GENERAL MOTORS

LATEST CHANGES & CORRECTIONS

Check these pages for updated information
in this and previous manuals.

See Chrysler Motors and Ford Motor Co. volume for information on these manufacturers and for all General Information.

1991 MITCHELL® DOMESTIC CARS SERVICE & REPAIR

The Leader in Professional Estimating and Repair Information.

Mitchell International

ACKNOWLEDGMENT

Mitchell International thanks the domestic manufacturers, distributors and dealers for their generous cooperation and assistance which make this manual possible.

Chrysler Motors
Ford Motor Company
General Motors Corporation

MARKETING

Senior Vice President
Dennis L. Bailey

Director
David R. Koontz

EDITORIAL

Senior Vice President
& Editor-in-Chief
Larry Laumann

Vice President
Steve Hansen

Senior Editors
Thomas L. Landis
Daniel D. Fleming
Chuck Vedra
Matthew Krimple
Ronald E. Garrett
Ramiro Gutierrez
John M. Fisher
Tom L. Hall
James A. Hawes

Technical Editors
Scott A. Olsen
Bob Reel
David W. Himes
Alex A. Solis
Donald T. Pellettera
David C. Rust
Serge G. Pirino
Reginald L. Baldwin
Michael C. May
KC Rosendale
Scott A. Tiner
James R. Warren
James D. Boxberger
David M. Finley
Linda M. Murphy
Electrical Editors
Leonard McVicker
Santiago Llano
Harry Piper
Lloyd Adams
Richard B. Speake
Barbara N. Moorefield

QUALITY ASSURANCE

Daryl F. Visser
Trang Nguyen-Tran
Nick DiVerde
Brian W. Hutchins

BOOK PRODUCTION

Roger Leftridge

TECHNICAL LIBRARIAN

Charlotte "Charlie" Norris

PRODUCT SUPPORT

Patrick G. San Nicolas

GRAPHICS

Manager
Judie LaPierre
Supervisor
Ann Klimetz

Published By

MITCHELL INTERNATIONAL
9889 Willow Creek Road
P.O. Box 26260
San Diego, California 92196-0260

ISBN 0-8470-0562-3

Copyright © 1991 Mitchell International
All Rights Reserved

Customer Service Numbers:
Subscription/Billing Information:
1-800-648-8010 or 619-578-6550
Technical Information:
1-800-854-7030 or 619-578-6550
Or Write: P.O. Box 26260, San Diego, CA 92196-0260

GENERAL MOTORS

GENERAL INFORMATION [1]

ENGINE PERFORMANCE

ENGINE PERFORMANCE (Cont.)

WIRING DIAGRAMS

SAFETY EQUIPMENT

SAFETY EQUIPMENT (Cont.)

1991 MODEL COVERAGE

MODEL	BODY CODE	ENGINE [1]	ENGINE ID	FUEL SYSTEM	IGNITION SYSTEM
Beretta	L	2.2L (LM3)	G	TBI	DIS Magnetic
		2.3L (LG0)	A	PFI	IDI Magnetic
		3.1L (LH0)	T	PFI	DIS Magnetic
Bonneville	H	3.8L (LN3)	C	[2] PFI	C[3]I Hall Effect
Brougham	D	5.0L (LO3)	E	TBI	HEI Magnetic
		5.7L (LO5)	7	TBI	HEI Magnetic
Camaro	F	3.1L (LH0)	T	PFI	HEI Magnetic
		5.0L (LB9)	F	PFI	HEI Magnetic
		5.0L (LO3)	E	TBI	HEI Magnetic
		5.7L (L98)	8	PFI	HEI Magnetic
Caprice	B	5.0L (LO3)	E	TBI	HEI Magnetic
		5.7L (LO5)	7	TBI	HEI Magnetic
Cavalier	J	2.2L (LM3)	G	TBI	DIS Magnetic
		3.1L (LH0)	T	PFI	DIS Magnetic
Century	A	2.5L (LR8)	R	TBI	DIS Magnetic
		3.3L (LG7)	N	PFI	C[3]I Hall Effect
Corsica	L	2.2L (LM3)	G	TBI	DIS Magnetic
		3.1L (LH0)	T	PFI	DIS Magnetic
Corvette	Y	5.7L (L98)	8	PFI	HEI Magnetic
Custom Cruiser	B	5.0L (LO3)	E	TBI	HEI Magnetic
Cutlass Calais	N	2.3L (LG0)	A	PFI	IDI Magnetic
		2.3L (LD2)	D	PFI	IDI Magnetic
		2.5L (L68)	U	TBI	DIS Magnetic
		3.3L (LG7)	N	PFI	C[3]I Hall Effect
Cutlass Ciera	A	2.5L (LR8)	R	TBI	DIS Magnetic
		3.3L (LG7)	N	PFI	C[3]I Hall Effect
Cutlass Cruiser Wagon	A	2.5L (LR8)	R	TBI	DIS Magnetic
		3.3L (LG7)	N	PFI	C[3]I Hall Effect
Cutlass Supreme	W	2.3L (LD2)	D	PFI	IDI Magnetic
		3.1L (LH0)	T	PFI	DIS Magnetic
		3.4L (LQ1)	X	PFI	DIS Magnetic
DeVille	C	4.9L (L26)	B	[2] PFI	[3] HEI Magnetic
Eighty-Eight	H	3.8L (LN3)	C	[2] PFI	C[3]I Hall Effect
Eldorado	E	4.9L (L26)	B	[2] PFI	[3] HEI Magnetic
Firebird	F	3.1L (LH0)	T	PFI	HEI Magnetic
		5.0L (LB9)	F	PFI	HEI Magnetic
		5.0L (LO3)	E	TBI	HEI Magnetic
		5.7L (L98)	8	PFI	HEI Magnetic
Fleetwood	C	4.9L (L26)	B	[2] PFI	[3] HEI Magnetic
Grand Am	N	2.3L (LG0)	A	PFI	IDI Magnetic
		2.3L (LD2)	D	PFI	IDI Magnetic
		2.5L (L68)	U	TBI	DIS Magnetic
Grand Prix	W	2.3L (LD2)	D	PFI	IDI Magnetic
		3.1L (LH0)	T	PFI	DIS Magnetic
		3.4L (LQ1)	X	PFI	DIS Magnetic
LeSabre	H	3.8L (LN3)	C	[2] PFI	C[3]I Hall Effect
Lumina	W	2.5L (LR8)	R	TBI	DIS Magnetic
		3.1L (LH0)	T	PFI	DIS Magnetic
		3.4L (LQ1)	X	PFI	DIS Magnetic
Ninety-Eight	C	3.8L (L27)	L	[2] PFI	C[3]I Hall Effect
Park Avenue	C	3.8L (L27)	L	[2] PFI	C[3]I Hall Effect

[1] – Engine code is stamped on engine block. See ENGINE CODE LOCATION table.
[2] – Sequential fuel injection.
[3] – Hall Effect camshaft sensor.

1991 MODEL COVERAGE (Cont.)

MODEL	BODY CODE	ENGINE [1]	ENGINE ID	FUEL SYSTEM	IGNITION SYSTEM
Reatta	E	3.8L (LN3)	C	[2] PFI	C³I Hall Effect
Riviera	E	3.8L (LN3)	C	[2] PFI	C³I Hall Effect
Regal	W	3.1L (LH0)	T	PFI	DIS Magnetic
		3.8L (L27)	L	PFI	C³I Hall Effect
Roadmaster	B	5.0L (LO3)	E	TBI	HEI Magnetic
Seville	K	4.9L (L26)	B	[2] PFI	[3] HEI Magnetic
Skylark	N	2.3L (LD2)	D	PFI	IDI Magnetic
		2.5L (L68)	U	TBI	DIS Magnetic
		3.3L (LG7)	N	PFI	C³I Hall Effect
Sunbird	J	2.0L (LT2)	K	TBI	HEI Magnetic
		3.1L (LH0)	T	PFI	DIS Magnetic
Toronado	E	3.8L (LN3)	C	[2] PFI	C³I Hall Effect
Touring Sedan	C	3.8L (L27)	L	[2] PFI	C³I Hall Effect
Trofeo	E	3.8L (LN3)	C	[2] PFI	C³I Hall Effect
6000	A	2.5L (LR8)	R	TBI	DIS Magnetic
		3.1L (LH0)	T	PFI	DIS Magnetic

[1] – Engine code is stamped on engine block. See ENGINE CODE LOCATION table.
[2] – Sequential fuel injection.
[3] – Hall Effect camshaft sensor.

VIN DEFINITION

1G1GZ11AXMR100001
① ② ③ ④ ⑤ ⑥ ⑦ ⑧ ⑨ ⑩ ⑪ ⑫ ⑬ ⑭ ⑮ ⑯ ⑰

① Indicates Nation of Origin.
② Indicates Manufacturer.
③ Indicates Vehicle Division.
④ Indicates Carline Body Code.
⑤ Indicates Carline/Series.
⑥ Indicates Body Type.
⑦ Indicates Restraint System.
⑧ **Indicates Engine ID.**
⑨ Indicates Check Digit.
⑩ **Indicates Model Year.**
⑪ Indicates Assembly Plant.
⑫⑬⑭⑮⑯⑰ Indicate Plant Sequential Number.

MODEL YEAR VIN CODE APPLICATION

VIN Code	Model Year
L	1990
M	1991

ENGINE CODE LOCATION [1]

LB9 – On engine block, near oil filter.
LD2 – On engine block, near starter.
LG0 – On engine block, near starter.
LG5 – On engine block, near starter.
LG7 – On left front of engine block, below cylinder head.
LH0 – On engine block, near starter.
LKO – Information not available.
LLO – Information not available.
LM3 – On left rear of engine block, on bellhousing flange.
LN3 – On left front of engine, below cylinder head.
LO3 – On right front of engine, below cylinder head. On engine block, near oil filter.
LO5 – On left front of engine block, below cylinder head. On engine block, near oil filter.
LQ1 – On engine block, near starter.
LR8 – On left front of engine block, below cylinder head.
LT2 – On left rear of engine block, on edge of flange casting.
LT3 – On left rear of engine block, on edge of flange casting.
LV2 – On left front of engine block, below cylinder head. On engine block, near oil filter.
L26 – On left rear of engine block, below cylinder head.
L27 – On left front of engine, below cylinder head.
L68 – On left rear of engine block, below cylinder head mating surface.
L98 – On engine block, near starter. On right front of engine block, below cylinder head.

[1] – See ENGINE in 1991 MODEL COVERAGE table for engine code location prefix (RPO).

1991 ENGINE PERFORMANCE
Emission Applications

1991 GENERAL MOTORS EMISSION SYSTEMS

Engine & Fuel System	Emission Control Systems & Devices	Remarks
2.0L (122") 4-Cyl. TBI (VIN K)	**PCV, EVAP, TWC, BP/EGR,** [1] **SPK, O₂, CEC,** [1] **SES,** EVAP-CAN, [1] SPK-EST	[1] – ECM controlled.
2.2L (135") 4-Cyl. TBI (VIN G)	**PCV, EVAP, TWC, BP/EGR,** [1] **SPK, O₂, CEC,** [1] **SES,** EVAP-CAN, [2][1] SPK-ESC, [1] SPK-EST	[2] – Cavalier only.
2.3L (140") 4-Cyl. PFI (VIN A & D)	**CVS, EVAP, TWC,** [1][3] **EGR-DC,** [1] **SPK, O₂, CEC,** [1] **SES,** EVAP-CAN, [1] EVAP-CPS, [4] TP-CV, [1] SPK-ESC, [1] SPK-EST	[3] – Cutlass Supreme & Grand Prix only.
2.5L (151") 4-Cyl. TBI (VIN R & U)	**PCV, EVAP, TWC, BP/EGR,** [1] **SPK, O₂, CEC,** [1] **SES,** EVAP-CAN, [1] SPK-EST	[4] – In fuel tank.
3.1L (181") V6 PFI (VIN T)	**PCV, EVAP, TWC,** [1] **EGR-DC,** [1] **SPK,** [5][6] **AP, O₂, CEC,** [1] **SES,** EVAP-CAN, [1] EVAP-CPS, [7] TP-CV, [1] SPK-ESC, [1] SPK-EST	[5] – "W" body with M/T only.
3.3L (204") V6 PFI (VIN N)	**PCV, EVAP, TWC,** [1] **SPK, O₂, CEC,** [1] **SES,** EVAP-CAN, [1] EVAP-CPS, [1] SPK-EST, [1] SPK-ESC	[6] – Brougham, Camaro & Firebird only.
3.4L (204") V6 PFI (VIN X)	**PCV, EVAP, TWC,** [1] **EGR-DC,** [1] **SPK,** [1][5] **AP, O₂, CEC,** [1] **SES,** EVAP-CAN, [1] EVAP-CPS, [4] TP-CV, [1] SPK-ESC, [1] SPK-EST, [1][5] EADV, [1][5] EAP, [5] AP-CV, [1][5] AP-RLY, [8] DV, [1][5][6] EADV, [5][6] AP-CV	[7] – Located in fuel tank on "J" & "W" bodies. [8] – Camaro & Firebird only. [9] – Sequential fuel injection.
3.8L (231") V6 [9] PFI (VIN C)	**PCV, EVAP, TWC,** [1][10] **EGR-DC,** [1] **SPK, O₂, CEC,** [1] **SES,** EVAP-CAN, [1] EVAP-CPS, [1] SPK-ESC, [1] SPK-EST	[10] – "H" body only. [11] – "B" body only.
3.8L (231") V6 [9] PFI (VIN L)	**PCV, EVAP, TWC,** [1] **SPK, O₂, CEC,** [1] **SES,** EVAP-CAN, [1] EVAP-CPS, [7] TP-CV, [1] SPK-ESC, [1] SPK-EST	
4.9L (275") V8 [9] PFI (VIN B)	**PCV, EVAP, TWC, BP/EGR,** [1] **SPK, O₂, CEC,** [1] **SES,** EVAP-CAN, [1] EVAP-CPS, TP-CV, [1] SPK-EST	
5.0L (305") V8 TBI (VIN E) & 5.7L (350") V8 TBI (VIN 7)	**PCV, TAC, EVAP, TWC,** [8] **TWC/OC, BP/EGR, AP,** [1] **SPK, O₂, CEC,** [1] **SES,** [6] TAC-VM, [11] TAC-WP, EVAP-CAN, [1] EVAP-CPS, TP-CV, [1] EGR-CS, [1] EADV, [1][8] AMgV, AP-CV, [1] SPK-ESC, [1] SPK-EST	
5.0L (305") V8 PFI (VIN F) & 5.7L (350") V8 PFI (VIN 8)	**PCV, EVAP, TWC/OC, BP/EGR, AP,** [1] **SPK, O₂, CEC,** [1] **SES,** EVAP-CAN, [1] EVAP-CPS, TP-CV, [1] EGR-CS, [1] AMgV, AP-CV, [1] SPK-ESC, [1] SPK-EST	

NOTE: Major emission control systems are listed in bold type; components are listed in light type.

AMgV – Air Management Valve
AP – Air Pump
AP-CV – Air Pump Check Valve
AP-RLY – Electric Air Pump Relay
BP/EGR – Backpressure EGR Valve
CEC – Computerized Engine Controls
CVS – Crankcase Ventilation System
DV – Diverter Valve
EADV – Electric Air Control Divert Valve
EAP – Electric Air Pump
EGR – Exhaust Gas Recirculation
EGR-CS – EGR Control Solenoid
EGR-DC – EGR Digital Control
EVAP – Fuel Evaporation System
EVAP-CAN – EVAP Canister
EVAP-CPS – EVAP Canister Purge Solenoid

O₂ – Oxygen Sensor
PCV – Positive Crankcase Ventilation
PFI – Port Fuel Injection
SES – Service Engine Soon Light
SPK – Spark Controls
SPK-ESC – Electronic Spark Control (Retard)
SPK-EST – Electronic Spark Timing
TAC – Thermostatic Air Cleaner
TAC-VM – Thermostatic Air Cleaner Vacuum Motor
TAC-WP – Thermostatic Air Cleaner Wax Pellet Type Motor
TBI – Throttle Body Injection
TP-CV – Tank Pressure Control Valve
TWC – Three-Way Catalyst
TWC/OC – Three-Way Catalyst/ Oxidation Catalyst

1991 ENGINE PERFORMANCE
Service & Adjustment Specifications

Beretta, Bonneville, Brougham, Camaro, Caprice, Cavalier, Century, Corsica, Corvette, Custom Cruiser, Cutlass Calais, Cutlass Ciera, Cutlass Cruiser, Cutlass Supreme, DeVille, Eighty-Eight, Eldorado, Firebird, Fleetwood, Grand Am, Grand Prix, LeSabre, Lumina, Ninety-Eight, Park Avenue, Reatta, Regal, Riviera, Roadmaster, Seville, Skylark, Sunbird, Toronado, Touring Sedan, Trofeo, 6000

INTRODUCTION

Use this article to quickly find specifications related to servicing and on-vehicle adjustments. Use this article for quick reference when you are familiar with proper adjustment procedures and only need a specification.

CAPACITIES

BATTERY SPECIFICATIONS

Application	Cold Crank Amps @ 0°F (-18°C)	Reserve Capacity Minutes
2.0L (VIN K)	630	90
2.2L (VIN G)	630	90
2.3L (VIN A & D)	630	90
2.5L (VIN R & U)	630	90
3.1L (VIN T)	630	90
3.3L (VIN N)	630	90
3.4L (VIN X)	690	90
3.8L (VIN C & L)		
Standard	630	90
Heavy Duty	770	115
4.9L (VIN B)	[1]	[1]
5.0L (VIN E & F)		
Standard	525	90
Heavy Duty	730	115
5.7L (VIN 7)		
Standard	525	90
Heavy Duty	730	115
5.7L (VIN 8)	525	90

[1] – Information is not available from manufacturer.

FLUID CAPACITIES

Application	[1] Quantity Qts. (L)
Crankcase [2]	
2.0L (VIN K)	4.0 (3.8)
2.2L (VIN G)	4.0 (3.8)
2.3L (VIN A & D)	4.0 (3.8)
2.5L (VIN R & U)	4.0 (3.8)
3.1L (VIN T)	4.0 (3.8)
3.3L (VIN N)	4.0 (3.8)
3.4L (VIN X)	4.0 (3.8)
3.8L (VIN C & L)	4.0 (3.8)
4.9L (VIN B)	[3]
5.0L (VIN E & F)	4.0 (3.8)
5.7L (VIN 7)	4.0 (3.8)
5.7L (VIN 8)	4.0 (3.8)

[1] – Fluid capacities listed are approximate. Always fill to FULL mark.
[2] – Does not include filter capacity.
[3] – Information is not available from manufacturer.

FLUID CAPACITIES (Cont.)

Application	[1] Quantity Qts. (L)
Cooling System (Includes Heater)	
2.0L (VIN K)	11.7 (11.1)
2.2L (VIN G)	11.7 (11.1)
2.3L (VIN A & D)	9.2 (8.7)
2.5L (VIN R)	9.9 (9.4)
2.5L (VIN U)	7.8 (7.4)
3.1L (VIN T)	14.0 (13.2)
3.3L (VIN N)	13.0 (12.3)
3.4L (VIN X)	13.0 (12.3)
3.8L (VIN C & L)	13.0 (12.3)
4.9L (VIN 3)	[2]
5.0L (VIN E & F)	18.0 (17.0)
5.7L (VIN 7)	15.0 (14.2)
5.7L (VIN 8)	17.0 (16.0)
Automatic Transaxle/Transmission [3][4]	
2.0L (VIN K)	4.0 (3.8)
2.2L (VIN G)	4.0 (3.8)
2.3L (VIN D)	
3T40	7.0 (6.6)
4T60	6.0 (5.7)
2.5L (VIN R)	
3T40	7.0 (6.6)
4T60	6.0 (5.7)
2.5L (VIN U)	4.0 (3.8)
3.1L (VIN T)	
3T40	7.0 (6.6)
4L60	6.0 (5.7)
3.3L (VIN N)	
3T40	7.0 (6.6)
4T60	6.0 (5.7)
3.4L (VIN X)	
3T40	7.0 (6.6)
4L60	6.0 (5.7)
3.8L (VIN C & L)	6.0 (5.7)
4.9L (VIN B)	6.0 (5.7)
5.0L (VIN E & F)	4.9 (4.6)
5.0L (VIN 8)	5.0 (4.7)
5.7L (VIN 7)	5.0 (4.7)
Manual Transaxle/Transmission	
2.0L (VIN K)	[5] 2.0 (1.9)
2.2L (VIN G)	[5] 2.0 (1.9)
2.3L (VIN A & D)	[5] 2.0 (1.9)
2.5L (VIN U)	[5] 2.0 (1.9)
3.1L (VIN T)	
"F" Body	[4] 3.0 (2.8)
All Others	[5] 1.9 (1.8)
3.4 (VIN X)	[5] 2.0 (1.9)
5.0L (VIN F)	[4] 3.0 (2.8)
5.7L (VIN 8)	[6] 2.2 (2.1)

[1] – Fluid capacities listed are approximate. Always fill to FULL mark.
[2] – Information is not available from manufacturer.
[3] – Drain and refill capacity only. Does not include torque converter.
[4] – Dexron-II
[5] – Synchromesh Transmission Fluid (GM 12345349)
[6] – SAE 5W-30

QUICK-SERVICE

SERVICE INTERVALS & SPECIFICATIONS

REPLACEMENT INTERVALS

Component	Miles
Oil & Filter	7500
Air Filter	30,000
Cam Timing Belt	[1]
Coolant	30,000
Fuel Filter	[1]
Spark Plugs	30,000

[1] – No scheduled replacement interval given by manufacturer. Check and replace as necessary.

BELT ADJUSTMENT

Application	[1] Tension Lbs. (kg)
Serpentine Belt [2]	
2.0L (VIN K)	225 (102)
2.2L (VIN G)	63-77 (29-40)
2.3L (VIN A & D)	50 (23)
2.5L (VIN R)	[3]
3.1L (VIN T)	
"F" Body	
With A/C	85-110 (39-50)
Without A/C	95-140 (43-64)
All Others	50-70 (23-32)
3.4L (VIN X)	[3]
3.3L (VIN N)	[3]
3.8L (VIN C & L)	[3]
4.9L (VIN B)	
"C" Body	70-110 (32-50)
"E" & "K" Body	[3]
5.0L (VIN E)	105-125 (48-57)
5.0L (VIN F)	99-121 (45-55)
5.7L (VIN 7)	99-121 (45-55)
5.7L (VIN 8)	60-90 (27-41)
"V" Belt	
2.3L (VIN A)	
Power Steering	110 (50)
2.5L (VIN U)	
A/C Compressor	165 (75)
Alternator	165 (75)
Power Steering	180 (82)
Water Pump	180 (82)

[1] – Specifications are for new belts only. Measure tension with belt tension gauge.
[2] – Engines with serpentine belts have automatic tensioner. If tension reading is not as specified, check belt's operating length or tensioner's operating range. Replace belt as necessary.
[3] – Information is not available from manufacturer.

MECHANICAL CHECKS

ENGINE COMPRESSION

Check engine compression under the following conditions: engine at normal operating temperature and specified cranking speed, all spark plugs removed, and throttle wide open.

COMPRESSION SPECIFICATIONS

Application	Specification
Compression Ratio	
2.0L (VIN K)	8.8:1
2.2L (VIN G)	8.9:1
2.3L (VIN A & D)	9.5:1
2.5L (VIN R & U)	8.3:1
3.1L (VIN T)	
"F" Body	8.5:1
All Others	8.8:1
3.3L (VIN N)	9.0:1
3.4L (VIN X)	9.25-9.50:1
3.8L (VIN C & L)	8.5:1
4.9L (VIN B)	9.5:1
5.0L (VIN E & F)	9.3:1
5.7L (VIN 7)	9.8:1
5.7L (VIN 8)	10.25:1
Normal Compression Pressure	
4.9L (VIN B)	140-165 psi (10-12 kg/cm²)
All Others	[1]
Minimum Compression Pressure	[1]

[1] – The lowest compression reading should not be less than 70 percent of the highest compression reading. No cylinder compression reading should be less than 100 psi (7 kg/cm²).

VALVE CLEARANCE

NOTE: All models are equipped with hydraulic lifters. No adjustment is required.

IGNITION SYSTEM

IGNITION COIL

PICK-UP COIL RESISTANCE

Application	Ohms
All Models With HEI-EST	500-1500

HIGH TENSION WIRE RESISTANCE

HIGH TENSION WIRE RESISTANCE

Application [1]	Ohms
All Models	30,000 Maximum

[1] – Not applicable to direct ignition systems.

SPARK PLUGS

SPARK PLUG TYPE

Application	AC Spark Plug
2.0L (VIN K)	R44XLS
2.2L (VIN G)	R44LTSM
2.3L (VIN A & D)	FR3LS
2.5L (VIN R)	R43TS6
2.5L (VIN U)	R43TS6
3.1L (VIN T)	
"F" Body	R43TSK
"J" Body	R44LTSM
All Others	R43LTSE
3.3L (VIN N)	R45LTS6
3.4L (VIN X)	R42LTSM
3.8L (VIN C & L)	R44LTS6
4.9L (VIN B)	R45LTS6K
5.0L (VIN E & F)	R45TS
5.7L (VIN 7)	R45TS
5.7L (VIN 8)	FR5LS

SPARK PLUG SPECIFICATIONS

Application	Gap In. (mm)	Torque Ft. Lbs. (N.m)
2.0L (VIN K)	.045 (1.14)	15 (20)
2.2L (VIN G)	.035 (0.89)	11 (15)
2.3L (VIN A & D)	.035 (0.89)	17 (23)
2.5L (VIN R & U)	.060 (1.52)	20 (27)
3.1L (VIN T)	.045 (1.14)	15 (20)
3.3L (VIN N)	.060 (1.52)	20 (27)
3.4L (VIN X)	.045 (1.14)	11 (15)
3.8L (VIN C & L)	.060 (1.52)	20 (27)
4.9L (VIN B)	.060 (1.52)	20 (27)
5.0L (VIN E & F)	.035 (0.89)	22 (30)
5.7L (VIN 7 & 8)	.035 (0.89)	22 (30)

1991 ENGINE PERFORMANCE
Service & Adjustment Specifications (Cont.)

FIRING ORDER & TIMING MARKS

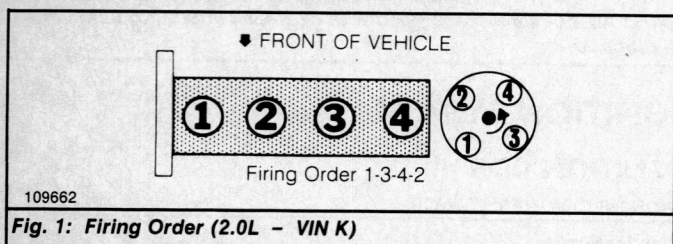

109662
Fig. 1: Firing Order (2.0L – VIN K)

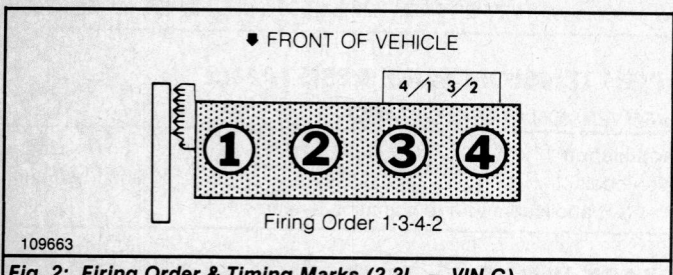

109663
Fig. 2: Firing Order & Timing Marks (2.2L – VIN G)

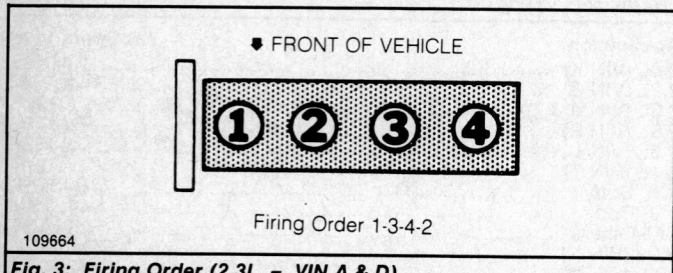

109664
Fig. 3: Firing Order (2.3L – VIN A & D)

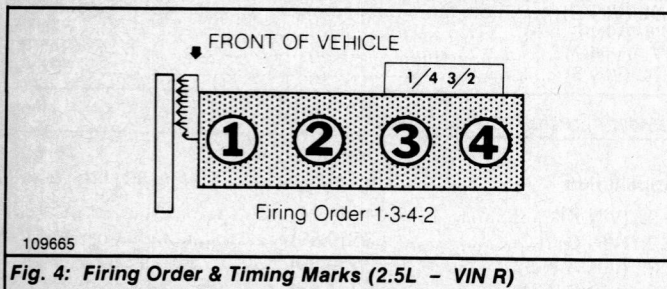

109665
Fig. 4: Firing Order & Timing Marks (2.5L – VIN R)

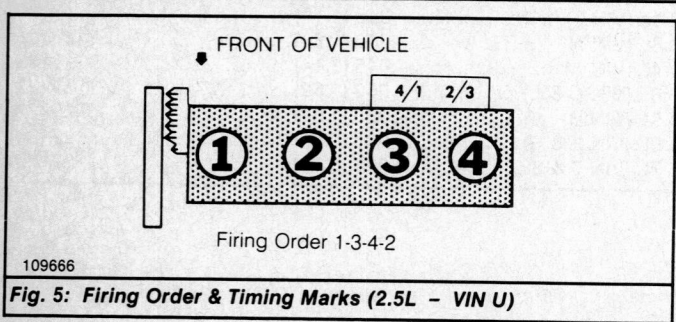

109666
Fig. 5: Firing Order & Timing Marks (2.5L – VIN U)

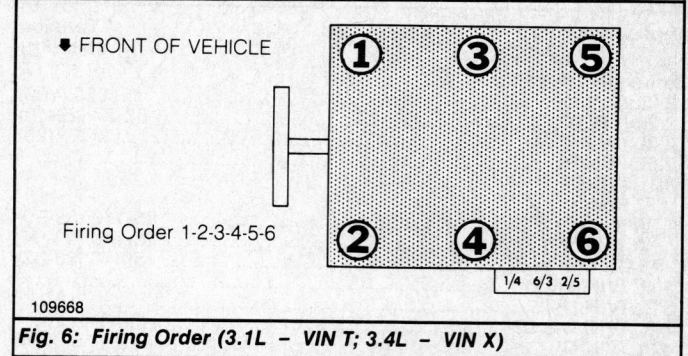

109668
Fig. 6: Firing Order (3.1L – VIN T; 3.4L – VIN X)

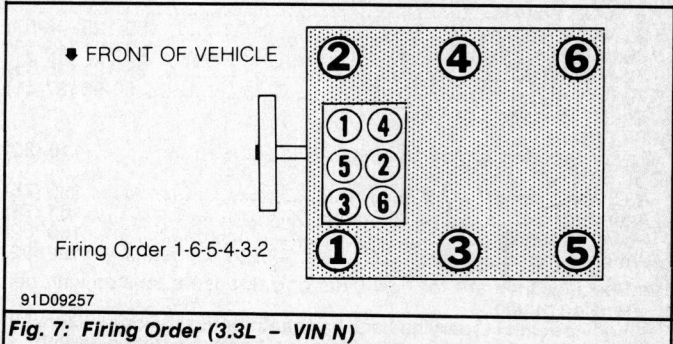

91D09257
Fig. 7: Firing Order (3.3L – VIN N)

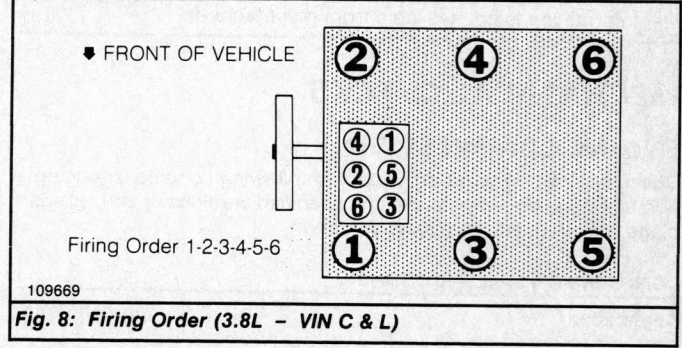

109669
Fig. 8: Firing Order (3.8L – VIN C & L)

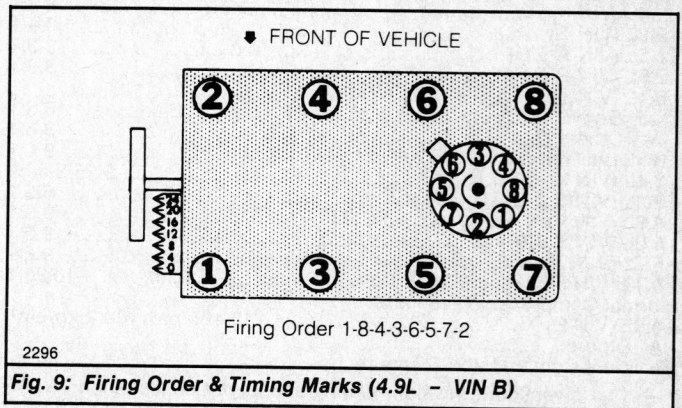

2296
Fig. 9: Firing Order & Timing Marks (4.9L – VIN B)

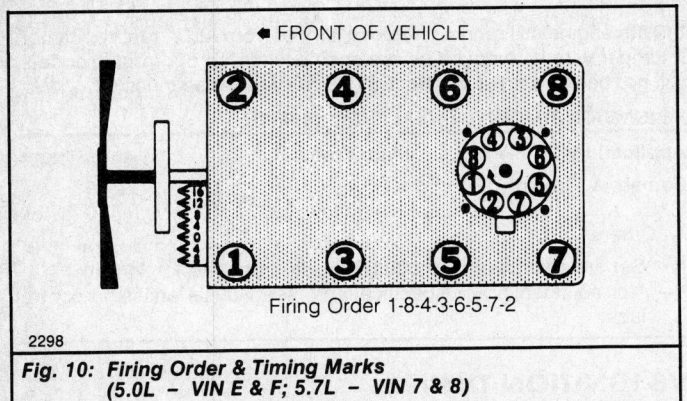

◄ FRONT OF VEHICLE

Firing Order 1-8-4-3-6-5-7-2

2298

Fig. 10: *Firing Order & Timing Marks (5.0L – VIN E & F; 5.7L – VIN 7 & 8)*

IGNITION TIMING

NOTE: For timing procedures, see ON-VEHICLE ADJUSTMENTS article.

IGNITION TIMING (Degrees BTDC @ RPM)

Application	Man. Trans.	Auto. Trans.
2.0L (VIN K)	8 @ Idle	8 @ Idle
2.2L (VIN G)	[1]	[1]
2.3L (VIN A & D)	[1]	[1]
2.5L (VIN R & U)	[1]	[1]
3.1L (VIN T)		
"F" Body	10 @ Idle	10 @ Idle
All Others	[1]	[1]
3.4L (VIN X)	[1]	[1]
3.3L (VIN N)	[1]	[1]
3.8L (VIN C & L)	[1]	[2]
4.9L (VIN B)		[2]
5.0L (VIN E)	[3]	[3]
5.0L (VIN F)	[3]	[3]
5.7L (VIN 7)	[3]	[3]
5.7L (VIN 8)	[3]	[3]

[1] – Not adjustable.
[2] – Information is not available from manufacturer.
[3] – Refer to Vehicle Emission Control Label.

FUEL SYSTEM

FUEL PUMP

NOTE: Fuel pump performance is a measurement of fuel pressure and volume availability, not regulated fuel pressure.

FUEL PUMP PERFORMANCE

Application	Specification psi (kg/cm²)
2.0L (VIN K)	9-13 (0.63-0.91)
2.2L (VIN G)	9-13 (0.63-0.91)
2.3L (VIN A & D)	41-47 (2.88-3.30)
2.5L (VIN R)	9-13 (0.63-0.91)
3.1L (VIN T)	41-47 (2.88-3.30)
3.3L (VIN N)	41-47 (2.88-3.30)
3.4L (VIN X)	32-47 (2.25-3.30)
3.8L (VIN C & L)	40-47 (2.81-3.30)
4.9L (VIN B)	40-50 (2.81-3.52)
5.0L (VIN E)	9-13 (0.63-0.91)
5.0L (VIN F)	41-47 (2.88-3.30)
5.7L (VIN 7)	9-13 (0.63-0.91)
5.7L (VIN 8)	41-47 (2.88-3.30)

INJECTOR RESISTANCE

INJECTOR RESISTANCE SPECIFICATIONS [1]

Application	Ohms
2.0L (VIN K)	1.6
2.2L (VIN G)	1.6
2.3L (VIN A & D)	1.9-2.1
2.5L (VIN R & U)	1.6
3.1L (VIN T)	
"W" Body	12.0-12.4
All Others	8.0
3.3L (VIN N)	11.8-12.6
3.4L (VIN X)	12.0-12.4
3.8L (VIN C & L)	[2]
4.9L (VIN B)	[2]
5.0L (VIN E)	1.2
5.0L (VIN F)	10.0
5.7L (VIN 7)	1.2
5.7L (VIN 8)	10.0

[1] – Injector resistance specification is at 140°F (60°C).
[2] – Information is not available from manufacturer.

IDLE SPEED & MIXTURE

NOTE: Idle mixture is controlled by the Electronic Control Module (ECM). Idle mixture adjustment is neither required nor possible on fuel-injected models.

THROTTLE POSITION SENSOR (TPS)

NOTE: On 4-cylinder models, TPS is not adjustable. For further testing, refer to SELF-DIAGNOSTICS article.

TPS ADJUSTMENT VOLTAGE

Application	[1] Volts
3.1L (VIN T)	
"A" & "J" Body	[2] .29-4.8
All Others	[2] .50-4.8
3.3L (VIN N)	.33-.46
3.4L (VIN X)	[2] .50-4.8
3.8L (VIN C & L)	.33-.46
4.9L (VIN B)	[3]
5.0L (VIN E)	[2]
5.0L (VIN F)	[2]
5.7L (VIN 7)	[2]
5.7L (VIN 8)	[2]

[1] – At idle RPM.
[2] – Not adjustable.
[3] – Information is not available from manufacturer.

1991 ENGINE PERFORMANCE
On-Vehicle Adjustments

Beretta, Bonneville, Brougham, Camaro, Caprice, Cavalier, Century, Corsica, Corvette, Custom Cruiser, Cutlass Calais, Cutlass Ciera, Cutlass Cruiser, Cutlass Supreme, DeVille, Eighty-Eight, Eldorado, Firebird, Fleetwood, Grand Am, Grand Prix, LeSabre, Lumina, Ninety-Eight, Park Avenue, Reatta, Regal, Riviera, Roadmaster, Seville, Skylark, Sunbird, Toronado, Touring Sedan, Trofeo, 6000

ENGINE MECHANICAL

Before performing any on-vehicle adjustments to fuel or ignition systems, ensure engine mechanical condition is okay.

VALVE CLEARANCE

NOTE: All models use hydraulic lifters. No adjustments are required.

IGNITION TIMING

NOTE: Procedures for timing adjustment are for engines equipped with HEI-EST distributors only. All other models are equipped with either C³I, DIS or IDI ignition system. Timing on these systems is not adjustable.

4-CYLINDER IGNITION TIMING

2.0L (VIN K) – **1)** Set parking brake and block drive wheels. Warm engine to normal operating temperature. Ensure all accessories are off. Ensure SERVICE ENGINE SOON (SES) light is off. Using a jumper, ground ALDL test connector. ALDL test connector is located under driver's side of dash. Start engine. The SES light should flash.
2) Connect timing light to No. 1 spark plug wire and record position of timing mark. Move timing light to No. 4 spark plug wire. Check timing and record position of timing mark.
3) To obtain average timing, add both timing figures and divide by 2. If timing is not as specified, adjust average timing by turning distributor. See 4-CYLINDER IGNITION TIMING table.
4) Remove jumper from ALDL test connector. Check SES light. If SES light stays on, remove Electronic Control Module (ECM) fuse from fuse block or disconnect ECM pigtail at battery for about 10 seconds.

4-CYLINDER IGNITION TIMING (Degrees BTDC @ RPM)

Application	Man. Trans.	Auto. Trans.
2.0L (VIN K)	8 @ Idle	[1] 8 @ Idle
2.2L (VIN G)	[2]	[2]
2.3L (VIN A & D)	[2]	[2]
2.5L (VIN R & U)	[2]	[2]

[1] – Set timing at less than 800 RPM with transmission in Park.
[2] – Not adjustable. For specifications, see vehicle emission control label.

V6 IGNITION TIMING

NOTE: Some engines are equipped with a socket for a magnetic probe timing meter, located 9.5 degrees ATDC. DO NOT use this location for setting timing with a conventional timing light.

3.1L (Camaro & Firebird) – **1)** Warm engine to normal operating temperature. Disconnect Electronic Spark Timing (EST) connector located on wiring harness near distributor, or ground ALDL test connector using a jumper. ALDL is located under driver's side of dash.
2) Connect timing light to No. 1 spark plug wire. Set timing to specification. See V6 IGNITION TIMING table. Tighten distributor and recheck timing.

3) With engine still running, remove jumper from ALDL test connector. If jumper wire is removed before engine is turned off, trouble code(s) will not be stored. Reconnect EST connector if disconnected.

V6 IGNITION TIMING (Degrees BTDC @ RPM)

Application	Man. Trans.	Auto. Trans.
Camaro & Firebird 3.1L	10 @ Idle	[1] 10 @ Idle
All Others	[2]	[2]

[1] – Set timing at less than 800 RPM with transmission in Park.
[2] – Not adjustable. For specifications, see vehicle emission control label.

V8 IGNITION TIMING

NOTE: Some engines are equipped with a socket for a magnetic probe timing meter, located 9.5 degrees ATDC. DO NOT use this location for setting timing with a conventional timing light.

4.9L (VIN B) – **1)** Place transmission in Park. Ensure engine is at normal operating temperature. Turn A/C and all accessories off. Ensure system is not in diagnostic mode.
2) Jumper ALDL test terminals "A" and "B". Connect timing light to No. 1 spark plug wire. Check ignition timing and adjust if necessary. Set timing to specification. See V8 IGNITION TIMING SPECIFICATIONS table. Tighten distributor and recheck timing. Remove jumper from ALDL test connector.
5.0L (VIN E & F) & 5.7L (VIN 7 & 8) – **1)** Place transmission in Park. Start and warm engine to normal operating temperature. Turn A/C and all accessories off. Ensure CHECK ENGINE light is off.
2) Put Electronic Spark Timing (EST) into by-pass mode by unplugging Set-Timing connector. Connector is a single wire in the wiring harness near distributor. DO NOT unplug 4-wire connector at distributor.
3) Connect timing light to No. 1 spark plug wire. Loosen distributor hold-down bolt. Set timing to specification. See V8 IGNITION TIMING SPECIFICATIONS table. Tighten distributor and recheck timing. Reconnect Set-Timing connector. Clear Electronic Control Module (ECM) trouble code by momentarily disconnecting ECM power source.

V8 IGNITION TIMING SPECIFICATIONS

Application	Degrees BTDC @ RPM
4.9L (VIN B)	6-10 @ Idle
5.0L (VIN E & F)	[1]
5.7L (VIN 7 & 8)	[1]

[1] – Refer to vehicle emission control label.

IDLE SPEED & MIXTURE

NOTE: Idle mixture is controlled by the Electronic Control Module (ECM). Adjustment is not possible.

4-CYLINDER IDLE SPEED

NOTE: Idle speed is controlled by ECM. Slight fluctuations in idle speed are considered normal. Start and run engine for at least 7 minutes to re-establish ECM control of idle.

NOTE: Incorrect idle speeds are normally caused by dirty throttle plate or vacuum leaks. Ensure all vacuum components are functioning properly.

2.0L (VIN K) & 2.5L (VIN R & U) – **1)** Ensure engine is at normal operating temperature. Ground ALDL test connector located under driver's side dash. With ignition on and engine off, wait 30 seconds for Idle Air Control (IAC) valve to seat in throttle body.

2) Disconnect IAC valve electrical connector. Connect tachometer or "Scan" tester to monitor engine RPM. Disconnect ground from ALDL test connector.

3) With transaxle in Park or Neutral, start engine and allow engine RPM to stabilize. Ensure all accessories are turned off. Observe idle speed. See MINIMUM IDLE SPEED (4 CYLINDERS) table.

4) If idle speed is incorrect, remove air cleaner to gain access to throttle body (if necessary). Plug any disconnected hoses. Disconnect throttle cable and kickdown cable (A/T vehicles). Use an awl to pierce cover of minimum idle stop screw. Apply leverage to remove cover.

5) Using minimum idle stop screw, adjust engine idle speed to specification. If minimum idle speed correction requires more than 1/2 turn (in or out) of idle stop screw, check for vacuum leaks or dirty throttle plate.

2.2L (VIN G) – Idle speed is ECM controlled and is not adjustable.

2.3L (VIN A & D) – **1)** Install "Scan" tester to ALDL test connector. Start and run engine to normal operating temperature. Observe IAC counts. See MINIMUM IDLE SPEED (4 CYLINDERS) table.

2) If idle speed is incorrect, use an awl to pierce cover of minimum idle stop screw. Apply leverage to remove cover. Turn idle stop screw out until screw clears linkage. Turn screw in until screw touches linkage. Turn screw in an additional 1 1/2 turns.

3) Turn idle stop screw in to decrease IAC counts. Turn screw out to increase IAC counts. If minimum idle speed correction requires more than 1/2 turn (in or out) of idle stop screw, check for vacuum leaks or dirty throttle plate. Clear any trouble codes.

MINIMUM IDLE SPEED (4 CYLINDERS)

Application	RPM
2.0L (VIN K)	450-650
2.2L (VIN G)	[1]
2.3L (VIN A & D)	[2]
2.5L (VIN R & U)	550-650

[1] – Idle speed is ECM controlled and is not adjustable.
[2] – Idle RPM should be 15-45 counts on "Scan" tester.

4-CYLINDER IDLE MIXTURE

NOTE: Idle mixture is controlled by the Electronic Control Module (ECM). No adjustment is required or possible.

V6 IDLE SPEED

NOTE: Incorrect idle speeds are normally caused by dirty throttle plate or vacuum leaks. Ensure all vacuum components are functioning properly.

All Models – **1)** Install "Scan" tester to ALDL test connector located under driver's side of dash. Start and run engine to normal operating temperature. Observe Idle Air Control (IAC) counts. See MINIMUM IDLE SPEED (V6) table.

2) If IAC counts are incorrect, use an awl to pierce cover of minimum idle stop screw. Apply leverage to remove cover. Turn idle stop screw out until screw clears linkage. Turn screw in until screw touches linkage. Turn screw in an additional 1 1/2 turns.

3) Turn idle stop screw in to decrease IAC counts. Turn screw out to increase IAC counts. If minimum idle speed correction requires more than 1/2 turn (in or out) of idle stop screw, check for vacuum leaks or dirty throttle plate. Clear any trouble codes.

MINIMUM IDLE SPEED (V6)

Application	IAC Counts
All Models	10-20

V6 IDLE MIXTURE

NOTE: Idle mixture is controlled by the Electronic Control Module (ECM). No adjustment is possible.

V8 IDLE SPEED

Minimum Idle (DeVille & Fleetwood) – **1)** Warm engine to normal operating temperature. Turn A/C and all accessories off. With key on and engine off, select Powertrain Control Module (PCM) override E.5.3., Idle Speed Control (ISC) motor. See ENTERING SELF-DIAGNOSTICS in SELF-DIAGNOSTICS – DEVILLE & FLEETWOOD PCM/BCM article.

2) Press the WARMER button on Electronic Climate Control (EEC) panel. The fuel data center should alternately display E.5.3. and 99, indicating override function has started. The ISC will extend to maximum extend position.

3) With ISC at maximum extension, Throttle Position Sensor (TPS) voltage should be 1.15-1.20 volts. If TPS voltage is less than 1.15 volts, go to next step. If TPS voltage is greater than 1.20 volts, go to step 5).

4) Adjust ISC plunger out by turning plunger counterclockwise until TPS parameter reads 1.18 volts.

5) Adjust ISC plunger in by turning plunger clockwise until TPS parameter reads 1.18 volts.

6) Recheck ISC maximum extension setting. Press COOLER button to retract ISC plunger. Wait 5 seconds. Press the WARMER button and read TPS voltage. Adjust ISC plunger again if necessary.

7) After all adjustments are made and while still in diagnostic mode, turn ignition off. Allow approximately 20 seconds for ISC motor to retract and perform a TPS learn routine.

8) Re-enter diagnostics and repeat step 7). It takes 2 cycles for a successful TPS learn to occur. Remove alternator disable ground wire (Green harness connector plug). Start engine and check for proper ISC motor operation.

Minimum Idle (Eldorado & Seville) – **1)** Warm engine to normal operating temperature. Turn A/C and all accessories off. Enter diagnostics and select Powertrain Control Module (PCM) override ES03, Idle Speed Control (ISC) motor. See ENTERING SELF-DIAGNOSTICS in SELF-DIAGNOSTICS – ELDORADO & SEVILLE PCM/BCM article.

2) This action disengages the A/C compressor, command EGR off and turn off alternator. The Electronic Climate Control (ECC) panel will display 50 to 00. The ISC motor will slowly move to a fully retracted position (20 seconds).

3) Ensure throttle lever is resting on the minimum idle speed screw. With ISC plunger fully retracted, disconnect ISC harness. The plunger should not be touching the throttle lever. If contact is noted, adjust ISC plunger.

4) If engine stalls, check throttle blades for deposits that might restrict airflow. Clean throttle bores and area behind and around throttle plates. Check minimum idle speed displayed on Driver Information Center (DIC). Use average RPM reading to set minimum idle speed. See MINIMUM IDLE SPEED (V8 – 4.9L) table. Check for vacuum leaks.

MINIMUM IDLE SPEED (V8 – 4.9L)

Application	Idle Speed (RPM)
DeVille, Eldorado, Fleetwood & Seville	500-550

NOTE: On 5.0L (VIN E & F) and 5.7L (VIN 7 & 8) engines, idle speed is controlled by ECM and will normally vary; adjustment is normally not required. The following adjustment is for minimum idle speed only.

5.0L (VIN E & F) & 5.7L (VIN 7 & 8) – **1)** Pierce idle stop screw plug with an awl and remove. With Idle Air Control (IAC) motor connected, ground ALDL test connector located under driver's side of dash. Disconnect distributor Set-Timing connector located by the distributor.

2) Turn ignition on, but DO NOT start engine. Wait 45 seconds. With ignition on, disconnect IAC connector. Remove jumper from ALDL test connector and start engine. Allow engine to go into Closed Loop mode.

3) Adjust idle screw to specifications. See MINIMUM IDLE SPEED (V8 – 5.0L & 5.7L) table. Turn ignition off and reconnect IAC motor. Check TPS adjustment. See THROTTLE POSITION SENSOR (TPS) in this article. Start engine and check for proper idle operation.

MINIMUM IDLE SPEED (V8 – 5.0L & 5.7L)

Application	RPM
5.0L (VIN E & F)	400-450
5.7L (VIN 7 & 8)	400-450

Maximum ISC Extension (DeVille & Fleetwood) – 1) Before adjusting maximum Idle Speed Control (ISC) extension, check minimum idle and Throttle Position Sensor (TPS) adjustment. See MINIMUM IDLE under V8 IDLE SPEED. Also, see THROTTLE POSITION SENSOR (TPS).
2) With ignition on and engine off, select ISC MOTOR override E.5.3. See ENTERING SELF-DIAGNOSTICS in SELF DIAGNOSTICS –DEVILLE & FLEETWOOD PCM/BCM article. Fully extend ISC motor by pressing WARMER button on the Electronic Control Center (ECC) on dash. Fuel data center should alternately display E.5.3 and 99, indicating override function has started.
3) ISC should extend to maximum extend position. With ISC at maximum extended position, TPS voltage should be 1.15-1.20 volts. If TPS voltage is NOT 1.15-1.20 volts, adjust ISC plunger. Adjust ISC plunger, clockwise or counterclockwise, until TPS parameter reads 1.18 volts.
4) Recheck maximum extend setting. Press COOLER button to retract ISC plunger. Wait 5 seconds. Press WARMER button and check TPS voltage. Readjust ISC plunger if necessary.
Maximum ISC Extension (Eldorado & Seville) – 1) Before adjusting maximum Idle Speed Control (ISC) extension, check minimum idle and Throttle Position Sensor (TPS) adjustment. See MINIMUM IDLE under V8 IDLE SPEED. Also, see THROTTLE POSITION SENSOR (TPS).
2) With ignition on and engine off, select ECM ISC MOTOR override ES03. See ENTERING SELF-DIAGNOSTICS in SELF-DIAGNOSTICS – ELDORADO & SEVILLE PCM/BCM article.
3) Fully extend ISC motor by pressing WARMER button on the Electronic Control Center (ECC) on dash. Fuel data center display should alternately change from 50 or 00 to 99, indicating override function has started.
4) ISC should extend to maximum extend position. With ISC at maximum extended position, TPS parameter should read 13.0-13.8 degrees on Driver Information Center (DIC). If TPS is NOT 13.0-13.8 degrees, adjust ISC plunger. Adjust ISC plunger, clockwise or counterclockwise, until TPS parameter reads 13.4 degrees on DIC.
5) Recheck maximum extend setting. Press COOLER button to retract ISC plunger. Wait 5 seconds. Press WARMER button and check TPS voltage. Readjust ISC plunger if necessary.

V8 IDLE MIXTURE

NOTE: Idle mixture is controlled by the Electronic Control Module (ECM). No adjustment is required or possible.

THROTTLE POSITION SENSOR (TPS)

4-CYLINDER THROTTLE POSITION SENSOR

NOTE: TPS is not adjustable. For further testing procedures, refer to appropriate SELF-DIAGNOSTICS or SYSTEM & COMPONENT TESTING article.

V6 THROTTLE POSITION SENSOR

NOTE: Not all TPS are adjustable. For further testing procedures, refer to appropriate SELF-DIAGNOSTICS or SYSTEM & COMPONENT TESTING article.

Throttle Position Sensor (TPS) can be adjusted using "Scan" tester or the following procedure.
1) Ensure engine is at normal operating temperature. Install 3 jumper wires between TPS and TPS wiring harness connector.
2) Turn ignition on with engine off. Connect a DVOM to Dark Blue and Black wire terminals. With throttle at closed position, adjust TPS to obtain specified voltage. See TPS ADJUSTMENT VOLTAGE table.
3) Tighten screws and recheck readings. Turn ignition off. Remove jumper wires and reconnect harness connector to TPS.

TPS ADJUSTMENT VOLTAGE (V6)

Application	[1] Voltage
3.1L (VIN T)	
Cavalier, Sunbird & 6000	[2] .29-4.8
All Others	[2] .50-4.8
3.3L (VIN N)	.33-.46
3.4L (VIN X)	[2] .50-4.8
3.8L (VIN C & L)	.33-.46

[1] – At idle RPM or closed throttle.
[2] – Not adjustable.

V8 THROTTLE POSITION SENSOR

NOTE: All testing procedures are made with engine at normal operating temperature. Not all TPS are adjustable. For further testing procedures, refer to appropriate SELF-DIAGNOSTICS or SYSTEM & COMPONENT TESTING article.

4.9L (VIN B) – 1) Turn ignition on with engine off. Install TPS Jumper Harness (J-38490) and connect DVOM. Enter diagnostic mode and select PCM override E.5.3., ISC Motor. See ENTERING SELF-DIAGNOSTICS in SELF-DIAGNOSTICS – DEVILLE & FLEETWOOD PCM/BCM or SELF-DIAGNOSTICS – ELDORADO & SEVILLE PCM/BCM article.
2) Press the COOLER button to retract ISC motor to minimum air setting. Loosen TPS screws enough to permit sensor to be rotated. Open throttle slightly and allow throttle lever to snap shut against minimum air screw.
3) Adjust TPS. See TPS ADJUSTMENT VOLTAGE (V8) table. Tighten TPS mounting screws. Recheck voltage reading.

TPS ADJUSTMENT VOLTAGE (V8)

Application	[1] Voltage
4.9L (VIN B)	.45-.55
5.0L (VIN E & F)	[2] .36-.96
5.7L (VIN 7)	[2] .36-.96
5.7L (VIN 8)	[2]

[1] – At idle RPM or closed throttle.
[2] – Not adjustable.

Beretta, Bonneville, Brougham, Camaro, Caprice, Cavalier, Century, Corsica, Corvette, Custom Cruiser, Cutlass Calais, Cutlass Ciera, Cutlass Cruiser, Cutlass Supreme, DeVille, Eighty-Eight Eldorado, Firebird, Fleetwood, Grand Am, Grand Prix, LeSabre, Lumina, Ninety-Eight, Park Avenue, Reatta, Regal, Riviera, Roadmaster, Seville, Skylark, Sunbird, Toronado, Touring Sedan, Trofeo, 6000

INTRODUCTION

This article covers basic description and operation of engine performance-related systems and components. Read this article before diagnosing vehicles or systems with which you are not completely familiar.

AIR INDUCTION SYSTEM

AIRFLOW SENSING

Mass Airflow (3.3L & 3.8L) – Sensor measures flow of air entering the engine in grams per second. This measurement of airflow is a reflection of engine load (throttle opening and air volume), similar to the relationship of engine load to MAP or vacuum sensor signal. Mass Airflow (MAF) signal should remain relatively constant at cruise, gradually changing with throttle angle and rapidly changing on sudden acceleration. The ECM uses this information to control fuel delivery. Sensor produces a frequency signal that cannot be easily measured in testing (32-150 Hertz). This varying signal is proportional to airflow.

Speed Density (Except 3.3L & 3.8L) – On models equipped with MAP and MAT sensors, the speed density method is used to compute the airflow rate. Manifold pressure and temperature are used to calculate the airflow rate to the ECM. The MAP sensor responds to manifold vacuum changes due to engine load and speed changes.

The ECM sends a voltage signal to the MAP sensor. Manifold pressure changes result in resistance changes in the MAP sensor. By monitoring MAP sensor output voltage, the ECM determines manifold pressure. If MAP sensor fails, the ECM will supply a fixed MAP value and use the TPS to control fuel.

COMPUTERIZED ENGINE CONTROLS

The computerized engine control system monitors and controls a variety of engine/vehicle functions. The computerized engine control system is primarily an emission control system which is designed to maintain a 14.7:1 air/fuel ratio under most operating conditions. When the ideal air/fuel ratio is maintained, the 3-way catalytic converter can control oxides of nitrogen (NOx), hydrocarbon (HC) and carbon monoxide (CO) emissions.

The computerized engine control system consists of the following sub-systems: Electronic Control Module (ECM), input devices (sensors and switches) and output signals.

ELECTRONIC CONTROL MODULE (ECM)

NOTE: Some models use what is termed a Powertrain Control Module (PCM). The only difference between an ECM and PCM is that, in addition to electronic engine controls, the PCM also controls electronic transmission internals and cruise control system. Unless specifically stated, references to ECM also apply to PCM equipped vehicles.

On most vehicles, ECM is located in passenger compartment. For exact location of ECM, see ECM LOCATION in appropriate SELF-DIAGNOSTICS article, or COMPONENT LOCATIONS in SYSTEM & COMPONENT TESTING article. The ECM consists of the Arithmetic Logic Unit (ALU), Central Processing Unit (CPU), power supply and system memories.

The ECM has a "learning" ability which allows it to make minor corrections for fuel system variations. If battery power is interrupted, a vehicle performance change may be noticed. This will correct itself and normal performance will return if vehicle is allowed to "relearn" optimum control conditions. This is accomplished by driving vehicle at normal operating temperature, under part throttle, moderate acceleration and idle conditions.

Arithmetic Logic Unit (ALU) – This internal component of the ECM converts electrical signals, received by ECM from various engine sensors, into digital signals for use by the CPU.

Central Processing Unit (CPU) – Digital signals received by CPU are used to perform all mathematical computations and logic functions necessary to deliver proper air/fuel mixture. CPU also calculates spark timing and idle speed. The CPU commands operation of emission control, "closed loop" fuel control and diagnostic system.

Power Supply – Power for ECM reference output signals (5 volts) and control devices (12 volts) is received from the battery (through ignition circuit when ignition switch is in ON position). Keep alive memory power is received directly from the battery.

Memories – The 5 types of memories used in ECMs are: Read Only Memory (ROM), Random Access Memory (RAM), Programmable Read Only Memory (PROM), fuel system CALPAC and Memory Calibration unit (MEM-CAL).

- **Read Only Memory (ROM)** – ROM is programmed information that can only be read by ECM. The ROM program cannot be changed. If battery voltage is removed, ROM information will be retained.

- **Random Access Memory (RAM)** – RAM is the scratch pad for the CPU. Data input, diagnostic codes and results of calculations are constantly updated and temporarily stored in RAM. If battery voltage is removed from ECM, all information stored in RAM is lost.

- **Programmable Read Only Memory (PROM)** – PROM is factory programmed engine calibration data which "tailors" ECM for specific transmission, engine, emission, vehicle weight and rear axle ratio application. The PROM can be removed from ECM. If battery voltage is removed, PROM information will be retained.

- **CALPAC** – Some fuel injected models use a PROM and a device called a CALPAC. The CALPAC provides fuel delivery back-up so engine will run in case of a PROM or ECM failure. Any time ECM is replaced, PROM and CALPAC must both be installed into replacement ECM. If battery voltage is removed, CALPAC information will be retained.

- **MEM-CAL** – Vehicles with fuel injection may also use another type of ECM containing a Memory Calibration unit (MEM-CAL). This assembly contains functions of PROM and CALPAC and, on some models, the ESC control module. If power to ECM is removed, MEM-CAL information will be retained.

NOTE: Components are grouped into 2 categories. The first category covers INPUT DEVICES, which control or produce voltage signals monitored by the control unit. The second category covers OUTPUT SIGNALS, which are components controlled by the control unit.

INPUT DEVICES

Vehicles are equipped with different combinations of input devices. Not all devices are used on all models. To determine the input device usage on a specific model, see appropriate wiring diagram in WIRING DIAGRAMS article in ENGINE PERFORMANCE. The available input signals include the following:

A/C "On" Switch – The air conditioner "on" switch is mounted in instrument panel. This switch provides a simple "on" or "A/C request" signal which is monitored by the ECM. The ECM uses this signal to determine control of the A/C clutch relay (if equipped) and to adjust idle speed when air conditioner compressor clutch is engaged. On some models, ECM may also activate radiator cooling fan when this signal is present. If this signal is not present on A/C-equipped vehicles, vehicle may idle rough when A/C compressor cycles. To check function of the A/C switch, perform functional check of switch. See SYSTEM & COMPONENT TESTING article.

A/C Pressure Sensor – Some models are equipped with an air conditioner pressure sensor which is used to inform ECM of A/C system pressure levels. Low pressure signal will cause ECM to disengage the A/C compressor to prevent system damage. High pressure levels cause ECM to energize high speed fans while A/C compressor clutch is engaged. Extremely high pressure levels will cause ECM to disengage A/C compressor clutch to prevent system damage.

A/C Pressure Switches – A/C high and low pressure switches may be used in the ECM-monitored A/C request circuit. Switches are normally closed, completing the circuit between ignition and ECM. ECM will engage or disengage A/C clutch relay based upon status of this circuit. When system freon pressure increases beyond a certain point, high side switch will open, causing A/C request line voltage to drop. If system freon level decreases, causing freon pressure to drop below normal, low side pressure switch will open, once again causing A/C request line voltage to drop. Switches may be used as normal clutch cycling devices or as safety devices which prevent compressor damage in the event of excessively high or low freon pressure.

A/C Temperature Sensors (Cadillac 4.9L) – Cadillac models (except Brougham) are equipped with air conditioner high side and low side temperature sensors which are used to inform ECM of A/C system temperature levels. Low temperature signal will cause A/C compressor to disengage. High temperature levels help ECM determine control of A/C compressor relative to cooling fans and idle speed.

Battery Voltage – Battery voltage is monitored by ECM (and BCM on Eldorado and Seville). If battery voltage swings low, a weak spark or improper fuel control may result. To compensate for low battery voltage, ECM may increase idle speed, advance ignition timing, increase ignition dwell or enrichen the air/fuel mixture. If voltage swings excessively high or low, ECM may set a charging system fault code and turn on SERVICE ENGINE SOON light.

Brake Switch Feedback – Models equipped with cruise control systems may monitor the brake switch circuit to determine when to engage and disengage cruise control. On vehicles equipped with a Torque Converter Clutch (TCC) or Viscous Converter Clutch (VCC), one circuit of brake switch is in series with the power supply for the TCC or VCC solenoid located in the transmission/transaxle.

Coolant Temperature Sensor (CTS) – The CTS is a thermistor (temperature sensitive resistor) located in an engine coolant passage. The ECM supplies and monitors a 5-volt signal to CTS. This monitored 5-volt signal is then reduced by resistance of the CTS. When coolant temperatures are low, CTS resistance is high, and a high monitored voltage signal is seen by the ECM. When coolant temperatures are high, CTS resistance is low, and a low monitored voltage is seen by the ECM. When fully warmed, CTS should reflect a temperature of at least 185°F (85°C).

Coolant temperature input is used in the control of fuel delivery, ignition timing, idle speed, cooling fan operation, emission control devices and converter clutch application. A CTS which is out of calibration will not set a trouble code, but will cause fuel delivery and driveability problems. A coolant sensor circuit problem (open or short to ground) will swing monitored voltage high or low and should set a related trouble code.

Camshaft Position Sensor (C³I System) – A Hall Effect camshaft position sensor is used on 3.8L C³I-equipped models, while 3.3L C³I-equipped models use a combination cam and crank Hall Effect sensor. The 4.9L engine uses a Hall Effect camshaft sensor located inside of the HEI distributor.

The cam sensor provides ECM with a TDC No. 1 signal used to compute the exact position of valves. This allows ECM to properly time ignition and fuel injection operation on PFI equipped models. A fault in the cam sensor circuit (no cam sensor signal) will result in a no-start condition (except 4.9L) and should set a related trouble code. For additional information, see COMPUTER CONTROLLED COIL IGNITION (C³I) SYSTEM and HEI-EST DISTRIBUTOR under IGNITION SYSTEM.

Crankshaft Position Sensor – Crankshaft position sensor, used on 3.3L and 3.8L engines, utilizes a Hall Effect switch mounted near vibration damper. The sensor monitors vibration damper position (crankshaft position) and sends signals to ignition module. These signals provide ECM with a TDC position reference for each piston, as well as supplying an engine speed (RPM) signal.

The 2.2L, 2.5L, 3.1L, and 3.4L Direct Ignition System (DIS) and 2.3L Integrated Direct Ignition (IDI) system crankshaft position sensor protrudes through side of engine block, to within .05" (1.3 mm) of an internally-mounted crankshaft reluctor ring. The reluctor ring is a special trigger wheel cast into the crankshaft. As crankshaft rotates, 7 notches in the reluctor ring change the magnetic field at the tip of the position sensor. This creates an induced AC voltage signal in the sensor windings, resulting in reference signals which are sent to ECM by ignition module. This allows ECM to compute crankshaft position and Vehicles equipped with HEI-EST distributor systems use the RPM reference signal from the ignition module in the distributor for a crankshaft position signal. Although there is no differentiation between TDC intake and TDC exhaust, this is not necessary on non-sequential fuel injected or carbureted engines. Signal is used on fuel injected vehicles to trigger fuel injector(s). For additional information, see COMPUTER CONTROLLED COIL IGNITION (C³I) SYSTEM and DIRECT IGNITION SYSTEM (DIS) & INTEGRATED DIRECT IGNITION SYSTEM (IDIS) under IGNITION SYSTEM.

Fuel Pump Feedback – On some models, the fuel pump circuit between the relay and fuel pump is monitored by ECM. This enables ECM to determine when the fuel pump relay is energized and voltage is being delivered to fuel pump. Voltage monitored on this circuit is also used in calculations to determine changes in idle speed, air/fuel ratio and ignition dwell. A failure in this monitored circuit will result in the setting of a related trouble code in ECM memory.

Gear Switches – Gear switches are located inside automatic transmission. Switches may be normally open or closed and change status depending upon internal hydraulic pressures. High gear switch information is used by ECM in controlling emission components and engagement of Torque Converter Clutch (TCC), or Viscous Converter Clutch (VCC) on Cadillac (except Brougham).

Ignition/Crank Signal – The ECM looks at the initial cranking (RPM) signal on circuit No. 430 to determine when the engine is being started. This information is used for starting enrichment. If this signal is intermittent or not available, hard starting or a no-start condition may result.

Knock Sensor – The knock sensor is a piezoelectric device which detects abnormal engine vibrations (spark knock) in the engine. This vibration results in the production of a very low AC signal which is sent from the knock sensor back to the ESC controller, or to the MEM-CAL portion of the ECM on models not equipped with a controller. The ECM will then retard ignition timing until the engine knock ceases.

For additional information on knock sensor operation, see ESC DETONATION RETARD OPERATION under IGNITION TIMING SYSTEMS.

A fault in the ESC circuit may set a related trouble code. When a related trouble code is not present and the ESC system is suspected as the cause of a driveability problem, perform functional check of ESC system. See SYSTEMS & COMPONENT TESTING article.

Manifold Absolute Pressure (MAP) Sensor (Except 3.3L & 3.8L) – The MAP sensor measures changes in manifold pressure. Changes in manifold pressure result from engine load and speed changes. The MAP sensor converts these changes in manifold pressure into a voltage output signal to ECM (about 1.5 volts at idle to about 4.5 volts at WOT). The ECM can monitor these signals and adjust air/fuel ratio and ignition timing under various operating conditions.

If MAP sensor fails, the ECM will substitute a fixed MAP value and will use the TPS to control fuel delivery. A fault in the MAP circuit should set a related trouble code. If a related trouble code is not present and MAP sensor is suspected of causing a driveability problem, perform functional check of MAP sensor. See SYSTEM & COMPONENT TESTING article.

Mass Airflow (MAF) Sensor (3.3L & 3.8L) – The MAF sensor measures flow of air entering the engine in grams per second. This measurement of airflow is a reflection of engine load (throttle opening and air volume), similar to the relationship of engine load to MAP or vacuum sensor signal. MAF signal should remain relatively constant at cruise, gradually changing with throttle angle and rapidly changing on sudden acceleration. The ECM uses this information to control fuel delivery.

This frequency generator type MAF sensor produces a frequency signal that cannot be easily measured in testing (32-150 Hertz). This varying signal is proportional to airflow. A fault in the MAF sensor circuit should set a related trouble code.

Manifold Air Temperature (MAT) Sensor – The MAT sensor (may also be referred to as an intake air temperature sensor) is a thermistor (temperature sensitive resistor) mounted in the intake manifold. Low intake air temperature produces high internal sensor resistance, while high temperature causes low internal sensor resistance. The ECM supplies and monitors a 5-volt signal to sensor through a resistor in ECM. By monitoring this voltage, ECM determines manifold air temperature. After a vehicle has sat overnight, MAT and CTS signals (resistance and temperature) should be close to same reading. Failure in MAT sensor circuit (open or short to ground) will cause monitored voltage to swing high or low and should set a related trouble code.

Oil Temperature (Engine) Sensor – Corvette is equipped with an oil temperature sensor. If sensor indicates oil temperature is high when it should be low, or low when it should be high, a trouble Code 52 (low) or 62 (high) will set in ECM memory; however, sensor will not cause driveability problems. Sensor information is sent from ECM to be used by Central Control Module (CCM) to determine oil life expectancy. If an oil temperature sensor code is set in memory, CCM has been calculating oil life from inaccurate ECM input. Oil and filter must be changed, code must be cleared and oil life monitor must be reset.

To reset oil life monitor, turn ignition on. Depress ENG MET button on trip monitor and release. Within 5 seconds, depress and release ENG MET button again. Within 5 seconds, depress and hold the RANGE button on trip monitor. The CHANGE OIL light should flash.

Hold the RANGE button depressed until the CHANGE OIL light stops flashing and goes out. When the light goes out, the engine oil life monitor is reset. This should take about 10 seconds. If the light does not reset, turn the ignition off and repeat the procedure.

Oxygen (O₂) Sensor – The O_2 sensor is mounted in the exhaust system where it monitors oxygen content of exhaust gases. Two oxygen sensors are used on some Cadillac models. The oxygen content causes the Zirconia/Platinum-tipped O_2 sensor to produce a voltage signal which is proportional to exhaust gas oxygen concentration (0-3%) compared to outside oxygen (20-21%). This voltage signal is low (about .1 volt) when a lean mixture is present and high (about 1.0 volt) when a rich mixture is present. As ECM compensates for a lean or rich condition, this voltage signal constantly fluctuates between high and low crossing a .45-volt reference voltage supplied by ECM on the O_2 signal line. This is referred to as "cross counts".

The O_2 sensor will not function properly (produce voltage) until its temperature reaches 600°F (316°C). At temperatures less than the normal operating range of the sensor, vehicle will function in "open loop" mode and ECM will not make air/fuel adjustments based upon O_2 sensor signals but will use TPS and MAP or MAF values to determine air/fuel ratio from a table built into memory. When ECM reads a voltage signal greater than .45 volt from the O_2 sensor, ECM will begin to alter commands to injector to produce either a leaner or richer mixture.

Once vehicle has entered "closed loop", a fault in the O_2 circuit (cooled-down sensor or open or shorted O_2 sensor circuit) is the only thing which can return it to "open loop". A problem in the O_2 sensor circuit should set a related trouble code.

CAUTION: DO NOT attempt to measure O_2 sensor output voltage with a conventional voltmeter. Current drain of voltmeter could damage sensor. Oxygen sensor voltage signal can be measured using a 10-megohm (minimum input impedance) digital voltmeter.

Park/Neutral Switch (P/N) – This switch is connected to transmission gear selector. The switch signals ECM when transmission is in Park or Neutral. Information from P/N switch is used by ECM for determining control of ignition timing, converter clutch and idle speed. To check function of P/N switch, perform functional check of switch. See SYSTEM & COMPONENT TESTING article.

Power Steering (P/S) Pressure Switch – This switch informs ECM of engine load conditions which exist when steering wheel is turned from center to full lock position. Information is used by ECM to help control idle speed and also A/C clutch on some models. To check function of P/S switch, perform functional check of switch. See SYSTEM & COMPONENT TESTING article.

RPM Reference Signal – The RPM is monitored by ECM through ignition module tach/pulse signals (circuit No. 430) produced by either the HEI module (tach reference line of 4-wire EST connector) or crankshaft position sensor signal (Hall Effect signal on C³I, PM generator signal on DIS and IDI). These signals are used by ECM for determining control of timing, fuel delivery, EGR function and idle speed.

Throttle Position Sensor (TPS) – The TPS is a variable mechanical resistor connected either directly to the throttle shaft linkage. The TPS has 3 wires connected to it. One is connected to a 5-volt reference voltage supply from ECM. The second is connected to ECM ground and the third is the signal return which is monitored by ECM. The voltage signal from the TPS varies from closed throttle (.5-1.0 volt) to wide open throttle (4.5-5 volts). This signal is used by ECM for determining control of fuel, idle speed, spark timing and converter clutch. A problem in the TPS circuit may set a related trouble code.

Throttle Switch (Cadillac 4.9L) – On Cadillac models using an Idle Speed Control (ISC) motor, an idle switch is incorporated into ISC motor. This switch informs ECM when throttle lever is contacting ISC plunger. This allows ECM to determine when to control idle speed. When throttle is open sufficiently to relieve pressure from the ISC plunger, switch will open and ECM will no longer attempt to control idle speed.

Vehicle Speed Sensor (VSS) – Depending upon vehicle application, VSS is either a Permanent Magnet (PM) generator mounted in transmission or a Light Emitting Diode (LED) mounted in instrument panel cluster, behind speedometer. The VSS sends a pulsing signal to ECM, which ECM converts into miles per hour (MPH). This sensor input is used by ECM in controlling converter clutch engagement.

OUTPUT SIGNALS

NOTE: Vehicles are equipped with different combinations of computer-controlled components. Not all components listed below are used on every vehicle. For theory and operation on each output component, refer to the system indicated after component.

A/C Clutch – See MISCELLANEOUS CONTROLS.
Air Injection Control Solenoid – See EMISSION SYSTEMS.
Canister Purge Solenoid – See EMISSION SYSTEMS.
Computer Controlled Coil Ignition (C³I) – See IGNITION SYSTEM.
Cooling Fan Relay – See MISCELLANEOUS CONTROLS.
Digital EGR Valve – See EMISSION SYSTEMS.
Direct Ignition System (DIS) – See IGNITION SYSTEM.
EGR Control Solenoid – See EMISSION SYSTEMS.
ESC Timing Retard – See IGNITION SYSTEM.
EST Timing Control – See IGNITION SYSTEM.
Fuel Injectors – See FUEL CONTROL.
Fuel Pump & Fuel Pump Relay – See FUEL DELIVERY.
HEI-EST Ignition – See IGNITION SYSTEM.
HOT Light or Coolant TEMP Light – See MISCELLANEOUS CONTROLS.
Idle Air Control (IAC) Valve – See IDLE SPEED.
Idle Speed Control (ISC) Motor (Fuel Injected 4.9L Cadillac) – See IDLE SPEED.
Integrated Direct Ignition System (IDIS) – See IGNITION SYSTEM.
Self-Diagnostics – See SELF-DIAGNOSTICS.
Serial Data – See SELF-DIAGNOSTICS.
SERVICE ENGINE SOON Light – See SELF-DIAGNOSTICS.
Shift Light – See MISCELLANEOUS CONTROLS.
Torque Converter Clutch – See MISCELLANEOUS CONTROLS.

FUEL SYSTEM

FUEL DELIVERY

Fuel Pump – An in-tank electric fuel pump delivers fuel to injector(s) through an in-line fuel filter. The pump is designed to supply fuel pressure in excess of vehicle requirements. The pressure relief valve in the fuel pump, controls maximum fuel pump pressure.

A pressure regulator mounted in fuel rail (port injection systems) or on throttle body unit (throttle body injection systems) keeps fuel available to injector(s) at a constant pressure. Excess fuel is returned to fuel tank through pressure regulator return line. For fuel pressure specifications, see SERVICE & ADJUSTMENT SPECIFICATIONS article.

When the ignition switch is turned to the ON position, ECM will turn on the electric fuel pump by energizing the fuel pump relay. The ECM will continue to energize relay if the engine is running or cranking (ECM is receiving reference pulses from the ignition module). If there are no reference pulses, ECM de-energizes fuel pump relay within 2 seconds after key is turned on. For additional information, see FUEL PUMP RELAY in this article.

Fuel Pressure Regulator (TBI) – On TBI systems, a constant fuel pressure is maintained by a factory preset, nonadjustable, spring loaded diaphragm contained within the throttle body. Spring tension maintains a constant fuel pressure to injector regardless of engine load.

Fuel Pressure Regulator (PFI) – Fuel pressure regulator is a diaphragm-operated relief valve with injector pressure on one side and manifold pressure (vacuum) on the other. Pressure regulator compensates for engine load by increasing fuel pressure when low manifold vacuum is experienced.

During periods of high manifold vacuum, regulator-to-fuel tank return orifice is fully open, keeping fuel pressure on the low side of its regulated range. As throttle valve opens, vacuum to regulator diaphragm decreases, allowing spring tension to gradually close off return passage. At wide open throttle when vacuum is at its lowest, return orifice is restricted, providing maximum fuel volume and maintaining constant fuel pressure to injectors.

Fuel Pump Relay – When the ignition switch is turned to the ON position, ECM will turn on the electric fuel pump by energizing the fuel pump relay. The ECM will keep the relay energized if the engine is running or cranking (ECM is receiving reference pulses from the ignition module). If there are no reference pulses, ECM turns pump off within 2 seconds after key on.

As a back-up system to fuel pump relay, fuel pump is also activated by the oil pressure switch. The oil pressure switch is normally open until oil pressure reaches approximately 4 psi (.28 kg/cm²). If fuel pump relay fails, the oil pressure switch closes when oil pressure is obtained, operating the fuel pump. An inoperative fuel pump relay may result in extended cranking times due to the time required to build up oil pressure. Oil pressure switch may be combined into a single unit with an oil pressure gauge sender or sensor.

For additional information on fuel pump activation, see BASIC DIAGNOSTIC PROCEDURES and SYSTEM & COMPONENT TESTING articles.

FUEL CONTROL

The ECM, using input signals, determines adjustments to the air/fuel mixture in order to provide the optimum ratio for proper combustion under all operating conditions. One of 2 types of fuel control systems are used: throttle body injection or port fuel injection. These systems can operate in the "open loop" or "closed loop" mode. Description of these modes is as follows:

Open Loop – When engine is cold and engine speed is greater than 400 RPM, ECM operates in "open loop" mode. In "open loop", ECM calculates air/fuel ratio based upon coolant temperature and Manifold Absolute Pressure (MAP) or Mass Airflow (MAF) sensor readings. Engine will remain in "open loop" operation until O_2 sensor reaches operating temperature, coolant temperature reaches preset temperature, and a specific period of time has elapsed after engine starts.

Closed Loop – When oxygen sensor has reached operating temperature, coolant temperature has reached a preset temperature and a specific period of time has passed since engine start-up, ECM operates in "closed loop". In "closed loop", ECM controls air/fuel ratio based upon O_2 sensor signals (in addition to other input parameters) to maintain as close to a 14.7:1 air/fuel mixture as possible. If oxygen sensor cools off (due to excessive idling) or a fault occurs in the oxygen sensor circuit, vehicle will once again enter "open loop" mode.

Battery Voltage Correction – ECM compensates for low battery voltage by increasing injector pulse width and increasing idle RPM. ECM is able to perform these commands because of a built-in memory/learning function.

Fuel Cut-Off – Injectors are de-energized when ignition is turned off so that dieseling is prevented. Injectors will not be energized if RPM reference pulses are not received by the ECM, even with ignition on. This prevents flooding before starting. Fuel cut-off will also occur at high engine RPM to prevent internal damage to engine. Some fuel injected models may also cut off fuel injector signals during periods of high speed, closed throttle deceleration (when fuel is not needed).

Throttle Body Injection (TBI) – Injector is located in throttle body unit. Dual injectors are used on 5.0L (VIN E) and 5.7L (VIN 7) engines. Battery voltage is supplied to the injector when the ignition is on. ECM energizes solenoid by providing a ground path through its internal circuitry. By regulating the injector ground circuit, ECM controls injector "on" time (pulse width) to provide proper amount of fuel to engine.

Pressure to injector is maintained at a constant level by the pressure regulator. Excess fuel passes through pressure regulator and is returned to fuel tank.

In the "run" mode, ECM uses tach (RPM) signal to determine when to pulse injector. Fuel injectors are pulsed once for each engine revolution, each spray providing 1/2 the fuel required for the combustion process. Thus, 2 injections of fuel (2 rotations of crankshaft) are mixed with incoming air to produce the fuel charge for each combustion cycle. On models equipped with dual injectors in the throttle body, injectors are pulsed alternately.

During starting, clear flood mode, deceleration and heavy acceleration, fuel delivery is controlled by internal ECM calibration.

- **Starting** – During engine starts, ECM delivers one injector pulse for each distributor reference pulse received (synchronized mode). Injector pulse width is based upon coolant temperature and throttle position. Air/fuel ratio is determined by ECM when throttle position is less than 80 percent open. Engine starting air/fuel ratio ranges from 1.5:1 at -33°F (-36°C) to 14.7:1 at 201°F (94°C). At lower coolant temperatures, injector pulse width is longer (richer air/fuel mixture ratio). When coolant temperature is high, injector pulse width becomes shorter (leaner air/fuel ratio).

- **Clear Flood** – If engine is flooded, driver must depress accelerator pedal to Wide Open Throttle (WOT) position. At this position, ECM adjusts injector pulse width equal to an air/fuel ratio of 20:1. This air/fuel ratio will be maintained as long as throttle remains in wide open position and engine speed is less than 600 RPM. If throttle position becomes less than 80 percent open and/or engine speed exceeds 600 RPM, ECM changes injector pulse width to that used during engine starting (based upon coolant temperature and manifold vacuum).

- **Heavy Acceleration** – Fuel enrichment during heavy acceleration is provided by ECM. Sudden opening of throttle valve causes rapid increase in MAP signal. Pulse width is directly related to MAP, throttle position and coolant temperature. Higher MAP and wider throttle angles give wider injector pulse width (richer mixture). During enrichment, injector pulses are non-synchronized (not in proportion to distributor reference signals). Any reduction in throttle angle cancels fuel enrichment.

- **Deceleration** – During normal deceleration, fuel output is reduced. This reduction in available fuel serves to remove residual fuel from intake manifold. During sudden deceleration, when MAP, throttle position and engine speed are reduced to preset levels, fuel flow is cut-off completely. This deceleration fuel cut-off overrides normal deceleration mode. During either deceleration mode, injector pulses are not in proportion to distributor reference signals.

Port Fuel Injection (PFI) – Individual, electrically pulsed injectors (one per cylinder) are located in intake manifold fuel rails. These injectors are next to intake valves in cylinder head.

Standard PFI systems feature simultaneous double-fire injection. Fuel injectors are pulsed once for each engine revolution, each spray providing 1/2 the fuel required for the combustion process. Thus, 2 injections of fuel (2 rotations of crankshaft) are mixed with incoming air to produce the fuel charge for each combustion cycle.

The 3.8L and 4.9L models use Sequential Fuel Injection (SFI). Injectors on these models are pulsed sequentially in spark plug firing order. Main differences between sequential and simultaneous systems are injectors, wiring and the ECM.

In all systems, constant fuel pressure is maintained to the injectors. Air/fuel mixture is regulated by the time that injector stays open (pulse width). Various sensors provide information to the ECM to control pulse width.

IDLE SPEED

Engine idle speed is controlled by the ECM depending upon engine operating conditions. The ECM senses engine operating conditions and determines the best idle speed.

Idle Air Control Valve (Fuel Injection – Except 4.9L Cadillac) – The Idle Air Control (IAC) valve controls engine idle speed during engine load changes to prevent stalling. The IAC valve is mounted on throttle body and controls the amount of air by-passed around the throttle plate. The IAC valve moves its pintle in and out in steps referred to as "counts" (0 counts-fully seated, 255 counts-fully retracted) to control engine idle speed. Counts can be measured using a "Scan" tester plugged into the Assembly Line Data Link (ALDL).

If engine RPM is too low, pintle is retracted and more air is by-passed around the throttle plate to increase engine RPM. If engine RPM is too high, pintle is extended and less air is by-passed around the throttle plate to decrease engine RPM. Normal counts on an idling engine should be 4-60. When engine is idling, ECM determines proper positioning of IAC valve based on battery voltage, coolant temperature, engine load and engine RPM.

If IAC valve is disconnected or connected with engine running, IAC loses its reference point and has to be reset. Resetting of IAC is accomplished on some models by turning ignition on and off. On other models, it may be necessary to drive vehicle (at normal operating temperature) over 35 MPH with circuit properly connected. Problems in IAC circuit should set a related code.

The IAC valve affects only the idle system. If valve is stuck fully open, excessive airflow into the manifold creates a high idle speed. Valve stuck closed allows insufficient airflow, resulting in low idle speed. For calibration purposes, several different design IAC valves are used. Ensure proper design valve is used during replacement.

Idle Speed Control (ISC) Motor (Fuel Injection – 4.9L Cadillac) – The ISC, mounted to the throttle body, is an electrically driven actuator which changes throttle angle according to ECM demands. An internal idle switch by-passes this function when throttle is opened enough to allow TPS to move from idle position. The ISC motor is factory calibrated and should not be disassembled. Replace as complete assembly only.

IGNITION SYSTEM

All vehicles are equipped with a high energy ignition system capable of producing in excess of 50,000 volts. Vehicles except those using a C³I (3.3L and 3.8L), IDI (2.3L) or DIS (2.2L, 2.5L, 3.4L and some 3.1L) system are equipped with a High Energy Ignition Electronic Spark Timing (HEI-EST) distributor.

HEI-EST DISTRIBUTOR

The Delco-Remy High Energy Ignition Electronic Spark Timing (HEI-EST) system consists of distributor housing, rotor, cap, 7 or 8-terminal ignition module, magnetic pick-up, pole piece, pick-up coil, connecting harness and the EST portion of the ECM. The distributor is connected to the EST system by means of a 4-wire connector, leading to Electro-

nic Control Module (ECM).

On some models, the ignition coil is contained within the distributor cap, while others have an externally mounted coil. A capacitor is installed in the distributor for radio noise suppression.

No vacuum or centrifugal advance mechanisms are used. All spark timing changes are controlled by the Electronic Control Module (ECM) based upon monitored input signals. Some models use an additional Electronic Spark Control (ESC) ignition retard system in the event of engine detonation (knock). Most models are equipped with sealed ignition coil and ignition module connectors.

When the external teeth on the timing core approach, align with, and pass the pick-up coil windings, an alternating current is produced in the pick-up coil windings. In the cranking mode, this alternating current signals switching transistors in the HEI module to make or break the ignition coil primary ground circuit. Once the engine has started, ECM takes control of primary ground circuit (EST mode).

When the primary ground circuit is removed, the magnetic field created by the flow of current in the primary windings collapses across the primary and secondary windings of the coil. This induces a high-voltage surge in the secondary windings of the coil. Secondary voltage is then discharged to the rotor, which distributes it to the appropriate spark plug terminal. The distributor module may have either a 7-terminal ignition module or an 8-terminal ignition module (sealed connector module), depending on application.

The 4.9L HEI-EST system is also equipped with a Hall Effect switch inside of the distributor. The Hall Effect switch produces a camshaft signal which is used by the ECM to determine the proper firing sequence for the injectors on the sequential fuel injection system. Loss of the camshaft signal will result in the fuel injection operating in a non-sequential mode and the setting of a related trouble code.

COMPUTER CONTROLLED COIL IGNITION (C³I)

The Computer Controlled Coil Ignition (C³I) system, used on 3.3L and 3.8L PFI engines, eliminates the need for a mechanical distributor. The C³I ignition system consists of a coil pack (3 coils), ignition module, camshaft and crankshaft (3.8L) or combination (3.3L) sensor, wiring harness, and the Electronic Spark Timing (EST) portion of the Electronic Control Module (ECM).

In the C³I system, each cylinder is paired with the cylinder that is opposite it in the firing order. Cylinders No. 1/4, 5/2, and 3/6 are paired. Spark occurs simultaneously in the cylinder coming up on the compression stroke and in the cylinder coming up on the exhaust stroke. The cylinder on the exhaust stroke requires less voltage for the spark plug to fire. This leaves the bulk of the available voltage to fire the spark plug for the cylinder on the compression stroke. The process is repeated when the cylinders reverse roles. Each cylinder pair is fired by its own ignition coil.

Input from the Hall Effect combination sensor (3.3L) or cam and crank sensors (3.8L) is used by the ignition module to determine when to trigger the appropriate coil pack. On 3.8L models, module passes on camshaft sync-pulse signal to the ECM so that sequential fuel injector timing can be initialized.

Type II Ignition Coil Pack (3.3L) – On type II ignition coil pack, 3 separate twin tower coils are independently mounted over the C³I ignition module. Each coil provides the spark for 2 simultaneously paired spark plugs. Each coil can be replaced separately.

Type III Ignition Coil Pack (3.8L) – On type III ignition coil pack, 3 twin tower coils are combined into a single coil pack. Coil pack is mounted directly over the C³I ignition module. Each coil provides the spark for 2 simultaneously paired spark plugs. All 3 coils must be replaced as a unit. Although old-style type I coil pack will physically fit on ignition module, the No. 1/4 coil pack is in a different location in relation to module connector.

Combination Sensor (3.3L) – The combination cam/crank sensor actually consists of 2 Hall Effect sensors mounted, in a single unit, near the harmonic balancer. Since the 3.3L engine uses a double-fire simultaneous injection system rather than a sequential fuel injection system, it does not require a distinctive (TDC No. 1 piston compression) camshaft signal. Instead, each engine revolution, camshaft portion of the combination sensor generates TDC signal for the No. 1/4 cylinder pair. Each engine revolution, the second sensor (crankshaft) generates RPM information and signals for the following cylinder pairs: 1/4, 2/5 and 3/6.

Camshaft Position Sensor (3.8L) – The 3.8L camshaft sensor is located on the timing cover, behind and below water pump. The ECM uses camshaft "sync-pulse" signals (passed to ECM by the ignition module) to determine the exact position of the No. 1 piston. Signal is used by ECM to properly initialize fuel injector firing. If camshaft sensor signal is lost, Code 41 (E041 on some models) will be set. The engine can be restarted and will run in sequential mode; however, without the camshaft signal, there is a 1 in 6 chance of injectors spraying correctly. This provides "walk home" protection against cam sensor failure.

Combination 3X & 18X Sensors (3.8L) – In addition to the camshaft sensor, the 3.8L engine contains sensors which are similar to the combination sensor used on the 3.3L engine; however, the interrupter rings on the back side of the balancer differ in configuration and purpose. The outside ring contains 18 evenly spaced interrupters, producing 18 pulses per crankshaft revolution. The inner ring has 3 interrupters spaced at irregular intervals (10 degrees, 20 degrees and 30 degrees apart).

The ignition module monitors signals generated by the 2 interrupter rings. The 18X ring will change state once during the 10 degree gap of the 3X ring, twice during the 20 degree gap, and 3 times during the 30 degree gap. The changing relationship between the 2 rings allows the ignition module to identify the correct ignition coil to fire within the first 120 degrees of crankshaft rotation. This system provides for a faster start and a more accurate measurement of the crankshaft sensor signals.

If the 3X signal to ignition module is lost while the engine is running, the fuel injection system will continue to run in sequential mode; however, loss of the 3X, or the 18X signal, will not allow the vehicle to restart.

Fuel Control Signal (3.8L) – In addition to the RPM reference (18X) signal and fuel sync (camshaft) signals generated by the ignition module on 3.8L models, a fuel control reference signal must also be passed on to the ECM in order to inform ECM that proper signals are being generated to the ignition module. The fuel control signal is generated by the C³I module from calculations involving signals from the 18X and the 3X pulse rings.

DIRECT IGNITION SYSTEM (DIS) & INTEGRATED DIRECT IGNITION SYSTEM (IDIS)

DIS is a distributorless system used on 2.2L, 2.5L, 3.4L and some 3.1L models. On the 2.3L, a similar system is referred to as the Integrated Direct Ignition System (IDIS). The operation of both DIS and IDI is quite similar to that of C³I system. Systems consist of 2 or 3 ignition coils (4-cylinder or V6), spark plug wires, ignition module (located under coil pack), a crankshaft position sensor, necessary wiring and the Electronic Spark Timing (EST) portion of the Electronic Control Module (ECM). On 2.3L models, coils, module and spark plug connectors are all combined into one unit which plugs directly onto spark plugs.

Rather than a crankshaft position sensor mounted at crankshaft pulley (such as C³I), spark is timed by a signal sent from a crankshaft sensor mounted through side of engine block. This signal is received by ECM (through ignition module), and is used to trigger each coil at the proper time. See CRANKSHAFT POSITION SENSOR under INPUT SIGNALS. As with the C³I system, each cylinder is fired consecutively with the cylinder opposite it in the firing order. On V6 engines, cylinders No. 1/4, 3/6 and 2/5 are paired. On 4-cylinder engines, cylinders No. 1/4 and 2/3 are paired. Each pair of cylinders is fired by its own ignition coil.

The crankshaft position sensor is mounted on the bottom of the DIS ignition module or near the ignition module. The sensor protrudes through the side of engine block to within .05" (1.3 mm) of an internally-mounted crankshaft reluctor ring. Sensor position is not adjustable.

The reluctor is a special piece of metal, cast with the crankshaft. It has 7 slots machined into it, 6 of which are equally spaced (60 degrees apart). A seventh slot is spaced about 10 degrees from one of the other slots and generates a synchronization pulse signal. As crankshaft

rotates, notches in the reluctor ring change the magnetic field at the tip of position sensor. This creates an induced AC voltage signal in the sensor windings, resulting in RPM reference signals which are sent to ECM by ignition module. This allows ECM to compute crankshaft position and RPM.

IGNITION TIMING SYSTEMS

Ignition Timing Advance – At engine speeds less than 400 RPM, the ignition module controls spark advance by triggering coil(s) at a predetermined interval based on engine speed only. At engine speeds greater than 400 RPM (EST mode), the ECM takes over control of the ignition timing. On 3.8L engines, when in EST mode, ECM also changes fuel injection timing to a sequential mode.

Ignition timing is controlled by the ECM based upon input signals from the engine RPM reference line (ignition module), coolant temperature sensor, manifold air temperature sensor, throttle position sensor, knock sensor, vehicle speed sensor, gear position switch, and the MAF or MAP sensor.

The PROM/MEM-CAL portion of the ECM has a programmed spark advance curve based on engine speed. Spark timing is calculated by ECM whenever an ignition pulse is present. Spark advance is controlled only when engine is running (not during cranking). Input signal values are used by ECM to modify PROM/MEM-CAL information, increasing or decreasing spark advance to achieve maximum performance with minimum emissions. To check ignition system operation, see BASIC DIAGNOSTIC PROCEDURES or SYSTEM & COMPONENT TESTING articles.

Although several types of ignition systems are used, all ignition systems use the same 4 basic ignition circuits. Models may use a conventional HEI/EST distributor system or one of 3 types of distributorless ignition systems. The C³I uses the same ignition module-to-ECM circuits that IDI, DIS and distributor type ignition systems use with the addition of fuel control and fuel sync (camshaft) signals on 3.8L engines. For description of fuel control and sync signals, see IGNITION SYSTEM.

The ignition module is connected to ECM by 4 EST circuits. Circuits perform the following functions:

- **Reference (RPM)** – Alternating current signals from the pick-up coil (HEI distributor), PM generator (DIS and IDI) or Hall Effect sensors (C³I and Cadillac 4.9L) are converted by the ignition module converter to digital signals for use by the ECM. This supplies RPM data and crankshaft position reference to the ECM. Since the signal on this circuit is used as an injector trigger reference on fuel injected vehicles, if circuit is open or grounded, engine will not run.

- **By-Pass** – When an engine speed signal of approximately 400 RPM is received by the ECM, ECM considers engine to be running and applies 5 volts to the ignition module on the by-pass wire. This causes ignition module to switch timing control over to the variable timing control circuit in the ECM. On some models, this by-pass wire contains a connector located between the 4-wire connector and the ECM. This is disconnected when adjusting base timing. On all models, an open or grounded by-pass circuit will set a related trouble code in ECM memory. The engine will run at base timing plus a small amount of advance built into the HEI module.

- **EST** – When 5 volts is present on the by-pass circuit and ignition module has turned control of engine timing over to ECM, the ECM advances or retards spark on this circuit based on calculations involving the reference signal and other sensor input signals. If base timing is incorrectly set, entire advance curve will be incorrect.

- **Ground** – This is the reference ground circuit. It is grounded at distributor and ECM, ensuring there is no voltage drop in the EST circuit which could affect ignition operation.

ESC Detonation Retard Operation – In conjunction with the HEI-EST system, an Electronic Spark Control (ESC) retard system is used on some models. System consists of the following: a detonation (knock) sensor, a high energy ignition system, an ESC controller (some models), and the ECM. On some models, the function of the ESC controller is built into the Memory Calibration (MEM-CAL) unit of the ECM.

When detonation (engine knock) occurs, detonation sensor produces a low voltage AC signal. This signal goes to the ESC controller or directly to the MEM-CAL unit inside the ECM, depending upon application.

On models using an ESC controller, controller supplies the ECM with a 12-volt signal. When detonation occurs, controller grounds the 12-volt signal to the ECM, pulling the signal down to near zero volts. The ECM interprets this as a need to retard timing. The ECM then retards spark timing until the ESC controller returns the 12-volt signal. If signal wire were to become open or grounded on models utilizing ESC controller, ECM would continuously provide full ignition timing retard.

On vehicles using ECMs containing MEM-CAL units, the ECM supplies a 5-volt DC reference signal on the knock sensor signal line. Internal circuitry of the knock sensor will pull this voltage down to about 2.5 volts. When knock occurs, the knock sensor produces an AC voltage signal which rides on the 2.5-volt DC signal back to the ECM. The voltage and frequency of this signal depend upon knock signals received by the sensor. The ECM will retard spark timing until signals from detonation sensor cease.

A malfunction in the ESC circuit should set a related trouble code. If a code is not present and ESC system is suspected as the cause of driveability problems, perform functional check of ESC system. See SYSTEM & COMPONENT TESTING article.

EMISSION SYSTEMS

NOTE: To determine emission systems usage, see EMISSION APPLICATIONS article at beginning of ENGINE PERFORMANCE.

AIR INJECTION SYSTEM

This system helps reduce hydrocarbon (HC) and carbon monoxide (CO) exhaust emissions by injecting air into the exhaust system. The induction of additional air promotes further oxidation (combustion) of unburned and partially burned exhaust gases. During cold engine operation air is injected into exhaust manifold. This quickly warms up catalytic converter and oxygen sensor. When vehicle warms up, air is diverted to atmosphere, or on models with a TWC/OC, to the catalytic converter. See CATALYTIC CONVERTER.

Air Pump (Except 3.4L "W" Body Man. Trans,) – The air pump is a belt driven, positive displacement vane-type pump. Air drawn into pump is purged of dirt and contaminates by a centrifugal filter mounted behind the pulley. The air pump is permanently lubricated and requires no periodic service.

Air Pump (3.4L "W" Body Man. Trans.) – Air pump is an electric-motor type located in the right front corner of the engine compartment. Pump is energized by an ECM-controlled relay which is activated when fuel system is functioning in open loop mode and/or less than 80 seconds has passed since relay was energized.

NOTE: Always cover centrifugal filter fan before cleaning engine to prevent liquid from entering air pump. DO NOT oil air pump.

Check Valve – The check valve prevents the backflow of exhaust gases into the air injection system. The check valve closes when exhaust gas pressure in exhaust manifold exceeds pressure delivered by pump. This occurs when air pump by-passes at high speeds, air delivery is switched to catalytic converter, air is diverted to atmosphere or air cleaner, or when air pump malfunctions.

Air Injection Reaction Management System – When ECM energizes the air control (divert) and air switching valves on a cold vehicle, air is allowed to flow through the control valve to the air switching valve. The air switching valve then directs this air to the exhaust port.

During warm engine operation (closed loop), ECM de-energizes the air switching valve. This causes air switching valve to direct air to the catalytic converter.

If air control (divert) valve detects a rapid increase in manifold vacuum (deceleration condition), or if high RPM operation causes pump output pressure to exceed normal operating range, air is mechanically diverted to the air cleaner by the air control (divert) valve. If ECM detects any failure in the computerized engine control system, air control (divert) valve will be de-energized, also causing air to be diverted to

the air cleaner or atmosphere. To check function of AIR system, perform functional check of system. See SYSTEM & COMPONENT TESTING article.

NOTE: Air control (divert) valve and air switching valve may be separate or combined into a single assembly.

Electric Air Divert/Electric Air Switching Valves – Electric divert and electric switching valves are used on Federal vehicles (except 3.1L and 3.4L with manual transaxle). System may combine both divert function and air switching function into one integral component.

The valves are electrically controlled by the ECM and operated by air pump pressure. The operation of the valves is not dependent on intake manifold vacuum.

For cold engine (open loop) operation, the divert solenoid is energized and air flows to exhaust ports. In warm engine (closed loop) operation, the divert solenoid is de-energized and switching solenoid is energized. This forces airflow to the converter. In the divert mode, both solenoids are de-energized and airflow is allowed to vent to atmosphere.

Divert will occur during rich operating condition, when the ECM recognizes a problem and turns on the SERVICE ENGINE SOON light, during deceleration (high vacuum) and during heavy acceleration when air pressure exceeds the setting of the relief valve in the air divert valve.

Electric Air Divert Valve (EADV) – The Electric Air Divert Valve (EADV) is used on California vehicles and 3.1L and 3.4L Cutlass Supreme, Grand Prix and Lumina with manual transaxle. Valve performs normal diverter valve operation and may provide air divert to the air cleaner for catalytic converter protection during wide open throttle and high temperature conditions.

The ECM de-energizes EADV solenoid (located in EADV), preventing manifold vacuum from entering the chamber during the above conditions. Spring tension against the lower diaphragm pushes the diaphragm up, diverting air to air cleaner. Air from the air pump is always shut off from the engine unless ECM grounds EADV circuit (solenoid energized).

Electric Air Pump Relay (3.4L Man. Trans.) – On 3.4L with manual transmission, an electric air pump relay is used. When vehicle is cold (open loop mode), ECM provides a ground for the EADV solenoid and relay. When relay is energized, power is supplied to the electric air pump. When fuel system goes into "closed loop", or electric air pump has been on for more than 80 seconds, the ECM opens the ground circuit. When solenoid is de-energized, air is diverted to the atmosphere until air pump stops swimming.

CATALYTIC CONVERTER

A 3-way catalytic (TWC) converter is used on all vehicles to reduce exhaust emissions. This type of converter reduces hydrocarbon (HC), carbon monoxide (CO) and oxides of nitrogen (NOx) levels.

TWC (Except Camaro, Corvette & Firebird) – Converter contains a reducing agent (Rhodium and Platinum) to reduce NOx and an oxidizing agent (Paladium and Platinum) to oxidize HC and CO. This causes HC and CO to oxidize (break down with the addition of oxygen and heat) into the harmless base elements water (H_2O) and carbon dioxide (CO_2). Oxygen is removed from NOx causing it to reduce to the harmless base elements nitrogen (N) and oxygen (O_2).

TWC/OC (Camaro, Corvette & Firebird) – In addition to the standard TWC features, this converter contains a second Oxidizing Catalyst (OC) bed which continues to oxidize carbon monoxide and hydrocarbons. An air tube from the air injection system injects additional air between the 2 beds. This allows the second converter bed to oxidize any remaining HC and CO to efficiently reduce exhaust emissions.

EXHAUST GAS RECIRCULATION (EGR)

The Exhaust Gas Recirculation (EGR) system is designed to reduce oxides of nitrogen (NOx) emissions by lowering combustion temperatures. This is accomplished when a metered amount of exhaust gas is recirculated into the intake manifold and mixed with the air/fuel mixture.

There are 3 types of EGR systems used: pulse width modulated backpressure (positive and negative) EGR using an EGR solenoid (V8), backpressure EGR (positive and negative) without EGR solenoid control (4-cylinder TBI), and digital EGR (2.3L, 3.1L & 3.4L).

On computer-controlled EGR systems using a solenoid, ECM controls ported vacuum to EGR valve through solenoid valve. Solenoid may be normally open or normally closed, depending upon application.

ECM uses coolant temperature, throttle position and manifold pressure signals to determine vacuum solenoid operation. During cold engine operation and idle, EGR is not desired; ECM causes solenoid to block vacuum to EGR valve. During warm engine operation and at speeds greater than idle, vacuum is allowed through solenoid, opening EGR valve. To check function of EGR system, perform functional check of system. See SYSTEM & COMPONENT TESTING article.

Pulse Width Modulated (PWM) EGR System – This type EGR system is controlled entirely by the ECM. ECM regulates EGR vacuum signal by controlling an electrical signal to a solenoid vacuum valve. The ECM controlled vacuum solenoid valve is located in series between vacuum source and EGR valve. The solenoid is pulsed at a rate of up to 32 times per second. The ECM uses a ported vacuum signal to determine the flow rate signal to the solenoid. PWM systems also use a backpressure EGR valve to prevent EGR function until engine loads are present. See EXHAUST BACKPRESSURE EGR SYSTEM.

Digital EGR System (2.3L) – The digital EGR valve is designed to accurately supply EGR to engine, independent of intake manifold vacuum. The valve controls EGR flow from exhaust to intake manifold through 2 internally-mounted solenoids. When each solenoid is energized, a pintle is lifted to allow exhaust gas to flow through valve. Solenoids are energized individually or together in different combinations to tailor EGR flow to specific engine requirements.

Digital EGR System (3.1L & 3.4L) – The digital EGR valve is designed to accurately supply EGR to engine, independent of intake manifold vacuum. The valve controls EGR flow from exhaust to intake manifold through 3 internally-mounted solenoids. When each solenoid is energized, a pintle is lifted to allow exhaust gas to flow through valve. Solenoids are energized individually, in pairs, or together to provide 7 different EGR flow ratios. This enables ECM to tailor EGR flow to specific engine requirements.

Exhaust Backpressure EGR System – Two types of backpressure EGR valves are used: positive and negative backpressure valves. These valves may be identified by the letter in the last position of part number. Letter "P" designates a positive backpressure valve; letter "N", a negative backpressure valve. Backpressure EGR may also use an ECM-controlled solenoid to regulate vacuum signal to EGR valve.

- **Positive Backpressure EGR Valve** – A control valve, located in EGR valve, acts as a vacuum regulator valve. Control valve regulates amount of vacuum to EGR diaphragm chamber by bleeding vacuum to atmosphere during certain operating conditions.

  When control valve receives a backpressure signal, through the hollow shaft of EGR valve, pressure on bottom of control valve closes control valve. When control valve closes, maximum vacuum signal is applied directly to EGR valve allowing exhaust gas recirculation.

- **Negative Backpressure EGR Valve** – Vacuum is applied to upper EGR diaphragm via a hose connected intake manifold vacuum. Manifold vacuum is also applied to lower EGR diaphragm (through intake port at base of EGR valve).

  When manifold vacuum in lower chamber is insufficient to overcome spring tension on lower diaphragm, bleed valve will be closed, allowing vacuum in upper chamber to open EGR valve. With engine at idle, or under light load, high manifold vacuum applied to lower chamber opens air bleed valve in lower diaphragm. This bleeds off vacuum in upper chamber, keeping the EGR valve closed.

EVAPORATIVE EMISSION CONTROL

Carbon canister storage is used for evaporative fuel control on all vehicles. The function of evaporative emission control system is to store gasoline fumes from fuel tank in a carbon canister until fumes can be drawn into engine for burning during combustion process.

There are 3 basic components used in evaporative emission system:
- Activated carbon canister (may be sealed or open at top or bottom for fresh air intake).
- ECM-controlled solenoid (mounted on canister or remotely).
- Tank pressure control valve (mounted internal or external of fuel tank).

For specific component application see EMISSION APPLICATIONS article at front of ENGINE PERFORMANCE. For vacuum hose routing, see VACUUM DIAGRAMS article.

Carbon Canister – Evaporative fumes from the fuel tank are vented through hose(s) into a canister containing activated carbon. The activated carbon absorbs and holds fuel vapors when the engine is not operating. When the engine is started and engine speed is greater than idle (purge at idle would cause too rich a mixture), engine vacuum draws fuel vapors from the canister into the engine. Regulation of vapors through this purge line may be controlled by a vacuum canister purge valve, an ECM-controlled solenoid, or both.

Carbon canisters are either open or closed in design. When the engine is started on open canister models, engine vacuum draws outside air into canister either through the top or through a filter in bottom of canister. This helps to purge vapors from the activated carbon.

Purge Solenoid Valve – Purge solenoid valve is controlled by the Electronic Control Module (ECM). Current is supplied to solenoid when the ignition is on. Solenoid is energized when ECM provides a ground circuit for solenoid. Solenoid may be normally closed or normally open. When solenoid valve is open, charcoal canister is purged using manifold or ported vacuum. When solenoid valve is closed, purge vacuum to canister is blocked.

The ECM will allow vacuum to pass through solenoid when engine has been running for more than one minute, coolant temperature is above 176°F (80°C), vehicle speed is greater than 5 MPH and throttle is off idle. This solenoid (if used) is located in the purge line between the charcoal canister and the vacuum purge port or on top of the canister.

Fuel Tank Pressure Control Valve – Fuel tank pressure control valve is a vacuum regulated/pressure control valve located in the fuel tank, or in the vapor delivery hose between fuel tank and carbon canister. When engine is not running and tank pressure is less than .9 psi (.06 kg/cm²), internal spring pressure holds valve in the closed position.

This causes fuel tank low-pressure vapors to be vented through a restriction in valve. This restriction will retain most of fuel tank vapors in fuel tank. When tank pressure rises and overrides spring tension, fumes are vented to the carbon canister. When engine is running, vacuum is applied to upper port of valve, opening passage between fuel tank and carbon canister, which is purged by engine vacuum.

NOTE: Models without fuel tank pressure control valves may utilize a special pressure/vacuum relief fuel tank filler cap or other external relief device.

POSITIVE CRANKCASE VENTILATION (PCV)

Except 2.3L – The PCV system is used to provide more effective elimination of crankcase vapors. Fresh air from the air filter housing is supplied to the crankcase where it is mixed with blow-by gases and passed through a PCV valve into the intake manifold. This mixture is then passed into the combustion chamber and burned.

The PCV valve provides primary control in this system by metering the flow of the blow-by vapors, according to manifold vacuum. When manifold vacuum is high (at idle) the PCV restricts the flow to maintain a smooth idle condition.

Under conditions where abnormal amounts of blow-by gases are produced (such as worn cylinders or rings), the system is designed to allow the excess gases to flow back through crankcase vent hose into the air inlet and be consumed during normal combustion.

2.3L – Unlike conventional crankcase ventilation systems, the 2.3L does not have a fresh air inlet to the crankcase. All blow-by gases are drawn from the crankcase through an oil/air separator. Flow is limited by a .060" (1.52 mm) orifice in the manifold intake nipple. Oil suspended in the blow-by gases is trapped in the separator and returned to the crankcase.

THERMOSTATIC AIR CLEANER (TAC)

Many models are equipped with a system for preheating the air entering the throttle body during cold engine operation.

This system maintains incoming air temperature to a point where the fuel injection system can maintain lean air/fuel ratios to reduce hydrocarbon (HC) and carbon monoxide (CO) emissions. There are 2 types of TAC systems used: vacuum controlled and wax pellet controlled.

Vacuum Motor Controlled (Brougham, Camaro & Firebird TBI) –This system consists of an air cleaner assembly with integral air control door, vacuum control temperature sensor, vacuum motor, heat shroud (on exhaust manifold), heated air tube and vacuum hoses.

- **Vacuum Control Temperature Sensor** – The vacuum control temperature sensor controls the operation of the air control door. During initial start-up situations, this valve directs engine vacuum to the air control vacuum motor. The motor closes the air intake door, allowing the intake of heated manifold air. When the intake air temperature reaches a precalibrated value, this valve opens, allowing the intake of cooler outside air.
- **Air Control Door** – The air control door temperature sensor closes when the temperature of air entering the air cleaner is less than the calibrated temperature of the temperature sensor. This allows engine vacuum to operate the air control door vacuum motor, and warm manifold air to be routed to the throttle body.
- **Vacuum Motor** – When engine vacuum is applied to the vacuum motor, the air control door closes off the intake of outside air. Air is then drawn into the air cleaner from around the exhaust manifold.

As air inside the air cleaner warms, the temperature sensor begins to open, bleeding off vacuum to the vacuum motor. As vacuum to vacuum motor decreases, the air control door begins to open.

As air control door opens, outside air is allowed to enter air cleaner assembly. When air entering air cleaner reaches a predetermined temperature, the air control door opens completely, and closes off the intake of heated air.

Wax Pellet Controlled (Caprice, Custom Cruiser & Roadmaster) – The air regulator damper (hot/cold air delivery door) is controlled by means of a self-contained, wax pellet actuated assembly mounted in the air cleaner. When incoming air is cold, wax material sealed in the actuator is in a solid contracted state. As incoming air warms, wax material expands by changing to a liquid state. This forces piston outward, repositioning air regulator damper and allowing cold and hot air to mix, or all cold air to enter engine.

SELF-DIAGNOSTICS

The ECM is equipped with a self-diagnostic system which detects system failures or abnormalities. When a malfunction occurs, ECM will illuminate the SERVICE ENGINE SOON light located on instrument panel. When malfunction is detected and light is turned on, a corresponding trouble code will be stored in ECM memory. Malfunctions are designated as either "hard failures" or as "intermittent failures". To retrieve stored codes, see appropriate SELF-DIAGNOSTICS article.

"Hard Failures" – Hard failures cause SERVICE ENGINE SOON light to glow and remain on until the malfunction is repaired. On models using digital display on dash to indicate codes, when recalled, codes may be accompanied by a "current" or "history" indication for intermittent and hard codes. If light comes on and remains on during vehicle operation, cause of malfunction must be determined using diagnostic charts located in SELF-DIAGNOSTICS article. If a sensor fails, ECM will use a substitute value in its calculations to continue engine operation. In this condition, vehicle is functional, but loss of good driveability will most likely be encountered.

"Intermittent Failures" – Intermittent failures cause SERVICE ENGINE SOON light to flicker or illuminate and go out about 10 seconds after the intermittent fault goes away. The corresponding

trouble code, however, will be retained in ECM memory. On models using digital display on dash to indicate codes, when recalled, codes may be accompanied by a "current" or "history" indication for intermittent and hard codes. If related fault does not reoccur within 50 engine restarts, related trouble code will be erased from ECM memory. Intermittent failures may be caused by sensor, connector or wiring related problems. See TROUBLE SHOOTING – NO CODES article.

SERVICE ENGINE SOON LIGHT

As a bulb and system check, SERVICE ENGINE SOON light will glow when ignition switch is turned to ON position and engine is not running. When engine is started, light should go out. If not, a malfunction has been detected in the computerized engine control system or SERVICE ENGINE SOON light circuit is faulty. Light may be used on some models to display stored trouble codes. To access codes using "Scan" or "Non-Scan" methods, see appropriate SELF-DIAGNOSTICS article.

SERIAL DATA

ECM is equipped with a serial data line. Serial data is a stream of electrical impulses which can be interpreted by special testers of other control modules. On some models, serial data must be accessed using special Scan testers connected to the Assembly Line Data Link (ALDL). Update intervals and information contained within the data stream vary with model application.

On models utilizing an ECM and Body Control Module (BCM), serial data may be accessed using the Driver Information Center (DIC) and Climate Control Panel (CCP). On these models, serial data may be shared with BCM, A/C controller, supplemental restraint controller, anti-lock brake controller, or even cruise control unit.

MISCELLANEOUS CONTROLS

NOTE: Although not considered true engine performance-related systems, some controlled devices may affect driveability if they malfunction.

A/C CLUTCH

On many models ECM regulates operation of the A/C clutch through an ECM controlled relay. This allows the ECM to disengage the A/C compressor when compressor load on engine may cause driveability problems (i.e. during hot restart, idle, low speed steering maneuvers, and wide open throttle operation), or if A/C freon pressure drops below or rises above normal operating levels.

Freon pressure sensing may be accomplished through the monitoring of high and low pressure switches or a pressure sensor which will register either high or low pressure levels. Power steering load is monitored through a power steering pressure switch. Hot restart is monitored through the coolant temperature sensor. For component application and related wiring, see wiring schematics in MISCELLANEOUS ECM CONTROLS in SYSTEM & COMPONENT TESTING article.

A/C Pressure Sensor – Some models are equipped with an air conditioner pressure sensor which is used to inform ECM of A/C system pressure levels. Low pressure signal will cause A/C compressor to disengage to prevent system damage. High pressure levels cause ECM to engage high speed fans while A/C compressor clutch is engaged. Extremely high pressure levels will cause ECM to disengage A/C compressor clutch to prevent system damage.

A/C Pressure Switches – A/C high and low pressure switches may be used in the ECM-monitored A/C request circuit. Switches are normally closed, completing the circuit between ignition and ECM. ECM will engage or disengage A/C clutch relay based upon status of this circuit. When system freon pressure increases beyond a certain point, high side switch will open, causing A/C request line voltage to drop.

If system freon level decreases, causing freon pressure to drop below normal, low side pressure switch will open, once again causing A/C request line voltage to drop. Switches may be used as normal clutch cycling devices or as safety devices which prevent compressor damage in the event of excessively high or low freon pressure.

COOLING FAN

On many models, ECM regulates operation of the electric cooling fan through an ECM controlled relay which controls the ground circuit or power circuit for the cooling fan. This allows the ECM to operate the cooling fan based upon engine temperature.

Most systems will engage the electric cooling fan whenever the A/C clutch is engaged, regardless of engine temperature. As a back-up system, many models utilize a coolant override switch which will also engage the cooling fan in the event that the ECM fails to energize the cooling fan relay, or the cooling fan relay malfunctions. A malfunction of the cooling fan will cause engine overheating and possible detonation.

Some models utilize more than one cooling fan. The second fan may function as an auxiliary cooling device when A/C is engaged, or (on models utilizing freon temperature sensors or high pressure switches) during periods of engine overheating or high A/C freon pressures.

For component application and related wiring, see wiring schematics under MISCELLANEOUS ECM CONTROLS in SYSTEM & COMPONENT TESTING article.

HOT LIGHT OR COOLANT TEMPERATURE LIGHT

When engine coolant temperature sensor input indicates temperature exceeds prespecified range, the ECM will turn on the TEMP or HOT light by providing a ground for the light circuit. As a bulb check, the ECM also supplies a ground to turn on light when the ignition is first turned on.

TRANSMISSION

Torque Converter Clutch (ECM Type) – The purpose of the transmission/transaxle converter clutch feature is to eliminate power loss of torque converter stage when vehicle is in a cruise condition. This allows convenience of automatic transmission/transaxle and fuel economy of a manual transmission.

Fused battery ignition is supplied to converter solenoid through a brake switch. On some models, 2nd, 3rd and 4th gear hydraulic apply switches (located within the transmission) may also be in series with solenoid power or ground circuit. On other models, switch status may only be monitored by the ECM, without sharing power or ground with the converter solenoid. For wiring reference, see wiring schematics under MISCELLANEOUS ECM CONTROLS in SYSTEM & COMPONENT TESTING article.

Converter clutch will engage when vehicle is moving greater than a precalibrated speed, engine is at normal operating temperature, throttle position sensor output is not changing (indicating a steady road speed), transmission 3rd gear or high gear switch is closed (if equipped), and brake switch is closed.

When vehicle speed is great enough (about 20-45 MPH as indicated by the vehicle speed sensor), ECM energizes converter clutch solenoid mounted in transmission. This allows torque converter to directly connect engine to the transmission. When operating conditions indicate that transmission should operate as normal, converter clutch solenoid is de-energized.

This allows transmission to return to normal automatic operation. Since power for the converter solenoid is delivered through the brake switch, transmission will also return to normal automatic operation when brake pedal is depressed. To check function of converter clutch system, perform functional check of system. See MISCELLANEOUS ECM CONTROLS in SYSTEM & COMPONENT TESTING article.

Torque Converter Clutch (PCM Type w/4T60E Transaxle) – The PCM type torque converter clutch functions similar to the ECM type except that instead of a single internal solenoid, the PCM type uses 2 solenoids. A standard TCC solenoid is used in conjunction with a Pulse Width Modulated (PWM) solenoid which regulates hydraulic pressure to make locking and unlocking of the TCC smoother.

Shift Light (Except Corvette) – The shift light is used on vehicles equipped with manual transmission. Light indicates the best transmission shift point for maximum fuel economy. Power for light is supplied through the GAUGES fuse. Light is illuminated when the ECM supplies a ground circuit for the bulb. For wiring reference, see MISCELLANEOUS ECM CONTROLS in SYSTEMS & COMPONENT TESTING article.

1-4 Shift Light (Corvette) – The shift light is used on vehicles equipped with manual transmission. Light indicates when driver should shift transmission from first gear to fourth gear for maximum fuel economy. Power for light is supplied through the 10-amp AIR BAG fuse. Light is illuminated when the ECM supplies a ground circuit for the bulb. For wiring reference, see MISCELLANEOUS ECM CONTROLS in SYSTEM & COMPONENT TESTING article.

1-4 Shift Light Relay (Corvette) – Power for the relay winding is supplied by the GAUGES fuse. When ECM determines that driver should shift transmission from first gear to fourth gear for maximum fuel economy, ECM will provide a ground for the 1-4 upshift relay. When relay is energized, voltage supplied by the TURN/BACK-UP fuse will pass through relay and energize the 1-4 upshift solenoid mounted in the transmission. When solenoid is energized, transmission is locked out from shifting from first gear into any gear other than fourth. For wiring reference, see MISCELLANEOUS ECM CONTROLS in SYSTEM & COMPONENT TESTING article.

Beretta, Bonneville, Brougham, Camaro, Caprice, Cavalier, Century, Corsica, Corvette, Custom Cruiser, Cutlass Calais, Cutlass Ciera, Cutlass Cruiser, Cutlass Supreme, DeVille, Eighty-Eight Eldorado, Firebird, Fleetwood, Grand Am, Grand Prix, LeSabre, Lumina, Ninety-Eight, Park Avenue, Reatta, Regal, Riviera, Roadmaster, Seville, Skylark, Sunbird, Toronado, Touring Sedan, Trofeo, 6000

INTRODUCTION

The following diagnostic steps will help prevent overlooking a simple problem. This is also where to begin diagnosis for a no-start condition.

The first step in diagnosing any driveability problem is verifying the customer's complaint with a test drive under the conditions during which the problem reportedly occurred.

Before entering self-diagnostics, perform a careful and complete visual inspection. Most engine control problems result from mechanical breakdowns, poor electrical connections or damaged/misrouted vacuum hoses. Before condemning the computerized system, perform each test listed in this article.

PRELIMINARY INSPECTION & ADJUSTMENTS

VISUAL INSPECTION

Visually inspect all electrical wiring, looking for chafed, stretched, cut or pinched wiring. Ensure electrical connectors fit tightly and are not corroded. Ensure vacuum hoses are properly routed and not pinched or cut. See VACUUM DIAGRAMS article to verify routing and connections (if necessary). Inspect air induction system for possible vacuum leaks.

MECHANICAL INSPECTION

Compression – Check engine mechanical condition with a compression gauge, vacuum gauge, or an engine analyzer. See engine analyzer manual for specific instructions. For compression specifications, see SERVICE & ADJUSTMENT SPECIFICATIONS article.

WARNING: DO NOT use ignition switch during compression tests on fuel injected vehicles. Use a remote starter to crank engine. Fuel injectors on many models are triggered by ignition switch during cranking mode, which can create a fire hazard or contaminate the engine's oiling system.

Exhaust System Backpressure – Before replacing any components, check exhaust system for restrictions. The exhaust system can be checked with a vacuum gauge or a low pressure (0-5 psi) pressure gauge.

If a vacuum gauge is used, connect vacuum gauge hose to intake manifold vacuum port and start engine. Observe vacuum gauge. Open throttle part way and hold steady. If vacuum gauge reading slowly drops after stabilizing, exhaust system should be checked for a restriction.

- **Check at AIR Pipe** – Remove rubber hose at exhaust manifold AIR pipe check valve and remove check valve. Install pressure gauge to hose and nipple via Propane Enrichment Device (J26911). Nipple should be inserted into exhaust manifold AIR pipe.
- **Check at O₂ Sensor** – Remove O_2 sensor. Install backpressure tester in place of O_2 sensor. After test is completed, coat O_2 sensor threads with anti-seize compound.
- **Diagnosis** – 1) Start engine and bring to operating temperature. Increase engine speed to 2000-2500 RPM and note gauge. Reading should not exceed 1.25 psi (.09 kg/cm²). Exhaust system is restricted if specification is exceeded.
  2) Check exhaust system for collapsed pipe, heat distress and possible internal muffler failure. If none of these conditions exist, check for restricted catalytic converter. Replace as required.

NOTE: Perform all voltage tests with a Digital Volt-Ohmmeter (DVOM) with a minimum 10-megohm input impedance, unless stated otherwise in test procedure.

IMPORTANT: The following table provides the location of commonly used diagnostic information. These former "A" and "C" charts are now written in text and inserted into the appropriate location in the new Engine Performance workflow. To familiarize yourself with the Engine Performance workflow, see HOW TO USE THE ENGINE PERFORMANCE SECTION in GENERAL INFORMATION.

GENERAL MOTORS A & C CHART REFERENCE TABLE

System or Component	Diagnostic Information Location
A-1 & A-2, SERVICE ENGINE SOON Light	See DIAGNOSTIC CIRCUIT CHECK in BASIC DIAGNOSTIC PROCEDURES
A-3, No Start	See NO START – ENGINE CRANKS OKAY in BASIC DIAGNOSTIC PROCEDURES
A-5, Fuel Pump Relay	See RELAYS, SOLENOIDS & MOTORS in SYSTEMS & COMPONENT TESTING
A-7, Fuel System Diagnosis	See BASIC FUEL SYSTEM CHECKS in BASIC DIAGNOSTIC PROCEDURES
C-1, MAP Sensor	See ENGINE SENSORS & SWITCHES in SYSTEMS & COMPONENT TESTING
C-1, Power Steering Pressure Switch	See ENGINE SENSORS & SWITCHES in SYSTEMS & COMPONENT TESTING
C-1, Park/Neutral Switch	See ENGINE SENSORS & SWITCHES in SYSTEMS & COMPONENT TESTING
C-2, Injector Balance Test	See FUEL CONTROL in SYSTEMS & COMPONENT TESTING
C-2, IAC Motor	See IDLE CONTROL SYSTEM in SYSTEMS & COMPONENT TESTING
C-2, ISC Motor	See IDLE CONTROL SYSTEM in SYSTEMS & COMPONENT TESTING
C-3, Canister Purge System	See EMISSION SYSTEMS & SUB-SYSTEMS in SYSTEMS & COMPONENT TESTING
C-4, EST Ignition Check	See BASIC IGNITION SYSTEM CHECKS in BASIC DIAGNOSTIC PROCEDURES
C-5, ESC Ignition Check	See IGNITION SYSTEM in SYSTEMS & COMPONENT TESTING
C-6, Air Injection System	See EMISSION SYSTEMS & SUB-SYSTEMS in SYSTEMS & COMPONENT TESTING
C-7, EGR System	See EMISSION SYSTEMS & SUB-SYSTEMS in SYSTEMS & COMPONENT TESTING
C-8, Torque Converter Clutch	[1] See MISCELLANEOUS ECM CONTROLS in SYSTEMS & COMPONENT TESTING
C-8, Manual Transmission Shift Lights	[1] See MISCELLANEOUS ECM CONTROLS in SYSTEMS & COMPONENT TESTING
C-10, A/C Clutch Control	[2] See MISCELLANEOUS ECM CONTROLS in SYSTEMS & COMPONENT TESTING
C-12, Electric Cooling Fan Control	[3] See MISCELLANEOUS ECM CONTROLS in SYSTEMS & COMPONENT TESTING

[1] – Covered in entirety in Mitchell's 1991-92 TRANSMISSION SERVICE & REPAIR manual for Domestic vehicles.
[2] – Covered in entirety in Mitchell's 1991 AIR CONDITIONING & HEATING SERVICE & REPAIR supplement for Domestic vehicles.
[3] – Covered in entirety in ENGINE COOLING in Mitchell's 1991 DOMESTIC CARS SERVICE & REPAIR manual and ENGINE, CLUTCH & DRIVE AXLE supplement, and in Mitchell's 1991 AIR CONDITIONING & HEATING SERVICE & REPAIR supplement for Domestic vehicles.

NO START DIAGNOSIS (A-3)

NOTE: Some vehicles are equipped with anti-theft systems (VATS or PASS-KEY) which will not allow vehicle to be started if improper starting techniques or improperly coded ignition keys are used. Both fuel injection and cranking systems will be disabled. Loss of fuel enable signal from anti-theft decoder module should set a trouble code in ECM memory.

Definition – No start is defined as engine cranks properly, but does not start. Engine may fire a few times.

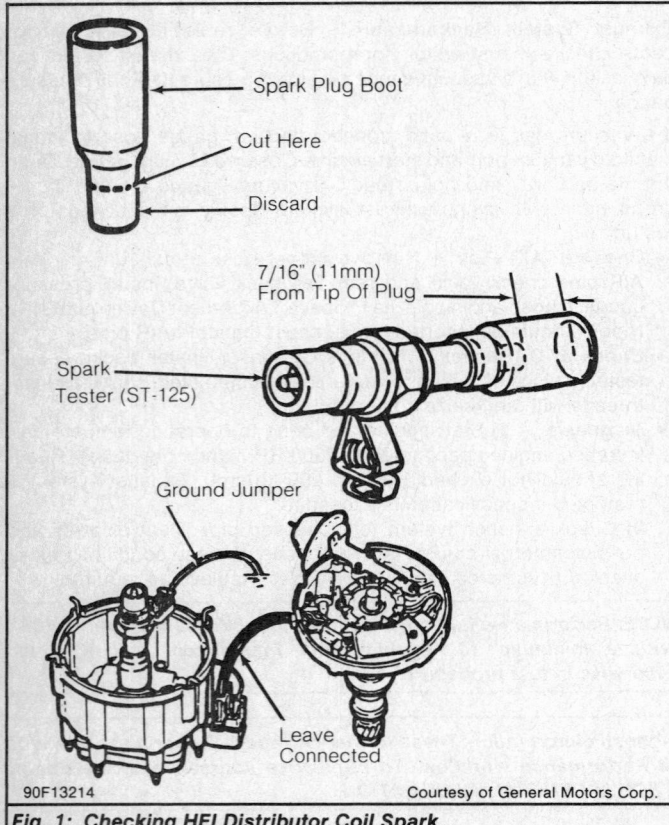

90F13214   Courtesy of General Motors Corp.

Fig. 1: Checking HEI Distributor Coil Spark

NO START – ENGINE CRANKS OKAY
(THROTTLE BODY INJECTION WITH HEI)

NOTE: Check battery condition, engine cranking speed and fuel supply before performing the following tests.

General Inspection – 1) Make sure proper starting procedure is being used.
2) Visually check vacuum hoses for splits, kinks and proper connections, as shown on underhood Vehicle Emission Control Information label. Check ignition wires for cracking, hardness and proper connections at both distributor cap and spark plugs.
3) Remove spark plugs. Check and replace as necessary.
4) Remove distributor cap and check for moisture, dust, cracks, burns and arcing to ground through coil mounting screws or rotor.
5) Try to turn distributor shaft by hand. Drive gear pin may be broken.
6) In very cold temperatures, ensure oil is proper viscosity and not contaminated with gasoline.
Ignition System – 1) Disconnect tachometer wire at distributor TACH terminal (if equipped). A shorted tachometer or tachometer circuit will not allow vehicle to start.
2) Check for battery voltage at BAT terminal at distributor with ignition on. Repair as necessary.
3) Connect ST-125 spark tester to end of one plug wire and crank engine. If spark occurs, check fuel delivery.

4) If spark does not occur, disconnect 4-wire EST connector at distributor. If spark now occurs, replace pick-up coil in distributor.
5) If spark does not occur, reconnect EST connector and check voltage at TACH terminal at distributor with ignition on.
6) If voltage is less than one volt, repair faulty coil connection or replace faulty coil. If voltage is 1-10 volts, replace ignition module and recheck for spark. If spark still does not occur, replace ignition coil.
7) If voltage reading at TACH terminal of distributor is greater than 10 volts, remove and invert distributor cap with wires connected. Fabricate an HEI coil spark tester by trimming a spark plug boot and connecting it to ST-125 spark tester. *See Fig. 1.* Crank engine.
8) If spark occurs, check cap for cracks, water or other defects. Check pick-up coil connector and ignition coil lead wire colors. Ignition coil with Yellow and Red wires should be used with a Yellow pick-up coil connector. Ignition coil with White and Red wires should be used with a Clear or Black pick-up coil connector.
9) If spark does not occur, turn ignition off and disconnect pick-up coil leads from module. Turn ignition on. With voltmeter connected to distributor TACH terminal and fabricated coil spark tester connected, momentarily touch test light, connected to a remote voltage source (1.5-8.0 volts), to ignition module terminal "P".
10) If voltage at TACH terminal does not drop, check ignition module ground and for open in wires from ignition coil to module. If all is okay, replace ignition module.
11) If voltage at TACH terminal does drop, check for spark at spark tester as test light is removed from terminal "P". If spark occurs, check pick-up coil connections and check for 500-1500 ohms resistance at pick-up coil leads. Repair as necessary.
12) If spark does not occur, test ignition module with module tester. If module tests okay, check ignition coil wire. If module tester is not available, replace ignition coil and again touch terminal "P." If spark occurs, system is okay. If spark does not occur, reinstall original ignition coil and replace ignition module.

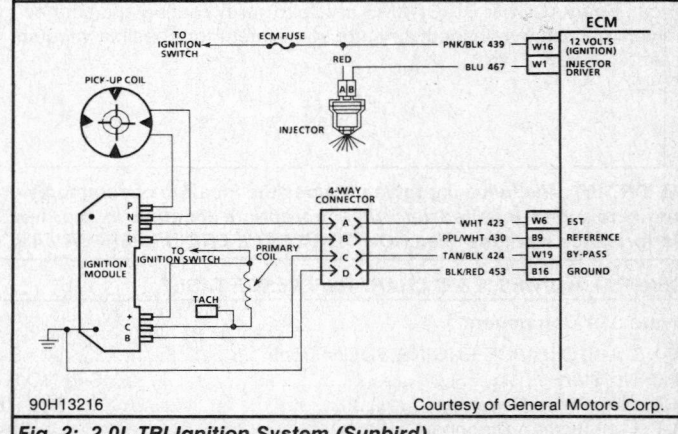

90H13216   Courtesy of General Motors Corp.

Fig. 2: 2.0L TBI Ignition System (Sunbird)

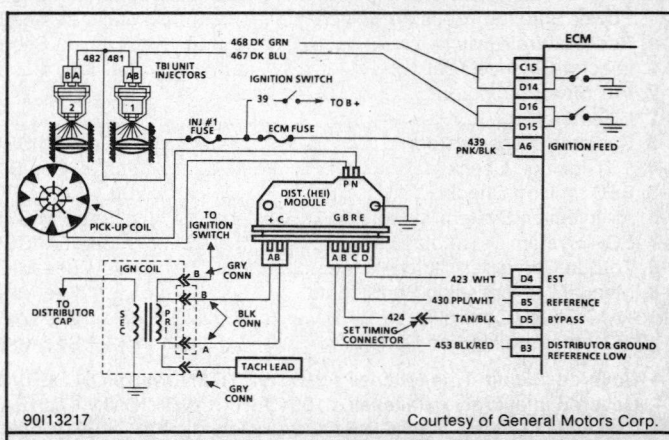

90I13217   Courtesy of General Motors Corp.

Fig. 3: 5.0L TBI Ignition System (Camaro & Firebird)

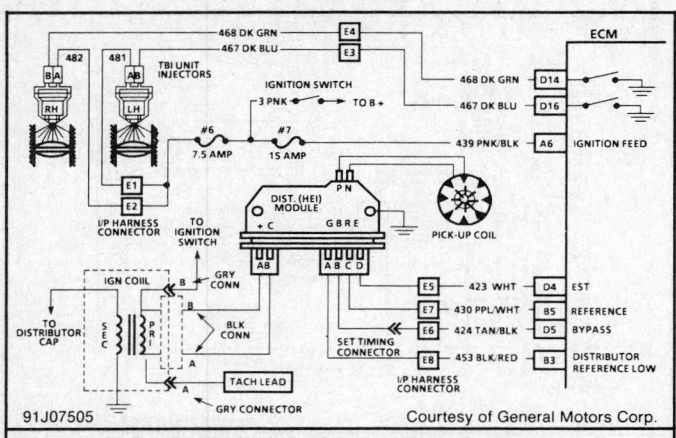

Fig. 4: 5.0L & 5.7L TBI Ignition System (Brougham)

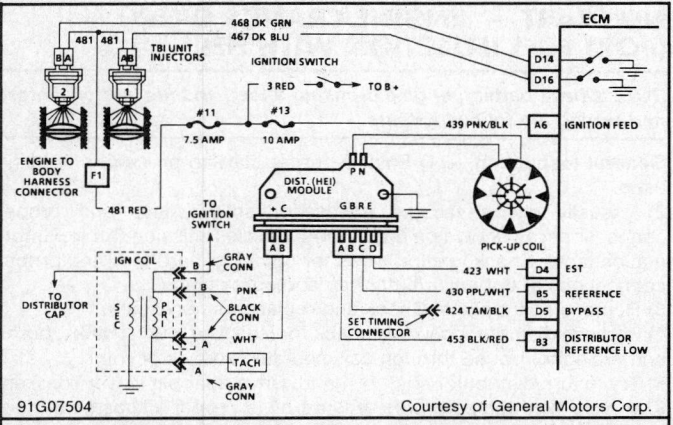

Fig. 5: 5.0L & 5.7L TBI Ignition System (Caprice, Custom Cruiser & Roadmaster)

Fuel System – 1) Prior to checking fuel system for a no-start condition, check ignition for adequate spark. Check for proper fuel pump pressure (9-13 psi or .6-.9 kg/cm²) and capacity (1 pt. or .47L in 30 seconds). See BASIC FUEL SYSTEM CHECKS.

2) Crank engine and watch for injector spray. If injector spray occurs, go to step 5). If no spray occurs, disconnect injector harness and check for battery voltage at harness. Battery voltage should be present on one of the injector terminals. If battery voltage is not present, check for blown injector power fuse. If battery voltage is present on both terminals, check for wires shorted to one another.

3) If battery voltage is present on only one terminal, connect injector test light to injector harness. Crank engine and note light. If light flashes, check for stored ECM codes. If no codes are present, refer to HARD START symptom in TROUBLE SHOOTING – NO CODES article. If light does not flash, momentarily touch test light from battery voltage to ECM RPM reference terminal (circuit No. 430).

4) Each time test light is removed from ECM RPM reference terminal, injector test light should flash. If test light does not flash, check for open in RPM reference wire, injector drive (ground) circuit, or replace faulty ECM.

5) If injector spray occurred while cranking engine, disconnect injector harness and crank engine. If injector spray or leakage occurs, this could cause a no-start condition due to excessive fuel being delivered during cranking. Repair faulty injector or injector seal. If no spray or leakage occurs, refer to HARD START symptom in TROUBLE SHOOTING – NO CODES article.

NO START – ENGINE CRANKS OKAY (THROTTLE BODY INJECTION WITH DIS)

NOTE: Check battery, engine cranking speed and fuel supply before performing the following tests.

General Inspection – 1) Ensure proper starting procedure is being used.

2) Visually check vacuum hoses for splits, kinks and proper connections, as shown on Vehicle Emission Control Information label. Check ignition wires for cracking, hardness and proper connections at both coil pack and spark plugs.

3) Remove spark plugs. Check and replace as necessary.

4) In very cold temperatures, ensure oil is proper viscosity and not contaminated with gasoline.

Ignition System – 1) Disconnect tachometer wire (if equipped). A shorted tachometer or tachometer circuit will not allow vehicle to start.

2) With ignition on, check for battery voltage at Pink or Pink/Black wire of 2-wire connector at ignition module. Check for continuity to ground on Black/White wire of 2-wire connector. Repair as necessary.

3) Connect ST-125 spark tester to end of one plug wire and crank engine. Leave matching plug wire connected to spark plug. If spark occurs, check spark on matching wire. If spark occurs on both wires, check fuel system. If spark occurs on only one wire, go to step 5).

4) If spark does not occur on both wires, remove crankshaft sensor and check resistance. On 2.5L engine, it is necessary to remove ignition module in order to remove sensor. Resistance should be 800-900 ohms at room temperature. Lay a flat piece of metal on tip of sensor to determine if sensor is still magnetized. Replace if necessary. If sensor is okay, check wiring harness to and from ignition module for opens or shorts. If harness is okay, replace ignition module.

5) If spark occurred on only one wire in step 3), note which wire had no spark. Turn ignition off and remove ignition coils. Check for carbon tracking or faulty connections between coil and ignition module. Repair or replace as necessary. If no problems are noticeable, switch coil positions on module and recheck for spark.

6) If same plug wire has no spark, replace ignition module. If spark now occurs on plug wire which previously had no spark and no spark occurs on a different plug wire, replace defective ignition coil.

Fuel System – 1) Prior to checking fuel system for a no-start condition, check ignition for adequate spark. Check for proper fuel pump pressure (9-13 psi) and capacity (one pint in 30 seconds). See BASIC FUEL SYSTEM CHECKS.

2) Crank engine and watch for injector spray. If injector spray occurs, go to step 5). If no spray occurs, disconnect injector harness and check for battery voltage at harness with ignition on. Battery voltage should be present on the Red or Pink/Black wire of the injector harness. If battery voltage is not present, check for blown injector power fuse. If battery voltage is present on both injector harness terminals, check for wires shorted to one another.

3) If battery voltage is present on only one terminal, connect injector test light to injector harness. Crank engine and note light. If light flashes, check for stored ECM codes. If no codes are present, refer to HARD START symptom in TROUBLE SHOOTING – NO CODES article. If light does not flash, momentarily touch test light connected to battery voltage to ECM RPM reference terminal (circuit No. 430). See Figs. 6-10.

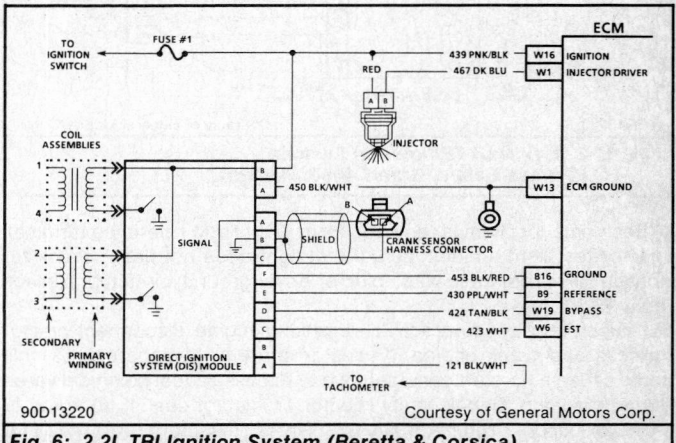

Fig. 6: 2.2L TBI Ignition System (Beretta & Corsica)

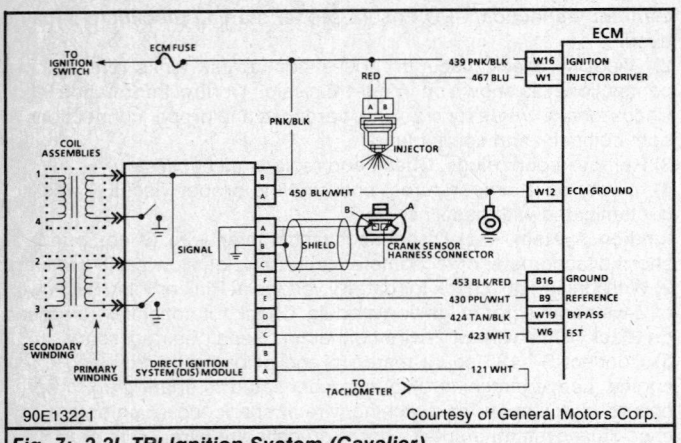

Fig. 7: 2.2L TBI Ignition System (Cavalier)

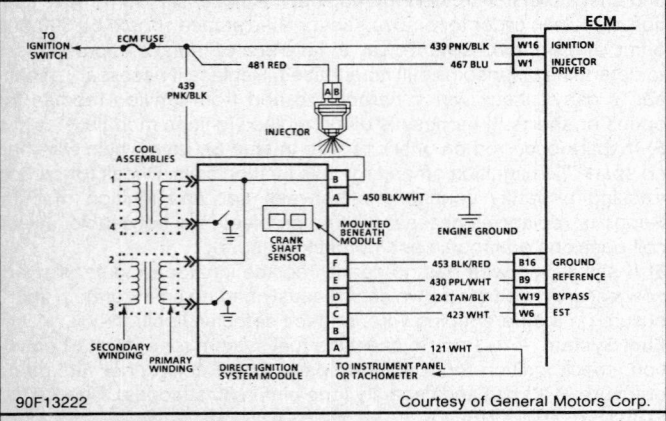

Fig. 8: 2.5L (VIN R) TBI Ignition System (Century & Cutlass Cruiser)

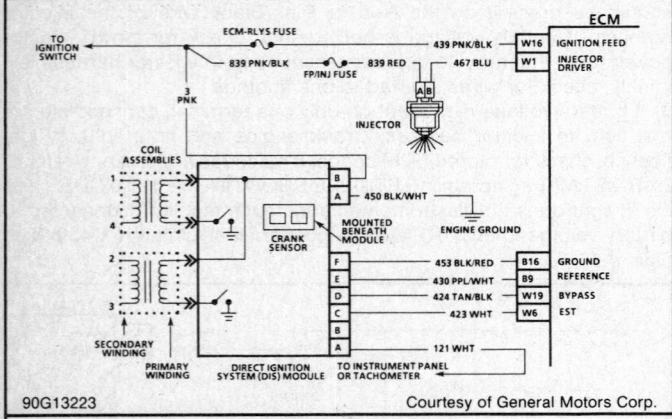

Fig. 9: 2.5L (VIN U) TBI Ignition System (Cutlass Calais, Grand Am & Skylark)

4) Each time test light is removed from ECM RPM reference terminal, injector test light should flash. If test light does not flash, check for open in RPM reference wire, injector drive (ground) circuit, or replace faulty ECM.

5) If injector spray occurred while cranking engine, disconnect injector harness and crank engine. If injector spray or leakage occurs, this could cause a no-start condition due to excessive fuel being delivered during cranking. Repair faulty injector or injector seal. If no spray or leakage occurs, refer to HARD START symptom in TROUBLE SHOOTING – NO CODES article.

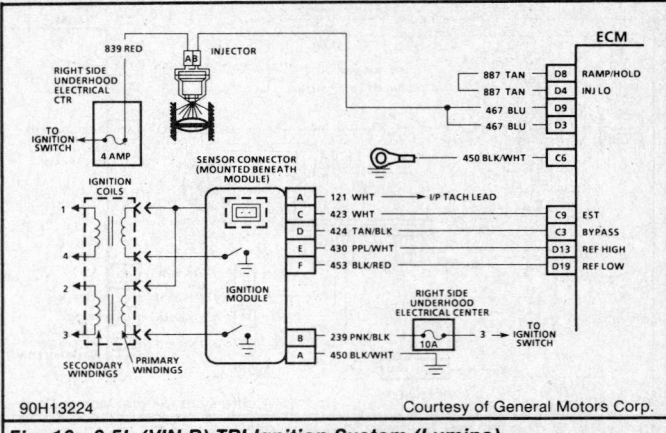

Fig. 10: 2.5L (VIN R) TBI Ignition System (Lumina)

NO START – ENGINE CRANKS OKAY (PORT FUEL INJECTION WITH HEI)

NOTE: Check battery, engine cranking speed and fuel supply before performing the following tests.

General Inspection – 1) Ensure proper starting procedure is being used.
2) Visually check vacuum hoses for splits, kinks and proper connections, as shown on underhood Vehicle Emission Control Information label. Check ignition wires for cracking, hardness and proper connections at both distributor cap and spark plugs.
3) Remove spark plugs. Check and replace as necessary.
4) Remove distributor cap and check for moisture, dust, cracks, burns and arcing to ground through coil mounting screws or rotor.
5) Try to turn distributor shaft by hand. Drive gear pin may be broken.
6) In very cold temperatures, ensure oil is proper viscosity and not contaminated with gasoline.

Ignition System (Remote Coil) – 1) Disconnect tachometer wire at coil (if equipped). If tachometer lead is not used, it may be taped against harness near coil. A shorted tachometer or tachometer circuit will not allow vehicle to start.
2) Disconnect 2-wire connector at distributor. Turn ignition on. Check voltage on "C" and "+" terminals of harness. If voltage to terminal "C" is less than 10 volts, check for open or ground in wire between terminal "C" at distributor and ignition coil. If wire is okay, fault is in ignition coil or ignition coil connector.
3) If voltage at both terminals is less than 10 volts, repair wire from module "+" terminal to ignition coil or repair primary circuit to ignition coil.
4) If voltage at both terminals is 10 volts or more, reconnect 2-wire connector at distributor. Check voltage at tachometer terminal at coil with ignition on. Tachometer connector may be taped back against harness. If voltage is greater than 10 volts, go to step **5)**. If voltage is less than one volt, repair open in tachometer lead and repeat voltage check. If voltage is 1-10 volts, replace ignition module and check for spark from coil wire. If spark occurs, system is okay. If spark does not occur, replace ignition coil also.
5) Connect a test light from tach terminal to ground. Crank engine. If test light illuminates and does not flash, go to step **6)**. If test light flashes, replace ignition coil and recheck for spark with tester. If spark is still not present, replace ignition module and retest.
6) If test light was on steady in last step, turn ignition off and remove 4-wire connector at distributor. Remove distributor cap and disconnect pick-up coil leads from ignition module. Turn ignition on. With voltmeter connected to tachometer terminal of distributor, momentarily touch test light connected to a remote voltage source (1.5-8.0 volts) to terminal "P" of ignition module.
7) If voltage at tachometer terminal does not drop, check ignition module ground. If all is okay, replace ignition module.
8) If voltage at tachometer terminal does drop, check for spark at spark tester connected to coil wire. If spark occurs as test light is

removed from terminal "P", check pick-up coil connections and check for 500-1500 ohms resistance at pick-up coil leads. Check if pole piece is still magnetized. Repair connections or replace pick-up coil as necessary.

9) If spark does not occur, test ignition module with module tester. If module tests okay, check ignition coil wire. If module tester is not available, replace ignition coil and again touch terminal "P". If spark occurs, system is okay. If spark does not occur, reinstall original ignition coil and replace ignition module.

Ignition System (Integral Coil) – 1) Disconnect tachometer wire at distributor (if equipped). A shorted tachometer or tachometer circuit will not allow vehicle to start.

2) Check for battery voltage at BAT terminal at distributor with ignition on. Repair as necessary.

3) Connect ST-125 spark tester to end of one plug wire and crank engine. Check for spark at several plug wires. If spark occurs, check fuel delivery system.

4) If spark does not occur, check voltage at distributor BAT terminal while cranking engine. If voltage is less than 7 volts, repair primary circuit to ignition switch. If voltage is 7 volts oe more, check voltage to distributor TACH terminal. If voltage is greater than 10 volts, go to step **6)**. If voltage is less than one volt, repair faulty ignition coil connection or replace defective ignition coil.

5) If voltage is 1-10 volts, replace ignition module and recheck for spark. If spark occurs, system is okay. If spark does not occur, replace ignition coil also.

6) If voltage reading at TACH terminal of distributor is greater than 10 volts, remove and invert distributor cap with wires connected. Fabricate an HEI coil spark tester by trimming a spark plug boot and connecting it to ST-125 spark tester. *See Fig. 1.* Crank engine.

7) If spark occurs, check cap for cracks, water or other defects. Check for rotor burn-through. Check pick-up coil connector and ignition coil lead wire colors. Ignition coil with Yellow and Red wires should be used with Yellow pick-up coil connector. Ignition coil with White and Red wires should be used with Clear or Black pick-up coil connector.

8) If spark does not occur, turn ignition off and disconnect pick-up coil leads from module. Turn ignition on. With voltmeter connected to TACH terminal of distributor and fabricated coil spark tester connected, momentarily touch test light, connected to battery voltage, to terminal "P" of ignition module. DO NOT touch test light to terminal "P" for more than 5 seconds.

9) If voltage at TACH terminal does not drop, check ignition module ground and for open in wires from ignition coil to module. If wiring is okay, replace ignition module.

10) If voltage at TACH terminal does drop, check for spark at spark tester as test light is removed from terminal "P". If spark occurs, check pick-up coil connections and check for 500-1500 ohms resistance at pick-up coil leads. Repair connections or replace pick-up coil as necessary.

11) If spark does not occur, test ignition module with module tester. If module tests okay, check ignition coil wire. If module tester is not available, replace ignition coil and again touch terminal "P". If spark occurs, system is okay. If spark does not occur, reinstall original ignition coil and replace ignition module.

Fuel System – 1) Prior to checking fuel system for a no-start condition, check ignition for proper spark. Check for proper fuel pump pressure (approximately 40-47 psi or 2.8-3.3 kg/cm²) and capacity (1 pt. or .47L in 30 seconds). See BASIC FUEL SYSTEM CHECKS.

2) Disconnect injector harness. Turn ignition on and check for battery voltage at each injector harness. *See Figs. 11-15.* Battery voltage should be present on one side of each injector. If battery voltage is not present, check for blown injector power fuse. If battery voltage is present on both injector terminals, check for wires shorted together.

3) If battery voltage is present on only one terminal, connect injector test light to injector harness. Crank engine and note light. Repeat on other injector connectors. If light flashes, check for stored ECM codes. If no codes are present, refer to HARD START symptom in TROUBLE SHOOTING – NO CODES article.

4) If light does not flash, disconnect distributor 4-wire (5-wire on Cadillac) connector. Momentarily touch test light from battery voltage to ECM RPM reference wire (circuit No. 430) of 4-wire connector. Each

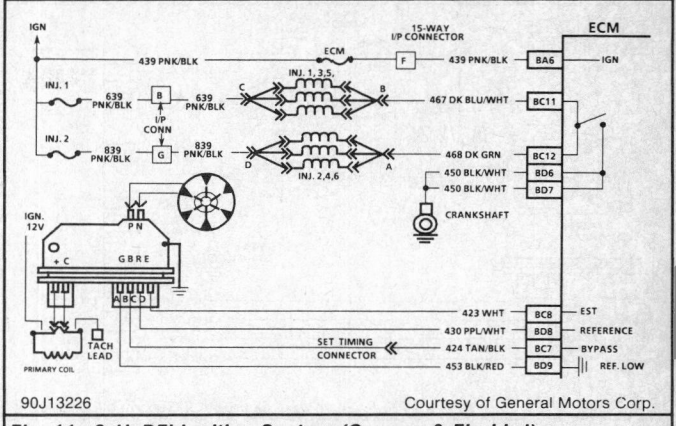
Fig. 11: 3.1L PFI Ignition System (Camaro & Firebird)

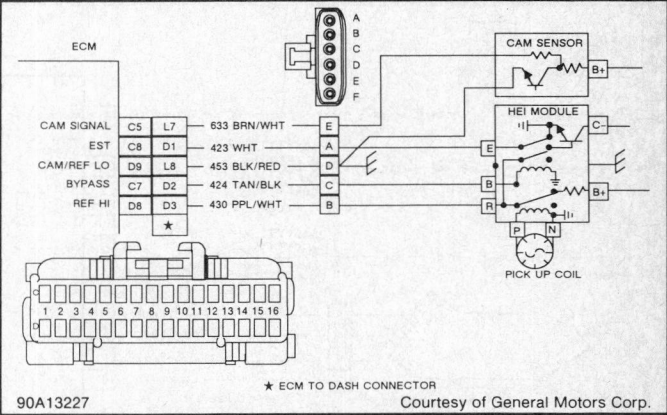
Fig. 12: 4.9L PFI Ignition System (Cadillac)

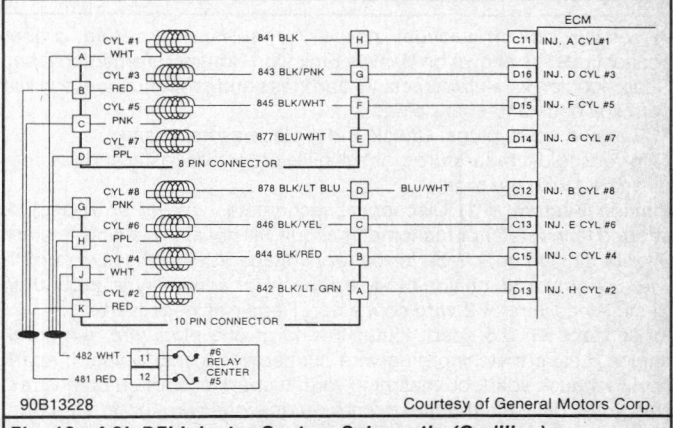
Fig. 13: 4.9L PFI Injector System Schematic (Cadillac)

time test light is removed from ECM RPM reference terminal, injector test light should flash. If test light does not flash, check for open in RPM reference wire, injector drive (ground) circuit or replace faulty ECM.

NO START – ENGINE CRANKS OKAY (PORT FUEL INJECTION WITH DIS)

NOTE: Check battery, engine cranking speed and fuel supply before performing the following tests.

General Inspection – 1) Ensure proper starting procedure is being used.

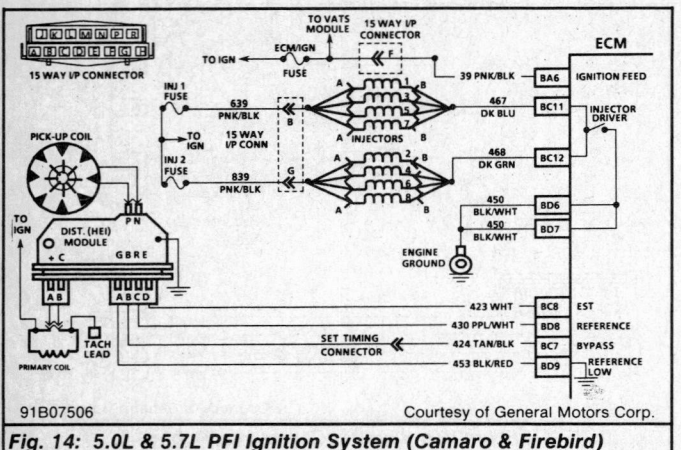

91B07506 Courtesy of General Motors Corp.

Fig. 14: 5.0L & 5.7L PFI Ignition System (Camaro & Firebird)

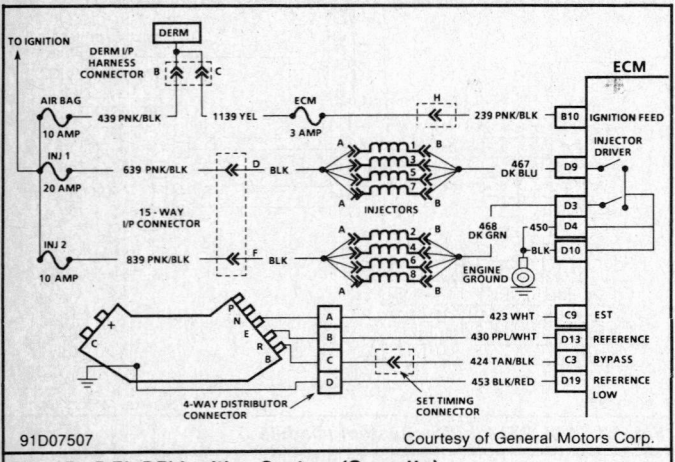

91D07507 Courtesy of General Motors Corp.

Fig. 15: 5.7L PFI Ignition System (Corvette)

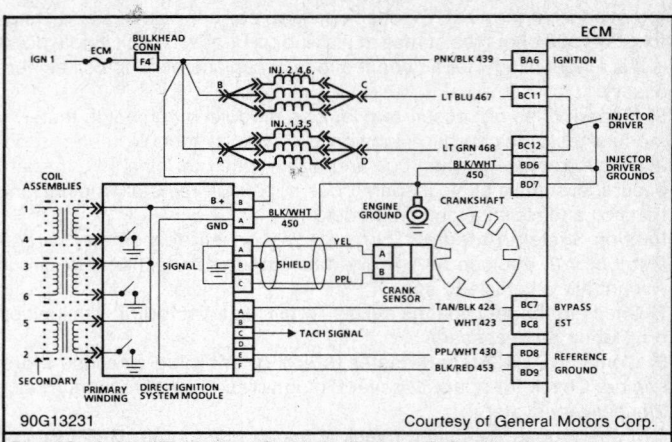

90G13231 Courtesy of General Motors Corp.

Fig. 16: 3.1L PFI Ignition System (Beretta & Corsica)

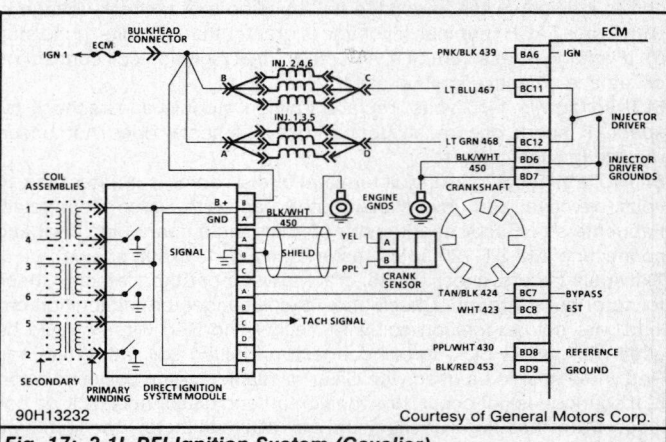

90H13232 Courtesy of General Motors Corp.

Fig. 17: 3.1L PFI Ignition System (Cavalier)

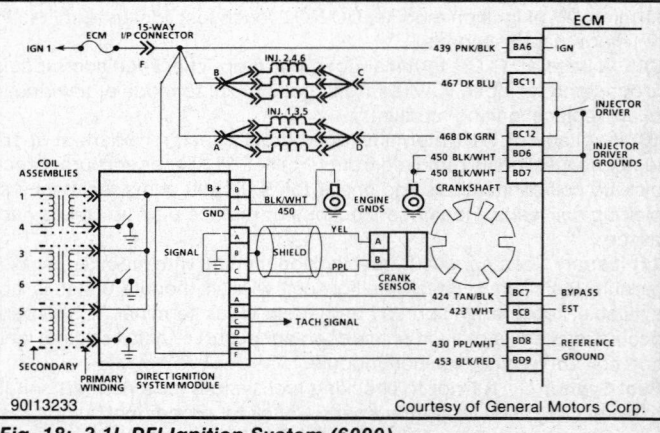

90I13233 Courtesy of General Motors Corp.

Fig. 18: 3.1L PFI Ignition System (6000)

2) Visually check vacuum hoses for splits, kinks and proper connections, as shown on Vehicle Emission Control Information label. Check ignition wires for cracking, hardness and proper connections at both coil pack and spark plugs.

3) Remove spark plugs. Check and replace as necessary.

4) In very cold temperatures, check oil is proper viscosity and not contaminated with gasoline.

Ignition System – 1) Disconnect tachometer wire (if equipped). A shorted tachometer or tachometer circuit will not allow vehicle to start.

2) With ignition on, check for battery voltage at Pink/Black wire of 2-wire connector at ignition module. Check for continuity to ground on Black/White wire of 2-wire connector. Repair as necessary.

3) Connect ST-125 spark tester to end of one plug wire and crank engine. Leave matching plug wire connected to spark plug. If spark occurs, check spark on matching wire. If spark occurs on both wires, check fuel delivery. If spark occurs on only one wire, go to step 5).

4) If spark does not occur on either wire, remove crankshaft sensor and check resistance. Resistance should be 900-1200 ohms at room temperature. Lay a flat piece of metal on tip of sensor to determine if sensor is still magnetized. Replace if necessary. If sensor is okay, check wiring harness to and from ignition module for opens or shorts. If harness is okay, replace ignition module.

5) If spark occurred on only one wire in step **3)**, note which wire had no spark. Turn ignition off and remove ignition coils. Check for evidence of carbon tracking or faulty connections between coil and ignition module. Repair or replace as necessary. If no problems are noticeable, switch coil positions on module and recheck for spark.

6) If same plug wire has no spark, replace ignition module. If spark now occurs on plug wire which previously had no spark and no spark occurs on a different plug wire, replace defective ignition coil.

Fuel System – 1) Prior to checking fuel system for a no-start condition, check ignition for adequate spark. Check for proper fuel pump

pressure (approximately 40-47 psi or 2.8-3.3 kg/cm²; 32-47 psi or 2.3-3.3 kg/cm² on 3.4L) and capacity (1 pt. or .47L in 30 seconds). See BASIC FUEL SYSTEM CHECKS.

2) Disconnect injector harness. Turn ignition on and check for battery voltage at each injector harness terminal. Battery voltage should be present on one injector harness terminal at each injector. If battery voltage is not present, check for blown injector power fuse. If battery voltage is present on both terminals, check for wires shorted to one another.

3) If battery voltage is present on only one terminal, connect injector test light to injector harness. Crank engine and note light. Repeat on other injector connectors. If light flashes, check for stored ECM codes. If no codes are present, refer to HARD START symptom in TROUBLE SHOOTING – NO CODES article.

4) If light does not flash, turn ignition off. Disconnect ignition module 6-wire connector. Turn ignition on. Momentarily touch test light from battery voltage to ECM RPM reference wire (circuit No. 430) of 6-wire connector. Each time test light is removed from ECM RPM reference terminal, injector test light should flash. If test light does not flash, check for open in RPM reference wire, injector drive (ground) circuit or replace faulty ECM.

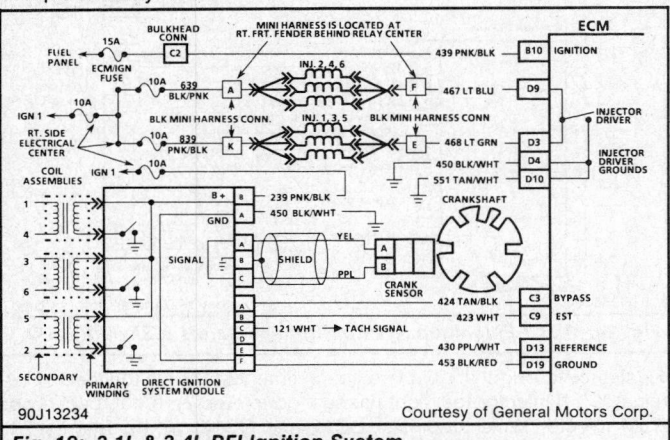

Fig. 19: 3.1L & 3.4L PFI Ignition System
(Cutlass Supreme, Grand Prix, Lumina & Regal)

NO START – ENGINE CRANKS OKAY (PORT FUEL INJECTION WITH IDI)

NOTE: Check battery, engine cranking speed and fuel supply before performing the following tests.

General Inspection – 1) Ensure proper starting procedure is being used. Visually check vacuum hoses for splits, kinks and proper connections, as shown on Vehicle Emission Control Information label. Check ignition wires for cracking, hardness and proper connections at both coil pack and spark plugs.

2) Remove spark plugs. Check and replace as necessary. In very cold temperatures, ensure oil is proper viscosity and not contaminated with gasoline.

Ignition System – 1) Disconnect tachometer wire from IDI module (if equipped). A shorted tachometer or tachometer circuit will not allow vehicle to start. Temporarily remove IDI assembly and install spark plug Jumper Wires (J-36012). Check for adequate spark with Spark Tester (ST-125). Check for spark on 2 adjacent plug wires (1-2 or 3-4, not 2-3). Leave matching plug wire connected while checking for spark. If spark jumps tester on both plug wires, check fuel system. If spark did not jump tester on either plug wire, go to step **4)**.

2) If spark jumped tester on only one plug wire, disconnect plug jumper wires and remove coil housing. Disconnect coil harness connector

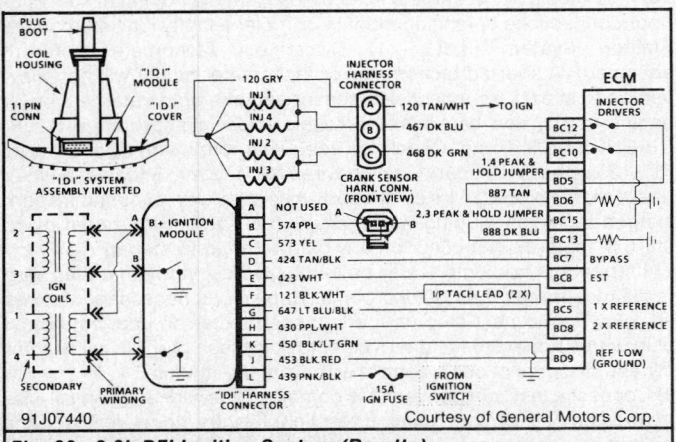

Fig. 20: 2.3L PFI Ignition System (Beretta)

at module. Install test light between module terminal "A" and control terminal for coil which did not spark. *See Figs. 20-22.*

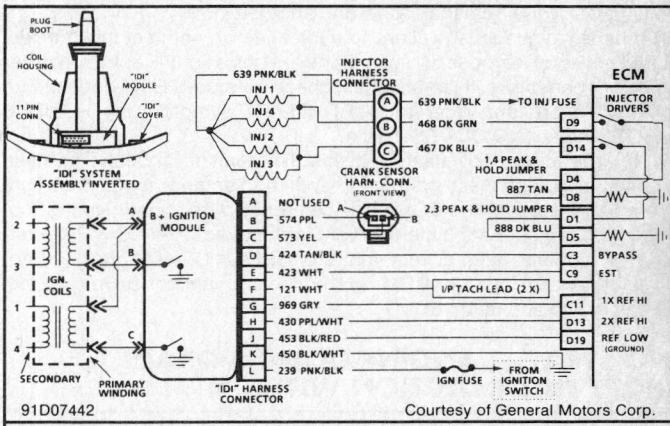

Fig. 21: 2.3L PFI Ignition System (Cutlass Supreme & Grand Prix)

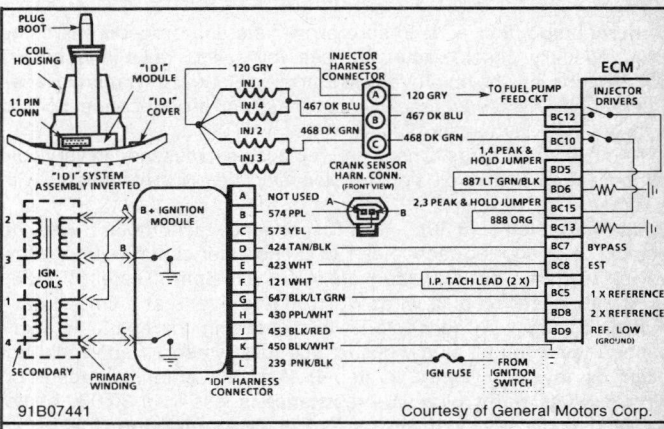

Fig. 22: 2.3L PFI Ignition System (Cutlass Calais, Grand Am & Skylark)

3) Crank engine and note test light. If test light blinks at both test terminals, repair faulty harness, poor connection or replace faulty coil. If test light did not blink on both terminals, repair module connections or replace faulty module.

4) If spark did not occur on either plug wire in step **1)**, turn ignition off. Disconnect 11-pin connector at module. Turn ignition on and connect test light between terminals "K" and "L" at harness. If test light is not on, repair open or short in module ground or power supply.

5) If test light is on in step **4)**, install injector test light in any injector. Connect a test light to battery voltage and repeatedly touch to IDI module terminal "H". Injector test light should flash. If test light flashes, go to step **6)**. If not, check injector drive circuits for open or short to voltage. If ground circuits are okay, check injector power supply. If power supply is okay, repair poor connections at ECM or replace faulty ECM.

6) Connect DVOM between terminals "B" and "C" of IDI module harness connector. Place DVOM on 2-volt AC scale. Crank engine and note voltage. Voltmeter should read greater than 20mV. If voltage is correct, replace IDI module. If voltage is not correct, remove crankshaft sensor from block. Measure sensor resistance. Resistance should be 500-900 ohms. Place a flat piece of metal on tip of sensor to verify sensor is still magnetized. Inspect sensor harness. Repair or replace as necessary.

Fuel System – 1) Prior to checking fuel system for a no-start condition, check injectors for proper spark. Check for proper fuel pump pressure (40-47 psi or 2.8-3.3 kg/cm²) and capacity (1 pt. or .47L in 30 seconds). See BASIC FUEL SYSTEM CHECKS.

2) Disconnect injector harness. Turn ignition on and check for battery voltage at each injector harness. Battery voltage should be present on one of the injector terminals. If battery voltage is not present, check for blown injector power fuse. If battery voltage is present on both terminals, check for wires shorted to one another.

3) If battery voltage is present to each injector, connect injector test light to injector harness. Crank engine and note light. Repeat on other injector connectors. If light flashes, check for stored ECM codes. If no codes are present, refer to HARD START symptom in TROUBLE SHOOTING – NO CODES article.

4) If light does not flash, access IDI ignition module harness connector. Disconnect connector and momentarily touch test light from battery voltage to ECM RPM reference wire (circuit No. 430) of module harness. Each time test light is removed from ECM RPM reference terminal, injector test light should flash. If test light does not flash, check for open in RPM reference wire, injector drive (ground) circuit or replace faulty ECM.

NO START – ENGINE CRANKS OKAY (PORT FUEL INJECTION WITH C³I)

NOTE: Before performing following tests, check battery condition, engine cranking speed, and for adequate fuel in the tank.

General Inspection – 1) Ensure proper starting procedure is being used. Visually check vacuum hoses for splits, kinks and proper connections, as shown on Vehicle Emission Control Information label. Check ignition wires for cracking, hardness and proper connections at both coil pack and spark plugs.

2) Remove spark plugs. Check and replace as necessary. In very cold temperatures, ensure oil is proper viscosity and not contaminated with gasoline.

Ignition System (3.3L) – 1) Disconnect tachometer wire (if equipped). A shorted tachometer or tachometer circuit will not allow vehicle to start. Check for adequate spark with Spark Tester (ST-125). Check for spark on plug wires No. 1, 3 and 5 (one at a time). Leave matching plug wire connected while checking for spark. If spark jumped tester on all plug wires, check fuel system. If spark did not occur on any plug wire, go to step **4)**. If spark did not jump tester on all plug wires, verify plug wire resistance is less than 30,000 ohms. Replace as necessary. If wires are okay, go to next step.

2) If spark jumped tester on one, but not all plug wires, remove 2 fasteners holding effected coil assembly. Remove coil from module. Connect a test light to 2 exposed terminals on the module. Crank engine. If test light flashes, check for poor coil to module connections. If connections are okay, replace faulty coil.

3) If test light does not flash, replace ignition module. Also, check primary coil resistance (.5-.9 ohm). Replace coil if necessary.

4) Turn ignition off. Disconnect ignition module connector. Turn ignition on. Check for battery voltage on terminal "M" of ignition module harness. *See Figs. 23 and 24.* Repair open or short, or replace ignition fuse as necessary. If battery voltage is present, turn ignition off and disconnect fuel pump relay. Install injector test light in injector har-

ness connector. Connect test light to battery voltage and repeatedly touch to terminal "C" of the ignition module harness connector.

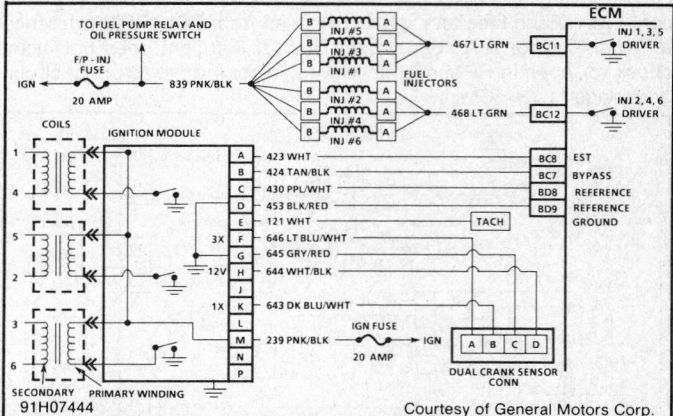

91H07444   Courtesy of General Motors Corp.

Fig. 24: 3.3L PFI Ignition System (Cutlass Calais & Skylark)

5) Injector test light should flash each time test light is touched to terminal "C". If injector test light flashes, go to step **7)**. If not, backprobe ECM injector drive terminals (BC11 and BC12) with a test light to ground. If light is off, check for loss of power to fuel injector harness or open between injectors and drive terminals. If test light is on, disconnect ALL injectors. With test light connected to ground, check for voltage on both terminals of each injector harness.

6) If voltage is present on both wires of any or all injectors, check for short to voltage on injector drive circuit. If battery voltage is present on only one wire of each injector harness, check for open or shorted circuit No. 430 (RPM reference high), poor connections at ECM terminals BC11 and BC12 or a faulty ECM.

7) Turn ignition off and reconnect ignition module connector. Disconnect dual crank (combination) sensor. Turn ignition on. Using a DVOM, measure voltage between sensor harness terminals "C" and "D." If 10-12 volts are not present, check for poor connections at ignition module, open or short in combination sensor harness or replace faulty ignition module.

8) If 10-12 volts are present at combination sensor connector, turn ignition off. Disconnect No. 6 spark plug wire from coil tower. NEVER crank engine with a spark plug wire off coil. Damage to coil or ignition module may occur. Attach Spark Tester (ST-125) to coil tower. Install injector test light in any injector harness.

9) Turn ignition on. Jumper dual crank sensor connector terminal "A" to terminal "B". Using a test light connected to ground, momentarily touch terminal "A". If injector test light flashes and spark tester sparks, check for poor connections at dual crank sensor. If connections are okay, replace faulty dual crank sensor. Inspect dual crank sensor and pulley for signs of rubbing.

10) If spark did not occur and injector test light did not flash, check for poor connections at ignition module or replace faulty ignition module.

Ignition System (3.8L) – 1) Disconnect tachometer wire (if equipped). A shorted tachometer or tachometer circuit will not allow vehicle to start. Disconnect cam sensor and attempt to start engine. If engine starts, see cam sensor trouble code in appropriate SELF-DIAGNOSTICS article. Check for adequate spark with Spark Tester (ST-125). Check for spark on plug wires No. 1, 3 and 5 (one at a time). Leave matching plug wire connected while checking for spark. If spark jumped tester on all plug wires, check fuel system for cause of no start. If spark did not occur on any plug wire, go to step **4)**.

2) If spark did not jump tester on all plug wires, verify that plug wire resistance is less than 30,000 ohms. Replace as necessary. If wires are okay, go to next step. If spark jumped tester on one, but not all plug wires, remove 6 fasteners holding coil assembly. Tilt coil assembly and disconnect coil's control wire from the module.

3) Connect a test light between the common Blue wire and control wire of affected coil. Crank engine. If test light flashes, check for poor coil to module connections. If connections are okay, replace faulty coil. If test light does not flash, replace ignition module. Also, check primary coil resistance (.5-.9 ohm). Replace coil if necessary.

91F07443   Courtesy of General Motors Corp.

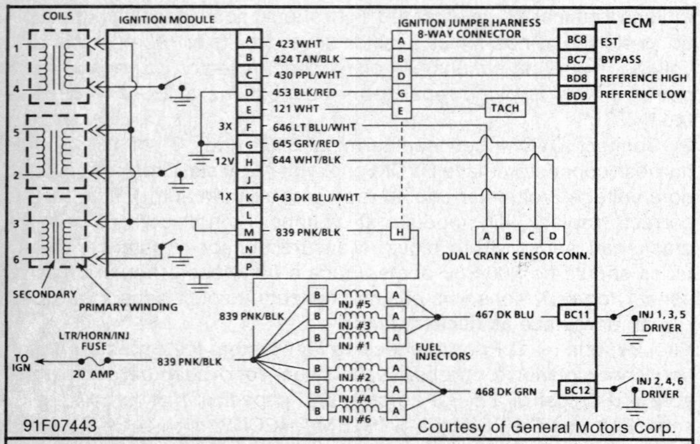

Fig. 23: 3.3L PFI Ignition System (Century, Cutlass Ciera & Cutlass Cruiser)

4) Turn ignition off. Disconnect ignition module connector. Turn ignition on. Check for battery voltage on terminal "P" of ignition module harness. *See Figs. 25-28.* Repair open or short, or replace ignition fuse as necessary. If battery voltage is present, turn ignition off and disconnect fuel pump relay. Install injector test light in injector harness connector. Connect test light to battery voltage and repeatedly touch terminal "D" of the ignition module harness connector.

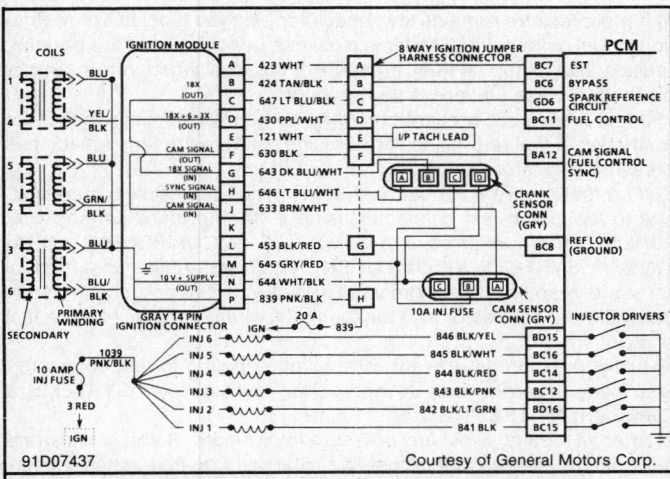

Fig. 25: 3.8L PFI Ignition System (Bonneville, Eighty-Eight, Ninety-Eight, LeSabre, Park Avenue, & Touring Sedan)

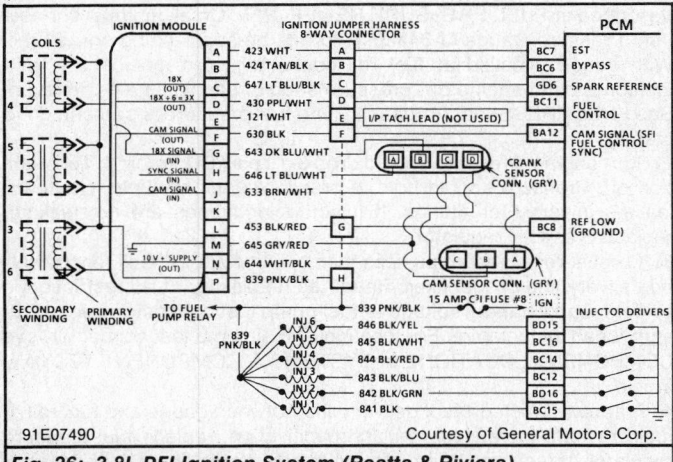

Fig. 26: 3.8L PFI Ignition System (Reatta & Riviera)

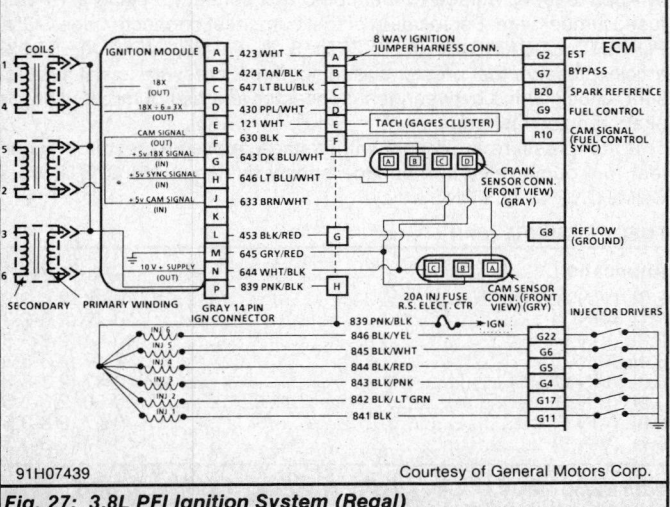

Fig. 27: 3.8L PFI Ignition System (Regal)

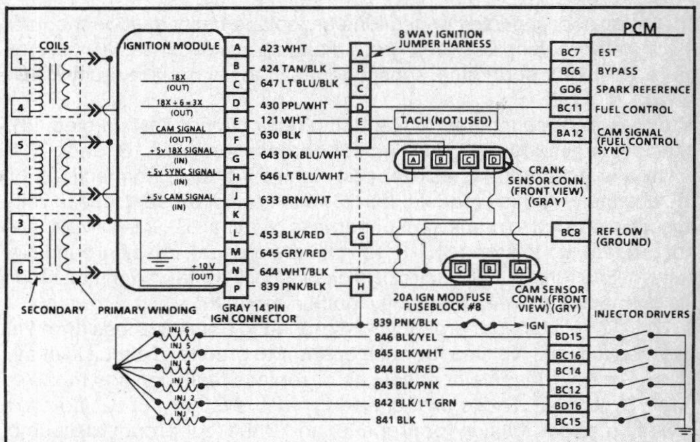

Fig. 28: 3.8L PFI Ignition System (Toronado & Trofeo)

5) Injector test light should flash each time test light is touched to terminal "C". If injector test light flashes, go to step **7)**. If not, backprobe ECM injector drive terminals with a test light to ground. If light is off, check for loss of power to fuel injector harness or open between injectors and drive terminals. If test light is on, disconnect ALL injectors. With test light connected to ground, check for voltage on both terminals of each injector harness.

6) If voltage is present on both wires of any or all injectors, check for short to voltage on injector drive circuit. If battery voltage is present on only one wire of each injector harness, check for open or shorted circuit No. 430 (RPM reference high), poor connections at ECM injector drive terminals or a faulty ECM.

CAUTION: In step 7), keep hands clear of pulleys and belts when jumpering sensor terminals. Slight belt/pulley movement may occur.

7) Turn ignition off and reconnect ignition module connector. Disconnect crank sensor. Turn ignition on. Momentarily jumper crank sensor harness terminals "A" and "C". Reconnect crank sensor harness connector to sensor. Crank engine. If injector test light does not flash, go to step **8)**. If injector test light flashes, check voltage to crank sensor harness terminal "D". If reading is more than 10 volts, check for poor crank sensor connections or replace faulty crank sensor. If reading is less than 10 volts, check for open in power circuit (No. 644) to cam and crank sensors. If power circuit is okay, replace ignition module.

8) If injector test light did not flash in step **7)**, check voltage between crank sensor harness terminals "A" and "C" using a DVOM. If 9-12 volts are present, go to step **10)**. If 9-12 volts are not present, check voltage from ground to crank sensor harness terminal "A". If 9-12 volts are now present, check circuit No. 645 for an open. If circuit is okay, check for faulty ignition module connections or replace faulty ignition module.

9) If 9-12 volts are not present from terminal "A" to ground, check circuit No. 646 for an open or short to ground. Verify battery voltage is present at terminal "P" of ignition module. If battery voltage is present at terminal "P" and circuit No. 646 is not open or shorted to ground, check for poor ignition module connections or replace faulty ignition module.

CAUTION: In step 10), keep fingers and hands clear of pulleys and belts when jumpering sensor terminals. Slight belt/pulley movement may occur.

10) With ignition on, momentarily jumper crank sensor harness terminals "A" to "C". Install a test light between fuel pump test connector and ground. Repeatedly jumper crank sensor harness terminals "B" to "C". As these 2 terminals are jumpered, test light on fuel pump test connector should flash. If test light does not flash, go to step **12)**.

11) If test light on fuel pump test connector did flash, check voltage between ground and terminal "D" of crank sensor harness connector. If reading is less than 10 volts, check crank and cam sensor power feed circuit (No. 644) for an open or short to ground. If circuit is okay, check for poor module connections or replace faulty ignition module. If voltmeter reading between ground and terminal "D" was 10 volts or more, check for poor crank sensor connections or replace faulty crank sensor.

12) If test light connected to fuel pump relay did not flash in step **10)**, check voltage between crank sensor harness terminals "B" and "C". If voltage is 9-12 volts, check for poor ignition module connections or replace faulty ignition module. If 9-12 volts are not present, check voltage from ground to crank sensor harness terminal "B". If 9-12 volts are not present, go to step **13)**. If 9-12 volts are present, check ground circuit No. 645 for an open. If circuit is okay, check for faulty ignition module connections or replace faulty ignition module.

13) If 9-12 volts are not present from ground to crank harness terminal "B", check circuit No. 643 for open or short to ground. If circuit is okay, check for poor module connections or replace faulty ignition module.

Fuel System – 1) Before checking fuel system for a no-start condition, check ignition for proper spark. Check for proper fuel pump pressure (40-44 psi or 2.8-3.1 kg/cm² for 3.3L; 40-47 psi or 2.8-3.3 kg/cm² for 3.8L) and capacity (1 pt. or .47L in 30 seconds). See BASIC FUEL SYSTEM CHECKS.

2) Disconnect injector harness. Turn ignition on and check for battery voltage at each injector harness. Battery voltage should be present on one of the injector terminals. If battery voltage is not present, check for blown injector power fuse. If battery voltage is present on both terminals, check for injector drive circuit shorted to voltage.

3) If battery voltage is present to each injector, connect injector test light to injector harness. Turn ignition on. DO NOT crank engine. If light is off, go to step **4)**. If injector test light illuminates without cranking engine, turn ignition off. Disconnect ECM C-D connector. If light is off, replace faulty ECM. If light is still on, check for short to ground in injector drive circuit.

4) Crank engine and note light. Repeat on other injector connectors. If light flashes, check for stored ECM codes. If no codes are present, refer to HARD START symptom in TROUBLE SHOOTING – NO CODES article.

5) If light does not flash, disconnect ignition module connector and momentarily touch test light from battery voltage to ECM RPM reference wire (circuit No. 430) of module harness. Each time test light is removed from ECM RPM reference terminal, injector test light should flash. If test light does not flash, check for open in RPM reference wire, injector drive (ground) circuit, or replace faulty ECM.

BASIC FUEL SYSTEM CHECKS (A-7)
FUEL SYSTEM PRESSURE TEST

CAUTION: Fuel system trouble shooting and diagnosis begins with checking fuel injection system pressure. High fuel pressure may be present in fuel lines and component parts. Relieve fuel pressure before disconnecting any fuel system components.

Fuel Pressure Relief (TBI) – Disconnect negative battery cable. Remove fuel filler cap. Since these TBI units contain an internal bleed-down feature, after a short time, system fuel pressure should dissipate.

Fuel Pressure Relief (PFI) – Fuel system is under pressure. Pressure must be relieved prior to servicing fuel system. Fuel pressure may be relieved by using one of the following methods.

- Disconnect fuel pump at rear body connector. Start engine and run engine until it stalls. Crank starter for 3 seconds to remove remaining fuel from fuel lines. Reconnect rear body connector.
- Install Fuel Pressure Gauge (J-34730-1) on fuel pressure connector of fuel rail. Wrap shop towel around pressure connection when installing fuel pressure gauge to absorb fuel leakage. Install gauge bleed hose in container. Open bleed valve to bleed fuel pressure.

Fuel Pressure Check (TBI) – 1) Relieve fuel pressure (if necessary). Remove air cleaner and plug thermal vacuum port on throttle body. When removing fuel line, always use 2 wrenches. Install Fuel Pressure Gauge (J-29658B or BT-8205) and Adapter (J-29658-85) in fuel line between steel line and flexible hose.

2) Turn ignition on and observe fuel pressure reading. Fuel pressure should read 9-13 psi (.6-.9 kg/cm²). If no fuel pressure is indicated, go

to step **5)**. If fuel pressure is okay but engine will not start, proceed to NO START DIAGNOSIS. If fuel pressure is present but is too high, go to step **4)**. If fuel pressure is present but is too low, gradually pinch off fuel return line to fuel tank.

NOTE: It should not be necessary to completely restrict fuel return line to observe a pressure increase. DO NOT damage return line.

3) If fuel pressure remains low, check for plugged fuel filter or restriction in fuel delivery line. If filter is okay and no restrictions are present, replace fuel pump. If fuel pressure increases when return line is pinched, replace fuel pressure regulator.

4) If fuel pressure is present but is higher than specification, check for restriction in fuel return line. If return line is not restricted, replace fuel pressure regulator.

5) If no fuel pressure is observed, turn ignition off. Apply battery voltage to fuel pump test connector using a 10-amp fused jumper wire. For location of fuel pump test connector, see COMPONENT LOCATIONS in SYSTEMS & COMPONENT TESTING article. Observe fuel pressure reading. If fuel pressure is still not evident, check wiring between test connector and fuel pump. If wiring is okay, replace fuel pump.

6) If fuel pressure is present with voltage applied to test connector, test fuel pump relay and voltage supply to relay. See SYSTEMS & COMPONENT TESTING article.

7) After all repairs, allow fuel pressure to dissipate. Remove fuel pressure gauge and reconnect fuel line. Start engine and watch for fuel system leaks. For further details on fuel pressure testing, proceed to SYSTEMS & COMPONENT TESTING article.

Fuel Pressure Check (PFI) – 1) Relieve fuel pressure as previously described in FUEL PRESSURE RELIEF (PFI). On all models, connect Fuel Pressure Gauge (J-34730-1) to fuel pressure fitting on fuel rail. With gauge installed at fuel rail connector, turn ignition on. With ignition on and engine off, pressure should read within specification. See FUEL PRESSURE (PFI) table. If no fuel pressure is present, go to step **5)**.

2) Start engine. Pressure should drop 3-10 psi (.2-7 kg/cm²). Turn ignition off. Pressure should hold. If pressure does not hold, check for leaking injectors or fittings. If injectors or fittings are not leaking, replace pressure regulator.

3) If pressure is present but less than specification, check for restricted delivery line or fuel filter. Repair as necessary. If no restriction is evident, apply battery voltage to fuel pump test connector using a 10-amp fused jumper wire. For location of fuel pump test connector, see COMPONENT LOCATIONS in SYSTEMS & COMPONENT TESTING article.

4) Gradually pinch off fuel delivery line between gauge and fuel rail. If fuel pressure increase to within specification, replace fuel pressure regulator. If fuel pressure does not increase with line pinched, check for faulty in-tank fuel pump or partial blocked fuel strainer.

5) Apply battery voltage to fuel pump test connector using a 10-amp fused jumper wire. For location of fuel pump test connector, see COMPONENT LOCATIONS in SYSTEMS & COMPONENT TESTING article. Observe fuel pressure reading. If fuel pressure is still not present, check wiring between test connector and fuel pump. If wiring is okay, replace fuel pump.

6) If fuel pressure is present with voltage applied to test connector, test fuel pump relay and voltage supply to relay. See SYSTEMS & COMPONENT TESTING article.

FUEL PRESSURE (PFI)

Application	psi (kg/cm²)
2.3L (VIN A & D)	40-47 (2.8-3.3)
3.1L (VIN T)	40-47 (2.8-3.3)
3.3L (VIN N)	40-44 (2.8-3.3)
3.4L (VIN X)	32-47 (2.3-3.3)
3.8L (VIN C & L)	40-47 (2.8-3.3)
4.9L (VIN B)	40-50 (2.8-3.5)
5.0L (VIN F)	40-47 (2.8-3.3)
5.7L (VIN 8)	40-47 (2.8-3.3)

Fuel Pump Relay – See MOTORS, RELAYS & SOLENOIDS in SYSTEMS & COMPONENT TESTING article.

Fuel Pump Relay By-Pass Procedure – See FUEL DELIVERY in SYSTEMS & COMPONENT TESTING article.

FIELD SERVICE MODE CHECK (EXCEPT PFI CADILLAC)

NOTE: Oxygen sensor may cool off while engine is idling. This causes system to go into "open loop". To restore "closed loop" mode, run engine at part throttle several minutes and accelerate from idle to part throttle several times. For field service mode check on PFI Cadillac vehicles, see appropriate SELF-DIAGNOSTICS article.

Field service mode check confirms proper fuel system operation and verifies "closed loop" operation. Clear codes and perform this test after any repair is completed. When performing this check, always engage parking brake and block DRIVE wheels. Parking brake on FWD models does NOT hold drive wheels.

1) Start engine. With engine running, ground "test" terminal "B" of the ALDL diagnostic connector. *See Fig. 31.* In "closed loop" mode, SERVICE ENGINE SOON light will flash once a second.

2) In "open loop", light will flash 2.5 times a second. If light is off most of the time, a lean exhaust is indicated. If light is on most of the time, a rich exhaust is indicated.

BASIC IGNITION SYSTEM CHECKS (C-4)

HEI-EST DISTRIBUTOR

NOTE: The only adjustments that can be made to HEI/EST ignition system are basic ignition timing (on distributor-type ignitions) and spark plug gap.

Spark – **1)** If factory tachometer is connected to ignition coil tachometer terminal, disconnect it before performing tests. When removing spark plug wire from spark plug, twist and pull on boot, NOT on wire.

2) Using Spark Tester (ST-125), check for spark at coil wire (if applicable) and at each spark plug wire using spark tester. Check spark plug wire resistance on suspect wires. Resistance should be no greater than 30,000 ohms.

Ignition Coil Power Source – **1)** Turn ignition on. Using voltmeter, check voltage between terminal "B" of ignition coil and ground on models with remote-mounted coil.

2) On models equipped with integral ignition coil, check voltage between "BAT" terminal and ground at distributor. Battery voltage should exist. If not, check for open circuit, blown ignition fuse or defective ignition switch.

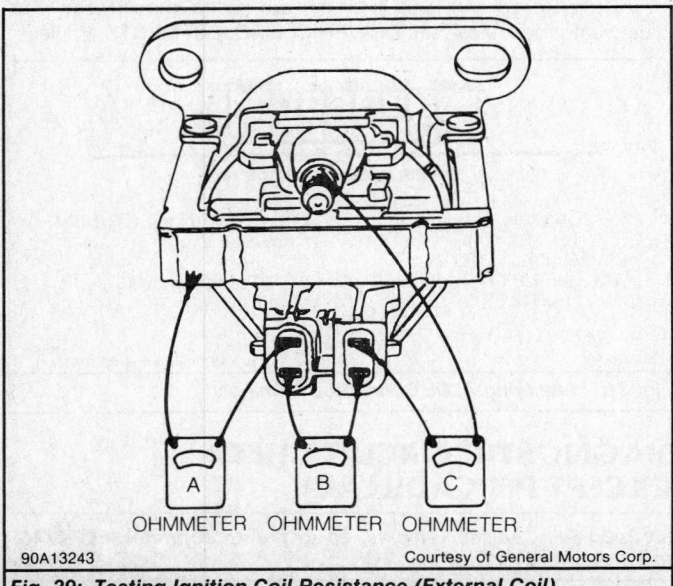

90A13243   Courtesy of General Motors Corp.

Fig. 29: Testing Ignition Coil Resistance (External Coil)

Ignition Coil Resistance (Externally Mounted) – **1)** Remove coil connectors and secondary coil wire. In test "A", use high ohmmeter scale. *See Fig. 29.* Resistance value should be very high (infinite). If not, replace coil.

2) In test "B", use low ohmmeter scale. Reading should be approximately zero ohms or replace coil. In test "C", use high ohmmeter scale. If there is no continuity, replace coil.

Ignition Coil Resistance (Internally Mounted) – **1)** Turn ignition off. Remove the distributor cap and coil assembly. Turn cap upside down. *See Fig. 30.* Set ohmmeter to low scale. Connect leads to coil BAT and TACH terminals. If resistance is more than zero, replace ignition coil.

2) Set ohmmeter on high scale. Connect one lead to coil secondary terminal and other lead first to TACH terminal and then to ground terminal. If resistance reading in BOTH instances is infinite, replace ignition coil.

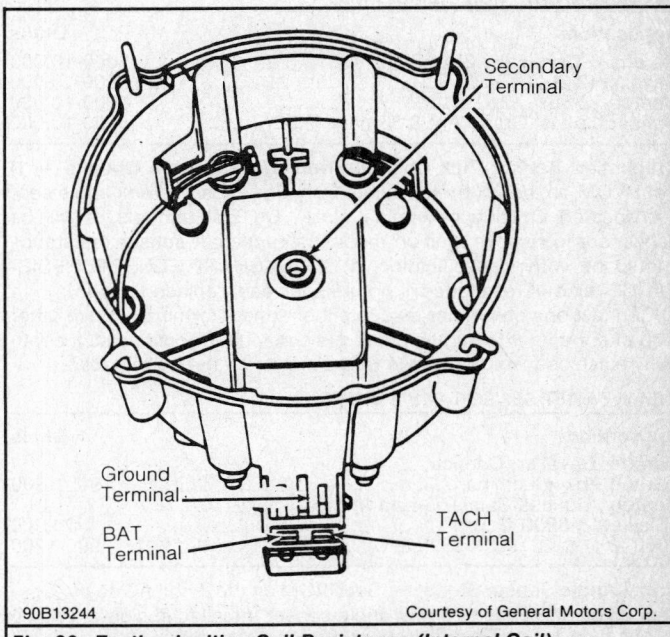

90B13244   Courtesy of General Motors Corp.

Fig. 30: Testing Ignition Coil Resistance (Internal Coil)

Distributor Pick-Up Coil Short & Resistance Checks – **1)** Disconnect pick-up coil leads from HEI/EST module terminals "N" and "P". Set ohmmeter to middle scale. Connect one ohmmeter lead to either pick-up coil lead and the other lead to distributor housing. Flex pick-up coil leads by hand to check for intermittent shorts to ground. Reading should be infinity at all times. If resistance is not infinite, replace pick-up coil.

2) Connect ohmmeter between both pick-up coil leads. Check for intermittent opens by flexing wires and connectors. Resistance should be 500-1500 ohms. If resistance is not as specified, replace pick-up coil.

Tach Pulse (RPM) Signal – Connect a "Scan" tester to the ALDL diagnostic connector. RPM should be indicated on tester when engine is cranked or running. If "Scan" tester is unavailable, tach pulse (RPM reference from ignition module) will be indicated as a voltage signal on a DVOM (with a minimum 10-megohm input impedance) when DVOM is touched to circuit No. 430 ECM terminal with engine cranking.

A tach pulse signal may be simulated (to test ECM response) by connecting a test light in series between battery and circuit No. 430 ECM terminal. Each time test light is touched to and removed from circuit No. 430, ECM will see this as a tach signal. For circuit and terminal reference, see appropriate schematic in NO START – ENGINE CRANKS OKAY in this article.

DIS

Spark – **1)** If factory tachometer is connected to ignition coil tachometer terminal, disconnect it before performing tests. When removing spark plug wire from spark plug, twist and pull on boot, NOT on wire.

2) Using Spark Tester (ST-125), check for spark at each spark plug wire using spark tester. Leave opposed firing plug connected while checking for spark. Check spark plug wire resistance on suspect wires. Resistance should be no greater than 30,000 ohms.

Ignition Coil Power Source – Turn ignition on and check Pink or Pink/Black wire of ignition module for battery voltage. If battery voltage is not present, check ignition or ECM fuse. If fuse is not blown, check for open between fuse and ignition module.

Ignition Coil Resistance – 1) Disconnect leads from ignition coil. Using an ohmmeter, check secondary ignition coil resistance. See DIS SECONDARY COIL RESISTANCE table.

2) Primary resistance values, and secondary resistance values on models not listed in DIS SECONDARY COIL RESISTANCE table, are not supplied by manufacturer.

DIS SECONDARY COIL RESISTANCE

Application	Ohms
Beretta & Corsica (2.2L & 3.1L)	5000-10,000
Cavalier (2.2L)	5000-10,000
Century (2.5L)	5000-10,000
Cutlass Calais, Grand Am & Skylark (2.5L)	5000-10,000

Crankshaft Sensor Pick-Up Coil Short & Resistance Checks – 1) Set DVOM on the 2000-ohm scale. Connect leads to crank angle sensor, located on side of engine block. On 2.5L models, it will be necessary to remove ignition module. Crankshaft sensor resistance should be within specification in CRANKSHAFT SENSOR RESISTANCE table. If resistance is not as specified, replace sensor.

2) Connect one ohmmeter lead to either sensor terminal. Touch other lead of ohmmeter to engine block. No continuity should exist. If continuity exists, sensor is shorted to ground and must be replaced.

CRANKSHAFT SENSOR RESISTANCE

Application	Ohms
Beretta, Cavalier, Corsica, Grand Prix & Lumina	900-1200
Century, Cutlass Calais, Grand Am, Skylark & 6000 (2.5)	800-900
6000 (3.1)	900-1200

Crank Angle Sensor Signal – Set DVOM on the 2-volt AC scale. Connect voltmeter leads to crank angle sensor installed in side of engine block. On 2.5L models it will be necessary to remove ignition module. Crank engine and observe voltmeter reading. Crank angle sensor should generate a voltage signal of about .05 volt at slow cranking speed to greater than .1 volt (100 mV) at high cranking speed.

Tach Pulse (RPM) Signal – Connect "Scan" tester to ALDL diagnostic connector. RPM should be indicated on tester when engine is cranked or running. Tach pulse (RPM reference) will be indicated as a voltage signal when a DVOM (with a minimum 10-megohm input impedance) is connected in series between battery and circuit No. 430 ECM terminal. For circuit and terminal reference, see appropriate schematic in NO START – ENGINE CRANKS OKAY in this article.

IDI

Spark – Disconnect tachometer wire from IDI module (if equipped). A shorted tachometer will not allow vehicle to start. Temporarily remove IDI assembly and install spark plug Jumper Wires (J-36012). Check for adequate spark with Spark Tester (ST-125). Check for spark on 2 adjacent plug wires (1-2 or 3-4, not 2-3). Leave matching plug wire connected while checking for spark. When removing spark plug wire from spark plug, twist and pull on boot. DO NOT pull on wire.

Ignition Coil Power Source – Turn ignition on. Check for battery voltage on Pink/Black wire to ignition module. If battery voltage is not present, check for blown ignition fuse. If fuse is not blown, check for open between fuse and ignition module.

Ignition Coil Resistance – Disconnect leads from ignition coil. Using an ohmmeter, check ignition coil secondary resistance. Secondary resistance should be less than 10,000 ohms on all models.

Crankshaft Sensor Pick-Up Coil Short & Resistance Checks – 1) Set DVOM on the 2000-ohm scale. Connect leads to crank angle sensor installed in side of engine block. Crankshaft sensor resistance

should be 500-900 ohms on all models. If resistance is not as specified, replace sensor.

2) Connect one ohmmeter lead to either sensor terminal. Touch other ohmmeter lead to engine block. No continuity should exist. If continuity exists, sensor is shorted to ground and must be replaced.

Crank Angle Sensor Signal – Set DVOM on the 2-volt AC scale. Connect voltmeter leads to crank angle sensor, located on side of engine block. Crank engine and observe voltmeter reading. Crank angle sensor should generate a voltage signal of about .01 volt at slow cranking speed to greater than .02 volt (20 mV) at high cranking speed.

Tach Pulse (RPM) Signal – Connect "Scan" tester to ALDL diagnostic connector. RPM should be indicated on tester when engine is cranked or running. Tach pulse (RPM reference) will be indicated as a voltage signal when a DVOM (with a minimum 10-megohm input impedance) is connected in series between battery and circuit No. 430 ECM terminal. For circuit and terminal reference, see appropriate schematic in NO START – ENGINE CRANKS OKAY in this article.

C³I

Spark – Disconnect tachometer wire (if equipped). A shorted tachometer will not allow vehicle to start. Disconnect cam sensor and attempt to start engine. If engine starts, see cam sensor trouble code in appropriate SELF-DIAGNOSTICS article. Check for adequate spark with Spark Tester (ST-125). Check for spark on plug wires No. 1, 3 and 5 (one at a time). Leave matching plug wire connected while checking for spark. When removing spark plug wire from spark plug, twist and pull on boot. DO NOT pull on wire.

Ignition Coil Power Source – Turn ignition on. Check for battery voltage on Pink/Black wire to ignition module. If battery voltage is not present, check for blown ignition fuse. If fuse is not blown, check for open between fuse and ignition module.

Ignition Coil Resistance – Disconnect ignition coil leads. Use an ohmmeter to check ignition coil resistance. Primary resistance should be .5-.9 ohm. Secondary resistance should be 5000-10,000 ohms. Replace ignition coil if not within specification.

Tach Pulse (RPM Reference) Signal – Connect "Scan" tester to ALDL diagnostic connector. RPM should be indicated on tester when engine is cranked or running. Tach pulse (RPM reference) will be indicated as a voltage signal when a DVOM (with a minimum 10-megohm input impedance) is connected in series between battery and circuit No. 430 ECM terminal. For circuit and terminal reference, see appropriate schematic in NO START – ENGINE CRANKS OKAY in this article.

IDLE SPEED & IGNITION TIMING

Ensure idle speed and ignition timing are set to specification. For adjustment procedures, see ON-VEHICLE ADJUSTMENTS article.

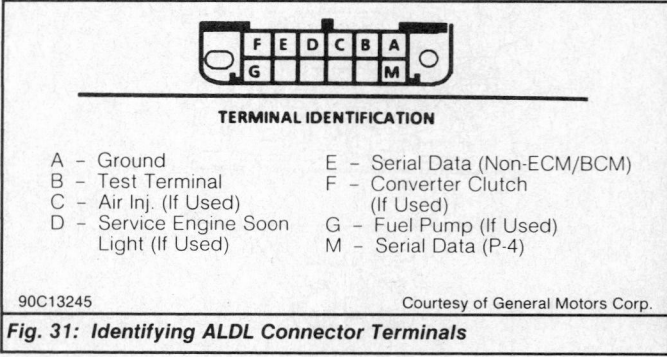

TERMINAL IDENTIFICATION

A – Ground	E – Serial Data (Non-ECM/BCM)
B – Test Terminal	F – Converter Clutch
C – Air Inj. (If Used)	(If Used)
D – Service Engine Soon	G – Fuel Pump (If Used)
Light (If Used)	M – Serial Data (P-4)

90C13245   Courtesy of General Motors Corp.

Fig. 31: Identifying ALDL Connector Terminals

DIAGNOSTIC CIRCUIT CHECK (EXCEPT PFI CADILLAC)

NOTE: On PFI Cadillac vehicles, go to the appropriate SELF-DIAG-NOSTICS article.

The Diagnostic Circuit Check determines:
- If SERVICE ENGINE SOON light works.
- If ECM is operating and can recognize a fault.
- If any codes are stored.

After performing procedures in PRELIMINARY INSPECTION & ADJUSTMENTS, BASIC FUEL SYSTEM CHECKS and BASIC IGNITION SYSTEM CHECKS, this is the starting point for utilizing the self-diagnostic system for determining computer-related problems. After

performing necessary tests as described in the diagnostic circuit check, if no codes are indicated and driveability problems still exist, see TROUBLE SHOOTING – NO CODES article and SCAN TESTER USAGE in SELF-DIAGNOSTICS – ECM/PCM EXCEPT CADILLAC article.

1) Check operation of SERVICE ENGINE SOON light. Turn ignition on with engine off. SERVICE ENGINE SOON light should be on steady. If light illuminates and stays on steady, go to next step. If light does not

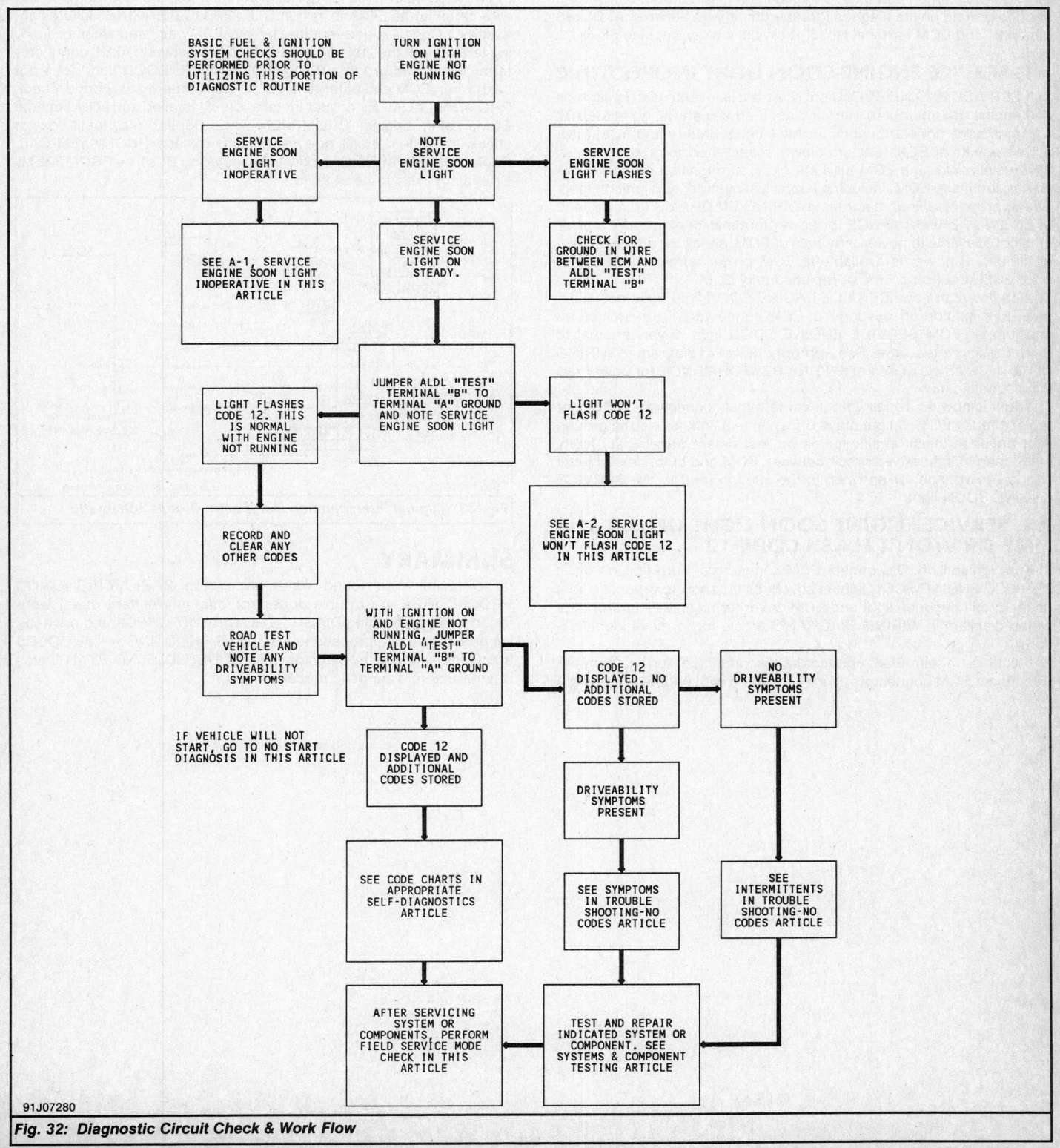

Fig. 32: *Diagnostic Circuit Check & Work Flow*

91J07280

illuminate, go to A1, SERVICE ENGINE SOON LIGHT INOPERATIVE. If light flashes, go to step **3)**.

2) Grounding the ALDL "test" terminal "B" at this time should cause SERVICE ENGINE SOON light to flash a Code 12, followed by any codes stored in ECM memory. *See Fig. 31.* If light goes from bright to dim, this is not considered a code. If light dims or remains on, and does not flash Code 12, see A2, SERVICE ENGINE SOON LIGHT ON STEADY OR WON'T FLASH CODE 12.

3) If light begins to flash as soon as ignition is turned on, check for a short to ground on the diagnostic test terminal wire between ALDL terminal "B" and ECM terminal No. 5. If circuit is okay, replace ECM.

A1, SERVICE ENGINE SOON LIGHT INOPERATIVE

1) If SERVICE ENGINE SOON light does not illuminate with ignition on and engine off, attempt to start engine. If engine starts, go to step **3)**. If engine does not start, check fusible links at battery and ECM fuse. If fusible links or ECM fuse are blown, repair short to ground.

2) If fusible links and ECM fuse are okay, turn ignition on and check power circuits to ECM, including keep alive memory and ignition feed. See appropriate wiring diagram in WIRING DIAGRAMS article at end of ENGINE PERFORMANCE for power terminal identification. If power is not available to power terminals of ECM, check for opens in power circuits. If power is available to ECM power terminals, check for poor ECM ground circuits, or replace faulty ECM.

3) If engine starts and SERVICE ENGINE SOON light does not illuminate, turn ignition off. Disconnect ECM connectors. Turn ignition on and jumper ECM SERVICE ENGINE SOON light driver terminal to ground using a test light. See appropriate wiring diagram in WIRING DIAGRAMS article at end of ENGINE PERFORMANCE for power terminal identification.

4) If light is now on, repair light driver terminal connections at ECM or replace faulty ECM. If light stays off when test light is used to ground light driver terminal, check for blown instrument panel fuse, faulty bulb, open in light driver circuit between ECM and bulb, driver circuit shorted to voltage, or an open in the ignition feed to the SERVICE ENGINE SOON light.

A2, SERVICE ENGINE SOON LIGHT ON ALL THE TIME OR WON'T FLASH CODE 12

1) Turn ignition off. Disconnect ECM connectors. Turn ignition on. If SERVICE ENGINE SOON light is on, check for short to ground in light driver circuit between light and ECM driver terminal. See appropriate wiring diagram in WIRING DIAGRAMS article for terminal identification.

2) If light is off with ECM connectors disconnected, turn ignition off. Reconnect ECM connectors. Turn ignition on with engine off. Using a DVOM, check voltage at ALDL "test" terminal "B". *See Fig. 31.* If voltage is greater than 9 volts, check for a short to voltage on ALDL terminal "B" wire between ECM and ALDL connector. If voltage is 5-6 volts, proceed to next step. If voltage is less than 5 volts, backprobe appropriate ECM terminal with DVOM. See appropriate wiring diagram in WIRING DIAGRAMS at end of ENGINE PERFORMANCE. If 5-6 volts is now present, repair open or short in wire between ECM and ALDL terminal "B".

3) If voltage at terminal "B" of ALDL connector is 5-6 volts, jumper that wire terminal at ECM to ground. If SERVICE ENGINE SOON light flashes a Code 12, and terminal "A" of ALDL was used when grounding terminal "B" the first time, check for open between ALDL connector terminal "A" and ground. If SERVICE ENGINE SOON light does not flash when ECM end of terminal "B" wire is jumpered to ground, check PROM/MEM-CAL for proper installation. If installed correctly, replace ECM, using original PROM/MEM-CAL. Repeat diagnostic circuit check. If Code 12 still does not flash, replace PROM/MEM-CAL. Replace PROM/MEM-CAL only after replacing ECM, as PROM/MEM-CAL is not likely to be at fault.

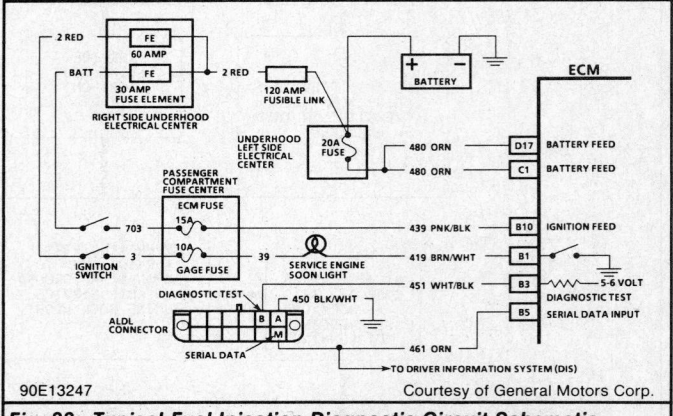

90E13247   Courtesy of General Motors Corp.

Fig. 33: Typical Fuel Injection Diagnostic Circuit Schematic

SUMMARY

If no faults were found while performing BASIC DIAGNOSTIC PROCEDURES, no trouble codes (or only intermittent ones) were found while performing DIAGNOSTIC CIRCUIT CHECK and driveability problems exist, proceed to TROUBLE SHOOTING – NO CODES article for diagnosis by symptom (i.e., ROUGH IDLE, NO-START, etc.) or intermittent diagnostic procedures.

Beretta, Bonneville, Brougham, Camaro,
Caprice, Cavalier, Century, Corsica,
Corvette, Custom Cruiser, Cutlass Calais,
Cutlass Ciera, Cutlass Cruiser,
Cutlass Supreme, Eighty-Eight, Firebird,
Grand Am, Grand Prix, LeSabre, Lumina,
Ninety-Eight, Park Avenue, Riviera,
Reatta, Regal, Roadmaster, Skylark, Sunbird,
Toronado, Touring Sedan, Trofeo, 6000

NOTE: This article does not apply to Cadillac self-diagnostics or to the BCM function on Reatta, Riviera, Toronado and Trofeo models. For information on these systems, see appropriate SELF-DIAGNOSTICS article.

INTRODUCTION

Most engine control problems are the result of mechanical breakdowns, poor electrical connections or damaged vacuum hoses. Before considering the computer system as a possible cause of problems, perform checks and inspections covered in BASIC DIAGNOSTIC PROCEDURES article. Failure to do so may result in lost diagnostic time.

If no faults were found while performing BASIC DIAGNOSTIC PROCEDURES, proceed with DIAGNOSTIC PROCEDURE. If no fault codes or only a non-running Code 12 is present and driveability problems exist, proceed to TROUBLE SHOOTING – NO CODES article for diagnosis by symptom (i.e. ROUGH IDLE, NO START, etc.). If only intermittent codes are present, see INTERMITTENTS in TROUBLE SHOOTING – NO CODES article.

SELF-DIAGNOSTIC SYSTEM
SELF-DIAGNOSTICS DIRECTORY

All vehicle are equipped with either an Electronic Control Module (ECM) or Powertrain Control Module (PCM). Unless specifically stated, references to ECM also apply to PCM equipped vehicles. Control module is equipped with a self-diagnostic system, which detects system failures or abnormalities. When a malfunction occurs, control module will illuminate the SERVICE ENGINE SOON light located on instrument panel. When malfunction is detected and light is turned on, a corresponding trouble code will be stored in control module memory. To retrieve stored codes, see RETRIEVING CODES (NON-SCAN) in this article. Malfunctions are recorded as HARD FAILURES or as INTERMITTENT FAILURES.

Hard Failures – Hard failures cause SERVICE ENGINE SOON light to illuminate and remain on until the malfunction is repaired. If light comes on and remains on (light may flash) during vehicle operation, cause of malfunction must be determined using diagnostic (code) charts. If a sensor fails, control module will use a substitute value in its calculations to continue engine operation. In this condition, vehicle is functional, but most likely degraded driveability will be encountered.

Intermittent Failures – Intermittent failures cause SERVICE ENGINE SOON light to flicker or illuminate and go out about 10 seconds after the intermittent fault goes away. The corresponding trouble code, however, will be retained in control module memory. If related fault does not reoccur within 50 engine restarts, related trouble code will be erased from control module memory. Intermittent failures may be caused by sensor, connector or wiring related problems. See INTERMITTENTS in TROUBLE SHOOTING – NO CODES article.

DIAGNOSTIC PROCEDURE

Diagnosis of the computerized engine control system should be performed in the following order:
1) Make sure all engine systems not related to the computer system are operating properly. Do not proceed with testing unless all other problems have been repaired. DIAGNOSTIC CIRCUIT CHECK must be performed prior to utilizing trouble code charts. See BASIC DIAGNOSTIC PROCEDURES article.
2) If trouble codes were displayed (other than Code 12), decide whether codes are hard or intermittent trouble codes. Hard codes will cause the SERVICE ENGINE SOON light to illuminate continuously while engine is running. See HARD OR INTERMITTENT TROUBLE CODE DETERMINATION in this article. For diagnosing hard codes, proceed to appropriate trouble code chart in this article. For diagnosing intermittent codes, proceed to INTERMITTENTS in TROUBLE SHOOTING – NO CODES article. Exceptions are Code 13, 15, 24, 44 and 45 charts, which may be used to help diagnose intermittent codes.
3) If no trouble codes were displayed and a driveability problem exists, refer to SYMPTOMS in TROUBLE SHOOTING – NO CODES article. The comments there will send you to the proper system or component to check in SYSTEMS & COMPONENT TESTING article.
4) After any repairs are made, clear any trouble codes and perform FIELD SERVICE MODE check in BASIC DIAGNOSTIC PROCEDURES article.

RETRIEVING CODES (NON-SCAN)

NOTE: For information on retrieving codes using a "Scan" tester, refer to owners manual supplied with "Scan" tester. On Reatta, Riviera, Toronado and Trofeo, codes can also be retrieved through the Electronic Climate Control Panel (ECCP). For additional information on ECCP function, see SELF-DIAGNOSTICS – BCM EXCEPT CADILLAC article.

1) Turn ignition on. Do not start engine. SERVICE ENGINE SOON light should glow. Locate Assembly Line Data Link (ALDL) connector attached to control module wiring harness. Most ALDL connectors are located under dash on driver's side of vehicle. For exact location of ALDL, see appropriate COMPONENT LOCATIONS illustration in SYSTEMS & COMPONENT TESTING article. Turn ignition on with engine not running. Insert jumper wire from terminal "B" (diagnostic test terminal) to terminal "A" (ground) of ALDL connector. *See Fig. 1.*

NOTE: Inserting jumper wire into test and ground terminals of ALDL connector with engine running will cause fuel injected vehicles to enter field service mode. Flashes of the SERVICE ENGINE SOON light will not indicate codes if this is done. See FIELD SERVICE MODE in BASIC DIAGNOSTIC PROCEDURES article.

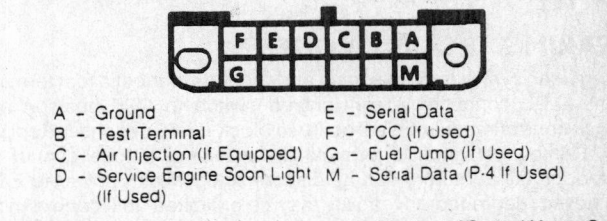

A – Ground
B – Test Terminal
C – Air Injection (If Equipped)
D – Service Engine Soon Light (If Used)
E – Serial Data
F – TCC (If Used)
G – Fuel Pump (If Used)
M – Serial Data (P-4 If Used)

90B01199   Courtesy of General Motors Corp.

Fig. 1: ALDL Connector Terminal Identification

2) SERVICE ENGINE SOON light should begin to flash codes. Each code will be repeated 3 times. If codes are not flashed or SERVICE ENGINE SOON light does not illuminate, perform DIAGNOSTIC CIRCUIT CHECK in BASIC DIAGNOSTIC PROCEDURES article. To exit diagnostic mode, turn ignition off and remove jumper wire from ALDL connector.

READING TROUBLE CODES

The control module stores component failure information under a related trouble code which can be recalled for diagnosis and repair. Trouble codes may be read by counting flashes of the SERVICE ENGINE SOON light, or by reading the output of a diagnostic "Scan" tester connected to the ALDL connector. The tester is faster to use, more accurate, and capable of reading information which otherwise would necessitate testing individual control module and sensor/solenoid connector terminals with a digital voltmeter. See SCAN TESTER USAGE and tables under SCAN DATA in this article.

NOTE: When using a "Scan" tester, there is a time delay between serial data updates. For instantaneous response, a digital voltmeter must be used.

If "Scan" tester is not available, it is possible to read flashes of the SERVICE ENGINE SOON light by grounding the diagnostic test terminal "B" of the ALDL with ignition on and engine off. For example, FLASH, FLASH, pause, FLASH, longer pause, identifies Code 21. The first series of flashes are the first digit of trouble code. The second series of flashes are the second digit of trouble code. Trouble codes are displayed starting with the lowest numbered code. Each code is displayed 3 times. Codes will continue to repeat as long as ALDL test terminal is grounded.

NOTE: Trouble codes will be recorded at various operating times. Some codes require operation of that sensor or switch for 5 seconds; others may require operation for 5 minutes or longer at normal operating temperature, road speed and load. Therefore, some codes may not set in a service bay operational mode and may require road testing vehicle in order to duplicate condition under which code will set.

HARD OR INTERMITTENT
TROUBLE CODE DETERMINATION

During any diagnostic procedure, it must be determined if codes are hard failure codes or intermittent failure codes. Diagnostic charts will not usually help analyze intermittent codes. To determine hard codes and intermittent codes, proceed as follows:

1) MANUALLY enter diagnostic mode. Read and record all stored trouble codes. Exit diagnostic mode and clear trouble codes. See CLEARING TROUBLE CODES.

2) Apply parking brake and place transmission in Neutral or Park. Block drive wheels and start engine. SERVICE ENGINE SOON light should go out. Run warm engine at specified curb idle for 2 minutes and note SERVICE ENGINE SOON light.

3) If SERVICE ENGINE SOON light comes on, MANUALLY enter diagnostic mode. Read and record trouble codes. This will reveal hard failure codes. Codes 13, 15, 24, 44, 45 and 55 may require a road test to reset hard failure after trouble codes were cleared.

4) If SERVICE ENGINE SOON light does not come on, all stored trouble codes were intermittent failures. Exceptions are noted under DIAGNOSTIC PROCEDURE.

CLEARING TROUBLE CODES

Turn ignition switch to ON position and ground diagnostic test terminal "B" at ALDL connector. Turn ignition switch to OFF position and remove control module fuse from fuse block for 10 seconds. Replace fuse. Remove diagnostic terminal ground lead. If fuse cannot be located, pigtail at battery can be disconnected. When power to ECM is removed, degraded driveability may be exhibited until control module "relearns" optimum operational parameters.

ECM/PCM LOCATION

On most vehicles the engine control module is located behind the right or left side of the dash, or behind the right or left kick panel. On the Grand Prix and Lumina, the control module is located on the right side of the engine compartment. On Corvette, the control module is located in the left rear corner of the engine compartment, next to the battery. For illustration of engine control module locations see COMPONENT LOCATIONS in SYSTEMS & COMPONENT TESTING article.

DIAGNOSTIC MATERIALS

Diagnostic Aids – Diagnostic aids (located in many trouble code charts) are additional tips used to help diagnose trouble codes when inspected circuit checks out okay. Diagnostic aids may help lead to a definitive solution to that trouble code problem.

TROUBLE CODE DEFINITION

ECM/PCM TROUBLE CODE DEFINITION

Code No.	Circuit Affected
12 [1]	No RPM Reference Pulse
13	Open Oxygen Sensor Circuit
14	CTS Signal Voltage Low
15	CTS Signal Voltage High
16	System Voltage High
17	RPM Signal Problem (3.8L C Body)
21	TPS Signal Voltage High
22	TPS Signal Voltage Low
23	MAT Sensor Signal Voltage High
24	Vehicle Speed Sensor Circuit
25	MAT Sensor Signal Voltage Low
26	Quad-Driver Error
27, 28 & 29	Gear Switch Problem (3.3L & 3.8L)
31	Park/Neutral Switch (3.3L & 3.8L)
32	EGR System Error
33	MAP Sensor Signal Voltage High
34	MAP Sensor Signal Voltage Low
	MAF Sensor Signal Voltage Low (3.3L & 3.8L)
35	IAC Idle Speed Error
36	[2] Trans. Shift Circuit
38	Brake Switch (3.3L & 3.8L)
39	TCC (3.3L & 3.8L)
41	Cam Sensor Loss (3.3L & 3.8L)
	Cylinder Select Error (3.1L)
	1X Signal Loss (2.3L)
42	EST Circuit Open Or Grounded
43	ESC Error
44	Lean Exhaust Indication
45	Rich Exhaust Indication
46	Anti-Theft System Fault
	Power Steering Pressure Switch
47	PCM-BCM Data Loss (3.8L E Body)
48	Misfire Diagnosis (3.3L & 3.8L)
51	Faulty PROM, MEM-CAL or ECM/PCM
52	Faulty/Missing CALPAC or MEM-CAL
	Low Engine Oil Temperature (Corvette)
53	System Overvoltage
	Anti-Theft System Fault
54	Fuel Pump Voltage Low
55	ECM/PCM Error
58	Anti-Theft System Fault (3.8L)
61	Degraded O$_2$ Sensor (3.1L & 4.3L)
	[2] Cruise Vent Solenoid
62	Gear Switch Error (3.1L & 3.4L)
	High Engine Oil Temperature (Corvette)
	[2] Cruise Vacuum Solenoid
63, 64 or 65	EGR Flow Check Error (3.8L H Body)
65	Fuel Injector Current Low (2.3L)
	[2] Cruise servo position
66	A/C Pressure Sensor Voltage Out Of Specification
	Low A/C Refrigerant Charge (3.8L)
67	[2] Cruise Engage Switches
68	[2] Cruise System Problem
69	A/C Head Pressure Switch (3.8L)

[1] – Display of a Code 12 is normal when no reference pulses are received by control module (engine not running).

[2] – PCM equipped models.

NOTE: Trouble code charts should only be used if SERVICE ENGINE SOON light is illuminated (indicating a current problem exists). Exceptions are Code 13, 15, 24, 44 and 45 charts, which may be used to help diagnose intermittent codes. Anytime control module-related Codes 51, 52 or 55 are displayed with another code, start with 50-series code first, then proceed to low profile numbered codes.

Field Service Mode Check – If ALDL test terminal "B" is grounded with engine running, SERVICE ENGINE SOON light will indicate operational mode of engine. This test confirms proper operation of fuel system and verifies closed loop operation. Clear codes and perform this test after any repair is completed. Field service mode check can be found by proceeding to FIELD SERVICE MODE CHECK in BASIC DIAGNOSTIC PROCEDURES article.

1991 ENGINE PERFORMANCE
Self-Diagnostics – ECM/PCM Except Cadillac (Cont.)

GM
1-37

SPECIAL TOOLS (DIAGNOSTIC)

NOTE: Special "Scan" testers plugged into the ALDL may be used to read trouble codes and check voltages in the system on the serial data line (terminal "E", or terminal "M" on P-4 systems). These testers can save a great deal of time. For additional information, see SCAN TESTER USAGE and tables under SCAN DATA in this article.

The computerized engine control system is most easily diagnosed using a "Scan" tester; however, other tools may aid in diagnosing problems if a "Scan" tester is unavailable. These tools are a tachometer, test light, ohmmeter, digital voltmeter with 10-megohm input impedance (minimum), vacuum pump, vacuum gauge, fuel injector test lights (for both TBI and PFI) and 6 jumper wires 6" long (one wire with female connectors at both ends, one wire with male connector at both ends and 4 wires with male and female connectors at opposite ends). A test light, rather than a voltmeter, must be used when indicated by a diagnostic chart.

SCAN TESTER USAGE

NOTE: Prior to connection of "Scan" tester to vehicle, diagnostic system should be checked to determine if system is operating properly and if information received by "Scan" tester will be accurate. This is done by performing DIAGNOSTIC CIRCUIT CHECK located in BASIC DIAGNOSTIC PROCEDURES article. If vehicle does not pass diagnostic circuit check, information received by "Scan" tester may be invalid.

The "Scan" tester is a specialized tester which, when plugged into ALDL, can be used to diagnose on-board computer control systems by providing instant access to circuit voltage information without need to crawl under dash or hood to backprobe sensors and connectors. "Scan" testers cut down diagnostic time dramatically by furnishing input data (voltage signals) which can be compared to specification parameters. See tables under SCAN DATA in this article. They may also furnish information on output device (solenoids and motors) status. However, status parameters are only an indication that output signals have been sent to devices by the control module. It does not indicate if devices have responded properly to that signal. This will need to be verified at output device using a voltmeter or test light.

NOTE: Code 12 should always exist when ALDL is grounded with key on and engine not running, but may not be indicated by all makes of "Scan" testers.

If trouble codes are not present, this is not an indication that there is not a problem. Driveability related problems with codes displayed occur about 20 percent of the time, while driveability problems without codes occur about 80 percent of the time. Sensors that are out of specification WILL NOT set a trouble code but WILL cause driveability problems. Using a "Scan" tester is the easiest method of checking sensor specifications and other data parameters. Tester is also useful in finding intermittent wiring problems by wiggling wiring harnesses and connections (key on, engine off) while observing data parameters. See tables under SCAN DATA in this article.

NOTE: Information obtained by "Scan" tester is only as accurate as the tester itself. If erroneous voltage signals are suspected, it will be necessary to verify tester information using a digital voltmeter and wiring schematic. If non-existent codes are displayed, turn ignition off, remove tester, turn ignition on and ground ALDL test terminal "B". If same codes are not flashed by SERVICE ENGINE SOON light that were indicated by "Scan" tester, tester cannot be used on vehicle and information obtained by it will not be guaranteed accurate.

SCAN DATA

NOTE: Information contained in the following tables is typical of readings taken on vehicle with engine idling, upper radiator hose hot, closed throttle, transmission in Park or Neutral, closed loop status achieved and all accessories off (except as noted in tables). Data parameters are updated every 1 1/4 seconds. On systems using P-4 computers, parameter updates are more often. Not all devices and systems are used on all models and the following lists represent only the most commonly used parameters. For additional information, refer to owners manual furnished with tester.

THROTTLE BODY INJECTION

Tester Position	Units Measured	Nominal Data Value
A/C Clutch	On/Off	Off (On With A/C)
A/C Request	Yes/No	No/Yes (With Request)
AIR Divert Sol.	On/Off	On (Air To Switching Sol.) Off (Air To Atmosphere)
AIR Switching Sol.	On/Off	On (To Exhaust Manifold) Off (To Catalytic Converter)
BARO	Volts	3-4.5
Battery Voltage	Volts	13.5-14.5
Block Learn	Counts	118-138 (128 Normal)
Brake Switch	On/Off	On When Engaged
Canister Purge Sol.	On/Off	On/Engine Cold (Idle Some)
Clear Flood	On/Off	***See Tester Manual***
Coolant Fan	On/Off	Off Below 216°F (102°C)
Coolant Temp.	°C	85-105° (Norm. Temperature)
Crank RPM	RPM	100-900
Cross Counts	Counts	0-255
Cruise Cont. Sw.	On/Off	On When Engaged
EGR Solenoid	On/Off	On When Energized
EGR Duty Cycle	0-100%	0/closed-100/Fully Open
Fan Relay	On/Off	On When Energized
Fan Request	On/Off	On With Request
Fuel Back-Up	Yes/No	Yes When Engaged
IAC	Counts	0-50
Ignition/Crank	On/Off	On With Ignition/Crank
Injector Pulse Width	Mil./Sec	.8-3.0
INT (Integrator)	Counts	110-145 (128 Normal)
Knock Retard (ESC)	Counts	0-255
Knock Signal	Yes/No	Yes When Knock Exists
MAT	°C	10-90°
MAP	Volts	1 (Idle) to 4.5 (WOT)
Open/Closed Loop Status	OI/CI	Closed/Open During Extended Idle
O₂ Sensor	Millivolts	100 (Lean) To 999 (Rich)
P/N Switch	P/N/RDL	Park/Neutral
P/S Switch	Norm/Hi	Normal
PROM I.D.	PROM #	Original Factory Number
RPM	RPM	Spec. ±25 RPM Drive (A/T) Spec. ±50 RPM Neut. (M/T)
Spark Advance	No. Deg.	Varies
TCC	On/Off	Off (On With Command)
TPS	Volts	1.25 (Idle) to 5.0 (WOT)
Throttle Angle	0-100%	0 (Idle) to 110 (WOT)
Trouble Codes	Code #	No Codes
Upshift Light (Man. Trans.)	On/Off	Off
VSS or MPH	MPH	0-Actual
3rd Gear Switch	On/Off	On/3rd & 4th Gear
4th Gear Switch	On/Off	On/4th Gear

PORT FUEL INJECTION

Tester Position	Units Measured	Nominal Data Value
A/C Clutch	On/Off	Off (On With A/C)
A/C Request	Yes/No	No/Yes (With Request)
AIR Divert Sol.	On/Off	On (Air To Switching Sol.) Off (Air To Atmosphere)
AIR Switching Sol.	On/Off	On (To Exhaust Manifold) Off (To Catalytic Converter)
BARO	Volts	3-4.5
Battery Voltage	Volts	13.5-14.5
Block Learn	Counts	118-138 (128 Normal)
Canister Purge Sol.	On/Off	On/Engine Cold (Idle Some)
Clear Flood	On/Off	***See Tester Manual***
Coolant Fan	On/Off	Off below 216°F (102°C)
Coolant Temp.	°C	85-105° (Norm. Temperature)
Crank RPM	RPM	100-900
Cross Counts	Counts	0-255
EGR Solenoid	On/Off	On When Energized
EGR Duty Cycle	0-100%	0/Closed-100/fully Open
Fan Relay	On/Off	On When Energized
Fan Request	On/Off	On With Request
Fuel Back-Up	Yes/No	Yes When Engaged
IAC	Counts	0-50
Ignition/Crank	On/Off	On With Ignition/Crank
Injector Pulse Width	Mil./Sec	.8-3.0
INT (Integrator)	Counts	110-145 (128 Normal)
Knock Retard (ESC)	Counts	0-255
Knock Signal	Yes/No	Yes When Knock Exists
MAT	C°	10-90°
MAP	Volts	1 (Idle) to 4.5 (WOT)
Open/Closed Loop Status	OI/CI	Closed/Open During Extended Idle

PORT FUEL INJECTION (Cont.)

Tester Position	Units Measured	Nominal Data Value
O$_2$ Sensor	Millivolts	100 (Lean) To 999 (Rich)
P/N Switch	P/N/RDL	Park/Neutral
P/S Switch	Norm/Hi	Normal
PROM I.D.	PROM #	Original Factory Number
RPM	RPM	Spec. ±25 RPM Drive (Auto.) Spec. ±50 RPM Neut. (Man.)
Spark Advance	No. Deg.	Varies
TCC	On/Off	Off (On With Command)
TPS	Volts	1.25 (Idle) to 5.0 (WOT)
Throttle Angle	0-100%	0 (Idle) To 100 (WOT)
Trouble Codes	Code #	No Codes
Upshift Light (Man. Trans.)	On/Off	Off
VSS or MPH	MPH	0-Actual
Water Injection	On/Off	On When Injecting
1st Gear Switch	On/Off	On/1st Gear Only
3rd Gear Switch	On/Off	On/3rd & 4th Gear
4th Gear Switch	On/Off	On/4th Gear

SUMMARY

If no hard fault codes are present, driveability symptoms exist or intermittent codes exist, proceed to TROUBLE SHOOTING – NO CODES article for diagnosis by symptom (i.e. ROUGH IDLE, NO START, etc.), or intermittent diagnostic procedures.

NOTE: In the following diagnostic flow charts, mini-schematics are supplied courtesy of General Motors Corp.

1991 ENGINE PERFORMANCE
Self-Diagnostics – ECM/PCM Except Cadillac (Cont.)

GM
1-39

CODE 13, OPEN OXYGEN SENSOR CIRCUIT

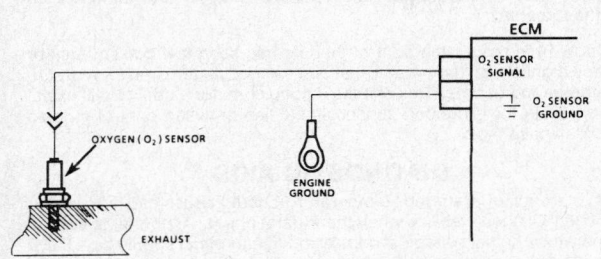

CODE 13 ECM TERMINAL & CIRCUIT WIRING IDENTIFICATION

Application	ECM Terminal	Wire Color
2.0L, 2.2L &		
2.5L A & N Bodies		
O₂ Signal	B2	Purple
O₂ Ground	B23	Tan
2.3L L Body		
O₂ Signal	GE14	Black
O₂ Ground	GE15	Tan
2.3L N Body, 3.1L F, J & L Bodies		
O₂ Signal	GE14	Purple
O₂ Ground	GE15	Tan
2.3L W Body, 2.5L W Body,		
3.1L W Body, 3.4L W Body		
& 5.7L Y Body		
O₂ Signal	A16	Purple
O₂ Ground	A22	Tan
3.1L A Body		
O₂ Signal	GE14	Purple
O₂ Ground	GE15	Black
3.3L		
O₂ Signal	YE14	Purple
O₂ Ground	YE15	Tan
3.8L C & E Bodies		
O₂ Signal	BD3	Purple
O₂ Ground	BD2	Tan
3.8L H Body		
O₂ Signal	YD2	Purple
O₂ Ground	YD3	Tan
3.8L W Body		
O₂ Signal	R16	Purple
O₂ Ground	R21	Tan
5.0L & 5.7L TBI		
O₂ Signal	D7	Purple
O₂ Ground	D6	Tan
5.0L & 5.7L PFI F Body		
O₂ Signal	GE14	Purple
O₂ Ground	GE15	Tan/White

NOTE: Test numbers refer to test numbers on diagnostic chart.

1) This tests if problem still exists. Vehicle cannot enter closed loop mode if oxygen sensor circuit is open. Code 13 indicates an open in the O₂ sensor circuit. Code will set if:
- Engine is at normal operating temperature.
- Neither Code 21 nor Code 22 are stored.
- O₂ sensor voltage is constant within a specified range (.34-.55 volt).
- Throttle angle is greater than idle.
- A precalibrated amount of time has elapsed since start-up.
- All conditions have existed for a precalibrated amount of time.

2) Determines if O₂ sensor, wiring or control module is at fault. If wiring is good, grounding oxygen sensor wire will cause .45 volt reference supplied by the control module to pull low.
3) This tests O₂ sensor circuit wiring. Use only a high impedance (10-megohm minimum) digital voltmeter.

DIAGNOSTIC AIDS

Control module will not go into closed loop if Code 13 is set. Code 13 may set if vehicle runs out of fuel or stalls while vehicle is in motion. If oxygen sensor ground becomes loose, a false oxygen sensor reading will occur. This can result in a Code 13 being set.

---

1 RUN ENGINE TO OPERATING TEMPERATURE. INCREASE RPM AND HOLD FOR 2 MINUTES. VERIFY CLOSED LOOP OPERATION WHILE IN FIELD SERVICE MODE. CLOSED LOOP OPERATION? → YES

CODE IS INTERMITTENT. IF NO OTHER CODES ARE STORED, GO TO TROUBLE SHOOTING-NO CODES ARTICLE. ALSO SEE DIAGNOSTIC AIDS

NO

2 DISCONNECT OXYGEN SENSOR AND JUMPER ECM SIDE OF HARNESS CONNECTOR TO GROUND. SCAN TESTER SHOULD DISPLAY LESS THAN .3 VOLT. DOES IT? SEE NOTE. → YES

NOTE: IF SCAN TESTER IS NOT AVAILABLE, BACKPROBE OXYGEN SENSOR SIGNAL TERMINAL AT ECM WITH A 10-MEGOHM DVOM

FAULTY OXYGEN SENSOR OR SENSOR CONNECTION

NO

3 TURN IGNITION OFF. DISCONNECT JUMPER. TURN IGNITION ON WITH ENGINE OFF. USING A DVOM, CHECK VOLTAGE ON OXYGEN SENSOR HARNESS CONNECTOR FROM ECM. → LESS THAN .3 VOLT

.3-.6 VOLT → FAULTY ECM

GREATER THAN .6 VOLT → OPEN SENSOR GROUND OR FAULTY ECM CONNECTION OR FAULTY ECM

OPEN SENSOR SIGNAL LINE OR FAULTY ECM CONNECTION OR FAULTY ECM

CODE 14, COOLANT TEMPERATURE SENSOR SIGNAL VOLTAGE LOW

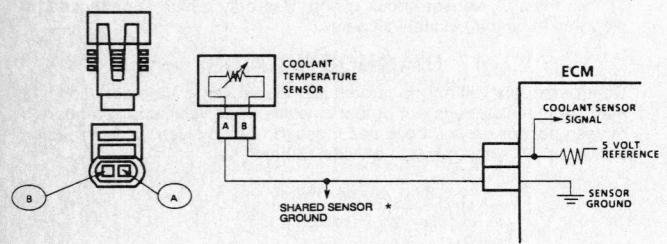

* – For shared sensor ground tie-offs, see appropriate diagram in WIRING DIAGRAMS.

CODE 14 ECM TERMINAL & CIRCUIT WIRING IDENTIFICATION

Application	ECM Terminal	Wire Color
2.0L, 2.2L J Body & 2.5L A & N Bodies		
CTS Signal	B8	Yellow
CTS Ground	B12	Black
2.2L L Body		
CTS Signal	B8	Gray
CTS Ground	B12	Purple
2.3L W Body, 2.5L W Body,		
CTS Signal	C16	Yellow
CTS Ground	C10	Black
2.3L N Body, 3.1L J Body, & 5.0L & 5.7L PFI F Body		
CTS Signal	GE16	Yellow
CTS Ground	BB6	Black
3.1L A & F Bodies		
CTS Signal	GE16	Yellow
CTS Ground	BB6	Purple
3.1L L Body		
CTS Signal	GE16	Gray
CTS Ground	BB6	Purple
3.1L W Body, 3.4L W Body & 5.7L Y Body		
CTS Signal	C16	Yellow
CTS Ground	C10	Black
3.3L A & N Bodies		
CTS Signal	YE16	Yellow
CTS Ground	BB6	Black
3.8L C & E Bodies		
CTS Signal	BB9	Yellow
CTS Ground	BA8	Black
3.8L H Body		
CTS Signal	YD4	Yellow
CTS Ground	YD5	Black
3.8L W Body		
CTS Signal	R13	Yellow
CTS Ground	R7	Black
5.0L & 5.7L TBI		
CTS Signal	C10	Yellow
CTS Ground	A11	Black

NOTE: This chart assumes engine cooling system is functioning properly (not overheating). Test numbers refer to test numbers on diagnostic chart.

1) Code 14 indicates the control module has seen low coolant sensor voltage signal (high temperature) at control module terminal for a precalibrated period of time. This checks if conditions for Code 14 still exist.
2) This tests for grounded sensor signal line between control module and coolant sensor.

DIAGNOSTIC AIDS

After the engine is started, temperature should rise steadily to about 190°F (88°C), then stabilize when thermostat opens. At normal operating temperature, signal voltage at control module terminal should be 1.5-2.0 volts. Check sensor for shifted calibration by using sensor TEMPERATURE-TO-RESISTANCE VALUES table. When Code 14 is set, control module will turn on electric cooling fan(s), if equipped.

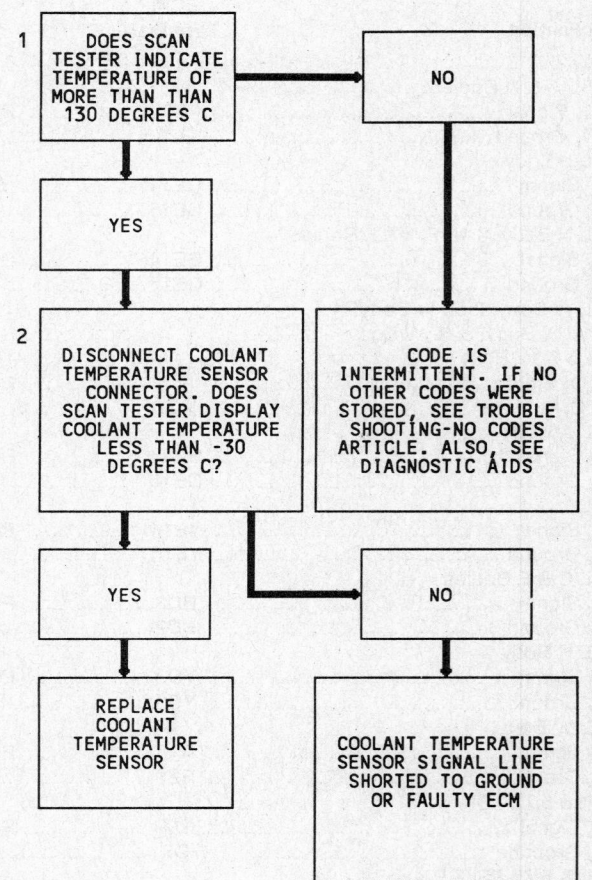

TEMPERATURE-TO-RESISTANCE VALUES [1]

Temperature °F (°C)	Ohms
210 (100)	185
160 (70)	450
100 (38)	1800
70 (20)	3400
20 (-7)	13,500
0 (-18)	25,000
-40 (-40)	100,700

[1] – Measure resistance across sensor terminals.

1991 ENGINE PERFORMANCE
Self-Diagnostics – ECM/PCM Except Cadillac (Cont.)

GM
1-41

CODE 15, COOLANT TEMPERATURE SENSOR SIGNAL VOLTAGE HIGH

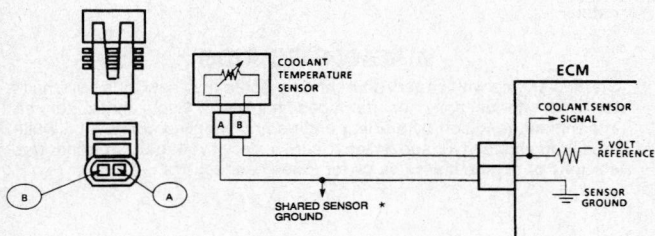

* – For shared sensor ground tie-offs, see appropriate diagram in WIRING DIAGRAMS.

CODE 15 ECM TERMINAL & CIRCUIT WIRING IDENTIFICATION

Application	ECM Terminal	Wire Color
2.0L, 2.2L J Body & 2.5L A & N Bodies		
CTS Signal	B8	Yellow
CTS Ground	B12	Black
2.2L L Body		
CTS Signal	B8	Gray
CTS Ground	B12	Purple
2.3L W Body, 2.5L W Body,		
CTS Signal	C16	Yellow
CTS Ground	C10	Black
2.3L N Body, 3.1L J Body, & 5.0L & 5.7L PFI F Body		
CTS Signal	GE16	Yellow
CTS Ground	BB6	Black
3.1L A & F Bodies		
CTS Signal	GE16	Yellow
CTS Ground	BB6	Purple
3.1L L Body		
CTS Signal	GE16	Gray
CTS Ground	BB6	Purple
3.1L W Body, 3.4L W Body & 5.7L Y Body		
CTS Signal	C16	Yellow
CTS Ground	C10	Black
3.3L A & N Bodies		
CTS Signal	YE16	Yellow
CTS Ground	BB6	Black
3.8L C & E Bodies		
CTS Signal	BB9	Yellow
CTS Ground	BA8	Black
3.8L H Body		
CTS Signal	YD4	Yellow
CTS Ground	YD5	Black
3.8L W Body		
CTS Signal	R13	Yellow
CTS Ground	R7	Black
5.0L & 5.7L TBI		
CTS Signal	C10	Yellow
CTS Ground	A11	Black

NOTE: Test numbers refer to test numbers on diagnostic chart.

1) Code 15 indicates control module has seen high resistance in coolant sensor circuit. This could be due to high resistance (cold temperature) or high voltage at coolant sensor terminal at control module for a precalibrated period of time. This checks if conditions for Code 15 still exist.
2) This test simulates conditions for a Code 14. If control module recognizes the low voltage signal, "Scan" tester will display greater than 130°C. This indicates the control module and wiring are not at fault.
3) This test determines if coolant sensor ground or signal circuit is open.

DIAGNOSTIC AIDS

After the engine is started, temperature should rise steadily to about 190°F (88°C), then stabilize when thermostat opens. At normal operating temperature, voltage at control module sensor signal line should be 1.5-2.0 volts. Check sensor for shifted calibration by using sensor temperature-to-resistance table. When Code 14 is set, control module will turn on electric cooling fan(s), if equipped.

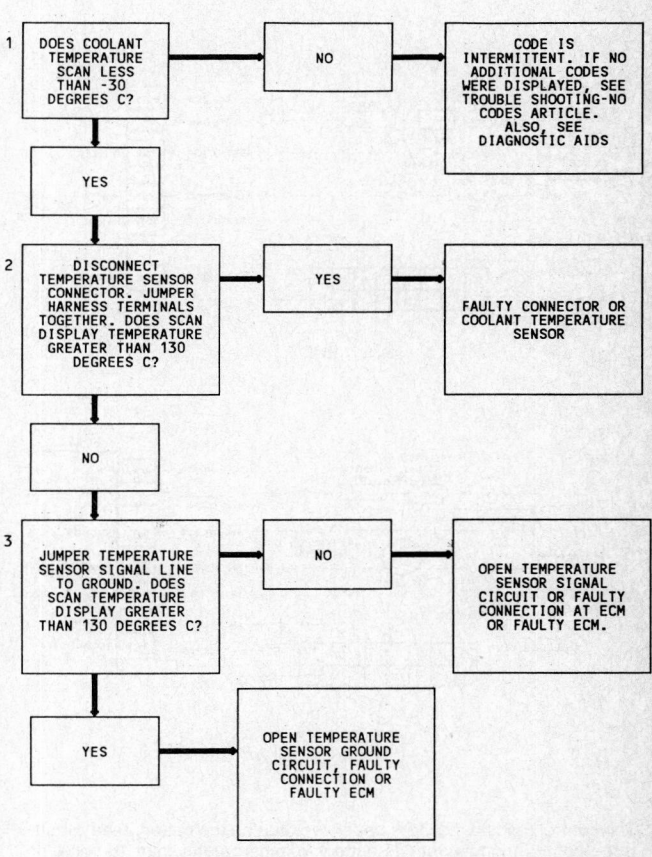

TEMPERATURE-TO-RESISTANCE VALUES [1]

Temperature °F (°C)	Ohms
210 (100)	185
160 (70)	450
100 (38)	1800
70 (20)	3400
20 (-7)	13,500
0 (-18)	25,000
-40 (-40)	100,700

[1] – Measure resistance across sensor terminals.

GM
1-42

1991 ENGINE PERFORMANCE
Self-Diagnostics — ECM/PCM Except Cadillac (Cont.)

CODE 16, SYSTEM VOLTAGE HIGH
3.3L A & N BODIES & 3.8L H BODY

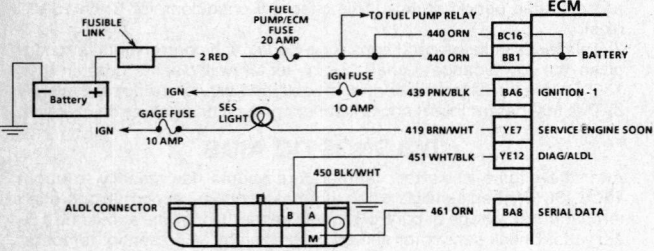

3.3L A BODY

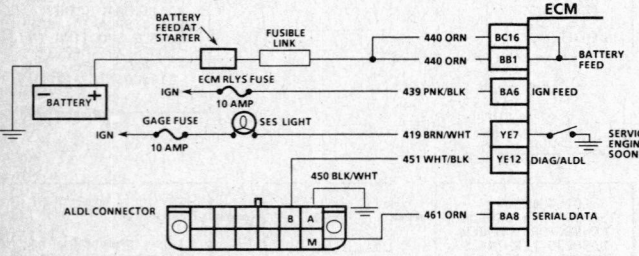

3.3L N BODY

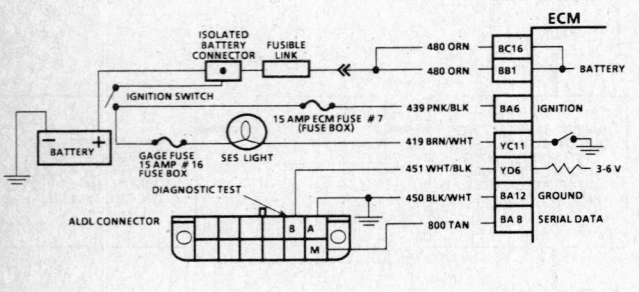

3.8L H BODY

The control module monitors battery voltage on the battery feed circuit. If the control module detects battery voltage greater than 16 volts for more than 10 seconds, it will set a Code 16 in memory.

NOTE: Test numbers refer to test numbers on diagnostic chart.

1) Test alternator output to determine proper operation of voltage regulator. Increase engine speed to a moderate level and measure voltage across battery terminals. If reading is greater than 16 volts, service alternator.

DIAGNOSTIC AIDS

Starting engine with battery charger connected may set Code 16. Check for poor connections or damaged harness. Also, check for an intermittent condition by starting engine and wiggling connection while monitoring battery voltage on the "Scan" tester. If voltage status changes abruptly or engine stalls, check for loose connections.

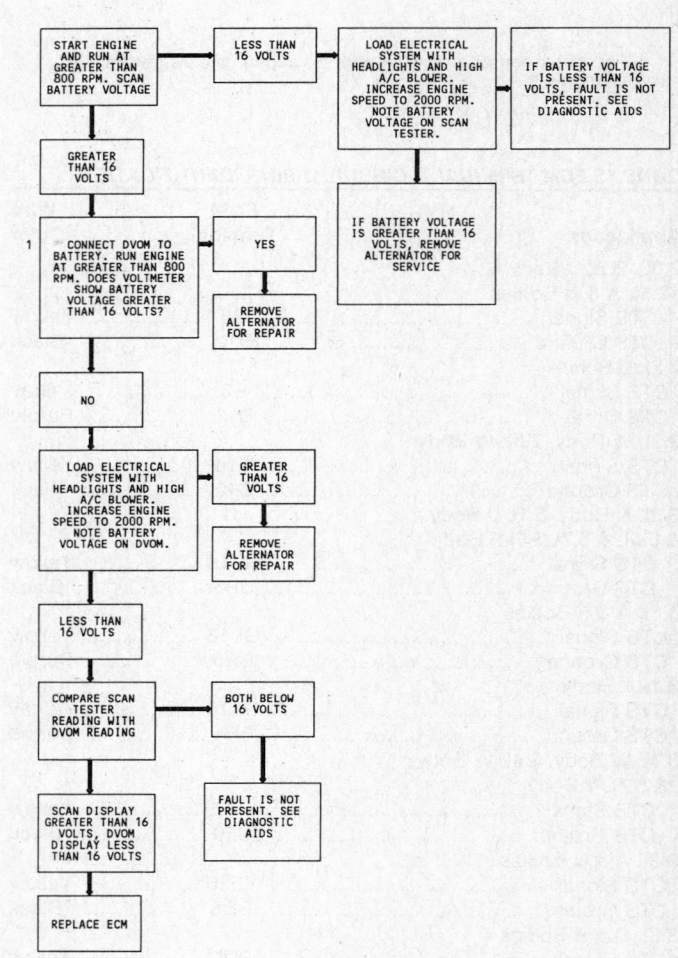

1991 ENGINE PERFORMANCE
Self-Diagnostics – ECM/PCM Except Cadillac (Cont.)

GM
1-43

CODE 16, SYSTEM VOLTAGE HIGH/LOW 3.8L C, E & W BODIES

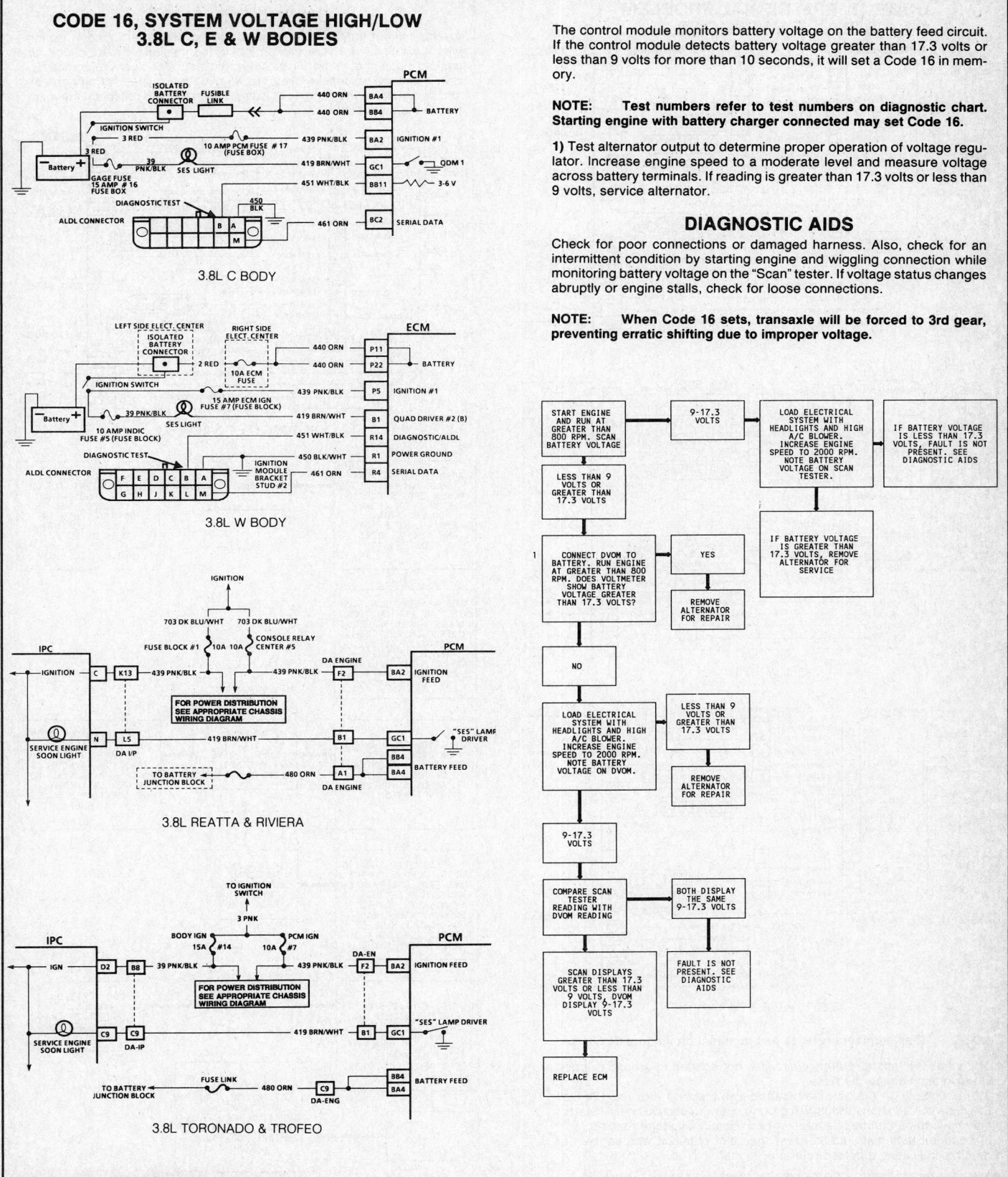

3.8L C BODY

3.8L W BODY

3.8L REATTA & RIVIERA

3.8L TORONADO & TROFEO

The control module monitors battery voltage on the battery feed circuit. If the control module detects battery voltage greater than 17.3 volts or less than 9 volts for more than 10 seconds, it will set a Code 16 in memory.

NOTE: Test numbers refer to test numbers on diagnostic chart. Starting engine with battery charger connected may set Code 16.

1) Test alternator output to determine proper operation of voltage regulator. Increase engine speed to a moderate level and measure voltage across battery terminals. If reading is greater than 17.3 volts or less than 9 volts, service alternator.

DIAGNOSTIC AIDS

Check for poor connections or damaged harness. Also, check for an intermittent condition by starting engine and wiggling connection while monitoring battery voltage on the "Scan" tester. If voltage status changes abruptly or engine stalls, check for loose connections.

NOTE: When Code 16 sets, transaxle will be forced to 3rd gear, preventing erratic shifting due to improper voltage.

GM
1-44

1991 ENGINE PERFORMANCE
Self-Diagnostics – ECM/PCM Except Cadillac (Cont.)

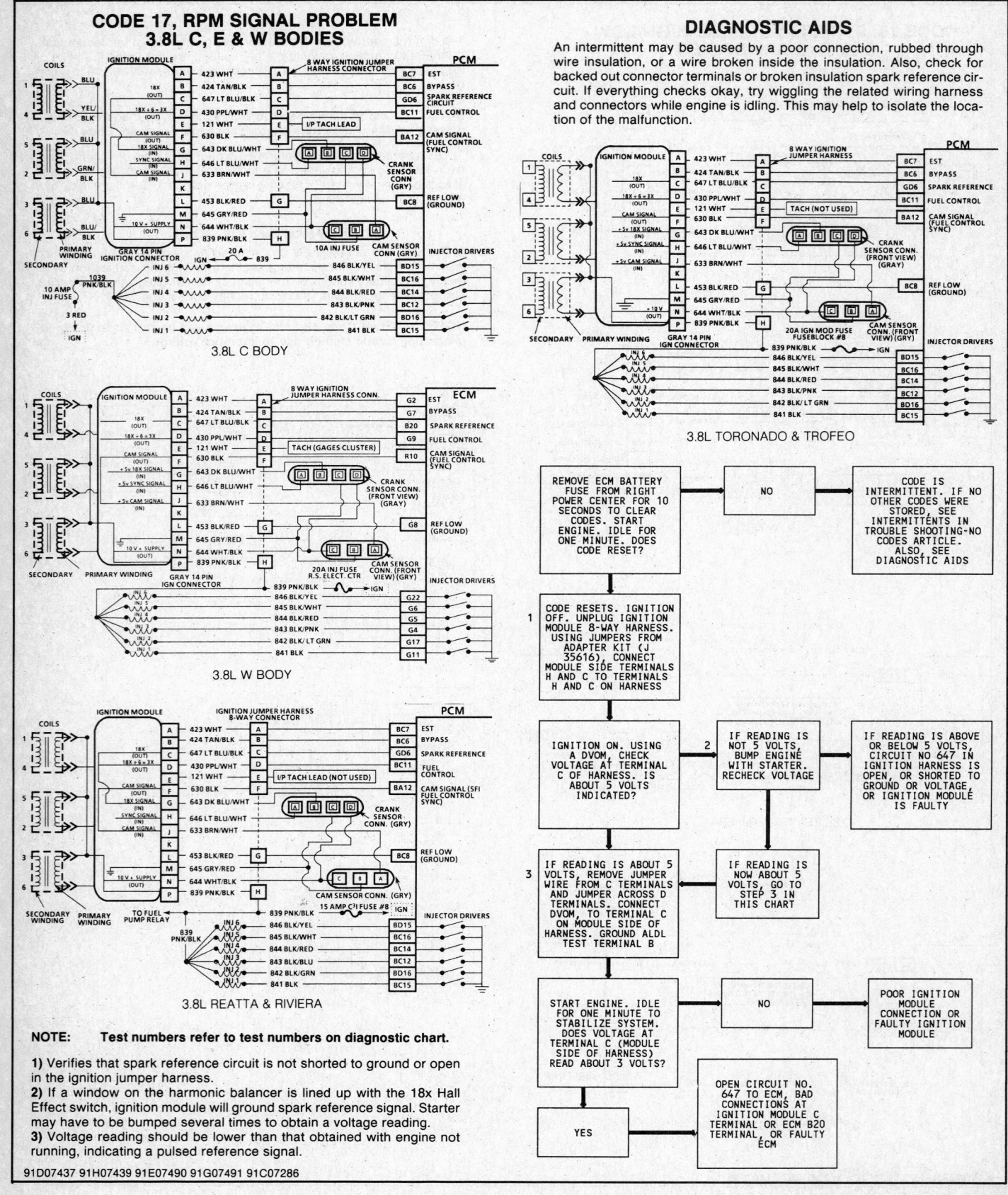

CODE 17, RPM SIGNAL PROBLEM 3.8L C, E & W BODIES

3.8L C BODY

3.8L W BODY

3.8L REATTA & RIVIERA

DIAGNOSTIC AIDS

An intermittent may be caused by a poor connection, rubbed through wire insulation, or a wire broken inside the insulation. Also, check for backed out connector terminals or broken insulation spark reference circuit. If everything checks okay, try wiggling the related wiring harness and connectors while engine is idling. This may help to isolate the location of the malfunction.

3.8L TORONADO & TROFEO

NOTE: Test numbers refer to test numbers on diagnostic chart.

1) Verifies that spark reference circuit is not shorted to ground or open in the ignition jumper harness.
2) If a window on the harmonic balancer is lined up with the 18x Hall Effect switch, ignition module will ground spark reference signal. Starter may have to be bumped several times to obtain a voltage reading.
3) Voltage reading should be lower than that obtained with engine not running, indicating a pulsed reference signal.

1991 ENGINE PERFORMANCE
Self-Diagnostics – ECM/PCM Except Cadillac (Cont.)

GM
1-45

CODE 21, THROTTLE POSITION SENSOR SIGNAL VOLTAGE HIGH

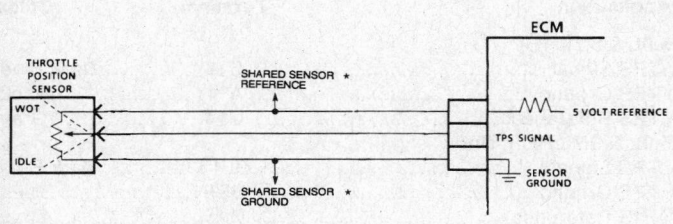

* – For shared sensor reference and shared sensor ground tie-offs, see appropriate diagram in WIRING DIAGRAMS.

CODE 21 ECM TERMINAL & CIRCUIT WIRING IDENTIFICATION

Application	ECM Terminal	Wire Color
2.0L, 2.2L J Body & 2.5L A & N Bodies		
TPS Signal	B19	Dark Blue
TPS Ground	B12	Black
TPS Reference	W11	Gray
2.2L Body		
TPS Signal	B19	Dark Blue
TPS Ground	W14	Black
TPS Reference	W11	Gray
2.3L L & N Bodies		
TPS Signal	GF13	Dark Blue
TPS Ground	BB6	Black
TPS Reference	BA5	Gray
2.3L W Body		
TPS Signal	C15	Dark Blue
TPS Ground	C10	Black
TPS Reference	C12	Gray
2.5L W Body, 3.1L W Body, 3.4W Body & 5.7L Y Body		
TPS Signal	C15	Dark Blue
TPS Ground	C10	Black
TPS Reference	C7	Gray
3.1L A, F, J & L Bodies		
TPS Signal	GF13	Dark Blue
TPS Ground	BB5	Black
TPS Reference	BA5	Gray
3.3L		
TPS Signal	YF13	Dark Blue
TPS Ground	BB6	Black
TPS Reference	BA4	Gray
3.8L C Body		
TPS Signal	BB10	Dark Blue
TPS Ground	BB8	Black
TPS Reference	BB3	Gray
3.8L E Body		
TPS Signal	BB10	Dark Blue
TPS Ground	BA8	Black
TPS Reference	BB3	Gray
3.8L H Body		
TPS Signal	YD13	Dark Blue
TPS Ground	YD5	Black
TPS Reference	BC14	Gray

CODE 21 ECM TERMINAL & CIRCUIT WIRING IDENTIFICATION (Cont.)

Application	ECM Terminal	Wire Color
3.8L W Body		
TPS Signal	R19	Dark Blue
TPS Ground	R7	Black
TPS Reference	P4	Gray
5.0L & 5.7L TBI		
TPS Signal	C13	Dark Blue
TPS Ground	A11	Black
TPS Reference	C14	Gray
5.0L & 5.7L PFI F Body		
TPS Signal	GF13	Dark Blue
TPS Ground	BB5	Black
TPS Reference	BA5	Gray

NOTE: Test numbers refer to test numbers on diagnostic chart.

1) This test checks if code is the result of a hard failure or an intermittent condition.

2) This test simulates conditions for a Code 22. If control module recognizes the change of state, the control module and wiring are okay.

3) This step isolates a faulty sensor, control module or open sensor ground circuit. If sensor ground is shared by another sensor, there may be an accompanying code related to that sensor.

DIAGNOSTIC AIDS

A "Scan" tester displays throttle position in volts. Closed throttle voltage should be low. Voltage should increase gradually to about 4.5 volts at a steady rate, as throttle angle is increased. If code is intermittent, see INTERMITTENTS in TROUBLE SHOOTING – NO CODES article.

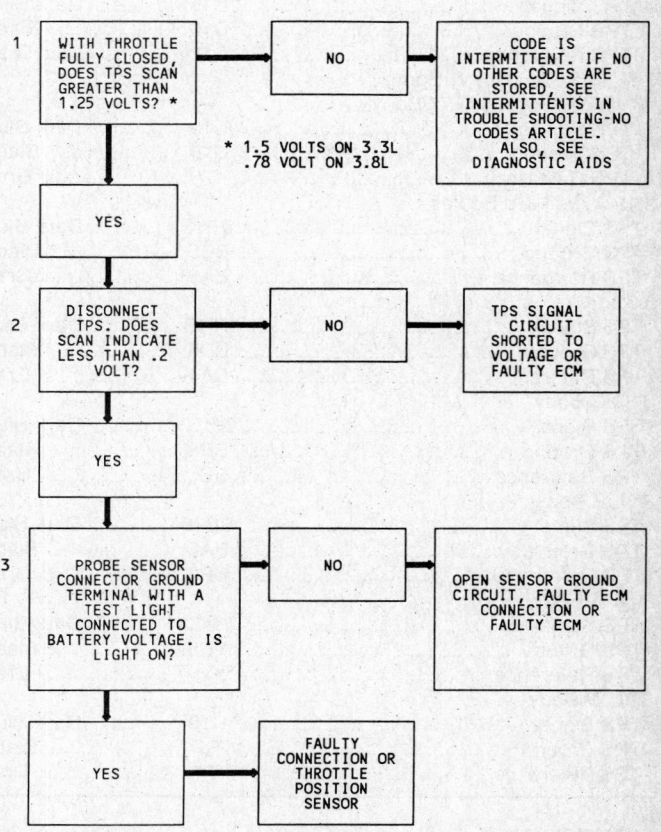

GM
1-46

1991 ENGINE PERFORMANCE
Self-Diagnostics — ECM/PCM Except Cadillac (Cont.)

CODE 22, THROTTLE POSITION SENSOR SIGNAL VOLTAGE LOW

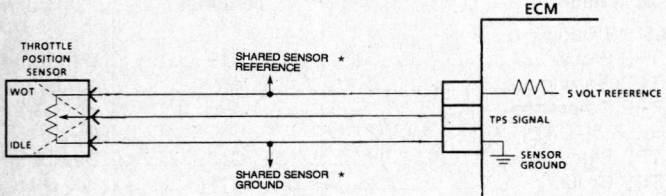

* – For shared sensor reference and shared sensor ground tie-offs, see appropriate diagram in WIRING DIAGRAMS.

CODE 22 ECM TERMINAL & CIRCUIT WIRING IDENTIFICATION

Application	ECM Terminal	Wire Color
2.0L, 2.2L J Body & 2.5L A & N Bodies		
TPS Signal	B19	Dark Blue
TPS Ground	B12	Black
TPS Reference	W11	Gray
2.2L Body		
TPS Signal	B19	Dark Blue
TPS Ground	W14	Black
TPS Reference	W11	Gray
2.3L L & N Bodies		
TPS Signal	GF13	Dark Blue
TPS Ground	BB6	Black
TPS Reference	BA5	Gray
2.3L W Body		
TPS Signal	C15	Dark Blue
TPS Ground	C10	Black
TPS Reference	C12	Gray
2.5L W Body, 3.1L W Body, 3.4L W Body & 5.7L Y Body		
TPS Signal	C15	Dark Blue
TPS Ground	C10	Black
TPS Reference	C7	Gray
3.1L A, F, J & L Bodies		
TPS Signal	GF13	Dark Blue
TPS Ground	BB5	Black
TPS Reference	BA5	Gray
3.3L		
TPS Signal	YF13	Dark Blue
TPS Ground	BB6	Black
TPS Reference	BA4	Gray
3.8L C Body		
TPS Signal	BB10	Dark Blue
TPS Ground	BB8	Black
TPS Reference	BB3	Gray
3.8L E Body		
TPS Signal	BB10	Dark Blue
TPS Ground	BA8	Black
TPS Reference	BB3	Gray
3.8L H Body		
TPS Signal	YD13	Dark Blue
TPS Ground	YD5	Black
TPS Reference	BC14	Gray
3.8L W Body		
TPS Signal	R19	Dark Blue
TPS Ground	R7	Black
TPS Reference	P4	Gray

CODE 22 ECM TERMINAL & CIRCUIT WIRING IDENTIFICATION (Cont.)

Application	ECM Terminal	Wire Color
5.0L & 5.7L TBI		
TPS Signal	C13	Dark Blue
TPS Ground	A11	Black
TPS Reference	C14	Gray
5.0L & 5.7L PFI F Body		
TPS Signal	GF13	Dark Blue
TPS Ground	BB5	Black
TPS Reference	BA5	Gray

NOTE: Test numbers refer to test numbers on diagnostic chart.

1) This test checks if code is the result of a hard failure or an intermittent condition.

2) This test simulates conditions for a Code 21. If control module recognizes the change of state, the control module and wiring are okay.

3) This simulates a high signal voltage to check for an open in the TPS signal line to control module. "Scan" tester should recognize this signal and display high TPS voltage.

DIAGNOSTIC AIDS

A "Scan" tester displays throttle position in volts. Closed throttle voltage should be low. Voltage should increase gradually to about 4.5 volts at a steady rate, as throttle angle is increased. If code is intermittent, see INTERMITTENTS in TROUBLE SHOOTING – NO CODES article.

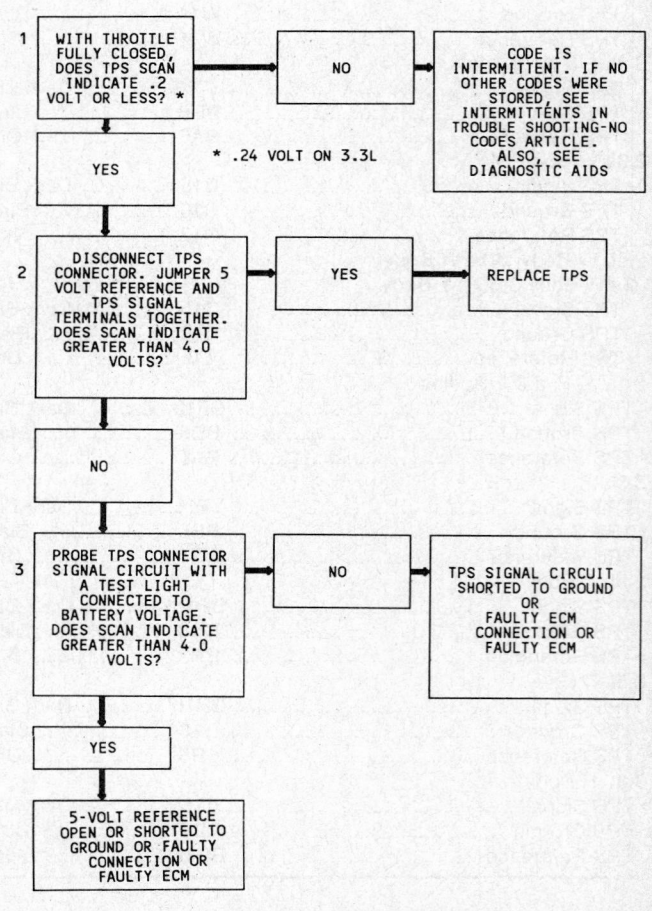

1991 ENGINE PERFORMANCE
Self-Diagnostics — ECM/PCM Except Cadillac (Cont.)

GM
1-47

CODE 23, MAT SENSOR SIGNAL VOLTAGE HIGH

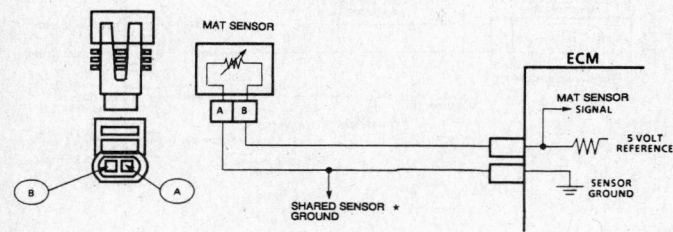

* – For shared sensor ground tie-offs, see appropriate diagram in WIR-ING DIAGRAMS.

NOTE: Test numbers refer to test numbers on diagnostic chart.

1) This checks if code is the result of a hard failure or an intermittent condition. Code 23 will set if engine has been running for a precalibrated period of time, has reached operating temperature and signal voltage indicates a MAT temperature less than -22°F (-30°C).

2) This simulates conditions for a Code 25. If the "Scan" tester displays a high temperature, the control module and wiring are not at fault.

3) This checks for continuity of sensor signal and ground circuits. If ground circuit is shared by other sensors and ground circuit is open, accompanying codes related to those sensors may be present.

DIAGNOSTIC AIDS

If the engine is allowed to cool overnight, the coolant and MAT sensors should read close to each other, when measured with a "Scan" tester. A Code 23 will result if signal and ground circuits become open. Check sensor for shifted calibration by using sensor TEMPERATURE-TO-RESISTANCE VALUES table.

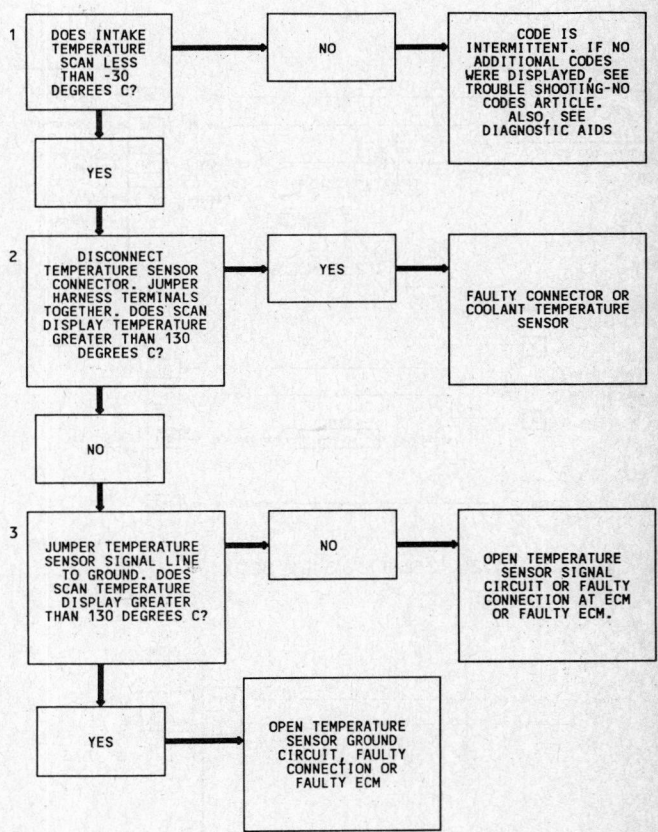

CODE 23 ECM TERMINAL & CIRCUIT WIRING IDENTIFICATION

Application	ECM Terminal	Wire Color
2.0L, 2.2L J Body & 2.5L A & N Bodies		
MAT Signal	B5	Tan
MAT Ground	W14	Black/Orange
2.2L L Body		
MAT Signal	B5	Black/Pink
MAT Ground	W14	Black
2.3L L Body		
MAT Signal	GF16	Black/Pink
MAT Ground	BB5	Black
2.3L W Body, 2.5L W Body & 3.1L W Body & 3.4L W Body		
MAT Signal	C4	Tan
MAT Ground	C5	Black
3.1L A, F & J Bodies, & 5.0L & 5.7L PFI F Body		
MAT Signal	GF16	Tan
MAT Ground	BB5	Black
3.1L L Body		
MAT Signal	GF16	Pink/Black
MAT Ground	BB5	Black
3.8L C & E Bodies		
MAT Signal	BB7	Tan
MAT Ground	BA7	Black
3.8L H Body		
MAT Signal	YD11	Tan
MAT Ground	YD5	Black
3.8L W Body		
MAT Signal	R12	Tan
MAT Ground	R2	Black/White
5.0L & 5.7L TBI		
MAT Signal	C12	Tan
MAT Ground	A11	Black
5.7L Y Body		
MAT Signal	C4	Tan
MAT Ground	C5	Black/Pink

TEMPERATURE-TO-RESISTANCE VALUES [1]

Temperature °F (°C)	Ohms
210 (100)	185
160 (70)	450
100 (38)	1800
70 (20)	3400
20 (-7)	13,500
0 (-18)	25,000
-40 (-40)	100,700

[1] – Measure resistance across sensor terminals.

91E07386 91I07289

GM
1-48

1991 ENGINE PERFORMANCE
Self-Diagnostics — ECM/PCM Except Cadillac (Cont.)

CODE 24, VEHICLE SPEED SENSOR (VSS)
2.0L, 2.2L L BODY, 2.3L L, N & W BODIES,
2.5L A, N & W BODIES, 3.1L A, F, J,
L & W BODIES, 3.4L W BODY, 3.8L W BODY
& V8 PFI F & Y BODIES

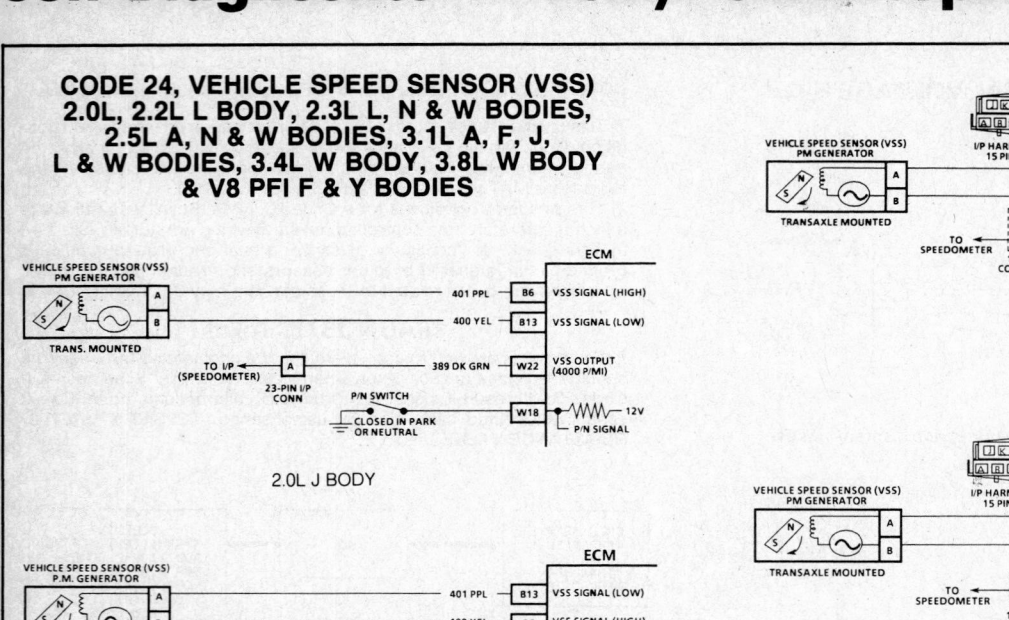

2.0L J BODY

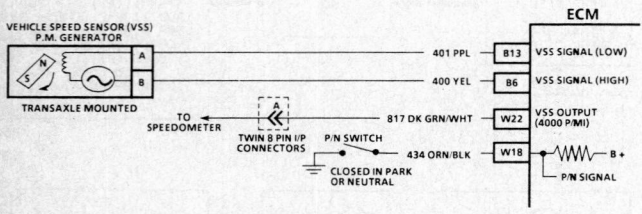

2.2L L BODY

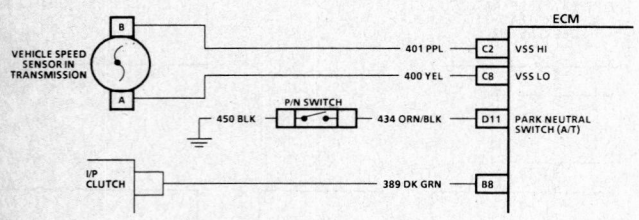

2.3L, 2.5L, 3.1L & 3.4L W BODY

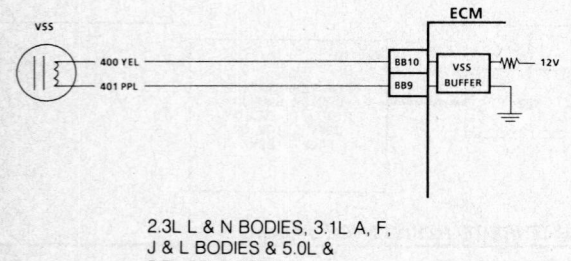

2.3L L & N BODIES, 3.1L A, F,
J & L BODIES & 5.0L &
5.7L PFI F BODY

2.5L A BODY

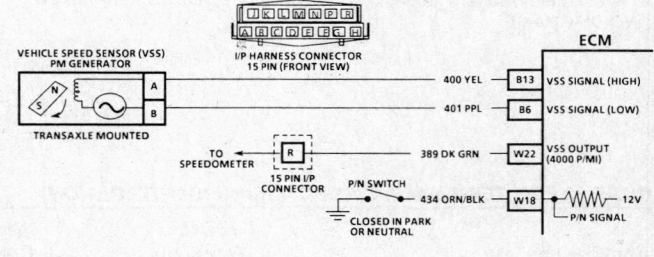

2.5L N BODY

3.8L W BODY

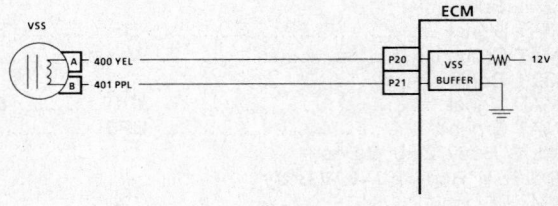

The speed sensor, which is a Permanent Magnet (PM) generator, provides the control module with vehicle speed information. The PM generator, mounted in the transmission, produces a pulsing voltage signal whenever the vehicle speed is more than 3 MPH. The voltage level and pulses increase with vehicle speed. The control module converts the pulsing voltage to MPH, which is used by the control module in calculations to determine vehicle adjustments.

91G07387 91I07388 91A07389 91C07390 91E07391 91G07392 91D07395

1991 ENGINE PERFORMANCE
Self-Diagnostics — ECM/PCM Except Cadillac (Cont.)

GM
1-49

CODE 24, VEHICLE SPEED SENSOR (VSS)
2.0L, 2.2L L BODY, 2.3L L, N & W BODIES,
2.5L A, N & W BODIES, 3.1L A, F, J,
L & W BODIES, 3.4L W BODY, 3.8L W BODY
& V8 PFI F & Y BODIES (Cont.)

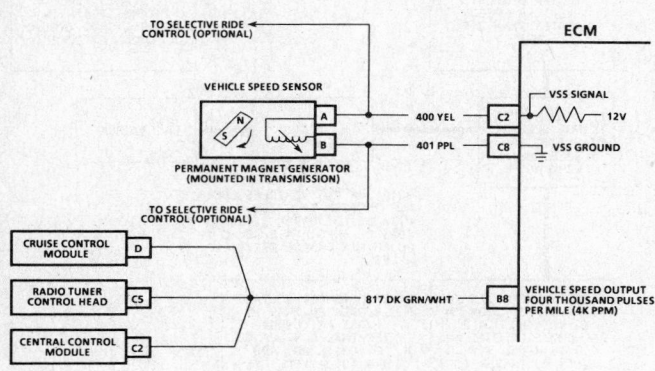

5.7L Y BODY

NOTE: **Test numbers refer to test numbers on diagnostic chart.**

1) A Code 24 will set when MPH reads zero, transmission is not in Park or Neutral, engine speed indicates vehicle is in a cruise mode (1200-4400) RPM, TPS indicates closed throttle and high manifold vacuum is sensed by the MAP sensor. All of these conditions must be met for 2-5 seconds. The PM generator only produces a voltage signal if drive wheels are turning greater than 3 MPH.
2) Before replacing the control module, PROM/MEM-CAL should be checked for correct application.

91I07393 91A07290

DIAGNOSTIC AIDS

A faulty or misadjusted park/neutral switch may set a false Code 24. Use "Scan" tester and check for proper signal in Drive, while wiggling shifter. Code 24 may set if vehicle is power braked (brakes applied and throttle depressed) for more than 10 seconds.

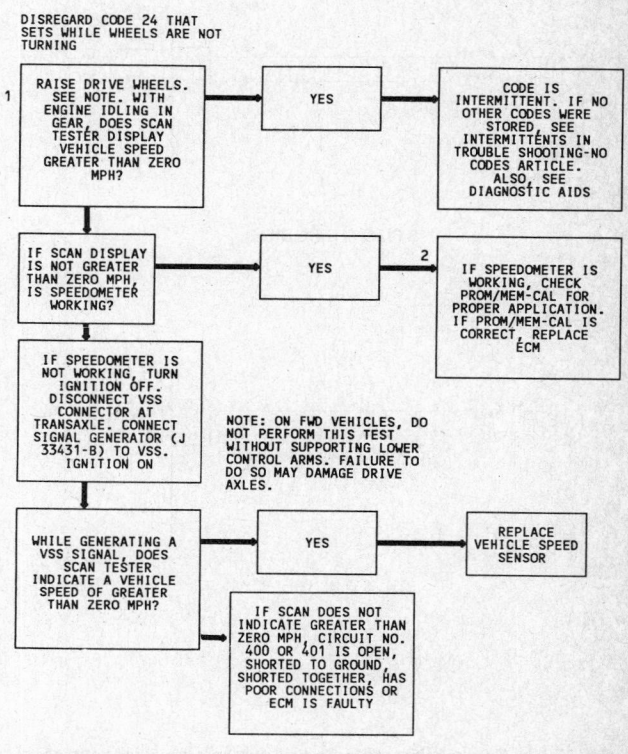

CODE 24, VEHICLE SPEED SENSOR (VSS)
2.2L J BODY

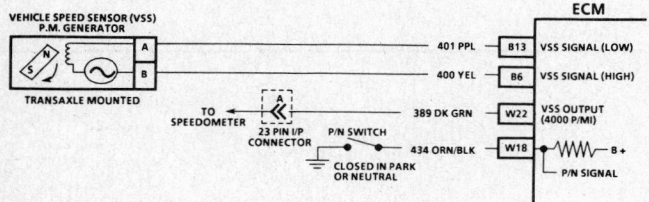

NOTE: **Test numbers refer to test numbers on diagnostic chart.**

1) Code 24 will set if vehicle speed is less than 2 MPH with engine speed at 1125-4400 RPM, transmission is not in Park or Neutral, MAP indicates a road load deceleration condition and these conditions have been met for 5 seconds.

DIAGNOSTIC AIDS

A faulty or misadjusted park/neutral switch may set a false Code 24. Use "Scan" tester and check for proper signal in Drive, while wiggling shifter.

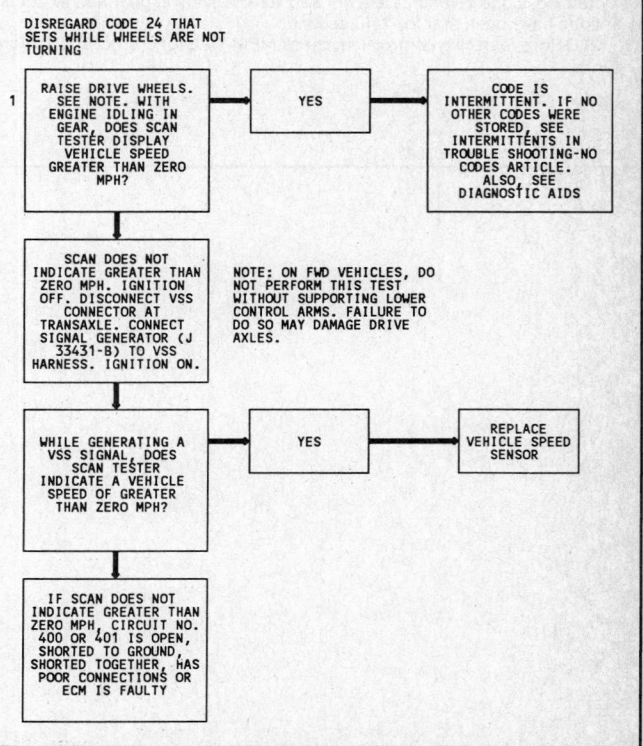

91A07394 91C07291

GM
1-50

1991 ENGINE PERFORMANCE
Self-Diagnostics — ECM/PCM Except Cadillac (Cont.)

**CODE 24, VEHICLE SPEED SENSOR (VSS)
3.3L & 3.8L C, E & H BODIES**

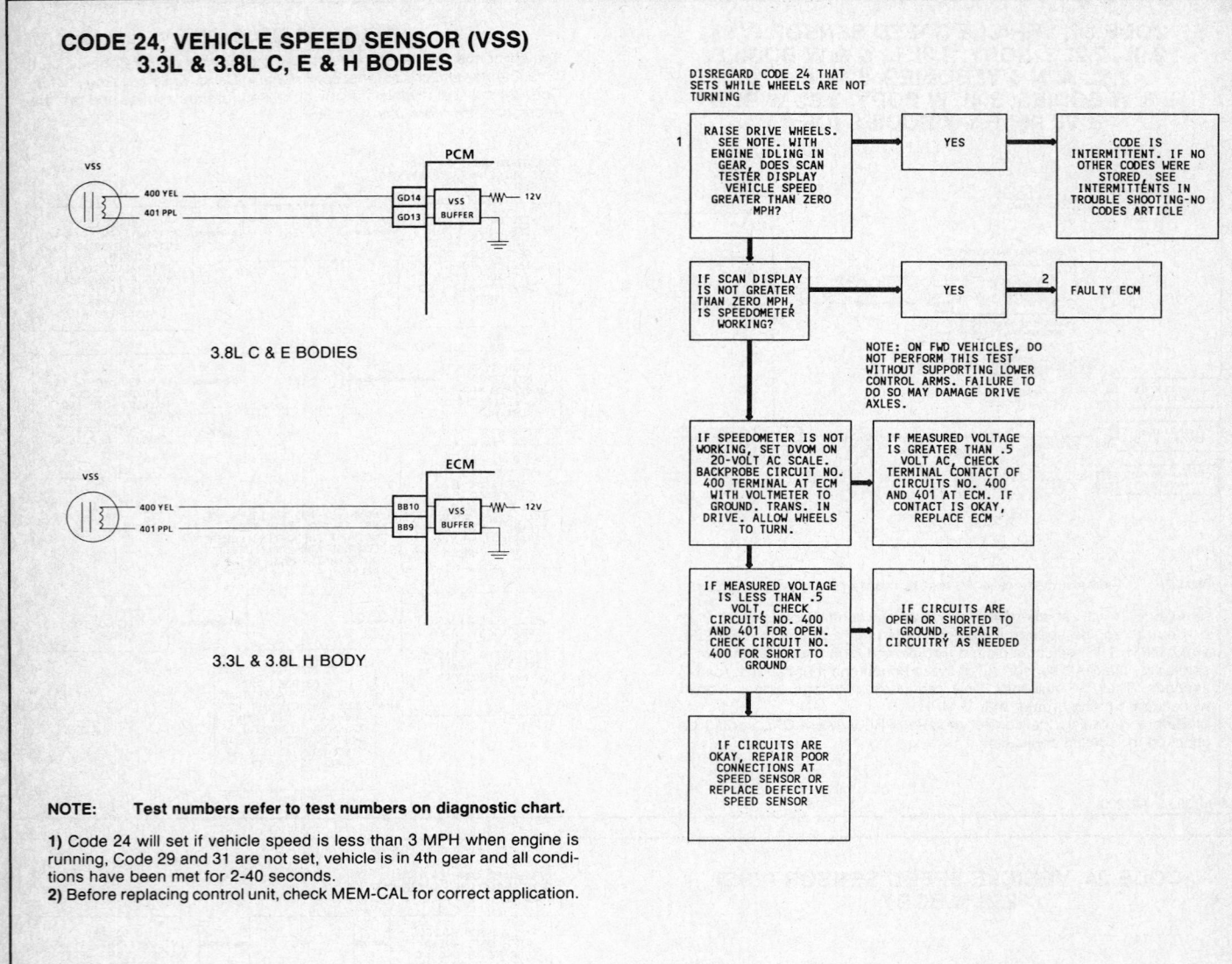

3.8L C & E BODIES

3.3L & 3.8L H BODY

NOTE: Test numbers refer to test numbers on diagnostic chart.

1) Code 24 will set if vehicle speed is less than 3 MPH when engine is running, Code 29 and 31 are not set, vehicle is in 4th gear and all conditions have been met for 2-40 seconds.

2) Before replacing control unit, check MEM-CAL for correct application.

1991 ENGINE PERFORMANCE
Self-Diagnostics — ECM/PCM Except Cadillac (Cont.)

GM
1-51

CODE 24, VEHICLE SPEED SENSOR (VSS)
5.0L & 5.7L TBI B, D & F BODIES

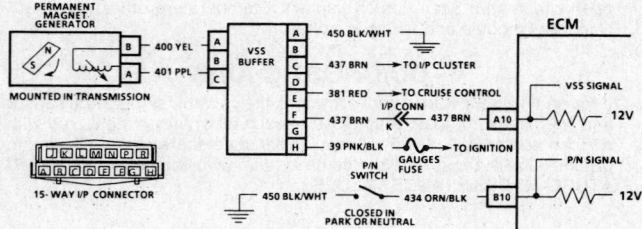

5.0L TBI F BODY

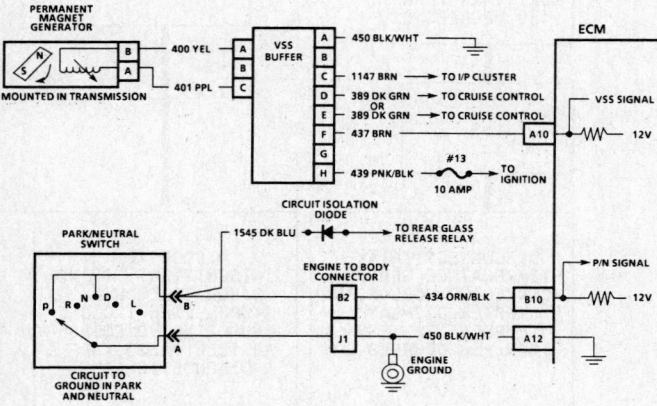

5.0L & 5.7L TBI B BODY

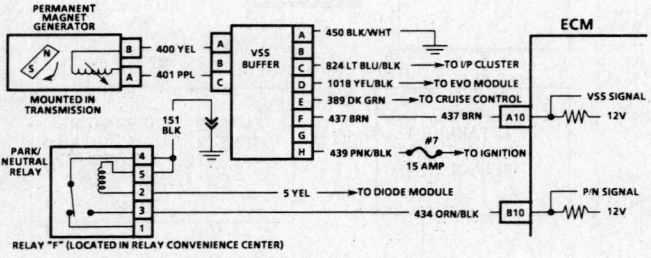

5.0L & 5.7L TBI D BODY

NOTE: Test numbers refer to test numbers on diagnostic chart.

1) Code 24 will set if VSS signal circuit voltage is constant, engine speed is 1200-4400 RPM, TPS indicates throttle is near idle position, transmission is not in Park or Neutral and all conditions have been met for at least 4 seconds.

2) A voltage of less than one volt at the instrument panel connector indicates that VSS signal circuit wire may be shorted to ground. Disconnect signal wire at the VSS buffer. If voltage remains less than 10 volts, circuit is shorted to ground or open. If circuit is not open or shorted to ground, check for poor control module connection or faulty control module.

DIAGNOSTIC AIDS

A faulty or misadjusted park/neutral switch may set a false Code 24. Use "Scan" tester and check for proper signal in Drive, while wiggling shifter.

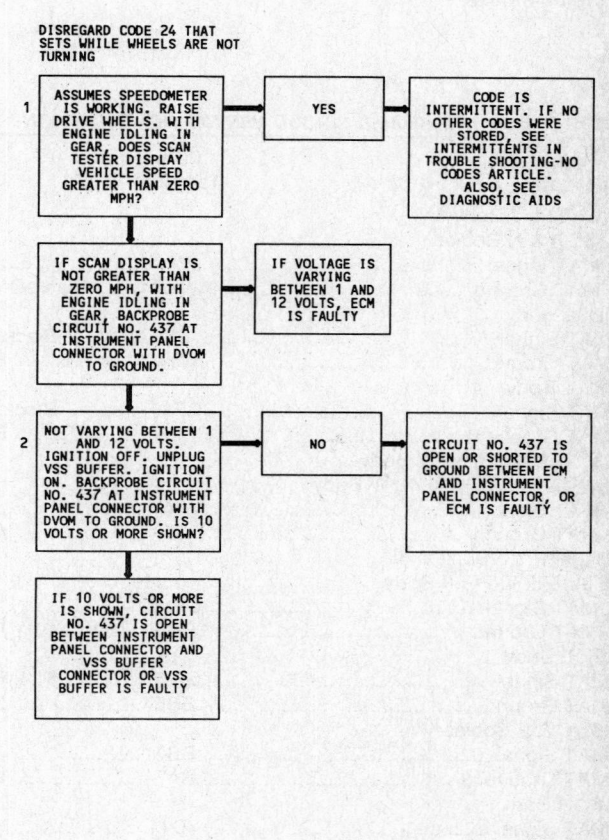

91H07397 91J07398 91B07399 91G07293

CODE 25, MAT SENSOR SIGNAL VOLTAGE LOW

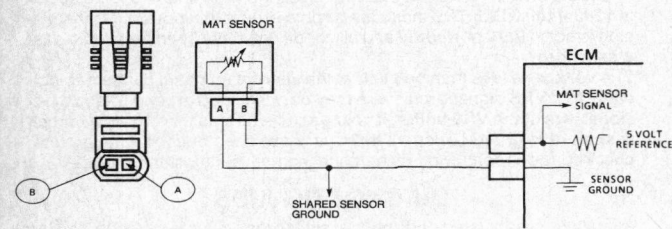

* – For shared sensor ground tie-offs, see appropriate diagram in WIRING DIAGRAMS.

CODE 25 ECM TERMINAL & CIRCUIT WIRING IDENTIFICATION

Application	ECM Terminal	Wire Color
2.0L, 2.2L J Body &		
2.5L A & N Bodies		
MAT Signal	B5	Tan
MAT Ground	W14	Black/Orange
2.2L L Body		
MAT Signal	B5	Black/Pink
MAT Ground	W14	Black
2.3L L Body		
MAT Signal	GF16	Black/Pink
MAT Ground	BB5	Black
2.3L W Body, 2.5L W Body		
& 3.1L W Body & 3.4L W Body		
MAT Signal	C4	Tan
MAT Ground	C5	Black
3.1L A, F & J Bodies, &		
5.0L & 5.7L PFI F Body		
MAT Signal	GF16	Tan
MAT Ground	BB5	Black
3.1L L Body		
MAT Signal	GF16	Pink/Black
MAT Ground	BB5	Black
3.8L C & E Bodies		
MAT Signal	BB7	Tan
MAT Ground	BA7	Black
3.8L H Body		
MAT Signal	YD11	Tan
MAT Ground	YD5	Black
3.8L W Body		
MAT Signal	R12	Tan
MAT Ground	R2	Black/White
5.0L & 5.7L TBI		
MAT Signal	C12	Tan
MAT Ground	A11	Black
5.7L Y Body		
MAT Signal	C4	Tan
MAT Ground	C5	Black/Pink

NOTE: Test numbers refer to test numbers on diagnostic chart.

1) This checks if the code is a hard failure or an intermittent condition. Code 25 will set if a MAT temperature greater than 266°F (130°C) is sensed for more than a precalibrated period.

2) This simulates condition for Code 23. if control module recognizes the open circuit and "Scan" tester displays a temperature of less than -30° C, control module and wiring are okay.

DIAGNOSTIC AIDS

If the engine is allowed to cool overnight, the coolant temperature sensor and MAT sensor should read close to each other, when measured with a "Scan" tester. A Code 25 will result if sensor signal circuit is shorted to ground. Check sensor for shifted calibration by using sensor TEMPERATURE-TO-RESISTANCE VALUES table.

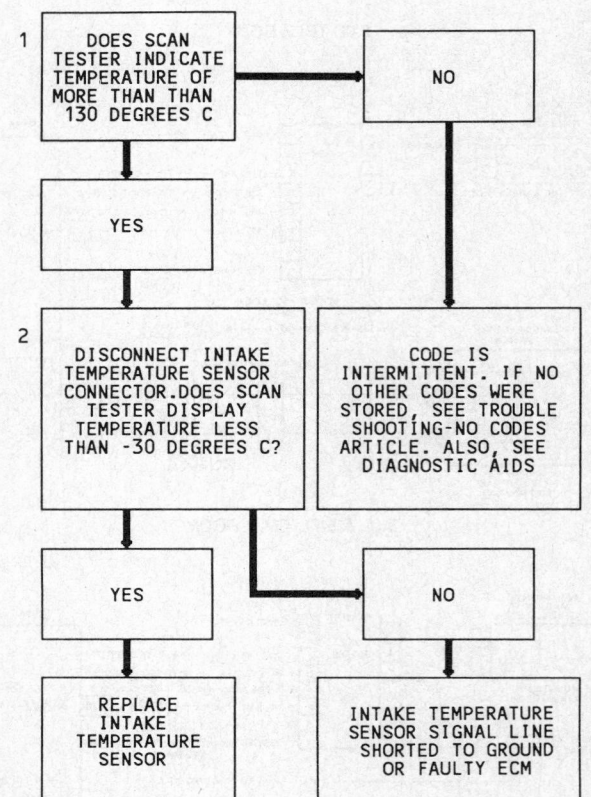

TEMPERATURE-TO-RESISTANCE VALUES [1]

Temperature °F (°C)	Ohms
210 (100)	185
160 (70)	450
100 (38)	1800
70 (20)	3400
20 (-7)	13,500
0 (-18)	25,000
-40 (-40)	100,700

[1] – Measure resistance across sensor terminals.

1991 ENGINE PERFORMANCE
Self-Diagnostics — ECM/PCM Except Cadillac (Cont.)

GM
1-53

CODE 26, QUAD-DRIVER ERROR
2.3L N BODY (1 OF 3)

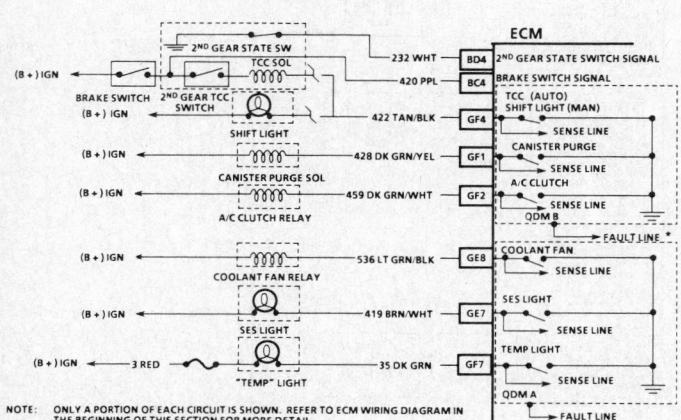

NOTE: ONLY A PORTION OF EACH CIRCUIT IS SHOWN. REFER TO ECM WIRING DIAGRAM IN THE BEGINNING OF THIS SECTION FOR MORE DETAIL.

The control module controls most components with electronic switches, completing a ground circuit when actuated. These switches are arranged in groups of 4, called Quad-Driver Modules (QDMs), which can independently control up to 4 outputs (control module terminals). When an output is actuated, the terminal is grounded and its voltage normally will be low. When an output is off, its terminal voltage will normally be high, except for the Torque Converter Clutch (TCC), which depends on the brake switch and 2nd gear TCC switch.

QDMs are fault protected. If a relay or solenoid coil is shorted, having very low resistance, or if control side of circuit is shorted to voltage, it would allow too much current into QDM. The QDM senses this and turns the output off, or its internal resistance increases to limit current flow and protect the QDM. The result is high output terminal voltage when it should be low. If the circuit from battery voltage or the component is open, or the control side of circuit is shorted to ground, terminal voltage will be low, even when output is turned off. Either of these conditions is considered to be a QDM fault.

Each QDM has a separate fault line to indicate the presence of a current fault to control module's central processor. A "Scan" tester displays the status of each of these fault lines as "low equals okay" or "high equals fault".

Because of the brake and 2nd gear switches in the TCC circuit, Code 26 is set under different conditions for QDM A and QDM B. Those conditions are as described:
• QDM A fault line equals "high" for 20 seconds or more.
• QDM B fault line equals "high" for 20 seconds or more and brake switch signal indicates switch is closed,
  2nd gear switch indicates transaxle is in 2nd or 3rd gear
  or TCC is commanded on.

NOTE: QDM B fault line on an automatic transaxle vehicle will normally be "high" when the vehicle is stopped. The control module ignores the QDM B fault line except under conditions noted above.

DIAGNOSTIC AIDS

Intermittent faults must be continuously present for at least 20 seconds to cause Code 26 to set. QDM controlled circuits should be inspected for poor terminal contact or damaged harness. The TCC circuit should be checked with the transaxle at operating temperature if Code 26 sets intermittently and no other cause is found, as a defective TCC solenoid resistance can drop too low (below 20 ohms) at high temperature. QDM faults can be detected as noted above and when outputs are on or off as follows:
• With open circuit or control circuit short to ground – output commanded off.
• With shorted device or control circuit short to voltage – output commanded on.

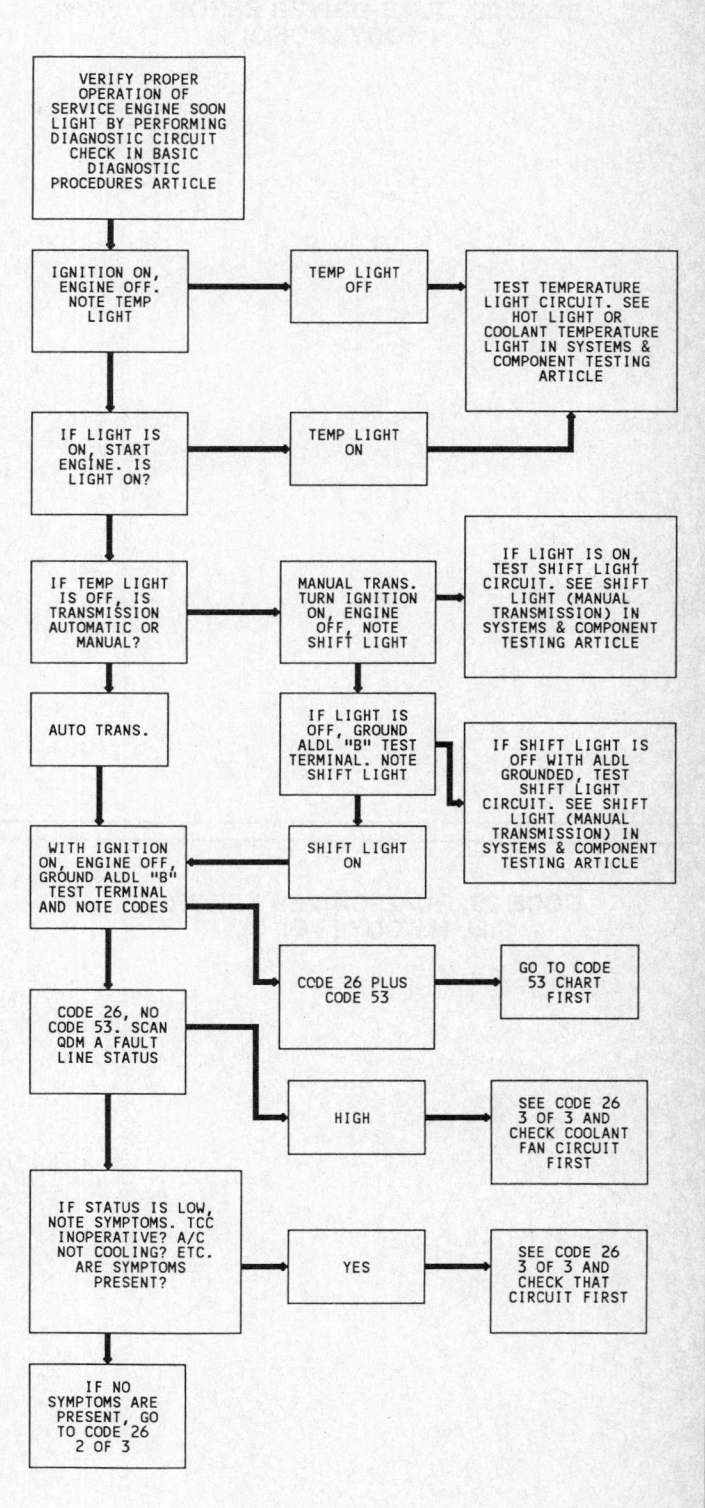

GM
1-54

1991 ENGINE PERFORMANCE
Self-Diagnostics — ECM/PCM Except Cadillac (Cont.)

CODE 26, QUAD-DRIVER ERROR
2.3L N BODY (2 OF 3)

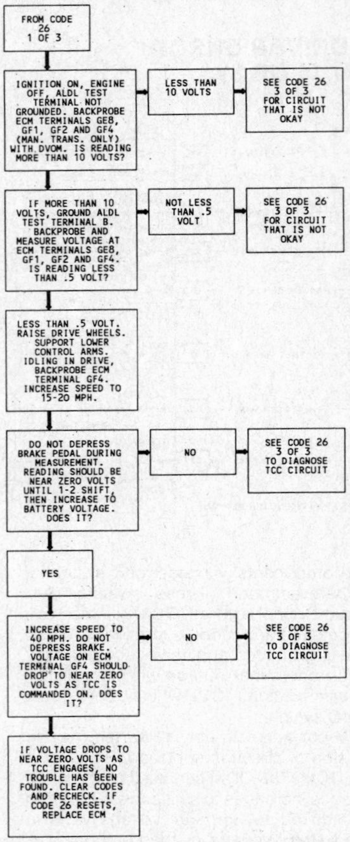

FROM CODE
26
1 OF 3

IGNITION ON, ENGINE OFF, ALDL TEST TERMINAL NOT GROUNDED. BACKPROBE ECM TERMINALS GE8, GF1, GF2 AND GF4 (MAN. TRANS. ONLY) WITH DVOM. IS READING MORE THAN 10 VOLTS?

LESS THAN 10 VOLTS → SEE CODE 26 3 OF 3 FOR CIRCUIT THAT IS NOT OKAY

IF MORE THAN 10 VOLTS, GROUND ALDL TEST TERMINAL B. BACKPROBE AND MEASURE VOLTAGE AT ECM TERMINALS GE8, GF1, GF2 AND GF4. IS READING LESS THAN .5 VOLT?

NOT LESS THAN .5 VOLT → SEE CODE 26 3 OF 3 FOR CIRCUIT THAT IS NOT OKAY

LESS THAN .5 VOLT. RAISE DRIVE WHEELS. SUPPORT LOWER CONTROL ARMS. IDLING IN DRIVE, BACKPROBE ECM TERMINAL GF4. INCREASE SPEED TO 15-20 MPH.

DO NOT DEPRESS BRAKE PEDAL DURING MEASUREMENT. READING SHOULD BE NEAR ZERO VOLTS UNTIL 1-2 SHIFT THEN INCREASE TO BATTERY VOLTAGE. DOES IT?

NO → SEE CODE 26 3 OF 3 TO DIAGNOSE TCC CIRCUIT

YES

INCREASE SPEED TO 40 MPH. DO NOT DEPRESS BRAKE. VOLTAGE ON ECM TERMINAL GF4 SHOULD DROP TO NEAR ZERO VOLTS AS TCC IS COMMANDED ON. DOES IT?

NO → SEE CODE 26 3 OF 3 TO DIAGNOSE TCC CIRCUIT

IF VOLTAGE DROPS TO NEAR ZERO VOLTS AS TCC ENGAGES, NO TROUBLE HAS BEEN FOUND. CLEAR CODES AND RECHECK. IF CODE 26 RESETS, REPLACE ECM

91D07296

CODE 26, QUAD-DRIVER ERROR
2.3L N BODY (3 OF 3)

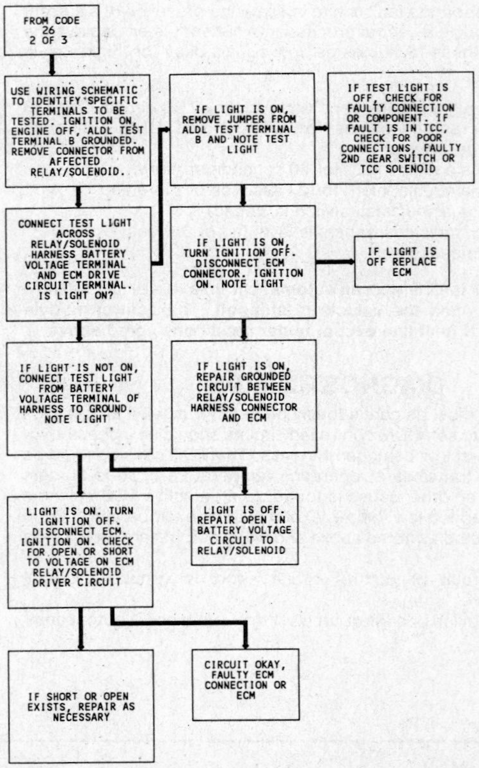

FROM CODE
26
2 OF 3

USE WIRING SCHEMATIC TO IDENTIFY SPECIFIC TERMINALS TO BE TESTED. IGNITION ON, ENGINE OFF, ALDL TEST TERMINAL B GROUNDED. REMOVE CONNECTOR FROM AFFECTED RELAY/SOLENOID.

IF LIGHT IS ON, REMOVE JUMPER FROM ALDL TEST TERMINAL B AND NOTE TEST LIGHT

IF TEST LIGHT IS OFF, CHECK FOR FAULTY CONNECTION OR COMPONENT. IF FAULT IS IN TCC, CHECK FOR POOR CONNECTIONS, FAULTY 2ND GEAR SWITCH OR TCC SOLENOID

CONNECT TEST LIGHT ACROSS RELAY/SOLENOID HARNESS BATTERY VOLTAGE TERMINAL AND ECM DRIVE CIRCUIT TERMINAL. IS LIGHT ON?

IF LIGHT IS ON, TURN IGNITION OFF. DISCONNECT ECM CONNECTOR. IGNITION ON. NOTE LIGHT

IF LIGHT IS OFF REPLACE ECM

IF LIGHT IS NOT ON, CONNECT TEST LIGHT FROM BATTERY VOLTAGE TERMINAL OF HARNESS TO GROUND. NOTE LIGHT

IF LIGHT IS ON, REPAIR GROUNDED CIRCUIT BETWEEN RELAY/SOLENOID HARNESS CONNECTOR AND ECM

LIGHT IS ON. TURN IGNITION OFF. DISCONNECT ECM. IGNITION ON. CHECK FOR OPEN OR SHORT TO VOLTAGE ON ECM RELAY/SOLENOID DRIVER CIRCUIT

LIGHT IS OFF. REPAIR OPEN IN BATTERY VOLTAGE CIRCUIT TO RELAY/SOLENOID

IF SHORT OR OPEN EXISTS, REPAIR AS NECESSARY

CIRCUIT OKAY, FAULTY ECM CONNECTION OR ECM

91F07297

1991 ENGINE PERFORMANCE
Self-Diagnostics — ECM/PCM Except Cadillac (Cont.)

GM
1-55

CODE 26, QUAD-DRIVER ERROR
2.3L W BODY (1 OF 3)

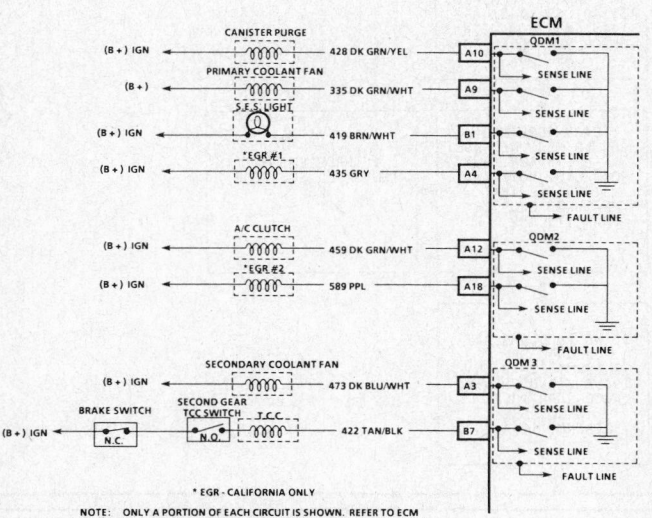

NOTE: ONLY A PORTION OF EACH CIRCUIT IS SHOWN. REFER TO ECM
WIRING DIAGRAMS IN THE BEGINNING OF THIS SECTION FOR MORE DETAIL.

The control module controls most components with electronic switches completing a ground circuit when actuated. These switches are arranged in groups of 4, called Quad-Driver Modules (QDM's), which can independently control up to 4 outputs (control module terminals). When an output is actuated, the terminal is grounded and its voltage normally will be low. When an output is off, its terminal voltage normally will be high, except for the TCC, which depends on the brake and 2nd gear TCC switches.

QDM's are fault protected. If a relay or solenoid coil is shorted, having very low resistance, or if control side of circuit is shorted to voltage, it would allow too much current into QDM. The QDM senses this and turns the output off, or its internal resistance increases to limit current flow and protect the QDM. The result is high output terminal voltage when it should be low. If the circuit from battery voltage or the component is open, or the control side of circuit is shorted to ground, terminal voltage will be low, even when output is turned off. Either of these conditions is considered to be a QDM fault.

The control module ignores the fault line signal from QDM 3 to prevent false setting of Code 26 due to brake or 2nd gear TCC series switches. As a result, QDM 3 circuit problems will not cause a Code 26 although the circuits are fault protected and operate the same as QDMs 1 and 2.

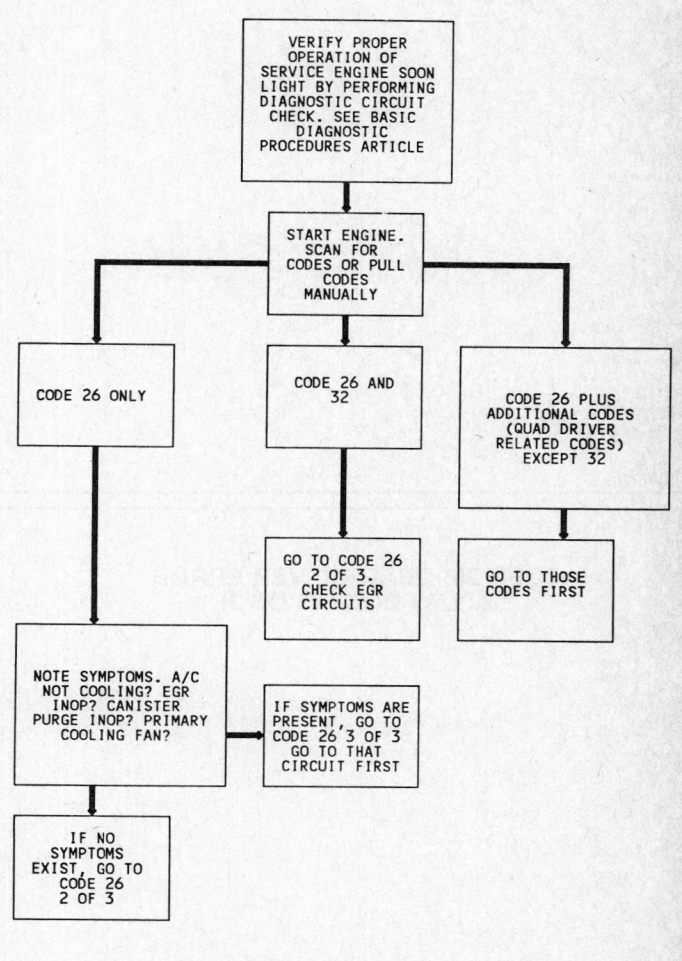

91H07401 91H07298

GM
1-56

1991 ENGINE PERFORMANCE
Self-Diagnostics — ECM/PCM Except Cadillac (Cont.)

CODE 26, QUAD-DRIVER ERROR
2.3L W BODY (2 OF 3)

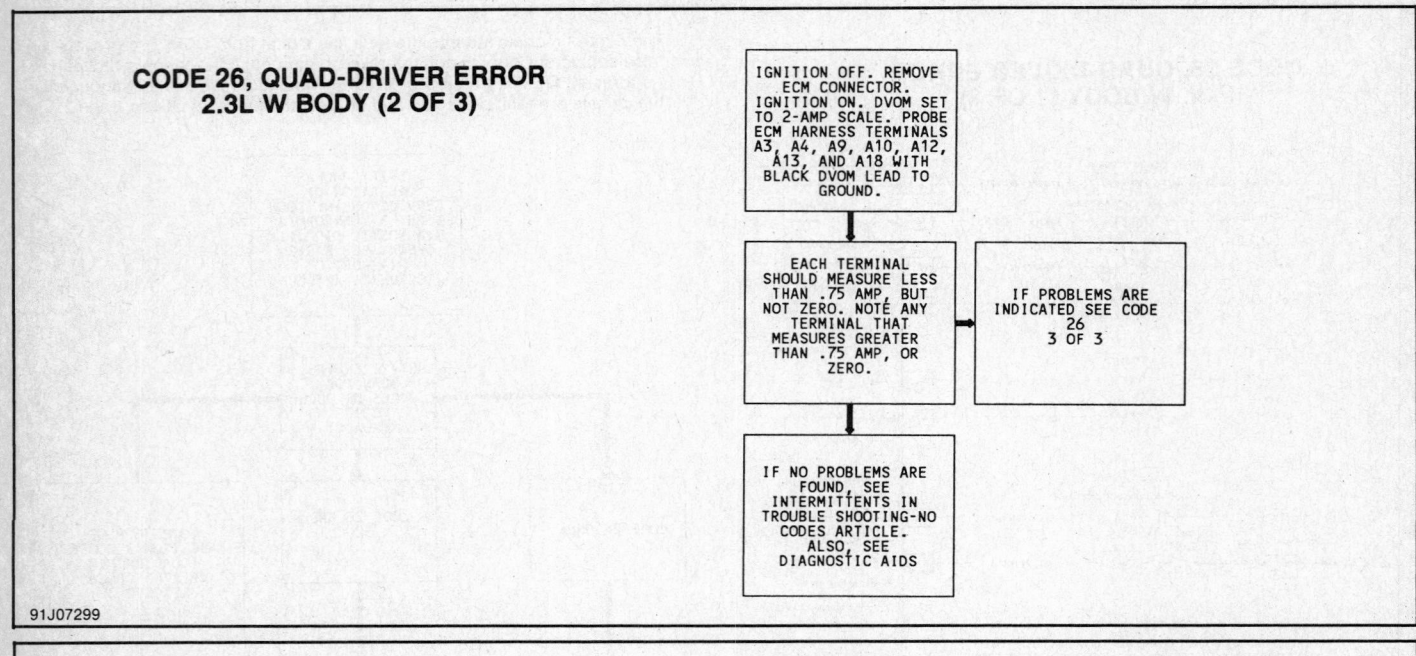

IGNITION OFF. REMOVE ECM CONNECTOR. IGNITION ON. DVOM SET TO 2-AMP SCALE. PROBE ECM HARNESS TERMINALS A3, A4, A9, A10, A12, A13, AND A18 WITH BLACK DVOM LEAD TO GROUND.

EACH TERMINAL SHOULD MEASURE LESS THAN .75 AMP, BUT NOT ZERO. NOTE ANY TERMINAL THAT MEASURES GREATER THAN .75 AMP, OR ZERO.

IF PROBLEMS ARE INDICATED SEE CODE 26 3 OF 3

IF NO PROBLEMS ARE FOUND, SEE INTERMITTENTS IN TROUBLE SHOOTING-NO CODES ARTICLE. ALSO, SEE DIAGNOSTIC AIDS

91J07299

CODE 26, QUAD-DRIVER ERROR
2.3L W BODY (3 OF 3)

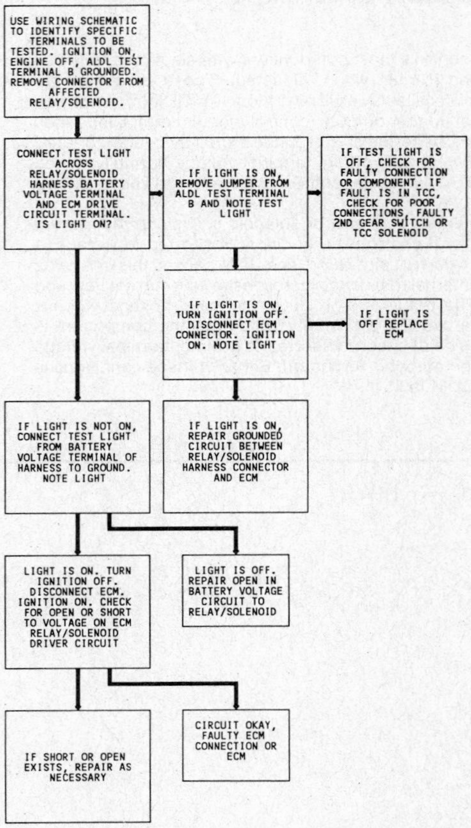

USE WIRING SCHEMATIC TO IDENTIFY SPECIFIC TERMINALS TO BE TESTED. IGNITION ON, ENGINE OFF, ALDL TEST TERMINAL B GROUNDED. REMOVE CONNECTOR FROM AFFECTED RELAY/SOLENOID.

CONNECT TEST LIGHT ACROSS RELAY/SOLENOID HARNESS BATTERY VOLTAGE TERMINAL AND ECM DRIVE CIRCUIT TERMINAL. IS LIGHT ON?

IF LIGHT IS ON, REMOVE JUMPER FROM ALDL TEST TERMINAL B AND NOTE TEST LIGHT

IF TEST LIGHT IS OFF, CHECK FOR FAULTY CONNECTION OR COMPONENT. IF FAULT IS IN TCC, CHECK FOR POOR CONNECTIONS, FAULTY 2ND GEAR SWITCH OR TCC SOLENOID

IF LIGHT IS ON, TURN IGNITION OFF. DISCONNECT ECM CONNECTOR. IGNITION ON. NOTE LIGHT

IF LIGHT IS OFF REPLACE ECM

IF LIGHT IS NOT ON, CONNECT TEST LIGHT FROM BATTERY VOLTAGE TERMINAL OF HARNESS TO GROUND. NOTE LIGHT

IF LIGHT IS ON, REPAIR GROUNDED CIRCUIT BETWEEN RELAY/SOLENOID HARNESS CONNECTOR AND ECM

LIGHT IS ON. TURN IGNITION OFF. DISCONNECT ECM. IGNITION ON. CHECK FOR OPEN OR SHORT TO VOLTAGE ON ECM RELAY/SOLENOID DRIVER CIRCUIT

LIGHT IS OFF. REPAIR OPEN IN BATTERY VOLTAGE CIRCUIT TO RELAY/SOLENOID

IF SHORT OR OPEN EXISTS, REPAIR AS NECESSARY

CIRCUIT OKAY, FAULTY ECM CONNECTION OR ECM

91D07300

1991 ENGINE PERFORMANCE
Self-Diagnostics — ECM/PCM Except Cadillac (Cont.)

GM
1-57

CODE 26, QUAD-DRIVER CIRCUIT
3.8L W BODY (1 OF 4)

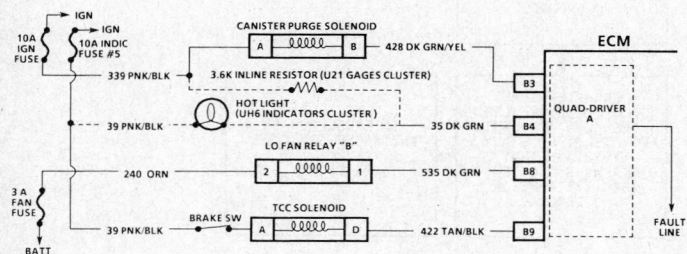

Each ECM Quad-Driver has a fault line which is monitored by the ECM. The ECM compares voltage values of the fault line with acceptable values in ECM memory. If the ECM senses other than accepted values, a Code 26 will set.

NOTE: Test numbers refer to test numbers on diagnostic chart.

1) The ECM does not know which controlled circuit set the Code 26 so this chart will go through each circuit to determine which is at fault. On vehicles equipped with an ECM controlled hot light, this test checks hot light driver and hot light circuit.

2) QDM SYMPTOMS
- TCC inoperative, Code 39
- Hot light on all the time, off during bulb check.
- Cooling fans on low speed all of the time or will not come on at all.
- Poor driveability due to 100 percent canister purge.

DIAGNOSTIC AIDS

The coolant temperature sensor, in rare cases, may fail to indicate the correct coolant temperature without setting a malfunction code (Code 14 or 15). This could result in turning on the hot light without having an overheating condition. It could also result in engine overheating without turning on the hot light. Check coolant sensor temperature-to-resistance values in SENSOR OPERATING RANGES article.

HOT LIGHT DIAGNOSIS

NOTE: These checks assume vehicle is not overheating. Verify proper operation of cooling system prior to diagnosing hot light.

Hot light is powered by the 10-amp INDIC fuse. Light will turn on when ECM provides a ground for the circuit. If circuit grounds between light and ECM, light will illuminate any time the ignition is turned on.

1) Turn ignition on with engine off (bulb test position). If hot light illuminates, go to step **3)**. If hot light does not illuminate, check the following:
- 10-amp INDIC fuse.
- Faulty instrument cluster bulb
- Open circuit between fuse and hot light.

2) Backprobe terminal B4 at ECM with a test light to battery voltage. Turn ignition on. If test light does not illuminate, ECM terminal connection is bad or ECM is faulty. If test light illuminates, turn ignition off. Disconnect ECM connectors. Jumper terminal B4 to ground. Turn ignition on. If hot light does not illuminate, check for open circuit between hot light and ECM. If light does not illuminate and all circuits are intact and power is available to light, instrument cluster must be replaced.

3) Start engine. If test light goes off, no problem is evident. See DIAGNOSTIC AIDS. If test light is on, turn ignition off. Disconnect ECM connector. Probe ECM harness terminal B4 with a test light to battery voltage. If light is off, replace ECM. If light is on, repair short to ground in circuit No. 35. If no short is present, replace instrument cluster.

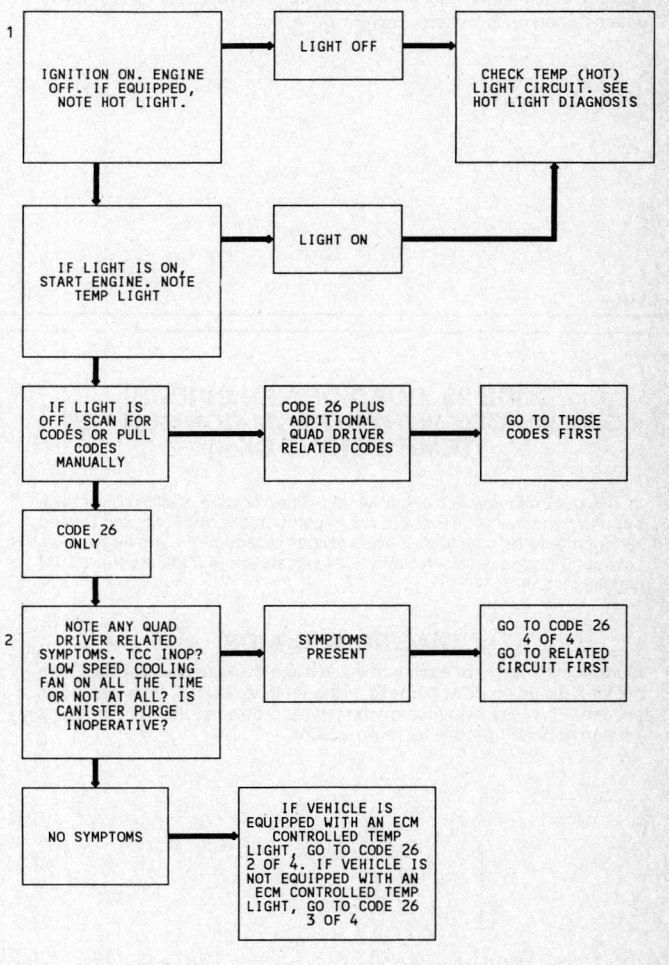

91J07402 91F07301

GM
1-58

1991 ENGINE PERFORMANCE
Self-Diagnostics — ECM/PCM Except Cadillac (Cont.)

CODE 26, QUAD-DRIVER CIRCUIT 3.8L W BODY WITH ECM-CONTROLLED TEMP LIGHT (2 OF 4)

3) This determines which circuit is out of specification.

DIAGNOSTIC AIDS

Monitor the voltage of each terminal while moving related harness connectors, including ECM harness. If the fault is induced, the voltage will change. This may help locate intermittent problems. If code reappears with no apparent problems, replace ECM.

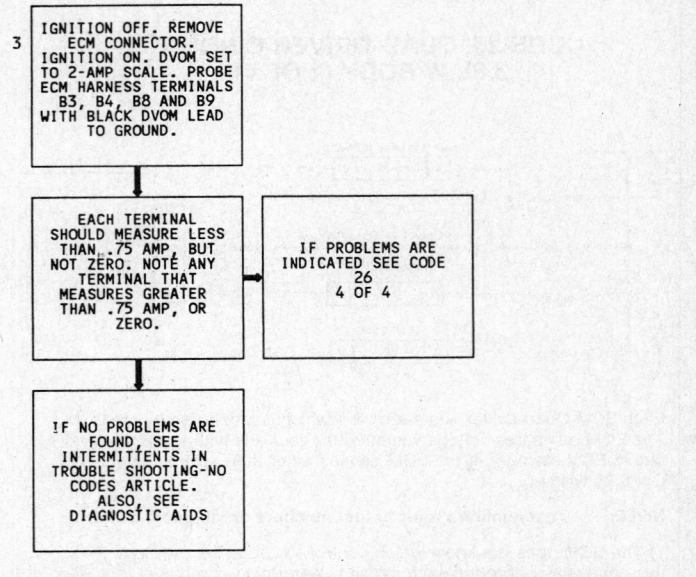

91H07302

CODE 26, QUAD-DRIVER CIRCUIT 3.8L W BODY WITHOUT ECM-CONTROLLED TEMP LIGHT (3 OF 4)

3) This determines which circuit is out of specification. If all circuits check out okay, the in-line resistor (used in place of the hot light) and related wiring should be checked. In-line resistor is taped into engine harness between right power center and ECM pigtail, about 2 inches from ECM pigtail junction.

DIAGNOSTIC AIDS

Monitor the voltage of each terminal while moving related harness connectors, including ECM harness. If the fault is induced, the voltage will change. This may help locate intermittent problems. If code reappears with no apparent problems, replace ECM.

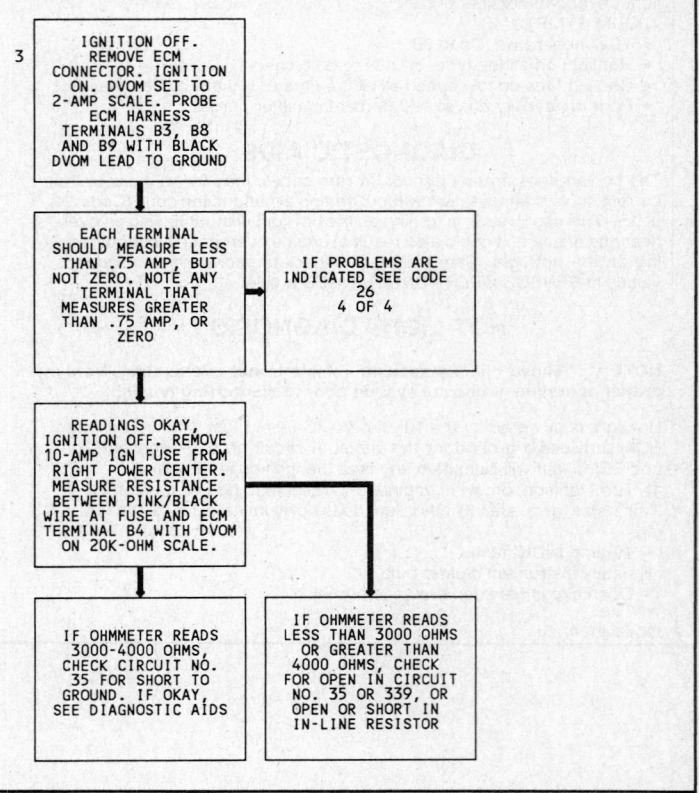

91J07303

1991 ENGINE PERFORMANCE
Self-Diagnostics — ECM/PCM Except Cadillac (Cont.)

GM
1-59

CODE 26, QUAD-DRIVER CIRCUIT
3.8L W BODY (4 OF 4)

4) This determines if the problem is the circuit or the component. Factory-installed ECM has an internal fuse and it's unlikely ECM needs replacing.

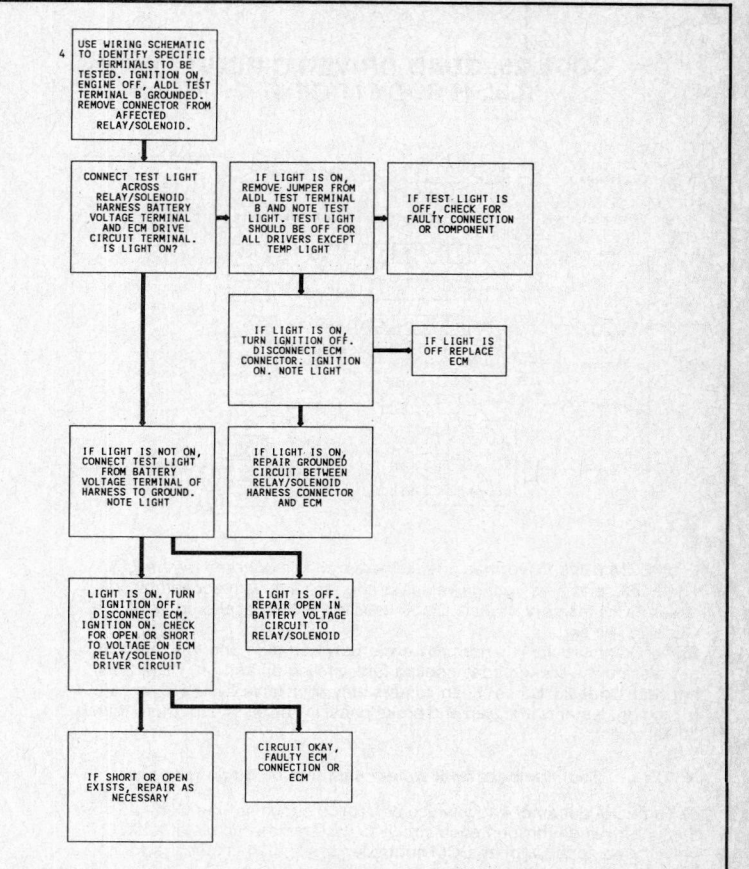

91B07304

CODE 26, QUAD-DRIVER CIRCUIT
3.8L H BODY (1 OF 3)

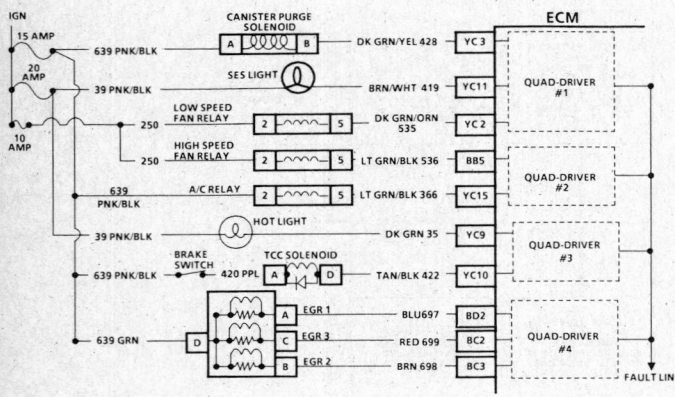

Each ECM Quad-Driver has a fault line which is monitored by the ECM. The ECM compares voltage values of the fault line with acceptable values in ECM memory. If the ECM senses other than accepted values, a Code 26 will set.

Some QDM circuits will normally cycle between high and low, such as depressing the brake pedal, cooling fans cycling on and off. QDM 2 will not set a Code 26. Some "Scan" testers may set a false Code 26 if engine is running, tester is installed and brake pedal is depressed for more than 30 seconds.

NOTE: Test numbers refer to test numbers on diagnostic chart.

1) The ECM does not know which controlled circuit set the Code 26 so this chart will go through each circuit to determine which is at fault. On vehicles equipped with an ECM controlled hot light, this test checks hot light driver and hot light circuit.
2) QDM SYMPTOMS
- TCC inoperative, Code 39
- EGR inoperative, Codes 63, 64 and 65.
- Hot light on all the time, off during bulb check.
- Cooling fan on low speed all of the time or will not come on at all.
- Poor driveability due to 100 percent canister purge.

DIAGNOSTIC AIDS

The coolant temperature sensor, in rare cases, may fail to indicate the correct coolant temperature without setting a malfunction code (Code 14 or 15). This could result in turning on the hot light without having an over-heating condition. It could also result in engine overheating without turning on the hot light. Check coolant sensor temperature-to-resistance values in SENSOR OPERATING RANGES article.

HOT LIGHT DIAGNOSIS

NOTE: These checks assume vehicle is not overheating. Verify proper operation of cooling system prior to diagnosing hot light.

Hot light is powered by the 10-amp INDIC fuse. Light will turn on when ECM provides a ground for the circuit. If circuit grounds between light and ECM, light will illuminate any time the ignition is turned on.
1) Turn ignition on with engine off (bulb test position). If hot light illuminates, go to step **3)**. If hot light does not illuminate, check the following:
- 10-amp INDIC fuse.
- Faulty instrument cluster bulb
- Open circuit between fuse and hot light.
2) Backprobe terminal YC9 at ECM with a test light to battery voltage. Turn ignition on. If test light does not illuminate, ECM terminal

connection is bad or ECM is faulty. If test light illuminates, turn ignition off. Disconnect ECM connectors. Jumper terminal YC9 to ground. Turn ignition on. If hot light does not illuminate, check for open circuit between hot light and ECM. If light does not illuminate and all circuits are intact and power is available to light, instrument cluster must be replaced.
3) Start engine. If test light goes off, no problem is evident. See DIAGNOSTIC AIDS. If test light is on, turn ignition off. Disconnect ECM connector. Probe ECM harness terminal YC9 with a test light to battery voltage. If light is off, replace ECM. If light is on, repair short to ground in circuit No. 35. If no short is present, replace instrument cluster.

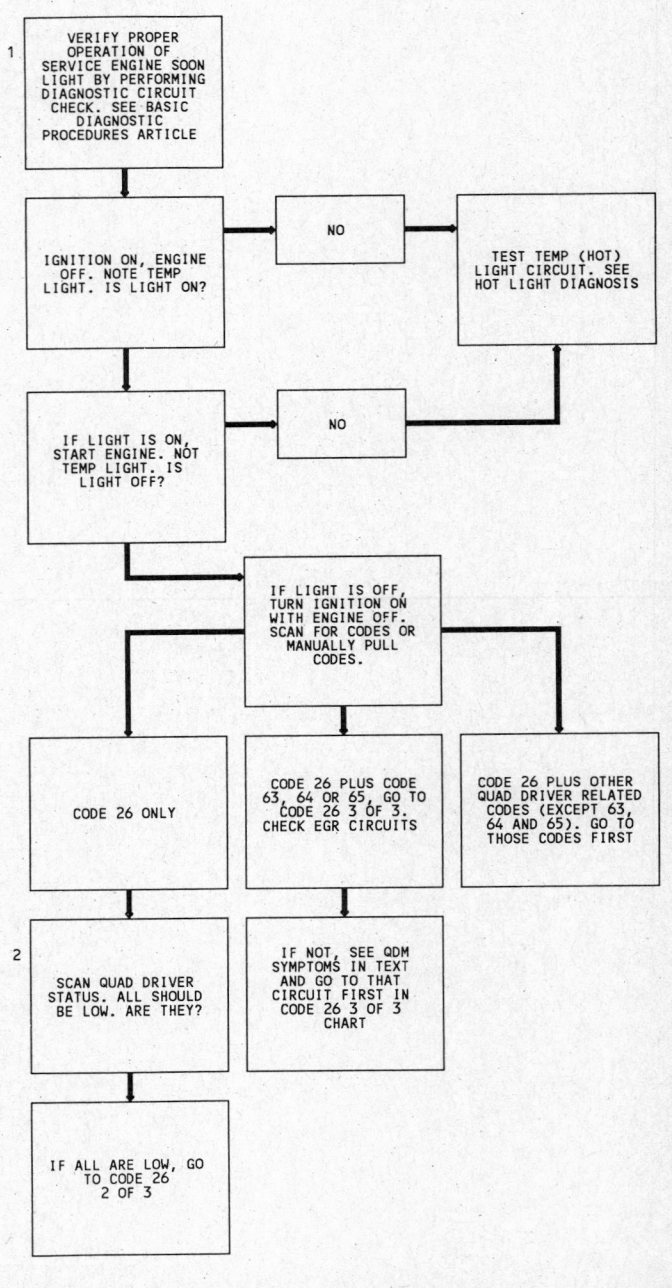

1991 ENGINE PERFORMANCE
Self-Diagnostics — ECM/PCM Except Cadillac (Cont.)

GM
1-61

CODE 26, QUAD-DRIVER CIRCUIT
3.8L H BODY (2 OF 3)

3) This determines which circuit is out of specification. All circuits except SERVICE ENGINE SOON light and hot light should have battery voltage with engine running and ALDL test terminal "B" not grounded.

DIAGNOSTIC AIDS

Monitor the voltage of each terminal while moving related harness connectors, including control module harness. If the fault is induced, the voltage will change. This may help locate intermittent problems. If code reappears with no apparent problems, replace control module.

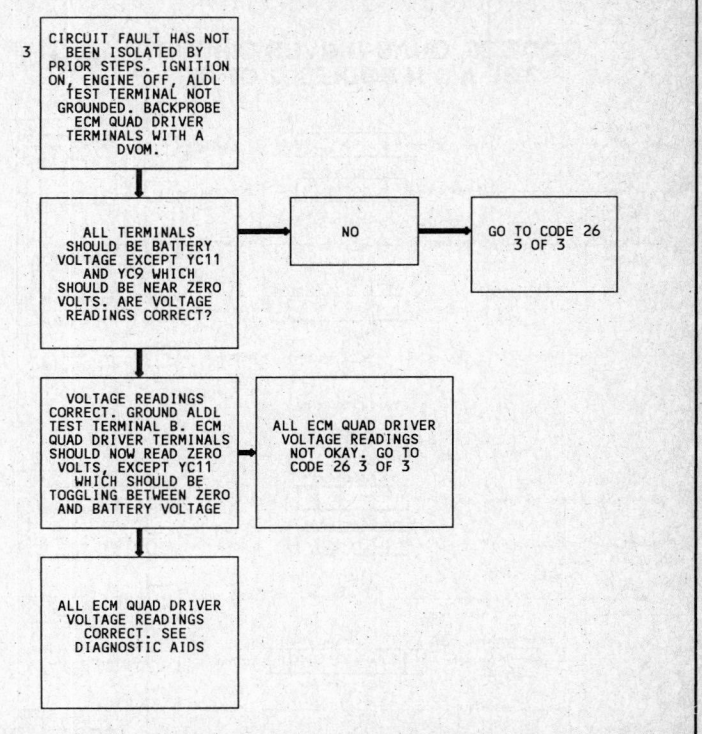

91G07306

CODE 26, QUAD-DRIVER CIRCUIT
3.8L H BODY (3 OF 3)

4) This determines if the problem is the circuit or the component. Factory-installed ECM has an internal fuse and it's unlikely ECM needs replacing.

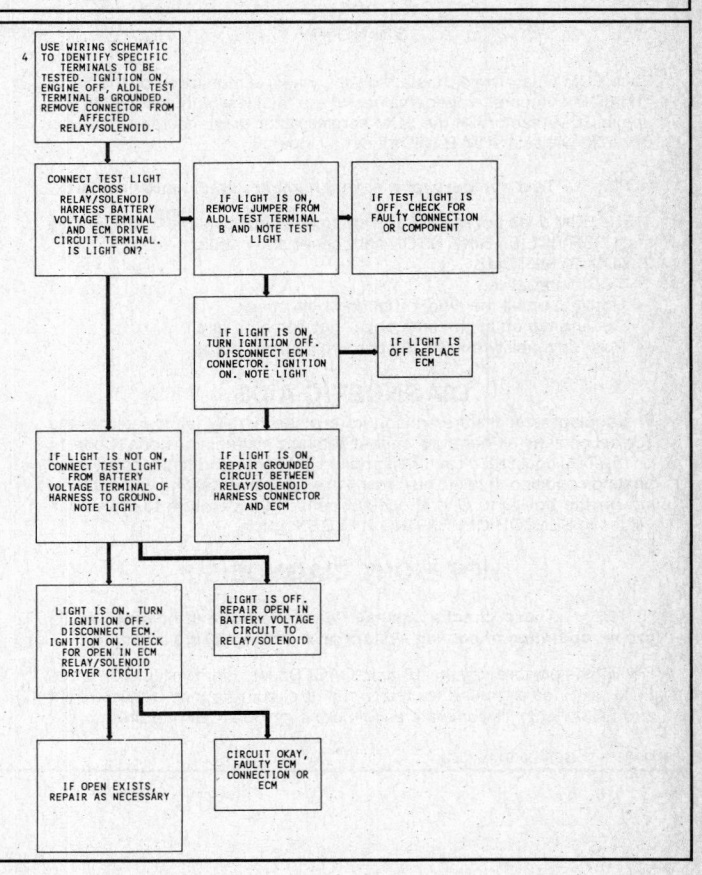

91I07307

CODE 26, QUAD-DRIVER CIRCUIT
3.3L A & N BODIES (1 OF 3)

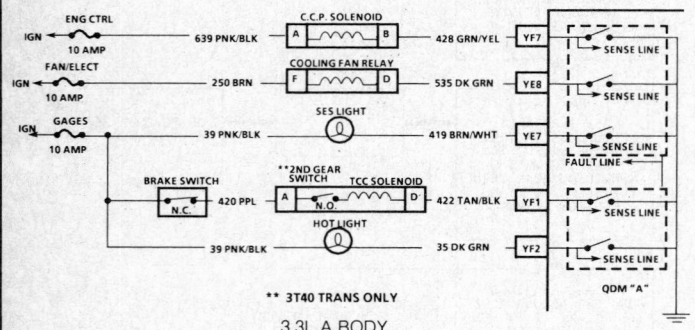

3.3L A BODY

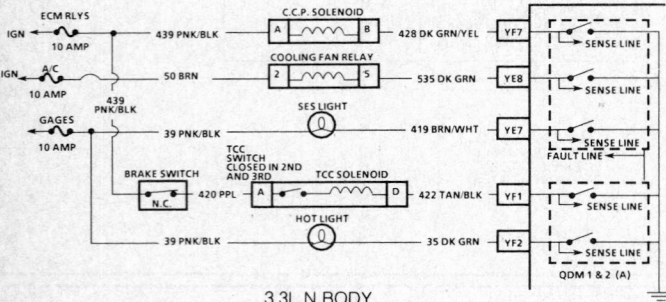

3.3L N BODY

Each ECM Quad-Driver has a fault line which is monitored by the ECM. The ECM compares voltage values of the fault line with acceptable values in ECM memory. If the ECM senses other than accepted values, a Code 26 will set. QDM B will not set a Code 26.

NOTE: Test numbers refer to test numbers on diagnostic chart.

1) The ECM does not know which controlled circuit set the Code 26. This tests SERVICE ENGINE SOON light driver and circuit.
2) QDM SYMPTOMS
- TCC inoperative.
- Hot light on all the time, off during bulb check.
- Cooling fan on all the time or will not come on at all.
- Poor driveability due to 100 percent canister purge.

DIAGNOSTIC AIDS

The coolant temperature sensor, in rare cases, may fail to indicate the correct coolant temperature without setting a malfunction code (Code 14 or 15). This could result in turning on the hot light without having an overheating condition. It could also result in engine overheating without turning on the hot light. Check coolant sensor temperature-to-resistance values in SENSOR OPERATING RANGES article.

HOT LIGHT DIAGNOSIS

NOTE: These checks assume vehicle is not overheating. Verify proper operation of cooling system prior to diagnosing hot light.

Hot light is powered by the 10-amp GAGES fuse. Light will turn on when ECM provides a ground for the circuit. If circuit grounds between light and ECM, light will illuminate any time the ignition is turned on.

91D07404 91G07405 91A07308

1) Turn ignition on with engine off (bulb test position). If hot light illuminates, go to step 3). If hot light does not illuminate, check the following:
- 10-amp GAGES fuse.
- Faulty instrument cluster bulb
- Open circuit between fuse and hot light.

2) Backprobe terminal YE2 (A body) or YF2 (N body) at ECM with a test light to battery voltage. Turn ignition on. If test light does not illuminate, ECM terminal connection is bad or ECM is faulty. If test light illuminates, turn ignition off. Disconnect ECM connectors. Jumper terminal YE2 (A body) or YF2 (N body) to ground. Turn ignition on. If hot light does not illuminate, check for open circuit between hot light and ECM. If light does not illuminate and all circuits are intact and power is available to light, instrument cluster must be replaced.

3) Start engine. If test light goes off, no problem is evident. See DIAGNOSTIC AIDS. If test light is on, turn ignition off. Disconnect ECM connector. Probe ECM harness terminal YE2 (A body) or YF2 (N body) with a test light to battery voltage. If light is off, replace ECM. If light is on, repair short to ground in circuit No. 35. If no short is present, replace instrument cluster.

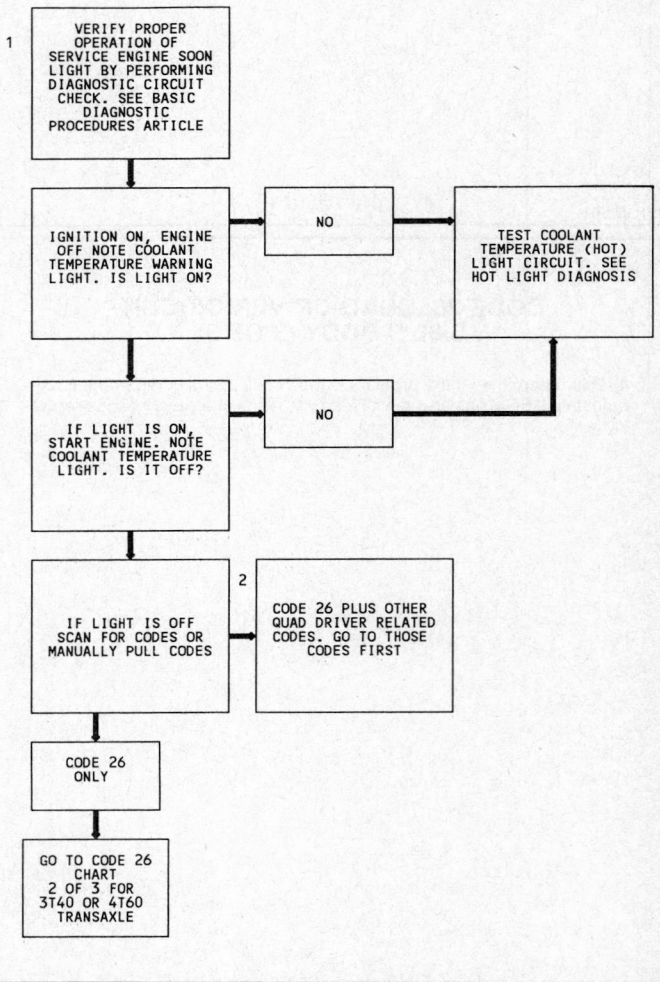

1991 ENGINE PERFORMANCE
Self-Diagnostics — ECM/PCM Except Cadillac (Cont.)

GM
1-63

CODE 26, QUAD-DRIVER CIRCUIT
3.3L A & N BODIES WITH 3T40 TRANS.
(2 OF 3)

On vehicle with a 3T40 transmission, QDM A fault status on "Scan" tester should read HIGH until 2nd gear switch is closed or brake is applied. To simulate driving in 2nd gear and change status to LOW, disconnect TCC connector and connect test light between harness terminals A and D.

NOTE: Test numbers refer to test numbers on diagnostic chart.

3) This step determines which circuit is out of specification.

DIAGNOSTIC AIDS

Monitor the voltage of each terminal while moving related harness connectors, including ECM harness. If the fault is induced, the voltage will change. This may help locate intermittent problems. If code reappears with no apparent problems, replace ECM.

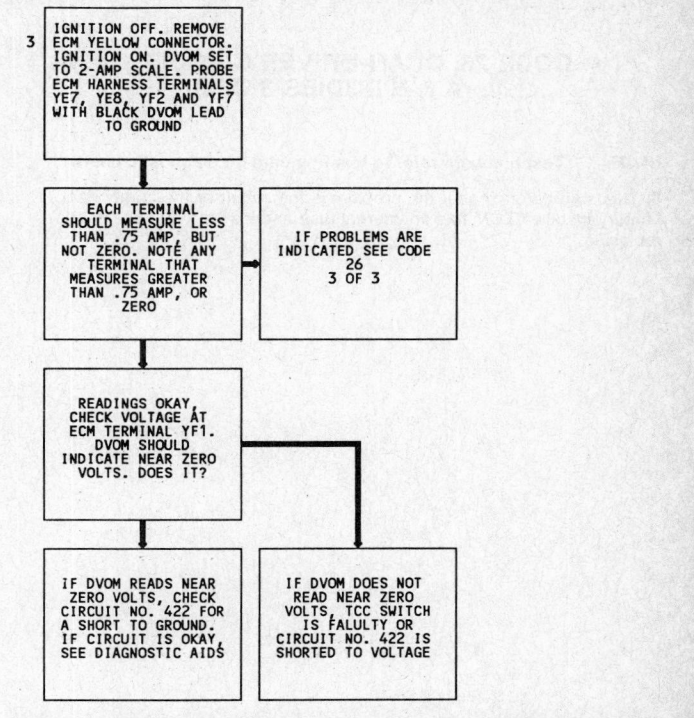

91C07309

CODE 26, QUAD-DRIVER CIRCUIT
3.3L A & N BODIES WITH 4T60 TRANS.
(2 OF 3)

NOTE: Test numbers refer to test numbers on diagnostic chart.

3) This step determines which circuit is out of specification.

DIAGNOSTIC AIDS

Monitor the voltage of each terminal while moving related harness connectors, including ECM harness. If the fault is induced, the voltage will change. This may help locate intermittent problems. If code reappears with no apparent problems, replace ECM.

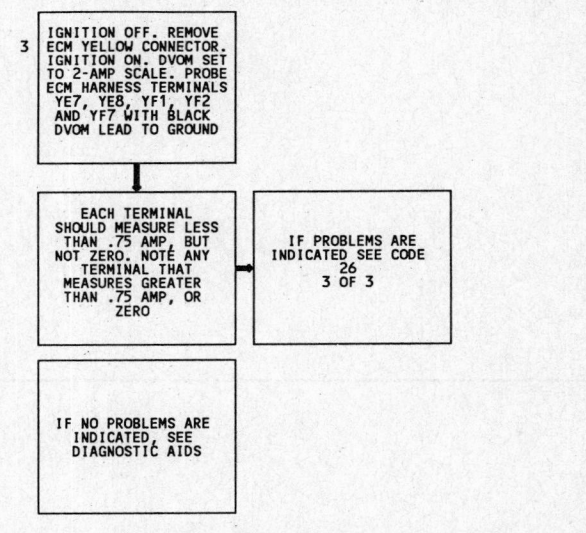

91E07310

GM
1-64

1991 ENGINE PERFORMANCE
Self-Diagnostics — ECM/PCM Except Cadillac (Cont.)

CODE 26, QUAD-DRIVER CIRCUIT
3.3L (A & N BODIES 3 OF 3)

NOTE: Test numbers refer to test numbers on diagnostic chart.

4) This step determines if the problem is the circuit or the component. Factory-installed ECM has an internal fuse and it's unlikely ECM needs replacing.

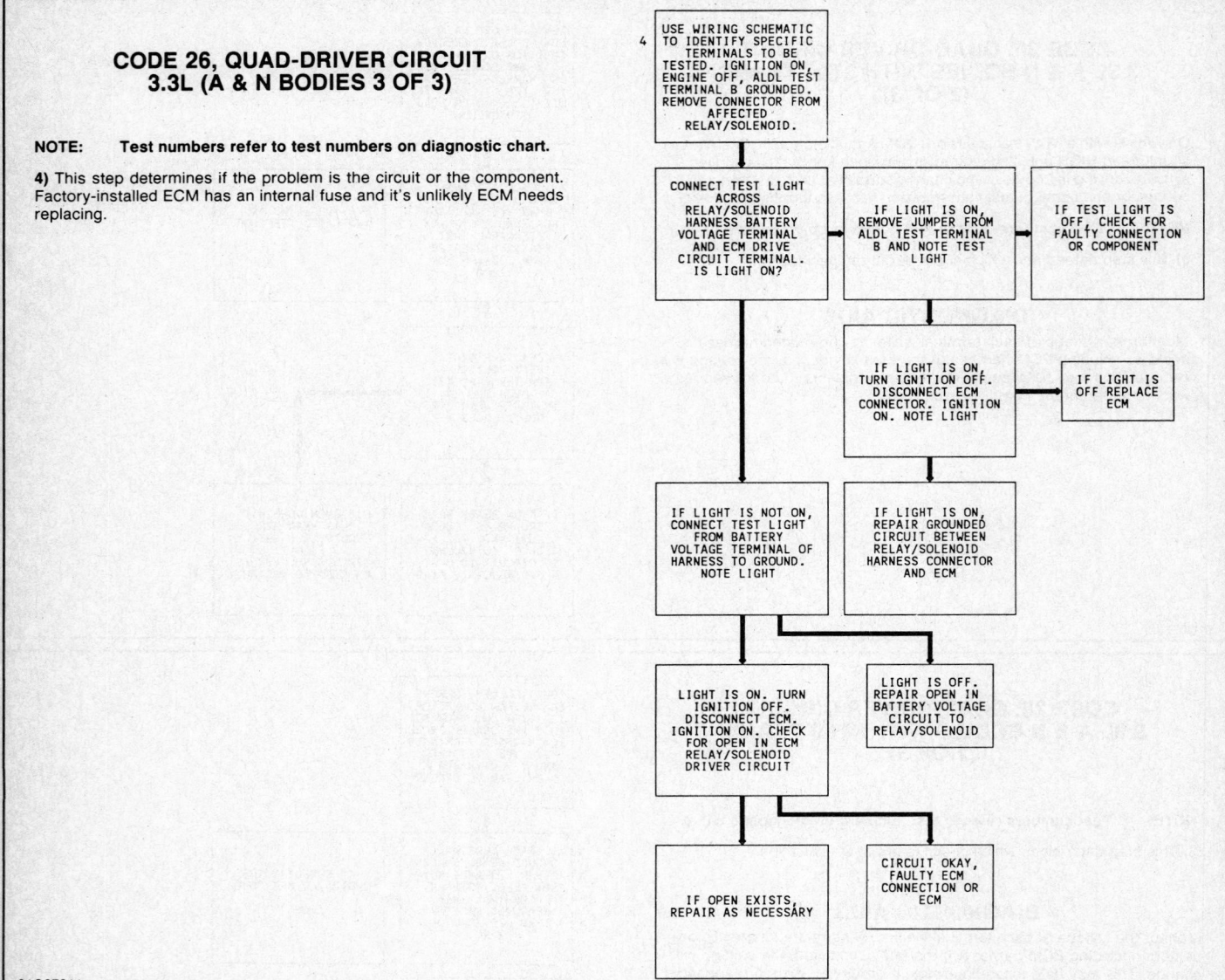

91G07311

1991 ENGINE PERFORMANCE
Self-Diagnostics — ECM/PCM Except Cadillac (Cont.)

GM
1-65

CODE 26, QUAD-DRIVER CIRCUIT
2.3L L BODY (1 OF 3)

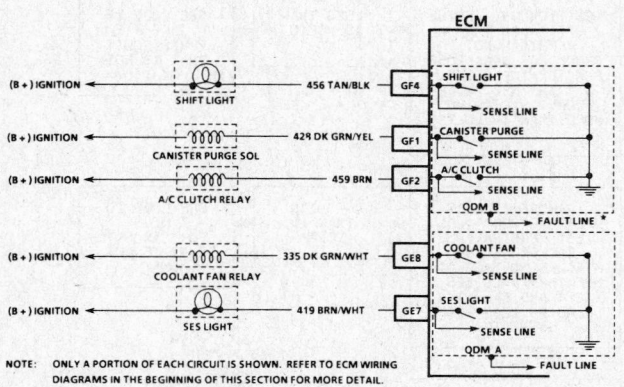

NOTE: ONLY A PORTION OF EACH CIRCUIT IS SHOWN. REFER TO ECM WIRING DIAGRAMS IN THE BEGINNING OF THIS SECTION FOR MORE DETAIL.

The ECM controls most components with electronic switches completing a ground circuit when actuated. These switches are arranged in groups of 4, called Quad-Driver Modules (QDMs), which can independently control up to 4 outputs (control module terminals). When an output is actuated, the terminal is grounded and its voltage normally will be low. When an output is off, its terminal voltage will normally be high.

QDMs are fault protected. If a relay or solenoid coil is shorted, having very low resistance, or if control side of circuit is shorted to voltage, it would allow too much current into QDM. The QDM senses this and turns the output off, or its internal resistance increases to limit current flow and protect the QDM. The result is high output terminal voltage when it should be low. If the circuit from battery voltage or the component is open, or the control side of circuit is shorted to ground, terminal voltage will be low, even when output is turned off. Either of these conditions is considered to be a QDM fault.

Each QDM has a separate fault line to indicate the presence of a current fault to control module's central processor. A "Scan" tester displays the status of each of these fault lines as "low equals okay" or "high equals fault".

DIAGNOSTIC AIDS

Intermittent faults must be continuously present for at least 20 seconds to cause Code 26 to set. QDM controlled circuits should be inspected for poor terminal contact or damaged harness. QDM faults can be detected as noted above and when outputs are on or off as follows:

- Open circuit or control circuit short to ground – output commanded off.
- Shorted device or control circuit short to voltage – output commanded on.

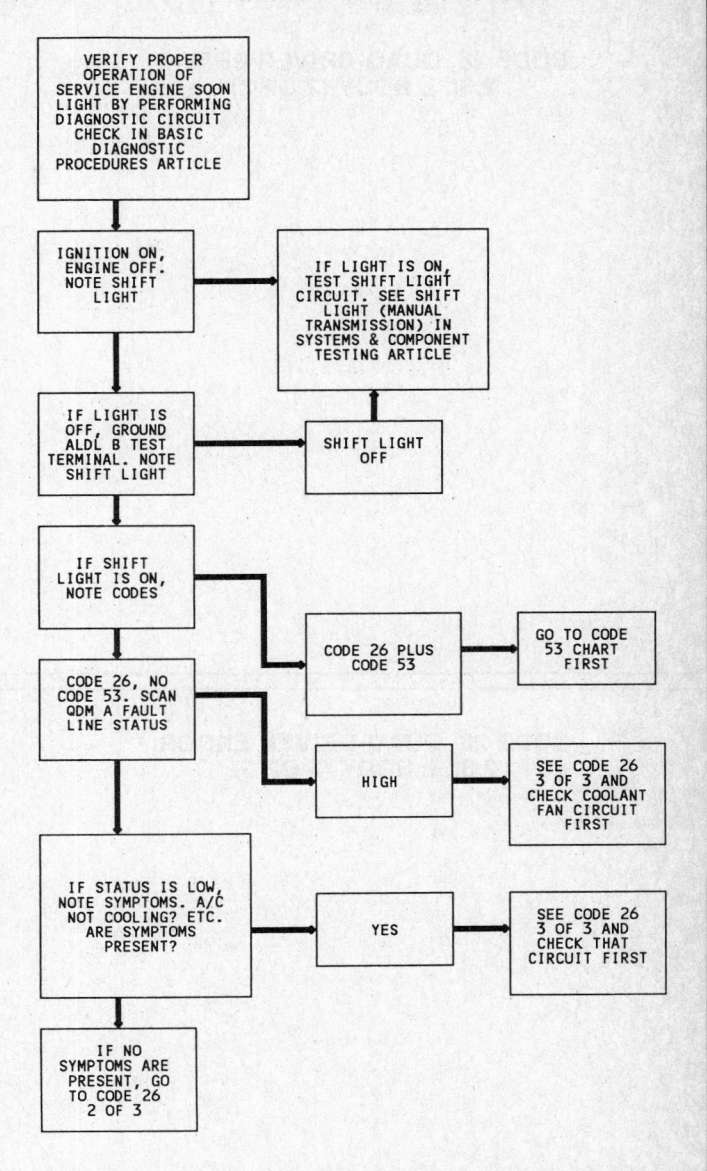

91I07406 91I07312

CODE 26, QUAD-DRIVER ERROR
2.3L L BODY (2 OF 3)

CODE 26, QUAD-DRIVER ERROR
2.3L L BODY (3 OF 3)

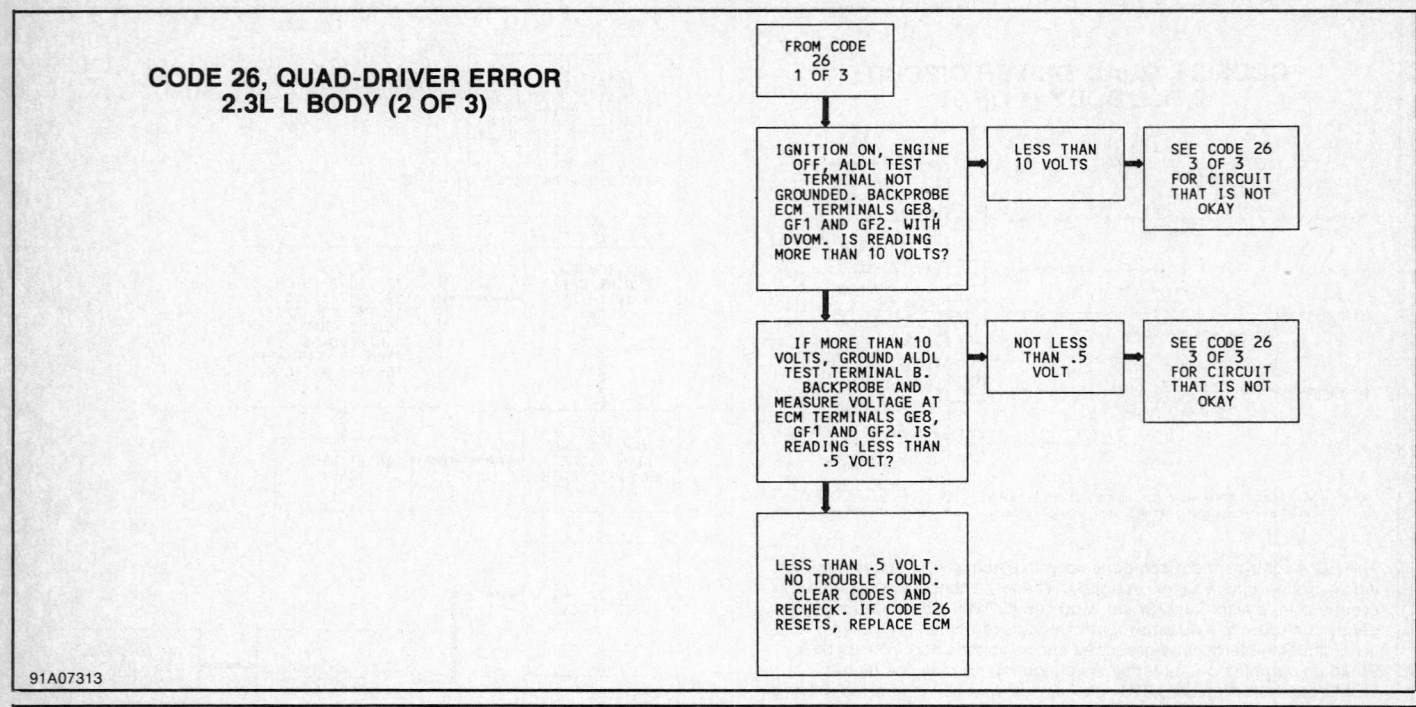

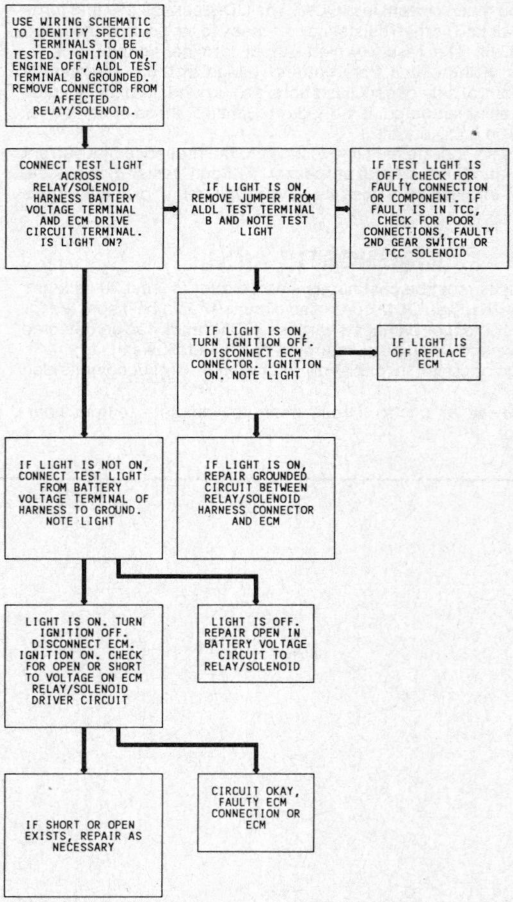

FROM CODE 26 1 OF 3

IGNITION ON, ENGINE OFF, ALDL TEST TERMINAL NOT GROUNDED. BACKPROBE ECM TERMINALS GE8, GF1 AND GF2. WITH DVOM. IS READING MORE THAN 10 VOLTS?

LESS THAN 10 VOLTS

SEE CODE 26 3 OF 3 FOR CIRCUIT THAT IS NOT OKAY

IF MORE THAN 10 VOLTS, GROUND ALDL TEST TERMINAL B. BACKPROBE AND MEASURE VOLTAGE AT ECM TERMINALS GE8, GF1 AND GF2. IS READING LESS THAN .5 VOLT?

NOT LESS THAN .5 VOLT

SEE CODE 26 3 OF 3 FOR CIRCUIT THAT IS NOT OKAY

LESS THAN .5 VOLT. NO TROUBLE FOUND. CLEAR CODES AND RECHECK. IF CODE 26 RESETS, REPLACE ECM

91A07313

USE WIRING SCHEMATIC TO IDENTIFY SPECIFIC TERMINALS TO BE TESTED. IGNITION ON, ENGINE OFF, ALDL TEST TERMINAL B GROUNDED. REMOVE CONNECTOR FROM AFFECTED RELAY/SOLENOID.

CONNECT TEST LIGHT ACROSS RELAY/SOLENOID HARNESS BATTERY VOLTAGE TERMINAL AND ECM DRIVE CIRCUIT TERMINAL. IS LIGHT ON?

IF LIGHT IS ON, REMOVE JUMPER FROM ALDL TEST TERMINAL B AND NOTE TEST LIGHT

IF TEST LIGHT IS OFF, CHECK FOR FAULTY CONNECTION OR COMPONENT. IF FAULT IS IN TCC, CHECK FOR POOR CONNECTIONS, FAULTY 2ND GEAR SWITCH OR TCC SOLENOID

IF LIGHT IS ON, TURN IGNITION OFF. DISCONNECT ECM CONNECTOR. IGNITION ON, NOTE LIGHT

IF LIGHT IS OFF REPLACE ECM

IF LIGHT IS NOT ON, CONNECT TEST LIGHT FROM BATTERY VOLTAGE TERMINAL OF HARNESS TO GROUND. NOTE LIGHT

IF LIGHT IS ON, REPAIR GROUNDED CIRCUIT BETWEEN RELAY/SOLENOID HARNESS CONNECTOR AND ECM

LIGHT IS ON. TURN IGNITION OFF. DISCONNECT ECM. IGNITION ON. CHECK FOR OPEN OR SHORT TO VOLTAGE ON ECM RELAY/SOLENOID DRIVER CIRCUIT

LIGHT IS OFF. REPAIR OPEN IN BATTERY VOLTAGE CIRCUIT TO RELAY/SOLENOID

IF SHORT OR OPEN EXISTS, REPAIR AS NECESSARY

CIRCUIT OKAY, FAULTY ECM CONNECTION OR ECM

91C07314

1991 ENGINE PERFORMANCE
Self-Diagnostics — ECM/PCM Except Cadillac (Cont.)

GM
1-67

CODE 26, QUAD-DRIVER CIRCUIT
3.8L C & E BODIES (1 OF 3)

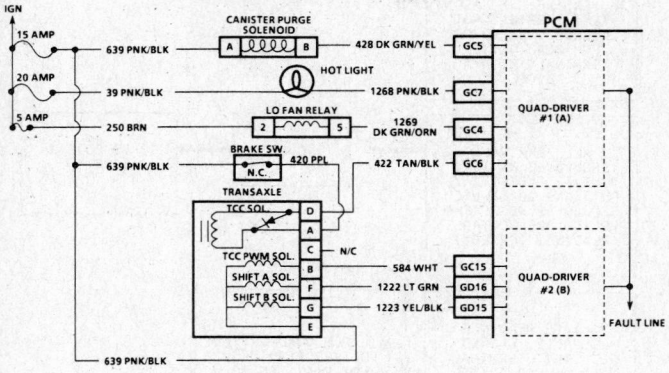

3.8L C BODY

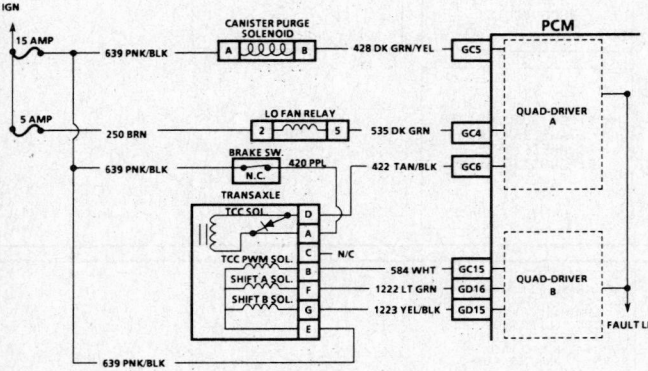

3.8L E BODY (REATTA & RIVIERA)

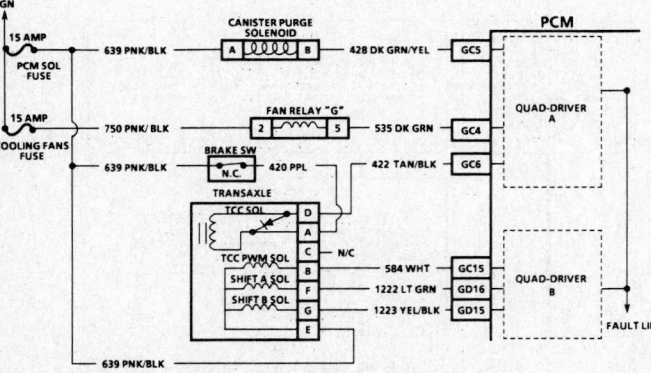

3.8L E BODY (TORONADO & TROFEO)

Each PCM Quad-Driver has a fault line which is monitored by the PCM. The PCM compares voltage values of the fault line with acceptable values in PCM memory. If the PCM senses other than accepted values, a Code 26 will set.

Some QDM circuits will normally cycle between high and low, such as depressing the brake pedal. Some "Scan" testers may set a false Code 26 if engine is running, tester is installed and brake pedal is depressed for more than 30 seconds.

NOTE: Test numbers refer to test numbers on diagnostic chart.

1) The PCM does not know which controlled circuit set the Code 26 so this chart will go through each of the circuits to determine which is at fault. This step tests SERVICE ENGINE SOON light driver and circuit.

QDM SYMPTOMS
- Hot light (C body) on all the time, off during bulb check.
- Cooling fan on low speed all of the time or will not come on at all.
- Poor driveability due to 100 percent canister purge.

DIAGNOSTIC AIDS

The coolant temperature sensor, in rare cases, may fail to indicate the correct coolant temperature without setting a malfunction code (Code 14 or 15). This could result in turning on the hot light without having an overheating condition. It could also result in engine overheating without turning on the hot light. Check coolant sensor temperature-to-resistance values in SENSOR OPERATING RANGES article.

HOT LIGHT DIAGNOSIS (C BODY)

NOTE: These checks assume vehicle is not overheating. Verify proper operation of cooling system prior to diagnosing hot light.

Hot light is powered by a 15 or 20-amp fuse No. 6 (depending upon instrument cluster option). Light will turn on when PCM provides a ground for the circuit. If circuit grounds between light and PCM, light will illuminate any time the ignition is turned on.

1) Turn ignition on with engine off (bulb test position). If hot light illuminates, go to step **3)**. If hot light does not illuminate, check the following:
- 15 or 20-amp fuse No. 6 in I.P. fuse panel.
- Faulty instrument cluster bulb.
- Open circuit between fuse and hot light.

2) Backprobe terminal GC7 at PCM with a test light to battery voltage. Turn ignition on. If test light does not illuminate, PCM terminal connection is bad or PCM is faulty. If test light illuminates, turn ignition off. Disconnect ECM connectors. Jumper terminal GC7 to ground. Turn ignition on. If hot light does not illuminate, check for open circuit between hot light and PCM. If light does not illuminate and all circuits are intact and power is available to light, instrument cluster must be replaced.

3) Start engine. If test light goes off, no problem is evident. See DIAGNOSTIC AIDS. If test light is on, turn ignition off. Disconnect PCM connector. Probe ECM harness terminal GC7 with a test light to battery voltage. If light is off, replace PCM. If light is on, repair short to ground in circuit No. 1268. If no short is present, replace instrument cluster.

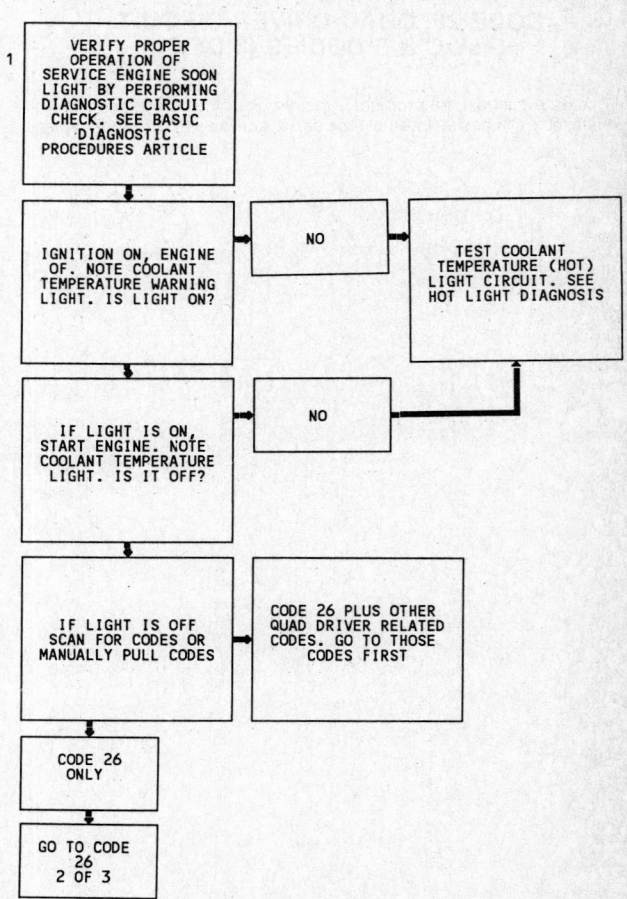

GM
1-68

1991 ENGINE PERFORMANCE
Self-Diagnostics — ECM/PCM Except Cadillac (Cont.)

CODE 26, QUAD-DRIVER CIRCUIT
3.8L C & E BODIES (2 OF 3)

2) This determines which circuit is out of specification. All circuits except GD16 and GD15 should have battery voltage with ignition on, engine not running and ALDL test terminal not grounded.

DIAGNOSTIC AIDS

Monitor the voltage of each terminal while moving related harness connectors, including PCM harness. If the fault is induced, the voltage will change. This may help locate intermittent problems. If code reappears with no apparent problems, replace PCM.

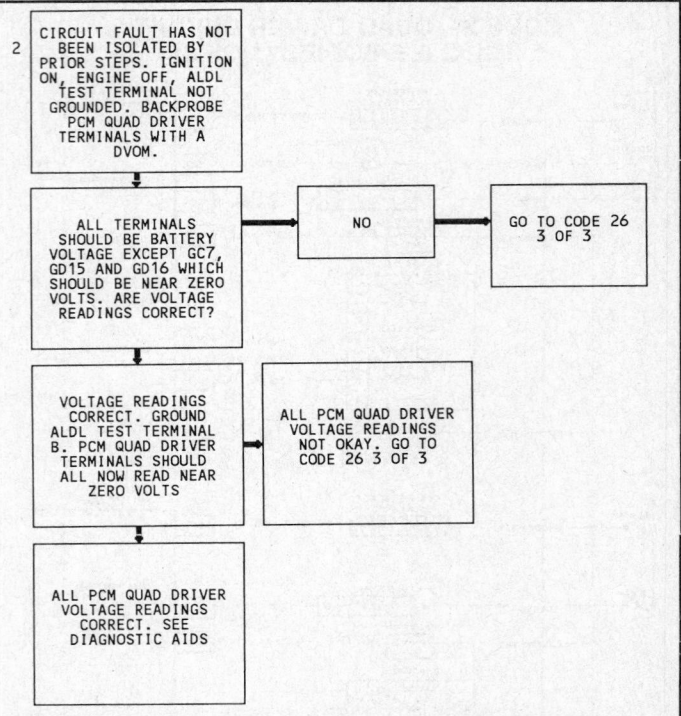

91H07316

CODE 26, QUAD-DRIVER CIRCUIT
3.8L C & E BODIES (3 OF 3)

3) This determines if the problem is the circuit or the component. Factory-installed PCM has an internal fuse and it's unlikely PCM needs replacing.

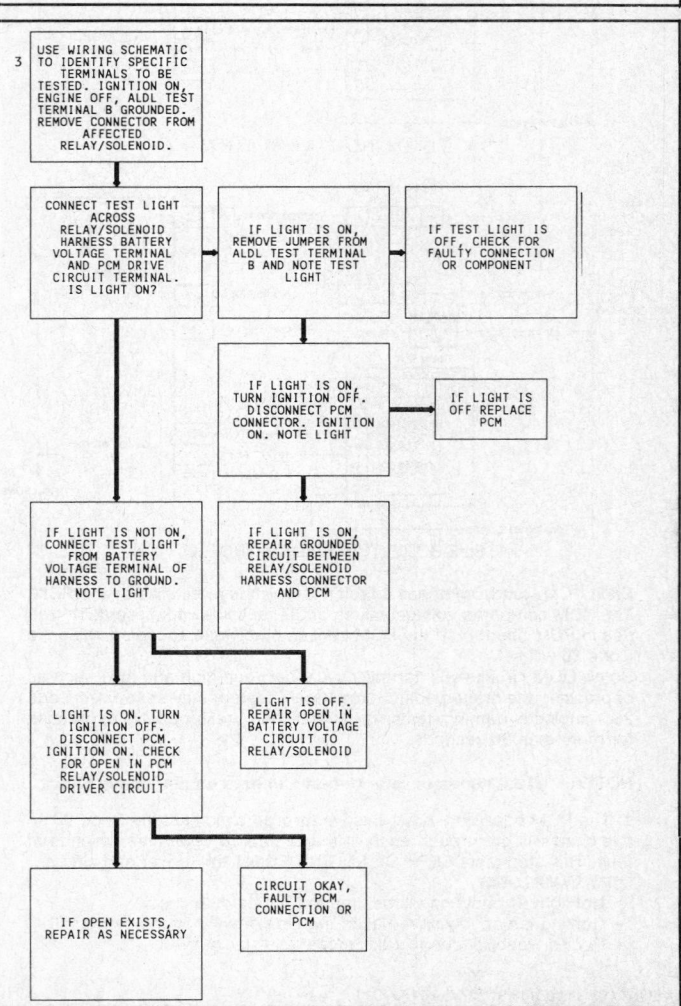

91J07317

1991 ENGINE PERFORMANCE
Self-Diagnostics — ECM/PCM Except Cadillac (Cont.)

GM
1-69

CODE 27 OR 28, GEAR SWITCH CIRCUITS 3.3L WITH 3T40 TRANSAXLE

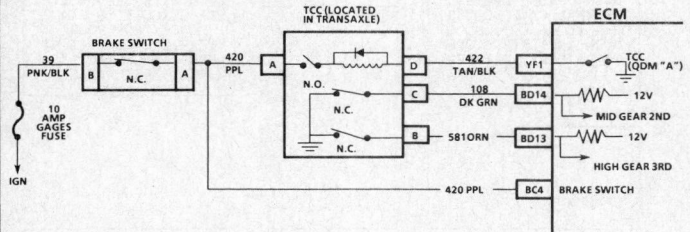

3.3L A BODY

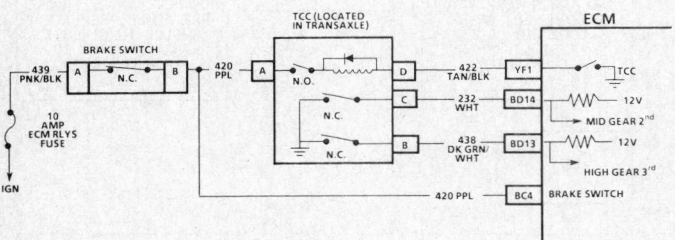

3.3L N BODY

The gear switches are located inside the transaxle. Switches are normally closed. As road speed increases, hydraulic pressure applies the specific gear clutches and the gear switch opens. The ECM uses the gear switches to control fuel delivery and TCC operation.

Code 27 will set if circuit No. 108 indicates ground or closed switch for 12 seconds when the vehicle is in 3rd gear or if circuit No. 108 indicates an open when engine is first started.

Code 28 will set if circuit No. 581 indicates ground or closed switch for 10 seconds when the vehicle is in 3rd gear or if circuit No. 581 indicates an open when engine is first started.

NOTE: **Test numbers refer to test numbers on diagnostic chart.**

1) A digital volt-ohmmeter must be used in this test. A test light will not work due to the low voltage supplied by the ECM.
2) Checks if the circuit is grounded through the switch.
3) Checks for a good, properly operating switch and checks circuit within transaxle for an improper ground.

DIAGNOSTIC AIDS

Check for poor connections at ECM pins. Inspect harness for incorrect routing (too close to high voltage wiring) or chafing. Monitor the voltage of each terminal while moving related harness connectors. If the failure is induced, the voltage reading will change.

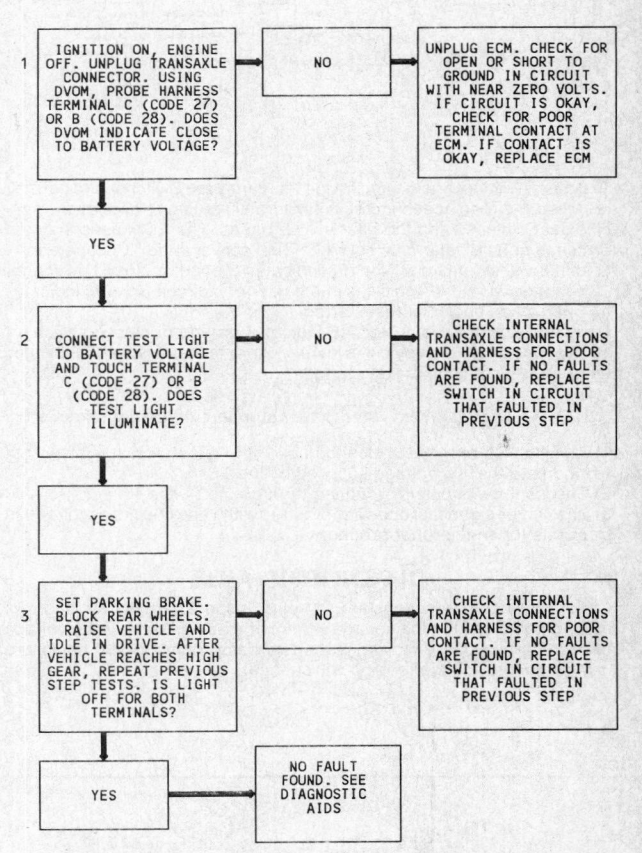

91C07408 91E07409 91B07318

GM
1-70

1991 ENGINE PERFORMANCE
Self-Diagnostics — ECM/PCM Except Cadillac (Cont.)

CODE 28 OR 29, GEAR SWITCH CIRCUITS
3.3L A BODY WITH 4T60 TRANSAXLE

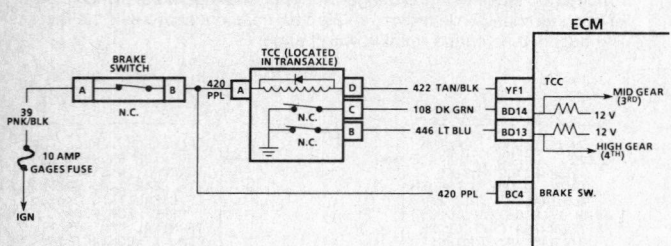

The gear switches are located inside the transaxle. Switches are normally closed. As road speed increases, hydraulic pressure applies the specific gear clutches and the gear switch opens. The ECM uses the gear switches to help determine control of fuel delivery and TCC operation. Code 28 will set if circuit No. 108 indicates ground or closed switch for 12 seconds when the vehicle is in 4th gear or if circuit No. 108 indicates an open when engine is first started.

Code 29 will set if circuit No. 446 indicates ground or closed switch for 10 seconds when the vehicle is in 4th gear or if circuit No. 446 indicates an open when engine is first started.

NOTE: **Test numbers refer to test numbers on diagnostic chart.**

1) A digital volt-ohmmeter must be used in this test. A test light will not work due to the low voltage supplied by the ECM.
2) Checks if the circuit is grounded through the switch.
3) Checks for a good, properly operating switch and checks circuit within transaxle for an improper ground.

DIAGNOSTIC AIDS

Check for poor connections at ECM pins. Inspect harness for incorrect routing (too close to high voltage wiring) or chafing. Monitor the voltage of each terminal while moving related harness connectors. If the failure is induced, the voltage reading will change.

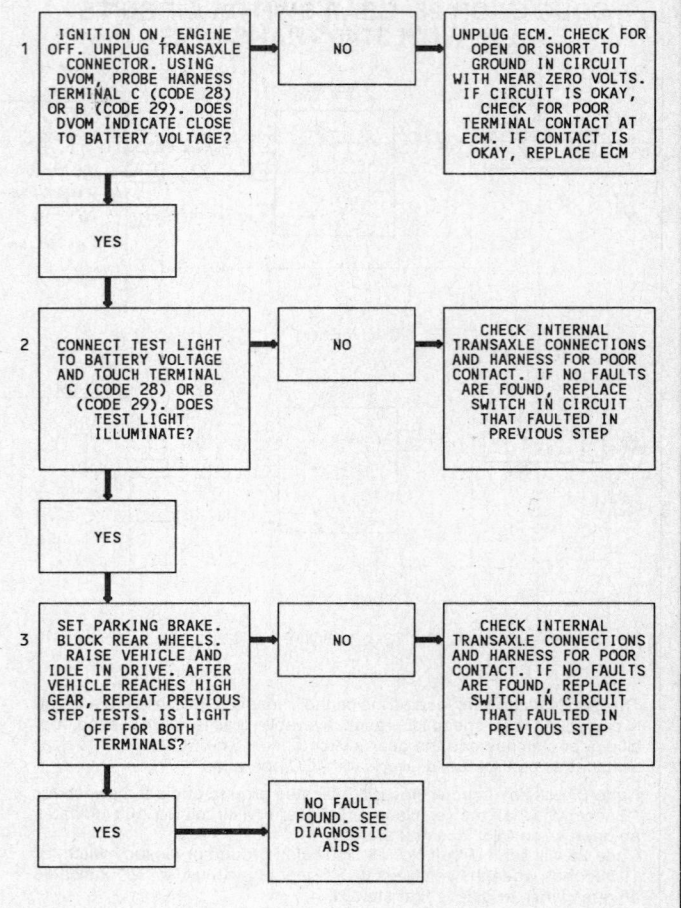

91G07410 91D07319

1991 ENGINE PERFORMANCE
Self-Diagnostics — ECM/PCM Except Cadillac (Cont.)

GM
1-71

CODE 27, 28 OR 29,
GEAR SWITCH CIRCUITS 3.8L

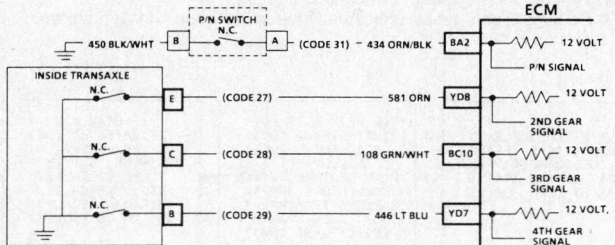

3.8L H BODY

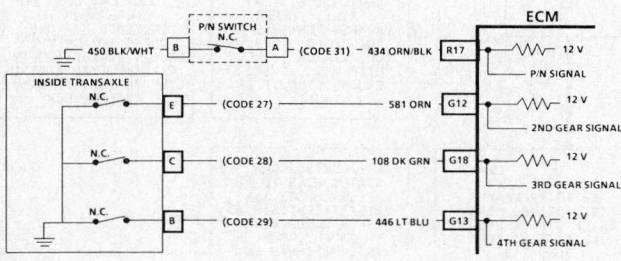

3.8L W BODY

The gear switches are located inside the transaxle. Switches are normally closed. As road speed increases, hydraulic pressure applies the specific gear clutches and the gear switch opens. The ECM uses the gear switches to help determine control of fuel delivery and TCC operation. Code 27 will set if no Code 29 is present, circuit No. 581 indicates ground or closed switch for 10 seconds when vehicle is in 4th gear, or circuits No 581 or No. 446 indicate an open when the engine is first started. Code 28 will set if circuit No. 108 indicates ground or closed switch for 10 seconds when the vehicle is in 4th gear, or circuits No. 108 or No. 446 indicate an open when engine is first started.

Code 29 will set if circuit No. 446 indicates ground or closed switch for 10 seconds when the vehicle is in 4th gear (TCC locked and brake not applied) or if circuit No. 446 indicates an open when engine is first started.

NOTE: Test numbers refer to test numbers on diagnostic chart.

1) A digital volt-ohmmeter must be used in this test. A test light will not work due to the low voltage supplied by the ECM.
2) Checks if the circuit is grounded through the switch.
3) Checks for a good, properly operating switch and checks circuit within transaxle for an improper ground.

DIAGNOSTIC AIDS

Check for poor connections at ECM pins. Inspect harness for incorrect routing (too close to high voltage wiring) or chafing. Monitor the voltage of each terminal while moving related harness connectors. If the failure is induced, the voltage reading will change.

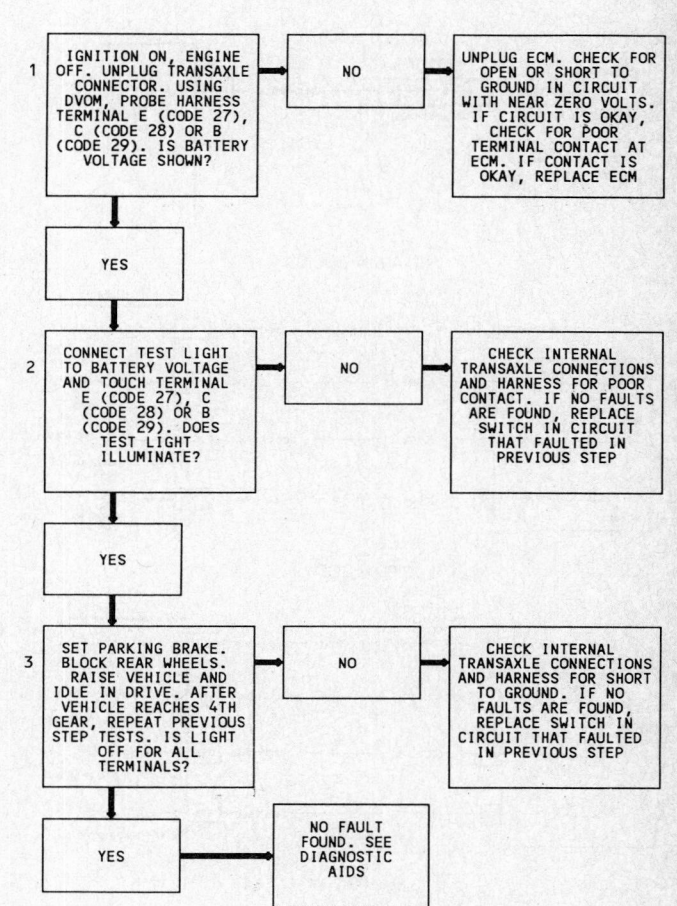

CODE 31, PARK/NEUTRAL SWITCH CIRCUIT 3.3L & 3.8L

NOTE: Complete diagnosis of Code 31 for 3.8L (VIN L) C and E body vehicles requires the use of a GM Tech 1 "Scan" tester which is capable of indicating status of all 4 park/neutral switch positions. This chart does not apply to 3.8L (VIN L) C and E body vehicles.

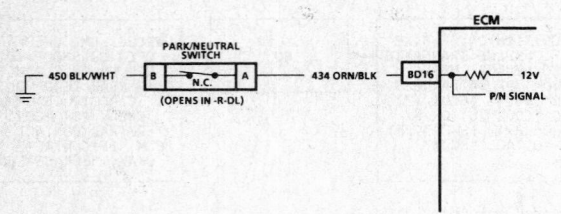

3.3L A & N BODIES

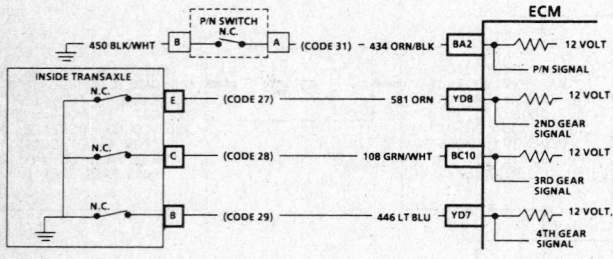

3.8L H BODY

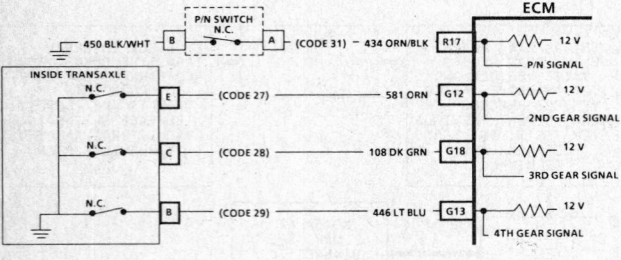

3.8L W BODY

The park/neutral switch contacts are part of the neutral start switch. The contacts close to ground in Park or Neutral and open in Drive. Code 31 will set if park/neutral signal circuit indicates an open for 3-4 consecutive starts or if conditions occur as follows:
- No Code 38 (3.3L) or 29 (3.8L) exists.
- Circuit No. 434 indicates ground.
- Transmission is in high gear.
- TCC is locked on 4T60 trans. only.
- Vehicle speed is greater than 45 MPH and TPS is less than 15 percent (.94 volt) on 3T40 trans. only.
- All above conditions have been met for at least 12 seconds.

91C07413 91I07411 91A07412 91H07321

NOTE: Test numbers refer to test numbers on diagnostic chart.

1) This tests for a closed switch to ground in Park.
2) This tests for an open switch in Drive.
3) Be sure "Scan" tester indicates Drive, even when wiggling shifter.

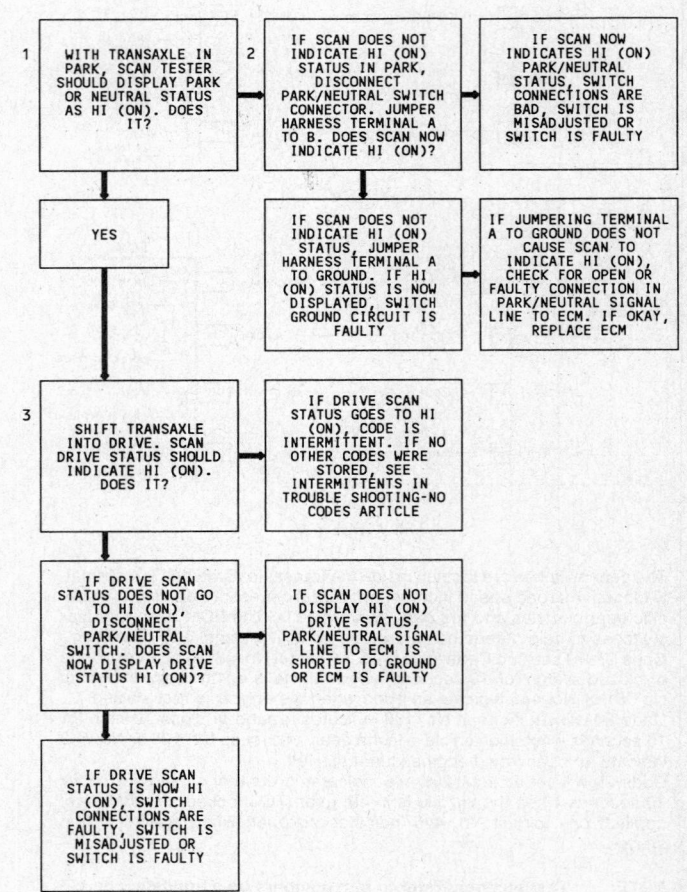

1991 ENGINE PERFORMANCE
Self-Diagnostics — ECM/PCM Except Cadillac (Cont.)

GM
1-73

CODE 32, EGR SYSTEM ERROR
2.0L, 2.2L J & L BODIES &
2.5L A, N & W BODIES

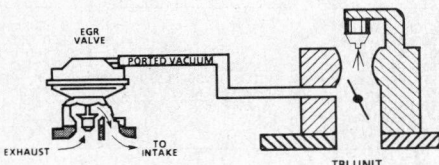

A properly operating EGR will directly affect the air/fuel mixture requirements of the engine. Since the exhaust gas introduced into the airflow is an inert gas (contains little or no oxygen), less fuel is required to maintain a correct air/fuel mixture. If the EGR system were to become inoperative, the inert exhaust gas would be replaced with oxygen and the air/fuel mixture would become leaner. This would be reflected in an increased block learn value.

The engine control system operates within 2 block learn cells: a closed throttle cell and an open throttle cell. The block learn value of these 2 cells should be close to the same. The open throttle cell is affected by the operation of a functional EGR system. If the EGR system malfunctions, the open throttle cell block learn would increase, but the block learn for the closed throttle cell would remain unchanged. When the change becomes too great, the ECM will set a Code 32.

DIAGNOSTIC AIDS

The Code 32 chart is a functional check of the EGR system. If the EGR system works properly and a Code 32 is set, check for other causes for an increased open throttle block learn value.

- Check for a blocked/restricted EGR passage.
- Check the MAP sensor function. See SYSTEMS & COMPONENT TESTING article. A MAP sensor may shift enough in calibration to affect the air/fuel mixture without setting a MAP-related code.

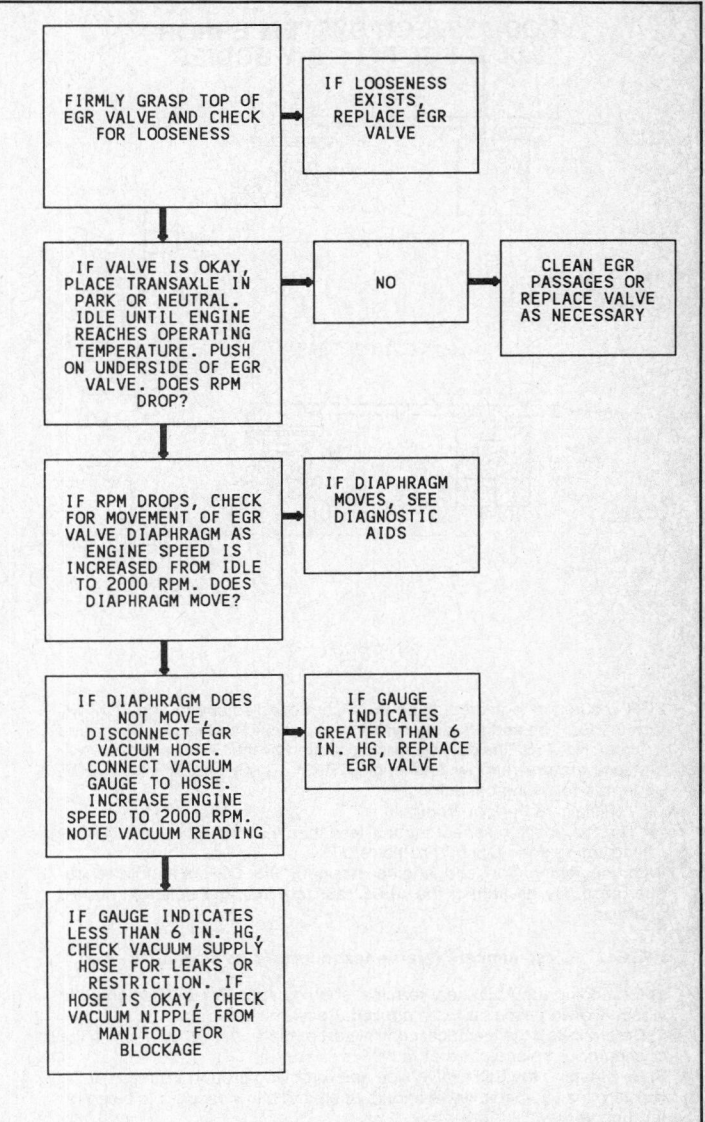

91J07416 91J07322

CODE 32, EGR SYSTEM ERROR
5.0L & 5.7L PFI F & Y BODIES

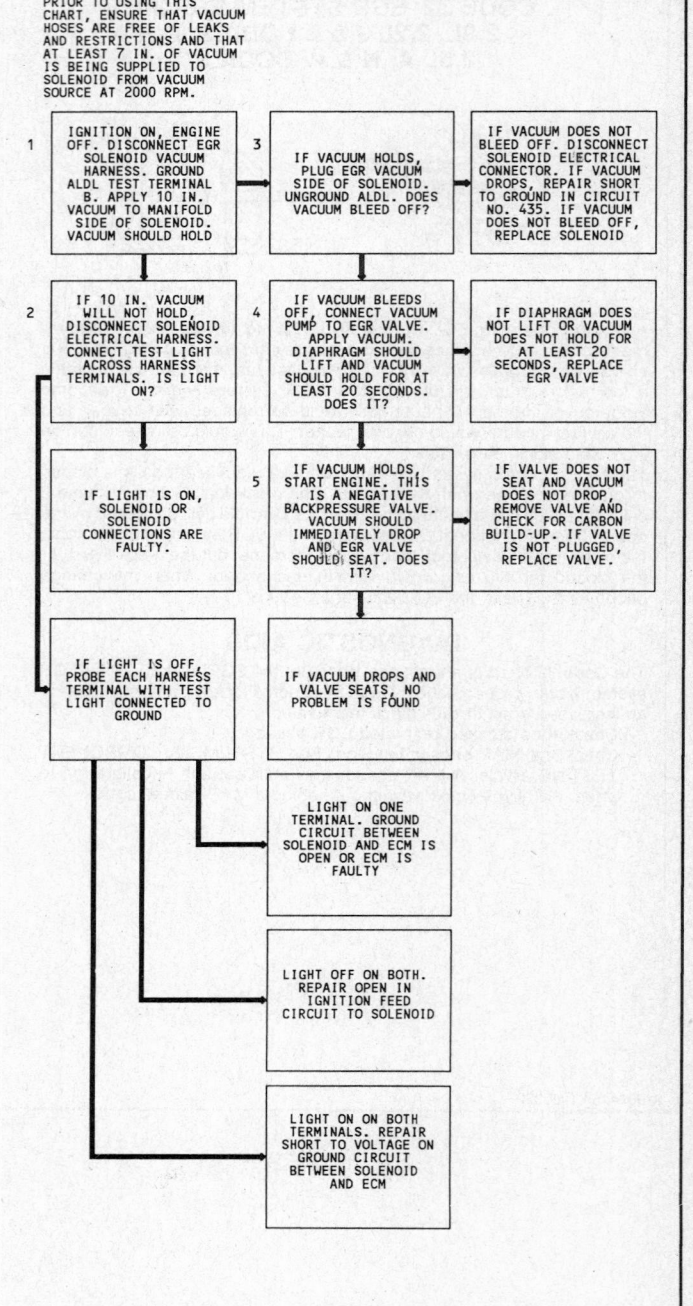

5.0L & 5.7L PFI F BODY

5.7L Y BODY

EGR vacuum is regulated by an ECM-controlled solenoid. The ECM will turn the EGR on and off (duty cycle) by grounding and removing ground to circuit No. 435. The duty cycle is calculated by the ECM based on coolant temperature, airflow and engine RPM. There should be no EGR under the following conditions:

• Vehicle is in Park or Neutral
• Throttle position sensor input is less than a specified value or TPS is indicating Wide Open Throttle (WOT).

With the ignition on and engine stopped, the EGR solenoid is de-energized. By grounding the ALDL test terminal, the solenoid should energize.

NOTE: Test numbers refer to test numbers on diagnostic chart.

1) Grounding the ALDL test terminal should cause the EGR solenoid to close, allowing vacuum to be applied. Vacuum should hold.
2) Determines if the electrical control part of the system is at fault or if the connector or solenoid are at fault.
3) By plugging the EGR valve side and removing ground from the ALDL test terminal, solenoid valve should open and allow vacuum to bleed off through vent.
4) With the engine not running and vacuum applied to valve, valve should move to the fully open position.
5) System uses negative backpressure to open EGR valve. Valve should close when the engine is cranked.

91D07418 91F07419 91B07323

1991 ENGINE PERFORMANCE
Self-Diagnostics — ECM/PCM Except Cadillac (Cont.)

GM
1-75

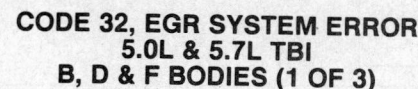

CODE 32, EGR SYSTEM ERROR
5.0L & 5.7L TBI
B, D & F BODIES (1 OF 3)

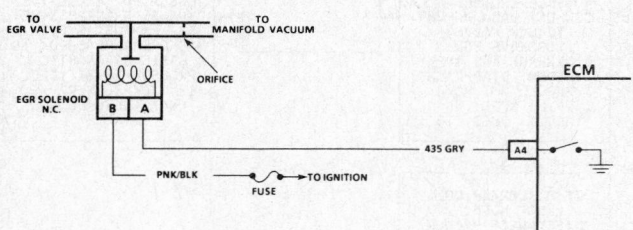

ECM operates a normally closed solenoid to regulate vacuum to EGR valve. When ECM provides a path to ground for the EGR solenoid winding, solenoid opens, allowing vacuum to pass through to EGR valve. ECM monitors EGR effectiveness by shutting off vacuum to EGR valve during a steady cruise above 50 MPH, and monitoring the change in MAP sensor vacuum signal. If vacuum signal change is not within a pre-calibrated window, Code 32 will be set.

NOTE: **Test numbers refer to test numbers on diagnostic chart.**

1) Plugged Intake Passage – Shut off engine and remove EGR valve. Plug exhaust side port with a shop rag or suitable plug. Attempt to start engine. If engine runs at a very high idle (up to 3000 RPM is possible) or if engine starts and stalls, EGR intake passage is not plugged. If vehicle starts and idles normally, intake side passage is plugged.
Plugged Exhaust Passage – With EGR valve removed, plug intake manifold side passage with a suitable plug. Start engine and listen for exhaust noise. If no exhaust gas escapes from open EGR port, exhaust passage is plugged.
2) By grounding ALDL test terminal B, EGR solenoid should energize and allow vacuum to be applied to gauge. Vacuum at gauge may or may not slowly bleed off; however, what is important is that gauge is able to read amount of vacuum being applied.
3) When ALDL test terminal is ungrounded, gauge vacuum should bleed off through a vent in the solenoid. Pump gauge vacuum may or may not bleed off but this does not indicate a problem.
4) This test determines if electrical control part of system is at fault or if the connector or solenoid is at fault.
5) EGR valves used with this engine are stamped with a P for positive backpressure or an N for negative backpressure. F body uses negative backpressure only. Proceed to the appropriate chart for the valve being tested.

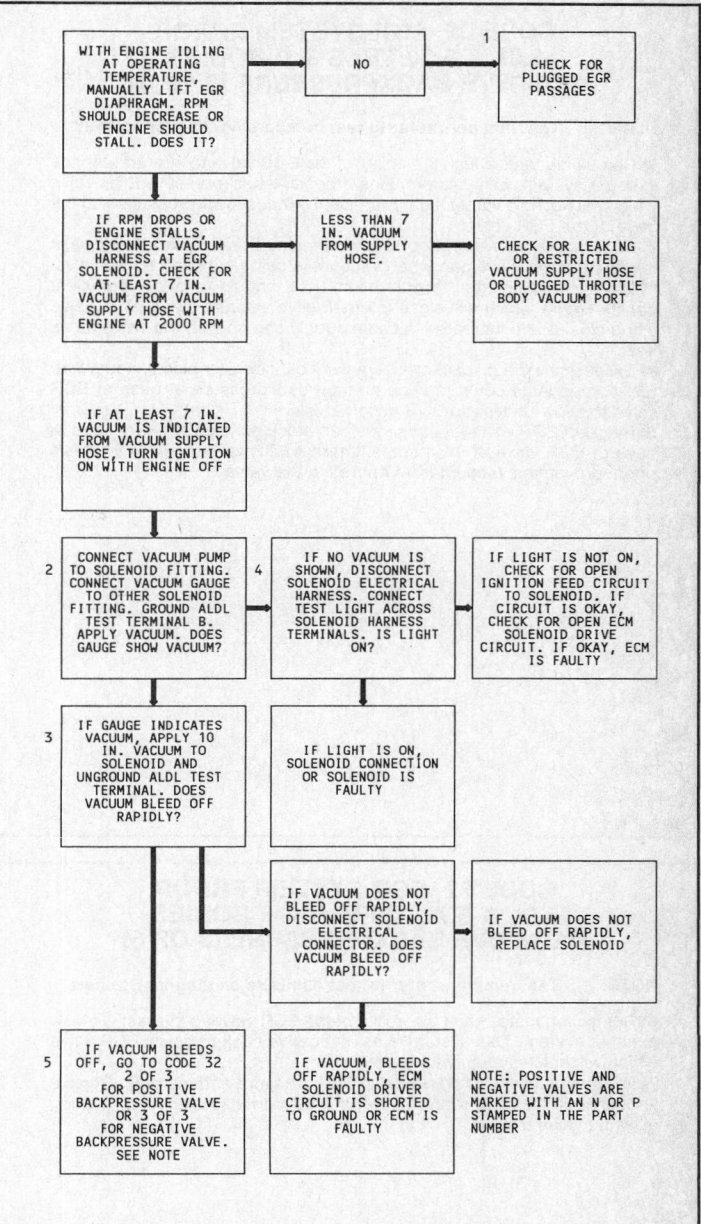

91B07417 91D07324

GM
1-76

1991 ENGINE PERFORMANCE
Self-Diagnostics — ECM/PCM Except Cadillac (Cont.)

CODE 32, EGR SYSTEM ERROR
5.0L & 5.7L TBI B & D BODIES
POSITIVE BACKPRESSURE (2 OF 3)

NOTE: **Test numbers refer to test numbers on diagnostic chart.**

6) Remaining tests check the ability of the EGR valve to interact with the exhaust system. This system uses a positive backpressure EGR valve which will not hold vacuum until sufficient exhaust backpressure is at the base of the EGR valve.

7) EGR valve diaphragm should move when sufficient backpressure is at the base of the valve and when vacuum is being supplied to the valve. Rapidly snapping the throttle from idle should provide sufficient backpressure which will close internal valve vacuum bleed. With valve bleed closed, the jumpered vacuum supply can now lift the valve off its seat.

8) Excessive exhaust backpressure from bent or restricted exhaust system components could provide enough backpressure at base of EGR valve to allow undesired EGR action at idle.

9) Plugged EGR exhaust passages can block exhaust backpressure at base of EGR valve. If this occurs, internal EGR valve bleed will remain open, preventing vacuum from operating the valve.

91G07325

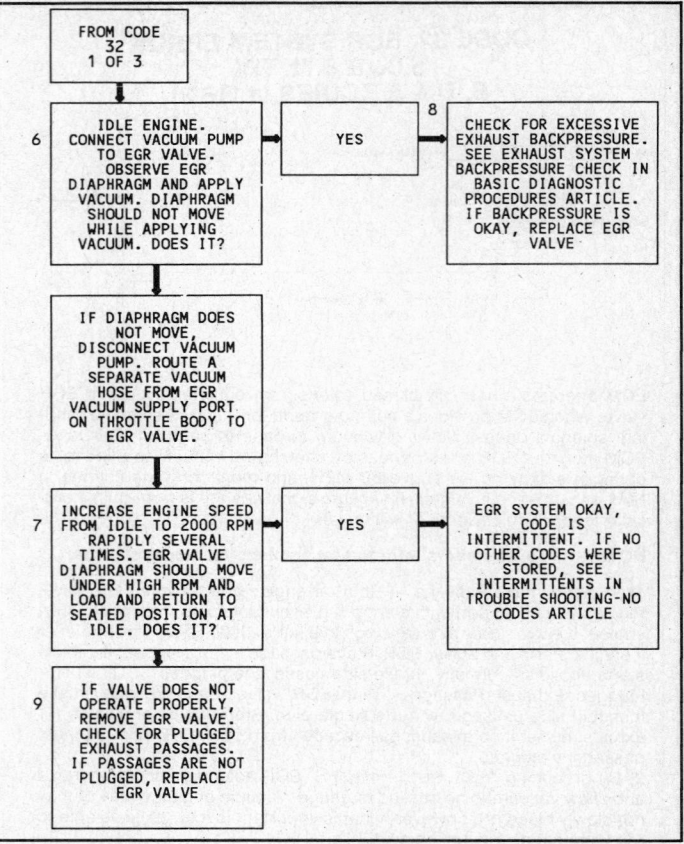

CODE 32, EGR SYSTEM ERROR
5.0L & 5.7L TBI B, D & F BODIES
NEGATIVE BACKPRESSURE (3 OF 3)

NOTE: **Test numbers refer to test numbers on diagnostic chart.**

6) Remaining tests check the ability of the EGR valve to interact with the exhaust system. This system uses a negative backpressure EGR valve which will hold vacuum with engine off.

7) When engine is started, exhaust backpressure at base of EGR valve should open the valve's internal bleed. This will vent the applied vacuum, allowing valve to seat.

91I07326

NEGATIVE BACKPRESSURE
VALVE CAN BE IDENTIFIED
BY THE PRESENCE OF THE
LETTER N IN PART NUMBER

6
```
IGNITION OFF.
CONNECT VACUUM PUMP
TO EGR VALVE. APPLY
VACUUM. DIAPHRAGM
SHOULD LIFT AND
VACUUM SHOULD HOLD
FOR AT LEAST 20
SECONDS. DOES IT?
```
→
```
IF DIAPHRAGM DOES
NOT LIFT OR VACUUM
DOES NOT HOLD FOR
AT LEAST 20
SECONDS, REPLACE
EGR VALVE
```

7
```
IF VACUUM HOLDS,
START ENGINE.
VACUUM SHOULD
IMMEDIATELY DROP
AND EGR VALVE
SHOULD SEAT. DOES
IT?
```
→
```
IF VALVE DOES NOT
SEAT AND VACUUM
DOES NOT DROP,
REMOVE VALVE AND
CHECK FOR CARBON
BUILD-UP. IF VALVE
IS NOT PLUGGED,
REPLACE VALVE.
```

```
IF VACUUM DROPS AND
VALVE SEATS, NO
PROBLEM IS FOUND
```

1991 ENGINE PERFORMANCE
Self-Diagnostics — ECM/PCM Except Cadillac (Cont.)

GM
1-77

CODE 32, EGR SYSTEM ERROR
2.3L W BODY

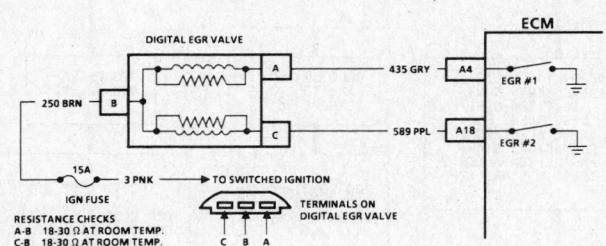

Digital EGR valve controls EGR flow through 2 different sized orifices which are normally closed by pintles held down by springs. Orifice No. 1 is smaller than No. 2. Independent solenoids lift the pintles off of the seats when ECM allows current to flow through solenoids by providing a ground for the solenoid windings. Electric circuit problems should result in a Code 26 setting. ECM test EGR operating by quickly opening the EGR pintles during stable idle conditions and monitoring changes in the MAP sensor vacuum signal. If change does not occur, this test is repeated several times before setting Code 32. Test occurs so quickly that it should not be noticeable to driver.

NOTE: Test numbers refer to test numbers on diagnostic chart.

1) Code 26 indicates an electrical problem is likely. This can be diagnosed using Code 26 chart.

2) This step actuates each solenoid and should result in a momentary drop in RPM or engine roughness if EGR flows at idle. The No. 2 solenoid should have a greater effect than the No. 1 solenoid.

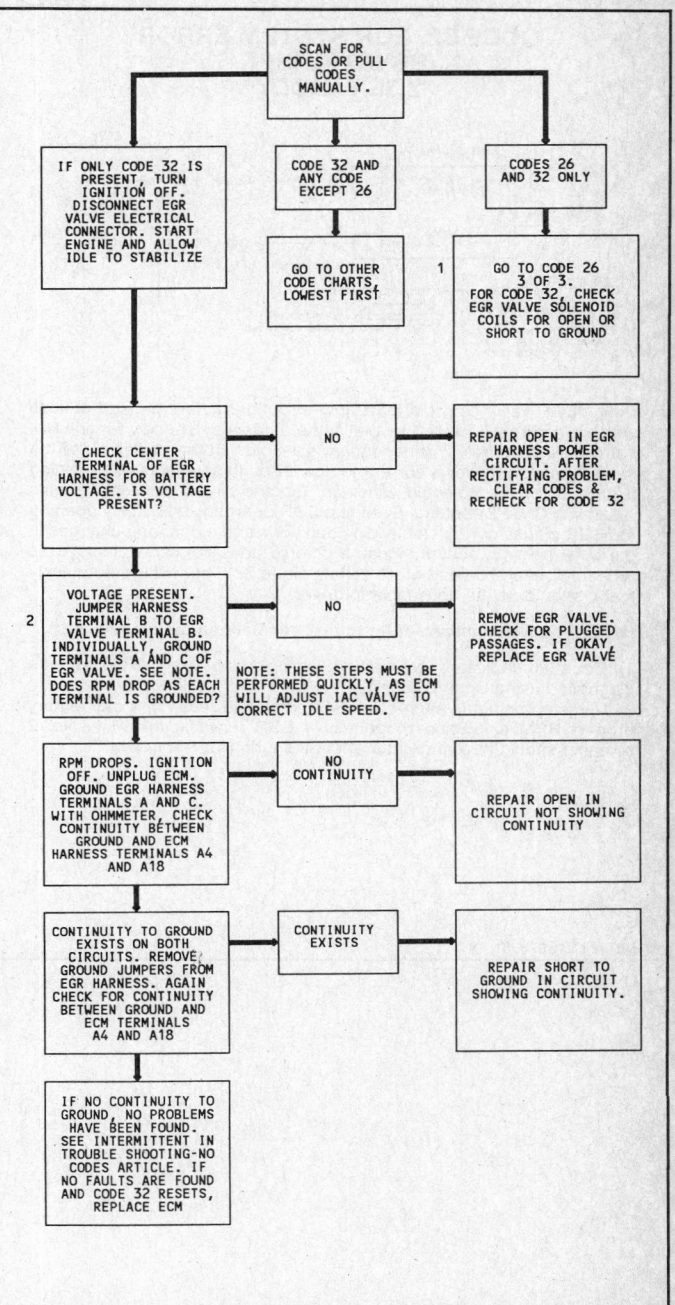

91H07420 91A07327

CODE 32, EGR SYSTEM ERROR USING TECH I 2.3L W BODY

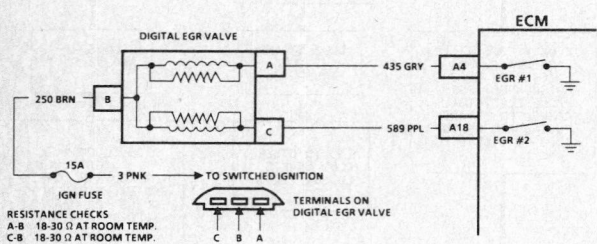

Digital EGR valve controls EGR flow through 2 different sized orifices which are normally closed by pintles held down by springs. Orifice No. 1 is smaller than No. 2. Independent solenoids lift the pintles off of the seats when ECM allows current to flow through solenoids by providing a ground for the solenoid windings. Electric circuit problems should result in a Code 26 setting. ECM test EGR operating by quickly opening the EGR pintles during stable idle conditions and monitoring changes in the MAP sensor vacuum signal. If change does not occur, this test is repeated several times before setting Code 32. Test occurs so quickly that it should not be noticeable to driver.

NOTE: Test numbers refer to test numbers on diagnostic chart.

1) Code 26 indicates an electrical problem is likely. This can be diagnosed using Code 26 chart.

2) This step actuates each solenoid and should result in a momentary drop in RPM or engine roughness if EGR flows at idle. The No. 2 solenoid should have a greater effect than the No. 1 solenoid.

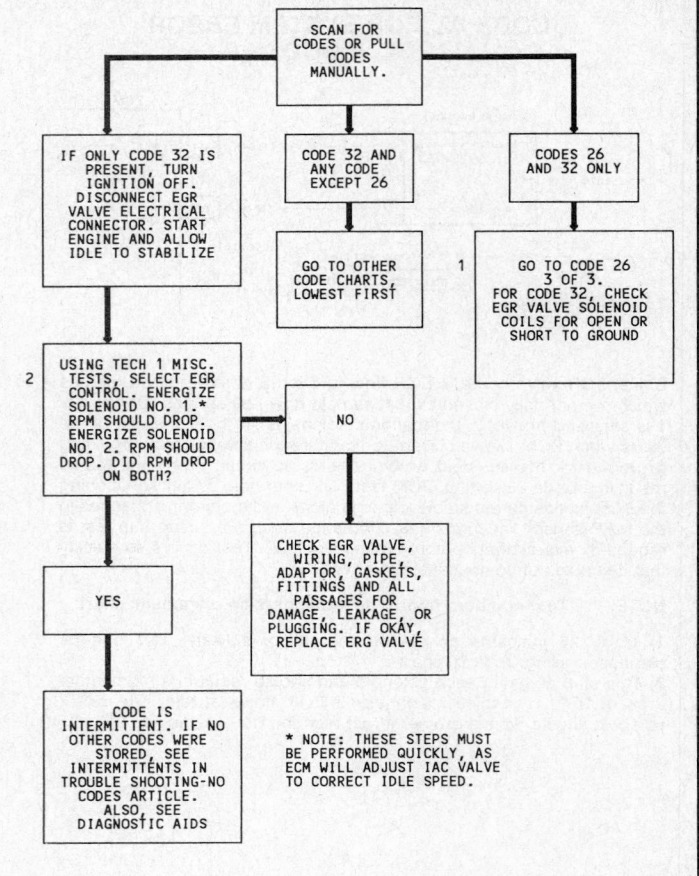

91H07420 91C07328

1991 ENGINE PERFORMANCE
Self-Diagnostics — ECM/PCM Except Cadillac (Cont.)

GM
1-79

CODE 32, EGR SYSTEM ERROR
3.1L A, F, J, L & W BODIES
& 3.4L W BODY

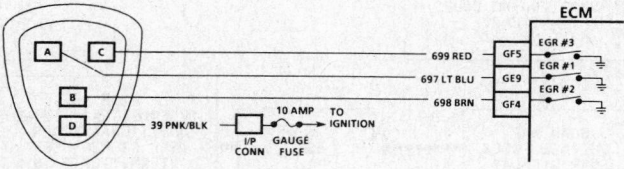

3.1L A, F, J & L BODIES

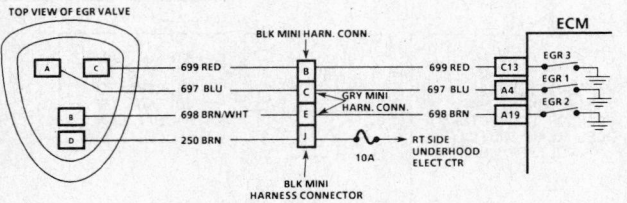

3.1L & 3.4L W BODY

Code 32 represents an EGR flow test error. During a closed throttle coastdown, ECM will cycle 3 internal EGR valve solenoids on and off individually while monitoring for changes in engine RPM and oxygen sensor activity.

NOTE: Test numbers refer to test numbers on diagnostic chart.

1) This test determine if there is power to the EGR valve.
2) This test will determine if there is an open circuit in the EGR wiring or if the EGR valve is at fault.
3) This test will determine if there is a short to ground in any circuit going to the EGR valve or if the ECM is at fault.

USE ACCOMPANYING SCHEMATIC TO IDENTIFY TERMINALS REFERENCED IN FLOW CHART.

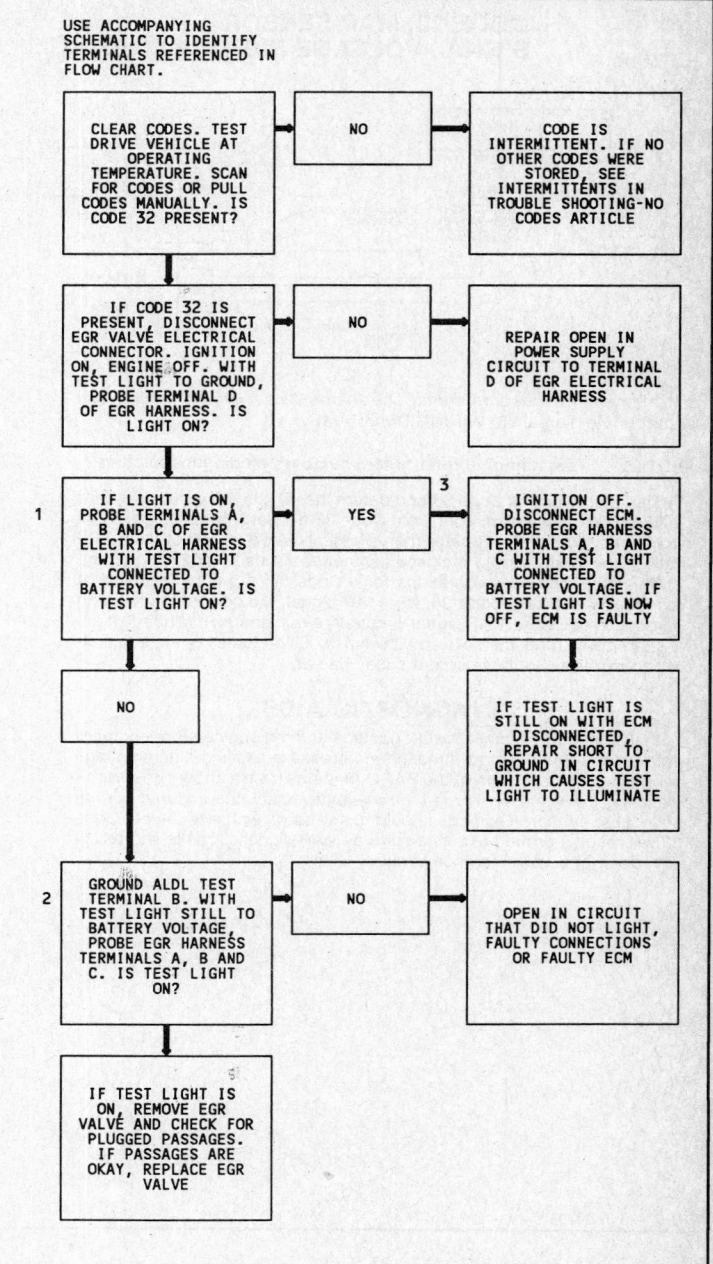

91J07421 91B07422 91E07329

CODE 33, MAP SENSOR SIGNAL VOLTAGE HIGH

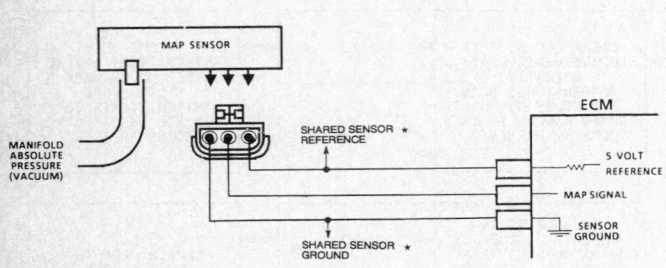

* – For shared sensor reference and shared sensor ground tie-offs, see appropriate diagram in WIRING DIAGRAMS.

NOTE: Test numbers refer to test numbers on diagnostic chart.

1) This test confirms Code 33 and determines if it is the result of a hard failure or an intermittent condition. Code 33 will set when voltage signal reading is too high for greater than a precalibrated period of time, TPS voltage indicates throttle is closed and neither Code 21 or 22 is present.
2) This step simulates conditions for a Code 34. If the control module recognizes and sets Code 34, low MAP signal, the control module and 5-volt reference and MAP signal circuits are not at fault. If ground circuit is shared with other sensors and ground circuit becomes open, additional codes related to these sensors may be set.

DIAGNOSTIC AIDS

With the ignition switch in the ON position and the engine stopped, manifold pressure is equal to atmospheric pressure and the signal voltage will be high. Comparison of the BARO readings from a known good vehicle using the same sensor is a good way to check the accuracy of the suspected sensor. Readings should be the same within ± .4 volt. Code 33 will result if ground circuit is open or MAP signal circuit is shorted to voltage or to 5-volt reference circuit.

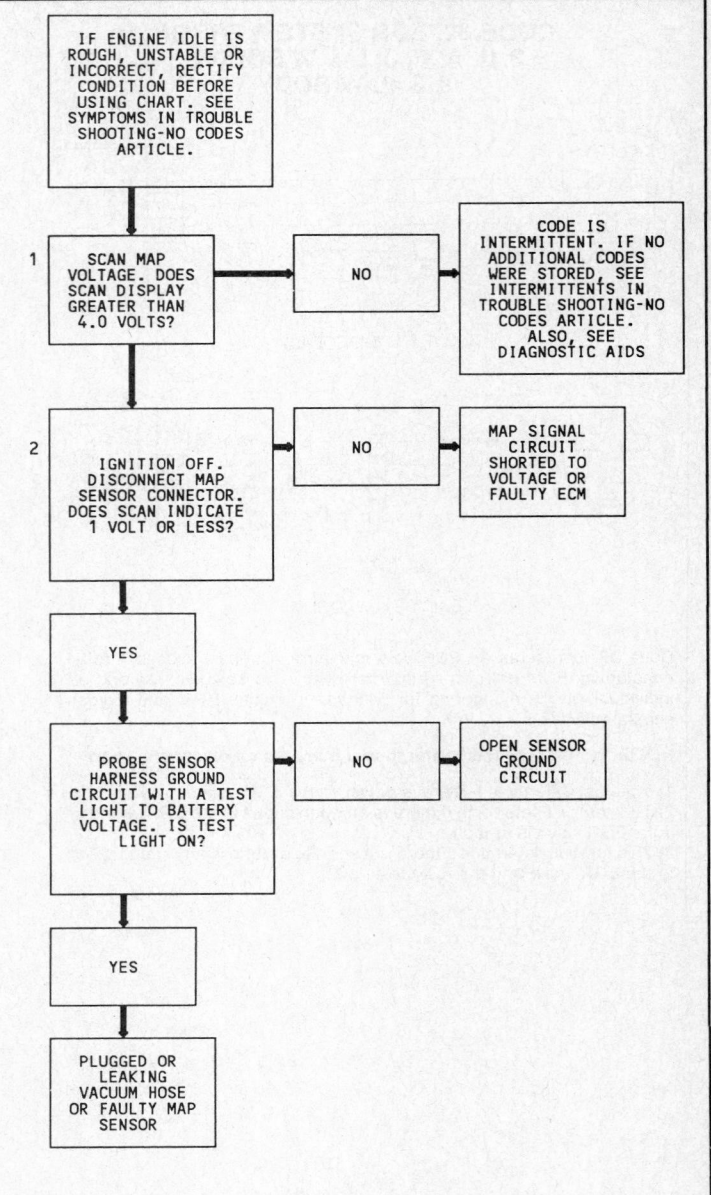

91D07423 91G07330

1991 ENGINE PERFORMANCE
Self-Diagnostics — ECM/PCM Except Cadillac (Cont.)

GM
1-81

CODE 34, MAP SENSOR SIGNAL VOLTAGE LOW

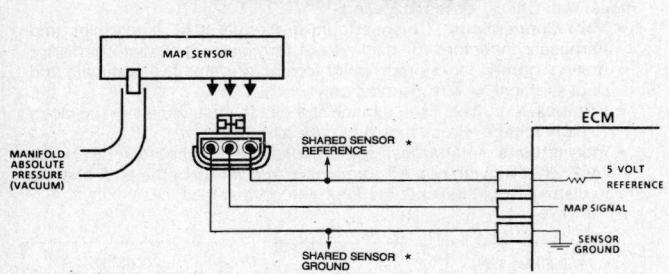

* – For shared sensor reference and shared sensor ground tie-offs, see appropriate diagram in WIRING DIAGRAMS.

NOTE: Test numbers refer to test numbers on diagnostic chart.

1) This confirms Code 34 and determines if code was caused by a hard failure or an intermittent fault. Code 34 will set when ignition is on and MAP signal voltage is low. On some systems, engine must be running to set code.

2) Jumpering MAP signal to 5-volt reference at MAP harness connector will determine if sensor is at fault or if there is a problem with the control module or wiring.

3) "Scan" tester may not display 12 volts. The important thing is the control module recognizes the voltage as greater than 4 volts (high MAP voltage signal), indicating the control module and MAP signal circuit are not at fault.

DIAGNOSTIC AIDS

With the ignition switch in the ON position and the engine stopped, manifold pressure is equal to atmospheric pressure and the signal voltage will be high. Compare BARO readings with a known good vehicle using the same sensor is a good way to check the accuracy of the suspected sensor. Readings should be the same within ± .4 volt. A Code 34 will also result if 5-volt reference and MAP signal circuits are open or shorted to ground.

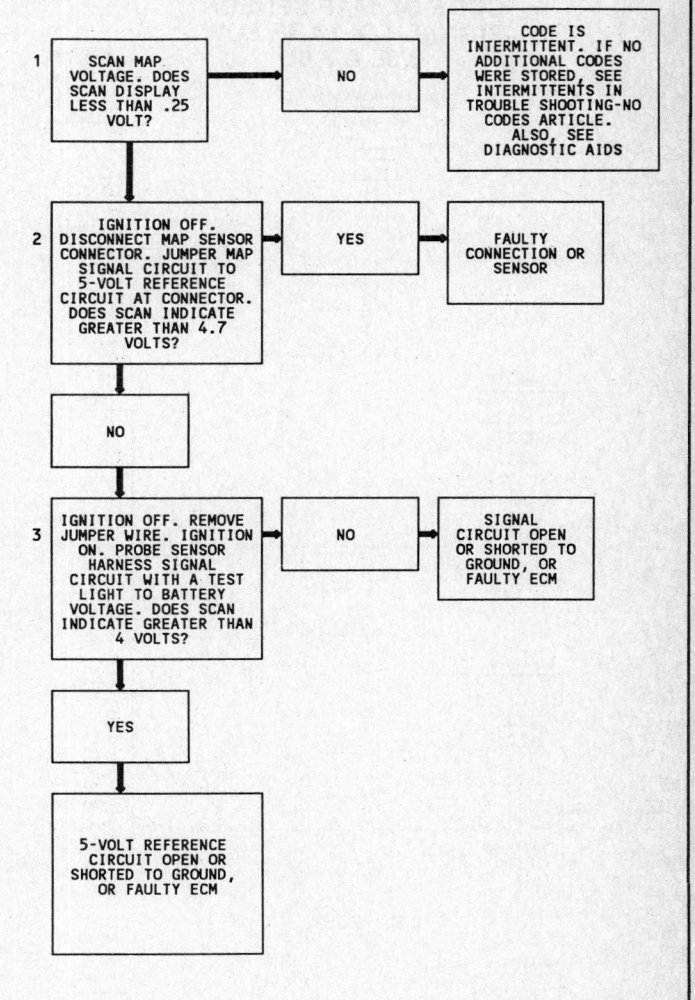

91D07423 91I07331

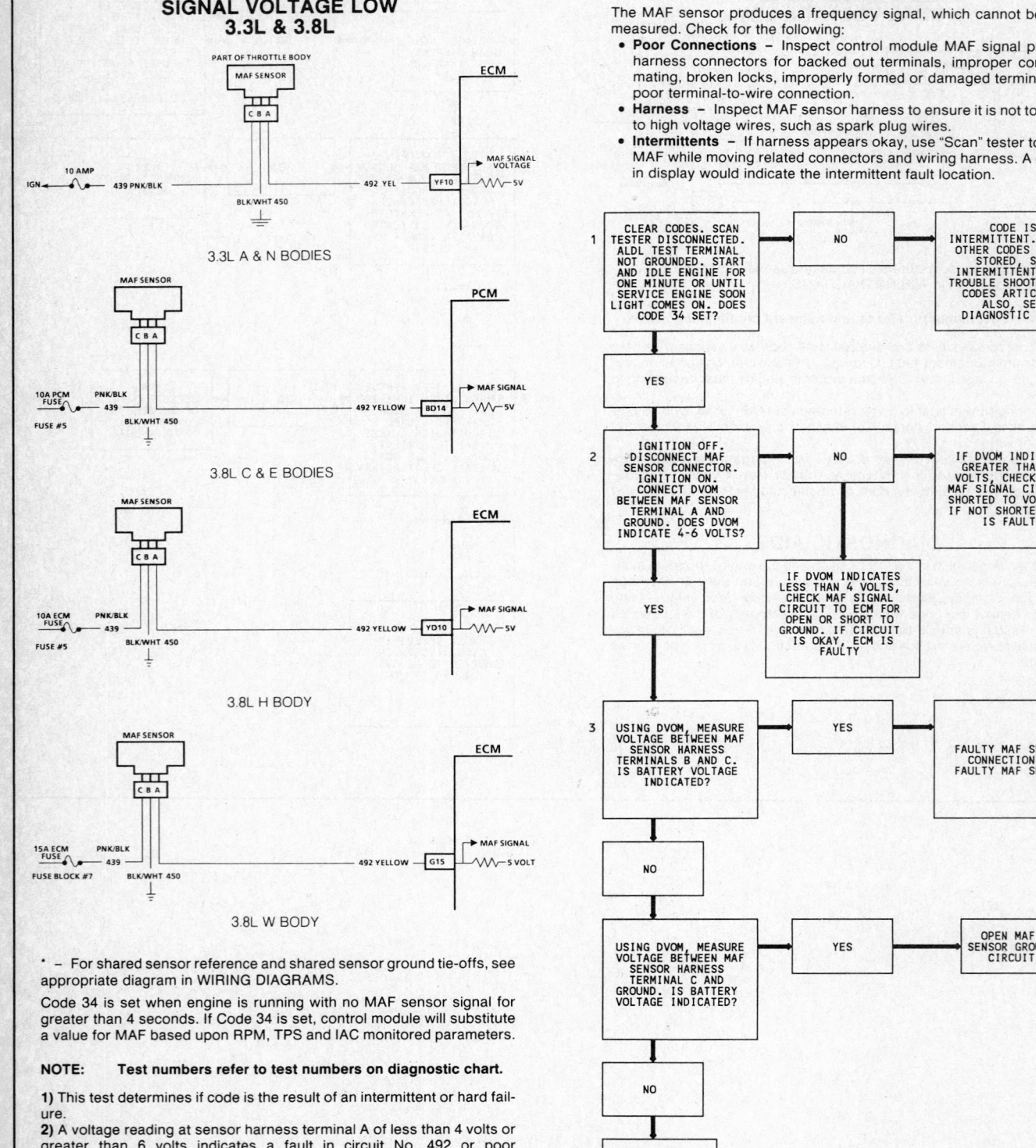

CODE 34, MAF SENSOR SIGNAL VOLTAGE LOW 3.3L & 3.8L

PART OF THROTTLE BODY

MAF SENSOR

C B A

ECM

10 AMP

IGN

439 PNK/BLK

492 YEL

YF10

MAF SIGNAL VOLTAGE

5V

BLK/WHT 450

3.3L A & N BODIES

MAF SENSOR

C B A

PCM

10A PCM FUSE

PNK/BLK

439

492 YELLOW

BD14

MAF SIGNAL

5V

BLK/WHT 450

FUSE #5

3.8L C & E BODIES

MAF SENSOR

C B A

ECM

10A ECM FUSE

PNK/BLK

439

492 YELLOW

YD10

MAF SIGNAL

5V

BLK/WHT 450

FUSE #5

3.8L H BODY

MAF SENSOR

C B A

ECM

15A ECM FUSE

PNK/BLK

439

492 YELLOW

G15

MAF SIGNAL

5 VOLT

BLK/WHT 450

FUSE BLOCK #7

3.8L W BODY

* – For shared sensor reference and shared sensor ground tie-offs, see appropriate diagram in WIRING DIAGRAMS.

Code 34 is set when engine is running with no MAF sensor signal for greater than 4 seconds. If Code 34 is set, control module will substitute a value for MAF based upon RPM, TPS and IAC monitored parameters.

NOTE: **Test numbers refer to test numbers on diagnostic chart.**

1) This test determines if code is the result of an intermittent or hard failure.
2) A voltage reading at sensor harness terminal A of less than 4 volts or greater than 6 volts indicates a fault in circuit No. 492 or poor connections.
3) Verifies both ignition voltage and a good ground are available.

DIAGNOSTIC AIDS

The MAF sensor produces a frequency signal, which cannot be easily measured. Check for the following:
- **Poor Connections** – Inspect control module MAF signal pins and harness connectors for backed out terminals, improper connector mating, broken locks, improperly formed or damaged terminals and poor terminal-to-wire connection.
- **Harness** – Inspect MAF sensor harness to ensure it is not too close to high voltage wires, such as spark plug wires.
- **Intermittents** – If harness appears okay, use "Scan" tester to check MAF while moving related connectors and wiring harness. A change in display would indicate the intermittent fault location.

1. CLEAR CODES. SCAN TESTER DISCONNECTED. ALDL TEST TERMINAL NOT GROUNDED. START AND IDLE ENGINE FOR ONE MINUTE OR UNTIL SERVICE ENGINE SOON LIGHT COMES ON. DOES CODE 34 SET?

NO → CODE IS INTERMITTENT. IF NO OTHER CODES WERE STORED, SEE INTERMITTENTS IN TROUBLE SHOOTING-NO CODES ARTICLE. ALSO, SEE DIAGNOSTIC AIDS

YES

2. IGNITION OFF. DISCONNECT MAF SENSOR CONNECTOR. IGNITION ON. CONNECT DVOM BETWEEN MAF SENSOR TERMINAL A AND GROUND. DOES DVOM INDICATE 4-6 VOLTS?

NO → IF DVOM INDICATES GREATER THAN 6 VOLTS, CHECK FOR MAF SIGNAL CIRCUIT SHORTED TO VOLTAGE. IF NOT SHORTED, ECM IS FAULTY

IF DVOM INDICATES LESS THAN 4 VOLTS, CHECK MAF SIGNAL CIRCUIT TO ECM FOR OPEN OR SHORT TO GROUND. IF CIRCUIT IS OKAY, ECM IS FAULTY

YES

3. USING DVOM, MEASURE VOLTAGE BETWEEN MAF SENSOR HARNESS TERMINALS B AND C. IS BATTERY VOLTAGE INDICATED?

YES → FAULTY MAF SENSOR CONNECTION OR FAULTY MAF SENSOR

NO

USING DVOM, MEASURE VOLTAGE BETWEEN MAF SENSOR HARNESS TERMINAL C AND GROUND. IS BATTERY VOLTAGE INDICATED?

YES → OPEN MAF SENSOR GROUND CIRCUIT

NO

OPEN MAF SENSOR POWER SUPPLY CIRCUIT

1991 ENGINE PERFORMANCE
Self-Diagnostics — ECM/PCM Except Cadillac (Cont.)

GM
1-83

CODE 35, IAC IDLE SPEED ERROR

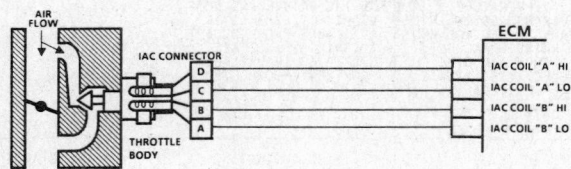

Code 35 will set when closed throttle engine speed is 150 RPM greater or less than correct idle speed for 20 seconds.

NOTE: Test numbers refer to test numbers on diagnostic chart.

1) IAC driver is used to extend and retract IAC valve. Movement is verified by an engine speed change. If no change in speed occurs, valve can be retested when removed from throttle body.

2) Checks IAC movement quality from step **1)**. Between 700-1500 RPM, engine speed should change smoothly with each flash of the tester light in both extend and retract. If IAC valve is retracted beyond the control range (about 1500 RPM), it may take many flashes in the extend position before engine speed begins to drop. This is normal on certain engines. Fully extending the IAC may cause engine to stall. This may be normal.

3) Steps **1)** and **2)** verified proper IAC valve operation while this step checks the IAC circuits. Each light on the node light should flash Red and Green while the IAC valve is cycled. While the sequence of color is not important if either light is off or does not flash Red and Green, check the circuits for faults beginning with poor terminal contacts.

DIAGNOSTIC AIDS

A slow, unstable idle may be caused by a system problem that cannot be overcome by IAC. "Scan" counts will be greater than 60 if too low, and zero counts, if too high. If idle is too high, stop engine. Fully extend IAC with driver. Start engine. If idle speed is greater than 800 RPM, look for possible vacuum leaks.

System Too Lean – If air/fuel ratio is too lean, the idle speed may be either too high (check for vacuum leaks) or too low. Engine speed may vary up and down and disconnecting the IAC may not help. "Scan" and/or digital voltmeter (10-megohm) will read an oxygen sensor output less than 300 mv (.3 volt). Check for low fuel pressure or water in the fuel. A contaminated O_2 sensor (caused by silicone) will produce lean air/fuel mixtures with an oxygen sensor output fixed greater than 800 mv (.8 volt). This may also set Code 45.

System Too Rich – If air/fuel ratio is too rich, idle speed will be too low and "Scan" tester counts will usually be greater than 80. The system may be obviously rich, with Black smoke from the tailpipe. "Scan" tester and/or voltmeter will read an oxygen sensor voltage signal fixed greater than 800 mv (.8 volt). Look for high fuel pressure or injectors leaking or sticking. Remove IAC and inspect bore for foreign material or evidence of IAC valve dragging the bore.

Throttle Body – Remove IAC and inspect bore for evidence of IAC valve dragging.

IAC Valve Connections – Inspect carefully for loose or corroded connections.

PCV Valve – An incorrect PCV valve may cause incorrect idle speed.

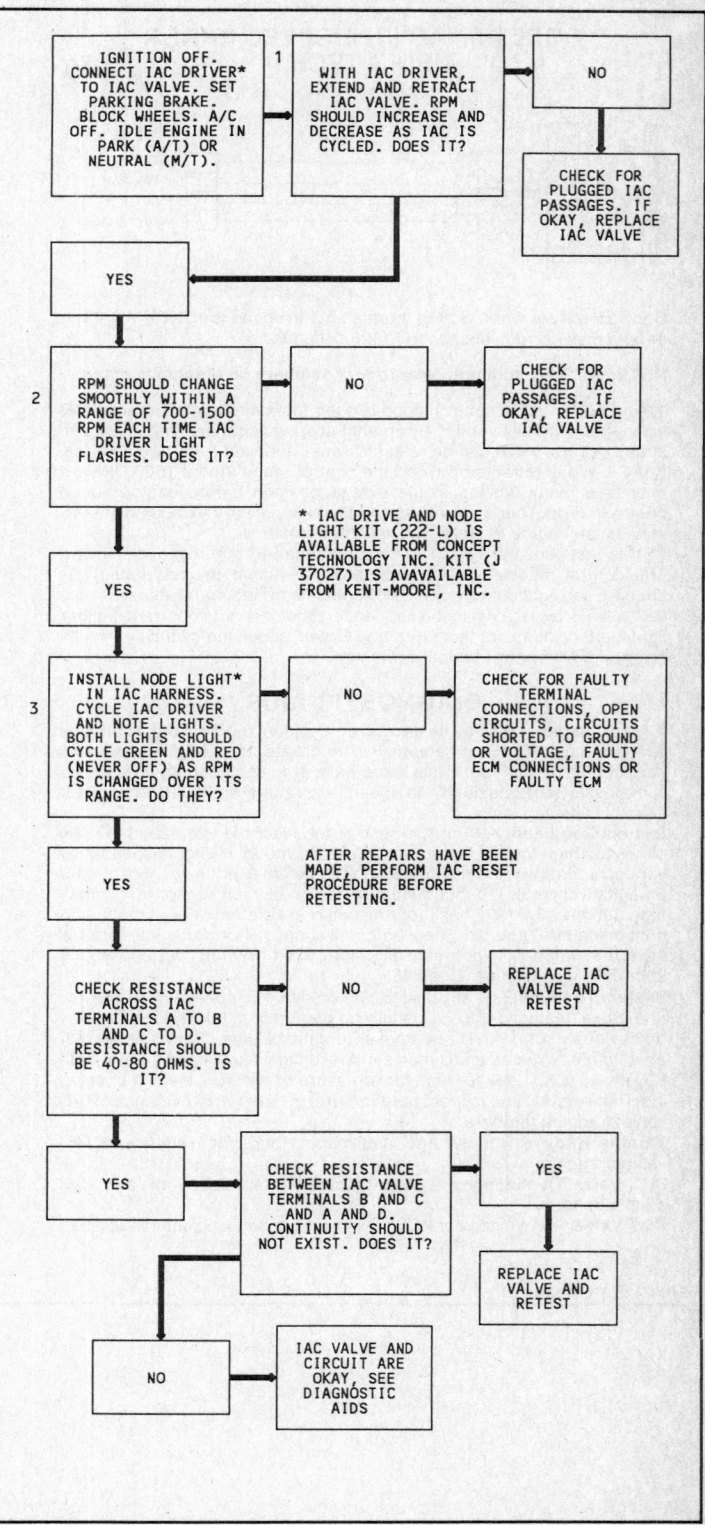

91E07428 91C07333

CODE 35, IAC IDLE SPEED ERROR USING TECH I

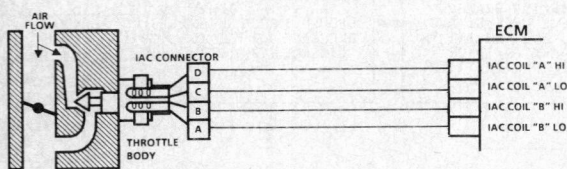

Code 35 will set when closed throttle engine speed is 150 RPM greater or less than correct idle speed for 20 seconds.

NOTE: Test numbers refer to test numbers on diagnostic chart.

1) The Tech 1 RPM control mode is used to extend and retract the IAC valve. Movement is verified by an engine speed change. If no change in speed occurs, valve can be retested when removed from throttle body. If IAC valve is retracted beyond the control range (about 1500 RPM), it may take many flashes in the extend position before engine speed begins to drop. This is normal on certain engines. Fully extending the IAC may cause engine to stall. This may be normal.

2) This test uses the Tech 1 to command the IAC controlled idle speed. The control module issues commands to obtain the requested idle speed. Each light on the node light should flash Red and Green while the IAC valve is cycled. While the sequence of color is not important if either light is off or does not flash Red and Green, check the circuits for faults beginning with poor terminal contacts.

DIAGNOSTIC AIDS

A slow, unstable idle may be caused by a system problem that cannot be overcome by IAC. "Scan" counts will be greater than 60 if too low, and zero counts, if too high. If idle is too high, stop engine. Fully extend IAC with driver. Start engine. If idle speed is greater than 800 RPM, look for possible vacuum leaks.

System Too Lean – If air/fuel ratio is too lean, the idle speed may be either too high (check for vacuum leaks) or too low. Engine speed may vary up and down and disconnecting the IAC may not help. "Scan" and/ or digital voltmeter (10-megohm) will read an oxygen sensor output less than 300 mv (.3 volt). Check for low fuel pressure or water in the fuel. A contaminated O_2 sensor (caused by silicone) will produce lean air/fuel mixtures with an oxygen sensor output fixed greater than 800 mv (.8 volt). This may also set Code 45.

System Too Rich – If air/fuel ratio is too rich, idle speed will be too low and "Scan" tester counts will usually be greater than 80. The system may be obviously rich, with Black smoke from the tailpipe. "Scan" tester and/ or voltmeter will read an oxygen sensor voltage signal fixed greater than 800 mv (.8 volt). Look for high fuel pressure or injectors leaking or sticking. Remove IAC and inspect bore for foreign material or evidence of IAC valve dragging the bore.

Throttle Body – Remove IAC and inspect bore for evidence of IAC valve dragging.

IAC Valve Connections – Inspect carefully for loose or corroded connections.

PCV Valve – An incorrect PCV valve may cause incorrect idle speed.

91E07428 91E07334

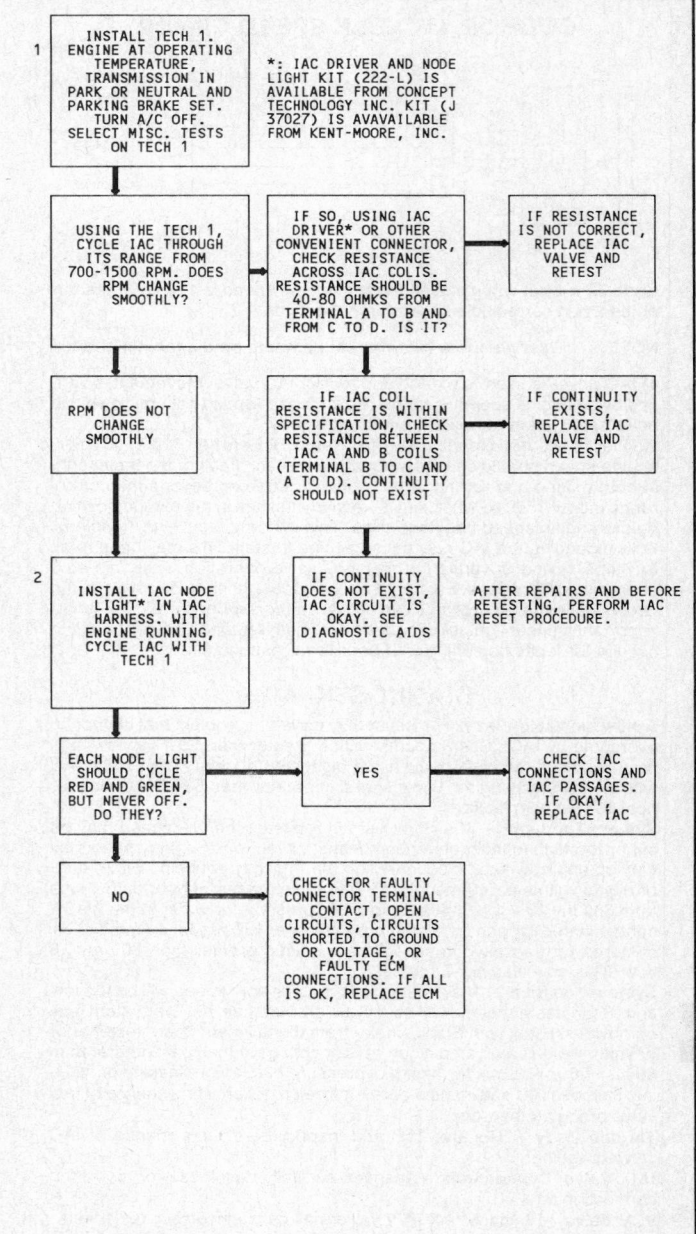

1991 ENGINE PERFORMANCE
Self-Diagnostics – ECM/PCM Except Cadillac (Cont.)

GM
1-85

CODE 36, SHIFT CONTROL PROBLEM
3.8L C & E BODIES WITH 4T60E TRANSAXLE

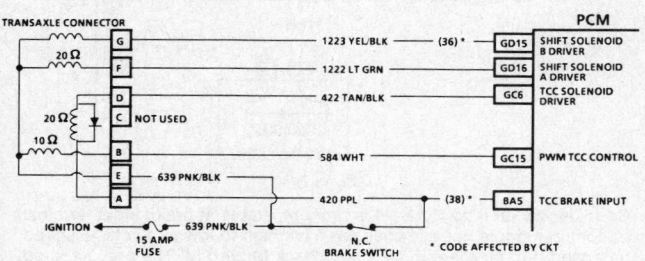

The 4T60E transaxle is electronically shifted. Within transaxle are 4 solenoids. Solenoid A is used for 1st and 4th gear operation only. Solenoid b is used for 1st and 2nd gear operation. The remaining 2 solenoids are for TCC operation only. All PRNDL indications are ignored as far as transaxle shifting is concerned except manual low. Code 36 will set if solenoid "B" failed in the off position, which will cause the transaxle to be in 3rd gear and desired gear is 1st, TPS is greater than 5 percent, VSS is greater than 5 MPH and no code 21, 22 or 24 is present. Code will also set if solenoid "B" failed in the on position, which will cause transaxle to be in 1st gear and desired gear is 4th, PRNDL is in 3rd or 4th, TPS is greater than 10 percent and no Code 31, 21 or 22 is present.

DIAGNOSTIC AIDS

When Code 36 is set, transaxle will be forced into 3rd gear. If code sets due to a grounded circuit No. 1223, 1st and 2nd gear operation will be available only. If circuit No. 1223 is open, 3rd and 4th gear operation will be available only. If fault goes away, normal operation will be resumed for the duration of the key cycle.

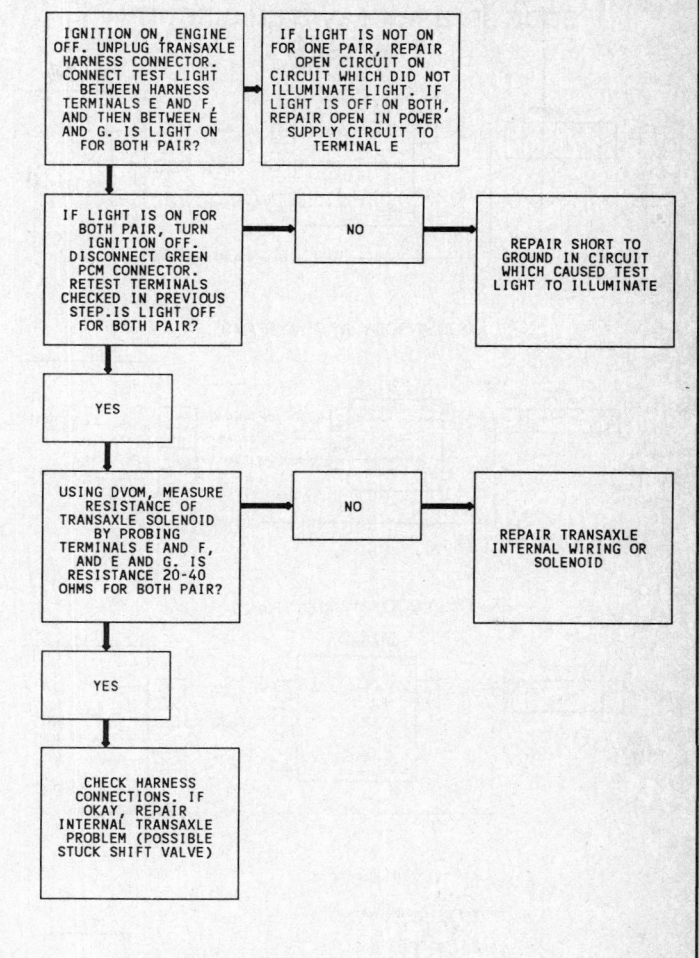

91G07429 91H07335

GM
1-86

1991 ENGINE PERFORMANCE
Self-Diagnostics – ECM/PCM Except Cadillac (Cont.)

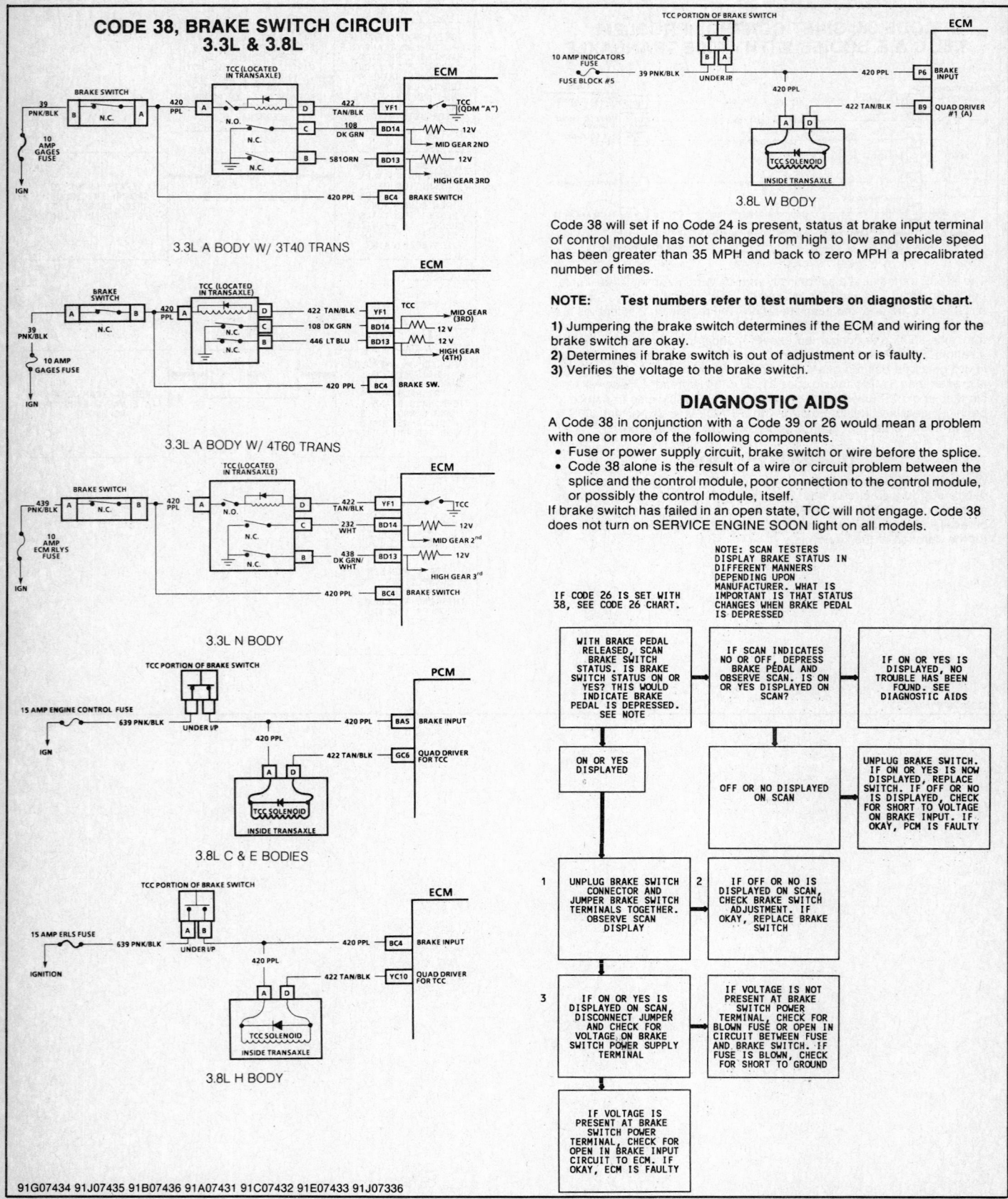

CODE 38, BRAKE SWITCH CIRCUIT 3.3L & 3.8L

3.3L A BODY W/ 3T40 TRANS

3.3L A BODY W/ 4T60 TRANS

3.3L N BODY

3.8L C & E BODIES

3.8L H BODY

3.8L W BODY

Code 38 will set if no Code 24 is present, status at brake input terminal of control module has not changed from high to low and vehicle speed has been greater than 35 MPH and back to zero MPH a precalibrated number of times.

NOTE: Test numbers refer to test numbers on diagnostic chart.

1) Jumpering the brake switch determines if the ECM and wiring for the brake switch are okay.
2) Determines if brake switch is out of adjustment or is faulty.
3) Verifies the voltage to the brake switch.

DIAGNOSTIC AIDS

A Code 38 in conjunction with a Code 39 or 26 would mean a problem with one or more of the following components.
- Fuse or power supply circuit, brake switch or wire before the splice.
- Code 38 alone is the result of a wire or circuit problem between the splice and the control module, poor connection to the control module, or possibly the control module, itself.

If brake switch has failed in an open state, TCC will not engage. Code 38 does not turn on SERVICE ENGINE SOON light on all models.

1991 ENGINE PERFORMANCE
Self-Diagnostics – ECM/PCM Except Cadillac (Cont.)

GM
1-87

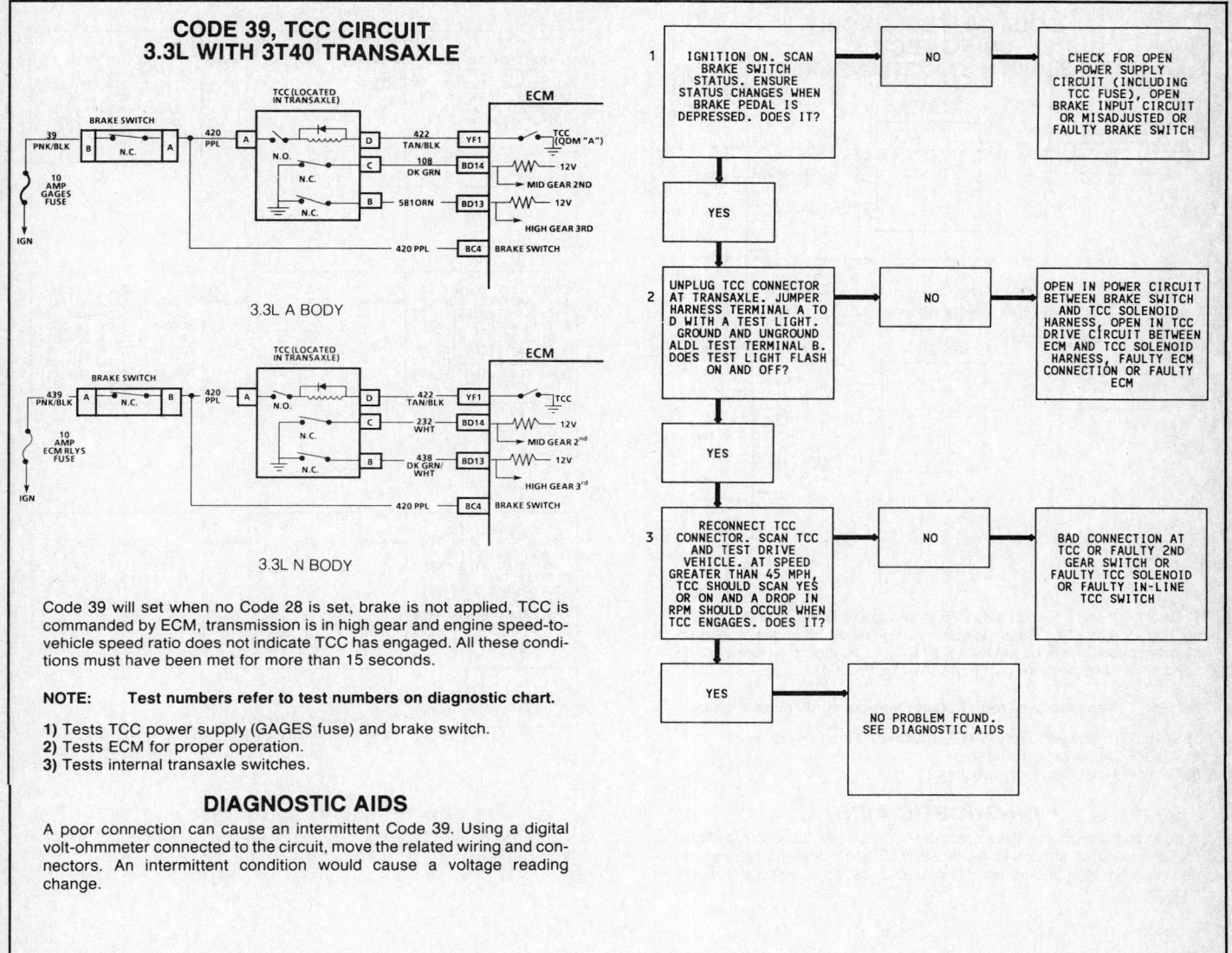

CODE 39, TCC CIRCUIT
3.3L WITH 3T40 TRANSAXLE

3.3L A BODY

3.3L N BODY

Code 39 will set when no Code 28 is set, brake is not applied, TCC is commanded by ECM, transmission is in high gear and engine speed-to-vehicle speed ratio does not indicate TCC has engaged. All these conditions must have been met for more than 15 seconds.

NOTE: Test numbers refer to test numbers on diagnostic chart.

1) Tests TCC power supply (GAGES fuse) and brake switch.
2) Tests ECM for proper operation.
3) Tests internal transaxle switches.

DIAGNOSTIC AIDS

A poor connection can cause an intermittent Code 39. Using a digital volt-ohmmeter connected to the circuit, move the related wiring and connectors. An intermittent condition would cause a voltage reading change.

1 IGNITION ON. SCAN BRAKE SWITCH STATUS. ENSURE STATUS CHANGES WHEN BRAKE PEDAL IS DEPRESSED. DOES IT? → NO → CHECK FOR OPEN POWER SUPPLY CIRCUIT (INCLUDING TCC FUSE), OPEN BRAKE INPUT CIRCUIT OR MISADJUSTED OR FAULTY BRAKE SWITCH

YES

2 UNPLUG TCC CONNECTOR AT TRANSAXLE. JUMPER HARNESS TERMINAL A TO D WITH A TEST LIGHT. GROUND AND UNGROUND ALDL TEST TERMINAL B. DOES TEST LIGHT FLASH ON AND OFF? → NO → OPEN IN POWER CIRCUIT BETWEEN BRAKE SWITCH AND TCC SOLENOID HARNESS, OPEN IN TCC DRIVE CIRCUIT BETWEEN ECM AND TCC SOLENOID HARNESS, FAULTY ECM CONNECTION OR FAULTY ECM

YES

3 RECONNECT TCC CONNECTOR. SCAN TCC AND TEST DRIVE VEHICLE. AT SPEED GREATER THAN 45 MPH, TCC SHOULD SCAN YES OR ON AND A DROP IN RPM SHOULD OCCUR WHEN TCC ENGAGES. DOES IT? → NO → BAD CONNECTION AT TCC OR FAULTY 2ND GEAR SWITCH OR FAULTY TCC SOLENOID OR FAULTY IN-LINE TCC SWITCH

YES → NO PROBLEM FOUND. SEE DIAGNOSTIC AIDS

91G07434 91B07436 91B07337

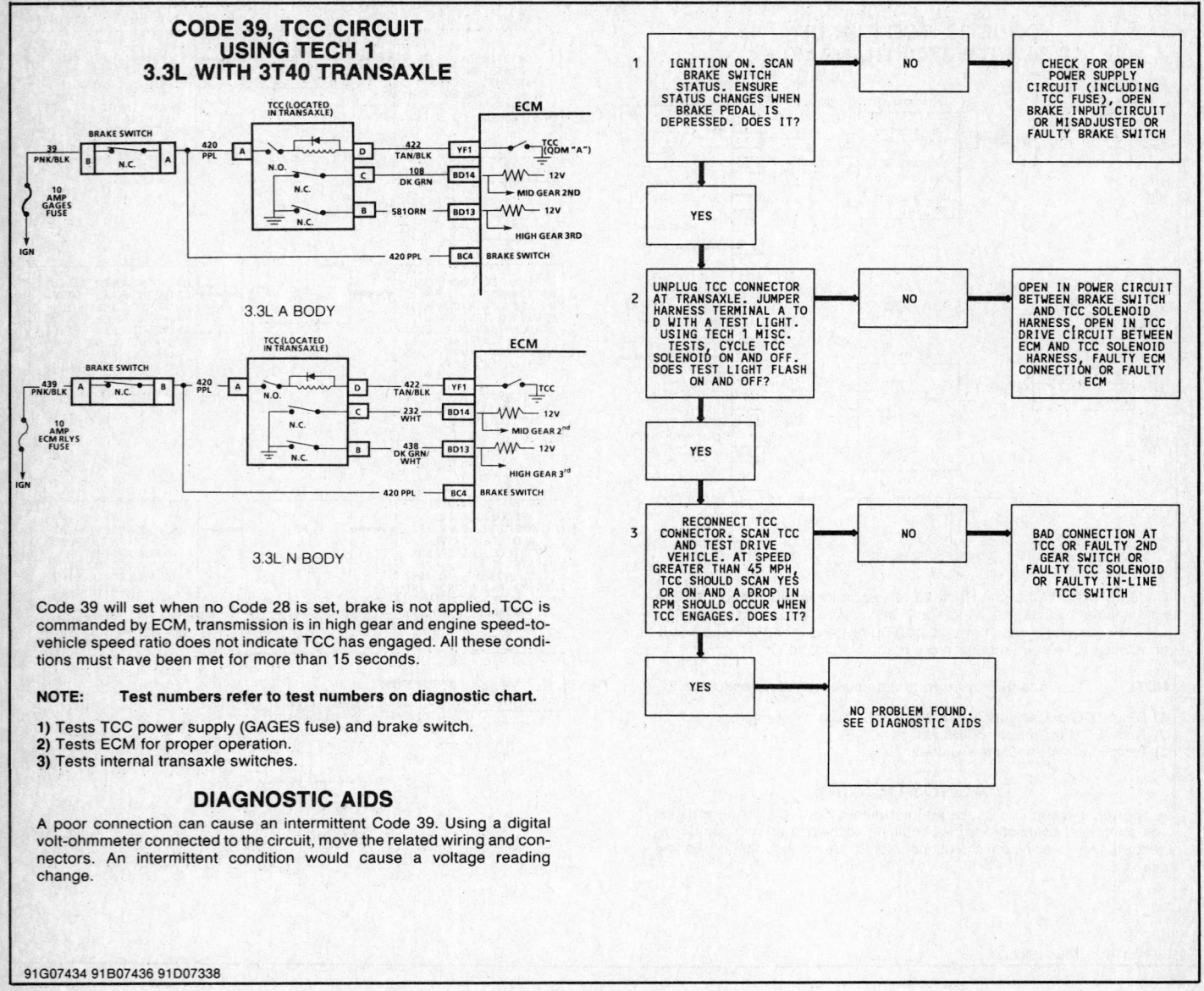

CODE 39, TCC CIRCUIT
USING TECH 1
3.3L WITH 3T40 TRANSAXLE

3.3L A BODY

3.3L N BODY

Code 39 will set when no Code 28 is set, brake is not applied, TCC is commanded by ECM, transmission is in high gear and engine speed-to-vehicle speed ratio does not indicate TCC has engaged. All these conditions must have been met for more than 15 seconds.

NOTE: Test numbers refer to test numbers on diagnostic chart.

1) Tests TCC power supply (GAGES fuse) and brake switch.
2) Tests ECM for proper operation.
3) Tests internal transaxle switches.

DIAGNOSTIC AIDS

A poor connection can cause an intermittent Code 39. Using a digital volt-ohmmeter connected to the circuit, move the related wiring and connectors. An intermittent condition would cause a voltage reading change.

91G07434 91B07436 91D07338

1991 ENGINE PERFORMANCE
Self-Diagnostics – ECM/PCM Except Cadillac (Cont.)

GM 1-89

CODE 39, TCC CIRCUIT
3.3L & 3.8L WITH 4T60 (440-T4) TRANSAXLE

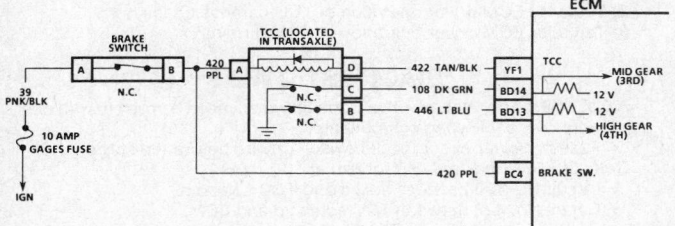

3.3L A BODY

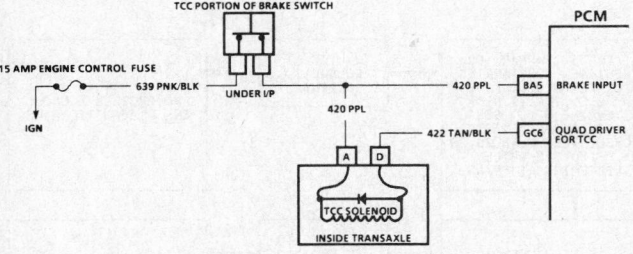

3.8L C & E BODY

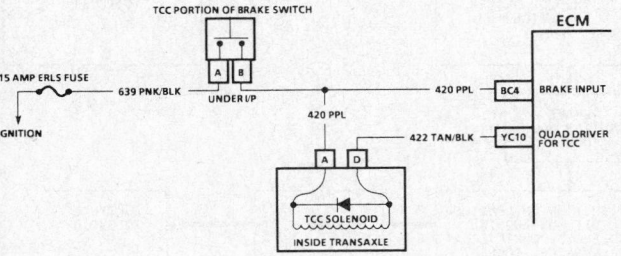

3.8L H BODY

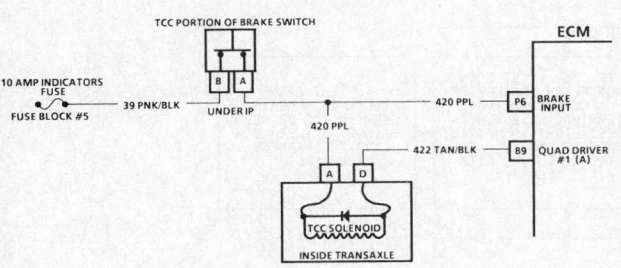

3.8L W BODY

Code 39 will set when no Code 28 or 29 is set, brake is not applied, TCC is commanded by ECM, transmission is in high gear and engine speed-to-vehicle speed ratio does not indicate TCC has engaged. All these conditions must have been met for more than 15 seconds.

NOTE: Test numbers refer to test numbers on diagnostic chart.

1) Tests fuse, brake switch and battery power circuit to the TCC solenoid.
2) Tests for ECM driver operation at TCC harness connector.
3) Tests for ECM driver operation at ECM terminal.

DIAGNOSTIC AIDS

A Code 39 in conjunction with a Code 38 would mean a problem with one or more of the following components.

• Fuse or power circuit, brake switch or wire before the splice.

Code 39 alone indicates a problem at:

• Circuit No. 420 between splice and TCC solenoid.
• Circuit No. 422 between TCC solenoid and ECM.
• Poor connection to the ECM or ECM, itself.

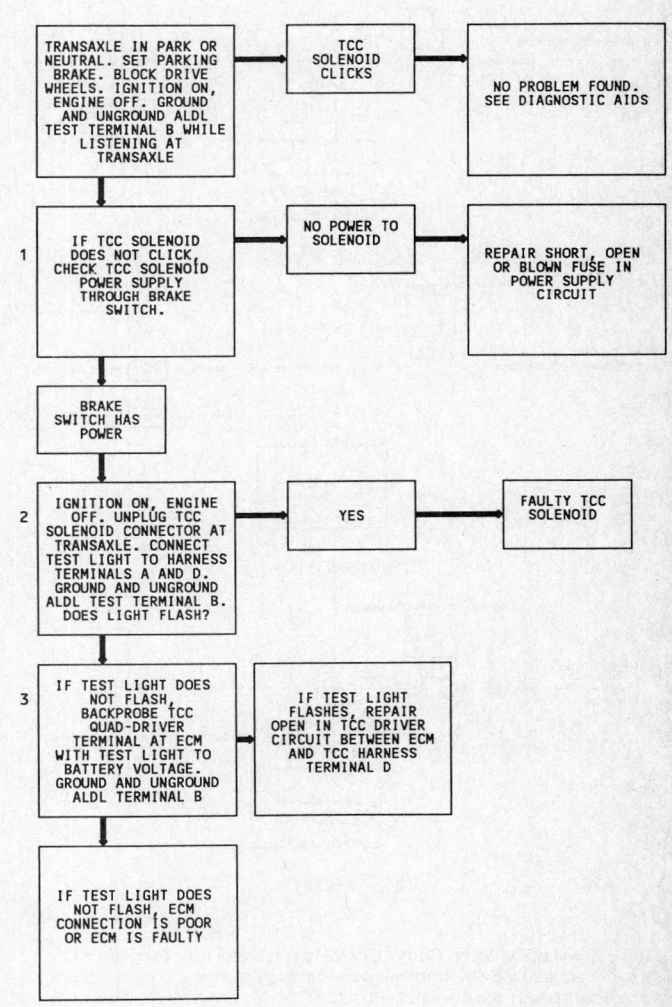

CODE 39, TCC CIRCUIT
USING TECH 1
3.3L & 3.8L WITH 4T60 (440-T4) TRANSAXLE

3.3L A BODY

3.8L C & E BODY

3.8L H BODY

3.8L W BODY

Code 39 will set when no Code 28 or 29 is set, brake is not applied, TCC is commanded by ECM, transmission is in high gear and engine speed-to-vehicle speed ratio does not indicate TCC has engaged. All these conditions must have been met for more than 15 seconds.

NOTE: Test numbers refer to test numbers on diagnostic chart.

1) Tests fuse, brake switch and battery power circuit to the TCC solenoid.
2) Tests for ECM driver operation at TCC harness connector.
3) Tests for ECM driver operation at ECM terminal.

DIAGNOSTIC AIDS

A Code 39 in conjunction with a Code 38 would mean a problem with one or more of the following components.

• Fuse or power circuit, brake switch or wire before the splice.

Code 39 alone indicates a problem at:

• Circuit No. 420 between splice and TCC solenoid.
• Circuit No. 422 between TCC solenoid and ECM.
• Poor connection to the ECM or ECM, itself.

1991 ENGINE PERFORMANCE
Self-Diagnostics — ECM/PCM Except Cadillac (Cont.)

GM
1-91

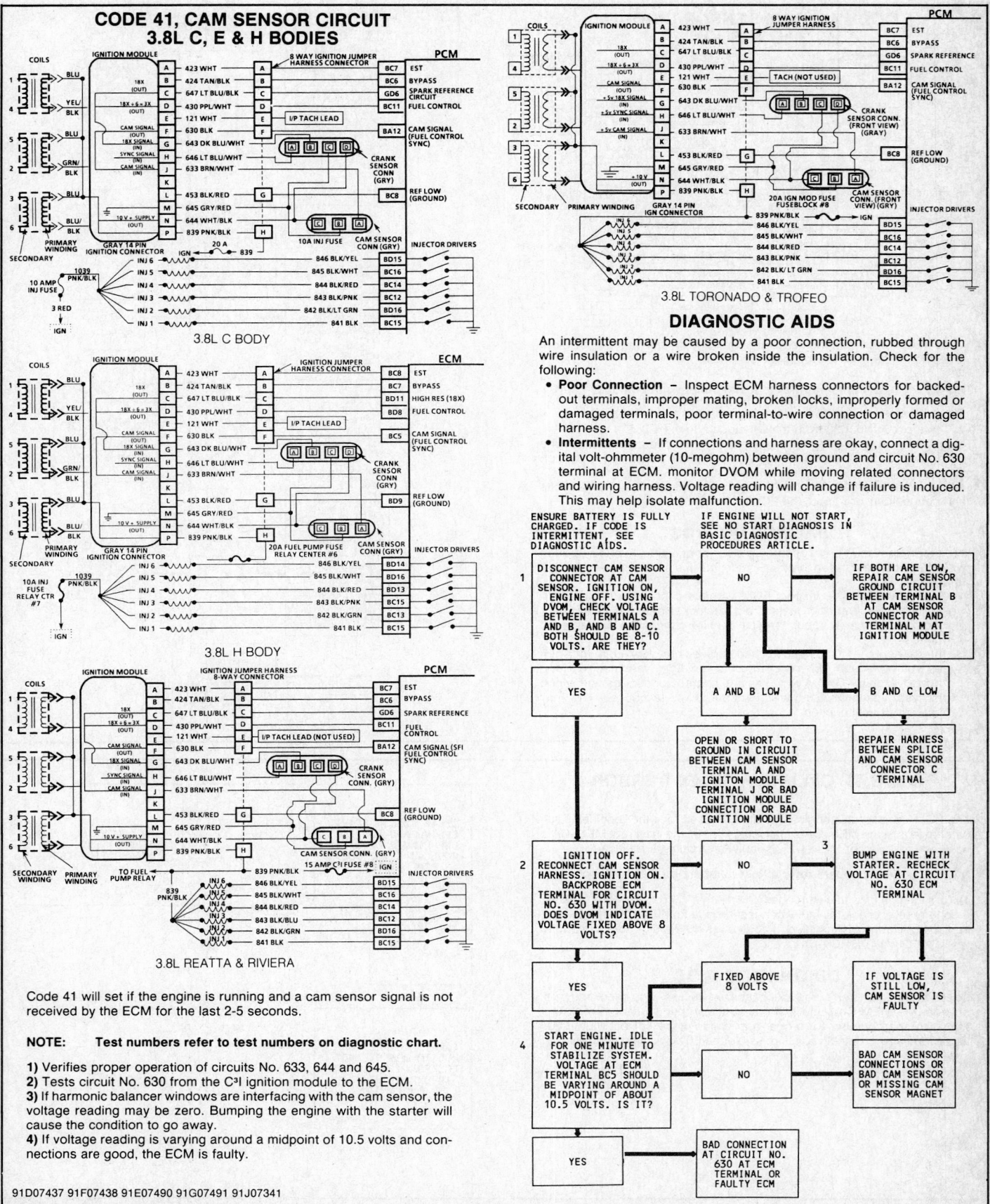

CODE 41, CAM SENSOR CIRCUIT 3.8L C, E & H BODIES

3.8L C BODY

3.8L H BODY

3.8L REATTA & RIVIERA

3.8L TORONADO & TROFEO

Code 41 will set if the engine is running and a cam sensor signal is not received by the ECM for the last 2-5 seconds.

NOTE: Test numbers refer to test numbers on diagnostic chart.

1) Verifies proper operation of circuits No. 633, 644 and 645.
2) Tests circuit No. 630 from the C³ ignition module to the ECM.
3) If harmonic balancer windows are interfacing with the cam sensor, the voltage reading may be zero. Bumping the engine with the starter will cause the condition to go away.
4) If voltage reading is varying around a midpoint of 10.5 volts and connections are good, the ECM is faulty.

DIAGNOSTIC AIDS

An intermittent may be caused by a poor connection, rubbed through wire insulation or a wire broken inside the insulation. Check for the following:

- **Poor Connection** – Inspect ECM harness connectors for backed-out terminals, improper mating, broken locks, improperly formed or damaged terminals, poor terminal-to-wire connection or damaged harness.
- **Intermittents** – If connections and harness are okay, connect a digital volt-ohmmeter (10-megohm) between ground and circuit No. 630 terminal at ECM. monitor DVOM while moving related connectors and wiring harness. Voltage reading will change if failure is induced. This may help isolate malfunction.

CODE 41, CAM SENSOR CIRCUIT
3.8L W BODY

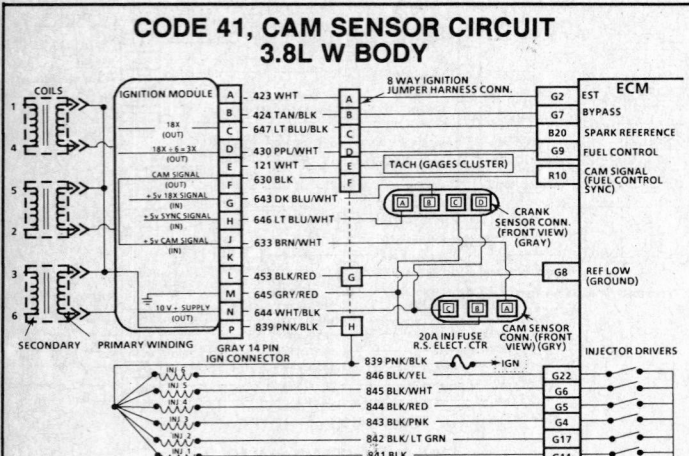

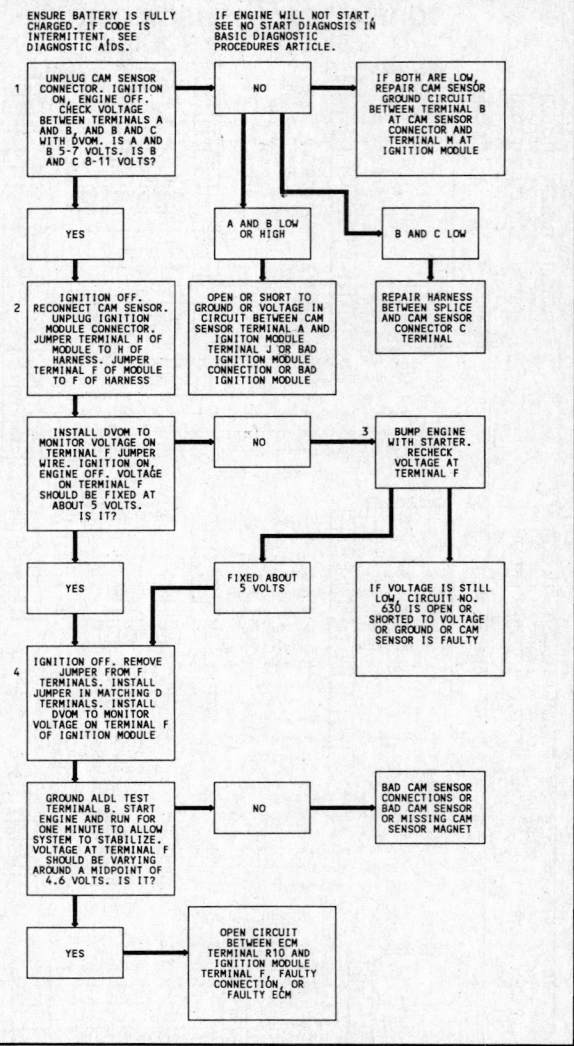

Code 41 will set if the engine is running and a cam sensor signal is not received by the ECM for the last 2 seconds.

NOTE: Test numbers refer to test numbers on diagnostic chart.

1) Verifies proper operation of circuits No. 633, 644 and 645.
2) Tests circuit No. 630 from the C³I module to the ECM.
3) If camshaft gear magnet is interfacing with the cam sensor, the voltage reading will be zero. Bumping the engine will cause the condition to go away.
4) If voltage reading is constantly varying around a midpoint of 4.6 volts and connections are good, the ECM is faulty.

DIAGNOSTIC AIDS

An intermittent may be caused by a poor connection, rubbed through wire insulation or a wire broken inside the insulation. Check for the following:

- **Poor Connection** – Inspect ECM harness connectors for backed-out terminals, improper mating, broken locks, improperly formed or damaged terminals, poor terminal-to-wire connection or damaged harness.
- **Intermittents** – If connections and harness are okay, connect a digital volt-ohmmeter (10-megohm) between ECM terminal R10 and ground. Monitor DVOM while moving related connectors and wiring harness. Voltage reading will change if failure is induced. This may help isolate malfunction.

91H07439 91B07342

CODE 41, CYLINDER SELECT ERROR
3.1L

The ECM used for this engine can also be used for other engines. The difference is in the MEM-CAL. If a Code 41 sets, the incorrect MEM-CAL has been installed or MEM-CAL is faulty and must be replaced.

NOTE: Test numbers refer to test numbers on diagnostic chart.

1) Turn ignition off and clear codes. Start engine and run for one minute. If code resets, check for faulty connection due to MEM-CAL not locked in place or incorrectly installed. If code does not recur, code is intermittent. See DIAGNOSTIC AIDS.

DIAGNOSTIC AIDS

Check MEM-CAL to be sure locking tabs are secure. Also check the pins on both the MEM-CAL and ECM to verify proper contact. Check the MEM-CAL part number for proper application. If the correct MEM-CAL is installed and is defective, it is possible the ECM will also need replacing.

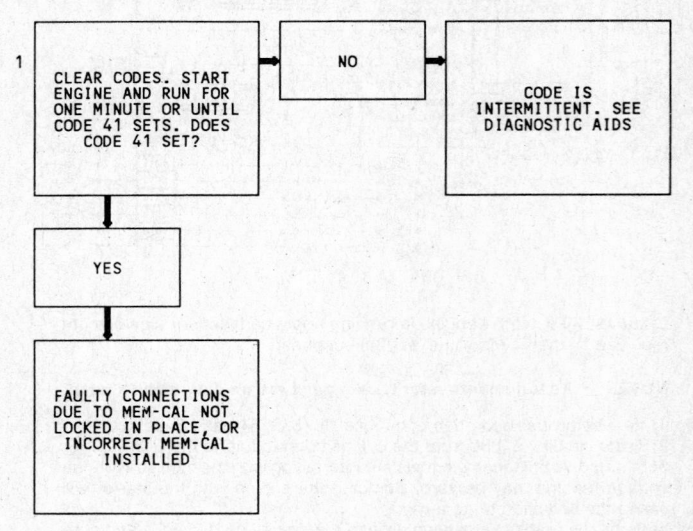

91D07343

1991 ENGINE PERFORMANCE
Self-Diagnostics — ECM/PCM Except Cadillac (Cont.)

GM
1-93

CODE 41, 1X REFERENCE CIRCUIT 2.3L

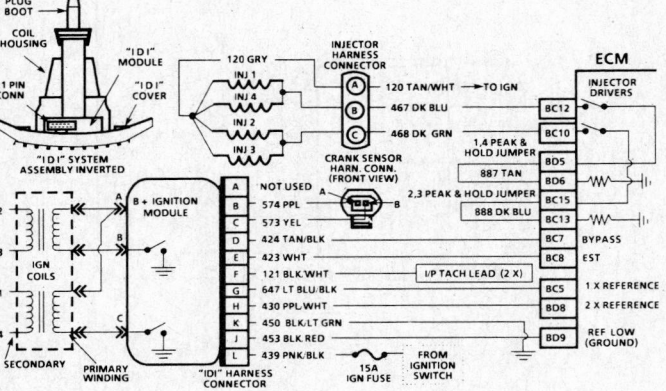

L BODY

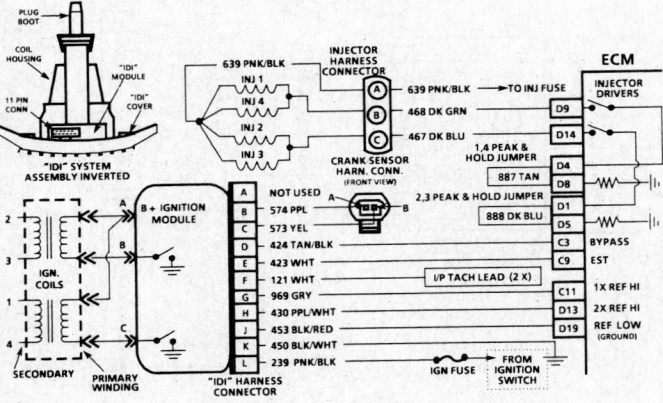

N BODY

W BODY

The ignition module sends a signal to ECM once per revolution to indicate crankshaft position. The ECM uses this information to determine when to pulse injectors for cylinders No. 2 and 3. This signal can be described as a synchronization signal and is called 1X reference, because it occurs one time per revolution.

The ignition module applies 5 volts from terminal G to ECM terminal BC5 (L & N Body) or C11 (W Body) and in effect, switches this circuit to ground for a short period of time, 125 degrees before TDC of cylinders

No. 2 and 3. Code 41 is set if ECM receives (8) 2X reference pulses without a 1X reference pulse. When Code 41 is present, ECM pulses injectors in the simultaneously mode.

NOTE: Test numbers refer to test numbers on diagnostic chart.

1) This determines if ECM recognizes a fault. If a Code 41 is not set here, problem is intermittent and could be caused by a loose connection.
2) This step simulates 1X signal. If circuit and ECM are okay, ECM should recognize the voltage drop as test light probe is removed. This step will only give accurate results if:
- Chart sequence is used (ignition off or ignition on).
- "Scan" tester is set to 1X reference.
- Terminal "G" is contacted using test light probe.

The ECM will only recognize up to 4 simulated 1X pulses under this test condition.
3) If ECM did not recognize simulation of 1X signal, circuit No. 969 (L and W Bodies) or No. 647 (N Body) may be open or shorted to ground or voltage. If circuit is okay, ECM is faulty.
4) Step 2 indicated 1X circuit is okay and ECM is capable of recognizing simulated 1X reference pulse. This indicates either a poor connection at ignition module terminal "G" or a faulty ignition module caused Code 41 to occur.

DIAGNOSTIC AIDS

An intermittent may be caused by a poor connection, rubbed through wire insulation or a wire broken inside the insulation. Inspect ECM harness 1X connector terminal and ignition module terminal "G" for improperly formed or damaged terminals, poor terminal to wire connection and damaged harness. Code 41 will set if a 1988 ignition module is installed.

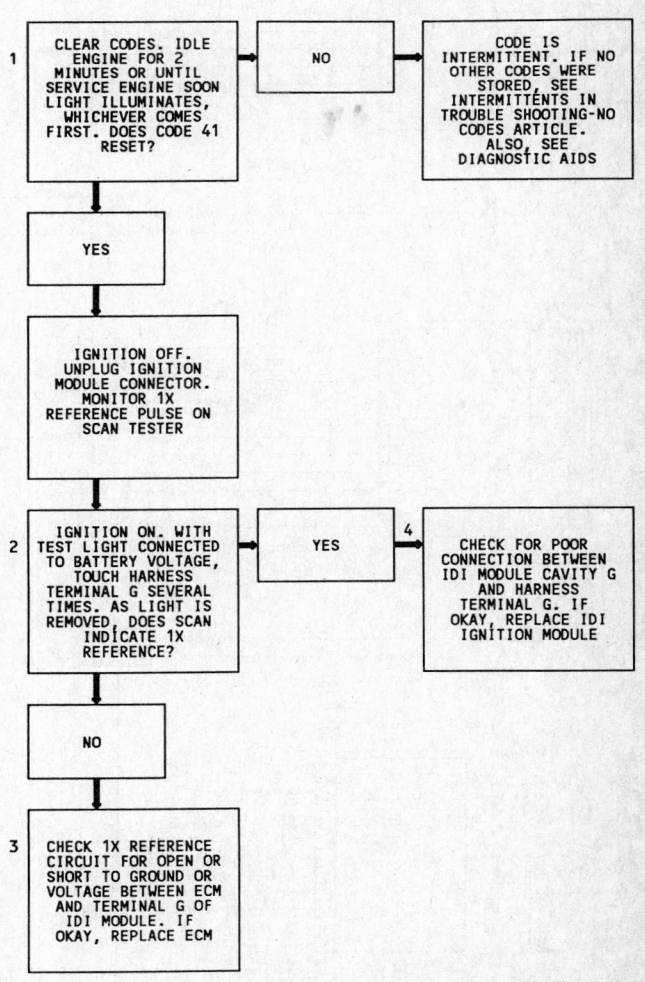

GM
1-94

1991 ENGINE PERFORMANCE
Self-Diagnostics — ECM/PCM Except Cadillac (Cont.)

**CODE 42, EST CIRCUIT OPEN OR GROUNDED
ALL EXCEPT 2.3L, 3.3L & 3.8L**

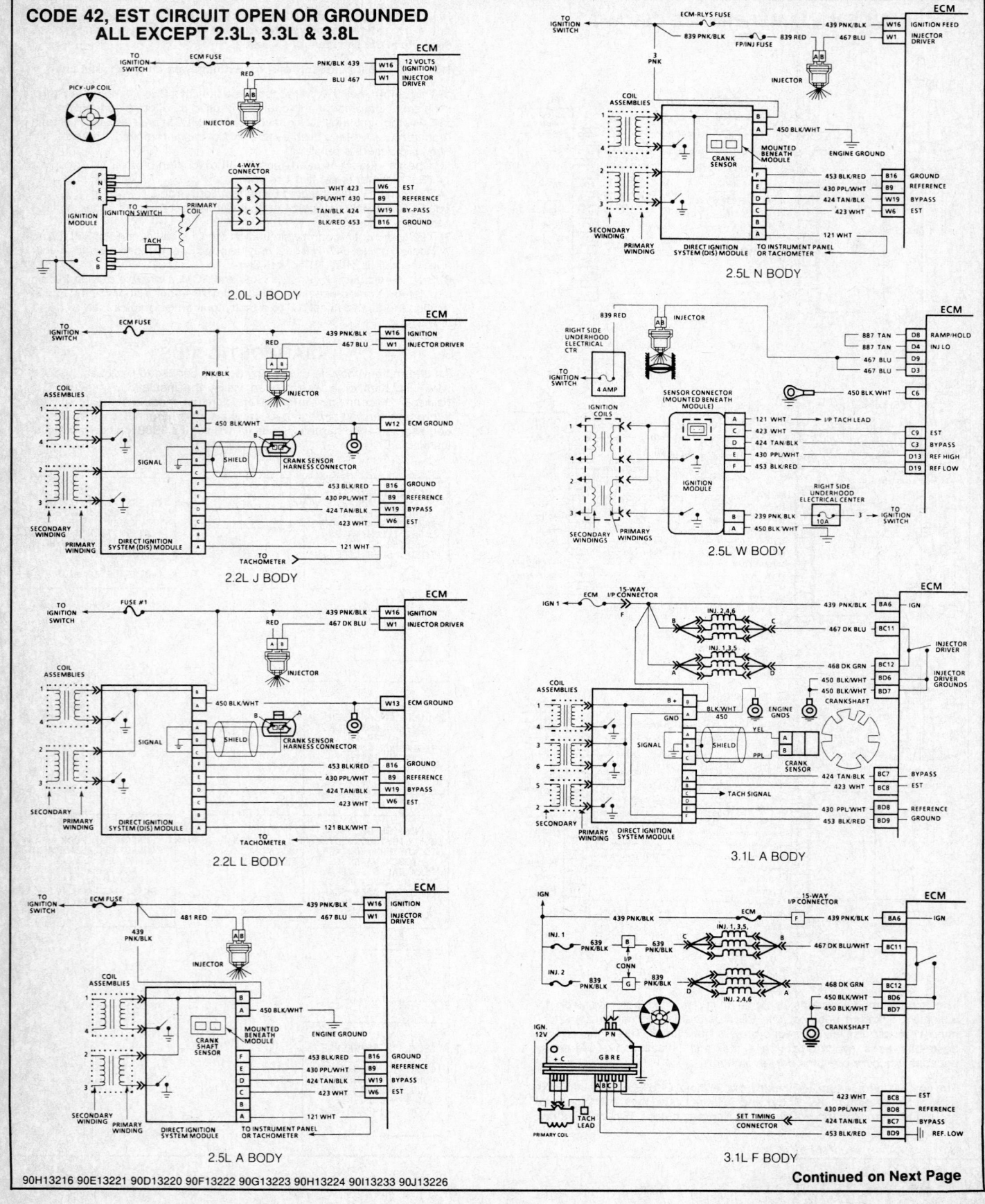

2.0L J BODY

2.2L J BODY

2.2L L BODY

2.5L A BODY

2.5L N BODY

2.5L W BODY

3.1L A BODY

3.1L F BODY

Continued on Next Page

1991 ENGINE PERFORMANCE
Self-Diagnostics — ECM/PCM Except Cadillac (Cont.)

GM
1-95

CODE 42, EST CIRCUIT OPEN OR GROUNDED
ALL EXCEPT 2.3L, 3.3L & 3.8L (Cont.)

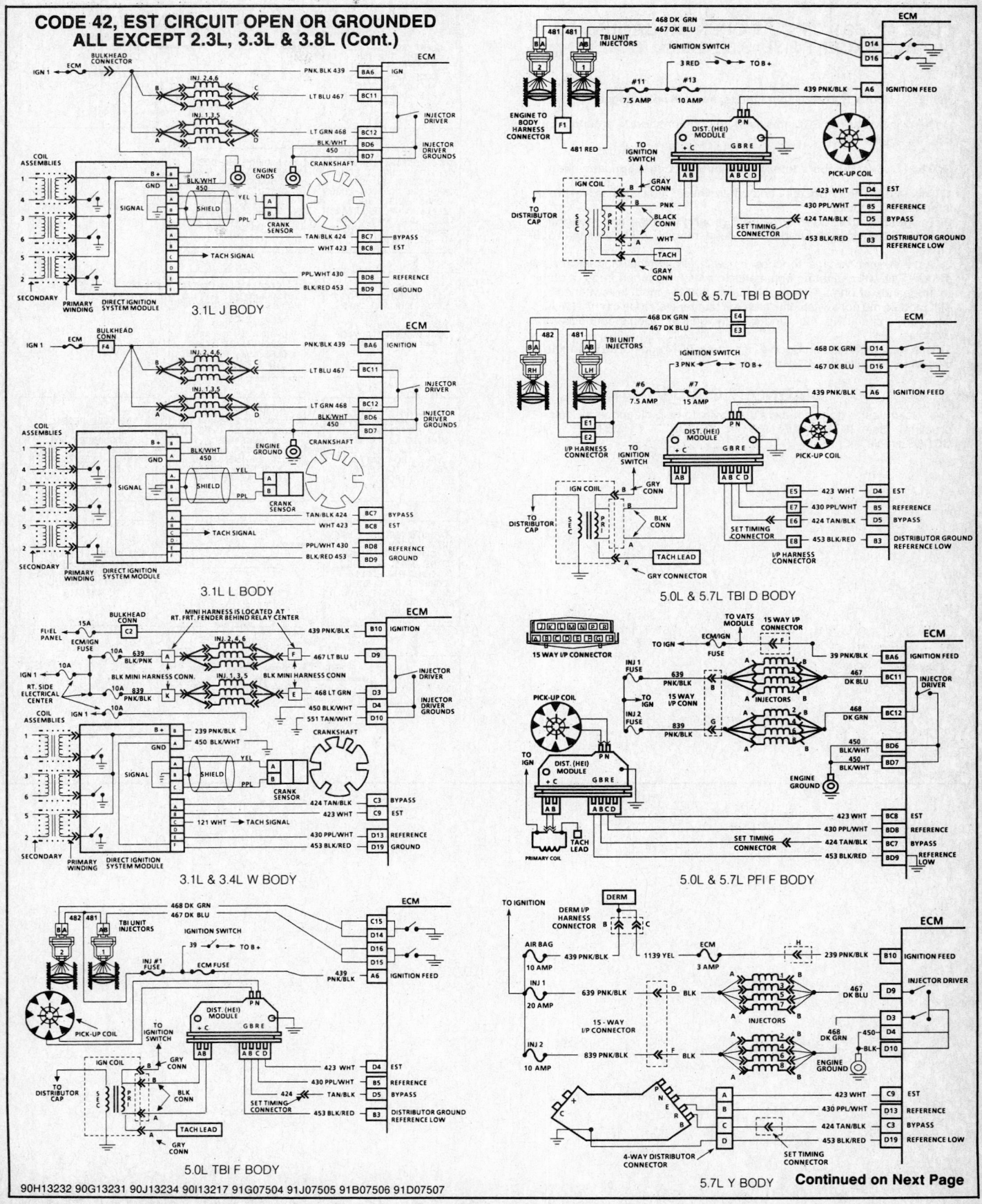

3.1L J BODY

3.1L L BODY

3.1L & 3.4L W BODY

5.0L TBI F BODY

5.0L & 5.7L TBI B BODY

5.0L & 5.7L TBI D BODY

5.0L & 5.7L PFI F BODY

5.7L Y BODY

Continued on Next Page

90H13232 90G13231 90J13234 90I13217 91G07504 91J07505 91B07506 91D07507

CODE 42, EST CIRCUIT OPEN OR GROUNDED ALL EXCEPT 2.3L, 3.3L & 3.8L (Cont.)

NOTE: For applicable schematics, see previous pages.

Code 42 indicates the ECM has seen an open or short to ground in HEI EST or by-pass circuit.

NOTE: Test numbers refer to test numbers on diagnostic chart.

1) This test confirms Code 42 and determines if fault is a hard failure or intermittent condition.

2) This test checks for a normal EST ground path through the ignition module. If EST circuit is shorted to ground, reading will be less than 500 ohms.

3) As test light voltage touches by-pass circuit, the module should switch. This will cause the ohmmeter to switch from hundreds of ohms to thousands of ohms. This test assures that the module "switched".

4) If module did not switch, this step will test for a short in circuit No. 423, an open in circuit No. 424, and a faulty ignition module connection or module.

5) This step confirms that Code 42 is a faulty ECM and not an intermittent problem in circuits No. 423 and 424.

DIAGNOSTIC AIDS

The "Scan" tester does not have the ability to help diagnose a Code 42 problem. See INTERMITTENTS in TROUBLE SHOOTING – NO CODES article.

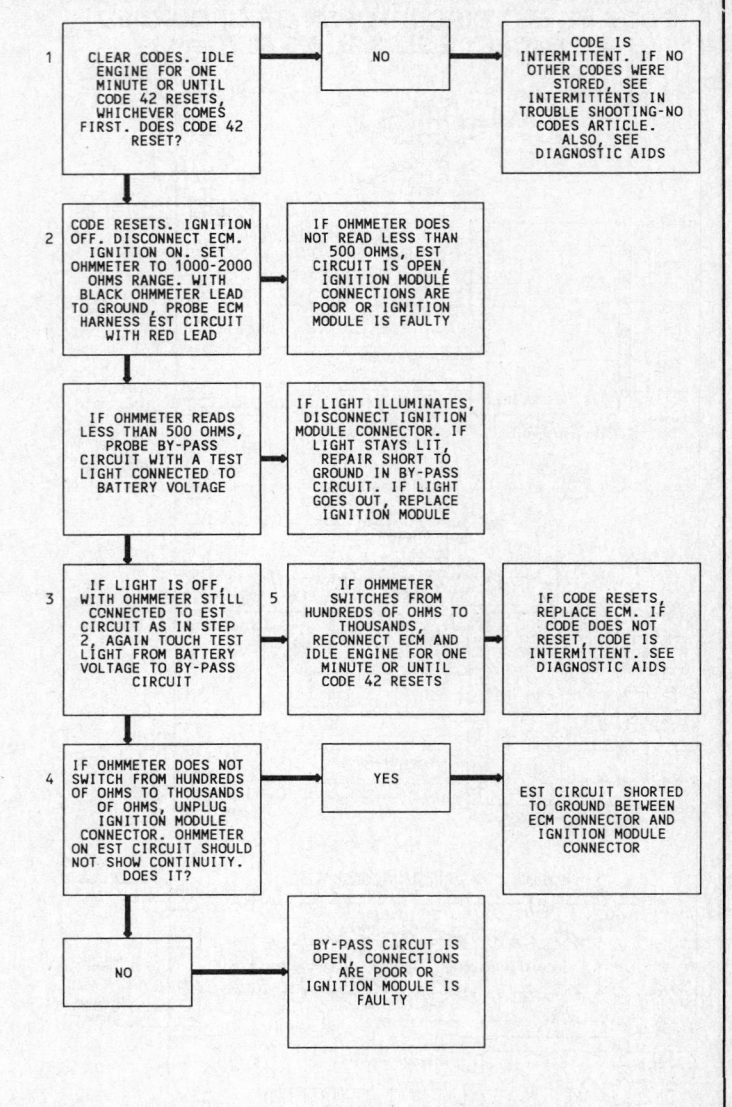

91I07345

1991 ENGINE PERFORMANCE
Self-Diagnostics — ECM/PCM Except Cadillac (Cont.)

GM
1-97

CODE 42, EST CIRCUIT OPEN OR GROUNDED
2.3L

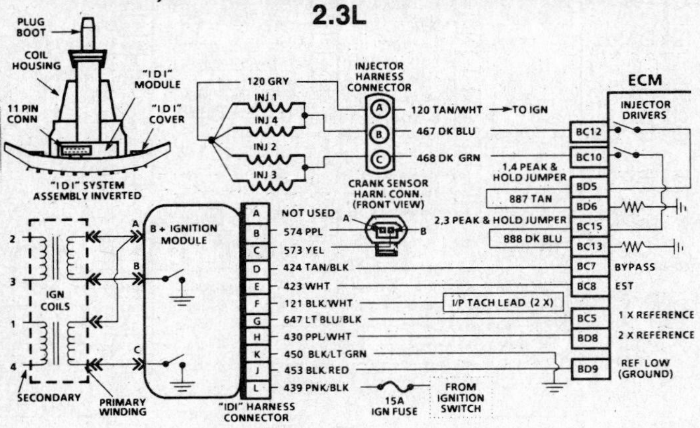

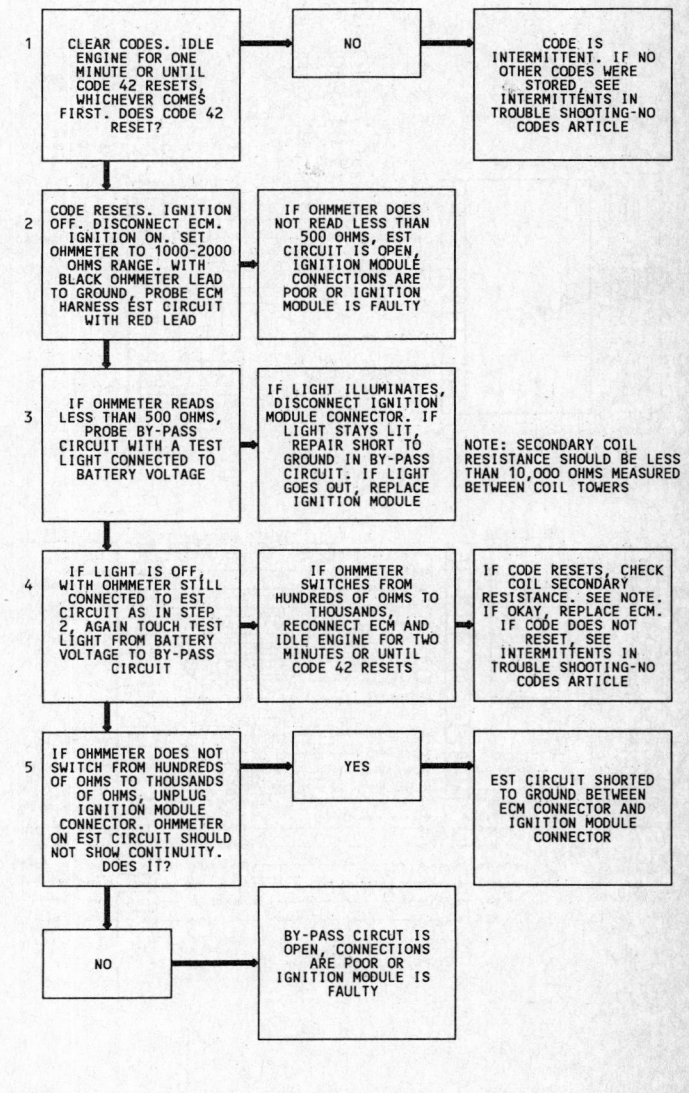

2.3L L BODY

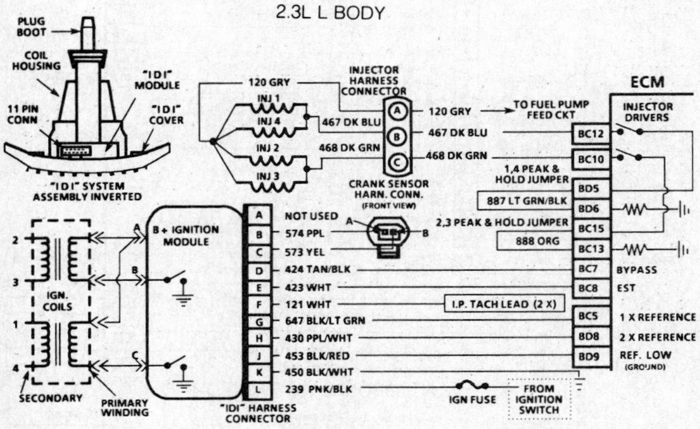

2.3L N BODY

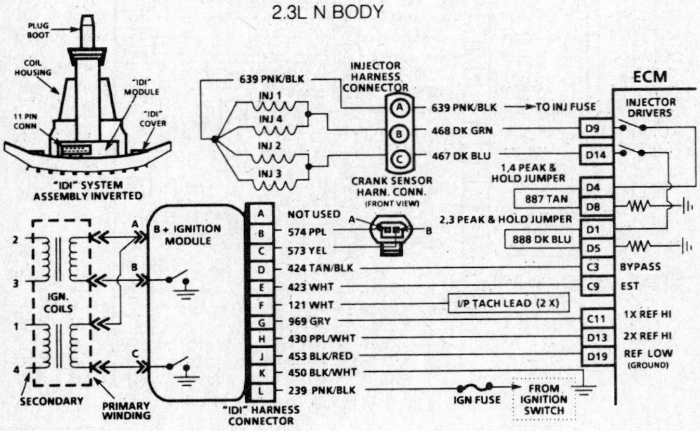

2.3L W BODY

Code 42 indicates the ECM has seen an open or short to ground in HEI EST or by-pass circuit.

NOTE: Test numbers refer to test numbers on diagnostic chart.

1) Checks if ECM recognizes a fault. If a Code 42 is not set here, an intermittent problem exists and could be caused by a loose connection.
2) With ECM disconnected, ohmmeter should indicate less than 500 ohms, which is normal resistance for the ignition module. A higher resistance indicates a fault in circuit No. 423, poor ignition module connection or faulty ignition module.
3) If test light was illuminated when connected from 12 volts to ECM harness by-pass terminal either circuit No. 423 is shorted to ground or ignition module is faulty.
4) Checks if ignition module switches when bypass circuit is energized by 12 volts through test light. If ignition module switches, ohmmeter reading should switch from less than 500 ohms to greater than 8000 ohms.
5) Disconnecting ignition module should cause ohmmeter to indicate as if it were monitoring an open circuit (infinite reading). If ohmmeter reads anything other than infinity, circuit No. 423 is shorted to ground.

DIAGNOSTIC AIDS

An intermittent may be caused by a poor connection, rubbed through wire insulation or wire broken inside insulation. Inspect ECM harness connectors for backed-out by-pass or EST terminals, improper mating, broken locks, improperly formed or damaged terminals, poor terminal-to-wire connection or damaged harness.

1 CLEAR CODES. IDLE ENGINE FOR ONE MINUTE OR UNTIL CODE 42 RESETS, WHICHEVER COMES FIRST. DOES CODE 42 RESET? → NO → CODE IS INTERMITTENT. IF NO OTHER CODES WERE STORED, SEE INTERMITTENTS IN TROUBLE SHOOTING-NO CODES ARTICLE

2 CODE RESETS. IGNITION OFF. DISCONNECT ECM. IGNITION ON. SET OHMMETER TO 1000-2000 OHMS RANGE. WITH BLACK OHMMETER LEAD TO GROUND. PROBE ECM HARNESS EST CIRCUIT WITH RED LEAD

IF OHMMETER DOES NOT READ LESS THAN 500 OHMS, EST CIRCUIT IS OPEN, IGNITION MODULE CONNECTIONS ARE POOR OR IGNITION MODULE IS FAULTY

3 IF OHMMETER READS LESS THAN 500 OHMS, PROBE BY-PASS CIRCUIT WITH A TEST LIGHT CONNECTED TO BATTERY VOLTAGE

IF LIGHT ILLUMINATES, DISCONNECT IGNITION MODULE CONNECTOR. IF LIGHT STAYS LIT, REPAIR SHORT TO GROUND IN BY-PASS CIRCUIT. IF LIGHT GOES OUT, REPLACE IGNITION MODULE

NOTE: SECONDARY COIL RESISTANCE SHOULD BE LESS THAN 10,000 OHMS MEASURED BETWEEN COIL TOWERS

4 IF LIGHT IS OFF WITH OHMMETER STILL CONNECTED TO EST CIRCUIT AS IN STEP 2, AGAIN TOUCH TEST LIGHT FROM BATTERY VOLTAGE TO BY-PASS CIRCUIT

IF OHMMETER SWITCHES FROM HUNDREDS OF OHMS TO THOUSANDS, RECONNECT ECM AND IDLE ENGINE FOR TWO MINUTES OR UNTIL CODE 42 RESETS

IF CODE RESETS, CHECK COIL SECONDARY RESISTANCE. SEE NOTE. IF OKAY, REPLACE ECM. IF CODE DOES NOT RESET, SEE INTERMITTENTS IN TROUBLE SHOOTING-NO CODES ARTICLE

5 IF OHMMETER DOES NOT SWITCH FROM HUNDREDS OF OHMS TO THOUSANDS OF OHMS, UNPLUG IGNITION MODULE CONNECTOR. OHMMETER ON EST CIRCUIT SHOULD NOT SHOW CONTINUITY. DOES IT? → YES → EST CIRCUIT SHORTED TO GROUND BETWEEN ECM CONNECTOR AND IGNITION MODULE CONNECTOR

→ NO → BY-PASS CIRCUT IS OPEN, CONNECTIONS ARE POOR OR IGNITION MODULE IS FAULTY

GM
1-98

1991 ENGINE PERFORMANCE
Self-Diagnostics – ECM/PCM Except Cadillac (Cont.)

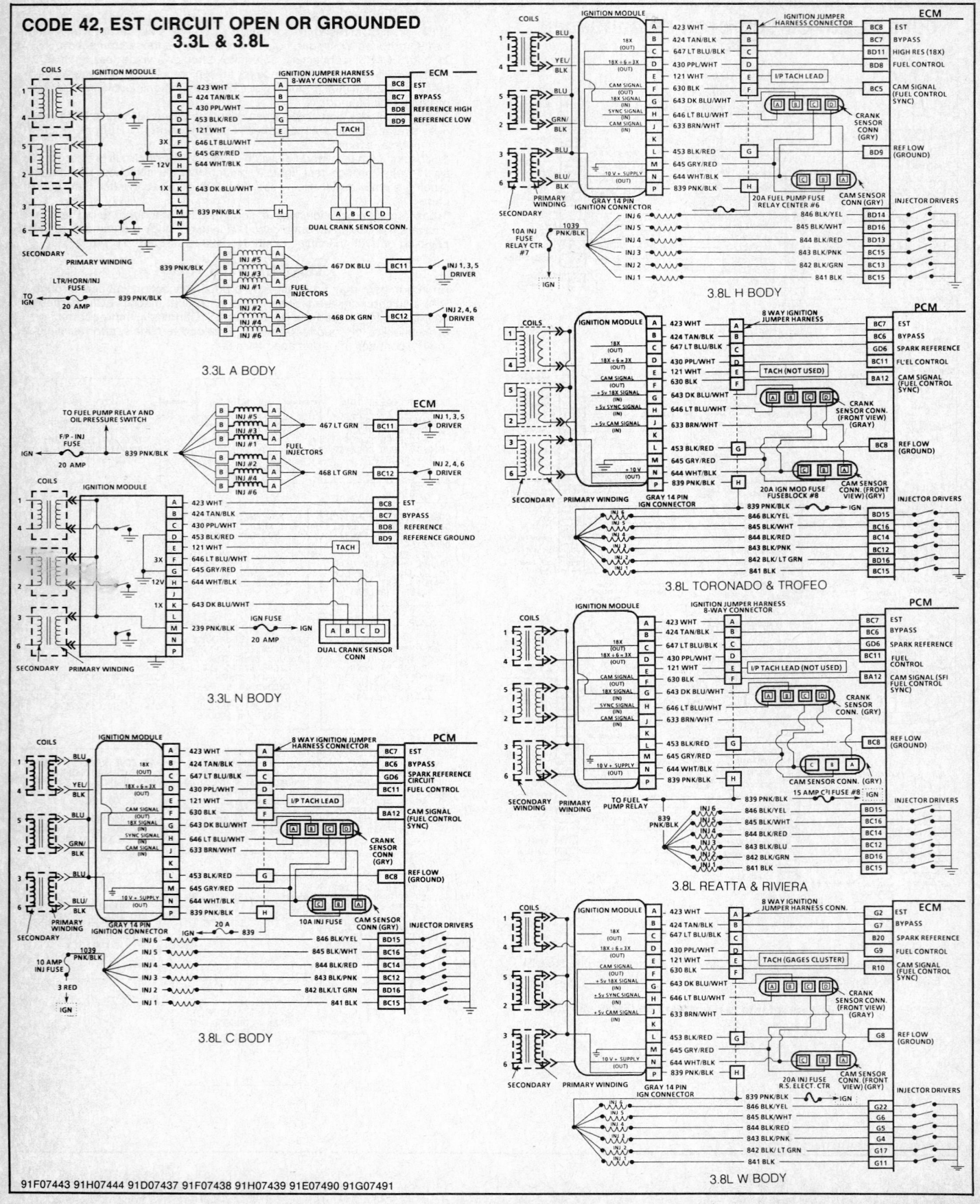

CODE 42, EST CIRCUIT OPEN OR GROUNDED 3.3L & 3.8L

3.3L A BODY

3.3L N BODY

3.8L C BODY

3.8L H BODY

3.8L TORONADO & TROFEO

3.8L REATTA & RIVIERA

3.8L W BODY

1991 ENGINE PERFORMANCE
Self-Diagnostics – ECM/PCM Except Cadillac (Cont.)

GM
1-99

CODE 42, EST CIRCUIT OPEN OR GROUNDED
3.3L & 3.8L (Cont.)

NOTE: For applicable schematic, see previous page.

Code 42 will set if EST or by-pass circuit is open or grounded at time of engine start-up.

NOTE: Test numbers refer to test numbers on diagnostic chart.

1) Tests if ECM recognizes a problem. If it doesn't set Code 42 at this point, it is an intermittent problem. Check for a loose connection.
2) With the ECM disconnected, the digital volt-ohmmeter should read less than 200 ohms. This is normal EST circuit resistance through the ignition module. A higher resistance would indicate a fault in circuit No. 423, a poor ignition module connection or a faulty ignition module.
3) If test light was on when connected from 12 volts to ECM harness by-pass circuit, either circuit No. 424 is shorted to ground or the ignition module is faulty.
4) Tests if ignition module switches when by-pass circuit is energized by 12 volts through test light. If ignition module switches, the resistance reading should switch from less than 200 ohms to more than 6000 ohms.
5) Disconnecting the ignition module should make the ohmmeter read as if it were monitoring an open circuit (infinite reading). Otherwise, circuit No. 423 is shorted to ground.

DIAGNOSTIC AIDS

An intermittent may be caused by a poor connection, rubbed through wire insulation or a wire broken inside the insulation.
- **Poor Connection** – Inspect ECM harness connectors for backed-out terminals, improper mating, broken locks, improperly formed or damaged terminals, poor terminal-to-wire connection or damaged harness.
- **Intermittents** – If connections and harness are okay, connect a digital volt-ohmmeter between affected terminal to ground and monitor meter while moving related connectors and wiring harness. If the failure is induced, the voltage reading will change.

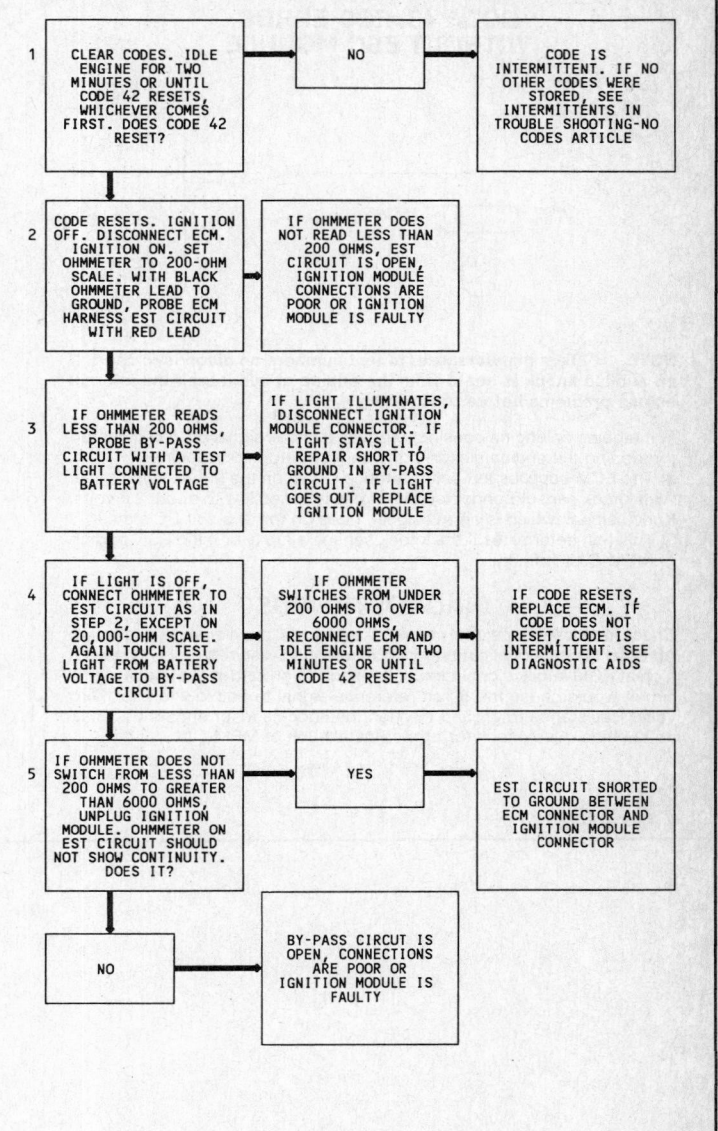

91C07347

CODE 43, ESC ERROR
WITHOUT ESC MODULE

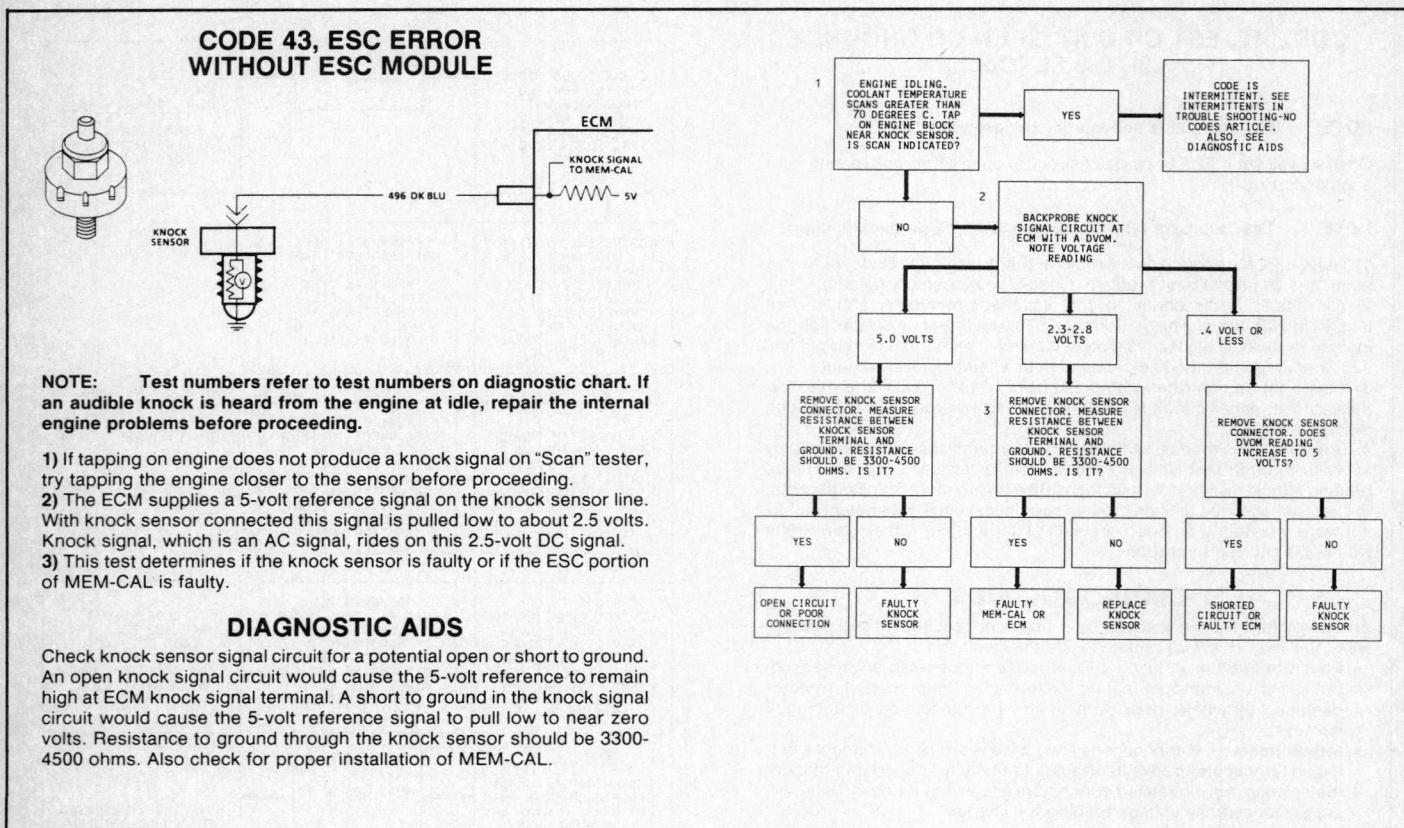

NOTE: Test numbers refer to test numbers on diagnostic chart. If an audible knock is heard from the engine at idle, repair the internal engine problems before proceeding.

1) If tapping on engine does not produce a knock signal on "Scan" tester, try tapping the engine closer to the sensor before proceeding.

2) The ECM supplies a 5-volt reference signal on the knock sensor line. With knock sensor connected this signal is pulled low to about 2.5 volts. Knock signal, which is an AC signal, rides on this 2.5-volt DC signal.

3) This test determines if the knock sensor is faulty or if the ESC portion of MEM-CAL is faulty.

DIAGNOSTIC AIDS

Check knock sensor signal circuit for a potential open or short to ground. An open knock signal circuit would cause the 5-volt reference to remain high at ECM knock signal terminal. A short to ground in the knock signal circuit would cause the 5-volt reference signal to pull low to near zero volts. Resistance to ground through the knock sensor should be 3300-4500 ohms. Also check for proper installation of MEM-CAL.

91A07445 91E07348

1991 ENGINE PERFORMANCE
Self-Diagnostics — ECM/PCM Except Cadillac (Cont.)

GM
1-101

CODE 43, ESC ERROR
V8 TBI WITH ESC MODULE

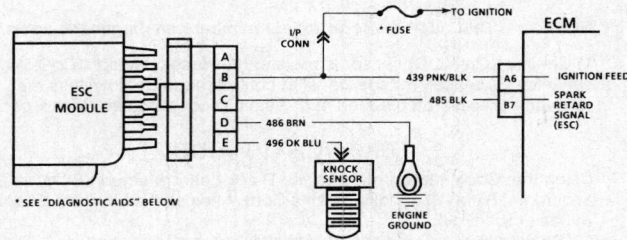

5.0L & 5.7L TBI B & F BODIES

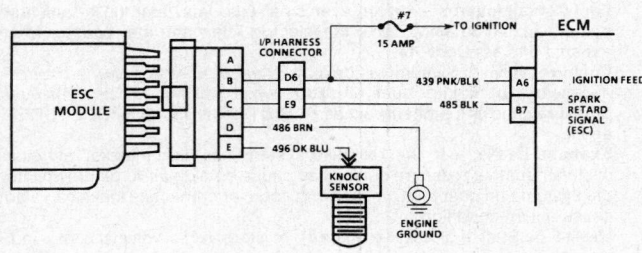

5.0L & 5.7L TBI D BODY

NOTE: Test numbers refer to test numbers on diagnostic chart.

1) If conditions for a Code 43 exist, "Scan" tester will indicate knock signal presence. There should not be a knock signal at idle unless an internal or system problem exists.

2) Determines if system is functioning at this time. Usually, a knock signal can be generated by tapping on the exhaust manifold. If no knock signal is generated, try tapping on engine block closer to sensor.

3) Because Code 43 sets when the signal voltage on the spark retard line remains low, this test should cause the signal on that line to go high. The 12-volt signal should be seen by the control module as a "no knock" signal if the control module and wiring are okay.

4) This test will determine if the knock signal is being detected on the sensor-to-controller line or if the ESC module is at fault.

5) If sensor line is routed too close to secondary ignition wires, the ESC module may see induced interference as a knock signal.

6) This checks ground circuit to module. An open ground will cause the voltage on the monitored line to constantly remain about 12 volts. This would cause the Code 43 functional test to fail.

7) Contacting the sensor-to-controller wire with a test light connected to 12 volts will generate a knock signal to the controller. This will determine if the ESC controller is operating correctly.

91C07446 91E07447 91G07349

DIAGNOSTIC AIDS

Code 43 can be caused by a faulty connection at the knock sensor, at the ESC module or at the control module. Check the controller-to-control module signal line for an open or short to ground. Check for poor connections or damaged harness. Inspect control module harness connectors for backed-out sensor signal and ECM input signal terminals, improper mating, broken locks, improperly formed or damaged terminals or damaged harness. If connections and harness check out okay, monitor knock signal parameter using "Scan" tester, while moving related connectors and wiring harness. If failure is induced, knock signal will abruptly change. This may help to isolate the malfunction.

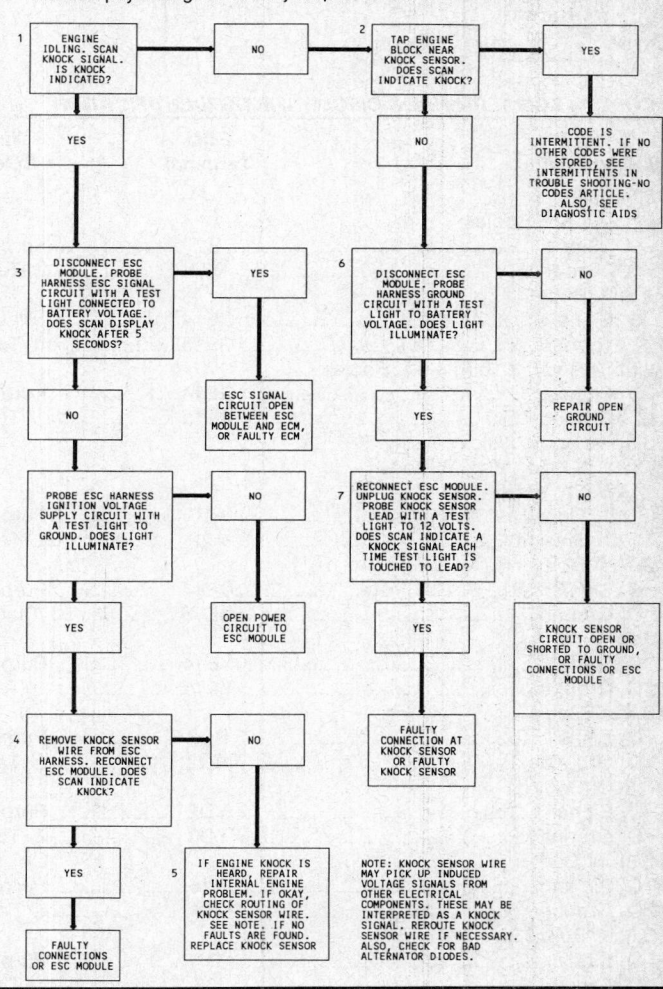

CODE 44, LEAN EXHAUST INDICATION

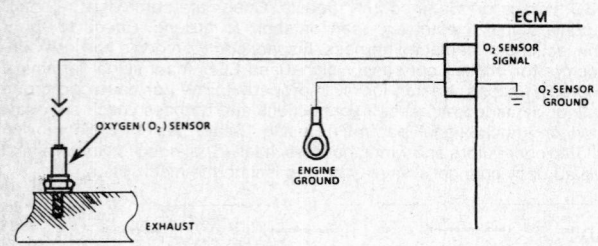

CODE 44 ECM TERMINAL & CIRCUIT WIRING IDENTIFICATION

Application	ECM Terminal	Wire Color
2.0L, 2.2L &		
2.5L A & N Bodies		
O₂ Signal	B2	Purple
O₂ Ground	B23	Tan
2.3L L Body		
O₂ Signal	GE14	Black
O₂ Ground	GE15	Tan
2.3L N Body, 3.1L F, J & L Bodies		
O₂ Signal	GE14	Purple
O₂ Ground	GE15	Tan
2.3L W Body, 2.5L W Body,		
3.1L W Body, 3.4L W Body		
& 5.7L Y Body		
O₂ Signal	A16	Purple
O₂ Ground	A22	Tan
3.1L A Body		
O₂ Signal	GE14	Purple
O₂ Ground	GE15	Black
3.3L		
O₂ Signal	YE14	Purple
O₂ Ground	YE15	Tan
3.8L C Body		
O₂ Signal	BD3	Purple
O₂ Ground	BD2	Tan
3.8L H Body		
O₂ Signal	YD2	Purple
O₂ Ground	YD3	Tan
3.8L W Body		
O₂ Signal	R16	Purple
O₂ Ground	R21	Tan
5.0L & 5.7L TBI		
O₂ Signal	D7	Purple
O₂ Ground	D6	Tan
5.0L & 5.7L PFI F Body		
O₂ Signal	GE14	Purple
O₂ Ground	GE15	Tan/White

Oxygen sensor acts like an open sensor circuit and produces no voltage when exhaust temperature is less than 600°F (316°C). An open sensor circuit or cold sensor causes "open loop" operation.

NOTE: Test numbers refer to test numbers on diagnostic chart.

1) Checks to see if O₂ sensor is registering a lean condition. Code 44 is set when O₂ sensor voltage signal at control module is low (less than .3 volt) for a precalibrated period and system is operating in "closed loop".

DIAGNOSTIC AIDS

Using the "Scan" tester, observe the Block Learn Memory (BLM) value at different RPMs. If conditions for a Code 44 exist, the block learn value will be around 150.

O² Sensor Wire – O₂ sensor wire may be mispositioned and laying against the exhaust manifold. Check for ground between sensor and wire connector.

Fuel Contamination – Water, even small amounts, near the in-tank fuel pump inlet can be delivered to the injector. The water may cause a lean exhaust and set Code 44.

Fuel Pressure – System will be lean if fuel pressure is low. It may be necessary to monitor fuel pressure while driving vehicle. For fuel pressure checking procedure, see BASIC DIAGNOSTIC PROCEDURES article.

Exhaust Leaks – If the exhaust system has large leaks, exhaust system negative pressure pulses can cause outside air to be drawn into the system and past the O₂ sensor. Vacuum or crankcase leaks can also cause a lean condition.

Misfire or Stall – If engine misfires or stalls while vehicle is moving, including running out of fuel, a Code 44 may set. If Code 44 is intermittent, see INTERMITTENTS in TROUBLE SHOOTING – NO CODES article.

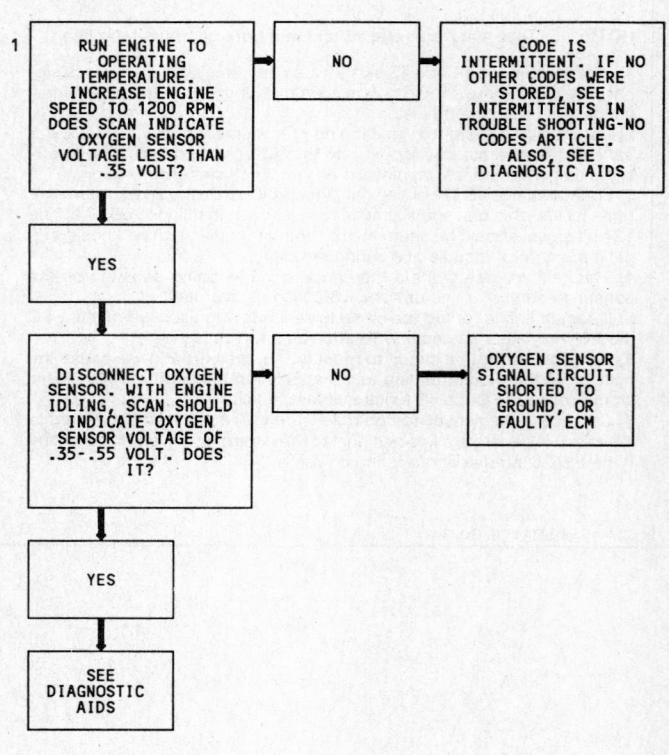

1991 ENGINE PERFORMANCE
Self-Diagnostics – ECM/PCM Except Cadillac (Cont.)

GM
1-103

CODE 45, RICH EXHAUST INDICATION

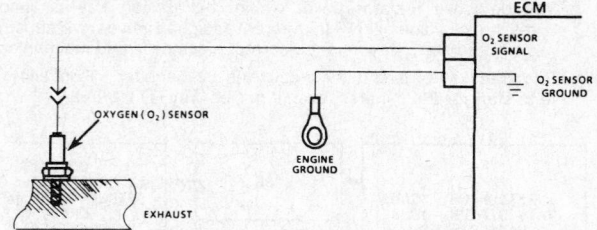

CODE 45 ECM TERMINAL & CIRCUIT WIRING IDENTIFICATION

Application	ECM Terminal	Wire Color
2.0L, 2.2L & 2.5L A & N Bodies		
O₂ Signal	B2	Purple
O₂ Ground	B23	Tan
2.3L L Body		
O₂ Signal	GE14	Black
O₂ Ground	GE15	Tan
2.3L N Body, 3.1L F, J & L Bodies		
O₂ Signal	GE14	Purple
O₂ Ground	GE15	Tan
2.3L W Body, 2.5L W Body, 3.1L W Body, 3.4L W Body & 5.7L Y Body		
O₂ Signal	A16	Purple
O₂ Ground	A22	Tan
3.1L A Body		
O₂ Signal	GE14	Purple
O₂ Ground	GE15	Black
3.3L		
O₂ Signal	YE14	Purple
O₂ Ground	YE15	Tan
3.8L C Body		
O₂ Signal	BD3	Purple
O₂ Ground	BD2	Tan
3.8L H Body		
O₂ Signal	YD2	Purple
O₂ Ground	YD3	Tan
3.8L W Body		
O₂ Signal	R16	Purple
O₂ Ground	R21	Tan
5.0L & 5.7L TBI		
O₂ Signal	D7	Purple
O₂ Ground	D6	Tan
5.0L & 5.7L PFI F Body		
O₂ Signal	GE14	Purple
O₂ Ground	GE15	Tan/White

Oxygen sensor acts like an open sensor circuit and produces no voltage when exhaust temperature is less than 600°F (316°C). An open sensor circuit or cold sensor causes "open loop" operation.

Code 45 indicates a rich exhaust and diagnosis should begin with these items: fuel pressure, leaking injector, HEI shielding (ground), vapor canister fuel saturation, coolant sensor, MAP sensor, O₂ sensor contamination and TPS intermittent output.

NOTE: Test numbers refer to test numbers on diagnostic chart.

1) Test checks to see if O₂ sensor is registering a rich condition. Code 45 is set when vehicle is at operating temperature (in "closed loop"), throttle angle is greater than idle, O₂ sensor signal at control module is greater than .7 volt for a precalibrated period and time since engine start is one minute or more.

DIAGNOSTIC AIDS

If other codes of lower number are set with Code 45, use those charts first. Malfunction in the MAP or TPS sensor circuits can cause a Code 45 to set. If other codes are not set, Code 45, rich exhaust, is most likely caused by one of the following:

Fuel Pressure High – If fuel pressure is too high, air/fuel ratios will be rich. For fuel pressure checking procedure, see BASIC DIAGNOSTIC PROCEDURES article. The control module can compensate for slight increases but if air/fuel ratio becomes too rich a Code 45 will be set.

Ignition Ground – If an open occurs at circuit No. 453, HEI induced electrical "noise" may result, causing simulated reference pulses to be picked up by control module on reference line of EST harness. Additional pulses result in a higher than actual engine speed signal. The control module will increase injector pulse width ("on" time) to match the increased RPM signal. "Scan" tester will show higher than actual RPM, which can help in diagnosing this problem.

Evaporative Fuel Canister – Fuel saturation of the charcoal canister will cause a rich air/fuel ratio. If full of fuel, check canister control valves and hoses.

MAP Sensor – An output that causes the control module to sense a higher than normal manifold pressure (low vacuum) can cause the system to go rich. Disconnecting the MAP sensor will allow the control module to substitute a fixed value for the MAP sensor. If the condition disappears, substitute a different MAP sensor and continue testing.

TPS – An intermittent TPS output will cause the system to operate rich due to a false indication of engine acceleration.

O₂ Sensor Contamination – O₂ sensor contamination, caused by silicone in certain fuels or use of improper RTV sealant, may cause a White powdery coating to cover the exterior of the O₂ sensor. The false high signal voltage (low oxygen content sensed) produced is interpreted by the control module as a rich mixture, causing the control module to set Code 45.

EGR Problem – EGR valve sticking open at idle is usually accompanied by a rough idle and/or stalling.

Also check for shorted or leaking injector, or fuel contaminated oil. If Code 45 is intermittent, see INTERMITTENTS in TROUBLE SHOOTING – NO CODES article.

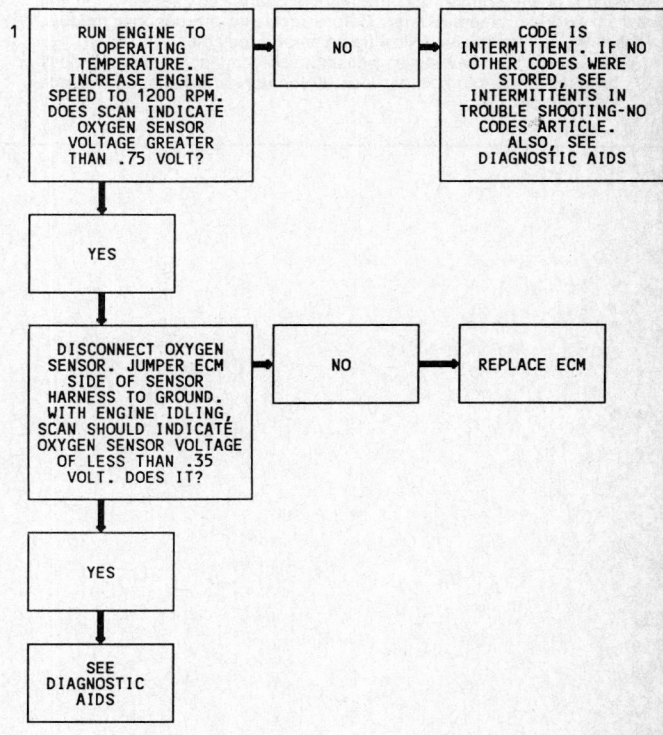

GM
1-104

1991 ENGINE PERFORMANCE
Self-Diagnostics — ECM/PCM Except Cadillac (Cont.)

CODE 46, VEHICLE ANTI-THEFT SYSTEM 3.1L, 5.0L & 5.7L PFI F BODY

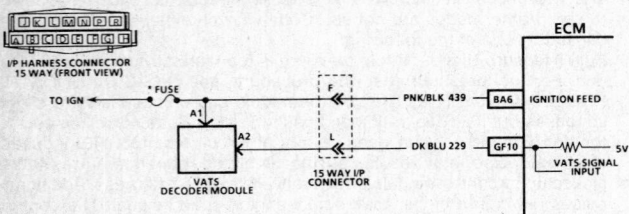

The Vehicle Anti-Theft System (VATS) is designed to disable vehicle operation if an incorrect ignition key or starting procedure is used. The anti-theft decoder module sends a signal to the ECM if the correct key is used. If the proper signal does not reach the ECM on circuit No. 229, the ECM will not pulse the injectors and the vehicle will not start. Code 46 will set.

NOTE: Test numbers refer to test numbers on diagnostic chart.

1) If the engine cranks and a Code 46 is stored, it indicates the VATS decoder module, which generates the signal to the ECM, is not operating or circuit No. 229 is open or shorted to ground. If VATS decoder module is okay, the ECM may be at fault, but this is not likely.

2) If Code 46 is stored and the engine will not start, it indicates an anti-theft system problem, or an incorrect ignition key or starting procedure is being used.

NOTE: Fuse for the VATS is the ECM/IGN fuse. If condition is intermittent, see INTERMITTENTS in TROUBLE SHOOTING – NO CODES article.

VATS DIAGNOSIS

The VATS is a sophisticated system which interfaces the ECM and starter with a power source, decoder module, starter enable relay, ignition switch and instrument cluster. Before replacing the decoder module, check the system for the following common problems.

- Check ignition key pellet sensing contacts in the ignition lock cylinder. Look into cylinder lock. If contacts are damaged, replace cylinder lock.

91G07448 91C07352

- Check ECM/IGN and GAGES fuses
- Check security indicator bulb in the instrument panel.
- A defective resistor pellet within the ignition key or incorrect resistance value of key (15 different assigned values) will cause vehicle not to start. Key must be correct electrically and mechanically.

If incorrect key is used to try to start vehicle, decoder will not allow vehicle to start for 2-4 minutes, even if correct key is inserted.

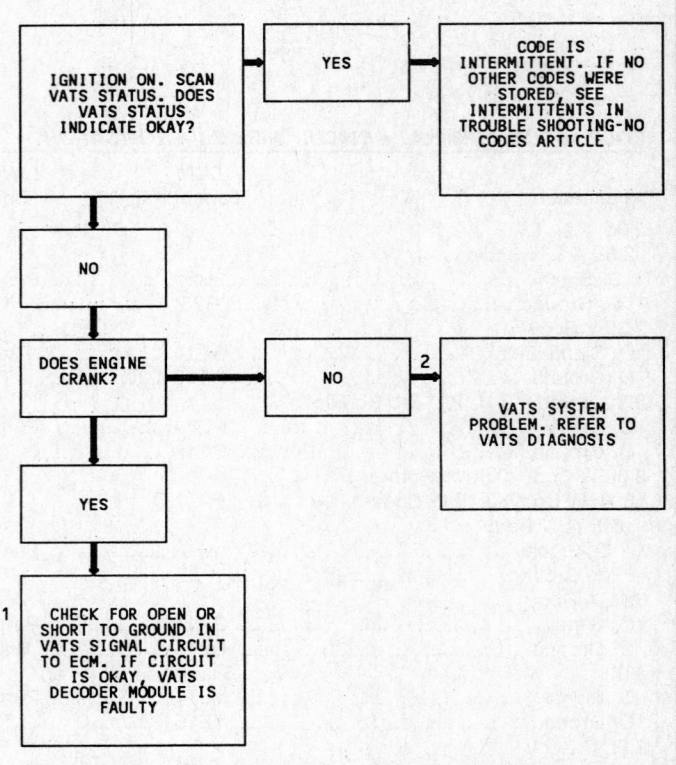

1991 ENGINE PERFORMANCE
Self-Diagnostics — ECM/PCM Except Cadillac (Cont.)

GM
1-105

CODE 46, POWER STEERING PRESSURE SWITCH 3.3L & 3.8L

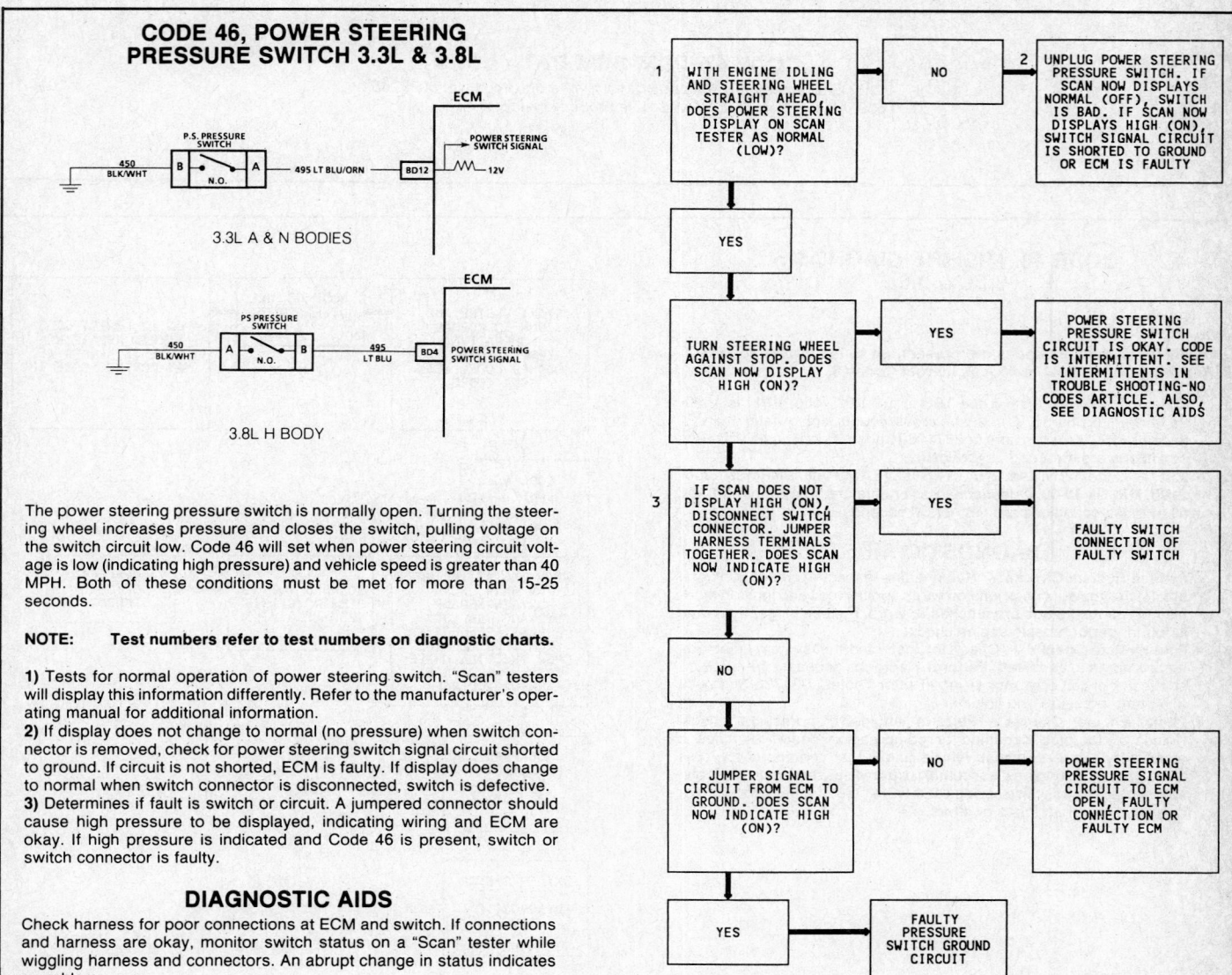

3.3L A & N BODIES

3.8L H BODY

The power steering pressure switch is normally open. Turning the steering wheel increases pressure and closes the switch, pulling voltage on the switch circuit low. Code 46 will set when power steering circuit voltage is low (indicating high pressure) and vehicle speed is greater than 40 MPH. Both of these conditions must be met for more than 15-25 seconds.

NOTE: Test numbers refer to test numbers on diagnostic charts.

1) Tests for normal operation of power steering switch. "Scan" testers will display this information differently. Refer to the manufacturer's operating manual for additional information.

2) If display does not change to normal (no pressure) when switch connector is removed, check for power steering switch signal circuit shorted to ground. If circuit is not shorted, ECM is faulty. If display does change to normal when switch connector is disconnected, switch is defective.

3) Determines if fault is switch or circuit. A jumpered connector should cause high pressure to be displayed, indicating wiring and ECM are okay. If high pressure is indicated and Code 46 is present, switch or switch connector is faulty.

DIAGNOSTIC AIDS

Check harness for poor connections at ECM and switch. If connections and harness are okay, monitor switch status on a "Scan" tester while wiggling harness and connectors. An abrupt change in status indicates a problem.

91I07449 91A07450 91E07353

GM
1-106

1991 ENGINE PERFORMANCE
Self-Diagnostics — ECM/PCM Except Cadillac (Cont.)

CODE 47, PCM-BCM DATA LOSS

Check for momentary loss of BCM's 7 volts on circuit No. 807, 750 or 555. Also, ensure that MEM-CAL is properly installed.

CODE 48, MISFIRE DIAGNOSIS
3.3L & 3.8L

NOTE: If multiple codes are present, go to the lowest code first. Repairing Code 13, 44 or 45 may correct Code 48.

- **3.3L** – Code 48 will set if the TPS is .58-1.02 volts, RPM is 1500-2500, MPH is 50-60, O_2 sensor cross counts are greater than 32 (except 4T60 transmission) or 26 (4T60 transmission) and all of these conditions are met for 30 seconds.
- **3.8L** – Code 48 will set if the TPS is .48-1.30 volts, RPM is 1300-2100, MPH is 50-60, O_2 sensor cross counts are greater than 21 and all of these conditions are met for 30 seconds.

DIAGNOSTIC AIDS

- **Ignition System Checks** – Remove and inspect each spark plug. If plug(s) are fouled, check ignition wires, ignition coil and ignition module operation. If plugs are cracked or worn, replace plugs. If no fault is found, perform basic engine checks.
- **Fuel System Checks** – Check for restricted fuel system (injectors, fuel pump, lines and filter). Perform injector balance test. Verify proper injector circuit operation using Injector Tester (J-34730-3). Check fuel pump pressure and volume.
- **Basic Engine Checks** – Perform engine compression check. Unless spark plug condition or compression check identifies a specific cylinder, road test vehicle under test conditions to verify Code 48 prior to engine disassembly. Upon disassembly, inspect pistons, rings, valves, valve springs and valve guides. Check for worn or damaged camshaft lobes or lifters.

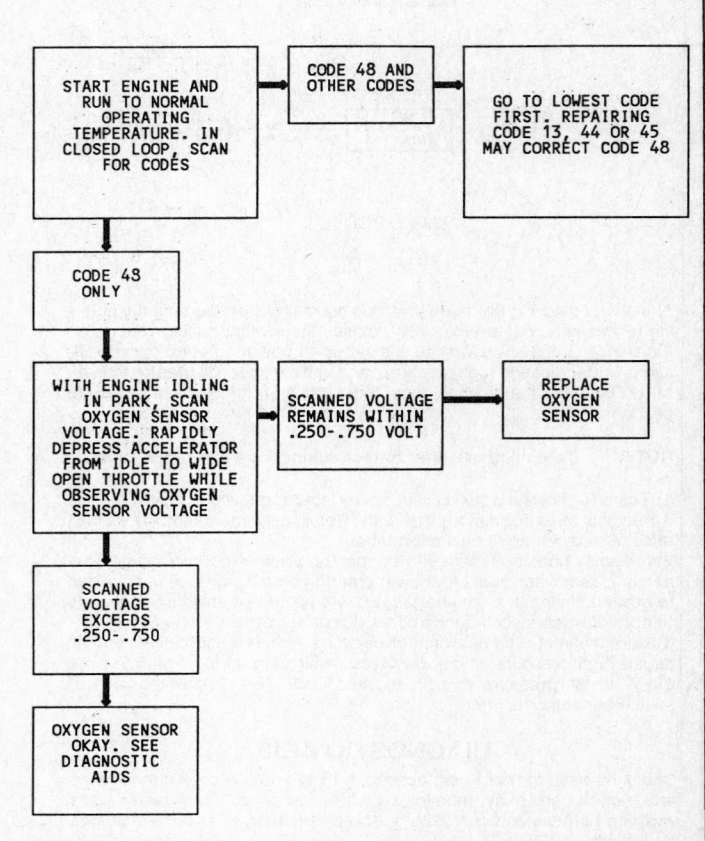

91J07355

CODE 51, FAULTY PROM/MEM-CAL

Check that all pins are fully inserted in socket. If okay, replace PROM/MEM-CAL, clear memory and recheck. If Code 51 reappears, replace control module.

CODE 52, FAULTY CALPAK

Check that all pins are fully inserted in socket. If okay, replace CALPAK, clear memory and recheck. If Code 51 reappears, replace control module.

1991 ENGINE PERFORMANCE
Self-Diagnostics — ECM/PCM Except Cadillac (Cont.)

GM
1-107

CODE 46, PASS-KEY SYSTEM
5.7L Y BODY

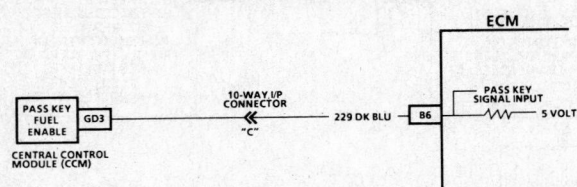

The Personal Automotive Security System (PASS-KEY) is designed to disable vehicle operation if an incorrect ignition key or starting procedure is used. The ECM applies and monitors a 5-volt signal to the Central Control Module (CCM). When CCM determines proper key and starting technique is being used, it will complete the PASS-KEY circuit, modifying the ECM-monitored voltage signal and enabling the starter relay. ECM will then allow enablement of the fuel injector circuits and permit vehicle to start and run. If monitored circuit No. 229 becomes open or shorted to ground, Code 46 will set and vehicle will not start.

NOTE: Test numbers refer to test numbers on diagnostic chart.

1) If the engine cranks and a Code 46 is stored, it indicates the CCM, which modifies the ECM-monitored signal, is not operating or circuit No. 229 is open or shorted to ground. If CCM is okay and circuit No. 229 is not open or shorted to ground, the ECM may be at fault, but this is not likely.

2) If Code 46 is stored and the engine will not start, it indicates an anti-theft system problem, an incorrect ignition key or starting procedure is used.

NOTE: If condition is intermittent, see INTERMITTENTS in TROUBLE SHOOTING — NO CODES article

PASS-KEY DIAGNOSIS

PASS-KEY is a sophisticated system which interfaces the CCM, ECM and starter with a power source, starter enable relay, ignition switch and instrument cluster. Before replacing the CCM, check the system for the following common problems.

- Check ignition key pellet sensing contacts in the ignition lock cylinder. Look into cylinder lock. If contacts are damaged, replace cylinder lock.
- Check ECM and GAGES fuses
- Check security indicator bulb in the instrument panel.
- A defective resistor pellet within the ignition key or incorrect resistance value of key (15 different assigned values) will cause vehicle not to start. Key must be correct electrically and mechanically.

91C07451 91G07354

If incorrect key is used to try to start vehicle, decoder will not allow vehicle to start for 2-4 minutes, even if correct key is inserted.

NOTE: Testing and servicing CCM requires special test equipment and documentation.

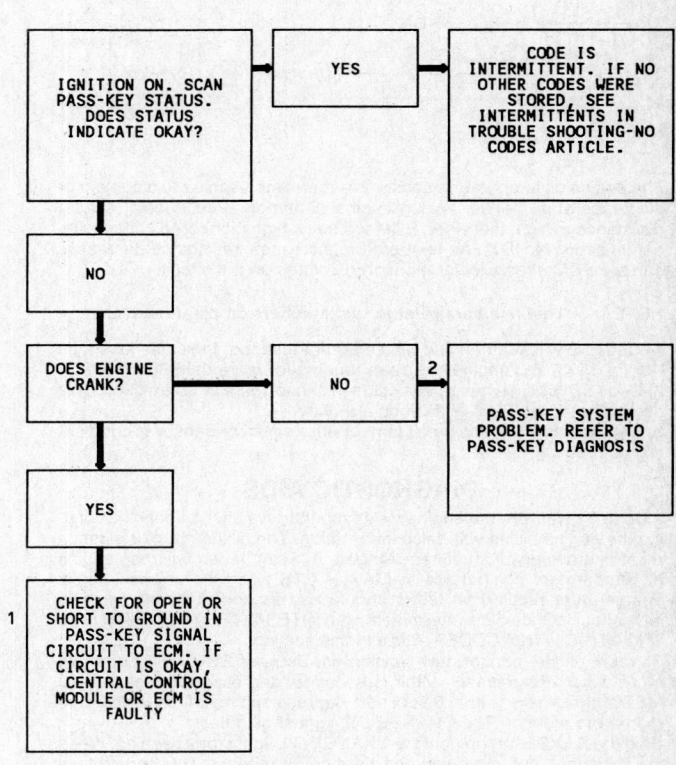

CODE 52, LOW ENGINE OIL TEMPERATURE 5.7L Y BODY

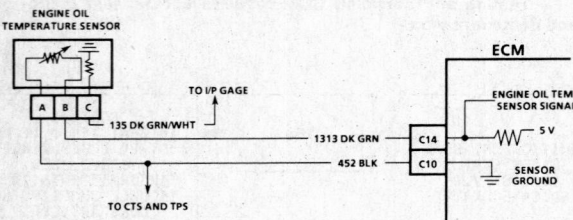

The engine oil temperature sensor is a thermistor, similar to a coolant or air temperature sensor. When engine oil temperature is cold, sensor resistance is high, therefore, ECM will see a high monitored voltage signal on circuit No. 901. As temperature increases, resistance decreases and the ECM sees a lower monitored voltage on the circuit.

NOTE: Test numbers refer to test numbers on diagnostic chart.

1) Code 52 will set if engine oil temperature sensor indicates less than -31°F (-35°C) and engine has been running for more than 30 minutes.
2) Code 52 will set when open occurs in sensor, wire or connection. This determines if the ECM and wiring are okay.
3) Determines if the engine oil temperature signal or sensor ground circuit is open.

DIAGNOSTIC AIDS

If Code 52 was set, the engine oil life monitor system has been calculating the engine oil life with false information. The oil life monitor must be reset and engine oil and filter changed. A "Scan" tester will read engine oil temperature comparable to MAT or CTS when the engine is cold. Temperature reading on tester should rise as engine oil temperature increases. If Code 52 is intermittent, see INTERMITTENTS in TROUBLE SHOOTING – NO CODES article in this section.

To reset oil life monitor, turn ignition on. Depress ENG MET button on trip monitor and release. Within 5 seconds, depress and release ENG MET button again. Within 5 seconds, depress and hold the RANGE button on trip monitor. The CHANGE OIL light should flash.

Hold the RANGE button until the CHANGE OIL light stops flashing. When the light goes out, the engine oil life monitor is reset. This should take about 10 seconds. If the light does not reset, turn the ignition off and repeat procedure.

91E07452 91B07356

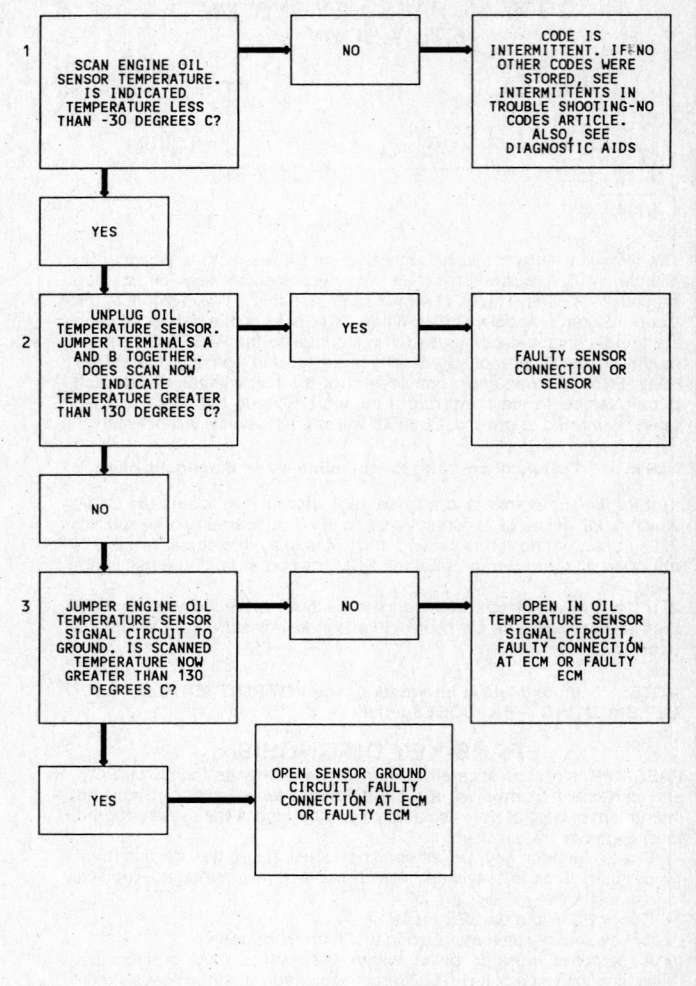

CODE 53, SYSTEM OVERVOLTAGE
2.0L, 2.3L, 2.5L, 3.1L, 3.4L & 5.7L Y BODY

This code indicates a basic charging system problem. Code 53 will set when voltage at control module terminal is greater or less than specification for a precalibrated time. If voltage at ECM battery voltage terminal is not within specification, check and repair charging system.

CHARGING SYSTEM SPECIFICATIONS

Application	Minimum Charge	Maximum Charge
2.0L		16.9
2.3L	10.0	17.1
2.5L		16.9
3.1L		[1] 16.9
3.4L W Body		17.1
5.7L Y Body	8.0	17.1

[1] – A & W Body 3.1L maximum voltage is 17.1 volts.

91D07357

1991 ENGINE PERFORMANCE
Self-Diagnostics — ECM/PCM Except Cadillac (Cont.)

GM
1-109

CODE 53, VEHICLE ANTI-THEFT SYSTEM 5.0L TBI F BODY

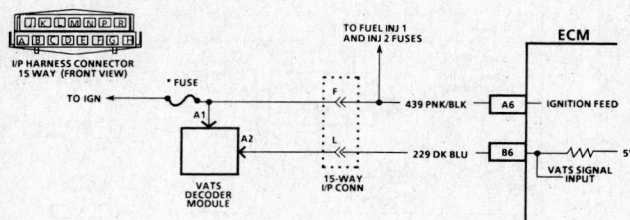

The Vehicle Anti-Theft System (VATS) is designed to disable vehicle operation if an incorrect ignition key or starting procedure is used. The anti-theft decoder module sends a signal to the ECM if the correct key is used. If the proper signal does not reach the ECM on circuit No. 229, the ECM will not pulse the injectors and the vehicle will not start. Code 53 will set.

NOTE: Test numbers refer to test numbers on diagnostic chart.

1) If the engine cranks and a Code 53 is stored, it indicates the VATS decoder module, which generates the signal to the ECM, is not operating or circuit No. 229 is open or shorted to ground. If VATS decoder module is okay, the ECM may be at fault, but this is not likely.

2) If Code 53 is stored and the engine will not start, it indicates an anti-theft system problem, an incorrect ignition key or starting procedure is used.

NOTE: Power fuse for VATS is the ECM fuse. If condition is intermittent, see INTERMITTENTS in TROUBLE SHOOTING – NO CODES article.

VATS DIAGNOSIS

The VATS is a sophisticated system which interfaces the ECM and starter with a power source, decoder module, starter enable relay, ignition switch and instrument cluster. Before replacing the decoder module, check the system for the following common problems.

- Check ignition key pellet sensing contacts in the ignition lock cylinder. Look into cylinder lock. If contacts are damaged, replace cylinder lock.
- Check ECM and GAGES fuses
- Check security indicator bulb in the instrument panel.
- A defective resistor pellet within the ignition key or incorrect resistance value of key (15 different assigned values) will cause vehicle not to start. Key must be correct electrically and mechanically.

If incorrect key is used to try to start vehicle, decoder will not allow vehicle to start for 2-4 minutes, even if correct key is inserted.

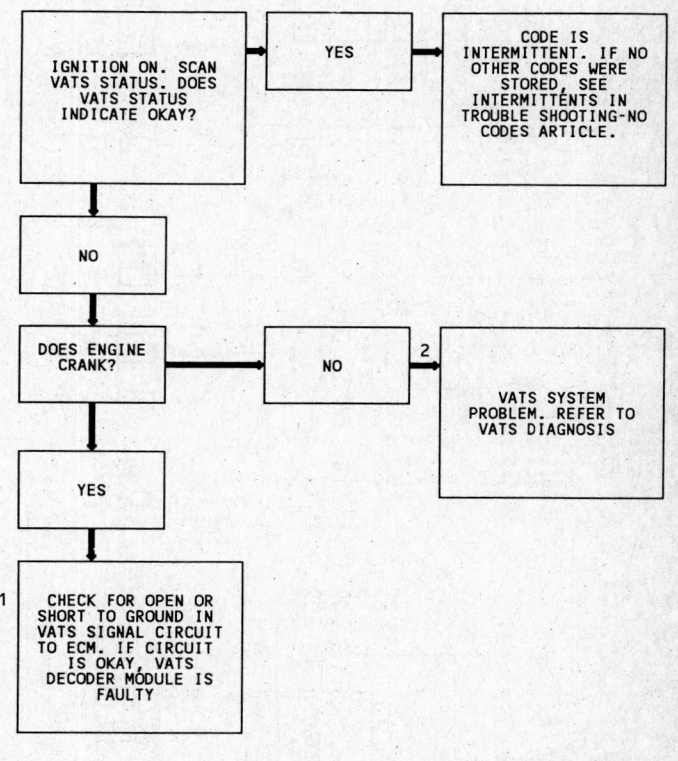

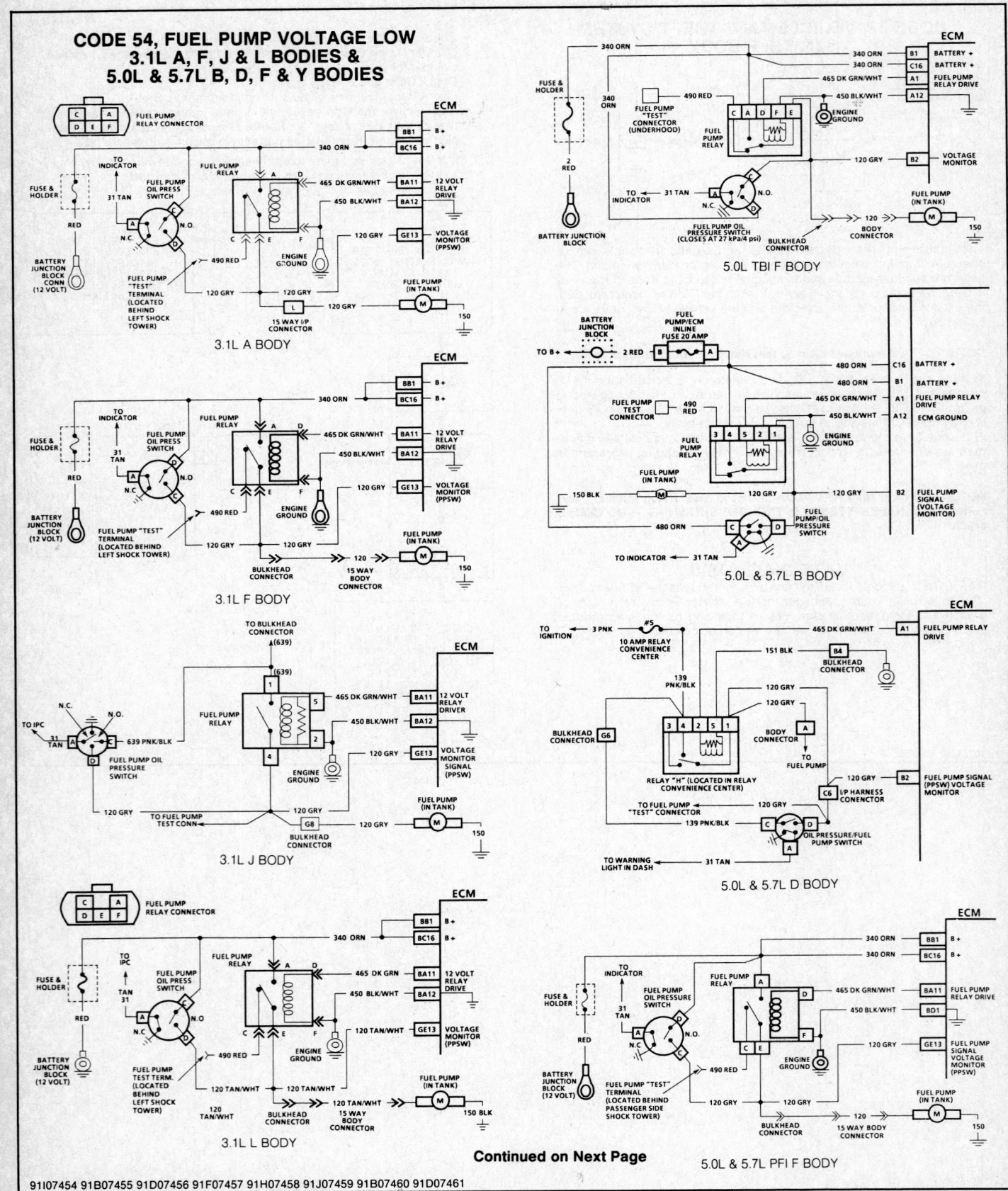

CODE 54, FUEL PUMP VOLTAGE LOW
3.1L A, F, J & L BODIES &
5.0L & 5.7L B, D, F & Y BODIES

3.1L A BODY

3.1L F BODY

3.1L J BODY

3.1L L BODY

5.0L TBI F BODY

5.0L & 5.7L B BODY

5.0L & 5.7L D BODY

5.0L & 5.7L PFI F BODY

Continued on Next Page

1991 ENGINE PERFORMANCE
Self-Diagnostics — ECM/PCM Except Cadillac (Cont.)

GM
1-111

CODE 54, FUEL PUMP VOLTAGE LOW
3.1L A, F, J & L BODIES &
5.0L & 5.7L B, D, F & Y BODIES (Cont.)

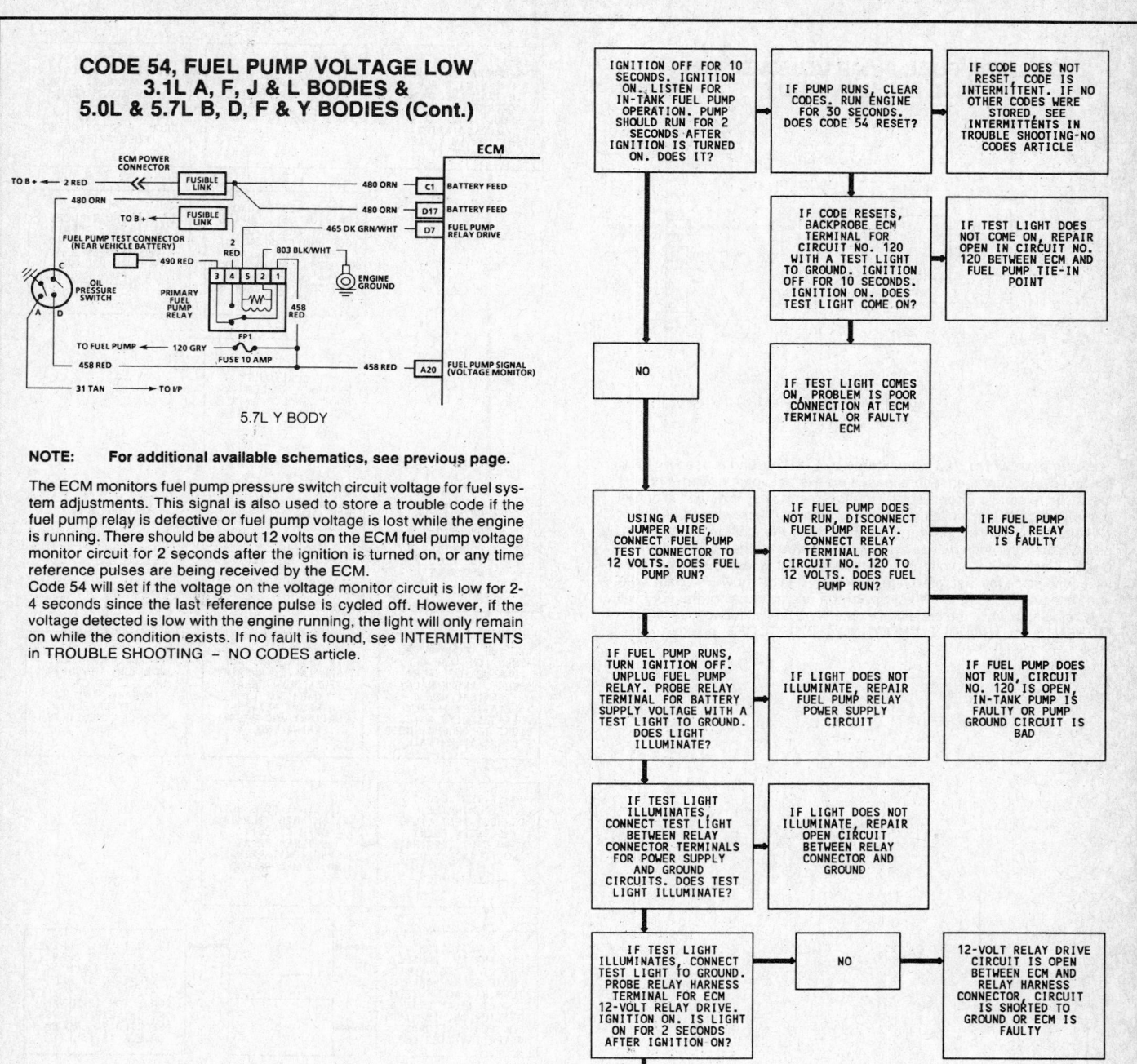

5.7L Y BODY

NOTE: For additional available schematics, see previous page.

The ECM monitors fuel pump pressure switch circuit voltage for fuel system adjustments. This signal is also used to store a trouble code if the fuel pump relay is defective or fuel pump voltage is lost while the engine is running. There should be about 12 volts on the ECM fuel pump voltage monitor circuit for 2 seconds after the ignition is turned on, or any time reference pulses are being received by the ECM.

Code 54 will set if the voltage on the voltage monitor circuit is low for 2-4 seconds since the last reference pulse is cycled off. However, if the voltage detected is low with the engine running, the light will only remain on while the condition exists. If no fault is found, see INTERMITTENTS in TROUBLE SHOOTING – NO CODES article.

91F07462 91F07358

GM
1-112

1991 ENGINE PERFORMANCE
Self-Diagnostics – ECM/PCM Except Cadillac (Cont.)

CODE 54, FUEL PUMP VOLTAGE LOW
3.1L & 3.4L W BODY

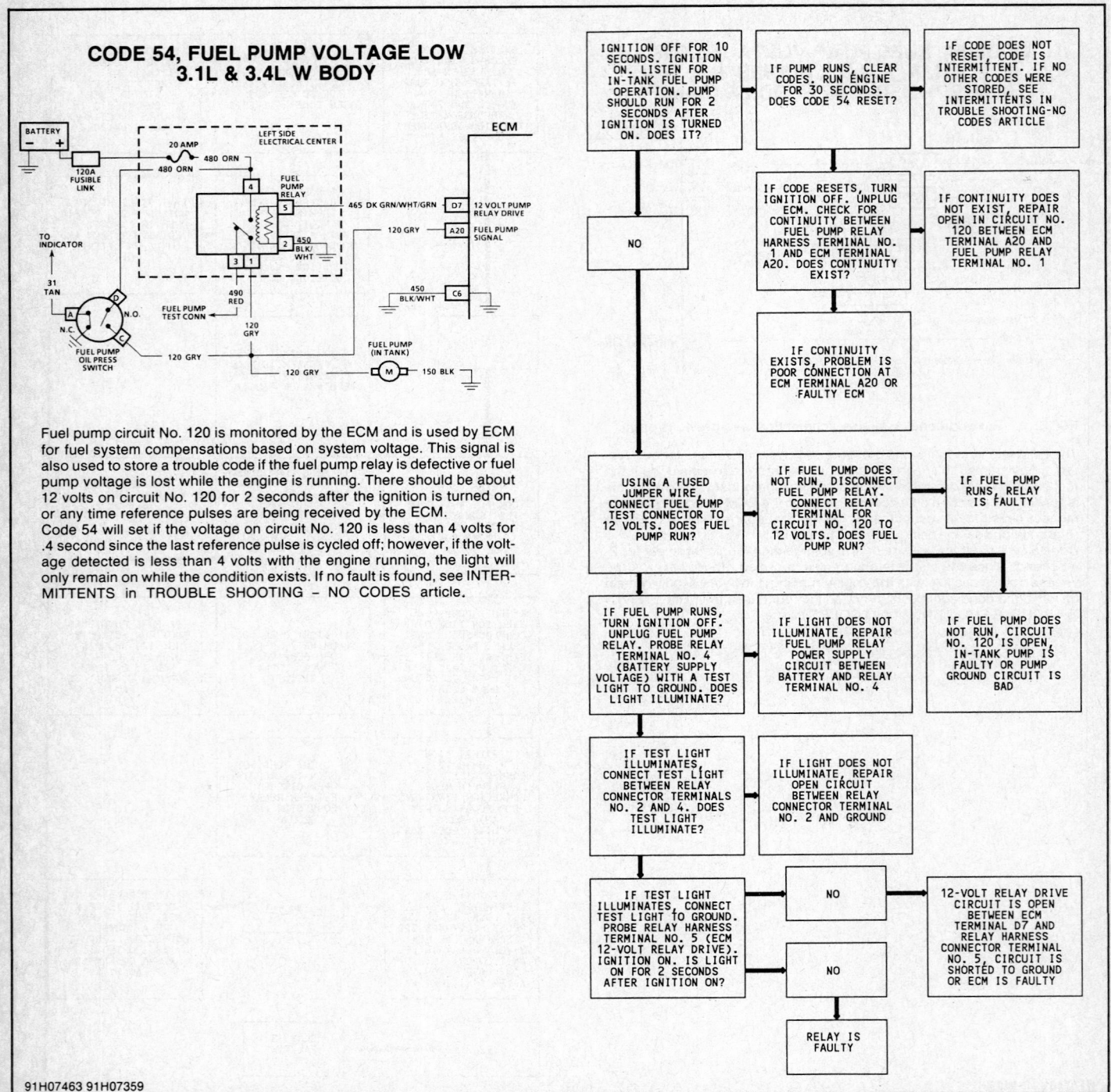

Fuel pump circuit No. 120 is monitored by the ECM and is used by ECM for fuel system compensations based on system voltage. This signal is also used to store a trouble code if the fuel pump relay is defective or fuel pump voltage is lost while the engine is running. There should be about 12 volts on circuit No. 120 for 2 seconds after the ignition is turned on, or any time reference pulses are being received by the ECM.

Code 54 will set if the voltage on circuit No. 120 is less than 4 volts for .4 second since the last reference pulse is cycled off; however, if the voltage detected is less than 4 volts with the engine running, the light will only remain on while the condition exists. If no fault is found, see INTERMITTENTS in TROUBLE SHOOTING – NO CODES article.

91H07463 91H07359

CODE 55, ECM ERROR
5.0L & 5.7L

Ensure correct MEM-CAL or PROM is being used and that it is properly installed. If so, replace control module. Clear codes, confirm closed loop operation and check operation of SERVICE ENGINE SOON light.

1991 ENGINE PERFORMANCE
Self-Diagnostics — ECM/PCM Except Cadillac (Cont.)

GM
1-113

CODE 58, PASS-KEY FUEL ENABLE CIRCUIT
3.8L C & E BODIES

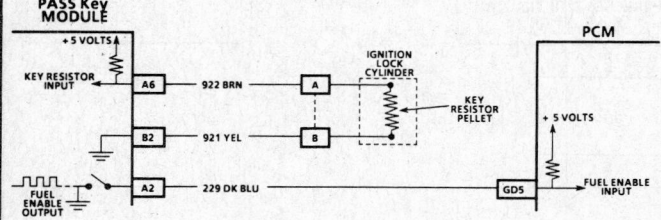

Personal Automotive Security System (PASS-KEY) is designed to disable vehicle operation if an incorrect ignition key or starting procedure is used. If correct key and starting technique is used, PASS-KEY decoder module sends a fuel enable signal to the PCM and also energizes starter enable relay. If the proper signal does not reach the PCM on circuit No. 229, the PCM will not pulse the injectors and the vehicle will not start and Code 58 will set.

NOTE: Test numbers refer to test numbers on diagnostic chart.

1) If vehicle will not crank with Code 58 stored, problem affects entire PASS-KEY system and is not isolated to fuel enable circuit.
2) The PCM applies and monitors a 5-volt signal on circuit No. 229. Decoder module will pulse this signal to ground when proper key and starting technique is used. This test ensures that PCM is supplying the 5-volt signal and that circuit is not open or shorted to ground.
3) Checks PWM signal from PASS-KEY module. Since the 5 volts supplied by the PCM is being pulsed to ground, voltage on circuit No. 229 should measure about 2.5 volts.
4) Checks for a faulty PCM or intermittent condition by clearing code. Since the PCM ignores the absence of a fuel enable signal only when Code 58 is stored, vehicle should not start if the problem is present and Code 58 is not.

PASS-KEY DIAGNOSIS

PASS-KEY is a sophisticated system which interfaces the PASS-KEY decoder module, PCM and starter with a power source, starter enable relay, ignition switch, instrument cluster and Remote Accessory Control (RAC) module.

NOTE: Testing and servicing PASS-KEY decoder module requires special test equipment and documentation.

Before replacing the decoder module, check the system for the following common problems.
- Check ignition key pellet sensing contacts in the ignition lock cylinder. Look into cylinder lock. If contacts are damaged, replace cylinder lock.
- Check fuse No. 11 in instrument panel fuse block.
- Check fuse No. 4 in right underhood fuse block.
- Check fuse No. 8 in relay center.
- Check security indicator bulb in the instrument panel.

91J07464 91J07360

- A defective resistor pellet within the ignition key or incorrect resistance value of key (15 different assigned values) will cause vehicle not to start. Key must be correct electrically and mechanically.

If incorrect key is used to try to start vehicle, decoder will not allow vehicle to start for 2-4 minutes, even if correct key is inserted.

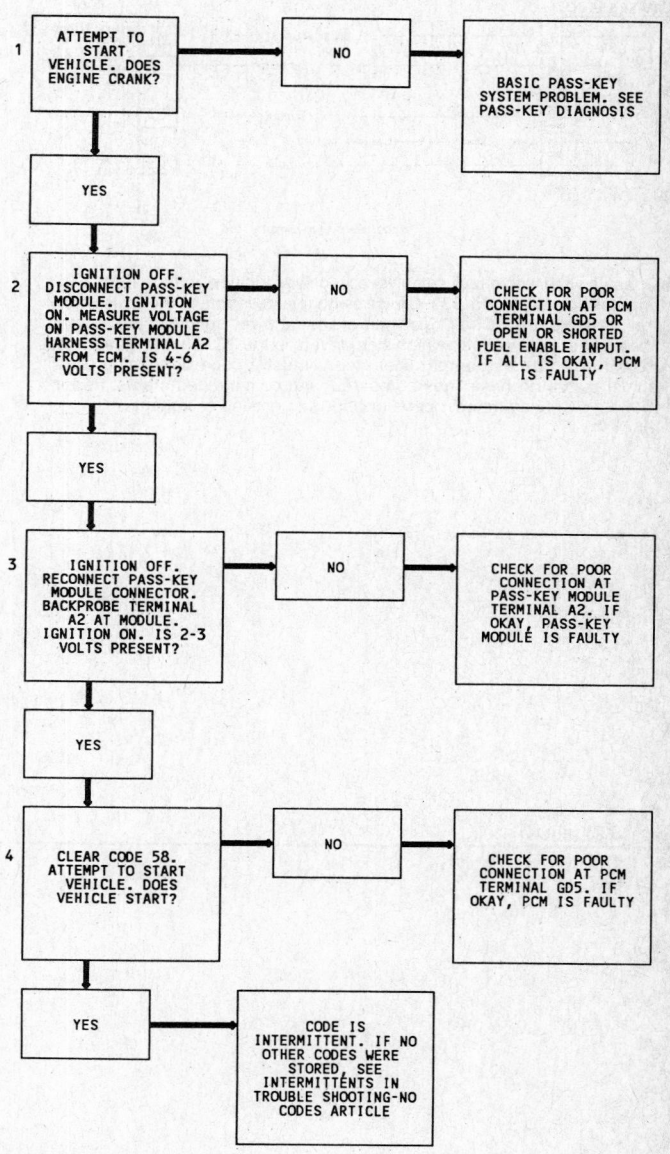

CODE 61, DEGRADED OXYGEN SENSOR
3.1L & 3.4L

If a Code 61 is stored in memory, the ECM has determined the oxygen sensor is contaminated or degraded because the voltage change time (cross counts) is slow or sluggish.

The ECM performs the oxygen sensor response time test when the coolant temperature is more than 185°F (85°C), MAT temperature is greater than 50°F (10°C), system is in closed-loop or in a decel fuel cut-off mode.

If Code 61 is stored, the oxygen sensor should be replaced.

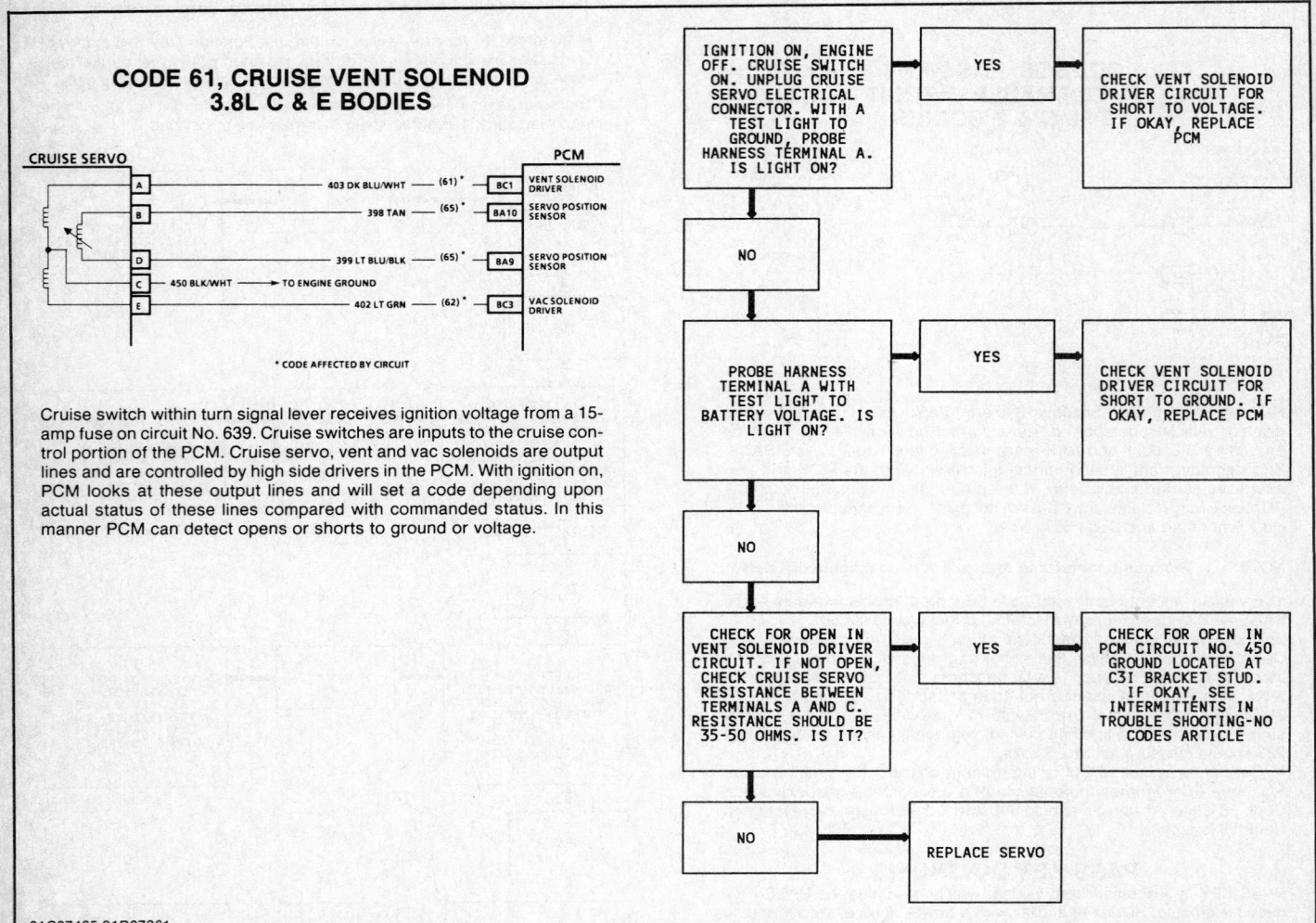

CODE 61, CRUISE VENT SOLENOID 3.8L C & E BODIES

Cruise switch within turn signal lever receives ignition voltage from a 15-amp fuse on circuit No. 639. Cruise switches are inputs to the cruise control portion of the PCM. Cruise servo, vent and vac solenoids are output lines and are controlled by high side drivers in the PCM. With ignition on, PCM looks at these output lines and will set a code depending upon actual status of these lines compared with commanded status. In this manner PCM can detect opens or shorts to ground or voltage.

91C07465 91B07361

1991 ENGINE PERFORMANCE
Self-Diagnostics — ECM/PCM Except Cadillac (Cont.)

GM
1-115

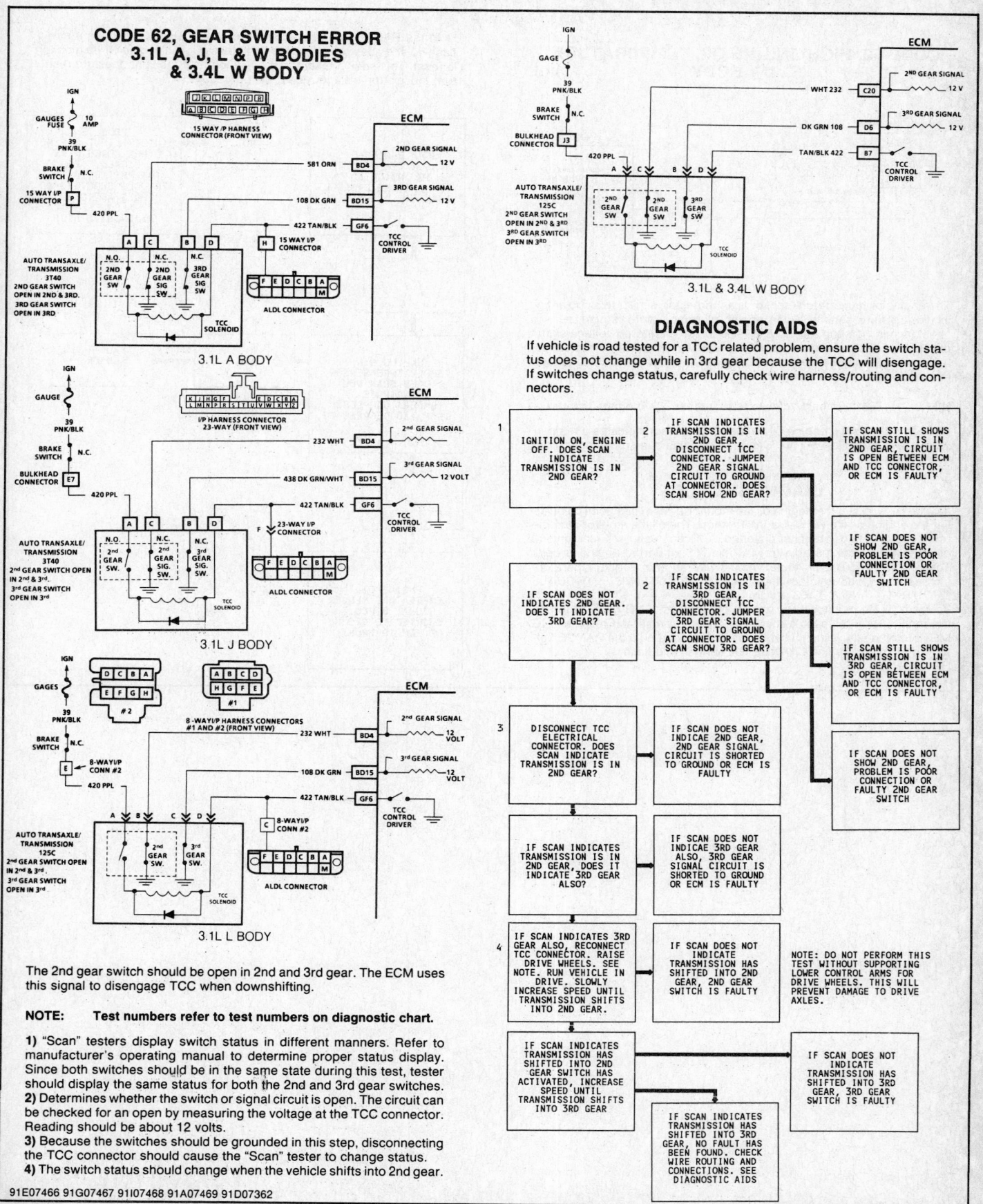

CODE 62, GEAR SWITCH ERROR
3.1L A, J, L & W BODIES
& 3.4L W BODY

DIAGNOSTIC AIDS

If vehicle is road tested for a TCC related problem, ensure the switch status does not change while in 3rd gear because the TCC will disengage. If switches change status, carefully check wire harness/routing and connectors.

The 2nd gear switch should be open in 2nd and 3rd gear. The ECM uses this signal to disengage TCC when downshifting.

NOTE: **Test numbers refer to test numbers on diagnostic chart.**

1) "Scan" testers display switch status in different manners. Refer to manufacturer's operating manual to determine proper status display. Since both switches should be in the same state during this test, tester should display the same status for both the 2nd and 3rd gear switches.

2) Determines whether the switch or signal circuit is open. The circuit can be checked for an open by measuring the voltage at the TCC connector. Reading should be about 12 volts.

3) Because the switches should be grounded in this step, disconnecting the TCC connector should cause the "Scan" tester to change status.

4) The switch status should change when the vehicle shifts into 2nd gear.

CODE 62, HIGH ENGINE OIL TEMPERATURE 5.7L Y BODY

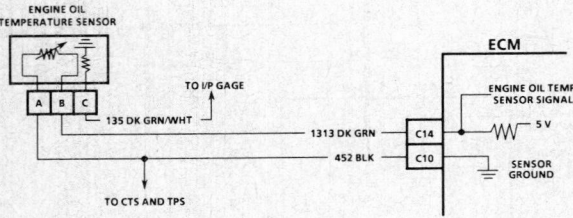

The engine oil temperature sensor is a thermistor, similar to a coolant or air temperature sensor. When engine oil temperature is cold, sensor resistance is high and the ECM will see a high monitored voltage signal on engine oil temperature sensor circuit. As temperature increases, resistance decreases and the ECM sees a lower monitored voltage engine oil temperature sensor circuit.

NOTE: Test numbers refer to test numbers on diagnostic chart.

1) Code 62 will set if engine oil temperature sensor indicates a temperature greater than 291°F (144°C) and engine has been running for more than 30 minutes.

DIAGNOSTIC AIDS

If Code 62 was set, the engine oil life monitor system has been calculating the engine oil life with false information. The oil life monitor must be reset and engine oil and filter changed. A "Scan" tester will read engine oil temperature comparable to MAT or CTS when the engine is cold. Temperature reading on tester should rise as engine oil temperature increases. If Code is intermittent, see INTERMITTENTS in TROUBLE SHOOTING – NO CODES article.

To reset oil life monitor, turn ignition on. Depress ENG MET button on trip monitor and release. Within 5 seconds, depress and release ENG MET button again. Within 5 seconds, depress and hold the RANGE button on trip monitor. The CHANGE OIL light should flash.

91E07452 91F07363

Hold the RANGE button depressed until the CHANGE OIL light stops flashing and goes out. When the light goes out, the engine oil life monitor is reset. This should take about 10 seconds. If the light does not reset, turn the ignition off and repeat the procedure.

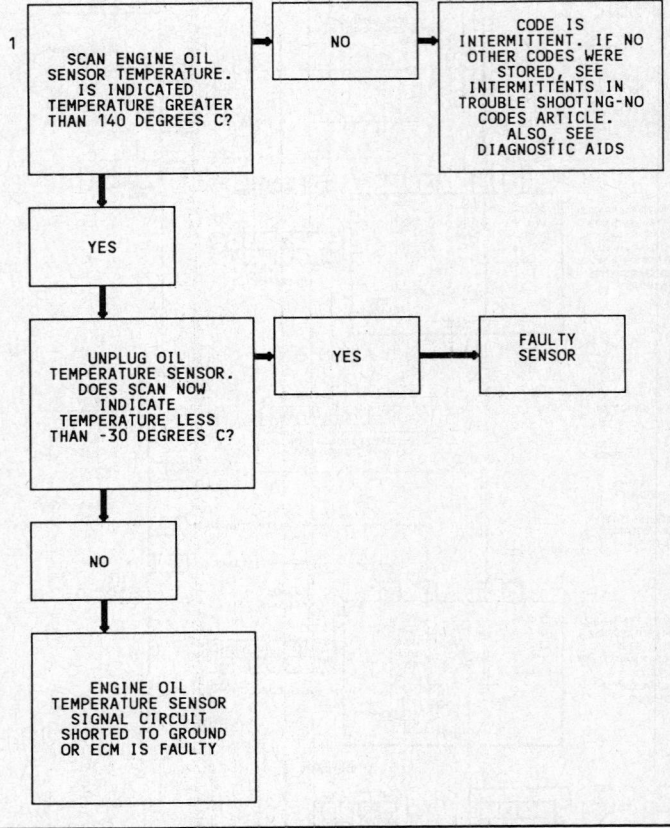

1991 ENGINE PERFORMANCE
Self-Diagnostics — ECM/PCM Except Cadillac (Cont.)

GM
1-117

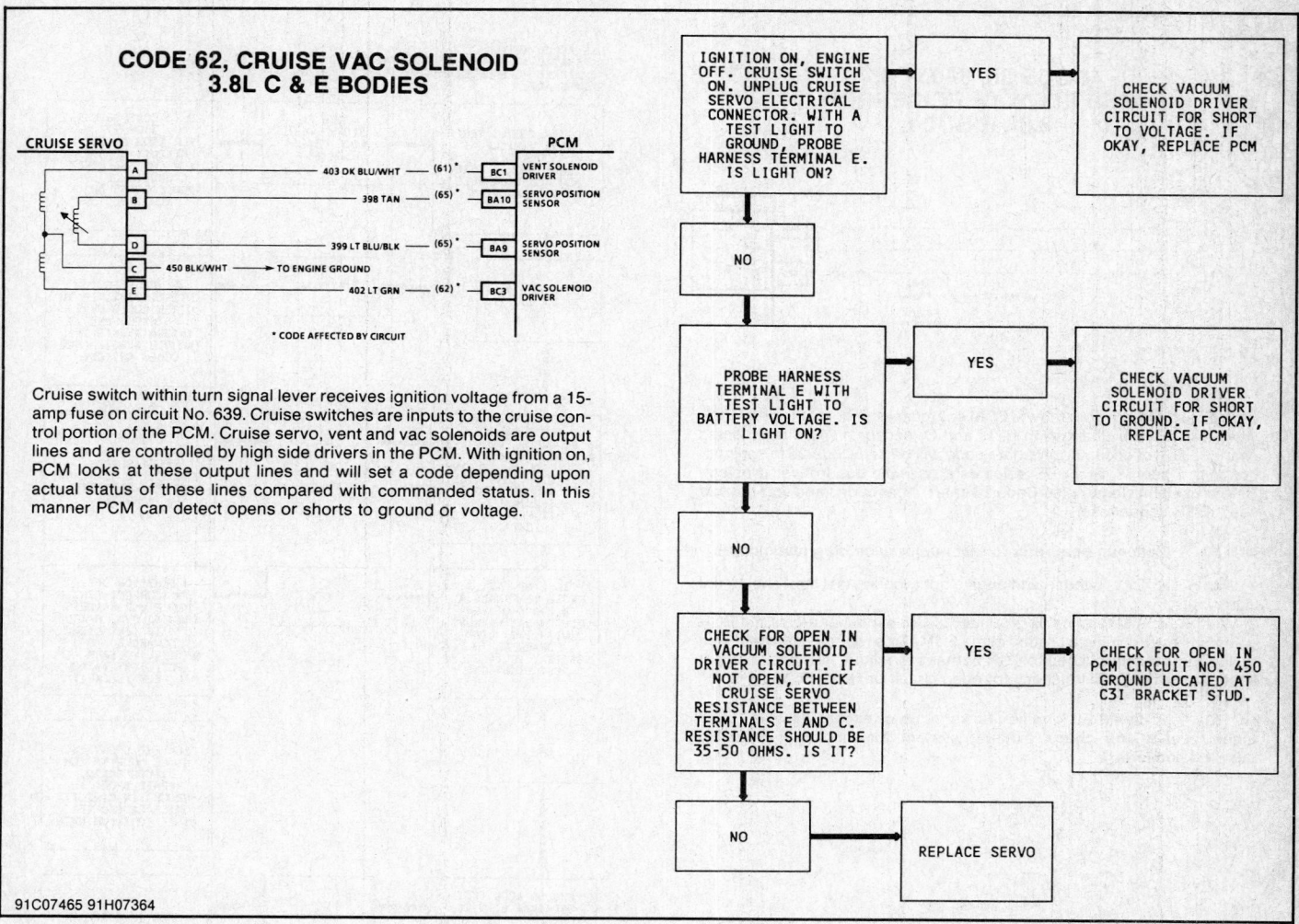

CODE 62, CRUISE VAC SOLENOID
3.8L C & E BODIES

CRUISE SERVO

			PCM	
A	403 DK BLU/WHT	(61)*	BC1	VENT SOLENOID DRIVER
B	398 TAN	(65)*	BA10	SERVO POSITION SENSOR
D	399 LT BLU/BLK	(65)*	BA9	SERVO POSITION SENSOR
C	450 BLK/WHT → TO ENGINE GROUND			
E	402 LT GRN	(62)*	BC3	VAC SOLENOID DRIVER

* CODE AFFECTED BY CIRCUIT

Cruise switch within turn signal lever receives ignition voltage from a 15-amp fuse on circuit No. 639. Cruise switches are inputs to the cruise control portion of the PCM. Cruise servo, vent and vac solenoids are output lines and are controlled by high side drivers in the PCM. With ignition on, PCM looks at these output lines and will set a code depending upon actual status of these lines compared with commanded status. In this manner PCM can detect opens or shorts to ground or voltage.

IGNITION ON, ENGINE OFF. CRUISE SWITCH ON. UNPLUG CRUISE SERVO ELECTRICAL CONNECTOR. WITH A TEST LIGHT TO GROUND, PROBE HARNESS TERMINAL E. IS LIGHT ON?

→ YES → CHECK VACUUM SOLENOID DRIVER CIRCUIT FOR SHORT TO VOLTAGE. IF OKAY, REPLACE PCM

↓ NO

PROBE HARNESS TERMINAL E WITH TEST LIGHT TO BATTERY VOLTAGE. IS LIGHT ON?

→ YES → CHECK VACUUM SOLENOID DRIVER CIRCUIT FOR SHORT TO GROUND. IF OKAY, REPLACE PCM

↓ NO

CHECK FOR OPEN IN VACUUM SOLENOID DRIVER CIRCUIT. IF NOT OPEN, CHECK CRUISE SERVO RESISTANCE BETWEEN TERMINALS E AND C. RESISTANCE SHOULD BE 35-50 OHMS. IS IT?

→ YES → CHECK FOR OPEN IN PCM CIRCUIT NO. 450 GROUND LOCATED AT C3I BRACKET STUD.

↓ NO → REPLACE SERVO

91C07465 91H07364

GM
1-118

1991 ENGINE PERFORMANCE
Self-Diagnostics — ECM/PCM Except Cadillac (Cont.)

CODE 63, 64 OR 65
EGR FLOW CHECK ERROR
3.8L H BODY

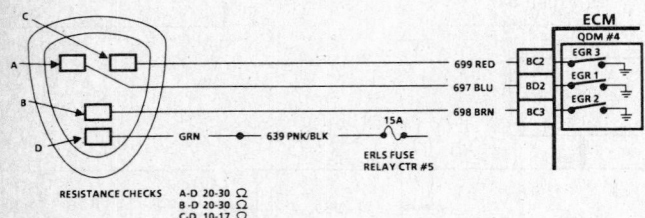

On a closed throttle coastdown, ECM energizes solenoids inside of EGR valve and monitor changes in RPM and O_2 sensor activity. If expected changes do not occur, appropriate code will be set. Code 26 in conjunction with Code 63, 64 or 65 indicates a possible quad-driver problem. Before using this chart, use Code 26 chart, clear codes and test drive to see if EGR codes reset.

NOTE: Test numbers refer to test numbers on diagnostic chart.

1) With ALDL not grounded and engine not running, test light should not illuminate.
2) With ALDL test terminal B grounded, ECM should energize the EGR solenoids by providing a ground at the ECM/ This will cause the test light to illuminate when touched to EGR harness terminals A, B and C. If test light does not illuminate, check for open circuit or faulty ECM.

NOTE: If digital EGR valve shows signs of excessive heat (i.e. a melted condition), check exhaust system for blockage (possible plugged converter).

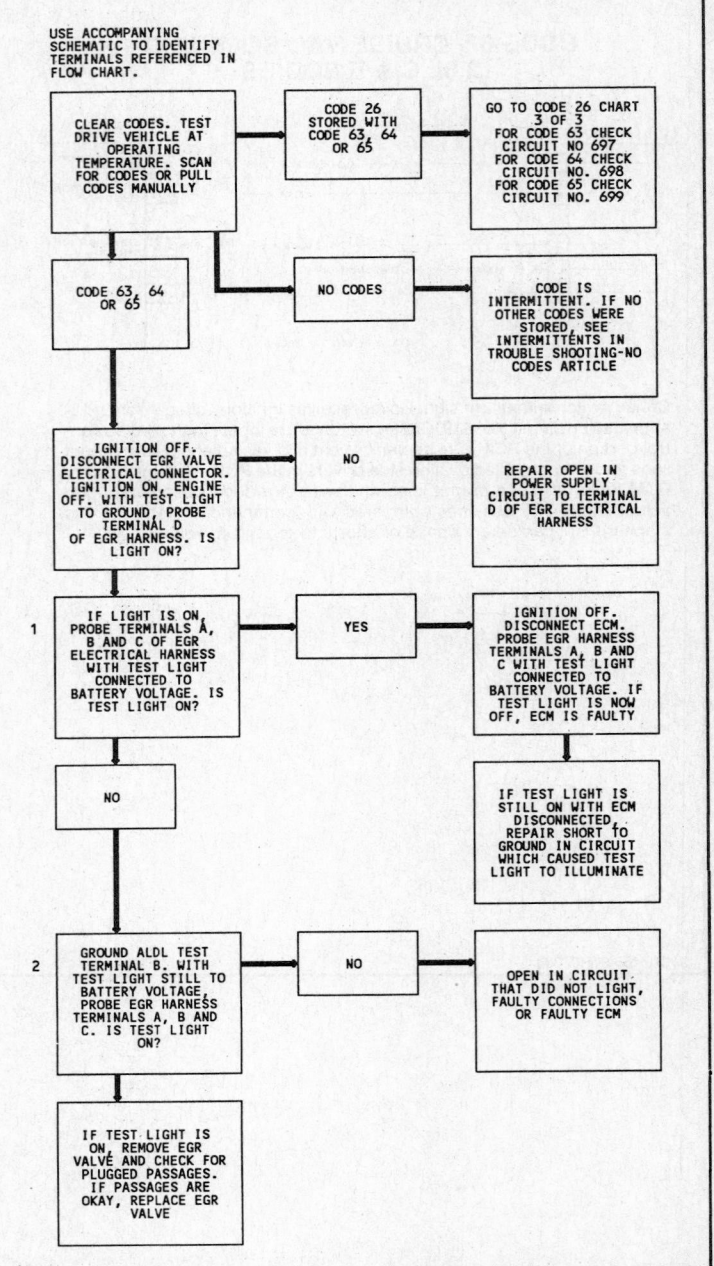

91C07470 91A07365

1991 ENGINE PERFORMANCE
Self-Diagnostics — ECM/PCM Except Cadillac (Cont.)

GM
1-119

CODE 63, 64 OR 65
EGR FLOW CHECK ERROR USING TECH 1
3.8L H BODY

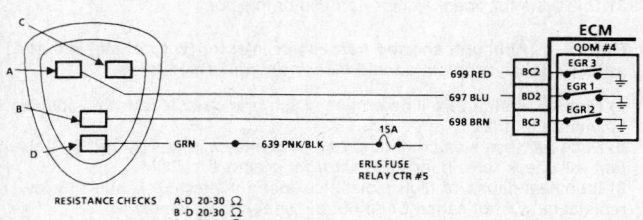

RESISTANCE CHECKS
A-D 20-30 Ω
B-D 20-30 Ω
C-D 10-17 Ω

On a closed throttle coastdown, ECM energizes solenoids inside of EGR valve and monitor changes in RPM and O_2 sensor activity. If expected changes do not occur, appropriate code will be set. Code 26 in conjunction with Code 63, 64 or 65 indicates a possible quad-driver problem. Before using this chart, use Code 26 chart, clear codes and test drive to see if EGR codes reset.

NOTE: Test numbers refer to test numbers on diagnostic chart.

1) A noticeable change in RPM should occur as each solenoid is cycled on. Solenoid No. 1 should cause the smallest change in RPM and solenoid No. 3 should cause the largest change and may even stall the engine.
2) Checks for an open circuit in harness between EGR valve and ECM, faulty ECM connection or faulty ECM.

NOTE: If digital EGR valve shows signs of excessive heat (i.e. a melted condition), check exhaust system for blockage (possible plugged converter).

USE ACCOMPANYING SCHEMATIC TO IDENTIFY TERMINALS REFERENCED IN FLOW CHART.

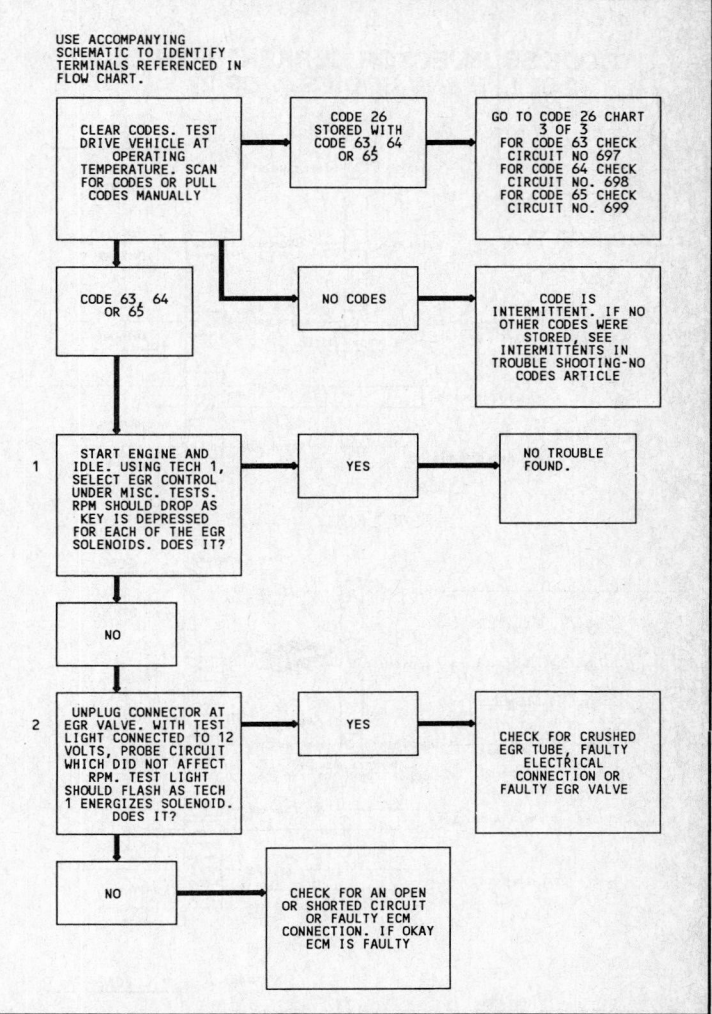

91C07470 91C07366

GM
1-120

1991 ENGINE PERFORMANCE
Self-Diagnostics — ECM/PCM Except Cadillac (Cont.)

CODE 65, INJECTOR CURRENT LOW
2.3L L, N & W BODIES (1 OF 2)

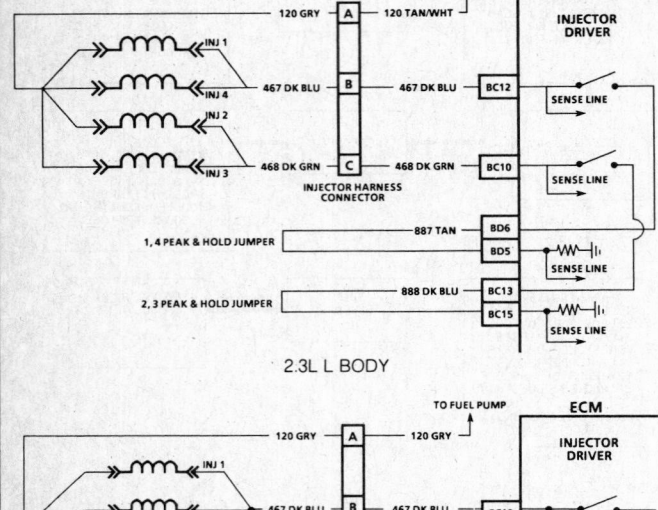

2.3L L BODY

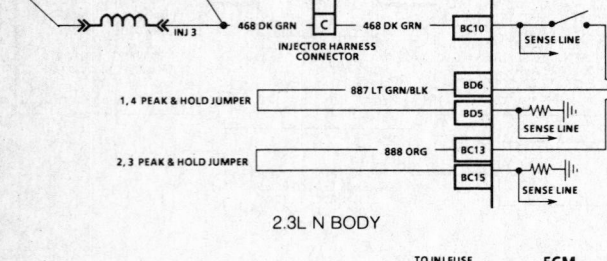

2.3L N BODY

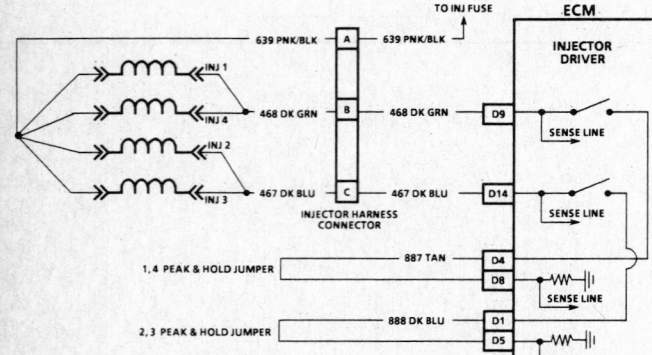

2.3L W BODY

The ECM has 2 injector driver circuits, each controlling a pair of injectors (1 and 4, or 2 and 3). The ECM monitors current of each injector driver circuit by measuring voltage drop through a fixed resistor. The ECM is able to control voltage drop. The current through each driver is allowed to rise to a peak of 4 amps, enabling injectors to open quickly, and is then reduced to one amp, holding them open. This is called, "peak and hold". If current can't reach a 4-amp peak, Code 65 is set. This code is also set if an injector driver circuit is shorted to voltage.

NOTE: Test numbers refer to test numbers on diagnostic chart.

91E07471 91G07472 91I07473 91E07367

1) The following conditions must be present to set a Code 65:
   • The 4-amp injector current was not reached on each circuit.
   • Battery voltage greater than 9 volts.
   • Injectors pulsed on longer than calibrated pulse width.
   • The above conditions met for 20 seconds.
2) Checks ECM and harness wiring to 3-terminal injector harness connector.
3) This tests for open injector harness or injector.

NOTE: Although shorted harness or injector (zero ohms) will not set a Code 65, problem should be corrected if discovered.

4) Results of step 2) will determine which branch to follow on Code 65 flow chart (2 of 2).
5) Each harness was confirmed as being okay in steps 2) and 3). This test will check remainder of circuit from injectors to ECM.
6) Identifies cause of high resistance found in step 3). A short or low resistance will not cause Code 65, but should be corrected.
7) This tests for grounded "peak and hold" jumpers. This condition would allow injectors to pulse, but would NOT allow "peak and hold" operation as current would not flow through resistor in ECM.

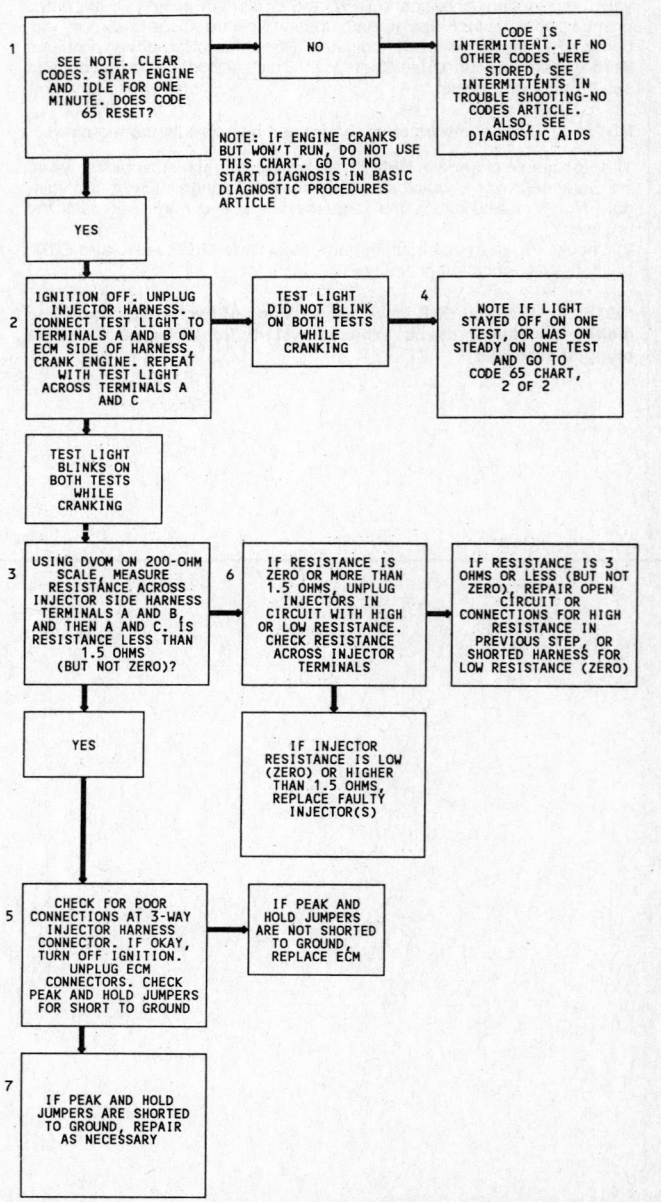

1991 ENGINE PERFORMANCE
Self-Diagnostics — ECM/PCM Except Cadillac (Cont.)

GM
1-121

CODE 65, INJECTOR CURRENT LOW
2.3L L, N & W BODIES (2 OF 2)

DIAGNOSTIC AIDS

An open in injector drive or "peak and hold" circuits, or ECM drive circuits shorted to voltage will cause a Code 65 to be set and also cause misfire due to an inoperative pair of injectors. "Peak and hold" circuits shorted to ground will cause a Code 65 to set, while allowing injectors to pulse. An intermittent problem would have to be present for at least 20 seconds to set Code 65.

NOTE: **Test numbers refer to test numbers on diagnostic chart.**

8) This checks for short to voltage in injector driver circuits.
9) Determines if injector driver circuits are shorted to ground.
10) This checks the output at the ECM to determine if injector driver circuits are okay.
11) Checks for proper continuity of "peak and hold" jumpers circuits.

FROM CODE 65 CHART 1 OF 2 → **TEST LIGHT ON STEADY ON ONE TEST** → **9) IGNITION OFF. UNPLUG ECM. WITH TEST LIGHT CONNECTED TO BATTERY VOLTAGE, PROBE ECM HARNESS TERMINAL FOR CIRCUIT WHICH PREVIOUSLY CAUSED LIGHT TO ILLUMINATE. IS TEST LIGHT ON?**

TEST LIGHT OFF ON ONE TEST

IF TEST LIGHT IS ON, REPAIR SHORT TO GROUND IN THAT CIRCUIT

IF TEST LIGHT IS OFF, REPLACE ECM

8) CONNECT TEST LIGHT TO GROUND. TOUCH INJECTOR HARNESS TERMINAL WHICH DID NOT CAUSE TEST LIGHT TO BLINK. CRANK ENGINE. DOES LIGHT REMAIN OFF WHILE CRANKING? → **NO** → **REPAIR SHORT TO BATTERY VOLTAGE ON THAT CIRCUIT**

YES

10) CONNECT TEST LIGHT TO GROUND. BACKPROBE ECM TERMINAL FOR CIRCUIT WHICH DID NOT CAUSE TEST LIGHT TO BLINK. CRANK ENGINE. DOES TEST LIGHT BLINK? → **YES** → **REPAIR OPEN IN CIRCUIT BETWEEN ECM TERMINAL AND INJECTOR 3-WAY HARNESS CONNECTOR**

NO

11) IGNITION OFF. UNPLUG ECM. USING DVOM, CHECK PEAK AND HOLD JUMPER RESISTANCE AT ECM HARNESS TERMINALS. RESISTANCE SHOULD BE LESS THAN ONE OHM. IS IT? → **NO** → **REPAIR OPEN CIRCUIT OR FAULTY CONNECTION IN PEAK AND HOLD JUMPER**

YES → **CHECK FOR POOR CONNECTIONS AT ECM HARNESS PEAK AND HOLD JUMPER TERMINALS. IF CONNECTIONS ARE OKAY, REPLACE ECM**

91G07368

CODE 65, CRUISE SERVO POSITION
3.8L C & E BODIES

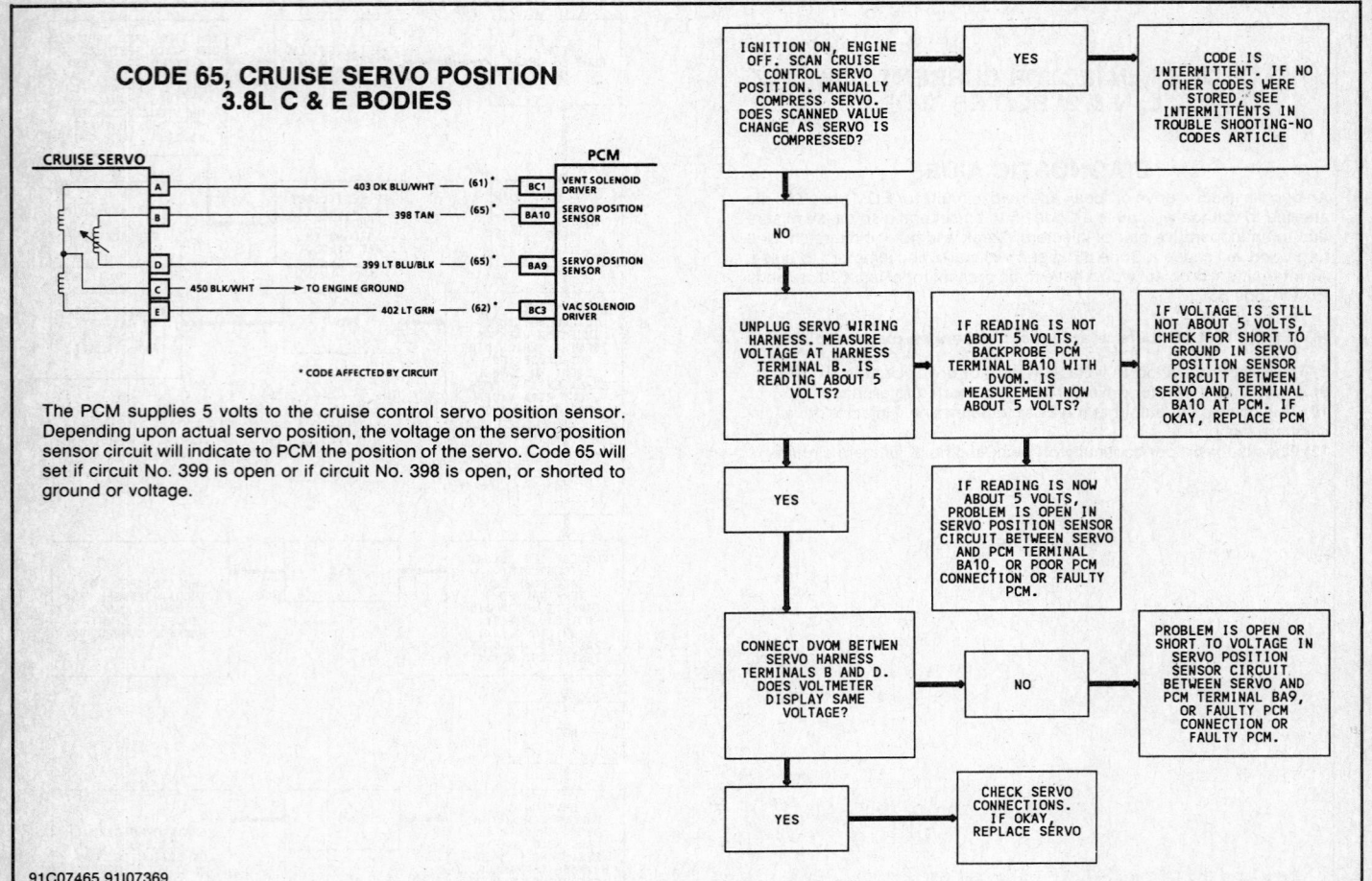

* CODE AFFECTED BY CIRCUIT

The PCM supplies 5 volts to the cruise control servo position sensor. Depending upon actual servo position, the voltage on the servo position sensor circuit will indicate to PCM the position of the servo. Code 65 will set if circuit No. 399 is open or if circuit No. 398 is open, or shorted to ground or voltage.

IGNITION ON, ENGINE OFF. SCAN CRUISE CONTROL SERVO POSITION. MANUALLY COMPRESS SERVO. DOES SCANNED VALUE CHANGE AS SERVO IS COMPRESSED?

→ YES → **CODE IS INTERMITTENT. IF NO OTHER CODES WERE STORED, SEE INTERMITTENTS IN TROUBLE SHOOTING-NO CODES ARTICLE**

NO

UNPLUG SERVO WIRING HARNESS. MEASURE VOLTAGE AT HARNESS TERMINAL B. IS READING ABOUT 5 VOLTS?

→ **IF READING IS NOT ABOUT 5 VOLTS, BACKPROBE PCM TERMINAL BA10 WITH DVOM. IS MEASUREMENT NOW ABOUT 5 VOLTS?**

→ **IF VOLTAGE IS STILL NOT ABOUT 5 VOLTS, CHECK FOR SHORT TO GROUND IN SERVO POSITION SENSOR CIRCUIT BETWEEN SERVO AND TERMINAL BA10 AT PCM. IF OKAY, REPLACE PCM**

IF READING IS NOW ABOUT 5 VOLTS, PROBLEM IS OPEN IN SERVO POSITION SENSOR CIRCUIT BETWEEN SERVO AND PCM TERMINAL BA10, OR POOR PCM CONNECTION OR FAULTY PCM.

YES

CONNECT DVOM BETWEN SERVO HARNESS TERMINALS B AND D. DOES VOLTMETER DISPLAY SAME VOLTAGE?

→ NO → **PROBLEM IS OPEN OR SHORT TO VOLTAGE IN SERVO POSITION SENSOR CIRCUIT BETWEEN SERVO AND PCM TERMINAL BA9, OR FAULTY PCM CONNECTION OR FAULTY PCM.**

YES → **CHECK SERVO CONNECTIONS. IF OKAY, REPLACE SERVO**

91C07465 91I07369

1991 ENGINE PERFORMANCE
Self-Diagnostics — ECM/PCM Except Cadillac (Cont.)

GM
1-123

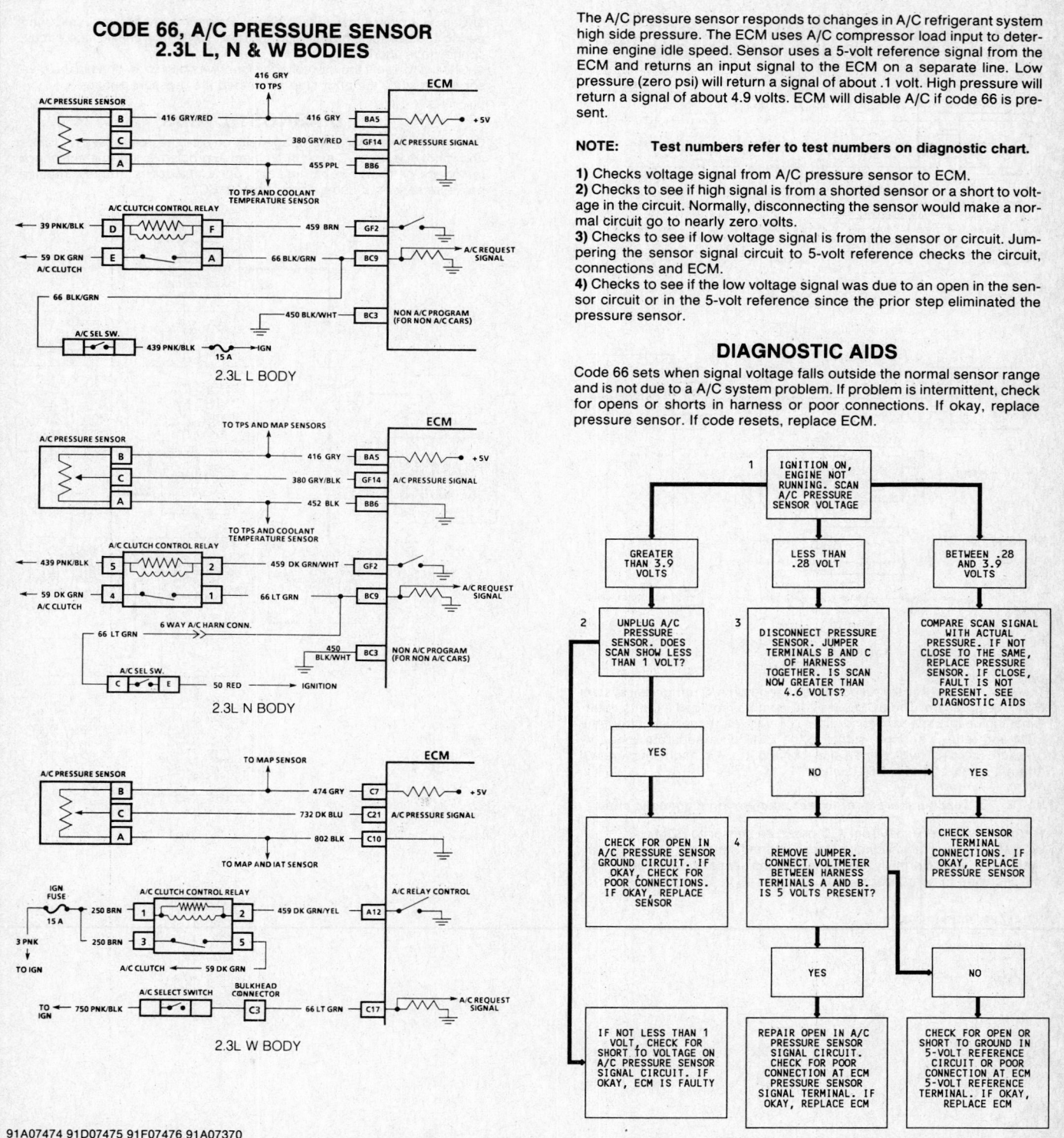

CODE 66, A/C PRESSURE SENSOR 2.3L L, N & W BODIES

The A/C pressure sensor responds to changes in A/C refrigerant system high side pressure. The ECM uses A/C compressor load input to determine engine idle speed. Sensor uses a 5-volt reference signal from the ECM and returns an input signal to the ECM on a separate line. Low pressure (zero psi) will return a signal of about .1 volt. High pressure will return a signal of about 4.9 volts. ECM will disable A/C if code 66 is present.

NOTE: **Test numbers refer to test numbers on diagnostic chart.**

1) Checks voltage signal from A/C pressure sensor to ECM.
2) Checks to see if high signal is from a shorted sensor or a short to voltage in the circuit. Normally, disconnecting the sensor would make a normal circuit go to nearly zero volts.
3) Checks to see if low voltage signal is from the sensor or circuit. Jumpering the sensor signal circuit to 5-volt reference checks the circuit, connections and ECM.
4) Checks to see if the low voltage signal was due to an open in the sensor circuit or in the 5-volt reference since the prior step eliminated the pressure sensor.

DIAGNOSTIC AIDS

Code 66 sets when signal voltage falls outside the normal sensor range and is not due to a A/C system problem. If problem is intermittent, check for opens or shorts in harness or poor connections. If okay, replace pressure sensor. If code resets, replace ECM.

91A07474 91D07475 91F07476 91A07370

CODE 66, A/C PRESSURE SENSOR
3.1L J, L & W BODIES, & 3.4L W BODY

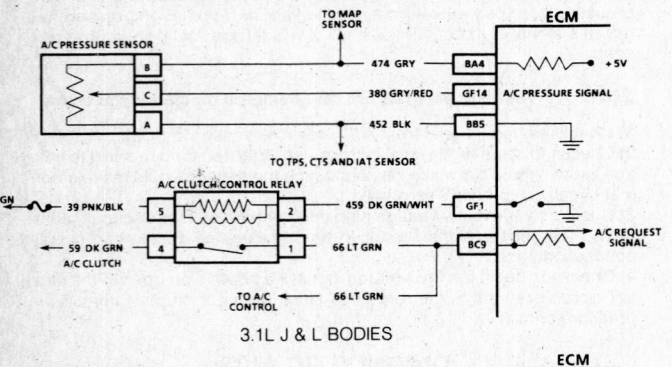

3.1L J & L BODIES

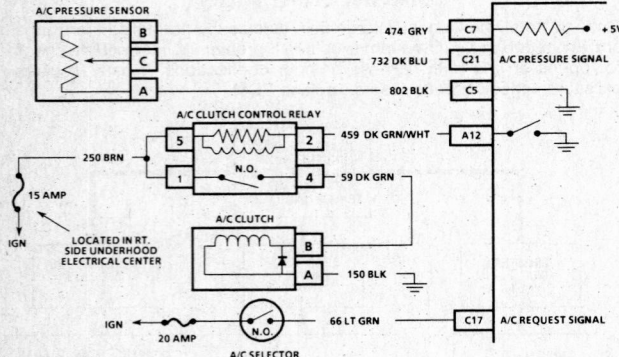

3.1L & 3.4L W BODY

The A/C pressure sensor responds to changes in A/C refrigerant system high side pressure. The ECM uses A/C compressor load input to determine engine idle speed. Sensor uses a 5-volt reference signal from the ECM and returns an input signal to the ECM on a separate line. Low pressure (zero psi) will return a signal of about .1 volt. High pressure will return a signal of about 4.6 volts.

NOTE: Test numbers refer to test numbers on diagnostic chart.

1) Checks voltage signal from A/C pressure sensor to ECM.
2) Checks to see if high signal is from a shorted sensor or a short to voltage in the circuit. Normally, disconnecting the sensor would make a normal circuit go to nearly zero volts.

3) Checks to see if low voltage signal is from the sensor or circuit. Jumpering the sensor signal circuit to 5-volt reference checks the circuit, connections and ECM.
4) Checks to see if the low voltage signal was due to an open in the sensor circuit since the prior step eliminated the pressure sensor.

DIAGNOSTIC AIDS

Code 66 sets when signal voltage falls outside the normal sensor range and is not due to a A/C system problem. If problem is intermittent, check for opens or shorts in harness or poor connections. If okay, replace pressure sensor. If code resets, replace ECM.

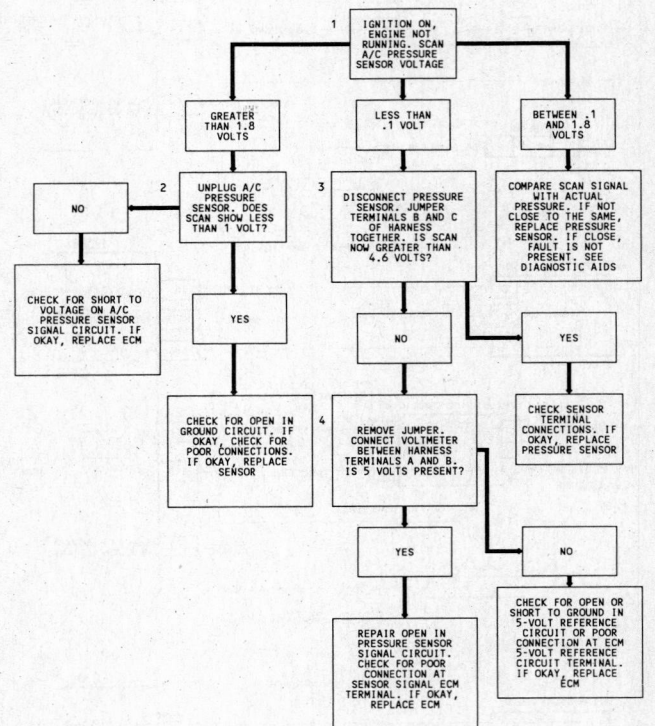

91H07477 91J07478 91C07371

1991 ENGINE PERFORMANCE
Self-Diagnostics — ECM/PCM Except Cadillac (Cont.)

GM
1-125

CODE 66, A/C PRESSURE SENSOR
3.3L N BODY

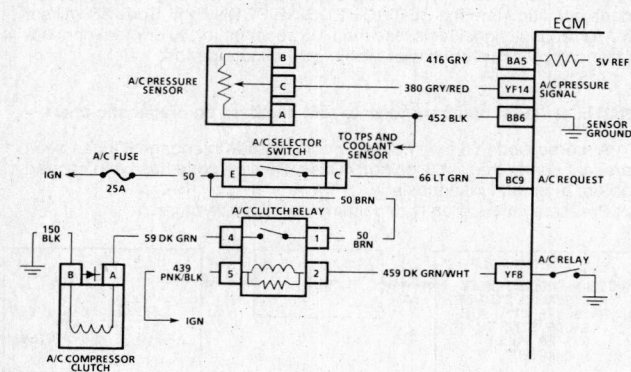

The A/C pressure sensor responds to changes in A/C refrigerant system high side pressure. The ECM uses A/C compressor load input to determine engine idle speed. Sensor uses a 5-volt reference signal from the ECM and returns an input signal to the ECM on a separate line. Low pressure (zero psi) will return a signal of about .1 volt. High pressure will return a signal of about 4.9 volts.

NOTE: **Test numbers refer to test numbers on diagnostic chart.**

1) Checks voltage signal from A/C pressure sensor to ECM.
2) Checks to see if high signal is from a shorted sensor or a short to voltage in the circuit. Normally, disconnecting the sensor would make a normal circuit go to nearly zero volts.
3) Checks to see if low voltage signal is from the sensor or circuit. Jumpering the sensor signal circuit to 5-volt reference checks the circuit, connections and ECM.
4) Checks to see if the low voltage signal was due to an open in the sensor circuit or 5-volt reference circuit since the prior step eliminated the pressure sensor.

91B07479 91E07372

DIAGNOSTIC AIDS

Code 66 sets when signal voltage falls outside the normal sensor range and is not due to a A/C system problem. If problem is intermittent, check for opens or shorts in harness or poor connections. If okay, replace pressure sensor. If code resets, replace ECM.

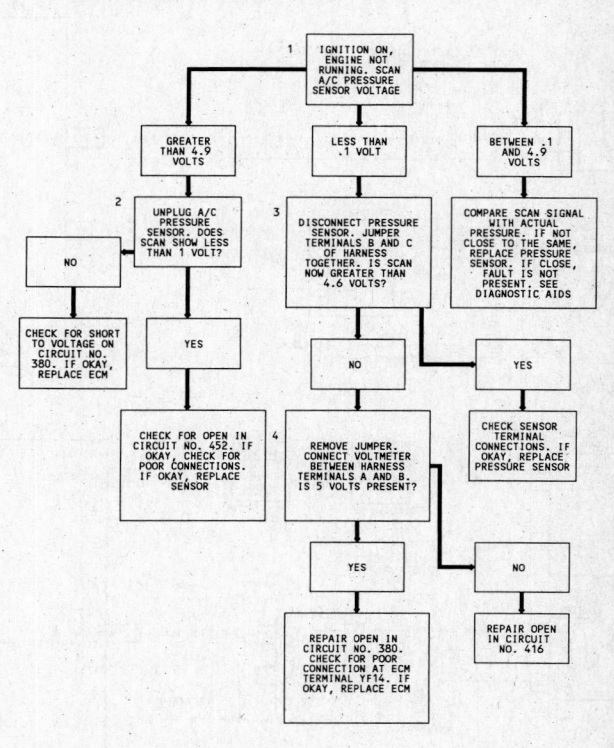

**CODE 66, LOW A/C REFRIGERANT CHARGE
3.8L C BODY (WITHOUT DIGITAL DISPLAY)
& 3.8L W BODY**

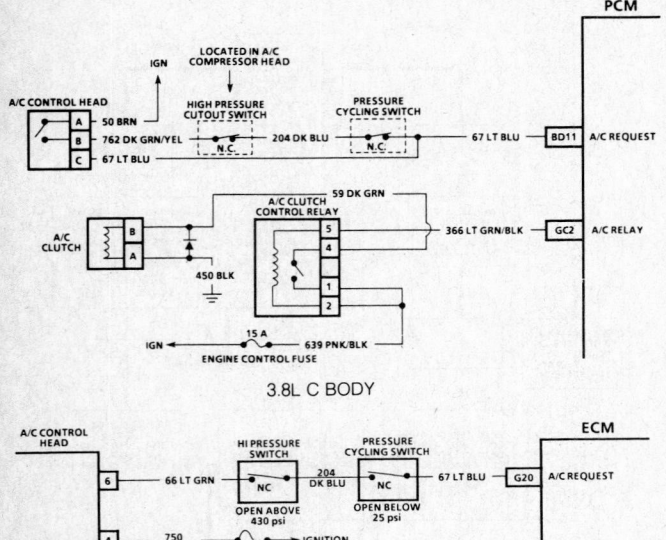

3.8L C BODY

3.8L W BODY

The ECM monitors A/C request and completes the ground for the A/C relay when an A/C mode is selected at control head and refrigerant pressure is sufficient to close pressure cycling switch. If A/C pressure is low

and clutch cycles too often, ECM will protect compressor by disabling the A/C relay and setting Code 66. Relay will be disabled until next ignition cycle. If Code 66 is set during 3 consecutive ignition cycles, A/C relay will be disabled until Code 66 is cleared from memory. Code 66 does not illuminate the SERVICE ENGINE SOON light. Code 66 will set if A/C request signal lasts less than 1.5 seconds for 10 or more consecutive compressor "on" cycles within a 15 minute period.

NOTE: Test numbers refer to test numbers on diagnostic chart.

1) A stored Code 66 may not allow compressor to engage if it has been present during the last 3 ignition cycles. Be sure code has been cleared before attempting diagnosis.
2) Pressure varies greatly depending upon temperature.

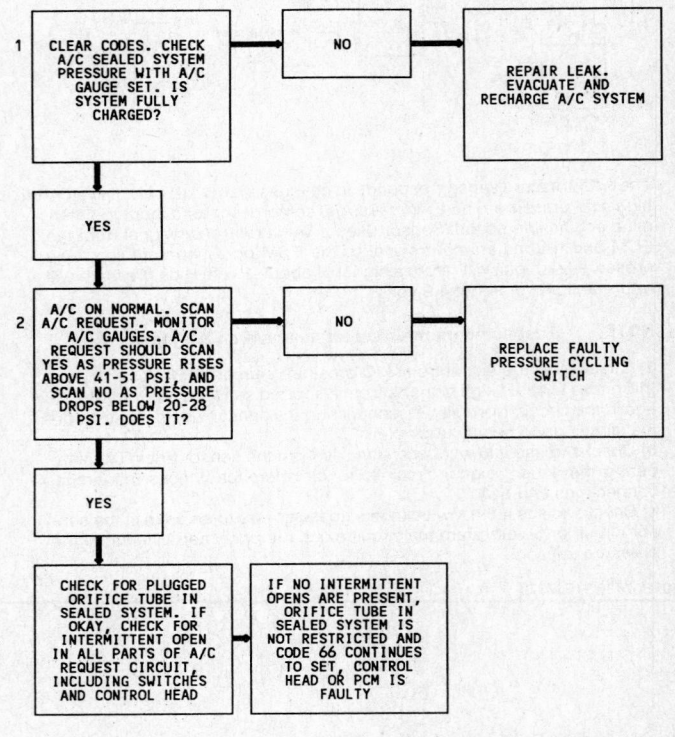

91D07480 91F07481 91G07373

1991 ENGINE PERFORMANCE
Self-Diagnostics — ECM/PCM Except Cadillac (Cont.)

GM
1-127

CODE 66, LOW A/C REFRIGERANT CHARGE
3.8L C BODY (WITH DIGITAL DISPLAY)

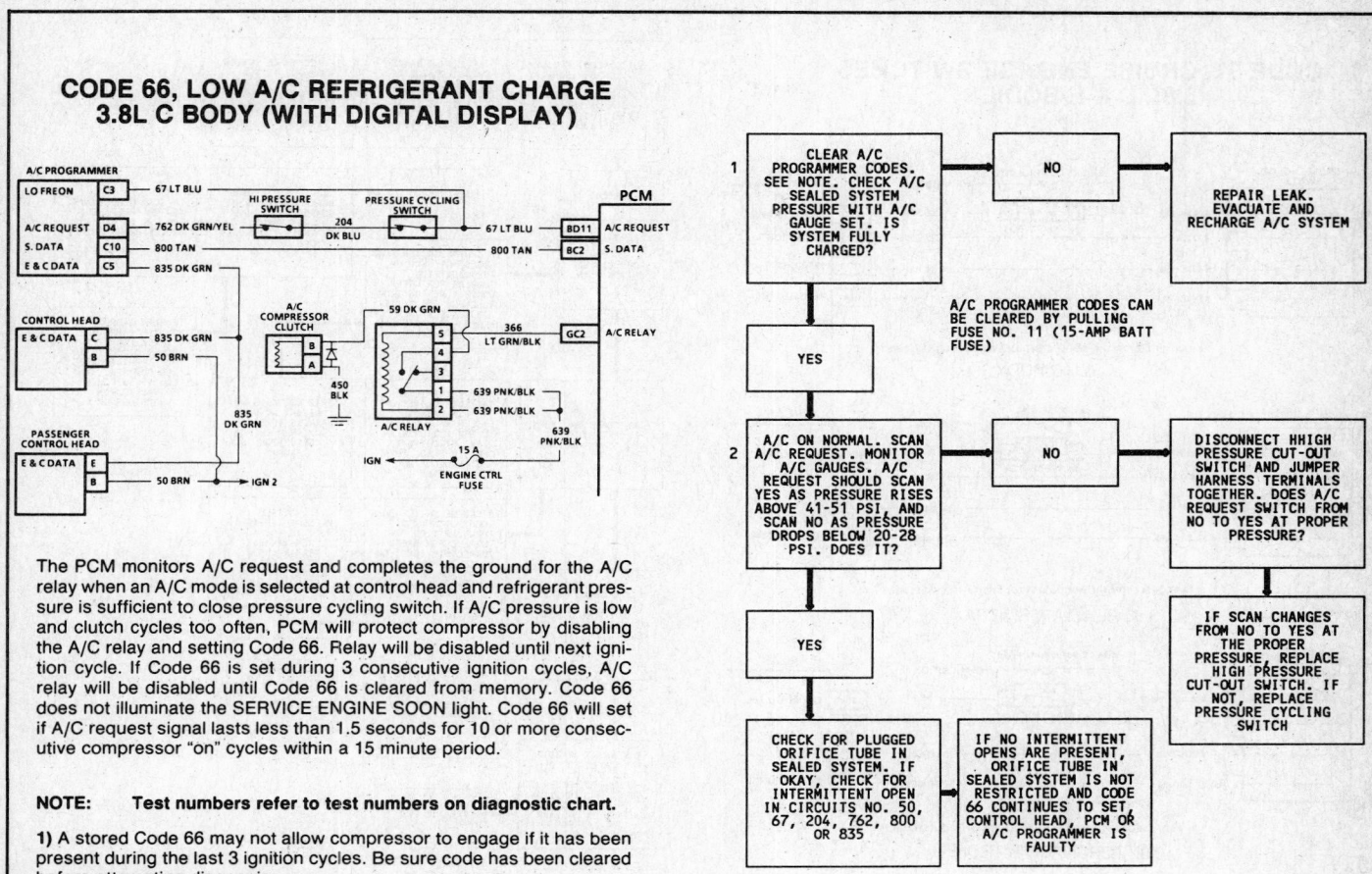

The PCM monitors A/C request and completes the ground for the A/C relay when an A/C mode is selected at control head and refrigerant pressure is sufficient to close pressure cycling switch. If A/C pressure is low and clutch cycles too often, PCM will protect compressor by disabling the A/C relay and setting Code 66. Relay will be disabled until next ignition cycle. If Code 66 is set during 3 consecutive ignition cycles, A/C relay will be disabled until Code 66 is cleared from memory. Code 66 does not illuminate the SERVICE ENGINE SOON light. Code 66 will set if A/C request signal lasts less than 1.5 seconds for 10 or more consecutive compressor "on" cycles within a 15 minute period.

NOTE: Test numbers refer to test numbers on diagnostic chart.

1) A stored Code 66 may not allow compressor to engage if it has been present during the last 3 ignition cycles. Be sure code has been cleared before attempting diagnosis.
2) Pressure varies greatly depending upon temperature.

91H07482 91I07374

GM
1-128

1991 ENGINE PERFORMANCE
Self-Diagnostics — ECM/PCM Except Cadillac (Cont.)

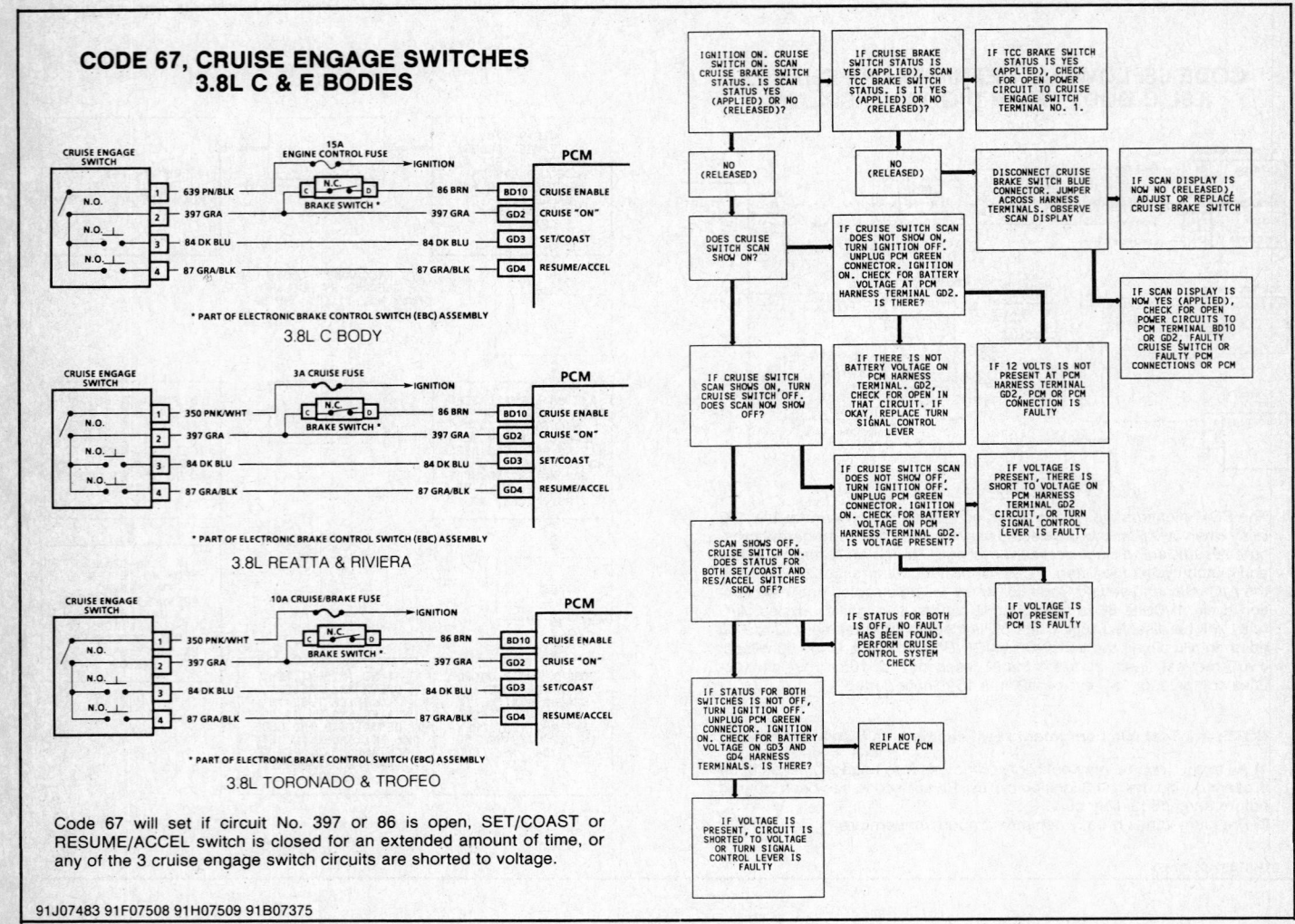

CODE 67, CRUISE ENGAGE SWITCHES
3.8L C & E BODIES

3.8L C BODY

* PART OF ELECTRONIC BRAKE CONTROL SWITCH (EBC) ASSEMBLY

3.8L REATTA & RIVIERA

* PART OF ELECTRONIC BRAKE CONTROL SWITCH (EBC) ASSEMBLY

3.8L TORONADO & TROFEO

* PART OF ELECTRONIC BRAKE CONTROL SWITCH (EBC) ASSEMBLY

Code 67 will set if circuit No. 397 or 86 is open, SET/COAST or RESUME/ACCEL switch is closed for an extended amount of time, or any of the 3 cruise engage switch circuits are shorted to voltage.

91J07483 91F07508 91H07509 91B07375

1991 ENGINE PERFORMANCE
Self-Diagnostics — ECM/PCM Except Cadillac (Cont.)

GM
1-129

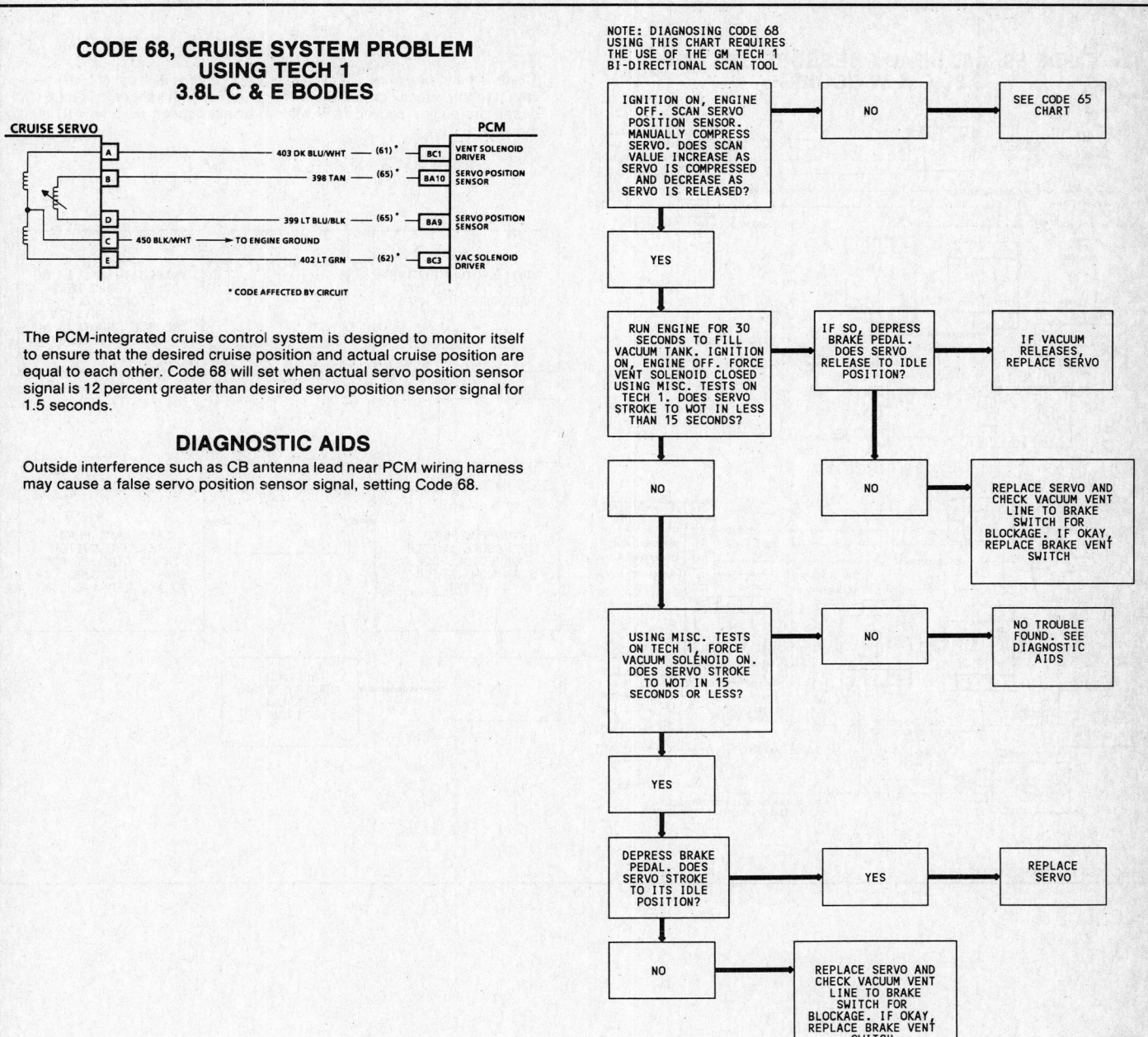

CODE 68, CRUISE SYSTEM PROBLEM USING TECH 1 3.8L C & E BODIES

CRUISE SERVO

* CODE AFFECTED BY CIRCUIT

The PCM-integrated cruise control system is designed to monitor itself to ensure that the desired cruise position and actual cruise position are equal to each other. Code 68 will set when actual servo position sensor signal is 12 percent greater than desired servo position sensor signal for 1.5 seconds.

DIAGNOSTIC AIDS

Outside interference such as CB antenna lead near PCM wiring harness may cause a false servo position sensor signal, setting Code 68.

NOTE: DIAGNOSING CODE 68 USING THIS CHART REQUIRES THE USE OF THE GM TECH 1 BI-DIRECTIONAL SCAN TOOL

IGNITION ON, ENGINE OFF. SCAN SERVO POSITION SENSOR. MANUALLY COMPRESS SERVO. DOES SCAN VALUE INCREASE AS SERVO IS COMPRESSED AND DECREASE AS SERVO IS RELEASED? → NO → SEE CODE 65 CHART

YES

RUN ENGINE FOR 30 SECONDS TO FILL VACUUM TANK. IGNITION ON, ENGINE OFF. FORCE VENT SOLENOID CLOSED USING MISC. TESTS ON TECH 1. DOES SERVO STROKE TO WOT IN LESS THAN 15 SECONDS? → IF SO, DEPRESS BRAKE PEDAL. DOES SERVO RELEASE TO IDLE POSITION? → IF VACUUM RELEASES, REPLACE SERVO

NO → NO → REPLACE SERVO AND CHECK VACUUM VENT LINE TO BRAKE SWITCH FOR BLOCKAGE. IF OKAY, REPLACE BRAKE VENT SWITCH

USING MISC. TESTS ON TECH 1, FORCE VACUUM SOLENOID ON. DOES SERVO STROKE TO WOT IN 15 SECONDS OR LESS? → NO → NO TROUBLE FOUND. SEE DIAGNOSTIC AIDS

YES

DEPRESS BRAKE PEDAL. DOES SERVO STROKE TO ITS IDLE POSITION? → YES → REPLACE SERVO

NO → REPLACE SERVO AND CHECK VACUUM VENT LINE TO BRAKE SWITCH FOR BLOCKAGE. IF OKAY, REPLACE BRAKE VENT SWITCH

91C07465 91D07376

**CODE 69, A/C HEAD PRESSURE SWITCH
3.8L C & W BODIES**

The A/C head pressure switch closes to ground at 210 psi (14.77 kg/cm²). When switch is closed, fans should run at high speed. If Code 69 is set, the engine cooling fans will run at high speed anytime A/C is requested.

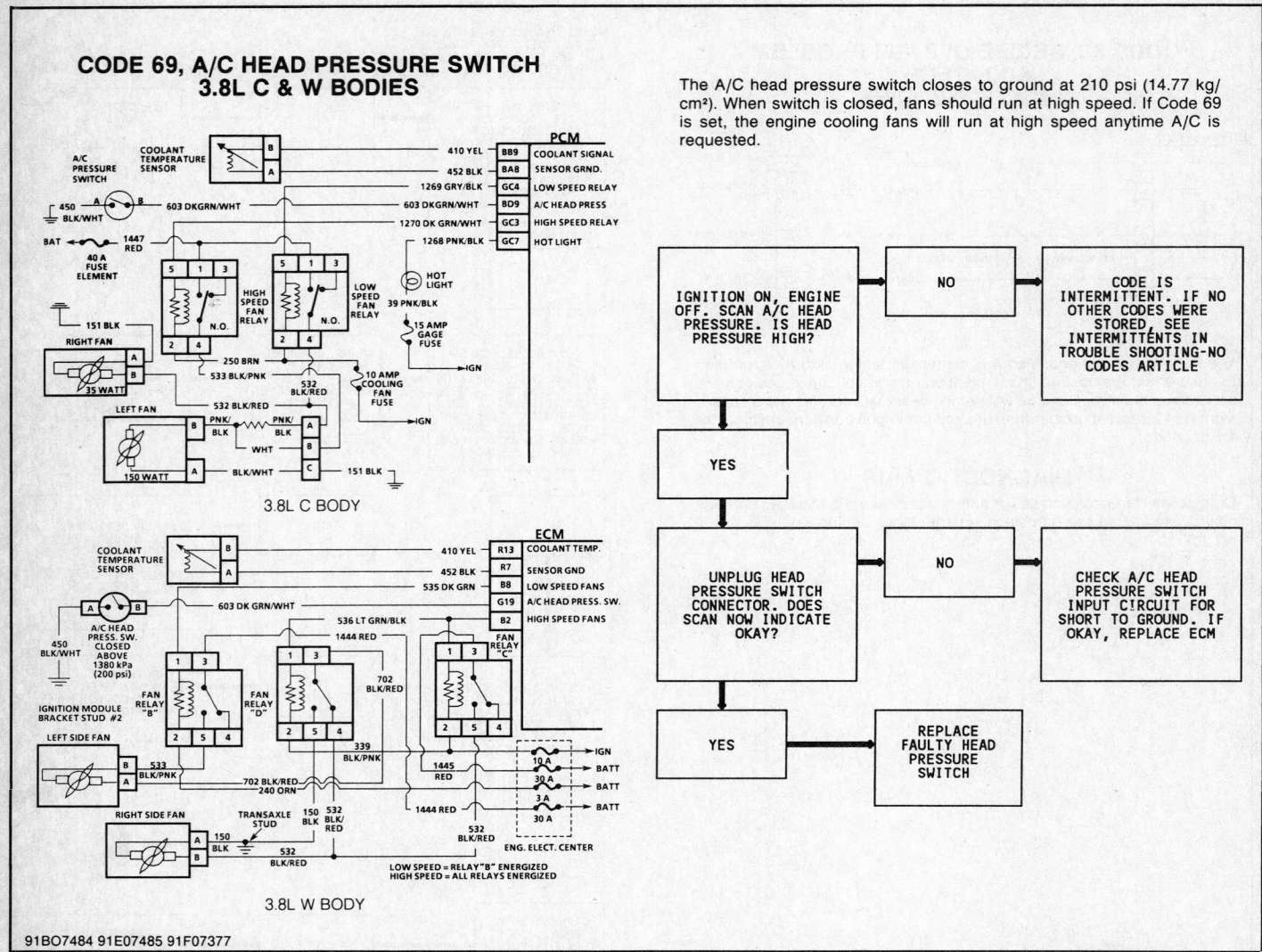

3.8L C BODY

3.8L W BODY

LOW SPEED = RELAY "B" ENERGIZED
HIGH SPEED = ALL RELAYS ENERGIZED

91BO7484 91E07485 91F07377

INTRODUCTION

NOTE: If no trouble codes were found while performing BASIC DIAGNOSTIC PROCEDURES, proceed with ENTERING SELF-DIAGNOSTICS. If no trouble codes or only pass codes are present after entering self-diagnostics, proceed to TROUBLE SHOOTING – NO CODES article for diagnosis by symptom (i.e. ROUGH IDLE, NO START, etc.).

DEVILLE & FLEETWOOD BCM/PCM CHART DIRECTORY

SELF-DIAGNOSTIC SYSTEM

NOTE: The terms Electronic Control Module (ECM) and Powertrain Control Module (PCM) refer to the same system and are often used interchangeably.

The Body Control Module (BCM) and the Powertrain Control Module (PCM) are the 2 major components of the self-diagnostic system. The BCM is the heart of the system, controlling a multitude of vehicle functions through monitored sensors and switch inputs. In addition, the BCM provides self-diagnostic capabilities. Likewise, the PCM provides control and self-diagnostic capabilities in relation to the various engine and emission related components it monitors.

Between the BCM and PCM, a communication process has been incorporated which allows these units to communicate with each other and share information. The BCM, upon receiving information from the PCM or one of its own related subsystems, compares the received information with programmed instructions within system memory. In this way, the BCM provides monitoring of the individual subsystems and their related sensors and switches.

Should a subsystem exceed pre-programmed limits, the BCM will recognize a malfunction and, in response, may act to control the malfunctioning subsystem. To control a particular subsystem, the BCM rapidly switches an internal circuit between zero and 5 volts, converting programmed control information into a series of pulses which represent coded data messages. These messages are transmitted to the malfunctioning component, which interprets the information and responds accordingly.

As a result of interactions between the BCM and a malfunctioning component, an alpha-numeric code, known as a trouble code, is often set in the BCM's memory. This trouble code identifies the malfunctioning component and can be accessed by a service technician as an aid to diagnostic procedures. All trouble codes are displayed on the Fuel Data Center (FDC). *See Fig. 2.*

In addition to monitoring the self-diagnostic system and displaying trouble codes, the BCM can be programmed by the service technician to perform specific diagnostic tests on individual components and systems. Depressing the appropriate buttons on the Electronic Climate Control Panel (ECCP) will request BCM to provide specific diagnostic information for display on the Fuel Data Center (FDC). *See Fig. 2.*

SELF-DIAGNOSTICS

ENTERING SELF-DIAGNOSTICS

1) Turn ignition switch on. Simultaneously depress OFF and WARMER buttons on Electronic Climate Control Panel (ECCP) and hold until all segments of the Fuel Data Center (FDC) and ECCP illuminate. This indicates beginning of diagnostic readout. *See Figs. 1 and 2.*

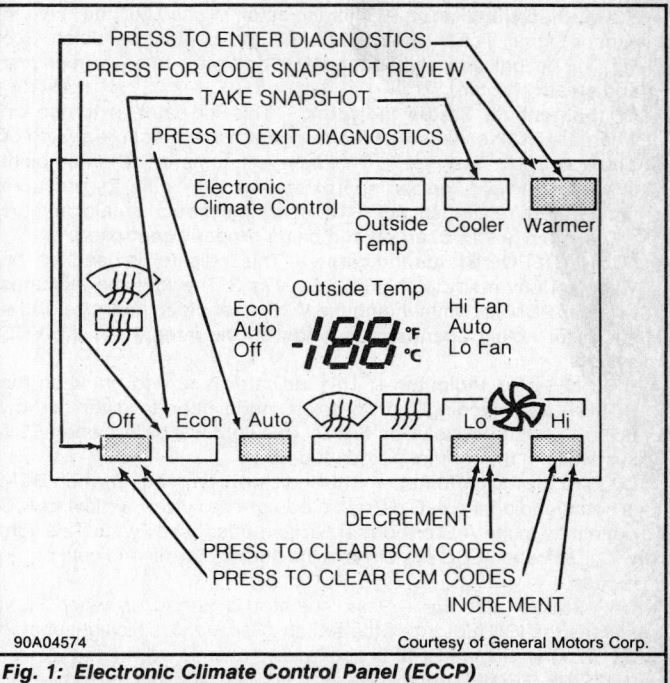

Fig. 1: Electronic Climate Control Panel (ECCP)

90A04574   Courtesy of General Motors Corp.

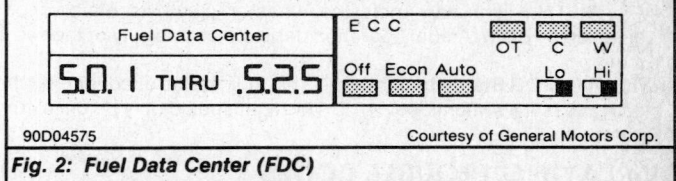

90D04575   Courtesy of General Motors Corp.

Fig. 2: Fuel Data Center (FDC)

2) Illuminating the FDC and ECCP ensures all segments of the displays are working properly. If all segments illuminate, proceed to DISPLAYING TROUBLE CODES.

3) If any of the segment(s) fail to illuminate, diagnosis should not be attempted, as this could lead to inaccurate test results. An inoperative panel must be replaced before proceeding with the self-diagnostic process.

NOTE: Following the completion of the segment check, system automatically enters self-diagnostic mode.

STATUS LIGHTS DISPLAY

While in self-diagnostic mode, the mode indicators on the ECCP automatically indicate system operating modes, the different modes of operation being indicated by illuminated or non-illuminated status lights. Following is a description of the various status lights and their meaning in relation to system operations.

- **AUTO Status Indicator** – This indicator is turned on whenever the PCM is operating in closed-loop fuel control. *See Fig. 3.* This light should come on after the coolant and oxygen sensors have reached normal operating temperatures.

NOTE: Extended clutch interval is inhibited during diagnostic mode.

- **AUTO FAN Status Indicator** – This status indicator is turned on when signal from the coolant fan control relays indicates that fans are commanded on. *See Fig. 3.* This light should be off when the fans are commanded off.
- **°C (Centigrade) Status Light** – This indicator is turned on when the BCM is commanding the heater valve to block coolant flow through the heater core. *See Fig. 3.* This light should remain off except when the air mix door is being commanded to the maximum A/C position (0%).

GM
1-132

1991 ENGINE PERFORMANCE
Self-Diagnostics – DeVille & Fleetwood PCM/BCM (Cont.)

- **ECON Status Indicator** – This indicator is used for the oxygen sensor signal. The indicator is on for rich exhaust condition. *See Fig. 3*. The indicator should toggle on and off with a warm engine and steady throttle.
- **°F (Fahrenheit) Status Indicator** – This indicator is turned on when the BCM senses that the refrigerant low pressure switch or circuit is open. *See Fig. 3*. This light will come on when ambient temperature falls below approximately -5°F due to pressure temperature relationship of R-12. This light should remain off if the A/C system is fully charged and being properly controlled.
- **FRONT DEFOG Status Indicator** – This indicator is used for the Viscous Converter Clutch (VCC). *See Fig. 3*. The light only indicates whether PCM is commanding the VCC solenoid to energize or de-energize. Actual operation depends on the integrity of the VCC system.
- **HI FAN Status Indicator** – This indicator is turned on when the BCM is commanding the up-down mode door to divert airflow down to heater outlet. *See Fig. 3*. This light will be off when ECC system is in the normal purge modes.
- **LO FAN Status Indicator** – This indicator is turned on when BCM is commanding the A/C defrost mode door to divert airflow to A/C outlets as in the A/C or normal purge modes. *See Fig. 3*. This light will be off when ECC system is in the heater defrost and cold purge modes.
- **OFF Status Indicator** – This indicator is turned on when PCM senses the ISC motor throttle switch . *See Fig. 3*. This light should be off when engine RPM is above idle.
- **OUTSIDE TEMP Status Indicator** – This indicator is turned on when BCM is requesting A/C compressor clutch to engage. *See Fig. 3*. This light only indicates whether clutch is enabled or disabled by BCM. Actual operation depends on integrity of the system.
- **REAR DEFOG Status Indicator** – This indicator is used for the 4th gear pressure switch. *See Fig. 3*. This light should only be on in 4th gear.

DISPLAYING TROUBLE CODES

Following the segment check (see ENTERING SELF-DIAGNOSTICS under SELF-DIAGNOSTICS in this article), the numerals "8.8.8." appear on the FDC for one second. The display of these 3 numerals signals that the trouble code display is about to begin.

PCM Trouble Codes Display – **1)** Following the one second display of "8.8.8.", the letter "E" appears on the FDC. The letter "E" indicates 2 passes through the PCM trouble code display cycle are about to begin. The first pass through the PCM trouble code cycle displays trouble codes stored in memory, including history and current trouble codes. The second pass displays only current trouble codes.

2) History trouble codes are those set in response to a malfunction that occurred during the past 50 key cycles, but not during the present key cycle. Current trouble codes represent malfunctions currently taking place. All trouble codes displayed during this cycle are prefixed with the letter "E". If no "E" codes are present, display will be bypassed.

3) Immediately following the first pass through the cycle of PCM trouble codes, the second pass begins, during which only current trouble codes are displayed. These codes are prefixed by the letters ".E.E.", indicating the related malfunction is currently taking place.

BCM Trouble Codes Display – Following the display of PCM trouble codes, 2 cycles of BCM trouble codes will be displayed. BCM trouble codes are prefixed by the letter(s) "F" or "F.F.". A single "F" precedes the first pass of BCM trouble codes which is a display of both history and current trouble codes. The letters "F.F." precede the second pass of BCM trouble codes which is a display of current trouble codes only.

NOTE: After the display of all PCM and BCM trouble codes, ".7.0" will be displayed on the FDC. ".7.0" indicates the system is ready for a diagnostic feature to be selected. See DIAGNOSTIC TESTING.

CLEARING TROUBLE CODES

NOTE: If PCM codes are cleared, all snapshot code data will be cleared. See PCM CODE & INSTANT SNAPSHOT and EXITING DIAGNOSTICS.

Clearing PCM Trouble Codes – **1)** PCM trouble codes stored in memory may be cleared (erased) by entering diagnostic mode (see ENTERING SELF-DIAGNOSTICS under SELF DIAGNOSTICS in this article) and simultaneously depressing OFF and HI buttons on ECCP until "E.O.O" appears.

2) After the "E.O.O" display appears, release buttons and ".7.0" will appear. With ".7.0" displayed, turn ignition off for at least 10 seconds.

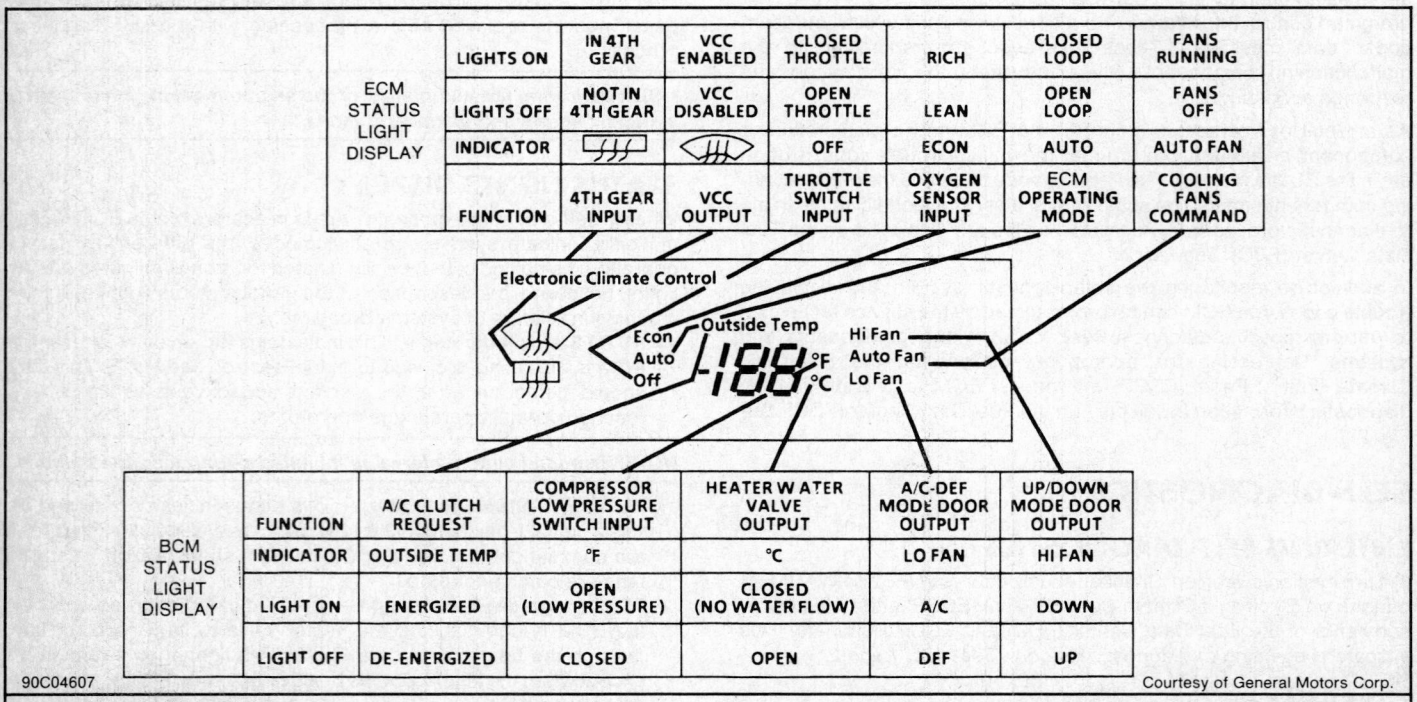

ECM STATUS LIGHT DISPLAY	LIGHTS ON	IN 4TH GEAR	VCC ENABLED	CLOSED THROTTLE	RICH	CLOSED LOOP	FANS RUNNING
	LIGHTS OFF	NOT IN 4TH GEAR	VCC DISABLED	OPEN THROTTLE	LEAN	OPEN LOOP	FANS OFF
	INDICATOR			OFF	ECON	AUTO	AUTO FAN
	FUNCTION	4TH GEAR INPUT	VCC OUTPUT	THROTTLE SWITCH INPUT	OXYGEN SENSOR INPUT	ECM OPERATING MODE	COOLING FANS COMMAND

BCM STATUS LIGHT DISPLAY	FUNCTION	A/C CLUTCH REQUEST	COMPRESSOR LOW PRESSURE SWITCH INPUT	HEATER WATER VALVE OUTPUT	A/C-DEF MODE DOOR OUTPUT	UP/DOWN MODE DOOR OUTPUT
	INDICATOR	OUTSIDE TEMP	°F	°C	LO FAN	HI FAN
	LIGHT ON	ENERGIZED	OPEN (LOW PRESSURE)	CLOSED (NO WATER FLOW)	A/C	DOWN
	LIGHT OFF	DE-ENERGIZED	CLOSED	OPEN	DEF	UP

90C04607

Courtesy of General Motors Corp.

Fig. 3: Status Lights Display

Codes are now cleared. To exit diagnostics without erasing trouble codes, see EXITING DIAGNOSTICS.

Clearing BCM Trouble Codes – To clear BCM trouble codes, follow the preceding PCM procedure using the LO button (rather than the HI button) on the ECCP.

EXITING DIAGNOSTICS

To exit from the diagnostic mode, depress AUTO button or turn ignition switch off for 10 seconds. The temperature setting will reappear in the display panel. Trouble code(s) are not erased when this is done.

PCM TROUBLE CODES

Code	Circuit Affected
E12 [1]	No Distributor Signal
E13 [1]	Oxygen Sensor Not Ready
E14 [1]	Shorted Coolant Sensor
E15 [1]	Open Coolant Sensor Circuit
E16 [2]	Alternator Voltage Out Of Range
E19 [2]	Shorted Fuel Pump Circuit
E20 [2]	Open Fuel Pump Circuit
E21 [1]	Shorted Throttle Position Sensor (TPS) Circuit
E22 [1]	Open TPS circuit
E23 [1]	Elec. Spark Timing (EST) By-Pass Circuit Problem
E24 [1]	VSS Circuit Protection
E26 [1]	Shorted Throttle Switch Circuit
E27 [1]	Open Throttle Switch Circuit
E30 [1]	ISC RPM Error Too Great
E31 [1]	Shorted MAP Sensor Circuit
E32 [1]	Open MAP Sensor Circuit
E34 [1]	Map Sensor Signal Too High
E37 [1]	Shorted Mat Sensor Circuit
E38 [1]	Open Mat Sensor Circuit
E39 [1]	VCC Engagement Problem Electrical Check
E40 [1]	Power Steering Pressure Circuit
E41 [1]	No Cam Sensor Signal
E44 [1]	Oxygen Sensor Signal Lean
E45 [1]	Oxygen Sensor Signal Rich
E47 [1]	PCM-BCM Data Problem
E48 [1]	EGR System Problem
E52 [3]	PCM Memory Reset Indicator
E53 [3]	Distributor Signal Interrupt
E55 [3]	TPS Misadjusted
E58 [1]	Pass Key Control Problem
E60 [3]	Cruise-Transmission Not In Drive
E61 [3]	Cruise Vent Solenoid Circuit Problem
E62 [3]	Cruise Vacuum Solenoid Circuit
E63 [3]	Cruise-Vehicle Speed Difference
E64 [3]	Cruise-Vehicle Acceleration Out Of Range
E65 [3]	Cruise-Servo Position Sensor Failure
E66 [3]	Cruise-Engine RPM Too High
E67 [3]	Set/Coast-Resume/Accel Switch Short
E68 [3]	Cruise Control Command Problem
E70 [3]	Intermittent TPS Signal
E71 [3]	Intermittent MAP Sensor Signal
E73 [3]	Intermittent Coolant Sensor Signal
E74 [3]	MAT Signal Interrupt
E75 [3]	VSS Signal Interrupt
E80 [1]	Fuel System Rich
E85 [1]	Throttle Body Service Required
E90 [2]	VCC Brake Switch Input Problem
E91 [2]	Park/Neutral Switch Problem
E92 [2]	Heated Windshield Request Problem
E96 [3]	Torque Converter Overstress
E97 [3]	P/N to D/R Engagement Problem
E98 [3]	P/N to D/R in ISC Range Problem
E99 [3]	Cruise Servo Applied Not In Cruise

[1] – This fault turns on SERVICE ENGINE SOON light.
[2] – This fault turns on SERVICE VEHICLE SOON light.
[3] – This fault does not turn on any light.

DIAGNOSTIC TESTING

NOTE: Diagnostic testing is intended for use in conjunction with the TROUBLE CODE CHARTS in this article. Prior to using trouble code charts, it will be necessary to become completely familiar with the procedures in DIAGNOSTIC TESTING.

BCM TROUBLE CODES

Code	Circuit Affected
F10	Outside Temperature Sensor Circuit Problem
F11 [1]	A/C High Side Temperature Sensor Circuit
F12 [2]	A/C Low Side Temperature Sensor Circuit
F13	In-Car Temperature Sensor Circuit
F15	Solar Sensor Circuit Failure
F30 or F31	Display Panels-To-BCM Data Problem
F32	PCM-To-BCM Data Circuit
F40	Air Mix Door Problem
F46 [3]	Refrigerant System Problem
F47 [3][4]	Refrigerant System Problem
F48 [3][4]	Refrigerant System Problem
F49	A/C Clutch Disengagement (Overheating)
F51	BCM PROM Error

[1] – Turns on cooling fans when A/C clutch is engaged.
[2] – Disengages A/C clutch.
[3] – Turns on SERVICE AIR COND light.
[4] – Switches from AUTO to ECON mode.

INTRODUCTION TO DIAGNOSTIC TESTING

To select a desired diagnostic feature, the diagnostic system must first be programmed to display ".7.0" on the FDC. ".7.0" indicates system is ready for a diagnostic feature to be selected. To cause ".7.0" to be displayed on the FDC, See ENTERING SELF-DIAGNOSTICS and DISPLAYING TROUBLE CODES under SELF-DIAGNOSTICS in this article. With ".7.0" displayed, technician may select any of the following diagnostic tests appearing in this article:

- **PCM Switch Tests** – To select, see PCM SWITCH TESTS under DIAGNOSTIC TESTING.
- **PCM Data Parameters** – To select, see PCM DATA PARAMETERS under DIAGNOSTIC TESTING.
- **PCM Code Snapshot** – To select, see PCM CODE & INSTANT SNAPSHOT under DIAGNOSTIC TESTING.
- **PCM Instant Snapshot** – To select, see PCM CODE & INSTANT SNAPSHOT under DIAGNOSTIC TESTING.
- **PCM Output Cycling** – To select, see PCM OUTPUT CYCLING under DIAGNOSTIC TESTING.
- **PCM Output Overrides** – To select, see PCM OUTPUT OVERRIDES under DIAGNOSTIC TESTING.
- **BCM Data Parameters** – To select, see BCM DATA PARAMETERS under DIAGNOSTIC TESTING.
- **ECCP Program Override** – To select, see ECCP PROGRAM OVERRIDE under DIAGNOSTIC TESTING.
- **Clear Codes** – See CLEARING TROUBLE CODES under SELF-DIAGNOSTICS.
- **Exit Diagnostics** – See EXITING DIAGNOSTICS under SELF-DIAGNOSTICS.

PCM SWITCH TESTS

NOTE: If cruise on/off switch or cruise brake switch has failed, entering switch test mode is not possible.

Entering Switch Test – **1)** With ".7.0" displayed on the FDC, the PCM switch test is initiated by placing cruise control switch in the ON position and depressing the brake pedal. To display ".7.0" on the FDC, see INTRODUCTION TO DIAGNOSTIC TESTING under DIAGNOSTIC TESTING.

2) After brake pedal has been depressed, FDC will display "E.7.0". At this point, the HI and LO buttons on the ECCP can be used to select the specific switch test desired. See step **3)** for a complete list of PCM switch tests.

3) When a specific switch test has been selected and that switch has been activated, the display will alternately display the code for the test and "00" to confirm switch is working. Following is a list of PCM switch tests accompanied by a test description:

- **"E.7.0" Cruise Control Brake Switch** — This test detects the opening and closing of the cruise control brake switch at PCM terminal C2. To activate test, turn cruise switch to the ON position, turn ignition on and enter self diagnostics. Depress brake pedal.

GM
1-134

1991 ENGINE PERFORMANCE
Self-Diagnostics – DeVille & Fleetwood PCM/BCM (Cont.)

- **"E.7.1" Viscous Converter Clutch (VCC) Brake Switch** – This test detects the opening and closing of the VCC brake switch at PCM terminal C4. *See Fig. 4.* To activate test, depress brake pedal.
- **"E.7.2" Throttle Switch** – This test detects the opening and closing of Idle Speed Control (ISC) nose switch (PCM terminal A7). *See Fig. 4.* To activate test, depress accelerator pedal.
- **"E.7.3" Not A Valid Test** – FDC will display E.7.3
- **"E.7.5" Cruise Control On/Off Switch** – This test detects the opening and closing of the cruise switch, mounted on dash (PCM terminal D2). *See Fig. 4.* To activate test, place switch in the ON position.

NOTE: The cruise control switch must be in ON position to perform this test.

- **"E.7.6" Cruise Control Set/Coast Switch** – This test detects the operation of set-coast switch located in the turn signal lever (PCM terminal D3). *See Fig. 4.* To activate test, depress the SET/COAST button.

NOTE: The cruise control switch must be in ON position to perform this test.

- **"E.7.7" Cruise Control Resume/Acceleration Switch** – This test detects the closing of the RESUME/ACCEL switch in the turn signal lever (PCM terminal C3). *See Fig. 4.* To activate test, slide the RESUME/ACCEL switch.
- **"E.7.8" Power Steering Pressure Switch (PSPS)** – This test detects the opening and closing of the power steering switch located on steering gear (PCM terminal C9). *See Fig. 4.* To perform test, start engine and turn wheels from straight ahead position to full right or left and then return to straight ahead position. While this action is being performed, PCM checks power steering pressure switch for proper operation.

Exiting PCM Switch Test Mode – To exit PCM switch test mode at any time and return to ".7.0", complete the procedures for clearing PCM or BCM trouble codes. See CLEARING CODES under SELF-DIAGNOSTICS.

PCM DATA PARAMETERS

PCM data parameters displays allow technician to compare the present operating specifications of the malfunctioning vehicle with the specifications of a known good vehicle.

Entering PCM Data Parameters Display – **1)** With ".7.0" displayed on the FDC, (to cause ".7.0" to be displayed on the FDC, see INTRODUCTION TO DIAGNOSTIC TESTING under DIAGNOSTIC TESTING), depress and release the LO button on the ECCP. This will switch display from ".7.0" to "E.9.0", signaling the start of the PCM data parameters display. Data parameter displays are prefixed with the letter "P". **2)** To advance system to a higher numbered data parameters display, depress the HI button on the ECCP. To return to a lower numbered data parameters display, depress the LO button on the ECCP. For complete list of data parameter displays, see PCM DATA PARAMETERS table.

Exiting Data Parameter Series Mode – To exit data parameter series at any time and return to ".7.0", complete the procedures for clearing PCM or BCM trouble codes. See CLEARING CODES under SELF-DIAGNOSTICS.

PCM CODE & INSTANT SNAPSHOT

PCM CODE snapshot permits review of PCM data parameter values which were present at the time a code was set. If more than one code

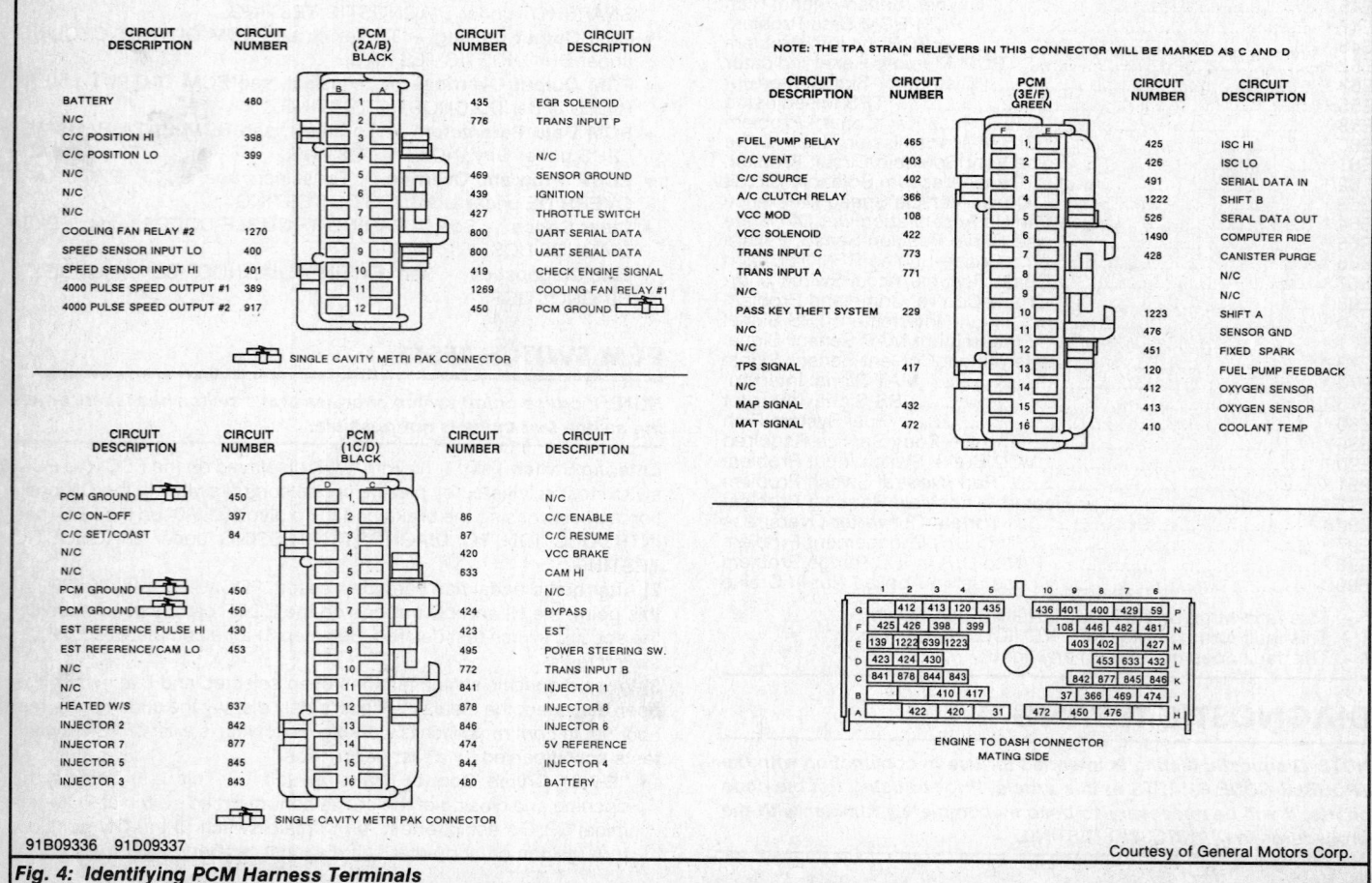

Fig. 4: Identifying PCM Harness Terminals

91B09336   91D09337

1991 ENGINE PERFORMANCE
Self-Diagnostics – DeVille & Fleetwood PCM/BCM (Cont.)

GM
1-135

PCM DATA PARAMETERS

Display	Parameter	Range
P.0.1	TPS Opening	-9° to 90°
P.0.2	MAP	14-108 kPa
P.0.3	BARO	[1] 60-102 kPa
P.0.4	CTS	-40° to 151°C
P.0.5	MAT	40° to 151°C
P.0.6	Spark Advance	0-90 degrees
P.0.7	Battery Voltage	0-25.6 volts
P.0.8	Engine Speed	0-6370 RPM
P.0.9	Vehicle Speed	0-255 MPH
P.1.2	Inj. Pulse Width	0-99.6 mS
P.1.4	O_2 Sensor Voltage	[2] 0-.99 volts
P.1.6	O_2 Cross Counts	[2] 0-255
P.1.8	Integrator	[3] 20-255
P.2.0	Block Learn	[4] 0-255
P.2.1	Cruise Feedback	[5] 0-99
P.2.2	PRNDL Sw. Status	[6] 0-1
P.2.3	PRNDL Sw. Status	[6] 0-1
P.2.4	Ignition Cycles	1-50
P.2.5	PROM ID Code	[7]

[1] – The BARO reading is taken with key on and is corrected at wide open throttle.

[2] – Measured in cross counts which are the number of times the voltage crosses the reference voltage of .45 volts.

[3] – Normal count position for integrator is "128", indicating engine is operating normally. A count greater than 128 indicates time is being added to the injector pulse width, adding more fuel to the engine. A count less than 128 indicates time is being subtracted from the injector pulse width, reducing the amount of fuel to the engine.

[4] – Normal count position is "128" and indicates engine is operating normally. The block learn value is based on integrator learned values. Readings greater than 128 indicate time is being added to the injector pulse width. Readings less than 128 indicate time is being subtracted from the injector pulse width.

[5] – "0" equals full extend and "99" equals full retract.

[6] – "0" indicates that the switch is closed and "1" indicates that the switch is open.

[7] – Display shows a 3 digit code identifying the PROM.

was set, the values associated with the last code will be stored. All displayed data will be prefixed by the letter "L".

The PCM INSTANT snapshot feature permits technician initiated recording of PCM data parameters at a particular instant, as chosen. All displayed information will be prefixed by the letter "S".

Entering PCM Code Snapshot – With ".7.0" displayed on the FDC (to cause ".7.0" to be displayed on the FDC, see INTRODUCTION TO DIAGNOSTIC TESTING under DIAGNOSTIC TESTING), depress and release the LO button on ECCP. This will switch display from ".7.0" to "E.9.0". With "E.9.0" displayed, depress ECON and WARMER buttons on ECCP. Display will now enter PCM code snapshot mode and the displayed codes will be prefixed by the letter "L".

Selecting PCM Code Snapshot – To scroll through available codes, depress HI button on ECCP to advance to higher numbers. Depress LO button on ECCP to return to lower numbers.

Exiting PCM Code Snapshot – To exit PCM Code Snapshot at any time and return to ".7.0", complete the procedures for clearing PCM or BCM trouble codes. See CLEARING CODES under SELF-DIAGNOSTICS.

Entering Instant Snapshot – With ".7.0" displayed on the FDC (to cause ".7.0" to be displayed on the FDC, see INTRODUCTION TO DIAGNOSTIC TESTING under DIAGNOSTIC TESTING in this article), depress and release the LO button on ECCP. This will switch display from ".7.0" to "E.9.0". System is now ready to record an instant snapshot.

Recording & Reviewing An Instant Snapshot – 1) With "E.9.0" displayed, depress ECON and COOLER buttons on ECCP. Display will now enter PCM instant snapshot and display "5.9.0" the moment the snapshot is taken and recorded.

2) Pressing the HI button on ECCP will start a review of the data parameters at the instant the snapshot was requested. This data will be prefixed by the letter "S". This "S" looks similar to the number 5 on the display.

Exiting PCM Instant Snapshot – To exit instant snapshot at any time and return to ".7.0", complete the procedures for clearing PCM or BCM trouble codes. See CLEARING CODES under SELF-DIAGNOSTICS.

PCM OUTPUT CYCLING

Entering PCM Output Cycling – To enter PCM output cycling, complete the following:

- Start engine and allow to idle.
- Move cruise control switch to ON position.
- Turn engine off. Within 2 seconds, turn ignition on.
- Enter diagnostics and display "E.9.5."
- Depress LO button to initiate the output cycling mode. The FDC will alternately display "E.1.2" and "E.9.6" and all of the following devices will be cycled on and off at 3 second intervals:

PCM OUTPUT CYCLING

Display	Parameter
E.0.0	No Outputs Cycled
E.0.1	Canister Purge Solenoid
E.0.2	VCC Solenoid
E.0.3	EGR Solenoid
E.0.6	ISC Motor
E.0.7	Cruise Vent Solenoid
E.0.8	Cruise Vac. Solenoid
E.0.9	Shift Solenoid "A"
E.1.0	Shift Solenoid "B"
E.1.1	A/C Clutch Relay
E.1.2	Cycle All Devices

- Devices can by cycled individually by repeatedly depressing HI to advance to the next displayed parameter number or LO to return to a lower parameter number. "E.0.0" (no outputs cycled) can also be selected in this manner. No outputs are cycled with "E.0.0" displayed.

Exiting PCM Output Cycling – To exit PCM output cycling series at any time and return to ".7.0", complete procedures for clearing PCM or BCM trouble codes. See CLEARING CODES under SELF-DIAGNOSTICS.

PCM OUTPUT OVERRIDES

This mode allows technician to test various PCM controlled components by overriding operating requirements of a selected component. **Entering PCM Output Overrides – 1)** With ".7.0" displayed on the FDC (to cause ".7.0" to be displayed on the FDC, see INTRODUCTION TO DIAGNOSTIC TESTING under DIAGNOSTIC TESTING), depress HI button on ECCP and display will change from ".7.0" to "E.9.5". Simultaneously depress ECON and WARMER button on ECCP and display will advance from "E.9.5" to "E.5.0", signaling the beginning of the output override cycle.

2) To advance display to higher numbered override, depress HI button on ECCP. If test conditions are not appropriate for performing test, ECCP will display "8.8.8." until test conditions are corrected or test is by-passed. To return to a lower numbered output override, depress the LO button on the ECCP.

3) Following is a listing of the available overrides, each with an accompanying explanation:

- **"E.5.0" No Override**.
- **"E.5.1" Viscous Converter Clutch (VCC) Override –** Upon selecting this mode, PCM controls the VCC at normal operating parameters. Technician can initiate an override by pushing the WARMER button on the ECCP to switch on the VCC solenoid or by pushing the COOLER button on ECCP to turn off the VCC solenoid. Override continues only while button is depressed.
- **"E.5.2" EGR Override –** While in this mode, PCM displays the amount of EGR flow on a scale of "00" (no flow) to "99" (full flow). If the WARMER button on ECCP is depressed, the EGR is commanded on until the button is released. If COOLER button on ECCP is depressed, the EGR is commanded off until the button is

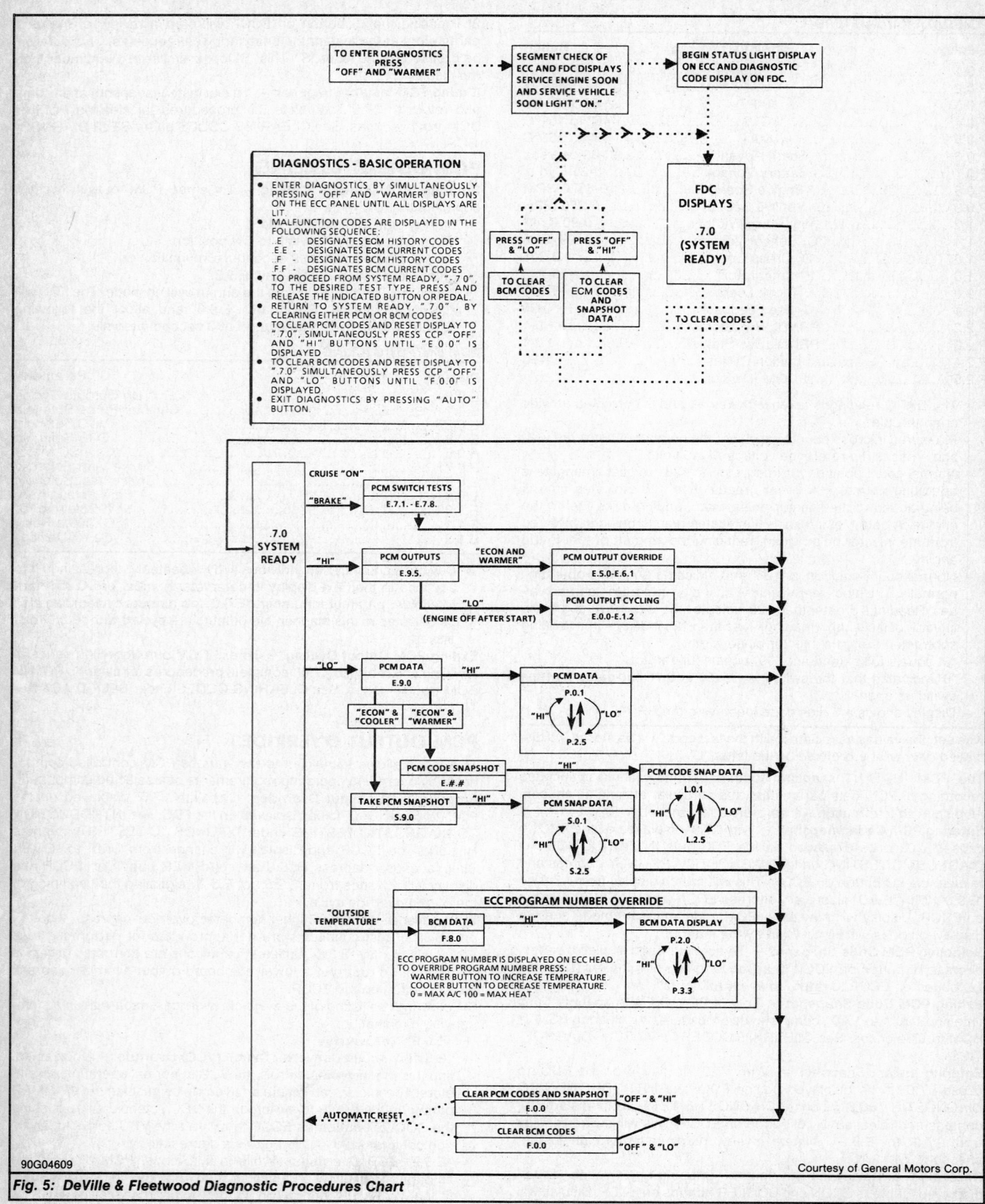

90G04609

Courtesy of General Motors Corp.

Fig. 5: DeVille & Fleetwood Diagnostic Procedures Chart

1991 ENGINE PERFORMANCE
Self-Diagnostics – DeVille & Fleetwood PCM/BCM (Cont.)

GM
1-137

released. The PCM controls the EGR at normal operating parameters when no button is depressed.

NOTE: *The EGR test will have little significance with the engine at idle. This is because a positive backpressure type of EGR valve is used.*

- **"E.5.3" ISC Override** – While in this mode, the Idle Speed Control (ISC) motor can be commanded and held to a fully retracted position through the use of ECCP COOLER and WARMER buttons. Vehicle must be standing still and transmission in Park or Neutral.

Depressing COOLER button on ECCP causes ISC to retract and remain in this position while button is depressed, FDC will display "00". Depressing WARMER button on ECCP causes ISC motor to extend until throttle switch closes. The ECCP will display "99". When throttle switch closes, normal control of the ISC is restored.

NOTE: *During this test the A/C compressor clutch is commanded off, EGR is commanded off and spark advance is fixed.*

- **"E.5.4" Injectors 1-8 Override** – While in this mode, each of the 8 fuel injectors can be individually selected and turned off using the ECCP WARMER and COOLER BUTTONS. Transmission must be in Park or Neutral.

Depressing WARMER button on ECCP selects injector number to be tested. With WARMER button depressed and held down, injector number will increment at a rate of one per second and displayed on FDC. Depressing COOLER button on ECCP turns off the selected injector and "00" is displayed on the FDC. The selected injector will remain off while COOLER button remains depressed.

- **"E.5.5" Fuel Pump Relay Override** – While in this mode, fuel pump relay is commanded off using ECCP COOLER button. Transmission must be in Park or Neutral. Depressing and holding the COOLER button on ECCP causes FDC to display "00", indicating fuel pump relay has been de-energized. Releasing COOLER button causes "99" to be displayed and normal control of fuel pump relay is resumed.

- **"E.5.7" Cruise Servo Feedback Override** – While in this mode, cruise control servo position can be changed using the ECCP WARMER and COOLER buttons.

Depressing the WARMER button on ECCP retracts cruise servo and increases commanded servo position one percent at a time to a maximum of 100 percent. Depressing COOLER button on ECCP will command a decrease in servo position and extend cruise servo one percent at a time to a minimum of zero percent. The FDC will display the current commanded cruise control servo position in percent.

NOTE: *To ensure sufficient vacuum is available to operate the cruise control servo, engine should be run and then turned off immediately prior to using the cruise control override. The cruise override test cannot be performed with engine running.*

- **"E.5.8" Coolant Fans Override** – While in this mode, the COOLER button on ECCP is depressed to invert the state of the low speed fan relay. "00" is displayed on FDC with fans not running. With fans running at low speed and low speed relay energized, FDC displays "10". Depressing WARMER button on ECCP will invert high speed fans operation. With fans running at high speed, "11" will be displayed on the FDC, indicating the high and low speed fan relays are energized.

- **"E.5.9" Fixed Spark Override** – While in this mode, spark advance is controlled manually and displayed on the FDC in degrees. The first time the COOLER button on FDC panel is depressed and released, spark angle is fixed at 10° BTDC. The second and subsequent times COOLER button is depressed, spark timing is retarded 1-2 degrees until 0° TDC is reached.

Each time the WARMER button on ECCP is depressed, spark is advanced 1-2 degrees until the PCM controlled spark advance that

was present when override was initiated is again reached. Spark advance cannot be advanced beyond original setting and attempt to do so will cause FDC to display "888".

- **"E.6.0" Injector Flow Override** – While in this mode, each of the fuel injectors can be individually selected and energized once per engine run cycle. The injector to be tested is selected by depressing and holding the COOLER button on ECCP. The FDC will display injector number which it will increment at a rate of one per second.

Depressing the WARMER button on ECCP energizes the displayed injector for 500 milliseconds. Each injector can be energized only once per engine cycle to avoid possible engine flooding. "888" will be displayed and override disabled if an attempt is made to energize an injector which has already been energized.

- **"E.6.1" Transaxle Override** – While in this mode, transaxle can be downshifted by depressing the COOLER button and upshifted by depressing the WARMER button. On speed greater than 30 MPH, transaxle will not downshift from 2nd to 1st gear at speeds greater than 30 MPH, or from 3rd to 2nd gear at speeds greater than 60 MPH.

Exiting PCM Output Overrides – To exit PCM output overrides series at any time and return to ".7.0", complete procedures for clearing PCM or BCM trouble codes. See CLEARING CODES under SELF-DIAGNOSTICS.

BCM DATA PARAMETERS

BCM data parameters displays allow technician to compare the present operating specifications of malfunctioning vehicle with specifications of a known good vehicle.

Entering BCM Data Display - 1) With ".7.0" displayed on FDC (to cause ".7.0" to be displayed on the FDC, see INTRODUCTION TO DIAGNOSTIC TESTING under DIAGNOSTIC TESTING), depress and release OUTSIDE TEMP button on ECCP. BCM data series begins as display switches from ".7.0" to "F.8.0".

2) To advance display, depress HI button on ECCP. To return to a lower numbered display or jump directly from "F.8.0" to the end of display list, "P.3.1", depress LO button on ECCP.

3) When trouble shooting a malfunction, BCM data display can be used to compare the vehicle with problems to a vehicle that is functioning properly. See BCM DATA PARAMETERS table for list of BCM data parameters.

4) When BCM data display is first initiated, FDC will display a parameter check (P.2.0 or P.3.1) for one second and then a number will be displayed for 9 seconds to indicate parameter value. The display will continue to repeat this sequence of events until another parameter is selected.

BCM DATA PARAMETERS

Display	Parameter
P.2.0	Blower Voltage
P.2.1	Coolant Temperature
P.2.2	Air Mix Door Position Angle
P.2.3	Actual Air Mix Door Position
P.2.4	[1] Air Delivery Mode
P.2.5	In-Vehicle Temperature
P.2.6	Actual Outside Temperature
P.2.7	Condenser Output
P.2.8	Evaporator Input
P.2.9	Fuel Level
P.3.0	Ignition Cycles
P.3.1	Oil Life Monitor Reset (Miles)
P.3.2	Sunload Sensor Value
P.3.3	BCM PROM I.D.

[1] – Each number is a code which represents the following air delivery modes:

0 – Max A/C	5 – Off
1 – A/C	6 – Normal Purge
2 – Bi-Level	7 – Cold Purge
3 – Heater/Defrost	8 – Front Defogger
4 – Heater	

Exiting BCM Data Display - To exit BCM Data Display series at any time and return to ".7.0", complete procedures for clearing PCM or

GM
1-138

1991 ENGINE PERFORMANCE
Self-Diagnostics – DeVille & Fleetwood PCM/BCM (Cont.)

BCM trouble codes. See CLEARING CODES under SELF-DIAGNOS-TICS.

ECCP PROGRAM OVERRIDE

ECCP Program Override – 1) During display of BCM data on FDC panel (See BCM DATA DISPLAY under SELF-DIAGNOSTICS in this article), ECCP will display a 2-digit number that represents various levels of heating and cooling effort. As "F.8.0" first appears on the FDC, ECCP will begin displaying the program number currently being used by the climate control system. As operating conditions change, number will automatically change in response.

2) Automatic calculation of program number can be by-passed using the manual override feature, initiated by depressing WARMER and COOLER buttons on ECCP. This manual override system allows service technician to control program number between "0" (maximum A/C) and "100" (maximum heat), and simultaneously observe reaction of any BCM data parameter.

Exiting ECCP Program Override – To exit ECCP Program Override series at any time and return to ".7.0", complete the procedures for clearing PCM or BCM trouble codes. See CLEARING CODES under SELF-DIAGNOSTICS.

PFI SYSTEM CHECK

The PFI SYSTEM CHECK should be the starting point for all diagnosis. It is an organized approach for identifying a problem caused by PFI system. Driver comments normally fall into one of the following: steady Engine Control System Fault telltale, driveability problems, engine will not start or engine stalls after start.

NOTE: Test numbers refer to test numbers on diagnostic chart.

1) The SERVICE ENGINE SOON light will remain illuminated after the bulb check or after engine has started if there are one or more current codes present. The SERVICE ENGINE SOON light will turn off after 2 seconds if no current code(s) is present.
2) PFI Chart A-2 diagnoses a faulty SERVICE ENGINE SOON light control circuit, the PCM or system that turns on the light but cannot communicate diagnostic codes.

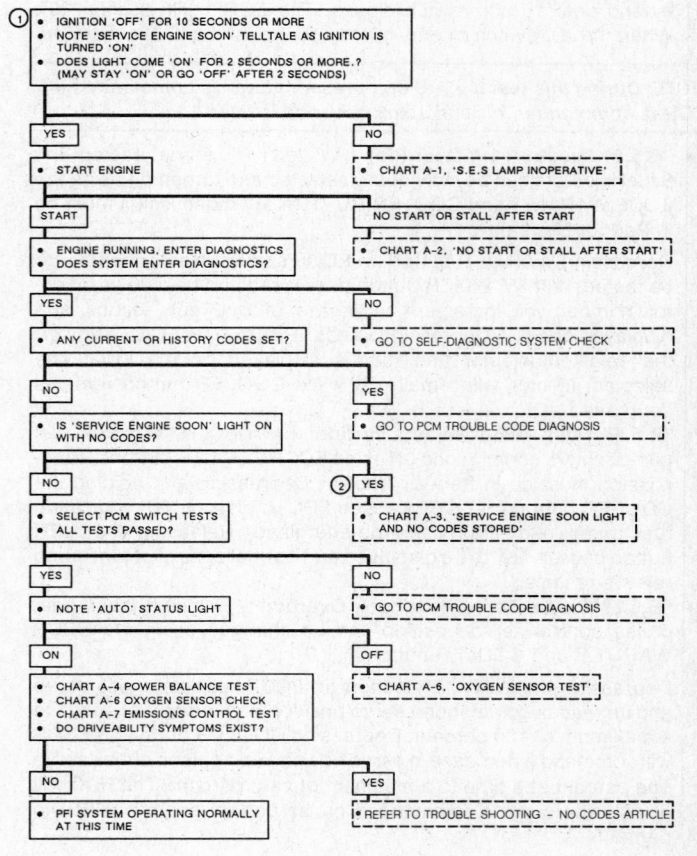

Courtesy of General Motors Corp.

1991 ENGINE PERFORMANCE
Self-Diagnostics – DeVille & Fleetwood PCM/BCM (Cont.)

GM
1-139

PFI CHART A-1,
SERVICE ENGINE SOON LIGHT INOPERATIVE

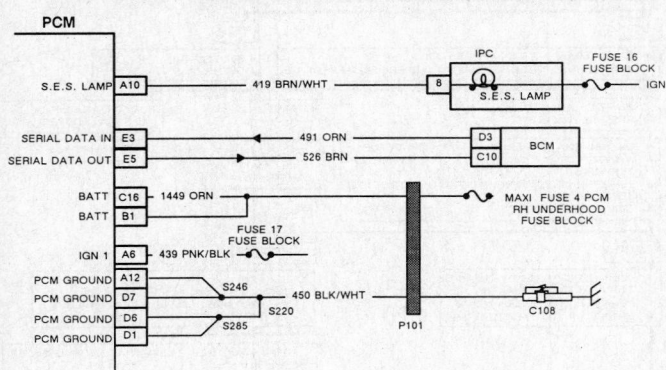

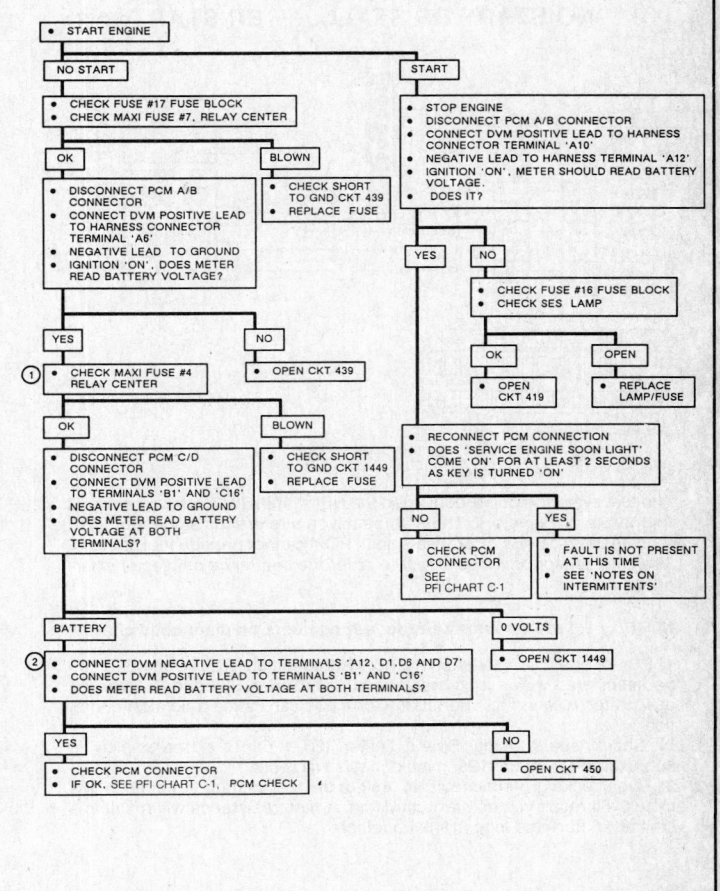

The SERVICE ENGINE SOON light is controlled by the PCM and will turn on for 2 seconds when ignition switch is turned to RUN position. When engine is cranked, SERVICE ENGINE SOON light will be off. After ignition is returned to the RUN position, light will turn on for another 2 seconds and turn off if there are no current code(s) that would cause light to stay on.

NOTE: Test numbers refer to test numbers on diagnostic chart.

1) Maxi fuses are located in underhood fuse/relay block.

2) Circuits D6, D7 and A12 are PCM grounds. Circuits B1 and C16 are battery positive to the PCM. The PCM will function with only one power and ground connection, but all should be tested.

Note On Intermittents – Temporarily disconnect MAT sensor to turn on SERVICE ENGINE SOON light. Turn ignition on and manipulate circuit No. 419 while observing SERVICE ENGINE SOON light. If light flashes on and off, repair intermittent open in circuit No. 419. Reconnect MAT sensor connector and clear codes.

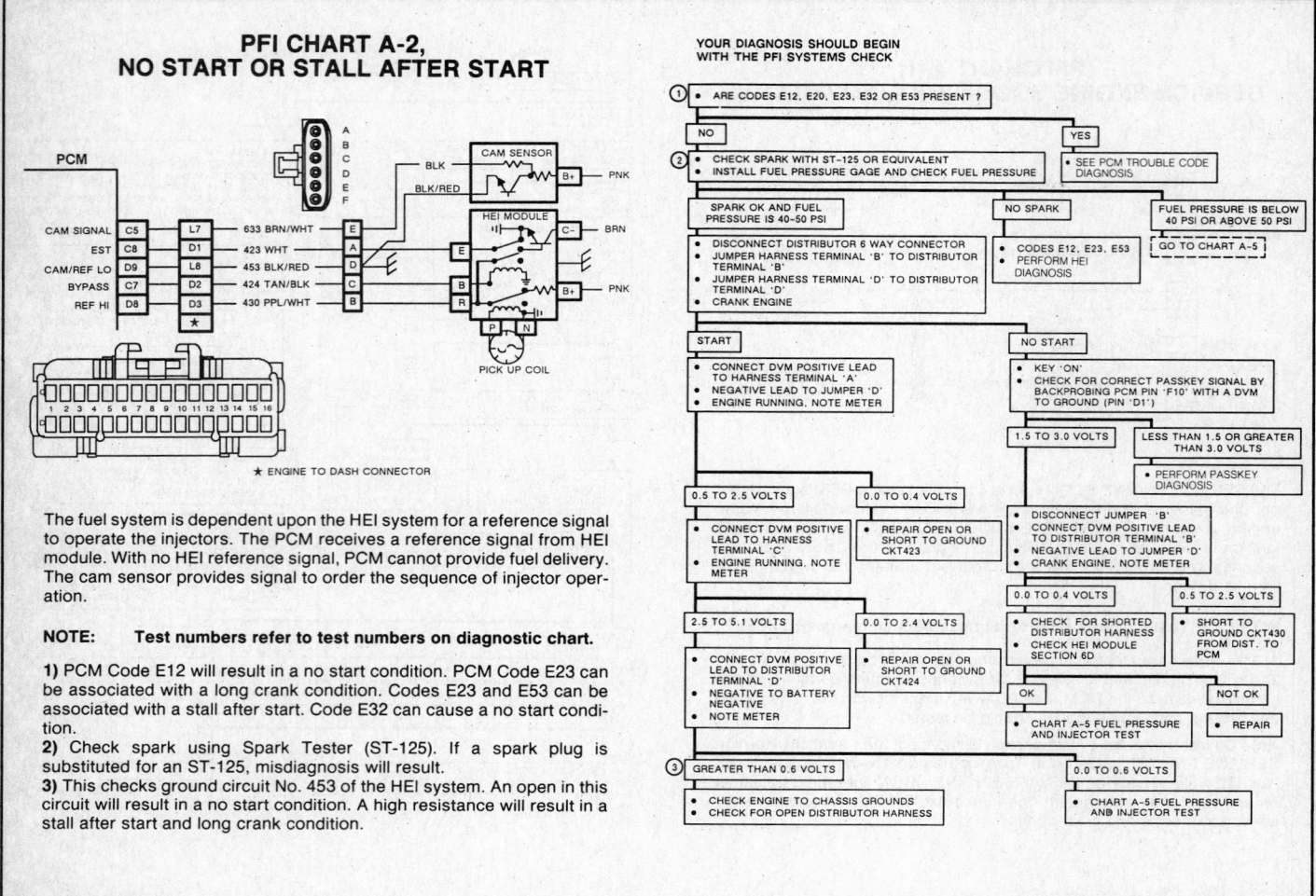

**PFI CHART A-2,
NO START OR STALL AFTER START**

The fuel system is dependent upon the HEI system for a reference signal to operate the injectors. The PCM receives a reference signal from HEI module. With no HEI reference signal, PCM cannot provide fuel delivery. The cam sensor provides signal to order the sequence of injector operation.

NOTE: Test numbers refer to test numbers on diagnostic chart.

1) PCM Code E12 will result in a no start condition. PCM Code E23 can be associated with a long crank condition. Codes E23 and E53 can be associated with a stall after start. Code E32 can cause a no start condition.
2) Check spark using Spark Tester (ST-125). If a spark plug is substituted for an ST-125, misdiagnosis will result.
3) This checks ground circuit No. 453 of the HEI system. An open in this circuit will result in a no start condition. A high resistance will result in a stall after start and long crank condition.

91C07663   91E07664

Courtesy of General Motors Corp.

1991 ENGINE PERFORMANCE
Self-Diagnostics – DeVille & Fleetwood PCM/BCM (Cont.)

GM
1-141

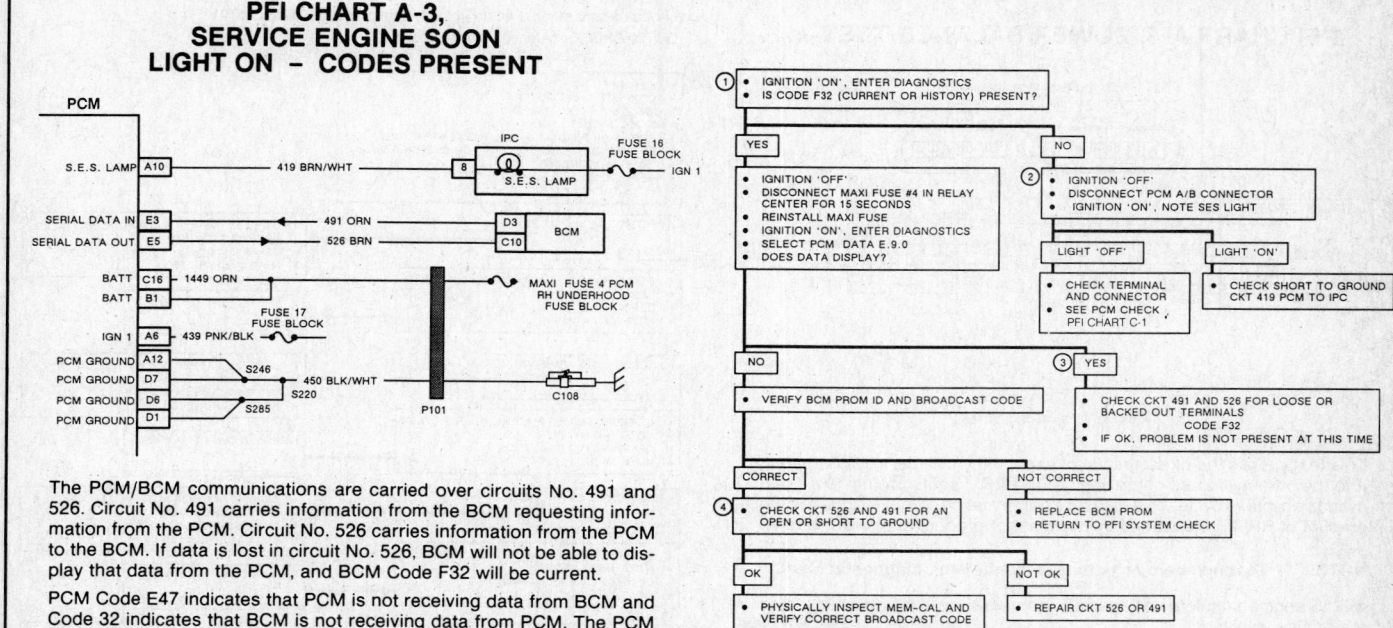

**PFI CHART A-3,
SERVICE ENGINE SOON
LIGHT ON – CODES PRESENT**

The PCM/BCM communications are carried over circuits No. 491 and 526. Circuit No. 491 carries information from the BCM requesting information from the PCM. Circuit No. 526 carries information from the PCM to the BCM. If data is lost in circuit No. 526, BCM will not be able to display that data from the PCM, and BCM Code F32 will be current.

PCM Code E47 indicates that PCM is not receiving data from BCM and Code 32 indicates that BCM is not receiving data from PCM. The PCM MEM-CAL encodes data from the BCM. A failure or misapplication of MEM-CAL will set Code E47. A failure or misapplication of the BCM PROM will set BCM Code F32. Check MEM-CAL and PROM for proper application by checking broadcast code on both components.

NOTE: Test numbers refer to test numbers on diagnostic chart.

1) Interruption of power or ground to either the PCM or BCM can also cause the codes to set.
2) Removal of Maxi fuse No. 4, interrupts power to the PCM and BCM and should cause both components to reset.
3) BCM Code F32 is intermittent at this point.
4) If instantaneous fuel economy varies while driving, circuit No. 526 (PCM to BCM data) is okay. Check circuit No. 491 for an open or short to ground.

91I07661   91J07666

Courtesy of General Motors Corp.

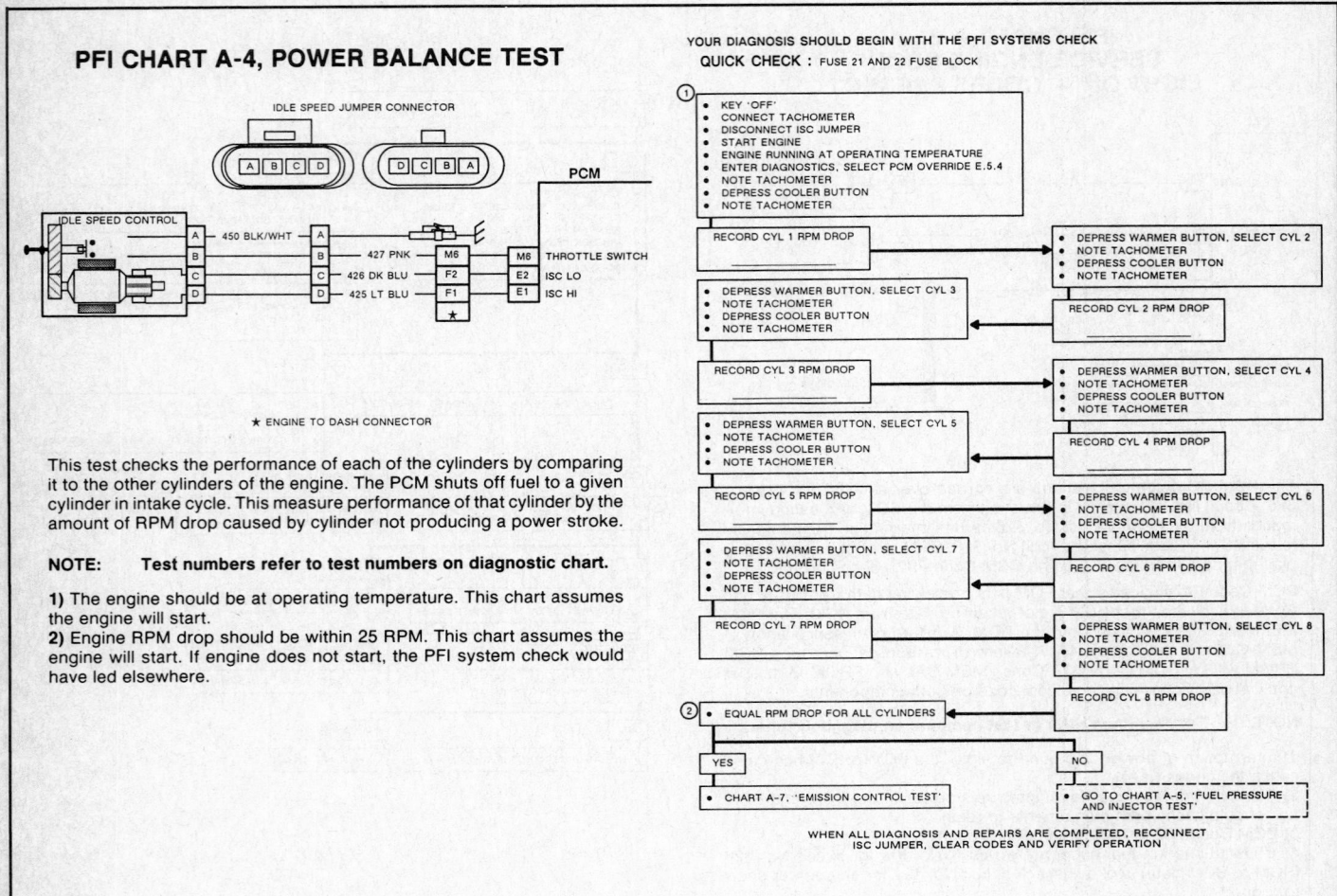

PFI CHART A-4, POWER BALANCE TEST

★ ENGINE TO DASH CONNECTOR

This test checks the performance of each of the cylinders by comparing it to the other cylinders of the engine. The PCM shuts off fuel to a given cylinder in intake cycle. This measure performance of that cylinder by the amount of RPM drop caused by cylinder not producing a power stroke.

NOTE: **Test numbers refer to test numbers on diagnostic chart.**

1) The engine should be at operating temperature. This chart assumes the engine will start.
2) Engine RPM drop should be within 25 RPM. This chart assumes the engine will start. If engine does not start, the PFI system check would have led elsewhere.

YOUR DIAGNOSIS SHOULD BEGIN WITH THE PFI SYSTEMS CHECK
QUICK CHECK : FUSE 21 AND 22 FUSE BLOCK

WHEN ALL DIAGNOSIS AND REPAIRS ARE COMPLETED, RECONNECT ISC JUMPER, CLEAR CODES AND VERIFY OPERATION

91B07667   91D07668

Courtesy of General Motors Corp.

1991 ENGINE PERFORMANCE
Self-Diagnostics – DeVille & Fleetwood PCM/BCM (Cont.)

GM
1-143

PFI CHART A-5,
FUEL PRESSURE & INJECTOR FLOW (1 OF 3)

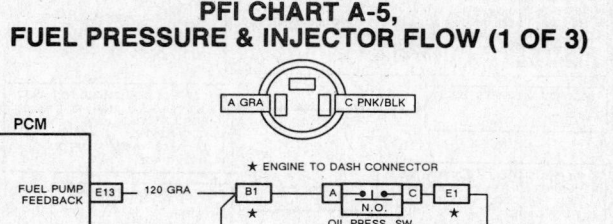

A GRA   C PNK/BLK

★ ENGINE TO DASH CONNECTOR

PCM

FUEL PUMP FEEDBACK   E13 — 120 GRA — B1 ... A ●|●|● C E1 ★
                              N.O.
                              OIL PRESS. SW.
                              FUEL PUMP PRIME
                              490 RED

TO FUEL PUMP — 120 GRA
              — 120 GRA   139 PNK/BLK   FUSE 6
FUEL PUMP RELAY   F1 — 465 DK GRN/WHT   450 BLK/WHT   RELAY CENTER

RELAY CENTER
LOCATION H

Tests for fuel pump's ability to deliver fuel to the injector fuel rail, the fuel injectors ability to deliver metered quantity of fuel, and for the presence of vacuum signal to the regulator to control fuel pressure.

NOTE: Test numbers refer to test numbers on diagnostic chart.

1) This test determines if a weak cylinder (no RPM drop) in the power balance test is caused by fuel flow or spark. Use a remote starter in this test to actuate fuel pump through the fuel pump prime connector.
2) This test determines whether the excessively high fuel pressure is caused by the pressure regulator or a restricted fuel line.
3) This test determines whether fuel pump or pressure regulator is the cause of the low fuel pressure. Pressurize fuel system by turning ignition on, engine off. If fuel pump can produce 50 psi (3.5 kg/cm²) pressure, and the pressure holds, this verifies the fuel pump and internal check valves are working. If fuel pump cannot produce at least 40 psi (2.8 kg/cm²) pressure, the cause can be a faulty fuel pump, faulty pulsator damper, a restricted line or filter, or a leaking injector.
4) A leaky injector is indicated by a rich exhaust (smoke or rotten egg smell) with low fuel pressure indicated in the above test. A leaking injector is indicated by a cylinder which does not produce an RPM drop during the power balance test. Replace affected injector. If injectors are okay, check fuel pump and pulsator damper.

91F07669   91H07670

QUICK CHECK : FUSE 2 RELAY CENTER

① • INSTALL FUEL PRESSURE GAGE AT TEST PORT ON FUEL RAIL
  • IGNITION 'ON', ENGINE 'OFF', NOTE GAGE

| BELOW 40 PSI AND/OR DOES NOT HOLD PRESSURE | ABOVE 50 PSI | BETWEEN 40 AND 50 PSI |

③ • INSTALL J 37287-2 IN-LINE WITH RETURN LINE
  • CLOSE SHUT OFF VALVE
  • CHECK PRESSURE WITH IGNITION 'ON', ENGINE 'OFF'

② • INSTALL FEMALE END OF J 37287-2 IN PRESSURE REGULATOR SIDE OF RETURN LINE
  • PLACE OTHER END OF TOOL IN SUITABLE CONTAINER FOR FLAMMABLE LIQUIDS
  • CHECK PRESSURE WITH IGNITION 'ON'

GO TO CHART A-5, (2 OF 3)

| ABOVE 50 PSI | BELOW 45 PSI |
| REPLACE FUEL PRESSURE REGULATOR | REPAIR RESTRICTION IN RETURN LINE |

| LESS THAN 40 PSI | GREATER THAN 50 PSI |

• DISCONNECT CONNECTOR TO FUEL SENDING UNIT
• CONNECT TEST LIGHT BETWEEN HARNESS CONNECTORS 'B' AND 'G'
• DOES TEST LIGHT COME ON FOR 2 SECONDS WHEN IGNITION IS TURNED 'ON'?

• REPLACE FUEL PRESSURE REGULATOR

| YES | NO |

• CHECK FUEL FILTER AND LINES FOR RESTRICTION

• GO TO   CODE 20, REGARDLESS OF WHETHER OR NOT CODE IS SET

| OK | RESTRICTION |

• DOES CAR START

• REPAIR RESTRICTION OR BLOCKAGE

| YES | NO |

④ • DOES EXHAUST INDICATE RICH CONDITIONS?

• CHECK CIRCUITS FROM FUEL PUMP TO SENDING UNIT CONNECTOR
• IF OK, REPLACE FUEL PUMP AND RETEST
• IF STILL LESS THAN 40 PSI, REPLACE PULSATOR DAMPER

| NO | YES |

• DOES CHART A-4 INDICATE CYLINDERS WITHOUT AN RPM DROP IN DURING POWER BALANCE TEST?

• REPLACE LEAKING INJECTOR(S) AS INDICATED BY THOSE CYLINDERS THAT DO NOT PRODUCE AN RPM DROP IN CHART A-4

| NO | YES |

• CHECK CIRCUITS FROM FUEL PUMP TO SENDING UNIT CONNECTOR
• IF OK, REPLACE FUEL PUMP AND RETEST
• IF STILL LESS THAN 40 PSI, REPLACE PULSATOR DAMPER

• REPLACE LEAKING INJECTOR(S) AS INDICATED BY THOSE CYLINDERS THAT DO NOT PRODUCE AN RPM DROP IN CHART A-4

Courtesy of General Motors Corp.

GM
1-144

1991 ENGINE PERFORMANCE
Self-Diagnostics – DeVille & Fleetwood PCM/BCM (Cont.)

PFI CHART A-5,
FUEL PRESSURE & INJECTOR FLOW (2 OF 3)

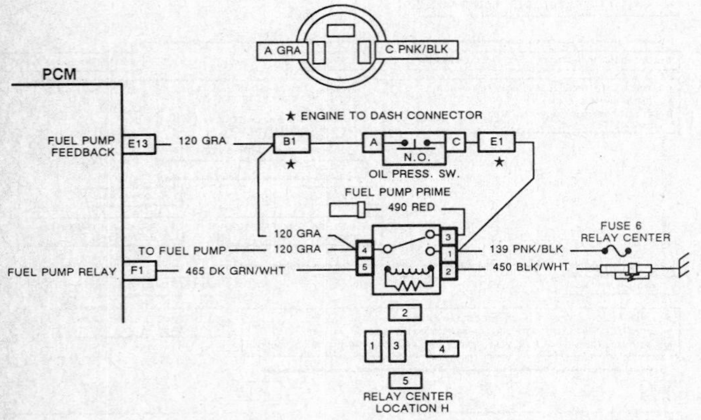

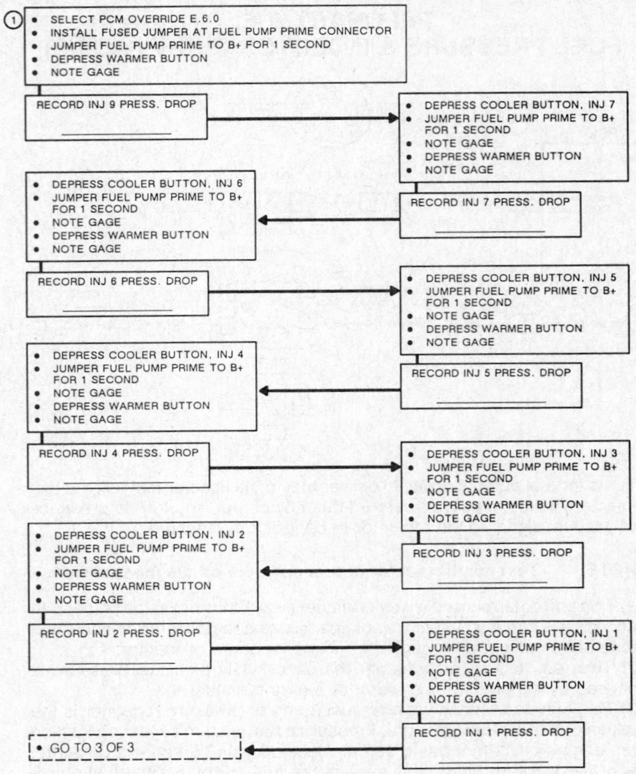

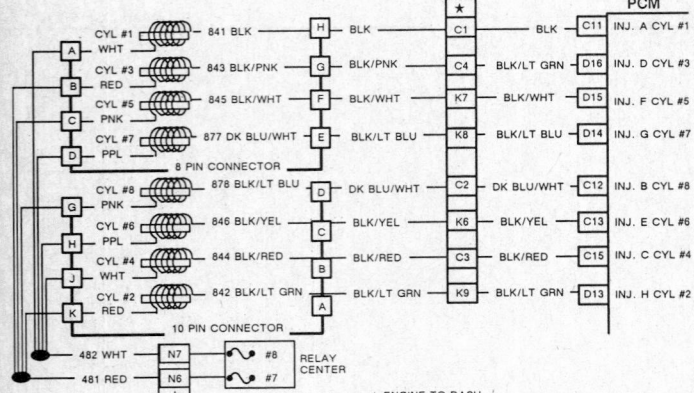

NOTE: Test numbers refer to test numbers on diagnostic chart.

1) Fuel pressure is okay at this point. This test determines if a weak cylinder (no RPM drop) in the power balance test is caused by fuel flow or spark. A remote starter switch can be used to actuate fuel pump through the fuel pump prime connector.

- SELECT PCM OVERRIDE E.6.0
- INSTALL FUSED JUMPER AT FUEL PUMP PRIME CONNECTOR
- JUMPER FUEL PUMP PRIME TO B+ FOR 1 SECOND
- DEPRESS WARMER BUTTON
- NOTE GAGE

RECORD INJ 9 PRESS. DROP

- DEPRESS COOLER BUTTON, INJ 7
- JUMPER FUEL PUMP PRIME TO B+ FOR 1 SECOND
- NOTE GAGE
- DEPRESS WARMER BUTTON
- NOTE GAGE

RECORD INJ 7 PRESS. DROP

- DEPRESS COOLER BUTTON, INJ 6
- JUMPER FUEL PUMP PRIME TO B+ FOR 1 SECOND
- NOTE GAGE
- DEPRESS WARMER BUTTON
- NOTE GAGE

RECORD INJ 6 PRESS. DROP

- DEPRESS COOLER BUTTON, INJ 5
- JUMPER FUEL PUMP PRIME TO B+ FOR 1 SECOND
- NOTE GAGE
- DEPRESS WARMER BUTTON
- NOTE GAGE

RECORD INJ 5 PRESS. DROP

- DEPRESS COOLER BUTTON, INJ 4
- JUMPER FUEL PUMP PRIME TO B+ FOR 1 SECOND
- NOTE GAGE
- DEPRESS WARMER BUTTON
- NOTE GAGE

RECORD INJ 4 PRESS. DROP

- DEPRESS COOLER BUTTON, INJ 3
- JUMPER FUEL PUMP PRIME TO B+ FOR 1 SECOND
- NOTE GAGE
- DEPRESS WARMER BUTTON
- NOTE GAGE

RECORD INJ 3 PRESS. DROP

- DEPRESS COOLER BUTTON, INJ 2
- JUMPER FUEL PUMP PRIME TO B+ FOR 1 SECOND
- NOTE GAGE
- DEPRESS WARMER BUTTON
- NOTE GAGE

RECORD INJ 2 PRESS. DROP

- DEPRESS COOLER BUTTON, INJ 1
- JUMPER FUEL PUMP PRIME TO B+ FOR 1 SECOND
- NOTE GAGE
- DEPRESS WARMER BUTTON
- NOTE GAGE

RECORD INJ 1 PRESS. DROP

- GO TO 3 OF 3

91F07669   91J07671

Courtesy of General Motors Corp.

PFI CHART A-5,
FUEL PRESSURE & INJECTOR FLOW (3 OF 3)

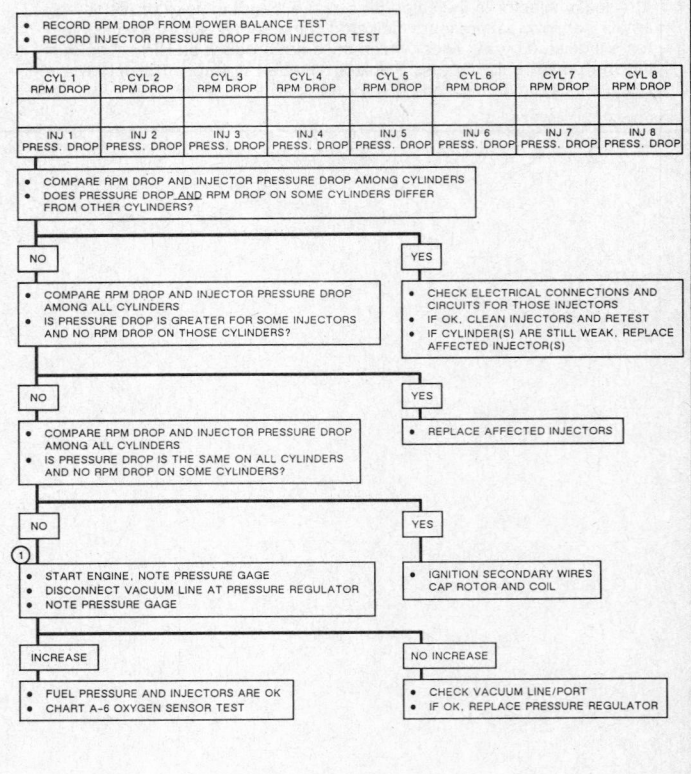

This chart analyzes the comparisons between power balance test and injector flow test, to determine condition of fuel injectors. If fuel injectors are in good condition, ignition secondary may be the cause of problem.

NOTE: Test numbers refer to test numbers on diagnostic chart.

1) Fuel pressure should be 32-38 psi (2.3-2.7 kg/cm²), depending on engine load and altitude. By disconnecting vacuum hose from pressure regulator, fuel pressure should rise to approximately 45 psi (3.2 kg/cm²). If pressure is greater than 50 psi, replace regulator. If pressure is less than 40 psi (2.8 kg/cm²), check fuel pump operation and electrical circuits.

- RECORD RPM DROP FROM POWER BALANCE TEST
- RECORD INJECTOR PRESSURE DROP FROM INJECTOR TEST

CYL 1 RPM DROP	CYL 2 RPM DROP	CYL 3 RPM DROP	CYL 4 RPM DROP	CYL 5 RPM DROP	CYL 6 RPM DROP	CYL 7 RPM DROP	CYL 8 RPM DROP
INJ 1 PRESS. DROP	INJ 2 PRESS. DROP	INJ 3 PRESS. DROP	INJ 4 PRESS. DROP	INJ 5 PRESS. DROP	INJ 6 PRESS. DROP	INJ 7 PRESS. DROP	INJ 8 PRESS. DROP

- COMPARE RPM DROP AND INJECTOR PRESSURE DROP AMONG CYLINDERS
- DOES PRESSURE DROP AND RPM DROP ON SOME CYLINDERS DIFFER FROM OTHER CYLINDERS?

NO / **YES**

YES:
- CHECK ELECTRICAL CONNECTIONS AND CIRCUITS FOR THOSE INJECTORS
- IF OK, CLEAN INJECTORS AND RETEST
- IF CYLINDER(S) ARE STILL WEAK, REPLACE AFFECTED INJECTOR(S)

- COMPARE RPM DROP AND INJECTOR PRESSURE DROP AMONG ALL CYLINDERS
- IS PRESSURE DROP IS GREATER FOR SOME INJECTORS AND NO RPM DROP ON THOSE CYLINDERS?

NO / **YES**

YES:
- REPLACE AFFECTED INJECTORS

- COMPARE RPM DROP AND INJECTOR PRESSURE DROP AMONG ALL CYLINDERS
- IS PRESSURE DROP IS THE SAME ON ALL CYLINDERS AND NO RPM DROP ON SOME CYLINDERS?

NO / **YES**

YES:
- IGNITION SECONDARY WIRES CAP ROTOR AND COIL

- START ENGINE, NOTE PRESSURE GAGE
- DISCONNECT VACUUM LINE AT PRESSURE REGULATOR
- NOTE PRESSURE GAGE

INCREASE / **NO INCREASE**

INCREASE:
- FUEL PRESSURE AND INJECTORS ARE OK
- CHART A-6 OXYGEN SENSOR TEST

NO INCREASE:
- CHECK VACUUM LINE/PORT
- IF OK, REPLACE PRESSURE REGULATOR

91B07672   91D07673

Courtesy of General Motors Corp.

1991 ENGINE PERFORMANCE
Self-Diagnostics – DeVille & Fleetwood PCM/BCM (Cont.)

GM
1-145

PFI CHART A-6, OXYGEN SENSOR TEST

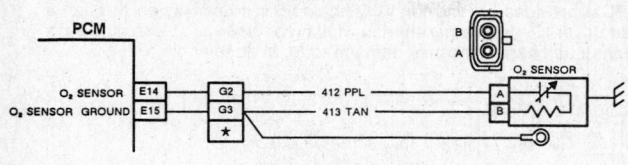

★ ENGINE TO DASH CONNECTOR

PCM provides a .45-volt reference to oxygen sensor on circuit No. 412. When warm, a properly operating oxygen sensor will drive .45-volt reference lower (below .45 volt) to indicate lean mixture and higher (more than .45 volt) to indicate rich mixture.

Oxygen sensor must be able to generate a counter voltage which is .15 volts greater or less than the .45-volt reference in order for the PCM to register a cross count of rich to lean or lean to rich. The oxygen sensor must generate cross counts to cause the system to go to closed loop operation.

The oxygen sensor test checks that the PCM is receiving sufficient voltage signals to generate cross counts.

NOTE: Test numbers refer to test numbers on diagnostic chart.

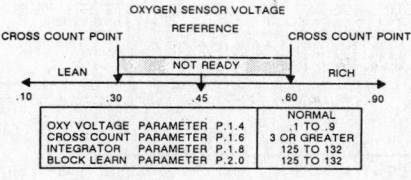

1) Contamination of the oxygen sensor can slow the reaction time of the sensor. PCM Codes E13, E44 and E54 are designed to detect a sensor fault. The slow reaction time of the sensor may cause a driveability problem.

2) Oxygen sensor must be able to generate sufficient voltage and cross counts to cause the system to go into closed loop operation. PCM data P.1.4 will display oxygen sensor voltage. With engine at normal operating temperature, oxygen sensor voltage should be constantly changing. If sensor voltage is fixed at zero volt, this would indicate a short in circuit No. 412. If sensor voltage is fixed between .42 and .48 volt, this would indicate an open in circuit No. 412 or No. 413.

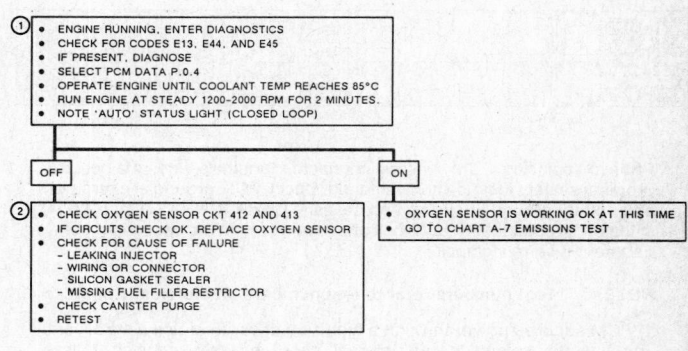

91F07674   91I07680   91I07675

Courtesy of General Motors Corp.

PFI CHART A-7,
EMISSIONS PERFORMANCE TEST

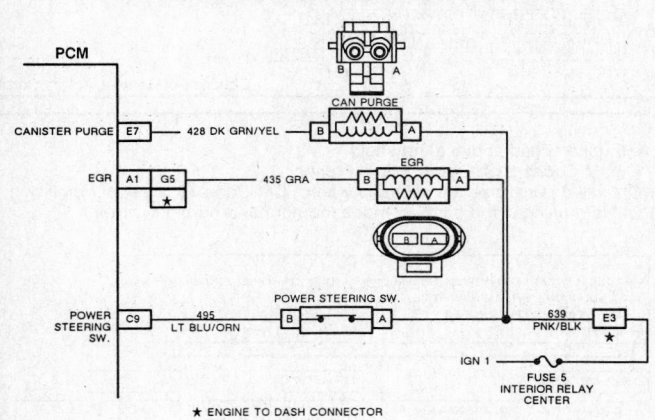

★ ENGINE TO DASH CONNECTOR

This test checks operation of canister purge valve, AIR valve mode and switches, EGR valve and control solenoid. This test provides a quick analysis of components operation. For complete diagnosis of each of the components and its systems, refer to PFI CHART C-3, CANISTER PURGE DIAGNOSIS and PFI CHART C-7, EGR SYSTEM DIAGNOSIS.

NOTE: Test numbers refer to test numbers on diagnostic chart.

1) If driveability problems such as hesitation, surge, lack of power and other conditions are present, refer to TROUBLE SHOOTING – NO CODES article.

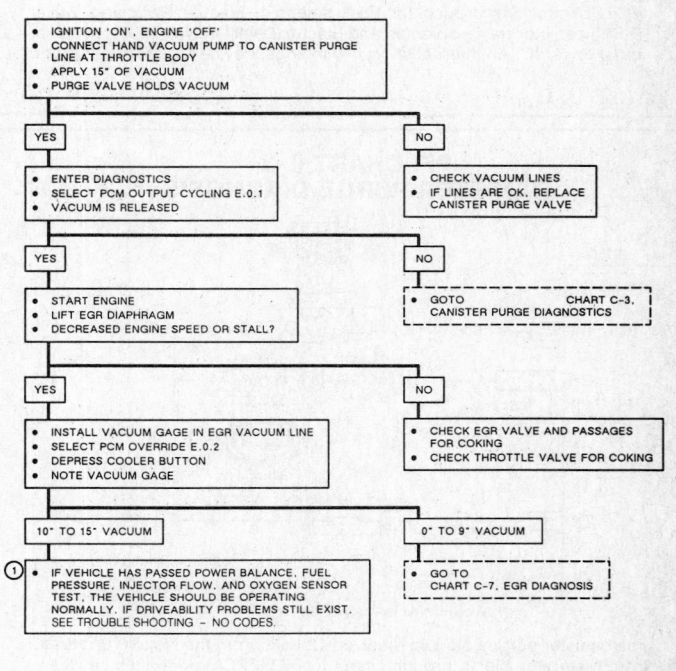

91A07676   91C07677

Courtesy of General Motors Corp.

GM
1-146

1991 ENGINE PERFORMANCE
Self-Diagnostics – DeVille & Fleetwood PCM/BCM (Cont.)

PFI CHART C-1
PCM REPLACEMENT CHECK

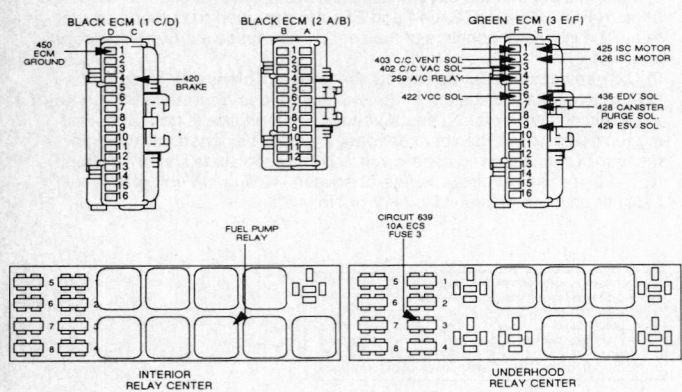

BLACK ECM (1 C/D)   BLACK ECM (2 A/B)   GREEN ECM (3 E/F)

450 ECM GROUND
420 BRAKE

403 C/C VENT SOL
402 C/C VAC SOL
259 A/C RELAY
422 VCC SOL

425 ISC MOTOR
426 ISC MOTOR
436 EDV SOL
428 CANISTER PURGE SOL
429 ESV SOL

FUEL PUMP RELAY

CIRCUIT 639
10A ECS
FUSE 3

INTERIOR RELAY CENTER   UNDERHOOD RELAY CENTER

Prior to replacing PCM, ensure connector terminals and retainer are properly seated, locked and positioned. Check PCM ground at alternator and battery ground at engine and chassis. Check IGN 1-ISO fuse No. 4 in the underhood fuse/relay block and fuse No. 17 in the passenger compartment fuse/relay block.

NOTE: Test numbers refer to test numbers on diagnostic chart.

1) PCM supplies power through a high side driver to cruise control vent and vacuum solenoids. An internal short in servo causing a low resistance or short in wiring harness may damage PCM or cause servo or solenoids to fail.
2) PCM supplies power to fuel pump relay through high side driver. An initial short in relay winding causing a low resistance or short in wiring harness may cause damage to PCM or relay to fail.
3) PCM supplies power to ISC through an internal switching IC that will change polarity of circuit. An internal short in ISC motor armature windings or short in wiring harness may cause damage to PCM or ISC motor to fail.
4) PCM provides ground for EGR solenoid, Electric Switching Valve (ESV), canister purge solenoid and Electric Divert Valve (EDV) through a quad driver IC. An internal short in windings, device resistor or short in

wiring harness may cause damage to PCM or Emission Control System (ECS) device.
5) PCM provides ground for VCC solenoid in transmission through a quad driver IC. An internal short in winding or diode of solenoid or short in wiring harness may cause damage to PCM or solenoid to fail.

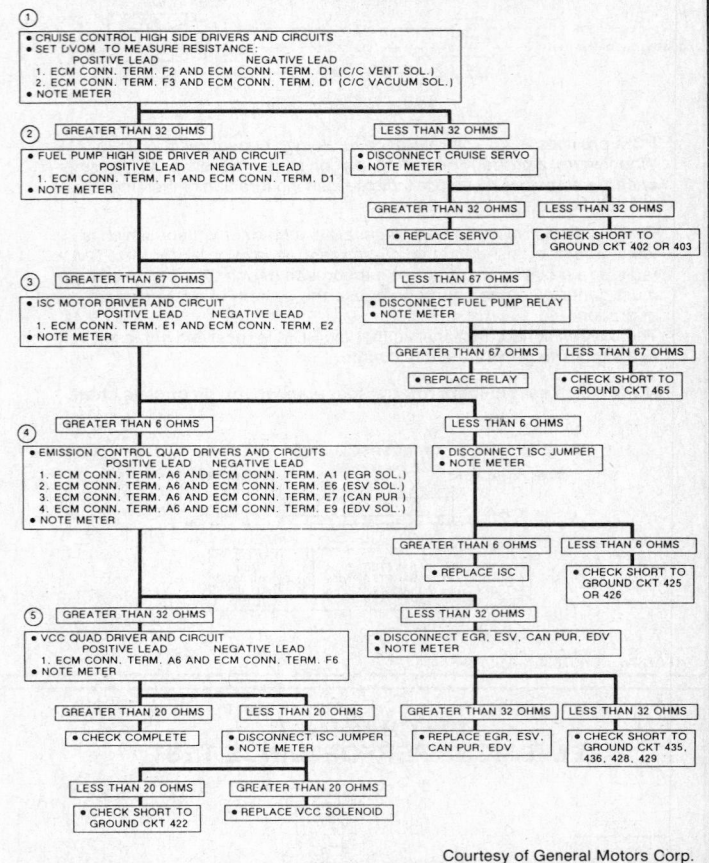

90A16162   90D13907

Courtesy of General Motors Corp.

PFI CHART C-3
CANISTER PURGE DIAGNOSIS

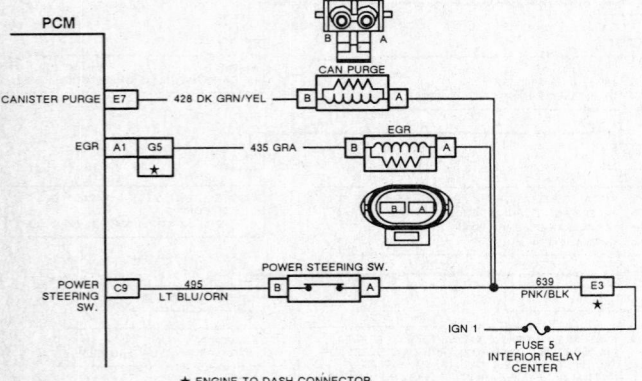

The canister purge solenoid receives 12 volts from the No. 5 (10A) fuse from fuse/relay block through circuit No. 639. PCM energizes canister purge solenoid by grounding pin E7 (circuit No. 428). When solenoid is energized, it allows the canister to purge.

Canister is commanded to purge when:
• Coolant temperature is greater than 176°F (80°C)
• System in closed loop for at least 30 seconds
• Throttle switch is open
• Vehicle speed greater than 10 MPH

• Engine speed above a threshold
• PCM Codes E13, E44 or E45 is present
PCM will de-energize the solenoid when PCM Code 16 is set or when PCM is running in the back-up mode (no normal program control).

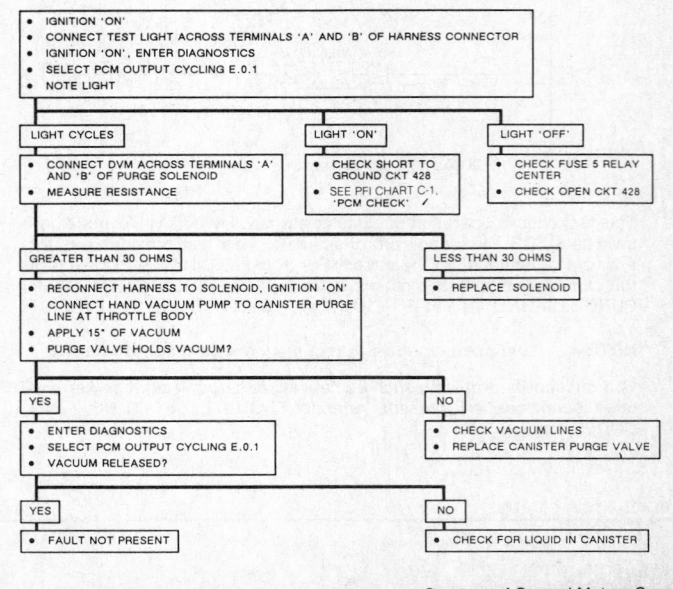

91A07676   91E07678

Courtesy of General Motors Corp.

1991 ENGINE PERFORMANCE
Self-Diagnostics – DeVille & Fleetwood PCM/BCM (Cont.)

GM
1-147

PFI CHART C-7
EGR SYSTEM DIAGNOSIS

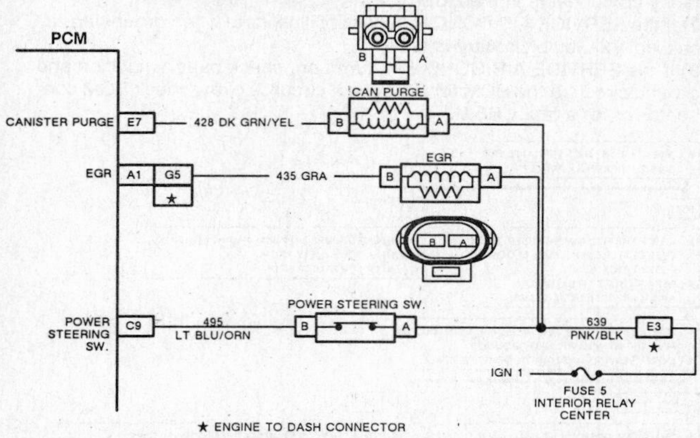

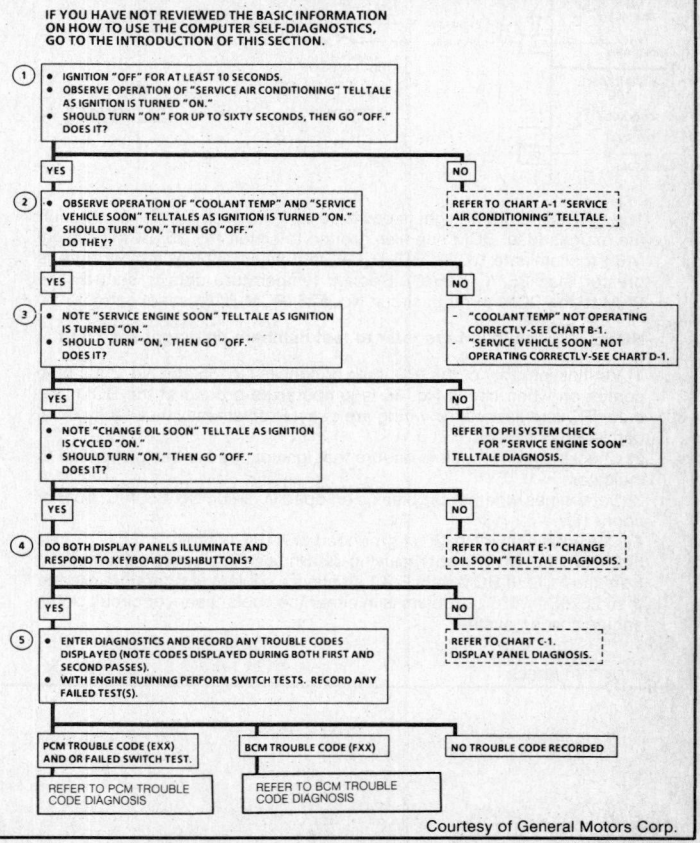

Before starting diagnosis, check fuse No. 5 (10A) in underhood fuse/relay block. Measure EGR resistance (20-100 ohms).

EGR is a positive backpressure valve which limits EGR flow with low exhaust backpressure (i.e. idle, deceleration). Ensure exhaust tubes to EGR is disconnected when diagnosing EGR system.

The following vacuum test procedures are used to test EGR:

1) Connect vacuum gauge to source side of EGR solenoid. Start engine. Manifold vacuum should be present. If vacuum is not present, repair leaks or obstruction between EGR solenoid and throttle body.

2) Connect vacuum gauge to EGR valve vacuum supply. With engine at idle, no vacuum should be present. If vacuum is present, follow PFI Chart C-7 for diagnosis.

3) With vacuum gauge still connected to EGR vacuum source, disconnect EGR solenoid connector. Gauge should read more than 8 inches of vacuum. If not, repair leak or obstruction in EGR vacuum hose.

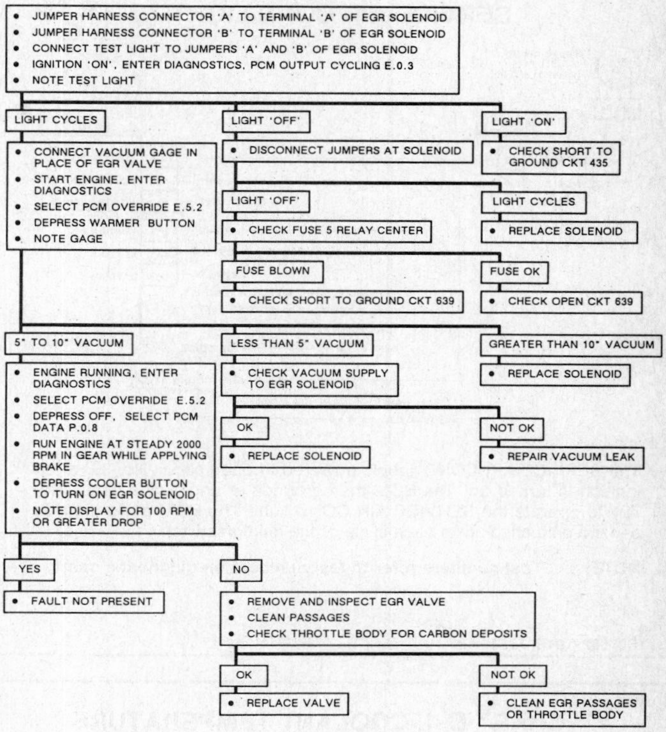

91A07676   91G07679

Courtesy of General Motors Corp.

SELF-DIAGNOSTIC SYSTEM CHECK

The Self-Diagnostic System Check is an organized approach to identifying a problem caused by the on-vehicle computer controlled electronics. Understanding the chart and using it correctly will reduce diagnostic time and prevent unnecessary parts replacement.

Codes displayed during the first pass are history or intermittent codes and may require a visual or physical inspection of circuitry to isolate problem. Codes displayed during the second pass are current or hard codes which can be diagnosed using procedures outlined in PCM TROUBLE CODE DIAGNOSIS or BCM TROUBLE CODE DIAGNOSIS. The Self-Diagnostic System Check should be used to begin diagnosis if any customer complaint does not directly relate to a specific subsystem.

NOTE: Test numbers refer to test numbers on diagnostic chart.

1) A 2-second bulb check of SERVICE AIR COND light with key on and after crank, confirms battery, ignition and ground integrity to the BCM.

2) Verifies proper operation of the COOLANT TEMP and SERVICE ENGINE SOON light.

3) A 2-second bulb check of the SERVICE ENGINE SOON light verifies battery, ignition and ground integrity to the PCM.

4) The Electronic Climate Control Panel (ECCP) and Fuel Data Center (FDC) must be functional in order to use the self-diagnostic system. Check if panels illuminate and respond when buttons are depressed.

5) After entering diagnostics, record all displayed trouble codes and note those displayed during both the first and second pass.

91A07681

Courtesy of General Motors Corp.

GM
1-148

1991 ENGINE PERFORMANCE
Self-Diagnostics – DeVille & Fleetwood PCM/BCM (Cont.)

CHART A-1, INOPERATIVE SERVICE AIR COND LIGHT

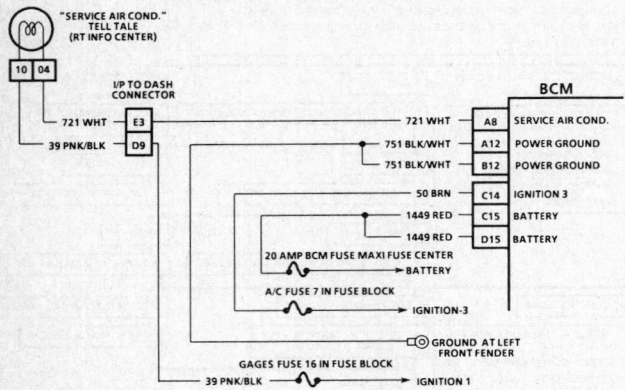

The SERVICE AIR COND light is powered through circuit No. 39, when ignition is turned on. The BCM then grounds or ungrounds circuit No. 721 to operate the SERVICE AIR COND light. The BCM performs a 2-second bulb check with each cycle of the ignition switch.

NOTE: Test numbers refer to test numbers on diagnostic chart.

1) If the SERVICE AIR COND light does not illuminate with ignition on and display shows "c", "d" or "-151", the BCM's microprocessor is not functioning properly, which can be due to improper PROM insertion or faulty components in the BCM.

2) If the SERVICE AIR COND light will not illuminate when grounding circuit No. 721, bulb circuitry is faulty.

3) If the SERVICE AIR COND light turns on, check battery, ignition and ground circuit to the BCM for integrity. If circuit is okay, check BCM connector or for a faulty BCM.

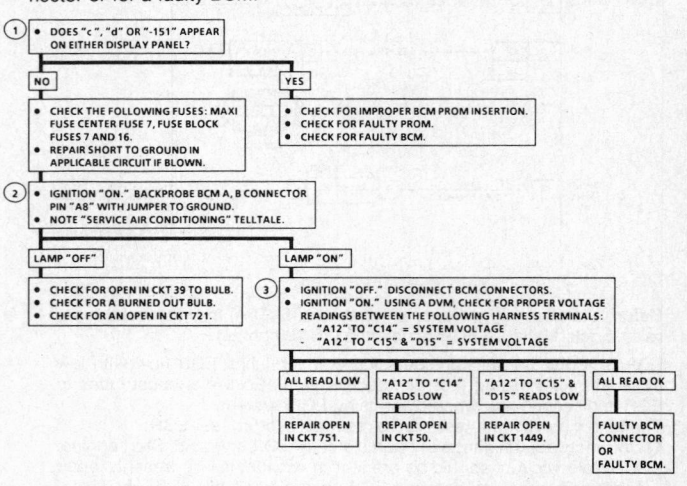

91C07682 91E07683

Courtesy of General Motors Corp.

CHART B-1, COOLANT TEMPERATURE LIGHT DIAGNOSIS

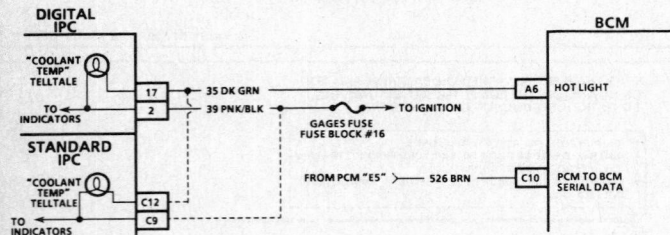

The COOLANT TEMP light is powered by ignition circuit No. 39 through the gauges fuse. BCM supplies ground to circuit No. 35 (BCM terminal "A6") to illuminate COOLANT TEMP light when coolant temperature is greater than 257°F (125°C). Coolant temperature data is sent by the PCM to the BCM through circuit No. 526 (PCM-BCM serial data).

NOTE: Test numbers refer to test numbers on diagnostic chart.

1) Verifies integrity of the IPC, bulb or circuits No. 35 and No. 39. If bulb comes on when circuit No. 35 is jumpered to ground at the BCM, the bulb, IPC and associated wiring are okay. Problem may be a faulty BCM connection or BCM.

2) Checks circuit No. 39 to ensure that ignition feed is being supplied to indicators.

3) Determines whether problem is an open in circuit No. 35, IPC, bulb or connector.

4) Checks if circuit No. 35 is grounded or if IPC is faulty.

5) Ensure that BCM is not receiving data indicating an overheat condition from the PCM. If BCM data P.2.1 displays a coolant temperature greater than 257°F (125°C), problem is in either the coolant sensor circuit or the engine cooling system.

91G07684 91J07685

Courtesy of General Motors Corp.

1991 ENGINE PERFORMANCE
Self-Diagnostics – DeVille & Fleetwood PCM/BCM (Cont.)

GM
1-149

CHART C-1, DISPLAY PANEL DIAGNOSIS (1 OF 6)

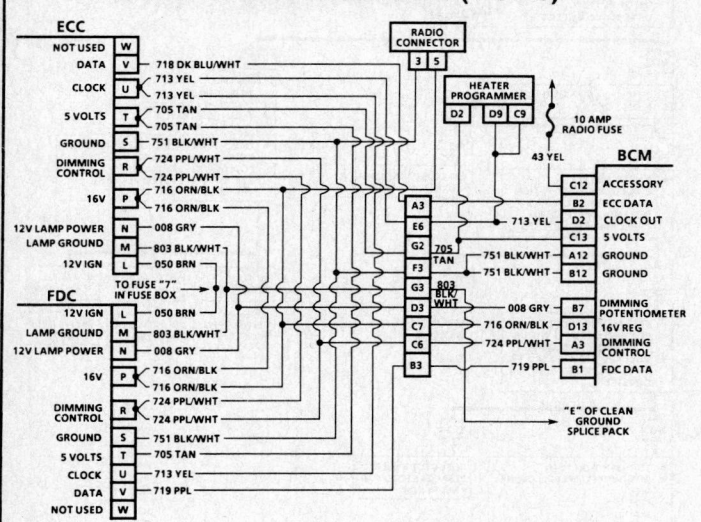

1) A "c" displayed on one or both panels indicates a loss of the clock signal to the affected panel.

2) A "d" displayed on either panel indicates a loss of the data signal to the affected panel.

3) If one panel is affected, only branches of the critical circuits to that panel require investigation.

4) If both panels are affected, several circuits require investigation. If depressing the OFF button on ECCP does not result in blower turning off, panels are not in communication with BCM. This could be caused by a loss of 5 volts or ground to panels. If blower turns off, all remaining critical circuits must be checked.

- SELF-DIAGNOSTIC SYSTEM CHECK MUST BE PERFORMED FIRST
- TURN IGNITION "ON." TURN HEADLAMPS "OFF."

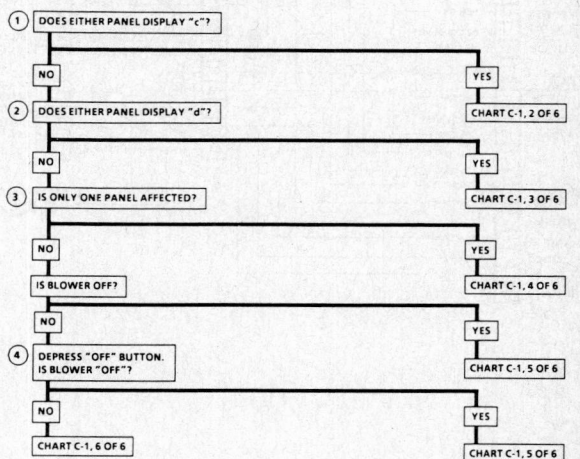

The BCM supplies the FDC and ECCP with information. The BCM sends data to the FDC through circuit No. 719. The BCM supplies the FDC with a 5-volt reference through circuit No. 705. The BCM supplies a reference ground through circuit No. 751. A clock signal is provided to the FDC and ECCP through circuit No. 713. The BCM supplies a 16-volt source to the FDC and ECCP through circuit No. 716. The BCM sends data through circuit No. 718 to the ECCP.

NOTE: Test numbers refer to test numbers on diagnostic chart.

91B07686   90A13904

CHART C-1, DISPLAY PANEL DIAGNOSIS (2 OF 6)

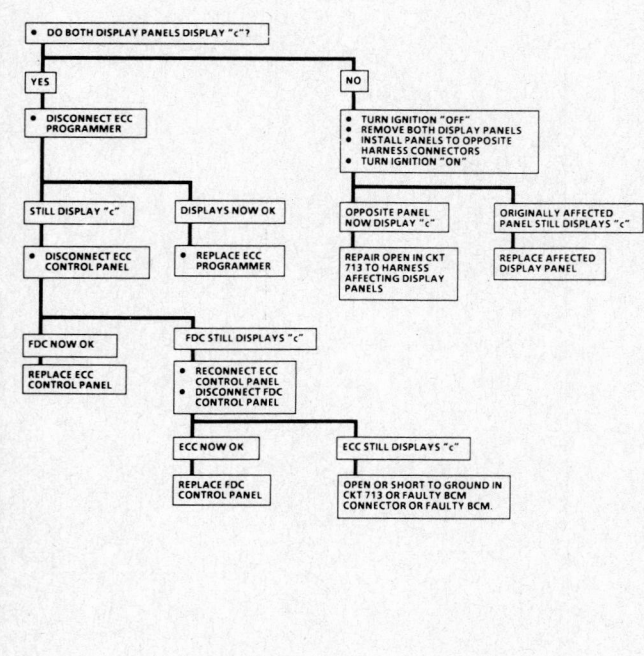

CHART C-1, DISPLAY PANEL DIAGNOSIS (3 OF 6)

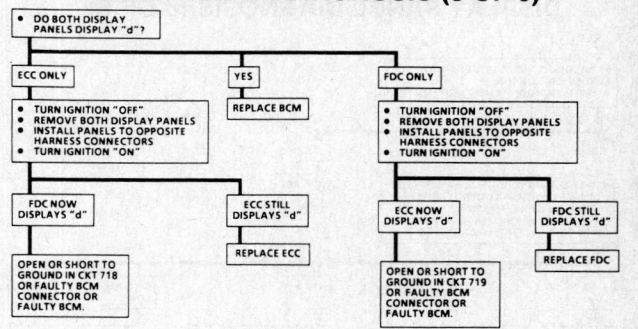

CHART C-1, DISPLAY PANEL DIAGNOSIS (4 OF 6)

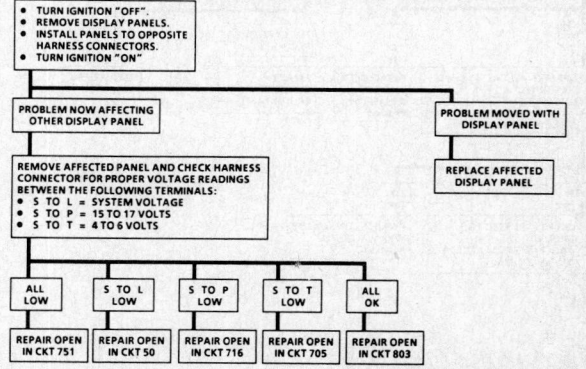

90B13905   90B17252   91H07689

CHART C-1, DISPLAY PANEL DIAGNOSIS (5 OF 6)

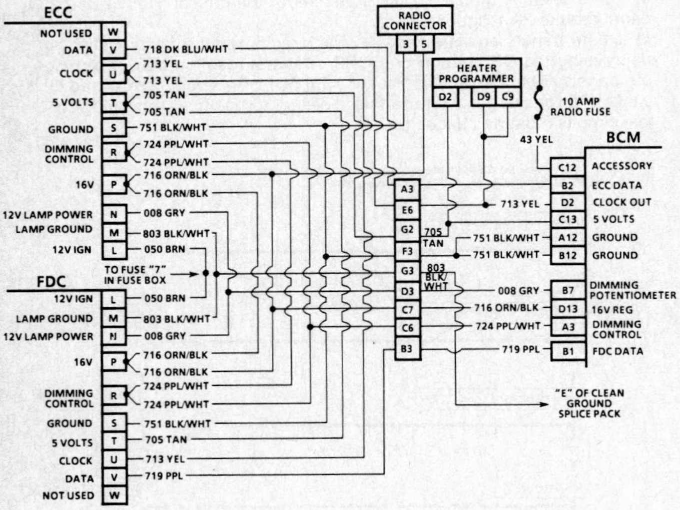
ECC
NOT USED W
DATA V 718 DK BLU/WHT
CLOCK U 713 YEL
713 YEL
5 VOLTS T 705 TAN
705 TAN
GROUND S 751 BLK/WHT
DIMMING CONTROL R 724 PPL/WHT
724 PPL/WHT
16V P 716 ORN/BLK
716 ORN/BLK
12V LAMP POWER N 008 GRY
LAMP GROUND M 803 BLK/WHT
12V IGN L 050 BRN
TO FUSE "7" IN FUSE BOX
FDC
12V IGN L 050 BRN
LAMP GROUND M 803 BLK/WHT
12V LAMP POWER N 008 GRY
16V P 716 ORN/BLK
716 ORN/BLK
DIMMING CONTROL R 724 PPL/WHT
724 PPL/WHT
GROUND S 751 BLK/WHT
5 VOLTS T 705 TAN
CLOCK U 713 YEL
DATA V 719 PPL
NOT USED W
RADIO CONNECTOR 3 5
HEATER PROGRAMMER D2 D9 C9
10 AMP RADIO FUSE
43 YEL
A3 E6 G2 F3 G3 D3 C7 C6 B3
705 TAN
803 BLK/WHT
BCM
C12 ACCESSORY
B2 ECC DATA
713 YEL D2 CLOCK OUT
C13 5 VOLTS
751 BLK/WHT A12 GROUND
751 BLK/WHT B12 GROUND
008 GRY B7 DIMMING POTENTIOMETER
716 ORN/BLK D13 16V REG
724 PPL/WHT A3 DIMMING CONTROL
719 PPL B1 FDC DATA
"E" OF CLEAN GROUND SPLICE PACK

- TURN IGNITION "ON" AND PUSH FRONT DEFOG BUTTON. DOES BLOWER OPERATE?
  - **NO:**
    - CHECK 10 AMP RADIO FUSE
    - IS FUSE OK?
      - **YES:**
        - BACKPROBE BCM CONNECTOR "C13" WITH A VOLTMETER TO GROUND. DOES VOLTMETER READ APPROXIMATELY 5 VOLTS?
          - **YES:**
            - BACKPROBE BCM C-D CONNECTOR "D13" WITH A VOLTMETER TO GROUND.
            - VOLTAGE SHOULD READ 15 TO 17 VOLTS. DOES IT?
              - **NO:**
                - TURN IGNITION "OFF."
                - DISCONNECT THE FOLLOWING: -ECC -FDC -RADIO -DIGITAL CLUSTER
                - TURN IGNITION "ON."
                - OBSERVE VOLTMETER. DID VOLTAGE INCREASE?
                  - **NO:** CKT 716 SHORTED TO GROUND OR FAULTY BCM CONNECTOR OR FAULTY BCM.
                  - **YES:**
                    - RECONNECT ONE COMPONENT AT A TIME AND OBSERVE VOLTMETER.
                    - REPLACE COMPONENT WHICH AFFECTS READING.
              - **YES:** CHECK FOR FAULTY BCM CONNECTOR OR FAULTY BCM
          - **NO:** REPAIR OPEN IN CKT 705.
      - **NO:** REPAIR GROUNDED CKT 43 AND REPLACE FUSE.
  - **YES:**
    - TURN IGNITION "OFF."
    - DISCONNECT THE ECC.
    - TURN IGNITION "ON."
    - CHECK ECC CONNECTOR FOR PROPER VOLTAGE READINGS BETWEEN THE FOLLOWING TERMINALS
      M TO L = SYSTEM VOLTAGE
      M TO P = 15 TO 17 VOLTS
      - **M TO P READS LOW:** REPAIR OPEN IN CKT 716
      - **BOTH READ LOW:** REPAIR OPEN IN CKT 803
      - **M TO L READS LOW:** REPAIR OPEN IN CKT 50

91B07686 91J07690 Courtesy of General Motors Corp.

CHART C-1, DISPLAY PANEL DIAGNOSIS (6 OF 6)

- DISCONNECT ECC PANEL HARNESS.
- TURN IGNITION "ON."
- DOES FDC NOW OPERATE PROPERLY?
  - **NO:**
    - USING A DVM, CHECK ECC HARNESS FOR PROPER VOLTAGE READINGS BETWEEN THE FOLLOWING TERMINALS:
      S TO L = BATTERY VOLTAGE
      S TO T = 4 TO 6 VOLTS
      - **S TO T LOW:**
        - BACKPROBE BCM CONNECTOR "C13" WITH VOLTMETER TO GROUND. VOLTAGE SHOULD READ 4 TO 6 VOLTS.
          - **LOW:**
            - OBSERVE VOLTMETER WHILE DISCONNECTING THE FOLLOWING: - FDC - ECC PROGRAMMER
              - **LOW:** - CKT 705 SHORTED TO GROUND. - FAULTY BCM CONNECTOR OR FAULTY BCM.
              - **OK:** REPLACE COMPONENT WHICH AFFECTED READING.
          - **OK:** REPAIR OPEN IN CKT 705 TO DISPLAY PANELS
      - **BOTH LOW:**
        - BACKPROBE BCM CONNECTOR "B12" AND/OR "A12" WITH A JUMPER TO GROUND.
          - **FDC OPERATES PROPERLY:** FAULTY CONNECTOR OR FAULTY BCM.
          - **FDC STILL AFFECTED:** REPAIR OPEN IN CKT 751
      - **S TO L LOW:** REPAIR OPEN IN CKT 50
      - **BOTH OK:** REPAIR OPEN IN CKT 803
  - **YES:** REPLACE ECC

91B07691 Courtesy of General Motors Corp.

1991 ENGINE PERFORMANCE
Self-Diagnostics – DeVille & Fleetwood PCM/BCM (Cont.)

GM
1-151

CHART D-1,
SERVICE VEHICLE SOON LIGHT DIAGNOSIS

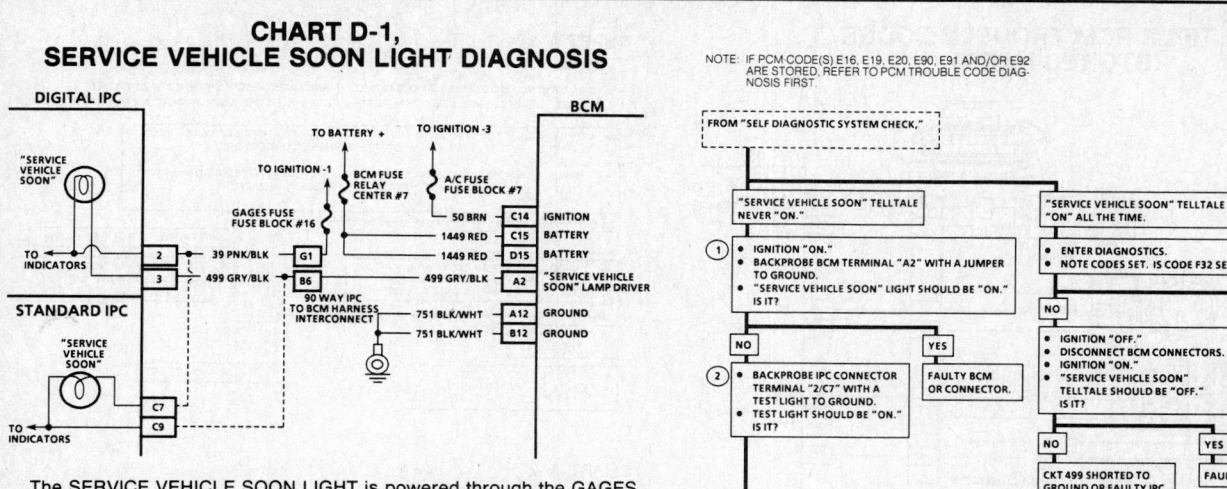

NOTE: IF PCM CODE(S) E16, E19, E20, E90, E91 AND/OR E92 ARE STORED, REFER TO PCM TROUBLE CODE DIAGNOSIS FIRST.

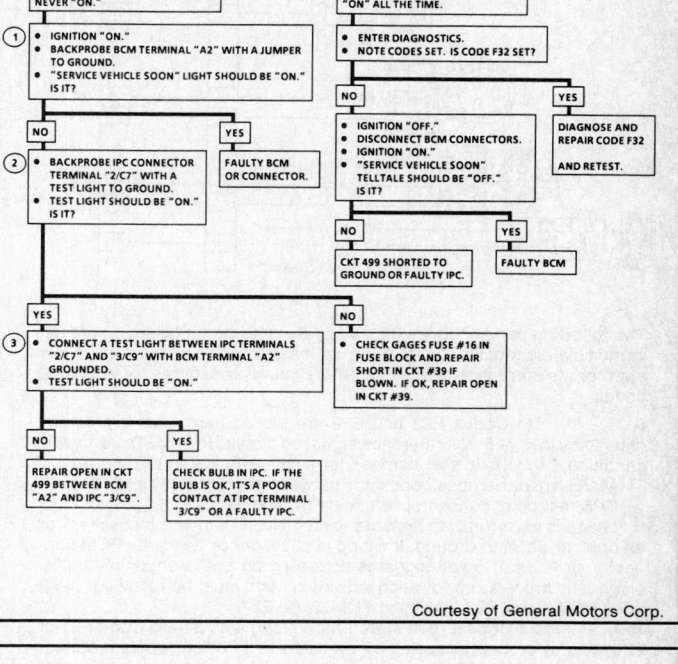

The SERVICE VEHICLE SOON LIGHT is powered through the GAGES fuse (No. 16, in fuse/relay block). The BCM grounds circuit No. 499 to illuminate SERVICE VEHICLE SOON light, if conditions for setting BCM Code F32 or PCM Codes E16, E19, E20, E90, E91 or E92 are present. These codes are explained in the beginning of this article. The BCM also grounds circuit No. 499 to illuminate SERVICE VEHICLE SOON light at key up for a 2 second bulb check.

NOTE: **Test numbers refer to test numbers on diagnostic chart.**

1) Grounding BCM terminal A2, completes the SERVICE VEHICLE SOON light circuit. If SERVICE VEHICLE SOON light turns on when terminal A2 is shorted to ground, the circuit is okay and problem is at the BCM.
2) Checks circuit No. 39 and GAGES fuse.
3) Checks for an open in circuit No. 499 or a fault at the IPC.

91D07692   91F07693

Courtesy of General Motors Corp.

CHART E-1,
CHANGE OIL SOON LIGHT DIAGNOSIS

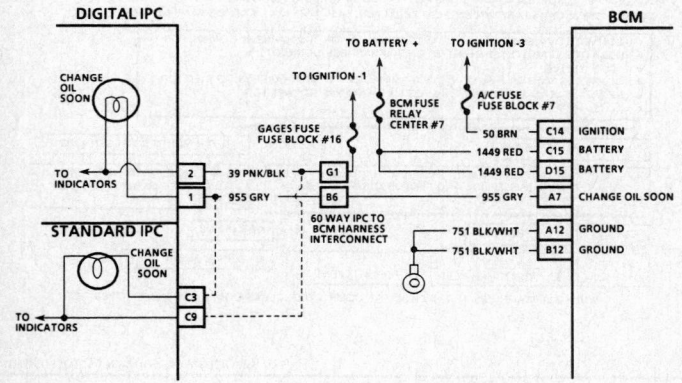

Always reset the oil life monitor system to zero after oil has been changed. To reset system, depress and hold RESET and RANGE button on the FDC for 5 seconds. Release buttons. CHANGE OIL SOON light will flash 4 times, indicating that reset is complete. If CHANGE OIL SOON light is on (steady) for 5 seconds and RESET and RANGE buttons were not depressed long enough, repeat reset procedure.

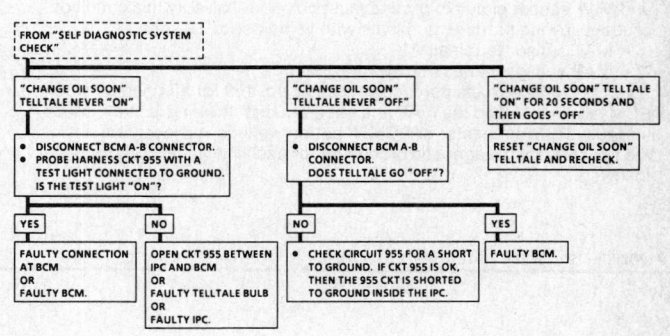

BCM monitors odometer and engine revolutions to determine when the CHANGE OIL SOON light should be turned on. When odometer reaches a count of 7000 miles or when engine has made approximately 18 million revolutions, the BCM grounds circuit No. 955.
The CHANGE OIL SOON light will stay on for 20 seconds every time ignition switch is cycled when its time to change oil.

91H07694   91A07695

Courtesy of General Motors Corp.

GM
1-152

1991 ENGINE PERFORMANCE
Self-Diagnostics – DeVille & Fleetwood PCM/BCM (Cont.)

MULTIPLE PCM TROUBLE CODES (STORED HARD)

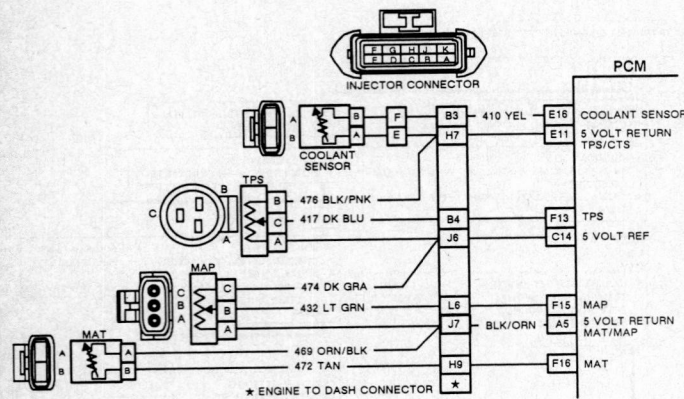

The following conditions are caused by a single circuit failure, yet result in multiple diagnostic codes. If any of these conditions are met, follow appropriate correction procedure before using procedures for individual codes:

A-1) – If PCM Codes E22 and E32 are stored hard, this is probably caused by loss of 5-volt reference signal on circuit No. 474. To verify this condition, probe following harness terminals with voltmeter to ground:
- MAP sensor harness connector between terminals "A" and "C".
- TPS test point connector terminals "A" and "B".

If voltage is zero for both sensors, circuit No. 474 must be checked for an open or short to ground. If wiring is okay, check for faulty PCM connector or PCM. If 5-volt signal is observed on both sensor terminals, diagnostic procedures for each individual code must be followed. Diagnose PCM Code E22 first, then PCM Code E32.

A-2) – If PCM Code E15 is stored hard along with a hard Code E21 or E26, this is probably caused by an open in TPS and coolant sensor ground circuit No. 476. To verify, probe the following harness terminals with voltmeter to 12 volts:
- Coolant temperature sensor terminal "A".
- TPS test point connector terminal "B" (Black/Pink wire).

If voltage is zero for both sensors, check for open in circuit No. 476. If wiring is okay, check for faulty PCM connector or PCM. If battery voltage is observed on sensors, diagnostic procedures for each individual code must be followed. Diagnose Code E15 followed by Code E21, then Code E26.

A-3) – If PCM Code E34 is stored hard along with hard Code E38, MAP and MAT sensor circuit to ground must be open. To verify this condition, probe following harness terminals with voltmeter to 12 volts:
- MAT sensor terminal "A".
- MAP sensor harness terminal "A".

If sensor voltage reads zero, check circuit No. 469 for an open between PCM terminal A5 and the MAP and MAT sensors. If wiring is okay, check for faulty PCM connector or PCM. If battery voltage is present on any of the sensors, then diagnostic procedure for each individual code must be followed.

CHART A-1

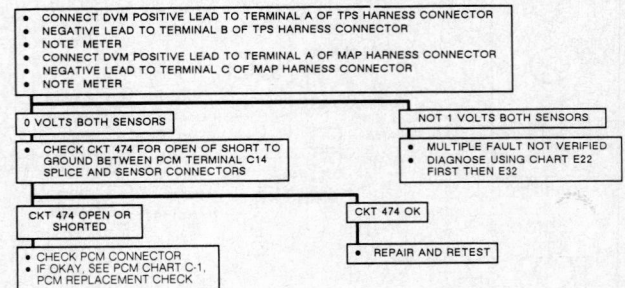

CHART A-2

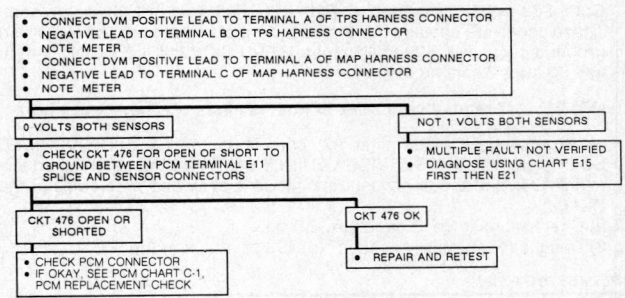

WHEN ALL DIAGNOSIS AND REPAIRS ARE COMPLETED, CLEAR CODES AND VERIFY OPERATION

CHART A-3 – MULTIPLE PCM CODES STORED CURRENT

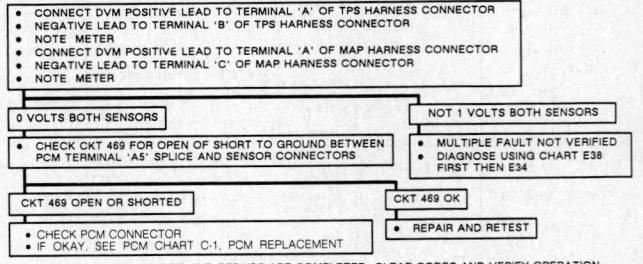

WHEN ALL DIAGNOSIS AND REPAIRS ARE COMPLETED, CLEAR CODES AND VERIFY OPERATION

1991 ENGINE PERFORMANCE
Self-Diagnostics – DeVille & Fleetwood PCM/BCM (Cont.)

GM
1-153

PCM CODE E12, NO DISTRIBUTOR (TACH) SIGNAL

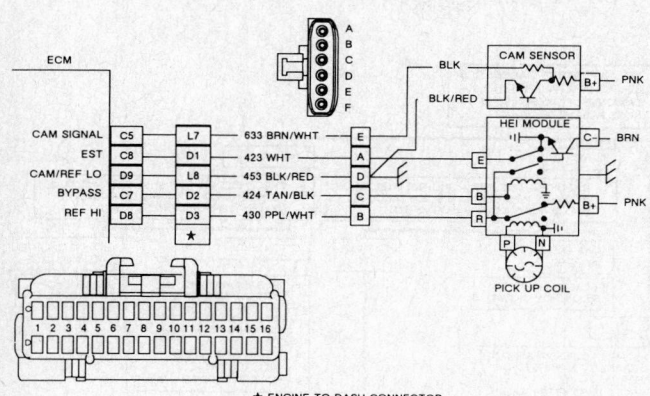

★ ENGINE TO DASH CONNECTOR

Note On Intermittents – If PCM Code E12 is stored as a hard code, start engine and allow to idle. Manipulating circuits No. 430 and No. 453. An intermittent open will cause engine to stumble or quit when PCM loses distributor reference.

If wiring and PCM connectors are okay, check HEI pick-up coil leads for intermittent open circuit.

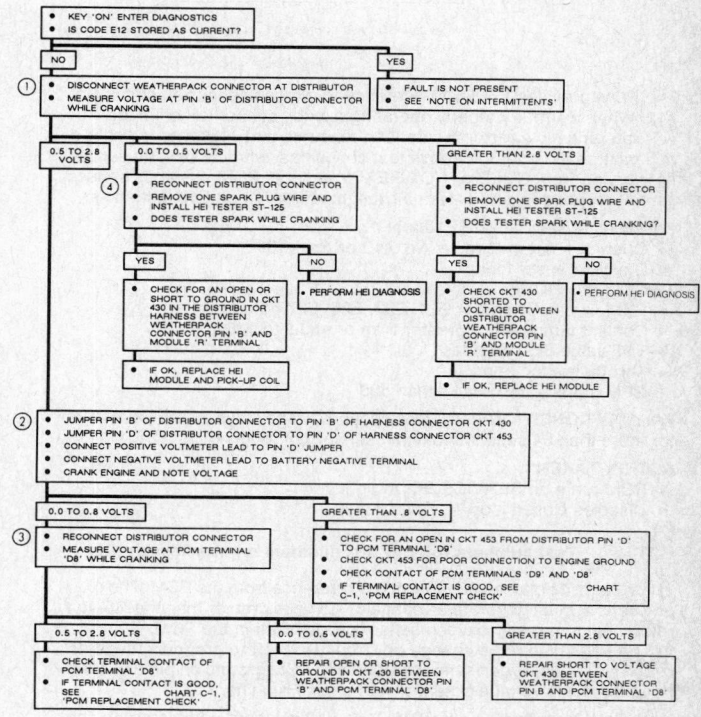

WHEN ALL DIAGNOSIS AND REPAIRS ARE COMPLETED, CLEAR CODES AND VERIFY OPERATION

TEST CONDITIONS: PCM Code E41 not set. Code E12 is tested during engine cranking (crank input to PCM at system voltage).

FAILURE CONDITIONS: If PCM does not see distributor reference pulses for 4 seconds with cam reference input to PCM at system voltage, current Code E12 will be set.

ACTION: PCM turns on SERVICE ENGINE SOON light

Possible causes of PCM Code E12 are:
- Open or short on circuit No. 430 from module to 5-way weatherpack to PCM
- HEI module unable to process pick-up coil signals
- Defective pick-up coil
- Poor connection of grounding screw, located on metal tab attached to plastic fitting of 5-wire harness

NOTE: Test numbers refer to test numbers on diagnostic chart.

1) Check for proper HEI voltage output. If voltmeter shows .5-2.8 volts, HEI is producing reference pulses.
2) Check for proper ground connection between PCM and engine, and PCM and HEI.
3) Check for proper voltage through circuit No. 430 from HEI to PCM. If PCM terminal D8 sees 0.5-2.8 volts, PCM is receiving reference pulses.
4) If HEI will produce spark, pick-up coil and HEI module are okay. Check circuit No. 430 for open or short to ground, from module terminal "R" to terminal "B" of 5-way weatherpack.

90F17256   91C07700

PCM CODE E13, OXYGEN SENSOR NOT READY

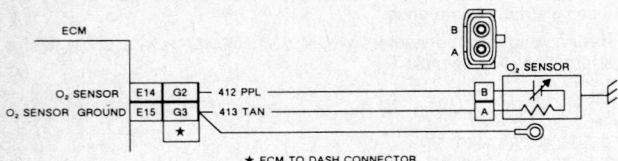

The PCM provides a .45-volt reference to oxygen sensor on circuit No. 412. When warm, a properly operating oxygen sensor will drive the .45-volt reference lower to indicate lean mixtures and higher to indicate a rich mixture. If under the above test conditions, with the oxygen sensor not varying from COLD or NOT READY voltage, PCM assumes sensor cannot respond to rich or lean air/fuel mixtures. Code E13 is then set.

Possible causes of Code E13 are:
* Open or short on circuits No. 412 or No. 413
* Oxygen sensor faulty

TEST CONDITIONS:
* PCM Codes E14, E15, E21, E22, E26, E27 not set
* Coolant temperature greater than or equal to 136°F (58°C)
* TPS value 6-30 degrees
* Throttle switch open
* RPM equal to or greater than 800

FAILURE CONDITIONS: Oxygen sensor voltage stays at .307-.609 volts for more than 64 seconds (oxygen sensor not toggling)

ACTION TAKEN:
* PCM turns on SERVICE SOON light
* Disables closed loop

NOTE: Test numbers refer to test numbers on diagnostic chart.

1) A voltage display of .42-.48 volt is a reference from the PCM. The oxygen sensor must generate a voltage of .15 volts greater than the .45-volt reference, to register oxygen sensor cross count in the PCM.

2) The PCM compares voltage on circuit No. 412 to ground voltage on circuit No. 413. Oxygen sensor ground and PCM ground on pin E15 must be at the same voltage potential with engine running.

Note On Intermittents – If PCM Code E13 is a hard code, start engine and enter diagnostics. Operate engine at fast idle until AUTO closed loop status light is turned on. Observe parameter while manipulating circuits No. 412 and No. 413 wiring. If parameter P.1.4 stops fluctuating and stays fixed at approximately .45 volt, repair intermittent open circuit.

Check circuit No. 413 (ground to engine) for proper installation (clean, tight and star washer installed). Ground for circuit No. 413 is attached to rear of right cylinder head.

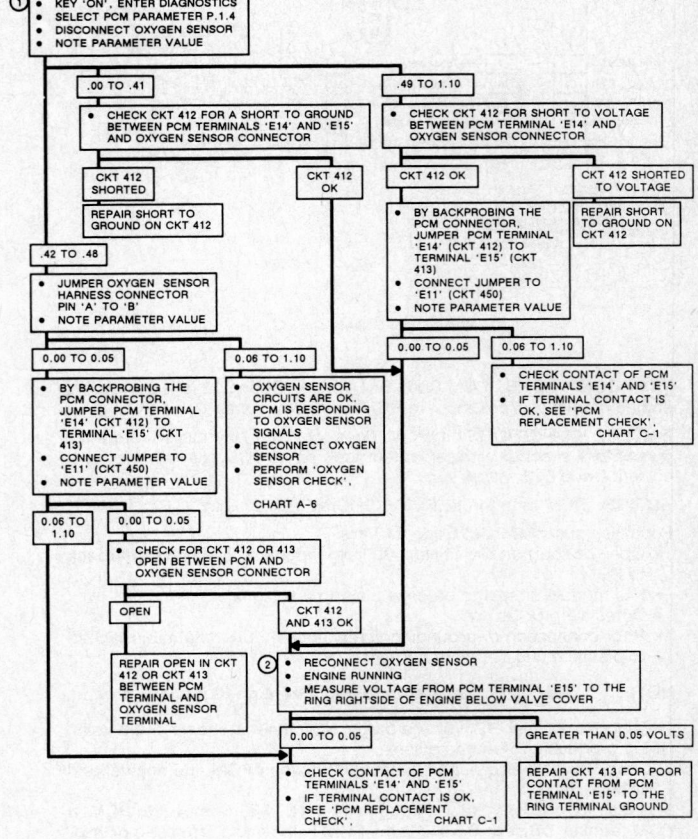

90B17260 91E07701

Courtesy of General Motors Corp.

1991 ENGINE PERFORMANCE
Self-Diagnostics – DeVille & Fleetwood PCM/BCM (Cont.)

GM
1-155

PCM CODE E14,
SHORTED COOLANT SENSOR CIRCUIT

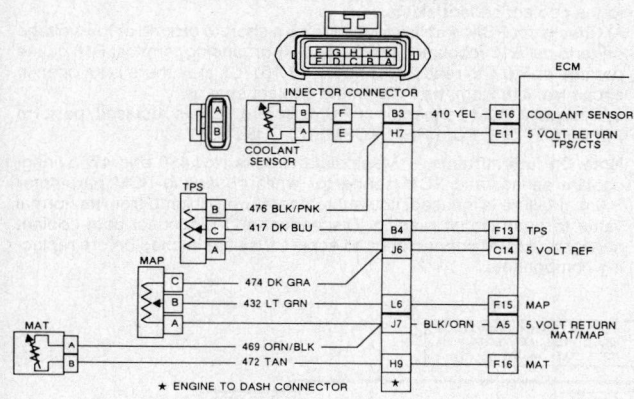

The coolant sensor is a thermistor (temperature-sensitive resistor). Sensor uses a 2-wire harness. Sensor signal voltage comes from PCM to terminal "B" on circuit No. 410. Sensor reference ground comes to terminal "A" from PCM on circuit No. 476.

As temperature of sensor increases, sensor resistance is lower. The monitored signal voltage from PCM to terminal "B" decreases as sensor temperature increases and current flows through the sensor element to terminal "A" sensor ground.

PCM Code E14 sets because PCM assumes that coolant temperature cannot be greater than 299°F (148°C) when MAT temperature is less than 212°F (100°C).

TEST CONDITIONS:
- PCM Codes E37 and E38 not set
- MAT sensor value less than or equal to 212°F (100°C)

FAILURE CONDITIONS: Coolant sensor value greater than 298°F (148°C)

ACTION TAKEN:
- PCM turns on SERVICE ENGINE SOON light
- PCM uses MAT sensor value in place of coolant sensor value for the first 4 minutes of engine operation, then the value of 194°F (90°C) is used

90F17264   90J14745

NOTE: Test numbers refer to test numbers on diagnostic chart.

1) With sensor or wiring shorted, PCM parameter P.1.4 should read 298°F (148°C) or greater. If not, the sensor is not shorted. See NOTE ON INTERMITTENTS.

2) Checks for shorted sensor or circuit No. 410. If parameter value stays at 288°F (142°C) or greater with sensor unplugged, the short is in circuit No. 410 between sensor pin "B" and PCM terminal "E16".

3) Fault is most likely at PCM connector or PCM. Before replacing PCM, perform PFI CHART C-1, PCM REPLACEMENT CHECK.

Note On Intermittents – Manipulate circuit No. 410 wiring, coolant sensor and PCM connectors while observing PCM parameter P.0.4. If failure is induced, coolant temperature will jump from its normal value to shorted readings of 288°F (142°C) or greater. Remove and replace both coolant sensor and PCM connectors and ensure they are latched before replacing components.

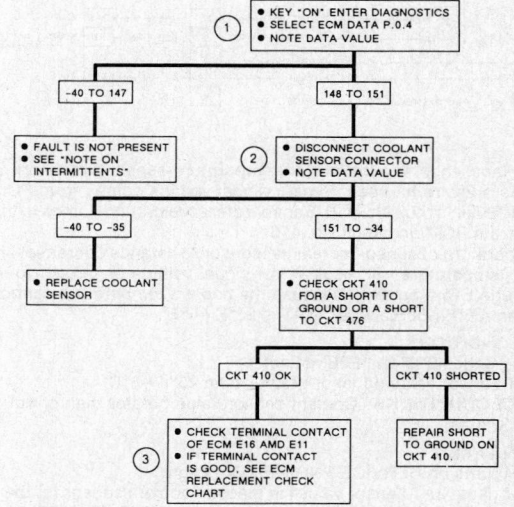

WHEN ALL DIAGNOSIS AND REPAIRS ARE COMPLETED, CLEAR CODES AND VERIFY OPERATION

Courtesy of General Motors Corp.

GM
1-156

1991 ENGINE PERFORMANCE
Self-Diagnostics – DeVille & Fleetwood PCM/BCM (Cont.)

PCM CODE E15, OPEN COOLANT SENSOR CIRCUIT

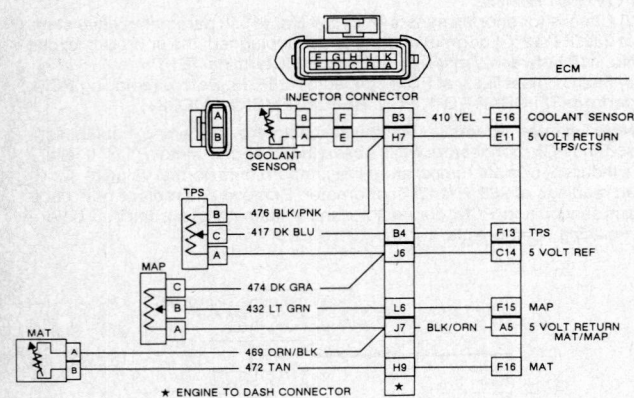

The coolant sensor is a thermistor (temperature-sensitive resistor). Sensor uses a 2-wire harness. Sensor signal voltage comes from PCM to terminal "B" on circuit No. 410. Sensor reference ground comes to terminal "A" from PCM on circuit No. 476.

As temperature of sensor increases, sensor resistance decreases. High coolant temperature will result in low signal voltage on circuit No. 410. PCM Code E15 then sets, because the coolant temperature cannot be less than -36°F (-38°C) when MAT is 23°F (-5°F).

TEST CONDITIONS:
- PCM Codes E37 and E38 not set
- MAT sensor value equal or greater than 23°F (-5°C)

FAILURE CONDITIONS: Coolant sensor value greater than or equal to -36°F (-38°C)

ACTION TAKEN:
- PCM turns on SERVICE ENGINE SOON light
- PCM uses MAT sensor values in place of coolant sensor for the first 4 minutes of engine operation, then the value of 194°F (90°C) is used

NOTE: Test numbers refer to test numbers on diagnostic chart.

1) If coolant sensor or wiring is open, parameter P.0.4 will read -26°F (-32°C) or less. If not, sensor signal is not open. See NOTE ON INTERMITTENTS.

2) Checks for open sensor signal circuit No. 410 from PCM to sensor connector. If parameter P.0.4 reads 298-304°F (148-151°C) with connector shorted, circuits No. 410 and No. 476 are okay.

3) Checks for open sensor ground circuit No. 476 from sensor pin "A" to the ground splice. If shorting pin "A" to ground causes parameter P.0.4 to read 298-304°F (148-151°C), an open in circuit No. 410 from the PCM to the coolant sensor exists.

4) Checks for PCM's ability to recognize a short to ground or low voltage on terminal E16 (coolant sensor input). If grounding terminal E16 cause parameter P.0.4 to read 298-304°F (148-151°C), then there is an open in circuit No. 410 from the PCM to the coolant sensor.

5) Fault is at PCM connector or PCM. Before PCM is replaced, perform PFI CHART C-1, PCM REPLACEMENT CHECK.

Note On Intermittents – Manipulate circuits No. 410 and 476 wiring, coolant sensor and PCM connector while observing PCM parameter P.0.4. If failure is induced, coolant temperature will jump from its normal value to open circuit reading. Disconnect and reconnect both coolant sensor and PCM connectors and ensure they are latched before replacing components.

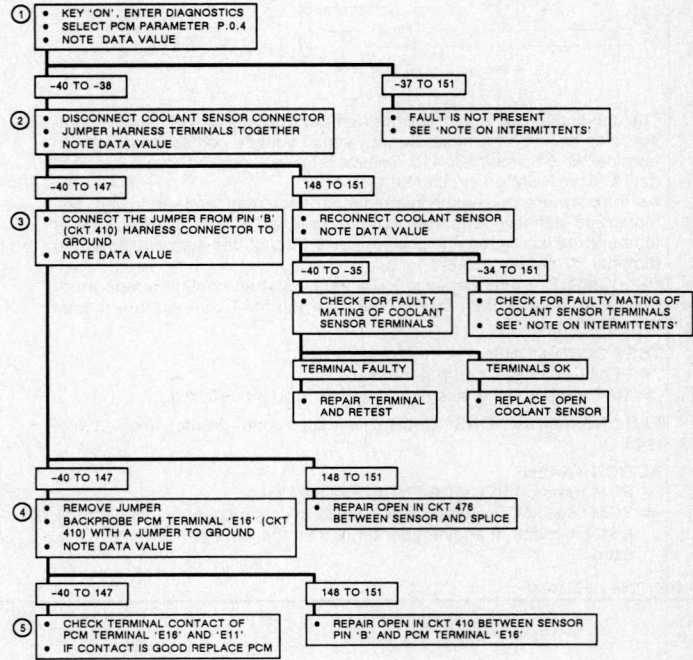

WHEN ALL DIAGNOSIS AND REPAIRS ARE COMPLETED, CLEAR CODES AND VERIFY OPERATION

90F17264 91G07702

1991 ENGINE PERFORMANCE
Self-Diagnostics – DeVille & Fleetwood PCM/BCM (Cont.)

GM
1-157

PCM CODE E16, ALTERNATOR VOLTAGE OUT OF RANGE

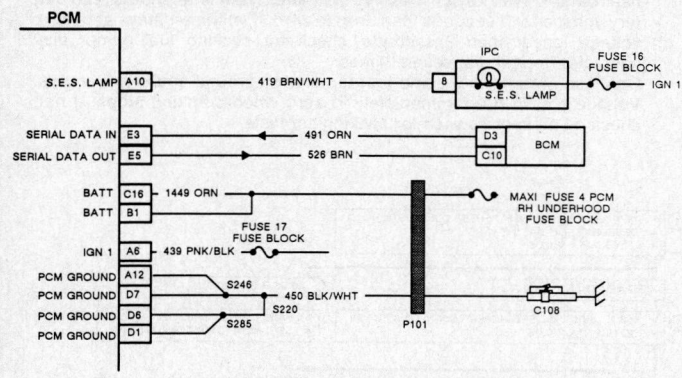

The PCM monitors vehicle electrical system voltage or battery voltage indirectly by monitoring voltage on fuel pump feedback to the PCM. This code will set if system voltage drops below 10 volts or goes greater than 16 volts with engine running at greater than 500 RPM.
If ignition voltage goes to zero (open circuit), engine will not run since PCM does not have the ignition signal.

TEST CONDITIONS: RPM greater than or equal to 500

FAILURE CONDITIONS: Ignition voltage less than 10 volts or greater than 16 volts for 5 seconds or more

ACTION TAKEN:
- PCM turns on SERVICE VEHICLE SOON light
- Canister purge solenoid is disabled
- Cruise control is disabled
- VCC solenoid is de-energized
- Transmission shift solenoids de-energized (3rd gear operation)

NOTE: Test numbers refer to test numbers on diagnostic chart.

1) Checks PCM Snap Shot Data for parameter P.0.7. If voltage is 16 volts or greater, voltage regulator is not controlling voltage.
2) Checks for proper charging system operation.
3) Checks for proper charging system regulation with no electrical loads on alternator.

91I07661   90B14747

Note On Intermittents – PCM Code E16 may be stored as a history code if the battery charge was low. Load test battery and check for proper operation of charging system. Check for loose battery connections at starter motor.

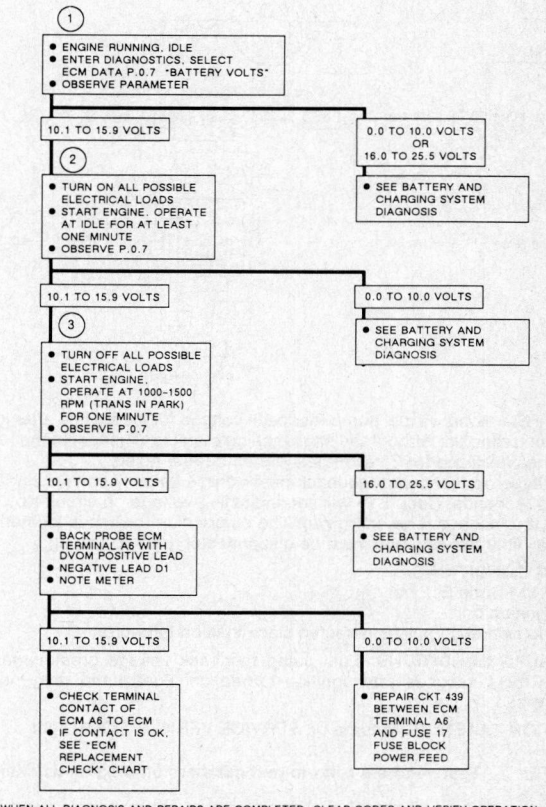

WHEN ALL DIAGNOSIS AND REPAIRS ARE COMPLETED, CLEAR CODES AND VERIFY OPERATION

Courtesy of General Motors Corp.

PCM CODE E19, SHORTED FUEL PUMP CIRCUIT

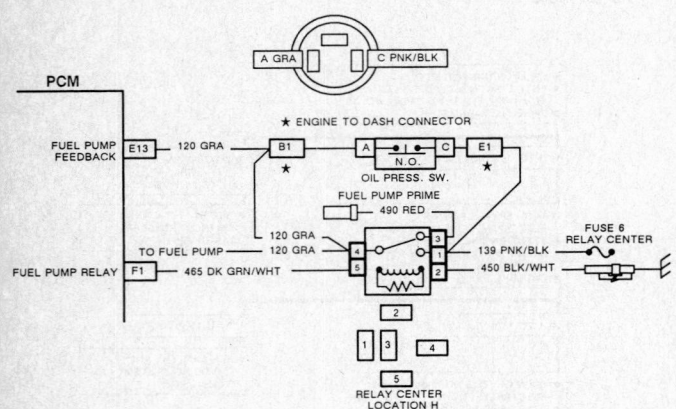

Note On Intermittents – Probe fuel pump test terminal with a voltmeter to ground. Fuel pump test terminal is located on left inner fender panel, near battery. With key on, observe voltmeter. Voltmeter should read battery voltage for 2 seconds then drop to zero. If voltmeter stays at battery voltage longer than 2 seconds, check for sticking fuel pump relay contacts. Repeat test several times.

Continue probing fuel pump test terminal to ground and crank engine. Voltage should drop immediately to zero when cranking stops. If not, check oil pressure switch for sticking contacts.

The PCM monitors fuel pump feedback voltage for 4 seconds after ignition is turned on, without the engine being cranked. The fuel pump relay will be energized for 2 seconds and then de-energized.

If voltage on fuel pump feedback never drops below 7 volts during the first 4 seconds, Code E19 will set, indicating voltage on circuit No. 120 with the fuel pump de-energized. The oil pressure switch is located on the oil filter housing and must be disconnected prior to testing.

TEST CONDITIONS:
- PCM Code E12 not set
- Ignition on
- No reference pulses detected since ignition turned on

FAILURE CONDITIONS: Fuel pump feedback voltage greater than 7 volts for 4 seconds after ignition turned on. Fuel pump relay never energized

ACTION TAKEN: PCM turns on SERVICE VEHICLE SOON light

NOTE: Test numbers refer to test numbers on diagnostic chart.

1) With key on, engine off, fuel pump should not be running and fuel pump feedback (PCM parameter P.0.7) should show zero volts. If P.0.7 shows more than 7 volts, cause of voltage on circuit No. 120 must be repaired.

2) Checks for shorted oil pressure switch. A shorted oil pressure switch will cause Code E19 to set.

3) Checks for shorted fuel pump relay.

4) Checks for voltage on circuit No. 120 at PCM.

5) Checks for proper control of fuel pump relay by the PCM.

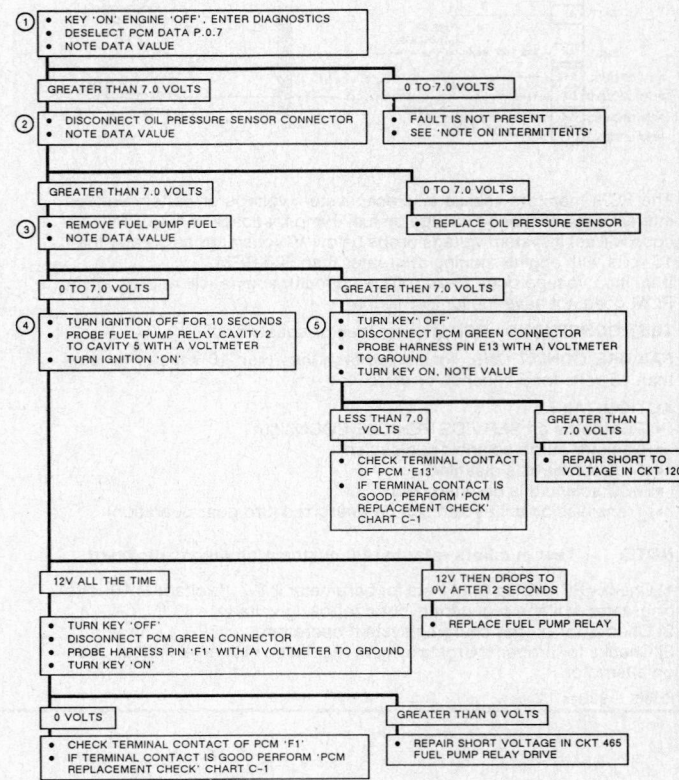

WHEN ALL DIAGNOSIS AND REPAIRS ARE COMPLETED, CLEAR CODES AND VERIFY OPERATION

91F07669   91A07704

Courtesy of General Motors Corp.

1991 ENGINE PERFORMANCE
Self-Diagnostics – DeVille & Fleetwood PCM/BCM (Cont.)

GM
1-159

PCM CODE E20, OPEN FUEL PUMP CIRCUIT (1 OF 3)

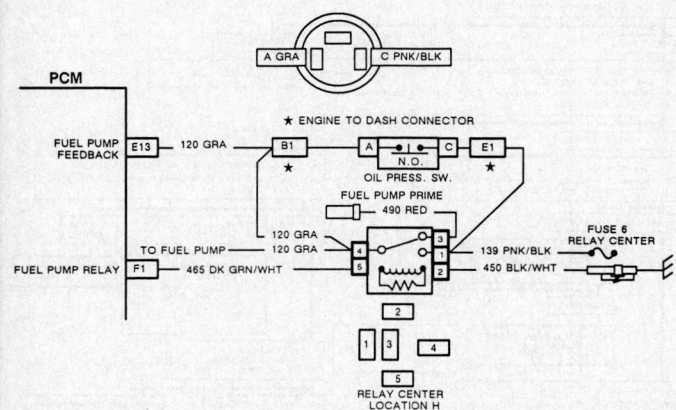

The PCM monitors voltage on fuel pump power circuit No. 120 to detect fuel pump voltage supply faults. Code E20 is set when PCM sees fuel pump not energized (zero volts on feedback) with engine cranking or running. The code is designed to detect a fuel pump relay fault. Relay is not powering fuel pump.

TEST CONDITIONS: Engine RPM greater than or equal to 24 RPM

FAILURE CONDITIONS: Fuel pump feedback voltage less than or equal to 2 volts for one second

ACTION TAKEN: PCM commands BCM to turn on SERVICE VEHICLE SOON light

NOTE: Test numbers refer to test numbers on diagnostic chart.

1) Checking for engine to start with fuel pump powered through fuel pump relay.
2) A reading of zero volts with engine running indicates an open in fuel pump power circuit to PCM fuel pump feedback. Fuel pump relay is not at fault.

Note On Intermittents – If PCM Code E20 is stored as current, unplug oil pressure switch, start engine and allow to idle. Manipulate affected

wiring, ensure PCM P1 (C/D) connector is latched and check relay for proper installation into relay center socket. If fault is induced, engine will stall. Code E20 will set. If Code E20 sets without engine stalling, cause is intermittent open in circuit No. 120 between PCM pin E13 and splice to fuel pump relay.

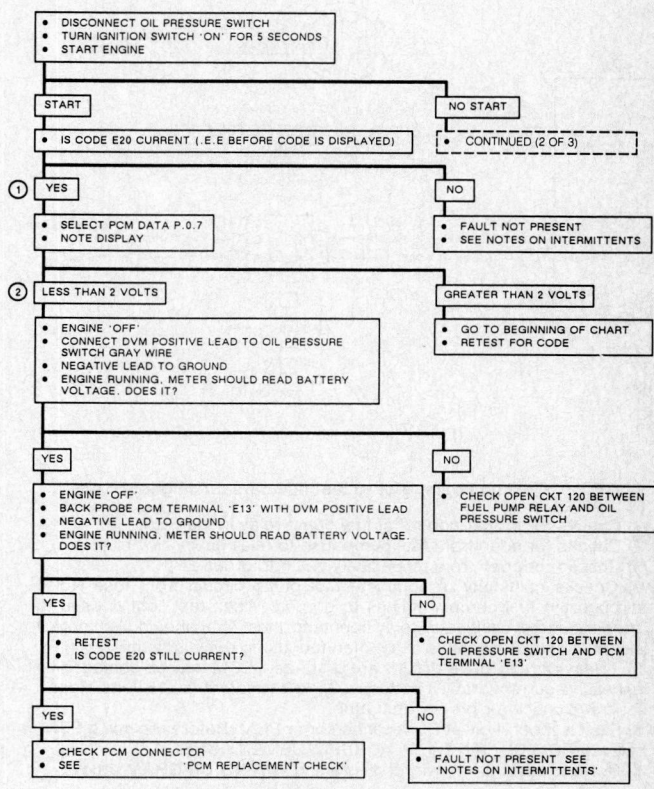

91F07669   91D07705

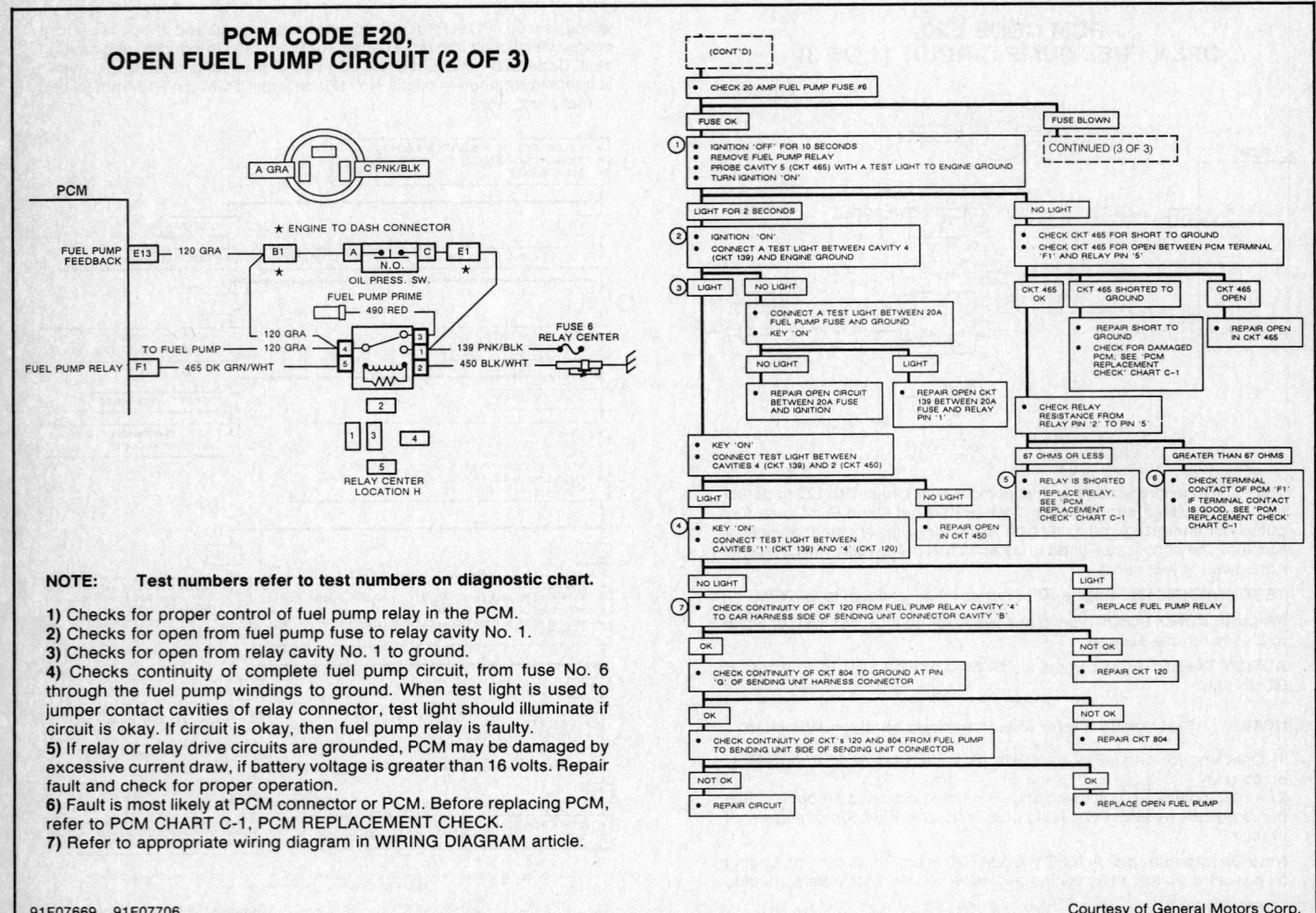

PCM CODE E20,
OPEN FUEL PUMP CIRCUIT (2 OF 3)

NOTE: Test numbers refer to test numbers on diagnostic chart.

1) Checks for proper control of fuel pump relay in the PCM.
2) Checks for open from fuel pump fuse to relay cavity No. 1.
3) Checks for open from relay cavity No. 1 to ground.
4) Checks continuity of complete fuel pump circuit, from fuse No. 6 through the fuel pump windings to ground. When test light is used to jumper contact cavities of relay connector, test light should illuminate if circuit is okay. If circuit is okay, then fuel pump relay is faulty.
5) If relay or relay drive circuits are grounded, PCM may be damaged by excessive current draw, if battery voltage is greater than 16 volts. Repair fault and check for proper operation.
6) Fault is most likely at PCM connector or PCM. Before replacing PCM, refer to PCM CHART C-1, PCM REPLACEMENT CHECK.
7) Refer to appropriate wiring diagram in WIRING DIAGRAM article.

91F07669   91F07706

1991 ENGINE PERFORMANCE
Self-Diagnostics — DeVille & Fleetwood PCM/BCM (Cont.)

GM
1-161

PCM CODE E20, OPEN FUEL PUMP CIRCUIT (3 OF 3)

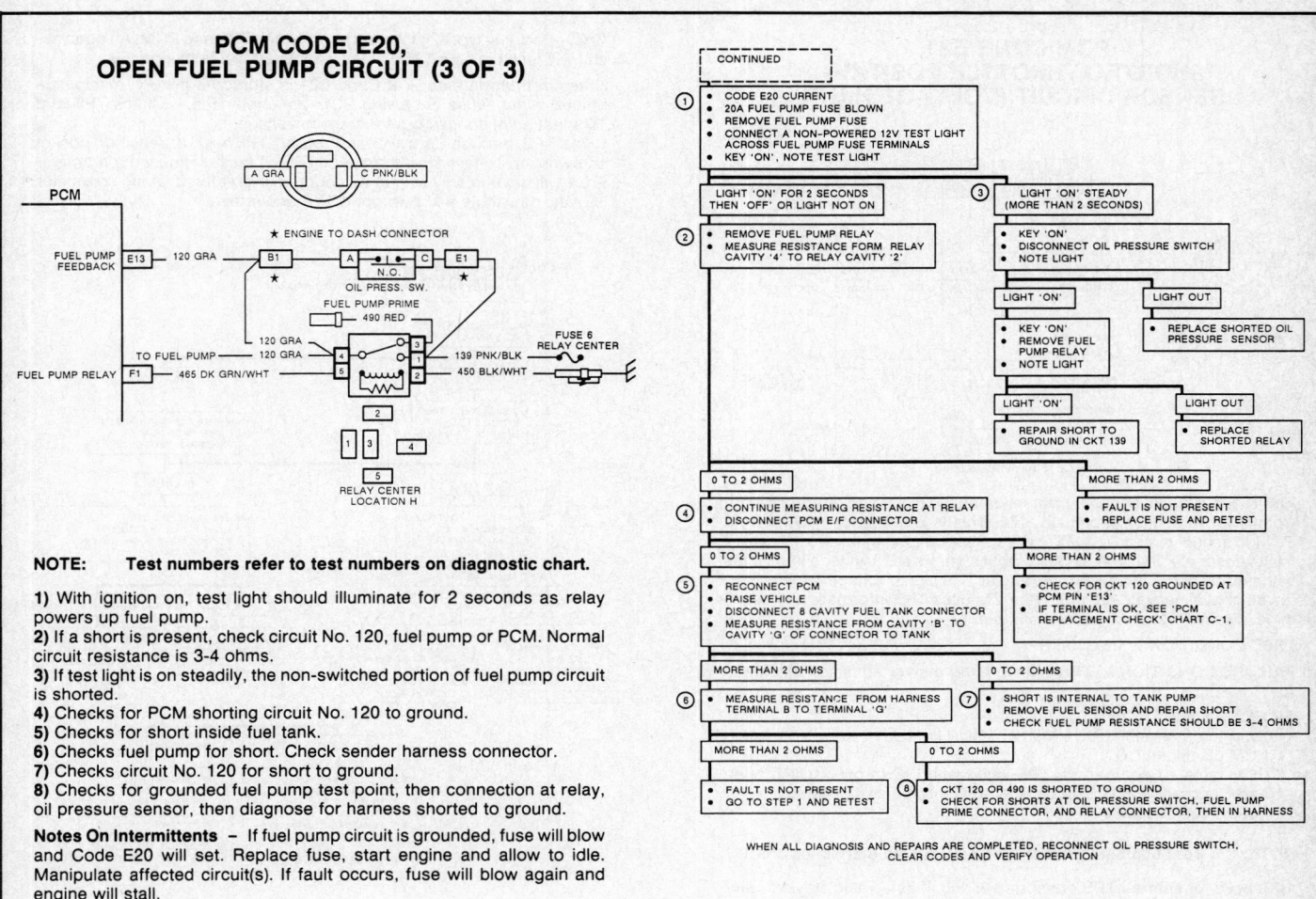

NOTE: Test numbers refer to test numbers on diagnostic chart.

1) With ignition on, test light should illuminate for 2 seconds as relay powers up fuel pump.

2) If a short is present, check circuit No. 120, fuel pump or PCM. Normal circuit resistance is 3-4 ohms.

3) If test light is on steadily, the non-switched portion of fuel pump circuit is shorted.

4) Checks for PCM shorting circuit No. 120 to ground.

5) Checks for short inside fuel tank.

6) Checks fuel pump for short. Check sender harness connector.

7) Checks circuit No. 120 for short to ground.

8) Checks for grounded fuel pump test point, then connection at relay, oil pressure sensor, then diagnose for harness shorted to ground.

Notes On Intermittents – If fuel pump circuit is grounded, fuse will blow and Code E20 will set. Replace fuse, start engine and allow to idle. Manipulate affected circuit(s). If fault occurs, fuse will blow again and engine will stall.

91F07669   91H07707

GM
1-162

1991 ENGINE PERFORMANCE
Self-Diagnostics – DeVille & Fleetwood PCM/BCM (Cont.)

PCM CODE E21, SHORTED THROTTLE POSITION SENSOR CIRCUIT (VOLTAGE HIGH)

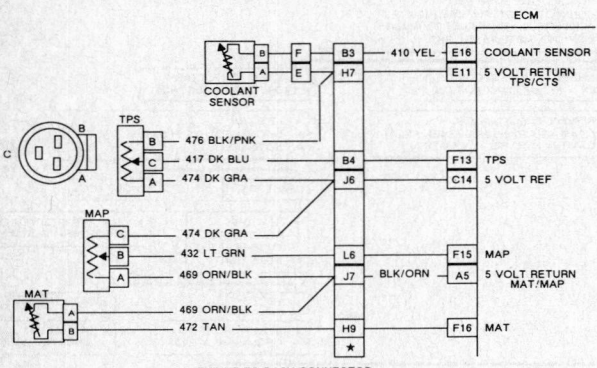

★ ENGINE TO DASH CONNECTOR

The TPS is a 3-wire sensor or potentiometer with a 5-volt reference input from PCM to sensor circuit No. 474. This is a reference ground from PCM to sensor circuit No. 476 and a sensor output signal circuit No. 417 from sensor to PCM. The sensor output signal is a DC voltage that varies with throttle angle. At low throttle angle, TPS signal voltage is low (about .5 volt at minimum air setting). The PCM uses TPS information to determine idle, WOT and proper fuel mixture.

TEST CONDITIONS: 25-3000 RPM

FAILURE CONDITIONS: TPS value greater than or equal to 72 degrees for .7 seconds

ACTION TAKEN:
- PCM turns on SERVICE ENGINE SOON light
- PCM disables VCC
- PCM uses 13 degrees for TPS value with ISC throttle switch open and 6 degrees for TPS value when ISC throttle switch closes
- Fourth gear disabled.

NOTE: Test numbers refer to test numbers on diagnostic chart.

1) Checks for shorted TPS or shorted wiring. If data value stays greater than -7 with TPS disconnected, problem is in wiring.

90F17264   90J14752

2) Check circuit No. 476 for an open between TPS and PCM. An open circuit will result in high TPS values whenever TPS is plugged in.

Note On Intermittents – If Code E21 is stored as history, manipulate related wiring while observing PCM parameter P.0.1. Check TPS and TPS test point connectors for short to voltage.
Cycle TPS through its travel and tap on TPS with a pencil or pocket screwdriver, to test for intermittent TPS. If fault is induced, parameter P.0.1 will momentarily skip to 72 degrees or greater. If wiring connector is okay, substitute a known good TPS and retest.

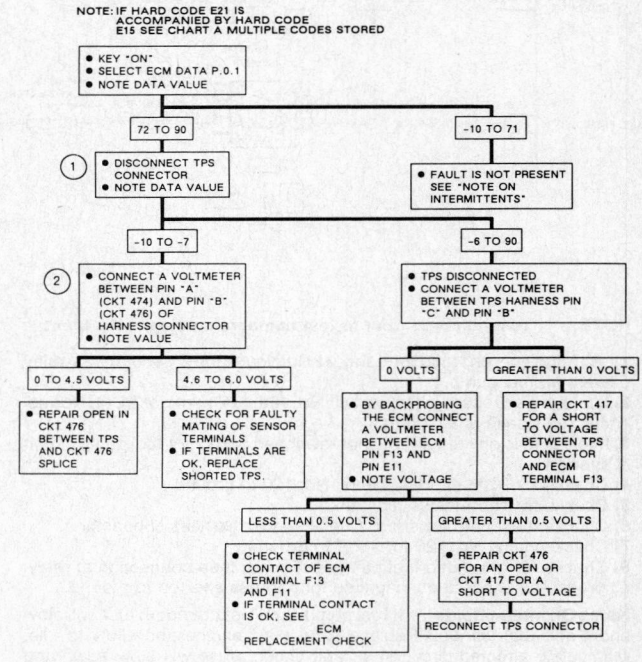

WHEN ALL DIAGNOSIS AND REPAIRS ARE COMPLETED. CLEAR CODES AND VERIFY OPERATION

Courtesy of General Motors Corp.

1991 ENGINE PERFORMANCE
Self-Diagnostics – DeVille & Fleetwood PCM/BCM (Cont.)

GM
1-163

PCM CODE E22, OPEN
THROTTLE POSITION SENSOR CIRCUIT

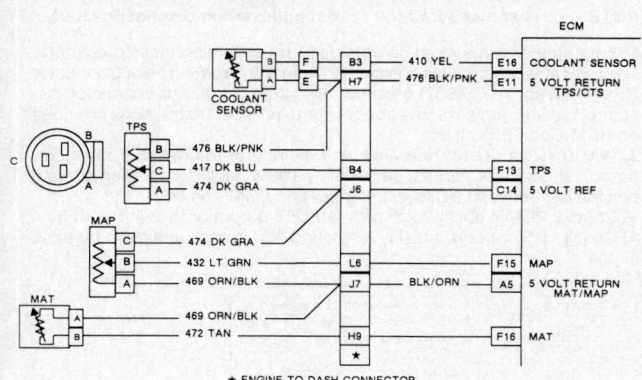

Note On Intermittents – If PCM Code E22 is stored as history, manipulate related wiring while observing PCM parameter P.0.1. Check TPS test point for short to ground. Cycle TPS through its travel and tap on TPS with a pencil or pocket screwdriver to test for intermittent TPS. If fault is induced, PCM data P.0.1 will momentarily skip to 72 degrees or greater. If wiring is okay, substitute known good TPS and retest.

NOTE: IF A HARD CODE E22 IS ACCOMPANIED BY HARD CODE E32, SEE PCM CHART A, 'MULIPLE PCM CODES STORED HARD'

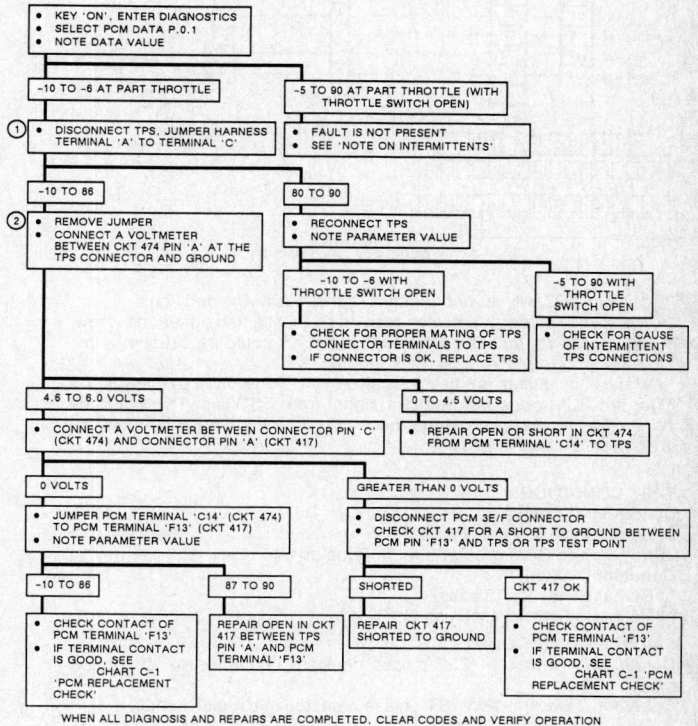

WHEN ALL DIAGNOSIS AND REPAIRS ARE COMPLETED, CLEAR CODES AND VERIFY OPERATION

The TPS is a 3-wire sensor or potentiometer with 5-volt reference input from PCM to sensor circuit No. 474. Ground is provided on circuit No. 476. The TPS signal circuit No. 417 varies between ground and 5 volts, based on the position of throttle plates. At low throttle angle, TPS signal voltage is low. The PCM uses TPS information to determine idle, WOT and proper air/fuel mixture.

TEST CONDITIONS: RPM greater than or equal to 600

FAILURE CONDITIONS: TPS of 1.3 degrees or less for .7 seconds

ACTION TAKEN:
- PCM turns on SERVICE SOON light
- PCM disables VCC
- PCM uses 13 degrees for TPS value with ISC throttle switch open and 6 degrees for TPS value when ISC throttle switch closes

NOTE: Test numbers refer to test numbers on diagnostic chart.

1) Checks for shorted TPS or shorted wiring. If data value stays greater than -7 with TPS disconnected, problem is in wiring.
2) Checks circuit No. 476 for an open between TPS and PCM. An open in circuit No. 476 will result in high TPS values whenever TPS is plugged in.

GM
1-164

1991 ENGINE PERFORMANCE
Self-Diagnostics – DeVille & Fleetwood PCM/BCM (Cont.)

PCM CODE E23, EST CIRCUIT PROBLEM (1 OF 2)

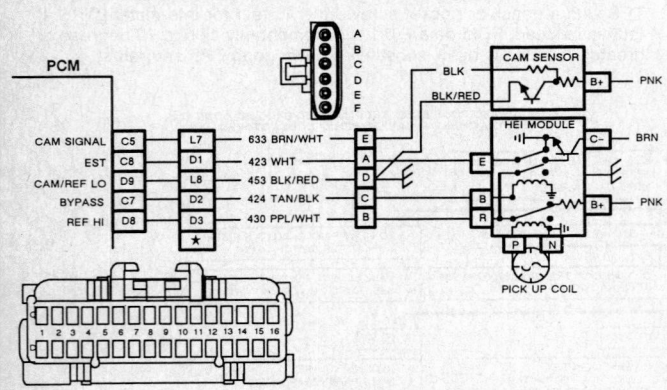

★ ENGINE TO DASH CONNECTOR

PCM Code E23 will set under either of the following conditions:
• Reference pulses are being received by PCM and by-pass line is low, but PCM detects pulses on the EST line. This could be caused by by-pass line shorted to voltage at distributor.
• Reference pulses are being received by PCM and the by-pass line is high, but PCM does not detect a signal from EST line. This could be caused by an open or shorted ground circuit on EST line or by-pass line is open or shorted to ground.

TEST CONDITIONS:
Condition 1 (Crank)
1) By-pass line low (zero volts)
2) Key on and RPM greater than or equal to 648
Condition 2 (Run)
1) By-pass line high (5 volts)
2) Reference pulses received by PCM

FAILURE CONDITIONS:
Condition 1 (Crank) – EST pulses detected on circuit No. 423 in by-pass
Condition 2 (Run) – No EST pulses detected in circuit No. 423

90F17256   90B14754

ACTION TAKEN:
• PCM turns on SERVICE ENGINE SOON light
• PCM controlled spark is disabled for ignition cycle

NOTE: Test numbers refer to test numbers on diagnostic chart.

1) Four jumper wires must be obtained for use in diagnostic procedure. The jumper wires should be about 12" long with Weatherpack Connector (12014836 and 12014837) on either end. With distributor connector disconnected, use jumpers to reconnect terminals per instructions provided on PCM Code E23 chart.
2) With only distributor reference and distributor reference ground jumpered, engine will run at back-up spark. Check for proper ground connection between PCM and engine, and PCM and HEI.
3) Checks PCM's ability to provide an EST output on circuit No. 423.
4) Checks HEI module's ability to ground EST signal with open by-pass circuit.

NOTE: USE ESSENTIAL TOOL J35616 TO JUMPER HARNESS CONNECTORS.

① • DISCONNECT 6-WAY WEATHERPACK CONNECTOR AT DISTRIBUTOR
• JUMPER DISTRIBUTOR PIN "B" TO HARNESS PIN "B" (DISTRIBUTOR REFERENCE)
• JUMPER DISTRIBUTOR PIN "D" TO HARNESS PIN "D" (DISTRIBUTOR REFERENCE GROUND)
• START ENGINE AND IDLE UNTIL WARM
• USE KENT-MOORE J-34029-A DVOM SET TO 20 VOLT SCALE
② • MEASURE VOLTAGE FROM PIN "D" JUMPER TO BATTERY NEGATIVE TERMINAL

VOLTAGE IS -0.8 TO +0.8 GROUNDS ARE OK

VOLTAGE LESS THAN -0.8 OR GREATER THAN +0.8

③ • ENGINE RUNNING. MEASURE VOLTAGE FROM HARNESS PIN "A" (EST SIGNAL) TO GROUND
• VOLTAGE SHOULD BE .5 TO 2.0 VOLTS

• REPAIR POOR GROUND FROM ECM TERMINALS D1, A12, D7 (CKT 450) TO BATTERY NEGATIVE
• CHECK CKT 453 FOR GOOD CONNECTION TO ECM TERMINAL D9 AND TO DISTRIBUTOR BASE AT CAPACITOR HOLD DOWN SCREW

VOLTAGE OK   VOLTAGE NOT OK

• CHECK FOR OPEN/GROUNDED CKT 423 FROM ECM TERMINAL C8 TO DISTRIBUTOR HARNESS PIN "A"
• CHECK CONTACT OF TERMINAL C8 TO ECM
• IF CONTACT IS OK, SEE "ECM PEPLACEMENT CHECK"

④ • ENGINE RUNNING. JUMPER DISTRIBUTOR PIN "A" TO HARNESS PIN "A"
• MEASURE VOLTAGE FROM PIN "A" JUMPER TO GROUND
• VOLTAGE SHOULD BE LESS THAN .5 VOLTS

VOLTAGE OK

CONTINUE ON CHART E23
2 of 2

• VOLTAGE NOT OK.
• MODULE NOT GROUNDING EST CIRCUIT WITH BYPASS OPEN

• CHECK FOR OPEN BETWEEN DISTRIBUTOR PIN "A" TO MODULE PIN "E"
• CHECK FOR PROPER MODULE PART NUMBER
• IF CIRCUIT IS OK, REPLACE IGNITION MODULE AND RETEST

WHEN ALL DIAGNOSIS AND REPAIRS ARE COMPLETED, CLEAR CODES AND VERIFY OPERATION

Courtesy of General Motors Corp.

PCM CODE E23, EST CIRCUIT PROBLEM (2 OF 2)

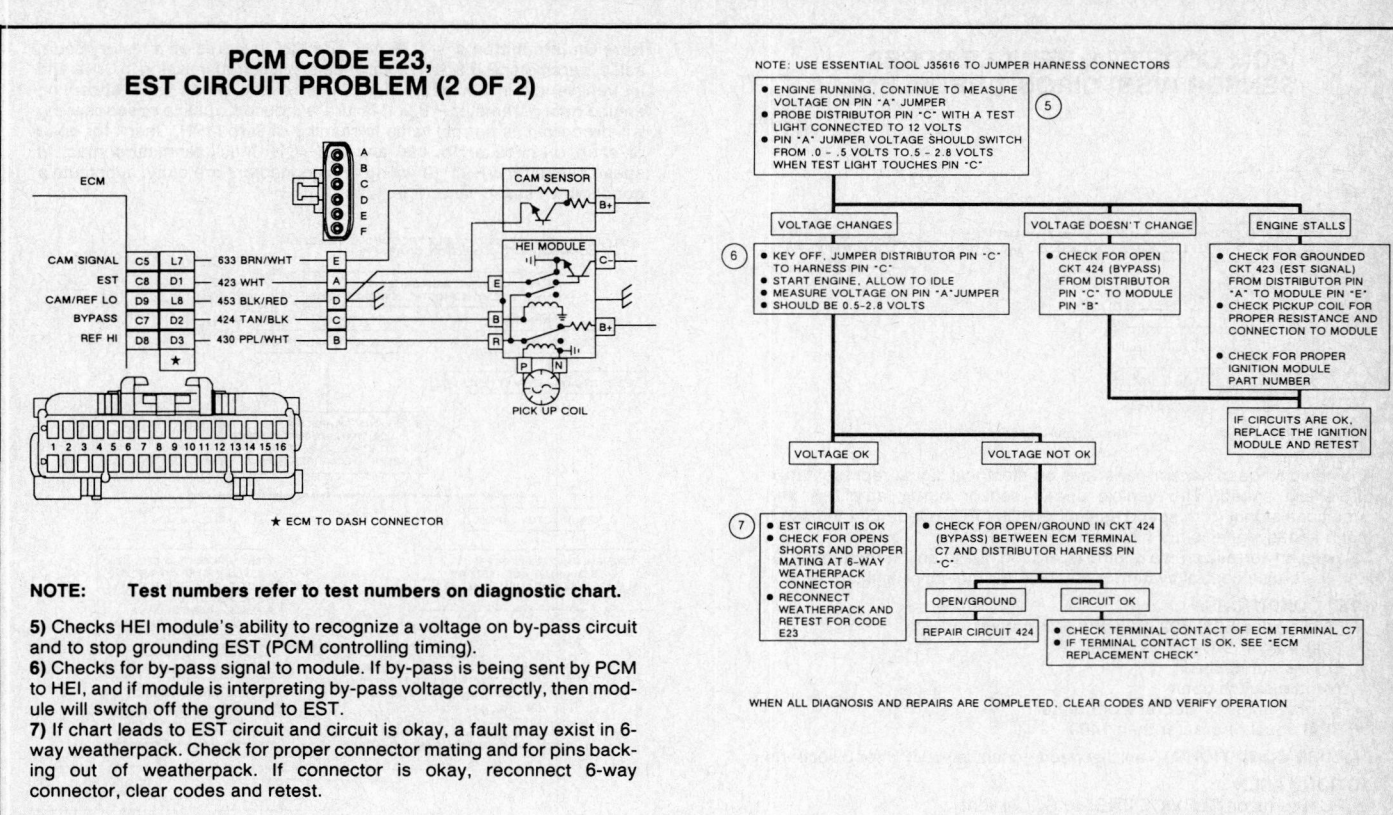

NOTE: Test numbers refer to test numbers on diagnostic chart.

5) Checks HEI module's ability to recognize a voltage on by-pass circuit and to stop grounding EST (PCM controlling timing).

6) Checks for by-pass signal to module. If by-pass is being sent by PCM to HEI, and if module is interpreting by-pass voltage correctly, then module will switch off the ground to EST.

7) If chart leads to EST circuit and circuit is okay, a fault may exist in 6-way weatherpack. Check for proper connector mating and for pins backing out of weatherpack. If connector is okay, reconnect 6-way connector, clear codes and retest.

90F17256   90C14755

Courtesy of General Motors Corp.

GM
1-166

1991 ENGINE PERFORMANCE
Self-Diagnostics – DeVille & Fleetwood PCM/BCM (Cont.)

PCM CODE E24, VEHICLE SPEED SENSOR (VSS) CIRCUIT PROBLEM

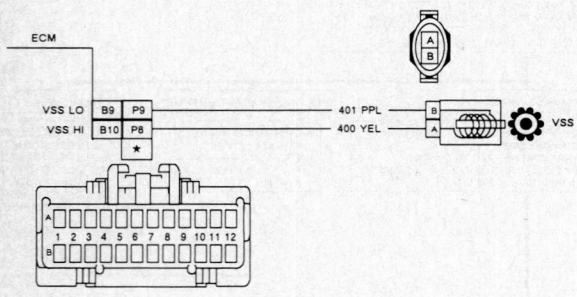

★ ENGINE TO DASH CONNECTOR

The vehicle speed sensor generates an electrical signal representative of vehicle speed. The vehicle speed sensor buffer amplifies and conditions signal from speed sensor to PCM. PCM Code E24 indicates that a speed signal is not being received by PCM.

To avoid any erratic cruise control operation due to an intermittent problem, the cruise control system is disabled for the entire ignition cycle.

TEST CONDITIONS:
- PCM Codes E21, E22, E26 and E27 not set
- Gear shift in Drive or Reverse
- Brakes not applied
- Throttle switch open
- Throttle angle 17 degrees or greater
- RPM equal or greater than 1400

FAILURE CONDITIONS: Vehicle speed equals zero MPH for 3 seconds

ACTION TAKEN:
- PCM turns on SERVICE ENGINE SOON light
- Disables VCC and cruise for entire key cycle
- 3rd and 4th gear disabled

NOTE: Test numbers refer to test numbers on diagnostic chart.

1) Vehicle speed sensor provides an AC voltage signal to PCM depending on vehicle speed. With wheels turning, signal to PCM should be greater than .5 volt AC.

90J17268   90D14756

Note On Intermittents – If PCM Code E24 is stored as a history code, select parameter P.0.9. Lift drive wheels, place transmission in Drive and let vehicle idle in low gear. Manipulate related wiring while observing engine data parameter P.0.9. If failure is induced, vehicle speed reading will drop from its normal value to reading of zero MPH. Check for open or short on circuits No. 400 and No. 401. Check terminal contact at speed sensor and PCM. If wiring and connectors are okay, substitute a good known sensor and repeat test.

NOTE: DO NOT USE THIS TROUBLE TREE WHILE VEHICLE IS
CONNECTED TO A BATTERY CHARGER.

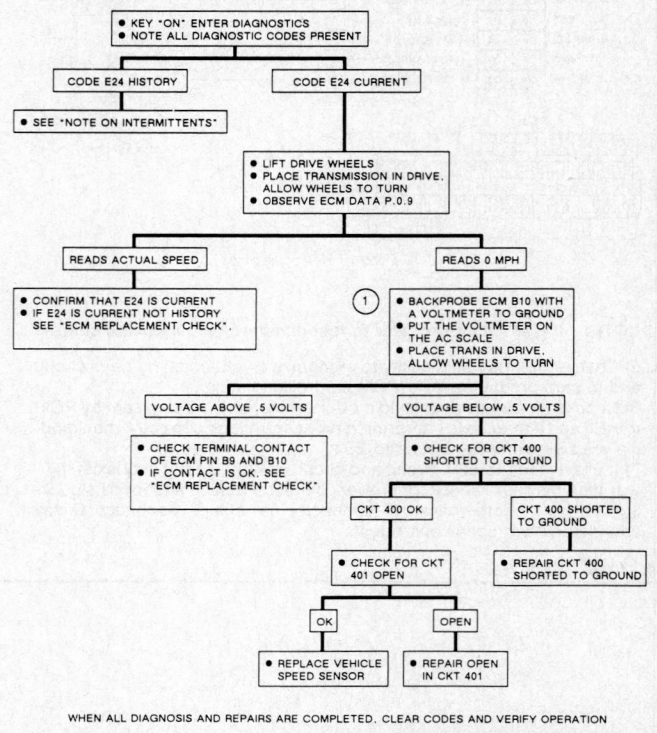

WHEN ALL DIAGNOSIS AND REPAIRS ARE COMPLETED, CLEAR CODES AND VERIFY OPERATION

Courtesy of General Motors Corp.

1991 ENGINE PERFORMANCE
Self-Diagnostics – DeVille & Fleetwood PCM/BCM (Cont.)

GM
1-167

PCM CODE E26, SHORTED THROTTLE SWITCH CIRCUIT

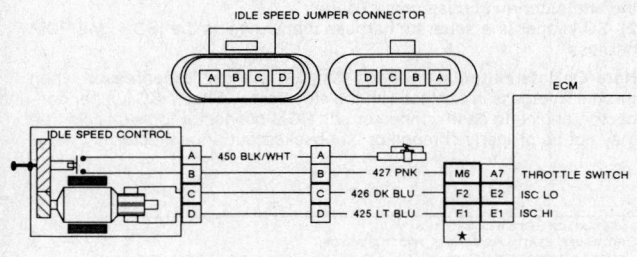

★ ENGINE TO DASH CONNECTOR

The throttle switch is part of ISC motor assembly. Terminal "B" of ISC motor 4-way weatherpack connector is throttle switch input to PCM. The PCM provides a 5-volt signal to circuit No. 427. When throttle lever contacts ISC plunger, throttle switch closes. When throttle switch is closed, input voltage is low. Code E26 sets when PCM detects a TPS signal greater than 20 degrees with throttle switch in closed position.

TEST CONDITIONS:
- PCM Codes E21 and E22 not set
- TPS value 20-75 degrees

FAILURE CONDITIONS: Throttle switch input to PCM grounded for 1.8 seconds

ACTION TAKEN:
- PCM turns on SERVICE ENGINE SOON light
- PCM assumes throttle switch is closed if brakes are applied and TPS is less than 18 degrees
- PCM assumes throttle switch is open if brakes are not applied, or TPS is greater than 18 degrees

NOTE: Test numbers refer to test numbers on diagnostic chart.

1) If PCM does not detect that throttle switch has opened or closed, the Fuel Data Center (FDC) will display E.7.2.
2) When PCM detects that switch opens and closes, the FDC will alternately display E.7.2 and 00.
3) Checks for high TPS voltage. Check TPS or TPS circuit.

4) If TPS and TPS circuit are okay, check PCM. Before PCM is replaced, perform PFI CHART C-1, PCM REPLACEMENT CHECK.

Note On Intermittents – Select PCM switch test. Manipulate ISC connector, ISC wiring and PCM connector. Observe display. If throttle switch state changes momentarily, 00 will appear on the display. Check for intermittent open or short in TPS wiring. Manipulate TPS connector and wiring while observing PCM data P.0.1 and watch for TPS value to jump to greater than 20 degrees at closed throttle.

NOTE: TO ENTER ECM SWITCH TEST THE CRUISE CONTROL ON/OFF SWITCH MUST BE IN THE ON POSITION BEFORE DEPRESSING THE BRAKE PEDAL.

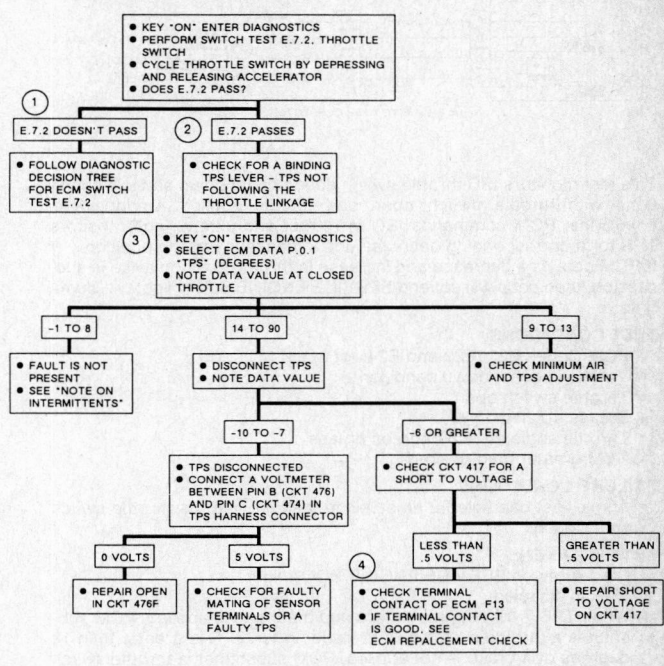

WHEN ALL DIAGNOSIS AND REPAIRS ARE COMPLETED, CLEAR CODES AND VERIFY OPERATION

90B17667   90E14757

Courtesy of General Motors Corp.

GM
1-168

1991 ENGINE PERFORMANCE
Self-Diagnostics – DeVille & Fleetwood PCM/BCM (Cont.)

PCM CODE E27,
OPEN THROTTLE SWITCH CIRCUIT

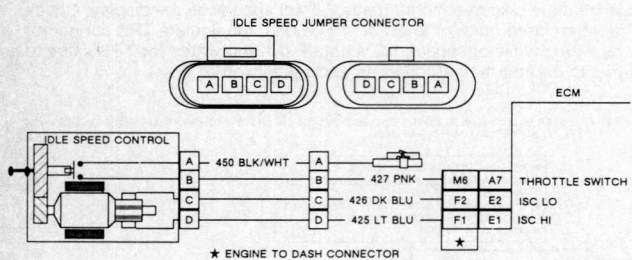

This test monitors ISC throttle switch during coast down and idle conditions with throttle switch open and brakes applied. Under these conditions, PCM commands ISC to retract and extend, and monitors TPS for a corresponding decrease and increase in throttle position.
If PCM detects a decrease and increase in throttle position twice in succession, then code will set and SERVICE ENGINE SOON light will illuminate.

TEST CONDITIONS:
- PCM Codes E21, E22 and E24 not set
- Vehicle in coast down condition
- Throttle switch open
- Brakes applied
- Throttle angle at 16.5 degrees or less
- RPM greater than desired

FAILURE CONDITIONS:
- Above test has failed 2 times since the last time the throttle switch was closed

ACTION TAKEN:
- PCM turns on SERVICE ENGINE SOON light
- EGR is disabled
- When TPS is 18 degrees or less and the brake is applied, PCM substitutes a throttle switch closed value. When TPS is greater than 18 degrees or if brake is not applied, PCM substitutes a throttle switch open value.

NOTE: **Test numbers refer to test numbers on diagnostic chart.**

1) The PCM harness connector for the ISC jumper is located between the alternator and cruise control servo.
2) ISC jumper is a separate harness that connects the ISC to the PCM harness.

Note On Intermittents – Check that ISC plunger is depressed when throttle linkage is in contact with the stop screw. Check ISC jumper connector, engine to dash connector and PCM connector for terminals that may not be properly crimped or has backed out of connector.

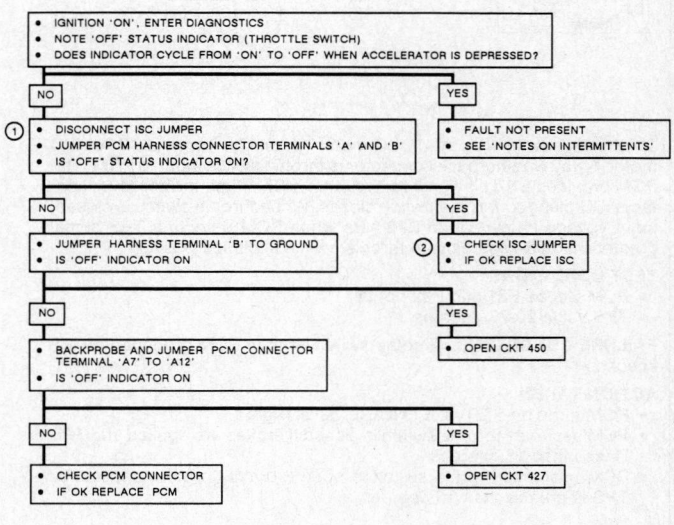

WHEN ALL DIAGNOSIS AND REPAIRS ARE COMPLETED, CLEAR CODES AND VERIFY OPERATION

90A17269   91D07710

Courtesy of General Motors Corp.

1991 ENGINE PERFORMANCE
Self-Diagnostics – DeVille & Fleetwood PCM/BCM (Cont.)

GM
1-169

PCM CODE E30, IDLE SPEED CONTROL CIRCUIT PROBLEM

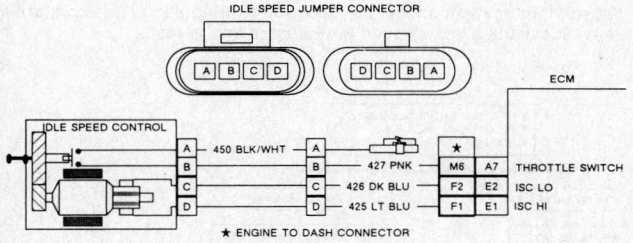

IDLE SPEED JUMPER CONNECTOR

The PCM controls engine idle by increasing or decreasing throttle opening using ISC motor. The ISC will control idle speed anytime throttle switch is closed.

PCM Code E30 sets because the actual RPM never reaches the desired RPM, signifying a slow or failed ISC motor. ISC motor connector is located behind alternator.

TEST CONDITIONS:
- PCM Codes E21, E22, E24, E26 and E27 not set
- Throttle switch closed
- Vehicle speed is zero
- Battery voltage greater than or equal to 11.0 volts
- Actual RPM and command RPM difference is 152 RPM or greater
- Engine has been running more than 7 seconds
- Engine not receiving power steering load
- PCM is not commanding an anticipated idle speed

FAILURE CONDITIONS:
- TPS at 14 degrees or greater and ISC is retracting for 15 seconds
- TPS at 2 degrees and ISC is extending for 15 seconds

ACTION TAKEN: PCM turns on SERVICE ENGINE SOON light for entire key cycle

NOTE: Test numbers refer to test numbers on diagnostic chart.

1) Checks for proper throttle switch, brake switch and park/neutral switch operation. The PCM must receive accurate switch status information in order to control idle.

2) Checks for proper ISC motor operation.

3) Many engine fuel and emissions system faults may cause unstable idle. If base engine idle is not steady, ISC may not be able to control idle speed to within 152 RPM of commanded idle speed.

Note On Intermittents – Display PCM parameter P.0.1. Manipulate TPS wiring and connectors. Watch for TPS valve to jump or skip. Enter output cycling and manipulate ISC wiring and connectors. Watch for ISC to stop cycling. Enter diagnostics and observe throttle switch status light (OFF). Check for binding throttle linkage or weak throttle return spring. If status light flashes, check for intermittent open circuit on circuit No. 427. Verify minimum air RPM, ISC and TPS are set to specification.

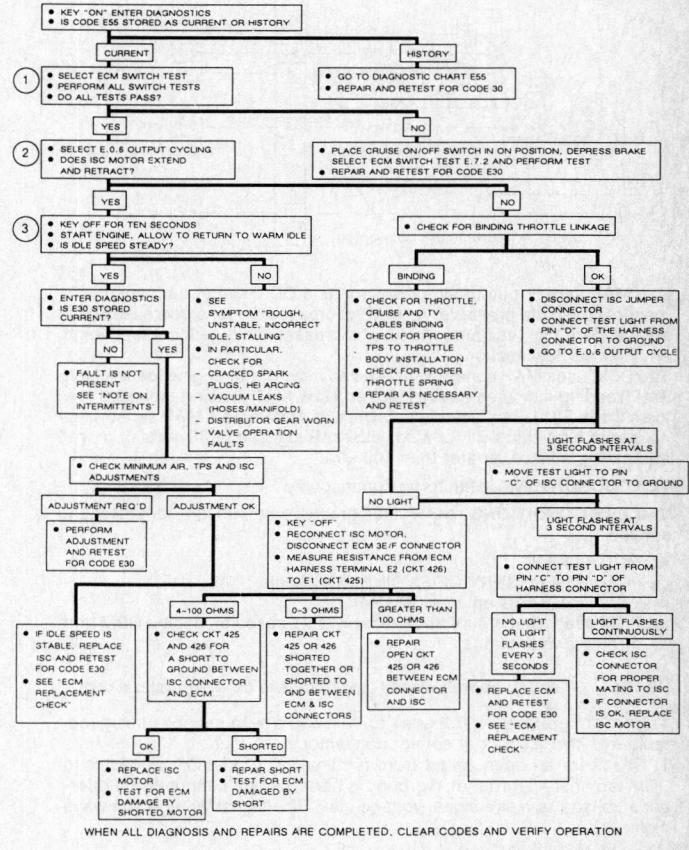

WHEN ALL DIAGNOSIS AND REPAIRS ARE COMPLETED, CLEAR CODES AND VERIFY OPERATION

90A17269   90J14760

GM
1-170

1991 ENGINE PERFORMANCE
Self-Diagnostics – DeVille & Fleetwood PCM/BCM (Cont.)

PCM CODE E31, SHORTED MAP SENSOR CIRCUIT

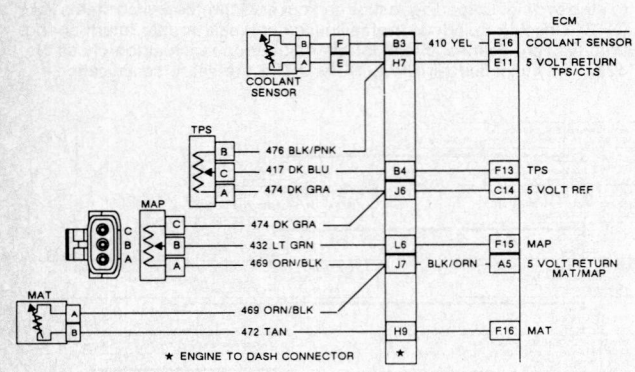

The MAP sensor output signal voltage is a DC voltage that varies with manifold absolute pressure. As MAP decreases, voltage decreases (low engine load, high vacuum). As MAP increases, voltage increases (high engine load, low vacuum).

The PCM uses MAP sensor values as an indicator of engine load. A high MAP reading indicates heavy load, and low MAP reading indicates low load. Code E31 is designed to set when PCM detects a MAP sensor signal out of high side limit, or also with MAP signal at 4.85 volts or more, and having a value greater than 108 kPa.

TEST CONDITIONS: Monitored continuously

FAILURE CONDITIONS: MAP value greater than 108 kPa for at least .2 second

ACTION TAKEN:
- PCM turns on SERVICE ENGINE SOON light
- PCM sets BARO equal to 92 kPa
- PCM uses a substitute MAP sensor value based on engine RPM and throttle switch status

NOTE: Test numbers refer to test numbers on diagnostic chart.

1) If PCM parameter P.0.2 goes to 14-16 kPa with sensor unplugged, fault is at MAP sensor or sensor connector.
2) Check for an open circuit from terminal "A" of sensor connector to PCM terminal A5 (ground). If ground is open, sensor cannot divide reference voltage to make signal voltage vary. The signal voltage is always high.

90F17264   90A14761

Note On Intermittents – Manipulate affected wiring and connectors while observing PCM parameter P.0.2. Apply and release vacuum to MAP sensor vacuum port using a vacuum source. If PCM parameter P.0.2 displays greater than 108 kPa, condition has been induced and cause of intermittent should be repaired. If wiring and connectors are okay, substitute a known good MAP sensor and re-test.

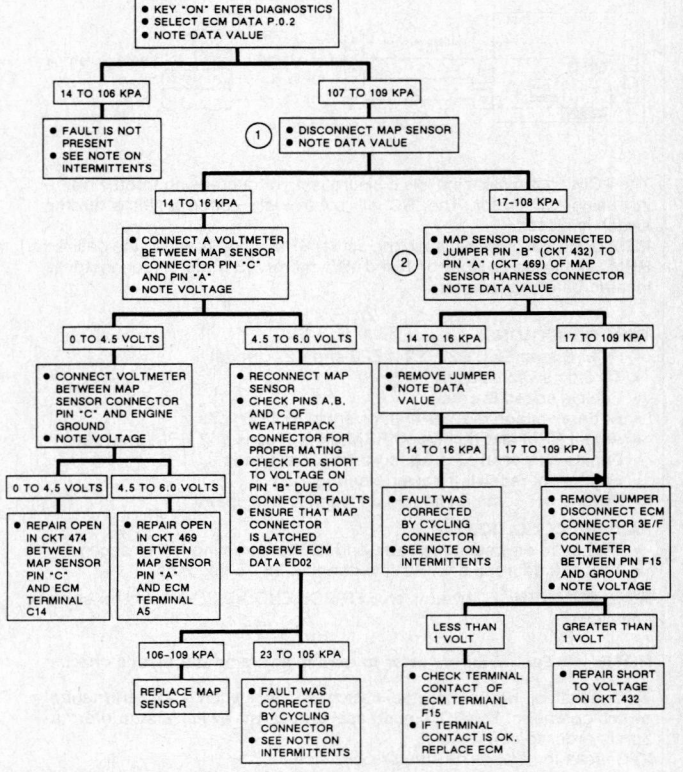

WHEN ALL DIAGNOSIS AND REPAIRS ARE COMPLETED, CLEAR CODES AND VERIFY OPERATION

1991 ENGINE PERFORMANCE
Self-Diagnostics – DeVille & Fleetwood PCM/BCM (Cont.)

GM
1-171

PCM CODE E32, OPEN MAP SENSOR CIRCUIT

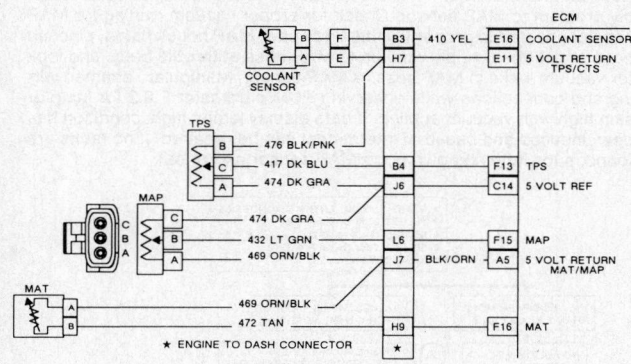

The MAP sensor changes resistance based upon manifold vacuum. PCM provides a 5 volt reference and ground. The MAP signal varies between ground and 5 volts as manifold vacuum varies. PCM Code E32 sets when PCM detects a MAP sensor signal that is too low.

TEST CONDITIONS:

Condition 1:
- RPM less than or equal to 700
- TPS 13 degrees or greater
- Throttle switch closed

Condition 2:
- RPM less than or equal to 1800
- TPS 13 degrees or greater
- Throttle switch open
- Not in Park or Neutral

FAILURE CONDITIONS: MAP value 15 kPa or less for .2 second

ACTION TAKEN:
- PCM turns on SERVICE ENGINE SOON light
- PCM sets BARO to 92 kPa
- PCM uses a substitute MAP sensor value based on engine RPM and throttle switch status (open or closed)

NOTE: Test numbers refer to test numbers on diagnostic chart.

1) Checks for sensor/PCM circuitry ability to respond to a 5-volt signal on MAP input. A reading of 106-109 kPa means wiring and PCM are okay.

2) Checks for 5-volt reference signal at sensor connector.
3) Checks circuit No. 432 for short to ground.
4) Checks PCM's ability to respond to a 5-volt signal voltage on MAP input.
5) Fault is most likely at PCM connector or PCM. Before PCM is replaced, perform PFI CHART C-1, PCM REPLACEMENT CHECK in this article.

Note On Intermittents – Manipulate affected wiring and connectors while observing PCM parameter P.0.2. Apply and release vacuum to MAP sensor vacuum port using a vacuum source. If PCM parameter P.0.2 displays less than 15 kPa, condition has been induced and cause of intermittent can be repaired.

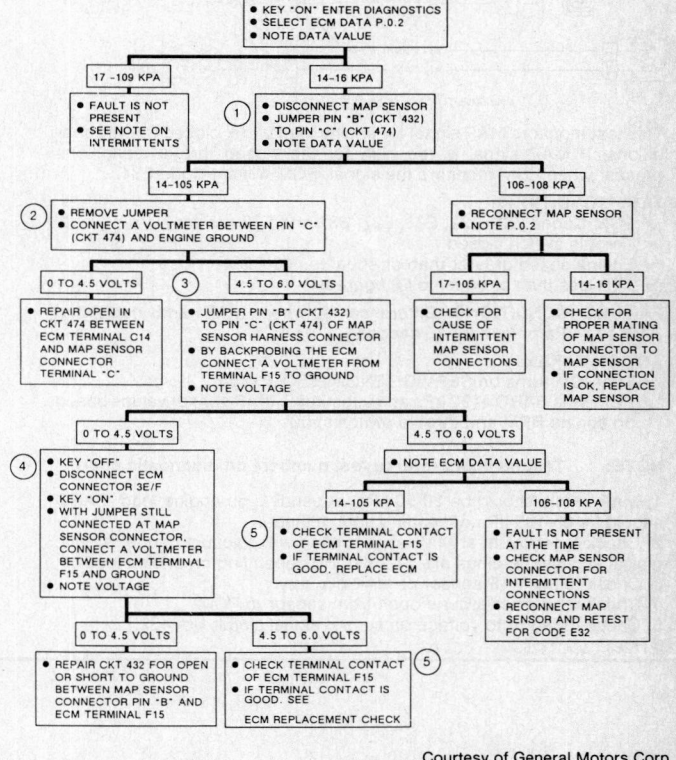

90F17264   90B14762

GM
1-172

1991 ENGINE PERFORMANCE
Self-Diagnostics – DeVille & Fleetwood PCM/BCM (Cont.)

PCM CODE E34,
MAP SIGNAL TOO HIGH

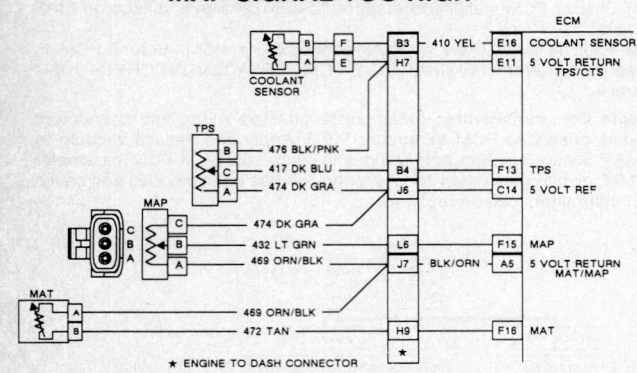

★ ENGINE TO DASH CONNECTOR

This test monitors MAP signal for engine load under closed throttle conditions. If MAP signal is too high for the closed throttle conditions present when PCM monitors the signal, PCM will set Code E34.

TEST CONDITIONS:
- PCM Codes E21, E22, E26, E27, E31 and E32 not set
- Throttle switch closed
- Engine speed greater than or equal to 400 RPM
- TPS less than or equal to 18 degrees

FAILURE CONDITIONS: Difference between MAP and calculated BARO 11 kPa or less for 15 seconds

ACTION TAKEN:
- The PCM turns on SERVICE ENGINE SOON light
- PCM sets BARO at 92 kPa and substitutes MAP sensor values based on engine RPM and throttle switch status

NOTE: Test numbers refer to test numbers on diagnostic chart.

1) MAP at idle should be 30-50 kPa, depending on engine load. BARO should be 85-105 kPa depending upon altitude.
2) Check for vacuum at MAP sensor hose with vacuum gauge. At idle, typical vacuum readings are 14-20 in. Hg depending on engine load.
3) Check faulty MAP sensor or MAP circuitry.
4) Check for sensor ground open from sensor to PCM.
5) Check for short to voltage on sensor signal circuit No. 432.

90F17264   90C14763

6) Fault is most likely at PCM connector or PCM. Before PCM is replaced, perform PFI CHART C-1, PCM REPLACEMENT CHECK in this article.

Note On Intermittents – PCM Code E34 is usually set by a vacuum supply problem to MAP sensor. Check for proper vacuum routing for MAP hose connected to proper throttle body port, MAP hose chafed, pinched hose or cut hose. Apply vacuum to MAP hose at throttle body, and look for vacuum leaks in MAP hose or MAP sensor. Manipulate affected wiring and connections while observing PCM parameter P.0.2 for jump or skip high with vacuum applied. If data display jumps high, condition has been induced and cause of intermittent can be repaired. If no faults are found, substitute a known good MAP sensor and retest.

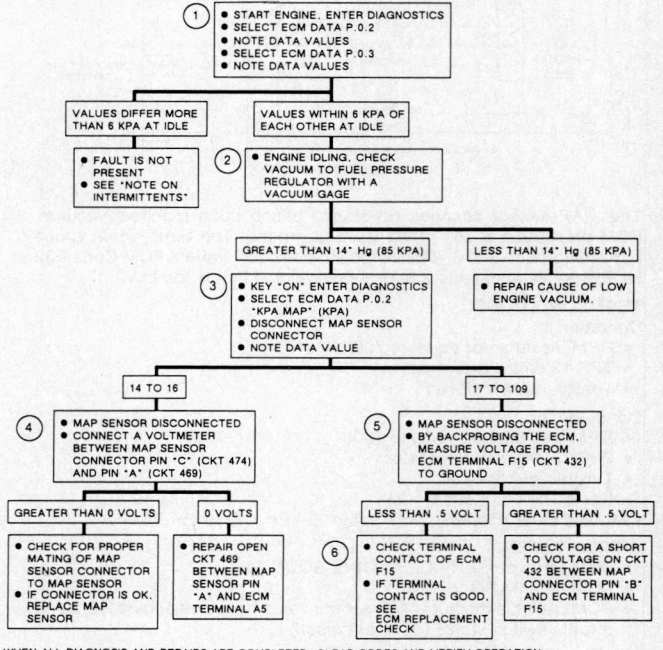

WHEN ALL DIAGNOSIS AND REPAIRS ARE COMPLETED, CLEAR CODES AND VERIFY OPERATION

Courtesy of General Motors Corp.

1991 ENGINE PERFORMANCE
Self-Diagnostics – DeVille & Fleetwood PCM/BCM (Cont.)

GM
1-173

PCM CODE E37, SHORTED MAT SENSOR CIRCUIT

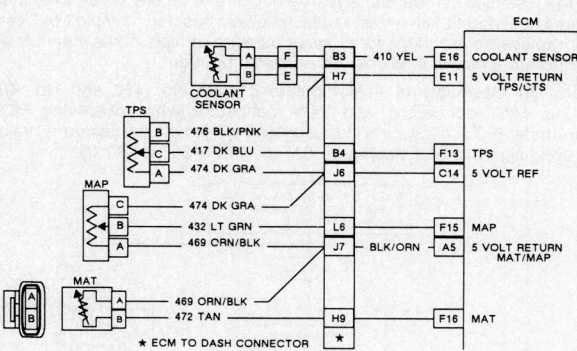

The MAT sensor is a thermistor (temperature sensitive resistor) that varies resistance with changes in temperature. As temperature of the sensor increases, resistance decreases. High temperature will result in low signal voltage.

PCM Code E37 sets when PCM sees a MAT sensor reading of 298°F (148°C) when coolant temperature is less than 212°F (100°C). The MAT sensor connector is located on right rear top of engine, behind the alternator.

TEST CONDITIONS:
- PCM Codes E14 and E15 not set
- Coolant temperature sensor less than or equal to 212°F (100°C)

FAILURE CONDITIONS: MAT sensor value greater than or equal to 298°F (148°C)

ACTION TAKEN:
- PCM turns on SERVICE ENGINE SOON light
- PCM substitutes 104°F (40°C) for MAT when coolant temperature is greater than or equal to 104°F (40°C)
- PCM uses coolant temperature for MAT when coolant temperature is less than or equal to 104°F (40°C)

NOTE: Test numbers refer to test numbers on diagnostic chart.

90F17264   90D14764

1) If MAT sensor is shorted, PCM parameter P.0.5 should read 298°F (148°C) or greater. If not, sensor is not shorted. See NOTE ON INTERMITTENTS.

2) Checks for shorted sensor or shorted circuit No. 472. If PCM parameter P.0.5 stays at 288°-304°F (142°-151°C) with sensor unplugged, short is in circuit No. 472.

3) MAT sensor can be damaged by a backfire in intake. If vehicle has had more than one MAT sensor replaced, check for signs of backfire or high intake manifold temperatures due to improper valve train operation.

4) Fault is most likely at PCM connector or PCM. Before PCM is replaced, perform PFI CHART C-1, PCM REPLACEMENT CHECK in this article.

Note On Intermittents – Manipulate circuit No. 472 wiring, the MAT sensor and PCM connector while observing PCM parameter P.0.5. If failure is induced, manifold air temperature will jump from its normal value to shorted reading of 288°-304°F (142°-151°C).

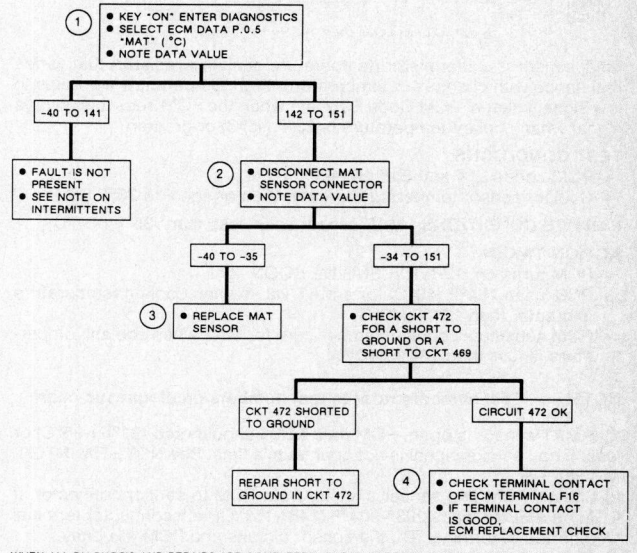

WHEN ALL DIAGNOSIS AND REPAIRS ARE COMPLETED, CLEAR CODES AND VERIFY OPERATION

Courtesy of General Motors Corp.

GM
1-174

1991 ENGINE PERFORMANCE
Self-Diagnostics – DeVille & Fleetwood PCM/BCM (Cont.)

PCM CODE E38,
OPEN MAT SENSOR CIRCUIT

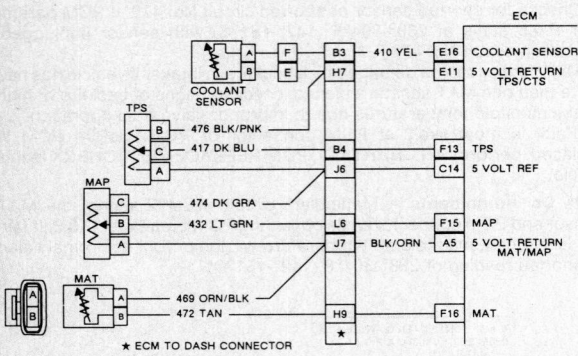

MAT sensor is a thermistor (temperature sensitive resistor) that varies resistance with changes in temperature. High temperature will result in low signal voltage. PCM Code E38 sets when the PCM sees low voltage signal when coolant temperature is 23°F (-5°C) or greater.

TEST CONDITIONS:
- PCM codes E14 and E15 not set
- Coolant sensor temperature greater than or equal to 23°F (-5°C)

FAILURE CONDITIONS: MAT sensor value less than -35°F (-37°C)

ACTION TAKEN:
- PCM turns on SERVICE ENGINE SOON light
- PCM uses 104°F (40°C) for a MAT value when coolant temperature is greater than 104°F (40°C)
- PCM substitutes coolant temperature for MAT when coolant temperature is less than 104°F (40°C)

NOTE: Test numbers refer to test numbers on diagnostic chart.

1) If MAT sensor is open, PCM data ED05 should read -31°F (-35°C) or less. If not, sensor signal is not open at this time. See NOTE ON INTERMITTENTS.
2) Checks PCM and sensor circuitry from PCM to sensor connector. If PCM data ED05 reads 293°-304°F (148°-151°C) with connector terminal "A" shorted to terminal "B", the sensor circuits and PCM are okay.
3) Checks for open sensor ground.

90F17264   90E14765

4) Checks PCM's ability to recognize short to ground on MAT input.
5) Fault is most likely at PCM connector or PCM. Before PCM is replaced, perform PFI CHART C-1, PCM REPLACEMENT CHECK in this article.
6) MAT sensor can be damaged by backfire in intake, or by excessive intake heat due to valve train faults. If vehicle has had multiple MAT sensor replacements, check for signs of backfire or high intake manifold air temperature due to improper valve train operation.

Note On Intermittents – Manipulate circuits No. 472 and No. 469 wiring, MAT connector, and PCM connector while observing PCM parameter P.0.5. If failure is induced, MAT will jump from its normal value to open signal circuit reading of -31° to -40°F (-35° to -40°C).

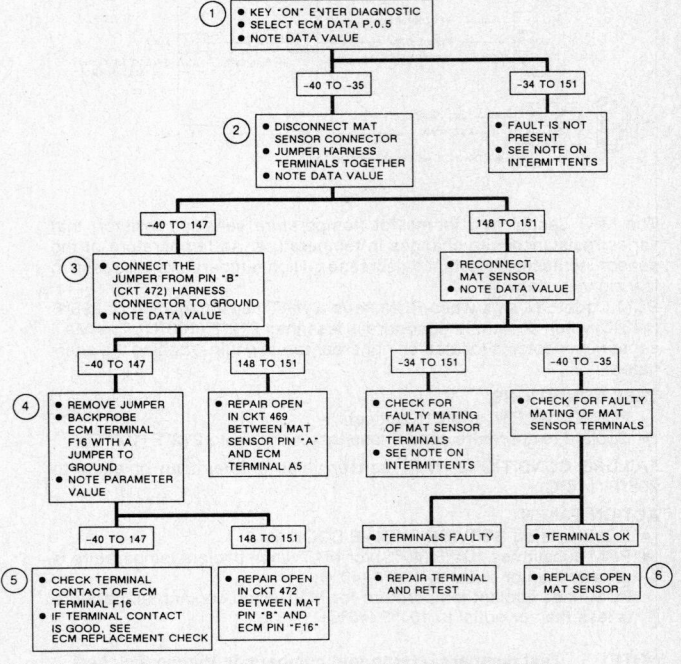

WHEN ALL DIAGNOSIS AND REPAIRS ARE COMPLETED, CLEAR CODES AND VERIFY OPERATION

Courtesy of General Motors Corp.

1991 ENGINE PERFORMANCE
Self-Diagnostics – DeVille & Fleetwood PCM/BCM (Cont.)

GM
1-175

PCM CODE E39, VCC ENGAGEMENT PROBLEM (1 OF 2)

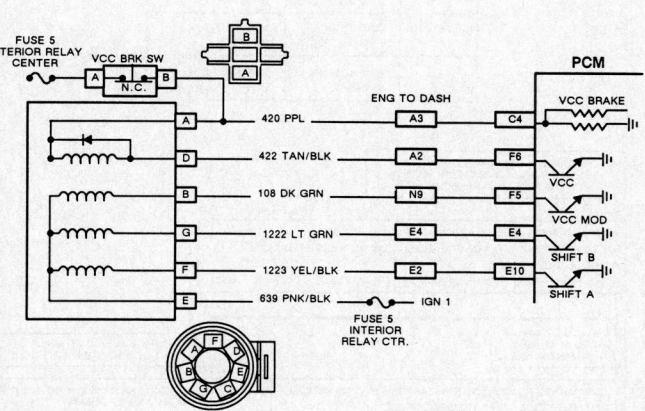

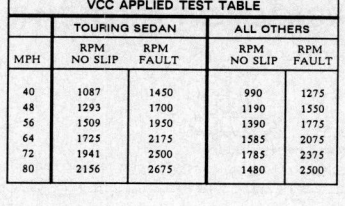

VCC APPLIED TEST TABLE				
	TOURING SEDAN		ALL OTHERS	
MPH	RPM NO SLIP	RPM FAULT	RPM NO SLIP	RPM FAULT
40	1087	1450	990	1275
48	1293	1700	1190	1550
56	1509	1950	1390	1775
64	1725	2175	1585	2075
72	1941	2500	1785	2375
80	2156	2675	1480	2500

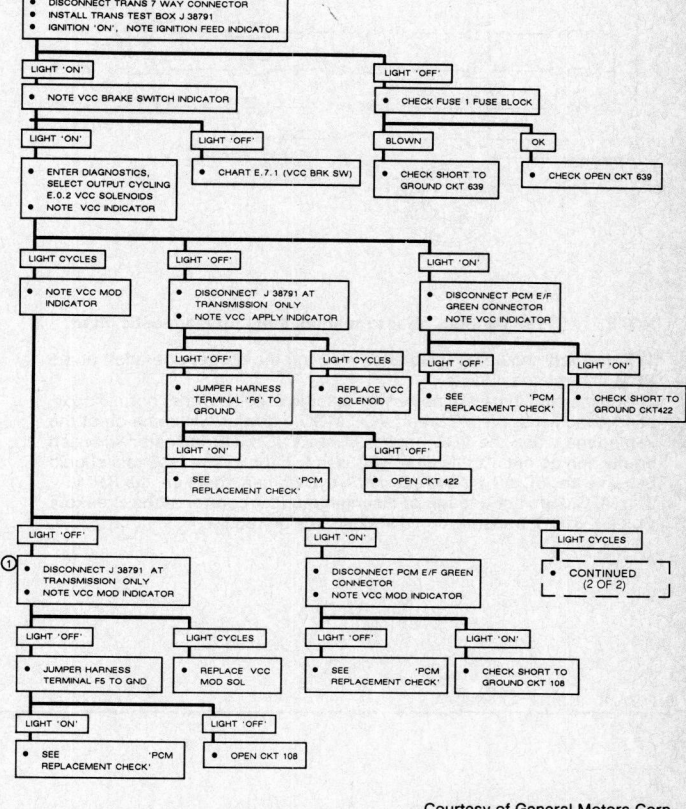

This test monitors VCC engagement for a problem, by comparing engine speed to a speed which should not be possible to achieve unless the viscous clutch is slipping excessively.

TEST CONDITIONS:
- PCM codes E26, E27, E31, E32 and E34 not set
- Transmission is in 4th gear and brake not applied
- Engine speed at 3100 RPM or less
- System in closed loop
- MAP between 29 and 80 kPa
- VCC engaged
- VCC solenoid at 100 percent duty cycle

FAILURE CONDITIONS: Code sets when engine RPM is greater than RPM fault. See VCC APPLIED TEST table

ACTION TAKEN:
- PCM turns on SERVICE ENGINE SOON light and remains on for entire key cycle
- VCC disabled through entire key cycle

NOTE: Test numbers refer to test numbers on diagnostic chart.

1) Testing resistance of VCC solenoids and wiring inside transmission. The road test checks for proper transmission operation.

91F07711 91H07712 91J07713

Courtesy of General Motors Corp.

GM
1-176

1991 ENGINE PERFORMANCE
Self-Diagnostics – DeVille & Fleetwood PCM/BCM (Cont.)

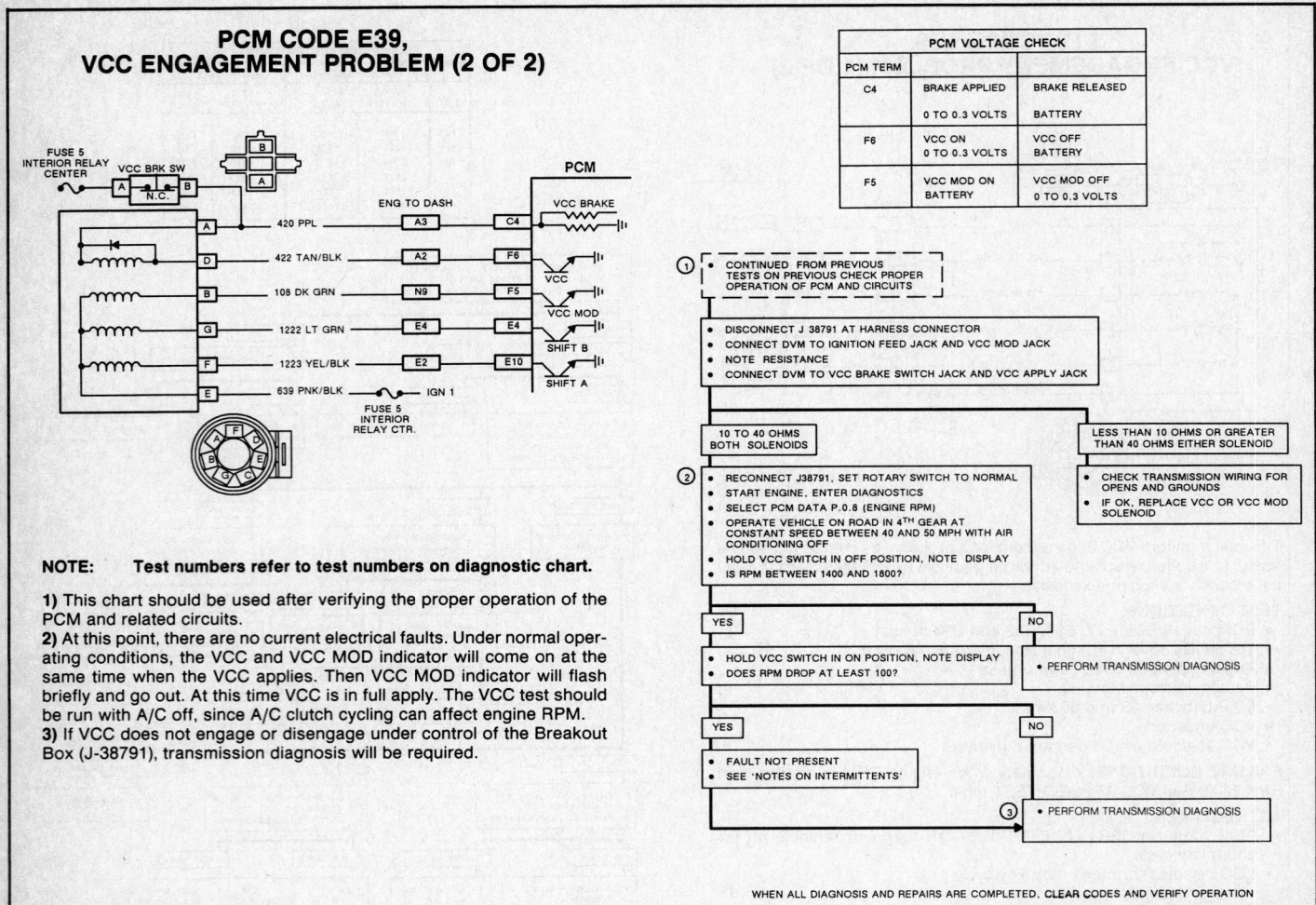

PCM CODE E39, VCC ENGAGEMENT PROBLEM (2 OF 2)

PCM VOLTAGE CHECK		
PCM TERM		
C4	BRAKE APPLIED	BRAKE RELEASED
	0 TO 0.3 VOLTS	BATTERY
F6	VCC ON	VCC OFF
	0 TO 0.3 VOLTS	BATTERY
F5	VCC MOD ON	VCC MOD OFF
	BATTERY	0 TO 0.3 VOLTS

NOTE: Test numbers refer to test numbers on diagnostic chart.

1) This chart should be used after verifying the proper operation of the PCM and related circuits.

2) At this point, there are no current electrical faults. Under normal operating conditions, the VCC and VCC MOD indicator will come on at the same time when the VCC applies. Then VCC MOD indicator will flash briefly and go out. At this time VCC is in full apply. The VCC test should be run with A/C off, since A/C clutch cycling can affect engine RPM.

3) If VCC does not engage or disengage under control of the Breakout Box (J-38791), transmission diagnosis will be required.

① CONTINUED FROM PREVIOUS TESTS ON PREVIOUS CHECK PROPER OPERATION OF PCM AND CIRCUITS

- DISCONNECT J 38791 AT HARNESS CONNECTOR
- CONNECT DVM TO IGNITION FEED JACK AND VCC MOD JACK
- NOTE RESISTANCE
- CONNECT DVM TO VCC BRAKE SWITCH JACK AND VCC APPLY JACK

10 TO 40 OHMS BOTH SOLENOIDS

LESS THAN 10 OHMS OR GREATER THAN 40 OHMS EITHER SOLENOID

②
- RECONNECT J38791, SET ROTARY SWITCH TO NORMAL
- START ENGINE, ENTER DIAGNOSTICS
- SELECT PCM DATA P.0.8 (ENGINE RPM)
- OPERATE VEHICLE ON ROAD IN 4TH GEAR AT CONSTANT SPEED BETWEEN 40 AND 50 MPH WITH AIR CONDITIONING OFF
- HOLD VCC SWITCH IN OFF POSITION, NOTE DISPLAY
- IS RPM BETWEEN 1400 AND 1800?

CHECK TRANSMISSION WIRING FOR OPENS AND GROUNDS
- IF OK, REPLACE VCC OR VCC MOD SOLENOID

YES ... **NO**

- HOLD VCC SWITCH IN ON POSITION, NOTE DISPLAY
- DOES RPM DROP AT LEAST 100?

PERFORM TRANSMISSION DIAGNOSIS

YES ... **NO**

- FAULT NOT PRESENT
- SEE 'NOTES ON INTERMITTENTS'

③ PERFORM TRANSMISSION DIAGNOSIS

WHEN ALL DIAGNOSIS AND REPAIRS ARE COMPLETED, CLEAR CODES AND VERIFY OPERATION

1991 ENGINE PERFORMANCE
Self-Diagnostics – DeVille & Fleetwood PCM/BCM (Cont.)

GM
1-177

PCM CODE E40, POWER STEERING PRESSURE SWITCH CIRCUIT

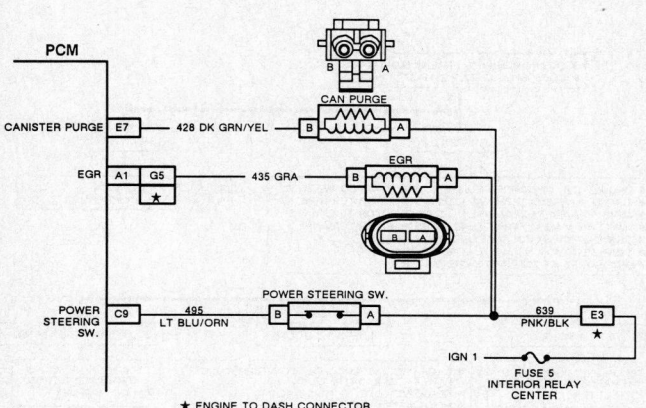

NOTE: TO ENTER ECM SWITCH TEST THE CRUISE CONTROL ON/OFF SWITCH MUST BE IN THE ON POSITION BEFORE DEPRESSING THE BRAKE PEDAL.

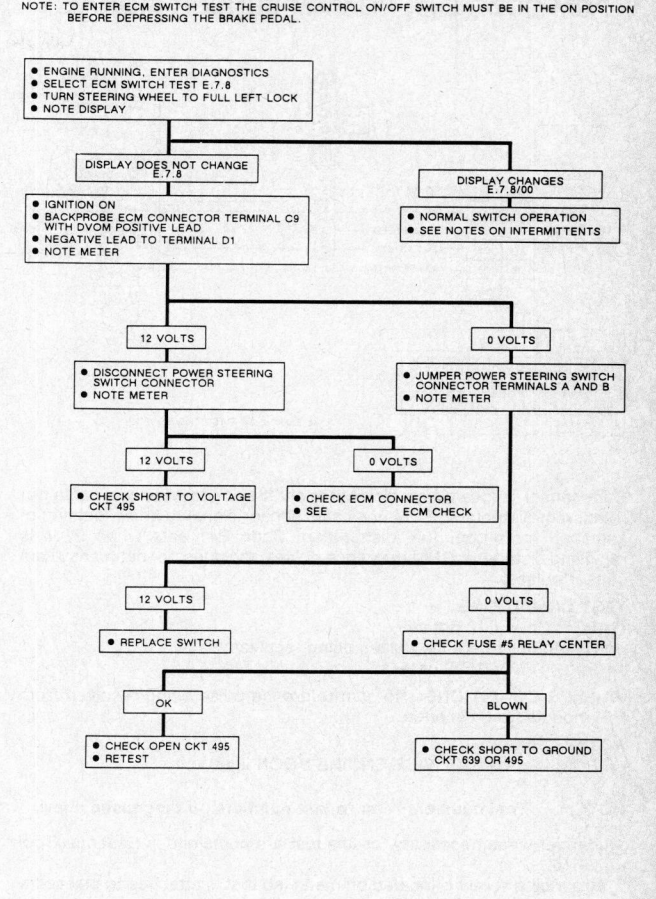

This test monitors the Power Steering Pressure Switch (PSPS). When a load is placed in the power steering, i.e. full lock position, the switch opens. PCM Code E40 sets when vehicle speed is greater than 45 MPH and switch is open. The PSPS is located on rack and pinion assembly.

TEST CONDITIONS: Vehicle speed greater than or equal to 45 MPH

FAILURE CONDITIONS: Power steering switch opens with vehicle speed greater than or equal to 45 MPH

ACTION TAKEN: PCM turns on SERVICE ENGINE SOON light

Note On Intermittents – With key on, backprobe PCM terminal C9 to ground with a 12-volt test light. The light should remain on unless steering is turned to full lock. Manipulate power steering pressure switch connector, circuit No. 495 wiring and PCM terminal C9 connector, while observing test light. If light goes out, repair intermittent open or short to ground.

91A07676   90H14768

**GM
1-178**

1991 ENGINE PERFORMANCE
Self-Diagnostics – DeVille & Fleetwood PCM/BCM (Cont.)

PCM CODE E41, NO CAM SENSOR SIGNAL

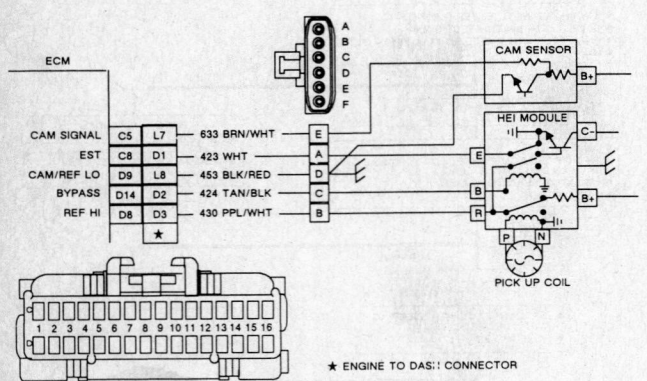

Cam sensor is located on distributor shaft and provides one pulse per rotation of distributor. PCM uses cam sensor signal to know location of camshaft for proper fuel distribution. Code E41 sets when PCM is receiving distributor RPM reference pulses and does not detect any cam sensor pulses.

TEST CONDITIONS:
- PCM Code E12 not set
- Distributor reference pulses being received
- Engine RPM 1600 or less

FAILURE CONDITIONS: No cam reference pulse being received from HEI module for 5 seconds

ACTION TAKEN:
- PCM turns on SERVICE ENGINE SOON light

NOTE: Test numbers refer to test numbers on diagnostic chart.

1) Jumper wires necessary for this test are contained in Essential Tool (J-35616).
2) Grounding screw is located on metal tab that is attached to plastic fitting on distributor harness.

90F17256   90I14769

Note On Intermittents – With engine running, manipulate affected wiring. If fault is induced, code will set and wiring should be repaired for intermittent open or short to ground. Disconnect and reconnect distributor connector and PCM connector and ensure they are latched.

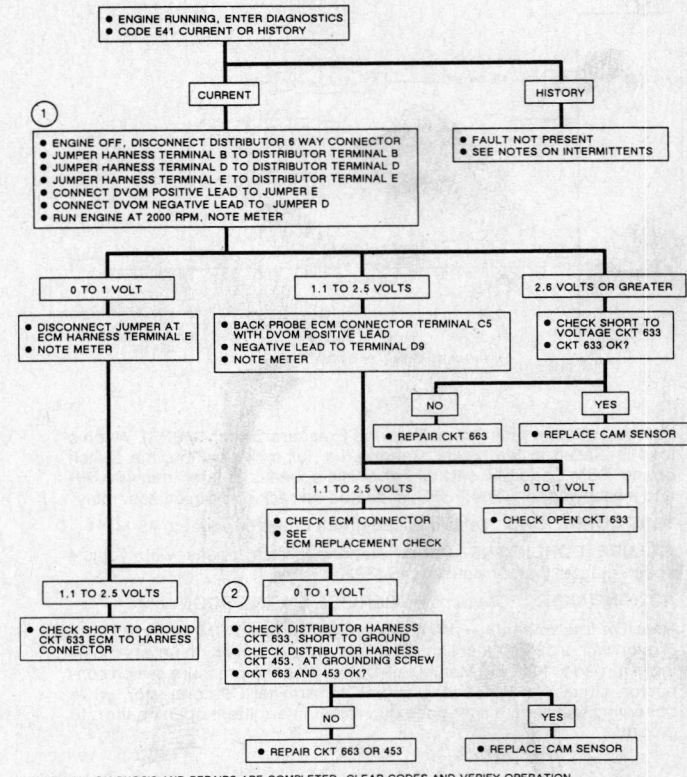

WHEN ALL DIAGNOSIS AND REPAIRS ARE COMPLETED, CLEAR CODES AND VERIFY OPERATION

Courtesy of General Motors Corp.

1991 ENGINE PERFORMANCE
Self-Diagnostics – DeVille & Fleetwood PCM/BCM (Cont.)

GM
1-179

PCM CODE E44, OXYGEN SENSOR LEAN EXHAUST SIGNAL

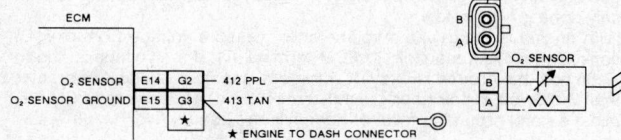

The PCM provides a .45-volt reference signal to oxygen sensor on circuit No. 412. When oxygen sensor is cold, less than 392°F (200°C), oxygen sensor signal voltage will be about .45 volt. The PCM will keep system in open loop operation. When oxygen sensor is warm, greater than 392°F (200°C), oxygen sensor signal voltage will swing from rich to lean rapidly. At least one swing every 2 seconds will happen if PCM is in good control of air/fuel mixture.

When PCM sees that oxygen is varying from cold voltage of .45 volt, it will send system into closed loop operation. In closed loop operation, PCM will adjust fuel delivery rate to engine based on oxygen sensor readings.

Code E44 is designed so that if oxygen sensor stays at lean voltage for more than 51 seconds during test conditions, Code E44 will set. Code E44 will set when:
- There is an oxygen sensor circuit fault giving a false lean indication.
- When air/fuel ratio is actually lean due to a vacuum leak or fuel control system fault.

TEST CONDITIONS:
- PCM Codes E14, E15, E16, E21, E22, E26, E27, E31, E32 and E34 not set
- Throttle switch open
- TPS between 6 and 30 degrees
- Coolant temperature greater than or equal to 136°F (58°C)
- Oxygen sensor ready (closed loop)
- RPM greater than or equal to 800
- Canister purge has purged at full duty cycle for 10 minutes since engine was running with coolant 176°F (80°C) and TPS indicates 10 degrees or greater

FAILURE CONDITIONS: Oxygen sensor status remains lean for more than 50 seconds

ACTION TAKEN:
- PCM turns on SERVICE ENGINE SOON light
- PCM enables canister purge

NOTE: Test numbers refer to test numbers on diagnostic chart.

1) With oxygen sensor disconnected, parameter P.1.4 should remain at reference voltage (.38-.63 volt).
2) Checks ability of sensor circuitry to record rich readings. The DVOM set on volts will provide a few billionths of an amp to drive circuit No. 412 to greater than .64 volt (rich). Similar results may be obtained by placing one finger on oxygen sensor circuit No. 412 harness terminal and another finger on positive battery terminal.

3) The PCM compares oxygen sensor signal voltage received on circuit No. 412 to ground voltage on circuit No. 413. If PCM does not have a good ground to engine on circuit No. 413, oxygen sensor reading can falsely appear high or low.

With engine running, use a voltmeter to measure voltage from oxygen sensor at exhaust manifold to PCM terminal A1. If the voltage is -.05 to +.05 volt, the ground is okay. If voltage is less than -.05 volt or greater than +.05 volt, repair poor ground on circuit No. 413 between PCM terminal A1 and ground at front of engine (right rear of cylinder head).

Note On Intermittents – With engine running, manipulate oxygen sensor, PCM wiring and connectors while observing PCM parameter P.1.4. If fault is induced, P.1.4 will jump to less than .37 volt, and ECON status light will go off. Manipulate circuit No. 413 ground to engine, and look for a loose ground eyelet or ground eyelet installed at wrong location. If lean engine operation is suspected, perform PFI SYSTEM CHECK.

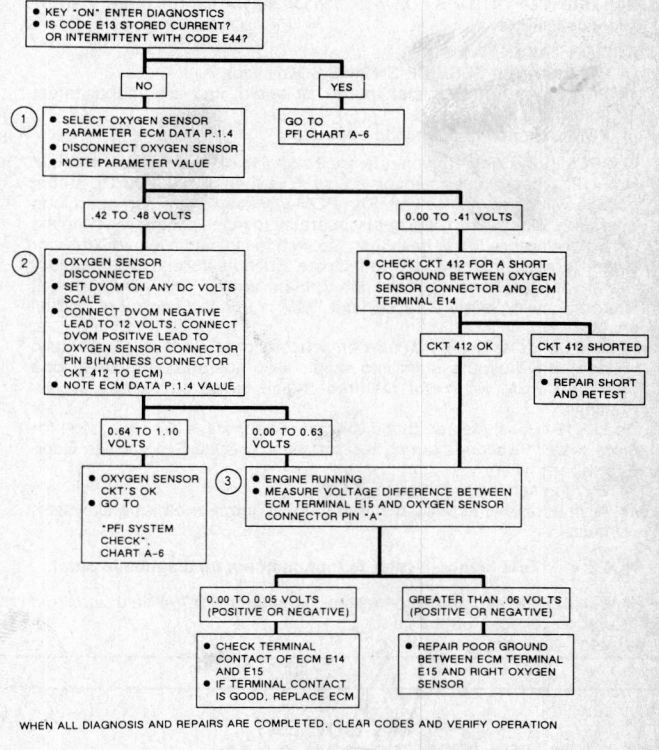

PCM CODE E45, OXYGEN SENSOR RICH EXHAUST SIGNAL

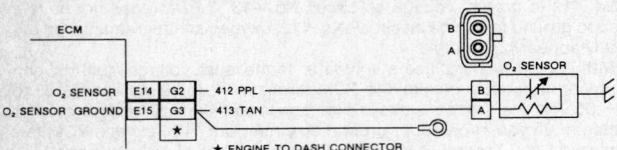

TEST CONDITIONS:
- Codes E14, E15, E16, E21, E22, E26, E27, E31, E32 and E34 not set
- Throttle switch open
- TPS between 6 and 29 degrees
- Coolant sensor greater than or equal to 176°F (80°C)
- Oxygen sensor ready (closed loop)
- Not accelerating or decelerating
- RPM greater than or equal to 800

FAILURE CONDITIONS: Oxygen sensor stays rich for more than 51 seconds

ACTION TAKEN:
- PCM turns on SERVICE ENGINE SOON light
- PCM turns off canister purge solenoid and air management solenoids.
- PCM switches to open loop operation

The PCM provides a .45-volt reference signal to oxygen sensor on circuit No. 412. When oxygen sensor is cold, less than 392°F (200°C), output voltage will be about .45 volt. The PCM will keep system in open loop operation. When warm, a properly operating oxygen sensor will drive the .45-volt reference lower (less than .45 volt) to indicate a lean mixture; or higher (greater than .45 volt) to indicate a rich mixture. Oxygen sensor signal voltage will swing from rich to lean rapidly. This will happen at least one swing every 2 seconds, if PCM is in good control of air/fuel mixture.

When PCM determines that oxygen sensor signal is not at .45 volt (cold voltage), it will send system into closed loop operation. In closed loop operation, PCM will meter fuel into engine based on oxygen sensor readings.

Code E45 is designed so that if oxygen sensor stays at rich voltage for more than 51 seconds during test conditions, Code E45 will set. Code E45 will set when:
- Oxygen sensor circuit faults
- Air/fuel ratio is actually rich due to fuel control or emissions system fault

NOTE: Test numbers refer to test numbers on diagnostic chart.

1) With oxygen sensor disconnected, parameter P.0.7 should remain at reference voltage (.38-.63 volt).

90B17260   90C14771

2) Checks for PCM ability to recognize lean input on oxygen sensor signal circuit No. 412.

3) The PCM compares oxygen sensor signal voltage received on circuit No. 412 to ground voltage on circuit No. 413. If PCM does not have a good ground to engine on circuit No. 413, oxygen sensor reading can falsely appear high or low.

With engine running, use a voltmeter to measure voltage from oxygen sensor at exhaust manifold to PCM terminal A1. If the voltage is -.05 to +.05 volt, the ground is okay. If voltage is less than -.05 volt or greater than +.05 volt, repair poor ground on circuit No. 413 between PCM terminal A1 and ground at front of right cylinder head.

Note On Intermittents – With engine running, manipulate oxygen sensor, PCM wiring and connectors while observing PCM parameter P.0.7. If fault is induced, P.0.7 will be greater than .63 volt, and ECON status light will go on. Manipulate circuit No. 413 ground to engine, and look for a loose ground eyelet or ground eyelet installed at wrong location. If lean engine operation is suspected, perform PFI SYSTEM CHECK.

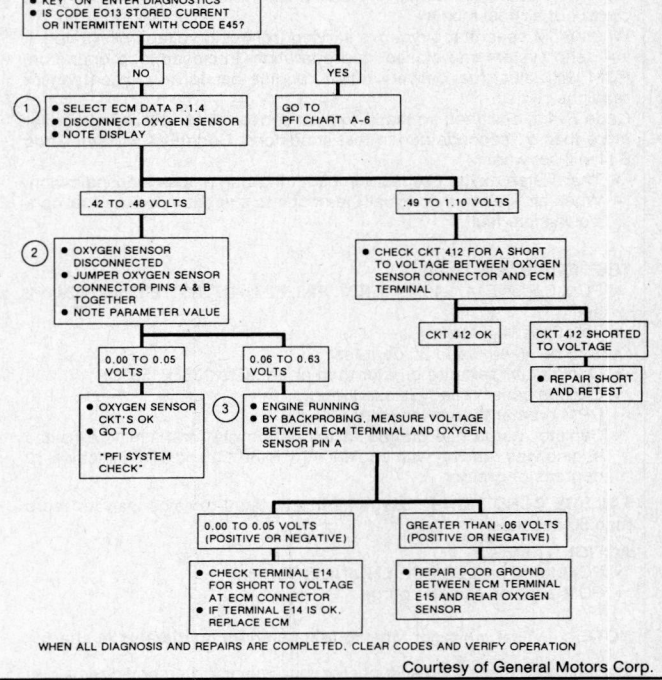

WHEN ALL DIAGNOSIS AND REPAIRS ARE COMPLETED, CLEAR CODES AND VERIFY OPERATION

Courtesy of General Motors Corp.

PCM CODE E47, BCM TO PCM DATA

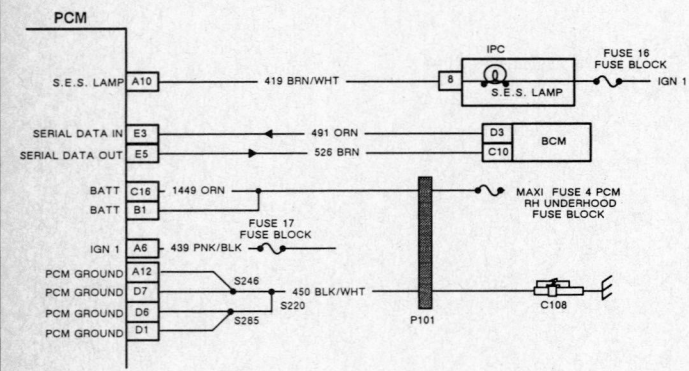

This test monitors the BCM to PCM serial data for a problem. A faulty ignition switch can cause PCM Code E47 to set, due to the switch powering the PCM before it powers the BCM. PCM Code E47 and BCM Code F32 can be stored together. Refer to BCM CODE F32 for diagnosis.

TEST CONDITIONS: PCM Code E12 is not set, engine speed is greater than 500 RPM for 5 seconds

FAILURE CONDITIONS: PCM receives bad data or interrupt in serial data input

ACTION TAKEN:
- PCM turns on SERVICE ENGINE SOON light

91I07661

Courtesy of General Motors Corp.

1991 ENGINE PERFORMANCE
Self-Diagnostics – DeVille & Fleetwood PCM/BCM (Cont.)

GM
1-181

PCM CODE E48, EGR SYSTEM FAULT (1 OF 2)

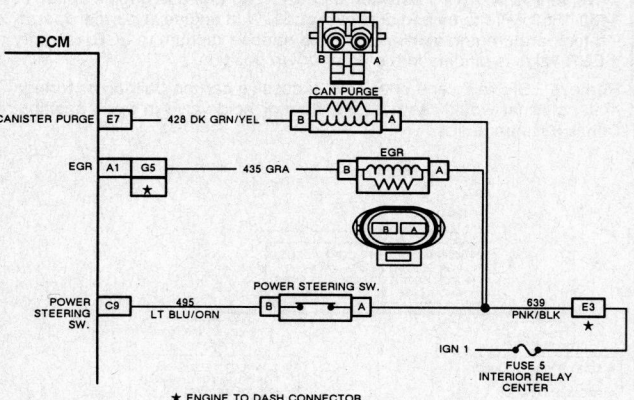

★ ENGINE TO DASH CONNECTOR

PCM Code E48 is designed to set if there is an EGR system fault. The test for Code E48 is performed under conditions where EGR is normally allowing exhaust gas to flow into intake.

To perform test, PCM turns off EGR flow to engine and monitors oxygen sensor (closed loop) integrator. With EGR turned off, integrator should swing to a higher value, reflecting leaner air/fuel mixtures. If not, PCM assumes either EGR was turned off before test started, or EGR is flowing and PCM does not have ability to turn it off.

TEST CONDITIONS:
- PCM Codes E13, E14, E15, E21, E22, E31, E32, E34, E44 and E45 not set
- Coolant temperature 185°-230°F (85°-110°C)
- TPS between 7 and 14 degrees
- RPM 1450-1650
- Oxygen sensor output switching (closed loop operation)
- MPH greater than 35
- 10 minute time lapse since vehicle start
- Steady throttle

NOTE: In test conditions, the PCM turns off EGR and looks for a leaner mixture signal from oxygen sensor. The PCM performs this test up to 6 times in a given key cycle.

FAILURE CONDITIONS: If oxygen sensor fails to indicate a leaner mixture in at least 3 of 5 tests, PCM Code E48 is set

ACTION TAKEN:
- PCM turns on SERVICE ENGINE SOON light and stays on for entire key cycle
- EGR is disabled for entire key cycle

91A07676   90E14773

NOTE: Test numbers refer to test numbers on diagnostic chart.

1) Checks for EGR operation using PCM override.
2) Checks for EGR gases to enter intake manifold by raising the EGR valve off its seat.
3) Checks for EGR solenoid vacuum flow.

Vacuum Test – 1) Connect a vacuum gauge to source side of EGR solenoid. Start engine and check that manifold vacuum is present. If not, repair vacuum circuit between EGR solenoid and throttle body.
2) Connect vacuum gauge to the EGR valve vacuum supply. No vacuum should be present when engine is at idle. If vacuum is present, go to PCM CODE E48, EGR SYSTEM FAULT (2 OF 2).
3) With vacuum gauge hooked to EGR valve vacuum supply, disconnect EGR valve solenoid connector. There should be 8 in. Hg at gauge. If not, repair leak or obstruction in EGR valve vacuum hose.

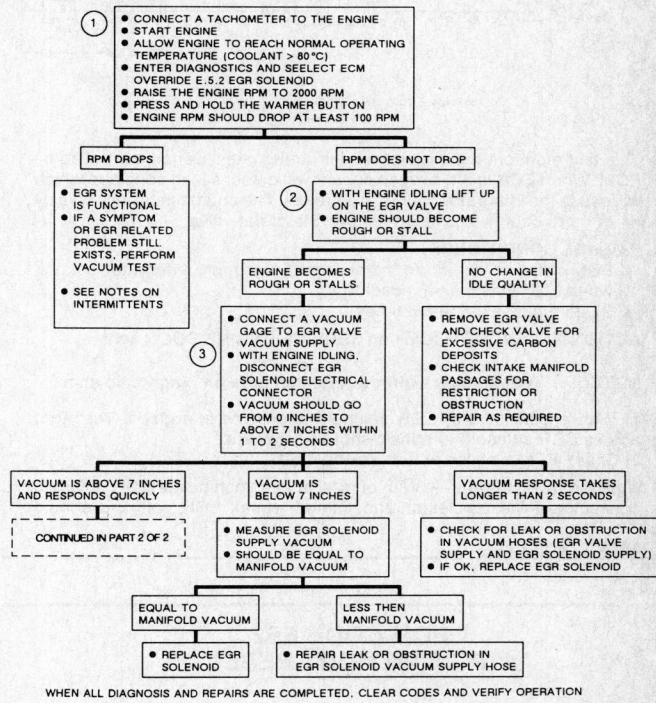

WHEN ALL DIAGNOSIS AND REPAIRS ARE COMPLETED, CLEAR CODES AND VERIFY OPERATION

Courtesy of General Motors Corp.

PCM CODE E48,
EGR SYSTEM FAULT (2 OF 2)

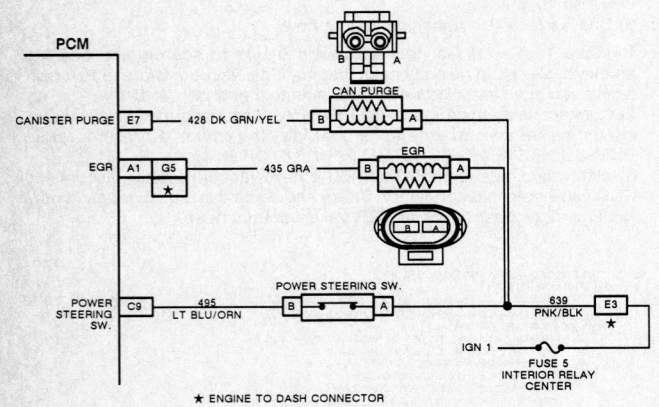

★ ENGINE TO DASH CONNECTOR

This test monitors the oxygen sensor during a test period controlled by PCM. When EGR is off, oxygen sensor will detect a lean condition which will cause the integrator counts to increase. The counts must increase by 14 or more counts to check the flow rate of the valve.

FAILURE CONDITIONS:
- PCM failed to detect an increase of 14 or more integrator counts, when EGR was commanded off
- System has failed test 3 times

ACTION TAKEN: PCM turns on SERVICE ENGINE SOON light

NOTE: Test numbers refer to test numbers on diagnostic chart.

1) With engine at idle, EGR solenoid should be energized. Test light across EGR solenoid terminals should illuminate.
2) Check PCM's ability to turn solenoid off.

Note On Intermittents – With engine at idle, manipulate EGR solenoid connector, PCM connector and related wiring. EGR solenoid should

remain energized (circuit No. 435 grounded) to block vacuum to EGR. Listen for a change in idle quality.

Drive vehicle with TPS between 8 and 15 degrees and engine speed at 1450-1650 RPM to try and duplicate code. With engine at normal operating temperature and at idle, apply and release vacuum to EGR, to verify if EGR valve is binding in the up or down position.

Remove EGR valve and check for excessive carbon buildup or foreign materials that would restrict EGR flow or hold valve in open position. Check vacuum hoses.

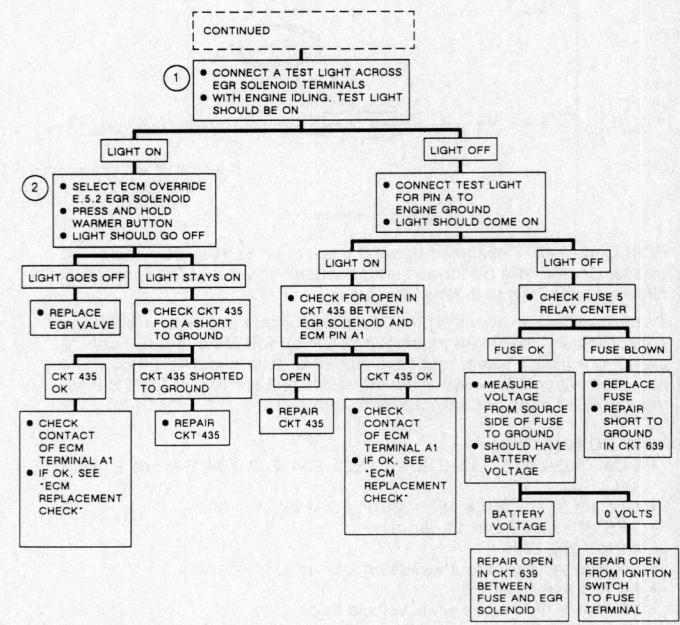

WHEN ALL DIAGNOSIS AND REPAIRS ARE COMPLETED, CLEAR CODES AND VERIFY OPERATION

91A07676   90F14774

PCM CODE E52,
PCM MEMORY RESET

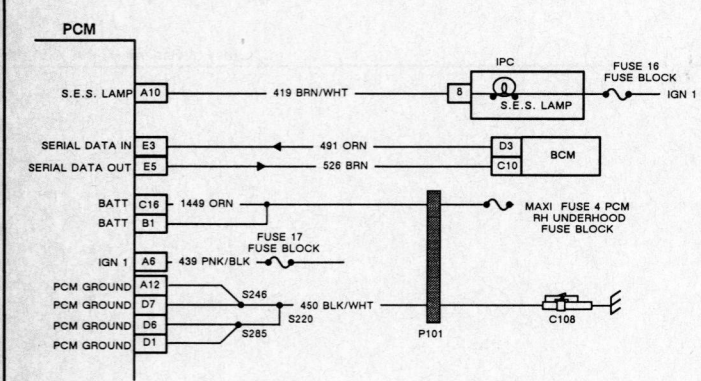

This test monitors the PCM's long term memory for loss of data. If the battery power or ground is disconnected, code will set.

ACTION TAKEN:
- PCM Code E52 will set
- SERVICE ENGINE SOON light off

FAILURE CONDITIONS:
- Loss of primary battery power to the PCM
- Loss of data from PCM

Notes On Intermittents – If battery has been disconnected, PCM Code 52 will set. The PCM keeps a running check on the memory. If memory changes, it resets.

91I07661

1991 ENGINE PERFORMANCE
Self-Diagnostics – DeVille & Fleetwood PCM/BCM (Cont.)

GM 1-183

PCM CODE E53, DISTRIBUTOR SIGNAL INTERRUPT

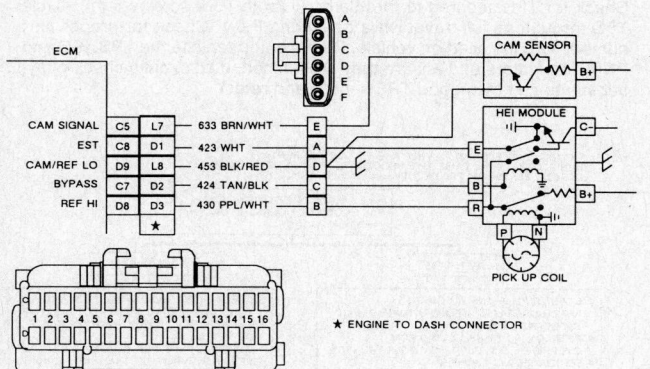

★ ENGINE TO DASH CONNECTOR

PCM Code E53 is set if PCM does not receive distributor reference pulses from HEI for more than .4 second. Since PFI system requires HEI pulses in order to fire the injectors, most occurrences of Code E53 will be accompanied by a stall.

TEST CONDITIONS: PCM Code E19 not set

FAILURE CONDITIONS: Engine speed greater than 568 RPM followed by no distributor reference pulses for .4 second

ACTION TAKEN: PCM Code E53 is stored as an intermittent code and no SERVICE ENGINE SOON light are illuminated

NOTE: Test numbers refer to test numbers on diagnostic chart.

1) Jumper wires necessary for this test are contained in Essential Tool (J-35616). Also necessary are 2 patch cords and 2 each of Flexible Connectors (J-35616-28) and (J-35616-29).

Note On Intermittents – DO NOT attempt to diagnose Code E53 unless there are complaints of stumble, stall, miss or other driveability conditions that could be caused by loss of spark or fuel. Code E53 can be caused by:

- Loss of ground on circuit No. 453.
- Loss of battery power to BAT terminal of distributor.
- Pick up coil has an intermittent short, open or poor connection at module.
- Check PCM connector for improperly seated terminals and mating to PCM connector.

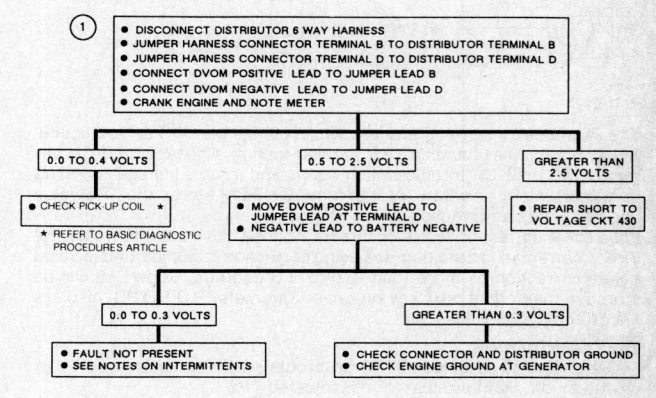

90F17256   90I14777

Courtesy of General Motors Corp.

**GM
1-184**

1991 ENGINE PERFORMANCE
Self-Diagnostics – DeVille & Fleetwood PCM/BCM (Cont.)

PCM CODE E55,
TPS OUT OF ADJUSTMENT

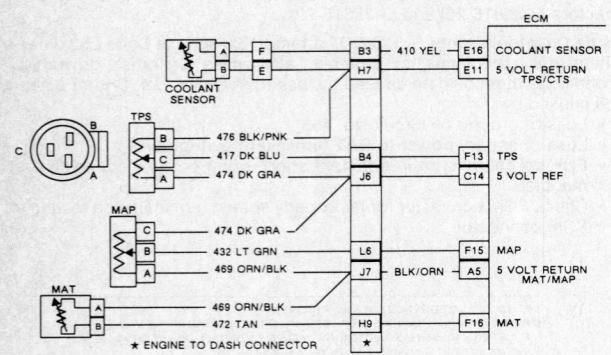

The PCM uses a learning process which makes the TPS self-adjusting. At key off, PCM executes a TPS learning routine. After key off, PCM will retract ISC until ISC throttle switch opens and throttle linkage is resting on the minimum air screw. At that time, the PCM stores the TPS value and calculates a correction.

If the same correction factor occurs on 2 consecutive key-off cycles, the TPS is corrected to zero degrees using correction factor learned. If value needs correction by more than -2.9 to +3 degrees, Code E55 will be stored in memory at next key on cycle. Parameter P.0.1 (TPS) displays uncorrected TPS values.

TEST CONDITIONS:
- No problems detected in TPS or throttle switch circuits
- At key off, PCM will test for misadjusted TPS

FAILURE CONDITIONS: If TPS correction needed is -2.9 to +3 degrees, the TPS out-of-adjustment flag is set

ACTION TAKEN: At next key on, the PCM will see TPS out-of-adjustment flag, and log PCM Code E55 as current. No light or service message will appear

NOTE: Test numbers refer to test numbers on diagnostic chart.

1) Checks TPS adjustment. PCM parameter P.0.1 (TPS) displays uncorrected TPS so that it can be used to check TPS adjustment.
2) TPS adjustment is okay.
3) If TPS adjustment is okay, ISC and throttle switch operation needs to be thoroughly checked. Throttle linkage needs to be checked for proper operation, throttle, cruise and TV cables not binding, proper throttle return spring operation, and throttle shaft and blades free to move.

Note On Intermittents – Enter diagnostics. Manipulate ISC wiring while observing OFF throttle switch status light and ISC operation during PCM output cycling. Manipulate TPS wiring and connector while observing PCM parameter P.0.1 for jumps, skips and intermittent behavior.

Check for TPS secured to throttle body (both Torx screws tight). Cycle TPS through its full travel while observing P.0.1. Check for proper part number TPS installed on vehicle. Remove and replace the TPS, ISC and PCM connectors and ensure they are latched. If all circuits check okay, substitute a known good TPS sensor and retest.

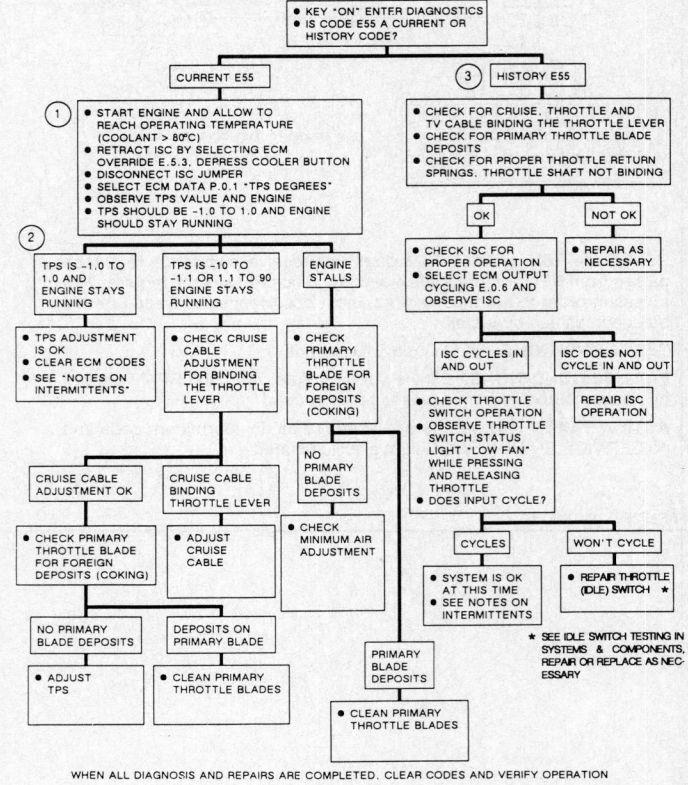

1991 ENGINE PERFORMANCE
Self-Diagnostics – DeVille & Fleetwood PCM/BCM (Cont.)

GM
1-185

PCM CODE E58, PASS KEY FUEL ENABLE PROBLEM

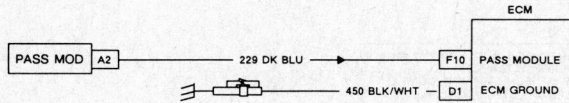

PCM Code E58 is an indication that Pass Key Fuel Enable Input has failed after a good signal was received in a given engine run cycle. Pass Key system enables engine operation by:
- Allowing starter motor to engage
- Issuing a Fuel Enable signal to PCM

Once engine is running, PCM continuously monitors Fuel Enable signal, testing for a circuit or Pass Key module failure that would prohibit a positive fuel enable on future ignition cycles. PCM will not cancel fuel injection after it has been approved within a given ignition cycle. Therefore, a stalling condition cannot be caused by Pass Key system failures.

TEST CONDITIONS: Engine has been running for a predetermined amount of time

FAILURE CONDITIONS: Pass Key Fuel Enable Input is not correct but has been correct within this engine run cycle

ACTION TAKEN:
- PCM turns on SERVICE VEHICLE SOON light
- Enable fuel injection on future ignition cycles without regard for Pass Key Fuel Enable Input status

NOTE: Test numbers refer to test numbers on diagnostic chart.

1) If engine will crank, problem has been isolated to Pass Key Module, PCM or Fuel Enable circuit. If engine will not crank, problem is in Pass Key System.
2) Checking voltage input to PCM will identify if PCM is at fault. Typical signal will be approximately 2.5 volts.
3) Voltage is too low – could be faulty Pass Key Module, a poor connection at PCM or a short to ground in Fuel Enable circuit.
4) Voltage is too high – could be faulty Pass Key Module, a poor connection at Pass Key Module or a short to voltage or an open in Fuel Enable circuit.

90A14779

Notes on Intermittents – If Code E58 is set intermittently, problem could be caused by:
- Intermittent short to ground or voltage on circuit No. 229.
- Intermittent open on circuit No. 229.
- Intermittent loss of power or ground to Pass Key Module. Pass Key Module reads ignition key once each ignition cycle, when ignition is first turned on. Faults in key pellet and circuits can cause a no-start condition but cannot cause a stall or set a Code E58.

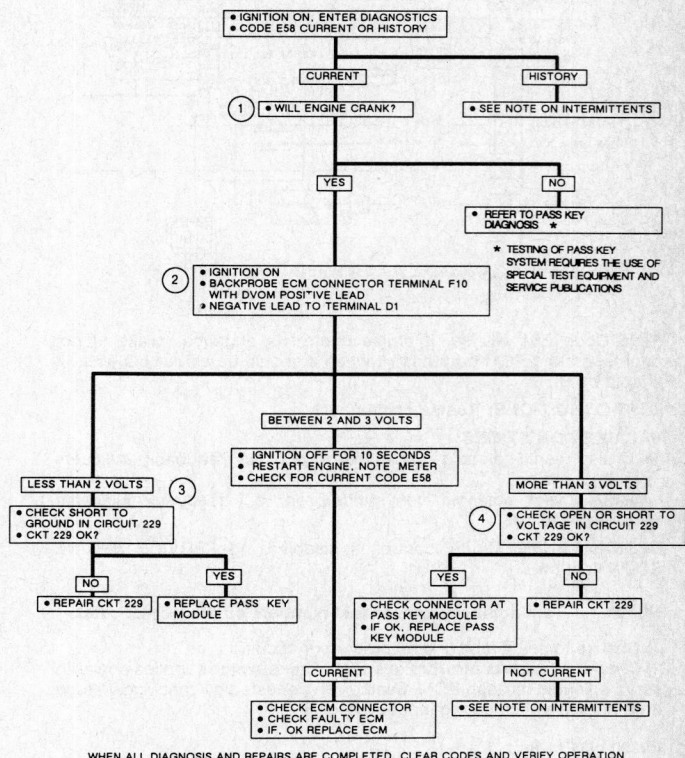

Courtesy of General Motors Corp.

PCM CODE E60, CRUISE CONTROL ENGAGED WITH TRANSMISSION IN PARK OR NEUTRAL

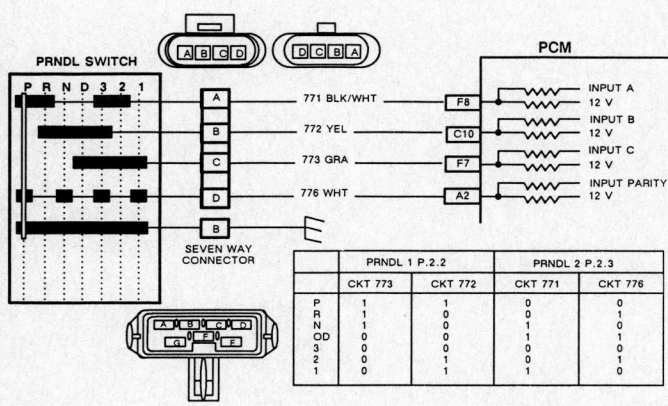

PCM Code E60 is designed to prevent excessive engine RPM due to cruise control being engaged when transmission is not in Drive. Code E60 may be set if park/neutral switch is out of adjustment, or if vehicle operation places the transmission in Park or Neutral with cruise control engaged.

TEST CONDITIONS: Cruise control on and engaged

FAILURE CONDITIONS: Transmission in Park or Neutral

ACTION TAKEN: Disengage cruise control

Note On Intermittents – If Code E60 is stored as intermittent, select PCM data P.2.2 and P.2.3. Manipulate harness while observing the switch status. If the switch changes status while wire is being manipulated, repair affected circuit.

If no trouble was found, code must have been induced if transmission was inadvertently shifted into Neutral while cruise control was engaged.

	PRNDL 1 P.2.2		PRNDL 2 P.2.3	
	CKT 773	CKT 772	CKT 771	CKT 776
P	1	1	0	0
R	1	0	0	1
N	0	1	1	0
OD	0	0	1	1
3	0	0	1	0
2	0	0	1	0
1	0	1	0	1

91C07719

Courtesy of General Motors Corp.

**GM
1-186**

1991 ENGINE PERFORMANCE
Self-Diagnostics – DeVille & Fleetwood PCM/BCM (Cont.)

PCM CODE E61, CRUISE CONTROL VENT SOLENOID CIRCUIT

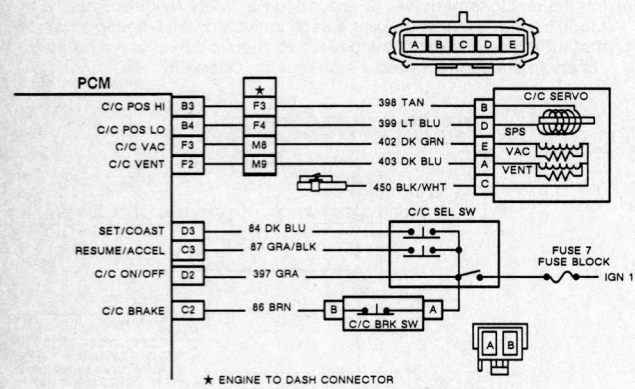

★ ENGINE TO DASH CONNECTOR

PCM Code E61 will set if cruise control is engaged, brake is not depressed and PCM output is HI when it should be LO, or LO when it should be HI.

TEST CONDITIONS: Tested continuously

FAILURE CONDITIONS:
- Cruise vent solenoid commanded off, but feedback indicates solenoid is on
- Cruise vent solenoid commanded on, but feedback indicates solenoid is off

ACTION TAKEN: Cruise control is disabled; no SERVICE ENGINE SOON light on

NOTE: Test numbers refer to test numbers on diagnostic chart.

1) Checks to see if fault is due to servo or circuit.
2) Checking cruise control brake switch. Brake switch supplies power to servo solenoid through PCM. Switch can be tested by checking voltage drop across switch during input cycling.

91E07720   90E14781

Note On Intermittents – Start engine to charge vacuum reservoir. With engine OFF, select PCM override E.5.7, depress warmer button and fully apply servo. Manipulate wiring and connectors and observe servo. If servo does not remain applied, there is an intermittent open in circuit.

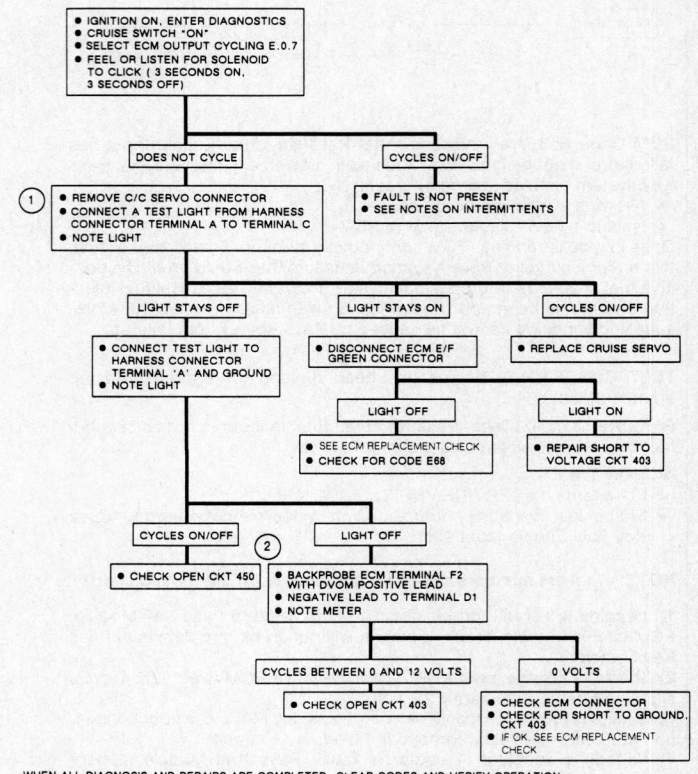

WHEN ALL DIAGNOSIS AND REPAIRS ARE COMPLETED, CLEAR CODES AND VERIFY OPERATION

Courtesy of General Motors Corp.

1991 ENGINE PERFORMANCE
Self-Diagnostics – DeVille & Fleetwood PCM/BCM (Cont.)

GM
1-187

PCM CODE E62, CRUISE CONTROL VACUUM SOLENOID CIRCUIT

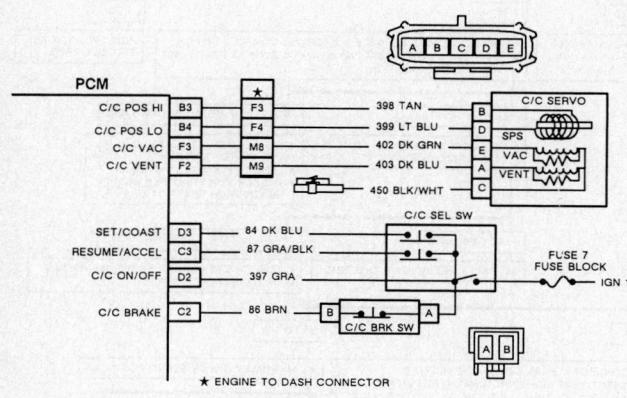

★ ENGINE TO DASH CONNECTOR

Code E62 will set if cruise control is engaged, brake is not depressed and PCM output is HI when it should be LO, or LO when it should be HI.

TEST CONDITIONS: Always tested

FAILURE CONDITIONS:
- Cruise vent solenoid commanded off, but feedback indicates solenoid is on
- Cruise vent solenoid commanded on, but feedback indicates solenoid is off

ACTION TAKEN: Disengage cruise control; no SERVICE ENGINE SOON light illuminated

NOTE: Test numbers refer to test numbers on diagnostic chart.

1) Checks to see if fault is due to servo or circuit.
2) Checking cruise control brake switch. Brake switch supplies power to servo solenoid through PCM. Switch can be tested by checking voltage drop across switch during input cycling.

Note On Intermittents – Start engine to charge vacuum reservoir. With engine OFF, select PCM override E.5.7, depress warmer button and fully apply servo. Manipulate wiring and connectors and observe servo. If servo does not remain applied, there is an intermittent open in circuit.

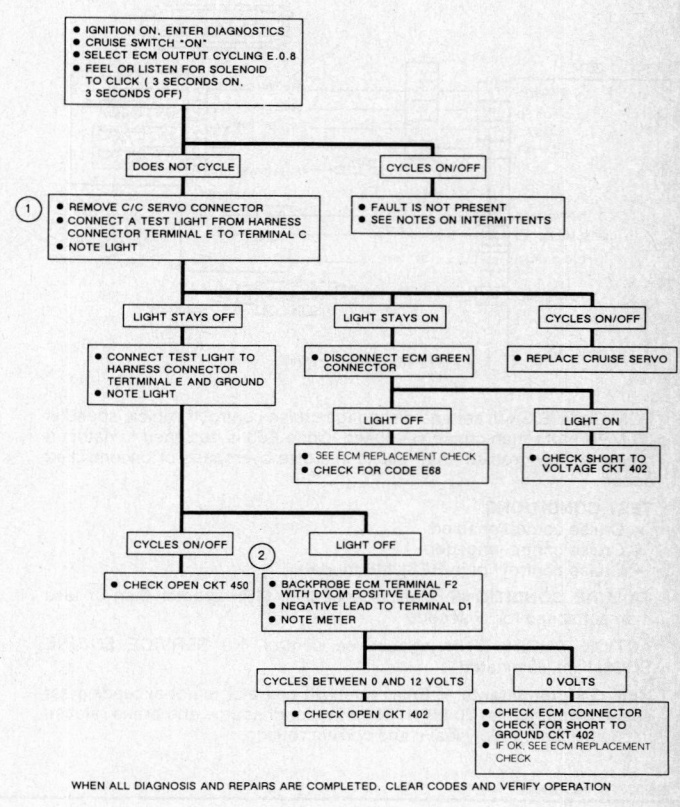

WHEN ALL DIAGNOSIS AND REPAIRS ARE COMPLETED, CLEAR CODES AND VERIFY OPERATION

91E07720   90F14782

Courtesy of General Motors Corp.

GM
1-188

1991 ENGINE PERFORMANCE
Self-Diagnostics – DeVille & Fleetwood PCM/BCM (Cont.)

PCM CODE E63, CRUISE CONTROL CIRCUIT VEHICLE SPEED & SET SPEED DIFFERENTIAL EXCEEDED

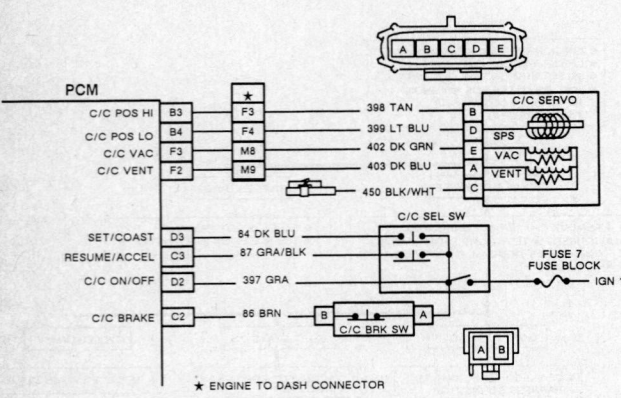

PCM Code E63 will set and disengage cruise control if vehicle speed is 20 MPH more than cruise set speed. Code E63 is designed to detect a cruise control problem that results in cruise overspeed or uncontrolled speed.

TEST CONDITIONS:
- Cruise control enabled
- Cruise control engaged
- Cruise control not in RESUME mode

FAILURE CONDITIONS: Vehicle speed 20 MPH greater than or less than set speed for .5 second

ACTION TAKEN: Disengage cruise control. No SERVICE ENGINE SOON light illuminated

Note On Intermittents – Ensure vehicle operator is not exceeding set speed by more than 20 MPH. Check vacuum source and brake release vacuum lines for slow leaks and correct routing.

- START ENGINE, IDLE FOR 2 MINUTES
- TURN ENGINE 'OFF'
- TURN IGNITION SWITCH 'ON', ENTER DIAGNOSTICS
- SELECT PCM DATA P.2.1 (CRUISE FEEDBACK)
- NOTE DISPLAY

30 TO 100	7 TO 30	0 TO 6
• DEPRESS BRAKE PEDAL FULLY • NOTE DISPLAY	• SELECT PCM OVERRIDE E.5.7 (CRUISE CONTROL SERVO) • DEPRESS COOLER BUTTON UNTIL ECC DISPLAY READS '99' • NOTE SERVO POSITION	FOLLOW CODE E65 TROUBLE TREE

FULL RETRACTION	NONE TO PARTIAL RETRACTION
• DEPRESS WARMER BUTTON UNTIL ECC DISPLAYS '0'	• CHECK FOR AT LEAST 10 In. Hg OF SUPPLY VACUUM • CHECK FOR VACUUM LEAKS • CHECK FOR THROTTLE CABLE BINDING OR RESTRICTIONS

FULLY RELAXED	PARTIAL TO FULL RETRACTION
NO FAULT PRESENT AT THIS TIME	• CHECK CKT 403 FOR SHORT TO VOLTAGE • IF OK, REPLACE SERVO

0 TO 30	30 TO 100
• DISCONNECT CRUISE SERVO CONNECTOR • CONNECT TEST LIGHT FROM HARNESS PIN 'A' TO 'C' • SELECT PCM OUTPUT E.0.8 (CRUISE VENT SOLENOID) • NOTE LIGHT	• MANUALLY CHECK SERVO POSITION

CYCLES ON/OFF	STAYS ON OR OFF	RETRACTED	RELAXED
• RECONNECT SERVO CONNECTOR • LISTEN OR FEEL FOR VENT SOLENOID CYCLING	FOLLOW CODE E061 TROUBLE TREE	• CHECK BRAKE VACUUM RELEASE FOR RESTRICTION • CHECK CKT 403 FOR SHORT TO VOLTAGE	REPLACE SERVO

SOLENOID CYCLES ON/OFF	SOLENOID DOES NOT CYCLE	OK	NOT OK
• NO ELECTRICAL FAULT PRESENT • CHECK FOR POSSIBLE BINDING OF CRUISE LINKAGE OR THROTTLE CABLE	REPLACE SERVO	REPLACE SERVO	REPAIR

91E07720   91G07721

Courtesy of General Motors Corp.

PCM CODE E64, VEHICLE ACCELERATION OUT OF RANGE

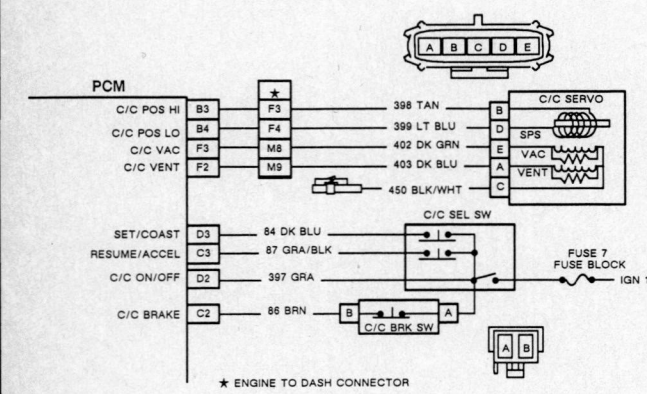

PCM Code E64 sets when vehicle wheel speed increases at an extremely rapid rate. This is a protective measure to prevent wheel spin on icy roads when cruise control is in operation.

TEST CONDITIONS: Tested when cruise is enabled and engaged

FAILURE CONDITIONS: Vehicle speed increases more than 4 MPH in .25 second

ACTION TAKEN: Disengage cruise control; no SERVICE ENGINE SOON light are illuminated

Note On Intermittents – If Code E64 is stored as an intermittent code and operator complains of frequent loss of cruise control function, drive vehicle while observing PCM data parameter ED12 (vehicle speed). If displayed speed is erratic, check speed sensor unit. If Code E64 is found with no other codes stored, clear code and road test. If Code E64 resets without wheelspin, see CHART C-1, PCM REPLACEMENT CHECK in this article.

91E07720

Courtesy of General Motors Corp.

1991 ENGINE PERFORMANCE
Self-Diagnostics – DeVille & Fleetwood PCM/BCM (Cont.)

GM
1-189

PCM CODE E65, CRUISE CONTROL SERVO POSITION SENSOR FAILURE

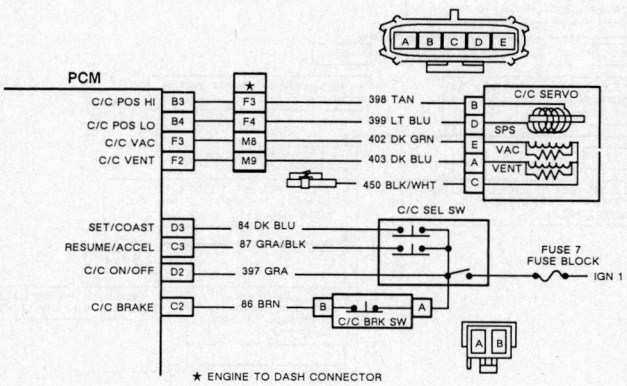

★ ENGINE TO DASH CONNECTOR

PCM Code E65 will detect a cruise control servo position sensor shorted to ground. Cruise servo position sensor is a potentiometer that changes resistance with servo position. Code E65 sets when PCM detects a low voltage indicating a short to ground in cruise servo position sensor circuit.

TEST CONDITIONS: Always tested

FAILURE CONDITIONS: Servo position 6.3 percent or less for one second

ACTION TAKEN: Disengage cruise control; no SERVICE ENGINE SOON light illuminated

91E07720 91I07722

Note on Intermittents – Manipulate PCM connector, 56-pin engine-to-dash connector, servo connector and affected wiring. Note display for rapid change in servo position.

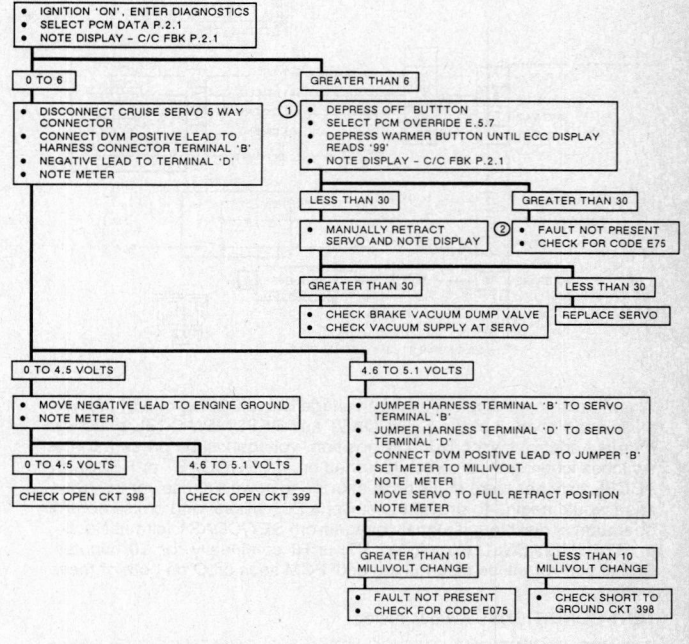

Courtesy of General Motors Corp.

PCM CODE E66, ENGINE RPM TOO HIGH WITH CRUISE ENGAGED

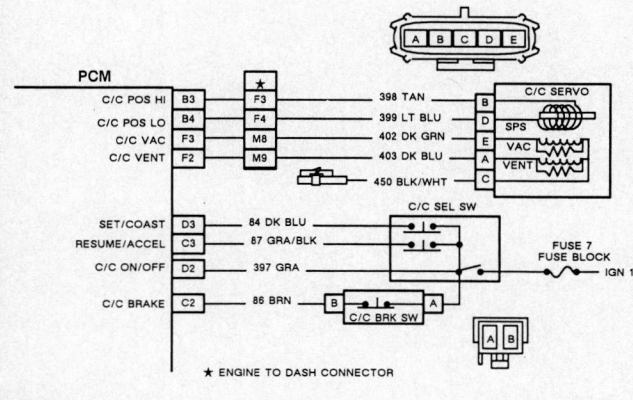

★ ENGINE TO DASH CONNECTOR

91E07720

PCM Code E66 will set when engine RPM is greater than 4800 RPM with cruise control engaged. This may occur on slippery pavement, extended wide open throttle acceleration or for some mechanical problems (such as transmission slippage). Under these conditions, Code E66 is normal. No SERVICE ENGINE SOON light will illuminate. If Code E66 is accompanied by Code E60, it is likely Code E66 was caused by transmission being shifted to Neutral while driving.

TEST CONDITIONS: Tested when cruise is enabled and engaged

FAILURE CONDITIONS: Engine RPM 4800 or greater for .25 second

ACTION TAKEN: Disengage cruise control; no SERVICE ENGINE SOON light illuminated

Courtesy of General Motors Corp.

GM
1-190

1991 ENGINE PERFORMANCE
Self-Diagnostics – DeVille & Fleetwood PCM/BCM (Cont.)

PCM CODE E67, SET/COAST OR RESUME/ACCEL CIRCUITS SHORTED

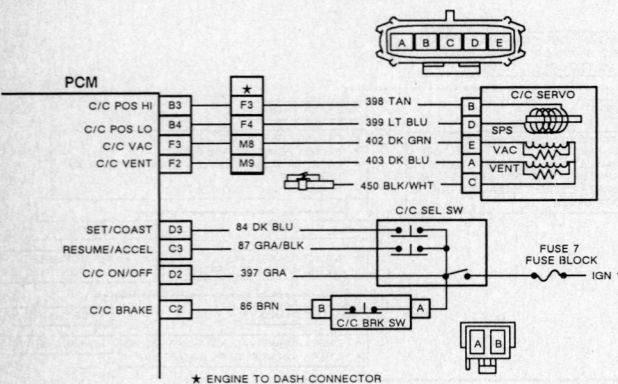

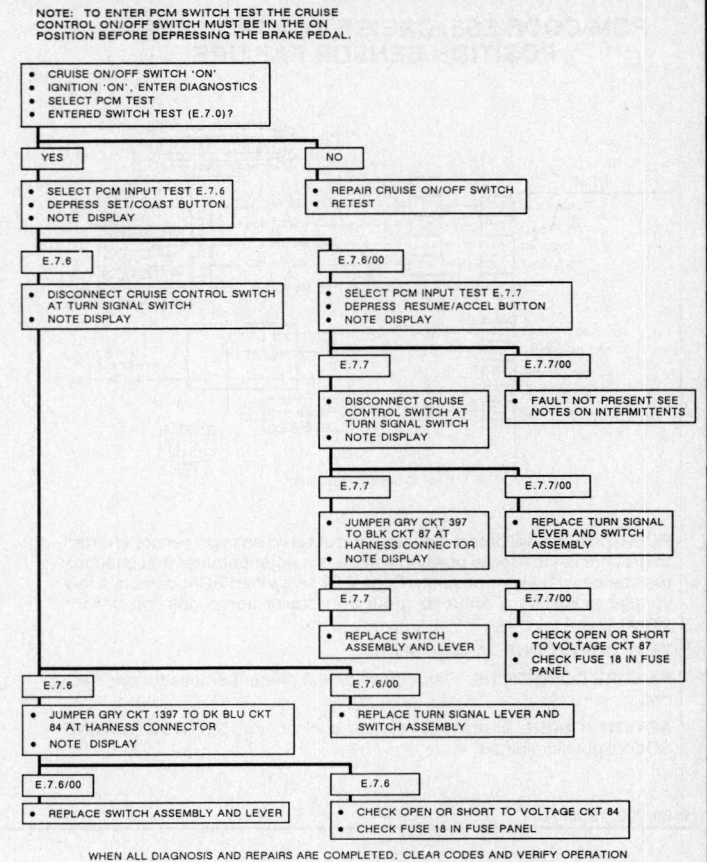

When cruise control is on, system voltage is available at one of the normally open contact of the SET/COAST and RESUME/ACCEL switches. If cruise control switch is in ON position, voltage will be present to the switches when ignition switch is turned on. If SET/COAST or RESUME/ACCEL switches were stuck on or shorted to power, cruise control operation would begin. To prevent this, Code E67 will set and cruise control operation is disabled, if signal voltage from SET/COAST (circuit No. 84) or RESUME/ACCEL (circuit No. 87) is HI continually for 10 minutes. Cruise control will be disengaged until PCM sees a LO on both of these signals.

TEST CONDITIONS: Always tested

FAILURE CONDITIONS: SET/COAST and RESUME/ACCEL switches are both closed for 10 minutes

ACTION TAKEN: Disengage cruise control; no SERVICE ENGINE SOON light illuminated.

91E07720   91A07723

1991 ENGINE PERFORMANCE
Self-Diagnostics – DeVille & Fleetwood PCM/BCM (Cont.)

GM
1-191

PCM CODE E68, CRUISE CONTROL COMMAND PROBLEM

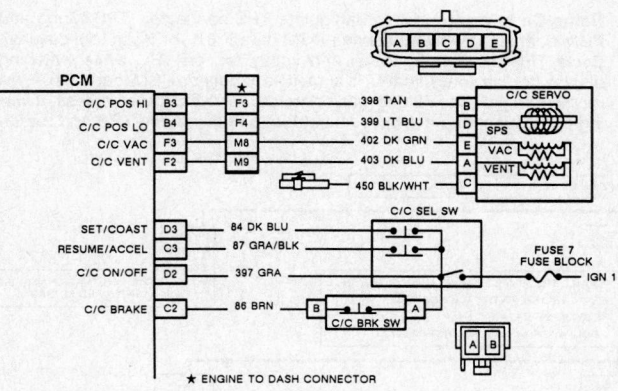

PCM continuously compares cruise control servo position sensor to throttle position. This diagnostic test monitors for a throttle position greater than 20 degrees and servo position greater than commanded by PCM for 2 seconds.

TEST CONDITIONS: Tested with cruise control engaged

FAILURE CONDITIONS: Throttle angle greater than 20 degrees and servo position sensor indicating a stroke greater than commanded

ACTION TAKEN: Disengages cruise control for key cycle; no SERVICE ENGINE SOON light illuminated.

Note on Intermittents – Manipulate PCM connector, 56-pin engine-to-dash connector, servo connectors and affected wiring. Note display for rapid change in servo position. Check for circuit No. 403 for intermittent short to power.

91E07720 91C07724

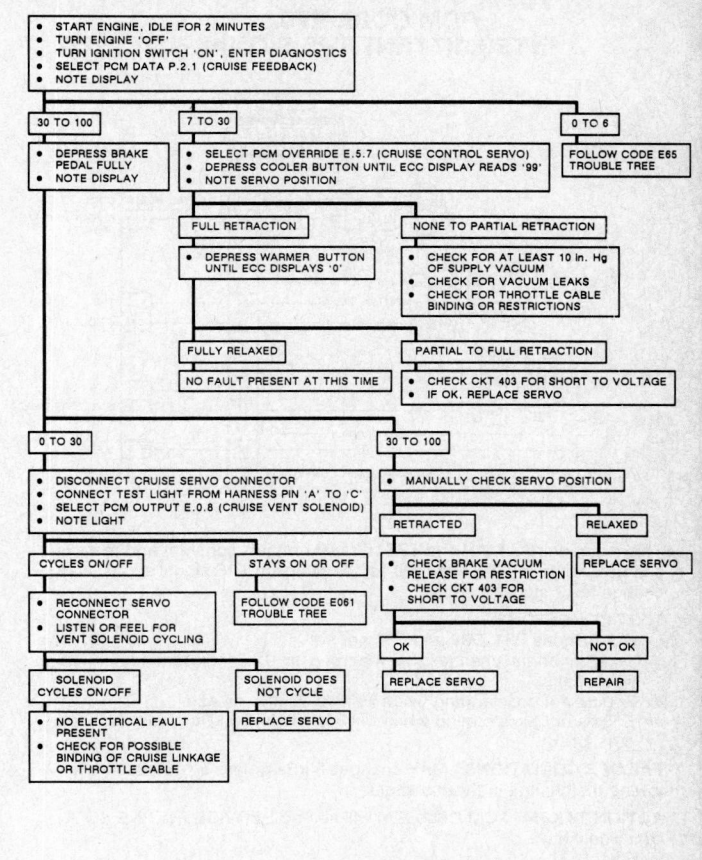

PCM CODE E70, INTERMITTENT TPS SIGNAL

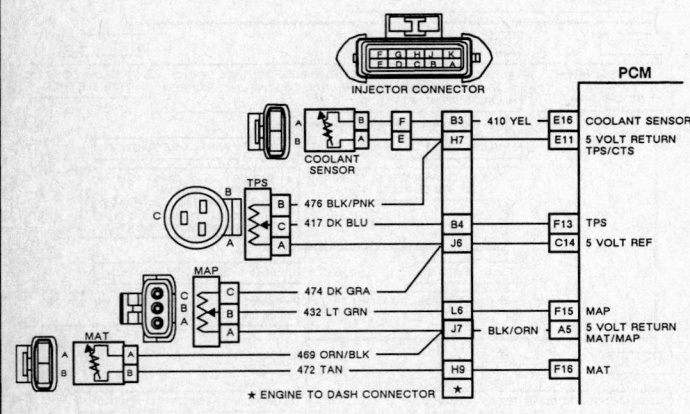

This test monitors MAP and TPS. If MAP remains constant and there is a large change in TPS, code will set. A change in TPS signal should also change MAP signal.

TEST CONDITIONS:
- PCM Codes E31, E32 and E34 not set
- Throttle angle changes 3.5 degrees in 12.5 milliseconds (.0125 seconds)
- Engine not decelerating when MAP is 22 kPa or less
- Engine not accelerating when MAP is within 7.4 kPa of atmospheric pressure

FAILURE CONDITIONS: MAP changes 3 kPa or less in .16 second, following the change in throttle angle

ACTION TAKEN: PCM Code E70 will set; no SERVICE ENGINE SOON light illuminated.

NOTE: Test numbers refer to test numbers on diagnostic chart.

1) PCM Code E70 is not present at this time, unless PCM Codes E21, E22, E31, E32 or E34 is present. This code indicates an unacceptable high rate of TPS change.

2) For this test a high impedance needle-type voltmeter should be used, as the quick deflection of the needle is easier to observe than that of a digital meter.

3) If throttle blades/valves does return to the idle stop, the throttle blades/valves may be coked or is binding. These conditions may cause Codes E55 and E85 to set.

4) Improper TPS adjustment, such as forcing or tapping on TPS without loosening screws, will damage TPS and can cause Code E70 to set.

Notes On Intermittents – Manipulate TPS connector, TPS wiring and PCM connector while observing PCM data P.0.1 (or Scan tool display). Cycle TPS through its travel and lightly tap on TPS while watching display for an intermittent. If a fault is induced, PCM data P.0.1 will momentarily skip to 72 degrees or greater, or 1.3 degrees or less. If wiring and connectors are okay, substitute a known good TPS and retest.

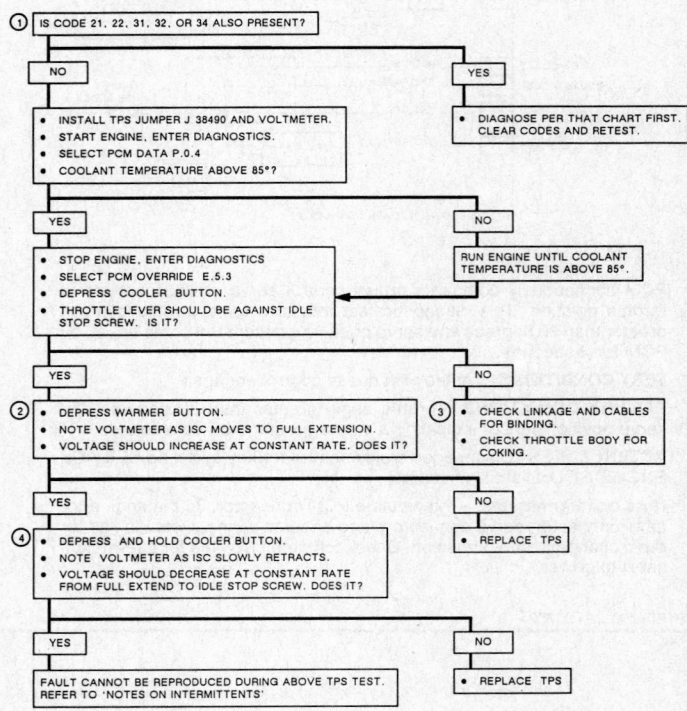

WHEN ALL DIAGNOSIS AND REPAIRS ARE COMPLETED, CLEAR CODES AND VERIFY OPERATION

91F07688   91H07726

1991 ENGINE PERFORMANCE
Self-Diagnostics – DeVille & Fleetwood PCM/BCM (Cont.)

GM
1-193

PCM CODE E71, INTERMITTENT MAP SENSOR

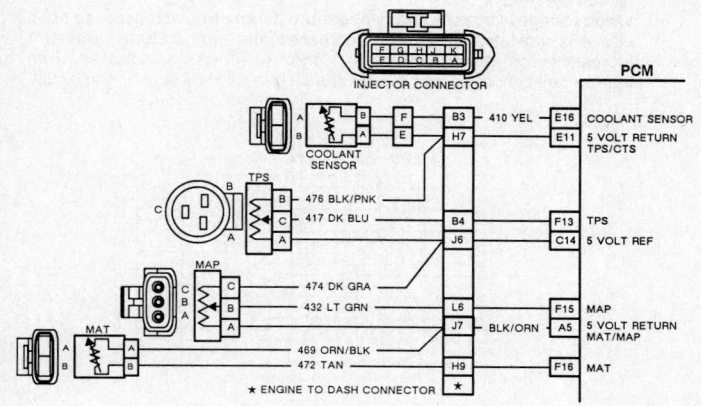

INJECTOR CONNECTOR

PCM

B3	410 YEL — E16	COOLANT SENSOR
H7		E11 5 VOLT RETURN TPS/CTS
B4 — 476 BLK/PNK		F13 TPS
— 417 DK BLU		C14 5 VOLT REF
J6		
— 474 DK GRA		
L6 — 432 LT GRN		F15 MAP
J7 BLK/ORN		A5 5 VOLT RETURN MAT/MAP
— 469 ORN/BLK		
H9 — 472 TAN		F16 MAT

COOLANT SENSOR

TPS

MAP

MAT

★ ENGINE TO DASH CONNECTOR

This test monitors TPS, RPM, MAP, EGR flow and A/C clutch. If TPS, RPM, EGR flow and A/C clutch remains constant, but a rapid change in MAP sensor occurs, code will set. Engine operation requires that a large change in manifold pressure must be preceded by a change in throttle angle.

TEST CONDITIONS:
- PCM Codes E21 and E22 not set
- TPS does not change more than .8 degrees for 1.01 seconds
- RPM does not change more than 100 RPM for 1.01 seconds
- EGR does not change more than 4 percent for 1.01 seconds
- A/C clutch is not commanded on or off.

FAILURE CONDITIONS: MAP sensor reading changes more than 5.5 kPa in 12.5 milliseconds (.0125 second)

ACTION TAKEN: PCM Code 71 will set; no SERVICE ENGINE SOON light illuminated

Note On Intermittent – Check terminal crimp to the wire and ensure terminals are properly seated in their connectors.

91F07688   91I07736   91J07727

The 5-volt reference can be tested by connecting jumpers between harness connector and MAP sensor terminal. Connect DVOM positive lead to jumper "C" and negative lead to jumper "A". Turn ignition on and apply vacuum to sensor. Tap lightly on sensor, voltage reading should remain between 4.6 and 5.1 volts.

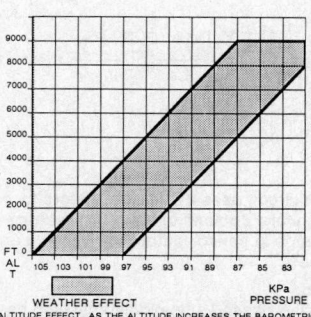

WEATHER EFFECT

KPa PRESSURE

ALTITUDE EFFECT, AS THE ALTITUDE INCREASES THE BAROMETRIC PRESSURE WILL DECREASE.
WEATHER EFFECT, CHANGES IN CONDITIONS SUCH AS A STORM WILL CAUSE A LOW PRESSURE AND FAIR CONDITIONS PRODUCE HIGH PRESSURES.
BAROMETRIC PRESSURE GIVEN IN A WEATHER REPORT IS ONE CORRECTED TO SEA LEVEL.

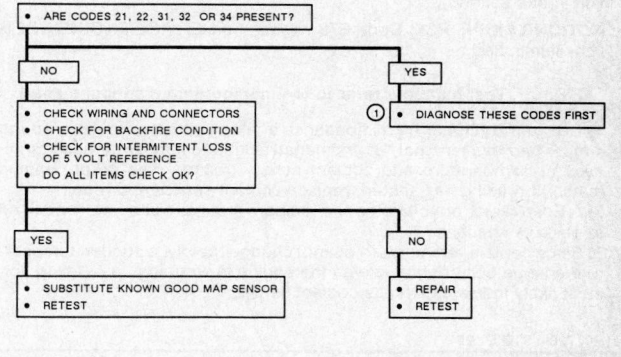

- ARE CODES 21, 22, 31, 32 OR 34 PRESENT?

NO

YES

- CHECK WIRING AND CONNECTORS
- CHECK FOR BACKFIRE CONDITION
- CHECK FOR INTERMITTENT LOSS OF 5 VOLT REFERENCE
- DO ALL ITEMS CHECK OK?

① — DIAGNOSE THESE CODES FIRST

YES

NO

- SUBSTITUTE KNOWN GOOD MAP SENSOR
- RETEST

- REPAIR
- RETEST

Courtesy of General Motors Corp.

GM
1-194

1991 ENGINE PERFORMANCE
Self-Diagnostics – DeVille & Fleetwood PCM/BCM (Cont.)

PCM CODE E73, INTERMITTENT COOLANT TEMPERATURE SENSOR SIGNAL

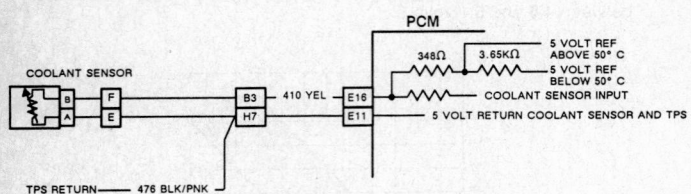

The coolant sensor circuit uses 2 pull-up resistors for temperature sensing. This test monitors coolant temperature sensor voltage. If PCM detects a large change in sensor output voltage in a one second period of time, code will set.

TEST CONDITIONS:
- Two seconds have passed since ignition switch has been turned on
- Two seconds have passed since PCM shifted coolant temperature pull-up resistors. This occurs when sensor resistance indicates 122°F (50°C)

FAILURE CONDITIONS: Coolant temperature voltage has changed .3 volt in one second

ACTION TAKEN: PCM Code E73 will set; no SERVICE ENGINE SOON light illuminated.

NOTE: Test numbers refer to test numbers on diagnostic chart.

1) Connect DVOM or high impedance analog voltmeter positive lead to jumper harness terminal "B" and negative lead to jumper harness terminal "A". Temperature and coolant sensor voltage (see graph) should match. If reading has shifted, replace coolant sensor and retest.
2) A Scan tester or voltmeter and jumper wires, can alternately be used to observe changes.
3) Since coolant temperature cannot change rapidly, a sudden temperature change occurring at idle as the engine is warming up or idling hot, most likely indicates a faulty coolant sensor.

91B07728   91D07729

Notes On Intermittents – Manipulate wiring, coolant sensor connector, engine to dash connector and PCM connector while observing PCM data P.0.4 or meter. If a failure is induced, the data or meter will change from its current reading.

When voltage increases and temperature parameter decreases, an open circuit is indicated. If voltage decreases and temperature parameter increases from its current value, a short to ground is indicated. If an intermittent cannot be found, substitute a known good sensor and retest.

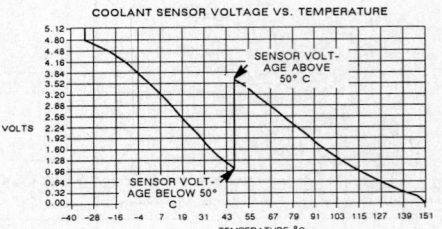

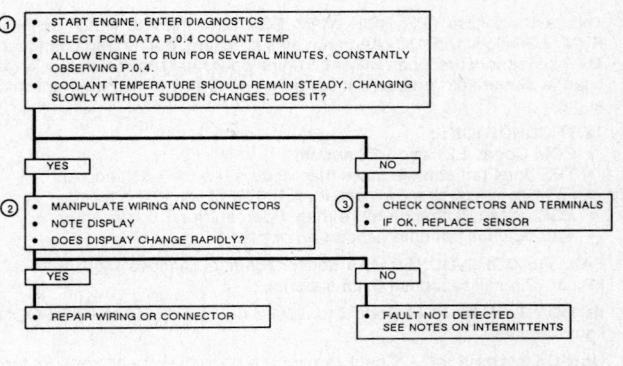

Courtesy of General Motors Corp.

PCM CODE E74, MAT SENSOR SIGNAL INTERRUPT

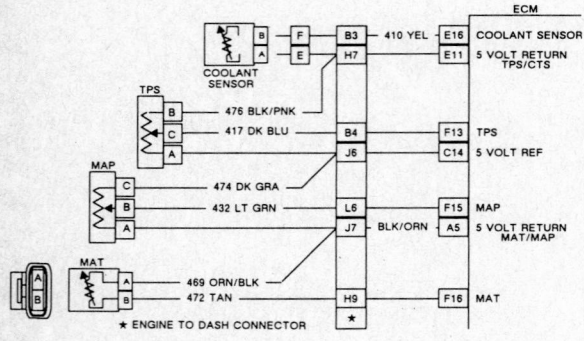

This test monitors MAT signal for a rapid change of 7 degrees or more in temperature, in a short period of time.

TEST CONDITIONS: Engine running

FAILURE CONDITIONS: MAT signal change of 7 degrees or more in 250 milliseconds (.250 second)

ACTION TAKEN: PCM Code E74 will set; no SERVICE ENGINE SOON light illuminated.

Note On Intermittents – This code can be caused by an open, short to ground or short to voltage on circuit No. 472 and/or 469. Also check for open or short in sensor connector, engine-to-dash connector or PCM connector. If no problems are found in wiring or connectors, substitute a known good sensor and retest.

90F17264

Courtesy of General Motors Corp.

1991 ENGINE PERFORMANCE
Self-Diagnostics – DeVille & Fleetwood PCM/BCM (Cont.)

GM
1-195

PCM CODE E75, VSS SIGNAL INTERRUPT

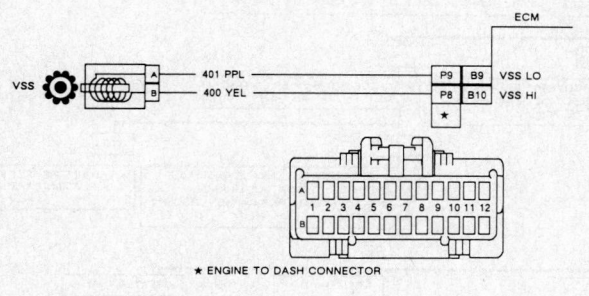

★ ENGINE TO DASH CONNECTOR

90J17268

This test compares vehicle speed to manifold pressure. A corresponding change in MAP reading and vehicle speed should exist. PCM will ignore test if conditions for engine idle are present.

TEST CONDITIONS: PCM Codes E31, E32 and E34 not set, engine running and brakes not applied

FAILURE CONDITIONS: Vehicle speed change of 8 MPH or more in a one-second time period with a corresponding MAP change of 2 kPa or less.

ACTION TAKEN: PCM Code E75 will set. No SERVICE ENGINE SOON light illuminated

Note On Intermittents – Manipulate VSS wiring and connectors and verify that wiring is not close to spark plug wires. Code can be caused by an open, short to ground or short to voltage on circuits No. 400 or No. 401. Also, check for an open or shorted sensor connector, engine-to-dash connector, PCM connector or a defective sensor. If wiring and connectors check out okay, substitute with a known good sensor and retest.

Courtesy of General Motors Corp.

PCM CODE E80, FUEL SYSTEM RICH

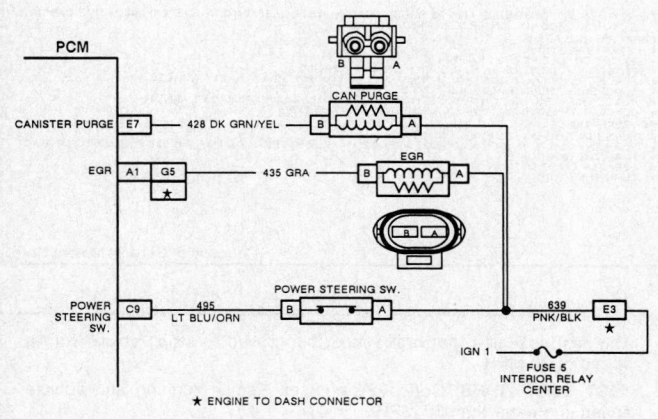

★ ENGINE TO DASH CONNECTOR

91A07676

This test monitors a rich condition caused by the fuel injection system or by the evaporative fuel canister that is purging continuously and causing the rich condition. The code can only be set during sustained steady driving or when block learn is still 104 or less.

TEST CONDITIONS:
- PCM Codes E14, E15, E16, E21, E22, E26, E27, E31, E32 or E34 not set
- System in closed loop
- Throttle switch open
- Throttle angle 6-30 degrees
- Coolant temperature greater than 180°F (82°C)
- Canister has been at a purge duty cycle of 94 percent at a throttle angle of 10 degrees or greater for 10 minutes

FAILURE CONDITIONS: Block learn is at 104 or less for 25 seconds

ACTION TAKEN: PCM Code E80 will set; PCM turns on SERVICE ENGINE SOON light

Courtesy of General Motors Corp.

PCM CODE E85,
THROTTLE BODY SERVICE REQUIRED

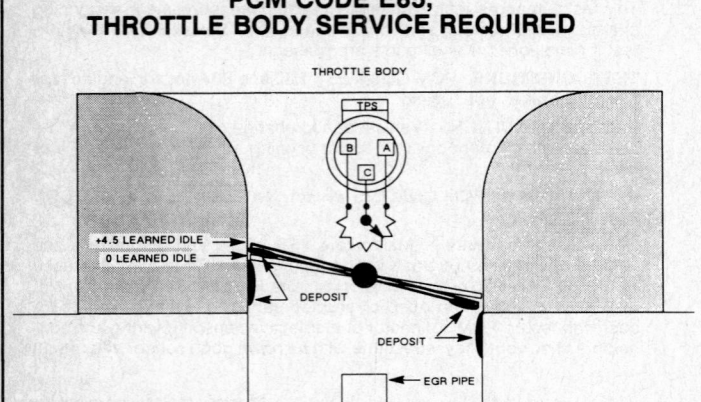

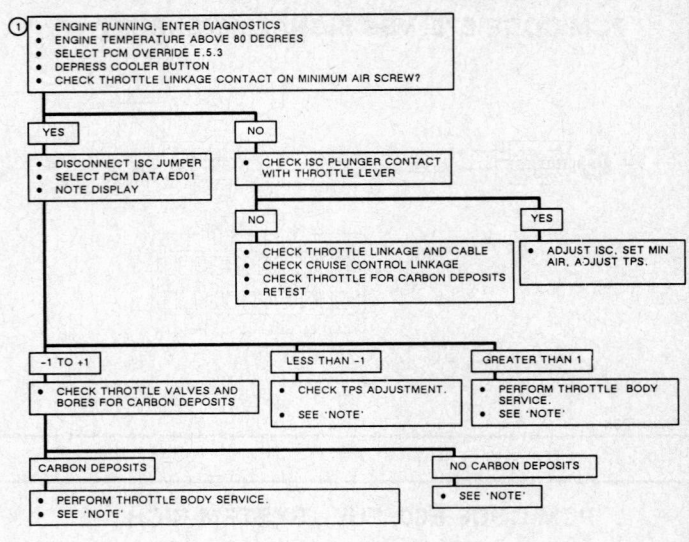

The PCM constantly learns base idle position. This base idle position is the relationship of engine RPM to throttle position. PCM is limited to fixed amount of learned throttle angle it can apply. When limit is reached, code will set. A build up of deposits in the throttle body will cause an increase in learned throttle angle.

TEST CONDITIONS: Constantly monitored

FAILURE CONDITIONS: Coast-down throttle angle offset is greater than 5 degrees from learned value

ACTION TAKEN: PCM Code E85 will set; SERVICE ENGINE SOON light turns on

NOTE: Test numbers refer to test numbers on diagnostic chart.

1) If engine stalls, continue the test. The stall may be caused by carbon deposits on the throttle valves and in throttle bores.

90E17271   91H07731

NOTE: WHEN ALL DIAGNOSIS AND REPAIRS ARE COMPLETE, DISCONNECT BATTERY NEGATIVE CABLE FOR 10 SECONDS AND RECONNECT.
TO PERFORM IDLE LEARN
  • START THE ENGINE
  • ALLOW TO IDLE FOR 13 MINUTES
  • PLACE TRANSMISSION IN DRIVE WITH BRAKES APPLIED
  • PLACE THE CLIMATE CONTROL IN THE 'OFF' POSITION FOR AT LEAST 1 MINUTE
  • MAKE SURE THE OUTSIDED AIR TEMPERATURE IS ABOVE 50°F
  • PLACE THE CLIMATE CONTROL IN THE 'AUTO' POSITION FOR AT LEAST 1 MINUTE
  • PLACE TRANSMISSION IN PARK AND TURN IGNITION OFF
TO PERFORM TPS LEARN
  • TURN IGNITION ON, ENTER DIAGNOSTICS
  • TURN THE IGNITION 'OFF' AND WAIT APPROXIMATELY 20 SECONDS FOR THE ISC MOTOR TO RETRACT
  • TURN THE IGNITION 'ON'
  • REENTER DIAGNOSTICS
  • TURN THE IGNITION OFF

Courtesy of General Motors Corp.

PCM CODE E90,
VCC BRAKE SWITCH INPUT PROBLEM

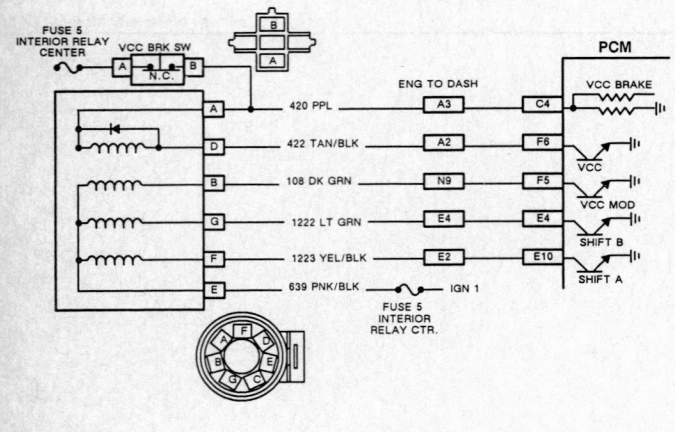

This test assumes that brake must be applied to stop vehicle from a speed of 30 MPH.

TEST CONDITIONS: Code E24 not set. Engine running and vehicle speed is greater than 30 MPH

FAILURE CONDITIONS: Vehicle speed cycles from 30 MPH or greater to zero MPH with no VCC brake switch input. PCM must record 10 of these occurrences to set code

ACTION TAKEN: PCM will set Code E90 and turns on SERVICE ENGINE SOON light

NOTE: Test numbers refer to test numbers on diagnostic chart.

1) When test is successfully completed, the Fuel Data Center (FDC) will alternately display E.7.1 and 00.

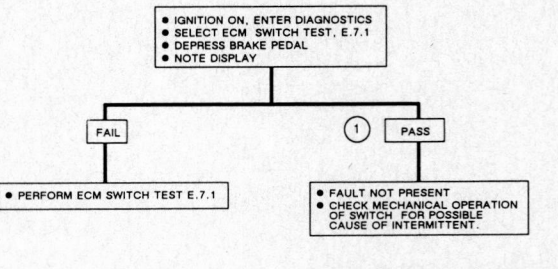

91F07711   91J07732

Courtesy of General Motors Corp.

1991 ENGINE PERFORMANCE
Self-Diagnostics – DeVille & Fleetwood PCM/BCM (Cont.)

GM
1-197

PCM CODE E91,
PARK/NEUTRAL SWITCH PROBLEM (1 OF 2)

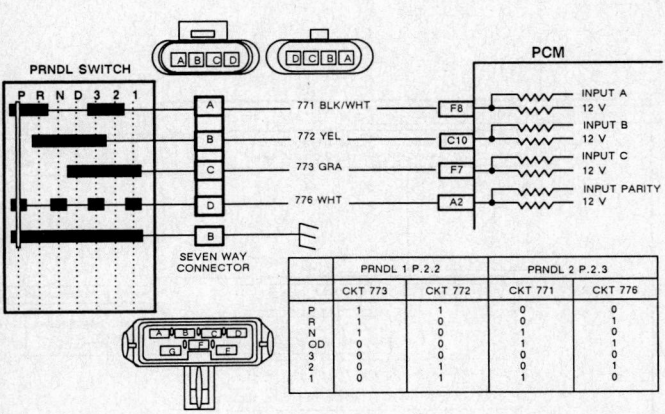

PRNDL SWITCH

771 BLK/WHT — F8 — INPUT A 12 V
772 YEL — C10 — INPUT B 12 V
773 GRA — F7 — INPUT C 12 V
776 WHT — A2 — INPUT PARITY 12 V

PCM

SEVEN WAY CONNECTOR

	PRNDL 1 P.2.2		PRNDL 2 P.2.3	
	CKT 773	CKT 772	CKT 771	CKT 776
P	1	1	0	0
R	1	0	0	1
N	1	0	1	0
OD	0	0	1	1
3	0	0	0	1
2	0	1	1	0
1	0	1	1	0

TEST CONDITIONS: Constantly monitored

FAILURE CONDITIONS:
- An open or short to ground in one or more switches or circuits that would generate an invalid binary code
- An engine start with a code recognized by the PCM as one for a forward or reverse gear

ACTION: PCM will set Code E91; SERVICE VEHICLE SOON light illuminated

Note On Intermittents – The PCM data displays P.2.2 and P.2.3 indicating status of each of the 4 circuits. A pull-up resistor produces a battery voltage signal at the PCM terminal when circuit is open and no signal when circuit is to ground. See table in Code E91 electrical schematic.

PCM VOLTAGE CHECK		
PCM TERM	SW CLOSED	SW OPEN
F8	0 TO 0.3 Volts	BATTERY
C10	0 TO 0.3 VOLTS	BATTERY
F7	0 TO 0.3 VOLTS	BATTERY
A2	0 TO 0.3 VOLTS	BATTERY

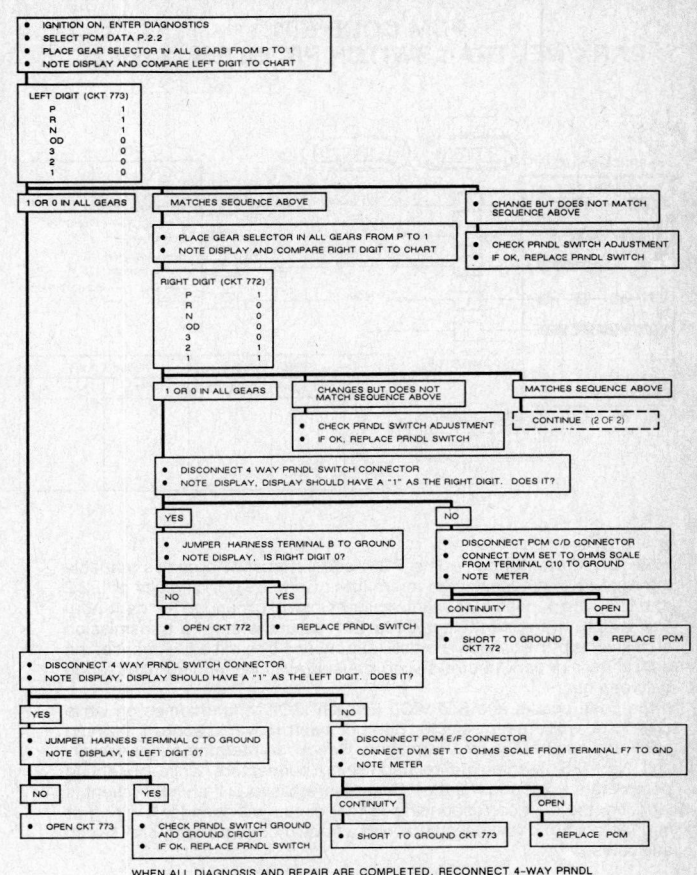

- IGNITION ON, ENTER DIAGNOSTICS
- SELECT PCM DATA P.2.2
- PLACE GEAR SELECTOR IN ALL GEARS FROM P TO 1
- NOTE DISPLAY AND COMPARE LEFT DIGIT TO CHART

LEFT DIGIT (CKT 773)
P 1
R 1
N 1
OD 0
3 0
2 0
1 0

1 OR 0 IN ALL GEARS — **MATCHES SEQUENCE ABOVE** — **CHANGE BUT DOES NOT MATCH SEQUENCE ABOVE**

- PLACE GEAR SELECTOR IN ALL GEARS FROM P TO 1
- NOTE DISPLAY AND COMPARE RIGHT DIGIT TO CHART

CHECK PRNDL SWITCH ADJUSTMENT
IF OK, REPLACE PRNDL SWITCH

RIGHT DIGIT (CKT 772)
P 1
R 0
N 0
OD 0
3 0
2 1
1 1

1 OR 0 IN ALL GEARS — **CHANGES BUT DOES NOT MATCH SEQUENCE ABOVE** — **MATCHES SEQUENCE ABOVE**

- CHECK PRNDL SWITCH ADJUSTMENT
- IF OK, REPLACE PRNDL SWITCH

CONTINUE (2 OF 2)

- DISCONNECT 4 WAY PRNDL SWITCH CONNECTOR
- NOTE DISPLAY, DISPLAY SHOULD HAVE A "1" AS THE RIGHT DIGIT. DOES IT?

YES
- JUMPER HARNESS TERMINAL B TO GROUND
- NOTE DISPLAY, IS RIGHT DIGIT 0?

NO

NO — OPEN CKT 772
YES — REPLACE PRNDL SWITCH

- DISCONNECT PCM C/D CONNECTOR
- CONNECT DVM SET TO OHMS SCALE FROM TERMINAL C10 TO GROUND
- NOTE METER

CONTINUITY — SHORT TO GROUND CKT 772
OPEN — REPLACE PCM

- DISCONNECT 4 WAY PRNDL SWITCH CONNECTOR
- NOTE DISPLAY, DISPLAY SHOULD HAVE A "1" AS THE LEFT DIGIT. DOES IT?

YES
- JUMPER HARNESS TERMINAL C TO GROUND
- NOTE DISPLAY, IS LEFT DIGIT 0?

NO — OPEN CKT 773
YES
- CHECK PRNDL SWITCH GROUND AND GROUND CIRCUIT
- IF OK, REPLACE PRNDL SWITCH

NO
- DISCONNECT PCM E/F CONNECTOR
- CONNECT DVM SET TO OHMS SCALE FROM TERMINAL F7 TO GND
- NOTE METER

CONTINUITY — SHORT TO GROUND CKT 773
OPEN — REPLACE PCM

WHEN ALL DIAGNOSIS AND REPAIR ARE COMPLETED, RECONNECT 4-WAY PRNDL CONNECTOR, CLEAR CODES, AND VERIFY OPERATION

91C07719 91A07737 91B07733

Courtesy of General Motors Corp.

PCM CODE E91, PARK/NEUTRAL SWITCH PROBLEM (2 OF 2)

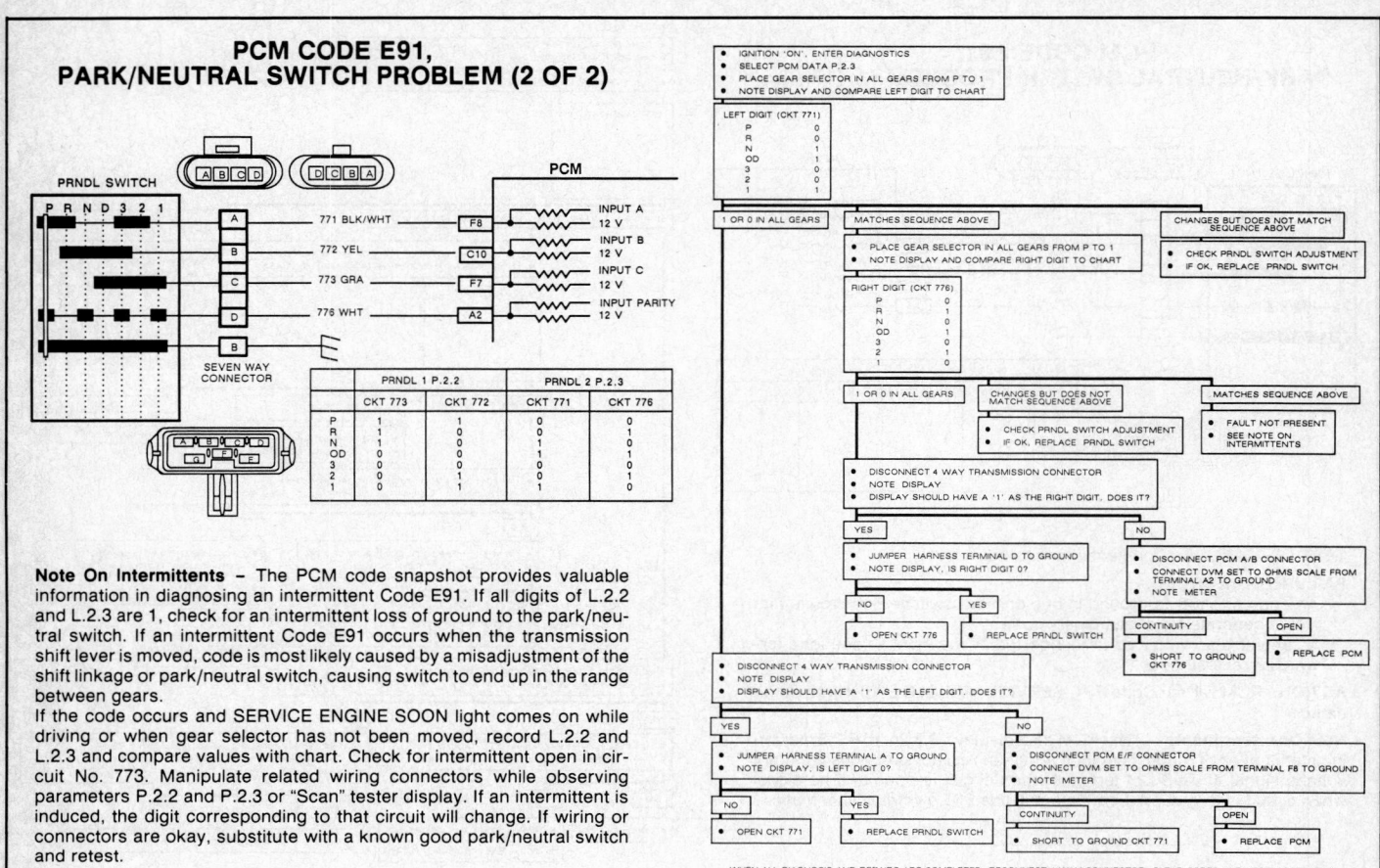

	PRNDL 1 P.2.2		PRNDL 2 P.2.3	
	CKT 773	CKT 772	CKT 771	CKT 776
P	1	1	0	0
R	1	1	0	1
N	1	0	0	0
OD	0	0	1	0
3	0	0	1	0
2	0	1	1	0
1	0	1	0	0

Note On Intermittents – The PCM code snapshot provides valuable information in diagnosing an intermittent Code E91. If all digits of L.2.2 and L.2.3 are 1, check for an intermittent loss of ground to the park/neutral switch. If an intermittent Code E91 occurs when the transmission shift lever is moved, code is most likely caused by a misadjustment of the shift linkage or park/neutral switch, causing switch to end up in the range between gears.

If the code occurs and SERVICE ENGINE SOON light comes on while driving or when gear selector has not been moved, record L.2.2 and L.2.3 and compare values with chart. Check for intermittent open in circuit No. 773. Manipulate related wiring connectors while observing parameters P.2.2 and P.2.3 or "Scan" tester display. If an intermittent is induced, the digit corresponding to that circuit will change. If wiring or connectors are okay, substitute with a known good park/neutral switch and retest.

91C07719   91D07734

Courtesy of General Motors Corp.

PCM CODE E92, HEATED WINDSHIELD REQUEST PROBLEM

PCM will increase idle speed to compensate for the electrical load placed in the alternator when the heated windshield is turned on.

TEST CONDITIONS: Engine running

FAILURE CONDITIONS: Heated windshield request present at PCM for more than 10 minutes

ACTION TAKEN: PCM Code E92 will set; BCM turns on SERVICE VEHICLE SOON light

91F07730   91C07738

Courtesy of General Motors Corp.

1991 ENGINE PERFORMANCE
Self-Diagnostics – DeVille & Fleetwood PCM/BCM (Cont.)

GM
1-199

PCM CODE E96, TORQUE CONVERTER OVERSTRESS

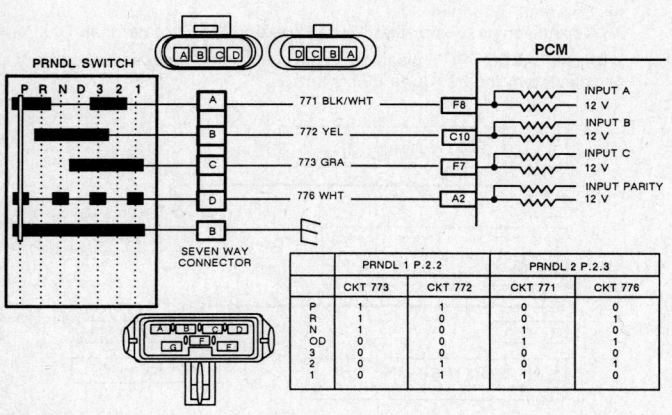

This test monitors throttle position and vehicle speed with brakes applied, to detect an action of the driver that could damage the vehicle drivetrain or create an unsafe condition.

TEST CONDITIONS: PCM Codes E21, E22 and E24 not set

FAILURE CONDITIONS: • Brakes applied
• Transmission in Drive or Reverse
• Vehicle speed 5 MPH or less
• Throttle angle greater than 65 degrees for 12 seconds

ACTION TAKEN: PCM will set Code E96; no SERVICE ENGINE SOON light illuminated.

91C07719

Courtesy of General Motors Corp.

PCM CODE E97, PARK/NEUTRAL TO DRIVE/REVERSE AT HIGH THROTTLE ANGLE

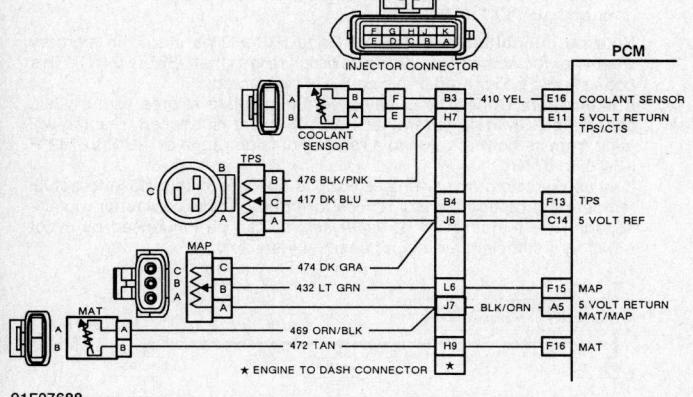

TEST CONDITIONS: PCM Codes E21 and E22 not set

FAILURE CONDITIONS:
• Gear selector from Park or Neutral to Drive or Reverse
• Vehicle speed less than 6 MPH
• Engine speed greater than 2000 RPM
• Throttle angle of 20 degrees or greater

ACTION TAKEN: PCM will disable selected injectors and set Code E97; no SERVICE ENGINE SOON light illuminated

91F07688

Courtesy of General Motors Corp.

PCM CODE E98, PARK/NEUTRAL TO DRIVE/REVERSE WHILE OUTSIDE OF ISC CONTROL RANGE

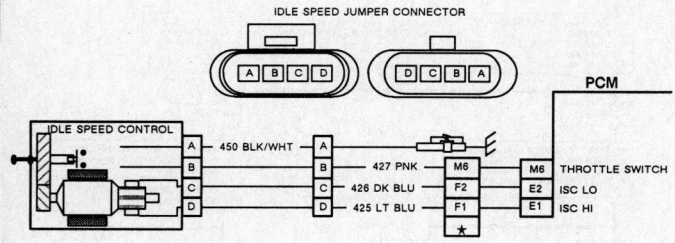

TEST CONDITIONS: PCM Codes E21 and E22 not set.

FAILURE CONDITIONS:
• Engine running
• Gear selector moved from Park or Neutral to Drive or Reverse or vise versa
• Engine speed at 600 RPM greater than desired
• Throttle angle of 20 degrees or less
• Vehicle speed less than 6 MPH

ACTION TAKEN: PCM will retard ignition timing and set Code E98. No SERVICE ENGINE SOON light illuminated

Note On Intermittents – Code is most likely induced by driver shifting from Neutral to Drive while depressing accelerator. Check driver habits to help determine how code was set.

★ ENGINE TO DASH CONNECTOR

91B07667

Courtesy of General Motors Corp.

GM
1-200

1991 ENGINE PERFORMANCE
Self-Diagnostics – DeVille & Fleetwood PCM/BCM (Cont.)

PCM CODE E99, CRUISE SERVO APPLIED NOT IN CRUISE

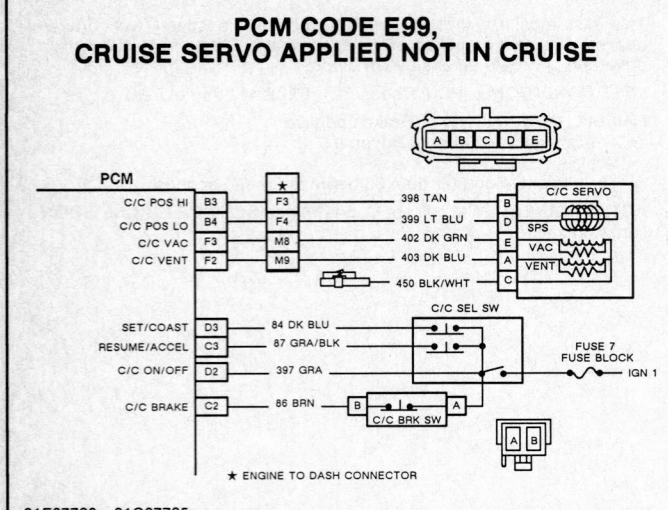

TEST CONDITIONS: Constantly monitored

FAILURE CONDITIONS:
- Cruise control disengaged for 2 seconds
- Servo still engaged
- Throttle angle greater than 20 degrees and MAP greater than 70 kPa

ACTION TAKEN: PCM disables cruise control and reduces fuel delivery to selected cylinders. Code E99 is set

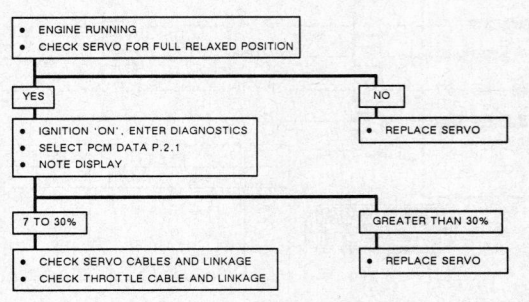

91E07720   91G07735

Courtesy of General Motors Corp.

BCM CODE CHARTS

BCM CODE F10, OUTSIDE AIR TEMPERATURE SENSOR CIRCUIT

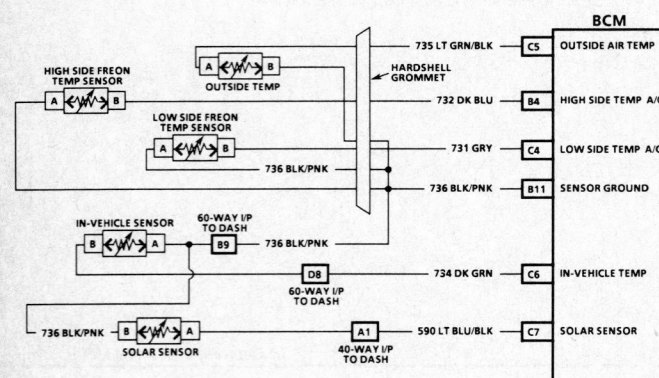

3) By applying ground to various points in circuits, an open can be isolated when temperature display changes from less than -29°F (-34°C) to greater than 189°F (87°C).

Note on Intermittents – A BCM Code F10 will be stored in memory whenever the ambient temperature drops to less than -29°F (-34°C). This code should be ignored if this cause is suspected.

If intermittent Code F10 is being set, manipulate related wiring while observing BCM data parameter P.2.6. If failure is induced, reading will jump from its normal value to a reading outside range of -29°F to 189°F (-34°C to 87°C).

If value displayed by parameter P.2.6 is not reasonably close to actual temperature of air at sensor, check for poor terminal contact or replace sensor. The temperature of air at sensor can be influenced by a hot radiator, if sufficient air is not passing by sensor.

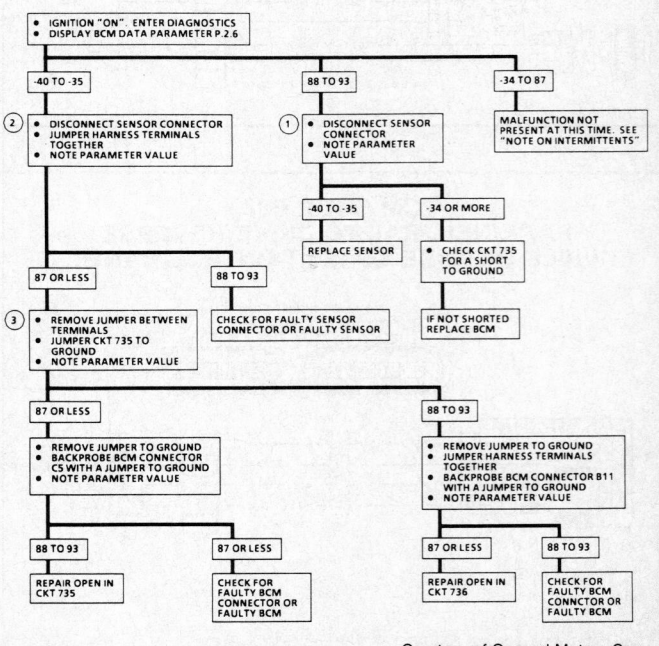

NOTE: If this code is not displayed during second pass of diagnostic codes, it is an intermittent failure and cannot be diagnosed using this procedure. Refer to NOTE ON INTERMITTENTS at end of this text.

The outside air temperature sensor uses a thermistor to control signal voltage to BCM. The BCM applies and monitors voltage on circuit No. 735 to sensor. When sensor is cold, its resistance is high; therefore, BCM will see a high monitored voltage. As sensor warms, its resistance becomes less and signal voltage is pulled low through sensor ground circuit No. 736. This signal voltage will vary between 5 volts (open circuit) and zero volts (shorted circuit).

BCM Code F10 will set if temperature is less than -29°F (-34°C) (circuit open), or temperature is greater than 189°F (87°C) (circuit shorted). These conditions can be observed in BCM data display (parameter P.2.6) as a reading outside the range of -29°F to 189°F (-34°C to 87°C).

NOTE: Test numbers refer to test numbers on diagnostic chart.

1) If temperature reading changes after disconnecting sensor, BCM and wiring are okay.

2) If temperature reading changes after jumpering sensor terminals, BCM and wiring are okay.

91E07739   90G13736

Courtesy of General Motors Corp.

1991 ENGINE PERFORMANCE
Self-Diagnostics – DeVille & Fleetwood PCM/BCM (Cont.)

GM
1-201

BCM CODE F11, A/C HIGH SIDE TEMPERATURE SENSOR CIRCUIT

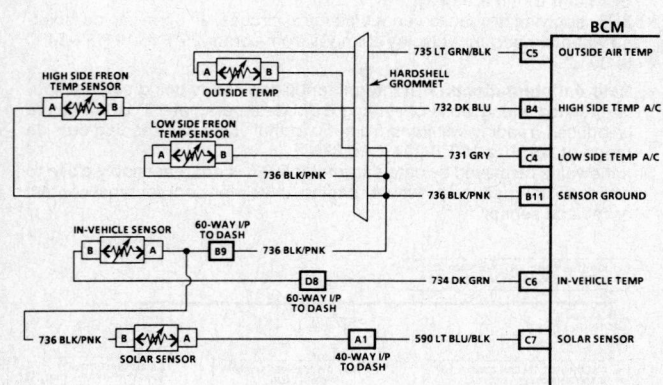

NOTE: If this code is not displayed during second pass of diagnostic codes, it is an intermittent failure and cannot be diagnosed using this procedure. Refer to NOTE ON INTERMITTENTS at end of this text.

The A/C high side temperature sensor uses a thermistor to control signal voltage to BCM. The BCM applies and monitors voltage on circuit No. 732 to sensor. When sensor is cold, its resistance is high; therefore, BCM will see a high signal voltage. As sensor warms, its resistance becomes less and monitored signal voltage is pulled low through sensor ground, circuit No. 736. This signal voltage will vary between 5 volts (circuit open) and zero volts (circuit shorted).

BCM Code F11 will set if signal voltage indicates an open circuit 16°F (-9°C), or a shorted circuit, 408°F (209°C). These conditions can be observed in BCM data display (parameter P.2.7) as a reading outside the range of 16°F to 408°F (-9°C to 209°C).

NOTE: Test numbers refer to test numbers on diagnostic chart.

1) If temperature reading changes after disconnecting sensor, BCM and wiring are okay.

2) If temperature reading changes after jumpering sensor terminals, BCM and wiring are okay.

3) By applying ground to various points in circuits, an open can be isolated when temperature display changes from about 59°F to 392°F (-15°C to 200°C).

Note on Intermittents – If intermittent BCM Code F11 is being set, manipulate related wiring while observing BCM data parameter P.2.7. If failure is induced, reading will jump from its normal value to a reading outside range of 16°F to 408°F (-9°C to 209°C).

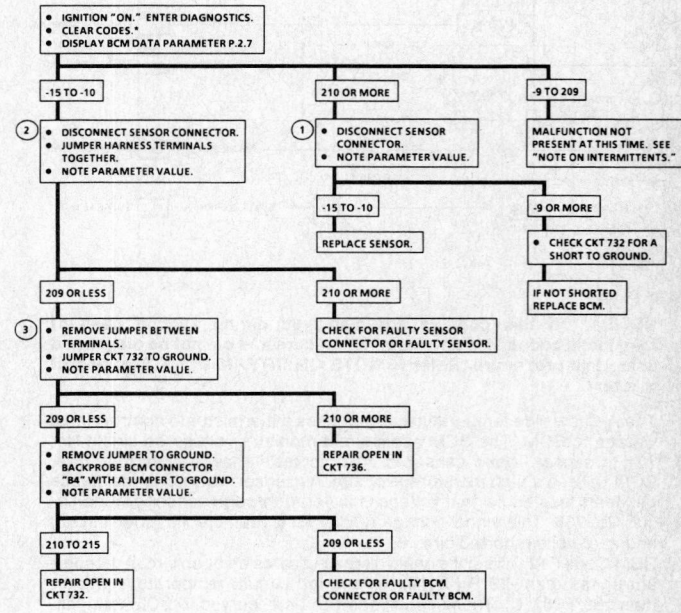

* IF A FAULT OCCURS BEFORE DIAGNOSTICS ARE ENTERED THE DISPLAY PARAMETER P.2.7 WILL DISPLAY THE DEFAULT VALUE OF 56. CLEARING THE CODES WILL ALLOW THE ACTUAL VALUE TO BE DISPLAYED.

91E07739 91B07747

GM
1-202

1991 ENGINE PERFORMANCE
Self-Diagnostics – DeVille & Fleetwood PCM/BCM (Cont.)

BCM CODE F12, A/C LOW SIDE TEMPERATURE SENSOR CIRCUIT

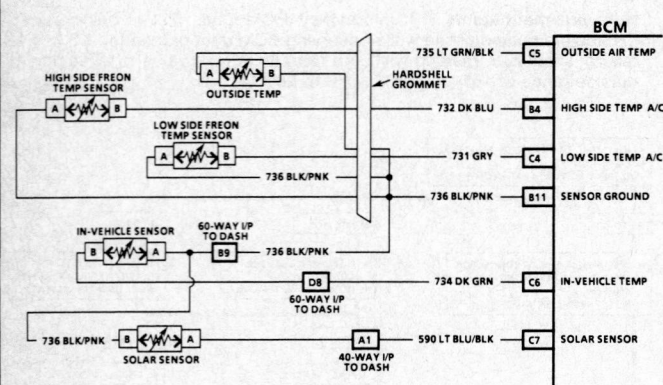

NOTE: If this code is not displayed during second pass of diagnostic codes, it is an intermittent failure and cannot be diagnosed using this procedure. Refer to NOTE ON INTERMITTENTS at end of this text.

The A/C low side temperature sensor uses a thermistor to control signal voltage to BCM. The BCM applies and monitors voltage on circuit No. 731 to sensor. When sensor is cold, its resistance is high; therefore, BCM will see a high monitored voltage. As sensor warms, its resistance becomes less and signal voltage is lowered through sensor ground circuit No. 736. This signal voltage will vary between 5 volts (open circuit) and zero volts (shorted circuit).

BCM Code F12 will set if signal voltage indicates an open circuit, temperature less than -29°F (-34°C); or shorted circuit, temperature greater than 189°F (87°C). These conditions can be observed in BCM data display (parameter P.2.8) as a reading outside the range of -29°F to 189°F (-34°C to 87°C).

NOTE: Test numbers refer to test numbers on diagnostic chart.

1) If temperature reading changes after disconnecting sensor, BCM and wiring are okay.

2) If temperature reading changes after jumpering sensor terminals, BCM and wiring are okay.

3) By applying ground to various points in circuits, an open can be isolated when temperature display changes from about -29°F to 194°F (-34°C to 90°C).

Note on Intermittents – If intermittent Code F12 is being set, manipulate related wiring while observing BCM data parameter P.2.8. If failure is induced, reading will jump from its normal value to a reading outside range of -29°F to 189°F (-34°C to 87°C).

If the value displayed by data parameter P.2.8 is not reasonably close to corresponding gauge pressure reading, check for poor terminal contact or replace sensor.

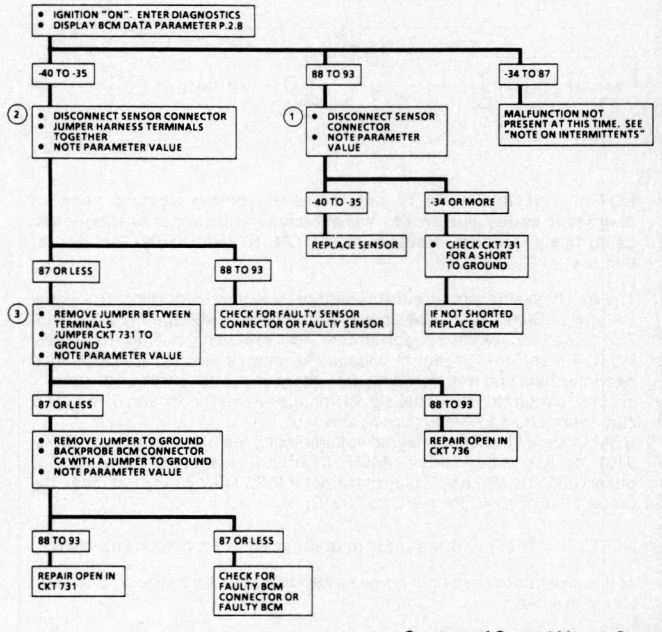

91E07739   90I13738

Courtesy of General Motors Corp.

1991 ENGINE PERFORMANCE
Self-Diagnostics – DeVille & Fleetwood PCM/BCM (Cont.)

GM
1-203

BCM CODE F13, IN-VEHICLE TEMPERATURE SENSOR

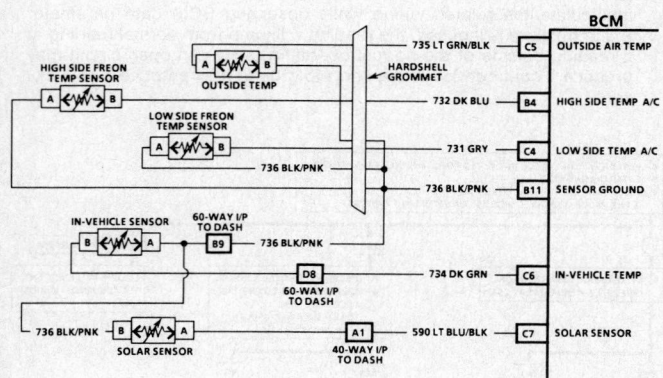

NOTE: If this code is not displayed during second pass of diagnostic codes, it is an intermittent failure and cannot be diagnosed using this procedure. Refer to NOTE ON INTERMITTENTS at end of this text.

The in-vehicle temperature sensor uses a thermistor to control signal voltage to BCM. BCM applies and monitors voltage on circuit No. 734 to sensor. When sensor is cold, its resistance is high (BCM will read a high monitored voltage). As sensor warms, its resistance decreases and the signal voltage is pulled low through sensor ground circuit No. 736. This signal will vary between 5 volts (open circuit) and zero volts (shorted circuit). Code F13 will set if signal voltage indicates less than -29°F (-34°C) or greater than 205°F (96°C). These conditions can be observed in BCM data display as an in-vehicle temperature reading (parameter P.2.5) outside range.

NOTE: Test numbers refer to test numbers on diagnostic chart.

1) If temperature reading changes after disconnecting sensor, the BCM and wiring are okay.

2) If temperature reading changes after jumpering sensor terminals, the BCM and wiring are okay.

3) By applying a ground to various points in circuit, an open can be isolated when display changes to outside the range of -29°F to 194°F (-34°C to 90°C).

Note on Intermittents – If an intermittent Code F13 is being set, manipulate related wiring while observing BCM data parameter P.2.5. If failure is induced, reading will jump from its normal value to a reading outside range of -29°F to 204°F (-34°C to 96°C).

If value displayed by parameter P.2.5 is not reasonably close to actual air temperature at sensor, check for poor terminal contact or replace sensor. To obtain an accurate reading of in-car temperature, the aspirator must draw in-vehicle air past sensor.

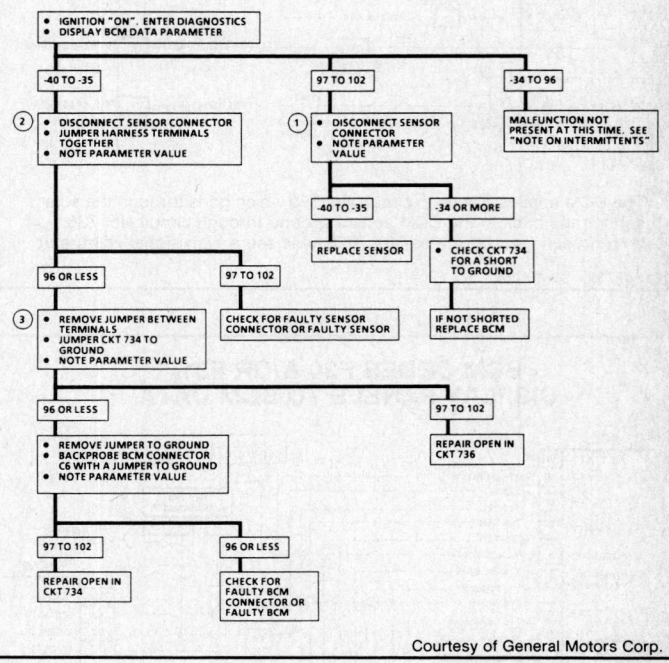

Courtesy of General Motors Corp.

91E07739   90J13739

BCM CODE F15, SOLAR SENSOR CIRCUIT FAILURE

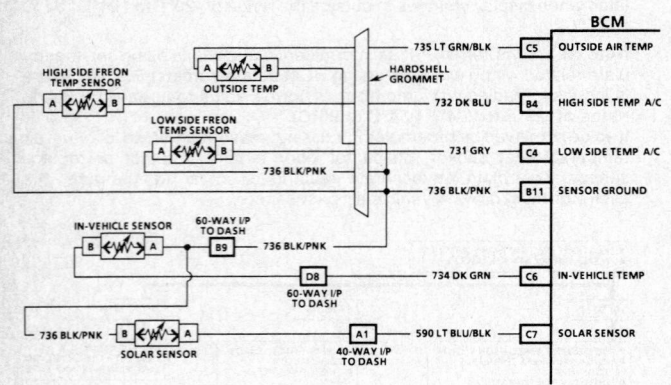

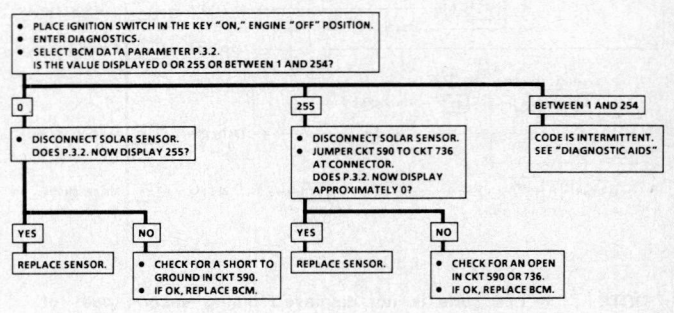

BCM terminal C7. With a full sun load, the voltage at BCM terminal C7 will drop low. BCM Code F15 will set if circuit No. 590 is open or shorted to ground.

Notes On Intermittents – If an intermittent Code F15 is being set, manipulate the related wiring while observing BCM data parameter P.3.2. If failure is induced, the reading will jump from normal reading to a reading outside of the normal operating range. An open circuit may produce a count of 255 and a short to ground may produce a count of zero.

The BCM applies 5 volts to circuit No. 590 which goes through the solar sensor and back to the BCM sensor ground through circuit No. 736. With no sun load on the sensor, BCM will see a high signal voltage at

91E07739 91D07748

BCM CODES F30 &/OR F31, DISPLAY PANELS TO BCM DATA

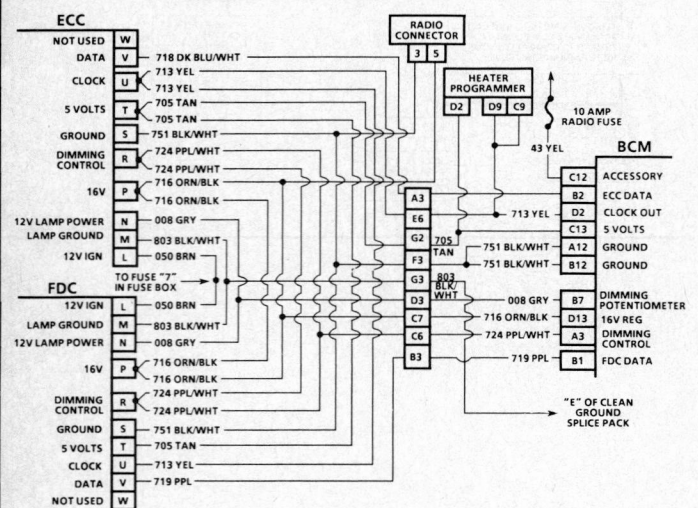

BCM Code F30 is set if BCM is unable to receive data from Electronic Climate Control Panel (ECCP). Code F31 indicates that same condition exists between BCM and Fuel Data Center (FDC). If malfunction should occur in circuit common to both display panels, both codes will be stored in BCM memory.

Due to failure modes of Codes F30 and F31, they will only be displayed if the problem is intermittent. When these codes are currently failing, displays do not function properly, which prohibits use of diagnostics. One or more of the symptoms (listed in SYMPTOMS OF MALFUNCTIONS table by corresponding number) is associated with each circuit malfunction and is referenced in parentheses.

91B07686

SYMPTOMS OF MALFUNCTIONS

Number in Parentheses	Display Symptom
1	Panel Displays "D"
2	Panel Displays "C"
3	Panel Frozen, Dim Or Blank
4	Displays Flash On And Off

Code F30 Only
- Circuit No. 718 open or short to ground (1)
- ECCP branch of circuit No. 713 open (2)
- ECCP branch of circuit No. 751B open (3)
- ECCP branch of circuit No. 705 open (3)
- Faulty ECCP (1, 2, 3 or 4)
- Faulty BCM (1)

Code F31 Only
- Circuit No. 719 open or short to ground (1)
- FDC branch of circuit No. 713 open (2)
- FDC branch of circuit No. 751B open (3)
- FDC branch of circuit No. 705 open (3)
- Faulty FDC (1, 2, 3 or 4)
- Faulty BCM (1)

Both Codes
- Common branch of circuit No. 713 open (2)
- Circuit No. 713 short to ground (2)
- Common branch of circuit No. 751B open (3)
- Common branch of circuit No. 705 open (3)
- Circuit No. 705 short to ground (3, 4)
- Faulty BCM (1, 2, 3, 4)

Note on Intermittents – If intermittent Code F30 and/or F31 is being set, manipulate related wiring while observing display panels. If failure is induced, associated symptom will appear. This will help to isolate location of malfunction. If failure is induced, but cannot be isolated to a given circuit, follow SELF-DIAGNOSTIC SYSTEM CHECK chart, which is designed to locate display malfunctions that are currently failing.

1991 ENGINE PERFORMANCE
Self-Diagnostics – DeVille & Fleetwood PCM/BCM (Cont.)

GM
1-205

BCM CODE F32, BCM-TO-PCM DATA PROBLEM

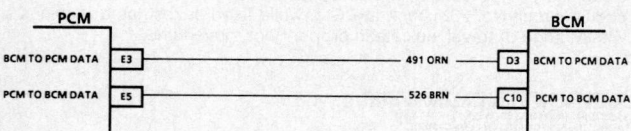

NOTE: If this code is not displayed during second pass of diagnostic codes, it is an intermittent failure and cannot be diagnosed using this procedure. Refer to NOTE ON INTERMITTENTS at end of this text.

BCM Code F32 is set if a problem is detected as data is being transferred back and forth between BCM and PCM. If a hard Code F32 is displayed upon entering self-diagnostics, one of the following conditions exists:

BCM To PCM Data Malfunction In Circuit No. 526
If BCM fails to receive data from PCM terminal C10 on circuit No. 526, Code F32 will be set immediately and the BCM will stop sending data to PCM on circuit No. 491. When PCM stops receiving data on circuit No. 491, it will set Code E47 in its memory.
However, this code will not be displayed since it would have to be sent on circuit No. 526 to BCM. The loss of data to BCM will result in a faulty instantaneous fuel economy reading of "0" MPG at all times.

BCM To PCM Data Malfunction In Circuit No. 491
If PCM fails to receive data from BCM terminal D3 on circuit No. 491, Code E47 will be set immediately by the PCM. Data will continue to be sent to BCM on circuit No. 526. Since BCM continues to receive data, Code F32 is not set immediately and instantaneous fuel economy reading will be accurate.
Upon entering self-diagnostics, the BCM will attempt to request diagnostic data from PCM, but cannot due to malfunction in circuit No. 491. If diagnostic data is not received by BCM, Code F32 will set. The BCM will be unable to display Code E47 stored in PCM memory.

PCM MEM-CAL Malfunction
If PCM fails to receive data from MEM-CAL, the PCM will stop sending data on circuit No. 526 and Code F32 will be set immediately. See BCM TO PCM DATA MALFUNCTION IN CIRCUIT NO. 526.
If hard Code F32 is displayed, first check to see if PCM can illuminate its service telltales while cranking engine. If not, the PCM is not operating

properly and should be checked using SELF-DIAGNOSTIC SYSTEM CHECK chart.
If telltales work properly, observe instantaneous fuel economy display while vehicle is moving. A malfunction in circuit No. 526 will result in a constant reading of "0" MPG.
If reading varies normally, the cause of Code F32 is a malfunction in circuit No. 491. If no circuit problem can be found, one or both modules is unable to process data and should be replaced.

Note on Intermittents – The following conditions will result in intermittent BCM Code F32 and/or PCM Code E47:
- Momentary open or short in circuit No. 526 resulting in both Code F32 and E47.
- Momentary open or short in circuit No. 491 resulting in Code E47 only
- Momentary loss of ignition (circuit No. 50), battery (circuit No. 840) or ground (circuit No. 751A) to BCM resulting in Code E47 and intermittent display panel operation
- Momentary loss of ignition (circuit No. 439) to PCM resulting in Code F32 and intermittent engine operation
- Momentary loss of battery (circuit No. 480) or ground (circuit No. 450) to PCM resulting in Codes F32, E52 and intermittent engine operation.
- Momentary BCM PROM problem resulting in Codes E47, F51 and intermittent display of "-151" on ECCP

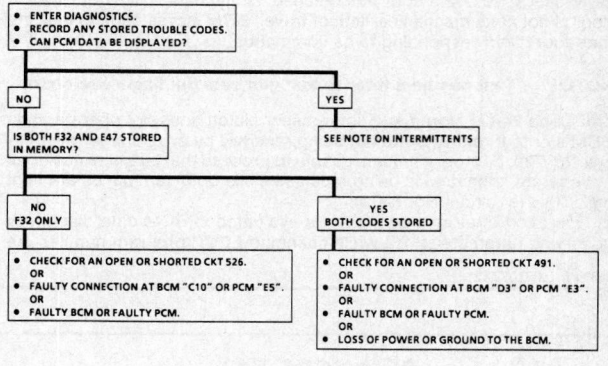

91G07740   91A07742

BCM CODE F40, AIR-MIX DOOR PROBLEM (1 OF 2)

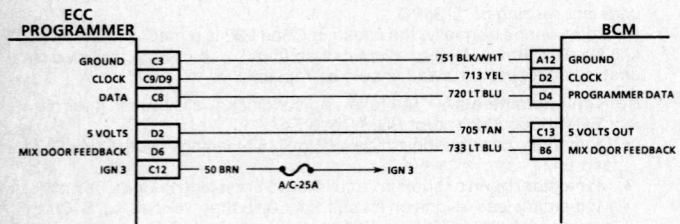

NOTE: If no malfunction is uncovered using this procedure, it will indicate that PFI system is okay at this time.

BCM Code F40 is set by BCM if it is unable to move air-mix door. The BCM requests door to move over data circuit (circuit No. 720) to programmer. The programmer then supplies voltage to DC motor which drives air-mix door. The BCM monitors feedback pot on DC motor which varies between zero and 5 volts, depending on its position.
If door is requested to move, but feedback voltage does not change, BCM checks to see if door has reached its mechanical limit of travel. If door is not at its mechanical limit of travel, BCM stores code to indicate that door is not responding to its commands.

NOTE: Test numbers refer to test numbers on diagnostic chart.

1) If Code F40 is stored and compressor clutch does not operate, then BCM's output requests are not being received by programmer over circuit No. 720, or programmer is unable to process the data. If clutch does not operate, then data is being received since both commands are sent by BCM over circuit No. 720.
2) Operation of air-mix door can be evaluated in BCM data display by observing parameter P.2.3 while changing ECCP program number. As

program number is changed from zero (maximum A/C) to 100 (maximum heat), door position should vary between its mechanical limits of travel (less than 20 percent and greater than 97 percent).
Readings of 0 percent or 100 percent indicate malfunction in feedback circuit (circuit No. 733) back to BCM, while fixed or restricted readings within range of travel indicate improper door movement.

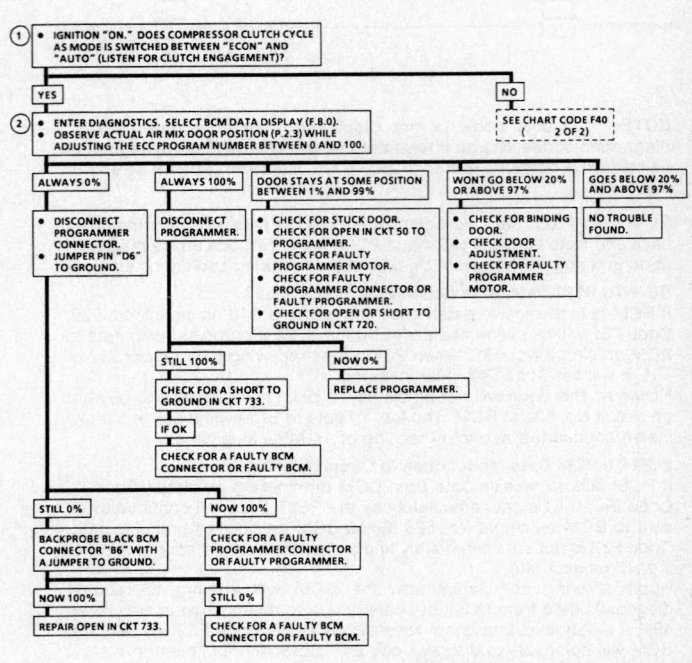

91I07741   91C07743

Courtesy of General Motors Corp.

BCM CODE F40, AIR-MIX DOOR PROBLEM (2 OF 2)

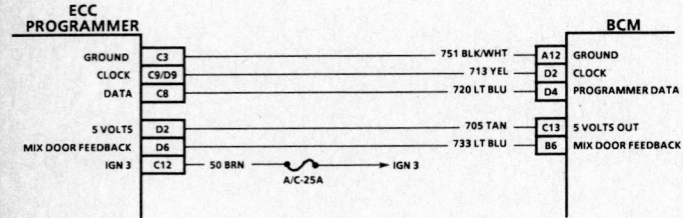

NOTE: Test numbers refer to test numbers on diagnostic chart.

3) Checks circuits No. 707, 713 and 751 for a fault between BCM and programmer.
4) Verifies programmer is receiving data from BCM. If programmer is receiving data from BCM commanding it to reposition air-mix door and does not do so, programmer is faulty. If it is not receiving data, circuit No. 720 is open or shorted, or BCM is faulty.

Note on Intermittents – If intermittent Code F40 is being set, manipulate related wiring while observing parameter P.2.3. If failure is induced, door reading will either stop or jump to an extreme value (0 percent or 100 percent). This will help to isolate location of malfunction.

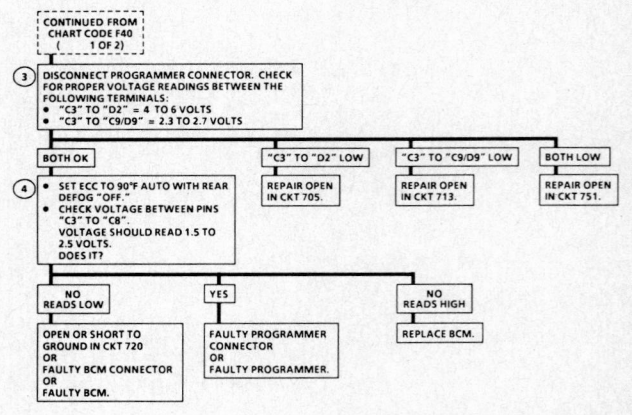

91I07741   91E07744

Courtesy of General Motors Corp.

1991 ENGINE PERFORMANCE
Self-Diagnostics – DeVille & Fleetwood PCM/BCM (Cont.)

GM
1-207

BCM CODES F46, F47 &/OR F48, REFRIGERANT SYSTEM PROBLEMS

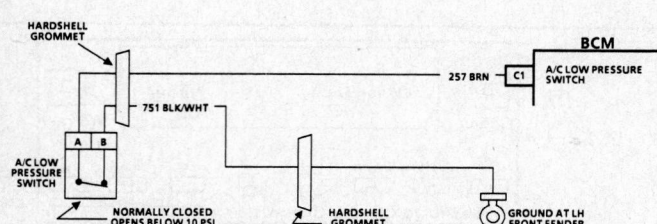

In process of controlling compressor clutch, BCM monitors certain system inputs for an indication of low refrigerant charge. If system's refrigerant state of charge should fall below about 1/3 of its capacity, the BCM is capable of detecting this condition and will illuminate SERVICE AIR COND light to warn operator. In addition to illuminating the light, the BCM will store a diagnostic code in memory. These codes all indicate that a low refrigerant condition was detected.

If low pressure status indicator (°F) appears upon entering diagnostics, this indicates either a complete loss of refrigerant or malfunction in A/C low pressure switch circuit. This chart is designed to isolate loss of ground signal which is normally provided to BCM through pressure switch contacts. These contacts open at less than about 10 psi.

If low pressure status indicator does not appear, then some refrigerant remains in system. Fault lies in air conditioning system controls.

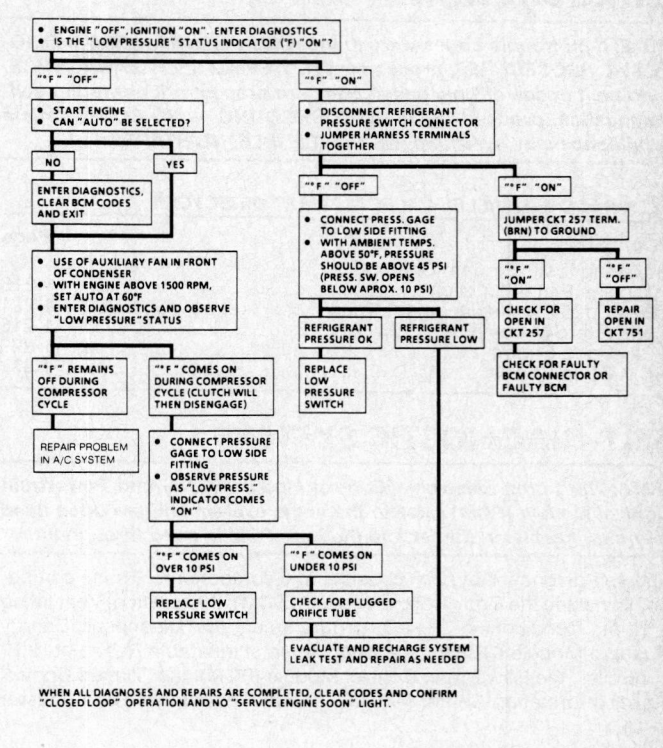

91H07745   90G13744

INTRODUCTION

NOTE: If no trouble codes were found while performing BASIC DIAGNOSTIC PROCEDURES, proceed with ENTERING SELF-DIAGNOSTICS. If no fault codes or only pass codes are present after entering self-diagnostics, proceed to TROUBLE SHOOTING – NO CODES article for diagnosis by symptom (i.e. ROUGH IDLE, NO START, etc.).

ELDORADO & SEVILLE PCM/BCM CHART DIRECTORY

SELF-DIAGNOSTIC SYSTEM

NOTE: The terms Electronic Control Module (ECM) and Powertrain Control Module (PCM) refer to the same system and are often used interchangeably. In this article the term PCM is used throughout.

The self-diagnostic system consists of 6 components. These components include the Body Control Module (BCM), the Heating, Ventilating and Air Conditioning (HVAC) programmer, the Diagnostic Energy Reserve Module (DERM), the Supplemental Inflatable Restraint (SIR) controller, the Powertrain Control Module (PCM), the Climate Control Driver Information Center (CCDIC) and the Instrument Panel Cluster (IPC).

In addition to monitoring a particular set of sensors and switches, the BCM functions as the heart of the self-diagnostic system, maintaining continuous communication with each of the other 5 components of the system. These other 5 components, known as subsystems, also monitor sensors and switches, reporting system conditions to the BCM.

The BCM, upon receiving information from a subsystem, compares the received information with programmed instructions within its memory, monitor individual subsystems and their related sensors and switches.

Should a subsystem exceed pre-programmed limits, the BCM will recognize a malfunction and, in response, may act to control the malfunctioning subsystem. To control a particular subsystem, the BCM rapidly switches an internal circuit between zero and 5 volts, converting programmed control information into a series of pulses which represent coded data messages. These messages are transmitted to the malfunctioning component, which interprets the information and responds accordingly.

As a result of interactions between the BCM and a malfunctioning component, an alphanumeric code, known as a trouble code, is often set in the BCM's memory. This trouble code identifies the malfunctioning component and can be accessed by a service technician as an aid to diagnostic procedures. All trouble codes are displayed on the CCDIC.

In addition to monitoring the self-diagnostic system and displaying trouble codes, the BCM can be programmed by the service technician to perform specific diagnostic tests on individual components and systems. The results of these tests are displayed on the CCDIC. This article covers accessing trouble codes and programming the self-diagnostic system to perform specific diagnostic tests on system components.

ENTERING SELF-DIAGNOSTICS

NOTE: The Electronic Climate Control (ECC) panel and Driver Information Center (DIC) make up the Climate Control Driver Information Center (CCDIC). See Fig. 1.

1) Turn ignition on. Simultaneously push OFF and WARMER buttons on ECC panel. *See Fig. 1.* Continue to push OFF and WARMER buttons until the segment check appears on the Instrument Panel Cluster (IPC) and CCDIC (approximately 3 seconds). *See Figs. 1 and 2.*

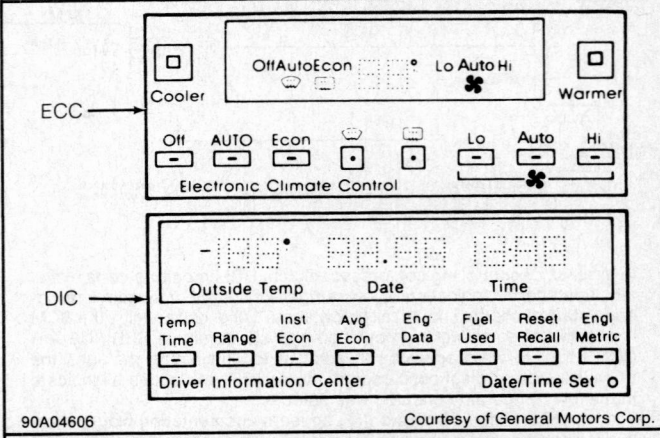

90A04606   Courtesy of General Motors Corp.

Fig. 1: Climate Control Driver Information Center (CCDIC)

90B04579   Courtesy of General Motors Corp.

Fig. 2: Instrument Panel Cluster (IPC)

2) When the segment check appears (all segments illuminate), system has entered self-diagnostic mode. Release both buttons.
3) Illuminating the segments of the IPC and CCDIC ensures all segments of the vacuum fluorescent displays are working properly. On the IPC, however, the turn signal indicators do not light during this check.
4) If all IPC and CCDIC segments appear, proceed to DISPLAYING TROUBLE CODES. Failure of any segment to illuminate may result in inaccurate test results. Any inoperative segments of the CCDIC display must be replaced before proceeding with the self-diagnostic process. If any segment of the IPC requires repair, see IPC SYSTEM SELF-DIAGNOSTICS.

CAUTION: Accessing self-diagnostics for 30 minutes or longer without running engine will cause battery to discharge, resulting in a possible no-start condition. To ensure proper operation, attach battery charger to battery.

DISPLAYING TROUBLE CODES

1) Powertrain Control Module (PCM), Body Control Module (BCM) and Supplemental Inflatable Restraint (SIR) trouble codes automatically display after system enters self-diagnostics.
2) PCM trouble codes are displayed first. They appear in ascending (3-digit) numerical order and are prefixed with the letter "E". For complete list of available PCM trouble codes, see PCM TROUBLE CODES table. If no PCM trouble codes are stored, a NO PCM CODES message will be displayed.
3) BCM trouble codes are displayed immediately following the PCM trouble code display. BCM trouble codes appear in ascending (3-digit) numerical order and are prefixed with the letter "B". For complete list of available BCM trouble codes, see BCM TROUBLE CODES table. If no BCM trouble codes are stored in memory, a NO BCM CODES message is displayed.

4) SIR system trouble codes are displayed last. These codes are displayed in ascending (3-digit) numerical order and are prefixed with the letter "R". The SIR system is not covered in this article. See appropriate AIR BAG article in SAFETY EQUIPMENT.

NOTE: If no codes are present or the communication link between a component and the BCM is not operating, a NO X DATA message will be displayed, indicating the BCM could not communicate with the particular component (X = the particular component).

5) During the actual trouble codes display cycle, all BCM and PCM trouble codes are followed by the letter "C" or "H". The letter "C" stands for current and indicates a trouble code related fault presently exists. The letter "H" stands for history and indicates the system failure was not present during the last key cycle but was present during one of the previous 50 key cycles. For example: Code B410H is BCM code number 410, set in response to a malfunction that occurred in the past (history).

6) At any time during the display of trouble codes, if the RESET/RECALL button on the DIC is depressed, the system will exit service mode and go back to normal vehicle operation.

NOTE: After all trouble codes have been displayed, depressing the OFF button on the ECC will activate a repeat of the trouble code display.

BCM TROUBLE CODES

Code	Circuit Affected
B110	Outside Temperature Sensor Circuit
B111	A/C High Side Temperature Sensor Circuit
B112	A/C Low Side Temperature Sensor Circuit
B113	In-Car Temperature Sensor Circuit
B115	Sunload Temperature Sensor Circuit
B119	Twilight Photocell Circuit
B120	Twilight Delay Pot Circuit
B121	Twilight Enable Switch Circuit
B122	Panel Light Dimming Pot Circuit
B123	Courtesy Light Panel Switch Circuit
B333	Loss Of SIR Data
B334	Loss Of PCM Data
B335	Loss Of CCDIC Data
B336	Loss Of IPC Data
B337	Loss Of A/C-Heater Programmer Data
B410	Charging System Circuit
B411	Battery Voltage Too Low
B412	Battery Voltage Too High
B420	Relay Circuits
B440	A/C-Heater System Air Mix Door
B446	Low Refrigerant Charge
B447	Low Refrigerant Charge
B448	Low Refrigerant Pressure
B449	A/C High Side Temperature Too High
B450	HVAC-Coolant Temperature Too High
B552	Keep Alive Memory Error
B556	Odometer EEPROM Error

PCM TROUBLE CODES

Code	Test Condition
EO12	No Distributor (Tach) Signal
EO13	Right Oxygen Sensor Not Ready
EO14	Shorted Coolant Sensor Circuit
EO15	Open Coolant Sensor Circuit
EO16	Alternator Voltage Out Of Range
EO17	Left Oxygen Sensor Not Ready
EO19	Shorted Fuel Pump Circuit
EO20	Open Fuel Pump Circuit
EO21	Shorted TPS Circuit
EO22	Open TPS Circuit
EO23	EST Signal Problem
EO24	Vehicle Speed Sensor Circuit
EO26	Shorted Throttle Switch Circuit
EO27	Open Throttle Switch Circuit
EO30	Idle Speed Control (ISC) Circuit
EO31	Shorted MAP Sensor Circuit
EO32	Open MAP Sensor Circuit
EO34	MAP Sensor Signal Out Of Range
EO37	Shorted MAT Sensor Circuit

PCM TROUBLE CODES (Cont.)

Code	Test Condition
EO38	Open MAT Sensor Circuit
EO39	Viscous Clutch Converter (VCC) Engagement Problem
EO40	Power Steering Pressure Switch Circuit Problem
EO41	Cam Sensor Circuit Problem
EO42	Left Oxygen Sensor Lean
EO43	Left Oxygen Sensor Rich
EO44	Right Oxygen Sensor Lean
EO45	Right Oxygen Sensor Rich
EO46	Right To Left Bank Fueling Problem
EO47	BCM/PCM Data Problem
EO48	EGR Control Problem
EO51	MEM-CAL Error
EO52	PCM Memory Reset Indicator
EO53	Distributor Signal Interrupt
EO55	TPS Misadjusted
EO59	Pass Key Control Problem
EO60	Cruise Control Transaxle Not In Drive
EO61	Cruise Control Vent Solenoid Problem
EO62	Cruise Control Vacuum Solenoid Problem
EO63	Vehicle Speed-To-Set Speed Too High
EO64	Cruise Control/Acceleration Too High
EO65	Cruise Control Servo Position Sensor Failure
EO66	Cruise Control/Engine RPM Too High
EO67	Cruise Control Switch Shorted
EO68	Cruise Control Command Problem
EO70	Intermittent TPS
EO71	Intermittent MAP Sensor
EO73	Intermittent Coolant Sensor
EO74	Intermittent MAT Sensor
EO75	Intermittent Vehicle Speed Sensor (VSS) Signal
EO80	Fuel System Rich
EO85	Throttle Body Service Required
EO90	Viscous Clutch Converter Brake Switch Input Problem
EO91	PRNDL Switch Problem
EO92	Heated Windshield Problem
EO96	Torque Converter Overstress
EO97	High RPM P/N to D/R Shift
EO98	High RPM P/N To D/R Shift Under Idle Speed Control
EO99	Cruise Servo Apply Problem

OPERATION OF SERVICE MODE

NOTE: This function of the system is intended for use in conjunction with the TROUBLE CODE CHARTS section of this article. Prior to using trouble code charts, it will be necessary to become completely familiar with the procedures in OPERATION OF SERVICE MODE.

SELECTING THE SYSTEM

After trouble codes have been displayed, the Service Mode can be used to perform several tests on different systems one at a time. Upon completion of trouble code(s) display, a specific system may be selected for testing. *See Fig. 3.*

Following the display of trouble codes, the first available system will be displayed (i.e. PCM?). While selecting a system to test, any of the following actions may be taken to control the display:

1) Depressing OFF button on the ECC will stop the system selection process and return the display to the beginning of the trouble code sequence.

2) Depressing LO button on the ECC will display the next available system selection. This allows the display to be stepped through all system choices. This list of systems can be repeated following the end of the system list.

3) Depressing the HI button on the ECC will select the displayed system for testing.

4) Depressing RESET/RECALL button on the DIC will halt diagnostics and return to normal display and operation.

SELECTING THE TEST TYPE

Having selected a system, the first available test type will be displayed (i.e. ECM DERM?). While selecting a specific test type, any of the following actions may be taken to control the display:

GM
1-210

1991 ENGINE PERFORMANCE
Self-Diagnostics – Eldorado & Seville PCM/BCM (Cont.)

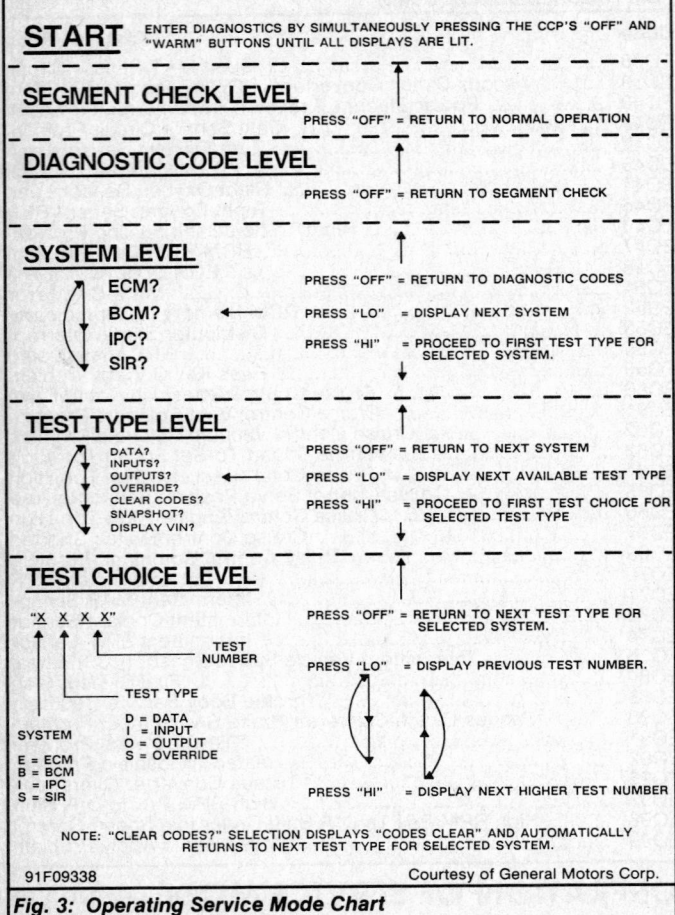

Fig. 3: Operating Service Mode Chart

1) Depressing OFF button on the ECC will stop the test type selection process and return the display to the available system selection.
2) Depressing LO button on the ECC will display the next available test type for the selected system. This allows display to be stepped through all available test type choices. This list of test types can be repeated following the display of the last test type.
3) Depressing HI button on the ECC will select the displayed test type. At this point the first of the several specific tests will appear.
4) Depressing RESET/RECALL button on the DIC will halt diagnostics and system will return to normal display and operation.

SELECTING THE TEST

Selection of the DATA?, INPUTS?, OUTPUTS? or OVERRIDE? test types will result in the first available test being displayed. If dashes appears in ECC, this indicates that test is not allowed with the engine running. While selecting a specific test, any of the following actions may be taken to control the display:
1) Depressing OFF button on the ECC will stop the test selection process and return the display to the next available test type for the selected system.
2) Depressing LO button on the ECC will display the next smaller test number for the selected test type. If this button is pressed with the lowest test number displayed, the highest test number will then appear.
3) Depressing HI button on the ECC will display the next highest test number for the selected test type. If this button is pressed with the highest test number displayed, the lowest test number will then appear.
4) Depressing RESET/RECALL button on the DIC will halt diagnostics and return system to normal display and operation.

SELECTING CLEAR CODES?

NOTE: Clearing codes will result in loss of any Snapshot data taken when code is set. Codes should only be cleared after diagnosis is complete.

NOTE: Code RO51 (SIR code) cannot be cleared without the use of a Scan tester.

Selection of CLEAR CODES? test type will result in the message CODES CLEAR being displayed along the selected system name. This message will appear for 3 seconds to indicate that all stored trouble codes have been erased from memory. After 3 seconds, display will automatically return to the next available test type for the selected system.
After a code has been cleared, a complete ignition cycle and possible test drive should be made. Recheck for codes to ensure that code does not reset.

SELECTING SNAPSHOTS

For selection of snapshot data, *See Fig. 4.*

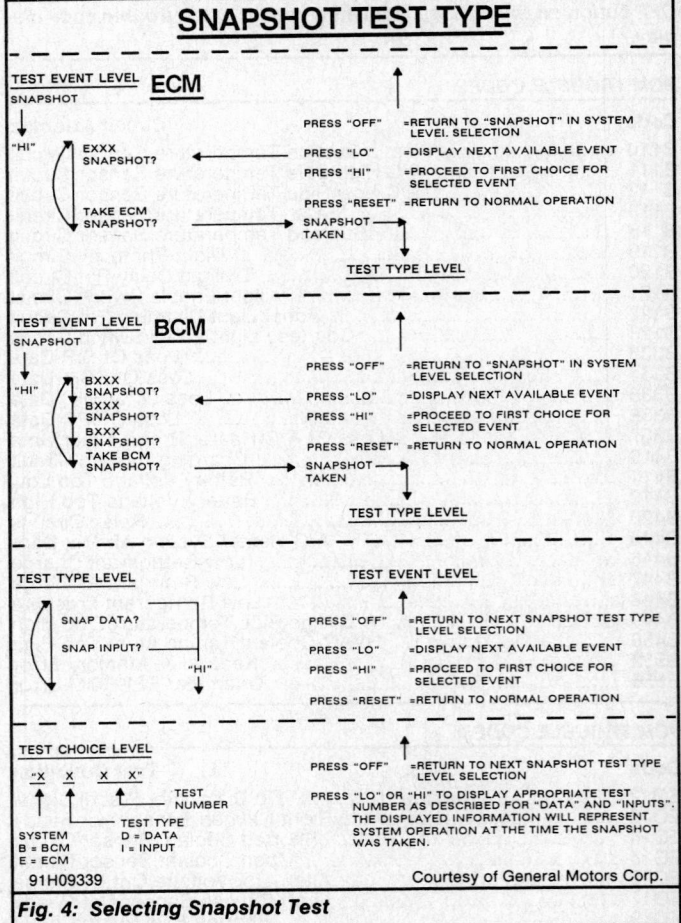

Fig. 4: Selecting Snapshot Test

BCM SNAPSHOT

Selection of SNAPSHOT test type while in the BCM system level will allow the recall of up to 3 snapshots recorded at time of the setting of BCM code(s). Additionally, one may trigger the recording of a snapshot upon demand. By pushing HI button on the ECC while in the BCM mode, will result in the display of BXXX (XXX being the 3-digit trouble code that recorded the snapshot).

1991 ENGINE PERFORMANCE
Self-Diagnostics – Eldorado & Seville PCM/BCM (Cont.)

GM
1-211

While selecting the snapshot, any of the following actions may be taken to control the display:

1) Depressing OFF button on the ECC will stop the test type selection process and return the display to the next available system selection.

2) Depressing LO button will allow scrolling through the list of BCM diagnostic codes that the BCM has stored a snapshot for. After the last BCM diagnostic code or the third if there are more than 3 codes, pressing the LO button will result in TAKE BCM SNAPSHOT? display. Responding LO will return to the first BXXX SNAPSHOT? display.

3) Depressing HI button will cause the BCM SNAP DATA? or BCM SNAP INPUTS? to be displayed and will select the test type. At this point display is controlled as it would be for non-snapshot data and input displays, however, all values and status information represents memorized vehicle conditions.

PCM SNAPSHOT

Selection of SNAPSHOT test type while in PCM mode will allow the recall of snapshot recorded at time of the setting of the last PCM trouble code. Additionally, one may trigger the setting of a snapshot upon demand. Selecting snapshot (by pushing HI button) while in PCM mode will display EXXX (XXX being the 3-digit code that recorded snapshot).

While selecting snapshot, any of the following actions may be taken to control the display.

1) Depressing the OFF button on the ECC will stop test type selection process and return the display to the next available system selection.

2) Depressing the LO button will allow scrolling through the list of PCM diagnostic codes that the PCM has stored a snapshot for. Pressing the LO button will result in the TAKE PCM SNAPSHOT? display. Responding LO will return to the first EOXX SNAPSHOT? display.

3) Depressing HI button will cause PCM SNAP DATA? or PCM SNAP INPUTS to be displayed and will select that test type. At this point the display is controlled as it would be for non-snapshot data and input displays, however, all values and status information represents memorized vehicle conditions.

EXITING SERVICE MODE

Depressing the RESET/RECALL button on the DIC at any time during self-diagnostic procedures will halt diagnostics and return to normal display and operation.

DIAGNOSTIC PARAMETERS

STATUS LIGHTS DISPLAY

While in the BCM and PCM system level in the diagnostic service mode, the mode indicators on the CCDIC are used to indicate status of certain operating modes. The different modes of operation are indicated by status light being turned on or turned off.

BCM STATUS LIGHTS DISPLAY

1) OFF Status Indicator Light – The OFF indicator is illuminated whenever the BCM is commanding the RECIRC mode valve to the recirculation position. This indicator light is off when the BCM is commanding use of outside air. The light does not indicate that the valve has responded to the BCM's command. Actual operation depends on the integrity of the mode valve system.

2) AUTO Indicator Light – This indicator illuminates whenever the BCM is requesting the PCM to engage the A/C compressor clutch. This indicator light is not an indication of whether or not the A/C clutch is actually enabled or disabled by the PCM. Actual operation depends on the PCM and the integrity of the compressor clutch system.

3) ECON Indicator Light – This indicator illuminates whenever the BCM senses the low refrigerant pressure switch is open. The light should remain off if the refrigerant system is fully charged and being properly controlled. If however ambient temperature drops below approximately -5°F (-21°C), the light will come on due to the pressure temperature relationship of refrigerant R-12.

4) LO Status Indicator – This indicator is illuminated whenever BCM is commanding the upper mode valve to divert air flow to A/C outlets. This occurs in the BI-LEVEL or normal purge modes. The indicator light will be off when the ECC system is in the heater intermediate, defrost or cold purge modes.

5) HI Status Indicator – This indicator is illuminated whenever the BCM is commanding the LOWER mode valve to divert air flow up, away from the heater outlet. This indicator light will be off when the ECC system is in the heater BI-LEVEL, intermediate or normal purge mode.

PCM STATUS LIGHTS DISPLAY

Upon entering the PCM system level of the self-diagnostic mode, the indicator lights on the ECC panel of the CCDIC automatically indicate the operational status of the Viscous Converter Clutch (VCC), certain emission control components and A/C compressor operation. Operational status of these components is indicated by their corresponding status light being on or off. See Fig. 5 for diagram of relationship between status lights and specific components.

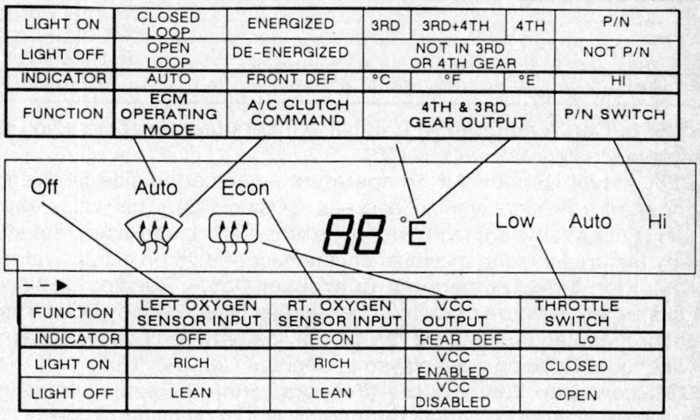

LIGHT ON	CLOSED LOOP	ENERGIZED	3RD	3RD+4TH	4TH	P/N
LIGHT OFF	OPEN LOOP	DE-ENERGIZED		NOT IN 3RD OR 4TH GEAR		NOT P/N
INDICATOR	AUTO	FRONT DEF	°C	°F	°E	HI
FUNCTION	ECM OPERATING MODE	A/C CLUTCH COMMAND		4TH & 3RD GEAR OUTPUT		P/N SWITCH

FUNCTION	LEFT OXYGEN SENSOR INPUT	RT. OXYGEN SENSOR INPUT	VCC OUTPUT	THROTTLE SWITCH
INDICATOR	OFF	ECON	REAR DEF.	Lo
LIGHT ON	RICH	RICH	VCC ENABLED	CLOSED
LIGHT OFF	LEAN	LEAN	VCC DISABLED	OPEN

90F04604   Courtesy of General Motors Corp.

Fig. 5: PCM Status Lights Display

DATA DISPLAYS

Data displays are operated as defined under SELECTING THE TEST. When troubleshooting a malfunction, the BCM and PCM data display can be used to compare vehicle with problems to a vehicle which is functioning properly. See SPECIFIC TEST TYPE AVAILABILITY.

SPECIFIC TEST TYPE LETTER CODE

Code	System	Test Type
BD	BCM	Data
BI	BCM	Input
BO	BCM	Output
BS	BCM	Override
ED	PCM	Data
EI	PCM	Input
EO	PCM	Output
ES	PCM	Override
II	IPC	Input

SPECIFIC TEST TYPE AVAILABILITY

BCM SPECIFIC DATA (BD) TESTS

BD20: Commanded Blower Voltage – Display exhibits the command blower voltage reading that is sent from the BCM to the Heating Ventilating and Air Conditioning (HVAC) programmer in order to control blower speed.

BD21: Coolant Temperature – Displayed in degrees Celsius (°C). Value is sent from PCM to BCM. If circuit malfunctions, as determined by PCM, the PCM will send a substitute value for display.

GM
1-212

1991 ENGINE PERFORMANCE
Self-Diagnostics – Eldorado & Seville PCM/BCM (Cont.)

BD22: Commanded Air-Mix Door – The commanded A/C-heater system air-mix door position is displayed in percentage. A value close to 0 represents a cold air-mix. A value close to 100 represents a warm (heated) air-mix.

BD23: Actual Air-Mix Door Position – The actual A/C-heater system air-mix door position is displayed in percentage. This value should closely follow commanded air position (BD22), except when door is commanded beyond its mechanical limit of travel.

BD24: Air Delivery Mode – The A/C-heater system air delivery mode is displayed as a number from "0"-"9". Each number is a code which represents an air delivery mode. See AIR DELIVERY CODE IDENTIFICATION table.

AIR DELIVERY CODE IDENTIFICATION

Code Number	Air Delivery Mode
"0"	Maximum A/C
"1"	Normal A/C
"2"	Bi-Level
"3"	Heater/Defrost
"4"	Heater
"5"	Off
"6"	Normal Purge
"7"	Cold Purge
"8"	Front Defrost
"9"	A/C Purge

BD25: In-Car Temperature – In-car temperature sensor reading is displayed in degrees Celsius (°C).

BD26: Actual Outside Air Temperature – Actual outside (ambient) temperature is displayed in degrees Celsius (°C). This value represents actual ambient temperature sensor reading and is not restricted by features used to minimize engine heat effects on display value.

BD27: High Side Temperature Condenser Out – Reading displays high side temperature of A/C refrigerant that is received by BCM from sensor mounted in the liquid refrigerant line between condenser and orifice tube. Reading is displayed in degrees Celsius (°C).

BD28: Low Side Temperature (Evaporator In) – Reading displays low side temperature of A/C refrigerant as it is received by the BCM from a sensor mounted in the refrigerant line between the orifice tube and the evaporator. Reading is in degrees Celsius (°C).

BD32: Sun Load Temperature – The heat load induced in the vehicle by the sun is received by the BCM from a sensor mounted under the defroster grille. Sensor is mounted at the center of the grille at the base of the windshield. Reading is displayed in degrees Celsius (°C) from -41° to 102°C.

BD40: Actual Fuel Level – Actual fuel level is read in gallons. Value represents actual sensor position and is not restricted by the features used to eliminate fuel slosh effects on display value. Information is received by the BCM from an in-tank sensor.

BD42: Dimming Pot – The dimming pot value of the I/P light intensity control is displayed in percentage. A value close to zero represents daylight. A value close to 100 represents maximum brightness. Signal to the BCM is from a potentiometer mounted in the headlight (left) switch assembly.

BD43: Twilight Delay Pot – The twilight delay pot value is displayed as a percentage. A value close to zero represents daylight. A value close to 100 represents darkness. Signal is sent to the BCM from a potentiometer mounted above the headlight switch on the I/P.

BD44: Twilight Photocell – The twilight photocell value is displayed in a percentage. A value close to zero represents daylight. A value close to 100 represents darkness. The signal to the BCM is sent from a photo-voltaic sensor mounted in the front defroster grille.

BD50: Battery Charge – Battery state of charge is displayed in volts. The BCM receives this information from the central power supply. Display range is zero to 16.3 volts.

BD51: Alternator Field – Alternator field value is displayed as a percentage. A value close to zero represents minimum regulator on time. A value close to 100 represents maximum regulator on time.

BD60: Vehicle Speed – Displayed in MPH from zero to 159.

BD61: Engine Speed – Displayed in RPM from zero to 6375.

BD90: Option 1 EEPROM – This is the option bit "1" reading the BCM receives from the EEPROM. It contains the USA, Canadian and export

status for which the vehicle was built. Each number is a code that represents the status of the vehicle. To determine proper option "1" value, start with "0" and use table below. See VEHICLE DESTINATION CODE IDENTIFICATION table.

VEHICLE DESTINATION CODE IDENTIFICATION

Destination & Vehicle	Add
U.S. Cars	128
Heated Windshield	32
Seville (Canadian)	1

BD91: Option 2 EEPROM – This is the option bit "2" display the BCM receives from the EEPROM. It is not used for this production year. For all cars a "0" should be stored for this option bit.

BD98: Ignition Cycle Counter – Value is the number of times the BCM has been turned off since a BCM trouble code was last detected. After 100 ignition cycles without any malfunction being detected, all stored BCM codes are cleared.

BD99: BCM PROM ID – The BCM Programmable Read-Only Memory (PROM) identification number is displayed as a 4-digit number.

BCM SPECIFIC INPUT (BI) TESTS

BI01: Courtesy Light Panel Switch – Display is LO when courtesy lights are turned on from switch.

BI02: Parking Light Switch – Display is LO when parking light switch is in the OFF position.

BI03: Driver Front Door Ajar Switch – Display is LO when the driver's (front) door is ajar (open).

BI04: Passenger's Rear Door Ajar Switch – Display is LO when the passenger's (rear) door is ajar (open).

BI05: Door Jamb Switch – Display is LO when any door is open.

BI06: Door Handle Switch – Display is momentarily LO when either front outside door handle button is depressed.

BI07: Trunk Open Switch – Display is LO when trunk is open.

BI08: A/C Low Refrigerant Pressure Switch – Display is LO when system is low on refrigerant.

BI09: Windshield Washer Fluid Level Switch – Display is LO when vehicle is low on washer fluid.

BI30: Temp/Time Switch – Display is LO when button is depressed.

BI51: Alternator Feedback – Display is LO when there is an alternator problem or engine is not running.

BI55: CCR Fault Line – The Computer Command Ride (CCR) fault line display is LO at speeds below 5 MPH and HI at speeds greater than 15 MPH.

BCM SPECIFIC OUTPUT (BO) TESTS

BO00: No Outputs – The CYCLE NONE display will not display HI or LO because this is a resting spot where no outputs will be cycled.

BO03: Retained Accessory Power (RAP) Relay – Display is LO when relays are energized.

BO04: Courtesy Light Relay – Display is LO when relay is energized.

BO05: Twilight Relays – Display is LO when relays are energized.

BO06: Hi/Lo Beam Headlight Relays – Display is LO when relays are energized.

BO07: Daytime Running Light Relays – Display is LO when relays are energized.

BCM SPECIFIC OVERRIDE (BS) TESTS

BS00: None – This test will display a NONE message because no overrides are active at this point.

BS01: ECC Program Number – The program number override can be controlled from zero (maximum A/C) to 98 (maximum heating). The display will hold the override value upon release of WARMER or COOLER button.

BS02: Vacuum Fluorescent (VF) Dimming – The VF dimming override can be controlled from zero (maximum dimming) to 99 (maximum brightness). The display will hold the override value upon release of WARMER or COOLER button.

BS03: Incandescent Bulb Dimming – The incandescent bulb dimming override can be controlled from zero (maximum dimming) to 99

1991 ENGINE PERFORMANCE
Self-Diagnostics – Eldorado & Seville PCM/BCM (Cont.)

GM
1-213

(maximum brightness) if parking lights are turned on. The display will hold the override value upon release of WARMER or COOLER button.

BS08: Option 1 – The option "1" override will control the export status bit. See VEHICLE DESTINATION CODE IDENTIFICATION table. To override, press WARMER button on ECC to increase value or COOLER button on ECC to decrease value. To overwrite the value in the EEPROM, hold the ECON (climate control) button and the INST/ECON button for 3 seconds.

BS09: Option 2 – The option "2" override will be "2" for all cars.

PCM SPECIFIC DATA (ED) TESTS

ED01: Throttle Position Sensor (TPS) – Display shows degrees of throttle opening from -9 to 90 degrees.

ED02: Manifold Air Pressure – Sensor reading is displayed in Kilopascals (kPa) from 14 to 108 kPa.

ED03: Computed Barometric Pressure – Reading is displayed in Kilopascals (kPa) from 60 to 102 kPa. Note: BARO pressure reading is taken with key on and is corrected at Wide Open Throttle (WOT).

ED04: Coolant Temperature – Display shows temperature in degrees Celsius (°C) from -40° to 151°C.

ED05: Manifold Air Temperature (MAT) Sensor – Reading is displayed in degrees Celsius (°C) from -40° to 151°C.

ED08: Spark Advance – Displayed in degrees BTDC as generated by the Electronic Spark Timing (EST) signal from the PCM. Range of display is zero to 90 degrees. If base timing is properly adjusted (10 degrees before TDC), readings from a timing light should agree.

ED10: Battery State Of Charge – Displayed in volts from zero to 25.6 volts. This is voltage measured at fuel pump feedback terminal F1.

ED11: Engine Speed – Displayed in RPM from zero to 6370.

ED12: Vehicle Speed – Displayed in MPH from zero to 255.

ED30: Left Injector Pulse Width – Display shows pulse width in milliseconds (mS) from zero to 99.6 mS.

ED31: Right Injector Pulse Width – Display shows pulse width in milliseconds (mS) from zero to 99.6 mS.

ED32: Left Oxygen Sensor Voltage – Display shows volts from zero to .99 volts.

ED33: Right Oxygen Sensor Voltage – Display shows volts from zero to .99 volts.

ED34: Left Oxygen Sensor Cross Counts – Display counts from zero to 255. Cross counts are the number of times the voltage crosses the reference voltage of .45 in one second.

ED35: Right Oxygen Sensor Cross Counts – Display counts from zero to 255. Cross counts are the number of times the voltage crosses the reference voltage of .45 in one second.

ED36: Left Fuel Integrator – Display shows counts from zero to 255. Normal injector count position is 128, indicating engine is operating normally. A count greater than 128 indicates time is being added to injector pulse width, which adds more fuel to the engine. A count less than 128 indicates time is being subtracted from the injector pulse width, reducing the amount of fuel to the engine.

ED37: Right Fuel Integrator – Display shows counts from zero to 255. Normal injector count position is 128, indicating engine is operating normally. A count greater than 128 indicates time is being added to injector pulse width, which adds more fuel to the engine. A count less than 128 indicates time is being subtracted from the injector pulse width, reducing the amount of fuel to the engine.

ED38: Left Block Learn Display – Display shows counts from zero to 255. Normal count position for block learn is 128, indicating engine is operating normally. Block value is based on integrator learned values. A count greater than 128 indicates time is being added to the injector pulse width, resulting in more fuel to the engine. A count less than 128 indicates time is being subtracted from the injector pulse width, resulting in reducing amount of fuel to the engine.

ED39: Right Block Learn Display – Display functions identically to the left block learn display. See ED38: LEFT BLOCK LEARN DISPLAY.

ED70: Cruise Control Feedback – Display shows percentage of servo apply as measured by the servo position sensor. Zero equals no vacuum and 99 equals full vacuum (full apply).

ED71: PRNDL 1 Status – Display shows the status of the Park/Neutral switch for circuits No. 772 and No. 773, which are inputs "B" and "C" to the PCM. "0" indicates the switch is closed and "1" indicates switch is open.

ED72: PRNDL 2 Status – Display shows the status of the Park/Neutral switch for circuits No. 771 and No. 776, which are inputs "A" and "P" to the PCM. "0" indicates the switch is closed and "1" indicates switch is open.

ED98: Ignition Cycles – Display shows counts from 1 to 50. The count increases by one with each on to off cycle. When a trouble code sets, the counter is set to zero. If the trouble code becomes history, the counter will increment with each key cycle until another code is set or until the key has been cycled 50 times, at which point the code will be erased.

ED99: PCM Programmable Read Only Memory (PROM) Identification Code – Display shows a 3-digit code that identifies the PROM of the MEM-CAL unit.

PCM SPECIFIC INPUT (EI) TESTS

EI70: Cruise Control Brake Switch – Test detects the open and close of cruise control brake switch at terminal C2 of the PCM. See Fig. 6. HI means brake switch is closed and PCM has 12 volts at the cruise brake switch input (cruise switch must be on). LO means brake switch is open and PCM has zero volts at the input. "X" means the brake pedal has been depressed and a change in switch state has been detected.

EI71: Viscous Converter Clutch (VCC) Brake Switch – Test detects the opening and closing of the VCC brake switch at terminal C4 of the PCM. See Fig. 6. HI means brake switch is closed and PCM has 12 volts at the VCC brake switch input. LO means brake switch is open and PCM has zero volts at its input. "X" means brake pedal has been depressed and a change in switch state has been detected.

EI72: Throttle Switch Display – Test detects the opening and closing of the Idle Speed Control (ISC) nose switch at terminal A7 of the PCM. See Fig. 6. HI means throttle switch is open and PCM has 5 volts at the throttle switch input. LO means throttle switch is closed and PCM has zero volts at the throttle switch input. "X" means throttle pedal has been depressed and a change in switch state has been detected.

EI79: – Not valid.

EI82: Cruise Control ON/OFF Switch – Test detects the opening and closing of CRUISE switch mounted on the turn signal lever at terminal D2 of PCM. See Fig. 6. To activate test, turn cruise control switch on. HI means ON/OFF switch is on and PCM has 12 volts at the cruise enable input. LO means ON/OFF switch is off and PCM has zero volts at the cruise enable input. "X" means ON/OFF switch has been turned on or off and a change in switch state has been detected.

EI83: Cruise Control SET/COAST Switch – Test detects closing of SET/COAST switch in the turn signal lever at terminal D8 of PCM. See Fig. 6. To activate test, depress SET/COAST button. The cruise control switch must be on. HI means SET/COAST button is closed (depressed) and PCM has 12 volts on the set/coast input. LO means SET/COAST button is open (not depressed) and PCM has zero volts on the set/coast input. "X" means SET/COAST switch has been depressed and a change in switch state has been detected.

EI84: Cruise Control RESUME/ACCEL Switch – This test detects closing of the RESUME/ACCEL switch in the turn signal lever at terminal C3 of the PCM. See Fig. 6. To activate test, slide RESUME/ACCEL switch. The cruise control switch must be on to perform this test. HI means RESUME/ACCEL button is closed (pushed) and PCM has 12 volts on the resume/accel input. LO means RESUME/ACCEL button is open (not pushed) and PCM has zero volts on the resume/accel input. "X" means RESUME/ACCEL switch has been disengaged and a change in switch state has been detected.

EI85: POWER STEERING Switch – HI designates that power steering switch is closed and PCM is receiving battery voltage. LO means that power steering switch is open and PCM is not receiving battery voltage. "X" means that power steering switch has cycled and passed the input test.

GM
1-214

1991 ENGINE PERFORMANCE
Self-Diagnostics – Eldorado & Seville PCM/BCM (Cont.)

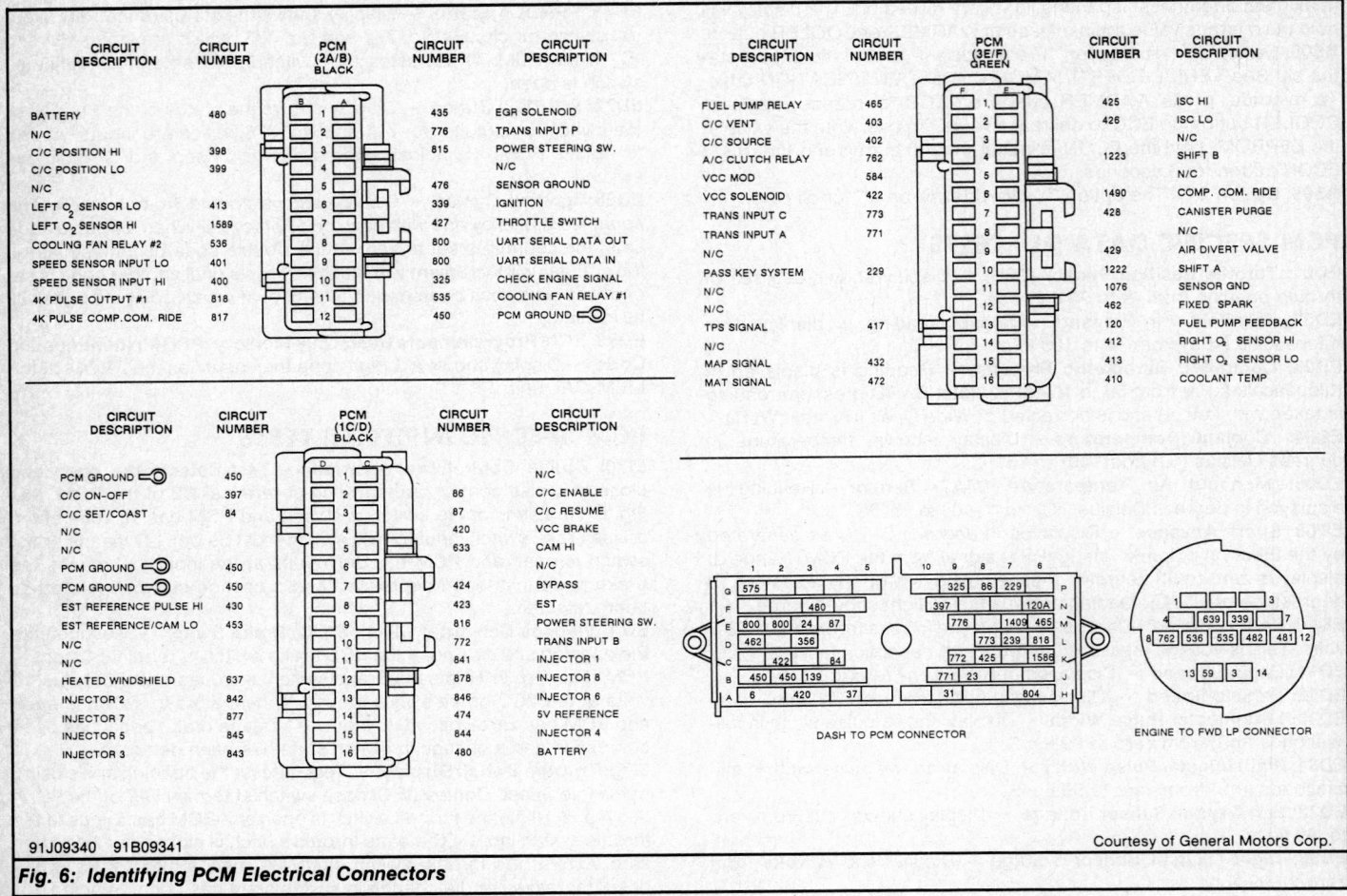

91J09340 91B09341

Courtesy of General Motors Corp.

Fig. 6: Identifying PCM Electrical Connectors

PCM SPECIFIC OUTPUT (EO) TESTS

NOTE: All PCM specific output tests are to be performed with key on, engine off.

EO00: No Outputs – No outputs are cycled.

EO01: Canister Purge – Canister purge solenoid.

EO02: Viscous Converter Clutch (VCC) – VCC solenoid and modulating solenoid.

EO03: EGR Solenoid – Electronic Vacuum Regulator Valve (EVRV).

EO05: Air Switch – Not valid.

EO06: Air Divert – Not valid.

EO07: ISC Motor – Idle Speed Control (ISC) motor.

EO08: Cruise Control Vent – Cruise control vent solenoid.

EO09: Cruise Control Vacuum – Cruise control vacuum solenoid.

EO10: Shift A – Transmission shift solenoid.

EO11: Shift B – Transmission shift solenoid.

EO20: A/C Relay – A/C clutch control relay.

EO99: Cycle All – All previously mentioned outputs are cycled.

PCM SPECIFIC OVERRIDE TESTS

ES00: No Overrides – No overrides are active at this point.

ES01: Viscous Converter Clutch (VCC) Solenoid – VCC solenoid is energized by the WARMER button and deactivated by the COOLER button. The ECC will display 99 for on and 00 for off.

ES02: EGR Solenoid – The EGR valve solenoid is de-energized when WARMER button on the ECC is depressed, causing EGR valve to receive a vacuum signal and the ECC to display 99. Depressing COOLER button on ECC will energize solenoid, causing no vacuum signal to EGR valve and ECC to display 00.

ES03: Idle Speed Control (ISC) Motor – **1)** Test conditions: Vehicle in Park or Neutral, PCM commanding A/C relay off and EGR solenoid de-energized. When ISC motor is stopped, the ECC displays 50 and TPS reads 4 degrees or less.

2) With engine off, depress WARMER button on ECC, ISC plunger will extend until it ratchets once. The ECC will display 99. With engine on, "--" will be displayed when WARMER button is depressed.

3) With engine off, depressing COOLER button on ECC will retract ISC and the display will read 00. With engine on, ISC will retract to base idle (550 RPM).

ES04: Injector Cutout (Power Balance) – **1)** Test conditions: Engine running and transmission in Park or Neutral. Desired engine RPM should be selected before selecting this override, as the ISC will stay at a selected RPM.

2) Depressing WARMER button will select an injector and will increment at the rate of one selection per second. ECC panel will display injector selected. Depressing COOLER button will cause injector cut-off and ECC panel will display injector 00.

ES05: Fuel Pump Relay – Depressing COOLER button with engine on and relay off causes ECC panel to display 00. Display will return to 99 when button is released. With vehicle in Park or Neutral and engine on, ECC panel will display 99.

ES07: Cruise Control Servo – **1)** Prior to testing, engine should be run to charge vacuum reservoir. Transmission in Park or Neutral and engine off. With no buttons depressed, system remains at selected override.

2) Depressing WARMER button will cause servo to retract. ECC panel will display 00 to 99. Depressing COOLER button will cause servo to extend. ECC panel will display 99 to 00".

ES08: Cooling Fan – **1)** Each time COOLER button on ECC is

1991 ENGINE PERFORMANCE
Self-Diagnostics – Eldorado & Seville PCM/BCM (Cont.)

GM
1-215

depressed, state of low relay will change. A "1" as the left digit indicates relay is energized. A "0" indicates relay is de-energized. To properly energize the circuit for low speed operation, ECC should display 10.

2) Depressing WARMER button on ECC changes state of relay each time button is depressed. A "1" as the right digit indicates relay is energized. A "0" indicates relay is de-energized. To properly energize circuit for high speed operation, ECC should display 11.

3) During testing procedures, both cooling fans will run in high and low speeds. The series, series parallel and parallel relays are energized together to produce high speed.

ES09: Fixed Spark – **1)** Transaxle in Park or Neutral and engine running. A calculated advance will be displayed when this test is selected. The first time COOLER button on ECC is depressed, PCM will fix the spark advance to 10 degrees BTDC; ECC will display 10.

2) Depressing COOLER button the second time, PCM will calculate a 1-2 degree timing retard. Depressing WARMER button, PCM will calculate a 1-2 degree timing advance. If an advance is selected greater than calculated value, "--" will be displayed.

ES10: Injector Flow – Depressing COOLER button, display will increment at the rate of one injector pulse per second. PCM will energize injector for 50 milliseconds. An individual injector can be tested only once per cycle. To prevent engine damage, engine must be run before the flow test for that injector can be performed again.

ES11: Transaxle Shift – **1)** Transmission in Drive. This override places transmission in selected gear until the WARMER or COOLER buttons are depressed to change gear selection.

2) The PCM will prevent a downshift from second to first gear at speeds greater than 30 MPH and from third to second gear at speeds greater than 60 MPH. When no button is depressed, transmission remains at selected override position.

3) Each time COOLER button is depressed, transmission will downshift one gear. The ECC will display the gear number/position selected.

4) Each time WARMER button is depressed, transmission will upshift one gear. The ECC will display the gear number/position selected.

IPC SYSTEM SELF-DIAGNOSTICS

ENTERING IPC SYSTEM SELF-DIAGNOSTICS

NOTE: Although there are no IPC system trouble codes, all trouble codes in memory must be displayed as part the procedure for entering the IPC self-diagnostic system.

The Instrument Panel Cluster (IPC) does not produce trouble codes in relation to system malfunctions. The IPC does, however, have self-diagnostic capabilities. To access self-diagnostic capabilities of the IPC system, complete the following:

* Enter self-diagnostics. See ENTERING SELF-DIAGNOSTICS under SELF-DIAGNOSTIC SYSTEM.
* Display diagnostic codes displayed in memory. See DISPLAYING TROUBLE CODES under SELF-DIAGNOSTIC SYSTEM.
* Select IPC system for testing. *See Fig. 4.* Refer to IPC SPECIFIC INPUT (II) CODES for list of available IPC specific input tests.

IPC SPECIFIC INPUT (II) CODES

I178: Headlights Switch – Display is HI whenever headlights are on.
I179: High Beam Switch – Display is LO as long as lever is pulled in.
I182: Twilight Enable Switch – Display is LO whenever system is on.
I183: Oil Pressure Switch – Display is LO whenever engine is running.

BCM LOCATION
BCM is located behind glove box.

PCM LOCATION
PCM is located behind dashboard on passenger side of vehicle.

SUMMARY
If no hard fault codes (or only pass codes) are present, driveability symptoms exist or intermittent codes exist, proceed to TROUBLE SHOOTING – NO CODES article for diagnosis by symptom (i.e. ROUGH IDLE, NO START, etc.) or intermittent diagnostic procedures.

GM
1-216

1991 ENGINE PERFORMANCE
Self-Diagnostics – Eldorado & Seville PCM/BCM (Cont.)

SELF-DIAGNOSTIC SYSTEM CHECK

The Self-Diagnostic System Check is an organized approach to identifying a computer-controlled electronics problem. Understanding the chart and using it correctly will reduce diagnostic time and prevent unnecessary parts replacement.

The Self-Diagnostic System Check should be used to begin diagnosis if any customer complaint does not directly relate to a specific subsystem. If the SERVICE ENGINE SOON light fails to illuminate during cranking, then the problem could be in the power supply circuit of the BCM/PCM computer system. The Self-Diagnostic System Check will direct technician to an appropriate diagnostic chart.

If the CCDIC display is not operating properly, BCM/PCM COMPUTER SYSTEM SELF-DIAGNOSTICS mode CANNOT be used and the SELF-DIAGNOSTIC SYSTEM CHECK will direct technician to an appropriate diagnostic chart.

If a trouble code is identified by the BCM/PCM computer system self-diagnostics mode, problem can be corrected following the appropriate numbered code chart(s). If no code has been identified, the SELF-DIAGNOSTIC SYSTEM CHECK will direct technician to an appropriate diagnostic chart.

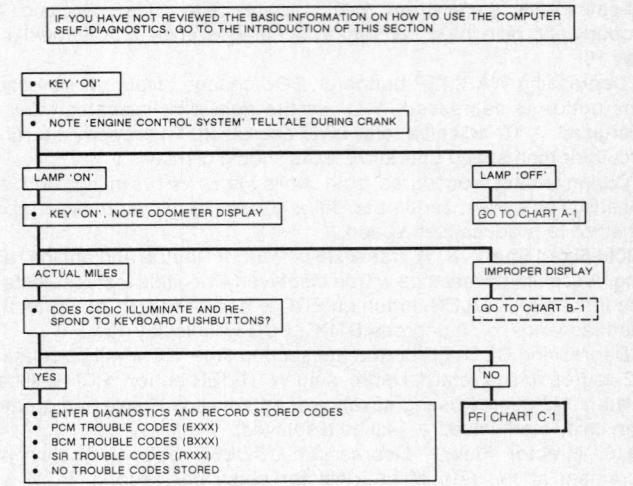

91F09362

Courtesy of General Motors Corp.

PFI CHART A-1, INOPERATIVE SERVICE ENGINE SOON LIGHT

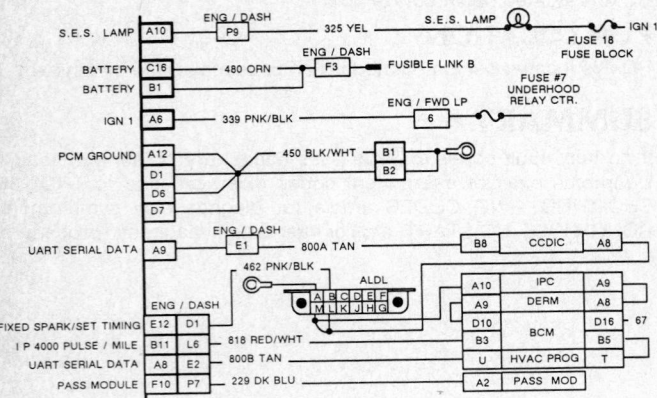

The SERVICE ENGINE SOON light is controlled by the PCM and will turn on for 2 seconds when ignition switch in turned to the RUN position. When engine is cranked, SERVICE ENGINE SOON light will be off. After the key is returned to RUN position, SERVICE ENGINE SOON light will turn on for another 2 seconds.

NOTE: Test numbers refer to test numbers on diagnostic chart.

1) Terminals D1, D6, D7 and A12 are PCM ground. Terminals B1 and C16 are battery positive to the PCM. The PCM will function only one power and ground connection, but all should be tested.

91D09342   91F09343

Courtesy of General Motors Corp.

1991 ENGINE PERFORMANCE
Self-Diagnostics – Eldorado & Seville PCM/BCM (Cont.)

GM
1-217

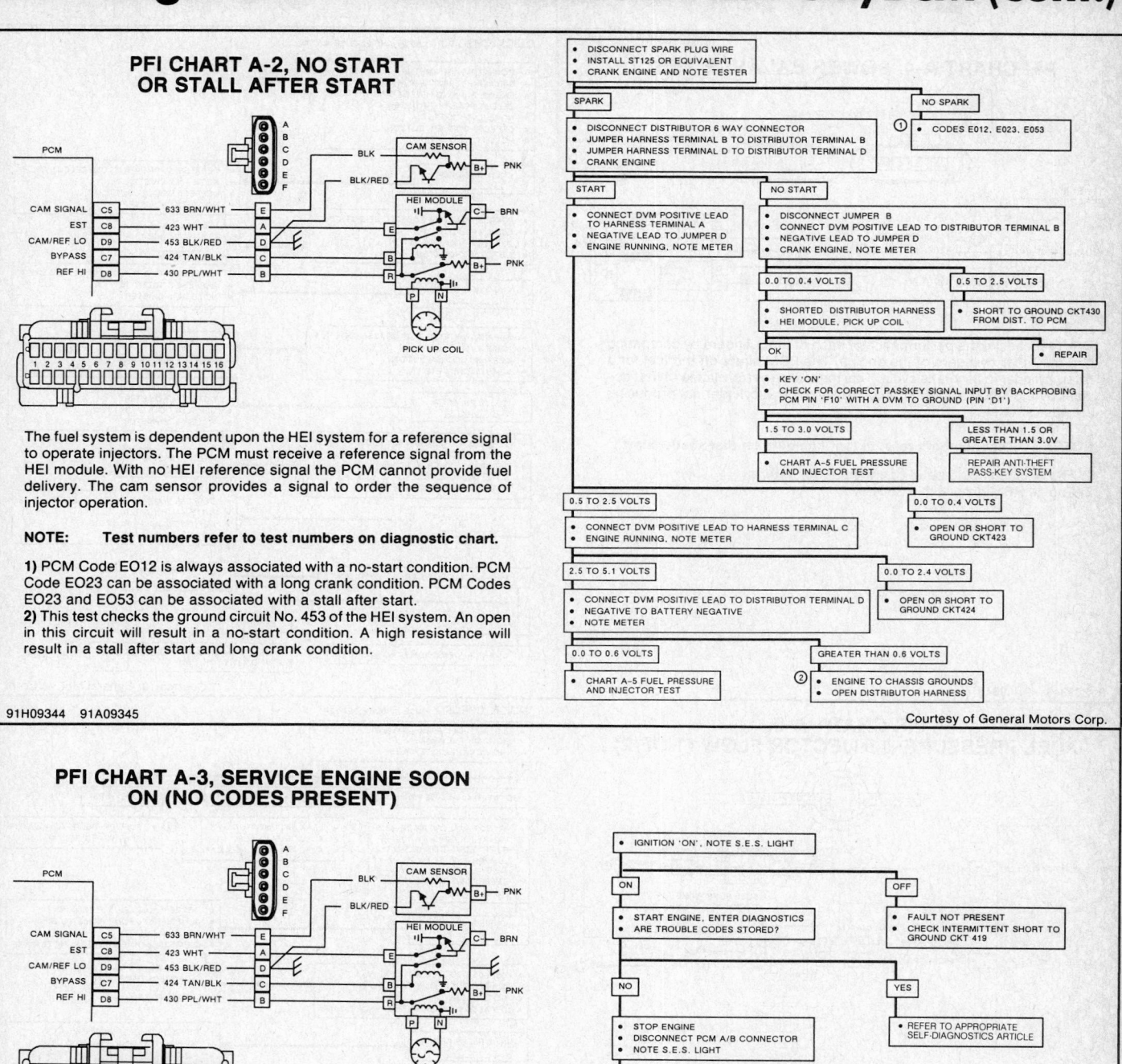

PFI CHART A-2, NO START OR STALL AFTER START

The fuel system is dependent upon the HEI system for a reference signal to operate injectors. The PCM must receive a reference signal from the HEI module. With no HEI reference signal the PCM cannot provide fuel delivery. The cam sensor provides a signal to order the sequence of injector operation.

NOTE: Test numbers refer to test numbers on diagnostic chart.

1) PCM Code EO12 is always associated with a no-start condition. PCM Code EO23 can be associated with a long crank condition. PCM Codes EO23 and EO53 can be associated with a stall after start.

2) This test checks the ground circuit No. 453 of the HEI system. An open in this circuit will result in a no-start condition. A high resistance will result in a stall after start and long crank condition.

91H09344   91A09345

Courtesy of General Motors Corp.

PFI CHART A-3, SERVICE ENGINE SOON ON (NO CODES PRESENT)

If BCM Code B334 is present, diagnose using BCM Code 334, Loss of PCM Data.

91H09344   91E09347

Courtesy of General Motors Corp.

GM
1-218

1991 ENGINE PERFORMANCE
Self-Diagnostics – Eldorado & Seville PCM/BCM (Cont.)

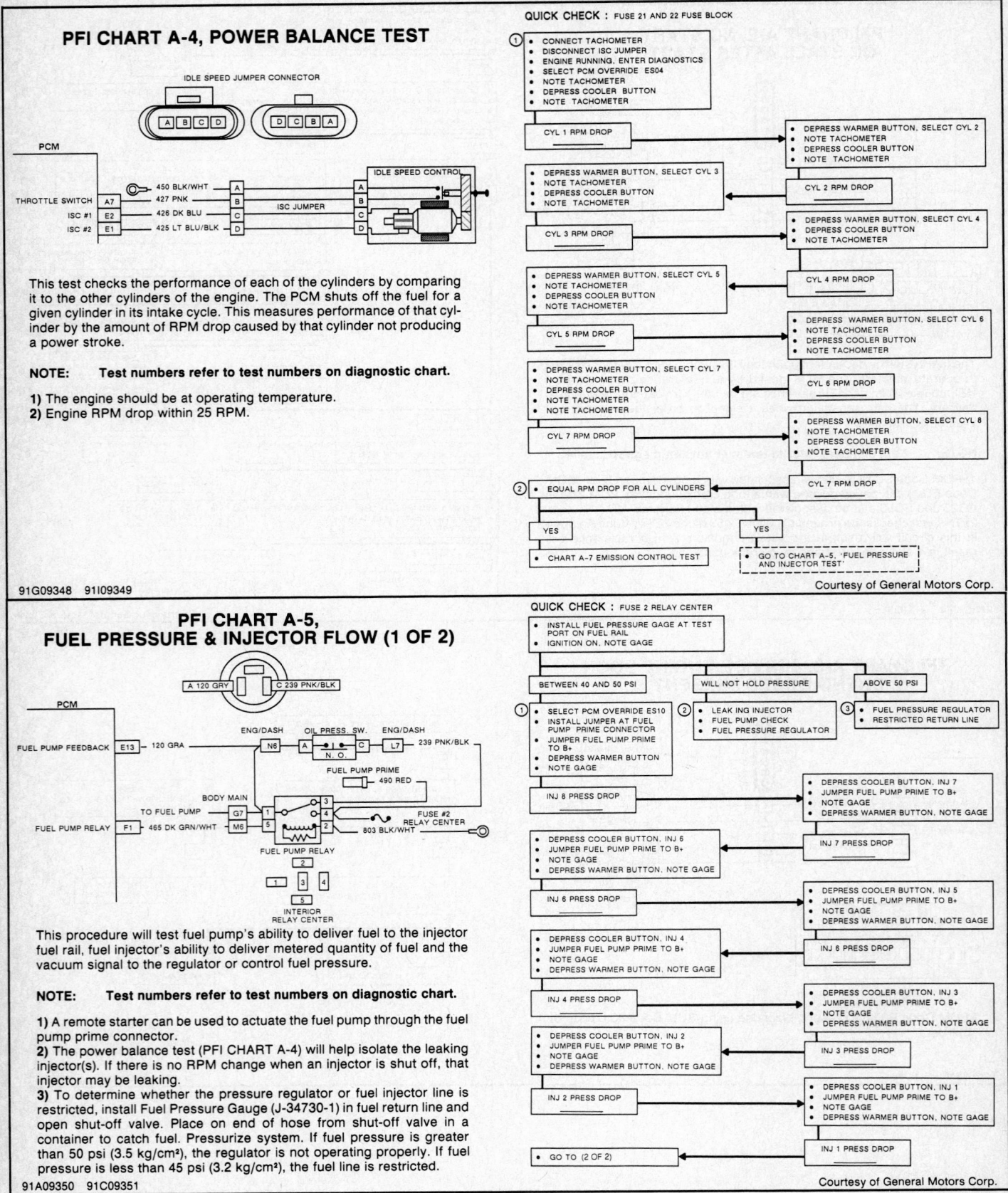

PFI CHART A-4, POWER BALANCE TEST

This test checks the performance of each of the cylinders by comparing it to the other cylinders of the engine. The PCM shuts off the fuel for a given cylinder in its intake cycle. This measures performance of that cylinder by the amount of RPM drop caused by that cylinder not producing a power stroke.

NOTE: Test numbers refer to test numbers on diagnostic chart.

1) The engine should be at operating temperature.
2) Engine RPM drop within 25 RPM.

91G09348   91I09349

Courtesy of General Motors Corp.

PFI CHART A-5,
FUEL PRESSURE & INJECTOR FLOW (1 OF 2)

This procedure will test fuel pump's ability to deliver fuel to the injector fuel rail, fuel injector's ability to deliver metered quantity of fuel and the vacuum signal to the regulator or control fuel pressure.

NOTE: Test numbers refer to test numbers on diagnostic chart.

1) A remote starter can be used to actuate the fuel pump through the fuel pump prime connector.
2) The power balance test (PFI CHART A-4) will help isolate the leaking injector(s). If there is no RPM change when an injector is shut off, that injector may be leaking.
3) To determine whether the pressure regulator or fuel injector line is restricted, install Fuel Pressure Gauge (J-34730-1) in fuel return line and open shut-off valve. Place on end of hose from shut-off valve in a container to catch fuel. Pressurize system. If fuel pressure is greater than 50 psi (3.5 kg/cm²), the regulator is not operating properly. If fuel pressure is less than 45 psi (3.2 kg/cm²), the fuel line is restricted.

91A09350   91C09351

Courtesy of General Motors Corp.

1991 ENGINE PERFORMANCE
Self-Diagnostics – Eldorado & Seville PCM/BCM (Cont.)

GM
1-219

PFI CHART A-5, FUEL PRESSURE & INJECTOR FLOW (2 OF 2)

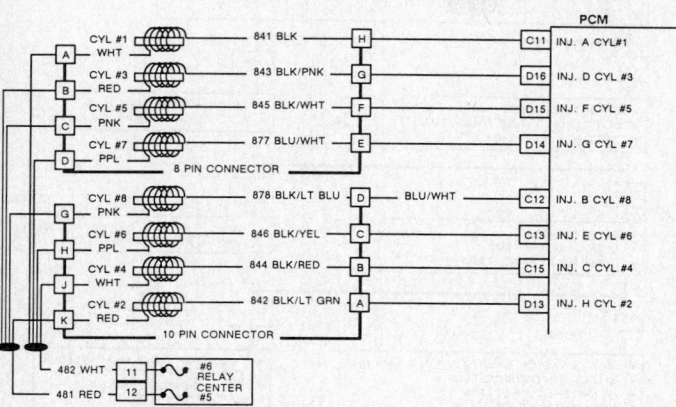

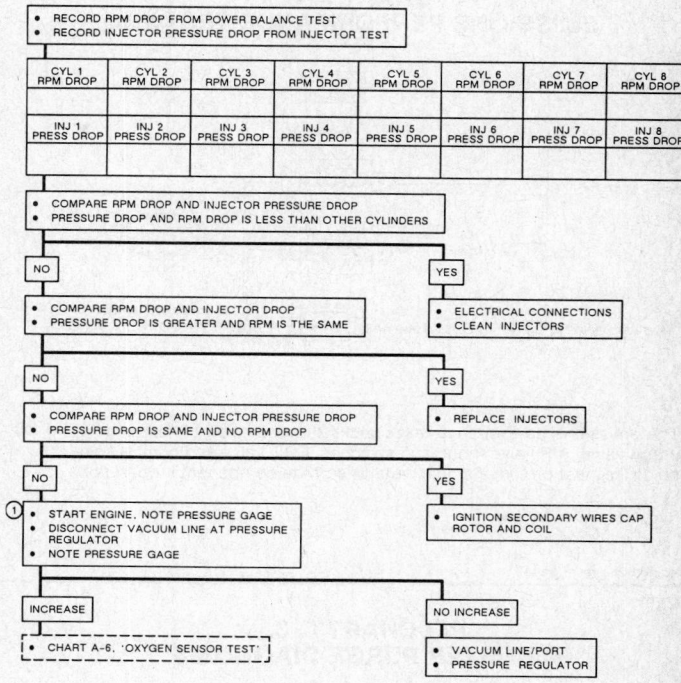

This chart analyzes the comparisons between the Power Balance Test (PFI CHART A-4) and injector flow test to determine the condition of the fuel injectors. If the fuel injectors are in good condition, the ignition secondary may be the cause of the problem.

NOTE: Test numbers refer to test numbers on diagnostic chart.

1) Fuel pressure should be 32-38 psi (2.2-2.7 kg/cm²) depending on engine load and altitude. By disconnecting the vacuum hose, engine load compensation is taken away from the fuel pressure regulator. Fuel pressure should rise to approximately 45 psi (3.1 kg/cm²). If pressure is greater than 50 psi (3.5 kg/cm²), replace regulator. If pressure is less than 40 psi (2.8 kg/cm²), check fuel pump operation, fuel filter and electrical circuits.

91E09352   91G09353

Courtesy of General Motors Corp.

PFI CHART A-6, OXYGEN SENSOR TEST

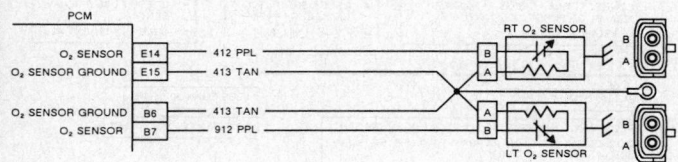

OXYGEN SENSOR OPERATING RANGE

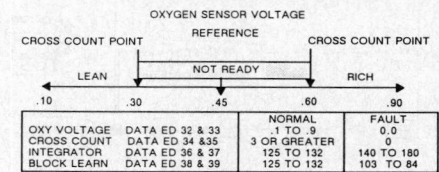

		NORMAL	FAULT
OXY VOLTAGE	DATA ED 32 & 33	1 TO .9	0.0
CROSS COUNT	DATA ED 34 &35	3 OR GREATER	0
INTEGRATOR	DATA ED 36 & 37	125 TO 132	140 TO 180
BLOCK LEARN	DATA ED 38 & 39	125 TO 132	103 TO 84

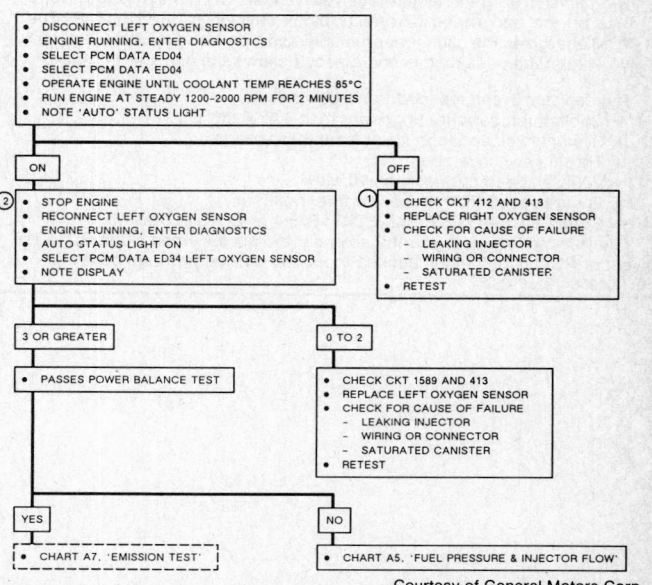

PCM provides a .45-volt reference to oxygen sensor. When warm, a properly operating oxygen sensor will drive .45-volt reference lower (less than .45 volt) to indicate lean mixture and higher (more than .45 volt) to indicate rich mixture.

The oxygen sensor must be able to generate a counter voltage of greater than .15 volt or less than .45-volt reference to cause PCM to register a cross count of rich to lean or lean to rich. The oxygen sensor must generate cross counts to enable the system to go to closed loop operation.

The oxygen sensor test checks that the PCM is receiving voltage signals of sufficient range from the sensor to generate a cross count.

NOTE: Test numbers refer to test numbers on diagnostic chart.

1) PCM trouble Code EO13, EO44 and EO45 are designed to detect a sensor fault. The slow reaction time of the sensor may cause a driveability problem. PCM data ED32 and ED33 will display oxygen sensor voltage. With engine at normal operating temperature, O₂ sensor voltage should be constantly changing. A fixed voltage at zero volts, indicate a shorted circuit No. 412 for the right O₂ sensor and circuit No. 912 for the left O₂ sensor. A fixed voltage between .42-.48 volt, indicate an open in circuits No. 412 or No. 413 for the right O₂ sensor and circuits No. 413 or No. 912 for the left O₂ sensor.
2) If the system cannot go to closed loop operation, both the O₂ sensors are not functioning.

91I09354   91C07540   91B09355

Courtesy of General Motors Corp.

GM
1-220

1991 ENGINE PERFORMANCE
Self-Diagnostics – Eldorado & Seville PCM/BCM (Cont.)

PFI CHART A-7, EMISSIONS PERFORMANCE TEST

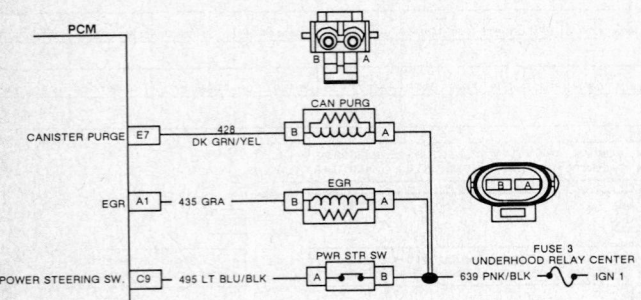

The emissions performance test checks the operation of the canister purge valve, AIR valve mode and switches, EGR valve and control sole-noid. This test provides a quick analysis of the component's operation.

91D09356   91F09357

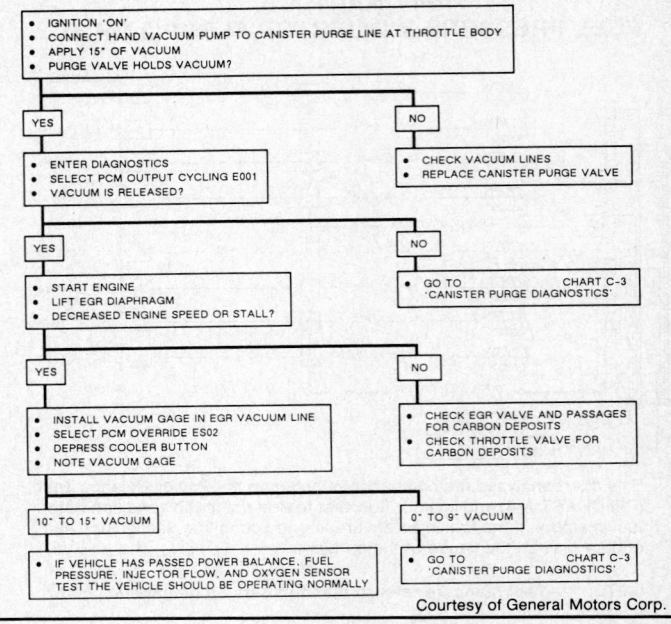

Courtesy of General Motors Corp.

PFI CHART C-3, CANISTER PURGE DIAGNOSIS

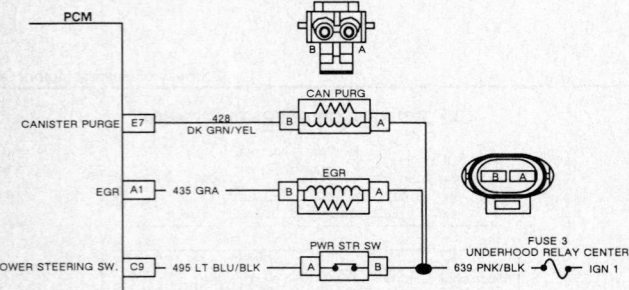

The canister purge solenoid receives 12 volts from the 10-amp. No. 3 fuse on the underhood fuse/relay block through circuit No. 639. The PCM energizes the canister purge solenoid by grounding PIN E7 (circuit No. 428). When solenoid is energized, it allows the canister to purge.

The canister is commanded to purge when:
- Coolant temperature is greater than 176°F (80°C).
- System in closed loop for at least 30 seconds.
- Throttle switch is open.
- Vehicle speed greater than 10 MPH.
- Engine speed (RPM) above a threshold.
- Code EO13, EO17, EO42, EO43, EO44 or EO45 is present.

The PCM will de-energize the solenoid (no purge) when Code EO16 is set or PCM is running in backup mode (no normal program control).

91D09356   91J09359

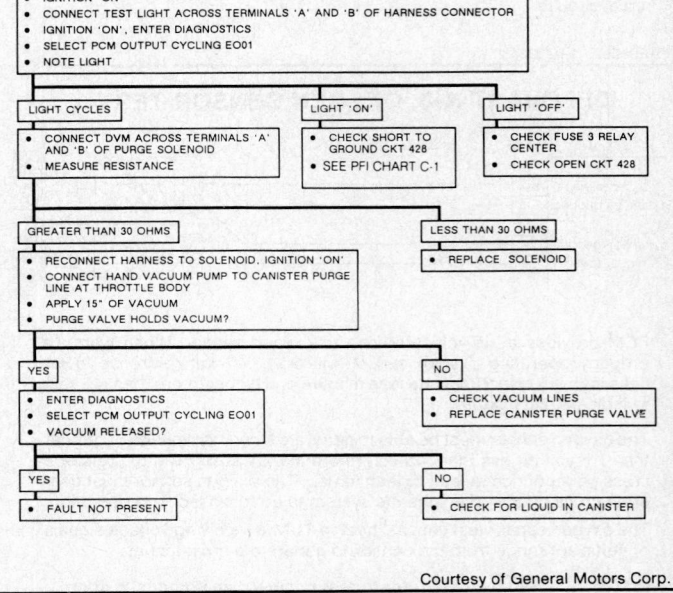

Courtesy of General Motors Corp.

1991 ENGINE PERFORMANCE
Self-Diagnostics – Eldorado & Seville PCM/BCM (Cont.)

GM
1-221

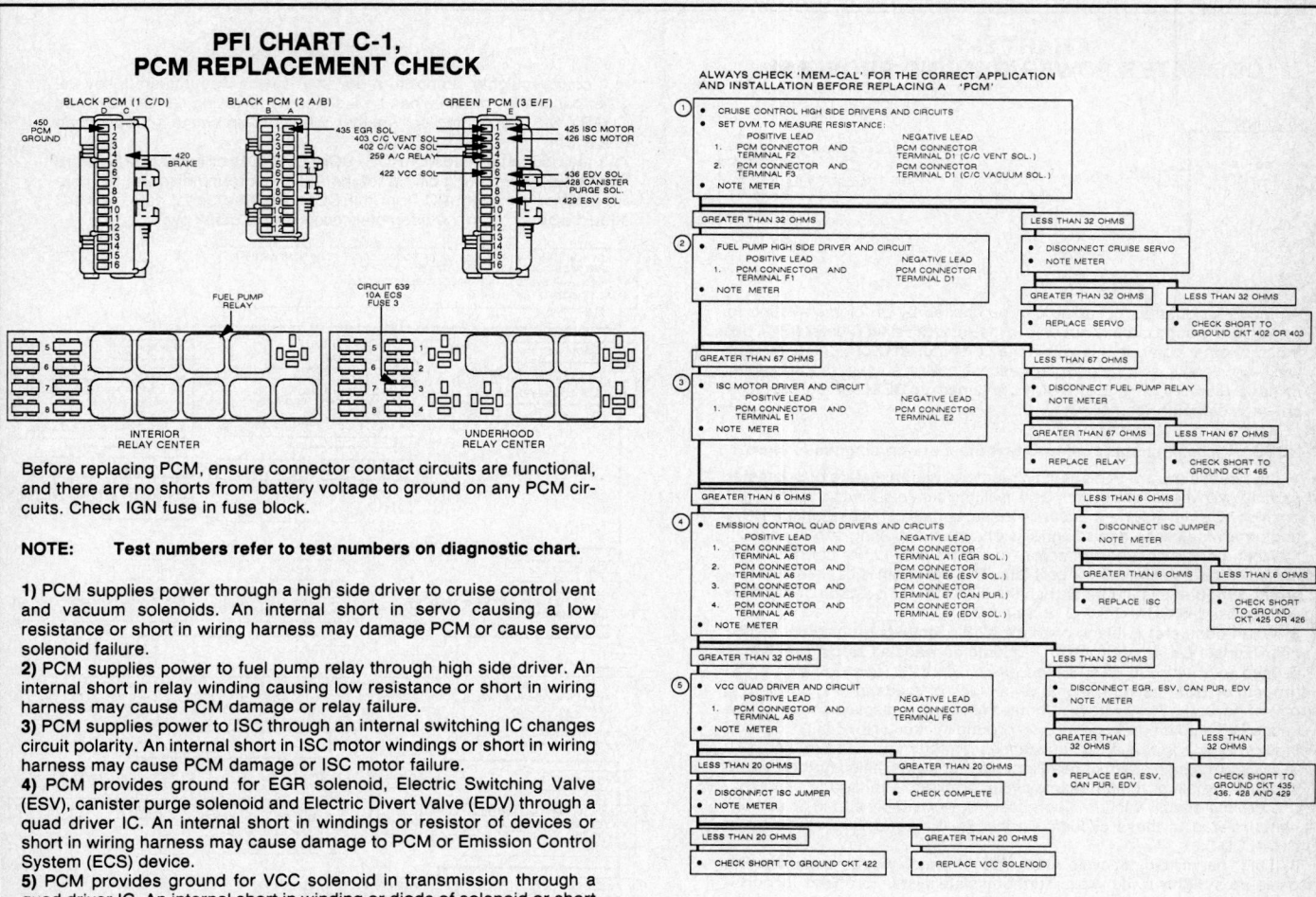

PFI CHART C-1, PCM REPLACEMENT CHECK

Before replacing PCM, ensure connector contact circuits are functional, and there are no shorts from battery voltage to ground on any PCM circuits. Check IGN fuse in fuse block.

NOTE: Test numbers refer to test numbers on diagnostic chart.

1) PCM supplies power through a high side driver to cruise control vent and vacuum solenoids. An internal short in servo causing a low resistance or short in wiring harness may damage PCM or cause servo solenoid failure.

2) PCM supplies power to fuel pump relay through high side driver. An internal short in relay winding causing low resistance or short in wiring harness may cause PCM damage or relay failure.

3) PCM supplies power to ISC through an internal switching IC changes circuit polarity. An internal short in ISC motor windings or short in wiring harness may cause PCM damage or ISC motor failure.

4) PCM provides ground for EGR solenoid, Electric Switching Valve (ESV), canister purge solenoid and Electric Divert Valve (EDV) through a quad driver IC. An internal short in windings or resistor of devices or short in wiring harness may cause damage to PCM or Emission Control System (ECS) device.

5) PCM provides ground for VCC solenoid in transmission through a quad driver IC. An internal short in winding or diode of solenoid or short in wiring harness may cause PCM damage or solenoid failure.

91B09360   91D09361

Courtesy of General Motors Corp.

GM
1-222

1991 ENGINE PERFORMANCE
Self-Diagnostics – Eldorado & Seville PCM/BCM (Cont.)

CHART B-1,
ODOMETER POWER/GROUND PROBLEM

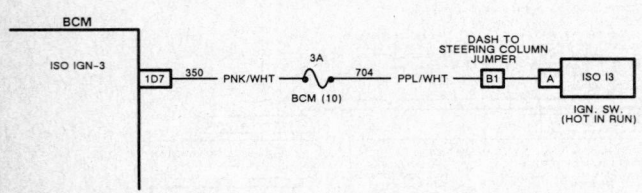

An incorrect odometer reading can be caused by problems relating to power and ground circuits not only in Instrument Panel Cluster (IPC), but those of other components within the computer network, the computer wake-up signals, the vacuum fluorescent power supply, the odometer mileage memory chip (EEPROM) contained in BCM, or by data link between computer components.

NOTE: Test numbers refer to test numbers on diagnostic chart.

1) If no codes are set in diagnostic memory, observe state of odometer reading with headlight switch and twilight sentinel switch in the OFF position. This is important because these signals can wake-up the BCM and otherwise cause a misdiagnosis of a malfunctioning primary circuit.
2) When odometer reads all zeros, actuating the interior courtesy light switch helps isolate cause of problem. This symptom is caused by a failure in computer system other than the IPC. Further isolation of this fault is diagnosed in CHARTS B-2, B-3 and B-4.
3) When odometer is blank or reads all 8's, actuating headlight switch helps isolate cause of problem. If odometer reads all zeros, problem is caused by faulty ISO IGN-3 feed circuit to BCM (open or shorted to ground) or BCM itself. If odometer is blank or reads all 8's, problem is one of several others within computer network. If display is normal, the cause is due to an open or short to ground in circuit No. 588 (16-volt VF input to radio) or circuit No. 8 (incandescent bulb output from IPC).
4) Cycling the high beam or headlight dimmer switch helps further isolate cause of problem. If high beams cycle, problem is related to IPC itself, IPC ground circuit, vacuum fluorescent power supply circuit or components related to these circuits. Further fault diagnosis is contained in CHART B-5.
5) If high beams did not cycle when dimmer switch was actuated, turning on courtesy lights switch helps further isolate system problem. If courtesy lights turn on, problem is related to IPC itself, the Central Power Supply (CPS) to IPC logic circuits ground, the 12-volt power circuits from CPS to IPC, or the CPS itself. Further problem isolation is contained in CHART B-6.

6) If courtesy lights did not turn on when switch was actuated, several other causes for problem can be isolated by following CHART B-7 and CHART B-8, depending on whether the lights-on chime sounds when test is run.
7) If the odometer reads ERROR, BCM EEPROM or internal IPC failure is indicated. Jumpering pin "M" of the ALDL to ground disables the data line and isolates the IPC from the BCM. With no serial data, the IPC should display "0" in the odometer following the crank cycle.

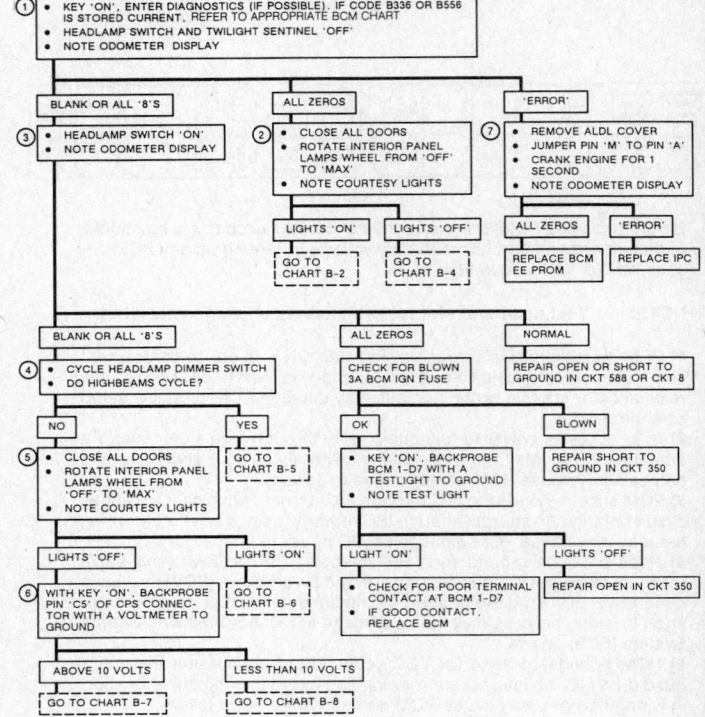

WHEN ALL THE DIAGNOSIS AND REPAIRS ARE COMPLETED, CLEAR CODES AND VERIFY OPERATION

* TO AVOID ENGINE STARTING, THE 7.5 AMP INJECTOR FUSES MAY BE REMOVED FROM THE UNDERHOOD RELAY CENTER

1991 ENGINE PERFORMANCE
Self-Diagnostics – Eldorado & Seville PCM/BCM (Cont.)

GM
1-223

CHART B-2, BCM-TO-IPC COMMUNICATION PROBLEM

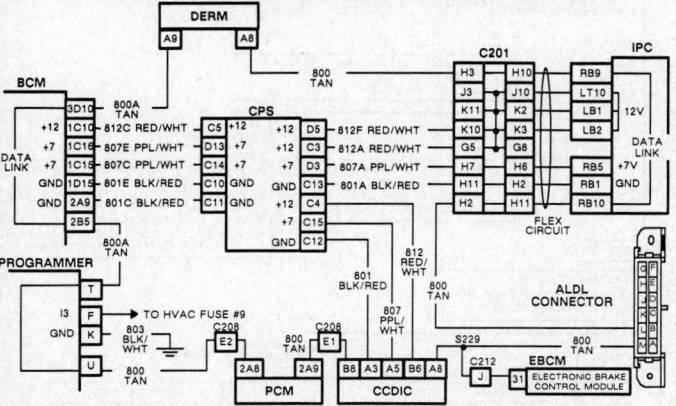

You are at this chart because odometer, with key on, read all zeroes and courtesy lights turned on when switch was actuated. These symptoms indicate a loss of BCM data communication to Instrument Panel Cluster (IPC), which can be caused by several different problems.

NOTE: Test numbers refer to test numbers on diagnostic chart.

1) If ALDL connector cover is off or loose, this could cause a break in data circuit, cutting off BCM communication to IPC under certain electrical conditions. Should this be the case, securely connect ALDL cover and return to beginning of SELF-DIAGNOSTIC SYSTEM CHECK.
2) This step isolates ALDL connector, the PCM and programmer from data circuit in order to find fault. If odometer reads actual accumulated miles, the fault lies within network between ALDL connector, the PCM and programmer.
3) If the CCP portion of the CCDIC has displays, the data line between the BCM and CCDIC has been verified good. A blank CCP indicates a problem in this segment of the circuit.
4) This determines if condition is caused by the DERM by isolating it from the circuit.

91C09365   91E09366

5) From the preceding steps, the problem must exist between the DERM pin A8 and ALDL pin "L". Removing IPC and reconnecting ALDL cover will add only the data line circuit from IPC terminal RB10 to ALDL pin "L", the known good circuit. If the CCP blanks out when this is done, this circuit is the source of the fault.
6) This step determines if fault is in the last section of circuit No. 800 or the IPC. Jumper around the IPC to isolate the last section of circuit No. 800 and connect it with a known good circuit.

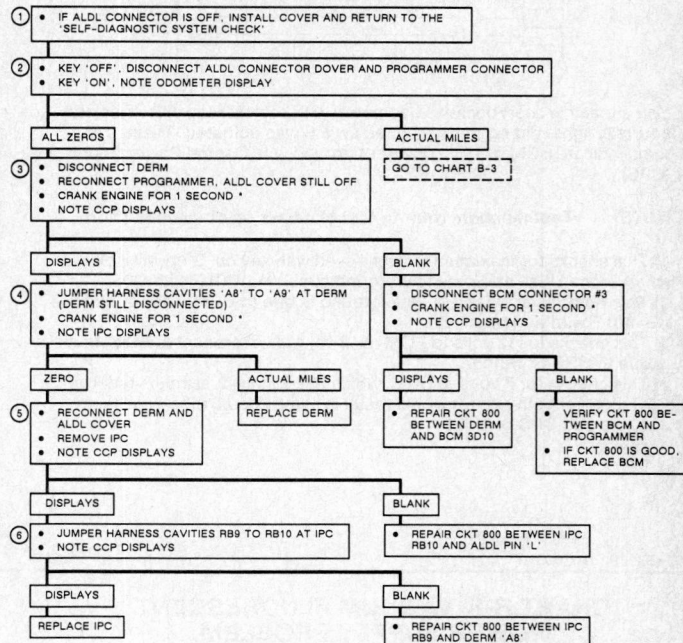

WHEN ALL THE DIAGNOSIS AND REPAIRS ARE COMPLETED, CLEAR CODES AND VERIFY OPERATION

* TO AVOID ENGINE STARTING, THE 7.5 AMP INJECTOR FUSES MAY BE REMOVED FROM THE UNDERHOOD RELAY CENTER

Courtesy of General Motors Corp.

CHART B-3, CCDIC PROBLEM

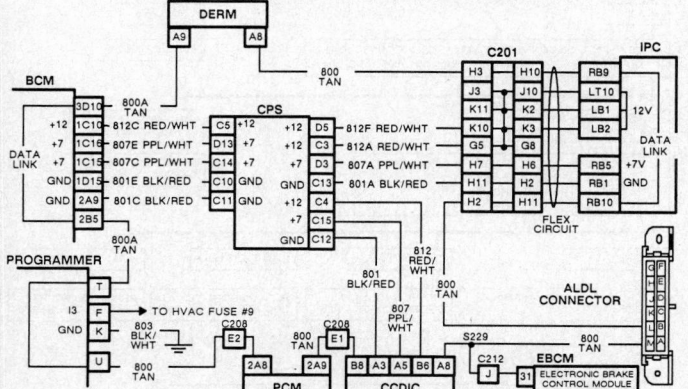

You are here because the odometer problem has been isolated to the programmer, BCM, CCDIC components or related data link circuitry.

NOTE: Test numbers refer to test numbers on diagnostic chart.

1) This step restores circuit No. 800 between PCM pin No. 2A9 and ALDL into the data circuit. If odometer reads zero, the circuit is shorted to ground or voltage.
2) This step isolates problem to the area between programmer and BCM (including data circuit).
3) This step isolates the area between PCM pin 2A9 and ALDL pin "M". Disconnecting the CCDIC will verify circuit No. 800 between CCDIC pin A8 and ALDL pin "M".
4) This step isolates the fault to the CCDIC or circuit No. 800.

91C09365   91I09368

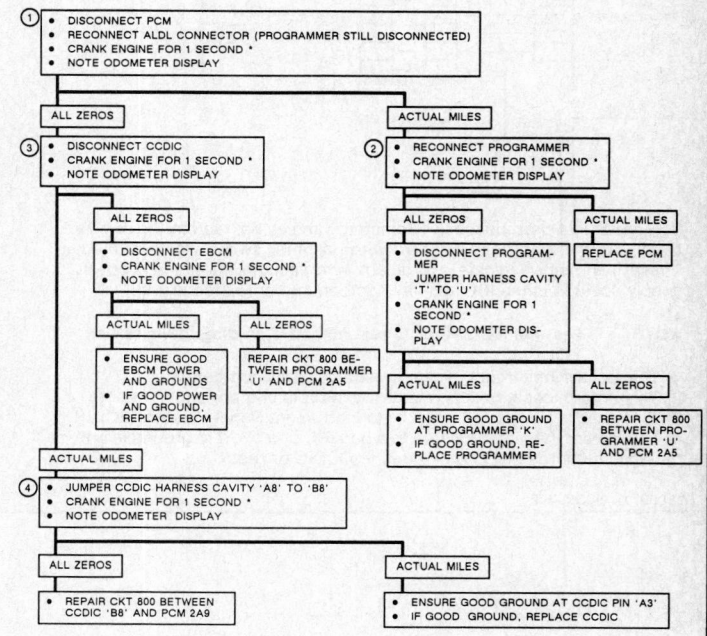

WHEN ALL THE DIAGNOSIS AND REPAIRS ARE COMPLETED, CLEAR CODES AND VERIFY OPERATION

* TO AVOID ENGINE STARTING, THE 7.5 AMP INJECTOR FUSES MAY BE REMOVED FROM THE UNDERHOOD RELAY CENTER

Courtesy of General Motors Corp.

CHART B-4, BCM-TO-CPS POWER/GROUND PROBLEM

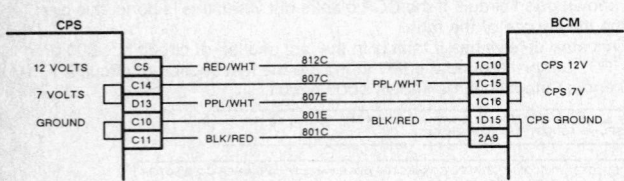

You are at this chart because odometer, with key on, read all zeroes and courtesy lights did not turn on when switch was actuated. These symptoms indicate BCM has lost power or ground with Central Power Supply (CPS).

NOTE: Test numbers refer to test numbers on diagnostic chart.

1) This checks for maximum blower speed with key on. Step will indicate whether the BCM has lost logic ground circuit No. 801E with CPS.
2) This determines if loss of logic ground is due to BCM, CPS or circuit No. 801E wire and terminals.
3) This checks for 12 volts to BCM. If 12 volts is not present at BCM, fault is due to CPS or wiring.
4) This checks for 7 volts to BCM, which has 2 individual inputs fed from CPS. Loss of both signals would result in system fault, otherwise fault is due to a bad CPS or BCM.

91A09369 91C09370

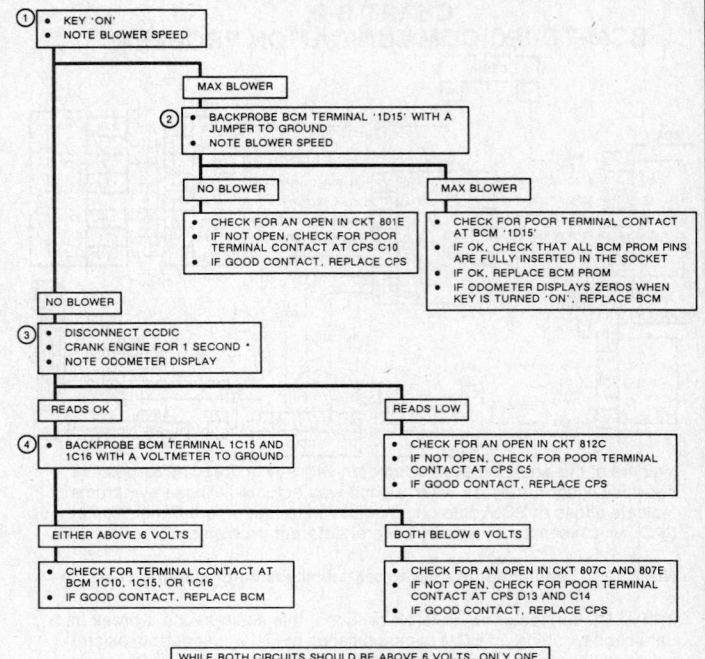

WHILE BOTH CIRCUITS SHOULD BE ABOVE 6 VOLTS, ONLY ONE CIRCUIT IS REQUIRED TO MAINTAIN SYSTEM OPERATION

WHEN ALL THE DIAGNOSIS AND REPAIRS ARE COMPLETED, CLEAR CODES AND VERIFY OPERATION

Courtesy of General Motors Corp.

CHART B-5, VACUUM FLUORESCENT POWER SUPPLY PROBLEM

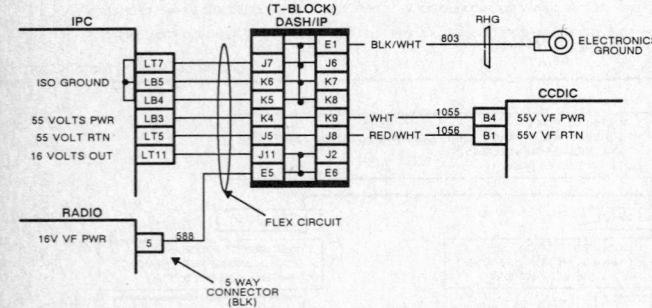

You are at this chart because odometer, with key on, read all 8's or was blank, but the high beams cycled when dimmer switch was activated. These symptoms indicate a problem with vacuum fluorescent power supply, located in the IPC, display components or related wiring.

NOTE: Test numbers refer to test numbers on diagnostic chart.

1) This determines if fault is due to a bad CCDIC component.
2) This determines if fault is due to a bad radio component.
3) This checks for ground integrity to Instrument Panel Cluster (IPC).
4) This determines if fault is due to a bad IPC or a short to ground in one of vacuum fluorescent power wires to CCDIC or radio.

91E09371 91G09372

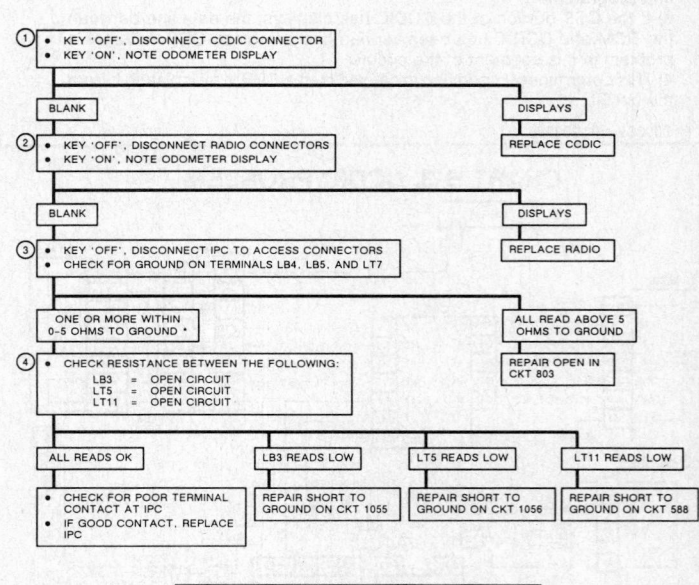

* WHILE ALL CIRCUITS SHOULD BE NEAR GROUND, ONLY ONE CIRCUIT IS REQUIRED TO MAINTAIN SYSTEM OPERATION

WHEN ALL THE DIAGNOSIS AND REPAIRS ARE COMPLETED, CLEAR CODES AND VERIFY OPERATION

Courtesy of General Motors Corp.

1991 ENGINE PERFORMANCE
Self-Diagnostics – Eldorado & Seville PCM/BCM (Cont.)

GM
1-225

CHART B-6,
IPC-TO-CPS POWER/GROUND PROBLEM

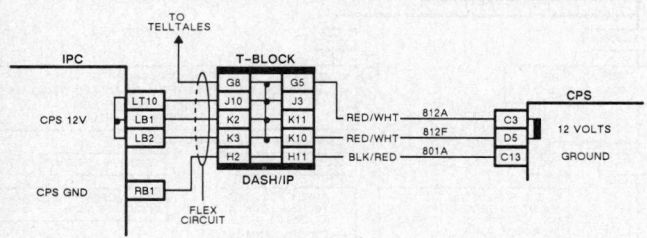

You are at this chart because odometer, with key on, read all 8's or was blank, the high beams would not cycle, but courtesy light came on when switch was activated. These symptoms indicate Instrument Panel Cluster (IPC) has lost 12-volt power feed or ground with Central Power Supply (CPS).

NOTE: Test numbers refer to test numbers on diagnostic chart.

1) Checking CCDIC display indicates whether IPC has ground.
2) Disconnecting IPC and checking resistance in circuit No. 801A determines if fault is due to IPC, wiring and terminals, or the CPS.
3) This checks if 12 volts is available from the CPS. If not, fault is due to wiring or CPS.
4) With 12 volts available from CPS, this checks if fault is due to IPC or flex circuit between transition block and IPC.

91I09373   91A09374

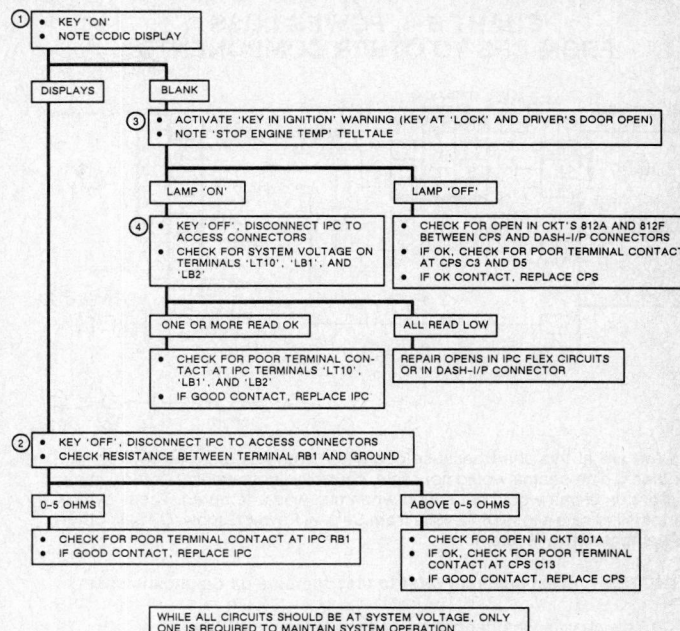

CHART B-7,
BCM-TO-CPS WAKE-UP SIGNAL PROBLEM

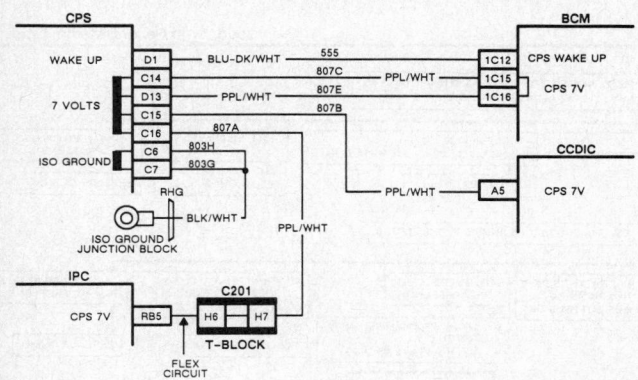

You are at this chart because odometer, with key on, read all 8's, was blank, high beams would not cycle, courtesy lights would not turn on, but lights on chime would sound when activated. These symptoms indicate a loss of 7 volts from Central Power Supply (CPS) to data network components, used to power the microprocessor chip, or CPS has lost system wake-up signal from BCM, which is used to turn on 7-volt power supply.

NOTE: Test numbers refer to test numbers on diagnostic chart.

1) This checks circuit No. 555, CPS wake-up signal, for a short to ground, a fault in BCM or BCM connector, or a bad CPS.
2) This checks for an open in circuit No. 555.
3) This checks for an open circuit in CPS ground, which will disable 7-volt power supply.
4) This checks for short to ground in each 7-volt circuit from CPS, for a faulty component in network or a faulty CPS.

91D09375   91F09376

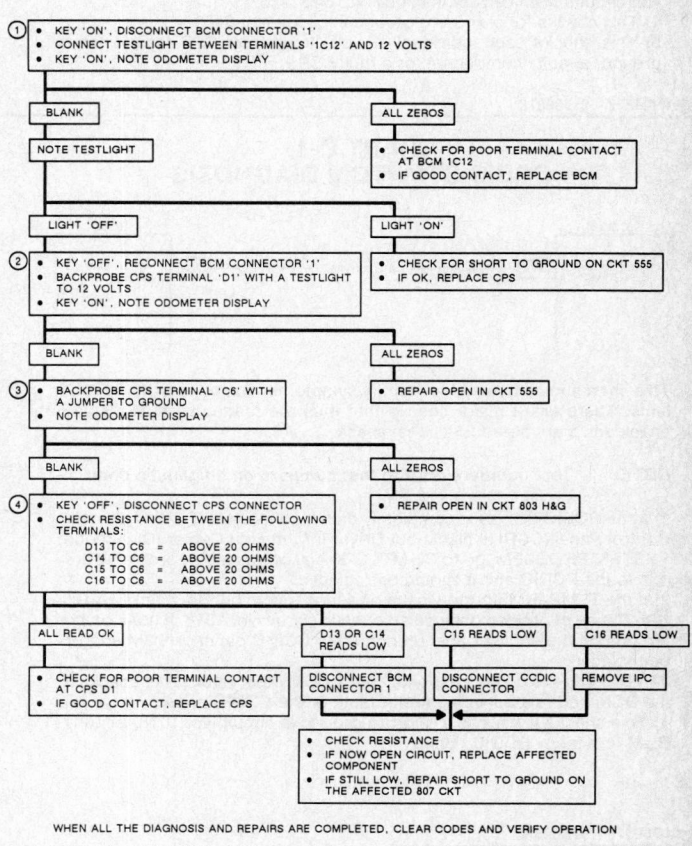

CHART B-8, POWER LOSS FROM CPS TO OTHER COMPONENTS

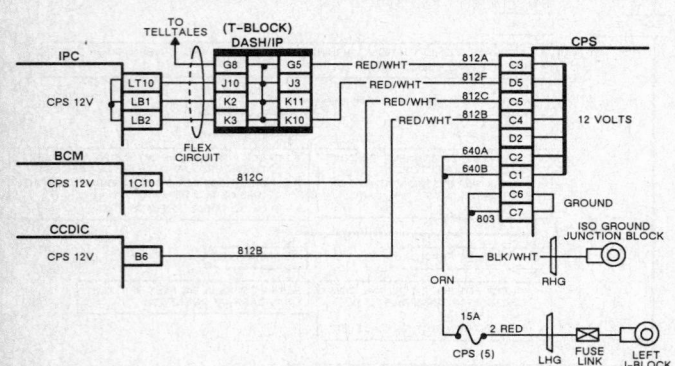

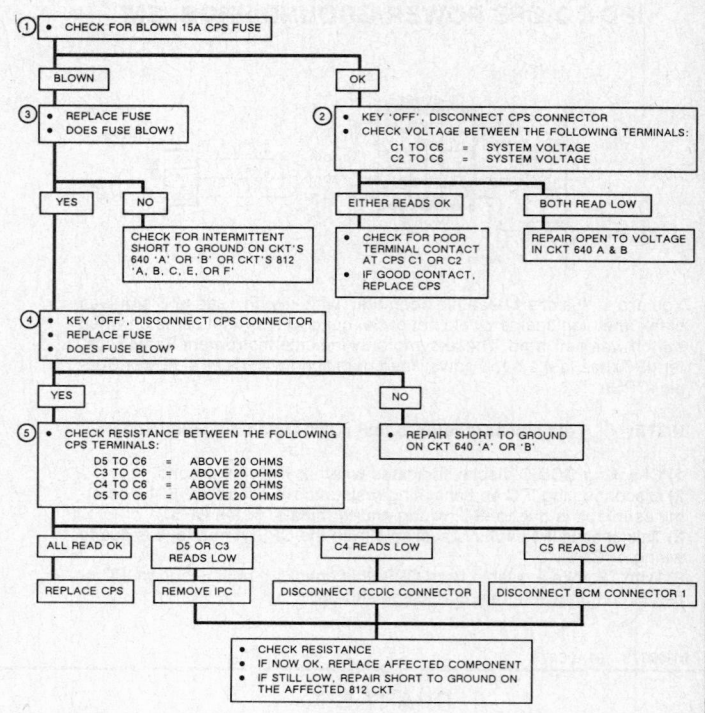

You are at this chart because odometer, with key on, read all 8's, was blank, high beams would not cycle, courtesy lights would not turn on, or light on chime would not sound when test was attempted. These symptoms indicate a loss of 12 volts from Central Power Supply (CPS) to other components in system.

NOTE: Test numbers refer to test numbers on diagnostic chart.

1) This checks whether battery voltage is feeding CPS.
2) This checks for an open in circuit No. 640, CPS battery feed, poor terminal contact, or a faulty CPS.
3) This checks for an intermittent short to ground condition on any of 12-volt circuits from CPS or in circuit No. 640 feed.
4) This checks for a short to ground in circuit No. 640.
5) This checks each individual 12-volt circuit from CPS for a short to ground, a faulty component, or a faulty CPS.

WHEN ALL THE DIAGNOSIS AND REPAIRS ARE COMPLETED, CLEAR CODES AND VERIFY OPERATION

91H09377   91J09378

Courtesy of General Motors Corp.

CHART C-1, CCDIC SYMPTOM DIAGNOSIS

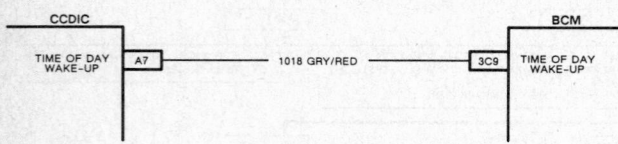

This chart should be used to identify symptoms relating to CCDIC problems. There are 2 major checks that must be made: a visual display check and a keyboard functional check.

NOTE: Test numbers refer to test numbers on diagnostic chart.

1) If the CCDIC display is completely blank, go to CHART C-2. If Climate Control Panel (CCP) is blank, but Driver Information Center (DIC) reads SYSTEM PROBLEM, go to CHART C-3. Any other display problems are due to the CCDIC and it should be replaced.
2) If the TEMP/TIME button is the only inoperative button, go to CHART C-4. Cause of problem may be an open in circuit No. 1018. If none of the buttons on the engine panel respond, the CCDIC panel or BCM should be replaced.
3) If DIC buttons do not respond, check BCM input B130. This checks if the BCM and related wiring are at fault, or the CCDIC panel.
4) This checks if there is a short to ground in circuit No. 1018, a faulty BCM or a faulty CCDIC panel.

WHEN ALL THE DIAGNOSIS AND REPAIRS ARE COMPLETED, CLEAR CODES AND VERIFY OPERATION

Courtesy of General Motors Corp.

91B09379   91D09380

1991 ENGINE PERFORMANCE
Self-Diagnostics – Eldorado & Seville PCM/BCM (Cont.)

GM
1-227

CHART C-2,
CCDIC COMPLETELY BLANK

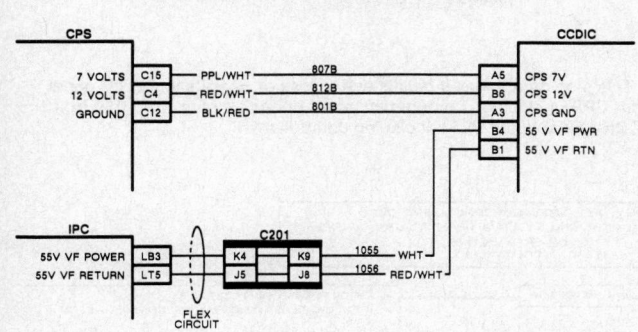

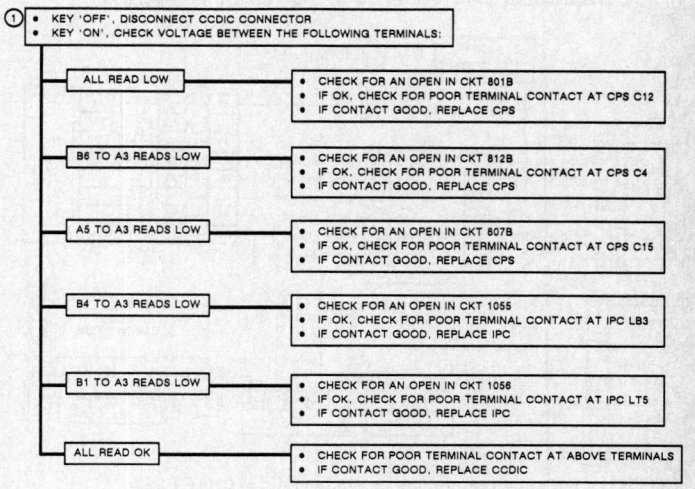

You are at this chart because the CCDIC display is completely blank. Cause for this problem could be a loss of Central Power Supply (CPS) power or ground, or loss of vacuum fluorescent power from Instrument Panel Cluster (IPC).

NOTE: **Test numbers refer to test numbers on diagnostic chart.**

1) Unplugging the CCDIC connector and performing individual circuit checks will determine if wiring connector, terminals or component is faulty.

WHEN ALL THE DIAGNOSIS AND REPAIRS ARE COMPLETED, CLEAR CODES AND VERIFY OPERATION

91F09381   91H09382

Courtesy of General Motors Corp.

CHART C-3,
CCDIC DISPLAY READS SYSTEM PROBLEM

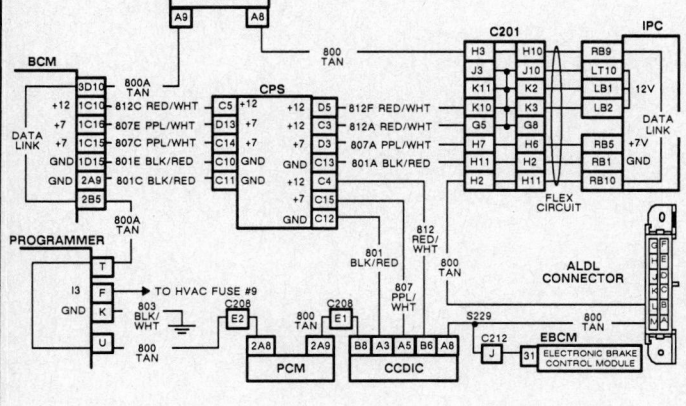

1) This checks if data link or the CCDIC panel is faulty.
2) This checks where problem exists in data link, including the CCDIC panel.
3) If the ALDL cover does not provide a good jumper between pin "L" and "M", an open will develop in the data line circuit. If the jumper is good, the problem is in the CCDIC.

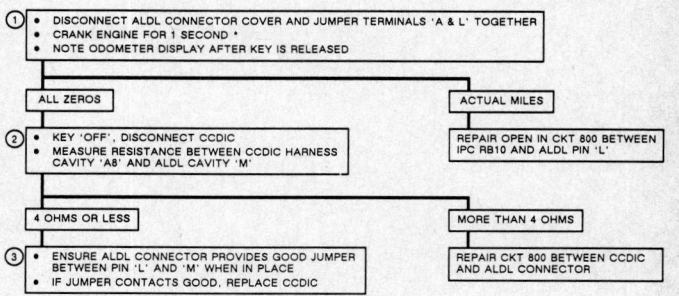

You are at this chart because the CCDIC display reads SYSTEM PROBLEM. This symptom is the result of a data link problem.

NOTE: **Test numbers refer to test numbers on diagnostic chart.**

* TO AVOID ENGINE STARTING, THE 7.5 AMP INJECTOR FUSES MAY BE REMOVED FROM THE UNDERHOOD RELAY CENTER

WHEN ALL THE DIAGNOSIS AND REPAIRS ARE COMPLETED, CLEAR CODES AND VERIFY OPERATION

91C09365   91B09384

Courtesy of General Motors Corp.

CHART C-4,
CCDIC DISPLAY READS SYSTEM PROBLEM

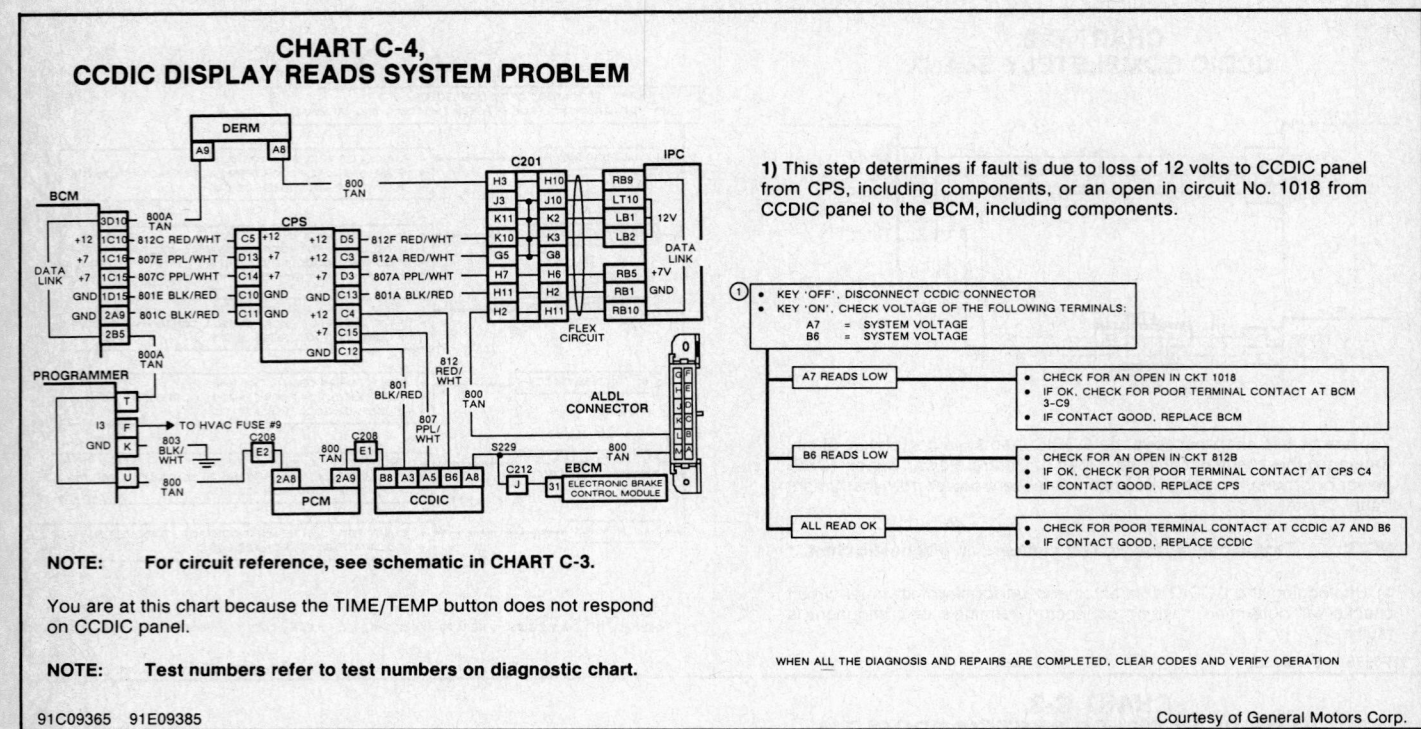

1) This step determines if fault is due to loss of 12 volts to CCDIC panel from CPS, including components, or an open in circuit No. 1018 from CCDIC panel to the BCM, including components.

① • KEY 'OFF', DISCONNECT CCDIC CONNECTOR
  • KEY 'ON', CHECK VOLTAGE OF THE FOLLOWING TERMINALS:
    A7 = SYSTEM VOLTAGE
    B6 = SYSTEM VOLTAGE

| A7 READS LOW | → | • CHECK FOR AN OPEN IN CKT 1018 • IF OK, CHECK FOR POOR TERMINAL CONTACT AT BCM 3-C9 • IF CONTACT GOOD, REPLACE BCM |

| B6 READS LOW | → | • CHECK FOR AN OPEN IN CKT 812B • IF OK, CHECK FOR POOR TERMINAL CONTACT AT CPS C4 • IF CONTACT GOOD, REPLACE CPS |

| ALL READ OK | → | • CHECK FOR POOR TERMINAL CONTACT AT CCDIC A7 AND B6 • IF CONTACT GOOD, REPLACE CCDIC |

NOTE: For circuit reference, see schematic in CHART C-3.

You are at this chart because the TIME/TEMP button does not respond on CCDIC panel.

NOTE: Test numbers refer to test numbers on diagnostic chart.

WHEN ALL THE DIAGNOSIS AND REPAIRS ARE COMPLETED, CLEAR CODES AND VERIFY OPERATION

91C09365   91E09385

Courtesy of General Motors Corp.

1991 ENGINE PERFORMANCE
Self-Diagnostics – Eldorado & Seville PCM/BCM (Cont.)

GM
1-229

PCM CODE CHARTS

PCM CHART A, MULTIPLE CODES STORED (HARD)

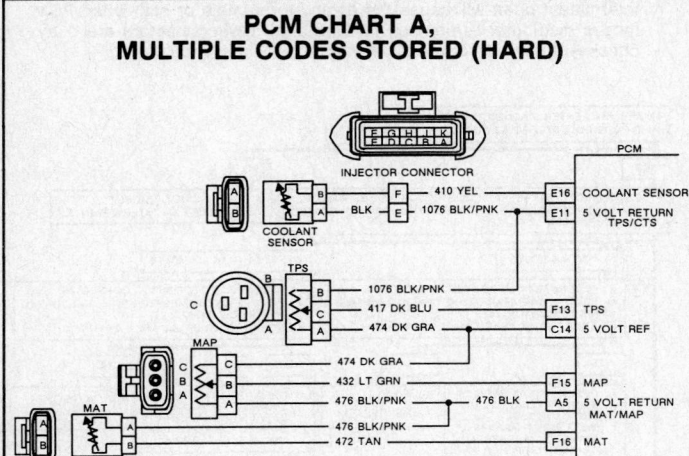

The conditions, diagnosed by this chart, are caused by a single circuit failure and result in multiple diagnostic codes. If any of these conditions are met, follow the appropriate correction procedure before using the procedures for individual codes.

Chart A-1 – If Codes EO22 and EO32 are stored, the cause is probably a loss of 5 volts to circuit No. 474, the 5-volt reference to MAP sensor and Throttle Position Sensor (TPS). To verify this condition, probe the following harness terminals with a voltmeter to ground: MAP sensor harness connector terminal "C" and TPS connector terminal "C".

If voltage is zero for both circuits, check circuit No. 474 for an open or short to ground. If wiring is okay, either the PCM connector or the PCM itself is faulty. If 5-volt reference signal is available on both sensor's terminals, go to the diagnostic chart for each individual code.

Chart A-2 – If a Code EO15 is stored along with a Code EO21, the cause is probably an open in sensor ground circuit No. 976 (coolant sensor and TPS). To verify this condition, probe the following harness terminals with a voltmeter to 12 volts: coolant temperature sensor terminal "A" (Black/Pink wire) and TPS connector terminal "B" (Black/Pink wire).

If voltage is zero at both sensors, check circuit No. 976 for an open. If wiring is okay, either the PCM connector or the PCM itself is faulty. If 5 volts are present at either sensor, follow the diagnostic chart for each individual code. Diagnose Code EO15 first, and then Code EO21.

Chart A-3 – If Code EO34 is stored hard along with Code EO38, this condition is probably caused by an open in ground circuit No. 469 for the MAP and MAT sensors. To verify this condition, probe the following harness terminals with a voltmeter to 12 volts: MAT sensor terminal "A" and MAP sensor harness terminal "A".

If voltage is zero at sensors, check for an open between PCM and splice. If 5 volts is present at sensors, follow the diagnostic chart for each individual code. Diagnose Code EO34 first and Code EO38 last.

CHART A-1 E022 – E032

- CONNECT DVOM POSITIVE LEAD TO TERMINAL A OF TPS HARNESS CONNECTOR
- NEGATIVE LEAD TO TERMINAL B OF TPS HARNESS CONNECTOR
- NOTE METER
- CONNECT DVOM POSITIVE LEAD TO TERMINAL A OF MAP HARNESS CONNECTOR
- NEGATIVE LEAD TO TERMINAL C OF MAP HARNESS CONNECTOR
- NOTE METER

0 VOLTS BOTH SENSORS	NOT 0 VOLTS BOTH SENSORS
• CHECK CKT 474 FOR OPEN OR SHORT TO GROUND BETWEEN ECM TERMINAL C14 SPLICE AND SENSOR CONNECTORS	• MULTIPLE FAULT NOT VERIFIED • DIAGNOSE USING CHART E022 FIRST THEN E032

CKT 474 OPEN OR SHORTED	CKT 474 OK
• REPAIR AND RETEST	• CHECK ECM CONNECTOR • SEE ECM REPLACEMENT CHECK.

CHART A-2 E015 – E021

- CONNECT DVOM POSITIVE LEAD TO TERMINAL A OF TPS HARNESS CONNECTOR
- NEGATIVE LEAD TO TERMINAL B OF TPS HARNESS CONNECTOR
- NOTE METER
- CONNECT DVOM POSITIVE LEAD TO TERMINAL A OF CTS HARNESS CONNECTOR
- NEGATIVE LEAD TO TERMINAL B OF CTS HARNESS CONNECTOR
- NOTE METER

0 VOLTS BOTH SENSORS	NOT 0 VOLTS BOTH SENSORS
• CHECK CKT 476 FOR OPEN OR SHORT TO GROUND BETWEEN ECM TERMINAL E11 SPLICE AND SENSOR CONNECTORS	• MULTIPLE FAULT NOT VERIFIED • DIAGNOSE USING CHART E015 FIRST THEN E021

CKT 476 OPEN OR SHORTED	CKT 476 OK
• REPAIR AND RETEST	• CHECK ECM CONNECTOR • SEE ECM REPLACEMENT CHECK.

WHEN ALL DIAGNOSIS AND REPAIRS ARE COMPLETED, CLEAR CODES AND VERIFY OPERATION

CHART A-3 E034 – E038

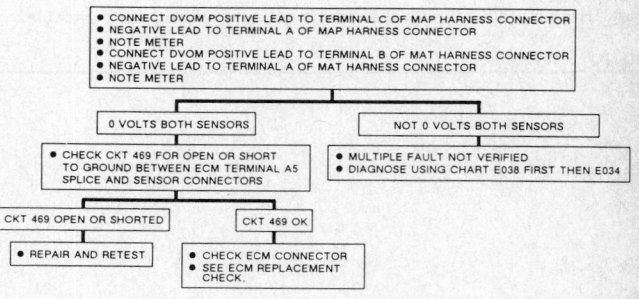

- CONNECT DVOM POSITIVE LEAD TO TERMINAL C OF MAP HARNESS CONNECTOR
- NEGATIVE LEAD TO TERMINAL A OF MAP HARNESS CONNECTOR
- NOTE METER
- CONNECT DVOM POSITIVE LEAD TO TERMINAL B OF MAT HARNESS CONNECTOR
- NEGATIVE LEAD TO TERMINAL A OF MAT HARNESS CONNECTOR
- NOTE METER

0 VOLTS BOTH SENSORS	NOT 0 VOLTS BOTH SENSORS
• CHECK CKT 469 FOR OPEN OR SHORT TO GROUND BETWEEN ECM TERMINAL A5 SPLICE AND SENSOR CONNECTORS	• MULTIPLE FAULT NOT VERIFIED • DIAGNOSE USING CHART E038 FIRST THEN E034

CKT 469 OPEN OR SHORTED	CKT 469 OK
• REPAIR AND RETEST	• CHECK ECM CONNECTOR • SEE ECM REPLACEMENT CHECK.

WHEN ALL DIAGNOSIS AND REPAIRS ARE COMPLETED, CLEAR CODES AND VERIFY OPERATION

GM
1-230

1991 ENGINE PERFORMANCE
Self-Diagnostics – Eldorado & Seville PCM/BCM (Cont.)

PCM CODE EO12, NO DISTRIBUTOR (TACH) SIGNAL

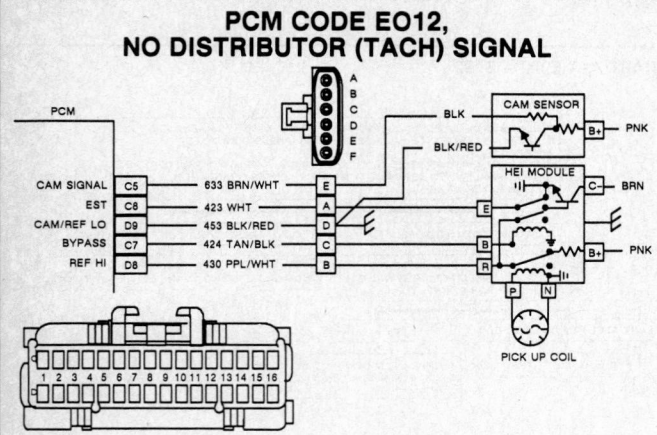

TEST CONDITIONS: Code EO12 is tested anytime cam sensor signals are being received during engine cranking operation (crank input to PCM at system voltage) and Code EO41 is not set.

FAILURE CONDITIONS: If PCM does not see distributor reference pulses for 4 seconds with crank input to PCM at system voltage, Code EO12 will be set.

ACTION: PCM turns on SERVICE ENGINE SOON light.

Possible causes of no distributor reference pulses are open pick-up coil, HEI module unable to process pick-up coil signals, or open or shorts on circuit No. 430 from module 5-wire connector to PCM.

NOTE: **Test numbers refer to test numbers on diagnostic chart.**

1) This checks for proper voltage of HEI system. If voltmeter shows .5-2.8 volts, HEI module is receiving pick-up coil signal and producing reference pulses.
2) This checks for proper ground connections between PCM and engine, and between PCM and HEI.
3) This checks for proper voltage through circuit No. 430 from HEI to PCM. If PCM terminal D8 sees .5-2.8 volts, then PCM is receiving reference pulses.
4) If HEI will produce spark, then fault is not within pick-up coil or module.

Note On Intermittents – If Code EO12 is stored as a history code, start engine and allow it to idle. Manipulate circuits No. 430 and No. 453. An intermittent open will cause the engine to stumble or stall when PCM looses distributor reference. If wiring and PCM connectors are okay, check HEI pick-up coil leads for intermittent open circuit.

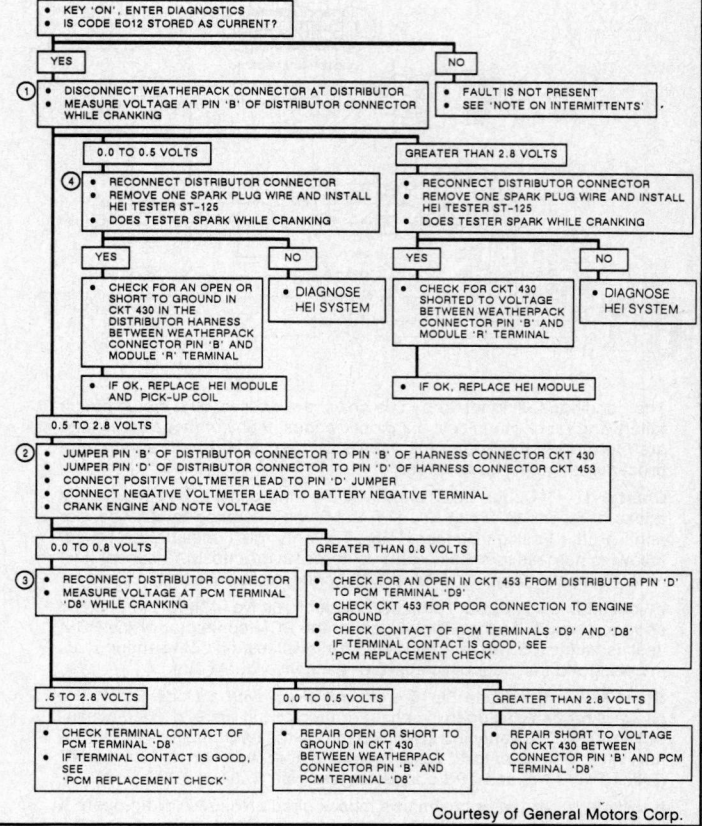

1991 ENGINE PERFORMANCE
Self-Diagnostics – Eldorado & Seville PCM/BCM (Cont.)

GM
1-231

PCM CODE EO13, RIGHT OXYGEN SENSOR NOT READY

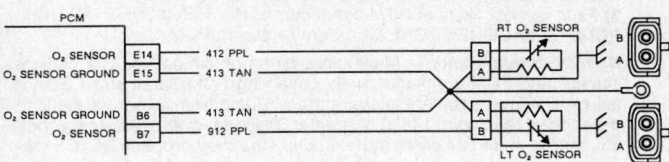

TEST CONDITIONS: Codes EO14, EO15, EO21, EO22, EO26 and EO27 are not set. Coolant temperature greater than or equal to 136°F (58°C). TPS value of 6-30 degrees. Throttle switch open. RPM at least 800.

FAILURE CONDITIONS: Oxygen sensor voltage stays between .307-.609 volt for more than 64 seconds (not toggling).

ACTION: PCM turns on SERVICE ENGINE SOON light and closed loop is disabled. When warm, a properly operating oxygen sensor will drive the PCM's .45-volt reference signal lower (less than .45 volt) to indicate a lean mixture, and higher (greater than .45 volt) to indicate a rich mixture. If under test conditions, when the oxygen sensor does not vary from the cold or not-ready voltage, PCM assumes sensor cannot respond to air/fuel mixture changes and sets a Code EO13.

NOTE: Test numbers refer to test numbers on diagnostic chart.

1) A voltage of .42-.48 displayed is a reference from the PCM. Oxygen sensor must generate .15 volt greater than the .45 reference voltage to register a cross count in the PCM.

2) The PCM compares voltage on circuit No. 412 to the ground voltage on circuit No. 413. It is essential oxygen sensor ground and PCM ground on terminal E15 indicate good continuity (no voltage difference), with engine running.

Note On Intermittents – If Code EO13 is stored as a history code, start engine and enter diagnostics. Operate engine at fast idle until AUTO closed loop status light is turned on. Observe parameter of ED33 while manipulating wiring on circuits No. 412 and No. 413. If parameter ED33 changes from a fluctuating voltage to fixed .45 volt, repair intermittent open circuit.

Check circuit No. 413 for a good ground to engine (clean and tighten star washer). Ground for circuit No. 413 is located at right side of engine or rear of cylinder head.

91I07543   91A07544

① • KEY 'ON', ENTER DIAGNOSTICS
• SELECT PCM PARAMETER ED33
• DISCONNECT OXYGEN SENSOR
• NOTE PARAMETER VALUE

.00 TO .41 → CHECK CKT 412 FOR A SHORT TO GROUND BETWEEN PCM TERMINALS 'E14' AND 'E15' AND OXYGEN SENSOR CONNECTOR

.49 TO 1.10 → CHECK CKT 412 FOR SHORT TO VOLTAGE BETWEEN PCM TERMINAL 'E14' AND OXYGEN SENSOR CONNECTOR

CKT 412 SHORTED → REPAIR SHORT TO GROUND ON CKT 412

CKT 412 OK

CKT 412 OK → • BY BACKPROBING THE PCM CONNECTOR, JUMPER PCM TERMINAL 'E14' TO TERMINAL 'E15'
• CONNECT JUMPER TO 'E11'
• NOTE PARAMETER VALUE

CKT 412 SHORTED TO VOLTAGE → REPAIR SHORT TO GROUND ON CKT 412

.42 TO .48 → • JUMPER OXYGEN SENSOR HARNESS CONNECTOR PIN 'A' TO 'B'
• NOTE PARAMETER VALUE

0.00 TO 0.05 → • CHECK CONTACT OF PCM TERMINALS 'E14' AND 'E15'
• IF TERMINAL CONTACT IS OK, SEE 'PCM REPLACEMENT CHECK',

0.06 TO 1.10

0.06 TO 1.10 → • BY BACKPROBING THE PCM CONNECTOR, JUMPER PCM TERMINAL 'E14' (CKT 412) TO TERMINAL 'E15' (CKT 413)
• CONNECT JUMPER TO 'E11' (CKT 976)
• NOTE PARAMETER VALUE

0.00 TO 0.05 → • OXYGEN SENSOR CIRCUITS ARE OK. PCM IS RESPONDING TO OXYGEN SENSOR SIGNALS
• RECONNECT OXYGEN SENSOR
• PERFORM 'OXYGEN SENSOR CHECK'.
CHART A-6

0.06 TO 1.10

0.00 TO 0.05 → • CHECK FOR CKT 412 OR 413 OPEN BETWEEN PCM AND OXYGEN SENSOR CONNECTOR

OPEN → REPAIR OPEN IN CKT 412 OR CKT 413 BETWEEN PCM TERMINAL AND OXYGEN SENSOR TERMINAL

CKT 412 AND 413 OK

② • RECONNECT OXYGEN SENSOR
• ENGINE RUNNING
• MEASURE VOLTAGE FROM PCM TERMINAL 'E15' TO THE RING RIGHTSIDE OF ENGINE BELOW VALVE COVER

0.00 TO 0.05 → • CHECK CONTACT OF PCM TERMINALS 'E14' AND 'E15'
• IF TERMINAL CONTACT IS OK, SEE 'PCM REPLACEMENT CHECK',

GREATER THAN 0.05 VOLTS → REPAIR CKT 413 FOR POOR CONTACT FROM PCM TERMINAL 'E15' TO THE RING TERMINAL GROUND

GM
1-232

1991 ENGINE PERFORMANCE
Self-Diagnostics – Eldorado & Seville PCM/BCM (Cont.)

PCM CODE EO14,
SHORTED COOLANT SENSOR CIRCUIT

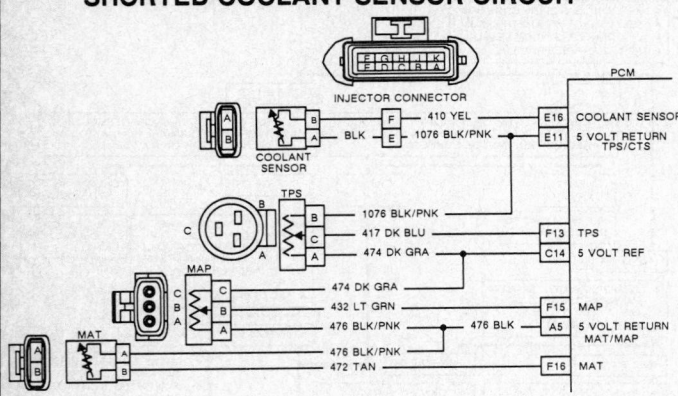

TEST CONDITIONS: Codes EO37 and EO38 are not set and MAT sensor value is less than or equal to 212°F (100°C).

FAILURE CONDITIONS: Coolant sensor value greater than or equal to 298°F (148°C).

ACTION: PCM turns on SERVICE ENGINE SOON light and uses MAT sensor value in place of coolant sensor value for all calculations for the first 4 minutes of operation. Then a value of 194°F (90°C) is used.

The coolant sensor is a 2-wire sensor with signal voltage coming from PCM to sensor terminal "B" (circuit No. 410), and a sensor reference ground on terminal "A" (circuit No. 976).

As sensor temperature increases, resistance decreases. Signal voltage from PCM to terminal "A" decreases as sensor temperature increases and current flows through sensor element to terminal "A" (sensor ground). Code EO14 sets because PCM assumes coolant temperature cannot be 298°F (148°C) or greater when MAT is 212°F (100°C) or less.

NOTE: Test numbers refer to test numbers on diagnostic chart.

1) With coolant sensor shorted, PCM parameter ED04 should read 148°C or more. If not, sensor is not shorted. See NOTE ON INTERMITTENTS.

2) This checks for a shorted coolant sensor or a short in circuit No. 410. If parameter stays at 142°C or greater with sensor unplugged, then short is in circuit No. 410, between pin "B" and PCM terminal E16.

3) Fault is most likely at PCM connector or PCM. See PFI CHART C-1, PCM REPLACEMENT CHECK before replacing PCM.

Note On Intermittents – Manipulate wiring on circuit No. 410, coolant sensor, and PCM connector while observing PCM parameter ED04. If failure is induced, coolant temperature will jump from its normal value to the shorted reading of 148°C or greater. Disconnect and reconnect coolant sensor and PCM connectors, and ensure they properly latch. If wiring and connectors are okay, substitute a known good sensor and retest.

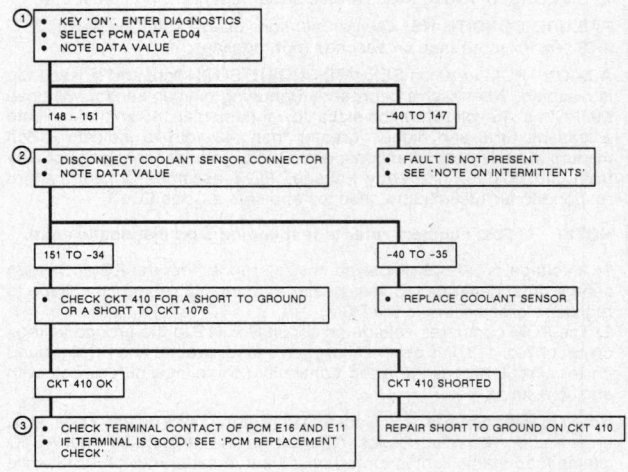

WHEN ALL DIAGNOSIS AND REPAIRS ARE COMPLETED, CLEAR CODES AND VERIFY OPERATION

91E07541   91F07546

Courtesy of General Motors Corp.

1991 ENGINE PERFORMANCE
Self-Diagnostics – Eldorado & Seville PCM/BCM (Cont.)

GM
1-233

PCM CODE EO15,
OPEN COOLANT SENSOR CIRCUIT

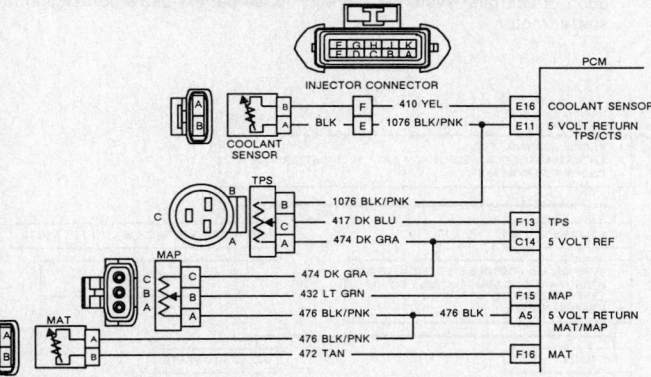

TEST CONDITIONS: Codes EO37 and EO38 not set and MAT sensor value is greater than or equal to 23°F (-5°C).

FAILURE CONDITIONS: Coolant sensor value is -36°F (-38°C) or greater.

ACTION: PCM turns on SERVICE ENGINE SOON light and uses MAT sensor value in place of coolant sensor value for all calculations for the first 4 minutes of operation. Then a value of 194°F (90°C) is used.

The coolant sensor is a variable thermistor. The coolant sensor is a 2-wire sensor with a signal voltage coming from the PCM to sensor terminal "B" (circuit No. 410), and a sensor reference ground on terminal "A" (circuit No. 976).

As temperature of sensor decreases, sensor resistance increases. Signal voltage from PCM to terminal "B" increases as sensor temperature decreases and less current flows through sensor element to terminal "A" (sensor ground). Code EO15 sets because PCM assumes coolant temperature cannot be -36°F (-38°C) or less when MAT is 23°F (-5°C) or greater.

NOTE: Test numbers refer to test numbers on diagnostic chart.

1) If sensor is open, PCM parameter ED04 should read -38°C or less. If not, then sensor signal is not open. See NOTE ON INTERMITTENTS.
2) This checks for open sensor signal in circuit No. 410 from PCM to sensor connector. If parameter ED04 reads 148-151°C with connector shorted, then circuit No. 410 is okay.

3) This checks for open in the sensor ground (circuit No. 1076 from sensor pin "A" to ground splice). If shorting pin "A" to ground causes parameter ED04 to read 148-151°C, then there is an open in circuit No. 976.
4) This checks if PCM can recognize a short to ground or low voltage on terminal E16, coolant temperature signal. If grounding terminal E16 causes ED04 to read 148-151°C, then there is an open circuit in circuit No. 410 from the PCM to the coolant sensor.
5) Fault is most likely at PCM connector or PCM. See PFI CHART C-1, PCM REPLACEMENT CHECK before replacing PCM.

Note On Intermittents – Manipulate wiring on circuits No. 410 and No. 976 (coolant temperature sensor and PCM connector), while observing PCM parameter ED04. If failure is induced, coolant temperature will jump from normal value to the open reading (-38°C or less). Disconnect and reconnect coolant sensor and PCM connectors, and ensure they properly latch. If wiring and connectors are okay, substitute a known good sensor and retest.

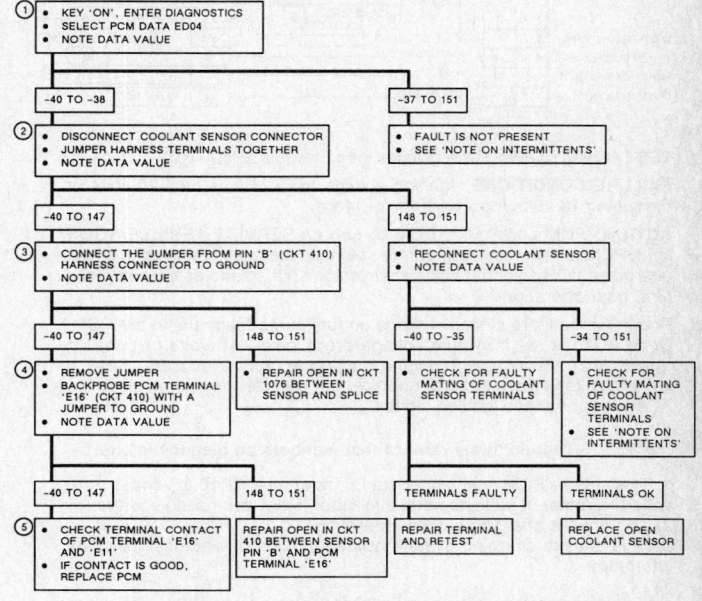

WHEN ALL DIAGNOSIS AND REPAIRS ARE COMPLETED, CLEAR CODES AND VERIFY OPERATION

Courtesy of General Motors Corp.

91E07541   91J07548

PCM CODE EO16, ALTERNATOR VOLTAGE OUT OF RANGE

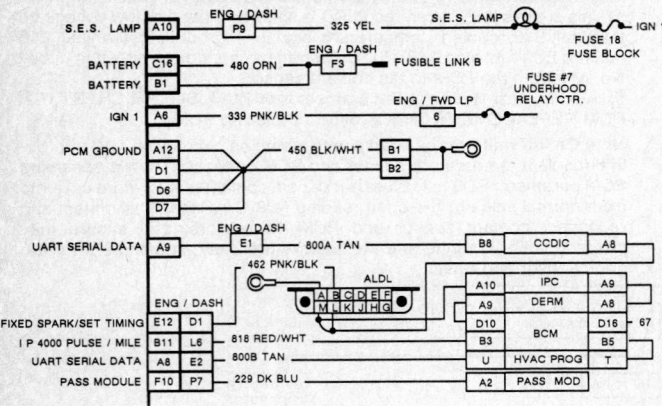

TEST CONDITIONS: RPM greater than or equal to 500 RPM.

FAILURE CONDITIONS: Ignition voltage to PCM less than 10 volts or more than 16 volts for 5 seconds or more.

ACTION: PCM commands BCM to turn on SERVICE VEHICLE SOON light. PCM turns off canister purge solenoid, disables cruise control, de-energizes VCC solenoid and transmission shift solenoids de-energized (3rd. gear operation).

The PCM monitors system voltage on fuel pump feedback to the PCM. Code EO16 is set if system voltage drops below 10 volts or goes up greater than 16 volts, with engine running at greater than 500 RPM. If ignition voltage goes to zero (open circuit), vehicle will not run since the PCM does not have ignition signal.

NOTE: Test numbers refer to test numbers on diagnostic chart.

1) This checks PCM snap shot data for parameter ED10. If voltage is 16 volts or greater, it indicates that alternator is not controlling voltage.
2) This checks charging system operation.
3) This checks charging system operation without electrical loads on alternator.

Note On Intermittents – Code EO16 may be stored as a history code if the battery charge was low. Load test battery and check for proper operation of charging system. Check for loose battery cable connection at starter motor.

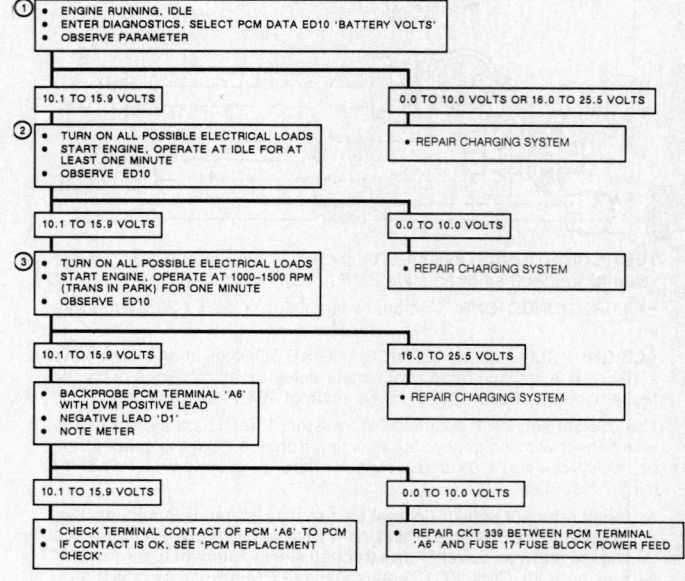

WHEN ALL DIAGNOSIS AND REPAIRS ARE COMPLETED, CLEAR CODES AND VERIFY OPERATION

91D09342   91D07550

Courtesy of General Motors Corp.

1991 ENGINE PERFORMANCE
Self-Diagnostics – Eldorado & Seville PCM/BCM (Cont.)

GM
1-235

PCM CODE EO17,
LEFT OXYGEN SENSOR NOT READY

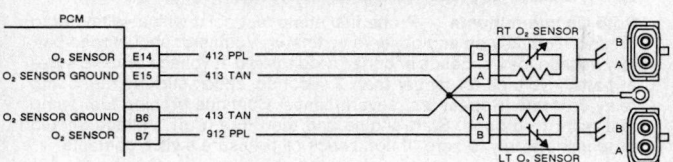

TEST CONDITIONS: Codes EO14, EO15, EO21, EO22, EO26 and EO27 are not set. Coolant temperature greater than or equal to 136°F (58°C). TPS value of 6-30 degrees. Throttle switch open. RPM at least 800 or greater.

FAILURE CONDITIONS: Oxygen sensor voltage stays between .307-.609 volt for more than 64 seconds (not toggling).

ACTION: PCM turns on SERVICE ENGINE SOON light and closed loop is disabled.

When warm, a properly operating oxygen sensor will drive the PCM's .45-volt reference signal lower (less than .45 volt) to indicate a lean mixture, and higher (greater than .45 volt) to indicate a rich mixture. If under test conditions, if the oxygen sensor does not vary from the cold or not ready voltage, PCM assumes sensor cannot respond to air/fuel mixture changes and sets a Code EO17.

Possible causes of setting Code EO17 are:
• Open in circuits No. 912 or No. 413.
• Short to voltage on circuits No. 912 or No. 413.
• Oxygen sensor that cannot respond.

NOTE: Test numbers refer to test numbers on diagnostic chart.

1) A voltage of .42-.48 displayed is a reference voltage from the PCM. Oxygen sensor must generate .15 volt greater than the .45 reference to register a cross count in the PCM.

2) The PCM compares voltage on circuit No. 912 to the ground voltage on circuit No. 413. It is essential that oxygen sensor ground and PCM ground on terminal E15 indicate good continuity (no voltage difference) with engine running.

Note On Intermittents – If Code EO17 is stored as a history code, start engine and enter diagnostics. Operate engine at fast idle until AUTO closed loop status light is turned on. Observe parameter of ED33 while manipulating wiring on circuits No. 912 and No. 413. If parameter ED34

changes from a fluctuating voltage to fixed .45 volt, repair intermittent open circuit.

Check circuit No. 413 for a good ground to engine (clean and tighten star washer). Ground for circuit No. 413 is located at right or rear of cylinder head.

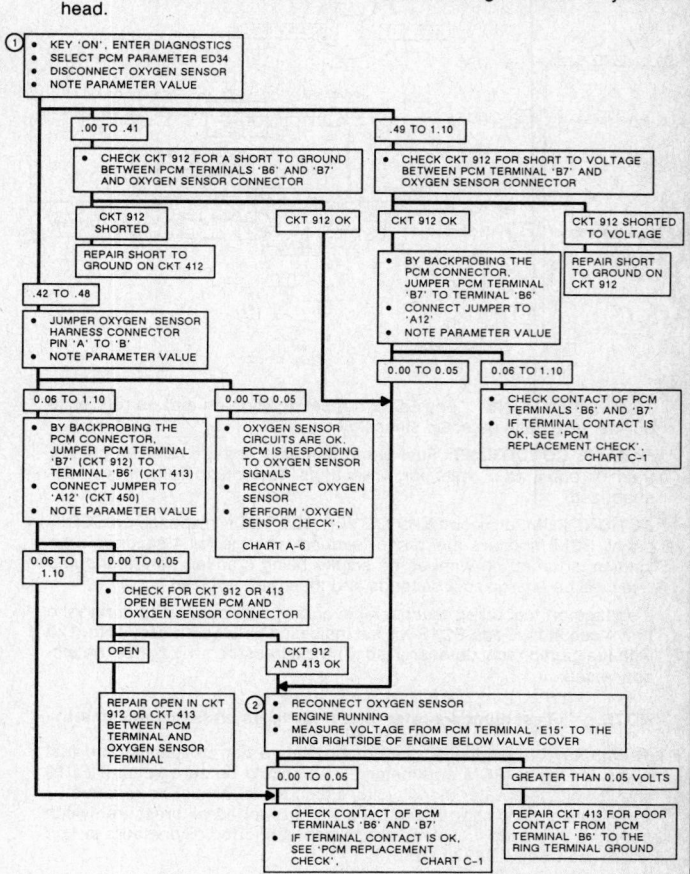

91I09354   91H07627

GM
1-236

1991 ENGINE PERFORMANCE
Self-Diagnostics – Eldorado & Seville PCM/BCM (Cont.)

PCM CODE EO19, SHORTED FUEL PUMP CIRCUIT

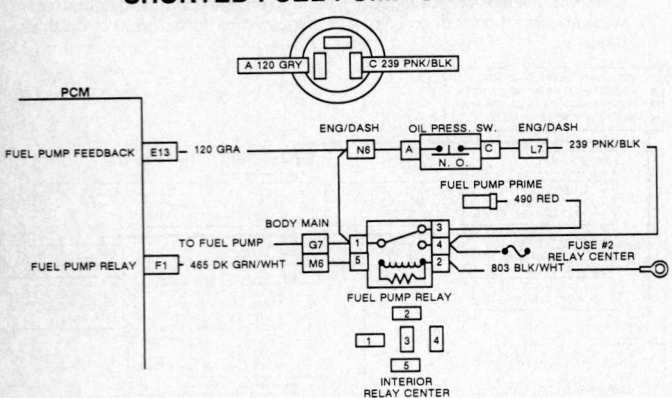

TEST CONDITIONS: Code EO12 not set. Ignition on and no reference pulses have been detected since key on.

FAILURE CONDITIONS: Fuel pump feedback voltage remains greater than or equal to 7 volts for 4 seconds (fuel pump relay never de-energized).

ACTION: PCM turns on SERVICE VEHICLE SOON message on CCDIC panel. PCM monitors fuel pump feedback voltage for 4 seconds after ignition is turned on without the engine being cranked. The fuel pump relay will be energized 2 seconds and then de-energized.

If voltage on fuel pump feedback never drops below 7 volts during the first 4 seconds, Code EO19 will set indicating voltage on circuit No. 120 with fuel pump relay de-energized. The oil pressure switch must be disconnected.

NOTE: Test numbers refer to test numbers on diagnostic chart.

1) With key on, engine off, fuel pump should not be running and fuel pump feedback (PCM parameter ED10) should be zero volts. If ED10 shows voltage greater than 7 volts, circuit No. 120 must be repaired.
2) This diagnostic chart branch checks for shorted oil pressure switch contacts, powering fuel pump at all times. A shorted oil pressure switch will cause Code EO19 to set.

3) This checks for shorted fuel pump relay.
4) This checks for voltage on circuit No. 120 at PCM.
5) This checks for proper control of the fuel pump relay by the PCM.

Note On Intermittents – Probe fuel pump test point with a voltmeter to ground. Turn key on and observe voltmeter. Voltmeter should read battery voltage for 2 seconds and then drop to zero. If voltage reading stays at battery voltage for longer than 2 seconds, check sticking fuel pump relay contacts. Repeat test several times. Continue probing fuel pump test point to ground. Start engine and then turn it off. Voltage should drop immediately to zero. If not, check oil pressure switch contacts.

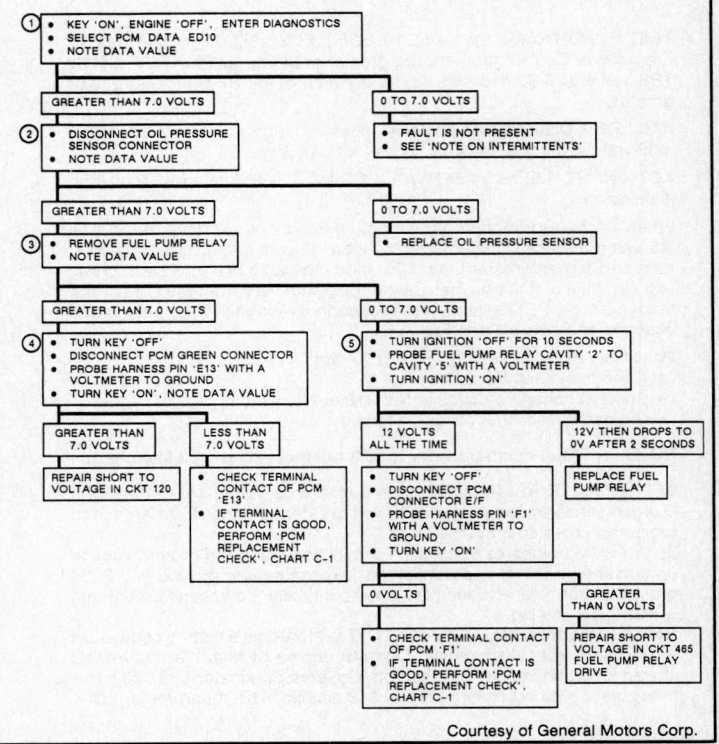

91A09350   91J07553

Courtesy of General Motors Corp.

1991 ENGINE PERFORMANCE
Self-Diagnostics – Eldorado & Seville PCM/BCM (Cont.)

GM
1-237

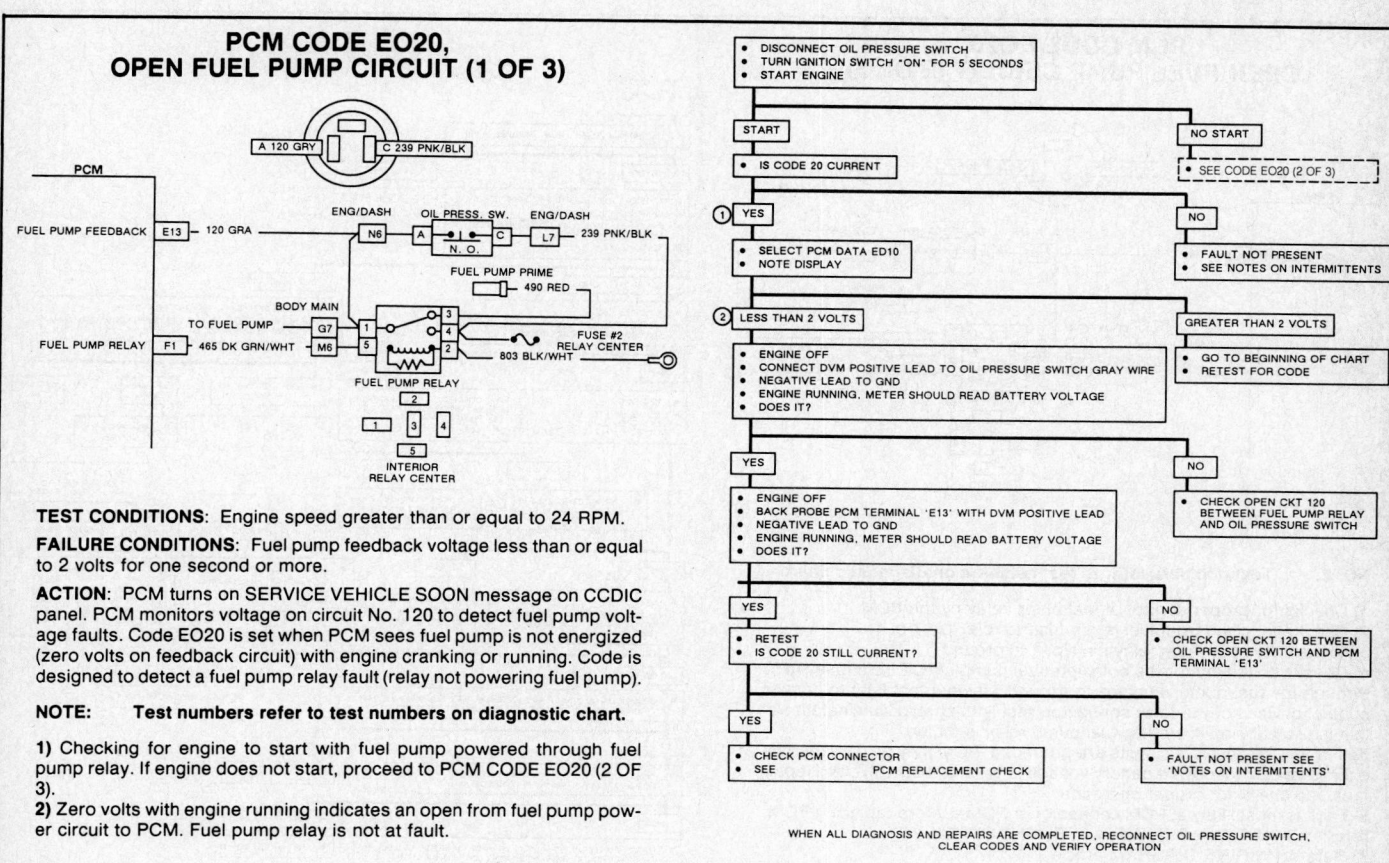

PCM CODE EO20, OPEN FUEL PUMP CIRCUIT (1 OF 3)

TEST CONDITIONS: Engine speed greater than or equal to 24 RPM.

FAILURE CONDITIONS: Fuel pump feedback voltage less than or equal to 2 volts for one second or more.

ACTION: PCM turns on SERVICE VEHICLE SOON message on CCDIC panel. PCM monitors voltage on circuit No. 120 to detect fuel pump voltage faults. Code EO20 is set when PCM sees fuel pump is not energized (zero volts on feedback circuit) with engine cranking or running. Code is designed to detect a fuel pump relay fault (relay not powering fuel pump).

NOTE: Test numbers refer to test numbers on diagnostic chart.

1) Checking for engine to start with fuel pump powered through fuel pump relay. If engine does not start, proceed to PCM CODE EO20 (2 OF 3).
2) Zero volts with engine running indicates an open from fuel pump power circuit to PCM. Fuel pump relay is not at fault.

WHEN ALL DIAGNOSIS AND REPAIRS ARE COMPLETED, RECONNECT OIL PRESSURE SWITCH, CLEAR CODES AND VERIFY OPERATION

91A09350   91B07554

Courtesy of General Motors Corp.

PCM CODE E020, OPEN FUEL PUMP CIRCUIT (2 OF 3)

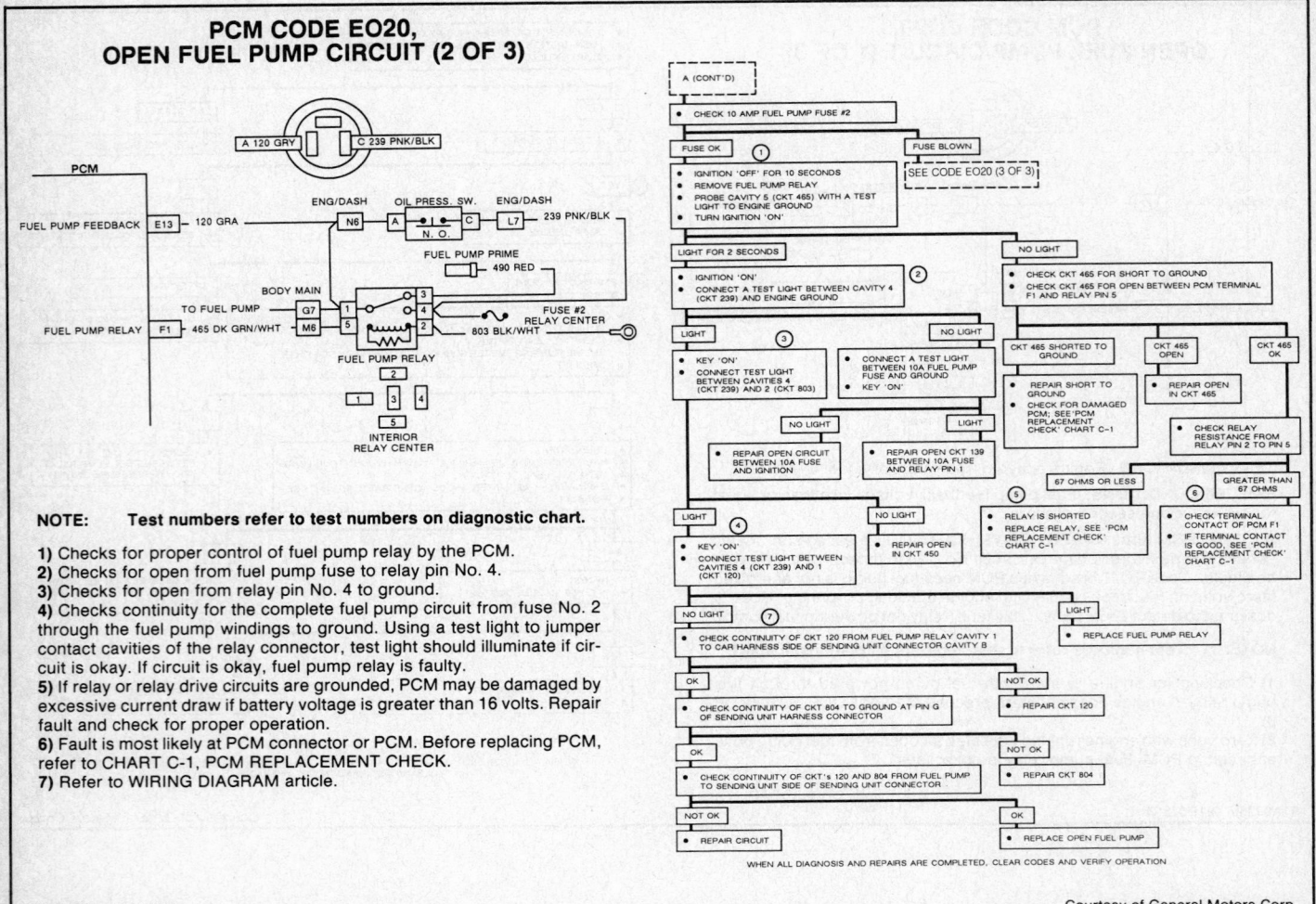

NOTE: Test numbers refer to test numbers on diagnostic chart.

1) Checks for proper control of fuel pump relay by the PCM.
2) Checks for open from fuel pump fuse to relay pin No. 4.
3) Checks for open from relay pin No. 4 to ground.
4) Checks continuity for the complete fuel pump circuit from fuse No. 2 through the fuel pump windings to ground. Using a test light to jumper contact cavities of the relay connector, test light should illuminate if circuit is okay. If circuit is okay, fuel pump relay is faulty.
5) If relay or relay drive circuits are grounded, PCM may be damaged by excessive current draw if battery voltage is greater than 16 volts. Repair fault and check for proper operation.
6) Fault is most likely at PCM connector or PCM. Before replacing PCM, refer to CHART C-1, PCM REPLACEMENT CHECK.
7) Refer to WIRING DIAGRAM article.

91A09350   91E07555

Courtesy of General Motors Corp.

1991 ENGINE PERFORMANCE
Self-Diagnostics – Eldorado & Seville PCM/BCM (Cont.)

GM
1-239

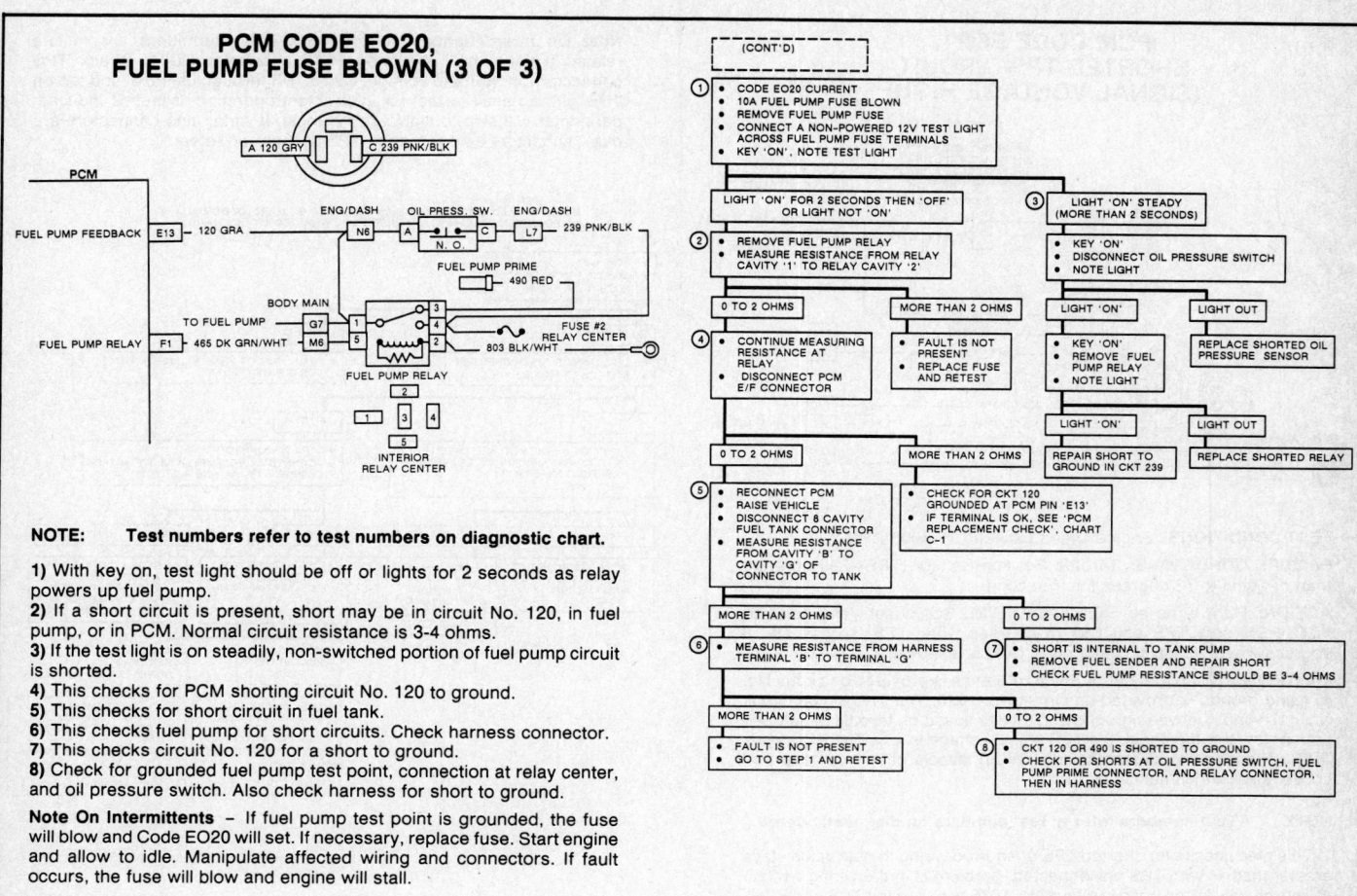

PCM CODE EO20, FUEL PUMP FUSE BLOWN (3 OF 3)

NOTE: Test numbers refer to test numbers on diagnostic chart.

1) With key on, test light should be off or lights for 2 seconds as relay powers up fuel pump.

2) If a short circuit is present, short may be in circuit No. 120, in fuel pump, or in PCM. Normal circuit resistance is 3-4 ohms.

3) If the test light is on steadily, non-switched portion of fuel pump circuit is shorted.

4) This checks for PCM shorting circuit No. 120 to ground.

5) This checks for short circuit in fuel tank.

6) This checks fuel pump for short circuits. Check harness connector.

7) This checks circuit No. 120 for a short to ground.

8) Check for grounded fuel pump test point, connection at relay center, and oil pressure switch. Also check harness for short to ground.

Note On Intermittents – If fuel pump test point is grounded, the fuse will blow and Code EO20 will set. If necessary, replace fuse. Start engine and allow to idle. Manipulate affected wiring and connectors. If fault occurs, the fuse will blow and engine will stall.

91A09350   91G07556

Courtesy of General Motors Corp.

GM
1-240

1991 ENGINE PERFORMANCE
Self-Diagnostics – Eldorado & Seville PCM/BCM (Cont.)

PCM CODE EO21, SHORTED TPS CIRCUIT (SIGNAL VOLTAGE HIGH)

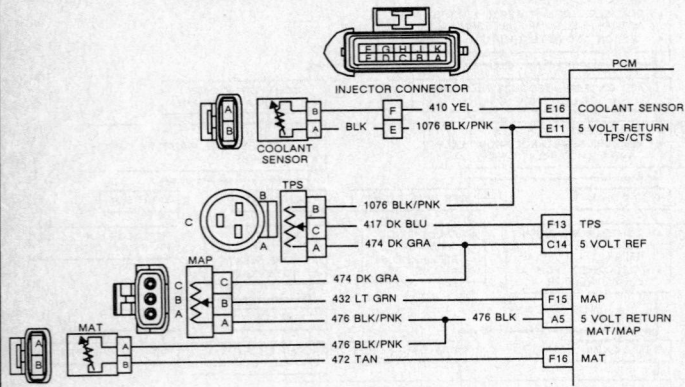

Note On Intermittents – If Code EO21 is intermittent, manipulate related wiring while observing PCM parameter ED01. Check TPS connector for shorts to voltage. Cycle TPS through its travel and tap on TPS with a pencil to test for intermittent operation. If fault is induced, parameter will skip to high throttle angle. If wiring and connectors are okay, substitute a known good TPS sensor and retest.

NOTE: IF HARD CODE EO21 IS ACCOMPANIED BY HARD CODE EO15 OR EO40: SEE DFI CHART A 'MULTIPLE PCM CODES STORES HARD'

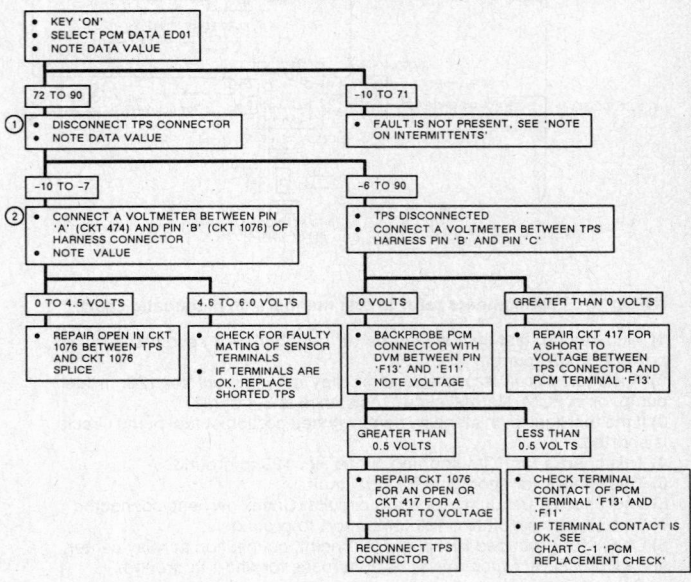

TEST CONDITIONS: Engine speed between 25-3000 RPM.

FAILURE CONDITIONS: Throttle Position Sensor (TPS) value greater than or equal to 72 degrees for .7 second.

ACTION: PCM turns on SERVICE ENGINE SOON light and disables VCC. PCM sets TPS equal to 13 degrees when TPS is open and 6 degrees when TPS is closed. Fourth gear is disabled.

The TPS is a potentiometer. A 5-volt reference is provided on circuit No. 474 and ground is provided on circuit No. 1076. The TPS signal circuit No. 417 varies between ground and 5 volts based on throttle plate position. At low throttle angle, the TPS signal voltage is low. The PCM uses TPS information to determine idle, WOT, deceleration leanness and acceleration enrichment.

NOTE: Test numbers refer to test numbers on diagnostic chart.

1) This step checks for shorted TPS or shorted wiring. If data value stays greater than -7 with TPS disconnected, problem is in the wiring circuit.
2) This checks for an open in circuit No. 1076 between the TPS and PCM. An open in circuit No. 1076 will result in high TPS values whenever the TPS is plugged in.

WHEN ALL DIAGNOSIS AND REPAIRS ARE COMPLETED, CLEAR CODES AND VERIFY OPERATION

91E07541 91A07558

Courtesy of General Motors Corp.

1991 ENGINE PERFORMANCE
Self-Diagnostics – Eldorado & Seville PCM/BCM (Cont.)

GM
1-241

PCM CODE EO22, OPEN TPS CIRCUIT (SIGNAL VOLTAGE LOW)

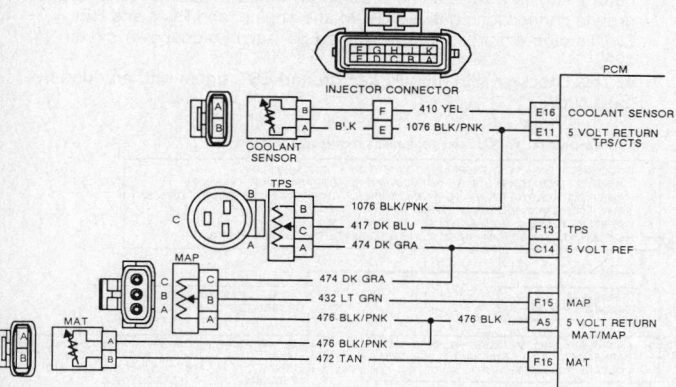

Note On Intermittents – If Code EO21 is intermittent, manipulate related wiring, while observing PCM parameter ED01. Check TPS connector for short to voltage. Cycle TPS through its travel and tap on TPS with a pencil to test for intermittent operation. If fault is induced, parameter will skip to high throttle angle. If wiring and connectors are okay, substitute a known good TPS sensor and retest.

NOTE: IF A HARD CODE E022 IS ACCOMPANIED BY HARD CODE E032; SEE PCM CHART A, 'MULIPLE PCM CODES STORED HARD', LOCATED EARLIER IN THIS SECTION.

TEST CONDITIONS: Engine speed is at least 600 RPM or greater.

FAILURE CONDITIONS: TPS value is less than 1.3 degrees for .7 second.

ACTION: PCM turns on SERVICE ENGINE SOON light and disables VCC. PCM uses 6 degrees for TPS value when ISC throttle switch closes. PCM sets TPS equal to 13 degrees when TPS is open and 6 degrees when TPS is closed. Fourth gear disabled.

The TPS is a potentiometer. A 5-volt reference is provided on circuit No. 474 and ground is provided on circuit No. 1076. The TPS signal circuit No. 417 varies between ground and 5 volts based on throttle plate position. At low throttle angle, TPS signal voltage is low. The PCM uses TPS information to determine idle, WOT, deceleration leanness and acceleration enrichment.

NOTE: Test numbers refer to test numbers on diagnostic chart.

1) Checks for shorted TPS or wiring. If data value stays greater than -7 with TPS disconnected, problem is in the wiring circuit.
2) Checks for an open in circuit No. 1076 between TPS and PCM. An open in circuit No. 1076 will cause TPS signal to be always high whenever the TPS is plugged in.

Diagnostic Flow Chart

- KEY 'ON', ENTER DIAGNOSTICS
- SELECT PCM DATA ED01
- NOTE DATA VALUE

-10 TO -6 AT PART THROTTLE → (1)
- DISCONNECT TPS, JUMPER HARNESS TERMINAL 'A' TO TERMINAL 'C'

-5 TO 90 AT PART THROTTLE (WITH THROTTLE SWITCH OPEN)
- FAULT IS NOT PRESENT
- SEE 'NOTE ON INTERMITTENTS'

-10 TO 86 → (2)
- REMOVE JUMPER
- CONNECT A VOLTMETER BETWEEN CKT 474 PIN 'A' AT THE TPS CONNECTOR AND GROUND

80 TO 90
- RECONNECT TPS
- NOTE PARAMETER VALUE

-10 TO -6 WITH THROTTLE SWITCH OPEN
- CHECK FOR PROPER MATING OF TPS CONNECTOR TERMINALS TO TPS
- IF CONNECTOR IS OK. REPLACE TPS

-5 TO 90 WITH THROTTLE SWITCH OPEN
- CHECK FOR CAUSE OF INTERMITTENT TPS CONNECTIONS

4.6 TO 6.0 VOLTS
- CONNECT A VOLTMETER BETWEEN CONNECTOR PIN 'C' (CKT 474) AND CONNECTOR PIN 'A' (CKT 417)

0 TO 4.5 VOLTS
- REPAIR OPEN OR SHORT IN CKT 474 FROM PCM TERMINAL 'C14' TO TPS

0 VOLTS
- JUMPER PCM TERMINAL 'C14' (CKT 474) TO PCM TERMINAL 'F13' (CKT 417)
- NOTE PARAMETER VALUE

GREATER THAN 0 VOLTS
- DISCONNECT PCM 3E/F CONNECTOR
- CHECK CKT 417 FOR A SHORT TO GROUND BETWEEN PCM PIN 'F13' AND TPS OR TPS TEST POINT

-10 TO 86
- CHECK CONTACT OF PCM TERMINAL 'F13'
- IF TERMINAL CONTACT IS GOOD, SEE CHART C-1 'PCM REPLACEMENT CHECK'

87 TO 90
- REPAIR OPEN IN CKT 417 BETWEEN TPS PIN 'A' AND PCM TERMINAL 'F13'

SHORTED
- REPAIR CKT 417 SHORTED TO GROUND

CKT 417 OK
- CHECK CONTACT OF PCM TERMINAL 'F13'
- IF TERMINAL CONTACT IS GOOD, SEE CHART C-1 'PCM REPLACEMENT CHECK'

WHEN ALL DIAGNOSIS AND REPAIRS ARE COMPLETED, CLEAR CODES AND VERIFY OPERATION

91E07541   91C07559

Courtesy of General Motors Corp.

GM
1-242

1991 ENGINE PERFORMANCE
Self-Diagnostics – Eldorado & Seville PCM/BCM (Cont.)

PCM CODE EO23, EST CIRCUIT PROBLEM (1 OF 2)

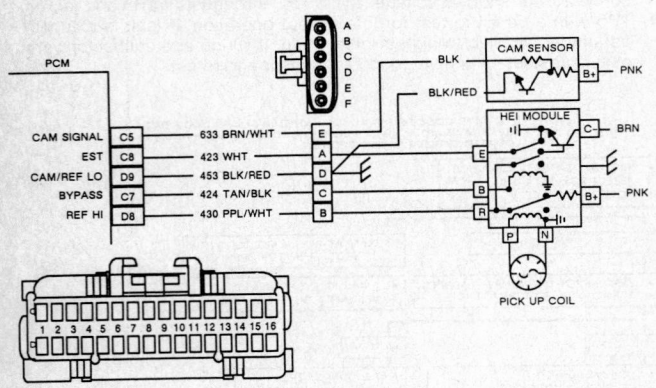

TEST CONDITIONS (CRANK): By-pass line low (zero volts) and reference pulses are sent to PCM from HEI module.

FAILURE CONDITIONS (CRANK): EST pulses are detected in circuit No. 423 in by-pass.

TEST CONDITIONS (RUN): By-pass line high (5 volts) and reference pulses being sent to PCM from HEI module.

FAILURE CONDITIONS (RUN): No EST pulses being detected on circuit No. 423.

ACTION: PCM turns on SERVICE ENGINE SOON light and will not enable spark timing control. The engine will start and run on base timing.

NOTE: Test numbers refer to test numbers on diagnostic chart.

90H21722   91G07561

1) When circuit No. 423 is shorted to ground, engine will have a long crank and hard start. When PCM detects grounded circuit, by-pass line will be shifted low.

2) With only distributor reference (distributor reference ground jumpered), engine will run on back-up spark control. This checks for proper ground connections between PCM and engine, and PCM and HEI.

3) This step ensures PCM provides EST output signal over circuit No. 423.

4) This checks if HEI module can ground EST signal with an open by-pass circuit.

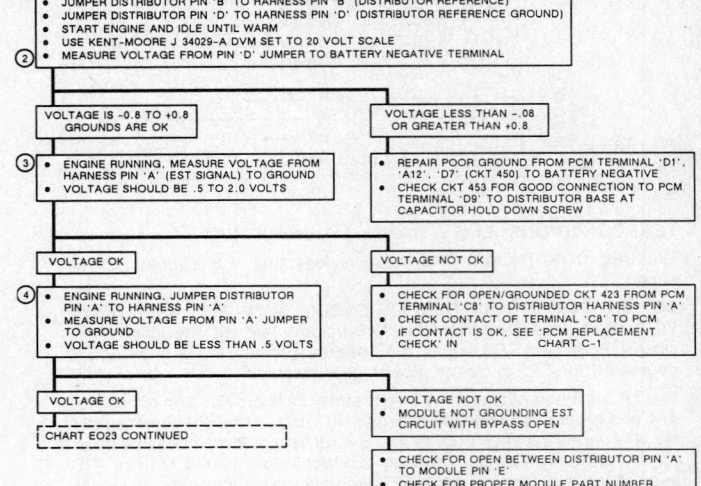

NOTE: USE ESSENTIAL TOOL J 35616 TO JUMPER HARNESS CONNECTORS

Courtesy of General Motors Corp.

PCM CODE EO23, EST CIRCUIT PROBLEM (2 OF 2)

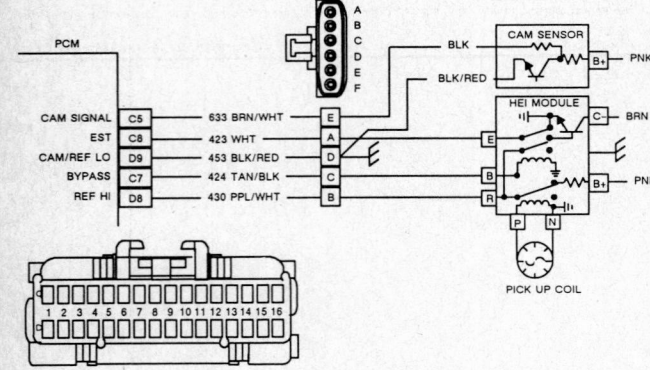

NOTE: USE ESSENTIAL TOOL J 35616 TO JUMPER HARNESS CONNECTORS

5) This checks if HEI module can recognize a voltage on by-pass circuit and stop grounding EST (PCM-controlled timing).

6) This checks for by-pass signal to module. If by-pass signal is being sent by PCM to HEI, and if module is interpreting by-pass voltage correctly, then module will switch off ground to EST.

7) If chart leads to EST CIRCUIT is okay, then a fault may exist in the 6-way connector. Check connector and terminals for damage. If connector is okay, plug in connector and retest for Code EO23.

90H21722   91I07562

WHEN ALL DIAGNOSIS AND REPAIRS ARE COMPLETED, CLEAR CODES AND VERIFY OPERATION

Courtesy of General Motors Corp.

1991 ENGINE PERFORMANCE
Self-Diagnostics – Eldorado & Seville PCM/BCM (Cont.)

GM
1-243

PCM CODE EO24, SPEED SENSOR CIRCUIT PROBLEM

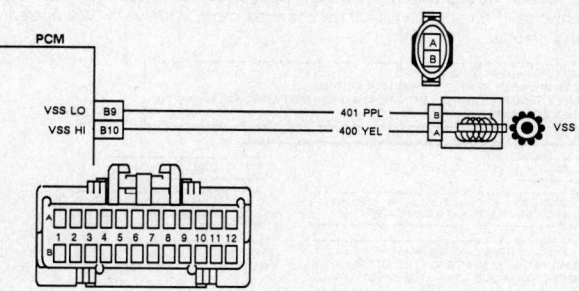

TEST CONDITIONS: Codes EO21, EO22, EO26 and EO27 not set. Transmission in Reverse or Drive and brake switch off. Throttle switch open. Throttle angle greater than 17 degrees. Engine speed greater or at least 1400 RPM.

FAILURE CONDITIONS: Vehicle speed equals zero MPH for 3 seconds.

ACTION: PCM turns on SERVICE ENGINE SOON light and disables Viscous Converter Clutch (VCC) and cruise control. Third and fourth gears disabled. The Vehicle Speed Sensor (VSS) is a permanent magnet pulse generator mounted in transaxle. The PCM uses VSS input for VCC apply-and-release determinations, to select between RPM and throttle angle control of ISC, and as a test condition for many codes.

NOTE: Test numbers refer to test numbers on diagnostic chart.

1) Vehicle speed sensor provides 0-36 volts AC signal to the PCM, depending upon vehicle speed. With tires moving, signal to PCM should be at least .5 volt AC.

Note On Intermittents – If Code EO24 is stored as a history code, select parameter ED12. Lift drive wheels, place transmission in Drive and allow wheels to turn. Manipulate affected wiring while observing parameter ED12. If fault is induced, parameter ED12 will momentarily drop to zero MPH. Check for intermittent opens or shorts to ground on circuits No. 400 and No. 401. Check terminal contact at VSS and at PCM connector.

NOTE: DO NOT USE THIS TROUBLE TREE WHILE VEHICLE IS CONNECTED TO A BATTERY CHARGER.

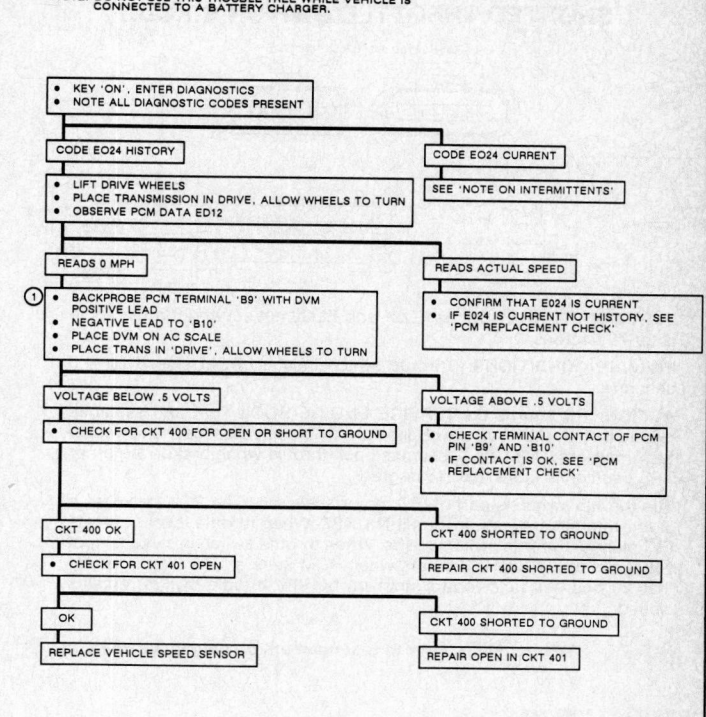

WHEN ALL DIAGNOSIS AND REPAIRS ARE COMPLETED. CLEAR CODES AND VERIFY OPERATION

91A07563   91C07564

Courtesy of General Motors Corp.

PCM CODE EO26, SHORTED THROTTLE SWITCH CIRCUIT

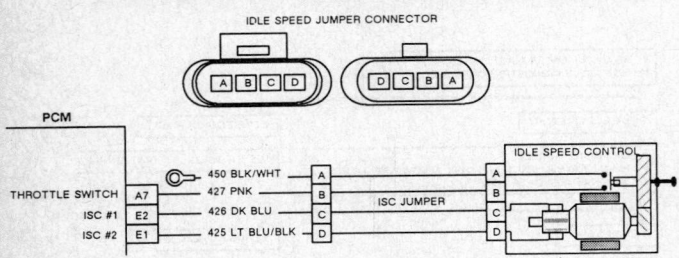

TEST CONDITIONS: Codes EO21 and EO22 not set and throttle angle is 20-75 degrees.

FAILURE CONDITIONS: Throttle switch input to PCM closed for 1.8 seconds.

ACTION: PCM turns on SERVICE ENGINE SOON light and assumes closed throttle if brakes are applied or TPS position is less than or equal to 18 degrees. PCM also assumes open throttle when brakes are off or TPS position is more than 18 degrees.

The throttle switch is part of ISC motor assembly. The PCM provides a 5-volt reference signal on circuit No. 427. When throttle lever contacts ISC plunger, throttle switch closes. When throttle switch is closed, input voltage is low. Code EO26 sets when PCM sees a TPS signal greater that 20 degrees (accelerator applied) but the throttle switch remains closed.

NOTE: Test numbers refer to test numbers on diagnostic chart.

91G09348 91H07566

1) Code EO26 can be caused by a sticking or binding TPS.

Note On Intermittents – Select PCM input switch test. Manipulate affected wiring and connectors and look for throttle switch status change. If throttle switch state changes momentarily, "X" will appear on the display.

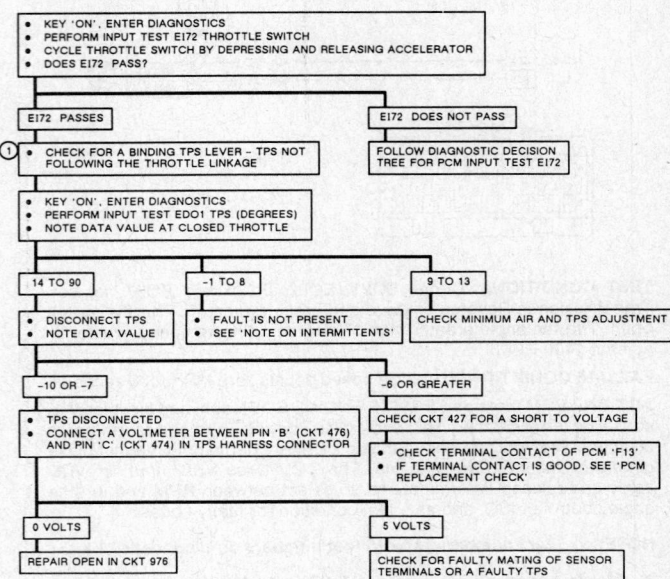

WHEN ALL DIAGNOSIS AND REPAIRS ARE COMPLETED, CLEAR CODES AND VERIFY OPERATION

Courtesy of General Motors Corp.

PCM CODE EO27, OPEN THROTTLE SWITCH CIRCUIT

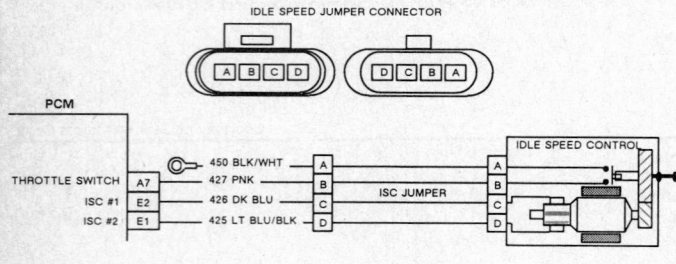

TEST CONDITIONS: Codes EO21, EO22 and EO24 are not set. Vehicle in coast down condition. Throttle switch open, brakes applied, throttle angle is 16.5 degrees or less and RPM is greater than desired.

Under these conditions, the PCM commands the ISC to retract and extend and monitors the TPS for a corresponding decrease and increase in throttle position.

If PCM detects a decrease and increase in throttle position twice in succession, then the code will set and SERVICE ENGINE SOON light will turn on.

FAILURE CONDITIONS: Test has failed twice since the last time throttle switch was closed.

ACTION: PCM turns on SERVICE ENGINE SOON light. EGR is disabled. PCM substitutes a throttle switch value when TPS is 18 degrees or less and brake pedal is applied. When TPS value is greater than 18 degrees or if brake is not applied, PCM substitutes a throttle switch open value.

NOTE: Test number refers to test number on diagnostic chart.

91G09348 91J07567

1) ISC 4-way connector is located at a jumper connector near the alternator and cruise control servo.

2) The ISC jumper is a separate harness that connects the ISC to the PCM harness.

Note On Intermittents – Check that ISC plunger is depressed when throttle linkage is in contact with the stop screw. Check ISC jumper connectors and PCM connector for terminals that are loose or not properly crimped.

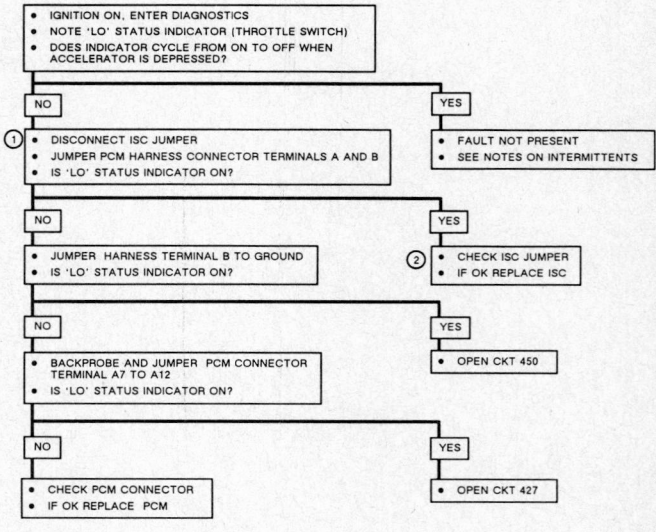

Courtesy of General Motors Corp.

1991 ENGINE PERFORMANCE
Self-Diagnostics – Eldorado & Seville PCM/BCM (Cont.)

GM
1-245

PCM CODE E030, ISC RPM OUT OF RANGE

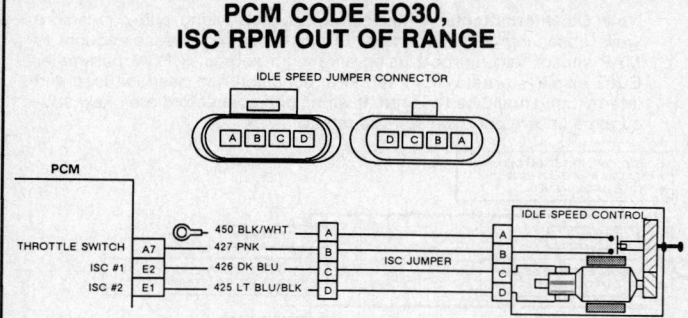

IDLE SPEED JUMPER CONNECTOR

TEST CONDITIONS: Codes E021, E022, E024, E026 and E027 not set, vehicle speed equals zero with throttle switch closed, battery voltage greater than or equal to 11 volts, desired RPM is 152 RPM greater than actual RPM, engine has been running for more than 7 seconds, no power steering load and PCM not commanding and idle speed anticipate.

FAILURE CONDITIONS: TPS is 14 degrees or greater and ISC is retracting for 15 seconds. TPS position less than or equal to 2 degrees and ISC extending for 15 seconds.

ACTION: PCM turns on SERVICE ENGINE SOON light and keeps it on for the entire ignition cycle.

PCM controls engine idle by increasing or decreasing throttle opening with Idle Speed Control (ISC) motor. The ISC controls idle speed any time throttle switch is closed. Code E030 detects engine RPM out of limits.

NOTE: Test numbers refer to test numbers on diagnostic chart.

1) This checks for proper throttle switch, power steering switch and P/N switch operation. The PCM must receive accurate switch status information to control idle.

2) This checks for proper ISC motor operation.

3) Many engine fuel and emissions system faults may cause unstable idle. If base engine idle is not steady, ISC may not be able to control idle to within 152 RPM of desired idle.

Note On Intermittents – Display PCM parameter ED01, manipulate TPS wiring and connectors, and see if TPS jumps or skips. Enter PCM

input E172, observe throttle switch status light and check for binding throttle linkage or weak throttle return spring. Verify minimum air rate RPM, ISC and TPS are set to specifications.

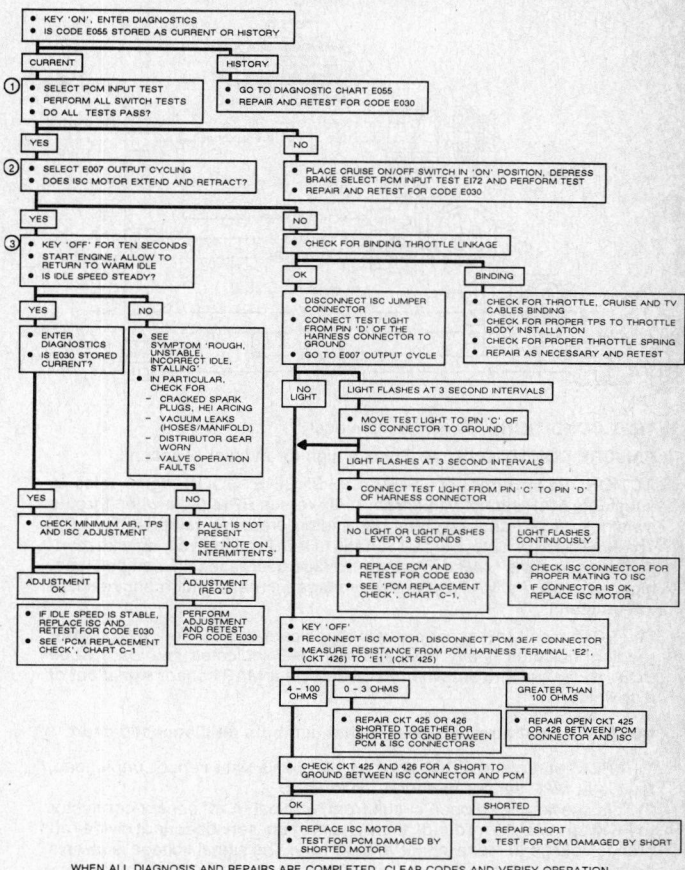

WHEN ALL DIAGNOSIS AND REPAIRS ARE COMPLETED, CLEAR CODES AND VERIFY OPERATION

Courtesy of General Motors Corp.

91G09348   91B07568

GM
1-246

1991 ENGINE PERFORMANCE
Self-Diagnostics – Eldorado & Seville PCM/BCM (Cont.)

PCM CODE EO31, SHORTED MAP SENSOR CIRCUIT

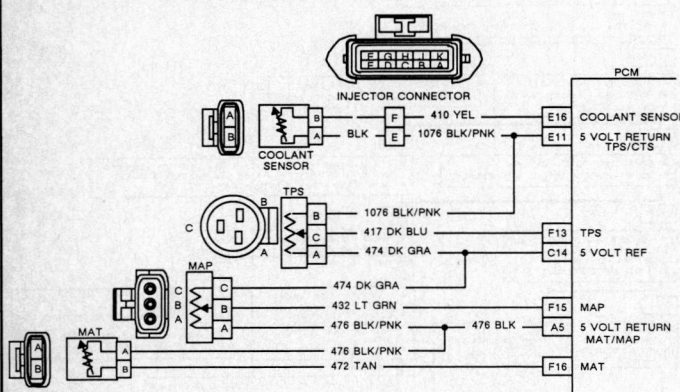

Note On Intermittents – Manipulate affected wiring and connectors while observing PCM parameter ED02. Apply and release vacuum to MAP sensor vacuum port using a vacuum source. If PCM parameter ED02 displays greater than 108 kPa, condition has been induced and intermittent should be repaired. If wiring and connectors are okay, substitute a known good sensor and retest.

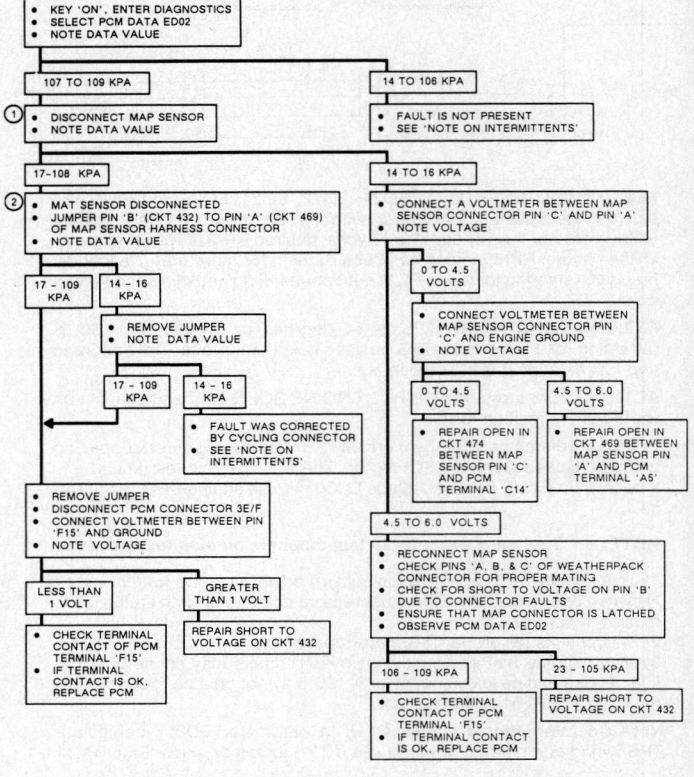

TEST CONDITIONS: Tested continuously.

FAILURE CONDITIONS: MAP value high for at least .2 second.

ACTION: PCM turns on SERVICE ENGINE SOON light, uses a substitute MAP sensor value from MAP versus RPM table when throttle switch is closed and assumes barometric pressure value is 92.2 kPa. The MAP sensor output signal voltage is a DC voltage varying with manifold pressure. As MAP decreases, voltage decreases (low engine load, high vacuum). As MAP increases, voltage increases (high engine load, low vacuum).

The PCM uses MAP sensor values to indicate engine load. A high MAP reading indicates heavy load and low MAP indicates low load. Code EO31 is designed to set when PCM detects a MAP sensor signal out of high limits.

NOTE: Test numbers refer to test numbers on diagnostic chart.

1) If PCM parameter ED02 goes to 14-16 kPa with sensor unplugged, fault is at MAP sensor or sensor connector.
2) This checks for an open circuit from terminal "A" of sensor connector to PCM terminal A5 (ground). If ground is open, sensor cannot divide reference voltage to make signal voltage vary. The signal voltage is always high.

91E07541   91F07570

WHEN ALL DIAGNOSIS AND REPAIRS ARE COMPLETED, CLEAR CODES AND VERIFY OPERATION

1991 ENGINE PERFORMANCE
Self-Diagnostics – Eldorado & Seville PCM/BCM (Cont.)

GM 1-247

PCM CODE EO32, OPEN MAP SENSOR CIRCUIT

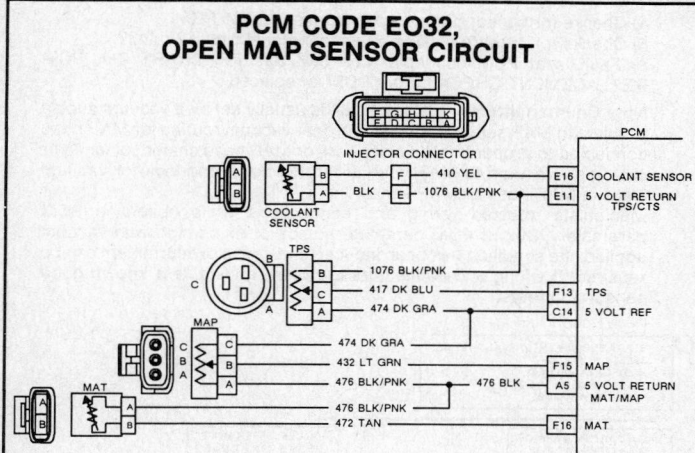

Note On Intermittents – Code EO32 can be set by an open 5-volt reference signal between PCM and sensor, an open MAP signal between sensor and PCM or a defective MAP sensor. Manipulate affected wiring and connectors while observing PCM parameter ED02. Apply and release vacuum to MAP sensor vacuum port using a vacuum source. If PCM parameter ED02 displays less than 15 kPa, condition has been induced and cause of intermittent can be repaired. If wiring and connectors are okay, substitute a known good sensor and retest.

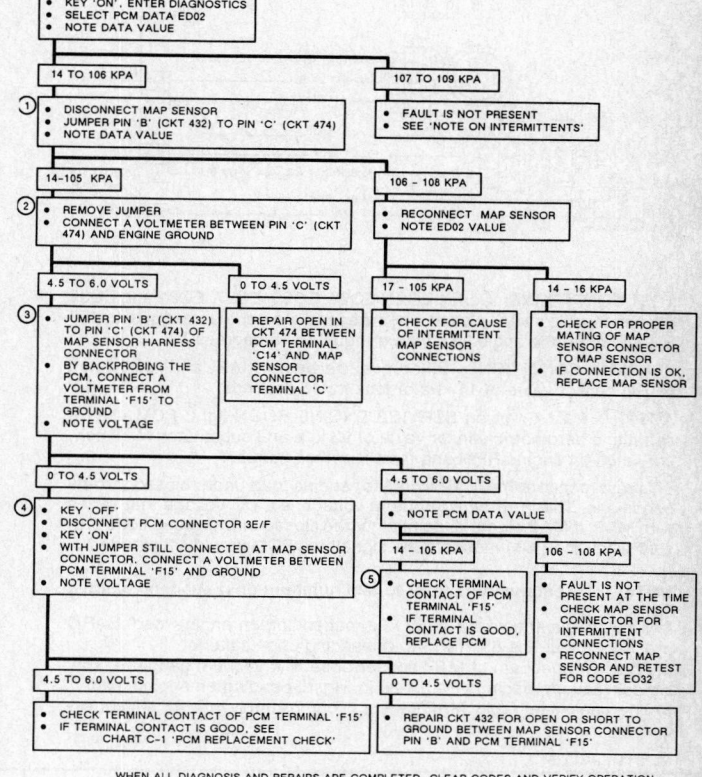

TEST CONDITIONS (1): Engine speed at less than or equal to 700 RPM, throttle angle less than or equal to 18 degrees and TPS closed.

TEST CONDITIONS (2): Engine speed at less than or equal to 1800 RPM, throttle angle less than or equal to 18 degrees, TPS open and transmission not in Park or Neutral.

FAILURE CONDITIONS: MAP value less than 16 kPa for .2 second.

ACTION: PCM turns on SERVICE ENGINE SOON light. PCM uses a substitute MAP value from a MAP versus RPM table when throttle switch is closed. PCM uses a substitute barometric pressure value of 92 kPa.

MAP sensor changes resistance based upon manifold vacuum. PCM provides a 5-volt reference and ground. MAP signal varies between ground and 5 volts as manifold vacuum varies. Code EO32 sets when PCM detects that MAP sensor signal is too low.

NOTE: Test numbers refer to test numbers on diagnostic chart.

1) This checks PCM's ability to respond to a 5-volt signal on MAP input. A reading of 106-109 kPa means wiring and PCM are okay.
2) This checks for 5-volt reference signal present at sensor connector.
3) This checks circuit No. 432 for short to ground.
4) This checks PCM's ability to respond to a 5-volt signal voltage on MAP input.
5) Fault is most likely at PCM connector or PCM. See CHART C-1, PCM REPLACEMENT CHECK, before PCM is replaced.

WHEN ALL DIAGNOSIS AND REPAIRS ARE COMPLETED, CLEAR CODES AND VERIFY OPERATION

91E07541   91H07571

GM
1-248

1991 ENGINE PERFORMANCE
Self-Diagnostics – Eldorado & Seville PCM/BCM (Cont.)

PCM CODE EO34, MAP SIGNAL TOO HIGH

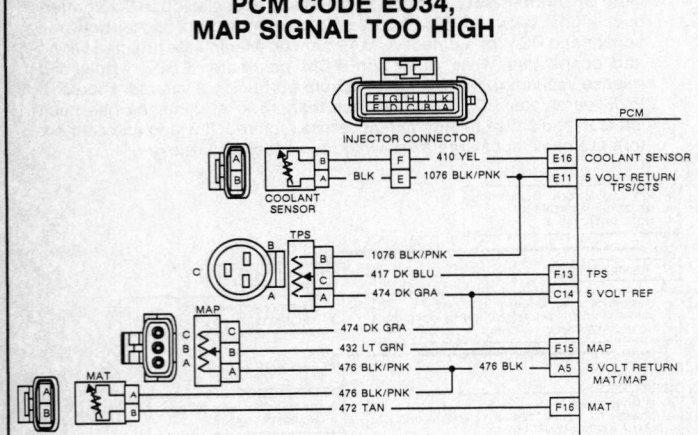

TEST CONDITIONS: Codes EO21, EO22, EO26, EO27, EO31 and EO32 not set, throttle switch closed, engine speed greater than or equal to 400 RPM and throttle angle less than or equal to 18 degrees.

FAILURE CONDITIONS: Difference between MAP and calculated BARO sensor value of 11 kPa or less for 15 seconds.

ACTION: PCM turns on SERVICE ENGINE SOON light. PCM uses a substitute barometric sensor value of 92 kPa and substitutes MAP sensor value on engine RPM and throttle switch status.

This test monitors the MAP signal for engine load under closed throttle conditions. The MAP sensor output voltage is a DC voltage that varies with MAP. If MAP signal is too high for the closed throttle conditions present when the PCM monitors the signal, the PCM would set a code.

NOTE: Test numbers refer to test numbers on diagnostic chart.

1) MAP at idle should be 30-50 kPa, depending on engine load. BARO pressure should be 85-105 kPa, depending upon altitude.
2) Check for vacuum at MAP sensor hose with vacuum gauge. At idle, typical vacuum readings are 14-20 in. Hg, depending on engine load.
3) This checks for faulty MAP sensor vacuum supply or MAP sensor circuitry.

4) Checks for sensor ground open from sensor to PCM.
5) Checks for short to voltage on sensor signal circuit No. 432.
6) Fault is at PCM connector or PCM. See PFI CHART C-1, PCM REPLACEMENT CHECK before PCM is replaced.

Note On Intermittents – Code EO34 is usually set by a vacuum supply problem to MAP sensor. Check for proper vacuum routing for MAP hose connected to proper throttle body port, or MAP hose chafed, pinched or cut. Apply vacuum to MAP hose at throttle body, and look for vacuum leaks in MAP hose or MAP sensor.
Manipulate affected wiring and connections while observing PCM parameter ED02. If PCM parameter jumps or skips high with vacuum applied, the condition has been induced and cause of intermittent can be repaired. If wiring and connectors are okay, substitute a known good sensor and retest.

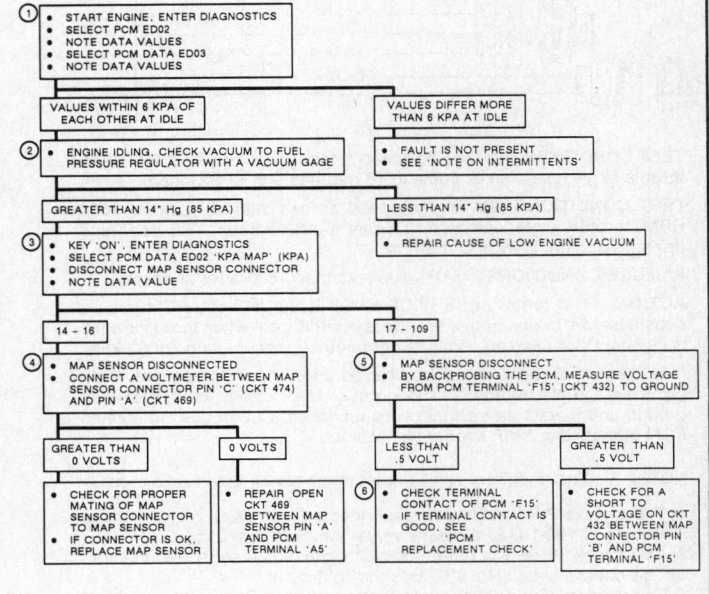

WHEN ALL DIAGNOSIS AND REPAIRS ARE COMPLETED, CLEAR CODES AND VERIFY OPERATION

1991 ENGINE PERFORMANCE
Self-Diagnostics – Eldorado & Seville PCM/BCM (Cont.)

GM
1-249

PCM CODE E037, SHORTED MAT SENSOR CIRCUIT

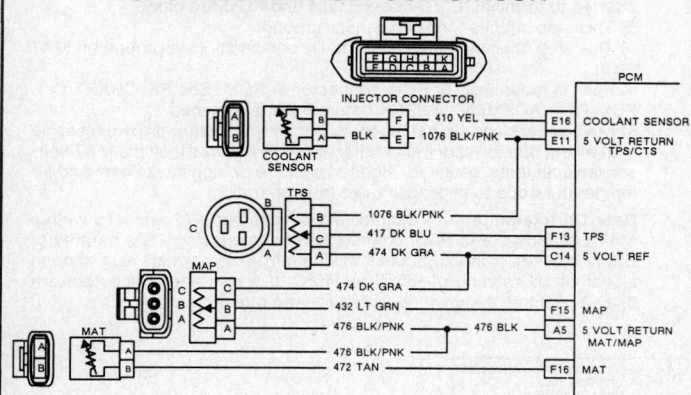

NOTE: Test numbers refer to test numbers on diagnostic chart.

1) With a shorted MAT sensor, PCM parameter ED05 should read 148°C or greater. If not, sensor is not shorted. See NOTE ON INTERMITTENTS.

2) Check for sensor short or circuit No. 472 shorted. If PCM parameter ED05 stays at 142-151°C with sensor unplugged, then circuit No. 472 is shorted to ground.

3) MAT sensors can be damaged by a backfire in the intake. If vehicle has had more than one MAT sensor replaced, check for signs of backfire or high intake manifold temperatures due to improper valve train operation.

4) Fault is most likely at PCM connector or PCM. See PFI CHART C-1, PCM REPLACEMENT CHECK before PCM is replaced.

Note On Intermittents – Manipulate circuit No. 472 wiring, MAT sensor and PCM connector while observing PCM parameter ED05. If failure is induced, manifold air temperature will jump from its normal value to shorted reading of 142-151°C. If wiring and connectors are okay, substitute a known good sensor and retest.

TEST CONDITIONS: Codes E014 and E015 not set. Coolant sensor temperature less than or equal to 212°F (100°C).

FAILURE CONDITIONS: MAT sensor value greater than or equal to 298°F (148°C).

ACTION: PCM turns on SERVICE ENGINE SOON light. PCM substitutes 104°F (40°C) for MAT when coolant temperature is greater than or equal to 104°F (40°C). PCM substitutes coolant temperature for MAT when coolant temperature is less than or equal to 104°F (40°C).

The MAT sensor is a thermistor that varies its resistance with temperature. The MAP sensor is a 2-wire sensor with a 5-volt reference voltage coming from the PCM to sensor terminal "B" over circuit No. 472, and a sensor reference ground on terminal "A" over circuit No. 469.

As temperature of sensor increases, sensor resistance is lower. The monitored signal voltage from PCM to terminal "B" decreases as sensor temperature increases, current flows from terminal "B" through sensor element to terminal "A", sensor ground.

High temperature means low signal voltage on circuit No. 472. Low temperature means high signal voltage on circuit No. 472. Code E037, shorted MAT sensor, sets because PCM assumes that MAT cannot be 288°F (142°C) or greater with a coolant temperature of less than 221°F (105°C).

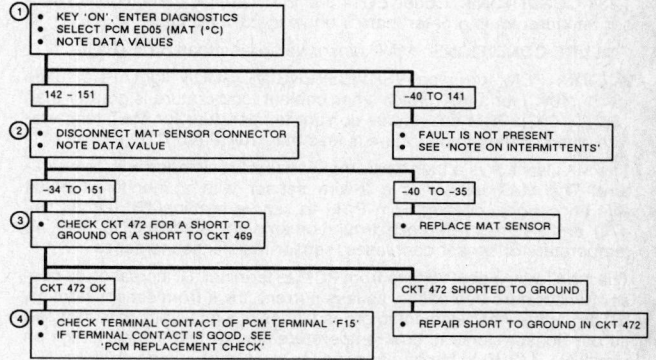

91E07541   91B07573

GM
1-250

1991 ENGINE PERFORMANCE
Self-Diagnostics – Eldorado & Seville PCM/BCM (Cont.)

PCM CODE EO38, OPEN MAT SENSOR CIRCUIT

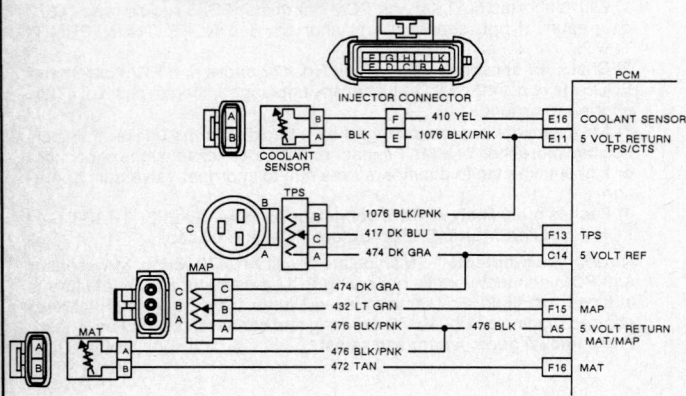

TEST CONDITIONS: Codes EO14 and EO15 are clear and coolant sensor temperature is greater than or equal to 23°F (-5°C).

FAILURE CONDITIONS: MAT sensor value less than 35°F (2°C).

ACTION: PCM turns on SERVICE ENGINE SOON light. PCM uses 104°F (40°C) for a MAT value when coolant temperature is greater than 104°F (40°C). PCM substitutes coolant temperature for MAT temperature when coolant temperature is less than 104°F (40°C).

The MAT sensor is a thermistor that varies its resistance with temperature. The MAT sensor is a 2-wire sensor with a monitored 5-volt reference signal coming from PCM to sensor terminal "B" (circuit No. 472), and a sensor reference ground on terminal "A" (circuit No. 469). As temperature of sensor decreases, sensor resistance increases.

The monitored signal voltage from PCM to terminal "B" increases as sensor temperature decreases, as less current flows from sensor terminal "B" through sensor element to ground. Less of signal voltage is dropped across sensor element. Low temperature means high signal voltage on circuit No. 472. High temperature means low voltage on circuit No. 472.

Code EO38, open MAT sensor, sets because PCM assumes that MAT cannot be -31°F to -40°F (-35°C to -40°C) with a coolant temperature of 23°F (-5°C) or greater.

NOTE: Test numbers refer to test numbers on diagnostic chart.

1) If sensor is open, PCM parameter ED05 should read -35°C or less. If not, sensor signal is not open at this time. See NOTE ON INTERMITTENTS.

91E07541   91D07574

2) Check PCM and sensor circuitry from PCM to sensor connector. If PCM parameter ED05 reads 148-151°C with connector terminal "A" shorted to terminal "B", sensor circuits and PCM are okay.

3) This step checks for open sensor ground.

4) This step checks PCM's ability to recognize short to ground on MAT input.

5) Fault is most likely at PCM connector or PCM. See PFI CHART C-1, PCM REPLACEMENT CHECK before PCM is replaced.

6) MAT sensor can be damaged by backfire in intake, or by excessive intake heat due to valve train faults. If vehicle has had multiple MAT sensor replacements, check for signs of backfire or high intake manifold air temperature due to improper valve train operation.

Note On Intermittents – Manipulate circuits No. 472 and 476 wiring, MAT connector, and PCM connector while observing PCM parameter ED05. If failure is induced, MAT will jump from its normal value to open signal circuit reading of -35°C to -40°C. If wiring and connectors are okay, substitute a known good sensor and retest.

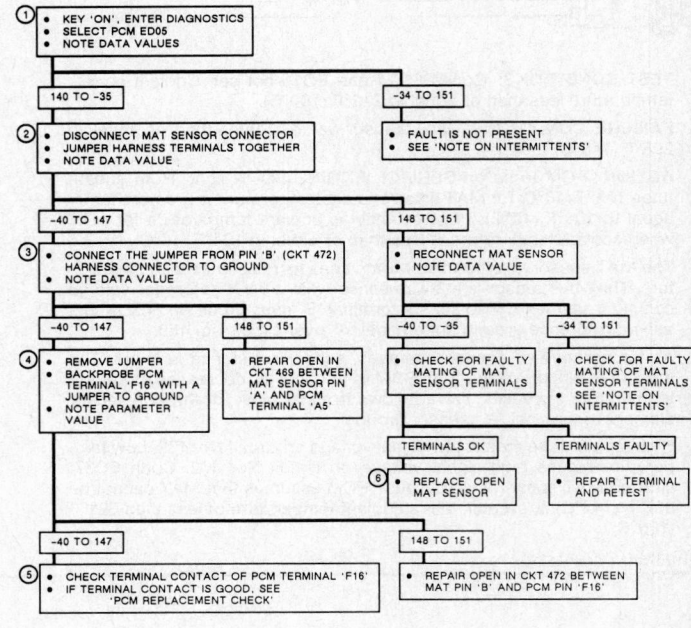

WHEN ALL DIAGNOSIS AND REPAIRS ARE COMPLETED, CLEAR CODES AND VERIFY OPERATION

Courtesy of General Motors Corp.

1991 ENGINE PERFORMANCE
Self-Diagnostics – Eldorado & Seville PCM/BCM (Cont.)

GM
1-251

PCM CODE EO39, VCC ENGAGEMENT PROBLEM (1 OF 2)

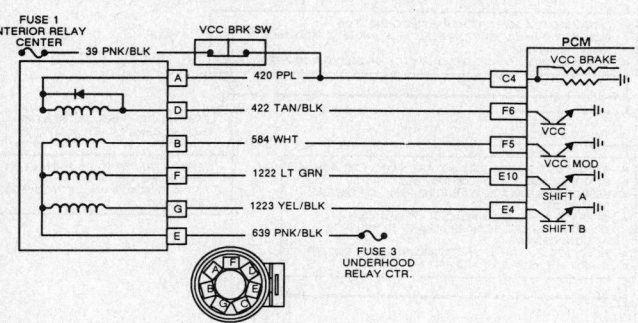

TEST CONDITIONS: Codes EO26, EO27, EO31, EO32 and EO34 not set, transmission in 4th gear and brake off. Engine speed at 3100 RPM or less, system in closed loop, MAP between 29-80 kPa. VCC commanded on and VCC module solenoid at 100 percent duty cycle.

FAILURE CONDITIONS: If engine RPM exceeds RPM for speed listed in table for 5 seconds, Code EO39 will set.

ACTION: PCM turns on SERVICE ENGINE SOON light and remains on for the ignition cycle. The VCC is disabled for the ignition cycle.

This test monitors VCC engagement for a problem by comparing the engine speed to a speed which should not be possible to achieve unless the viscous clutch is slipping excessively.

If a VCC failure has occurred, the failure is more likely to be observed under high road load (high MAP) conditions.

NOTE: Test numbers refer to test numbers on diagnostic chart.

1) The test chart will test resistance of the VCC solenoid and wiring inside the transmission. The road test checks for proper transmission operation.

Diagnostic flow chart (right side):

- DISCONNECT TRANS 7 WAY CONNECTOR
- INSTALL TRANS TEST BOX J 38791
- IGNITION ON, NOTE IGNITION FEED INDICATOR

LIGHT ON → NOTE VCC BRAKE SWITCH INDICATOR

LIGHT OFF → CHECK FUSE 1 FUSE BLOCK → BLOWN → CHECK SHORT TO GROUND CKT 39 ; OK → CHECK OPEN CKT 39

LIGHT ON → ENTER DIAGNOSTICS, SELECT OUTPUT CYCLING E.O.0.2 VCC SOLENOIDS, NOTE VCC INDICATOR

LIGHT OFF → CHART E.1.7.1 (VCC BRK SW)

LIGHT CYCLES → NOTE VCC MOD INDICATOR

LIGHT OFF → DISCONNECT J38791 AT TRANSMISSION ONLY, NOTE VCC APPLY INDICATOR
- LIGHT OFF → JUMPER HARNESS TERMINAL F6 TO GND → LIGHT ON → SEE PCM REPLACEMENT CHECK ; LIGHT OFF → OPEN CKT 422
- LIGHT CYCLES → REPLACE VCC SOL.

LIGHT ON → DISCONNECT PCM E/F GREEN CONNECTOR, NOTE VCC INDICATOR
- LIGHT OFF → SEE PCM REPLACEMENT CHECK
- LIGHT ON → CHECK SHORT TO GROUND CKT422

LIGHT CYCLES → CONTINUED ①

LIGHT OFF → DISCONNECT J 38791 AT TRANSMISSION ONLY, NOTE VCC MOD INDICATOR
- LIGHT OFF → JUMPER HARNESS TERMINAL F5 TO GND → LIGHT ON → SEE PCM REPLACEMENT CHECK ; LIGHT OFF → OPEN CKT 584
- LIGHT CYCLES → REPLACE VCC MOD SOL

LIGHT ON → DISCONNECT PCM E/F GREEN CONNECTOR, NOTE VCC MOD INDICATOR
- LIGHT OFF → SEE PCM REPLACEMENT CHECK
- LIGHT ON → CHECK SHORT TO GROUND CKT 108

	3.33 FINAL RATIO		2.97 FINAL RATIO	
MPH	RPM NO SLIP	RPM FAULT	RPM NO SLIP	RPM FAULT
40	1200	1550	1090	1450
48	1450	1850	1300	1700
56	1700	2125	1500	1950
64	1950	2375	1700	2175
72	2200	2650	2000	2500
80	2400	2850	2200	2675

PCM VOLTAGE CHECK		
PCM TERM.		
C4	BRAKE APPLIED 0 TO 0.3 Volts	BRAKE RELEASED BATTERY
F6	VCC ON 0 TO 0.3 VOLTS	VCC OFF BATTERY
F5	VCC MOD ON 0 TO 0.3 VOLTS	VCC MOD OFF BATTERY

GM
1-252

1991 ENGINE PERFORMANCE
Self-Diagnostics – Eldorado & Seville PCM/BCM (Cont.)

PCM CODE EO39,
VCC ENGAGEMENT PROBLEM (2 OF 2)

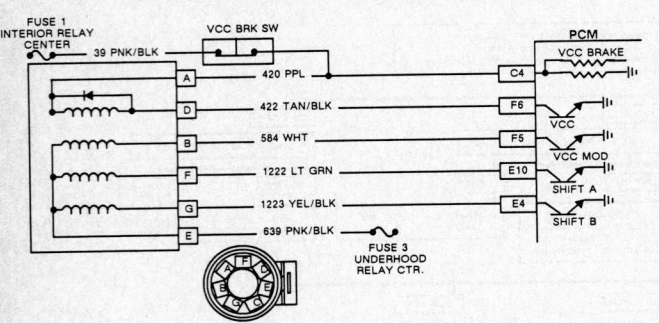

NOTE: Test numbers refer to test numbers on diagnostic chart.

1) This chart should be used after verifying proper operation of the PCM and circuits.

2) At this point there are no current electrical faults. Under normal operating conditions the VCC and VCC MOD indicator will come on at the same time when the VCC applies. Then the VCC MOD indicator will flash briefly and go out. At this time VCC is in full apply. The VCC test should be run with A/C off, since A/C cycling can affect engine RPM.

3) If the VCC does not engage or disengage under control of the Break Out Box (J-38791), diagnosis of transmission in indicated.

PCM VOLTAGE CHECK		
PCM TERM		
C4	BRAKE APPLIED 0 TO 0.3 VOLTS	BRAKE RELEASED BATTERY
F6	VCC ON 0 TO 0.3 VOLTS	VCC OFF BATTERY
F5	VCC MOD ON BATTERY	VCC MOD OFF 0 TO 0.3 VOLTS

91G07575   91J07628   91E07579

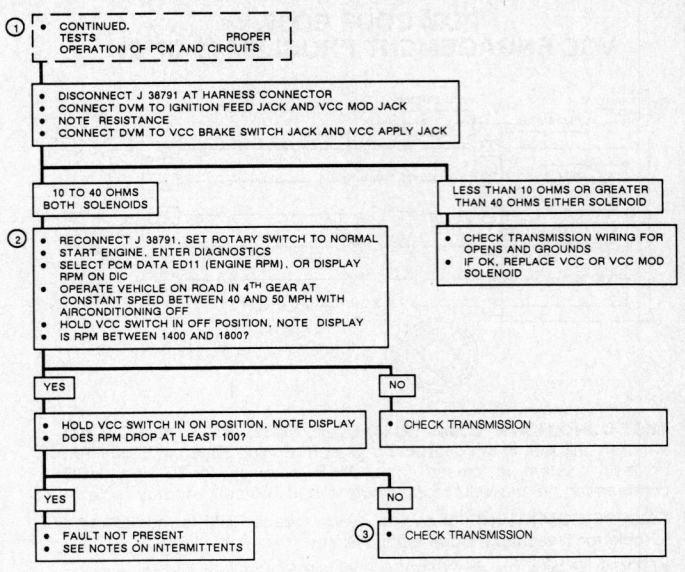

WHEN ALL DIAGNOSIS AND REPAIRS ARE COMPLETED, CLEAR CODES AND VERIFY OPERATION

Courtesy of General Motors Corp.

PCM CODE EO40,
OPEN PSPS CIRCUIT

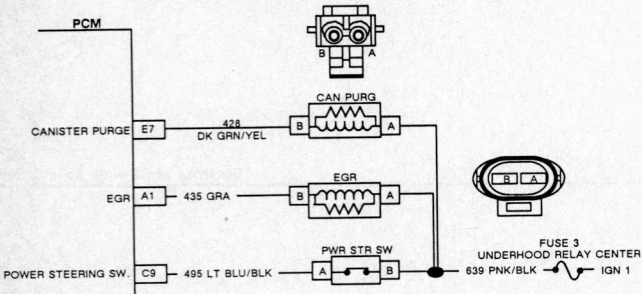

TEST CONDITIONS: Vehicle speed greater than or equal to 45 MPH.

FAILURE CONDITIONS: Power steering switch open with vehicle speed greater than or equal to 45 MPH.

ACTION: PCM turns on SERVICE ENGINE SOON light.

This test monitors the power steering pressure switch. When a load is placed on the power steering, such as full lock, the switch opens. Code EO40 sets when vehicle speed is greater than 45 MPH and pressure switch is open.

Note On Intermittents – Manipulate power steering pressure switch connector with engine running. If intermittent is created, code will set. Disconnect and reconnect power steering connector to ensure they are properly latched.

- ENGINE RUNNING, ENTER DIAGNOSTICS
- SELECT PCM INPUT TEST EI85
- TURN STEERING WHEEL TO FULL LEFT LOCK
- NOTE DISPLAY

DISPLAY DOES NOT CHANGE	DISPLAY CHANGES
HI '0' OR LO '0'	HI '0' OR LO '0'

DISPLAY DOES NOT CHANGE HI '0' OR LO '0':
- IGNITION 'ON'
- BACKPROBE PCM CONNECTOR TERMINAL 'C9' WITH DVM POSITIVE LEAD
- NEGATIVE LEAD TO TERMINAL 'D1'
- NOTE METER

DISPLAY CHANGES HI '0' OR LO '0':
- NORMAL SWITCH OPERATION
- CHECK SWITCH CONNECTOR FOR CAUSE OF INTERMITTENT

0 VOLTS:
- JUMPER POWER STEERING SWITCH CONNECTOR TERMINALS 'A' AND 'B'
- NOTE METER

12 VOLTS:
- DISCONNECT POWER STEERING SWITCH CONNECTOR
- NOTE DISPLAY

0 VOLTS:
- CHECK FUSE #5 RELAY CENTER

12 VOLTS:
- REPLACE SWITCH

0 VOLTS:
- CHECK PCM CONNECTOR
- SEE 'PCM REPLACEMENT CHECK'

12 VOLTS:
- CHECK SHORT TO VOLTAGE CKT 639

OK:
- CHECK OPEN CKT 639 OR 495
- RETEST

BLOWN:
- CHECK SHORT TO GROUND CKT 639 OR 495

91D09356   91I07581

Courtesy of General Motors Corp.

1991 ENGINE PERFORMANCE
Self-Diagnostics – Eldorado & Seville PCM/BCM (Cont.)

GM
1-253

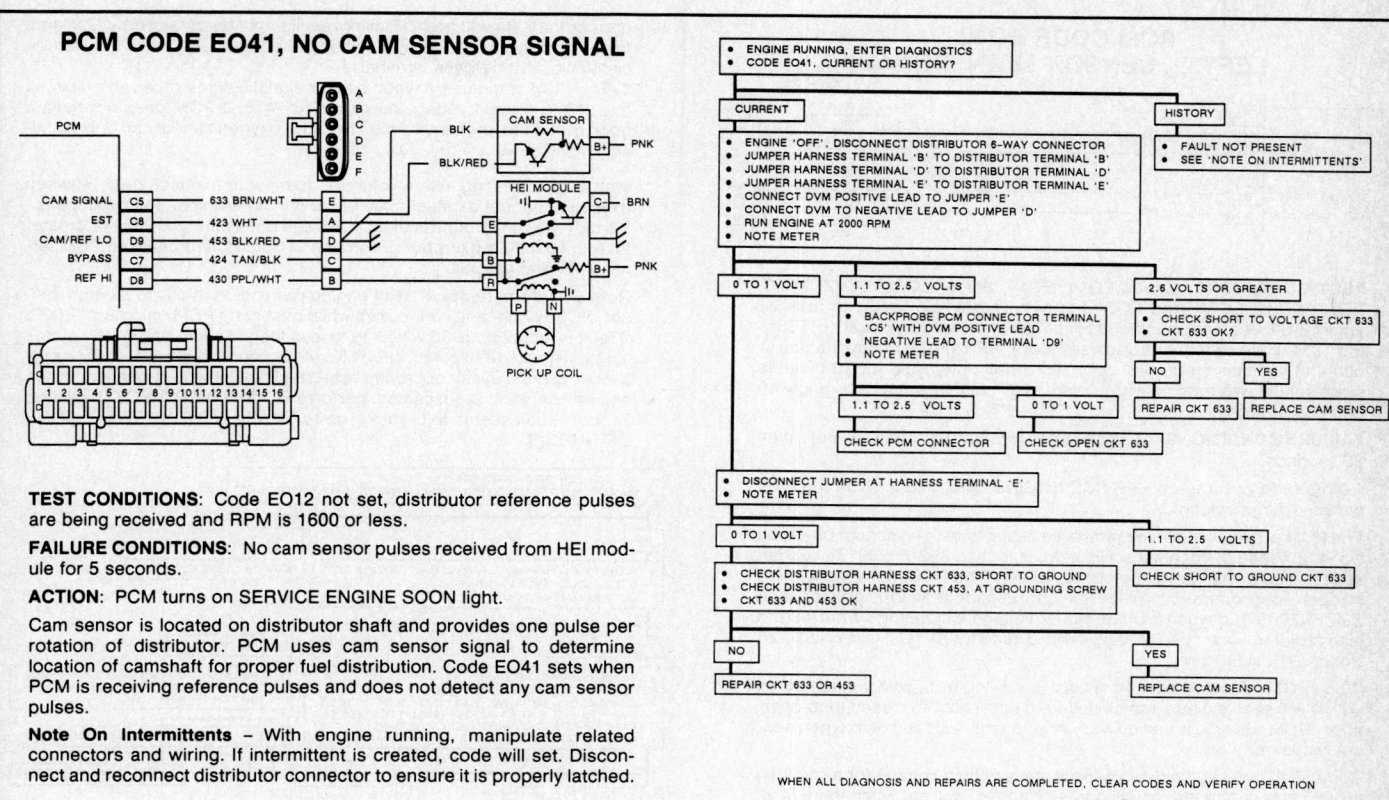

PCM CODE EO41, NO CAM SENSOR SIGNAL

TEST CONDITIONS: Code EO12 not set, distributor reference pulses are being received and RPM is 1600 or less.

FAILURE CONDITIONS: No cam sensor pulses received from HEI module for 5 seconds.

ACTION: PCM turns on SERVICE ENGINE SOON light.

Cam sensor is located on distributor shaft and provides one pulse per rotation of distributor. PCM uses cam sensor signal to determine location of camshaft for proper fuel distribution. Code EO41 sets when PCM is receiving reference pulses and does not detect any cam sensor pulses.

Note On Intermittents – With engine running, manipulate related connectors and wiring. If intermittent is created, code will set. Disconnect and reconnect distributor connector to ensure it is properly latched.

WHEN ALL DIAGNOSIS AND REPAIRS ARE COMPLETED, CLEAR CODES AND VERIFY OPERATION

90H21722   91C07583

Courtesy of General Motors Corp.

PCM CODE EO42, LEFT O₂ SENSOR LEAN SIGNAL

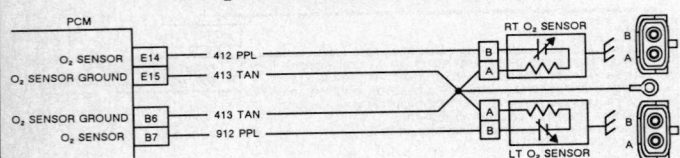

TEST CONDITIONS: Codes EO14, EO15, EO16, EO21, EO22, EO26, EO27, EO31, EO32, and EO34 not set. Throttle switch open, throttle angle 6-30 degrees, coolant sensor greater than or equal to 136°F (58°C), oxygen sensor ready (closed loop), RPM greater than or equal to 800 and canister purge has occurred at full duty cycle for 10 minutes since engine was running with coolant 176°F (80°C) and throttle angle 10 degrees or greater.

FAILURE CONDITIONS: Oxygen sensor status stays lean for more than 50 seconds.

ACTION: PCM turns on SERVICE ENGINE SOON light. PCM turns on canister purge solenoid.

The PCM provides a .45-volt reference signal to oxygen sensor on circuit No. 412. When oxygen sensor is cold, less than 392°F (200°C), oxygen sensor signal voltage will be about .45 volt. The PCM will keep system in open loop operation. When oxygen sensor is warm, greater than 392°F (200°C), oxygen sensor signal voltage will change from rich to lean rapidly (at least one change every 2 seconds) if PCM is in good control of air/fuel mixture.

When PCM sees that oxygen sensor is varying from cold voltage of .45 volt, it will send system into closed loop operation. In closed loop operation, PCM will adjust fuel delivery rate to engine based on oxygen sensor readings.

Code EO42 will set if oxygen sensor stays at lean voltage for more than 50 seconds during test conditions. Code EO42 will set when there is an oxygen sensor circuit fault giving a false lean indication, or when air/fuel ratio is actually lean due to a vacuum leak or fuel control system fault.

NOTE: Test numbers refer to test numbers on diagnostic chart.

1) With oxygen sensor disconnected, parameter ED32 should remain at reference voltage (.38-.63 volt).
2) Checks for sensor circuitry ability to record rich readings. The DVOM set on volts will provide a small current source to drive circuit No. 912 to

greater than .64 volt (rich). Similar results may be obtained by placing a finger on battery positive terminal and another finger on oxygen sensor circuit No. 912 harness terminal.

3) The PCM compares oxygen sensor signal voltage received on circuit No. 912 to ground voltage on circuit No. 413. If PCM does not have a good ground to engine on circuit No. 413, oxygen sensor can appear falsely high or low.

With engine running, use a voltmeter to measure voltage drop between oxygen sensor at exhaust manifold and PCM terminal B6. If voltage is -.05 to +.05 volt, ground is okay. If voltage is less than -.05 volt or greater than +.05 volt, repair poor ground on circuit No. 413 between PCM terminal B6 and ground.

Note On Intermittents – With engine running, manipulate oxygen sensor, PCM wiring, and connectors while observing PCM parameter ED32. If fault is induced, ED32 will jump to less than .37 volt, and ECON status light will go off. Manipulate circuit No. 413 ground to engine, and look for a loose ground eyelet or ground eyelet installed at wrong location. If lean engine operation is suspected, perform PFI SYSTEM CHECK. If oxygen sensor circuit seems to be okay, go to CHART A-9, OXYGEN SENSOR DIAGNOSIS.

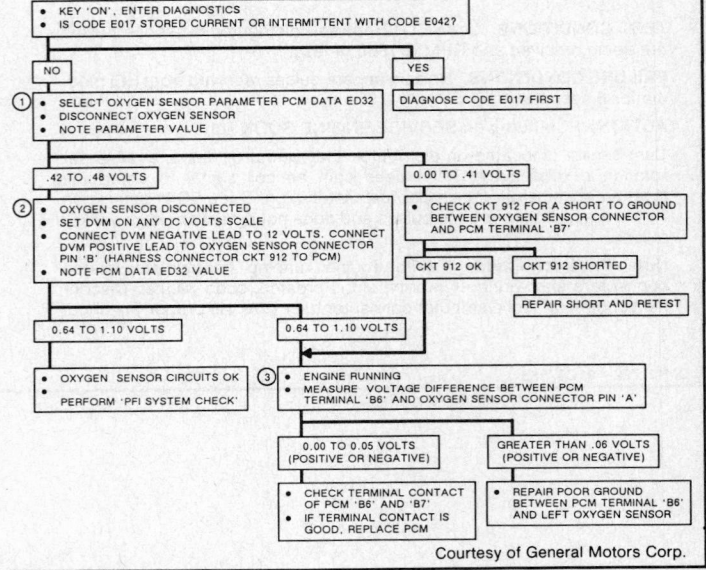

91I09354   91H07585

Courtesy of General Motors Corp.

1991 ENGINE PERFORMANCE
Self-Diagnostics – Eldorado & Seville PCM/BCM (Cont.)

GM
1-255

PCM CODE EO43, LEFT O₂ SENSOR RICH SIGNAL

TEST CONDITIONS: Codes EO14, EO15, EO16, EO21, EO22, EO26, EO27, EO31, EO32, and EO34 not set, throttle switch open, throttle angle 6-30 degrees, coolant sensor greater than or equal to 136°F (58°C), oxygen sensor ready (closed loop), vehicle not accelerating or decelerating, engine speed greater than or equal to 800 RPM and canister purge has occurred at full duty cycle for 10 minutes since engine was running with coolant temperature of 176°F (80°C) and throttle angle at 10 degrees or greater.

FAILURE CONDITIONS: Oxygen sensor stays rich for more than 50 seconds.

ACTION: PCM turns on SERVICE ENGINE SOON light. PCM turns on canister purge solenoid.

The PCM provides a .45-volt reference signal to oxygen sensor on circuit No. 912. When oxygen sensor is cold, less than 392°F (200°C), output voltage will be about .45 volt and PCM will keep system in open loop operation. When warm, a properly operating oxygen sensor will drive the .45-volt reference higher (greater than .45 volt) to indicate a rich mixture. Oxygen sensor signal voltage will swing from rich to lean rapidly. This will produce at least one swing every 2 seconds, if PCM is in good control of air/fuel mixture.

When PCM sees that oxygen sensor is not at cold voltage of .45 volt, it will send system into closed loop operation. In closed loop operation, PCM will meter fuel based on oxygen sensor readings.

Code EO43 will set if oxygen sensor stays at rich voltage for more than 45 seconds during test conditions. Code EO43 will set when oxygen sensor circuit fails, or when air/fuel ratio is actually rich due to fuel control or emissions system fault.

NOTE: Test numbers refer to test numbers on diagnostic chart.

1) With oxygen sensor disconnected, parameter ED33 should remain at reference voltage (.38-.63 volt).

91I09354   91J07586

2) This checks oxygen sensor circuitry to record lean readings.

3) The PCM compares oxygen sensor signal voltage received on circuit No. 912 to ground voltage on circuit No. 413. If PCM does not have a good ground to engine on circuit No. 413, oxygen sensor can appear falsely high or low.

With engine running, use a voltmeter to measure voltage between oxygen sensor at exhaust manifold and PCM terminal B6. If the voltage is -.05 to +.05 volt, ground is okay. If voltage is less than -.05 volt or greater than +.05 volt, repair poor ground on circuit No. 413 between PCM terminal B6 and ground at front of engine on right cylinder head.

Note On Intermittents – With engine running, manipulate oxygen sensor, PCM wiring, and connectors while observing PCM parameter ED33. If fault is induced, ED33 will jump to greater than .63 volt, and ECON status light will illuminate. Manipulate circuit No. 413 (ground to engine), and look for a loose ground eyelet or ground eyelet installed at wrong location. If oxygen sensor circuit is okay or lean engine operation is suspected, perform PFI SYSTEM CHECK.

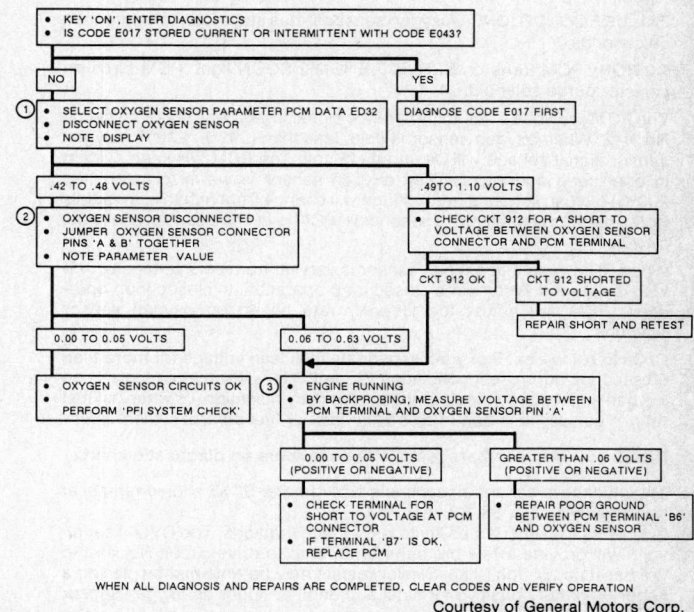

WHEN ALL DIAGNOSIS AND REPAIRS ARE COMPLETED, CLEAR CODES AND VERIFY OPERATION

Courtesy of General Motors Corp.

PCM CODE EO44, RIGHT O₂ SENSOR LEAN SIGNAL

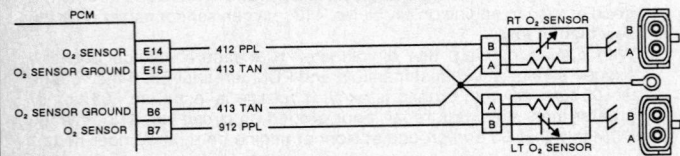

TEST CONDITIONS: Codes EO14, EO15, EO16, EO21, EO22, EO26, EO27, EO31, EO32, and EO34 not set. Throttle switch open, throttle angle 6-30 degrees, coolant sensor greater than or equal to 136°F (58°C), oxygen sensor ready (closed loop), RPM greater than or equal to 800 and canister purge has occurred at full duty cycle for 10 minutes since engine was running with coolant 176°F (80°C) and throttle angle 10 degrees or greater.

FAILURE CONDITIONS: Oxygen sensor status stays lean for more than 50 seconds.

ACTION: PCM turns on SERVICE ENGINE SOON light. PCM turns on canister purge solenoid.

The PCM provides a .45-volt reference signal to oxygen sensor on circuit No. 412. When oxygen sensor is cold, less than (392°F) 200°C, oxygen sensor signal voltage will be about .45 volt. The PCM will keep system in open loop operation. When oxygen sensor is warm (greater than 200°C) oxygen sensor signal voltage will change from rich to lean rapidly (at least one change every 2 seconds) if PCM is in good control of air/fuel mixture.

When PCM sees that oxygen sensor is varying from cold voltage of .45-volt, it will send system into closed loop operation. In closed loop operation, PCM will adjust fuel delivery rate based on oxygen sensor readings.

Code EO44 will set if oxygen sensor stays at lean voltage for more than 50 seconds during test conditions. Code EO44 will set when there is an oxygen sensor circuit fault giving a false lean indication, or when air/fuel ratio is actually lean due to a vacuum leak or fuel control system fault.

NOTE: Test numbers refer to test numbers on diagnostic chart.

1) With oxygen sensor disconnected, parameter ED33 should remain at reference voltage (.38-.63 volt).
2) Checks for sensor's ability to record rich readings. The DVOM set on volts will provide a few billionths of an amp to drive circuit No. 412 to greater than .64 volt (rich). Similar results may be obtained by placing a finger on battery positive terminal and another finger on oxygen sensor circuit No. 412 harness terminal.

91I09354   91G07587

3) The PCM compares oxygen sensor signal voltage received on circuit No. 412 and to ground voltage on circuit No. 413. If PCM does not have a good ground to engine on circuit No. 413, oxygen sensor can appear falsely high or low.

With engine running, use a voltmeter to measure voltage drop between oxygen sensor at exhaust manifold and PCM terminal E15. If voltage is -.05 to +.05 volt, ground is okay. If voltage is less than -.05 volt or greater than +.05 volt, repair poor ground on circuit No. 413 between PCM terminal E15 and ground.

Note On Intermittents – With engine running, manipulate oxygen sensor, PCM wiring and connectors while observing PCM parameter ED33. If fault is induced, ED33 will jump to less than .37 volt and ECON status light will go off. Manipulate ground to engine circuit No. 413, and look for a loose ground eyelet or ground eyelet installed at wrong location. If lean engine operation is suspected, perform PFI SYSTEM CHECK. If oxygen sensor circuit seems to be okay, go to CHART A-9, OXYGEN SENSOR DIAGNOSIS.

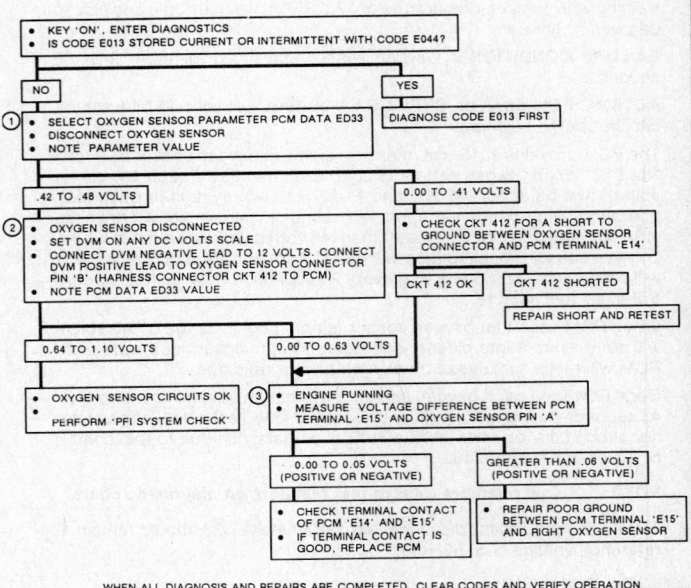

WHEN ALL DIAGNOSIS AND REPAIRS ARE COMPLETED, CLEAR CODES AND VERIFY OPERATION

Courtesy of General Motors Corp.

1991 ENGINE PERFORMANCE
Self-Diagnostics – Eldorado & Seville PCM/BCM (Cont.)

GM
1-257

PCM CODE EO45, RIGHT O₂ SENSOR RICH SIGNAL

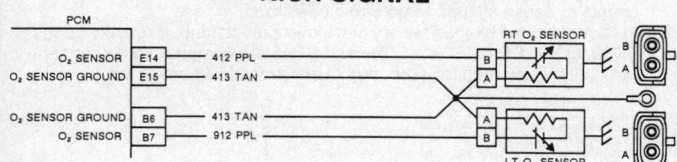

TEST CONDITIONS: Codes EO14, EO15, EO16, EO21, EO22, EO26, EO27, EO31, EO32, and EO34 not set. Throttle switch open, throttle angle 6-30 degrees, coolant temperature greater than or equal to 136°F (58°C), oxygen sensor ready (closed loop), engine speed greater than or equal to 800 RPM and canister purge has occurred at full duty cycle for 10 minutes since engine was running with coolant 176°F (80°C) and throttle angle 10 degrees or greater.

FAILURE CONDITIONS: Oxygen sensor stays rich for more than 50 seconds.

ACTION: PCM turns on SERVICE ENGINE SOON light. PCM turns on canister purge solenoid.

The PCM provides a .45-volt reference signal to oxygen sensor on circuit No. 412. When oxygen sensor is cold, less than 392°F (200°C), output voltage will be about .45 volt and PCM will keep system in open loop operation. When warm, a properly operating oxygen sensor will drive the .45-volt reference higher (greater than .45 volt) to indicate rich mixture. Oxygen sensor signal voltage will swing from rich to lean rapidly. This will produce at least one swing every 2 seconds, if PCM is in good control of air/fuel mixture.

When PCM sees that oxygen sensor is not at cold voltage of .45 volt, it will send system into closed loop operation. In closed loop operation, PCM will meter fuel into engine based on oxygen sensor readings.

Code EO45 will set if oxygen sensor stays at rich voltage for more than 45 seconds during test conditions. Code EO45 will set when oxygen sensor circuit fails, or when air/fuel ratio is actually rich due to fuel control or emissions system fault.

NOTE: Test numbers refer to test numbers on diagnostic chart.

1) With oxygen sensor disconnected, parameter ED33 should remain at reference voltage (.38-.63 volt).
2) This step checks PCM's ability to recognize lean input readings.

91I09354   91D07588

3) The PCM compares oxygen sensor signal voltage received on circuit No. 412 to ground voltage on circuit No. 413. If PCM does not have a good ground to engine on circuit No. 413, oxygen sensor can appear falsely high or low.

With engine running, use a voltmeter to measure voltage between oxygen sensor at exhaust manifold and PCM terminal E15. If voltage is -.05 to +.05 volt, ground is okay. If voltage is less than -.05 volt or greater than +.05 volt, repair poor ground on circuit No. 413 between PCM terminal E15 and ground at front of engine on right cylinder head.

Note On Intermittents – With engine running, manipulate oxygen sensor, PCM wiring, and connectors while observing PCM parameter ED33. If fault is induced, ED33 will jump to greater than .63 volt, and ECON status light will go on. Manipulate circuit No. 413 ground to engine, and look for a loose ground eyelet or ground eyelet installed at wrong location. If oxygen sensor circuit is okay or lean engine operation is suspected, perform PFI SYSTEM CHECK.

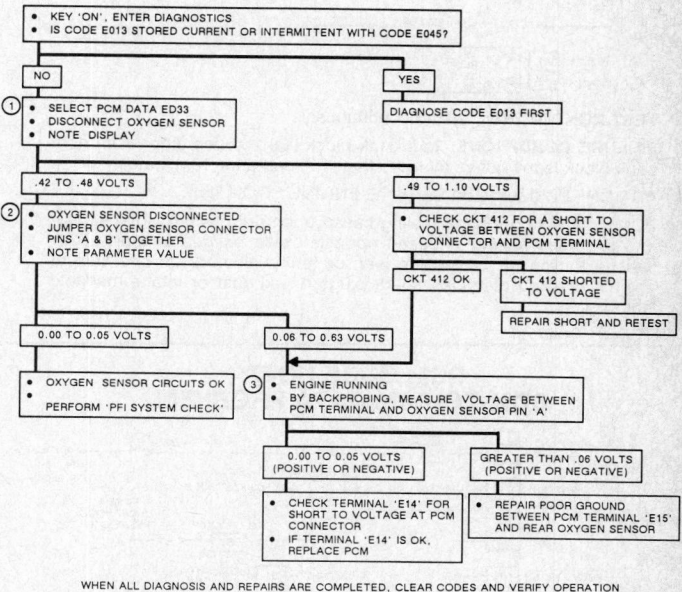

WHEN ALL DIAGNOSIS AND REPAIRS ARE COMPLETED, CLEAR CODES AND VERIFY OPERATION

Courtesy of General Motors Corp.

GM
1-258

1991 ENGINE PERFORMANCE
Self-Diagnostics – Eldorado & Seville PCM/BCM (Cont.)

PCM CODE EO46,
RIGHT TO LEFT BANK FUELING IMBALANCE

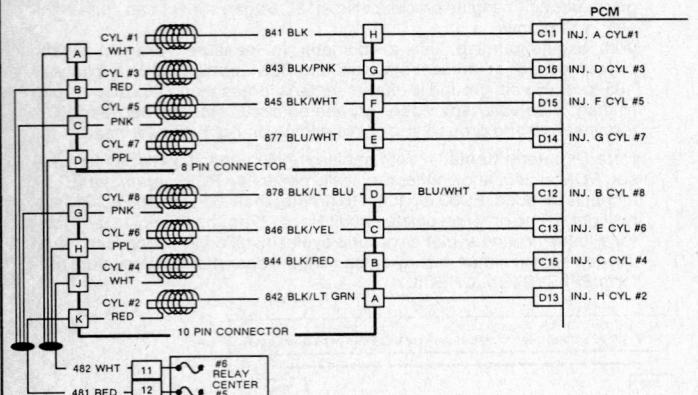

TEST CONDITIONS: Tested continuously.

FAILURE CONDITIONS: Left bank block learn values differ from right bank block learn values by more than 15 counts for 10 minutes.

ACTION: PCM turns on SERVICE ENGINE SOON light.

PCM controls right bank fueling based upon right side oxygen sensor and left bank fueling is based upon left side oxygen sensor. Likely causes for imbalance include lean or faulty injectors on one side of engine, cracked or fouled spark plugs or exhaust or intake manifold leaks.

91E09352   91J07591

NOTE: Test numbers refer to test numbers on diagnostic chart.

1) Oxygen sensor must be able to generate sufficient voltage and cross counts to cause system to go into closed loop.
2) Contaminated oxygen sensor can slow reaction time of sensor. Codes EO13, EO17, EO42, EO43, EO44 and EO45 are designed to detect sensor faults. Slow reaction time may cause driveability problems.

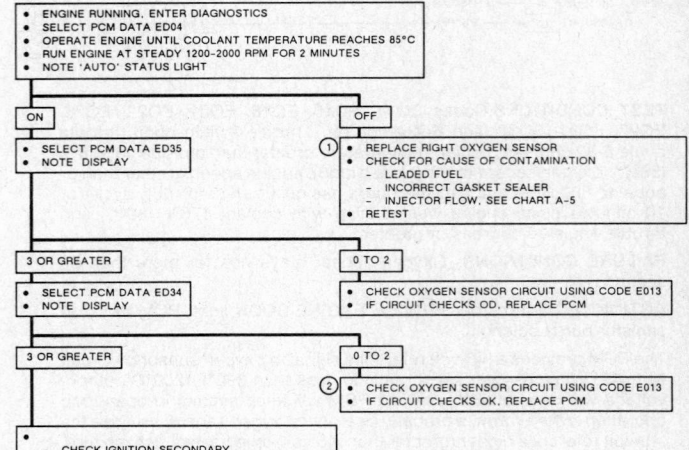

PCM CODE EO47,
BCM-TO-PCM DATA PROBLEM

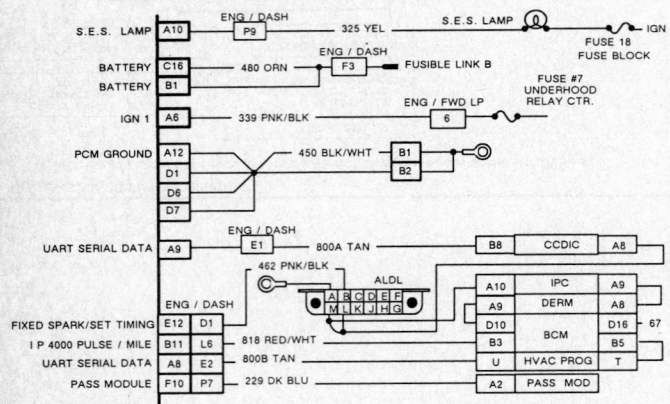

TEST CONDITIONS: Code EO12 is not set, ignition is on and engine speed is greater than 500 RPM for 20 seconds.

FAILURE CONDITIONS: PCM receives bad data or no data from BCM for 3 seconds.

ACTION: PCM clears all BCM data from PCM memory, disables A/C clutch and turns on SERVICE ENGINE SOON light.

The PCM and BCM share information through the PCM-BCM data through the Universal Asynchronous Receiver Transmitter (UART). The BCM is in control of data link and data is only transmitted at the BCM's request. Data is sent in 8 character words at a rate of 8192 characters per second.

91B07549

The data from the PCM to BCM contains engine operating information. The PCM-BCM data includes CTS, RPM and injector pulse width values so that the BCM can control cooling fans, display RPM and calculate MPG for display at the CCDIC. The BCM sends the PCM air conditioning status to be used for idle speed control and ambient temperature for use in VCC application and release decisions.

Code EO47 is set in the PCM in event of a UART failure. If fault is a current failure, PCM will not be able to communicate with the BCM and Code B334 will be displayed as current. Code EO47 is current in the PCM but cannot be sent (displayed) to BCM because of UART fault. If the UART fault is corrected, both Code EO47 and B334 will be displayed as history codes.

Code EO47 can only be displayed as an intermittent. If fault is present, Code B334 will be current. Two failures can result in a Code EO47:
• Open in circuits No. 800E and No. 800F. The symptoms will be:
  A – SYSTEM FAULT message on CCDIC panel.
  B – SERVICE ENGINE SOON and CHECK INFO CENTER lights on.
  C – Diagnostics entered and NO PCM DATA is displayed on CCDIC panel.
  D – When repaired, Codes EO47 and B334 will show as history codes.
• Grounded circuit No. 800 at any point. Symptoms will be:
  A – SYSTEM FAULT message on CCDIC panel.
  B – SERVICE ENGINE SOON light on.
  C – Instrument panel gauges will flash.
  D – Climate control panel goes blank.
  E – Engine cooling fans go high.
  E – Diagnostics disabled, SYSTEM FAULT message stays on CCDIC panel.
  F – When repaired, diagnostics will show Codes EO47, B334, B335, B336 and B337 as history codes.

1991 ENGINE PERFORMANCE
Self-Diagnostics – Eldorado & Seville PCM/BCM (Cont.)

GM
1-259

PCM CODE EO48, EGR SYSTEM FAULT (1 OF 2)

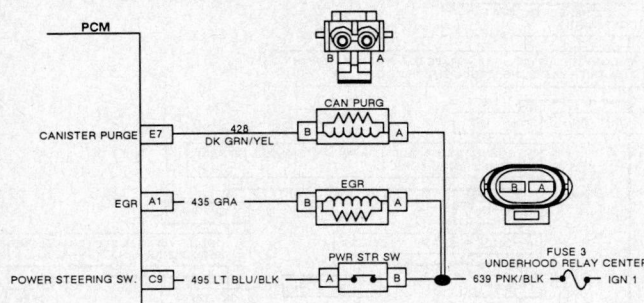

TEST CONDITIONS: Codes EO13, EO14, EO15, EO21, EO22, EO31, EO32, EO34, EO44, and EO45 not set. Coolant temperature 185-230°F (85-110°C), throttle angle 7-14 degrees, RPM 1450-1650 and oxygen sensor in closed loop operation at greater than 35 MPH, 10 minute timer after start-up expired and throttle steady.

FAILURE CONDITIONS: If oxygen sensor fails to indicate a leaner mixture in at least 3 of 5 tests during the key cycle, Code EO48 is set.

ACTION: PCM turns on SERVICE ENGINE SOON light for entire key cycle and EGR is disabled for the entire key cycle.

To perform test, PCM turns off EGR flow to engine and monitors oxygen sensor (closed loop) integrator. With EGR off, the integrator should swing to a higher value, reflecting leaner air/fuel mixtures. If not, PCM assumes that either EGR was turned off before test started, or that EGR is flowing and PCM does not have ability to turn it off. The PCM tests EGR 5 times in a given key cycle. If EGR does not respond 3 or more times during a key cycle, Code EO48 is set.

NOTE: Test numbers refer to test numbers on diagnostic chart.

1) Checks for EGR operation using PCM override.
2) Checking for EGR gases to enter intake manifold by raising EGR valve off of its seat.
3) Checking for EGR solenoid able to pass vacuum.

Vacuum Test – 1) Connect vacuum gauge to source side of EGR solenoid. Start engine. Manifold vacuum should be present. If not, repair leaks or obstruction between EGR solenoid and throttle body.

2) Connect vacuum gauge to EGR valve vacuum supply hose. There should be no vacuum with engine at idle. If vacuum is present, go to PCM CODE EO48 (2 OF 2).
3) With gauge attached to EGR valve vacuum supply hose, disconnect EGR solenoid connector. With engine at idle, vacuum reading should be greater than 8 in. Hg. If not, repair leak or obstruction in EGR valve vacuum hose.

NOTE: THIS PROCEDURE CANNOT
BE USED IF CODE E016 IS CURRENT

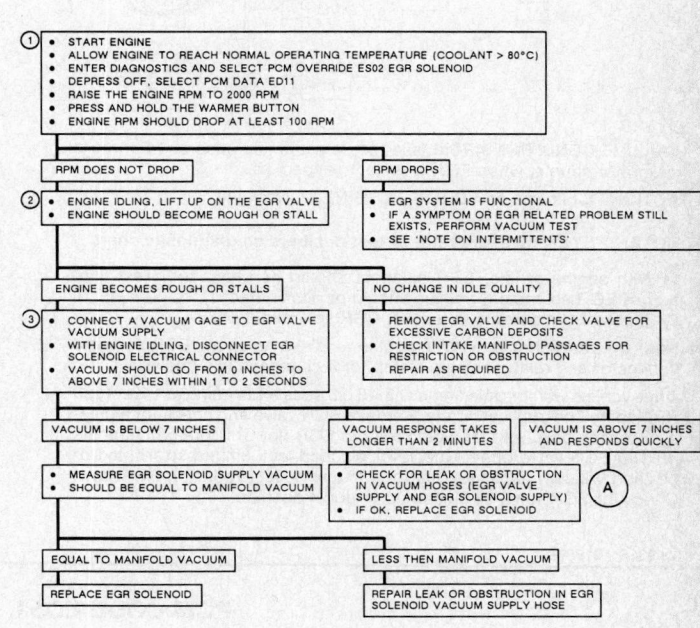

WHEN ALL DIAGNOSIS AND REPAIRS ARE COMPLETED, CLEAR CODES AND VERIFY OPERATION

91D09356   91D07593

Courtesy of General Motors Corp.

GM
1-260

1991 ENGINE PERFORMANCE
Self-Diagnostics – Eldorado & Seville PCM/BCM (Cont.)

PCM CODE EO48, EGR SYSTEM FAULT (2 OF 2)

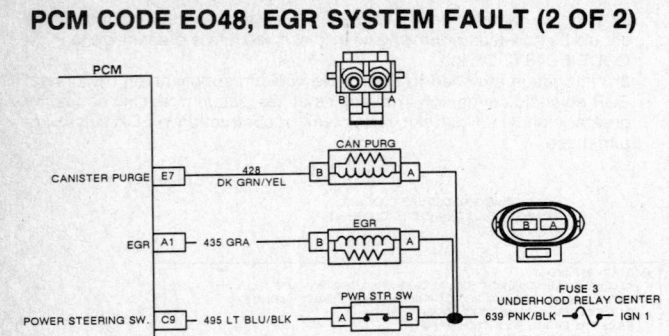

FAILURE CONDITIONS: PCM failed to detect an increase of 14 or more integrator counts, when EGR was commanded off.

ACTION: PCM turns on SERVICE ENGINE SOON light.

NOTE: Test numbers refer to test numbers on diagnostic chart.

1) With engine at idle, EGR solenoid should be energized. Test light across EGR solenoid terminals should be illuminated.
2) Checks PCM's ability to turn off EGR solenoid.

Note On Intermittents – With engine at idle, manipulate EGR solenoid connector and related wiring. Listen for a change in idle quality.

Drive vehicle with throttle angle at 8-15 degrees and engine at 1450-1650 RPM to try and duplicate code. Remove EGR valve and check for excessive carbon build-up that would restrict EGR flow, or foreign materials holding EGR valve open. Check for pinched, cut, kinked, misrouted or blocked vacuum passages and/or vacuum hoses, reducing EGR flow. Check for EGR valve binding in up or down position.

91D09356   91F07594

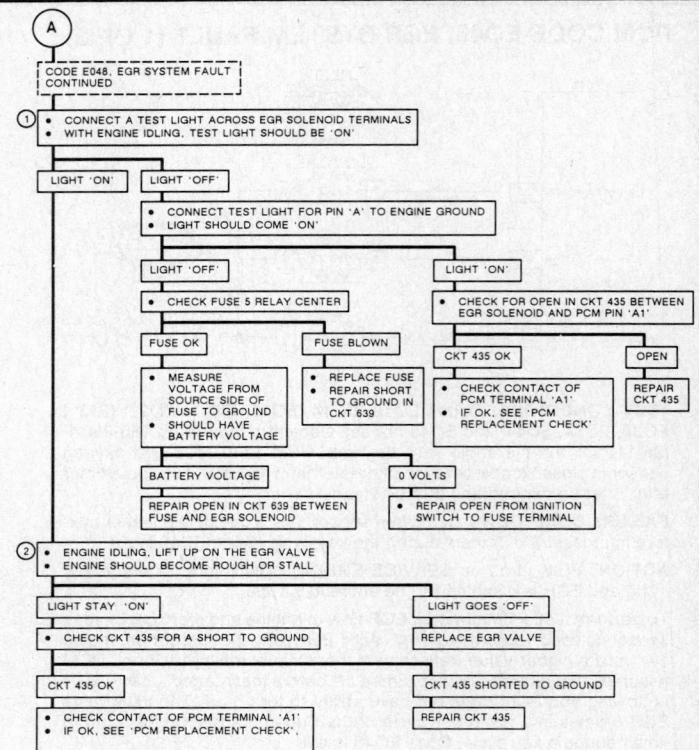

Courtesy of General Motors Corp.

PCM CODE EO51, MEM-CAL ERROR

Check that MEM-CAL is fully inserted in socket. If okay, replace MEM-CAL, clear memory and recheck. If Code EO51 reappears, replace PCM.

See cautions under POWERTRAIN CONTROL MODULE (PCM) in REMOVAL, OVERHAUL & INSTALLATION article when replacing MEM-CAL or PCM.

PCM CODE EO52, PCM MEMORY RESET

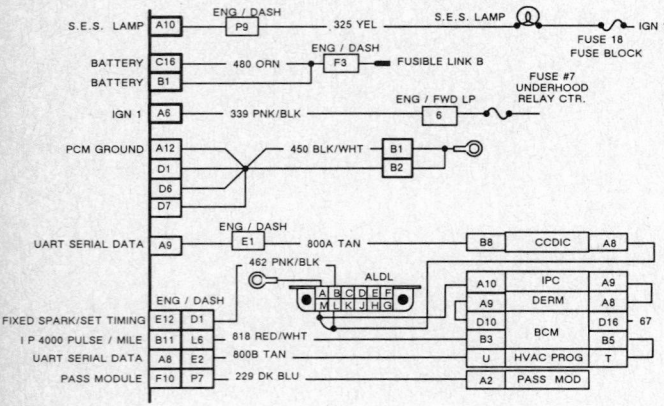

TEST CONDITIONS: Tested continuously.

FAILURE CONDITIONS: Loss of primary battery power and data to PCM.

ACTION: Code EO52 is set. SERVICE ENGINE SOON light not illuminated.

This test monitors the PCM's long term memory for loss of data. If battery power or ground is disconnected, Code EO52 will set.

The PCM keeps a running check on the memory. If memory changes, it resets.

91D09342

Courtesy of General Motors Corp.

1991 ENGINE PERFORMANCE
Self-Diagnostics – Eldorado & Seville PCM/BCM (Cont.)

GM
1-261

PCM CODE EO53, DISTRIBUTOR SIGNAL INTERRUPT

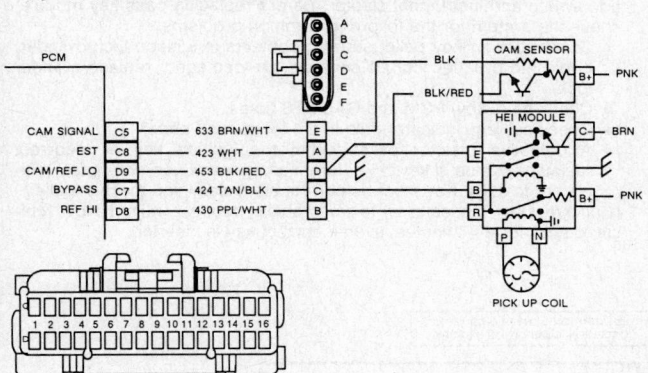

TEST CONDITIONS: Code EO19 not set.

FAILURE CONDITIONS: Engine speed is greater than 568 RPM, followed by no distributor reference pulses for .4 second.

ACTION: Code EO53 is set. SERVICE ENGINE SOON light not illuminated.

91H09344   91C07597

Code EO53 is set if PCM does not receive distributor reference pulses from HEI for more than .4 second. Since PFI system requires HEI pulses in order to fire the injectors, most occurrences of Code EO53 will be accompanied by a stall.

NOTE: Test numbers refer to test numbers on diagnostic chart.

1) A set of jumper wires is required on these test.

Note On Intermittents – DO NOT attempt to diagnose Code EO53 unless there are complaints of stumble, stall, miss or other driveability conditions that could be caused by loss of spark or fuel. Code EO53 can be caused by: loss of ground on circuit No. 453, loss of distributor reference signal on circuit No. 430, loss of battery power to "B+" terminal of distributor, or ignition switch circuit.

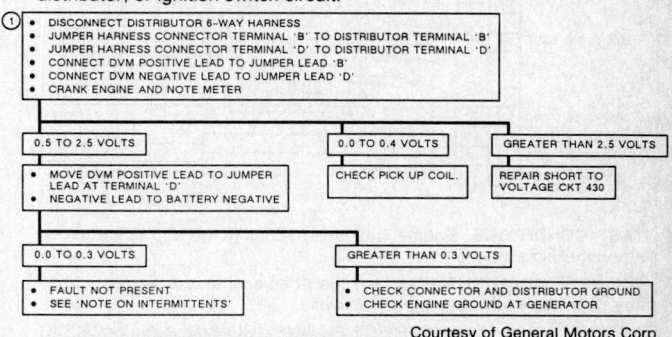

Courtesy of General Motors Corp.

PCM CODE EO55, TPS OUT OF ADJUSTMENT

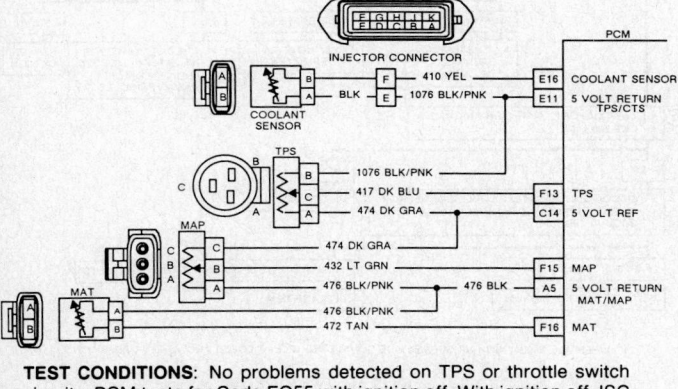

TEST CONDITIONS: No problems detected on TPS or throttle switch circuits. PCM tests for Code EO55 with ignition off. With ignition off, ISC will retract until throttle switch opens, TPS value is read by PCM, and a correction factor is stored. If correction value is the same on 2 consecutive key off cycles, TPS setting is relearned.

FAILURE CONDITIONS: "Learned" TPS is less than -2.9 degrees or greater than 3 degrees.

ACTION: At next key on, PCM will log Code EO55 as current. No diagnostic light or service message will appear.

The TPS is self-adjusting. With key off, the PCM executes a TPS learning routine. After turning key off, the PCM will retract ISC until the ISC throttle switch opens and throttle linkage is resting on the minimum air screw. At that time, PCM stores TPS value and calculates a correction.

If the same correction factor occurs on 2 consecutive key off cycles, TPS is corrected to zero degrees using correction factor learned. If value needs correction by more than -2.9 degrees or +3.0 degrees, Code EO55 will be stored in memory at next key on cycle. Parameter ED01 displays uncorrected TPS values.

NOTE: Test numbers refer to test numbers on diagnostic chart.

1) This step checks for TPS adjustment. PCM parameter ED01 displays uncorrected TPS so that it can be used to check TPS adjustment.
2) TPS adjustment is okay.
3) If TPS adjustment is okay, ISC and throttle switch operation need to be thoroughly checked. The throttle linkage needs to be checked for proper operation. Throttle and cruise cables, throttle valves not binding, proper throttle return spring operation, and throttle shaft and blades free to move.

91E07541   91E07598

Note On Intermittents – Manipulate ISC wiring while observing PCM input EI72 and while observing ISC operation during PCM output EO07. Manipulate TPS wiring and connector while observing PCM parameter ED01 for jumps, skips, and/or intermittent behavior.

Check that TPS is secured to throttle body (both screws tight). Cycle TPS through its full travel while observing parameter ED01 for erratic behavior. Check for proper TPS part number installed on vehicle. Unplug and plug the TPS, ISC and PCM connectors and ensure that they are latched properly.

NOTE: IF CODES E021, E026, E027, OR E030 ARE STORED CURRENT OR HISTORY, DO NOT USE THIS PROCEDURE. REPAIR USING CODE E021, E026, OR E030 PROCEDURES IN THIS SECTION

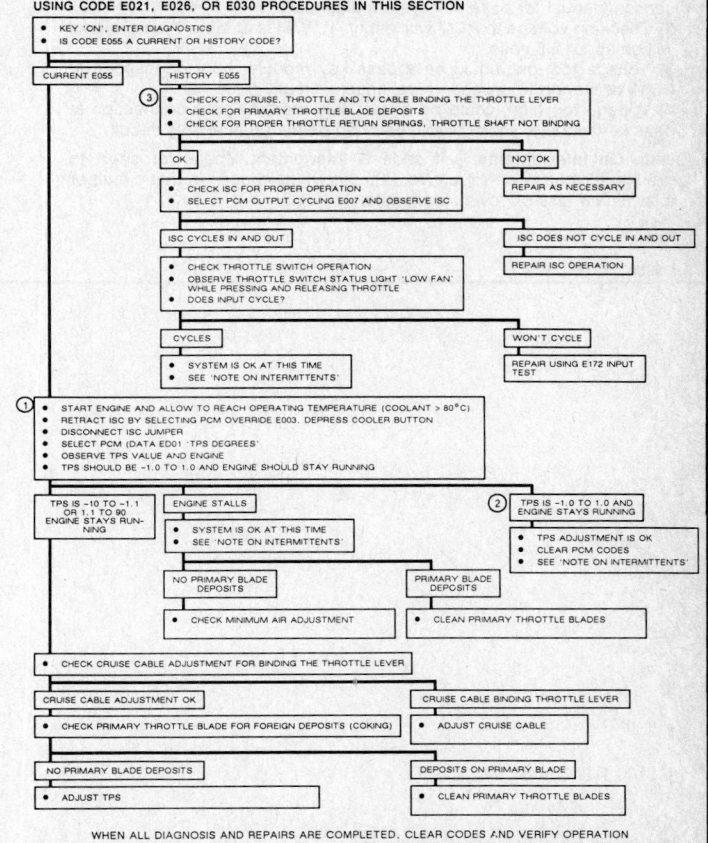

WHEN ALL DIAGNOSIS AND REPAIRS ARE COMPLETED, CLEAR CODES AND VERIFY OPERATION

Courtesy of General Motors Corp.

GM
1-262

1991 ENGINE PERFORMANCE
Self-Diagnostics – Eldorado & Seville PCM/BCM (Cont.)

PCM CODE E058,
PASS KEY CONTROL PROBLEM

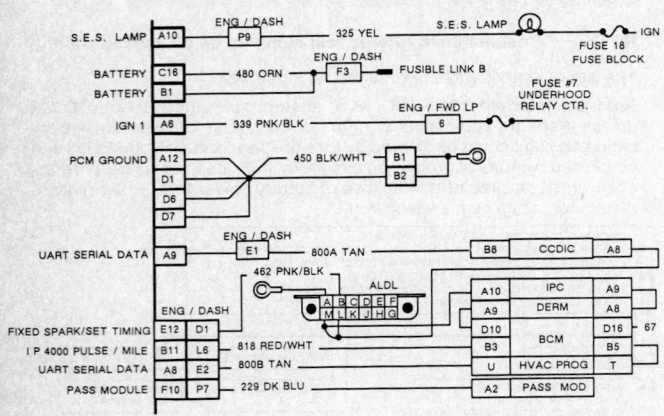

TEST CONDITIONS: Engine has been running for a predetermined amount of time.

FAILURE CONDITIONS: Pass key fuel enable input is incorrect but has been correct within this engine run cycle.

ACTION: PCM turns on SERVICE ENGINE SOON message on CCDIC panel and will enable fuel injection on future ignition cycles without regard for pass key fuel enable input status.

Once engine is running, PCM constantly monitors fuel enable signal from pass key module. PCM will not cancel fuel injection once it has seen a proper pass key module signal; therefore, stalling conditions cannot occur as a result of a pass key malfunction.

NOTE: Test numbers refer to test numbers on diagnostic chart.

1) If engine will crank, problem has been isolated to pass key module, PCM or fuel enable circuit. If engine will not crank, refer to appropriate service manual for pass key system diagnosis.
2) Checking voltage to PCM will identify if PCM is at fault. Typical signal will be about 2.5 volts.
3) Voltage too low, could be a pass key module, poor connection at PCM, or a short to ground in fuel enable circuit.
4) Voltage too high, could be a pass key module, poor connection at pass key module, short to voltage or an open in fuel enable circuit.

Note On Intermittents – If code is intermittent, check for short to ground or voltage on circuit No. 229, intermittent open in that circuit or intermittent loss of power to module.

Pass Key Diagnosis – The pass key system interfaces the PCM and starter with a power source, decoder module, starter enable relay, ignition switch and instrument cluster. Before replacing pass key module, check the system for the following common problems.
- Check ignition key pellet sensing contacts in ignition lock cylinder. Look into cylinder lock. If contacts are damaged, replace cylinder lock.
- Check pass key, PCM and GAUGES fuses.
- Check security indicator bulb in the instrument panel.
- A defective resistor pellet within the ignition key or incorrect resistance value of key (15 different assigned values) will cause vehicle not to start. Key must be correct electrically and mechanically.

If incorrect key is used to try to start vehicle, decoder will not allow vehicle to start for 2-4 minutes, even if correct key is inserted.

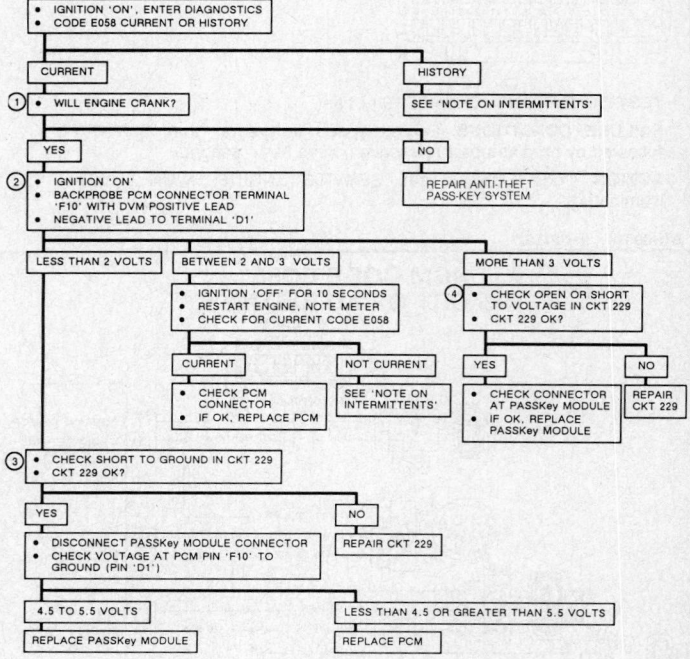

WHEN ALL DIAGNOSIS AND REPAIRS ARE COMPLETED, CLEAR CODES AND VERIFY OPERATION

1991 ENGINE PERFORMANCE
Self-Diagnostics – Eldorado & Seville PCM/BCM (Cont.)

GM
1-263

PCM CODE EO60, CRUISE CONTROL WITH TRANSMISSION NOT IN DRIVE

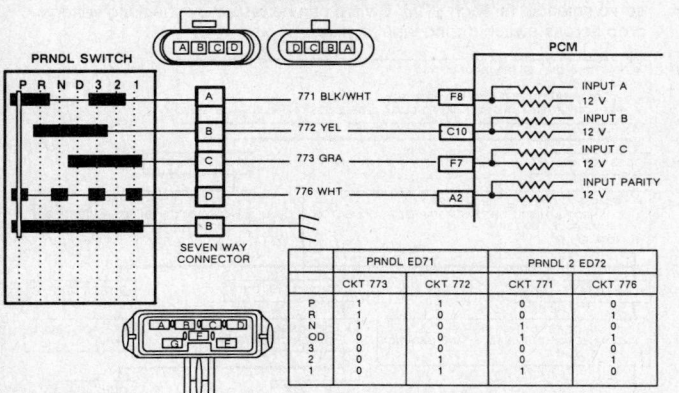

91A07600

TEST CONDITIONS: Cruise control on. Cruise control engaged.

FAILURE CONDITIONS: Transmission in Park or Neutral.

ACTION TAKEN: Disengage cruise control.

Code EO60 will set if the cruise control is engaged and the Park/Neutral switch is closed, indicating transmission is in Park or Neutral.

Note On Intermittents – If Code EO60 is stored as a history code, select PCM data ED71 and ED72. Manipulate harness while observing status of switch. If switch changes status as wiring is being manipulated, repair intermittent connections. If no trouble code is found, code may have been set if transmission was inadvertently put into Neutral while cruise control was engaged.

Courtesy of General Motors Corp.

PCM CODE EO61, CRUISE CONTROL VENT SOLENOID CIRCUIT

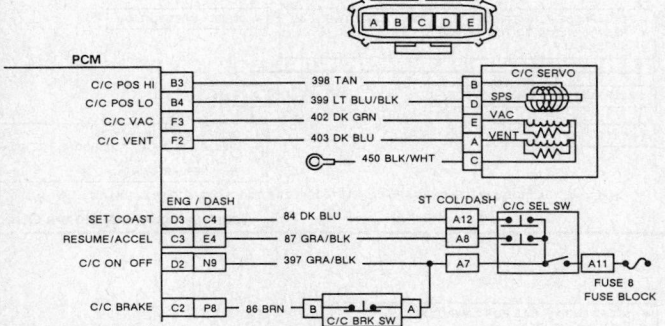

TEST CONDITIONS: Tested continuously.

FAILURE CONDITIONS:
- Cruise vent solenoid commanded off, but feedback indicates solenoid is on.
- Cruise vent solenoid commanded on, but feedback indicates solenoid is off.

ACTION TAKEN: Disengage cruise control.

Code EO61 will set if cruise control is engaged, brake is not depressed and PCM output is HI when it should be LO, or LO when it should be HI.

NOTE: Test numbers refer to test numbers on diagnostic chart.

1) Checks to see if fault is due to servo or circuit.
2) Checking cruise control brake switch. Brake switch supplies power to servo solenoid through PCM. Switch can be tested by checking voltage drop across switch during input cycling.

91C07601   91E07602

Note On Intermittents – If an intermittent Code EO61 is being set, manipulate wiring while in output function ED08. Listen for solenoid to cycle or stop cycling. This must be done slowly as function cycles solenoid on and off every 3 seconds.

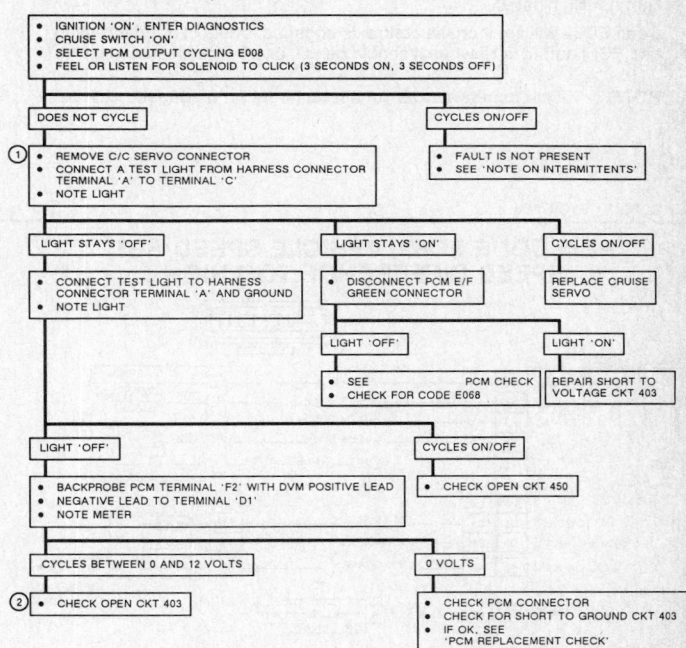

WHEN ALL DIAGNOSIS AND REPAIRS ARE COMPLETED, CLEAR CODES AND VERIFY OPERATION

Courtesy of General Motors Corp.

PCM CODE EO62, CRUISE CONTROL VACUUM SOLENOID CIRCUIT

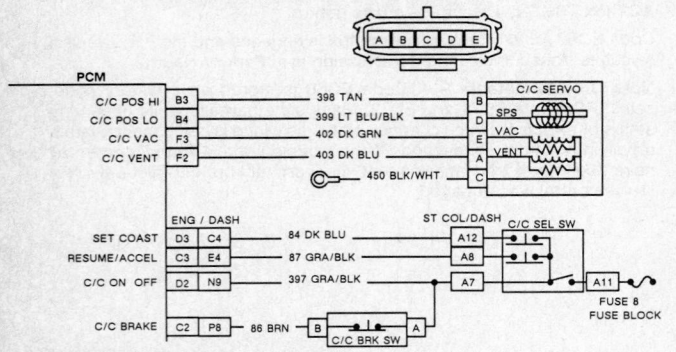

TEST CONDITIONS: Tested continuously.

FAILURE CONDITIONS:
- Cruise vent solenoid commanded off, but feedback indicates solenoid is on.
- Cruise vent solenoid commanded on, but feedback indicates solenoid is off.

ACTION TAKEN: Disengage cruise control. SERVICE ENGINE SOON light not illuminated.

Code EO62 will set if cruise control is engaged, brake is not depressed and PCM output is HI when it should be LO, or LO when it should be HI.

NOTE: Test numbers refer to test numbers on diagnostic chart.

91C07601   91G07603

1) Checks to see if fault is due to servo or circuit.
2) Checking cruise control brake switch. Brake switch supplies power to servo solenoid through PCM. Switch can be tested by checking voltage drop across switch during input cycling.

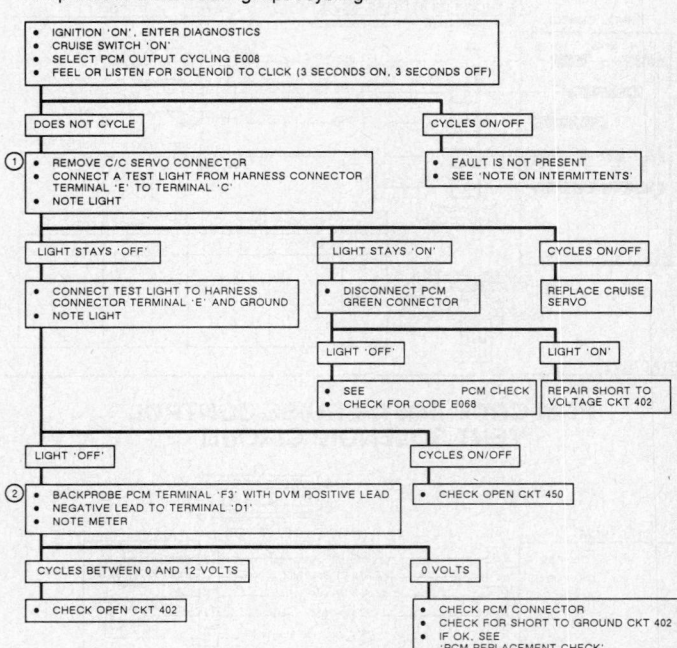

Courtesy of General Motors Corp.

PCM CODE EO63, VEHICLE SPEED/SET SPEED DIFFERENCE TOO HIGH

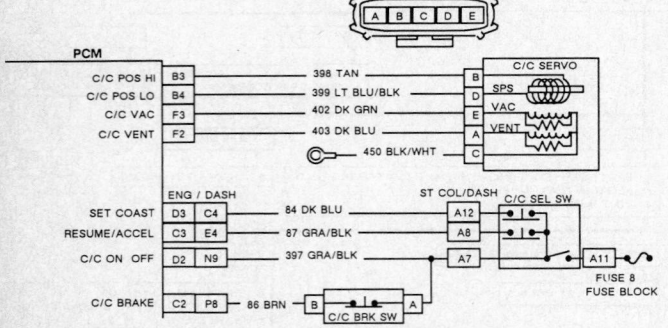

TEST CONDITIONS: Tested when cruise is enabled and engaged, and cruise control servo position is at 39 percent or greater.

FAILURE CONDITIONS: Vehicle speed 20 MPH greater than set speed for .5 second.

ACTION TAKEN: Disengage cruise control.

Code EO63 will set and disengage cruise control if vehicle speed is 20 MPH more than cruise set speed. Code EO63 is designed to detect a cruise control problem that results in cruise overspeed or cannot hold speed.

NOTE: Test numbers refer to test numbers on diagnostic chart.

1) PCM data value ED70 displays servo position. Range is approximately 4-94 percent. If servo will not go to full stroke, the vacuum supply, servo, or vacuum brake release circuit are leaking.
2) Code EO63 will not be caused by vacuum leaks or vacuum supply problems. If can only be set by the vehicle exceeding set speed by 20 MPH.
3) Jumper cruise control servo terminal.

91C07601   91I07604

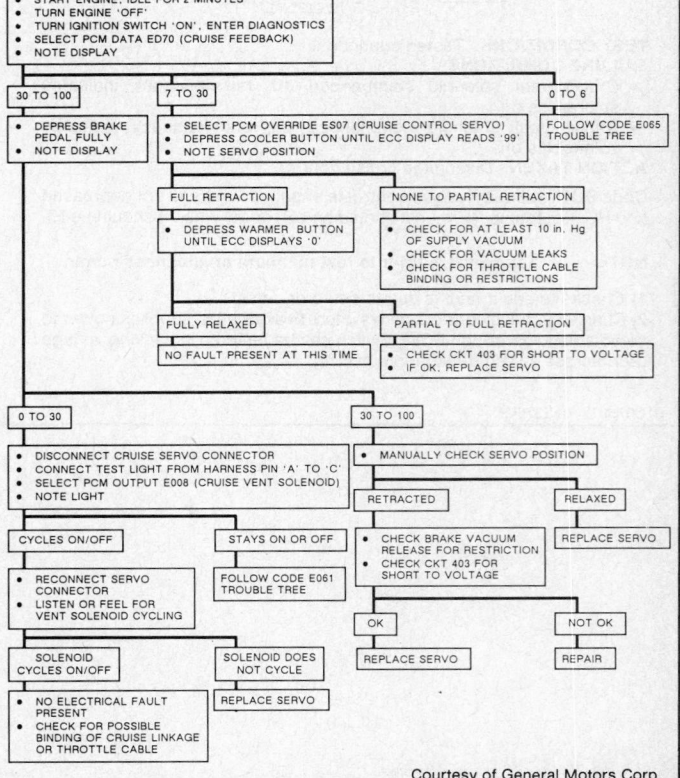

Courtesy of General Motors Corp.

1991 ENGINE PERFORMANCE
Self-Diagnostics – Eldorado & Seville PCM/BCM (Cont.)

GM
1-265

PCM CODE EO64, ACCELERATION TOO HIGH

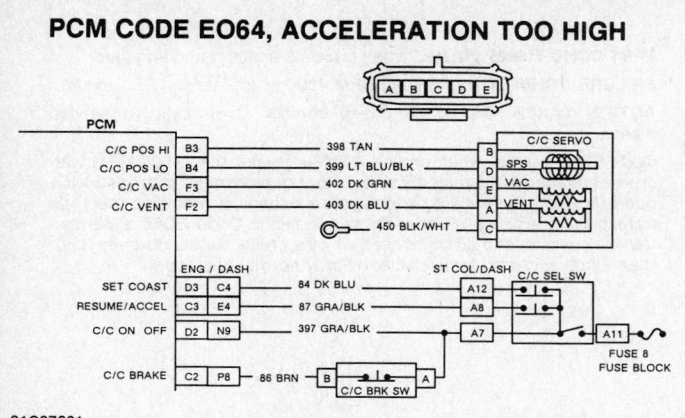

TEST CONDITIONS: Tested when cruise is enabled and engaged.

FAILURE CONDITIONS: Vehicle speed increases more than 4 MPH in .25 second.

ACTION TAKEN: Disengage cruise control. No warning lights are illuminated.

Code EO64 is set. Code EO64 is designed to set when vehicle speed is increasing at a rapid rate (wheel spin). This is a protective measure to prevent wheel spin on icy roads when cruise control is in operation.

91C07601

Courtesy of General Motors Corp.

PCM CODE EO65, CRUISE CONTROL SERVO POSITION SENSOR FAILURE

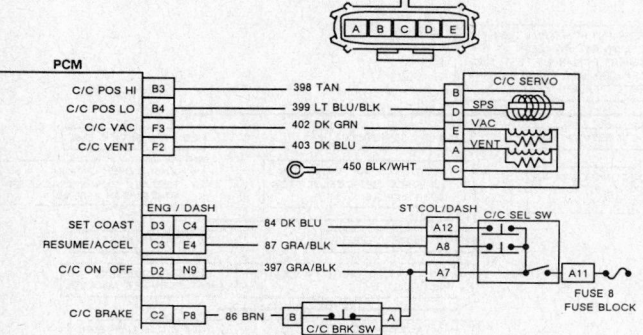

TEST CONDITIONS: Tested continuously.

FAILURE CONDITIONS: Servo position 6.3 percent or less for one second.

ACTION TAKEN: Disengage cruise control. Code set. No service message.

Code EO65 will detect a cruise control servo position sensor shorted to ground. Cruise servo position sensor is a potentiometer that changes resistance with servo position. Code EO65 sets when PCM detects a low voltage indicating a short to ground in cruise servo position sensor circuit.

NOTE: Test numbers refer to test numbers on diagnostic chart.

1) PCM data value ED70 displays servo position. Range is approximately 4-94 percent. If servo will not go to full stroke, the vacuum supply, servo, or vacuum brake release circuit are leaking.
2) Check dash to engine connector as possible source of intermittent in signal line.

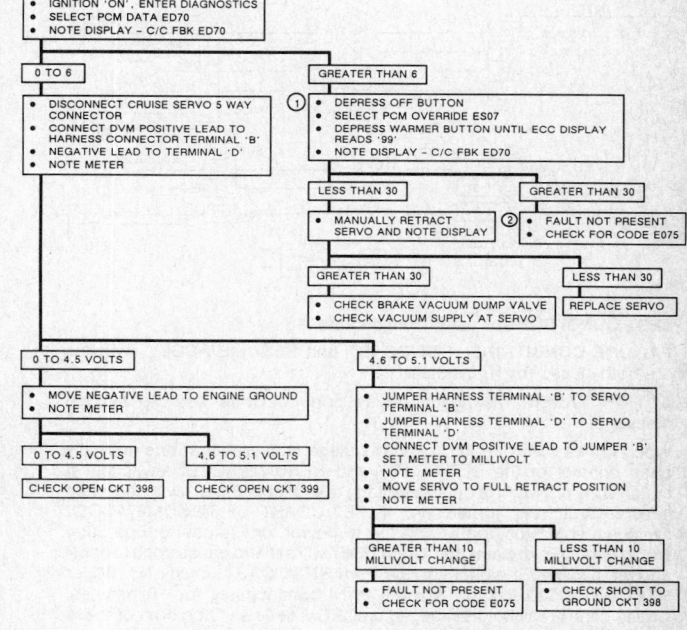

91C07601   91B07605

Courtesy of General Motors Corp.

PCM CODE EO66, ENGINE RPM TOO HIGH WITH CRUISE ENGAGED

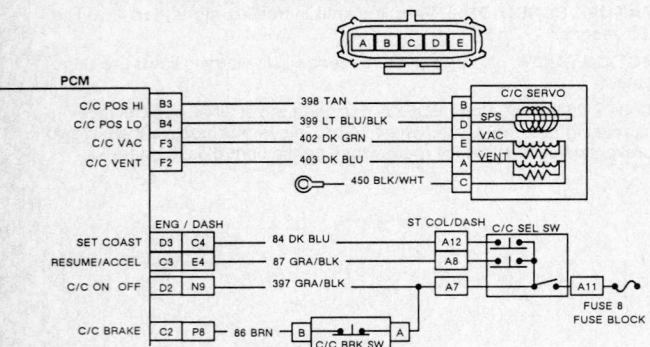

TEST CONDITIONS: Tested when cruise is enabled and engaged.

FAILURE CONDITIONS: Engine RPM 4800 or greater for .25 second.

ACTION TAKEN: Disengage cruise control. Code set. No service message.

Code EO66 will set when engine RPM is greater than 4800 RPM with cruise engaged. This may occur on slippery pavement, extended wide open throttle acceleration or for some mechanical problems (such as transmission slippage). Under these conditions Code EO66 is normal. Vehicle operator should be advised why the cruise control de-energized. Clear code and road test vehicle to verify normal operation.

91C07601

PCM CODE EO67, SET/COAST OR RESUME/ACCEL SWITCH SHORTED

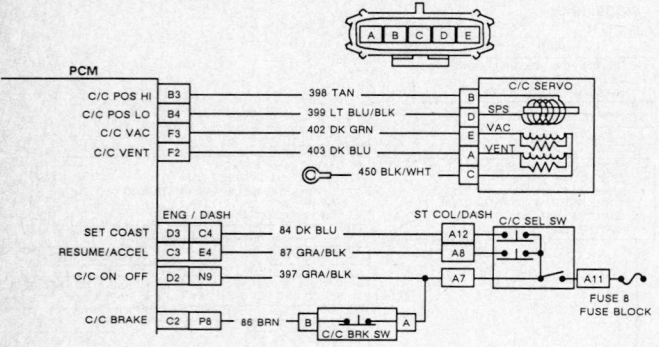

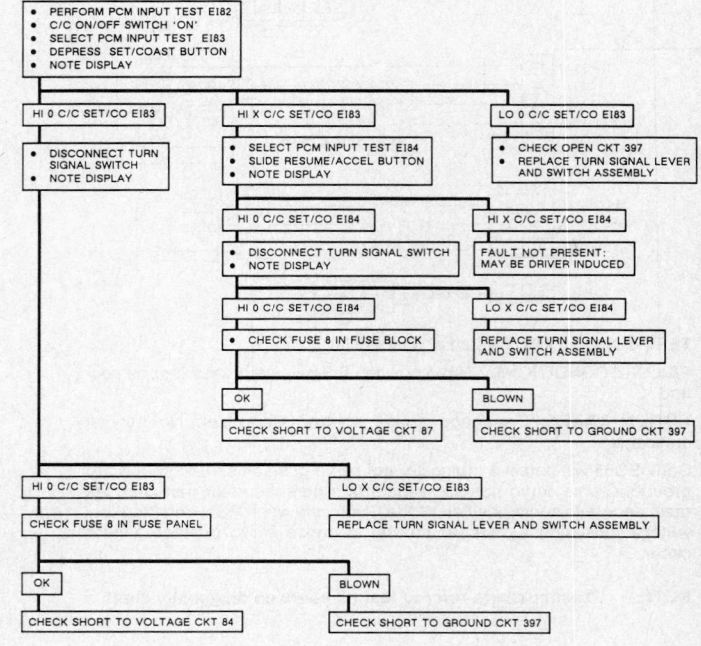

WHEN ALL DIAGNOSIS AND REPAIRS ARE COMPLETED, CLEAR CODES AND VERIFY OPERATION

TEST CONDITIONS: Tested continuously.

FAILURE CONDITIONS: SET/COAST and RESUME/ACCEL switches are both closed for 10 minutes.

ACTION TAKEN: Disengage cruise control. Code set. No service message.

When cruise control is on, system voltage is available at one normally open contact of the SET/COAST and RESUME/ACCEL switches. If cruise control switch is on, this voltage is available to the switches when ignition switch is turned on. If SET/COAST or RESUME/ACCEL switches were stuck on or shorted to power, cruise control operation would begin. To prevent this, Code EO67 will set and cruise control operation is disabled if signal voltage from SET/COAST (circuit No. 84) or RESUME/ACCEL (circuit No. 87) is HI continuously for 10 minutes. Cruise control will be disengaged until PCM sees a LO on both of these signals.

91C07601   91D07606

1991 ENGINE PERFORMANCE
Self-Diagnostics – Eldorado & Seville PCM/BCM (Cont.)

GM
1-267

PCM CODE E068, CRUISE CONTROL COMMAND PROBLEM

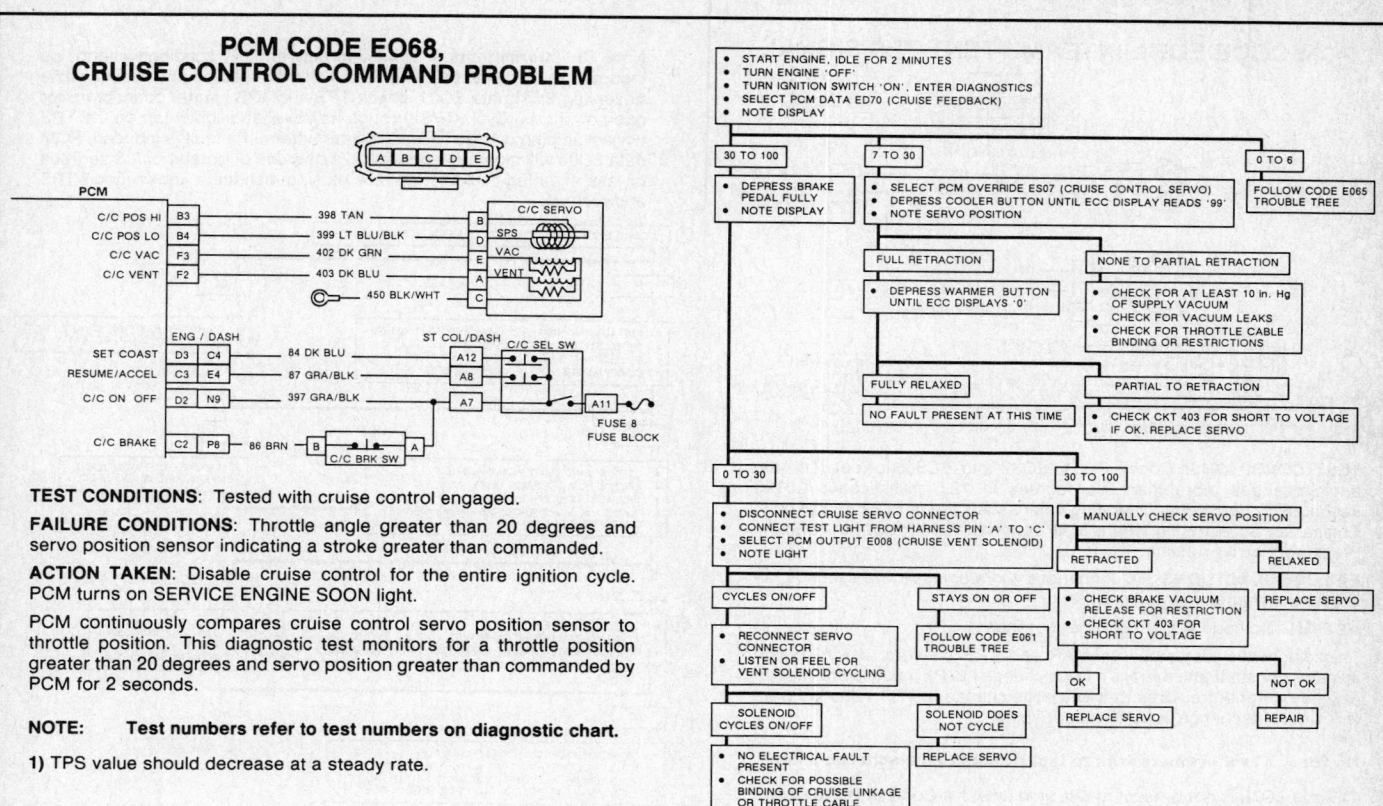

TEST CONDITIONS: Tested with cruise control engaged.

FAILURE CONDITIONS: Throttle angle greater than 20 degrees and servo position sensor indicating a stroke greater than commanded.

ACTION TAKEN: Disable cruise control for the entire ignition cycle. PCM turns on SERVICE ENGINE SOON light.

PCM continuously compares cruise control servo position sensor to throttle position. This diagnostic test monitors for a throttle position greater than 20 degrees and servo position greater than commanded by PCM for 2 seconds.

NOTE: Test numbers refer to test numbers on diagnostic chart.

1) TPS value should decrease at a steady rate.

91C07601   91F07607

Courtesy of General Motors Corp.

GM
1-268

1991 ENGINE PERFORMANCE
Self-Diagnostics – Eldorado & Seville PCM/BCM (Cont.)

PCM CODE EO70, INTERMITTENT TPS SIGNAL

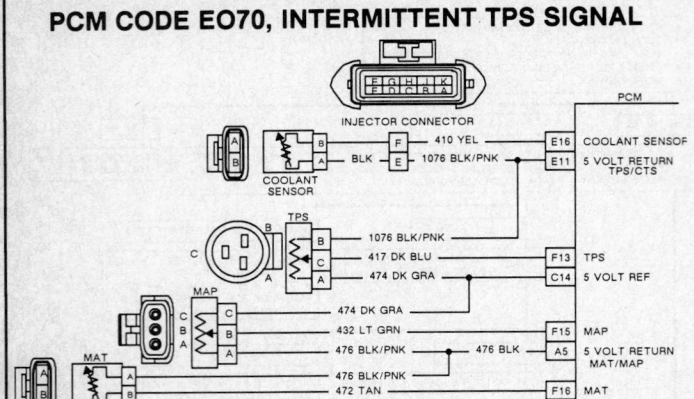

TEST CONDITIONS: Codes EO31, EO32 and EO34 not set. Throttle angle changes more than 3.5 degrees in 12.5 milliseconds (.0125 seconds). Engine not decelerating where MAP drops to 22 kPa or less. Engine not accelerating where MAP is within 7.4 kPa of atmospheric pressure. Engine running.

FAILURE CONDITIONS: MAP changes 4 kPa or less in .16 seconds following the change in throttle angle.

ACTION: No code set. No service message.

This diagnostic test monitors MAP and TPS sensors. If MAP value remains constant and there is a large change in TPS value, code will set. Engine operation requires that any large change in TPS value must be followed by a change in MAP sensor value.

NOTE: Test numbers refer to test numbers on diagnostic chart.

1) Code EO70 is not present at this time unless a Code 21, 22, 31 or 34 is current. This code indicates an unacceptable high rate of TPS change.
2) As the ISC extends, TPS voltage as measured at the TPS jumper should increase at a steady rate. A dead spot in the TPS will cause voltage to jump erratically as the ISC moves the TPS past that spot. Use a high impedance needle-type voltmeter for this test.
3) If the throttle blade cannot return to the idle stop, the throttle valves may be coked or binding. These conditions may set Codes EO55 and EO58.
4) Improper TPS adjustment, such as forcing or tapping on the TPS without loosening the attaching screws, will damage the TPS and can cause Code EO70 to set.

Note On Intermittents – If an intermittent TPS condition cannot be induced, manipulate the TPS and PCM connector and wiring while observing PCM data ED01. check TPS and TPS jumper connectors for open or shorts. Cycle TPS through its travel and lightly tap on the TPS while watching display to test for intermittent. If a fault is induced, PCM data ED01 will momentarily skip to 72 degrees or greater or 1.3 degrees or less. If wiring or connector are okay, substitute a known good TPS and recheck.

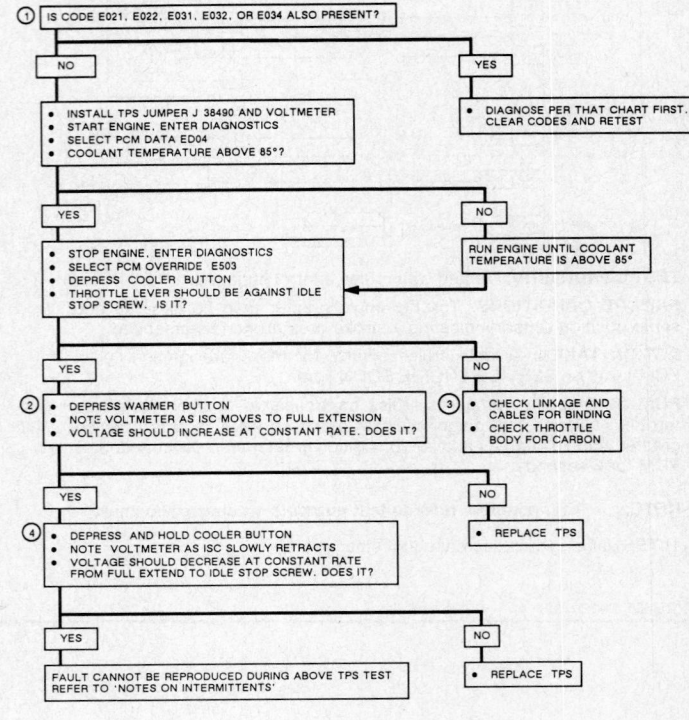

WHEN ALL DIAGNOSIS AND REPAIRS ARE COMPLETED, CLEAR CODES AND VERIFY OPERATION

91E07541   91A07582

Courtesy of General Motors Corp.

1991 ENGINE PERFORMANCE
Self-Diagnostics – Eldorado & Seville PCM/BCM (Cont.)

GM
1-269

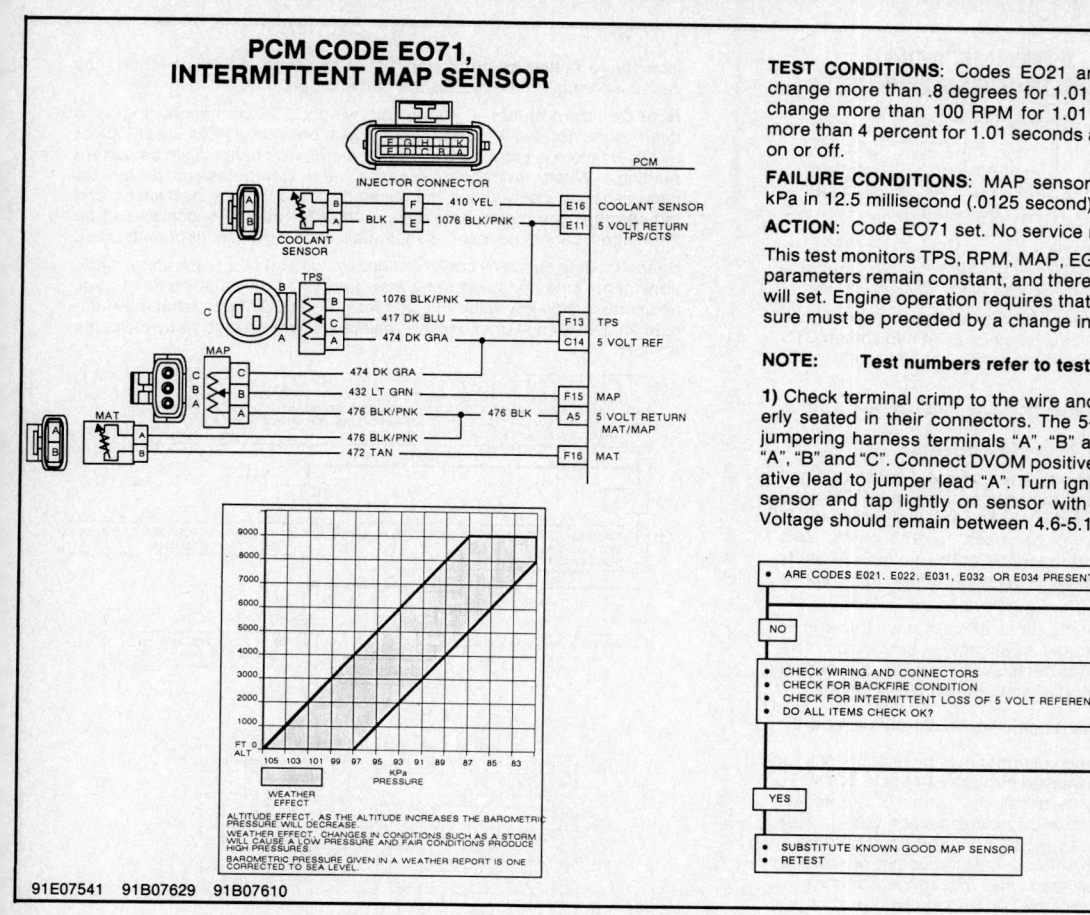

PCM CODE EO71, INTERMITTENT MAP SENSOR

TEST CONDITIONS: Codes EO21 and EO22 not set. TPS does not change more than .8 degrees for 1.01 seconds. Engine speed does not change more than 100 RPM for 1.01 seconds. EGR does not change more than 4 percent for 1.01 seconds and A/C clutch is not commanded on or off.

FAILURE CONDITIONS: MAP sensor reading changes more than 5.5 kPa in 12.5 millisecond (.0125 second).

ACTION: Code EO71 set. No service message.

This test monitors TPS, RPM, MAP, EGR flow and A/C clutch. If all these parameters remain constant, and there is a rapid change in MAP, a code will set. Engine operation requires that a large change in manifold pressure must be preceded by a change in throttle angle.

NOTE: Test numbers refer to test numbers on diagnostic chart.

1) Check terminal crimp to the wire and ensure that terminals are properly seated in their connectors. The 5-volt reference can be tested by jumpering harness terminals "A", "B" and "C" to MAP sensor terminals "A", "B" and "C". Connect DVOM positive lead to jumper lead "C" and negative lead to jumper lead "A". Turn ignition on. Apply vacuum signal to sensor and tap lightly on sensor with a pencil or pocket screwdriver. Voltage should remain between 4.6-5.1 volts, when sensor is tapped.

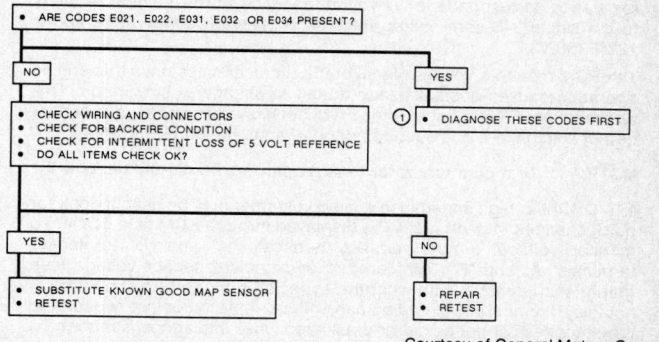

ALTITUDE EFFECT. AS THE ALTITUDE INCREASES THE BAROMETRIC PRESSURE WILL DECREASE.
WEATHER EFFECT. CHANGES IN CONDITIONS SUCH AS A STORM WILL CAUSE A LOW PRESSURE AND FAIR CONDITIONS PRODUCE HIGH PRESSURES
BAROMETRIC PRESSURE GIVEN IN A WEATHER REPORT IS ONE CORRECTED TO SEA LEVEL.

91E07541   91B07629   91B07610

PCM CODE EO73, INTERMITTENT COOLANT SENSOR SIGNAL

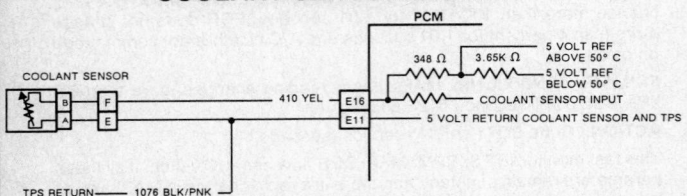

TEST CONDITIONS: 2 seconds have passed since ignition switch has been turned on and 2 seconds have passed since PCM had shifted CTS pull-up resistors. This occurs when sensor resistance indicates 122°F (50°C).

FAILURE CONDITIONS: CTS voltage has changes .3 volt in one second.

ACTION: Code EO73 has been set. No service message.

The CTS circuit uses 2 pull-up resistors for temperature sensing. When sensor resistance is high (indicating low temperatures), the PCM uses the 3.65K and 348-ohm resistor in series. As temperature increases to 122°F (50°C), sensor resistance will decrease to 973 ohms. This resistance corresponds to .97 volt at the PCM. At this point PCM shifts to the single 348-ohm pull-up resistor to measure temperature above 122°F (50°C).

The PCM monitors voltage signal of the circuit and assumes that engine operation causes coolant temperatures to change at slow rates. This test monitors CTS voltage. If the PCM detects a large change in sensor output voltage in a one second period of time, the code will set.

NOTE: Test numbers refer to test numbers on diagnostic chart.

1) A DVOM or high impedance analog voltmeter may be used to look for quick changes that too fast to be displayed through PCM data EDO4. To monitor voltage, jumper harness terminals "A" and "B" to sensor terminals "A" and "B". Temperature and coolant sensor voltage (see graph) should match with what the expected temperature should be at hot idle. If temperature reading has shifted, replace coolant sensor and retest (codes cannot be set or duplicated while in diagnostic mode).
2) A "Scan" tester or DVOM can alternately be used to observe changes in readings.
3) Since coolant temperature cannot change rapidly, a sudden change which occurs at idle as the engine is warming up or idling hot most likely indicates a faulty coolant sensor. A loose terminal or connection may cause a change in the resistance of the circuit.

Note On Intermittents – Manipulate wiring, CTS connector, engine to dash connector and PCM connector, while observing PCM data ED04 or meter. If failure is induced, the data or meter will change from its current reading. When voltage increases and temperature parameter decreases, an open circuit is indicated. When voltage decreases and temperature parameter increases, a short to ground is indicated. If an intermittent cannot be found, substitute a known good sensor and retest.

Snapshot data captures coolant sensor value and other operating conditions at the time code was set. While it provides only one frame of data, an unexpectedly low value of ED04 from Code EO73 snapshot may indicate an open circuit or excessive resistance, while a high value indicates a short.

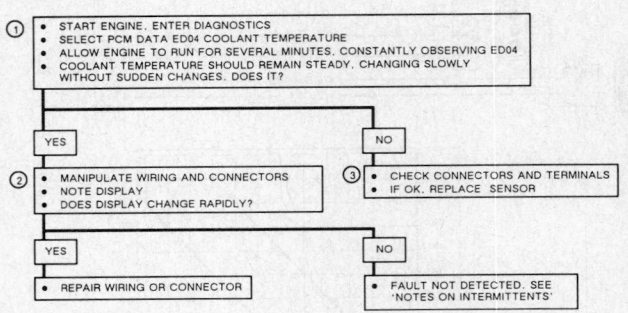

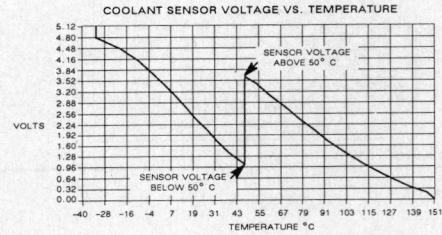

COOLANT SENSOR VOLTAGE VS. TEMPERATURE

91D07611   91F07612

Courtesy of General Motors Corp.

1991 ENGINE PERFORMANCE
Self-Diagnostics – Eldorado & Seville PCM/BCM (Cont.)

GM
1-271

PCM CODE EO74, INTERMITTENT MAT SENSOR SIGNAL

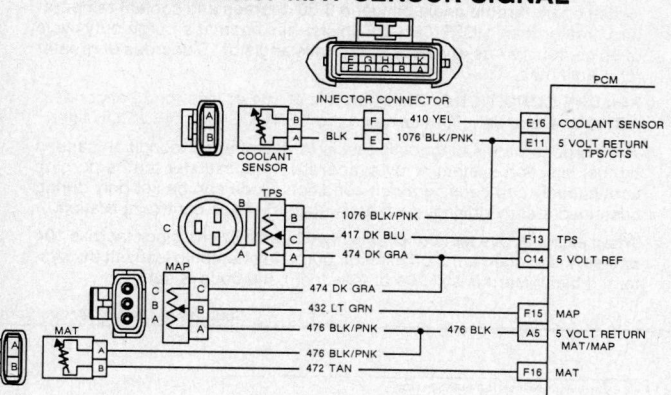

- JUMPER HARNESS CONNECTOR 'A' TO SENSOR CONNECTOR 'A'
- JUMPER HARNESS CONNECTOR 'B' TO SENSOR CONNECTOR 'B'
- CONNECT DVM POSITIVE LEAD TO JUMPER 'B'
- NEGATIVE LEAD TO JUMPER 'A'
- START ENGINE, ENTER DIAGNOSTICS
- SELECT PCM DATA ED05
- COMPARE DISPLAY TO METER
- DOES VOLTAGE AND DISPLAY AGREE AS ENGINE TEMPERATURE INCREASES?

YES	NO

- MANIPULATE WIRING AND CONNECTORS
- NOTE METER OR DISPLAY
- DOES METER OR DISPLAY CHANGE RAPIDLY

① ▸ REPLACE SENSOR

YES	NO

- REPAIR WIRING OR CONNECTOR
- FAULT NOT DETECTED. SEE 'NOTES ON INTERMITTENTS'

TEST CONDITIONS: Engine running.

FAILURE CONDITIONS: MAT change of 7 degrees or more in 250 milliseconds.

ACTION: PCM will set Code EO74. No service message.

Note On Intermittents – This code can be caused by an open, short to ground or short to voltage on circuits No. 472 and/or 469, an open or short in sensor connector, engine-to-dash connector or PCM connector. If no problems are found in wiring or connectors, substitute a known good sensor and retest.

91E07541   91H07613

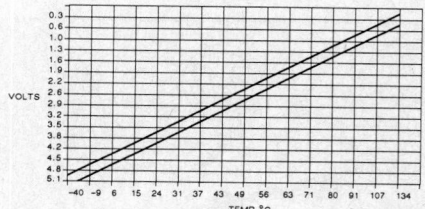

PCM CODE EO75, VSS SIGNAL INTERRUPT

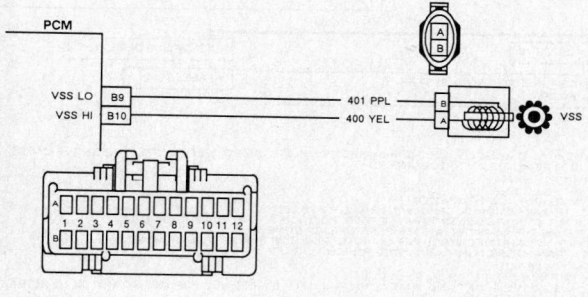

TEST CONDITIONS: Codes EO31, EO32 and EO34 not set, engine running and brakes not applied.

FAILURE CONDITIONS: Vehicle speed change of 8 MPH or more in a one second time period with a corresponding MAP change of 2 kPa or less.

ACTION: PCM will set Code EO75.

This test compares vehicle speed to manifold pressure. There must be a corresponding change in MAP with a change in vehicle speed. PCM will ignore test if conditions for engine idle are present.

Note On Intermittents – Manipulate VSS wiring and connectors and verify wiring is not close too spark plug wires. Code can be caused by an open, short to ground, or short to voltage on circuit No. 400 or 401. Also, check for an open or shorted sensor connector, engine-to-dash connector, PCM connector or a defective sensor. If wiring and connectors check out okay, substitute a known good sensor and retest.

91J07614

PCM CODE EO80, FUEL SYSTEM RICH

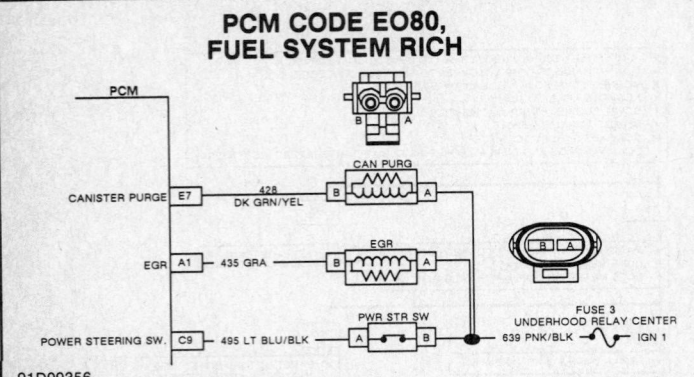

91D09356

TEST CONDITIONS: Codes EO14, EO15, EO16, EO21, EO22, EO26, EO27, EO31, EO32 or EO34 not set. System in closed loop, throttle switch open, throttle angle between 6-30 degrees and coolant temperature greater than 180°F (82°C). Canister has been at a purge duty cycle of 94 percent (purge enabled) at a throttle angle of 10 degrees or greater for 10 minutes.

FAILURE CONDITIONS: Block learn is at 104 or less for 25 seconds.
ACTION: Code set. PCM turns on the SERVICE ENGINE SOON light.

The purpose of this diagnostic test is to detect a rich condition caused by fuel injection system or by evaporative fuel canister that is purging continuously and causing a rich condition. Code can be set only during sustained steady driving, such as sustained cruise control operation.

When all the above test conditions have been met and block learn is 104 or less, the system turns off canister purge to attempt to lean out the system. If block learn is still 104 or less (rich), the code is set.

Courtesy of General Motors Corp.

PCM CODE EO85, THROTTLE BODY SERVICE REQUIRED

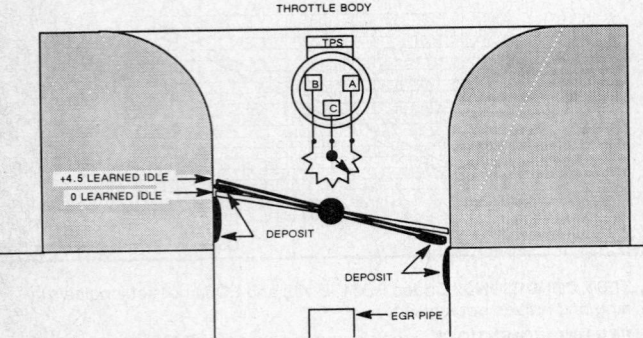

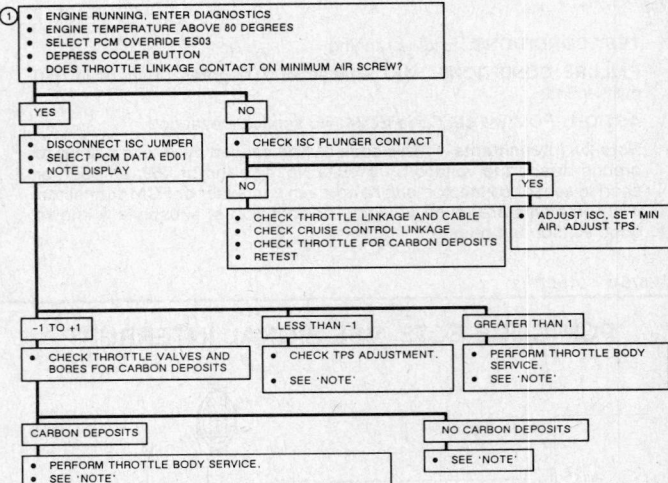

TEST CONDITIONS: Constantly monitored.

FAILURE CONDITIONS: Coast down throttle angle offset is greater than 5 degrees from learned value.

ACTION: PCM will set Code EO85 and turn on SERVICE ENGINE SOON light.

NOTE: Test numbers refer to test numbers on diagnostic chart.

1) If engine stalls, continue the test. The stall may be caused by the carbon deposits on the throttle valves and in the throttle bores.

NOTE: WHEN ALL DIAGNOSIS AND REPAIRS ARE COMPLETE, DISCONNECT BATTERY NEGATIVE CABLE FOR 10 SECONDS AND RECONNECT.
TO PERFORM IDLE LEARN
- START THE ENGINE
- ALLOW TO IDLE FOR 13 MINUTES
- PLACE TRANSMISSION IN DRIVE WITH BRAKES APPLIED
- PLACE THE CLIMATE CONTROL IN THE 'OFF' POSITION FOR AT LEAST 1 MINUTE
- MAKE SURE THE OUTSIDED AIR TEMPERATURE IS ABOVE 50°F
- PLACE THE CLIMATE CONTROL IN THE 'AUTO' POSITION FOR AT LEAST 1 MINUTE
- PLACE TRANSMISSION IN PARK AND TURN IGNITION OFF
TO PERFORM TPS LEARN
- TURN IGNITION ON, ENTER DIAGNOSTICS
- TURN THE IGNITION 'OFF' AND WAIT APPROXIMATELY 20 SECONDS FOR THE ISC MOTOR TO RETRACT
- TURN THE IGNITION 'ON'
- REENTER DIAGNOSTICS
- TURN THE IGNITION OFF

Courtesy of General Motors Corp.

91C07615   91E07616

1991 ENGINE PERFORMANCE
Self-Diagnostics – Eldorado & Seville PCM/BCM (Cont.)

GM
1-273

PCM CODE EO90, VCC BRAKE SWITCH INPUT PROBLEM

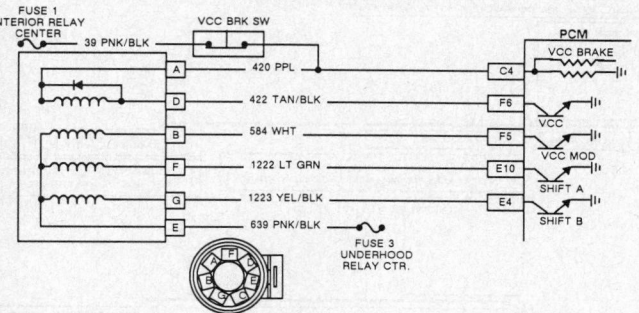

91F07631   91G07617

TEST CONDITIONS: Code EO24 not set, engine running and vehicle speed is greater than 30 MPH.

FAILURE CONDITIONS: Vehicle speed cycles from 30 MPH or greater to zero MPH with no VCC brake switch input. PCM must record 10 of these events to set code.

ACTION: PCM will set Code EO90 and turn on SERVICE ENGINE SOON light.

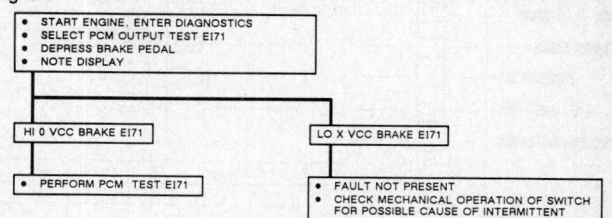

Courtesy of General Motors Corp.

PCM CODE EO91, PARK/NEUTRAL SWITCH PROBLEM (1 OF 2)

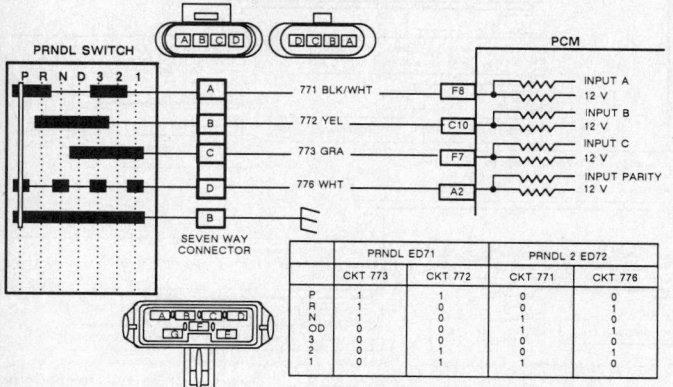

PRNDL ED71		PRNDL 2 ED72	
CKT 773	CKT 772	CKT 771	CKT 776

	CKT 773	CKT 772	CKT 771	CKT 776
P	1	1	0	0
R	1	1	0	1
N	1	0	1	0
OD	0	0	1	1
3	0	1	1	0
2	0	0	0	1
1	0	1	1	0

PCM VOLTAGE CHECK

PCM TERM	SW CLOSED	SW OPEN
F8	0 TO 0.3 Volts	BATTERY
C10	0 TO 0.3 VOLTS	BATTERY
F7	0 TO 0.3 Volts	BATTERY
A2	0 TO 0.3 Volts	BATTERY

TEST CONDITIONS: Constantly monitored.

FAILURE CONDITIONS: An open or short to ground in one or more switches or circuits that would generate an invalid binary code. An engine start with a code recognized by the PCM as one for a forward or reverse gear.

ACTION: Code EO91 is set. PCM turns on SERVICE VEHICLE SOON message.

Note On Intermittents – Drive vehicle and observe park/neutral parameter display. Stop vehicle and wiggle shifter. If display changes, check for defective switch or intermittent short to ground.

91I07618   91A07619   91C07620

- IGNITION 'ON', ENTER DIAGNOSTICS
- SELECT PCM DATA ED71
- PLACE GEAR SELECTOR IN ALL GEARS FROM 'P' TO '1'
- NOTE DISPLAY AND COMPARE LEFT DIGIT TO CHART

LEFT DIGIT (CKT 773)

P	1
R	1
N	1
OD	0
3	0
2	0
1	0

1 OR 0 IN ALL GEARS → MATCHES SEQUENCE ABOVE / CHANGE BUT DOES NOT MATCH SEQUENCE ABOVE

- PLACE GEAR SELECTOR IN ALL GEARS FROM 'P' TO '1'
- NOTE DISPLAY AND COMPARE RIGHT DIGIT TO CHART

- CHECK PRNDL SWITCH ADJUSTMENT
- IF OK, REPLACE PRNDL SWITCH

RIGHT DIGIT (CKT 772)

P	1
R	1
N	0
OD	0
3	0
2	0
1	1

1 OR 0 IN ALL GEARS / CHANGES BUT DOES NOT MATCH SEQUENCE ABOVE / MATCHES SEQUENCE ABOVE

- CHECK PRNDL SWITCH ADJUSTMENT
- IF OK, REPLACE PRNDL SWITCH

CONTINUED IN   2 OF 2

- DISCONNECT 4 WAY PRNDL SWITCH CONNECTOR
- NOTE DISPLAY, DISPLAY SHOULD HAVE A '1' AS THE RIGHT DIGIT. DOES IT?

YES / NO

- JUMPER HARNESS TERMINAL 'B' TO GROUND
- NOTE DISPLAY, IS RIGHT DIGIT '0'?

- DISCONNECT PCM C/D CONNECTOR
- CONNECT DVM SET TO OHMS SCALE FROM TERMINAL 'C10' TO GROUND
- NOTE METER

NO / YES

- OPEN CKT 772 / REPLACE PRNDL SWITCH

CONTINUITY / OPEN

SHORT TO GROUND CKT 772 / REPLACE PCM

- DISCONNECT 4 WAY PRNDL SWITCH CONNECTOR
- NOTE DISPLAY, DISPLAY SHOULD HAVE A '1' AS THE LEFT DIGIT. DOES IT?

YES / NO

- JUMPER HARNESS TERMINAL 'C' TO GROUND
- NOTE DISPLAY, IS LEFT DIGIT '0'?

- DISCONNECT PCM E/F CONNECTOR
- CONNECT DVM SET TO OHMS SCALE FROM TERMINAL 'F7' TO GROUND
- NOTE METER

NO / YES

- OPEN CKT 773 / CHECK PRNDL SWITCH GROUND AND GROUND CIRCUIT
- IF OK, REPLACE PRNDL SWITCH

CONTINUITY / OPEN

SHORT TO GROUND CKT 773 / REPLACE PCM

WHEN ALL DIAGNOSIS AND REPAIR ARE COMPLETED, RECONNECT 4-WAY PRNDL CONNECTOR, CLEAR CODES, AND VERIFY OPERATION

Courtesy of General Motors Corp.

PCM CODE EO91, PARK/NEUTRAL SWITCH PROBLEM (2 OF 2)

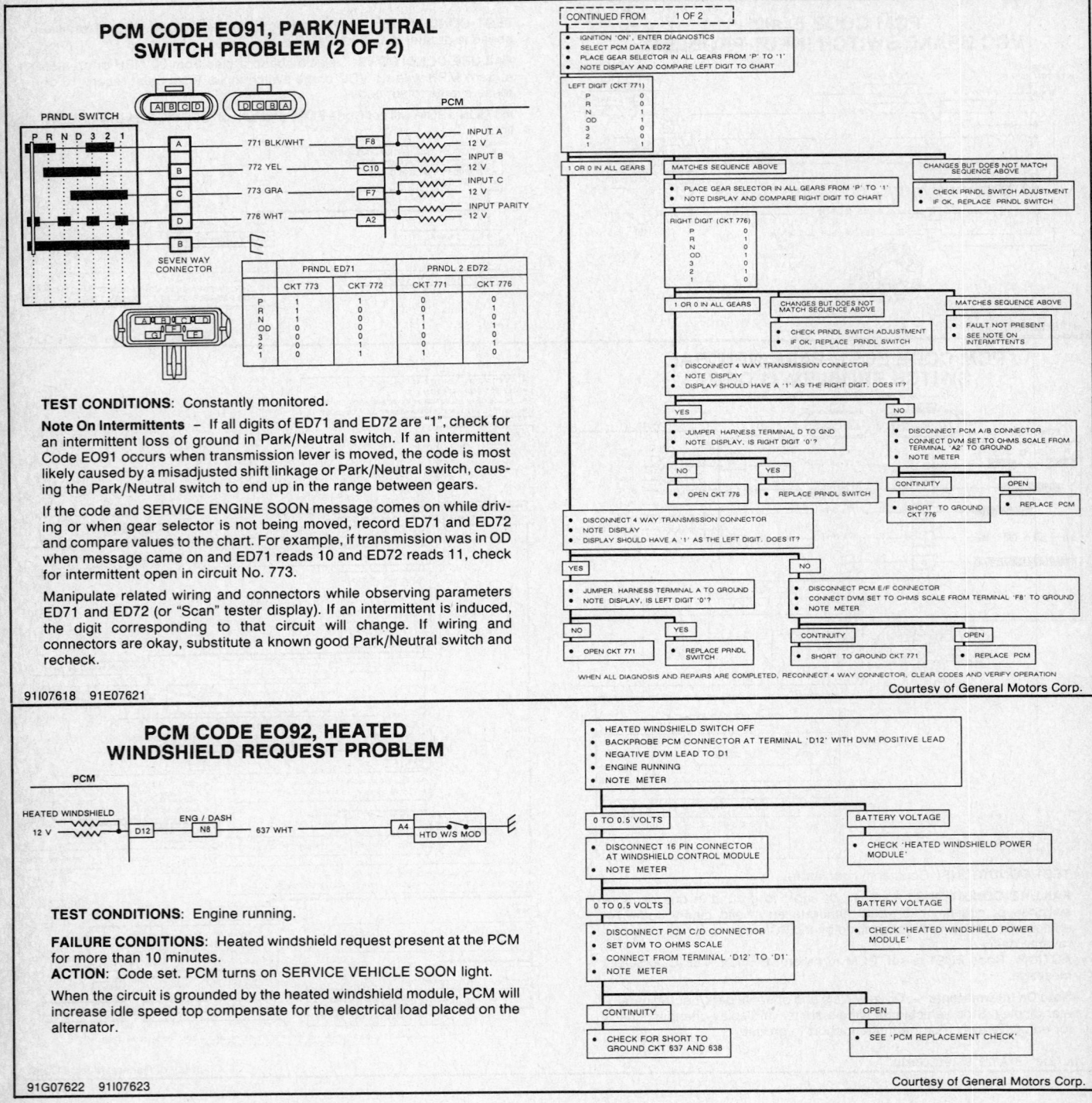

	PRNDL ED71		PRNDL 2 ED72	
	CKT 773	CKT 772	CKT 771	CKT 776
P	1	1	0	0
R	1	0	0	1
N	1	0	1	0
OD	0	0	1	1
3	0	1	1	0
2	0	1	0	1
1	0	1	1	0

TEST CONDITIONS: Constantly monitored.

Note On Intermittents – If all digits of ED71 and ED72 are "1", check for an intermittent loss of ground in Park/Neutral switch. If an intermittent Code EO91 occurs when transmission lever is moved, the code is most likely caused by a misadjusted shift linkage or Park/Neutral switch, causing the Park/Neutral switch to end up in the range between gears.

If the code and SERVICE ENGINE SOON message comes on while driving or when gear selector is not being moved, record ED71 and ED72 and compare values to the chart. For example, if transmission was in OD when message came on and ED71 reads 10 and ED72 reads 11, check for intermittent open in circuit No. 773.

Manipulate related wiring and connectors while observing parameters ED71 and ED72 (or "Scan" tester display). If an intermittent is induced, the digit corresponding to that circuit will change. If wiring and connectors are okay, substitute a known good Park/Neutral switch and recheck.

91I07618   91E07621

WHEN ALL DIAGNOSIS AND REPAIRS ARE COMPLETED, RECONNECT 4 WAY CONNECTOR, CLEAR CODES AND VERIFY OPERATION

Courtesy of General Motors Corp.

PCM CODE EO92, HEATED WINDSHIELD REQUEST PROBLEM

TEST CONDITIONS: Engine running.

FAILURE CONDITIONS: Heated windshield request present at the PCM for more than 10 minutes.

ACTION: Code set. PCM turns on SERVICE VEHICLE SOON light.

When the circuit is grounded by the heated windshield module, PCM will increase idle speed top compensate for the electrical load placed on the alternator.

91G07622   91I07623

Courtesy of General Motors Corp.

1991 ENGINE PERFORMANCE
Self-Diagnostics – Eldorado & Seville PCM/BCM (Cont.)

GM
1-275

PCM CODE EO96, TORQUE CONVERTER OVERSTRESS

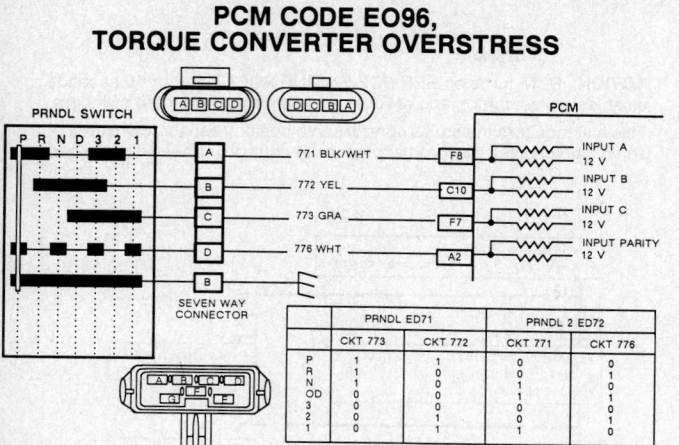

91I07618

TEST CONDITIONS: Codes EO21, EO22 and EO24 not set.

FAILURE CONDITIONS: Brake applied, transmission in Drive or Reverse, vehicle speed 5 MPH or less and throttle angle greater than 65 degrees for 12 seconds.

ACTION: PCM will set Code EO96.

Courtesy of General Motors Corp.

PCM CODE EO97, PARK/NEUTRAL TO DRIVE/REVERSE AT HIGH THROTTLE ANGLE

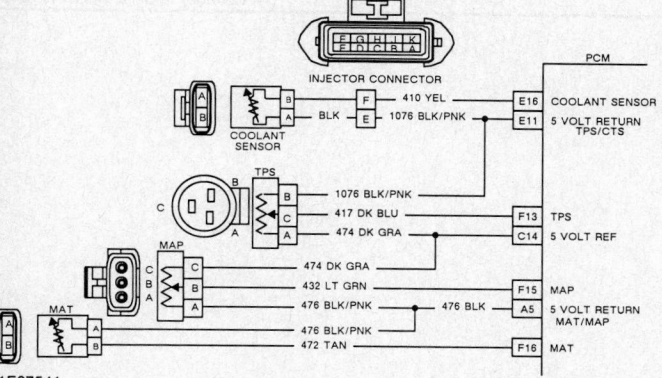

91E07541

TEST CONDITIONS: Codes EO21 and EO22 clear.

FAILURE CONDITIONS: Engine speed greater than 2000 RPM, gear selector moved from Park or Neutral to Drive or Reverse, vehicle speed less than 6 MPH and throttle angle is 20 percent or greater.

ACTION: PCM will disable selected injectors, set Code EO97 and no service message.

Courtesy of General Motors Corp.

PCM CODE EO98, PARK/NEUTRAL TO DRIVE/REVERSE WHILE OUTSIDE OF ISC CONTROL RANGE

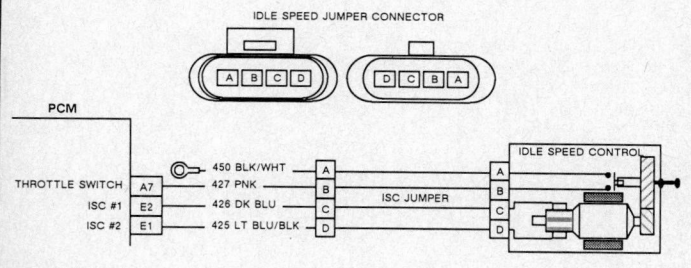

91G09348

TEST CONDITIONS: Codes EO21 and EO22 not set.

FAILURE CONDITIONS: Engine running and gear selector moved from Park or Neutral to Drive or Reverse. Engine speed 600 RPM greater than engine speed determined by PCM. Throttle angle or 20 degrees or less and vehicle speed less than 6 MPH.

ACTION: PCM will retard ignition timing and set Code EO98. No service message.

This test monitors idle speed and gear selection from Park or Neutral to Drive or Reverse when the throttle is in ISC speed range. If idle speed is greater than desired, PCM will retard spark advance and set the code.

Courtesy of General Motors Corp.

GM
1-276

1991 ENGINE PERFORMANCE
Self-Diagnostics – Eldorado & Seville PCM/BCM (Cont.)

PCM CODE EO99,
CRUISE SERVO APPLIED NOT IN CRUISE

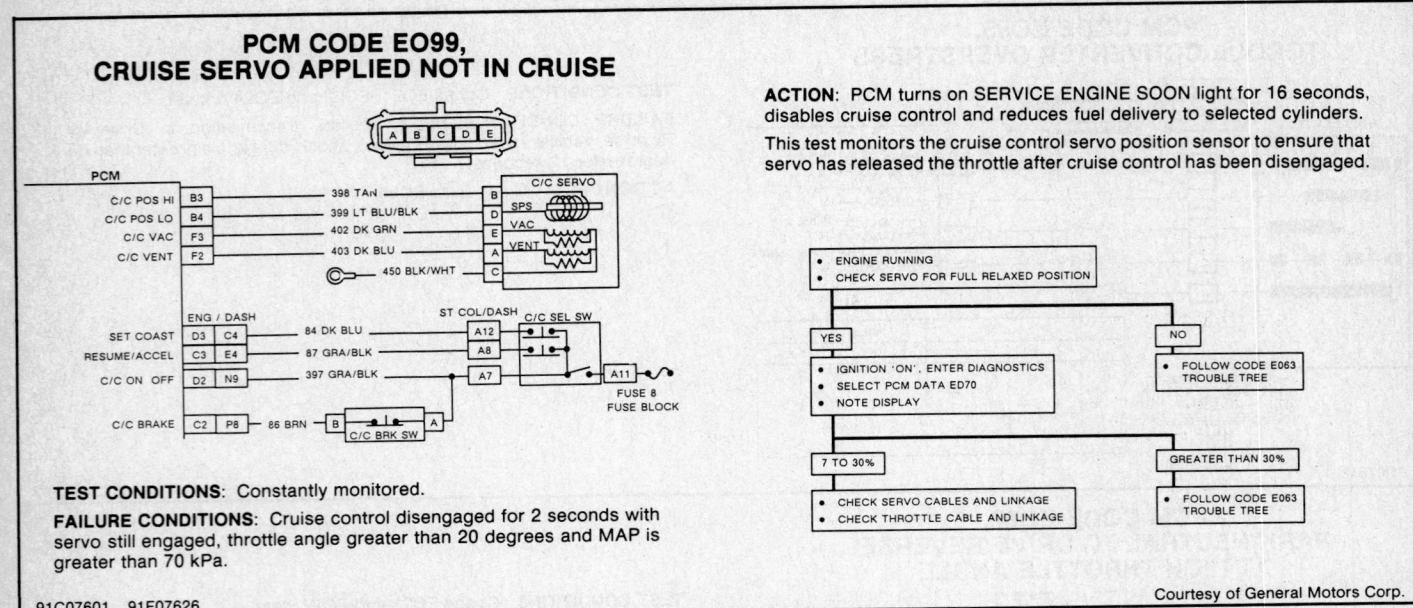

ACTION: PCM turns on SERVICE ENGINE SOON light for 16 seconds, disables cruise control and reduces fuel delivery to selected cylinders.

This test monitors the cruise control servo position sensor to ensure that servo has released the throttle after cruise control has been disengaged.

TEST CONDITIONS: Constantly monitored.

FAILURE CONDITIONS: Cruise control disengaged for 2 seconds with servo still engaged, throttle angle greater than 20 degrees and MAP is greater than 70 kPa.

91C07601   91F07626

Courtesy of General Motors Corp.

1991 ENGINE PERFORMANCE
Self-Diagnostics – Eldorado & Seville PCM/BCM (Cont.)

GM
1-277

BCM CODE CHARTS

BCM CODE B110, OUTSIDE AIR TEMPERATURE SENSOR CIRCUIT

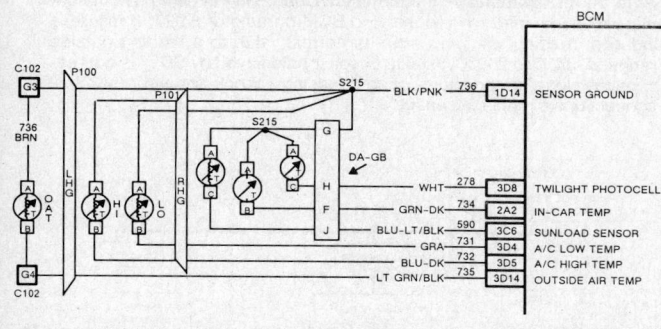

The outside air temperature sensor is a thermistor that controls the signal voltage to BCM. The BCM supplies voltage on circuit No. 735 to sensor. When sensor is cold, its resistance is high, therefore BCM will see a high monitored signal voltage. As sensor warms, its resistance becomes less and signal voltage is pulled low through sensor ground, circuit No. 736. This signal voltage will vary between 5 volts (open circuit) and zero volts (shorted circuit).

Code B110 will set if signal voltage indicates air temperature is less than -34°C (open circuit) or more than 87°C (shorted circuit). During a failure, a substitute temperature reading will be used to allow continued operation of A/C-heater system and compressor will not run continuously at idle.

NOTE: Test numbers refer to test numbers on diagnostic chart.

1) BCM data BD26 will display actual sensor reading. The normal range is from -34°C to 87°C.
2) Checks to see if open circuit reading is due to circuit or sensor. If open circuit reading changes to a shorted circuit reading after jumping sensor terminals, BCM and wiring are okay.
3) By applying a ground to various points in circuits, an open can be isolated by observing whether parameter display can be changed from open reading to shorted reading.
4) Check to see if shorted circuit reading is caused by circuit or sensor. If shorted circuit reading changes to an open circuit reading after disconnecting sensor, BCM and wiring are okay.

91G07636   90G05454

Note On Intermittents – A Code B110 will be stored in memory whenever the ambient temperature drops to less than -29°F (-34°C). This code should be ignored if this cause is suspected.

If intermittent Code B110 is being set, manipulate related wiring while observing BCM parameter BD26. If failure is induced, reading will jump from its normal value to a reading outside range of -34°C to 87°C.

If value displayed by BD26 is not reasonably close to actual temperature of air at sensor, check for poor terminal connections or replace sensor.

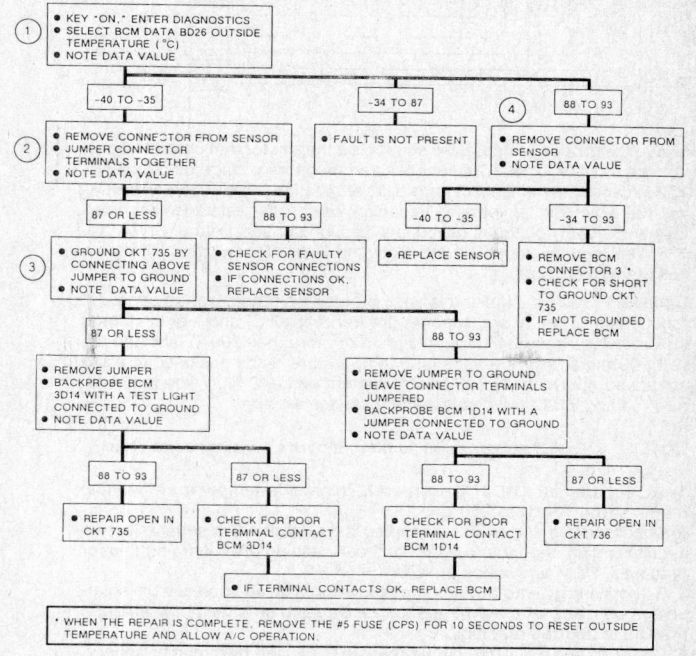

WHEN ALL DIAGNOSIS AND REPAIRS ARE COMPLETED, CLEAR CODES AND VERIFY PROPER OPERATION

Courtesy of General Motors Corp.

GM
1-278

1991 ENGINE PERFORMANCE
Self-Diagnostics – Eldorado & Seville PCM/BCM (Cont.)

BCM CODE B111, A/C HIGH SIDE TEMPERATURE SENSOR CIRCUIT

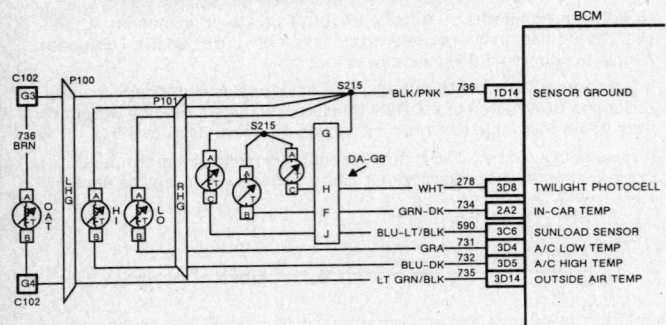

Note On Intermittents – If intermittent Code B111 is being set, manipulate related wiring while observing BCM parameter BD27. If failure is induced, reading will jump from its normal value to a reading outside range of -34°C to 209°C. If value of sensor displayed by BD27 is not reasonably close to pressure gauge reading, check for poor terminal connections or replace sensor.

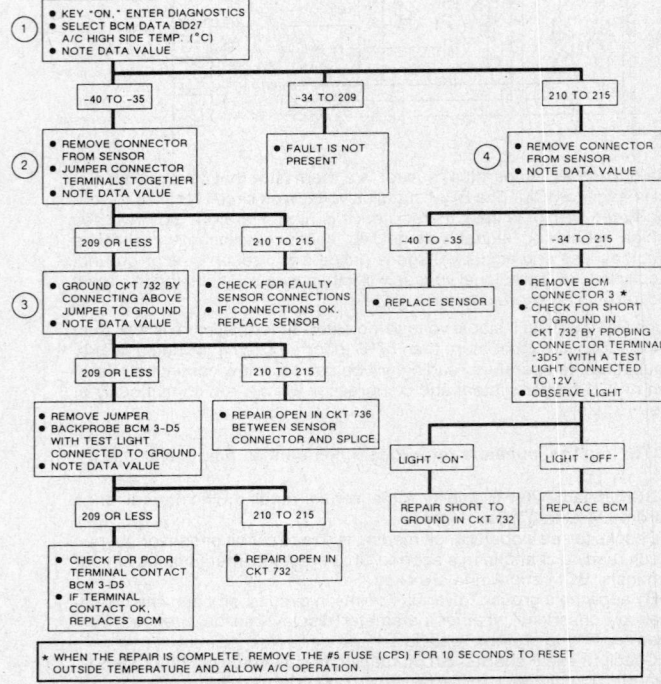

The A/C high side temperature sensor is a thermistor that controls signal voltage to BCM. The BCM supplies and monitors voltage on circuit No. 732 to sensor. When sensor is cold, its resistance is high, therefore BCM will see a high signal voltage. As sensor warms, its resistance becomes less and signal voltage is pulled low through sensor ground, circuit No. 736. This signal voltage will vary between 5 volts (open circuit) and zero volts (shorted circuit).

Code B111 will set if ignition is on, the outside air temperature sensor is functioning properly and reading greater than 0°C, and signal voltage indicates less than -34°C (open circuit) or more than 209°C (shorted circuit). During a failure, a substitute temperature reading is used to allow continued operation of A/C-heater system and A/C high side temperature reading BD27 will display actual sensor reading.

NOTE: Test numbers refer to test numbers on diagnostic chart.

1) BCM parameter BD27 displays A/C high side temperature. Normal range is from -34°C to 209°C.

2) Checks to see if open circuit reading is due to circuit or sensor. If open circuit reading changes to shorted circuit reading after jumping sensor terminals, BCM and wiring are okay.

3) By applying ground to various points in circuits, an open can be isolated by observing whether parameter display can be changed from open reading to shorted reading.

4) Check to see if shorted circuit reading is caused by circuit or sensor. If shorted circuit reading changes to an open circuit reading after disconnecting the sensor, BCM and wiring are okay.

91G07636   90A09265

Courtesy of General Motors Corp.

1991 ENGINE PERFORMANCE
Self-Diagnostics – Eldorado & Seville PCM/BCM (Cont.)

GM
1-279

BCM CODE B112, A/C LOW SIDE TEMPERATURE SENSOR CIRCUIT

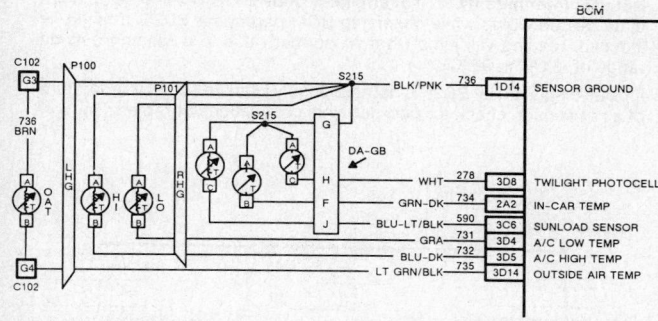

The A/C low side temperature sensor is a thermistor that controls signal voltage to BCM. The BCM supplies and monitors voltage on circuit No. 731 to sensor. When sensor is cold, its resistance is high; therefore, BCM will see a high signal voltage. As sensor warms, its resistance becomes less and signal voltage is pulled low through sensor ground, circuit No. 736. This signal voltage will vary between 5 volts (open circuit) and zero volts (shorted circuit).

Code B112 will set if signal voltage indicates less than -34°C (open circuit) or more than 87°C (shorted circuit). During a failure, a substitute temperature reading (ambient temperature reading) is used to allow continued operation of climate control system. The A/C compressor clutch will also be disabled and A/C low side temperature reading BD28 will display actual sensor reading.

NOTE: Test numbers refer to test numbers on diagnostic chart.

1) BCM parameter BD28 displays A/C low side temperature. Normal range is from -34°C to 87°C.
2) Check to see if open circuit reading is caused by circuit or sensor. If open circuit reading changes to shorted circuit reading after disconnecting sensor, BCM and wiring are okay.
3) By applying ground to various points in circuits, an open can be isolated by seeing if parameter display can be changed from open reading to shorted reading.
4) Checks to see if shorted circuit reading is caused by circuit or sensor. If shorted circuit reading changes to an open circuit reading after disconnecting sensor, BCM and wiring are okay.

91G07636   90C09266

Note On Intermittents – If intermittent Code B112 is being set, manipulate related wiring while observing BCM parameter BD28. If failure is induced, reading will jump from its normal value to a reading outside range of -34°C to 87°C.

If value displayed by data parameter BD28 is not reasonably close to corresponding pressure gauge reading, check for poor terminal connections or replace sensor.

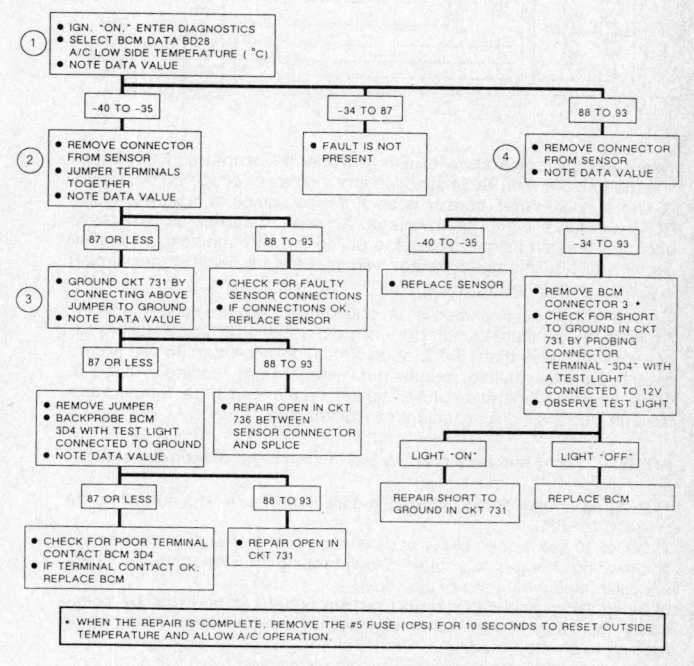

BCM CODE B113, IN-CAR TEMPERATURE SENSOR CIRCUIT

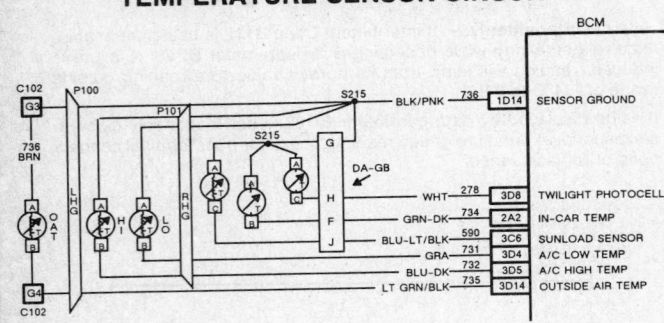

Note On Intermittents – If intermittent Code B113 is being set, manipulate related wiring while observing BCM parameter BD25. If failure is induced, reading will jump from its normal value to a reading outside range of -34°C to 96°C.

If value displayed by BD25 is not reasonably close to actual temperature of air at sensor, check for poor terminal connections or replace sensor.

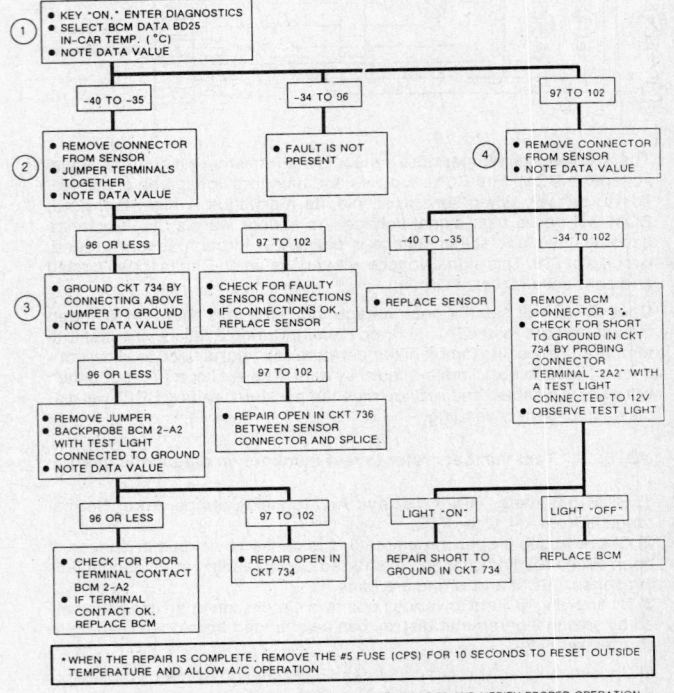

The in-car air temperature sensor is a thermistor that controls signal voltage to BCM. The BCM supplies and monitors voltage on circuit No. 734 to sensor. When sensor is cold, its resistance is high; therefore, BCM will see a high signal voltage. As sensor warms, its resistance becomes less and signal voltage is pulled low through sensor ground, circuit No. 736. This signal voltage will vary between 5 volts (open circuit) and zero volts (shorted circuit).

Code B113 will set if ignition is on, outside temperature sensor is working properly, ambient temperature is greater than -18°C and signal voltage indicates less than -34°C (open circuit) or more than 96°C (shorted circuit). During a failure, a substitute temperature reading is used to allow continued operation of A/C-heater system and in-car temperature reading BD25 will display actual sensor reading.

NOTE: Test numbers refer to test numbers on diagnostic chart.

1) BCM parameter BD25 displays in-car temperature. The normal range is -34°C to 96°C.
2) Check to see if open circuit is caused by circuit or sensor. If open circuit reading changes to shorted circuit reading after disconnecting sensor, BCM and wiring are okay.
3) By applying ground to various points in circuits, an open can be isolated by observing whether parameter display can be changed from open reading to shorted reading.
4) Check to see if shorted circuit reading is caused by circuit or sensor. If short circuit reading changes to an open circuit reading after disconnecting sensor, BCM and wiring are okay.

*WHEN THE REPAIR IS COMPLETE, REMOVE THE #5 FUSE (CPS) FOR 10 SECONDS TO RESET OUTSIDE TEMPERATURE AND ALLOW A/C OPERATION

WHEN ALL DIAGNOSIS AND REPAIRS ARE COMPLETED, CLEAR CODES AND VERIFY PROPER OPERATION

Courtesy of General Motors Corp.

91G07636   90E09267

1991 ENGINE PERFORMANCE
Self-Diagnostics – Eldorado & Seville PCM/BCM (Cont.)

GM
1-281

BCM CODE B115, SUNLOAD TEMPERATURE SENSOR

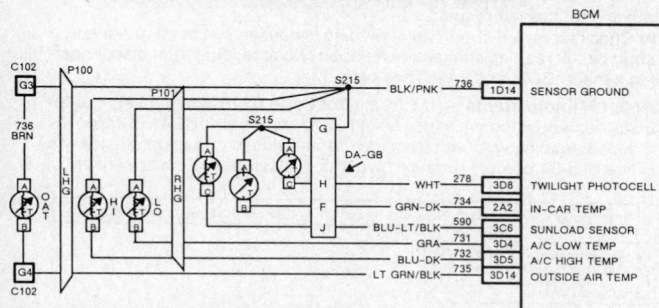

The sunload sensor uses a thermistor to control signal voltage to BCM. The BCM supplies and monitors voltage on circuit No. 590 to sensor. When sensor is cold, resistance is high; therefore, BCM will see high signal voltage. As sensor warms, resistance is lowered, signal voltage is pulled low through circuit No. 736 to ground. Signal voltage will vary between 5 volts (open circuit) and zero volts (short circuit).

Code B115 will set when ignition is on, outside temperature sensor is working properly, ambient temperature is more than -18°C and signal voltage indicates less than -34°C (open circuit) or more than 96°C (short circuit). During a failure, a substitute temperature reading will be used to allow continued operation of A/C-heater system and sunload temperature reading BD32 will display actual sensor reading.

NOTE: **Test numbers refer to test numbers on diagnostic chart.**

1) BCM parameter BD32 displays sunload temperature. Normal range is -34°C to 96°C.
2) Check to see if open circuit is caused by circuit or sensor. If open circuit reading changes to shorted circuit reading after jumping sensor terminals, BCM and wiring are okay.
3) By applying ground to various points in circuits, an open can be isolated by observing whether parameter display can be changed from open reading to shorted reading.
4) Check to see if short circuit reading is caused by circuit or sensor. If short circuit reading changes to an open circuit reading after disconnecting sensor, BCM and wiring are okay.

91G07636   90G09268

Note On Intermittents – If intermittent Code B115 is being set, manipulate related wiring while observing BCM parameter BD32. If failure is induced, reading will jump from its normal value to a reading outside range of -34°C to 96°C.

If value displayed by BD32 is not reasonably close to actual thermometer reading, check for poor terminal connections or replace sensor.

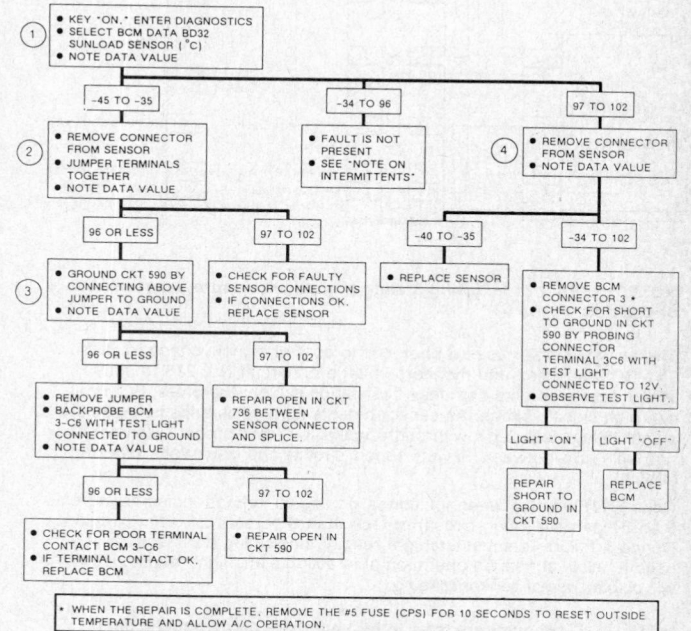

WHEN ALL DIAGNOSIS AND REPAIRS ARE COMPLETED. CLEAR CODES AND VERIFY PROPER OPERATION

Courtesy of General Motors Corp.

GM
1-282

1991 ENGINE PERFORMANCE
Self-Diagnostics – Eldorado & Seville PCM/BCM (Cont.)

BCM CODE B119, TWILIGHT PHOTOCELL CIRCUIT

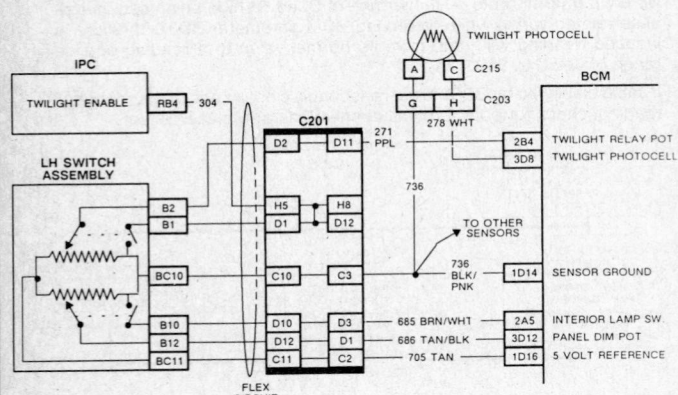

NOTE: Prior to following testing procedure, ensure sensor is not obstructed.

The twilight sensor uses a photocell to control signal voltage to BCM. The BCM supplies and monitors voltage on circuit No. 278 to sensor. When sensor detects darkness, resistance is high; therefore, BCM will see high signal voltage. As sensor detects light, resistance is lowered, signal voltage is pulled low through circuit No. 736 to ground. Signal voltage will vary between 5 volts (open circuit) and zero volts (shorted circuit).

Code B119 will set when ignition is on, signal voltage indicates more than 94 percent (open circuit) or less than 6 percent (shorted circuit). During a failure, a substitute light reading (indicating darkness) will be used to allow continued operation of headlights and light reading BD44 will display actual sensor reading.

NOTE: Test numbers refer to test numbers on diagnostic chart.

1) BCM parameter BD44 displays light level. Normal range is 6-94 percent.
2) Checks to see if open circuit is caused by circuit or sensor. If open circuit reading changes to shorted circuit reading after jumping sensor terminals, BCM and wiring are okay.

3) By applying ground to various points in circuits, an open can be isolated by observing whether parameter display can be changed from open reading to shorted reading.
4) Checks to see if short circuit reading is caused by circuit or sensor. If short circuit reading changes to an open circuit reading after disconnecting sensor, BCM and wiring are okay.

Note On Intermittents – If intermittent Code B119 is being set, manipulate related wiring while observing BCM parameter BD44. If failure is induced, reading will jump from its normal value to a reading outside the range of 6-94 percent. Ensure owner is advised not to cover sensor.

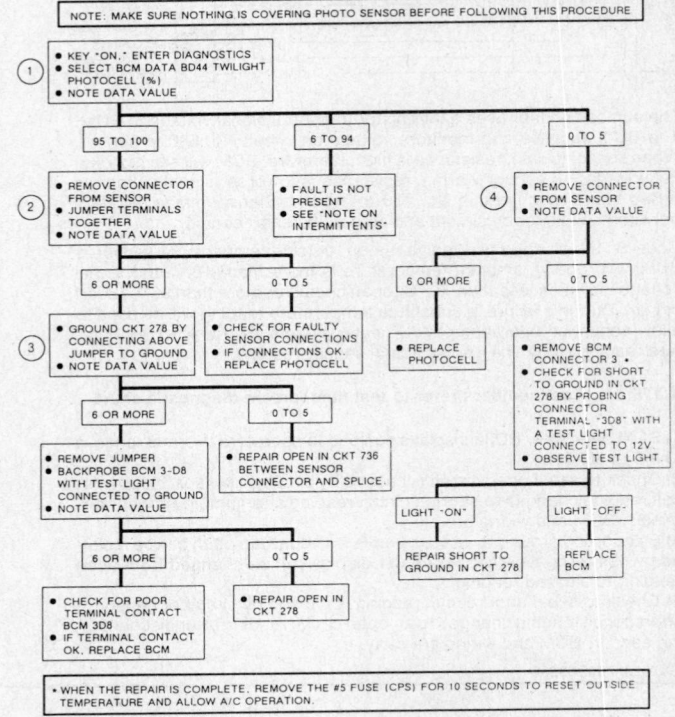

• WHEN THE REPAIR IS COMPLETE, REMOVE THE #5 FUSE (CPS) FOR 10 SECONDS TO RESET OUTSIDE TEMPERATURE AND ALLOW A/C OPERATION.

WHEN ALL DIAGNOSIS AND REPAIRS ARE COMPLETED, CLEAR CODES AND VERIFY PROPER OPERATION

Courtesy of General Motors Corp.

90A21741 90I09269

1991 ENGINE PERFORMANCE
Self-Diagnostics – Eldorado & Seville PCM/BCM (Cont.)

GM
1-283

BCM CODE B120, TWILIGHT DELAY POT CIRCUIT

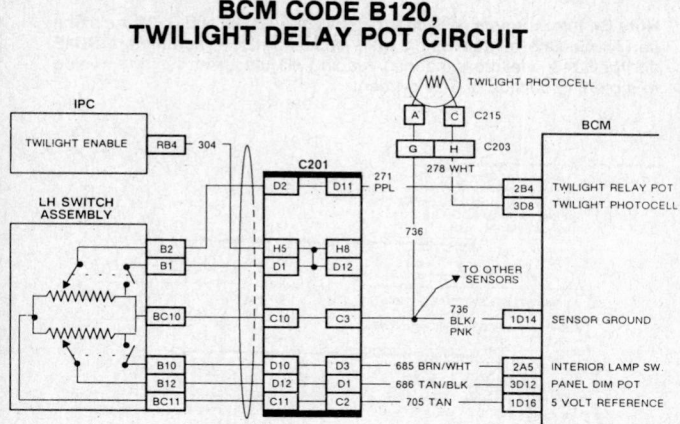

The twilight delay uses a potentiometer to control signal voltage to BCM. The BCM supplies voltage on circuit No. 705 to resistor in left switch assembly and grounds through circuit No. 736 to BCM. The wiper supplies voltage signal to BCM on circuit No. 271 indicating position of slider and delay time. When slider is moved toward maximum position, resistance is low; therefore, BCM will see high signal voltage. When slider is moved toward minimum position, resistance increases and signal voltage decreases. Signal voltage varies between zero volts (open or grounded circuit) and 5 volts (shorted voltage).

Code B120 will set when ignition is on, signal voltage indicates less than 6 percent (open or grounded circuit) or more than 94 percent (shorted to voltage). During a failure, a substitute delay time (minimum delay) is used to allow continued operation of twilight system and reading from BD43 will display actual reading.

NOTE: Test numbers refer to test numbers on diagnostic chart.

1) BCM parameter BD43 displays twilight delay. Normal range is 6-94 percent.
2) Checks to see if open circuit is caused by circuit or switch assembly. If open or grounded circuit reading changes to a short to voltage reading after jumping switch assembly terminals, BCM and wiring are okay.

3) Measuring voltage between circuit No. 705 (5 volts) and circuit No. 271 will determine if circuit No. 271 is open or shorted to ground.
4) Checks to see if short to voltage circuit reading is caused by circuit or switch assembly. If a short to voltage reading changes to an open circuit reading after disconnecting switch assembly, BCM and wiring are okay.

Note On Intermittents – If intermittent Code B120 is being set, manipulate related wiring while observing BCM parameter BD43. If failure is induced, reading will jump from its normal value to a reading outside the range of 6-94 percent.

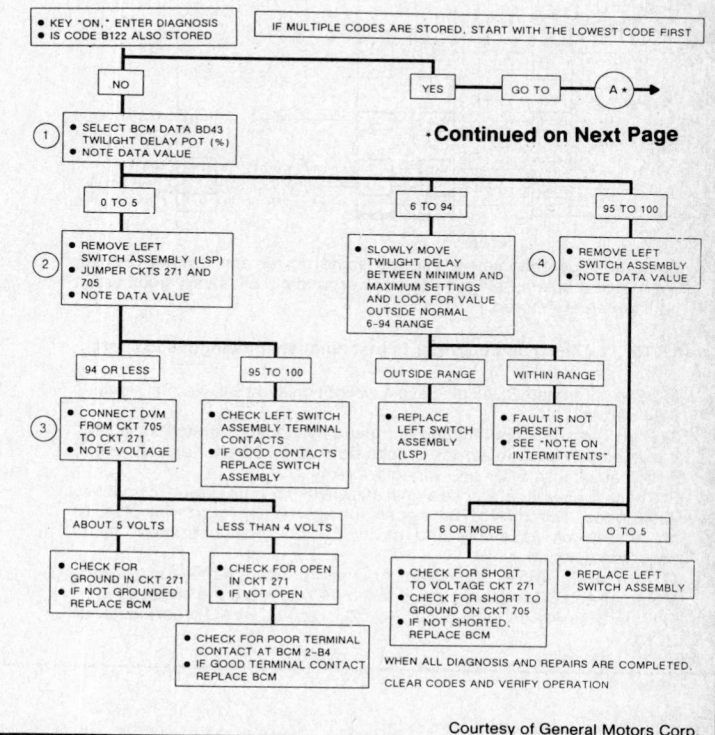

·Continued on Next Page

GM
1-284

1991 ENGINE PERFORMANCE
Self-Diagnostics – Eldorado & Seville PCM/BCM (Cont.)

BCM CODES B120 & B122, TWILIGHT DELAY & PANEL DIMMING

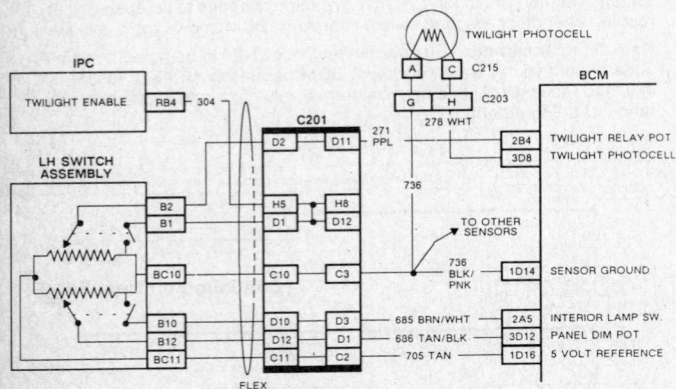

Note On Intermittents – If intermittent Codes B120 and B122 are being set, manipulate related wiring while observing BCM parameters BD42 and/or BD43. If failure is induced, reading will jump from its normal value to a reading outside of 6-94 percent.

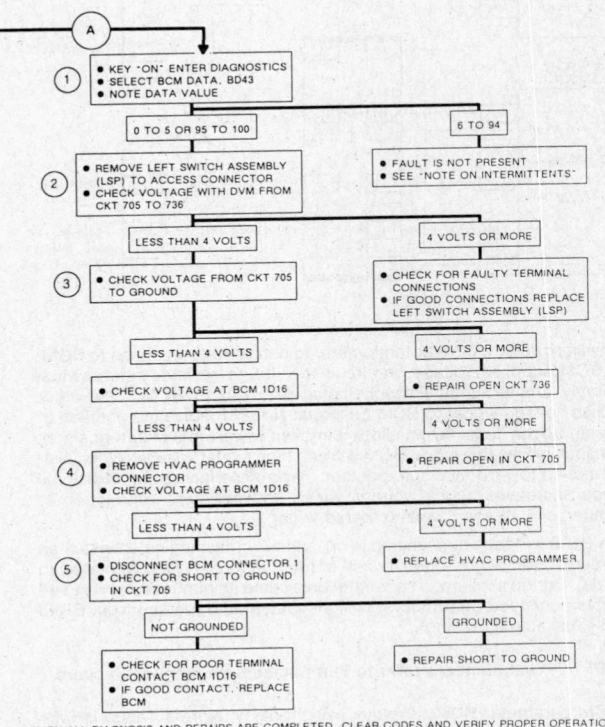

Since both potentiometers use the same power and ground circuits, chance of problem being in power or ground circuit is very good when both codes are stored.

NOTE: Test numbers refer to test numbers on diagnostic chart.

1) BCM parameter BD43 displays a twilight delay value. Normal range is 6-94 percent.

2) Check to see if open circuit is caused by circuit or switch assembly. If voltage can be read across circuits No. 705 & 736 after disconnecting switch assembly, BCM and wiring are okay.

3) Check for 5-volt reference signal at switch. If 5 volts is read, circuit No. 736 is open. If circuit No. 736 is open, the open is between terminal BC10 on left switch assembly and cavity C3 on dash/instrument panel transition connector.

4) If circuit No. 705 is suspected of being grounded, remove HVAC programmer and BCM connectors prior to making a ground check.

5) If there is no ground on circuit No. 705, replace HVAC programmer or BCM.

WHEN ALL DIAGNOSIS AND REPAIRS ARE COMPLETED, CLEAR CODES AND VERIFY PROPER OPERATION

Courtesy of General Motors Corp.

90A21741   90C09271

1991 ENGINE PERFORMANCE
Self-Diagnostics – Eldorado & Seville PCM/BCM (Cont.)

GM
1-285

BCM CODE B121, TWILIGHT ENABLE SWITCH

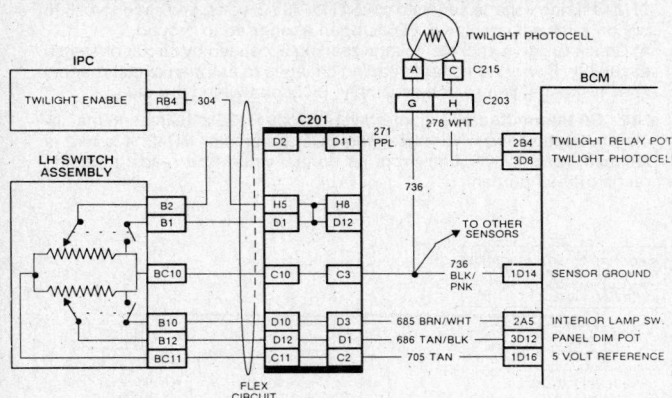

The twilight enable switch uses a physical control as the delay potentiometer. Inside left switch assembly, the enable switch contacts close when the time delay slider is moved to OFF position. The Instrument Panel Cluster (IPC) supplies voltage on circuit No. 304 to switch. When slider is moved from OFF position, the switch contacts close and signal voltage is pulled low through circuit No. 736 to ground.

Code B121 will set when ignition is on, twilight delay potentiometer is working properly (Code B120) and signal voltage is high when the delay slider is moved from OFF position (open circuit), or signal voltage is low when the delay slider is in OFF position (shorted circuit).

NOTE: Test numbers refer to test numbers on diagnostic chart.

1) IPC input parameter I182 displays voltage state of circuit No. 304 at IPC. These conditions can be observed in IPC input display as readings of high or low when delay slider is moved.

2) Check to see if LO reading is caused by circuit or switch assembly. If display changes from LO to HI when the switch assembly is disconnected, IPC is okay.

3) Check to see if HI reading is caused by circuit or switch assembly. If display changes from HI to LO when switch terminals are jumped together, the IPC and wiring are okay.

Note On Intermittents – When IPC I182 input change-of-state indicator displays an "X", check circuit for an intermittent open. Cycle twilight control between OFF and MAX delay. If BCM parameter BD43 does not read 6-94 percent, replace left switch assembly.

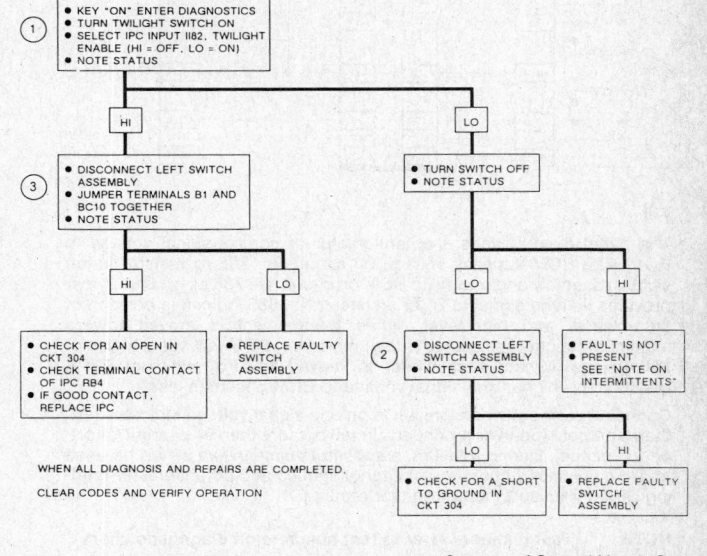

GM
1-286

1991 ENGINE PERFORMANCE
Self-Diagnostics – Eldorado & Seville PCM/BCM (Cont.)

BCM CODE B122,
PANEL LIGHT DIMMING POT CIRCUIT

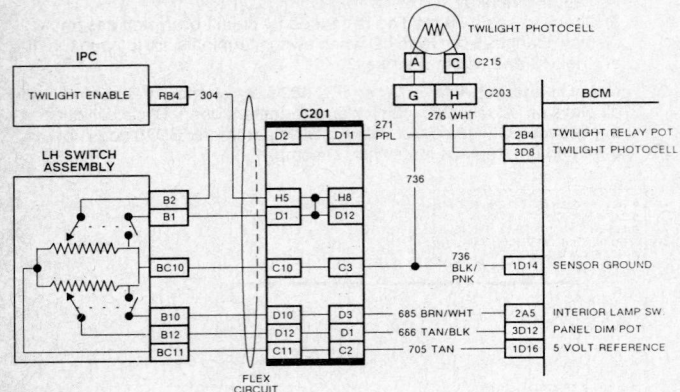

The panel dimmer uses a potentiometer to control signal voltage to BCM. The BCM supplies voltage on circuit No. 705 to resistor in left switch assembly and returns to BCM on circuit No. 736 as ground. Wiper provides voltage signal to BCM on circuit No. 686 indicating position of thumbwheel and dim level. When thumbwheel is moved toward maximum (bright), resistance is low; therefore, BCM will see a high signal voltage. When thumbwheel is moved toward minimum (dim), resistance is higher and signal voltage to BCM becomes less.

Code B122 will set when ignition is on and signal voltage indicates less than 6 percent (open or grounded circuit) or more than 94 percent (shorted to voltage). During a failure, a substitute dimming value will be used to allow continued operation of interior lighting and potentiometer reading BD42 will display actual sensor reading.

NOTE: Test numbers refer to test numbers on diagnostic chart.

1) BCM parameter BD42 displays amount of panel dimming. Normal range is 6-94 percent.
2) Check to see if open circuit is caused by circuit or switch assembly. If open or grounded circuit reading changes to shorted to voltage reading after jumping switch terminals, BCM and wiring are okay.

3) Measuring voltage between circuit No. 705 (5 volts) and circuit No. 686 will determine if circuit No. 686 is open or shorted to ground.
4) Check to see if short to voltage reading is caused by circuit or switch assembly. If short to voltage reading changes to an open circuit reading after disconnecting switch assembly, BCM and wiring are okay.

Note On Intermittents – If intermittent Code B122 is being set, manipulate related wiring while observing BCM parameter BD42. If failure is induced, reading will jump from its normal value to a reading outside range of 6-94 percent.

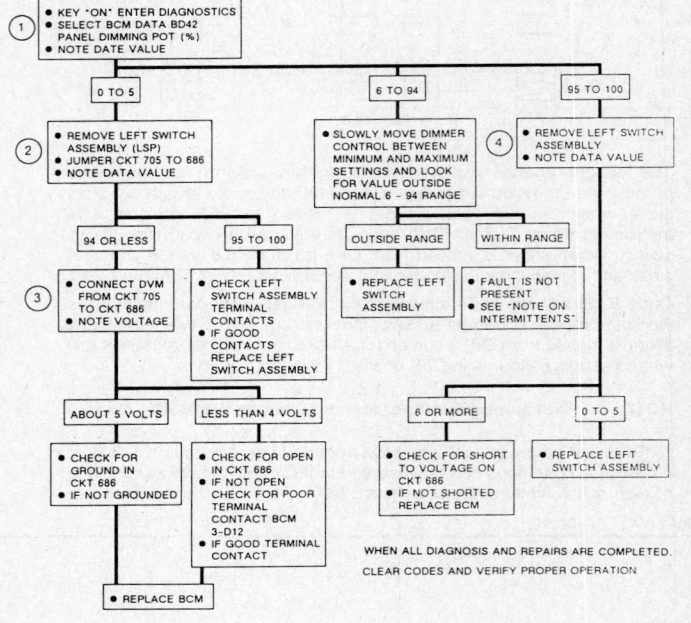

WHEN ALL DIAGNOSIS AND REPAIRS ARE COMPLETED, CLEAR CODES AND VERIFY PROPER OPERATION

Courtesy of General Motors Corp.

1991 ENGINE PERFORMANCE
Self-Diagnostics – Eldorado & Seville PCM/BCM (Cont.)

**GM
1-287**

BCM CODE B123, COURTESY LIGHT SWITCH

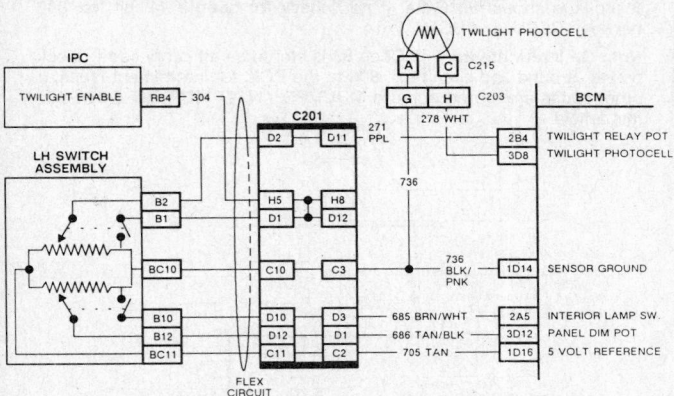

The courtesy lights panel switch is part of dimmer control potentiometer. In left switch assembly, the COURTESY LIGHTS ENABLE switch closes when dimmer is moved to extreme right. The BCM supplies signal voltage on circuit No. 685, which is pulled to ground through circuit No. 736 when switch contact is closed.

Code B123 will set when ignition is on, dimming potentiometer is working properly (Code B122) and signal voltage is high when dimmer is moved to enable position or signal voltage is low when dimmer is moved to maximum dim position.

NOTE: Test numbers refer to test numbers on diagnostic chart.

1) BCM input parameter B101 displays voltage state of circuit No. 685 at BCM.

90A21741   90I09274

2) Check to see if open circuit reading is caused by circuit or switch assembly. If display changes from HI to LO when switch terminals are jumped together, BCM and wiring are okay.
3) Check to see if open circuit reading is caused by BCM or wiring.
4) With courtesy lights switch off, checks if short to ground reading is due to switch assembly or wiring.

Note On Intermittents – If intermittent Code B123 is being set, manipulate circuit No. 685. When BCM input B101 change-of-state indicator displays an "X", check circuit at that location for intermittent fault.

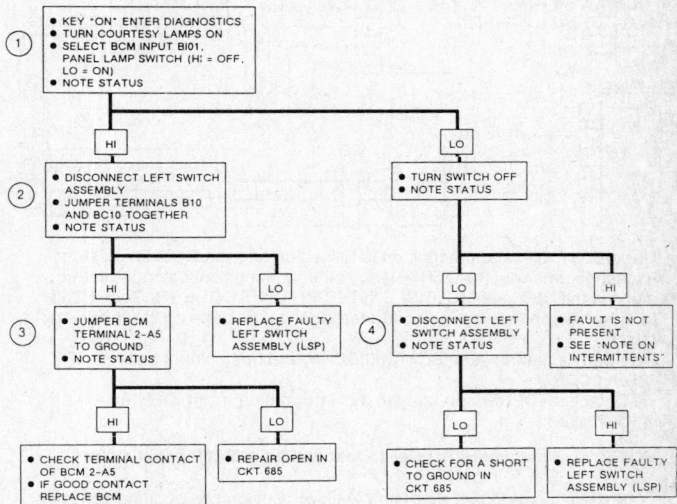

WHEN ALL DIAGNOSIS AND REPAIRS ARE COMPLETED. CLEAR CODES AND VERIFY OPERATION

Courtesy of General Motors Corp.

MULTIPLE INTERMITTENT CODES

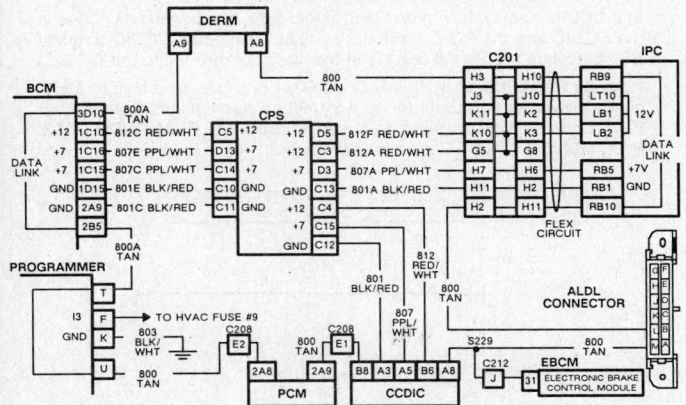

History Codes EO47, B333, B334, B335, B336 or B337
This chart should be used if 2 or more dataline history codes are retrieved.

NOTE: Test numbers refer to test numbers on diagnostic chart.

1) Checks for open in dataline circuit by measuring resistance of the loop. The first steps ensure BCM RAP has timed out and voltage is not present on the dataline during resistance checks.
2) If 10 ohms or more are present, an open in the dataline circuit is indicated. Check the codes set to determine which section of circuit No. 800 to inspect.

91H07632   90J09279

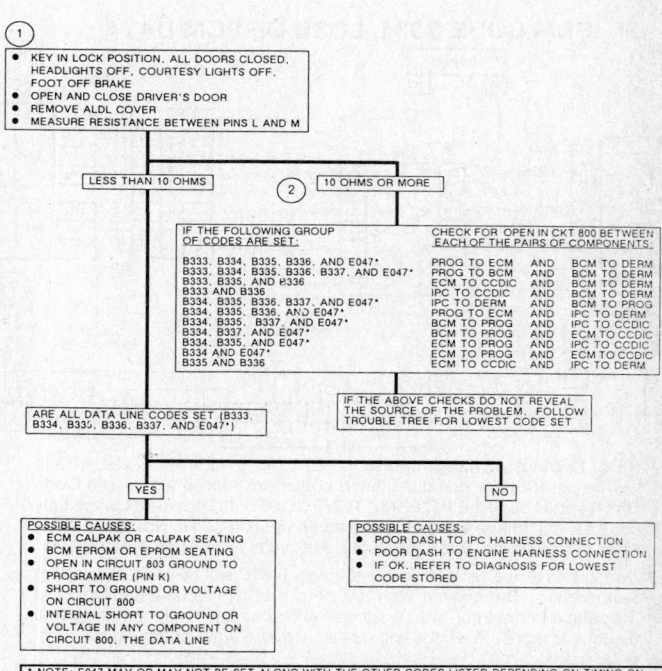

WHEN ALL DIAGNOSIS AND REPAIRS ARE COMPLETED. CLEAR CODES AND VERIFY PROPER OPERATION

Courtesy of General Motors Corp.

BCM CODE B333, LOSS OF SIR (DERM) DATA

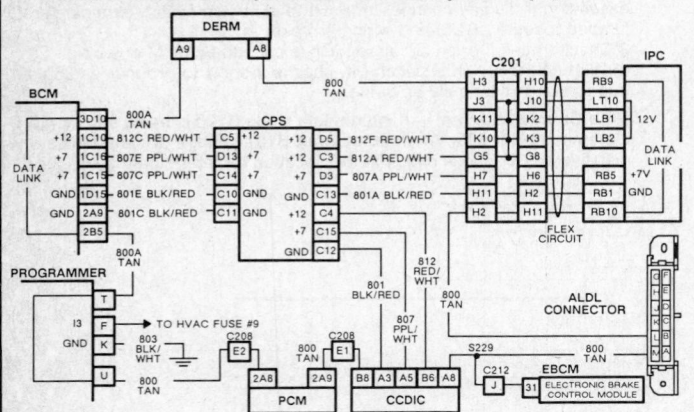

Code B333 will set if the ignition is turned on and the BCM is unable to exchange data with the DERM. If any other communication codes are set along with B333, see MULTIPLE INTERMITTENT CODES. If Code B333 is the only communication code stored, check for one of the following faults:

- Open circuit between BCM and DERM and open circuit between IPC and DERM.
- Defective DERM (no diagnostic information from DERM will be displayed.)

NOTE: Test numbers refer to test numbers on diagnostic chart.

1) DERM should cycle the telltale 7-9 times with ignition on. If not, check for defective power circuit, ground circuit, or internal DERM failure.

2) If multiple codes are present, refer to MULTIPLE INTERMITTENT CODES.

91H07632   90B09280

3) Voltage should fluctuate. If not, check for open in circuit No. 800 between DERM and BCM.

Note On Intermittents – If Code 33 is stored as a history code, check power, ground and circuit No. 800 to the BCM for intermittent faults. If other codes are stored, refer to MULTIPLE INTERMITTENT CODES in this article.

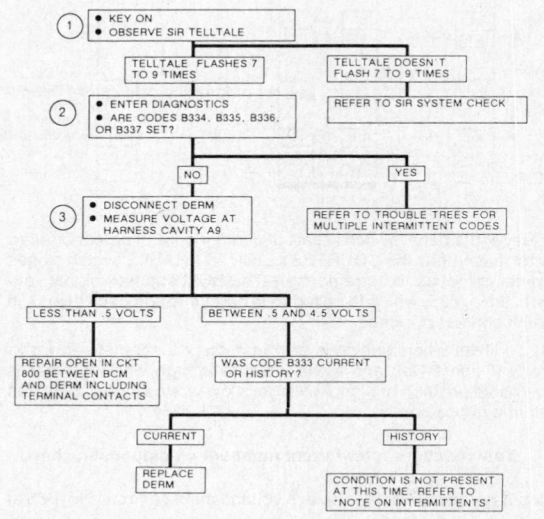

WHEN ALL DIAGNOSIS AND REPAIRS ARE COMPLETED, CLEAR CODES AND VERIFY PROPER OPERATION

Courtesy of General Motors Corp.

BCM CODE B334, LOSS OF PCM DATA

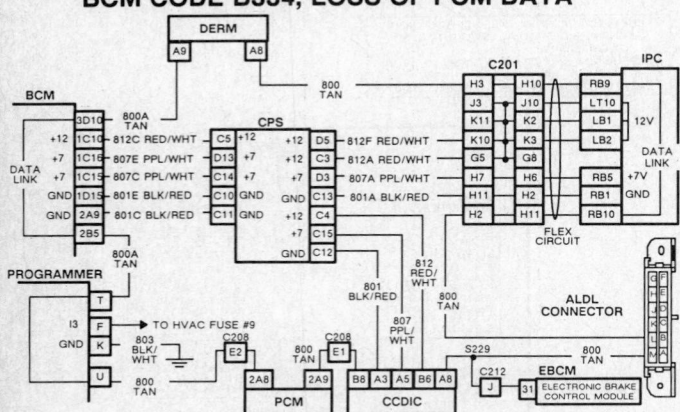

If BCM cannot exchange data with PCM and ignition is on, Code B334 will be set. If other communication codes are stored along with Code B334, see MULTIPLE INTERMITTENT CODES. If Code B334 is the only code stored, failure will be located as an open in circuit No. 800H, or an open in circuits No. 800J and 800G, or a faulty PCM or PCM MEM-CAL.

During a failure a fail soft value equal to 100°C will be used for coolant temperature. The cooling fans will be ran at high speed and no PCM diagnostic information will be available for display. While in the service diagnostic mode, this code will remain active, always checking for proper operation.

NOTE: Test numbers refer to test numbers on diagnostic chart.

1) Checks for intermittent operating conditions.

2) Check to see if open is in circuit No. 800 between PCM and CCDIC. If CCDIC blanks, dataline connections are good.

91H07632   90D09281

3) If CCDIC display did not go blank in this step, an open exists between the CCDIC and the PCM in the data circuit. Grounding CCDIC terminal B8 will isolate problem if open is in the circuit or internal to the CCDIC.

Note On Intermittents – If only Code B334 is stored as a history code, check power and grounds for an intermittent open in circuit No. 800. If PCM Code EO52 is also set as a history code, see PCM CODE EO52, PCM MEMORY RESET chart in this article.

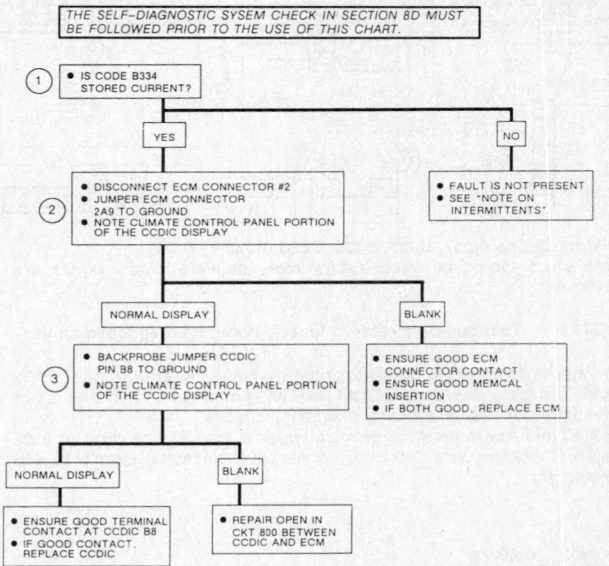

WHEN ALL DIAGNOSIS AND REPAIRS ARE COMPLETED, CLEAR CODES AND VERIFY OPERATION

Courtesy of General Motors Corp.

1991 ENGINE PERFORMANCE
Self-Diagnostics – Eldorado & Seville PCM/BCM (Cont.)

GM
1-289

BCM CODE B335, LOSS OF CCDIC DATA

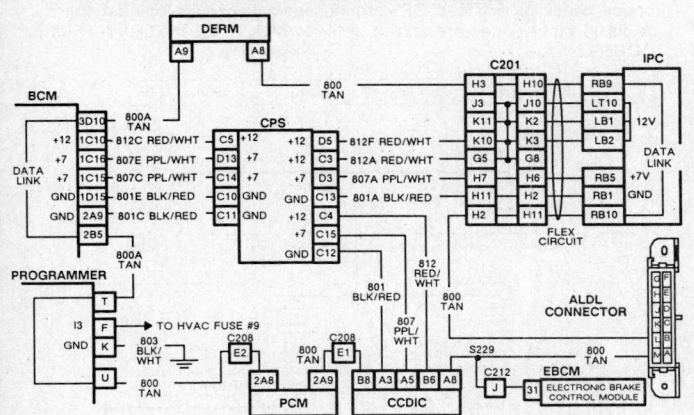

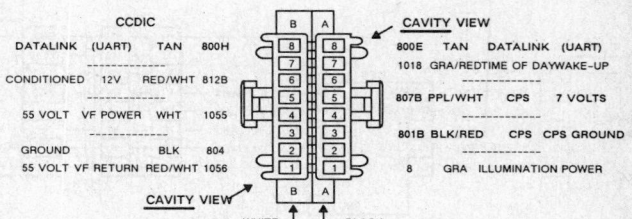

IF INTERMITTENT PROBLEMS PERSIST, REPLACE CCDIC (ONLY AFTER VERIFING WIRING INTEGRITY).

Since a loss of data communication with CCDIC will result in SYSTEM PROBLEM display, this code can only be recognized as a history code. During a failure, the A/C-heater programmer will default to 75°F set temperature, front defrost air delivery and automatic blower control.

With a 2-way, redundant communication ability built into this system, a double open in data line must occur to set fault. A single fault; however, in the CCDIC power or ground would also cause this code to set.

WHEN ALL DIAGNOSIS AND REPAIRS ARE COMPLETED, CLEAR CODES AND VERIFY OPERATION

91H07632   91J07633

Courtesy of General Motors Corp.

BCM CODE B336, LOSS OF IPC DATA

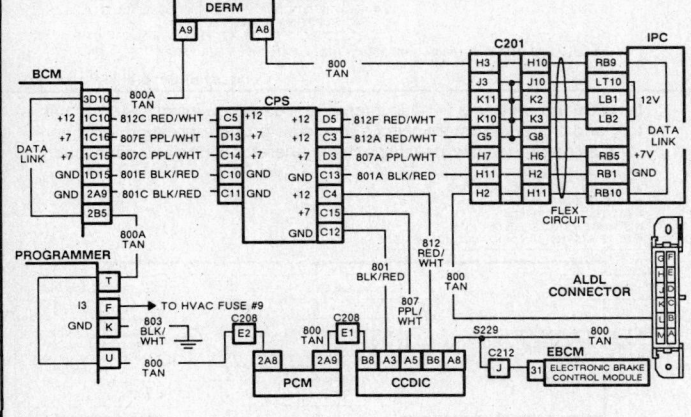

If BCM loses data communication with IPC and ignition is on, Code B336 will be set. The problem is a result of 7-volt or ground fault to IPC or double open circuit in data communication line between IPC and BCM. If this failure occurs, cruise control will disengage (if engaged) and headlights (if on) will function on low beam.

Note On Intermittents – Ensure good terminal contact at IPC for data line, power and ground connections. Also, watch for intermittent at transition block and in the flex circuit portion of the IPC carrier assembly. If wiring is good and intermittents continue, replace IPC.

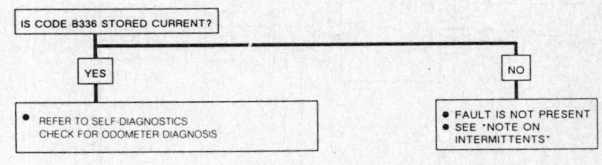

WHEN ALL DIAGNOSIS AND REPAIRS ARE COMPLETED, CLEAR CODES AND VERIFY OPERATION

91H07632   90H09283

Courtesy of General Motors Corp.

GM
1-290

1991 ENGINE PERFORMANCE
Self-Diagnostics – Eldorado & Seville PCM/BCM (Cont.)

BCM CODE B337, LOSS OF A/C-HEATER PROGRAMMER DATA

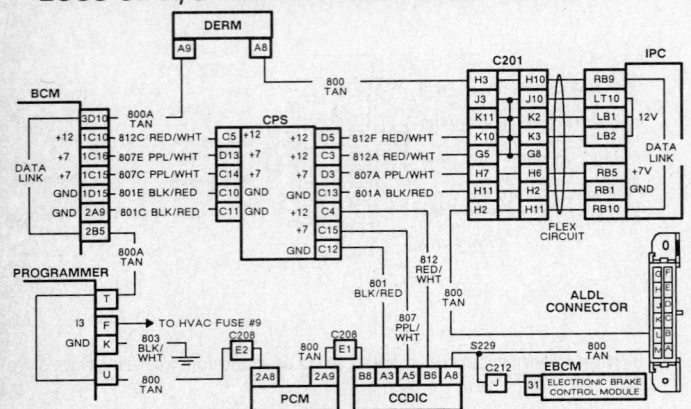

Note On Intermittents – If B337 shows as a history code, without other codes, check ignition feed, CPS ground, and data circuits for intermittent faults. If other codes are stored, refer to MULTIPLE INTERMITTENT CODES.

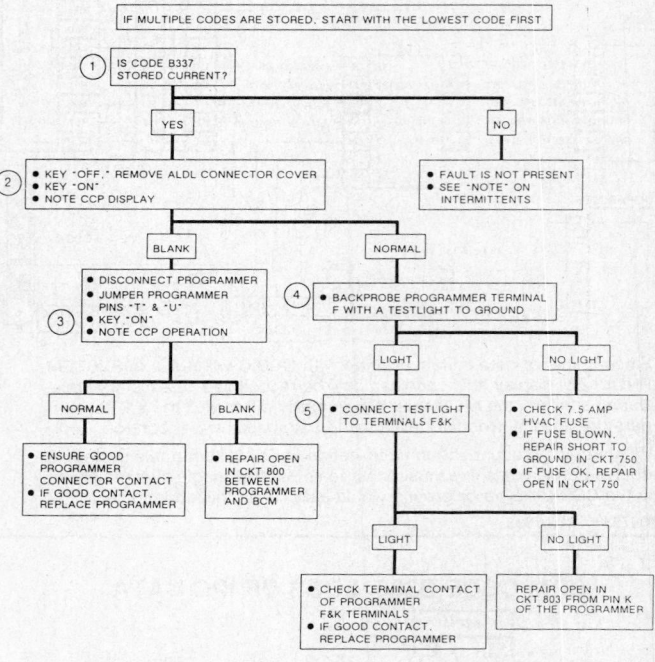

Code B337 will set if ignition is on and BCM has lost data communication with A/C-heater programmer. Fault can be caused by a loss of 12-volt power, ground to programmer or a double open in programmer data line, one on each side of component. During a failure, A/C clutch is disabled and blower motor runs at a constant 6 volts.

NOTE: Test numbers refer to test numbers on diagnostic chart.

1) Ensure code is not intermittent.
2) Determines if fault is due to power or ground circuits or data line.
3) Determines if data line fault is due to wiring or programmer.
4) Checks for IGN 3 to programmer.
5) Determines if loss of ground is due to programmer, wiring or CPS.

91H07632   90J09284

WHEN ALL DIAGNOSIS AND REPAIRS ARE COMPLETED, CLEAR CODES AND VERIFY OPERATION

Courtesy of General Motors Corp.

BCM CODE B410, CHARGING SYSTEM CIRCUIT

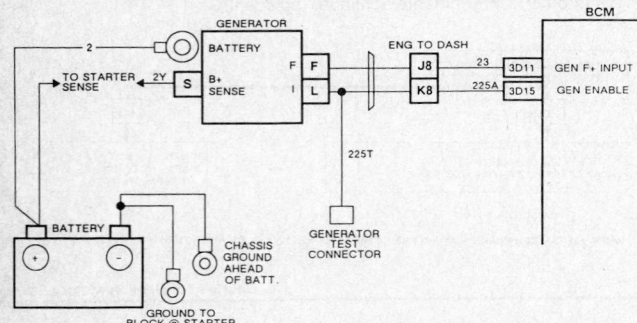

Note On Intermittents – If an intermittent condition exists, perform battery and charging system checks to assure proper operation. Also perform a comprehensive visual check of generator wiring and connection.

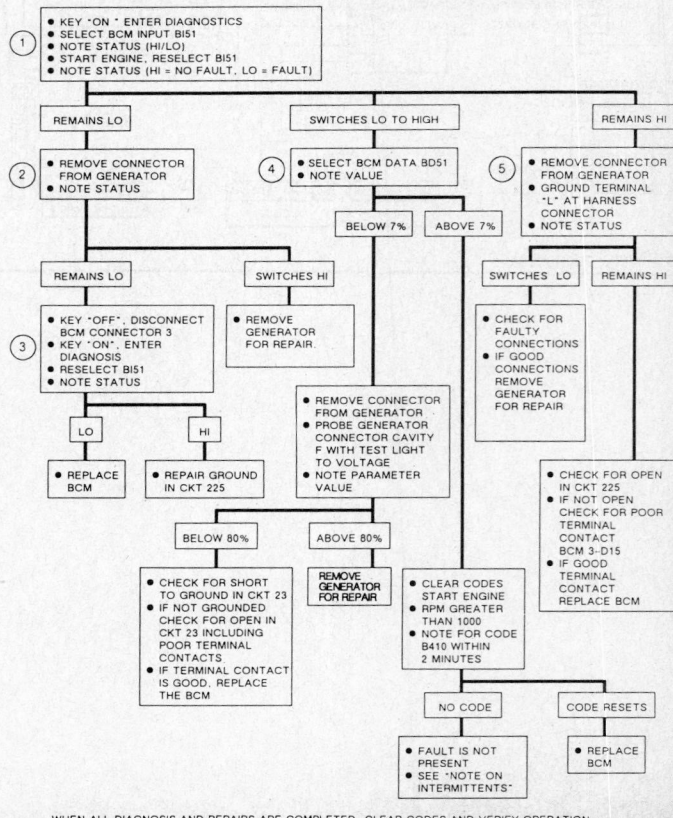

The alternator has fault detection capability built into the regulator. BCM will supply 12 volts to regulator over circuit No. 225 (terminal "L") and monitor field voltage of generator by using a PWM signal over circuit No. 23 (terminal "F").

Code B410 will set if there is either an open or short to ground on circuits No. 23 and 225, a belt break, or if an undervoltage or overvoltage condition exists. If there is a short to ground on circuit No. 225, BATTERY NO CHARGE telltale light will illuminate on IPC.

NOTE: Test numbers refer to test numbers on diagnostic chart.

1) BCM input Code BI51 displays generator voltage as HI or LO depending on voltage state at BCM. Normally, with ignition on and engine off, circuit No. 225 will be pulled low by generator and BI51 will read LO.
2) Check to see if LO reading is due to circuit No. 225 or generator. If reading changes from LO to HI when generator is disconnected, circuit No. 225 and BCM are okay.
3) Determines if fault is due to BCM or circuit No. 225.
4) BCM parameter BD51 displays amount of generator field activity. Under normal conditions, a reading less than 7 percent would indicate a fault in field circuit or BCM.
5) Removing generator connector will determine if fault is due to generator or an open in circuit No. 225 including BCM and interface connector.

WHEN ALL DIAGNOSIS AND REPAIRS ARE COMPLETED, CLEAR CODES AND VERIFY OPERATION

90D21744   90C09285

Courtesy of General Motors Corp.

1991 ENGINE PERFORMANCE
Self-Diagnostics – Eldorado & Seville PCM/BCM (Cont.)

GM
1-291

BCM CODES B411 & B412, BATTERY VOLTAGE LOW OR HIGH

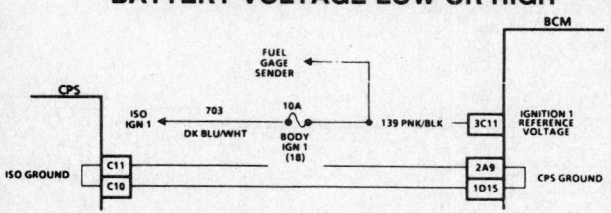

The BCM monitors IGN 1 voltage on terminal 3C11 as a reference for fuel control. Codes B411 and B412 are set when ignition is on, engine speed more than 800 RPM and IGN 1 voltage is less than 10 volts, Code B411 is set. If IGN 1 voltage is more than 16 volts, Code B412 is set.

During a failure, cruise control will disengage. The cause of Codes B411 and B412 should be corrected before diagnosing any other code that has set because high or low voltage can set false codes. A current Code B411 or B412 can be observed in BCM data display BD50 outside the range of 10-16 volts.

NOTE: Test numbers refer to test numbers on diagnostic chart.

1) BCM parameter BD50 displays battery voltage. Normal range is 10.6-16 volts.
2) Check to see if low voltage reading is caused by circuit or battery. If voltage is less than 10 volts with engine running, BCM and wiring are okay.
3) Check to see if low voltage reading is caused by the circuit or BCM. If voltage at BCM is less than 10 volts, BCM is okay.
4) Check to see if high voltage reading is caused by alternator or faulty BCM.
5) Check to see if charging voltage goes too high with higher engine RPM or electrical load.

Note On Intermittents – If an intermittent Code B411 or B412 is being set, observe BCM parameter BD50. This voltage reading is monitored from IGN 1 fuse, fuel reference voltage. If code is being set due to a high

current draw from a vehicle component, this can be observed by reading BD50. Operate various components while watching for reading to be less than 10 volts or more than 16 volts. Code B411 may be caused by intermittent open in circuit No. 39 which may be observed by manipulating the wire to BCM while watching parameter BD50 for a value less than 10 volts.

NOTE: IF FUEL GAGE READS FLASHING "E" ALONG WITH CODE B411, CHECK FOR BLOWN 10 AMP. IGNITION 1 FUSE OR SHORT TO GROUND IN CIRCUIT #139/239.

① • ENGINE RUNNING ABOVE 800 RPM
• SELECT BCM DATA BD50 BATTERY VOLTAGE (VOLTS)
• NOTE DATA VALUE

BELOW 10 VOLTS — ABOVE 16 VOLTS

② • CHECK BATTERY VOLTAGE AT BATTERY
④ • CHECK BATERY VOLTAGE AT BATTERY

ABOVE 10 VOLTS — BELOW 10 VOLTS
ABOVE 16 VOLTS — BELOW 16 VOLTS

③ • CHECK VOLTAGE FROM BCM TERMINAL 3-C11 TO 2-A9
• CHECK FOR PROPER GENERATOR OUTPUT OR RECHARGE AND TEST BATTERY AS NECESSARY

REMOVE GENERATOR FOR REPAIR.
REPLACE BCM

ABOVE 10 VOLTS — BELOW 10 VOLTS

BETWEEN 10 AND 16 VOLTS

• FAULT IS POOR TERMINAL CONTACT AT BCM 3-C11, 2-A9, OR 1-D15
• IF GOOD CONTACT, REPLACE BCM

• REPAIR OPEN IN CKT 139 OR 801

⑤ • RAISE ENGINE RPM TO 2000
• LOAD ELECTRICAL SYSTEM WITH HEADLAMPS AND HIGH ECC BLOWER
• NOTE DATA VALUE

ABOVE 16 VOLTS — BELOW 16 VOLTS

REMOVE GENERATOR FOR REPAIR.

FAULT IS NOT PRESENT. SEE "NOTE ON INTERMITTENTS." ALSO CHECK FOR IMPROPER BELT TENSION, POOR OR DIRTY BATTERY CONNECTIONS, ETC.

Courtesy of General Motors Corp.

90E21745 91B07634

GM
1-292

1991 ENGINE PERFORMANCE
Self-Diagnostics – Eldorado & Seville PCM/BCM (Cont.)

BCM CODE B420, RELAY CIRCUITS (1 OF 5)

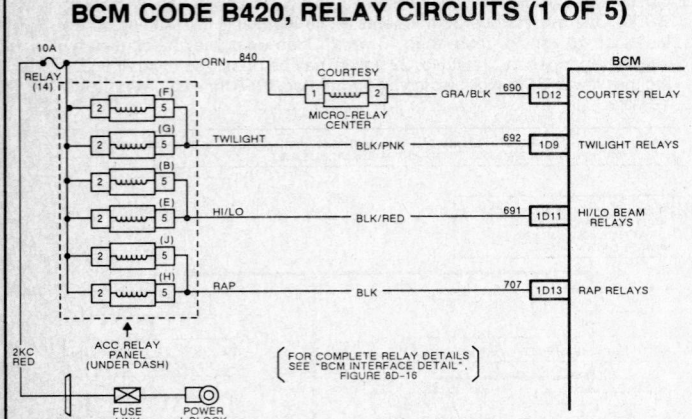

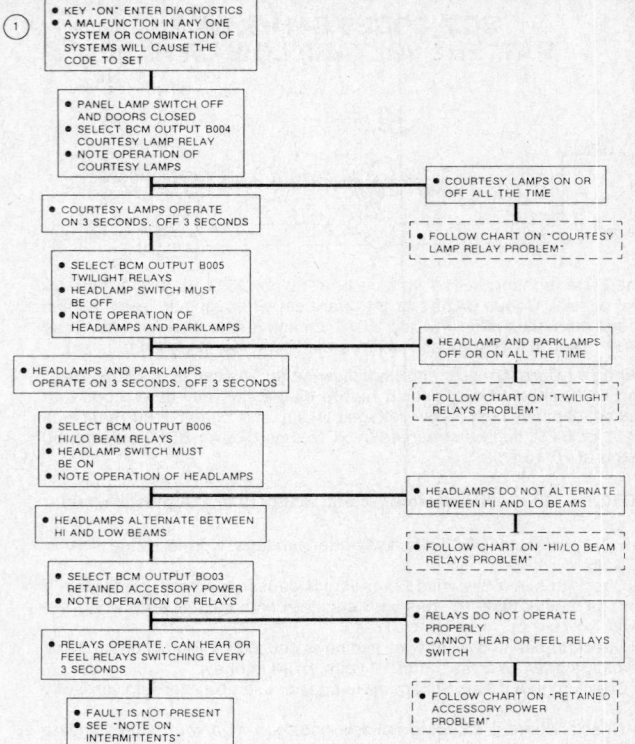

The BCM operates twilight, retained accessory power, high/low beam and courtesy light relays by providing a ground for the coils. When relay or relays are on, BCM output will be low. When relays are off, BCM output will be high. Code B420 will set if ignition is on and output voltage at BCM is low when high has been commanded.

NOTE: Test number refers to test number on diagnostic chart.

1) To determine which system has failed, select BCM output function in diagnostics. As individual outputs cycle on and off, observe their actual operation.

Note On Intermittents – Since all 4 groups of relays can cause an intermittent condition, see NOTE ON INTERMITTENTS for courtesy light relay, twilight relays, high/low beam relays, or retained accessory power relays.

91E07635   90E09286

WHEN ALL DIAGNOSIS AND REPAIRS ARE COMPLETED, CLEAR CODES AND VERIFY OPERATION

Courtesy of General Motors Corp.

BCM CODE B420,
COURTESY LIGHT RELAY CIRCUIT (2 OF 5)

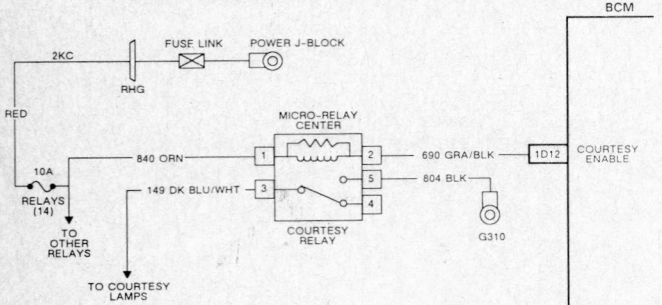

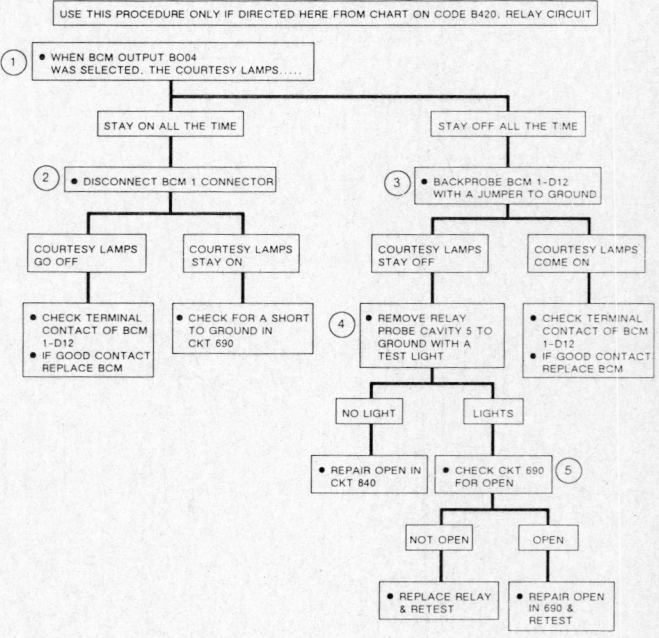

If courtesy lights did not cycle on and off when BO04 was selected, then courtesy lights relay have set Code B420.

NOTE: Test numbers refer to test numbers on diagnostic chart.

1) Checks to see if fault is due to an open circuit or a short to ground in the circuit. If courtesy lights are always on, then there is a short in control circuit. If courtesy lights never turn on, then there is an open in one of the circuits.
2) Checks to see if short to ground is due to circuit or BCM.
3) Checks to see if open circuit is due to circuit or BCM.
4) Checks to see if open circuit is on power side of relay.
5) Checks if open circuit is on ground side of relay or if relay is at fault.

Note On Intermittents – If an intermittent Code B420 is being set, manipulate related wiring in output function and watch for relays to cycle.

90F21746   90G09287

WHEN ALL DIAGNOSIS AND REPAIRS ARE COMPLETED, CLEAR CODES AND VERIFY OPERATION

Courtesy of General Motors Corp.

1991 ENGINE PERFORMANCE
Self-Diagnostics – Eldorado & Seville PCM/BCM (Cont.)

**GM
1-293**

BCM CODE B420, TWILIGHT RELAYS CIRCUIT (3 OF 5)

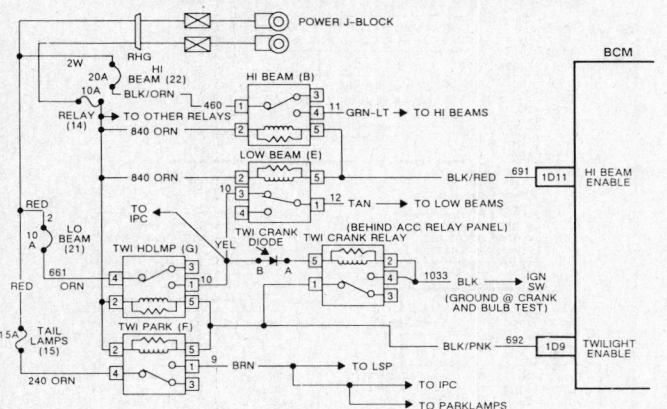

Note On Intermittents – If an intermittent Code B420 is being set, manipulate related wiring in output function and watch for relays to cycle.

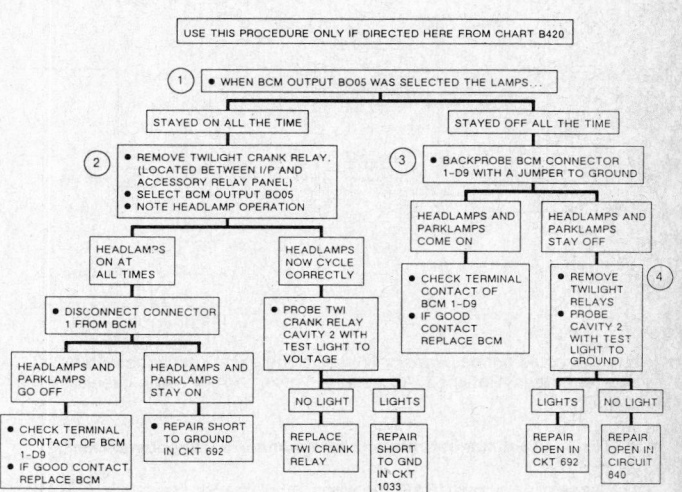

USE THIS PROCEDURE ONLY IF DIRECTED HERE FROM CHART B420

WHEN ALL DIAGNOSIS AND REPAIRS ARE COMPLETED, CLEAR CODES AND VERIFY OPERATION

If headlights and parklights did not cycle on and off when BO05 was selected, then this is the system that set Code B420.

NOTE: Test numbers refer to test numbers on diagnostic chart.

1) Checks to see if fault is caused by an open circuit or a short to ground. If headlights and parklights are always on, then there is a short to ground in control circuit. If headlights are never on, then there is an open in one of the circuits.
2) Checks to see if short to ground is due to circuit or BCM.
3) Checks to see if open circuit is due to circuit or BCM.
4) Checks to see if open circuit is on power or ground side of relay.

90G21747   90I09288

Courtesy of General Motors Corp.

BCM CODE B420, HIGH/LOW BEAM RELAYS CIRCUIT (4 OF 5)

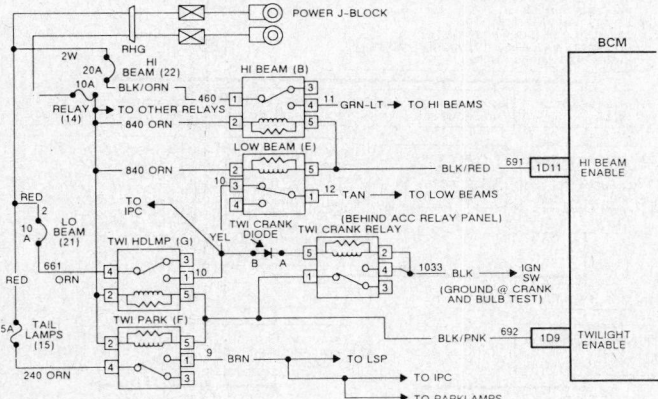

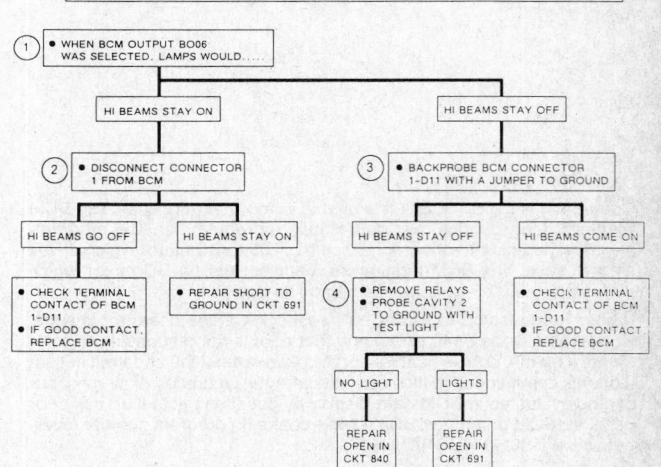

USE THIS PROCEDURE ONLY IF DIRECTED HERE FROM CHART ON CODE B420 , RELAY CIRCUIT. IF NO RELAYS ARE WORKING, CHECK FOR OPEN IN CKT 840.

WHEN ALL DIAGNOSIS AND REPAIRS ARE COMPLETED, CLEAR CODES AND VERIFY OPERATION

If high/low beam did not cycle on and off when BO06 was selected, then this is the system that set Code B420.

NOTE: Test numbers refer to test numbers on diagnostic chart.

1) Checks to see if fault is caused by an open circuit or short to ground. If high beams are always on, then there is a short to ground. If high beams never turn on, then there is an open in one of the circuits.
2) Checks to see if short to ground is due to circuit or BCM.
3) Checks to see if open circuit is due to circuit or BCM.
4) Checks to see if open circuit is on the power or ground side of relay.

Note On Intermittents – If an intermittent Code B420 is being set, manipulate related wiring in output function and watch for relays to cycle.

90G21747   90A09289

Courtesy of General Motors Corp.

BCM CODE B420, RETAINED ACCESSORY POWER RELAYS CIRCUIT (5 OF 5)

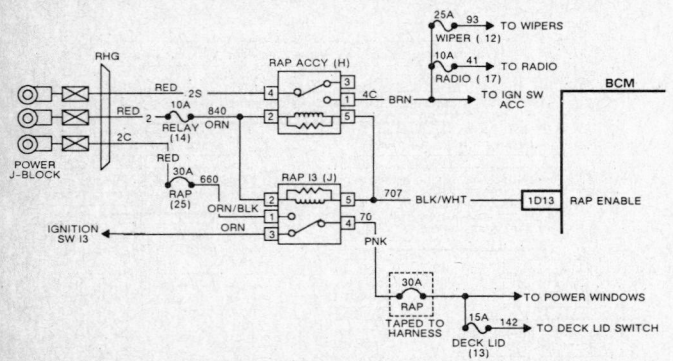

USE THIS PROCEDURE ONLY IF DIRECTED HERE FROM CHART ON CODE B420, "RELAY CIRCUIT"

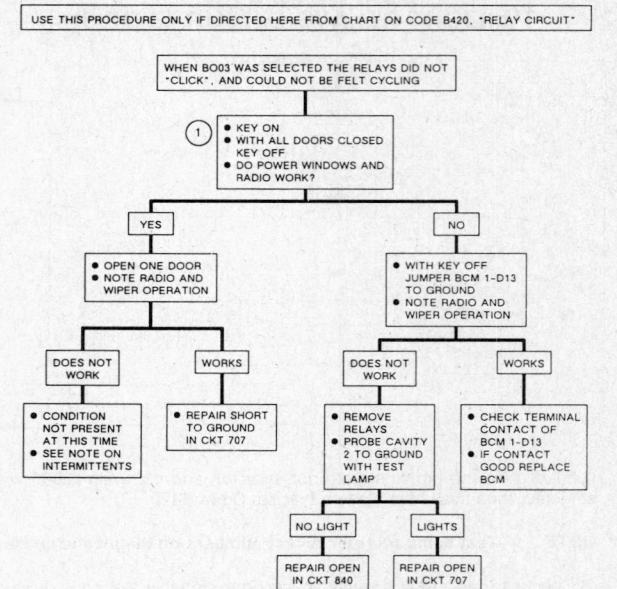

If relays could not be heard or felt switching each 3 seconds with BO03 selected, then Retained Accessory Power (RAP) relay circuits are suspect.

NOTE: Test number refers to test number on diagnostic chart.

1) Checks for normal RAP functions, and checks for faults in RAP circuits.

Note On Intermittents – If an intermittent Code B420 is being set, manipulate related wiring in output function and watch for relays to cycle.

90H21748   90C09290

Courtesy of General Motors Corp.

BCM CODE B440, A/C-HEATER AIR MIX DOOR CIRCUIT PROBLEM

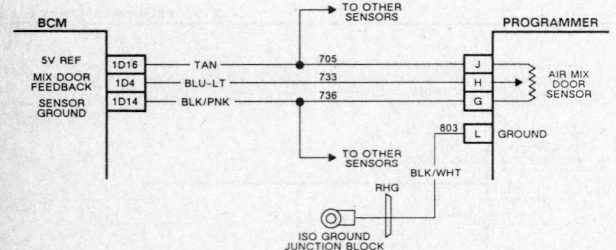

Note On Intermittents – If intermittent Code B440 is being set, manipulate related wiring while observing BD23. If failure is induced, door reading will either stop or jump to an extreme value 0% or 100%. This will help to isolate location of malfunction.

Exit diagnostics. Select maximum heating 90°F and maximum cooling 60°F using normal A/C-heater controls, waiting a minimum of 2 minutes in each mode to see if code sets.

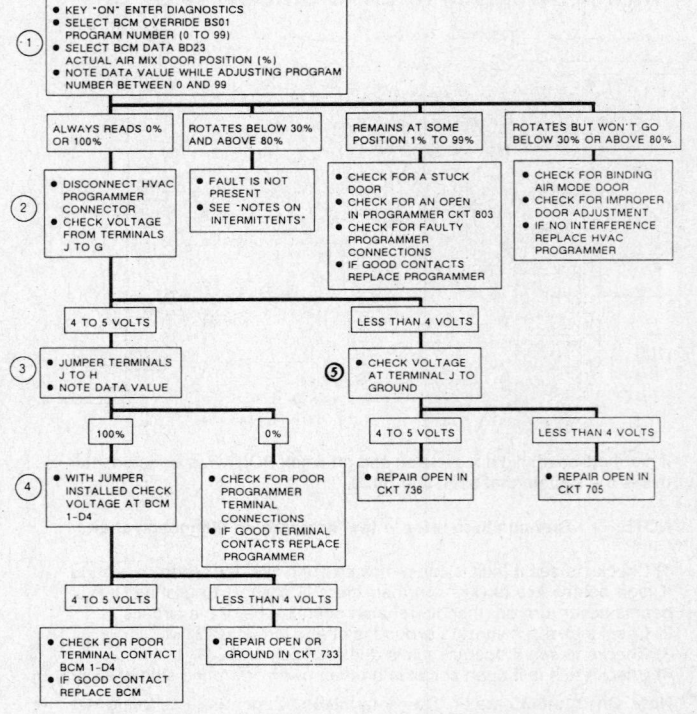

Code B440 is set by BCM if it is unable to move air mix door. The BCM requests door to move over data circuit to programmer. The programmer then supplies 5 volts from circuit No. 705 to DC motor which drives air mix door. The BCM monitors a feedback pot on DC motor which varies between 0-5 volts, depending on its position.

If door is requested to move, but feedback voltage does not change, BCM stores Code B440 to indicate that door is not responding to command. If air mix door is near its hot or cold extreme, the code will not set if door is commanded to move to that extreme. Operation of air mix door can be evaluated in BCM data display by observing actual air mix door position (BCM parameter BD23) while changing program number (override value BS01) PROGRAM NO.

NOTE: Test numbers refer to test numbers on diagnostic chart.

1) BCM parameter BD23 displays actual air mix door position. Normal range is 1-99 percent. BCM override value BS01 is for program number.
2) Checks to see if fault could be due to 5-volt reference and ground circuit or sensor circuit.
3) Checks to see if fault is due to programmer or sensor circuit.
4) Checks to see if fault is due to circuit or BCM.
5) Checks to see if open circuit reading is due to circuits No. 736 or No. 705.

90I21749   90E09291

Courtesy of General Motors Corp.

1991 ENGINE PERFORMANCE
Self-Diagnostics – Eldorado & Seville PCM/BCM (Cont.)

GM
1-295

BCM CODES B446 & B447, LOW REFRIGERANT PRESSURE

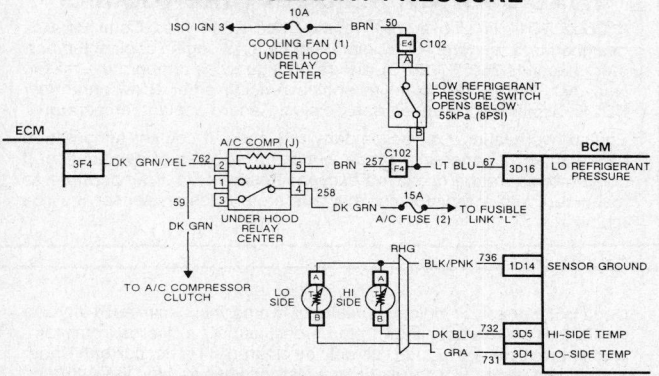

In the process of controlling compressor clutch, BCM monitors certain system inputs for an indication of low refrigerant charge. If system's refrigerant state of charge should fall to less than 1/3 of capacity, the BCM can detect this condition and illuminates LOW A/C REFRIGERANT-A/C COMPRESSOR OFF on CCDIC panel. BCM determines state of charge by monitoring low side temperature sensor. In addition to message, the BCM will store a diagnostic Code B446 or B447 in memory. These codes indicate a low refrigerant condition was detected. If B446 or B447 is detected, compressor clutch will disengage and remain disengaged until diagnostic codes are cleared.

NOTE: Test numbers refer to test numbers on diagnostic chart.

1) Checks for intermittent open or short in pressure switch circuit.
2) Checks for restriction causing intermittent low pressure condition.
3) Checks for restriction within refrigerant system.
4) An offset in the BCM temperature sensors BD26 (actual outside temperature) or BD28 (low side temperature) may trigger a false code. After

90C21750 90G09292

a long cold soak (preferably overnight), enter diagnostics without starting engine and monitor sensor readings. All readings should agree within 2°C.

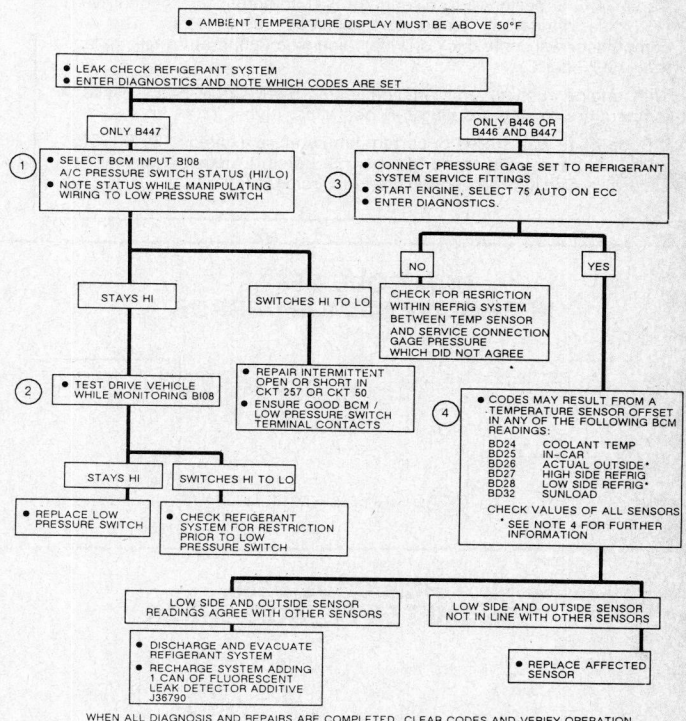

WHEN ALL DIAGNOSIS AND REPAIRS ARE COMPLETED, CLEAR CODES AND VERIFY OPERATION

Courtesy of General Motors Corp.

BCM CODE B448, LOW REFRIGERANT PRESSURE

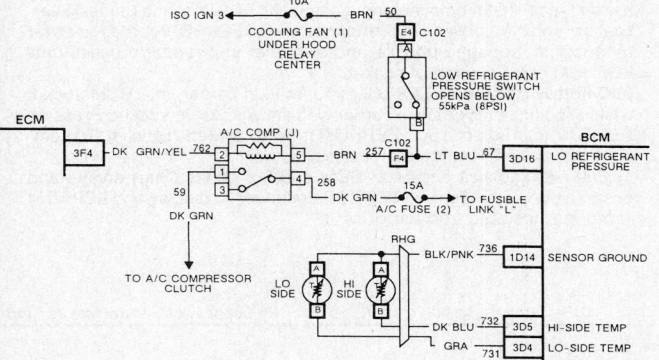

In the process of controlling compressor clutch, BCM monitors certain system inputs for low refrigerant charge indication. This code indicates a low refrigerant condition was detected. If B448 is detected, compressor clutch will disengage and remain disengaged until diagnostic code is cleared.

NOTE: Test numbers refer to test numbers on diagnostic chart.

1) Checks current state of low pressure switch
2) Checks circuits to low pressure switch
3) Checks refrigerant system pressure
4) Checks for restriction in refrigerant system
5) Checks for intermittent short or open

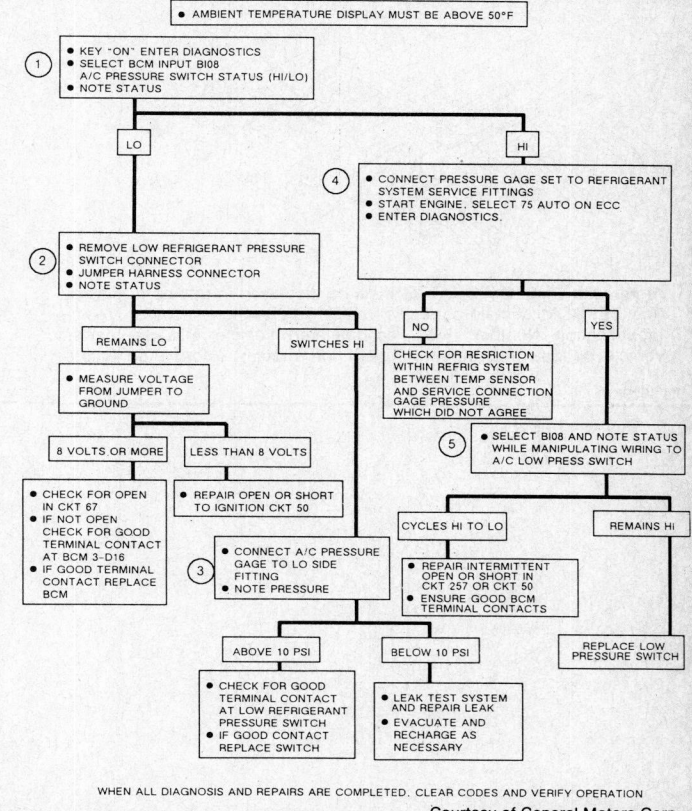

WHEN ALL DIAGNOSIS AND REPAIRS ARE COMPLETED, CLEAR CODES AND VERIFY OPERATION

90C21750 90I09293

Courtesy of General Motors Corp.

BCM CODE B449, A/C-HEATER HIGH SIDE TEMPERATURE TOO HIGH

Code B449 is designed to disengage A/C compressor clutch in event high side refrigerant temperature exceeds 199°F (93°C). The A/C compressor will come back on when high side temperature falls to less than 199°F (93°C).

With engine running and A/C on, enter BCM Code BD27. Record temperature displayed during A/C operation.

If Code B449 was stored or current temperature exceeds 199°F (93°C) and A/C pressure exceeds 380 psi (27 kg/cm²), possible causes for excessive high A/C head pressure must be checked.

BCM CODE B450, HVAC COOLANT TEMPERATURE TOO HIGH

If Code EO14 is also stored, repair Code EO14 first. Code B450 is designed to disengage A/C compressor clutch if engine coolant temperature exceeds 261°F (126°C), and re-engage when temperature falls to less than 248°F (120°C). With engine running enter BCM parameter BD21. Display will be in degrees Celsius. Record coolant temperature.

Engine overheating may accompany this code. If coolant temperature exceeds normal operating range, check for sources of overheating. If coolant temperature displayed exceeds actual coolant temperature as measured with a radiator coolant temperature tester, sensor may be faulty.

BCM CODE B552, KEEP ALIVE MEMORY ERROR

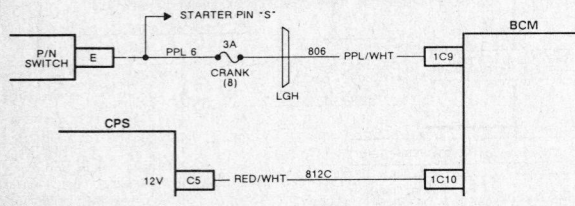

Code B552 does not indicate a fault but is a normal occurrence anytime power to BCM has been interrupted. Code cannot be cleared from memory in normal manner. Code can only be cleared if it is not current. Under normal conditions, code will become history when ignition key is turned to LOCK position, wait 5 seconds and turn key to ON position. Then, re-enter diagnostics. This code should now be history, and can be cleared in normal manner.

This code will also set if following conditions are met: ignition is cranked; and/or, no system voltage signal to BCM terminal 1C9. The purpose of crank circuit is to signal BCM to shut off when cranking so normal voltage variations during starting do not affect electronic devices.

90D09295   Courtesy of General Motors Corp.

BCM CODE B556, ODOMETER EEPROM ERROR

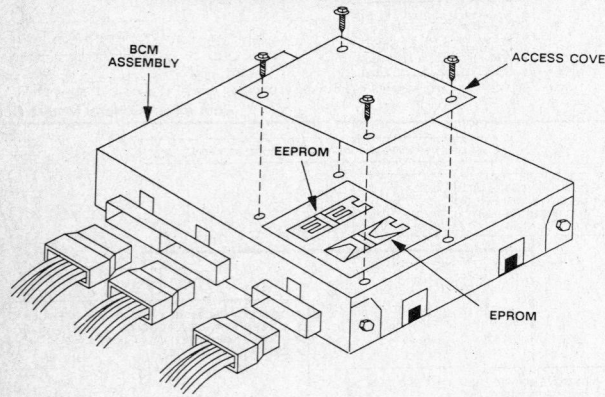

Along with Code B556, ERROR will be displayed in odometer display. The EEPROM contains specific vehicle information such as: Vehicle Identification Number (VIN), accumulated vehicle mileage, certain vehicle options and other pertinent information. Information is pro-grammed for the specific vehicle in which it is installed and CANNOT be exchanged or used in any other vehicle. Replacement EEPROMs must be obtained through any authorized Delco Electronics Service Center.

NOTE: **New EEPROM will have to be adjusted to current mileage by an authorized Delco Electronics Service Center.**

Replacement Procedure:
1) Remove instrument panel compartment door. Detach and move aside relay bracket assembly and fuse panel. With ignition off, disconnect BCM harness. Loosen BCM to bracket retaining nuts. Remove BCM.
2) Remove 4 screws from EEPROM access cover. Remove cover. Using rocker type PROM remover, engage one end of carrier and press on vertical bar end of remover. Rock engaged end of EEPROM carrier up as far as possible. Engage opposite end of carrier and repeat process until EEPROM carrier is free of socket.
3) Carefully install new EEPROM (mounted in carrier) into BCM socket while aligning small notch in carrier with small notch in socket. Press on EEPROM (carrier only) until EEPROM is firmly seated in socket. To complete installation, reverse removal procedure.
4) Enter diagnostics and clear BCM code or codes. Start engine and observe odometer display. If ERROR continues to display and EEPROM is properly installed, replace BCM.

90F09296   Courtesy of General Motors Corp.

DESCRIPTION

Reatta and Riviera models use several electronic components which can be controlled by the service technician to provide valuable self-diagnostic information. The components are part of an electrical network designed to control various engine and body subsystems. This article will provide a description of the overall electronic network and the on-board diagnostic capabilities which have been designed to aid the service technician in system diagnosing and testing.

At the heart of the computer system is the Body Control Module (BCM). The BCM is located behind the glove box and has an integral microprocessor, which is the center for communication with all other components in the system. All sensors and switches are monitored by the BCM or by one of the following major components:

- Electronic Heater and A/C Control Panel (ECCP)
- Instrument Panel Cluster (IPC)
- Programmer-Heating and A/C (HVAC)
- SIR Diagnostic Energy Reserve Module (DERM) controller
- Electronic Control Module (ECM)

NOTE: The Electronic Control Module (ECM) may be referred to as the Powertrain Control Module (PCM) in some diagnostic charts and figures. The 2 terms may be used interchangeably.

Vehicle utilizes an Electronic Climate Control Panel (ECCP) with LED digital display area for climate control/temperatures and override mode values. ECCP is used to access BCM diagnostics and display them in the IPC Driver Information Center (DIC) located in odometer/trip odometer display.

OPERATION

Inputs from major components, sensors and switches are used in calculations by BCM and combined with program instructions within system memory. This provides accurate control over all subsystems involved. When a subsystem circuit exceeds preprogrammed limits, a system malfunction is indicated and back-up functions may be provided.

The BCM controls subsystems through direct outputs or through data transmitted along the serial data line to one of the other major components. The process of receiving, storing, testing and controlling information is continuous. The data communication also gives the BCM control over the ECM's, IPC's, and DERM's self-diagnostic capabilities. Between the BCM and the other major components of the computer system, a data line communication process has been incorporated. This allows devices to share information and thereby provide for additional control capability.

In order to access and control the BCM self-diagnostic features, 2 electronic components are used, the Instrument Panel Cluster (IPC) and the Electronic Climate Control Panel (ECCP). *See Fig. 1.* The SERVICE MODE for diagnostic information incorporates odometer/trip odometer as Driver Information Center (DIC) display. When a malfunction is sensed by the BCM, the Service Engine Soon (SES) light will illuminate on IPC and stay on (with engine running) until code is cleared from BCM.

When the SERVICE MODE is entered, various BCM, ECM or IPC faults can be displayed. In addition to the parameters, fault codes, inputs and outputs, and other features such as override commands, snapshot, display VIN and code clearing capabilities can be accessed and displayed when commanded through the ECCP.

Certain system malfunctions cause computer controlled diagnostic messages and/or telltales to appear, indicating that service is

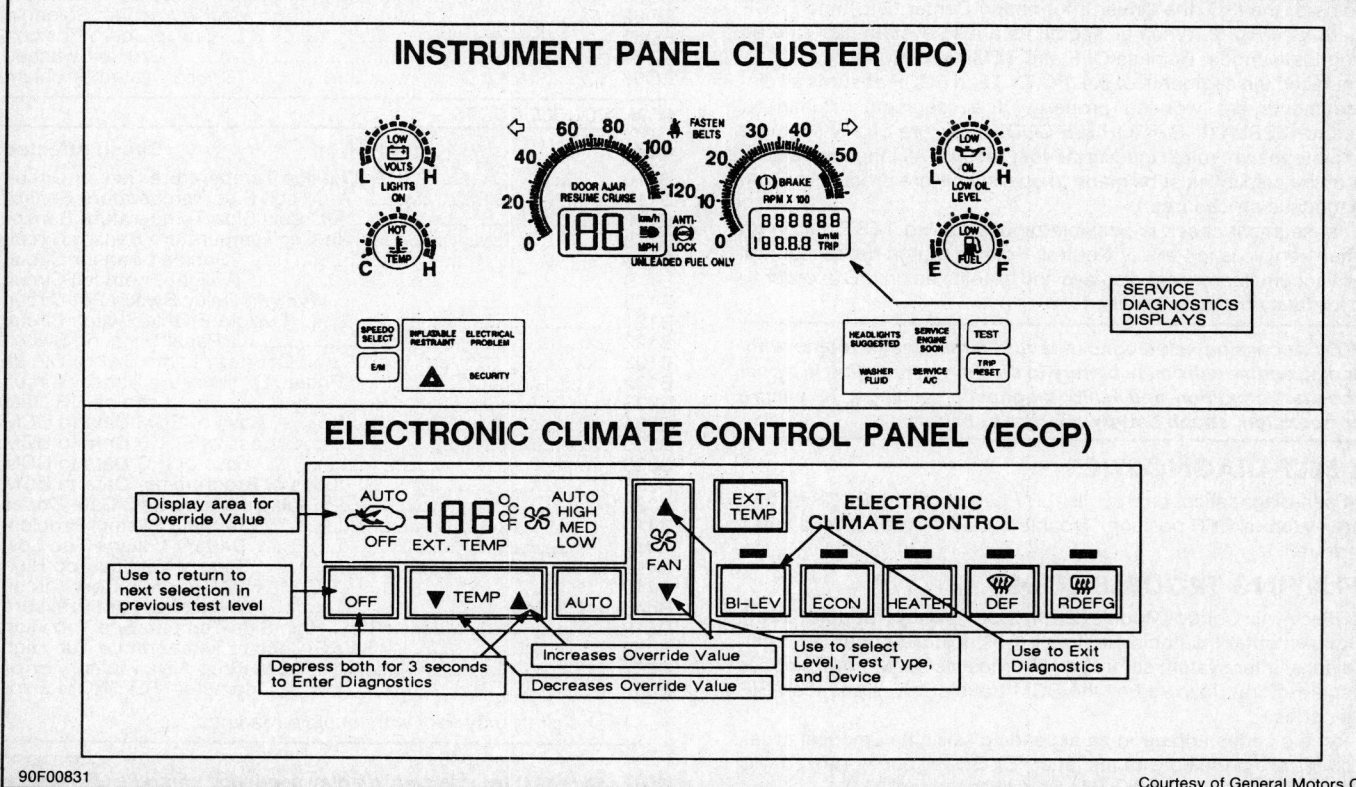

90F00831

Courtesy of General Motors Corp.

Fig. 1: Instrument Panel Cluster (Analog Gauges) & Electronic Climate Control Panel (ECCP)

GM
1-298

1991 ENGINE PERFORMANCE
Self-Diagnostics – Reatta & Riviera PCM/BCM (Cont.)

required. When a subsystem circuit exceeds preprogrammed limits, a system malfunction is indicated and the BCM provides certain back-up functions known as "failsoft". A typical failsoft action would be the substitution of a fixed input value when a sensor is detected to be open or shorted.

The ECCP becomes the controller by which to enter and access self-diagnostics. By pressing the appropriate buttons on the ECCP, data messages can be sent to the BCM, requesting specific diagnostic features. This communication process allows BCM to transfer any of its available diagnostic information to the instrument panel DIC display during SERVICE MODE operation. When in override mode of BCM diagnostics, information is displayed at the ECCP temperature LED display.

Below is a list of computer controlled subsystems.
- Alternator/Starter System
- Chime
- Climate Control
- Courtesy Lights
- Cruise Control
- Dimming (Lighting)
- Driver Diagnostics
- ECM Subsystems
- E & C Data
- Gauges
- Illuminated Entry
- Instrument Panel Displays
- Radio
- Self-Diagnostics System
- Supplemental Inflatable Restraint (SIR) System
- Twilight Sentinel

ENTERING SELF-DIAGNOSTICS
IPC SEGMENT CHECK
1) Turn ignition switch on. Simultaneously depress OFF and TEMP▲ buttons on the Electronic Climate Control Panel (ECCP). *See Fig. 1.*
2) Continue to depress OFF and TEMP▲ buttons until all segments and bulbs of the IPC, the Driver Information Center (DIC) and ECCP illuminate. *See Fig. 2.* When all segments are lit, system has entered self-diagnostic mode. Release OFF and TEMP▲ button.
3) Illuminating the segments of the IPC, DIC and ECCP ensures all display segments are working properly. If all segments illuminate, proceed to DISPLAYING TROUBLE CODES. Failure of any segment to illuminate may result in inaccurate test results. All inoperative segments of the display must be made to operate before proceeding with self-diagnostic procedures.
4) Partial segment check is possible by depressing TEST button on IPC when vehicle is in Park or Neutral. Holding button depressed will light all vacuum fluorescent displays and all telltales on IPC in order to check for faulty bulbs or panels.

CAUTION: Accessing self-diagnostics for 30 minutes or longer without running engine will cause battery to discharge, resulting in a possible no-start condition and faulty diagnostic readings. To ensure proper operation, attach battery charger to battery.

EXIT SELF-DIAGNOSTICS
To exit self-diagnostics, depress BI-LEV button on the ECCP or turn ignition switch to OFF position. Trouble codes are not erased when this is done.

DISPLAYING TROUBLE CODES
1) The Electronic Control Module (ECM), Body Control Module (BCM), and Supplemental Inflatable Restraint (SIR) trouble codes automatically display after system enters self-diagnostics. ECM trouble codes are displayed first, followed by the BCM trouble codes and then SIR trouble codes.
2) All trouble codes appear in an ascending (3 digit) numerical order. ECM codes are prefixed with the letter "E", BCM Codes prefixed with the letter "B", and SIR codes prefixed with the letter "R".

3) In addition, all trouble codes are followed by the letter "C" or "H". Letter "C" stands for current and indicates a trouble code related fault presently exists. Letter "H" stands for history and indicates the system failure was not present the last time the code was accessed.
4) For example: Code E016H is ECM trouble code number 016, set in response to a malfunction that occurred in the past (history). Code B410C is BCM trouble code number 410, set in response to a malfunction that is currently taking place.
5) If no ECM, BCM or SIR trouble codes are stored in memory, respectively, a NO E CODE, NO B CODE or NO R CODE message is displayed. Should the communication link between a component and the ECM or BCM fail, a NO B DATA, NO E DATA, or NO R DATA message will be displayed.
6) Trouble code display can be by-passed at any time by depressing FAN▼ button on ECCP.

ECM TROUBLE CODES

Code	Circuit Affected
EO13	Open O_2 Sensor Circuit
EO14	Coolant Sensor Temperature Too High
EO15	Coolant Sensor Temperature Too Low
EO16	Battery System Voltage Too High
EO17	Spark Reference Circuit
EO21	TPS Signal Voltage High
EO22	TPS Signal Voltage Low
EO23	MAT Sensor Circuit Temperature Low
EO24	Vehicle Speed Sensor (VSS) Circuit
EO25	MAT Sensor Circuit Temperature High
EO26	Quad-Driver Circuit
EO31	Park/Neutral Switch Circuit
EO34	MAF Sensor Circuit
EO36	Shift Control Problem
EO38	Brake Switch Circuit
EO41	Cam Sensor Circuit
EO42	Electronic Spark Timing (EST) Circuit
EO43	Electronic Spark Control (ESC) Circuit
EO44	Oxygen Sensor Circuit Lean
EO45	Oxygen Sensor Circuit Rich
EO47	ECM-BCM Data
EO51	MEM-CAL Error
EO58	VATS Fuel Enable Circuit
EO61	Cruise Vent Solenoid
EO62	Cruise Vacuum Solenoid
EO65	Cruise Servo Position
EO67	Cruise Switches
EO68	Cruise System Problem

BCM TROUBLE CODES

Code	Circuit Affected
B110	Outside Temperature Sensor Circuit
B111	A/C High Side Temperature Sensor
B112	A/C Low Side Temperature Sensor
B113	In-Car Temperature Sensor Circuit
B115	Sunload Sensor Circuit
B119	Twilight Photocell Circuit
B120	Twilight Delay Switch Pot Circuit
B121	Twilight Enable Switch Circuit
B122	Panel Dimming Switch
B123	Courtesy Lamp Switch Circuit
B132	Engine Oil Pressure Sensor Circuit
B333	Loss of SIR Data
B334	Loss of ECM Data to BCM
B335	Loss of ECCP Data to BCM
B336	Loss of IPC Data to BCM
B337	Loss of Programmer Data to BCM
B33*[1]	Multiple Intermittent Data Codes
B410	Charging System Problem
B411	Battery Voltage Too Low
B412	Battery Voltage Too High
B440	HVAC-Air Mix Door Circuit
B446, 447 & 448	Low Refrigerant Pressure
B449	HVAC-High Side Temperature Too High
B450	HVAC-Coolant Temperature Too High
B552	BCM Keep Alive Memory Error
B556	Odometer (EE) PROM Error

[1] – Last digit (*) may vary with multiple readings.

NOTE: To repeat trouble code display sequence, depress OFF button on ECCP.

1991 ENGINE PERFORMANCE
Self-Diagnostics — Reatta & Riviera PCM/BCM (Cont.)

GM
1-299

CLEARING TROUBLE CODES

See CLEAR CODES under TEST TYPE SELECTION.

MANUAL OPERATION OF SERVICE MODE

NOTE: Manual operation of service mode system is to be used with the TROUBLE CODE CHARTS portion of this article. Prior to using flow charts, it will be necessary to become completely familiar with the procedures in MANUAL OPERATION OF SERVICE MODE.

SYSTEM SELECTION

1) After all trouble codes have been displayed, the SERVICE MODE system can be directed to perform specific system diagnostic tests. See DISPLAYING TROUBLE CODES. Following the trouble code display, the first system available for testing will automatically be displayed. For example: ECM? may now be present on the display.
2) To select the desired system, (ECM, BCM, IPC, or SIR), advance and stop the DIC display as follows:
Depressing the FAN▼ button on the ECCP will cycle the system selection list. When the desired diagnostic system is displayed, depress FAN▲ button on ECCP and the displayed system will be selected for testing.
3) Depressing BI-LEV button on ECCP will exit diagnostics and return to normal IPC and ECCP operation.

NOTE: To cancel a system selection and activate a repeat of the system selection process, depress the OFF button on the ECCP.

TEST TYPE SELECTION

1) After the diagnostic system has been selected for testing, 6 test types are now made available for selection. The menu choices are: CLEAR CODES?, DATA?, INPUTS?, OUTPUTS?, OVERRIDE? and SNAPSHOT?. The Season Odometer/DIC display may be showing any one of these 6 test type choices. The Trip Odometer will display selected value as seen by computer. See Figs. 2-7.
2) To advance the display, depress FAN▼ button on the ECCP.
3) When the desired test type is displayed, depress the FAN▲ button on the ECCP.

NOTE: To cancel a test type selection and activate a repeat of the test type selection process, depress the OFF button on ECCP. To exit diagnostics without clearing codes, depress the BI-LEV button on ECCP.

The 6 test types are explained as follows:

- **CLEAR CODES** – Selection of CLEAR CODES? will result in the message CODES CLEAR or CODES NOT CLEAR being displayed, indicating whether the codes were successfully cleared. This message appears for 3 seconds, indicating all stored trouble codes have been erased from that system's memory. After 3 seconds, the display will automatically return to the next test type available for testing. See Figs. 2, 4 and 6.

NOTE: After trouble code has been cleared, test drive vehicle and recheck to ensure code did not reset.

- **DATA** – Data test displays component/system present specifications which can be compared with specifications of a properly functioning system. Trip Odometer/DIC displays data values.
- **INPUTS** – 1) Input test displays the voltage level of the circuit being tested as HI or LO. Input test display is shown in Trip Odometer/DIC panel.
2) HI or LO refers to input terminal voltage for the particular circuit. The display also indicates if an input reading has changed since the test was selected. This feature permits technician to activate or deactivate any listed device/circuit and then return to the display to see if voltage reading has changed.

3) If a voltage reading change occurs, an X will appear next to the HI/LO indicator; otherwise, a "0" will remain displayed indicating no change occurred. The X will only appear once per selected input. The HI/LO indicator will continue to change as the input changes.

- **OUTPUTS** – Output test displays the voltage level of selected device/circuit as HI or LO. After 3 seconds, this level will cycle between HI and LO voltage. Output test display is shown in Trip Odometer/DIC panel.
- **OVERRIDE** – Override test is represented as a percentage of the tested functions' full range during its current operation. This percentage value is displayed in the ECCP temperature display area. The display will alternate between the override percentage value ("--") and the normal operation value. This alternating display is a reminder that the tested function IS NOT being overridden. Pressing TEMP▲ and TEMP▼ buttons simultaneously on ECCP begins override of function. Alternating display will stop, and show override value.
Pressing TEMP▲ button increases value, pressing TEMP▼ button decreases value.

Normal program control is resumed in one of the following 3 ways:

1 – Selection of another override will cancel current override.
2 – Selection of another system (ECM, BCM, IPC or SIR) will cancel current override.
3 – Overriding the value beyond either extreme (0 or 90) will display "--" momentarily before resuming value. Releasing control button while "--" is displayed will resume normal program and display will start alternating.

Override test is unique in that while in override test, another test (i.e. DATA, INPUTS, or OUTPUTS) can be selected and be active at the same time with override test. After selecting override test, press the OFF button, to allow selection of another test type. ECCP will continue to display selected override. By pressing OFF and TEMP▲ or TEMP▼ buttons at same time, it is possible to monitor effect of override on different parameter.

To exit diagnostics without clearing codes, depress the BI-LEV button on ECCP.

- **SNAPSHOT** – Snapshot is a test type that will record all BCM or ECM data and inputs at one instant for review at a later time. Snapshot also permits a technician triggered recording of specific current BCM/ECM data and input parameters for review at a later time. BCM and ECM have slightly different types of snapshot.

NOTE: Proceed to SNAPSHOT after selecting snapshot test type.

EXPLANATION OF SPECIFIC TEST SELECTION

Following test type selection, the first of many specific tests will be made available for selection. The 4 characters of this display represent a test code. The first 2 characters of the test code are alphabetic letters which identify both the system and test type already selected. Study the following examples:

- If the BCM system and DATA test type were selected, BD will be the first 2 characters of the display. BD stands for BCM DATA. The last 2 characters numerically identify the specific test selection. For example: BD51 designates BCM DATA, test 51.
- If the ECM system and Data test type were selected, ED will be the first 2 characters of the display. ED stands for ECM DATA. The numerals following these 2 characters will represent the particular specific test selection.
- When BI appears as the first 2 characters of the test code, this signifies the BCM system and INPUT test type were selected. The last 2 characters numerically identify the specific test selection. For example: BI51 designates BCM INPUT, test 51.

MAKING SPECIFIC TEST SELECTION

Scrolling to a lower specific test number is done by depressing the FAN▼ button. Scrolling to a higher specific test number is done by depressing the FAN▲ button. The system will automatically display the values for whatever specific test number is displayed.

GM
1-300

1991 ENGINE PERFORMANCE
Self-Diagnostics — Reatta & Riviera PCM/BCM (Cont.)

NOTE: To cancel a specific test type selection and activate a repeat of the specific test type selection process, depress the OFF button on ECCP.

BCM SNAPSHOT

NOTE: If directed here from TEST TYPE SELECTION under MANUAL OPERATION OF SERVICE MODE, go to step 2).

1) Snapshot allows the recall of system operating specifications present at the exact time a BCM malfunction code was set. Up to 3 snapshots may be recalled. In addition, one snapshot may be triggered on demand by depressing FAN▲ button when DO B SNAP is displayed. See Fig. 5.
To enter snapshot, complete the following:
- Enter self-diagnostics. See ENTERING SELF-DIAGNOSTICS.
- Display trouble codes stored in memory. See DISPLAYING TROUBLE CODES.
- Select BCM system for testing. See SYSTEM SELECTION under MANUAL OPERATION OF SERVICE MODE.
- Select SNAPSHOT test type. See TEST TYPE SELECTION under MANUAL OPERATION OF SERVICE MODE.

NOTE: To cancel snapshot test type selection and activate a repeat of the specific test type selection process, depress the OFF button on ECCP.

2) Immediately following the selection of SNAPSHOT?, the system will display BXXX. B stands for BCM. XXX is used here to represent the 3-digit trouble code stored in BCM snapshot memory.
3) With BXXX displayed, depressing the LO button on the ECCP will permit scrolling through the list of BCM diagnostic codes for which the BCM has stored a snapshot. See BCM TROUBLE CODES for list of BCM trouble codes which may be present in snapshot.

NOTE: A trouble code displayed during the trouble code display cycle may NOT be present as a snapshot trouble code. If this is the case, exit SNAPSHOT by depressing the OFF button on the ECCP. This will return the display to the next available system selection.

4) After display of the last BCM trouble code for which a snapshot does exist, pressing the FAN▼ button on the ECCP will result in the DO B SNAP display.
5) Responding to this display by depressing the FAN▼ button on the ECCP will return the display to the first BXXX SNAP? display. Responding to the DO B SNAP display by depressing the HI button with SNAP DATA? or SNAP INPUTS? displayed, will select that test type for display.
6) At this point the display is controlled as it would be for non-snapshot data and inputs display; however, all values and status information represents memorized vehicle conditions. See EXPLANATION OF SPECIFIC TEST SELECTION and MAKING SPECIFIC TEST SELECTION under MANUAL OPERATION OF SERVICE MODE.
7) Depressing the HI button again with DO B SNAP? displayed will change DIC to display the SNAP DONE message to indicate new information has been stored in memory.

ECM SNAPSHOT

NOTE: If directed here from TEST TYPE SELECTION under MANUAL OPERATION OF SERVICE MODE, go to step 2).

1) SNAPSHOT allows the recall of system operating specifications present at the exact time an ECM malfunction code was set. Up to 3 snapshots may be recalled. In addition, one snapshot may be triggered on demand. To enter snapshot, complete the following:
- Enter self-diagnostics. See ENTERING SELF-DIAGNOSTICS.
- Display trouble codes stored in memory. See DISPLAYING TROUBLE CODES.
- Select ECM system for testing. See SYSTEM SELECTION under MANUAL OPERATION OF SERVICE MODE.
- Select SNAPSHOT test type. See TEST TYPE SELECTION under MANUAL OPERATION OF SERVICE MODE.

NOTE: To cancel snapshot test type selection and activate a repeat of the specific test type selection process, depress the OFF button on ECCP.

2) Immediately following the selection of SNAPSHOT?, the system will display the message SNAP DONE. This message appears for 3 seconds to indicate all ECM data and inputs have been stored in memory. Following this 3 second information storage verification, the display will automatically proceed to the first available snapshot test type (i.e., SNAP DATA? or SNAP INPUTS?).
3) At this point, depressing the FAN▼ button will display the next available snapshot test type. Display may be toggled between SNAP DATA? and SNAP INPUTS?.
4) Depressing the FAN▲ button with SNAP DATA? or SNAP INPUTS? displayed will select that particular test type.
5) At this point, the display is controlled as it would be for non-snapshot data and inputs displays; however, all values and status information represents memorized vehicle conditions. See EXPLANATION OF SPECIFIC TEST SELECTION and MAKING SPECIFIC TEST SELECTION under MANUAL OPERATION OF SERVICE MODE.
6) Depressing the FAN▲ button, with SNAP EC? displayed, will display the SNAP DONE message to indicate that new information has been stored in memory.

STATUS LIGHT INDICATORS

During self-diagnostics, the status light display on ECC Panel is used to indicate switchable parameter status. Each different mode of operation is indicated by it's status light being turned on or off. Status light indicators are relative to system level being tested (ECM or BCM). See Figs. 3 and 5.

Following are brief summaries of each systems status light indicators, starting with the ECM status light indicators:
- HIGH indicator light will be on when ECM is in closed loop fuel control. Light comes on only after coolant and O_2 sensors reach operating temperature.
- MED indicator light only indicates whether TCC is enabled (ON) or disabled (OFF) by ECM. Actual working operation depends on TCC system being in working order.
- LOW indicator light stays ON when oxygen sensor signals rich exhaust condition to ECM. Light will flash on and off during warm engine, steady throttle, and proper fuel mix condition.
- OFF indicator light will be on when ECM senses 4th gear pressure switch open. Light should only be on in 4th gear.
- Left-side AUTO indicator light will be on when ECM senses 3rd gear pressure switch open. Light should only be on in 3rd or 4th gear.
- "C" indicator light will be on when ECM senses 2nd gear pressure switch open. Light should only be on in 2nd, 3rd or 4th gear.
- A/C Compressor Command UPPER ARROW indicator light will be on only when ECM allows A/C clutch engagement through A/C relay. Light will also be on if BCM requests ECM to turn clutch on during test sequence. Light should be off if ECM commands disengagement.

Following are brief summaries of BCM system status light indicators:
- LOWER ARROW indicator light will be on if BCM senses low refrigerant pressure switch is open. Light will remain off if A/C system is fully charged and operational. However, light will come on when outside vehicle ambient temperature is less than –5°F (–21°C), this is due to temperature-pressure relationship of R-12 refrigerant.
- OFF indicator light will be on when BCM commands air recirculation.
- MED indicator light will be on when BCM commands airflow out the A/C vents. Light should also be on in A/C and BI-LEV modes.
- LOW indicator light will be on when BCM commands airflow out defroster outlets or when in defrost and A/C modes.
- HIGH indicator light will be on when BCM commands airflow out floor outlets. Light should be on in heater mode.
- Left-side AUTO indicator light will be on when BCM requests ECM to engage A/C compressor clutch.

1991 ENGINE PERFORMANCE
Self-Diagnostics – Reatta & Riviera PCM/BCM (Cont.)

GM
1-301

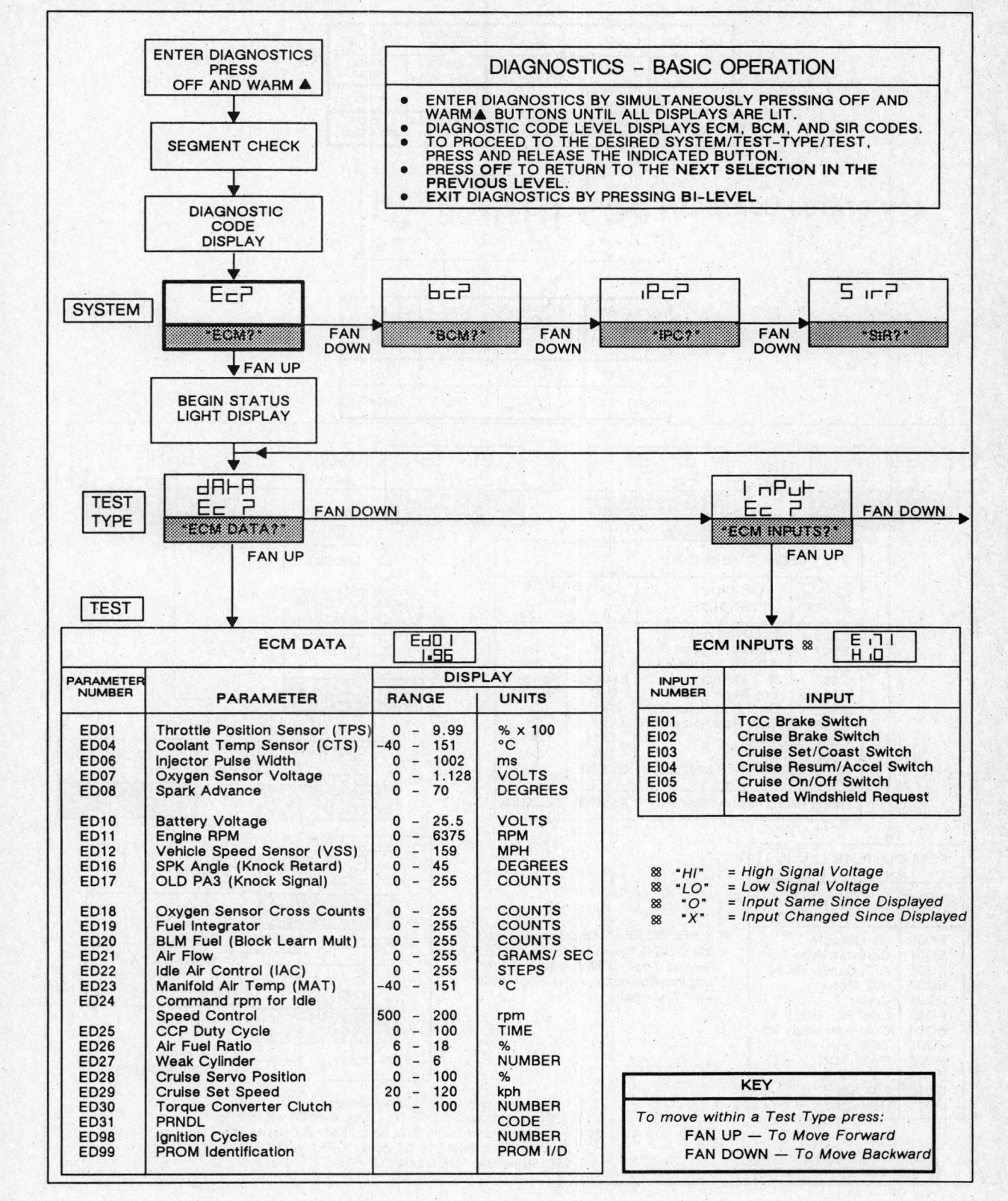

Fig. 2: ECM System Diagnostic Flow Chart (1 of 2)

GM
1-302

1991 ENGINE PERFORMANCE
Self-Diagnostics – Reatta & Riviera PCM/BCM (Cont.)

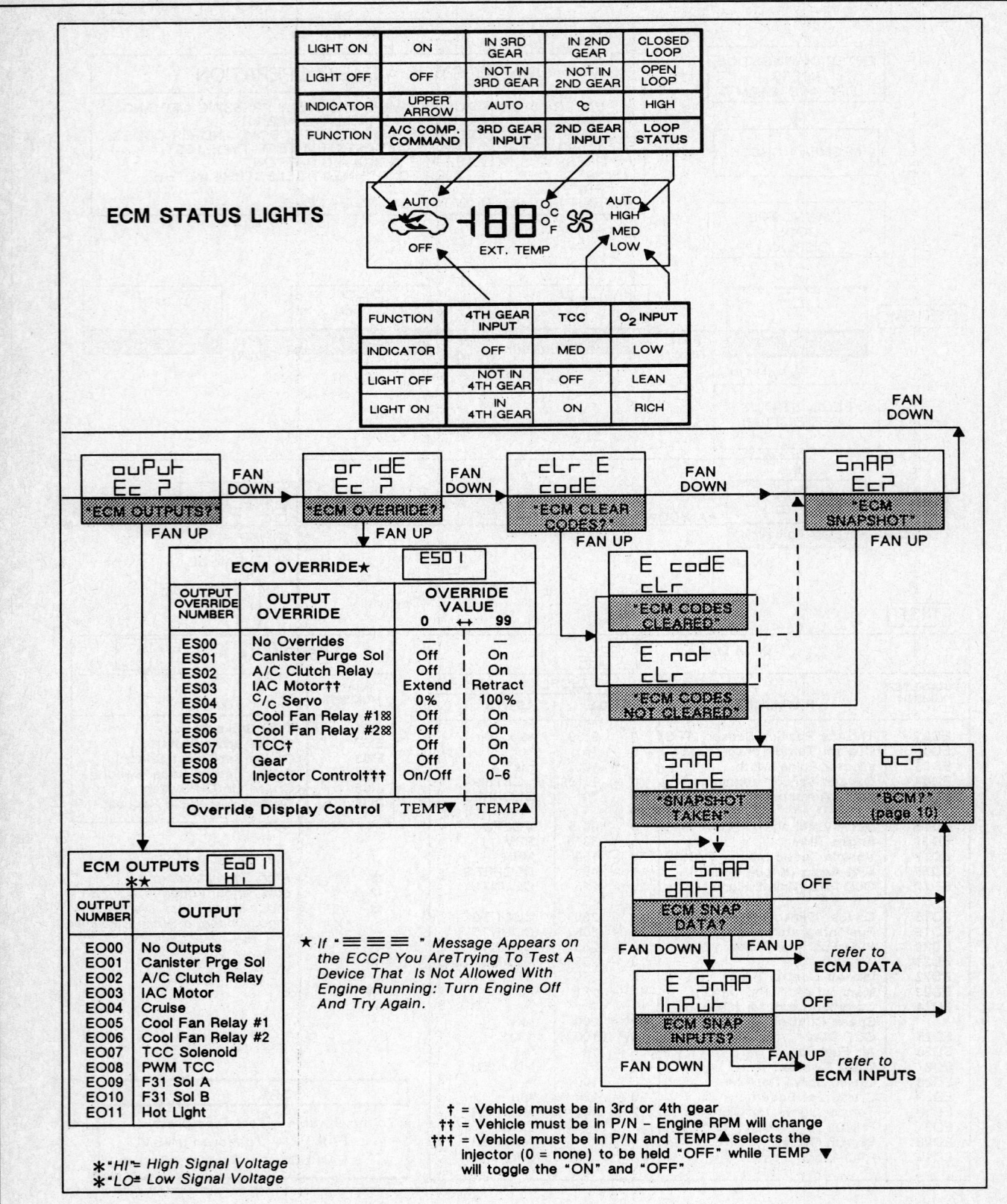

LIGHT ON	ON	IN 3RD GEAR	IN 2ND GEAR	CLOSED LOOP
LIGHT OFF	OFF	NOT IN 3RD GEAR	NOT IN 2ND GEAR	OPEN LOOP
INDICATOR	UPPER ARROW	AUTO	°C	HIGH
FUNCTION	A/C COMP. COMMAND	3RD GEAR INPUT	2ND GEAR INPUT	LOOP STATUS

ECM STATUS LIGHTS

FUNCTION	4TH GEAR INPUT	TCC	O₂ INPUT
INDICATOR	OFF	MED	LOW
LIGHT OFF	NOT IN 4TH GEAR	OFF	LEAN
LIGHT ON	IN 4TH GEAR	ON	RICH

ECM OVERRIDE★ ES01

OUTPUT OVERRIDE NUMBER	OUTPUT OVERRIDE	OVERRIDE VALUE 0 ↔ 99	
ES00	No Overrides	—	—
ES01	Canister Purge Sol	Off	On
ES02	A/C Clutch Relay	Off	On
ES03	IAC Motor††	Extend	Retract
ES04	C/C Servo	0%	100%
ES05	Cool Fan Relay #1⊗	Off	On
ES06	Cool Fan Relay #2⊗	Off	On
ES07	TCC†	Off	On
ES08	Gear	Off	On
ES09	Injector Control†††	On/Off	0–6
Override Display Control		TEMP▼	TEMP▲

ECM OUTPUTS ** EoO1 Hi

OUTPUT NUMBER	OUTPUT
EO00	No Outputs
EO01	Canister Prge Sol
EO02	A/C Clutch Relay
EO03	IAC Motor
EO04	Cruise
EO05	Cool Fan Relay #1
EO06	Cool Fan Relay #2
EO07	TCC Solenoid
EO08	PWM TCC
EO09	F31 Sol A
EO10	F31 Sol B
EO11	Hot Light

★ *If " ≡ ≡ ≡ " Message Appears on the ECCP You AreTrying To Test A Device That Is Not Allowed With Engine Running: Turn Engine Off And Try Again.*

★ "HI"= High Signal Voltage
★ "LO= Low Signal Voltage

ouPut Ec ? "ECM OUTPUTS?"
FAN DOWN / FAN UP

or idE Ec ? "ECM OVERRIDE?"
FAN DOWN / FAN UP

cLr E codE "ECM CLEAR CODES?"
FAN DOWN / FAN UP

SnAP EcP "ECM SNAPSHOT"
FAN UP

E codE cLr "ECM CODES CLEARED"

E not cLr "ECM CODES NOT CLEARED"

SnAP donE "SNAPSHOT TAKEN"

bcP "BCM?" (page 10)

E SnAP dAtA "ECM SNAP DATA?" OFF
FAN DOWN   FAN UP   *refer to* ECM DATA

E SnAP InPut "ECM SNAP INPUTS?" OFF
FAN DOWN   FAN UP   *refer to* ECM INPUTS

† = Vehicle must be in 3rd or 4th gear
†† = Vehicle must be in P/N – Engine RPM will change
††† = Vehicle must be in P/N and TEMP▲ selects the injector (0 = none) to be held "OFF" while TEMP ▼ will toggle the "ON" and "OFF"

91H07750

Fig. 3: *ECM System Diagnostic Flow Chart (2 of 2)*

1991 ENGINE PERFORMANCE
Self-Diagnostics — Reatta & Riviera PCM/BCM (Cont.)

GM
1-303

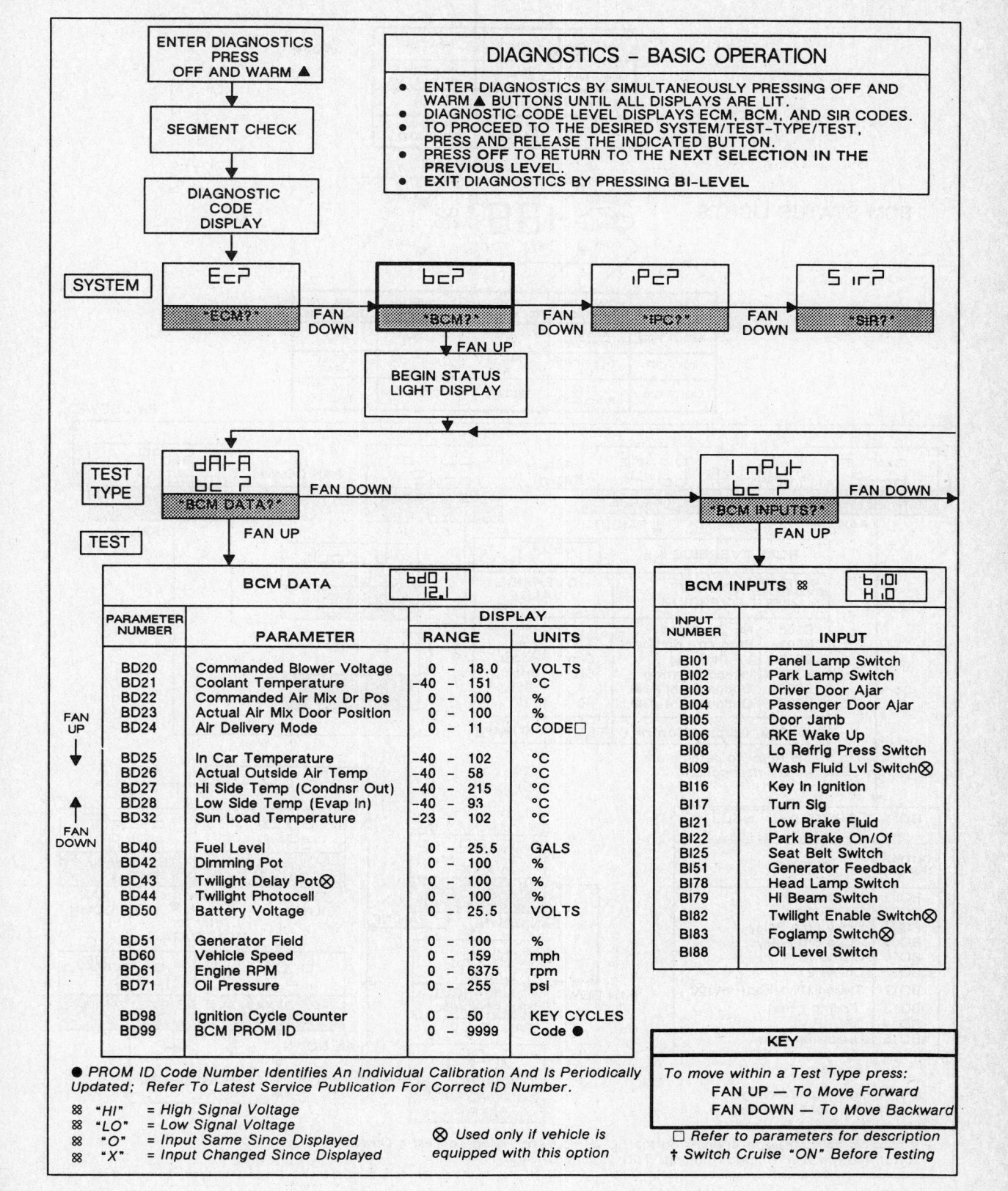

Fig. 4: BCM System Diagnostic Flow Chart (1 of 2)

GM
1-304

1991 ENGINE PERFORMANCE
Self-Diagnostics — Reatta & Riviera PCM/BCM (Cont.)

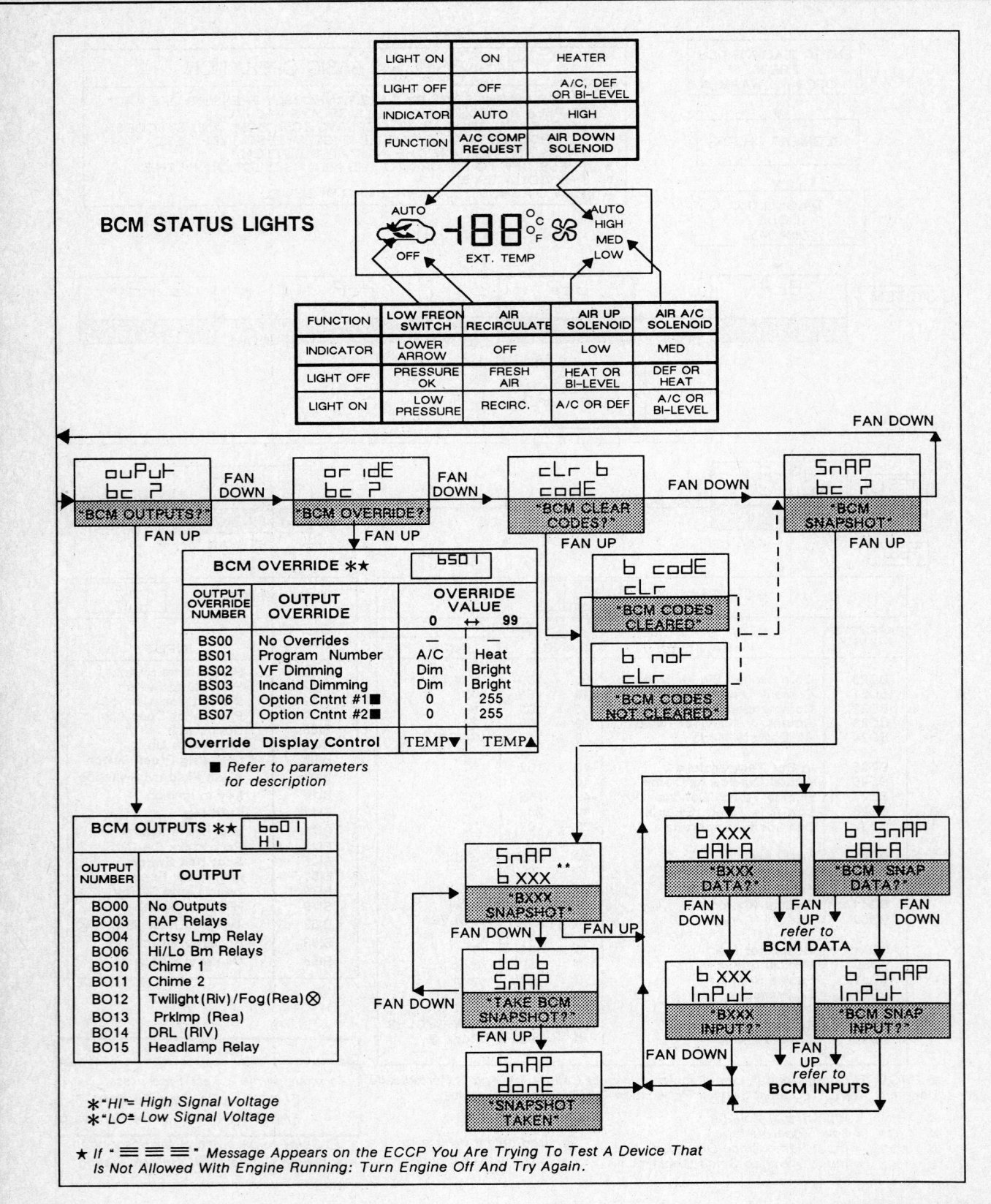

LIGHT ON	ON	HEATER
LIGHT OFF	OFF	A/C, DEF OR BI-LEVEL
INDICATOR	AUTO	HIGH
FUNCTION	A/C COMP REQUEST	AIR DOWN SOLENOID

BCM STATUS LIGHTS

FUNCTION	LOW FREON SWITCH	AIR RECIRCULATE	AIR UP SOLENOID	AIR A/C SOLENOID
INDICATOR	LOWER ARROW	OFF	LOW	MED
LIGHT OFF	PRESSURE OK	FRESH AIR	HEAT OR BI-LEVEL	DEF OR HEAT
LIGHT ON	LOW PRESSURE	RECIRC.	A/C OR DEF	A/C OR BI-LEVEL

BCM OVERRIDE ★★

OUTPUT OVERRIDE NUMBER	OUTPUT OVERRIDE	OVERRIDE VALUE 0 ↔ 99	
BS00	No Overrides	—	—
BS01	Program Number	A/C	Heat
BS02	VF Dimming	Dim	Bright
BS03	Incand Dimming	Dim	Bright
BS06	Option Cntnt #1■	0	255
BS07	Option Cntnt #2■	0	255
Override Display Control		TEMP▼	TEMP▲

■ Refer to parameters for description

BCM OUTPUTS ★★

OUTPUT NUMBER	OUTPUT
BO00	No Outputs
BO03	RAP Relays
BO04	Crtsy Lmp Relay
BO06	Hi/Lo Bm Relays
BO10	Chime 1
BO11	Chime 2
BO12	Twilight (Riv)/Fog (Rea)⊗
BO13	Prklmp (Rea)
BO14	DRL (RIV)
BO15	Headlamp Relay

★ "HI" = High Signal Voltage
★ "LO" = Low Signal Voltage

★ If "≡≡≡≡" Message Appears on the ECCP You Are Trying To Test A Device That Is Not Allowed With Engine Running: Turn Engine Off And Try Again.

91B07752

Courtesy of General Motors Corp.

Fig. 5: BCM System Diagnostic Flow Chart (2 of 2)

1991 ENGINE PERFORMANCE
Self-Diagnostics — Reatta & Riviera PCM/BCM (Cont.)

GM
1-305

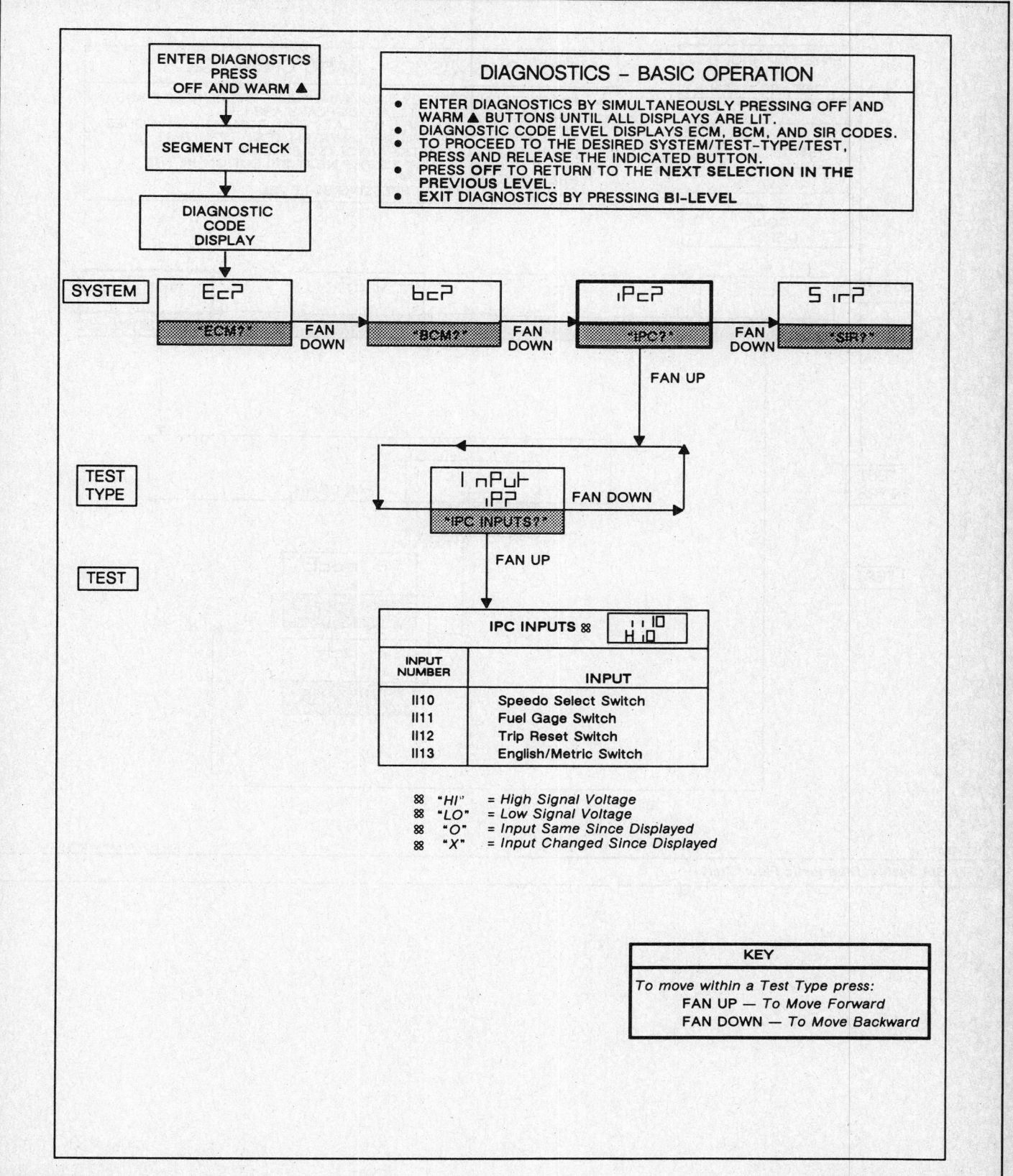

Fig. 6: IPC System Diagnostic Flow Chart

91D07753

Courtesy of General Motors Corp.

GM
1-306

1991 ENGINE PERFORMANCE
Self-Diagnostics – Reatta & Riviera PCM/BCM (Cont.)

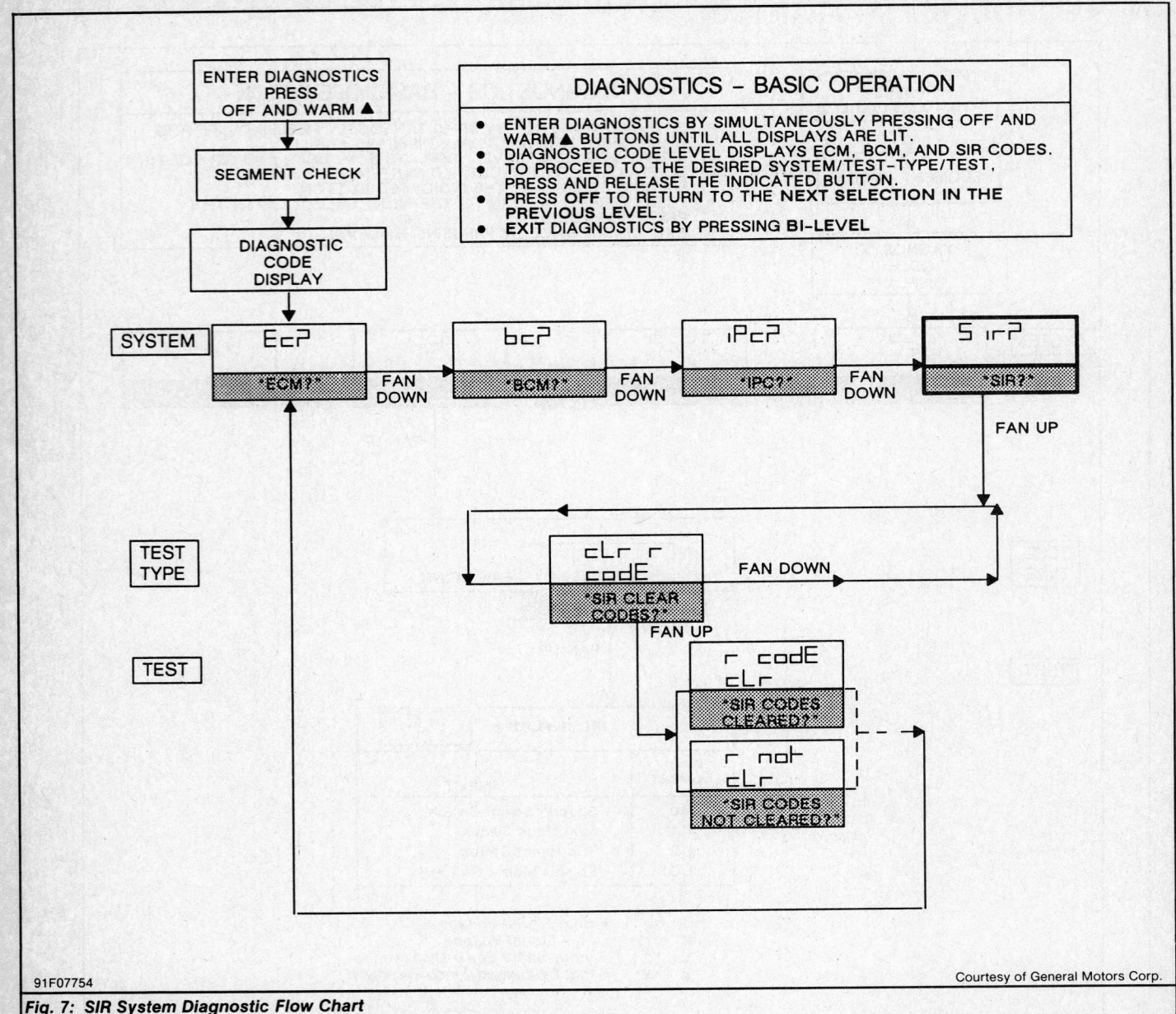

DIAGNOSTICS – BASIC OPERATION

- ENTER DIAGNOSTICS BY SIMULTANEOUSLY PRESSING OFF AND WARM ▲ BUTTONS UNTIL ALL DISPLAYS ARE LIT.
- DIAGNOSTIC CODE LEVEL DISPLAYS ECM, BCM, AND SIR CODES.
- TO PROCEED TO THE DESIRED SYSTEM/TEST-TYPE/TEST, PRESS AND RELEASE THE INDICATED BUTTON.
- PRESS OFF TO RETURN TO THE NEXT SELECTION IN THE PREVIOUS LEVEL.
- EXIT DIAGNOSTICS BY PRESSING BI-LEVEL

91F07754

Courtesy of General Motors Corp.

Fig. 7: SIR System Diagnostic Flow Chart

1991 ENGINE PERFORMANCE
Self-Diagnostics — Reatta & Riviera PCM/BCM (Cont.)

GM
1-307

DATA DISPLAY CODES

Brief summary of each DATA parameter is as follows:
ECM DATA PARAMETERS:

ED01 – Throttle position displayed in volts from 0 to 5.10.

ED04 – Coolant temperature displayed in degrees Celsius (°C) from –40 to 151.

ED06 – Injector pulse width displayed in milliseconds (ms) from 0 to 100.2.

ED07 – Oxygen sensor voltage displayed in volts from 0 to 1.128.

ED08 – Spark advance displayed in degrees from 0 to 70, similar to engine timing in degrees.

ED10 – Battery voltage read in volts from 0 to 25.5.

ED11 – Engine speed displayed in RPM from 0 to 6375. (May display 20 with ignition on and engine off).

ED12 - Vehicle speed displayed in MPH from 0 to 159.

ED16 - Knock retard displayed in degrees of timing pulled out from 0 to 45.

ED17 - Knock sensor activity displayed as counts, an arbitrary number that increases from 0 to 9999 according to amount of activity from knock sensor.

ED18 - Oxygen sensor cross counts displayed as number of times O_2 sensor voltage crossed .45-volt reference each second.

ED19 - Fuel integrator displayed in counts from 0 to 255.

ED20 - Block learn multiplier displayed in counts from 0 to 255.

ED21 - Mass airflow sensor displayed in grams per second of air flow from 0 to 255.

ED22 - Idle air control displayed in steps of travel from 0 to 255.

ED23 - Manifold air temperature displayed in degrees Celsius (°C) from –40 to 152.

ED24 - Command RPM for idle speed is displayed in RPM from 500 to 2000.

ED25 - Canister purge delay is displayed in percent from zero to 100.

ED26 - Air/fuel ratio is displayed in percent from 6 to 18.

ED27 - Weak cylinder display displays the number of the weak cylinder.

ED28 - Cruise servo position is displayed in percent from zero to 100.

ED29 - Cruise set speed is displayed in KPH from 20 to 120.

ED30 - Torque converter clutch duty cycle is displayed in percent from zero to 100. Zero indicates clutch is not engaged.

ED31 - PRNDL status is displayed in a 4-digit binary number as follows:

P=0110	D=0000
R=0011	2=0101
N=1010	1=1100
D=1001	

ED98 - Ignition cycle counter value is number of times the ignition has been cycled to OFF since ECM trouble code was last detected. After 50 ignition cycles without any malfunctions being detected, all stored ECM codes are cleared.

ED99 - ECM Prom ID displayed as number up to 4 digits long which can be used to identify MEM-CAL/PROM installed in ECM.

BCM DATA PARAMETERS:

BD20 - Commanded blower voltage in volts from 0 to 18.0 volts.

BD21 - Coolant temperature displayed in degrees Celsius (°C) from –40 to 151. This value is sent from ECM to BCM. If circuit malfunctions, ECM will send BCM a failsoft default value for display.

BD22 - Commanded air mix door position displayed in percent. Value close to 0% represents cold air mix and value close to 100% represents warm air mix.

BD23 - Actual air mix door position displayed in percent. This value should follow commanded air mix door position (BD22) except when door is commanded beyond its mechanical limits of travel.

BD24 - Air delivery mode displayed as number from 0 to 11. Each number is code which represents these air delivery modes:

0 – Auto-Recirc/MAX A/C outlets
1 – Auto-A/C outlets
2 – Auto-Bi-Level outlets
3 – Auto-Heater-Def outlets
4 – Auto-Heater outlets
5 – Off
6 – Normal purge
7 – Cold (DEF) purge
8 – Forced/Def outlets
9 – Forced (Fan) Heater outlets
10 – Forced (Fan) Bi-Level outlets
11 – A/C Purge

BD25 - In-car temperature is displayed in degrees Celsius (°C) from –40 to 102.

BD26 - Actual outside temperature displayed in degrees Celsius (°C) from –40 to 58. This value represents actual sensor temperature and is not buffered by software.

BD27 - A/C High side temperature (condenser output) displayed in degrees Celsius (°C) from –40 to 215.

BD28 - A/C Low side temperature (evaporator input) displayed in degrees Celsius (°C) from –40 to 93.

BD32 - Sunload temperature sensor displayed in degrees Celsius (°C) from –40 to 102.

BD40 - Actual fuel level read in gallons between 0 to 25.5. Value represents actual sensor position and is not restricted by features used to eliminate fuel slosh affects on IPC display value.

BD42 - Dimming pot displayed in percent. Value close to 0% represents maximum dimming and value close to 100% represents maximum brightness.

BD43 - Twilight delay pot displayed in percent. Value close to 0% represents minimum delay time and value close to 100% represents maximum delay time.

BD44 - Twilight Photocell displayed in percent. Value close to 0% represents daylight and value close to 100% represents darkness.

BD50 - Battery voltage read in volts between 0 and 25.5.

BD51 - Generator field displayed in percent. Value close to 0% represents minimum regulator on time and value close to 100% represents maximum regulator on time.

BD60 - Vehicle speed displayed in MPH from 0 to 159.

BD61 - Engine speed displayed in RPM from 0 to 6375.

BD71 - Oil pressure sensor displayed in PSI from 0 to 80.

BD98 - Ignition cycle value is the number of times that the BCM has been turned OFF since BCM trouble code was last detected. After 99 ignition cycles, (where each off, crank, off cycle counts as 2), without any malfunction being detected, all BCM codes are cleared.

BD99 - BCM PROM I.D. displayed as number, up to four digits long, which can be used to verify that proper PROM was installed in BCM.

INPUT DISPLAY CODES

Brief summary of each systems INPUT parameters is as follows.
ECM INPUT PARAMETERS:

EI01 - TCC brake switch display is LO when brake pedal is depressed.

EI02 - Cruise brake switch display is LO when brake pedal is depressed.

EI03 - Cruise SET/COAST switch display is HI when cruise ON/OFF switch is on and SET/COAST switch is depressed.

EI04 - Cruise RESUME/ACCEL switch display is HI when cruise ON/OFF switch is on and RESUME/ACCEL switch is depressed.

EI05 - Cruise ON/OFF switch display is HI when switch is on.

EI06 - HEATED WINDSHIELD switch display is HI when switch is on.

GM
1-308

1991 ENGINE PERFORMANCE
Self-Diagnostics — Reatta & Riviera PCM/BCM (Cont.)

BCM INPUT PARAMETERS:

BI01 - Panel light switch display is LO when panel light switch is in off position.

BI02 - Park light switch display is LO when park light switch is in off position.

BI03 - Driver door ajar switch display is LO when driver's front door is ajar.

BI04 - Passenger door ajar switch display is LO when passenger's door is open.

BI05 - Door jamb switch display is LO when any door is open.

BI06 - RKE WAKE UP display is LO when an unlock signal is recognized by the RKE receiver module.

BI08 - Low refrigerant pressure switch display is LO when system is low on refrigerant.

BI09 - Washer fluid level switch display is LO when vehicle is low on washer fluid.

BI16 - Key in ignition display is LO "only" when key is in LOCK position. (With ignition on, display will always read HI.)

BI17 - Turn signal switch display is LO when switch is on.

BI21 - Low brake fluid display is LO when brake fluid is low.

BI22 - Park brake switch display is LO when parking brake is applied.

BI25 - Seat belt switch display is HI when drivers seat belt is fastened.

BI51 - Generator feedback display is LO when there is generator problem or engine is not running.

BI78 - Headlights display is HI whenever headlight switch is on.

BI79 - High beam switch display is LO as long as lever is pulled in.

BI82 - Twilight enable switch display is LO whenever twilight sentinel headlight switch is on (Riviera only).

BI83 - Fog light switch display is HI whenever fog lights switch is on (Reatta only) .

BI88 - Low oil level switch display will be HI when engine oil level is low.

IPC INPUT PARAMETERS:

II10 - Speedo select switch display is HI as long as switch on IPC is depressed.

II11 - Fuel gauge switch display is HI as long as switch on IPC is depressed.

II12 - Trip reset switch display is HI as long as switch on IPC is depressed.

II13 - English/Metric switch display is HI as long as switch on IPC is depressed.

OUTPUT DISPLAY CODES

Brief summary of each systems OUTPUT parameters is as follows.

ECM OUTPUT PARAMETERS:

EO000 - No outputs display will not show HI or LO . This is normal resting code where no outputs will be cycled.

EO001 - Canister purge solenoid display will be LO when solenoid is energized.

EO002 - A/C clutch display is LO when clutch is engaged.

EO003 - IAC motor display will be LO when pintle is extended and HI when it is retracted.

EO004 - Cruise control servo display will display servo position.

EO005 - #1 coolant fan relay (FAN REL 1) display is LO when coolant fan is energized.

EO006 - #2 coolant fan relay (FAN REL 2) display is LO when coolant fan is energized.

EO007 - Torque Converter Clutch display will be LO when TCC solenoid is energized.

EO008 - Torque Converter Clutch modulated solenoid display will be LO when solenoid is energized.

EO009 - Torque Converter Clutch shift solenoid A display will be LO when solenoid is energized.

EO010 - Torque Converter Clutch shift solenoid B display will be LO when solenoid is energized.

EO011 - HOT light display will be LO when light is on.

BCM OUTPUT PARAMETERS:

BO00 - No outputs display will not show HI or LO. This is normal resting code where no outputs will be cycled.

BO03 - Retained Accessory Power (RAP) relays display is LO when relays are energized.

BO04 - Courtesy lights relay display is LO when relay is energized.

BO06 - Hi/Lo beam relay display is LO when relay is energized and hi beams ON.

BO10 - CHIME 1 display is LO when fast chime is sounding.

BO11 - CHIME 2 display is LO when slow chime is sounding.

BO12 - Fog light Daytime Running Lights (DRL) display is LO when fog light relay is on (Reatta only).

BO13 - Twilight display (Riviera) is LO when relay is energized. (Reatta) Park lights display is LO when lights are on.

BO14 - DRL (Daytime Running Lights) – Display is LO when relays are energized or lights on (Riviera only)

BO15 - Headlight relay display is LO when relay is energized.

OVERRIDE DISPLAY CODES

Brief summary of each OVERRIDE parameter is as follows.

ECM OVERRIDE PARAMETERS:

ES00 – No Overrides display will not show any value in display area on ECCP, as no overrides are active at this point. This is normal resting code where no overrides will be controlled. This code can be used to stop override control without having to go back to system selections.

ES01 – Canister purge solenoid can be turned OFF (00) by pressing TEMP▼ button or turned ON (99) by pressing TEMP▲ button.

ES02 – A/C RELAY can be turned OFF (00) by pressing TEMP▼ button or turned ON (99) by pressing TEMP▲ button.

ES03 – IAC MOTOR display will show position IAC motor is being commanded to in percentage of travel. Vehicle must be in Park or Neutral. TEMP▼ button will retract motor (increasing RPM) and TEMP▲ button will extend motor.

ES04 – Cruise control servo switch must be on for this test to work. This manual override allows by-passing of the cruise control automatic calculation function. Cruise control position can be controlled by percentage from zero to 99. This allows technician to compare requested cruise position with cruise servo position (ED28). The 2 should agree with each other within 3 percent. Since this test is not allowed with engine running, there will be only enough vacuum available to stroke servo one time. Pressing TEMP▲ button will increase cruise percentage and pressing TEMP▼ button will decrease cruise percentage.

ES05 – Cooling fan relay No.1 can be turned off (00) by pressing TEMP▼ button or turned ON (99) by pressing TEMP▲ button.

ES06 – Cooling fan relay No. 2 can be turned off (00) by pressing TEMP▼ button or turned ON (99) by pressing TEMP▲ button.

ES07 – TCC solenoid display will show commanded state of TCC solenoid (00–not engaged, 99–engaged). Pressing TEMP▲ button will engage TCC and pressing TEMP▼ button will disengage TCC. Vehicle must be in 3rd or 4th gear for override to operate.

ES08 – This override places transmission in current gear selected and remains in that gear until TEMP▲ (upshift) or TEMP▼ (downshift) button is depressed to change gear selection. ECM will allow 1st gear only up to 35 MPH, 2nd gear up to 50 MPH and 3rd gear up to 60 MPH.

ES09 – Injector control override will work only when vehicle is in Park or Neutral. When entering override, display will show "0", all injectors will be working normally. TEMP▲ button will increment display by one, up to 6 (or to 8, for 8 cylinder engine), and then return to "0". Display number indicates cylinder injector number that is being held off. Injector will continue to be held off until TEMP▼ button is used to turn

1991 ENGINE PERFORMANCE
Self-Diagnostics – Reatta & Riviera PCM/BCM (Cont.)

GM
1-309

injector back on. TEMP▼ button is used to toggle injector, on and off.

BCM OVERRIDE PARAMETERS:

BS00 – No Overrides display will not show any value in display area on ECCP, as no overrides are active at this point. This is normal resting code where no overrides will be controlled. This code can be used to stop override control without having to go back to system selections.

BS01 – Program Number will automatically change as heating and A/C operating conditions change. Program number can be manually overridden using TEMP▲ and TEMP▼ buttons. TEMP▲ button will increase number at controlled rate until MAX HEAT mode value of "99" is reached. TEMP▼ button will decrease number at controlled rate until MAX A/C mode value of "0" is reached. Manual override will continue until override code is canceled. This manual override control allows technician to alter and observe reactions of system change on other BCM data parameters.

BS02 – Vacuum Fluorescent (VF) Dimming Number will automatically change as dimming switch position is moved (only if exterior lights are ON). Using override controls, TEMP▲ and TEMP▼ buttons, automatic dimming can be manually controlled. Use "99" to represent maximum brightness of VF displays and "0" to represent maximum dimming of VF displays, (exterior lights need not be on when overriding dimming).

BS03 – Bulb Dimming – As dimming switch position is moved, incandescent dimming number will automatically change (only if exterior lights ON). Using override controls, TEMP▲ and TEMP▼ buttons, automatic dimming can be manually controlled. Using "99" to represent maximum brightness and "0" to represent maximum dimming of incandescent lighting, (exterior lights need not be on when overriding dimming).

BS06 – Option Content No. 1 – This override allows the ability to change contents of which options the vehicle's BCM has stored in its EEPROM. This option content is displayed in trip odometer as a number from 0 to 255. Each number is a code which represents option content. BCM uses this value to determine how to operate the displays and electronic controls. Incorrect option values cause many different problems. To determine proper option value, add up following options that vehicle is equipped with:

- U.S. vehicle (not Canadian or export model) – 128
- Reatta body style – 16
- Export displays (export car, option code NM8) – 32
- Twilight sentinel – 2

Take total of actual options vehicles has from above list and compare it with Option 1 value on ECCP display. If the two are different, correct Option 1 value using following procedure.

To change option content number press TEMP▲ or TEMP▼ button for override control until desired number appears, (corresponding to total of actual options vehicle does have). Next, press and hold HEATER and DEFROST buttons simultaneously for 3 seconds. This will reprogram BCM EEPROM to number of options displayed on the IPC odometer.

BS07 – Option Content No. 2 – This override allows the ability to change contents of which options the vehicle's BCM has stored in its EEPROM. This option content is displayed in trip odometer as number from 0 to 255. Each number is a code which represents option content. BCM uses this value to determine how to operate the displays and electronic controls. Incorrect option values cause many different problems. To determine proper option value add up following options that vehicle is equipped with:

- Oil level sensor (All vehicles) – 4
- Anti-lock brakes (option code JL9) – 32
- Washer fluid level sensor (All vehicles) – 128
- Universal Theft Deterrent – 64

(This is NOT Pass-Key Theft Deterrent System that comes standard with vehicle)

Take total of actual options vehicle has from above list and compare it with Option 2 value on ECCP display. If the 2 are different, correct Option 2 value using following procedure:

To change option content number press TEMP▲ or TEMP▼ button for override control until desired number appears, (number corresponding to total of actual options vehicle does have). Next, press and hold both HEATER and DEFROST buttons for 3 seconds. This will reprogram BCM EEPROM to number of options displayed on the IPC odometer.

SELF-DIAGNOSTIC SYSTEM CHECK

The self-diagnostic system check is an organized approach for identifying a problem caused by on-vehicle computer controlled electronics. Understanding this chart and using it correctly will reduce diagnostic time, prevent unnecessary replacement of parts, and reduce comebacks. To review the basic information on how to use the computer self-diagnostics, go to beginning of this article.

ALWAYS START ELECTRICAL OR ELECTRONIC DIAGNOSIS HERE

1) SERVICE ENGINE SOON telltale light at key ON confirms battery, ignition, and ground integrity to ECM and also verifies Ignition 1 power feed to IPC.

2) IPC odometer is primary display device for diagnosis and must be functional in order to use self-diagnostic system.

3) ECCP serves as access for onboard diagnosis and must be functional in order to use self-diagnostic system. A display other than standard temperature indicates fault that must be corrected before diagnostics can be entered.

4) After entering diagnostics, record all displayed trouble codes and note if they display as CURRENT or HISTORY. Codes displayed as current may be diagnosed using the procedures outlined in this article, but those codes displayed as HISTORY are not presently failing and may require visual inspection of circuitry to isolate. To diagnose intermittent codes, see INTERMITTENTS in TROUBLE SHOOTING – NO CODES article.

5) Failure of SERVICE ENGINE SOON light to go out in the expected time period indicates ECM problem.

6) If no fault is found and driveability problems exist, go to TROUBLE SHOOTING – NO CODES article for diagnosis by SYMPTOM.

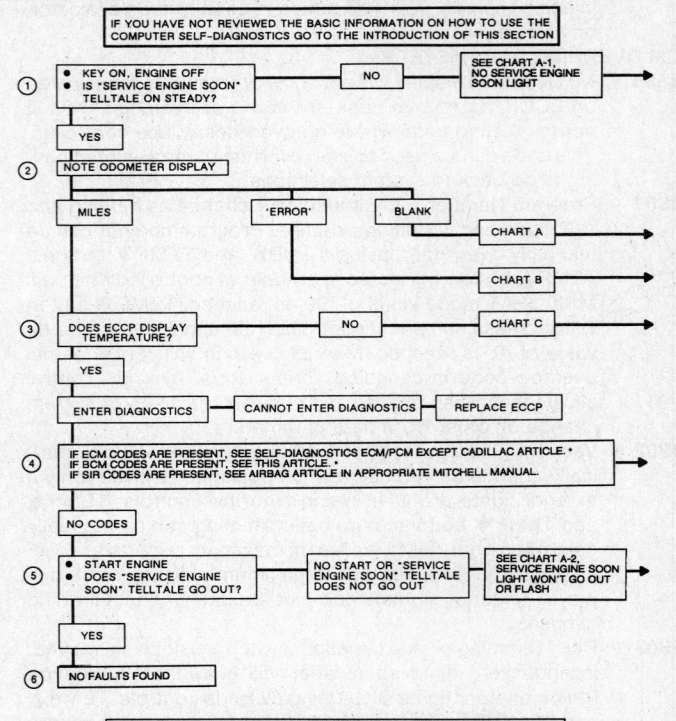

90C00838

WHEN ALL DIAGNOSIS AND REPAIRS ARE COMPLETED, CLEAR CODES AND VERIFY OPERATION

Courtesy of General Motors Corp.

CHART A-1, NO SERVICE ENGINE SOON LIGHT

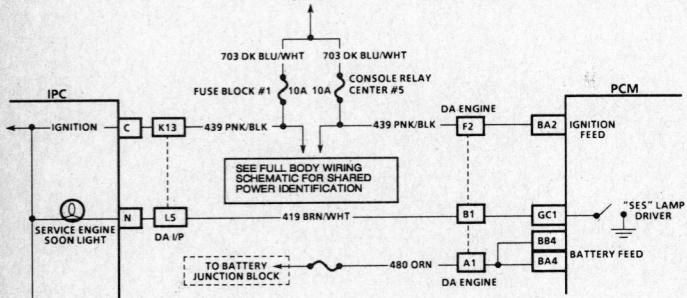

The SERVICE ENGINE SOON light is attached to the IPC. It is powered by CPS circuit No. 439. PCM completes the ground to turn the light on. The light will be on while engine is not running. With the engine running, a steady light indicates a PCM code is set

NOTE: Test numbers refer to numbers on diagnostic chart.

1) SERVICE ENGINE SOON light should be on.

2) Using a test light connected to battery voltage, probe each of the system ground circuits to be sure a good ground is present. See WIRING DIAGRAMS article in ENGINE PERFORMANCE to identify system ground circuits.

DIAGNOSTIC AIDS

If engine runs okay, check:
- Faulty light bulb.
- PCM drive circuit open.
- 10-amp ignition fuse open.

If engine cranks, but will not run:
- Continuous battery-fusible link open.
- Ignition feed to PCM open.
- Open fuse No. 5 in console relay center.
- Poor connection to PCM.

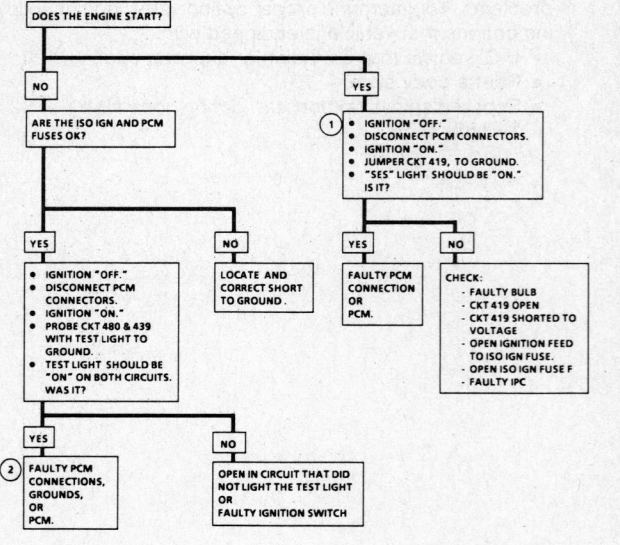

"AFTER REPAIRS," CONFIRM "CLOSED LOOP" OPERATION AND NO "SERVICE ENGINE SOON" LIGHT.

91I07755 91A07756

Courtesy of General Motors Corp.

1991 ENGINE PERFORMANCE
Self-Diagnostics — Reatta & Riviera PCM/BCM (Cont.)

GM
1-311

CHART A-2, SERVICE ENGINE SOON LIGHT WON'T GO OUT OR FLASH

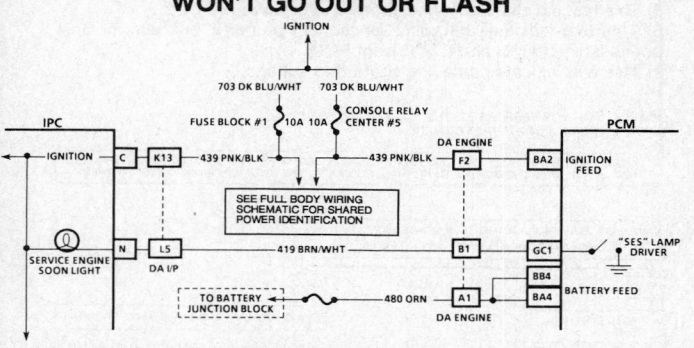

The SERVICE ENGINE SOON light is attached to the IPC. It is powered by CPS circuit No. 439. PCM completes the ground to turn the light on. The light will be on while engine is not running. With the engine running, a steady light indicates a PCM code is set

NOTE: Test numbers refer to numbers on diagnostic chart.

1) If the light goes off when PCM connector is unplugged, PCM drive circuit is not shorted to ground.

2) If there is a problem with PCM that causes a "Scan" tester to not read serial data, PCM should not flash Code 12. If Code 12 does flash, be sure that the tester is working properly by trying it on another vehicle. If tester is working properly and circuit No. 800 is okay, MEM-CAL or PCM or another component which uses the serial data line may be at fault for the NO ALDL problem.

3) This step will check for an open diagnostic circuit No. 451 (terminal "B" of ALDL).

4) At this point, SERVICE ENGINE SOON light wiring is okay. The problem is a faulty PCM or MEM-CAL. If Code 12 does not flash, PCM should be replaced using original MEM-CAL. Replace MEM-CAL only after trying a PCM, as a defective MEM-CAL is an unlikely cause of the problem.

91I07755 91C07757

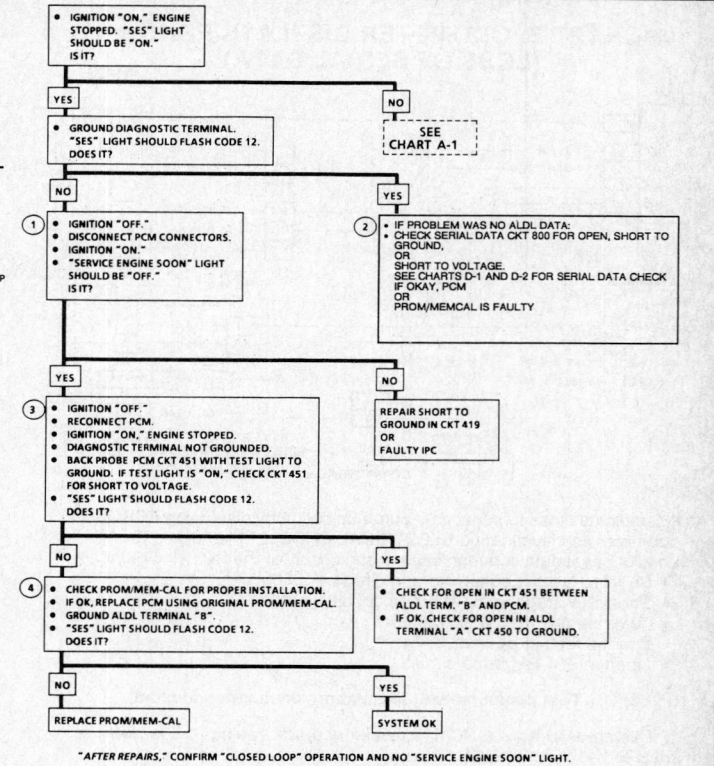

"AFTER REPAIRS," CONFIRM "CLOSED LOOP" OPERATION AND NO "SERVICE ENGINE SOON" LIGHT.

Courtesy of General Motors Corp.

CHART A, BLANK ODOMETER DISPLAY

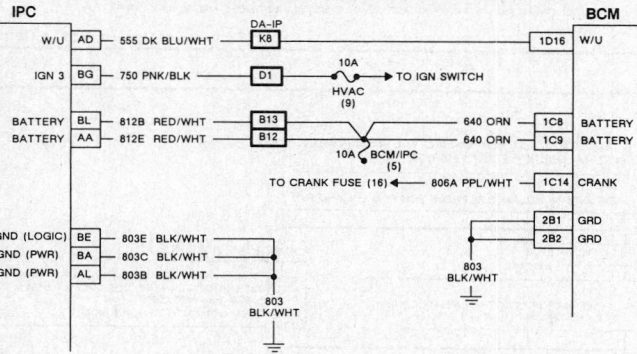

Loss of IPC display and messages can result from the following:

- Loss of 12 volt power to IPC (circuit No. 812).
- Loss of ground to IPC (circuit No. 803).
- Internal fault in CPS or IPC.

NOTE: Test numbers refer to numbers on diagnostic chart.

1) This test checks the IPC power and grounds.

2) Power, Ignition 3 and ground circuits to IPC are functioning properly; therefore, fault is either in terminal contacts or internal to the IPC.

3) The 12-volt feed to the IPC is not functioning. Check for open in circuit No. 640.

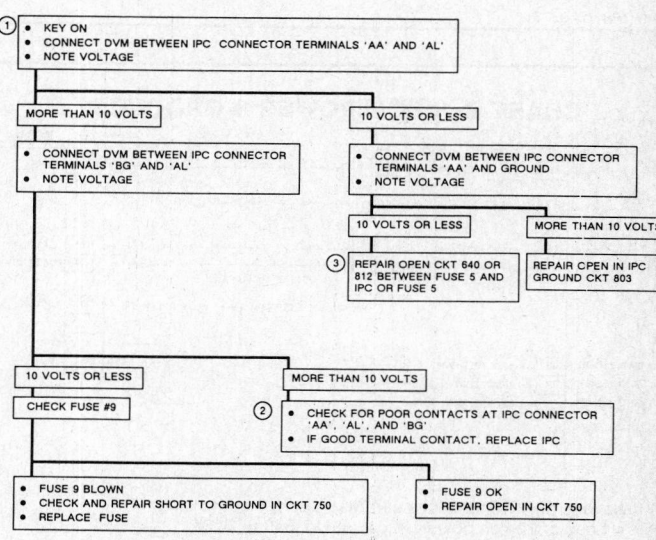

IF YOU HAVE NOT PERFORMED THE 'SELF-DIAGNOSTIC SYSTEM CHECK', START THERE FIRST

WHEN ALL DIAGNOSIS AND REPAIRS ARE COMPLETE, CLEAR CODES AND VERIFY OPERATION

91E07758 91G07759

Courtesy of General Motors Corp.

GM
1-312

1991 ENGINE PERFORMANCE
Self-Diagnostics – Reatta & Riviera PCM/BCM (Cont.)

CHART B, ODOMETER DISPLAYS ERROR (LOSS OF SERIAL DATA)

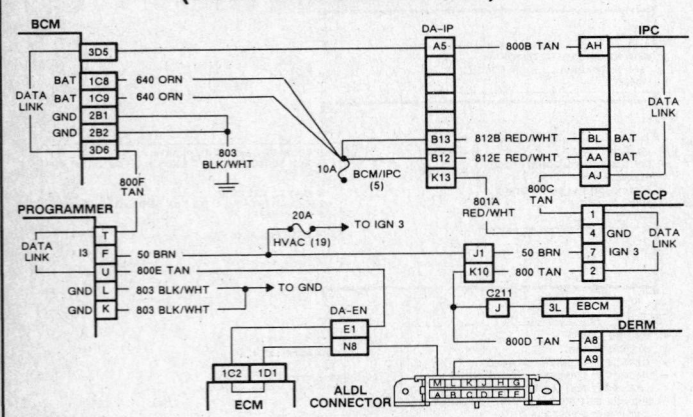

IPC indicates loss of serial data communication by displaying ERROR in odometer and illuminating ELECTRICAL PROBLEM telltale light.
Loss of serial data communications can occur for the following reasons:
- Short to ground somewhere in circuit No. 800.
- Short to voltage somewhere in circuit No. 800.
- Two opens in circuit No. 800.
- Internal fault in BCM or IPC.
- Open in ECCP ground circuit.

NOTE: **Test numbers refer to numbers on diagnostic chart.**

1) This steps checks if BCM is awake and functioning. If it is not, use chart B-1 to isolate fault.
2) This step checks if ECC head has lost data communication along with IPC.
3) Code B556 indicates IPC EEPROM error. Odometer will display ERROR, but diagnostics will be accessible.
4) Since IPC lost data communications, creating an open in data line at ALDL connector should remove data communications from ECCP as well. If not, IPC is receiving data but is unable to communicate due to poor connection or internal problem.

91I07760 91A07761

5) This test indicates data line shorted to ground.
6) This test indicates data line functioning properly, but with multiple opens isolating IPC and ECCP from BCM.
7) This test indicates data line shorted to voltage.

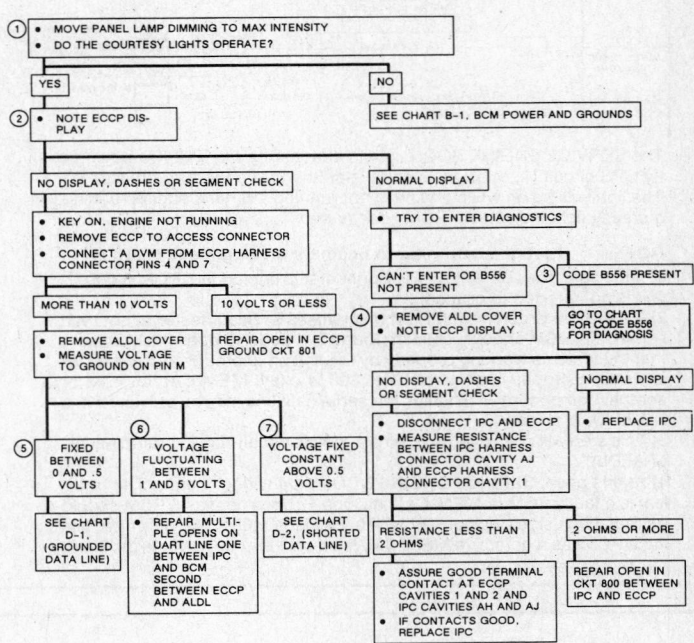

WHEN ALL DIAGNOSIS AND REPAIRS ARE COMPLETED, CLEAR CODES AND VERIFY OPERATION

Courtesy of General Motors Corp.

CHART B-1, BCM POWER & GROUNDS

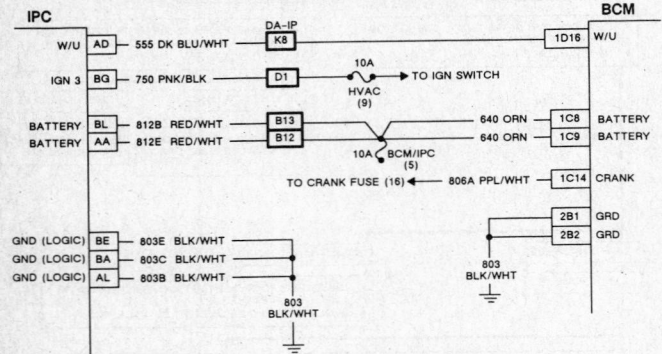

The loss of BCM functions can result from the following:
- Loss of 12-volt power on circuit No. 640 to BCM.
- Loss of ground on circuit No. 803 to BCM.
- Internal BCM fault.

NOTE: **Test numbers refer to numbers on diagnostic chart.**

1) BCM is not receiving 12-volt input. Check power and ground supply to BCM.
2) This step checks for short to ground in any part of circuit No. 640.
3) Checks to see if the short to ground is inside a component or in the circuit itself.

91E07758 91C07762

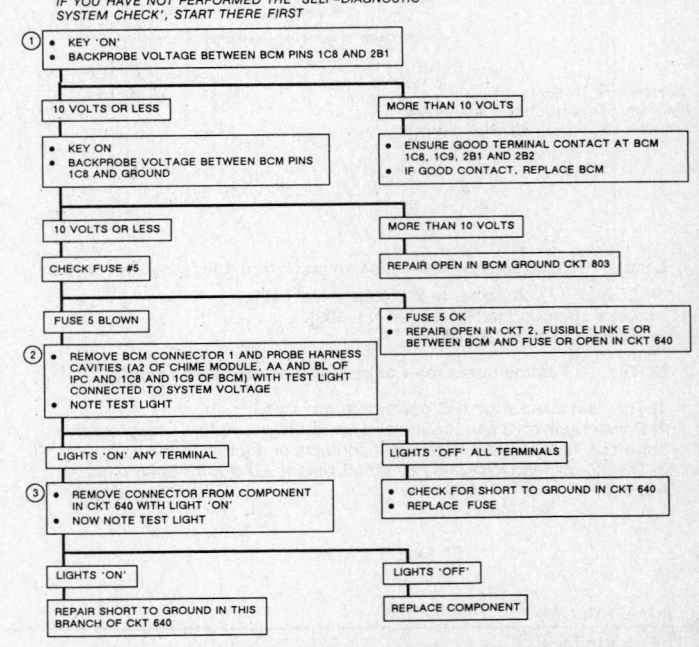

WHEN ALL DIAGNOSIS AND REPAIRS ARE COMPLETE, CLEAR CODES AND VERIFY OPERATION

Courtesy of General Motors Corp.

1991 ENGINE PERFORMANCE
Self-Diagnostics — Reatta & Riviera PCM/BCM (Cont.)

GM
1-313

CHART C, ECCP DISPLAY PROBLEMS (LOSS OF ECCP COMMUNICATIONS)

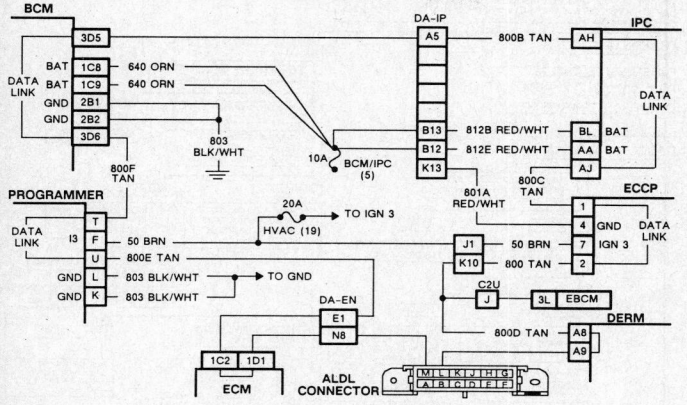

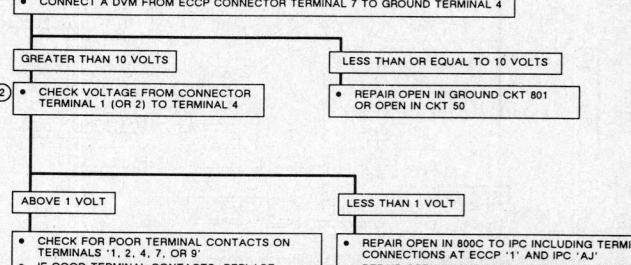

IF YOU HAVE NOT PERFORMED THE 'SELF-DIAGNOSTIC SYSTEM CHECK', START THERE FIRST

MAKE CERTAIN THE ALDL COVER IS PROPERLY INSTALLED. IF PROPER INSTALLATION OF THE ALDL COVER RETURNS THE DISPLAY TO NORMAL. RETURN TO THE 'SELF-DIAGNOSTIC SYSTEM CHECK'.

① • REMOVE ECCP TO ACCESS CONNECTOR
   • KEY 'ON', ENGINE NOT RUNNING
   • CONNECT A DVM FROM ECCP CONNECTOR TERMINAL 7 TO GROUND TERMINAL 4

GREATER THAN 10 VOLTS / LESS THAN OR EQUAL TO 10 VOLTS

② CHECK VOLTAGE FROM CONNECTOR TERMINAL 1 (OR 2) TO TERMINAL 4
   • REPAIR OPEN IN GROUND CKT 801 OR OPEN IN CKT 50

ABOVE 1 VOLT / LESS THAN 1 VOLT

• CHECK FOR POOR TERMINAL CONTACTS ON TERMINALS '1, 2, 4, 7, OR 9'
• IF GOOD TERMINAL CONTACTS, REPLACE ECCP

• REPAIR OPEN IN 800C TO IPC INCLUDING TERMINAL CONNECTIONS AT ECCP '1' AND IPC 'AJ'
• REPAIR OPEN IN CKT 800 TO DERM INCLUDING TERMINAL CONNECTIONS AT ECCP '2', DERM 'A8' AND EBCM '3L'

SOME AUTO-RANGING DVM'S WILL NOT MEASURE SERIAL DATA LINE VOLTAGE IN AUTO MODE. WHEN USING AN AUTO-RANGING DVM, USE THE FIXED VOLTAGE RANGE SCALE.

WHEN ALL DIAGNOSIS AND REPAIRS ARE COMPLETE, CLEAR CODES AND VERIFY OPERATION

When ECC communications are lost, service diagnostics usually cannot be entered, but a quick scan of panel will usually help isolate source of fault. Loss of serial data will result in 3 dashes being shown on the panel VF display. This indicates power and ground are okay. If panel displays normal exterior or interior set temperature, power, ground and serial data communications are being received and panel replacement is indicated.

NOTE: Test numbers refer to numbers on diagnostic chart.

1) This step checks for power and ground to panel. Voltage should be HI for both power to ground checks.
2) This step checks for serial data voltage. Normal voltage should be more than one volt and varying. Steady voltage indicates second open exists, or ALDL cover is off.

91I07760 91E07763

Courtesy of General Motors Corp.

CHART D-1, GROUNDED SERIAL DATA CIRCUIT

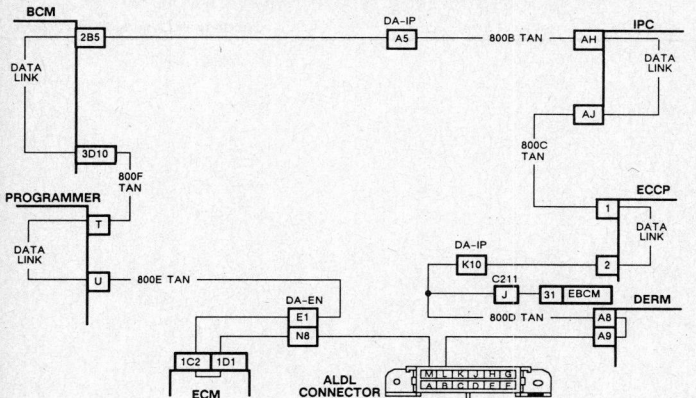

IF YOU HAVE NOT PERFORMED THE 'SELF-DIAGNOSTIC SYSTEM CHECK', START THERE FIRST

① • REMOVE ALDL COVER
   • DISCONNECT THE IPC
   • KEY 'ON', ENGINE NOT RUNNING
   • MEASURE VOLTAGE FROM CAVITY "M" OF THE ALDL TO GROUND

FIXED BETWEEN 0 AND 0.5 VOLTS / FLUCTUATES BETWEEN 0.5 AND 5 VOLTS

• DISCONNECT PROGRAMMER
• RECONNECT IPC
• NOTE IPC ODOMETER DISPLAY

"ERROR" / MILES

• REINSTALL ALDL COVER
• NOTE ODOMETER DISPLAY

"ERROR" / MILES

• DISCONNECT ECM
• NOTE ODOMETER DISPLAY

REPLACE PROGRAMMER

MILES / "ERROR"

• RECONNECT PROGRAMMER
• NOTE ODO DISPLAY

REPAIR SHORT TO GROUND IN CKT 800 BETWEEN ECM AND ALDL PIN M

MILES / "ERROR"

REPLACE ECM

REPAIR SHORT TO GROUND IN CKT 800 BETWEEN ECM AND PROGRAMMER

• DISCONNECT BCM CONNECTOR #3
• NOTE IPC ODOMETER DISPLAY

"ERROR" / MILES

• REINSTALL ALDL COVER
• REINSTALL PROGRAMMER
• REINSTALL BCM CONN #3
• DISCONNECT BCM CONN #2
• DISCONNECT IPC
• NOTE ECCP DISPLAY

REPAIR SHORT TO GROUND IN CKT 800 BETWEEN BCM AND PROGRAMMER

DASHES OR SEGMENT CHECK / SET TEMP

REPLACE BCM

REPAIR SHORT TO GROUND IN CKT 800 BETWEEN BCM AND IPC

• NOTE ECCP DISPLAY

DASHES OR SEGMENT CHECK / SET TEMP

• REMOVE ECCP
• REINSTALL IPC AND NOTE IPC ODOMETER DISPLAY

REPLACE IPC

"ERROR" / MILES

• REMOVE ALDL COVER
• MEASURE VOLTAGE AT ECCP HARNESS CAVITY 1

REPLACE ECCP

FLUCTUATES BETWEEN 0.5 AND 5 VOLTS / FIXED BETWEEN 0 AND 0.5 VOLTS

• DISCONNECT EBCM
• REINSTALL ECCP
• WITH ALDL COVER REMOVED, MEASURE VOLTAGE AT EBCM HARNESS CAVITY 31

REPAIR SHORT TO GROUND IN CKT 800 BETWEEN ECCP AND IPC

FLUCTUATES BETWEEN 0.5 AND 5 VOLTS / FIXED BETWEEN 0 AND 0.5 VOLTS

• REINSTALL ALDL COVER
• NOTE ODOMETER DISPLAY

REPAIR SHORT TO GROUND BETWEEN ECCP AND EBCM

"ERROR" / MILES

• REMOVE ALDL COVER
• DISCONNECT DERM
• MEASURE VOLTAGE AT DERM HARNESS CAVITY A8

REPLACE EBCM

FLUCTUATES BETWEEN 0.5 AND 5 VOLTS / FIXED BETWEEN 0 AND 0.5 VOLTS

• REINSTALL ALDL COVER
• MEASURE VOLTAGE AT DERM HARNESS CAVITY A9

REPAIR SHORT TO GROUND IN CKT 800 BETWEEN ECCP AND DERM AND EBCM

FLUCTUATES BETWEEN 0.5 AND 5 VOLTS / FIXED BETWEEN 0 AND 0.5 VOLTS

REPLACE DERM

REPAIR SHORT TO GROUND IN CKT 800 BETWEEN DERM AND ALDL PIN L

With grounded serial data circuit, BCM will not be able to communicate with any other devices in system. Voltage measured anywhere in circuit will zero. IPC will display ELECTRICAL PROBLEM; ECCP will display dashes ("---").

NOTE: Test numbers refer to numbers on diagnostic chart.

1) This step splits the system in half to help isolate source of grounded serial data line. If taking IPC out of the system allows both halves of serial data line to rise more than one volt, source of short has been located. The remaining steps follow same pattern in that components are removed from serial data line until normal voltage range is again measured. When section of circuit is isolated, a simple check of wire for short to ground will differentiate between grounded wire or ground in a device remote.

WHEN ALL DIAGNOSIS AND REPAIRS ARE COMPLETE, CLEAR CODES AND VERIFY OPERATION

91G07764 91J07765

Courtesy of General Motors Corp.

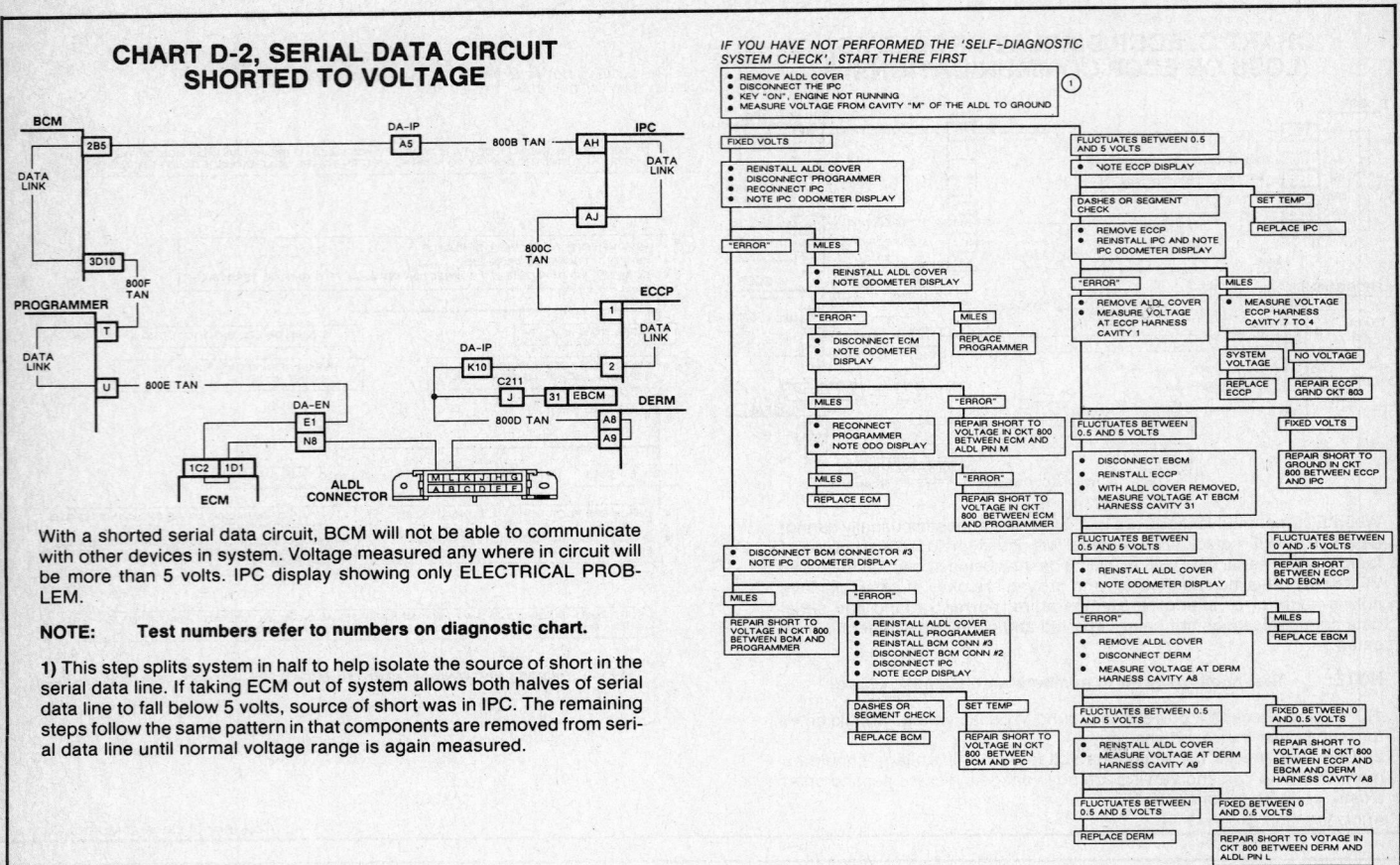

CHART D-2, SERIAL DATA CIRCUIT SHORTED TO VOLTAGE

With a shorted serial data circuit, BCM will not be able to communicate with other devices in system. Voltage measured any where in circuit will be more than 5 volts. IPC display showing only ELECTRICAL PROBLEM.

NOTE: Test numbers refer to numbers on diagnostic chart.

1) This step splits system in half to help isolate the source of short in the serial data line. If taking ECM out of system allows both halves of serial data line to fall below 5 volts, source of short was in IPC. The remaining steps follow the same pattern in that components are removed from serial data line until normal voltage range is again measured.

91G07764 91B07766

1991 ENGINE PERFORMANCE
Self-Diagnostics — Reatta & Riviera PCM/BCM (Cont.)

GM
1-315

CODE B110, OUTSIDE TEMPERATURE SENSOR CIRCUIT

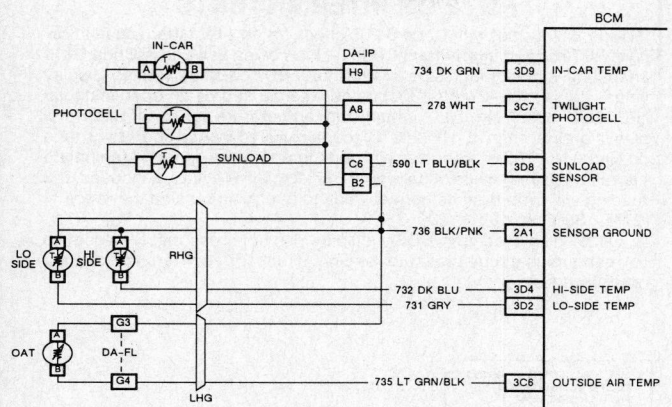

The outside air temperature sensor is a thermistor located behind grill. The BCM applies and monitors a 5-volt signal to sensor on circuit No. 735. When sensor is cold, its resistance is high, therefore BCM will see a high monitored voltage. As sensor warms, its resistance becomes less and signal voltage is pulled low through sensor ground, circuit No. 736. This signal voltage will vary between 5 volts (open circuit) and zero volts (shorted circuit).

Code B110 will set if ignition is on and signal voltage indicates less than -31°F (-35°C), which is open circuit voltage or greater than 137°F (58°C), which is shorted circuit voltage. During time failure is present, a substitute temperature reading will be used to allow continued operation of the climate control system, and continuous compressor at idle will be disabled. The outside air temperature reading BD26 display will indicate the actual sensor reading.

NOTE: Test numbers refer to numbers on diagnostic chart.

1) Checks to see if open circuit reading is due to circuit or sensor. If open circuit reading changes to a shorted circuit reading after jumping sensor terminals, BCM and wiring are okay.

2) By applying a ground to various points in the circuits, an open can be isolated by observing whether parameter display can be changed from an open reading to shorted reading.

3) Checks to see if shorted circuit reading is due to circuit or sensor. If shorted circuit reading changes to an open circuit reading after disconnecting sensor, BCM and wiring are okay.

NOTE ON INTERMITTENTS

If ambient temperature drops to less than about -31°F (-35°C), this code should be ignored. If B110 is set with any of the following codes: B119, B120, B122, B132 or B440, the most likely cause is an intermittent open in circuit No. 736.

If an intermittent Code B110 is being set, check B110 snap data value for outside temperature BD26. If BD26 value is less than -29°F (-34°C), code was caused by an open circuit No. 735 or 736, or outside temperature sensor. If BD26 value is greater than 135°F (57°C), code was caused by a short to ground on circuit No. 735 or a shorted outside temperature sensor. Manipulate related wiring while observing BCM display BD26. If failure is induced, reading will jump from its normal value to a reading outside the range of -31°F (-35°C) to 137°F (58°C).

If value indicated by BD26 display is not reasonably close to actual temperature of air at sensor, check for poor terminal contact or replace sensor.

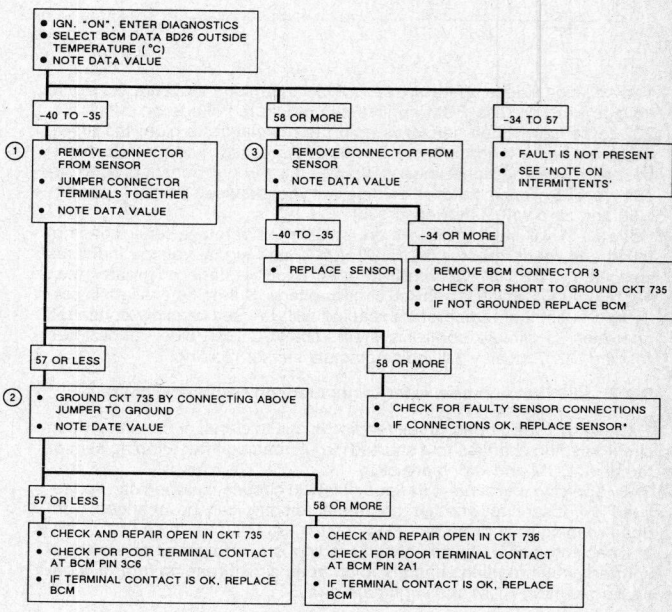

WHEN ALL DIAGNOSIS AND REPAIRS ARE COMPLETED, CLEAR CODES AND VERIFY PROPER OPERATION

91D07767 91F07768

Courtesy of General Motors Corp.

CODE B111, A/C HIGH SIDE TEMPERATURE SENSOR CIRCUIT

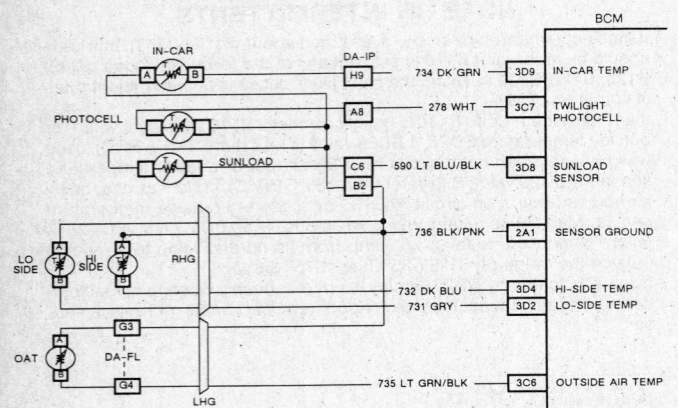

The A/C high side temperature sensor is a thermistor that controls signal voltage to BCM. The BCM applies and monitors voltage on circuit No. 732 to sensor. When sensor is cold, its resistance is high; therefore, BCM will see a high monitored voltage. As sensor warms, resistance becomes less and signal voltage is pulled low through sensor ground circuit No. 736. This monitored voltage will vary between 5 volts (open circuit) and zero volts (shorted circuit).

Code B111 will set if ignition is on, outside temperature sensor has not failed and reads greater than 32°F (0°C), and signal voltage indicates less than -24°F (-31°C), which is open circuit voltage or greater than 408°F (209°C), which is shorted circuit voltage. During time failure is present, a substitute temperature reading will be used to allow continued operation of climate control system. The A/C high side temperature reading BD27 display will indicate actual sensor reading.

NOTE: Test numbers refer to numbers on diagnostic chart.

1) Checks to see if open circuit reading is due to circuit or sensor. If open circuit reading changes to a shorted circuit reading after jumping sensor terminal, BCM and wiring are okay.

2) By applying a ground to various points in circuits, an open can be isolated by observing whether parameter display can be changed from open reading to shorted reading.

3) Checks to see if shorted circuit reading is due to circuit or sensor. If shorted circuit reading changes to an open circuit reading after disconnecting sensor, BCM and wiring are okay.

NOTE ON INTERMITTENTS

If Code B111 is set with Code B112, check for an intermittent open in circuit No. 736. If an intermittent Code B111 is being set, check Code B111 snap data value for high side temperature, BD27 display. If BD27 display value is less than -27°F (-33°C), code was caused by an open in circuit No. 732 or circuit No. 736, or high side temperature sensor. If BD27 display is greater than 408°F (209°C), code resulted from a short to ground on circuit No. 732 or a shorted high side temperature sensor. Manipulate the related wiring while observing BD27 display. If failure is induced, the reading will jump from its normal value to a reading outside the range of -27°F (-33°C) to 408°F (209°C).

If value displayed by BD27 display is not reasonably close to corresponding gauge pressure reading, check for poor terminal contact or replace sensor.

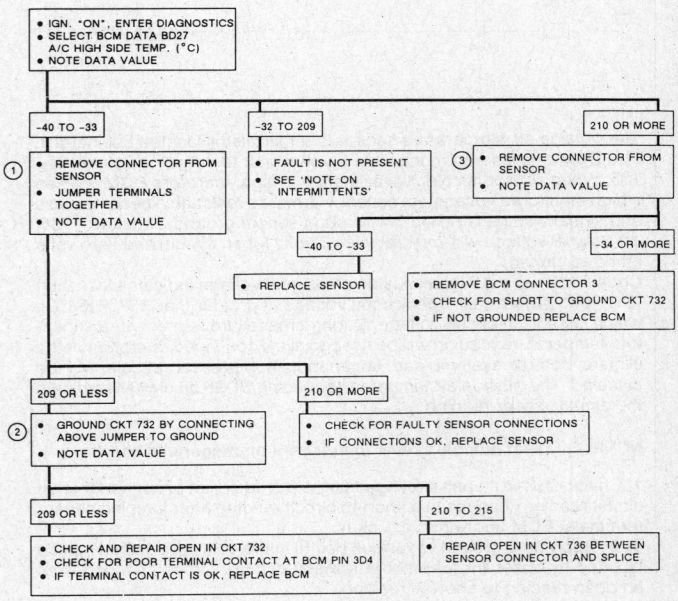

WHEN ALL DIAGNOSIS AND REPAIRS ARE COMPLETED, CLEAR CODES AND VERIFY PROPER OPERATION

91D07767 91H07769

Courtesy of General Motors Corp.

1991 ENGINE PERFORMANCE
Self-Diagnostics – Reatta & Riviera PCM/BCM (Cont.)

GM
1-317

CODE B112, A/C LOW SIDE TEMPERATURE SENSOR CIRCUIT

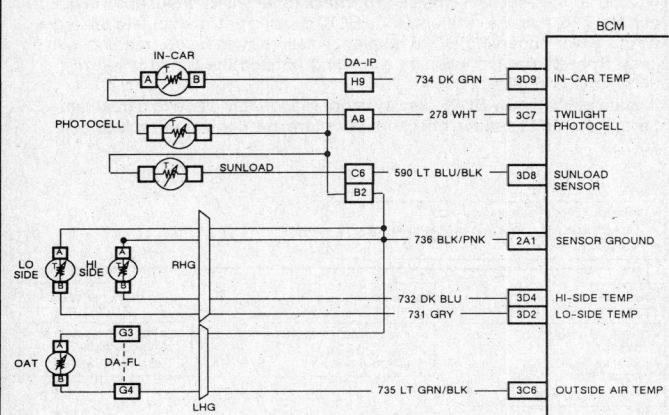

The A/C low side temperature sensor is a thermistor that controls signal voltage to BCM. The BCM applies and monitors voltage on circuit No. 731 to sensor. When sensor is cold, its resistance is high; therefore, BCM will see a high monitored voltage. As sensor warms, its resistance becomes less and signal voltage is pulled low through sensor ground, circuit No. 736. This monitored voltage will vary between 5 volts (open circuit) and zero volts (shorted circuit).

Code B112 will set if ignition is on, outside temperature sensor has not failed and reads greater than 32°F (0°C), and signal voltage indicates less than -29°F (-34°C), which is open circuit voltage, or greater than 209°F (85°C), which is shorted circuit voltage. During time failure is present, a substitute temperature reading (same value as outside air temperature) will be used to allow continued operation of climate control system and compressor clutch will be disabled. The A/C low side temperature reading BD28 display will display actual sensor reading.

NOTE: Test numbers refer to numbers on diagnostic chart.

1) Checks to see if open circuit reading is due to circuit or sensor. If open circuit reading changes to a shorted circuit reading after jumping sensor terminals, BCM and wiring are okay.

2) By applying a ground to various points in circuits, an open can be isolated by observing whether parameter display can be changed from open reading to shorted reading.

3) Checks to see if shorted circuit reading is due to circuit or sensor. If shorted circuit reading changes to an open circuit reading after disconnecting sensor, BCM and wiring are okay.

NOTE ON INTERMITTENTS

If an intermittent Code B112 is being set, manipulate the related wiring while observing BD28 display. If failure is induced, the reading will jump from its normal value to a reading outside the range of -29°F (-34°C) to 209°F (85°C).

If value indicated by BD28 display is not reasonably close to corresponding gauge pressure reading, check for poor terminal contact or replace sensor.

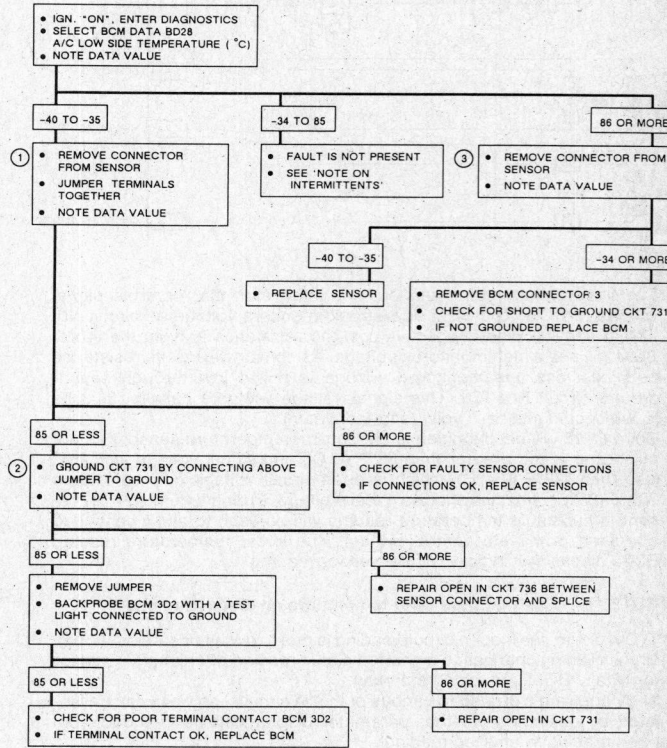

WHEN ALL DIAGNOSIS AND REPAIRS ARE COMPLETED, CLEAR CODES AND VERIFY PROPER OPERATION

91D07767 91J07770

GM
1-318

1991 ENGINE PERFORMANCE
Self-Diagnostics — Reatta & Riviera PCM/BCM (Cont.)

CODE B113, IN-CAR TEMPERATURE SENSOR CIRCUIT

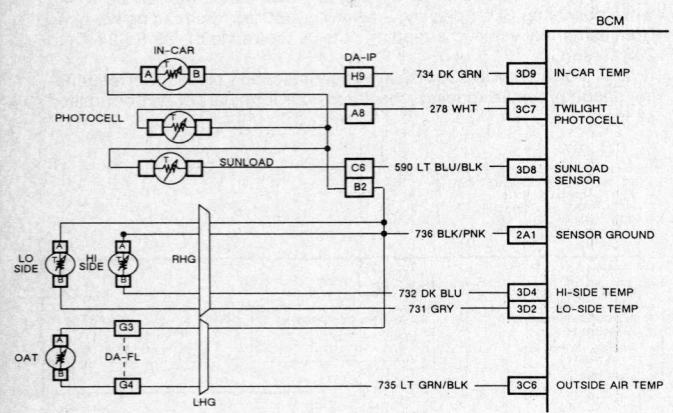

The in-car temperature sensor is a thermistor that controls signal voltage to BCM. The BCM applies and monitors voltage on circuit No. 734 to sensor. When sensor is cold, its resistance is high; therefore, BCM will see a high monitored voltage. As sensor warms, its resistance becomes less and monitored voltage is pulled low through sensor ground circuit No. 736. This signal voltage will vary between 5 volts (open circuit) and zero volts (shorted circuit).

Code B113 will set if ignition is on, outside temperature sensor has not failed and reads greater than 32°F (0°C), and signal voltage indicates less than -29°F (-34°C), which is open circuit voltage or greater than 209°F (85°C), which is shorted circuit voltage. During time failure is present, a substitute temperature reading will be used to allow continued operation of climate control system. The in-car temperature reading BD25 display will indicate actual sensor reading.

NOTE: Test numbers refer to numbers on diagnostic chart.

1) Checks to see if open circuit reading is due to circuit or sensor. If open circuit reading changes to a shorted circuit reading after jumping sensor terminals, BCM and wiring are okay.
2) By applying a ground to various points in circuits, an open can be isolated by observing whether parameter display can be changed from open reading to shorted reading.
3) Checks to see if shorted circuit reading is due to circuit or sensor. If shorted circuit reading changes to an open circuit reading after disconnecting sensor, BCM and wiring are okay.

NOTE ON INTERMITTENTS

If Code B113 is set with Code B115, check for an intermittent open in circuit No. 736. If an intermittent Code B113 is being set, manipulate related wiring while observing BD25 display. If failure is induced, reading will jump from its normal value to a reading outside the range of -29°F (-34°C) to 209°F (85°C).

If value indicated by BD25 display is not reasonably close to actual temperature of air at sensor, check for poor terminal contact or replace sensor.

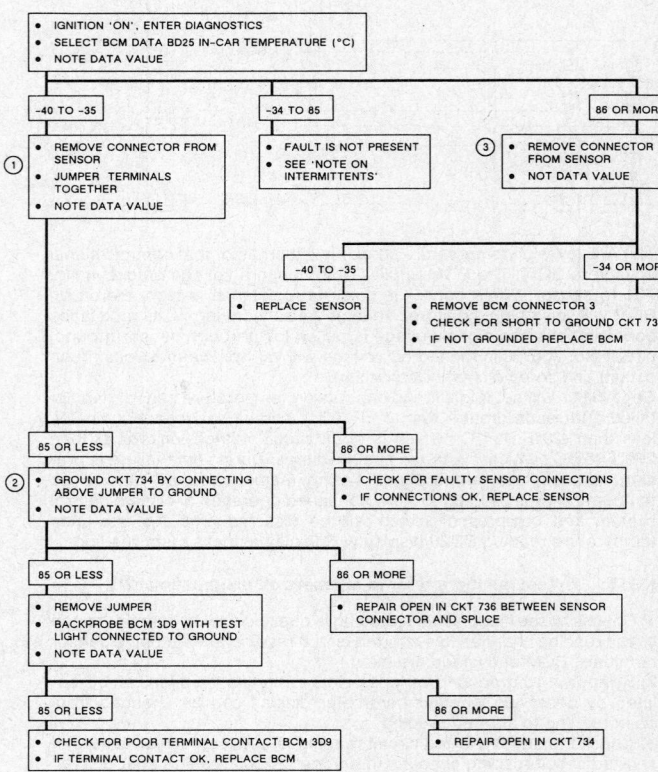

WHEN ALL DIAGNOSIS AND REPAIRS ARE COMPLETED, CLEAR CODES AND VERIFY PROPER OPERATION

91D07767 91B07771

Courtesy of General Motors Corp.

1991 ENGINE PERFORMANCE
Self-Diagnostics – Reatta & Riviera PCM/BCM (Cont.)

GM
1-319

CODE B115, SUN LOAD SENSOR CIRCUIT

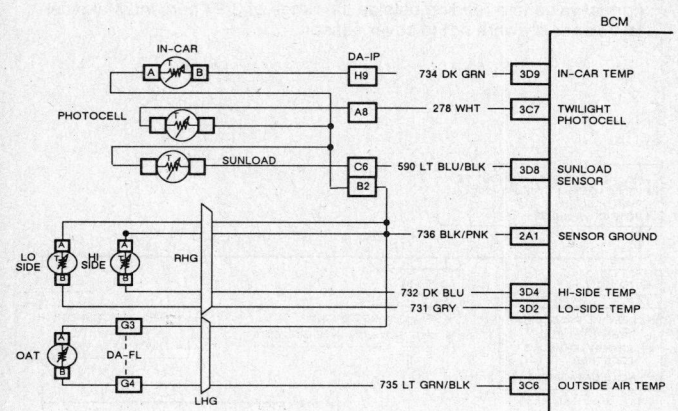

The sun load sensor is a thermistor that controls signal voltage to BCM. The BCM applies and monitors voltage on circuit No. 590 to sensor. When sensor is cold, its resistance is high; therefore, BCM will see a high monitored voltage. As sensor warms, its resistance becomes less and monitored voltage is pulled low through sensor ground circuit No. 736. This monitored voltage will vary between 5 volts (open circuit) and zero volts (shorted circuit).

Code B115 will set if ignition is on, outside temperature sensor has not failed and reads greater than 32°F (0°C), and signal voltage indicates less than -29°F (-34°C), which is open circuit voltage, or greater than 209°F (85°C), which is shorted circuit voltage. During time failure is present, a substitute temperature reading will be used to allow continued operation of climate control system. The sun load temperature reading BD32 display will indicate actual sensor reading.

NOTE: Test numbers refer to numbers on diagnostic chart.

1) Checks to see if open circuit reading is due to circuit or sensor. If open circuit reading changes to a shorted circuit reading after jumping sensor terminals, BCM and wiring are okay.

2) By applying a ground to various points in circuits, an open can be isolated by observing whether parameter display can be changed from open reading to shorted reading.

3) Checks to see if shorted circuit reading is due to circuit or sensor. If shorted circuit reading changes to an open circuit reading after disconnecting sensor, BCM and wiring are okay.

91D07767 91D07772

NOTE ON INTERMITTENTS

If an intermittent Code B115 is being set, check B115 snap data value for sun load temperature, BD32 display. If BD32 display value is less than -29°F (-34°C), code resulted from an open in circuit No. 590 or 736, or sun load temperature sensor. If BD32 display value is greater than 85°C, code resulted from a short to ground on circuit No. 590 or shorted sun load temperature sensor. Manipulate related wiring while observing BD32 display. If failure is induced, reading will jump from its normal value to a reading outside the range of -29°F (-34°C) to 209°F (85°C).

If value displayed by BD32 display is not reasonably close to a corresponding thermometer reading, check for poor terminal contact or replace sensor.

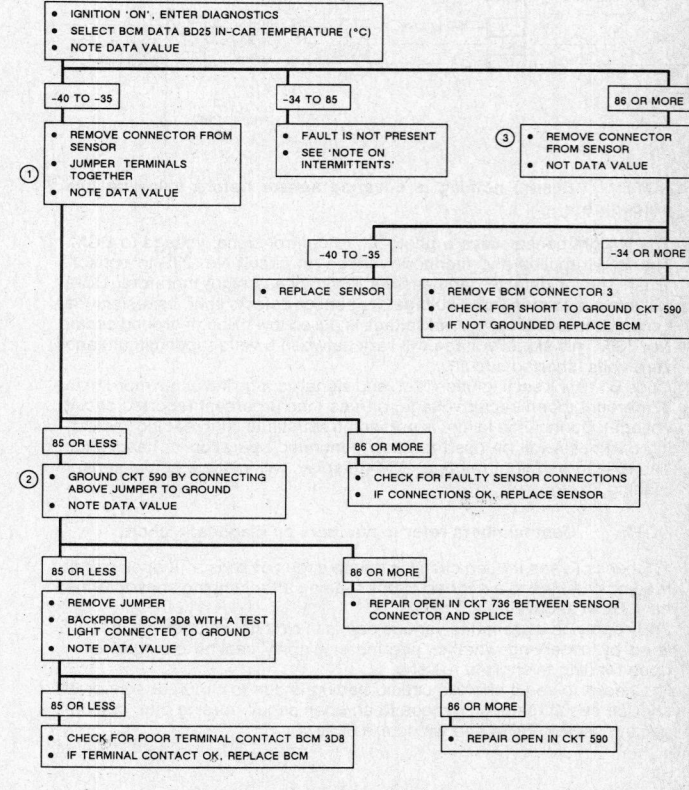

WHEN ALL DIAGNOSIS AND REPAIRS ARE COMPLETED, CLEAR CODES AND VERIFY PROPER OPERATION

Courtesy of General Motors Corp.

GM
1-320

1991 ENGINE PERFORMANCE
Self-Diagnostics — Reatta & Riviera PCM/BCM (Cont.)

CODE B119, TWILIGHT PHOTOCELL CIRCUIT

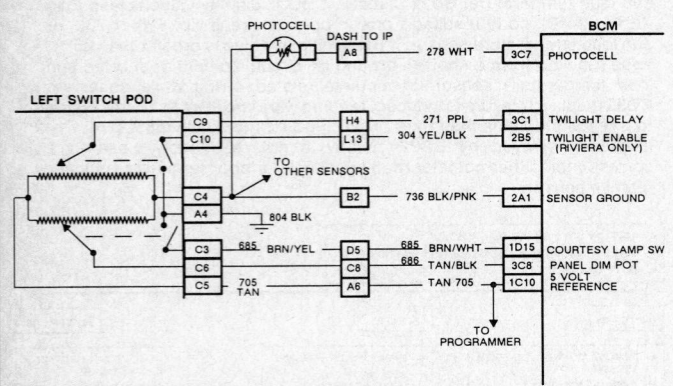

NOTE: Ensure nothing is covering sensor before following this procedure.

The twilight sensor uses a photocell to control signal voltage to BCM. The BCM applies and monitors voltage on circuit No. 278 to sensor. When sensor detects darkness, its resistance is high; therefore, BCM will see a high monitored voltage. As sensor detects light, its resistance becomes less and monitored voltage is pulled low through ground circuit No. 736. This signal voltage will vary between 5 volts (open circuit) and zero volts (shorted circuit).

Code B119 will set if ignition is on and signal voltage indicates more than 97 percent (open circuit voltage) or less than 3 percent (shorted circuit voltage). During time failure is present, a substitute light reading (indicating darkness) will be used to allow continued operation of headlights. The measure of light reading, BD44 display, will indicate actual sensor reading.

NOTE: Test numbers refer to numbers on diagnostic chart.

1) Checks to see if open circuit is due to circuit or sensor. If open circuit reading changes to a shorted circuit reading after jumping sensor terminals, BCM and wiring are okay.
2) By applying a ground to various points in circuits, an open can be isolated by observing whether parameter display can be changed from open reading to shorted reading.
3) Checks to see if shorted circuit reading is due to circuit or sensor. If shorted circuit reading changes to an open circuit reading after disconnecting sensor, BCM and wiring are okay.

NOTE ON INTERMITTENTS

If an intermittent Code B119 is being set, manipulate related wiring while observing BD44 display. If failure is induced, reading will jump from its normal value to a reading outside the range of 3-97 percent. Make certain owner is aware not to cover sensor.

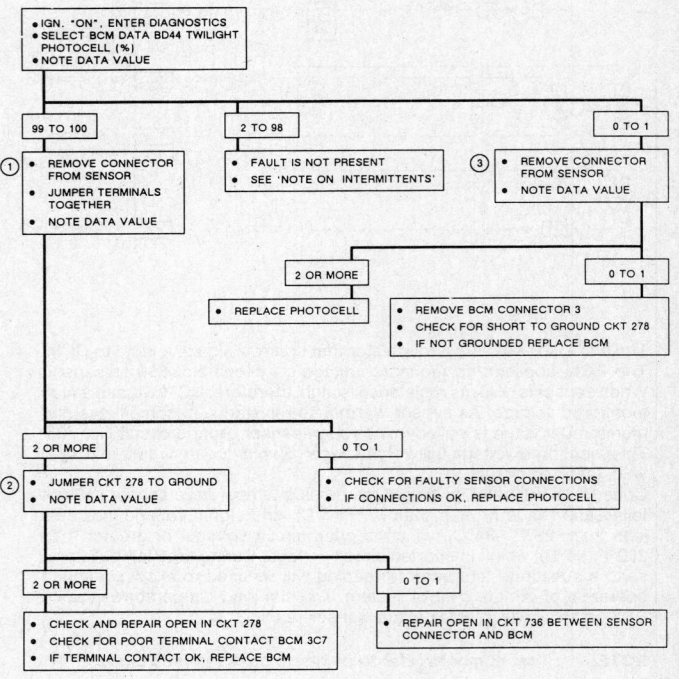

WHEN ALL DIAGNOSIS AND REPAIRS ARE COMPLETED, CLEAR CODES AND VERIFY PROPER OPERATION

1991 ENGINE PERFORMANCE
Self-Diagnostics — Reatta & Riviera PCM/BCM (Cont.)

GM
1-321

CODE B120, TWILIGHT DELAY POTENTIOMETER

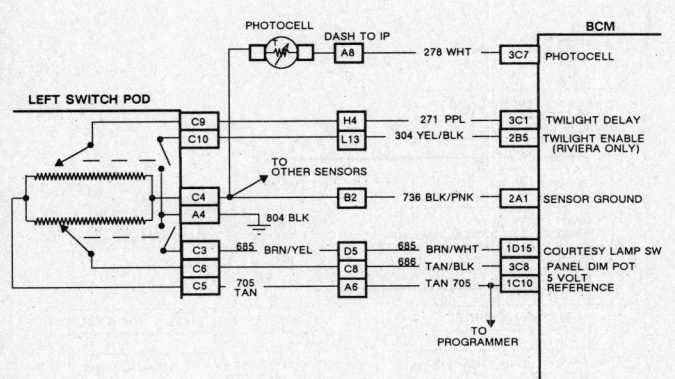

The twilight delay uses a potentiometer to control signal voltage to BCM. The BCM supplies voltage on circuit No. 705 to resistor in left switch assembly and returns as a ground to BCM on circuit No. 736. The wiper provides voltage signal to BCM on circuit No. 271. When slider is moved toward maximum position (maximum delay), resistance is low; therefore BCM will see a high signal voltage. As slider is moved toward minimum position (minimum delay), its resistance increases and signal voltage decreases. This signal voltage will vary between zero volts (open or grounded circuit) and 5 volts (shorted to voltage circuit).
Code B120 will set if vehicle is equipped with twilight sentinel, ignition is on and signal voltage indicates less than 2 percent (open or grounded circuit) or greater than 98 percent (shorted to voltage). During time failure is present, a substitute delay time (minimum delay) will be implemented, allowing continued operation of twilight system. The reading from potentiometer BD43 display will indicate actual reading.

NOTE: Test numbers refer to numbers on diagnostic chart.

1) BD43 displays twilight delay time. The normal range is 2-98 percent.
2) Checks to see if open or grounded circuit reading is due to circuit or switch. If open or grounded circuit reading changes from a short to voltage reading after jumping switch assembly terminals, BCM and wiring are okay.
3) Measuring between circuit No. 705 (5 volts) and circuit No. 736 will determine if circuit No. 705 or 271 is open or shorted to ground.

NOTE ON INTERMITTENTS

If an intermittent Code B120 is being set, check B120 snap data value for twilight delay BD43 display. If BD43 display value is greater than 98 percent, code resulted from an open in circuit No. 271 or 736, or left switch pod. If BD43 display value is less than 2 percent, code resulted from a short in left switch pod. Manipulate related wiring while observing BCM data parameter BD43 display. If failure is induced, reading will jump from its normal value to a reading outside range of 2-98 percent.

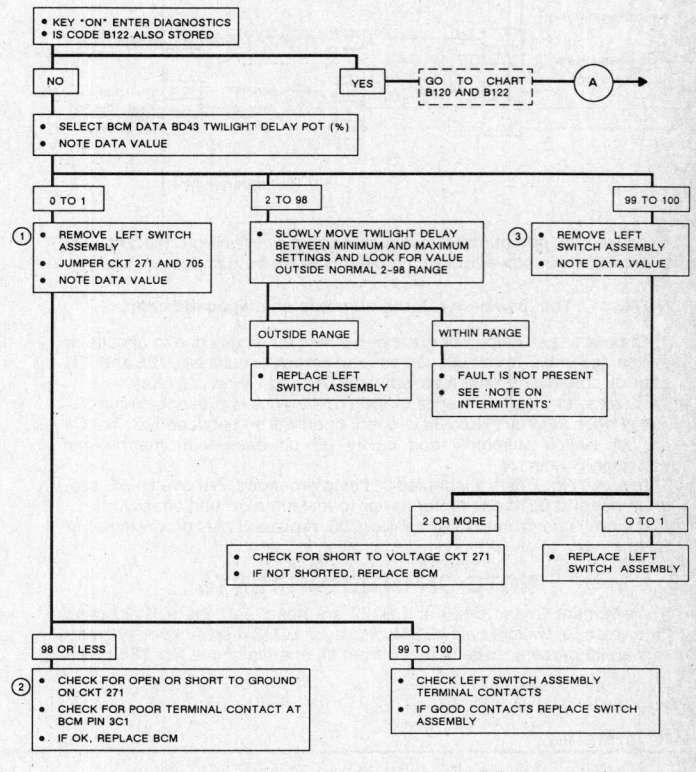

WHEN ALL DIAGNOSIS AND REPAIRS ARE COMPLETED, CLEAR CODES AND VERIFY OPERATION

91F07773 91J11857

Courtesy of General Motors Corp.

GM
1-322

1991 ENGINE PERFORMANCE
Self-Diagnostics — Reatta & Riviera PCM/BCM (Cont.)

CODE B120 & B122, TWILIGHT DELAY & PANEL DIMMING

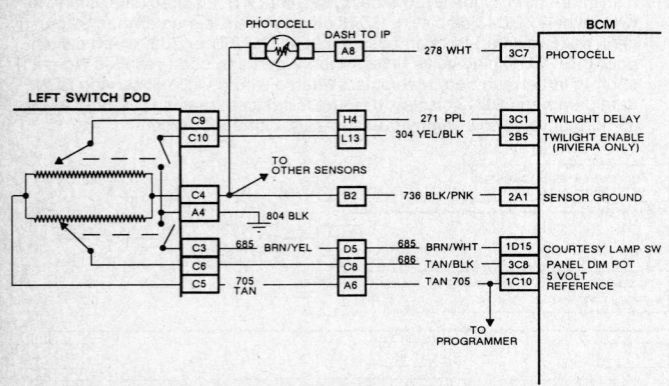

Because both potentiometers use the same power and ground, problem is most likely in power or ground circuits when both codes are stored.

NOTE: Test numbers refer to numbers on diagnostic chart.

1) Checks to see if open or grounded circuit reading is due to circuits or switch assembly. If voltage can be read across circuits No. 705 and 736 after disconnecting switch assembly, BCM and wiring are okay.

2) Checks for 5-volt reference at switch. If 5 volts is present, circuit No. 736 is open. If circuit No. 736 is open, open will be between terminal C4 on left switch assembly and cavity B2 on dash instrument panel transition connector.

3) If circuit No. 705 is suspected of being grounded, remove HVAC programmer and BCM connectors prior to making a ground check.

4) If there is no ground in circuit No. 705, replace HVAC programmer or BCM.

NOTE ON INTERMITTENTS

If intermittent Codes B120 and B122 are being set, check B120 snap data value for twilight delay BD43 display. If BD43 display value is greater than 98 percent, code resulted from an open in circuit No. 736 or left switch pod. If BD43 display value is less than 2 percent, code resulted from a short in circuit No. 705 or short in left switch pod. Manipulate related wiring while observing BD43 display. If failure is induced, reading will jump from its normal value to a reading outside the range of 2-98 percent.

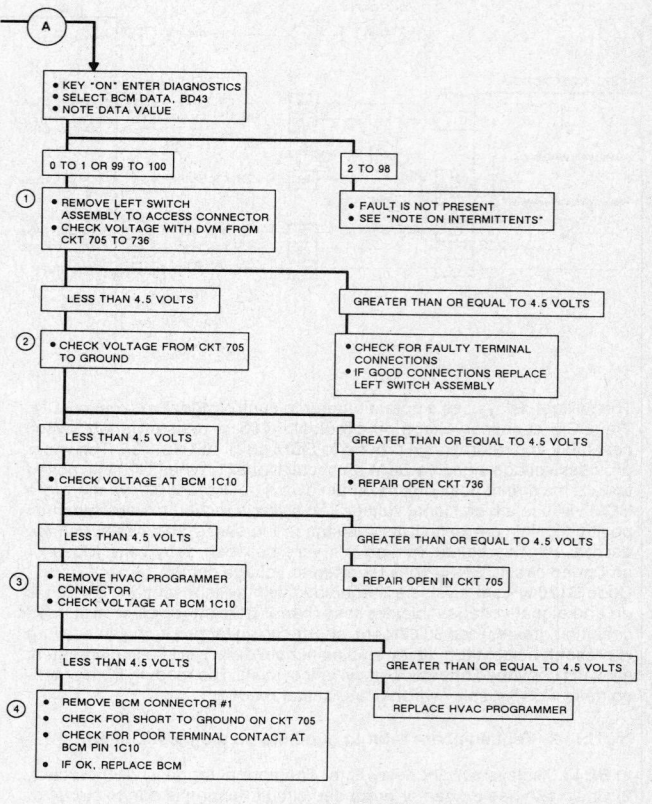

WHEN ALL DIAGNOSIS AND REPAIRS ARE COMPLETED, CLEAR CODES AND VERIFY PROPER OPERATION

1991 ENGINE PERFORMANCE
Self-Diagnostics — Reatta & Riviera PCM/BCM (Cont.)

GM
1-323

CODE B121, TWILIGHT ENABLE SWITCH CIRCUIT

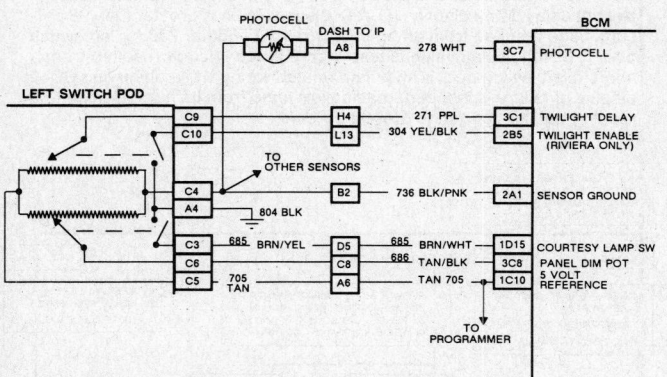

The twilight enable switch uses the same physical control as delay pot. Inside left switch assembly, enable switch contacts close as soon as time delay slider is moved off of its extreme minimum (off) position. The BCM supplies a voltage on circuit No. 304 to switch. When slider is moved from off position, switch contacts close and signal voltage is pulled low through ground circuit No. 804.

Code B121 will set if vehicle is equipped with twilight sentinel, twilight delay pot has not failed (Code B120), and signal voltage is high when delay slider is greater than 2 seconds delay (twilight sentinel on), or signal voltage is low when delay slider is less than 3 seconds (twilight sentinel off). During time failure is present, twilight sentinel will operate based on delay input. Whenever delay is greater than 2 seconds, BCM will assume twilight sentinel is on.

NOTE: Test numbers refer to numbers on diagnostic chart.

1) BI82 displays voltage state of circuit at BCM. These conditions can be observed in BI82 display as readings of HI or LO when slider is moved.
2) Checks to see if HI reading is due to circuit or switch assembly. If display changes from HI to LO when switch terminals are jumpered together, both BCM and wiring are okay. If display changes from HI to LO when a known good ground is provided, circuit No. 804 is open.
3) Checks to see if LO reading is due to circuit or switch assembly. If display changes from LO to HI when switch assembly is disconnected, BCM and wiring are okay.

NOTE ON INTERMITTENTS

If an intermittent Code B121 is being set, manipulate related wiring. When BI82 displays change-of-state, an "X" will be indicated. Check circuit for an intermittent open or short.

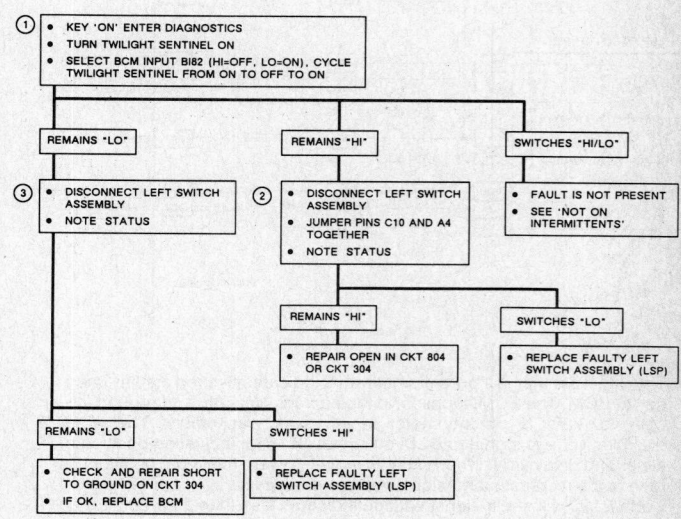

WHEN ALL DIAGNOSIS AND REPAIRS ARE COMPLETED, CLEAR CODES AND VERIFY PROPER OPERATION

91F07773 91A11858

Courtesy of General Motors Corp.

GM
1-324

1991 ENGINE PERFORMANCE
Self-Diagnostics — Reatta & Riviera PCM/BCM (Cont.)

CODE B122, PANEL DIMMING POTENTIOMETER CIRCUIT

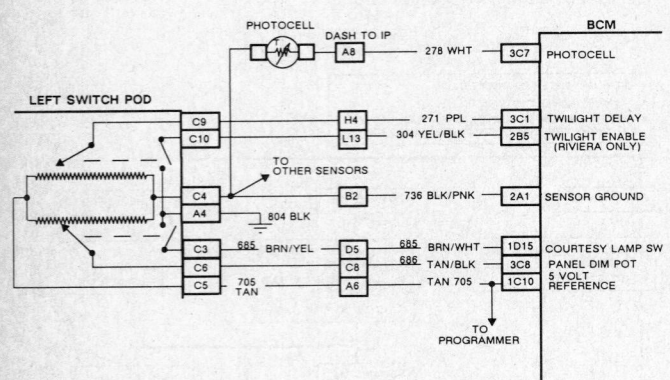

NOTE ON INTERMITTENTS

If an intermittent Code B122 is being set, check B122 snap data value for twilight delay BD42 display. If BD42 display value is greater than 98 percent, code resulted from an open in circuit No. 686 or 736, or left switch pod. If BD42 display value is less than 2 percent, code resulted from a short in left switch pod. Manipulate related wiring while observing BD42 display. If failure is induced, reading will jump from its normal value to a reading outside the range of 2-98 percent.

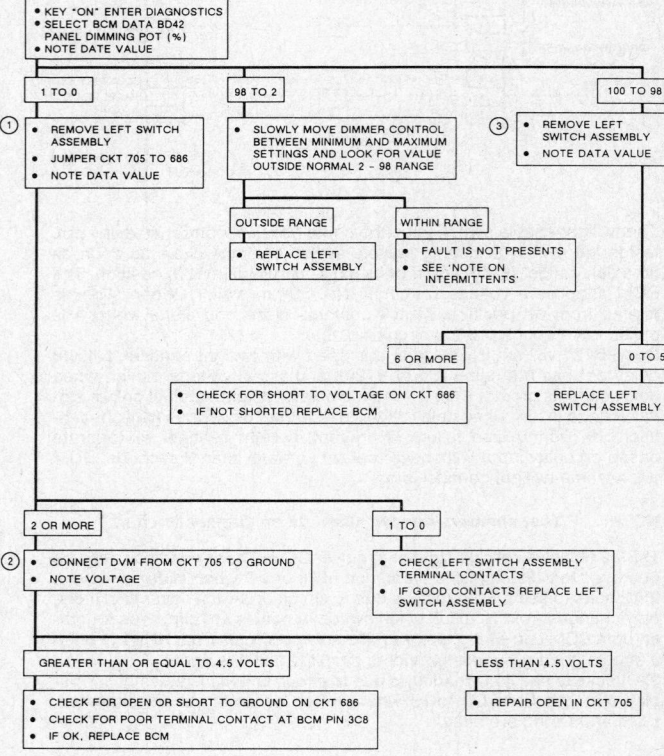

The panel dimmer is a potentiometer that indicates desired display intensity to BCM. The BCM supplies voltage (circuit No. 705) and ground (circuit No. 736) to potentiometer in left switch assembly. The wiper provides voltage signal to BCM on circuit No. 686, indicating position of slider and delay time. When slider is moved toward minimum position, its resistance increases and signal voltage decreases.

Code B122 will set, if signal voltage indicates less than 2 percent (open or grounded circuit), or greater than 98 percent (shorted to voltage). During time failure is present, a substitute delay time will be implemented to allow continued operation of interior lighting. The reading from potentiometer BD42 display will indicate actual reading.

NOTE: **Test numbers refer to numbers on diagnostic chart.**

1) Checks to see if open or grounded circuit reading is due to circuits or switch assembly. If open or grounded circuit reading changes to a short to voltage reading after jumpering switch assembly terminals, BCM and wiring are okay.

2) Measuring voltage between circuit No. 705 (5 volts) and circuit No. 736 will determine if problem is in circuit No. 705 or 686.

3) Checks to see if short to voltage circuit reading is due to circuit or an open in circuit No. 736 and switch assembly. If a short to voltage reading changes to an open circuit reading after disconnecting switch assembly, BCM and circuit No. 686 are okay.

WHEN ALL DIAGNOSIS AND REPAIRS ARE COMPLETED, CLEAR CODES AND VERIFY PROPER OPERATION

1991 ENGINE PERFORMANCE
Self-Diagnostics — Reatta & Riviera PCM/BCM (Cont.)

GM
1-325

CODE B123, COURTESY LAMP SWITCH CIRCUIT

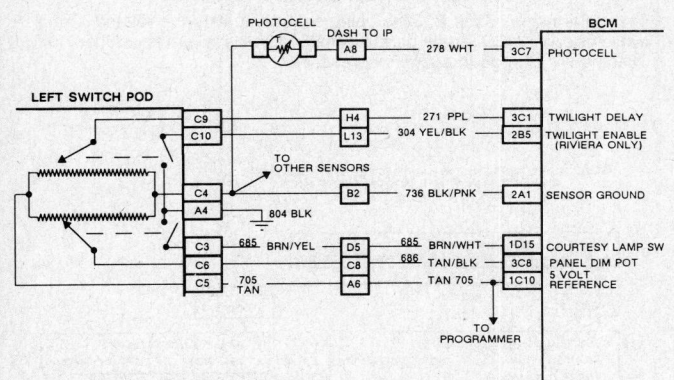

Inside left switch assembly, panel light switch contacts close when dimming slider is moved to its extreme maximum position. The BCM supplies a voltage on circuit No. 685 to switch. When signal is pulled to ground, BCM turns courtesy light on.

Code B123 will set if panel dimming pot has not failed and BCM sees circuit No. 685 grounded while dimmer switch position was less than a value for maximum panel light brightness. A grounded circuit No. 685 will not only set Code B123, but will also turn courtesy lights on at all times and drain battery.

NOTE: Test numbers refer to numbers on diagnostic chart.

1) BI01 display, dimmer switch input, will read LO if dimming slider is at maximum "up" position. BI01 display will read HI if dimming slider is not at maximum position.

2) By removing switch assembly, a shorted switch can be detected by observing BI01 display.

3) By removing BCM connector, short to ground can be isolated as being wire or BCM.

NOTE ON INTERMITTENTS

If circuit No. 685 were intermittently grounded, Code B123 could be stored. Manipulate circuit No. 685 while observing BI01 display with dimmer at a low setting. If short occurs, value will switch from HI to LO. Also check BD42 display. Cycle panel dimming control from minimum to maximum. If BD42 display does not range between 2 and 98 percent, or never reads more than 75 percent, replace left switch assembly.

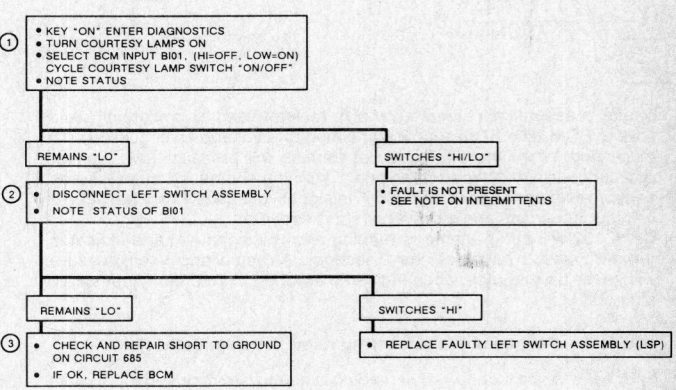

WHEN ALL DIAGNOSIS AND REPAIRS ARE COMPLETED, CLEAR CODES AND VERIFY OPERATION

CODE B132, ENGINE OIL
PRESSURE SENSOR CIRCUIT FAULTY

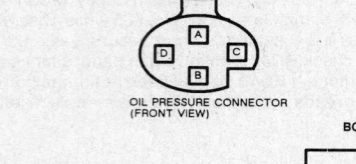

OIL PRESSURE CONNECTOR
(FRONT VIEW)

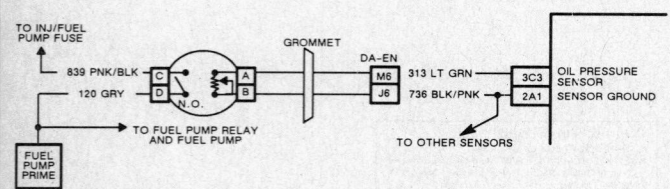

The oil pressure indicator is a variable resistor used to indicate oil pressure to BCM. The BCM supplies and monitors voltage on circuit No. 313 to sensor. When the engine is not running (oil pressure low), sensor resistance is low. When the engine is running (increased oil pressure), sensor resistance becomes high. The signal voltage will vary between 5 volts (open circuit) and zero volts (short circuit).

Code 132 will set if engine is running and the signal voltage indicates greater than 120 psi for at least 2 seconds. As actual engine oil pressure will never be that high, code indicates an open circuit, faulty sensor or faulty BCM.

NOTE: Test numbers refer to numbers on diagnostic chart.

1) Checks to see if open circuit reading is due to circuit or sensor. If open circuit reading changes to a shorted circuit reading after jumping sensor terminals, BCM and wiring are okay.

2) By applying a ground to various points in the circuits, an open can be isolated by observing whether the parameter display changes to a short circuit reading.

NOTE ON INTERMITTENTS

If an intermittent Code B132 is being set, manipulate the related wiring while observing BCM data parameter BD71. If the failure is induced, the reading will change to a high oil pressure.

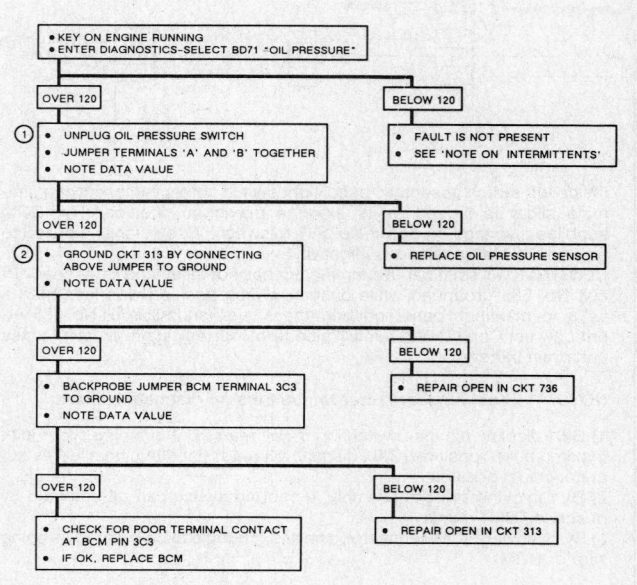

1991 ENGINE PERFORMANCE
Self-Diagnostics – Reatta & Riviera PCM/BCM (Cont.)

GM
1-327

CODE B333, LOSS OF SUPPLEMENTAL INFLATABLE RESTRAINT (SIR) DATA

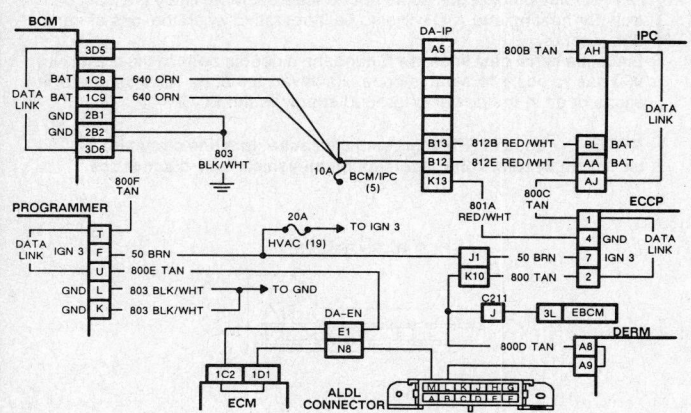

Code B333 will set if communication between DERM (SIR controller) and BCM is lost. When this code is set, ELECTRICAL PROBLEM and INFLATABLE RESTRAINT warning lights will illuminate.

NOTE: Test numbers refer to numbers on diagnostic chart.

1) Checks if other data line components are experiencing communications problems.
2) Checks status of data line at compass module. Normal data line voltage is .1-4.5 volts.

NOTE ON INTERMITTENTS

If an intermittent Code B333 is being stored, manipulate relating wiring at DERM (SIR controller). An ELECTRICAL PROBLEM message indicates loss of data and may help locate fault.

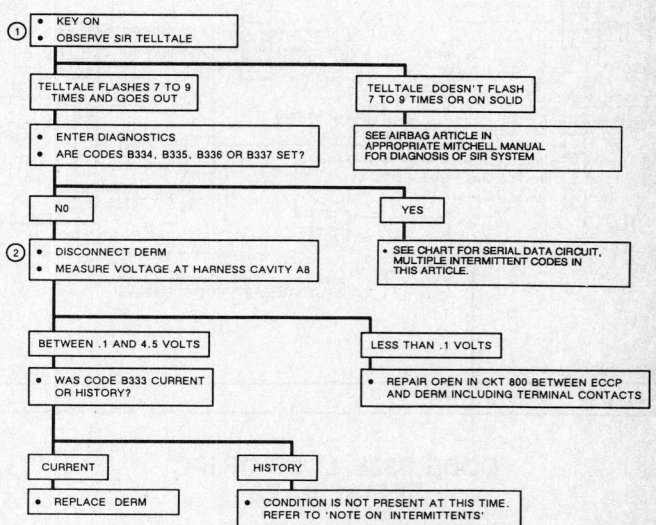

WHEN ALL DIAGNOSIS AND REPAIRS ARE COMPLETED, CLEAR CODES AND VERIFY PROPER OPERATION

Courtesy of General Motors Corp.

CODE B334, LOSS OF ECM DATA

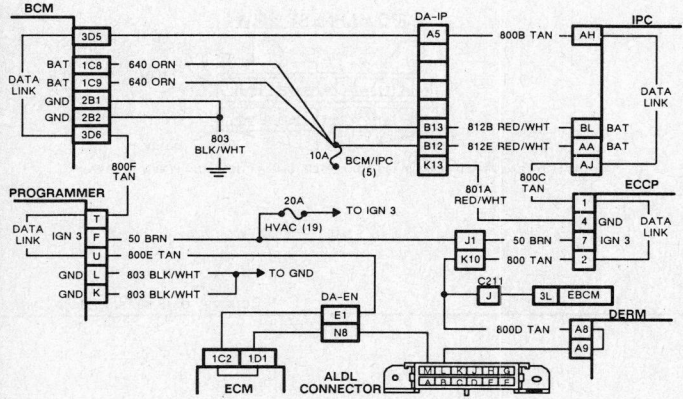

Code B334 will set if communication between ECM and BCM is lost. If the ECM remains powered and only serial communication is lost, the vehicle will still run; however, with ignition key on (engine not running), an ELECTRICAL PROBLEM message will illuminate.

NOTE: Test numbers refer to numbers on diagnostic chart.

1) If the ECM looses power or ground, code will set since ECM cannot communicate. It is important to note that engine will not start.
2) Since prior checks eliminated an open circuit, fault is poor terminal contact at ECM terminal 1C2, a faulty MEM-CAL connection or a faulty ECM.

NOTE ON INTERMITTENTS

If an intermittent Code B334 is being set, manipulate the related wiring at ECM. With the ignition key on (engine not running), an ELECTRICAL PROBLEM warning light will indicate loss of ECM communication, and possibly help to isolate the intermittent without having to look for the code. Also check ECM and MEM-CAL connections.

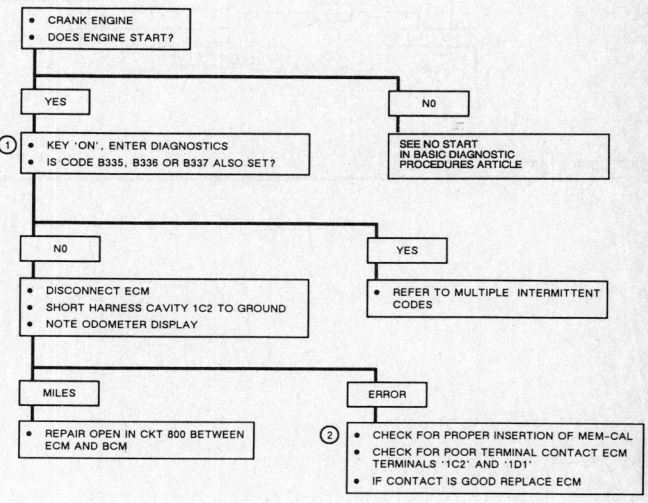

WHEN ALL DIAGNOSIS AND REPAIRS ARE COMPLETED, CLEAR CODES AND VERIFY PROPER OPERATION.

Courtesy of General Motors Corp.

CODE B335, LOSS OF ECCP SERIAL DATA

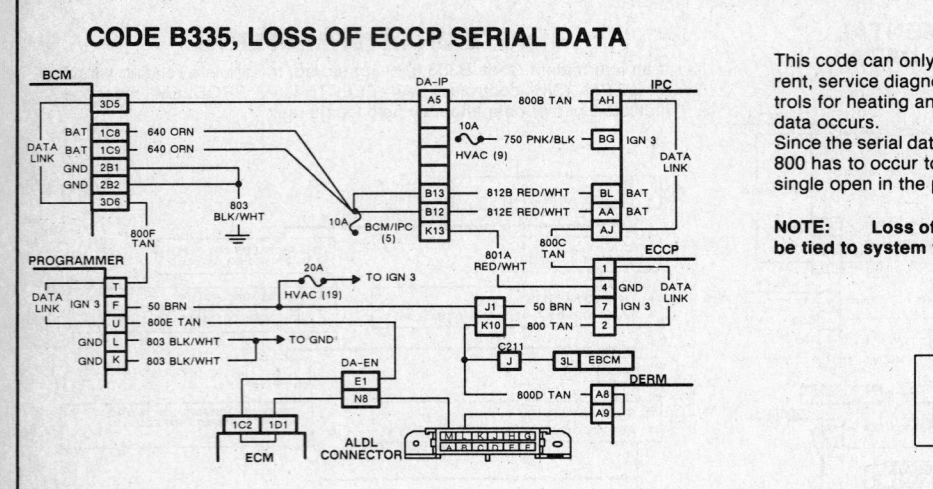

This code can only be viewed as a "history" code because if it was current, service diagnostics could not be entered. Most likely the ECC controls for heating and A/C will also be inoperative when the loss of serial data occurs.

Since the serial data lines are redundant, a double open in the circuit No. 800 has to occur to set this code. However, the code will also set for a single open in the power or ground supply to the ECCP.

NOTE: Loss of ECCP ground will cause data line circuit No. 800 to be tied to system voltage, disabling all vehicle self-diagnostics.

ECCP HARNESS VIEW

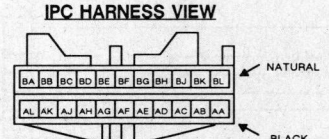

91I07760 90D14616   Courtesy of General Motors Corp.

CODE B336, LOSS OF IPC SERIAL DATA

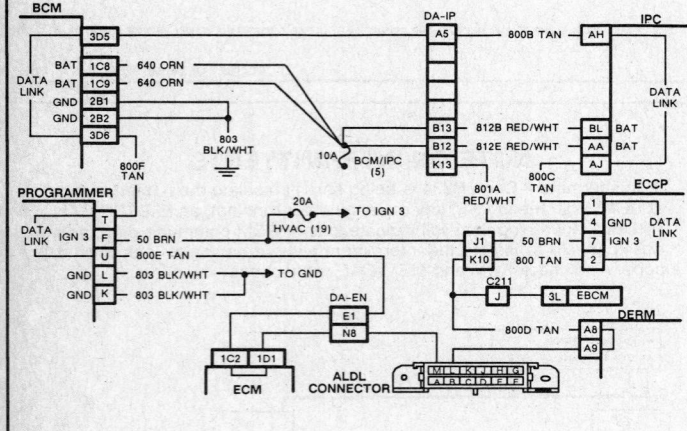

This code can only be viewed as a "history" code because if it were current, service diagnostics could not be entered. Since serial data and ground terminals are redundant, it would take a double open in any of those circuits to set the code. A single intermittent open in circuit No. 750 would also set this code.

If codes are intermittent, check all terminal contacts carefully prior to replacing any parts.

IPC HARNESS VIEW

WHEN ALL DIAGNOSIS AND REPAIRS ARE COMPLETED, CLEAR CODES AND VERIFY OPERATION

91I07760 90E14617   Courtesy of General Motors Corp.

1991 ENGINE PERFORMANCE
Self-Diagnostics – Reatta & Riviera PCM/BCM (Cont.)

GM
1-329

CODE B337, LOSS OF HVAC PROGRAMMER DATA

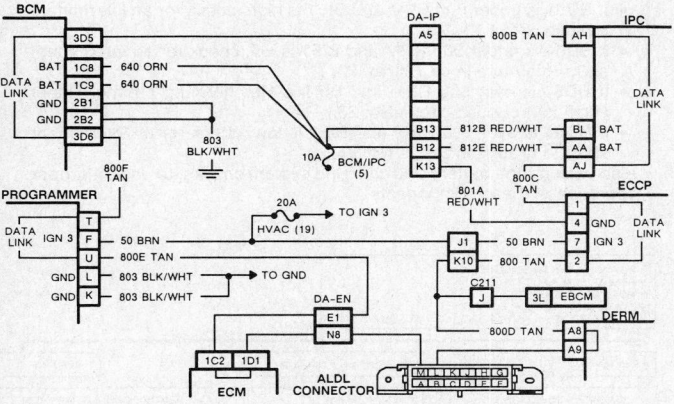

Code B337 will set if communication between the programmer and BCM is lost. This can occur if the HVAC loses ignition, ground or both serial data circuits.

NOTE: Test numbers refer to numbers on diagnostic chart.

1) Checks for power and ground up to the programmer. The test light should be on when connected from ignition source to both grounds.
2) Since power and ground are available to the programmer, the source for failure is either a double open in the circuit No. 800 or faulty terminal contacts.

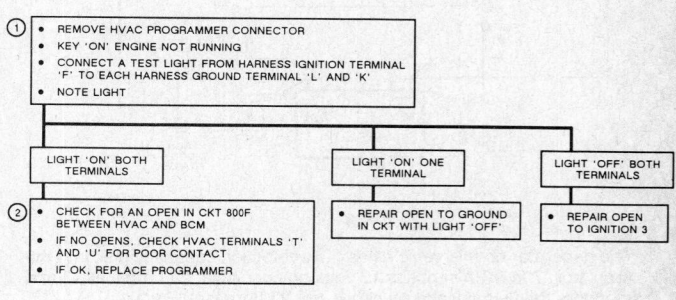

WHEN ALL DIAGNOSIS AND REPAIRS ARE COMPLETED, CLEAR CODES AND VERIFY OPERATION

91I07760 90F14618

Courtesy of General Motors Corp.

SERIAL DATA CIRCUIT MULTIPLE INTERMITTENT CODES

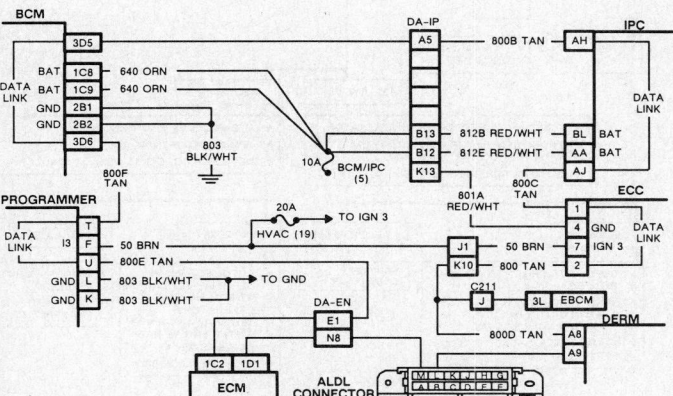

A damaged data line circuit or one of the components connected to the data line may cause multiple or intermittent setting of data line Codes B333, B334, B335, B336 and/or B337. When operating normally, serial data line voltage will continually fluctuate between .1 and 5.0 volts. If serial data line has been shorted to ground, voltage at the ALDL will be zero volts. If it has been shorted to voltage, it will be greater than 5.0 volts. If one of the components on the serial data line is affecting the data line voltage, serial data voltage at the ALDL connector will be a steady value anywhere between .1 and 5.0 volts.

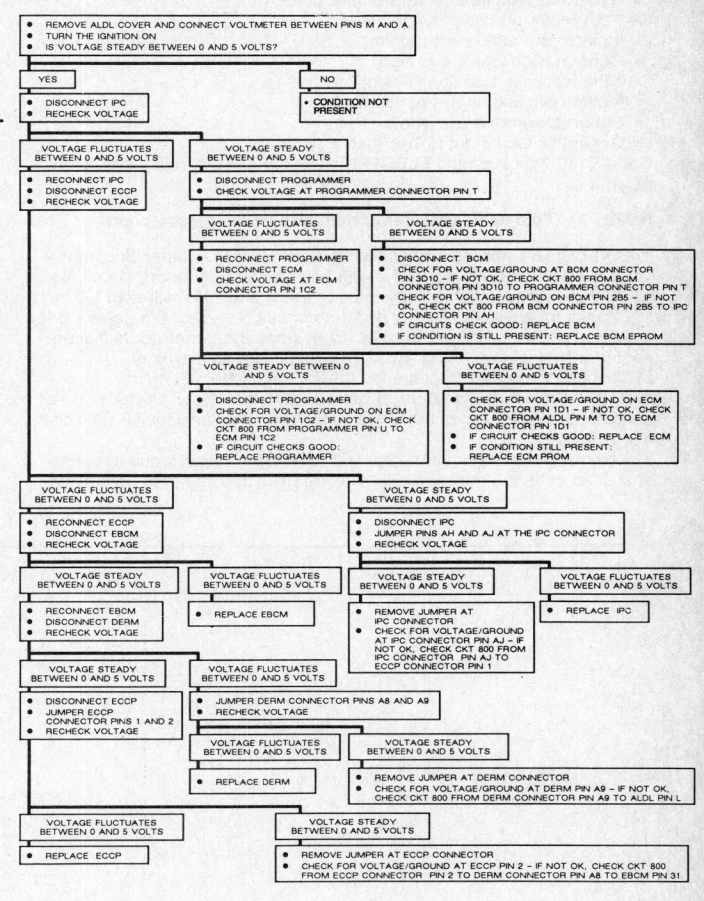

91I07760 91H11863

Courtesy of General Motors Corp.

CODE B410, CHARGING SYSTEM CIRCUIT FAULT

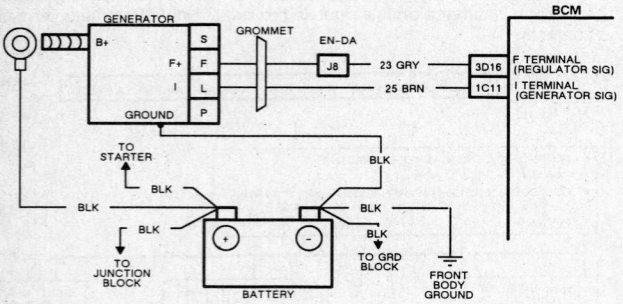

The generator on this vehicle has fault detection capability built into the regulator. The BCM supplies 12 volts on circuit No. 25 (terminal "I") and monitors the field voltage on circuit No. 23 (terminal "F+").
Code B410 will set if the following conditions exist:
• Engine running
• Generator enable line is low
Or if the following conditions exist:
• Engine running
• Generator enable line high
• Generator field input is less than 2 percent
Or if the following conditions exist:
• Ignition on, engine not running
• Generator enable line is high
Or if the following conditions exist
• Ignition on, engine not running
• Generator enable line is low
• Generator field input is less than 2 percent
Code B140 will cause the ELECTRICAL PROBLEM warning light to illuminate.

NOTE: **Test numbers refer to numbers on diagnostic chart.**

1) BI51 displays generator signal voltage as HI or LO, depending on the voltage state at BCM. Normally, with key on and engine off, circuit No. 25 voltage will be pulled low by the generator and BI51 will read LO.
2) Checks to see if LO reading is due to circuit No. 25 or the generator. If display reading changes from LO to HI when the generator is disconnected with engine running, BCM and circuit No. 25 are okay.
3) Checks to see if fault is due to BCM or circuit No. 25.
4) BD51 displays the amount of generator field activity. Under normal conditions, a reading less than 7 percent would indicate a fault in field circuit or BCM.
5) Removing generator connector will determine if fault is due to generator or an open in circuit No. 25, including BCM and interface connector.

NOTE ON INTERMITTENTS

If an intermittent condition exists, check B410 snap data parameters BD61 and BI51. Also check for the following conditions:
• If BD61 is under 500 RPM and BI51 is high, check for an intermittent open in circuit No. 25.
• If BD61 is under 500 RPM and BI51 is LO, check for an intermittent short to ground in circuit No. 23.
• If BD61 is over 500 RPM and BI51 is HI, check for an intermittent short to ground in circuit No. 23.
• If BD61 is over 500 RPM and BI51 is low, check for an intermittent short to ground in circuit No. 25.
Also perform the battery and charging system checks, to ensure proper operation of these components.

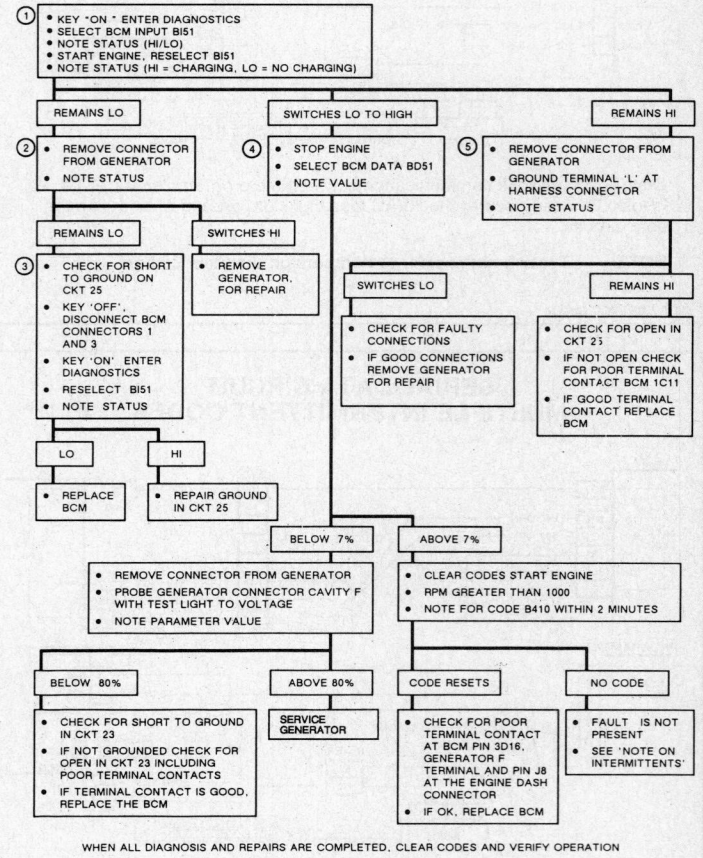

WHEN ALL DIAGNOSIS AND REPAIRS ARE COMPLETED, CLEAR CODES AND VERIFY OPERATION

91J11865 91A11866

1991 ENGINE PERFORMANCE
Self-Diagnostics — Reatta & Riviera PCM/BCM (Cont.)

GM
1-331

CODE B411 OR B412, BATTERY VOLTAGE TOO HIGH OR TOO LOW

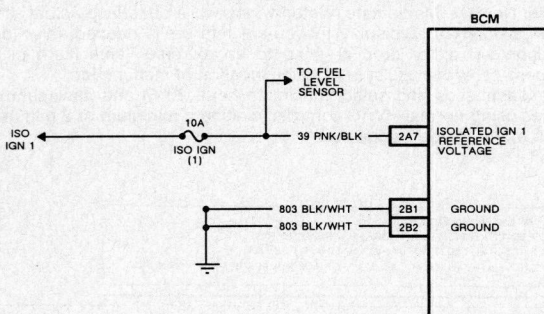

The BCM monitors ignition No. 1 voltage on terminal No. 2A7 as a reference for fuel control. Code B411 will set when ignition is on and the engine RPM is greater than 800 and the BCM sees an ignition No. 1 reference voltage of less than 10.6 volts. Code B412 will be set if the BCM sees voltage greater than 16 volts. Both B411 and B412 will cause the GENERATOR PROBLEM message to be displayed on IPC.

NOTE: Test numbers refer to numbers on diagnostic chart.

1) BD50 displays battery voltage. The normal range is 10.6-16 volts.
2) Checks to see if low voltage reading is due to circuit or battery. With engine running, and if voltage is less than 10 volts, BCM and wiring are okay.
3) Checks to see if low voltage reading is due to circuit or BCM. If voltage reading at BCM is less than 10.6 volts, BCM is okay.
4) Checks to see if high voltage reading is due to generator or faulty BCM.
5) Checks to see if charging voltage goes too high with increased engine RPM or electrical load.

NOTE ON INTERMITTENTS

If an intermittent Code B411 or B412 is being set, observe BD50 display. This battery voltage reading is monitored from 15-amp ISO IGN 1 fuse, fuel level reference voltage. If code is being set due to a high current draw in a certain vehicle component, this can be observed by reading

BD50 display. Operate various components while watching for reading to drop to less than 10 volts or increase to greater than 16 volts. Code B411 could be caused by an intermittent open in circuit No. 39, which may be observed by manipulating wire to BCM while observing BD50 voltage for a drop below 10 volts.

NOTICE: IF FUEL GAGE READ EMPTY ERRONEOUSLY ALONG WITH A CODE B411, CHECK FOR
A BLOWN 10 AMP IGNITION 1 FUSE AND SHORT TO GROUND ON CKT 39

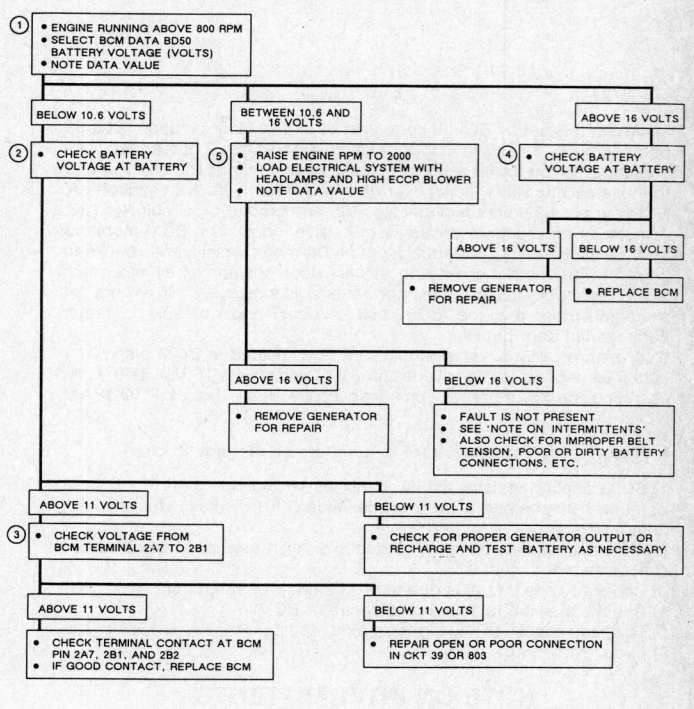

91B11867 91C11868

Courtesy of General Motors Corp.

CODE B440, AIR MIX VALVE (DOOR) CIRCUIT PROBLEM

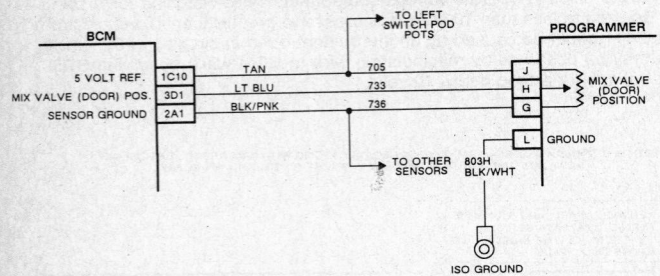

Code B440 is set by BCM if commanded air mix door position is 30-80 percent, but actual air mix door position is not within 2 percent of commanded position for 60 seconds. The BCM commands the programmer to move air mix valve (door) over data circuit No. 800. With ignition on, BCM supplies 5 volts on circuit No. 705 and ground on circuit No. 736. A motor in programmer drives air mix valve (door). The BCM monitors door position through a feedback pot on DC motor which varies between zero and 5 volts depending on air mix door position. If air mix valve (door) feedback indicates it is near hot or cold extreme, code will not set since mix door may be at its limit of travel and not able to reach commanded door position.

Operation of air mix valve (door) can be evaluated in BCM display by actual air mix valve (door) position (BD23 display ACT MIX DR) while changing the programmer number (override BS01 display PROGRAM NO).

NOTE: Test numbers refer to numbers on diagnostic chart.

1) BD23 display indicates actual air mix valve (door) position. The normal range is 1-99 percent. BCM override value BS01 display is for program number.

2) Checks to see if fault could be due to 5-volt reference and ground circuit, or sensor circuit.

3) Checks to see if fault is due to programmer or sensor circuit.

4) Checks to see if fault is due to circuit or BCM.

5) This step checks to see if open circuit reading is due to circuit No. 736 or circuit No. 705.

NOTE ON INTERMITTENTS

If an intermittent Code B440 is being set, check B440 snap data BD23 display. If it was zero percent, check for an intermittent open in circuit No. 736. If it was 100 percent, check for an intermittent open in circuit No. 733 or circuit No. 705. If it was 1-99 percent, check for binding door movement throughout range of door travel and check for a poor ground

circuit No. 803. Manipulate related wiring while observing actual air mix door position (BD23 display) movement. If failure is induced, valve (door) position will either stop or jump to an extreme value (zero or 100 percent). This will assist in isolating location of malfunction.

Exit diagnostics and select maximum heat (90°F) and maximum cool (60°F) using normal HVAC controls, waiting a minimum of 2 minutes in each mode to see if code sets.

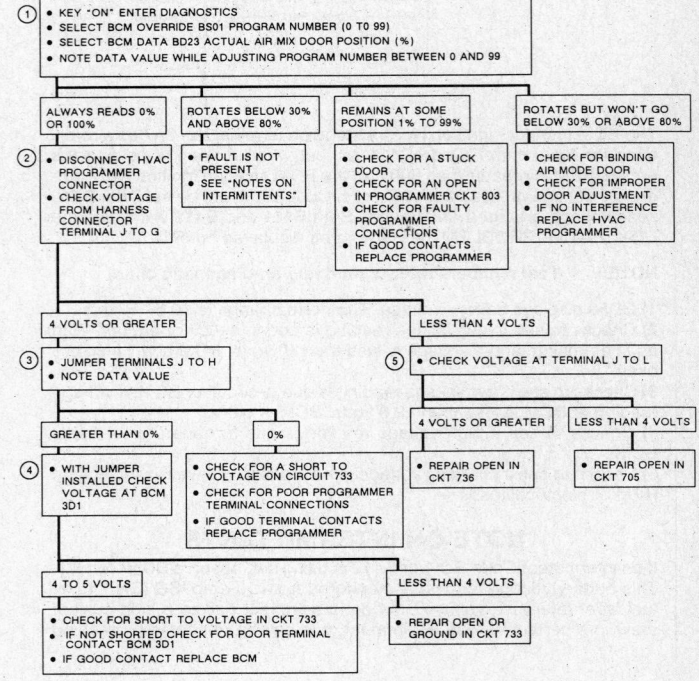

WHEN ALL DIAGNOSIS AND REPAIRS ARE COMPLETED, CLEAR CODES AND VERIFY OPERATION

91D11869 91G11870   Courtesy of General Motors Corp.

1991 ENGINE PERFORMANCE
Self-Diagnostics — Reatta & Riviera PCM/BCM (Cont.)

GM
1-333

CODES B446, B447 & B448, REFRIGERANT SYSTEM PROBLEM (1 OF 2)

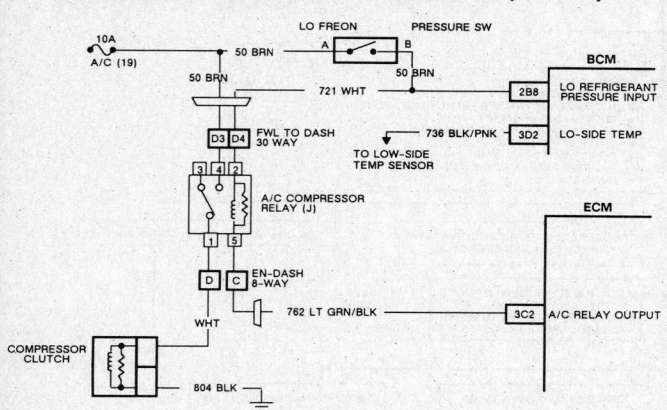

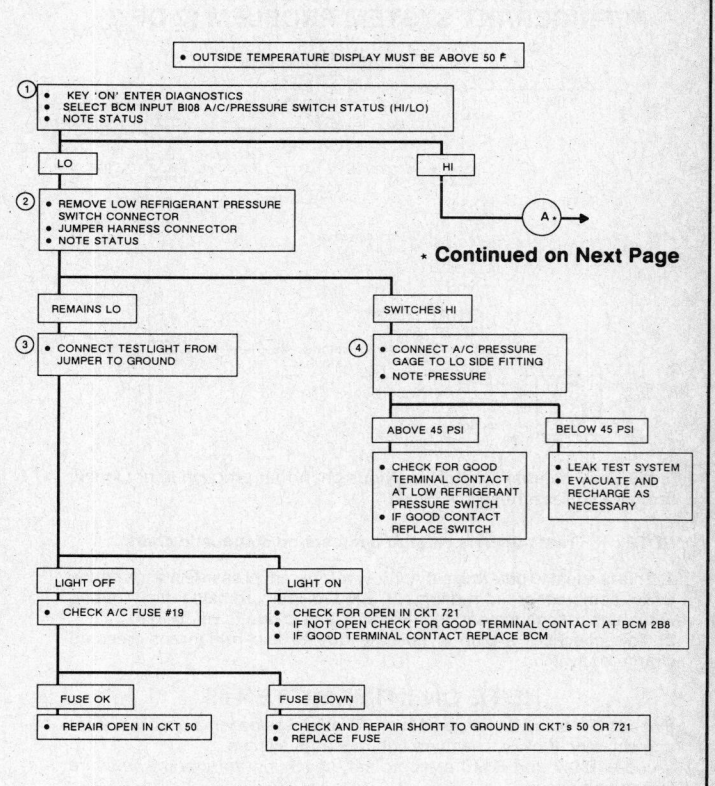

* **Continued on Next Page**

If system refrigerant state of charge falls to less than one third its capacity, BCM will detect this condition and display LOW A/C REFRIGERANT or VERY LOW A/C REFRIGERANT message to warn driver.

Code B446 will set if the low side temperature drops too quickly during compressor engagement. Code B447 will set if low side temperature drops much too quickly during compressor engagement or the low refrigerant pressure switch opens during compressor engagement. Code B448 will set if the low refrigerant pressure switch remains open for greater than 3 minutes.

NOTE: Test numbers refer to numbers on diagnostic chart.

1) BCM input value BI08 displays voltage state of circuit at BCM.
2) Checks to see if open circuit reading is due to circuit or switch.
3) Checks to see if fault is on ignition side or BCM side of switch circuit.
4) This step checks to see if fault is due to pressure switch or a low refrigerant charge.

WHEN ALL DIAGNOSIS AND REPAIRS ARE COMPLETED, CLEAR CODES AND VERIFY OPERATION

91H11871 90B14630

GM
1-334

1991 ENGINE PERFORMANCE
Self-Diagnostics – Reatta & Riviera PCM/BCM (Cont.)

CODES B446, B447 & B448,
REFRIGERANT SYSTEM PROBLEM (2 OF 2)

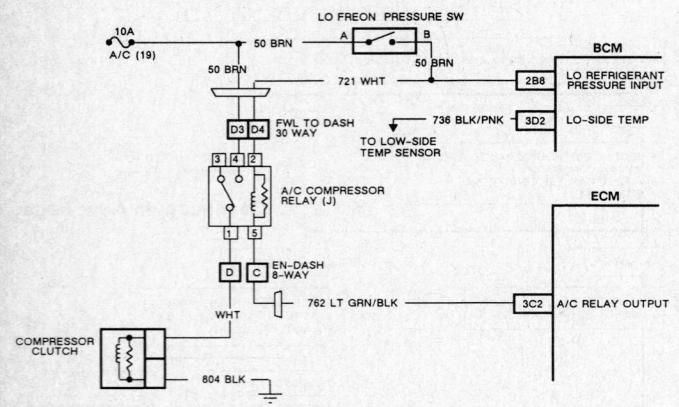

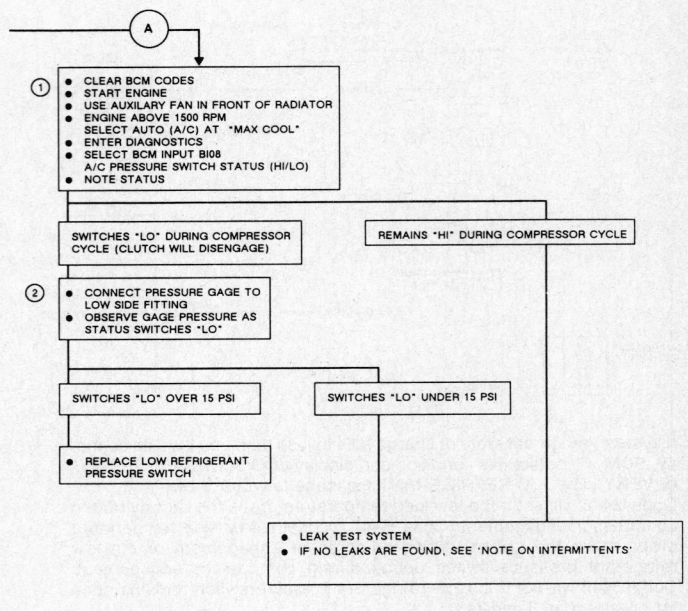

It has been determined from previous chart that problem is not in low refrigerant pressure switch circuit.

NOTE: Test numbers refer to numbers on diagnostic chart.

1) This is a test to determine if A/C low refrigerant pressure switch opens while compressor is running. If BI08 display remains high during compressor engagement, then system fault is due to refrigerant.

2) This checks if switch is opening due to low refrigerant pressure charge or switch.

NOTE ON INTERMITTENTS

If codes B446 and B447 are both set, check low side temperature sensor and circuitry. If okay, evacuate and recharge system.
If codes B447 and B448 are both set, check low refrigerant pressure switch and circuit.

WHEN ALL DIAGNOSIS AND REPAIRS ARE COMPLETED, CLEAR CODES AND VERIFY OPERATION

91H11871 90C14631

Courtesy of General Motors Corp.

CODES B449 & B450,
A/C HIGH SIDE TEMPERATURE TOO HIGH
COOLANT TEMPERATURE TOO HIGH

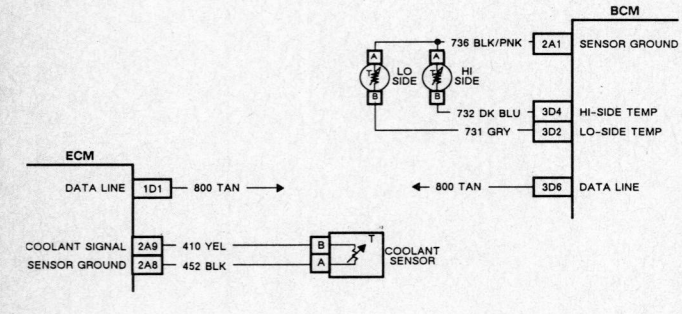

CODE B449,
A/C HIGH SIDE TEMPERATURE TOO HIGH

Code B449 is designed to disengage A/C compressor clutch in the event the high side refrigerant temperature exceeds 199°F (93°C). The A/C compressor clutch will reactivate once high side temperature falls to less than 199°F (93°C). Possible causes for excessively high A/C head pressures should be checked. Diagnose A/C system for refrigerant system performance.

CODE B450,
COOLANT TEMPERATURE TOO HIGH

Code B450 is designed to disengage A/C compressor clutch if engine coolant temperature exceeds 261°F (126°C) and re-engage clutch when coolant temperature falls to less than 248°F (120°C). If Code EO14 is also stored, follow diagnosis for that code first. See SELF-DIAGNOSTICS – ECM/PCM EXCEPT CADILLAC article. Engine overheating may accompany this code. If coolant temperature exceeds normal operating range, check for sources of overheating. Carefully check all sources of intermittent engine overheating, such as improper coolant fan operation, faulty belt or tension, low coolant level and restrictions or faulty hoses and/or routing.

91I11872

Courtesy of General Motors Corp.

1991 ENGINE PERFORMANCE
Self-Diagnostics — Reatta & Riviera PCM/BCM (Cont.)

GM
1-335

CODE B552,
BCM KEEP ALIVE MEMORY ERROR

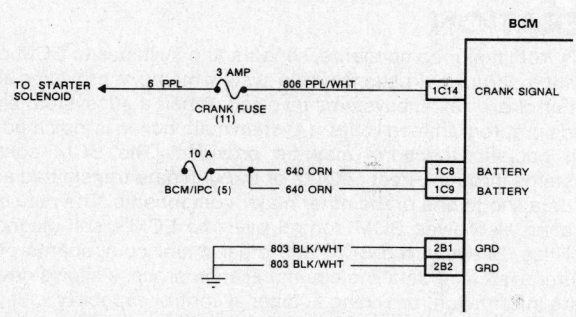

Code B552 does not necessarily indicate a fault, but is a normal occurrence anytime battery power or ground to BCM has been interrupted. Code B552 cannot be cleared from memory in the normal manner. Code B552 can only be cleared if it is not current. Under normal conditions, code will become "history" under the following conditions:

- Ignition in lock position
- Wait for 5 seconds
- Ignition key on, re-enter diagnostics

After the above conditions have taken place, code should now be "history", and can be cleared in the normal manner. This code could be set if the system voltage drops to less than 8 volts at BCM terminals No. 1C8 or 1C9. Possible causes for this are faulty charging system, starter system, extreme cold weather and jump starting vehicle.

NOTE: Test numbers refer to numbers on diagnostic chart.

1) This step is to change Code B552 from "current" to "history".
2) Checks to see if Code B552 was set due to a fault during cranking mode.

91J11873 91A11874

3) Checks for adequate system voltage at BCM terminals No. 1C8 and 1C9. System voltage must not drop to less than 8 volts during engine cranking. By removing C³ fuse, engine will not start and voltage during engine cranking can be observed.

CODE B552 INDICATES THAT THE KEEP ALIVE OR 'LONG TERM' MEMORY IN THE BCM HAS BEEN RESET. THIS WILL BE THE CASE WHENEVER POWER IS REMOVED FROM THE BCM, SUCH AS DISCONNECTING THE BATTERY CABLES OR DISCONNECTING THE BCM POWER CONNECTOR. THIS CODE SHOULD BE CLEARED FROM MEMORY AFTER RESTORING POWER TO THE BCM.

- VEHICLE MUST BE AT NORMAL OPERATING TEMPERATURE.
- CHARGING AND STARTER SYSTEM MUST BE IN GOOD OPERATING CONDITION.

①
- KEY IN "LOCK" POSITION
- WAIT 5 SECONDS
- KEY "ON", ENTER DIAGNOSTICS
- NOTE WHETHER CODE B552 IS CURRENT OR NOT

| B552 NOT CURRENT | B552 CURRENT |

②
- START ENGINE
- RE-ENTER DIAGNOSTICS
- NOTE WHETHER CODE B552 IS CURRENT OR NOT

- REPEAT STEP 1 ABOVE.
- IF CODE B552 RESETS CURRENT, REPLACE BCM.

| B552 CURRENT | B552 NOT CURRENT |

③
- REMOVE CCCI FUSE #8 (THIS ALLOWS FOR EXTENDED CRANK)
- BACKPROBE BCM PIN 1C8 WHILE ENGINE IS CRANKING
- IS VOLTAGE ABOVE 8 VOLTS DURING CRANK?

- NO TROUBLE FOUND
- CLEAR BCM CODES

| ABOVE 8 VOLTS | NOT ABOVE 8 VOLTS |

- CHECK FOR POOR TERMINAL CONTACT AT BCM PIN 1C8
- IF GOOD CONTACT, REPLACE BCM

REPAIR CHARGING OR STARTING SYSTEM FOR LOW VOLTAGE CONDITION

WHEN ALL DIAGNOSIS AND REPAIRS ARE COMPLETED, CLEAR CODES AND VERIFY OPERATION

CODE B556,
ODOMETER (EE) PROM ERROR

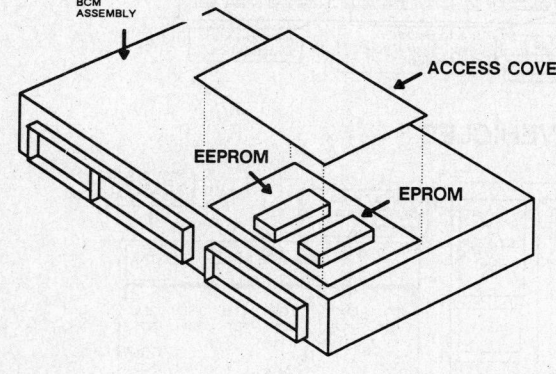

Code B556 indicates that EEPROM, which records elapsed odometer mileage, is not being read by BCM. Usually along with Code 556, ERROR will be displayed in the odometer display. The EEPROM contains specific vehicle information such as vehicle ID number, season odometer mileage and certain vehicle options. Since this information is programmed for the specific vehicle in which it is installed, an EEPROM cannot be transferred from one vehicle to another. Check for proper EEPROM installation. If the EEPROM is properly installed (no bent pins) but Code B556 persists, replace EEPROM. Obtain replacement EEPROMs through an authorized Delco Service Center.

90A14399

1991 ENGINE PERFORMANCE
Self-Diagnostics – Toronado & Trofeo PCM/BCM

TORONADO & TROFEO PCM/BCM CHART DIRECTORY

NOTE: The Electronic Control Module (ECM) may be referred to as the Powertrain Control Module (PCM) in some diagnostic charts and figures. The 2 terms may be used interchangeably.

DESCRIPTION

Self-diagnostic system uses several electronic components which can be controlled by service technician to provide valuable self-diagnostic information. Components are part of an electrical network designed to control various engine and body subsystems.

At the heart of the computer system is the Body Control Module (BCM). The BCM is located behind the glove box. All sensors and switches are monitored by the BCM or by one of the following major components:

- Cathode Ray Tube (CRT) Control Module (optional equipment)
- Electronic Control Module (ECM)
- Electronic Climate (Heater and A/C) Control Panel (ECCP)
- Instrument Panel Cluster (IPC)
- Heating and A/C (HVAC) Programmer
- SIR Diagnostic Energy Reserve Module (DERM) controller

The Cathode Ray Tube (CRT) is a touch sensitive color "monitor" located in climate control/radio center for setting temperature controls and accessing BCM diagnostic features. Non-CRT equipped units have an Electronic Climate Control Panel (ECCP) with LED digital display area for temperature and override mode values. Both CRT and ECCP are used to access BCM diagnostics and display them in IPC information center's 20 character LED display bar.

OPERATION

Signals from major components, sensors and switches to BCM combine with program instructions within system memory, providing accurate control over all subsystems involved. When a subsystem circuit exceeds preprogrammed limits, a system malfunction is indicated and certain back-up functions may be provided. The BCM controls subsystems through direct outputs or through data transmitted along serial data line to one of the other major components. The data communication also gives BCM control over the ECM's self-diagnostic capabilities. Between the BCM and other major components of the computer system, a data line communication process allows devices to share information, providing additional control capability.

In order to access and control BCM self-diagnostic features, 2 electronic components are used, the IPC and the ECCP (or optional CRT monitor). *See Figs. 1 and 2 .*

The "service mode" for diagnostic information incorporates a 20-character Driver Information Center (DIC) display. The DIC display is located on instrument panel cluster. When a malfunction is sensed by BCM computer system, one of the driver warning messages is illuminated on the DIC. When "service mode" is entered, data parameters, fault codes, inputs and outputs and other features such as override commands, snapshot and code clearing capabilities can be accessed and displayed through CRT or ECCP.

Certain system malfunctions cause computer controlled diagnostic messages and/or telltales to appear, indicating that service is required. When a subsystem circuit exceeds preprogrammed limits, a system malfunction is indicated and BCM provides certain back-up functions known as "failsoft". A typical "failsoft" action would be the substitution of a fixed input value when a sensor is detected to be open or shorted.

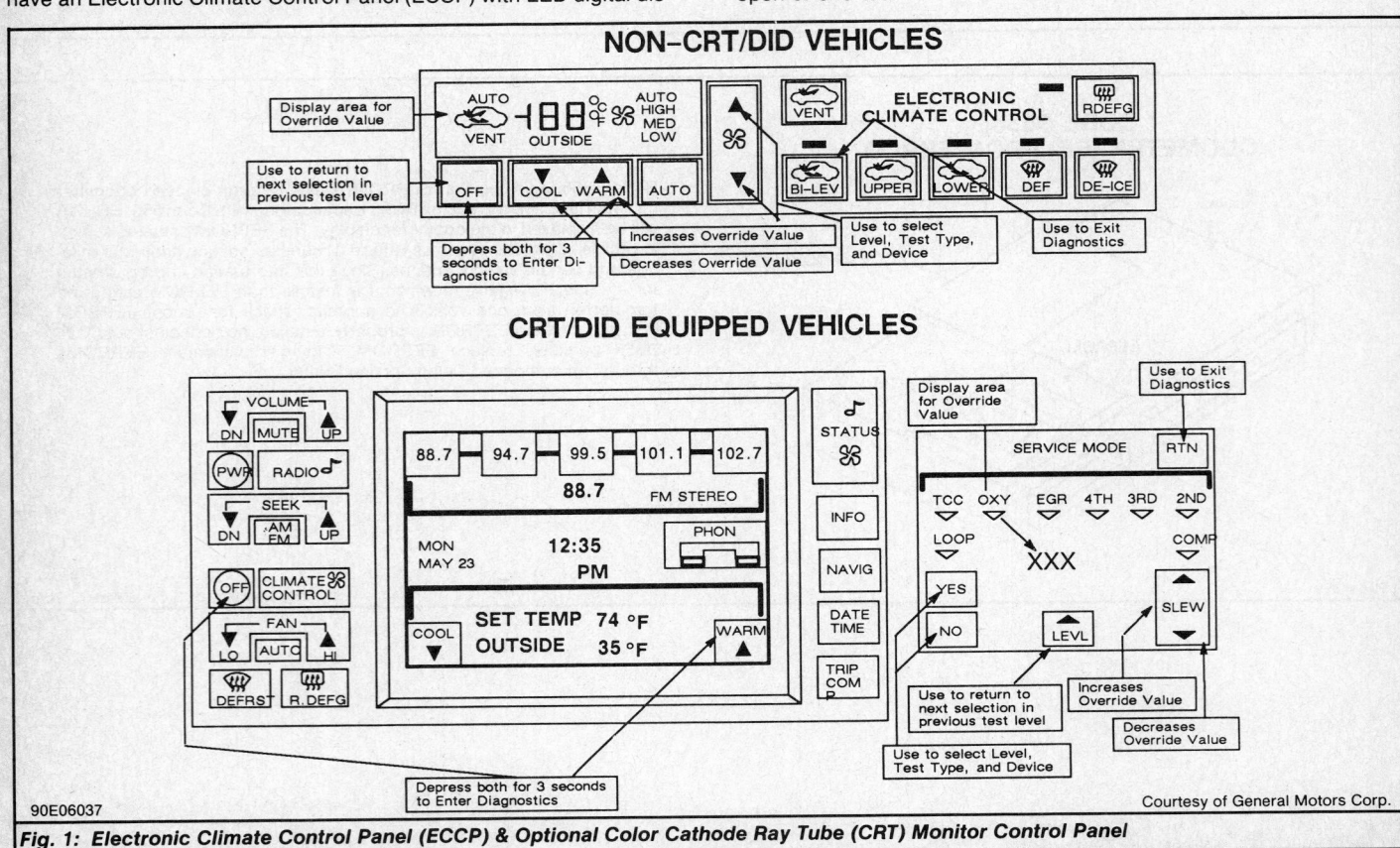

Fig. 1: Electronic Climate Control Panel (ECCP) & Optional Color Cathode Ray Tube (CRT) Monitor Control Panel

Courtesy of General Motors Corp.

1991 ENGINE PERFORMANCE
Self-Diagnostics – Toronado & Trofeo PCM/BCM (Cont.)

GM
1-337

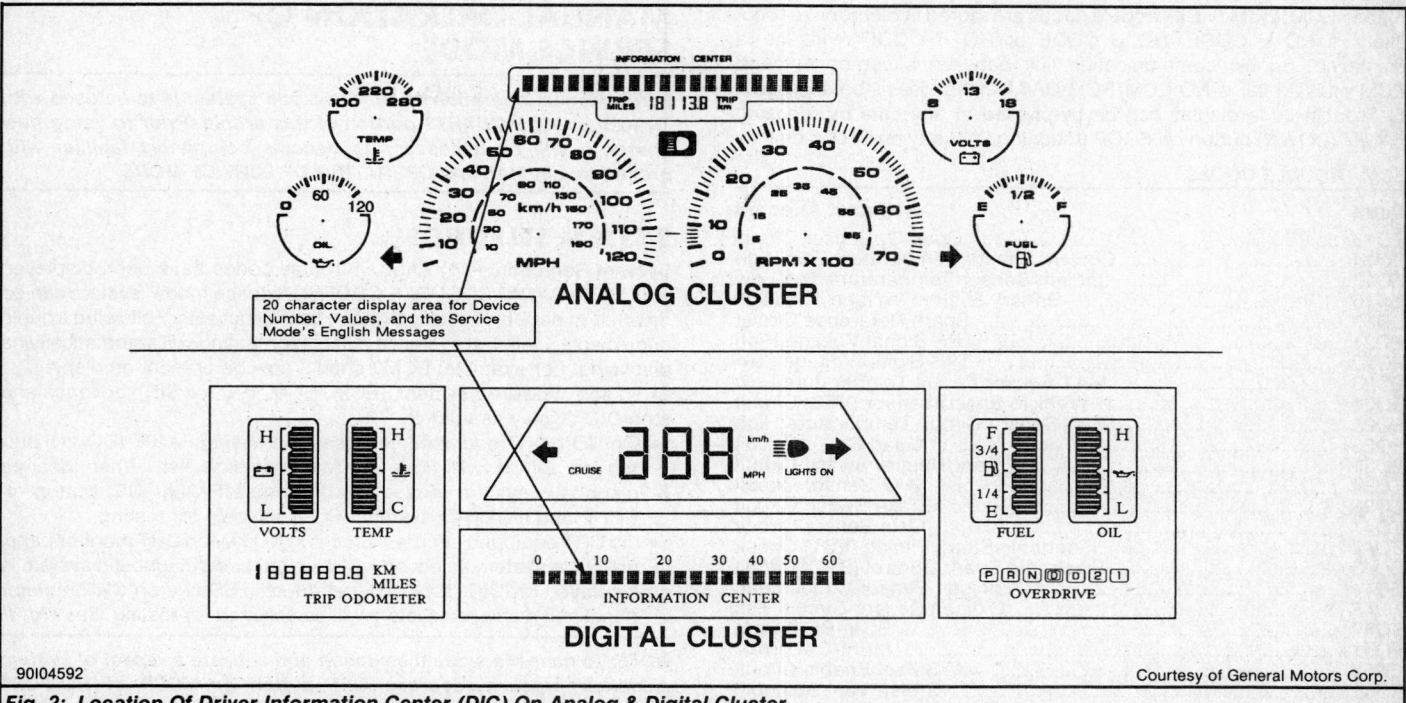

90I04592   Courtesy of General Motors Corp.

Fig. 2: Location Of Driver Information Center (DIC) On Analog & Digital Cluster

The CRT monitor or ECCP is the controller for entering diagnostics and accessing BCM self-diagnostics. By pressing or touching appropriate buttons on CRT monitor or ECCP, data messages can be sent to BCM, requesting specific diagnostic features. This communication process allows BCM to transfer any of its available diagnostic information to instrument panel's 20 character DIC display. When in override mode of BCM diagnostics, information is displayed at ECCP temperature LED display or on CRT monitor. The following is a list of computer controlled subsystems.

- Alternator/Starter System
- Chime
- Climate Control
- Courtesy Lights
- Cruise Control
- Dimming (Lighting)
- Driver Diagnostics
- ECM Subsystems
- Gauges
- Illuminated Entry
- Instrument Panel Displays
- Radio
- Self-Diagnostics System
- Twilight Sentinel

ENTERING SELF-DIAGNOSTICS

IPC SEGMENT CHECK

1) Turn ignition switch to ON position. On non-CRT equipped vehicles, simultaneously push OFF and WARM buttons on Electronic Climate Control Panel (ECCP). On CRT equipped vehicles, simultaneously push OFF button and touch WARM key on CRT monitor control panel. *See Fig. 1.*
2) On both non-CRT and CRT monitor equipped vehicles, continue to depress OFF and WARM button/key until all segments and bulbs of IPC, Driver Information Center (DIC) panel and ECCP illuminate. *See Fig. 2.* When all segments are lit, system has entered self-diagnostic mode. Release OFF and WARM button/key.
3) Illuminating segments of IPC, DIC and ECCP ensures all display segments are working properly. If all segments illuminate, proceed to

DISPLAYING TROUBLE CODES. Failure of any segment to illuminate may result in inaccurate test results. All segments of display must be made to operate before proceeding with self-diagnostic procedures.
4) Partial segment check is possible by depressing TEST button on IPC when transaxle is in Park or Neutral. Holding button depressed will light all vacuum fluorescent displays and all telltales on IPC in order to check for faulty bulbs or light panels.

CAUTION: Accessing self-diagnostics for 30 minutes or longer without running engine will cause battery to discharge, resulting in a possible no-start condition and faulty diagnostic readings. To ensure proper operation, attach battery charger to battery.

EXITING SELF-DIAGNOSTICS

During self-diagnostic procedures, it is possible to exit service mode without erasing trouble codes. On non-CRT equipped vehicles, exit service mode by depressing BI-LEV button on ECCP or by turning ignition switch to OFF position. On CRT monitor equipped vehicles, exit service mode by touching RTN key on CRT monitor panel or exit by turning ignition switch to OFF position.

DISPLAYING TROUBLE CODES

1) The Electronic Control Module (ECM), Body Control Module (BCM), and Supplemental Inflatable Restraint (SIR) trouble codes automatically display after system enters self-diagnostics. ECM trouble codes are displayed first, followed by BCM trouble codes and then SIR trouble codes.
2) All trouble codes appear in an ascending (3-digit) numerical order. ECM codes are prefixed with the letter "E", BCM Codes prefixed with the letter "B", and SIR codes prefixed with the letter "R".
3) In addition, all trouble codes are followed by the letter "C" or "H". Letter "C" stands for current and indicates a trouble code related fault presently exists. Letter "H" stands for history and indicates system failure was not present the last time code was accessed.
4) For example: E016H is ECM trouble code number 016, set in response to a malfunction that occurred in the past (history). Code B410C is BCM trouble code number 410, set in response to a malfunction that is currently taking place.

GM
1-338

1991 ENGINE PERFORMANCE
Self-Diagnostics – Toronado & Trofeo PCM/BCM (Cont.)

5) If no ECM, BCM or SIR trouble codes are stored in memory, respectively, a NO E CODE, NO B CODE or NO R CODE message is displayed. Should communication link between a component and ECM or BCM fail, a NO ECM/BCM DATA message will be displayed.
6) Trouble code display can be by-passed at any time by pressing FAN▼ (DOWN) button on ECCP (touching RTN key on CRT monitor).

ECM TROUBLE CODES

Code	Circuit Affected
EO13	Open O₂ Sensor Circuit
EO14	Coolant Sensor Temperature Too High
EO15	Coolant Sensor Temperature Too Low
EO16	Battery System Voltage Too High
EO17	Spark Reference Circuit
EO21	TPS Signal Voltage High
EO22	TPS Signal Voltage Low
EO23	MAT Sensor Circuit Temperature Low
EO24	Vehicle Speed Sensor (VSS) Circuit
EO25	MAT Sensor Circuit Temperature High
EO26	Quad-Driver Circuit
EO31	Park/Neutral Switch Circuit
EO34	MAF Sensor Circuit
EO38	Brake Switch Circuit
EO41	Cam Sensor Circuit
EO42	Electronic Spark Timing (EST) Circuit
EO43	Electronic Spark Control (ESC) Circuit
EO44	Oxygen Sensor Circuit Lean
EO45	Oxygen Sensor Circuit Rich
EO47	ECM-BCM Data
EO51	MEM-CAL Error
EO58	VATS Fuel Enable Circuit
EO61	Cruise Vent Solenoid
EO62	Cruise Vacuum Solenoid
EO65	Cruise Servo Position
EO67	Cruise Switches
EO68	Cruise System Problem

BCM TROUBLE CODES

Code	Circuit Affected
B110	Outside Temperature Sensor Circuit
B111	A/C High Side Temperature Sensor
B112	A/C Low Side Temperature Sensor
B113	In-Car Temperature Sensor Circuit
B115	Sunload Sensor Circuit
B119	Twilight Photocell Circuit
B120	Twilight Delay Switch Pot Circuit
B121	Twilight Enable Switch Circuit
B122	Panel Dimming Switch
B123	Courtesy Lamp Switch Circuit
B127	PRNDD21 Sensor
B132	Engine Oil Pressure Sensor Circuit
B140	Phone System Problem (CRT equipped)
B332	Loss of Compass Data to BCM (CRT equipped)
B333	Loss of SIR Data to BCM
B334	Loss of ECM Data to BCM
B335	Loss of ECCP Data or CRT Controller Data to BCM
B336	Loss of IPC Data to BCM
B337	Loss of Programmer Data to BCM
B410	Charging System Problem
B411	Battery Voltage Too Low
B412	Battery Voltage Too High
B440	HVAC-Air Mix Door Circuit
B446, 447 & 448	Low Refrigerant Pressure
B449	HVAC-High Side Temperature Too High
B450	HVAC-Coolant Temperature Too High
B552	BCM Keep Alive Memory Error
B556	Odometer (EE) PROM Error
C710	CRT-to-CTR Controller Communication Failure (CRT equipped)

NOTE: *To repeat trouble code display sequence, depress OFF button on ECCP of NON-CRT equipped vehicles. On CRT equipped vehicles, touch LEVL key on CRT monitor panel.*

CLEARING TROUBLE CODES

See CLEAR CODES under TEST TYPE SELECTION.

MANUAL OPERATION OF SERVICE MODE

NOTE: *Manual operation of service mode system is to be used with TROUBLE CODE CHARTS portion of this article. Prior to using flow charts, it will be necessary to become completely familiar with procedures in MANUAL OPERATION OF SERVICE MODE.*

SYSTEM SELECTION

System Selection – 1) After all trouble codes have been displayed (see DISPLAYING TROUBLE CODES), "service mode" system can be directed to perform specific system diagnostic tests. Following trouble code display, the first system available for testing will automatically be displayed. For example: ECM? should now be present on display.
2) To select desired system, (ECM, BCM, IPC, or SIR), advance and stop DIC display as follows:
- On NON-CRT equipped vehicles, depressing FAN▼ (DOWN) button on ECCP will cycle system selection list. When desired diagnostic system is displayed, depress FAN▲ (UP) button on ECCP and displayed system will be selected for testing.
- On CRT equipped vehicles, touching NO key on CRT monitor panel will cycle system selection list. When desired diagnostic system is displayed on DIC display panel, touch YES key on CRT monitor panel and displayed system will be selected for testing. *See Fig. 1.*

NOTE: *To cancel a system selection and activate a repeat of system selection process, depress OFF button on ECCP of NON-CRT equipped vehicles. On CRT equipped vehicles, touch LEVL key on CRT monitor panel.*

TEST TYPE SELECTION

Test Type Selection – 1) After diagnostic system has been selected for testing, 6 test types are now made available for selection. The menu choices are: CLEAR CODES?, DATA?, INPUTS?, OUTPUTS?, OVERRIDE? and SNAPSHOT?. The DIC display may be showing any one of these 6 test type choices.
2) To advance display, depress FAN▼ (DOWN) button on ECCP of NON-CRT equipped vehicles. On CRT equipped vehicles, touch NO key on CRT monitor panel.
3) When desired test type is displayed, depress FAN▲ (UP) button on ECCP (NON-CRT equipped). On CRT equipped vehicles, touch YES key on CRT monitor panel.

NOTE: *To cancel a test type selection and activate a repeat of test type selection process, depress OFF button on ECCP for NON-CRT equipped vehicles or for CRT equipped vehicles, touch LEVL key on CRT monitor panel. To exit diagnostics without clearing codes, depress BI-LEVEL button on ECCP or touch RTN key on CRT monitor panel.*

The 6 test types are explained as follows:
- **CLEAR CODES** – Selection of CLEAR CODES? will result in message CODES CLEAR or CODES NOT CLEAR being displayed, indicating whether codes were successfully cleared. This message appears for 3 seconds, indicating all stored trouble codes have been erased from that system's memory. After 3 seconds, display will automatically return to next test type available for testing.

NOTE: *After a trouble code has been cleared, a complete ignition cycle and preferably a test drive should be made, after which a recheck for codes should be made to ensure code did not reset.*

- **DATA** – Data test displays component/system present specifications which can be compared with specifications of a properly functioning system. Trip Odometer/DIC displays data values.
- **INPUTS** – **1)** Input test displays voltage level of the circuit being tested as HI or LO. Input test display is shown on DIC panel.
2) HI or LO refers to input terminal voltage for that particular circuit. The display also indicates if an input reading has changed since

1991 ENGINE PERFORMANCE
Self-Diagnostics – Toronado & Trofeo PCM/BCM (Cont.)

GM
1-339

test was selected. This feature permits technician to activate or deactivate any listed device/circuit and then return to display to see if voltage reading has changed.

3) If a voltage reading change occurs, an X will appear next to HI/LO indicator; otherwise a 0 will remain displayed, indicating no change occurred. The X will only appear once per selected input. HI/LO indicator will continue to change as input changes.

- **OUTPUTS** – Output test displays the voltage level of selected device/circuit as HI or LO. After 3 seconds, this level will cycle between HI and LO voltage. Output test display is shown on DIC panel.

- **OVERRIDE** – Override test is represented as a percentage of the tested functions' full range during its current operation. This percentage value is displayed in ECCP's temperature display area (NON-CRT), or on CRT monitor panel's "service mode" screen. Display will alternate between override percentage value ("--") and normal operation value. This alternating display is a reminder that tested function IS NOT being overridden.

Pressing WARM and COOL buttons simultaneously on ECCP (NON-CRT) begins override of function. Touching SLEW ▲ and SLEW ▼ keys simultaneously on CRT monitor panel begins override of function. Alternating display will stop, and show override value.

Pressing WARM button increases value, pressing COOL button decreases value (NON-CRT). Touching SLEW ▲ key on CRT monitor panel increases value, touching SLEW ▼ key decreases value.

Normal program control is resumed in one of the following 3 ways:
  1 – Selection of another override will cancel current override.
  2 – Selection of another system (ECM, BCM, IPC or SIR) will cancel current override.
  3 – An overriding value beyond either extreme (0 or 90) will display "--" momentarily before resuming value. Releasing control button while "--" is displayed will resume normal program and display will start alternating.

Override test is unique in that while in override test, another test (i.e. DATA, INPUTS, or OUTPUTS) can be selected and be active at the same time with override test. After selecting override test, press OFF button (NON-CRT equipped) or touch LEVL key (CRT equipped), to allow selection of another test type. ECCP (or CRT monitor) will continue to display selected override. By pressing OFF and WARM or COOL buttons at same time (NON-CRT equipped), or by touching LEVL and SLEW keys at the same time (CRT equipped) it is possible to monitor effect of override on different parameters.

To exit diagnostics without clearing codes, depress BI-LEV button on ECCP (NON-CRT) or touch RTN key on CRT monitor panel.

- **SNAPSHOT** – Snapshot test type will record all BCM or ECM data and inputs at one instant for review at a later time. BCM and ECM have slightly different types of snapshot.

NOTE: Proceed to ECM or BCM SNAPSHOT after selecting snapshot test type.

EXPLANATION OF SPECIFIC TEST SELECTION

Following test type selection, the first of many specific tests will be made available for selection. The 4 characters of this display represent a test code. The first 2 characters of test code are alphabetic letters which identify both system and test type already selected. Study the following examples:

- If BCM system and DATA test type were selected, BD will be the first 2 characters of display. BD stands for BCM DATA. The last 2 characters numerically identify specific test selection. For example: BD51 designates BCM DATA, test 51.
- If ECM system and Data test type were selected, ED will be the first 2 characters of display. ED stands for ECM DATA. The numerals following these 2 characters will represent the particular specific test selection.
- When BI appears as the first 2 characters of test code, this signifies BCM system and INPUT test type were selected. The last

2 characters numerically identify the specific test selection. For example: BI51 designates BCM INPUT, test 51.

MAKING SPECIFIC TEST SELECTION

1) On NON-CRT equipped vehicles, scrolling to a lower specific test number is done by depressing FAN▼ (DOWN) button. Scrolling to a higher specific test number is done by depressing FAN▲ (UP) button. The system will automatically display the value for whatever specific test number is displayed.

2) On CRT monitor equipped vehicles, scrolling to a lower specific test number is done by touching NO key on CRT monitor control panel. Scrolling to a higher number is done by touching YES key. The system will automatically display the value for whatever specific test number is displayed.

NOTE: To cancel a specific test type selection and activate a repeat of specific test type selection process, depress OFF button on ECCP of NON-CRT equipped vehicles or touch LEVL key on CRT monitor control panel of CRT equipped vehicles.

BCM SNAPSHOT (NON-CRT EQUIPPED VEHICLES)

NOTE: If directed here from TEST TYPE SELECTION under MANUAL OPERATION OF SERVICE MODE, go to step 2).

1) SNAPSHOT allows the recall of system operating specifications present at the exact time a BCM malfunction code was set. Up to 3 snapshots may be recalled. In addition, one snapshot may be triggered on demand by depressing FAN▲ (UP) button when DO B SNAP is displayed.
To enter snapshot perform the following:
- Enter self-diagnostics. See ENTERING SELF-DIAGNOSTICS.
- Display trouble codes stored in memory. See DISPLAYING TROUBLE CODES.
- Select BCM system for testing. See SYSTEM SELECTION under MANUAL OPERATION OF SERVICE MODE.
- Select SNAPSHOT test type. See TEST TYPE SELECTION under MANUAL OPERATION OF SERVICE MODE.

NOTE: To cancel snapshot test type selection and activate a repeat of specific test type selection process, depress OFF button on ECCP.

2) Immediately following the selection of SNAPSHOT?, system will display CODE BXXX SNAP SHOT. B stands for BCM. XXX is used here to represent 3-digit trouble code stored in BCM snapshot.
3) With BXXX displayed, depressing FAN▼ (DOWN) button on ECCP will permit scrolling through list of BCM diagnostic codes for which BCM has stored a snapshot. See DISPLAYING TROUBLE CODES for list of BCM trouble codes which may be present in snapshot.

NOTE: A trouble code displayed during trouble code display cycle may NOT be present as a snapshot trouble code. If this is the case, exit SNAPSHOT by depressing OFF button on ECCP. This will return display to the next available system selection.

4) After display of last BCM trouble code for which a snapshot does exist, pressing FAN▼ (DOWN) button on ECCP will result in DO B SNAP display.
5) Responding to this display by depressing FAN▼ (DOWN) button on ECCP will return display to first BXXX SNAP? display. Responding to DO B SNAP display by depressing FAN▲ (UP) button with SNAP DATA? or SNAP INPUTS? displayed, will select that test type for display.
6) At this point, display is controlled as it would be for non-snapshot data and inputs display; however, all values and status information represents memorized vehicle conditions. See EXPLANATION OF SPECIFIC TEST SELECTION and MAKING SPECIFIC TEST SELECTION under MANUAL OPERATION OF SERVICE MODE.
7) Depressing FAN▲ (UP) key again with DO B SNAP? displayed will change DIC to display SNAP DONE message to indicate new information has been stored in memory.

GM
1-340

1991 ENGINE PERFORMANCE
Self-Diagnostics – Toronado & Trofeo PCM/BCM (Cont.)

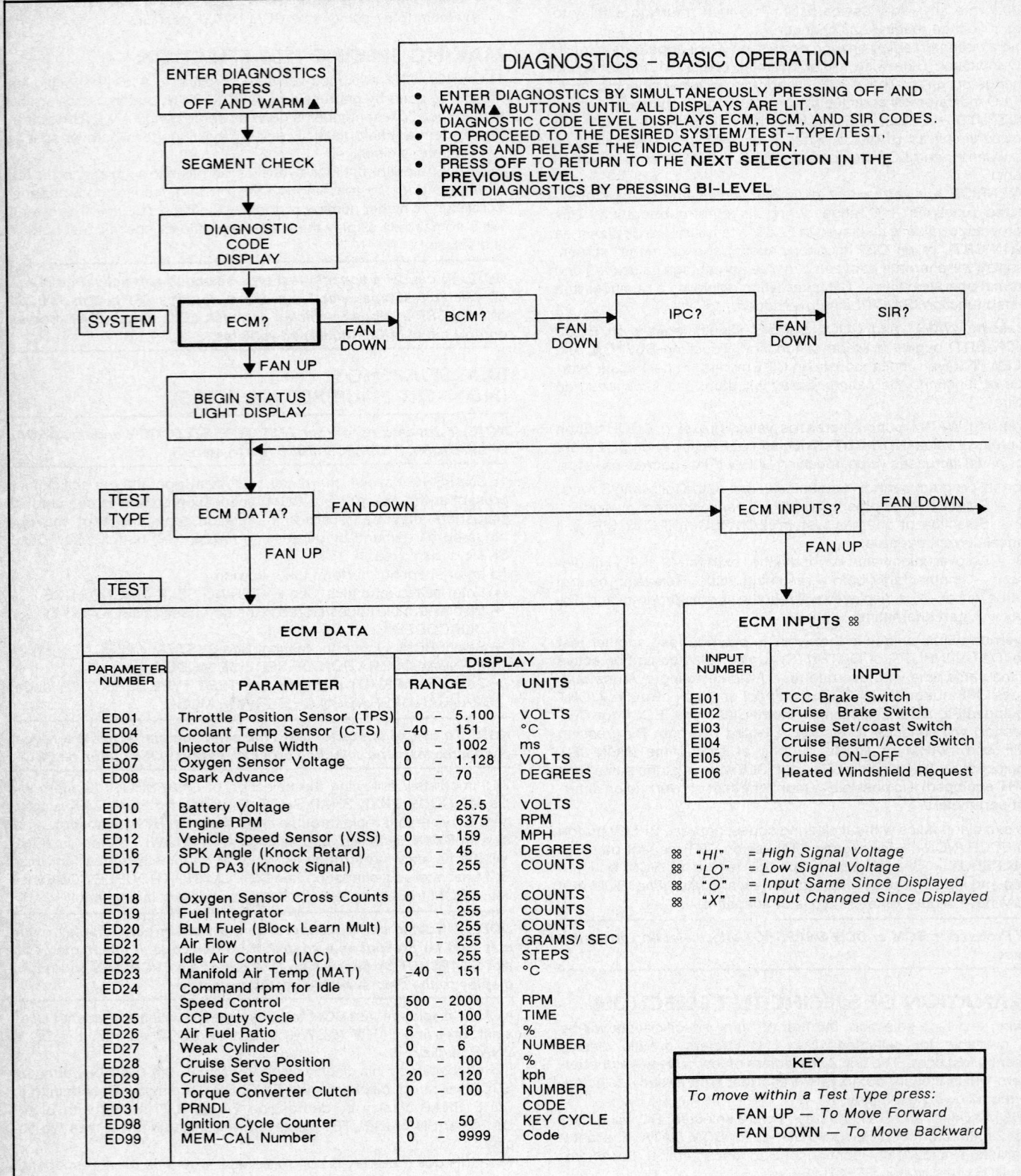

DIAGNOSTICS – BASIC OPERATION

- ENTER DIAGNOSTICS BY SIMULTANEOUSLY PRESSING OFF AND WARM▲ BUTTONS UNTIL ALL DISPLAYS ARE LIT.
- DIAGNOSTIC CODE LEVEL DISPLAYS ECM, BCM, AND SIR CODES.
- TO PROCEED TO THE DESIRED SYSTEM/TEST-TYPE/TEST, PRESS AND RELEASE THE INDICATED BUTTON.
- PRESS OFF TO RETURN TO THE NEXT SELECTION IN THE PREVIOUS LEVEL.
- EXIT DIAGNOSTICS BY PRESSING BI-LEVEL

ENTER DIAGNOSTICS PRESS OFF AND WARM▲

SEGMENT CHECK

DIAGNOSTIC CODE DISPLAY

SYSTEM — ECM? — FAN DOWN — BCM? — FAN DOWN — IPC? — FAN DOWN — SIR?

FAN UP

BEGIN STATUS LIGHT DISPLAY

TEST TYPE — ECM DATA? — FAN DOWN — ECM INPUTS? — FAN DOWN

FAN UP — FAN UP

TEST

ECM DATA

PARAMETER NUMBER	PARAMETER	DISPLAY		
		RANGE		UNITS
ED01	Throttle Position Sensor (TPS)	0 – 5.100		VOLTS
ED04	Coolant Temp Sensor (CTS)	–40 – 151		°C
ED06	Injector Pulse Width	0 – 1002		ms
ED07	Oxygen Sensor Voltage	0 – 1.128		VOLTS
ED08	Spark Advance	0 – 70		DEGREES
ED10	Battery Voltage	0 – 25.5		VOLTS
ED11	Engine RPM	0 – 6375		RPM
ED12	Vehicle Speed Sensor (VSS)	0 – 159		MPH
ED16	SPK Angle (Knock Retard)	0 – 45		DEGREES
ED17	OLD PA3 (Knock Signal)	0 – 255		COUNTS
ED18	Oxygen Sensor Cross Counts	0 – 255		COUNTS
ED19	Fuel Integrator	0 – 255		COUNTS
ED20	BLM Fuel (Block Learn Mult)	0 – 255		COUNTS
ED21	Air Flow	0 – 255		GRAMS/ SEC
ED22	Idle Air Control (IAC)	0 – 255		STEPS
ED23	Manifold Air Temp (MAT)	–40 – 151		°C
ED24	Command rpm for Idle Speed Control	500 – 2000		RPM
ED25	CCP Duty Cycle	0 – 100		TIME
ED26	Air Fuel Ratio	6 – 18		%
ED27	Weak Cylinder	0 – 6		NUMBER
ED28	Cruise Servo Position	0 – 100		%
ED29	Cruise Set Speed	20 – 120		kph
ED30	Torque Converter Clutch	0 – 100		NUMBER
ED31	PRNDL			CODE
ED98	Ignition Cycle Counter	0 – 50		KEY CYCLE
ED99	MEM-CAL Number	0 – 9999		Code

ECM INPUTS ※

INPUT NUMBER	INPUT
EI01	TCC Brake Switch
EI02	Cruise Brake Switch
EI03	Cruise Set/coast Switch
EI04	Cruise Resum/Accel Switch
EI05	Cruise ON-OFF
EI06	Heated Windshield Request

※ "HI" = High Signal Voltage
※ "LO" = Low Signal Voltage
※ "O" = Input Same Since Displayed
※ "X" = Input Changed Since Displayed

KEY

To move within a Test Type press:
FAN UP — To Move Forward
FAN DOWN — To Move Backward

91B11875

Fig. 3: ECM (PCM) System Diagnostic Flow Chart Without CRT (1 of 2)

1991 ENGINE PERFORMANCE
Self-Diagnostics – Toronado & Trofeo PCM/BCM (Cont.)

GM
1-341

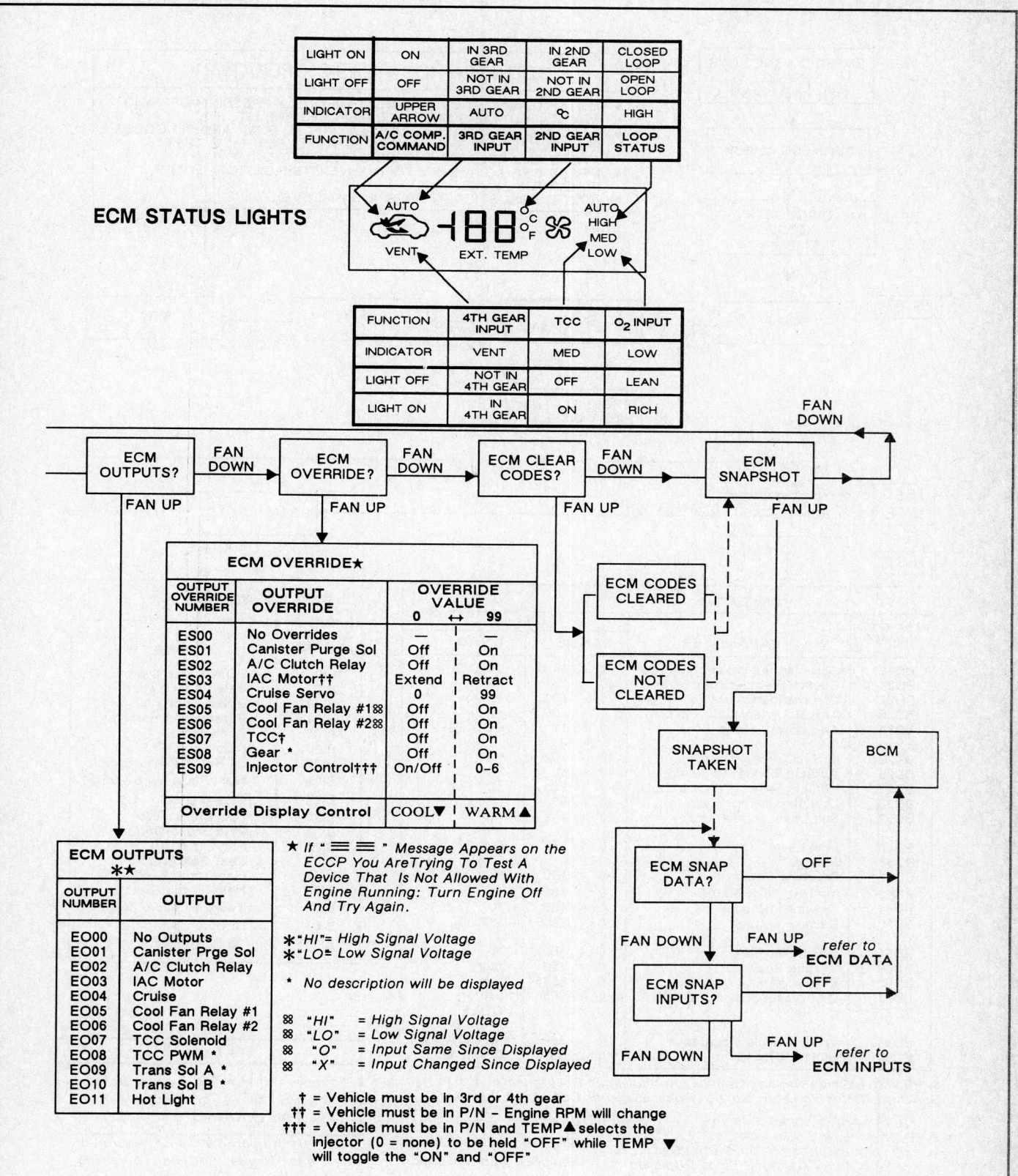

LIGHT ON	ON	IN 3RD GEAR	IN 2ND GEAR	CLOSED LOOP
LIGHT OFF	OFF	NOT IN 3RD GEAR	NOT IN 2ND GEAR	OPEN LOOP
INDICATOR	UPPER ARROW	AUTO	°C	HIGH
FUNCTION	A/C COMP. COMMAND	3RD GEAR INPUT	2ND GEAR INPUT	LOOP STATUS

ECM STATUS LIGHTS

FUNCTION	4TH GEAR INPUT	TCC	O₂ INPUT
INDICATOR	VENT	MED	LOW
LIGHT OFF	NOT IN 4TH GEAR	OFF	LEAN
LIGHT ON	IN 4TH GEAR	ON	RICH

ECM OVERRIDE★

OUTPUT OVERRIDE NUMBER	OUTPUT OVERRIDE	OVERRIDE VALUE 0 ↔ 99	
ES00	No Overrides	—	—
ES01	Canister Purge Sol	Off	On
ES02	A/C Clutch Relay	Off	On
ES03	IAC Motor††	Extend	Retract
ES04	Cruise Servo	0	99
ES05	Cool Fan Relay #1⊗⊗	Off	On
ES06	Cool Fan Relay #2⊗⊗	Off	On
ES07	TCC†	Off	On
ES08	Gear *	Off	On
ES09	Injector Control†††	On/Off	0–6
Override Display Control		COOL▼	WARM▲

ECM OUTPUTS ★★

OUTPUT NUMBER	OUTPUT
EO00	No Outputs
EO01	Canister Prge Sol
EO02	A/C Clutch Relay
EO03	IAC Motor
EO04	Cruise
EO05	Cool Fan Relay #1
EO06	Cool Fan Relay #2
EO07	TCC Solenoid
EO08	TCC PWM *
EO09	Trans Sol A *
EO10	Trans Sol B *
EO11	Hot Light

★ If " ☰ ☰ " Message Appears on the ECCP You Are Trying To Test A Device That Is Not Allowed With Engine Running: Turn Engine Off And Try Again.

★ "HI"= High Signal Voltage
★ "LO"= Low Signal Voltage

* No description will be displayed

⊗⊗ "HI" = High Signal Voltage
⊗⊗ "LO" = Low Signal Voltage
⊗⊗ "O" = Input Same Since Displayed
⊗⊗ "X" = Input Changed Since Displayed

† = Vehicle must be in 3rd or 4th gear
†† = Vehicle must be in P/N - Engine RPM will change
††† = Vehicle must be in P/N and TEMP▲ selects the injector (0 = none) to be held "OFF" while TEMP ▼ will toggle the "ON" and "OFF"

91C11876

Courtesy of General Motors Corp.

Fig. 4: ECM (PCM) System Diagnostic Flow Chart Without CRT (2 of 2)

GM
1-342

1991 ENGINE PERFORMANCE
Self-Diagnostics – Toronado & Trofeo PCM/BCM (Cont.)

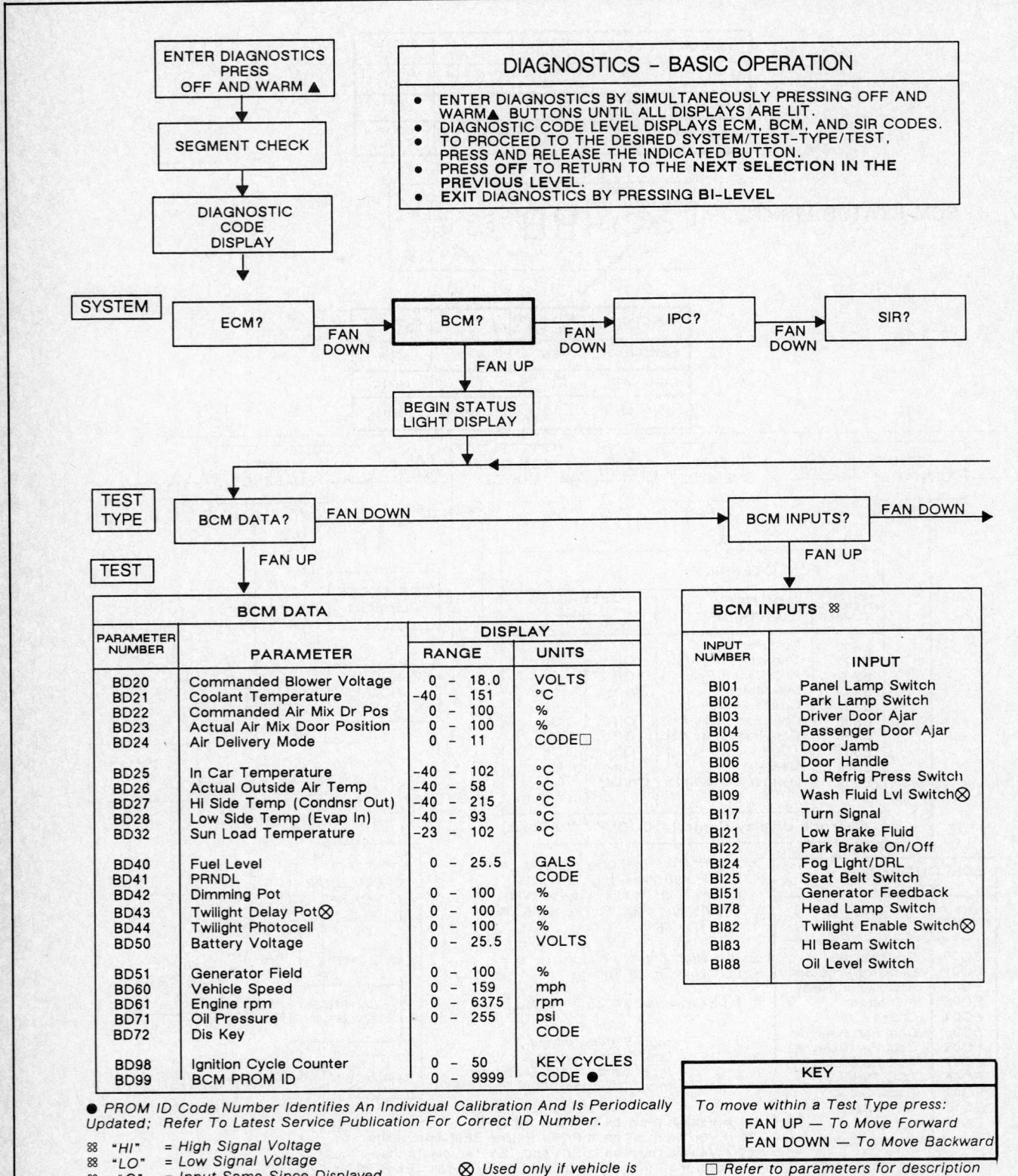

DIAGNOSTICS – BASIC OPERATION

- ENTER DIAGNOSTICS BY SIMULTANEOUSLY PRESSING OFF AND WARM▲ BUTTONS UNTIL ALL DISPLAYS ARE LIT.
- DIAGNOSTIC CODE LEVEL DISPLAYS ECM, BCM, AND SIR CODES.
- TO PROCEED TO THE DESIRED SYSTEM/TEST-TYPE/TEST, PRESS AND RELEASE THE INDICATED BUTTON.
- PRESS OFF TO RETURN TO THE NEXT SELECTION IN THE PREVIOUS LEVEL.
- EXIT DIAGNOSTICS BY PRESSING BI-LEVEL

BCM DATA

PARAMETER NUMBER	PARAMETER	DISPLAY		
		RANGE	UNITS	
BD20	Commanded Blower Voltage	0 – 18.0	VOLTS	
BD21	Coolant Temperature	-40 – 151	°C	
BD22	Commanded Air Mix Dr Pos	0 – 100	%	
BD23	Actual Air Mix Door Position	0 – 100	%	
BD24	Air Delivery Mode	0 – 11	CODE□	
BD25	In Car Temperature	-40 – 102	°C	
BD26	Actual Outside Air Temp	-40 – 58	°C	
BD27	Hi Side Temp (Condnsr Out)	-40 – 215	°C	
BD28	Low Side Temp (Evap In)	-40 – 93	°C	
BD32	Sun Load Temperature	-23 – 102	°C	
BD40	Fuel Level	0 – 25.5	GALS	
BD41	PRNDL		CODE	
BD42	Dimming Pot	0 – 100	%	
BD43	Twilight Delay Pot⊗	0 – 100	%	
BD44	Twilight Photocell	0 – 100	%	
BD50	Battery Voltage	0 – 25.5	VOLTS	
BD51	Generator Field	0 – 100	%	
BD60	Vehicle Speed	0 – 159	mph	
BD61	Engine rpm	0 – 6375	rpm	
BD71	Oil Pressure	0 – 255	psi	
BD72	Dis Key		CODE	
BD98	Ignition Cycle Counter	0 – 50	KEY CYCLES	
BD99	BCM PROM ID	0 – 9999	CODE ●	

BCM INPUTS ⊗⊗

INPUT NUMBER	INPUT
BI01	Panel Lamp Switch
BI02	Park Lamp Switch
BI03	Driver Door Ajar
BI04	Passenger Door Ajar
BI05	Door Jamb
BI06	Door Handle
BI08	Lo Refrig Press Switch†
BI09	Wash Fluid Lvl Switch⊗
BI17	Turn Signal
BI21	Low Brake Fluid
BI22	Park Brake On/Off
BI24	Fog Light/DRL
BI25	Seat Belt Switch
BI51	Generator Feedback
BI78	Head Lamp Switch
BI82	Twilight Enable Switch⊗
BI83	HI Beam Switch
BI88	Oil Level Switch

● PROM ID Code Number Identifies An Individual Calibration And Is Periodically Updated; Refer To Latest Service Publication For Correct ID Number.

⊗⊗ "HI" = High Signal Voltage
⊗⊗ "LO" = Low Signal Voltage
⊗⊗ "O" = Input Same Since Displayed
⊗⊗ "X" = Input Changed Since Displayed

⊗ Used only if vehicle is equipped with this option

KEY

To move within a Test Type press:
FAN UP — To Move Forward
FAN DOWN — To Move Backward

□ Refer to parameters for description
† Switch Cruise "ON" Before Testing

91D11877

Courtesy of General Motors Corp.

Fig. 5: BCM System Diagnostic Flow Chart Without CRT (1 of 2)

1991 ENGINE PERFORMANCE
Self-Diagnostics – Toronado & Trofeo PCM/BCM (Cont.)

GM
1-343

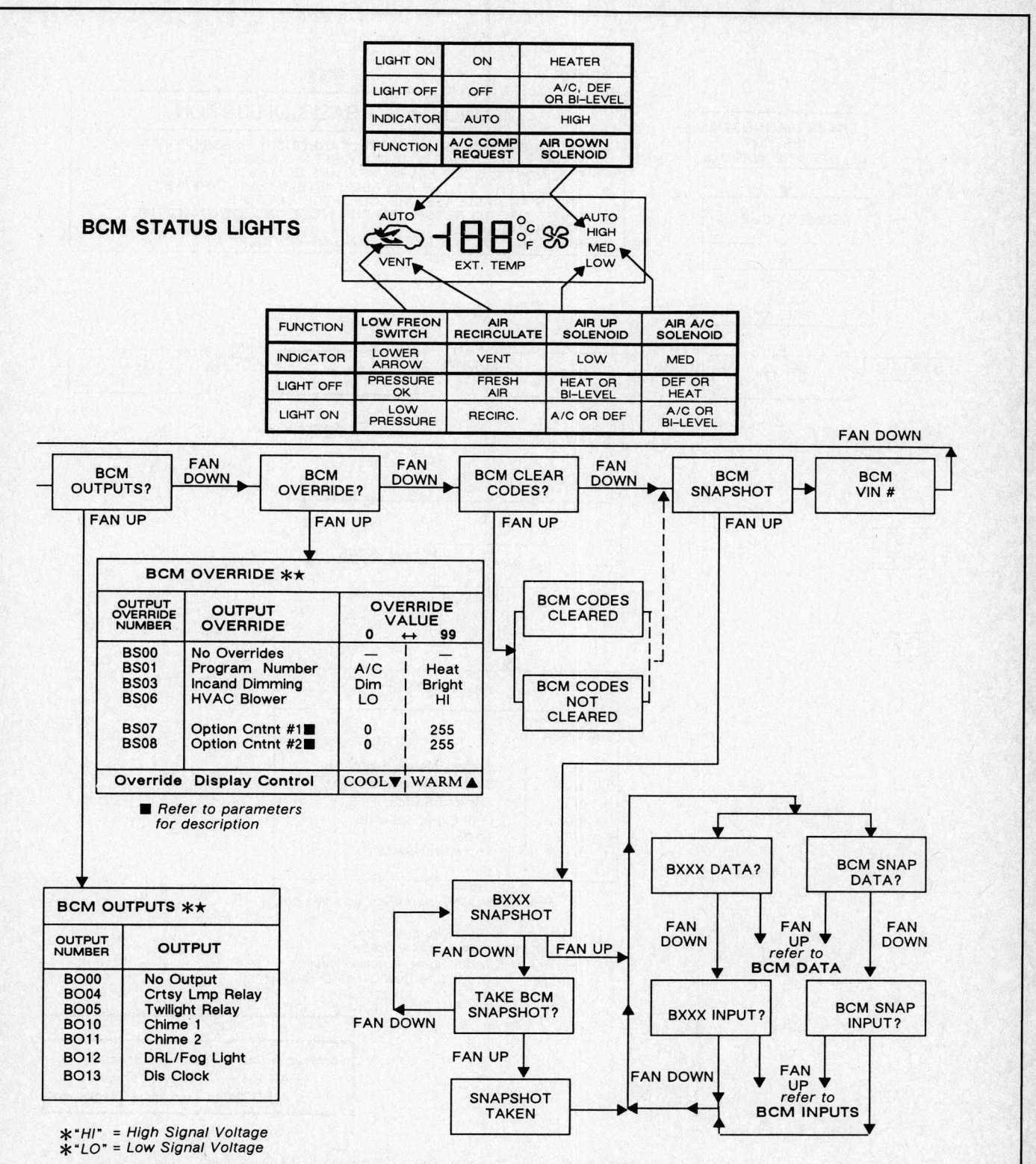

LIGHT ON	ON	HEATER
LIGHT OFF	OFF	A/C, DEF OR BI-LEVEL
INDICATOR	AUTO	HIGH
FUNCTION	A/C COMP REQUEST	AIR DOWN SOLENOID

BCM STATUS LIGHTS

FUNCTION	LOW FREON SWITCH	AIR RECIRCULATE	AIR UP SOLENOID	AIR A/C SOLENOID
INDICATOR	LOWER ARROW	VENT	LOW	MED
LIGHT OFF	PRESSURE OK	FRESH AIR	HEAT OR BI-LEVEL	DEF OR HEAT
LIGHT ON	LOW PRESSURE	RECIRC.	A/C OR DEF	A/C OR BI-LEVEL

BCM OVERRIDE ✶✶

OUTPUT OVERRIDE NUMBER	OUTPUT OVERRIDE	OVERRIDE VALUE 0 ↔ 99	
BS00	No Overrides	—	
BS01	Program Number	A/C	Heat
BS03	Incand Dimming	Dim	Bright
BS06	HVAC Blower	LO	HI
BS07	Option Cntnt #1■	0	255
BS08	Option Cntnt #2■	0	255
Override Display Control		COOL▼	WARM▲

■ *Refer to parameters for description*

BCM OUTPUTS ✶✶

OUTPUT NUMBER	OUTPUT
BO00	No Output
BO04	Crtsy Lmp Relay
BO05	Twilight Relay
BO10	Chime 1
BO11	Chime 2
BO12	DRL/Fog Light
BO13	Dis Clock

✶*"HI" = High Signal Voltage*
✶*"LO" = Low Signal Voltage*

★ *If "≡ ≡ ≡" Message Appears on the ECCP You Are Trying To Test A Device That Is Not Allowed With Engine Running: Turn Engine Off And Try Again.*

91E11878

Courtesy of General Motors Corp.

Fig. 6: BCM System Diagnostic Flow Chart Without CRT (2 of 2)

GM
1-344

1991 ENGINE PERFORMANCE
Self-Diagnostics – Toronado & Trofeo PCM/BCM (Cont.)

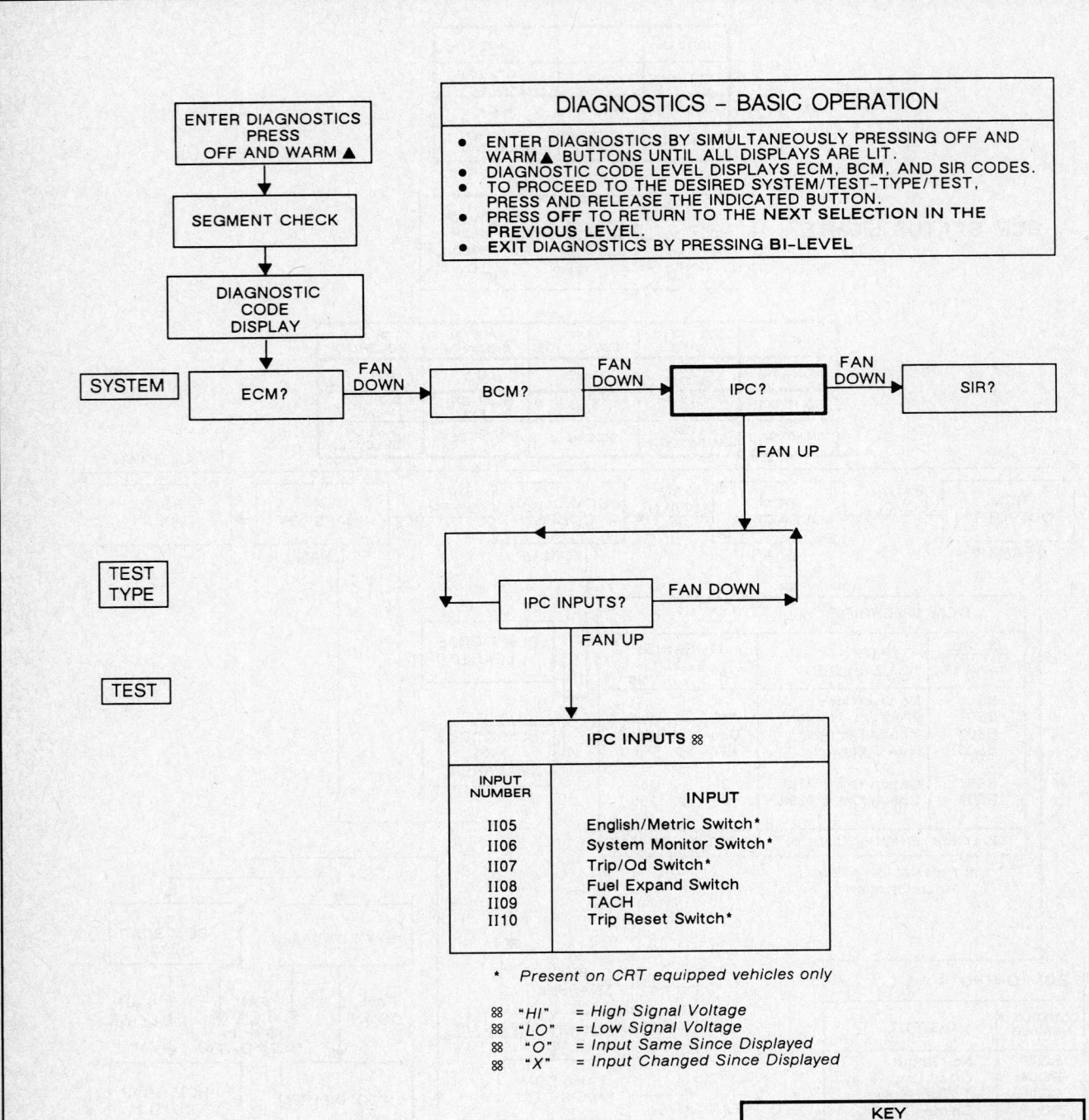

DIAGNOSTICS – BASIC OPERATION

- ENTER DIAGNOSTICS BY SIMULTANEOUSLY PRESSING OFF AND WARM▲ BUTTONS UNTIL ALL DISPLAYS ARE LIT.
- DIAGNOSTIC CODE LEVEL DISPLAYS ECM, BCM, AND SIR CODES.
- TO PROCEED TO THE DESIRED SYSTEM/TEST–TYPE/TEST, PRESS AND RELEASE THE INDICATED BUTTON.
- PRESS OFF TO RETURN TO THE NEXT SELECTION IN THE PREVIOUS LEVEL.
- EXIT DIAGNOSTICS BY PRESSING BI–LEVEL

IPC INPUTS ⊠

INPUT NUMBER	INPUT
II05	English/Metric Switch*
II06	System Monitor Switch*
II07	Trip/Od Switch*
II08	Fuel Expand Switch
II09	TACH
II10	Trip Reset Switch*

* *Present on CRT equipped vehicles only*

⊠ *"HI"* = *High Signal Voltage*
⊠ *"LO"* = *Low Signal Voltage*
⊠ *"O"* = *Input Same Since Displayed*
⊠ *"X"* = *Input Changed Since Displayed*

KEY

To move within a Test Type press:
FAN UP — *To Move Forward*
FAN DOWN — *To Move Backward*

91F11879

Courtesy of General Motors Corp.

Fig. 7: IPC System Diagnostic Flow Chart Without CRT

1991 ENGINE PERFORMANCE
Self-Diagnostics – Toronado & Trofeo PCM/BCM (Cont.)

GM
1-345

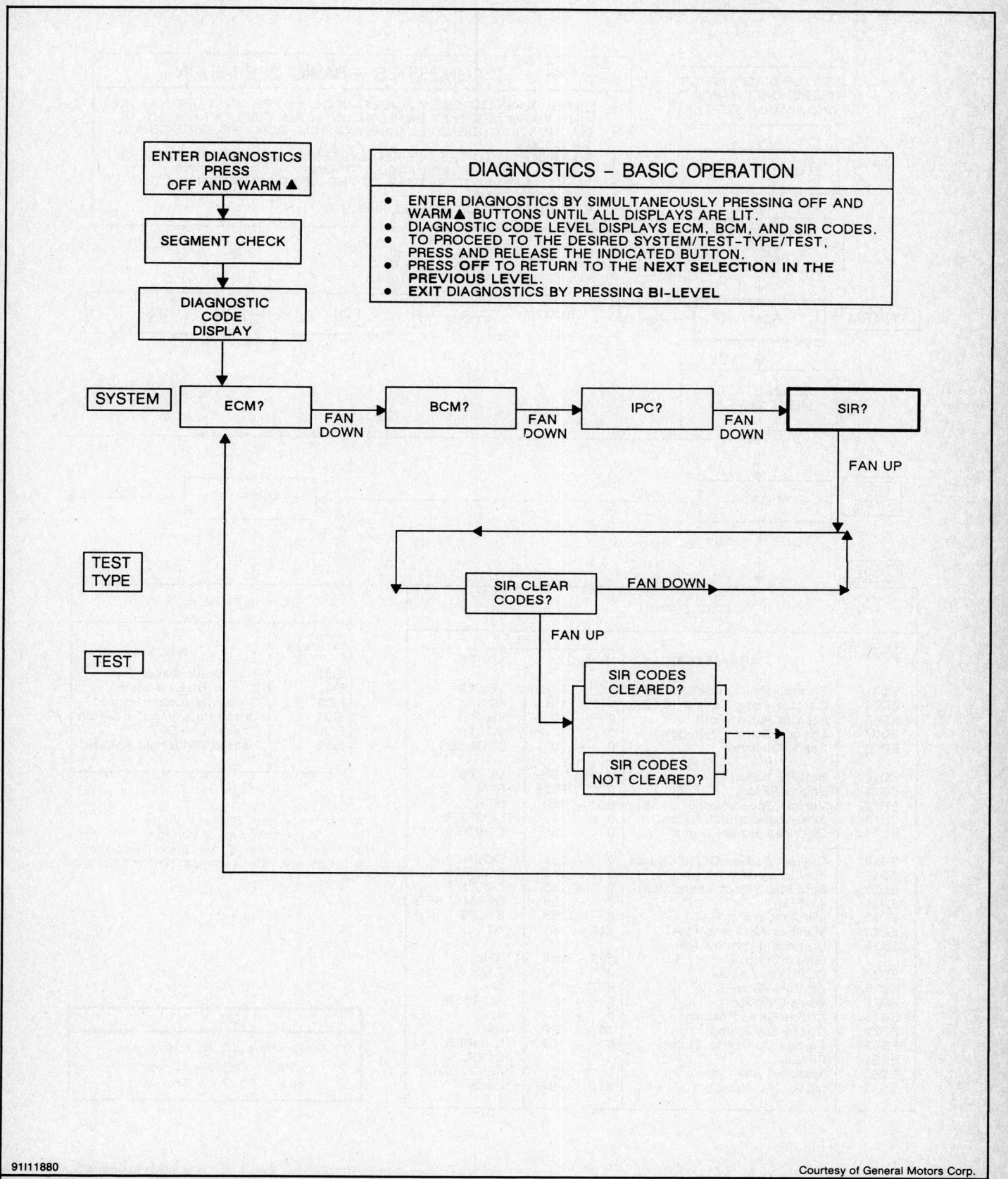

91I11880

Fig. 8: SIR System Diagnostic Flow Chart Without CRT

GM
1-346

1991 ENGINE PERFORMANCE
Self-Diagnostics – Toronado & Trofeo PCM/BCM (Cont.)

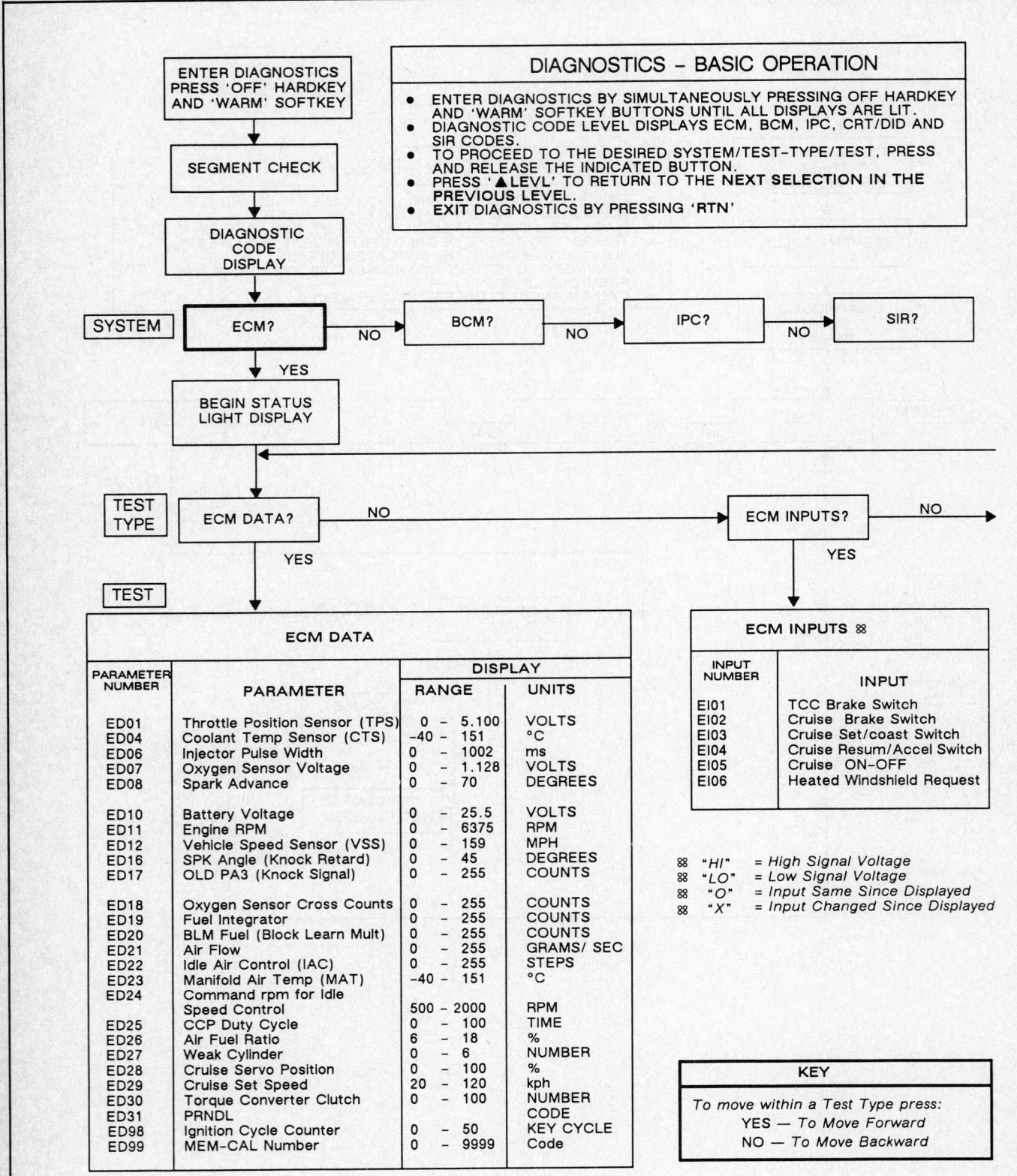

91J11881

Fig. 9: ECM (PCM) System Diagnostic Flow Chart With CRT (1 of 2)

1991 ENGINE PERFORMANCE
Self-Diagnostics – Toronado & Trofeo PCM/BCM (Cont.)

GM
1-347

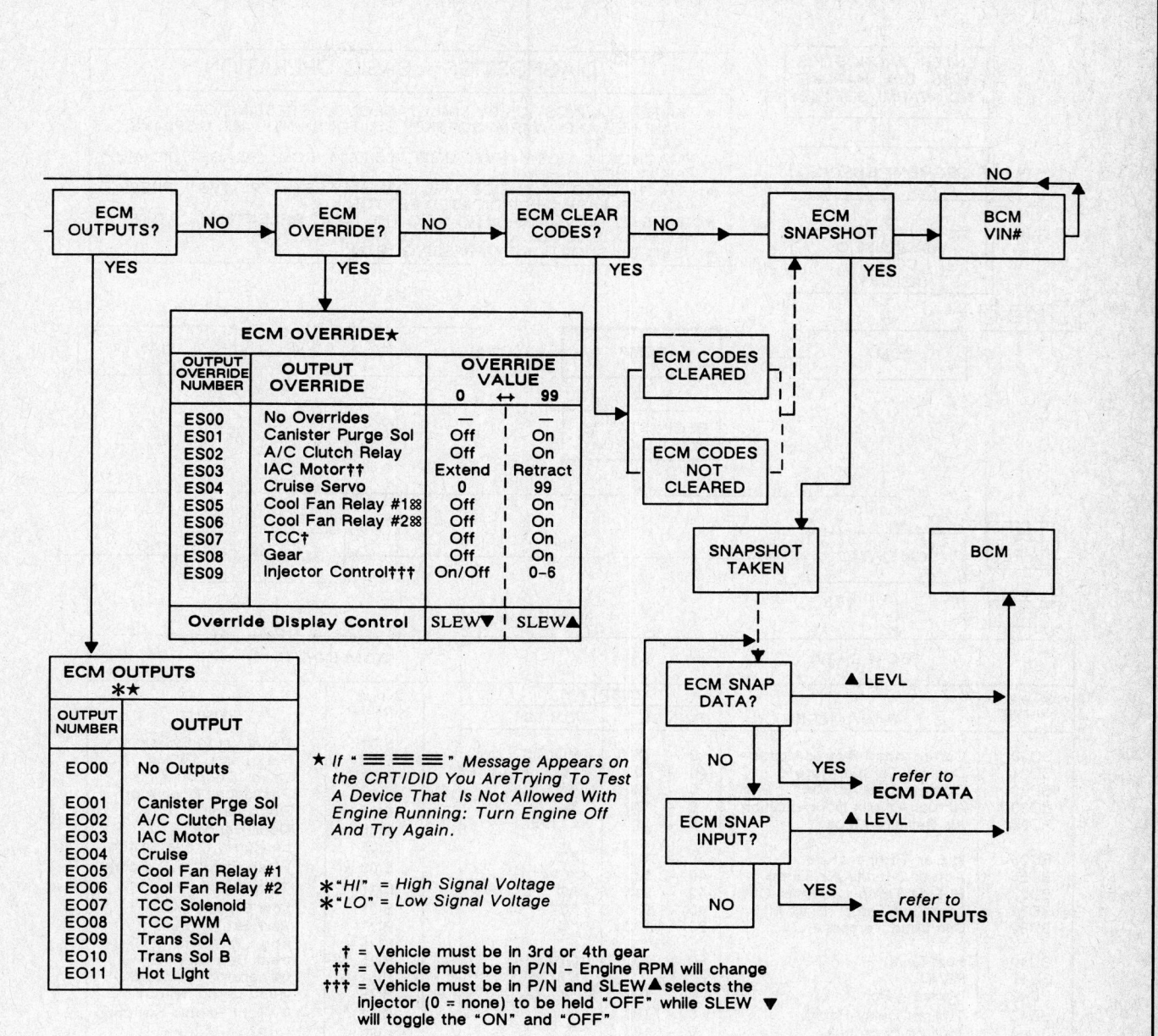

Courtesy of General Motors Corp.

Fig. 10: *ECM (PCM) System Diagnostic Flow Chart With CRT (2 of 2)*

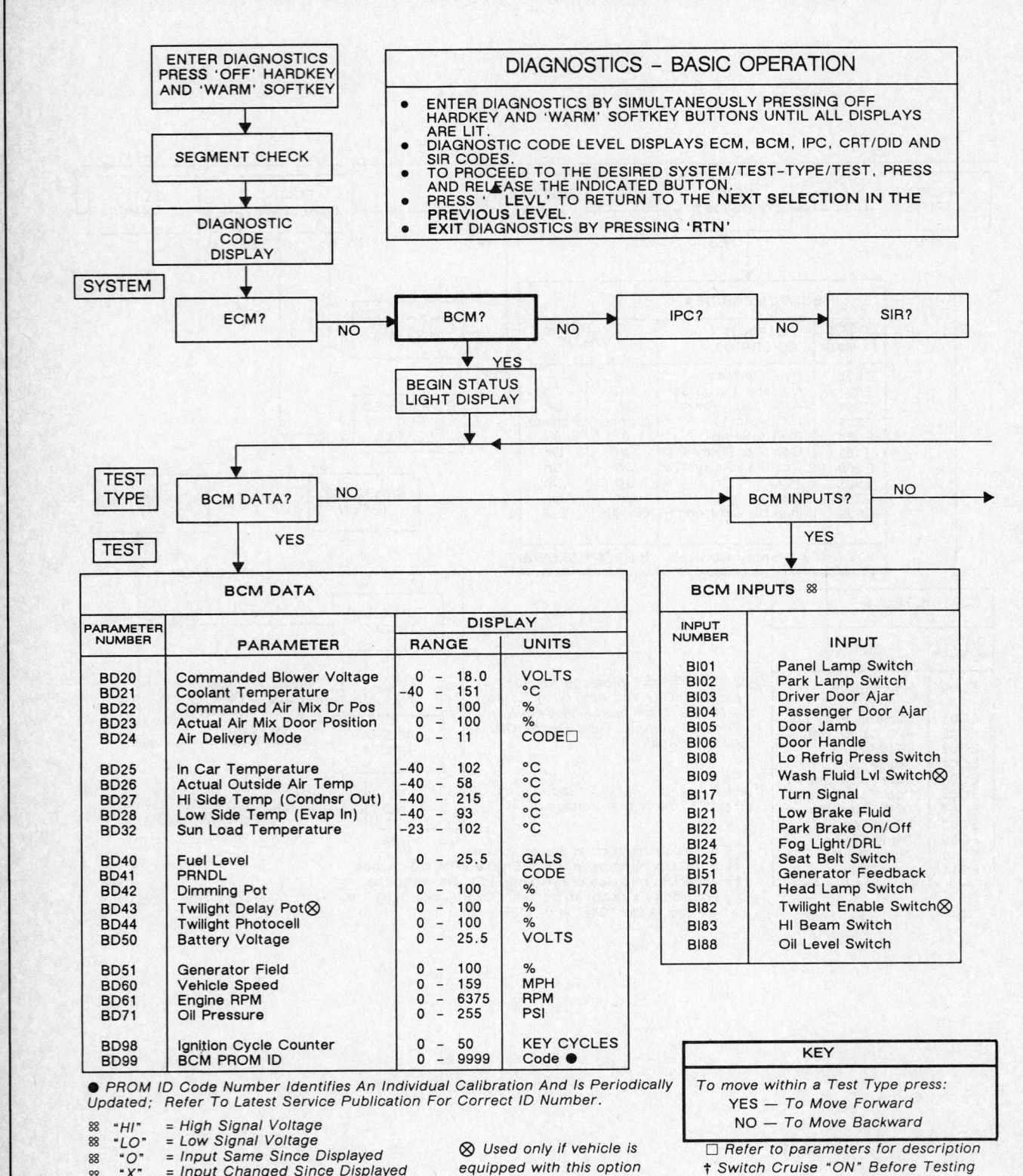

Fig. 11: BCM System Diagnostic Flow Chart With CRT (1 of 2)

1991 ENGINE PERFORMANCE
Self-Diagnostics – Toronado & Trofeo PCM/BCM (Cont.)

GM
1-349

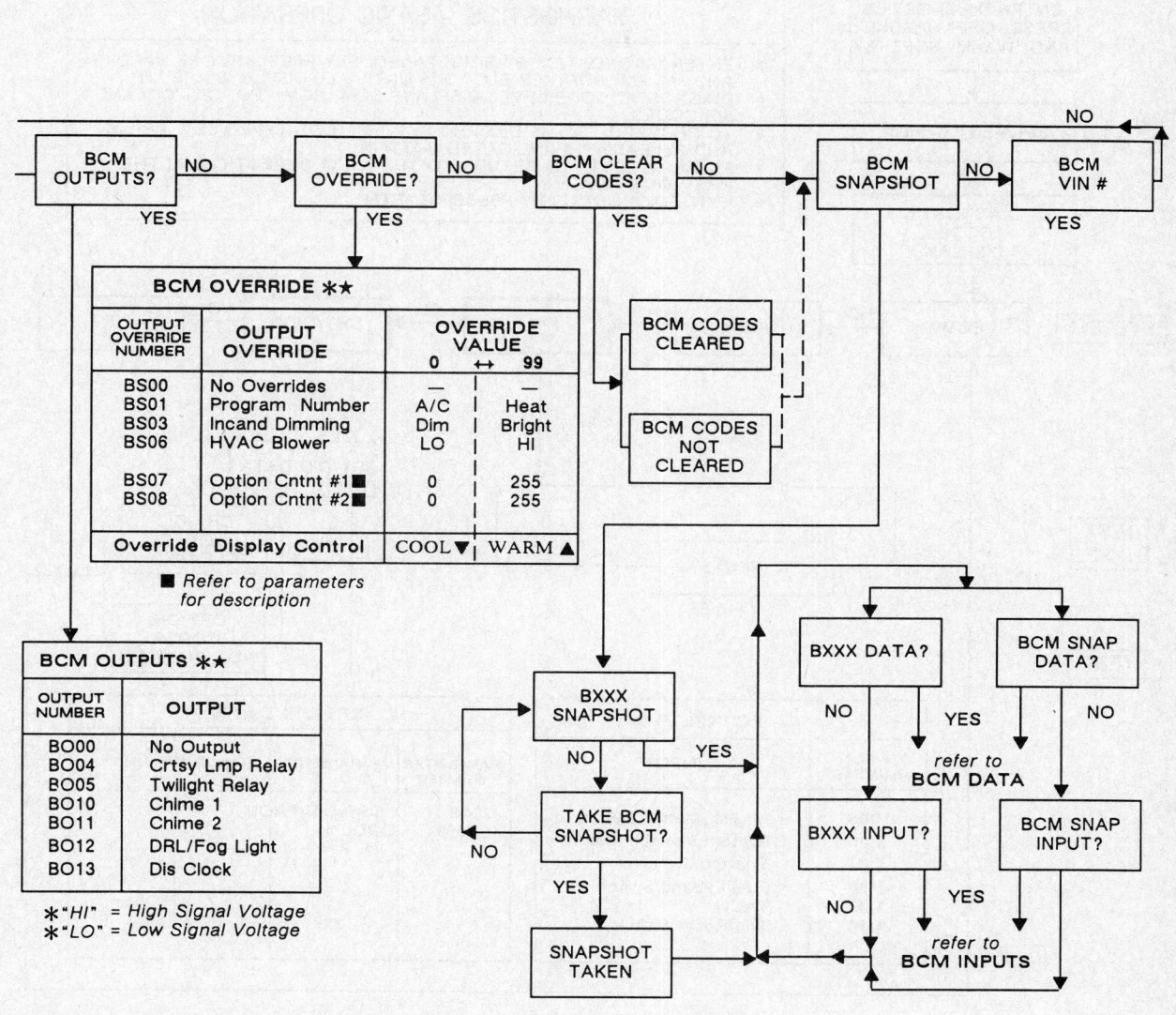

Fig. 12: BCM System Diagnostic Flow Chart With CRT (2 of 2)

GM
1-350

1991 ENGINE PERFORMANCE
Self-Diagnostics – Toronado & Trofeo PCM/BCM (Cont.)

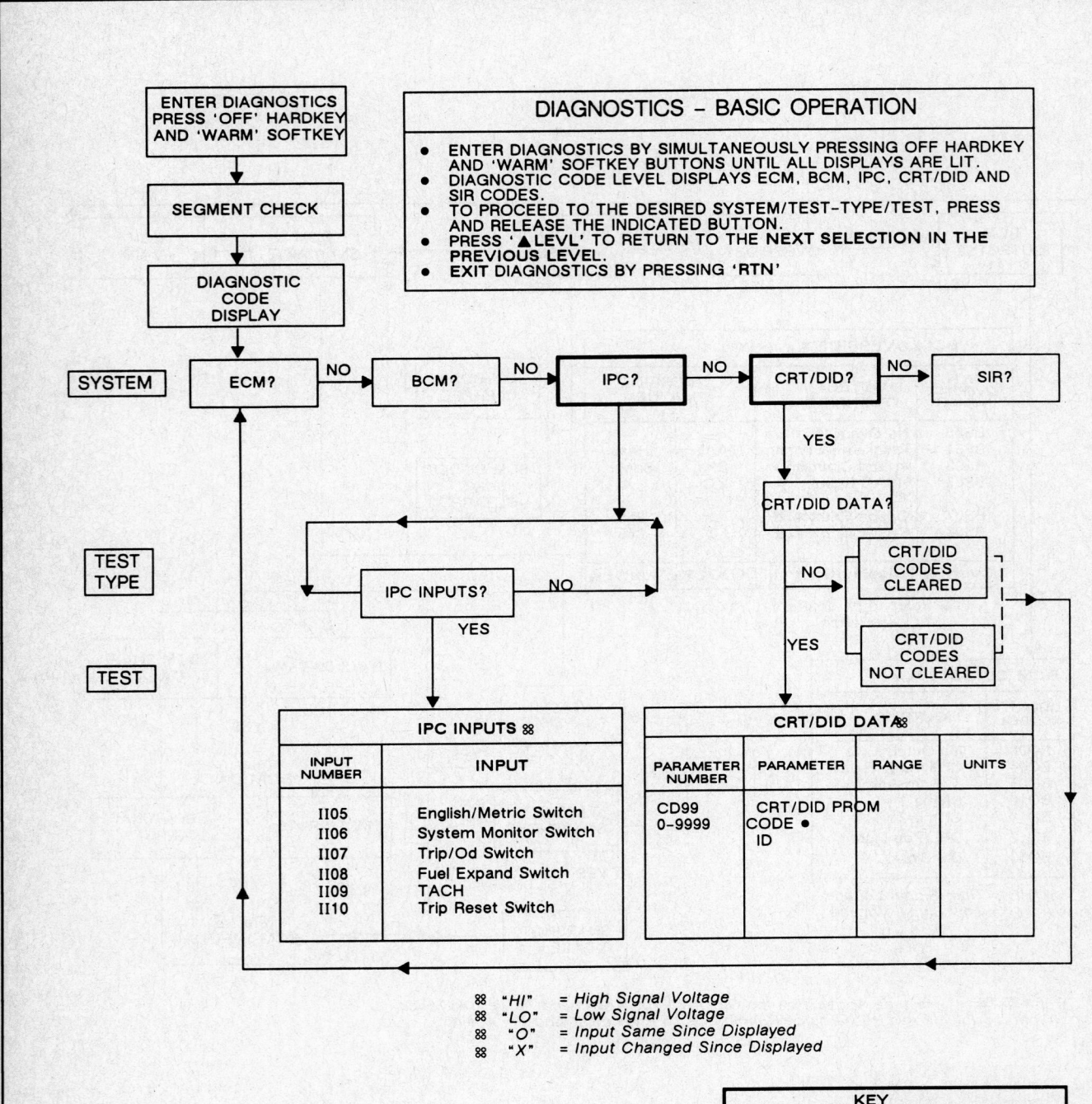

DIAGNOSTICS – BASIC OPERATION

- ENTER DIAGNOSTICS BY SIMULTANEOUSLY PRESSING OFF HARDKEY AND 'WARM' SOFTKEY BUTTONS UNTIL ALL DISPLAYS ARE LIT.
- DIAGNOSTIC CODE LEVEL DISPLAYS ECM, BCM, IPC, CRT/DID AND SIR CODES.
- TO PROCEED TO THE DESIRED SYSTEM/TEST–TYPE/TEST, PRESS AND RELEASE THE INDICATED BUTTON.
- PRESS '▲LEVL' TO RETURN TO THE NEXT SELECTION IN THE PREVIOUS LEVEL.
- EXIT DIAGNOSTICS BY PRESSING 'RTN'

88 "HI" = High Signal Voltage
88 "LO" = Low Signal Voltage
88 "O" = Input Same Since Displayed
88 "X" = Input Changed Since Displayed

KEY

To move within a Test Type press:
YES — To Move Forward
NO — To Move Backward

91D11885

Fig. 13: IPC System Diagnostic Flow Chart With CRT

1991 ENGINE PERFORMANCE
Self-Diagnostics – Toronado & Trofeo PCM/BCM (Cont.)

GM
1-351

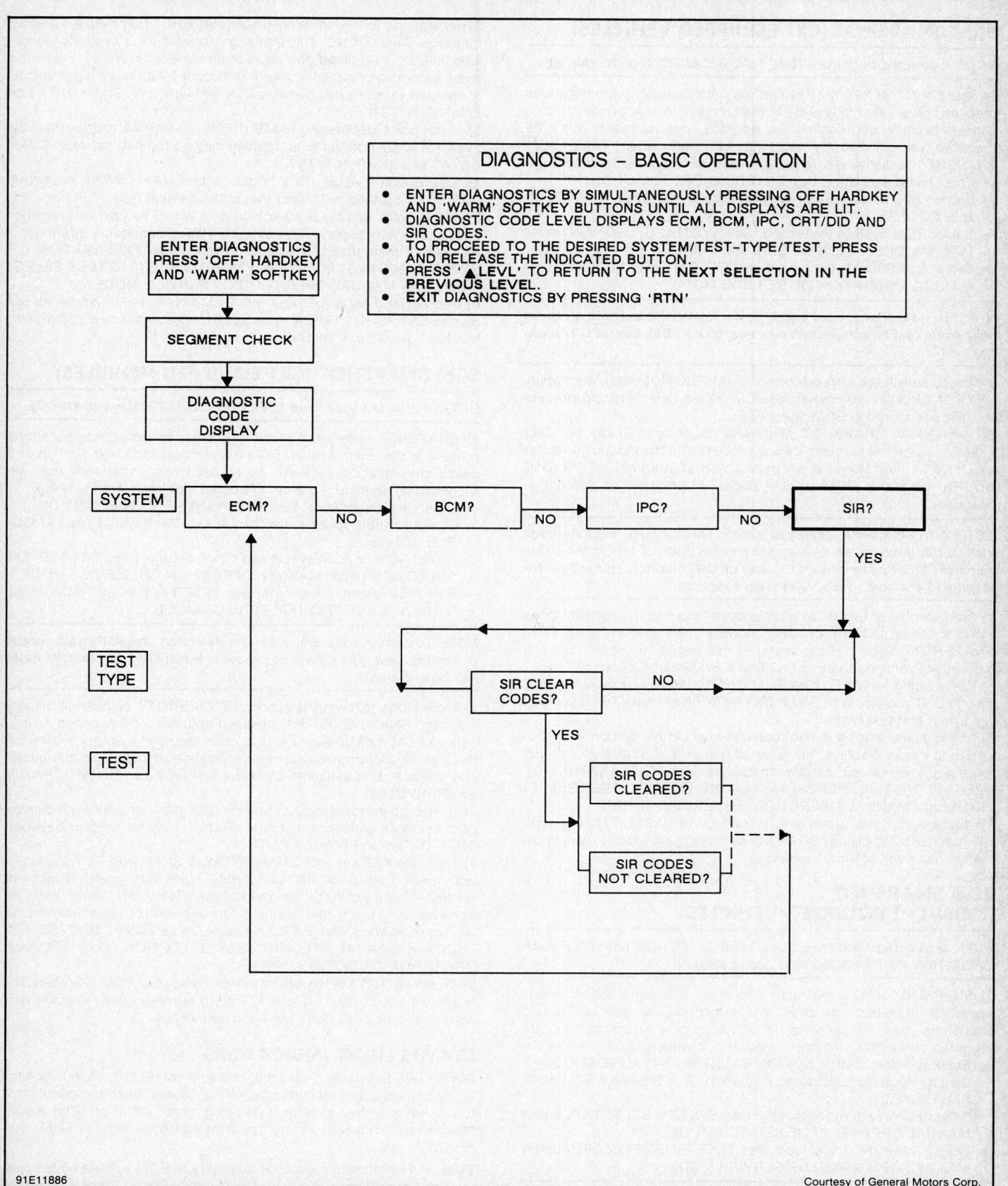

DIAGNOSTICS – BASIC OPERATION

- ENTER DIAGNOSTICS BY SIMULTANEOUSLY PRESSING OFF HARDKEY AND 'WARM' SOFTKEY BUTTONS UNTIL ALL DISPLAYS ARE LIT.
- DIAGNOSTIC CODE LEVEL DISPLAYS ECM, BCM, IPC, CRT/DID AND SIR CODES.
- TO PROCEED TO THE DESIRED SYSTEM/TEST–TYPE/TEST, PRESS AND RELEASE THE INDICATED BUTTON.
- PRESS '▲ LEVL' TO RETURN TO THE NEXT SELECTION IN THE PREVIOUS LEVEL.
- EXIT DIAGNOSTICS BY PRESSING 'RTN'

91E11886

Courtesy of General Motors Corp.

Fig. 14: SIR System Diagnostic Flow Chart With CRT

GM
1-352

1991 ENGINE PERFORMANCE
Self-Diagnostics – Toronado & Trofeo PCM/BCM (Cont.)

BCM SNAPSHOT (CRT EQUIPPED VEHICLES)

NOTE: If directed here from TEST TYPE SELECTION, go to step 2).

1) SNAPSHOT allows the recall of system operating specifications present at the exact time a BCM malfunction code was set. Up to 3 snapshots may be recalled. In addition, one snapshot may be triggered on demand by touching YES key when TAKE BCM SNAPSHOT is displayed. To enter snapshot complete the following:
- Enter self-diagnostics. See ENTERING SELF-DIAGNOSTICS.
- Display trouble codes stored in memory. See DISPLAYING TROUBLE CODES.
- Select BCM system for testing. See SYSTEM SELECTION under MANUAL OPERATION OF SERVICE MODE.
- Select SNAPSHOT test type. See TEST TYPE SELECTION under MANUAL OPERATION OF SERVICE MODE.

NOTE: To cancel snapshot test type selection and activate a repeat of specific test type selection process, touch LEVL key on CRT monitor.

2) Immediately following selection of SNAPSHOT?, system will display BXXX SNAPSHOT. "B" stands for BCM. XXX is used here to represent 3-digit code stored in BCM snapshot.
3) With BXXX SNAPSHOT displayed, touching NO key on CRT monitor will permit scrolling through list of BCM diagnostic codes for which BCM has stored a snapshot. See DISPLAYING TROUBLE CODES for list of BCM trouble codes which may be present in snapshot.

NOTE: A trouble code displayed during trouble code display cycle may not be present as a snapshot trouble code. If this is the case, exit SNAPSHOT by touching LEVL key on CRT monitor. This will return display to the next available system selection.

4) After display of last BCM trouble code for which a snapshot does exist, touching NO key on CRT monitor will result in TAKE BCM SNAPSHOT? display. Responding to this display by again touching NO key will return display to first BXXX SNAPSHOT? display.
5) Responding to TAKE BCM SNAPSHOT? display by touching YES key on CRT monitor with SNAP DATA? or SNAP INPUTS? displayed will select that test type.
6) At this point, display is controlled as it would be for non snapshot data and inputs displays; however all values and status information represent memorized vehicle conditions. See EXPLANATION OF SPECIFIC TEST SELECTION and MAKING SPECIFIC TEST SELECTION under MANUAL OPERATION OF SERVICE MODE.
7) Touching YES key again with TAKE BCM SNAPSHOT? displayed will change DIC to display SNAP DONE message to indicate new information has been stored in memory.

ECM SNAPSHOT
(NON-CRT EQUIPPED VEHICLES)

NOTE: If directed here from TEST TYPE SELECTION under MANUAL OPERATION OF SERVICE MODE, go to step 2).

1) SNAPSHOT allows the recall of system operating specifications present at the exact time an ECM malfunction code was set. Up to 3 snapshots may be recalled. In addition, one snapshot may be triggered on demand. To enter snapshot, complete the following:
- Enter self-diagnostics. See ENTERING SELF-DIAGNOSTICS.
- Display trouble codes stored in memory. See DISPLAYING TROUBLE CODES.
- Select ECM system for testing. See SYSTEM SELECTION under MANUAL OPERATION OF SERVICE MODE.
- Select SNAPSHOT test type. See TEST TYPE SELECTION under MANUAL OPERATION OF SERVICE MODE.

NOTE: To cancel snapshot test type selection and activate a repeat of specific test type selection process, depress OFF button on ECCP.

2) Immediately following selection of SNAPSHOT?, system will display message SNAP DONE. This message appears for 3 seconds to indicate all ECM data and inputs have been stored in memory. Following this 3 second information storage verification, display will automatically proceed to first available snapshot test type (i.e., SNAP DATA? or SNAP INPUTS?).
3) At this point, depressing FAN▼ (DOWN) button will display the next available snapshot test type. Display may be toggled between SNAP DATA? and SNAP INPUTS?.
4) Depressing FAN▲ (UP) button with SNAP DATA? or SNAP INPUTS? displayed will select that particular test type.
5) At this point, display is controlled as it would be for non-snapshot data and inputs displays; however, all values and status information represents memorized vehicle conditions. See EXPLANATION OF SPECIFIC TEST SELECTION and MAKING SPECIFIC TEST SELECTION under MANUAL OPERATION OF SERVICE MODE.
6) Depressing FAN▲ (UP) key with ECM SNAPSHOT? displayed will display SNAPSHOT TAKEN message to indicate that new information has been stored in memory.

ECM SNAPSHOT (CRT EQUIPPED VEHICLES)

NOTE: If directed here from TEST TYPE SELECTION, go to step 2).

1) SNAPSHOT allows the recall of system operating specifications present at the exact time an ECM malfunction code was set. Up to 3 snapshots may be recalled. In addition, one snapshot may be triggered on demand. To enter snapshot, complete the following:
- Enter self-diagnostics. See ENTERING SELF-DIAGNOSTICS.
- Display trouble codes stored in memory. See DISPLAYING TROUBLE CODES.
- Select BCM or ECM system (as desired) for testing. See SYSTEM SELECTION under MANUAL OPERATION OF SERVICE MODE.
- Select SNAPSHOT test type. See TEST TYPE SELECTION under MANUAL OPERATION OF SERVICE MODE.

NOTE: To cancel snapshot test type selection and activate a repeat of specific test type selection process, touch LEVL key on CRT monitor control panel.

2) Immediately following selection of SNAPSHOT?, system will display message SNAP DONE. This message appears for 3 seconds to indicate all ECM data and inputs have been stored in memory. Following this 3 second information storage verification, display will automatically proceed to first available snapshot test type (i.e., SNAP DATA? or SNAP INPUTS?).
3) At this point, touching NO key on CRT monitor panel will display next available snapshot test type. Display may be toggled between SNAP DATA? and SNAP INPUTS?.
4) Touching YES key with SNAP DATA? or SNAP INPUTS? displayed will select that particular test type. From this point, display is controlled as it would be for non-snapshot data and inputs displays; however, all values and status information represents memorized vehicle conditions. See EXPLANATION OF SPECIFIC TEST SELECTION and MAKING SPECIFIC TEST SELECTION under MANUAL OPERATION OF SERVICE MODE.
5) Touching YES key on CRT monitor panel with ECM SNAPSHOT? displayed will display SNAPSHOT TAKEN message to indicate that new information has been stored in memory.

STATUS LIGHT INDICATORS

During self-diagnostics, status light display on ECCP or CRT monitor is used to indicate switchable parameter status. Each parameter status is indicated by its status light being turned on or off. Status light indicators are relative to system level being tested (BCM or ECM). *See Fig. 15.*

ECM – The following is a brief summary of ECM system status light indicator operation.
- LOOP light (CRT equipped) or HIGH light (ECCP equipped) is on when ECM is in closed loop fuel control. Light comes on only after coolant and O_2 sensors reach operating temperature.

1991 ENGINE PERFORMANCE
Self-Diagnostics – Toronado & Trofeo PCM/BCM (Cont.)

GM
1-353

- TCC light (CRT equipped) or MED light (ECCP equipped) only indicates whether operation is enabled or disabled by ECM. Actual working operation depends on TCC system being in working order.
- OXY light (CRT equipped) or LOW light (ECCP equipped) stays on when oxygen sensor signals rich exhaust condition to ECM. Light will flash on and off during warm engine, steady throttle, and proper fuel mix condition.
- 4th Gear light (CRT equipped) or OFF light (ECCP equipped) will be on when ECM senses 4th gear pressure switch open. Light should only be on in 4th gear.
- 3rd Gear light (CRT equipped) or AUTO light (ECCP equipped) will be on when ECM senses 3th gear pressure switch open. Light should only be on in 3rd or 4th gear.
- 2nd Gear light (CRT equipped) or "°C" light (ECCP equipped) will be on when ECM senses 2nd gear pressure switch open. Light should only be on in 2nd, 3rd or 4th gear.
- A/C Compressor Command UPPER ARROW (ECCP equipped) or COMP light (CRT equipped) will be on only when ECM allows A/C clutch engagement through A/C relay. Light will also be on if BCM requests ECM to turn clutch on during test sequence. Light should be off if ECM commands disengagement.

- MED light (ECCP equipped) or A/C light (CRT equipped) will be on when BCM commands air flow out A/C vents. Light should also be on in A/C and BI/LEVEL modes.
- AIR UP light (CRT equipped) or LOW light (ECCP equipped) will be on when BCM commands air flow out defroster outlets. Light should also be on in defrost and A/C modes.
- AIR DOWN light (CRT equipped) or HIGH light (ECCP equipped) will be on when BCM commands air flow out floor outlets. Light should be on in heater mode.
- Left side AUTO light (ECCP equipped) or COMP light (CRT equipped) will be on when BCM requests ECM to engage A/C compressor clutch.

DATA DISPLAY CODES

Brief summary of each DATA parameter is as follows:

ECM DATA PARAMETERS:

ED01 – Throttle position (TPS) displayed in percent from 0 to 100.

ED04 – Coolant temperature (COOLANT TP) displayed in degrees Celsius (°C) from –40 to 151.

ED06 – Injector pulse width (MS INJ PW) displayed in milliseconds (ms) from 0 to 100.2.

ED07 – Oxygen sensor voltage (OXY SENSOR) displayed in volts from 0 to 1.14.

ED08 – Spark advance (DEG SPARK) displayed in degrees from 0 to 70, similar to engine timing in degrees.

ED10 – Battery voltage (BATT VOLTS) read in volts from 0 to 25.5.

ED11 - Engine speed (RPM) displayed in RPM from 0 to 6375.

ED12 - Vehicle speed (MPH) displayed in miles per hour from 0 to 159.

ED16 - Knock retard (SPK ANGLE) displayed in degrees of timing pulled out from 0 to 45.

ED17 - Knock sensor activity (OLD PA3) displayed as counts, an arbitrary number that increases from 0 to 9999 according to amount of activity from knock sensor.

ED18 - Oxygen sensor cross counts (CROSS CTS) displayed as number of times O_2 sensor crossed reference line each second.

ED19 - Fuel integrator (INT FUEL) displayed in counts from 0 to 255.

ED20 - Block learn multiplier (BLM FUEL) displayed in counts from 0 to 255.

ED21 - Mass airflow (AIR FLOW) sensor displayed in grams per second of air flow from 0 to 255.

ED22 - Idle air control (IAC MOTOR) displayed in steps of travel from 0 to 255.

ED23 - Manifold air temperature (MAT) displayed in degrees (°C) from –40 to 152.

ED24 - Command RPM for idle speed is displayed in RPM from 500 to 2000.

ED25 - Canister purge delay is displayed in percent from zero to 100.

ED26 - Air/fuel ratio is displayed in percent from 6 to 18.

ED27 - Weak cylinder display displays the number of the weak cylinder.

ED28 - Cruise servo position is displayed in percent from zero to 100.

ED29 - Cruise set speed is displayed in KPH from 20 to 120.

ED30 - Torque converter clutch duty cycle is displayed in percent from zero to 100. Zero indicates clutch is not engaged.

ED31 - PRNDL status is displayed in a 4-digit binary number as follows:

P=0110		D=0000
R=0011		2=0101
N=1010		1=1100
D=1001		

ED98 - Ignition cycle counter (IGN CYCLES) value is number of times the ignition has been cycled to off since ECM trouble code was last detected. After 50 ignition cycles (key OFF, ON, OFF is one cycle) without any malfunctions being detected, all stored ECM codes are cleared.

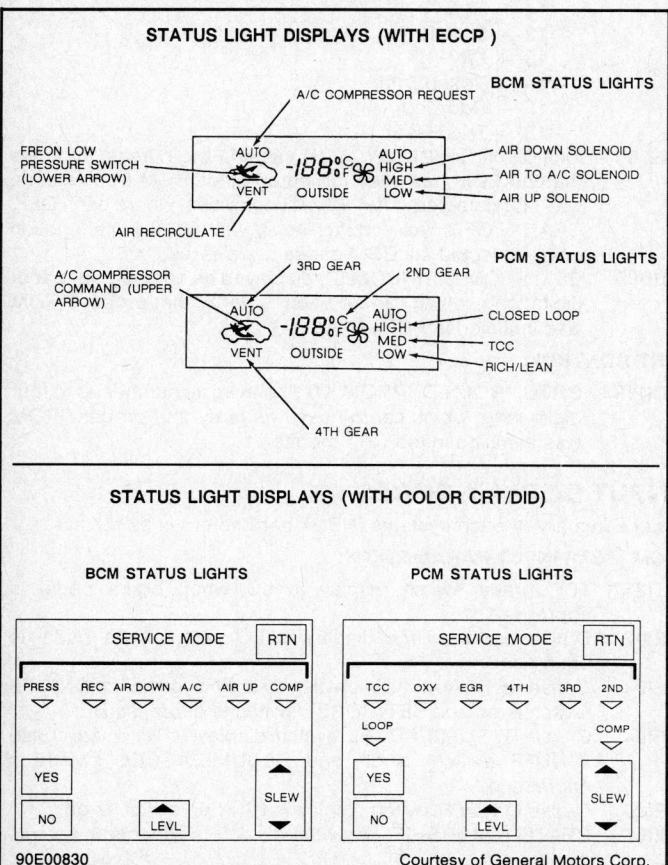

STATUS LIGHT DISPLAYS (WITH ECCP)

BCM STATUS LIGHTS

A/C COMPRESSOR REQUEST

FREON LOW PRESSURE SWITCH (LOWER ARROW)

AIR RECIRCULATE

AUTO — AIR DOWN SOLENOID
AUTO HIGH MED LOW — AIR TO A/C SOLENOID
VENT OUTSIDE — AIR UP SOLENOID
-188°C °F

PCM STATUS LIGHTS

A/C COMPRESSOR COMMAND (UPPER ARROW)

3RD GEAR   2ND GEAR

AUTO — CLOSED LOOP
AUTO HIGH MED LOW — TCC
VENT OUTSIDE — RICH/LEAN
-188°C °F

4TH GEAR

STATUS LIGHT DISPLAYS (WITH COLOR CRT/DID)

BCM STATUS LIGHTS

SERVICE MODE					RTN
PRESS	REC	AIR DOWN	A/C	AIR UP	COMP
YES					
NO		LEVL		SLEW	

PCM STATUS LIGHTS

SERVICE MODE					RTN
TCC	OXY	EGR	4TH	3RD	2ND
LOOP					COMP
YES					
NO		LEVL		SLEW	

90E00830   Courtesy of General Motors Corp.

Fig. 15: Status Light Displays

BCM – The following is a brief summary of BCM system status light indicator operation.

- PRESS light (CRT equipped) or LOWER ARROW light (ECCP equipped) will be on if BCM senses low refrigerant pressure switch is open. Light will remain off if A/C system is fully charged and operational. (However, light will come on when outside vehicle ambient temperature is less than –5°F (–21°C), this is due to temperature-pressure relationship of R-12 refrigerant.)
- OFF light (ECCP equipped) or REC light (CRT equipped) will be on when BCM commands air recirculation.

GM
1-354

1991 ENGINE PERFORMANCE
Self-Diagnostics — Toronado & Trofeo PCM/BCM (Cont.)

ED99 - ECM PROM ID (PROM ID) displayed as number up to 4 digits long which can bee used to identify MEM-CAL installed in ECM.

BCM DATA PARAMETERS:

BD20 - Commanded blower voltage (BLWR VOLTS) read in volts from 0 to 18.0.

BD21 - Coolant temperature (COOLANT TP) displayed in degrees Celsius (°C) from –40 to 151. This value is sent from ECM to BCM. If circuit malfunctions, ECM will send BCM a "failsoft" value for display.

BD22 - Commanded air mix door position (COM MIX DR) displayed in percent. Value close to 0% represents cold air mix and value close to 100% represents warm air mix.

BD23 - Actual air mix door position (ACT MIX DR) displayed in percent. This value should follow commanded air mix door position (BD22) except when door is commanded beyond its mechanical limits of travel.

BD24 - Air delivery mode (AIR MODE) displayed as a number from 0 to 12. Each number is code which represents the following air delivery modes:

    0 – Auto-Recirc Upper outlets
    1 – Auto-outside Upper outlets
    2 – Auto-Bi-Level outlets
    3 – Auto-Heater-Defog outlets
    4 – Auto-Lower outlets
    5 – OFF
    6 – Normal purge
    7 – Cold (DEF) purge
    8 – Defog
    9 – Forced (FAN) Lower outlets
    10 – Forced (FAN) Upper outlets
    11 – Forced (FAN) Bi-level outlets
    12 – Forced (FAN) De-fog outlets

BD25 - In-car temperature (IN CAR TP) displayed in degrees Celsius (°C) from –40 to 102.

BD26 - Actual outside temperature (OUTSIDE TP) displayed in degrees Celsius (°C) from –40 to 93. This value represents actual sensor temperature and is not buffered by software.

BD27 - A/C High side temperature (HI SIDE TP) (condenser output) displayed in degrees Celsius (°C) from –40 to 215.

BD28 - A/C Low side temperature (LO SIDE TP) (evaporator input) displayed in degrees Celsius (°C) from –40 to 93.

BD32 - Sunload temperature sensor (SUN TP) displayed in degrees Celsius (°C) from –40 to 102.

BD40 - Actual fuel level (FUEL LEVEL) read in gallons between 0 and 17.0. Value represents actual sensor position and is not restricted by features used to eliminate fuel slosh affects on IPC display value.

BD41 - PRNDD21 (PRND321) displayed as four digit binary number as follows:

    P – 0110
    R – 0011
    N – 1010
    D – 1001
    D – 0000
    2 – 0101
    1 – 1100

BD42 - Dimming pot (DIM POT) displayed in percent. Value close to 0% represents maximum dimming and value close to 100% represents maximum brightness.

BD43 - Twilight delay pot (TWI POT) displayed in percent. Value close to 0% represents minimum delay time and value close to 100% represents maximum delay time.

BD44 - Twilight Photocell (TWI PHOTO) displayed in percent. Value close to 0% represents daylight and value close to 100% represents darkness.

BD50 - Battery voltage (BATT VOLTS) read in volts between 0 and 25.5.

BD51 - Generator field (GEN F TERM) displayed in percent. Value close to 0% represents minimum regulator on time and value close to 100% represents maximum regulator on time.

BD60 - Vehicle speed (MPH) displayed in miles per hour from 0 to 159.

BD61 - Engine speed (RPM) displayed in RPM from 0 to 6375.

BD71 - Oil pressure sensor (OIL PRESS) displayed in psi from 0 to 80.

BD72 - DIS KEY displays unique code (defined below) received at the BCM from switch pod for each switch held. This code is for communication between computers and DOES NOT MATCH printed numbers on keys. This parameter is on NON-CRT vehicles only.

    2 – Disp ON/OFF
    3 – System Monitor
    4 – Econ
    5 – Fuel
    6 – Range
    7 – Speed
    8 – Eng Data
    9 – Date
    10 – Dist
    11 – ETA
    12 – Elap Time
    13 – E/M
    14 – Reset/Enter
    15 – Odo/Trip
    16 – Trip Reset

BD98 - Ignition cycle (IGN CYCLES) value is the number of times that the BCM has been turned off since BCM trouble code was last detected. After 99 ignition cycles, where each OFF, CRANK, OFF cycle counts as 2, without any malfunction being detected, all BCM codes are cleared.

BD99 - BCM PROM I.D. (PROM ID) displayed as number, up to four digits long, which can be used to verify that proper PROM was installed in BCM.

CRT CONTROL:

CD99 - CRTC PROM I.D. (PROM ID) displayed as number up to four digits long, which can be used to verify that proper PROM was installed in the CRT monitor.

INPUT DISPLAY CODES

Brief summary of each systems INPUT parameters is as follows.

ECM (PCM) INPUT PARAMETERS:

EI01 - TCC brake switch display is LO when brake pedal is depressed.

EI02 - Cruise brake switch display is LO when brake pedal is depressed.

EI03 - Cruise SET/COAST switch display is HI when cruise ON/OFF switch is on and SET/COAST switch is depressed.

EI04 - Cruise RESUME/ACCEL switch display is HI when cruise ON/OFF switch is on and RESUME/ACCEL switch is depressed.

EI05 - Cruise ON/OFF switch display is HI when switch is on.

EI06 - HEATED WINDSHIELD switch display is HI when switch is on.

BCM INPUT PARAMETERS:

BI01 - PANEL LAMP switch display is LO when panel light switch is in off position.

BI02 - PARK LAMP switch display is LO when park light switch is in off position.

BI03 - Driver door ajar switch (LT DR AJAR) display is LO when drivers front door is ajar.

BI04 - Passenger door ajar switch (RT DR AJAR) display is LO when passenger's rear door is open.

BI05 - DOOR JAMB switch display is LO when any door is open.

BI06 - Door handle switch (DOOR HNDLE) display is momentarily LO when either outside door handle button is depressed.

1991 ENGINE PERFORMANCE
Self-Diagnostics – Toronado & Trofeo PCM/BCM (Cont.)

GM
1-355

BI08 - Low refrigerant pressure switch (A/C PRESS) display is LO when system is low on refrigerant.

BI09 - Washer fluid level switch (WASH FLUID) display is LO when vehicle is low on washer fluid.

BI17 - TURN SIGNAL input (BLANK DISPLAY) is HI when turn signal switch is in OFF position. When either directional is on, input will toggle between LO and HI, with bulb illuminating in HI state.

BI21 - Low brake fluid (BRK FLUID) display is LO when brake fluid is low.

BI22 - PARK BRAKE switch display is LO when parking brake is applied.

BI24 - FOGLAMP switch display is LO whenever switch is pressed.

BI25 - SEAT BELT switch display is HI when driver's seat belt is fastened.

BI51 - GENERATOR FEEDBACK (I-TERM) display is LO when there is generator problem or engine is not running.

BI78 - HEADLAMPS display is HI whenever headlight switch is on.

BI82 - TWILIGHT display is LO whenever headlight switch is on.

BI83 - HI BEAM display is LO whenever hi beam switch is on.

BI88 - LOW OIL display will be HI when engine oil level is low.

IPC INPUT PARAMETERS:

II05 - ENG/MET display is LO whenever english-metric button is pressed (CRT only).

II06 - SYS MON display is LO whenever system monitor button is pressed (CRT only).

II07 - ODO/TRIP display is LO whenever trip odometer button is pressed (CRT only).

II08 - FUEL GAUGE display is LO whenever gauge button is pressed (Digital cluster only).

II09 - TACH display is LO whenever tachometer button is pressed (Digital cluster only).

II10 - TRIP RESET display is LO whenever trip reset button is pressed (CRT only).

OUTPUT DISPLAY CODES

Brief summary of each systems OUTPUT parameters is as follows.

ECM (PCM) OUTPUT PARAMETERS:

EO00 - No outputs display will not show HI or LO . This is normal resting code where no outputs will be cycled.

EO01 - Canister purge solenoid display will be LO when solenoid is energized.

EO02 - A/C clutch display is LO when clutch is engaged.

EO03 - IAC motor display will be LO when pintle is extended and HI when it is retracted.

EO04 - Cruise control servo display will display servo position.

EO05 - #1 coolant fan relay (FAN REL 1) display is LO when coolant fan is energized.

EO06 - #2 coolant fan relay (FAN REL 2) display is LO when coolant fan is energized.

EO07 - Torque Converter Clutch display will be LO when TCC solenoid is energized.

EO08 - Torque Converter Clutch modulated solenoid display will be LO when solenoid is energized.

EO09 - Torque Converter Clutch shift solenoid A display will be LO when solenoid is energized.

EO10 - Torque Converter Clutch shift solenoid B display will be LO when solenoid is energized.

EO11 - HOT light display will be LO when light is on.

BCM OUTPUT PARAMETERS:

BO00 - CYCLE NONE will display and will not show HI or LO. This is normal resting code where no outputs will be cycled.

BO04 - Courtesy lamps (COURT LMPS) display is LO when relay is on (energized).

BO05 - Twilight relay (TWILIGHT) display is LO when relays are on (energized).

BO10 - CHIME 1 display is LO when fast chime is on (sounding).

BO11 - CHIME 2 display is LO when slow chime is on (sounding).

BO12 - DRL FG LMP display is LO when foglights (DRL) are on.

BO13 - DIS CLOCK display is LO when clock line voltage is LO.

OVERRIDE DISPLAY CODES

Brief summary of each OVERRIDE parameter is as follows.

NOTE: For CRT equipped vehicles, substitute SLEW ▲ and SLEW ▼ keys for WARM or COOL buttons in the following ECM/BCM parameters.

ECM (PCM) OVERRIDE PARAMETERS:

ES00 – The NONE display will not show any value in display area on ECCP or CRT Monitor, as no overrides are active at this point. This is normal resting code where no overrides will be controlled. This code can be used to stop override control without having to go back to system selections.

ES01 – Canister purge solenoid (CAN PURG) can be turned off (00) by pressing COOL button or turned on (99) by pressing WARM button.

ES02 – A/C RELAY can be turned off (00) by pressing COOL button or turned on (99) by pressing WARM button.

ES03 – IAC MOTOR display will show position IAC motor is being commanded to in percentage of travel. Transaxle must be in Park or Neutral. COOL button will retract motor (increasing RPM) and WARM button will extend motor (decreasing RPM).

ES04 – Cruise control servo switch must be on for this test to work. This manual override allows by-passing of the cruise control automatic calculation function. Cruise control position can be controlled by percentage from zero to 99. This allows technician to compare requested cruise position with cruise servo position (BD70). The 2 should agree with each other within 3 percent. Since this test is not allowed with engine running, there is only enough vacuum available to stroke servo one time. Pressing WARM button will increase cruise percentage and pressing COOL button will decrease cruise percentage.

ES05 – Cooling fan relay No. 1 (FAN REL 1) can be turned off (00) by pressing COOL button or turned on (99) by pressing WARM button.

ES06 – Cooling fan relay No. 2 (FAN REL 2) can be turned off (00) by pressing COOL button or turned on (99) by pressing WARM button.

ES07 – TCC solenoid (TCC SOL) display will show commanded state of TCC solenoid ("00" – not engaged, "99" – engaged). Pressing WARM button will engage TCC and pressing COOL button will disengage TCC. Vehicle must be in 3rd or 4th gear for override to operate.

ES08 – This override places transmission in current gear selected and remains in that gear until COOL (downshift) or WARM (upshift) button is depressed to change gear selection. ECM will allow 1st gear only up to 35 MPH, 2nd gear up to 50 MPH and 3rd gear up to 60 MPH.

ES09 – Injector control override (INJECTOR) will work only when transaxle is in Park or Neutral. When entering override, display will show "0", all injectors will be working normally. WARM button will increment display by 1, up to 6, and then return to "0". Display number indicates cylinder injector number that is being held off. Injector will continue to be held off until COOL button is used to turn injector back on. COOL button is used to toggle on and off.

GM
1-356

1991 ENGINE PERFORMANCE
Self-Diagnostics – Toronado & Trofeo PCM/BCM (Cont.)

BCM OVERRIDE PARAMETERS:

BS00 – The NONE display will not show any value in display area on ECCP or CRT Monitor, as no overrides are active at this point. This is normal resting code where no overrides will be controlled. This code can be used to stop override control without having to go back to system selections.

BS01 – PROGRAM NUMBER – As heating and A/C operating conditions change, program number will automatically change. Program number can be manually overridden using WARM and COOL buttons. WARM button will increase number at controlled rate until MAX HEAT mode value of "99" is reached. COOL button will decrease number at controlled rate until MAX A/C mode value of "0" is reached. Manual override will continue until override code is canceled. This manual override control allows technician to alter and observe reactions of system change on other BCM data parameters.

BS03 – BULB DIM – As dimming switch position is moved, incandescent dimming number will automatically change (only if exterior lights are on). Using override controls, WARM and COOL buttons, automatic dimming can be manually controlled. Using "99" to represent maximum brightness and "0" to represent maximum dimming of incandescent lighting, (exterior lights need not be on when overriding dimming).

BS06 – BLOWER SPEED – WARM button will override control of HVAC blower to full speed (99 representing maximum blower) and COOL button will slow blower to minimum speed (0 representing blower off).

BS07 – OPTION CONTENT No. 1 – Option content No. 1 (OPTION 1) displayed as number from 0 to 255. Each number is a code which represents option content. BCM uses this value to determine how to operate the displays and electronic controls. Incorrect option values cause many different problems. To determine proper option value add up following options that vehicle is equipped with:
- U.S. vehicle (not Canadian or export model) – 128
- Heated windshield – 64
- Export displays (export car, option code NM8) – 32
- Analog cluster – 16
- Oil pressure sensor – 8
- Compass (option code UC3) – 4
- CD player – 1

Take total of actual options from above list and compare it with OPTION 1 value. If the 2 are different, correct OPTION 1 value using following procedure.

To change option content number press WARM or COOL button for override control until desired number appears, (corresponding to total of actual options). Next, press and hold LOWER air mode and DEF buttons simultaneously for 5 seconds, (CRT equipped vehicles use DEFRST and R.DEFG keys). This will reprogram BCM EEPROM to number of options displayed on the IPC.

BS08 – OPTION CONTENT No. 2 (OPTION 2) is displayed as number from 0 to 255. Each number is a code which represents option content. BCM uses this value to determine how to operate the displays and electronic controls. Incorrect option values cause many different problems. To determine proper option value add up following options that vehicle is equipped with:
- CRT/DID option – 128
- Oil level sensor (all vehicles) – 64
- Washer fluid level sensor (all vehicles) – 8
- Trofeo model – 4

Take total of actual options from above list and compare it with OPTION 2 value. If the two are different, correct OPTION 2 value using following procedure.

To change option content number press WARM or COOL button for override control until desired number appears, (number corresponding to total of actual options) Next, press and hold both LOWER air mode and DEF buttons for 5 seconds, (CRT equipped vehicles use DEFRST and R.DEFG keys). This will reprogram BCM EEPROM to number of options displayed on the IPC.

1991 ENGINE PERFORMANCE
Self-Diagnostics – Toronado & Trofeo PCM/BCM (Cont.)

GM
1-357

DISPLAY HEAD DIAGNOSTIC FLOW CHARTS

NOTE: The Electronic Control Module (ECM) may be referred to as the Powertrain Control Module (PCM) in diagnostic charts and figures. The 2 terms may be used interchangeably.

CHART A-1, NO SERVICE ENGINE SOON LIGHT

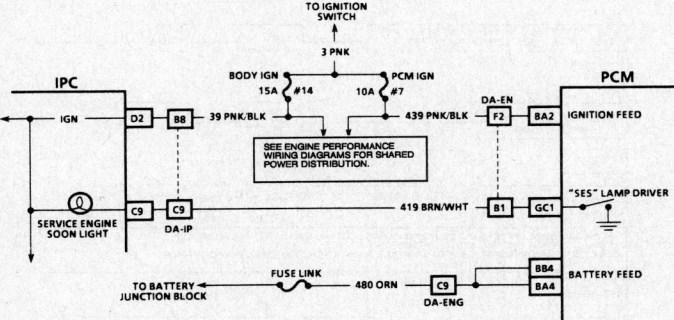

The SERVICE ENGINE SOON light is located in the IPC. Light is powered by Ignition 1, circuit No. 39 and PCM completes system ground to turn light on. With ignition on and engine not running, light should be on. If with engine running, light is on steady, this indicates a fault code is set.

NOTE: Test numbers refer to numbers on diagnostic chart.

1) SERVICE ENGINE SOON light should be on.
2) Using a test light connected to battery voltage, probe each of the system ground circuits to be sure a good ground is present. See WIRING DIAGRAMS in ENGINE PERFORMANCE to identify system ground circuits.

91F11887 91G11888

DIAGNOSTIC AIDS

If engine runs okay, check:
- Faulty light bulb.
- PCM drive circuit open.
- 15-amp BODY IGN fuse open.

If engine cranks, but will not run:
- Continuous battery-fusible link open.
- Ignition feed to PCM open.
- Open fuse No. 7 bad.
- Poor connection to PCM.

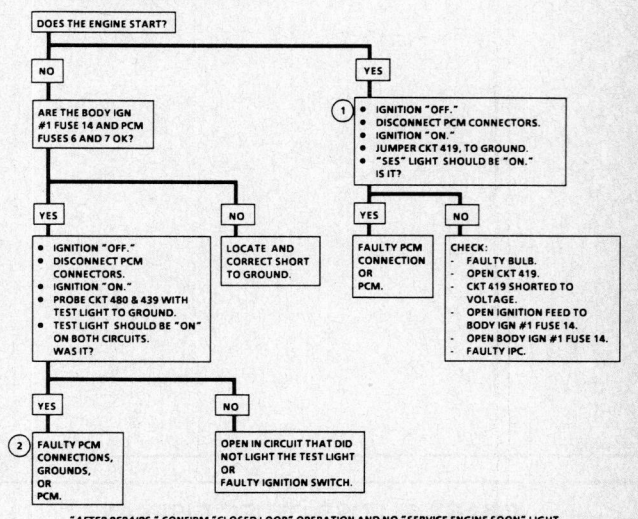

"*AFTER REPAIRS*," CONFIRM "CLOSED LOOP" OPERATION AND NO "SERVICE ENGINE SOON" LIGHT.

Courtesy of General Motors Corp.

CHART A-2, SERVICE ENGINE SOON LIGHT WILL NOT GO OUT OR FLASH

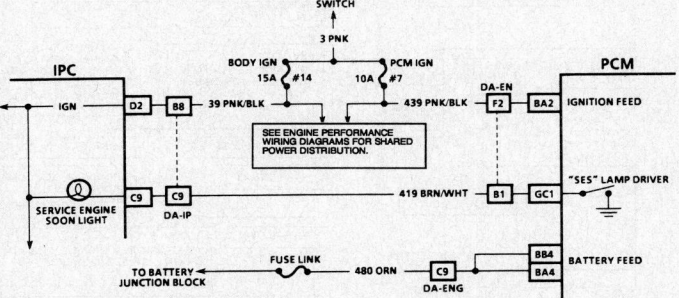

The SERVICE ENGINE SOON light is attached to the IPC. It is powered by circuit No. 39. PCM completes the ground to turn the light on. The light will be on while engine is not running. With the engine running, a steady light indicates a fault code is set

NOTE: Test numbers refer to numbers on diagnostic chart.

1) If the light goes off when PCM connector is unplugged, PCM drive circuit is not shorted to ground.
2) If there is a problem with PCM that causes a "Scan" tester to not read serial data, PCM should not flash Code 12. If Code 12 does flash, be sure that the tester is working properly by trying it on another vehicle. If tester is working properly and circuit No. 800 is okay, MEM-CAL or PCM or another component which uses the serial data line may be at fault for the NO ALDL problem.
3) This step will check for an open diagnostic circuit No. 451 (terminal "B" of ALDL).
4) At this point, SERVICE ENGINE SOON light wiring is okay. The problem is a faulty PCM or MEM-CAL. If Code 12 does not flash, PCM should

be replaced using original MEM-CAL. Replace MEM-CAL only after trying a PCM, as a defective MEM-CAL is an unlikely cause of the problem.

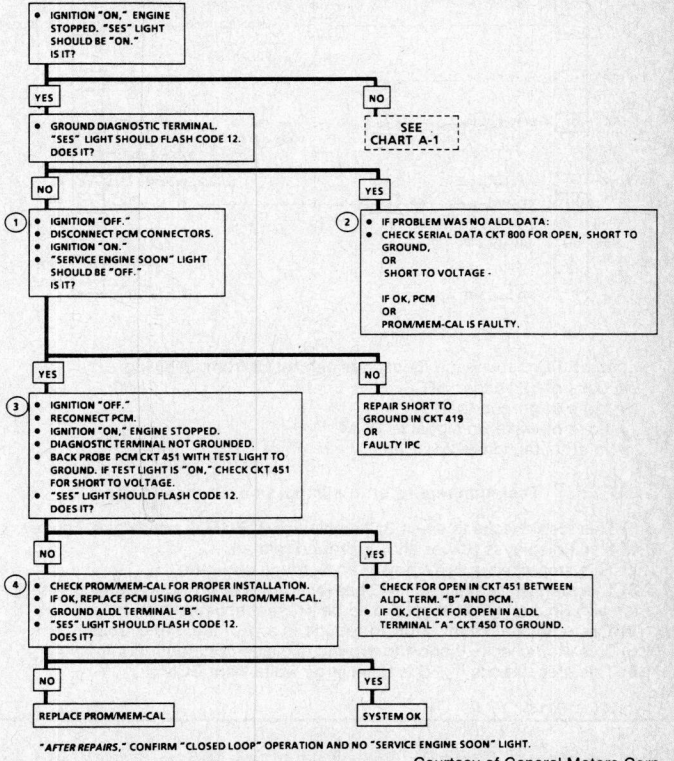

"*AFTER REPAIRS*," CONFIRM "CLOSED LOOP" OPERATION AND NO "SERVICE ENGINE SOON" LIGHT.

91F11887 91H11889

Courtesy of General Motors Corp.

SELF-DIAGNOSTIC SYSTEM CHECK
(NON-CRT EQUIPPED)

The Self-Diagnostic System Check is an organized approach for identifying problems caused by on-vehicle computer controlled electronics. Understanding this chart and using it correctly will reduce diagnostic time and prevent unnecessary replacement of components. If you have not reviewed the basic information on how to use computer self-diagnostics, go to beginning of this article.

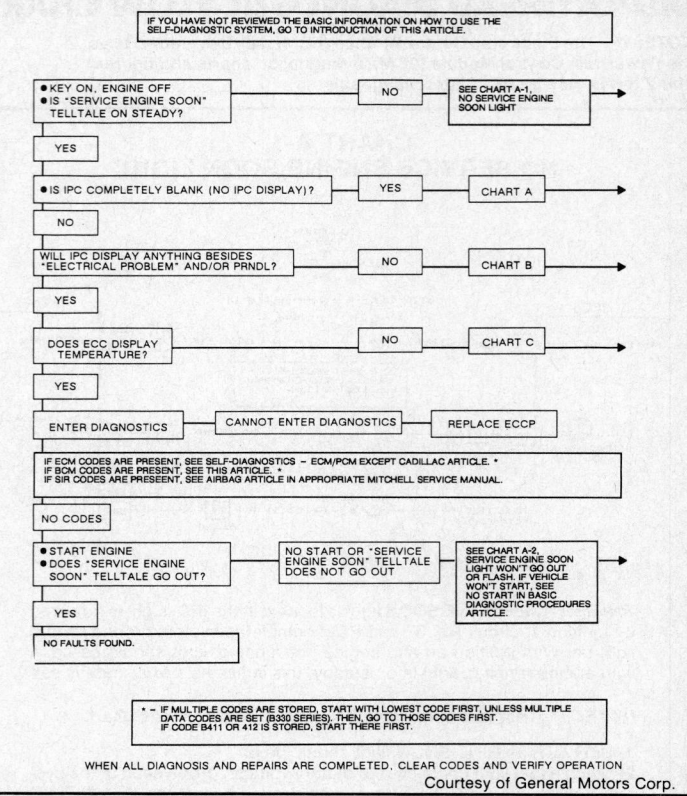

IF YOU HAVE NOT REVIEWED THE BASIC INFORMATION ON HOW TO USE THE SELF-DIAGNOSTIC SYSTEM, GO TO INTRODUCTION OF THIS ARTICLE.

- KEY ON, ENGINE OFF
- IS "SERVICE ENGINE SOON" TELLTALE ON STEADY? — NO → SEE CHART A-1, NO SERVICE ENGINE SOON LIGHT

YES

- IS IPC COMPLETELY BLANK (NO IPC DISPLAY)? — YES → CHART A

NO

- WILL IPC DISPLAY ANYTHING BESIDES "ELECTRICAL PROBLEM" AND/OR PRNDL? — NO → CHART B

YES

- DOES ECC DISPLAY TEMPERATURE? — NO → CHART C

YES

ENTER DIAGNOSTICS — CANNOT ENTER DIAGNOSTICS — REPLACE ECCP

IF ECM CODES ARE PRESENT, SEE SELF-DIAGNOSTICS – ECM/PCM EXCEPT CADILLAC ARTICLE. •
IF BCM CODES ARE PRESENT, SEE THIS ARTICLE. •
IF SIR CODES ARE PRESENT, SEE AIRBAG ARTICLE IN APPROPRIATE MITCHELL SERVICE MANUAL.

NO CODES

- START ENGINE
- DOES "SERVICE ENGINE SOON" TELLTALE GO OUT? — NO START OR "SERVICE ENGINE SOON" TELLTALE DOES NOT GO OUT → SEE CHART A-2, SERVICE ENGINE SOON LIGHT WON'T GO OUT OR FLASH. IF VEHICLE WON'T START, SEE NO START IN BASIC DIAGNOSTIC PROCEDURES ARTICLE.

YES

NO FAULTS FOUND.

• – IF MULTIPLE CODES ARE STORED, START WITH LOWEST CODE FIRST, UNLESS MULTIPLE DATA CODES ARE SET (B330 SERIES). THEN, GO TO THOSE CODES FIRST. IF CODE B411 OR 412 IS STORED, START THERE FIRST.

WHEN ALL DIAGNOSIS AND REPAIRS ARE COMPLETED, CLEAR CODES AND VERIFY OPERATION

90I13928

Courtesy of General Motors Corp.

CHART A, LOSS OF IPC DISPLAY
(NON-CRT EQUIPPED)

IF YOU HAVE NOT PERFORMED THE 'SELF-DIAGNOSTIC SYSTEM CHECK', START THERE FIRST

IPC / **BCM**

WAKE-UP	C3	DA-IP D7	555 DK BLU/WHT	1D16	IPC WAKE-UP
WAKE-UP	D3		TO IGN SW 10A IGN OFF (11)		
IGN OFF	C2	343 WHT/BLK — B5 C201	343 WHT/BLK	2A7	IGN
IGN	D2	39 PNK/BLK — B8	15A 806 PPL/WHT BODY IGN (14)	1C14	CRANK
			TO CRK FUSE (16)		
BATTERY	C1	640 ORN	DA-IP C201 E13	640 ORN	1C8	BATTERY
BATTERY	D1	640 ORN	10A ELECTRONICS BATTERY (5)	640 ORN	1C9	BATTERY
GND (LAMP)	C15	804 BLK				
GND (PWR)	C16				2B1	GND
GND (PWR)	D16	803 BLK/WHT	803 BLK/WHT	2B2	GND

① - MOVE PANEL LAMP DIMMING TO MAX INTENSITY
- DO THE COURTESY LIGHTS OPERATE?

YES → ③
- KEY ON
- CONNECT DVM BETWEEN IPC CONN CAVITY C16 AND CAVITIES C1, D1, D2, AND C2
- NOTE VOLTAGE

NO → ②
- KEY ON
- BACKPROBE VOLTAGE BETWEEN BCM PINS 1C8 AND 2B1

LESS THAN OR EQUAL TO 10 VOLTS
- KEY ON
- BACKPROBE VOLTAGE BETWEEN BCM PINS 1C8 AND GROUND

GREATER THAN 10 VOLTS
- ENSURE GOOD TERMINAL CONTACT AT BCM 1C8, 1C9, 2B1 AND 2B2
- IF GOOD CONTACT REPLACE BCM

10 VOLTS OR LESS → CHECK FUSE #5

MORE THAN 10 VOLTS → REPAIR OPEN IN BCM GROUND CKT 803

FUSE 5 BLOWN
- FUSE 5 OK
- REPAIR OPEN IN CKT 2. FUSIBLE LINK E OR BETWEEN BCM AND FUSE

ALL GREATER THAN 10 VOLTS / ALL LESS THAN 10 VOLTS / ONE LESS THAN 10 VOLTS → REPAIR CKT RELATED TO THIS CAVITY

⑥ - CONNECT DVM BETWEEN IPC CONN CAVITY C16 AND CAVITIES C3, AND D3
- NOTE VOLTAGE

REPAIR OPEN IN CKT 803

④ - REMOVE BCM CONNECTOR AND PROBE HARNESS CAVITIES (A2 OF CHIME MODULE, C1 AND D1 OF IPC AND 1C8 AND 1C9 OF BCM) WITH TEST LIGHT CONNECTED TO SYSTEM VOLTAGE
- NOTE TEST LIGHT

LIGHTS 'ON' ANY TERMINAL / LIGHTS 'OFF' ALL TERMINALS

⑤ - REMOVE CONNECTOR FROM COMPONENT IN CKT 640 WITH LIGHT 'ON'
- NOW NOTE TEST LIGHT

- CHECK FOR SHORT TO GROUND IN CKT 640
- REPLACE FUSE

ONE OR BOTH LESS THAN 10 VOLTS → CHECK VOLTAGE AT BCM PIN 1D16

ALL GREATER THAN 10 VOLTS
- CHECK FOR POOR TERMINAL CONTACT AT TERMINALS C1, C2, C3, D1, D2, D3 AND C16
- IF GOOD TERMINAL CONTACT. REPLACE IPC

LIGHTS 'ON' → REPAIR SHORT TO GROUND IN THIS BRANCH OF CKT 640

LIGHTS 'OFF' → REPLACE COMPONENT

10 VOLTS OR MORE → REPAIR CKT BETWEEN BCM AND IPC

LESS THAN 5 VOLTS
- CHECK BCM TERMINAL CONTACT
- IF GOOD CONTACT, REPLACE BCM

Loss of IPC display and messages can result from following:
- Loss of 12 volts to IPC
- Loss of ground to IPC
- Loss of wake-up signal to BCM
- Internal fault in BCM or IPC

NOTE: Test numbers refer to numbers on diagnostic chart.

1) This step checks to see if BCM is awake. If BCM is not awake, cause of blank display is power and/or ground related.
2) This step checks BCM power and ground sources.
3) This step checks to see if IPC has lost power or ground. Normally with ignition on, battery voltage should be present at listed terminals.
4) This step checks for short to ground in any of the 640 circuits.
5) This step checks if short to ground is inside component or in circuit.
6) This step checks if IPC is receiving 7 volts from BCM.

WHEN ALL DIAGNOSIS AND REPAIRS ARE COMPLETE, CLEAR CODES AND VERIFY OPERATION

91A11890 91B11891

Courtesy of General Motors Corp.

1991 ENGINE PERFORMANCE
Self-Diagnostics – Toronado & Trofeo PCM/BCM (Cont.)

GM
1-359

CHART B, LOSS OF SERIAL DATA (NON-CRT EQUIPPED)

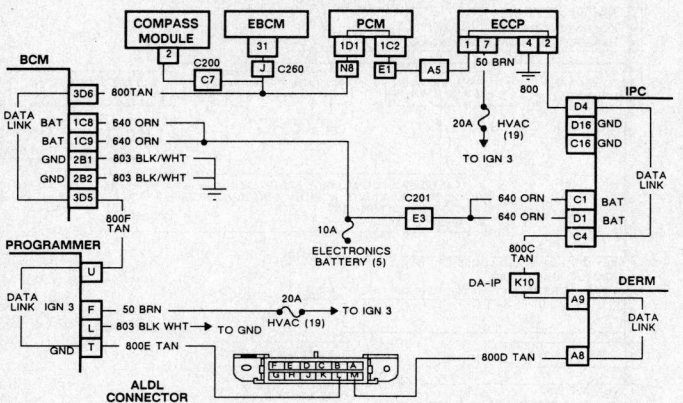

IPC indicates loss of serial data communication by displaying the message ELECTRICAL PROBLEM. All other segments are blank. If display is fully illuminated and ELECTRICAL PROBLEM message is displayed, enter diagnostics and proceed to appropriate code chart. DO NOT use CHART A. Loss of serial data communications can occur for the following reasons:

- Short to ground anywhere in circuit No. 800
- Short to voltage anywhere in circuit No. 800
- Two opens in circuit No. 800
- Internal BCM or IPC fault
- Open in ECCP ground circuit or IGN 3 circuit.

NOTE: Test numbers refer to numbers on diagnostic chart.

1) This step checks to see if ECCP has lost data communication along with IPC.

91C11892 91D11893

2) Since IPC has lost data communications, shorting terminal "M" at ALDL connector should NOT remove data communications from ECCP. If this does happen, IPC is receiving data but is unable to communicate due to poor connection or an internal problem.

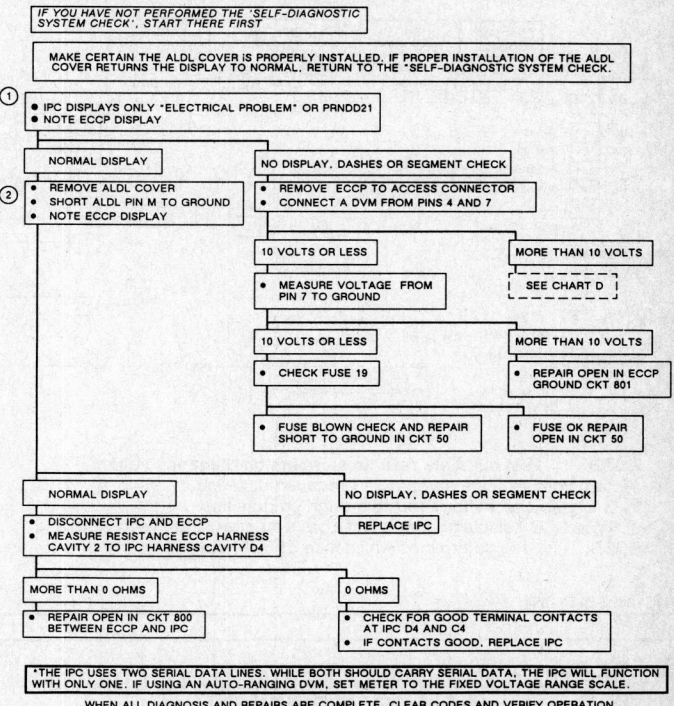

*THE IPC USES TWO SERIAL DATA LINES. WHILE BOTH SHOULD CARRY SERIAL DATA, THE IPC WILL FUNCTION WITH ONLY ONE. IF USING AN AUTO-RANGING DVM, SET METER TO THE FIXED VOLTAGE RANGE SCALE.

WHEN ALL DIAGNOSIS AND REPAIRS ARE COMPLETE, CLEAR CODES AND VERIFY OPERATION

Courtesy of General Motors Corp.

CHART C, LOSS OF ECCP COMMUNICATIONS (NON-CRT EQUIPPED)

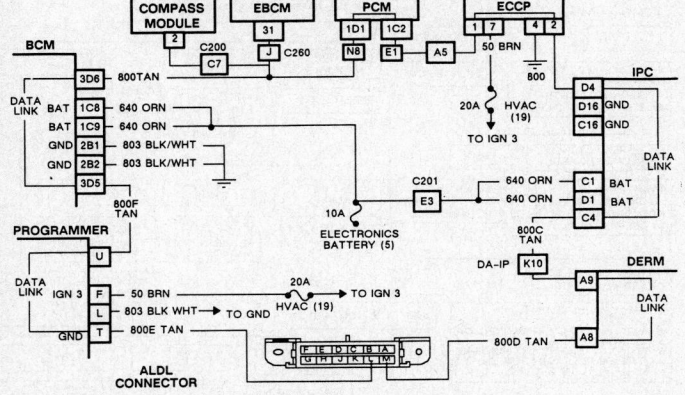

When ECCP communications are lost, service diagnostics usually cannot be entered, but a quick scan of panel will usually help isolate source of fault. ECCP is powered by ignition. If power source is lost, IPC will usually display ELECTRICAL PROBLEM. Loss of serial data will result in 3 dashes being shown on panel VF display. This indicates power and ground are okay. If the panel displays normal outside or interior set temperature, power, ground and serial communications are being received, indicating need to replace panel.

NOTE: Test numbers refer to numbers on diagnostic chart.

1) This step checks for power and ground to panel. Test light should be on for both power to ground checks.
2) This step checks for serial data voltage. Normal voltage should be above one volt and varying.

91C11892 90E13932

* SOME AUTO-RANGING DVM'S WILL NOT MEASURE SERIAL DATA LINE VOLTAGE IN AUTO MODE. WHEN USING AN AUTO-RANGING DVM USE THE FIXED VOLTAGE RANGE SCALE.

WHEN ALL DIAGNOSIS AND REPAIRS ARE COMPLETE, CLEAR CODES AND VERIFY OPERATION

Courtesy of General Motors Corp.

GM
1-360

1991 ENGINE PERFORMANCE
Self-Diagnostics – Toronado & Trofeo PCM/BCM (Cont.)

CHART D, LOSS OF COMMUNICATIONS
(NON-CRT EQUIPPED)

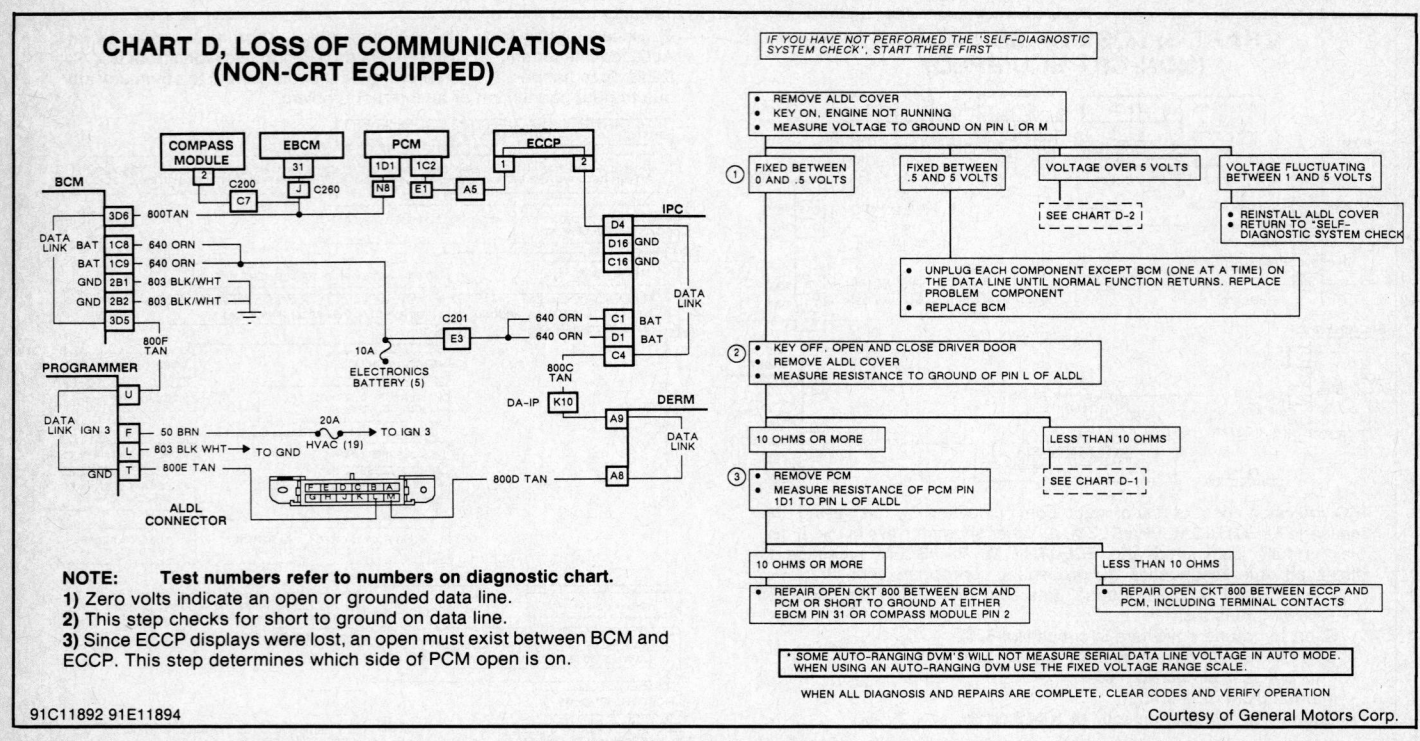

NOTE: Test numbers refer to numbers on diagnostic chart.
1) Zero volts indicate an open or grounded data line.
2) This step checks for short to ground on data line.
3) Since ECCP displays were lost, an open must exist between BCM and ECCP. This step determines which side of PCM open is on.

91C11892 91E11894

Courtesy of General Motors Corp.

CHART D-1, GROUNDED SERIAL DATA CIRCUIT
(NON-CRT EQUIPPED)

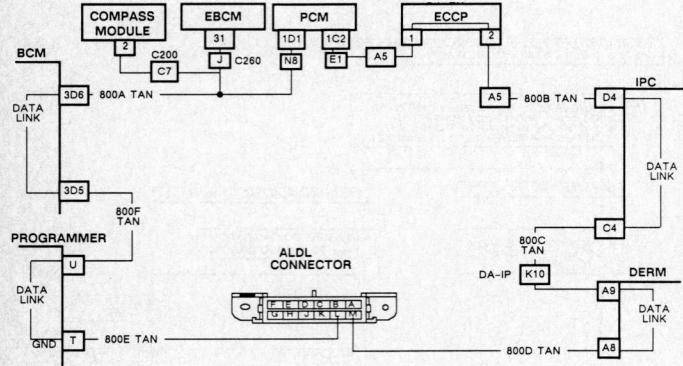

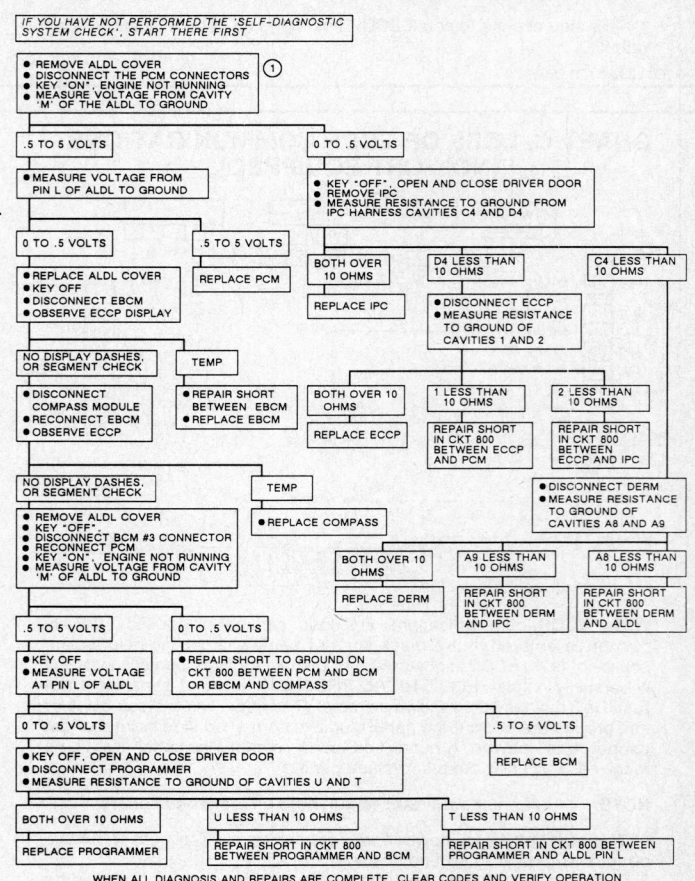

With grounded serial data circuit, BCM will not be able to communicate with any other devices in system. Voltage measured anywhere along circuit will be zero. Display on IPC will be ELECTRICAL PROBLEM and ECCP will display dashes "---".

NOTE: Test numbers refer to numbers on diagnostic chart.

1) This step splits system in half to help isolate the source of grounded serial data line. If taking PCM out of system allows both halves of serial data line to rise above one volt, the source of short has been located. The remaining steps of chart follow same pattern in that the components are removed from serial data line until normal voltage range is again measured. When section of circuit is isolated, a simple check of wire for short to ground differentiates between a grounded wire or a ground in the device.

91F11895 91G11896

Courtesy of General Motors Corp.

1991 ENGINE PERFORMANCE
Self-Diagnostics – Toronado & Trofeo PCM/BCM (Cont.)

GM
1-361

CHART D-2, SERIAL DATA CIRCUIT
SHORTED TO VOLTAGE (NON-CRT EQUIPPED)

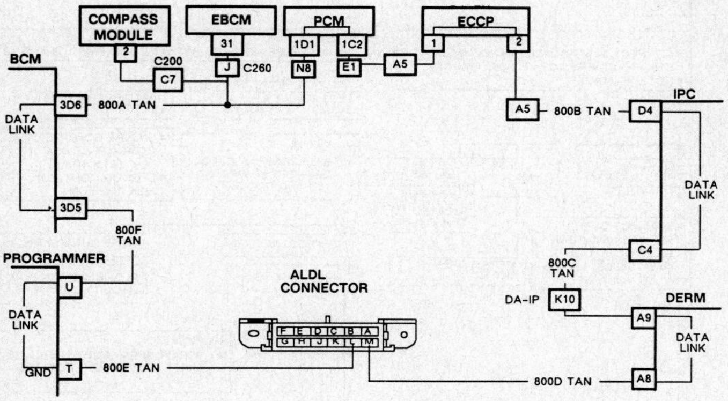

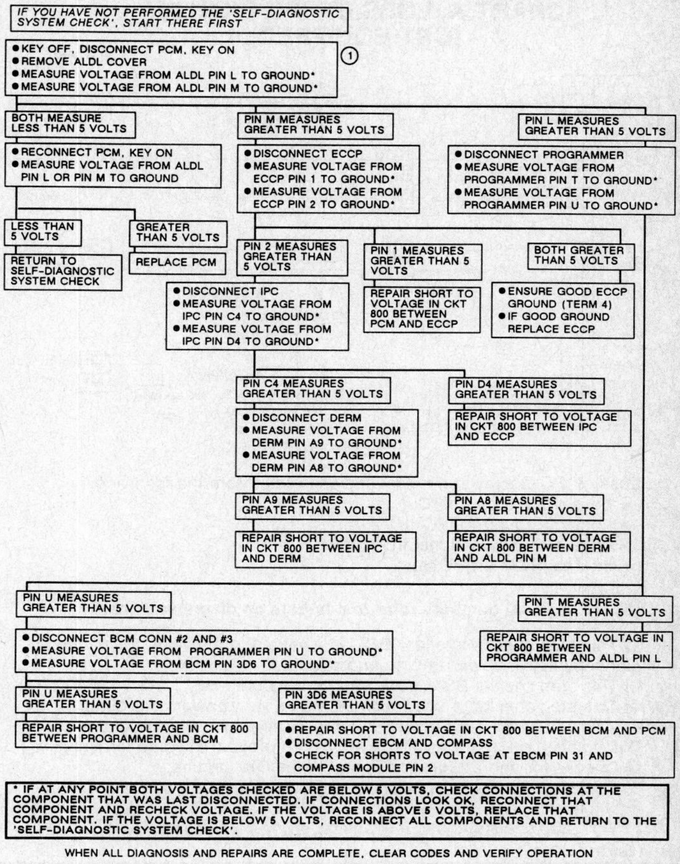

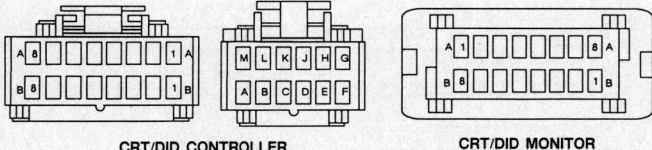

With shorted serial data circuit BCM will not be able to communicate with other devices in system. Voltage measured anywhere along circuit will be above 5 volts. IPC will display ELECTRICAL PROBLEM.

NOTE: Test numbers refer to numbers on diagnostic chart.

1) This step splits system in half to help isolate source of short in serial data line. If taking PCM out of system allows both halves of serial data line to fall below 5 volts, source of short was in PCM.
The remaining steps follow the same pattern in that components are removed from serial data line until normal voltage range is again measured.

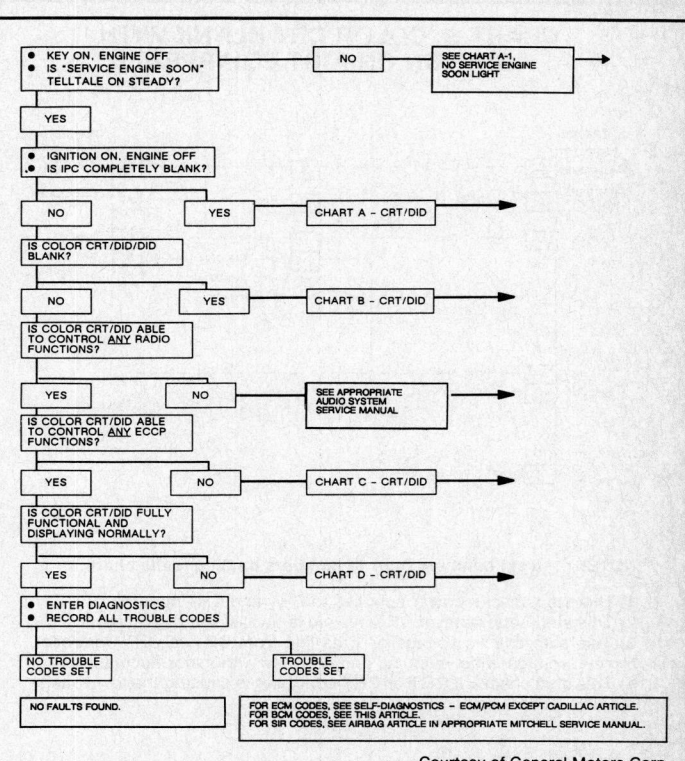

IF YOU HAVE NOT PERFORMED THE 'SELF-DIAGNOSTIC SYSTEM CHECK', START THERE FIRST

* IF AT ANY POINT BOTH VOLTAGES CHECKED ARE BELOW 5 VOLTS, CHECK CONNECTIONS AT THE COMPONENT THAT WAS LAST DISCONNECTED. IF CONNECTIONS LOOK OK, RECONNECT THAT COMPONENT AND RECHECK VOLTAGE. IF THE VOLTAGE IS ABOVE 5 VOLTS, REPLACE THAT COMPONENT. IF THE VOLTAGE IS BELOW 5 VOLTS, RECONNECT ALL COMPONENTS AND RETURN TO THE 'SELF-DIAGNOSTIC SYSTEM CHECK'.

WHEN ALL DIAGNOSIS AND REPAIRS ARE COMPLETE, CLEAR CODES AND VERIFY OPERATION

91F11895 91H11897

Courtesy of General Motors Corp.

SELF-DIAGNOSTIC SYSTEM CHECK
(CRT EQUIPPED)

CRT/DID CONNECTORS
(CAVITY VIEWS)

CRT/DID CONTROLLER
(CRTC/DIDC)

CRT/DID MONITOR
(CRTM/DIDM)

The Self-Diagnostic System Check is an organized approach for identifying problems caused by on-vehicle computer controlled electronics. Understanding this chart and using it correctly will reduce diagnostic time and prevent unnecessary replacement of components. If you have not reviewed the basic information on how to use computer self-diagnostics, go to beginning of this article.

* KEY ON, ENGINE OFF
* IS "SERVICE ENGINE SOON" TELLTALE ON STEADY?

NO → SEE CHART A-1, NO SERVICE ENGINE SOON LIGHT

YES

* IGNITION ON, ENGINE OFF
* IS IPC COMPLETELY BLANK?

NO   YES → CHART A – CRT/DID

IS COLOR CRT/DID/DID BLANK?

NO   YES → CHART B – CRT/DID

IS COLOR CRT/DID ABLE TO CONTROL ANY RADIO FUNCTIONS?

YES   NO → SEE APPROPRIATE AUDIO SYSTEM SERVICE MANUAL

IS COLOR CRT/DID ABLE TO CONTROL ANY ECCP FUNCTIONS?

YES   NO → CHART C – CRT/DID

IS COLOR CRT/DID FULLY FUNCTIONAL AND DISPLAYING NORMALLY?

YES   NO → CHART D – CRT/DID

* ENTER DIAGNOSTICS
* RECORD ALL TROUBLE CODES

NO TROUBLE CODES SET   TROUBLE CODES SET

NO FAULTS FOUND.

FOR ECM CODES, SEE SELF-DIAGNOSTICS – ECM/PCM EXCEPT CADILLAC ARTICLE.
FOR BCM CODES, SEE THIS ARTICLE.
FOR SIR CODES, SEE AIRBAG ARTICLE IN APPROPRIATE MITCHELL SERVICE MANUAL.

90I13936 90D21447

Courtesy of General Motors Corp.

GM
1-362

1991 ENGINE PERFORMANCE
Self-Diagnostics – Toronado & Trofeo PCM/BCM (Cont.)

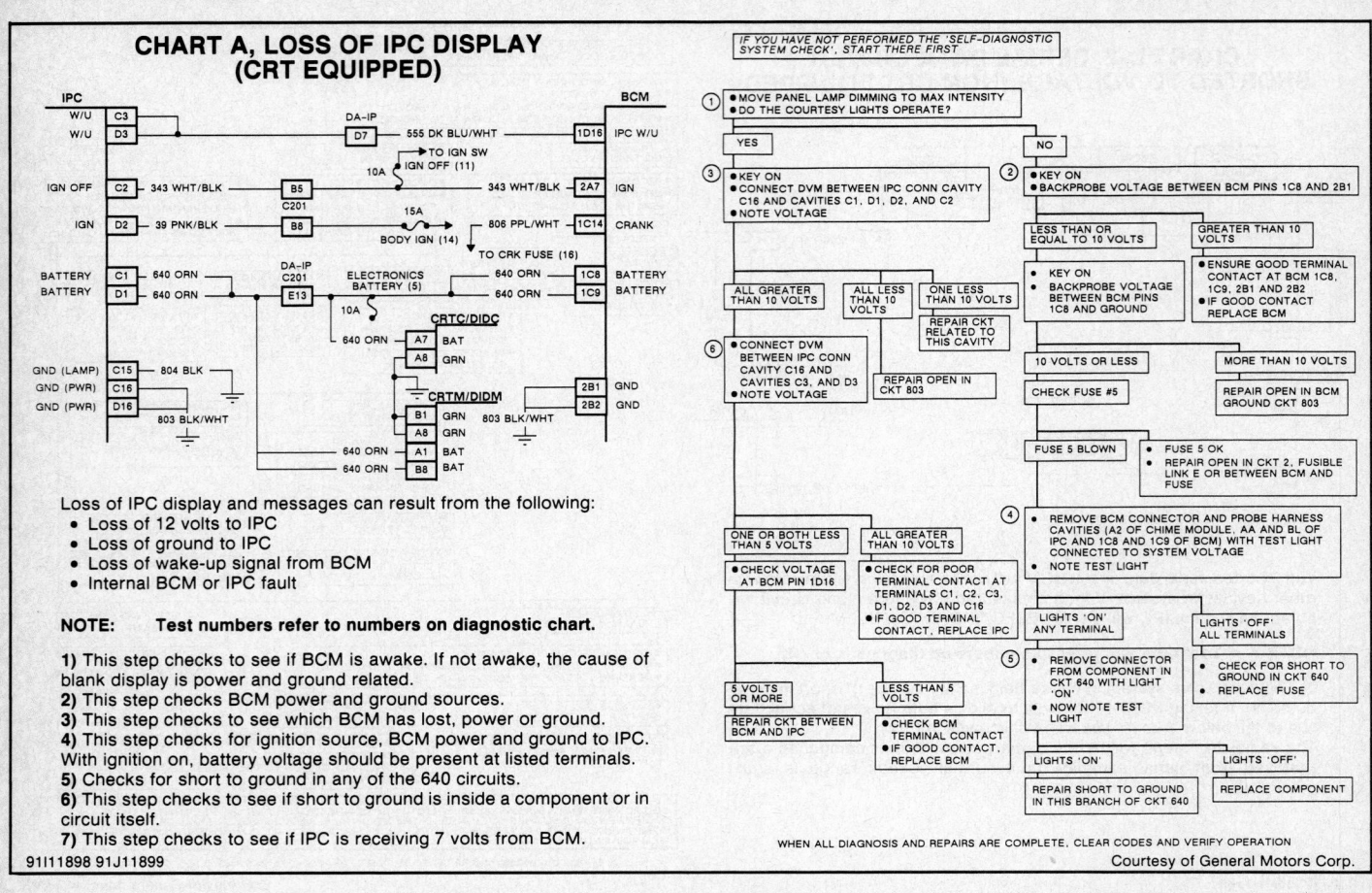

CHART A, LOSS OF IPC DISPLAY (CRT EQUIPPED)

Loss of IPC display and messages can result from the following:
- Loss of 12 volts to IPC
- Loss of ground to IPC
- Loss of wake-up signal from BCM
- Internal BCM or IPC fault

NOTE: Test numbers refer to numbers on diagnostic chart.

1) This step checks to see if BCM is awake. If not awake, the cause of blank display is power and ground related.
2) This step checks BCM power and ground sources.
3) This step checks to see which BCM has lost, power or ground.
4) This step checks for ignition source, BCM power and ground to IPC. With ignition on, battery voltage should be present at listed terminals.
5) Checks for short to ground in any of the 640 circuits.
6) This step checks to see if short to ground is inside a component or in circuit itself.
7) This step checks to see if IPC is receiving 7 volts from BCM.

91I11898 91J11899

WHEN ALL DIAGNOSIS AND REPAIRS ARE COMPLETE, CLEAR CODES AND VERIFY OPERATION

Courtesy of General Motors Corp.

CHART B, COLOR CRT BLANK WITH IGNITION ON (CRT EQUIPPED)

NOTE: Test numbers refer to numbers on diagnostic chart.

1) This step checks power supplies to CRT and CRT controller.
2) This step determines if CRT system is awake and operating.
3) This step checks voltage on data line from CRT to CRT controller. Normal voltage is between 1.5 and 4.5 volts with minor fluctuations.
4) This step checks if CRT or CRT controller is causing the low voltage reading on data line.

91C11900 91D11901

WHEN ALL DIAGNOSIS AND REPAIRS ARE COMPLETE, CLEAR CODES AND VERIFY OPERATION

Courtesy of General Motors Corp.

1991 ENGINE PERFORMANCE
Self-Diagnostics – Toronado & Trofeo PCM/BCM (Cont.)

GM
1-363

CHART C, COLOR CRT UNABLE TO CONTROL ECCP (CRT EQUIPPED)

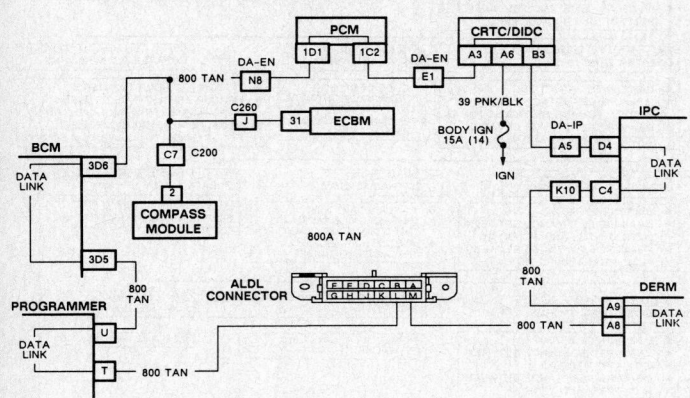

IPC indicates loss of serial data communication by displaying the message ELECTRICAL PROBLEM. All other segments are blank. If display is fully illuminated and ELECTRICAL PROBLEM message is displayed, enter diagnostics and proceed to appropriate code chart. DO NOT use CHART A. Loss of serial data communications can occur for the following reasons:

- Short to ground anywhere in circuit No. 800.
- Short to voltage anywhere in circuit No. 800.
- Two opens in circuit No. 800.
- Internal BCM or IPC fault.

NOTE: Test numbers refer to numbers on diagnostic chart.

1) If climate control page is accessible, CRTC is receiving ignition power and should be capable of communicating with BCM.
2) This step checks to see if CRTC has lost communication with BCM.
3) This step checks to see if IPC has lost communication with BCM also.
4) This step checks continuity of the data line (circuit No. 800). Since data line is a loop, resistance around it should be close to zero ohms.
5) This step checks for short to ground on data line.
6) This step checks voltage on data line under normal operating conditions. Normal data line voltage is a continual fluctuating between .1

and 5.0 volts. Voltage above 5.0 volts or non-fluctuating voltage indicates a problem in data line causing entire communications network to be inoperative.

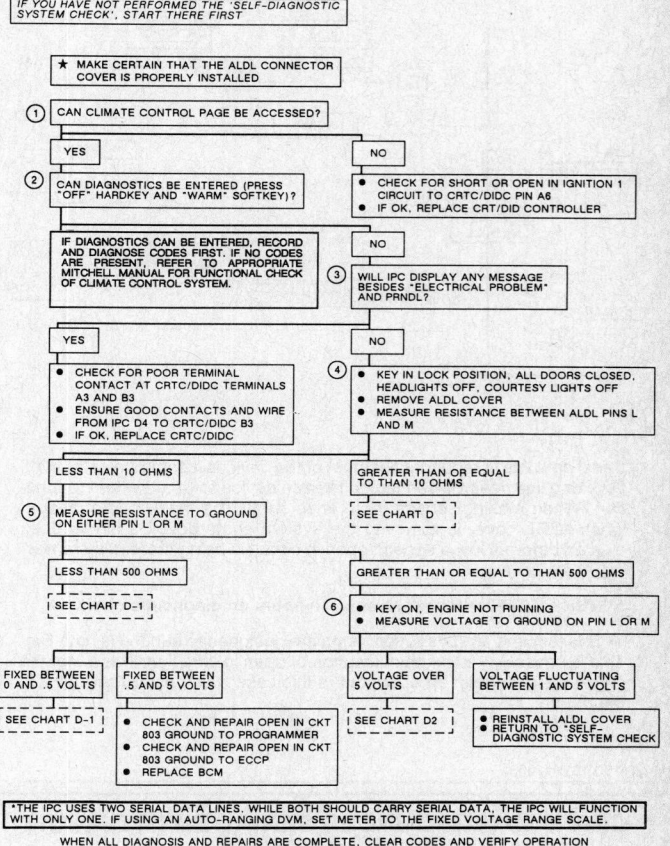

*THE IPC USES TWO SERIAL DATA LINES. WHILE BOTH SHOULD CARRY SERIAL DATA, THE IPC WILL FUNCTION WITH ONLY ONE. IF USING AN AUTO-RANGING DVM, SET METER TO THE FIXED VOLTAGE RANGE SCALE.

WHEN ALL DIAGNOSIS AND REPAIRS ARE COMPLETE, CLEAR CODES AND VERIFY OPERATION

91E11902 90E13940

Courtesy of General Motors Corp.

GM
1-364

1991 ENGINE PERFORMANCE
Self-Diagnostics – Toronado & Trofeo PCM/BCM (Cont.)

CHART D, SERIAL DATA CIRCUIT OPEN (CRT EQUIPPED)

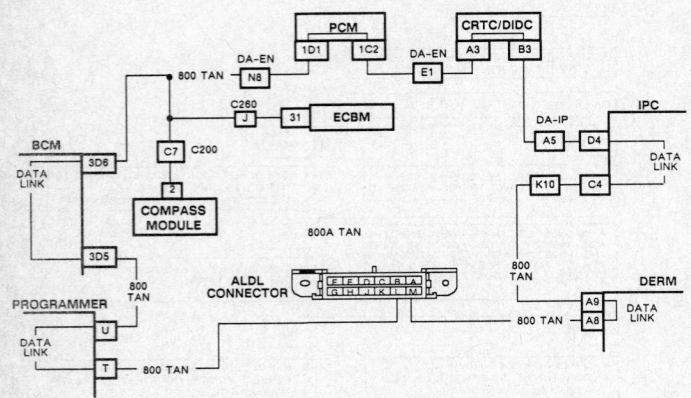

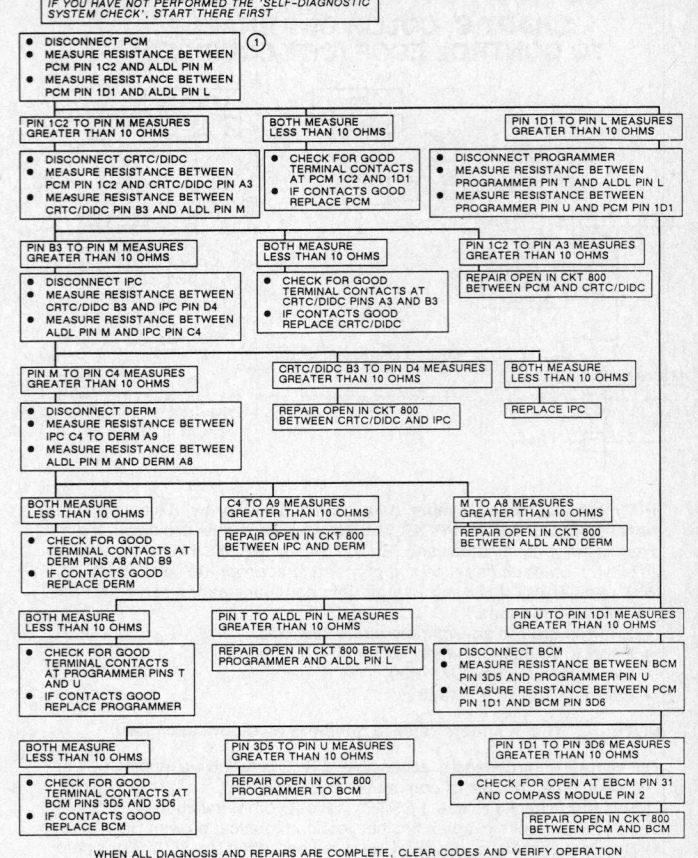

Serial data line is redundant at most of the devices it communicates with. Only one line need be connected to each device for that system to function. When making repairs, both lines should be made operational. If when ALDL cover is removed the system shuts down, a single open existed before. Now a second open in circuit is being created by removing ALDL cover.

NOTE: Test numbers refer to numbers on diagnostic chart.

1) This test and all subsequent tests are designed to subdivide data line. This is necessary to pinpoint location of open in data line. This is not the only way to pinpoint an open, but in this case, will most quickly lead to the open.

91E11902 91F11903

Courtesy of General Motors Corp.

CHART D-1, GROUNDED SERIAL DATA CIRCUIT (CRT EQUIPPED)

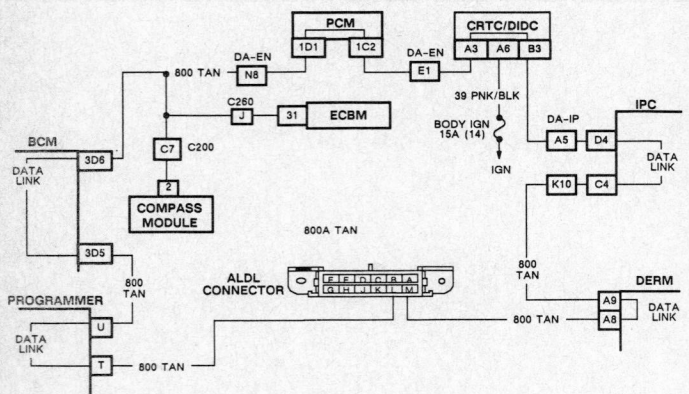

With grounded serial data circuit, BCM will not be able to communicate with any other devices in system. Voltage measured anywhere in circuit will be zero. IPC display will show ELECTRICAL PROBLEM, CRT will display normally and HVAC controls will not function.

NOTE: Test numbers refer to numbers on diagnostic chart.

1) This step splits the system in half to help isolate source of grounded serial data line. If taking PCM out of the system allows both halves of serial data line to rise above one volt, source of short has been located. The remaining steps follow same pattern in that components are removed from serial data line until normal voltage range is again measured. When section of circuit is isolated, a simple check of wire for short to ground will differentiate between grounded wire or ground in a device remote.

91E11902 91G11904

WHEN ALL DIAGNOSIS AND REPAIRS ARE COMPLETE, CLEAR CODES AND VERIFY OPERATION

Courtesy of General Motors Corp.

1991 ENGINE PERFORMANCE
Self-Diagnostics — Toronado & Trofeo PCM/BCM (Cont.)

GM
1-365

CHART D-2, SERIAL DATA CIRCUIT SHORTED TO VOLTAGE (CRT EQUIPPED)

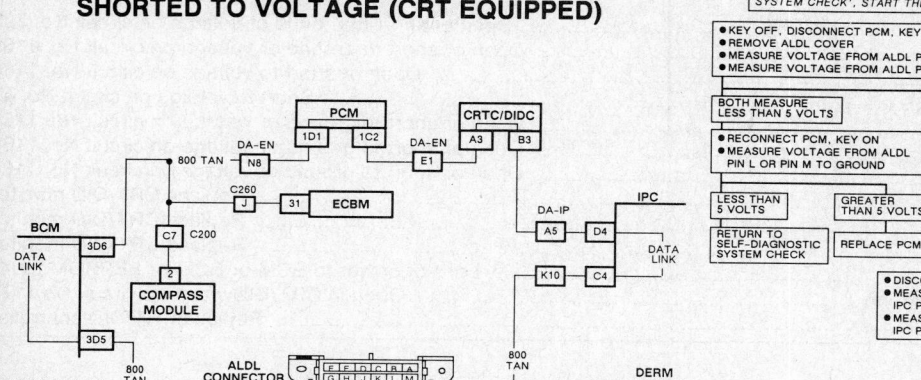

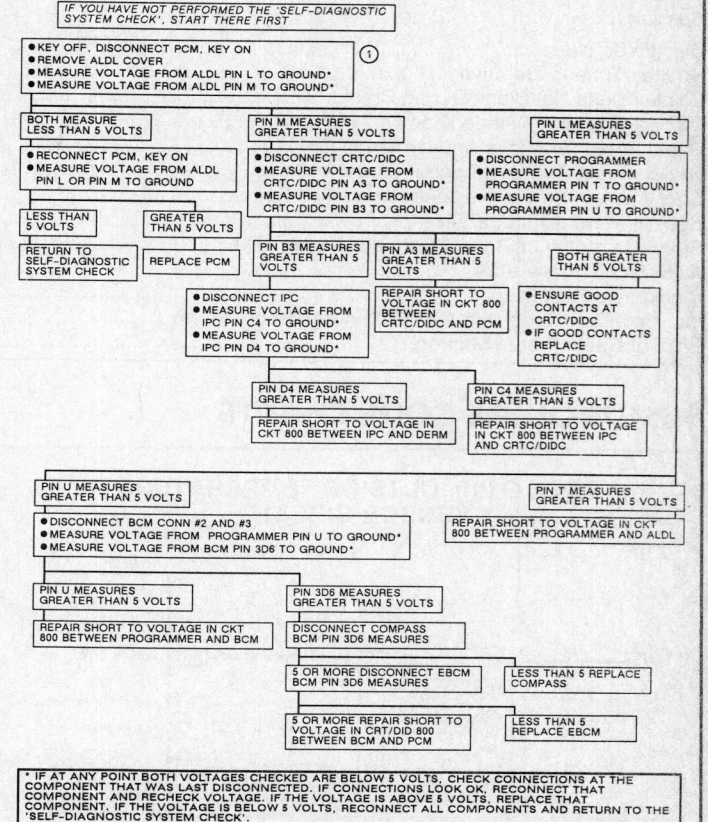

With a shorted serial data circuit, BCM will not be able to communicate with other devices in system. Voltage measured anywhere in circuit will be above 5 volts. IPC display showing only ELECTRICAL PROBLEM.

NOTE: Test numbers refer to numbers on diagnostic chart.

1) This step splits system in half to help isolate the source of short in the serial data line. If taking PCM out of system allows both halves of serial data line to fall below 5 volts, source of short was in PCM.
The remaining steps follow the same pattern in that components are removed from serial data line until normal voltage range is again measured.

91E11902 91H11905

Courtesy of General Motors Corp.

CHART E, COLOR CRT ABNORMALITIES (CRT EQUIPPED)

NOTE: If you have not performed the SELF-DIAGNOSTIC SYSTEM CHECK, start there first.

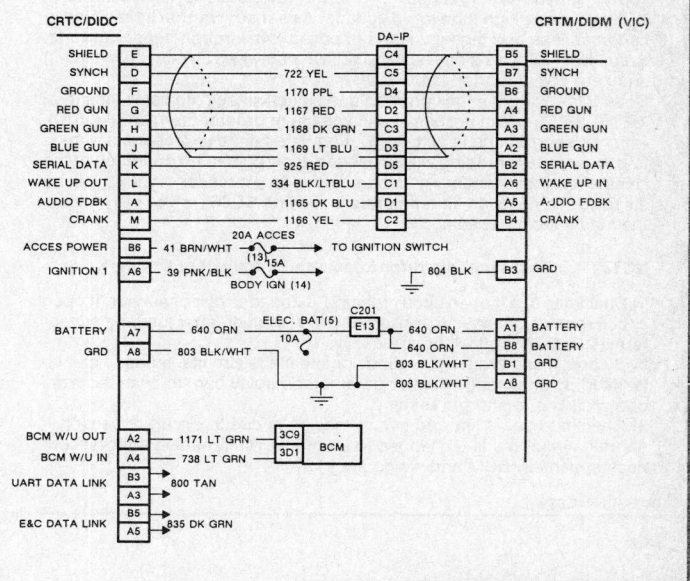

91I11906

Courtesy of General Motors Corp.

COLOR CRT/DID ABNORMALITIES

Condition	Possible Causes
Display Scrolls	Open or short to ground or voltage on circuit No. 722
Softkey Tone Inoperative	Open or short to ground or voltage on circuit No. 1165
Display Does Not Blank During Crank	Open or short to voltage on circuit No. 1166
Display Operates With Ignition Off	Short to voltage on circuit No. 41
Radio Preset Softkeys Appear Green (No Blue)	Open or short to ground or voltage on circuit No. 1169
Radio Preset Softkeys Appear Blue (No Green)	Open or short to ground or voltage on circuit No. 1168
Cool & Warm Softkeys Appear Green (No Red)	Open or short to ground or voltage on circuit No. 1167
Specific Hardkey Inoperative	Replace CRT/DID monitor
Specific Column or Row of Softkeys Inoperative	Replace CRT/DID monitor
All Softkeys Inoperative	Replace CRT/DID monitor
Clock/Date Resets	Loss of power to BCM or BCM or EEPROM faulty
Incorrect Date/Time with CRT/DID in Accessory Mode	Open in CRT/DID wake-up circuit No 1171
Loss of Radio Preset Memory	Replace CRT/DID controller

BCM TROUBLE CODE CHARTS

CODE B110, OUTSIDE TEMPERATURE SENSOR CIRCUIT

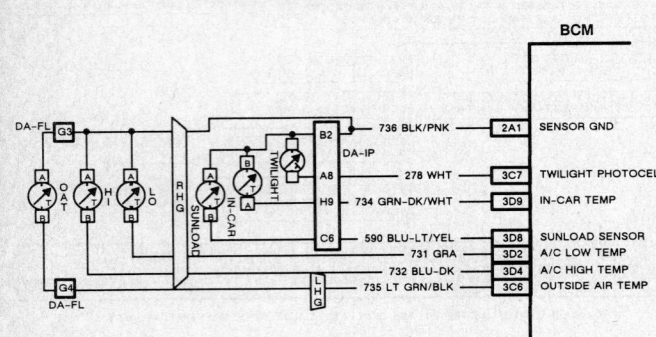

The outside air temperature sensor is a thermistor that controls signal voltage to BCM. The BCM applies and monitors voltage on circuit No. 735 to sensor. When sensor is cold, its resistance is high; therefore, BCM will see a high monitored voltage. As sensor warms, its resistance becomes less and signal voltage is pulled low through sensor ground, circuit No. 736. This signal voltage will vary between 5 volts (open circuit) and zero volts (shorted circuit).

Code B110 will set if ignition is on and signal voltage indicates less than -36°F (-38°C), which is open circuit voltage or greater than 131°F (55°C), which is shorted circuit voltage. During time failure is present, a substitute temperature reading will be used to allow continued operation of the climate control system, and continuous compressor at idle will be disabled. The outside air temperature reading BD26 display will indicate the actual sensor reading.

NOTE: Test numbers refer to numbers on diagnostic chart.

1) Checks to see if open circuit reading is due to circuit or sensor. If open circuit reading changes to a shorted circuit reading after jumping sensor terminals, BCM and wiring are okay.

2) By applying a ground to various points in the circuits, an open can be isolated by observing whether parameter display can be changed from open reading to shorted reading.

3) Checks to see if shorted circuit reading is due to circuit or sensor. If shorted circuit reading changes to an open circuit reading after disconnecting sensor, BCM and wiring are okay.

NOTE ON INTERMITTENTS

If ambient temperature drops to less than about -36°F (-38°C), this code should be ignored. If B110 is set with any of the following codes: B119, B120, B122, B132 or B440, the most likely cause is an intermittent open circuit No. 736.

If an intermittent Code B110 is being set, manipulate related wiring while observing BD26 display. If failure is induced, reading will jump from its normal value to a reading outside the range of -36°F (-38°C) to 131°F (55°C).

If value indicated by BD26 display is not reasonably close to actual temperature of air at sensor, check for poor terminal contact or replace sensor.

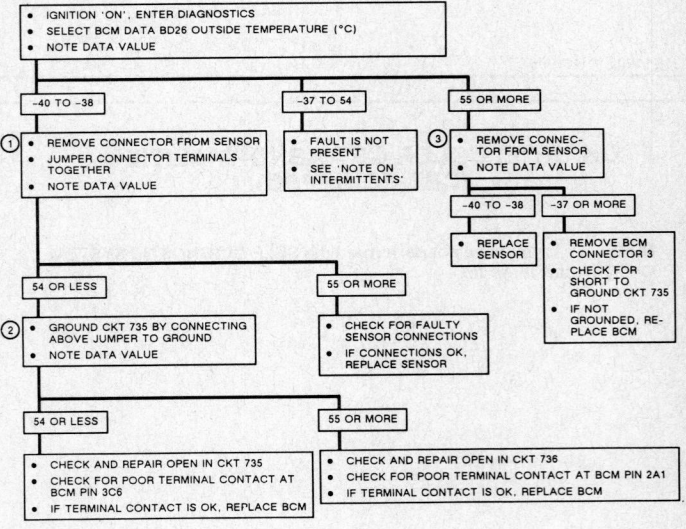

WHEN ALL DIAGNOSIS AND REPAIRS ARE COMPLETED, CLEAR CODES AND VERIFY OPERATION

91A05371 91C05942

Courtesy of General Motors Corp.

1991 ENGINE PERFORMANCE
Self-Diagnostics – Toronado & Trofeo PCM/BCM (Cont.)

GM
1-367

CODE B111, A/C HIGH SIDE TEMPERATURE SENSOR CIRCUIT

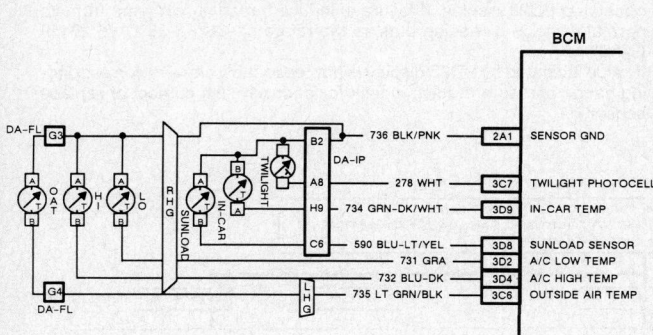

The A/C high side temperature sensor is a thermistor that controls signal voltage to BCM. The BCM applies and monitors voltage on circuit No. 732 to sensor. When sensor is cold, its resistance is high; therefore, BCM will see a high monitored voltage. As sensor warms, resistance becomes less and signal voltage is pulled low through sensor ground circuit No. 736. This monitored voltage will vary between 5 volts (open circuit) and zero volts (shorted circuit).

Code B111 will set if ignition is on, outside temperature sensor has not failed and reads greater than 32°F (0°C), and signal voltage indicates less than -22°F (-30°C), which is open circuit voltage or greater than 363°F (184°C), which is shorted circuit voltage. During time failure is present, a substitute temperature reading will be used to allow continued operation of climate control system. The A/C high side temperature reading BD27 display will indicate actual sensor reading.

NOTE: Test numbers refer to numbers on diagnostic chart.

1) Checks to see if open circuit reading is due to circuit or sensor. If open circuit reading changes to a shorted circuit reading after jumping sensor terminal, BCM and wiring are okay.

2) By applying a ground to various points in circuits, an open can be isolated by observing whether parameter display can be changed from open reading to shorted reading.

3) Checks to see if shorted circuit reading is due to circuit or sensor. If shorted circuit reading changes to an open circuit reading after disconnecting sensor, BCM and wiring are okay.

NOTE ON INTERMITTENTS

If an intermittent Code B111 is being set, check Code B111 snap data value for high side temperature, BD27 display. If BD27 display value is less than -22°F (-30°C), code was caused by an open in circuit No. 732, circuit No. 736 or high side temperature sensor. If BD27 display is greater than 363°F (184°C), code resulted from a short to ground on circuit No. 732 or a shorted high side temperature sensor. Manipulate related wiring while observing BD27 display. If failure is induced, reading will jump from its normal value to a reading outside the range of -22°F to 363°F (-30°C to 184°C).

If value displayed by BD27 is not reasonably close to corresponding gauge pressure reading, check for poor terminal contact or replace sensor.

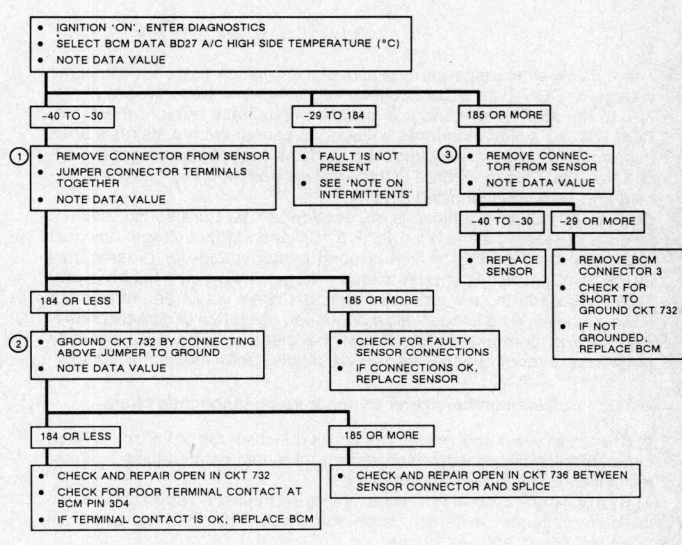

WHEN ALL DIAGNOSIS AND REPAIRS ARE COMPLETED, CLEAR CODES AND VERIFY OPERATION

GM
1-368

1991 ENGINE PERFORMANCE
Self-Diagnostics – Toronado & Trofeo PCM/BCM (Cont.)

CODE B112, A/C LOW SIDE TEMPERATURE SENSOR CIRCUIT

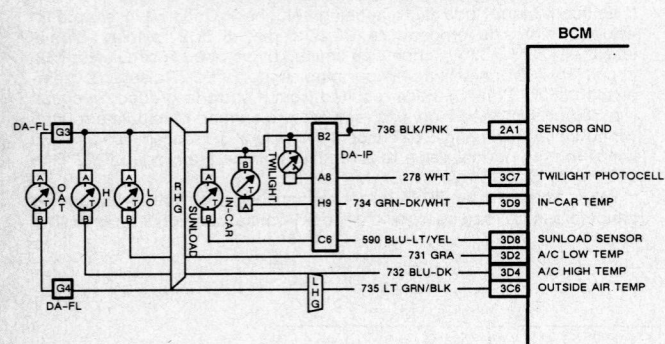

The A/C low side temperature sensor is a thermistor that controls signal voltage to BCM. The BCM applies and monitors voltage on circuit No. 731 to sensor. When sensor is cold, its resistance is high; therefore, BCM will see a high monitored voltage. As sensor warms, its resistance becomes less and signal voltage is pulled low through sensor ground circuit No. 736. This monitored voltage will vary between 5 volts (open circuit) and zero volts (shorted circuit).

Code B112 will set if ignition is on, outside temperature sensor has not failed and reads greater than 32°F (0°C), and signal voltage indicates less than -36°F (-38°C), which is open circuit voltage or greater than 201°F (94°C), which is shorted circuit voltage. During time failure is present, a substitute temperature reading (same value as outside air temperature) will be used to allow continued operation of climate control system and compressor clutch will be disabled. The A/C low side temperature reading BD28 display will display actual sensor reading.

NOTE: Test numbers refer to numbers on diagnostic chart.

1) Checks to see if open circuit reading is due to circuit or sensor. If open circuit reading changes to a shorted circuit reading after jumping sensor terminals, BCM and wiring are okay.
2) By applying a ground to various points in circuits, an open can be isolated by observing whether parameter display can be changed from open reading to shorted reading.
3) Checks to see if shorted circuit reading is due to circuit or sensor. If shorted circuit reading changes to an open circuit reading after disconnecting sensor, BCM and wiring are okay.

NOTE ON INTERMITTENTS

If an intermittent Code B112 is being set, manipulate related wiring while observing BD28 display. If failure is induced, reading will jump from its normal value to a reading outside the range of -36°F (-38°C) to 201°F (94°C).

If value indicated by BD28 display is not reasonably close to corresponding gauge pressure reading, check for poor terminal contact or replace sensor.

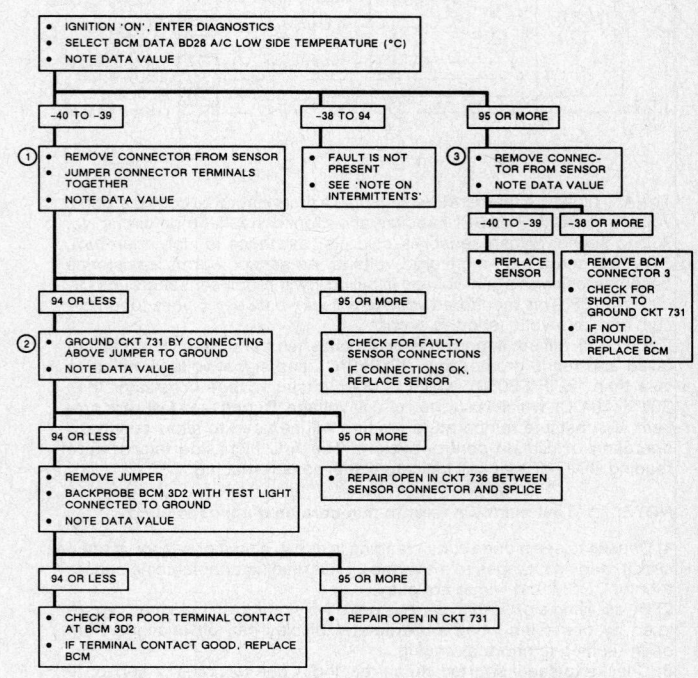

WHEN ALL DIAGNOSIS AND REPAIRS ARE COMPLETED, CLEAR CODES AND VERIFY OPERATION

91A05371 91E05373

Courtesy of General Motors Corp.

1991 ENGINE PERFORMANCE
Self-Diagnostics – Toronado & Trofeo PCM/BCM (Cont.)

GM
1-369

CODE B113, IN-CAR TEMPERATURE SENSOR CIRCUIT

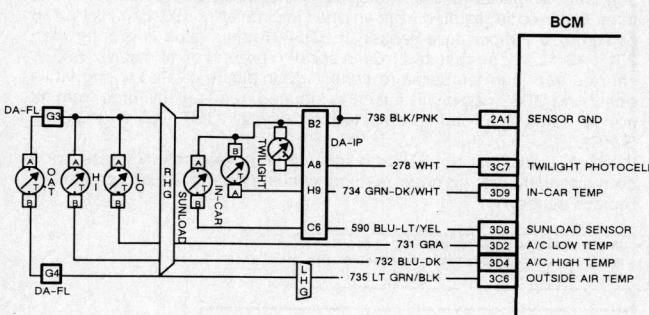

The in-car temperature sensor is a thermistor that controls signal voltage to BCM. The BCM applies and monitors voltage on circuit No. 734 to sensor. When sensor is cold, its resistance is high; therefore, BCM will see a high monitored voltage. As sensor warms, its resistance becomes less and monitored voltage is pulled low through sensor ground circuit No. 736. This signal voltage will vary between 5 volts (open circuit) and zero volts (shorted circuit).

Code B113 will set if ignition is on, outside temperature sensor has not failed and reads greater than 32°F (0°C), and signal voltage indicates less than -33°F (-36°C), which is open circuit voltage or greater than 206°F (97°C), which is shorted circuit voltage. During time failure is present, a substitute temperature reading will be used to allow continued operation of climate control system. The in-car temperature reading BD25 display will indicate actual sensor reading.

NOTE: **Test numbers refer to numbers on diagnostic chart.**

1) Checks to see if open circuit reading is due to circuit or sensor. If open circuit reading changes to a shorted circuit reading after jumping sensor terminals, BCM and wiring are okay.

2) By applying a ground to various points in circuits, an open can be isolated by observing whether parameter display can be changed from open reading to shorted reading.

3) Checks to see if shorted circuit reading is due to circuit or sensor. If shorted circuit reading changes to an open circuit reading after disconnecting sensor, BCM and wiring are okay.

91A05371 91G05374

NOTE ON INTERMITTENTS

If an intermittent Code B113 is being set, manipulate related wiring while observing BD25 display. If failure is induced, reading will jump from its normal value to a reading outside the range of -33°F (-36°C) to 206°F (97°C).

If value indicated by BD25 display is not reasonably close to actual temperature of air at sensor, check for poor terminal contact or replace sensor.

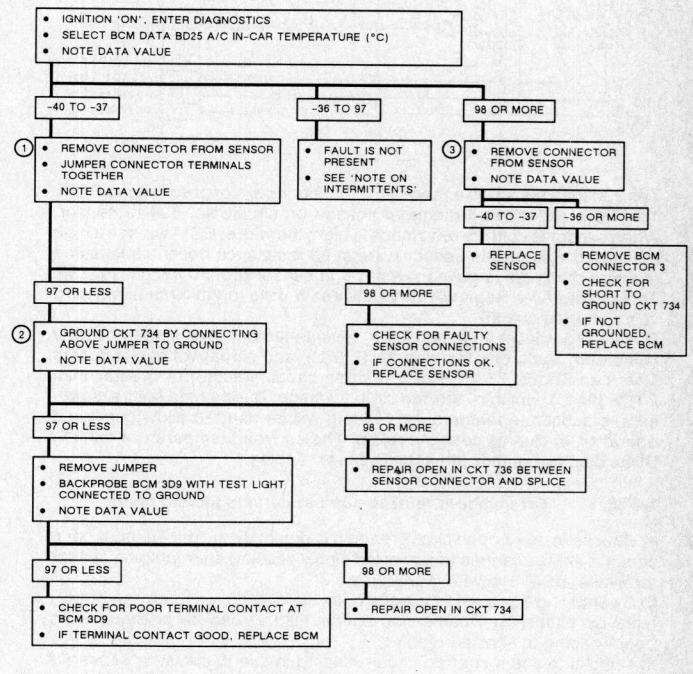

WHEN ALL DIAGNOSIS AND REPAIRS ARE COMPLETED, CLEAR CODES AND VERIFY OPERATION

GM
1-370

1991 ENGINE PERFORMANCE
Self-Diagnostics – Toronado & Trofeo PCM/BCM (Cont.)

CODE B115, SUN LOAD SENSOR CIRCUIT

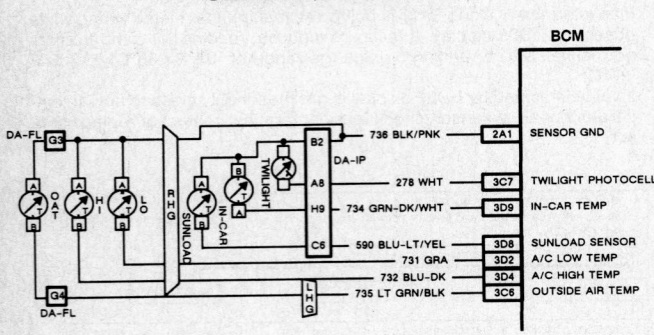

The sun load sensor is a thermistor that controls signal voltage to BCM. The BCM applies and monitors voltage on circuit No. 590 to sensor. When sensor is cold, its resistance is high; therefore, BCM will see a high monitored voltage. As sensor warms, its resistance becomes less and monitored voltage is pulled low through sensor ground circuit No. 736. This monitored voltage will vary between 5 volts (open circuit) and zero volts (shorted circuit).

Code B115 will set if ignition is on, outside temperature sensor has not failed and reads greater than 32°F (0°C), and signal voltage indicates less than -31°F (-35°C), which is open circuit voltage, or greater than 201°F (94°C), which is shorted circuit voltage. During time failure is present, a substitute temperature reading will be used to allow continued operation of climate control system. The sun load temperature reading BD32 display will indicate actual sensor reading.

NOTE: Test numbers refer to numbers on diagnostic chart.

1) Checks to see if open circuit reading is due to circuit or sensor. If open circuit reading changes to a shorted circuit reading after jumping sensor terminals, BCM and wiring are okay.

2) By applying a ground to various points in circuits, an open can be isolated by observing whether parameter display can be changed from open reading to shorted reading.

3) Checks to see if shorted circuit reading is due to circuit or sensor. If shorted circuit reading changes to an open circuit reading after disconnecting sensor, BCM and wiring are okay.

91A05371 91J05375

NOTE ON INTERMITTENTS

If an intermittent Code B115 is being set, check B115 snap data value for sun load temperature, BD32 display. If the BD32 display value is less than -35°C, code resulted from an open in circuit No. 590, circuit No. 736 or sun load temperature sensor. If BD32 display value is greater than 201°F (94°C), code resulted from a short to ground on circuit No. 590 or shorted sun load temperature sensor. Manipulate related wiring while observing BD32 display. If failure is induced, reading will jump from its normal value to a reading outside the range of -31°F (-35°C) to 201°F (94°C).

If value displayed by BD32 display is not reasonably close to a corresponding thermometer reading, check for poor terminal contact or replace sensor.

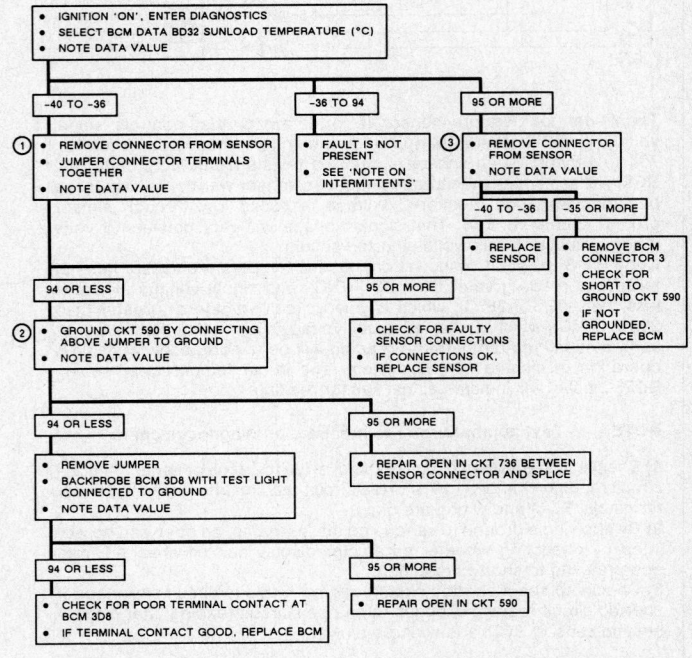

WHEN ALL DIAGNOSIS AND REPAIRS ARE COMPLETED, CLEAR CODES AND VERIFY OPERATION

Courtesy of General Motors Corp.

1991 ENGINE PERFORMANCE
Self-Diagnostics – Toronado & Trofeo PCM/BCM (Cont.)

GM
1-371

CODE B119, TWILIGHT PHOTOCELL CIRCUIT

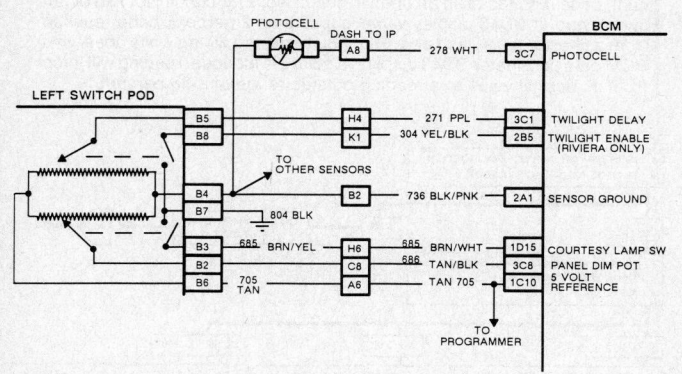

NOTE: Ensure nothing is covering sensor before following this procedure.

The twilight sensor uses a photocell to control signal voltage to BCM. The BCM applies and monitors voltage on circuit No. 278 to sensor. When sensor detects darkness, its resistance is high; therefore, BCM will see a high monitored voltage. As sensor detects light, its resistance becomes less and monitored voltage is pulled low through ground circuit No. 736. This signal voltage will vary between 5 volts (open circuit) and zero volts (shorted circuit).

Code B119 will set if ignition is on and signal voltage indicates more than 97 percent, open circuit voltage or less than 2 percent, which is shorted circuit voltage. During time failure is present, a substitute light reading (indicating darkness) will be used to allow continued operation of headlights. The measure of light reading, BD44 display, will indicate actual sensor reading.

NOTE: Test numbers refer to numbers on diagnostic chart.

1) Checks to see if open circuit is due to circuit or sensor. If open circuit reading changes to a shorted circuit reading after jumping sensor terminals, BCM and wiring are okay.
2) By applying a ground to various points in circuits, an open can be isolated by observing whether parameter display can be changed from open reading to shorted reading.
3) Checks to see if shorted circuit reading is due to circuit or sensor. If shorted circuit reading changes to an open circuit reading after disconnecting sensor, BCM and wiring are okay.

NOTE ON INTERMITTENTS

If an intermittent Code B119 is being set, manipulate related wiring while observing BD44 display. If failure is induced, reading will jump from its normal value to a reading outside the range of 3-97 percent. Make certain owner is aware not to cover sensor.

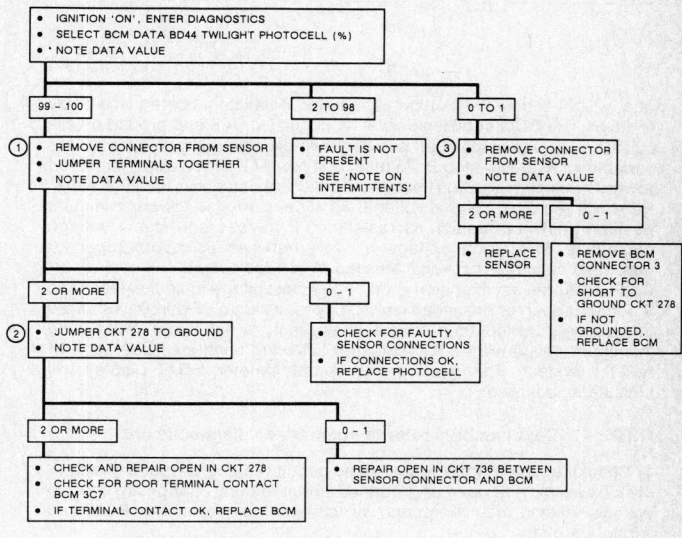

WHEN ALL DIAGNOSIS AND REPAIRS ARE COMPLETED, CLEAR CODES AND VERIFY OPERATION

Courtesy of General Motors Corp.

CODE B120, TWILIGHT DELAY POTENTIOMETER CIRCUIT

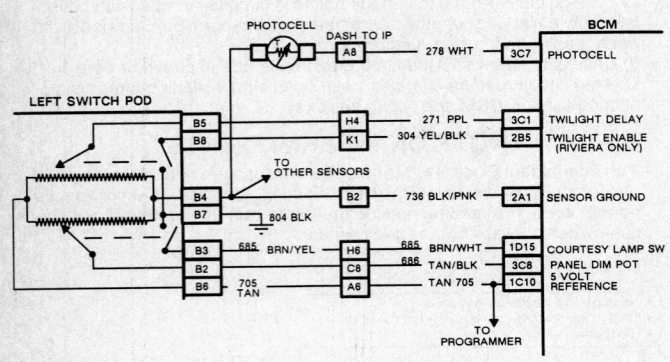

The twilight sentinel uses a potentiometer to indicate desired time delay to BCM. The BCM supplies 5 volts on circuit No. 705 and ground on circuit No. 736 to resistor in left switch assembly. The delay wiper provides variable voltage signal to BCM on circuit No. 271. When slider is moved toward maximum position (maximum delay), resistance is low; therefore, BCM will see a high signal voltage. As slider is moved toward minimum position (minimum delay), its resistance increases and signal voltage decreases. This signal voltage will vary between zero volts (open or grounded circuit) and 5 volts (shorted to voltage circuit).

Code B120 will set if ignition is on and signal voltage indicates less than 2 percent (open or grounded circuit) or greater than 98 percent (shorted to voltage). During time failure is present, a substitute delay time (minimum delay) will be implemented, allowing continued operation of twilight system. The reading from potentiometer BD43 display will indicate actual reading.

NOTE: Test numbers refer to numbers on diagnostic chart.

1) Checks to see if open or grounded circuit reading is due to circuit or switch assembly. If open or grounded circuit reading changes to short to voltage reading after jumpering switch assembly terminals, BCM and wiring are okay.

2) Measuring voltage between circuit No. 705 and circuit No. 271 checks to see if circuit No. 271 is open or shorted to ground.

3) Checks to see if short to voltage circuit reading is due to the circuit or switch assembly. If short to voltage reading changes to an open circuit after disconnecting switch, BCM and wiring are okay.

NOTE ON INTERMITTENTS

If an intermittent Code B120 is being set, check B120 snap data value for twilight delay BD43 display. If BD43 display value is greater than 98 percent, code resulted from an open in circuit No. 271, circuit No. 736 or left switch pod. If BD43 display value is less than 2 percent, code resulted from a short in left switch pod. Manipulate related wiring while observing BCM data parameter BD43 display. If failure is induced, reading will jump from its normal value to a reading outside range of 2-98 percent.

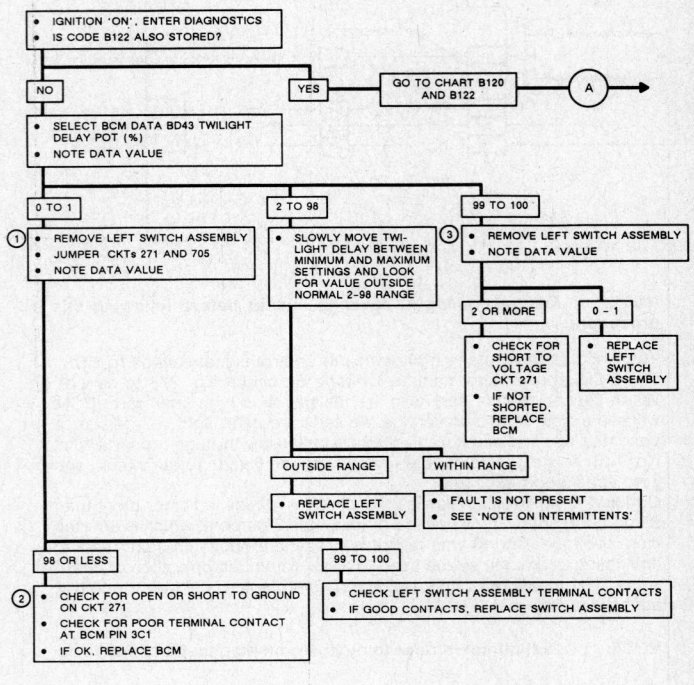

WHEN ALL DIAGNOSIS AND REPAIRS ARE COMPLETED, CLEAR CODES AND VERIFY OPERATION

1991 ENGINE PERFORMANCE
Self-Diagnostics – Toronado & Trofeo PCM/BCM (Cont.)

GM
1-373

CODE B121, TWILIGHT ENABLE SWITCH CIRCUIT

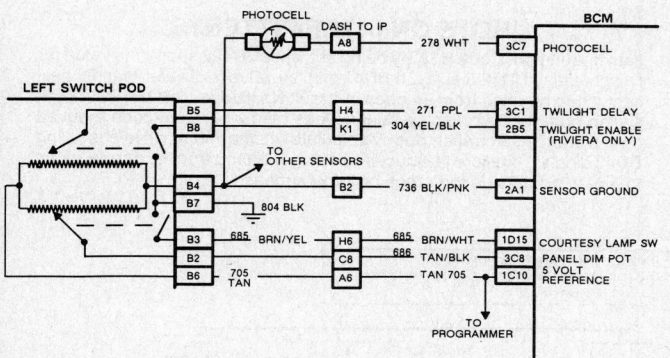

The twilight enable switch uses the same physical control as delay pot. Inside left switch assembly, enable switch contacts close as soon as time delay slider is moved off of its extreme minimum (off) position. The BCM supplies a voltage on circuit No. 304 to switch. When slider is moved from off position, switch contacts close and signal voltage is pulled low through ground circuit No. 804.

Code B121 will set if vehicle is equipped with twilight sentinel, twilight delay pot has not failed (Code B120), and signal voltage is high when delay slider is greater than 2 seconds (twilight sentinel on), or signal voltage is low when delay slider is less than 3 seconds (twilight sentinel off). During time failure is present, twilight sentinel will operate based on delay input. Whenever delay is greater than 2 seconds, BCM will assume twilight sentinel is on.

NOTE: Test numbers refer to numbers on diagnostic chart.

91A11908 91G11912

1) BI82 displays voltage state of circuit at BCM. These conditions can be observed in BI82 display as readings of HI or LO when slider is moved.
2) Checks to see if HI reading is due to circuit or switch assembly. If display changes from HI to LO after jumping switch assembly terminals, BCM and wiring are okay.
3) Checks to see if LO reading is due to circuit or switch assembly. If display changes from LO to HI when switch assembly is disconnected, both BCM and wiring are okay.

NOTE ON INTERMITTENTS

If an intermittent Code B121 is being set, manipulate related wiring. When BCM BI82 displays change-of-state, an "X" will be indicated. Check circuit for an intermittent open or short.

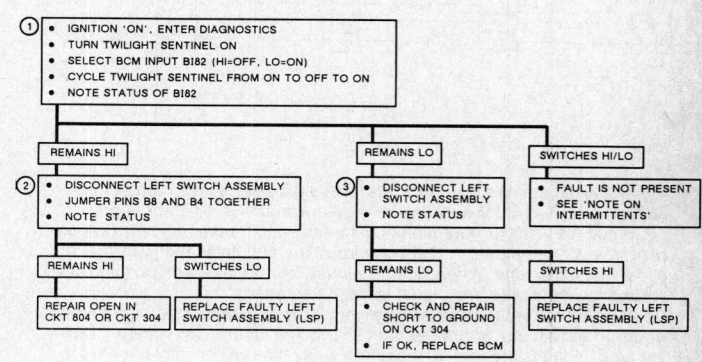

WHEN ALL DIAGNOSIS AND REPAIRS ARE COMPLETED, CLEAR CODES AND VERIFY OPERATION

Courtesy of General Motors Corp.

GM
1-374

1991 ENGINE PERFORMANCE
Self-Diagnostics – Toronado & Trofeo PCM/BCM (Cont.)

CODE B122, PANEL DIMMING POTENTIOMETER CIRCUIT

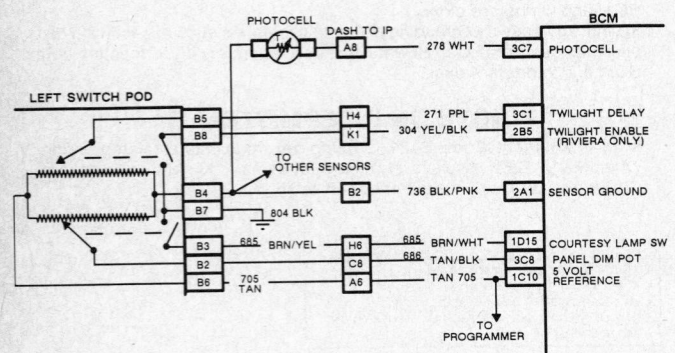

The panel dimmer is a potentiometer that indicates desired display intensity to BCM. The BCM supplies voltage on circuit No. 705 and a ground on circuit No. 736 to potentiometer in left switch assembly. The wiper provides voltage signal to BCM on circuit No. 686, indicating position of slider and delay time. When slider is moved toward minimum position, its resistance increases and signal voltage decreases.

Code B122 will set if signal voltage indicates less than 2 percent (open or grounded circuit), or greater than 98 percent (shorted to voltage). During time failure is present, a substitute delay time will be implemented to allow continued operation of interior lighting. The reading from potentiometer BD42 display will indicate actual reading.

NOTE: **Test numbers refer to numbers on diagnostic chart.**

1) Checks to see if open or grounded circuit reading is due to circuits or switch assembly. If open or grounded circuit reading changes to a short to voltage reading, after jumpering switch assembly terminals, BCM and wiring are okay.

2) Measuring voltage between circuit No. 705 and circuit No. 686 will determine if circuit No. 686 is open or shorted to ground.

3) Checks to see if short to voltage circuit reading is due to circuit or switch assembly. If a short to voltage reading changes to an open circuit reading after disconnecting switch assembly, BCM and wiring are okay.

NOTE ON INTERMITTENTS

If an intermittent Code B122 is being set, check B122 snap data value for twilight delay BD42 display. If BD42 display value is greater than 98 percent, code resulted from an open in circuit No. 686, circuit No. 736 or left switch pod. If BD42 display value is less than 2 percent, code resulted from a short in left switch pod. Manipulate related wiring while observing BD42 display. If failure is induced, reading will jump from its normal value to a reading outside the range of 2-98 percent.

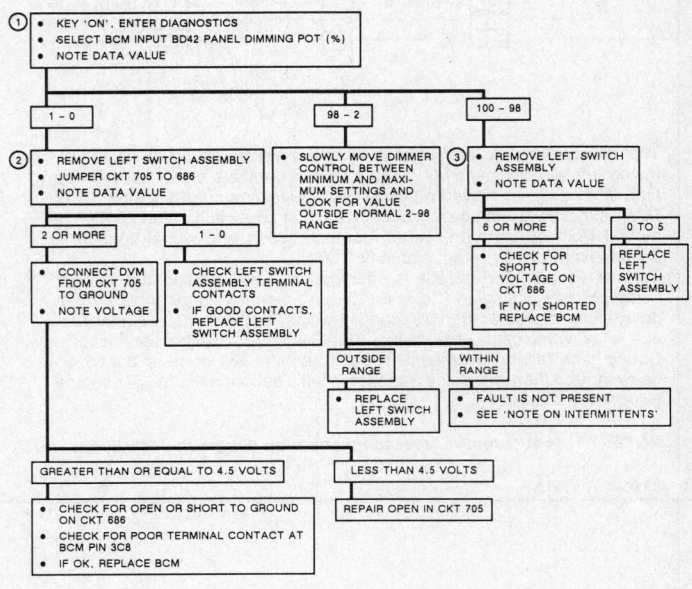

WHEN ALL DIAGNOSIS AND REPAIRS ARE COMPLETED, CLEAR CODES AND VERIFY OPERATION

1991 ENGINE PERFORMANCE
Self-Diagnostics – Toronado & Trofeo PCM/BCM (Cont.)

GM
1-375

CODE B120, TWILIGHT DELAY & B122, PANEL DIMMING (SIMULTANEOUSLY)

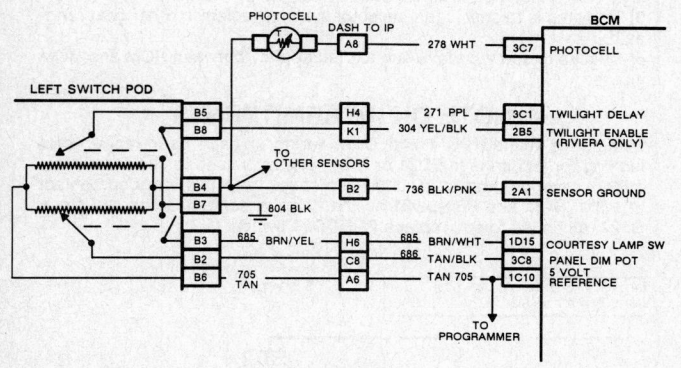

Since both potentiometers use same power and ground, problem is in power or ground circuit when both Codes B120 and B122 are stored.

NOTE: Test numbers refer to numbers on diagnostic chart.

1) Checks to see if open or grounded circuit reading is due to circuit or switch. If voltage can be read across circuits No. 705 and 736 after disconnecting switch assembly, BCM and wiring are okay.
2) Check for 5-volt reference at switch. If 5 volts are present, circuit No. 736 is open. If circuit No. 736 is open, open will be between terminal B4 on left switch and cavity B2 on dash-IP transition connector.
3) If circuit No. 705 is suspected of being grounded, remove HVAC programmer and BCM connectors prior to making ground check.
4) If there is no ground in circuit No. 705, replace HVAC programmer or BCM.

NOTE ON INTERMITTENTS

If an intermittent Code B120 and B122 are being set, check B120 snap data value for twilight delay BD43 display. If BD43 display value is greater than 98 percent, code resulted from an open in circuit No. 736 or left

91A11908 91F11911

switch pod. If BD43 display value is less than 2 percent, code resulted from an open in circuit No. 705 or short in left switch pod. Manipulate related wiring while observing BD43 display. If failure is induced, reading will jump from its normal value to a reading outside the range of 2-98 percent.

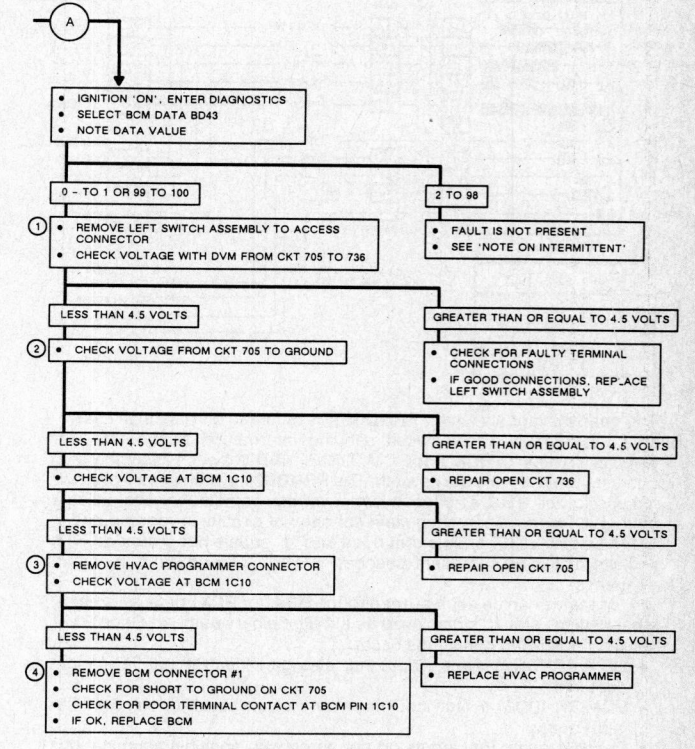

WHEN ALL DIAGNOSIS AND REPAIRS ARE COMPLETED, CLEAR CODES AND VERIFY OPERATION

Courtesy of General Motors Corp.

CODE B123, PANEL LAMP SWITCH CIRCUIT

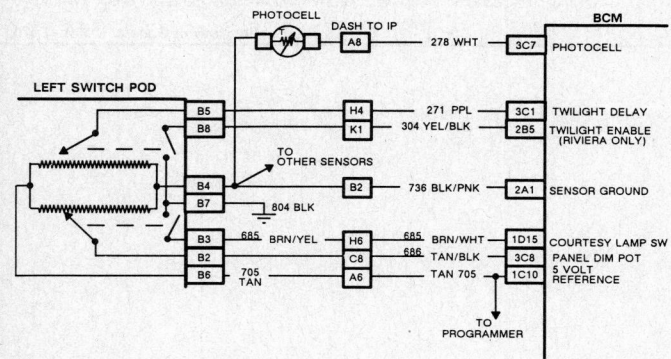

Inside left switch assembly, panel lamp switch contacts close when dimming slider is moved to its extreme maximum position. The BCM supplies a voltage on circuit No. 685 to switch. When signal is pulled to ground, BCM turns courtesy light on.
Code B123 will set if panel dimming pot has not failed and BCM sees circuit No. 685 grounded while dimmer switch position is less than a value for maximum panel light brightness. A grounded circuit No. 685 will not only set Code B123, but will also turn courtesy lights on at all times and drain battery.

NOTE: Test numbers refer to numbers on diagnostic chart.

91A11908 90I14371

1) BI01 display, dimmer switch input, will read LO if dimming slider is at maximum up position. BI01 display will read HI if dimming slider is not at maximum position.
2) By removing switch assembly, a shorted switch can be detected by observing BI01 display.
3) By removing BCM connector, short to ground can be isolated as being wire or BCM.

NOTE ON INTERMITTENTS

If circuit No. 685 was intermittently grounded, Code B123 could be stored. Manipulate circuit No. 685 while observing BI01 display with dimmer at a low setting. If short occurs, value will switch from HI to LO. Also check BD42 display. Cycle panel dimming control from minimum to maximum. If BD42 display does not range between 2-98 percent, or never reads more than 75 percent, replace left switch assembly.

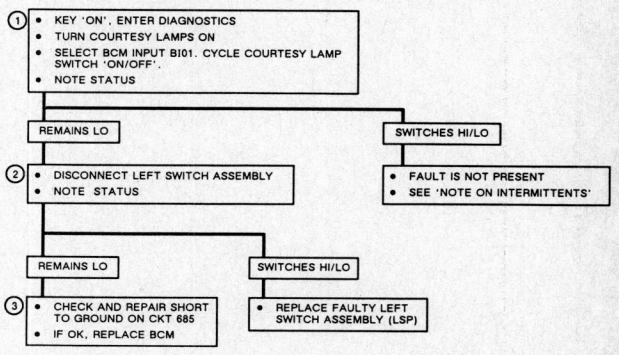

WHEN ALL DIAGNOSIS AND REPAIRS ARE COMPLETED, CLEAR CODES AND VERIFY OPERATION

Courtesy of General Motors Corp.

GM
1-376

1991 ENGINE PERFORMANCE
Self-Diagnostics – Toronado & Trofeo PCM/BCM (Cont.)

CODE B127, GEAR SELECTOR SWITCH CIRCUIT (1 OF 3)

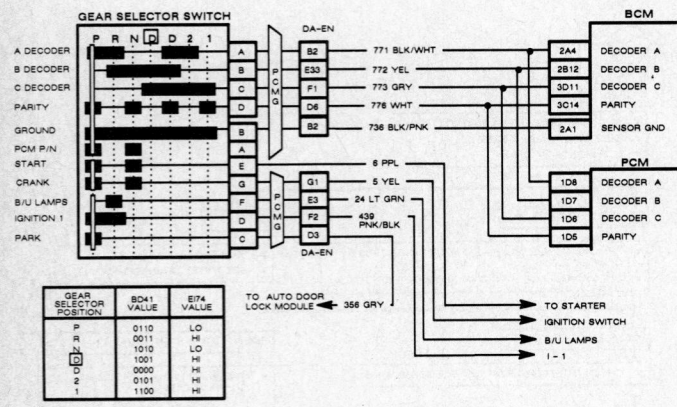

GEAR SELECTOR POSITION	BD41 VALUE	E174 VALUE
P	0110	LO
R	0011	HI
N	1010	LO
D̄	1001	HI
D	0000	HI
2	0101	HI
1	1100	HI

The gear selector switch (or PRNDD21) is mounted on transaxle assembly. It is a multi-signal switch sending information relative to gear selector position to BCM and PCM. The PRNDD21 switch assembly also contains the neutral safety switch. The PRNDD21 switch uses 4 discrete circuits to pull 4 BCM voltages low in various combinations to indicate each gear range. The voltage level of each of circuits is represented in BD41 display as "0" equals grounded and "1" equals not grounded. The 4 digits displayed represent decoder "A", "B", "C" and parity inputs in sequence.

Switch status can be seen by monitoring BD41 or ED31 data parameter, where switch status is displayed as a 4-digit binary number. Code B127 will set if following conditions occur:

- BCM PRNDD21 switch input indicates park/neutral, but PCM input does not.
- BCM PRNDD21 switch input does not indicate park/neutral, but PCM input does.
- Decoder and parity inputs do not agree with possible combinations per BD41 display values found in DATA DISPLAY in introduction portion of this article.

If Code B127 is set, Driver Information Center (DIC) will display warning message GEAR SELECT FAULT and IPC PRNDD21 display will flash.

NOTE: Test numbers refer to numbers on diagnostic chart.

1) Checks BCM inputs when only decoder "A" and parity circuit are pulled low.
2) Checks BCM inputs when only decoder "B" and "C" inputs are pulled low. This will complete HI/LO check of all 4 BCM inputs.
3) This step is to check gear selector switch problem in other gear ranges.
4) Checks to see if code is due to discrepancy between PCM and BCM inputs.

NOTE ON INTERMITTENTS

Manipulate related PCM and BCM wiring in each gear range while looking for a change in ED31 or BD41 display values to check for intermittent open or short to ground. Also check terminals for good contact at PCM, BCM and PRNDD21 switch. If good contact exists and Code B127 continues to set, replace PRNDD21 switch.

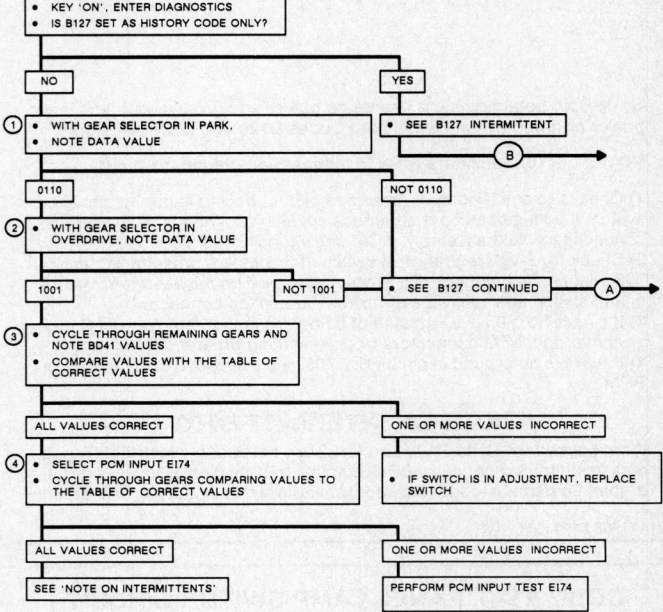

WHEN ALL DIAGNOSIS AND REPAIRS ARE COMPLETED, CLEAR CODES AND VERIFY OPERATION

1991 ENGINE PERFORMANCE
Self-Diagnostics – Toronado & Trofeo PCM/BCM (Cont.)

GM
1-377

CODE B127, GEAR SELECTOR SWITCH CIRCUIT (2 OF 3)

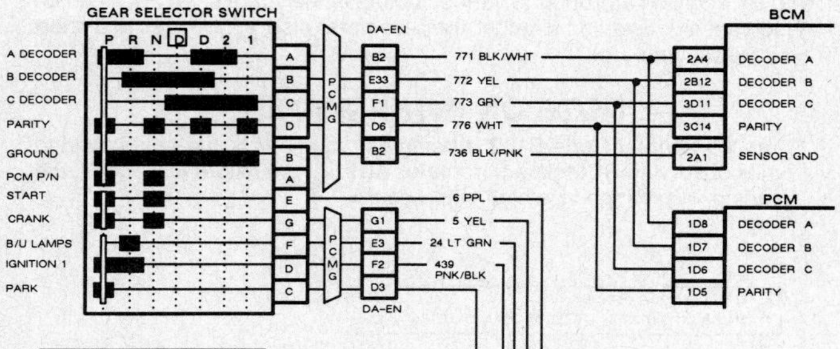

GEAR SELECTOR SWITCH

P R N D D 2 1

		DA–EN			BCM
A DECODER	A	B2	771 BLK/WHT	2A4	DECODER A
B DECODER	B	E33	772 YEL	2B12	DECODER B
C DECODER	C	F1	773 GRY	3D11	DECODER C
PARITY	D	D6	776 WHT	3C14	PARITY
GROUND	B	B2	736 BLK/PNK	2A1	SENSOR GND
PCM P/N	A				
START	E				PCM
CRANK	G	G1	6 PPL	1D8	DECODER A
B/U LAMPS	F	E3	5 YEL	1D7	DECODER B
IGNITION 1	D	F2	24 LT GRN	1D6	DECODER C
PARK	C	D3	439 PNK/BLK	1D5	PARITY

DA–EN

GEAR SELECTOR POSITION	BD41 VALUE	EI74 VALUE
P	0110	LO
R	0011	HI
N	1010	LO
D	1001	HI
D	0000	HI
2	0101	HI
1	1100	HI

TO AUTO DOOR LOCK MODULE ← 356 GRY

TO STARTER
IGNITION SWITCH
B/U LAMPS
I – 1

NOTE: Test numbers refer to numbers on diagnostic chart.

5) Checks for short to ground in gear selector switch to BCM circuits.
6) Checks for open in circuits to BCM.
7) Circuit shorted to ground will result in a "0" for that circuit.
8) Checks for open PRNDDD21 sensor ground.
9) Circuit with open will result in a "1" for that circuit.

Ⓐ

5)
- UNPLUG 4-WAY CONNECTOR FROM GEAR SELECTOR SWITCH
- NOTE BD41 VALUE

1111 → **6)**
NOT 1111 → **7)**

6)
- SHORT ALL 4 CAVITIES (A-D) OF HARNESS 4-WAY CONNECTOR TO A KNOWN GOOD GROUND
- NOTE BD41 VALUE

NOT 0000 → **8)**
0000

7)
- EACH DIGIT IN BD41 REPRESENTS A VOLTAGE LEVEL ON A CIRCUIT

1 1 1 1
- IF THIS DIGIT IS A 0 (ZERO), CHECK FOR SHORT TO GND IN CKT 776.
- IF THIS DIGIT IS A 0 (ZERO), CHECK FOR SHORT TO GND IN CKT 773.
- IF THIS DIGIT IS A 0 (ZERO), CHECK FOR SHORT TO GND IN CKT 772.
- IF THIS DIGIT IS A 0 (ZERO), CHECK FOR SHORT TO GND IN CKT 771.

8)
- UNPLUG 7-WAY CONNECTOR AT SWITCH
- CHECK FOR GROUND AT CAVITY B

GOOD GROUND → REPLACE SWITCH
NO GROUND → REPAIR CKT 736

9)
- EACH DIGIT IN BD41 REPRESENTS A VOLTAGE LEVEL ON A CIRCUIT

0 0 0 0
- IF THIS DIGIT IS A 1 (ONE), CHECK FOR AN OPEN OR POOR TERMINAL CONTACT IN CKT 776.
- IF THIS DIGIT IS A 1 (ONE), CHECK FOR AN OPEN OR POOR TERMINAL CONTACT IN CKT 773.
- IF THIS DIGIT IS A 1 (ONE), CHECK FOR AN OPEN OR POOR TERMINAL CONTACT IN CKT 772.
- IF THIS DIGIT IS A 1 (ONE), CHECK FOR AN OPEN OR POOR TERMINAL CONTACT IN CKT 771.

NO OPEN FOUND
- CHECK FOR SHORT TO VOLTAGE
- ENSURE GOOD CONTACT AT BCM CONNECTOR
- IF GOOD CONTACT, REPLACE BCM

OPEN FOUND → REPAIR CIRCUIT

WHEN ALL DIAGNOSIS AND REPAIRS ARE COMPLETED, CLEAR CODES AND VERIFY OPERATION

Courtesy of General Motors Corp.

CODE B127, GEAR SELECTOR SWITCH CIRCUIT (3 OF 3)

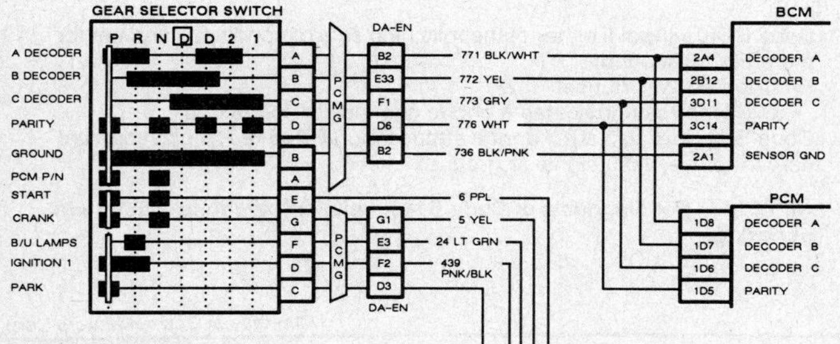

GEAR SELECTOR SWITCH

P R N D D 2 1

		DA–EN			BCM
A DECODER	A	B2	771 BLK/WHT	2A4	DECODER A
B DECODER	B	E33	772 YEL	2B12	DECODER B
C DECODER	C	F1	773 GRY	3D11	DECODER C
PARITY	D	D6	776 WHT	3C14	PARITY
GROUND	B	B2	736 BLK/PNK	2A1	SENSOR GND
PCM P/N	A				
START	E				PCM
CRANK	G	G1	6 PPL	1D8	DECODER A
B/U LAMPS	F	E3	5 YEL	1D7	DECODER B
IGNITION 1	D	F2	24 LT GRN	1D6	DECODER C
PARK	C	D3	439 PNK/BLK	1D5	PARITY

DA–EN

GEAR SELECTOR POSITION	BD41 VALUE	EI74 VALUE
P	0110	LO
R	0011	HI
N	1010	LO
D	1001	HI
D	0000	HI
2	0101	HI
1	1100	HI

TO AUTO DOOR LOCK MODULE ← 356 GRY

TO STARTER
IGNITION SWITCH
B/U LAMPS
I – 1

NOTE: Test numbers refer to numbers on diagnostic chart.

10) The snap data value of BD41 display will be value that BCM recognized when code was set. This is used to determine whether this value is valid. If it is a valid value, PCM park/neutral input must be incorrect to set code.

Ⓑ

10)
- SELECT SNAP DATA FOR CODE B127 AND RECORD PARAMETER BD41
- DOES THIS VALUE MATCH ANY OF THE FOLLOWING VALUES: 0110, 0011, 1010, 1001, 0101, 1100?

NO
BD41 SNAP VALUE READ...

YES
- CHECK THE CORRESPONDING VALUE OF EI174 IN THE TABLE
- IF THE CORRESPONDING VALUE OF EI174 IS HI, THIS CODE WAS PROBABLY CAUSED BY AN INTERMITTENT SHORT TO GROUND ON CKT 434
- IF THE CORRESPONDING VALUE OF EI174 IS LO, THIS CODE WAS PROBABLY CAUSED BY AN INTERMITTENT OPEN OR SHORT TO VOLTAGE ON CKT 434

1111
- THIS CODE WAS SET DUE TO AN OPEN IN CKT 736. REPAIR INTERMITTENT OPEN IN 736.

YES
- IF ACTUAL GEAR POSITION WHEN THE CODE SET IS KNOWN, COMPARE THE CORRECT BD41 VALUE FROM THE TABLE ON THE PRECEDING PAGE WITH THE SNAP DATA VALUE AND DETERMINE WHICH DIGIT IS INCORRECT.

1 1 1 1
- REPRESENTS CKT 776
- REPRESENTS CKT 773
- REPRESENTS CKT 772
- REPRESENTS CKT 771

IF THE INCORRECT DIGIT IS A ONE WHEN IT SHOULD BE A ZERO, CORRESPONDING CIRCUIT WAS OPEN WHEN THE CODE WAS SET OR SHORTED TO VOLTAGE.

IF THE INCORRECT DIGIT IS A ZERO WHEN IT SHOULD BE A ONE, CORRESPONDING CIRCUIT WAS GROUNDED WHEN THE CODE SET.

WHEN ALL DIAGNOSIS AND REPAIRS ARE COMPLETED, CLEAR CODES AND VERIFY OPERATION

Courtesy of General Motors Corp.

GM
1-378

1991 ENGINE PERFORMANCE
Self-Diagnostics – Toronado & Trofeo PCM/BCM (Cont.)

CODE B132, ENGINE OIL PRESSURE SENSOR CIRCUIT FAULTY

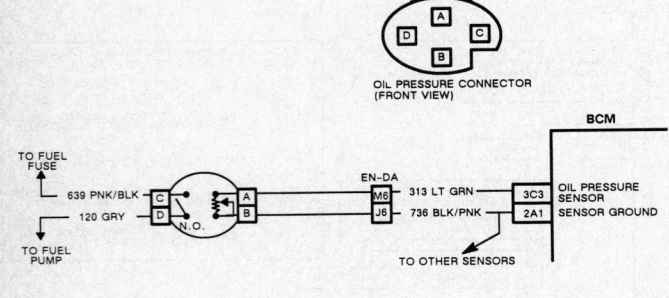

OIL PRESSURE CONNECTOR
(FRONT VIEW)

1) Checks to see if open circuit reading is due to circuit or sensor. If open circuit reading changes to a shorted circuit reading after jumping sensor terminals, BCM and wiring are okay.
2) By applying a ground to various points in the circuits, an open can be isolated by observing whether the parameter display changes to a short circuit reading.

NOTE ON INTERMITTENTS

If an intermittent Code B132 is being set, manipulate the related wiring while observing BCM data parameter BD71. If the failure is induced, the reading will change to a high oil pressure.

The oil pressure indicator is a variable resistor used to indicate oil pressure to BCM. The BCM supplies voltage on circuit No. 313 to sensor. When the engine is not running (oil pressure low), sensor resistance is low. When the engine is running (increased oil pressure), sensor resistance becomes high. The signal voltage will vary between 5 volts (open circuit) and zero volts (short circuit).
Code 132 will set if engine is running and the signal voltage indicates greater than 80 psi for at least 2 seconds. As actual engine oil pressure will never be that high, code indicates an open circuit, faulty sensor or faulty BCM.

NOTE: Test numbers refer to numbers on diagnostic chart.

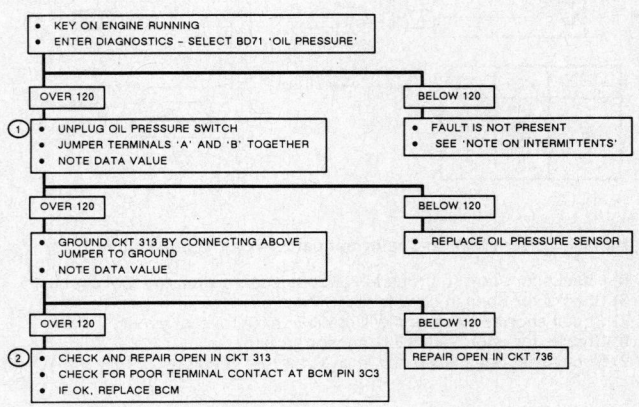

WHEN ALL DIAGNOSIS AND REPAIRS ARE COMPLETED, CLEAR CODES AND VERIFY OPERATION

91A11916 91B11917

Courtesy of General Motors Corp.

CODE B140, PHONE SYSTEM FAULT

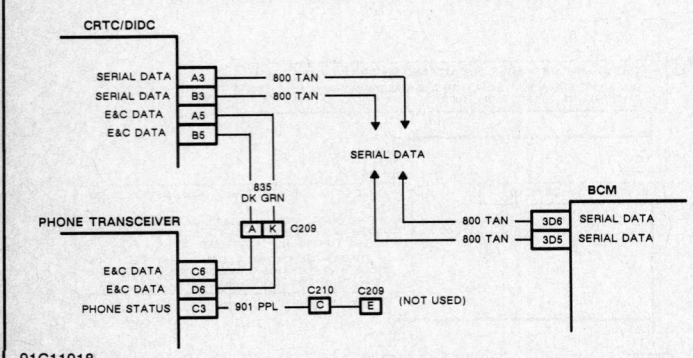

The BCM receives phone status information directly from the phone transceiver and from CRT controller across serial data line. The phone status input to BCM is a pulse width modulated signal that indicates the state of the phone (see BCM data parameter BD45). The phone status input from the CRT controller is a discrete indication of whether CRT is able to communicate with the phone transceiver across "E" & "C" data line.
Code B140 will set if either of the following sets of conditions are met for more than 2 seconds:
• Code B335 is not set
• CRT controller indicates a phone communication failure
Code B140 will also set if phone status input, BD45 is 7, indicating zero percent pulse width signal (a ground).

NOTE: For diagnosis of Code B140, cellular telephone will require servicing.

91C11918

Courtesy of General Motors Corp.

1991 ENGINE PERFORMANCE
Self-Diagnostics – Toronado & Trofeo PCM/BCM (Cont.)

GM
1-379

CODE B332, LOSS OF COMPASS DATA

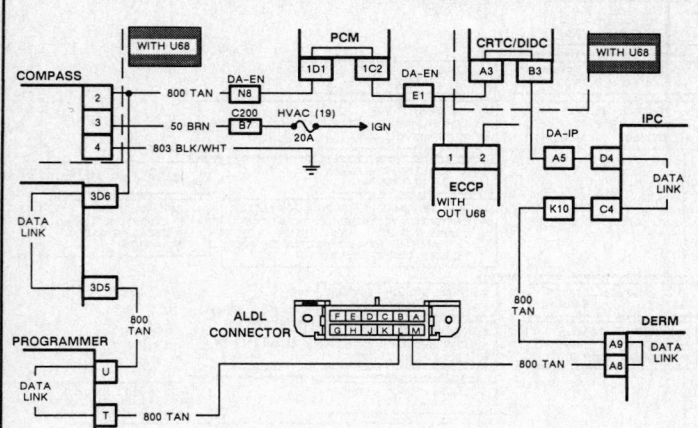

Code B332 will set if communication between the compass and BCM is lost. If Code B332 is set, an ELECTRICAL PROBLEM message will be displayed and the compass will display the last direction indicated until compass communication resumes.

NOTE: Test numbers refer to numbers on diagnostic chart.

1) Checks to see if other data line components are experiencing communications problems.
2) Checks status of data line at compass module. Normal data line voltage is between .1 and 4.5 volts.

91D11919 91G11920

NOTE ON INTERMITTENTS

If an intermittent Code B332 is stored, manipulate the related wiring at compass module and up to splice. An ELECTRICAL PROBLEM message indicates a loss of data and may help locate fault.

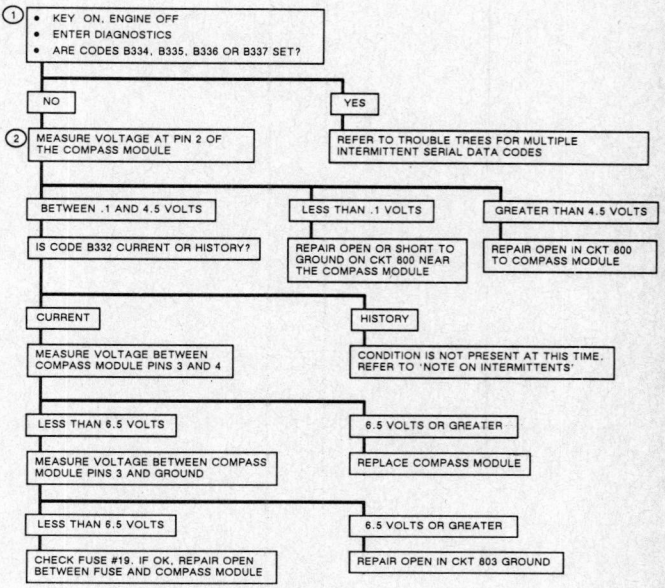

WHEN ALL DIAGNOSIS AND REPAIRS ARE COMPLETED, CLEAR CODES AND VERIFY PROPER OPERATION

Courtesy of General Motors Corp.

SERIAL DATA CIRCUIT
MULTIPLE INTERMITTENT CODES
NON-CRT/DID (1 OF 2)

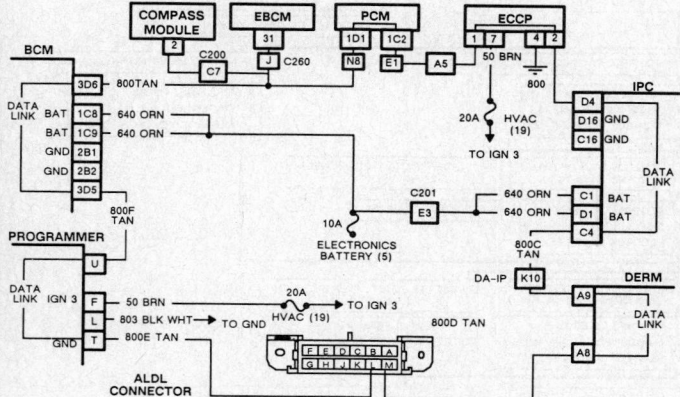

A damaged serial data line circuit or one of the components connected to the data line may cause multiple or intermittent setting of data line Codes B333, B334, B335, B336 and/or B337. When operating normally, the serial data line voltage should continually fluctuate from .1 to 5.0 volts.

If the serial data line has been shorted to ground, the voltage at the ALDL will be zero volts. If it has been shorted to voltage, it will be over 5 volts.

If one of the components on the serial data line is affecting the data line voltage, the serial data voltage at the ALDL connector will be a steady value anywhere between .1 and 5.0 volts.

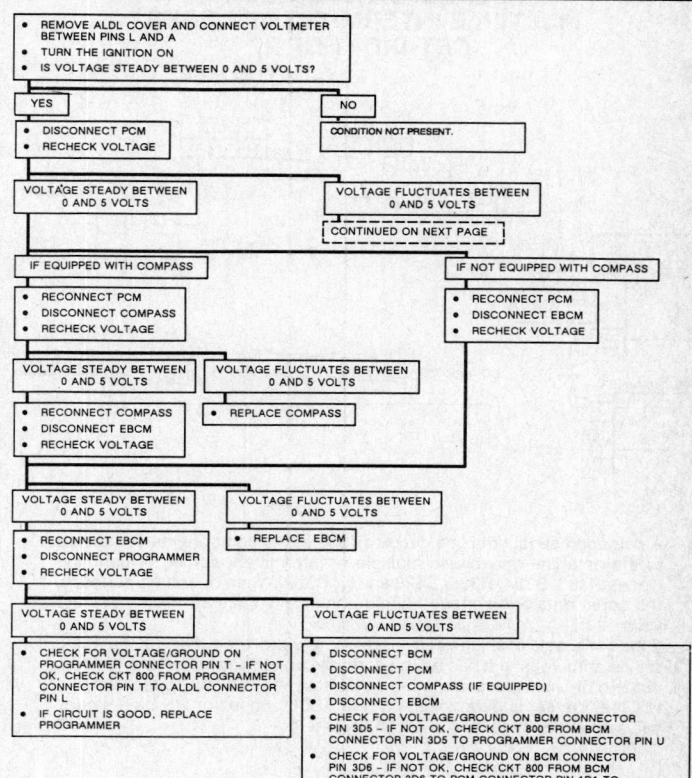

WHEN ALL DIAGNOSIS AND REPAIRS ARE COMPLETED, CLEAR CODES AND VERIFY PROPER OPERATION

91C11892 91J11923

Courtesy of General Motors Corp.

GM
1-380

1991 ENGINE PERFORMANCE
Self-Diagnostics – Toronado & Trofeo PCM/BCM (Cont.)

SERIAL DATA CIRCUIT MULTIPLE INTERMITTENT CODES NON-CRT/DID (2 OF 2)

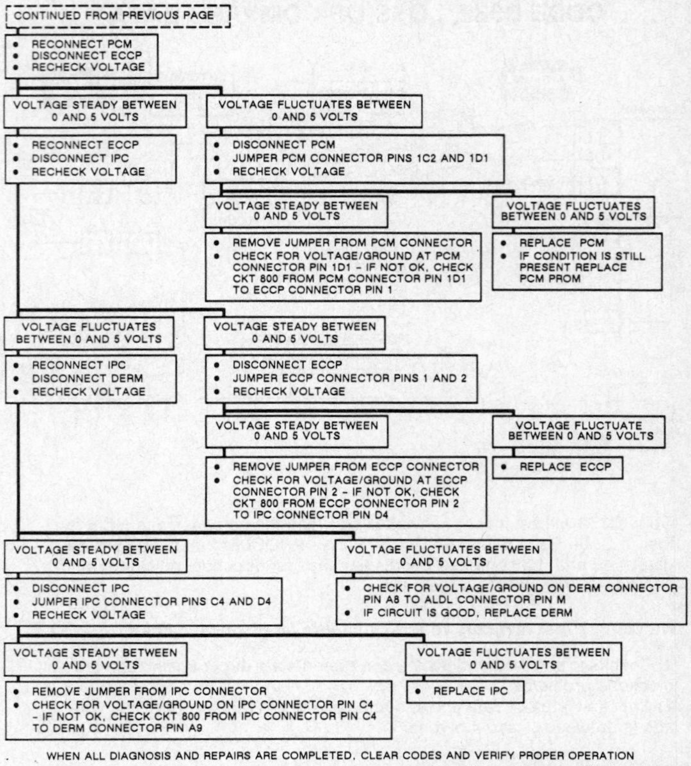

CONTINUED FROM PREVIOUS PAGE
- RECONNECT PCM
- DISCONNECT ECCP
- RECHECK VOLTAGE

VOLTAGE STEADY BETWEEN 0 AND 5 VOLTS

VOLTAGE FLUCTUATES BETWEEN 0 AND 5 VOLTS

- RECONNECT ECCP
- DISCONNECT IPC
- RECHECK VOLTAGE

- DISCONNECT PCM
- JUMPER PCM CONNECTOR PINS 1C2 AND 1D1
- RECHECK VOLTAGE

VOLTAGE STEADY BETWEEN 0 AND 5 VOLTS

VOLTAGE FLUCTUATES BETWEEN 0 AND 5 VOLTS

- REMOVE JUMPER FROM PCM CONNECTOR
- CHECK FOR VOLTAGE/GROUND AT PCM CONNECTOR PIN 1D1 – IF NOT OK, CHECK CKT 800 FROM PCM CONNECTOR PIN 1D1 TO ECCP CONNECTOR PIN 1

- REPLACE PCM
- IF CONDITION IS STILL PRESENT REPLACE PCM PROM

VOLTAGE FLUCTUATES BETWEEN 0 AND 5 VOLTS

VOLTAGE STEADY BETWEEN 0 AND 5 VOLTS

- RECONNECT IPC
- DISCONNECT DERM
- RECHECK VOLTAGE

- DISCONNECT ECCP
- JUMPER ECCP CONNECTOR PINS 1 AND 2
- RECHECK VOLTAGE

VOLTAGE STEADY BETWEEN 0 AND 5 VOLTS

VOLTAGE FLUCTUATE BETWEEN 0 AND 5 VOLTS

- REMOVE JUMPER FROM ECCP CONNECTOR
- CHECK FOR VOLTAGE/GROUND AT ECCP CONNECTOR PIN 2 – IF NOT OK, CHECK CKT 800 FROM ECCP CONNECTOR PIN 2 TO IPC CONNECTOR PIN D4

- REPLACE ECCP

VOLTAGE STEADY BETWEEN 0 AND 5 VOLTS

VOLTAGE FLUCTUATES BETWEEN 0 AND 5 VOLTS

- DISCONNECT IPC
- JUMPER IPC CONNECTOR PINS C4 AND D4
- RECHECK VOLTAGE

- CHECK FOR VOLTAGE/GROUND ON DERM CONNECTOR PIN A8 TO ALDL CONNECTOR PIN M
- IF CIRCUIT IS GOOD, REPLACE DERM

VOLTAGE STEADY BETWEEN 0 AND 5 VOLTS

VOLTAGE FLUCTUATES BETWEEN 0 AND 5 VOLTS

- REMOVE JUMPER FROM IPC CONNECTOR
- CHECK FOR VOLTAGE/GROUND ON IPC CONNECTOR PIN C4 – IF NOT OK, CHECK CKT 800 FROM IPC CONNECTOR PIN C4 TO DERM CONNECTOR PIN A9

- REPLACE IPC

WHEN ALL DIAGNOSIS AND REPAIRS ARE COMPLETED, CLEAR CODES AND VERIFY PROPER OPERATION

Courtesy of General Motors Corp.

91A11924

SERIAL DATA CIRCUIT MULTIPLE INTERMITTENT CODES CRT/DID (1 OF 2)

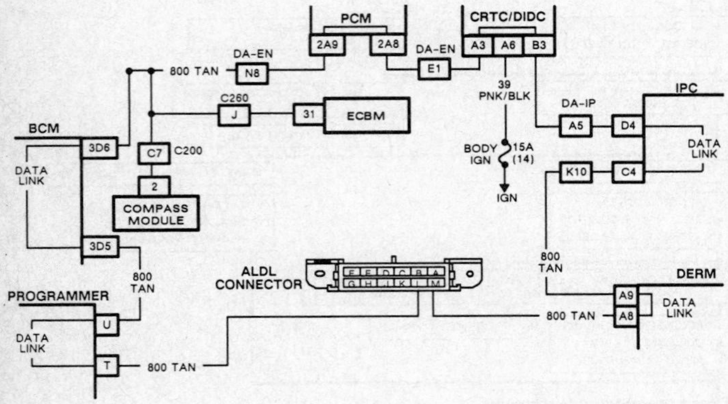

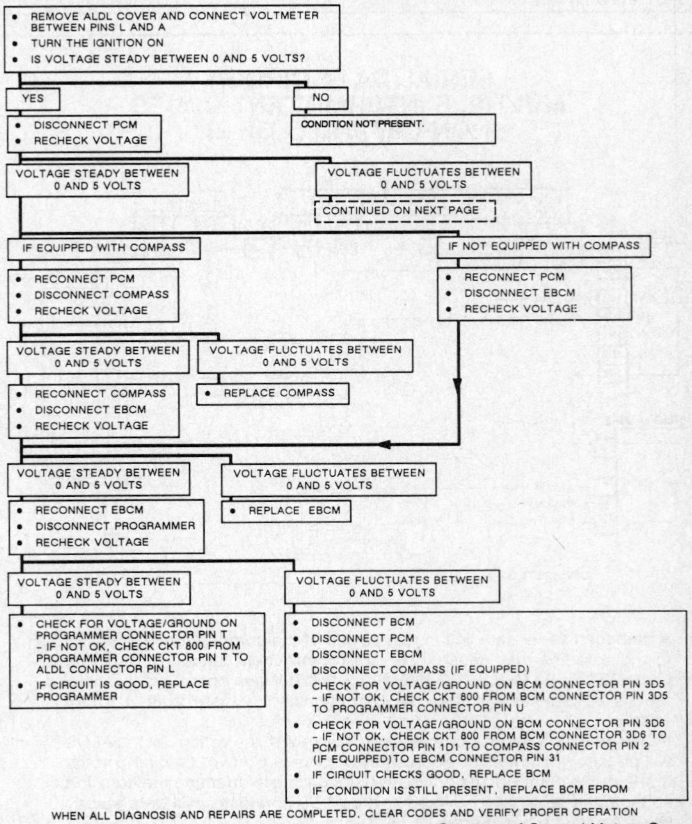

- REMOVE ALDL COVER AND CONNECT VOLTMETER BETWEEN PINS L AND A
- TURN THE IGNITION ON
- IS VOLTAGE STEADY BETWEEN 0 AND 5 VOLTS?

YES
- DISCONNECT PCM
- RECHECK VOLTAGE

NO
CONDITION NOT PRESENT.

VOLTAGE STEADY BETWEEN 0 AND 5 VOLTS

VOLTAGE FLUCTUATES BETWEEN 0 AND 5 VOLTS

CONTINUED ON NEXT PAGE

IF EQUIPPED WITH COMPASS
- RECONNECT PCM
- DISCONNECT COMPASS
- RECHECK VOLTAGE

IF NOT EQUIPPED WITH COMPASS
- RECONNECT PCM
- DISCONNECT EBCM
- RECHECK VOLTAGE

VOLTAGE STEADY BETWEEN 0 AND 5 VOLTS

VOLTAGE FLUCTUATES BETWEEN 0 AND 5 VOLTS

- RECONNECT COMPASS
- DISCONNECT EBCM
- RECHECK VOLTAGE

- REPLACE COMPASS

VOLTAGE STEADY BETWEEN 0 AND 5 VOLTS

VOLTAGE FLUCTUATES BETWEEN 0 AND 5 VOLTS

- RECONNECT EBCM
- DISCONNECT PROGRAMMER
- RECHECK VOLTAGE

- REPLACE EBCM

VOLTAGE STEADY BETWEEN 0 AND 5 VOLTS

VOLTAGE FLUCTUATES BETWEEN 0 AND 5 VOLTS

- CHECK FOR VOLTAGE/GROUND ON PROGRAMMER CONNECTOR PIN T – IF NOT OK, CHECK CKT 800 FROM PROGRAMMER CONNECTOR PIN T TO ALDL CONNECTOR PIN L
- IF CIRCUIT IS GOOD, REPLACE PROGRAMMER

- DISCONNECT BCM
- DISCONNECT PCM
- DISCONNECT EBCM
- DISCONNECT COMPASS (IF EQUIPPED)
- CHECK FOR VOLTAGE/GROUND ON BCM CONNECTOR PIN 3D5 – IF NOT OK, CHECK CKT 800 FROM BCM CONNECTOR PIN 3D5 TO PROGRAMMER CONNECTOR PIN U
- CHECK FOR VOLTAGE/GROUND ON BCM CONNECTOR PIN 3D6 – IF NOT OK, CHECK CKT 800 FROM BCM CONNECTOR 3D6 TO PCM CONNECTOR PIN 1D1 TO COMPASS CONNECTOR 2 (IF EQUIPPED)TO EBCM CONNECTOR PIN 31
- IF CIRCUIT CHECKS GOOD, REPLACE BCM
- IF CONDITION IS STILL PRESENT, REPLACE BCM EPROM

A damaged serial data line circuit or one of the components connected to the data line may cause multiple or intermittent setting of data line Codes B333, B334, B335, B336 and/or B337. When operating normally, the serial data line voltage should continually fluctuate from .1 to 5.0 volts.
If the serial data line has been shorted to ground, the voltage at the ALDL will be zero volts. If it has been shorted to voltage, it will be over 5 volts. If one of the components on the serial data line is affecting the data line voltage, the serial data voltage at the ALDL connector will be a steady value anywhere between .1 and 5.0 volts.

WHEN ALL DIAGNOSIS AND REPAIRS ARE COMPLETED. CLEAR CODES AND VERIFY PROPER OPERATION

Courtesy of General Motors Corp.

91E11902 91B11925

1991 ENGINE PERFORMANCE
Self-Diagnostics – Toronado & Trofeo PCM/BCM (Cont.)

GM
1-381

SERIAL DATA CIRCUIT
MULTIPLE INTERMITTENT CODES
CRT/DID (2 OF 2)

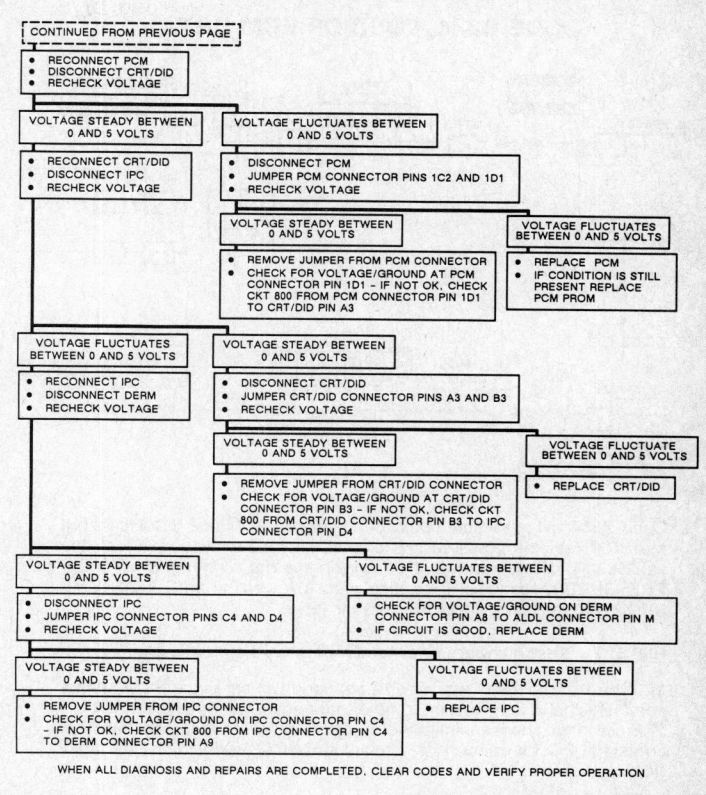

```
CONTINUED FROM PREVIOUS PAGE
  • RECONNECT PCM
  • DISCONNECT CRT/DID
  • RECHECK VOLTAGE

VOLTAGE STEADY BETWEEN        VOLTAGE FLUCTUATES BETWEEN
0 AND 5 VOLTS                  0 AND 5 VOLTS

  • RECONNECT CRT/DID          • DISCONNECT PCM
  • DISCONNECT IPC             • JUMPER PCM CONNECTOR PINS 1C2 AND 1D1
  • RECHECK VOLTAGE            • RECHECK VOLTAGE

              VOLTAGE STEADY BETWEEN          VOLTAGE FLUCTUATES
              0 AND 5 VOLTS                    BETWEEN 0 AND 5 VOLTS

              • REMOVE JUMPER FROM PCM CONNECTOR      • REPLACE PCM
              • CHECK FOR VOLTAGE/GROUND AT PCM       • IF CONDITION IS STILL
                CONNECTOR PIN 1D1 - IF NOT OK, CHECK    PRESENT REPLACE
                CKT 800 FROM PCM CONNECTOR PIN 1D1      PCM PROM
                TO CRT/DID PIN A3

VOLTAGE FLUCTUATES           VOLTAGE STEADY BETWEEN
BETWEEN 0 AND 5 VOLTS         0 AND 5 VOLTS

  • RECONNECT IPC             • DISCONNECT CRT/DID
  • DISCONNECT DERM           • JUMPER CRT/DID CONNECTOR PINS A3 AND B3
  • RECHECK VOLTAGE           • RECHECK VOLTAGE

              VOLTAGE STEADY BETWEEN          VOLTAGE FLUCTUATE
              0 AND 5 VOLTS                    BETWEEN 0 AND 5 VOLTS

              • REMOVE JUMPER FROM CRT/DID CONNECTOR   • REPLACE CRT/DID
              • CHECK FOR VOLTAGE/GROUND AT CRT/DID
                CONNECTOR PIN B3 - IF NOT OK, CHECK CKT
                800 FROM CRT/DID CONNECTOR PIN B3 TO IPC
                CONNECTOR PIN D4

VOLTAGE STEADY BETWEEN        VOLTAGE FLUCTUATES BETWEEN
0 AND 5 VOLTS                  0 AND 5 VOLTS

  • DISCONNECT IPC            • CHECK FOR VOLTAGE/GROUND ON DERM
  • JUMPER IPC CONNECTOR PINS C4 AND D4    CONNECTOR PIN A8 TO ALDL CONNECTOR PIN M
  • RECHECK VOLTAGE           • IF CIRCUIT IS GOOD, REPLACE DERM

VOLTAGE STEADY BETWEEN        VOLTAGE FLUCTUATES BETWEEN
0 AND 5 VOLTS                  0 AND 5 VOLTS

  • REMOVE JUMPER FROM IPC CONNECTOR       • REPLACE IPC
  • CHECK FOR VOLTAGE/GROUND ON IPC CONNECTOR PIN C4
    – IF NOT OK, CHECK CKT 800 FROM IPC CONNECTOR PIN C4
    TO DERM CONNECTOR PIN A9
```

WHEN ALL DIAGNOSIS AND REPAIRS ARE COMPLETED. CLEAR CODES AND VERIFY PROPER OPERATION

91C11926

Courtesy of General Motors Corp.

CODE B333, LOSS OF SIR DATA

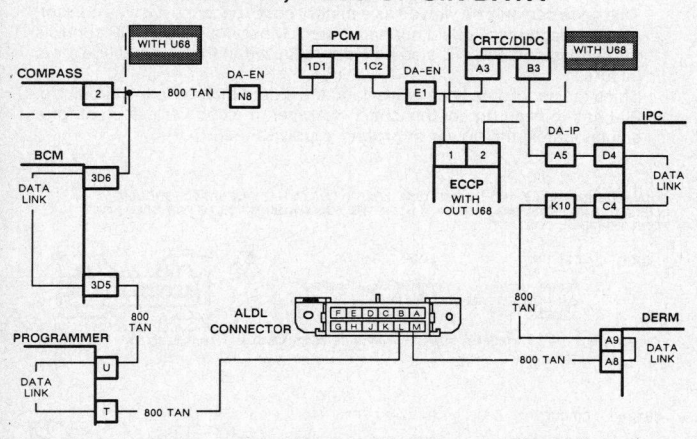

```
①  • KEY ON
    • OBSERVE SIR TELLTALE

TELLTALE FLASHES 7 TO 9 TIMES       TELLTALE DOESN'T FLASHES 7
AND GOES OUT                         TO 9 TIMES OR ON SOLID

②  • ENTER DIAGNOSTICS              REFER TO SIR SYSTEM CHECK
    • ARE CODES B334, B335, B336, OR B337 SET?

NO                                   YES

  • DISCONNECT DERM                  REFER TO TROUBLE TREES FOR SERIAL
  • MEASURE VOLTAGE AT HARNESS CAVITY A9    DATA CIRCUIT MULTIPLE INTERMITTENT
                                     CODES

BETWEEN .1 AND 4.5 VOLTS            LESS THAN .5 VOLTS

WAS CODE B333 CURRENT OR HISTORY?   REPAIR OPEN IN CKT 800 BETWEEN IPC AND
                                     DERM INCLUDING TERMINAL CONTACTS

CURRENT                 HISTORY

REPLACE DERM            CONDITION IS NOT PRESENT AT
                        THIS TIME. REFER TO 'NOTE ON
                        INTERMITTENTS'
```

Code B333 will set if communication between DERM (SIR controller) and BCM is lost. If code B333 is set, ELECTRICAL PROBLEM and INFLATABLE RESTRAINT telltales will be lit.

NOTE: Test numbers refer to numbers on diagnostic chart.

1) Checks to see if other data line components are experiencing communications problems.
2) Checks status of data line at compass module. Normal data line voltage is between .1 and 4.5 volts.

NOTE ON INTERMITTENTS
If an intermittent Code B333 is being stored, manipulate related wiring at DERM. An ELECTRICAL PROBLEM message indicates a loss of data and may help locate fault.

WHEN ALL DIAGNOSIS AND REPAIRS ARE COMPLETED. CLEAR CODES AND VERIFY PROPER OPERATION

91D11919 91H11921

Courtesy of General Motors Corp.

CODE B334, LOSS OF ECM DATA

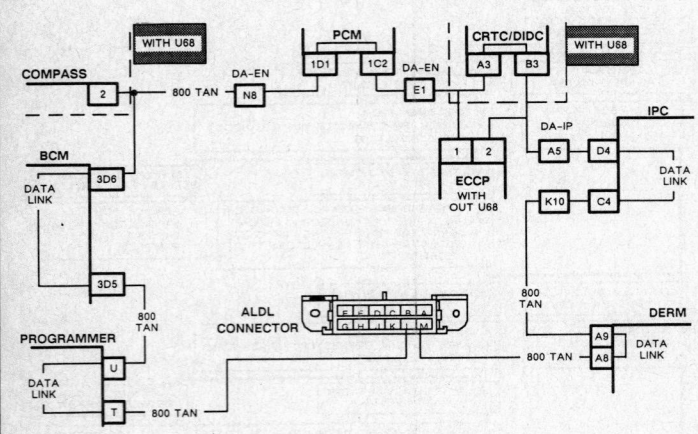

NOTE ON INTERMITTENTS

If an intermittent Code B334 is being set, manipulate the related wiring at PCM. With the ignition key on (engine not running), a LOW OIL PRESSURE message will indicate loss of PCM communication, and possibly help to isolate the intermittent without having to look for the code. Also check PCM and MEM-CAL connections.

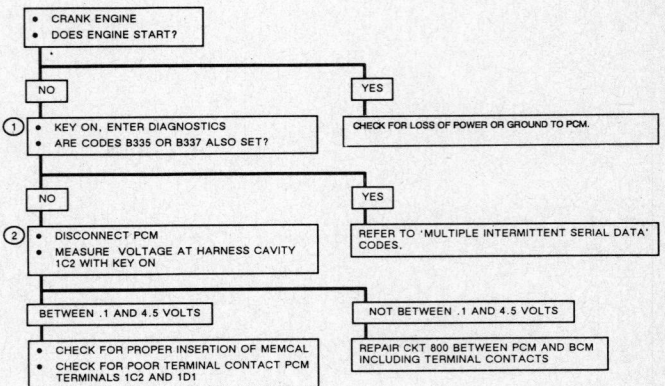

Code B334 will set if communication between PCM and BCM is lost. If the BCM remains powered and only serial communication is lost, the vehicle will still run, with ignition on (engine not running), a LOW OIL PRESSURE message will be displayed followed by an ELECTRICAL PROBLEM message about 25 seconds later.

NOTE: Test numbers refer to numbers on diagnostic chart.

1) If the PCM loses power or ground, code will set since PCM cannot communicate. It is important to note that engine will not start.
2) Since prior checks eliminated an open circuit, fault is poor terminal contact at PCM terminal 1C2, a faulty MEM-CAL connection or a faulty PCM.

WHEN ALL DIAGNOSIS AND REPAIRS ARE COMPLETED, CLEAR CODES AND VERIFY PROPER OPERATION

91D11919 91I11922

Courtesy of General Motors Corp.

CODE B335, LOSS OF ECCP OR CRT SERIAL DATA

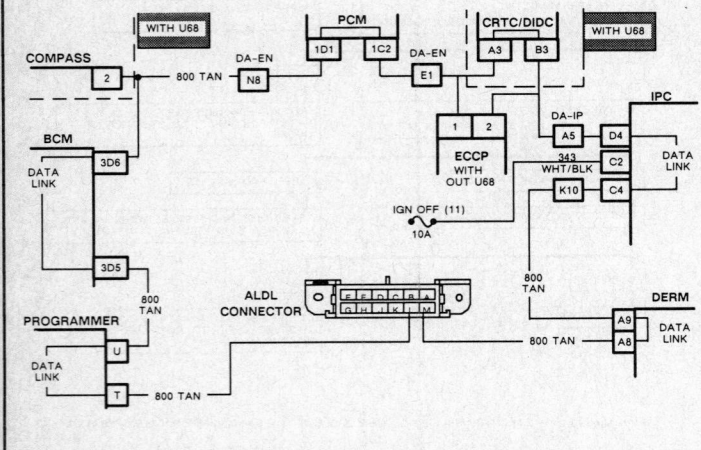

This code can only be viewed as a history code, because if it was current, service diagnostics could not be entered. Most likely the ECCP controls for heating and A/C will also be inoperative when the loss of serial data occurs.

Since the serial data lines are redundant, a double open in the circuit No. 800 has to occur to set this code. However, the code will also set for a single open in the power or ground supply to the ECCP.

CODE B335 INDICATES AN INTERMITTENT LOSS OF DATA HAS OCCURRED. SHOULD INTERMITTENT PROBLEMS PERSIST, CHECK THE FOLLOWING CIRCUITS FOR OPENS OR POOR TERMINAL CONTACT:

ECCP:	CIRCUIT	ECCP TERMINAL
	SERIAL DATA	TERMINALS 1 AND 2
	IGNITION 1 TERMINAL 7	
	GROUND	TERMINAL 4

IF INTERMITTENT PROBLEMS PERSIST, REPLACE ECCP HEAD.

ECCP CONNECTOR FRONT VIEW
HARNESS CAVITY VIEW

CRT/DID:	CIRCUIT	CRTC/DIDC TERMINAL
	SERIAL DATA	TERMINALS A3 AND B3
	IGNITION 1 TERMINAL A6	
	GROUND	TERMINALS A8

IF INTERMITTENT PROBLEMS PERSIST, REPLACE CRTC/DIDC.

CRT/DID CONTROLLER (CRTC/DIDC)
HARNESS CAVITY VIEW

91D11919 90B14382

Courtesy of General Motors Corp.

1991 ENGINE PERFORMANCE
Self-Diagnostics – Toronado & Trofeo PCM/BCM (Cont.)

GM
1-383

CODE B336, LOSS OF IPC SERIAL DATA

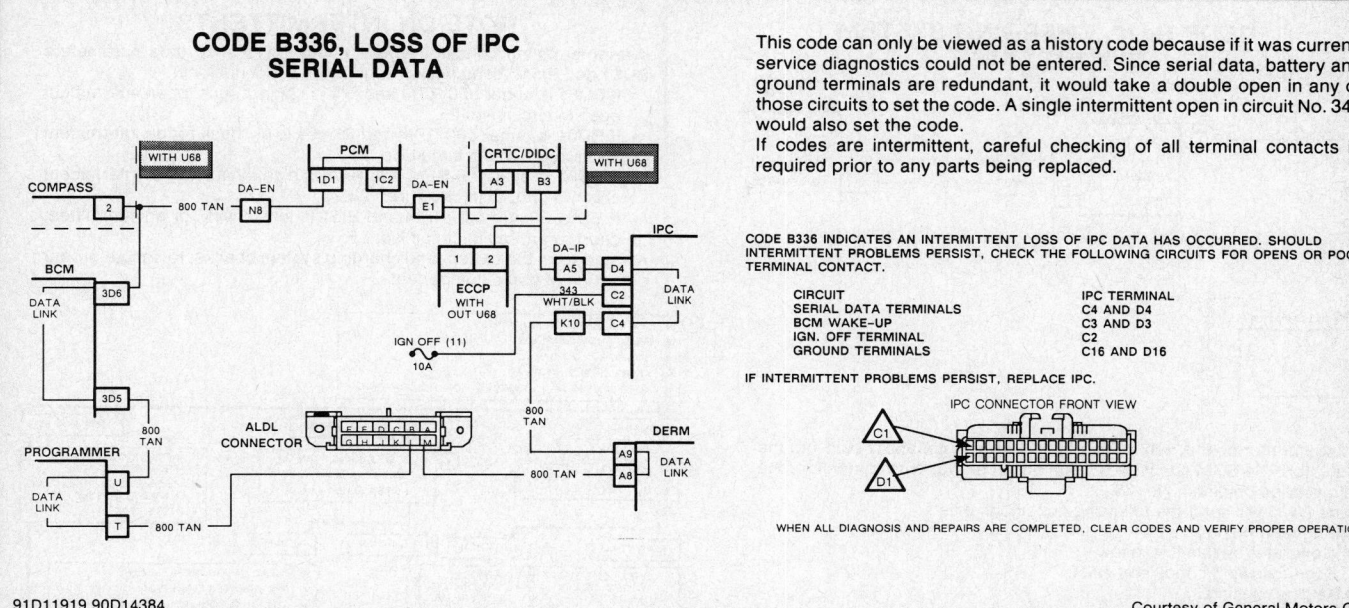

This code can only be viewed as a history code because if it was current, service diagnostics could not be entered. Since serial data, battery and ground terminals are redundant, it would take a double open in any of those circuits to set the code. A single intermittent open in circuit No. 343 would also set the code.

If codes are intermittent, careful checking of all terminal contacts is required prior to any parts being replaced.

CODE B336 INDICATES AN INTERMITTENT LOSS OF IPC DATA HAS OCCURRED. SHOULD INTERMITTENT PROBLEMS PERSIST, CHECK THE FOLLOWING CIRCUITS FOR OPENS OR POOR TERMINAL CONTACT.

CIRCUIT	IPC TERMINAL
SERIAL DATA TERMINALS	C4 AND D4
BCM WAKE-UP	C3 AND D3
IGN. OFF TERMINAL	C2
GROUND TERMINALS	C16 AND D16

IF INTERMITTENT PROBLEMS PERSIST, REPLACE IPC.

WHEN ALL DIAGNOSIS AND REPAIRS ARE COMPLETED, CLEAR CODES AND VERIFY PROPER OPERATION

91D11919 90D14384

Courtesy of General Motors Corp.

CODE B337, LOSS OF HVAC PROGRAMMER DATA

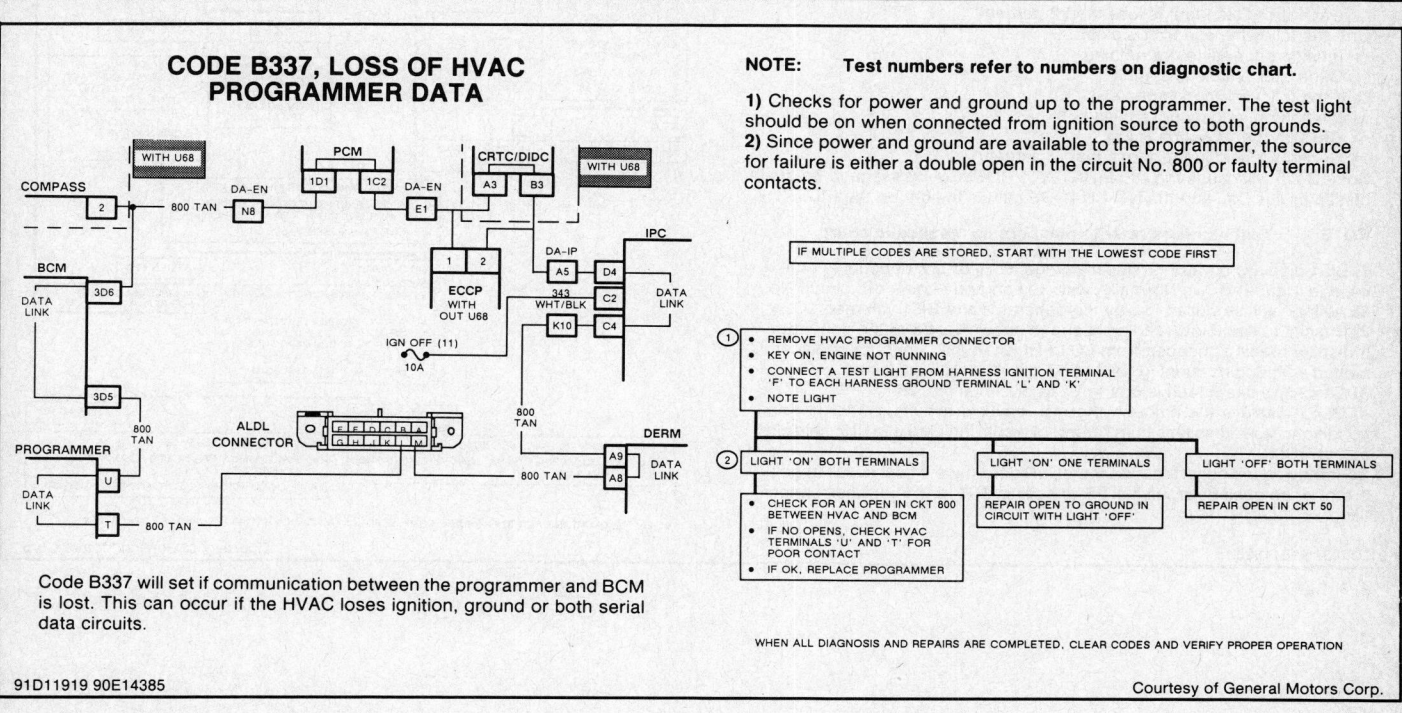

NOTE: Test numbers refer to numbers on diagnostic chart.

1) Checks for power and ground up to the programmer. The test light should be on when connected from ignition source to both grounds.
2) Since power and ground are available to the programmer, the source for failure is either a double open in the circuit No. 800 or faulty terminal contacts.

IF MULTIPLE CODES ARE STORED, START WITH THE LOWEST CODE FIRST

① • REMOVE HVAC PROGRAMMER CONNECTOR
• KEY ON, ENGINE NOT RUNNING
• CONNECT A TEST LIGHT FROM HARNESS IGNITION TERMINAL 'F' TO EACH HARNESS GROUND TERMINAL 'L' AND 'K'
• NOTE LIGHT

② LIGHT 'ON' BOTH TERMINALS | LIGHT 'ON' ONE TERMINALS | LIGHT 'OFF' BOTH TERMINALS

• CHECK FOR AN OPEN IN CKT 800 BETWEEN HVAC AND BCM
• IF NO OPENS, CHECK HVAC TERMINALS 'U' AND 'T' FOR POOR CONTACT
• IF OK, REPLACE PROGRAMMER

REPAIR OPEN TO GROUND IN CIRCUIT WITH LIGHT 'OFF'

REPAIR OPEN IN CKT 50

Code B337 will set if communication between the programmer and BCM is lost. This can occur if the HVAC loses ignition, ground or both serial data circuits.

WHEN ALL DIAGNOSIS AND REPAIRS ARE COMPLETED, CLEAR CODES AND VERIFY PROPER OPERATION

91D11919 90E14385

Courtesy of General Motors Corp.

CODE B410, CHARGING SYSTEM CIRCUIT FAULT

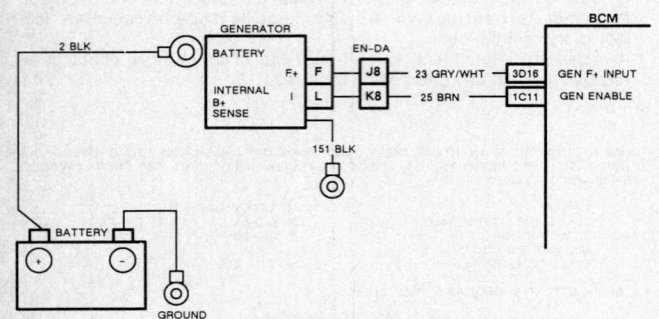

The generator on this vehicle has fault detection capability built into the regulator. The BCM supplies 12 volts on circuit No. 25 and monitors the field voltage on circuit No. 23.

Code B410 will set if the following conditions exist:
- Engine running
- Generator enable line is low

Or if the following conditions exist:
- Engine running
- Generator enable line high
- Generator field input is less than 2 percent

Or if the following conditions exist:
- Ignition on, engine not running
- Generator enable line is high

Or if the following conditions exist:
- Ignition on, engine not running
- Generator enable line is low
- Generator field input is less than 2 percent

Code B410 will cause the GENERATOR PROBLEM message to be displayed on the DIC and the NO CHARGE telltale to light on the IPC.

NOTE: Test numbers refer to numbers on diagnostic chart.

1) BI51 displays generator signal voltage as HI or LO, depending on the voltage state at BCM. Normally, with key on and engine off, circuit No. 25 voltage will be pulled low by the generator and BI51 will read LO.

2) Checks to see if low reading is due to circuit No. 25 or the generator. If display reading changes from LO to HI when the generator is disconnected with engine running, BCM and circuit No. 25 are okay.

3) Checks to see if fault is due to BCM or circuit No. 25.

4) BD51 displays the amount of generator field activity. Under normal conditions, a reading less than 7 percent would indicate a fault in field circuit at BCM.

5) Removing the generator connector will determine if fault is due to generator or an open in circuit No. 25, including BCM and interface connector.

NOTE ON INTERMITTENTS

If an intermittent condition exists, check B410 snap data parameters BD61 and BI51. Also check for the following conditions:
- If BD61 is under 500 RPM and BI51 is high, check for an intermittent open in circuit No. 25.
- If BD61 is under 500 RPM and BI51 is low, check for an intermittent short to ground in circuit No. 23.
- If BD61 is over 500 RPM and BI51 is high, check for an intermittent short to ground in circuit No. 23.
- If BD61 is over 500 RPM and BI51 is low, check for an intermittent short to ground in circuit No. 25.

Also perform the battery and charging system checks, to ensure proper operation of these components.

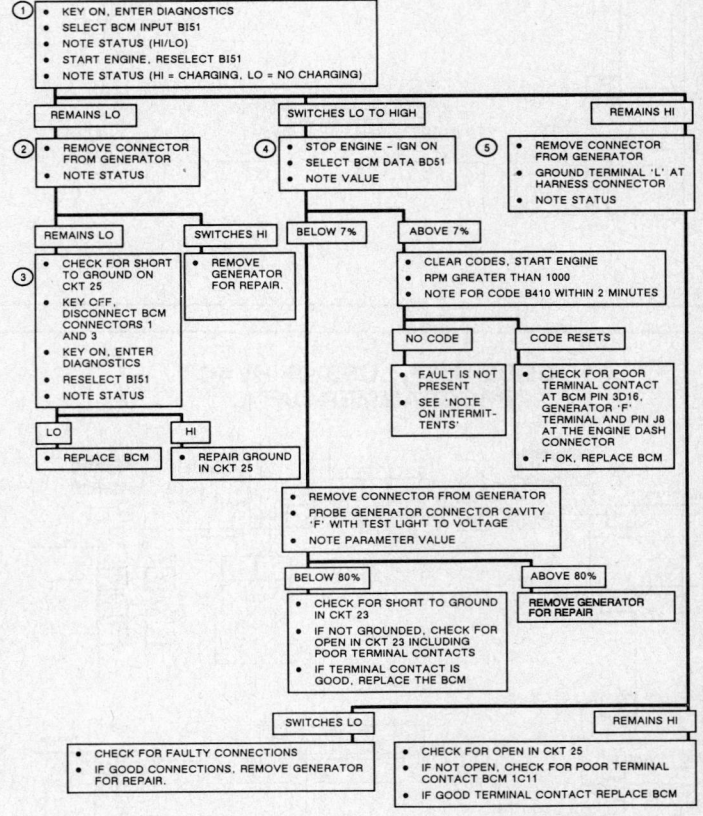

WHEN ALL DIAGNOSIS AND REPAIRS ARE COMPLETED, CLEAR CODES AND VERIFY PROPER OPERATION

91D11927 91E11928

Courtesy of General Motors Corp.

1991 ENGINE PERFORMANCE
Self-Diagnostics – Toronado & Trofeo PCM/BCM (Cont.)

GM
1-385

CODE B411 OR B412, BATTERY VOLTAGE TOO HIGH OR TOO LOW

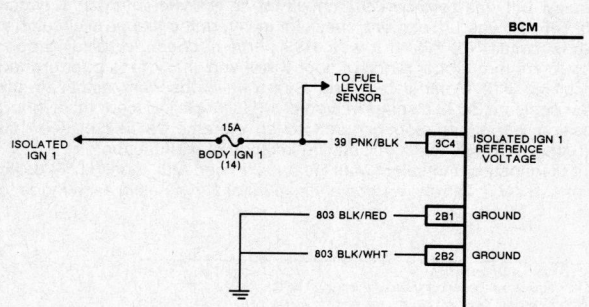

The BCM monitors IGN 1 voltage on terminal 3C4 as a reference for fuel control. Code B411 will set when ignition is on, engine RPM is greater than 800 and the BCM sees an IGN 1 reference voltage of less than 10.6 volts. Code B412 will be set if the BCM sees voltage over 16 volts. Both B411 and B412 will cause the GENERATOR PROBLEM message to be displayed on the IPC.

NOTE: Test numbers refer to numbers on diagnostic chart.

1) BD50 displays battery voltage. The normal range is 10.6-16 volts.
2) Checks to see if low voltage reading is due to circuit or battery. With engine running, if voltage is less than 10 volts, BCM and wiring are okay.
3) Checks to see if low voltage reading is due to circuit or BCM. If voltage reading at BCM is less than 10.6 volts, BCM is okay.
4) Checks to see if high voltage reading is due to generator or faulty BCM.
5) Checks to see if charging voltage goes too high with higher engine RPM or electrical load.

91F11929 91I11930

NOTE ON INTERMITTENTS

If an intermittent Code B411 or B412 is being set, observe BD50 display. This battery voltage reading is monitored from 15-amp ISO IGN 1 fuse, fuel reference voltage. If code is being set due to a high current draw in a certain vehicle component, this can be observed by reading BD50 display. Operate various components while watching for reading to drop to less than 10 volts or increase to greater than 16 volts.

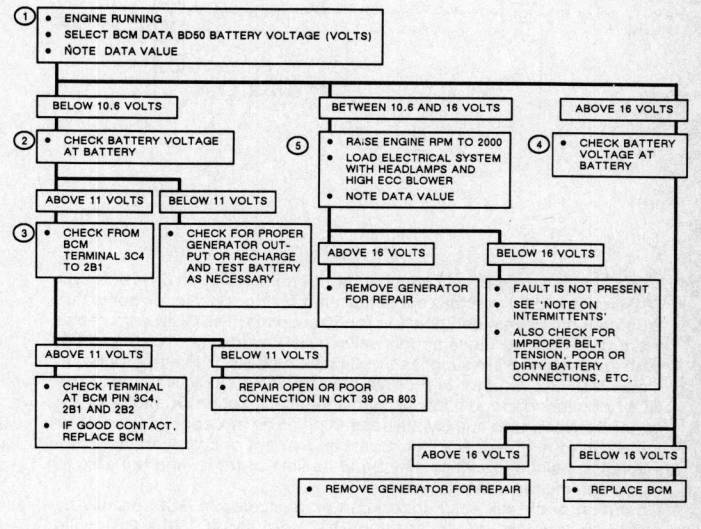

WHEN ALL DIAGNOSIS AND REPAIRS ARE COMPLETED, CLEAR CODES AND VERIFY PROPER OPERATION

GM
1-386

1991 ENGINE PERFORMANCE
Self-Diagnostics – Toronado & Trofeo PCM/BCM (Cont.)

CODE B440, AIR MIX VALVE (DOOR) CIRCUIT PROBLEM

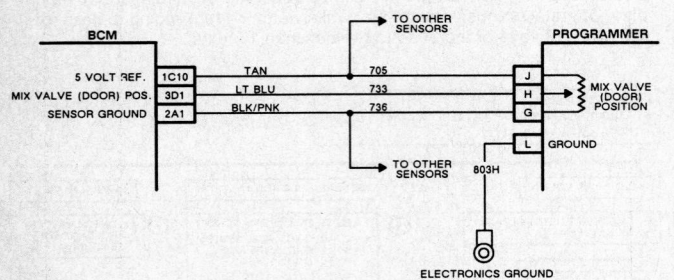

Code B440 is set by BCM if commanded air mix door position is between 30 percent and 80 percent, but actual air mix door position is not within 2 percent of commanded position for 60 seconds. The BCM commands the programmer to move air mix valve (door) over data circuit No. 800. With ignition on, BCM supplies 5 volts on circuit No. 705 and ground on circuit No. 736. A motor in programmer drives air mix valve (door). The BCM monitors door position through a feedback pot on DC motor which varies between zero and 5 volts depending on air mix door position. If air mix valve (door) feedback indicates it is near hot or cold extreme, code will not set since mix door may be at its limit of travel and not able to reach commanded door position.

Operation of air mix valve (door) can be evaluated in BCM display by actual air mix valve (door) position (BD23 display ACT MIX DR) while changing the programmer number (override BS01 display PROGRAM NO).

NOTE: Test numbers refer to numbers on diagnostic chart.

1) BD23 display indicates actual air mix valve (door) position. The normal range is 1-99 percent. BCM override value BS01 display is for program number.
2) Checks to see if fault could be due to 5-volt reference and ground circuit, or sensor circuit.
3) Checks to see if fault is due to programmer or sensor circuit.
4) Checks to see if fault is due to circuit or BCM.
5) This step checks to see if open circuit reading is due to circuit No. 736 or circuit No. 705.

NOTE ON INTERMITTENTS

If an intermittent Code B440 is being set, check B440 snap data BD23 display. If it was zero percent, check for an intermittent open in circuit No. 736. If it was 100 percent, check for an intermittent open in circuit No. 733 or circuit No. 705. If it was 1-99 percent, check for binding door movement throughout range of door travel and check for a poor ground circuit No. 803. Manipulate related wiring while observing actual air mix door position (BD23 display) movement. If failure is induced, valve (door) position will either stop or jump to an extreme value (zero to 100 percent). This will assist in isolating location of malfunction.

Exit diagnostics and select Max Heat (90°F) and Max Cool (60°F) using normal HVAC controls, waiting a minimum of 2 minutes in each mode to see if code sets.

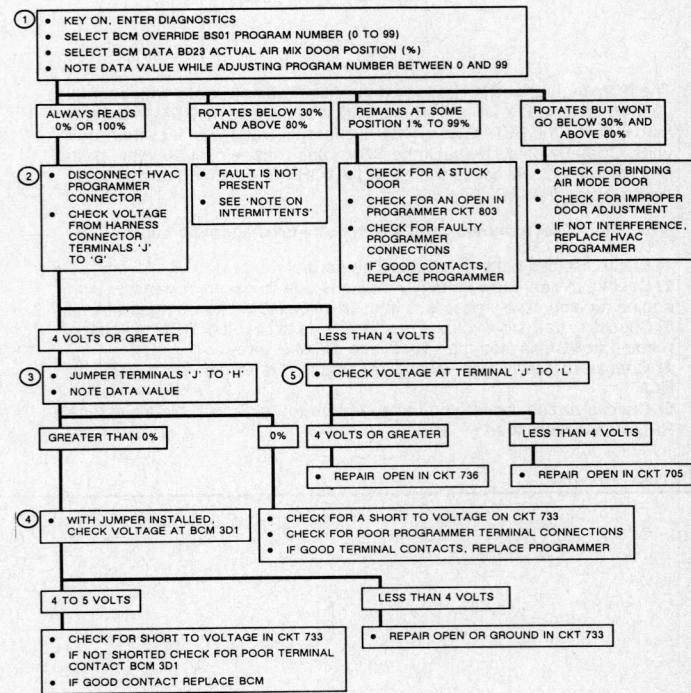

WHEN ALL DIAGNOSIS AND REPAIRS ARE COMPLETED, CLEAR CODES AND VERIFY PROPER OPERATION

Courtesy of General Motors Corp.

91B05376 91E05943

1991 ENGINE PERFORMANCE
Self-Diagnostics – Toronado & Trofeo PCM/BCM (Cont.)

GM
1-387

CODES B446, B447 & B448, REFRIGERANT SYSTEM PROBLEM (1 OF 2)

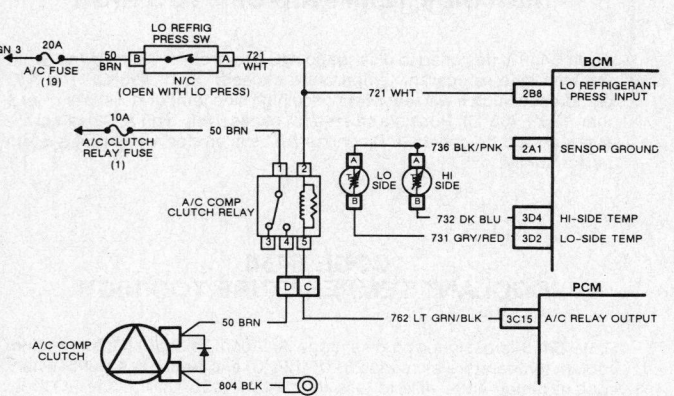

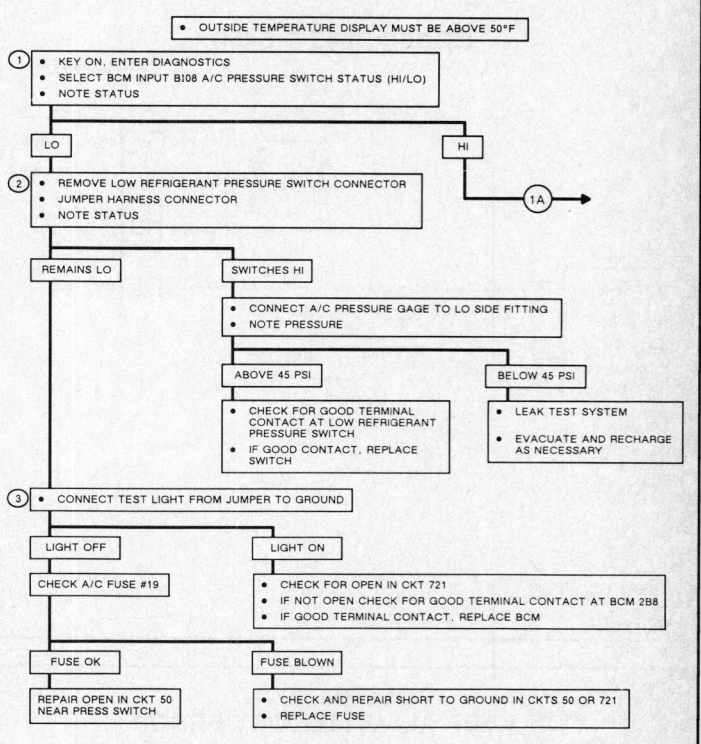

Code B446 will set if the low side temperature drops too quickly during compressor engagement. Code B447 will set if low side temperature drops much too quickly during compressor engagement or the low refrigerant pressure switch opens during compressor engagement. Code B448 will set if the low refrigerant pressure switch remains open for greater than 3 minutes.

NOTE: Test numbers refer to numbers on diagnostic chart.

1) BCM input value BI08 displays voltage state of circuit at BCM.
2) Checks to see if open circuit reading is due to circuit or switch.
3) Checks to see if fault is on ignition side or BCM side of switch circuit.

91D05377 91G05944

Courtesy of General Motors Corp.

CODES B446, B447 & B448 REFRIGERANT SYSTEM PROBLEM (2 OF 2)

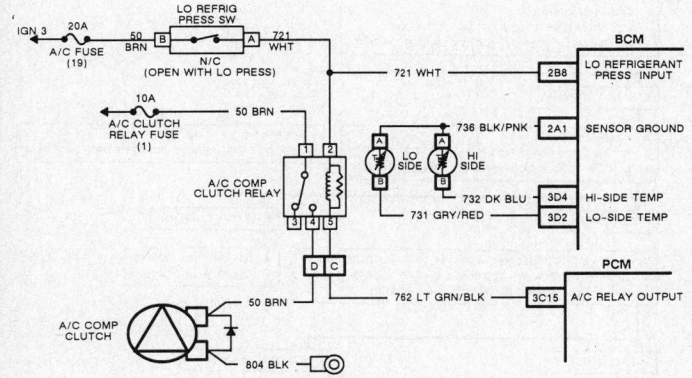

It has been determined from previous chart that problem is not in low refrigerant pressure switch circuit.

NOTE: Test numbers refer to numbers on diagnostic chart.

1) This is a test to determine if A/C low refrigerant pressure switch opens while compressor is running. If BI08 display remains HI during compressor engagement, then system fault is due to refrigerant.
2) This checks if switch is opening due to low refrigerant pressure charge or switch is faulty.

NOTE ON INTERMITTENTS

If Codes B446 and B447 are both set, check low side temperature sensor and circuitry. If okay, evacuate and recharge system. If Codes B447 and/or B448 are set, check low refrigerant pressure switch and circuit.

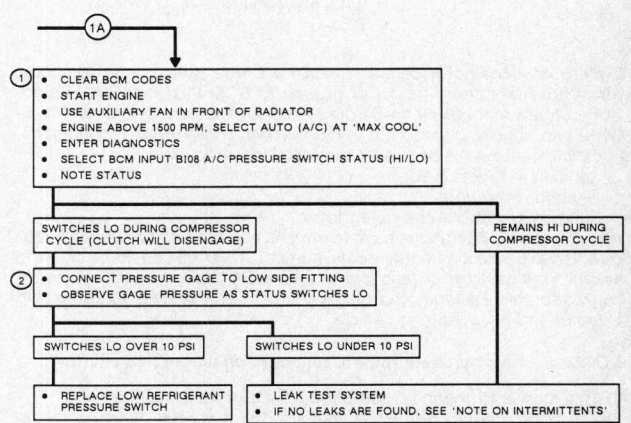

WHEN ALL DIAGNOSIS AND REPAIRS ARE COMPLETED, CLEAR CODES AND VERIFY PROPER OPERATION

91D05377 90G14395

Courtesy of General Motors Corp.

GM
1-388

1991 ENGINE PERFORMANCE
Self-Diagnostics – Toronado & Trofeo PCM/BCM (Cont.)

CODES B449 & B450

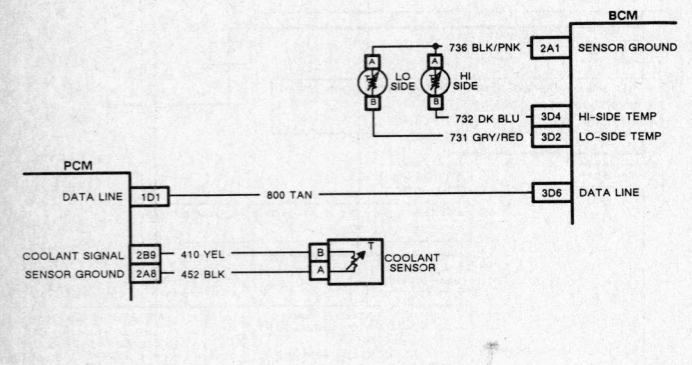

CODE B449,
HIGH SIDE TEMPERATURE TOO HIGH

Code B449 is designed to disengage A/C compressor clutch in the event the high side refrigerant temperature exceeds 199°F (93°C). The A/C compressor clutch will reactivate once high side temperature falls to less than 199°F (93°C). Possible causes for excessively high A/C head pressures should be checked. Diagnose A/C system for refrigerant system performance.

CODE B450,
COOLANT TEMPERATURE TOO HIGH

Code B450 is designed to disengage A/C compressor clutch if engine coolant temperature exceeds 261°F (126°C) and re-engage clutch when coolant temperature falls to less than 248°F (120°C). If Code EO14 is also stored, follow diagnosis for that code first. Engine overheating may accompany this code. If coolant temperature exceeds normal operating range, check for sources of overheating. Carefully check all sources of intermittent engine overheating, such as improper coolant fan operation, faulty belt or tension, low coolant level and restrictions or faulty hoses and/or routing.

91H05379

CODE B552,
BCM KEEP ALIVE MEMORY ERROR

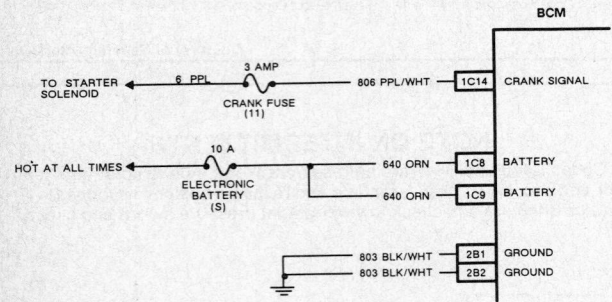

Code B552 does not necessarily indicate a fault, but is a normal occurrence anytime battery power or ground to BCM has been interrupted. Code B552 cannot be cleared from memory in the normal manner. Code B552 can only be cleared if it is not current. Under normal conditions, code will become history under the following conditions:
- Ignition in lock position
- Wait for 5 seconds
- Ignition key on, re-enter diagnosis

After the above conditions have taken place, code should now be history, and can be cleared in the normal manner. This code could be set if the system voltage drops to less than 8 volts at BCM terminal 1C8. Possible causes for this are faulty charging system, starter system, extreme cold weather and jump starting vehicle.

NOTE: Test numbers refer to numbers on diagnostic chart.

1) This step is to change Code B552 from current to history.
2) Checks to see if Code B552 was set due to a fault during cranking mode.

91J11931 91A11932

3) Checks for adequate system voltage at BCM terminal 1C8. System voltage must not drop to less than 8 volts during engine cranking. By removing fuel pump fuse, engine will not start and voltage during engine cranking can be observed.

CODE B552 INDICATES THAT THE KEEP ALIVE OR 'LONG TERM' MEMORY IN THE BCM HAS BEEN RESET. THIS WILL BE THE CASE WHENEVER POWER IS REMOVED FROM THE BCM, SUCH AS DISCONNECTING THE BATTERY CABLES OR DISCONNECTING THE BCM POWER CONNECTOR. THIS CODE SHOULD BE CLEARED FROM MEMORY AFTER RESTORING THE BCM POWER SUPPLY.

- VEHICLE MUST BE AT NORMAL OPERATING TEMPERATURE
- CHARGING AND STARTER SYSTEM MUST BE IN GOOD OPERATING CONDITION

① - KEY IN 'LOCK' POSITION
- WAIT 5 SECONDS
- KEY ON, ENTER DIAGNOSTICS
- NOTE WHETHER CODE B552 IS CURRENT OR NOT

B552 NOT CURRENT | B552 CURRENT

② - START ENGINE
- RE-ENTER DIAGNOSTICS
- NOTE WHETHER CODE B552 IS CURRENT OR NOT

- REPEAT STEP 1 ABOVE
- IF CODE B552 RESETS CURRENT, REPLACE BCM

B552 CURRENT | B552 NOT CURRENT

③ - REMOVE CCCI FUSE #8 (ALLOWS FOR EXTENDED CRANK)
- BACKPROBE BCM PIN 1C8 WHILE ENGINE IS CRANKING
- IS VOLTAGE ABOVE 8 VOLTS DURING CRANK?

- NO TROUBLE FOUND
- CLEAR BCM CODES

ABOVE 8 VOLTS | NOT ABOVE 8 VOLTS

- CHECK FOR POOR TERMINAL CONTACT AT BCM PIN 1C8 OR 1C9
- IF GOOD CONTACT, REPLACE BCM

- REPAIR CHARGING OR STARTING SYSTEM FOR LOW VOLTAGE CONDITION

WHEN ALL DIAGNOSIS AND REPAIRS ARE COMPLETED, CLEAR CODES AND VERIFY PROPER OPERATION

1991 ENGINE PERFORMANCE
Self-Diagnostics – Toronado & Trofeo PCM/BCM (Cont.)

GM
1-389

CODE B556, ODOMETER (EE) PROM ERROR

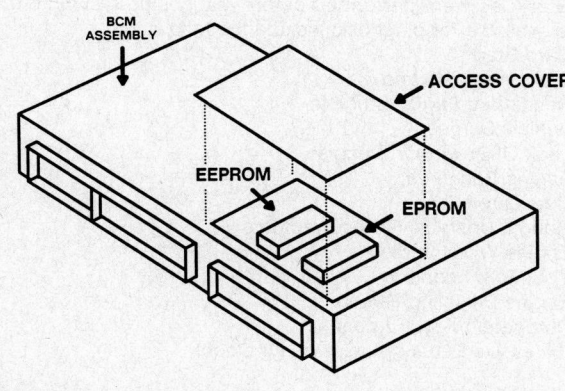

90A14399

Code B556 indicates that EEPROM, which records elapsed odometer mileage, is not being read by BCM. Usually along with Code 556, ERROR will be displayed in the odometer display. The EEPROM contains specific vehicle information such as vehicle ID number, season odometer mileage and certain vehicle options. Since this information is programmed for the specific vehicle in which it is installed, an EEPROM cannot be transferred from one vehicle to another. Check for proper EEPROM installation. If the EEPROM is properly installed, no bent pins, but Code B556 persists, replace EEPROM. Replacement EEPROMs must be obtained through an authorized Delco Service Center.

Courtesy of General Motors Corp.

CODE C710, CRTC SWITCHING CIRCUIT PROBLEM

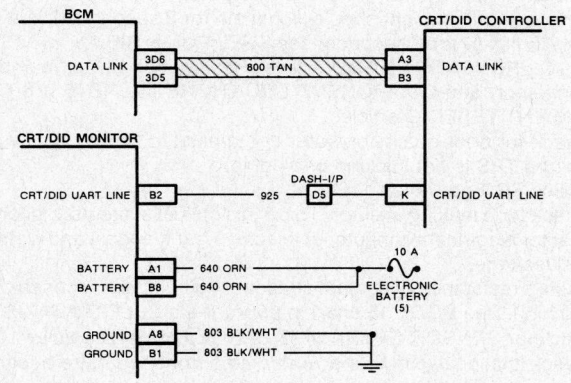

NOTE: Test numbers refer to numbers on diagnostic chart.

1) CRT/DID monitor needs communication from the CRT/DID controller to initially illuminate. Therefore, if CRT monitor lights initially, it is receiving signals from controller.
2) If CRT/DID is blank at times and Code C710 is set, monitor is not receiving data intermittently.
3) Checks voltage on CRT controller-to-CRT/DID data line. Normal voltage is between 1.5 and 4.5 volts and fluctuates some.
4) Checks whether CRT/DID or CRT controller is causing low voltage reading on data line.

91B11933 91C11934

NOTE ON INTERMITTENTS
Check connections at CRT/DID monitor and CRT controller. If both connections are clean and tight, either CRT/DID monitor or CRT controller could be at fault.

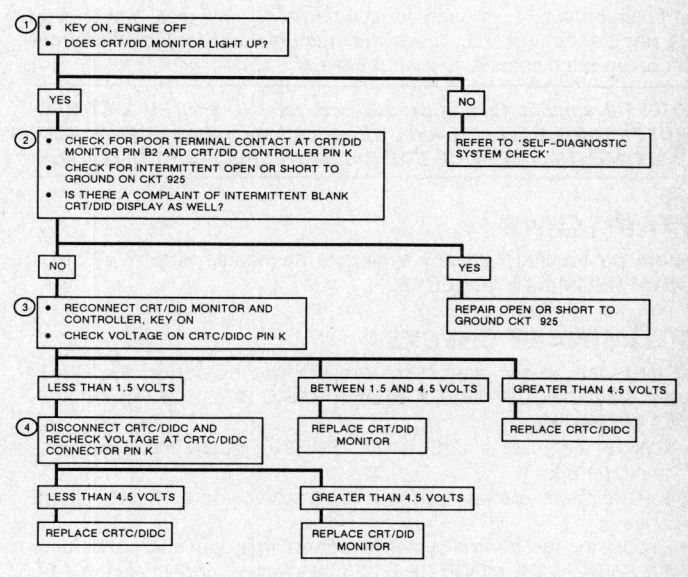

WHEN ALL DIAGNOSIS AND REPAIRS ARE COMPLETED, CLEAR CODES AND VERIFY PROPER OPERATION

Courtesy of General Motors Corp.

1991 ENGINE PERFORMANCE
Trouble Shooting – No Codes

Beretta, Bonneville, Brougham, Camaro, Caprice, Cavalier, Century, Corsica, Corvette, Custom Cruiser, Cutlass Calais, Cutlass Ciera, Cutlass Cruiser, Cutlass Supreme, DeVille, Eighty-Eight, Eldorado, Firebird, Fleetwood, Grand Am, Grand Prix, LeSabre, Lumina, Ninety-Eight, Park Avenue, Reatta, Regal, Riviera, Roadmaster, Seville, Skylark, Sunbird, Toronado, Touring Sedan, Trofeo, 6000

INTRODUCTION

Before attempting to diagnose symptoms or intermittent faults, ensure steps in BASIC DIAGNOSTIC PROCEDURES and SELF-DIAGNOSTICS articles have been performed. Use this article to diagnose driveability problems that exist when a hard-fault code is not present.

Symptom checks are intended to direct the technician to malfunctioning component(s) so that further diagnosis may be performed. A symptom should lead to further testing of specific components or systems, or verification of adjustment specifications.

Use intermittent test procedures to locate intermittent driveability problems that do not occur when the vehicle is being tested. These problems may cause a noticeable driveability problem or cause the malfunction warning light to illuminate on some vehicles.

It is also possible that certain driveability concerns have been rectified by the manufacturer through substitution of a revised calibration chip or computer control unit. Check with manufacturer for latest information on updated chips and control units.

NOTE: For specific testing procedures, refer to SYSTEM & COMPONENT TESTING article. To verify specifications, refer to ON-VEHICLE ADJUSTMENTS or SERVICE & ADJUSTMENT SPECIFICATIONS article.

SYMPTOMS

Before proceeding with any symptom diagnosis, perform all steps under PRELIMINARY CHECKS.

PRELIMINARY CHECKS

- Verify the on-car diagnostics are working by performing DIAGNOSTIC CIRCUIT CHECK chart in BASIC DIAGNOSTIC PROCEDURES article.
- Ensure the ECM and SERVICE ENGINE SOON light are functioning properly.
- Ensure there are no trouble codes stored, or only intermittent ones.
- Ensure the fuel control system is operating properly by performing FIELD SERVICE MODE CHECK (fuel injected models except 4.9L Cadillac) or PFI SYSTEM CHECK (Cadillac except Brougham) in BASIC DIAGNOSTIC PROCEDURES article.
- Perform fuel system pressure test in BASIC DIAGNOSTIC PROCEDURES article.
- Perform a careful visual inspection of all systems.

After all checks have been performed, verify customer complaint and locate correct symptom. Check items indicated under that symptom. Not all items listed under each symptom apply to all models and systems. These procedures will normally recommend testing of a system or component on vehicle, such as EGR, EST, TCC, etc. See SYSTEM & COMPONENT TESTING article for test procedures.

NOTE: If ECM displays data but engine fails to start, proceed to NO START – ENGINE CRANKS OKAY in BASIC DIAGNOSTIC PROCEDURES article.

SYMPTOM DIAGNOSIS

Symptom checks cannot be used properly unless the problem occurs while the vehicle is being tested. To reduce diagnostic time, ensure steps in BASIC DIAGNOSTIC PROCEDURES and SELF-DIAGNOSTICS articles were performed before diagnosing a symptom. Symptoms available for diagnosis include the following:

- Hard Start
- Stalls After Starting
- Hesitation, Sag or Stumble
- Vehicle Surges
- Lack Of Power Or Sluggish
- Engine Backfires
- Cuts Out, Misses
- Rough, Unstable Or Incorrect Idle
- Engine Will Not Idle
- Poor Fuel Economy
- Engine Dieseling/Run-On
- Detonation/Spark Knock
- Excessive Exhaust Emission Or Odors

HARD START

Symptom Definition – Engine cranks okay, but does not start for a long time. Engine eventually starts, and may die immediately or run okay.

Possible Cause & Correction – Check the following items.

- Check fuel pump relay by connecting test light between fuel pump test terminal (terminal "G" of ALDL on most vehicles) and ground. Turn ignition on. Light should illuminate for 2 seconds. If light does not illuminate for 2 seconds, see FUEL PUMP RELAY in SYSTEM & COMPONENT TESTING article. For location of fuel pump test connector, see COMPONENT LOCATIONS in SYSTEM & COMPONENT TESTING article.
- Check for poor quality or water contaminated fuel.
- Ensure TPS is not sticking or binding.
- Check EGR operation.
- Check for a leaking injector. To do this on TBI systems, disconnect injector electrical connector at injector. Crank engine and watch for fuel leakage.
- Ensure resistance of coolant sensor circuit or coolant sensor is not too high. See CODE 15 chart in appropriate SELF-DIAGNOSTICS article or SENSOR OPERATING RANGE CHARTS article.
- Check ignition system for a worn distributor shaft, bare or shorted wires, incorrect pick-up coil resistance, loose ignition coil ground or moisture in distributor cap. Check for adequate spark using Spark Tester (ST-125).
- Check for shorts by spraying plug wires with a fine mist of water.
- Remove spark plugs and check for wet plugs, cracks, improper gap, burned electrodes or heavy carbon deposits.
- Check for correct fuel pressure in all speed ranges.
- A faulty in-tank fuel pump check valve (PFI only) will allow fuel in lines to drain back to tank after engine is stopped. To check this condition, turn ignition off, disconnect fuel pressure line at fuel rail, remove filler cap, and connect a radiator test pump and apply 15 psi (1.0 kg/cm²) pressure. If pressure will hold for 60 seconds, check valve is okay.
- Ensure the installed PROM/MEM-CAL application is correct for that particular vehicle. Check with dealer for latest application information.
- Check for restricted exhaust system. See RESTRICTED EXHAUST SYSTEM CHECK in BASIC DIAGNOSTIC PROCEDURES article.

STALLS AFTER STARTING

Symptom Definition – Engine starts okay but dies after brief idle, dies as soon as any load is placed on engine (such as turning on air conditioner or engaging transmission), or on initial driveaway.

Possible Cause & Correction – Check the following items.

- Ensure hot air tube is connected to air cleaner.
- Check for proper operation of thermostatic air cleaner.

- Check for proper operation of Idle Air Control (IAC) system.
- Check PCV valve for proper operation.
- Unplug MAF or MAP sensor. ECM will substitute a default value for sensor signal. If stall condition is eliminated, replace sensor.
- Check EGR system for proper operation.
- If stall occurs when air conditioner is turned on, check air conditioner clutch signal (A/C request) to ECM terminal. Voltage at A/C terminal of ECM should be battery voltage when air conditioner compressor clutch is engaged. A high voltage surge due to a shorted compressor clutch diode could cause ECM shutdown.
- Check for an overcharged air conditioner system.
- Check for plugged or restricted fuel lines.
- Using Spark Tester (ST-125), check for a weak spark from ignition coil.

HESITATION, SAG OR STUMBLE

Symptom Definition – Momentary lack of response when accelerator is pushed down. Condition occurs at all vehicle speeds, or usually occurs when taking off from a stop.

Possible Cause & Correction – Check the following items.

- Visually check vacuum hoses for splits, kinks and proper connections as shown on Vehicle Emission Control Information label. Check ignition wires for cracking, hardness and proper connections at both distributor cap and spark plugs.
- Check wires for pinches, cuts, and proper connections.
- Ensure fuel pressure is correct at all speeds. Also, check for poor quality or water contaminated fuel.
- Check for fouled spark plugs.
- Ensure installed PROM/MEM-CAL is correct for that particular vehicle. Check with dealer for latest application information.
- Check for a binding or sticking TPS.
- Ensure initial ignition timing is properly set.
- Ensure ECM-controlled idle speed is correct.
- Check EGR system for proper operation.
- Disconnect fuel injector electrical connectors. Crank engine and check for injector leaks.
- Check engine cooling system thermostat for proper operation and application.
- Check for an open in HEI ground circuit.
- Check canister purge system for proper operation.
- Check charging system output. Repair charging system if voltage is less than 9 volts or more than 17 volts.
- On PFI vehicles, perform INJECTOR BALANCE TEST in SYSTEM & COMPONENT TESTING article.

VEHICLE SURGES

Symptom Definition – Engine power varies under steady throttle or cruise. Vehicle speeds up and slows down without changing position of accelerator pedal.

Possible Cause & Correction – Check the following items.

- Check operation of thermostatic air cleaner damper door.
- Ensure Park/Neutral switch is properly adjusted.
- Check for intermittent open or short to ground in Torque Converter Clutch (TCC) or HEI by-pass circuits.
- Check for proper operation of canister purge system.
- Check for proper operation of ESC system.
- Check for proper operation of EGR system.
- Ensure initial ignition timing is properly set.
- Check for adequate spark output using Spark Tester (ST-125).
- Check O_2 sensor for lead or RTV sealant contamination. This will cause a false high voltage signal to ECM. ECM will respond by leaning air/fuel ratio.
- Check in-line fuel filter and replace if dirty or clogged.
- Check fuel for water contamination. Ensure fuel system pressure is correct at all engine speeds.
- Remove spark plugs and check for wet plugs, cracks, improper gap, burned electrodes or heavy carbon deposits. Also, check condition of distributor cap, rotor and spark plug wires.
- Check charging system output. Repair charging system if voltage is less than 9 volts or more than 17 volts.
- Check A/C for excessive charge.

- Check for restricted exhaust system. See RESTRICTED EXHAUST SYSTEM CHECK in BASIC DIAGNOSTIC PROCEDURES article.

LACK OF POWER OR SLUGGISH

Symptom Definition – Engine delivers less power than expected. Little or no increase in speed when accelerator is pushed down.

Possible Cause & Correction – Check the following items.

- Ensure air filter and fuel filter are not plugged. Replace if necessary. Check for incorrect fuel pressure.
- Check for proper operation of thermostatic air cleaner damper door.
- Ensure initial ignition timing is properly set.
- Check for proper operation of TCC or VCC system.
- Check ESC system for excessive retard.
- Check EST system for proper operation.
- Ensure EGR valve is not open all the time.
- Check exhaust system for restrictions, such as a damaged or collapsed pipe, muffler or catalytic converter. See RESTRICTED EXHAUST SYSTEM CHECK in BASIC DIAGNOSTIC PROCEDURES article.
- Check charging system output. Repair charging system if voltage is less than 9 volts or more than 17 volts.
- Check for A/C clutch cutout at wide open throttle.
- Check MAP sensor output.
- Using Spark Tester (ST-125), check for available secondary voltage.
- Check engine valve timing and compression.
- Check ECM grounds for clean, tight connections.
- Check engine for a worn camshaft.

ENGINE BACKFIRES

Symptom Definition – Fuel ignites in intake manifold or in exhaust system, making a loud popping noise.

Possible Cause & Correction – Check the following items.

- Check for proper valve timing.
- Check for engine vacuum leaks and/or engine not tuned to specifications.
- Check for faulty air injection divert valve or check valve.
- Check for electric air switching valve or electric air divert valve not switching air pump discharge to air cleaner/atmosphere during engine starting or deceleration.
- Check EGR valve for leaking base gasket or valve hanging open.
- Check engine for sticking or leaking valves.
- Check for fuel or water in vacuum hose to MAP sensor. Also check for restricted hose.
- Using Spark Tester (ST-125), check available output voltage of ignition coil.
- Check for crossfire between spark plugs, distributor cap and spark plug wires.
- Check for an intermittent ignition system problem.
- Ensure initial ignition timing is properly set.

CUTS OUT, MISSES

Symptom Definition – Cuts out or misses is defined as a steady pulsation or jerking that follows engine speed, and is usually more pronounced as engine load increases. The exhaust may have a steady spitting sound at idle or low speed. Perform a careful visual inspection as described in BASIC DIAGNOSTIC PROCEDURES article.

Possible Cause & Correction – Check the following items.

- Check ignition wires for short or faulty insulation.
- Check distributor cap (if equipped) for moisture, dust or cracks. Spray spark plug wires with a fine mist of water to check for shorts.
- Connect Spark Tester ST-125 to spark plug and check for adequate spark.
- Check ignition system for faulty grounds.
- Ensure EST wiring harness is not routed too close to wiring which may cause induced voltage signals.
- Check ignition coil connections.

- Remove spark plugs and check for correct heat range, wear, cracks, wetness, improper gap or heavy deposits.
- Check for poor or contaminated (water) fuel.
- Check for improper fuel pressure.
- Check PFI vehicles for plugged injectors. See INJECTOR BALANCE TEST in SYSTEM & COMPONENT TESTING article.
- Check for EGR valve sticking open.
- Check ECM for proper ground circuits.
- Check TPS for sticking or binding. TPS voltage should be less than 1.25 volts at idle.
- Check for proper crank angle sensor (DIS and IDI) or pick-up coil (HEI distributor) resistance.
- Check for restricted exhaust. See RESTRICTED EXHAUST SYSTEM CHECK in BASIC DIAGNOSTIC PROCEDURES article.
- Check for bent push rods, broken valve springs or worn camshaft lobes.

Misfire Isolation (Fuel Injection) – 1) Start engine. Disconnect IAC motor. Using insulated pliers, remove one spark plug wire from a spark plug and ground it against the engine.
2) Note engine RPM as wire is grounded. Reconnect spark plug wire. Repeat procedure for all cylinders. Stop engine and reconnect IAC motor.
If engine speed dropped equally (within 50 RPM) on all cylinders, refer to ROUGH, UNSTABLE OR INCORRECT IDLE symptom. If there is no engine RPM drop or if there is excessive variation on one or more cylinder, check spark on the respective cylinder(s).

ROUGH, UNSTABLE OR INCORRECT IDLE

Symptom Definition – Engine runs unevenly at idle. If bad enough, vehicle will shake. Idle may vary in RPM. Engine idles at incorrect RPM.

Possible Cause & Correction – Check the following items.
- Ensure throttle linkage and/or TPS are not sticking or binding.
- Ensure initial ignition timing is properly set.
- Check engine idle speed (both base idle and ECM idle).
- Check Idle Air Control (IAC) system. Check for foreign material in IAC bore. See DIAGNOSTIC AIDS in CODE 35 chart in appropriate SELF-DIAGNOSTICS article.
- Check for proper operation of EGR system.
- Check P/N switch circuit. Ensure P/N switch is properly adjusted.
- Check power steering pressure switch circuit.
- Check exhaust system for restrictions, such as a damaged or collapsed pipe, muffler or catalytic converter. See RESTRICTED EXHAUST SYSTEM CHECK in BASIC DIAGNOSTIC PROCEDURES article.
- Check charging system output. Repair charging system if voltage is less than 9 volts or more than 17 volts.
- If rough idle only occurs when engine is hot, check PCV valve for proper operation. Check evaporative emission control system. Check for proper spark plug gap and check engine compression.
- On PFI vehicles, check for fuel in pressure regulator vacuum line. If fuel is present, replace regulator.

ENGINE WILL NOT IDLE

Symptom Definition – Engine starts but will not run at idle. Engine will run if accelerator is held at part throttle.
Possible Cause & Correction – Check the following items.
- Problem is most likely in Idle Air Control (IAC) system. See DIAGNOSTIC AIDS in CODE 35 chart in appropriate SELF-DIAGNOSTICS article.
- Check EGR system.
- Check P/N switch.
- On PFI vehicles, perform INJECTOR BALANCE TEST in SYSTEM & COMPONENT TESTING article.
- Disconnect MAF or MAP sensor. If condition is corrected, replace sensor.

POOR FUEL ECONOMY

Symptom Definition – Fuel economy, as measured by an actual road test, is noticeably lower than expected. Fuel economy is noticeably lower than was on this vehicle at one time.
Possible Cause & Correction – Check the following items.
- Check for proper operation of thermostatic air cleaner damper door. Also check for a clogged air filter.
- Check cooling system thermostat for proper heat range and operation.
- Check coolant sensor for shift in calibration. Use temperature-to-resistance table in SENSOR OPERATING RANGE CHARTS article.
- Check A/C for "full time" operation.
- Ensure initial ignition timing is properly set and check for proper operation of EST and ESC.
- Check for proper operation of TCC or VCC.
- On vehicles with TWC/OC, check for the following conditions: air pump output not shifting to catalytic converter upon signal from ECM, and/or faulty electrical and/or vacuum circuits.
- Check exhaust system for restrictions, such as a damaged or collapsed pipe, muffler or catalytic converter. See RESTRICTED EXHAUST SYSTEM CHECK in BASIC DIAGNOSTIC PROCEDURES article.
- Check oxygen sensor for silicone or lead contamination.
- Remove spark plugs and check for wet plugs, cracks, improper gap, burned electrodes or heavy carbon deposits.
- Ensure speedometer is properly calibrated.
- Check engine compression.
- Check for dragging brakes.

ENGINE DIESELING/RUN-ON

Symptom Definition – Engine continues to run after ignition is turned off but runs very rough. If engine runs smoothly, check ignition switch.
Possible Cause & Correction – Check the following items.
- Check for binding throttle linkage.
- Check for leaking injectors. On PFI vehicles, perform INJECTOR BALANCE TEST in SYSTEM & COMPONENT TESTING article.
- Check IAC system. See DIAGNOSTIC AIDS in CODE 35 chart in appropriate SELF-DIAGNOSTICS article.
- Check engine for overheating.

DETONATION/SPARK KNOCK

Symptom Definition – A mild to severe ping, usually worse under acceleration. The engine makes sharp metallic knocks that change with amount of acceleration.
Possible Cause & Correction – Check the following items.
- Check for obvious overheating problems.
- Ensure initial timing is correct.
- Check TPS adjustment and operation.
- Check fuel system for low pressure or volume. Also check for induction air leaks.
- Ensure ESC system is operating properly.
- Ensure EGR valve is not open all the time.
- Ensure TCC or VCC system is operating properly.
- Remove carbon from engine with top engine cleaner.
- If excessive carbon exists in combustion chamber, check for excessive oil burning due to leaking valve guide seals.
- Check for incorrect basic engine parts such as camshaft, cylinder heads and pistons.
- Ensure PROM/MEM-CAL in vehicle is correct for that particular vehicle. Check with dealer for latest application information.

EXCESSIVE EXHAUST EMISSION OR ODORS

Symptom Definition – Vehicle fails emission test. Vehicle may also have excessive "rotten egg" smell (hydrogen sulfide) being emitted from exhaust pipe. Excessive odors DO NOT necessarily indicate exhaust emissions are high.
Possible Cause & Correction – Check the following items.
- Check for lead contamination of catalytic converter. Look for removal/tampering at restrictor in fuel filler neck.

- Check cooling system thermostat for proper operation and application.
- Check cooling fan for proper operation.
- Ensure air is NOT diverted to exhaust manifold but diverted to catalytic converter (TWC/OC) or atmosphere during normal engine operation.
- If emission test shows excessive carbon monoxide (CO) and hydrocarbons (HC) emissions, and vehicle is also emitting excessive odor, check all systems and components that could cause engine to run rich. See DIAGNOSTIC AIDS in CODE 45 chart in appropriate SELF-DIAGNOSTICS article.
- Ensure PROM/MEM-CAL in vehicle is correct for that particular vehicle. Check with dealer for latest application information.
- If emission test shows excessive oxides of nitrogen (NOx) emissions, check all systems and components that could cause engine to run lean or to run too hot. See DIAGNOSTIC AIDS in CODE 44 chart in appropriate SELF-DIAGNOSTICS article.

INTERMITTENTS

INTERMITTENT PROBLEM DIAGNOSIS

Intermittent fault testing requires duplicating circuit or component failure to identify fault. These procedures may lead to the computer setting a fault code which may help in diagnosis.

If problem vehicle does not produce fault codes, monitor voltage or resistance values using a DVOM while attempting to reproduce conditions causing the intermittent fault. A status change on DVOM indicates a fault has been located.

Use DVOM to pinpoint faults. When monitoring voltage, ensure ignition is in ON position or vehicle is running. When monitoring resistance, ensure ignition switch is in the OFF position or negative battery is disconnected. A status change on DVOM while performing TEST PROCEDURES indicates area of fault.

TEST PROCEDURES

Intermittent Simulation – To reproduce the conditions causing intermittent fault, use the following methods:
- Lightly vibrate component.
- Heat component.
- Wiggle or bend wiring harness.
- Spray component with water.
- Remove or apply vacuum source.

Monitor circuit/component voltage or resistance while simulating intermittent. If vehicle is running, monitor for self-diagnostic codes. Use test results to identify a faulty component or circuit.

INTERMITTENT TROUBLE SHOOTING

Symptom Definition – SERVICE ENGINE SOON light comes on but does not stay on. A stored code may or may not exist.

Possible Cause & Correction – To track down possible causes of an intermittent SERVICE ENGINE SOON light, check the following items.
- Check for poor mating of one connector to another. Terminals may not be fully seated. Check for improperly formed or damaged terminals. Check wire to terminal connections.
- Check for poor connection from ignition coil to ground or arcing at spark plug wires or plugs.
- Check wire from SERVICE ENGINE SOON light to ECM for short to ground.
- Check wire from test terminal "B" of ALDL for intermittent short to ground.
- Check for poor connections in ECM ground terminals.
- Check for loss of trouble code memory. To check code memory on fuel injected models, disconnect TPS and run engine at idle until SERVICE ENGINE SOON light comes on. Code 22 should be stored and retained in memory when ignition is turned off. If Code 22 is not stored, ECM is faulty.
- Check for electrical system interference caused by a defective relay, or an ECM-driven solenoid or switch which may cause sharp electrical surge. This type of problem will normally occur when faulty component is operated.
- Check for aftermarket parts which may not have been produced to manufacturers' specifications. Solenoids without original-equipment diodes for circuit protection, and HEI-EST module or voltage regulator using transistors instead of silicon-chip circuitry may possibly cause voltage surges (up to 300 volts) in ECM wiring, causing temporary ECM shutdown. ECM shutdown is a normal response to system overvoltage (over 16 volts on most models). ECM will repower when condition no longer exists. This could cause a flickering SERVICE ENGINE SOON light with no codes set in memory.
- Check for improper installation of electrical accessories such as auxiliary lights or 2-way radios.
- Ensure EST wires are kept away from spark plug wires, distributor wires, distributor housing, ignition coil and generator. Ensure ground wire from ECM to distributor or ignition module is connected to a good ground.

1991 ENGINE PERFORMANCE
Systems & Component Testing

Beretta, Bonneville, Brougham, Camaro, Caprice, Cavalier, Century, Corsica, Corvette, Custom Cruiser, Cutlass Calais, Cutlass Ciera, Cutlass Cruiser, Cutlass Supreme, DeVille, Eighty-Eight Eldorado, Firebird, Fleetwood, Grand Am, Grand Prix, LeSabre, Lumina, Ninety-Eight, Park Avenue, Reatta, Regal, Riviera, Roadmaster, Seville, Skylark, Sunbird, Toronado, Touring Sedan, Trofeo, 6000

INTRODUCTION

Before testing separate components or systems, it is highly recommended that all procedures listed in BASIC DIAGNOSTIC PROCEDURES article be performed. Since many computer controlled and monitored components will set a trouble code if they malfunction, it is also recommended that self-diagnosis be performed. See appropriate SELF-DIAGNOSTICS article.

NOTE: Testing individual components does not isolate shorts or opens. Perform all voltage tests with a Digital Volt-Ohmmeter (DVOM) with a minimum 10-megohm input impedance, unless stated otherwise in test procedure. Use ohmmeter to isolate wiring harness shorts or opens.

COMPUTERIZED ENGINE CONTROLS

CONTROL UNIT

Ground Circuits – **1)** Using an ohmmeter, check for continuity to ground on control unit ground terminals. Use appropriate schematic in WIRING DIAGRAMS article to determine ECM ground terminals. Resistance to ground should be zero ohms. If reading is other than zero ohms, repair open to ground.
2) Using a DVOM, touch negative lead of voltmeter to a good ground. Touch positive lead of voltmeter to each ground terminal. With vehicle running, voltmeter should indicate less than one volt. If voltmeter reading is one volt or more, check for open, corrosion or loose connection on ground lead.

Power Circuits – **1)** Using a voltmeter, check for battery voltage between control unit constant battery power terminals and ground. If battery voltage is not present, check control unit power supply fuse. If fuse is okay, check for an open in power supply or control unit wiring.
2) Turn ignition switch to the ON position. Using a voltmeter, check for battery voltage between control unit ignition power terminals and ground. If battery voltage is not present, check power supply fuse(s). If fuse is okay, check for an open in wiring between fuse and control unit, or check for a defective ignition switch.
3) Connect voltmeter between ground and control unit start (crank) signal terminal. Turn ignition switch to the START position. Battery voltage should be present between control unit start terminal and ground ONLY when ignition switch is in the START position.
4) If voltage is not present, check fuse(s). If fuse is okay, check for an open in wiring between fuse and control unit, or check for a defective ignition switch.

ENGINE SENSORS & SWITCHES

NOTE: For additional sensor testing specifications, see SENSOR OPERATING RANGE CHARTS article.

A/C ON (A/C Request) Switch Test – **1)** Start engine and allow to idle. If a "Scan" tester is available, scan A/C request parameter. Move A/C mode selector back and forth between ON and OFF positions. Scan status should change.
2) If "Scan" tester is not available or scan status does not change, measure voltage between ground and ECM A/C request terminal. For wiring schematics, see mini-schematics in A/C CLUTCH under MISCELLANEOUS ECM CONTROLS.
3) With A/C mode selector in the ON position, 12 volts should be present. If 12 volts are not present, check for open between A/C mode select switch and ECM A/C request terminal, low A/C refrigerant level causing low pressure switch to open, bad A/C fuse, or bad A/C mode select switch.

IMPORTANT: The following table provides the location of commonly used diagnostic information. These former "A" and "C" charts are now written in text and inserted into the appropriate location in the new Engine Performance workflow. To familiarize yourself with the Engine Performance workflow, see HOW TO USE THE ENGINE PERFORMANCE SECTION in GENERAL INFORMATION.

GENERAL MOTORS A & C CHART REFERENCE TABLE

System or Component	Diagnostic Information Location
A-1 & A-2, SERVICE ENGINE SOON Light	See DIAGNOSTIC CIRCUIT CHECK in BASIC DIAGNOSTIC PROCEDURES
A-3, No Start	See NO START – ENGINE CRANKS OKAY in BASIC DIAGNOSTIC PROCEDURES
A-5, Fuel Pump Relay	See RELAYS, SOLENOIDS & MOTORS in SYSTEMS & COMPONENT TESTING
A-7, Fuel System Diagnosis	See BASIC FUEL SYSTEM CHECKS in BASIC DIAGNOSTIC PROCEDURES
C-1, MAP Sensor	See ENGINE SENSORS & SWITCHES in SYSTEMS & COMPONENT TESTING
C-1, Power Steering Pressure Switch	See ENGINE SENSORS & SWITCHES in SYSTEMS & COMPONENT TESTING
C-1, Park/Neutral Switch	See ENGINE SENSORS & SWITCHES in SYSTEMS & COMPONENT TESTING
C-2, Injector Balance Test	See FUEL CONTROL in SYSTEMS & COMPONENT TESTING
C-2, IAC Motor	See IDLE CONTROL SYSTEM in SYSTEMS & COMPONENT TESTING
C-2, ISC Motor	See IDLE CONTROL SYSTEM in SYSTEMS & COMPONENT TESTING
C-3, Canister Purge System	See EMISSION SYSTEMS & SUB-SYSTEMS in SYSTEMS & COMPONENT TESTING
C-4, EST Ignition Check	See BASIC IGNITION SYSTEM CHECKS in BASIC DIAGNOSTIC PROCEDURES
C-5, ESC Ignition Check	See IGNITION SYSTEM in SYSTEMS & COMPONENT TESTING
C-6, Air Injection System	See EMISSION SYSTEMS & SUB-SYSTEMS in SYSTEMS & COMPONENT TESTING
C-7, EGR System	See EMISSION SYSTEMS & SUB-SYSTEMS in SYSTEMS & COMPONENT TESTING
C-8, Torque Converter Clutch	[1] See MISCELLANEOUS ECM CONTROLS in SYSTEMS & COMPONENT TESTING
C-8, Manual Transmission Shift Lights	[1] See MISCELLANEOUS ECM CONTROLS in SYSTEMS & COMPONENT TESTING
C-10, A/C Clutch Control	[2] See MISCELLANEOUS ECM CONTROLS in SYSTEMS & COMPONENT TESTING
C-12, Electric Cooling Fan Control	[3] See MISCELLANEOUS ECM CONTROLS in SYSTEMS & COMPONENT TESTING

[1] – Covered in entirety in Mitchell's 1991-92 TRANSMISSION SERVICE & REPAIR manual for Domestic vehicles.
[2] – Covered in entirety in Mitchell's 1991 AIR CONDITIONING & HEATING SERVICE & REPAIR supplement for Domestic vehicles.
[3] – Covered in entirety in ENGINE COOLING in Mitchell's 1991 DOMESTIC CARS SERVICE & REPAIR manual and ENGINE, CLUTCH & DRIVE AXLE supplement, and in Mitchell's 1991 AIR CONDITIONING & HEATING SERVICE & REPAIR supplement for Domestic vehicles.

A/C Pressure Sensor (All 2.3L & 3.1L J & W Bodies) – A malfunction in A/C pressure sensor circuit will set a related trouble code. For testing procedures, see appropriate SELF-DIAGNOSTICS article. For wiring schematics, see mini-schematics in A/C CLUTCH under MISCELLANEOUS ECM CONTROLS.

A/C Pressure Switch – **1)** Connect A/C pressure gauges to system and start engine. Note high and low pressure readings. If pressures are normal, go to step **2)**. If pressures are less than normal, check system for leaks. Evacuate and recharge as necessary. If pressures are high, check for system overcharge, overheating or mechanical failure in freon delivery system.

2) Disconnect high and low pressure switches. Jumper across each switch harness connector to allow A/C system to function normally. Using an ohmmeter, check continuity between pressure switch terminals.

3) Continuity should be present on both high and low switches (if equipped). If continuity is not present, replace A/C pressure switch. For wiring schematics, see mini-schematics in A/C CLUTCH under MISCELLANEOUS ECM CONTROLS.

Brake Switch – Disconnect brake switch harness connector. Using an ohmmeter, check continuity between brake switch terminals. Continuity should be present. Depress brake pedal to activate brake switch, continuity should not be present.

Camshaft Sensor (3.8L VIN C) – A malfunction in the camshaft sensor circuit will set a related trouble code. For testing procedures, see appropriate SELF-DIAGNOSTICS article.

Camshaft Sensor (Cadillac Except Brougham) – See HALL EFFECT CAMSHAFT SENSOR.

Coolant Temperature Sensor (CTS) – If a coolant sensor related code is present, see appropriate SELF-DIAGNOSTICS article. An out-of-calibration sensor may not set a trouble code. Use following procedure to test sensor calibration. Disconnect coolant temperature sensor connector. Measure resistance between sensor terminals. Resistance should be high when engine is cold and drop as engine warms. See CTS RESISTANCE VALUES table.

CTS RESISTANCE VALUES

°F (°C)	Ohms
210 (100)	185
160 (70)	450
100 (38)	1800
70 (20)	3400
20 (-7)	13,500
0 (-18)	25,000
-40 (-40)	100,700

Crankshaft Position Sensor (2.3L IDI) – **1)** If a "Scan" tester is available, scan RPM parameter while cranking engine. If RPM is indicated, crankshaft position sensor is operating properly.

2) If "Scan" tester is not available, disconnect crankshaft sensor connector, located above oil filter. Set ohmmeter to 2-k/ohm position, measure resistance across sensor terminals. Resistance should be 500-900 ohms.

3) Set voltmeter on the 2-volt AC scale. Crank engine and measure voltage across sensor terminals. Voltmeter reading should be .1 volt or greater. If resistance reading is not as specified or sensor does not produce a voltage reading, replace faulty crank sensor. Also, check if sensor is still magnetized. Replace as necessary.

Crankshaft Position Sensor (DIS) – **1)** If a "Scan" tester is available, scan RPM parameter while cranking engine. If RPM is indicated, crankshaft position sensor is operating properly.

2) If "Scan" tester is not available, disconnect crankshaft sensor harness connector. Set ohmmeter to 2-k/ohm position, measure resistance across sensor terminals. Resistance should be 900-1200 ohms.

3) Set voltmeter on the 2-volt AC scale. Crank engine and measure voltage across sensor terminals. Voltmeter reading should be .1 volt or greater. If resistance reading is not as specified or sensor does not produce a voltage reading, repair faulty wiring or crank sensor.

Dual Crank (Combination) Sensor (3.3L C³I System) – This test should only be performed if vehicle will not start, injectors will not

pulse and spark plugs will not fire. This simulates a dual crank sensor signal. If spark and injector pulse occur, dual crank sensor or sensor connections are bad.

1) Turn ignition off. Disconnect No. 6 spark plug wire from coil tower. Install Spark Tester (ST-125) to coil tower. Install spark plug wire to spark tester.

2) Connect injector test light to any injector connector. Connect jumper wire across dual crank sensor connector terminals "A" and "B". See Figs. 1 and 2. Turn ignition on, engine off (DO NOT crank engine).

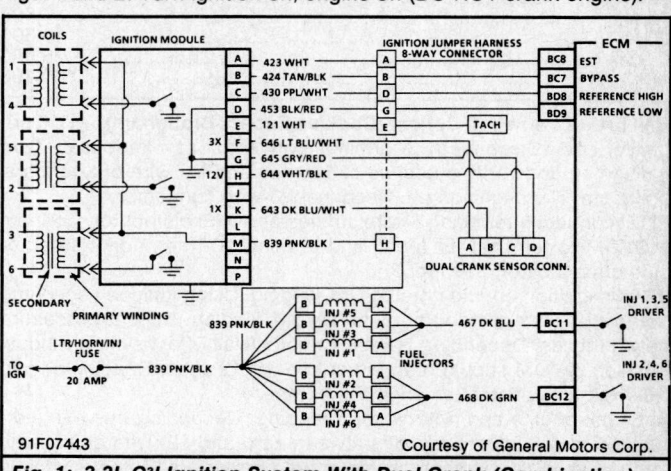

Fig. 1: 3.3L C³I Ignition System With Dual Crank (Combination) Sensor (Century, Cutlass Ciera & Cutlass Cruiser)

3) Using a test light connected to ground, momentarily touch dual crank sensor terminal "A". Note injector test light and spark tester. Test light should blink and spark should be present at spark tester.

NOTE: Repeatedly grounding terminal "A" at dual crank sensor or terminals "C" and "B" at C³I module may cause engine to flooded.

4) If spark was present and test light came on, check for poor connection at dual crank sensor terminal. If connections are okay, replace faulty dual crank sensor. If there was no spark and test light did not come on, check for poor connection at C³I module or replace faulty C³I module.

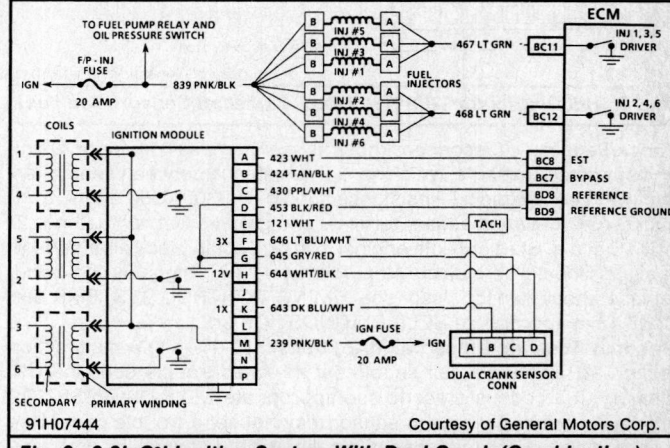

Fig. 2: 3.3L C³I Ignition System With Dual Crank (Combination) Sensor (Cutlass Calais & Skylark)

Engine Oil Temperature Sensor (Corvette) – If engine oil temperature sensor circuit malfunctions, a related code will be set. However, if sensor is out of calibration, this will not set a code. To check calibration, use following method.

Disconnect engine oil temperature sensor connector. Using an ohmmeter, measure resistance between sensor terminals. Resistance should be as specified. See ENGINE OIL TEMPERATURE SEN-SOR RESISTANCE table. Also see Code 52 and Code 62 in appropriate SELF-DIAGNOSTICS article.

ENGINE OIL TEMPERATURE SENSOR RESISTANCE

°F (°C)	Ohms
210 (100)	185
160 (70)	450
100 (38)	1800
70 (20)	3400
40 (4)	7500
20 (-7)	13,500
0 (-18)	25,000
-40 (-40)	100,700

Hall Effect Camshaft Sensor (Cadillac Except Brougham) – **1)** Turn ignition off. Disconnect 3-terminal connector at distributor. Turn ignition on and verify presence of 12 volts on Pink wire of 3-terminal connector. Turn ignition off. Reconnect 3-wire connector.

2) Disconnect 6-terminal, 5-wire connector at HEI distributor. Connect a DVOM to terminal "E" (pos.) and terminal "D" (neg.) on distributor side of connector. See Fig. 3.

3) Turn ignition on and note DVOM reading. Using ignition key, bump starter to rotate distributor. Note DVOM reading. Repeat procedure several times. Depending upon distributor/Hall Effect switch window position, DVOM should read either zero or 12 volts. Reading should NOT remain constant as engine is bumped.

4) Crank engine and note voltage reading. Depending on voltmeter, reading may fluctuate rapidly between zero and 12 volts or average about 6 volts. If voltmeter readings are correct, Hall Effect switch is okay. If voltmeter readings are not correct, replace Hall Effect switch.

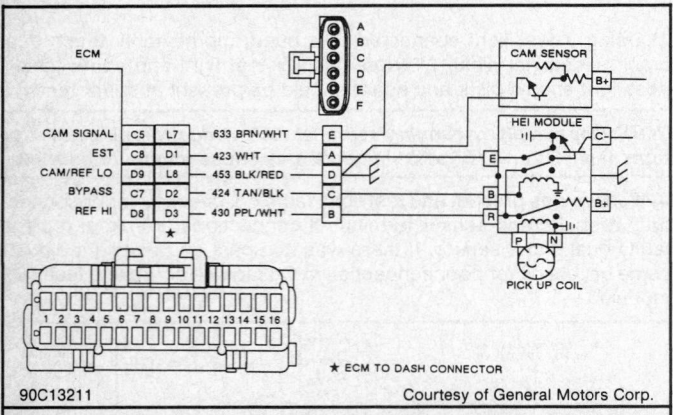

Fig. 3: HEI Distributor With Hall Effect Camshaft Sensor (Cadillac)

Knock Sensor – Disconnect knock sensor harness connector. Using an ohmmeter, measure knock sensor resistance between sensor terminal and engine block. Resistance should be 3300-4500 ohms. Connect DVOM between sensor terminal and ground. Set voltmeter to 2-volt AC scale. Start and idle engine. Tap on engine block near sensor. A signal should be indicated on voltmeter. If no signal is indicated, replace knock sensor. Also, see TIMING CONTROL SYSTEMS and Code 43 in appropriate SELF-DIAGNOSTICS article.

Manifold Absolute Pressure (MAP) Sensor (C-1) – **1)** A malfunction in the MAP sensor circuit should set a related trouble code in ECM memory. If a code is present, see appropriate SELF-DIAGNOSTICS article. An out-of-calibration sensor may not set a trouble code. Use following procedure to test sensor calibration. If driveability problems exist, MAP sensor failure is suspected and no MAP code is present, disconnect MAP sensor connector. If driveability condition improves, replace MAP sensor.

2) With ignition on and engine off, check MAP sensor parameter using a "Scan" tester connected to the ALDL connector. Voltage should be as specified in MAP SENSOR VOLTAGE RANGE table. If MAP sensor voltage is as specified, go to step **3)**. If voltage is not as specified, check for 5-volt reference supplied to sensor. Check harness integrity. If no problems are evident, replace MAP sensor.

3) Using a hand-held vacuum pump, apply 10 in. Hg to MAP sensor and note voltage change. Voltage should drop about 1.2-2.3 volts less than as specified in table. If voltage is not as specified or voltage reading does not immediately follow vacuum change, MAP sensor is faulty.

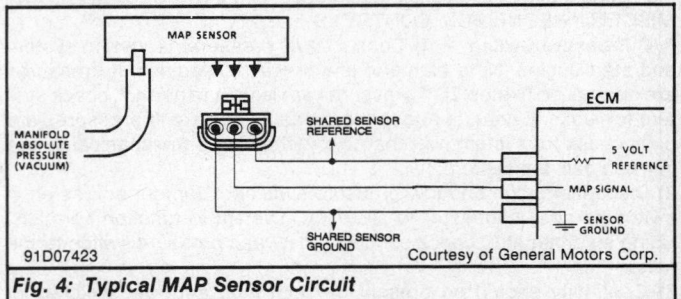

Fig. 4: Typical MAP Sensor Circuit

MAP SENSOR VOLTAGE RANGE

Altitude (Ft.)	Volts
Below 1000	3.8-5.5
1000-2000	3.6-5.3
2000-3000	3.5-5.1
3000-4000	3.3-5.0
4000-5000	3.2-4.8
5000-6000	3.0-4.6
6000-7000	2.9-4.5
7000-8000	2.8-4.3
8000-9000	2.6-4.2
9000-10,000	2.5-4.0

Manifold Air Temperature (MAT) Sensor – On some models, MAT sensor may also be referred to as a Intake Air Temperature (IAT) sensor. If a MAT sensor related code is present, see appropriate SELF-DIAGNOSTICS article. An out-of-calibration sensor may not set a trouble code. Use following procedure to test calibration. Disconnect MAT sensor harness connector. Connect ohmmeter between sensor terminals. Sensor resistance should be as specified. See MAT SENSOR RESISTANCE table. With vehicle sitting overnight, MAT sensor and coolant sensor should have close to the same resistance reading.

MAT SENSOR RESISTANCE

°F (°C)	Ohms
210 (100)	185
160 (70)	450
100 (38)	1800
70 (20)	3400
40 (4)	7500
20 (-7)	13,500
0 (-18)	25,000
-40 (-40)	100,700

Mass Airflow Sensor (3.3L & 3.8L) – A malfunction in the MAF sensor circuit will set a related trouble code. For testing procedures, see Code 34 in appropriate SELF-DIAGNOSTICS article. If driveability problems exist, MAF sensor failure is suspected and no Code 34 is present, disconnect MAF sensor connector. If driveability improves, replace MAF sensor.

Oxygen (O₂) Sensor – **1)** Start engine and warm to operating temperature. Disconnect oxygen sensor. Connect a DVOM between lead of oxygen sensor and ground. Place meter on the 2-volt scale. Voltmeter reading should increase to greater than .8 volt.

2) Using another DVOM on the 20-volt scale. Connect voltmeter in series between the O₂ wire from the ECM and the positive post of battery. Reading on voltmeter connected to oxygen sensor should decrease to a low voltage (less than .3 volt).

3) If a second DVOM is not available, install short jumper in O₂ wire from the ECM. Hold jumper in one hand and touch positive post of battery with other hand. This should cause oxygen sensor to produce less than .3 volt. For additional testing procedures, see appropriate SELF-DIAGNOSTICS article.

Park/Neutral (P/N) Switch (C-1) – **1)** Disconnect P/N switch harness connector. Connect ohmmeter between the P/N switch terminals. See

Fig. 5. Continuity should be present only when gear shift selector is in Park or Neutral. If continuity is not present, check P/N switch adjustment or replace defective P/N switch.

2) With park/neutral switch connector disconnected, turn ignition on. Check for 12 volts on the Orange/Black wire of park/neutral switch harness. If 12 volts are not present, check for open or short to ground between switch harness connector and ECM.

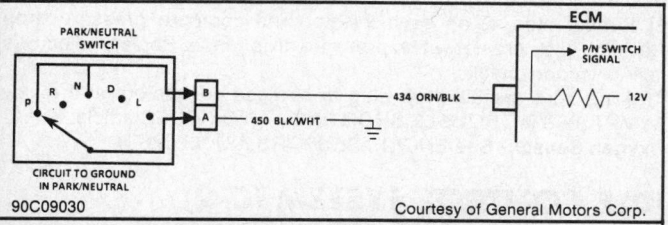

90C09030   Courtesy of General Motors Corp.

Fig. 5: Park/Neutral (P/N) Switch Circuit (Typical)

Power Steering (P/S) Pressure Switch (C-1) – 1) If "Scan" tester is available, scan power steering pressure switch status. Note status with engine running and wheels in straight-ahead position. Turn steering wheel to full left or right position and again note status. If status changed, power steering pressure switch is okay. If status did not change or "Scan" tester is not available, go to next step.

2) Turn ignition off. Disconnect P/S pressure switch harness connector. Connect ohmmeter between P/S pressure switch terminals. Start engine. With no-load on power steering, continuity should not be present. Turn steering wheel to full left or right position. Continuity should now be present. If readings are not as specified, replace P/S pressure switch.

3) With P/S pressure switch connector disconnected and ignition on, check for 12 volts on switch harness from ECM. If 12 volts are not present, check for open or short to ground in harness between switch connector and ECM.

Throttle Position Sensor (TPS) – Install jumper wires to enable connection of a DVOM in parallel between TPS harness connectors. Connect DVOM positive lead to Dark Blue TPS signal wire terminal. Connect negative lead to Black sensor ground wire terminal. *See Fig. 6.* Turn ignition on, engine off. Signal voltage should gradually change from less than one volt at closed throttle to about 5.0 volts at wide open throttle position. If reading is not as specified, adjust or replace TPS. See ON-VEHICLE ADJUSTMENTS article.

A malfunction in the TPS circuit should set a related trouble code. For further information, see appropriate SELF-DIAGNOSTICS article.

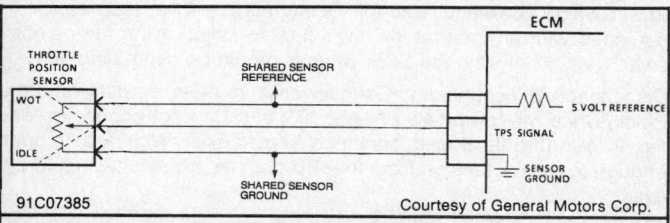

91C07385   Courtesy of General Motors Corp.

Fig. 6: Throttle Position Sensor Circuit (Typical)

Vehicle Speed Sensor (PM Generator Type) – Disconnect vehicle speed sensor harness connector (located in transaxle). Place gear selector in Neutral. Raise vehicle drive wheels off the ground. Turn drive wheels by hand (greater than 3 MPH). Measure AC signal voltage between sensor terminals. Voltage reading should be vary from 0.1-0.5 volt AC as the wheel is turned. If reading is not as specified, replace vehicle speed sensor.

Vehicle Speed Sensor (LED Type) – A speed sensor or buffer malfunction should set a related code in ECM memory. If a code is set, refer to appropriate SELF-DIAGNOSTICS article for diagnosis.

MOTORS, RELAYS & SOLENOIDS

MOTORS

Electric Air Pump (3.4L Man. Trans.) – Locate electric air pump in right front of engine compartment. Disconnect Orange and Black wire

connector. Apply ground to the Black wire terminal of air pump. Apply battery voltage with a fused jumper wire to Orange wire terminal of pump. Pump should run. If pump does not run, replace pump.

Idle Air Control (IAC) Motor & Idle Speed Control (ISC) Motor – See IDLE CONTROL SYSTEM.

RELAYS

A/C Clutch Relays – See MISCELLANEOUS CONTROLS.
Electric Air Pump Relay (3.4L Man. Trans.) – See EMISSION SYSTEMS & SUB-SYSTEMS.
Fuel Pump Relay – See FUEL SYSTEM.

SOLENOIDS

NOTE: All ECM-controlled solenoids should have at least 20 ohms of resistance.

Air Injection Solenoids – See EMISSION SYSTEMS & SUB-SYSTEMS.
Canister Purge Solenoid – See EMISSION SYSTEMS & SUB-SYSTEMS.
EGR Solenoid – See EMISSION SYSTEMS & SUB-SYSTEMS.

FUEL SYSTEM

FUEL DELIVERY

NOTE: For fuel system pressure testing, see BASIC DIAGNOSTIC PROCEDURES article.

Fuel Pressure Regulator (PFI) – 1) Install fuel pressure gauge to fuel rail fuel pressure test fitting. Remove vacuum hose from fuel pressure regulator. Turn ignition on and note fuel pressure on gauge.

2) Start engine. Check for manifold vacuum at pressure regulator vacuum hose. Repair as necessary. Reconnect vacuum hose to pressure regulator and note fuel pressure on gauge. Compare first and second reading. Fuel pressure reading should be 4-7 psi (.28-.49 kg/cm²) less with vacuum hose installed. Fuel pressure should decrease as vacuum increases. If results are unsatisfactory, replace fuel pressure regulator.

Fuel Pressure Regulator (TBI) – Fuel pressure regulator is mechanically controlled by internal spring pressure. Regulator is adjusted at factory and is not serviceable. If fuel pressure is too low, check for fuel filter, fuel pump pressure and volume. If fuel pressure is too high, check for restricted fuel tank return line. If no faults are found and pressure is too high or too low, replace fuel pressure regulator.

Fuel Pump Relay (A-5) – 1) Disconnect fuel pump relay connector. Refer to COMPONENT LOCATIONS at the end of this article to locate fuel pump relay. Apply battery voltage and ground to fuel pump relay winding terminals. To identify fuel pump relay terminals, see appropriate wiring diagram in WIRING DIAGRAMS article.

2) Using an ohmmeter, check for continuity between fuel pump relay power supply terminal and fuel pump drive terminal. Continuity should exist ONLY with relay energized. If relay does not test as indicated, replace relay.

3) To by-pass fuel pump relay (to test fuel pump and wiring when fuel pump is not energizing), see FUEL PUMP RELAY BY-PASS PROCEDURE.

Fuel Pump Relay By-Pass Procedure – 1) If fuel pump will not energize, relay may be by-passed to test fuel pump and related wiring. Turn ignition off. Disconnect fuel pump relay connector. Using a fused jumper wire, apply battery voltage to fuel pump test connector (located in engine compartment). For fuel pump test connector location, refer to COMPONENT LOCATIONS at end of this article. *See Figs. 85-113.*

2) If fuel pump runs and relay tests okay, check for faulty connections at relay. If fuel pump does not run, check for faulty wiring between relay and fuel pump or replace defective fuel pump.

Oil Pressure Switch Fuel Pump Back-Up – With engine idling, disconnect fuel pump relay. Engine should continue to run through oil

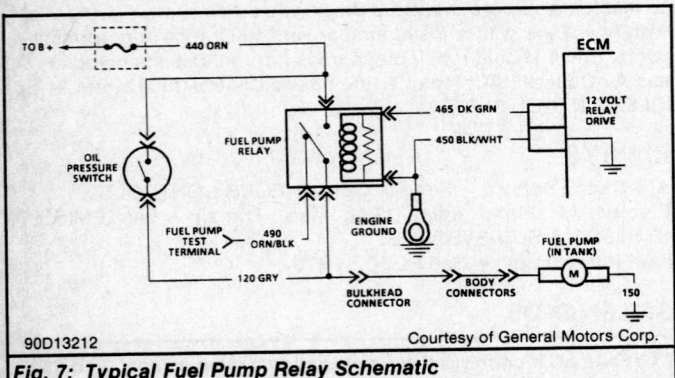

Fig. 7: Typical Fuel Pump Relay Schematic

pressure switch back-up circuit. If engine stalls, check oil pressure switch and related wiring.

FUEL CONTROL

Fuel Injector(s) – Disconnect fuel injector harness connector. Measure resistance across injector terminals at each injector. Resistance should be as specified. See FUEL INJECTOR RESISTANCE table.

FUEL INJECTOR RESISTANCE

Application	[1] Ohms
2.0L (VIN K)	1.6
2.2L (VIN G)	1.6
2.3L (VIN A & D)	1.9-2.1
2.5L (VIN R & U)	1.6
3.1L (VIN T)	12.0-12.4
3.3L (VIN N)	[2]
3.4L (VIN X)	12.0-12.4
3.8L (VIN C)	[2]
5.0L (VIN E)	1.2
5.0L (VIN F)	10.0
5.7L (VIN 7)	1.2
5.7L (VIN 8)	10.0

[1] – Injector resistance specification is at 140°F (60°C).
[2] – Information not available from manufacturer. Solenoid should have resistance; however, infinite resistance indicates an open injector winding.

NOTE: If injectors are dirty, they should be cleaned using approved injector cleaning procedure before performing INJECTOR BALANCE TEST.

PFI Injector Balance Test (C-2) – The injector balance test is used to pulse the injector for a precise amount of time, spraying a measured amount of fuel in the intake manifold. As each injector is pulsed, a drop in fuel rail pressure occurs. This pressure drop can be recorded and compared to other injectors. An injector with a pressure drop of 1.5 psi (.11 kg/cm²) or more, greater than or less than other injectors, should be considered faulty.

NOTE: Allow engine to cool down to avoid irregular readings due to "Hot Soak" fuel boiling. To prevent flooding, the INJECTOR BALANCE TEST should not be repeated more than once without starting and running engine.

CAUTION: To avoid possible vehicle fire, wrap a shop towel around fitting to avoid fuel spillage.

1) With ignition off, connect Fuel Pressure Gauge (J-34730-1) to pressure tap. Unplug harness connector at all injectors. Connect Injector Tester (J-34730-3) to one of the injectors.
2) Follow manufacturer's instructions when installing adapter harness. Ignition should be turned off at least 10 seconds to complete ECM shutdown cycle.
3) Turn ignition on. Fuel pump should run at least 2 seconds after ignition is turned on. Bleed air from gauge and hose to ensure accurate

gauge reading. Repeat this procedure until all air is bled from system. Turn ignition off for at least 10 seconds.
4) Turn ignition on again to bring fuel pressure to maximum. Record initial pressure reading. Energize tester one time and note pressure drop at lowest point.
5) Disregard any slight pressure drop after low point is reached. Subtracting second pressure reading from initial reading indicates amount of injector pressure drop.
6) Repeat step 4) on each injector and compare pressure drop. Recheck injectors not within pressure drop range. Replace injector(s) failing second check.
7) If injectors are all okay, plug in harness connectors and review SYMPTOMS in TROUBLE SHOOTING – NO CODES article.
Oxygen Sensor - See ENGINE SENSORS & SWITCHES.

IDLE CONTROL SYSTEM (C-2)

Idle Air Control (IAC) Motor – 1) Disconnect harness connector to motor. Check resistance across IAC coil terminals "A" and "B" (B coil) and "C" and "D" (A coil). Resistance should be 40-80 ohms. See Fig. 8. If resistance is as specified, go to next step. If resistance is not as specified, replace IAC motor.
2) Check resistance between IAC terminals "B" to "C" and "A" to "D". Resistance should be infinite. If resistance is not as specified, replace IAC motor.

NOTE: Additional testing of Idle Air Control (IAC) motor requires an IAC motor actuator and node light, or a "Scan" tester capable of cycling ECM output devices (General Motors Tech 1).

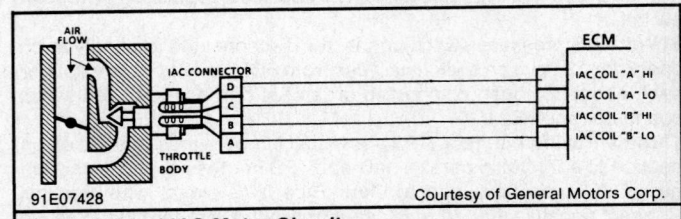

Fig. 8: Typical IAC Motor Circuit

Idle Speed Control (ISC) Motor (Cadillac Except Brougham) – A malfunction in the ISC circuit will set a trouble code. For testing procedures, see appropriate SELF-DIAGNOSTICS article. Also, see ISC minimum and maximum adjustment procedures in ON-VEHICLE ADJUSTMENTS article.
Idle Switch (Cadillac Except Brougham) – The ISC motor is equipped with an internal idle switch (also called a throttle or nose switch) which informs the ECM when it should be controlling idle.

Disconnect ISC connector. Connect an ohmmeter across Pink and Black/White wire terminals ("A" and "B") of ISC motor connector. See Fig. 9. With throttle closed, continuity should exist. With throttle open enough to relieve tension from the ISC plunger, continuity should not exist.

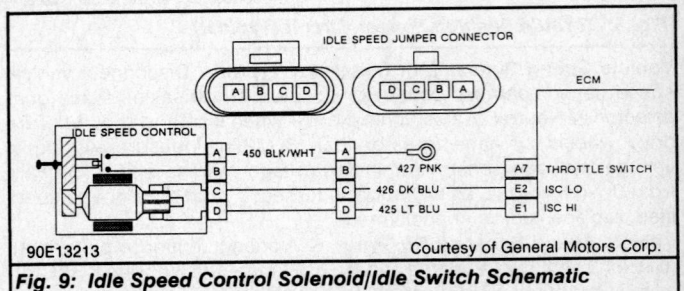

Fig. 9: Idle Speed Control Solenoid/Idle Switch Schematic

IGNITION SYSTEM

NOTE: For basic ignition system checks, see BASIC DIAGNOSTIC PROCEDURES article.

TIMING CONTROL SYSTEMS

Electronic Spark Timing (EST) Advance System – 1) A malfunction in the EST circuit should set a related trouble code. Start engine and warm to operating temperature. On vehicles equipped with a manual transmission, increase engine speed to about 2000 RPM. On vehicle equipped with an automatic transmission, slightly increase idle speed.
2) On all vehicles, ground "test" terminal "B" of ALDL. A noticeable change in engine speed should occur. If no change occurs, see DIAGNOSTIC CIRCUIT CHECK in BASIC DIAGNOSTIC PROCEDURES article.

Electronic Spark Control (ESC) Retard System, Without ESC Controller (C-5) – 1) An open or short circuit on the ESC wire to the ECM will set a related trouble code. A false detonation signal will not cause ECM to set a code.
2) If a "Scan" tester is available, connect it to the ALDL connector. Tap on engine next to knock sensor and note "knock" parameter. Knock should be indicated on "Scan" tester.
3) If a "Scan" tester is not available, connect tachometer to engine. Start engine and hold above idle. Using a metal object, tap on engine close to knock sensor. A noticeable decrease in engine RPM should occur. If no RPM decrease occurred, check knock sensor to ECM circuit.
4) On vehicles equipped with automatic transmission, it may be necessary to place transmission in Drive for timing change to occur. Also, see KNOCK SENSOR in ENGINE SENSORS & SWITCHES.

Electronic Spark Control (ESC) Retard System, With ESC Controller (C-5) – 1) An open or short circuit on the ESC wire to the ECM will cause a loss of the 12-volt ESC controller signal. This will cause the ECM to fully retard ignition timing.
2) If a "Scan" tester is available, connect it to the ALDL connector. Tap on engine next to knock sensor and note "knock" parameter. Knock should be indicated on "Scan" tester.
3) If a "Scan" tester is not available, connect a DVOM to the ECM ESC signal terminal. With engine idling, 12 volts should be present at this terminal. Using a metal object, tap on engine close to knock sensor. Voltage signal at ECM terminal should drop to zero volts, and return when knock signal ceases.
4) If signal does not respond as described, check knock sensor signal to ESC controller. On vehicles equipped with automatic transmission, it may be necessary to place transmission in Drive for timing change to occur. Also, see KNOCK SENSOR in ENGINE SENSORS & SWITCHES.

EMISSION SYSTEMS & SUB-SYSTEMS

AIR INJECTION (C-6)

Air Pump (Belt-Driven) – Accelerate engine to approximately 1500 RPM and observe airflow from hoses. If airflow increases as engine is accelerated, pump is working properly. If airflow does not increase, check hoses, pump belt tension, leaky valves or defective air injection pump.
Check Valve – Detach check valve and blow through valve in direction of check valve flow (to cylinder head). Attempt to suck back. Replace valve if airflow is allowed against the direction of flow.
Deceleration Valve (3.1L "F" Body) – 1) Remove air cleaner. Remove and plug vacuum hose to air cleaner. Connect tachometer to engine. With engine at idle, remove deceleration valve signal hose from vacuum port.
2) Reconnect signal hose to deceleration valve while listening for air flow through ventilation pipe into deceleration valve. Engine speed should drop when hose is reconnected.
3) If airflow lasts less than one second or engine speed does not drop, check for defective hose(s) or deceleration valve.

Electric Air Divert Valve (3.1L, 3.4L & 5.0L & 5.7L "B" & "D" Bodies) – With engine at idle, check for at least 10 in. Hg to valve. Run engine at part throttle (less than 2000 RPM). Air should go into exhaust ports until system goes into closed loop, then divert the air to atmosphere. If this does not occur, check terminal harness connector to valve, check for short to ground in air solenoid harness or replace defective valve. Regardless of open or closed loop operation, air should always divert to atmosphere on heavy deceleration.
Electric Air Pump Relay (3.4L Man. Trans.) – 1) Start engine. With engine fuel system operating in open loop, electric air pump should run and air should be routed through the EADV to the exhaust manifolds. Air pump should also run with ALDL "test" terminal "B" grounded with engine running.
2) If electric air pump is operating, allow engine to idle for at least 3 minutes. With vehicle in closed loop (or approximately 3 minutes after start), ECM should de-energize electric air pump relay and electric air pump should stop. If this does not occur, go to step 3). If air pump functions as described, relay is functioning properly.
3) Disconnect relay connector. Relay is located in right side electrical center. Connect ohmmeter across Orange wire terminals of relay. Apply battery voltage to Brown/White wire terminal of relay. Apply ground to Pink/Black wire terminal of relay.
4) Continuity should exist between Orange wire terminals of relay ONLY with relay energized. If relay does not test as indicated, replace relay.
Air Management System – Pressure Operated Electric Divert/Electric Switching (V8 "F" & "Y" Bodies) – 1) When engine is cold, port solenoid should be energized, allowing airflow to exhaust ports.
2) When engine is warmed up, port switch is de-energized (off) and converter solenoid should be energized, forcing airflow past the converter valve to the catalytic converter.
3) On the divert mode, both solenoids are de-energized, which opens the converter valve, allowing air out to divert/relief tube to atmosphere. If valves are not operating as specified, check circuit to solenoids. Repair or replace components as necessary.

EXHAUST GAS RECIRCULATION (C-7)

There are 3 types of EGR systems used: pulse width modulated backpressure EGR (positive and negative) with a control solenoid, pulse width modulated backpressure (positive and negative) EGR without a control solenoid, and digital EGR. To determine EGR system usage, see EGR SYSTEM IDENTIFICATION table.

EGR SYSTEM IDENTIFICATION

Application	System Type	Solenoid Type
2.0L, 2.2L & 2.5L TBI	BP/EGR	N/A
2.3L PFI	Digital	N/A
3.1 & 3.4L PFI	Digital	N/A
3.8L PFI "H" Body	Digital	N/A
4.9L PFI	BP/EGR	Normally Open
5.0 & 5.7L TBI	BP/EGR	Normally Closed
5.0L & 5.7L PFI "F" Body	BP/EGR	Normally Open
5.7L PFI "Y" Body	BP/EGR	Normally Open

System Test (Vacuum Operated) – Start and run engine to normal operating temperature. With engine at idle, push up on underside of EGR diaphragm. RPM should drop as EGR valve is opened. If RPM does not drop, remove EGR valve and check for blocked EGR passages. If RPM drops as diaphragm is lifted and EGR vacuum supply is regulated by an ECM-controlled solenoid, verify vacuum is available to solenoid at 2000 RPM and check solenoid using appropriate procedure. See EGR CONTROL SOLENOID.

CAUTION: Wear gloves if handling EGR valve when it is hot.

EGR Control Solenoid (Normally Closed) – 1) Disconnect EGR solenoid electrical harness connector and vacuum hoses. Connect a hand-held vacuum pump to solenoid vacuum source port. Connect vacuum gauge to solenoid EGR port. Pump up vacuum pump. Vacuum should not be present at port to EGR valve.

2) Activate EGR solenoid with a 12-volt power supply. Vacuum should now be present or registered at vacuum gauge. Solenoid should have at least 20 ohms of resistance.

EGR Control Solenoid (Normally Open) – 1) Disconnect solenoid harness connector. Install vacuum pump to vacuum source side of solenoid. Apply vacuum to solenoid. Vacuum should pass through when solenoid connector is disconnected.

2) Apply battery voltage and ground to solenoid terminals. With solenoid energized, apply vacuum to solenoid. Vacuum should not pass through solenoid. If results are not as specified, replace solenoid. Solenoid should have at least 20 ohms of resistance.

Digital EGR Valve (2.3L "W" Body) – 1) If an EGR-related code is set, go to appropriate SELF-DIAGNOSTICS article for diagnosis. Start and allow engine to idle. With engine at normal operating temperature, disconnect digital EGR valve solenoid harness connector. Using a 12-volt power source and a fused jumper wire, very quickly energize EGR solenoid No. 1. RPM should drop slightly. See Fig. 10.

2) Next, energize EGR solenoid No. 2. RPM should drop slightly more than step 1). If RPM drops as indicated, EGR is okay. If not, check for plugged EGR passages or defective digital EGR valve. Check EGR solenoid windings for opens or shorts.

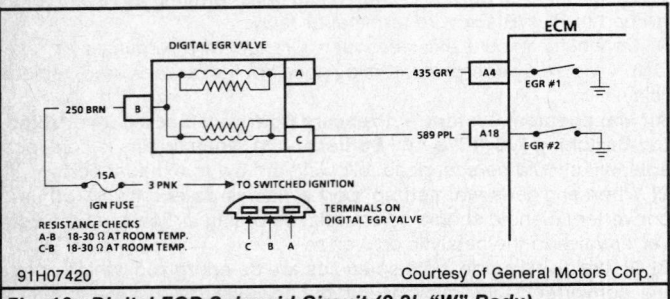

Fig. 10: Digital EGR Solenoid Circuit (2.3L "W" Body)

Digital EGR Valve (3.1L, 3.4L & 3.8L "H" Body) – 1) If an EGR-related code is set, go to appropriate SELF-DIAGNOSTICS article for diagnosis. Start and allow engine to idle. With engine at normal operating temperature, disconnect digital EGR valve solenoid harness connector.

2) Using a 12-volt power source and a fused jumper wire, very quickly energize EGR solenoid No. 1 Blue wire terminal on EGR valve. RPM should drop slightly. See Fig. 11. Next, energize EGR solenoid No. 2 Brown wire terminal on EGR valve. RPM should drop slightly more than step 1). Energize EGR solenoid No. 3 Red wire terminal on EGR valve.

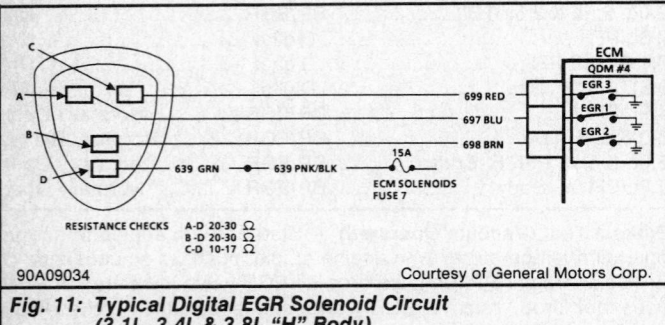

Fig. 11: Typical Digital EGR Solenoid Circuit (3.1L, 3.4L & 3.8L "H" Body)

3) RPM should drop more than step 1) or 2). If RPM drops as indicated, EGR is okay. If RPM drop is not as indicated, check for plugged EGR passages or defective digital EGR valve. Check EGR solenoid resistance. See DIGITAL EGR SOLENOID RESISTANCE table.

NOTE: For additional testing procedures, see appropriate SELF-DIAGNOSTICS article.

DIGITAL EGR SOLENOID RESISTANCE [1]

Terminals	Ohms
A-D	20-30
B-D	20-30
C-D	10-17

[1] – See Fig. 11 for terminal identification.

Positive Backpressure EGR Valve – 1) Place transmission in Park or Neutral. Set parking brake and block drive wheels. Connect tachometer. With engine running at normal operating temperature, run engine at 2000 RPM.

2) Disconnect vacuum hose from EGR valve and plug hose. EGR valve diaphragm should move down and engine RPM should increase.

NOTE: On some engines with ECM controlled solenoid, EGR vacuum is locked out in Park/Neutral and solenoid must be by-passed with vacuum supply hose.

3) Reconnect vacuum hose. EGR diaphragm should move up and engine RPM should decrease. A slight vibration of diaphragm plate may be noticed in backpressure EGR valves.

4) If engine RPM did not change and EGR diaphragm moved, the EGR valve is functioning properly. If engine RPM did not change and diaphragm did not move, remove EGR valve and apply 10 in. Hg to EGR vacuum signal port. EGR valve should not open.

5) If EGR valve opens, replace EGR valve. With vacuum still applied, direct a stream of air (15 psi maximum) into valve seat. EGR valve should open completely.

6) If air is not available, connect a short piece of hose over EGR valve seat. Connect vacuum pump to signal port. With thumb plugging intake port of EGR valve, operate vacuum pump while alternately blowing and pausing through hose.

7) With vacuum present at signal port, EGR valve should open while pressure is applied and should close when no vacuum is present.

Negative Backpressure EGR Valve – With engine off, disconnect vacuum hose to EGR valve. Connect vacuum pump to EGR and apply 10 in. Hg. EGR diaphragm should move up and stay up for 20 seconds. If valve does not operate as indicated, replace EGR valve.

FUEL EVAPORATION CONTROL (C-3)

NOTE: On 2.0L, 2.2L & 2.5L engines, no canister purge solenoid is used. Canister is purged by ported vacuum when engine is running above idle. On all other models, one of 2 types of solenoid is used: normally open or normally closed. See CANISTER PURGE SOLENOID IDENTIFICATION table.

CANISTER PURGE SOLENOID IDENTIFICATION

Application	Solenoid Type
2.0L, 2.2L & 2.5L TBI	N/A
2.3L	Normally Closed
3.1 & 3.4L	Normally Open
3.3L	Normally Closed
3.8L	Normally Closed
4.9L	Normally Closed
5.0 & 5.7L TBI	Normally Closed
5.0L & 5.7L PFI "F" Body	Normally Open
5.7L "Y" Body	Normally Closed

Canister Purge Solenoid (Normally Closed) – 1) Disconnect canister purge solenoid harness connector and vacuum hose. Apply 10 in. Hg to ported intake manifold vacuum side of solenoid valve. If vacuum holds, go to next step. If vacuum does not hold, replace canister purge solenoid.

2) Using a 12-volt power source, energize canister purge solenoid. Vacuum should release. If vacuum does not release, replace canister purge solenoid. Solenoid resistance should be at least 20 ohms.

Canister Purge Solenoid (Normally Open) – 1) Disconnect canister purge solenoid harness connector and vacuum hose. Apply vacuum to ported intake manifold vacuum side of solenoid valve. If vacuum holds, go to next step. If vacuum does not hold, replace canister purge solenoid.

2) Using a 12-volt power source, energize canister purge solenoid. Vacuum should release. If vacuum does not release, replace canister purge solenoid. Solenoid resistance should be at least 20 ohms.
Fuel Tank Pressure Control Valve – Apply approximately 15 in. Hg to tank pressure control valve. The diaphragm should hold vacuum for at least 20 seconds. If not, replace tank pressure control valve.

PCV

Required Service – The PCV system may require service for obstructions if any of the following conditions exist:
- Rough Idle
- Stalling or Slow Idle Speed
- Oil Leaks
- Oil in Air Cleaner
- Sludge in Engine

A leaking PCV valve or hose could cause:
- Rough Idle
- Stalling
- High Idle speed

If engine idles roughly, check for clogged PCV valve or plugged or broken hoses BEFORE adjusting idle. Check PCV valve application to ensure the correct valve is fitted. Replace PCV valve if required.
Checking PCV Valve Function – **1)** Remove PCV valve from rocker cover. Run engine at idle. Place thumb over open end of valve to check for vacuum. If there is no vacuum at valve, check for obstruction in manifold port, hoses or PCV valve. Repair or replace as necessary.
2) Turn engine off. Remove PCV valve. Shake valve and listen for rattle of check valve inside. If a clear rattle is not heard, replace PCV valve.
3) Visually inspect valve for varnish or deposits which may make PCV valve operation sticky, restricted or cause incomplete seating of valve. Replace if necessary.
4) An engine must be sealed for the PCV system to function as designed. If leakage, sludging or dilution of oil is noted and the PCV system is functioning properly, check engine for cause and repair as required to ensure PCV system will continue to function properly.
5) An engine operating without any crankcase ventilation can be damaged, so it is important to replace PCV valve and air cleaner breather at regular intervals (at least every 30,000 miles). Check all hoses and clamps for failure or deterioration.

THERMOSTATIC AIR CLEANER

Temperature Sensor (Vacuum Motor Type) – **1)** Air cleaner temperature should be less than 86°F (30°C). Place thermometer as close to sensor inside air cleaner. Start and idle engine. Damper door should close off outside air immediately.
2) When damper door starts to open snorkel passage, remove air cleaner cover and read thermometer temperature. Thermometer should read about 131°F (55°C).
3) If damper door does not open to outside air at the specified temperature, replace defective thermostatic air cleaner temperature sensor.
Vacuum Motor Diaphragm – **1)** Turn engine off. Disconnect vacuum hose to vacuum motor. Apply 7 in. Hg to vacuum motor. Damper door should close. If not, check if linkage is properly hooked up.
2) With vacuum still applied, trap vacuum in vacuum diaphragm motor by bending hose. Damper door should remain closed. If damper door does not remain closed, replace vacuum diaphragm motor assembly.
Damper Door – Wax Pellet Check ("B" Body) – **1)** Remove air cleaner assembly from vehicle and allow to cool to less than 40° F (4° C). Damper door should be closed to outside (cold) air.
2) Reinstall air cleaner assembly. Start engine and observe damper door. As air cleaner assembly warms up, wax pellet should expand, closing off hot air delivery and opening cold air delivery.
3) If door does not respond as indicated, ensure door is not binding and calibrated damper spring is installed properly.

MISCELLANEOUS CONTROLS

NOTE: Although some of the controlled devices listed here are not technically engine performance components, they can affect driveability if they malfunction.

A/C CLUTCH (C-10)

NOTE: A/C clutch control is also covered in greater detail in Mitchell's domestic AIR CONDITIONING & HEATING SERVICE & REPAIR supplement.

A/C Clutch Relay – **1)** Disconnect A/C clutch relay harness connector. Using proper mini-schematic and an ohmmeter, check continuity between A/C clutch relay winding terminals. Continuity should exist. Check continuity between clutch drive circuit terminals of relay. Continuity should not exist. *See Figs. 12-36.*
2) Using jumper wires, apply ground and battery voltage to relay winding of relay. Continuity should now exist between clutch drive circuit terminals of relay. Replace A/C clutch relay if readings are not as specified.

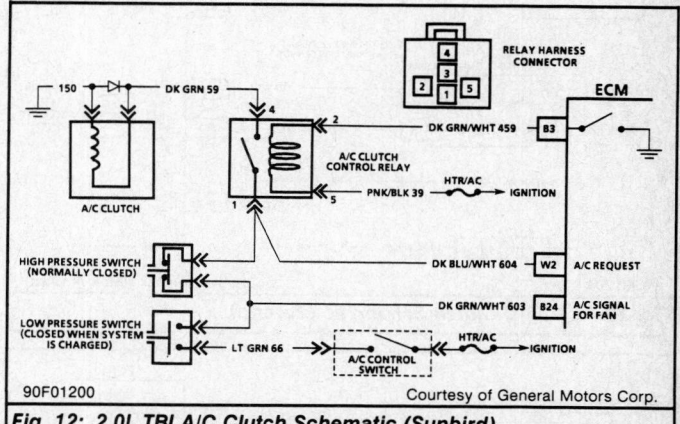

Courtesy of General Motors Corp.
Fig. 12: 2.0L TBI A/C Clutch Schematic (Sunbird)

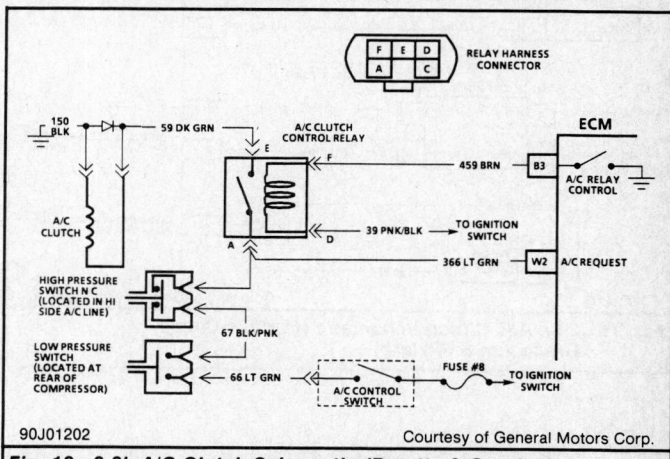

Courtesy of General Motors Corp.
Fig. 13: 2.2L A/C Clutch Schematic (Beretta & Corsica)

1991 ENGINE PERFORMANCE
Systems & Component Testing (Cont.)

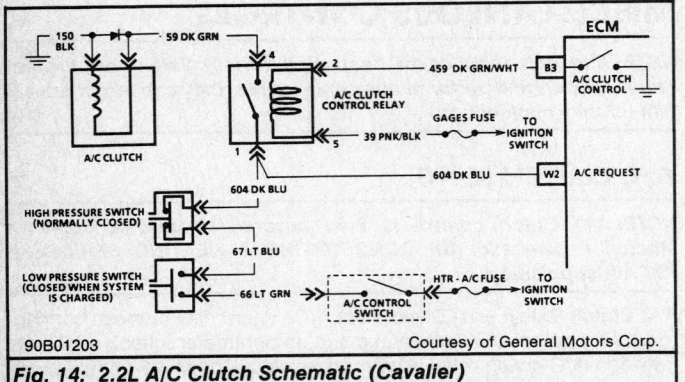

Fig. 14: 2.2L A/C Clutch Schematic (Cavalier)

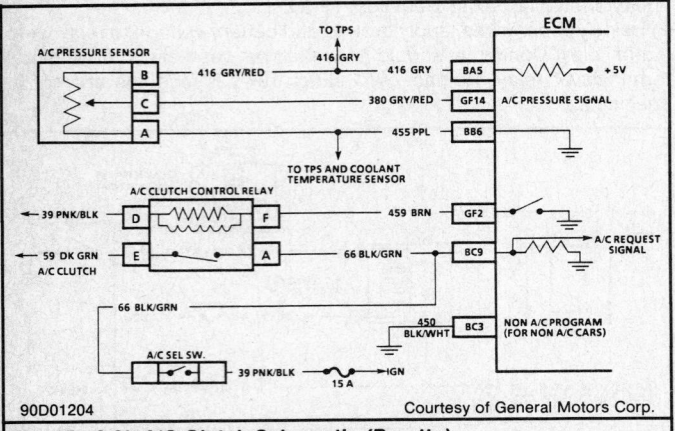

Fig. 15: 2.3L A/C Clutch Schematic (Beretta)

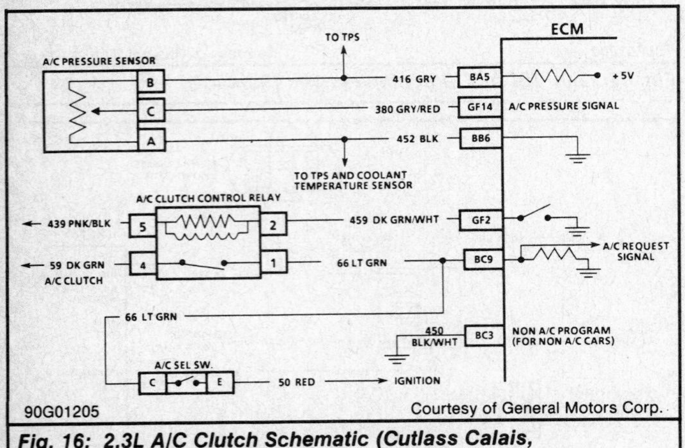

Fig. 16: 2.3L A/C Clutch Schematic (Cutlass Calais, Grand Am & Skylark)

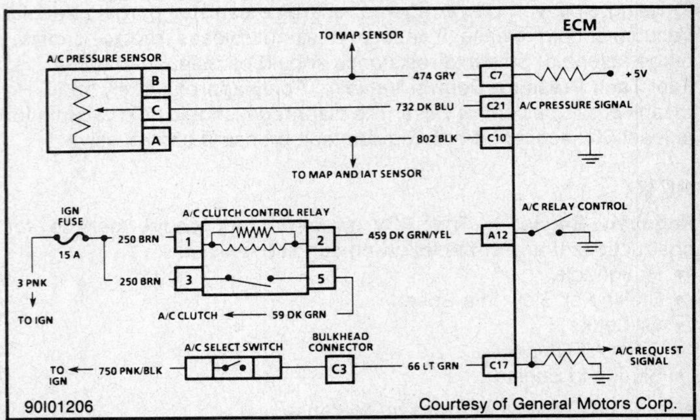

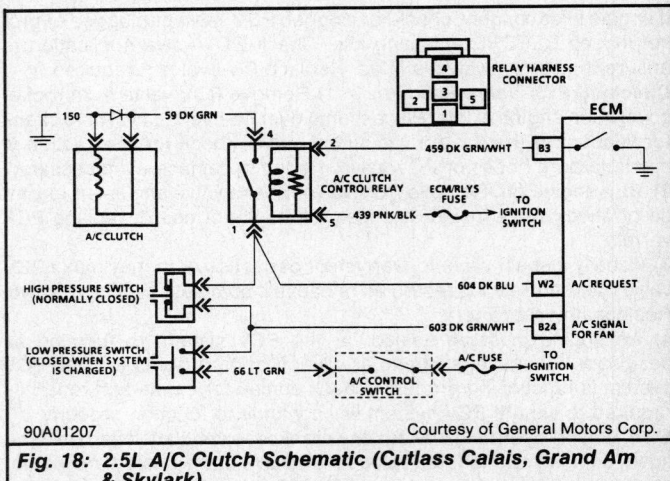

Fig. 17: 2.3L A/C Clutch Schematic (Cutlass Supreme & Grand Prix)

Fig. 18: 2.5L A/C Clutch Schematic (Cutlass Calais, Grand Am & Skylark)

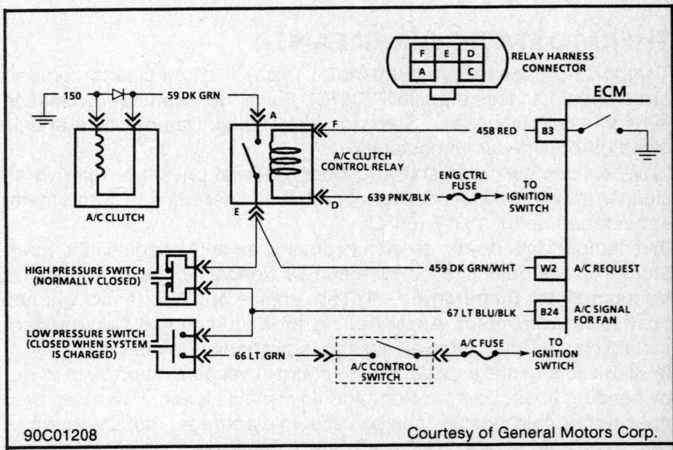

Fig. 19: 2.5L A/C Clutch Schematic (Century, Cutlass Ciera & Cutlass Cruiser)

91F05566 Courtesy of General Motors Corp.

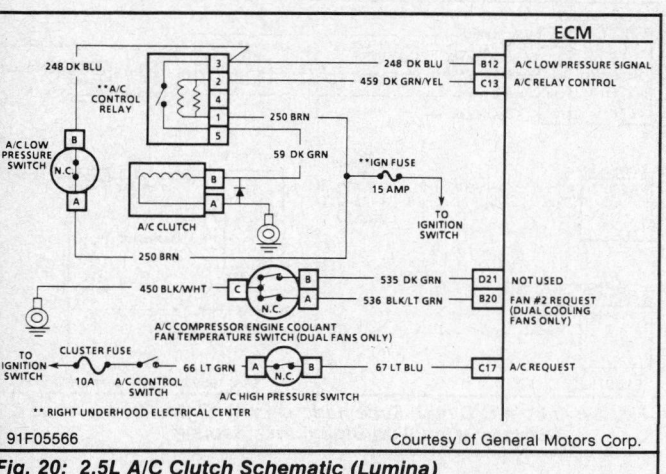

Fig. 20: 2.5L A/C Clutch Schematic (Lumina)

91G05576 Courtesy of General Motors Corp.

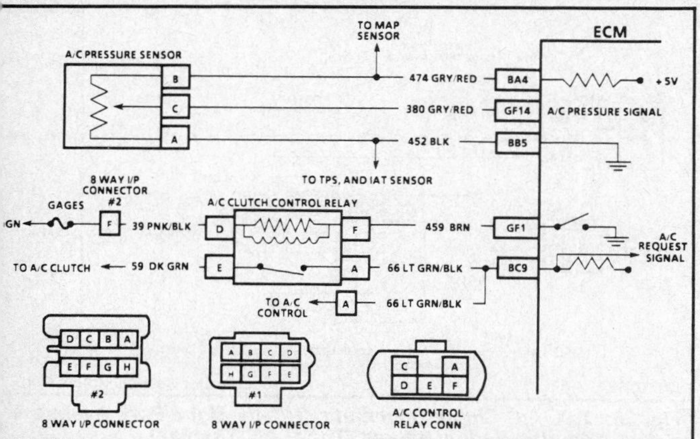

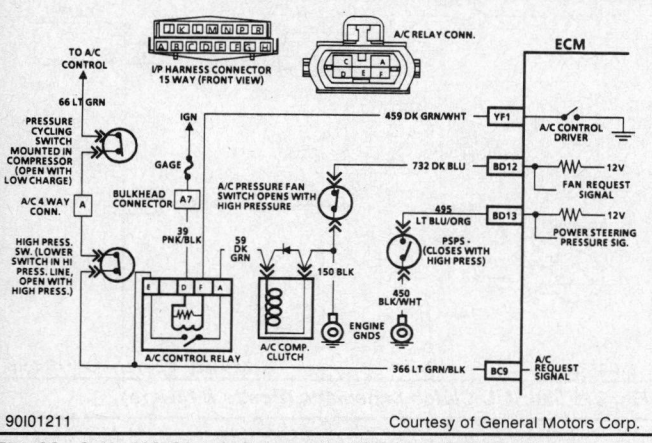

Fig. 21: 3.1L A/C Clutch Schematic (Beretta & Corsica)

90I01211 Courtesy of General Motors Corp.

Fig. 22: 3.1L A/C Clutch Schematic (Camaro & Firebird)

90A01212 Courtesy of General Motors Corp.

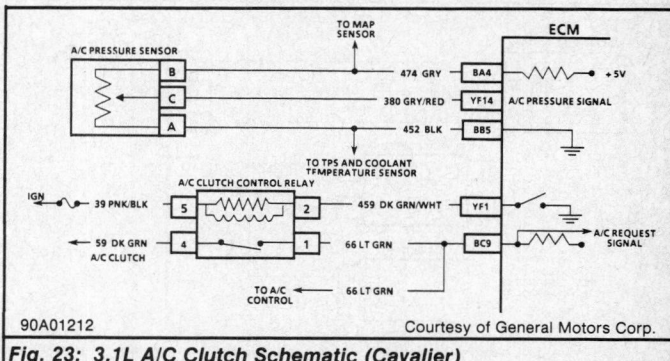

Fig. 23: 3.1L A/C Clutch Schematic (Cavalier)

90C01213 Courtesy of General Motors Corp.

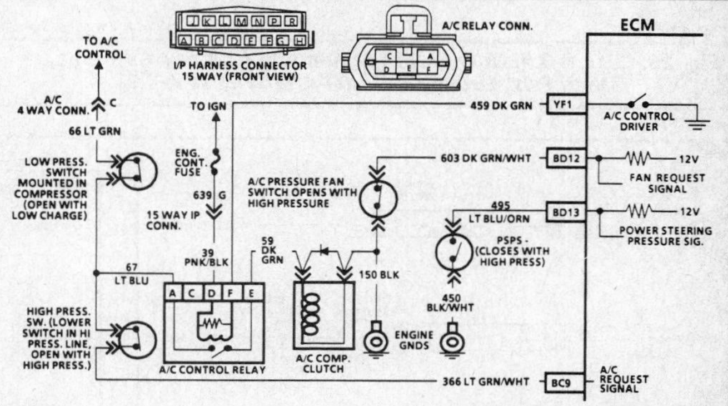

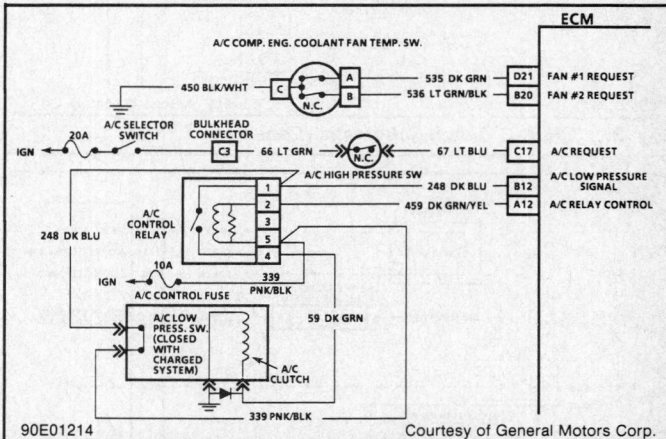

Fig. 24: 3.1L A/C Clutch Schematic (6000)

90E01214 Courtesy of General Motors Corp.

Fig. 25: 3.1L & 3.4L A/C Clutch Schematic (Regal Prior to VIN 800,000)

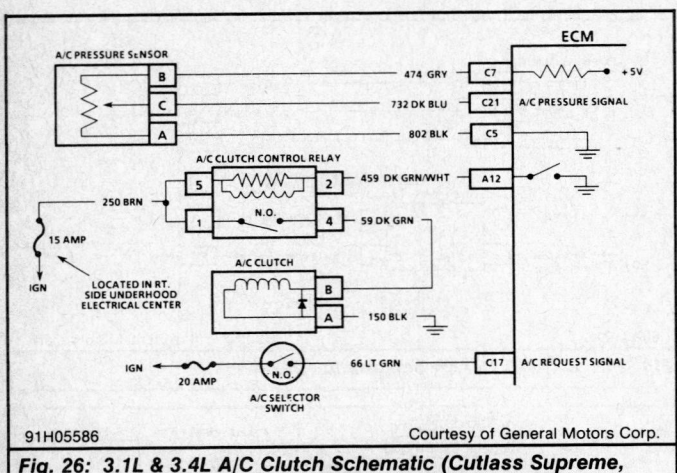

Fig. 26: 3.1L & 3.4L A/C Clutch Schematic (Cutlass Supreme, Grand Prix, Lumina & Regal After VIN 799,999)

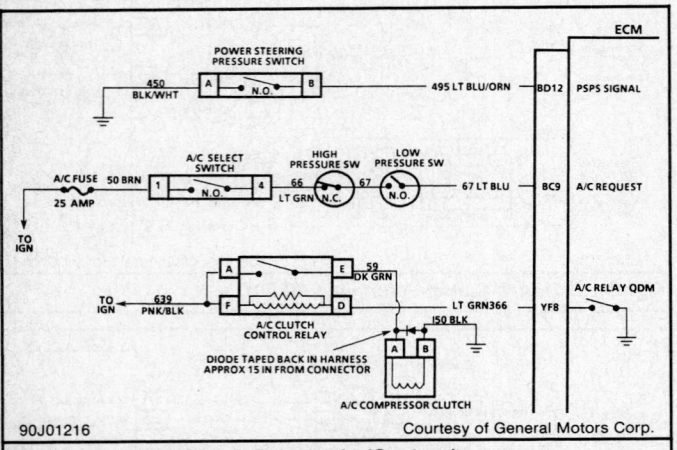

Fig. 27: 3.3L A/C Clutch Schematic (Century)

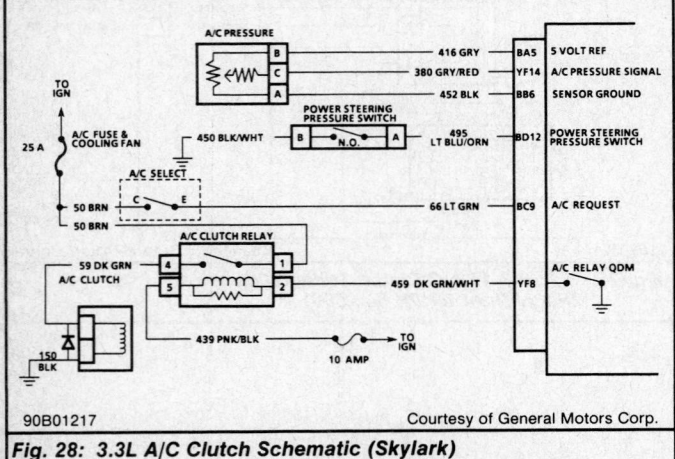

Fig. 28: 3.3L A/C Clutch Schematic (Skylark)

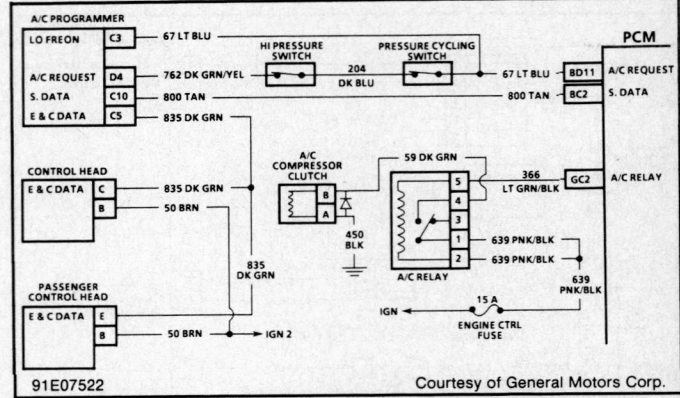

Fig. 29: 3.8L A/C Clutch Schematic (Ninety-Eight, Park Avenue & Touring Sedan With Digital A/C Display)

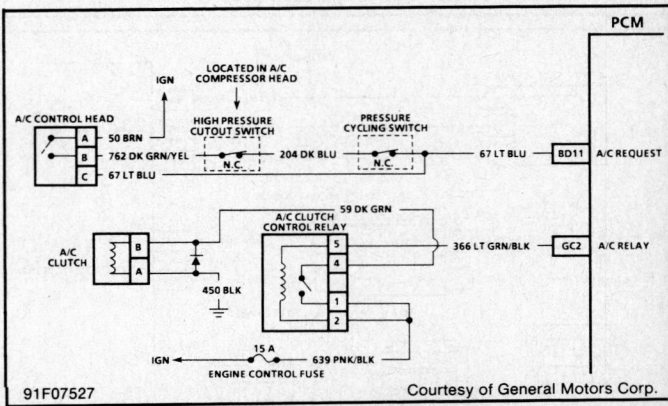

Fig. 30: 3.8L A/C Clutch Schematic (Ninety-Eight, Park Avenue & Touring Sedan Without Digital A/C Display)

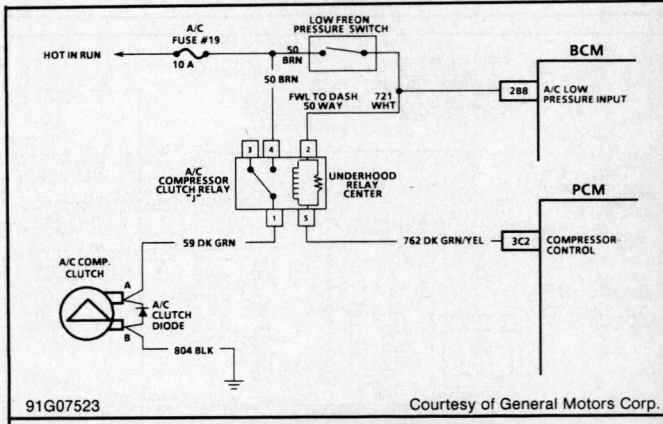

Fig. 31: 3.8L A/C Clutch Schematic (Reatta & Riviera)

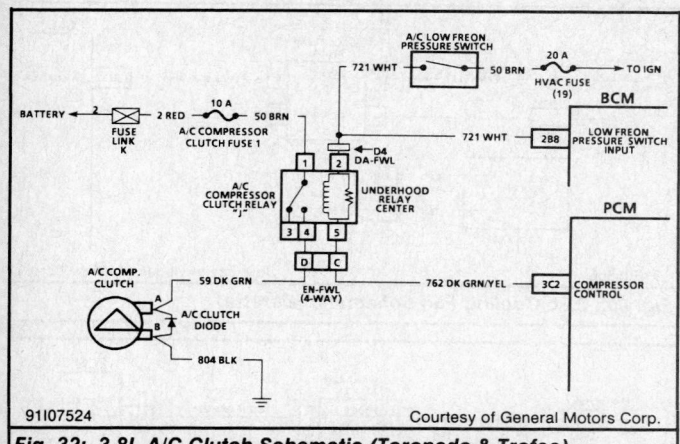

Fig. 32: 3.8L A/C Clutch Schematic (Toronado & Trofeo)

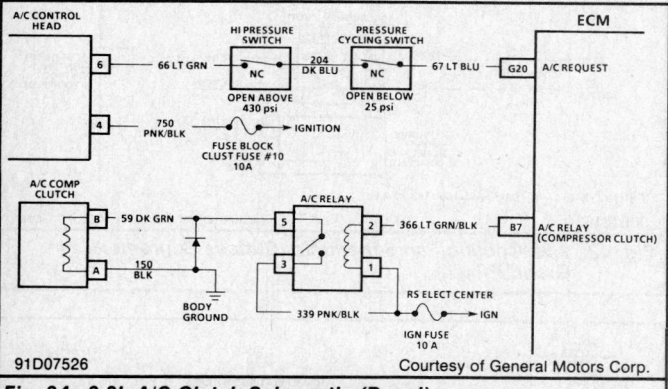

Fig. 33: 3.8L A/C Clutch Schematic (Bonneville, Eighty-Eight & LeSabre)

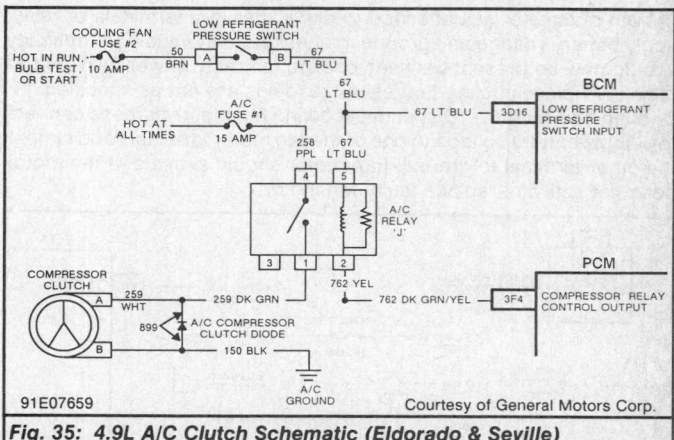

Fig. 35: 4.9L A/C Clutch Schematic (Eldorado & Seville)

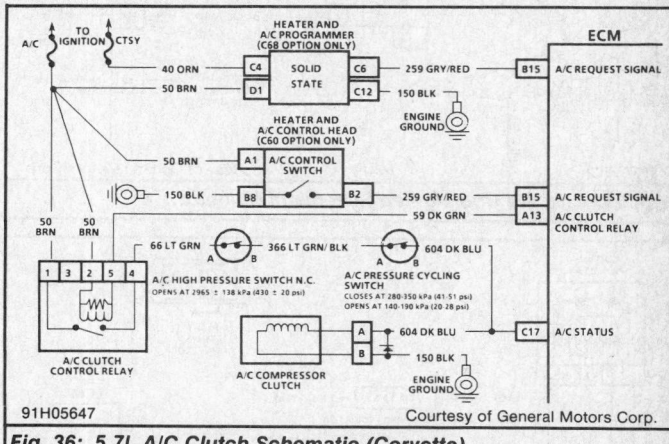

Fig. 36: 5.7L A/C Clutch Schematic (Corvette)

ELECTRIC COOLING FAN (C-12)

NOTE: For additional information on electric cooling fans, see ELECTRIC COOLING FANS article in ENGINE COOLING. Electric cooling fans are also covered in greater detail in Mitchell's domestic 1991 AIR CONDITIONING & HEATING SERVICE & REPAIR supplement.

Cooling Fan System & Quad-Driver Check – 1) Connect a test light to battery voltage. Touch test light probe to the cooling fan control driver terminal of the ECM. *See Figs. 37-59.* Disconnect coolant temperature sensor. This should set a code, causing ECM to engage cooling fan through relay. On some models it may be necessary to jumper the coolant temperature sensor harness connectors. On some models, grounding the ALDL with the ignition on and engine off will cause the ECM to activate the cooling fan control driver (ground circuit).

2) If test light illuminates and cooling fan does not come on, check cooling fan relay, power circuits, cooling fan motor, and relay and fan motor ground circuits. If test light does not illuminate, problem is a faulty ECM connector or ECM. Clear trouble code(s) from ECM memory after testing.

3) If cooling fan functions normally during testing but fails to operate under normal conditions, check ECM monitored inputs which affect cooling fan operation. These include the following: coolant temperature sensor, A/C request signal from A/C control switch and A/C pressure sensor or pressure/temperature switch signals (if equipped).

Cooling Fan Relay – 1) Disconnect cooling fan relay harness connector. Using an ohmmeter, check continuity of relay winding. *See Figs. 37-59.* Continuity should exist. Check continuity across power delivery terminals of relay. With relay not energized, no continuity should exist.

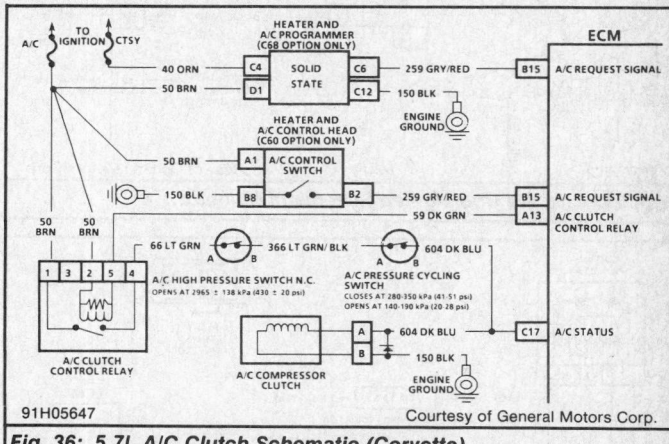

Fig. 34: 3.8L A/C Clutch Schematic (Regal)

2) With ohmmeter still attached to power delivery terminals of relay, apply battery voltage and ground to energize relay winding. Continuity should now be present between cooling fan relay power delivery terminals. Replace cooling fan relay if readings are not as specified.

Cooling Fan Motor – Disconnect cooling fan motor harness connector. Apply battery voltage to one of the fan motor terminals and jumper the other terminal to ground. Fan motor should activate. If fan motor does not activate, replace faulty fan motor.

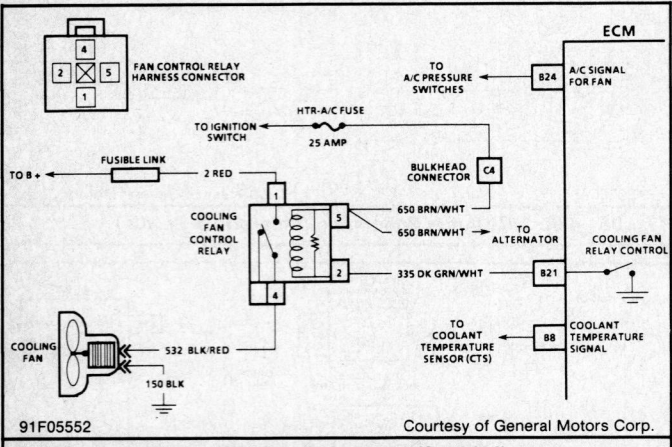

Fig. 37: 2.0L TBI Cooling Fan Schematic (Sunbird)

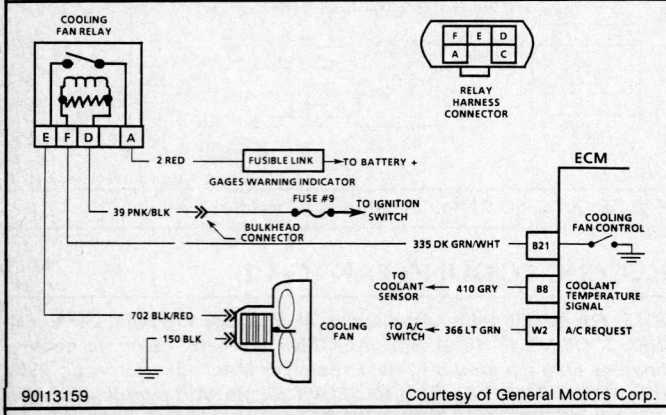

Fig. 38: 2.2L Cooling Fan Schematic (Beretta & Corsica)

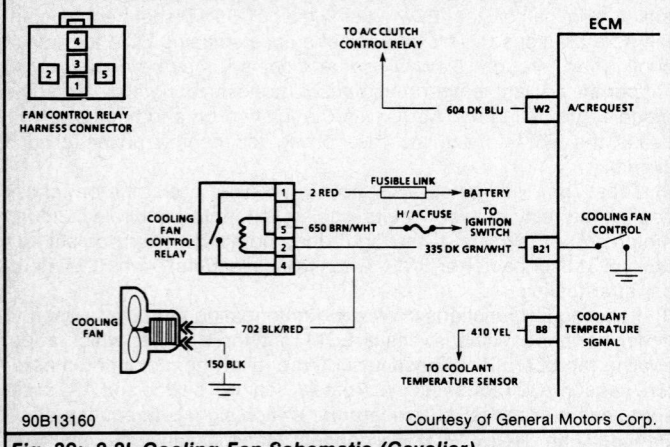

Fig. 39: 2.2L Cooling Fan Schematic (Cavalier)

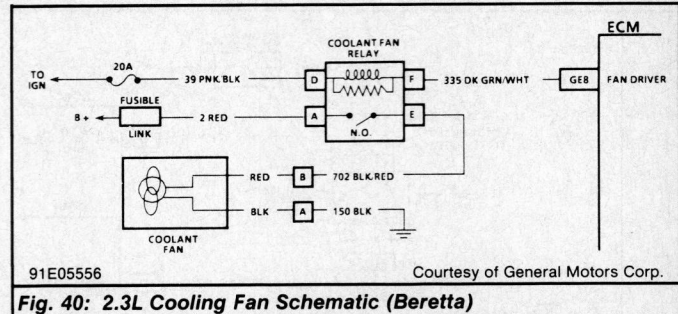

Fig. 40: 2.3L Cooling Fan Schematic (Beretta)

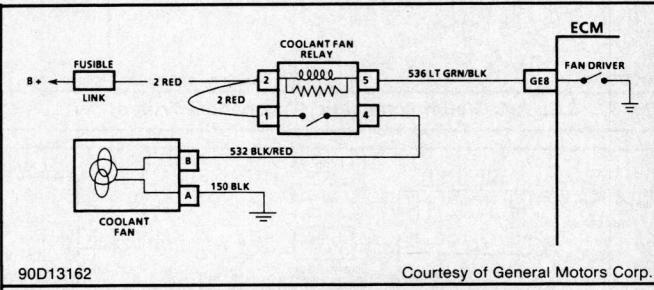

Fig. 41: 2.3L Cooling Fan Schematic (Cutlass Calais, Grand Am & Skylark)

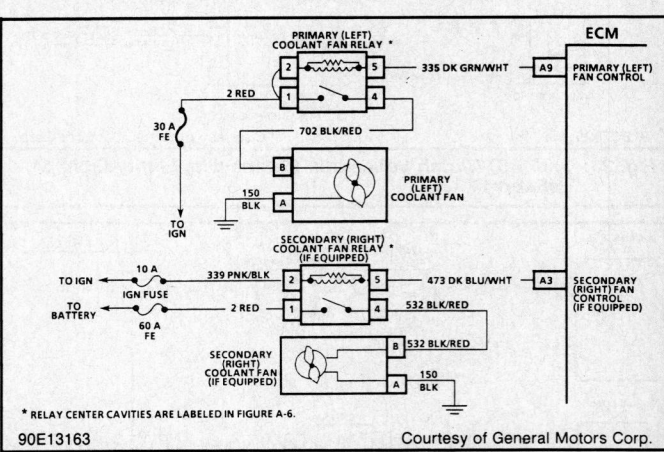

Fig. 42: 2.3L Cooling Fan Schematic (Cutlass Supreme & Grand Prix)

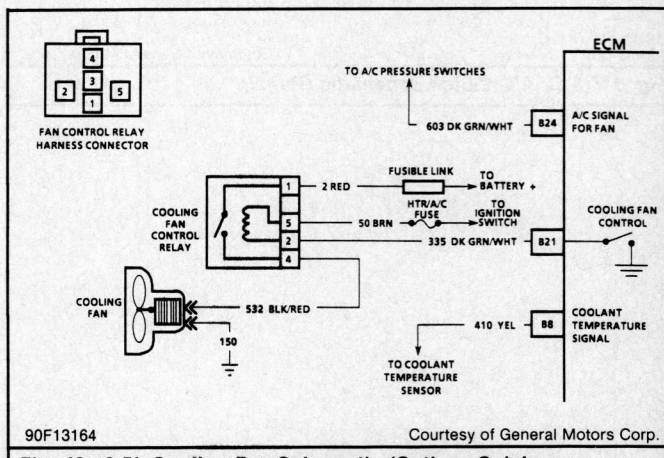

Fig. 43: 2.5L Cooling Fan Schematic (Cutlass Calais, Grand Am & Skylark)

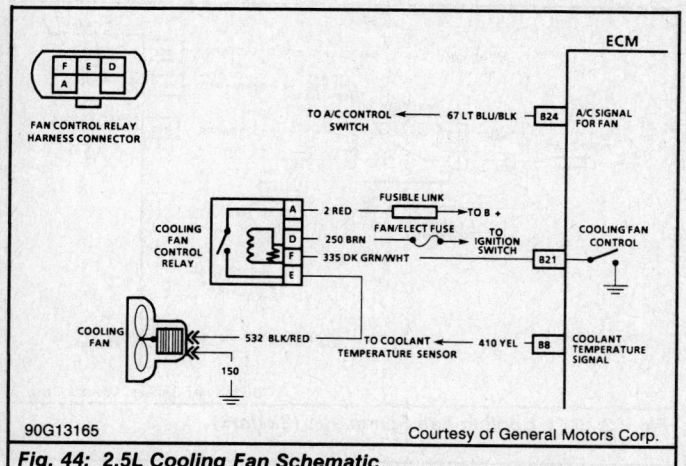

Fig. 44: 2.5L Cooling Fan Schematic
(Century, Cutlass Ciera, Cutlass Cruiser & 6000)

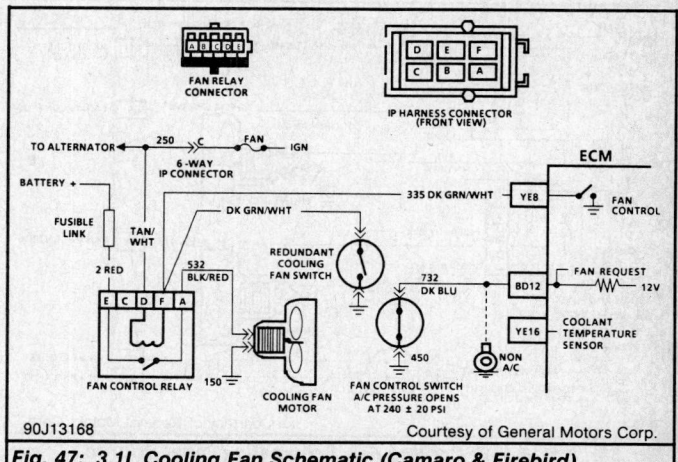

Fig. 47: 3.1L Cooling Fan Schematic (Camaro & Firebird)

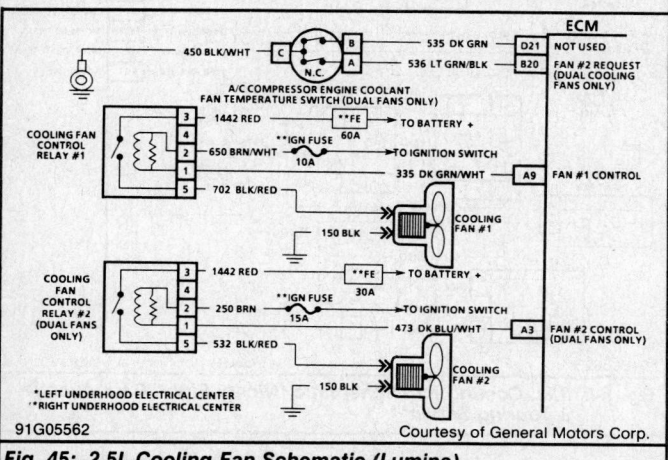

Fig. 45: 2.5L Cooling Fan Schematic (Lumina)

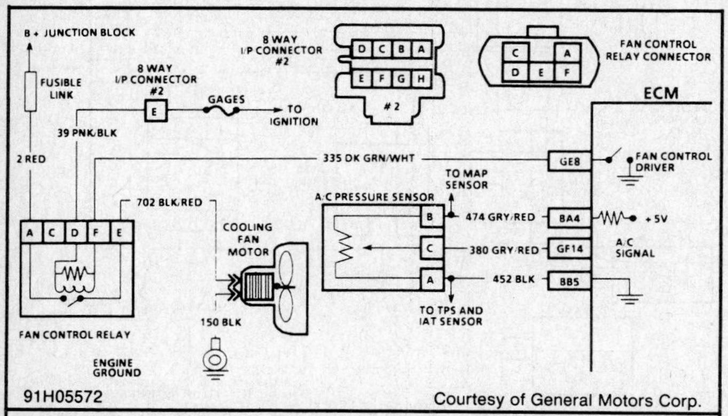

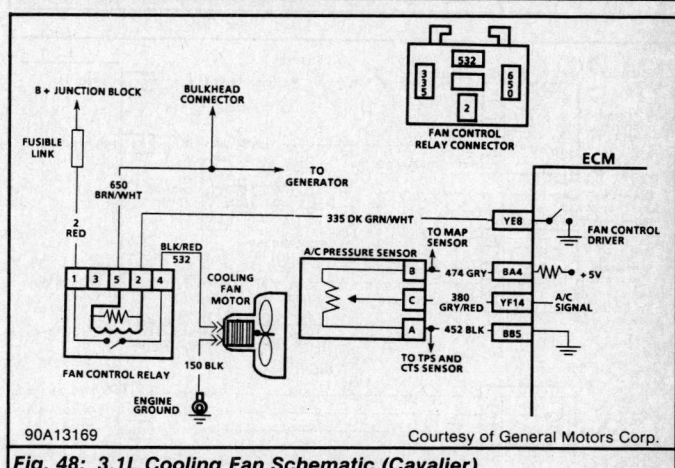

Fig. 48: 3.1L Cooling Fan Schematic (Cavalier)

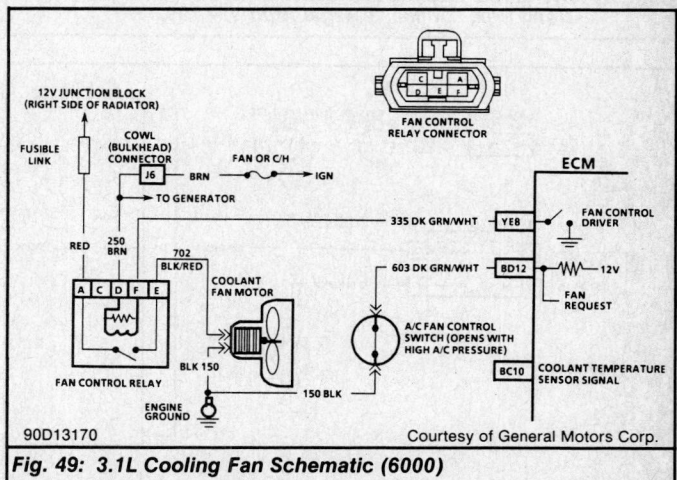

Fig. 46: 3.1L Cooling Fan Schematic (Beretta & Corsica)

Fig. 49: 3.1L Cooling Fan Schematic (6000)

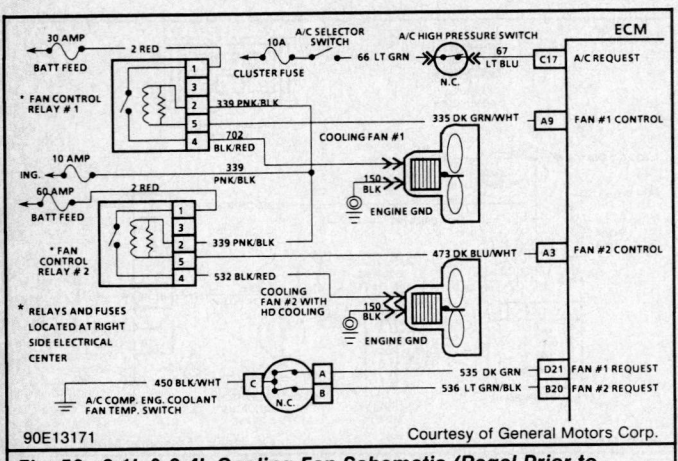

Fig. 50: *3.1L & 3.4L Cooling Fan Schematic (Regal Prior to VIN 800,000)*

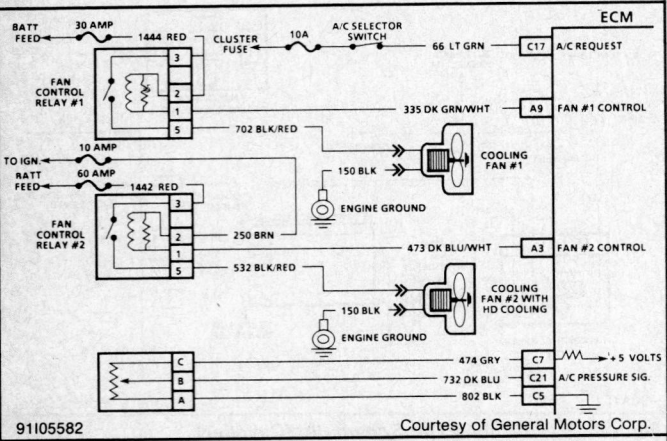

Fig. 51: *3.1L & 3.4L Cooling Fan Schematic (Cutlass Supreme, Grand Prix, Lumina, & Regal After VIN 799,999)*

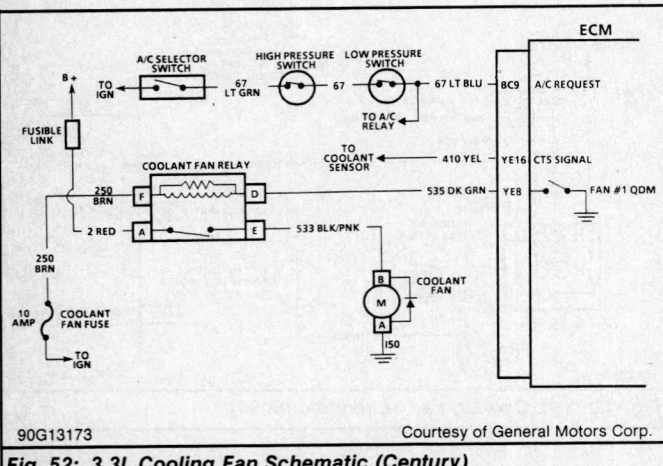

Fig. 52: *3.3L Cooling Fan Schematic (Century)*

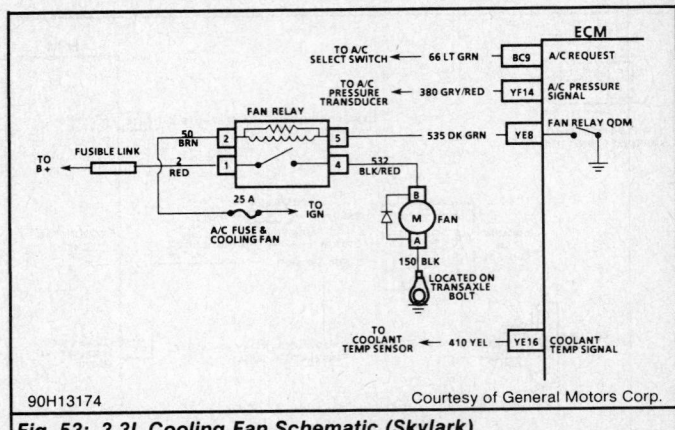

Fig. 53: *3.3L Cooling Fan Schematic (Skylark)*

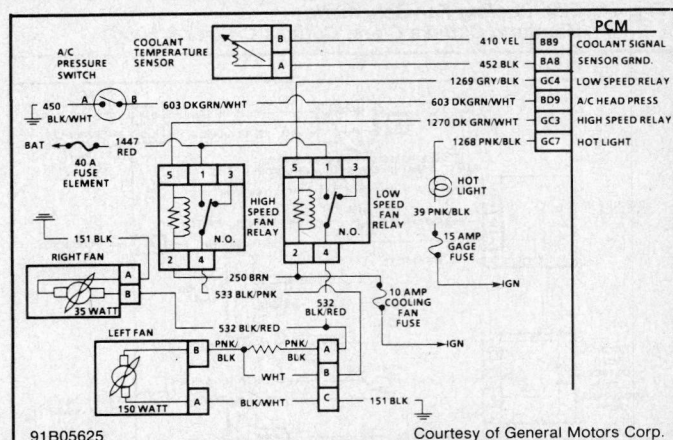

Fig. 54: *3.8L Cooling Fan Schematic (Ninety-Eight, Park Avenue & Touring Sedan)*

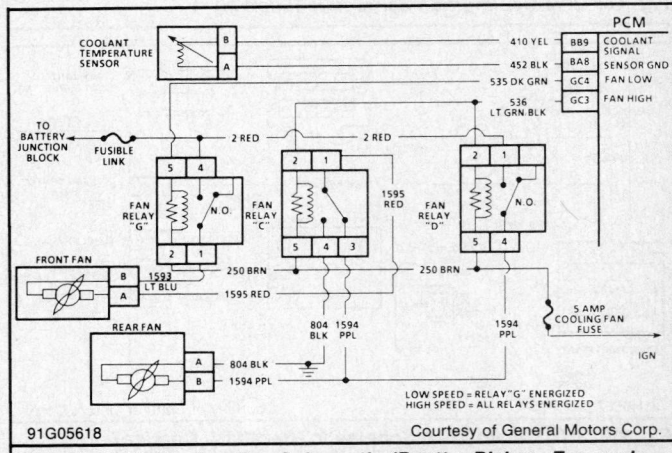

Fig. 55: *3.8L Cooling Fan Schematic (Reatta, Riviera, Toronado & Trofeo)*

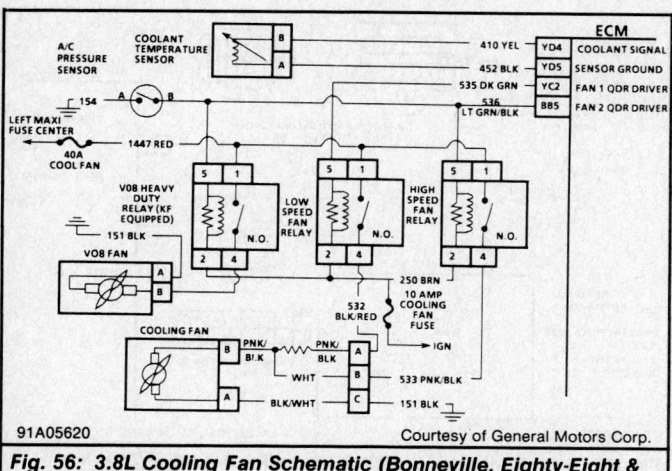

Fig. 56: 3.8L Cooling Fan Schematic (Bonneville, Eighty-Eight & LeSabre)

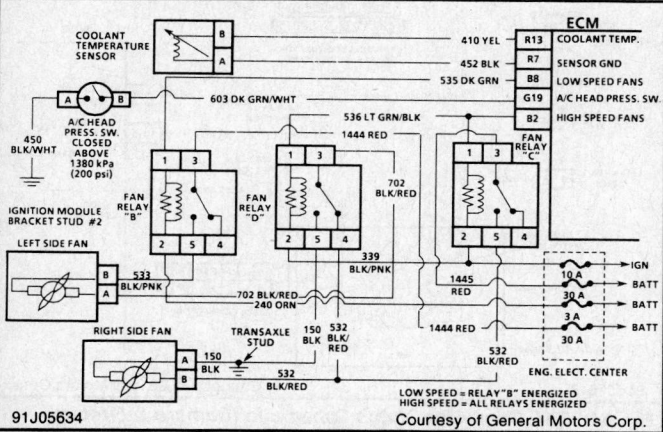

Fig. 57: 3.8L Cooling Fan Schematic (Regal)

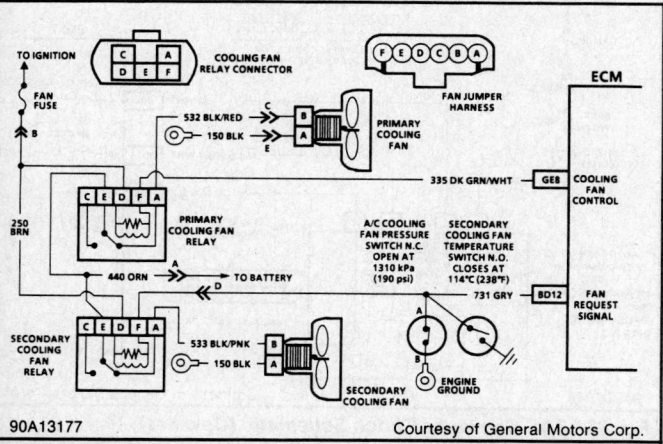

Fig. 58: 5.0L & 5.7L Cooling Fan Schematic (Camaro & Firebird)

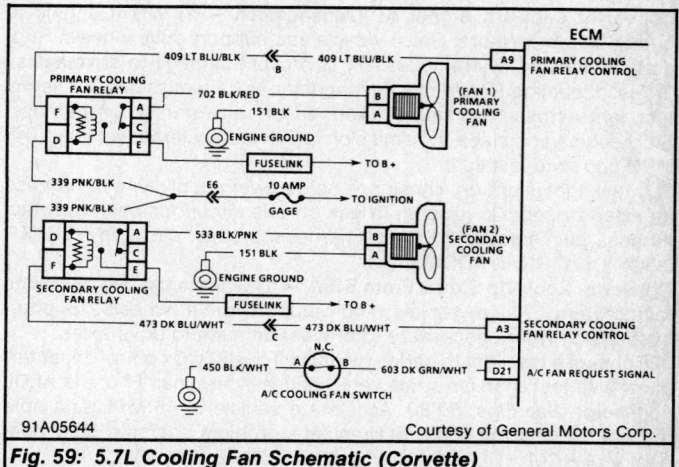

Fig. 59: 5.7L Cooling Fan Schematic (Corvette)

HOT LIGHT OR COOLANT TEMPERATURE LIGHT

NOTE: These checks assume vehicle is not overheating. Verify proper operation of cooling system prior to diagnosing hot light. The coolant temperature sensor, in rare cases, may fail to indicate the correct coolant temperature without setting a malfunction code (Code 14 or 15). This could result in turning on the hot light without having an overheating condition. It could also result in engine overheating without turning on the hot light. Check coolant sensor temperature-to-resistance values in SENSOR OPERATING RANGES article.

Hot light is powered by the 10-amp INDIC or GAGES fuse. Light will turn on when ECM provides a ground for the circuit. If circuit grounds between light and ECM, light will illuminate any time the ignition is turned on.

1) Turn ignition on with engine off (bulb test position). If hot light illuminates, go to step 3). If hot light does not illuminate, check the following:
- 10-amp INDIC OR GAGES fuse.
- Faulty instrument cluster bulb
- Open circuit between fuse and hot light.

2) Backprobe ECM hot light driver terminal with a test light to battery voltage. Turn ignition on. If test light does not illuminate, ECM terminal connection is bad or ECM is faulty. If test light illuminates, turn ignition off. Disconnect ECM connectors. Jumper ECM hot light driver harness terminal to ground. Turn ignition on. If hot light does not illuminate, check for open circuit between hot light and ECM. If light does not illuminate and all circuits are intact and power is available to light, instrument cluster must be replaced.

3) Start engine. If test light goes off, no problem is evident. If test light is on, turn ignition off. Disconnect ECM connector. Probe ECM hot light driver harness terminal with a test light to battery voltage. If light is off, replace ECM. If light is on, repair short to ground in hot light driver circuit. If no short is present, replace instrument cluster.

TRANSMISSION (C-8)

NOTE: ECM transmission controls are also covered in greater detail in Mitchell's domestic TRANSMISSION SERVICE & REPAIR manual.

Converter Clutch Solenoid – Disconnect harness connector to TCC solenoid. Measure resistance between TCC solenoid terminals "A" and "D". Solenoid resistance should be greater than 20 ohms.

NOTE: Some solenoids have an internal pressure switch in series with the solenoid winding and will not show continuity until that pressure switch is applied by transmission hydraulic pressure. See Figs. 60-80.

Converter Lock-Up Signal At Transmission – 1) Warm engine to operating temperature. Raise vehicle and support drive wheels. Support suspension where necessary to prevent damage to drive axles. **2)** Disconnect converter clutch connector at transmission. Connect a test light across terminals "A" and "D" of converter clutch harness. Start engine and place transmission in Drive. Accelerate vehicle to 45 MPH and note test light.

3) If test light is not on, check solenoid power supply wire of harness for open or short to ground. Check ground circuit for open between harness connector and ECM. If harness is okay, see CONVERTER LOCK-UP SIGNAL FROM ECM.

Converter Lock-Up Signal From ECM – 1) Warm engine to operating temperature. Raise vehicle and support drive wheels. Support suspension where necessary to prevent damage to drive axles.

2) Connect a test light to battery voltage. Touch TCC control driver terminal with test light. On some vehicles this is terminal "F" of the ALDL connector. *See Figs. 60-80.* Accelerate vehicle to 45 MPH and note test light. If test light does not illuminate, problem is a faulty ECM connector or ECM

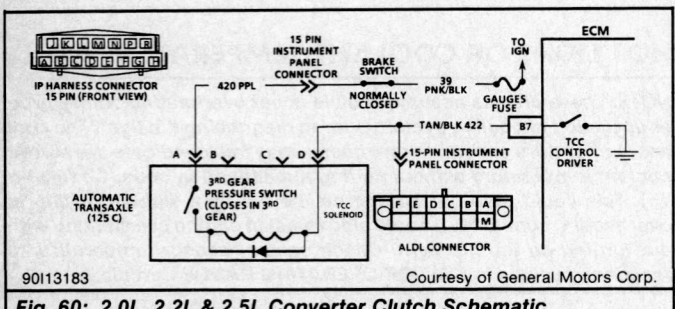

Courtesy of General Motors Corp.

Fig. 60: 2.0L, 2.2L & 2.5L Converter Clutch Schematic (Except 2.5L Lumina)

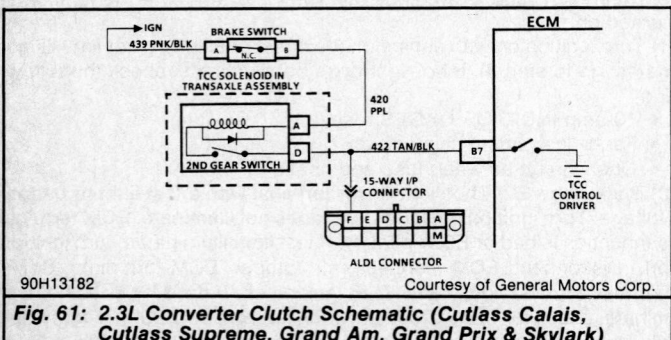

Courtesy of General Motors Corp.

Fig. 61: 2.3L Converter Clutch Schematic (Cutlass Calais, Cutlass Supreme, Grand Am, Grand Prix & Skylark)

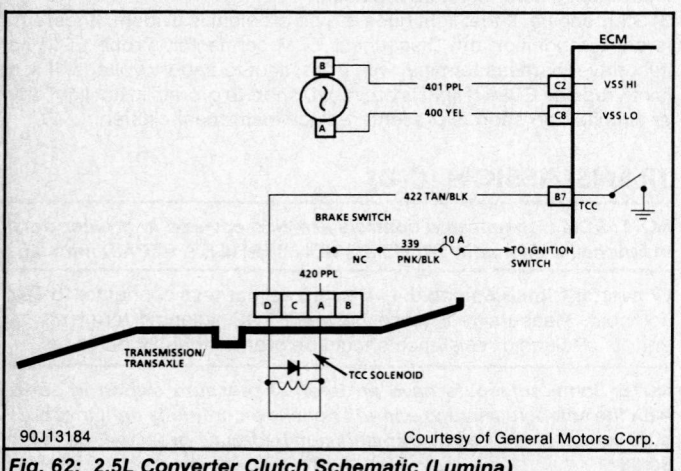

Courtesy of General Motors Corp.

Fig. 62: 2.5L Converter Clutch Schematic (Lumina)

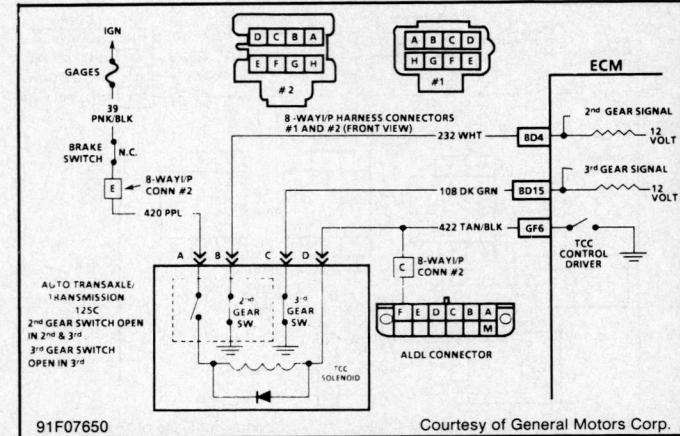

Courtesy of General Motors Corp.

Fig. 63: 3.1L Converter Clutch Schematic (Beretta & Corsica)

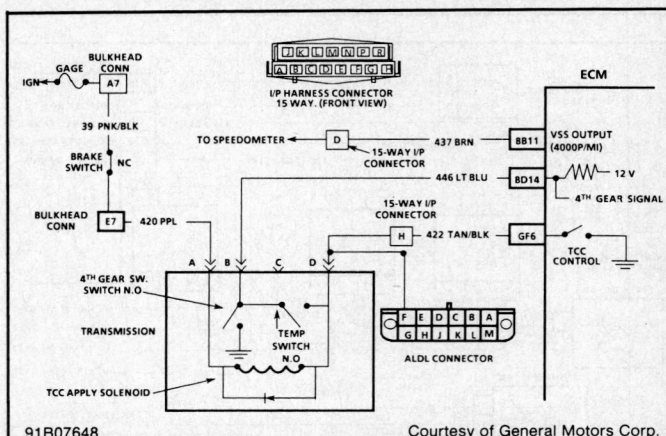

Courtesy of General Motors Corp.

Fig. 64: 3.1L Converter Clutch Schematic (Camaro & Firebird)

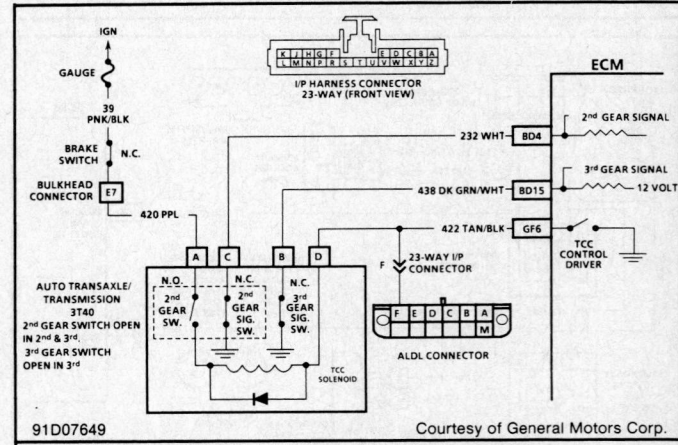

Courtesy of General Motors Corp.

Fig. 65: 3.1L Converter Clutch Schematic (Cavalier)

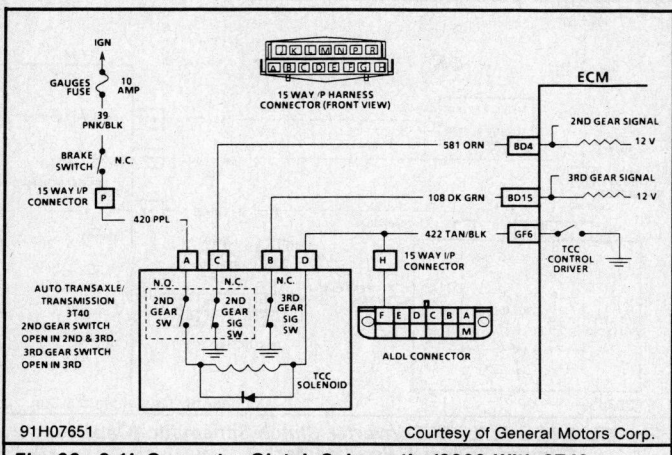

91H07651

Courtesy of General Motors Corp.

Fig. 66: 3.1L Converter Clutch Schematic (6000 With 3T40 Transaxle)

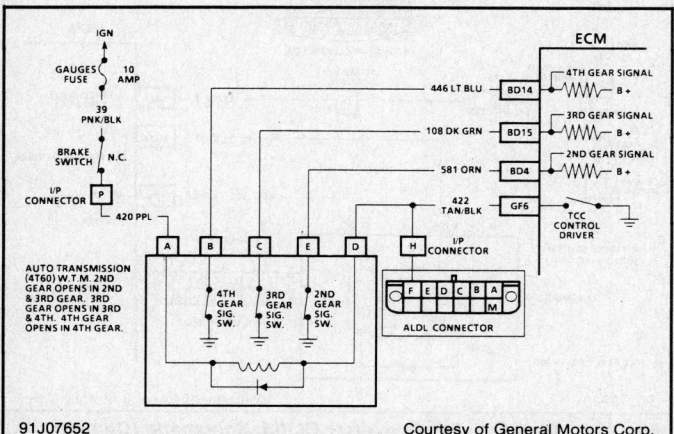

91J07652

Courtesy of General Motors Corp.

Fig. 67: 3.1L Converter Clutch Schematic (6000 With 4T60 Transaxle)

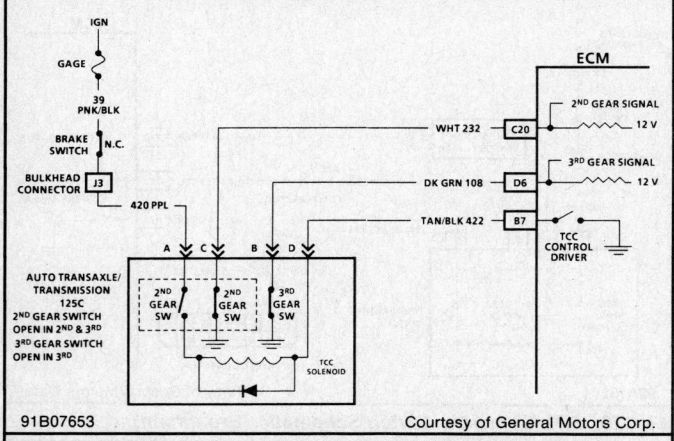

91B07653

Courtesy of General Motors Corp.

Fig. 68: 3.1L Converter Clutch Schematic (Lumina With 3T40 Transaxle)

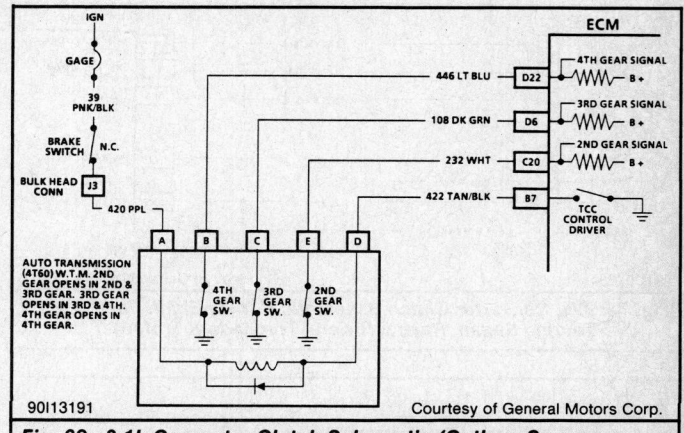

90I13191

Courtesy of General Motors Corp.

Fig. 69: 3.1L Converter Clutch Schematic (Cutlass Supreme, Grand Prix, Regal & Lumina With 4T60 Transaxle)

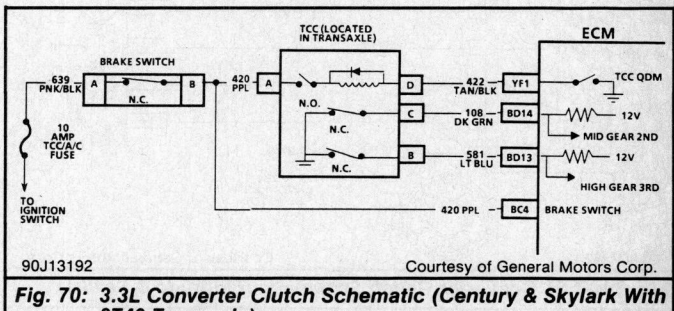

90J13192

Courtesy of General Motors Corp.

Fig. 70: 3.3L Converter Clutch Schematic (Century & Skylark With 3T40 Transaxle)

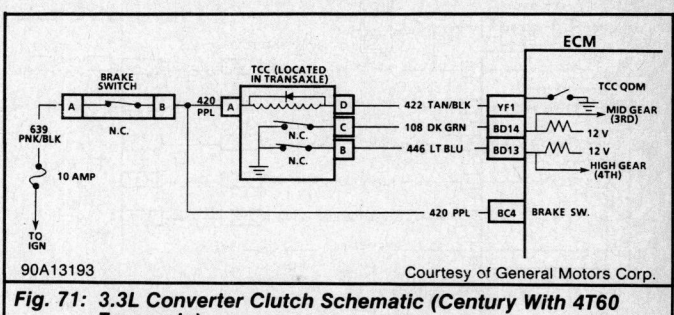

90A13193

Courtesy of General Motors Corp.

Fig. 71: 3.3L Converter Clutch Schematic (Century With 4T60 Transaxle)

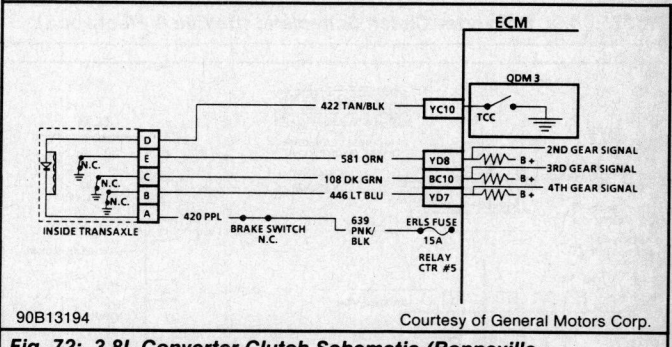

90B13194

Courtesy of General Motors Corp.

Fig. 72: 3.8L Converter Clutch Schematic (Bonneville, Eighty-Eight & LeSabre)

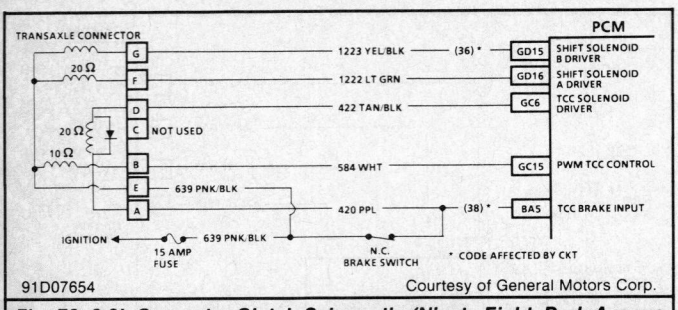

Fig. 73: 3.8L Converter Clutch Schematic (Ninety-Eight, Park Avenue, Touring Sedan, Reatta, Riviera, Toronado & Trofeo)

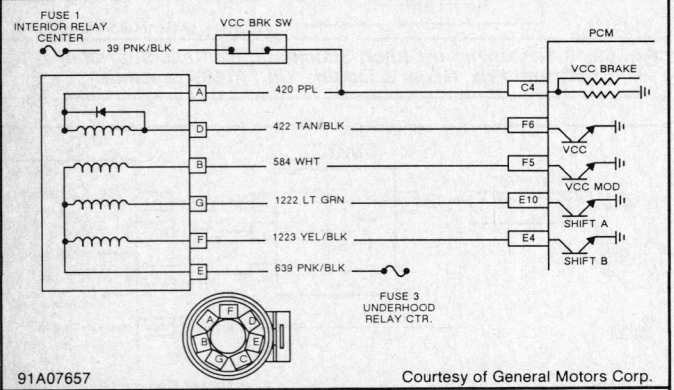

Fig. 74: 4.9L Converter Clutch Schematic (Eldorado & Seville)

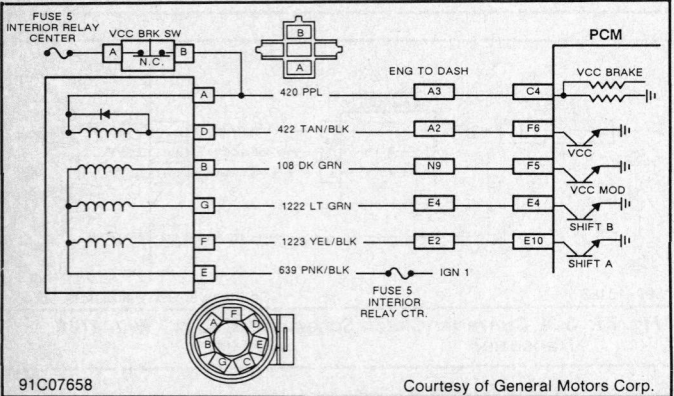

Fig. 75: 4.9L Converter Clutch Schematic (DeVille & Fleetwood)

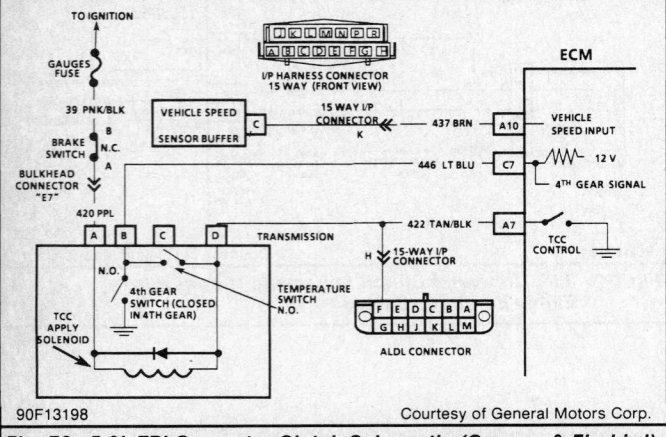

Fig. 76: 5.0L TBI Converter Clutch Schematic (Camaro & Firebird)

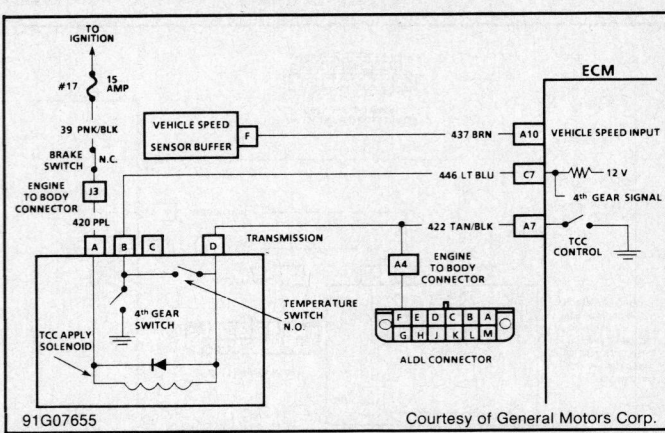

Fig. 77: 5.0L & 5.7L TBI Converter Clutch Schematic (Caprice, Custom Cruiser & Roadmaster)

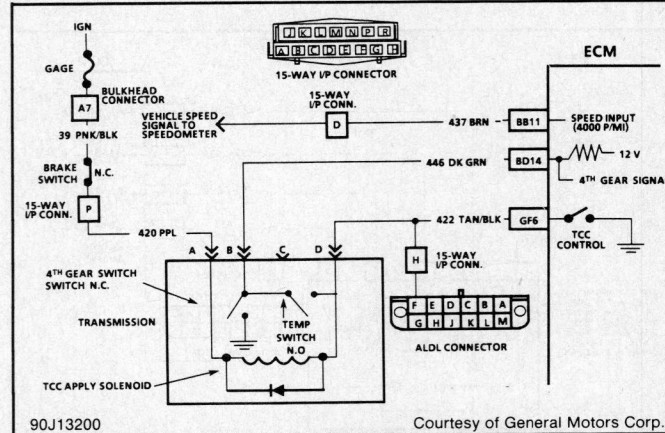

Fig. 78: 5.0L & 5.7L PFI Converter Clutch Schematic (Camaro & Firebird)

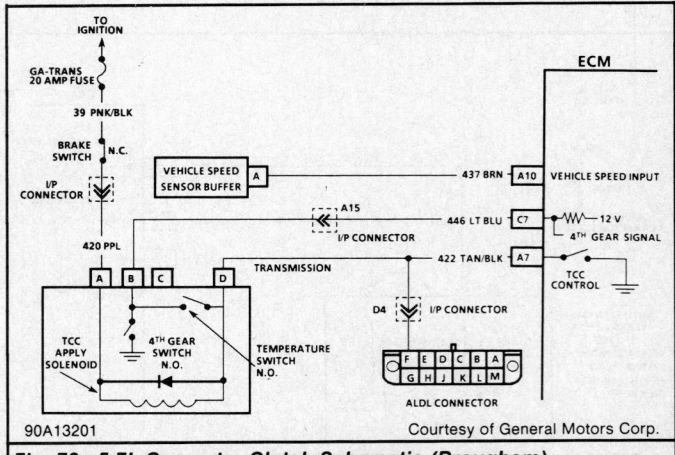

Fig. 79: 5.7L Converter Clutch Schematic (Brougham)

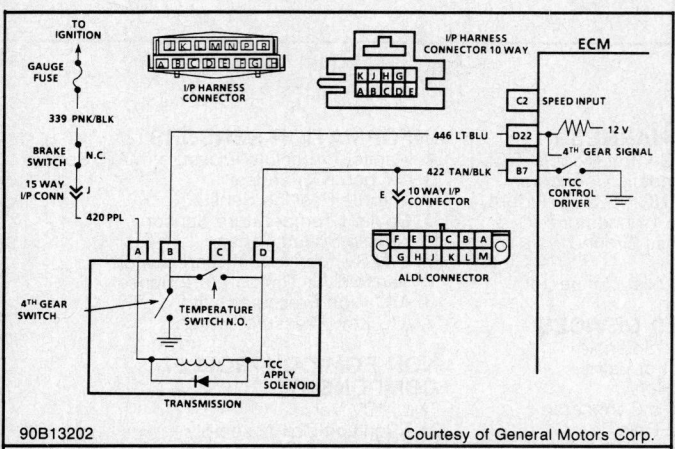

Fig. 80: 5.7L Converter Clutch Schematic (Corvette)

Shift Light (Man. Trans.) – 1) These tests assume a shift light problem exists. Use this procedure only if the light will not illuminate, or illuminates all of the time.

2) Turn ignition on, with engine off. Note shift light. Shift light should not be on. If light is on, check for a short to ground between the bulb and the ECM, or a bad ECM.

3) With ignition on and engine off, ground "test" terminal of ALDL connector. SERVICE ENGINE SOON light should start to flash and shift light should come on. If light comes on, go to next step. If SERVICE ENGINE SOON light does not flash, perform DIAGNOSTIC CIRCUIT CHECK as described in BASIC DIAGNOSTIC PROCEDURES article.

4) If shift light does not come on, ground Tan/Black wire at ECM terminal B7 (A12 on Corvette or GF4 on 2.3L Beretta, Cutlass Calais & Grand Am) using a jumper wire. If light still does not come on, check for blown GAUGES fuse (AIRBAG fuse on Corvette), blown bulb or open circuit between fuse and ECM. If light came on when grounding terminal B7 (or A12 or GF4) with a jumper wire, problem is a bad ECM connection or bad ECM.

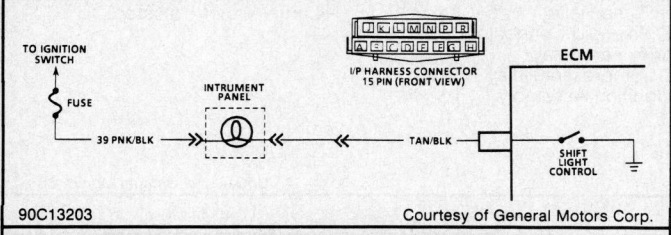

Fig. 81: Shift Light Schematic (Except Corvette)

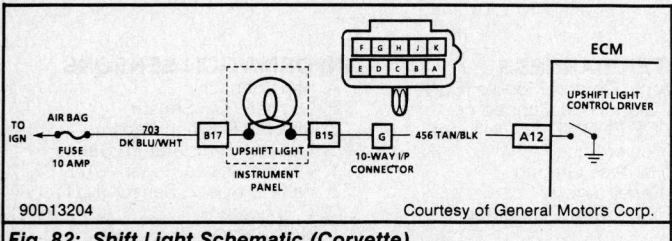

Fig. 82: Shift Light Schematic (Corvette)

1-4 Shift System Check (Man. Trans. – Corvette) – 1) With engine off, depress clutch and place transmission in 1st gear. Shift transmission into 2nd or 3rd gear. If transmission cannot be shifted into 2nd or 3rd gear, check for short to voltage on circuit between 1-4 shift relay and 1-4 shift solenoid, defective 1-4 shift solenoid, or internal mechanical transmission problem. *See Fig. 84.*

2) Turn ignition on with engine not running. Ground ALDL "test" terminal "B". Shift transmission into 2nd or 3rd gear. If transmission cannot be shifted into 2nd or 3rd gear, system is functioning correctly.

3) If transmission can be shifted into 2nd and 3rd gear, turn ignition off. Disconnect 1-4 shift relay connector. Turn ignition on and check for voltage from ground to harness terminals "D" and "E". If voltage is not present on both harness terminals, check for blown fuses or open circuit which did not illuminate test light.

4) If test light illuminated when touched to both terminals, ground ALDL "test" terminal "B" and connect test light from battery voltage to terminal "F" of 1-4 shift relay harness connector.

5) If test light does not illuminate, check for open in circuit No. 108 between relay and ECM, poor ECM terminal contact or defective ECM. If test light did illuminate, perform 1-4 SHIFT RELAY test procedures.

1-4 Shift Light (Man. Trans. – Corvette) – 1) This testing procedures assumes that a problem exists with the 1-4 shift light. Use this procedure only if the light will not illuminate, or illuminates all of the time.

2) Turn ignition on, with engine off. Note shift light. Shift light should not be on. If light is on, check for a short to ground between the bulb and the ECM, or a bad ECM.

3) With ignition on and engine off, ground "test" terminal "B" of ALDL connector. SERVICE ENGINE SOON light should start to flash and 1-4 shift light should come on. If light comes on, go to next step. If SERVICE ENGINE SOON light does not flash, perform DIAGNOSTIC CIRCUIT CHECK as described in BASIC DIAGNOSTIC PROCEDURES article.

4) If 1-4 shift light does not come on, ground ECM terminal C13 using a jumper wire. If light still does not come on, check for blown GAUGES fuse, blown bulb or open circuit between fuse and ECM. If light came on when grounding terminal C13 with a jumper wire, problem is a bad ECM connection or bad ECM.

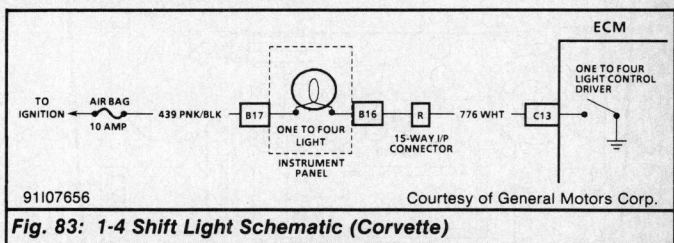

Fig. 83: 1-4 Shift Light Schematic (Corvette)

1-4 Shift Relay (Man. Trans. – Corvette) – 1) Turn ignition off. Disconnect 1-4 shift relay connector. Check for continuity between terminals "D" and "F" of relay. If continuity does not exist, replace relay. If continuity does exist, check for continuity between relay terminals "C" and "A". Continuity should also exist when relay is not energized. If not, replace relay.

2) Energize relay by applying battery voltage to terminal "D" of relay and ground to terminal "F". Check continuity between terminals "A" and "E". Continuity should exist while relay is energized. Replace relay if it does not test as described.

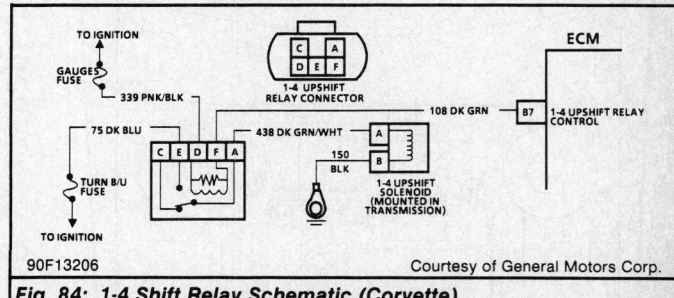

Fig. 84: 1-4 Shift Relay Schematic (Corvette)

COMPONENT LOCATIONS

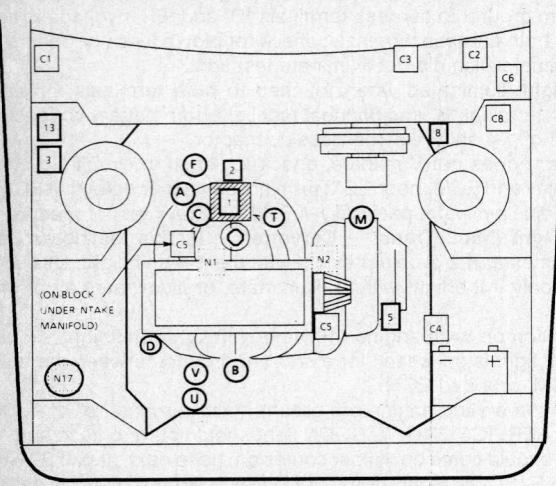

COMPUTER HARNESS
C1. Electronic Control Module (ECM)
C2. ALDL Diagnostic Connector
C3. SERVICE ENGINE SOON Light
C4. ECM Power Connector
C5. ECM Harness Ground
C6. Fuse Panel
C8. Fuel Pump Test Connector

CONTROLLED DEVICES
1. Fuel Injector Solenoid
2. Idle Air Control Valve
3. Fuel Pump Relay
5. TCC Solenoid Connector
8. Cooling Fan Relay
13. A/C Compressor Relay

INFORMATION SENSORS
A. Manifold Absolute Pressure (MAP) Sensor
B. Oxygen (O_2) Sensor
C. Throttle Position Sensor
D. Coolant Temperature Sensor
F. Vehicle Speed Sensor
M. P/N Switch/Neutral Start Switch
T. Manifold Air Temperature Sensor
U. A/C High Pressure Switch
V. A/C Low Pressure Switch

NON-ECM CONTROLLED COMPONENTS
N1. PCV Valve
N2. Ignition Coil Assembly
N17. Fuel Vapor Canister

91H07528

Courtesy of General Motors Corp.

Fig. 85: 2.0L (VIN K) Component Locations (J Body Vehicles)

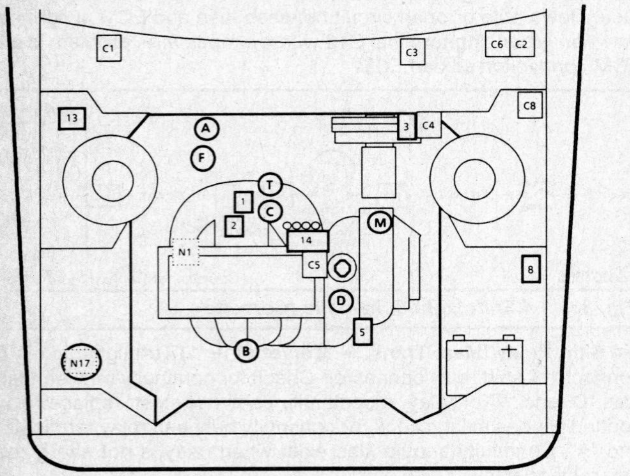

COMPUTER HARNESS
C1. Electronic Control Module (ECM)
C2. ALDL Diagnostic Connector
C3. SERVICE ENGINE SOON Light
C4. ECM Power Fuse
C5. ECM Harness Ground
C6. Fuse Panel
C8. Fuel Pump Test Connector

CONTROLLED DEVICES
1. Fuel Injector
2. Idle Air Control (IAC) Valve
3. Fuel Pump Relay
5. TCC Solenoid Connector
8. Cooling Fan Relay
13. A/C Compressor Relay
14. DIS Ignition Assembly

INFORMATION SENSORS
A. MAP Sensor
B. Oxygen (O_2) Sensor
C. Throttle Position Sensor
D. Coolant Temperature Sensor
F. Vehicle Speed Sensor
M. P/N Switch
T. MAT Sensor

NON-ECM CONTROLLED COMPONENTS
N1. PCV Valve
N4. Fuel Vapor Canister

90B09039

Courtesy of General Motors Corp.

Fig. 86: 2.2L (VIN G) Component Locations (J Body Vehicles)

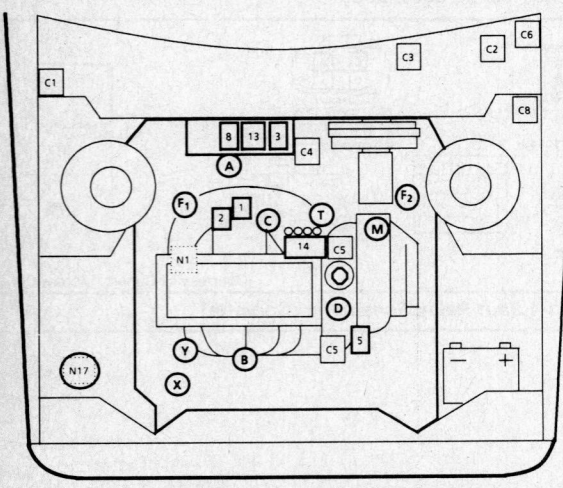

COMPUTER HARNESS
C1. Electronic Control Module (ECM)
C2. ALDL Diagnostic Connector
C3. SERVICE ENGINE SOON Light
C4. ECM Power Fuse
C5. ECM Harness Ground
C6. Fuse Panel
C8. Fuel Pump Test Connector

CONTROLLED DEVICES
1. Fuel Injector
2. Idle Air Control (IAC) Valve
3. Fuel Pump Relay
5. TCC Solenoid
8. Cooling Fan Relay
13. A/C Compressor Relay
14. DIS Assembly

INFORMATION SENSORS
A. MAP Sensor
B. Oxygen (O_2) Sensor
C. Throttle Position Sensor
D. Coolant Temperature Sensor
F1. Vehicle Speed Sensor (A/T)
F2. Vehicle Speed Sensor (M/T)
M. P/N Switch
T. MAT Sensor
X. A/C High Pressure Switch
Y. A/C Low Pressure Switch

NON-ECM CONTROLLED COMPONENTS
N1. PCV Valve
N17. Fuel Vapor Canister

90D09040

Courtesy of General Motors Corp.

Fig. 87: 2.2L (VIN G) Component Locations (L Body Vehicles)

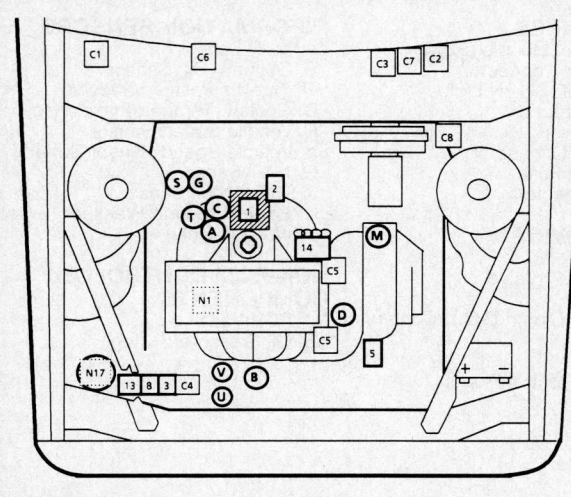

COMPUTER HARNESS
C1. Electronic Control Module (ECM)
C2. ALDL Diagnostic Connector
C3. SERVICE ENGINE SOON Light
C4. ECM Power Fuse
C5. ECM Harness Ground
C6. Fuse Panel
C7. Coolant Temperature Light
C8. Fuel Pump Test Connector

CONTROLLED DEVICES
1. Fuel Injector
2. Idle Air Control (IAC) Valve
3. Fuel Pump Relay
5. TCC Solenoid Connector
8. Cooling Fan Relay
13. A/C Compressor Relay
14. DIS Assembly

INFORMATION SENSORS
A. MAP Sensor
B. Oxygen (O_2) Sensor
C. Throttle Position Sensor
D. Coolant Temperature Sensor
G. Vehicle Speed Sensor/PM Generator
M. P/N Switch
S. Power Steering Pressure Switch
T. MAT Sensor
U. A/C High Pressure Switch
V. A/C Low Pressure Switch

NON-ECM CONTROLLED COMPONENTS
N1. PCV Valve
N17. Fuel Vapor Canister

91J07529

Courtesy of General Motors Corp.

Fig. 88: 2.5L (VIN R) Component Locations (A Body Vehicles)

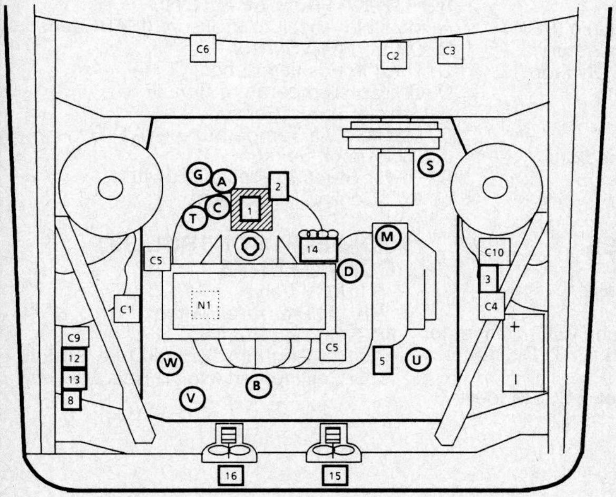

COMPUTER HARNESS
C1. Electronic Control Module (ECM)
C2. ALDL Diagnostic Connector
C3. SERVICE ENGINE SOON Light
C4. ECM Power Fuse
C5. ECM Harness Ground
C6. Fuse Panel
C9. Right Underhood Electrical Center
C10. Left Underhood Electrical Center

CONTROLLED DEVICES
1. Fuel Injector
2. Idle Air Control (IAC) Valve
3. Fuel Pump Relay
5. Torque Converter Clutch (TCC) Connector
8. A/C Compressor Relay
12. Secondary Cooling Fan Relay
13. Primary Cooling Fan Relay
14. DIS Assembly
15. Cooling Fan No. 1
16. Cooling Fan No. 2

INFORMATION SENSORS
A. MAP Sensor
B. Oxygen (O_2) Sensor
C. Throttle Position Sensor
D. Coolant Temperature Sensor
G. Vehicle Speed Sensor/PM Generator
M. P/N Switch/Neutral Start Switch
S. Power Steering Pressure Switch
T. MAT Sensor
U. A/C Compressor/Cooling Fan Temperature Switch
V. A/C Low Pressure Switch (On Compressor)
W. A/C High Pressure Switch (On Compressor)

NON-ECM CONTROLLED COMPONENTS
N1. PCV Valve
N17. Fuel Vapor Canister – Not Shown (Located At Rear Of Vehicle)

91D07531

Courtesy of General Motors Corp.

Fig. 89: 2.5L (VIN R) Component Locations (W Body Vehicles)

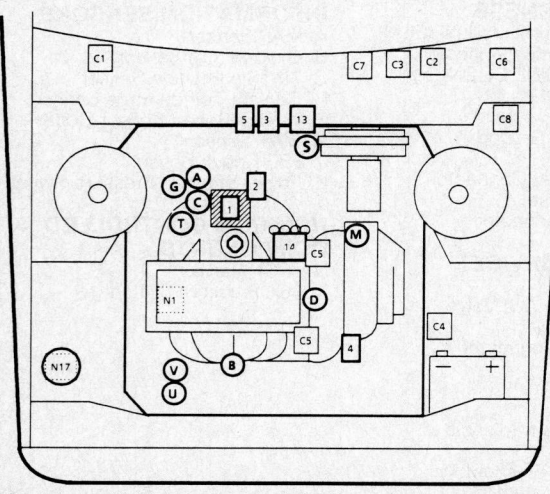

COMPUTER HARNESS
C1. Electronic Control Module (ECM)
C2. ALDL Diagnostic Connector
C3. SERVICE ENGINE SOON Light
C4. ECM Power Connector
C5. ECM Harness Ground
C6. Fuse Panel
C7. ECM-Controlled Warning Light
C8. Fuel Pump Test Connector

CONTROLLED DEVICES
1. Fuel Injector
2. Idle Air Control (IAC) Valve
3. Fuel Pump Relay
4. TCC Solenoid Connector
5. Cooling Fan Relay
13. A/C Compressor Relay
14. DIS Assembly

INFORMATION SENSORS
A. MAP Sensor
B. Oxygen (O_2) Sensor
C. Throttle Position Sensor
D. Coolant Temperature Sensor
G. Vehicle Speed Sensor
M. P/N Switch
S. Power Steering Pressure Switch
T. MAT Sensor
U. A/C High Pressure Switch (On Compressor)
V. A/C Low Pressure Switch (On Compressor)

NON-ECM CONTROLLED COMPONENTS
N1. PCV Valve
N17. Fuel Vapor Canister

91B07530

Courtesy of General Motors Corp.

Fig. 90: 2.5L (VIN U) Component Locations (N Body Vehicles)

1991 ENGINE PERFORMANCE
Systems & Component Testing (Cont.)

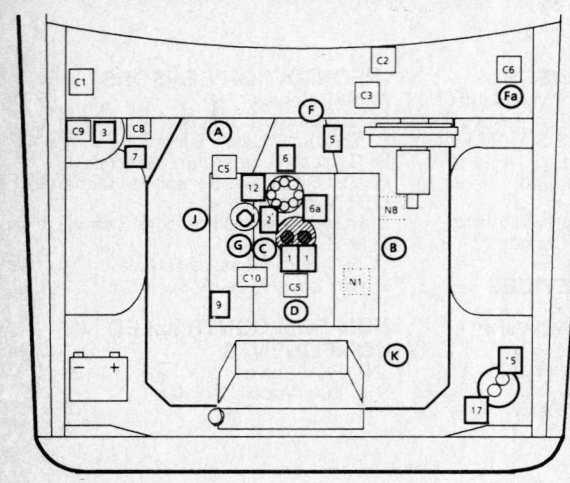

COMPUTER HARNESS
C1. Electronic Control Module (ECM)
C2. ALDL Diagnostic Connector
C3. SERVICE ENGINE SOON Light
C5. ECM Harness Ground
C6. Fuse Panel
C8. Fuel Pump Test Connector
C9. Fuel Pump/ECM Fuse
C10. Set Timing Connector

CONTROLLED DEVICES
1. Fuel Injector
2. Idle Air Control (IAC) Valve
3. Fuel Pump Relay
5. Torque Converter Clutch (TCC) Connector
6. EST Distributor
6a. Ignition Coil
7. Electronic Spark Control Module
9. AIR Port Solenoid
12. EGR Solenoid
15. Canister Purge Solenoid
17. Fuel Vapor Canister

INFORMATION SENSORS
A. MAP Sensor
B. Oxygen (O$_2$) Sensor
C. Throttle Position Sensor
D. Coolant Temperature Sensor
F. Vehicle Speed Sensor
Fa. Vehicle Speed Sensor Buffer
G. MAT Sensor
J. ESC Knock Sensor
K. Power Steering Pressure Switch
   (Wagon Only)

**NON-ECM CONTROLLED
COMPONENTS**
N1. PCV Valve
N8. Oil Pressure Switch

91F07532
Courtesy of General Motors Corp.

Fig. 91: 5.0L (VIN E) & 5.7L (VIN 7) Component Locations (B Body Vehicles)

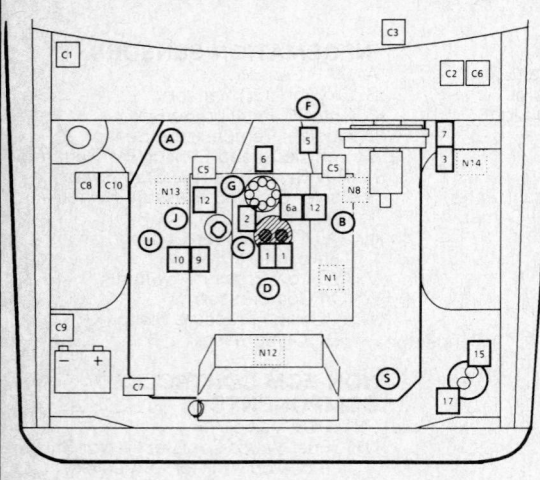

COMPUTER HARNESS
C1. Electronic Control Module (ECM)
C2. ALDL Diagnostic Connector
C3. SERVICE ENGINE SOON Light
C5. ECM Harness Ground
C6. Fuse Panel
C7. Battery Junction Box
C8. Fuel Pump Test Connector
C9. Fuel Pump/ECM Fuse
C10. Set Timing Connector

CONTROLLED DEVICES
1. Fuel Injector
2. Idle Air Control (IAC) Valve
3. Fuel Pump Relay
5. Torque Converter Clutch (TCC) Connector
6. Electronic Spark Timing (EST) Distributor
6a. Remote Ignition Coil
7. Electronic Spark Control (ESC) Module
9. AIR Port Solenoid
10. Air Converter Solenoid
12. EGR Solenoid
15. Canister Purge Solenoid
17. Fuel Vapor Canister

INFORMATION SENSORS
A. Manifold Absolute Pressure (MAP) Sensor
B. Oxygen (O$_2$) Sensor
C. Throttle Position Sensor (TPS)
D. Coolant Temperature Sensor
F. Vehicle Speed Sensor
G. Manifold Air Temperature (MAT) Sensor
J. ESC Knock Sensor
S. Power Steering Pressure Switch
U. A/C Cooling Fan Switch

**NON-ECM CONTROLLED
COMPONENTS**
N1. PCV Valve
N8. Oil Pressure Switch
N12. Cooling Fan (No. 1)
N13. Cooling Fan Temperature Switch
N14. Cooling Fan (No. 1) Relay

91J07534
Courtesy of General Motors Corp.

Fig. 92: 5.0L (VIN E) Component Locations (F Body Vehicles)

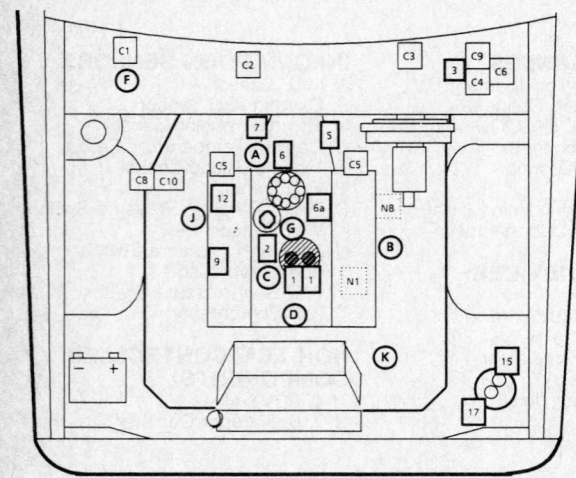

COMPUTER HARNESS
C1. Electronic Control Module (ECM)
C2. ALDL Diagnostic Connector
C3. SERVICE ENGINE SOON Light
C5. ECM Harness Ground
C4. ECM Fuse
C5. ECM Harness Grounds
C6. Fuse Panel
C8. Fuel Pump Test Connector
C9. Fuel Pump Fuse
C10. Set Timing Connector

CONTROLLED DEVICES
1. Fuel Injector
2. Idle Air Control (IAC) Valve
3. Fuel Pump Relay
5. TCC Solenoid Connector
6. EST Distributor
6a. Ignition Coil
7. ESC Control
9. Electric Air Divert Solenoid
12. EGR Solenoid
15. Canister Purge Solenoid
17. Fuel Vapor Canister

INFORMATION SENSORS
A. MAP Sensor
B. Oxygen (O$_2$) Sensor
C. Throttle Position Sensor
D. Coolant Temperature Sensor
F. Vehicle Speed Sensor/Buffer
G. MAT Sensor
J. ESC Knock Sensor
K. Power Steering Pressure Switch

**NON-ECM CONTROLLED
COMPONENTS**
N1. PCV Valve
N8. Oil Pressure Switch

91H07533
Courtesy of General Motors Corp.

Fig. 93: 5.0L (VIN E) & 5.7L (VIN 7) Component Locations (D Body Vehicles)

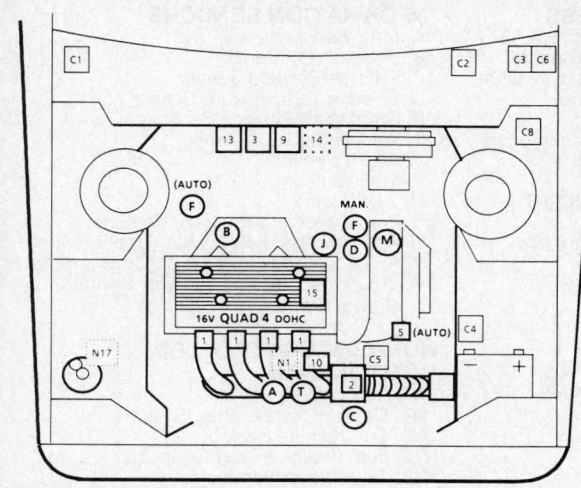

COMPUTER HARNESS
C1. Electronic Control Module (ECM)
C2. ALDL Diagnostic Connector
C3. SERVICE ENGINE SOON Light
C4. ECM Power Fuse
C5. ECM Harness Ground
C6. Fuse Panel
C8. Fuel Pump Test Connector

CONTROLLED DEVICES
1. Fuel Injector
2. Idle Air Control (IAC) Valve
3. Fuel Pump Relay
5. TCC Solenoid Connector
9. Cooling Fan Relay
10. Canister Purge Solenoid
13. A/C Compressor Relay
15. IDIS Module

INFORMATION SENSORS
A. MAP Sensor
B. Oxygen (O$_2$) Sensor
C. Throttle Position Sensor
D. Coolant Temperature Sensor
F. Vehicle Speed Sensor
J. Knock Sensor
M. P/N Switch
T. MAT Sensor

NON-ECM CONTROLLED COMPONENTS
N1. Crankcase Vent Oil/Air Separator
N14. A/C High Speed Fan Relay
N17. Fuel Vapor Canister

90A09048

Courtesy of General Motors Corp.

Fig. 94: 2.3L (VIN A & D) Component Locations (N Body Vehicles)

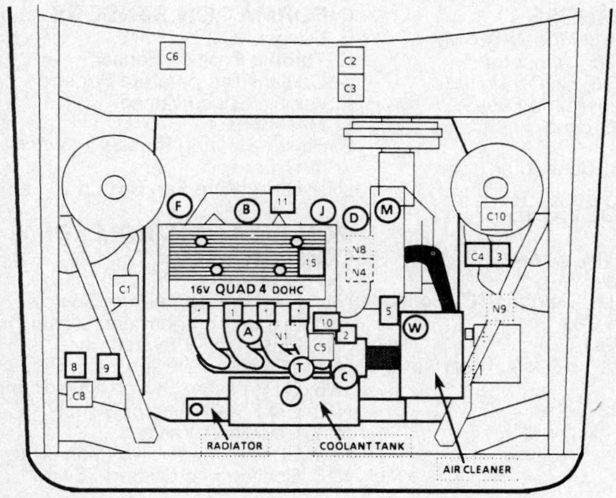

COMPUTER HARNESS
C1. Electronic Control Module (ECM)
C2. ALDL Diagnostic Connector
C3. SERVICE ENGINE SOON Light
C4. ECM Power
C5. ECM Harness Ground
C6. Fuse Panel
C8. Right Underhood Electrical Center
C10. Left Underhood Electrical Center

CONTROLLED DEVICES
1. Fuel Injector
2. Idle Air Control (IAC) Valve
3. Fuel Pump Relay
5. TCC Connector
8. Cooling Fan Relays
9. A/C Compressor Relay
10. Canister Purge Solenoid
11. EGR (Calif.)
15. Ignition Module (Under Cover)

INFORMATION SENSORS
A. MAP Sensor
B. Oxygen (O$_2$) Sensor
C. Throttle Position Sensor
D. Coolant Temperature Sensor
F. Vehicle Speed Sensor
M. P/N Switch
T. MAT Sensor
W. A/C Pressure Transducer

NON-ECM CONTROLLED COMPONENTS
N1. Crankcase Vent Oil/Air Separator
N4. Coolant Temp. Sensor/Switch
N8. Oil Pressure Switch
N9. Fuel Pump Prime/Test Connector

91E07536

Courtesy of General Motors Corp.

Fig. 95: 2.3L (VIN A & D) Component Locations (W Body Vehicles)

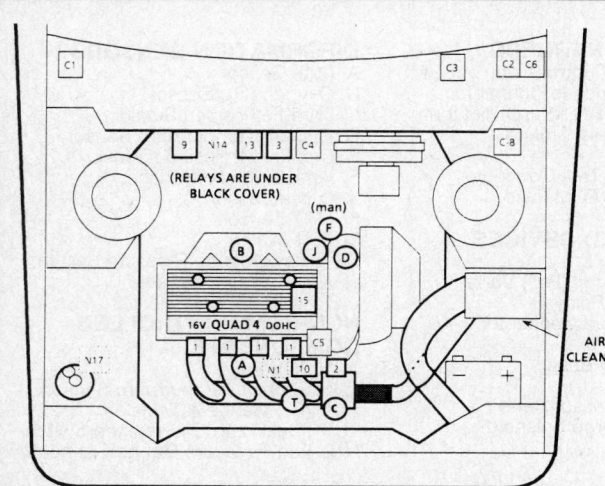

COMPUTER HARNESS
C1. Electronic Control Module (ECM)
C2. ALDL Diagnostic Connector
C3. SERVICE ENGINE SOON Light
C4. ECM Power Fuse
C5. ECM Harness Ground
C6. Fuse Panel
C8. Fuel Pump Test Connector

CONTROLLED DEVICES
1. Fuel Injector
2. Idle Air Control (IAC) Valve
3. Fuel Pump Relay
9. Cooling Fan Relay
10. Canister Purge Solenoid
13. A/C Compressor Relay
15. Ignition Module (Under Cover)

INFORMATION SENSORS
A. MAP Sensor
B. Oxygen (O$_2$) Sensor
C. Throttle Position Sensor
D. Coolant Temperature Sensor
F. Vehicle Speed Sensor
J. Knock Sensor
T. MAT Sensor

NON-ECM CONTROLLED COMPONENTS
N1. Crankcase Vent Oil/Air Separator
N14. A/C High Speed Fan Relay
N17. Fuel Vapor Canister

91C07535

Courtesy of General Motors Corp.

Fig. 96: 2.3L (VIN A) Component Locations (L Body Vehicles)

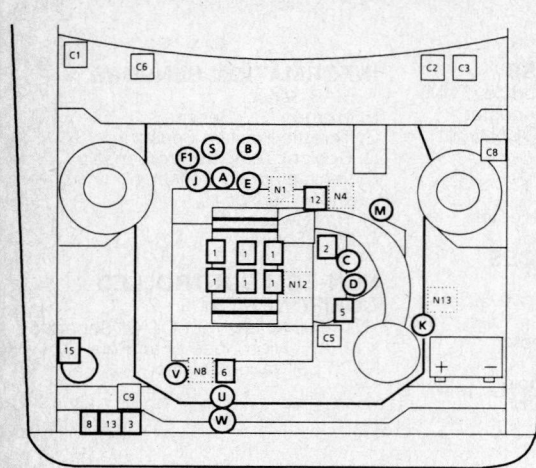

COMPUTER HARNESS
C1. Electronic Control Module (ECM)
C2. ALDL Diagnostic Connector
C3. SERVICE ENGINE SOON Light
C5. ECM Harness Ground
C6. Fuse Panel
C8. Fuel Pump Test Connector
C9. Fuel Pump/ECM Fuse

CONTROLLED DEVICES
1. Fuel Injector
2. Idle Air Control (IAC) Valve
3. Fuel Pump Relay
5. TCC Solenoid Connector
6. DIS Assembly
8. Cooling Fan Relay
12. EGR Valve
13. A/C Compressor Relay
15. Canister Purge Solenoid

INFORMATION SENSORS
A. MAP Sensor
B. Oxygen (O_2) Sensor
C. Throttle Position Sensor
D. Coolant Temperature Sensor
E. Crankshaft Position Sensor
F1. Vehicle Speed Sensor
J. Knock Sensor
K. MAT Sensor
M. P/N Switch
S. Power Steering Pressure Switch
U. A/C Pressure Fan Switch (Upper Switch)
V. A/C Low Pressure Switch (On Compressor)
W. A/C High Pressure Cut-Out Switch
   (Lower Switch)

NON-ECM CONTROLLED COMPONENTS
N1. PCV Valve
N4. Coolant Temperature Switch
N8. Oil Pressure Switch
N12. Fuel Pressure Test Connector
N13. 12-Volt Junction Block

91G07537

Courtesy of General Motors Corp.

Fig. 97: 3.1L (VIN T) Component Locations (A Body Vehicles)

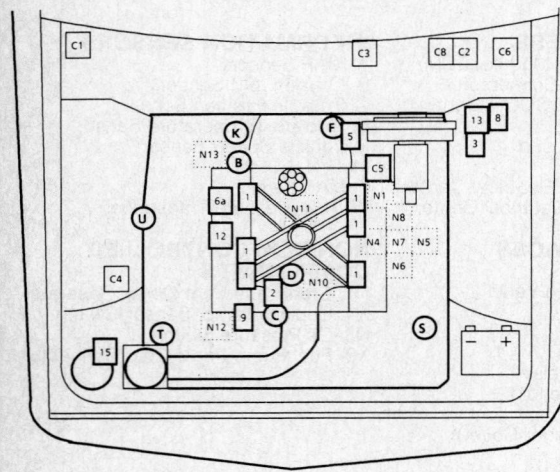

COMPUTER HARNESS
C1. Electronic Control Module (ECM)
C2. ALDL Diagnostic Connector
C3. SERVICE ENGINE SOON Light
C4. ECM Power/Fuel Pump Fuse
C5. ECM Harness Ground
C6. Fuse Panel
C7. Fuel Pump Test Connector

CONTROLLED DEVICES
1. Fuel Injector
2. Idle Air Control (IAC) Valve
3. Fuel Pump Relay
5. Torque Converter Clutch (TCC) Connector
6a. Remote Ignition Coil
8. Cooling Fan Relay
9. Air Control Solenoid (Man. Trans.)
12. EGR Valve
13. A/C Compressor Relay
15. Canister Purge Solenoid

INFORMATION SENSORS
B. Oxygen (O_2) Sensor
C. Throttle Position Sensor
D. Coolant Temperature Sensor
F. Vehicle Speed Sensor
K. MAP Sensor
S. Power Steering Pressure Switch
T. MAT Sensor
U. A/C Pressure Fan Switch

NON-ECM CONTROLLED COMPONENTS
N1. PCV Valve
N4. Engine Temperature Switch
N5. Engine Temperature Sensor
N6. Oil Pressure Switch
N7. Oil Pressure Sensor
N8. Oil Pressure Switch (Fuel Pump)
N10. Cold Start Injector Switch
N11. Cold Start Valve
N12. Deceleration Valve (Man. Trans.)
N13. Cooling Fan Override Switch

90A09053

Courtesy of General Motors Corp.

Fig. 98: 3.1L (VIN T) Component Locations (F Body Vehicles)

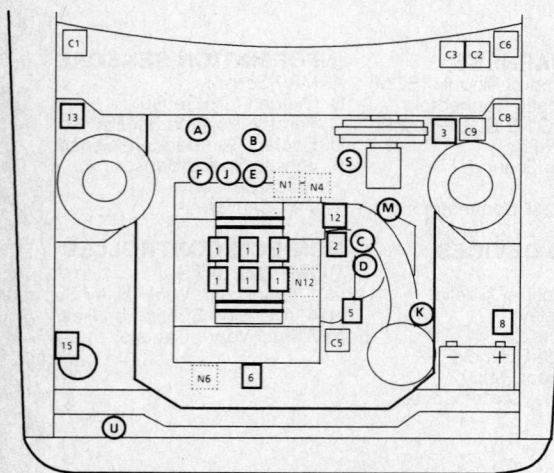

COMPUTER HARNESS
C1. Electronic Control Module (ECM)
C2. ALDL Diagnostic Connector
C3. SERVICE ENGINE SOON Light
C5. ECM Harness Ground
C6. Fuse Panel
C8. Fuel Pump Test Connector
C9. Fuel Pump/ECM Fuse

CONTROLLED DEVICES
1. Fuel Injector
2. Idle Air Control (IAC) Valve
3. Fuel Pump Relay
5. TCC Solenoid Connector
6. DIS System
8. Cooling Fan Relay
12. EGR Valve
13. A/C Compressor Relay
15. Canister Purge Solenoid

INFORMATION SENSORS
A. MAP Sensor
B. Oxygen (O_2) Sensor
C. Throttle Position Sensor
D. Coolant Temperature Sensor
E. Crankshaft Position Sensor
F. Vehicle Speed Sensor
J. Knock Sensor
K. MAT Sensor
M. P/N Switch
S. Power Steering Pressure Switch
U. A/C Pressure Sensor

NON-ECM CONTROLLED COMPONENTS
N1. PCV Valve
N4. Coolant Temperature Sensor
   (For Gauge & Telltale)
N6. Fuel Pump Oil Pressure Switch
N12. Fuel Pressure Gauge Connector

91I07538

Courtesy of General Motors Corp.

Fig. 99: 3.1L (VIN T) Component Locations (J Body Vehicles)

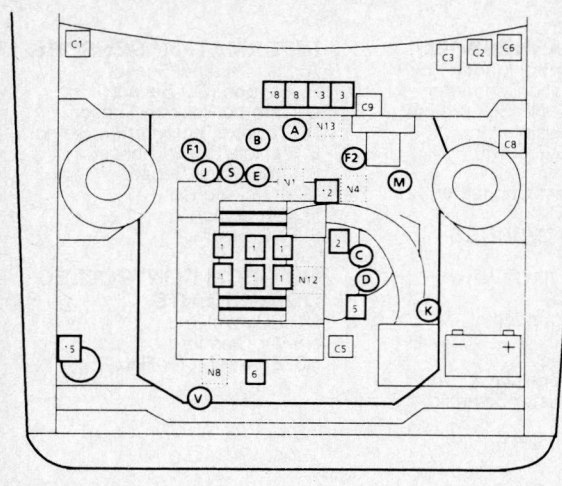

COMPUTER HARNESS
C1. Electronic Control Module (ECM)
C2. ALDL Diagnostic Connector
C3. SERVICE ENGINE SOON Light
C5. ECM Harness Ground
C6. Fuse Panel
C8. Fuel Pump Test Connector
C9. Fuel Pump/ECM Fuse

CONTROLLED DEVICES
1. Fuel Injector
2. Idle Air Control (IAC) Valve
3. Fuel Pump Relay
5. TCC Connector
6. DIS System
8. Cooling Fan Relay
12. EGR Valve
13. A/C Compressor Relay
15. Canister Purge Solenoid
18. A/C High Blower Relay

INFORMATION SENSORS
A. MAP Sensor
B. Oxygen (O_2) Sensor
C. Throttle Position Sensor
D. Coolant Temperature Sensor
E. Crankshaft Position Sensor
F1. Vehicle Speed Sensor (A/T)
F2. Vehicle Speed Sensor (M/T)
J. Knock Sensor
K. MAT Sensor
M. P/N Switch
S. Power Steering Pressure Switch
V. A/C Pressure Sensor

NON-ECM CONTROLLED COMPONENTS
N1. PCV Valve
N4. Coolant Temperature Sensor (For Gauge & Telltale)
N8. Fuel Pump Oil Pressure Switch
N12. Fuel Pressure Connector
N13. 12-Volt Junction Block

91A07539

Courtesy of General Motors Corp.

Fig. 100: 3.1L (VIN T) Component Locations (L Body Vehicles)

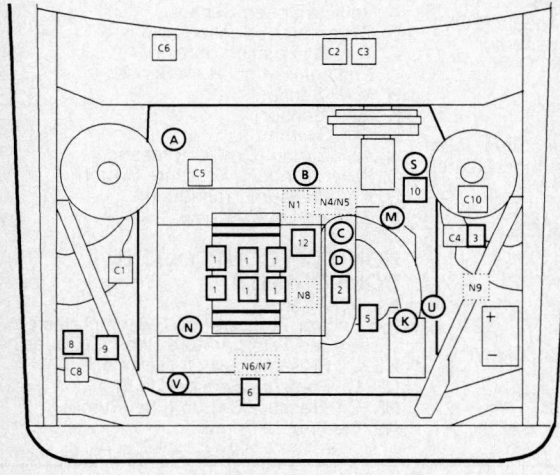

COMPUTER HARNESS
C1. Electronic Control Module (ECM)
C2. ALDL Diagnostic Connector
C3. SERVICE ENGINE SOON Light
C4. ECM Power
C5. ECM Harness Ground
C6. Fuse Panel
C8. Right Underhood Electrical Center
C10. Left Underhood Electrical Center
C11. ECM Mini Harness Connectors

CONTROLLED DEVICES
1. Fuel Injector
2. Idle Air Control (IAC) Valve
3. Fuel Pump Relay
5. TCC Connector
6. Ignition Module
8. Secondary Cooling Fan Relay
9. A/C Compressor Relay
10. Canister Purge Solenoid
12. Digital EGR Valve

INFORMATION SENSORS
A. Vehicle Speed Sensor
B. Oxygen (O_2) Sensor
C. Throttle Position Sensor
D. Coolant Temperature Sensor
H. MAP Sensor
K. MAT Sensor
M. P/N Switch
N. A/C Clutch
S. Power Steering Pressure Switch
U. A/C Pressure Transducer
V. Coolant Level Sensor

NON-ECM CONTROLLED COMPONENTS
N1. PCV Valve
N4. Coolant Temperature Switch (Telltale)
N5. Coolant Temperature Sensor (Gauge)
N6. Oil Pressure Switch (Telltale)
N7. Oil Pressure Sensor (Gauge)
N8. Fuel Pump Oil Pressure Switch
N9. Fuel Pump Prime/Test Connector

91I07637

Courtesy of General Motors Corp.

Fig. 101: 3.1L (VIN T) Component Locations (W Body Vehicles)

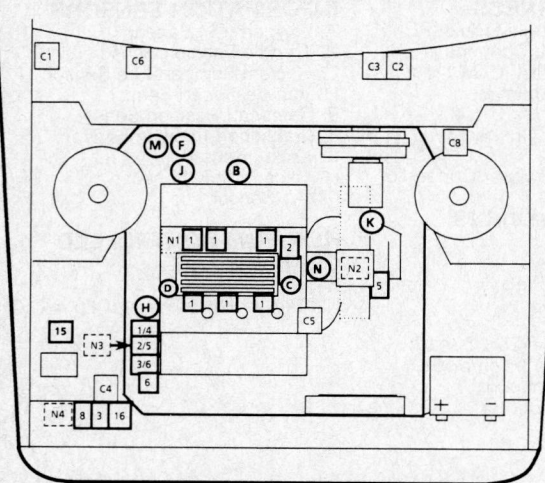

COMPUTER HARNESS
C1. Electronic Control Module (ECM)
C2. ALDL Diagnostic Connector
C3. SERVICE ENGINE SOON Light
C4. ECM Power/Fuel Pump Fuse
C5. ECM Harness Ground
C6. Fuse Panel
C8. Fuel Pump Test Connector

CONTROLLED DEVICES
1. Fuel Injector
2. Idle Air Control (IAC) Valve
3. A/C Compressor Relay
5. TCC Solenoid Connector
6. Ignition Module
8. Cooling Fan Relay
15. Canister Purge Solenoid
16. Fuel Pump Relay

INFORMATION SENSORS
B. Oxygen (O_2) Sensor
C. Throttle Position Sensor
D. Coolant Temperature Sensor
F. Vehicle Speed Sensor
H. Dual Crank Sensor
J. Knock Sensor
K. P/N Switch
M. Power Steering Pressure Switch
N. Mass Airflow Sensor

NON-ECM CONTROLLED COMPONENTS
N1. PCV Valve
N2. Air Cleaner
N3. Coil Assemblies
N4. Blower Motor Relay

91A07638

Courtesy of General Motors Corp.

Fig. 102: 3.3L (VIN N) Component Locations (A Body Vehicles)

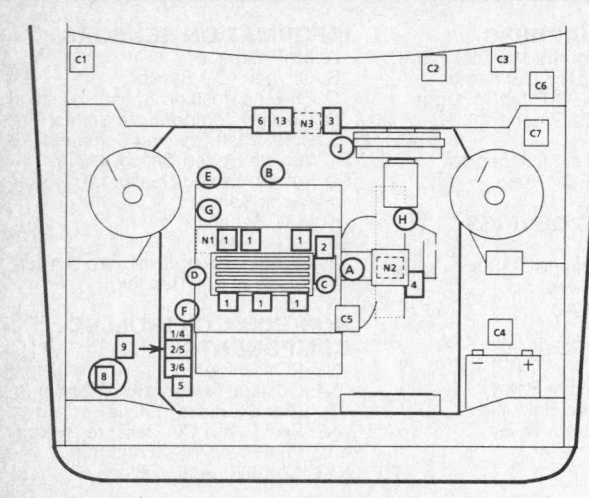

COMPUTER HARNESS
C1. Electronic Control Module (ECM)
C2. ALDL Diagnostic Connector
C3. SERVICE ENGINE SOON Light
C4. ECM Power Fusible Link
C5. ECM Harness Ground
C6. Fuse Panel
C7. Fuel Pump Test Connector

CONTROLLED DEVICES
1. Fuel Injector
2. Idle Air Control (IAC) Valve
3. Fuel Pump Relay
4. TCC Solenoid Connector
5. Ignition Coil
6. Cooling Fan Relay
7. A/C Compressor Relay
8. Fuel Vapor Canister Solenoid
9. Coil Assemblies

INFORMATION SENSORS
A. Mass Airflow Sensor
B. Oxygen (O_2) Sensor
C. Throttle Position Sensor
D. Coolant Temperature Sensor
E. Vehicle Speed Sensor
F. Dual Crank Sensor
G. Knock Sensor
H. P/N Switch
J. P/S Switch

NON-ECM CONTROLLED COMPONENTS
N1. PCV Valve
N2. Air Cleaner
N3. Blower Motor Relay

91C07639

Courtesy of General Motors Corp.

Fig. 103: 3.3L (VIN N) Component Locations (N Body Vehicles)

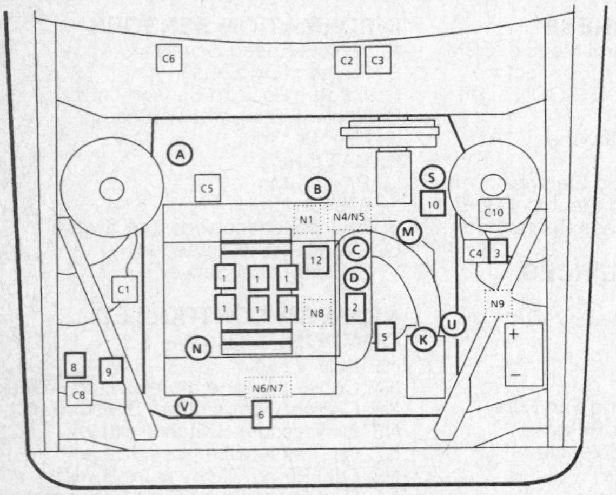

COMPUTER HARNESS
C1. Electronic Control Module (ECM)
C2. ALDL Diagnostic Connector
C3. SERVICE ENGINE SOON Light
C4. ECM Power
C5. ECM Harness Ground
C6. Fuse Panel
C8. Right Underhood Electrical Center
C10. Left Underhood Electrical Center
C11. ECM Mini Harness

CONTROLLED DEVICES
1. Fuel Injector
2. Idle Air Control (IAC) Valve
3. Fuel Pump Relay
5. TCC Connector
6. Ignition Module
8. Secondary Cooling Fan Relay
9. A/C Compressor Relay
10. Canister Purge Solenoid
11. Digital EGR

INFORMATION SENSORS
A. Vehicle Speed Sensor
B. Oxygen (O_2) Sensor
C. Throttle Position Sensor
D. Coolant Temperature Sensor
H. MAP Sensor
K. MAT Sensor
M. P/N Switch
N. A/C Clutch (On Compressor)
S. Power Steering Pressure Switch
U. A/C Pressure Transducer
V. Coolant Level Sensor

NON-ECM CONTROLLED COMPONENTS
N1. PCV Valve
N4. Engine Temperature Switch (Telltale)
N5. Engine Tem[perature Sensor (Gauge)
N6. Oil Pressure Switch (Telltale)
N7. Oil Pressure Sensor (Gauge)
N8. Oil Pressure Switch (Fuel Pump)
N9. Fuel Pump Prime

91H12044

Courtesy of General Motors Corp.

Fig. 104: 3.4L (VIN X) Component Locations (W Body Vehicles)

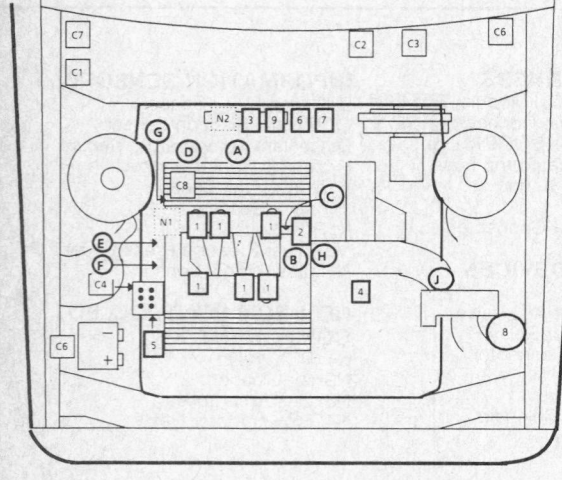

COMPUTER HARNESS
C1. Powertrain Control Module (PCM)
C2. ALDL Diagnostic Connector
C3. SERVICE ENGINE SOON Light
C4. PCM Harness Ground
C5. Fuse Panel
C6. Fuel Pump Test Connector
C7. Relay Center
C8. 8-Way Ignition Jumper Connector

CONTROLLED DEVICES
1. Fuel Injector
2. Idle Air Control (IAC) Valve
3. A/C Compressor Relay
4. TCC Solenoid Connector
5. Ignition Coil
6. Cooling Fan Relay (Low Speed)
7. Cooling Fan Relay (High Speed)
8. Canister Purge Solenoid
9. Maxi-Fuse Relay Center

INFORMATION SENSORS
A. Oxygen (O_2) Sensor
B. Throttle Position Sensor
C. Coolant Temperature Sensor
D. Vehicle Speed Sensor
E. Camshaft Position Sensor
F. Crankshaft Position Sensor
G. Knock Sensor
H. Mass Airflow Sensor
I. MAT Sensor

NON-ECM CONTROLLED COMPONENTS
N1. PCV Valve
N2. Blower Motor Relay (C60 A/C Only)

91E07640

Courtesy of General Motors Corp.

Fig. 105: 3.8L (VIN L) Component Locations (C Body Vehicles)

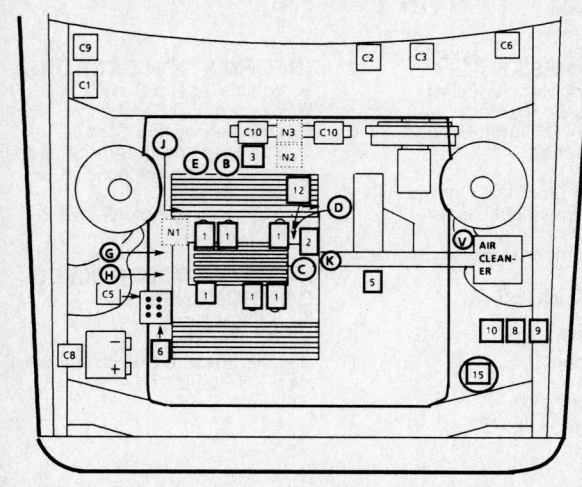

COMPUTER HARNESS
C1. Electronic Control Module (ECM)
C2. ALDL Diagnostic Connector
C3. SERVICE ENGINE SOON Light
C5. ECM Harness Ground
C6. Fuse Panel
C8. Fuel Pump Test Connector
C9. Relay Center
C10. Maxi-Fuse Center

CONTROLLED DEVICES
1. Fuel Injector
2. Idle Air Control (IAC) Valve
3. A/C Compressor Relay
5. TCC Solenoid Connector
6. C³I Ignition Coil
8. Cooling Fan Relay (Low Speed)
9. Cooling Fan Relay (High Speed)
10. Heavy Duty Fan Relay
12. Digital EGR Assembly
15. Canister Purge Solenoid

INFORMATION SENSORS
B. Oxygen (O₂) Sensor
C. Throttle Position Sensor
D. Coolant Temperature Sensor
E. Vehicle Speed Sensor
G. Camshaft Position Sensor
H. Crankshaft Position Sensor
J. Knock Sensor
K. Mass Airflow Sensor
V. MAT Sensor

NON-ECM CONTROLLED COMPONENTS
N1. PCV Valve
N2. Blower Motor Relay (C60 A/C Only)
N3. Isolated Battery Source

91G07641

Courtesy of General Motors Corp.

Fig. 106: 3.8L (VIN C) Component Locations (H Body Vehicles)

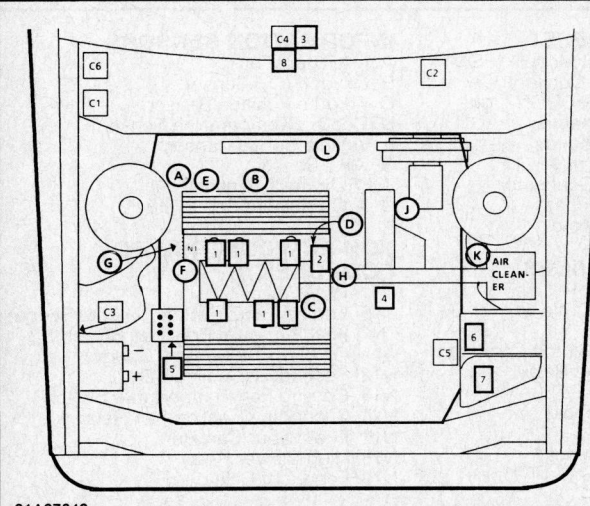

COMPUTER HARNESS
C1. Powertrain Control Module (PCM)
C2. SERVICE ENGINE SOON Light
C3. PCM Harness Ground
C4. Fuse Panel
C5. Fuel Pump Test Connector
C6. Engine/Dash Harness Connector

CONTROLLED DEVICES
1. Fuel Injector
2. Idle Air Control (IAC) Valve
3. Fuel Pump Relay
4. TCC Solenoid Connector
5. Ignition Module & Coil Assembly
6. Underhood Fuse/Relay Center
7. Canister Purge Solenoid
8. Console Relay Center

INFORMATION SENSORS
A. Oil Pressure Sensor/Switch
B. Oxygen (O₂) Sensor
C. Throttle Position Sensor
D. Coolant Temperature Sensor
E. Vehicle Speed Sensor
F. Cam/Crank Position Sensors
G. Knock Sensor
H. Mass Airflow Sensor
J. P/N Switch
K. MAT Sensor
L. A/C High Side Temperature Sensor

NON-ECM CONTROLLED COMPONENTS
N1. PCV Valve

91A07643

Courtesy of General Motors Corp.

Fig. 107: 3.8L (VIN L) Component Locations (E Body Reatta & Riviera)

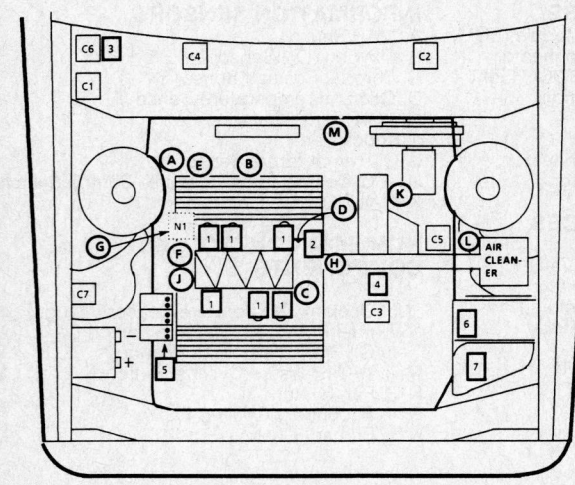

COMPUTER HARNESS
C1. Powertrain Control Module (PCM)
C2. SERVICE ENGINE SOON Light
C3. PCM Harness Ground
C4. Fuse Panel
C5. Fuel Pump Test Connector
C6. Engine/Dash Harness Connector
C7. Battery Junction Block

CONTROLLED DEVICES
1. Fuel Injector
2. Idle Air Control (IAC) Valve
3. Fuel Pump Relay
4. TCC Solenoid Connector
5. Ignition Module & Coil Assembly
6. Underhood Fuse/Relay Center
7. Canister Purge Solenoid

INFORMATION SENSORS
A. Oil Pressure Sensor/Switch
B. Oxygen (O₂) Sensor
C. Throttle Position Sensor
D. Coolant Temperature Sensor
E. Vehicle Speed Sensor
F. Cam Sensor
G. Knock Sensor
H. Mass Airflow Sensor
J. Crank Sensor
K. P/N Switch
L. MAT Sensor
M. A/C High Side Temperature Sensor

NON-ECM CONTROLLED COMPONENTS
N1. PCV Valve

91I07642

Courtesy of General Motors Corp.

Fig. 108: 3.8L (VIN L) Component Locations (E Body Toronado & Trofeo)

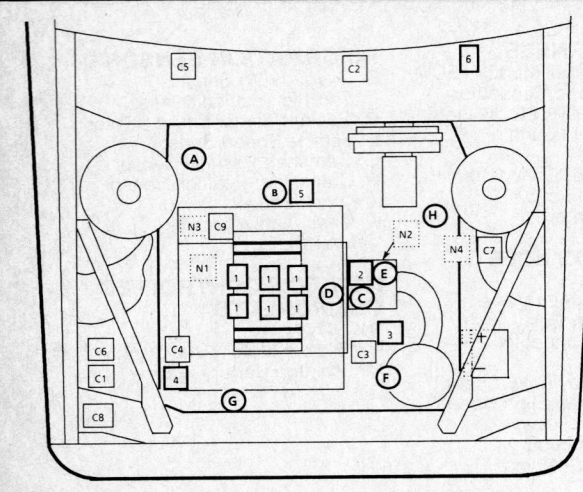

COMPUTER HARNESS
C1. Electronic Control Module (ECM)
C2. ALDL Diagnostic Connector
C3. Cooling Fans & A/C Clutch Ground
C4. ECM Harness Ground
C5. Fuse Panel
C6. Right Underhood Electrical Center
C7. Left Underhood Electrical Center
C8. ECM Mini Harness
C9. 8-Way Ignition Jumper Harness Connector

CONTROLLED DEVICES
1. Fuel Injector
2. Idle Air Control (IAC) Valve
3. TCC Solenoid Connector
4. Ignition Module
5. Canister Purge Solenoid
6. SERVICE ENGINE SOON Light

INFORMATION SENSORS
A. Vehicle Speed Sensor
B. Oxygen (O_2) Sensor
C. Throttle Position Sensor
D. Coolant Temperature Sensor
E. Mass Airflow Sensor
F. MAT Sensor
G. A/C Head Pressure Switch
H. P/N Switch

NON-ECM CONTROLLED COMPONENTS
N1. PCV Valve
N2. Throttle Body
N3. Oil Pressure Switch (Telltale)
N4. Fuel Pump Prime

91I12045
Courtesy of General Motors Corp.

Fig. 109: 3.8L (VIN L) Component Locations (W Body Vehicles)

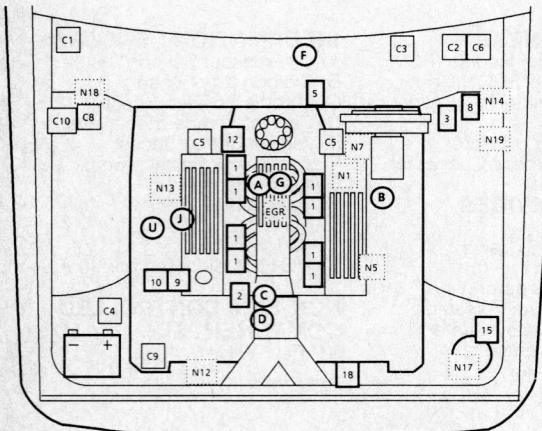

COMPUTER HARNESS
C1. Electronic Control Module (ECM)
C2. ALDL Diagnostic Connector
C3. SERVICE ENGINE SOON Light
C4. Power Feed Connector
C5. ECM Harness Grounds
C6. Fuse Panel
C8. Fuel Pump Test Connector
C9. Fuel Pump/ECM Fuse
C10. Set Timing Connector

CONTROLLED DEVICES
1. Fuel Injector
2. Idle Air Control (IAC) Valve
3. Fuel Pump Relay
5. Torque Converter Clutch Connector
8. Primary Cooling Fan Relay
9. AIR Port Solenoid
10. AIR Converter Solenoid
12. EGR Solenoid
15. Canister Purge Solenoid
18. Primary Cooling Fan

INFORMATION SENSORS
A. MAP Sensor
B. Oxygen (O_2) Sensor
C. Throttle Position Sensor
D. Coolant Temperature Sensor
F. Vehicle Speed Sensor
G. MAT Sensor
J. ESC Knock Sensor
U. A/C Pressure Fan Switch

NON-ECM CONTROLLED COMPONENTS
N1. PCV Valve
N5. Engine Temperature Sensor (Gauge)
N7. Fuel Pump Oil Pressure Switch & Oil Pressure Sensor (Gauge)
N12. Secondary Cooling Fan
N13. Cooling Fan Temperature Switch
N14. Secondary Cooling Fan Relay
N17. Fuel Vapor Canister
N18. High Blower Relay
N19. Fog Light Relay

91C07644
Courtesy of General Motors Corp.

Fig. 110: 5.0L (VIN F) & 5.7L (VIN 8) Component Locations (F Body Vehicles)

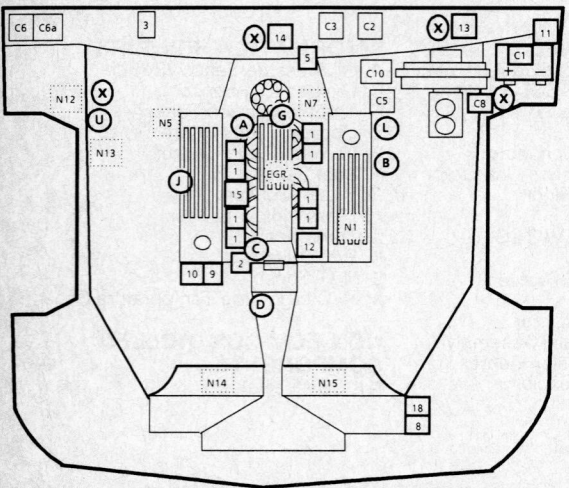

COMPUTER HARNESS
C1. Electronic Control Module (ECM)
C2. ALDL Diagnostic Connector
C3. SERVICE ENGINE SOON Light
C5. ECM Harness Ground
C6. Fuse Panel
C6a. Auxiliary Fuse Panel
C8. Fuel Pump Test Connector
C10. Set Timing Connector

CONTROLLED DEVICES
1. Fuel Injector
2. Idle Air Control (IAC) Valve
3. Fuel Pump Relay
5. TCC Solenoid Connector
8. Primary Cooling Fan Relay
9. AIR Port Solenoid
10. AIR Converter Solenoid
11. 1-4 Upshift Relay (M/T)
12. EGR Solenoid
13. A/C Clutch Control Relay
14. 1-4 Upshift Solenoid (M/T)
15. Canister Purge Solenoid
18. Secondary Cooling Fan Relay

INFORMATION SENSORS
A. MAP Sensor
B. Oxygen (O_2) Sensor
C. Throttle Position Sensor
D. Coolant Temperature Sensor
G. MAT Sensor
J. Knock Sensor
L. Oil Temperature Sensor
U. A/C Cooling Fan (Pressure) Control Switch
X. CAUTION SIR Components

NON-ECM CONTROLLED COMPONENTS
N1. PCV Valve
N5. Coolant Temperature Sensor (Gauge)
N7. Fuel Pump Oil Pressure Switch & Oil Pressure Sensor (Gauge)
N12. A/C Pressure Cycling Switch
N13. Fan Switch
N14. Secondary Cooling Fan
N15. Primary Cooling Fan

91F07645
Courtesy of General Motors Corp.

Fig. 111: 5.7L (VIN 8) Component Locations (Y Body Vehicles)

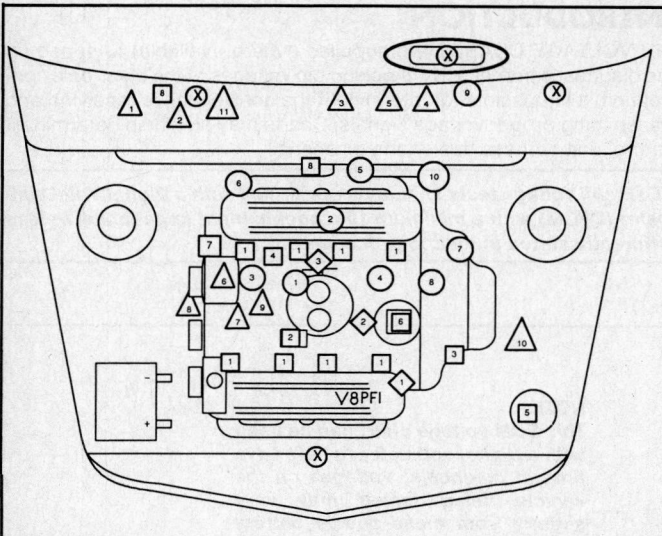

COMPUTER HARNESS
1. Powertrain Control Module (PCM)
2. Engine-Dash Connector
3. ALDL Connector
4. SERVICE ENGINE SOON/SERVICE VEHICLE SOON Light
5. Climate Control Panel
6. Ground Strap
7. ISC Jumper Connector
8. Oxygen (O_2) Sensor Ground
9. Alternator Disable Connector
10. Fuel Pump Prime/Test Connector
11. Fuse Panel

CONTROLLED DEVICES
1. Fuel Injector
2. Idle Speed Control Motor
3. VCC & Shift Solenoids
4. EGR Solenoid
5. Canister Purge Solenoid
6. Distributor
7. Cruise Control Unit
8. Relay Centers

MISCELLANEOUS
X. CAUTION SIR Components

INFORMATION SENSORS
1. Throttle Position Sensor
2. MAP Sensor
3. MAT Sensor
4. Coolant Temperature Sensor
5. Oxygen (O_2) Sensor
6. Vehicle Speed Sensor
7. P/N Switch
8. Oil Pressure Switch
9. Brake Switch
10. Power Steering Pressure Switch

NON-ECM CONTROLLED COMPONENTS
1. PCV Valve
2. Fuel Pressure Regulator
3. EGR Valve

Courtesy of General Motors Corp.

91H07646

Fig. 112: 4.9L (VIN B) Component Locations (C Body DeVille & Fleetwood)

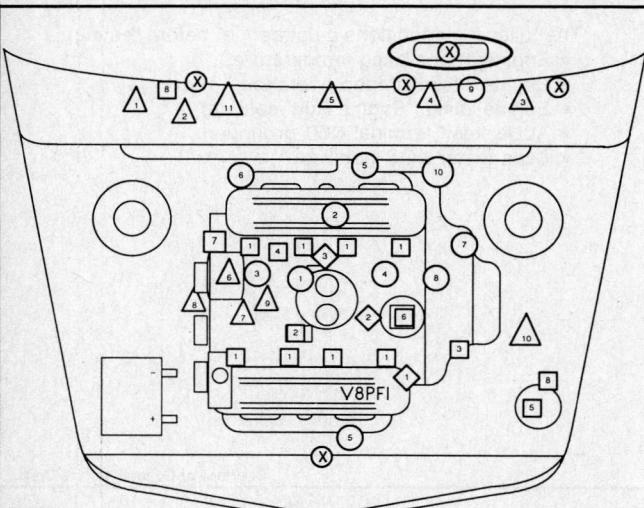

COMPUTER HARNESS
1. Powertrain Control Module (PCM)
2. Engine-Dash Connector
3. ALDL Connector
4. SERVICE ENGINE SOON Light
5. Climate Control Panel
6. Ground Strap
7. ISC Jumper Connector
8. Oxygen (O_2) Sensor Ground
9. Alternator Disable Connector
10. Fuel Pump Prime/Test Connector
11. Fuse Panel

CONTROLLED DEVICES
1. Fuel Injector
2. Idle Speed Control Motor
3. VCC Solenoids
4. EGR Solenoid
5. Canister Purge Solenoid
6. Distributor
7. Cruise Control Unit
8. Relay Centers

INFORMATION SENSORS
1. Throttle Position Sensor
2. MAP Sensor
3. MAT Sensor
4. Coolant Temperature Sensor
5. Oxygen (O_2) Sensor
6. Vehicle Speed Sensor
7. P/N Switch
8. Oil Pressure Switch
9. Brake Switch
10. Power Steering Pressure Switch

NON-ECM CONTROLLED COMPONENTS
1. PCV Valve
2. Fuel Pressure Regulator
3. EGR Valve

MISCELLANEOUS
X. CAUTION SIR Components

Courtesy of General Motors Corp.

91J07647

Fig. 113: 4.9L (VIN B) Component Locations (E Body Eldorado & K Body Seville)

1991 ENGINE PERFORMANCE
Pin Voltage Charts

Beretta, Bonneville, Brougham, Camaro, Caprice, Cavalier, Century, Corsica, Corvette, Custom Cruiser, Cutlass Calais, Cutlass Ciera, Cutlass Cruiser, Cutlass Supreme, DeVille, Eighty-Eight Eldorado, Firebird, Fleetwood, Grand Am, Grand Prix, LeSabre, Lumina, Ninety-Eight, Park Avenue, Reatta, Regal, Riviera, Roadmaster, Seville, Skylark, Sunbird, Toronado, Touring Sedan, Trofeo, 6000

INTRODUCTION

PIN VOLTAGE CHARTS are supplied (where available) to speed up the diagnostic process. By checking pin voltages at the electronic control unit, it is possible to determine if the control unit is receiving and transmitting proper voltage signals. Charts may also help determine if control unit harness has shorts or opens.

NOTE: All voltage tests should be performed with a Digital Volt-Ohmmeter (DVOM) with a minimum 10-megohm input impedance, unless differently stated in testing procedures.

WHITE (W) — 24 PIN CONNECTOR (BACK VIEW)

KEY "ON"	ENG. RUN	CIRCUIT	PIN	WIRE COLOR
B+	B+	INJECTOR DRIVER	W1	DK BLU
0*	0*	A/C REQUEST	W2	DK BLU
		NOT USED	W3	
		CRUISE R/A	W4	GRY/BLK
		NOT USED	W5	
0	1.1	EST	W6	WHT
④	④	IAC "A" HI	W7	LT BLU/WHT
④	④	IAC "B" LO	W8	LT GRN/BLK
④	④	IAC "B" HI	W9	LT GRN/WHT
B+	B+	BATTERY +	W10	ORN
5.0	5.0	5 VOLT SENSOR REFERENCE	W11	GRY
0*	0*	ECM GROUND	W12	BLK/WHT

WIRE COLOR	PIN	CIRCUIT	KEY "ON"	ENG. RUN
DK GRN/WHT	W24	FUEL PUMP	③	B+
	W23	NOT USED		
DK GRN	W22	VSS OUTPUT 4000 PPM	VARIES	VARIES
DK BLU	W21	CRUISE S/C		
GRY	W20	CRUISE ENABLE		
TAN/BLK	W19	IGNITION BYPASS	0*	4.7
ORN/BLK	W18	P/N SWITCH	0*	0*
LT BLU/BLK	W17	IAC "A" LO	④	④
PNK/BLK	W16	IGNITION	B+	B+
ORN	W15	BATTERY +	B+	B+
BLK/ORN	W14	MAP, IAT GROUND	0*	0*
TAN/WHT	W13	ECM GROUND	0*	0*

BLACK (B) — 24 PIN CONNECTOR

KEY "ON"	ENG. RUN	CIRCUIT	PIN	WIRE COLOR
3.9	3.9	SERIAL DATA	B1	ORN
.01-.55	.1-.9	OXYGEN (O₂) SENSOR SIGNAL	B2	PPL
B+	B+	A/C CLUTCH RELAY	B3	DK GRN/WHT
		NOT USED	B4	
2.6	3.0	IAT SIGNAL	B5	TAN
VARIES	VARIES	VSS SIGNAL (LOW)	B6	PPL
0* B+	0* B+	TCC OR SHIFT LIGHT	B7	TAN/BLK
1.9	1.9	CTS SIGNAL	B8	YEL
0*	.9	IGNITION REFERENCE HI	B9	PPL/WHT
		CRUISE VAC	B10	LT GRN
		CRUISE VENT	B11	DK BLU/WHT
0*	0*	CTS AND TPS GROUND	B12	BLK

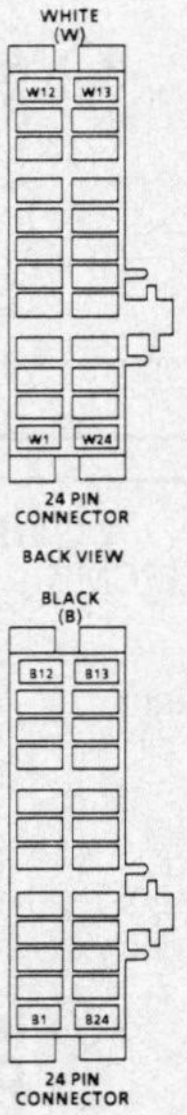

WIRE COLOR	PIN	CIRCUIT	KEY "ON"	ENG. RUN
DK GRN/WHT	B24	A/C SIGNAL FOR FAN	0*	0*
TAN	B23	OXYGEN (O₂) SENSOR GROUND	0*	0*
BRN/WHT	B22	"SERVICE ENGINE SOON" LIGHT	0*	B+
DK GRN/WHT	B21	ENGINE COOLING FAN	B+	B+
LT GRN	B20	MAP SIGNAL	4.8	1.1
DK BLU	B19	TPS SIGNAL	.6	.6
	B18	NOT USED		
	B17	NOT USED		
BLK/RED	B16	IGNITION GROUND	0*	0*
WHT/BLK	B15	ALDL DIAGNOSTIC TEST TERMINAL	5.0	5.0
BRN	B14	CRUISE/BRAKE SW		
YEL	B13	VSS SIGNAL (HIGH)	VARIES	VARIES

* All voltages shown "0" should read less than .5 volt.
① A/C, fan "OFF"
② Reads battery voltage for 2 seconds after ignition "ON" then should read 0 volts
③ Varies depending on temperature
④ Not useable

NOTE:
This ECM voltage chart can be used with a digital voltmeter to help save time in diagnosis. Voltages on the vehicle being tested may vary slightly from these due to battery voltage or alternator charging level.

The following conditions must be met before testing:
- Engine at operating temperature.
- Engine in closed loop operation.
- Engine idling ("Engine Run" column).
- ALDL "test" terminal NOT grounded.
- Scan tester NOT installed.

91F09258

Courtesy of General Motors Corp.

Fig. 1: *ECM Terminal Identification & Pin Voltages (2.0L VIN K Sunbird)*

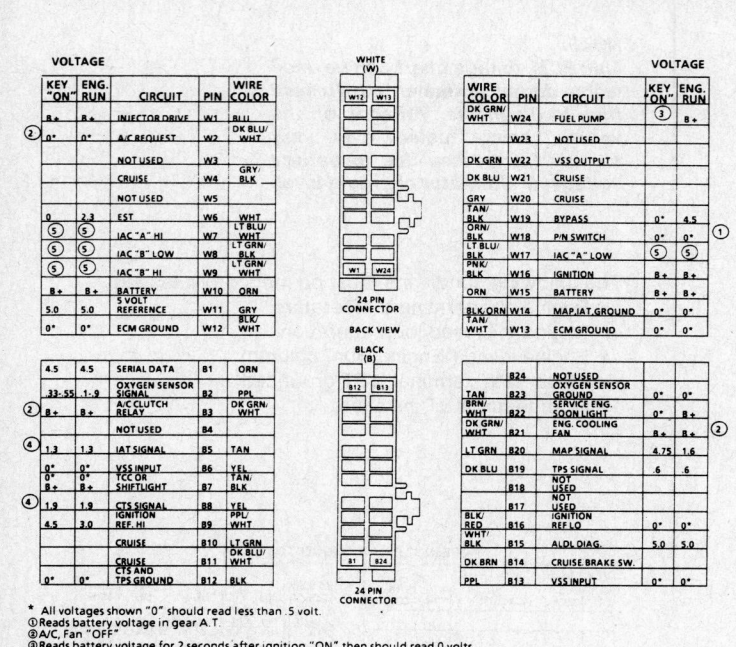

NOTE:
This ECM voltage chart can be used with a digital voltmeter to help save time in diagnosis. Voltages on the vehicle being tested may vary slightly from these due to battery voltage or alternator charging level.

The following conditions must be met before testing:
- Engine at operating temperature.
- Engine in closed loop operation.
- Engine idling ("Engine Run" column).
- ALDL "test" terminal NOT grounded.
- Scan tester NOT installed.

* All voltages shown "0" should read less than .5 volt.
① Reads battery voltage in gear A.T.
② A/C, Fan "OFF"
③ Reads battery voltage for 2 seconds after ignition "ON" then should read 0 volts
④ Varies depending on temperature
⑤ Not useable

91H09259

Courtesy of General Motors Corp.

Fig. 2: ECM Terminal Identification & Pin Voltages (2.2L VIN G Cavalier)

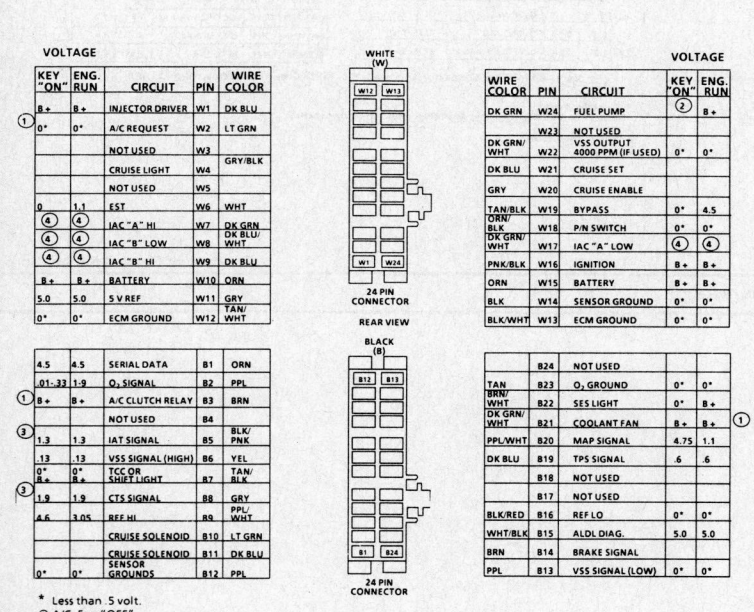

NOTE:
This ECM voltage chart can be used with a digital voltmeter to help save time in diagnosis. Voltages on the vehicle being tested may vary slightly from these due to battery voltage or alternator charging level.

The following conditions must be met before testing:
- Engine at operating temperature.
- Engine in closed loop operation.
- Engine idling ("Engine Run" column).
- ALDL "test" terminal NOT grounded.
- Scan tester NOT installed.

* Less than .5 volt.
① A/C, Fan "OFF"
② Reads battery voltage for 2 seconds after ignition "ON" then should read 0 volts
③ Varies depending on temperature
④ Not useable

91J09260

Courtesy of General Motors Corp.

Fig. 3: ECM Terminal Identification & Pin Voltages (2.2L VIN G Beretta & Corsica)

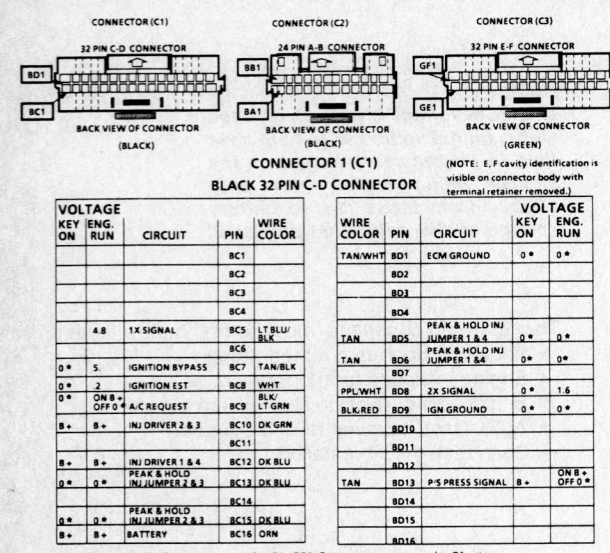

CONNECTOR (C1) 32 PIN C-D CONNECTOR BD1 BC1 BACK VIEW OF CONNECTOR (BLACK)

CONNECTOR (C2) 24 PIN A-B CONNECTOR BB1 BA1 BACK VIEW OF CONNECTOR (BLACK)

CONNECTOR (C3) 32 PIN E-F CONNECTOR GF1 GE1 BACK VIEW OF CONNECTOR (GREEN)

(NOTE: E, F cavity identification is visible on connector body with terminal retainer removed.)

NOTE:
This ECM voltage chart can be used with a digital voltmeter to help save time in diagnosis. Voltages on the vehicle being tested may vary slightly from these due to battery voltage or alternator charging level.

The following conditions must be met before testing:
- Engine at operating temperature.
- Engine in closed loop operation.
- Engine idling ("Engine Run" column).
- ALDL "test" terminal NOT grounded.
- Scan tester NOT installed.

CONNECTOR 1 (C1)
BLACK 32 PIN C-D CONNECTOR

VOLTAGE KEY ON	ENG. RUN	CIRCUIT	PIN	WIRE COLOR
			BC1	
			BC2	
			BC3	
			BC4	
	4.8	1X SIGNAL	BC5	LT BLU/BLK
			BC6	
0 *	5.	IGNITION BYPASS	BC7	TAN/BLK
0 *	2	IGNITION EST	BC8	WHT
0 *	ON B + OFF 0 *	A/C REQUEST	BC9	BLK/ LT GRN
B+	B+	INJ DRIVER 2 & 3	BC10	DK GRN
			BC11	
B+	B+	INJ DRIVER 1 & 4	BC12	DK BLU
0 *	0 *	PEAK & HOLD INJ JUMPER 2 & 3	BC13	DK BLU
			BC14	
0 *	0 *	PEAK & HOLD INJ JUMPER 2 & 3	BC15	DK BLU
B+	B+	BATTERY	BC16	ORN

WIRE COLOR	PIN	CIRCUIT	VOLTAGE KEY ON	ENG. RUN
TAN/WHT	BD1	ECM GROUND	0 *	0 *
	BD2			
	BD3			
	BD4			
TAN	BD5	PEAK & HOLD INJ JUMPER 1 & 4	0 *	0 *
TAN	BD6	PEAK & HOLD INJ JUMPER 1 & 4	0 *	0 *
	BD7			
PPL/WHT	BD8	2X SIGNAL	0 *	1.6
BLK/RED	BD9	IGN GROUND	0 *	0 *
	BD10			
	BD11			
	BD12			
TAN	BD13	P/S PRESS SIGNAL	B +	ON B + OFF 0 *
	BD14			
	BD15			
	BD16			

NOTE: BC1-Black connector, cavity C1; GE1-Green connector, cavity E1, etc.

* Less than .5 volt.
1. Varies from .60 to battery voltage depending on position of drive wheels.
2. Varies.
3. 12V first two seconds.
4. Varies with temperature.
5. Non A/C cars 0* volt, A/C cars should not have a wire in term. "BC3".

CONNECTOR 2 (C-2)
BLACK 24 PIN A-B CONNECTOR

VOLTAGE KEY ON	ENG. RUN	CIRCUIT	PIN	WIRE COLOR
			BA1	
			BA2	
			BA3	
5.0	5.0	+5V REFERENCE	BA4	GRAY/RED
5.0	5.0	+5V REFERENCE	BA5	GRAY
B+	B+	IGNITION FEED	BA6	PNK/BLK
			BA7	
②		SERIAL DATA/ALDL	BA8	ORN
			BA9	
			BA10	
③ 0 *	B+	FUEL PUMP	BA11	DK GRN
0 *	0 *	ECM GROUND	BA12	BLK/WHT

WIRE COLOR	PIN	CIRCUIT	VOLTAGE KEY ON	ENG. RUN
ORN	BB1	BATTERY	B +	B +
	BB2			
	BB3			
	BB4			
BLK	BB5	IAT & MAP GND	0 *	0 *
PPL	BB6	A/C.CTS.TPS GND	0 *	0 *
	BB7			
	BB8			
PPL	BB9	MAG. VSS LOW	0 *	0 *
YEL	BB10	MAG. VSS HIGH	0 *	0 *
DK GRN/WHT	BB11	4000 P/MI SPEED	4.85	5.3
	BB12			

GREEN 32 PIN E-F CONNECTOR 3 (C-3)

VOLTAGE KEY ON	ENG. RUN	CIRCUIT	PIN	WIRE COLOR
			GE1	
			GE2	
NOT USEABLE		IAC - A - HIGH	GE3	DK GRN
NOT USEABLE		IAC - A - LOW	GE4	DK GRN/WHT
NOT USEABLE		IAC - B - HIGH	GE5	DK BLU
NOT USEABLE		IAC - B - LOW	GE6	DK BLU/WHT
0 *	B -	SES LIGHT	GE7	BRN/WHT
B+	ON 0 * OFF B +	CLG FAN RLY	GE8	DK GRN/WHT
			GE9	
			GE10	
			GE11	
5.0	5.0	ALDL/DIAG TERM	GE12	WHT/BLK
			GE13	
② .3 - .5	.1 - .9	O₂ SIGNAL	GE14	BLK
0 *	0 *	O₂ GROUND	GE15	TAN
② 1.8	1.8	CLNT TEMP SIGNAL	GE16	GRY

WIRE COLOR	PIN	CIRCUIT	VOLTAGE KEY ON	ENG. RUN
GRN/YEL	GF1	CANISTER PURGE	B+	.3
BRN	GF2	A/C CLUTCH RELAY	B+	OFF B + ON 0 *
	GF3			
TAN/BLK	GF4	SHIFT LT	B+	OFF B + ON 0 *
	GF5			
	GF6			
	GF7			
	GF8			
DK BLU	GF9	KNOCK SIGNAL	2.3	2.3
	GF10			
	GF11			
	GF12			
DK BLU	GF13	TPS SIGNAL	54	54
GRY/RED	GF14	A/C PRESS SIGNAL	1.0	1.0 ②
PPL/WHT	GF15	MAP SIGNAL	4.7	1.4 ②
BLK/PNK	GF16	IAT SIGNAL	2.33	1.5 ②

Note: BA1 = Black Connector, cavity A1, etc. GE1 - Green Connector, cavity E1, etc.

* Less than .5 volt.
1. Varies from .60 to battery voltage depending on position of drive wheels.
2. Varies.
3. B + first two seconds.

91B09261   91D09262

Courtesy of General Motors Corp.

Fig. 4: *ECM Terminal Identification & Pin Voltages (2.3L VIN A Beretta)*

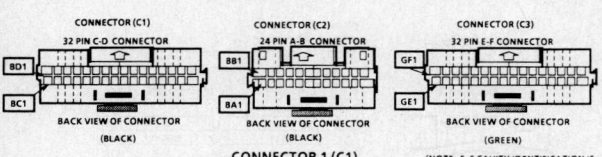

CONNECTOR (C1)
32 PIN C-D CONNECTOR
BD1
BC1
BACK VIEW OF CONNECTOR
(BLACK)

CONNECTOR (C2)
24 PIN A-B CONNECTOR
BB1
BA1
BACK VIEW OF CONNECTOR
(BLACK)

CONNECTOR (C3)
32 PIN E-F CONNECTOR
GF1
GE1
BACK VIEW OF CONNECTOR
(GREEN)

CONNECTOR 1 (C1)
BLACK 32 PIN C-D CONNECTOR

(NOTE: E, F CAVITY IDENTIFICATION IS VISIBLE ON CONNECTOR BODY WITH TERMINAL RETAINERS REMOVED.)

NOTE:
This ECM voltage chart can be used with a digital voltmeter to help save time in diagnosis. Voltages on the vehicle being tested may vary slightly from these due to battery voltage or alternator charging level.

The following conditions must be met before testing:
- Engine at operating temperature.
- Engine in closed loop operation.
- Engine idling ("Engine Run" column).
- ALDL "test" terminal NOT grounded.
- Scan tester NOT installed.

	VOLTAGE				
	KEY ON	ENG. RUN	CIRCUIT	PIN	WIRE COLOR
				BC1	
				BC2	
(5)	B+	B+	NON A/C PROG.	BC3	BLK/WHT
				BC4	
			1X SIGNAL	BC5	BLK/LT GRN
				BC6	
	0 *	5.	IGNITION BYPASS	BC7	TAN/BLK
	0 *	.2	IGNITION EST	BC8	WHT
	0 *	ON B+ OFF 0 *	A/C REQUEST	BC9	LT GRN
	B+	B+	INJ DRIVER 2 & 3	BC10	DK GRN
				BC11	
	B+	B+	INJ DRIVER 1 & 4	BC12	DK BLU
	0 *	0 *	PEAK & HOLD INJ JUMPER 2 & 3	BC13	ORG
				BC14	
	0*	0*	PEAK & HOLD INJ JUMPER 2 & 3	BC15	ORG
	B+	B+	BATTERY	BC16	RED

WIRE COLOR	PIN	CIRCUIT	VOLTAGE	
			KEY ON	ENG. RUN
TAN/WHT	BD1	ECM GROUND	0 *	0 *
	BD2			
	BD3			
WHT	BD4	2nd GEAR SW A/T	ON B+ OFF 0 *	ON B+ OFF 0 *
LT GRN/BLK	BD5	PEAK & HOLD INJ JUMPER 1 & 4	0 *	0 *
LT GRN/BLK	BD6	PEAK & HOLD INJ JUMPER 1 & 4	0 *	0 *
	BD7			
PPL/WHT	BD8	2X SIGNAL	0 *	2.9
BLK/RED	BD9	IGN GROUND	0 *	0 *
	BD10			
	BD11			
	BD12			
LT BLU/ORN	BD13	P/S PRESS SIGNAL	B+	ON + OFF 0 *
	BD14			
DK GRN/WHT	BD15	3rd GEAR SW A/T	ON 0 * OFF B +	ON 0 * OFF B +
ORN/BLK	BD16	P/N SWITCH A/T	ON 0 * OFF B +	ON 0 * OFF B +

NOTE: BC1-Black connector, cavity C1; GE1-Green connector, cavity E1, etc.

* Less than .5 volt.
(1) Varies from .60 to battery voltage depending on position of drive wheels.
(2) Varies.
(3) 12Volt first two seconds.
(4) Varies with temperature.
(5) Non A/C cars 0* volt. A/C cars should not have a wire in term. "BC3".

ENGINE - 2.3L / LD2/LG0
CARLINE - "N" Series

CONNECTOR 2 (C-2)
BLACK 24 PIN A-B CONNECTOR

	VOLTAGE				
	KEY ON	ENG. RUN	CIRCUIT	PIN	WIRE COLOR
				BA1	
				BA2	
				BA3	
	5.0	5.0	+5V REFERENCE	BA4	GRY
	5.0	5.0	+5V REFERENCE	BA5	GRY
	B+	B+	IGNITION FEED	BA6	PNK/BLK
				BA7	
(2)			SERIAL DATA/ALDL	BA8	ORN
				BA9	
				BA10	
(3)	0 *	B+	FUEL PUMP	BA11	DK GRN/WHT
	0 *	0 *	ECM GROUND	BA12	BLK/WHT

WIRE COLOR	PIN	CIRCUIT	VOLTAGE	
			KEY ON	ENG. RUN
RED	BB1	BATTERY	B+	B+
	BB2			
	BB3			
	BB4			
BLK/ORN	BB5	IAT & MAP GND	0 *	0 *
BLK	BB6	A/C,CTS,TPS GND	0 *	0 *
	BB7			
	BB8			
PPL	BB9	MAG. VSS LOW	0 *	0 *
YEL	BB10	MAG. VSS HIGH	0 *	0 *
DK GRN	BB11	4000 P/MI SPEED	10.0	11.4
	BB12			

GREEN 32 PIN E-F CONNECTOR 3 (C-3)

	VOLTAGE				
	KEY ON	ENG. RUN	CIRCUIT	PIN	WIRE COLOR
				GE1	
				GE2	
	NOT USEABLE		IAC - A - HIGH	GE3	LT BLU/WHT
	NOT USEABLE		IAC - A - LOW	GE4	LT BLU/BLK
	NOT USEABLE		IAC - B - HIGH	GE5	LT GRN/WHT
	NOT USEABLE		IAC - B - LOW	GE6	LT GRN/BLK
	0*	B+ ON 0 *	SES LIGHT	GE7	BRN/WHT
	B+	OFF B +	CLG FAN RLY	GE8	GRN/BLK
				GE9	
				GE10	
				GE11	
	5.0	5.0	ALDL/DIAG TERM	GE12	WHT/BLK
				GE13	
(2)	.3 - .5	.1 - .9	O2 SIGNAL	GE14	PPL
	0*	0*	O2 GROUND	GE15	TAN
(2)	1.8	1.8	CLNT TEMP SIGNAL	GE16	YEL

WIRE COLOR	PIN	CIRCUIT	VOLTAGE		
			KEY ON	ENG. RUN	
DK GRN/YEL	GF1	CANISTER PURGE	B+	.3	
DK GRN/WHT	GF2	A/C CLUTCH RELAY	B+	OFF B + ON 0 *	
	GF3				
TAN/BLK	GF4	TCC SHIFT LT	0 12	0 12	
	GF5				
	GF6				
DK GRN	GF7	COOLANT TEMP LIGHT			
	GF8				
DK BLU	GF9	KNOCK SIGNAL	2.3	2.3	
	GF10				
	GF11				
	GF12				
DK BLU	GF13	TPS SIGNAL	.54	.54	
GRY/BLK	GF14	A/C PRESS SIGNAL			(2)
LT GRN	GF15	MAP SIGNAL	4.7	1.4	(2)
TAN	GF16	IAT SIGNAL	3.6	1.5	(2)

Note: BA1 = Black Connector, cavity A1, etc. GE1 - Green Connector, cavity E1, etc.

* Less than .5 volt.
1. Varies from .60 to battery voltage depending on position of drive wheels.
2. Varies.
3. B+ first two seconds.

ENGINE - 2.3L / LD2/LG0
CARLINE - "N" Series

91F09263   91H09264

Courtesy of General Motors Corp.

Fig. 5: *ECM Terminal Identification & Pin Voltages (2.3L VIN A & D Cutlass Calais, Grand Am & Skylark)*

1991 ENGINE PERFORMANCE
Pin Voltage Charts (Cont.)

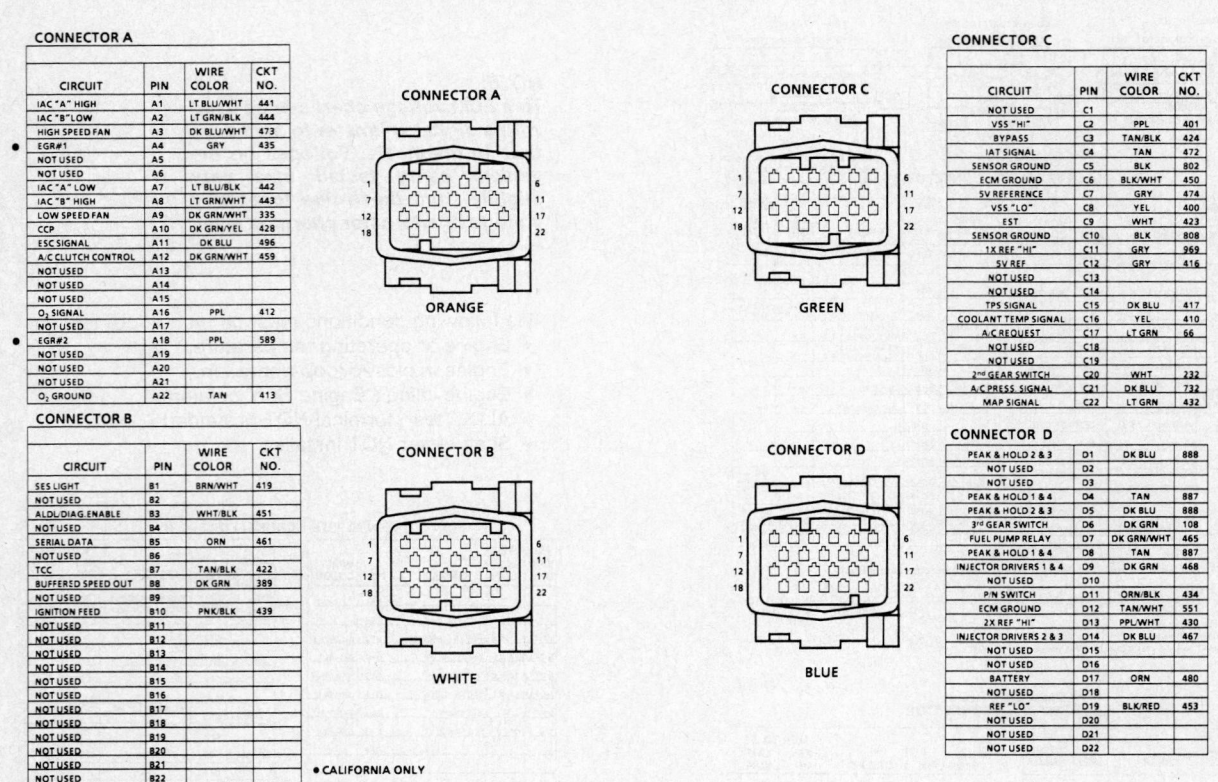

CONNECTOR A

CIRCUIT	PIN	WIRE COLOR	CKT NO.
IAC "A" HIGH	A1	LT BLU/WHT	441
IAC "B" LOW	A2	LT GRN/BLK	444
HIGH SPEED FAN	A3	DK BLU/WHT	473
• EGR#1	A4	GRY	435
NOT USED	A5		
NOT USED	A6		
IAC "A" LOW	A7	LT BLU/BLK	442
IAC "B" HIGH	A8	LT GRN/WHT	443
LOW SPEED FAN	A9	DK GRN/WHT	335
CCP	A10	DK GRN/YEL	428
ESC SIGNAL	A11	DK BLU	496
A/C CLUTCH CONTROL	A12	DK GRN/WHT	459
NOT USED	A13		
NOT USED	A14		
NOT USED	A15		
O2 SIGNAL	A16	PPL	412
NOT USED	A17		
• EGR#2	A18	PPL	589
NOT USED	A19		
NOT USED	A20		
NOT USED	A21		
O2 GROUND	A22	TAN	413

CONNECTOR B

CIRCUIT	PIN	WIRE COLOR	CKT NO.
SES LIGHT	B1	BRN/WHT	419
NOT USED	B2		
ALDL/DIAG.ENABLE	B3	WHT/BLK	451
NOT USED	B4		
SERIAL DATA	B5	ORN	461
NOT USED	B6		
TCC	B7	TAN/BLK	422
BUFFERED SPEED OUT	B8	DK GRN	389
NOT USED	B9		
IGNITION FEED	B10	PNK/BLK	439
NOT USED	B11		
NOT USED	B12		
NOT USED	B13		
NOT USED	B14		
NOT USED	B15		
NOT USED	B16		
NOT USED	B17		
NOT USED	B18		
NOT USED	B19		
NOT USED	B20		
NOT USED	B21		
NOT USED	B22		

• CALIFORNIA ONLY

CONNECTOR A — ORANGE

CONNECTOR B — WHITE

CONNECTOR C — GREEN

CONNECTOR D — BLUE

CONNECTOR C

CIRCUIT	PIN	WIRE COLOR	CKT NO.
NOT USED	C1		
VSS "HI"	C2	PPL	401
BYPASS	C3	TAN/BLK	424
IAT SIGNAL	C4	TAN	472
SENSOR GROUND	C5	BLK	802
ECM GROUND	C6	BLK/WHT	450
5V REFERENCE	C7	GRY	474
VSS "LO"	C8	YEL	400
EST	C9	WHT	423
SENSOR GROUND	C10	BLK	808
1X REF "HI"	C11	GRY	969
5V REF	C12	GRY	416
NOT USED	C13		
NOT USED	C14		
TPS SIGNAL	C15	DK BLU	417
COOLANT TEMP SIGNAL	C16	YEL	410
A/C REQUEST	C17	LT GRN	66
NOT USED	C18		
NOT USED	C19		
2nd GEAR SWITCH	C20	WHT	232
A/C PRESS SIGNAL	C21	DK BLU	732
MAP SIGNAL	C22	LT GRN	432

CONNECTOR D

CIRCUIT	PIN	WIRE COLOR	CKT NO.
PEAK & HOLD 2 & 3	D1	DK BLU	888
NOT USED	D2		
NOT USED	D3		
PEAK & HOLD 1 & 4	D4	TAN	887
PEAK & HOLD 2 & 3	D5	DK BLU	888
3rd GEAR SWITCH	D6	DK GRN	108
FUEL PUMP RELAY	D7	DK GRN/WHT	465
PEAK & HOLD 1 & 4	D8	TAN	887
INJECTOR DRIVERS 1 & 4	D9	DK GRN	468
NOT USED	D10		
P/N SWITCH	D11	ORN/BLK	434
ECM GROUND	D12	TAN/WHT	551
2X REF "HI"	D13	PPL/WHT	430
INJECTOR DRIVERS 2 & 3	D14	DK BLU	467
NOT USED	D15		
NOT USED	D16		
BATTERY	D17	ORN	480
NOT USED	D18		
REF "LO"	D19	BLK/RED	453
NOT USED	D20		
NOT USED	D21		
NOT USED	D22		

91A09265   91C09266

Courtesy of General Motors Corp.

Fig. 6: ECM Terminal Identification (2.3L VIN A & D Cutlass Supreme & Grand Prix)

VOLTAGE KEY "ON"	ENG. RUN	CIRCUIT	PIN	WIRE COLOR
B+	B+	INJECTOR DRIVER	W1	DK BLU
0*	0*	A/C REQUEST	W2	DK GRN/WHT
		NOT USED	W3	RED
		CRUISE R/A	W4	GRY/BLK
B+	B+	POWER STEERING SIGNAL	W5	LT BLU/ORN
0	1.1	EST	W6	WHT
④	④	IAC "A" HI	W7	LT BLU/WHT
④	④	IAC "B" LO	W8	LT GRN/BLK
④	④	IAC "B" HI	W9	LT GRN/WHT
B+	B+	BATTERY +	W10	ORN
5.0	5.0	5 VOLT SENSOR REFERENCE	W11	GRY
0*	0*	ECM GROUND	W12	BLK/WHT

VOLTAGE KEY "ON"	ENG. RUN	CIRCUIT	PIN	WIRE COLOR
4.5	4.5	SERIAL DATA	B1	ORN
.01-55	.1-9	OXYGEN SENSOR SIGNAL	B2	PPL
B+	B+	A/C CLUTCH RELAY	B3	RED
		CRUISE LIGHT (IF USED)	B4	WHT
1.3	1.3	IAT SIGNAL	B5	TAN
varies	varies	VSS SIGNAL (LOW)	B6	PPL
0*	0*	TCC	B7	TAN/BLK
1.9	1.9	CTS SIGNAL	B8	YEL
4.6	3.05	IGNITION REFERENCE HI	B9	PPL/WHT
		CRUISE VAC	B10	LT GRN
		CRUISE VENT	B11	DK BLU/WHT
0*	0*	CTS AND TPS GROUND	B12	BLK

WHITE (W)
24 PIN CONNECTOR
BACK VIEW

BLACK (B)
24 PIN CONNECTOR

WIRE COLOR	PIN	CIRCUIT	VOLTAGE KEY "ON"	ENG. RUN
DK GRN/WHT	W24	FUEL PUMP	③	B+
	W23	NOT USED		
BRN	W22	VSS OUTPUT 4000 PPM	varies	varies
DK BLU	W21	CRUISE S/C		
GRY	W20	CRUISE ENABLE		
TAN/BLK	W19	IGNITION BYPASS	0*	4.5
ORN/BLK	W18	P/N SWITCH	0*	0*
LT BLU/BLK	W17	IAC "A" LO	④	④
PNK/BLK	W16	IGNITION	B+	B+
ORN	W15	BATTERY +	B+	B+
BLK/ORN	W14	MAP, IAT GROUND	0*	0*
BLK/WHT	W13	ECM GROUND	0*	0*
LT BLU	B24	A/C SIGNAL FOR FAN	0*	0*
TAN	B23	OXYGEN SENSOR GROUND	0*	0*
BRN/WHT	B22	"SERVICE ENGINE SOON" LIGHT	0*	B+
DK GRN/WHT	B21	ENGINE COOLING FAN	B+	B+
LT GRN	B20	MAP SIGNAL	4.75	1.1
DK BLU	B19	TPS SIGNAL	.6	.6
DK GRN	B18	COOLANT TEMPERATURE LIGHT	0	B+
	B17	NOT USED		
BLK/RED	B16	IGNITION GROUND	0*	0*
WHT/BLK	B15	ALDL DIAGNOSTIC TEST TERMINAL	5.0	5.0
BRN	B14	CRUISE/BRAKE SW		
YEL	B13	VSS SIGNAL (HIGH)	varies	varies

NOTE:
This ECM voltage chart can be used with a digital voltmeter to help save time in diagnosis. Voltages on the vehicle being tested may vary slightly from these due to battery voltage or alternator charging level.

The following conditions must be met before testing:
- Engine at operating temperature.
- Engine in closed loop operation.
- Engine idling ("Engine Run" column).
- ALDL "test" terminal NOT grounded.
- Scan tester NOT installed.

* All voltages shown "0" should read less than .5 volt.
① A/C, Fan "OFF"
② Reads battery voltage for 2 seconds after ignition "ON" then should read 0 volts
③ Varies depending on temperature
④ Not useable
⑤ In "Park" or "Neutral"

91E09267

Courtesy of General Motors Corp.

Fig. 7: ECM Terminal Identification & Pin Voltages (2.5L VIN R Century, Cutlass Ciera & Cutlass Cruiser)

ECM CONNECTOR (A)

CIRCUIT	PIN	WIRE COLOR	CKT NO.
IDLE AIR CONTROL (IAC) "A" HI	A1	LT BLU/WHT	441
IDLE AIR CONTROL (IAC) "B" LO	A2	LT GRN/BLK	444
*COOLING FAN #2 CONTROL	A3	DK BLU/WHT	473
	A4		
	A5		
	A6		
IDLE AIR CONTROL (IAC) "A" LO	A7	LT BLU/BLK	442
IDLE AIR CONTROL (IAC) "B" HI	A8	LT GRN/BLK	443
COOLING FAN #1 CONTROL	A9	DK GRN/WHT	335
	A10		
	A11		
	A12		
	A13		
	A14		
	A15		
OXYGEN (O₂) SENSOR SIGNAL	A16	PPL	412
	A17		
	A18		
	A19		
	A20		
	A21		
OXYGEN (O₂) SENSOR GROUND	A22	TAN	413

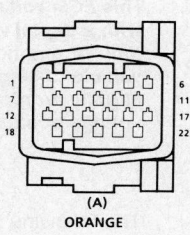

(A)
ORANGE

ECM CONNECTOR (B)

CIRCUIT	PIN	WIRE COLOR	CKT NO.
"SERVICE ENGINE SOON" LIGHT	B1	BRN/WHT	419
	B2		
DIAGNOSTIC ENABLE	B3	WHT/BLK	451
	B4		
SERIAL DATA/ALDL	B5	ORN	461
	B6		
TORQUE CONVERTER CLUTCH (TCC)	B7	TAN/BLK	422
4K VSS OUTPUT	B8	DK GRN	389
	B9		
IGNITION FEED	B10	PNK/BLK	439
	B11		
A/C LOW PRESSURE SIGNAL	B12	DK BLU	248
	B13		
	B14		
	B15		
	B16		
	B17		
	B18		
	B19		
*COOLING FAN #2 REQUEST	B20	LT GRN/BLK	536
	B21		
	B22		

* DUAL COOLING FANS ONLY

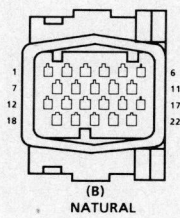

(B)
NATURAL

ECM CONNECTOR (C)

CIRCUIT	PIN	WIRE COLOR	CKT NO.
	C1		
VSS SIGNAL (HIGH)	C2	PPL	401
IGNITION BYPASS	C3	TAN/BLK	424
IAT SIGNAL	C4	TAN	472
MAP, IAT, GROUND	C5	BLK	802
SYSTEM GROUND	C6	BLK/WHT	450
MAP 5 VOLT REFERENCE	C7	GRY	474
VSS SIGNAL LOW	C8	YEL	400
EST CONTROL	C9	WHT	423
TPS, CTS, GROUND	C10	BLK	808
	C11		
TPS 5 VOLT REFERENCE	C12	GRY	416
A/C RELAY CONTROL	C13	DK GRN/YEL	459
	C14		
TPS SIGNAL	C15	DK BLU	417
COOLANT TEMP SIGNAL	C16	YEL	410
A/C REQUEST	C17	LT BLU	67
	C18		
	C19		
	C20		
	C21		
MAP SIGNAL	C22	LT GRN	432

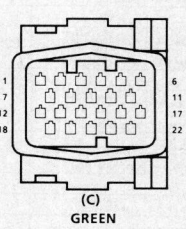

(C)
GREEN

ECM CONNECTOR (D)

CIRCUIT	PIN	WIRE COLOR	CKT NO.
	D1		
	D2		
	D3		
PEAK & HOLD JUMPER	D4	TAN	887
	D5		
	D6		
FUEL PUMP RELAY CONTROL	D7	DK GRN/WHT	465
PEAK & HOLD JUMPER	D8	TAN	887
INJECTOR DRIVER	D9	DK BLU	467
	D10		
PARK/NEUTRAL (P/N) SWITCH	D11	ORN/BLK	434
SYSTEM GROUND	D12		551
REFERENCE HIGH	D13	PPL/WHT	430
	D14		
	D15		
P/S PRESSURE SIGNAL	D16	LT BLU/ORN	495
BATTERY +	D17	ORN	480
	D18		
REFERENCE LOW	D19	BLK/RED	453
	D20		
NOT USED	D21	DK GRN	535
	D22		

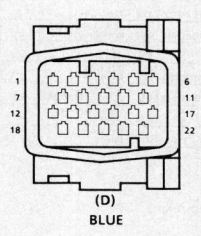

(D)
BLUE

91G09268   91I09269

Fig. 8: ECM Terminal Identification (2.5L VIN R Lumina)

VOLTAGE		CIRCUIT	PIN	WIRE COLOR
KEY "ON"	ENG. RUN			
B+	B+	INJECTOR DRIVER	W1	DK BLU
0*	0*	A/C REQUEST	W2	DK GRN/WHT
		NOT USED	W3	RED
		CRUISE R/A	W4	GRY/BLK
B+	B+	POWER STEERING SIGNAL	W5	LT BLU/WHT
0	1.1	EST	W6	WHT
④	④	IAC "A" HI	W7	LT BLU/WHT
④	④	IAC "B" LO	W8	LT GRN/BLK
④	④	IAC "B" HI	W9	LT GRN/WHT
B+	B+	BATTERY +	W10	ORN
5.0	5.0	5 VOLT SENSOR REFERENCE	W11	GRY
0*	0*	ECM GROUND	W12	BLK/WHT
4.5	4.5	SERIAL DATA	B1	ORN
.01-55	.1-9	OXYGEN SENSOR SIGNAL	B2	PPL
① B+	B+	A/C CLUTCH RELAY	B3	RED
		CRUISE LIGHT (IF USED)	B4	WHT
③ 1.3	1.3	IAT SIGNAL	B5	TAN
varies	varies	VSS SIGNAL (LOW)	B6	PPL
0*	0*	TCC	B7	TAN/BLK
③ 1.9	1.9	CTS SIGNAL	B8	YEL
4.6	3.05	IGNITION REFERENCE HI	B9	PPL/WHT
		CRUISE VAC	B10	LT GRN
		CRUISE VENT	B11	DK BLU/WHT
0*	0*	CTS AND TPS GROUND	B12	BLK

WIRE COLOR	PIN	CIRCUIT	VOLTAGE	
			KEY "ON"	ENG. RUN
DK GRN/WHT	W24	FUEL PUMP	③	B+
	W23	NOT USED		
BRN	W22	VSS OUTPUT 4000 PPM	varies	varies
DK BLU	W21	CRUISE S/C		
GRY	W20	CRUISE ENABLE		
TAN/BLK	W19	IGNITION BYPASS	0*	4.5
ORN/BLK	W18	P/N SWITCH	0*	0* ⑥
LT BLU/BLK	W17	IAC "A" LO	④	④
PNK/BLK	W16	IGNITION	B+	B+
ORN	W15	BATTERY +	B+	B+
BLK/ORN	W14	MAP, IAT GROUND	0*	0*
BLK/WHT	W13	ECM GROUND	0*	0*
LT BLU	B24	A/C SIGNAL FOR FAN	0*	0* ①
TAN	B23	OXYGEN SENSOR GROUND	0*	0*
BRN/WHT	B22	"SERVICE ENGINE SOON" LIGHT	0*	B+ ①
DK GRN/WHT	B21	ENGINE COOLING FAN	B+	B+ ①
LT GRN	B20	MAP SIGNAL	4.75	1.1
DK BLU	B19	TPS SIGNAL	6	6
DK GRN	B18	COOLANT TEMPERATURE LIGHT	0	B+
	B17	NOT USED		
BLK/RED	B16	IGNITION GROUND	0*	0*
WHT/BLK	B15	ALDL DIAGNOSTIC TEST TERMINAL	5.0	5.0
BRN	B14	CRUISE/BRAKE SW		
YEL	B13	VSS SIGNAL (HIGH)	varies	varies

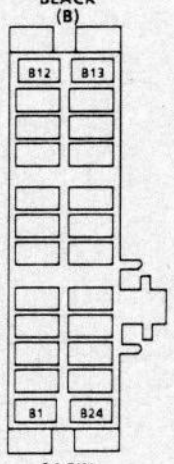

WHITE (W)

W12	W13

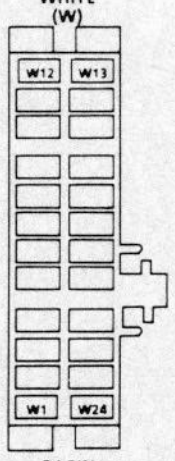

24 PIN CONNECTOR
BACK VIEW

| W1 | W24 |

BLACK (B)

| B12 | B13 |

| B1 | B24 |

24 PIN CONNECTOR

NOTE:
This ECM voltage chart can be used with a digital voltmeter to help save time in diagnosis. Voltages on the vehicle being tested may vary slightly from these due to battery voltage or alternator charging level.

The following conditions must be met before testing:
- Engine at operating temperature.
- Engine in closed loop operation.
- Engine idling ("Engine Run" column).
- ALDL "test" terminal NOT grounded.
- Scan tester NOT installed.

* All voltages shown "0" should read less than .5 volt.
① A/C, Fan "OFF"
⑥ Reads battery voltage for 2 seconds after ignition "ON" then should read 0 volts
③ Varies depending on temperature
④ Not useable
⑥ In "Park" or "Neutral"

91A09270

Fig. 9: ECM Terminal Identification & Pin Voltages (2.5L VIN R 6000)

VOLTAGE

KEY "ON"	ENG. RUN	CIRCUIT	PIN	WIRE COLOR
B+	B+	INJECTOR DRIVE	W1	DK BLU
① 0*	0*	A/C REQUEST	W2	DK BLU
		NOT USED	W3	
		CRUISE R/A	W4	GRY/BLK
B+	B+	POWER STEERING PRESSURE SIGNAL	W5	LT BLU/ORN
0	1.3	EST	W6	WHT
④	④	IAC "A" HI	W7	LT BLU/WHT
④	④	IAC "B" LO	W8	LT GRN/BLK
④	④	IAC "B" HI	W9	LT GRN/WHT
B+	B+	BATTERY +	W10	ORN
5.0	5.0	5 VOLT SENSOR REFERENCE	W11	GRY
0*	0*	ECM GROUND	W12	BLK/WHT

KEY "ON"	ENG. RUN	CIRCUIT	PIN	WIRE COLOR
4.5	4.5	SERIAL DATA	B1	ORN
.01-.55	.1-.9	OXYGEN (O2) SENSOR SIGNAL	B2	PPL
① B+	B+	A/C CLUTCH RELAY	B3	DK GRN/WHT
		CRUISE LIGHT (IF USED)	B4	WHT
③ 1.3	1.3	IAT SIGNAL	B5	TAN
VARIES	VARIES	VSS SIGNAL (LOW)	B6	PPL
0* B+	0* B+	TCC OR SHIFT LIGHT	B7	TAN/BLK
③ 1.9	1.9	CTS SIGNAL	B8	YEL
4.6	3.05	IGNITION REFERENCE HI	B9	PPL/WHT
		CRUISE VAC	B10	LT GRN
		CRUISE VENT	B11	DK BLU/WHT
0*	0*	CTS AND TPS GROUND	B12	BLK

WHITE (W) 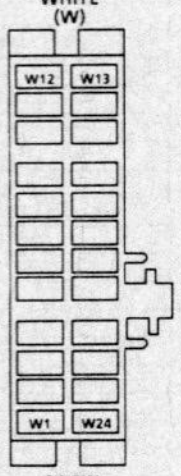
W12 W13 ... W1 W24
24 PIN CONNECTOR BACK VIEW

BLACK (B) 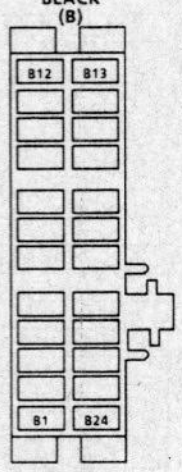
B12 B13 ... B1 B24
24 PIN CONNECTOR

VOLTAGE

WIRE COLOR	PIN	CIRCUIT	KEY "ON"	ENG. RUN	
DK GRN/WHT	W24	FUEL PUMP	②	B+	
	W23	NOT USED			
DK GRN	W22	VSS OUTPUT 4000 PPM	VARIES	VARIES	
DK BLU	W21	CRUISE S/C			
GRY	W20	CRUISE ENABLE			
TAN/BLK	W19	IGNITION BYPASS	0*	4.5	
ORN/BLK	W18	P/N SWITCH	0*	0*	
LT BLU/BLK	W17	IAC "A" LO	④	④	
PNK/BLK	W16	IGNITION	B+	B+	
ORN	W15	BATTERY +	B+	B+	
BLK/ORN	W14	MAP, IAT GROUND	0*	0*	
TAN/WHT	W13	ECM GROUND	0*	0*	

WIRE COLOR	PIN	CIRCUIT	KEY "ON"	ENG. RUN	
DK GRN/WHT	B24	A/C SIGNAL FOR FAN	0*	0*	①
TAN	B23	OXYGEN (O2) SENSOR GROUND	0*	0*	
BRN/WHT	B22	"SERVICE ENGINE SOON" LIGHT	0*	B+	
DK GRN/WHT	B21	ENGINE COOLING FAN	B+	B+	④
LT GRN	B20	MAP SIGNAL	4.75	1.1	
DK BLU	B19	TPS SIGNAL	.6	.6	
DK GRN	B18	ECM CONTROLLED WARNING LIGHT	0*	0*	
	B17	NOT USED			
BLK/RED	B16	IGNITION GROUND	0*	0*	
WHT/BLK	B15	ALDL DIAGNOSTIC "TEST" TERMINAL	5.0	5.0	
BRN	B14	CRUISE/BRAKE SWITCH			
YEL	B13	VSS SIGNAL (HIGH)	VARIES	VARIES	

NOTE:
This ECM voltage chart can be used with a digital voltmeter to help save time in diagnosis. Voltages on the vehicle being tested may vary slightly from these due to battery voltage or alternator charging level.

The following conditions must be met before testing:
- Engine at operating temperature.
- Engine in closed loop operation.
- Engine idling ("Engine Run" column).
- ALDL "test" terminal NOT grounded.
- Scan tester NOT installed.

* All voltages shown "0" should read less than .5 volt.
① A/C, fan "OFF"
② Reads battery voltage for 2 seconds after ignition "ON" then should read 0 volts
③ Varies depending on temperature
④ Not usable

91C09271

Fig. 10: ECM Terminal Identification & Pin Voltages (2.5L VIN U Cutlass Calais, Grand Am & Skylark)

NOTE:
This ECM voltage chart can be used with a digital voltmeter to help save time in diagnosis. Voltages on the vehicle being tested may vary slightly from these due to battery voltage or alternator charging level.

The following conditions must be met before testing:
- Engine at operating temperature.
- Engine in closed loop operation.
- Engine idling ("Engine Run" column).
- ALDL "test" terminal NOT grounded.
- Scan tester NOT installed.

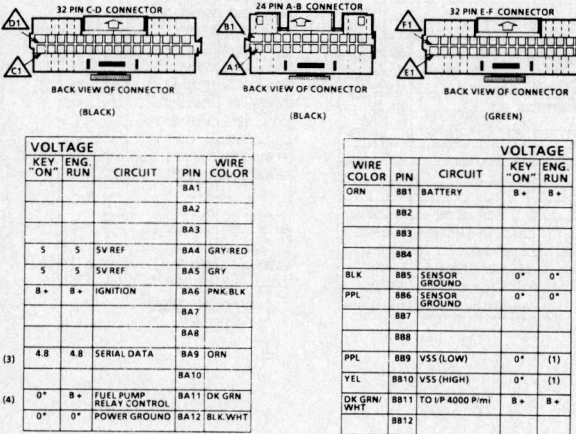

32 PIN C-D CONNECTOR	24 PIN A-B CONNECTOR	32 PIN E-F CONNECTOR
BACK VIEW OF CONNECTOR	BACK VIEW OF CONNECTOR	BACK VIEW OF CONNECTOR
(BLACK)	(BLACK)	(GREEN)

VOLTAGE

KEY "ON"	ENG. RUN	CIRCUIT	PIN	WIRE COLOR
			BA1	
			BA2	
			BA3	
5	5	5V REF	BA4	GRY-RED
5	5	5V REF	BA5	GRY
B+	B+	IGNITION	BA6	PNK-BLK
			BA7	
			BA8	
(3) 4.8	4.8	SERIAL DATA	BA9	ORN
			BA10	
(4) 0*	B+	FUEL PUMP RELAY CONTROL	BA11	DK GRN
0*	0*	POWER GROUND	BA12	BLK-WHT

VOLTAGE

WIRE COLOR	PIN	CIRCUIT	KEY "ON"	ENG. RUN
ORN	BB1	BATTERY	B+	B+
	BB2			
	BB3			
	BB4			
BLK	BB5	SENSOR GROUND	0*	0*
PPL	BB6	SENSOR GROUND	0*	0*
	BB7			
	BB8			
PPL	BB9	VSS (LOW)	0*	(1)
YEL	BB10	VSS (HIGH)	0*	(1)
DK GRN/WHT	BB11	TO I/P 4000 P/mi	B+	B+
	BB12			

VOLTAGE

KEY "ON"	ENG. RUN	CIRCUIT	PIN	WIRE COLOR
			BC1	
			BC2	
			BC3	
			BC4	
			BC5	
			BC6	
0*	4.7	BYPASS	BC7	TAN-BLK
0*	1.3	EST	BC8	WHT
B+	B+	WITH A/C "ON"		LT GRN/BLK
0*	0*	A/C REQUEST	BC9	
			BC10	
B+	B+	INJECTOR 2,4,6	BC11	DK BLU
B+	B+	INJECTOR 1,3,5	BC12	DK GRN
			BC13	
			BC14	
			BC15	
B+	B+	BATTERY	BC16	ORN

BLACK

VOLTAGE

WIRE COLOR	PIN	CIRCUIT	KEY "ON"	ENG. RUN
TAN-WHT	BD1	POWER GROUND	0*	0*
	BD2			
	BD3			
WHT	BD4	2ND GEAR SW	0*	0*
	BD5			
BLK-WHT	BD6	IN/DRIVE LOW	0*	0*
BLK-WHT	BD7	IN/DRIVE LOW	0*	0*
PPL-WHT	BD8	REFERENCE	0*	2.3
BLK-RED	BD9	REFERENCE LOW	0*	0*
	BD10			
	BD11			
	BD12			
LT BLU/ORN	BD13	PSPS	B+	B+
	BD14			
DK GRN	BD15	3RD GEAR SW	0*	0*
ORN-BLK	BD16	P/N SWITCH	0*	0*

VOLTAGE

KEY "ON"	ENG. RUN	CIRCUIT	PIN	WIRE COLOR
			GE1	
			GE2	
NOT USEABLE		IAC "A" HI	GE3	DK GRN
NOT USEABLE		IAC "A" LO	GE4	DK GRN/WHT
NOT USEABLE		IAC "B" HI	GE5	DK BLU
NOT USEABLE		IAC "B" LO	GE6	DK BLU/WHT
0*	B+	"SERVICE ENGINE SOON" LIGHT	GE7	BRN/WHT
B+	B+	FAN RELAY CONTROL	GE8	DK GRN/WHT
B+	B+	EGR SOL. #1	GE9	LT BLU
			GE10	
			GE11	
5	5	DIAG. TERMINAL	GE12	WHT-BLK
(4) 35-55	B+	FUEL PUMP SIGNAL	GE13	TAN/WHT
0*	(3)	O₂ SIGNAL	GE14	PPL
0*	0*	O₂ GROUND	GE15	TAN
(5)	(5)	COOLANT TEMP.	GE16	GRY

GREEN

(CODE Y)

VOLTAGE

WIRE COLOR	PIN	CIRCUIT	KEY "ON"	ENG. RUN
BRN	GF1	A/C RELAY CONTROL	B+	B+
	GF2			
	GF3			
BRN	GF4	EGR SOL. #2	B+	B+
RED	GF5	EGR SOL. #3	B+	B+
TAN/BLK	GF6	TCC CONTROL A/T SHIFT LIGHT M/T	B+	B+
DK GRN/YEL	GF7	PURGE CONTROL	0*	25
	GF8			
DK BLU	GF9	ISC SIGNAL	2.5	2.5
	GF10			
	GF11			
	GF12			
DK BLU	GF13	TPS SIGNAL	65	6
GRY-RED	GF14	A/C PRESSURE SIGNAL	(2)	(2)
PPL-WHT	GF15	MAP SIGNAL	4.5?	1.7
BLK-PNK	GF16	MAT SIGNAL	3.1	3.2

(3)
(3)
(5)

(1) Increases with vehicle speed (measure on A/C scale.)
(2) Normal operating temperature.
(3) Varies.
(4) 12 volts first two seconds.
(5) Varies with temperature.
* Less than 1 volt.

(1) Increases with vehicle speed (measure on A/C scale.)
(2) Normal operating temperature.
(3) Varies.
(4) 12V First two seconds.
(5) Varies with temperature.
* Less than 1 volt

91E09272   91G09273

Courtesy of General Motors Corp.

Fig. 11: ECM Terminal Identification & Pin Voltages (3.1L VIN T Beretta & Corsica)

NOTE:
This ECM voltage chart can be used with a digital voltmeter to help save time in diagnosis. Voltages on the vehicle being tested may vary slightly from these due to battery voltage or alternator charging level.

The following conditions must be met before testing:
- Engine at operating temperature.
- Engine in closed loop operation.
- Engine idling ("Engine Run" column).
- ALDL "test" terminal NOT grounded.
- Scan tester NOT installed.

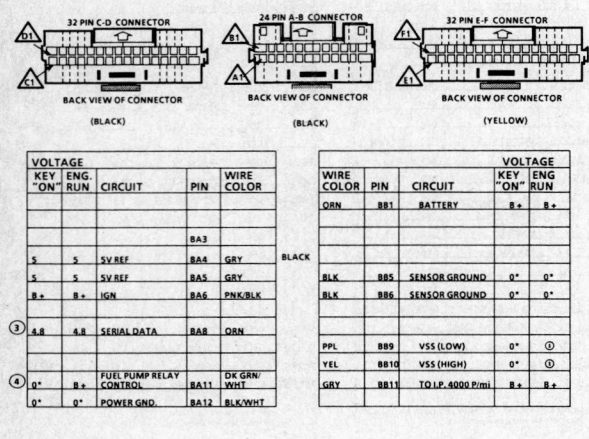

32 PIN C-D CONNECTOR — BACK VIEW OF CONNECTOR (BLACK)

24 PIN A-B CONNECTOR — BACK VIEW OF CONNECTOR (BLACK)

32 PIN E-F CONNECTOR — BACK VIEW OF CONNECTOR (YELLOW)

VOLTAGE (BC) — BLACK

KEY "ON"	ENG RUN	CIRCUIT	PIN	WIRE COLOR
0*		VSS BUFF	BC1	RED
0*	5	BYPASS	BC7	TAN/BLK
0*	1.3	EST	BC8	WHT
B+	B+	WITH A/C "ON"	BC9	LT GRN/BLK
0*	0*	A/C REQUEST		
B+	B+	INJECTOR 2,4,6	BC11	DK BLU
B+	B+	INJECTOR 1,3,5	BC12	GRN
B+	B+	BATTERY	BC16	ORN

① (marker for this table)

VOLTAGE (BD)

WIRE COLOR	PIN	CIRCUIT	KEY "ON"	ENG RUN
BLK/WHT	BD1	POWER GROUND	0*	0*
BLK/WHT	BD6	INJ DRIVE LOW	0*	0*
BLK/WHT	BD7	INJ DRIVE LOW	0*	0*
PPL/WHT	BD8	REFERENCE	0*	2.3
BLK/RED	BD9	REFERENCE LOW	0*	0*
DK BLU	BD12	A/C PRESS FAN SW.	0*	0*
LT BLU/ORN	BD13	PSPS	B+	B+
LT BLU	BD14	4TH GEAR	0*	0*
ORN/BLK	BD16	P/N SWITCH	0*	0*

VOLTAGE (GE) — GREEN

KEY "ON"	ENG RUN	CIRCUIT	PIN	WIRE COLOR
NOT USEABLE		IAC "A" HI	GE3	LT BLU/WHT
NOT USEABLE		IAC "A" LO	GE4	LT BLU/BLK
NOT USEABLE		IAC "B" HI	GE5	LT GRN/WHT
NOT USEABLE		IAC "B" LO	GE6	LT GRN/BLK
0*	B+	"SERVICE ENGINE SOON" LIGHT	GE7	BRN/WHT
0*	0*	"ON" FAN RELAY	GE8	DK GRN/WHT
B+	B+	"OFF" CONTROL		
B+	B+	EGR SOL #1	GE9	LT BLU
5	5	DIAG. TERMINAL	GE12	WHT/BLK
④	B+	FUEL PUMP SIGNAL	GE13	GRY
.35-.55	.1-.9	O₂ SIGNAL	GE14	PPL
0*	0*	O₂ GROUND	GE15	TAN
⑤	⑤	COOLANT TEMP.	GE16	YEL

③ ④ (markers for this table)

VOLTAGE (GF)

WIRE COLOR	PIN	CIRCUIT	KEY "ON"	ENG RUN
DK GRN/WHT	GF1	A/C RELAY "ON" CONTROL "OFF"	0* / B+	0* / B+
BRN	GF2	A/SW/SOL		
BRN	GF4	EGR SOL #2	B+	B+
RED	GF5	EGR SOL #3	B+	B+
TAN/BLK	GF6	TCC CONTROL A/T SHIFT LIGHT M/T	0* / B+	0* / B+
DK GRN/YEL	GF7	PURGE CONTROL	0*	0*
	GF8			
DK BLU	GF9	ESC SIGNAL	2.5	2.5
DK BLU	GF10	VATS MODULE		
DK BLU	GF13	TPS SIGNAL	.65	.65
LT GRN	GF15	MAP SIGNAL	4.57	③
TAN	GF16	MAT SIGNAL	⑤	⑤

VOLTAGE (BA) — BLACK

KEY "ON"	ENG RUN	CIRCUIT	PIN	WIRE COLOR
			BA3	
5	5	5V REF	BA4	GRY
5	5	5V REF	BA5	GRY
B+	B+	IGN	BA6	PNK/BLK
4.8	4.8	SERIAL DATA	BA8	ORN
0*	B+	FUEL PUMP RELAY CONTROL	BA11	DK GRN/WHT
0*	0*	POWER GND.	BA12	BLK/WHT

③ ④ (markers for this table)

VOLTAGE (BB)

WIRE COLOR	PIN	CIRCUIT	KEY "ON"	ENG RUN
ORN	BB1	BATTERY	B+	B+
BLK	BB5	SENSOR GROUND	0*	0*
BLK	BB6	SENSOR GROUND	0*	0*
PPL	BB9	VSS (LOW)	0*	①
YEL	BB10	VSS (HIGH)	0*	①
GRY	BB11	TO I.P. 4000 P/mi	B+	B+

1. Increases with vehicle speed (measure on A/C scale).
2. Normal operating temperature.
3. Varies.
4. 12V First two seconds.
5. Varies with temperature.
* Less than 1 volt.

1. Increases with vehicle speed (measure on A/C scale.)
2. Normal operating temperature.
3. Varies.
4. 12 volts first two seconds.
5. Varies with temperature.
* Less than 1 volt.

91I09274   91B09275

Fig. 12: ECM Terminal Identification & Pin Voltages (3.1L VIN T Camaro & Firebird)

NOTE:

This ECM voltage chart can be used with a digital voltmeter to help save time in diagnosis. Voltages on the vehicle being tested may vary slightly from these due to battery voltage or alternator charging level.

The following conditions must be met before testing:

- Engine at operating temperature.
- Engine in closed loop operation.
- Engine idling ("Engine Run" column).
- ALDL "test" terminal NOT grounded.
- Scan tester NOT installed.

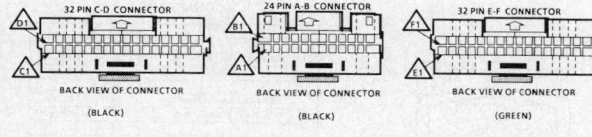

32 PIN C-D CONNECTOR — BACK VIEW OF CONNECTOR (BLACK)
24 PIN A-B CONNECTOR — BACK VIEW OF CONNECTOR (BLACK)
32 PIN E-F CONNECTOR — BACK VIEW OF CONNECTOR (GREEN)

VOLTAGE

KEY "ON"	ENG. RUN	CIRCUIT	PIN	WIRE COLOR
0*		VSS OUTPUT 2000 P/MI	BC1	RED
			BC2	
			BC3	
B+	B+	IF USED/BRAKE SWITCH	BC4	PPL
			BC5	
			BC6	
0*	5	BYPASS	BC7	TAN/BLK
0*	1.3	EST	BC8	WHT
0*	0*	A/C REQUEST	BC9	LT GRN
			BC10	
B+	B+	INJECTOR 2,4,6	BC11	DK BLU
B+	B+	INJECTOR 1,3,5	BC12	DK GRN
			BC13	
			BC14	
			BC15	
B+	B+	BATTERY	BC16	ORN

VOLTAGE

WIRE COLOR	PIN	CIRCUIT	KEY "ON"	ENG. RUN
TAN/WHT	BD1	SYSTEM GROUND	0*	0*
	BD2			
	BD3			
WHT	BD4	2ND GEAR SIGNAL	B+	B+
	BD5			
BLK/WHT	BD6	INJ DRIVE GROUND	0*	0*
BLK/WHT	BD7	INJ DRIVE GROUND	0*	0*
PPL/WHT	BD8	REFERENCE	0*	2.3
BLK/RED	BD9	REFERENCE GROUND	0*	0*
	BD10			
	BD11			
	BD12			
LT BLU/ORN	BD13	(WITH HIGH P/S PRESSURE) P.S.P.S.	0*	0*
	BD14			
DK GRN/WHT	BD15	3RD GEAR SIGNAL	B+	B+
ORN/BLK	BD16	P/N SWITCH	0*	0*

VOLTAGE

KEY "ON"	ENG. RUN	CIRCUIT	PIN	WIRE COLOR
			GE1	
			GE2	
NOT USEABLE		IAC "A" HIGH	GE3	LT BLU/WHT
NOT USEABLE		IAC "A" LOW	GE4	LT BLU/BLK
NOT USEABLE		IAC "B" HIGH	GE5	LT GRN/WHT
NOT USEABLE		IAC "B" LOW	GE6	LT GRN/BLK
0*	B+	SERVICE ENGINE SOON LIGHT	GE7	BRN/WHT
0* B+	0* B+	"ON" FAN CONTROL "OFF" RELAY	GE8	DK GRN/WHT
B+	B+	EGR SOL #1	GE9	LT BLU
			GE10	
			GE11	
5	5	DIAG TERMINAL	GE12	WHT/BLK
	B+	FUEL PUMP SIGNAL	GE13	GRY
35-55	1 ⑤ 3	O₂ SIGNAL	GE14	PPL
0*	0*	O₂ GND	GE15	TAN
⑤	⑤	COOLANT TEMP	GE16	YEL

VOLTAGE

WIRE COLOR	PIN	CIRCUIT	KEY "ON"	ENG. RUN
DK GRN/WHT	GF1	A/C RELAY "ON" CONTROL "OFF"	0* B+	0* B+
	GF2			
	GF3			
BRN	GF4	EGR SOL #2	B+	B+
RED	GF5	EGR SOL #3	B+	B+
TAN/BLK	GF6	TCC CONTROL A/T SHIFT LIGHT M/T	0* B+	0* B+
DK GRN/YEL	GF7	PURGE CONTROL	0*	0*
	GF8			
DK BLU	GF9	ESC SIGNAL	2.5	2.5 ③
	GF10			
	GF11			
	GF12			
DK BLU	GF13	TPS SIGNAL	.29-.98	.29-.98
GRY/RED	GF14	A/C PRESS. SENSOR	③	③
LT GRN	GF15	MAP SIGNAL	4.57	③
TAN	GF16	IAT SIGNAL	⑤	⑤

VOLTAGE

KEY "ON"	ENG. RUN	CIRCUIT	PIN	WIRE COLOR
			BA1	
			BA2	
			BA3	
5	5	5V REF (MAP)	BA4	GRY
5	5	5V REF (TPS)	BA5	GRY
B+	B+	IGNITION	BA6	PNK/BLK
			BA7	
			BA8	
③ 4.8	4.8	SERIAL DATA	BA9	ORN
			BA10	
④ 0*	B+	FUEL PUMP RELAY DRIVER	BA11	DK GRN/WHT
0*	0*	SYSTEM GROUND	BA12	BLK/WHT

VOLTAGE

WIRE COLOR	PIN	CIRCUIT	KEY "ON"	ENG. RUN
ORN	BB1	BATTERY	B+	B+
	BB2			
	BB3			
	BB4			
BLK	BB5	SENSOR GROUND	0*	0*
PPL	BB6	SENSOR GROUND	0*	0*
	BB7			
	BB8			
PPL	BB9	VSS (LOW)	0*	①
YEL	BB10	VSS (HIGH)	0*	①
DK GRN	BB11	VSS OUTPUT 4000 PMI	10	11.7
	BB12			

1. Increases with speed (measure on A/C scale)
2. Normal operating temperature.
3. Varies.
4. 12V First two seconds.
5. Varies with temperature.
* Less than 1 volt.

91D09276 91F09277

Fig. 13: ECM Terminal Identification & Pin Voltages (3.1L VIN T Cavalier & Sunbird)

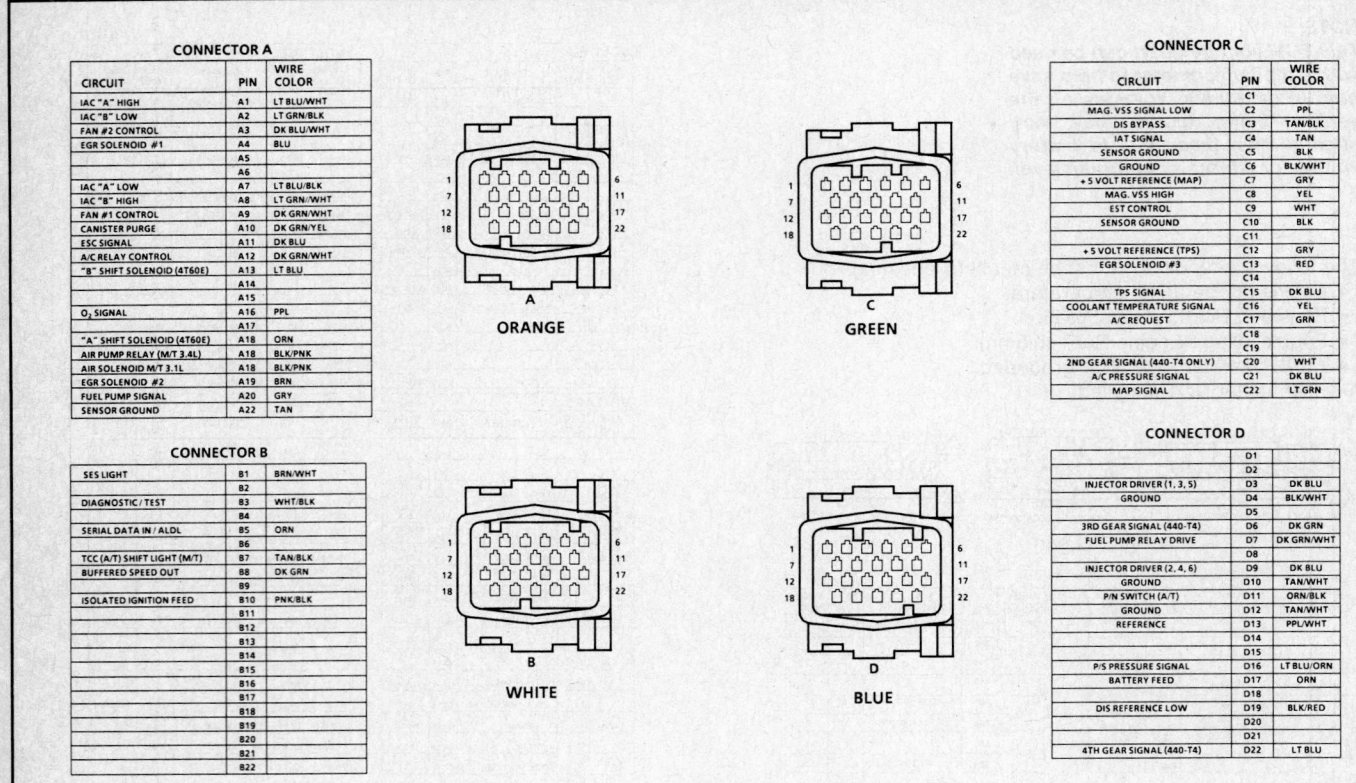

CONNECTOR A

CIRCUIT	PIN	WIRE COLOR
IAC "A" HIGH	A1	LT BLU/WHT
IAC "B" LOW	A2	LT GRN/BLK
FAN #2 CONTROL	A3	DK BLU/WHT
EGR SOLENOID #1	A4	BLU
	A5	
	A6	
IAC "A" LOW	A7	LT BLU/BLK
IAC "B" HIGH	A8	LT GRN/WHT
FAN #1 CONTROL	A9	DK GRN/WHT
CANISTER PURGE	A10	DK GRN/YEL
ESC SIGNAL	A11	DK BLU
A/C RELAY CONTROL	A12	DK GRN/WHT
"B" SHIFT SOLENOID (4T60E)	A13	LT BLU
	A14	
	A15	
O₂ SIGNAL	A16	PPL
	A17	
"A" SHIFT SOLENOID (4T60E)	A18	ORN
AIR PUMP RELAY (M/T 3.4L)	A18	BLK/PNK
AIR SOLENOID M/T 3.1L	A18	BLK/PNK
EGR SOLENOID #2	A19	BRN
FUEL PUMP SIGNAL	A20	GRY
SENSOR GROUND	A22	TAN

CONNECTOR C

CIRCUIT	PIN	WIRE COLOR
	C1	
MAG. VSS SIGNAL LOW	C2	PPL
DIS BYPASS	C3	TAN/BLK
IAT SIGNAL	C4	TAN
SENSOR GROUND	C5	BLK
GROUND	C6	BLK/WHT
+5 VOLT REFERENCE (MAP)	C7	GRY
MAG. VSS HIGH	C8	YEL
EST CONTROL	C9	WHT
SENSOR GROUND	C10	BLK
	C11	
+5 VOLT REFERENCE (TPS)	C12	GRY
EGR SOLENOID #3	C13	RED
	C14	
TPS SIGNAL	C15	DK BLU
COOLANT TEMPERATURE SIGNAL	C16	YEL
A/C REQUEST	C17	GRN
	C18	
	C19	
2ND GEAR SIGNAL (440-T4 ONLY)	C20	WHT
A/C PRESSURE SIGNAL	C21	DK BLU
MAP SIGNAL	C22	LT GRN

CONNECTOR B

CIRCUIT	PIN	WIRE COLOR
SES LIGHT	B1	BRN/WHT
	B2	
DIAGNOSTIC / TEST	B3	WHT/BLK
	B4	
SERIAL DATA IN / ALDL	B5	ORN
	B6	
TCC (A/T) SHIFT LIGHT (M/T)	B7	TAN/BLK
BUFFERED SPEED OUT	B8	DK GRN
	B9	
ISOLATED IGNITION FEED	B10	PNK/BLK
	B11	
	B12	
	B13	
	B14	
	B15	
	B16	
	B17	
	B18	
	B19	
	B20	
	B21	
	B22	

CONNECTOR D

CIRCUIT	PIN	WIRE COLOR
	D1	
	D2	
INJECTOR DRIVER (1, 3, 5)	D3	DK BLU
GROUND	D4	BLK/WHT
	D5	
3RD GEAR SIGNAL (440-T4)	D6	DK GRN
FUEL PUMP RELAY DRIVE	D7	DK GRN/WHT
	D8	
INJECTOR DRIVER (2, 4, 6)	D9	DK BLU
GROUND	D10	TAN/WHT
P/N SWITCH (A/T)	D11	ORN/BLK
GROUND	D12	TAN/WHT
REFERENCE	D13	PPL/WHT
	D14	
	D15	
P/S PRESSURE SIGNAL	D16	LT BLU/ORN
BATTERY FEED	D17	ORN
	D18	
DIS REFERENCE LOW	D19	BLK/RED
	D20	
	D21	
4TH GEAR SIGNAL (440-T4)	D22	LT BLU

ORANGE — A

GREEN — C

WHITE — B

BLUE — D

91H09278   91J09279

Courtesy of General Motors Corp.

Fig. 14: ECM Terminal Identification (3.1L VIN T Cutlass Supreme, Grand Prix & Lumina)

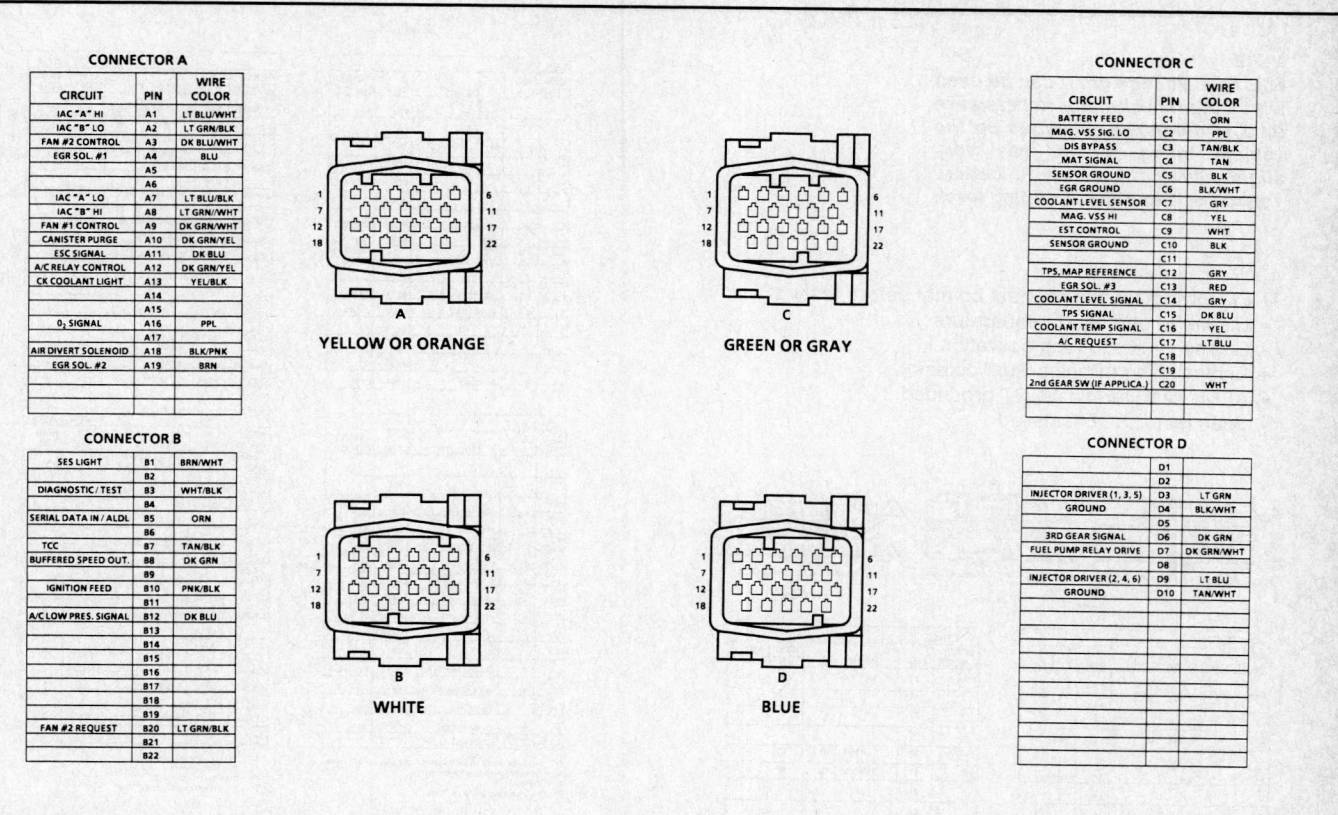

CONNECTOR A

CIRCUIT	PIN	WIRE COLOR
IAC "A" HI	A1	LT BLU/WHT
IAC "B" LO	A2	LT GRN/BLK
FAN #2 CONTROL	A3	DK BLU/WHT
EGR SOL. #1	A4	BLU
	A5	
	A6	
IAC "A" LO	A7	LT BLU/BLK
IAC "B" HI	A8	LT GRN/WHT
FAN #1 CONTROL	A9	DK GRN/WHT
CANISTER PURGE	A10	DK GRN/YEL
ESC SIGNAL	A11	DK BLU
A/C RELAY CONTROL	A12	DK GRN/YEL
CK COOLANT LIGHT	A13	YEL/BLK
	A14	
	A15	
O2 SIGNAL	A16	PPL
	A17	
AIR DIVERT SOLENOID	A18	BLK/PNK
EGR SOL. #2	A19	BRN

CONNECTOR C

CIRCUIT	PIN	WIRE COLOR
BATTERY FEED	C1	ORN
MAG. VSS SIG. LO	C2	PPL
DIS BYPASS	C3	TAN/BLK
MAT SIGNAL	C4	TAN
SENSOR GROUND	C5	BLK
EGR GROUND	C6	BLK/WHT
COOLANT LEVEL SENSOR	C7	GRY
MAG. VSS HI	C8	YEL
EST CONTROL	C9	WHT
SENSOR GROUND	C10	BLK
	C11	
TPS, MAP REFERENCE	C12	GRY
EGR SOL. #3	C13	RED
COOLANT LEVEL SIGNAL	C14	GRY
TPS SIGNAL	C15	DK BLU
COOLANT TEMP SIGNAL	C16	YEL
A/C REQUEST	C17	LT BLU
	C18	
	C19	
2nd GEAR SW (IF APPLICA.)	C20	WHT

A — **YELLOW OR ORANGE**

C — **GREEN OR GRAY**

CONNECTOR B

CIRCUIT	PIN	WIRE COLOR
SES LIGHT	B1	BRN/WHT
	B2	
DIAGNOSTIC / TEST	B3	WHT/BLK
	B4	
SERIAL DATA IN / ALDL	B5	ORN
	B6	
TCC	B7	TAN/BLK
BUFFERED SPEED OUT.	B8	DK GRN
	B9	
IGNITION FEED	B10	PNK/BLK
	B11	
A/C LOW PRES. SIGNAL	B12	DK BLU
	B13	
	B14	
	B15	
	B16	
	B17	
	B18	
	B19	
FAN #2 REQUEST	B20	LT GRN/BLK
	B21	
	B22	

CONNECTOR D

CIRCUIT	PIN	WIRE COLOR
	D1	
	D2	
INJECTOR DRIVER (1, 3, 5)	D3	LT GRN
GROUND	D4	BLK/WHT
	D5	
3RD GEAR SIGNAL	D6	DK GRN
FUEL PUMP RELAY DRIVE	D7	DK GRN/WHT
	D8	
INJECTOR DRIVER (2, 4, 6)	D9	LT BLU
GROUND	D10	TAN/WHT

B — **WHITE**

D — **BLUE**

91B09280   91D09281

Fig. 15: ECM Terminal Identification (3.1L VIN T Regal)

NOTE:
This ECM voltage chart can be used with a digital voltmeter to help save time in diagnosis. Voltages on the vehicle being tested may vary slightly from these due to battery voltage or alternator charging level.

The following conditions must be met before testing:
- Engine at operating temperature.
- Engine in closed loop operation.
- Engine idling ("Engine Run" column).
- ALDL "test" terminal NOT grounded.
- Scan tester NOT installed.

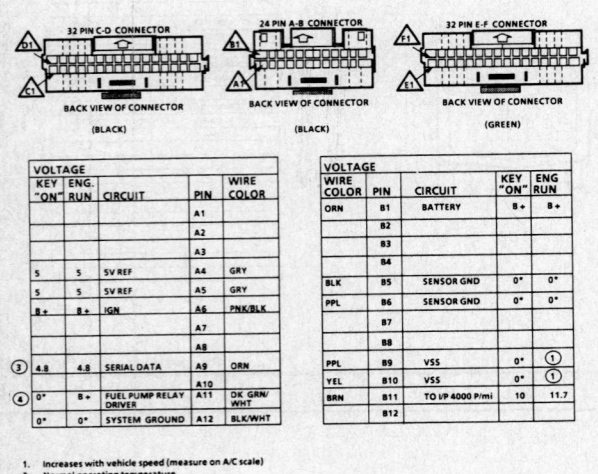

32 PIN C-D CONNECTOR
BACK VIEW OF CONNECTOR
(BLACK)

24 PIN A-B CONNECTOR
BACK VIEW OF CONNECTOR
(BLACK)

32 PIN E-F CONNECTOR
BACK VIEW OF CONNECTOR
(GREEN)

VOLTAGE

KEY "ON"	ENG. RUN	CIRCUIT	PIN	WIRE COLOR
			A1	
			A2	
			A3	
5	5	5V REF	A4	GRY
5	5	5V REF	A5	GRY
B+	B+	IGN	A6	PNK/BLK
			A7	
			A8	
③ 4.8	4.8	SERIAL DATA	A9	ORN
			A10	
④ 0*	B+	FUEL PUMP RELAY DRIVER	A11	DK GRN/WHT
0*	0*	SYSTEM GROUND	A12	BLK/WHT

VOLTAGE

WIRE COLOR	PIN	CIRCUIT	KEY "ON"	ENG RUN
ORN	B1	BATTERY	B+	B+
	B2			
	B3			
	B4			
BLK	B5	SENSOR GND	0*	0*
PPL	B6	SENSOR GND	0*	0*
	B7			
	B8			
PPL	B9	VSS	0*	①
YEL	B10	VSS	0*	①
BRN	B11	TO I/P 4000 P/mi	10	11.7
	B12			

1. Increases with vehicle speed (measure on A/C scale)
2. Normal operating temperature.
3. Varies.
4. 12 V First two seconds.
5. Varies with temperature.

* Less than .5 V

VOLTAGE

KEY "ON"	ENG. RUN	CIRCUIT	PIN	WIRE COLOR
		TO CRUISE 2000 P/mi	BC1	RED
			BC2	
			BC3	
			BC4	
			BC5	
			BC6	
0*	5	BYPASS	BC7	TAN/BLK
0*	1.3	EST	BC8	WHT
B+	B+	"ON"	BC9	LT GRN/BLK
0*	0*	"OFF" A/C REQUEST		
			BC10	
B+	B+	INJECTOR 1, 3, 5	BC11	DK BLU
B+	B+	INJECTOR 2, 4, 6	BC12	DK GRN
			BC13	
			BC14	
			BC15	
B+	B+	BATTERY	BC16	ORN

BLACK

VOLTAGE

WIRE COLOR	PIN	CIRCUIT	KEY "ON"	ENG RUN
TAN/WHT	BD1	SYSTEM GROUND	0*	0*
	BD2			
	BD3			
ORN	BD4	2ND GEAR SIG (3T40)	0*	0*
	BD5			
BLK/WHT	BD6	INJ DRIVER GND	0*	0*
BLK/WHT	BD7	INJ DRIVER GND	0*	0*
PPL/WHT	BD8	REFERENCE	0*	2.3
BLK/RED	BD9	REFERENCE GND	0*	0*
	BD10			
	BD11			
DK GRN/WHT	BD12	FAN REQUEST A/C PRESS SW SIG	0*	0*
LT BLU/ORN	BD13	P.S.P.S	B+	B+
LT BLU	BD14	4TH GEAR SIG (4T60)	0*	0*
DK GRN	BD15	3RD GEAR SIG (4T60)	0*	0*
ORN/BLK	BD16	P/N SWITCH	0*	0*

VOLTAGE

KEY "ON"	ENG. RUN	CIRCUIT	PIN	WIRE COLOR
			GE1	
			GE2	
NOT USEABLE		IAC "A" HI	GE3	LT BLU/WHT
NOT USEABLE		IAC "A" LO	GE4	LT BLU/BLK
NOT USEABLE		IAC "B" HI	GE5	LT GRN/WHT
NOT USEABLE		IAC "B" LO	GE6	LT GRN/BLK
0*	B+	"SERVICE ENGINE SOON" LIGHT	GE7	BRN/WHT
0*	0*	"ON" FAN RELAY	GE8	DK GRN/WHT
B+	B+	"OFF" CONTROL		
⑦ 0	0	EGR SOL. #1	GE9	LT BLU
			GE10	
			GE11	
5	5	DIAG. TERMINAL	GE12	WHT/BLK
④ 35-.55	.1-.9	FUEL PUMP SIGNAL	GE13	
③		O₂ SIGNAL	GE14	PPL
0*	0*	O₂ GROUND	GE15	BLK
⑤	⑤	COOLANT TEMP	GE16	YEL

GREEN

VOLTAGE

WIRE COLOR	PIN	CIRCUIT	KEY "ON"	ENG RUN
DK GRN/WHT	GF1	A/C RELAY "ON" CONTROL "OFF"	0*	0*
			B+	B+
	GF2			
	GF3			
BRN	GF4	EGR SOL #2 ⑦	0	0
RED	GF5	EGR SOL #3 ⑦	0	0
TAN/BLK	GF6	TCC CONTROL A/T ⑥	0*	0*
			B+	B+
DK GRN/YEL	GF7	PURGE CONTROL	0*	0*
	GF8			
DK BLU	GF9	ESC SIGNAL	2.5	2.5
	GF10			
	GF11			
	GF12			
DK BLU	GF13	TPS SIGNAL	.65	.65
	GF14			
LT GRN	GF15	MAP SIGNAL	4.57	③
TAN	GF16	IATS SIGNAL	⑤	⑤

1. Increases with vehicle speed (measure on A/C scale.)
2. Normal operating temperature.
3. Varies.
4. B+ First two seconds.
5. Varies with temperature.
6. B+ 4T60 Trans.
* Less than .5 V
7. B+ When commanded "ON"

91F09282   91H09283

Fig. 16: ECM Terminal Identification & Pin Voltages (3.1L VIN T 6000)

NOTE:
This ECM voltage chart can be used with a digital voltmeter to help save time in diagnosis. Voltages on the vehicle being tested may vary slightly from these due to battery voltage or alternator charging level.

The following conditions must be met before testing:
- Engine at operating temperature.
- Engine in closed loop operation.
- Engine idling ("Engine Run" column).
- ALDL "test" terminal NOT grounded.
- Scan tester NOT installed.

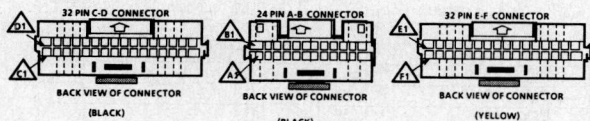

NOTICE: Before checking voltages, be sure ECM and engine grounds are located on the correct transaxle stud and are clean and tight.

BLACK 24 PIN A-B CONNECTOR

KEY "ON"	ENG. RUN	CIRCUIT	PIN	WIRE COLOR	WIRE COLOR	PIN	CIRCUIT	KEY "ON"	ENG. RUN
			A1		ORN	B1	BATTERY FEED	B+	B+
			A2			B2			
			A3			B3			
5.0	5.0	5 V REFERENCE	A4	GRY		B4			
			A5			B5			
B+	B+	IGNITION FEED	A6	PNK/BLK	BLK	B6	SENSOR GROUND	0*	0*
			A7			B7			
3.5	3.5	SERIAL DATA	A8	ORN		B8			
			A9		PPL	B9	VSS LOW	0*	0*
			A10		YEL	B10	VSS HI	*0	*0
*0 ③	B+	FUEL PUMP	A11	DK GRN/WHT	BRN	B11	4 K SPEEDO	0*·B+	0*·B+
0*	*0	ECM GROUND	A12	BLK/WHT	RED	B12	2K CRUISE	0*·B+	0*·B+

YELLOW 32 PIN E-F CONNECTOR

KEY "ON"	ENG. RUN	CIRCUIT	PIN	WIRE COLOR	WIRE COLOR	PIN	CIRCUIT	KEY "ON"	ENG. RUN
			E1		TAN/BLK	F1	TCC	B+	B+
			E2		DK GRN	F2	HOT LIGHT	0*	ON 0* OFF B+
NOT	USEABLE	IAC A HI	E3	LT BLU/WHT		F3			
NOT	USEABLE	IAC A LOW	E4	LT BLU/BLK		F4			
NOT	USEABLE	IAC B HI	E5	LT GRN/BLK		F5			
NOT	USEABLE	IAC B LOW	E6	LT GRN/BLK		F6			
*0	B+	SES LIGHT	E7	BRN/WHT	DK GRN/YEL	F7	CANISTER PURGE	B+	*0-B+ ①
B+	ON 0* OFF B+	COOLING FAN	E8	DK GRN	LT GRN/BLK	F8	A/C RELAY	B+	ON 0* OFF B+
			E9		DK BLU	F9	ESC SIGNAL	2.4	2.4
			E10		YEL	F10	MAF SIGNAL	5.0	2.4
			E11			F11			
5.0	5.0	DIAG/ALDL	E12	WHT/BLK		F12			
			E13		DK BLU	F13	TPS SIGNAL	.33-.46	.33-.46
0* ①	.1-.9	O₂ HI	E14	PPL		F14			
0*	0*	O₂ LOW	E15	TAN		F15			
1.8 ②	1.8	CTS SIGNAL	E16	YEL		F16			

** . VARIES AROUND 10 VOLTS.
* Less than .5V (500 mv).
① Varies within this range
② Varies with temperature
③ B+ for 2 sec. key up
④ 0* With brake applied

BLACK 32 PIN C-D CONNECTOR

KEY "ON"	ENG. RUN	CIRCUIT	PIN	WIRE COLOR	WIRE COLOR	PIN	CIRCUIT	KEY "ON"	ENG. RUN
			C1		BLK/WHT	D1	ECM GROUND	0*	0*
			C2			D2			
			C3			D3			
OPEN 0* CLOSE B+	OPEN 0* CLOSE B+	BRAKE SWITCH	C4	PPL		D4			
			C5			D5			
			C6		BLK/WHT	D6	INJ. GROUND	0*	0*
0*	5V	BYPASS	C7	TAN/BLK	BLK/WHT	D7	INJ. GROUND	0*	0*
0*	1.5V	EST	C8	WHT	PPL/WHT	D8	REFERENCE HIGH	0*	3.5V
ON B+ OFF 0*	ON B+ OFF 0*	A/C REQUEST	C9	LT BLU	BLK/RED	D9	REFERENCE LOW	0*	0*
			C10			D10			
B+	B+	INJ. 1, 3, 5	C11	DK BLU	YEL	D11	CRUISE ACTIVE	B+	B+
B+	B+	INJ. 2, 4, 6	C12	DK GRN	LT BLU/ORN	D12	PS PS	B+	OPEN B+ CLOSED 0*
			C13		LT BLU (4T60) ORN (3T40)	D13	HI GEAR SW.	0*	0* ②
			C14		DK GRN	D14	MID GEAR SW.	0*	0* ③
			C15			D15			
B+	B+	BATTERY FEED	C16	ORN	ORN/BLK	D16	P/N SWITCH	0*	0* ①

* Less than .5V (500mv).
1. 0 VOLT WHEN IN PARK/NUETRAL, B+ WHEN IN R-DL.
2. B+ WHEN HIGH GEAR IS ENGAGED.
3. B+ WHEN MID GEAR IS ENGAGED.

91J09284   91J09302

Fig. 17: ECM Terminal Identification & Pin Voltages (3.3L VIN N Century, Cutlass Ciera & Cutlass Cruiser)

NOTE:
This ECM voltage chart can be used with a digital voltmeter to help save time in diagnosis. Voltages on the vehicle being tested may vary slightly from these due to battery voltage or alternator charging level.

The following conditions must be met before testing:
- Engine at operating temperature.
- Engine in closed loop operation.
- Engine idling ("Engine Run" column).
- ALDL "test" terminal NOT grounded.
- Scan tester NOT installed.

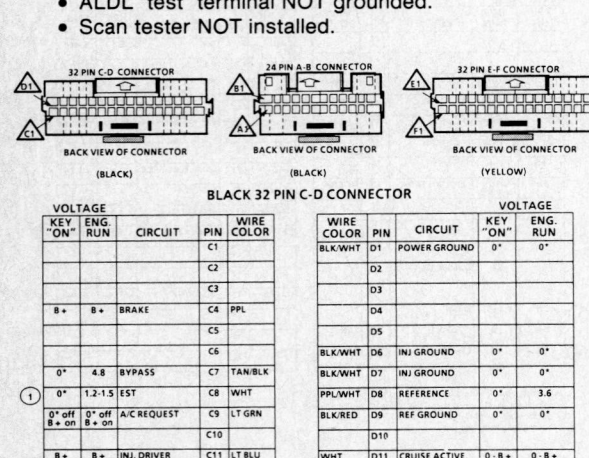

BLACK 24 PIN A-B CONNECTOR

VOLTAGE								VOLTAGE	
ENG. RUN	KEY "ON"	CIRCUIT	PIN	WIRE COLOR	WIRE COLOR	PIN	CIRCUIT	KEY "ON"	ENG. RUN
			A1		ORN	B1	BATTERY	B+	B+
			A2			B2			
			A3			B3			
5	5	5 VOLTS REF	A4	GRY		B4			
5	5	5 VOLTS REF	A5	GRY		B5			
B+	B+	IGNITION FEED	A6	PNK/BLK	BLK	B6	TPS, COOLANT A/C SENSOR GROUND	0*	0*
			A7			B7			
0*-5	0*-5	SERIAL DATA/ALDL	A8	ORN		B8			
			A9		PPL	B9	VSS LO	0*	0*
			A10		YEL	B10	VSS HI	0*-B+	0*-B+
0*	B+	FUEL PUMP	A11	DK GRN/WHT	DK GRN	B11	4K/MI SPEEDO	0*-B+	0*-B+
0*	0*	ECM GROUND	A12	BLK/WHT		B12			

(circled 3)

YELLOW 32 PIN E-F CONNECTOR

VOLTAGE								VOLTAGE	
ENG. RUN	KEY "ON"	CIRCUIT	PIN	WIRE COLOR	WIRE COLOR	PIN	CIRCUIT	KEY "ON"	ENG. RUN
			E1		TAN/BLK	F1	TCC	0*	0*
			E2		DK GRN	F2	HOT LIGHT	0*	B+
	NOT USEABLE	IAC A HI	E3	LT BLU/WHT		F3			
	NOT USEABLE	IAC A LO	E4	LT BLU/BLK		F4			
	NOT USEABLE	IAC B HI	E5	LT GRN/WHT		F5			
	NOT USEABLE	IAC B LO	E6	LT GRN/BKJ		F6			
0*		SES LIGHT	E7	BRN/WHT	DK GRN/YEL	F7	CANISTER PURGE	B+	0*-B+
B+	0* ON B+ OFF	FAN RELAY	E8	DK GRN	DK GRN/WHT	F8	A/C RELAY	B+	0* ON B+ OFF
			E9		DK BLU	F9	ESC SIGNAL	2.4	2.4
			E10		YEL	F10	MAF SIGNAL	5.0	2.4
			E11			F11			
5	5	DIAG/ALDL	E12	WHT/BLK		F12			
			E13		DK BLU	F13	TPS SIGNAL	.33-.46	.33-.46
0*	.1-.9	O₂ HI	E14	PPL	GRY/RED	F14	A/C PRESSURE SIGNAL	1	.2-4.5
0*	0*	O₂ LO	E15	TAN		F15			
1.8	1.8	CTS SIGNAL	E16	YEL		F16			

(circled 2)

★ LESS THAN 5v (500 mv).
1. VARIES WITHIN THIS RANGE.
2. VARIES WITH TEMPERATURE.
3. B+ FOR 1ˢᵗ 2 SECONDS.

BLACK 32 PIN C-D CONNECTOR

VOLTAGE									VOLTAGE	
KEY "ON"	ENG. RUN	CIRCUIT	PIN	WIRE COLOR	WIRE COLOR	PIN	CIRCUIT	KEY "ON"	ENG. RUN	
			C1		BLK/WHT	D1	POWER GROUND	0*	0*	
			C2			D2				
			C3			D3				
B+	B+	BRAKE	C4	PPL		D4				
			C5			D5				
			C6		BLK/WHT	D6	INJ GROUND	0*	0*	
0*	4.8	BYPASS	C7	TAN/BLK	BLK/WHT	D7	INJ GROUND	0*	0*	
0*	1.2-1.5	EST	C8	WHT	PPL/WHT	D8	REFERENCE	0*	3.6	
0* off B+ on	0* off B+ on	A/C REQUEST	C9	LT GRN	BLK/RED	D9	REF GROUND	0*	0*	
			C10			D10				
B+	B+	INJ. DRIVER 1,3,5	C11	LT BLU	WHT	D11	CRUISE ACTIVE	0-B+	0-B+	
B+	B+	INJ. DRIVER 2,4,6	C12	LT GRN	LT BLU/ORN	D12	PSPS	B+	B+ open 0* closed	
			C13		DK GRN/WHT	D13	3ʳᵈ GEAR	0*	0*	
			C14		WHT	D14	2ⁿᵈ GEAR	0*	0*	
			C15			D15				
B+	B+	BATTERY	C16	ORN	ORN/BLK	D16	P/N SWITCH	0*	0*	

(circled 1)

★ Less than .5V (500 mV).
1. Varies within this range.

91C09285   91E09286

Fig. 18: ECM Terminal Identification & Pin Voltages (3.3L VIN N Cutlass Calais & Skylark)

CONNECTOR A

CIRCUIT	PIN	WIRE COLOR
IAC "A" HIGH	A1	LT BLU/WHT
IAC "B" LOW	A2	LT GRN/BLK
FAN #2 CONTROL	A3	DK BLU/WHT
EGR SOLENOID #1	A4	BLU
	A5	
	A6	
IAC "A" LOW	A7	LT BLU/BLK
IAC "B" HIGH	A8	LT GRN/WHT
FAN #1 CONTROL	A9	DK GRN/WHT
CANISTER PURGE	A10	DK GRN/YEL
ESC SIGNAL	A11	DK BLU
A/C RELAY CONTROL	A12	DK GRN/WHT
"B" SHIFT SOLENOID (4T60E)	A13	LT BLU
	A14	
	A15	
O₂ SIGNAL	A16	PPL
	A17	
"A" SHIFT SOLENOID (4T60E)	A18	*ORN
AIR PUMP RELAY (M/T 3.4L)	A18	BLK/PNK
AIR SOLENOID M/T 3.1L	A18	BLK/PNK
EGR SOLENOID #2	A19	BRN
FUEL PUMP SIGNAL	A20	GRY
SENSOR GROUND	A22	TAN

CONNECTOR B

CIRCUIT	PIN	WIRE COLOR
SES LIGHT	B1	BRN/WHT
	B2	
DIAGNOSTIC / TEST	B3	WHT/BLK
	B4	
SERIAL DATA IN / ALDL	B5	ORN
	B6	
TCC (A/T) SHIFT LIGHT (M/T)	B7	TAN/BLK
BUFFERED SPEED OUT	B8	DK GRN
	B9	
ISOLATED IGNITION FEED	B10	PNK/BLK
	B11	
	B12	
	B13	
	B14	
	B15	
	B16	
	B17	
	B18	
	B19	
	B20	
	B21	
	B22	

CONNECTOR C

CIRCUIT	PIN	WIRE COLOR
	C1	
MAG. VSS SIGNAL LOW	C2	PPL
DIS BYPASS	C3	TAN/BLK
IAT SIGNAL	C4	TAN
SENSOR GROUND	C5	BLK
GROUND	C6	BLK/WHT
+ 5 VOLT REFERENCE (MAP)	C7	GRY
MAG. VSS HIGH	C8	YEL
EST CONTROL	C9	WHT
SENSOR GROUND	C10	BLK
	C11	
+ 5 VOLT REFERENCE (TPS)	C12	GRY
EGR SOLENOID #3	C13	RED
	C14	
TPS SIGNAL	C15	DK BLU
COOLANT TEMPERATURE SIGNAL	C16	YEL
A/C REQUEST	C17	LT BLU
	C18	
	C19	
4TH GEAR SIGNAL	C20	LT BLU
A/C PRESSURE SIGNAL	C21	DK BLU
MAP SIGNAL	C22	LT GRN

CONNECTOR D

CIRCUIT	PIN	WIRE COLOR
	D1	
	D2	
INJECTOR DRIVER (1, 3, 5)	D3	DK BLU
GROUND	D4	BLK/WHT
	D5	
	D6	
FUEL PUMP RELAY DRIVE	D7	DK GRN/WHT
	D8	
INJECTOR DRIVER (2, 4, 6)	D9	DK BLU
GROUND	D10	TAN/WHT
P/N SWITCH (A/T)	D11	ORN/BLK
GROUND	D12	TAN/WHT
REFERENCE	D13	PPL/WHT
	D14	
	D15	
P/S PRESSURE SIGNAL	D16	LT BLU/ORN
BATTERY FEED	D17	ORN
	D18	
DIS REFERENCE LOW	D19	BLK/RED
	D20	
	D21	
1ST GEAR SIGNAL	D22	RED

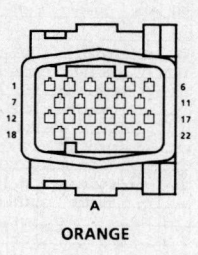

ORANGE

A

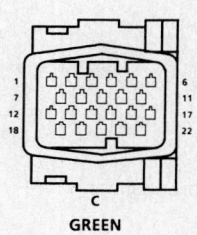

GREEN

C

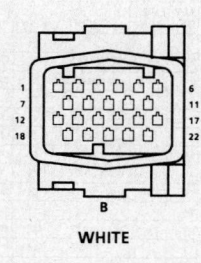

WHITE

B

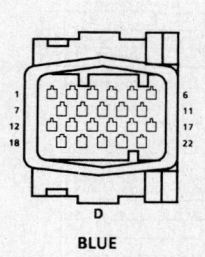

BLUE

D

91G09287   91I09288

Fig. 19: ECM Terminal Identification (3.4L VIN X Cutlass Supreme, Grand Prix & Lumina)

NOTE:
This ECM voltage chart can be used with a digital voltmeter to help save time in diagnosis. Voltages on the vehicle being tested may vary slightly from these due to battery voltage or alternator charging level.

The following conditions must be met before testing:
- Engine at operating temperature.
- Engine in closed loop operation.
- Engine idling ("Engine Run" column).
- ALDL "test" terminal NOT grounded.
- Scan tester NOT installed.

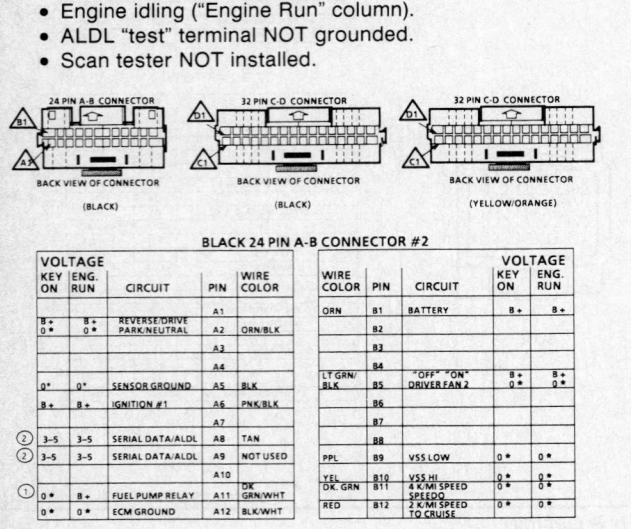

24 PIN A-B CONNECTOR	32 PIN C-D CONNECTOR	32 PIN C-D CONNECTOR
BACK VIEW OF CONNECTOR	BACK VIEW OF CONNECTOR	BACK VIEW OF CONNECTOR
(BLACK)	(BLACK)	(YELLOW/ORANGE)

BLACK 32 PIN C-D CONNECTOR #1

KEY ON	ENG. RUN	CIRCUIT	PIN	WIRE COLOR	WIRE COLOR	PIN	CIRCUIT	KEY ON	ENG. RUN
			C1		BLK/WHT	D1	ECM GROUND	0*	0*
B+	B+	EGR #3	C2	RED	BLU	D2	EGR #1	B+	B+
B+	B+	EGR #2	C3	BRN		D3			
B+	B+	BRAKE INPUT	C4	PPL	LT BLU/ORN	D4	PSPS	B+	B+
**	**	CAM SIGNAL	C5	BLK		D5			
			C6		BLK/WHT	D6	INJECTOR GROUND	0*	0*
0*	4.70	BYPASS	C7	TAN/BLK	BLK/WHT	D7	INJECTOR GROUND	0*	0*
0*	0-8+	EST	C8	WHT	PPL/WHT	D8	FUEL CONTROL	0*	6 V
Off-0 On-B+	Off-0 On-B+	A/C REQUEST	C9	LT BLU	BLK/RED	D9	REFLOW (GROUND)	0*	0*
0*	0*	3RD GEAR	C10	DK GRN	YEL	D10	CRUISE INPUT	B+	B+
			C11		LT BLU/BLK	D11	HIGH RES (18X)	0*	6 V
			C12			D12			
B+	B+	INJECTOR #2	C13	BLK/LT GRN	BLK/RED	D13	INJECTOR #4	B+	B+
5V	5V	+5V REF.	C14	GRY	BLK/YEL	D14	INJECTOR #6	B+	B+
B+	B+	INJECTOR #3	C15	BLK/PNK	BLK	D15	INJECTOR #1	B+	B+
B+	B+	BATTERY	C16	ORN	BLK/WHT	D16	INJECTOR #5	B+	B+

ORANGE 32 PIN C-D CONNECTOR #3

KEY ON	ENG. RUN	CIRCUIT	PIN	WIRE COLOR	WIRE COLOR	PIN	CIRCUIT	KEY ON	ENG. RUN
			C1			D1			
B+	B+	DRIVER FAN 1	C2	DK GRN	PPL	D2	O² SIGNAL	35-45	1-9 ①
B+	B+	CANISTER PURGE	C3	DKGRN/YEL	TAN	D3	O² GROUND	0*	0*
			C4		YEL	D4	COOLANT TEMP. SIGNAL	2.06	2.34 ②
① 0*	.8-12	IAC-A-HI	C5	LT BLU/WHT	BLK	D5	SENSOR GROUND	0*	0*
① B+	.8-12	IAC-A-LO	C6	LT BLU/BLK	WHT/BLK	D6	DIAG/ALDL	3-6V	3-6V
① 0*	.8-12	IAC-B-HI	C7	LT GRN/WHT	LT BLU	D7	4TH GEAR	0*	0*
① B+	.8-12	IAC-B-LO	C8	LT GRN/BLK	ORN	D8	2ND GEAR	0*	0*
0*	B+	HOT LIGHT	C9	DK GRN	DK BLU	D9	ESC SIGNAL	2.3	2.3
B+	B+	TCC	C10	TAN/BLK	YEL	D10	MAF SIGNAL	0*	2.3
0*	B+	SES LIGHT	C11	BRN/WHT	TAN	D11	MAT SIGNAL	2.06	2.34 ②
			C12			D12			
			C13		DK BLU	D13	TPS SIGNAL	33-46	33-46
			C14			D14			
0* B+	0* B+	"ON" "OFF" A/C CLUTCH DRIVER	C15	LT GRN/BLK		D15			
			C16			D16			

, VARIES AROUND 10 VOLTS.
* Less than .5v (500 mV).
① Varies within this range
② Varies with temperature.

BLACK 24 PIN A-B CONNECTOR #2

KEY ON	ENG. RUN	CIRCUIT	PIN	WIRE COLOR	WIRE COLOR	PIN	CIRCUIT	KEY ON	ENG. RUN
B+	B+	REVERSE/DRIVE	A1		ORN	B1	BATTERY	B+	B+
0*	0*	PARK/NEUTRAL	A2	ORN/BLK		B2			
			A3			B3			
			A4			B4			
0*	0*	SENSOR GROUND	A5	BLK	LT GRN/BLK	B5	"OFF" "ON" DRIVER FAN 2	B+ 0*	B+ 0*
B+	B+	IGNITION #1	A6	PNK/BLK		B6			
			A7			B7			
② 3-5	3-5	SERIAL DATA/ALDL	A8	TAN		B8			
② 3-5	3-5	SERIAL DATA/ALDL	A9	NOT USED	PPL	B9	VSS LOW	0*	0*
			A10		YEL	B10	VSS HI	0*	0*
① 0*	B+	FUEL PUMP RELAY	A11	DK GRN/WHT	DK. GRN	B11	4 K/MI SPEED SPEEDO	0*	0*
0*	0*	ECM GROUND	A12	BLK/WHT	RED	B12	2 K/MI SPEED TO CRUISE	0*	0*

* Less than .5V (500 mv).
① B + for first two seconds.
② Varies within this range.

NOTICE: Before closed loop operation can occur the following must take place:
1. Coolant temperature above 75°C.
2. O₂ Sensor voltage toggling.
3. Engine RPM greater than 800 for 15 consecutive seconds after 1 and 2 have occured.

91A09289 91C09290

Courtesy of General Motors Corp.

Fig. 20: ECM Terminal Identification & Pin Voltages (3.8L VIN C Bonneville, Eighty-Eight & LeSabre)

NOTE:
This ECM voltage chart can be used with a digital voltmeter to help save time in diagnosis. Voltages on the vehicle being tested may vary slightly from these due to battery voltage or alternator charging level.

The following conditions must be met before testing:

- Engine at operating temperature.
- Engine in closed loop operation.
- Engine idling ("Engine Run" column).
- ALDL "test" terminal NOT grounded.
- Scan tester NOT installed.

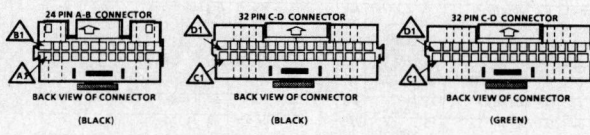

24 PIN A-B CONNECTOR / BACK VIEW OF CONNECTOR (BLACK)

32 PIN C-D CONNECTOR / BACK VIEW OF CONNECTOR (BLACK)

32 PIN C-D CONNECTOR / BACK VIEW OF CONNECTOR (GREEN)

BLACK 24 PIN A-B CONNECTOR #2

VOLTAGE KEY "ON"	VOLTAGE ENG. RUN	CIRCUIT	PIN	WIRE COLOR	CKT NUMBER	CKT NUMBER	WIRE COLOR	PIN	CIRCUIT	VOLTAGE KEY "ON"	VOLTAGE ENG. RUN
			A1					B1			
B+	B+	IGN #1	A2	PNK/BLK	439			B2			
			A3			416	GRY	B3	5 VOLT REF.	5	5
B+	B+	BATTERY	A4	ORN	480	480	ORN	B4	BATTERY	B+	B+
B+	B+	BRAKE	A5	PPL	420			B5			
0*	0*	PCM GROUND	A6	BLK/WHT	450	450	BLK/WHT	B6	PCM GROUND	0*	0*
0*	0*	SENSOR GROUND	A7	BLK/WHT	454	472	TAN	B7	IATS	2.0②	2.5②
0*	0*	SENSOR GROUND	A8	BLK	452	496	DK BLU	B8	ESC SIGNAL	2.4	2.4
0*	0*	SPS LO	A9	LT BLU/BLK	399	410	YEL	B9	CTS	1.8②	1.8②
0*	0*	SPS HI	A10	TAN	398	417	DK BLU	B10	TPS	.33-.46	.33-.46
			A11			451	WHT/BLK	B11	DIAG/ALDL	5	5
4.8	②	CAM HI	A12	BLK	630			B12			

* Less than .5 volt (500 mv).
① B+ for first two seconds.
② Varies.

BLACK 32 PIN C-D CONNECTOR #1

VOLTAGE KEY "ON"	VOLTAGE ENG. RUN	CIRCUIT	PIN	WIRE COLOR	CKT #	CKT #	WIRE COLOR	PIN	CIRCUIT	VOLTAGE KEY "ON"	VOLTAGE ENG. RUN
0*	0*	CC VENT	C1	DK BLU	403	800	TAN	D1	SERIAL DATA	3-5②	3-5②
3-5②	3-5②	SERIAL DATA	C2	TAN	800	413	TAN	D2	O² GND. REF.	0*	0*
0*	0*	CC VAC SOLENOID	C3	LT GRN	402	412	PPL	D3	O₂ SIGNAL	.3-.5	.1-.9②
0*	B+	FUEL PUMP RELAY	C4	DK GRN/WHT	465	637	WHT	D4	H/W REQUEST	8+	8+
			C5			776	WHT	D5	PRNDL P	0*	0*
0*	4.7	BYPASS	C6	TAN/BLK	424	773	GRY	D6	PRNDL C	8+	8+
0*	2.0②	EST	C7	WHT	423	772	YEL	D7	PRNDL B	8+	8+
0*	0*	REF. LO	C8	BLK/RED	453	771	BLK/WHT	D8	PRNDL A	0*	0*
			C9					D9			
			C10			86	BRN	D10	CRUISE ENABLE	0*	0*
4.8	2.4	FUEL CONTROL	C11	PPL/WHT	430			D11			
B+	B+	INJECTOR 3	C12	BLK/PNK	843			D12			
0*	0*	INJ GROUND	C13	BLK	450	450	BLK/WHT	D13	INJ GROUND	0*	0*
B+	B+	INJECTOR 4	C14	BLK/RED	844	492	YEL	D14	MAF SIGNAL	5	2.4②
B+	B+	INJECTOR 1	C15	BLK	841	846	BLK/YEL	D15	INJECTOR 6	8+	8+
B+	B+	INJECTOR 5	C16	BLK/WHT	845	842	BLK/LT GRN	D16	INJECTOR 2	8+	8+

GREEN 32 PIN C-D CONNECTOR #3

VOLTAGE KEY "ON"	VOLTAGE ENG. RUN	CIRCUIT	PIN	WIRE COLOR	CKT #	CKT #	WIRE COLOR	PIN	CIRCUIT	VOLTAGE KEY "ON"	VOLTAGE ENG. RUN
0*	B+	SES LIGHT	C1	BRN/WHT	419			D1			
B+	B+	A/C RELAY	C2	DK GRN/YEL	762	397	GRY	D2	CRUISE "ON/OFF"	0*	0*
B+	B+	HI FAN	C3	LT GRN/BLK	536	84	DK BLU	D3	SET/COAST	0*	0*
B+	B+	LO FAN	C4	DK GRN	535	87	GRY/BLK	D4	RESUME/ACCL	0*	0*
B+	B+	CCP	C5	DK GRN/YEL	428	229	DK BLU	D5	VATS	2.5	2.5
B+	B+	TCC	C6	TAN/BLK	422	647	LT BLU/BLK	D6	SPARK REFERENCE	0-5	3.0
			C7					D7			
			C8					D8			
			C9					D9			
			C10					D10	SPEEDO 4K/MI	8+	8+
②	②	IACA HI	C11	LT BLU/WHT	441	817	DK GRN/WHT	D10	SPEEDO 4K/MI	8+	8+
②	②	IACA LO	C12	LT BLU/BLK	442			D11			
②	②	IACB LO	C13	LT GRN/BLK	444			D12			
②	②	IACB HI	C14	LT GRN/WHT	443	401	PPL	D13	VSS LO	0*	0*
B+	B+	TCC PWM	C15	WHT	584	400	YEL	D14	VSS HI	0*	0*
			C16			1223	YEL/BLK	D15	SHIFT B	0*	0*
						1222	LT GRN	D16	SHIFT A	0*	0*

** VARIES AROUND 10 VOLTS * LESS THAN .5v (500 mv) ② VARIES

91E09291   91G09292

Courtesy of General Motors Corp.

Fig. 21: *ECM Terminal Identification & Pin Voltages (3.8L VIN C Reatta, Riviera, Toronado & Trofeo)*

NOTE:
This ECM voltage chart can be used with a digital voltmeter to help save time in diagnosis. Voltages on the vehicle being tested may vary slightly from these due to battery voltage or alternator charging level.

The following conditions must be met before testing:
- Engine at operating temperature.
- Engine in closed loop operation.
- Engine idling ("Engine Run" column).
- ALDL "test" terminal NOT grounded.
- Scan tester NOT installed.

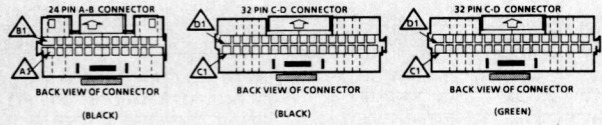

24 PIN A-B CONNECTOR
BACK VIEW OF CONNECTOR
(BLACK)

32 PIN C-D CONNECTOR
BACK VIEW OF CONNECTOR
(BLACK)

32 PIN C-D CONNECTOR
BACK VIEW OF CONNECTOR
(GREEN)

BLACK 24 PIN A-B CONNECTOR #2

KEY "ON"	ENG. RUN	CIRCUIT	PIN	WIRE COLOR	CKT NUMBER	CKT NUMBER	WIRE COLOR	PIN	CIRCUIT	KEY "ON"	ENG. RUN
			A1					B1			
B+	B+	IGN #1	A2	PNK/BLK	439			B2			
			A3			416	GRY	B3	5 VOLT REF.	5	5
B+	B+	BATTERY	A4	ORN	440	440	ORN	B4	BATTERY	B+	B+
B+	B+	BRAKE	A5	PPL	420			B5			
0*	0*	PCM GROUND	A6	BLK/WHT	450	450	BLK/WHT	B6	PCM GND	0*	0*
0*	0*	SENSOR GROUND	A7	BLK	454	472	TAN	B7	IATS	1.99②	2.45②
0*	0*	SENSOR GROUND	A8	BLK	452	496	DK BLU	B8	ESC SIGNAL	2.38	2.38
0*	0*	SPS LO	A9	LT BLU/BLK	399	410	YEL	B9	CTS	1.79②	1.75②
0*	0*	SPS HI	A10	TAN	398	417	DK BLU	B10	TPS	.33-.46	.33-.46
			A11			451	WHT/BLK	B11	DIAG. ALDL	5	5
4.80	②	CAM HI	A12	BLK	630			B12			

* Less than .5V (500 mV).
① B+ for first two seconds.
② Varies.

NOTICE: Before closed loop operation can occur the following must take place:
1. Coolant temperature above 75°C.
2. O₂ Sensor voltage toggling.
3. Engine RPM greater than 800 for 15 consecutive seconds after 1 and 2 have occured.

BLACK 32 PIN C-D CONNECTOR #1

KEY "ON"	ENG. RUN	CIRCUIT	PIN	WIRE COLOR	CKT #	CKT #	WIRE COLOR	PIN	CIRCUIT	KEY "ON"	ENG. RUN
0*	0*	CC VENT	C1	DK BLU/WHT	403			D1			
3-5②	3-5②	SERIAL DATA	C2	TAN	800	413	TAN	D2	O₂ LO	0*	0*
0*	0*	CC VAC SOLENOID	C3	LT GRN	402	412	PPL	D3	O₂ HI	3-.5②	3-.5②
0*	B+	FUEL PUMP RELAY	C4	DK GRN/WHT	465	637	WHT	D4	H/W REQUEST	B+	B+
②3-5	②3-5	SERIAL DATA	C5	TAN	800	776	WHT	D5	PRNDL P (PN)	0*	0*
0*	4.69	BYPASS	C6	TAN/BLK	424	773	GRY	D6	PRNDL C (2ND)	B+	B+
0*	2.09	EST	C7	WHT	423	772	YEL	D7	PRNDL B (3RD)	B+	B+
0*	0*	REFERENCE LO	C8	BLK	453	771	BLK/WHT	D8	PRNDL A (4TH)	0*	0*
			C9			603	DK GRN/WHT	D9	A/C PRESSURE SWITCH	B+	B+
			C10			86	BRN	D10	CRUISE ENABLE	0*	0*
4.80	2.42	FUEL CONTROL	C11	PPL/WHT	430	67	LT BLU	D11	A/C REQUEST	B+	B+
B+	B+	INJECTOR 3	C12	BLK/PNK	843			D12			
0*	0*	INJECTOR GROUND	C13	BLK/WHT	450	450	BLK/WHT	D13	INJ GROUND	0*	0*
B+	B+	INJECTOR 4	C14	BLK	844	492	YEL	D14	MAF SIGNAL	5	5②
B+	B+	INJECTOR 1	C15	BLK	841	846	BLK/YEL	D15	INJECTOR 6	B+	B+
B+	B+	INJECTOR 5	C16	BLK/WHT	845	842	BLK/LT GRN	D16	INJECTOR 2	B+	B+

GREEN 32 PIN C-D CONNECTOR #3

KEY "ON"	ENG. RUN	CIRCUIT	PIN	WIRE COLOR	CKT #	CKT #	WIRE COLOR	PIN	CIRCUIT	KEY "ON"	ENG. RUN
0*	B+	SES LIGHT	C1	BRN/WHT	419	85	WHT	D1	CRUISE LIGHT	0*	0*
B+	B+	A/C RELAY	C2	LT GRN/YEL	366	397	GRY	D2	CRUISE "ON"	0*	0*
B+	B+	HI FAN	C3	DK GRN/WHT	1270	84	DK BLU	D3	SET/COAST	0*	0*
B+	B+	LO FAN	C4	GRY/BLK	1269	87	GRY/BLK	D4	RESUME/ACCL	0*	0*
B+	B+	CCP	C5	DK GRN/YEL	428	229	DK BLU	D5	PASS-Key	5	5
B+	B+	TCC	C6	TAN/BLK	422	647	LT BLU/BLK	D6	18 X REF HI	0*	3.03
0*	0*	HOT LIGHT	C7	PNK/BLK	1268	1298	PNK	D7	C.C.R.	0*	0*
			C8					D8			
			C9					D9			
			C10			389	DK GRN	D10	VSS 4K/MI SPEED	B+	B+
②	②	IACA HI	C11	LT BLU/WHT	441	381	RED	D11	VSS TO CHIME MODULE	0*	0*
②	②	IACA LO	C12	LT BLU/BLK	442			D12			
②	②	IACB LO	C13	LT GRN/BLK	444	401	PPL	D13	VSS LO	0*	0*
②	②	IACB HI	C14	LT GRN/WHT	443	400	YEL	D14	VSS HI	0*	0*
B+	B+	TCC PWM	C15	DK BLU	1350	1223	BLK	D15	SHIFT B	0*	0*
②3-5	②3-5	SERIAL DATA	C16	TAN	800	1222	LT GRN	D16	SHIFT A	0*	0*

** VARIES AROUND 10 VOLTS   * LESS THAN .5v (500 mV)   ② VARIES   ENGINE - 3800/L27

Fig. 22: ECM Terminal Identification & Pin Voltages (3.8L VIN L Ninety-Eight, Park Avenue & Touring Sedan)

BROWN CONNECTOR

CIRCUIT	PIN	WIRE COLOR	CKT NO.
SERVICE ENGINE SOON	B1	BRN/WHT	419
HIGH SPEED FANS	B2	LT GRN/BLK	536
CANISTER PURGE	B3	DK GRN/YEL	428
HOT LIGHT	B4	DK GRN	35
N/C	B5	N/C	N/C
IAC "B" HIGH	B6	LT GRN/WHT	443
A/C RELAY	B7	LT GRN/BLK	366
LOW SPEED FANS	B8	DK GRN	535
TCC	B9	TAN/BLK	422
N/C	B10	N/C	N/C
N/C	B11	N/C	N/C
N/C	B12	N/C	N/C
N/C	B13	N/C	N/C
N/C	B14	N/C	N/C
N/C	B15	N/C	N/C
N/C	B16	N/C	N/C
IAC "B" LOW	B17	LT GRN/BLK	444
N/C	B18	N/C	N/C
N/C	B19	N/C	N/C
SPARK REFERENCE	B20	LT BLU/BLK	647
N/C	B21	N/C	N/C
N/C	B22	N/C	N/C

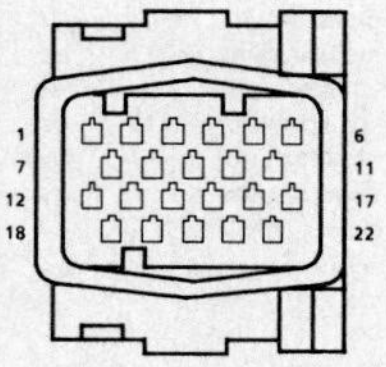

RED CONNECTOR

CIRCUIT	PIN	WIRE COLOR	CKT NO
ECM GROUND	R1	BLK/WHT	450
IAT SENSOR GROUND	R2	BLK/WHT	454
N/C	R3	N/C	N/C
SERIAL DATA	R4	ORN	461
N/C	R5	N/C	N/C
N/C	R6	N/C	N/C
TPS, CTS SENSOR GROUND	R7	BLK	452
N/C	R8	N/C	N/C
N/C	R9	N/C	N/C
CAM SIGNAL	R10	BLK	630
N/C	R11	N/C	N/C
INTAKE AIR TEMP.	R12	TAN	472
COOLANT TEMP. SIGNAL	R13	YEL	410
DIAG/ALDL	R14	WHT/BLK	451
N/C	R15	N/C	N/C
O2 HIGH	R16	PPL	412
P/N	R17	ORN/BLK	434
ESC SENSOR	R18	DK BLU	496
TPS SIGNAL	R19	DK BLU	417
N/C	R20	N/C	N/C
O2 LOW	R21	TAN	413
N/C	R22	N/C	N/C

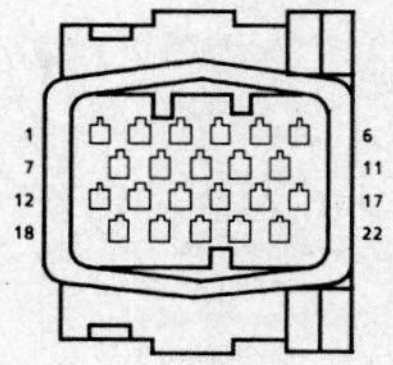

BROWN

RED

PURPLE CONNECTOR

CIRCUIT	PIN	WIRE COLOR	CKT NO.
ECM GROUND	P1	TAN/WHT	551
N/C	P2	N/C	N/C
IAC "A" HIGH	P3	LT BLU/WHT	441
5 VOLT REFERENCE	P4	GRY	416
IGN 1	P5	PNK/BLK	439
BRAKE	P6	PPL	420
N/C	P7	N/C	N/C
IAC "A" LOW	P8	LT BLU/BLK	442
N/C	P9	N/C	N/C
N/C	P10	N/C	N/C
BATTERY	P11	ORN	440
N/C	P12	N/C	N/C
CRUISE/SPEEDO 4 km/mi	P13	DK GRN	389
N/C	P14	N/C	N/C
N/C	P15	N/C	N/C
N/C	P16	N/C	N/C
N/C	P17	N/C	N/C
N/C	P18	N/C	N/C
N/C	P19	N/C	N/C
VSS HIGH	P20	YEL	400
VSS LOW	P21	PPL	401
BATTERY	P22	ORN	440

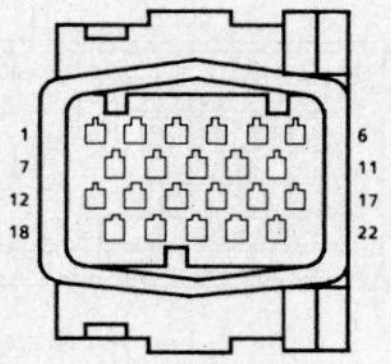

GRAY CONNECTOR

CIRCUIT	PIN	WIRE COLOR	CKT NO
FUEL PUMP RELAY	G1	DK GRN/WHT	465
EST	G2	WHT	423
N/C	G3	N/C	N/C
INJ #3	G4	BLK/PNK	843
INJ #4	G5	BLK/RED	844
INJ #5	G6	BLK/WHT	845
BYPASS	G7	TAN/BLK	424
REFERENCE LOW	G8	BLK/RED	453
REFERENCE HIGH	G9	PPL/WHT	430
INJ GROUND	G10	BLK/WHT	450
INJ #1	G11	BLK	841
2ND GEAR	G12	ORN	581
4TH GEAR	G13	LT BLU	446
CRUISE ACTIVE	G14	YEL	494
MAF SENSOR	G15	YEL	492
N/C	G16	N/C	N/C
INJ #2	G17	BLK/LT GRN	842
3RD GEAR	G18	DK GRN	108
A/C HEAD PRESSURE SW	G19	DK GRN/WHT	603
A/C REQUEST	G20	LT BLU	67
INJ GROUND	G21	BLK/WHT	450
INJ #6	G22	BLK/YEL	846

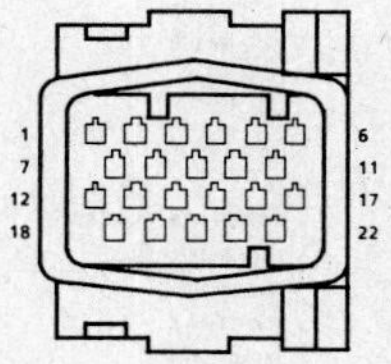

PURPLE

GRAY

91D09295   91F09296

Courtesy of General Motors Corp.

Fig. 23: ECM Terminal Identification (3.8L VIN L Regal)

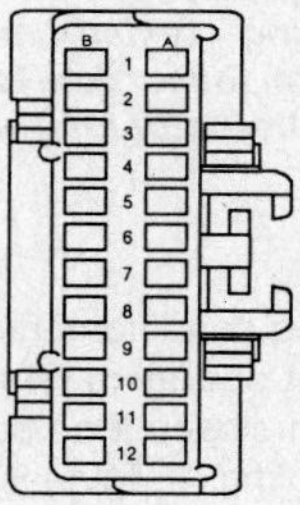

PCM (2A/B) BLACK

CIRCUIT DESCRIPTION	CIRCUIT NUMBER	PCM (2A/B) BLACK	CIRCUIT NUMBER	CIRCUIT DESCRIPTION
BATTERY	480	1 (B/A)	435	EGR SOLENOID
N/C		2	776	TRANS INPUT P
C/C POSITION HI	398	3		
C/C POSITION LO	399	4		N/C
N/C		5	469	SENSOR GROUND
N/C		6	439	IGNITION
N/C		7	427	THROTTLE SWITCH
COOLING FAN RELAY #2	1270	8	800	UART SERIAL DATA
SPEED SENSOR INPUT LO	400	9	800	UART SERIAL DATA
SPEED SENSOR INPUT HI	401	10	419	CHECK ENGINE SIGNAL
4000 PULSE SPEED OUTPUT #1	389	11	1269	COOLING FAN RELAY #1
4000 PULSE SPEED OUTPUT #2	917	12	450	PCM GROUND

SINGLE CAVITY METRI PAK CONNECTOR

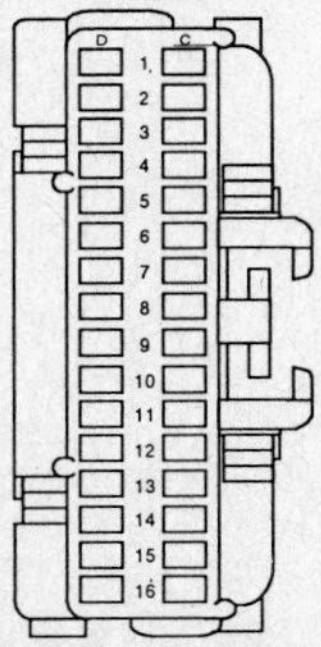

NOTE: THE TPA STRAIN RELIEVERS IN THIS CONNECTOR WILL BE MARKED AS C AND D

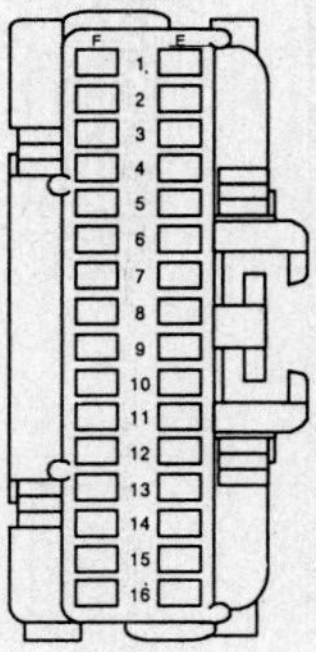

PCM (3E/F) GREEN

CIRCUIT DESCRIPTION	CIRCUIT NUMBER	PCM (3E/F) GREEN	CIRCUIT NUMBER	CIRCUIT DESCRIPTION
FUEL PUMP RELAY	465	1 (F/E)	425	ISC HI
C/C VENT	403	2	426	ISC LO
C/C SOURCE	402	3	491	SERIAL DATA IN
A/C CLUTCH RELAY	366	4	1222	SHIFT B
VCC MOD	108	5	526	SERAL DATA OUT
VCC SOLENOID	422	6	1490	COMPUTER RIDE
TRANS INPUT C	773	7	428	CANISTER PURGE
TRANS INPUT A	771	8		N/C
N/C		9		N/C
PASS KEY THEFT SYSTEM	229	10	1223	SHIFT A
N/C		11	476	SENSOR GND
N/C		12	451	FIXED SPARK
TPS SIGNAL	417	13	120	FUEL PUMP FEEDBACK
N/C		14	412	OXYGEN SENSOR
MAP SIGNAL	432	15	413	OXYGEN SENSOR
MAT SIGNAL	472	16	410	COOLANT TEMP

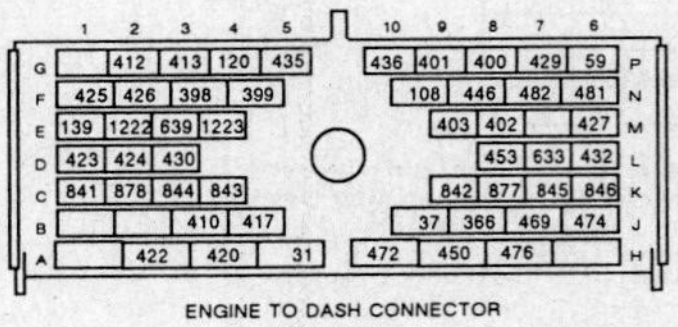

PCM (1C/D) BLACK

CIRCUIT DESCRIPTION	CIRCUIT NUMBER	PCM (1C/D) BLACK	CIRCUIT NUMBER	CIRCUIT DESCRIPTION
PCM GROUND	450	1 (D/C)		N/C
C/C ON-OFF	397	2	86	C/C ENABLE
C/C SET/COAST	84	3	87	C/C RESUME
N/C		4	420	VCC BRAKE
PCM GROUND	450	5	633	CAM HI
PCM GROUND	450	6		N/C
EST REFERENCE PULSE HI	430	7	424	BYPASS
EST REFERENCE/CAM LO	453	8	423	EST
N/C		9	495	POWER STEERING SW.
N/C		10	772	TRANS INPUT B
HEATED W/S	637	11	841	INJECTOR 1
INJECTOR 2	842	12	878	INJECTOR 8
INJECTOR 7	877	13	846	INJECTOR 6
INJECTOR 5	845	14	474	5V REFERENCE
INJECTOR 3	843	15	844	INJECTOR 4
		16	480	BATTERY

SINGLE CAVITY METRI PAK CONNECTOR

ENGINE TO DASH CONNECTOR MATING SIDE

	1	2	3	4	5		10	9	8	7	6	
G	412	413	120	435		436	401	400	429	59		P
F	425	426	398	399		108	446	482	481			N
E	139	1222	639	1223		403	402	427				M
D	423	424	430			453	633	432				L
C	841	878	844	843		842	877	845	846			K
B		410				37	366	469	474			J
A	422	420	31			472	450	476				H

91B09336   91D09337

Courtesy of General Motors Corp.

Fig. 24: ECM Terminal Identification (4.9L VIN B DeVille & Fleetwood)

PCM (2A/B) BLACK

CIRCUIT DESCRIPTION	CIRCUIT NUMBER	PIN	CIRCUIT NUMBER	CIRCUIT DESCRIPTION
BATTERY	480	B1 / A1	435	EGR SOLENOID
N/C		B2 / A2	776	TRANS INPUT P
C/C POSITION HI	398	B3 / A3	815	POWER STEERING SW.
C/C POSITION LO	399	B4 / A4		N/C
N/C		B5 / A5	476	SENSOR GROUND
LEFT O₂ SENSOR LO	413	B6 / A6	339	IGNITION
LEFT O₂ SENSOR HI	1589	B7 / A7	427	THROTTLE SWITCH
COOLING FAN RELAY #2	536	B8 / A8	800	UART SERIAL DATA OUT
SPEED SENSOR INPUT LO	401	B9 / A9	800	UART SERIAL DATA IN
SPEED SENSOR INPUT HI	400	B10 / A10	325	CHECK ENGINE SIGNAL
4K PULSE OUTPUT #1	818	B11 / A11	535	COOLING FAN RELAY #1
4K PULSE COMP. COM. RIDE	817	B12 / A12	450	PCM GROUND

PCM (3E/F) GREEN

CIRCUIT DESCRIPTION	CIRCUIT NUMBER	PIN	CIRCUIT NUMBER	CIRCUIT DESCRIPTION
FUEL PUMP RELAY	465	1	425	ISC HI
C/C VENT	403	2	426	ISC LO
C/C SOURCE	402	3		N/C
A/C CLUTCH RELAY	762	4	1223	SHIFT B
VCC MOD	584	5		N/C
VCC SOLENOID	422	6	1490	COMP. COM. RIDE
TRANS INPUT C	773	7	428	CANISTER PURGE
TRANS INPUT A	771	8	1222	SHIFT B
N/C		9	429	AIR DIVERT VALVE
PASS KEY SYSTEM	229	10	1222	SHIFT A
N/C		11	1076	SENSOR GND
N/C		12	462	FIXED SPARK
TPS SIGNAL	417	13	120	FUEL PUMP FEEDBACK
N/C		14	412	RIGHT O₂ SENSOR HI
MAP SIGNAL	432	15	413	RIGHT O₂ SENSOR LO
MAT SIGNAL	472	16	410	COOLANT TEMP

PCM (1C/D) BLACK

CIRCUIT DESCRIPTION	CIRCUIT NUMBER	PIN	CIRCUIT NUMBER	CIRCUIT DESCRIPTION
PCM GROUND	450	D1 / C1		N/C
C/C ON-OFF	397	D2 / C2	86	C/C ENABLE
C/C SET/COAST	84	D3 / C3	87	C/C RESUME
N/C		D4 / C4	420	VCC BRAKE
N/C		D5 / C5	633	CAM HI
PCM GROUND	450	D6 / C6		N/C
PCM GROUND	450	D7 / C7	424	BYPASS
EST REFERENCE PULSE HI	430	D8 / C8	423	EST
EST REFERENCE/CAM LO	453	D9 / C9	816	POWER STEERING SW.
N/C		D10 / C10	772	TRANS INPUT B
N/C		D11 / C11	841	INJECTOR 1
HEATED WINDSHIELD	637	D12 / C12	878	INJECTOR 8
INJECTOR 2	842	D13 / C13	846	INJECTOR 6
INJECTOR 7	877	D14 / C14	474	5V REFERENCE
INJECTOR 5	845	D15 / C15	844	INJECTOR 4
INJECTOR 3	843	D16 / C16	480	BATTERY

DASH TO PCM CONNECTOR

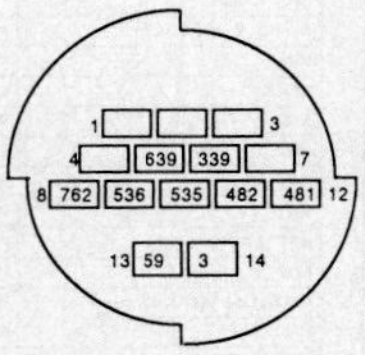

	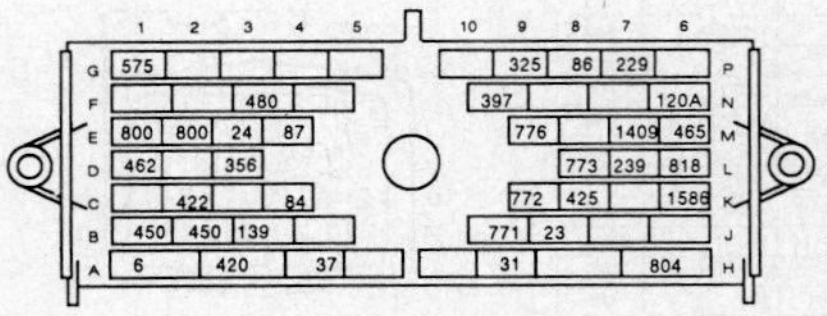 1	2	3			10	9	8	7	6	
G	575						325	86	229		P
F			480				397			120A	N
E	800	800	24	87			776		1409	465	M
D	462		356				773	239	818		L
C		422		84			772	425		1588	K
B	450	450	139				771	24			J
A	6		420		37			31		804	H

ENGINE TO FWD LP CONNECTOR

1	639	339	3
8	762	536	535	482	481	12
13	59	3	14

91H09297   91J09298

Courtesy of General Motors Corp.

Fig. 25: ECM Terminal Identification (4.9L VIN B Eldorado & Seville)

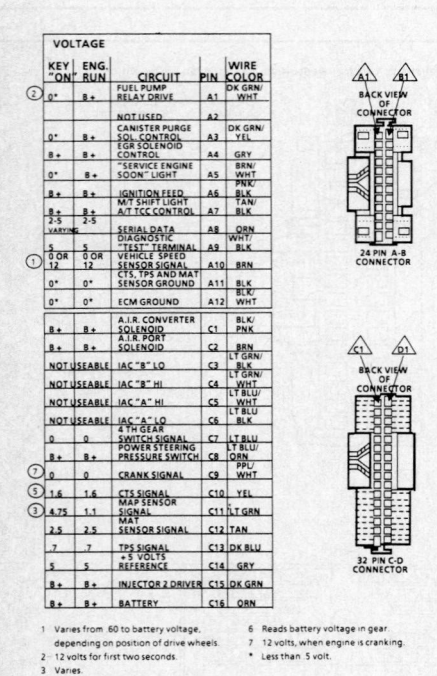

A-B CONNECTOR

VOLTAGE KEY "ON"	VOLTAGE ENG. RUN	CIRCUIT	PIN	WIRE COLOR
0*	B+	FUEL PUMP RELAY DRIVE	A1	DK GRN/WHT
		NOT USED	A2	
0*	B+	CANISTER PURGE SOL. CONTROL	A3	DK GRN/YEL
B+	B+	EGR SOLENOID CONTROL	A4	GRY
0*	B+	"SERVICE ENGINE SOON" LIGHT	A5	BRN/WHT
B+	B+	IGNITION FEED	A6	PNK/BLK
B+	B+	M/T SHIFT LIGHT A/T TCC CONTROL	A7	TAN/BLK
2-5 VARYING	2-5	SERIAL DATA	A8	ORN
5 0 OR 12	5 0 OR 12	DIAGNOSTIC "TEST" TERMINAL VEHICLE SPEED SENSOR SIGNAL	A9	WHT/BLK
0*	0*	CTS, TPS AND MAT SENSOR GROUND	A11	BLK
0*	0*	ECM GROUND	A12	BLK/WHT
B+	B+	A.I.R. CONVERTER SOLENOID	C1	BLK/PNK
B+	B+	A.I.R. PORT SOLENOID	C2	BRN
NOT USEABLE		IAC "B" LO	C3	BLK/LT GRN
NOT USEABLE		IAC "B" HI	C4	LT GRN/BLK
NOT USEABLE		IAC "A" HI	C5	LT BLU/WHT
NOT USEABLE		IAC "A" LO	C6	WHT/LT BLU
0	0	4TH GEAR SWITCH SIGNAL	C7	LT BLU
B+	B+	POWER STEERING PRESSURE SWITCH	C8	LT BLU/ORN
0	0	CRANK SIGNAL	C9	PPL/WHT
1.6	1.6	CTS SIGNAL	C10	YEL
4.75	1.1	MAP SENSOR SIGNAL	C11	LT GRN
2.5	2.5	MAT SENSOR SIGNAL	C12	TAN
.7	.7	TPS SIGNAL	C13	DK BLU
5	5	+5 VOLTS REFERENCE	C14	GRY
B+	B+	INJECTOR 2 DRIVER	C15	DK GRN
B+	B+	BATTERY	C16	ORN

C-D CONNECTOR

WIRE COLOR	PIN	CIRCUIT	VOLTAGE KEY "ON"	VOLTAGE ENG. RUN
ORN	B1	BATTERY	B+	B+
GRY	B2	FUEL PUMP SIGNAL	0	B+
BLK/RED	B3	DIST. GROUND REFERENCE LOW	0*	0*
	B4	NOT USED		
PPL/WHT	B5	REFERENCE	0	1.3
DK BLU	B6	VATS	5	5
LT	B7	SPARK RETARD SIGNAL (ESC)	9.2	9.3
BLU	B8	A/C REQUEST SIGNAL "OFF" "ON"	0 / B+	0 / B+
	B9	NOT USED		
ORN/BLK	B10	PARK/NEUTRAL SWITCH SIGNAL	0	0
	B11	NOT USED		
	B12	NOT USED		
BLK/WHT	D1	ECM GROUND	0	0
PPL	D2	MAP SENSOR GROUND	0	0
	D3	NOT USED		
WHT	D4	EST	0	1.3
TAN/BLK	D5	BYPASS	0	4.75
TAN	D6	O₂ SENSOR GROUND	0	0
PPL	D7	O₂ SENSOR SIGNAL	.3 - .5	.1 - .9
	D8	NOT USED		
	D9	NOT USED		
	D10	NOT USED		
	D11	NOT USED		
	D12	NOT USED		
	D13	NOT USED		
DK GRN	D14	INJECTOR 2 DRIVER	B+	B+
DK BLU	D15	INJECTOR 1 DRIVER	B+	B+
DK BLU	D16	INJECTOR 1 DRIVER	B+	B+

NOTE:
This ECM voltage chart can be used with a digital voltmeter to help save time in diagnosis. Voltages on the vehicle being tested may vary slightly from these due to battery voltage or alternator charging level.

The following conditions must be met before testing:
- Engine at operating temperature.
- Engine in closed loop operation.
- Engine idling ("Engine Run" column).
- ALDL "test" terminal NOT grounded.
- Scan tester NOT installed.

1 Varies from .60 to battery voltage, depending on position of drive wheels.
2 12 volts for first two seconds.
3 Varies.
4 12 volts when fuel pump is running.
5 Varies with temperature.
6 Reads battery voltage in gear.
7 12 volts, when engine is cranking.
* Less than 5 volt.

91B09299

Courtesy of General Motors Corp.

Fig. 26: ECM Terminal Identification & Pin Voltages (5.0L VIN E Camaro & Firebird)

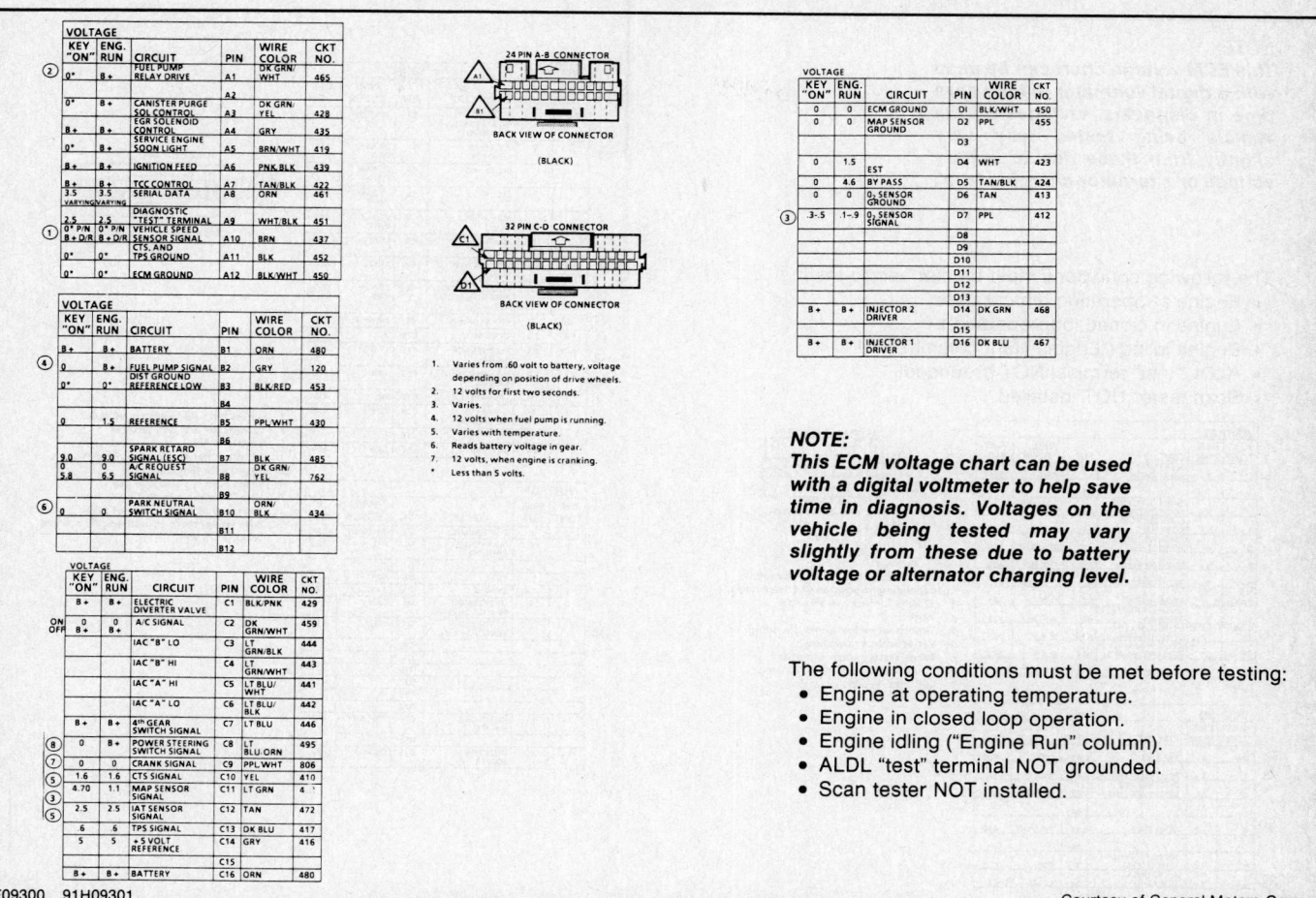

VOLTAGE

KEY "ON"	ENG. RUN	CIRCUIT	PIN	WIRE COLOR	CKT NO.
② 0*	B+	FUEL PUMP RELAY DRIVE	A1	DK GRN/WHT	465
			A2		
0*	B+	CANISTER PURGE SOL CONTROL	A3	DK GRN/YEL	428
B+	B+	EGR SOLENOID CONTROL	A4	GRY	435
0*	B+	SERVICE ENGINE SOON LIGHT	A5	BRN/WHT	419
B+	B+	IGNITION FEED	A6	PNK/BLK	439
B+	B+	TCC CONTROL	A7	TAN/BLK	422
3.5 VARYING	3.5 VARYING	SERIAL DATA	A8	ORN	461
① 2.5	2.5	DIAGNOSTIC "TEST" TERMINAL	A9	WHT/BLK	451
0* P/N B+ D/R	0* P/N B+ D/R	VEHICLE SPEED SENSOR SIGNAL	A10	BRN	437
0*	0*	CTS, AND TPS GROUND	A11	BLK	452
0*	0*	ECM GROUND	A12	BLK/WHT	450

VOLTAGE

KEY "ON"	ENG. RUN	CIRCUIT	PIN	WIRE COLOR	CKT NO.
B+	B+	BATTERY	B1	ORN	480
④ 0	B+	FUEL PUMP SIGNAL	B2	GRY	120
0*	0*	DIST GROUND REFERENCE LOW	B3	BLK/RED	453
			B4		
0	1.5	REFERENCE	B5	PPL/WHT	430
			B6		
9.0	9.0	SPARK RETARD SIGNAL (ESC)	B7	BLK	485
0	0	A/C REQUEST SIGNAL	B8	DK GRN/YEL	762
5.8	6.5				
			B9		
⑥ 0	0	PARK NEUTRAL SWITCH SIGNAL	B10	ORN/BLK	434
			B11		
			B12		

VOLTAGE

KEY "ON"	ENG. RUN	CIRCUIT	PIN	WIRE COLOR	CKT NO.
B+	B+	ELECTRIC DIVERTER VALVE	C1	BLK/PNK	429
ON 0 OFF B+	0 B+	A/C SIGNAL	C2	DK GRN/WHT	459
		IAC "B" LO	C3	LT GRN/BLK	444
		IAC "B" HI	C4	LT GRN/WHT	443
		IAC "A" HI	C5	LT BLU/WHT	441
		IAC "A" LO	C6	LT BLU/BLK	442
B+	B+	4TH GEAR SWITCH SIGNAL	C7	LT BLU	446
⑧ 0	B+	POWER STEERING SWITCH SIGNAL	C8	LT BLU/ORN	495
⑦ 0	0	CRANK SIGNAL	C9	PPL/WHT	806
⑤ 1.6	1.6	CTS SIGNAL	C10	YEL	410
③ 4.70	1.1	MAP SENSOR SIGNAL	C11	LT GRN	4
⑤ 2.5	2.5	IAT SENSOR SIGNAL	C12	TAN	472
.6	6	TPS SIGNAL	C13	DK BLU	417
5	5	+5 VOLT REFERENCE	C14	GRY	416
			C15		
B+	B+	BATTERY	C16	ORN	480

VOLTAGE

KEY "ON"	ENG. RUN	CIRCUIT	PIN	WIRE COLOR	CKT NO.
0	0	ECM GROUND	D1	BLK/WHT	450
0	0	MAP SENSOR GROUND	D2	PPL	455
			D3		
0	1.5	EST	D4	WHT	423
0	4.6	BY PASS	D5	TAN/BLK	424
0	0	O₂ SENSOR GROUND	D6	TAN	413
③ 3-5	.1-.9	O₂ SENSOR SIGNAL	D7	PPL	412
			D8		
			D9		
			D10		
			D11		
			D12		
			D13		
B+	B+	INJECTOR 2 DRIVER	D14	DK GRN	468
			D15		
B+	B+	INJECTOR 1 DRIVER	D16	DK BLU	467

24 PIN A-B CONNECTOR

BACK VIEW OF CONNECTOR

(BLACK)

32 PIN C-D CONNECTOR

BACK VIEW OF CONNECTOR

(BLACK)

1. Varies from .60 volt to battery, voltage depending on position of drive wheels.
2. 12 volts for first two seconds.
3. Varies.
4. 12 volts when fuel pump is running.
5. Varies with temperature.
6. Reads battery voltage in gear.
7. 12 volts, when engine is cranking.
* Less than 5 volts.

NOTE:
This ECM voltage chart can be used with a digital voltmeter to help save time in diagnosis. Voltages on the vehicle being tested may vary slightly from these due to battery voltage or alternator charging level.

The following conditions must be met before testing:
- Engine at operating temperature.
- Engine in closed loop operation.
- Engine idling ("Engine Run" column).
- ALDL "test" terminal NOT grounded.
- Scan tester NOT installed.

91F09300 91H09301

Courtesy of General Motors Corp.

Fig. 27: *ECM Terminal Identification & Pin Voltages (5.0L VIN E & 5.7L VIN 7 Brougham)*

1991 ENGINE PERFORMANCE
Pin Voltage Charts (Cont.)

NOTE:
This ECM voltage chart can be used with a digital voltmeter to help save time in diagnosis. Voltages on the vehicle being tested may vary slightly from these due to battery voltage or alternator charging level.

The following conditions must be met before testing:
- Engine at operating temperature.
- Engine in closed loop operation.
- Engine idling ("Engine Run" column).
- ALDL "test" terminal NOT grounded.
- Scan tester NOT installed.

	VOLTAGE KEY "ON"	ENG. RUN	CIRCUIT	PIN	WIRE COLOR	CKT NO.
(2)	0*	B+	FUEL PUMP RELAY DRIVE	A1	DK GRN/WHT	465
				A2		
	0*	B+	CANISTER PURGE SOL. CONTROL	A3	DK GRN/YEL	428
	B+	B+	EGR SOLENOID CONTROL	A4	GRY	435
	0*	B+	"SERVICE ENGINE SOON" LIGHT	A5	BRN/WHT	419
	B+	B+	IGNITION FEED	A6	PNK/BLK	439
	B+	B+	TCC CONTROL	A7	TAN/BLK	422
	3-5 VARYING	3-5	SERIAL DATA	A8	ORN	461
	5	5	DIAGNOSTIC "TEST" TERMINAL	A9	WHT/BLK	451
(1)	0 OR 12	0 OR 12	VEHICLE SPEED SENSOR SIGNAL	A10	BRN	437
	0*	0*	CTS, TPS AND IAT SENSOR GROUND	A11	BLK	452
	0*	0*	ECM GROUND	A12	BLK/WHT	450

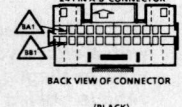

24 PIN A-B CONNECTOR

BACK VIEW OF CONNECTOR

(BLACK)

1 Varies from .60 to battery voltage, depending on position of drive wheels.
2 12 volts for first two seconds.
3 Varies.
4 12 volts when fuel pump is running.
5 Varies with temperature.
6 Reads battery voltage in gear.
7 12 volts, when engine is cranking.
* Less than 5 volts.

	VOLTAGE KEY "ON"	ENG. RUN	CIRCUIT	PIN	WIRE COLOR	CKT NO.
	B+	B+	BATTERY	B1	ORN	480
(4)	0	B+	FUEL PUMP SIGNAL	B2	GRY	120
	0*	0*	DIST GROUND REFERENCE LOW	B3	BLK/RED	453
				B4		
	0	1.5	REFERENCE	B5	PPL/WHT	430
				B6		
	9.0	9.0	SPARK RETARD SIGNAL (ESC)	B7	BLK	485
"OFF" "ON"	0 B+	0 B+	A/C REQUEST SIGNAL	B8	LT BLU	67
				B9		
(6)	0	0	PARK/NEUTRAL (P/N) SWITCH SIGNAL	B10	ORN/BLK	434
				B11		
				B12		

	VOLTAGE KEY "ON"	ENG. RUN	CIRCUIT	PIN	WIRE COLOR	CKT NO.
	B+	0	ELECTRIC DIVERTER VALVE SOLENOID	C1	BLK/PNK	429
(8)	0	0 B+	A/C RELAY CONTROL	C2	DK GRN/WHT	459
			IAC "B" LO	C3	LT GRN/BLK	444
			IAC "B" HI	C4	LT GRN/WHT	443
			IAC "A" HI	C5	LT BLU/WHT	441
			IAC "A" LO	C6	LT BLU/BLK	442
	B+	B+	4th GEAR SWITCH SIGNAL	C7	LT BLU	446
(9)	B+	0	POWER STEERING PRESSURE SWITCH (IF USED)	C8	LT BLU/ORN	495
(7)	0	0	CRANK SIGNAL	C9	PPL/WHT	806
(5)	1.6	1.6	CTS SIGNAL	C10	YEL	410
(3)	4.75	1.1	MAP SENSOR SIGNAL	C11	LT GRN	432
(5)	2.5	2.5	IAT SENSOR SIGNAL	C12	TAN	472
	.5	.5	TPS SIGNAL	C13	DK BLU	417
	5	5	+5 VOLTS REFERENCE	C14	GRY	416
				C15		
	B+	B+	BATTERY	C16	ORN	480

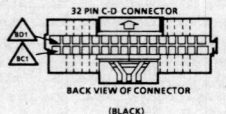

32 PIN C-D CONNECTOR

BACK VIEW OF CONNECTOR

(BLACK)

	VOLTAGE KEY "ON"	ENG. RUN	CIRCUIT	PIN	WIRE COLOR	CKT NO.
	0	0	ECM GROUND	D1	TAN/WHT	551
	0	0	MAP SENSOR GROUND	D2	PPL	455
				D3		
	0	1.1	EST	D4	WHT	423
	0	4.5	BYPASS	D5	TAN/BLK	424
	0	0	OXYGEN (O_2) SENSOR GROUND	D6	TAN	413
(3)	.3 - .5	.1 - .9	OXYGEN (O_2) SENSOR SIGNAL	D7	PPL	412
				D8		
				D9		
				D10		
				D11		
				D12		
				D13		
	B+	B+	INJECTOR 2 DRIVER	D14	DK GRN	468
				D15		
	B+	B+	INJECTOR 1 DRIVER	D16	DK BLU	467

1 Varies from .60 to battery voltage.
2 12 volts for first two seconds.
3 Varies.
4 12 volts when fuel pump is running.
5 Varies with temperature.
6 Reads battery voltage in gear.
7 12 volts, when engine is cranking.
8. With engine running and A/C "ON."
9. With power steering load, engine running.
* Less than .5 volt.

91B09303 91D09304

Courtesy of General Motors Corp.

Fig. 28: ECM Terminal Identification & Pin Voltages (5.0L VIN E Caprice, Custom Cruiser & Roadmaster; 5.7L VIN 7 Caprice)

| VOLTAGE | | | | | |
KEY "ON"	ENG. RUN	CIRCUIT	PIN	WIRE COLOR	CKT #
			BA1		
5	5	+5V REFERENCE (MAP)	BA4	GRY	474
5	5	+5V REFERENCE (TPS)	BA5	GRY	416
B+	B+	IGNITION FEED	BA6	PNK/BLK	439
② 4.8	4.8	SERIAL DATA	BA8	ORN	461
④ 0*	B+	FUEL PUMP RELAY DRIVE	BA11	DK GRN/WHT	465
0*	0*	ECM GROUND	BA12	BLK/WHT	450

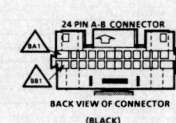

24 PIN A-B CONNECTOR

BACK VIEW OF CONNECTOR
(BLACK)

| VOLTAGE | | | | | |
KEY "ON"	ENG. RUN	CIRCUIT	PIN	WIRE COLOR	CKT #
B+	B+	BATTERY FEED	BB1	ORN	340
0*	0*	TPS & MAT SENSOR GROUND	BB5	BLK	452
0*	0*	CTS & MAP SENSOR GROUND	BB6	BLK	470
0*	①	VSS (LOW)	BB9	PPL	401
0*	①	VSS (HIGH)	BB10	YEL	400
B+	B+	VSS TO I/P 4000 P/MI	BB11	GRY	1019
			BB12		

| VOLTAGE | | | | | |
KEY "ON"	ENG. RUN	CIRCUIT	PIN	WIRE COLOR	CKT #
①		VEHICLE SPEED SIGNAL	BC1	RED	381
0*	5	BYPASS	BC7	TAN/BLK	424
0*	1.3	EST	BC8	WHT	423
B+/0*	B+/0*	WITH A/C "ON" A/C REQUEST	BC9	DK GRN	59
B+	B+	INJECTOR 1, 3, 5, 7	BC11	DK BLU	467
B+	B+	INJECTOR 2, 4, 6, 8	BC12	DK GRN	468
B+	B+	BATTERY FEED	BC16	ORN	340

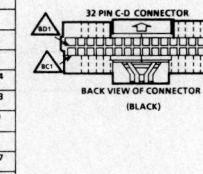

32 PIN C-D CONNECTOR

BACK VIEW OF CONNECTOR
(BLACK)

| VOLTAGE | | | | | |
KEY "ON"	ENG. RUN	CIRCUIT	PIN	WIRE COLOR	CKT #
0*	0*	ECM GROUND	BD1	BLK/WHT	450
0*	0*	INJECTOR GROUND	BD6	BLK/WHT	450
0*	0*	INJECTOR GROUND	BD7	BLK/WHT	450
0*	2.3	REFERENCE	BD8	PPL/WHT	430
0*	0*	REFERENCE LOW	BD9	BLK/RED	453
		FAN #2 REQUEST	BD12	GRY	731
0*	0*	4TH GEAR SWITCH	BD14	LT BLU	446
0*	0*	PARK/NEUTRAL (P/N) SWITCH SIG.	BD16	ORN/BLK	434

▽ Less than 1 volt.
* Less than .5 volt.
① Varies from .60 volt to Battery Voltage depending on position of drivewheels.
② Varies
③ Varies with temperature.
④ Battery Voltage for first two seconds.
⑤ Battery Voltage when fuel pump is running.
⑥ Reads battery voltage when in gear.

NOTE:
This ECM voltage chart can be used with a digital voltmeter to help save time in diagnosis. Voltages on the vehicle being tested may vary slightly from these due to battery voltage or alternator charging level.

The following conditions must be met before testing:
- Engine at operating temperature.
- Engine in closed loop operation.
- Engine idling ("Engine Run" column).
- ALDL "test" terminal NOT grounded.
- Scan tester NOT installed.

| VOLTAGE | | | | | |
KEY "ON"	ENG. RUN	CIRCUIT	PIN	WIRE COLOR	CKT #
			GE1		
NOT USEABLE		IAC "A" HIGH	GE3	LT BLU/WHT	441
NOT USEABLE		IAC "A" LOW	GE4	LT BLU/BLK	442
NOT USEABLE		IAC "B" HIGH	GE5	LT GRN/WHT	443
NOT USEABLE		IAC "B" LOW	GE6	LT GRN/BLK	444
0*	B+	"SERVICE ENGINE SOON LIGHT"	GE7	BRN/WHT	419
0*/B+	0*/B+	"ON" FAN RELAY "OFF" CONTROL	GE8	DK GRN/WHT	335
B+	1▽	EGR SOLENOID CONTROL	GE9	GRY	435
5	5	DIAGNOSTIC "TEST" TERMINAL	GE12	BLK/WHT	451
④	B+	FUEL PUMP SIGNAL PPSW	GE13	GRY	120
② .35 - .55	.1 - .9	OXYGEN (O₂) SENSOR SIGNAL	GE14	PPL	412
0*	0*	OXYGEN (O₂) SENSOR GROUND	GE15	TAN	413
③	③	CTS SIGNAL	GE16	YEL	410

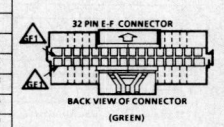

32 PIN E-F CONNECTOR

BACK VIEW OF CONNECTOR
(GREEN)

| VOLTAGE | | | | | |
KEY "ON"	ENG. RUN	CIRCUIT	PIN	WIRE COLOR	CKT #
0*/B+	0*/B+	M/T SHIFT LIGHT CONTROL	GF1	TAN/BLK	456
B+	B+	PORT (SWITCH) SOLENOID	GF2	BRN	436
B+	1▽	CONVERTER (DIVERT) SOLENOID	GF4	BLK/PNK	429
0*/B+	0*/B+	TCC CONTROL A/T	GF6	TAN/BLK	422
B+	B+	CANISTER PURGE SOL CONTROL	GF7	DK GRN/YEL	428
9.2	9.3	ESC KNOCK SENSOR SIGNAL	GF9	DK BLU	496
2.5	2.5	(PASS-KEY) VATS SIGNAL	GF10	DK BLU	229
.65	.65	TPS SIGNAL	GF13	DK BLU	417
4.57	③	MAP SIGNAL	GF15	LT GRN	432
③	③	MAT SIGNAL	GF16	TAN	472

▽ Less than 1 volt.
* Less than .5 volt.
① Varies from .60 volt to Battery Voltage depending on position of drivewheels.
② Varies
③ Varies with temperature.
④ Battery Voltage for first two seconds.
⑤ Battery Voltage when fuel pump is running.
⑥ Reads battery voltage when in gear.

Fig. 29: ECM Terminal Identification & Pin Voltages (5.0L VIN F & 5.7L VIN 8 Camaro & Firebird)

CONNECTOR A

CIRCUIT	PIN	WIRE COLOR
IAC COIL "A" HI	A1	LT BLU/WHT
IAC COIL "B" LO	A2	LT GRN/BLK
SECONDARY COOLING FAN	A3	DK BLU/WHT
EGR SOLENOID CONTROL	A4	GRY
	A5	
	A6	
IAC COIL "A" LO	A7	LT BLU/BLK
IAC COIL "B" HI	A8	LT GRN/WHT
PRIMARY COOLING FAN	A9	LT BLU/BLK
CANISTER PURGE CONTROL	A10	DK GRN/YEL
KNOCK SENSOR SIGNAL	A11	DK BLU
UPSHIFT LIGHT CONTROL	A12	TAN/BLK
A/C CLUTCH CONTROL	A13	DK GRN
	A14	
	A15	
OXYGEN SENSOR SIGNAL	A16	PPL
	A17	
A.I.R. EAS SOLENOID	A18	BRN
A.I.R. EAC SOLENOID	A19	BLK/PNK
FUEL PUMP SIGNAL	A20	RED
	A21	
OXYGEN SENSOR GROUND	A22	TAN

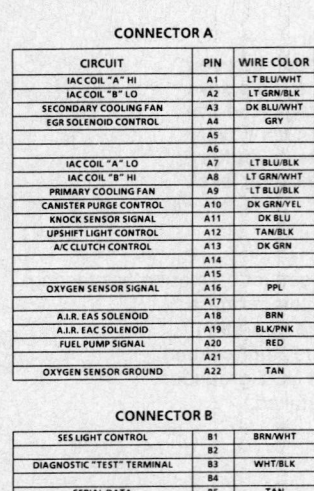
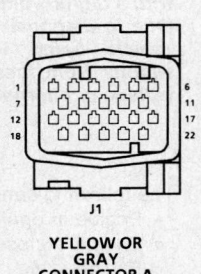

J1

YELLOW OR
GRAY
CONNECTOR A

CONNECTOR C

CIRCUIT	PIN	WIRE COLOR
BATTERY FEED	C1	ORN
VSS SIGNAL	C2	YEL
BYPASS	C3	TAN/BLK
IAT SENSOR SIGNAL	C4	TAN
MAP & IAT SENSOR GROUND	A5	BLK/PNK
ECM GROUND	A6	BLK/WHT
+ 5 VOLT REFERENCE	A7	GRY
VSS GROUND	A8	PPL
EST	A9	WHT
CTS, TPS & EOT SENSOR GROUND	A10	BLK
	A11	
+ 5 VOLT REFERENCE	A12	GRY
1-4 UPSHIFT LIGHT	A13	WHT
EOT SENSOR SIGNAL	A14	DK GRN
TPS SIGNAL	A15	DK BLU
CTS SIGNAL	A16	YEL
A/C STATUS	A17	DK BLU
	A18	
	A19	
	A20	
	A21	
MAP SIGNAL	A22	LT GRN

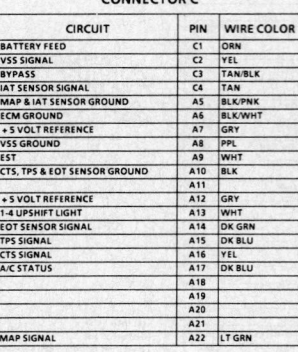
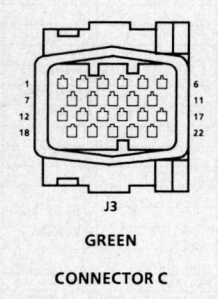

J3

GREEN

CONNECTOR C

CONNECTOR B

CIRCUIT	PIN	WIRE COLOR
SES LIGHT CONTROL	B1	BRN/WHT
	B2	
DIAGNOSTIC "TEST" TERMINAL	B3	WHT/BLK
	B4	
SERIAL DATA	B5	TAN
PASS-KEY® SIGNAL	B6	DK BLU
AT TCC OR MT 1-4 UPSHIFT	B7	TAN/BLK OR DK GRN
4K PPM-CCM, RADIO	B8	DK GRN/WHT
	B9	
IGNITION FEED	B10	PNK/BLK
SERIAL DATA	B11	TAN
	B12	
	B13	
	B14	
A/C REQUEST SIGNAL	B15	GRY/RED
	B16	
	B17	
	B18	
	B19	
	B20	
	B21	
	B22	

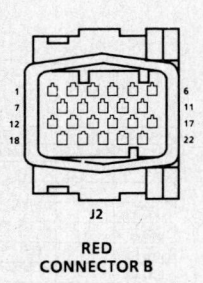

J2

RED
CONNECTOR B

CONNECTOR D

CIRCUIT	PIN	WIRE COLOR
	B1	
	B2	
INJECTORS 2, 4, 6, 8 DRIVER	B3	DK GRN
INJECTOR GROUND	B4	BLK/WHT
	B5	
	B6	
FUEL PUMP RELAY DRIVE	B7	DK GRN/WHT
	B8	
INJECTORS 1, 3, 5, 7 DRIVER	B9	DK BLU
INJECTOR GROUND	B10	BLK/WHT
PARK/NERTRAL SIGNAL	B11	ORN/BLK
ECM GROUND	B12	TAN/WHT
REFERENCE	B13	PPL/WHT
	B14	
	B15	
	B16	
BATTERY FEED	B17	ORN
	B18	
REFERENCE LOW	B19	BLK/RED
	B20	
A/C FAN REQUEST SIGNAL	B21	DK GRN/WHT
4TH GEAR SWITCH SIGNAL	B22	LT BLU

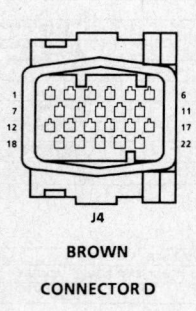

J4

BROWN

CONNECTOR D

91G09334   91J09335

Courtesy of General Motors Corp.

Fig. 30: ECM Terminal Identification (5.7L VIN 8 Corvette)

1991 ENGINE PERFORMANCE
Sensor Operating Range Charts

Beretta, Bonneville, Brougham, Camaro, Caprice, Cavalier, Century, Corsica, Corvette, Custom Cruiser, Cutlass Calais, Cutlass Ciera, Cutlass Cruiser, Cutlass Supreme, DeVille, Eighty-Eight Eldorado, Firebird, Fleetwood, Grand Am, Grand Prix, LeSabre, Lumina, Ninety-Eight, Park Avenue, Reatta, Regal, Riviera, Roadmaster, Seville, Skylark, Sunbird, Toronado, Touring Sedan, Trofeo, 6000

INTRODUCTION

Sensor operating range information can help determine if a sensor is out of calibration. An out-of-calibration sensor may not set a trouble code, but it will cause driveability problems.

NOTE: Unless stated otherwise in test procedure, perform all voltage tests with a Digital Volt-Ohmmeter (DVOM) with a minimum 10-megohm input impedance.

COOLANT TEMPERATURE RESISTANCE VALUES [1]

Temperature °F (°C)	Ohms
210 (100)	185
160 (70)	450
100 (38)	1800
70 (20)	3400
20 (-7)	13,500
0 (-18)	25,000
-40 (-40)	100,700

[1] – Measure resistance across sensor terminals.

MAP SENSOR VOLTAGE RANGE [1]

Altitude Feet	Volts
Below 1000	3.8-5.5
1000-2000	3.6-5.3
2000-3000	3.5-5.1
3000-4000	3.3-5.0
4000-5000	3.2-4.8
5000-6000	3.0-4.6
6000-7000	2.9-4.5
7000-8000	2.8-4.3
8000-9000	2.6-4.2
9000-10,000	2.5-4.0

[1] – Measured at sensor, or as seen on Scan tester.

MANIFOLD AIR TEMPERATURE SENSOR RESISTANCE VALUES [1]

Temperature °F (°C)	Ohms
210 (100)	185
160 (70)	450
100 (38)	1800
70 (20)	3400
40 (4)	7500
20 (-7)	13,500
0 (-18)	25,000
-40 (-40)	100,700

[1] – Measure resistance across sensor terminals.

OIL TEMPERATURE SENSOR RESISTANCE TEST (CORVETTE) [1]

Temperature °F (°C)	Ohms
210 (100)	185
160 (70)	450
100 (38)	1800
70 (20)	3400
40 (4)	7500
20 (-7)	13,500
0 (-18)	25,000
-40 (-40)	100,700

[1] – Measure resistance across sensor terminals.

OXYGEN SENSOR VOLTAGE TEST [1]

Condition	Volts
Lean	.1
Rich	.9

[1] – Measure voltage between O₂ sensor ground and signal terminals at ECM.

PRESSURE SENSOR VOLTAGE RANGE [1]

Altitude Feet	Volts
Below 1000	3.8-5.5
1000-2000	3.6-5.3
2000-3000	3.5-5.1
3000-4000	3.3-5.0
4000-5000	3.2-4.8
5000-6000	3.0-4.6
6000-7000	2.9-4.5
7000-8000	2.8-4.3
8000-9000	2.6-4.2
9000-10,000	2.5-4.0

[1] – Measured at sensor.

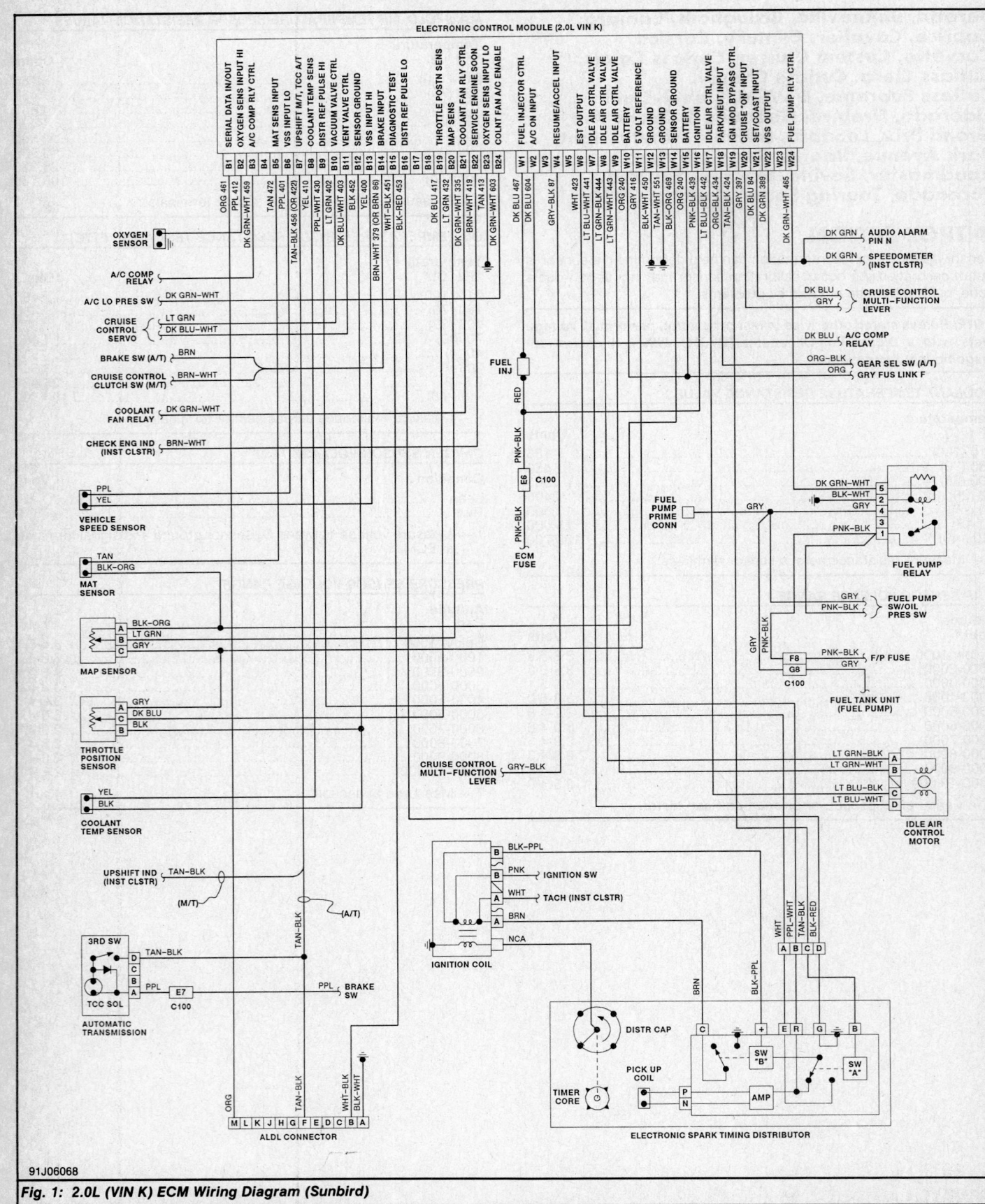

Fig. 1: 2.0L (VIN K) ECM Wiring Diagram (Sunbird)

91J06068

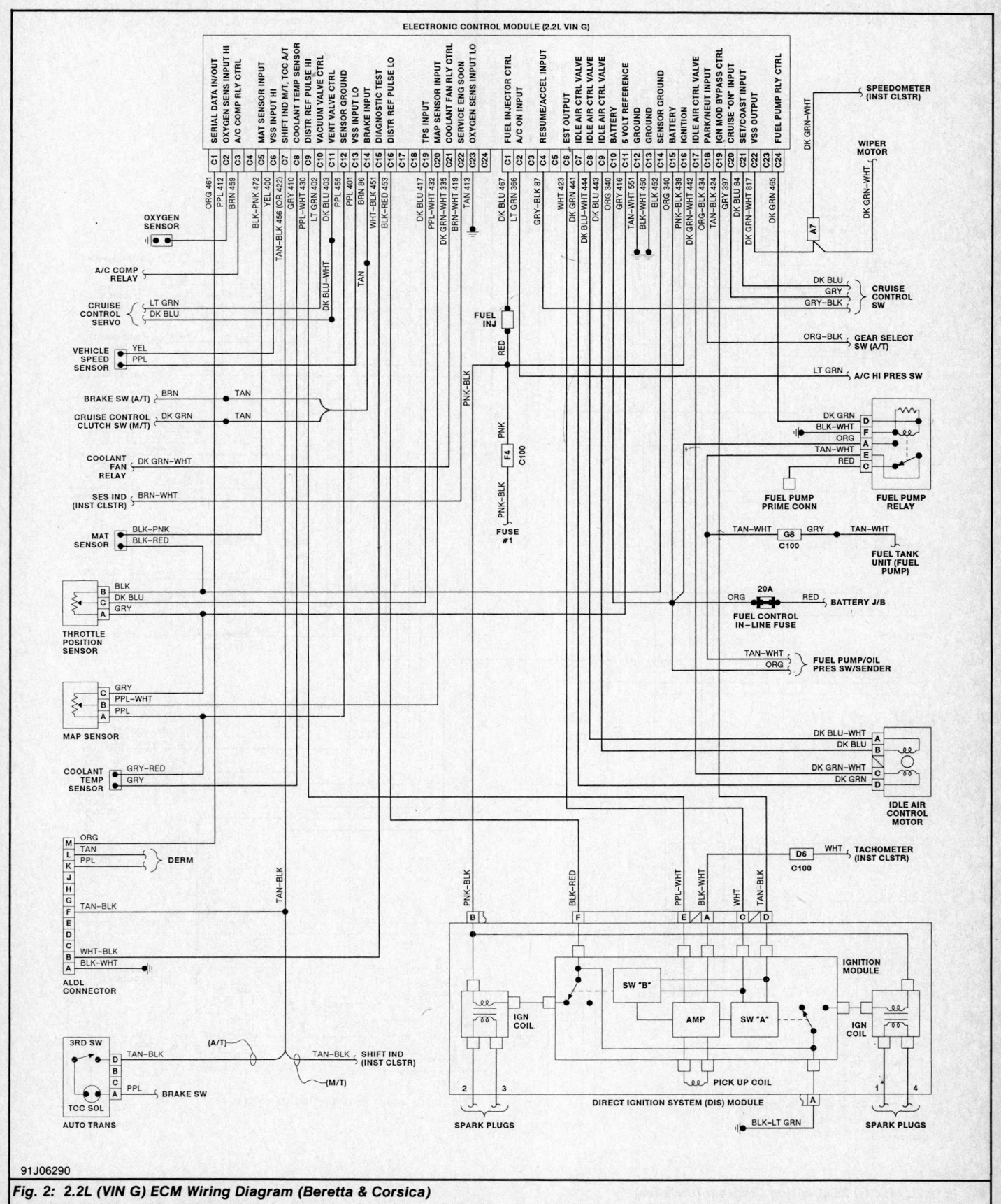

Fig. 2: 2.2L (VIN G) ECM Wiring Diagram (Beretta & Corsica)

91J06290

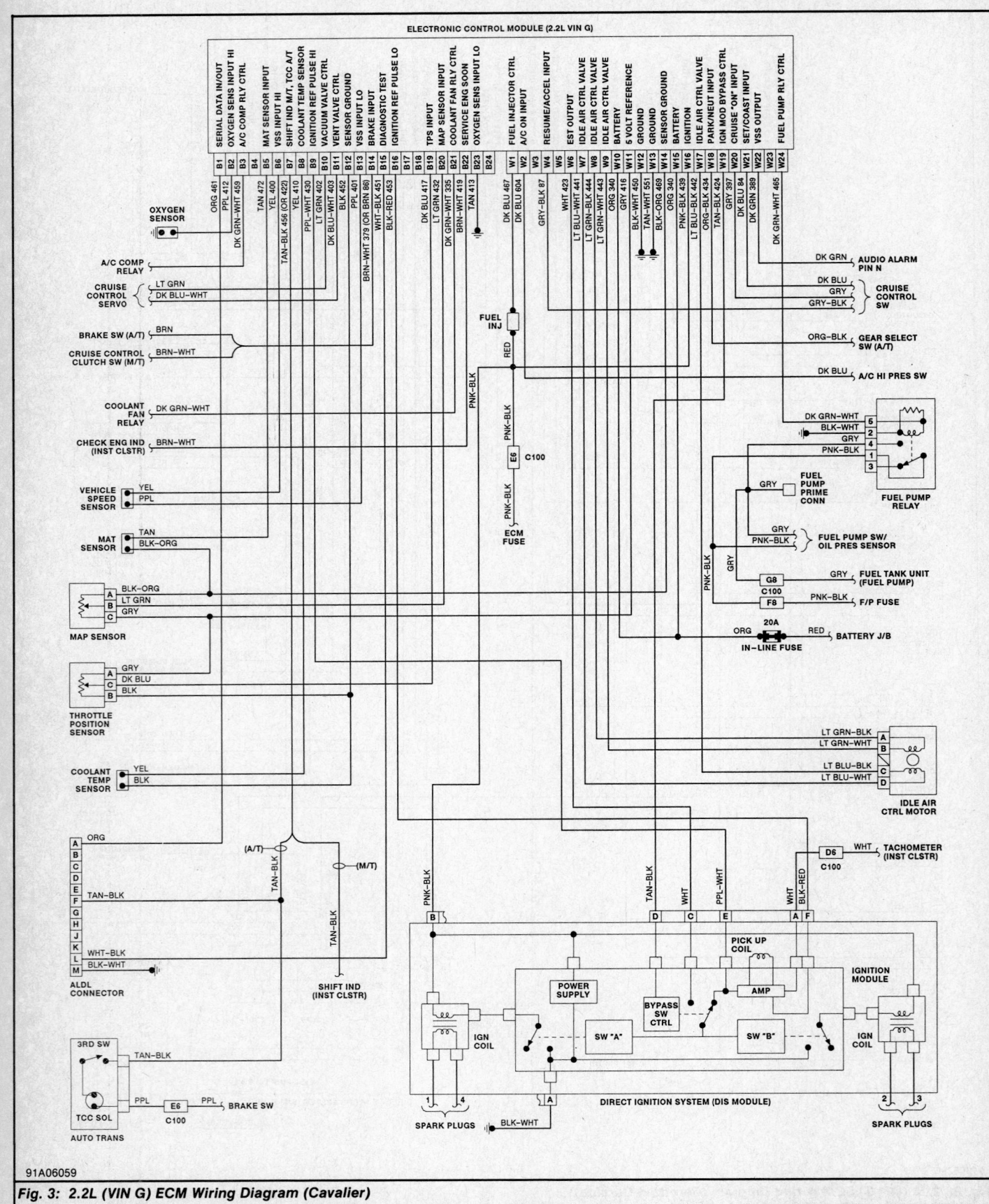

Fig. 3: 2.2L (VIN G) ECM Wiring Diagram (Cavalier)

91A06059

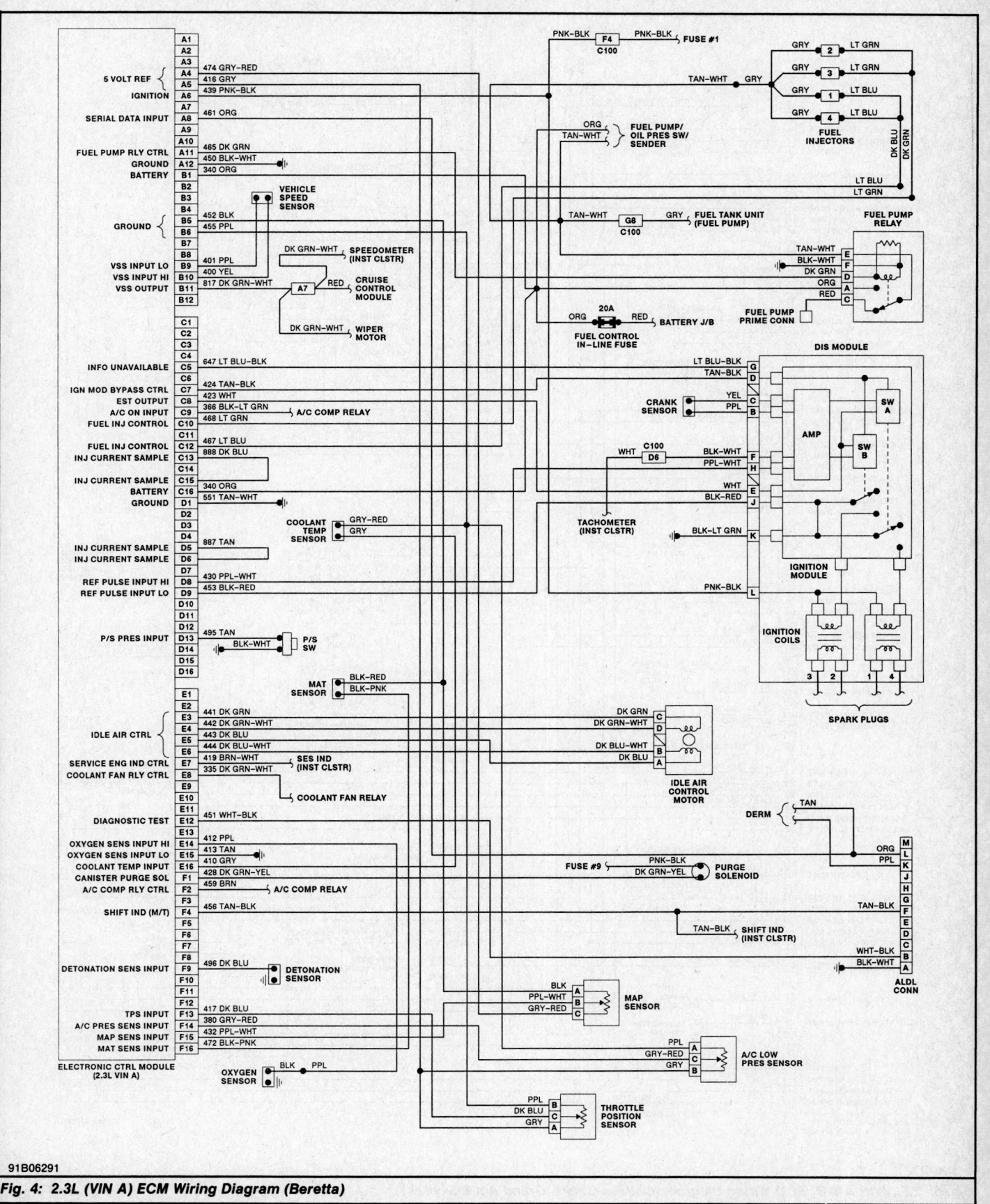

Fig. 4: 2.3L (VIN A) ECM Wiring Diagram (Beretta)

91B06291

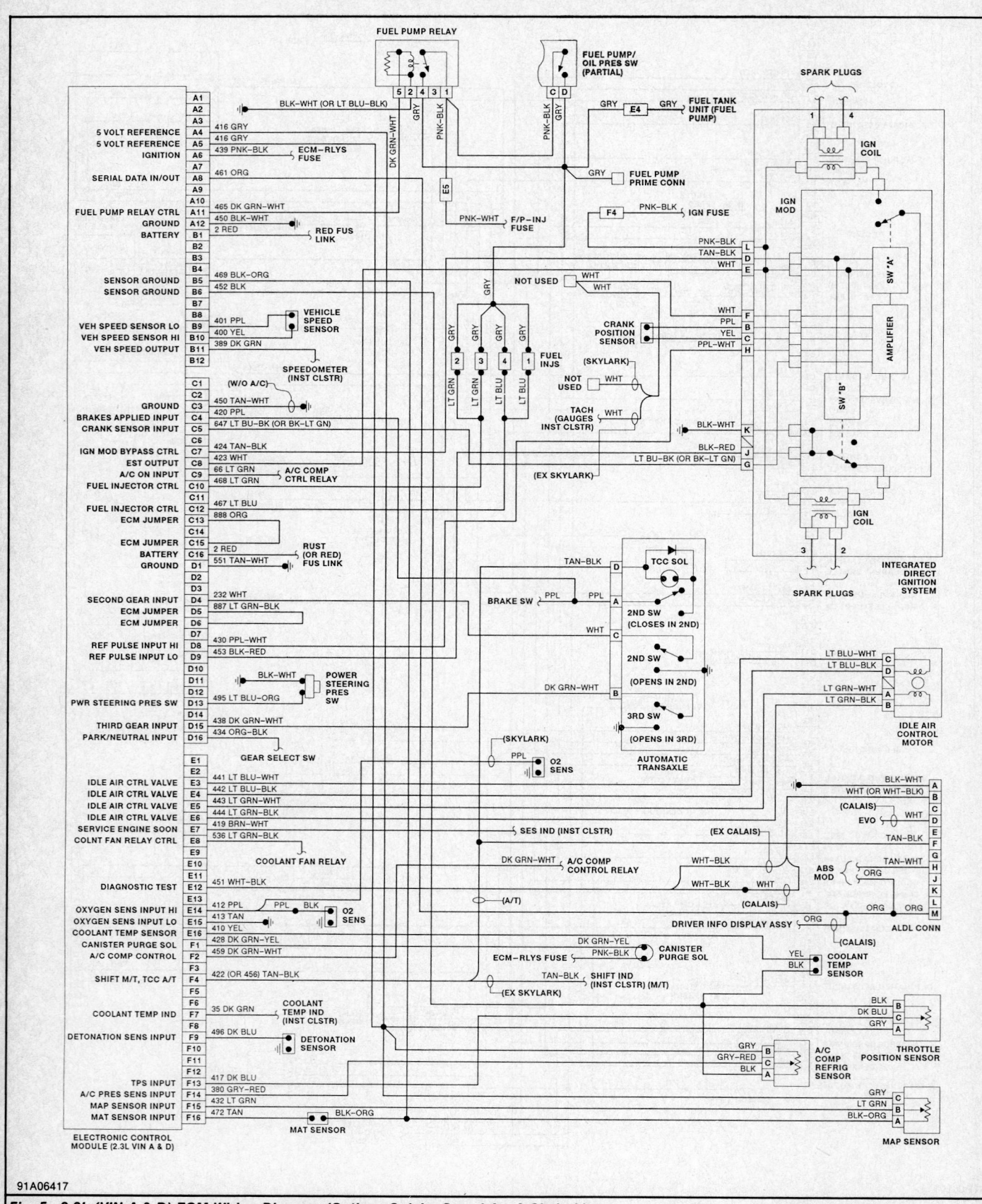

Fig. 5: *2.3L (VIN A & D) ECM Wiring Diagram (Cutlass Calais, Grand Am & Skylark)*

91A06417

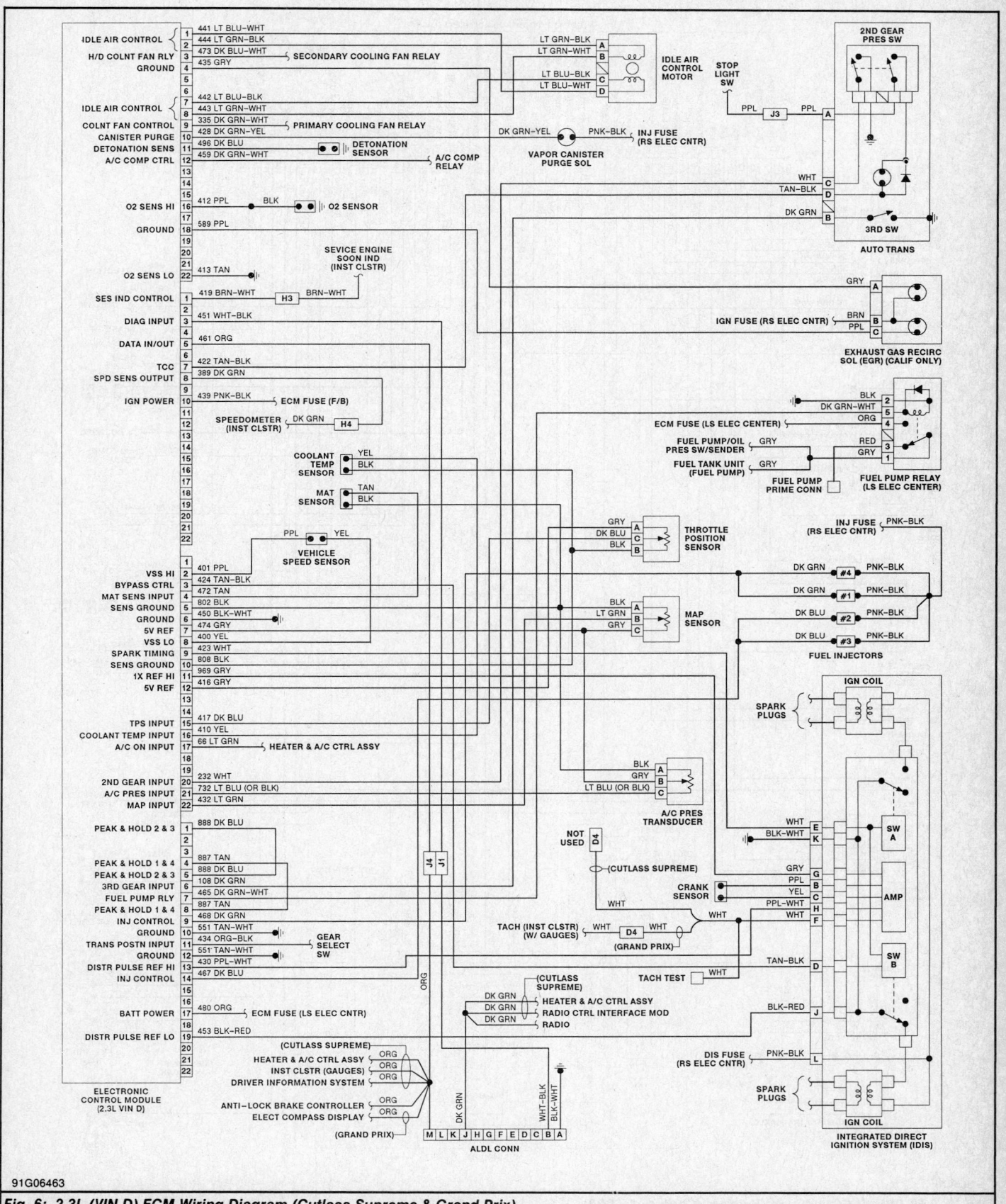

Fig. 6: 2.3L (VIN D) ECM Wiring Diagram (Cutlass Supreme & Grand Prix)

91G06463

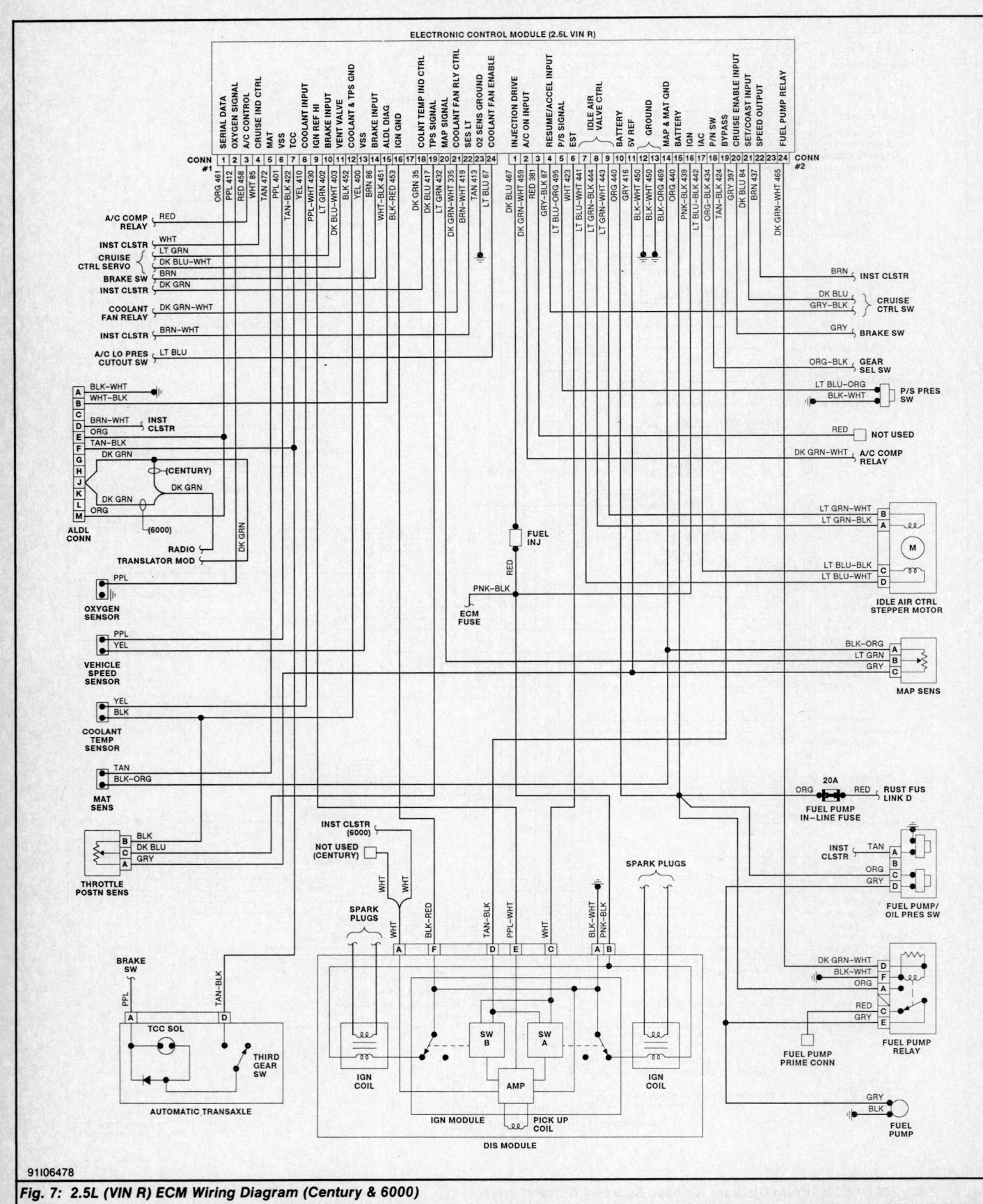

Fig. 7: 2.5L (VIN R) ECM Wiring Diagram (Century & 6000)

91I06478

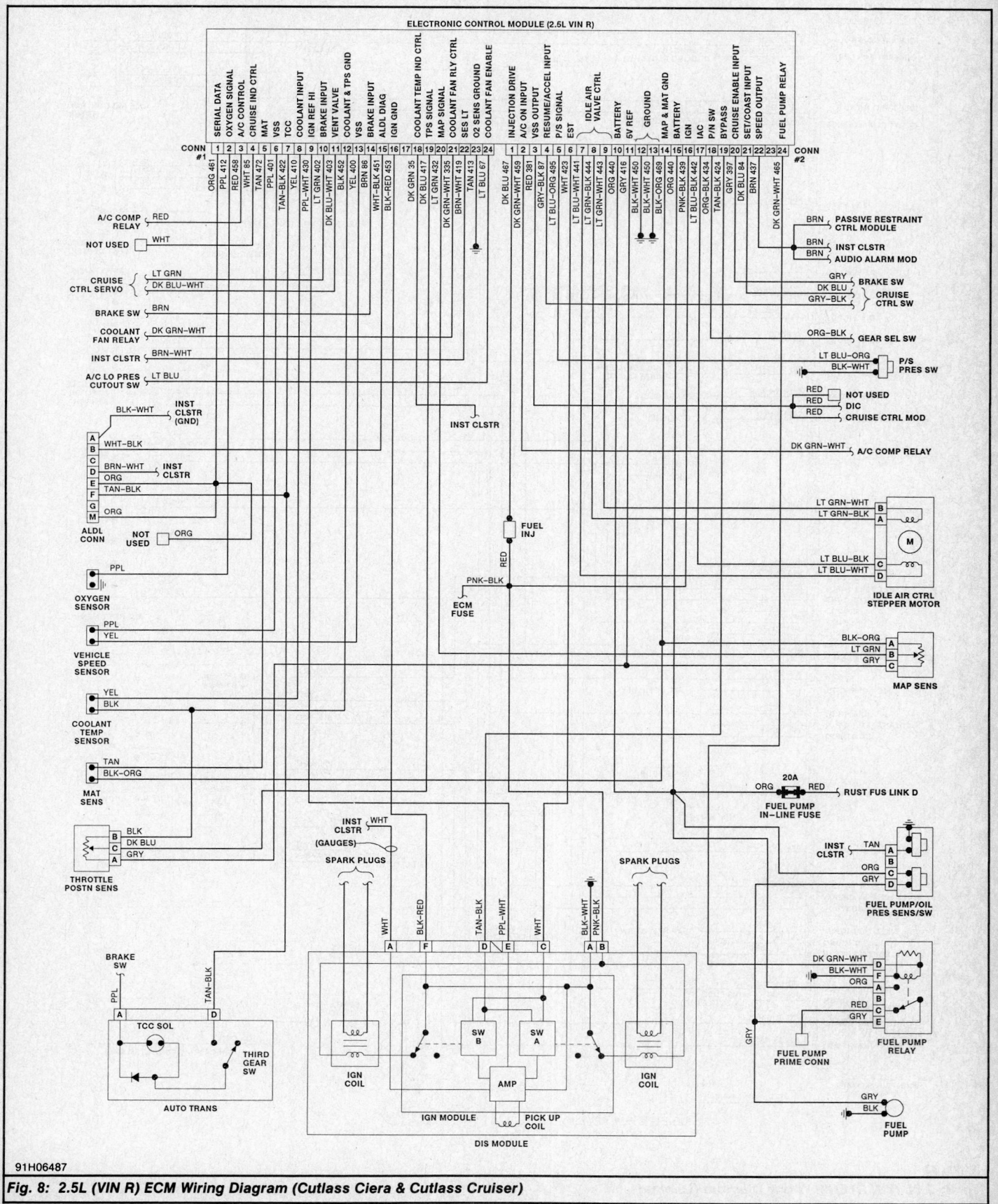

Fig. 8: 2.5L (VIN R) ECM Wiring Diagram (Cutlass Ciera & Cutlass Cruiser)

91H06487

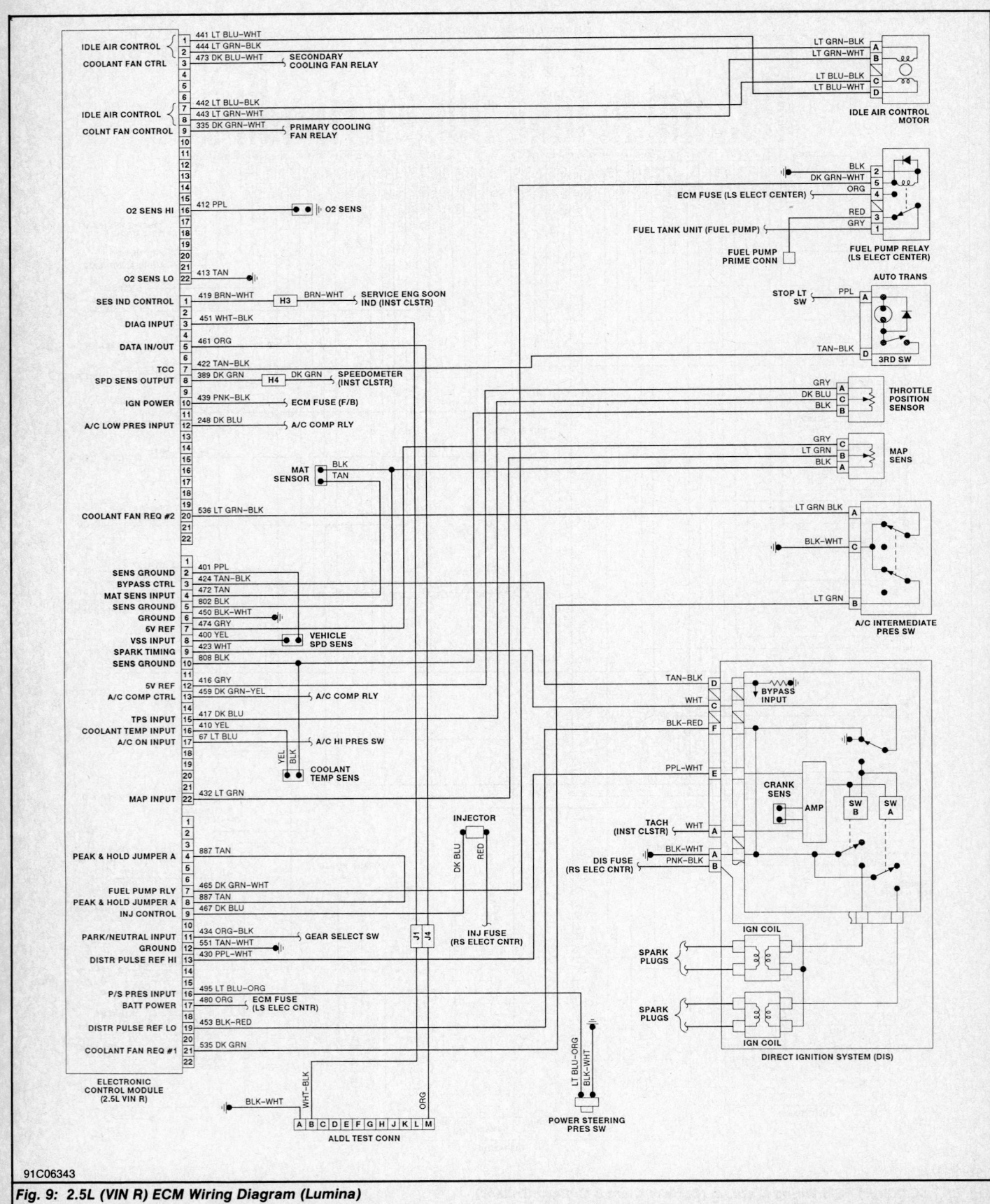

Fig. 9: *2.5L (VIN R) ECM Wiring Diagram (Lumina)*

91C06343

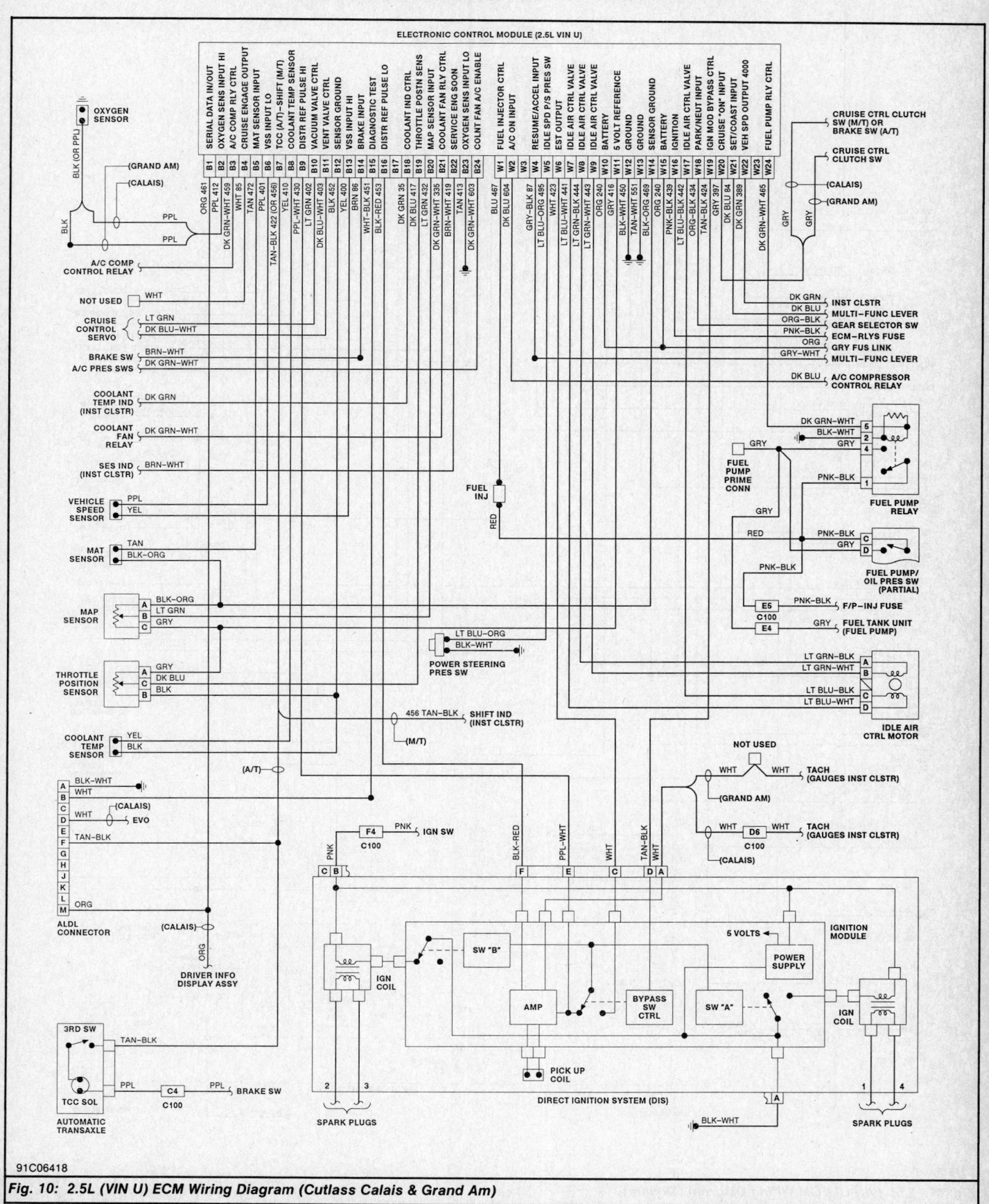

Fig. 10: *2.5L (VIN U) ECM Wiring Diagram (Cutlass Calais & Grand Am)*

91C06418

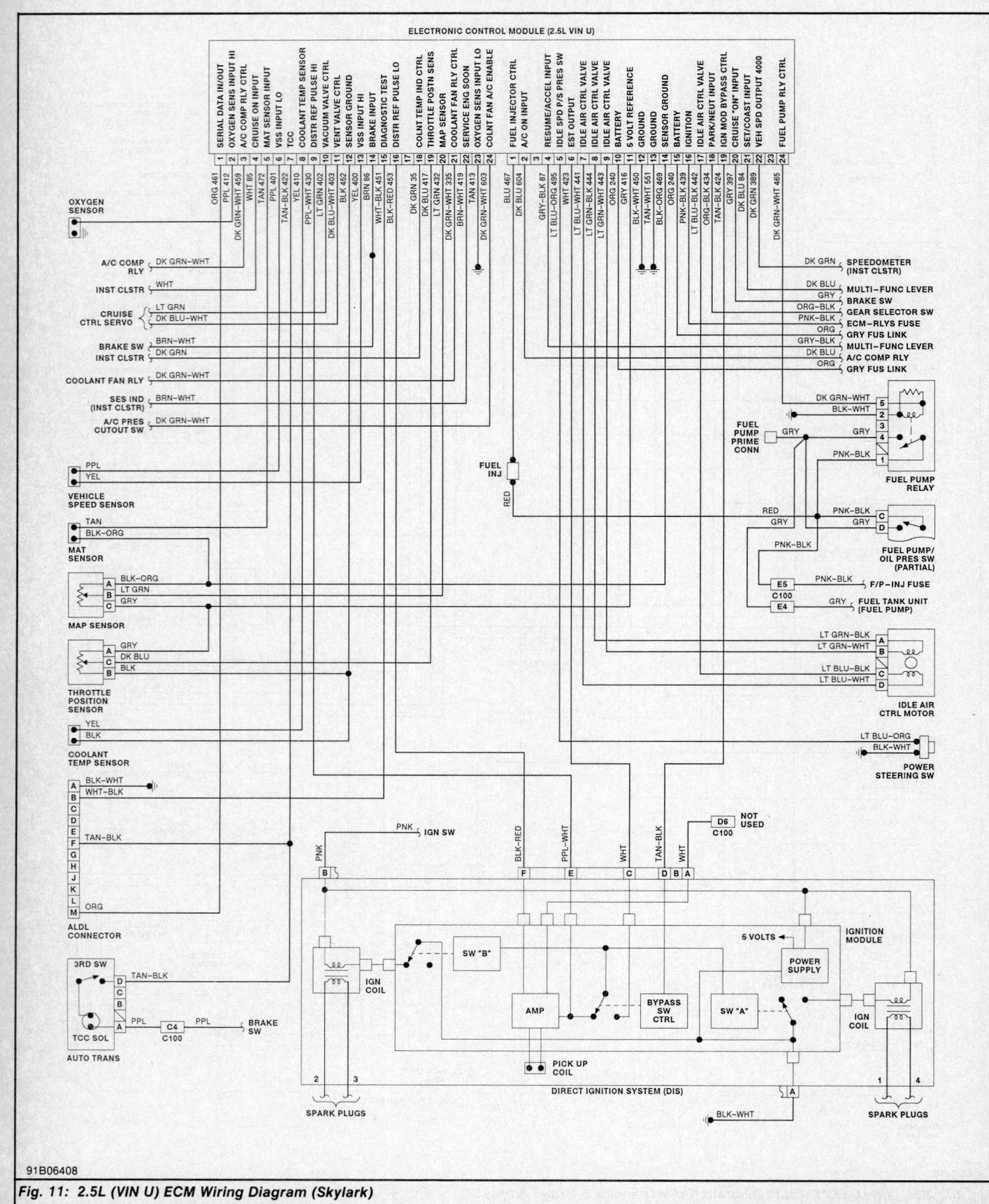

91B06408

Fig. 11: 2.5L (VIN U) ECM Wiring Diagram (Skylark)

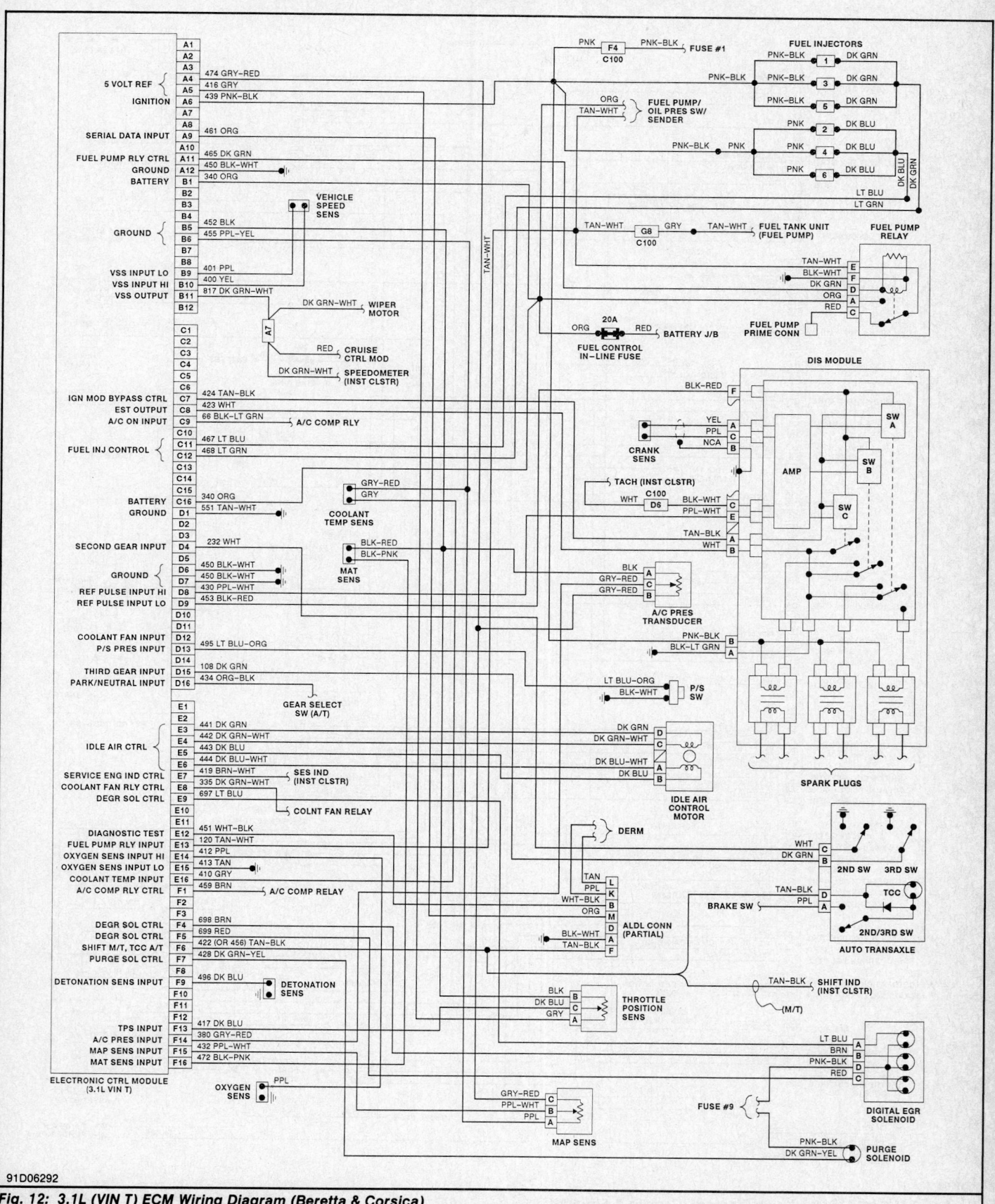

Fig. 12: 3.1L (VIN T) ECM Wiring Diagram (Beretta & Corsica)

91D06292

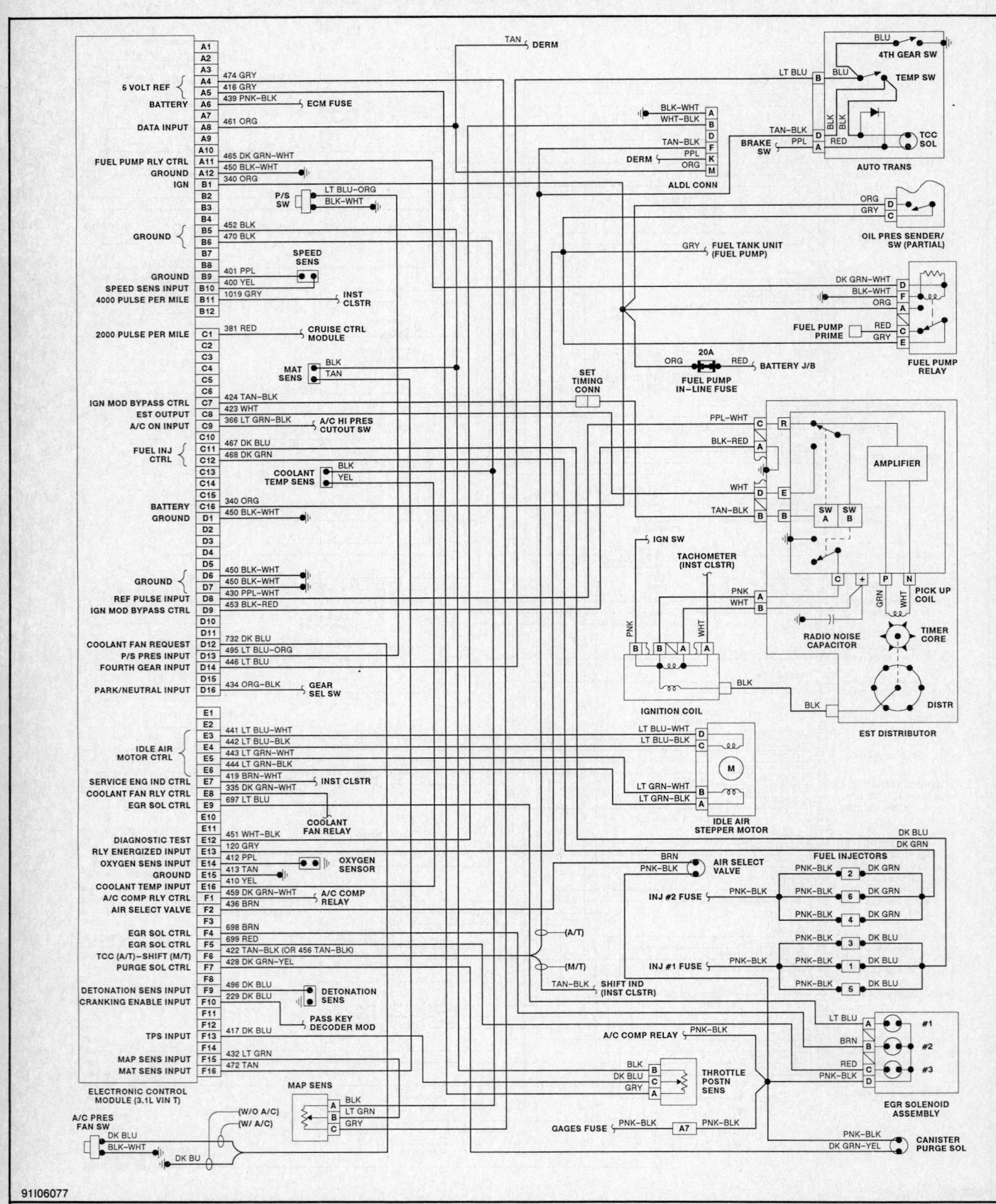

91I06077

Fig. 13: 3.1L (VIN T) ECM Wiring Diagram (Camaro & Firebird)

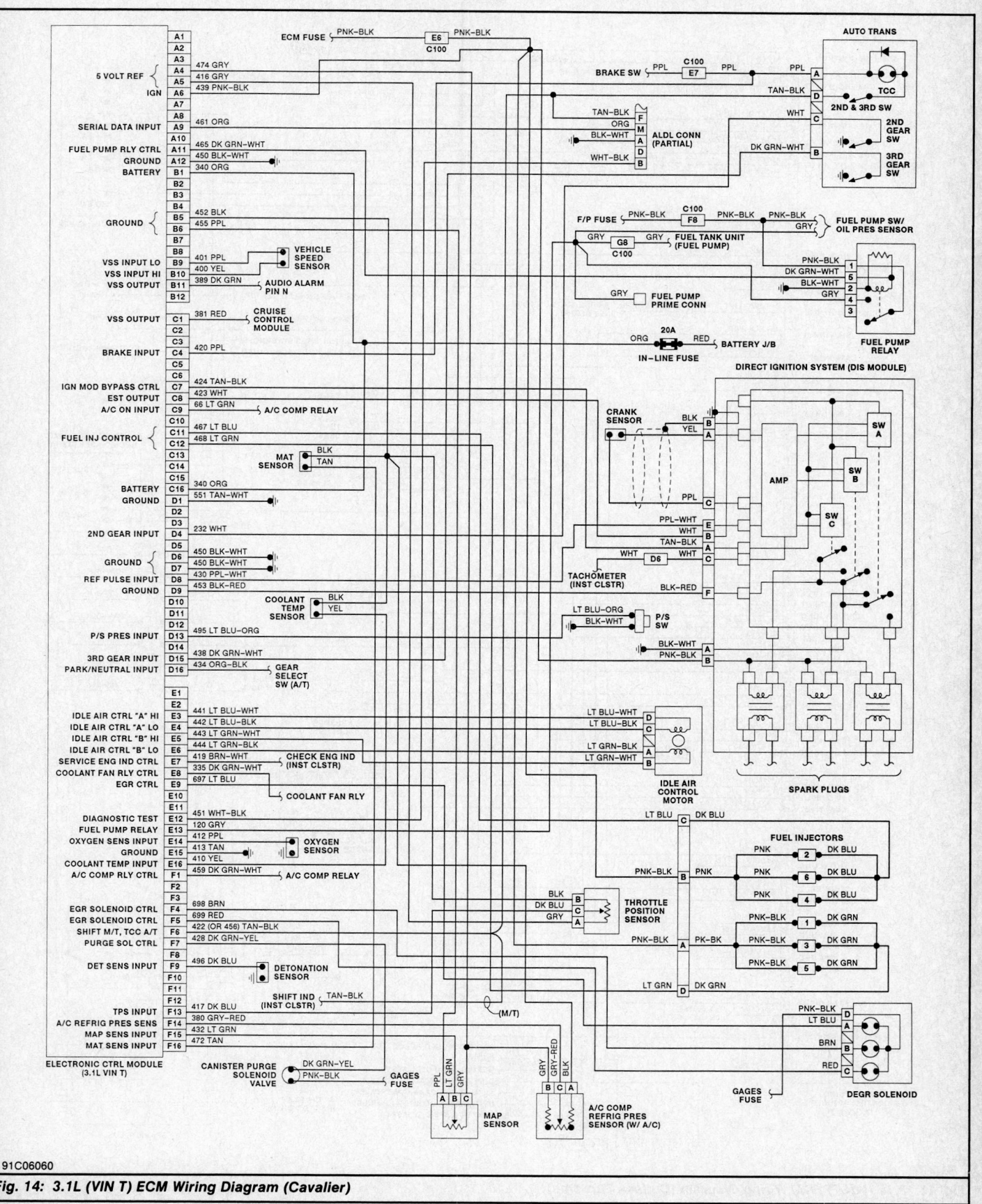

91C06060

Fig. 14: 3.1L (VIN T) ECM Wiring Diagram (Cavalier)

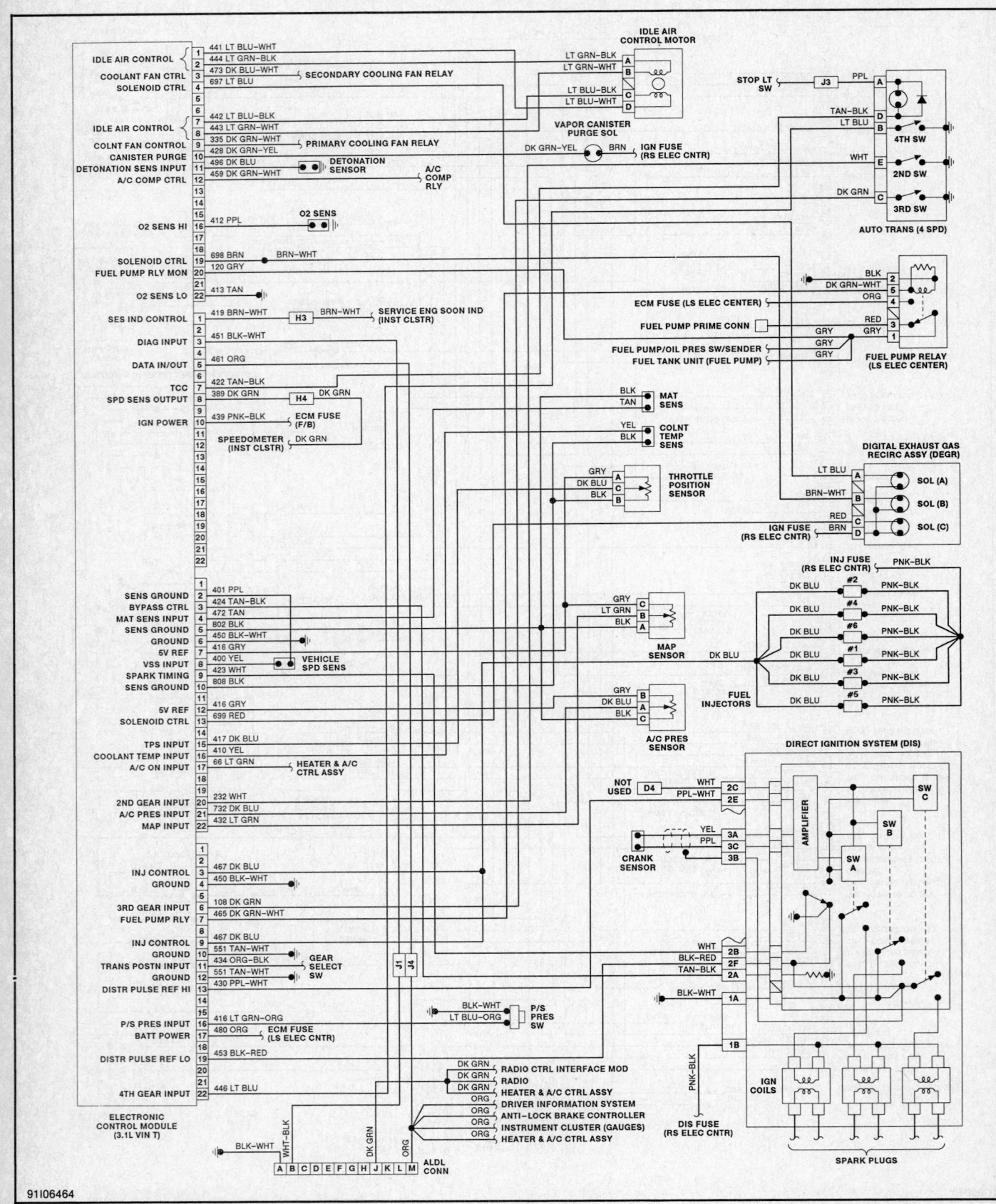

Fig. 15: 3.1L (VIN T) ECM Wiring Diagram (Cutlass Supreme)

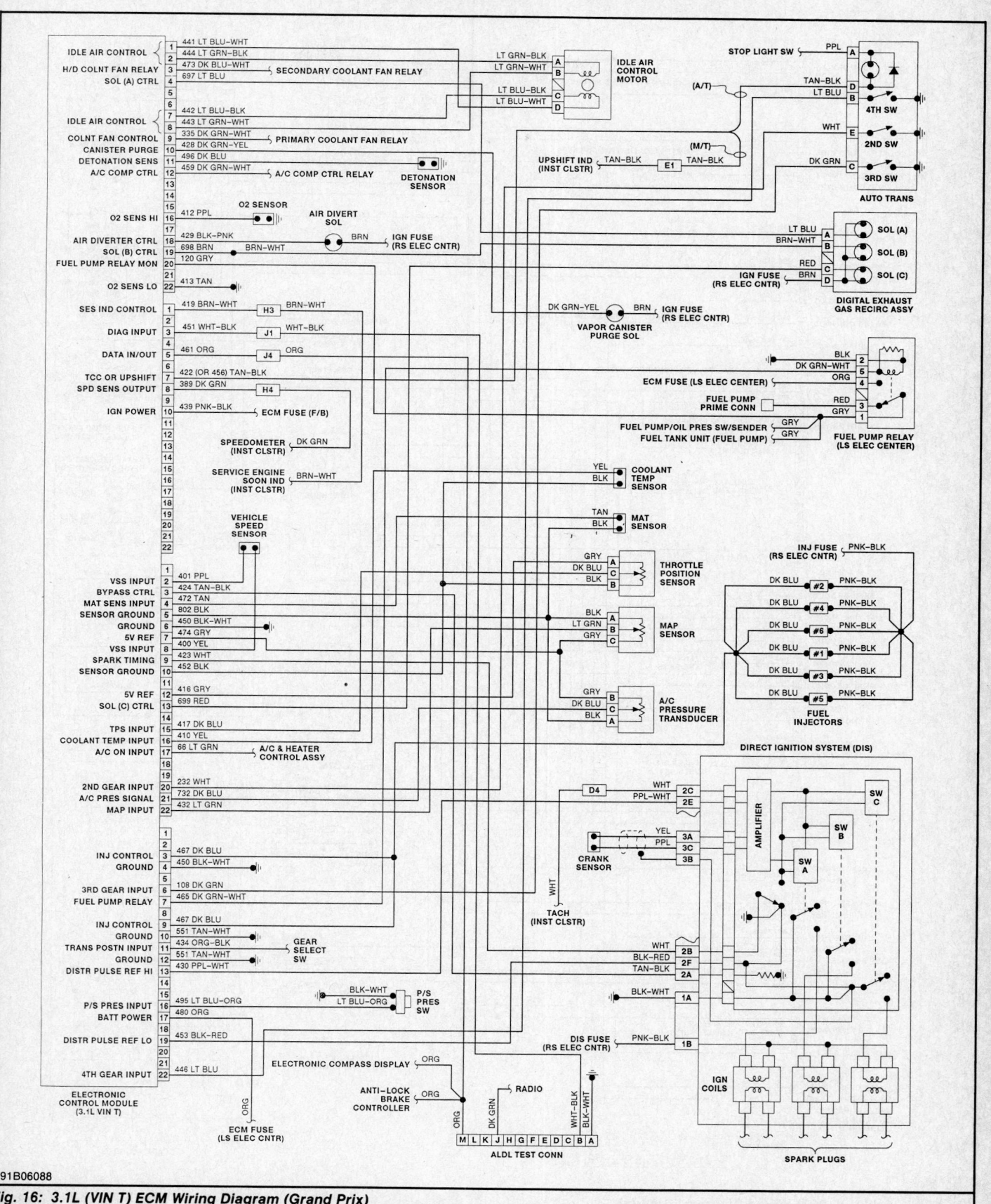

Fig. 16: 3.1L (VIN T) ECM Wiring Diagram (Grand Prix)

91B06088

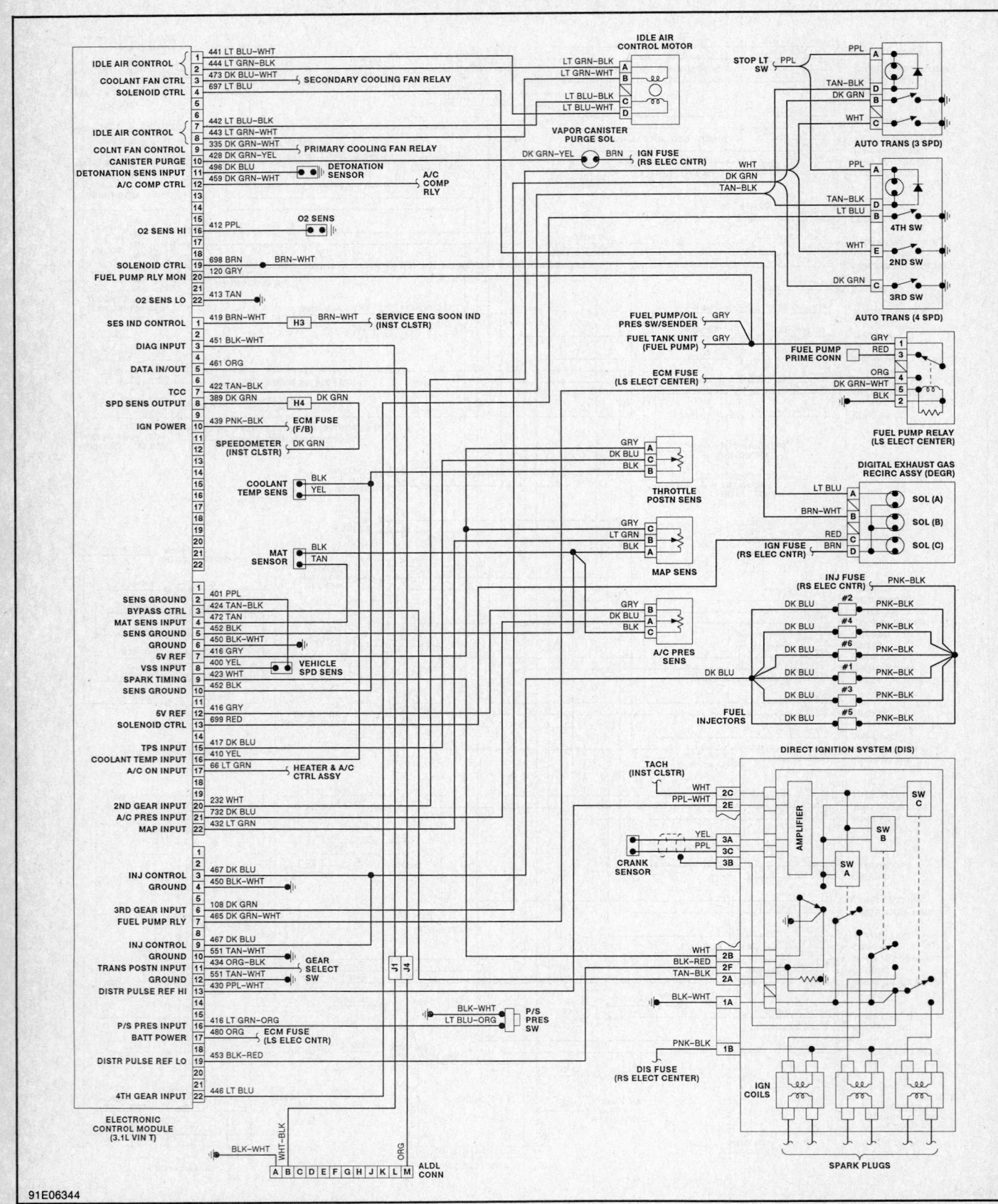

Fig. 17: 3.1L (VIN T) ECM Wiring Diagram (Lumina)

91E06344

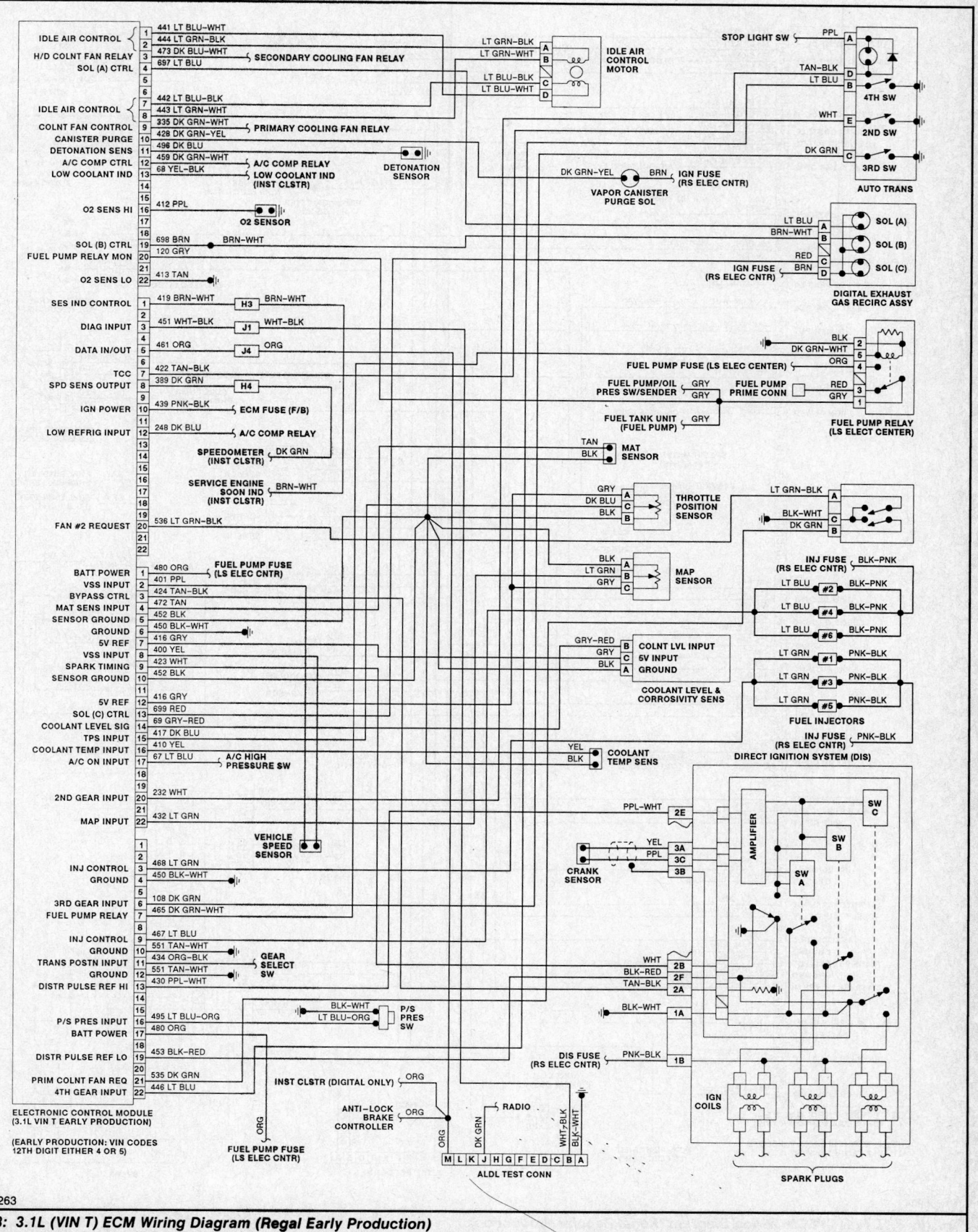

Fig. 18: 3.1L (VIN T) ECM Wiring Diagram (Regal Early Production)

91C06263

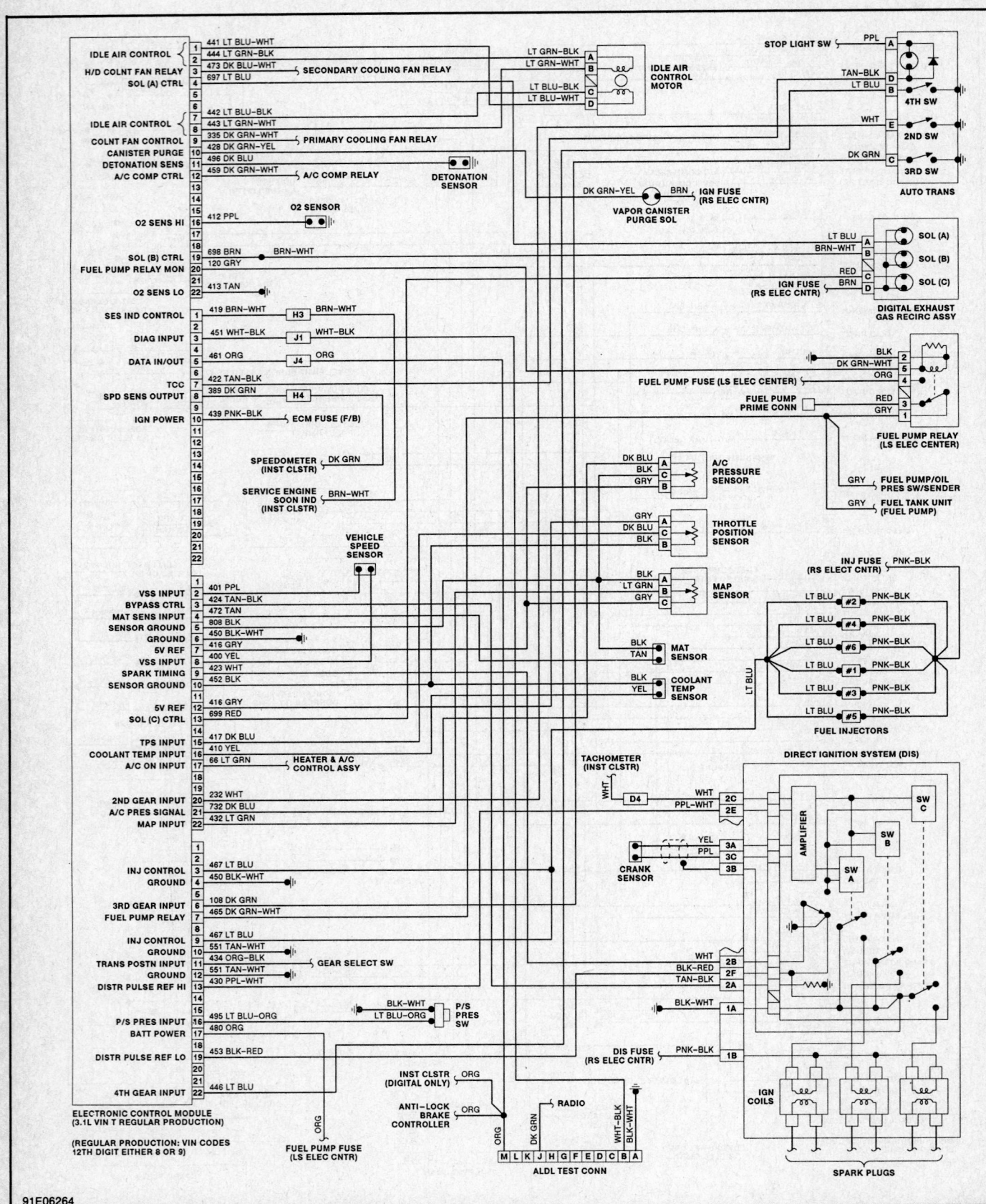

Fig. 19: 3.1L (VIN T) ECM Wiring Diagram (Regal Regular Production)

91E06264

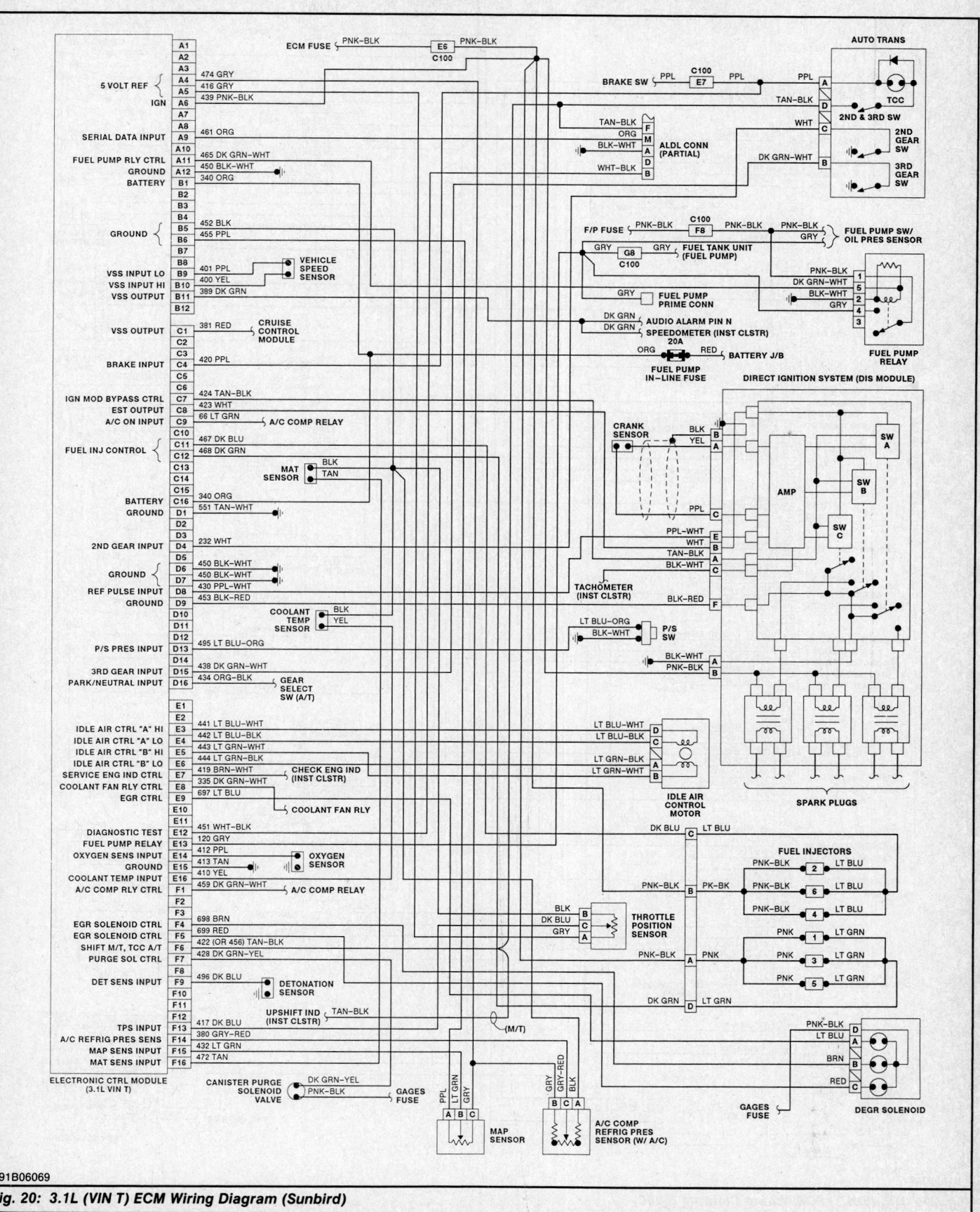

Fig. 20: 3.1L (VIN T) ECM Wiring Diagram (Sunbird)

91B06069

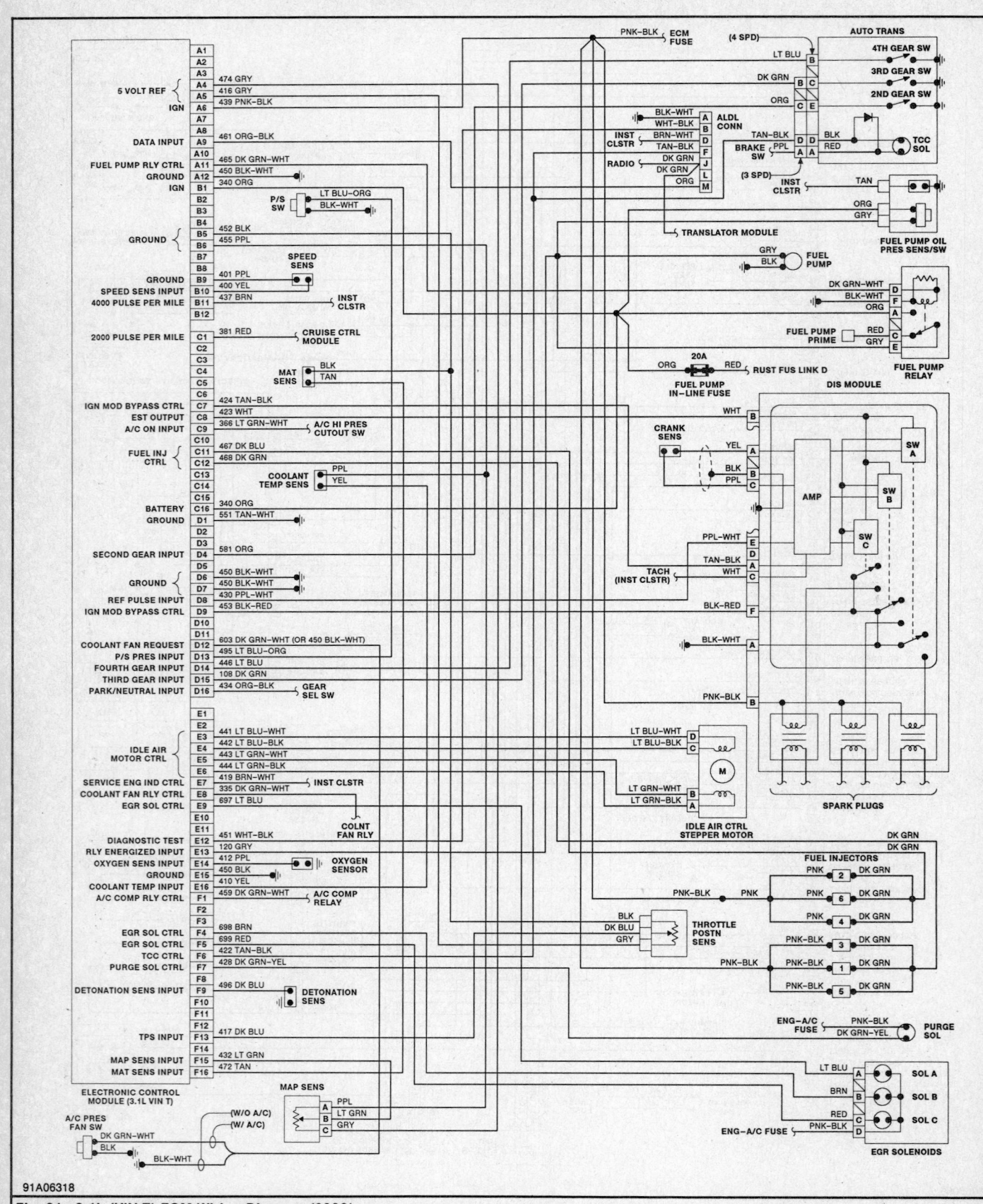

Fig. 21: *3.1L (VIN T) ECM Wiring Diagram (6000)*

91A06318

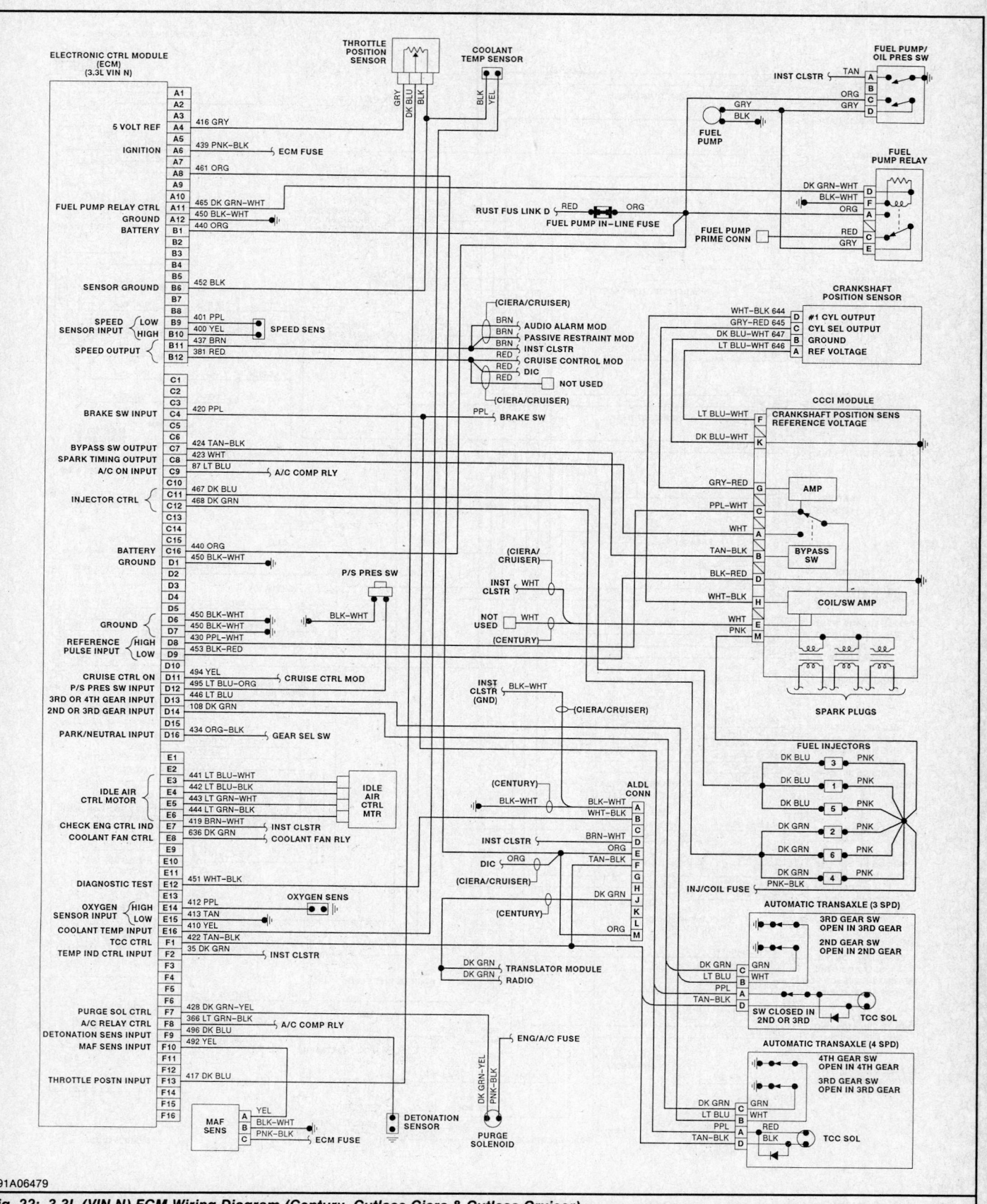

Fig. 22: 3.3L (VIN N) ECM Wiring Diagram (Century, Cutlass Ciera & Cutlass Cruiser)

91A06479

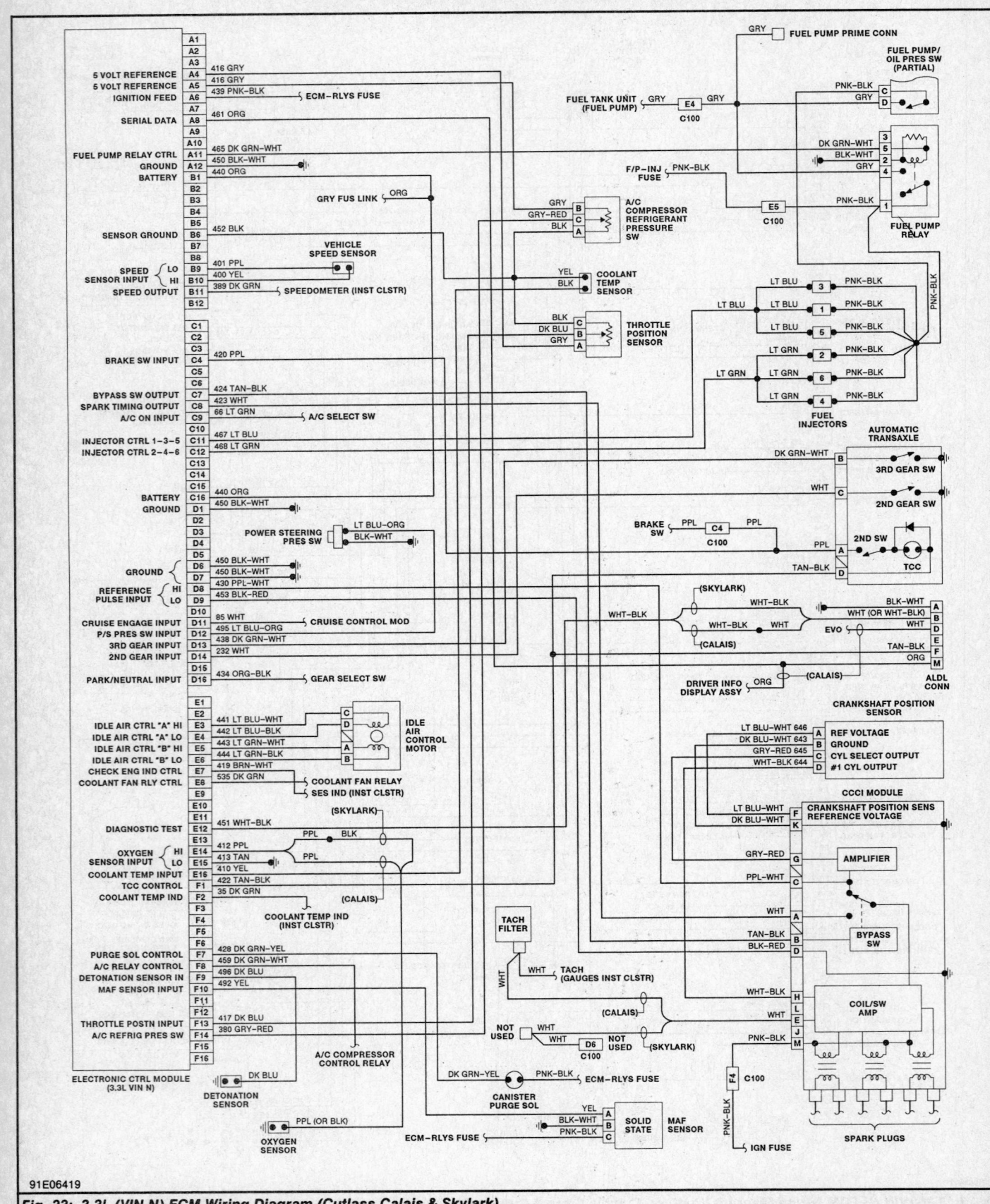

Fig. 23: 3.3L (VIN N) ECM Wiring Diagram (Cutlass Calais & Skylark)

91E06419

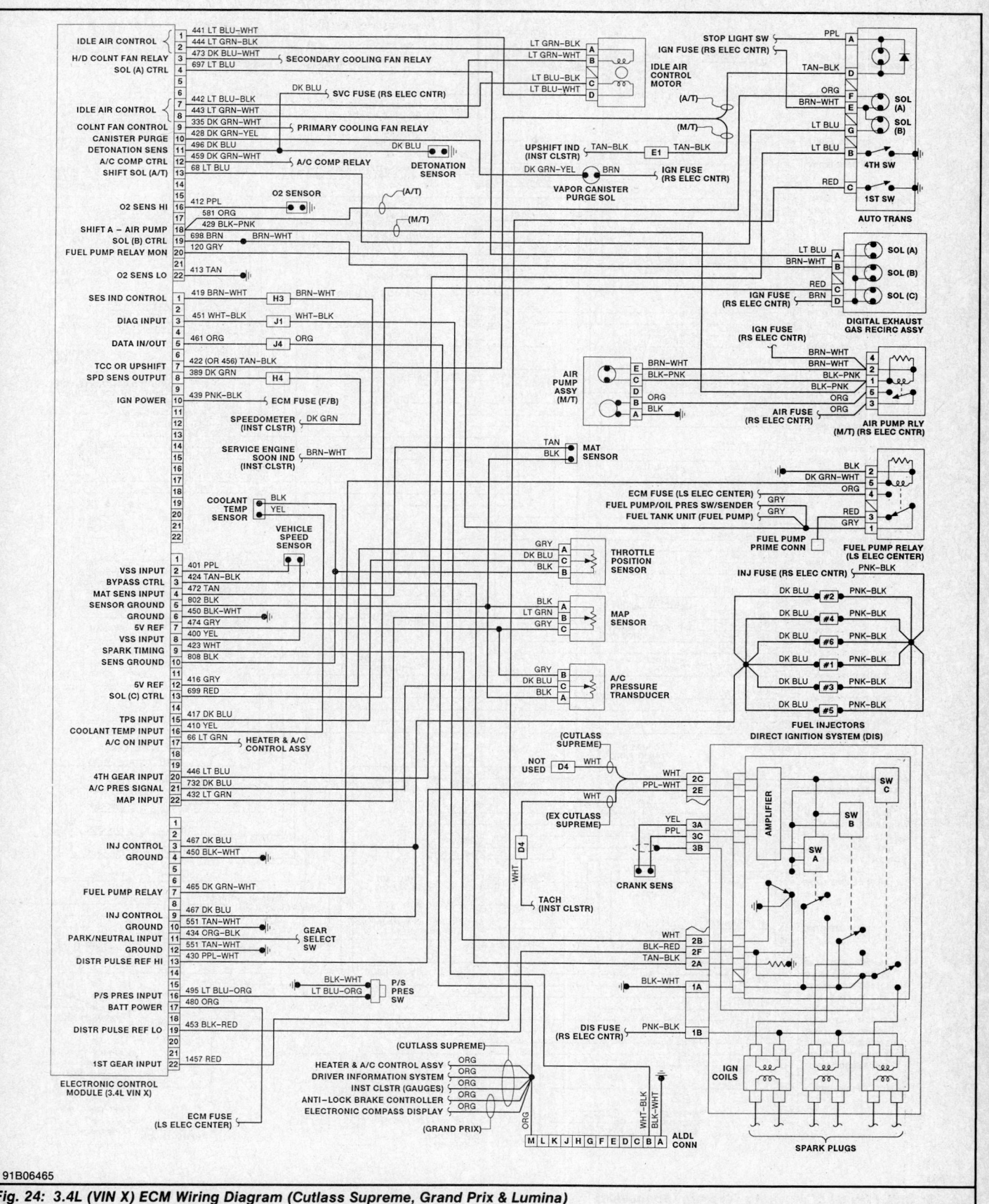

Fig. 24: 3.4L (VIN X) ECM Wiring Diagram (Cutlass Supreme, Grand Prix & Lumina)

91B06465

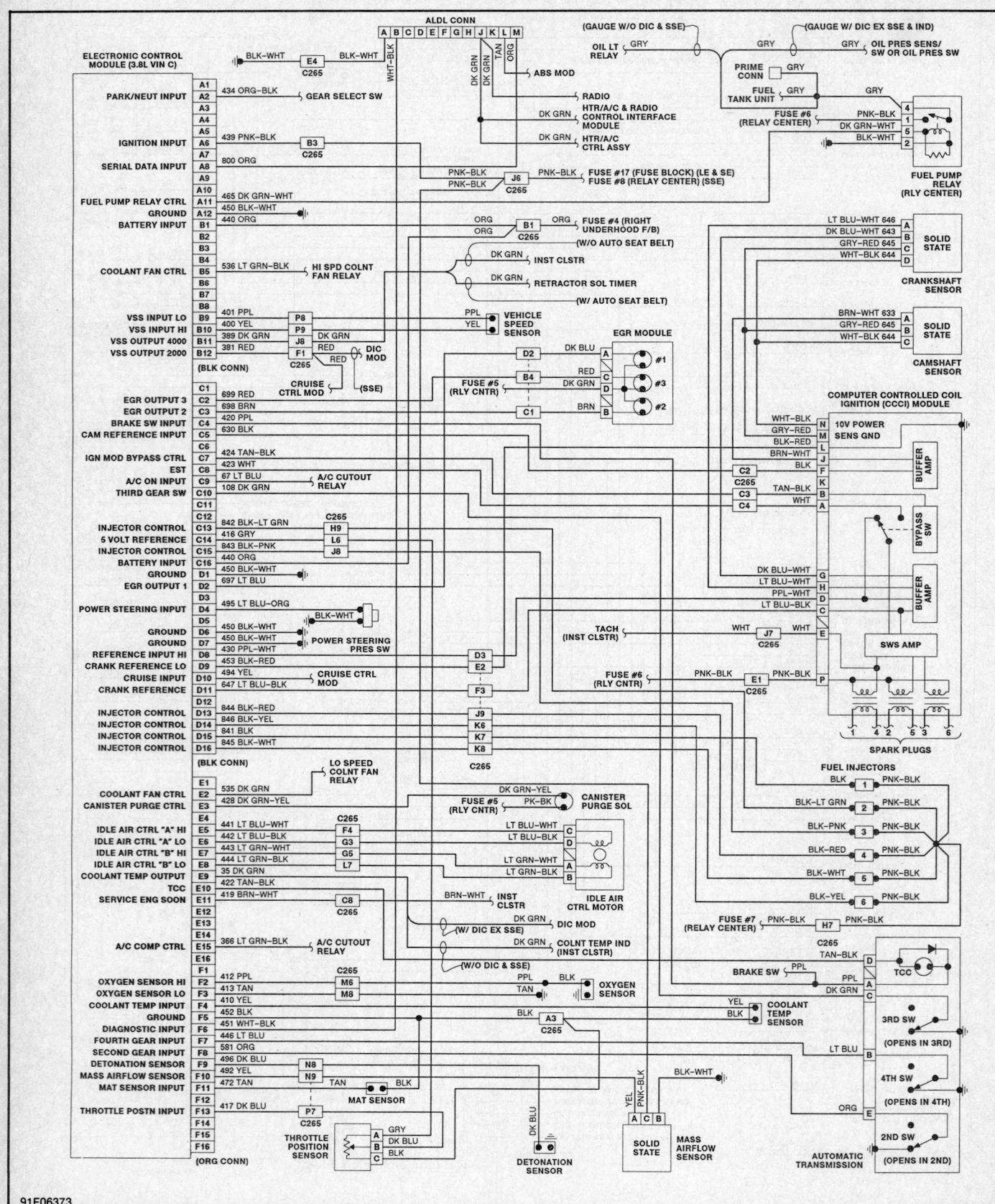

Fig. 25: 3.8L (VIN C) ECM Wiring Diagram (Bonneville)

91F06373

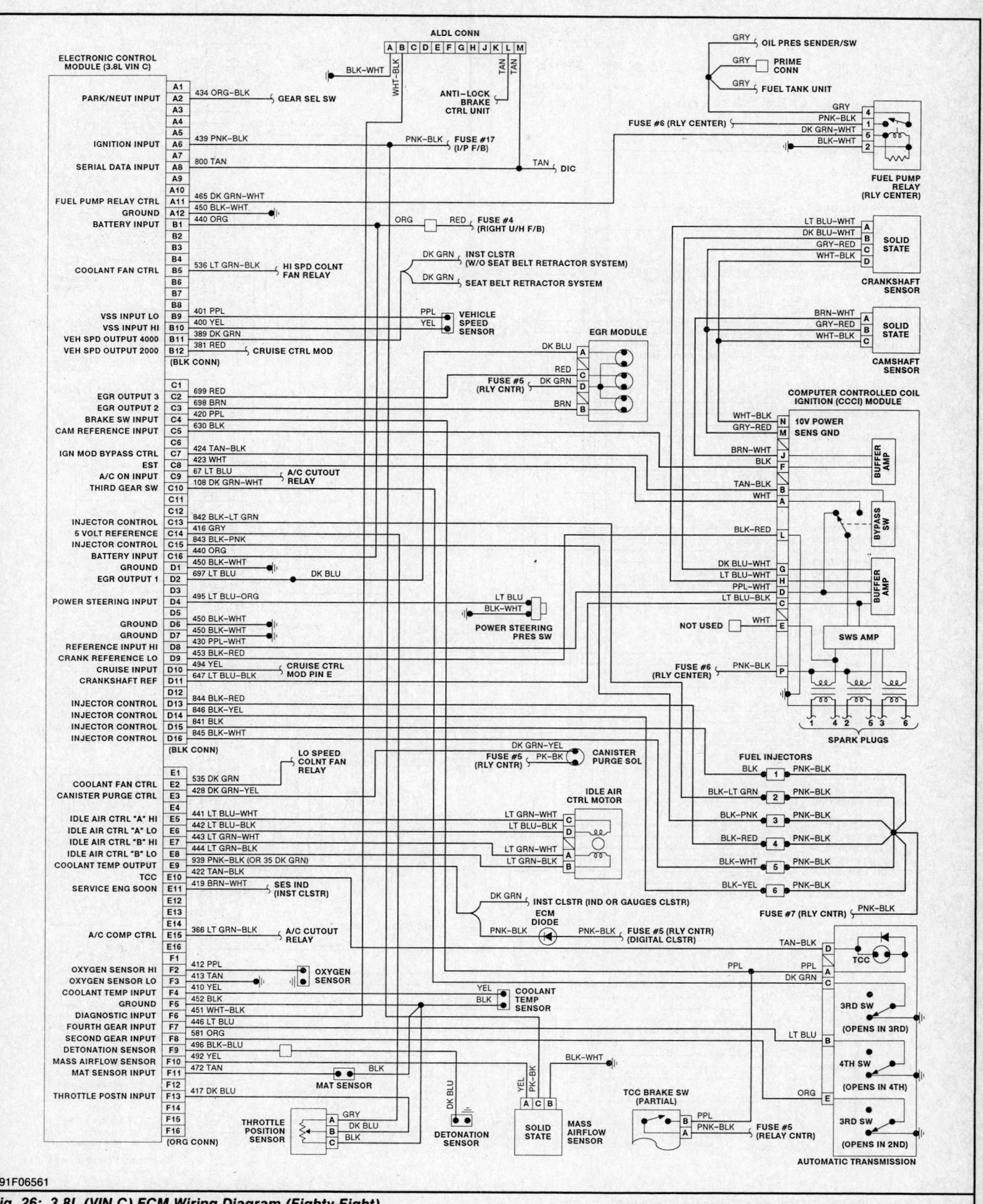

Fig. 26: *3.8L (VIN C) ECM Wiring Diagram (Eighty-Eight)*

91F06561

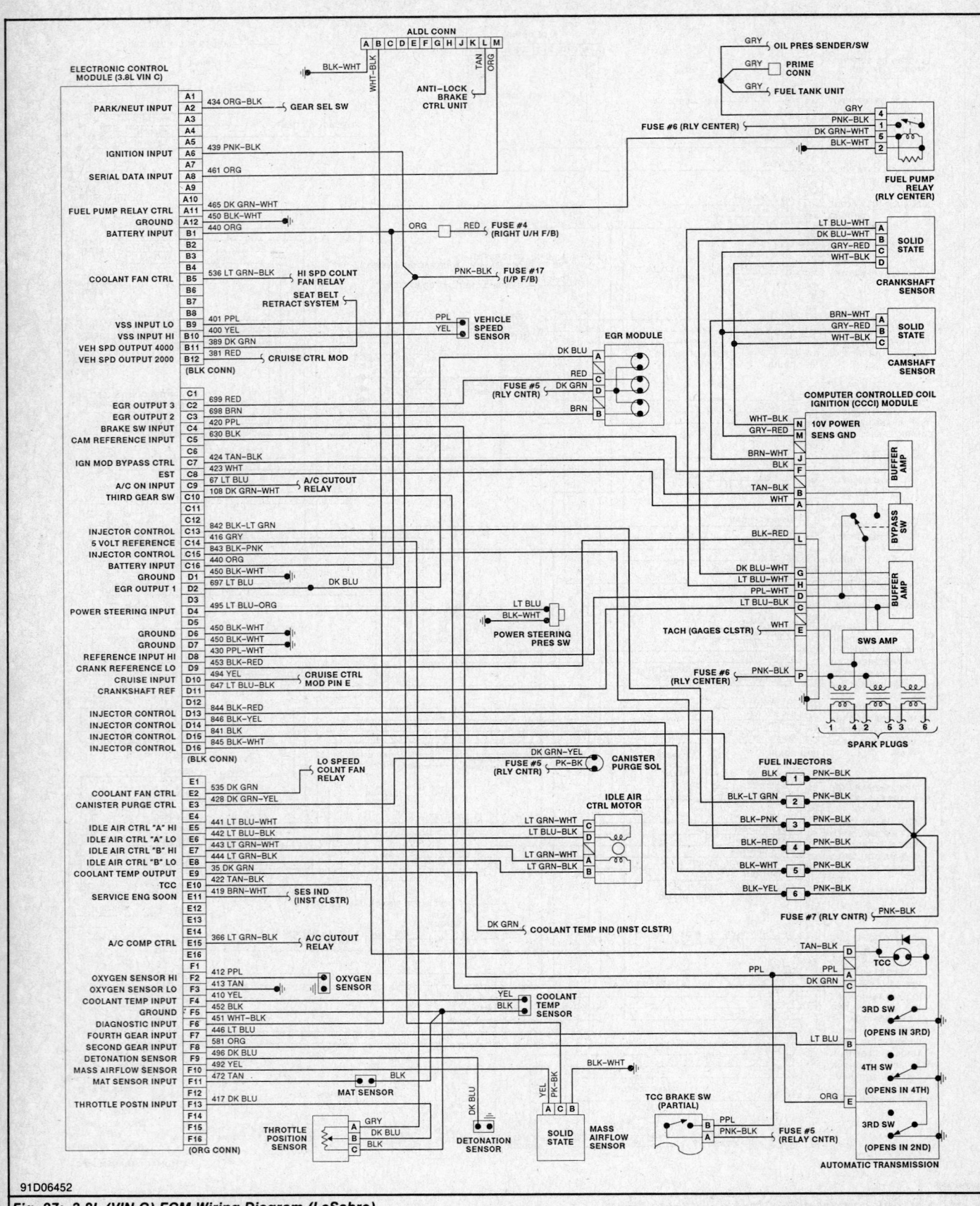

91D06452

Fig. 27: 3.8L (VIN C) ECM Wiring Diagram (LeSabre)

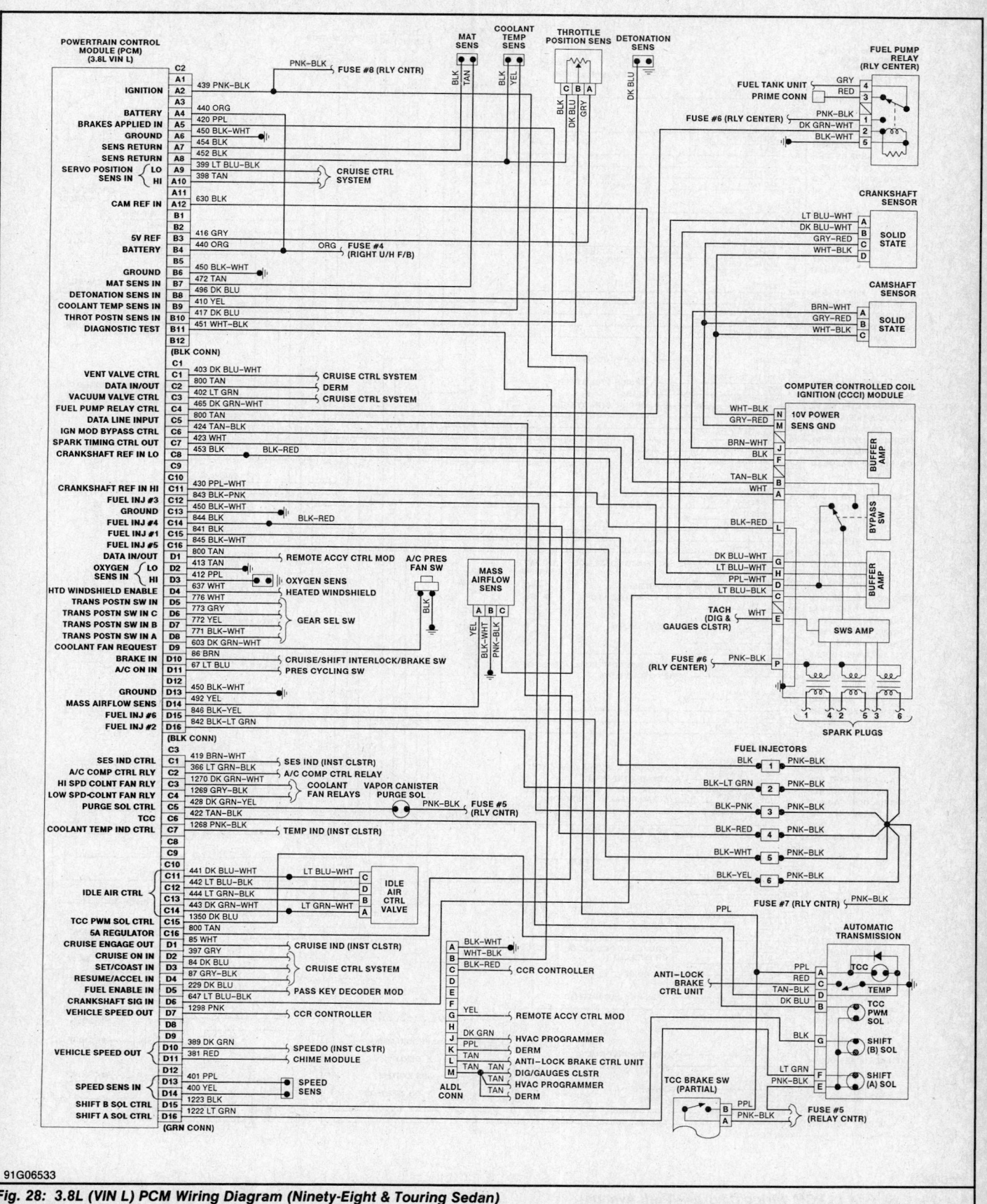

Fig. 28: 3.8L (VIN L) PCM Wiring Diagram (Ninety-Eight & Touring Sedan)

91G06533

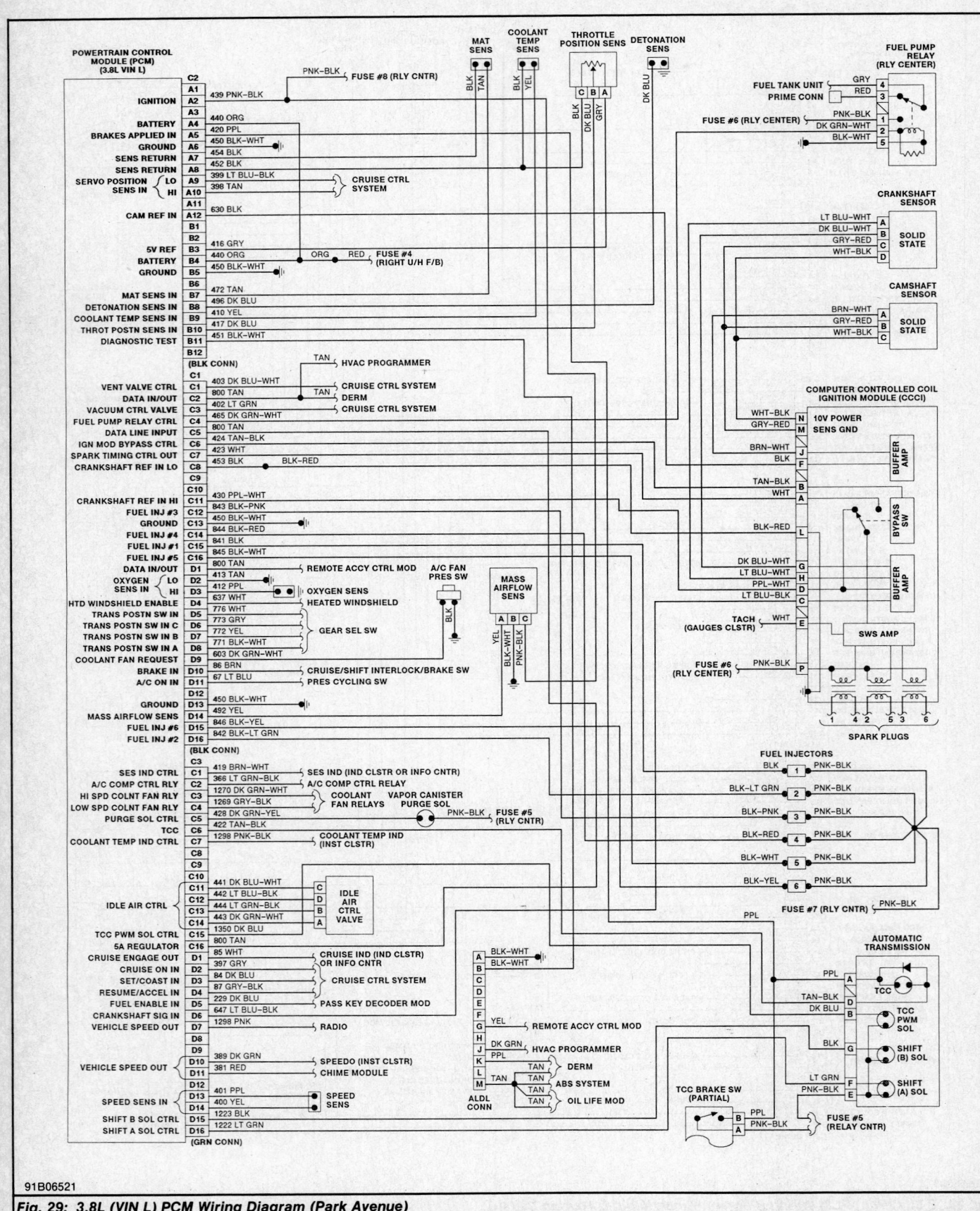

Fig. 29: 3.8L (VIN L) PCM Wiring Diagram (Park Avenue)

91B06521

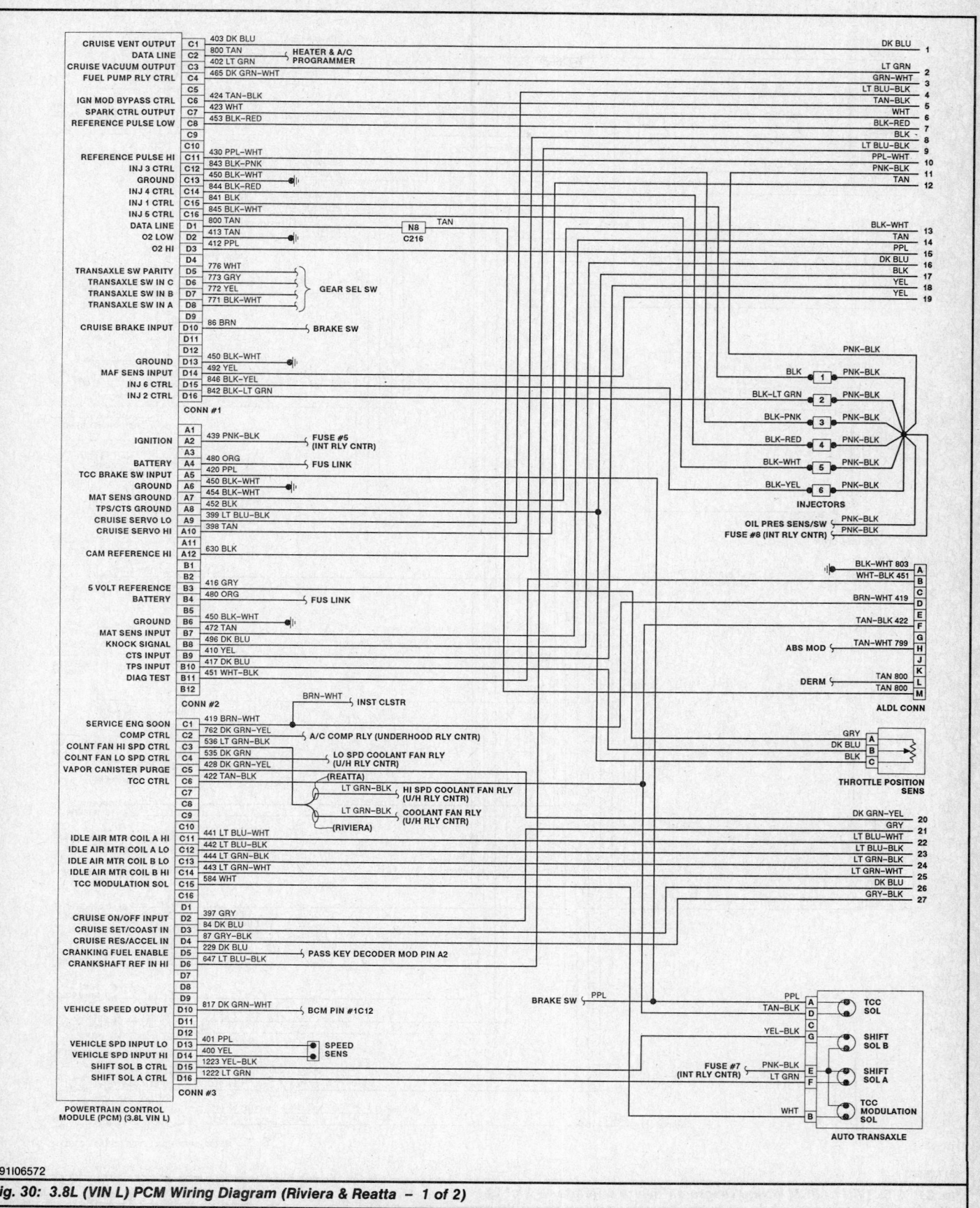

91I06572

Fig. 30: 3.8L (VIN L) PCM Wiring Diagram (Riviera & Reatta – 1 of 2)

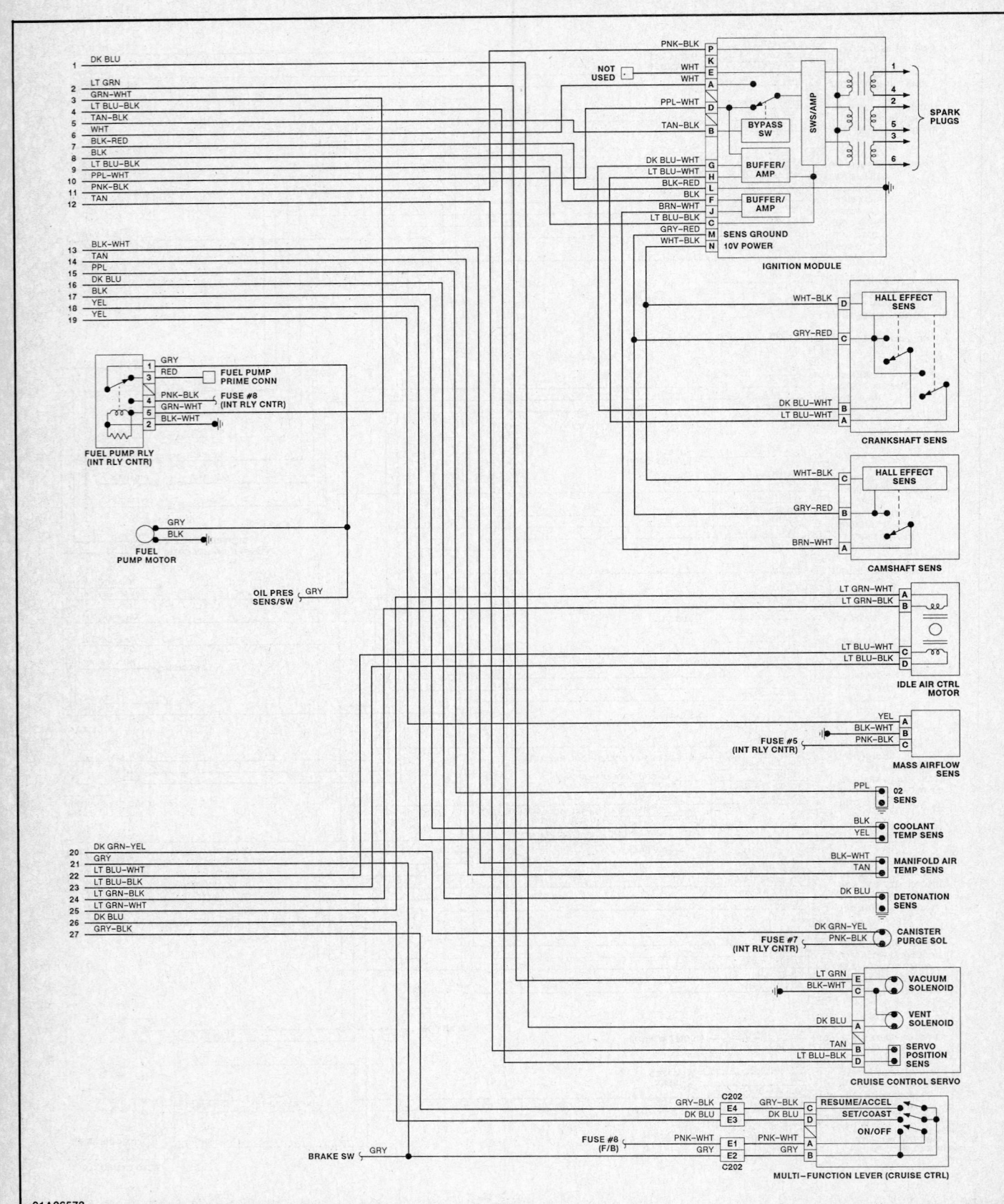

Fig. 31: 3.8L (VIN L) PCM Wiring Diagram (Riviera & Reatta – 2 of 2)

91A06573

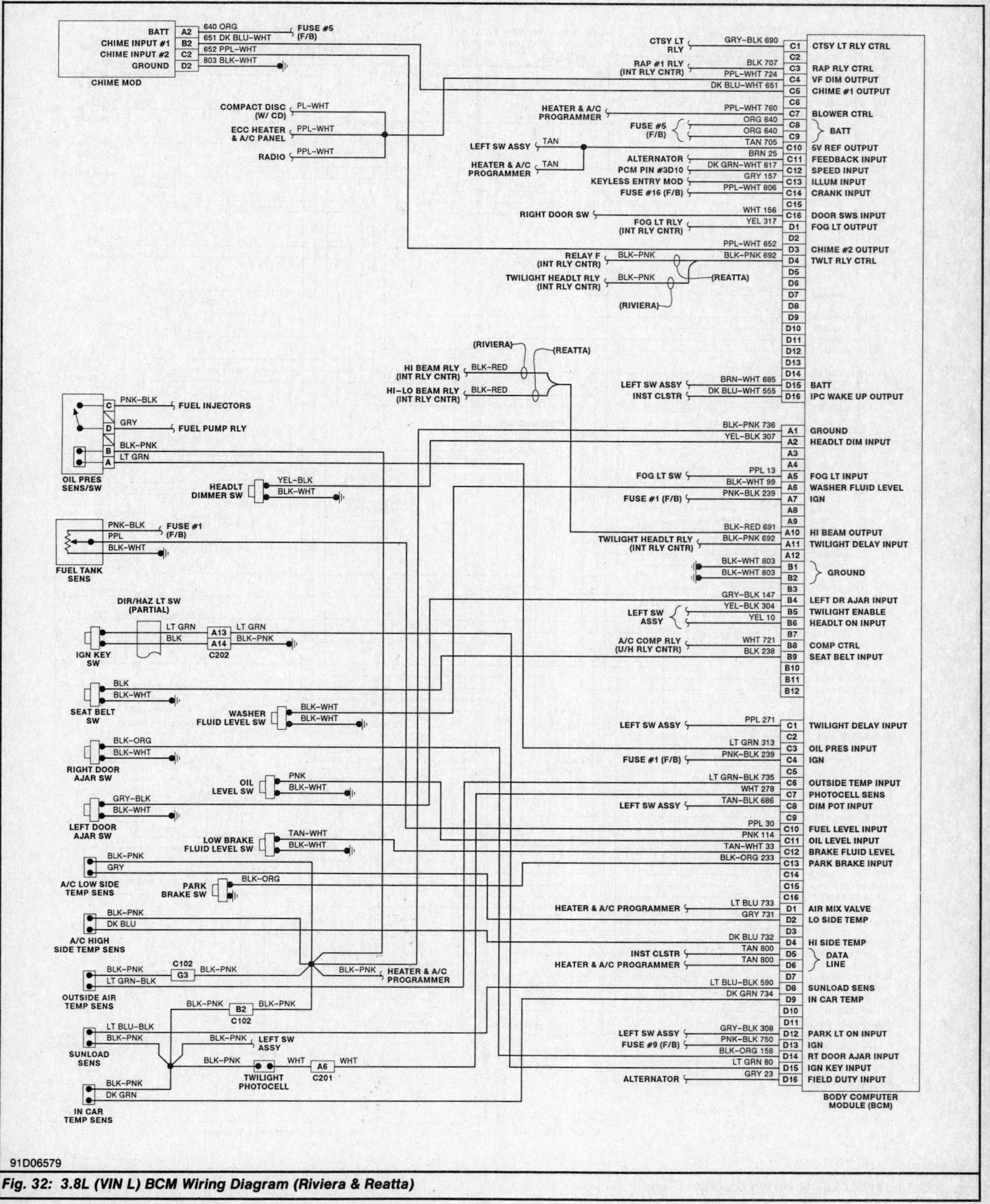

91D06579

Fig. 32: 3.8L (VIN L) BCM Wiring Diagram (Riviera & Reatta)

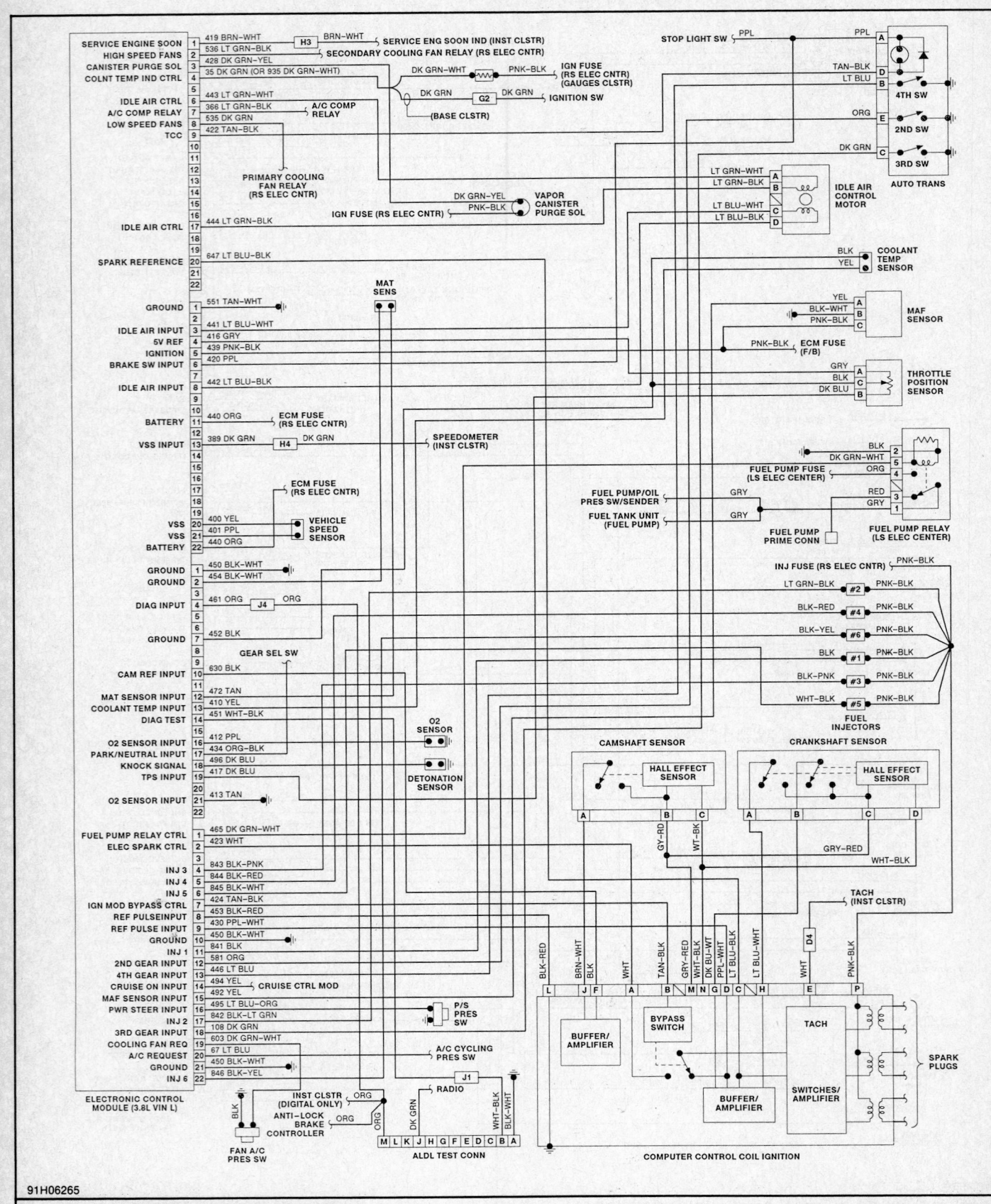

91H06265

Fig. 33: 3.8L (VIN L) ECM Wiring Diagram (Regal)

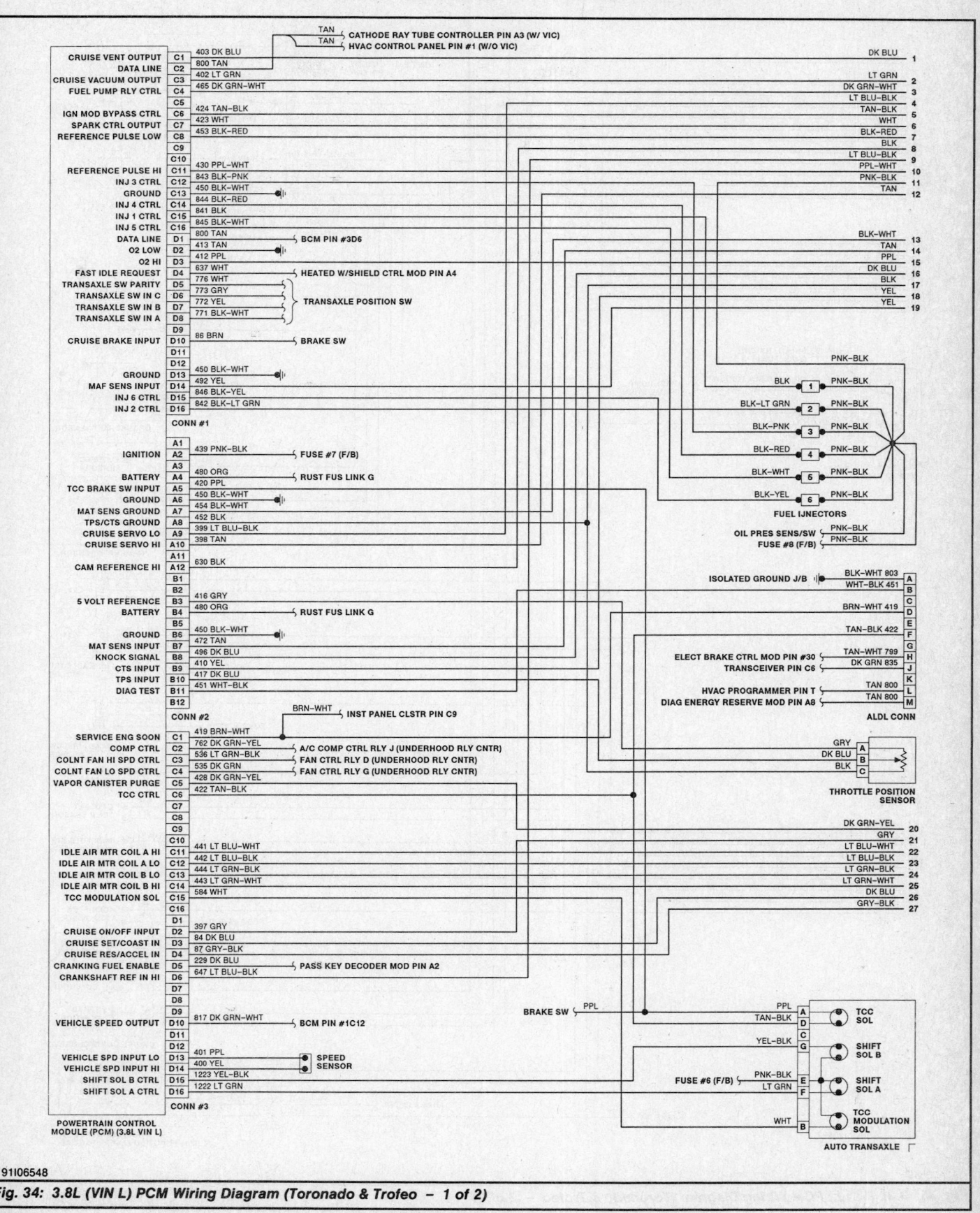

91I06548

Fig. 34: 3.8L (VIN L) PCM Wiring Diagram (Toronado & Trofeo – 1 of 2)

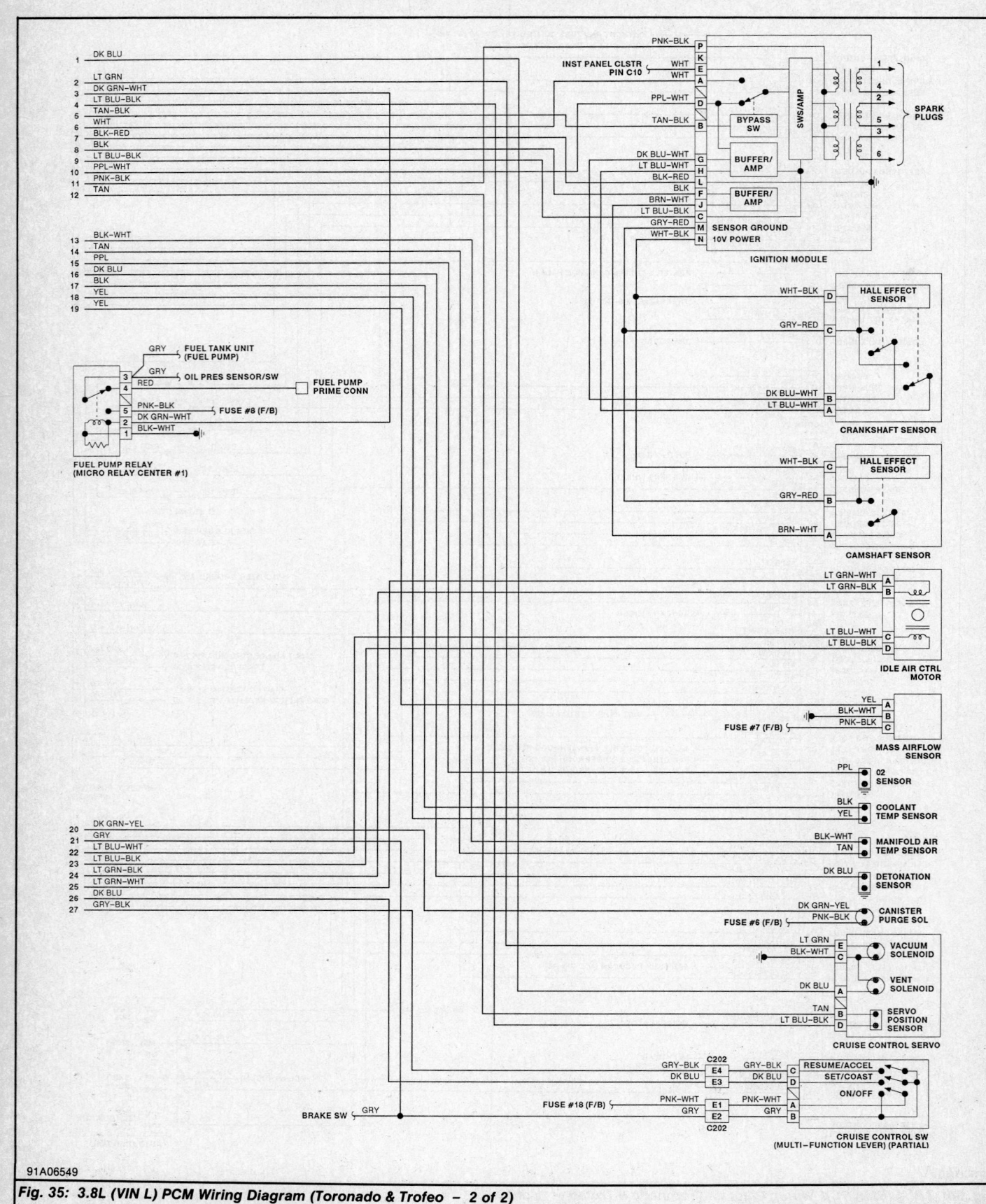

91A06549

Fig. 35: 3.8L (VIN L) PCM Wiring Diagram (Toronado & Trofeo – 2 of 2)

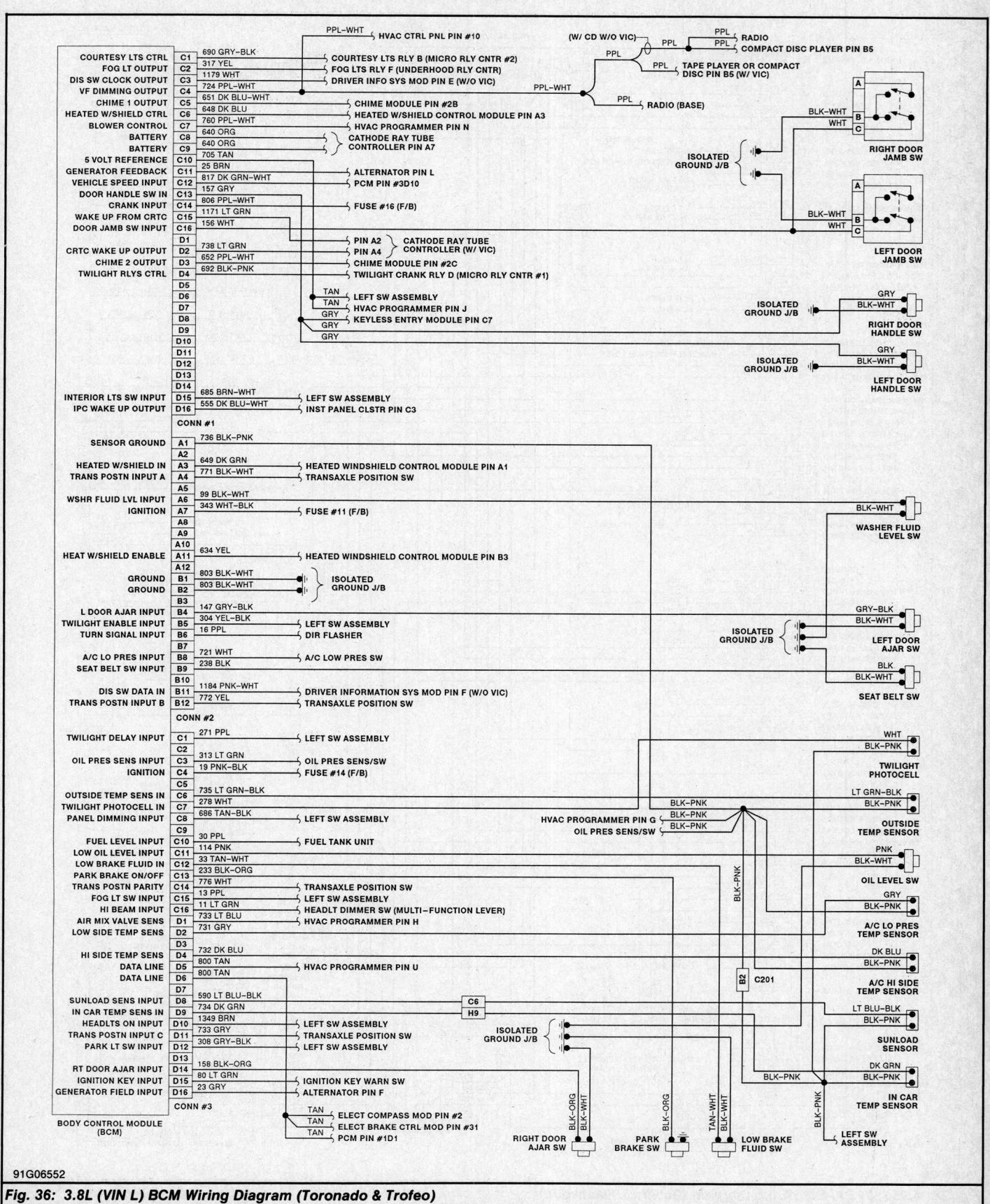

Fig. 36: 3.8L (VIN L) BCM Wiring Diagram (Toronado & Trofeo)

91G06552

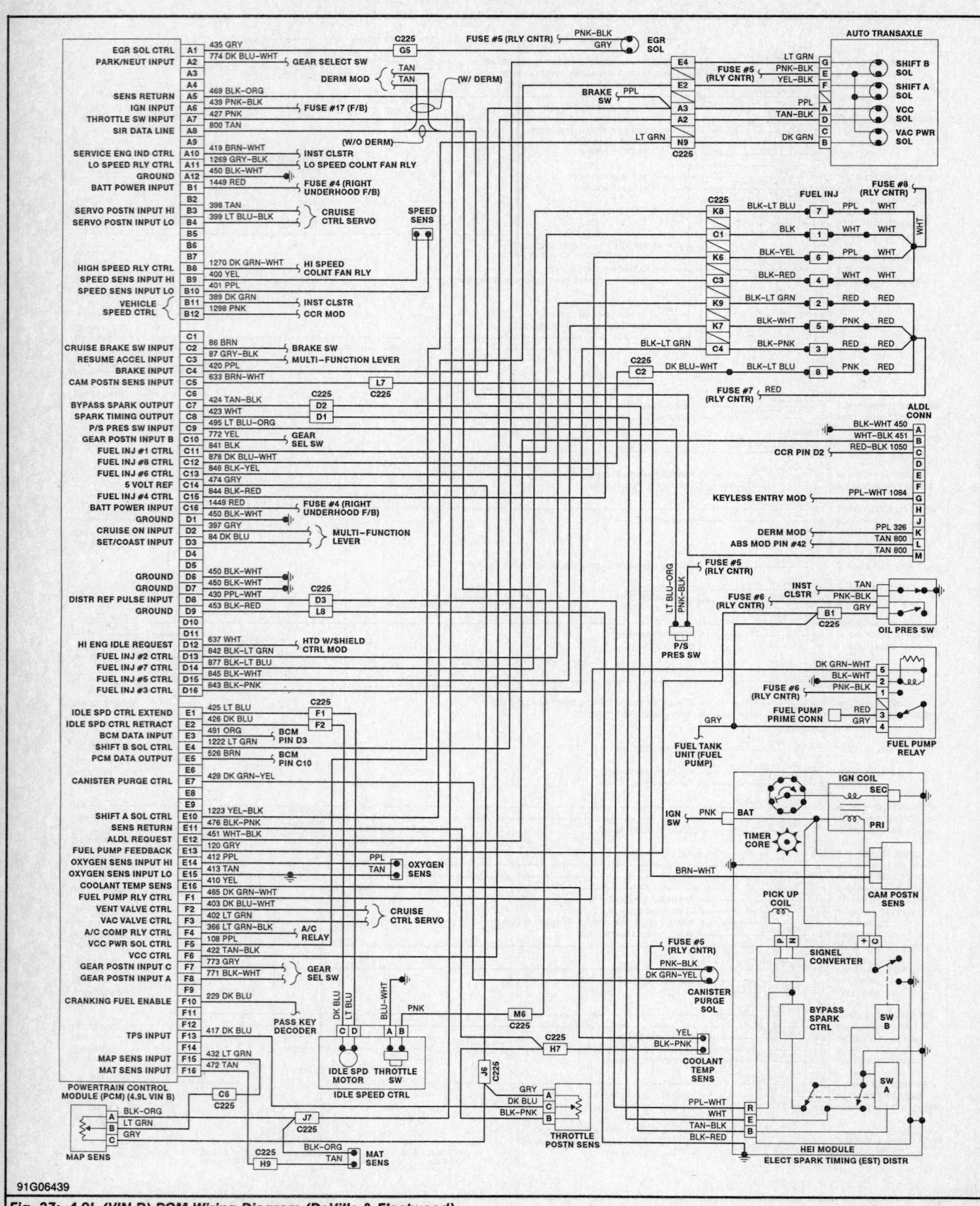

Fig. 37: 4.9L (VIN B) PCM Wiring Diagram (DeVille & Fleetwood)

91G06439

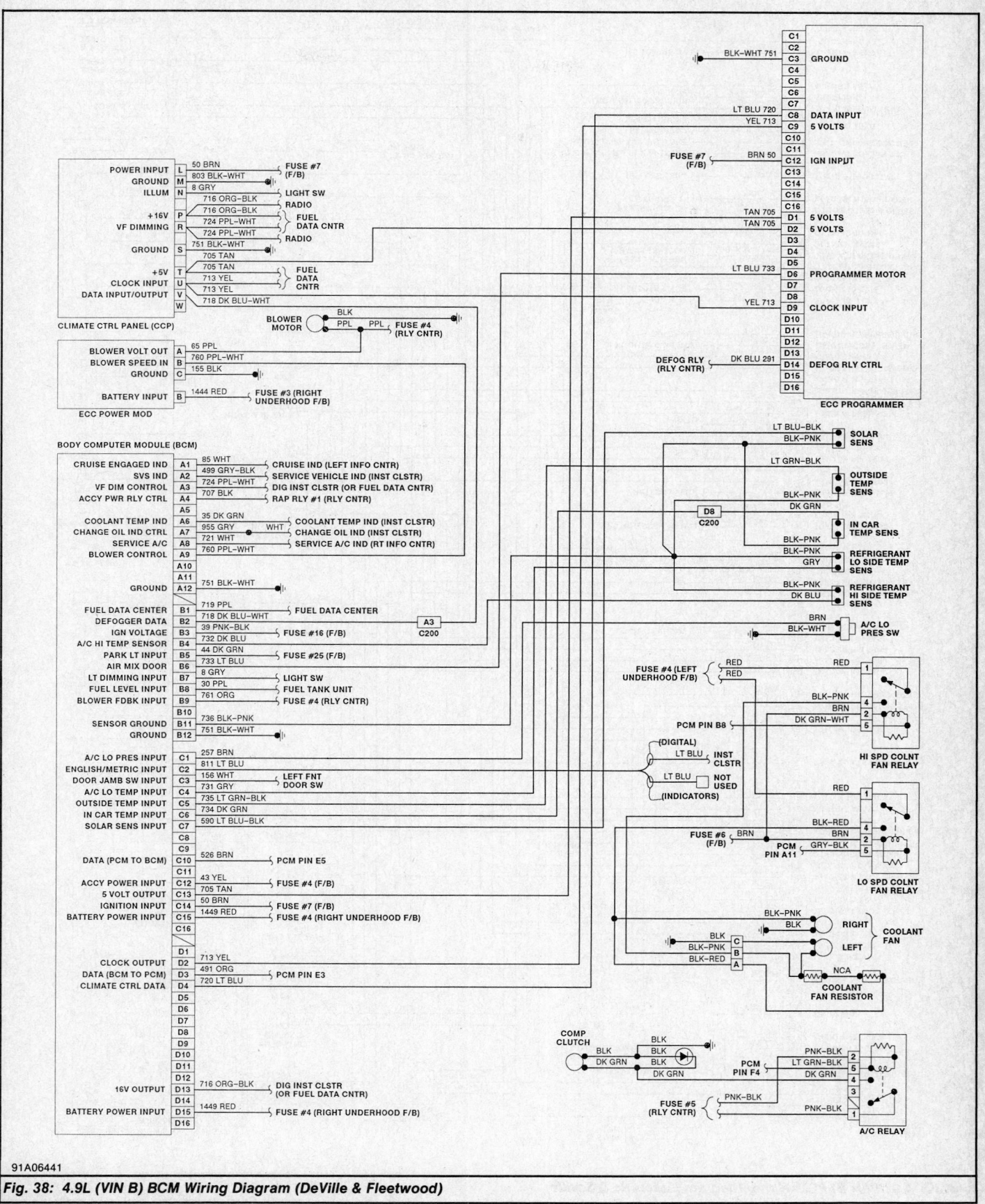

Fig. 38: 4.9L (VIN B) BCM Wiring Diagram (DeVille & Fleetwood)

91A06441

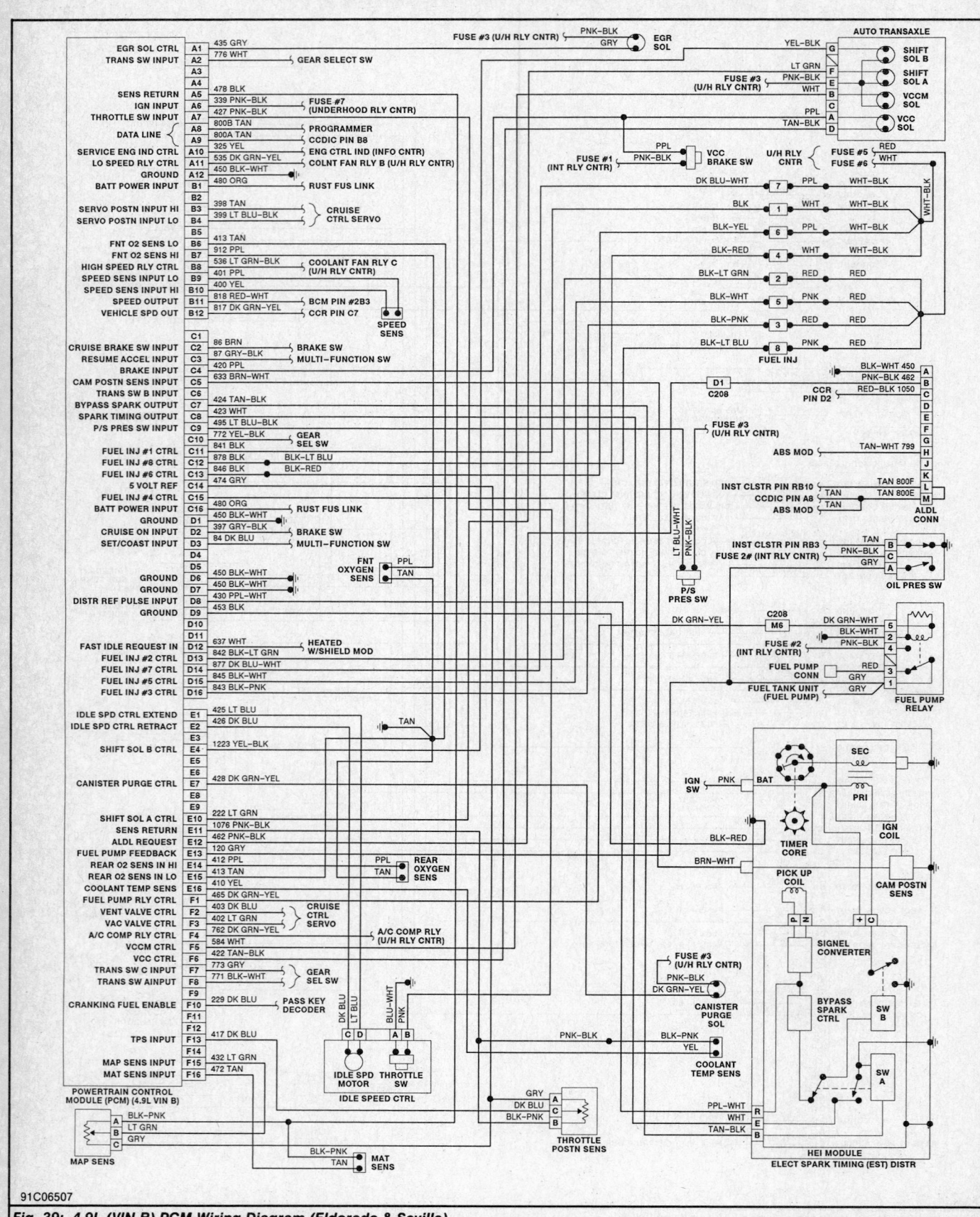

Fig. 39: 4.9L (VIN B) PCM Wiring Diagram (Eldorado & Seville)

91C06507

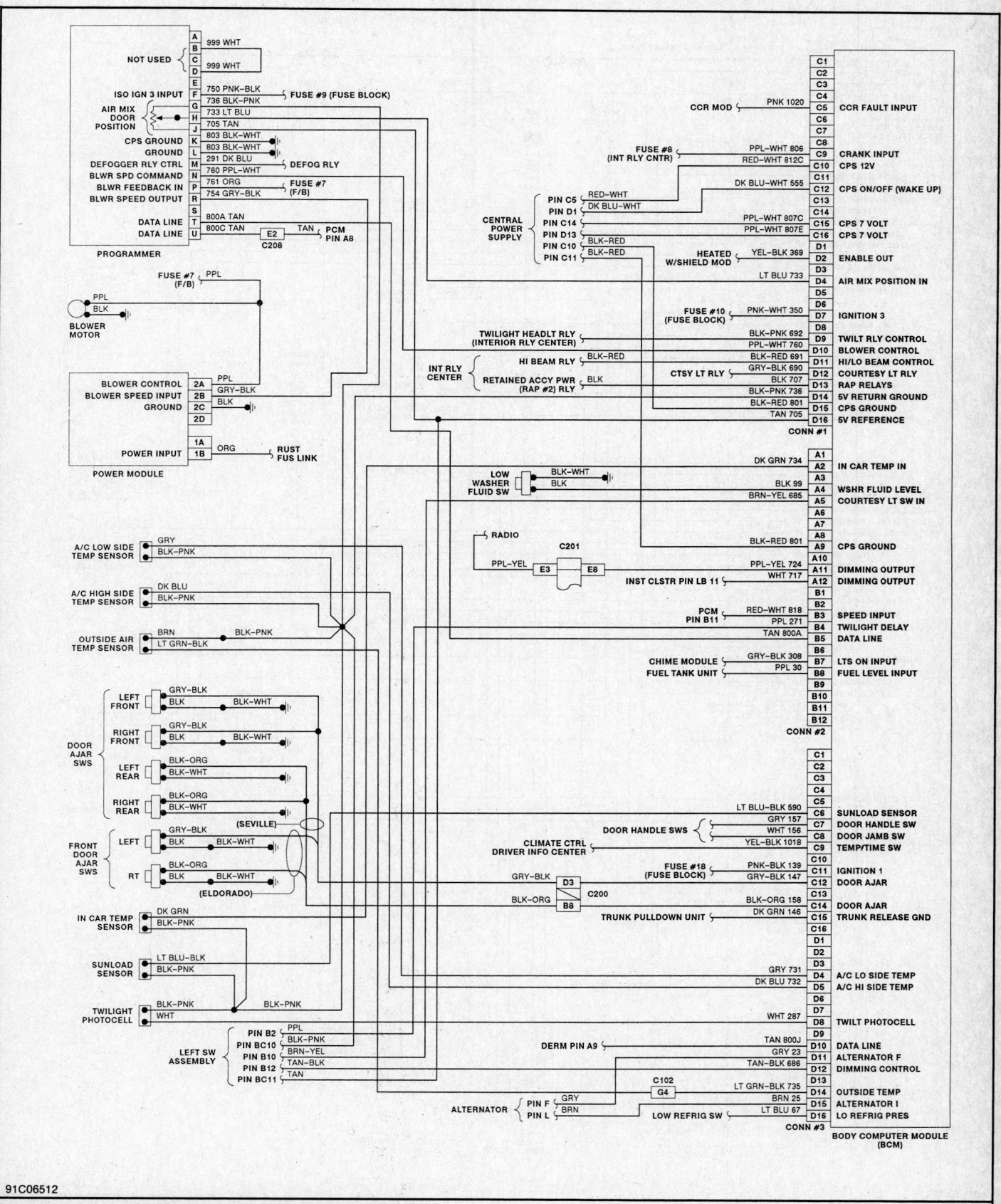

Fig. 40: 4.9L (VIN B) BCM Wiring Diagram (Eldorado & Seville)

91C06512

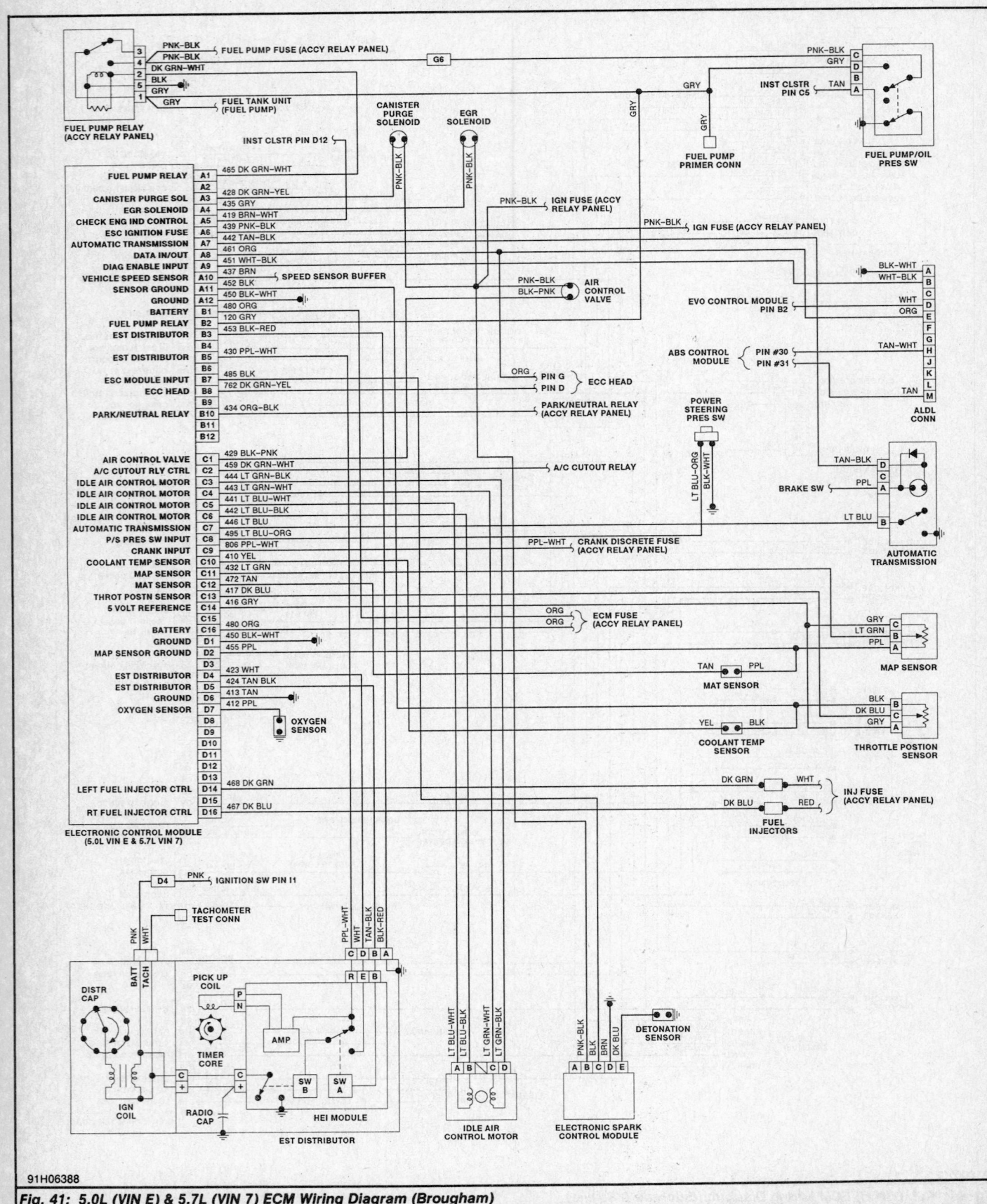

91H06388

Fig. 41: 5.0L (VIN E) & 5.7L (VIN 7) ECM Wiring Diagram (Brougham)

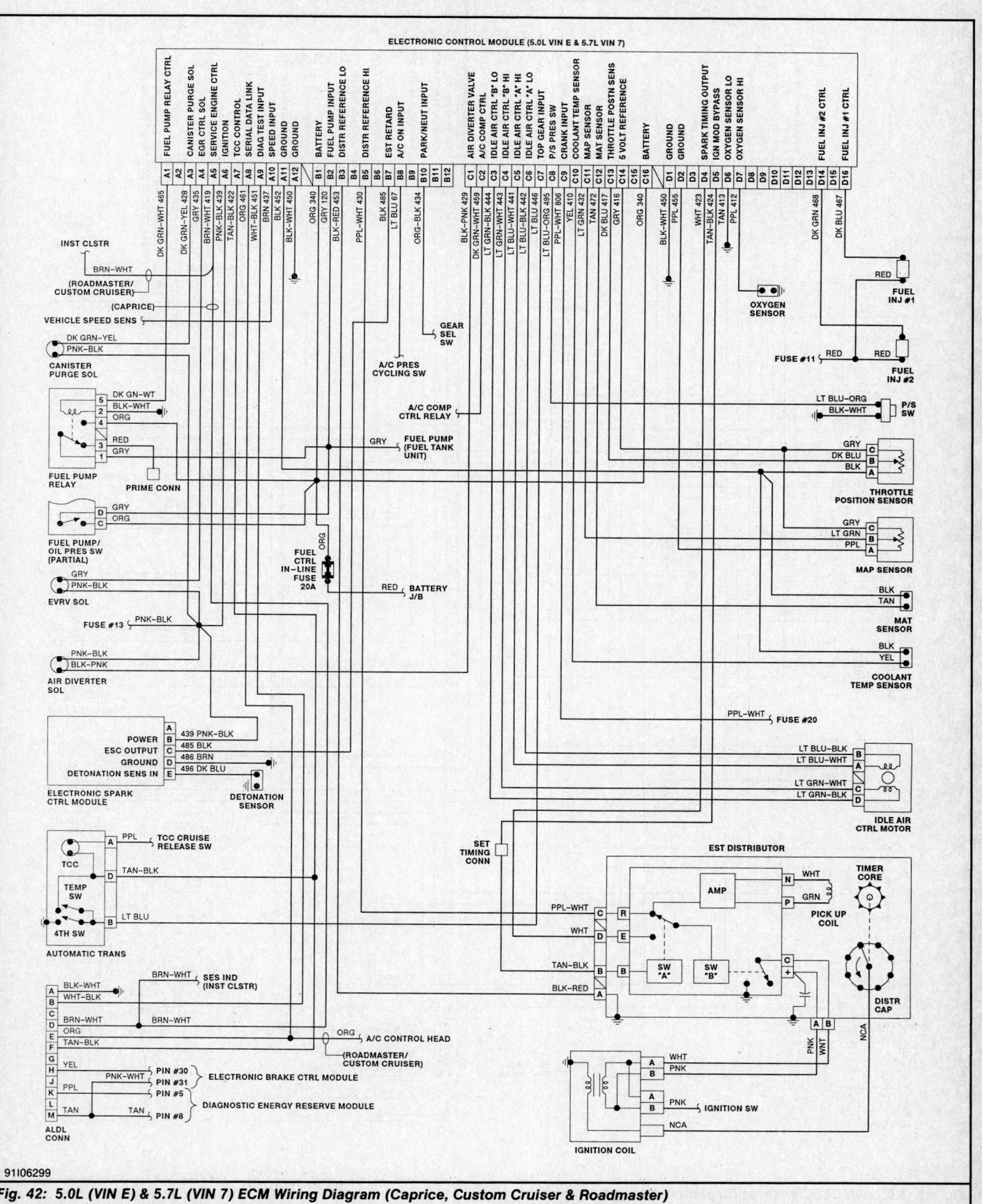

Fig. 42: 5.0L (VIN E) & 5.7L (VIN 7) ECM Wiring Diagram (Caprice, Custom Cruiser & Roadmaster)

91106299

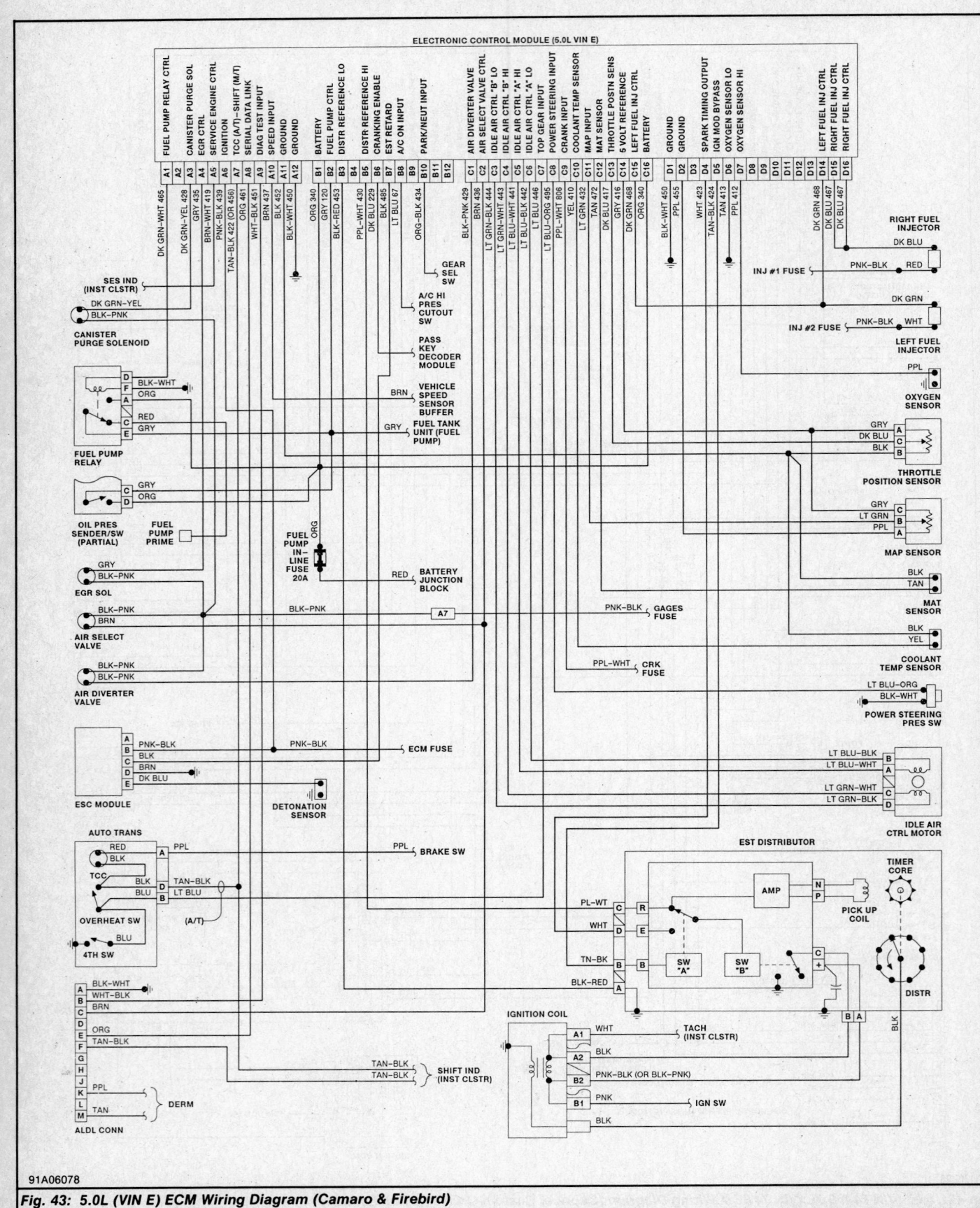

91A06078

Fig. 43: *5.0L (VIN E) ECM Wiring Diagram (Camaro & Firebird)*

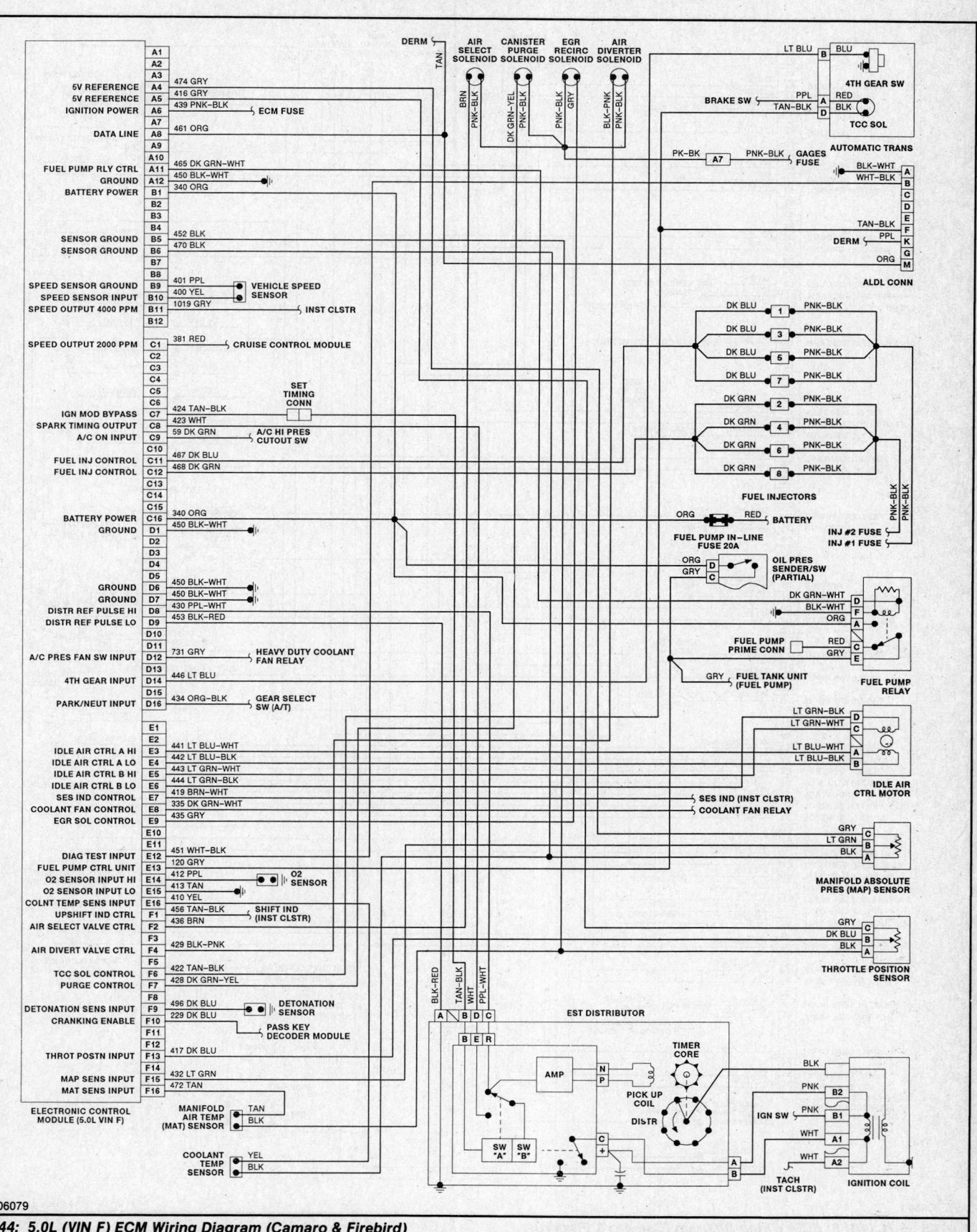

91C06079

Fig. 44: 5.0L (VIN F) ECM Wiring Diagram (Camaro & Firebird)

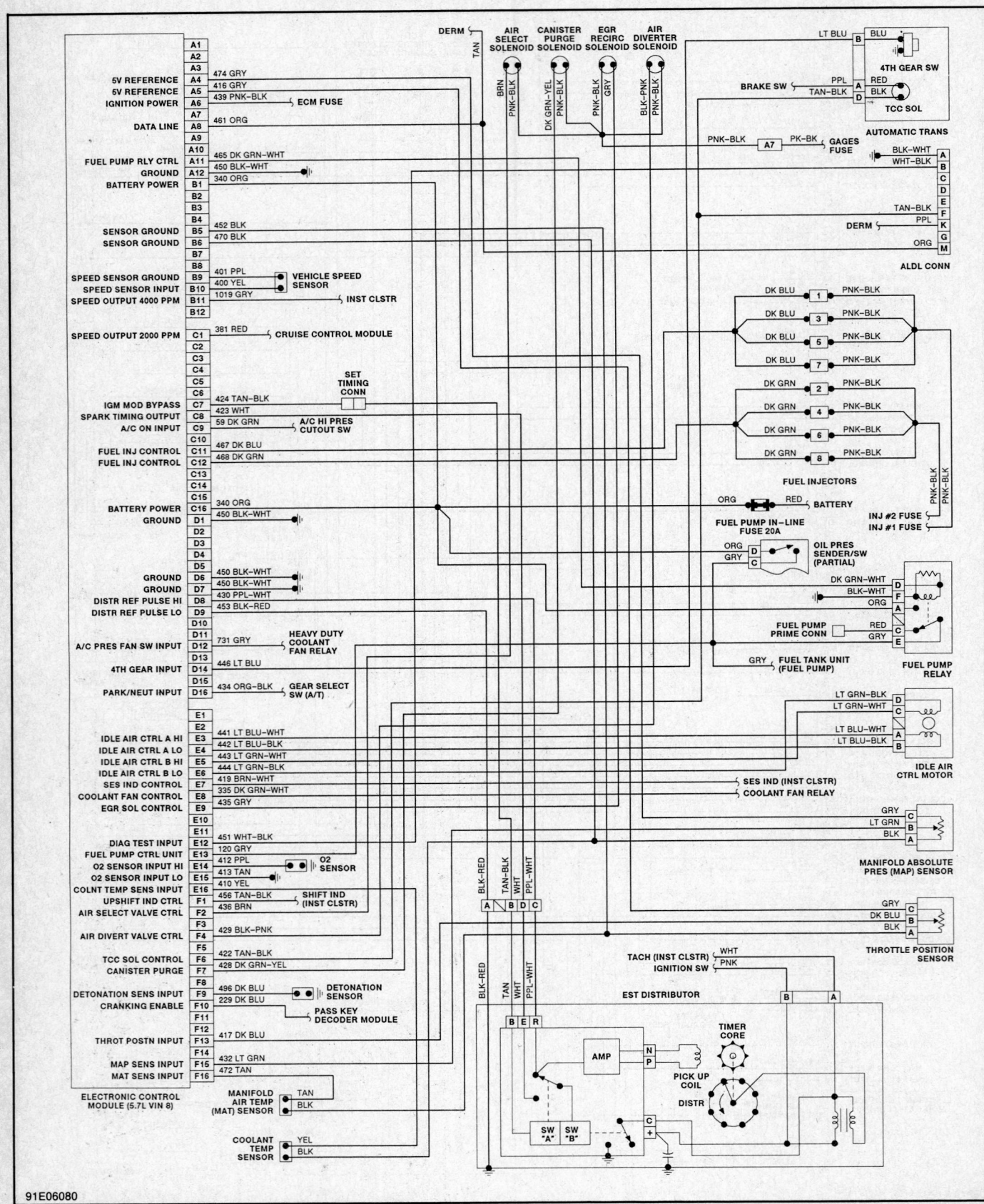

Fig. 45: 5.7L (VIN 8) ECM Wiring Diagram (Camaro & Firebird)

91E06080

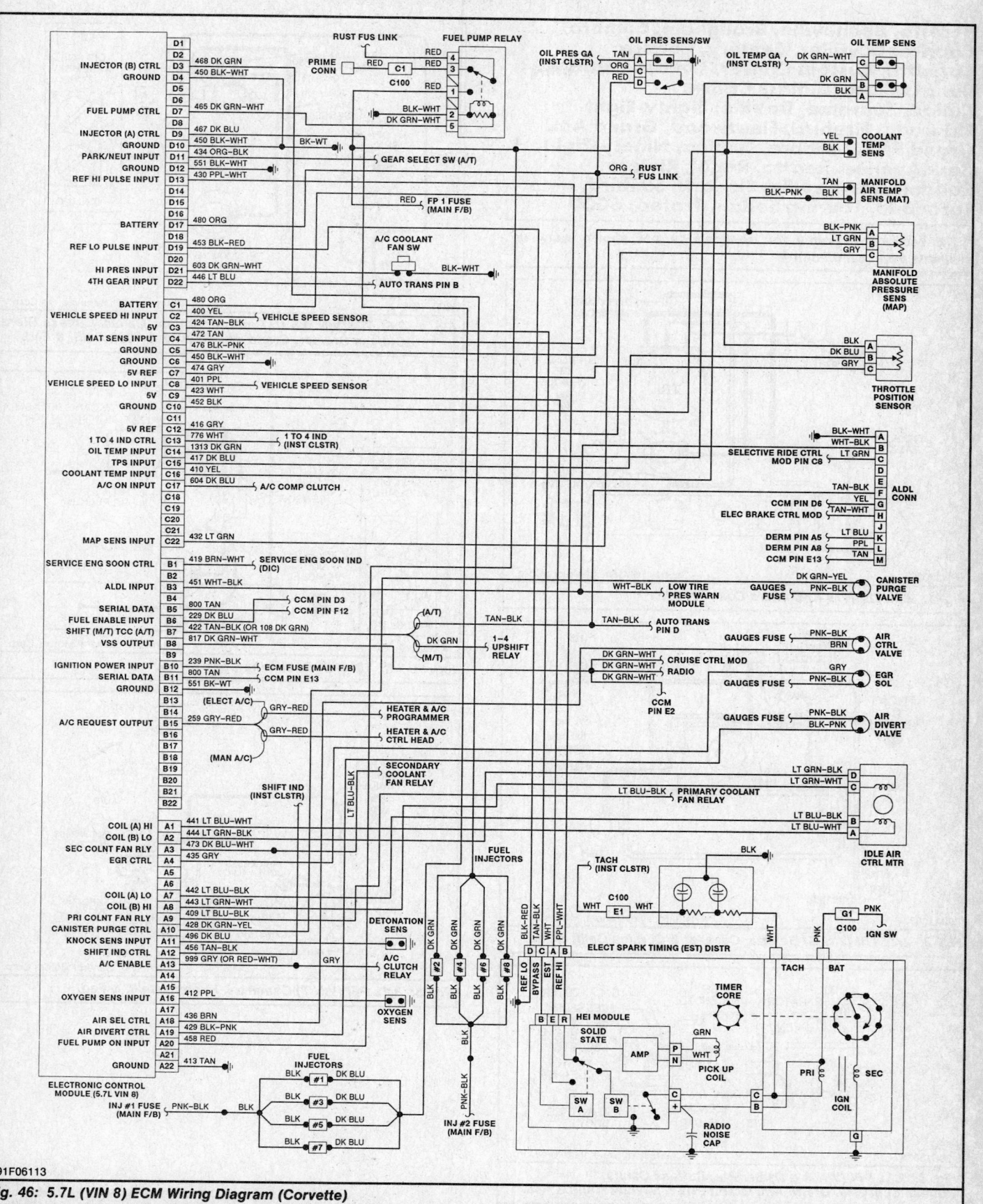

Fig. 46: 5.7L (VIN 8) ECM Wiring Diagram (Corvette)

91F06113

1991 ENGINE PERFORMANCE
Vacuum Diagrams

Beretta, Bonneville, Brougham, Camaro, Caprice, Cavalier, Century, Corsica, Corvette, Custom Cruiser, Cutlass Calais, Cutlass Ciera, Cutlass Cruiser, Cutlass Supreme, DeVille, Eighty-Eight Eldorado, Firebird, Fleetwood, Grand Am, Grand Prix, LeSabre, Lumina, Ninety-Eight, Park Avenue, Reatta, Regal, Riviera, Roadmaster, Seville, Skylark, Sunbird, Toronado, Touring Sedan, Trofeo, 6000

NOTE: Vacuum diagrams for applications not shown were not available from manufacturer.

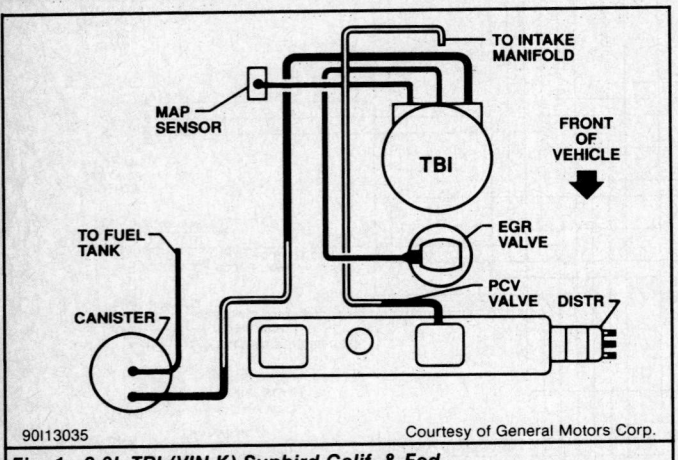

Fig. 1: 2.0L TBI (VIN K) Sunbird Calif. & Fed.

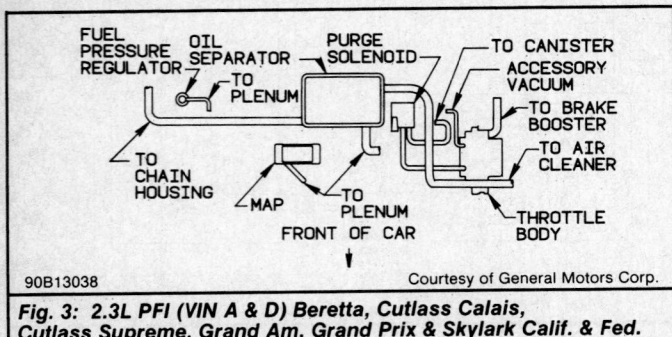

Fig. 2: 2.2L TBI (VIN G) Beretta, Cavalier & Corsica Calif. & Fed.

Fig. 3: 2.3L PFI (VIN A & D) Beretta, Cutlass Calais, Cutlass Supreme, Grand Am, Grand Prix & Skylark Calif. & Fed.

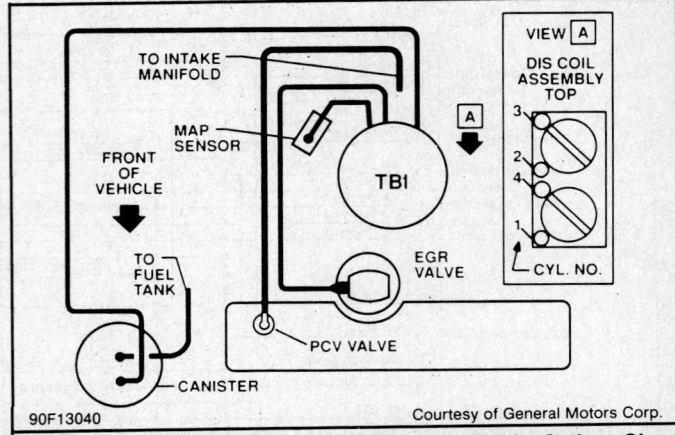

Fig. 4: 2.5L TBI (VIN R & U) Century, Cutlass Calais, Cutlass Ciera, Cutlass Cruiser, Grand Am, Skylark & 6000 Calif. & Fed.

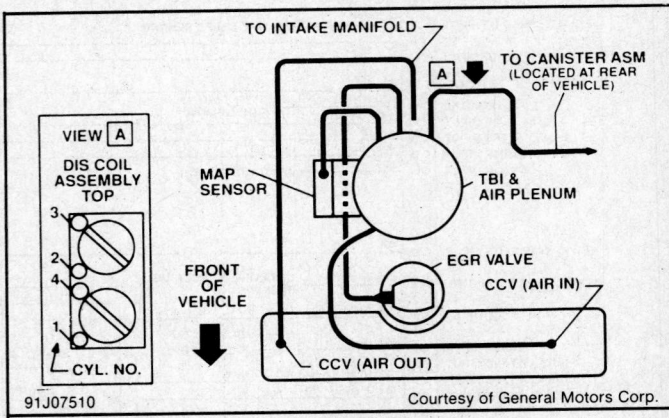

Fig. 5: 2.5L TBI (VIN R) Lumina Calif. & Fed.

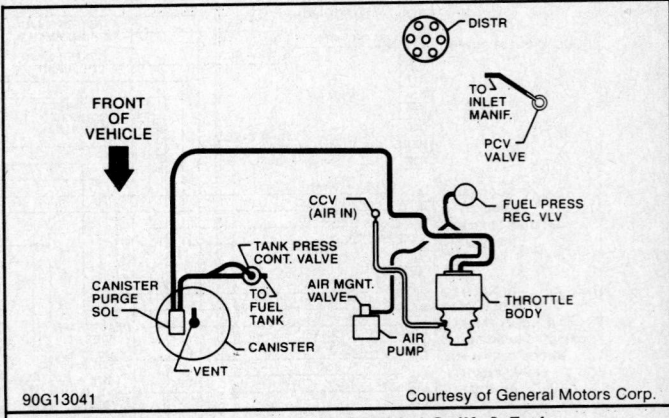

Fig. 6: 3.1L PFI (VIN T) Camaro & Firebird Calif. & Fed.

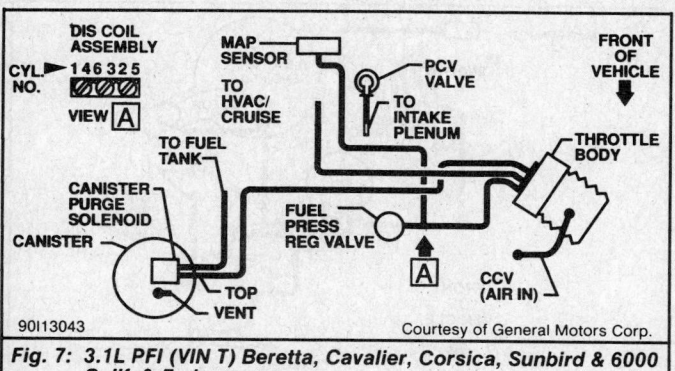

Fig. 7: 3.1L PFI (VIN T) Beretta, Cavalier, Corsica, Sunbird & 6000 Calif. & Fed.

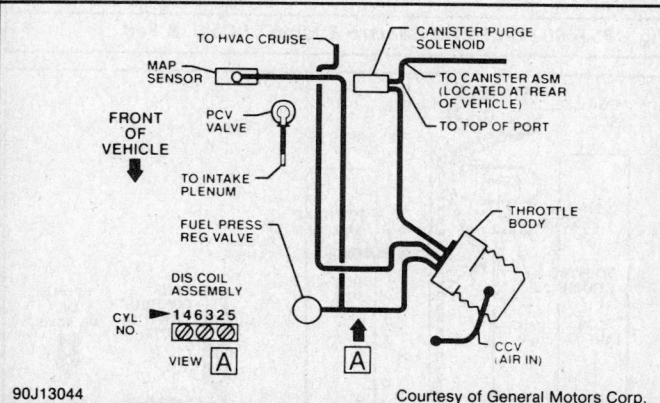

Fig. 8: 3.1L PFI (VIN T) Cutlass Supreme, Grand Prix, Lumina & Regal (Digital EGR) Calif. & Fed.

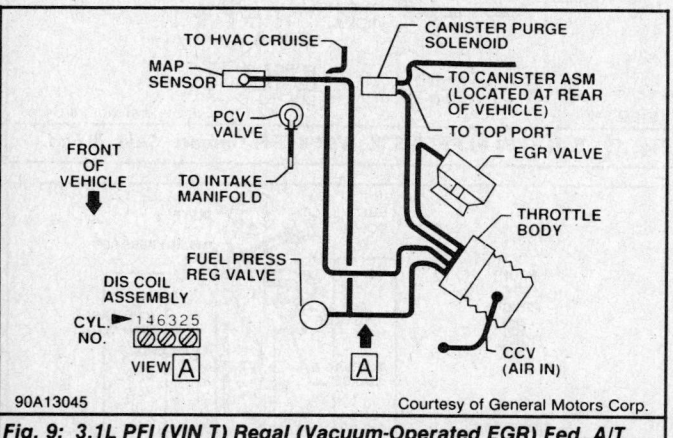

Fig. 9: 3.1L PFI (VIN T) Regal (Vacuum-Operated EGR) Fed. A/T

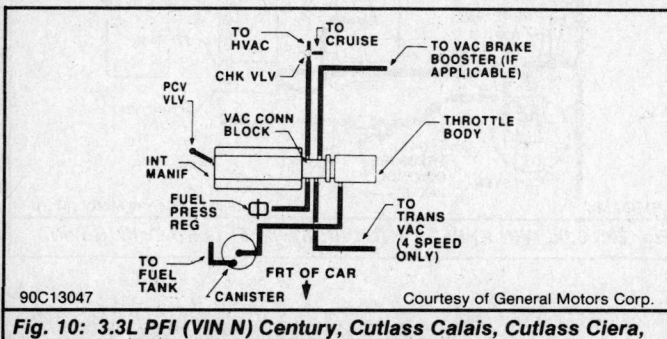

Fig. 10: 3.3L PFI (VIN N) Century, Cutlass Calais, Cutlass Ciera, Cutlass Cruiser & Skylark Calif. & Fed.

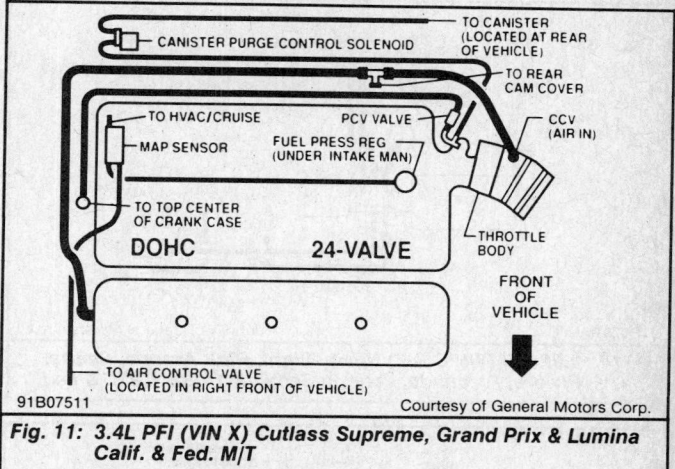

Fig. 11: 3.4L PFI (VIN X) Cutlass Supreme, Grand Prix & Lumina Calif. & Fed. M/T

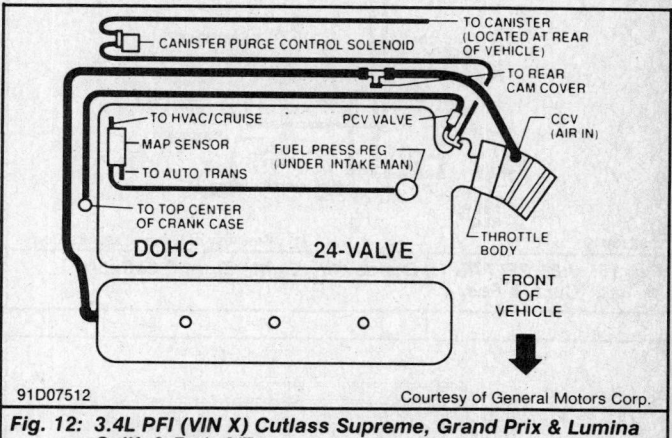

Fig. 12: 3.4L PFI (VIN X) Cutlass Supreme, Grand Prix & Lumina Calif. & Fed. A/T

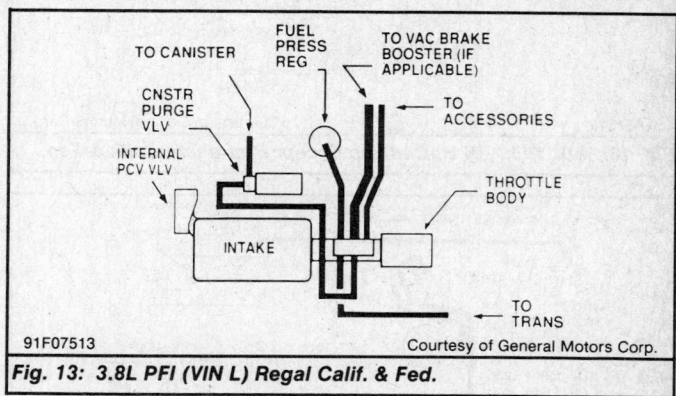

Fig. 13: 3.8L PFI (VIN L) Regal Calif. & Fed.

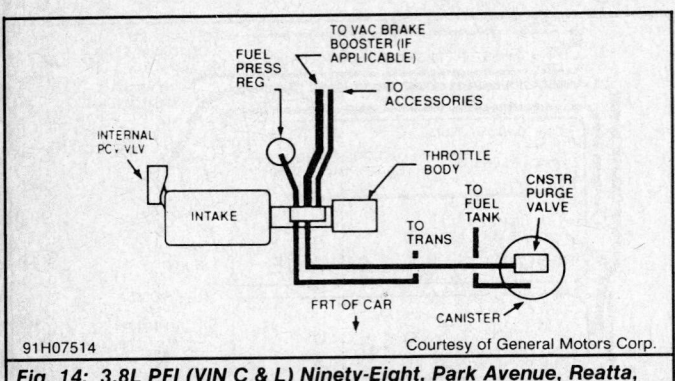

Fig. 14: 3.8L PFI (VIN C & L) Ninety-Eight, Park Avenue, Reatta, Riviera, Toronado, Touring Sedan & Trofeo Calif. & Fed.

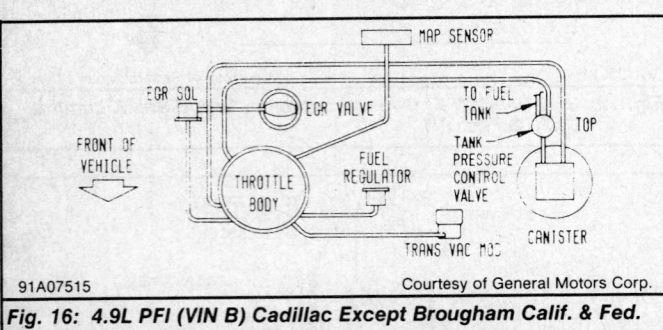

Fig. 15: 3.8L PFI (VIN C) Bonneville, Eighty-Eight & LeSabre Calif. & Fed.

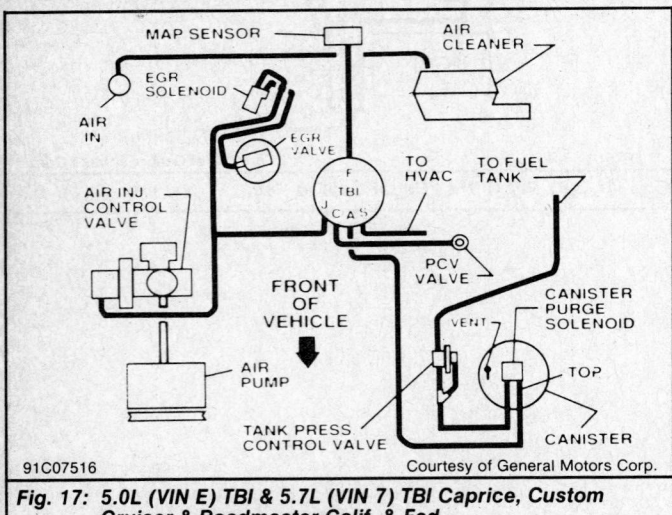

Fig. 16: 4.9L PFI (VIN B) Cadillac Except Brougham Calif. & Fed.

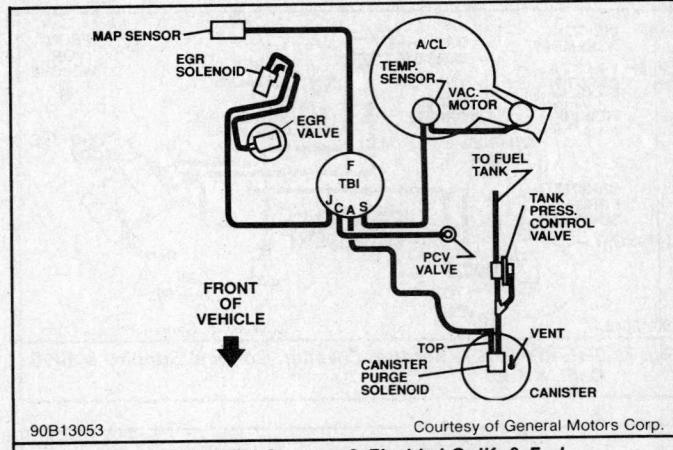

Fig. 18: 5.0L (VIN E) TBI Camaro & Firebird Calif. & Fed.

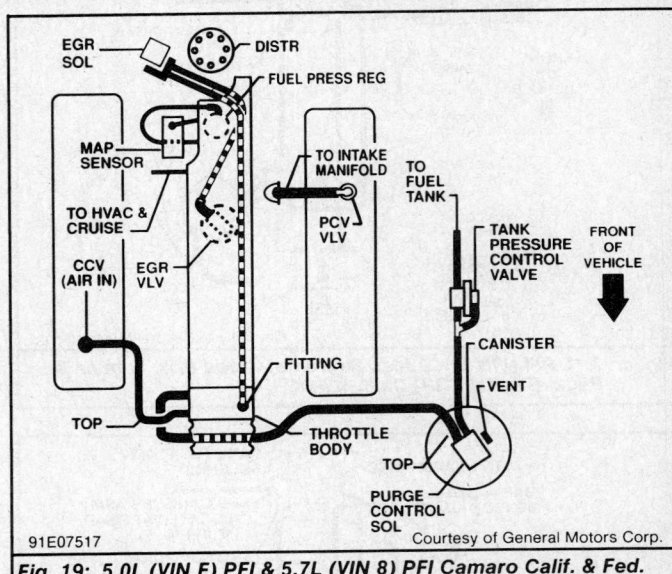

Fig. 19: 5.0L (VIN F) PFI & 5.7L (VIN 8) PFI Camaro Calif. & Fed.

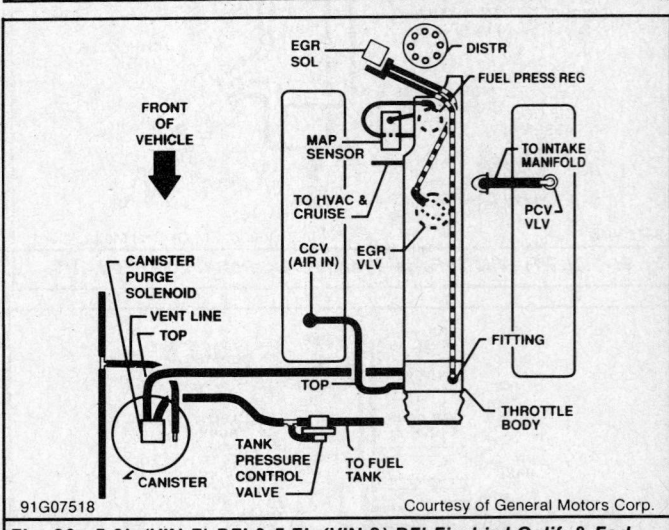

Fig. 20: 5.0L (VIN F) PFI & 5.7L (VIN 8) PFI Firebird Calif. & Fed.

Fig. 17: 5.0L (VIN E) TBI & 5.7L (VIN 7) TBI Caprice, Custom Cruiser & Roadmaster Calif. & Fed.

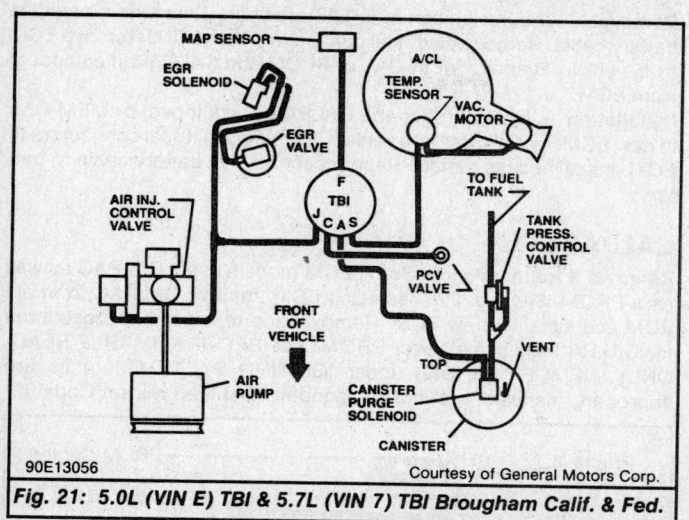

90E13056

Courtesy of General Motors Corp.

Fig. 21: 5.0L (VIN E) TBI & 5.7L (VIN 7) TBI Brougham Calif. & Fed.

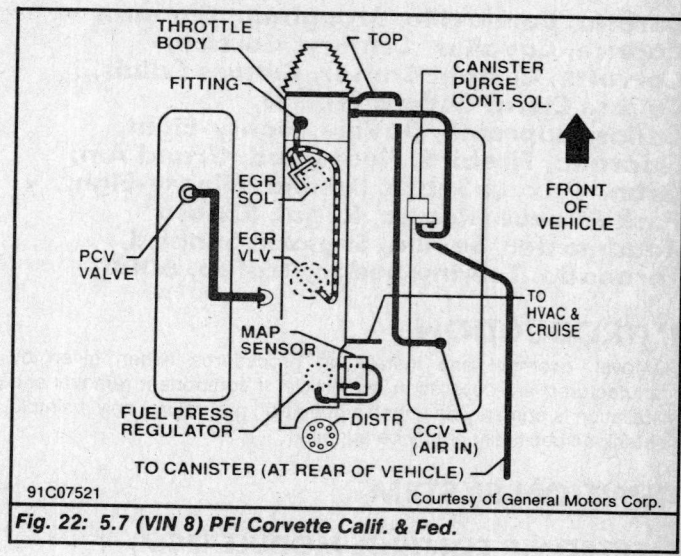

91C07521

Courtesy of General Motors Corp.

Fig. 22: 5.7 (VIN 8) PFI Corvette Calif. & Fed.

1991 ENGINE PERFORMANCE
Removal, Overhaul & Installation

Beretta, Bonneville, Brougham, Camaro, Caprice, Cavalier, Century, Corsica, Corvette, Custom Cruiser, Cutlass Calais, Cutlass Ciera, Cutlass Cruiser, Cutlass Supreme, DeVille, Eighty-Eight, Eldorado, Firebird, Fleetwood, Grand Am, Grand Prix, LeSabre, Lumina, Ninety-Eight, Park Avenue, Reatta, Regal, Riviera, Roadmaster, Seville, Skylark, Sunbird, Toronado, Touring Sedan, Trofeo, 6000

INTRODUCTION

Removal, overhaul and installation procedures (when given by manufacturer) are covered in this article. If component removal and installation is primarily an unbolt and bolt-on procedure, only a simple tightening specification may be supplied.

IGNITION SYSTEM

ELECTRONIC CONTROL MODULE (ECM)

CAUTION: Electronic components used in control systems are designed to carry very low voltages. As little as a 30-volt charge created by static electricity can cause a total or degrading failure in ECM or other electronic components containing integrated circuits. Before servicing ECM, ground yourself and ground the work area to discharge stored electricity.

STATIC CHARGE (VOLTS)

Movement	Relative Humidity 10-20%	Relative Humidity 65-90%
Handling Clear Plastic Bag	20,000	1200
Handling Vinyl Envelope	7000	600
Sliding On Velour Seat	15,000	400
Walking On Carpet	35,000	1500
Walking On Tile/Vinyl	12,000	50

CAUTION: DO NOT remove part from packaging until ready to install. Ground any static-proof package BEFORE opening. DO NOT touch electrical terminals of components unless properly grounded. DO NOT lay electrical components on car seat, carpeting or dashboard. Use electrostatic protection mat and ground strap whenever possible.

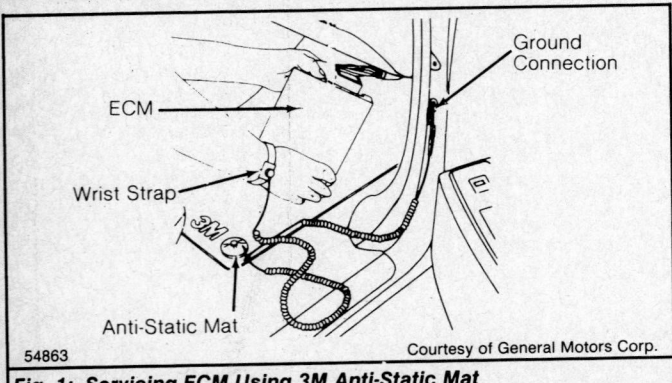

54863   Courtesy of General Motors Corp.

Fig. 1: Servicing ECM Using 3M Anti-Static Mat

NOTE: Before replacing ECM, carefully inspect all wiring and control components. Failure to test for short circuits may result in repeated ECM failure due to grounds and Quad-Driver failure. To prevent internal damage to ECM, ensure ignition is in OFF position when disconnecting or reconnecting ECM connectors or 12-volt components.

Removal – Ensure ignition is in OFF position. Disconnect negative battery cable. Remove electrical connectors from ECM. Remove ECM from vehicle. Remove MEM-CAL or PROM and CALPAC (if equipped) from ECM.

Installation – Install PROM and CALPAC (if equipped) or MEM-CAL in new ECM. Install ECM into vehicle. Connect electrical connectors to ECM. Install access panels. Reconnect negative battery cable to battery.

CALPAC

Removal & Installation – Some ECM models use a CALPAC as well as a PROM. *See Fig. 2.* If replacing ECM, remove CALPAC from old ECM and install in new ECM. Removal and replacement procedures for CALPAC are same as for PROM. See PROGRAMMABLE READ-ONLY MEMORY (PROM) under IGNITION SYSTEM. If units are improperly installed, grounding diagnostic test lead will set Code 52.

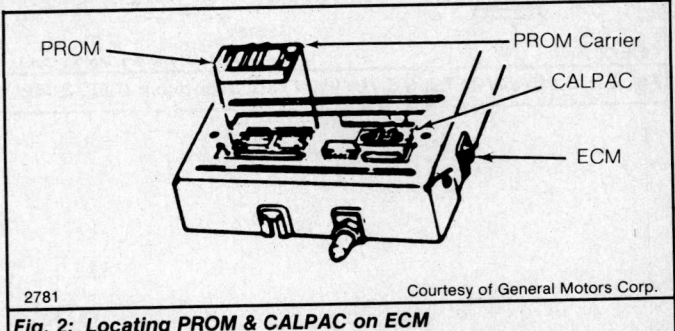

2781   Courtesy of General Motors Corp.

Fig. 2: Locating PROM & CALPAC on ECM

MEM-CAL

Removal – Disconnect negative battery cable. Remove ECM from vehicle. Using 2 fingers, push retaining clips back from MEM-CAL; at the same time, grasp MEL-CAL at both ends and lift out of socket. DO NOT remove MEM-CAL cover.

Installation – 1) Carefully align MEM-CAL pins with ECM pin holes. DO NOT press in middle of MEM-CAL. Push downward evenly on ends of MEM-CAL until retaining clips on ends of MEM-CAL snap into place.

2) Install ECM. Reconnect negative battery cable. Turn ignition on and ground ALDL connector. Code 12 should flash at least 4 times (if no other codes are present). If code(s) 42, 43, 51 or 52 is present, or if CHECK ENGINE light stays on constantly with code(s) present, MEM-CAL is not fully seated or is defective. If it is necessary to remove MEM-CAL, follow previous removal instructions.

PROGRAMMABLE READ-ONLY MEMORY (PROM)

Removal – 1) Remove ECM from vehicle. See ELECTRONIC CONTROL MODULE under IGNITION SYSTEM. Position ECM so bottom cover faces upward. Remove slide-off PROM access cover by depressing locking tab.

2) Using PROM removal tool, grasp PROM at narrow ends. Gently rock PROM from end to end while pulling up. If installing new PROM, remove old PROM from PROM carrier. *See Fig. 2.*

NOTE: Note reference notch locations in PROM, carrier and ECM for reassembly reference.

Installation – 1) Ensure new PROM has same service number as old one. Place new PROM in PROM carrier. Position PROM carrier squarely over ECM PROM socket. Press on PROM carrier until PROM is firmly seated in ECM.

NOTE: Ensure reference notches in both ECM and PROM are properly aligned. If PROM is installed backwards, PROM will be destroyed when ignition is turned on.

2) Install PROM access cover on ECM. Install ECM in vehicle. See ELECTRONIC CONTROL MODULE (ECM) under IGNITION SYSTEM. Start engine and ground ALDL diagnostic test connector. Watch for trouble Code 51 or 52.

3) If Code 51 or 52 occurs, PROM is either not fully seated in ECM, installed backwards, has bent pins, or is defective. If bent pins are cracked when trying to straighten, replace PROM. If PROM is installed backwards or is defective, replace PROM.

ELECTRONIC SPARK CONTROL (ESC) MODULE

NOTE: The ESC is mounted to firewall on a bracket behind the distributor.

Removal & Installation – Turn ignition off. Remove bracket-to-firewall screws. Rotate bracket to access ESC module. Disconnect ESC module harness connector. Remove ESC mounting screws and remove ESC. To install, reverse removal procedure.

IGNITION MODULE (DIS)

Removal & Installation (2.2L, 2.5L, 3.1L & 3.4L) – **1)** Disconnect negative battery cable. Unplug connectors at ignition module. Disconnect spark plug wires from coil pack. Remove ignition module from engine block. Remove coils and assembly plate.

2) On 2.5L engines, inspect crankshaft sensor "O" ring for wear, cracks or other damage. Replace as necessary. Lubricate new "O" ring with engine oil before installing.

3) To install, reverse removal procedure. Tighten ignition coil nuts and module to specification. See TORQUE SPECIFICATIONS table at end of article.

NOTE: If spark plug boots adheres to spark plugs, use Boot Remover (J-36011). Twist first and then pull upward. Boots must be in place on housing before installing ignition system assembly, or damage may result.

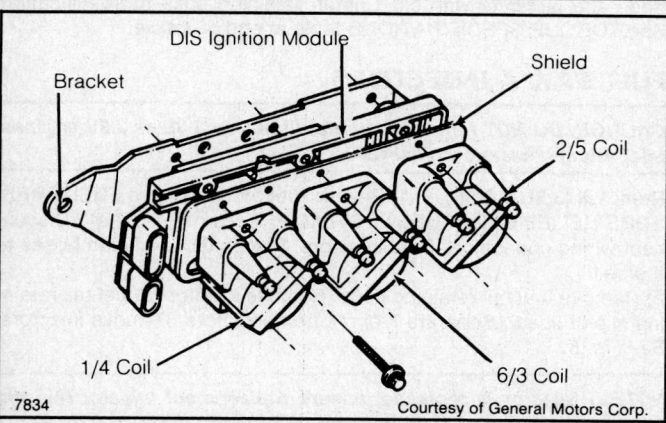

Fig. 3: Locating Distributorless Ignition Module Components (3.1L & 3.4L)

IGNITION MODULE (IDI)

Removal & Installation (2.3L) – **1)** Disconnect negative battery cable. Disconnect 11-pin harness connector. Remove 4 ignition module cover-to-cam carrier bolts.

2) Remove ignition system assembly from engine. Remove 4 housing cover screws. Remove housing cover. Remove coil harness connector from module. Remove module-to-cover screws. Remove module from cover. To install, reverse removal procedure.

NOTE: DO NOT wipe grease from module or coil if module is not being replaced. If installing a new module, spread silicone grease on metal face of module and on cover where module seats. Grease is included with new module and is necessary for module cooling purposes.

IGNITION MODULE (C³I)

Removal & Installation (3.3L & 3.8L) – Disconnect negative battery cable. Unplug 14-way connector at ignition module. Disconnect spark plug wires from coil pack. Remove nuts and washers securing ignition module to bracket. Remove coil-to-ignition module Torx screws. Note wire colors for reassembly. Unplug connectors between ignition coil and module. Remove module. To install, reverse removal procedure.

CRANKSHAFT/COMBINATION SENSOR (C³I)

Removal (3.3L & 3.8L) – **1)** Remove serpentine belt from crankshaft pulley. Raise vehicle on hoist. Remove right front tire and wheel assembly. Remove right inner fender access cover.

2) Using 28-mm socket, remove crankshaft harmonic balancer retaining bolt. Remove harmonic balancer. Remove foreign object deflector (DO NOT use pry bar). Disconnect sensor harness connector. Remove sensor and pedestal (as an assembly) from block. Remove sensor from pedestal.

Installation – **1)** Loosely install sensor on pedestal. Position sensor, with pedestal attached, onto Installer (J-37089). *See Fig. 4.* Position installer onto crankshaft.

2) Install pedestal-to-block bolts. Tighten bolts to 18-26 ft. lbs. (25-35 N.m). Tighten pedestal pinch bolt to 26-44 INCH lbs. (3-5 N.m). Remove installer. Install foreign object deflector. Place harmonic balancer onto installer. Rotate balancer on installer. If any vanes of interrupter rings contact installer, replace harmonic balancer.

3) Install balancer on crankshaft. To complete installation, reverse removal procedure. Tighten balancer retaining bolt to specification. See TORQUE SPECIFICATIONS table at end of article.

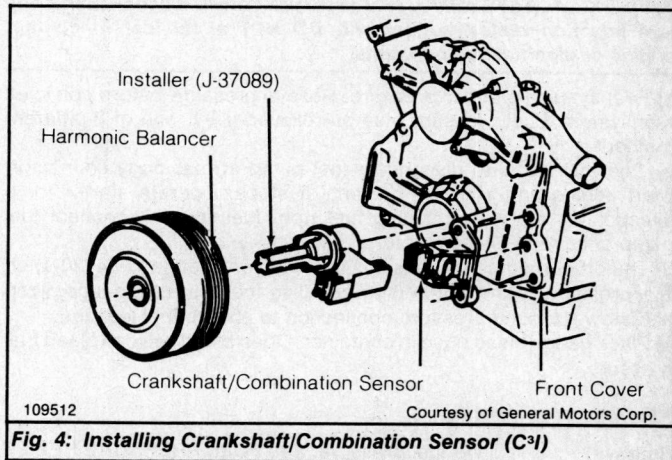

Fig. 4: Installing Crankshaft/Combination Sensor (C³I)

CAMSHAFT SENSOR (C³I)

Removal & Installation (3.3L & 3.8L) – Disconnect negative battery cable. Remove camshaft sensor attaching bolt. Disconnect wiring harness and remove sensor. To install, reverse removal procedure.

CRANKSHAFT POSITION SENSOR (DIS & IDI)

Removal & Installation (2.2L, 2.3L, 3.1L & 3.4L) – Disconnect sensor harness at IDI or DIS ignition module. Remove bolt and sensor from engine block. Inspect crankshaft sensor "O" ring for wear, cracks or other damage. Replace as necessary. Lubricate new "O" rings with engine oil before installing. To install, reverse removal procedure.

Removal & Installation (2.5L) – Remove DIS ignition module. Remove crankshaft sensor mounting screws and remove sensor from DIS module. Inspect "O" ring for wear before installing DIS module. Replace as necessary. To install, reverse removal procedure. Tighten screws to specification. See TORQUE SPECIFICATIONS table at end of article.

IGNITION COIL (C³I)

Removal & Installation (3.3L) – Disconnect negative battery cable. Remove spark plug wires from coil. Remove coil-to-module bolts.

Remove coil assembly. To install, reverse removal procedure. Tighten retaining bolts to specification. See TORQUE SPECIFICATIONS table at end of article.

Removal & Installation (3.8L) – Disconnect negative battery cable. Remove spark plug wires from coil pack. Remove coil-to-ignition module Torx screws. Tilt coil assembly back. Disconnect module connectors and remove coil pack. To install, reverse removal procedure. Tighten retaining bolts to specifications. See TORQUE SPECIFICATIONS table at end of article.

IGNITION COILS (DIS & IDI)

Removal & Installation (2.2L, 2.5L, 3.1L & 3.4L) – Disconnect negative battery cable. Remove spark plug wires from coils. Remove nuts or screws from ignition coils. Remove coils. To install, reverse removal procedure.

Removal & Installation (2.3L) – **1)** Disconnect negative battery cable. Disconnect 11-pin harness connector. Remove ignition cover-to-cam carrier bolts. Remove ignition system assembly from engine. Remove housing cover screws. Remove housing cover.

2) Remove coil harness connector from module. Remove module-to-cover screws. Remove module from cover. To install, reverse removal procedures. Tighten screws to specification. See TORQUE SPECIFICATIONS table at end of article.

FUEL SYSTEM (PFI)

FUEL PRESSURE RELIEF

WARNING: ALWAYS relieve fuel pressure before disconnecting any fuel injection-related component. DO NOT allow fuel to contact engine or electrical components.

1) Fuel system is under pressure. Relieve pressure before servicing fuel system. Fuel pressure may be relieved using one of 2 different methods.

2) One method is to disconnect fuel pump at rear body connector. Start engine and allow to run until it stops. Operate starter for 3 seconds to remove remaining fuel from fuel lines. Reconnect fuel pump once repair is complete.

3) The other method is to install Fuel Pressure Gauge (J-34730-1) on fuel pressure connection. When installing fuel pressure gauge, wrap shop towel around pressure connection to absorb fuel leakage.

4) Place gauge bleed hose in container. Open bleed valve to bleed fuel pressure.

THROTTLE BODY

Removal – **1)** Relieve fuel pressure. See FUEL PRESSURE RELIEF under FUEL SYSTEM (PFI). Remove air inlet ducts. Disconnect and mark electrical connections and vacuum hoses from throttle body. Disconnect control cables from throttle body.

2) Drain cooling system. Remove coolant hoses. Remove throttle body retaining bolts. Remove throttle body and gasket.

NOTE: Identification number is stamped on throttle body. Use identification number to order replacement components.

Installation – **1)** To install, reverse removal procedure; use new gasket. Tighten retaining bolts to specification. See TORQUE SPECIFICATIONS table at end of article. Refill cooling system.

2) If installing new Idle Air Control (IAC), ensure IAC pintle length setting before installing. See IDLE AIR CONTROL VALVE under FUEL SYSTEM (PFI). Adjust idle speed and TPS (if removed). See ON-VEHICLE ADJUSTMENTS article in ENGINE PERFORMANCE.

FUEL PRESSURE REGULATOR

Removal (2.3L, 3.3L, 3.8L & 4.9L) – **1)** Relieve fuel pressure. See FUEL PRESSURE RELIEF under FUEL SYSTEM (PFI). Disconnect pressure regulator-to-fuel rail hose. On 2.3L, remove fuel rail. See FUEL RAIL & INJECTORS under FUEL SYSTEM (PFI).

2) On all models, remove pressure regulator retaining bolts. Remove pressure regulator from fuel rail. On 2.3L, remove pressure regulator retainer and seal from fuel rail.

Installation – To install, reverse removal procedures. Always replace "O" rings. Lubricate fuel rail seal with oil and install in regulator. Tighten bolts to specification. See TORQUE SPECIFICATIONS table at end of article.

Removal (3.1L & 3.4L) – **1)** Relieve fuel pressure. See FUEL PRESSURE RELIEF under FUEL SYSTEM (PFI). Remove upper manifold or intake manifold plenum. On 3.1L models, remove fuel rails. See FUEL RAIL & INJECTORS under FUEL SYSTEM (PFI).

2) On all models, remove inlet and return fuel fittings and gaskets. Remove pressure regulator-to-bracket retaining bolts. Separate pressure regulator from fuel rail.

3) Remove pressure regulator base-to-fuel rail connector tubes from pressure regulator.

Installation – **1)** To install, reverse removal procedures. Lubricate new "O" rings with oil. Install fuel return "O" rings on fuel rails. Return "O" rings are larger in diameter than connector tube "O" rings.

2) Tighten bolts to specification. See TORQUE SPECIFICATIONS table at end of article.

Removal (5.0L & 5.7L) – **1)** Relieve fuel pressure, and remove fuel rails. See FUEL PRESSURE RELIEF and FUEL RAILS & INJECTORS under FUEL SYSTEM (PFI).

2) Remove front crossover tube retainer on right fuel rail. Remove rear crossover tube retainer at pressure regulator on right fuel rail. Separate fuel rail assemblies.

3) Remove pressure regulator bracket-to-fuel rail bolt. Remove bracket-to-regulator base bolt. Remove bracket. Remove fuel outlet tube-to-right fuel rail bolt. Remove base-to-right fuel rail bolt.

4) Remove pressure regulator assembly from fuel rail. Rotate pressure regulator and remove from outlet tube. Remove base-to-fuel rail connector tube. Remove "O" rings from connector tube, outlet tube and crossover tubes.

Installation – To install, reverse removal procedures. Install new "O" rings and lubricate with oil. Tighten retaining bolts to specification. See TORQUE SPECIFICATIONS table at end of article.

FUEL RAIL & INJECTORS

CAUTION: DO NOT remove fuel inlet fitting on 2.3L or 3.3L engines. Inlet fitting is staked to fuel rail.

Removal (3.3L & 3.8L) – **1)** Relieve fuel pressure. See FUEL PRESSURE RELIEF under FUEL SYSTEM (PFI). Turn ignition off. Disconnect wiring connectors from injectors. Disconnect and plug hoses to fuel rail.

2) Remove fuel rail retaining bolts. Remove injector-to-fuel rail retaining clip (if used). Separate fuel rail from injectors. Remove injectors. *See Fig. 5.*

NOTE: If injector is replaced, ensure replacement injector has the same part number as that removed.

Installation – To install, reverse removal procedure. Coat new "O" rings with oil. Install "O" rings on injectors. Tighten fuel rail retaining bolts to specification. See TORQUE SPECIFICATIONS table at end of article.

Removal (2.3L) – **1)** Relieve fuel pressure. See FUEL PRESSURE RELIEF under FUEL SYSTEM (PFI). Remove crankcase ventilation oil/separator.

2) Remove fuel lines from fuel rail. Remove vacuum line at pressure regulator. Disconnect wiring connector while pushing inward on connector. Remove fuel rail retaining bolts. Remove fuel rail. *See Fig. 6.*

3) Remove injector-to-fuel rail retaining clip. Remove injector from fuel rail. Remove injector "O" rings.

Installation – To install reverse removal procedure. Lubricate injector "O" rings with oil. Install injector-to-fuel rail retaining clip, with open end facing injector electrical connection. Tighten fuel rail retaining bolts.

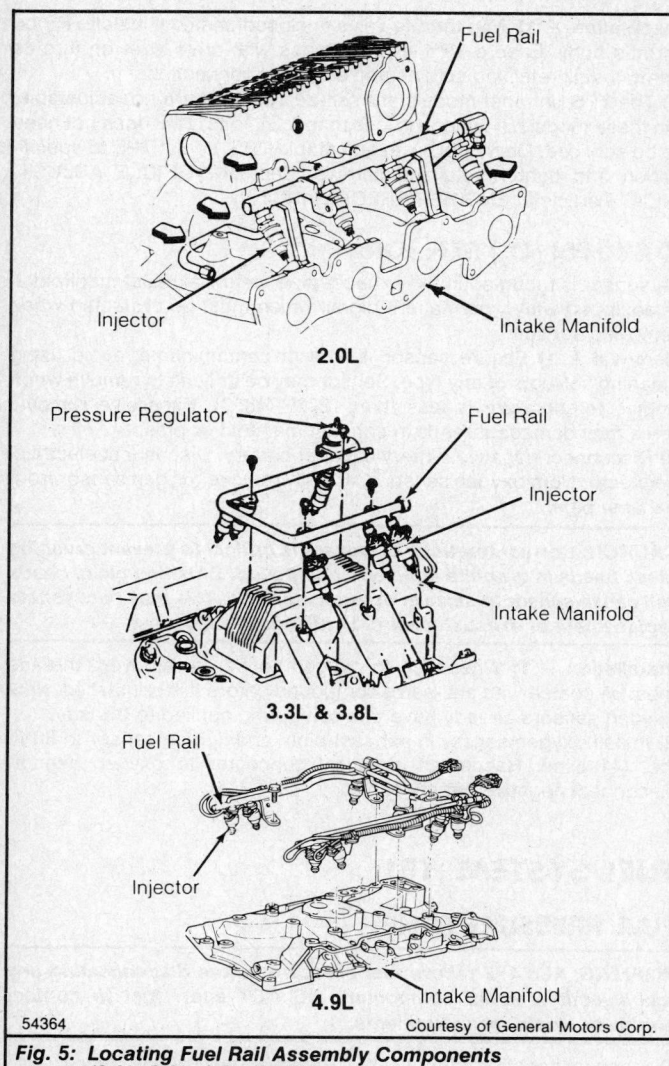

Fig. 5: Locating Fuel Rail Assembly Components (2.0L, 3.3L, 3.8L & 4.9L)

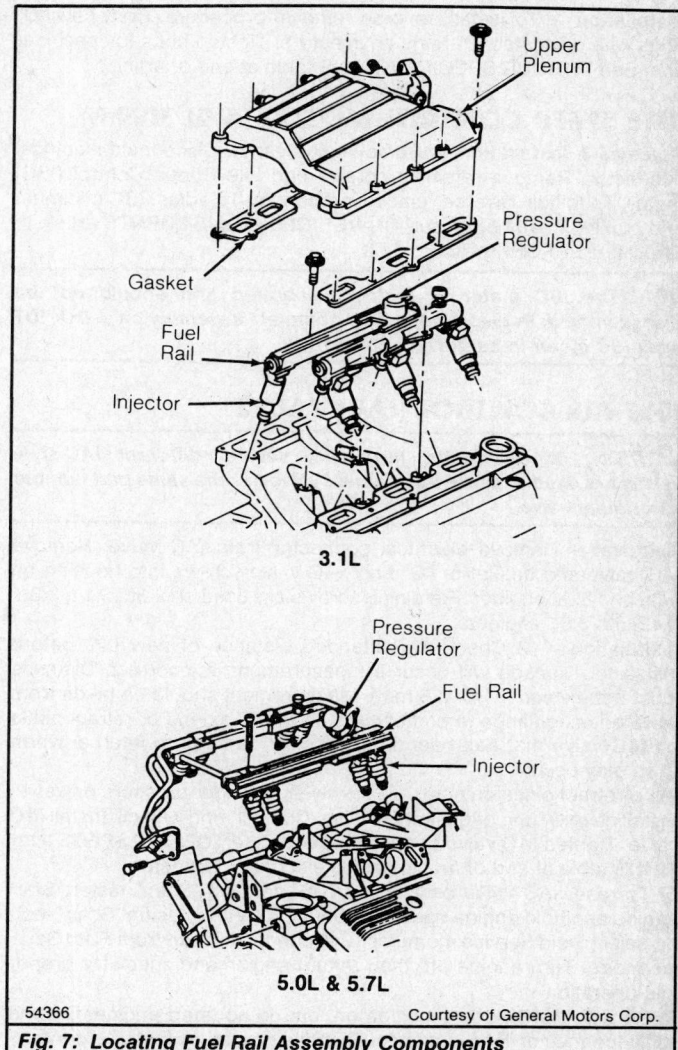

Fig. 7: Locating Fuel Rail Assembly Components (3.1L, 5.0L & 5.7L)

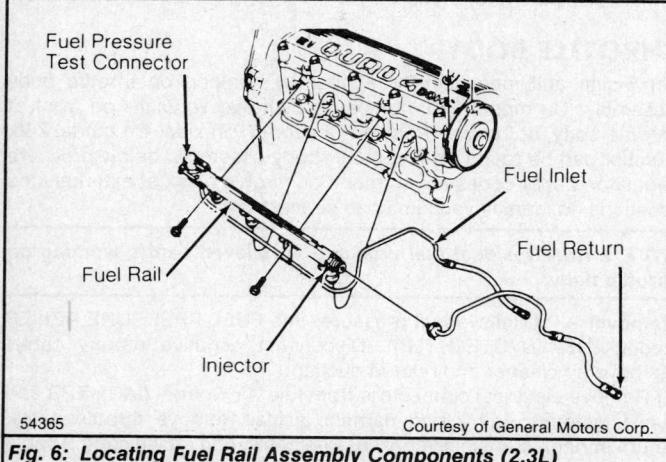

Fig. 6: Locating Fuel Rail Assembly Components (2.3L)

Removal (3.1L, 3.4L, 5.0L & 5.7L) – 1) Relieve fuel pressure. See FUEL PRESSURE RELIEF under FUEL SYSTEM (PFI). Disconnect negative battery cable. Remove intake manifold upper plenum. Disconnect and mark vacuum lines. Remove EGR-to-intake manifold retaining bolts. Some models use an EGR pipe which requires removal at EGR base.

2) Remove throttle cable bracket bolts. Disconnect cables and electrical wiring connections from throttle body. Remove throttle body from intake manifold. Remove plenum and gasket. See Fig. 7.

3) Disconnect vacuum hose to pressure regulator. Remove runners. Disconnect fuel lines from fuel rail. With ignition off, disconnect electrical connections from injectors.

4) Remove fuel rail retaining bolts. Remove fuel rail and injectors. On 5.0L and 5.7L, rotate injector retaining clip to unlock position. On all models, remove injectors from fuel rail. Remove "O" rings from injectors.

Installation – To install, reverse removal procedure. Coat new "O" rings with oil. Install "O" rings on injectors. Tighten bolts to specification. See TORQUE SPECIFICATIONS table at end of article.

Removal (4.9L) – 1) Remove air cleaner. Relieve fuel pressure. See FUEL PRESSURE RELIEF under FUEL SYSTEM (PFI). Disconnect negative battery cable. Remove power steering pump and set aside.

2) Disconnect vacuum hose to pressure regulator and base assembly. Disconnect accelerator cable, cruise control cable and bracket. Disconnect electrical connectors. Drain coolant and disconnect coolant hose to thermostat housing.

3) Wrap shop towel around fuel line, and disconnect fuel feed line from rear fuel rail assembly and fuel return line. Discard "O" rings. Disconnect EGR vacuum hose. Remove EGR valve. Remove fuel rail attaching bolts. Disconnect electrical connectors at front and rear fuel rail assemblies. Remove fuel rail from intake manifold. See Fig. 5.

Installation – To install, reverse removal procedure. Coat new "O" rings with oil. Install "O" rings on injectors. Tighten bolts to specification. See TORQUE SPECIFICATIONS table at end of article.

IDLE SPEED CONTROL MOTOR (4.9L VIN B)

Removal & Installation – Remove air cleaner. Disconnect electrical connector. Remove retaining screws and Idle Speed Control (ISC) motor. To install, reverse removal procedure. To adjust ISC minimum and maximum authority, see ON-VEHICLE ADJUSTMENTS article in ENGINE PERFORMANCE.

NOTE: The ISC motor is factory calibrated and should not be disassembled. Replace motor as a complete assembly only. DO NOT soak ISC motor in carburetor cleaner.

IDLE AIR CONTROL (IAC) VALVE

CAUTION: For calibration purposes, several different IAC-style valves are used. Ensure replacement valve has the same part number as original valve.

Removal – Remove electrical connector from IAC valve. Remove IAC valve and gasket or "O" ring. IAC valve screws into housing on 5.0L and 5.7L engines. Retaining screws are used on 2.3L, 3.1L, 3.3L, 3.4L and 3.8L engines.

Installation – **1)** Check the extended distance of new IAC before installing. Damage will occur if measurement is incorrect. Distance must not exceed 1 1/8" (28 mm). Measurement should be taken from valve housing flange to end of cone. DO NOT extend or retract pintle on IAC valve that has been in service, or damage to internal worm drive may occur.

2) To retract pintle on new IAC, slowly exert finger pressure on valve. Install new "O" ring or gasket on valve. Coat "O" ring with oil. Install IAC valve. Tighten IAC valve to specifications. See TORQUE SPECIFICATIONS table at end of article. Install electrical connector.

3) To reset IAC valve on 2.3L (VIN A), connect "Scan" tester. Start engine and hold engine speed at about 2000 RPM. Using "Scan" tester, select Field Service mode for 10 seconds then exit from Field Service mode. Turn engine off, then restart engine and check for proper idle operation.

4) On 2.3L (VIN D), turn ignition on, but do not start engine. Ground ALDL connector for 5 seconds. Remove ground from ALDL connector. Turn ignition on for 10 seconds. Start engine and check for proper idle operation.

5) On 3.1L & 3.4L, turn ignition on for 5 seconds, then turn ignition off for 10 seconds. Start engine and check for proper idle operation.

6) On 3.3L, turn ignition on, but do not start engine. Ground ALDL connector for 5 seconds. Remove ground from ALDL connector. Start engine and check for proper idle operation.

7) On 5.7L (VIN 8), depress accelerator slightly. Start and run engine for 5 seconds. Turn ignition off for 10 seconds. Restart engine and check for proper idle operation.

FUEL PUMP

Removal & Installation – **1)** Disconnect negative battery cable. Relieve fuel pressure. See FUEL PRESSURE RELIEF under FUEL SYSTEM (PFI). Remove filler neck. Lower fuel tank. Disconnect fuel lines and electrical connection.

2) Remove fuel level sending unit and fuel pump retaining bolts or cam lock ring. Lift assembly from fuel tank and remove fuel pump from sending unit.

3) Pull fuel pump upward while pulling outward away from bottom support. Use care not to damage rubber insulator and strainer. To install, reverse removal procedure; use new "O" ring and gasket.

THROTTLE POSITION SENSOR (TPS)

Removal – Disconnect electrical connection from TPS. Remove TPS retaining screws. Remove TPS.

Installation – **1)** With throttle valve in closed position, install TPS on throttle body. Ensure TPS lever engages with drive lever on throttle shaft. Install retaining screws and electrical connection.

2) The TPS on most models are self-zeroing and are not adjustable. On these models, if voltage is less than 1.25 volts, TPS does not need to be serviced. On models with adjustable TPS, adjust TPS to specification and tighten retaining screws. See ON-VEHICLE ADJUSTMENTS article in ENGINE PERFORMANCE.

OXYGEN (O₂) SENSOR

O_2 sensor is mounted in the exhaust pipe, below exhaust manifold. It is equipped with a permanent pigtail which must be protected when removing sensor.

Removal – **1)** Ensure sensor is free of contaminants; avoid using cleaning solvents of any type. Sensor may be difficult to remove when engine temperature is less than 120°F (48°C). Excessive removal force may damage threads in exhaust manifold or pipe.

2) Disconnect negative battery cable at battery. Disconnect electrical connector from oxygen sensor. Carefully remove oxygen sensor from exhaust pipe.

CAUTION: Correct torque of O_2 sensor is critical to prevent crushing glass beads in graphite anti-seize compound. Crushing glass beads will cause sensor to seize in exhaust manifold. This may necessitate replacement of exhaust manifold at the next removal.

Installation – **1)** Whenever an oxygen sensor is removed, threads must be coated with anti-seize compound before it is reinstalled. New oxygen sensors already have this compound applied to threads.

2) Install oxygen sensor in exhaust pipe, and tighten sensor to 30 ft. lbs. (41 N.m). Reconnect electrical connector to oxygen sensor. Reconnect negative battery cable.

FUEL SYSTEM (TBI)

FUEL PRESSURE RELIEF

WARNING: ALWAYS relieve fuel pressure before disconnecting any fuel injection-related component. DO NOT allow fuel to contact engine or electrical components.

Disconnect negative battery cable. Remove fuel filler cap. Since these TBI units contain an internal bleed-down feature, system fuel pressure should dissipate after a short time.

THROTTLE BODY

An 8-digit unit identification number is stamped on throttle body assembly. On model 220, number is stamped vertically on front of throttle body, at Throttle Position Sensor (TPS) side. On model 700, number can be found on fuel meter body assembly, below pressure regulator. Letter codes are stamped on throttle body, at external tube locations, to identify vacuum hose connections.

NOTE: Ensure residual fuel pressure is relieved before working on throttle body.

Removal – **1)** Relieve fuel pressure. See FUEL PRESSURE RELIEF under FUEL SYSTEM (TBI). Disconnect negative battery cable. Remove air cleaner and related ducting.

2) Remove electrical connectors from Idle Air Control (IAC), TPS and fuel injector(s). Lay wiring harness aside. Remove throttle cable, return springs, transmission/transaxle cable, and cruise control cable (if equipped). Label and remove vacuum hoses.

3) Remove fuel feed and return lines. Use 2 wrenches to prevent nuts in throttle body from coming loose. Remove fuel line "O" rings and discard. Remove throttle body retaining bolts. Remove TBI unit and base gasket. Discard base gasket.

CAUTION: Pressure regulator spring is under heavy tension, and can cause injury if released. DO NOT immerse cover in any type of cleaning solvent.

Disassembly (Throttle Body Cover – Model 220) – 1) Place throttle body on Holding Fixture (J-9789-118 or BT 30-15) to prevent damage to throttle valve. Remove cover-to-throttle body screws; note location of 2 short screws.

2) Remove throttle body cover. *See Fig. 9.* Throttle body cover and pressure regulator are serviced as an assembly. DO NOT remove pressure regulator-to-cover screws. Remove TPS and IAC assembly. Throttle valve screws are staked in position and should not be removed.

Disassembly (Fuel Meter Assembly – Model 700) – Remove fuel meter-to-throttle body retaining screws. Remove fuel meter assembly. *See Fig. 8.* Discard gasket. If fuel pressure regulator cover is removed, replace regulator diaphragm to prevent fuel leaks. Remove TPS and IAC assembly. Throttle valve screws are staked in position and should not be removed.

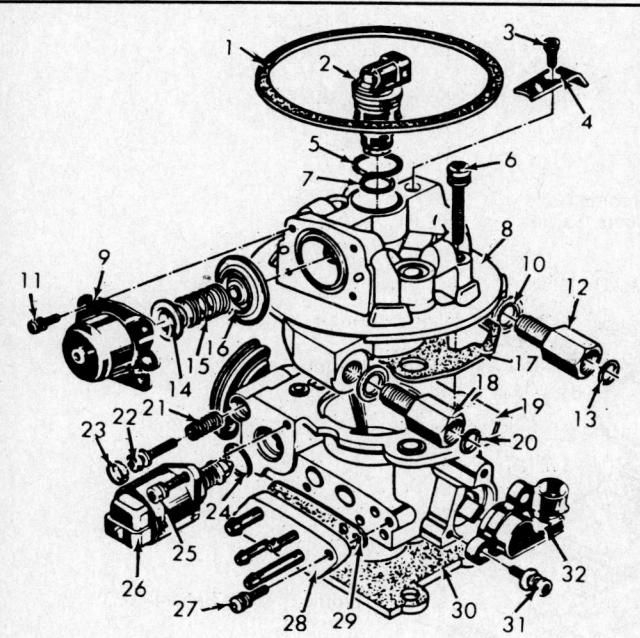

1. Air Filter Gasket
2. Fuel Injector
3. Injector Retainer Screw
4. Injector Retainer
5. Upper Injector "O" Ring
6. Fuel Meter Assembly Screw
7. Lower Injector "O" Ring
8. Fuel Meter Assembly
9. Pressure Regulator Cover
10. Fuel Nut Seal
11. Pressure Regulator Cover Screw
12. Fuel Feed Nut
13. Fuel Line "O" Ring
14. Regulator Spring Seat
15. Regulator Spring
16. Pressure Regulator Diaphragm
17. Fuel Meter Assembly Gasket
18. Fuel Return Nut
19. Throttle Body Assembly
20. Fuel Line "O" Ring
21. Idle Stop Screw Spring
22. Idle Stop Screw
23. Idle Stop Screw Plug
24. IAC "O" Ring
25. IAC Retaining Screw
26. IAC Valve
27. Vacuum Tube Assembly Retaining Screw
28. Vacuum Tube Assembly
29. Vacuum Tube Gasket
30. Base Gasket
31. TPS Mounting Screw
32. TPS

7758   Courtesy of General Motors Corp.

Fig. 8: Exploded View of Throttle Body Assembly (Model 700)

Cleaning & Inspection – 1) Clean all metal parts in a cold immersion-type cleaner such as Carbon X (X-55). Blow dry with compressed air.
2) DO NOT immerse the following in cleaner solvent: TPS, IAC, throttle body cover, fuel meter and pressure regulator assemblies, fuel injector, fuel filter, rubber parts and diaphragms.

3) Inspect mating surfaces for damage that may prevent gasket sealing. Repair or replace components as necessary.
Reassembly (Throttle Body Cover – Model 220) – 1) Install new dust seal into recess of throttle body. Install fuel outlet passage gasket on cover. Install throttle body cover gasket on throttle body. Install cover; ensure pressure regulator dust seal and cover gaskets are in place.
2) Apply thread locking compound to cover attaching screws. Install cover screws and lock washers. Tighten screws. Connect electrical lead to fuel injector and install air cleaner. To complete assembly, reverse disassembly procedure.
Reassembly (Fuel Meter Assembly – Model 700) – 1) Install new fuel meter-to-throttle body assembly gasket. Match cutout portions of gasket with openings in throttle body assembly.
2) Place fuel meter assembly on throttle body. Install fuel meter-to-throttle body retaining screws and washers (screws should be coated with locking compound). Tighten screws to specification. See TORQUE SPECIFICATIONS table at end of article.
3) Install new "O" rings on fuel lines. Using a back-up wrench on fuel fittings, tighten fuel line nuts to 20 ft. lbs. (27 N.m). To complete reassembly, reverse disassembly procedure.
Installation – 1) Install throttle body unit to intake manifold; use new gaskets. Tighten retaining bolts to specification. See TORQUE SPECIFICATIONS table at end of article. Install new "O" rings onto fuel lines.
2) Connect fuel feed and return lines throttle body. Use a back-up wrench to prevent fuel line fittings in throttle body from turning. Tighten fuel line nuts to specifications. See TORQUE SPECIFICATIONS table at end of article.

THROTTLE BODY INJECTOR

Removal (Model 220) – 1) Relieve fuel pressure. See FUEL PRESSURE RELIEF under FUEL SYSTEM (TBI). Remove throttle body cover, leaving cover gasket in place. Using screwdriver and fulcrum, carefully pry injector out. *See Fig. 10.* Remove small "O" ring from nozzle end of injector.
2) Carefully rotate injector fuel filter back and forth to remove fuel filter from base of injector. Remove and discard throttle body cover gasket. Remove large "O" ring and steel back-up washer from top counterbore of throttle body injector cavity.
Installation – 1) Install fuel filter on nozzle end of fuel injector. Ensure large end of filter faces injector so filter covers the raised rib at base of injector. Lubricate small "O" ring with ATF, and push "O" ring on nozzle end of injector until it presses against injector filter.
2) Install steel back-up washer in top counterbore of throttle body injector cavity. Lubricate large "O" ring with ATF, and install "O" ring directly over back-up washer. *See Fig. 9.* Ensure "O" ring is seated properly in cavity and is flush with top of throttle body casting.

CAUTION: Back-up washer and large "O" ring must be installed before injector. Improper seating of "O" ring will cause fuel leak.

3) Install "O" ring on injector. Install injector into cavity by aligning raised lug on injector base with cast-in notch of throttle body cavity. Push down on injector until fully seated. Electrical terminals of injector will be approximately parallel with throttle shaft. Install throttle body cover.
Removal (Model 700) – Relieve fuel pressure. See FUEL PRESSURE RELIEF under FUEL SYSTEM (TBI). Remove fuel injector retainer screw and remove retainer. Using screwdriver and fulcrum on side of injector opposite connector terminals, carefully pry injector out. *See Fig. 10.* Remove upper and lower "O" rings and discard.
Installation – 1) Lubricate new upper and lower "O" rings with engine oil, and place them on injector. Ensure upper ring is in groove and lower ring is flush against filter.
2) Position injector in fuel meter assembly, with electrical connector facing cutout for wire grommet.
3) Push injector down to seat in cavity. Install injector retainer. Coat injector retainer screw with thread locking compound and install. Tighten screw to 27 INCH lbs. (3.0 N.m).

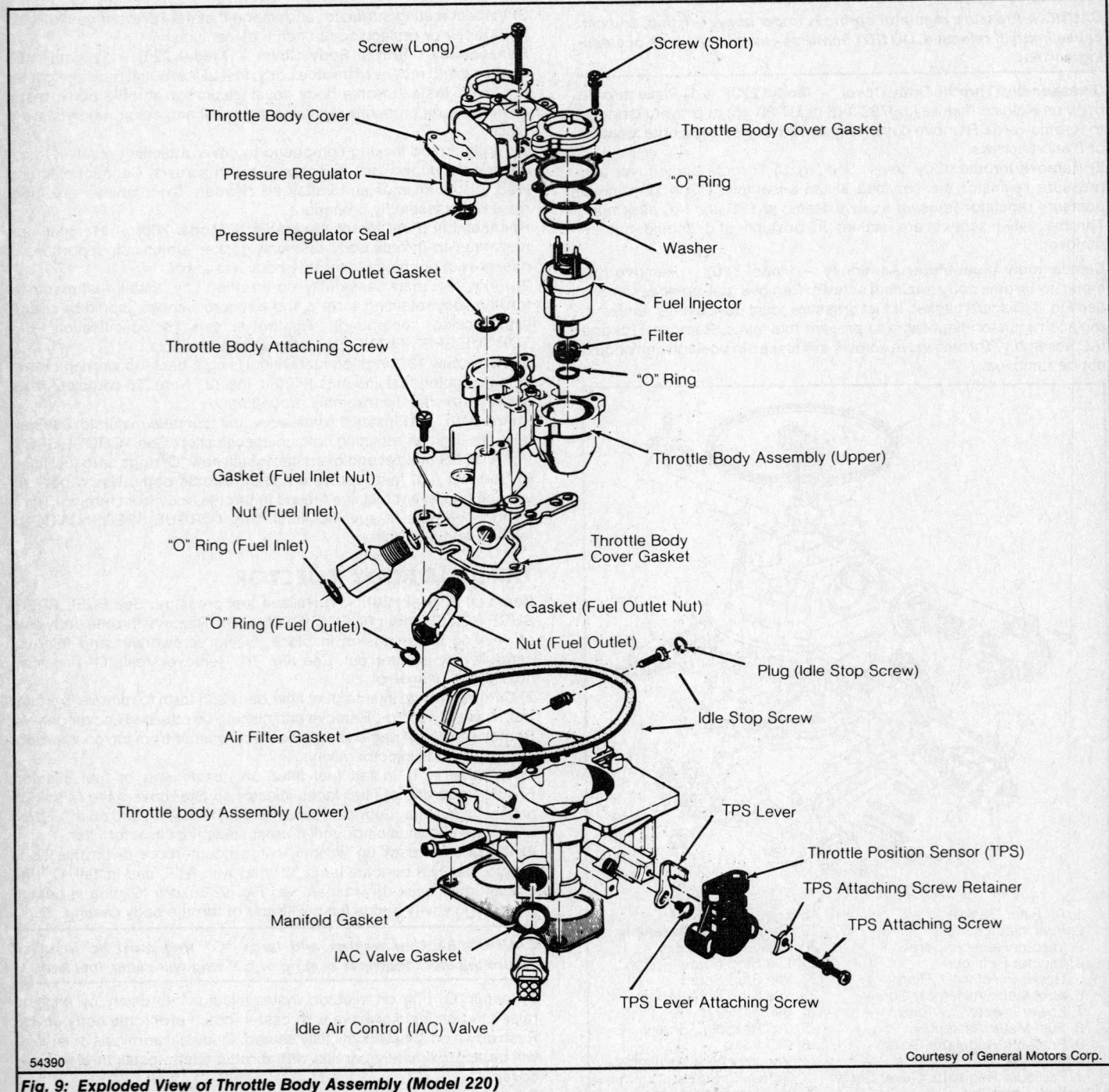

Fig. 9: Exploded View of Throttle Body Assembly (Model 220)

54390

Courtesy of General Motors Corp.

IDLE AIR CONTROL (IAC) VALVE

Removal – Remove air cleaner and related ducting. Remove Idle Air Control (IAC) electrical connector. On model 220, unscrew IAC valve. On model 700, remove IAC retaining screws and remove IAC valve. Replace as necessary.

Installation – **1)** Inspect gasket or "O" ring for damage. Replace as necessary. Measure distance from IAC contact flange to tip of pintle. Distance should not exceed 1 1/8" (28 mm). If valve is extended too far, valve will be damaged during installation.

2) To set IAC pintle length on new IAC, use finger pressure to slowly retract pintle. Lubricate new "O" ring with ATF and install new gasket. Install IAC valve on throttle body. Tighten IAC valve to specification. See TORQUE SPECIFICATIONS table at end of article.

CAUTION: DO NOT extend or retract pintle if IAC valve has been in service, or damage to worm gear will result.

3) Connect electrical lead to IAC valve, and install air cleaner. Start engine and hold engine speed at greater than 2000 RPM. Ground ALDL connector for 10 seconds then remove ground. Turn ignition off then restart engine. Check for proper idle operation.

FUEL PUMP

Removal & Installation – 1) Disconnect negative battery cable. Relieve fuel pressure. See FUEL PRESSURE RELIEF under FUEL SYSTEM (TBI). Remove filler neck. Lower fuel tank. Disconnect fuel lines and electrical connection.

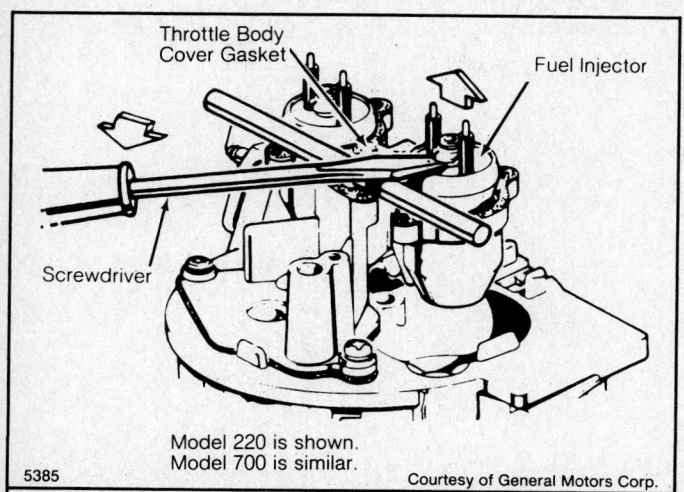

Model 220 is shown.
Model 700 is similar.

5385   Courtesy of General Motors Corp.

Fig. 10: Removing Throttle Body Injector (Typical)

2) Remove fuel level sending unit and fuel pump retaining bolts or cam lock ring. Lift assembly from fuel tank and remove fuel pump from sending unit.

3) Pull fuel pump upward while pulling outward away from bottom support. Use care not to damage rubber insulator and strainer. To install, reverse removal procedure; use new "O" ring and gasket.

THROTTLE POSITION SENSOR (TPS)

Removal – Disconnect electrical connection from TPS. Remove TPS retaining screws. Remove TPS.

Installation – **1)** With throttle valve in closed position, install TPS on throttle body. Ensure TPS lever engages with drive lever on throttle shaft. Install retaining screws and electrical connection.

2) The TPS on most models are self-zeroing and are not adjustable. On these models, if voltage is less than 1.25 volts, TPS does not need to be serviced. On models with adjustable TPS, adjust TPS to specification and tighten retaining screws. See ON-VEHICLE ADJUSTMENTS article in ENGINE PERFORMANCE.

OXYGEN (O₂) SENSOR

O_2 sensor is mounted in the exhaust pipe, below exhaust manifold. It is equipped with a permanent pigtail which must be protected when removing sensor.

Removal – **1)** Ensure sensor is free of contaminants; avoid using cleaning solvents of any type. Sensor may be difficult to remove when engine temperature is less than 120°F (48°C). Excessive removal force may damage threads in exhaust manifold or pipe.

2) Disconnect negative battery cable at battery. Disconnect electrical connector from oxygen sensor. Carefully remove oxygen sensor from exhaust pipe.

CAUTION: Correct torque of O_2 sensor is critical to prevent crushing glass beads in graphite anti-seize compound. Crushing glass beads will cause sensor to seize in exhaust manifold. This may necessitate replacement of exhaust manifold at the next removal.

Installation – **1)** Whenever an oxygen sensor is removed, threads must be coated with anti-seize compound before it is reinstalled. New oxygen sensors already have this compound applied to threads.

2) Install oxygen sensor in exhaust pipe, and tighten sensor to 30 ft. lbs. (41 N.m). Reconnect electrical connector to oxygen sensor. Reconnect negative battery cable.

TORQUE SPECIFICATIONS

TORQUE SPECIFICATIONS

Application	Ft. Lbs. (N.m)
Harmonic Balancer (C³I)	
3.3L & 3.8L	200-239 (270-325)

TORQUE SPECIFICATIONS (Cont.)

Application	Ft. Lbs. (N.m)
Ignition System	
DIS Module-To-Block Bolt	
2.2L, 2.5L, 3.1L & 3.4L	15-22 (20-30)
IDI Cover Assembly Bolt (4)	19 (26)
Oxygen Sensor	30 (41)
Fuel System (PFI)	
Fuel Inlet & Return Line Nuts	
2.0L	20 (27)
2.3L, 3.3L, 3.4L & 4.9L	22 (30)
3.1L	17 (23)
5.0L & 5.7L	20 (27)
Fuel Rail Bolt	
2.0L & 3.3L	15-20 (20-27)
2.3L	19 (26)
4.9L	18 (24)
5.0L & 5.7L	15 (20)
Fuel Inlet Fitting [1]	
3.1L	35 (47)
IAC Valve	
2.0L, 5.0L & 5.7L	13 (18)
Intake Runner Bolts	
5.0L & 5.7L	19 (26)
Plenum Bolts	
3.1L	16 (22)
5.0L & 5.7L	19 (26)
Throttle Body Bolt	
2.0L	10-15 (14-20)
2.3L, 3.1L, 5.0L & 5.7L	19 (26)
3.8L	11 (15)
4.9L	14 (19)
Throttle Body Nut	
3.3L	21 (28)
Fuel System (TBI)	
Fuel Inlet Fitting	30 (41)
Fuel Outlet Fitting (Model 220)	22 (30)
Fuel Outlet Fitting (Model 700)	30 (41)
Fuel Line Nut	20 (27)
Idle Air Control Valve (Model 220)	13 (18)
Throttle Body-To-Manifold Bolt	18 (24)

Application	INCH Lbs. (N.m)
Ignition System	
Coil-To-Cover Screws (4)	
2.3L	35 (4.0)
Crankshaft/Combination Sensor-To-Block Bolt	
2.2L	53-106 (6-12)
2.3L	89 (10)
3.1L	71 (8.0)
Crankshaft Sensor-To-Module Screws	
2.5L	20 (2.3)
Ignition Coil-To-Module Screws	
2.2L, 2.5L & 3.1L	41 (4.6)
Module-To-Cover Screws (3)	
2.3L	35 (4.0)
Fuel System (PFI)	
Coolant Cover Screws	
2.3L	9 (1.0)
3.1L	27 (3.0)
Crossover Tube Retainer Bolt	
5.0L & 5.7L	44 (4.9)
Fuel Rail Bolt	
3.1L	89 (10)
Fuel Return Line Clamp Bolt	
2.3L	53 (6.0)
IAC Valve Housing	
3.3L & 3.8L	27 (3.0)
IAC Valve Retaining Screw	
2.3L, 3.1L, 3.3L & 3.8L	18 (2.0)
Pressure Regulator Base-To-Rail Bolt	
5.0L & 5.7L	44 (4.9)
Pressure Regulator-To-Bracket Bolts	
5.0L & 5.7L	44 (4.9)
Fuel System (TBI)	
Fuel Injector Screw (Model 700)	27 (3.0)
Fuel Meter Assembly Screw (Model 700)	31 (3.5)
Idle Air Control Valve Retaining Screw (Model 700)	27 (3.0)
Lower Throttle Body-To-Upper	
Throttle Body Screw (Model 220)	35 (4.0)
Throttle Body Cover Screw (Model 220)	27 (3.0)
Throttle Position Sensor Screw	18 (2.0)
Vacuum Tube Assembly Screw (Model 700)	27 (3.0)

[1] – On 2.3L and 3.3L, fuel rail inlet fitting must not be removed from fuel rail. Fitting is staked in place.

DESCRIPTION

The CS144, 140-amp alternator is used in conjunction with a Body Control Module (BCM). CS stands for charging system and 144 denotes the outside diameter (in millimeters) of the alternator stator laminations.

The alternator and related charging system circuitry has self-diagnostic capacity. A communication process has been incorporated between the BCM and CS144 alternator. When the alternator circuit exceeds programmed limits, the malfunction may be indicated by the BATTERY NO CHARGE message on the telltale warning lamp cluster.

The voltage regulator is enclosed in a solid mold, mounted inside the alternator. A capacitor, mounted in the end frame, protects the rectifier bridge from high voltage and suppresses radio noise.

OPERATION

The voltage regulator controls the field with a Pulse Width Modulated (PWM) signal, measured in duty cycles. A PWM signal continuously cycles on and off. The "on" time can vary within each cycle.

When the ignition switch is turned to the RUN position, before engine is started, the BCM applies voltage to the regulator. The regulator is now in field strobe function and applies a small percentage of the duty cycle to the field windings, which produce a magnetic field. As alternator RPM increases, the field strobe function is disabled and normal regulation occurs.

When field current is on, the regulator switches the field current on and off at a fixed frequency of about 400 cycles per second. By varying the overall on and off time, correct average field current for proper system voltage control is achieved. At high speeds, the on time may be 10 percent. At low speeds, with a heavy electrical load, the on time may be as much as 90 percent.

The BCM monitors the regulator from the generator field terminal. If the PWM duty cycle falls below 7 percent "on" time, the BCM will sense a fault and indicate a problem, illuminating the CHARGE indicator.

SELF-DIAGNOSTICS

ENTERING SELF-DIAGNOSTICS

1) With ignition switch in ON position, simultaneously push OFF and WARMER buttons on Electronic Climate Control (ECC) panel. *See Fig. 1.* Continue to push OFF and WARMER buttons until all segments of the Fuel Data Center (FDC) and ECC illuminate. This is a segment illumination check. *See Figs. 1 and 2.*

2) Illuminating the FDC and ECC display panels ensures all display segments are working properly. If all segments illuminate, proceed to DISPLAYING TROUBLE CODES. Failure of any segment to illuminate may result in inaccurate test results. An inoperative display panel must be replaced before proceeding with the self-diagnostic process.

NOTE: System automatically enters self-diagnostic mode after segment check.

DISPLAYING TROUBLE CODES

Following the segment check, "8.8.8." is displayed on the FDC. These 3 numbers signal the trouble code display is about to begin. See ENTERING SELF-DIAGNOSTICS.

NOTE: ECM codes may also be referred to as PCM codes.

ECM History Codes Display – **1)** Within 3 seconds of "8.8.8." display, FDC switches to an "E" display, indicating start of ECM history trouble code display cycle. (History trouble codes are codes set in response to a malfunction, which occurred during the past 50 key cycles, not during this key cycle.)

2) During display cycle of ECM history trouble codes, all detected malfunctions, whether history or current, will be displayed. If no ECM history trouble codes are stored, the "E" display will be by-passed.

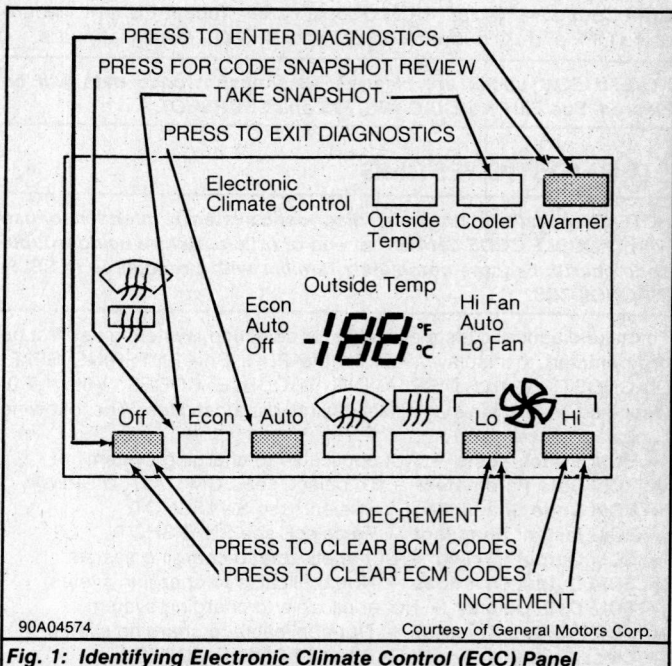

PRESS TO ENTER DIAGNOSTICS
PRESS FOR CODE SNAPSHOT REVIEW
TAKE SNAPSHOT
PRESS TO EXIT DIAGNOSTICS

Electronic Climate Control

Outside Temp   Cooler   Warmer

Econ Auto Off   Outside Temp -188 °F °C   Hi Fan Auto Lo Fan

Off   Econ   Auto   Lo   Hi

DECREMENT
PRESS TO CLEAR BCM CODES
PRESS TO CLEAR ECM CODES
INCREMENT

90A04574   Courtesy of General Motors Corp.

Fig. 1: Identifying Electronic Climate Control (ECC) Panel

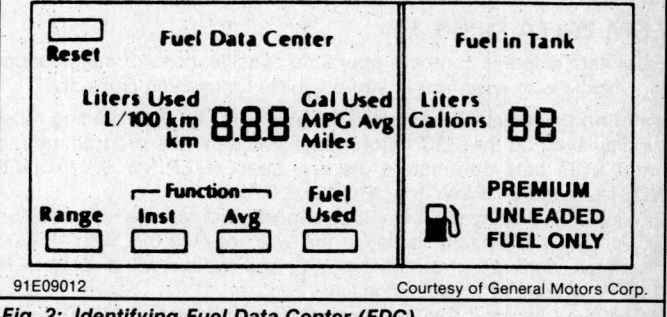

Reset   **Fuel Data Center**   **Fuel in Tank**

Liters Used L/100 km km 8.8.8 Gal Used MPG Avg Miles   Liters Gallons 88

Range   Function Inst Avg   Fuel Used   PREMIUM UNLEADED FUEL ONLY

91E09012   Courtesy of General Motors Corp.

Fig. 2: Identifying Fuel Data Center (FDC)

ECM History Code "E16" – This is history trouble code for alternator voltage out of range. No other ECM history trouble codes are charging system-related.

ECM Current Codes Display – Following history trouble code display, ECM displays current trouble codes. These codes are prefixed by the letters ".E.E." Any ".E.E." trouble codes that have been set indicate the related malfunction is currently occurring.

ECM Current Code ".E.E.16" – This is current trouble code for alternator voltage out of range. No other ECM current trouble codes are charging system-related.

BCM Codes Display – Following display of ECM trouble codes, 2 cycles of BCM trouble codes will be displayed. BCM trouble codes are prefixed by letter(s) "F" or "F.F." A single "F" precedes the cycle of BCM history trouble codes. The letters "F.F." precede the cycle of BCM current trouble codes. BCM does not set charging system trouble codes.

NOTE: After the display of all ECM and BCM trouble codes, ".7.0" will be displayed on FDC, indicating system is ready for next diagnostic feature to be selected. See DIAGNOSTIC TESTING.

CLEARING TROUBLE CODES

ECM Codes – **1)** ECM trouble codes stored in memory may be cleared (erased) by entering diagnostic mode and simultaneously depressing OFF and HI buttons on ECC panel until "E.O.O." appears.

2) After "E.O.O." display appears, release buttons, and ".7.0" appears. With ".7.0" displayed, turn ignition off for at least 10 seconds. Codes are now cleared. To exit diagnostics without erasing trouble codes, see EXITING DIAGNOSTICS.

BCM Codes – To clear BCM trouble codes, repeat ECM procedure using OFF and LO buttons on ECC until "F.O.O". display appears.

NOTE: If ECM codes are cleared, all snapshot code data will be cleared. See EXITING DIAGNOSTICS and SNAPSHOT.

DIAGNOSTIC TESTING

NOTE: Diagnostic testing using diagnostic system is intended for use with TROUBLE CODE CHARTS at end of article. Before using trouble code charts, become completely familiar with procedures in SELF-DIAGNOSTICS.

To make diagnostic tests available for selection, system must first be programmed to display ".7.0" on the FDC. See ENTERING SELF-DIAGNOSTICS and DISPLAYING TROUBLE CODES. With ".7.0" displayed, technician may select desired diagnostic test. The following choices are available:

- **ECM Switch Tests** – Not applicable to charging system.
- **ECM Data Parameters** – To select, see ECM DATA DISPLAY.
- **ECM Code Snapshot** – To select, see SNAPSHOT.
- **ECM Instant Snapshot** – To select, see SNAPSHOT.
- **ECM Output Cycling** – Not applicable to charging system.
- **ECM Output Overrides** – Not applicable to charging system.
- **BCM Data Display** – Not applicable to charging system.
- **ECC Program Override** – Not applicable to charging system.
- **Clear Codes** – See CLEARING TROUBLE CODES.
- **Exit Diagnostics** – See EXITING DIAGNOSTICS.

ECM DATA DISPLAY

ECM data displays compare operating specifications of malfunctioning vehicle with specifications of a vehicle functioning correctly.

Entering ECM Data Parameters Display – 1) A ".7.0" reading must be displayed on the FDC before diagnostics can be programmed to enter ECM data parameters display. See ENTERING SELF-DIAGNOSTICS and DISPLAYING TROUBLE CODES.
2) With ".7.0" displayed on the FDC, depress and release LO button on ECC. This will switch display from ".7.0" to "E.9.0.". With "E.9.0." displayed, depress HI button on ECC, and system will display ECM data Parameters ("P") selection list.
Selecting Charging System Data Parameter Tests – Depress HI button on ECC to scroll parameter list to a higher "P" number. Depress LO button to scroll display to lower "P" number. The available charging system data parameter displays are:
- **"P.0.7"** – This is the charging system data that displays battery voltage from 0 volts to 25.5 volts.
- **"P.2.4"** – This is the ignition cycle counter that shows the number of times the ignition has been cycled to OFF since an ECM trouble code was last detected.
Exiting Data Parameter Series – See EXITING DIAGNOSTICS.

SNAPSHOT

Snapshot mode lets you review the ECM data parameter values present when a code was set. In addition, snapshot permits a technician-initiated recording of ECM data parameters at a particular instant.
ECM Code Snapshot – When ECM code snapshot is selected, the parameters displayed are those stored in the keep-alive memory from the time the code was set. If more than one code has been set, the values associated with the last code will be stored.
Entering ECM Code Snapshot – 1) To enter ECM code snapshot, ".7.0" must first be displayed on the FDC. See ENTERING SELF-DIAGNOSTICS and DISPLAYING TROUBLE CODES.
2) With ".7.0" displayed on FDC display, depress and release LO button on ECC. This will switch display from ".7.0" to "E.9.0.". With "E.9.0." displayed, depress ECON and WARMER buttons on ECC. Display will now enter ECM code snapshot, and displayed codes will be prefixed by the letter "L".
Selecting An ECM Code Snapshot – To scroll through available codes, depress HI button on the ECC to advance to higher numbers. Depress LO button to return to lower numbers.
ECM Code Snapshot "L.0.7" – This is the ECM charging system out-of-range code snapshot. No other code snapshots relate to charging system malfunctions.
Exiting Code Snapshot – To exit ECM code snapshot, see EXITING DIAGNOSTICS.
Selecting An ECM Instant Snapshot – The instant ECM snapshot mode is similar to code snapshot, except technician can determine the instant the data is to be recorded.
Entering Instant Snapshot – 1) To enter ECM instant snapshot, ".7.0" must first be displayed on the FDC. See ENTERING SELF-DIAGNOSTICS and DISPLAYING TROUBLE CODES.
2) With ".7.0" displayed on FDC display, depress and release "LO" button on the ECC. This will switch display from ".7.0." to "E.9.0.". System is now ready to record an instant snapshot.
Recording & Reviewing An Instant Snapshot – 1) With "E.9.0." displayed, depress the ECON and COOLER buttons on the ECC. Display will now enter ECM instant snapshot and display "5.9.0." at the instant the snapshot is taken and recorded.
2) Pressing HI button will start a review of the data parameters at the instant snapshot was requested. This data will be prefixed by the letter "S", which looks similar to the number 5 on the display.
Exiting ECM Instant Snapshot – See EXITING DIAGNOSTICS.

EXITING SELF-DIAGNOSTICS

To exit diagnostics and return to ".7.0" without clearing trouble codes, depress AUTO button on ECC, or turn ignition switch to OFF position for 10 seconds. Temperature setting reappears on ECC panel.

BENCH TESTING

See ALTERNATORS – ALL OTHERS article.

OVERHAUL

See ALTERNATORS – ALL OTHERS article.

TROUBLE CODE CHARTS

CODE E16
ALTERNATOR VOLTAGE OUT OF RANGE

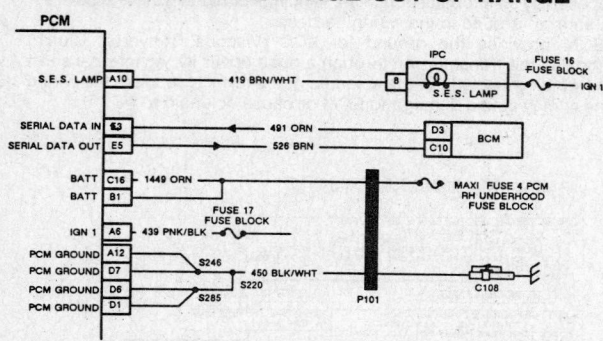

CIRCUIT DESCRIPTION: The PCM monitors system voltage on the fuel pump feedback to the PCM. With engine running at greater than 500 RPM, code E16 sets if system voltage is less than 10 volts or greater than 16 volts. If ignition voltage goes to 0 (open circuit), engine will not run, since the PCM does not receive ignition signal.

While a failure is present, PCM turns on SERVICE VEHICLE SOON telltale. Canister purge and cruise control are disabled. VCC (Viscous Converter Clutch) solenoid is de-energized. Transmission shift solenoids are de-energized.

NOTE: The following step numbers correspond to test numbers in trouble code chart

TEST DESCRIPTION:

1) Check PCM Snap Shot Data for parameter P.O.7 (battery voltage). Display shows voltage from 0 to 25.5 volts. If voltage is 16 volts or greater, alternator is not controlling voltage.

91C09011 91A11510

2) Check for proper charging system operation.
3) Check for proper charging system regulation with no electrical loads on the alternator.

NOTE ON INTERMITTENTS: Code E16 may be stored as a history code if the battery charge was low. Load test battery and check charging system operation. Check for loose battery cable connection at starter motor.

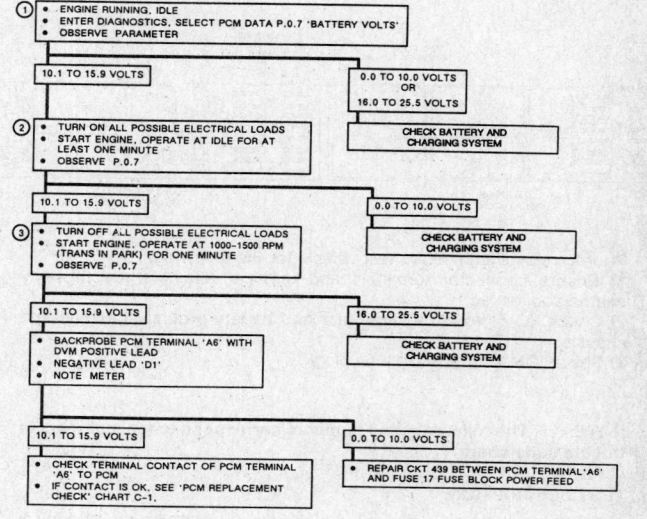

WHEN ALL DIAGNOSIS AND REPAIRS ARE COMPLETED, CLEAR CODES AND VERIFY OPERATION

Courtesy of General Motors Corp.

Fig. 3: *ECM Trouble Code E16 Flow Chart & Wiring Diagram*

CHART C-1
ECM REPLACEMENT CHECK

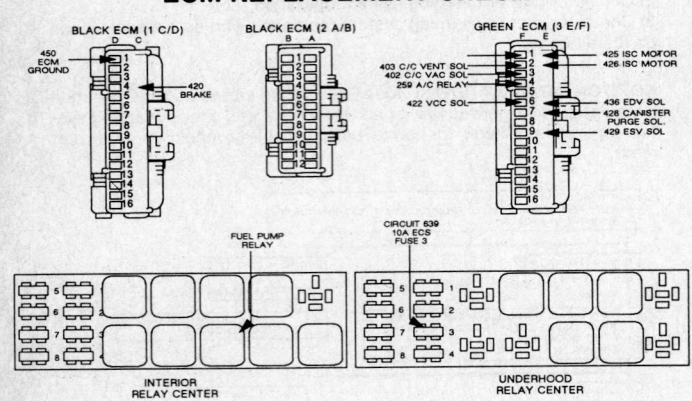

Prior to replacing an ECM, test vehicle for the following:

1) Ensure connector terminals and terminal retainers are properly seated and locked.

2) Check ECM ground at alternator and battery ground at engine and chassis.

3) Check IGN 1-IS0 fuse in fuse block.

NOTE: The following step numbers correspond to test numbers in trouble code chart

TEST DESCRIPTION:

1) ECM supplies power through a high-side driver to the cruise control vent and vacuum solenoids. An internal short in the servo, causing a low resistance or short to ground in the wiring harness, may damage the ECM or cause solenoid servos to fail.

2) ECM supplies power to the fuel pump relay through a high side driver. An internal short in the relay winding, causing a low resistance or short to ground in the wiring harness, may damage ECM or cause relay to fail.

3) ECM supplies power to the ISC through an internal switching IC that changes the polarity of the circuit. An internal short in the ISC motor armature windings or short to ground in the wiring harness may damage ECM or cause ISC motor to fail.

4) ECM provides the ground for EGR solenoid, Electric Switching Valve (ESV), canister purge solenoid and Electric Divert Valve (EDV) through a quad driver IC. Damage to the ECM or the emission control system may be caused by an internal short in the windings or resistors of the devices, or a short to ground in the wiring harness.

5) ECM provides the ground for VCC (Viscous Converter Clutch) solenoid in the transmission through a quad driver IC. An internal short in the winding or diode of the solenoid or a short to ground in the wiring harness may cause damage to ECM or cause solenoid to fail.

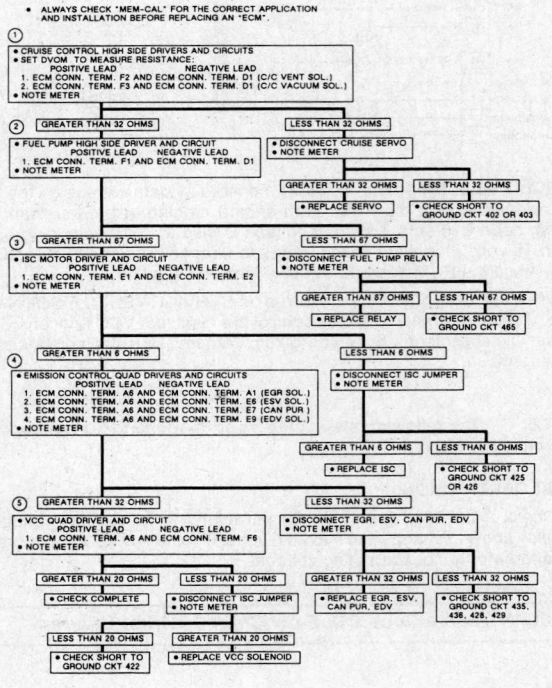

90G04586

Fig. 4: Chart C-1 — ECM Replacement Check

DESCRIPTION

The CS144, 140-amp alternator is used in conjunction with a Body Control Module (BCM). CS stands for charging system, and 144 denotes the outside diameter (in millimeters) of the alternator stator laminations.

The alternator and related charging system circuitry has self-diagnostic capacity. A communication process has been incorporated between the BCM and CS144 alternator. When the alternator circuit exceeds programmed limits, the malfunction may be indicated by the BATTERY NO CHARGE message on the telltale warning lamp cluster.

The voltage regulator is enclosed in a solid mold, mounted inside the alternator. A capacitor, mounted in the end frame, protects the rectifier bridge from high voltage, and suppresses radio noise.

OPERATION

The voltage regulator controls the field with a Pulse Width Modulated (PWM) signal, measured in duty cycles. A PWM signal continuously cycles on and off; the on time can vary within each cycle.

When the ignition switch is turned to the RUN position, the BCM applies voltage to the regulator before engine is started. The regulator is now in field strobe function, and applies a small percentage of the duty cycle to the field windings, which produce a magnetic field. As alternator RPM increases, the field strobe function is disabled, and normal regulation occurs.

When field current is on, the regulator switches the field current on and off at a fixed frequency of about 400 cycles per second. By varying the overall on and off time, correct average field current for proper system voltage control is achieved. At high speeds, the on time may be 10 percent. At low speeds, with a heavy electrical load, the on time may be as much as 90 percent.

The BCM monitors the regulator from the field terminal of the generator. If the PWM duty cycle falls below 7 percent on time, the BCM senses a fault, and indicates a problem by illuminating the BATTERY NO CHARGE telltale.

SELF-DIAGNOSTICS

ENTERING SELF-DIAGNOSTICS

1) With ignition switch in ON position, simultaneously push OFF and WARMER buttons on Electronic Climate Control (ECC) panel. *See Fig. 1.* Continue to push OFF and WARMER buttons until segment check appears on ECC panel, Driver Information Center (DIC) and Instrument Panel Cluster (IPC). *See Figs. 1 and 2.*

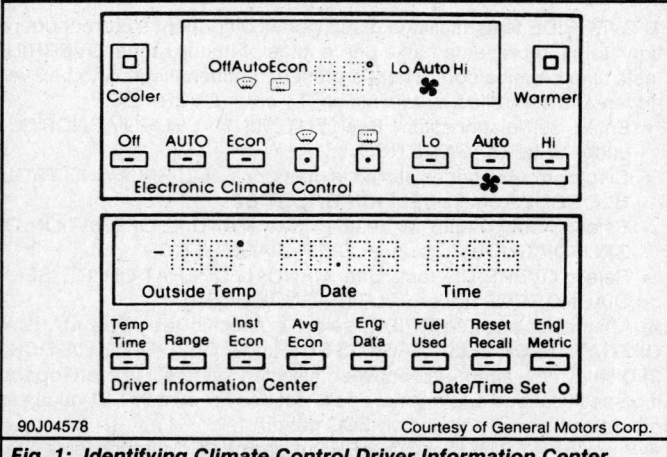

90J04578   Courtesy of General Motors Corp.

Fig. 1: Identifying Climate Control Driver Information Center (CCDIC)

2) When segment check appears, system has entered self-diagnostic mode. Release buttons. At any time during self-diagnostic proce-

90B04579   Courtesy of General Motors Corp.

Fig. 2: Identifying Instrument Panel Cluster (IPC)

dures, pressing RESET/RECALL button on DIC initiates immediate exit from self-diagnostics.

NOTE: ECC panel and DIC make up Climate Control Driver Information Center (CCDIC).

3) Illuminating segments of IPC and CCDIC ensures all segments of vacuum fluorescent displays work properly. On IPC, however, turn signal indicators do not light during this check.
4) If all CCDIC segments appear, proceed to DISPLAYING TROUBLE CODES. Failure of any segment to illuminate may result in inaccurate test results. Any inoperative segments of CCDIC display must be replaced before proceeding with self-diagnostic process.

CAUTION: Accessing self-diagnostics for 30 minutes without running engine will discharge battery, resulting in a possible no-start condition. To ensure proper operation, attach battery charger to battery.

NOTE: ECM codes may also be referred to as PCM codes.

DISPLAYING TROUBLE CODES

1) Electronic Control Module (ECM), Body Control Module (BCM) and Supplemental Inflatable Restraint (SIR) trouble codes automatically display after system enters self-diagnostics. ECM trouble codes are displayed first, and are prefixed with "E". If no ECM trouble codes are stored, a NO ECM CODES message displays. Charging system trouble codes are not set by ECM.
2) BCM sets trouble codes for charging system malfunctions. These trouble codes are displayed immediately following ECM display. BCM trouble codes appear in ascending (3 digit) numerical order, and are prefixed with "B".
3) All BCM trouble codes are followed by "C" or "H". "C" stands for current, and indicates a trouble code related fault presently exists. "H" stands for history, and indicates system failure was not present last time code was accessed. For example: B410H is BCM code 410, set in response to a past malfunction.
4) If no BCM trouble codes are stored in memory, a NO BCM CODES message displays. If communication link between a component and BCM is not operating, a NO BCM DATA message displays.
5) SIR system trouble codes are prefixed with "R". No charging system trouble codes are set by SIR.

NOTE: After all trouble codes have been displayed, depressing OFF button on ECC panel repeats trouble code display.

BCM CHARGING SYSTEM TROUBLE CODES

BCM charging system trouble codes are:
- **Code B410** – This code sets if there is an open or short to ground on circuit No. 23 or No. 225. See TROUBLE CODE CHARTS. A drive belt break or an undervoltage or overvoltage condition also causes this code to set. If a short to ground occurs on circuit No. 225, BATTERY NO CHARGE telltale lights on IPC.
- **Code B411** – This code sets if ignition voltage "1" is less than 10 volts. See TROUBLE CODE CHARTS.
- **Code B412** – This code sets if ignition voltage "1" is more than 16 volts. See TROUBLE CODE CHARTS.

ECM CHARGING SYSTEM TROUBLE CODES

- **Code E016** – This code sets if battery voltage is out of range. See TROUBLE CODE CHARTS.

NOTE: After system completes diagnostic code display cycle, system can test charging system components and/or circuitry indicated by trouble codes. See MANUAL OPERATION OF SELF-DIAGNOSTICS under SELF-DIAGNOSTICS.

MANUAL OPERATION OF SELF-DIAGNOSTICS

NOTE: Manual operation of self-diagnostic system is intended for use with TROUBLE CODE CHARTS. Before using flow charts, become completely familiar with procedures in MANUAL OPERATION OF SELF-DIAGNOSTICS.

System Selection – 1) After all trouble codes have displayed (see DISPLAYING TROUBLE CODES under SELF-DIAGNOSTICS), self-diagnostic system can perform specific diagnostic tests. After trouble code display, first system available for testing automatically displays. For example: ECM? may now be present on display.
2) Charging system tests are part of BCM system. To select BCM system, advance display until BCM? is displayed. Repeatedly depressing LO button on ECC panel cycles system selection list. See Fig. 1.
3) After selection list, selection sequence may be cycled again by continuing to depress LO button. When BCM? displays on ECC panel, release LO button. Depress HI button on ECC panel to select displayed BCM? system for testing.

NOTE: If necessary, depress OFF button on ECC panel to cancel a system selection and repeat system selection process.

Test Type Selection – 1) After BCM system has been selected for testing, select test type. Test types are CLEAR CODES?, DATA?, INPUTS?, OUTPUTS?, OVERRIDE? and SNAPSHOT?. System may now display any of these 6 test types.
2) Depress LO button on ECC panel to display next available BCM test type. List of test types can repeat following display of last test type.
3) When desired test type is displayed, depress HI button on ECC panel to select displayed test type. Should dashes appear, selected test type is not permitted with engine running.

NOTE: If necessary, depress OFF button on ECC panel to cancel a test type selection and repeat test type selection process.

- CLEAR CODES – Selection of CLEAR CODES? displays message CLEAR CODES along with selected system name. Message appears for 3 seconds, indicating all stored trouble codes have been erased from system's memory. After 3 seconds, display automatically returns to next available test type.
- DATA – DATA test displays compare malfunctioning system's present specifications with those of a properly functioning system.
- INPUTS – 1) INPUTS test displays determine if switched inputs can be properly interpreted. When one of various INPUTS tests is selected, state of device is displayed as HI or LO.
2) HI or LO refers to input terminal voltage for particular circuit. Display also indicates if an input reading has changed. This feature permits activating or deactivating any listed device and then returning to display to see if reading has changed.
3) If a reading change occurs, an "X" appears next to HI/LO indicator; otherwise an "0" appears. "X" will only appear once per selected input. HI/LO indication continues to change as input changes.
- OUTPUTS – OUTPUTS tests are not used for charging system diagnosis.
- OVERRIDE – OVERRIDE tests perform 2 functions. First, they display a component's current operational status, represented as a percentage of its full range. Second, they permit a component's present functional status to be overridden and controlled by technician.

NOTE: Proceed to OVERRIDE after selecting OVERRIDE test type.

- SNAPSHOT – SNAPSHOT recalls system operating specifications present at exact time a BCM malfunction code was set.

NOTE: Proceed to SNAPSHOT after selecting SNAPSHOT test type.

Specific Test Selection – 1) Following test type selection, first of many specific tests becomes available for selection. Characters of display represent a test code.
2) First 2 characters of test code are letters which identify both system and test type selected. For example: if BCM system and DATA test type are selected, BD is first 2 characters of display. BD stands for BCM DATA. Last 2 characters numerically identify specific test selection. For example: BD51 designates BCM DATA, test 51.
3) When BI appears as first 2 characters of test code, BCM system and INPUTS test type are selected. Last 2 characters numerically identify specific test selection. For example: BI51 designates BCM INPUTS, test 51.
4) When BS appears as first 2 characters of test code, BCM system and OVERRIDE test type are selected. Last 2 characters numerically identify specific test selection. For example: BS06 designates BCM OVERRIDE, test 06.
5) To scroll to specific test number, depress LO button on ECC panel, and system displays next lower specific test number. If this button is depressed with lowest test number displayed, highest test number appears.
6) Depress HI button on ECC panel to display next higher test number. If this button is pressed with highest test number displayed, lowest test number appears.

NOTE: If necessary, depress OFF button on ECC panel to cancel a specific test selection and repeat specific test selection process.

7) System malfunctions represented by specific test selection numbers are:
- BD50 – Battery voltage is read in volts between zero and 16.3.
- BD51 – Generator field is displayed in a percentage. A value close to zero percent represents MINIMUM voltage regulator on time and a value close to 100 percent represents MAXIMUM voltage regulator on time.
- BD61 – Engine speed is displayed in RPM from zero to 6375.
- BD98 – Ignition cycle value is number of times BCM has been turned OFF since a BCM trouble code was last detected. After 100 ignition cycles without any malfunction detected, all BCM trouble codes are cleared.
- BI51 – Alternator feedback display is LO when there is an alternator problem or engine is not running.

OVERRIDE

NOTE: If directed here from TEST TYPE SELECTION, proceed to step 2).

1) OVERRIDE tests facilitate display of a component's current operation status, represented as a percentage of its full range. OVERRIDE tests also permit a component's present functional status to be overridden and controlled by technician. To enter OVERRIDE:
- Enter self-diagnostics. See ENTERING SELF-DIAGNOSTICS under SELF-DIAGNOSTICS.
- Display trouble codes stored in memory. See DISPLAYING TROUBLE CODES under SELF-DIAGNOSTICS.
- Select BCM system for testing. See MANUAL OPERATION OF SELF-DIAGNOSTICS under SELF-DIAGNOSTICS.
- Select OVERRIDE test. See MANUAL OPERATION OF SELF-DIAGNOSTICS under SELF-DIAGNOSTICS.
2) After selecting OVERRIDE, select a specific test. See MANUAL OPERATION OF SELF-DIAGNOSTICS under SELF-DIAGNOSTICS.
3) Display now alternates between selected system's present operating specifications and normal specifications for system. All values for comparison are displayed on ECC panel.
4) Pressing WARMER or COOLER buttons on ECC panel begins override function, while simultaneously stopping alternating display of present and normal system operating values. Pressing WARMER button increases a value. Pressing COOLER button decreases a value.
5) Upon releasing COOLER or WARMER button, display may remain at an override value or automatically return to normal program control.

If display remains at override value, normal program control resumes by:
- Selecting another OVERRIDE test, cancelling current override.
- Selecting another system, cancelling current override.
- Overriding a value beyond extremes of zero or 99, causing display to alternate between out-of-range value and opposite extreme. If button is released while out-of-range value is displayed, normal program control resumes.

NOTE: While in OVERRIDE, another test type within selected system may also be active. After selecting an OVERRIDE test, press OFF button to select another test type. ECC panel, however, continues to display selected override. Pressing WARMER or COOLER allows monitoring effect of OVERRIDE on different vehicle parameters.

SNAPSHOT

NOTE: If directed here from TEST TYPE SELECTION, proceed to step 2).

1) SNAPSHOT recalls system operating specifications present at exact time a BCM malfunction code was set. Up to 3 snapshots may be recalled. To enter SNAPSHOT:
- Enter self-diagnostics. See ENTERING SELF-DIAGNOSTICS under SELF-DIAGNOSTICS.
- Display trouble codes stored in memory. See DISPLAYING TROUBLE CODES under SELF-DIAGNOSTICS.
- Select BCM system for testing. See MANUAL OPERATION OF SELF-DIAGNOSTICS under SELF-DIAGNOSTICS.
- Select SNAPSHOT test type. See MANUAL OPERATION OF SELF-DIAGNOSTICS under SELF-DIAGNOSTICS.

2) Immediately following selection of SNAPSHOT?, system displays BXXX. B stands for BCM. XXX represents 3-digit code stored in BCM snapshot. During actual BCM snapshot display, a 3-digit code appears in place of XXX.

3) Depressing LO button on ECC panel allows scrolling through list of BCM diagnostic codes for which BCM has stored a snapshot. See BCM CHARGING SYSTEM TROUBLE CODES under SELF-DIAGNOSTICS for list of BCM diagnostic charging system trouble codes. A desired charging system snapshot has possibly NOT been set. In this case, exit SNAPSHOT by depressing RESET/RECALL button on DIC.

4) After display of last BCM diagnostic code for which a snapshot exists, press LO button to display TAKE BCM SNAPSHOT?. Pressing LO button again returns display to first BXXX SNAPSHOT display. Pressing HI button causes BCM SNAP DATA? or BCM SNAP INPUTS? to display.

5) Press LO button on ECC panel to alternate display between BCM SNAP DATA? and BCM SNAP INPUTS?. Press HI button on ECC panel to select desired display for testing.

6) System automatically advances to specific test selection level. Display is now controlled as it would be for non-snapshot data and input displays. All values and status information displayed is snapshot information.

EXITING SELF-DIAGNOSTICS

To exit self-diagnostics and return to normal system operation, depress RESET/RECALL button on DIC. This button may be depressed at any time during code display.

BENCH TESTING

See ALTERNATORS — ALL OTHERS article.

OVERHAUL

See ALTERNATORS — ALL OTHERS article.

TROUBLE CODE CHARTS

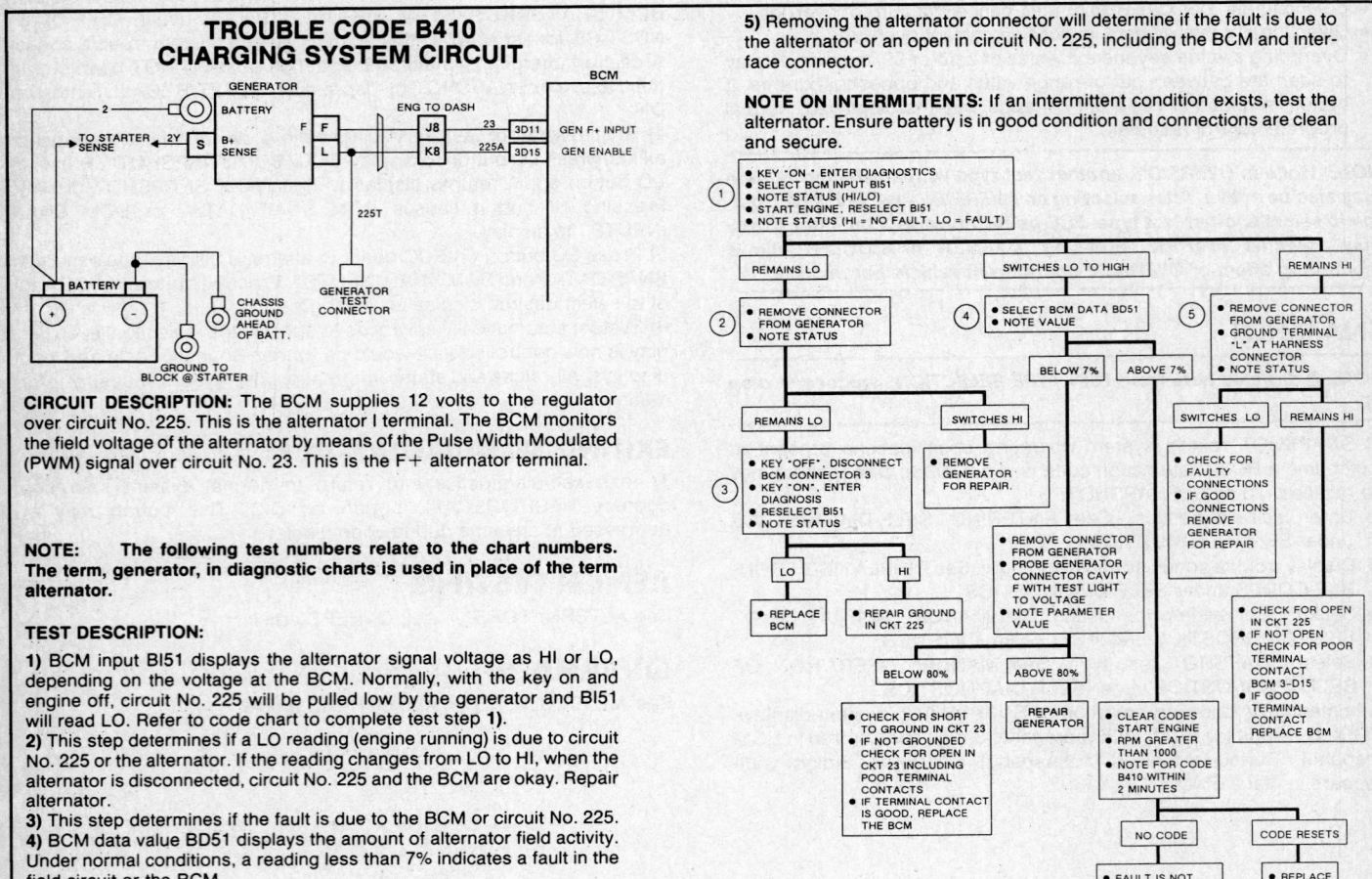

TROUBLE CODE B410
CHARGING SYSTEM CIRCUIT

CIRCUIT DESCRIPTION: The BCM supplies 12 volts to the regulator over circuit No. 225. This is the alternator I terminal. The BCM monitors the field voltage of the alternator by means of the Pulse Width Modulated (PWM) signal over circuit No. 23. This is the F+ alternator terminal.

NOTE: The following test numbers relate to the chart numbers. The term, generator, in diagnostic charts is used in place of the term alternator.

TEST DESCRIPTION:

1) BCM input BI51 displays the alternator signal voltage as HI or LO, depending on the voltage at the BCM. Normally, with the key on and engine off, circuit No. 225 will be pulled low by the generator and BI51 will read LO. Refer to code chart to complete test step **1)**.

2) This step determines if a LO reading (engine running) is due to circuit No. 225 or the alternator. If the reading changes from LO to HI, when the alternator is disconnected, circuit No. 225 and the BCM are okay. Repair alternator.

3) This step determines if the fault is due to the BCM or circuit No. 225.

4) BCM data value BD51 displays the amount of alternator field activity. Under normal conditions, a reading less than 7% indicates a fault in the field circuit or the BCM.

5) Removing the alternator connector will determine if the fault is due to the alternator or an open in circuit No. 225, including the BCM and interface connector.

NOTE ON INTERMITTENTS: If an intermittent condition exists, test the alternator. Ensure battery is in good condition and connections are clean and secure.

90D04580   90C1656

Courtesy of General Motors Corp.

Fig. 3: Trouble Code B410 Flow Chart & Wiring Diagram (Eldorado & Seville)

CODE B411 OR B412
BATTERY VOLTAGE TOO LOW OR TOO HIGH

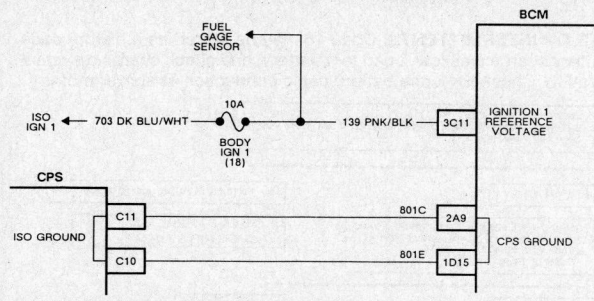

CIRCUIT DESCRIPTION: The BCM monitors ignition "1" voltage on terminal 3C11 as a reference for fuel control. Codes B411 and B412 are set when the ignition is ON and the engine speed is greater than 800 RPM as follows: Code B411 sets when ignition "1" is less than 10 volts. Code B412 sets when ignition voltage "1" is greater than 16 volts.

During the time a failure is present, the cruise control will be disengaged. The cause of these codes should be corrected before diagnosing any other code that has been set. This is necessary because low or high voltage can cause false setting of codes. A current B411 or B412 can be observed in BCM data display BD50 BATT VOLTS outside the range of 10-16 volts.

NOTE: The following test numbers relate to the chart numbers. The term, generator, in diagnostic charts is used in place of the term alternator.

TEST DESCRIPTION:

1) BCM data value BD50 displays battery voltage. The normal range is between 10.6 and 16 volts.
2) Ensure low voltage readings are due to circuitry or the battery. If voltage is less than 10 volts with engine running, BCM and related wiring are okay.
3) Ensure low voltage reading is due to the circuit or BCM. If voltage at BCM is less than 10.6 volts, BCM is okay.
4) Determine if high voltage reading is due to the alternator or faulty BCM.
5) Determine if charging voltage goes too high with higher engine RPM or electrical load.

90F04581

NOTE ON INTERMITTENTS: If an intermittent code B411 or B412 is being set, observe BCM data value BD50. This battery voltage reading is monitored from the 10-amp ISO ignition No. 1 fuse, fuel reference voltage.

If the code is being set due to high current draw in a particular vehicle component, this can be observed by reading the display for BD50. Operate the various components while watching for the reading to drop below 10 volts or go above 16 volts.

Code B411 could be due to an intermittent open in circuit No. 139, which may be observed by manipulating the wire to the BCM while watching BD50 for voltage to drop below 10 volts.

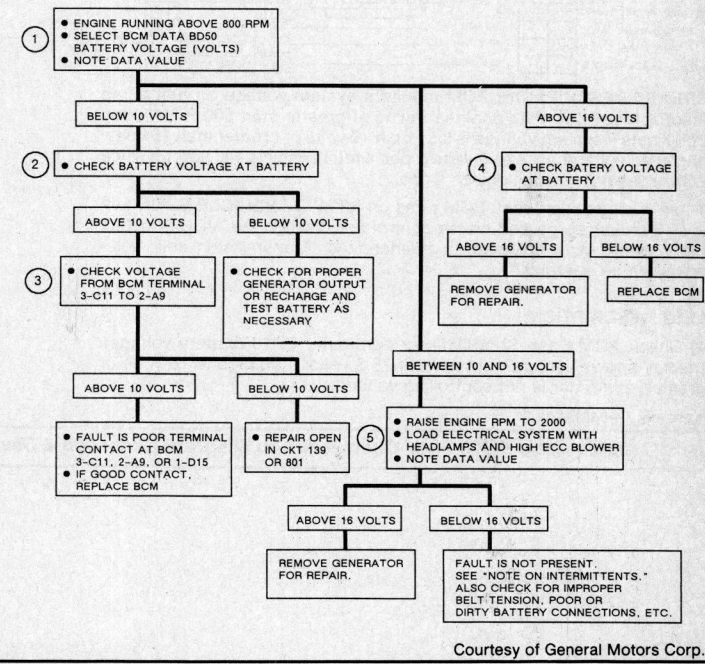

Courtesy of General Motors Corp.

Fig. 4: Trouble Codes B411/B412 Flow Chart & Wiring Diagram (Eldorado & Seville)

CODE EO16
BATTERY VOLTAGE OUT OF RANGE

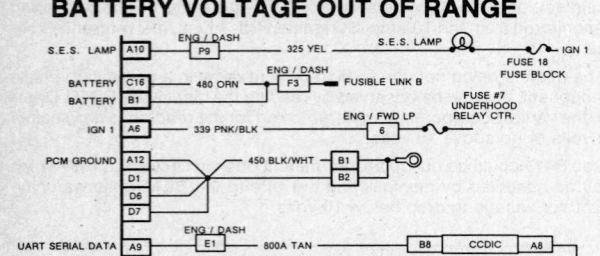

CIRCUIT DESCRIPTION: PCM monitors system voltage on fuel pump feedback to PCM. With engine running at greater than 500 RPM, code EO16 sets if system voltage is less than 10 volts or greater than 16 volts. If ignition voltage goes to 0 volts (open circuit), vehicle will not run since PCM does not receive ignition signal.

When a failure is present, PCM turns on SERVICE VEHICLE SOON tell-tale. Canister purge and cruise control are disengaged. VCC (Viscous Converter Clutch) solenoid is de-energized. Transmission shift solenoids are de-energized.

TEST DESCRIPTION:

1) Check PCM Snap Shot Data for parameter ED10 (battery voltage). Display shows voltage from zero to 25.5 volts. If voltage is 16 volts or greater, alternator is not controlling voltage.

2) Check for proper charging system operation.
3) Check for proper charging system regulation with no electrical loads on alternator.

NOTE ON INTERMITTENTS: Code 16 may be stored as a history code if battery charge was low. Load test battery, and check charging system operation. Check for loose battery cable connection at starter motor.

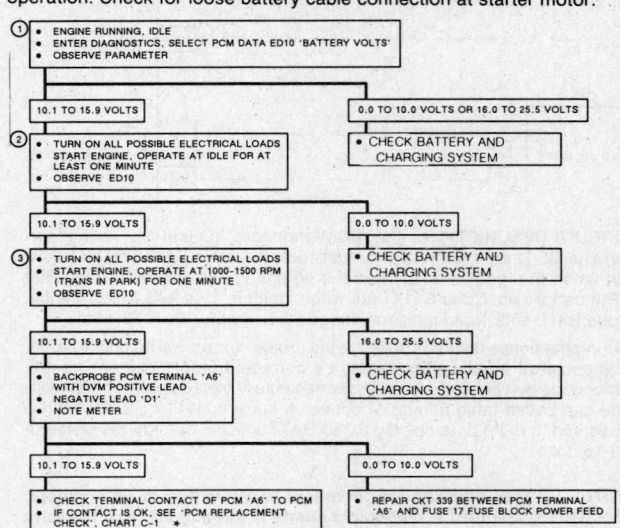

WHEN ALL DIAGNOSIS AND REPAIRS ARE COMPLETED, CLEAR CODES AND VERIFY OPERATION

*See SELF-DIAGNOSTICS – ELDORADO & SEVILLE BCM/PCM article in ENGINE PERFORMANCE.

91B07549 91B07550

Courtesy of General Motors Corp.

Fig. 5: Trouble Code EO16 Flow Chart & Wiring Diagram (Eldorado & Seville)

DESCRIPTION

The 120-amp, CS144 alternator is used in conjunction with a Body Control Module (BCM). CS stands for charging system and 144 denotes the outside diameter (in millimeters) of the alternator stator laminations.

The alternator and related charging system circuitry have self-diagnostic capability. A communication process exists between the BCM and CS144 alternator, which permits the alternator to interface with the BCM. When the alternator circuit exceeds programmed limits, the malfunction may be indicated by the ELECTRICAL PROBLEM message on the telltale warning light cluster.

The voltage regulator, enclosed in a solid mold, is mounted inside the alternator. A capacitor, mounted in the end frame, protects the rectifier bridge from high voltage and suppresses radio noise.

OPERATION

The voltage regulator controls the field with a Pulse Width Modulated (PWM) signal, measured in duty cycles. A PWM signal continuously cycles on and off; the on time can vary within each cycle.

When the ignition switch is turned to the RUN position, before engine is started, the BCM applies voltage to the regulator. The regulator is now in field strobe function and applies a small percentage of the duty cycle to the field winding, which produces a magnetic field. As alternator RPM increases, the field strobe function is disabled and normal regulation occurs.

When field current is on, the regulator switches the field current on and off at a fixed frequency of about 400 cycles per second. By varying the overall time field current is on and off, correct average field current for proper system voltage control is achieved. At high speeds, the time on may be 10 percent. At low speeds, with a heavy electrical load, the time on may be as much as 90 percent.

The BCM monitors the regulator from the alternator field terminal. If the PWM duty cycle falls below 7 percent on time, the BCM will sense a fault and indicate a problem, illuminating the ELECTRICAL PROBLEM telltale.

SELF-DIAGNOSTICS

ENTERING SELF-DIAGNOSTICS

1) Turn ignition switch to ON position. On the Electronic Climate Control (ECC) panel, simultaneously depress OFF button and the increase-temperature side of the TEMP button. *See Fig. 1.* Continue to depress OFF button and the increase-temperature side of the TEMP button until all display segments of the Instrument Panel Cluster (IPC) illuminate. *See Fig. 2.* When all segments illuminate, system has entered self-diagnostic mode. Release buttons.

2) Illuminating the IPC segments ensures all display segments are working properly. If all segments illuminate, proceed to DISPLAYING TROUBLE CODES. Failure of any segment to illuminate may result in inaccurate test results. Any inoperative segments of the display must be repaired before proceeding to self-diagnostic procedures.

CAUTION: Accessing self-diagnostics for 30 minutes without running engine will cause battery to discharge, resulting in a possible no-start condition. To ensure proper operation, attach battery charger to battery.

EXITING SELF-DIAGNOSTICS

To exit self-diagnostic mode, depress BI-LEV button on ECC panel or turn ignition switch to OFF position. Diagnostic mode can be exited at anytime during diagnostic procedures. Trouble codes are not erased from memory following this procedure.

DISPLAYING TROUBLE CODES

NOTE: ECM codes may also be referred to as PCM codes.

1) The Electronic Control Module (ECM), Body Control Module (BCM) and Supplemental Inflatable Restraint (SIR) trouble codes automatically display after system enters self-diagnostics. ECM trouble codes are displayed first, followed by the BCM trouble codes and finally the SIR trouble codes.

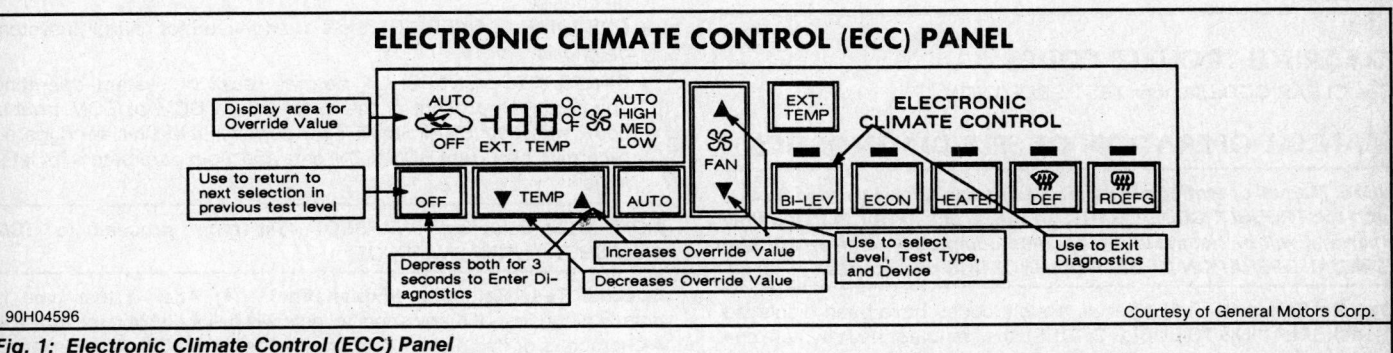

90H04596

Courtesy of General Motors Corp.

Fig. 1: Electronic Climate Control (ECC) Panel

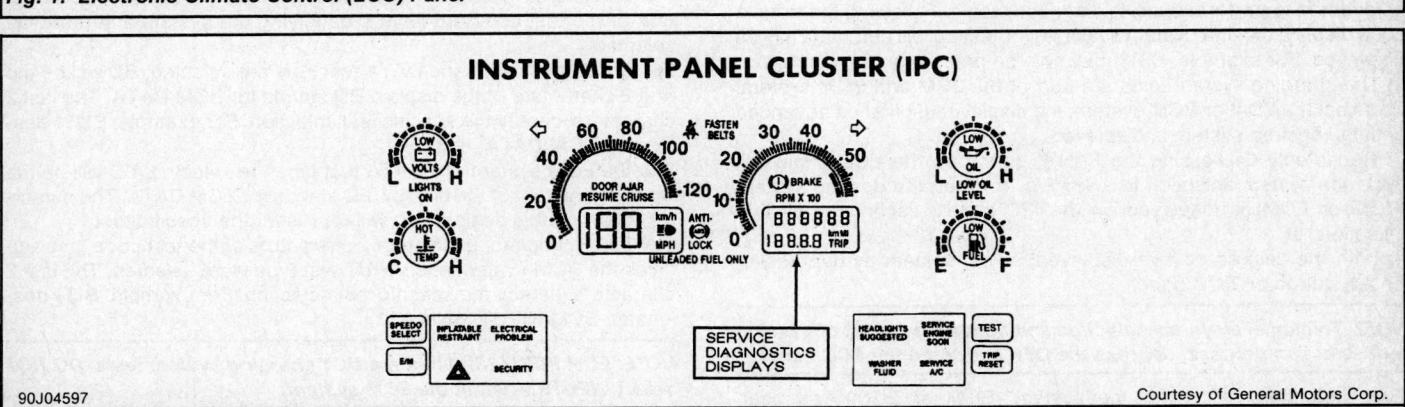

90J04597

Courtesy of General Motors Corp.

Fig. 2: Instrument Panel Cluster (IPC)

2) All trouble codes appear in an ascending (3 digit) numerical order. ECM codes are prefixed with "E", BCM Codes with "B" and SIR codes with "R".

3) In addition, all trouble codes are followed by "C" or "H". "C" stands for current and indicates a trouble code related fault presently exists. "H" stands for history and indicates the system failure was not present the last time the code was accessed.

4) For example: Code E016H is ECM trouble code number 016, set in response to a past malfunction (history). Code B410C is BCM trouble code number 410, set in response to a current malfunction.

5) If no ECM or BCM trouble codes are stored in memory, a NO E CODE or NO B CODE message is displayed respectively. Should the communication link between a component and the ECM or BCM fail, a NO BCM/ECM DATA message will be displayed.

6) SIR system trouble codes, prefixed with "R", are not covered in this article.

NOTE: The trouble code display can be repeated by depressing OFF button on ECC panel.

BCM CHARGING SYSTEM TROUBLE CODES

Up to 3 BCM charging system trouble codes may be set in response to charging system malfunctions:
- **Code B410** – Undervoltage or overvoltage condition. See TROUBLE CODE CHARTS.
- **Code B411** – Ignition voltage "1" is less than 10.6 volts. See TROUBLE CODE CHARTS.
- **Code B412** – Ignition voltage "1" is more than 16 volts. See TROUBLE CODE CHARTS.

ECM CHARGING SYSTEM TROUBLE CODES

- **Code EO16** – Battery voltage out of range. See TROUBLE CODE CHARTS.

NOTE: After system completes diagnostic code display cycle, it can be directed to test charging system components and/or circuitry indicated by trouble codes. See MANUAL OPERATION OF SELF-DIAGNOSTICS.

CLEARING TROUBLE CODES

See CLEAR CODES under TEST SELECTION.

MANUAL OPERATION OF SELF-DIAGNOSTICS

NOTE: Manual operation of self-diagnostic system is intended for use with the TROUBLE CODE CHARTS in this article. Prior to using flow charts, it will be necessary to become completely familiar with the MANUAL OPERATION OF SELF-DIAGNOSTICS procedures.

System Selection – 1) After all trouble codes have been displayed (see DISPLAYING TROUBLE CODES), the self-diagnostic system can be directed to perform specific diagnostic tests. Following the trouble code display, the first system available for testing will automatically be displayed. For example: SIR? may now be present on the display.

2) The charging system tests are part of the ECM and BCM system. To select the ECM or BCM system, the display must first be advanced until the desired system is displayed.

3) Repeatedly depressing the FAN▼ button on the ECC panel will cycle the system selection list. *See Fig. 1.* When the desired system (BCM or ECM) is displayed on the IPC panel, discontinue cycling selection list.

4) With the desired system displayed, select system by depressing FAN▲ button on ECC panel.

NOTE: To cancel a system selection and activate a repeat of the system selection process, depress the OFF button on the ECC panel.

Test Selection – 1) After the system (BCM or ECM) has been selected for testing, 6 test types are now made available for selection. The choices are: CLEAR CODES?, DATA?, INPUTS?, OUTPUTS?,

OVERRIDE? and SNAPSHOT?. The system may now be displaying any of these 6 test type choices.

2) To advance the display to next available test type, depress the FAN DOWN button on the ECC panel. The list of test types can be repeated.

3) When desired test type is displayed, select test type by depressing FAN▲ button.

NOTE: To cancel a test type selection and repeat test type selection process, depress OFF button on ECC panel.

- **CLEAR CODES** – Selection of CLEAR CODES will result in the message CODES CLEAR or X NOT CLEAR being displayed (X = a particular code), indicating whether a code has been successfully cleared. This message appears for 3 seconds, indicating all stored trouble codes have been erased from that system's memory. After 3 seconds, the display will automatically return to the next test available.

NOTE: After clearing a code has been cleared, complete ignition cycle and test vehicle. Recheck codes and ensure code does not reset.

- **DATA** – DATA test displays compare the malfunctioning system's present specifications with the specifications of a properly functioning system.
- **INPUTS** – **1)** INPUT test displays determine if switched inputs can be properly interpreted. When one of the various input tests is selected, the state of corresponding device is displayed as HI or LO.
  2) HI or LO refers to input terminal voltage for the particular circuit. The display also indicates if an input reading has changed. This feature permits technician to activate or deactivate any listed device and then return to the display to see if reading has changed (i.e. press FAN▲ and then FAN▼).
  3) If a reading change occurs, an X will appear next to the HI/LO indicator; otherwise a 0 will remain displayed. The X will only appear once per selected input. The HI/LO indication will continue to change as the input changes.
- **OUTPUTS** – OUTPUT tests are not used for charging system diagnosis.
- **OVERRIDE** – OVERRIDE tests are not used for charging system diagnosis.
- **SNAPSHOT** – SNAPSHOT permits recall of system operating specifications present at the exact time a BCM or ECM trouble code was set. SNAPSHOT also permits a technician-triggered recording of current BCM/ECM data and input parameters for later review.

NOTE: After selecting SNAPSHOT test type, proceed to ECM SNAPSHOT or BCM SNAPSHOT.

Specific Test Selection (Explanation) – 1) After a test type is selected, the first of many specific tests will be available to select. The 4 characters of this display represent a test code. The first 2 characters of the test code are letters identifying the system and test type selected.

2) If the BCM system and DATA test type are selected, BD will be the first 2 characters of the display. BD stands for BCM DATA. The last 2 characters identify the specific test selection. For example: BD51 designates BCM DATA, test 51.

3) If the ECM system and DATA test type are selected, ED will be the first 2 characters of the display. ED stands for ECM DATA. The numerals following this designation will represent the specific test.

4) When BI appears as the first 2 characters of the test code, this signifies the BCM system and INPUT test type were selected. The last 2 characters identify the specific test selection. For example: BI51 designates BCM INPUT, test 51.

NOTE: ECM INPUT (EI) tests are NOT charging system tests. DO NOT select INPUTS when in the ECM system.

Specific Test Selection (Making Selection) – **1)** Scroll to a lower specific test number by depressing the FAN▼ button. Scroll to a higher specific test number by depressing the FAN▲ button. The system will automatically display the values for whatever specific test number is displayed.

NOTE: To cancel or repeat test type selection process, depress the OFF button on ECC panel.

2) The following are charging system malfunctions shown by the specific test selection numbers:

- **BD50** – Battery voltage is read in volts between zero and 25.5 volts.
- **BD51** – The alternator field is displayed as a percentage. A value close to zero percent represents MINIMUM time voltage regulator is on and a value close to 100 percent represents MAXIMUM time voltage regulator is on.
- **BD61** – Engine speed is displayed in RPM from zero to 6375.
- **BD98** – The ignition cycle value is displayed as the number of times the BCM has been turned OFF since a BCM trouble code was last detected. After 50 ignition cycles without any malfunction detected, all BCM trouble codes are cleared.
- **BI51** – The alternator feedback display is LO when there is an alternator problem or when engine is not running.
- **ED10** – Battery voltage is read in volts between zero and 25.5 volts.

BCM SNAPSHOT

NOTE: If directed here from TEST SELECTION under MANUAL OPERATION OF SELF-DIAGNOSTICS, go to step 2).

1) SNAPSHOT allows the recall of system operating specifications when BCM malfunction code was set. Up to 3 snapshots may be recalled. In addition, one snapshot may be triggered on demand. To enter snapshot complete the following:

- Enter self-diagnostics. See ENTERING SELF-DIAGNOSTICS under SELF-DIAGNOSTICS.
- Display trouble codes stored in memory. See DISPLAYING TROUBLE CODES under SELF-DIAGNOSTICS.
- Select BCM or ECM system (as desired) for testing. See SYSTEM SELECTION under MANUAL OPERATION OF SELF-DIAGNOSTICS.
- Select SNAPSHOT test type. See TEST SELECTION under MANUAL OPERATION OF SELF-DIAGNOSTICS.

NOTE: To cancel snapshot test type selection and repeat test type selection process, depress the OFF button on ECC panel.

2) Immediately following the selection of SNAPSHOT?, the system will display BXXX. B stands for BCM. XXX is used here to represent the 3-digit code stored in BCM snapshot.

3) With BXXX displayed, depressing the FAN▼ button on the ECC panel will permit scrolling through the list of BCM diagnostic codes for which the BCM has stored a snapshot. For a list of BCM charging system trouble codes that may be present in snapshot, see BCM CHARGING SYSTEM TROUBLE CODES under SELF-DIAGNOSTICS.

NOTE: A trouble code displayed during the trouble code display cycle CANNOT also be present as a snapshot. To access such a code, exit SNAPSHOT by depressing the OFF button on the ECC. This will return the display to the next available system selection.

4) After display of the last BCM trouble code for which a snapshot does exist, pressing the FAN▼ button on the ECC will result in the DO B SNAP display.

5) Press the FAN▼ button on the ECC to return the display to the first BXXX SNAP? display. Responding to the DO B SNAP display by depressing the FAN▲ button with SNAP DATA? or SNAP INPUTS? displayed, selects that desired type.

6) Display is controlled now as it would be for non-snapshot data and inputs, however, all values and status information represents memorized vehicle conditions. See SPECIFIC TEST SELECTION (EXPLANATION) and SPECIFIC TEST SELECTION (MAKING SELECTION) under MANUAL OPERATION OF SELF-DIAGNOSTICS.

7) Depressing the FAN▲ button again with DO B SNAP? displayed will display the SNAP DONE message to indicate new information has been stored in memory.

ECM SNAPSHOT

NOTE: If directed here from TEST SELECTION under MANUAL OPERATION OF SELF-DIAGNOSTICS, go to step 2).

1) SNAPSHOT allows the recall of system operating specifications present at the exact time an ECM malfunction code was set. Up to 3 snapshots may be recalled. In addition, one snapshot may be triggered on demand. To enter snapshot, complete the following:

- Enter self-diagnostics. See ENTERING SELF-DIAGNOSTICS under SELF-DIAGNOSTICS.
- Display trouble codes stored in memory. See DISPLAYING TROUBLE CODES under SELF-DIAGNOSTICS.
- Select BCM or ECM system (as desired) for testing. See SYSTEM SELECTION under MANUAL OPERATION OF SELF-DIAGNOSTICS.
- Select SNAPSHOT test type. See TEST SELECTION under MANUAL OPERATION OF SELF-DIAGNOSTICS.

NOTE: To cancel snapshot test type selection and repeat test type selection process, depress the OFF button on ECC panel.

2) Immediately following the selection of SNAPSHOT?, the system will display the message SNAP DONE. This message appears for 3 seconds to indicate all ECM data and inputs have been stored in memory. Following this 3-second verification of information storage, the display will automatically proceed to the first available snapshot test type (i.e., SNAP DATA or SNAP INPUTS).

3) Now, depressing the FAN DOWN button will display the next available snapshot test type. Display may be switched between SNAP DATA and SNAP INPUTS.

4) Depress the FAN▲ button with SNAP DATA or SNAP INPUTS displayed to select desired test type.

5) Now, the display is controlled as it would be for non-snapshot data and inputs, however, all values and status information represents memorized vehicle conditions. See SPECIFIC TEST SELECTION (EXPLANATION) and SPECIFIC TEST SELECTION (MAKING SELECTION) under MANUAL OPERATION OF SELF-DIAGNOSTICS.

6) Depressing the FAN▲ button with SNAP EC displayed will display the SNAP DONE message to indicate that new information has been stored in memory.

BENCH TESTING

See ALTERNATORS – ALL OTHERS article.

OVERHAUL

See ALTERNATORS – ALL OTHERS article.

TROUBLE CODE CHARTS

TROUBLE CODE B410 CHARGING SYSTEM CIRCUIT

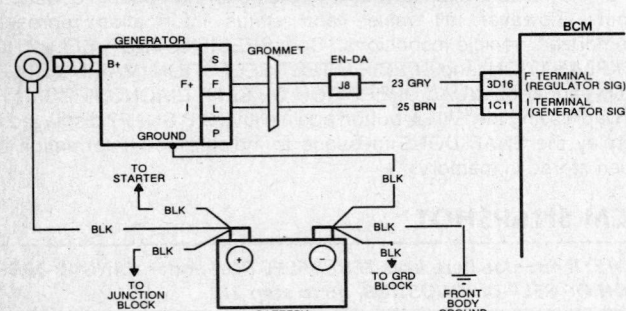

1) • KEY "ON" ENTER DIAGNOSTICS
   • SELECT BCM INPUT BI51
   • NOTE STATUS (HI/LO)
   • START ENGINE, RESELECT BI51
   • NOTE STATUS (HI = CHARGING, LO = NO CHARGING)

REMAINS LO — **SWITCHES LO TO HIGH** — **REMAINS HI**

2) • REMOVE CONNECTOR FROM GENERATOR
   • NOTE STATUS

4) • STOP ENGINE
   • SELECT BCM DATA BD51
   • NOTE VALUE

5) • REMOVE CONNECTOR FROM GENERATOR
   • GROUND TERMINAL 'L' AT HARNESS CONNECTOR
   • NOTE STATUS

REMAINS LO — **SWITCHES HI**

3) • CHECK FOR SHORT TO GROUND ON CKT 25
   • KEY 'OFF', DISCONNECT BCM CONNECTORS 1 AND 3
   • KEY 'ON' ENTER DIAGNOSTICS
   • RESELECT BI51
   • NOTE STATUS

• REMOVE GENERATOR FOR REPAIR

SWITCHES LO — **REMAINS HI**

• CHECK FOR FAULTY CONNECTIONS
• IF GOOD CONNECTIONS REMOVE GENERATOR FOR REPAIR

• CHECK FOR OPEN IN CKT 25
• IF NOT OPEN CHECK FOR POOR TERMINAL CONTACT BCM 1C11
• IF GOOD TERMINAL CONTACT REPLACE BCM

LO — **HI**

• REPLACE BCM

• REPAIR GROUND IN CKT 25

BELOW 7% — **ABOVE 7%**

• REMOVE CONNECTOR FROM GENERATOR
• PROBE GENERATOR CONNECTOR CAVITY F WITH TEST LIGHT TO VOLTAGE
• NOTE PARAMETER VALUE

• CLEAR CODES START ENGINE
• RPM GREATER THAN 1000
• NOTE FOR CODE B410 WITHIN 2 MINUTES

BELOW 80% — **ABOVE 80%** — **CODE RESETS** — **NO CODE**

• CHECK FOR SHORT TO GROUND IN CKT 23
• IF NOT GROUNDED CHECK FOR OPEN IN CKT 23 INCLUDING POOR TERMINAL CONTACTS
• IF TERMINAL CONTACT IS GOOD, REPLACE THE BCM

*

• CHECK FOR POOR TERMINAL CONTACT AT BCM PIN 3D16, GENERATOR F TERMINAL AND PIN J8 AT THE ENGINE DASH CONNECTOR
• IF OK, REPLACE BCM

• FAULTY IS NOT PRESENT
• SEE 'NOTE ON INTERMITTENTS'

WHEN ALL DIAGNOSIS AND REPAIRS ARE COMPLETED, CLEAR CODES AND VERIFY OPERATION

TROUBLE CODE SET CONDITIONS

Code B410 will set if the following conditions exist:

1) Engine is running and the alternator enable line is low or high and alternator field input is less than 2 percent.

2) Ignition on, engine not running and alternator enable line is high or low and alternator field input is less than 2 percent.

3) Code B410 will cause the ELECTRICAL PROBLEM telltale to light on the Instrument Panel Cluster (IPC).

CIRCUIT DESCRIPTION:

The alternator has fault detection capability built into the regulator. The BCM will supply 12 volts to the regulator over circuit No. 25, the "I" terminal, and monitor the field voltage of the alternator by way of a PWM signal over circuit No 23, the F+ terminal.

NOTE: Test numbers refer to numbers on diagnostic chart. The term "generator" in diagnostic chart is used in place of alternator. For location of BCM pins referred to in diagnostic chart, see Fig. 5.

TEST DESCRIPTION:

1) BCM input BI51 displays alternator signal voltage as HI or LO depending on the voltage state at the BCM. Normally with key on and engine off, circuit No.25 will be pulled LO by the alternator (BI51 reads LO).

2) This step checks if the LO reading is due to circuit No. 25 or the alternator. If the reading changes from LO to HI when the alternator is disconnected, circuit No. 25 and the BCM are okay.

3) This step determines if the fault is due to the BCM or circuit No. 25.

4) BCM data value BD51 displays the amount of alternator field activity. Under normal conditions, a reading less than 7 percent would indicate a fault in the field circuit or the BCM.

5) Removing the alternator connector will determine if the fault is due to the alternator or an open in circuit No. 25, including the BCM and interface connector.

NOTE ON INTERMITTENTS:

If an intermittent condition exists, check B410 snap data parameters, BD61 and BI51.

1) If BD61 is less than 500 RPM and BI51 is HI, check for an intermittent open in circuit No. 25.

2) If BD61 is less than 500 RPM and BI51 is LO, check for an intermittent short to ground in circuit No. 23.

3) If BD61 is more than 500 RPM and BI51 is HI, check for an intermittent short to ground in circuit No. 23.

4) If BD61 is more than 500 RPM and BI51 is LO, check for an intermittent short to ground in circuit No. 25.

* See ALTERNATORS – ALL OTHERS article.

91E09007 91H06604

Courtesy of General Motors Corp.

Fig. 3: Trouble Code B410 Flow Chart & Wiring Diagram

CODE B411 OR B412
BATTERY VOLTAGE TOO LOW OR TOO HIGH

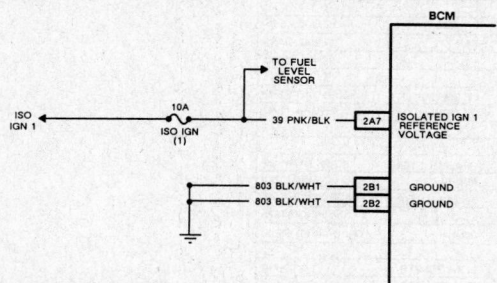

TROUBLE CODE SET CONDITIONS

Code B411 will set when ignition is on, engine speed is greater than 800 RPM and the BCM sees an ignition "1" reference voltage of less than 10.6 volts. Code B412 will set if BCM sees voltage greater than 16 volts. Both trouble codes B411 and B412 will cause the alternator problem message to be displayed on the IPC.

CIRCUIT DESCRIPTION:

The BCM monitors ignition "1" voltage on terminal 2A7 as a reference for fuel control. *See Fig. 5.*

NOTE: Test numbers refer to numbers on diagnostic chart. The term "generator" in diagnostic chart is used in place of alternator. For location of BCM pins referred to in diagnostic chart, see Fig. 5.

TEST DESCRIPTION:

1) BCM data value BD50 displays battery voltage. The normal range is between 10.6 and 16 volts.
2) Ensure low voltage readings are due to circuitry or the battery. If voltage is less than 10 volts with engine running, BCM and related wiring are okay.
3) Ensure low voltage reading is due to the circuit or BCM. If voltage at BCM is less than 10.6 volts, BCM is okay.
4) Determine if high voltage reading is due to the alternator or faulty BCM.
5) Determine if charging voltage is too high with higher engine RPM or electrical load.

NOTICE: IF FUEL GAGE READ EMPTY ERRONEOUSLY ALONG WITH A CODE B411, CHECK FOR A BLOWN 10 AMP IGNITION 1 FUSE AND SHORT TO GROUND ON CKT 39

① • ENGINE RUNNING ABOVE 800 RPM
• SELECT BCM DATA BD50 BATTERY VOLTAGE (VOLTS)
• NOTE DATA VALUE

BELOW 10.6 VOLTS → ② • CHECK BATTERY VOLTAGE AT BATTERY

BETWEEN 10.6 AND 16 VOLTS → ⑤ • RAISE ENGINE RPM TO 2000
• LOAD ELECTRICAL SYSTEM WITH HEADLAMPS AND HIGH ECCP BLOWER
• NOTE DATA VALUE

ABOVE 16 VOLTS → ④ • CHECK BATTERY VOLTAGE AT BATTERY

ABOVE 16 VOLTS → • REMOVE GENERATOR FOR REPAIR

BELOW 16 VOLTS → • REPLACE BCM

ABOVE 16 VOLTS → • REMOVE GENERATOR FOR REPAIR

BELOW 16 VOLTS → • FAULT IS NOT PRESENT
• SEE 'NOTE ON INTERMITTENTS'
• ALSO CHECK FOR IMPROPER BELT TENSION, POOR OR DIRTY BATTERY CONNECTIONS, ETC.

ABOVE 11 VOLTS → ③ • CHECK VOLTAGE FROM BCM TERMINAL 2A7 TO 2B1

BELOW 11 VOLTS → • CHECK FOR PROPER GENERATOR OUTPUT OR RECHARGE AND TEST BATTERY AS NECESSARY

ABOVE 11 VOLTS → • CHECK TERMINAL CONTACT AT BCM PIN 2A7, 2B1, AND 2B2
• IF GOOD CONTACT, REPLACE BCM

BELOW 11 VOLTS → • REPAIR OPEN OR POOR CONNECTION IN CKT 39 OR 803

NOTE ON INTERMITTENTS:

If an intermittent code B411 or B412 is set:
1) Observe BCM data value BD50. This battery voltage reading is monitored from the 15-amp ISO ignition No. 1 fuse, fuel level reference voltage.
2) If the code is set due to high current draw in a particular vehicle component, this can be observed by reading the display for BD50. Operate the various components while watching for the reading to drop to less than 10 volts or increase to greater than 16 volts.
3) Code B411 could be due to an intermittent open in circuit No. 39, which may be observed by manipulating the wire to the BCM while watching BD50 for voltage to drop below 10 volts.

91G09008 91A06605

Courtesy of General Motors Corp.

Fig. 4: Trouble Codes B411/B412 Flow Chart & Wiring Diagram

CKT DESC	/ COLOR /	CKT NO
TWILIGHT DELAY POT	PPL	271
OIL PRESSURE	LT GRN	313
IGNITION #1	PNK/BLK STR	239
OUTSIDE AIR TEMP	LT GRN/BLK STR	735
TWILIGHT PHOTOCELL	WHT	278
PANEL DIM POT	TAN/BLK STR	686
FUEL LEVEL WIPER	PPL	30
ENGINE OIL LEVEL	PNK	114
BRAKE BLUID SW	TAN/WHT STR	33
PARK BRAKE SW	BLK/ORN STR	233
SENSOR GND	BLK/PNK STR	736
HI BEAM SW	YEL/BLK STR	307
FOG LAMP SW	BLK/WHT	901
WASHER FLUID LEVEL	BLK/WHT STR	99
IGNITION #1 W/U	PNK/BLK STR	239
HI/LO BEAM RELAY	BLK/RED STR	691
HEADLAMP RELAY	PNK BLK STR	692
COURTESY LAMP	GRA/BLK STR	690
RAP RELAY	BLK	707
VF DIMMING	PPL/WHT STR	724
CHIME #1	DK BLU/WHT STR	651
BLOWER PWM	PPL/WHT STR	760
BATTERY	ORN	640
BATTERY	ORN	640
5V SENSOR REF	TAN	705
GENERATOR ENABLE	BRN	25
VSS FROM ECM	DK GRN/WHT STR	817
RKE W/U	GRA/WHT STR	157
CRANK	PPL/WHT STR	806
DOOR JAMB SW W/U	WHT	156

WIRE SIDE

CKT NO /	COLOR /	CKT DESC
733	LT BLU	AIR MIX DOOR
731	GRA	LO SIDE TEMP
732	DK BLU	HI SIDE TEMP
800	TAN	SERIAL DATA
800	TAN	SERIAL DATA
590	LT BLU/BLK STR	SUNLOAD TEMP
734	DK GRN	IN-CAR TEMP
308	GRA/BLK STR	PARK LAMP SW
750	PNK/BLK	IGNITION 3
158	BLK/ORN STR	PASS DOOR AJAR
80	LT GRN	KEY IN IGNITION
23	GRA	GENERATER FIELD
803	BLK/WHT STR	GROUND
803	BLK/WHT STR	GROUND
147	GRA/BLK STR	DRIVER DOOR AJAR
304	YEL/BLK STR	TWILIGHT ENABLE
10	YEL	HEADLAMP SW
721	WHT	LOW FREON SW
238	BLK	SEAT BELT SW
317	YEL	FOGLAMP/DRL
652	PPL/WHT STR	CHIME #2
692E	BLK/PNK	PARKLAMP RELAY
685	BRN/WHT STR	COURT PANEL LAMP
555	DK BLU/WHT STR	SYSTEM ON/OFF

WIRE SIDE

91109009

Courtesy of General Motors Corp.

Fig. 5: BCM Electrical Connector (Viewed From Wire Side)

CODE 16
SYSTEM VOLTAGE HIGH/LOW
3800 (VIN L), PFI

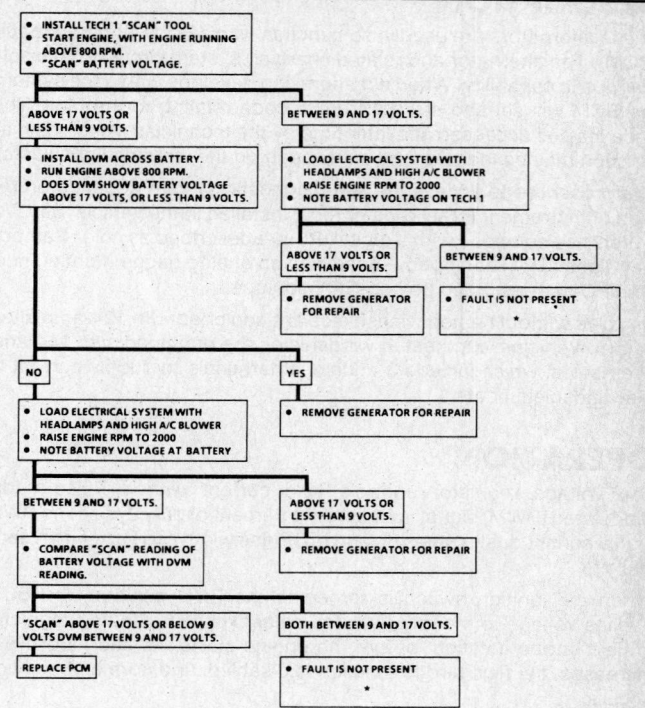

NOTE: Charging battery with a battery charger and starting engine may set a code 16. When code 16 is set, transaxle will be forced to third gear. This is to avoid erratic shifting due to improper voltages.

TROUBLE CODE SET CONDITIONS

If the PCM (Powertrain Control Module) detects more than 17 volts or less than 9 volts for more than 10 seconds on circuit No. 439, it will turn the SES (Service Engine Soon) light ON and set code 16 in memory.

CIRCUIT DESCRIPTION:

The PCM monitors battery voltage on circuit No. 439 to terminal BA2. If the PCM detects more than 17 volts or less than 9 volts for more than 10 seconds, it will turn SES light ON and set code 16 in memory.

NOTE: Test numbers refer to numbers on diagnostic chart. The term "generator" in diagnostic chart is used in place of alternator. For location of BCM pins referred to in diagnostic chart, see Fig. 5.

TEST DESCRIPTION:

Test alternator output. Run engine at moderate speed and measure voltage across the battery. If over 17 volts or under 9 volts, repair alternator. See ALTERNATORS – ALL OTHERS article.

NOTE ON INTERMITTENTS:

An intermittent may be caused by a poor connection, rubbed through insulation, a wire broken inside the insulation or poor PCM grounds.

Inspect for the following: PCM harness connectors for backed out terminal BA2, improper mating, broken locks, improperly formed or damaged terminals, poor terminal-to-wire connection and damaged harness.

INTERMITTENT TEST:

If connections and harness are okay, observe battery voltage while moving related connectors. If failure is induced, battery voltage abruptly changes. This may help isolate malfunction. An engine stall while manipulating harness indicates PCM has lost voltage at terminal BA2. Check for loose connectors in circuit No. 439.

* See NOTE ON INTERMITTENTS.

91G07486 91C06606

Fig. 6: *Trouble Code 16 Flow Chart & Wiring Diagram*

DESCRIPTION

These alternators are used in conjunction with a Body Control Module (BCM). The alternator and related charging system circuitry have self-diagnostic capability. When a malfunction develops within the system, the BCM will set and store a trouble code relating to the fault. This code may be accessed at a later time by the technician. Also, the malfunction may be indicated by a message on the warning light cluster.

The procedure to access the self-diagnostic system depends on the type of Instrument Panel Cluster (IPC) installed in the vehicle. See Fig. 1. Vehicles equipped with a digital IPC are described as color Cathode Ray Tube (CRT) equipped. Those with an analog gauge (floating needle) IPC are described as non-CRT equipped.

Vehicles without heated windshields are equipped with 124-amp alternators. Vehicles with heated windshields are equipped with 144-amp alternators, which include 3 additional terminals to supply current to the windshield heater.

OPERATION

The voltage regulator controls field current with a Pulse Width Modulated (PWM) signal, measured in percent of duty cycle. The PWM signal continuously cycles on and off. Pulse width can vary within each cycle.

When the ignition switch is turned to the RUN position, the BCM applies voltage to the regulator for initial excitation, setting regulator in field strobe function, before the engine starts. As alternator RPM increases, the field strobe function is disabled, and normal regulation occurs.

The regulator switches field current on and off at a fixed frequency of about 400 cycles per second. By varying pulse width, correct average field current for system voltage control is achieved. At high speeds, field-on time may be as low as 10 percent. At low speeds with a heavy electrical load, field-on time may be as much as 90 percent.

The BCM monitors the regulator from the alternator field terminal. If the PWM duty cycle falls below 7 percent, the BCM senses a fault, and indicates a problem by lighting the warning lamp on the instrument cluster.

SELF-DIAGNOSTICS

ENTERING SELF-DIAGNOSTICS

1) Turn ignition switch to ON position. On non-CRT equipped vehicles, simultaneously press OFF and WARM keys on Electronic Climate Control (ECC) panel, and hold them for 3 seconds. On CRT equipped vehicles, simultaneously press OFF and WARM keys on CRT control panel, and hold them for 3 seconds. See Fig. 2.

NOTE: See DESCRIPTION for description of non-CRT and CRT equipped vehicles.

2) On both non-CRT and CRT equipped vehicles, continue to simultaneously press OFF and WARM keys until all segments of Driver Information Center (DIC) light. See Fig. 1. When all segments are lit, system has entered self-diagnostic mode. Release OFF and WARM keys.

3) Lighting of all segments of DIC ensures all display segments are working properly. If all segments light, proceed to DISPLAYING TROUBLE CODES. Failure of any segment to light may result in inaccurate test results. Ensure all segments of display operate properly before proceeding with self-diagnostic procedures.

CAUTION: Accessing self-diagnostics for 30 minutes without running engine will discharge battery, resulting in a possible no-start condition. To ensure proper operation, connect charger to battery.

EXITING SELF-DIAGNOSTICS

On non-CRT equipped vehicles, exit self-diagnostic mode without erasing trouble codes by pressing BI-LEV button on ECC panel or by turning ignition switch to OFF position. On CRT equipped vehicles, exit self-diagnostic mode without erasing trouble codes by pressing RTN key on CRT control panel or by turning ignition switch to OFF position.

DISPLAYING TROUBLE CODES

1) Electronic Control Module (ECM), Body Control Module (BCM) and Supplemental Inflatable Restraint (SIR) trouble codes display automatically after system enters self-diagnostics. ECM trouble codes are displayed first, followed by BCM trouble codes, and finally SIR trouble codes.

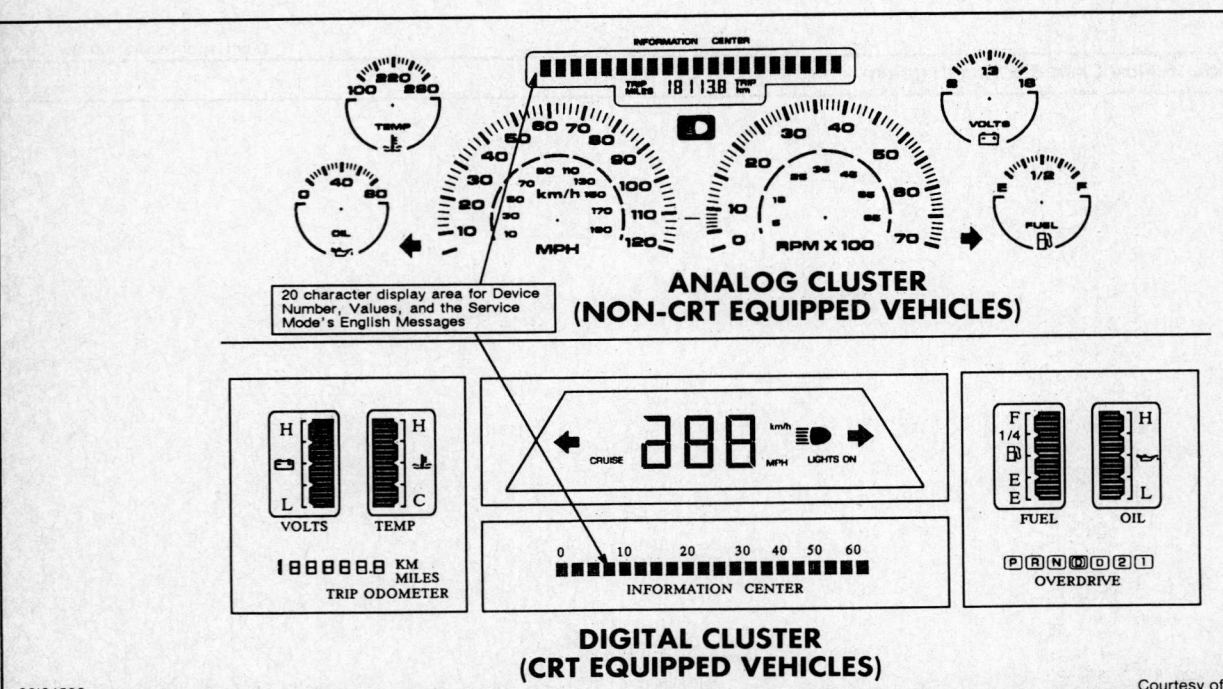

20 character display area for Device Number, Values, and the Service Mode's English Messages

ANALOG CLUSTER (NON-CRT EQUIPPED VEHICLES)

DIGITAL CLUSTER (CRT EQUIPPED VEHICLES)

Courtesy of General Motors Corp.

90I04592

Fig. 1: Locating Driver Information Center (DIC) On Analog & Digital Clusters (Toronado & Trofeo)

2) All trouble codes appear in ascending 3-digit order. ECM codes are prefixed with "E", BCM Codes with "B" and SIR codes with "R". SIR codes do not pertain to charging system.

3) All trouble codes are followed by "C" or "H". "C" stands for current, and indicates a fault presently exists. "H" stands for history, and indicates system malfunction was not present last time code was accessed.

4) For example, code E016H is ECM trouble code number 016, set in response to a past malfunction. Code B410C is BCM trouble code number 410, set in response to a current malfunction.

5) If no ECM or BCM trouble codes are stored in memory, NO E CODE or NO B CODE, respectively, is displayed. Should communication link between a component and ECM or BCM fail, NO BCM/ECM DATA is displayed.

NOTE: After all trouble codes have been displayed, trouble code display can repeat. To repeat trouble code display, press OFF button on ECC of non-CRT equipped vehicles or LEVL key on CRT control panel of CRT equipped vehicles.

BCM CHARGING SYSTEM TROUBLE CODES

BCM charging system trouble codes are:
- **Code B410** – Undervoltage or overvoltage condition. See TROUBLE CODE CHARTS at end of article.
- **Code B411** – Ignition voltage "1" is less than 10.6 volts. See TROUBLE CODE CHARTS at end of article.
- **Code B412** – Ignition voltage "1" is more than 16 volts. See TROUBLE CODE CHARTS at end of article.

ECM CHARGING SYSTEM TROUBLE CODE

ECM charging system trouble code is:
- **Code E016** – Battery voltage out of range. Code may set after charging battery with battery charger, and starting engine.

NOTE: After system completes trouble code display cycle, system can test charging system components and/or circuitry indicated by trouble codes. See MANUAL OPERATION OF SELF-DIAGNOSTICS.

CLEARING TROUBLE CODES

See TEST TYPE SELECTION under MANUAL OPERATION OF SELF-DIAGNOSTICS.

MANUAL OPERATION OF SELF-DIAGNOSTICS

NOTE: Use TROUBLE CODE CHARTS during manual operation of self-diagnostic system. Before using flow charts, become familiar with procedures in MANUAL OPERATION OF SELF-DIAGNOSTICS.

System Selection – 1) After all trouble codes have been displayed (see DISPLAYING TROUBLE CODES), system can perform specific diagnostic tests. After trouble codes display, first system available for testing automatically displays.

2) Charging system tests are part of ECM and BCM systems. To select ECM or BCM system, advance display until reaching desired system.

3) On non-CRT equipped vehicles, repeatedly press FAN DOWN button on ECC panel to cycle system selection list. *See Fig. 2.* On CRT equipped vehicles, repeatedly press NO key on CRT control panel to cycle system selection list. *See Fig. 2.*

4) When desired system (BCM or ECM) is displayed, discontinue cycling selection list. On non-CRT equipped vehicles, press FAN UP button on ECC panel until displayed system is selected for testing. On CRT equipped vehicles, press YES key on CRT control panel until displayed system is selected for testing.

NOTE: To cancel a system selection or repeat system selection process, press OFF button on ECC panel of non-CRT equipped vehicles or press LEVL key on CRT control panel of CRT equipped vehicles.

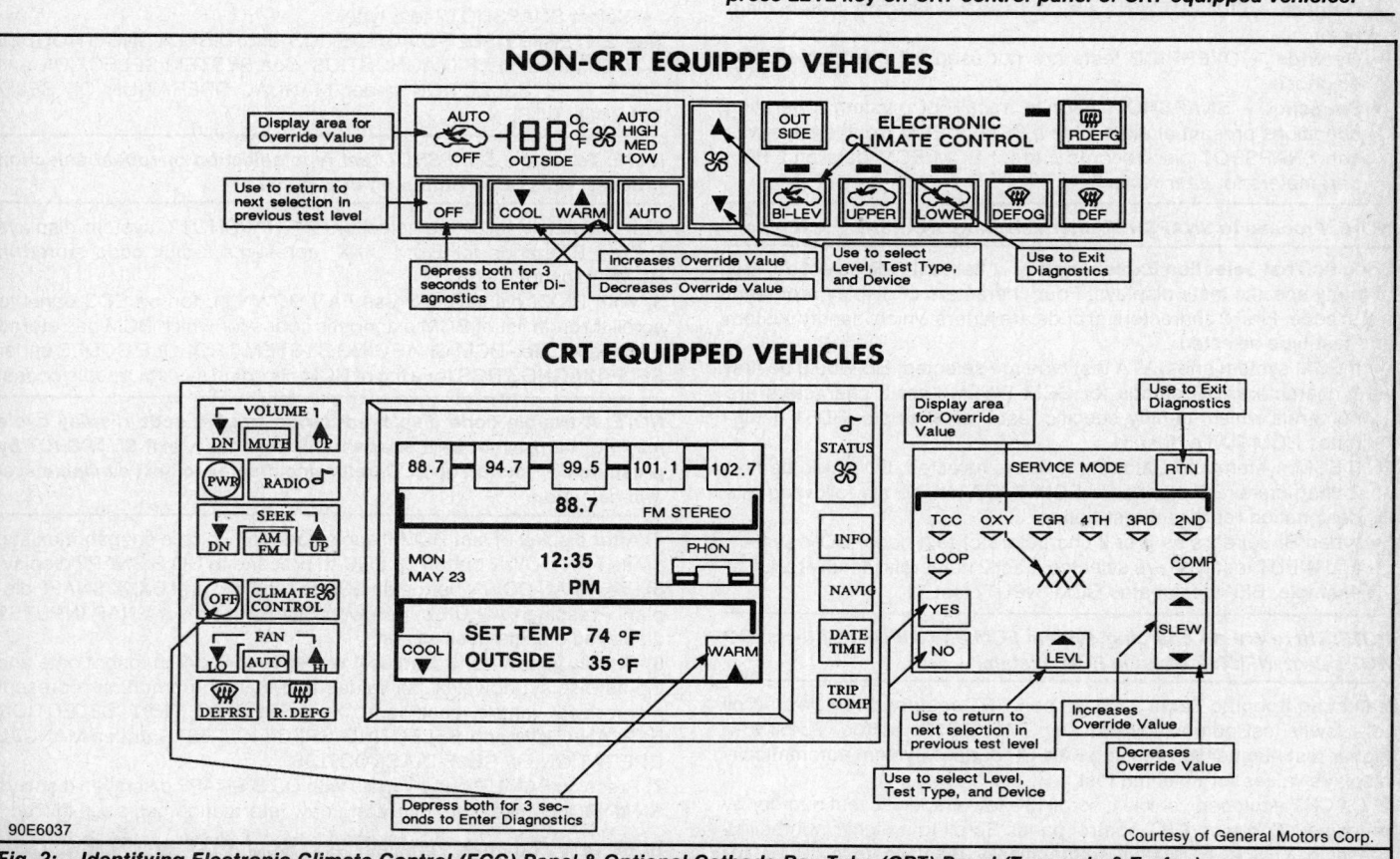

90E6037

Fig. 2: *Identifying Electronic Climate Control (ECC) Panel & Optional Cathode Ray Tube (CRT) Panel (Toronado & Trofeo)*

Test Type Selection – 1) After selecting system, select test type. Test types are CLEAR CODES?, DATA?, INPUTS?, OUTPUTS?, OVERRIDE? and SNAPSHOT?. System may display any of these test types.

2) To advance display to next available test type, press FAN DOWN button on ECC of non-CRT equipped vehicles or NO key on CRT control panel of CRT equipped vehicles. List of test types can be repeated after last test type.

3) When desired test type is displayed, press FAN UP button on ECC of non-CRT equipped vehicles or YES key on CRT control panel of CRT equipped vehicles.

- **Clear Codes** – Selection of CLEAR CODES? displays CODES CLEAR or CODES NOT CLEAR, indicating whether or not codes were successfully cleared. Message appears for 3 seconds, indicating all stored trouble codes have been erased from system's memory. After 3 seconds, display will automatically return to next available test type.

NOTE: After clearing trouble codes, ensure codes do not reset by rechecking after a complete ignition cycle and test drive.

- **Data** – DATA test displays compare malfunctioning system's present parameters with specifications of a properly functioning system.
- **Inputs – 1)** INPUT test displays determine if switched inputs can be properly interpreted. When one of various input tests is selected, state of device is displayed as HI or LO.

  2) HI or LO refers to input terminal voltage for particular circuit. Display also indicates if an input reading has changed. This feature permits activating or deactivating any listed device, and then returning to display to see if reading has changed.

  3) If a reading change occurs, an X will appear next to the HI/LO indicator; otherwise an 0 will appear. X will appear only once per selected input. HI/LO indication continues to change as input changes.
- **Outputs** – OUTPUT tests are not used for charging system diagnosis.
- **Override** – OVERRIDE tests are not used for charging system diagnosis.
- **Snapshot** – SNAPSHOT permits recall of system operating conditions present at exact time a BCM or ECM trouble code was set. SNAPSHOT also records current BCM/ECM data and input parameters for later review.

NOTE: Proceed to SNAPSHOT after selecting SNAPSHOT test type.

Specific Test Selection Explanation – After test type selection, first of many specific tests displays. Four characters of display represent a test code. First 2 characters of code are letters which identify system and test type selected.

- If BCM system and DATA test type are selected, BD would be first 2 characters. BD stands for BCM DATA. Last 2 characters are numerals which identify specific test. For example, BD51 designates BCM DATA, test 51.
- If ECM system and Data test type are selected, ED would be first 2 characters. ED stands for ECM DATA. Numerals following this designation represent test option.
- When BI appears as first 2 characters of test code, BCM system and INPUT test type are selected. Last 2 numerals identify test. For example, BI51 designates BCM INPUT, test 51.

NOTE: There are no charging system ECM and INPUT (EI) tests. DO NOT select INPUTS? when in ECM system.

Selecting Specific Tests – 1) On non-CRT equipped vehicles, scroll to a lower test number by pressing FAN DOWN button. Scroll to a higher test number by pressing FAN UP button. System automatically displays values for selected test.

2) On CRT equipped vehicles, scroll to a lower specific test number by pressing NO key on CRT control panel. Scroll to a higher number by pressing YES key. System automatically displays test values for selected test.

NOTE: To cancel a test selection and repeat test selection process, press OFF button on ECC panel of non-CRT equipped vehicles or LEVL key on CRT control panel of CRT equipped vehicles.

3) Charging system malfunctions represented by specific test selections are:
- **BD50** – Battery voltage is displayed between zero and 25.5 volts.
- **BD51** – Alternator field excitation is displayed as a percentage. A value close to zero represents minimum voltage regulator-on time; a value close to 100 represents maximum voltage regulator-on time.
- **BD61** – Engine speed is displayed in RPM from zero to 6375.
- **BD98** – Ignition cycle value is displayed as number of times BCM has been turned OFF since a BCM trouble code was last detected. After 100 ignition cycles without any malfunction detected, all BCM trouble codes are cleared.
- **BI51** – Alternator feedback display is LO when there is an alternator problem or engine is not running.
- **ED10** – Battery voltage is displayed between zero and 25.5 volts.

SNAPSHOT

NOTE: If directed here from TEST TYPE SELECTION under MANUAL OPERATION OF SELF-DIAGNOSTICS, go to step 2) of appropriate SNAPSHOT procedure.

BCM (Non-CRT Equipped Vehicles) – 1) BCM SNAPSHOT allows recall of system operating conditions present at exact time a BCM malfunction code was set. Up to 3 snapshots may be recalled. In addition, one snapshot may be triggered on command. To enter SNAPSHOT:
- Enter self-diagnostics. Simultaneously press OFF and WARM buttons on ECC panel until all segments light.
- Display trouble codes stored in memory.
- Select BCM for testing.
- Select SNAPSHOT? test type.

See ENTERING SELF-DIAGNOSTICS and DISPLAYING TROUBLE CODES under SELF-DIAGNOSTICS. See SYSTEM SELECTION and TEST TYPE SELECTION under MANUAL OPERATION OF SELF-DIAGNOSTICS.

NOTE: To cancel SNAPSHOT test type selection or repeat selection process, press OFF button on ECC panel.

2) Immediately following selection of SNAPSHOT?, system displays BXXX. "B" stands for BCM. XXX represents 3-digit code stored in BCM snapshot.

3) With BXXX displayed, press FAN DOWN button on ECC panel to scroll through list of BCM diagnostic codes for which BCM has stored a snapshot. See BCM CHARGING SYSTEM TROUBLE CODES under SELF-DIAGNOSTICS for a list of BCM charging system trouble codes.

NOTE: A trouble code displayed during trouble code display cycle may not be present as a snapshot. In this case, exit SNAPSHOT by pressing OFF button on ECC, returning display to next available system selection.

4) After display of last BCM trouble code for which a snapshot exists, press FAN DOWN button on ECC to proceed to DO B SNAP? display.

5) Press FAN DOWN button on ECC to return to first BXXX SNAP? display. Pressing FAN UP button with SNAP DATA? or SNAP INPUTS? displayed selects desired test.

6) Display is now controlled as it would be for non-snapshot data and inputs display; however, all values and status information represent memorized vehicle conditions. See SPECIFIC TEST SELECTION EXPLANATION and SELECTING SPECIFIC TESTS under MANUAL OPERATION OF SELF-DIAGNOSTICS.

7) Pressing FAN UP button again with DO B SNAP? displayed displays SNAP DONE message, indicating new information has been stored.

BCM (CRT Equipped Vehicles) – 1) BCM SNAPSHOT allows recall of system operating conditions present at exact time a BCM malfunction code was set. Up to 3 snapshots may be recalled. In addition, one snapshot may be triggered on command. To enter SNAPSHOT:

- Enter self-diagnostics. Simultaneously press OFF and WARM keys on CRT control panel until all segments light.
- Display trouble codes stored in memory.
- Select BCM for testing.
- Select SNAPSHOT? test type.

See ENTERING SELF-DIAGNOSTICS and DISPLAYING TROUBLE CODES under SELF-DIAGNOSTICS. See SYSTEM SELECTION and TEST TYPE SELECTION under MANUAL OPERATION OF SELF-DIAGNOSTICS.

NOTE: To cancel SNAPSHOT test type selection or repeat selection process, press LEVL key on CRT control panel.

---

2) Immediately following selection of SNAPSHOT?, system displays BXXX. "B" stands for BCM. XXX represents 3-digit code stored in BCM snapshot.

3) With BXXX displayed, press NO key on CRT control panel to scroll through list of BCM diagnostic codes for which BCM has stored a snapshot . See BCM CHARGING SYSTEM TROUBLE CODES under SELF-DIAGNOSTICS for a list of BCM charging system trouble codes.

NOTE: A trouble code displayed during trouble code display cycle may not be present as a snapshot. In this case, exit SNAPSHOT by pressing OFF key on CRT control panel, returning display to next available system selection.

---

4) After display of last BCM trouble code for which a snapshot exists, press NO key on CRT control panel to proceed to DO B SNAP? display.

5) Press NO key on CRT control panel to return to first BXXX SNAP? display. Pressing YES key on CRT control panel with either SNAP DATA? or SNAP INPUTS? displayed selects desired test.

6) Display is now controlled as it would be for non-snapshot data and inputs display; however, all values and status information represent memorized vehicle conditions. See SPECIFIC TEST SELECTION EXPLANATION and SELECTING SPECIFIC TESTS under MANUAL OPERATION OF SELF-DIAGNOSTICS.

7) Pressing YES key again with DO B SNAP? displayed displays SNAP DONE message, indicating new information has been stored.

ECM (Non-CRT Equipped Vehicles) – 1) ECM SNAPSHOT allows recall of system operating conditions present at exact time an ECM malfunction code was set. Up to 3 snapshots may be recalled. In addition, one snapshot may be triggered on command. To enter SNAPSHOT:

- Enter self-diagnostics. Simultaneously press OFF and WARM buttons on ECC panel until all segments light.
- Display trouble codes stored in memory.
- Select ECM for testing.
- Select SNAPSHOT? test type.

See ENTERING SELF-DIAGNOSTICS and DISPLAYING TROUBLE CODES under SELF-DIAGNOSTICS. See SYSTEM SELECTION and TEST TYPE SELECTION under MANUAL OPERATION OF SELF-DIAGNOSTICS.

NOTE: To cancel SNAPSHOT test type selection or repeat selection process, press OFF button on ECC panel.

---

2) Immediately following selection of SNAPSHOT?, system displays SNAP DONE, indicating all ECM data and inputs have been stored. Display will then automatically proceed to next available SNAPSHOT test type.

3) Press FAN DOWN button on ECC panel to display next available SNAPSHOT test type. Display may be toggled between SNAP DATA? and SNAP INPUTS?

4) Press FAN UP KEY button on ECC panel with SNAP DATA? or SNAP INPUTS? displayed to select desired test. Display is now controlled as it would be for non-snapshot data and inputs display; however, all values and status information represent memorized conditions.

5) Pressing FAN UP button on ECC panel with ECM SNAP SHOT? displayed displays SNAP SHOT TAKEN, indicating new information has been stored. Information may be accessed as previously described.

ECM (CRT Equipped Vehicles) – 1) ECM SNAPSHOT allows recall of system operating conditions present at exact time an ECM malfunction code was set. Up to 3 snapshots may be recalled. In addition, one snapshot may be triggered on command. To enter SNAPSHOT:

- Enter self-diagnostics. Simultaneously press OFF and WARM keys on CRT control panel until all segments light.
- Display trouble codes stored in memory.
- Select ECM for testing.
- Select SNAPSHOT? test type.

See ENTERING SELF-DIAGNOSTICS and DISPLAYING TROUBLE CODES under SELF-DIAGNOSTICS. See SYSTEM SELECTION and TEST TYPE SELECTION under MANUAL OPERATION OF SELF-DIAGNOSTICS.

NOTE: To cancel SNAPSHOT test type selection or repeat selection process, press LEVL key on CRT control panel.

---

2) Immediately following selection of SNAPSHOT?, system displays SNAP DONE, indicating all ECM data and inputs have been stored. Display will then automatically proceed to next available SNAPSHOT test type.

3) Press NO key on CRT control panel to display next available SNAPSHOT test type. Display may be toggled between SNAP DATA? and SNAP INPUTS?

4) Press YES key on CRT control panel with SNAP DATA? or SNAP INPUTS? displayed to select desired test. Display is now controlled as it would be for non-snapshot data and inputs display; however, all values and status information represent memorized conditions.

5) Pressing YES key on CRT control panel with ECM SNAP SHOT? displayed displays SNAP SHOT TAKEN, indicating new information has been stored. Information may be accessed as previously described.

BENCH TESTING

See ALTERNATORS – ALL OTHERS article.

OVERHAUL

See ALTERNATORS – ALL OTHERS article.

TROUBLE CODE CHARTS

CODE B410, CHARGING SYSTEM CIRCUIT FAULT

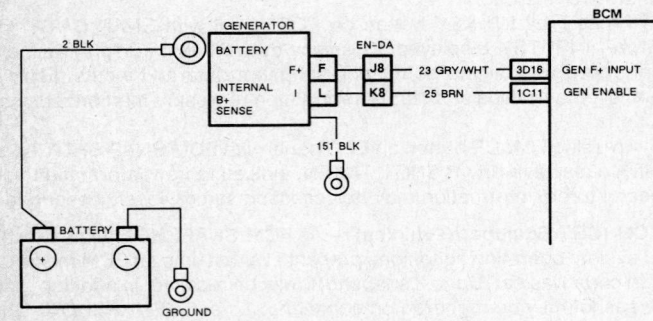

Generator on this vehicle has fault detection capability built into regulator. BCM supplies 12 volts on circuit No. 25, and monitors field voltage on circuit No. 23.
Code B410 sets if following conditions exist:
- Engine running
- Generator enable line is low
Or if following conditions exist:
- Engine running
- Generator enable line high
- Generator field input is less than 2 percent
Or if following conditions exist:
- Ignition on, engine not running
- Generator enable line is high
Or if following conditions exist:
- Ignition on, engine not running
- Generator enable line is low
- Generator field input is less than 2 percent
Code B410 causes GENERATOR PROBLEM message to be displayed on DIC and NO CHARGE telltale to light on IPC.

NOTE: Test numbers refer to numbers on diagnostic chart.

1) BI51 displays generator signal voltage as HI or LO, depending on voltage state at BCM. Normally, with key on and engine off, circuit No. 25 voltage will be pulled low by generator, and BI51 will read LO.
2) Checks to see if low reading is due to circuit No. 25 or generator. If display reading changes from LO to HI when the generator is disconnected with engine running, BCM and circuit No. 25 are okay.
3) Checks to see if fault is due to BCM or circuit No. 25.
4) BD51 displays amount of generator field activity. Under normal conditions, a reading less than 7 percent would indicate a fault in field circuit at BCM.
5) Removing generator connector determines if fault is due to generator or an open in circuit No. 25, including BCM and interface connector.

91D11927 91E11928

NOTE ON INTERMITTENTS

If an intermittent condition exists, check B410 snap data parameters BD61 and BI51. Also check for following conditions:
- If BD61 is under 500 RPM and BI51 is high, check for an intermittent open in circuit No. 25.
- If BD61 is under 500 RPM and BI51 is low, check for an intermittent short to ground in circuit No. 23.
- If BD61 is over 500 RPM and BI51 is high, check for an intermittent short to ground in circuit No. 23.
- If BD61 is over 500 RPM and BI51 is low, check for an intermittent short to ground in circuit No. 25.
Also perform battery and charging system checks to ensure proper operation of these components.

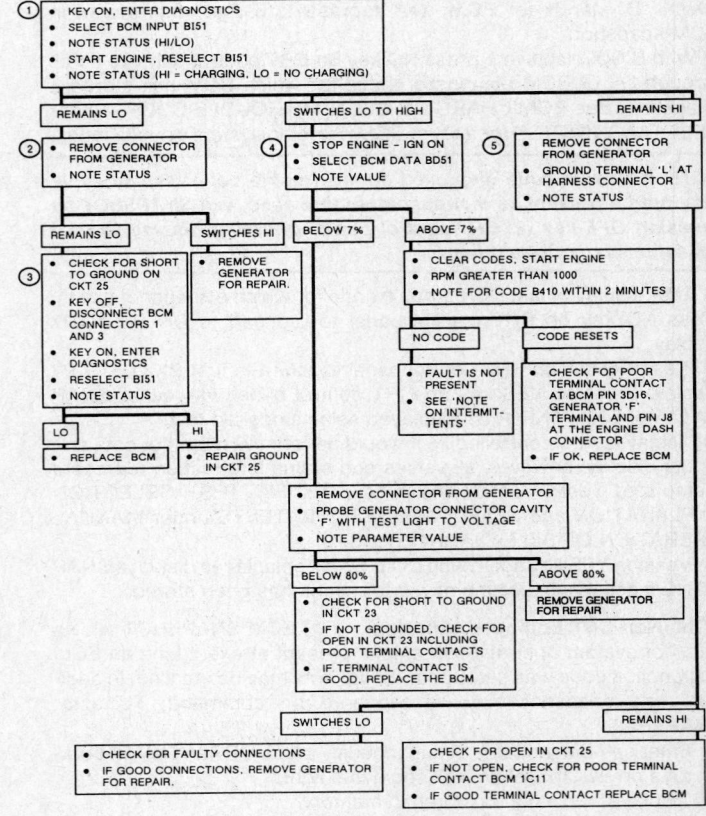

WHEN ALL DIAGNOSIS AND REPAIRS ARE COMPLETED, CLEAR CODES AND VERIFY PROPER OPERATION

Courtesy of General Motors Corp.

Fig. 3: Trouble Code B410 Flow Chart & Wiring Diagram (Toronado & Trofeo)

CODE B411 OR B412, BATTERY VOLTAGE TOO HIGH OR TOO LOW

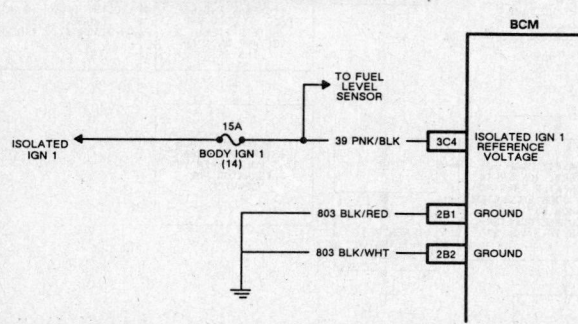

BCM monitors IGN 1 voltage on terminal 3C4 as a reference for fuel control. Code B411 sets when ignition is on, engine RPM is greater than 800 and BCM sees an IGN 1 reference voltage of less than 10.6 volts. Code B412 sets if BCM sees voltage over 16 volts. Both B411 and B412 cause GENERATOR PROBLEM message to be displayed on IPC.

NOTE: Test numbers refer to numbers on diagnostic chart.

1) BD50 displays battery voltage. Normal range is 10.6-16 volts.
2) Checks to see if low voltage reading is due to circuit or battery. With engine running, if voltage is less than 10 volts, BCM and wiring are okay.
3) Checks to see if low voltage reading is due to circuit or BCM. If voltage reading at BCM is less than 10.6 volts, BCM is okay.
4) Checks to see if high voltage reading is due to generator or faulty BCM.
5) Checks to see if charging voltage goes too high with higher engine RPM or electrical load.

91F11929 91I11930

NOTE ON INTERMITTENTS

If an intermittent Code B411 or B412 is being set, observe BD50 display. This battery voltage reading is monitored from 15-amp ISO IGN 1 fuse, fuel reference voltage. If code is being set due to a high current draw in a certain vehicle component, this can be observed by reading BD50 display. Operate various components while watching for reading to drop to less than 10 volts or increase to greater than 16 volts.

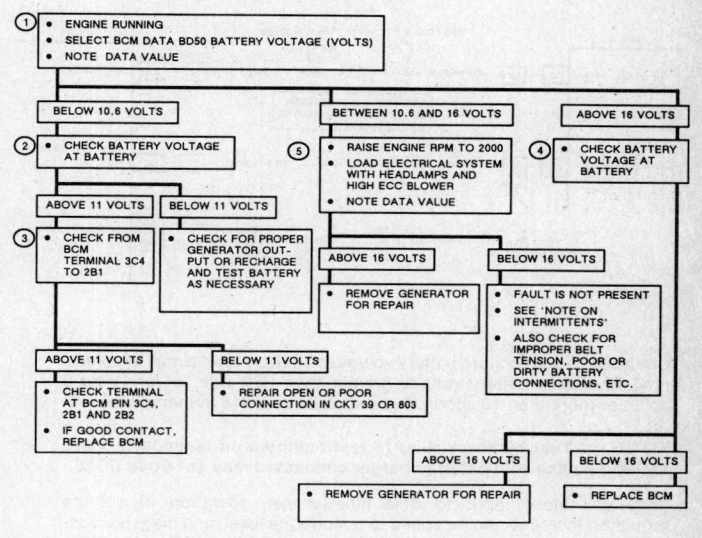

Courtesy of General Motors Corp.

Fig. 4: Trouble Codes B411 Or B412 Flow Chart & Wiring Diagram (Toronado & Trofeo)

CKT DESC	/ COLOR /	CKT NO	WIRE SIDE		CKT NO /	COLOR	/	CKT DESC
TWILIGHT DELAY POT	PPL	271	1 1	D 1	733	LT BLU		AIR MIX DOOR
			2 2		731	GRA		LO SIDE TEMP
OIL PRESSURE	LT GRN	313	3 3					
IGNITION #1	PNK/BLK	39C	4 4		732	DK BLU		HI SIDE TEMP
			5 5		800E	TAN		SERIAL DATA
OUTSIDE AIR TEMP	LT GRN/BLK	735	6 6	RED	800C	TAN		SERIAL DATA
TWILIGHT PHOTOCELL	WHT	278	7 7					
PANEL DIM POT	TAN/BLK	686	8 8		590	LT BLU/BLK		SUN LOAD TEMP
			9 9		734	DK GRN		IN-CAR TEMP
FUEL LEVEL SENDER	PPL	30	10 10		953	(13499) BRN		HEADLAMP SW
ENGINE OIL LEVEL	PNK	114	11 11		773	GRA		PRNDL DECODER C
BRAKE FLUID SW	TAN/WHT	33	12 12		308	GRA/BLK		PARKLAMPS SW WAKE-UP
PARK BRAKE SW	BLK/ORN	233	13 13					
PRNDL PARITY	WHT	776	14 14		158	BLK/ORN		PASS DOOR AJAR
FOG LAMP SW	PPL	13	15 15	D 1	80	LT GRN		KEY IN IGNITION
HI BEAM SW	LT GRN	11E	16 16	6	23	GRA		GENERATOR FIELD
5 VOLT RETURN	BLK/PNK	736C	1 1	B1	803A	BLK/WHT		GROUND
			2 2		803B	BLK/WHT		GROUND
HWS ON INPUT	DK GRN	649	3 3					
PRNDL DECODER	BLK/WHT	771	4 4		147	GRA/BLK		DRIVER DOOR AJAR
			5 5	BROWN	304	YEL/BLK		TWILIGHT ENABLE
WASHER FL LEVEL	BLK/WHT	99RV	6 6		16B	PPL		TURN SIGNAL
IGNITION OFF WAKE-UP	WHT/BLK	343B	7 7					
			8 8		721A	WHT		LOW FREON SW
			9 9		238	BLK		SEAT BELT SW
			10 10					
HEATED WINDSHIELD ENABLE/DISABLE	YEL	635	11 11		118A	PNK/WHT		DIS DATA
			12 12	B12	772	YEL		PRNDL DECODER B
COURTESY LAMP	GRA/BLK	690	1 1	D 1	738	LT GRN		CRT WARM-UP
FOG LAMP	YEL	317	2 2		652	PPL/WHT		CHIME #2
DIS CLOCK	WHT	1179	3 3		692C	BLK/PNK		TWILIGHT RELAYS
VF DIMMING	PPL/WHT	724C	4 4					
CHIME #1	DK BLU/WHT	651	5 5					
HWS CONTROL	DK BLU	648	6 6					
BLOWER PWM	PPL/WHT	760	7 7	BROWN				
BATTERY	ORN	640A	8 8					
BATTERY	ORN	640B	9 9					
5 VOLT REF	TAN	705B	10 10					
GENERATOR ENABLE	BRN	25	11 11					
VSS FROM ECM	DK GRN/WHT	817	12 12					
DOOR HANDLE W/U	GRA	157	13 13					
CRANK	PPL/WHT	806A	14 14					
CRTC WAKE-UP	LT GRN	1171	15 15	D 1	685	BRN/WHT		COURTESY LAMP SWITCH WAKE-UP
DOOR JAMB W/U	WHT	156	16 16	6	555	DK BLU/WHT		IPC WAKE-UP

WIRE SIDE
TORONADO

*ON COLOR CRT/DID EQUIPPED CARS ONLY

91J11337

Courtesy of General Motors Corp.

Fig. 5: Locating BCM Electrical Connector Pins (Viewed From Wire Side) – Toronado & Trofeo

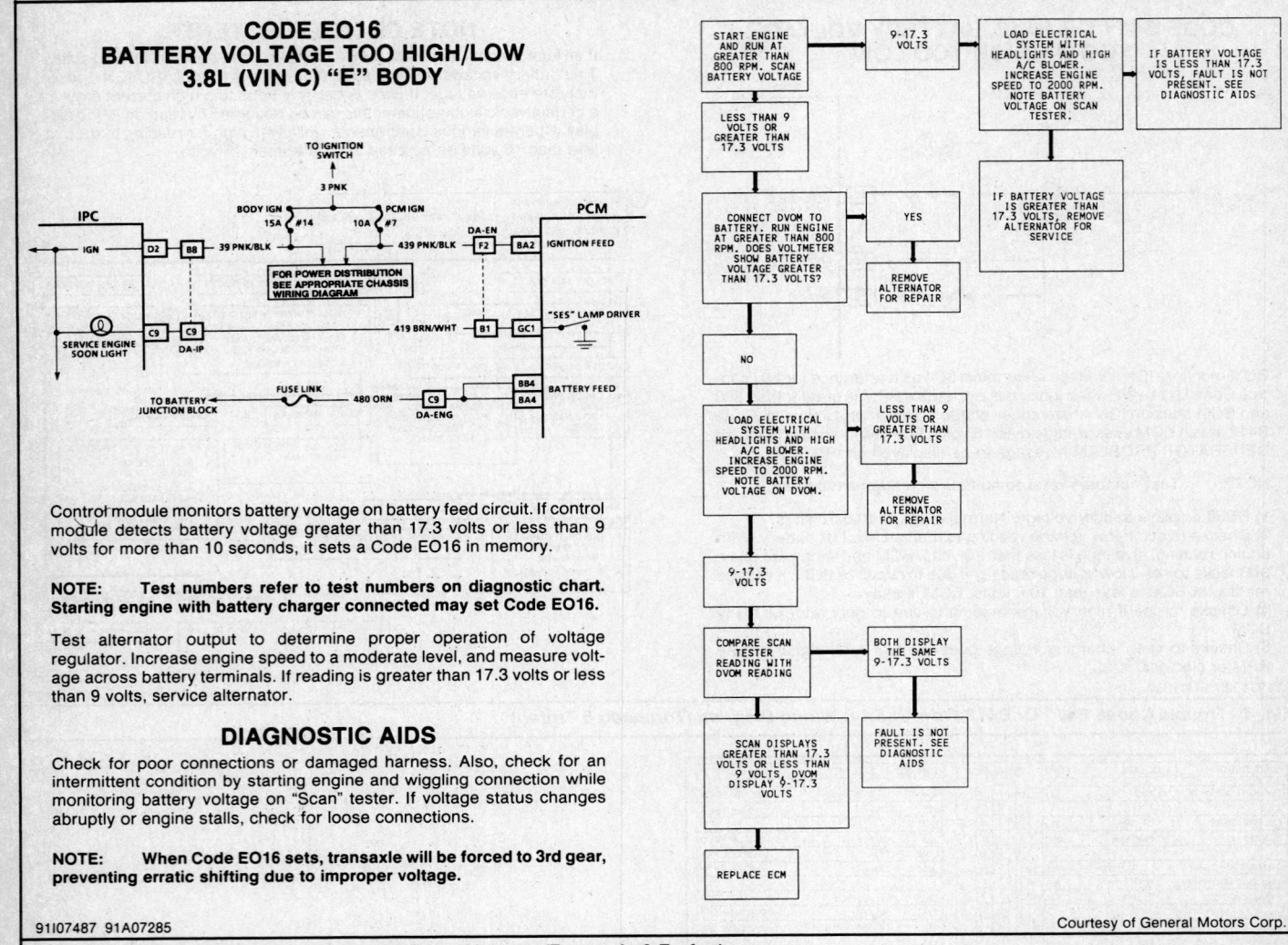

CODE EO16
BATTERY VOLTAGE TOO HIGH/LOW
3.8L (VIN C) "E" BODY

Control module monitors battery voltage on battery feed circuit. If control module detects battery voltage greater than 17.3 volts or less than 9 volts for more than 10 seconds, it sets a Code EO16 in memory.

NOTE: **Test numbers refer to test numbers on diagnostic chart. Starting engine with battery charger connected may set Code EO16.**

Test alternator output to determine proper operation of voltage regulator. Increase engine speed to a moderate level, and measure voltage across battery terminals. If reading is greater than 17.3 volts or less than 9 volts, service alternator.

DIAGNOSTIC AIDS

Check for poor connections or damaged harness. Also, check for an intermittent condition by starting engine and wiggling connection while monitoring battery voltage on "Scan" tester. If voltage status changes abruptly or engine stalls, check for loose connections.

NOTE: **When Code EO16 sets, transaxle will be forced to 3rd gear, preventing erratic shifting due to improper voltage.**

91I07487 91A07285

Courtesy of General Motors Corp.

Fig. 6: *Trouble Code E016 Flow Chart & Wiring Diagram (Toronado & Trofeo)*

Beretta, Bonneville, Brougham, Camaro, Caprice, Cavalier, Century, Corsica, Corvette, Custom Cruiser, Cutlass Calais, Cutlass Ciera, Cutlass Cruiser, Cutlass Supreme, Eighty-Eight, Firebird, Grand Am, Grand Prix, LeSabre, Lumina, Ninety-Eight, Park Avenue, Regal, Roadmaster, Skylark, Sunbird, Touring Sedan, 6000

DESCRIPTION

CS series alternators include a stator, rectifier bridge, and rotor with slip rings and brushes. A built-in regulator incorporates fault detection circuitry.

Most CS series alternators operate with 2 wire connections and a ground path through the mounting bracket. The first wire connection is the BAT (output) terminal. This terminal must be connected to the battery during operation. The second wire connection is through the charge indicator light or an external resistor to the terminal "L" of the regulator. This connection provides initial excitation at start-up.

Three other regulator terminals, "P", "I" and "S", are provided for optional use. Terminal "P" is connected to the stator and may be connected to a tachometer. Terminal "I" provides an alternative method for turning on the alternator without going through the indicator light or external resistor. Terminal "S" may be used to sense electrical system voltage at a remote point on the vehicle. If terminal "S" is not used, the regulator senses internal alternator voltage.

Some CS144 models have 3 auxiliary phase terminals which supply current to operate heated windshields on vehicles so equipped.

No periodic maintenance is necessary. CS144 alternators, except for those with 3 auxiliary phase terminals, can be disassembled and repaired. All CS121, CS130 and CS144 alternators with 3 auxiliary phase terminals are serviced by replacement.

TROUBLE SHOOTING

NOTE: For trouble shooting, see TROUBLE SHOOTING article in GENERAL INFORMATION.

ADJUSTMENTS

No adjustment or maintenance is required on alternator assembly. Regulator voltage is preset and no adjustment is possible.

ON-VEHICLE TESTING

VEHICLES WITH CHARGE WARNING LIGHT

1) Visually check alternator belt and wiring. Turn ignition switch to ON position (engine not running). Charge light should come on. If light does not illuminate, go to step 2). If light comes on, go to step 4).
2) Disconnect harness connector at alternator. Using a jumper wire, connect terminal "L" of alternator harness connector to ground. If light now illuminates, repair or replace alternator.
3) If light still does not illuminate, check bulb. If bulb is okay, repair open circuit between jumper wire connected in step 2) and ignition switch. Reconnect alternator harness connector.
4) Start engine, and run at moderate speed. Charge light should go off. If charge light stays on, disconnect alternator wiring connector. If light goes off, repair or replace alternator. If light stays on, check for grounded wire between terminal "L" of alternator harness connector and charge indicator light.

VEHICLES WITH GAUGES

1) Visually check alternator belt and wiring. With ignition off, disconnect harness connector at alternator. Turn ignition on. Connect negative lead of a voltmeter to a good engine ground. Connect positive voltmeter lead, in turn, to terminals "I" and "L" of alternator harness connector.
2) Meter should indicate battery voltage at at least one terminal. If power appears at either or both terminals, reconnect harness connector, then continue with UNDER- OR OVERCHARGED BATTERY test. If power is not present at both terminals, repair open circuit between harness connector and ignition switch.

UNDER- OR OVERCHARGED BATTERY

NOTE: Battery should be fully charged and in good condition before performing the following steps. If battery is not at (or near) a fully charged condition, or if its condition is questionable, substitute a known good battery before proceeding.

1) Perform tests under VEHICLES WITH CHARGE WARNING LIGHT or VEHICLES WITH GAUGES as appropriate. Connect positive voltmeter lead to positive battery post. Connect negative lead to negative battery post.
2) Start engine and run at moderate speed. If voltmeter indicates more than 16 volts, repair or replace alternator. If voltmeter indicates less than 16 volts, continue with CURRENT OUTPUT TEST.

CURRENT OUTPUT TEST

CAUTION: Never run engine with alternator output terminal disconnected from battery.

1) Connect an ammeter in series with alternator output cable. Connect positive voltmeter lead to positive battery post. Connect negative lead to negative battery post.

CAUTION: Carbon-pile testing is part of this procedure. To avoid battery explosion, turn carbon pile OFF before connecting or disconnecting to and from vehicle battery.

2) Ensure carbon pile control knob is in OFF position. Connect carbon pile to battery. Start engine and run at moderate speed.
3) Turn on all accessories except for heated windshield on vehicles so equipped. Load battery with carbon pile to obtain maximum alternator output. Adjust carbon pile to maintain voltage at 13 volts or more.
4) If ammeter reading is within 15 amps of rated output, alternator is okay. If ammeter reading is not within 15 amps of rated output, repair or replace alternator.

BENCH TESTING

ALTERNATOR OUTPUT TEST

CAUTION: Carbon-pile testing is part of this procedure. To avoid battery explosion, turn carbon pile OFF before connecting or disconnecting to and from test-stand battery.

1) Mount alternator on test stand. Set test stand controls to turn alternator clockwise. Ensure ground polarity of alternator and battery are the same. Ensure battery is fully charged. Connect voltmeter, ammeter and carbon pile (in OFF position). Connect 30-500 ohm resistor between battery and terminal "L" of alternator. See Fig. 1.
2) Slowly increase alternator speed while observing voltmeter. If output is uncontrolled and increases to more than 16 volts, rotor coil is shorted and/or regulator is defective. A shorted rotor coil can cause regulator failure.
3) If voltage is less than 16 volts, increase speed and adjust carbon pile to obtain maximum output current. Maintain voltage at 13 volts. If output is within 15 amps of rated output, alternator is okay. If output is not within 15 amps of rated output, repair or replace alternator.

ROTOR TEST

NOTE: When disassembling alternator, carefully note locations of insulated and uninsulated screws.

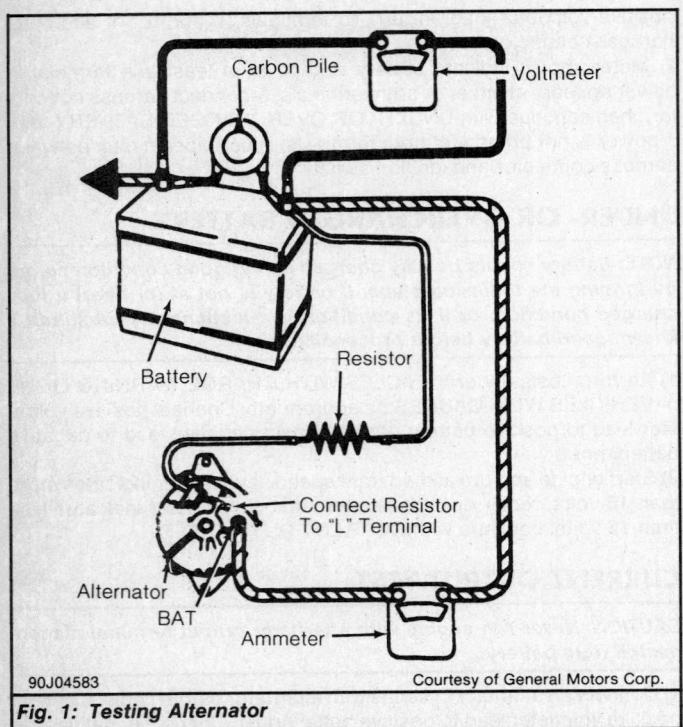

90J04583

Courtesy of General Motors Corp.

Fig. 1: Testing Alternator

CS144 – 1) Scribe end frames to facilitate reassembly. Remove through bolts and separate end frames.

2) With ohmmeter set to its lowest range, measure coil resistance between slip rings. *See Fig. 2.* Replace rotor if coil resistance is not 1.7-3.0 ohms at 70°F (21°C).

3) With ohmmeter set to its highest range, check for grounds between either slip ring and rotor pole piece. *See Fig. 2.* If reading is not close to infinite, replace rotor.

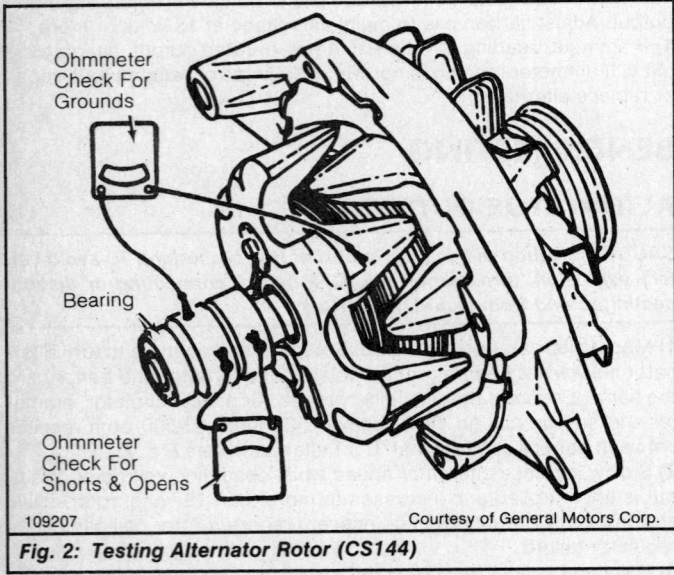

109207

Courtesy of General Motors Corp.

Fig. 2: Testing Alternator Rotor (CS144)

NOTE: Manufacturer recommends installing new bearing at slip ring end whenever alternator is reassembled.

4) To reassemble alternator, reverse disassembly procedure. Retain brushes with brush retaining pin during reassembly. *See Fig. 3.* Remove retaining pin after tightening through bolts.

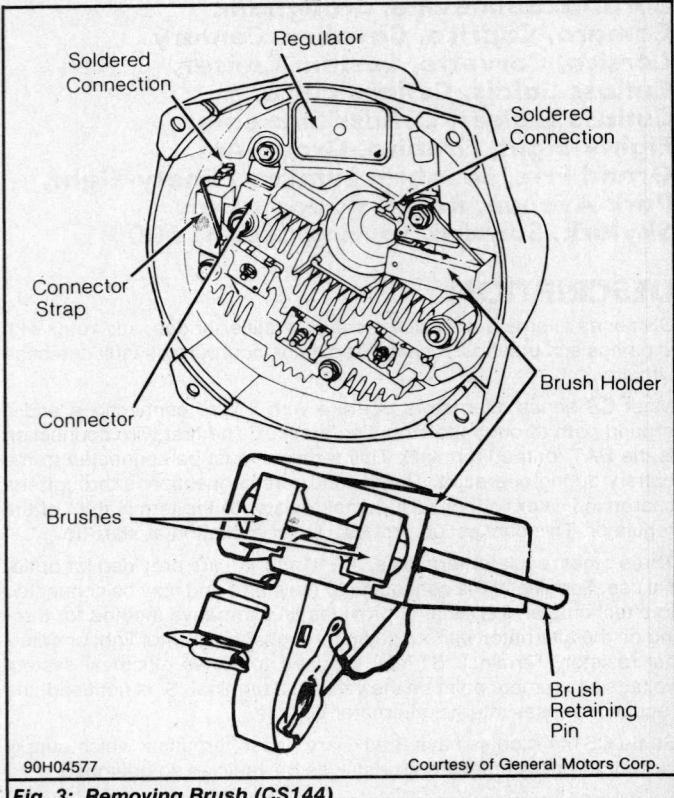

90H04577

Courtesy of General Motors Corp.

Fig. 3: Removing Brush (CS144)

STATOR TEST

CS144 – 1) Scribe end frames to facilitate reassembly. Remove through bolts and separate end frames. Remove stator lead attaching nuts and remove stator.

2) With ohmmeter set to its highest range, check that coil is not grounded to stator core. *See Fig. 4.* Ohmmeter should indicate infinite resistance. If ohmmeter does not indicate infinity, replace stator. Stator cannot be checked for opens or shorts with ohmmeter.

NOTE: Manufacturer recommends installing new bearing at slip ring end whenever alternator is reassembled.

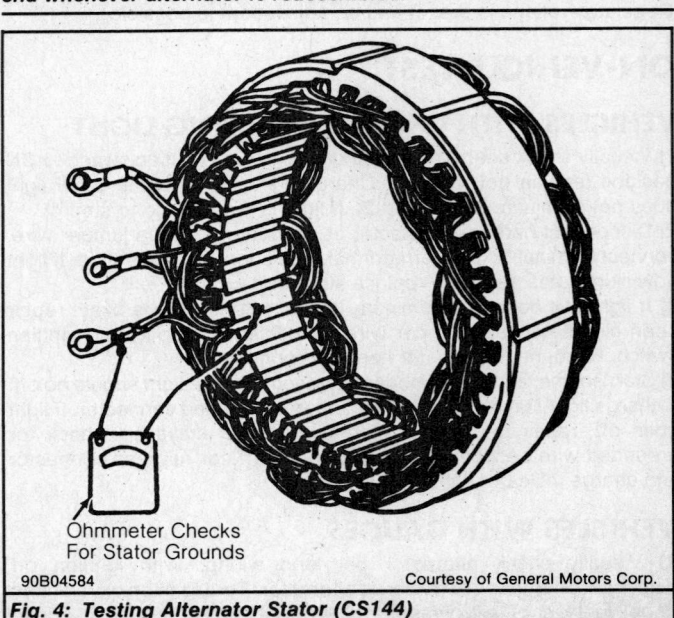

90B04584

Courtesy of General Motors Corp.

Fig. 4: Testing Alternator Stator (CS144)

3) To reassemble alternator, reverse disassembly procedure. Retain brushes with brush retaining pin during reassembly. *See Fig. 3.* Remove retaining pin after tightening through bolts.

RECTIFIER BRIDGE TEST

CS144 – 1) Scribe end frames to facilitate reassembly. Remove through bolts and separate end frames. Remove stator. Connect an ohmmeter between grounded heat sink and any one of 3 grounded flat metal rectifier bridge terminal connectors; note reading. *See Fig. 5.*

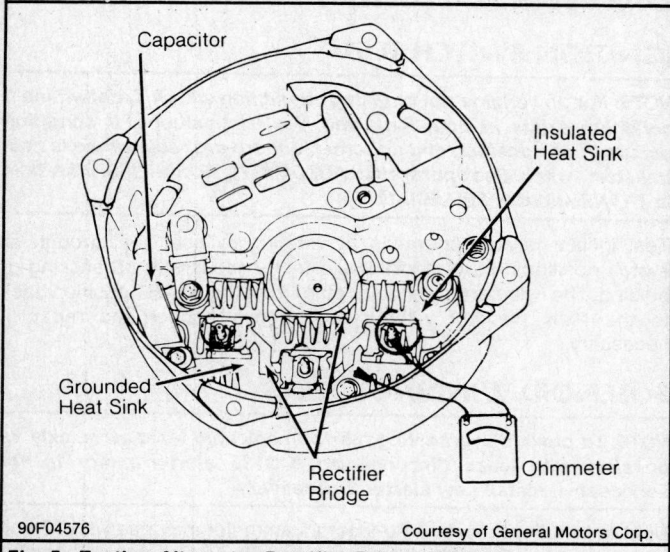

90F04576   Courtesy of General Motors Corp.

Fig. 5: Testing Alternator Rectifier Bridge (CS144)

2) Reverse meter leads. If both readings are the same, replace rectifier bridge. Repeat test between grounded heat sink and the other 2 flat metal terminal connectors. If readings are the same when leads are reversed at either connection, replace rectifier bridge.

3) Repeat test between insulated heat sink and its 3 flat rectifier bridge metal connectors. Replace rectifier bridge if test readings are the same when leads are reversed at any test connection.

NOTE: Manufacturer recommends installing new bearing at slip ring end whenever alternator is reassembled.

4) To reassemble alternator, reverse disassembly procedure. Retain brushes with brush retaining pin during reassembly. *See Fig. 3.* Remove retaining pin after tightening through bolts.

OVERHAUL

NOTE: Replacement parts are not available for CS121 and CS130 alternators. If alternator is defective, a new unit must be installed. CS144 alternators without auxiliary terminals for heated windshields may be disassembled for repair.

BRUSHES & REGULATOR

CS144 – 1) Scribe end frames to facilitate reassembly. Remove through bolts and separate end frames. Unsolder brush connections. Remove attaching screws and connectors. Remove regulator and brush holder. Clean new brushes with soft dry cloth.

2) Put brushes in holder and hold with brush retaining pin. *See Fig. 3.* Install brush holder into alternator by reversing removal procedure. To reassemble alternator, reverse disassembly procedure. Remove brush retainer pin after tightening through bolts.

NOTE: Manufacturer recommends installing new bearing at slip ring end whenever alternator is reassembled.

DRIVE-END BEARING

CS144 – 1) Scribe end frames to facilitate reassembly. Remove through bolts and separate end frames. Remove shaft nut while holding rotor with hex wrench inserted into shaft end. Push rotor from housing. Remove retainer plate and press bearing out. On some alternators, drive end bearing cannot be replaced.

2) To install new bearing, press against outer race until bearing seats. Bearing is sealed; no added lubricant is required. Assemble retainer and press rotor into end frame. Tighten shaft nut to 40-80 ft. lbs. (54-108 N.m).

NOTE: Manufacturer recommends installing new bearing at slip ring end whenever alternator is reassembled.

3) To reassemble alternator, reverse disassembly procedure. Retain brushes with brush retaining pin during reassembly. *See Fig. 3.* Remove retaining pin after tightening through bolts.

1991 ELECTRICAL
Starters – Delco-Remy

Beretta, Bonneville, Brougham, Camaro, Caprice, Cavalier, Century, Corsica, Corvette, Custom Cruiser, Cutlass Calais, Cutlass Ciera, Cutlass Cruiser, Cutlass Supreme, DeVille, Eighty-Eight Eldorado, Firebird, Fleetwood, Grand Am, Grand Prix, LeSabre, Lumina, Ninety-Eight, Park Avenue, Reatta, Regal, Riviera, Roadmaster, Seville, Skylark, Sunbird, Toronado, Touring Sedan, Trofeo, 6000

DESCRIPTION & OPERATION

The starter is part of the cranking circuit, which consists of the battery, ignition switch and related wiring. See Fig. 1. When the ignition switch is turned to the START position, the starter solenoid windings are energized. This causes the plunger to move the shift lever, which engages the pinion with the engine flywheel ring gear. The movement of the plunger also closes the main contacts, applying battery voltage to the starter.

When the engine starts, the pinion will overrun, protecting the armature from excessive speed and the flywheel from damage. When the ignition switch is released, the plunger return spring disengages the pinion.

TROUBLE SHOOTING

STARTER NOISE

CAUTION: Never operate starter for periods of more than 15 seconds. Excessive cranking can cause starter to overheat. Allow starter to cool for at least 2 minutes after each time operated.

1) A high-pitched whine, heard while cranking (before engine starts), indicates excessive distance between starter pinion and flywheel. If high-pitched whine is heard after engine starts and key is released, distance between starter pinion and flywheel is too short.
2) If loud, siren-like "whoop" sound is heard after the engine starts, clutch is likely defective. If "rumble", "growl" or "knock" is present as starter is coasting to a stop after starting engine, starter armature is bent or unbalanced.

3) If diagnosis indicates pinion should be closer to flywheel, remove one double .015" shim or add a single .015" shim to the outer bolt only. If noise persists, continue removing or adding shims to outside bolt as required. See STARTER under REMOVAL & INSTALLATION.
4) If diagnosis indicates pinion should be moved away from flywheel, add one .015" shim. If condition is not corrected, another .015" shim may be added. Do not exceed .045" shim thickness. See STARTER under REMOVAL & INSTALLATION.

ON-VEHICLE TESTING

IGNITION SWITCH TEST

NOTE: For an "engine not cranking" condition with A/T, determine if condition exists in both Park and Neutral positions. If condition occurs in one position and not other, a more probable cause is neutral start switch. See appropriate AUTOMATIC TRANSMISSION article in TRANSMISSION SERVICING.

Test ignition switch operation by rotating cylinder/key through all switch positions. Movement should feel smooth with no sticking or binding. The cylinder/key should return from the START position back to the RUN position without assistance. Inspect and repair if necessary.

SOLENOID WINDINGS TESTS

NOTE: To prevent overheating, perform solenoid tests as quickly as possible with leads disconnected. OG195 starter motor is not serviceable. Install new starter if necessary.

Hold-In Windings Test – Connect an ammeter in series with 12-volt battery and terminal "S" on solenoid. See Fig. 2. Connect a voltmeter between solenoid terminal "S" and ground. Connect a carbon pile rheostat across battery. Adjust voltage to 10 volts and check amperage reading. See HOLD-IN WINDINGS SPECIFICATIONS table.

HOLD-IN WINDINGS SPECIFICATIONS

Starter Motor	[1] Amperage
SD200	13-19
SD210	12-15
SD250, SD260 & SD300	13-19

[1] – At 10 volts.

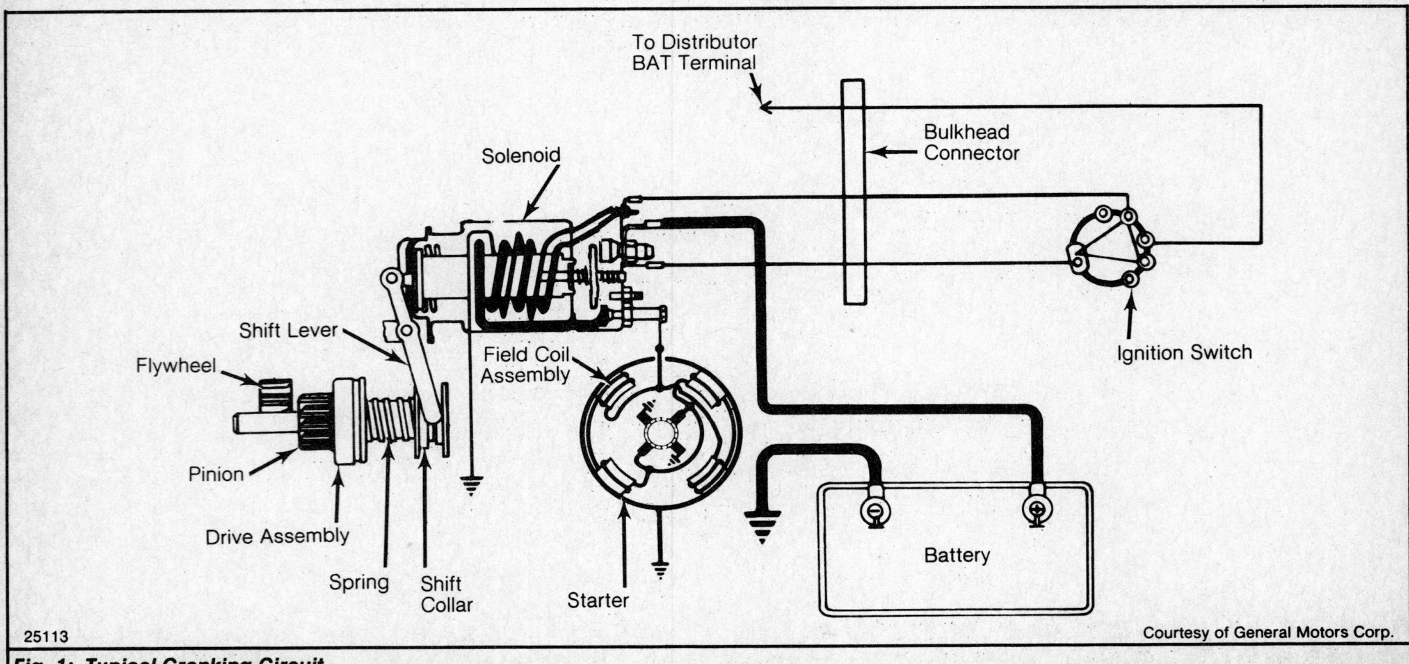

25113

Courtesy of General Motors Corp.

Fig. 1: Typical Cranking Circuit

Pull-In Windings Test – Connect test equipment. See HOLD-IN WINDINGS TEST. *See Fig. 2*. Ground terminal "M" of solenoid. Adjust voltage to 10 volts and note ammeter reading. See PULL-IN WINDINGS SPECIFICATIONS table.

NOTE: Current will decrease as windings heat up.

PULL-IN WINDINGS SPECIFICATIONS

Starter Motor	[1] Amperage
SD200	36-49
SD210	42-51
SD250	36-49
SD260	55-80
SD300	55-80

[1] – At 10 volts.

Test Results – If current draw reads greater than specification, short or ground is present in windings of solenoid. Low current draw indicates excessive resistance. No current indicates an open circuit. Check connections. Replace starter solenoid as necessary.

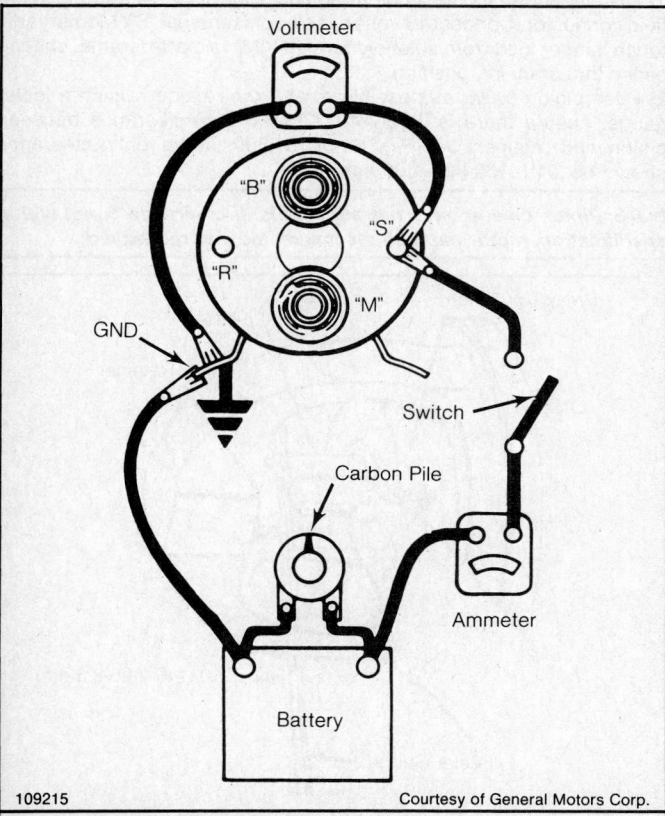

109215   Courtesy of General Motors Corp.

Fig. 2: Solenoid Winding Test Connections

STARTER NO-LOAD TEST

1) Connect test equipment to starter. *See Fig. 3*. Close switch and compare RPM, amperage and voltage readings with specifications. See STARTER NO-LOAD TEST SPECIFICATIONS table.

CAUTION: DO NOT apply more voltage than specified. Excessive voltage may cause armature to throw windings due to excessive speed.

2) If current draw and RPM meet specification, starter motor is okay. If test indicates low free speed and high current draw, unit may have tight, dirty or worn bearings, shorted or grounded armature, bent armature shaft, or grounded fields.

3) Failure to operate with high current draw indicates direct ground in terminal fields or frozen bearings. Failure to operate with no current

draw indicates an open field circuit, open solenoid windings, open armature coils or broken brush springs.

4) Low RPM and low current draw indicates high internal resistance due to poor connections, defective leads or dirty commutator. High free speed and high current draw indicate shorted fields.

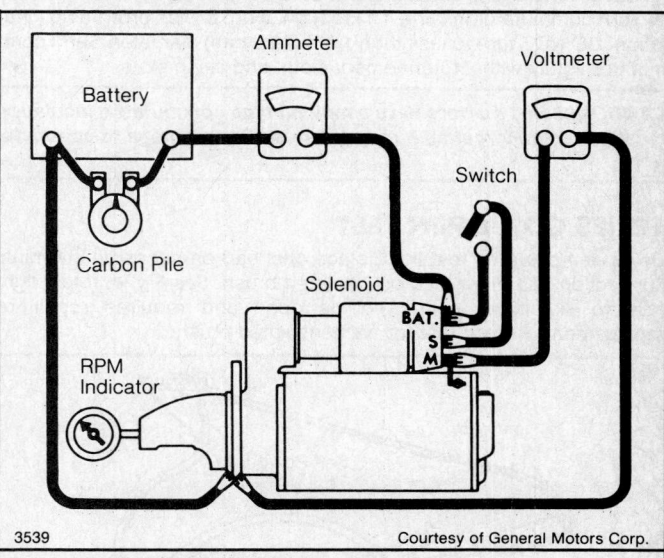

3539   Courtesy of General Motors Corp.

Fig. 3: Starter No-Load Test Connections

STARTER NO-LOAD TEST SPECIFICATIONS

Delco-Remy Part Number	Motor	Amps [1]	RPM
1998548	SD200	50-75	6000-11,900
1998579	SD300	70-110	6500-10,700
1998580	SD300	70-110	6500-10,700
1998591	SD300	70-110	6500-10,700
10455004	SD200	50-75	6000-11,900
10455006	SD250	45-74	8600-12,900
10455007	SD200	50-75	6000-11,900
10455010	SD210	55-85	7000-12,000
10455011	SD210	45-75	6000-11,000
10455012	SD260	45-75	6500-11,000
10455016	SD200	50-75	6000-11,900
10455017	SD200	50-75	6000-11,900
10455019	SD200	50-75	6000-11,900
10455021	SD200	55-85	6000-12,000
10455022	SD200	55-85	6000-12,000
10455024	SD250	45-74	8600-12,900
10455025	SD210	45-74	6000-11,000
10455044	SD200	52-76	6000-12,000
10455047	SD260	50-75	7000-11,000
10455049	SD200	52-76	3500-5000
10455702	N/A	45-90	3500-5000
10455704	N/A	45-90	3500-5000
10455706	OG195	90	3500

[1] – Starter No-Load Test at 10 volts.

BENCH TESTING

PRELIMINARY TESTS

Remove starter from vehicle. See STARTER under REMOVAL & INSTALLATION. Ensure pinion moves freely on screw shaft. Ensure armature rotates freely by prying pinion. If armature does not turn freely, disassemble motor for inspection. If armature rotates freely, motor should be given a no-load test before disassembly.

ARMATURE TEST

1) Test armature for shorted coils with growler. Check for grounded coils with test light. Place one lead on armature shaft and the other lead on commutator. Test light should not illuminate. If test light illuminates, armature is grounded and must be replaced.

2) Turn commutator in lathe if it is rough, worn or has protruding insulation. DO NOT turn to less than 1.65" (41.9 mm) diameter. Sand commutator lightly with 240 grit emery cloth, and clean slots.

CAUTION: Some starters have a molded-type commutator. Insulation must not be undercut as it may cause serious damage to commutator.

SERIES COIL OPEN TEST

Using self-powered test light, place one lead on series coil terminal connection and other lead on insulated brush. *See Fig. 4.* If test light fails to illuminate, series coil is open and requires repair or replacement. Repeat test for each insulated brush.

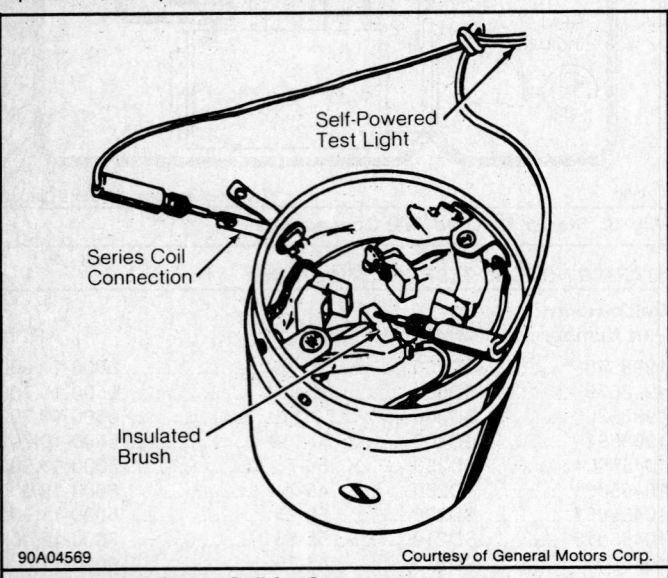

90A04569   Courtesy of General Motors Corp.

Fig. 4: Testing Series Coil for Open

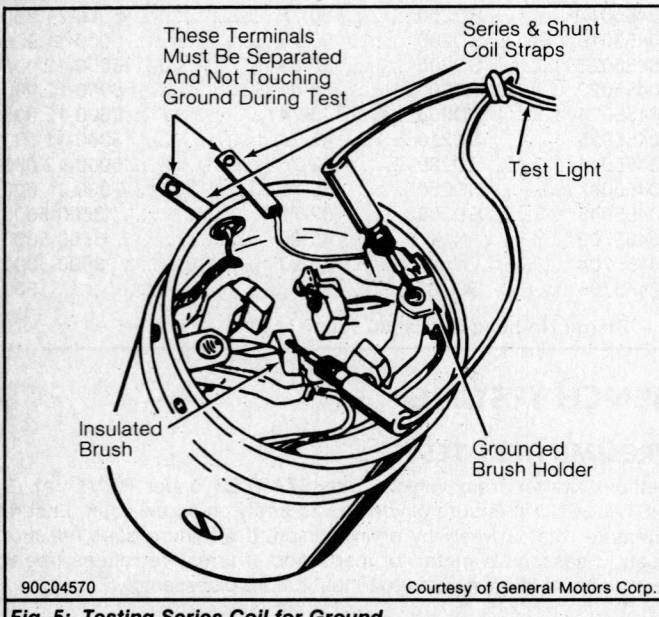

90C04570   Courtesy of General Motors Corp.

Fig. 5: Testing Series Coil for Ground

SERIES COIL GROUND TEST

On starters with shunt coil, separate series and shunt coil strap terminals during test. Using test light, place one lead on grounded brush holder and the other lead on either insulated brush. *See Fig. 5.* If test light glows, a grounded series coil is indicated and series coil must be repaired or replaced.

BRUSHES, SPRINGS & HOLDERS CHECK

Replace brushes if worn to 1/2 of original length or if oil-soaked or pitted. Check brush spring tension and replace springs if weak or distorted.

OVERRUNNING CLUTCH CHECK

Clutch pinion should turn freely in one direction only. Check pinion teeth for chips, cracks or excessive wear. Chipped teeth may indicate defective ring gear.

PINION CLEARANCE CHECK

1) Disconnect motor field coil at solenoid terminal "M", and insulate field connector. Connect 12 volts to solenoid terminal "S". Momentarily touch jumper lead from solenoid terminal "M" to starter frame, shifting pinion into cranking position.

2) Push pinion as far as possible away from retainer. Using a feeler gauge, ensure there is .010-.140" (.25-3.6 mm) clearance between pinion and retainer. *See Fig. 6.* On SD300 starter only, clearance should be .010-.160 (.25-4.06 mm).

NOTE: Pinion clearance is not adjustable. If clearance is not within specification, motor must be disassembled and rechecked.

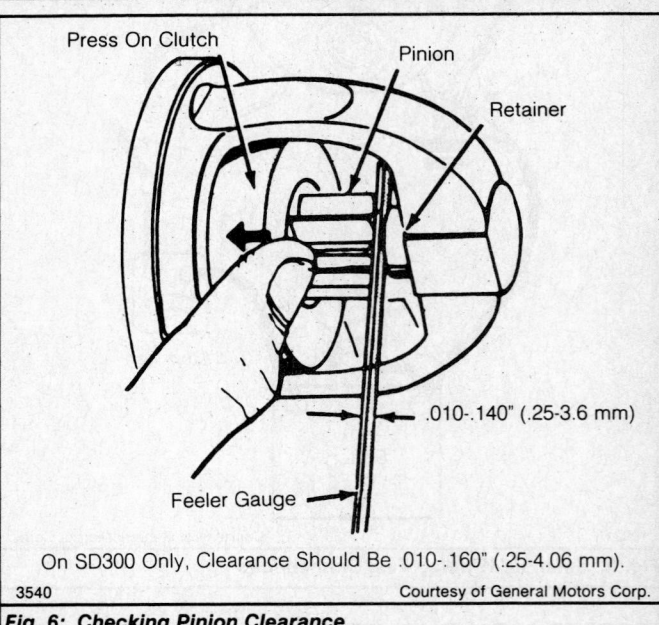

On SD300 Only, Clearance Should Be .010-.160" (.25-4.06 mm).

3540   Courtesy of General Motors Corp.

Fig. 6: Checking Pinion Clearance

REMOVAL & INSTALLATION
STARTER

Removal – 1) Disconnect negative battery cable. Raise and support vehicle. As required, remove nuts from A/C compressor and engine brace, adjacent to starter. Remove other items that may interfere with removal of starter.

2) If necessary, remove nut from engine cross brace. Using pry bar between upper engine mount and engine, pry rearward and support engine.

3) If necessary, remove oil filter. Disconnect wiring at starter, and note position. Remove starter mounting bolts and any shims. Remove starter. *See Figs. 7 and 10.*

Installation – Before installation, measure pinion-to-flywheel clearance. *See Fig. 8.* Clearance should be .020" (0.5 mm). Add or subtract shims as necessary. To complete installation, reverse removal procedure. Tighten mounting bolts to 32 ft. lbs. (43 N.m).

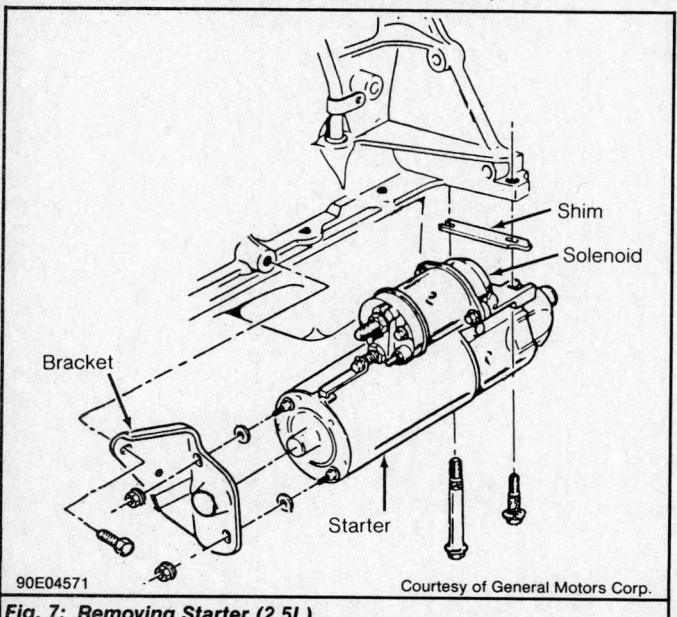

Shim
Solenoid
Bracket
Starter
90E04571
Courtesy of General Motors Corp.

Fig. 7: Removing Starter (2.5L)

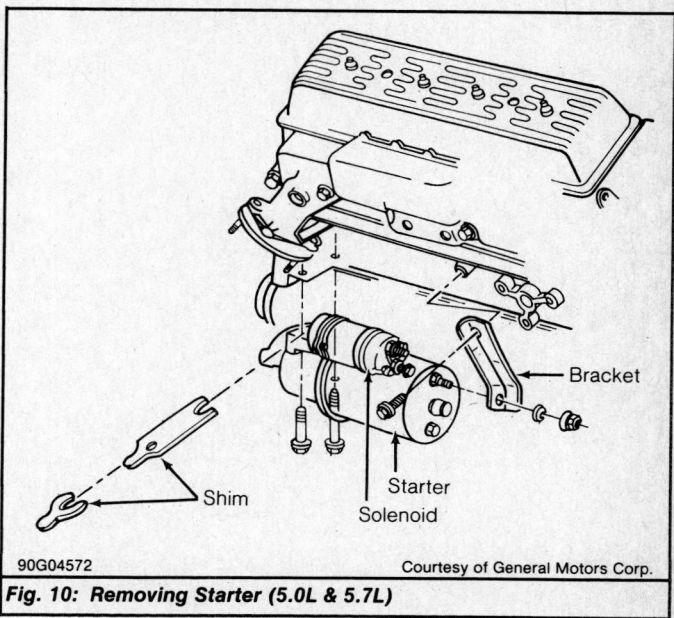

Bracket
Shim
Starter
Solenoid
90G04572
Courtesy of General Motors Corp.

Fig. 10: Removing Starter (5.0L & 5.7L)

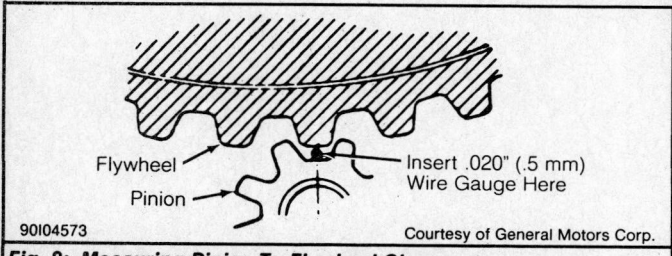

Flywheel
Pinion
Insert .020" (.5 mm) Wire Gauge Here
90I04573
Courtesy of General Motors Corp.

Fig. 8: Measuring Pinion-To-Flywheel Clearance

OVERHAUL

STARTER

CAUTION: DO NOT clean starter in degreasing tank or with grease dissolving solvents. This will remove lubricant from clutch mechanism.

Starter motors do not require lubrication, except during overhaul. Roll-type overrunning clutch requires no lubrication. Drive assembly, however, should be wiped clean and lubricated with silicon grease on shaft, underneath overrunning clutch assembly. *See Fig. 9.*

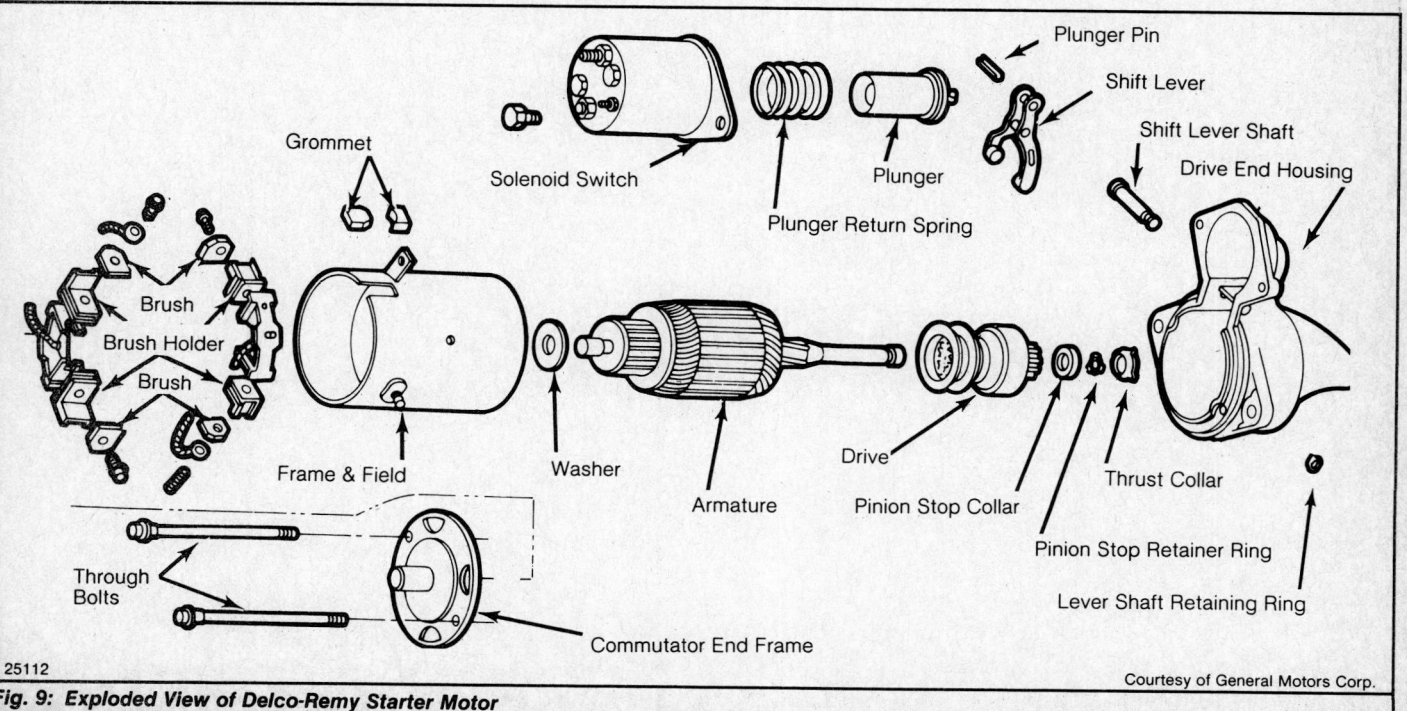

Grommet
Solenoid Switch
Plunger Return Spring
Plunger
Plunger Pin
Shift Lever
Shift Lever Shaft
Drive End Housing
Brush
Brush Holder
Brush
Frame & Field
Washer
Armature
Drive
Pinion Stop Collar
Thrust Collar
Pinion Stop Retainer Ring
Lever Shaft Retaining Ring
Through Bolts
Commutator End Frame
25112
Courtesy of General Motors Corp.

Fig. 9: Exploded View of Delco-Remy Starter Motor

1991 WIRING DIAGRAMS
Beretta & Corsica

COMPONENT LOCATOR:

A/C BLOWER RLY	C 21–22
A/C COMP RLY	A 23
A/C/HEATER CTRL ASSY	A–B 20
ALDL CONN (VIN A)	D–E 11
ALDL CONN (VIN G)	D–E 4
ALDL CONN (VIN T)	D–E 14
ALTERNATOR	B–C 2–3
ARMING SENS	D 31
AUDIO ALARM MODULE	C 24
AUTO TRANS (VIN G)	E 4
AUTO TRANS (VIN T)	D 15
BACK–UP LT SW	B 16
BEAM SEL SW	B 24
BLOWER RLY (W/O A/C)	B 21–22
BRAKE SW	E 23
CIG LTR	B 25–26
CLUTCH SW	A 16
CONVERTIBLE SW	A 27
COOLANT TEMP SENS/SW	A 28
CRUISE CTRL CLUTCH SW (M/T)	E 23
CRUISE CTRL SERVO	C 23
CRUISE CTRL SW	D 23
CRUISE CTRL UNIT	C–D 23
DEFOG SW	C 20
DERM	D–E 28
DIGITAL EGR SOL (VIN T)	E 15
DIR/HAZ SW	E 24–25
DIS MOD (VIN A)	B–C 11
DIS MOD (VIN G)	E 5–7
DIS MOD (VINT)	B–D 15
DOOR LOCK RLY	D–E 32–33
ECM (VIN A)	A–E 8
ECM (VIN G)	A 4–7
ECM (VIN T)	A–E 12
FOG LT RLY	C 2
FUEL CTRL IN–LINE FUSE (VIN A)	B 10
FUEL CTRL IN–LINE FUSE (VIN G)	C 7
FUEL CTRL IN–LINE FUSE (VIN T)	B 14
FUEL PUMP RLY (VIN A)	A–B 11
FUEL PUMP RLY (VIN G)	B–C 7
FUEL PUMP RLY (VIN T)	A 15
FUEL PUMP/OIL PRES SENS/SW	B 28
FUEL TANK UNIT	A 28
FUSE BLOCK	C–D 17–18
GEAR SEL SW	A–B 16
HAZ FLASHER	D 24
HEATER SW (W/O A/C)	B 23
HORN RLY	C 24
IGN SW	A 17–19
INST CLSTR	A–D 31
LIGHT SW	A–B 24
LOW COOLANT MOD	B–C 28–29
POWER WDO SYS	A–C 32–35
PURGE SOL (VIN A)	D 10–11
PURGE SOL (VIN T)	E 15
RELEASE RLY	C 28
RELEASE SW	C 30
STARTER	A 3
STOP LT SW	D 24
TRUNK LT	C 26
WIPER MOTOR	C–E 2–3
WIPER SW	D–E 20–21

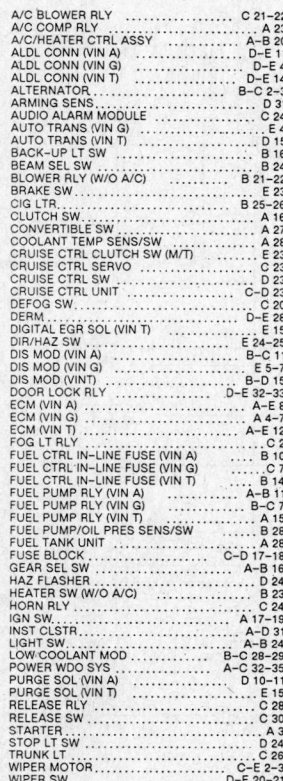

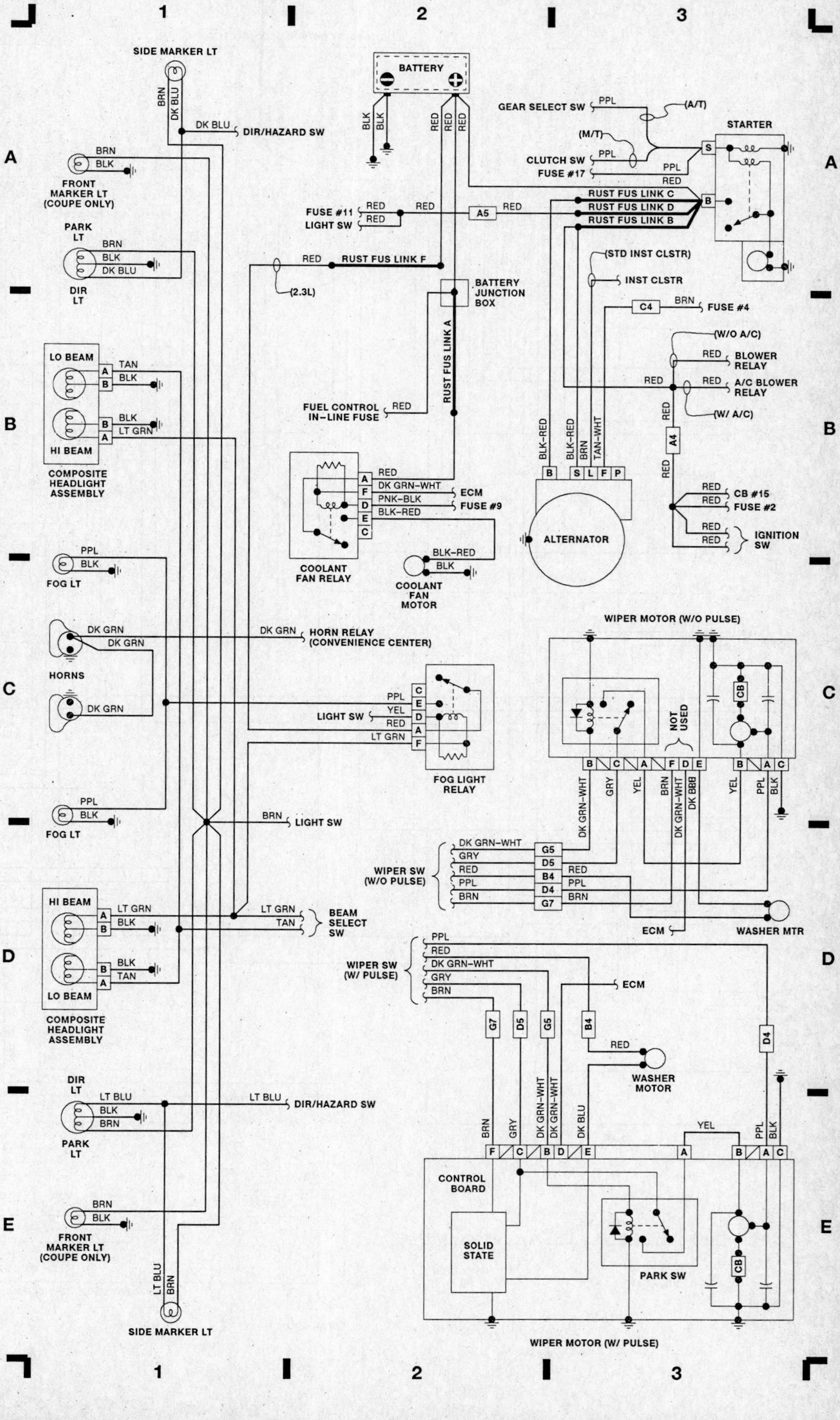

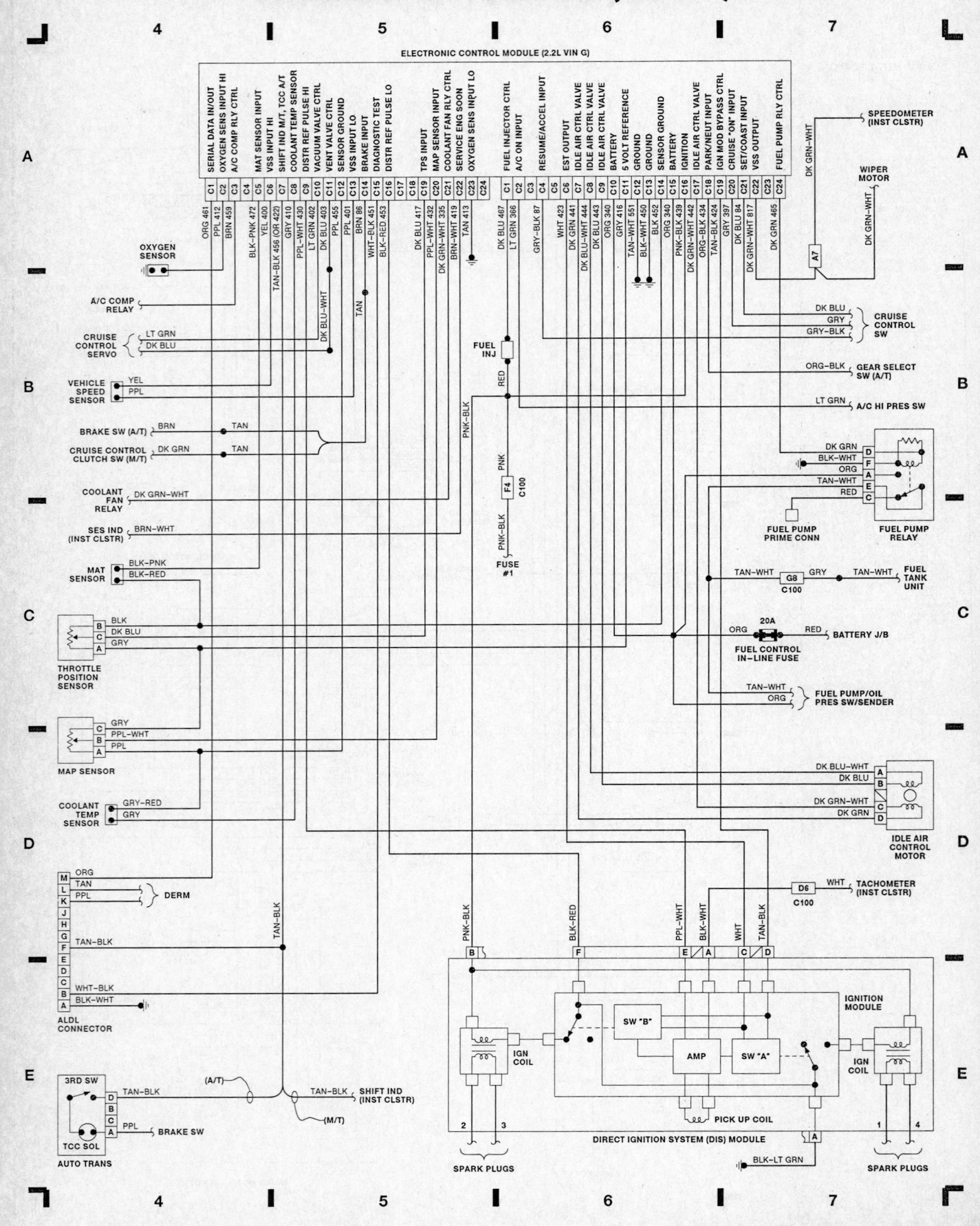

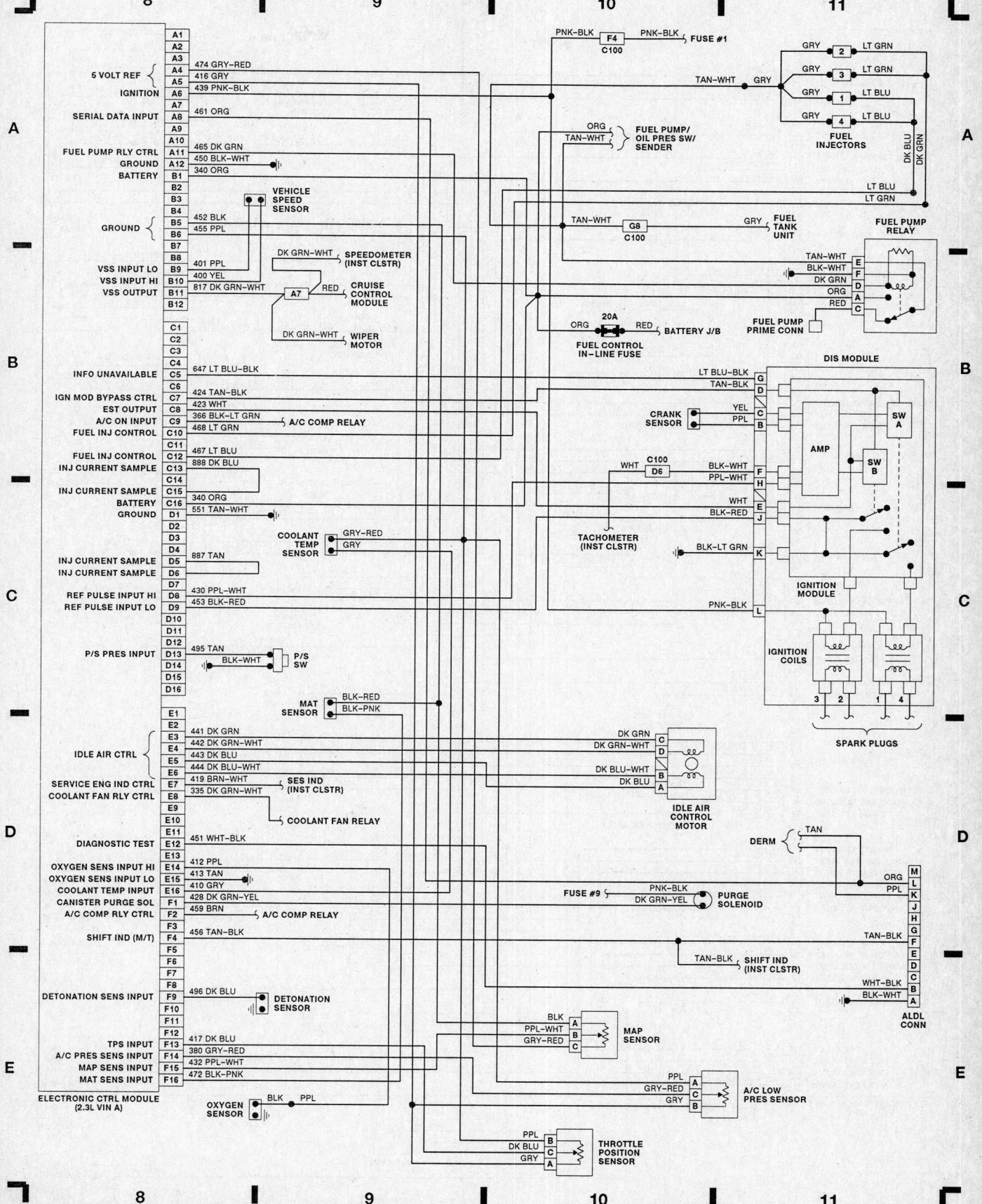

1991 WIRING DIAGRAMS
Beretta & Corsica (Cont.)

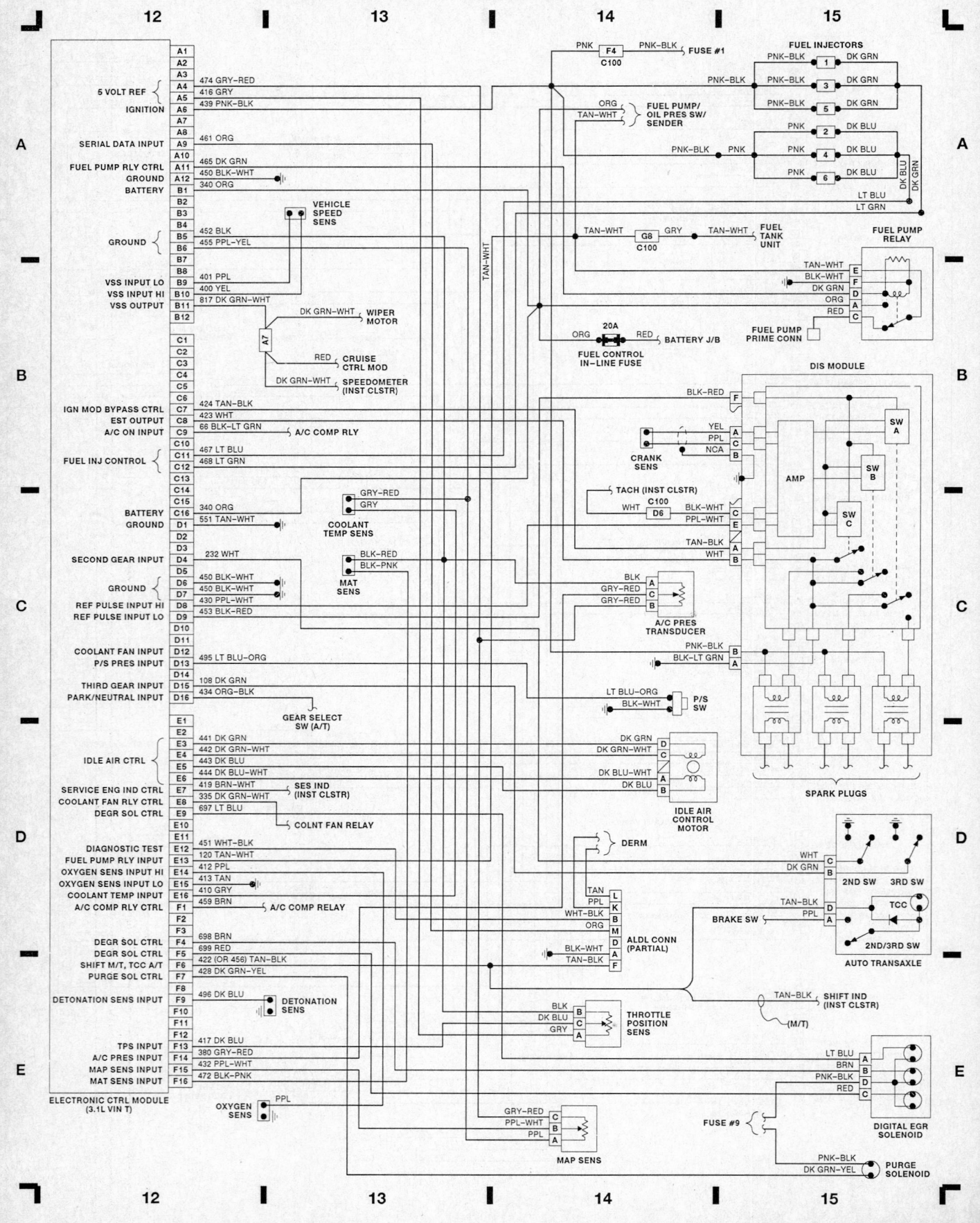

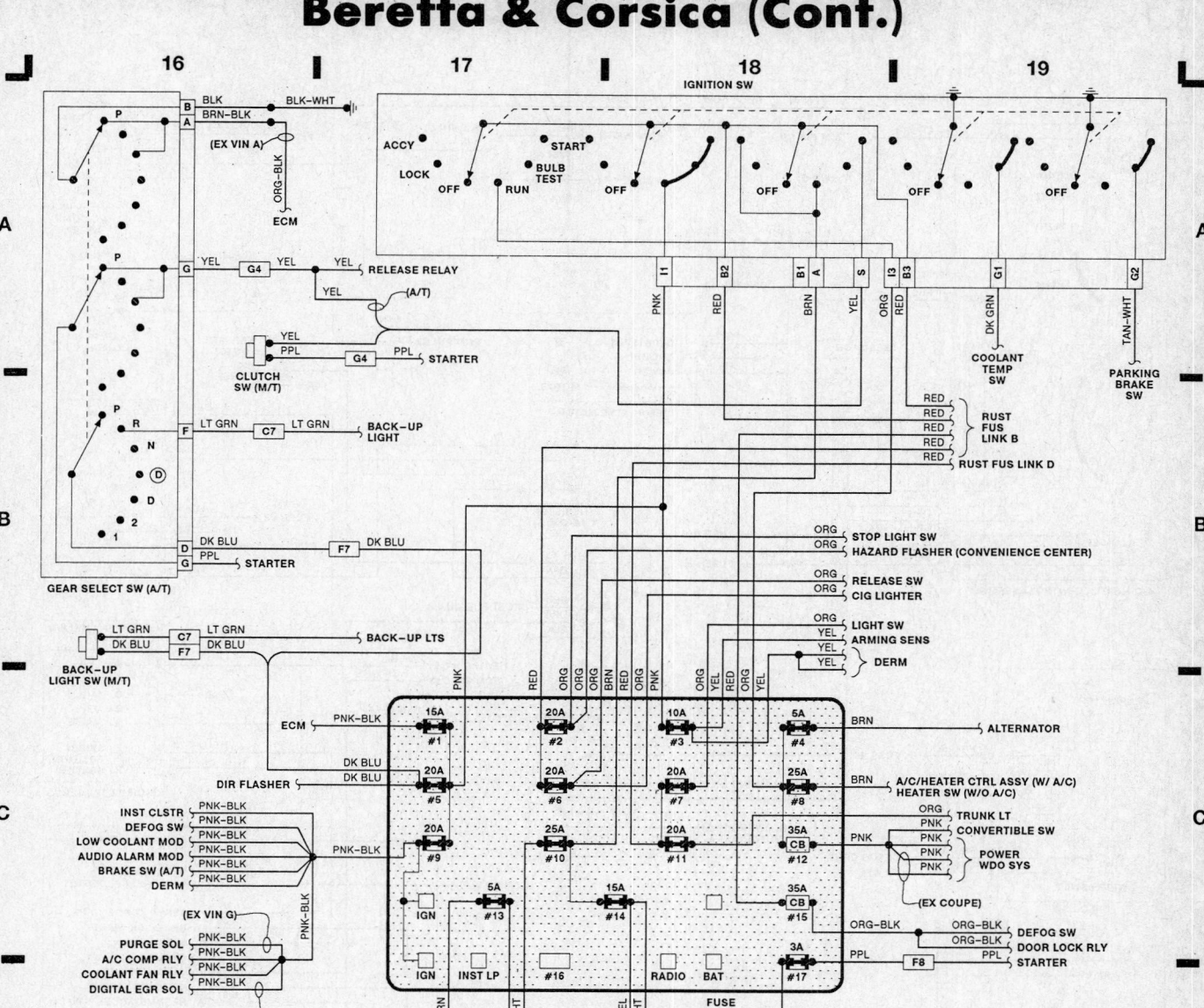

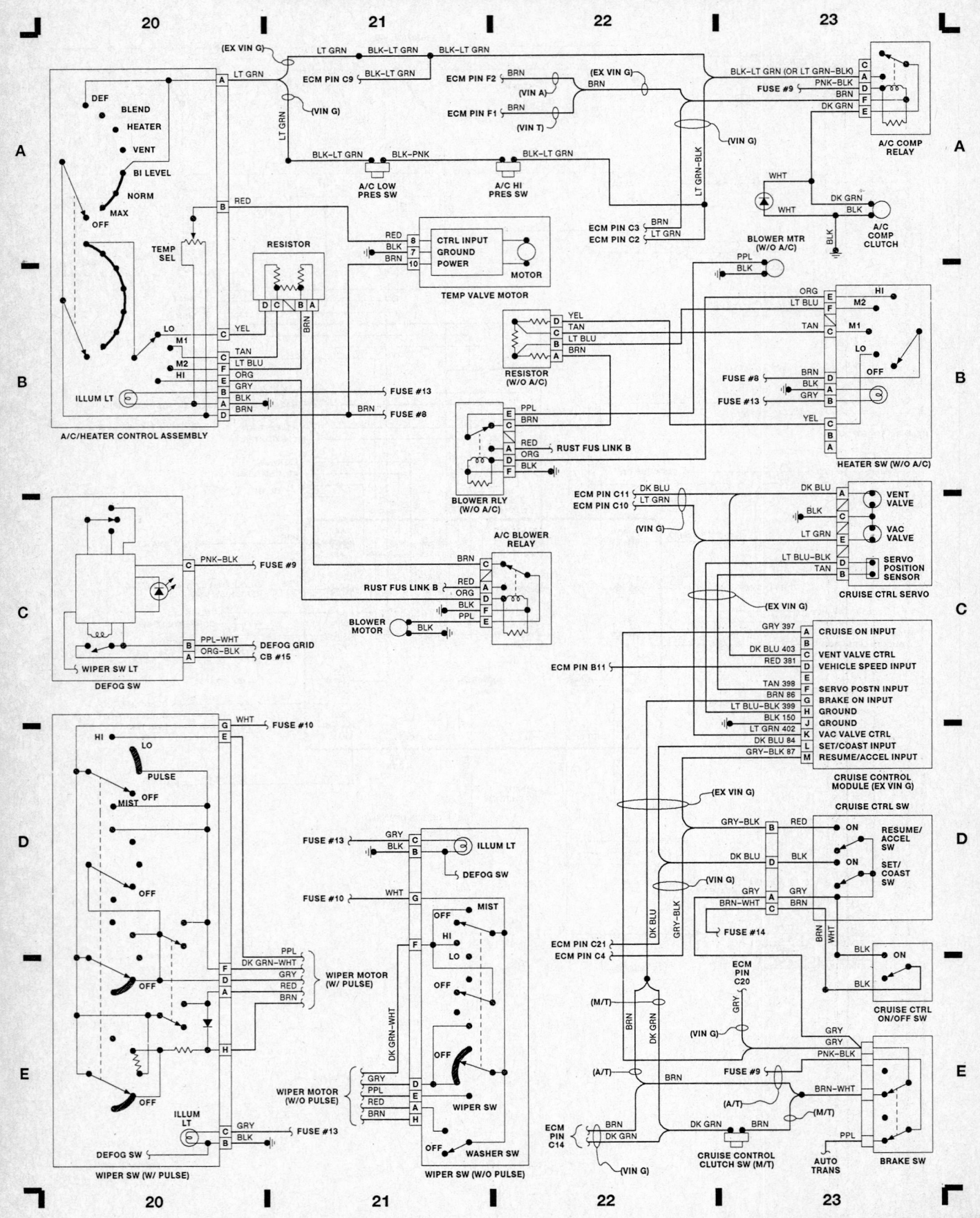

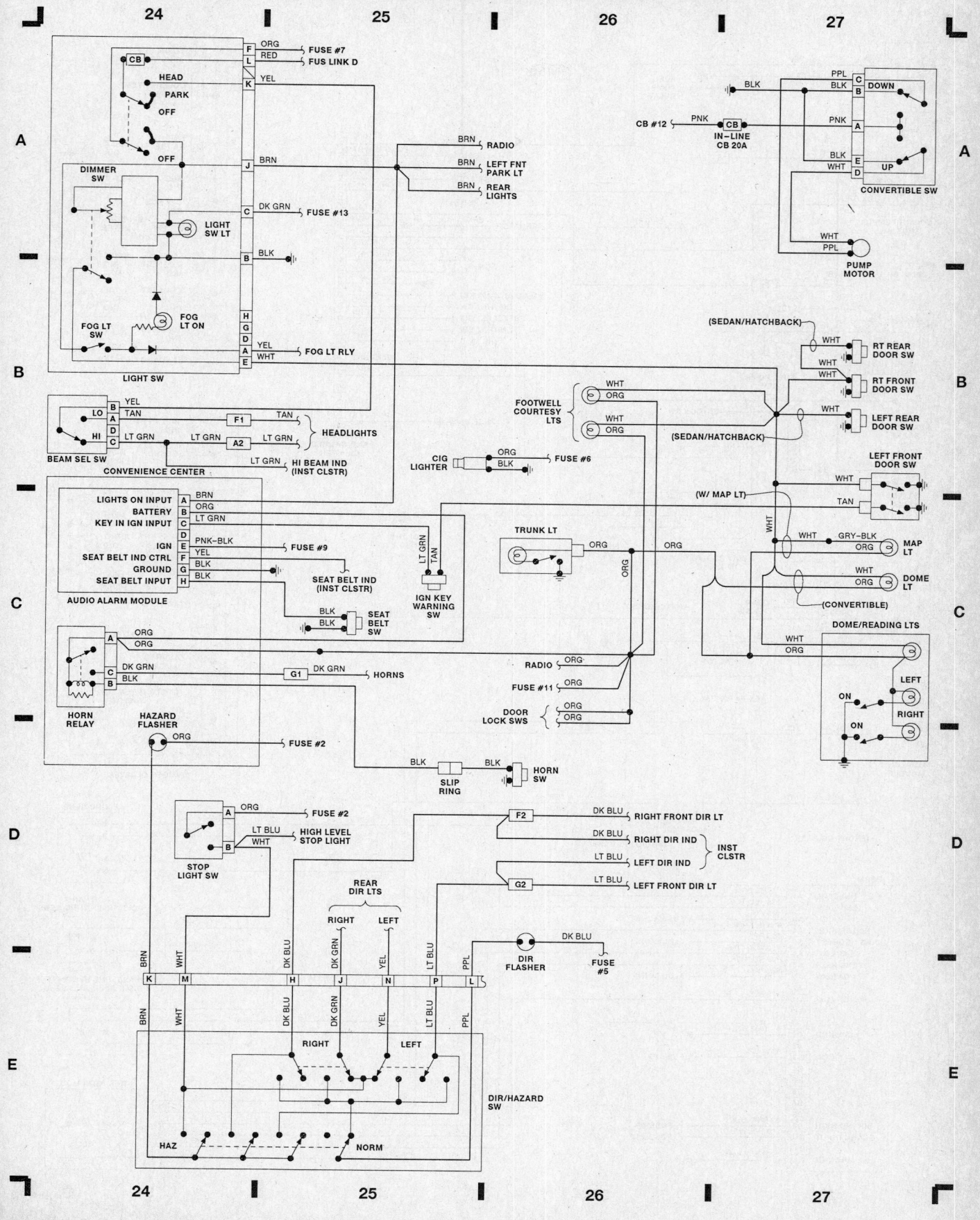

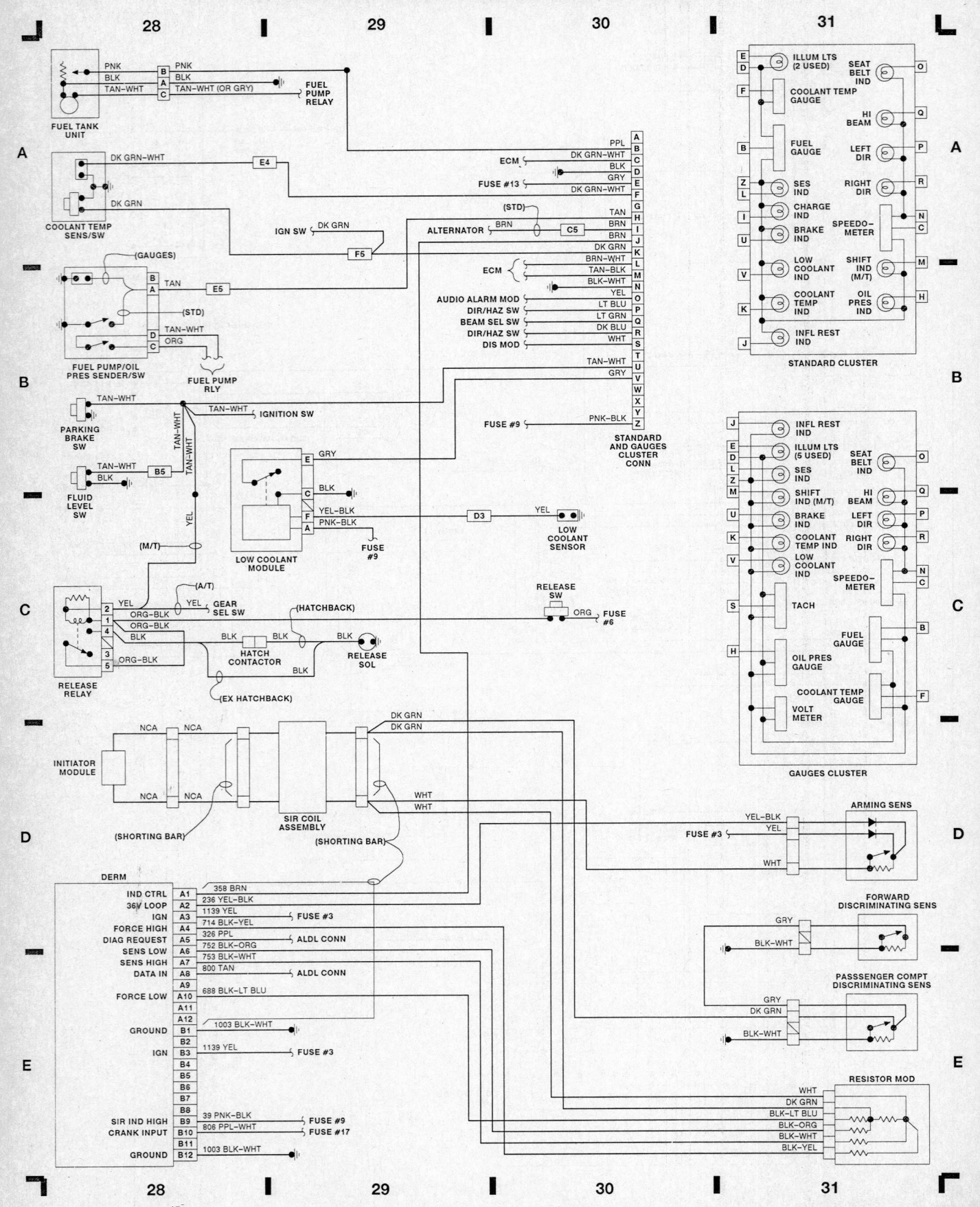

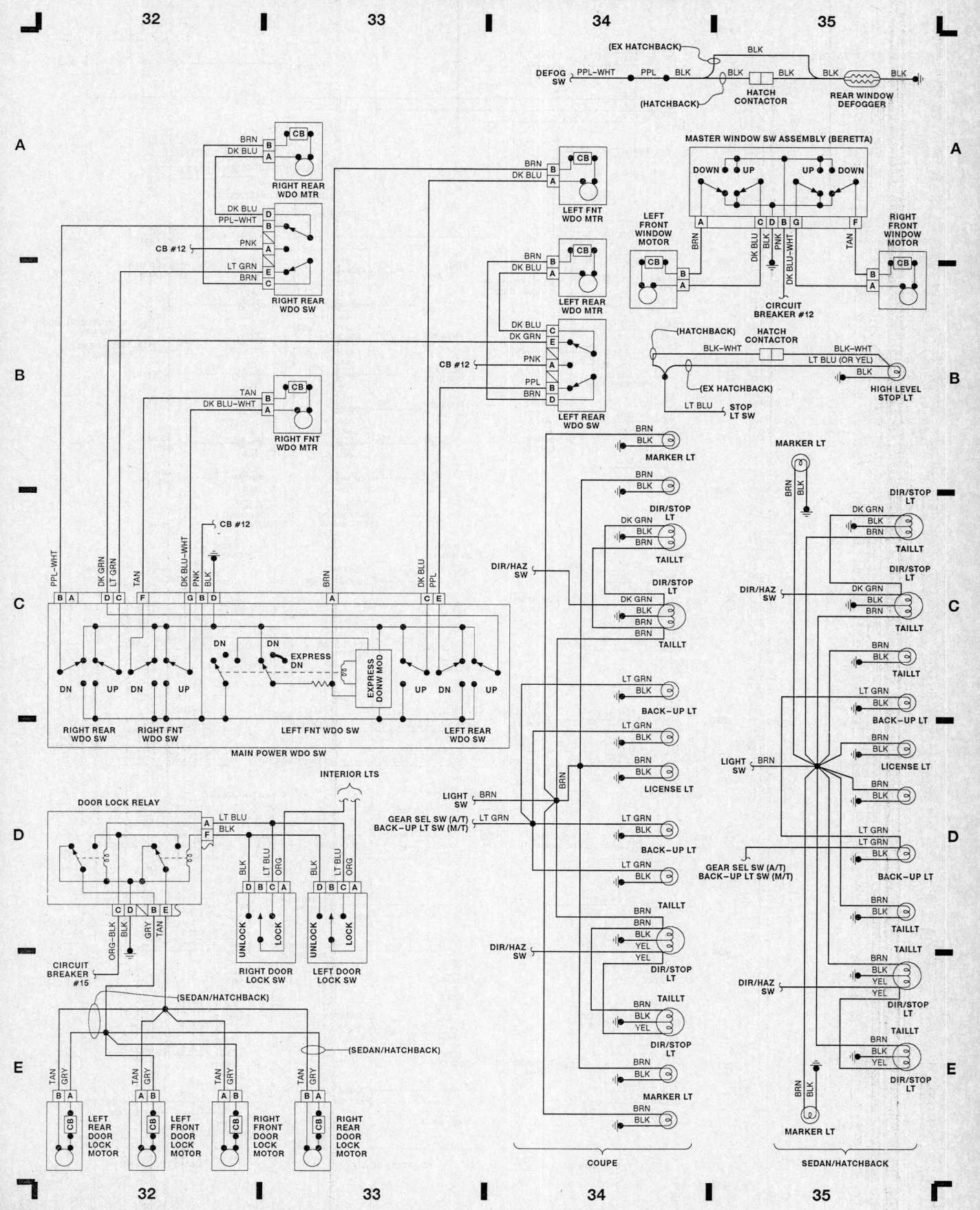

1991 WIRING DIAGRAMS
Bonneville

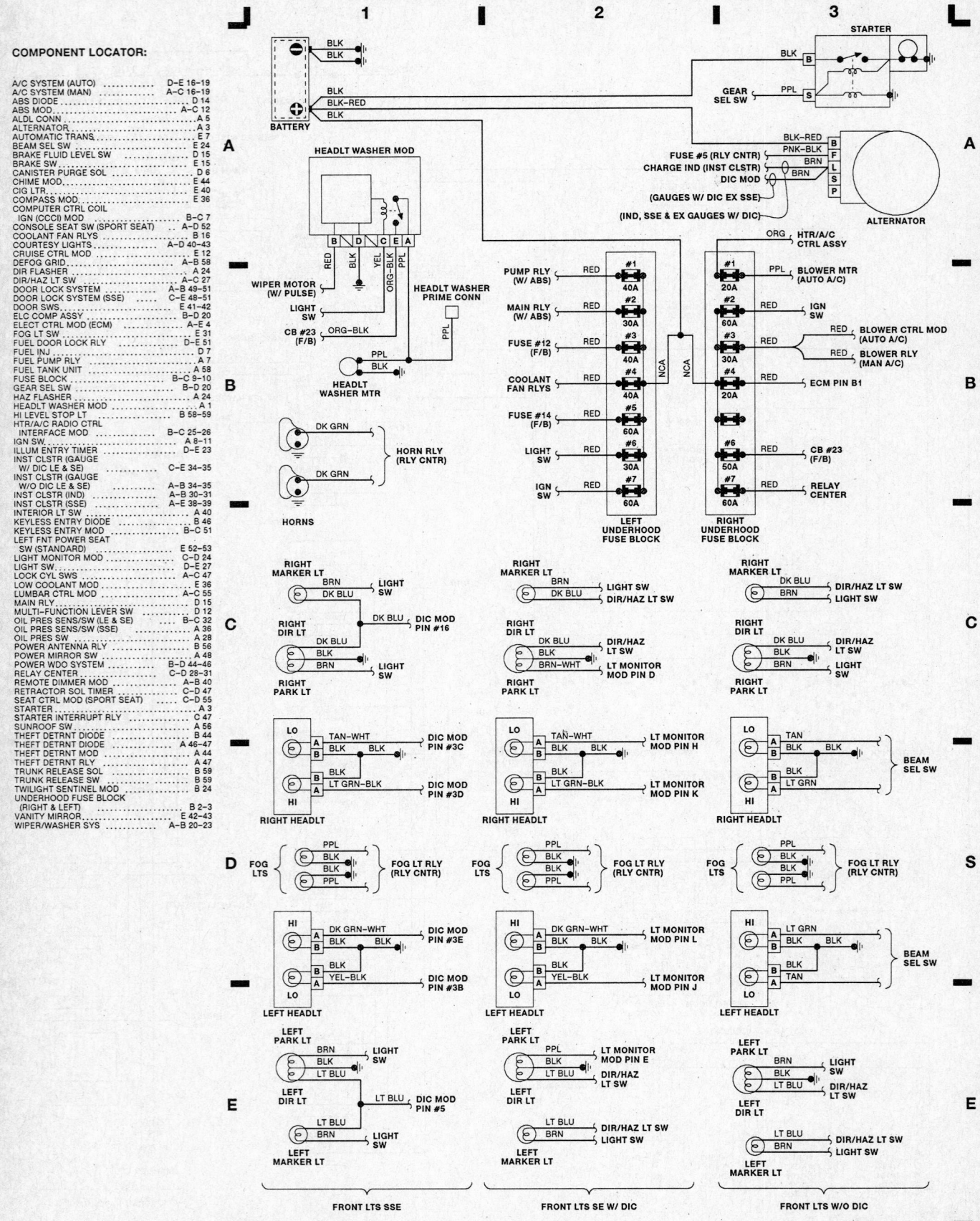

COMPONENT LOCATOR:

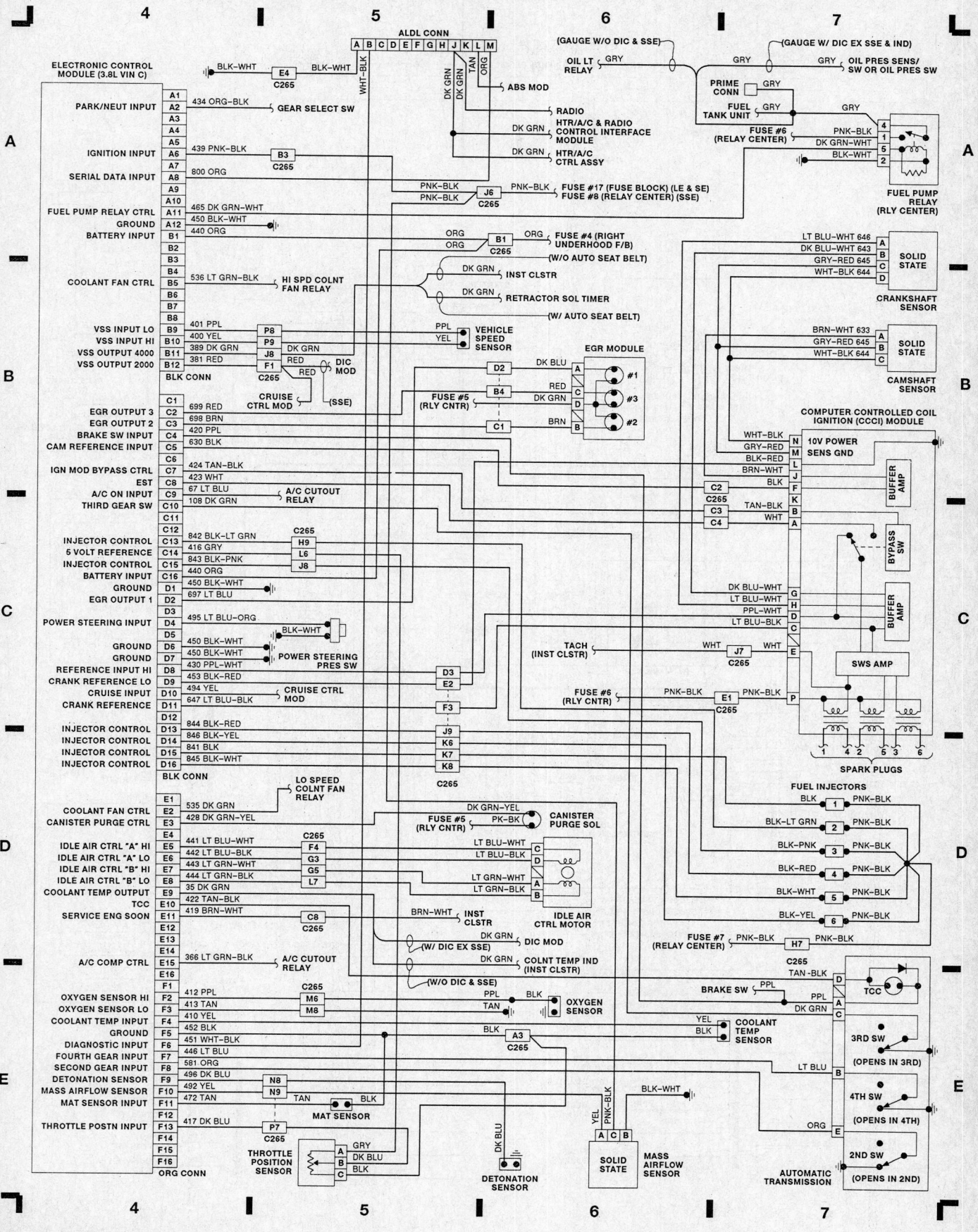

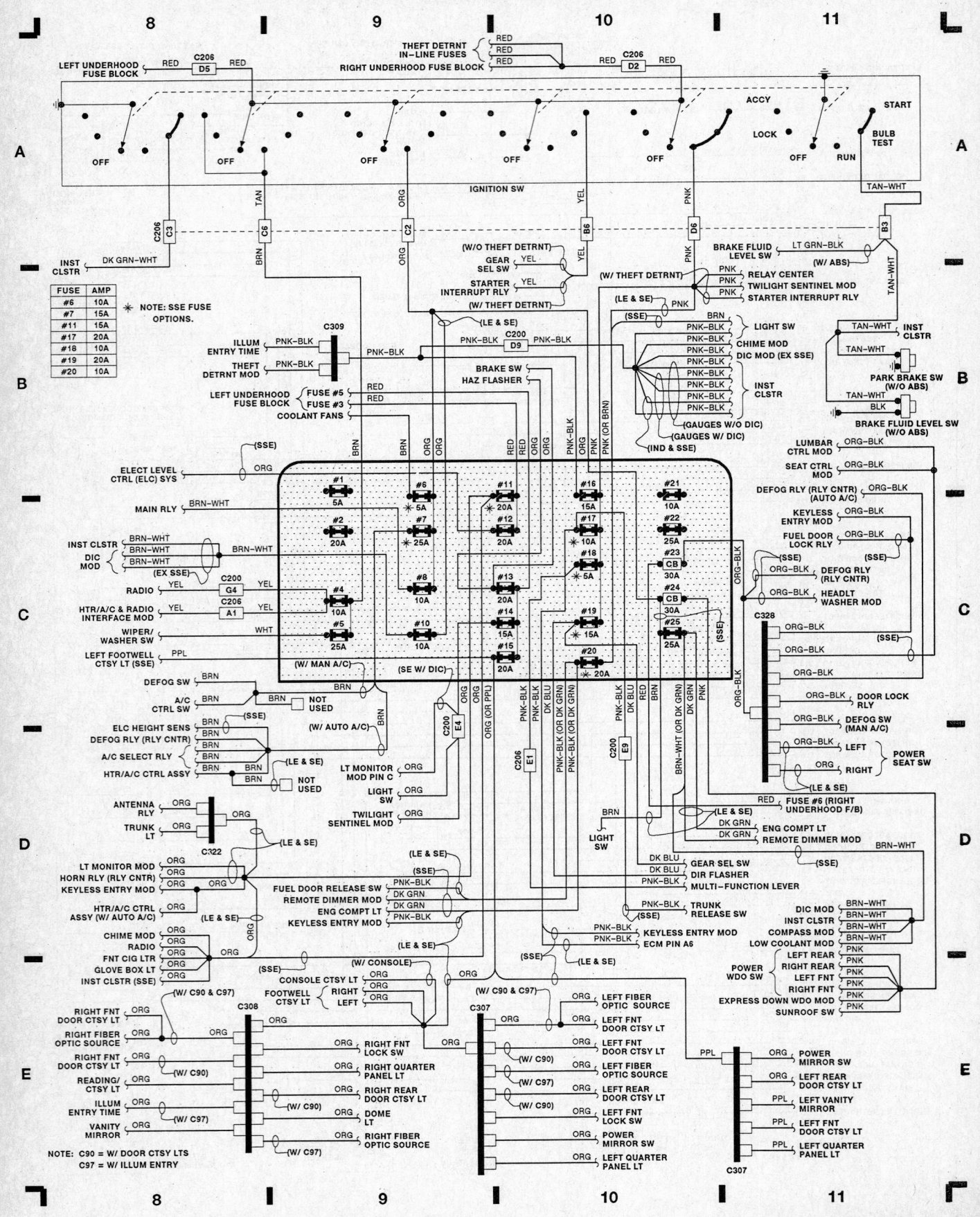

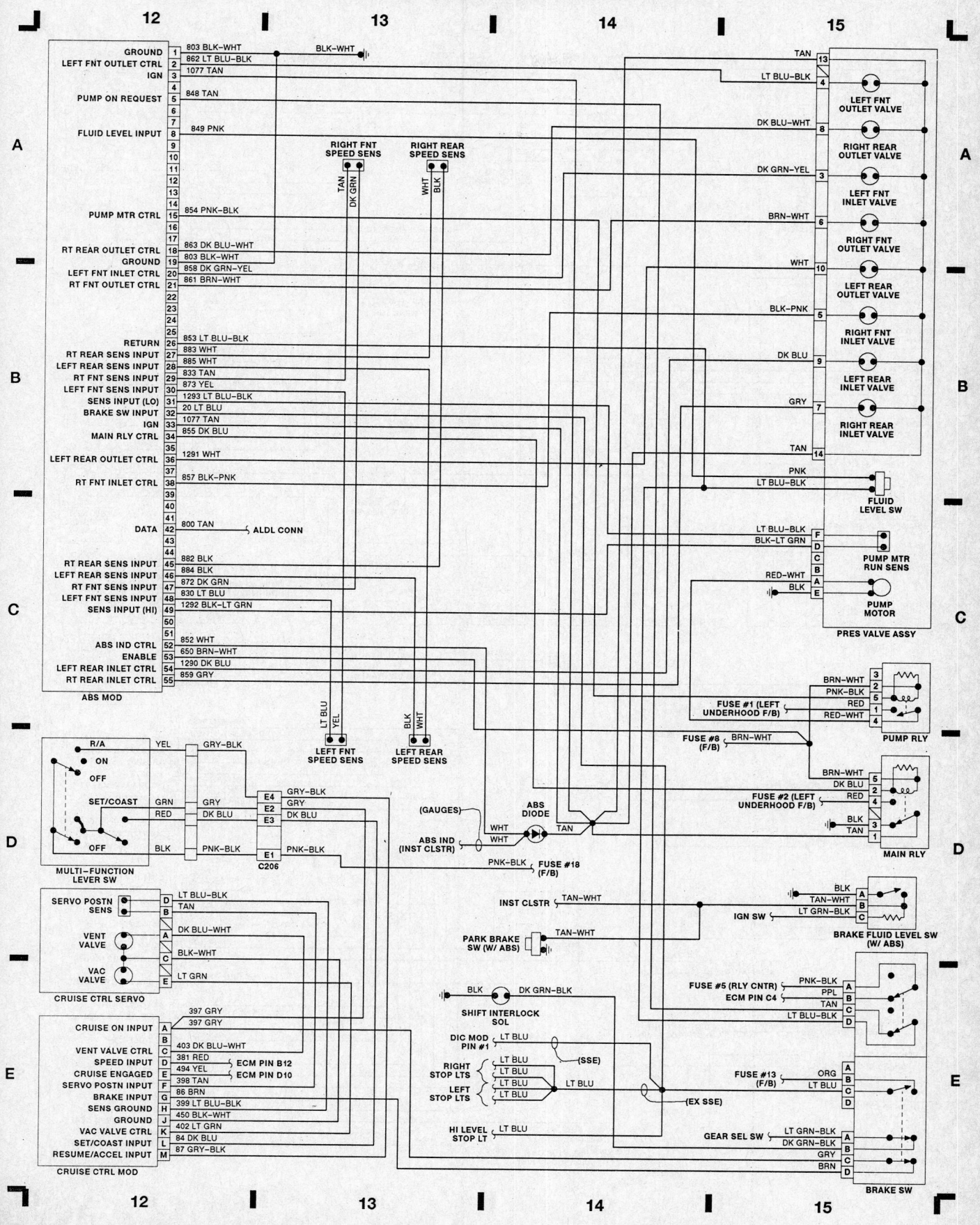

1991 WIRING DIAGRAMS
Bonneville (Cont.)

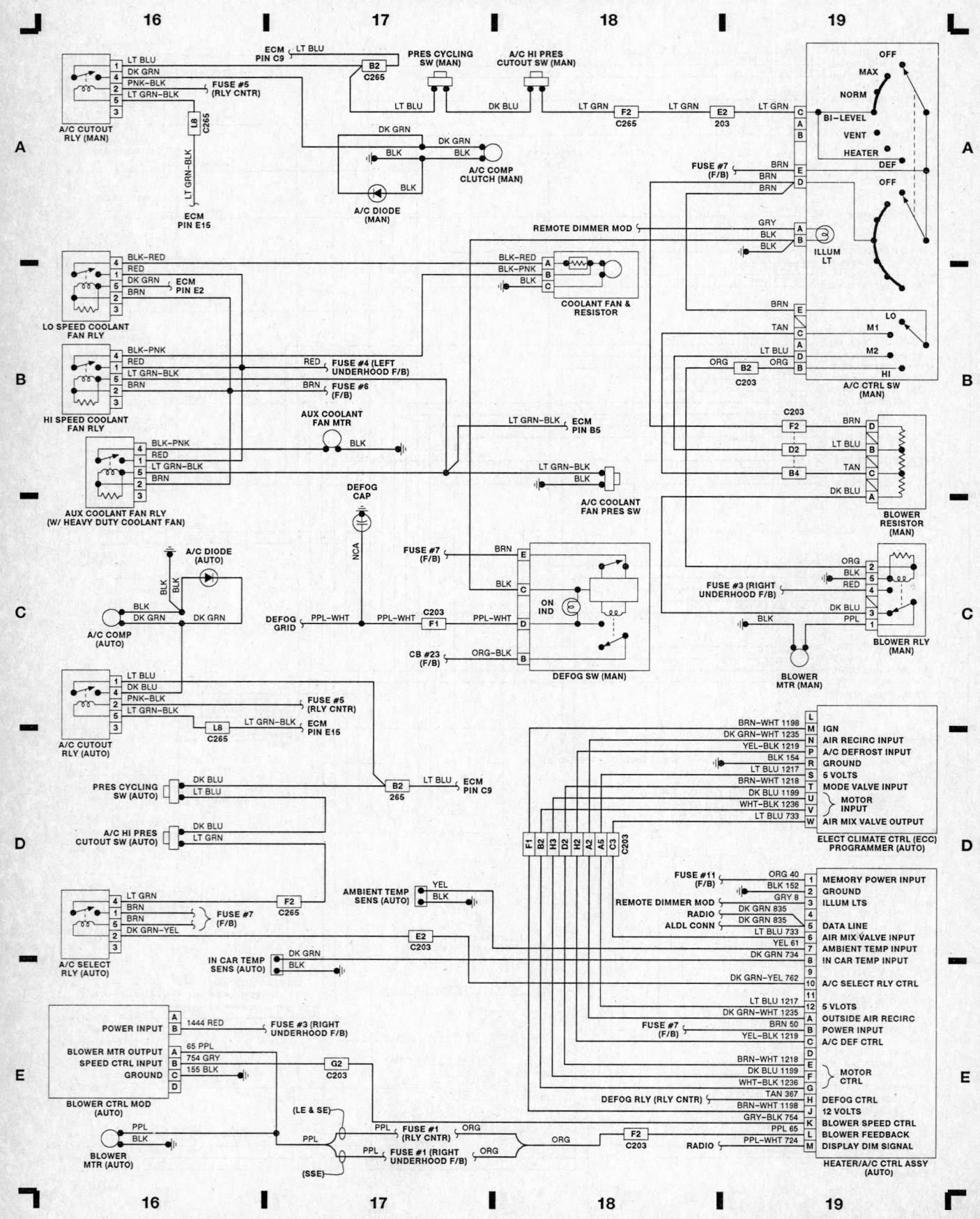

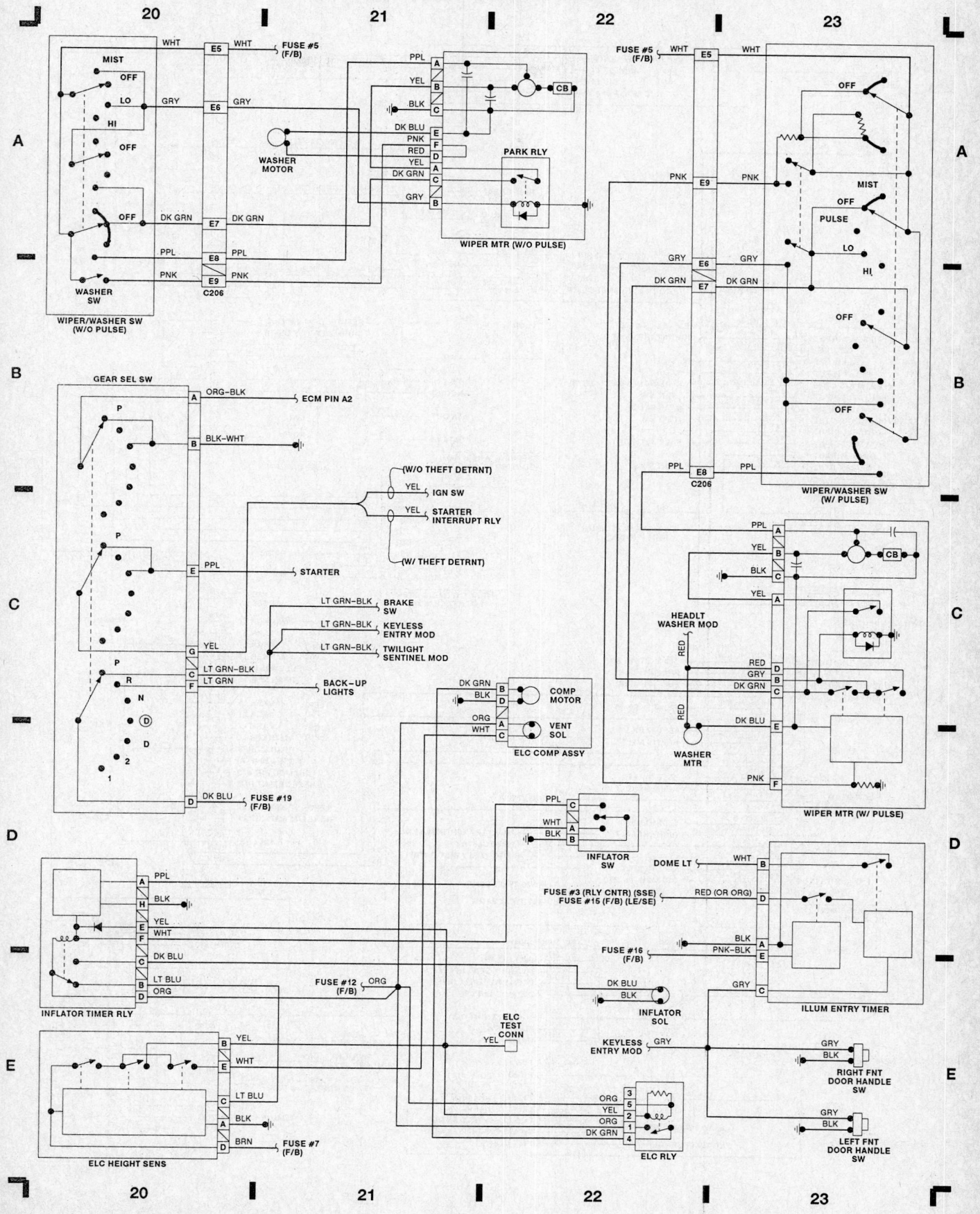

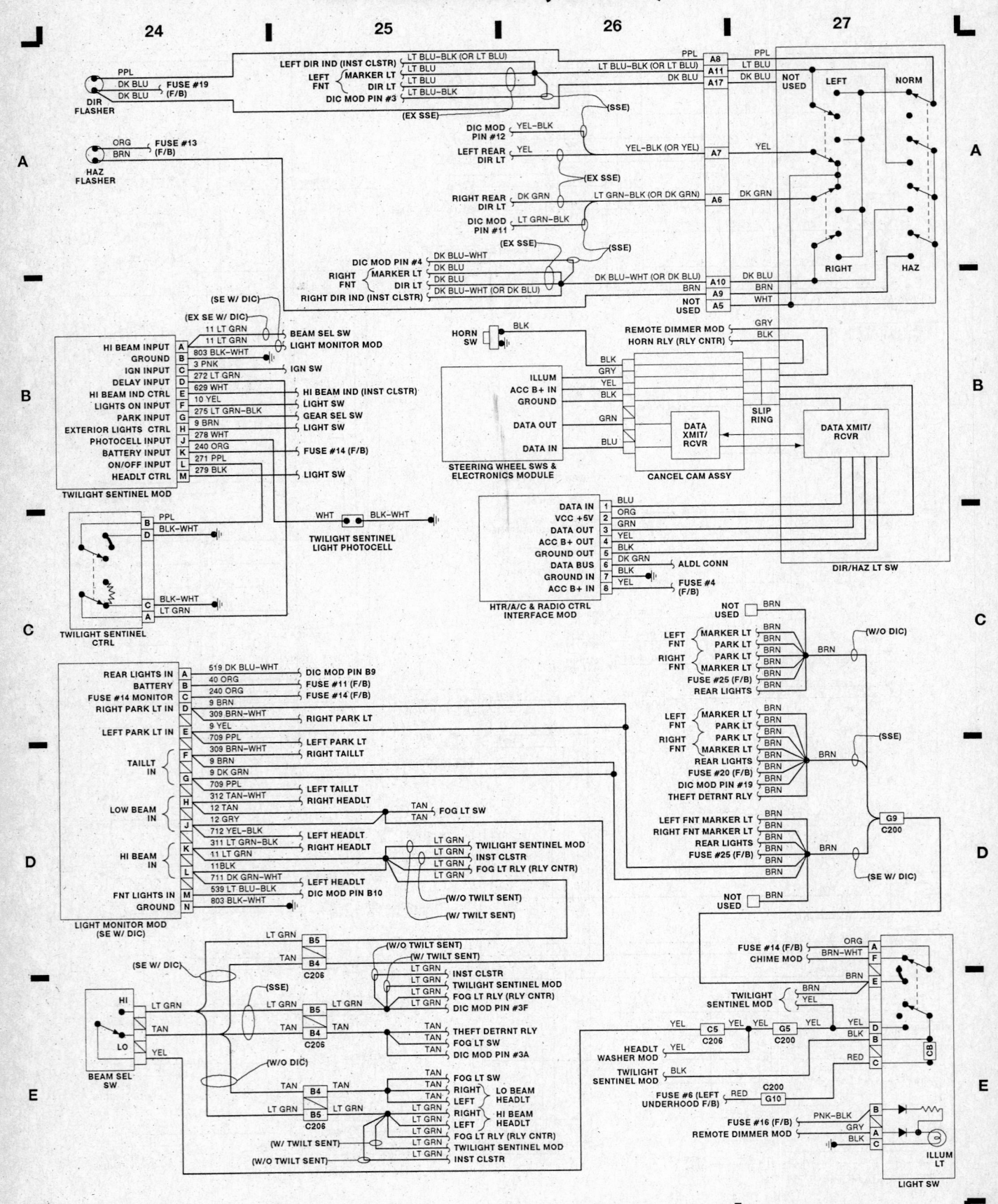

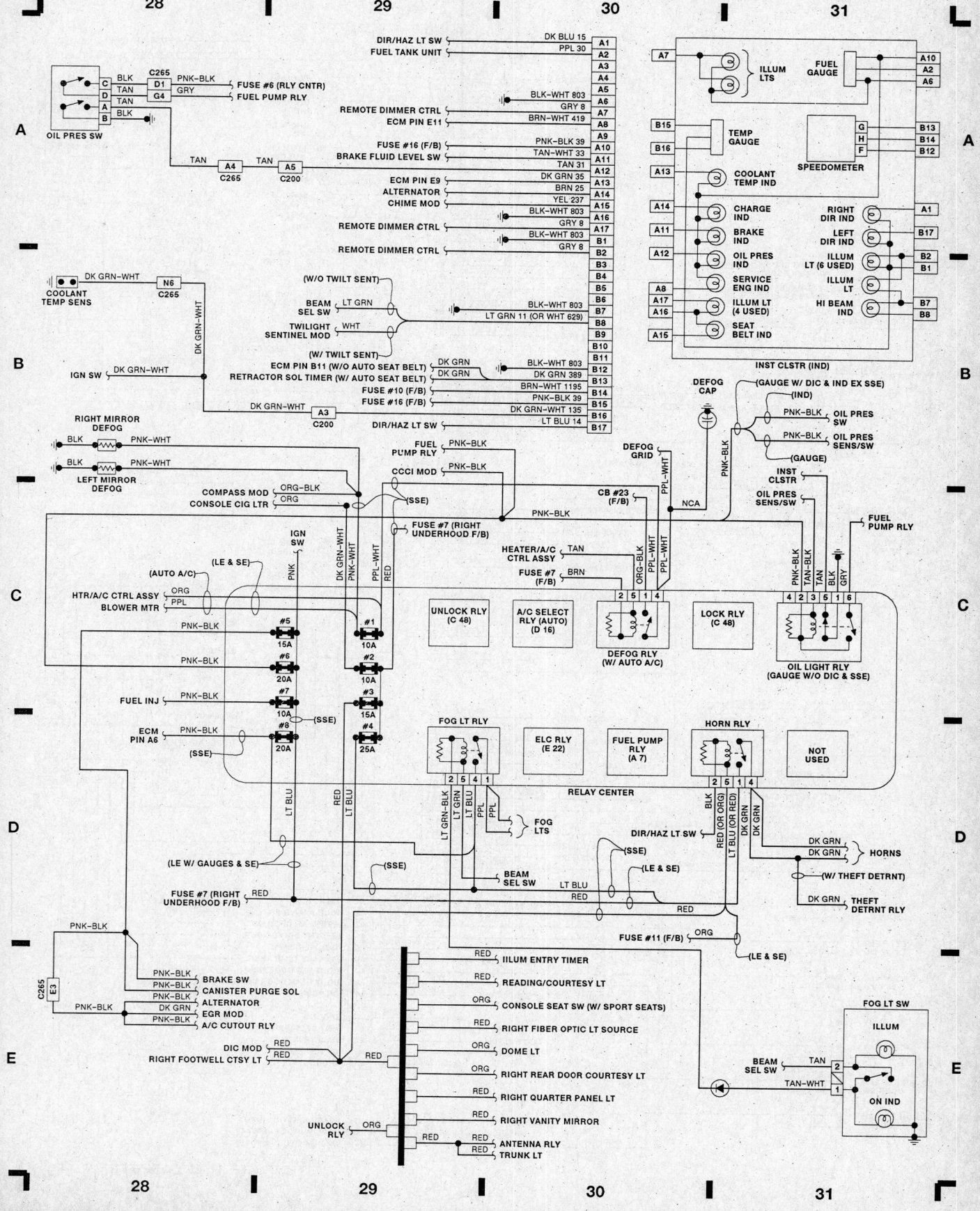

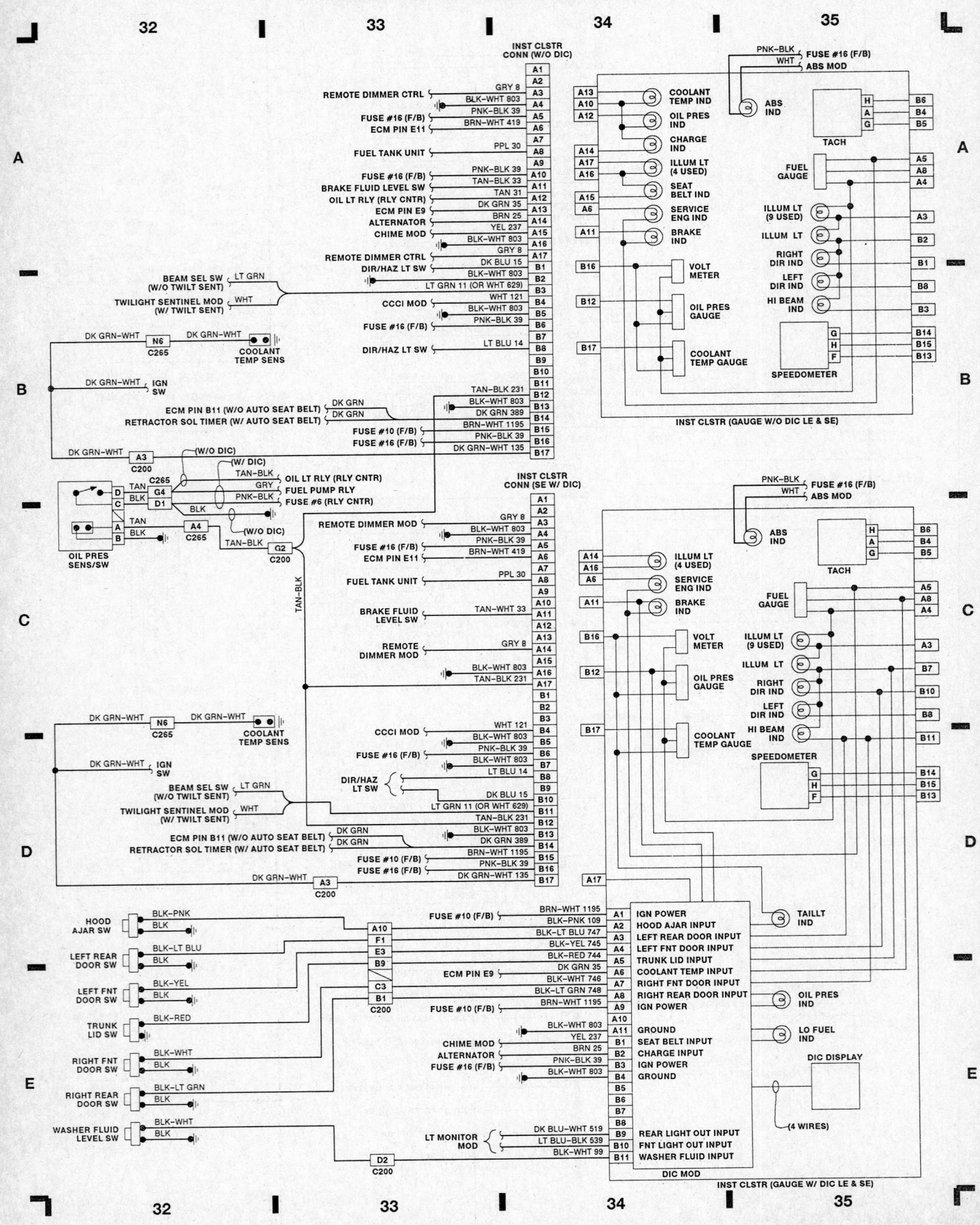

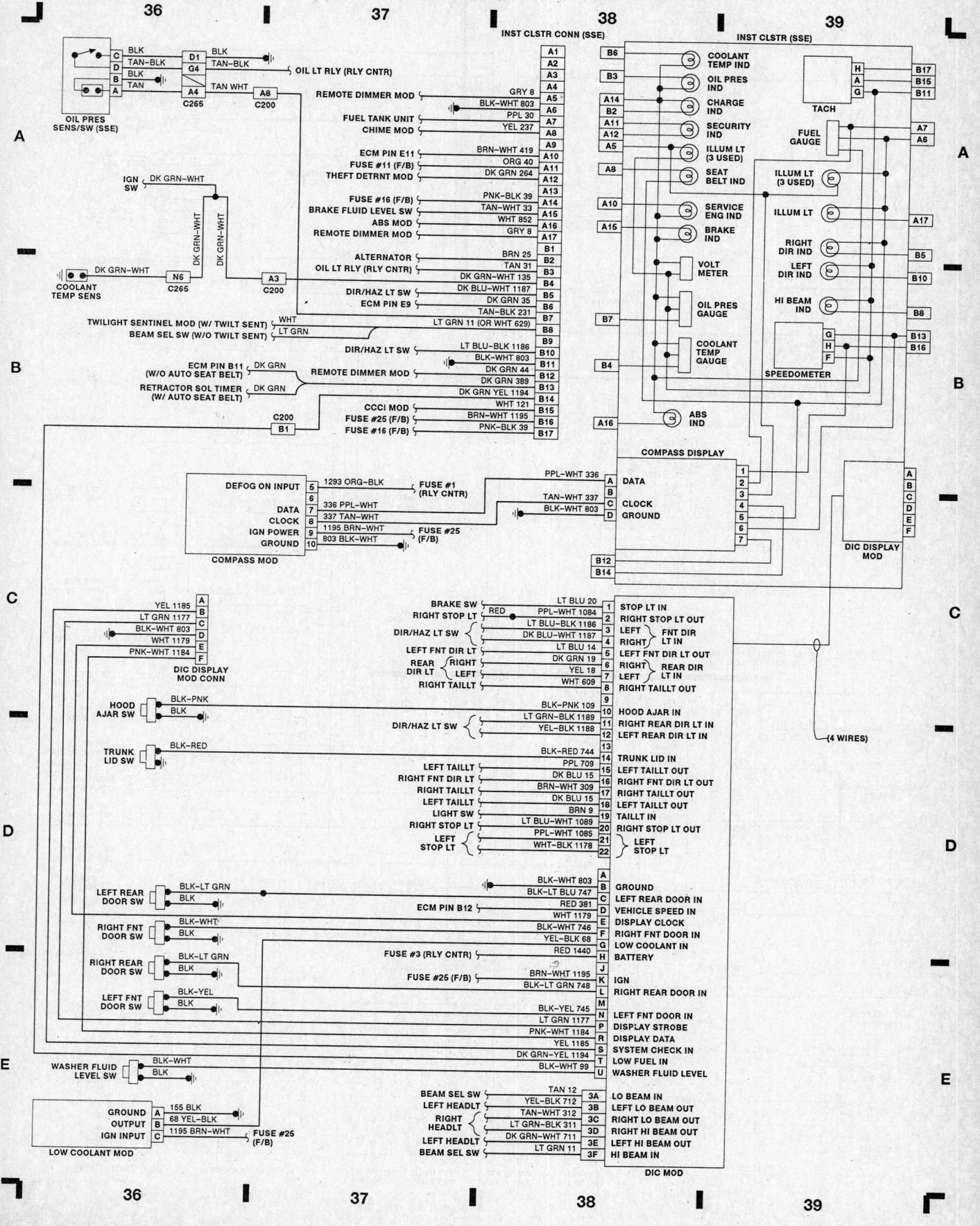

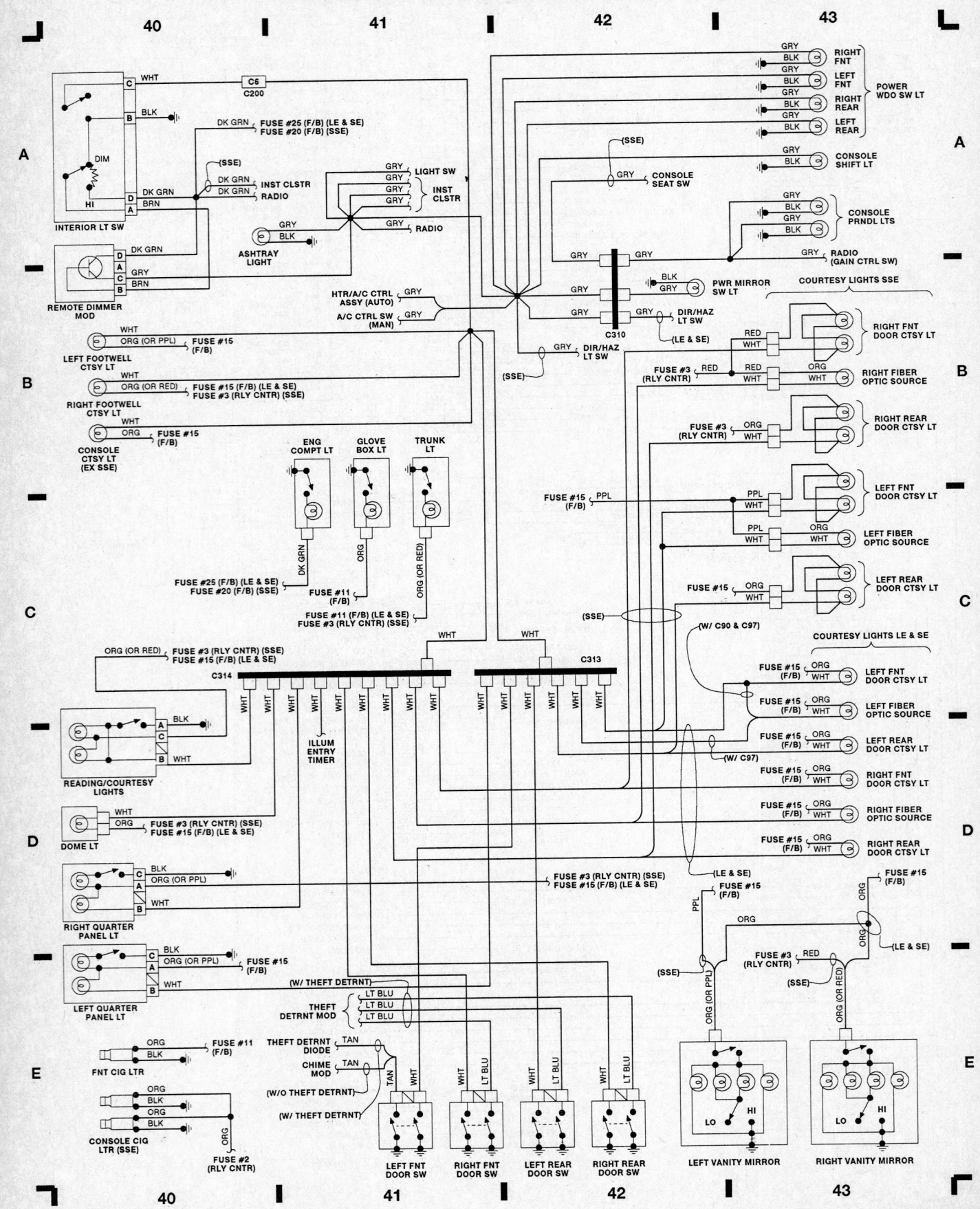

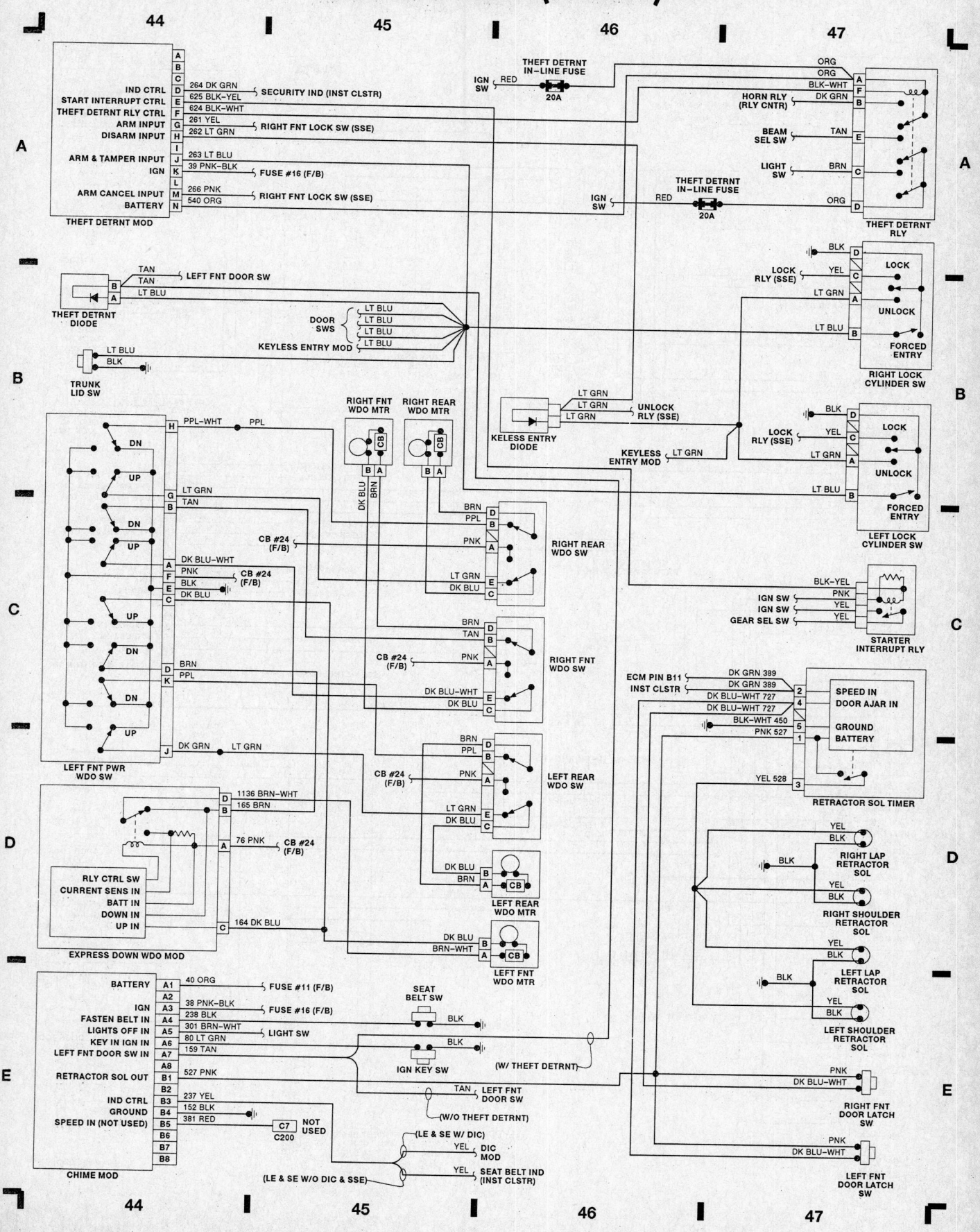

1991 WIRING DIAGRAMS
Bonneville (Cont.)

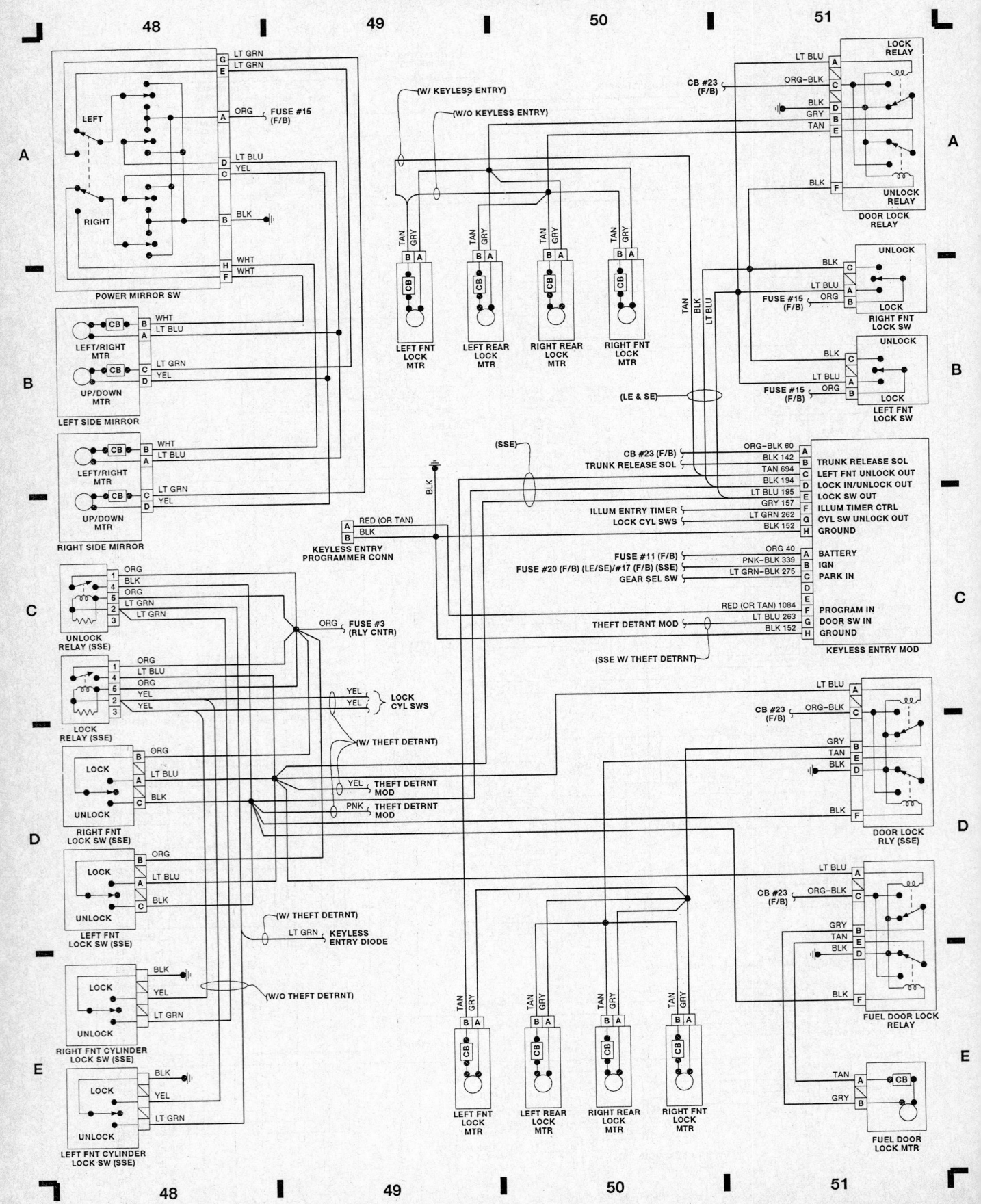

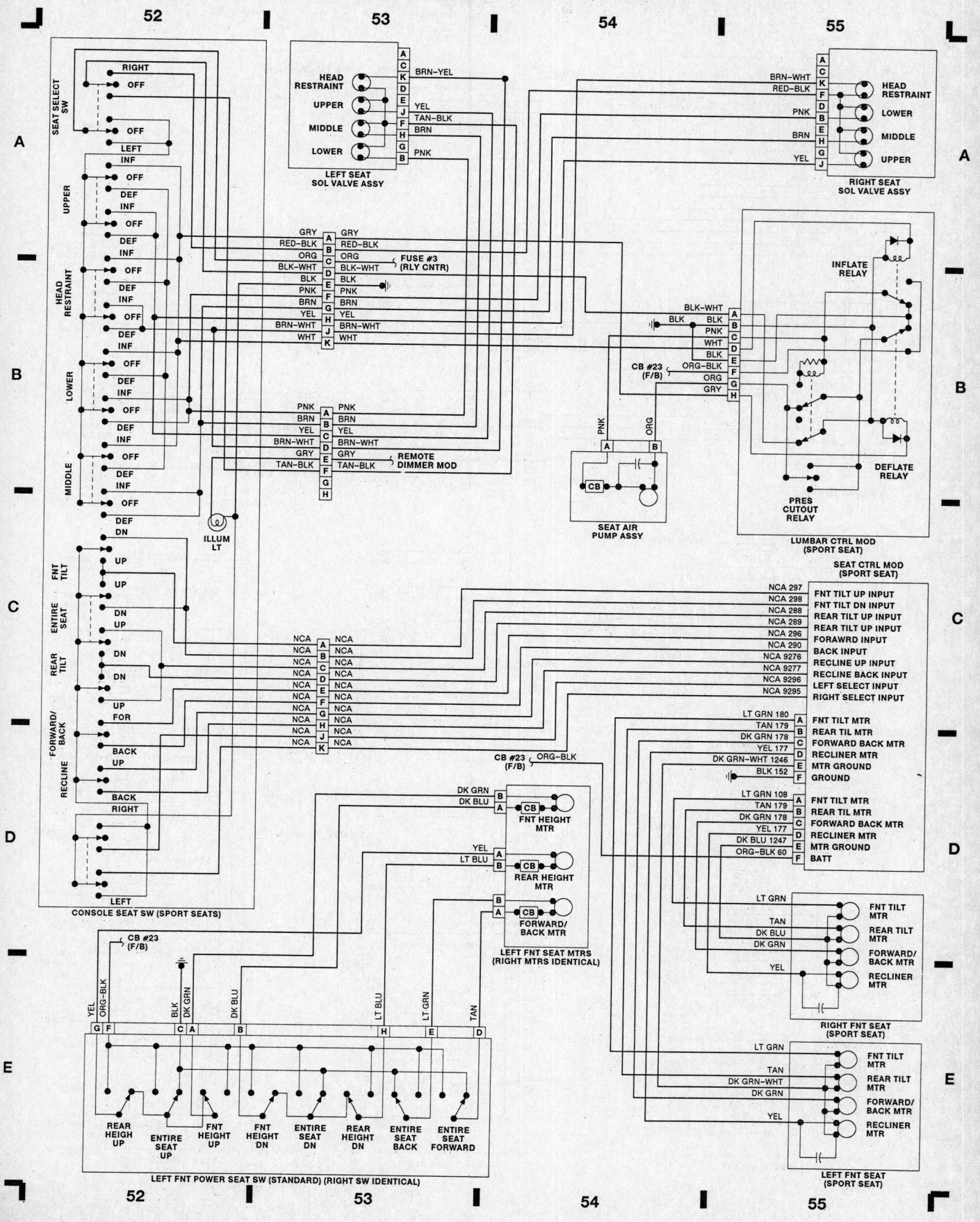

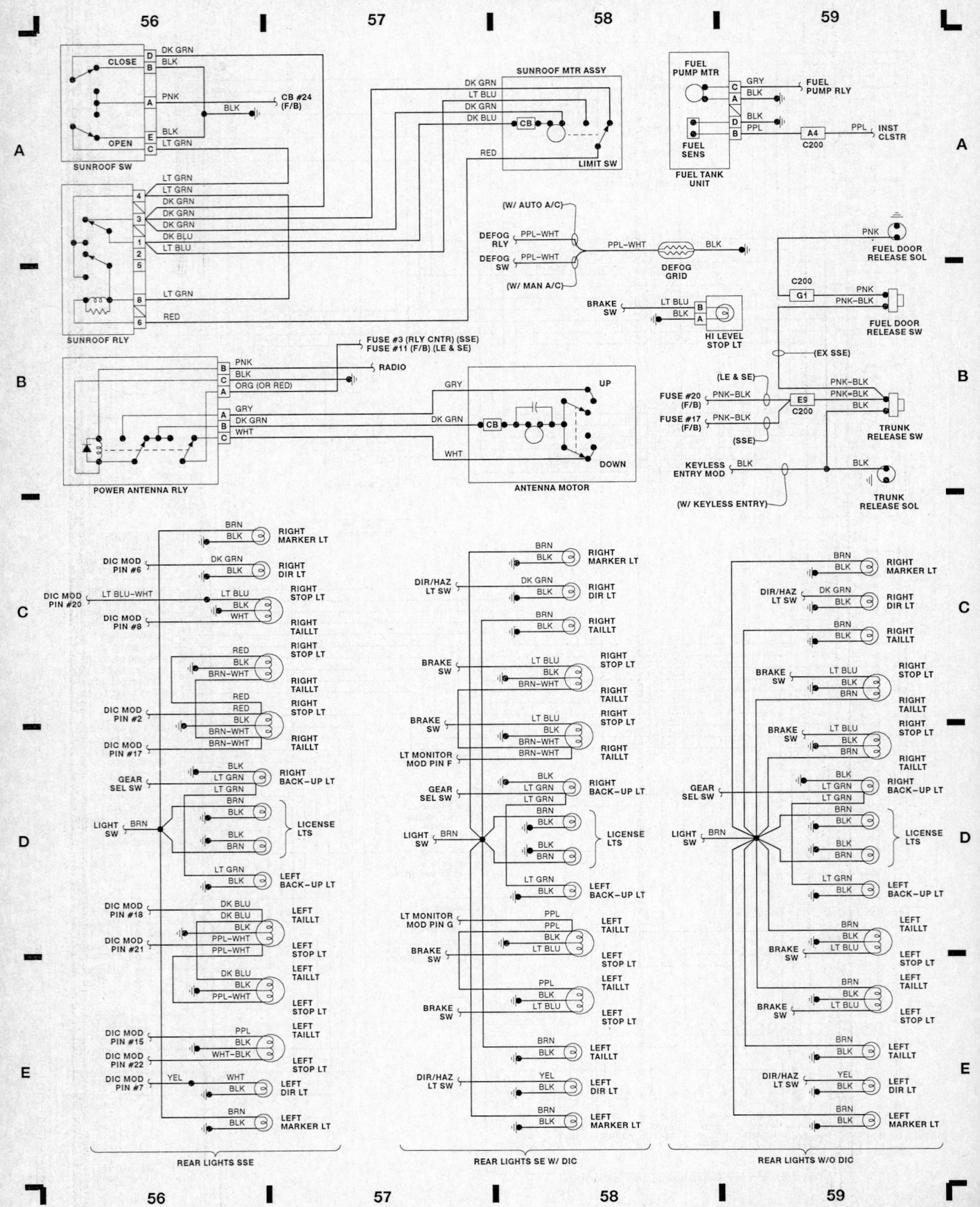

COMPONENT LOCATOR:

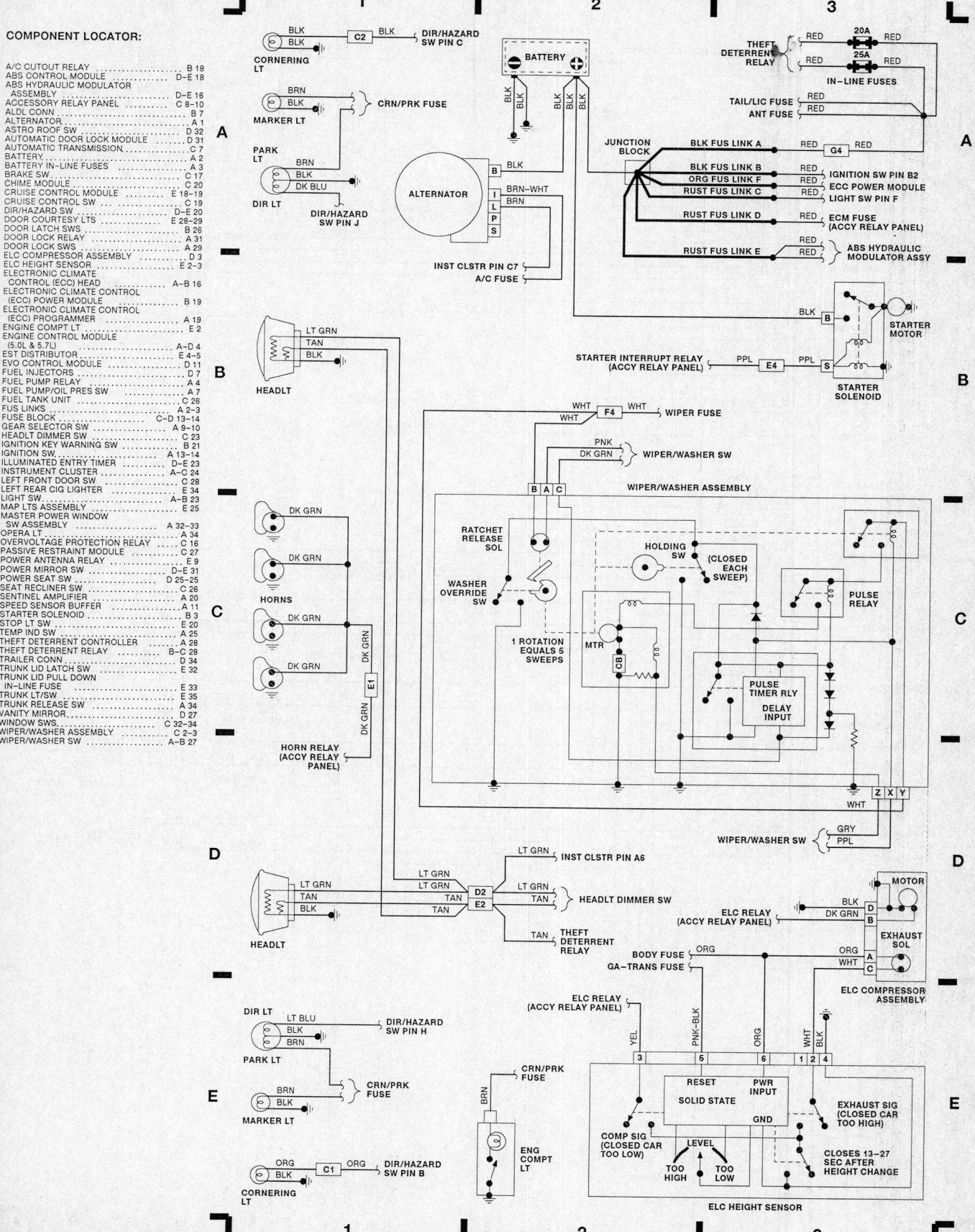

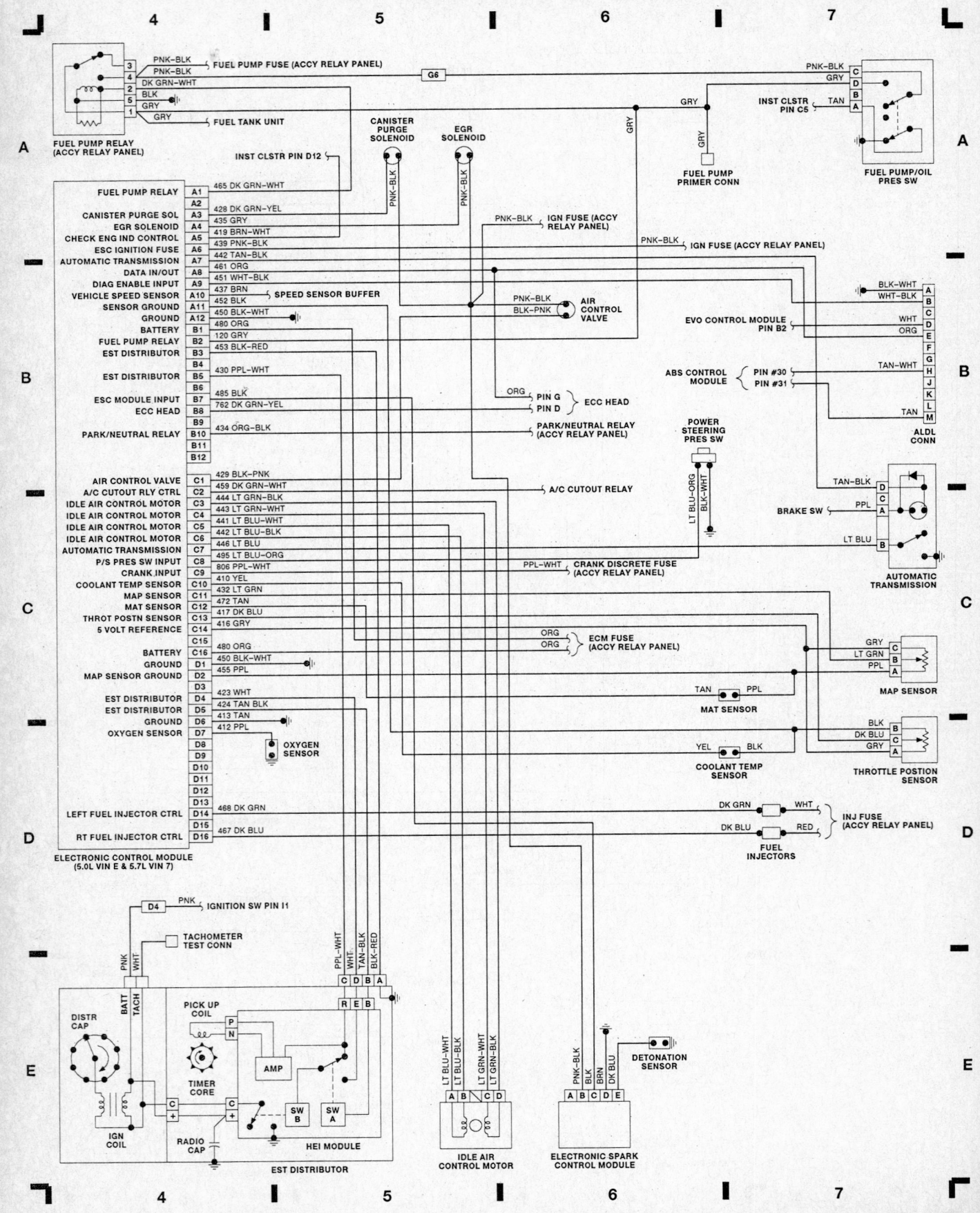

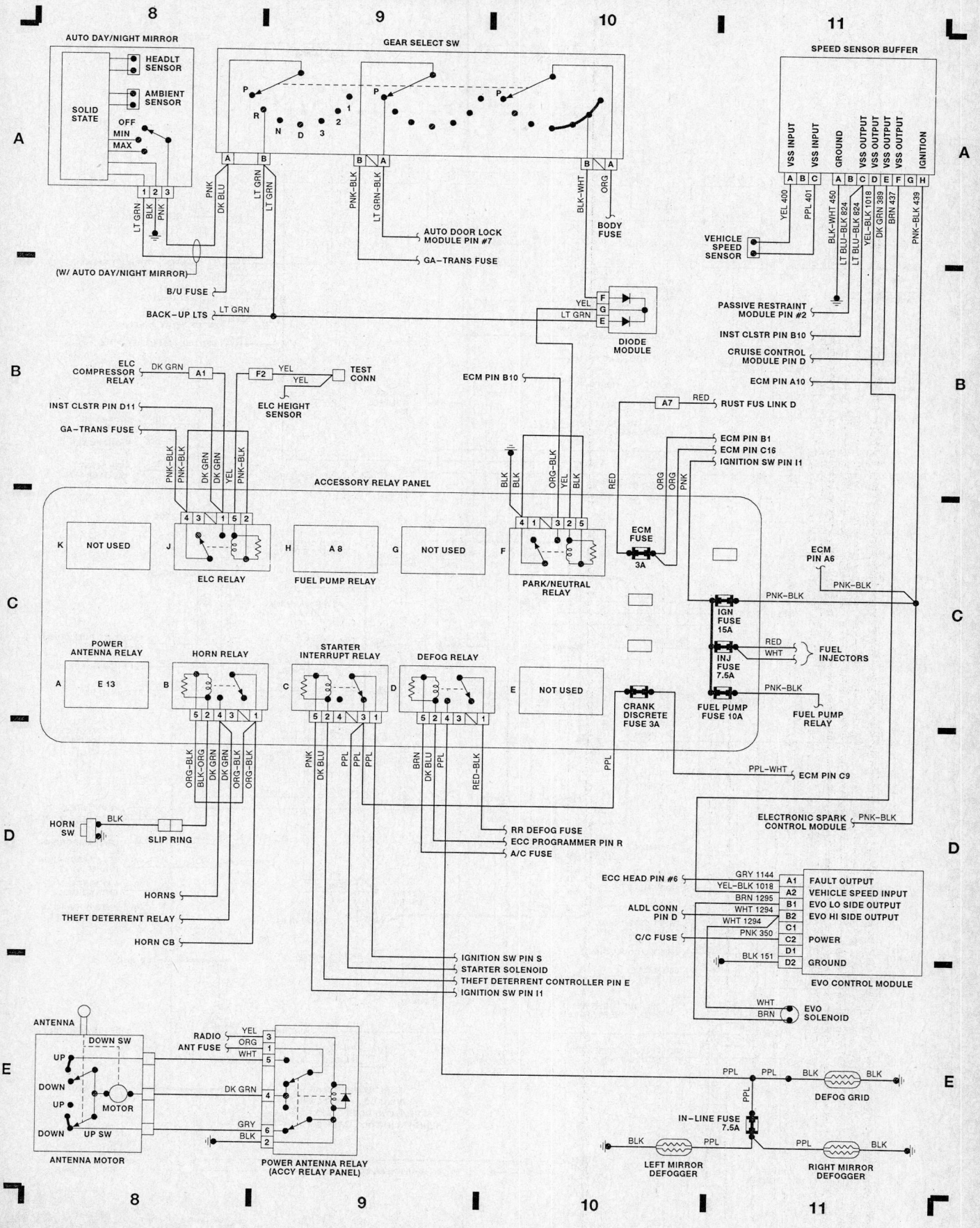

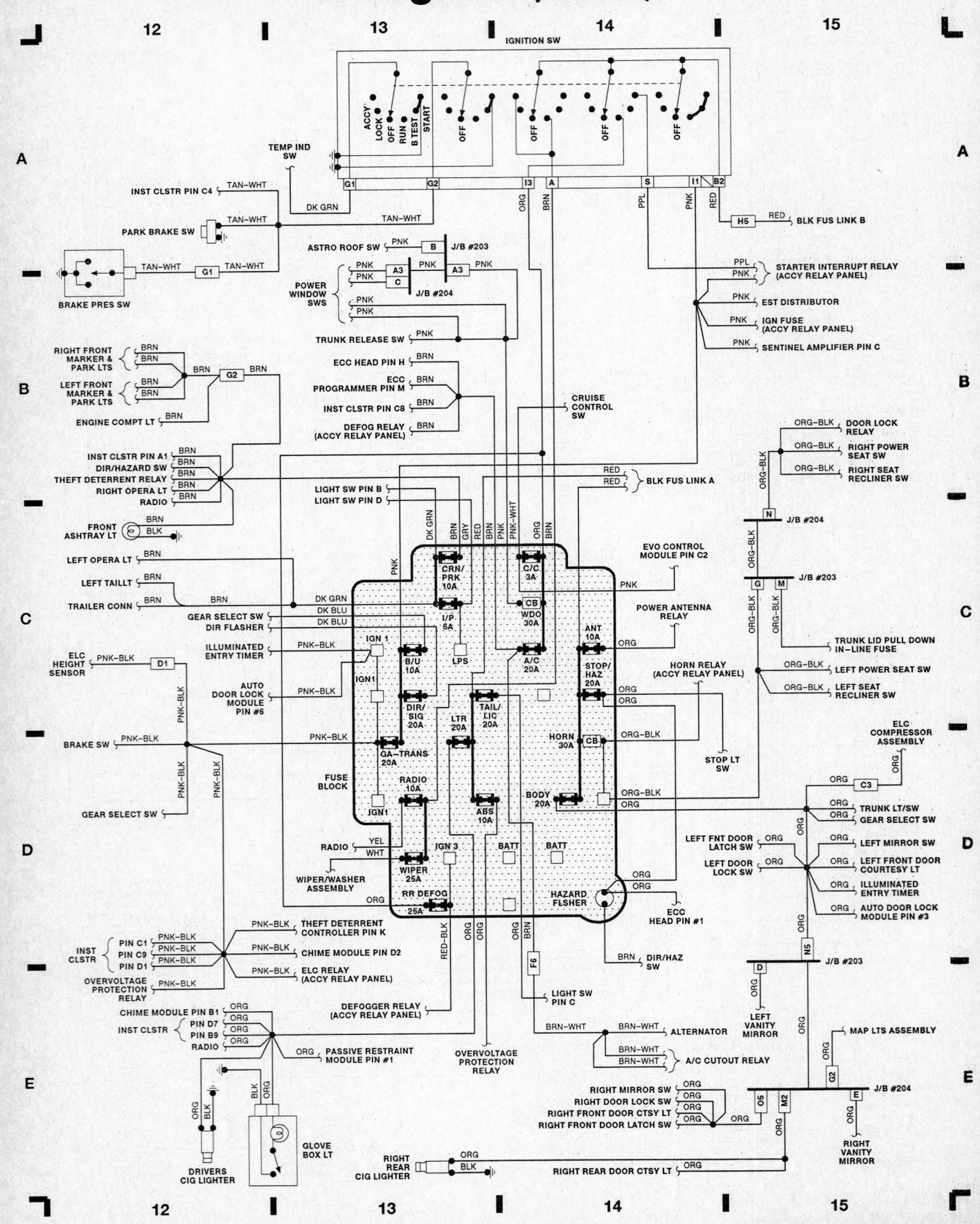

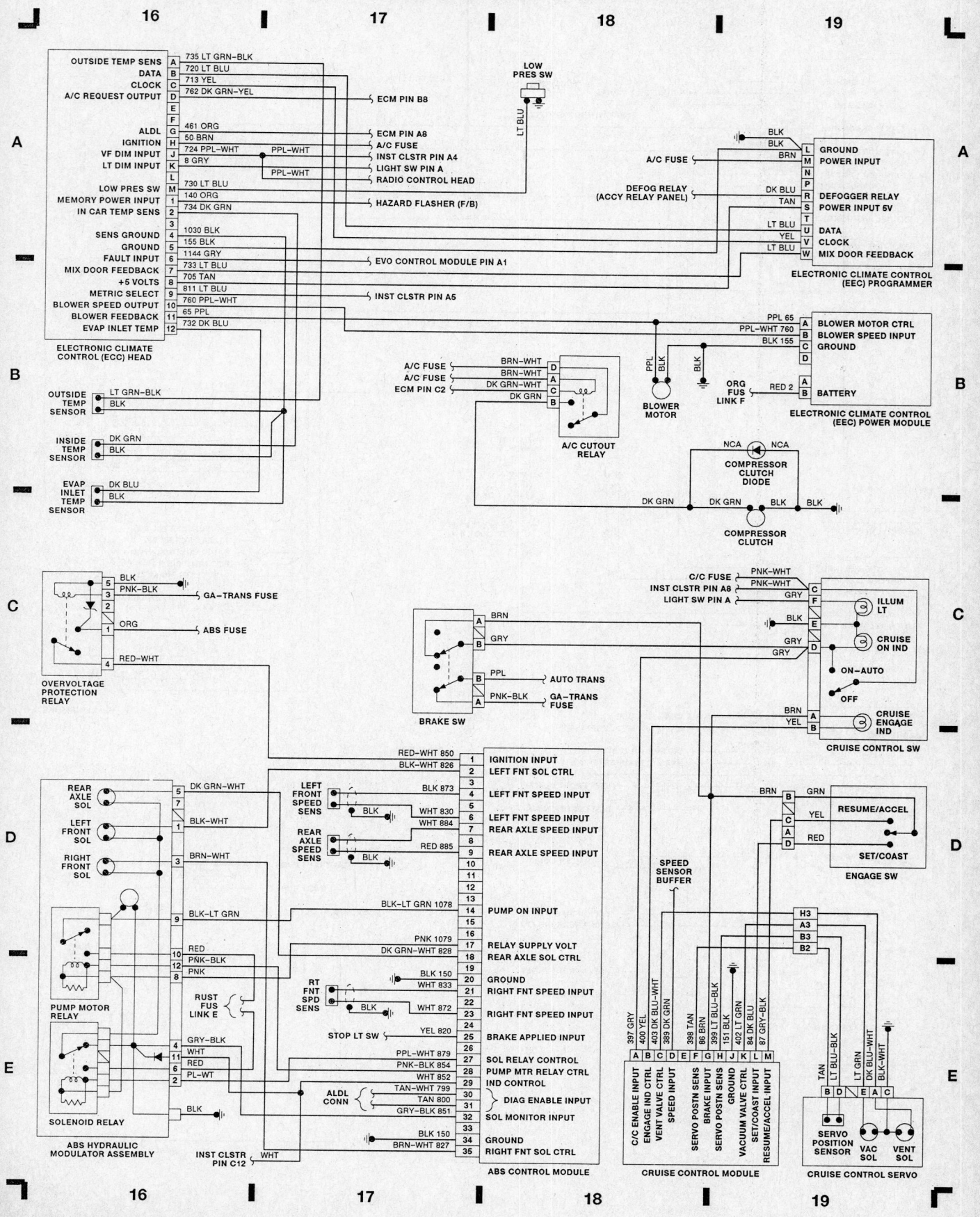

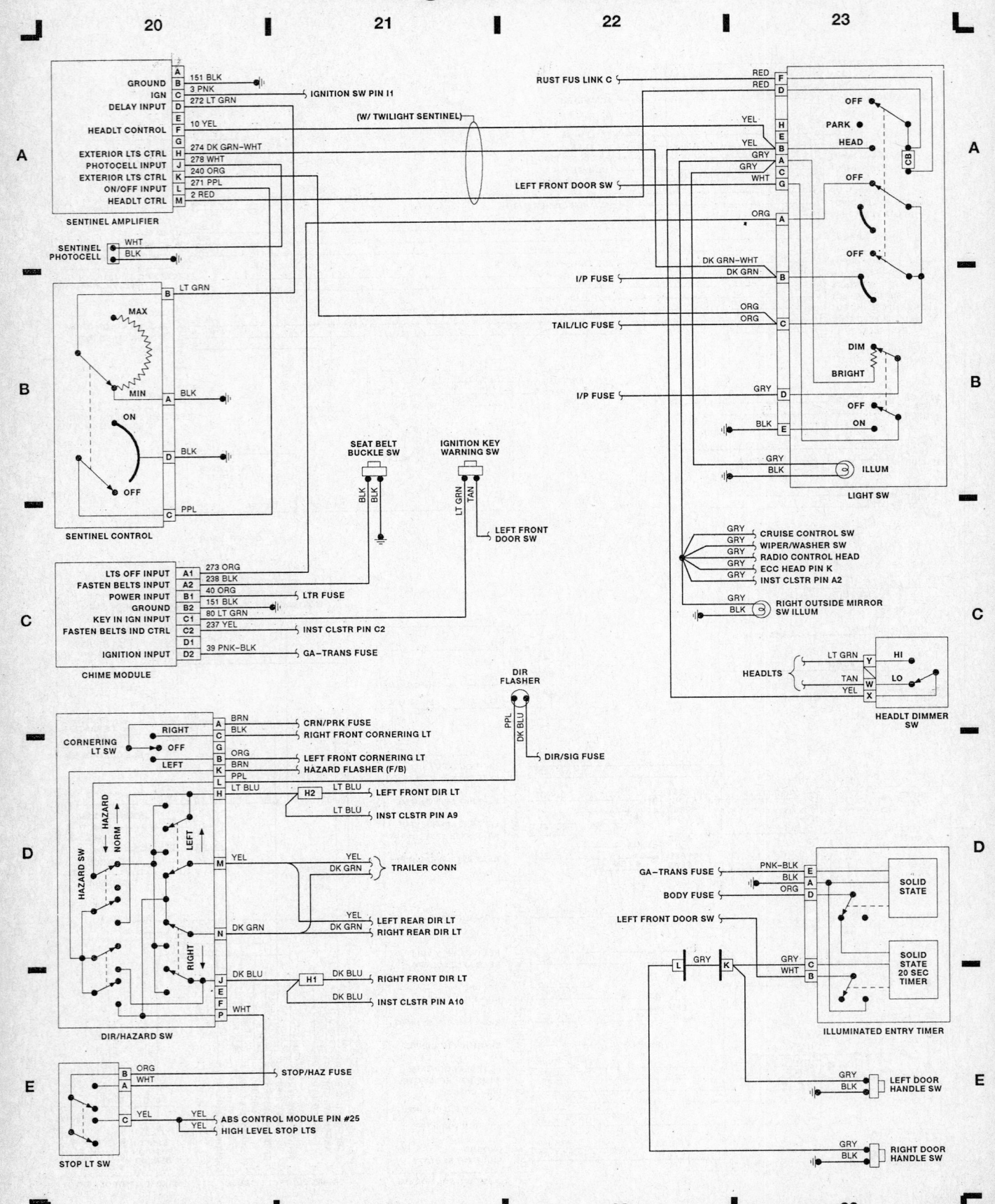

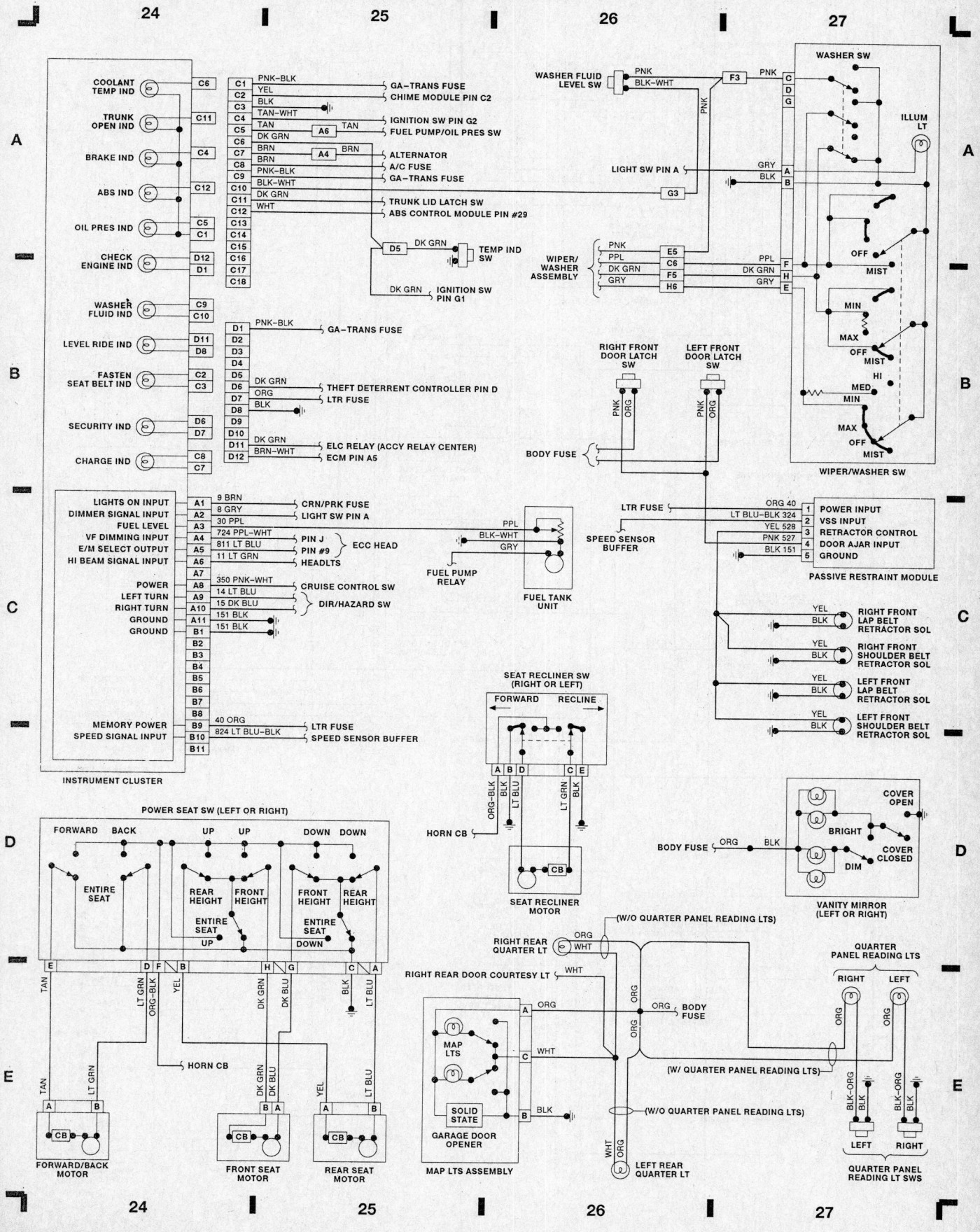

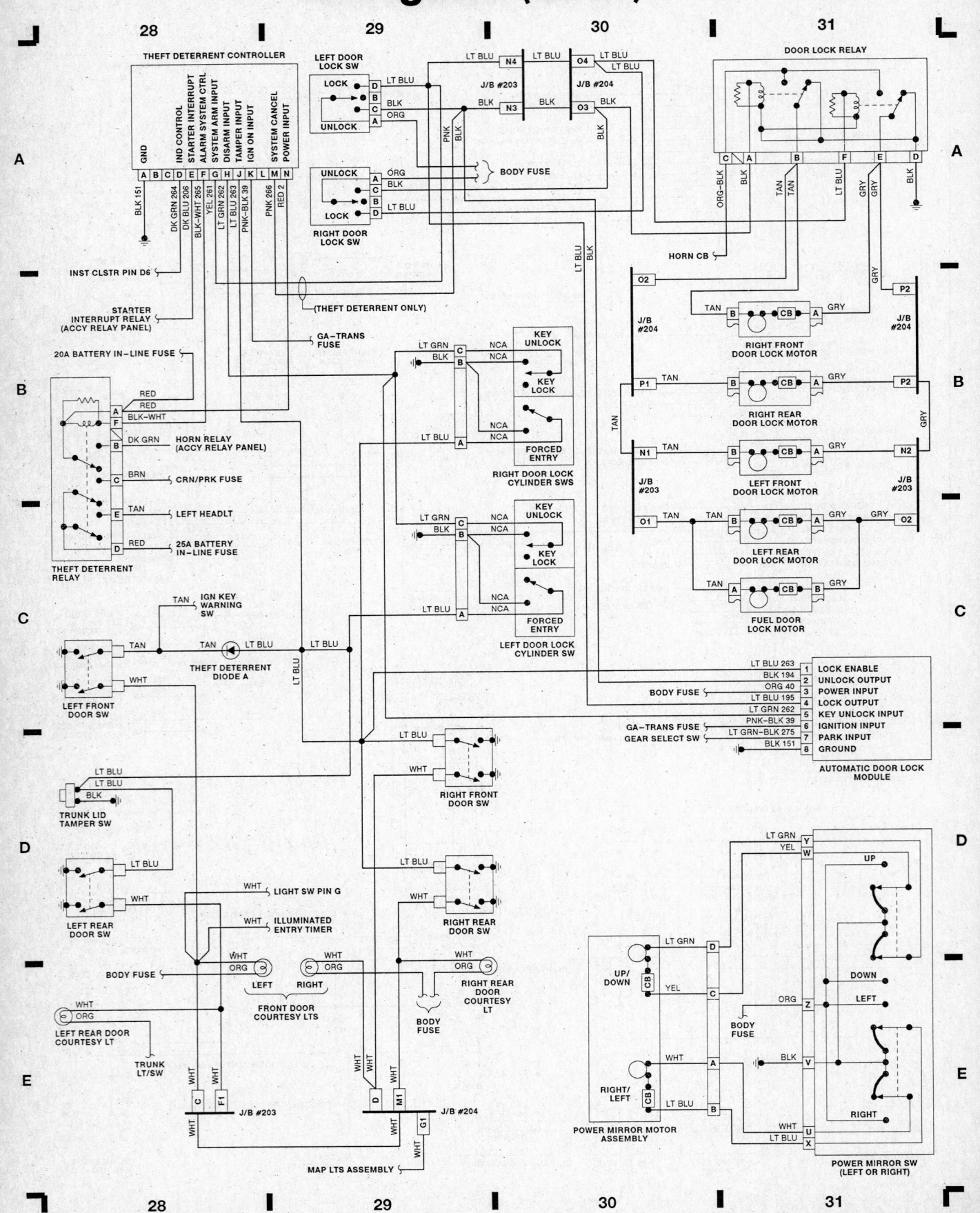

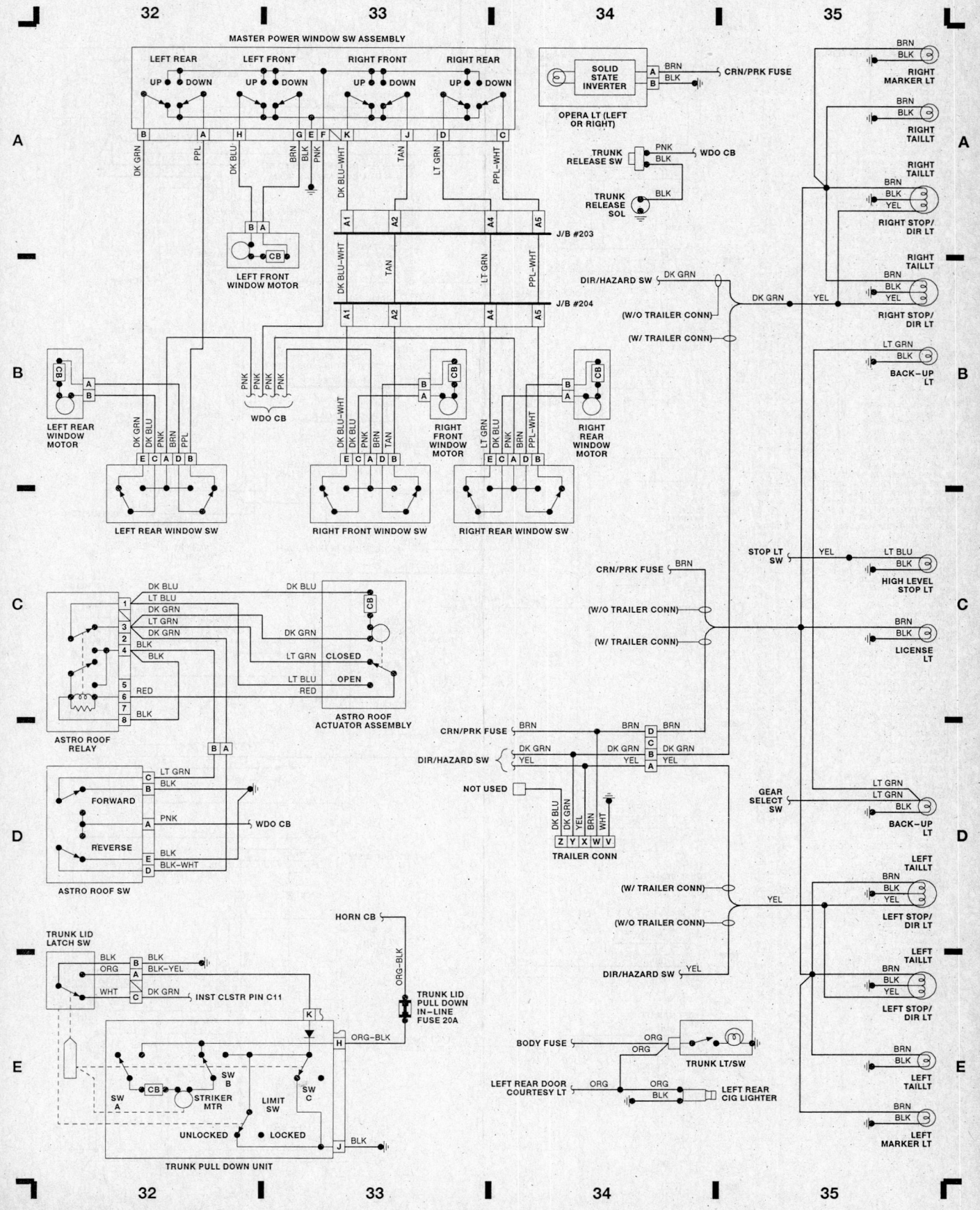

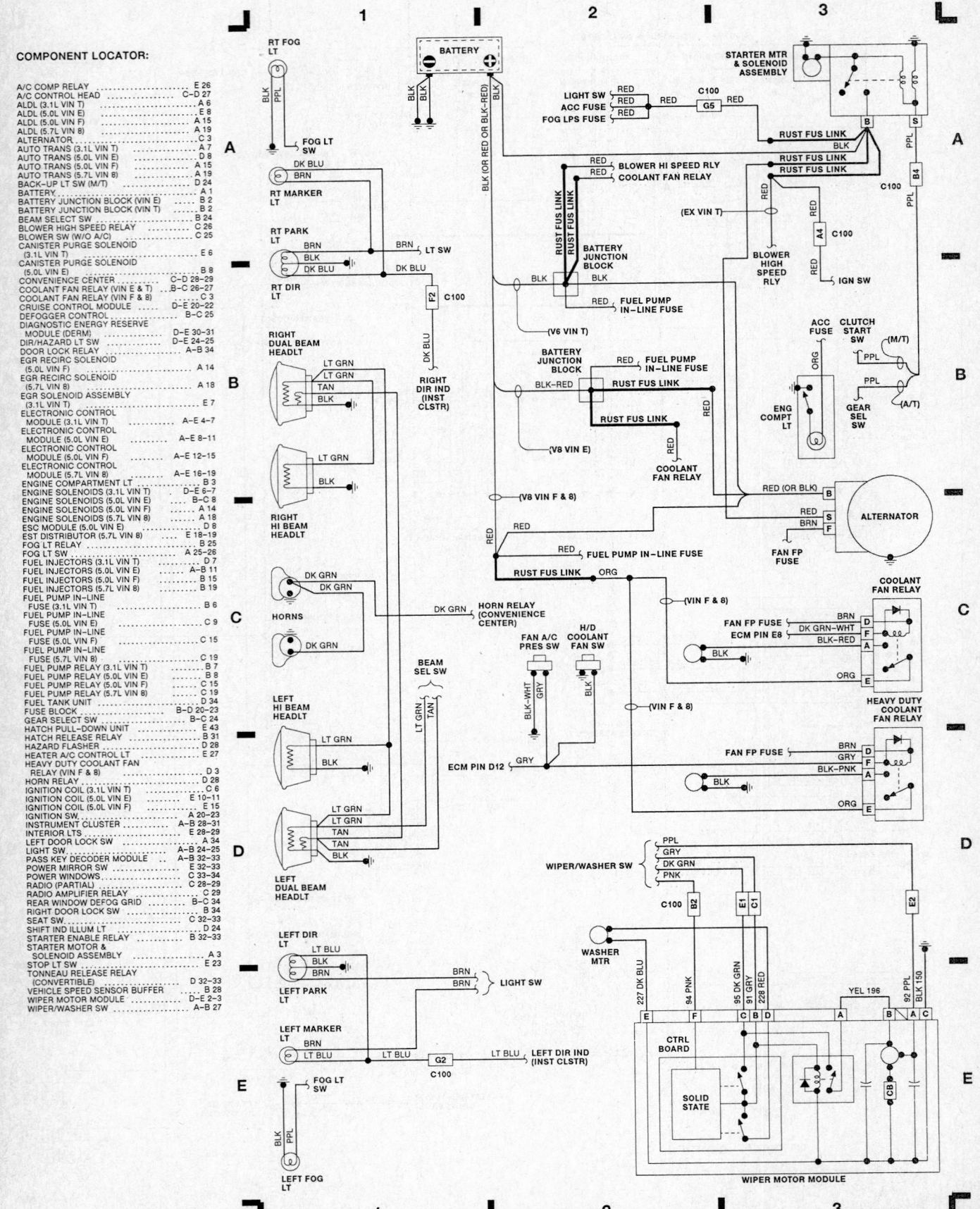

COMPONENT LOCATOR:

A/C COMP RELAY .... E 26
A/C CONTROL HEAD .... C-D 27
ALDL (3.1L VIN T) .... A 6
ALDL (5.0L VIN E) .... E 8
ALDL (5.0L VIN F) .... A 15
ALDL (5.7L VIN 8) .... A 19
ALTERNATOR .... C 3
AUTO TRANS (3.1L VIN T) .... A 7
AUTO TRANS (5.0L VIN E) .... D 8
AUTO TRANS (5.0L VIN F) .... A 15
AUTO TRANS (5.7L VIN 8) .... A 19
BACK-UP LT SW (M/T) .... D 24
BATTERY .... A 1
BATTERY JUNCTION BLOCK (VIN E) ..... B 2
BATTERY JUNCTION BLOCK (VIN T) ..... B 2
BEAM SELECT SW .... B 24
BLOWER HIGH SPEED RELAY ...... C 26
BLOWER SW (W/O A/C) .... C 25
CANISTER PURGE SOLENOID
    (3.1L VIN T) .... E 6
CANISTER PURGE SOLENOID
    (5.0L VIN E) .... B 8
CONVENIENCE CENTER .... C-D 28-29
COOLANT FAN RELAY (VIN E & T) ..B-C 26-27
COOLANT FAN RELAY (VIN F & 8) .... C 3
CRUISE CONTROL MODULE ...... D-E 20-22
DEFOGGER CONTROL .... B-C 25
DIAGNOSTIC ENERGY RESERVE
    MODULE (DERM) .... D-E 30-31
DIR/HAZARD LT SW .... D-E 24-25
DOOR LOCK RELAY .... A-B 34
EGR RECIRC SOLENOID
    (5.0L VIN F) .... A 14
EGR RECIRC SOLENOID
    (5.7L VIN 8) .... A 18
EGR SOLENOID ASSEMBLY
    (3.1L VIN T) .... E 7
ELECTRONIC CONTROL
    MODULE (3.1L VIN T) .... A-E 4-7
ELECTRONIC CONTROL
    MODULE (5.0L VIN E) .... A-E 8-11
ELECTRONIC CONTROL
    MODULE (5.0L VIN F) .... A-E 12-15
ELECTRONIC CONTROL
    MODULE (5.7L VIN 8) .... A-E 16-19
ENGINE COMPARTMENT LT .... B 3
ENGINE SOLENOIDS (3.1L VIN T) ..D-E 6-7
ENGINE SOLENOIDS (5.0L VIN E) ...B-C 8
ENGINE SOLENOIDS (5.0L VIN F) .. A 14
ENGINE SOLENOIDS (5.7L VIN 8) .. A 18
ESC MODULE (5.0L VIN E) .... D 8
EST DISTRIBUTOR (5.7L VIN 8) ... E 18-19
FOG LT RELAY .... D 7
FOG LT SW .... A 25-26
FUEL INJECTORS (3.1L VIN T) .... D 7
FUEL INJECTORS (5.0L VIN E) .... A-B 11
FUEL INJECTORS (5.0L VIN F) .... B 15
FUEL INJECTORS (5.7L VIN 8) .... B 19
FUEL PUMP IN-LINE
    FUSE (3.1L VIN T) .... B 6
FUEL PUMP IN-LINE
    FUSE (5.0L VIN E) .... C 9
FUEL PUMP IN-LINE
    FUSE (5.0L VIN F) .... C 15
FUEL PUMP IN-LINE
    FUSE (5.7L VIN 8) .... C 19
FUEL PUMP RELAY (3.1L VIN T) .. B 7
FUEL PUMP RELAY (5.0L VIN E) .. B 8
FUEL PUMP RELAY (5.0L VIN F) .. C 15
FUEL PUMP RELAY (5.7L VIN 8) .. C 19
FUEL TANK UNIT .... D 34
FUSE BLOCK .... B-D 20-23
GEAR SELECT SW .... B-C 24
HATCH PULL-DOWN UNIT .... E 43
HATCH RELEASE RELAY .... B 31
HAZARD FLASHER .... D 28
HEATER A/C CONTROL LT .... E 27
HEAVY DUTY COOLANT FAN
    RELAY (VIN F & 8) .... D 3
HORN RELAY .... D 28
IGNITION COIL (3.1L VIN T) .... C 6
IGNITION COIL (5.0L VIN E) .... E 10-11
IGNITION COIL (5.0L VIN F) .... E 15
IGNITION SW .... A 20-23
INSTRUMENT CLUSTER .... A-B 28-31
INTERIOR LTS .... E 28-29
LEFT DOOR LOCK SW .... A 34
LIGHT SW .... A-B 24-25
PASS KEY DECODER MODULE .... A-B 32-33
POWER MIRROR SW .... E 32-33
POWER WINDOWS .... C 33-34
RADIO (PARTIAL) .... C 28-29
RADIO AMPLIFIER RELAY .... C 29
REAR WINDOW DEFOG GRID ..... B-C 34
RIGHT DOOR LOCK SW .... B 34
SEAT SW .... C 32-33
SHIFT IND ILLUM LT .... D 24
STARTER ENABLE RELAY .... B 32-33
STARTER MOTOR &
    SOLENOID ASSEMBLY .... A 3
STOP LT SW .... E 23
TONNEAU RELEASE RELAY
    (CONVERTIBLE) .... D 32-33
VEHICLE SPEED SENSOR BUFFER .. B 28
WIPER MOTOR MODULE .... D-E 2-3
WIPER/WASHER SW .... A-B 27

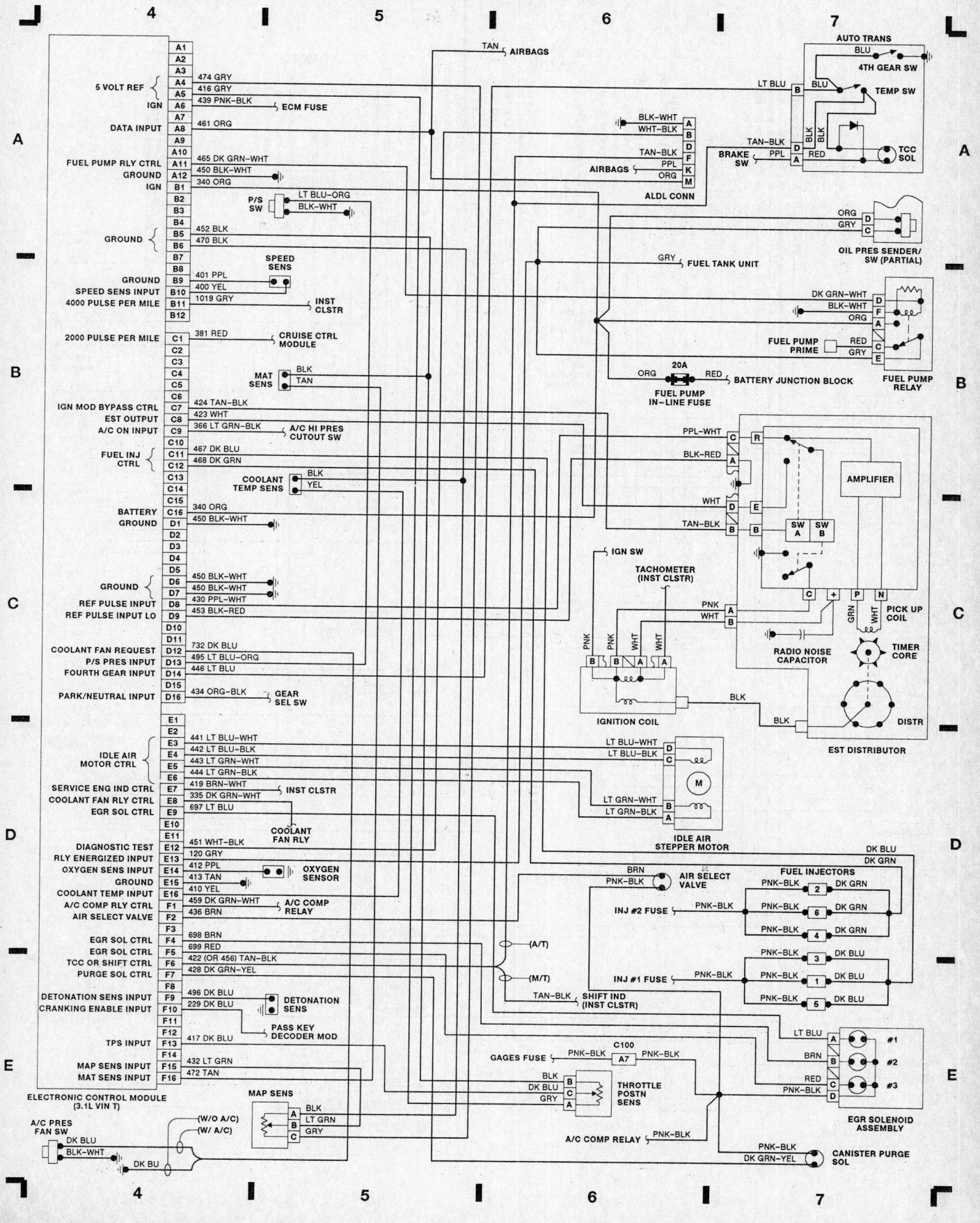

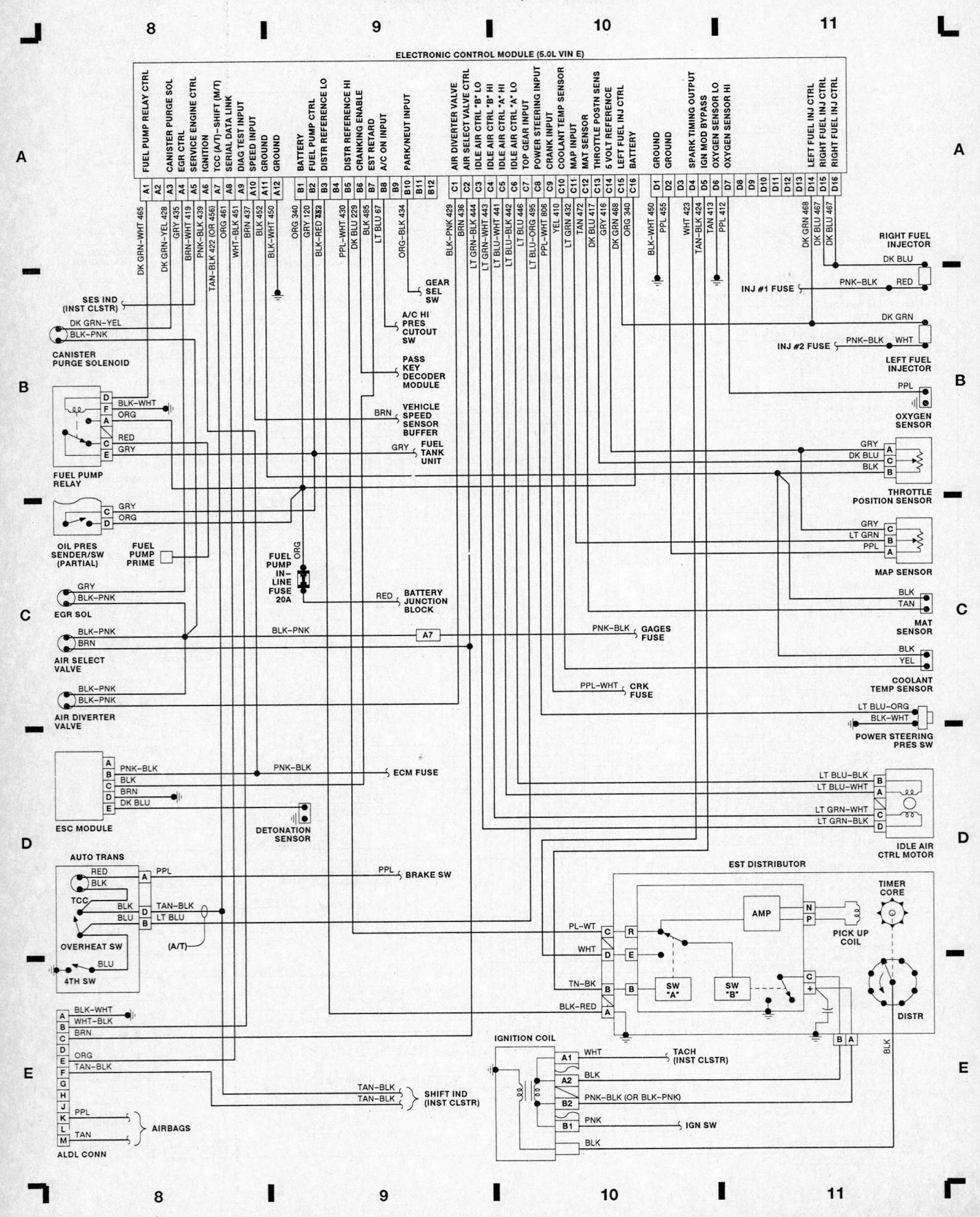

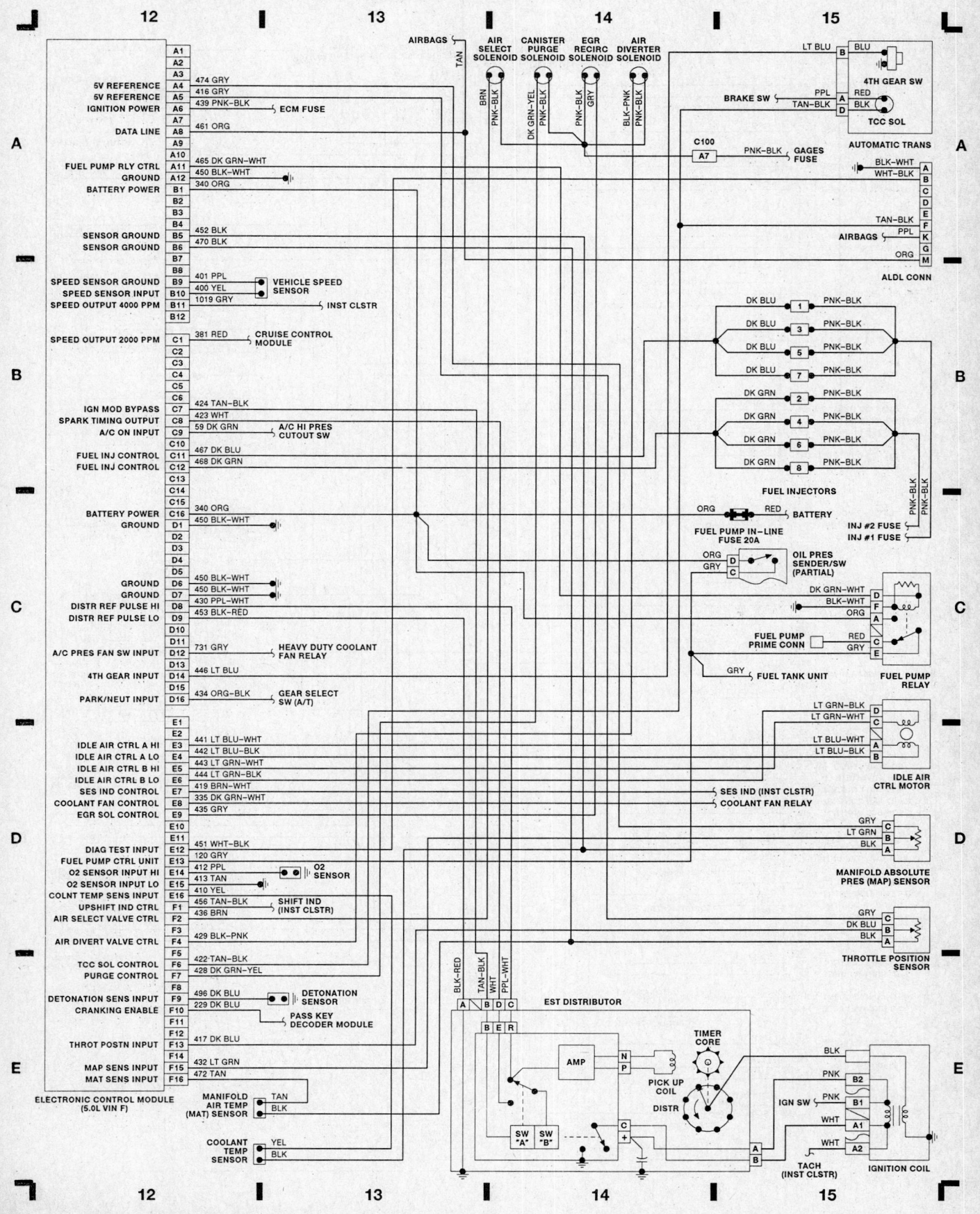

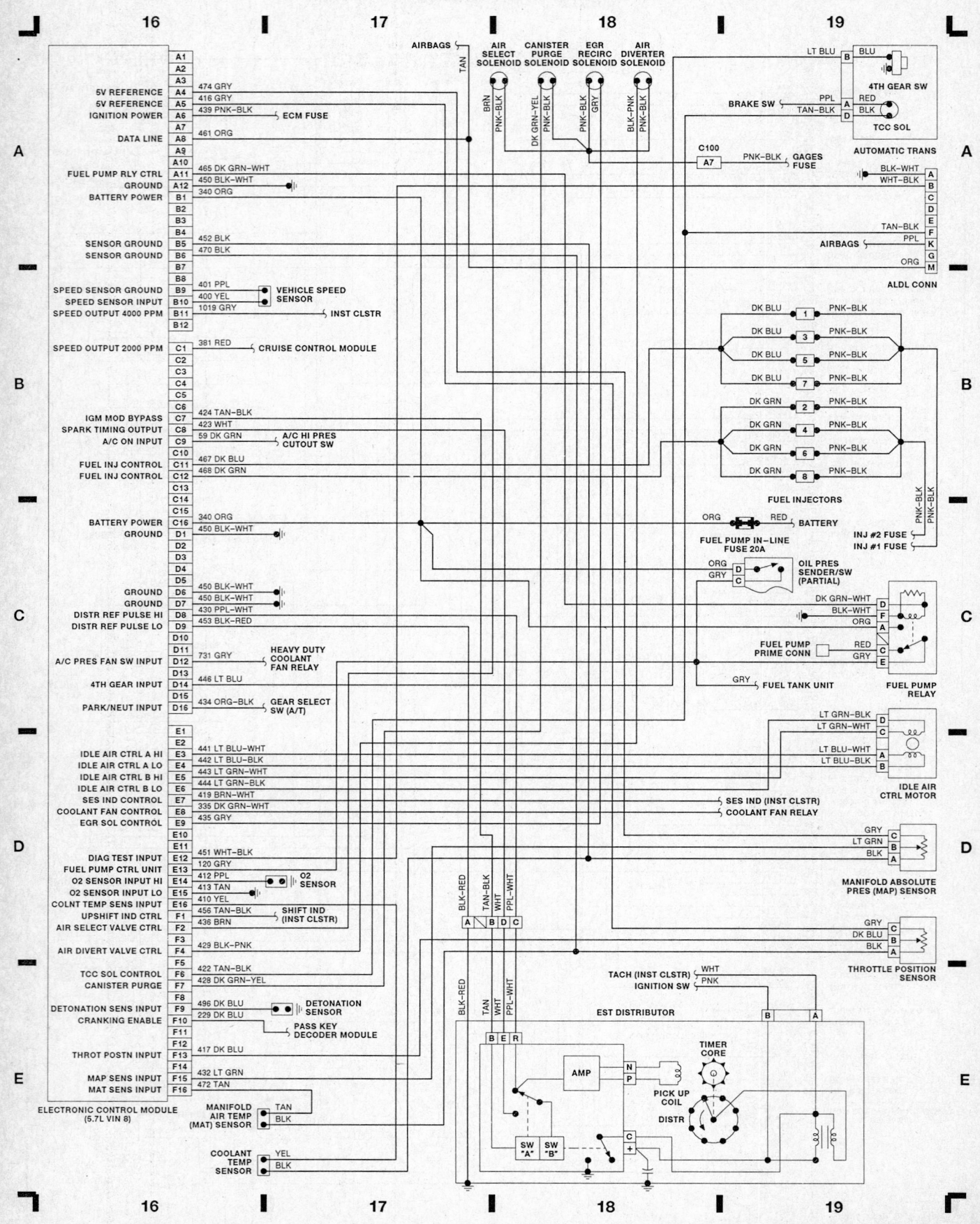

20   21   22   23

A

IGNITION SW

ACCY   START
LOCK   BULB TEST
OFF   OFF   RUN   OFF   OFF

A B C D E   A B C D

YEL PNK RED BRN   ORG RED DK GRN

STARTER ENABLE RELAY

RUST FUS LINK   RED

PARKING BRAKE SW

TAN-WHT   DK GRN   F5

COOLANT TEMP SENDER

DK GRN   INST CLSTR

RED

PNK   F4

PNK   IGN COIL (V6 VIN T, V8 VIN E & V8 VIN F) EST DISTRIBUTOR (V8 VIN 8)

FUEL INJECTORS   PNK-BLK / PNK-BLK
AIRBAGS   YEL

LIGHT SW   RUST FUS LINK

PNK   BRN   ORG   RED   RED   ORG

ECM PIN A6   PNK-BLK   PNK-BLK

BRN   C100   BRN   ALTERNATOR / COOLANT FAN RELAY

(VIN T)

B

PASS KEY DECODER   PNK-BLK

DIR FLASHER   (EX VIN E) DK BLU

ECM 20A   INJ #1 10A   LID 20A   FAN FP 25A

(EX VIN T)   BRN   BRN   ALTERNATOR
BRN   G8   BRN   COOLANT FAN RELAY
C100

BRN   HEAVY DUTY COOLANT FAN RELAY

TURN B/U 10A   INJ #2 10A   TAIL 20A   HTR/ A/C 30A

DIR FLASHER   DK BLU   (VIN E) DK BLU
GEAR SELECT SW   DK BLU
BACK-UP LT SW   DK BLU

BRN   BLOWER SW (W/O A/C) A/C CONTROL HEAD (W/ A/C)

GAGES 10A   SIR 10A   ACG 20A   WDO CB 30A

PNK   POWER WINDOWS

AIRBAGS   PNK-BLK
CRUISE CONTROL   PNK-BLK
BRAKE SW   PNK-BLK
AUDIO ALARM MOD PIN H   PNK-BLK
DEFOGGER CONTROL   PNK-BLK
VEHICLE SPEED SENSOR BUFFER   PNK-BLK
INST CLSTR   PNK-BLK

INST LPS 5A   RADIO 10A   PWR ACC CB 30A

ORG-BLK   DEFOGGER CONTROL
ORG-BLK   ORG-BLK   DOOR LOCK RELAY
ORG-BLK   POWER SEATS

C

ENGINE SOLS   PNK-BLK

IGN   INST LPS   BAT

STOP HAZ 20A

ORG   AUDIO ALARM MOD PIN C
ORG   HAZARD FLASHER
ORG

IGN   INST LPS   WPR 25A   BAT

RADIO ILLUM LT   GRY
HTR/A/C CONTROL LT   GRY
DEFOGGER CONTROL   GRY
ASHTRAY LT   GRY

LIGHT SW   DK GRN   GRY   WHT   YEL   RED-WHT   ORG   FUSE BLOCK

ORG   RIGHT DOOR LOCK SW
ORG   LEFT DOOR LOCK SW
ORG   POWER MIRRORS
ORG   TONNEAU RELEASE RLY
ORG   CIG LTR
ORG   DOME LT
ORG   HATCH RELEASE RELAY
ORG   ENG COMPT LT
ORG   HORN RELAY
ORG   RADIO AMP RELAY

WIPER/WASHER SW   WHT
RADIO   YEL
CARGO COMPT LT   RED-WHT

SHIFT IND ILLUM LT   GRY
FOG LT SW   GRY
INST CLSTR   GRY

RED   VATS 10A   ARC 20A   CRK 3A   FOG LPS 20A   RED

RUST FUS LINK

PASS KEY DECODER MODULE   ORG
RADIO   ORG

LT BLU   FOG LT RELAY
PPL   GEAR SELECT SW (A/T), CLUTCH START SW (M/T)

PPL-WHT   AIRBAGS
PPL-WHT   ECM PIN C9

PL-WT

D

CRUISE CONTROL SERVO

SERVO POSTN SENS

D   LT BLU-BLK
B   TAN

VENT VALVE
A   DK BLU-WHT
C   BLK
VACUUM VALVE
E   LT GRN

(EX V8 VIN E)
(V8 VIN E)   NOT USED

ECM PIN C1 (VIN T,F & 8) VEHICLE SPEED SENS BUFFER (VIN E)

GRY 397   A   CRUISE IN
B
DK BLU-WHT 403   C   VENT CTRL
RED 381   D   VSS IN
E
TAN 398   F   SPS IN
BRN 86   G   BRAKE IN
LT BLU-BLK 399   H
BLK 150   J   GROUND
LT GRN 402   K   VAC CTRL
DK BLU 84   L   SET/COAST
GRY-BLK 87   M   R/A IN

CRUISE CONTROL MOD

HIGH LEVEL STOP LT   YEL

LEFT STOP LT   LT BLU

E

R/A   GRY   L   GRY
ON
OFF

BLK   J   GRY-BLK
OFF
PNK   M   PNK-BLK   GAGES FUSE
SET SW
DK BLU   K   DK BLU

MULTI-FUNCTION SW

GAGES FUSE
AUTO TRANS   PPL   E7
BRN   PPL
CLUTCH SW   (A/T)
BRN   BRN-WHT
(M/T)   GRY

PNK-BLK

BRAKE SW

ORG   LT BLU   YEL
B   A   C

STOP LT SW

20   21   22   23

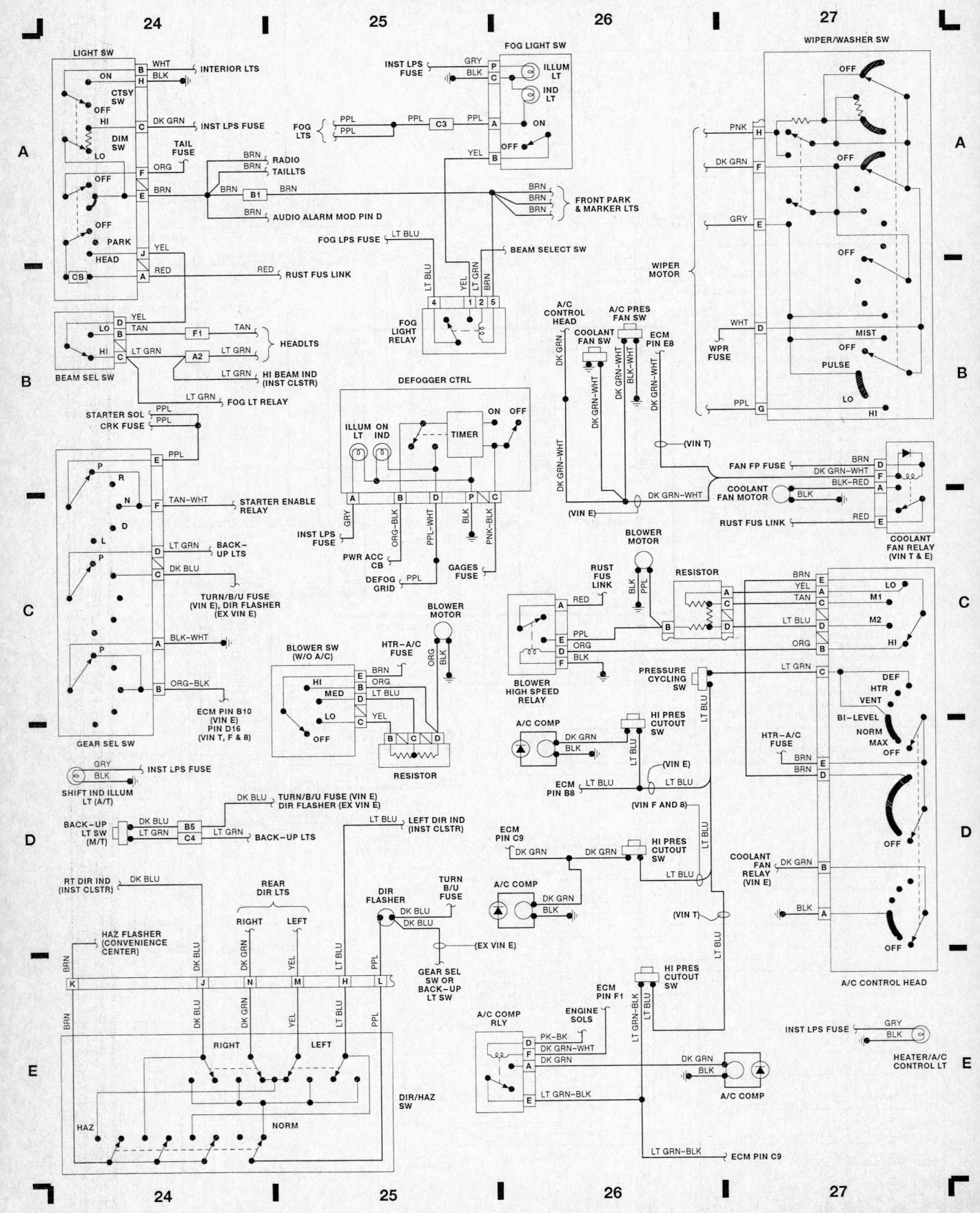

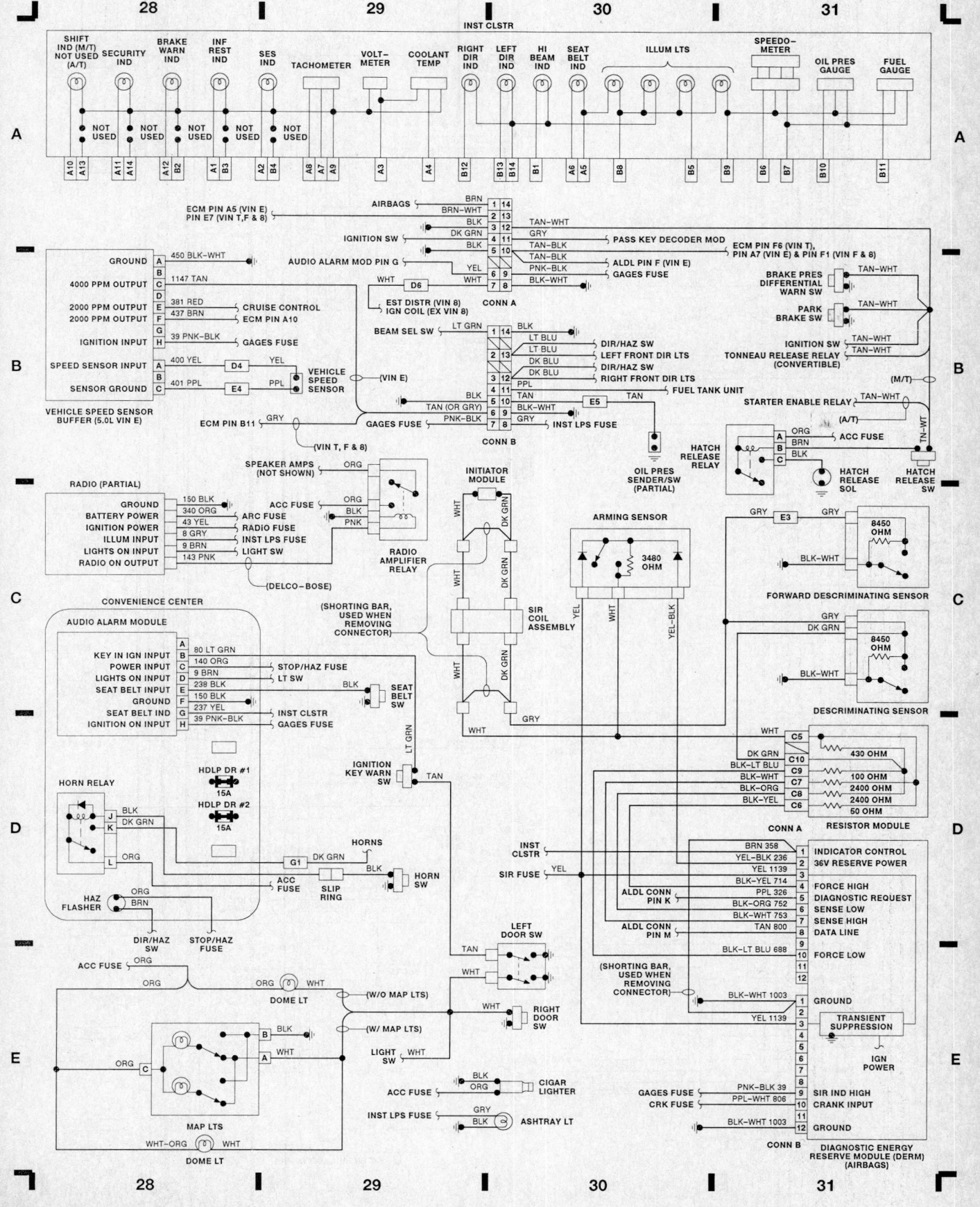

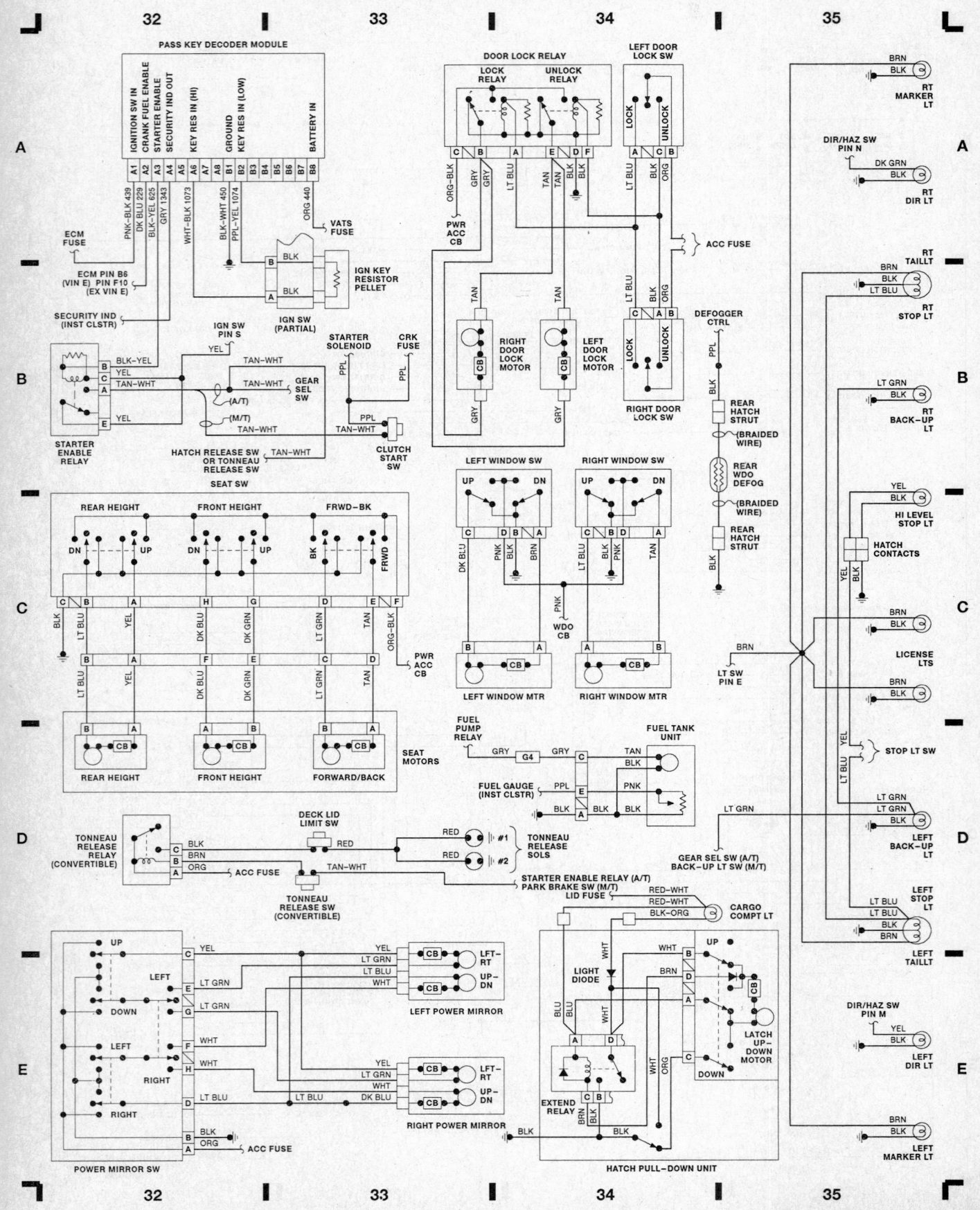

COMPONENT LOCATOR:

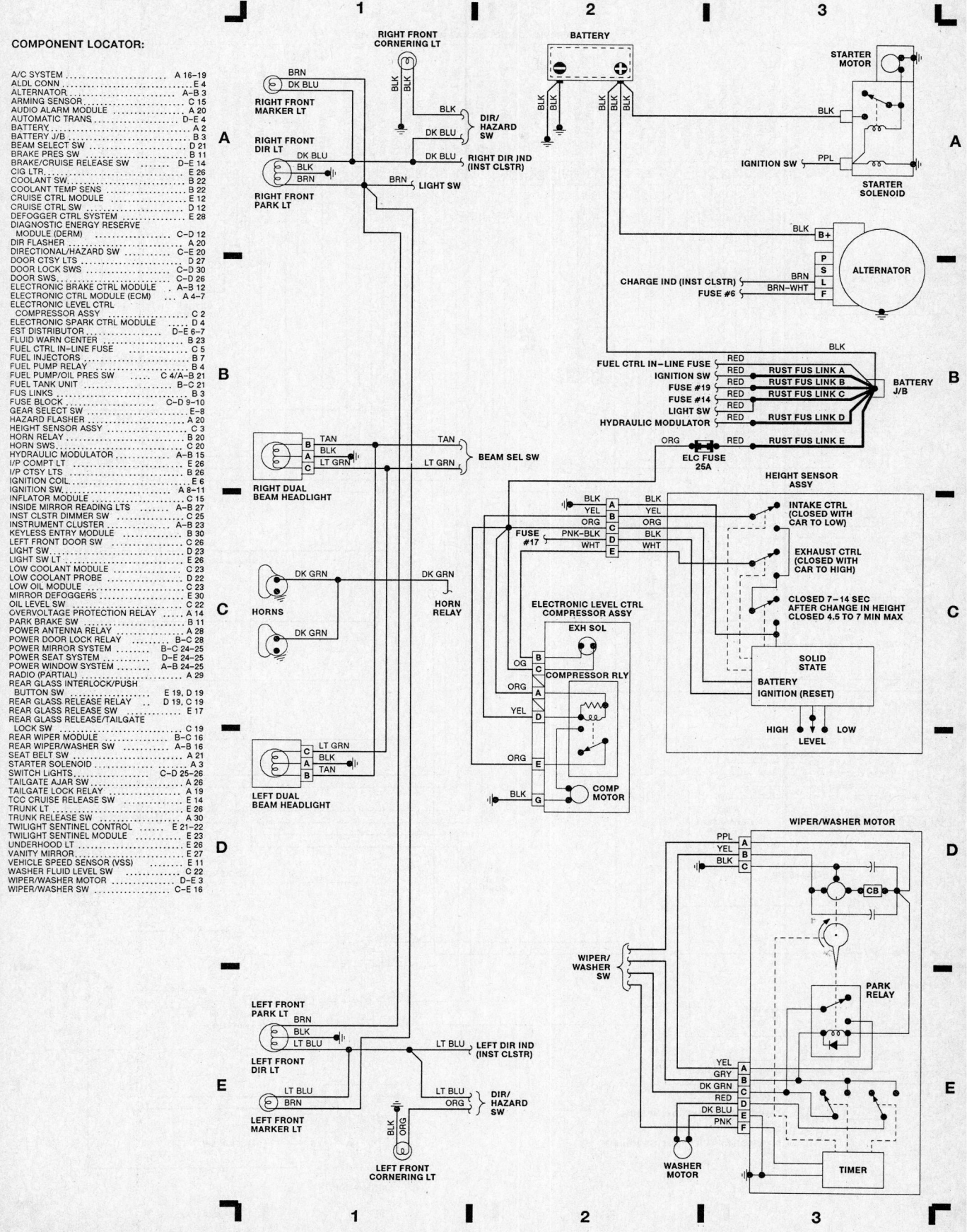

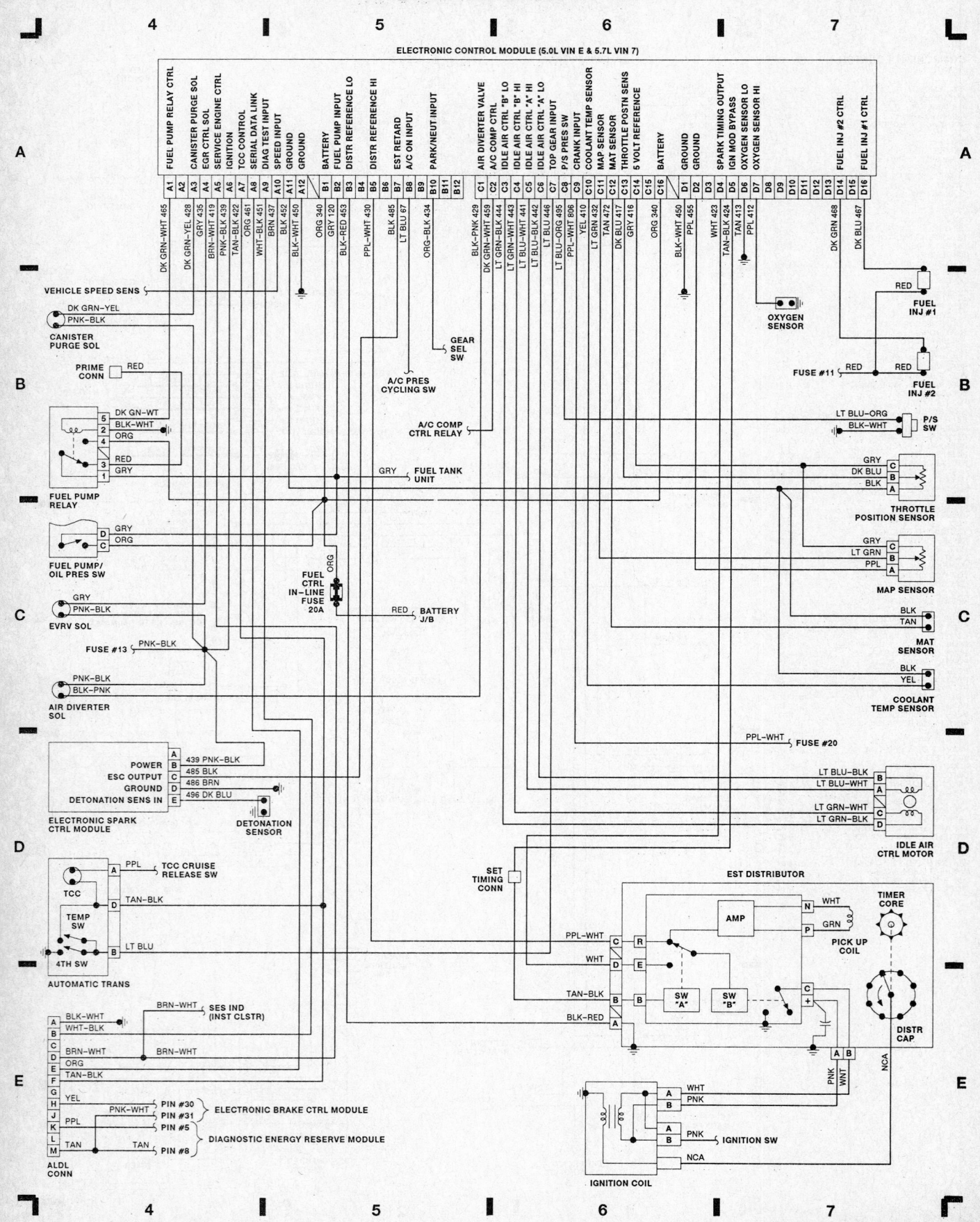

ELECTRONIC CONTROL MODULE (5.0L VIN E & 5.7L VIN 7)

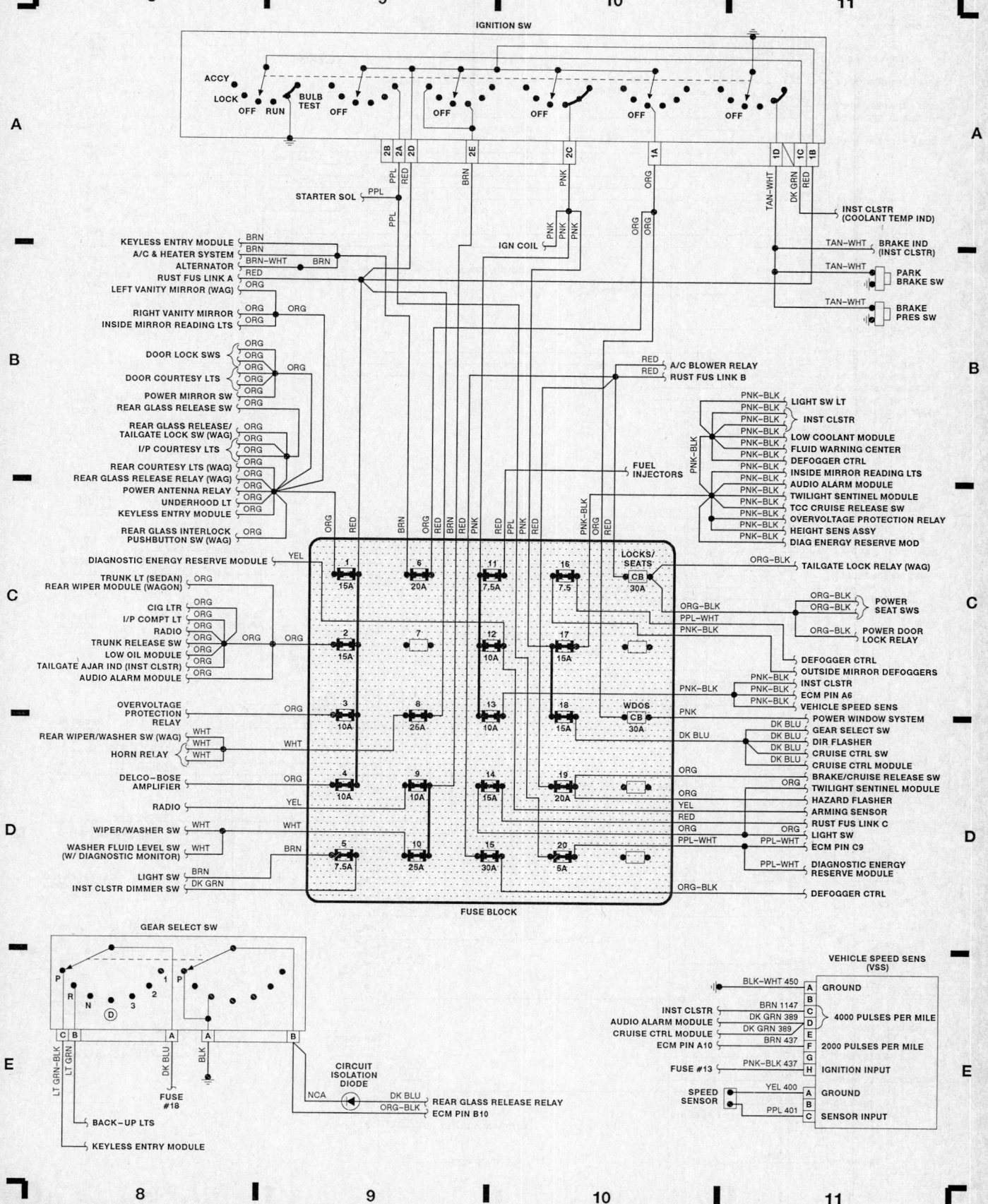

1991 WIRING DIAGRAMS
Caprice (Cont.)

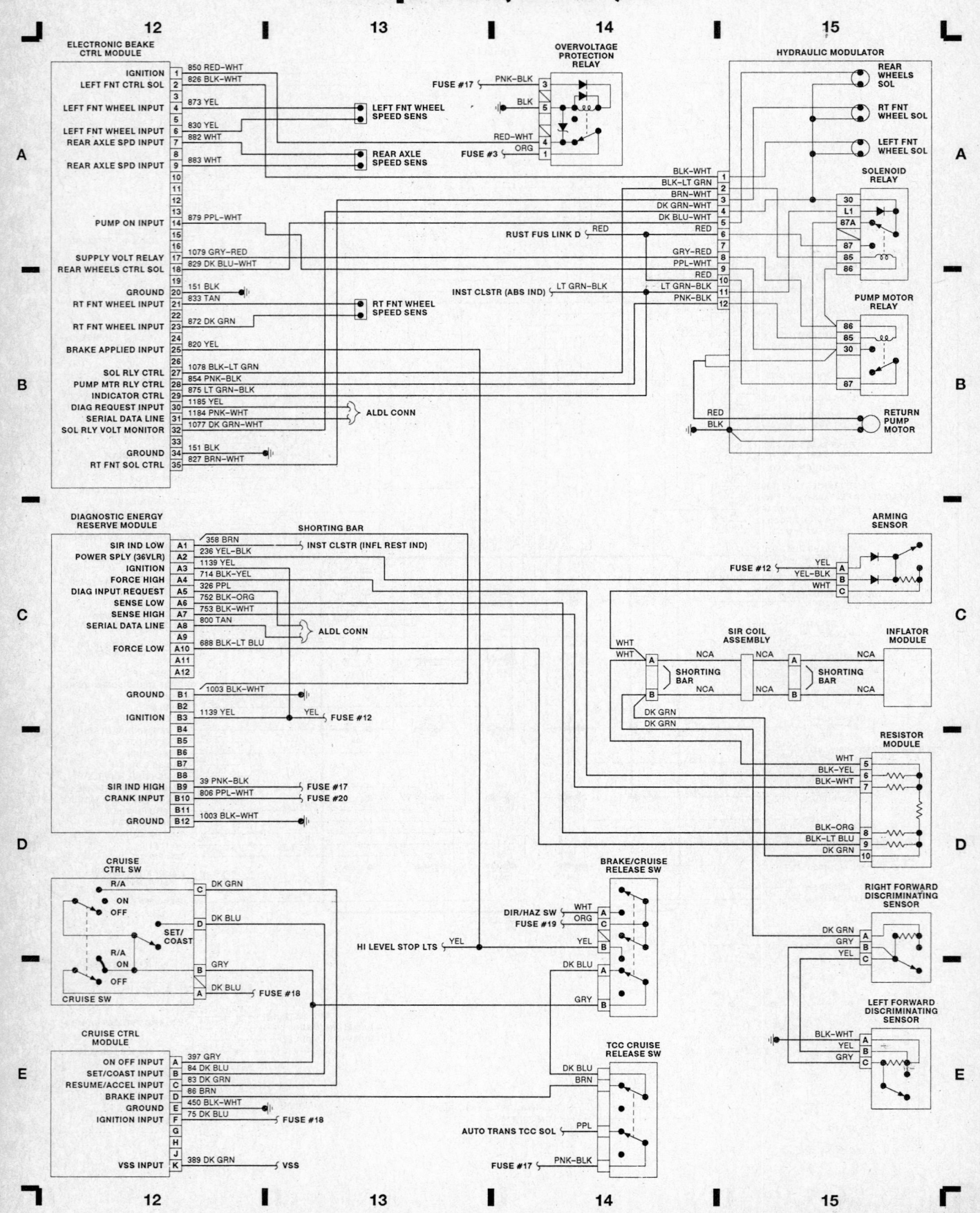

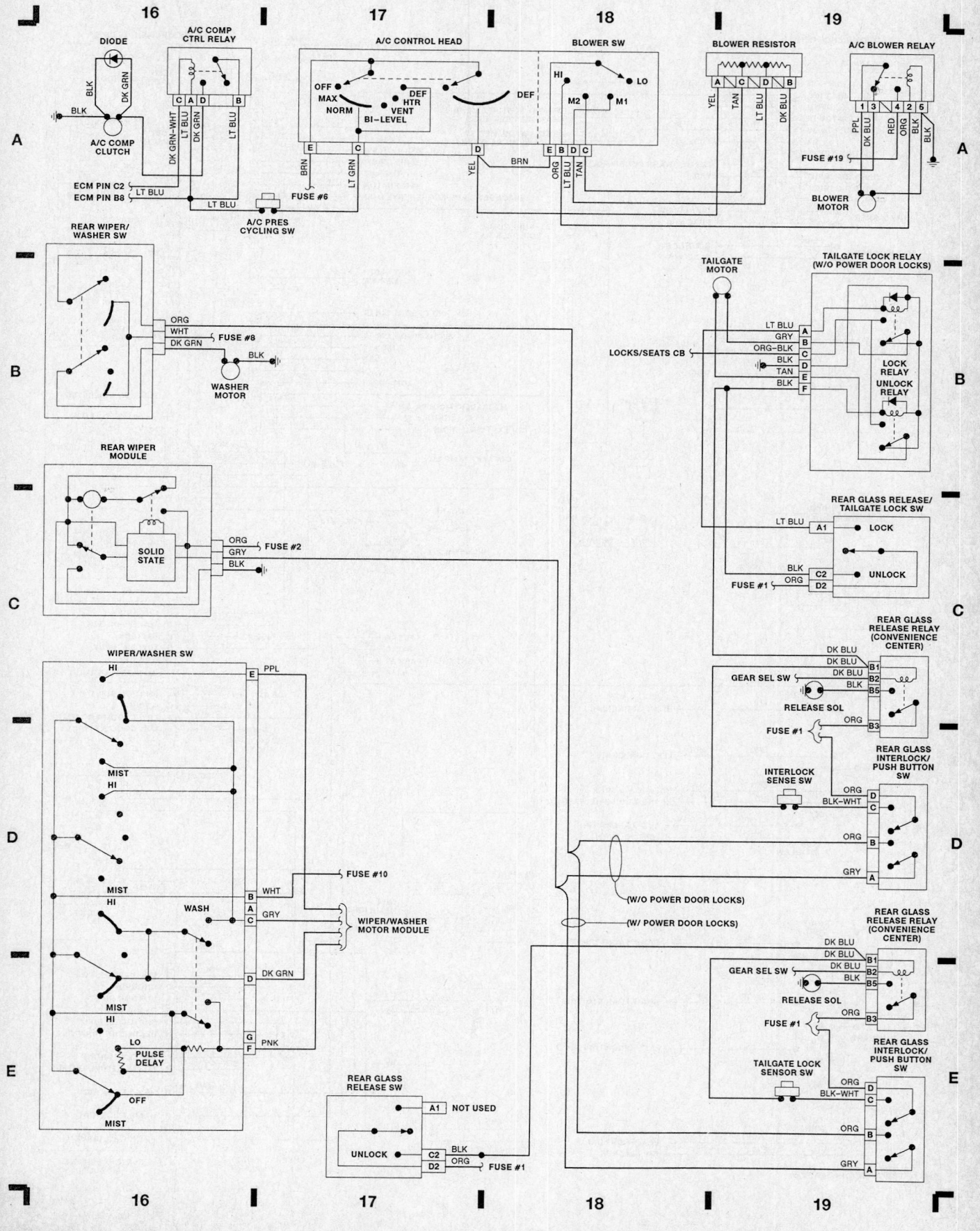

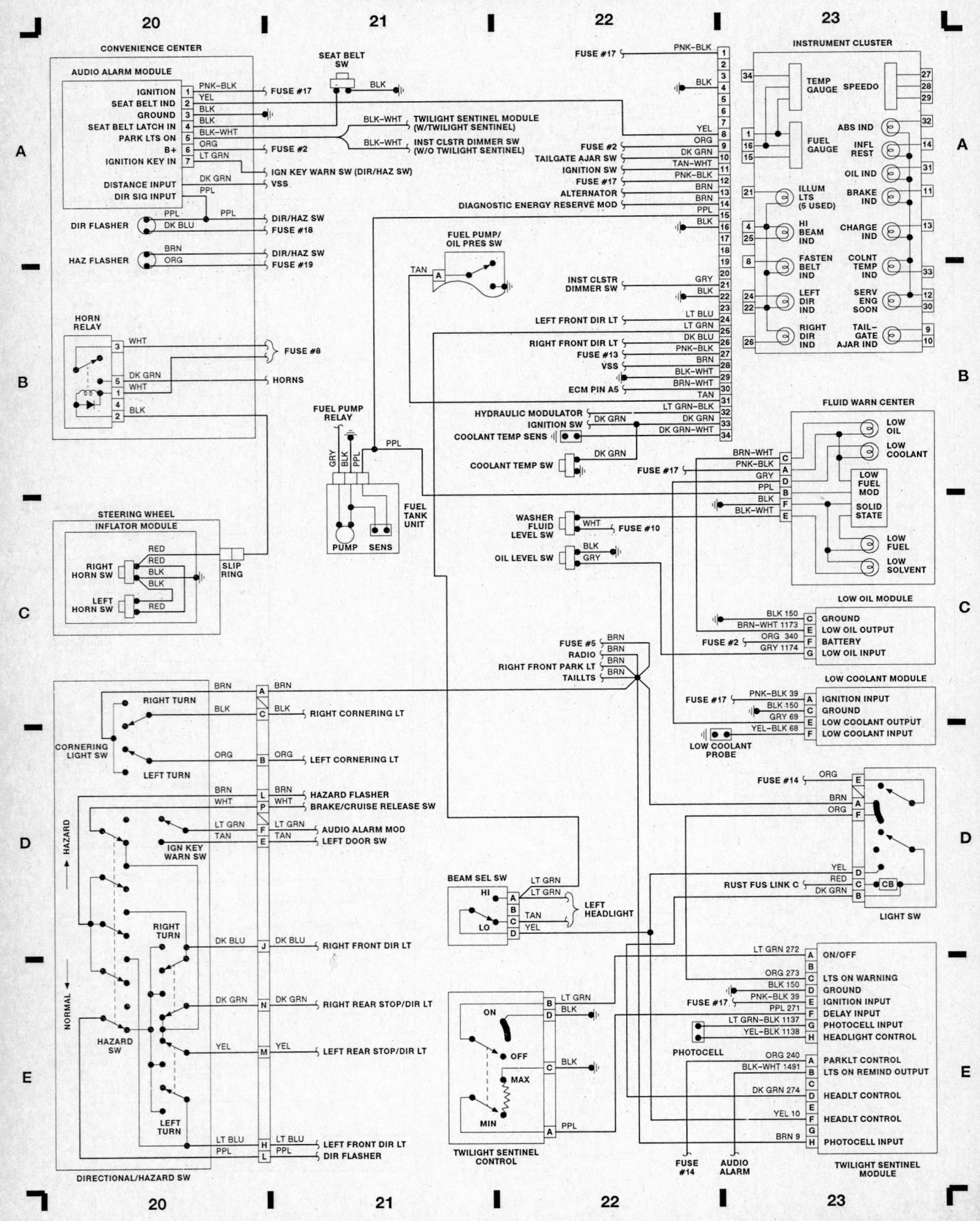

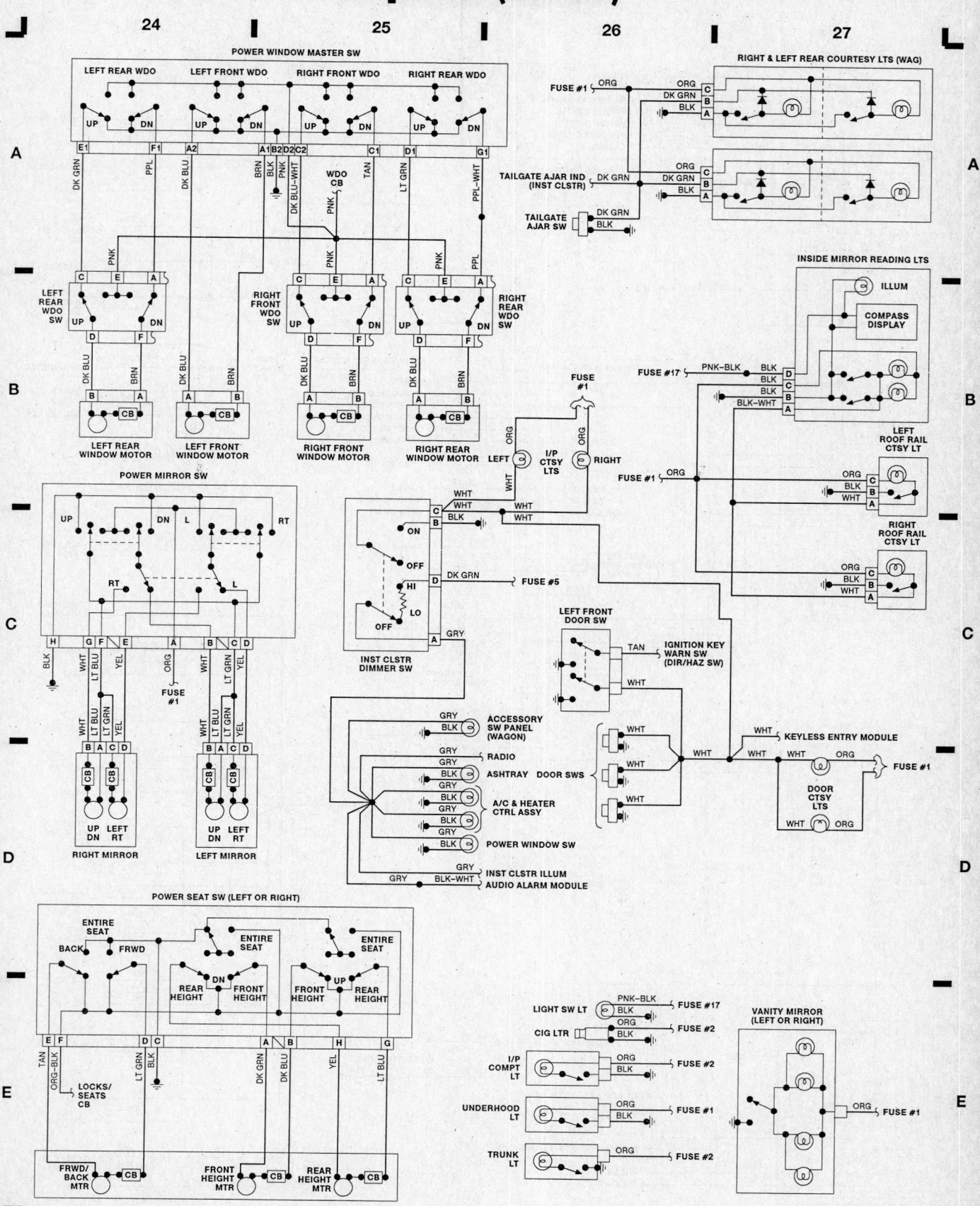

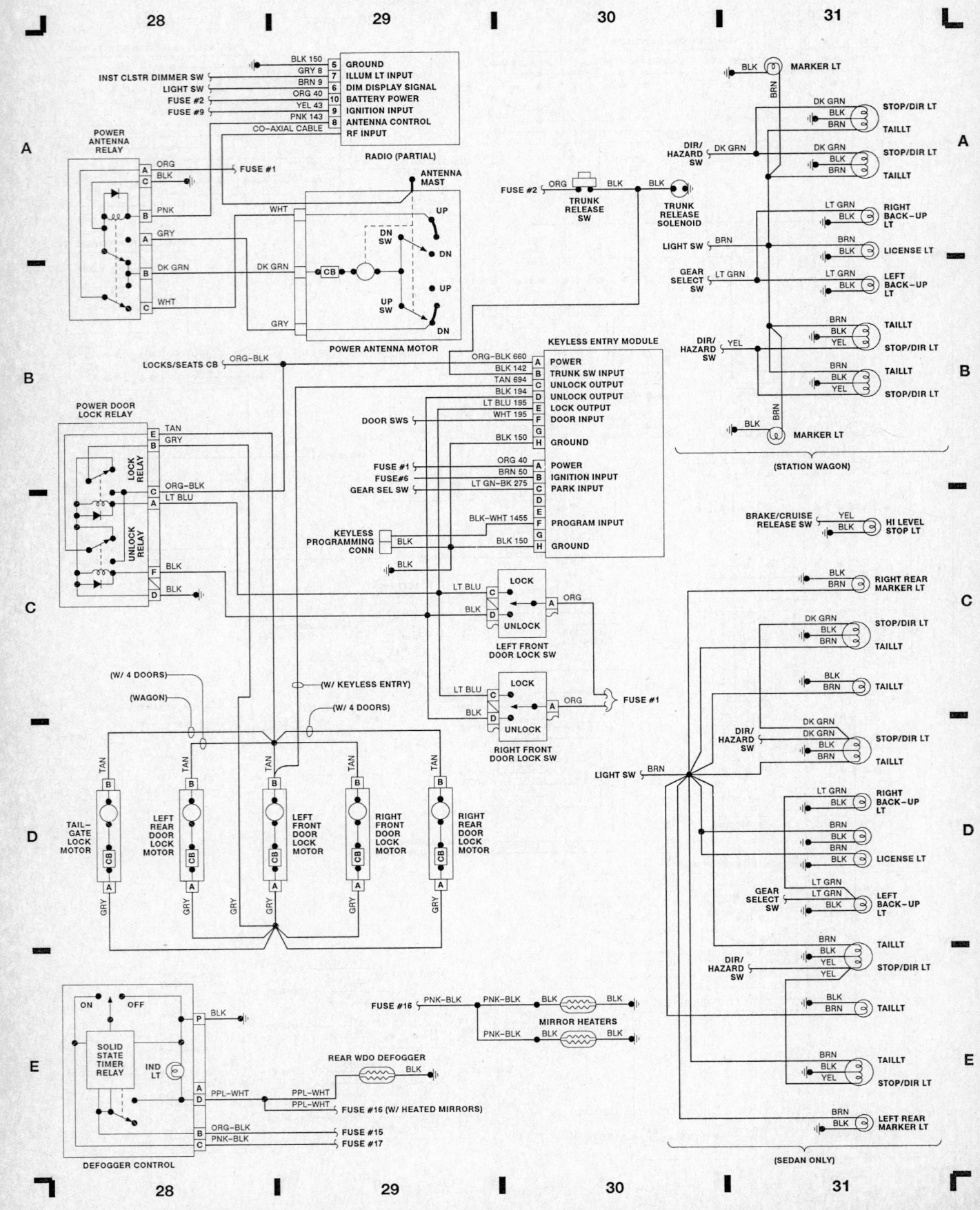

COMPONENT LOCATOR:

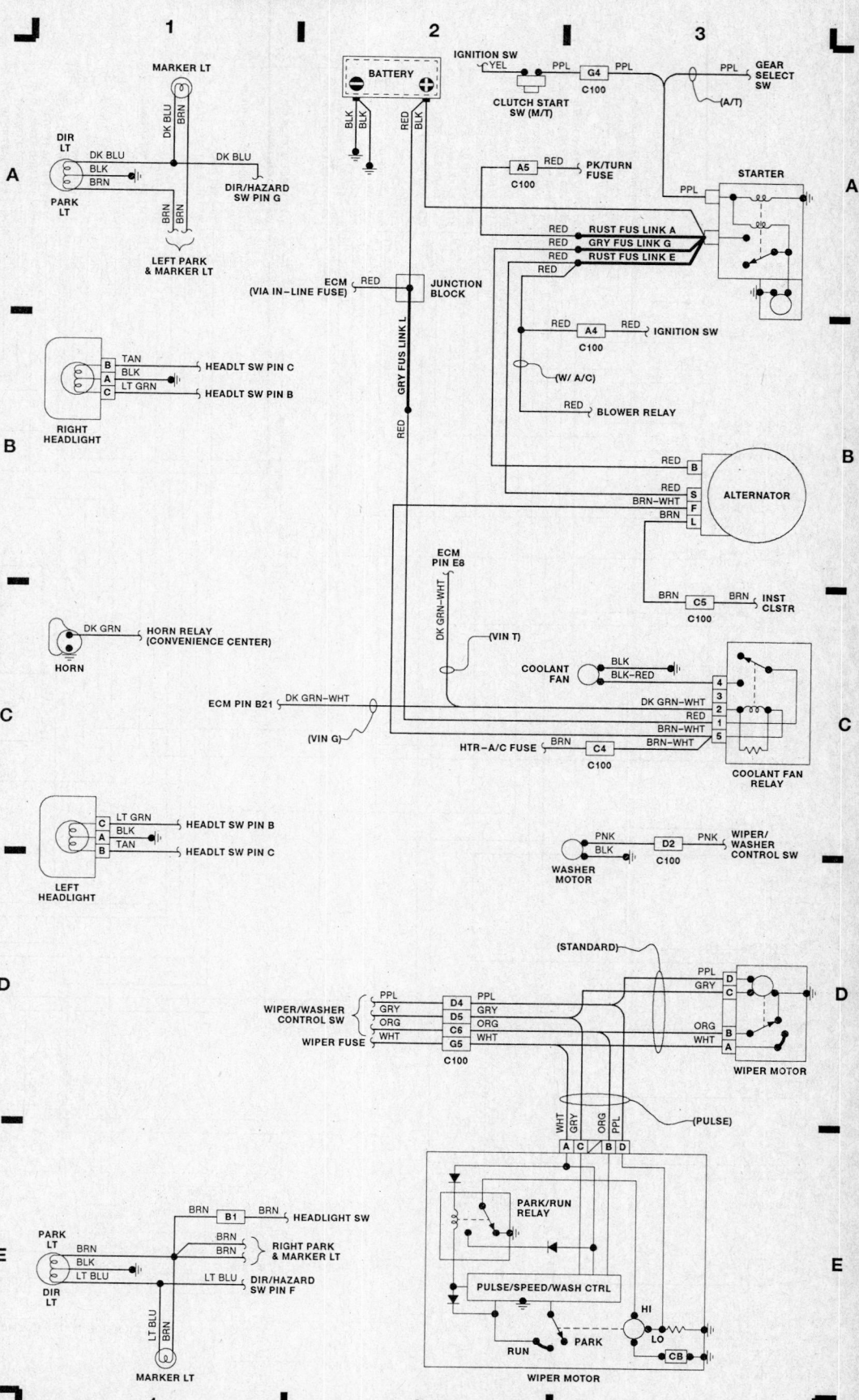

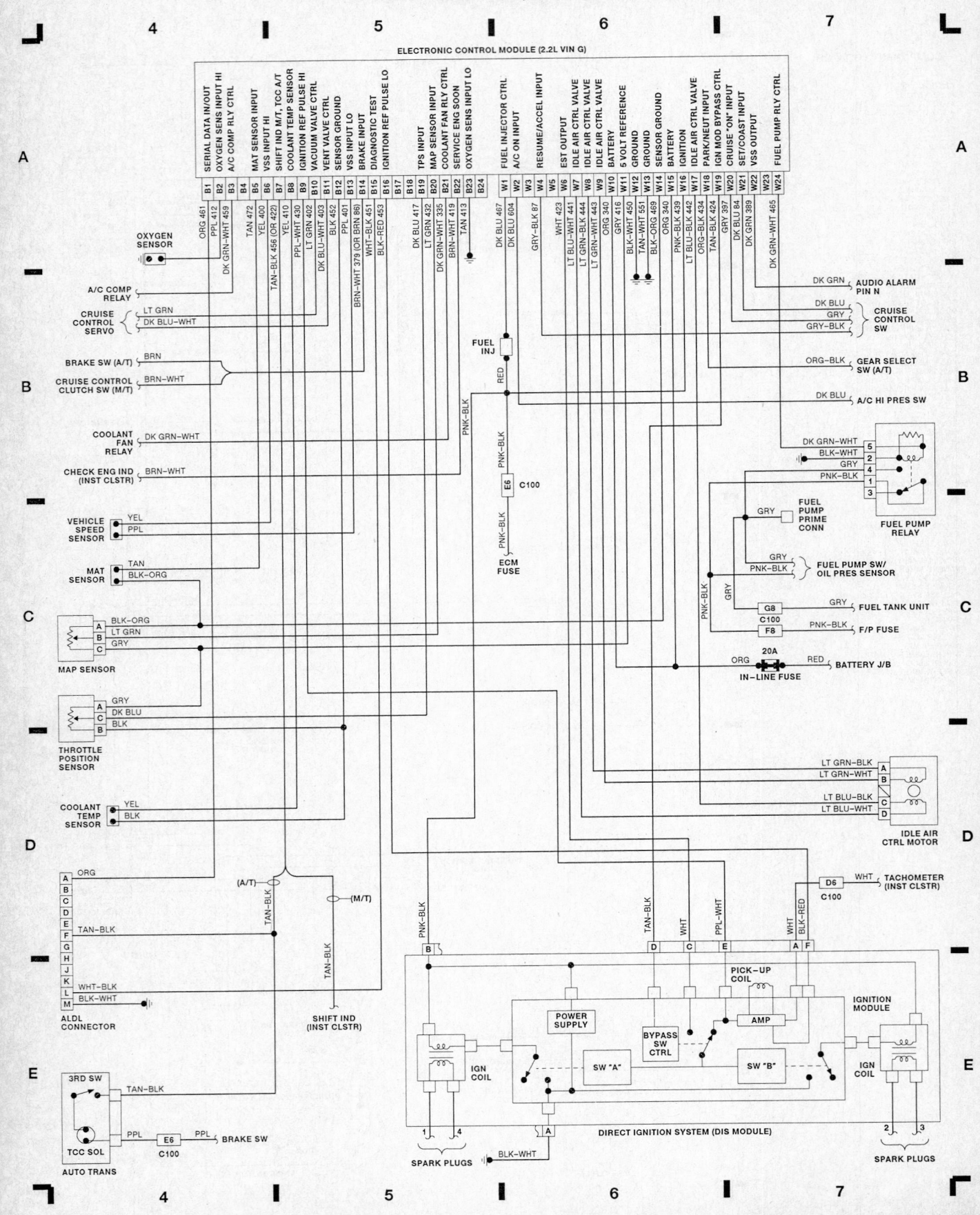

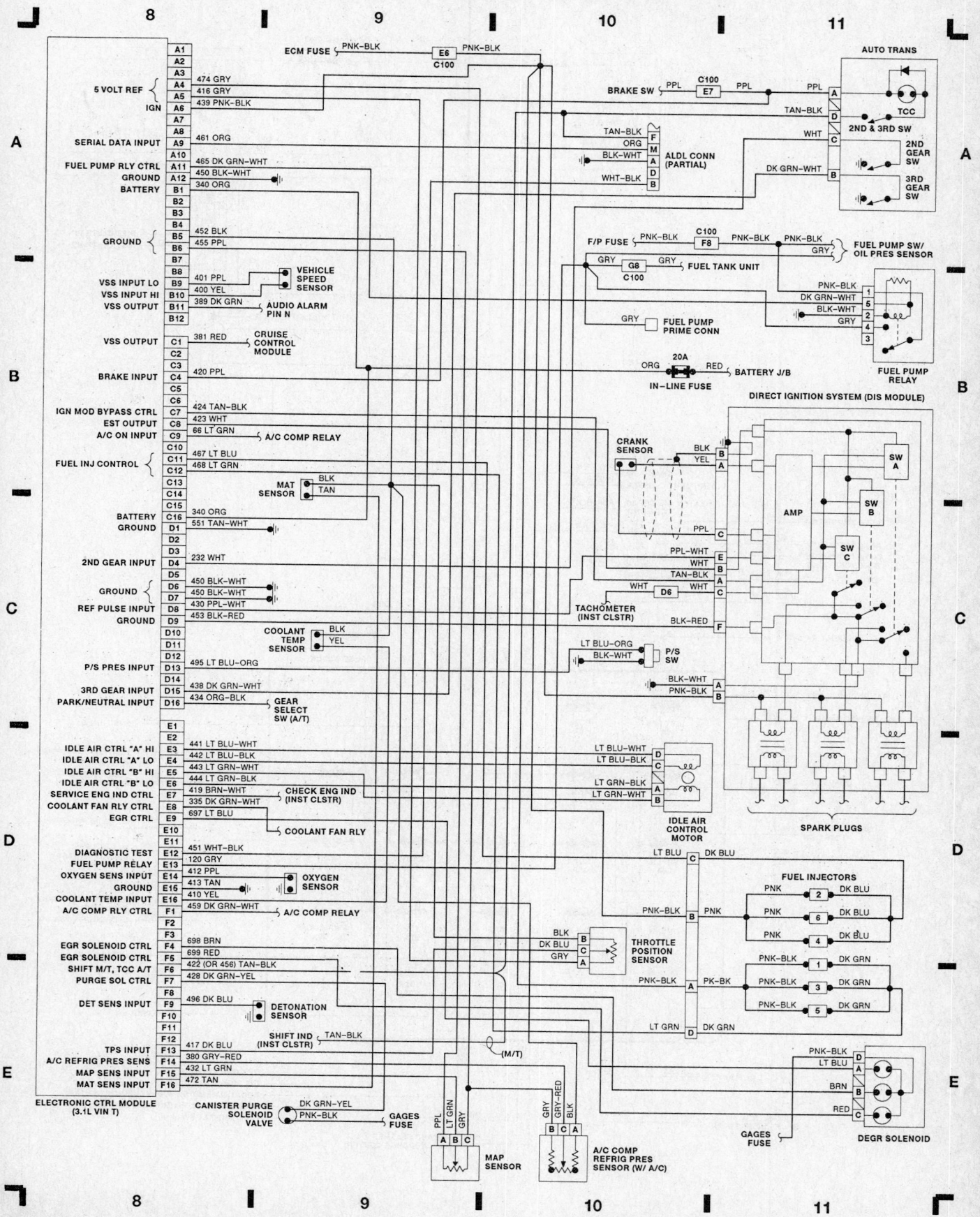

1991 WIRING DIAGRAMS
Cavalier (Cont.)

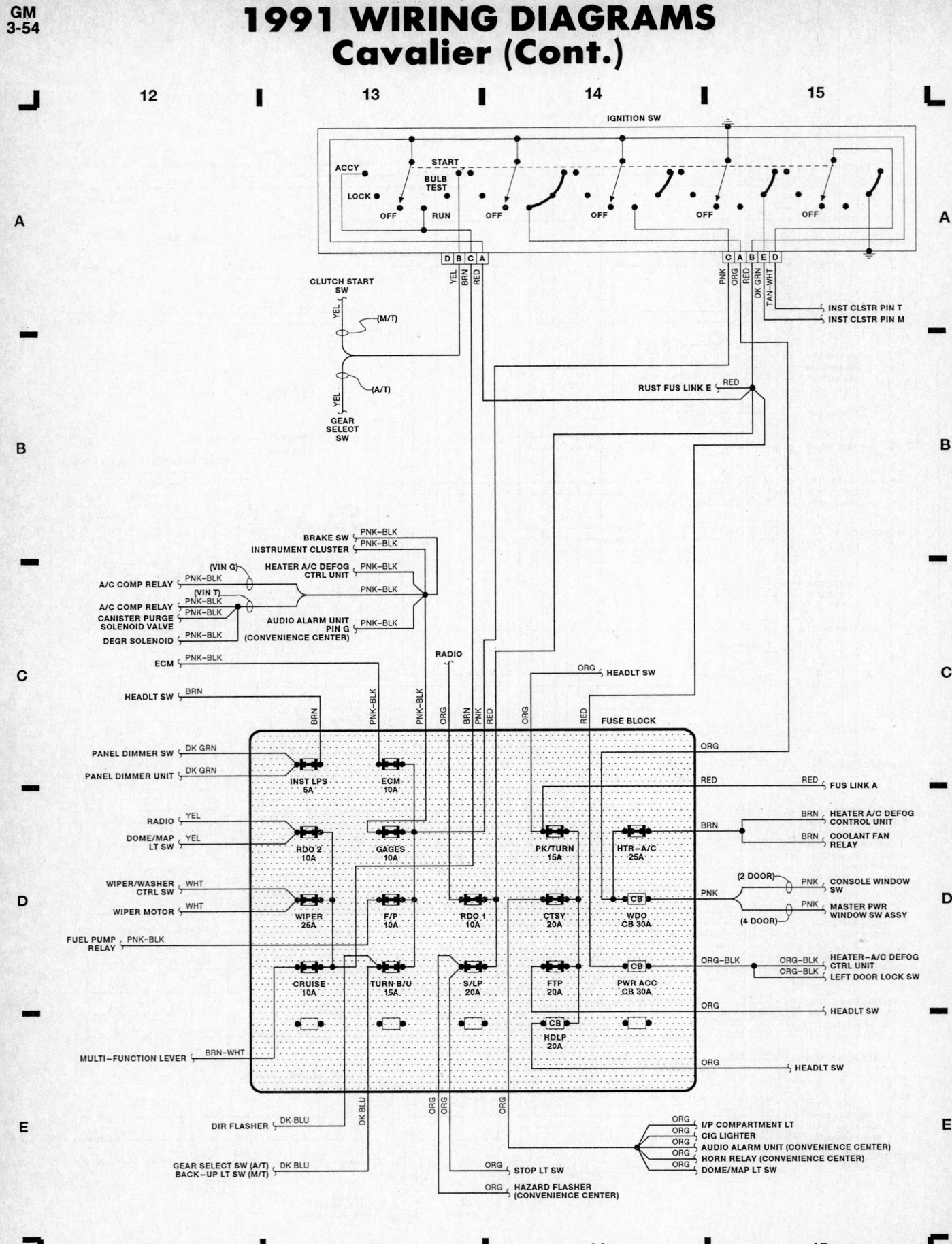

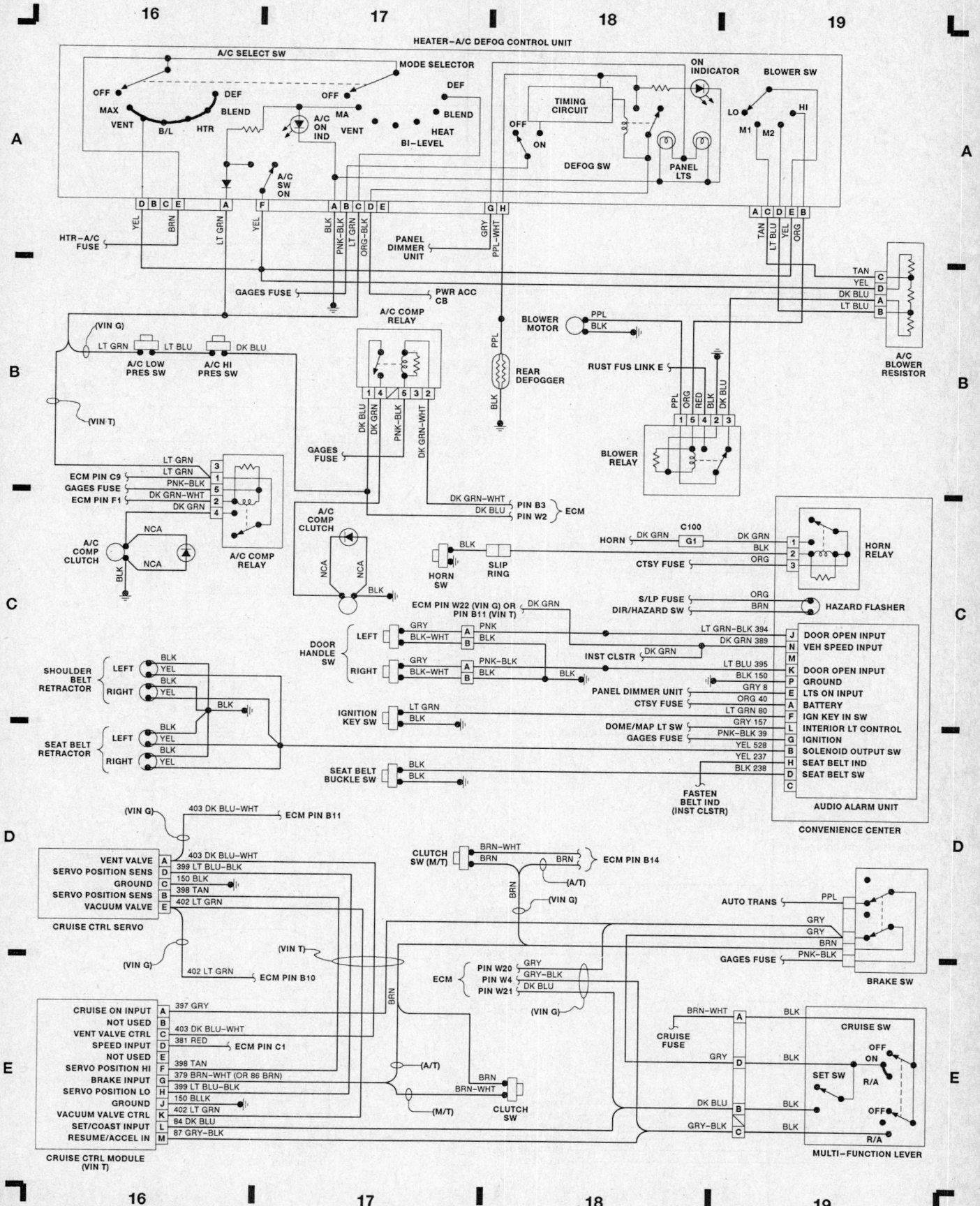

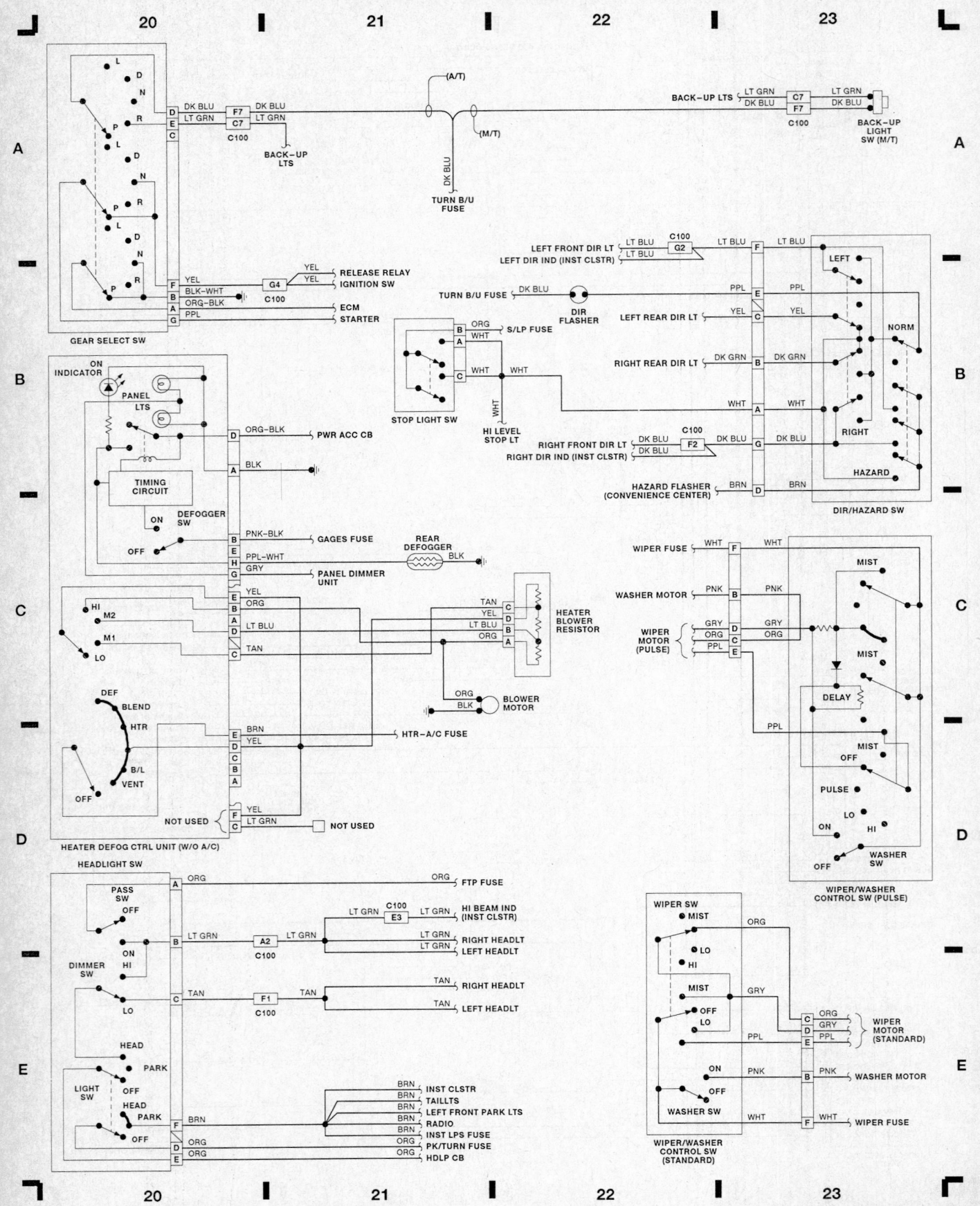

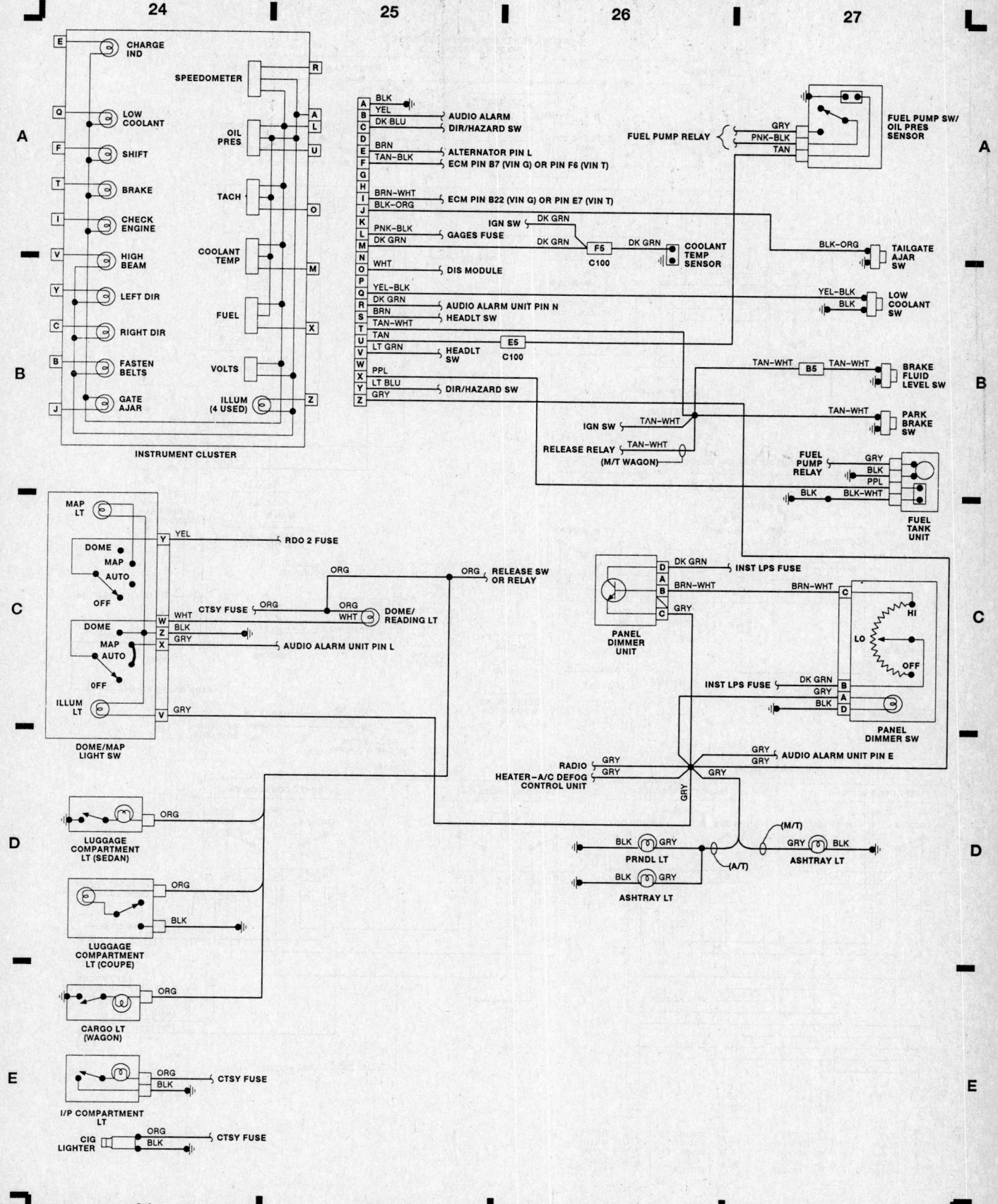

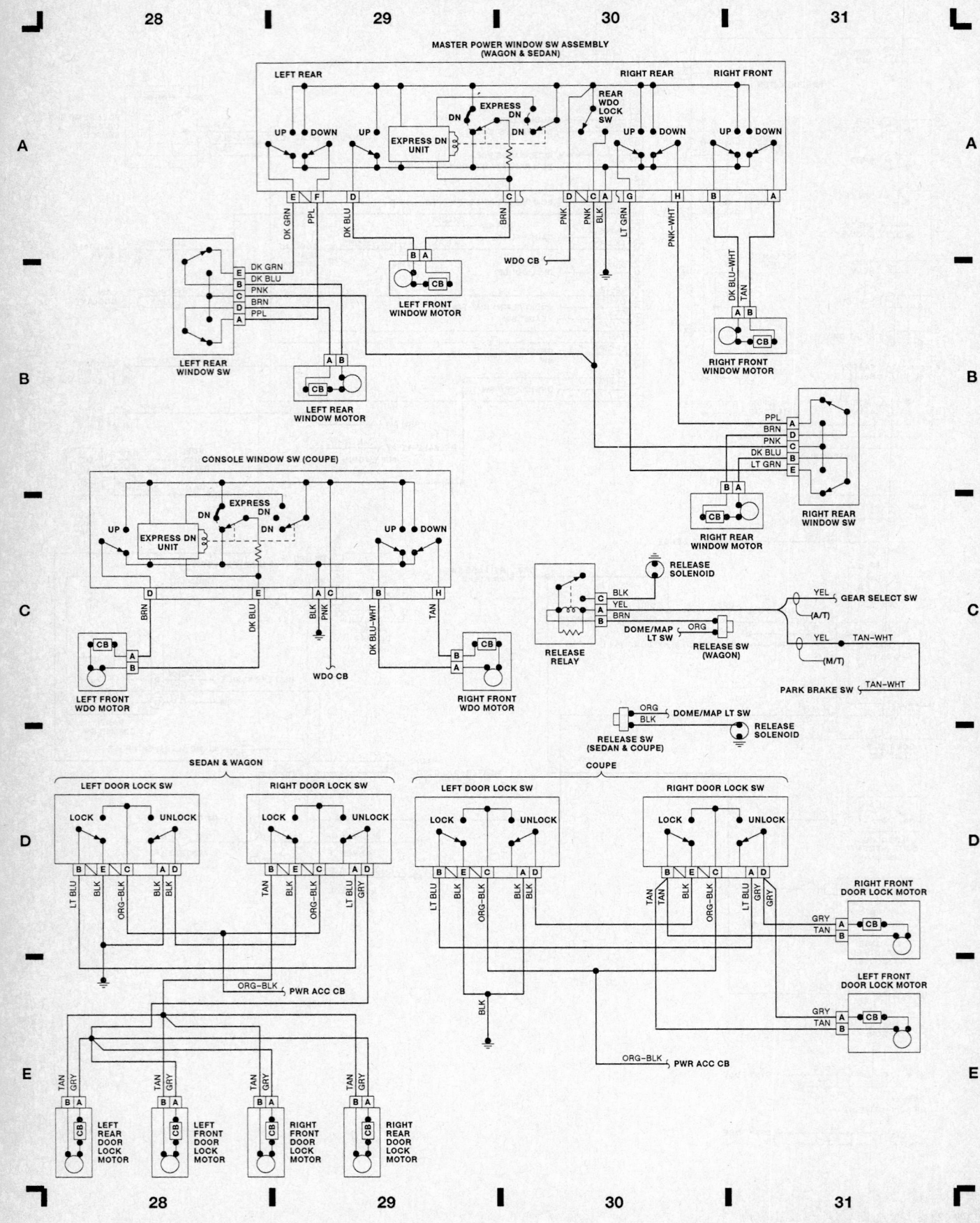

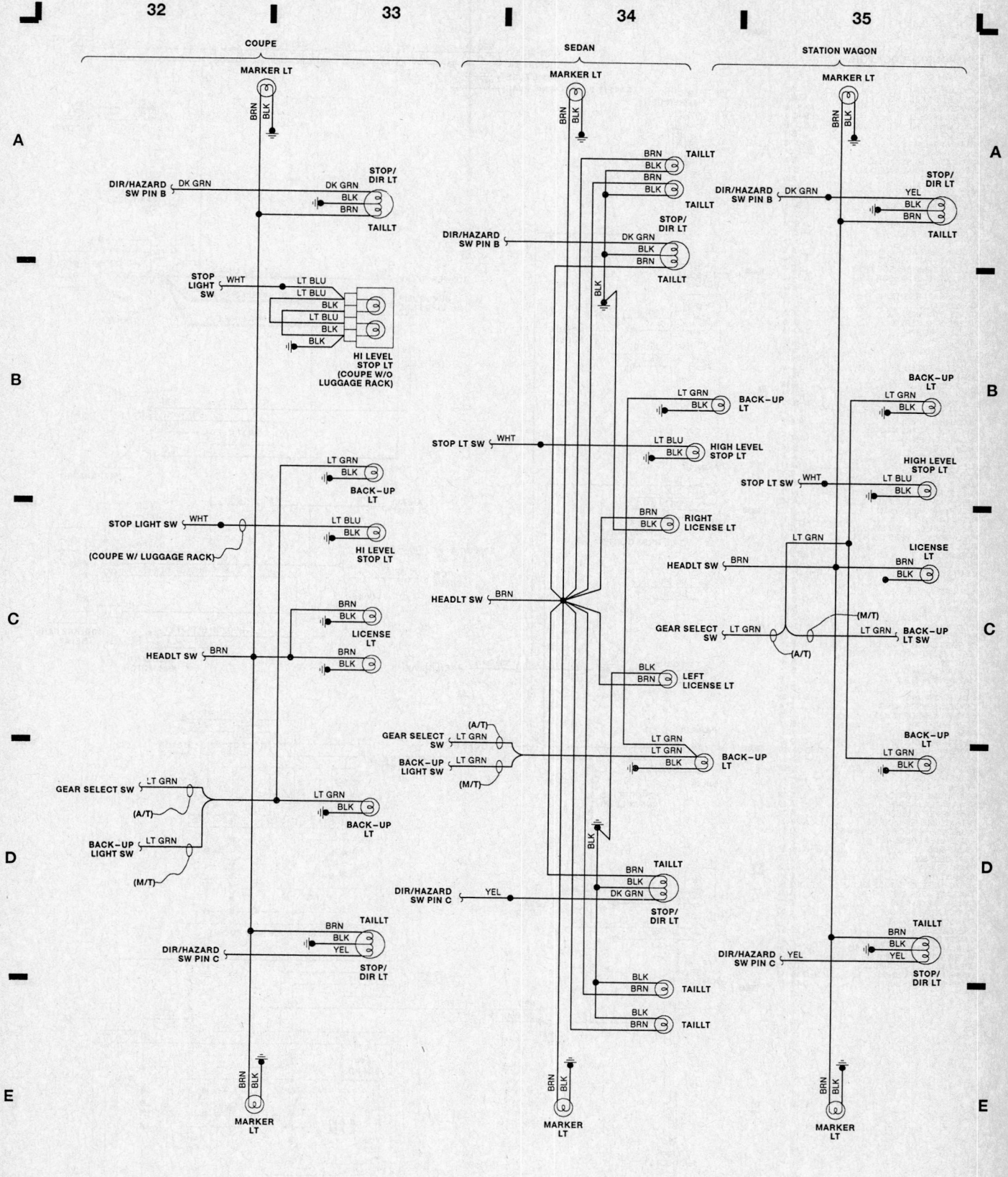

COUPE

SEDAN

STATION WAGON

MARKER LT

DIR/HAZARD SW PIN B — DK GRN

STOP/DIR LT

TAILLT

STOP LIGHT SW — WHT

HI LEVEL STOP LT (COUPE W/O LUGGAGE RACK)

BACK-UP LT

STOP LIGHT SW — WHT

HI LEVEL STOP LT

(COUPE W/ LUGGAGE RACK)

LICENSE LT

HEADLT SW — BRN

GEAR SELECT SW — LT GRN

(A/T)

BACK-UP LIGHT SW — LT GRN

(M/T)

BACK-UP LT

DIR/HAZARD SW PIN C — YEL

STOP/DIR LT — TAILLT

MARKER LT

MARKER LT

TAILLT

DIR/HAZARD SW PIN B — DK GRN

STOP/DIR LT

TAILLT

STOP LT SW — WHT

HIGH LEVEL STOP LT

BACK-UP LT

RIGHT LICENSE LT

HEADLT SW — BRN

GEAR SELECT SW

(A/T)

BACK-UP LIGHT SW

(M/T)

LT GRN

BACK-UP LT

LEFT LICENSE LT

DIR/HAZARD SW PIN C — YEL

STOP/DIR LT

TAILLT

TAILLT

MARKER LT

MARKER LT

DIR/HAZARD SW PIN B — DK GRN

STOP/DIR LT

TAILLT

BACK-UP LT

HIGH LEVEL STOP LT

STOP LT SW — WHT

LICENSE LT

HEADLT SW — BRN

(M/T)

GEAR SELECT SW — LT GRN

(A/T)

BACK-UP LT SW

BACK-UP LT

DIR/HAZARD SW PIN C — YEL

TAILLT

STOP/DIR LT

MARKER LT

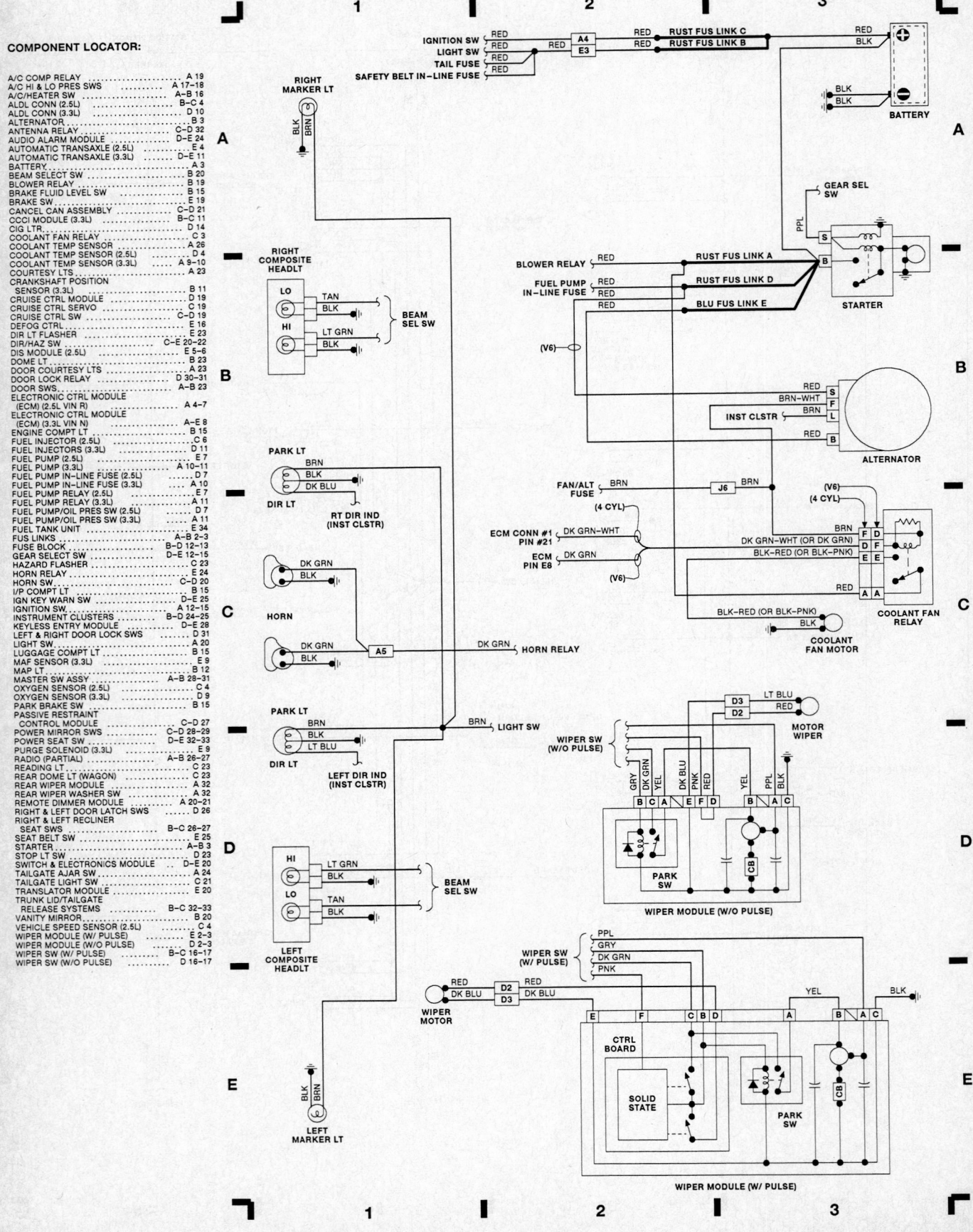

COMPONENT LOCATOR:

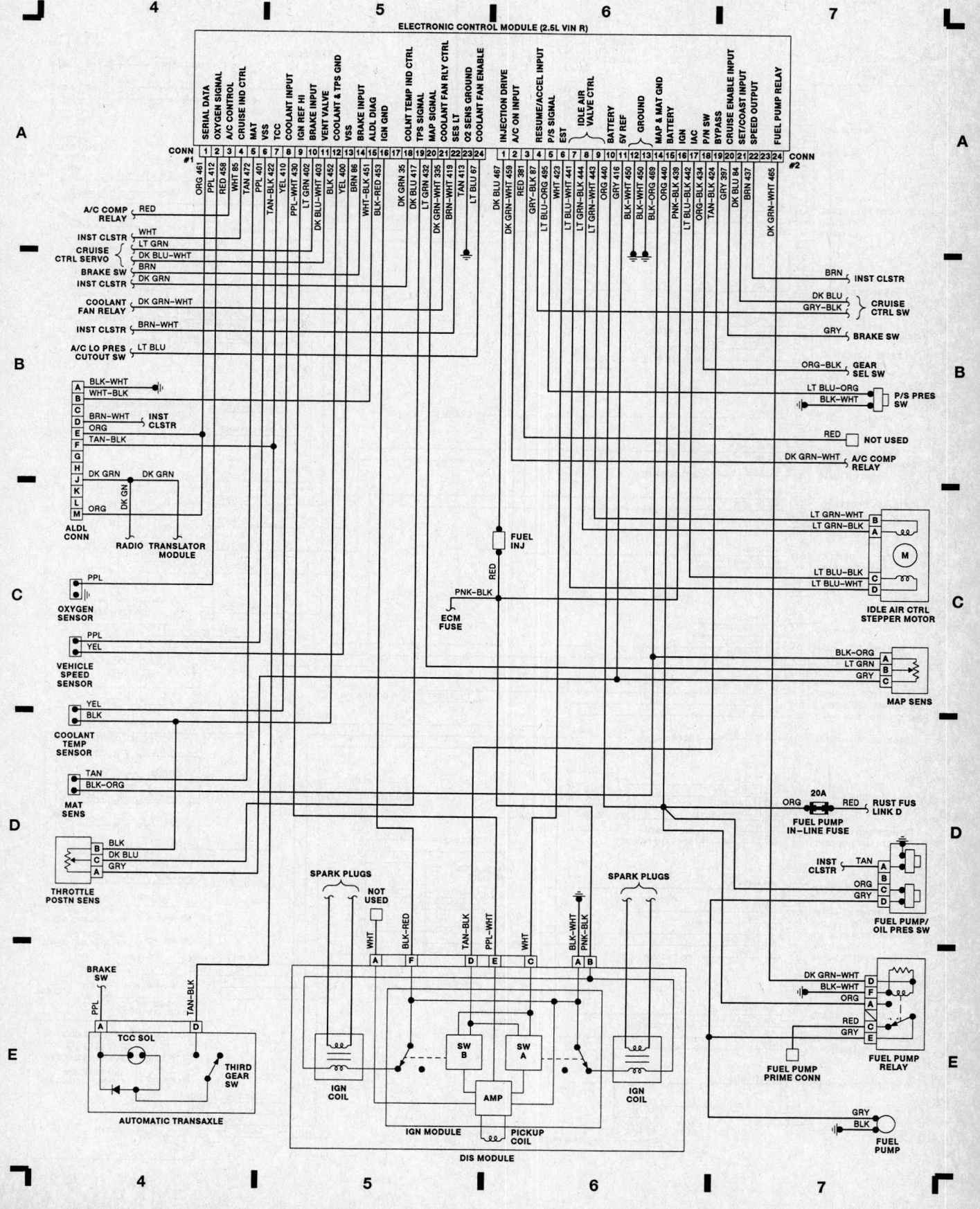

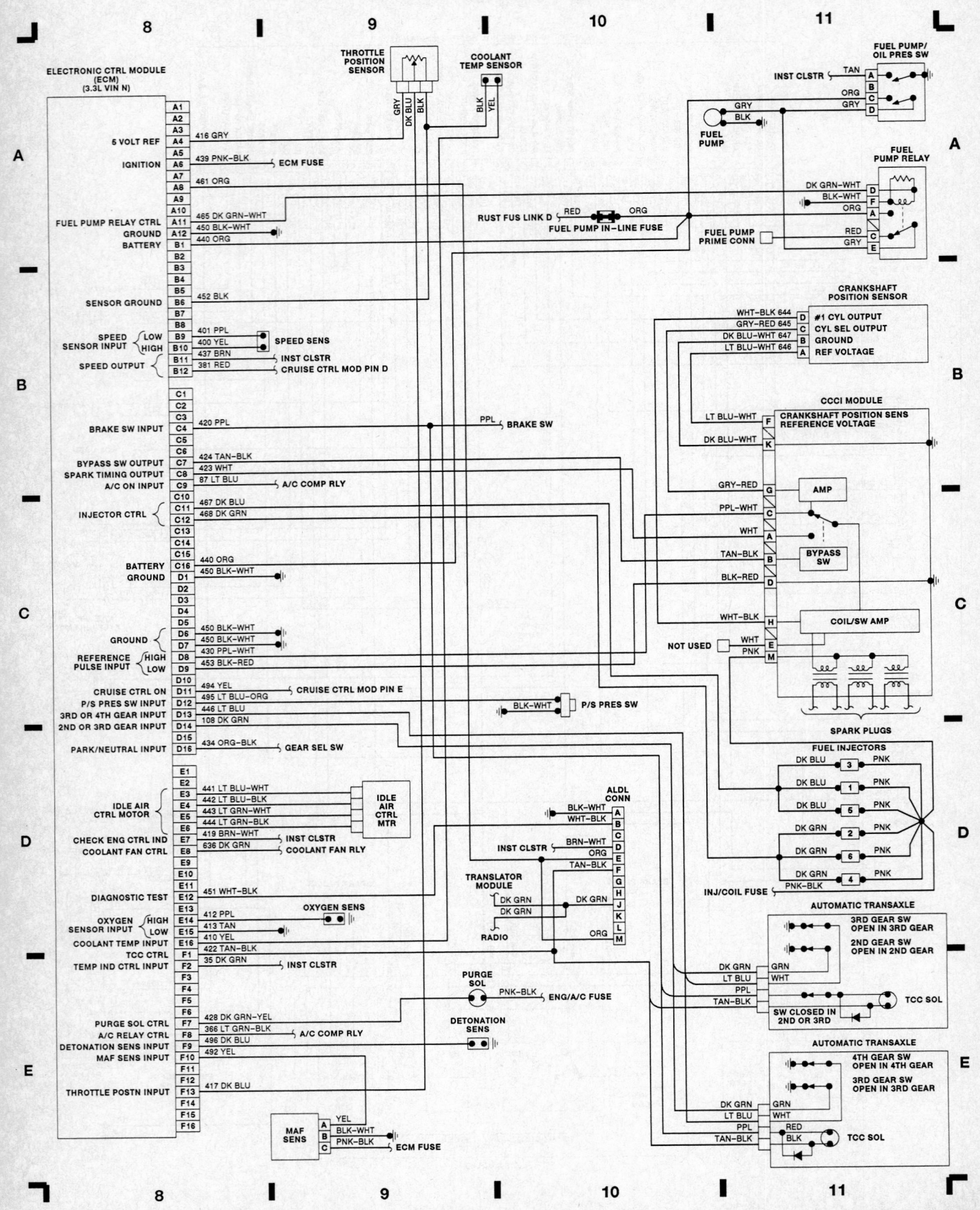

1991 Century wiring diagram (cont.): ignition switch, fuse block, gear select switch, and related circuits.

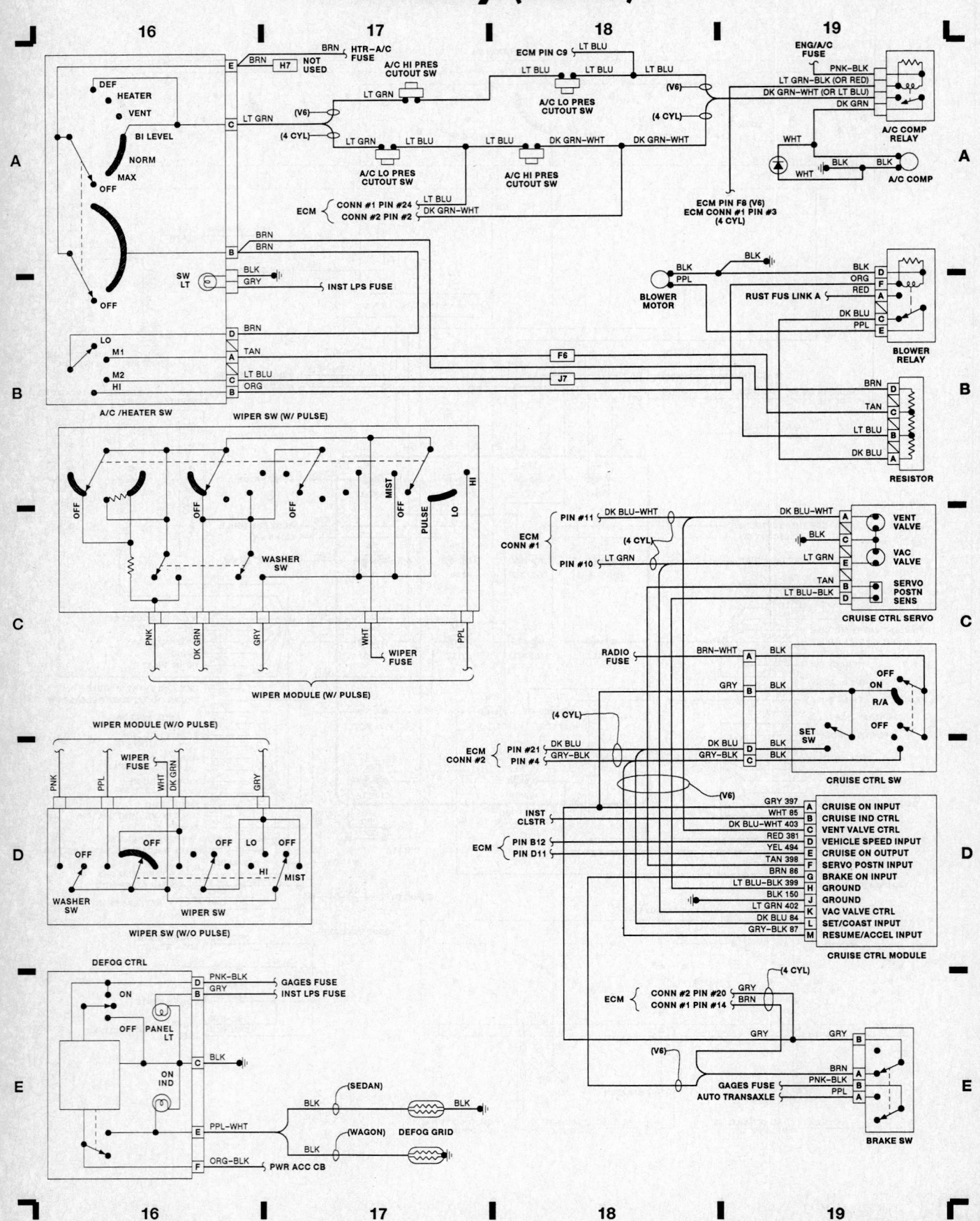

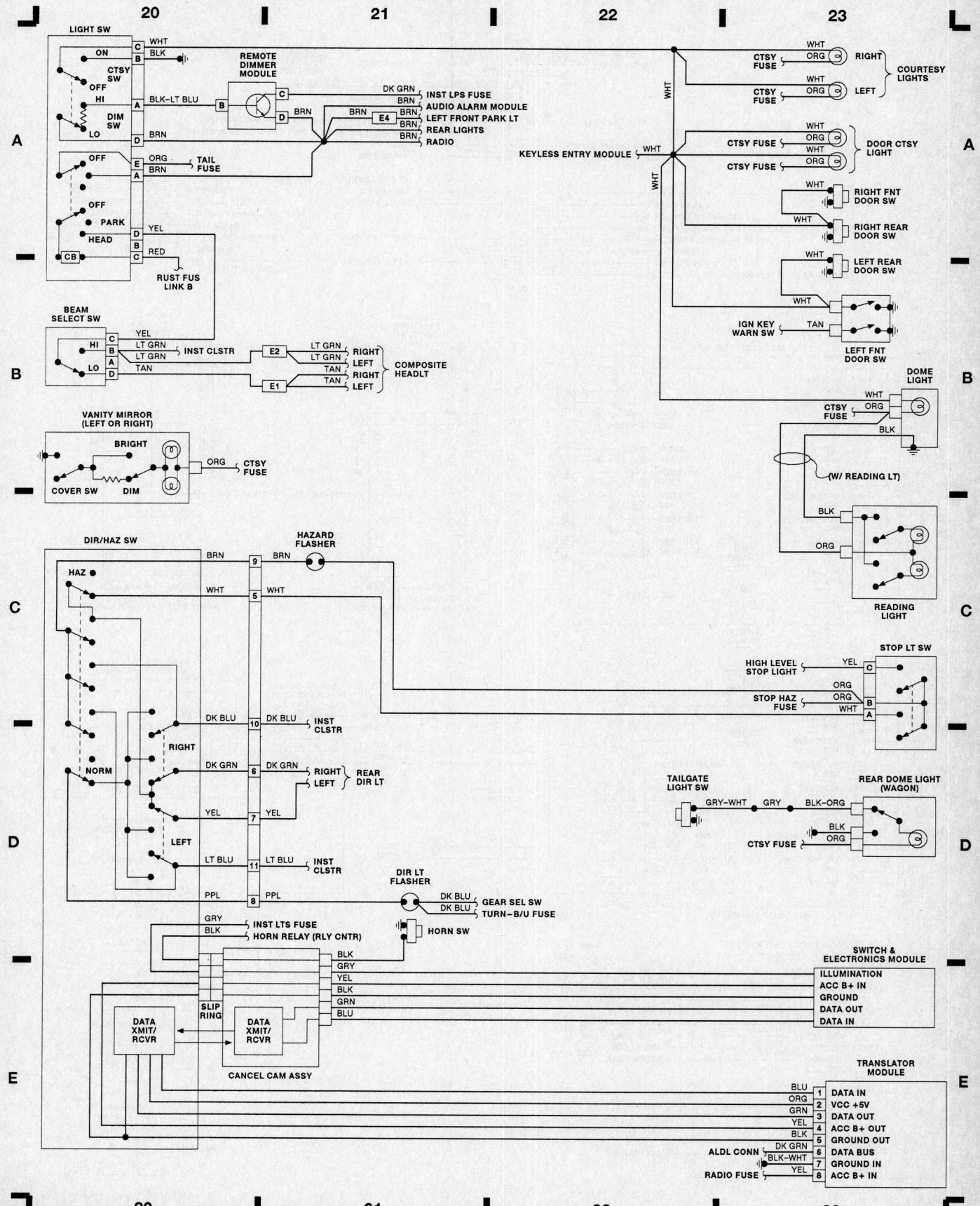

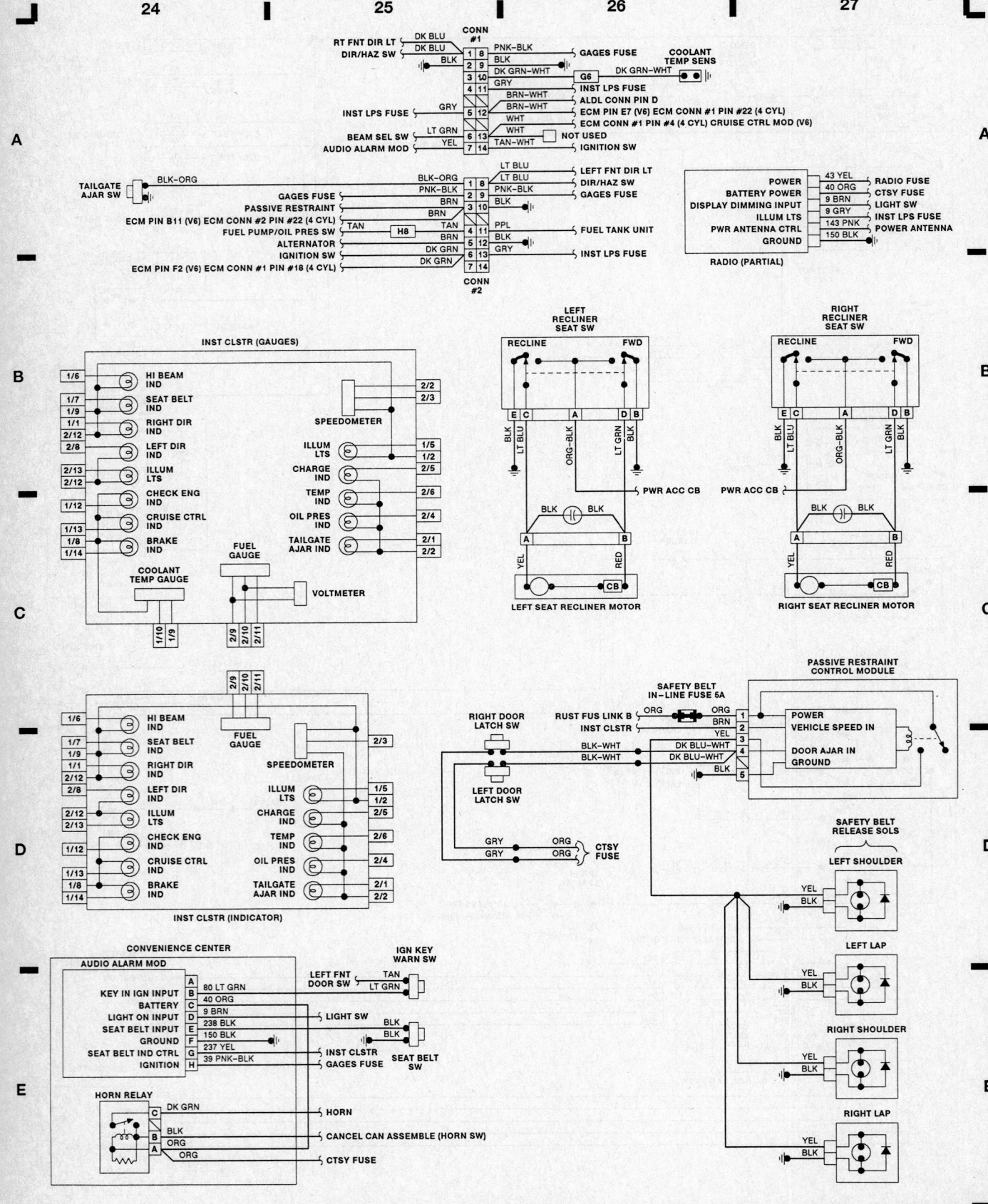

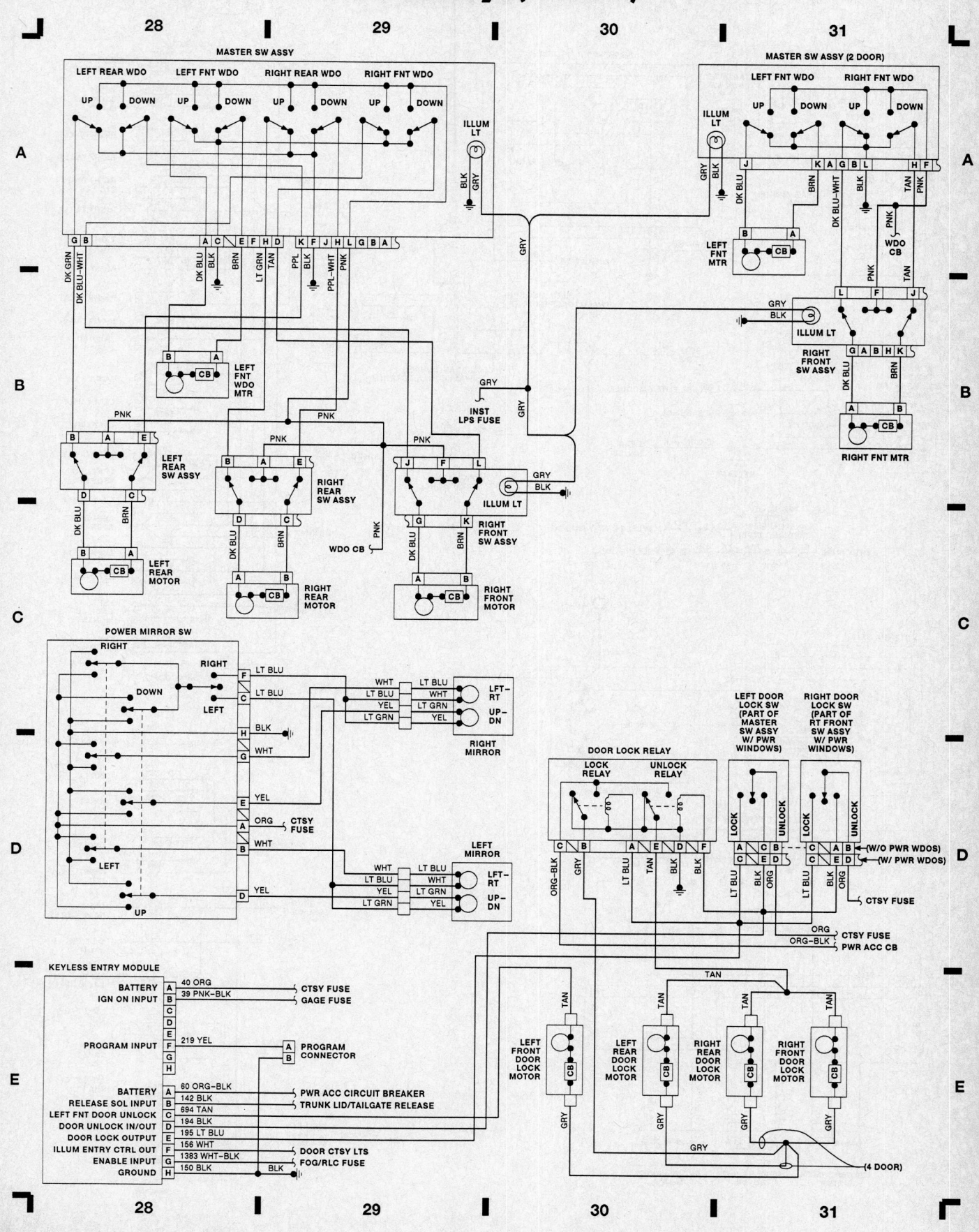

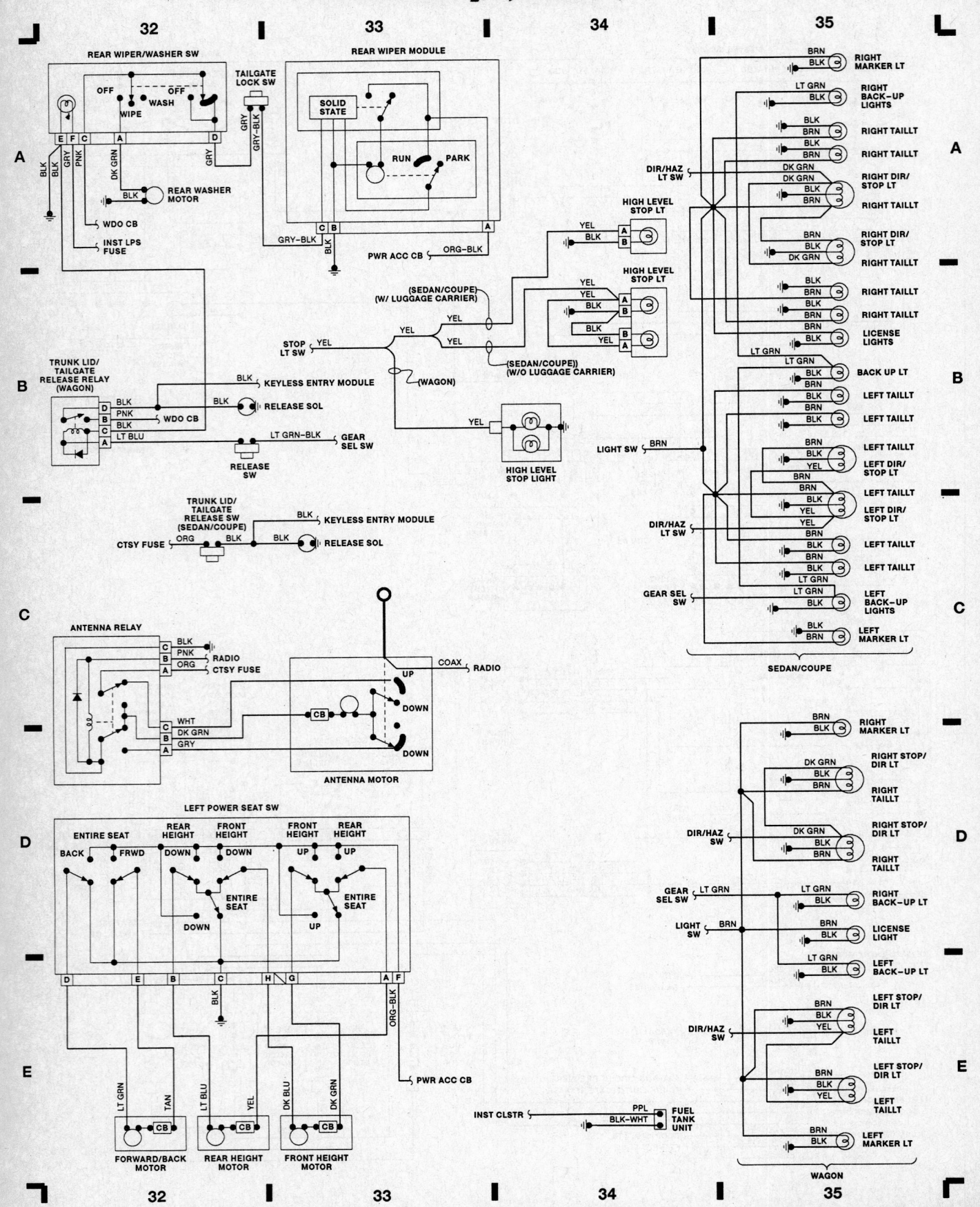

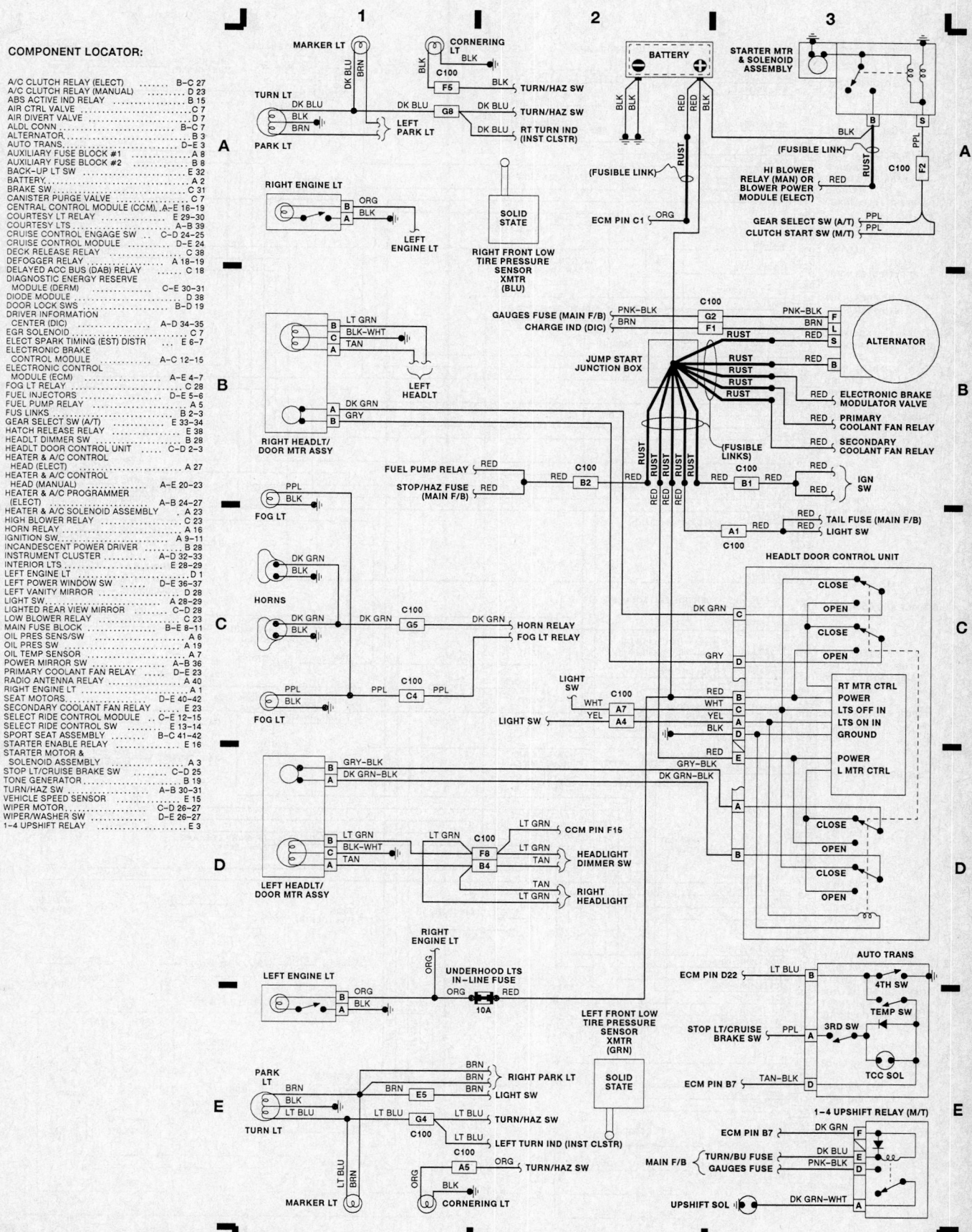

COMPONENT LOCATOR:

A/C CLUTCH RELAY (ELECT) .... B-C 27
A/C CLUTCH RELAY (MANUAL) .... D 23
ABS ACTIVE IND RELAY .... B 15
AIR CTRL VALVE .... C 7
AIR DIVERT VALVE .... D 7
ALDL CONN .... B-C 7
ALTERNATOR .... B 3
AUTO TRANS .... D-E 3
AUXILIARY FUSE BLOCK #1 .... A 8
AUXILIARY FUSE BLOCK #2 .... B 8
BACK-UP LT SW .... E 32
BATTERY .... A 2
BRAKE SW .... C 31
CANISTER PURGE VALVE .... C 7
CENTRAL CONTROL MODULE (CCM) .. A-E 16-19
COURTESY LT RELAY .... E 29-30
COURTESY LTS .... A-B 39
CRUISE CONTROL ENGAGE SW ... C-D 24-25
CRUISE CONTROL MODULE .... D-E 24
DECK RELEASE RELAY .... C 38
DEFOGGER RELAY .... A 18-19
DELAYED ACC BUS (DAB) RELAY ..... C 18
DIAGNOSTIC ENERGY RESERVE
  MODULE (DERM) .... C-E 30-31
DIODE MODULE .... D 38
DOOR LOCK SWS .... B-D 19
DRIVER INFORMATION
  CENTER (DIC) .... A-D 34-35
EGR SOLENOID .... C 7
ELECT SPARK TIMING (EST) DISTR ... E 6-7
ELECTRONIC BRAKE
  CONTROL MODULE .... A-C 12-15
ELECTRONIC CONTROL
  MODULE (ECM) .... A-E 4-7
FOG LT RELAY .... C 28
FUEL INJECTORS .... D-E 5-6
FUEL PUMP RELAY .... A 5
FUS LINKS .... B 2-3
GEAR SELECT SW (A/T) .... E 33-34
HATCH RELEASE RELAY .... E 38
HEADLT DIMMER SW .... B 28
HEADLT DOOR CONTROL UNIT .. C-D 2-3
HEATER & A/C CONTROL
  HEAD (ELECT) .... A 27
HEATER & A/C CONTROL
  HEAD (MANUAL) .... A-E 20-23
HEATER & A/C PROGRAMMER
  (ELECT) .... A-B 24-27
HEATER & A/C SOLENOID ASSEMBLY . A 23
HIGH BLOWER RELAY .... C 23
HORN RELAY .... A 16
IGNITION SW .... A 9-11
INCANDESCENT POWER DRIVER ..... B 28
INSTRUMENT CLUSTER .... A-D 32-33
INTERIOR LTS .... E 28-29
LEFT ENGINE LT .... D 1
LEFT POWER WINDOW SW .... D-E 36-37
LEFT VANITY MIRROR .... D 28
LIGHT SW .... A 28-29
LIGHTED REAR VIEW MIRROR ..... C-D 28
LOW BLOWER RELAY .... C 23
MAIN FUSE BLOCK .... B-E 8-11
OIL PRES SENS/SW .... A 6
OIL PRES SW .... A 19
OIL TEMP SENSOR .... A 7
POWER MIRROR SW .... A-B 36
PRIMARY COOLANT FAN RELAY .... D-E 23
RADIO ANTENNA RELAY .... A 40
RIGHT ENGINE LT .... A 1
SEAT MOTORS .... D-E 40-42
SECONDARY COOLANT FAN RELAY . E 23
SELECT RIDE CONTROL MODULE .. C-E 12-15
SELECT RIDE CONTROL SW ...... E 13-14
SPORT SEAT ASSEMBLY .... B-C 41-42
STARTER ENABLE RELAY .... E 16
STARTER MOTOR &
  SOLENOID ASSEMBLY .... A 3
STOP LT/CRUISE BRAKE SW ...... C-D 25
TONE GENERATOR .... B 19
TURN/HAZ SW .... A-B 30-31
VEHICLE SPEED SENSOR .... E 15
WIPER MOTOR .... C-D 26-27
WIPER/WASHER SW .... D-E 26-27
1-4 UPSHIFT RELAY .... E 3

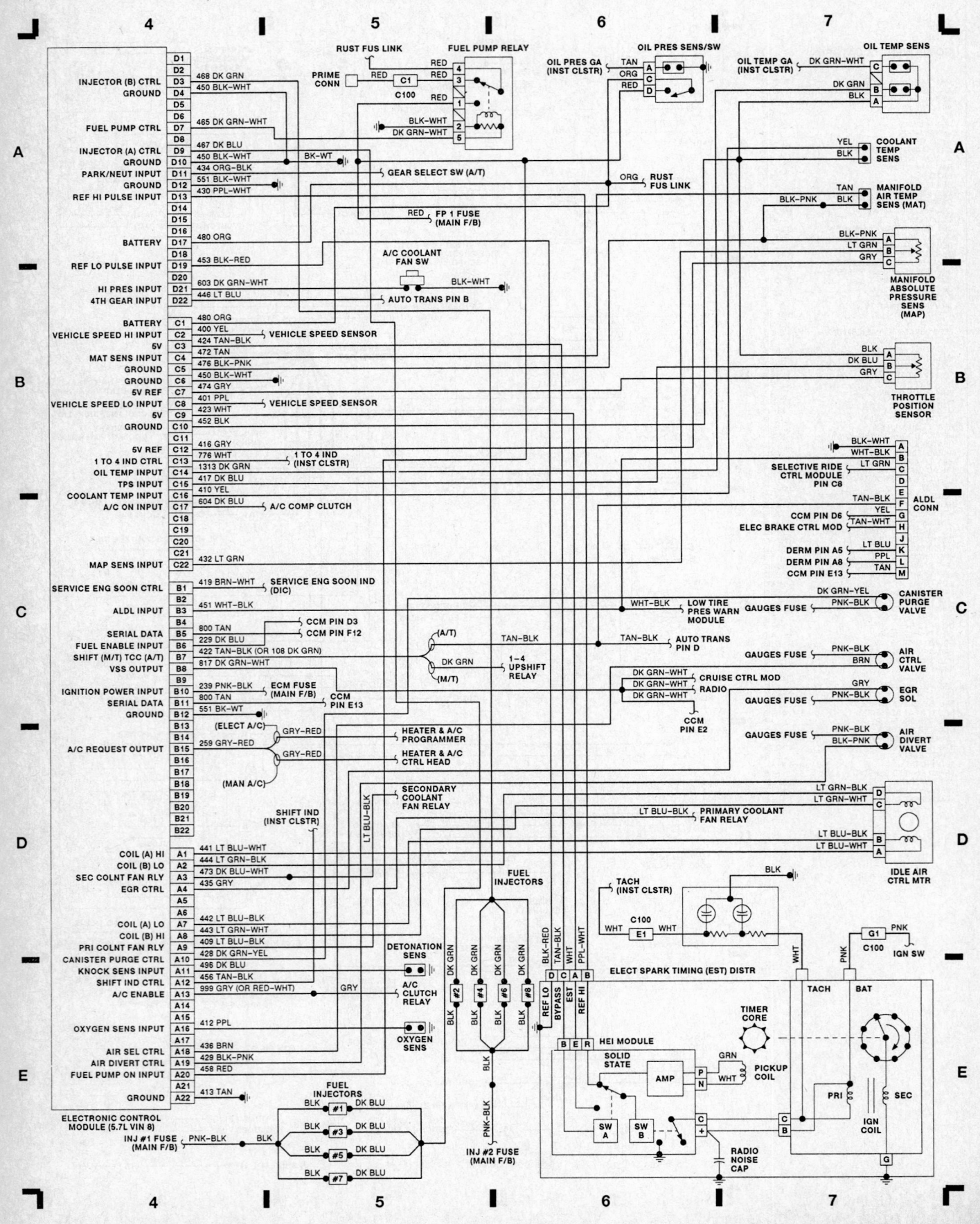

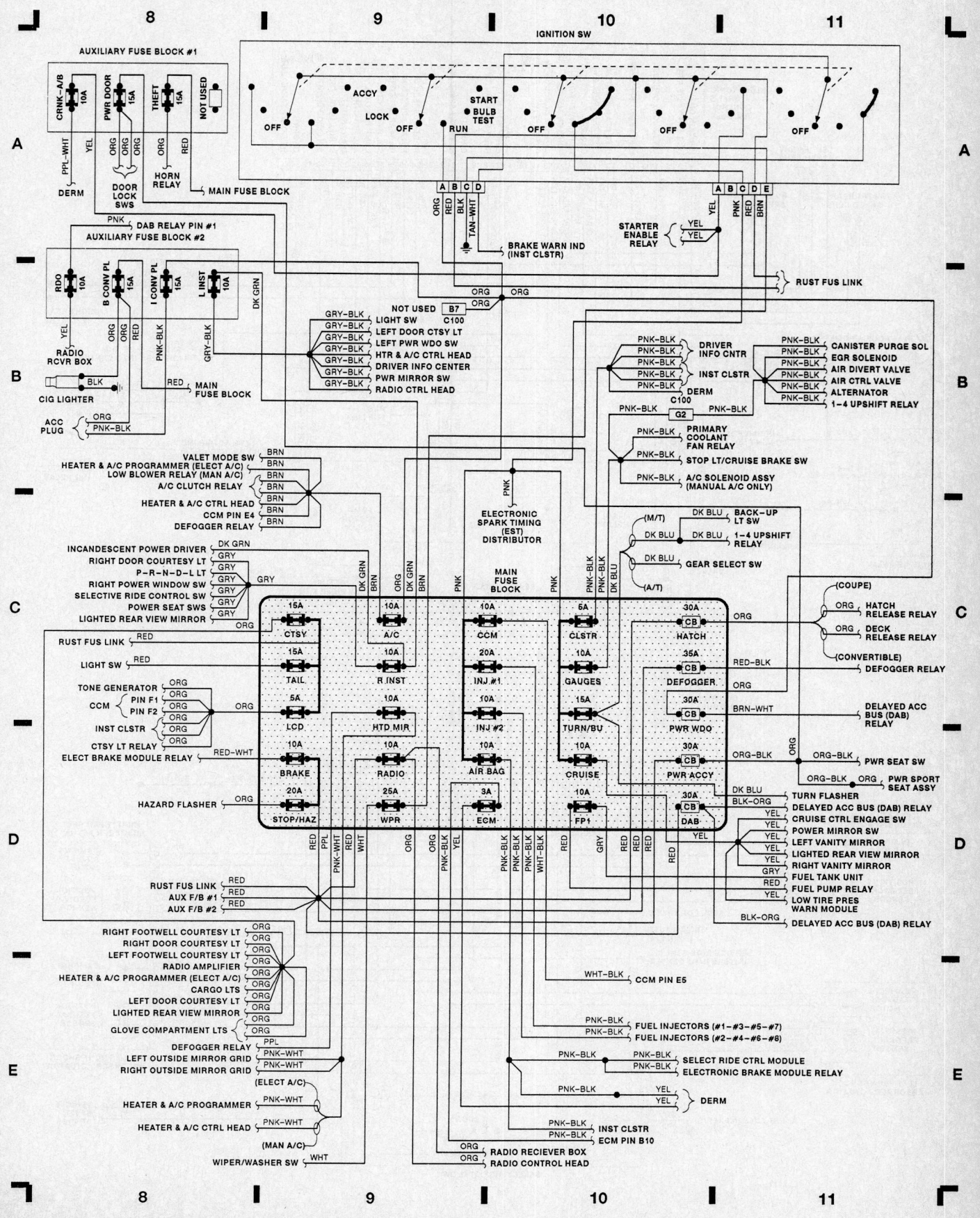

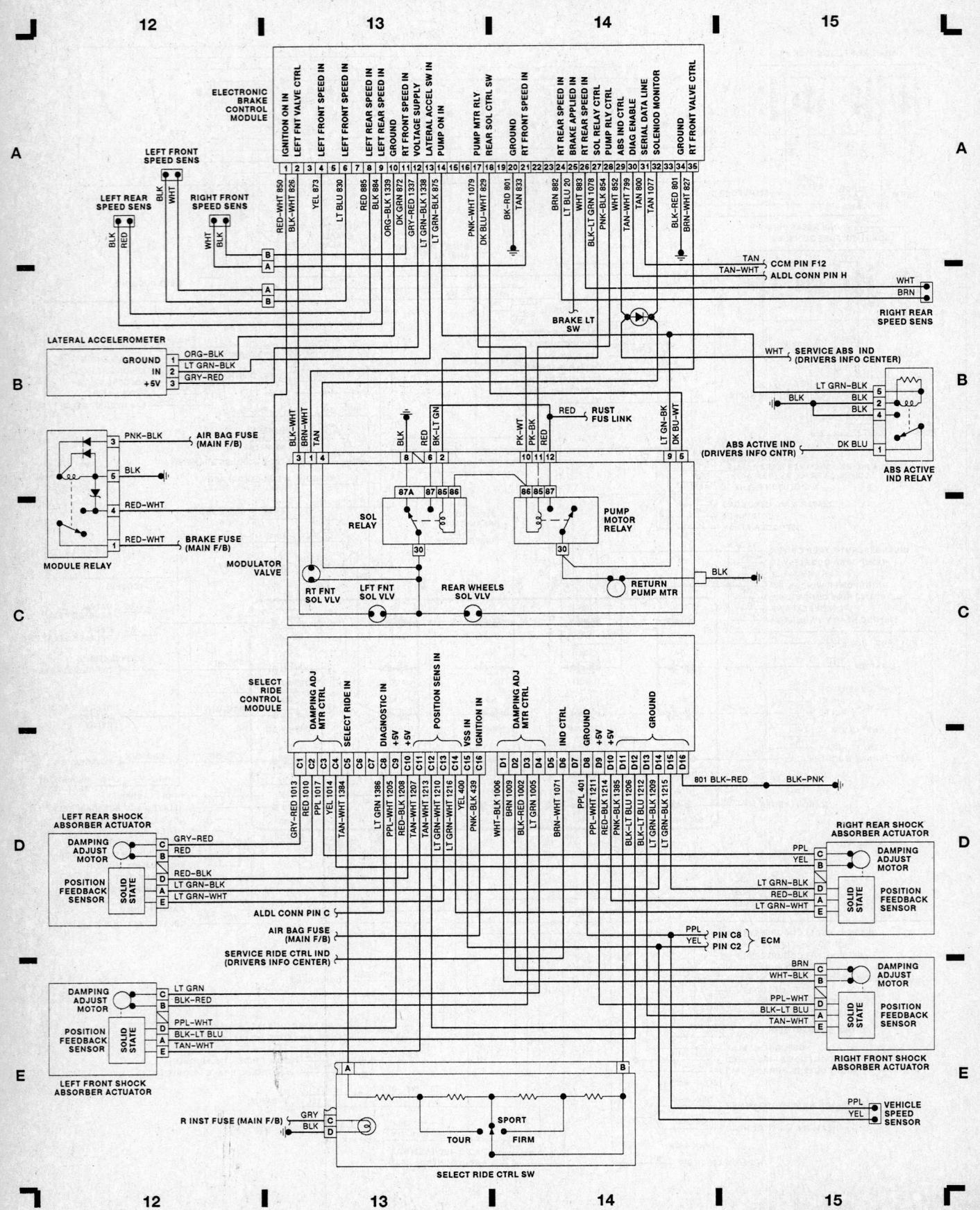

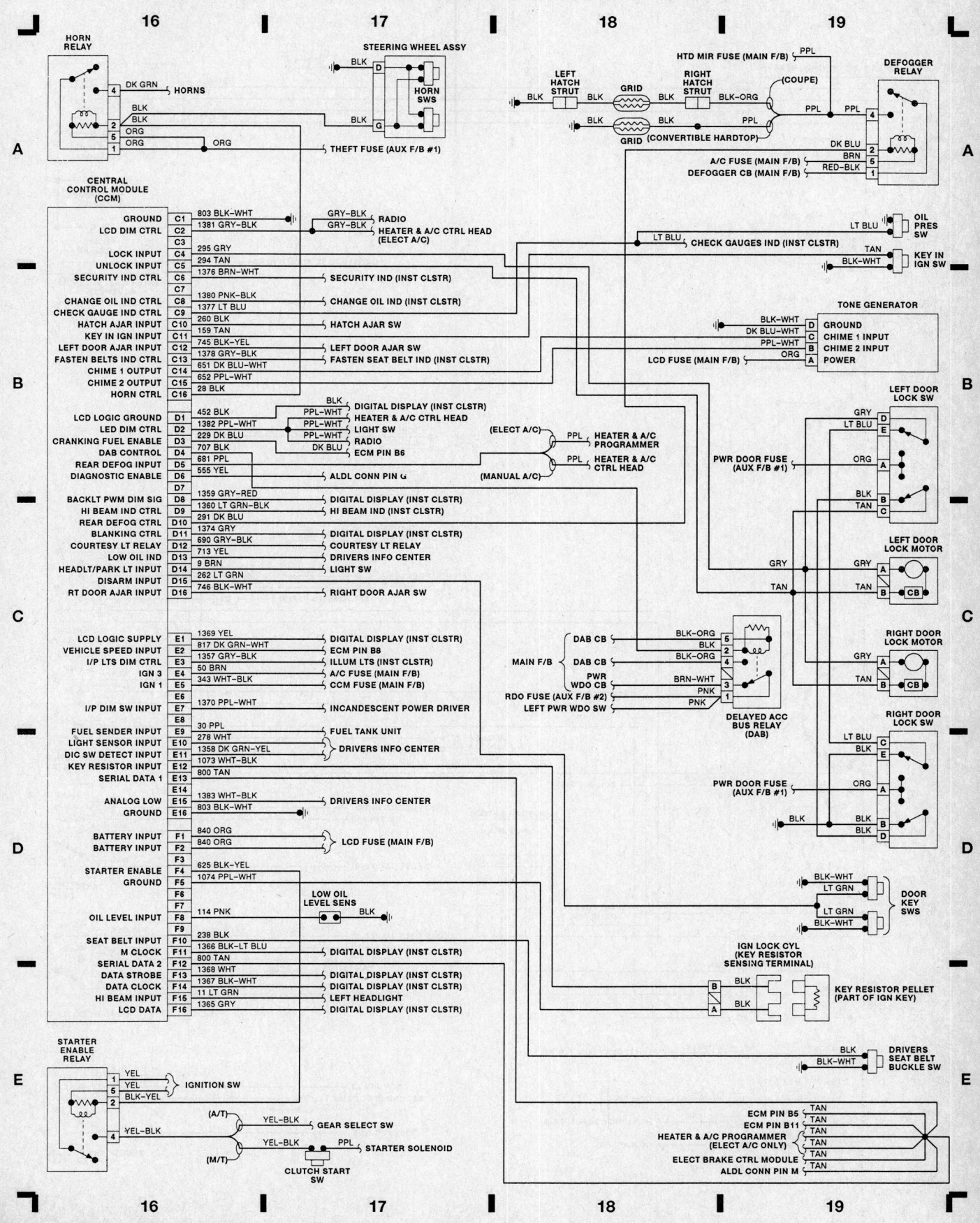

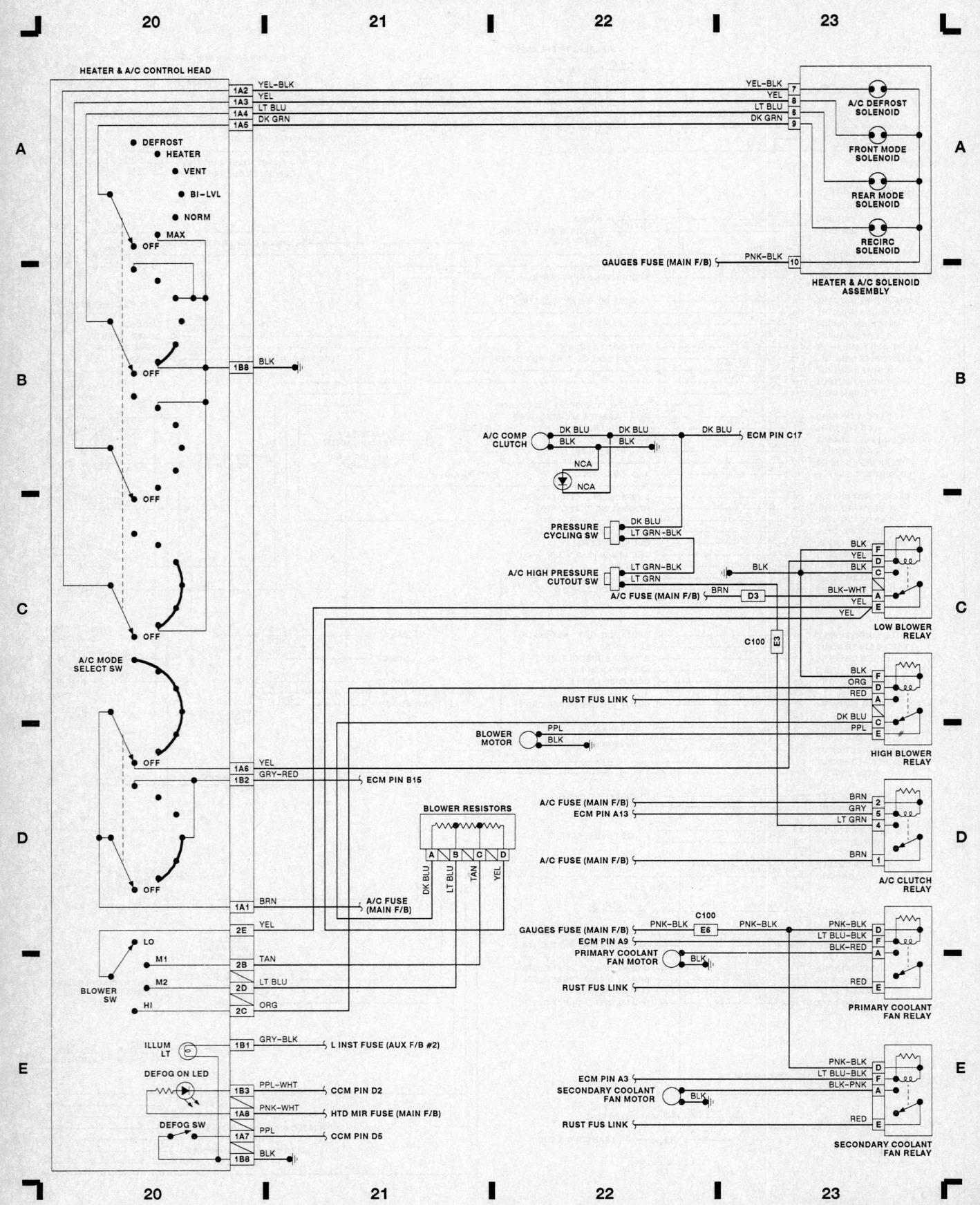

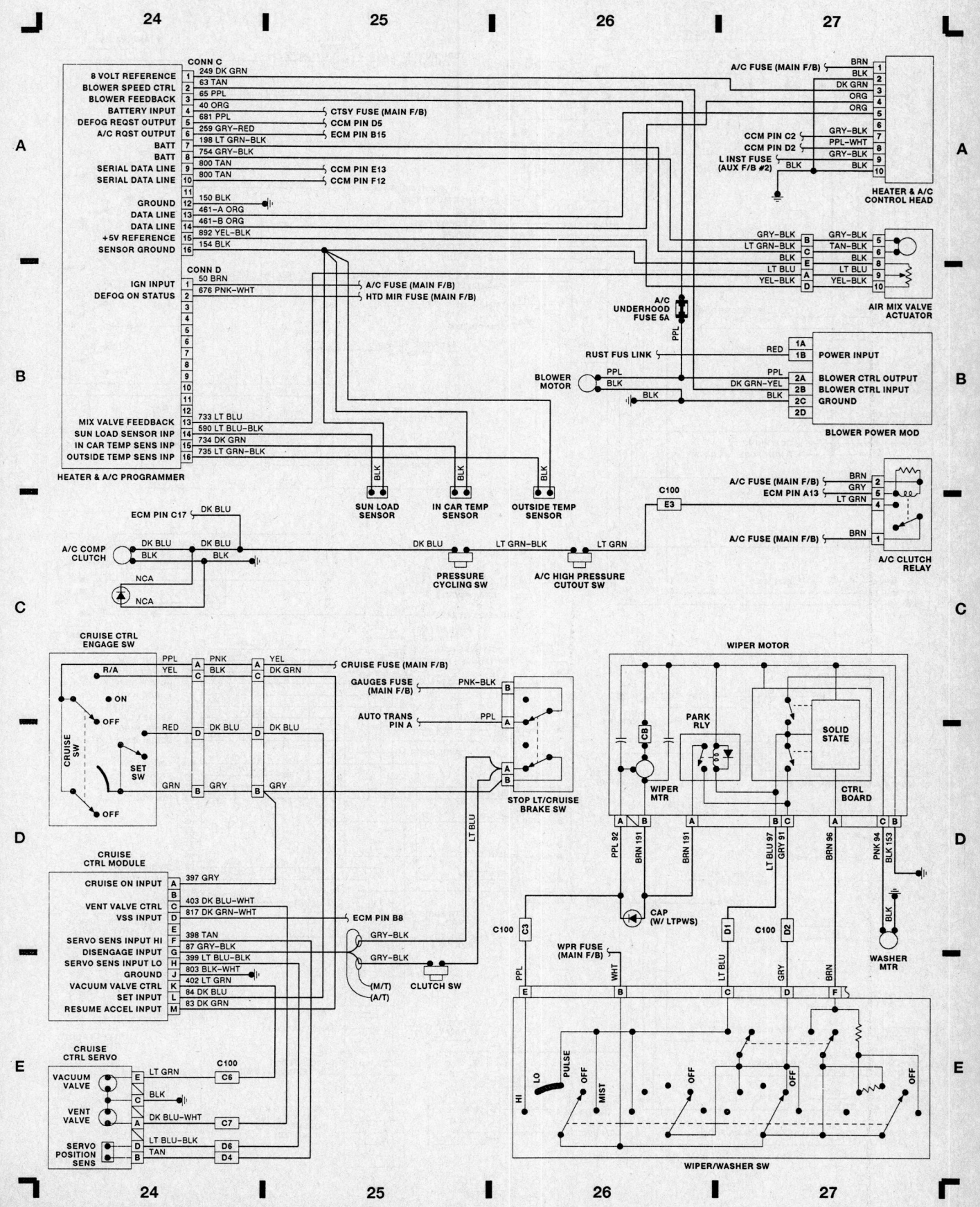

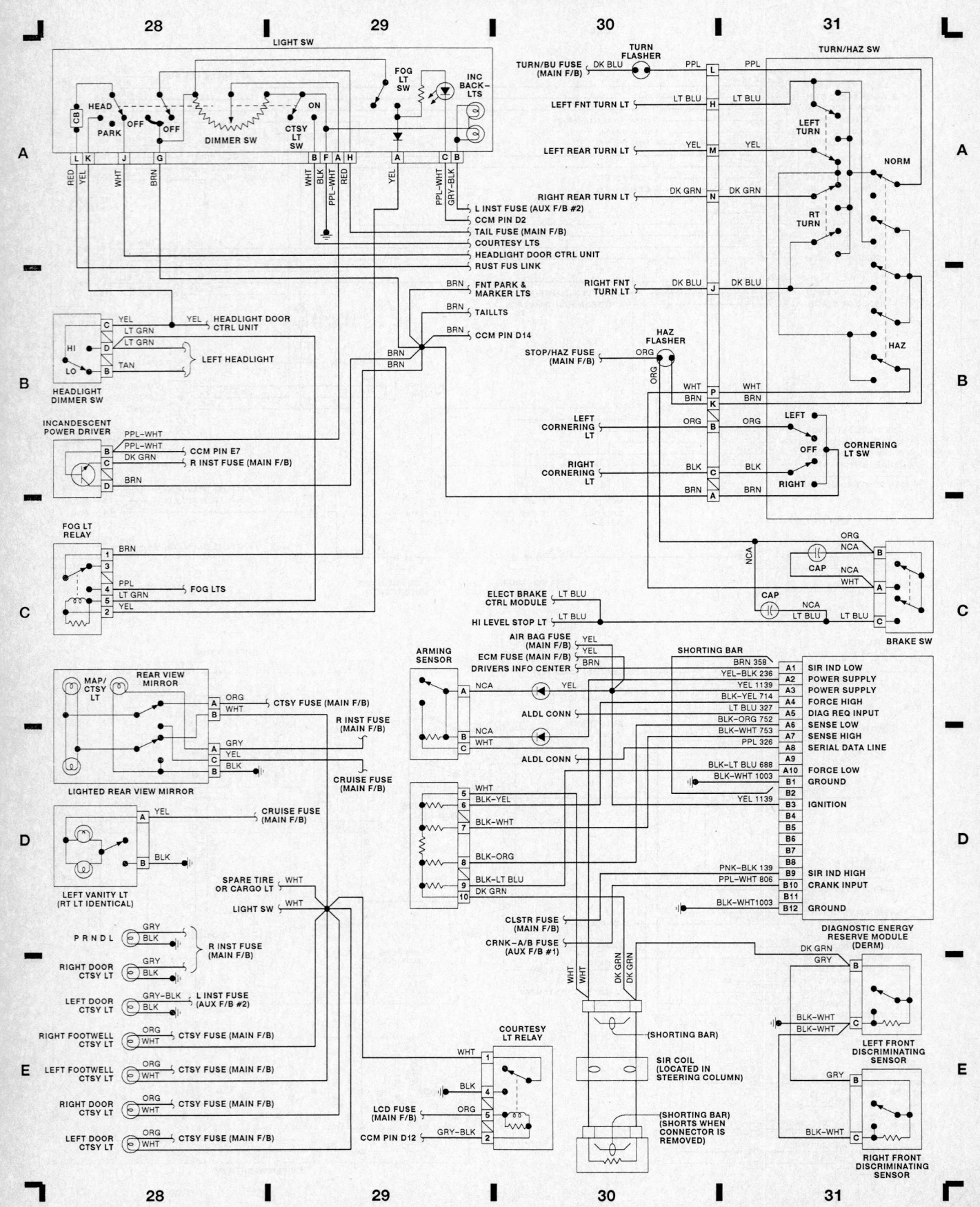

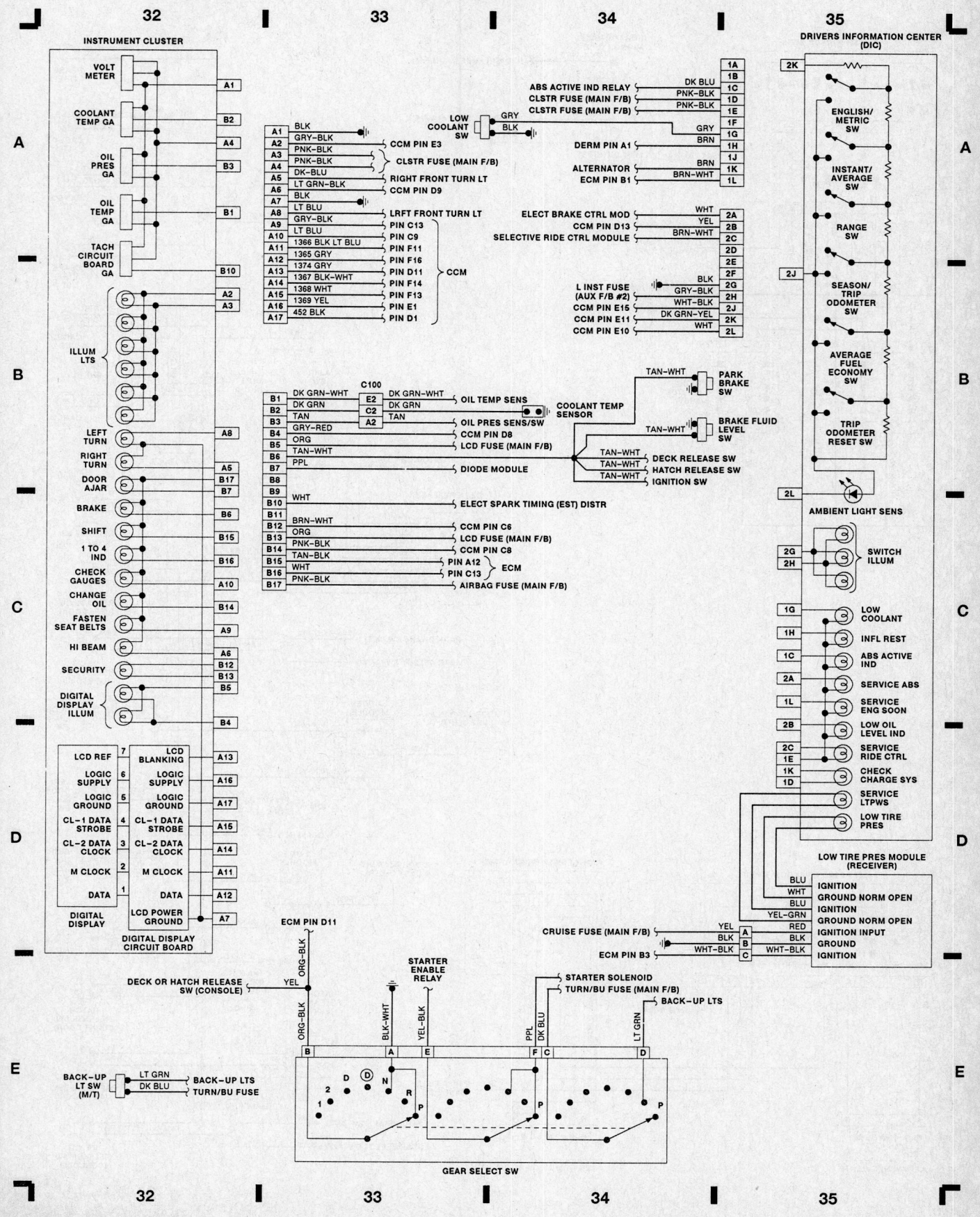

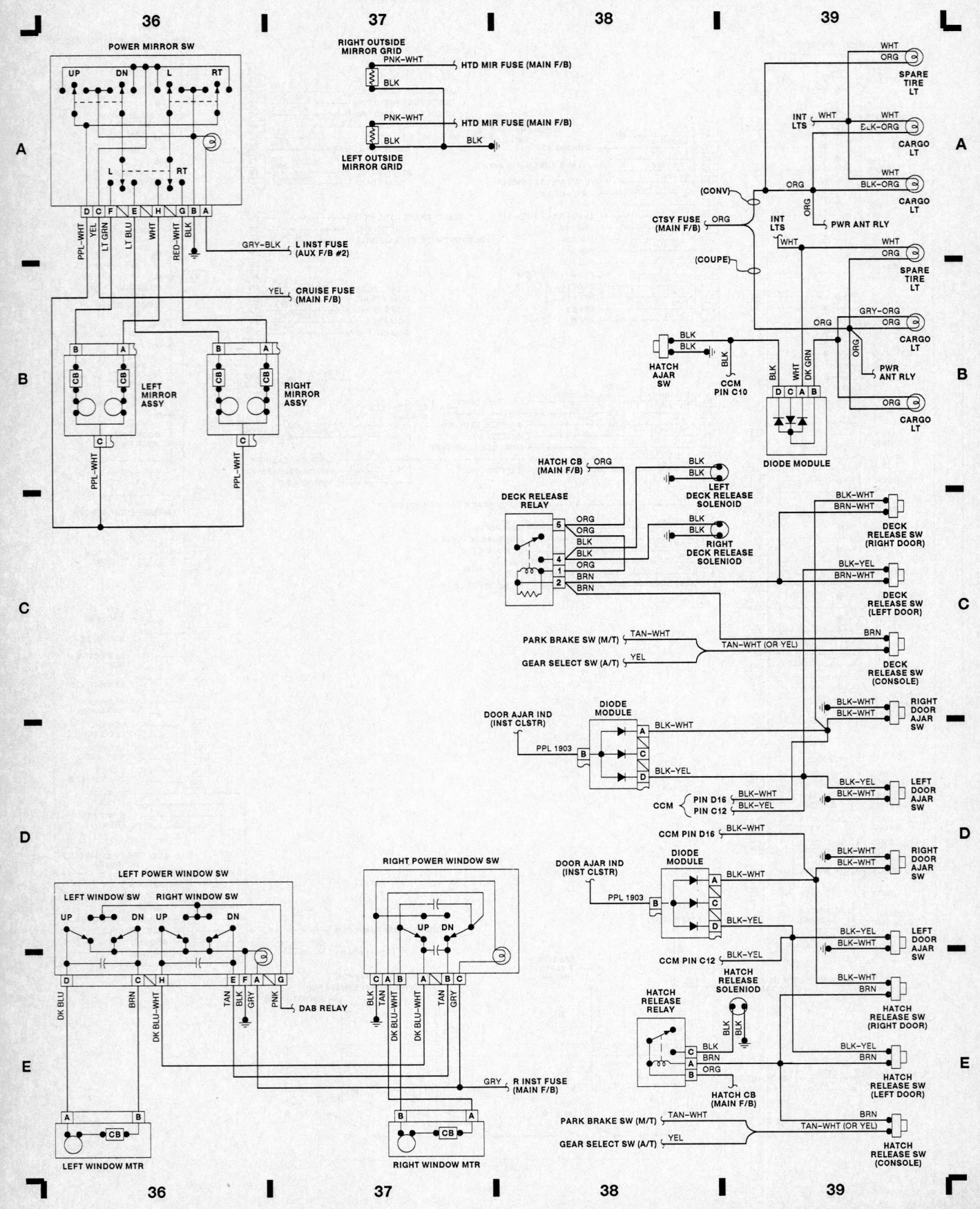

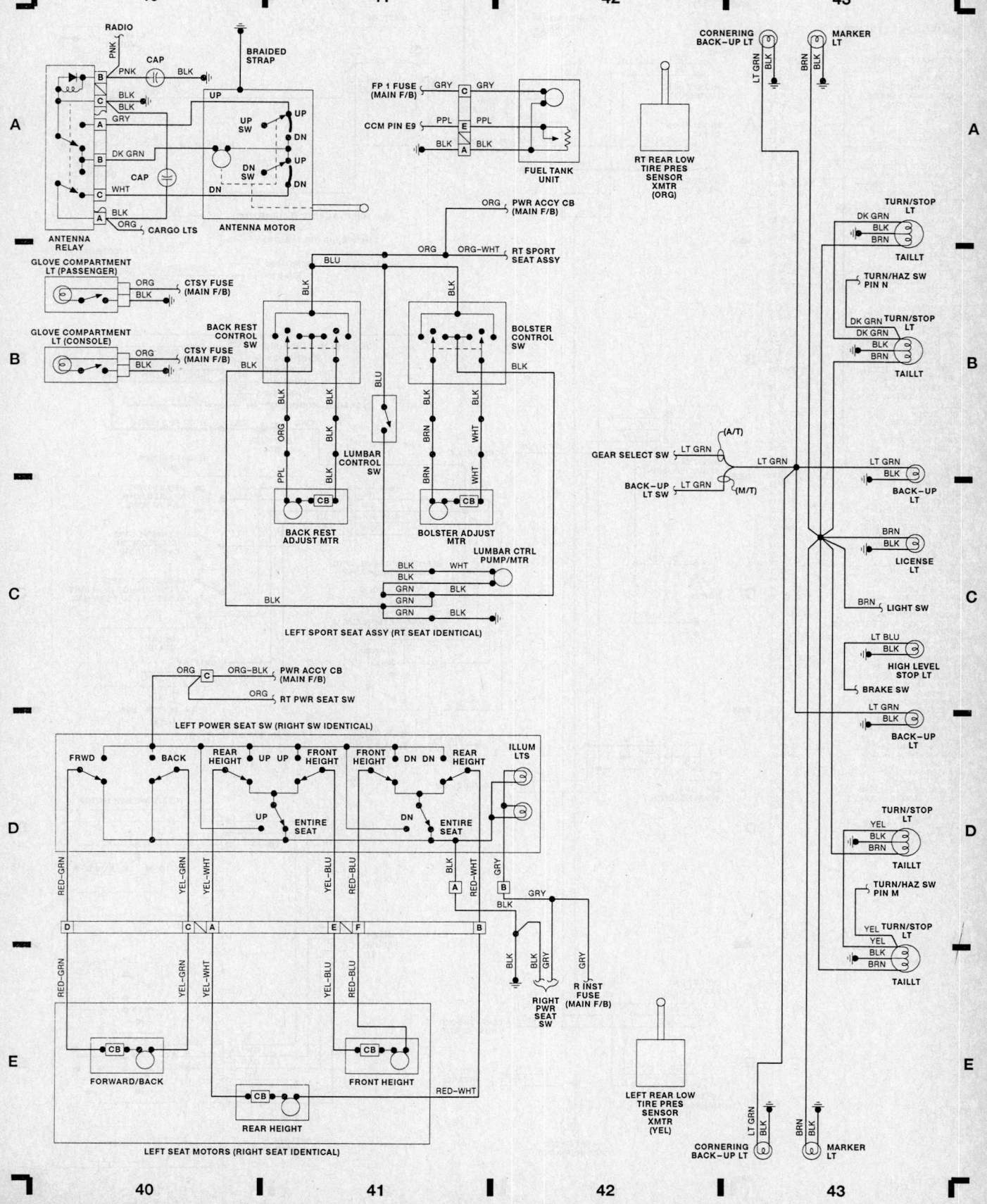

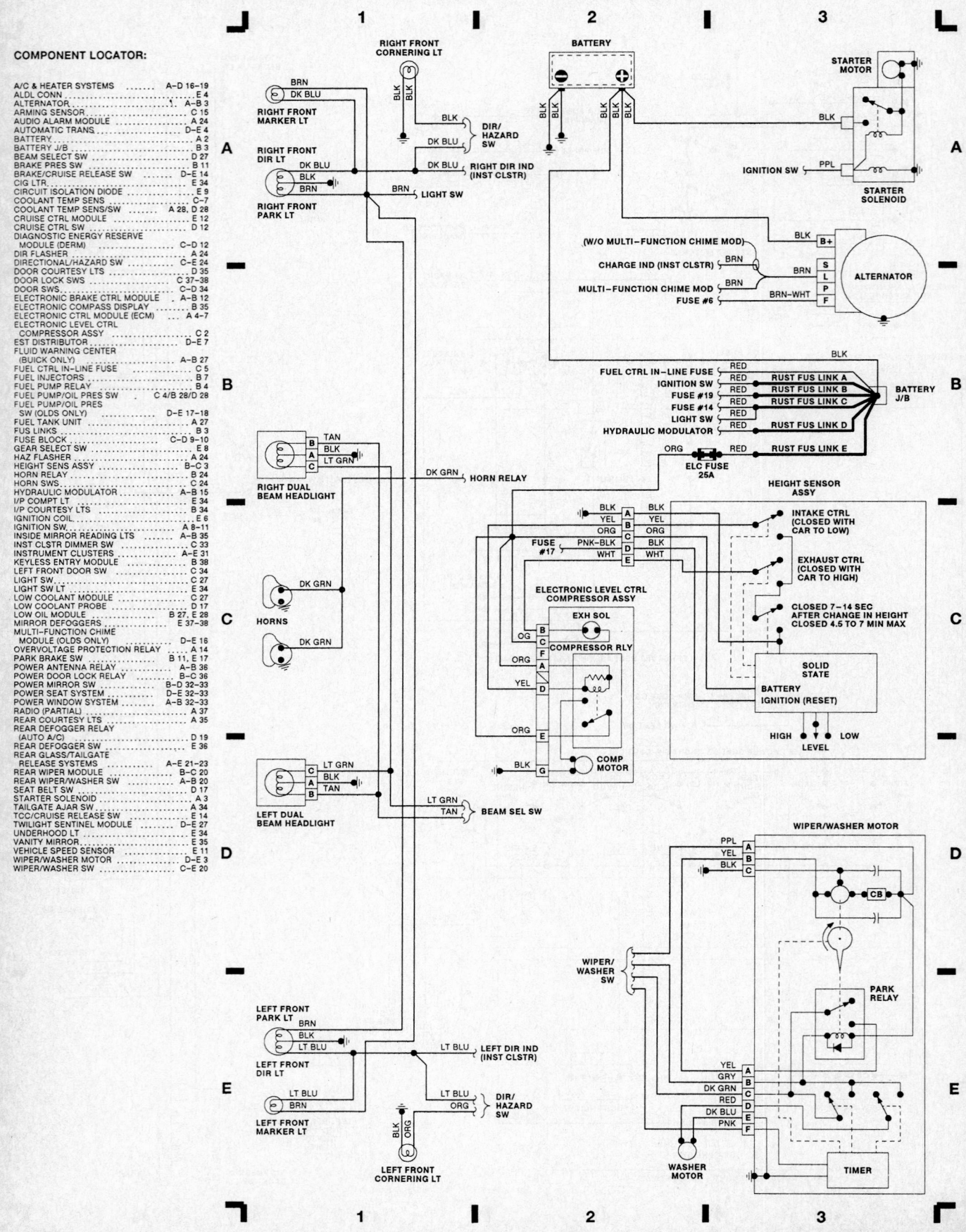

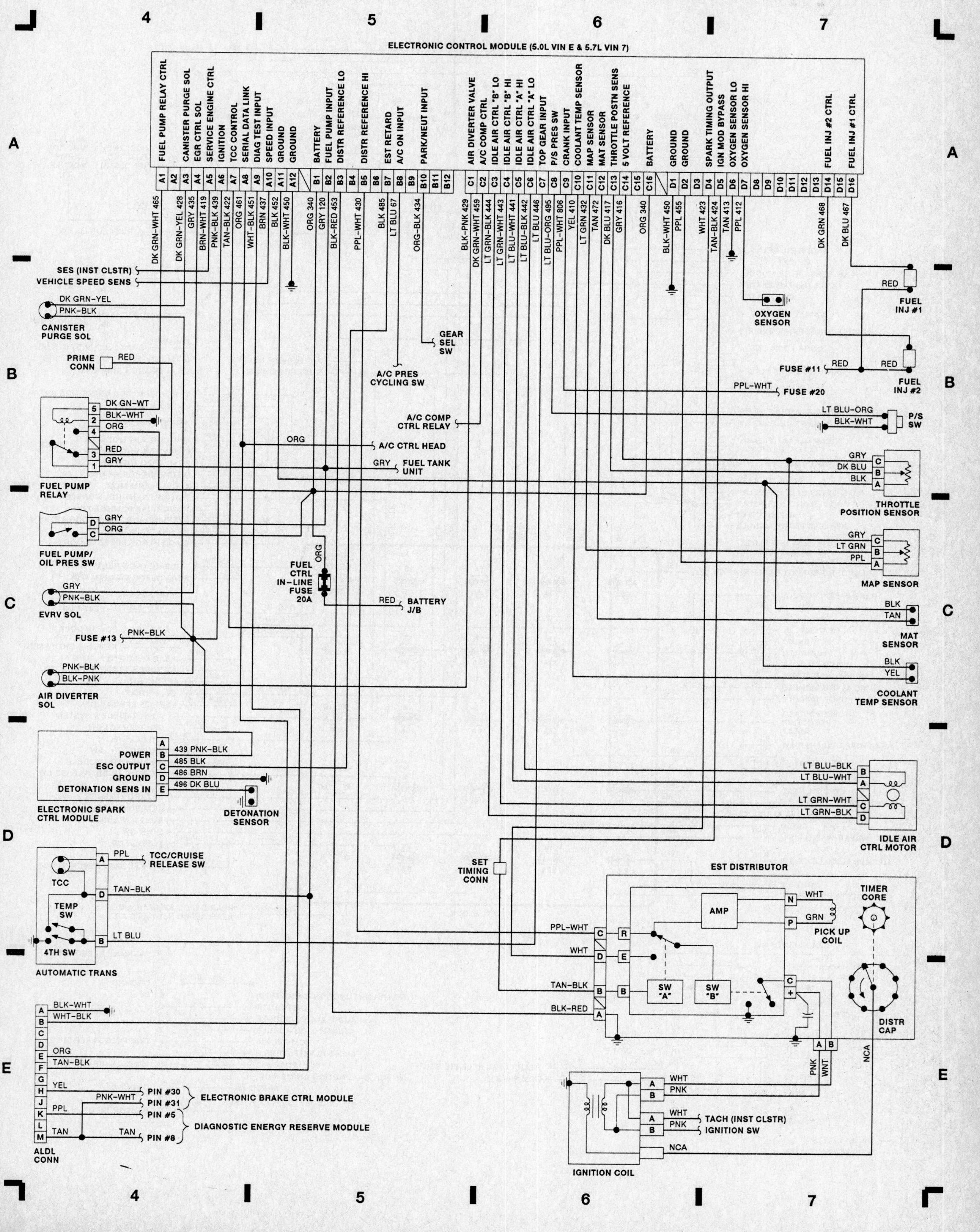

ELECTRONIC CONTROL MODULE (5.0L VIN E & 5.7L VIN 7)
FUEL PUMP RELAY CTRL
CANISTER PURGE SOL
EGR CTRL SOL
SERVICE ENGINE CTRL
IGNITION
TCC CONTROL
SERIAL DATA LINK
DIAG TEST INPUT
SPEED INPUT
GROUND
GROUND
BATTERY
FUEL PUMP INPUT
DISTR REFERENCE LO
DISTR REFERENCE HI
EST RETARD
A/C ON INPUT
PARK/NEUT INPUT
AIR DIVERTER VALVE
A/C COMP CTRL
IDLE AIR CTRL "B" LO
IDLE AIR CTRL "B" HI
IDLE AIR CTRL "A" HI
IDLE AIR CTRL "A" LO
TOP GEAR INPUT
P/S PRES SW
CRANK INPUT
COOLANT TEMP SENSOR
MAP SENSOR
MAT SENSOR
THROTTLE POSTN SENS
5 VOLT REFERENCE
BATTERY
GROUND
GROUND
SPARK TIMING OUTPUT
IGN MOD BYPASS
OXYGEN SENSOR LO
OXYGEN SENSOR HI
FUEL INJ #2 CTRL
FUEL INJ #1 CTRL
A1 A2 A3 A4 A5 A6 A7 A8 A9 A10 A11 A12
B1 B2 B3 B4 B5 B6 B7 B8 B9 B10 B11 B12
C1 C2 C3 C4 C5 C6 C7 C8 C9 C10 C11 C12 C13 C14 C15 C16
D1 D2 D3 D4 D5 D6 D7 D8 D9 D10 D11 D12 D13 D14 D15 D16
DK GRN-WHT 465
DK GRN-YEL 428
GRY 435
BRN-WHT 419
PNK-BLK 439
TAN-BLK 422
ORG 461
WHT-BLK 451
BRN 437
BLK 452
BLK-WHT 450
ORG 340
GRY 120
BLK-RED 453
PPL-WHT 430
BLK 485
LT BLU 67
ORG-BLK 434
BLK-PNK 429
DK GRN-WHT 459
LT GRN-BLK 444
LT GRN-WHT 443
LT BLU-WHT 441
LT BLU-BLK 442
LT BLU 446
LT BLU-ORG 495
PPL-WHT 806
YEL 410
LT GRN 432
TAN 472
DK BLU 417
GRY 416
ORG 340
BLK-WHT 450
PPL 455
WHT 423
TAN-BLK 424
TAN 413
PPL 412
DK GRN 468
DK BLU 467
SES (INST CLSTR)
VEHICLE SPEED SENS
DK GRN-YEL
PNK-BLK
CANISTER PURGE SOL
PRIME CONN
RED
DK GN-WT
BLK-WHT
ORG
RED
GRY
FUEL PUMP RELAY
GRY
ORG
FUEL PUMP/ OIL PRES SW
GRY
PNK-BLK
EVRV SOL
FUSE #13
PNK-BLK
PNK-BLK
BLK-PNK
AIR DIVERTER SOL
GEAR SEL SW
A/C PRES CYCLING SW
A/C COMP CTRL RELAY
ORG
A/C CTRL HEAD
GRY
FUEL TANK UNIT
ORG
FUEL CTRL IN-LINE FUSE 20A
RED
BATTERY J/B
OXYGEN SENSOR
RED
FUEL INJ #1
FUSE #11
RED
RED
FUEL INJ #2
PPL-WHT
FUSE #20
LT BLU-ORG
BLK-WHT
P/S SW
GRY
DK BLU
BLK
THROTTLE POSITION SENSOR
GRY
LT GRN
PPL
MAP SENSOR
BLK
TAN
MAT SENSOR
BLK
YEL
COOLANT TEMP SENSOR
POWER
ESC OUTPUT
GROUND
DETONATION SENS IN
439 PNK-BLK
485 BLK
486 BRN
496 DK BLU
ELECTRONIC SPARK CTRL MODULE
DETONATION SENSOR
LT BLU-BLK
LT BLU-WHT
LT GRN-WHT
LT GRN-BLK
IDLE AIR CTRL MOTOR
TCC
PPL
TCC/CRUISE RELEASE SW
TAN-BLK
TEMP SW
LT BLU
4TH SW
AUTOMATIC TRANS
SET TIMING CONN
EST DISTRIBUTOR
AMP
WHT
GRN
PICK UP COIL
TIMER CORE
PPL-WHT
WHT
TAN-BLK
BLK-RED
SW "A"
SW "B"
DISTR CAP
PNK
WNT
NCA
BLK-WHT
WHT-BLK
ORG
TAN-BLK
YEL
PNK-WHT
PPL
TAN
TAN
PIN #30
PIN #31
ELECTRONIC BRAKE CTRL MODULE
PIN #5
PIN #8
DIAGNOSTIC ENERGY RESERVE MODULE
ALDL CONN
WHT
PNK
WHT
PNK
TACH (INST CLSTR)
IGNITION SW
NCA
IGNITION COIL

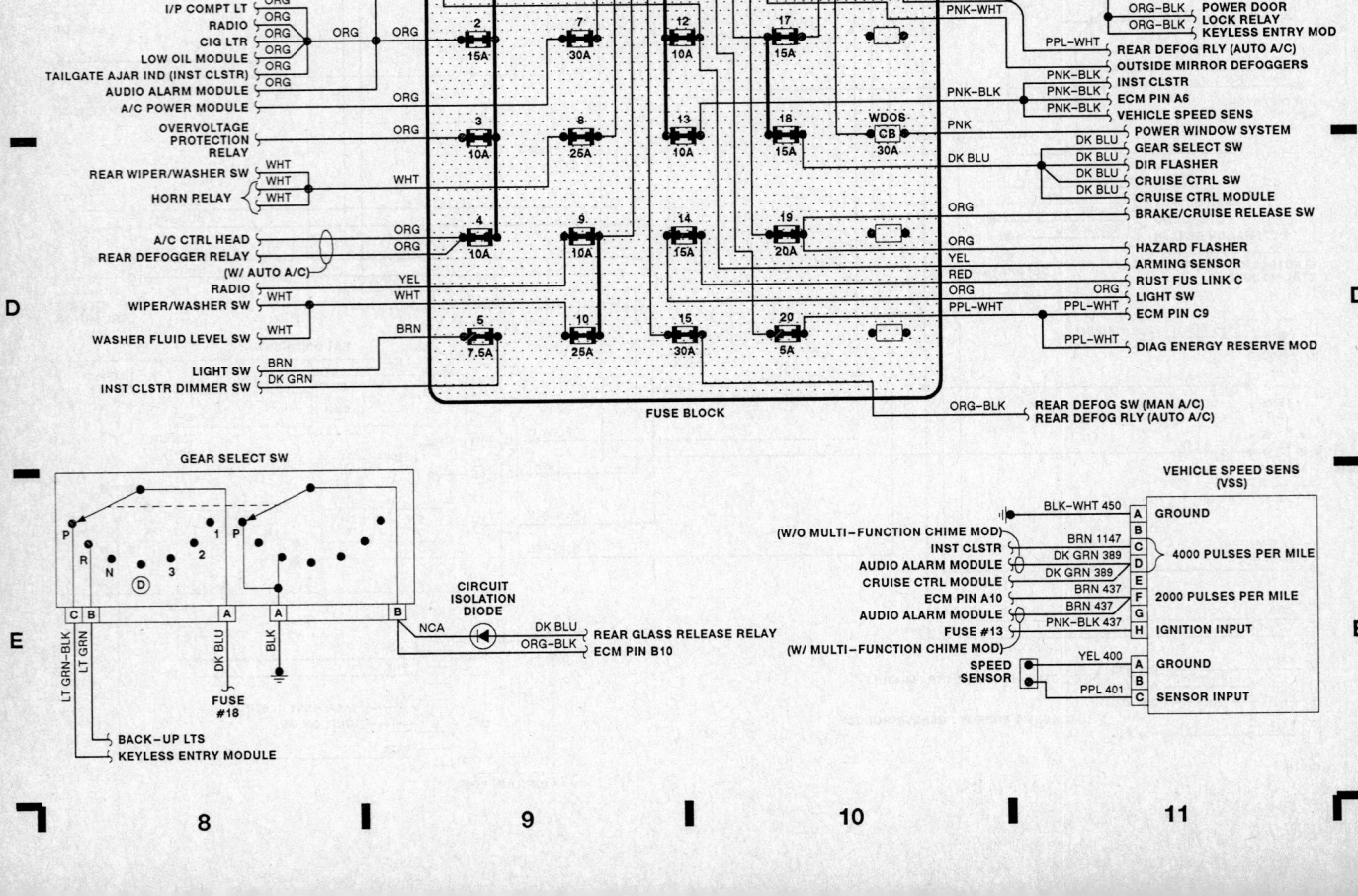

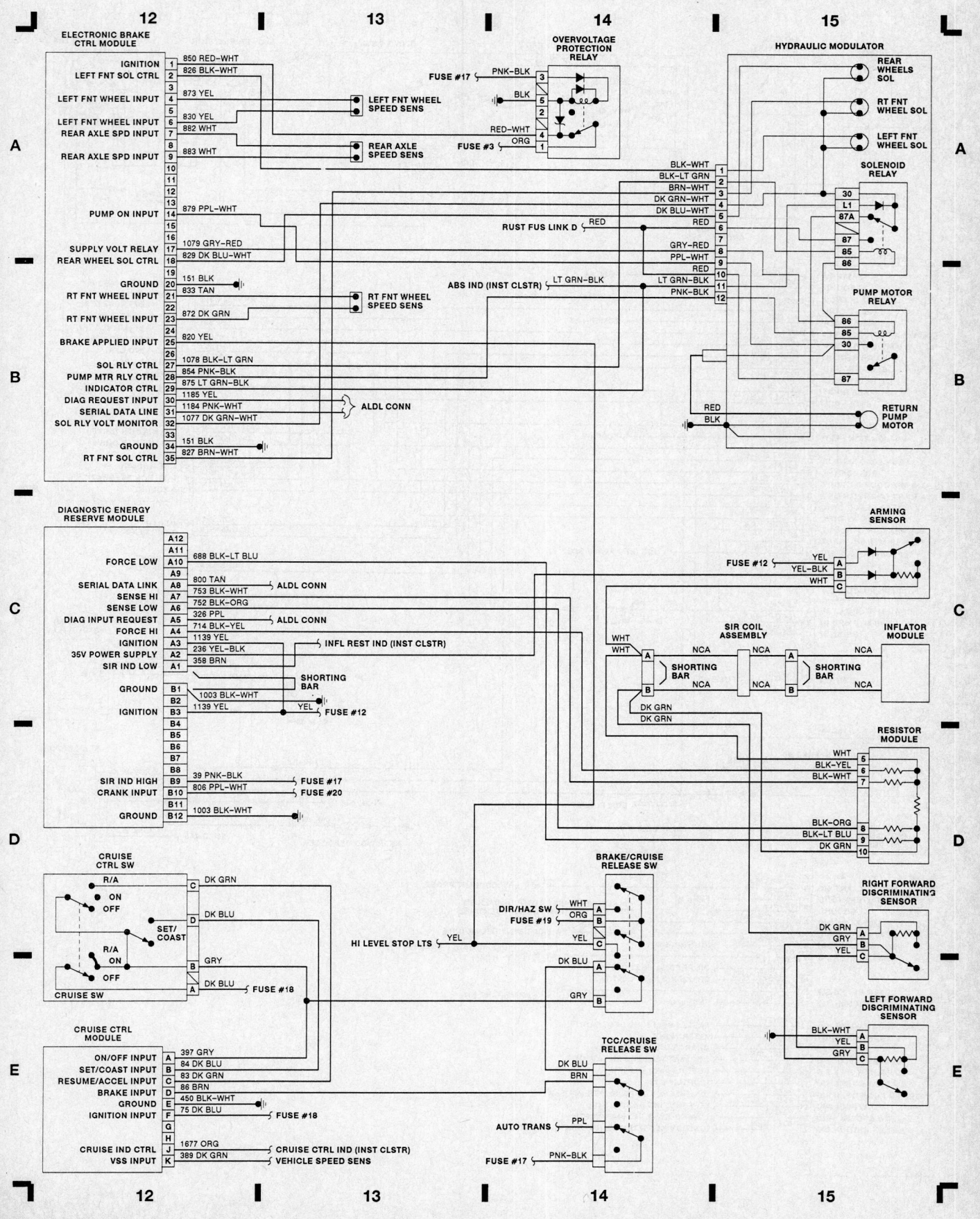

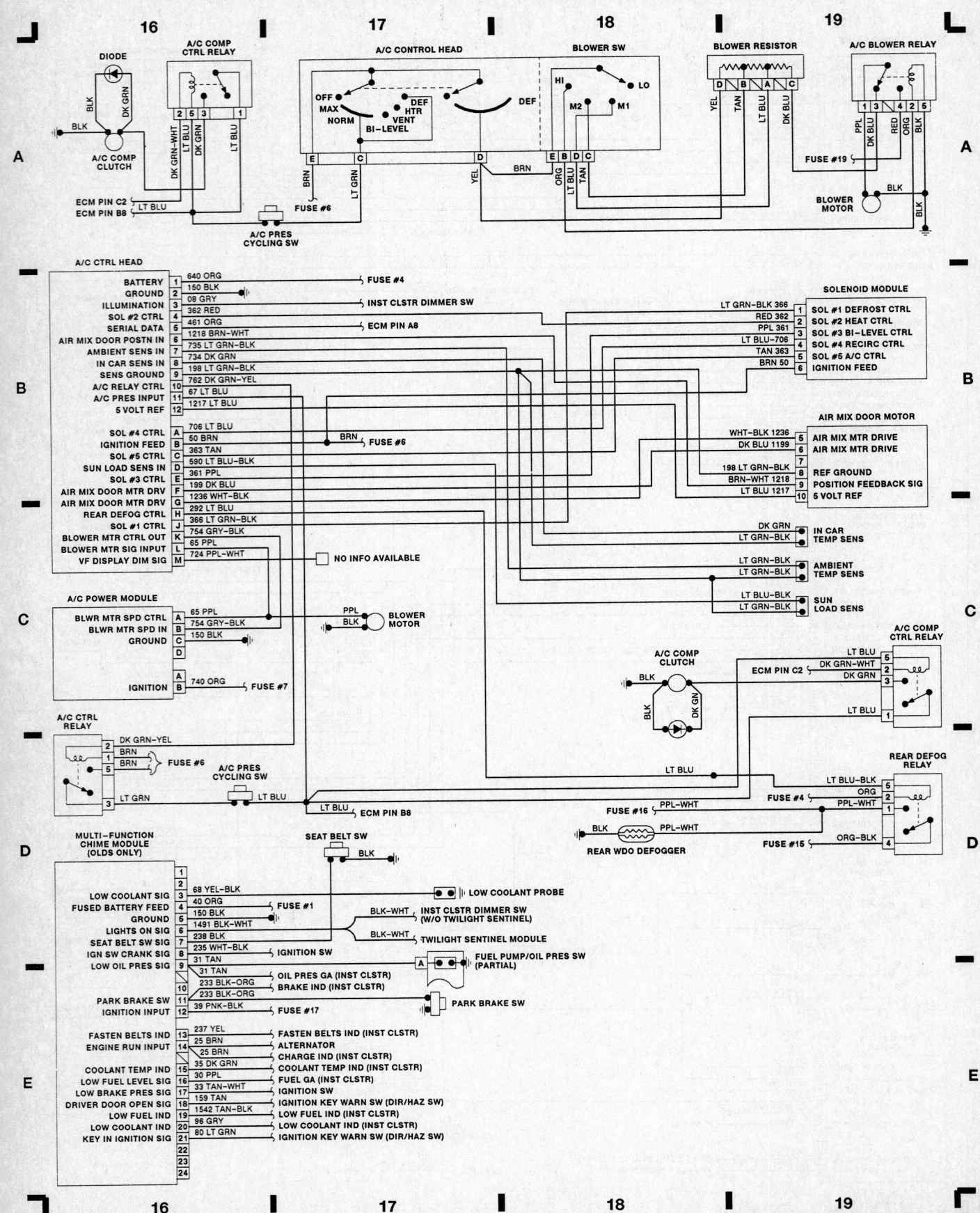

20   21   22   23

A

REAR WIPER/
WASHER SW

ORG
WHT
DK GRN — FUSE #8

BLK

WASHER
MOTOR

TAILGATE
MOTOR

TAILGATE LOCK RELAY
(W/O POWER DOOR LOCKS)

LT BLU — A
GRY — B
LOCKS/SEATS CB — ORG-BLK — C
BLK — D
TAN — E
BLK — F

LOCK
RELAY

UNLOCK
RELAY

A

B

REAR WIPER
MODULE

SOLID
STATE

ORG
GRY — FUSE #2
BLK

REAR GLASS RELEASE/
TAILGATE LOCK SW

LT BLU — A1 — LOCK

BLK — C2 — UNLOCK
FUSE #1 — ORG — D2

B

REAR GLASS
RELEASE RELAY
(CONVENIENCE
CENTER)

DK BLU
DK BLU
GEAR SEL SW — DK BLU — 1
2
BLK — 5
RELEASE SOL
ORG — 3
FUSE #1

REAR GLASS
INTERLOCK/
PUSH BUTTON
SW

INTERLOCK
SENSE SW
ORG — D
BLK-WHT — C
ORG — B
GRY — A

C

WIPER/WASHER SW

HI — E — PPL

MIST
HI

MIST
HI

WASH

B — WHT — FUSE #10
A — GRY
C

WIPER/WASHER
MOTOR

D — DK GRN

MIST
HI

LO
PULSE
DELAY

F — PNK

OFF

MIST

C

(W/O POWER DOOR LOCKS)

(W/ POWER DOOR LOCKS)

KEYLESS
ENTRY
MODULE — BLK

REAR GLASS
RELEASE RELAY
(CONVENIENCE
CENTER)

DK BLU
DK BLU
GEAR SEL SW — DK BLU — 1
2
BLK — 5
RELEASE SOL
ORG — 3
FUSE #1

TAILGATE LOCK
SENSOR SW

REAR GLASS
INTERLOCK/
PUSH BUTTON
SW

ORG — D
BLK-WHT — C
ORG — B
GRY — A

D

E

REAR GLASS
RELEASE SW

A1 — NOT USED

UNLOCK — C2 — BLK — DK BLU
D2 — ORG — FUSE #1

D

E

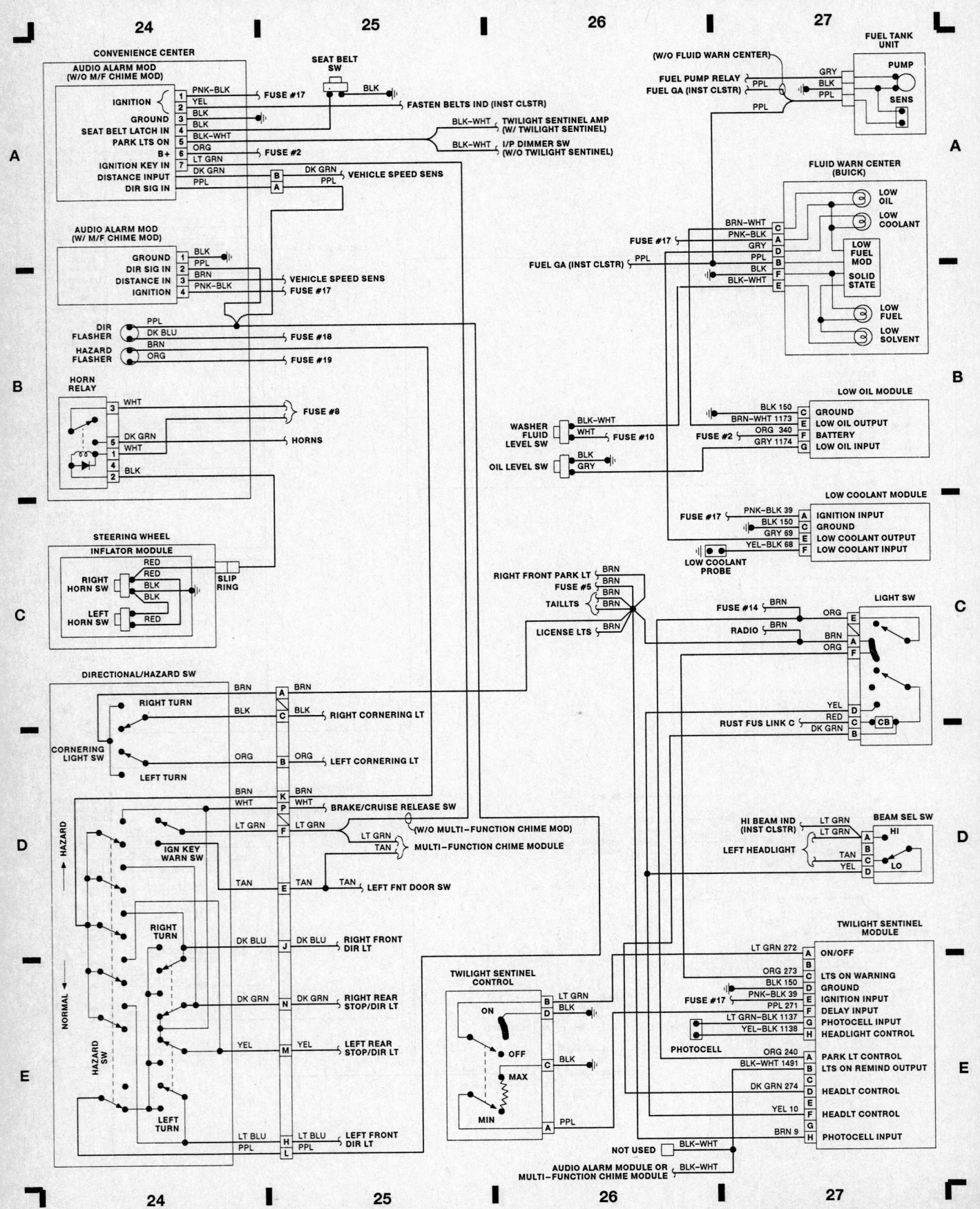

28   29   30   31

Top diagram (Buick):

C1

COOLANT TEMP SENS/SW

INST CLSTR DIMMER SW — GRY — A1 / A2
IGNITION SW — DK GRN — A3 / A4
DK GRN — A5
B — DK GRN
A — DK GRN–WHT — DK GRN
ALTERNATOR — BRN — A6 / A7
A8 / A9
FUSE #17 — PNK–BLK — A10
FUSE #13 — PNK–BLK — A11
DK GRN–WHT — B1
VEHICLE SPEED SENS — BRN — B2
B3
BLK–WHT — B4 / B5
B6 / B7
BLK — B8
LEFT FRONT DIR LT — LT BLU — B9
DIAGNOSTIC ENERGY RESERVE MOD — BRN — B10 / B11

FUEL PUMP/ OIL PRES SW (PARTIAL

A — TAN

C2
FUEL TANK UNIT — PPL — A1
TAN — A2
BLK — A3
PNK–BLK — A4
BEAM SEL SW — LT GRN — A5
AUDIO ALARM MOD — YEL — A6
RIGHT FRONT DIR LT — DK BLU — A7
HYDRAULIC MODULATOR — LT GRN–BLK — A8
A9 / A10 / A11
IGNITION COIL — WHT — B1 / B2
FUSE #17 — PNK–BLK — B3
IGNITION SW — TAN–WHT — B4
ECM PIN A5 — BRN–WHT — B5
CRUISE CTRL MOD — ORG — B6 / B7
TAILGATE AJAR SW — DK GRN — B8 / B9 / B10
FUSE #2 — ORG — B11

INSTRUMENT CLUSTER (BUICK)

C2 A2 — SOLID STATE
OIL
C2 A1 / C1 A11 / C2 B3 — FUEL GA
OIL PRES GA
C1 B2 — TEMP GA
C1 A2 — ILLUM LTS (5)
C1 B9 — HI BEAM
C2 A5 — FASTEN BELT
C2 A6
C1 B10 — LEFT DIR
C2 A3
C2 A7 — RIGHT DIR
C2 B11 — TAILGATE AJAR
C2 B8

SPEEDO — C2 A4 / C1 B3 / C1 B1 / C1 B5
VOLT GA
TACH — C2 B1
ABS — C2 A8
INFL REST — C1 B11
BRAKE — C2 B4
CHARGE — C1 A7
COLNT TEMP — C1 A5
SES — C2 B5
CRUISE CTRL — C2 B6

Bottom diagram (Olds):

C1

WASHER FLUID LEVEL SW
WHT
BLK–WHT — FUSE #10
INST CLSTR DIMMER SW — GRY — A1 / A2
BLK–WHT — A3
DK GRN — A4
DK GRN — A5
DK GRN
MULTI–FUNCTION CHIME MOD — BRN — A6 / A7 — GRY
ECM PIN A5 — BRN–WHT — A8 / A9

COOLANT TEMP SENS/SW
B — DK GRN — DK GRN — IGNITION SW
A — DK GRN–WHT
FUSE #17 — PNK–BLK — A10
FUSE #13 — PNK–BLK — A11
DK GRN–WHT — B1
B2
VEHICLE SPEED SENS — BRN — B3
B4
BLK–WHT — B5
B6 / B7 / B8
BLK — B9
LEFT FRONT DIR LT — LT BLU — B10
DIAGNOSTIC ENERGY RESERVE MOD — BRN — B11

FUEL PUMP/ OIL PRES SW
TAN — A
(W/O MULTI–FUNCTION CHIME MOD) MULTI–FUNCTION CHIME MOD — PPL
FUEL TANK UNIT — PPL

C2
PPL — A1
TAN — A2
BLK — A3
MULTI–FUNCTION CHIME MOD — TAN — PNK–BLK — A4
BEAM SEL SW — LT GRN — A5
AUDIO ALARM MOD OR MULTI–FUNCTION CHIME MOD — YEL — A6
RIGHT FRONT DIR LT — DK BLU — A7
HYDRAULIC MODULATOR — LT GRN–BLK — A8
MULTI–FUNCTION CHIME MOD — BLK–ORG — A9 / A10
IGNITION SW — TAN–WHT
(W/O MULTI–FUNCTION CHIME MOD)
(W/ MULTI–FUNCTION CHIME MOD) — IGNITION COIL — WHT — A11 / B1
FUSE #17 — PNK–BLK — B2
TAN–WHT (OR BLK–ORG) — B3
BRN–WHT — B4
B5 / B6
MULTI–FUNCTION CHIME MOD — TAN–BLK — B7
TAILGATE AJAR SW — DK GRN — B8 / B9 / B10
FUSE #2 — ORG — B11

LOW OIL MODULE
GROUND — C — BLK
BATTERY — F — ORG
LOW OIL OUTPUT — E — BRN–WHT — FUSE #2
LOW OIL INPUT — G — GRY

OIL LEVEL SW
GRY
BLK

INSTRUMENT CLUSTER (OLDS)

C2 A2 — SOLID STATE
OIL
C2 A1 / C1 A11 / C2 B3 — FUEL GA
OIL PRES GA
C1 B2 — TEMP GA
C1 A4 — LOW WASHER FLUID
C1 A2 — ILLUM LTS (5)
C1 B9 — HI BEAM
C2 A5 — FASTEN BELT
C2 A6
C1 B10 — LEFT DIR
C2 A3
C2 A7 — RIGHT DIR
C2 B11 — TAILGATE AJAR
C2 B8

SPEEDO — C2 A4 / C1 B3 / C1 B1 / C1 B5
VOLT GA
TACH — C2 B1
LOW OIL — C2 B5
ABS — C2 A8
INFL REST — C1 B11
BRAKE — C2 B4
CHARGE — C1 A7
COLNT TEMP — C1 A5
SES — C1 A9
LOW COOLANT — C1 A8
LOW FUEL — C2 B7

28   29   30   31

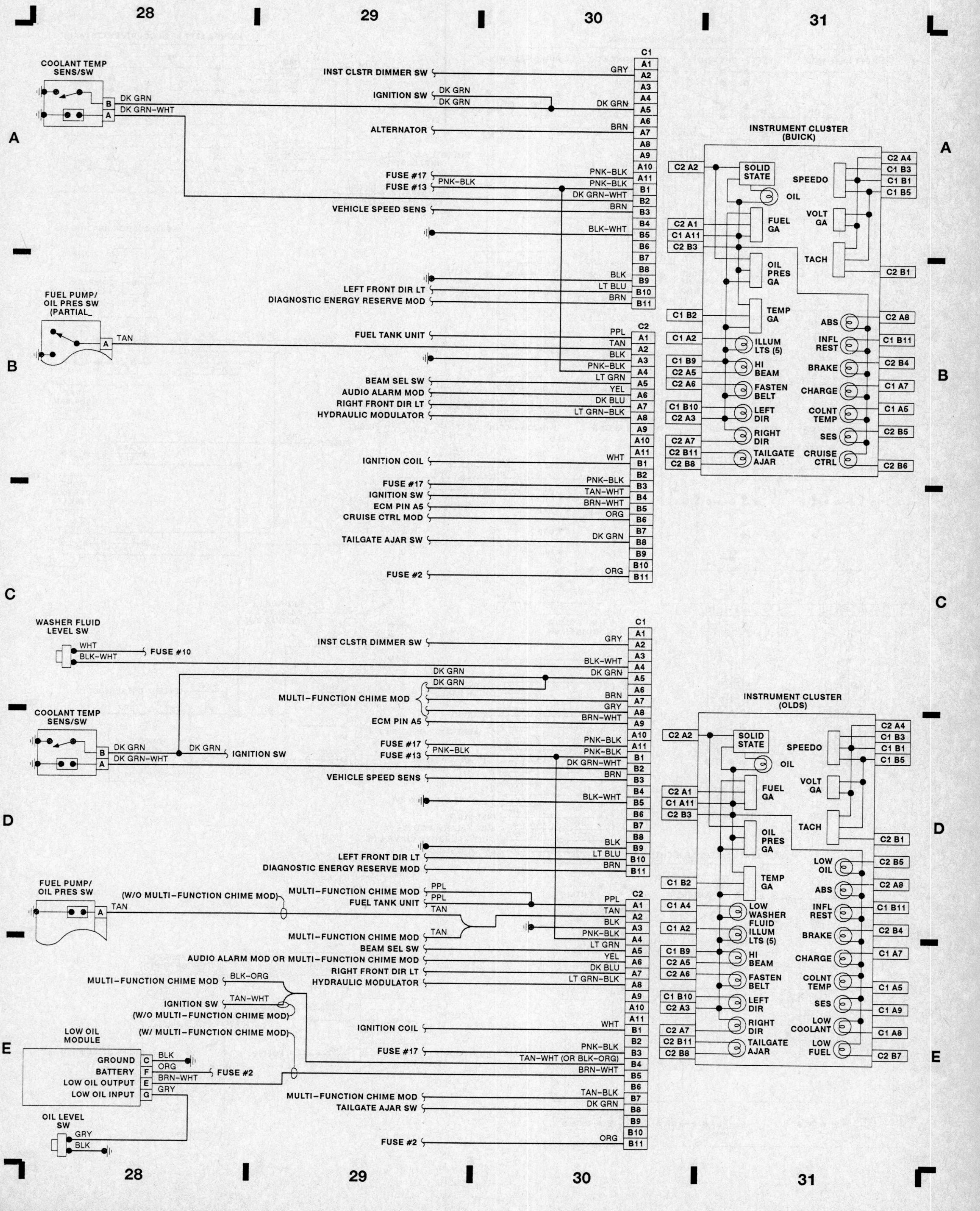

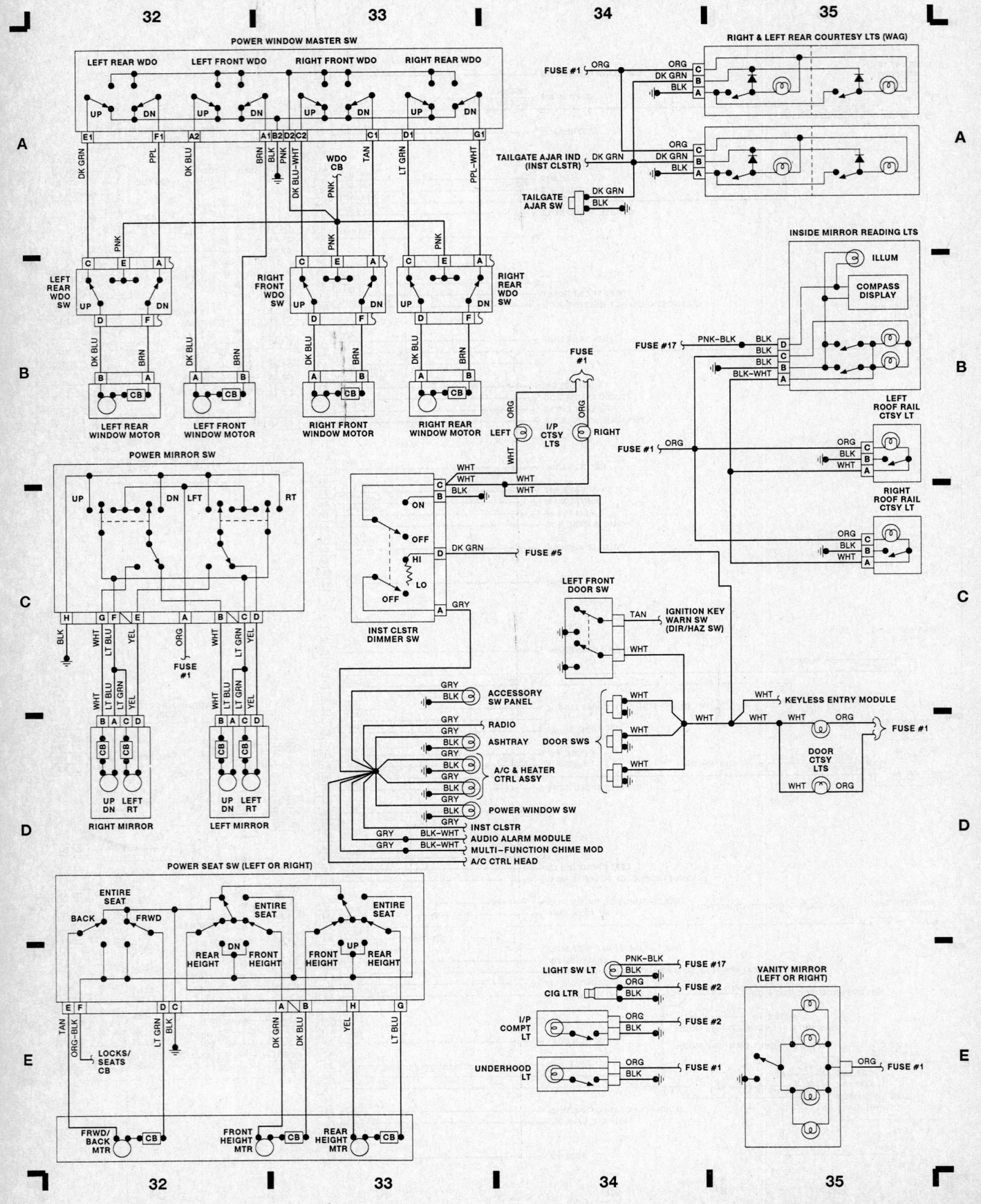

36   37   38   39

INST CLSTR DIMMER SW — BLK 150 — 5 — GROUND
LIGHT SW — GRY 8 — 7 — ILLUM LT INPUT
— BRN 9 — 6 — DIM DISPLAY SIGNAL
FUSE #2 — ORG 40 — 10 — BATTERY POWER
FUSE #9 — YEL 43 — 9 — IGNITION INPUT
— PNK 143 — 8 — ANTENNA CONTROL
CO-AXIAL CABLE — RF INPUT

RADIO (PARTIAL)

A

POWER ANTENNA RELAY
A — ORG — FUSE #1
C — BLK
B — PNK
A — GRY
B — DK GRN
C — WHT

WHT
DK GRN — DK GRN — CB
GRY

ANTENNA MAST
DN SW — UP / DN / DN
UP SW — UP / DN

POWER ANTENNA MOTOR

BLK — MARKER LT
BRN

DK GRN — STOP/DIR LT
BLK / BRN — TAILLT
DIR/HAZARD SW — DK GRN
DK GRN — STOP/DIR LT
LIGHT SW — BRN — BLK / BRN — TAILLT

A

LT GRN — RIGHT BACK-UP LT
BLK

B

KEYLESS ENTRY MODULE
LOCKS/SEATS CB — ORG-BLK — ORG-BLK — A — POWER
— ORG-BLK — BLK — B — TRUNK SW INPUT
REAR GLASS RELEASE SW — TAN — C — UNLOCK OUTPUT
— BLK — D — UNLOCK OUTPUT
— LT BLU — E — LOCK OUTPUT
DOOR SWS — WHT — F — DOOR INPUT
GEAR SEL SW — LT GRN-BLK — G — PARK INPUT
— BLK — H — GROUND
FUSE #1 — ORG — A — POWER
FUSE #6 — BRN — B — IGNITION INPUT
— C
— D
KEYLESS PROGRAMMING CONN — BLK-WHT — E — PROGRAM INPUT
— F
— G
— H

B

POWER DOOR LOCK RELAY
E — TAN
E — GRY
LOCK RELAY
A — ORG-BLK
A — LT BLU
UNLOCK RELAY
F — BLK
D — BLK

LIGHT SW — BRN — BRN — LICENSE LT
BLK
BRAKE/CRUISE RELEASE SW — YEL — HI LEVEL STOP LT
BLK
BRN — LICENSE LT
BLK

C

LT BLU — F — LOCK
BLK — D — UNLOCK
E — ORG
LEFT FRONT DOOR LOCK SW

(W/ 4 DOORS)
(WAGON)
(W/ KEYLESS ENTRY)
(W/ 4 DOORS)

LT BLU — F — LOCK
BLK — D — UNLOCK
E — ORG — FUSE #1
RIGHT FRONT DOOR LOCK SW

C

TAN — B — TAILGATE LOCK MOTOR — CB — A — GRY
TAN — B — LEFT REAR DOOR LOCK MOTOR — CB — A — GRY
TAN — B — LEFT FRONT DOOR LOCK MOTOR — CB — A — GRY
TAN — B — RIGHT FRONT DOOR LOCK MOTOR — CB — A — GRY
TAN — B — RIGHT REAR DOOR LOCK MOTOR — CB — A — GRY

D

GEAR SELECT SW — LT GRN — LT GRN — LEFT BACK-UP LT
BLK

D

REAR DEFOGGER SW
ON — OFF
SOLID STATE TIMER RELAY
IND LT
P — BLK
D — PPL-WHT — PPL-WHT
A / B / C
ORG-BLK — FUSE #15
PNK-BLK — FUSE #17
PPL-WHT — FUSE #16 (W/ HEATED MIRRORS)

FUSE #16 — PNK-WHT — PNK-WHT — BLK — BLK
MIRROR DEFOGGERS
PNK-WHT — BLK — BLK

REAR WDO DEFOGGER — BLK

LIGHT SW — BRN — BRN — TAILLT
BLK / YEL
DIR/HAZARD SW — YEL — STOP/DIR LT
BRN — TAILLT
BLK / YEL
STOP/DIR LT

BLK — BRN — MARKER LT

E

36   37   38   39

1991 WIRING DIAGRAMS
Cutlass Calais

COMPONENT LOCATOR:

A/C COMP CTRL RLY	C 26
A/C PRES SWS	B 25–26
A/C SELECT SW	A 25–27
ABS ENABLE RLY	B 23
ABS MOD	A–B 20
ALDL CONN (2.3L)	D 7
ALDL CONN (2.5L)	D 8
ALDL CONN (3.3L)	C 15
ALTERNATOR	B 3
AUDIO ALARM MOD	C–D 32
AUTOMATIC TRANSAXLE (2.3L)	C–D 6
AUTOMATIC TRANSAXLE (2.5L)	E 8
AUTOMATIC TRANSAXLE (3.3L)	B–C 15
BACK-UP LT SW	B 19
BRAKE SW	C–D 24
CANISTER PURGE SOL (2.3L)	E 6
CANISTER PURGE SOL (3.3L)	E 13–14
CIGARETTE LTR	B 39
CLUTCH START SW	B 18
COMPUTER CTRL COIL	
IGN (CCCI) MOD	D–E 15
CONSOLE SHIFT IND	E 18–19
COOLANT FAN RLY	A–C 24
COURTESY LTS	E 38
CRUISE CTRL MOD	E 24
CRUISE CTRL SERVO	D–E 24
DEFOG GRID	B 42
DIMMER MOD	C 38
DIR FLASHER	C 30
DIR HAZ SW	A–B 28
DIRECT IGN SYS (DIS)	D–E 9–11
DOME LT	D 37
DRIVER INFORMATION	
DISPLAY ASSY	E 32
ELECTRONIC CONTROL	
MODULE (ECM) (2.3L)	A–E 4
ELECTRONIC CONTROL	
MODULE (ECM) (2.5L)	A 8–11
ELECTRONIC CONTROL	
MODULE (ECM) (3.3L)	A–E 12
ELECTRONIC VARIABLE ORIFICE	
(EVO) STEERING	E 23
FOG LIGHT RLY	C 2
FUEL PUMP RLY (2.3L)	A 5
FUEL PUMP RLY (2.5L)	B–C 11
FUEL PUMP RLY (3.3L)	A 15
FUEL TANK UNIT	D 42
FUSE BLOCK	C–D 17–18
GEAR SELECT SW	C–D 28
GLOVE BOX LT	B 39
HAZ FLASHER	D 32
HEADER COURTESY/READING	
LTS ASSY	D 39
HEADLT SW	E 28–29
HEATER BLOWER SW	A 24
HI BEAM SELECT SW	D 29
HI BLOWER RLY	B 27
HORN RLY	D 32
IGN SW	A 16–19
INST CLSTR	A–D 35
INTEGRATED DIRECT	
IGN SYS (IDI SYS)	A–C 7
KEYLESS ENTRY MOD	E 36
LAMP MOD	B–C 23
MAF SENS (3.3L)	E 15
MASTER SW ASSY	A 40–42
MULTI-FUNCTION LEVER	E 27
POWER ANTENNA RLY	C 40
POWER DOOR SYS	D–E 40–42
POWER SEAT SW ASSY	A 36–38
REAR DEFOG CTRL SW	D–E 31
REAR DEFOG TIMER RLY	E 31
STARTER SOL	A 2–3
STOP LT SW	B 28
TRUNK LT	E 42
TRUNK RELEASE SW	D 40
WIPER/WASHER ASSY	C–E 3
WIPER/WASHER SW ASSY	A–D 31

MARKER LT

DIR LT

PARK LT

LEFT PARK & MARKER LT

DIR/HAZARD SW

RIGHT DIR IND (INST CLSTR)

BATTERY

STARTER SOLENOID

STARTER MOTOR

CLUTCH START SW (M/T)

GEAR SELECT SW (A/T)

RUST FUS LINK

RED FUS LINK

BLU (OR GRY) FUS LINK

GRY FUS LINK

IGN SW

ABS ENABLE RLY

ECM (2.5L/3.3L)

(2.3L/3.3L)

IGNITION SW
HI BLOWER RELAY
TAIL LPS FUSE
COOLANT FAN RELAY
ABS MOD
ECM

(2.5L/3.3L)
(W/ A/C)
(2.3L)

ALTERNATOR

ECM-RLYS FUSE
CHARGE IND (INST CLSTR)

RIGHT COMPOSITE HEADLIGHT

LO / HI

TAN
BLK–WHT
BLK–WHT
LT GRN

FOG LT

HORNS

HORN RELAY (CONVENIENCE CENTER)

FOG LT

HEADER COURTESY/ READING LTS ASSEMBLY

FOG LIGHT RELAY

WASHER MOTOR

WIPER/WASHER SW ASSY

WIPER/WASHER MOTOR ASSY (W/O PULSE)

HI BEAM IND (INST CLSTR)

LEFT COMPOSITE HEADLIGHT

HI / LO

HI BEAM SELECT SW

WIPER/WASHER SW ASSY

TIMER

WIPER/WASHER MOTOR ASSY (W/ PULSE)

RIGHT PARK & MARKER LT

DIR/ HAZARD SW

HEADLIGHT SW

PARK LT

DIR LT

LEFT DIR IND (INST CLSTR)

MARKER LT

ENG COMPT LT

WASHER MOTOR

4   5   6   7

FUEL PUMP RELAY

FUEL PUMP/ OIL PRES SW (PARTIAL)

SPARK PLUGS

1   4

IGN COIL

IGN MOD

SW "A"

AMPLIFIER

SW "B"

IGN COIL

3   2

INTEGRATED DIRECT IGNITION SYSTEM

SPARK PLUGS

Pin	Wire	Label
A1		
A2		
A3		
A4	416 GRY	5 VOLT REFERENCE
A5	416 GRY	5 VOLT REFERENCE
A6	439 PNK–BLK	IGNITION
A7		ECM–RLYS FUSE
A8	461 ORG	SERIAL DATA IN/OUT
A9		
A10	465 DK GRN–WHT	FUEL PUMP RELAY CTRL
A11	450 BLK–WHT	GROUND
A12	2 RED	BATTERY
B1		RED FUS LINK
B2		
B3		
B4	469 BLK–ORG	SENSOR GROUND
B5	452 BLK	SENSOR GROUND
B6		
B7		
B8	401 PPL	VEH SPEED SENSOR LO
B9	400 YEL	VEH SPEED SENSOR HI
B10	389 DK GRN	VEH SPEED OUTPUT
B11		
B12		

VEHICLE SPEED SENSOR

SPEEDOMETER (INST CLSTR)

Pin	Wire	Label
C1		(W/O A/C)
C2	450 TAN–WHT	GROUND
C3	420 PPL	BRAKES APPLIED INPUT
C4	647 LT BLU–BLK	CRANK SENSOR INPUT
C5		
C6	424 TAN–BLK	IGN MOD BYPASS CTRL
C7	423 WHT	EST OUTPUT
C8	66 LT GRN	A/C ON INPUT
C9	468 LT GRN	FUEL INJECTOR CTRL
C10		A/C COMP CTRL RELAY
C11	467 LT BLU	FUEL INJECTOR CTRL
C12	888 ORG	ECM JUMPER
C13		
C14		
C15	2 RED	ECM JUMPER
C16	551 TAN–WHT	BATTERY
D1		GROUND / RED FUS LINK
D2		
D3	232 WHT	SECOND GEAR INPUT
D4	887 LT GRN–BLK	ECM JUMPER
D5		ECM JUMPER
D6		
D7	430 PPL–WHT	REF PULSE INPUT HI
D8	453 BLK–RED	REF PULSE INPUT LO
D9		
D10	BLK–WHT	
D11		POWER STEERING PRES SW
D12	495 LT BLU–ORG	PWR STEERING PRES SW
D13		
D14	438 DK GRN–WHT	THIRD GEAR INPUT
D15	434 ORG–BLK	PARK/NEUTRAL INPUT
D16		GEAR SELECT SW

FUEL INJECTORS   2 3 4 1   LT GRN / LT GRN / LT BLU / LT BLU

NOT USED   WHT   TACHOMETER (GAUGES INST CLSTR)

CRANK POSITION SENSOR

PNK–BLK / TAN–BLK / WHT

PPL / YEL / PPL–WHT

BLK–WHT / BLK–RED / LT BLU–BLK

Pin	Wire	Label
E1		
E2		
E3	441 LT BLU–WHT	IDLE AIR CTRL VALVE
E4	442 LT BLU–BLK	IDLE AIR CTRL VALVE
E5	443 LT GRN–WHT	IDLE AIR CTRL VALVE
E6	444 LT GRN–BLK	IDLE AIR CTRL VALVE
E7	419 BRN–WHT	SERVICE ENGINE SOON
E8	536 LT GRN–BLK	COLNT FAN RELAY CTRL
E9		COOLANT FAN RELAY
E10		
E11	451 WHT–BLK	DIAGNOSTIC TEST
E12		
E13	412 PPL	OXYGEN SENS INPUT HI
E14	413 TAN	OXYGEN SENS INPUT LO
E15	410 YEL	COOLANT TEMP SENSOR
E16		
F1	428 DK GRN–YEL	CANISTER PURGE SOL
F2	459 DK GRN–WHT	A/C COMP CONTROL
F3		
F4	422 (OR 456) TAN–BLK	SHIFT M/T, TCC A/T
F5		
F6		
F7	35 DK GRN	COOLANT TEMP IND
F8		COOLANT TEMP IND (INST CLSTR)
F9	496 DK BLU	DETONATION SENS INPUT
F10		DETONATION SENSOR
F11		
F12		
F13	417 DK BLU	TPS INPUT
F14	380 GRY–RED	A/C PRES SENS INPUT
F15	432 LT GRN	MAP SENSOR INPUT
F16	472 TAN	MAT SENSOR INPUT

ELECTRONIC CONTROL MODULE (2.3L VIN A & D)

OXYGEN SENSOR (BLK)

MAT SENSOR (BLK–ORG)

AUTOMATIC TRANSAXLE

TCC SOL

BRAKE SW   PPL / PPL

2ND SW (CLOSES IN 2ND)

2ND SW (OPENS IN 2ND)

3RD SW (OPENS IN 3RD)

DK GRN–WHT

TAN–BLK / WHT

DK GRN–WHT   A/C COMP CONTROL RELAY

SES IND (INST CLSTR)

(A/T)

DRIVER INFO DISPLAY ASSY   ORG

DK GRN–YEL / PNK–BLK   CANISTER PURGE SOL

TAN–BLK   SHIFT IND (INST CLSTR)

(M/T)

IDLE AIR CONTROL MOTOR

LT BLU–WHT / LT BLU–BLK / LT GRN–WHT / LT GRN–BLK   (D C B A)

EVO   BLK–WHT / WHT / WHT / TAN–BLK / TAN–WHT

ABS MOD   ORG / WHT–BLK / ORG

ORG

ALDL CONN (A B C D E F G H J K L M)

COOLANT TEMP SENSOR   YEL / BLK

THROTTLE POSITION SENSOR   BLK / DK BLU / GRY (C B A)

A/C COMP REFRIG SENSOR   GRY / GRY–RED / BLK (B C A)

MAP SENSOR   GRY / LT GRN / BLK–ORG (C B A)

FUEL PUMP/ OIL PRES SW: C D

GRY   E4   GRY   **FUEL TANK UNIT**

PNK–BLK / GRY

GRY   **FUEL PUMP PRIME CONN**

DK GRN–WHT / BLK–WHT / GRY / PNK–BLK

E5

PNK–WHT   **F/P–INJ FUSE**

F4   PNK–BLK   **IGN FUSE**

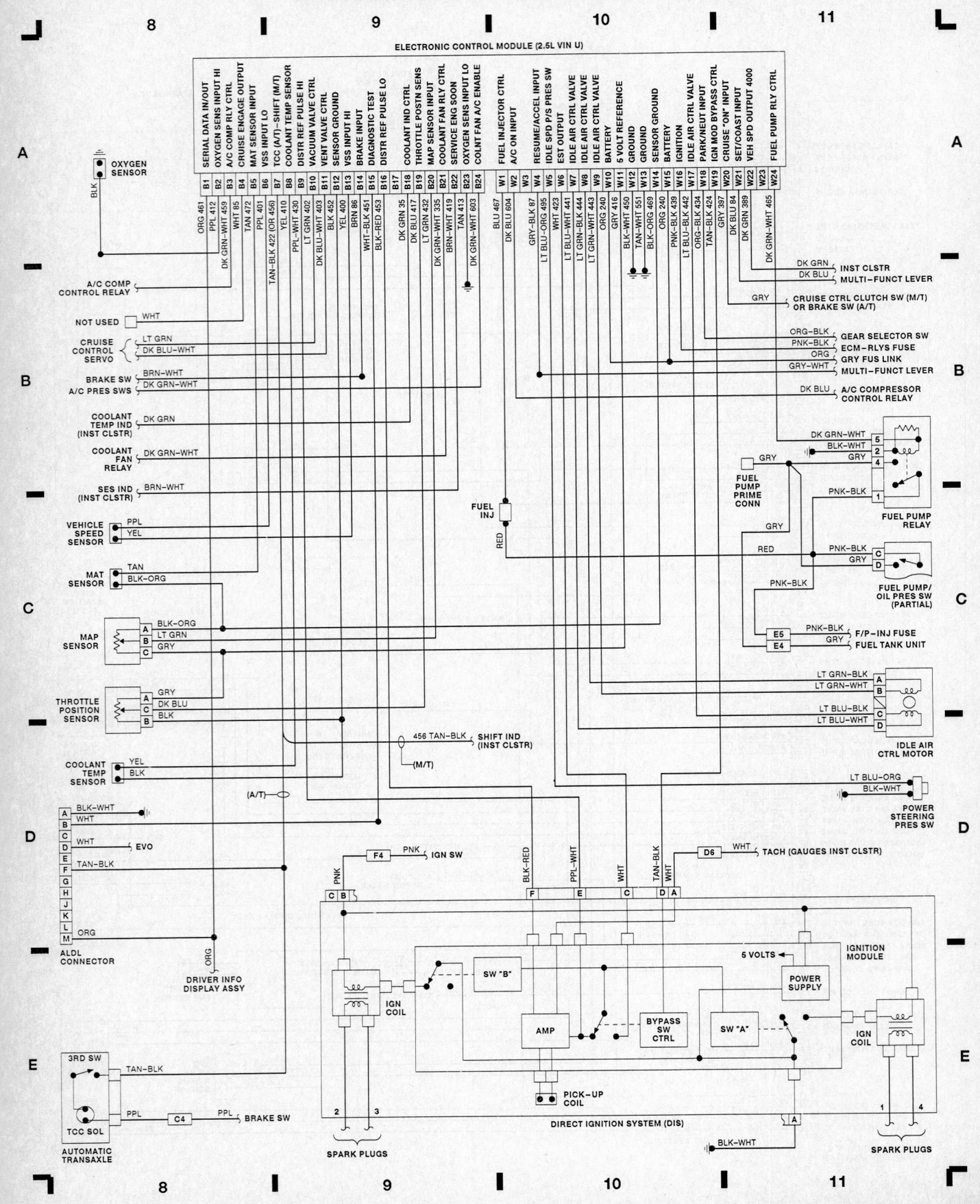

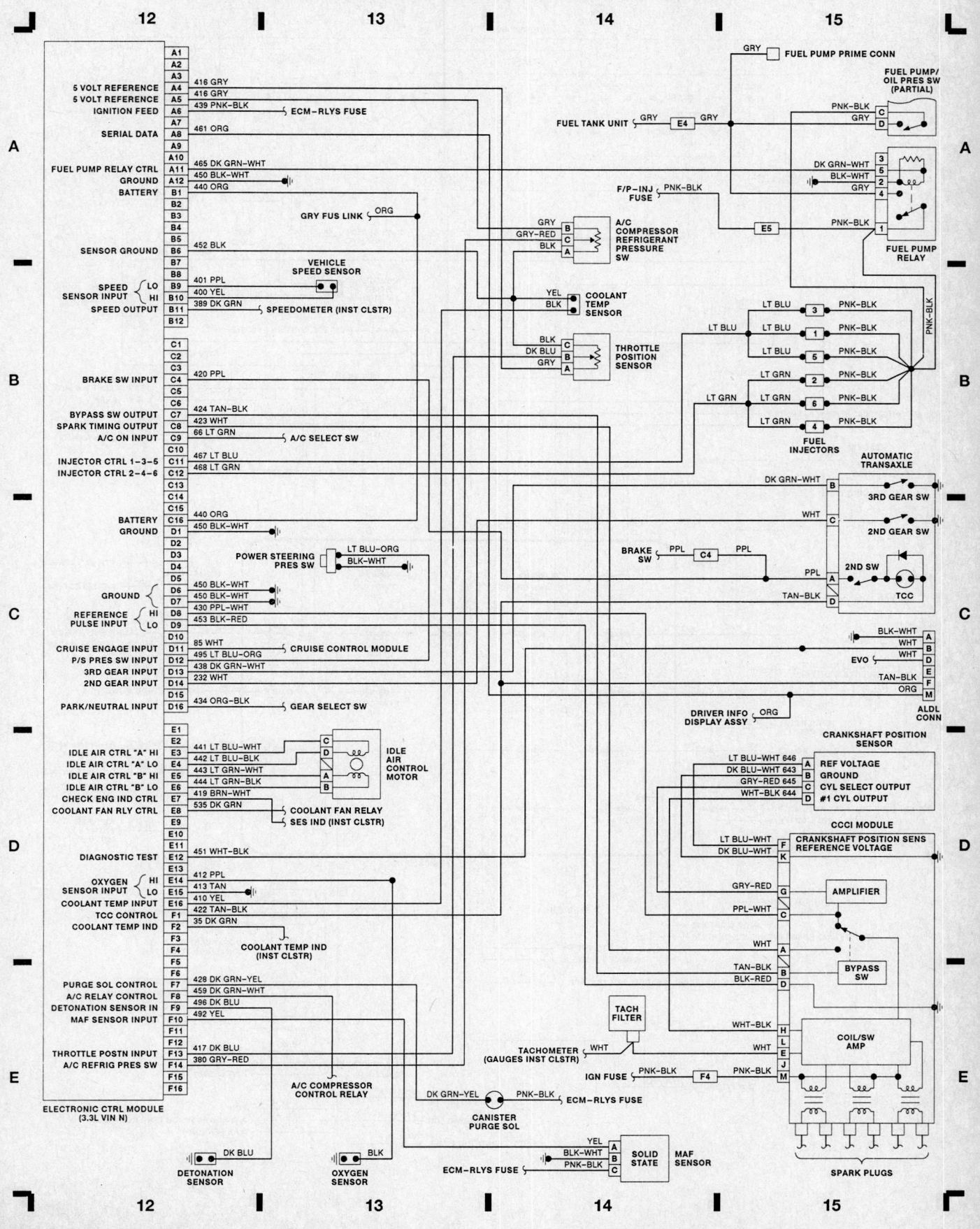

1991 WIRING DIAGRAMS
Cutlass Calais (Cont.)

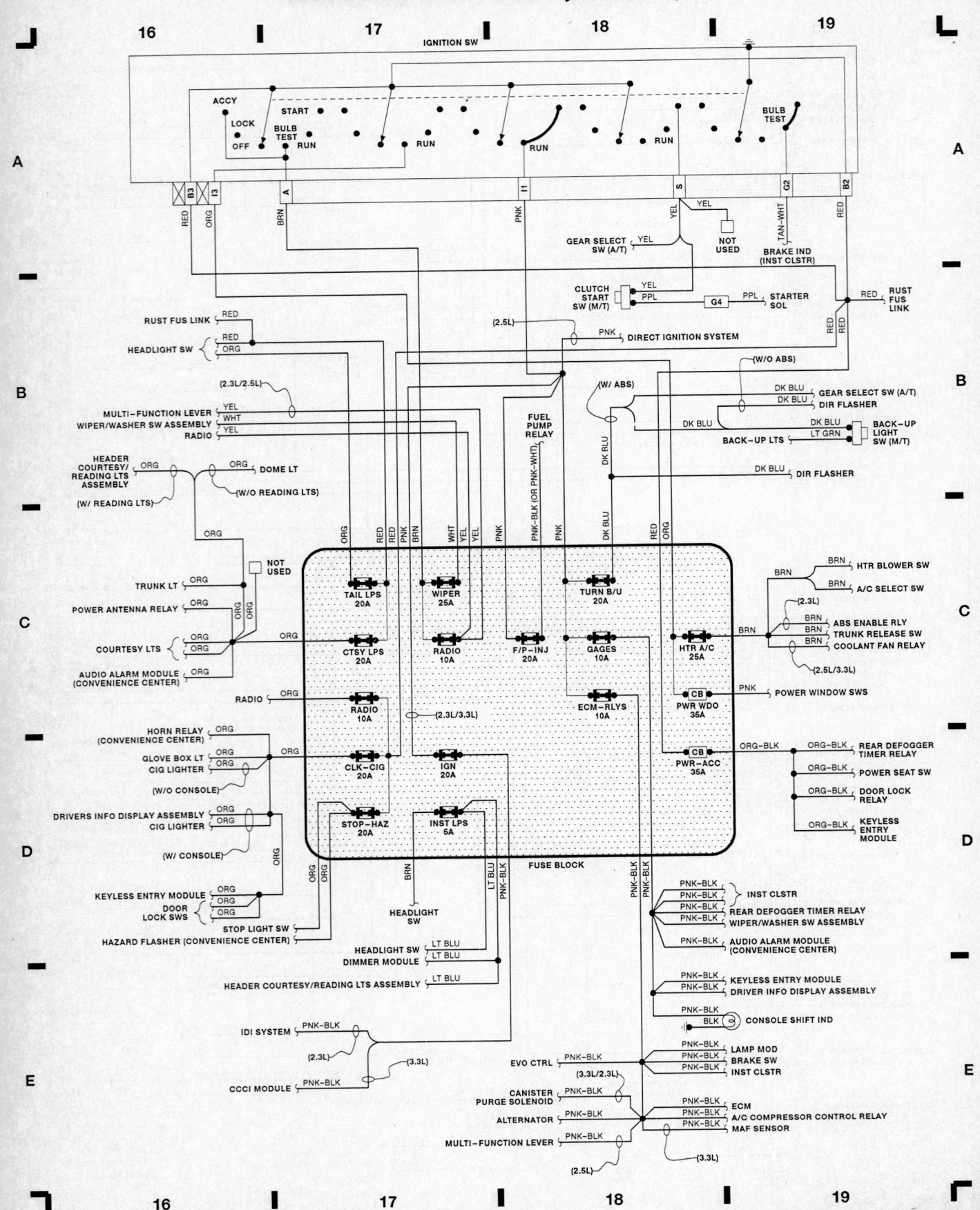

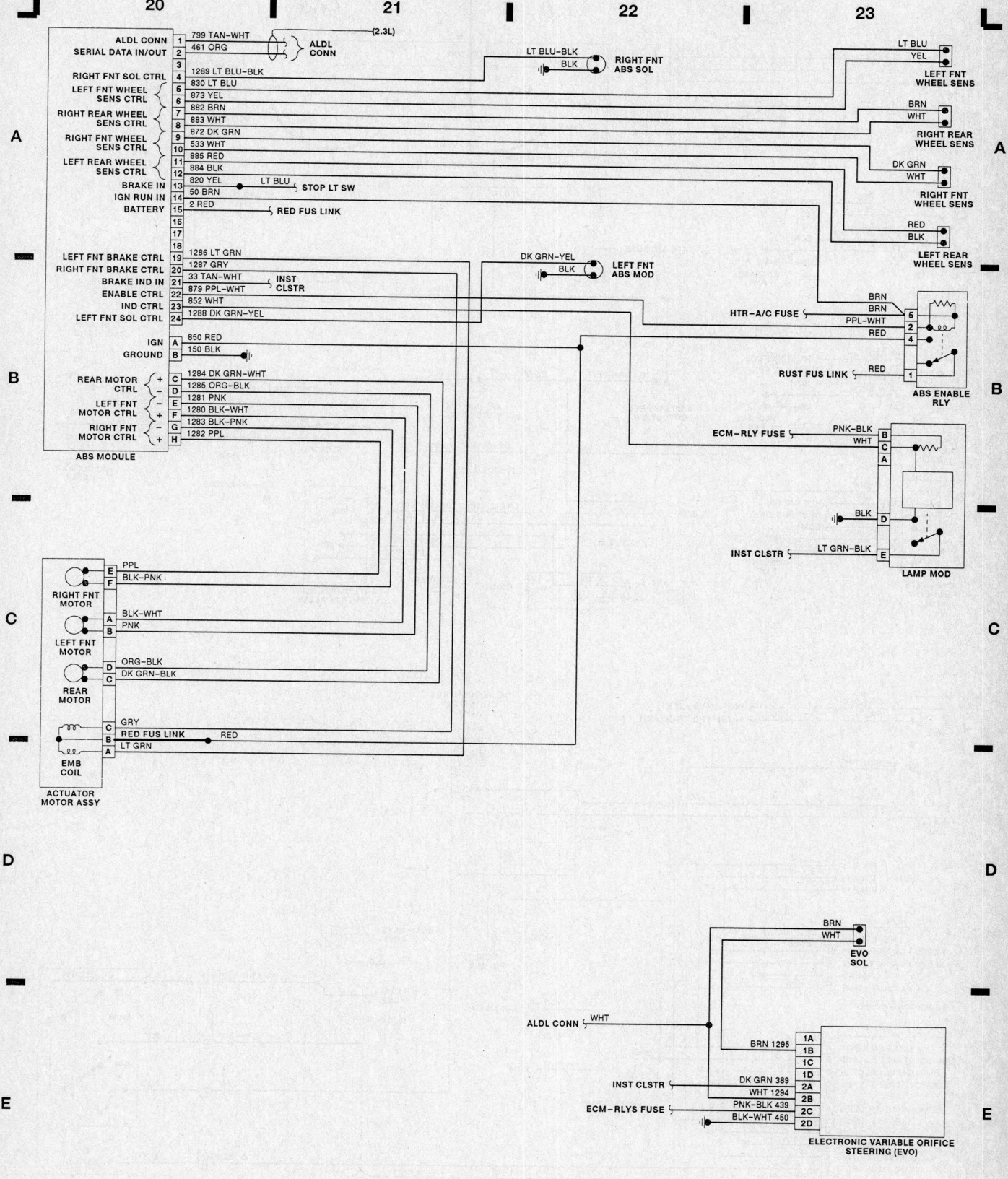

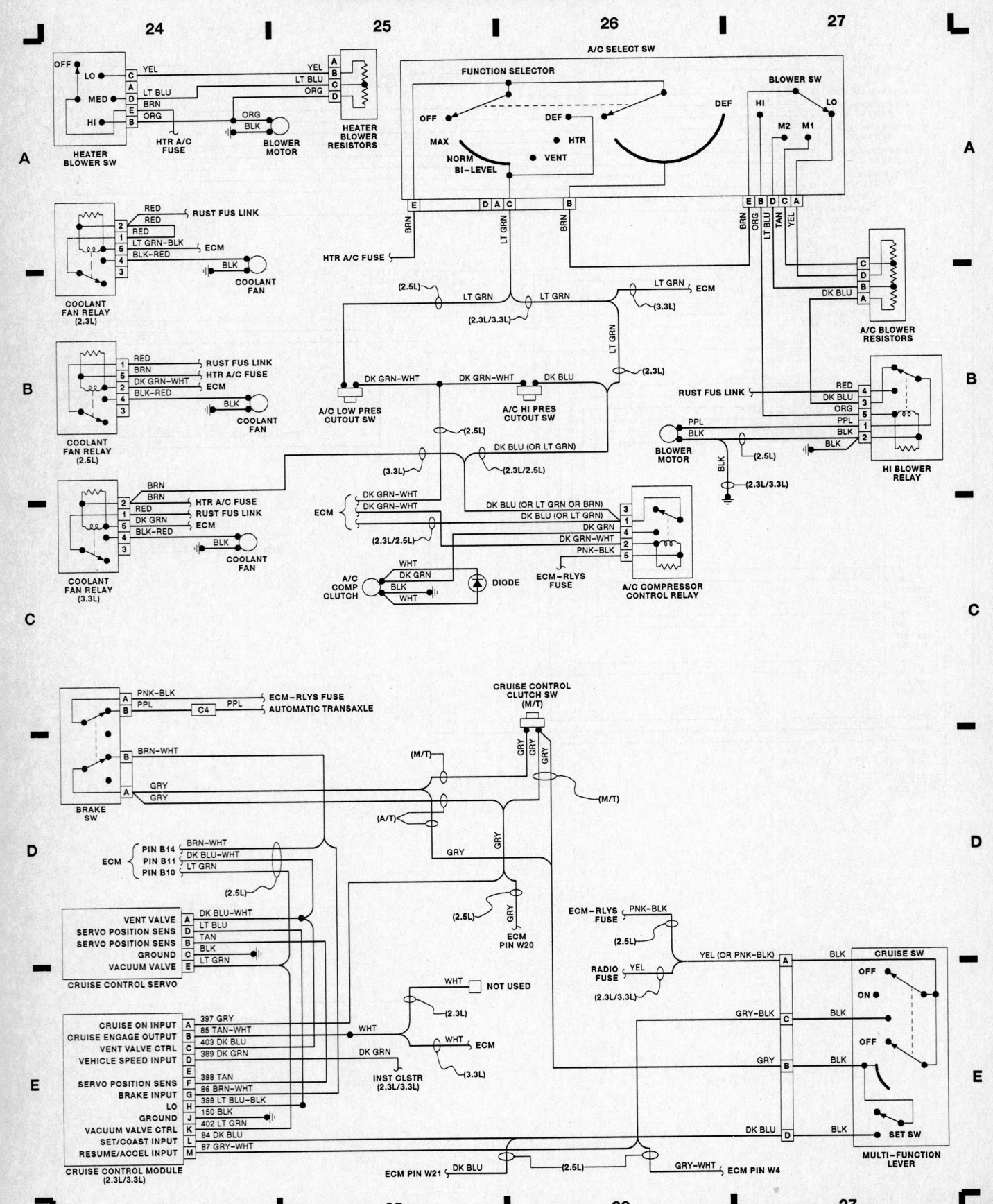

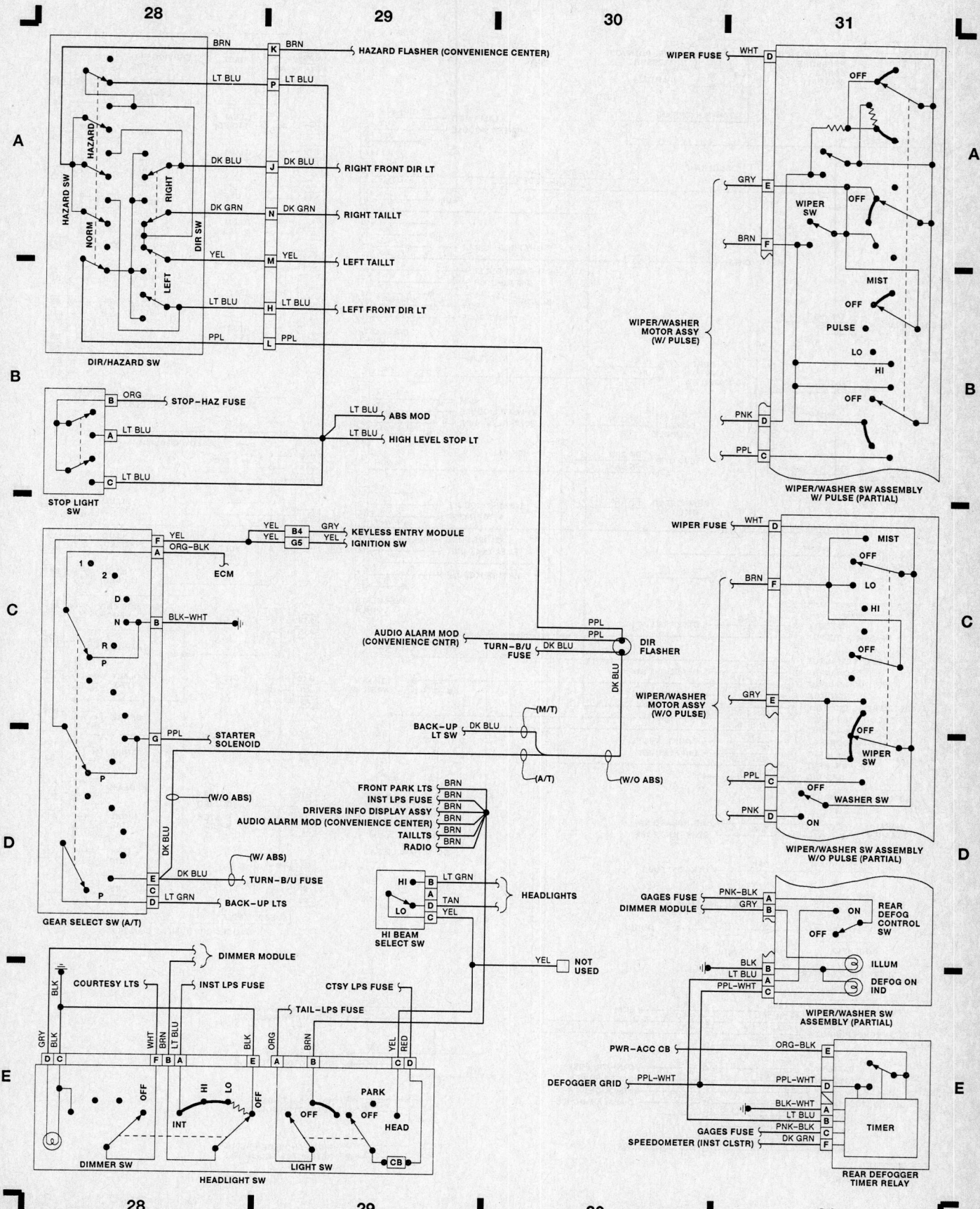

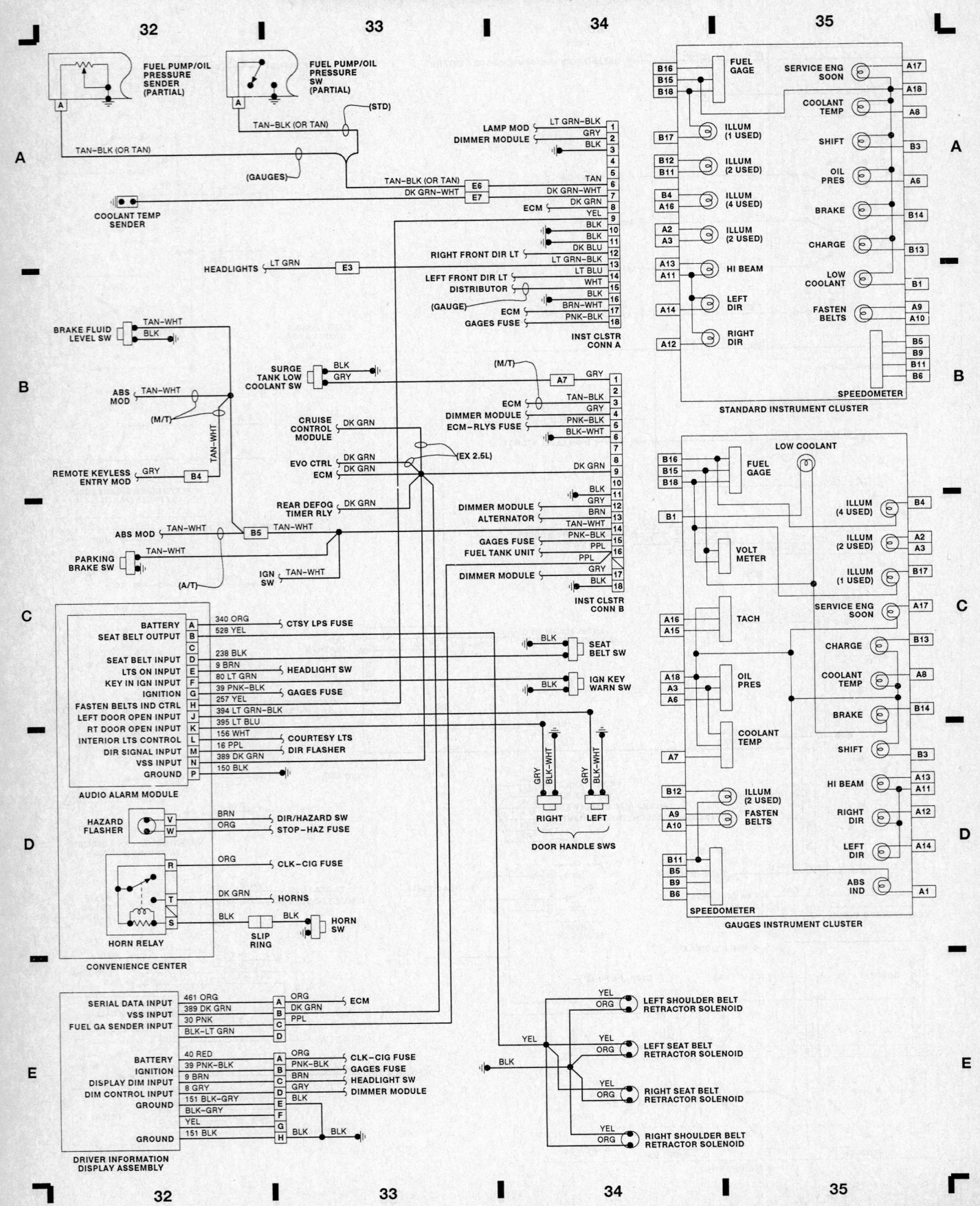

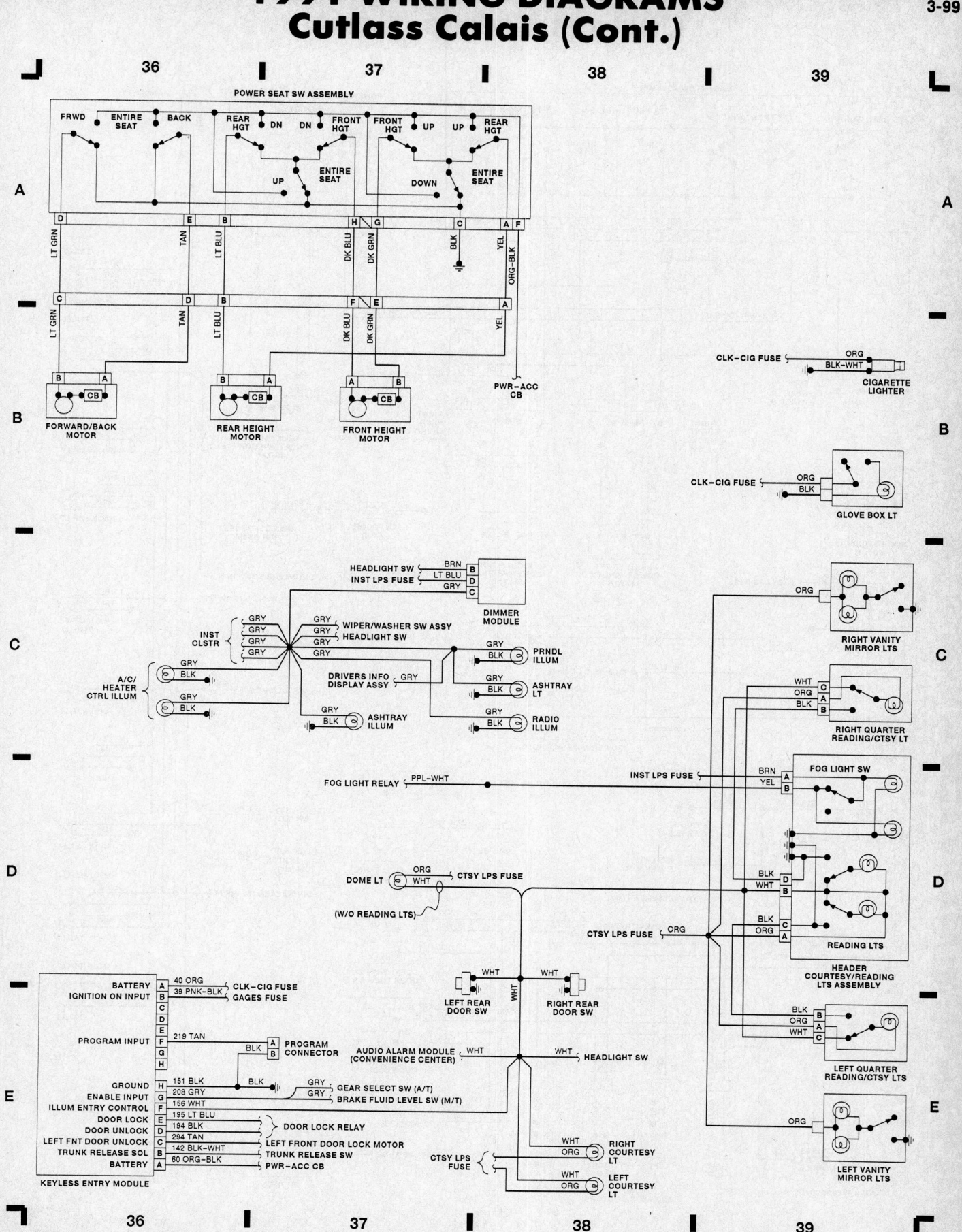

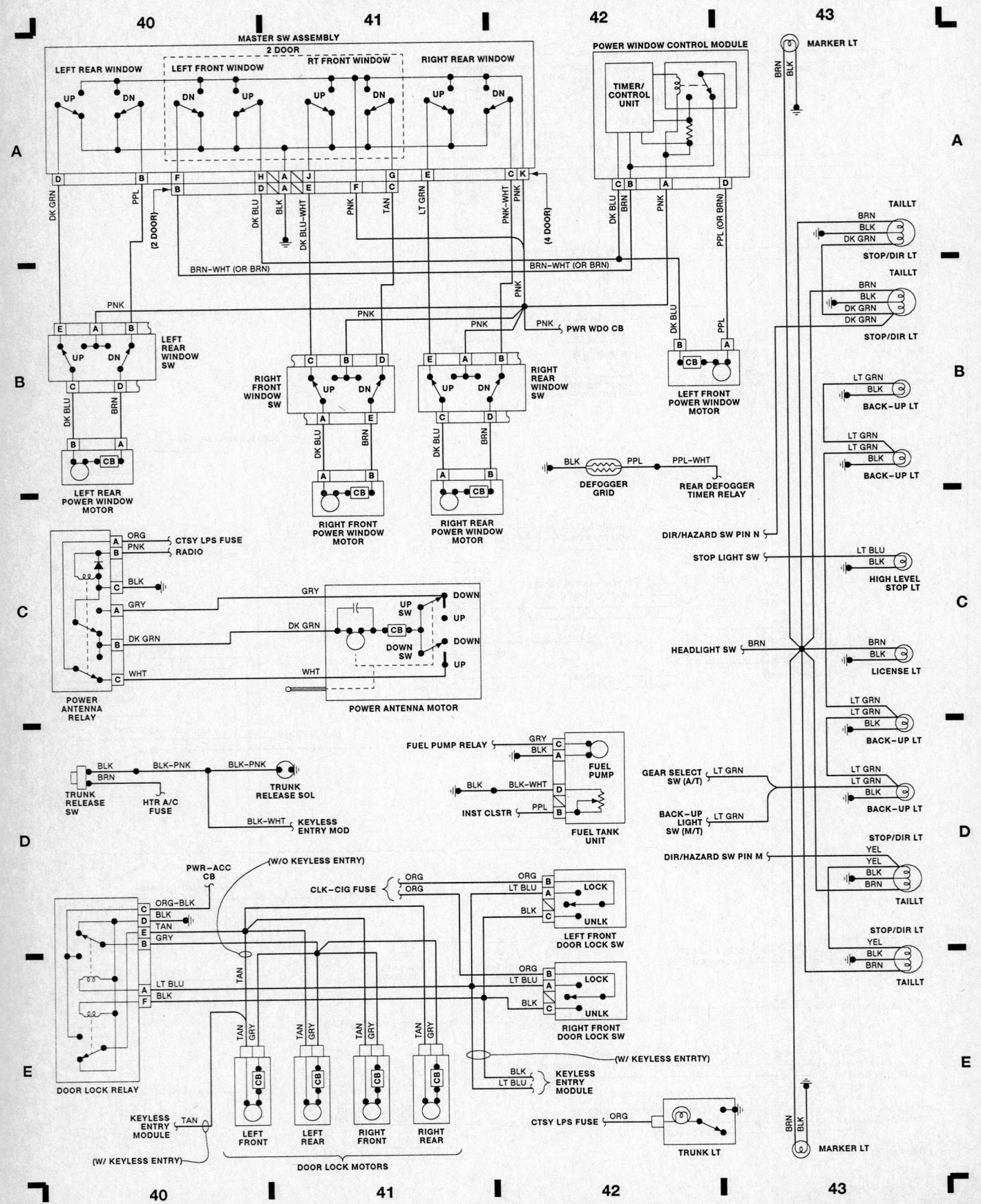

COMPONENT LOCATOR:

A/C & HEATER SYSTEM .... A–B 16–19
ALDL CONN (2.5L) .... B–C 4
ALDL CONN (3.3L) .... D 10
ALTERNATOR .... B 3
ASHTRAY LT .... D 12
AUDIO ALARM MODULE .... D–E 24
AUTO TRANS (2.5L) .... E 4
BATTERY .... A 3
BRAKE FLUID LEVEL SW .... C 27
BRAKE SW .... E 19
CIG LTR .... E 15
COMPUTER CONTROLLED COIL
  IGN (CCCI) MODULE (3.3L) .... B–C 11
CONSOLE ASHTRAY LT .... E 12
CONSOLE CIG LTR .... D 15
CONSOLE COURTESY LT .... B 23
CONSOLE SHIFT IND .... E 12
COOLANT FAN RELAY .... C 3
COOLANT TEMP SENDER .... B 27
COURTESY LTS .... A 23
CRUISE CTRL SYSTEM .... C–E 18–19
DEFOG SYSTEM .... C–D 20
DIR LT FLASHER .... E 22
DIR/HAZ SW .... E 20–21
DIS MODULE (2.5L) .... E 5–6
DOME LT .... B 23
DOOR LATCH SWS .... D 26
DOOR SWS .... A–B 23
DRIVER INFORMATION
  CENTER (DIC) .... C 31
ELECTRONIC CTRL MODULE
  (ECM) (2.5L VIN R) .... A 4–7
ELECTRONIC CTRL MODULE
  (ECM) (3.3L VIN N) .... A–E 8
ENG COMPT LT .... A 22
FOG LT RELAY .... B 20
FOG LT SW .... C 20
FUEL INJECTORS (3.3L) .... D 11
FUEL PUMP (2.5L) .... E 7
FUEL PUMP (3.3L) .... A 11
FUEL PUMP IN-LINE FUSE (2.5L) .. D 7
FUEL PUMP IN-LINE FUSE (3.3L) .. A 10
FUEL PUMP OIL PRES
  SENS/SW (2.5L) .... D 7
FUEL PUMP OIL PRES
  SENS/SW (3.3L) .... A 11
FUEL TANK UNIT .... B 27
FUS LINKS .... A–B 2–3
FUSE BLOCK .... C–D 13–14
GEAR SEL SW .... C–E 23
HAZARD FLASHER .... D 20
HEATER SW (W/O A/C) .... E 16–18
HORN RELAY .... E 24
HORN SW .... E 25
I/P COMPT LT .... B 15
IGN KEY WARN SW .... D 25
IGNITION SW .... A 12–15
INSTRUMENT CLUSTERS .... A–D 24–25
KEYLESS ENTRY MODULE .... A 28
LIGHT SW .... A 20
LIGHT SW LT .... C 12
MAF SENS (3.3L) .... E 9
OIL PRES SW .... D 27
PARK BRAKE SW .... C 27
PASSIVE RESTRAINT MODULE ..... D–E 26
POWER ANTENNA .... B 32
POWER DOOR LOCK SYSTEM ...... A–B 30–31
POWER RECLINER SEAT SYSTEM .. A 32–33
POWER SEAT SYSTEM .... D–E 32–33
POWER WINDOW SYSTEMS .... C–E 28–31
PURGE SOL (3.3L) .... E 9–10
RADIO (PARTIAL) .... B 27
REAR DOME LT (WAGON) .... C 21
SAFETY BELT IN-LINE FUSE .... D 26
SEAT BELT SW .... E 25
STARTER .... A–B 3
STOP LT SW .... D 22–23
TAILGATE AJAR SW .... C 27
TRUNK LID/TAILGATE
  RELEASE SYSTEMS .... B 28–29
TRUNK LT .... B 15
VANITY MIRROR LT .... B 15
WIPER MODULE (W/O PULSE) ...... D 2
WIPER MODULE W/ PULSE) .... E 2–3
WIPER/WASHER SWS .... B–D 16–17

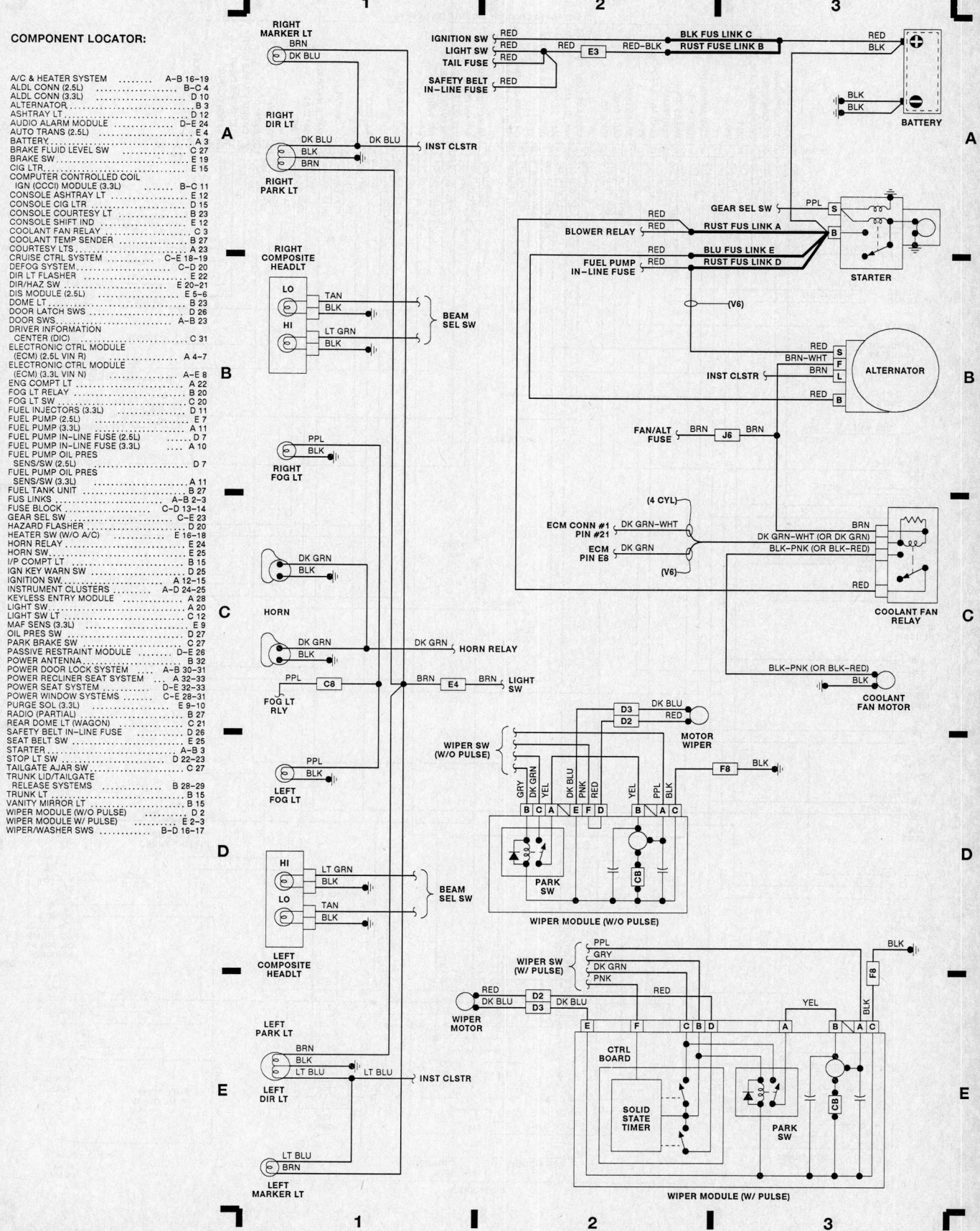

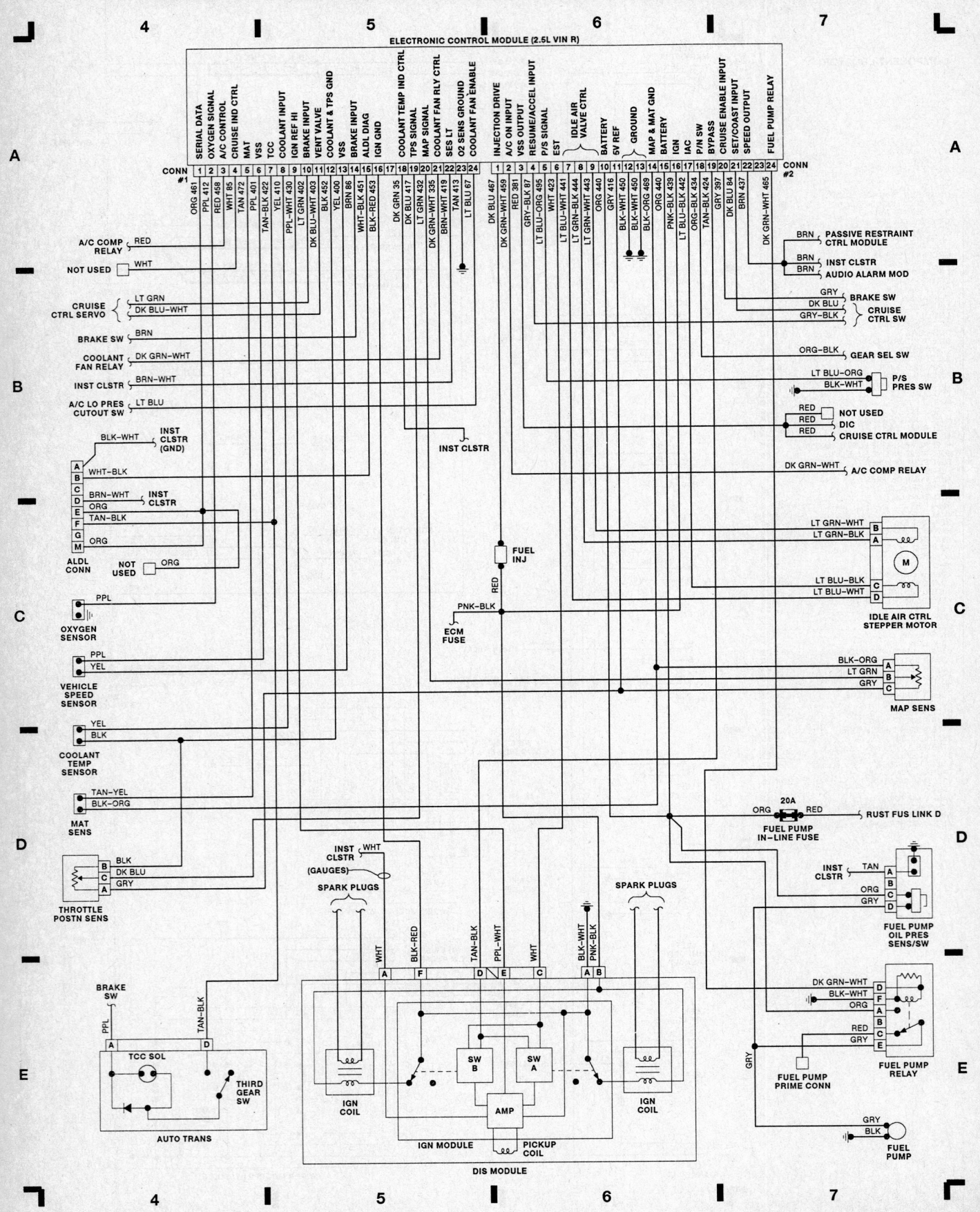

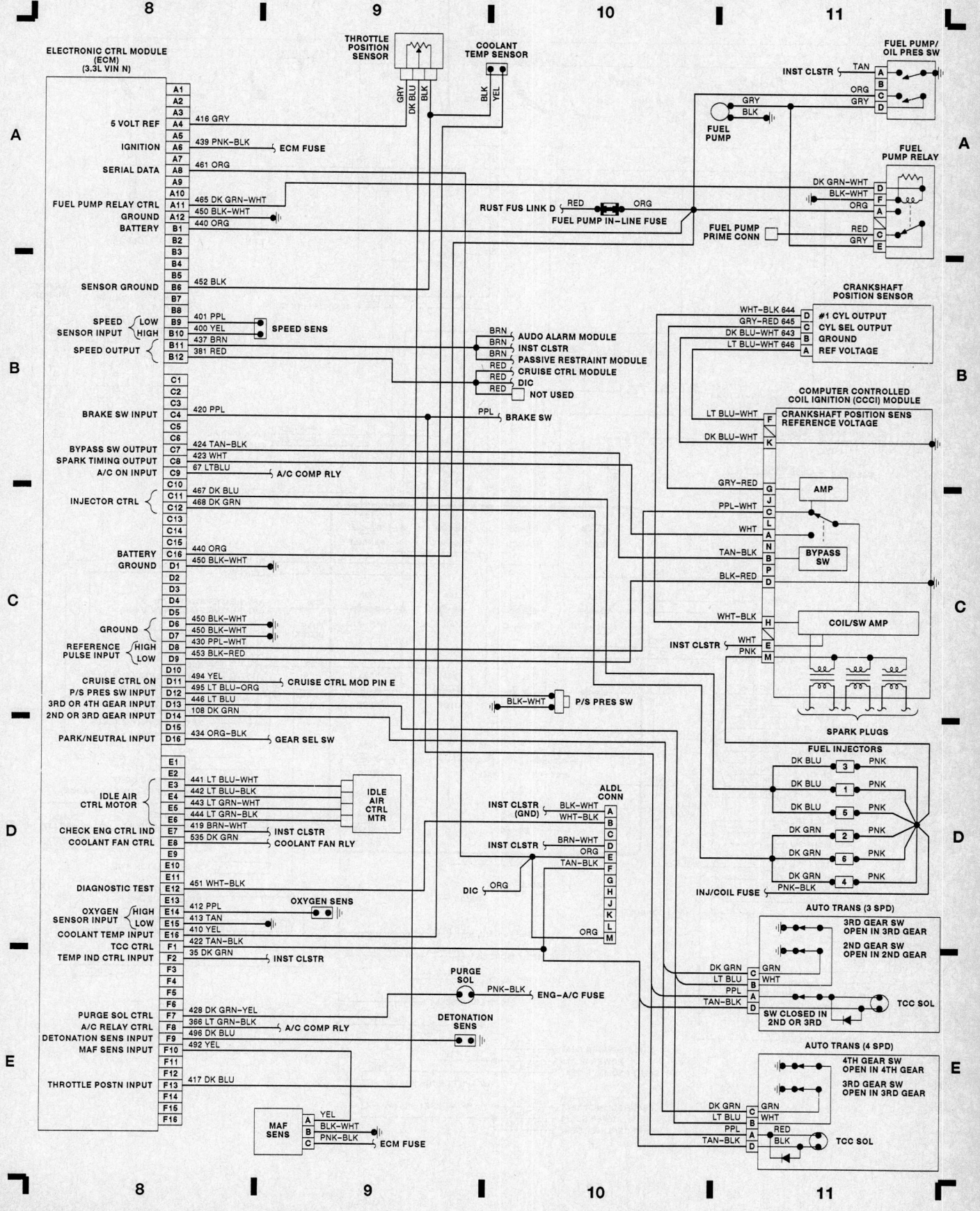

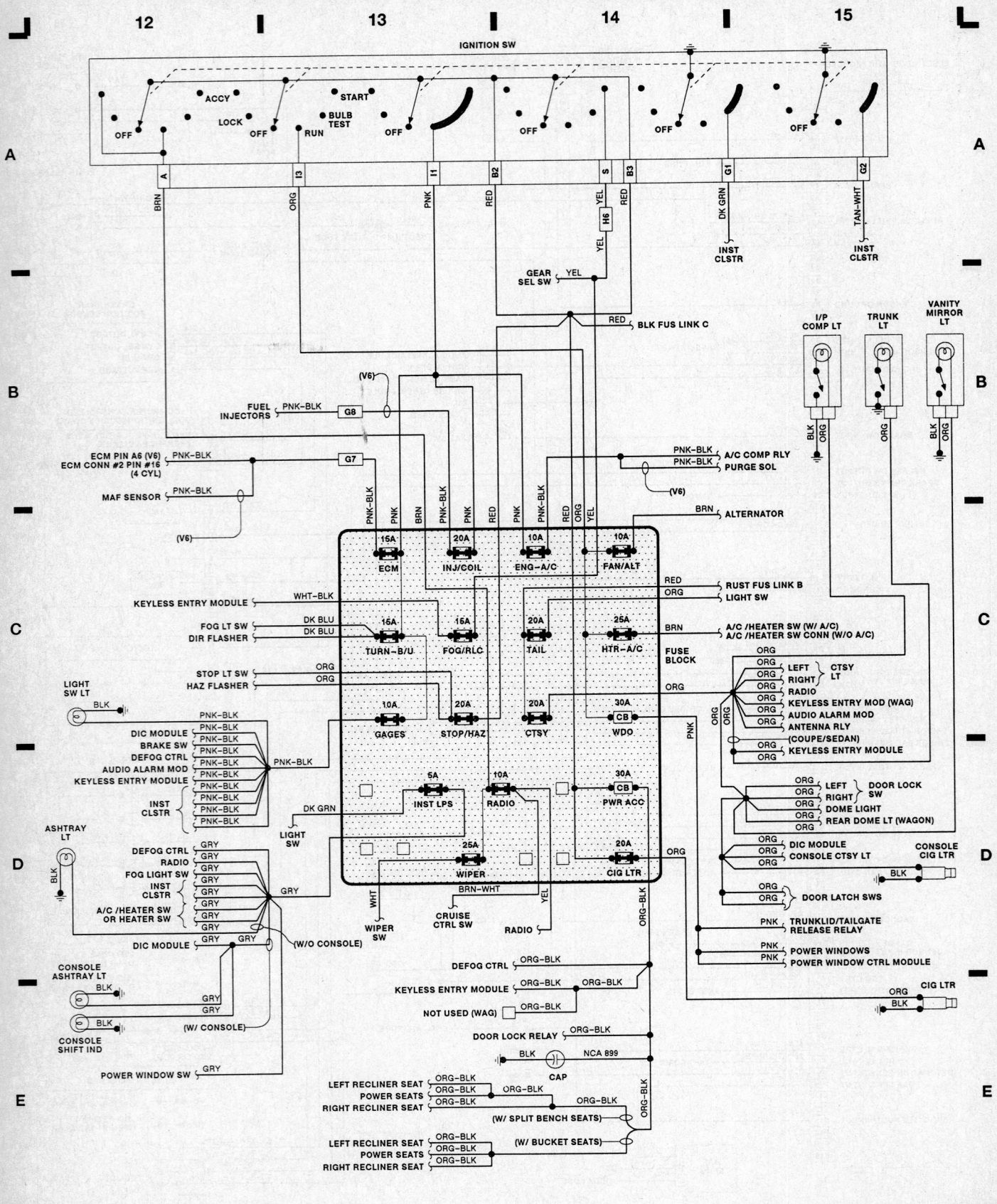

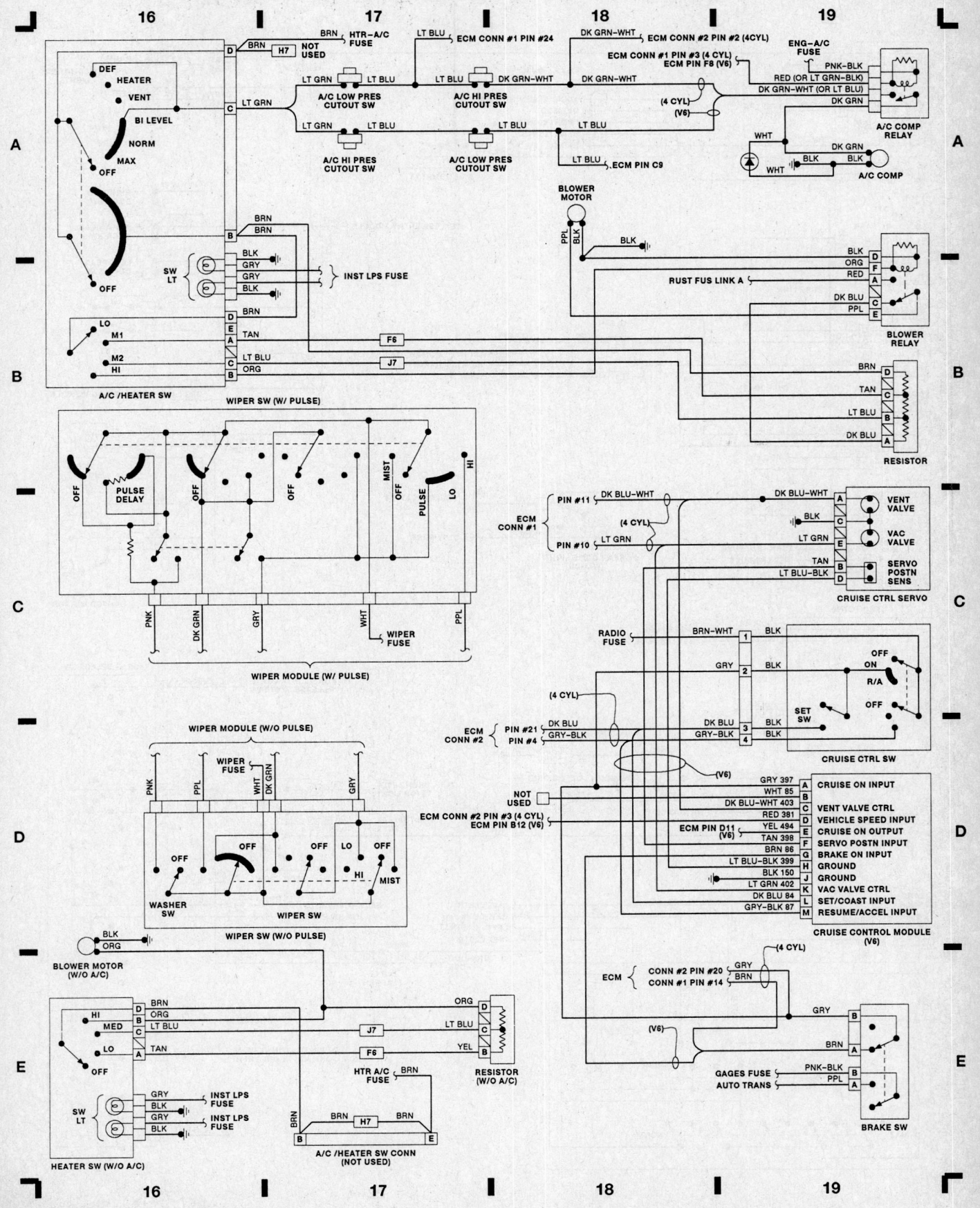

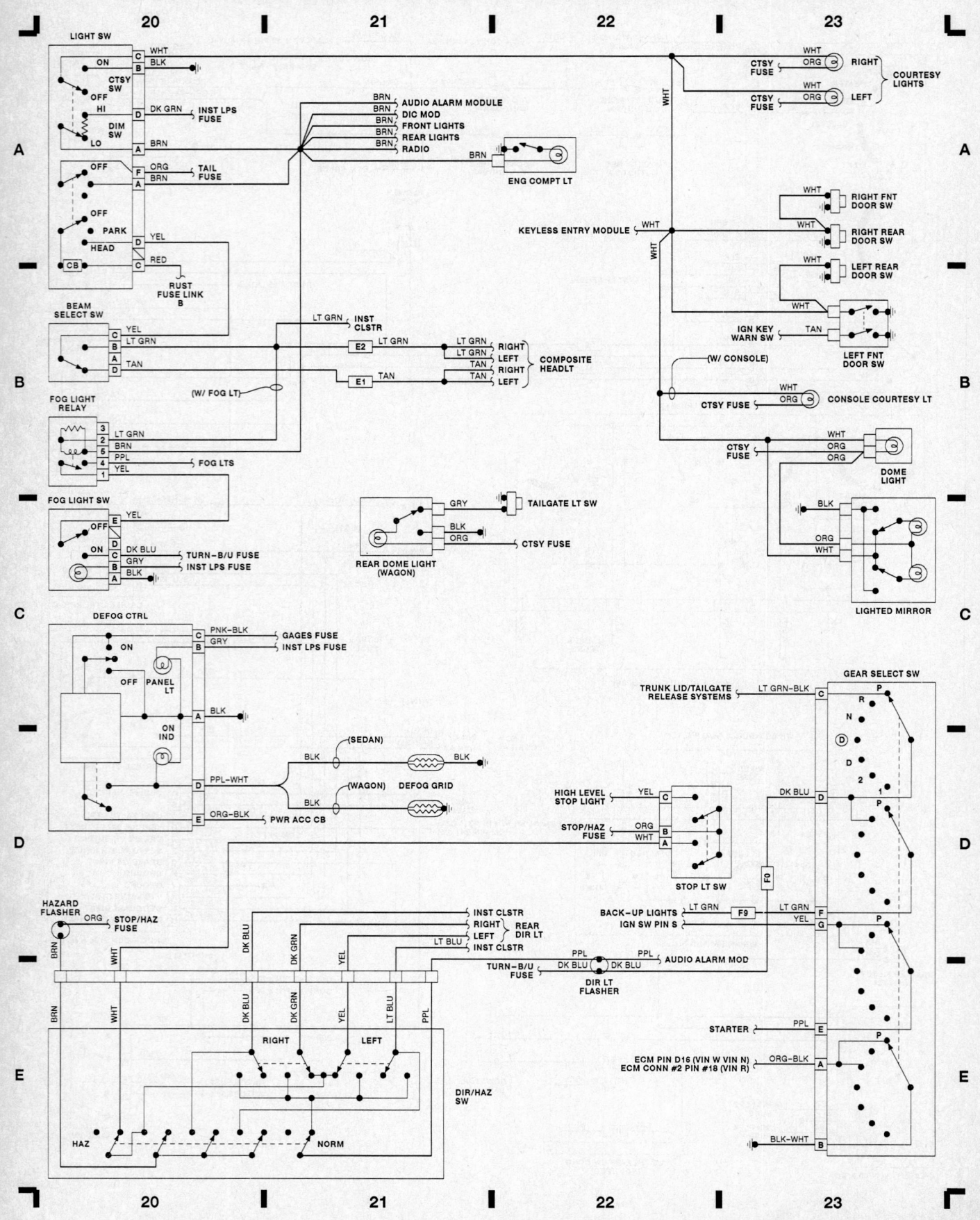

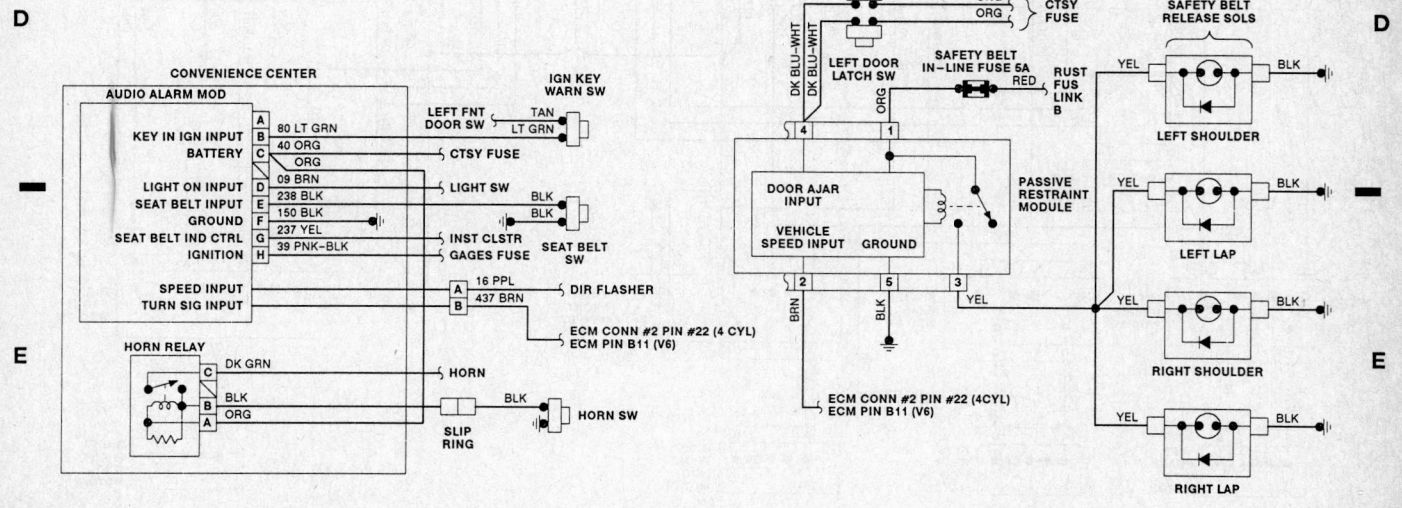

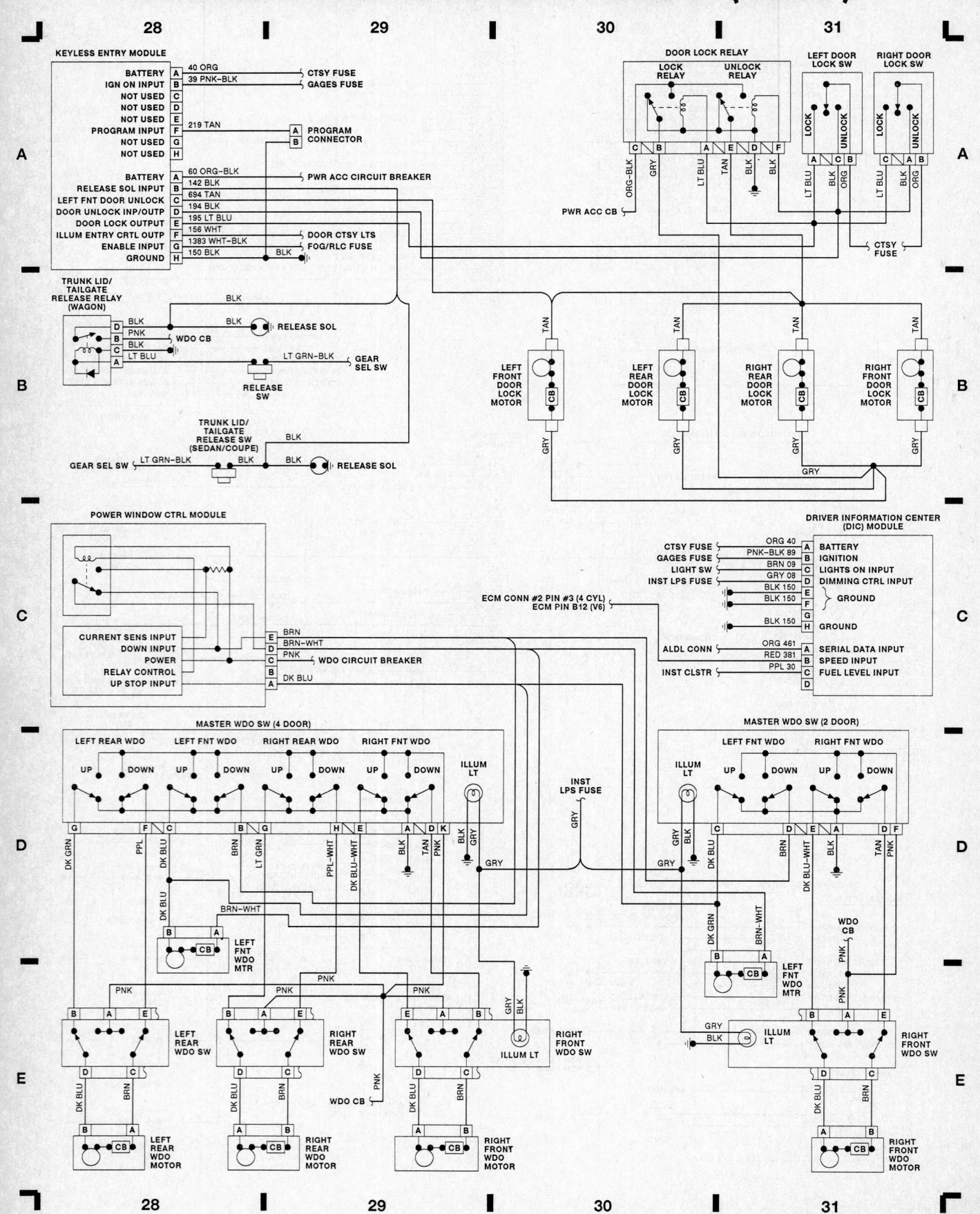

32　33　34　35

ORG-BLK — PWR ACC CB　PWR ACC CB — DK GRN

BRN / BLK — RIGHT MARKER LT

RECLINE　FWD　BLK　BLK

LT GRN / BLK — RIGHT BACK-UP LIGHTS

LEFT RECLINER SW　RIGHT RECLINING SEAT

BLK　BLK

A

LT BLU　LT GRN　LT BLU　LT GRN

BLK　BLK　BLK　BLK

YEL　RED　YEL　RED

CB　CB

LEFT SEAT RECLINER MOTOR　RIGHT SEAT RECLINER MOTOR

DIR/HAZ SW　DK GRN / DK GRN — RIGHT DIR/ STOP LT
BLK / BRN — RIGHT TAILLT
DK GRN / BLK / BRN — RIGHT DIR/ STOP LT
BRN — RIGHT TAILLT

LIGHT SW — BRN

BRN / BLK — LICENSE LIGHTS

BRN / BRN / BLK / YEL — LEFT TAILLT / LEFT DIR/ STOP LT
BRN / BLK / YEL — LEFT TAILLT / LEFT DIR/ STOP LT
YEL

B

ANTENNA RELAY　ANTENNA MOTOR

UP　COAX → RADIO

C — WHT

B — DK GRN　CB　DOWN

A — GRY　DOWN

C — BLK
B — PNK → RADIO
A — ORG → CTSY FUSE

GEAR SEL SW — LT GRN
LT GRN / BLK — LEFT BACK-UP LIGHTS
BLK / BRN — LEFT MARKER LT

DIR/HAZ SW

YEL
YEL
BLK　A
BLK　B
YEL　A

HIGH LEVEL STOP LIGHT

SEDAN/COUPE

C

YEL / BLK — HIGH LEVEL STOP LIGHT

(W/ LUGGAGE CARRIER)
(W/O LUGGAGE CARRIER)

YEL
STOP LT SW — YEL
YEL　(SEDAN/COUPE))

(WAGON)

LT BLU — HIGH LEVEL STOP LIGHT

BRN / BLK — RIGHT MARKER LT

DK GRN / BLK / BRN — RIGHT STOP/ DIR LT / RIGHT TAILLT

DIR/HAZ SW　DK GRN / BLK / BRN — RIGHT STOP/ DIR LT / RIGHT TAILLT

D

LEFT POWER SEAT SW

ENTIRE SEAT　REAR HEIGHT　FRONT HEIGHT　FRONT HEIGHT　REAR HEIGHT

BACK　FRWD　DOWN　DOWN　UP　UP

ENTIRE SEAT　ENTIRE SEAT

DOWN　UP

D　E　B　C　H　G　A　F

BLK　ORG-BLK

GEAR SEL SW — LT GRN / LT GRN / BLK — RIGHT BACK-UP LT

LIGHT SW — BRN / BRN / BLK — LICENSE LIGHT

LT GRN / BLK — LEFT BACK-UP LT

→ PWR ACC CB

E

LT GRN　TAN　LT BLU　YEL　DK BLU　DK GRN

CB　CB　CB

FORWARD/BACK MOTOR　REAR HEIGHT MOTOR　FRONT HEIGHT MOTOR

BRN / BLK / YEL — LEFT STOP/ DIR LT
DIR/HAZ SW　BRN / BLK — LEFT TAILLT
BRN / BLK / YEL — LEFT STOP/ DIR LT
BRN / BLK — LEFT TAILLT

BRN / BLK — LEFT MARKER LT

WAGON

32　33　34　35

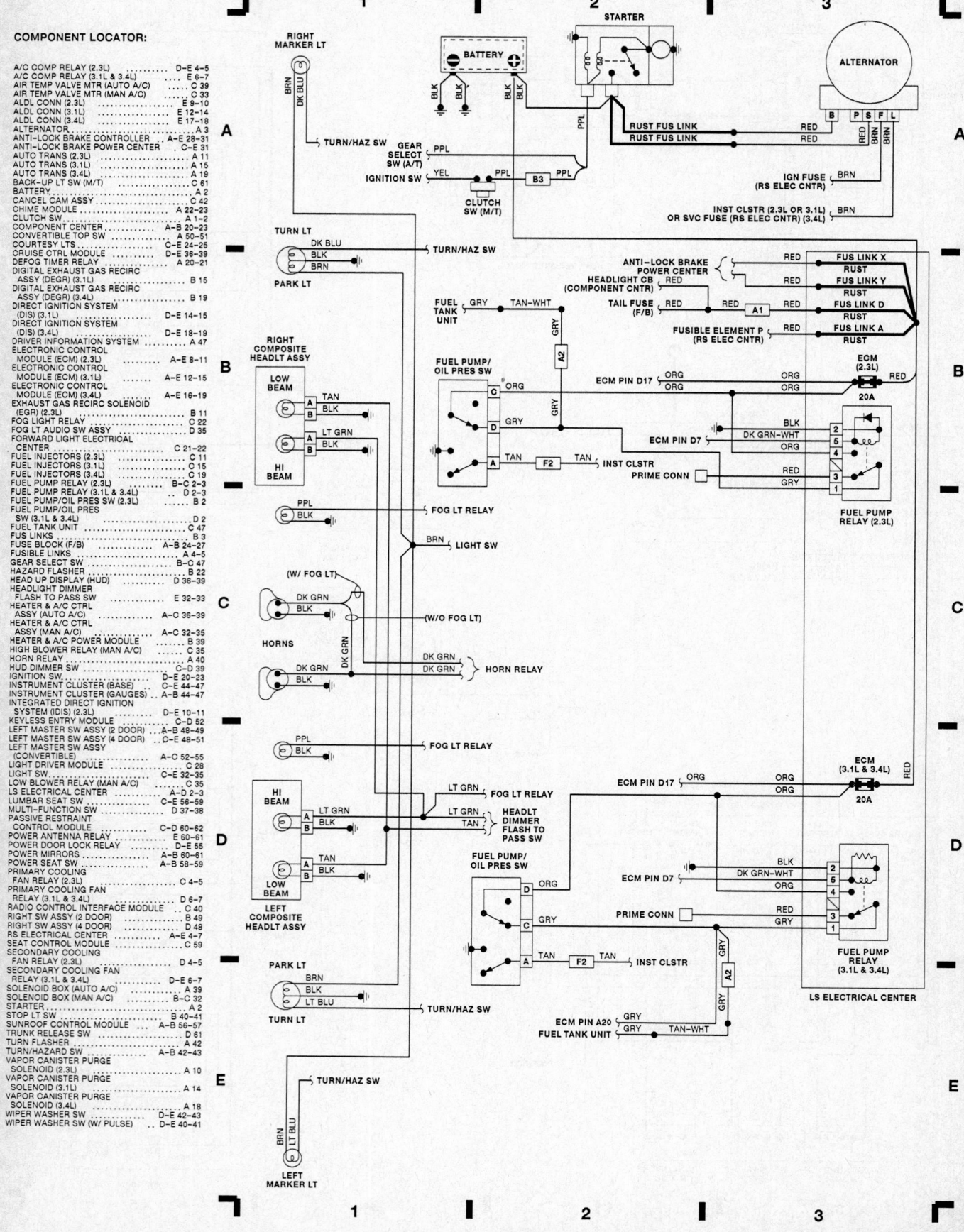

COMPONENT LOCATOR:

A/C COMP RELAY (2.3L) .... D-E 4-5
A/C COMP RELAY (3.1L & 3.4L) .... E 6-7
AIR TEMP VALVE MTR (AUTO A/C) ... C 39
AIR TEMP VALVE MTR (MAN A/C) .... C 33
ALDL CONN (2.3L) .... E 9-10
ALDL CONN (3.1L) .... E 12-14
ALDL CONN (3.4L) .... E 17-18
ALTERNATOR .... A 3
ANTI-LOCK BRAKE CONTROLLER .... A-E 28-31
ANTI-LOCK BRAKE POWER CENTER ... C-E 31
AUTO TRANS (2.3L) .... A 11
AUTO TRANS (3.1L) .... A 15
AUTO TRANS (3.4L) .... A 19
BACK-UP LT SW (M/T) .... C 61
BATTERY .... A 2
CANCEL CAM ASSY .... C 42
CHIME MODULE .... A 22-23
CLUTCH SW .... A 1-2
COMPONENT CENTER .... A-B 20-23
CONVERTIBLE TOP SW .... A 50-51
COURTESY LTS .... C-E 24-25
CRUISE CTRL MODULE .... D-E 36-39
DEFOG TIMER RELAY .... A 20-21
DIGITAL EXHAUST GAS RECIRC
ASSY (DEGR) (3.1L) .... B 15
DIGITAL EXHAUST GAS RECIRC
ASSY (DEGR) (3.4L) .... B 19
DIRECT IGNITION SYSTEM
(DIS) (3.1L) .... D-E 14-15
DIRECT IGNITION SYSTEM
(DIS) (3.4L) .... D-E 18-19
DRIVER INFORMATION SYSTEM ...... A 47
ELECTRONIC CONTROL
MODULE (ECM) (2.3L) .... A-E 8-11
ELECTRONIC CONTROL
MODULE (ECM) (3.1L) .... A-E 12-15
ELECTRONIC CONTROL
MODULE (ECM) (3.4L) .... A-E 16-19
EXHAUST GAS RECIRC SOLENOID
(EGR) (2.3L) .... B 11
FOG LIGHT RELAY .... C 22
FOG LT AUDIO SW ASSY .... D 35
FORWARD LIGHT ELECTRICAL
CENTER .... C 21-22
FUEL INJECTORS (2.3L) .... C 11
FUEL INJECTORS (3.1L) .... C 15
FUEL INJECTORS (3.4L) .... C 19
FUEL PUMP RELAY (2.3L) .... B-C 2-3
FUEL PUMP RELAY (3.1L & 3.4L) .. D 2-3
FUEL PUMP/OIL PRES SW (2.3L) ... B 2
FUEL PUMP/OIL PRES
SW (3.1L & 3.4L) .... D 2
FUEL TANK UNIT .... C 47
FUS LINKS .... B 3
FUSE BLOCK (F/B) .... A-B 24-27
FUSIBLE LINKS .... A 4-5
GEAR SELECT SW .... B-C 47
HAZARD FLASHER .... B 22
HEAD UP DISPLAY (HUD) .... D 36-39
HEADLIGHT DIMMER
FLASH TO PASS SW .... E 32-33
HEATER & A/C CTRL
ASSY (AUTO A/C) .... A-C 36-39
HEATER & A/C CTRL
ASSY (MAN A/C) .... A-C 32-35
HEATER & A/C POWER MODULE ...... B 39
HIGH BLOWER RELAY (MAN A/C) .... C 35
HORN RELAY .... A 40
HUD DIMMER SW .... C-D 39
IGNITION SW. .... D-E 20-23
INSTRUMENT CLUSTER (BASE) ...... C-E 44-47
INSTRUMENT CLUSTER (GAUGES) .... A-B 44-47
INTEGRATED DIRECT IGNITION
SYSTEM (IDIS) (2.3L) .... D-E 10-11
KEYLESS ENTRY MODULE .... C-D 52
LEFT MASTER SW ASSY (2 DOOR) ... A-B 48-49
LEFT MASTER SW ASSY (4 DOOR) ... C-E 48-51
LEFT MASTER SW ASSY
(CONVERTIBLE) .... A-C 52-55
LIGHT DRIVER MODULE .... C 28
LIGHT SW. .... C-E 32-35
LOW BLOWER RELAY (MAN A/C) ..... C 35
LS ELECTRICAL CENTER .... A-D 2-3
LUMBAR SEAT SW .... C-E 56-59
MULTI-FUNCTION SW .... D 37-38
PASSIVE RESTRAINT
CONTROL MODULE .... C-D 60-62
POWER ANTENNA RELAY .... E 60-61
POWER DOOR LOCK RELAY .... D-E 65
POWER MIRRORS .... A-B 60-61
POWER SEAT SW .... B 58-59
PRIMARY COOLING
FAN RELAY (2.3L) .... C 4-5
PRIMARY COOLING FAN
RELAY (3.1L & 3.4L) .... D 6-7
RADIO CONTROL INTERFACE MODULE .. C 40
RIGHT SW ASSY (2 DOOR) .... B 49
RIGHT SW ASSY (4 DOOR) .... D 48
RS ELECTRICAL CENTER .... A-E 4-7
SEAT CONTROL MODULE .... C 59
SECONDARY COOLING
FAN RELAY (2.3L) .... D 4-5
SECONDARY COOLING FAN
RELAY (3.1L & 3.4L) .... D-E 6-7
SOLENOID BOX (AUTO A/C) .... A 39
SOLENOID BOX (MAN A/C) .... B-C 32
STARTER .... A 2
STOP LT SW .... B 40-41
SUNROOF CONTROL MODULE .... A-B 56-57
TRUNK RELEASE SW .... D 61
TURN FLASHER .... A 42
TURN/HAZARD SW .... A-B 42-43
VAPOR CANISTER PURGE
SOLENOID (2.3L) .... A 10
VAPOR CANISTER PURGE
SOLENOID (3.1L) .... A 14
VAPOR CANISTER PURGE
SOLENOID (3.4L) .... A 18
WIPER WASHER SW .... D-E 42-43
WIPER WASHER SW (W/ PULSE) ..... D-E 40-41

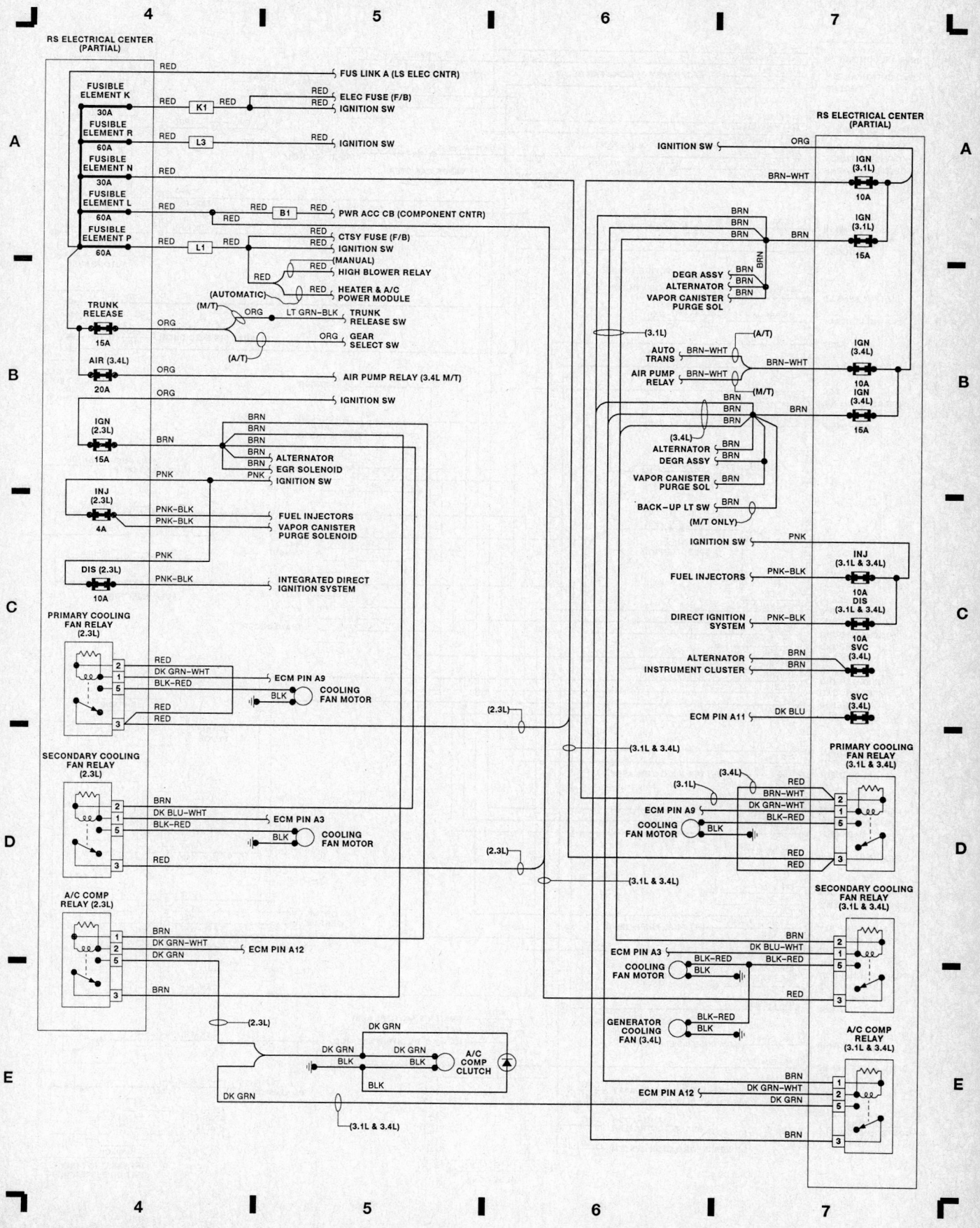

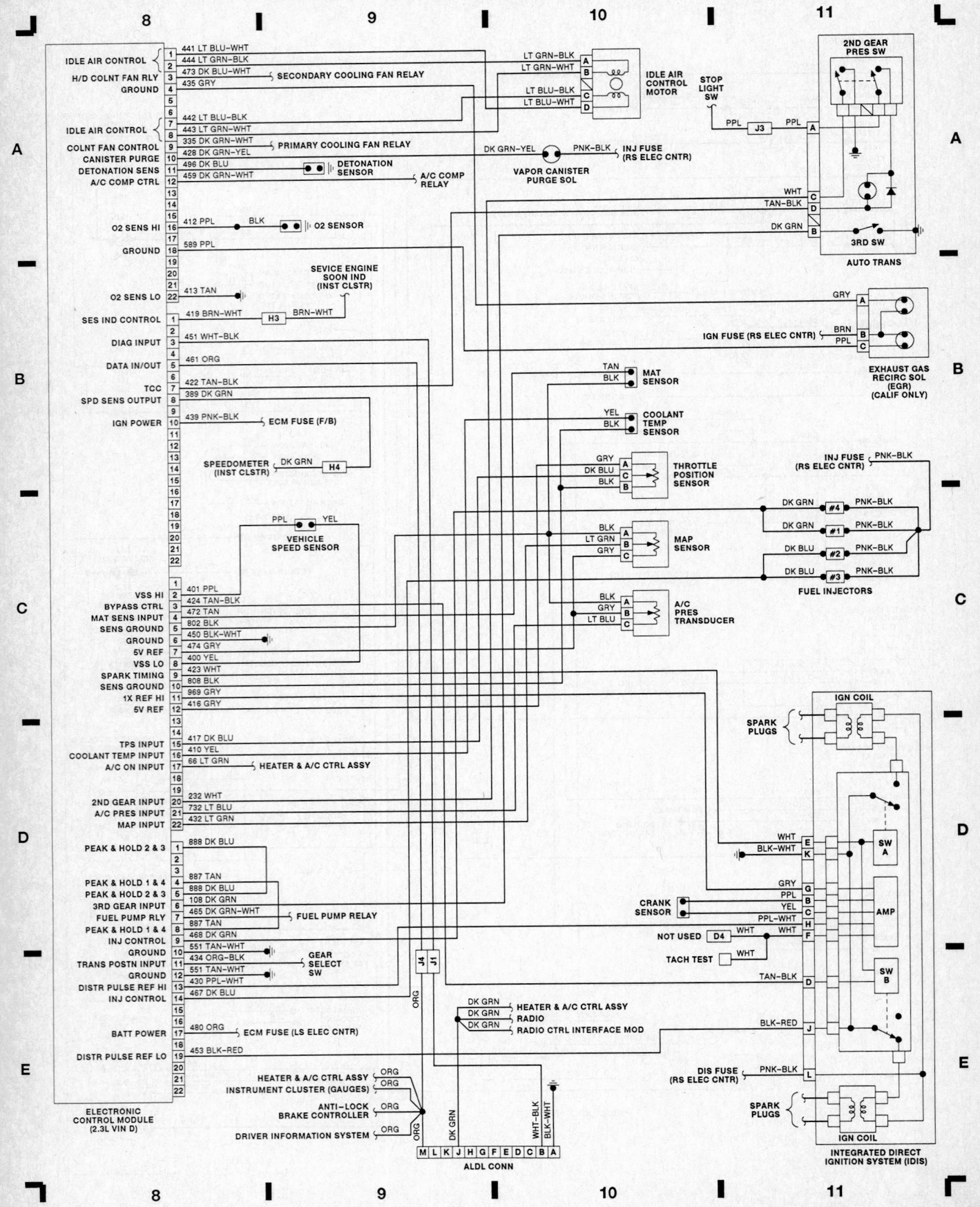

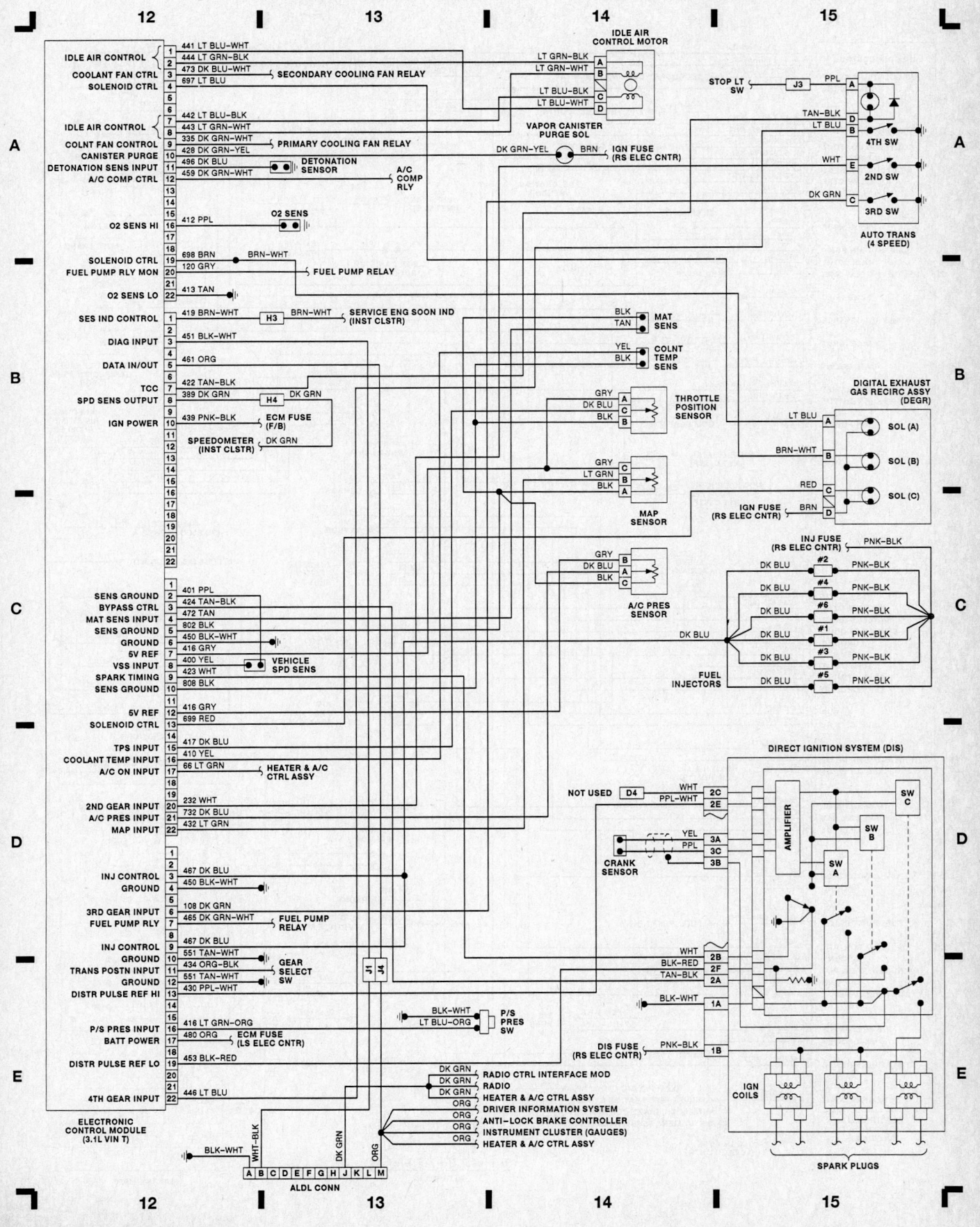

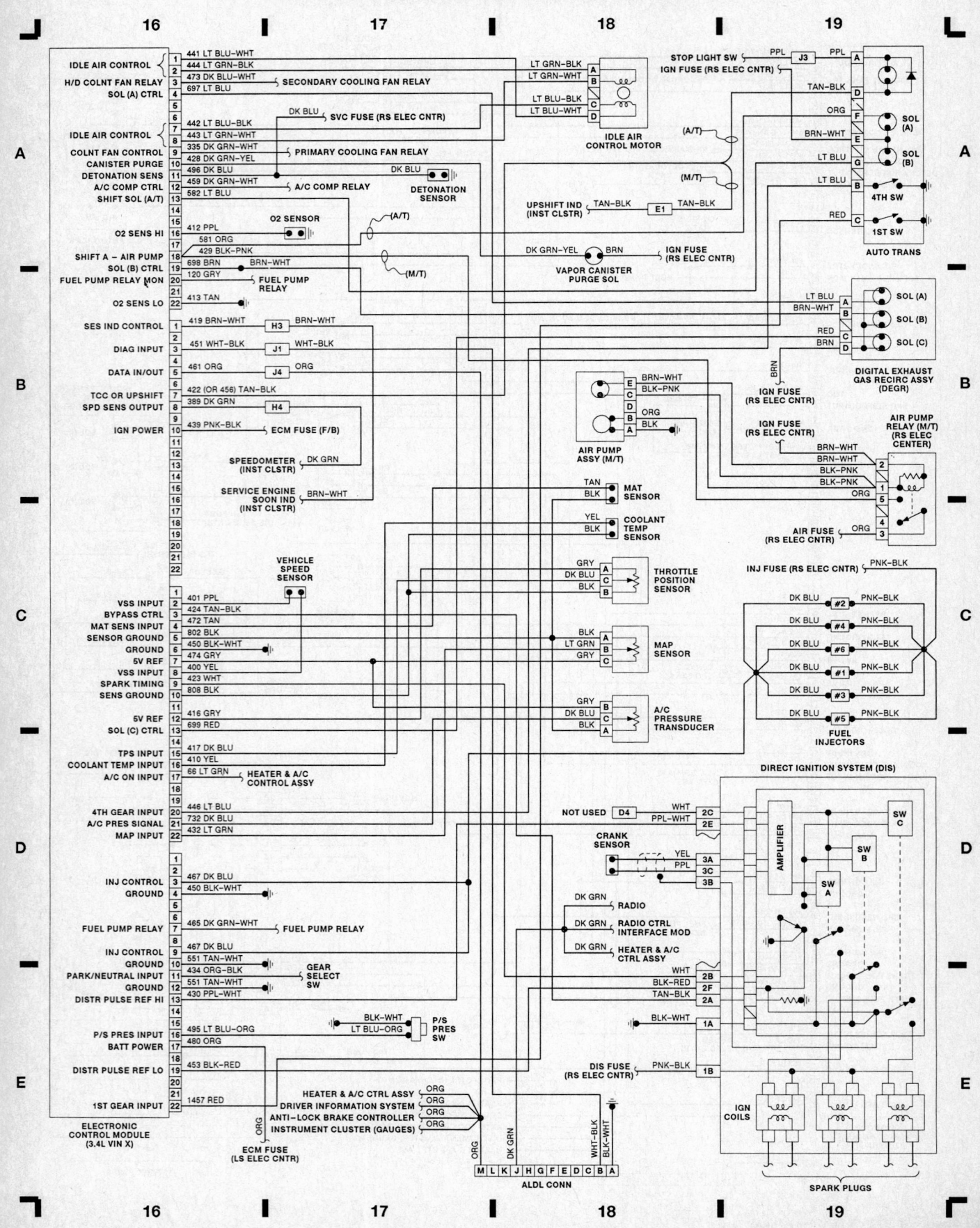

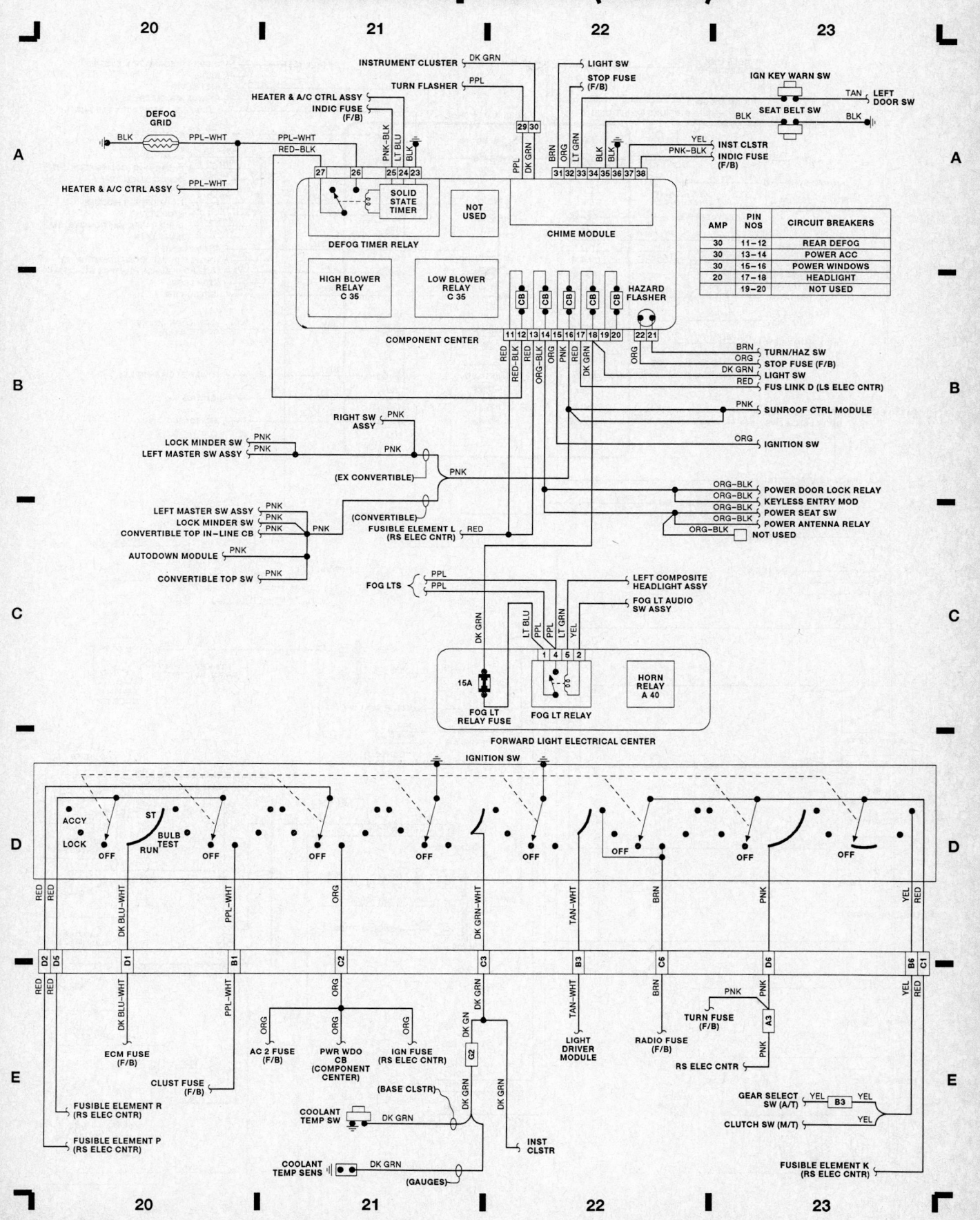

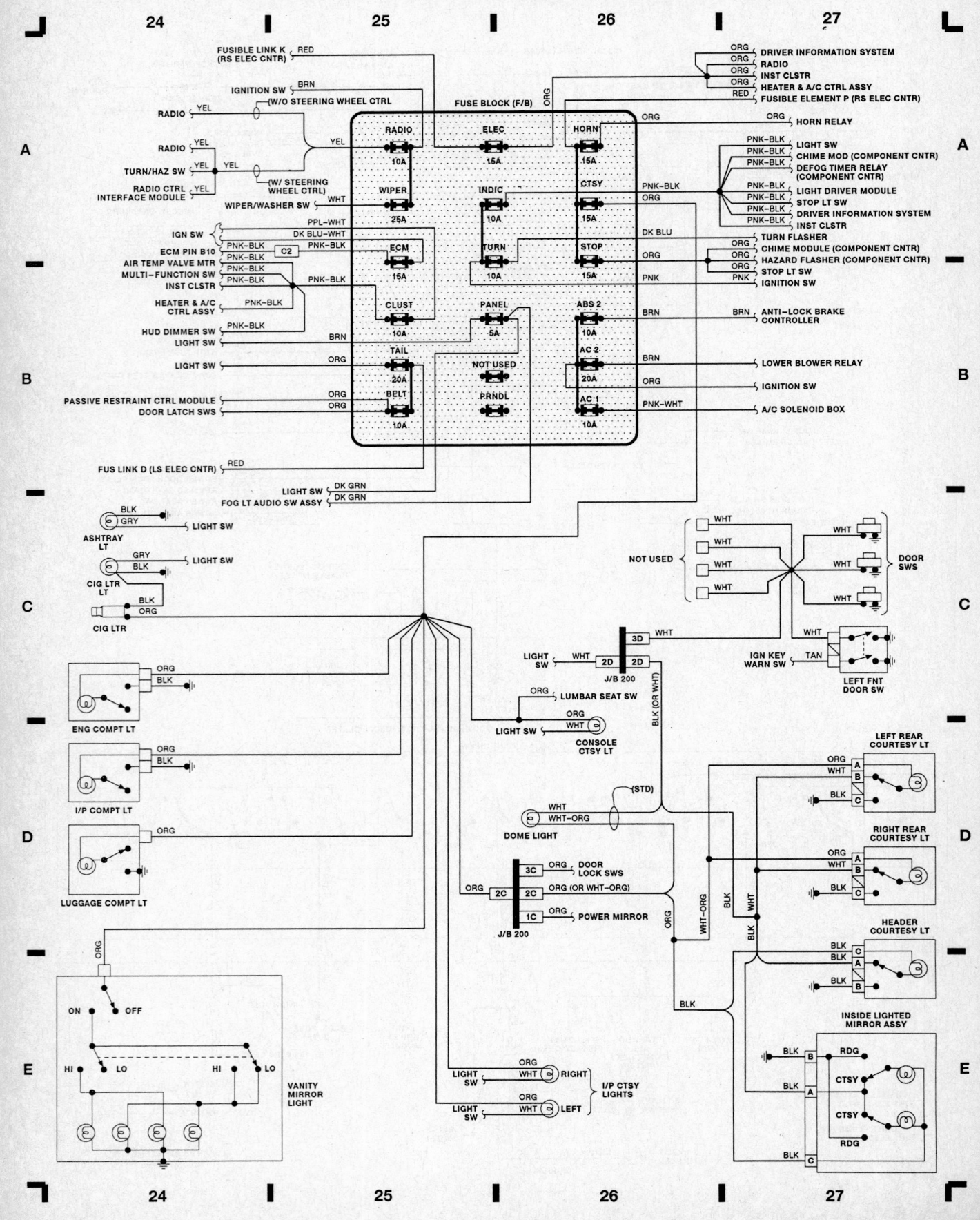

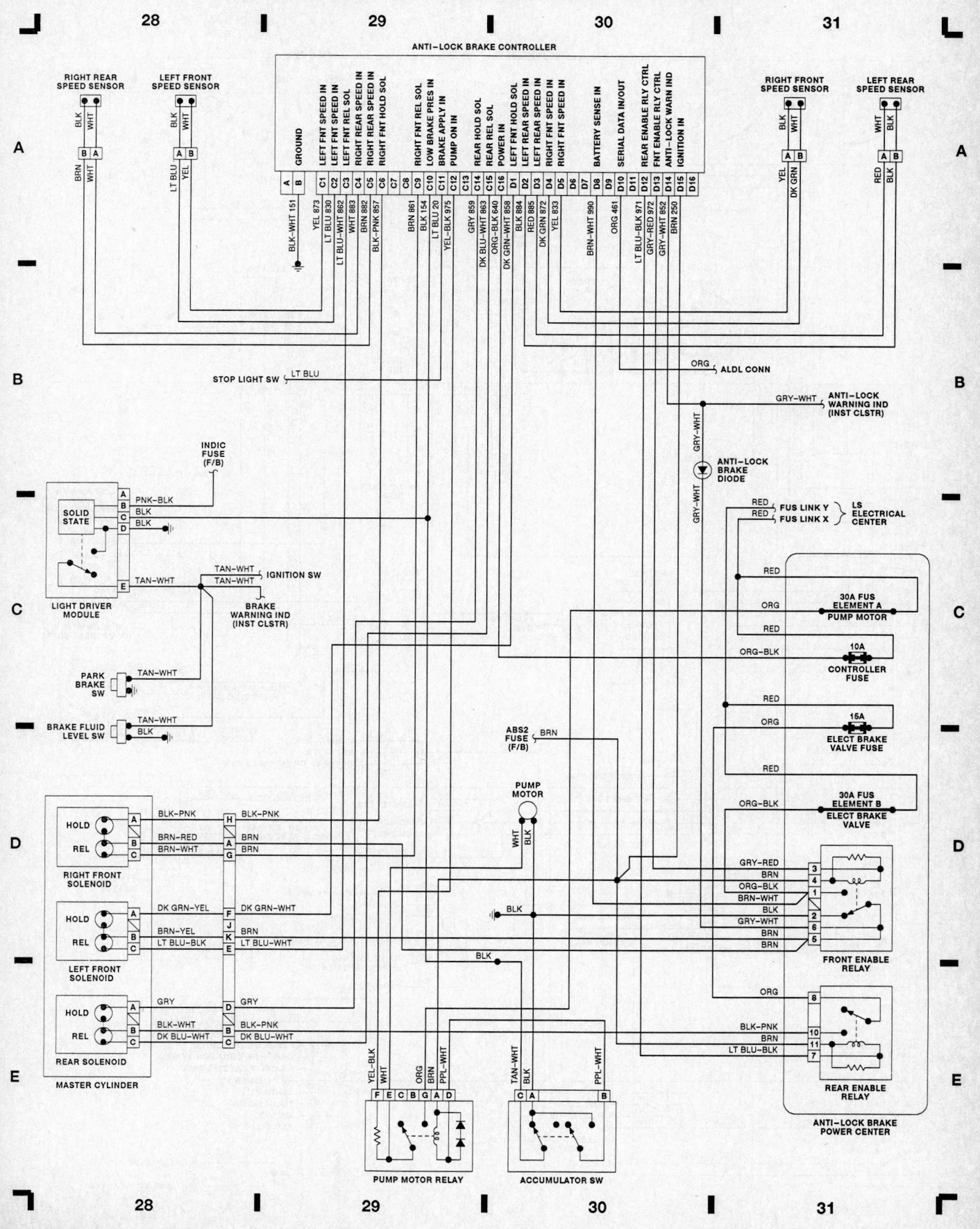

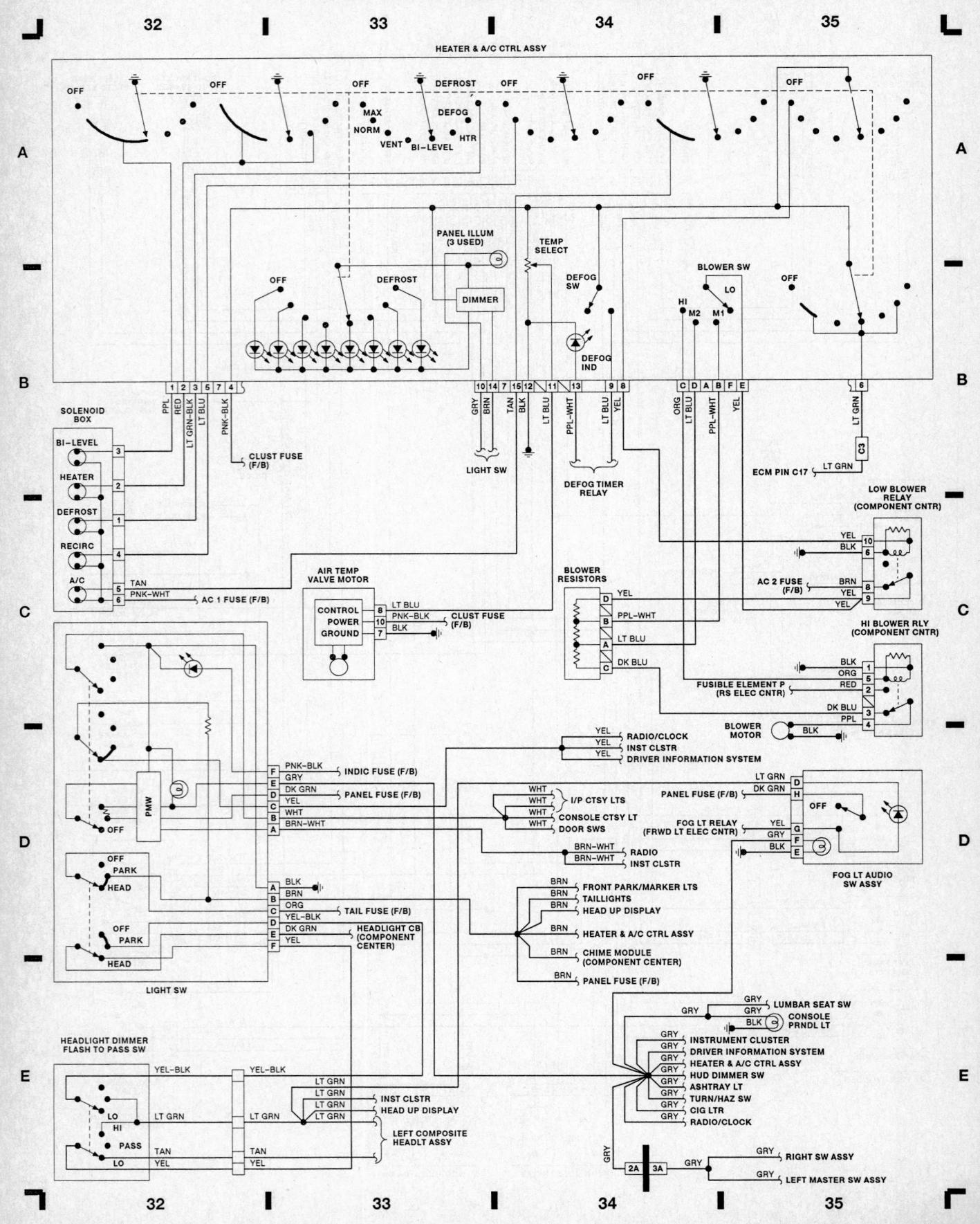

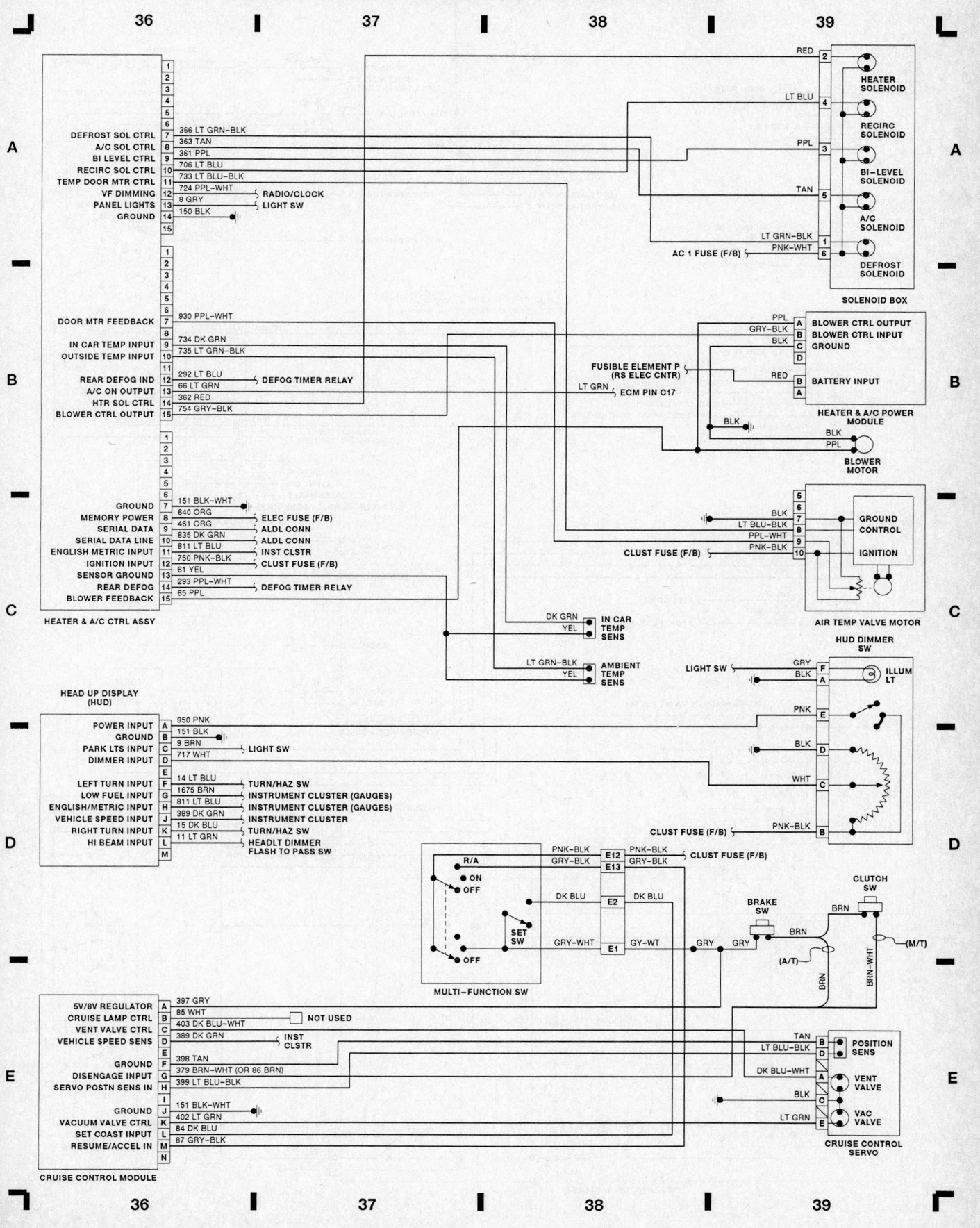

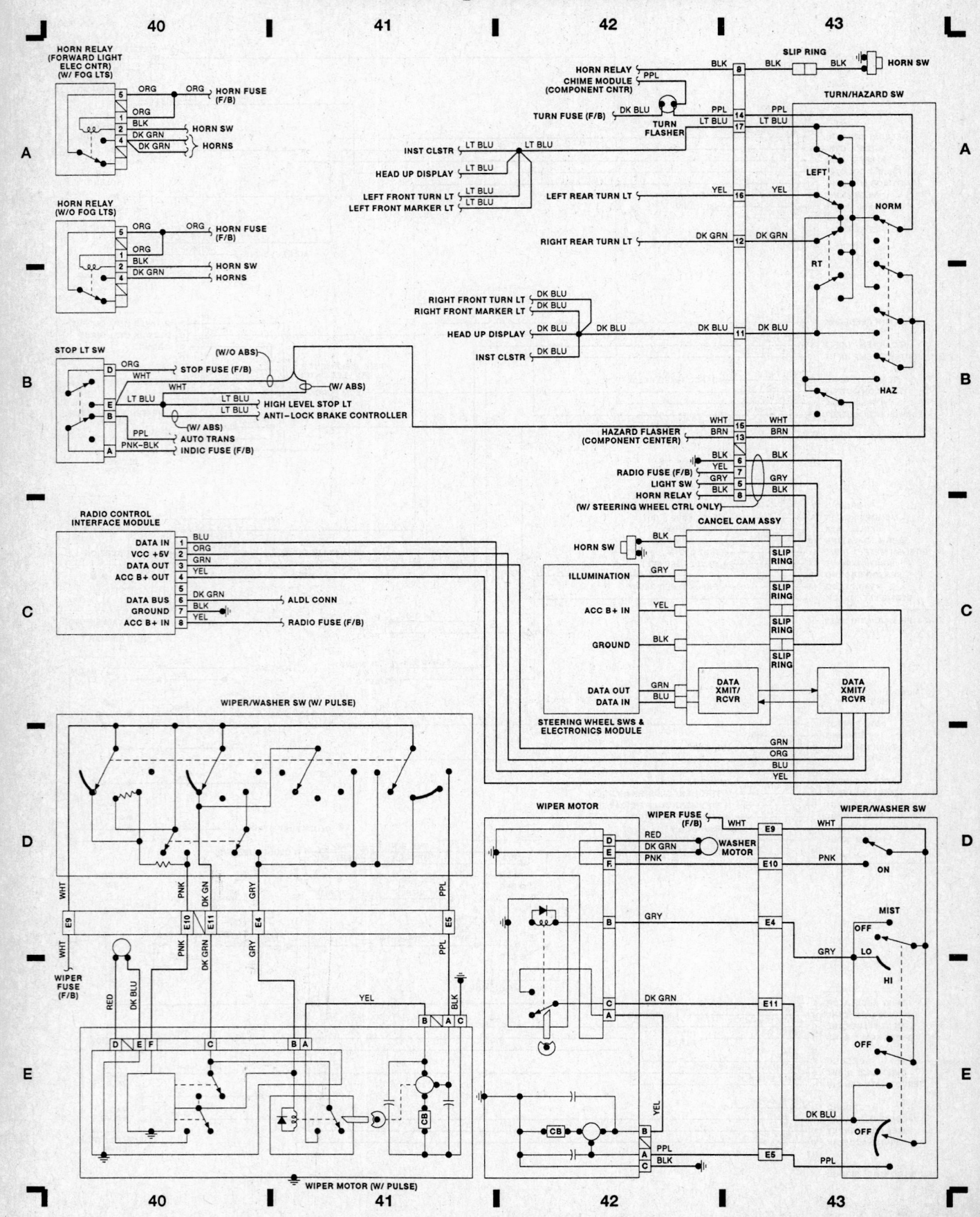

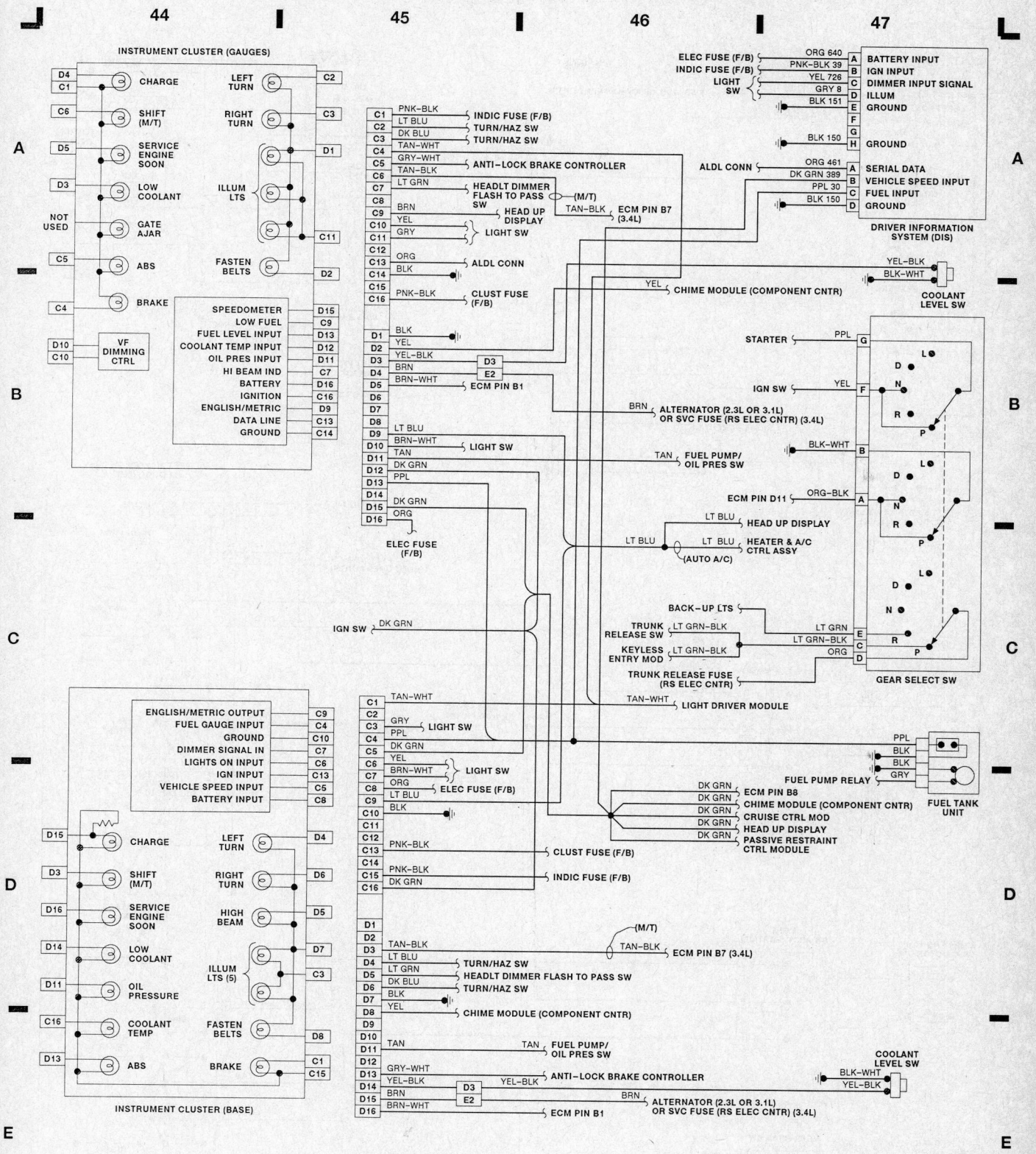

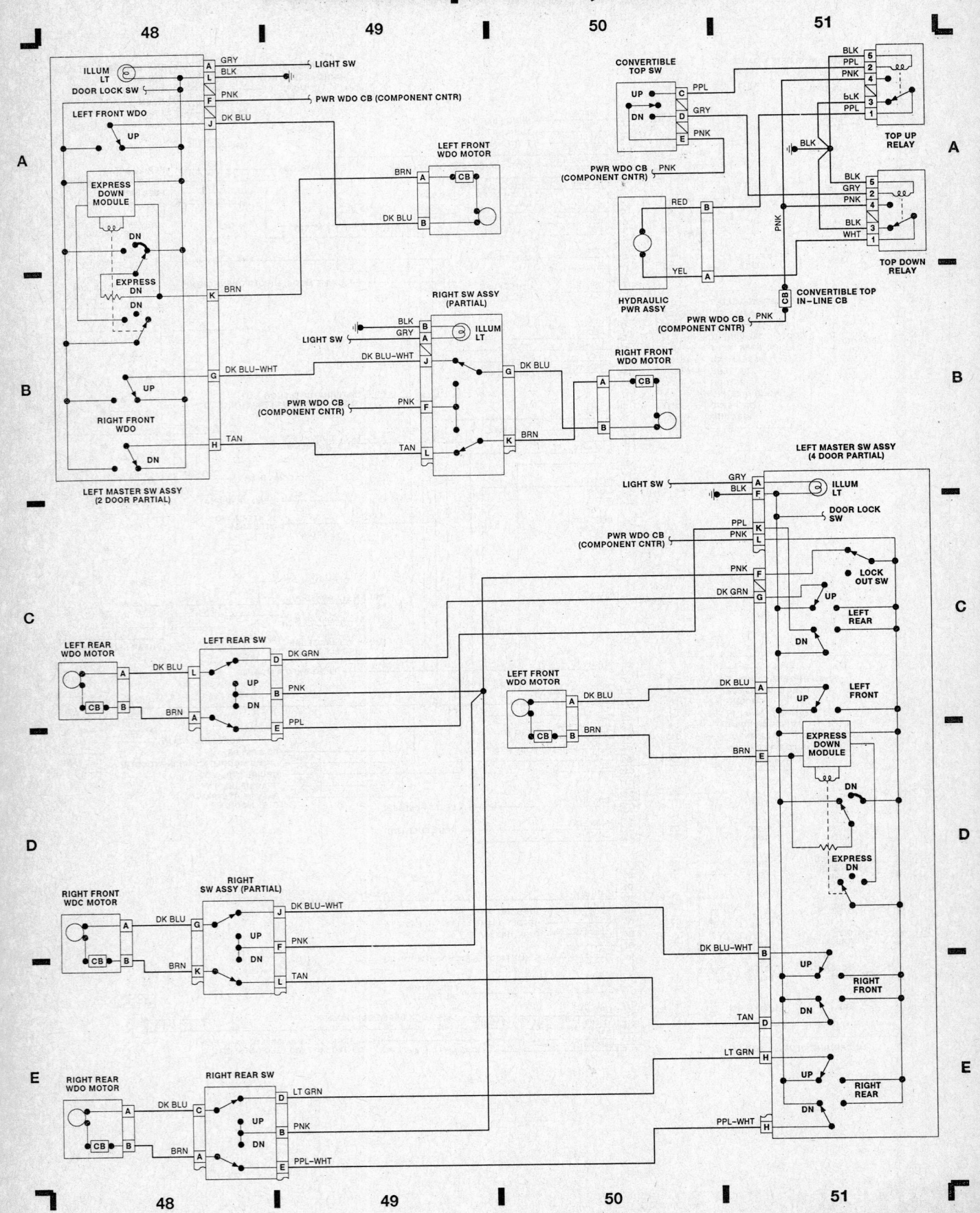

LEFT FRONT WDO MOTOR — DK BLU (A), BRN (B), CB

LIGHT SW — GRY — GRY — BLK — BLK — **ILLUM LT**

DOOR LOCK SW

PWR WDO CB (COMPONENT CNTR) — PNK / PNK

PPL — PPL K
PNK — PNK L
PNK — F
DK GRN — G

LOCK OUT SW

LEFT REAR UP / DN

LEFT REAR WDO MOTOR — DK BLU (A), BRN (B), CB

LEFT REAR SW — C, A — DK GRN (D), PNK (B) UP/DN, PPL (E)

AUTODOWN MODULE
- A PNK
- B PPL-WHT
- C PPL-WHT
- D DK BLU
- E DK BLU-WHT
- F LT GRN
- G DK GRN
- H PPL
- I PPL
- J TAN
- K DK BLU-WHT
- L BRN
- M BRN
- N BRN
- O BLK
- R BLK

DK BLU — A
LEFT FRONT UP / DN

BRN — E

RIGHT FRONT WDO MOTOR — DK BLU (A), BRN (B), CB

RIGHT SW ASSY (PARTIAL) — G, K — DK BLU-WHT (J), PNK (F) UP/DN, TAN (L)

BLK

TOP SW LT (INFORMATION UNAVAILABLE) — BLK

DK BLU-WHT — B
RIGHT FRONT UP / DN

TAN — D

RIGHT REAR WDO MOTOR — DK BLU (A), BRN (B), CB

RIGHT REAR SW — C, A — LT GRN (D), PNK (B) UP/DN, PPL-WHT (E)

LT GRN — H
RIGHT REAR UP / DN

PPL-WHT — H

LEFT MASTER SW ASSY (CONVERTIBLE)

D — LT GRN-BLK — **GEAR SELECT SW**
H — BLK — **TRUNK RELEASE SW**

B — TAN
E — BLK

G — BLK

F — LT BLU
A — ORG-BLK

KEYLESS ENTRY MODULE

POWER ACC CB (COMPONENT CENTER)

LEFT FRONT LOCK MOTOR — TAN (A), GRY (B), CB

(W/O KEYLESS ENTRY)

LEFT REAR LOCK MOTOR — TAN (A), GRY (B), CB

RIGHT FRONT LOCK MOTOR — TAN, GRY (A), CB

RIGHT REAR LOCK MOTOR — TAN (B), GRY (A), CB

PWR ACC CB (COMPONENT CNTR)

POWER DOOR LOCK RLY
- TAN — E
- BLK — F
- LT BLU — A
- ORG-BLK — C
- BLK — D
- GRY — B

LEFT MASTER SW ASSY (PARTIAL)
- UNLOCK — D — ORG
- C — BLK-LT BLU
- LOCK — LT BLU
- E — B — PNK-WHT
- **PWR WDO SW**

CTSY FUSE (F/B) — ORG

BLK — **LOCK MINDER SW**

PNK

PWR WDO CB (COMPONENT CNTR)

RIGHT SW ASSY (PARTIAL)
- ORG — D — UNLOCK
- BLK-LT BLU — C
- LT BLU — E — LOCK

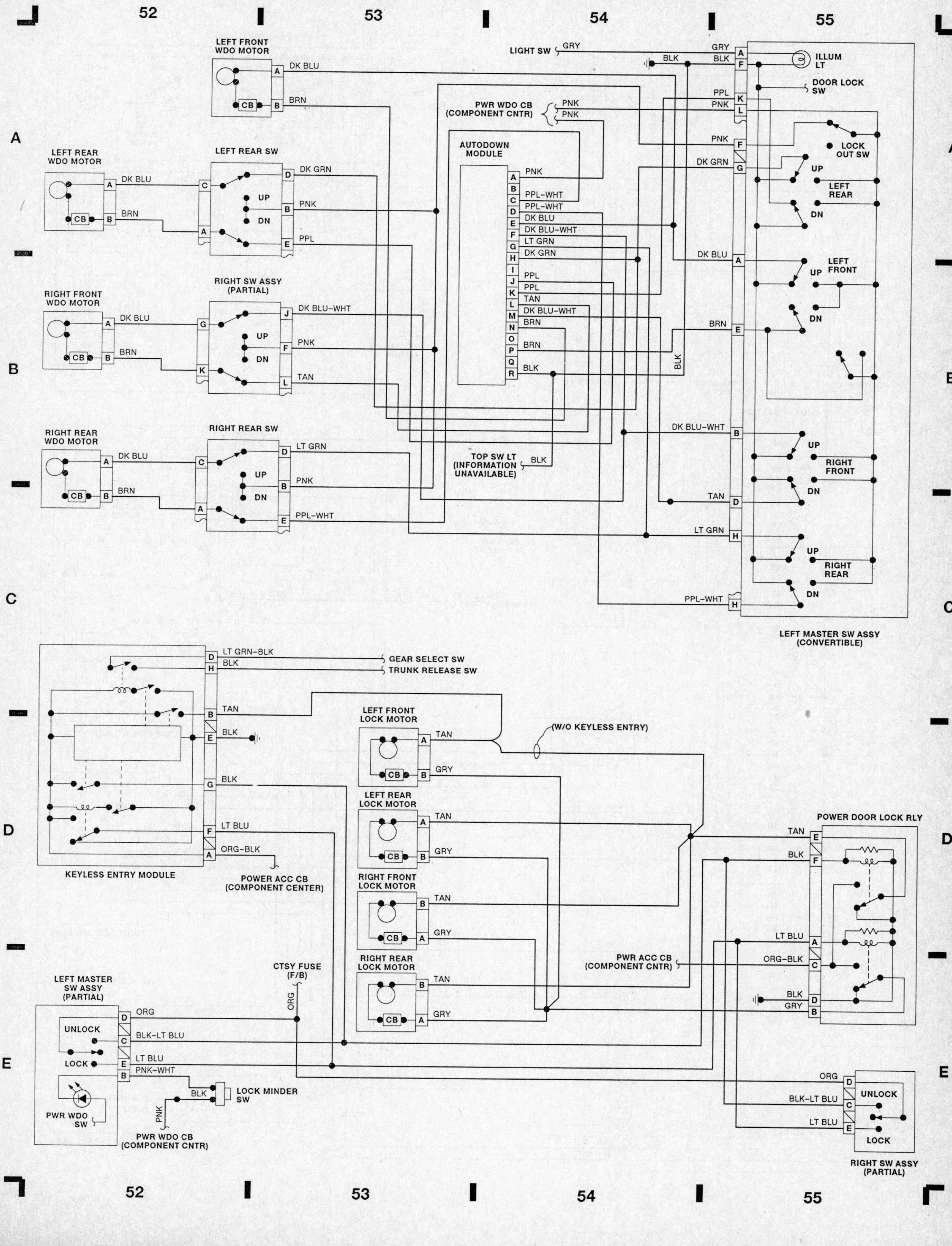

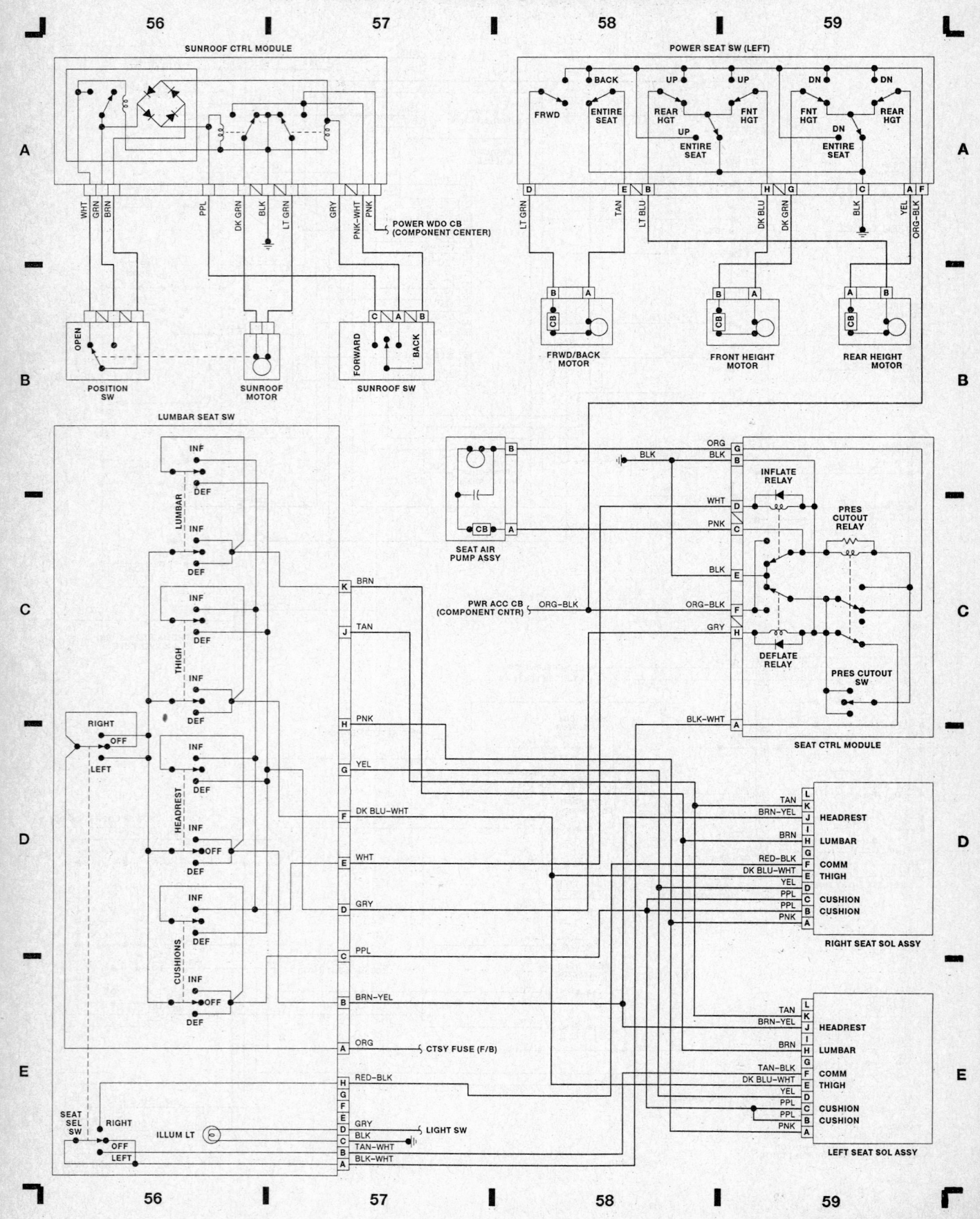

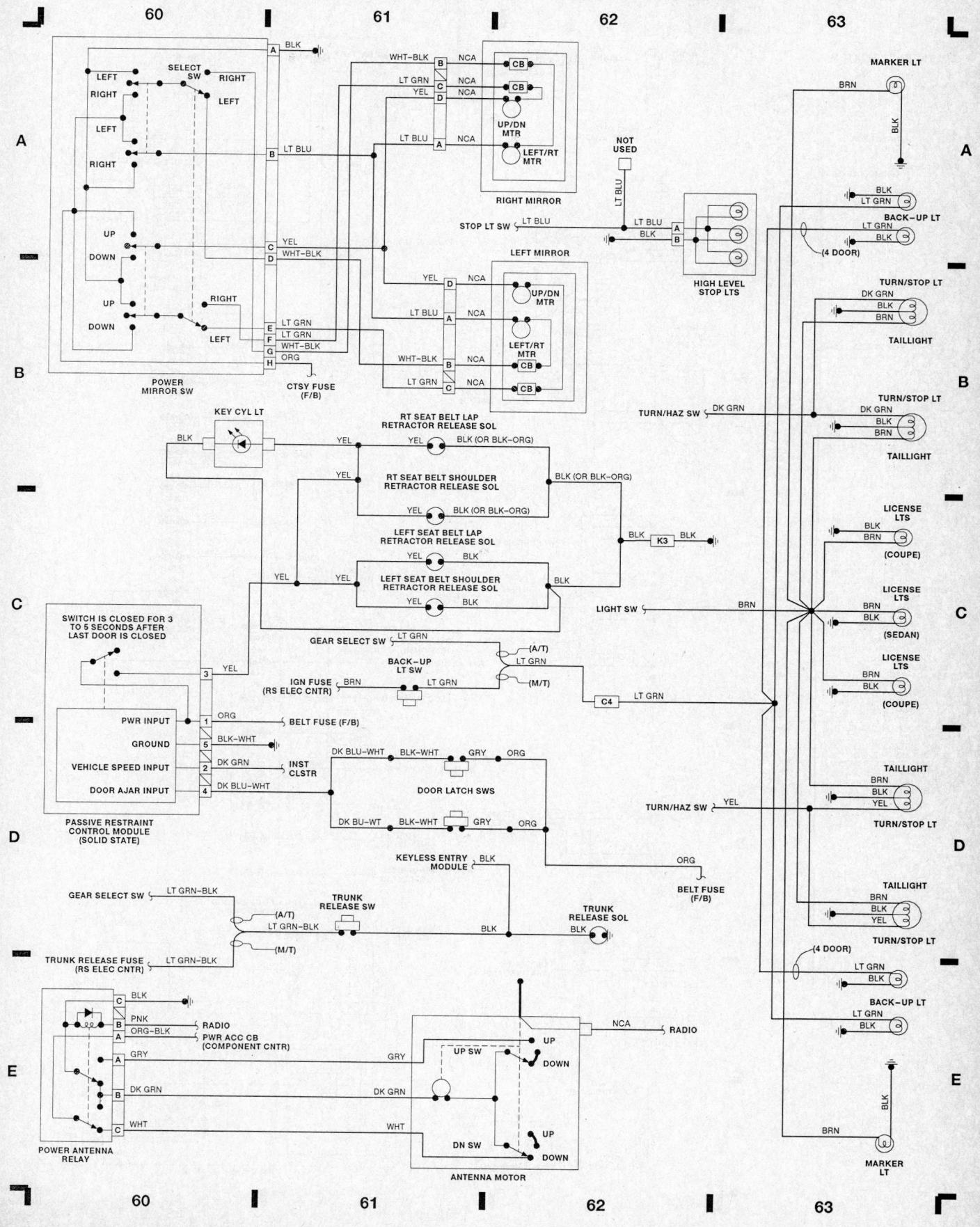

COMPONENT LOCATOR:

A/C RELAY .... E 15
ABS MOD. .... A–C 20
ABS PUMP RLY .... C 23
ALDL CONN .... B–C 7
ANTENNA RLY .... E 50–51
ASTRO ROOF MOD .... A 35
AUTO DAY/NIGHT MIRROR .... A 35
AUTO DOOR LOCK CTRL .... A 44
AUTO TRANSAXLE .... A 7
BEAM SELECT SW .... B 24
BODY COMPUTER MODULE (BCM) .... C–E 12
BRAKE SW .... D–E 23
CANISTER PURGE SOL .... E 6
CLIMATE CTRL PANEL (CCP) .... A–B 12
COMPUTER COMMAND
  RIDE (CCR) MOD .... A–B 16
COOLANT FAN RELAYS .... C–D 15
COURTESY LIGHTS .... D–E 33–34
CRUISE CTRL SERVO .... D 20
DIAGNOSTIC ENERGY
  RESERVE MOD (DERM) .... C–D 19
DIR/HAZ LT SW .... C–D 24
DOOR LOCK CYL SWS .... E 37–38
DOOR LOCK SWS .... A–B 47
DOOR SWS. .... D–E 32
DUAL SENS. .... C–D 16
ECC POWER MOD .... B 12
ECC PROGRAMMER .... A–B 15
ELC COMP ASSY .... D 27
ELC HEIGHT SENS .... C–D 26
ELECT SPARK TIMING (EST) DISTR ... D–E 7
ENG COMPT LT .... B 1
FNT CIG LTR .... B–C 33
FUEL DATA CNTR .... B–C 27
FUEL INJ .... A–B 7
FUEL PUMP RLY .... C–D 7
FUSE BLOCK .... C–D 9–10
GEAR SEL SW .... E 16–19
HEATED WINDSHIELD CTRL MOD .... A 32
HEATED WINDSHIELD PWR MOD .... B 32
HEATED WINDSHIELD SW .... A 34
IGNITION SW. .... A 8–11
ILLUM ENTRY TIMER .... E 48
INST CLSTR (DIG) .... A–B 30–31
INST CLSTR (IND) .... A 28–29
KEYLESS ENTRY MOD .... D–E 44
LEFT INFORMATION CNTR .... E 24
LIGHT SW. .... A–B 24
LOCK RLY ASSY .... B–C 47
MAIN RLY .... D 23
MULTI–FUNCTION CHIME (MFC) MOD ... B–C 32
MULTI–FUNCTION LEVER .... E 20
OIL PRES SW .... C 7
OPERA LTS .... C–D 36–37
P/S PRES SW .... C 6
PASS KEY DECODER .... D–E 36
PASSIVE RESTRAINT TIMER MOD ...... C 35
POWER MIRROR SYS .... A–C 38–39
POWER RECLINER SW .... D–E 49
POWER SEAT SYS .... A–C 48
POWER SEAT SYS (W/
  SIXTY SPECIAL SEAT) .... A–E 40–43
POWER SEAT SYS (W/O
  SIXTY SPECIAL SEAT) .... A–D 44–47
POWER WINDOW SW .... A–B 36
POWERTRAIN CTRL MOD (PCM) .... A–E 4
PULL DOWN UNIT .... A–B 50
REAR CIG LTR .... D–E 34
RELAY CENTER .... D 28–31
RIGHT INFORMATION CNTR .... E 27
STARTER. .... A 3
STARTER ENABLE RLY .... D 39
THEFT DETRNT SYS .... C–E 38–39
TRUNK AJAR SW .... C 49
TRUNK DOOR UNLOCK RLY .... B–C 50
TRUNK LT .... A 51
TRUNK UNLOCK SW .... C 50
TWILIGHT SENTINEL AMP .... B–D 2–3
UNDERHOOD FUSE BLOCKS .... B–D 9–10
VANITY MIRROR. .... D–E 35
WIPER MTR MOD .... E 2–3
WIPER/WASHER SW .... A–B 35

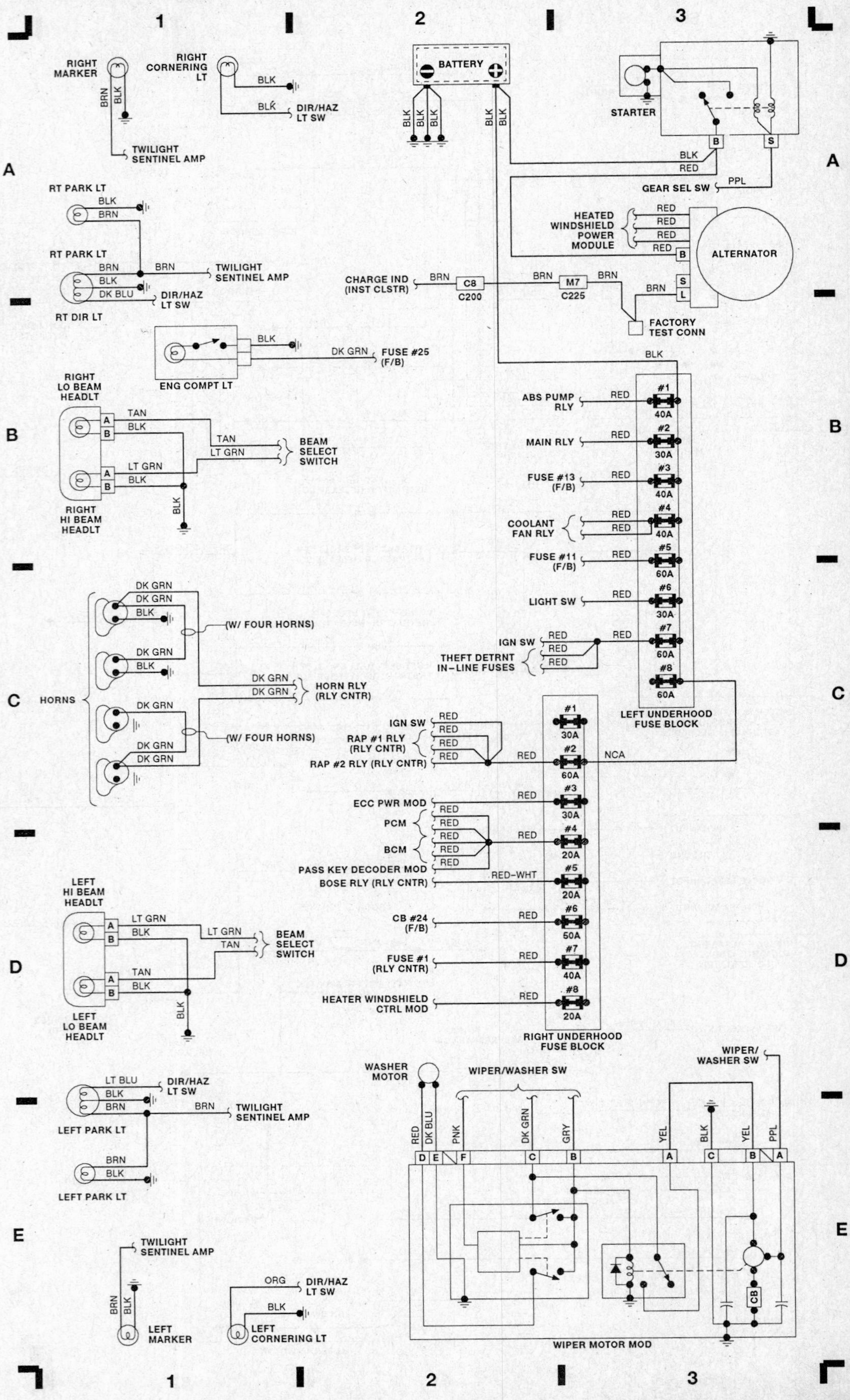

1

RIGHT
MARKER
BRN
BLK
TWILIGHT
SENTINEL AMP

RIGHT
CORNERING
LT
BLK
BLK
DIR/HAZ
LT SW

RT PARK LT
BLK
BRN

RT PARK LT
BRN
BRN
TWILIGHT
SENTINEL AMP
BLK
DK BLU
DIR/HAZ
LT SW
RT DIR LT

BLK
ENG COMPT LT
DK GRN
FUSE #25
(F/B)

RIGHT
LO BEAM
HEADLT
A
B
TAN
BLK
TAN
LT GRN
BEAM
SELECT
SWITCH
LT GRN
A
B
BLK
RIGHT
HI BEAM
HEADLT

HORNS
DK GRN
DK GRN
BLK
(W/ FOUR HORNS)
DK GRN
BLK
DK GRN
DK GRN
HORN RLY
(RLY CNTR)
DK GRN
DK GRN
(W/ FOUR HORNS)
DK GRN

LEFT
HI BEAM
HEADLT
A
B
LT GRN
BLK
LT GRN
TAN
BEAM
SELECT
SWITCH
A
B
TAN
BLK
BLK
LEFT
LO BEAM
HEADLT

LT BLU
DIR/HAZ
LT SW
BLK
BRN
BRN
TWILIGHT
SENTINEL AMP
LEFT PARK LT
BRN
BLK
LEFT PARK LT

TWILIGHT
SENTINEL AMP
BRN
BLK
LEFT
MARKER
ORG
DIR/HAZ
LT SW
BLK
LEFT
CORNERING LT

2

BATTERY
BLK BLK BLK
BLK BLK

CHARGE IND
(INST CLSTR)
BRN
C8
C200
BRN
M7
C225
BRN
BRN

ABS PUMP
RLY
RED
#1
40A
MAIN RLY
RED
#2
30A
FUSE #13
(F/B)
RED
#3
40A
COOLANT
FAN RLY
RED
RED
#4
40A
FUSE #11
(F/B)
RED
#5
60A
LIGHT SW
RED
#6
30A
IGN SW
RED
RED
#7
60A
THEFT DETRNT
IN–LINE FUSES
RED
RED
#8
60A
LEFT UNDERHOOD
FUSE BLOCK

IGN SW
RED
RAP #1 RLY
(RLY CNTR)
RED
RED
#1
30A
RAP #2 RLY (RLY CNTR)
RED
#2
60A
NCA
ECC PWR MOD
RED
#3
30A
PCM
RED
RED
#4
20A
BCM
RED
RED
PASS KEY DECODER MOD
RED
#5
20A
BOSE RLY (RLY CNTR)
RED–WHT
CB #24
(F/B)
RED
#6
50A
FUSE #1
(RLY CNTR)
RED
#7
40A
HEATER WINDSHIELD
CTRL MOD
RED
#8
20A
RIGHT UNDERHOOD
FUSE BLOCK

3

STARTER
B
S
BLK
RED
GEAR SEL SW
PPL
HEATED
WINDSHIELD
POWER
MODULE
RED
RED
RED
RED
B
ALTERNATOR
S
L
FACTORY
TEST CONN
BLK

WASHER
MOTOR
WIPER/WASHER SW
WIPER/
WASHER SW
RED DK BLU PNK DK GRN GRY YEL BLK YEL PPL
D E F C B A C B A
CB
WIPER MOTOR MOD

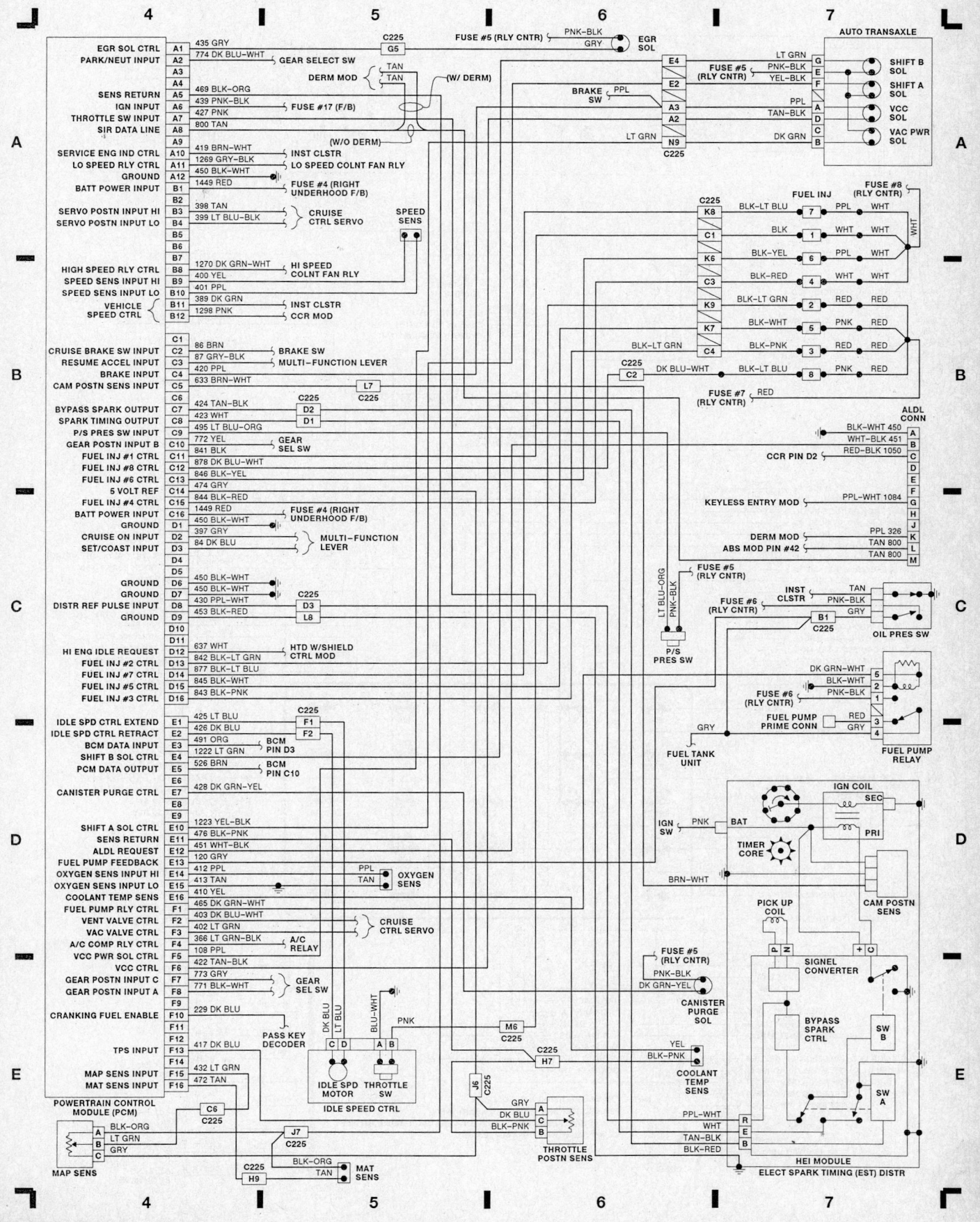

1991 WIRING DIAGRAMS
DeVille & Fleetwood (Cont.)

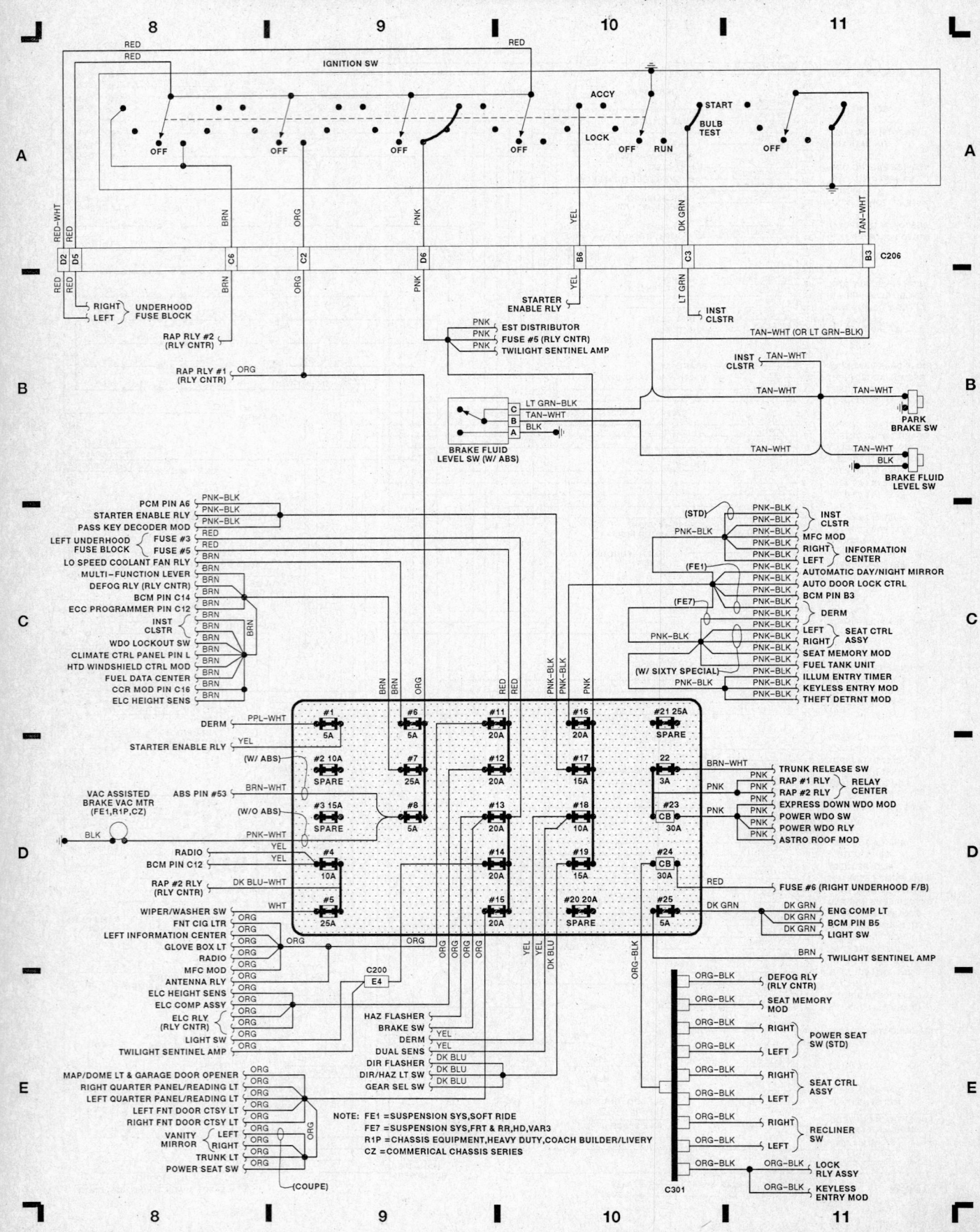

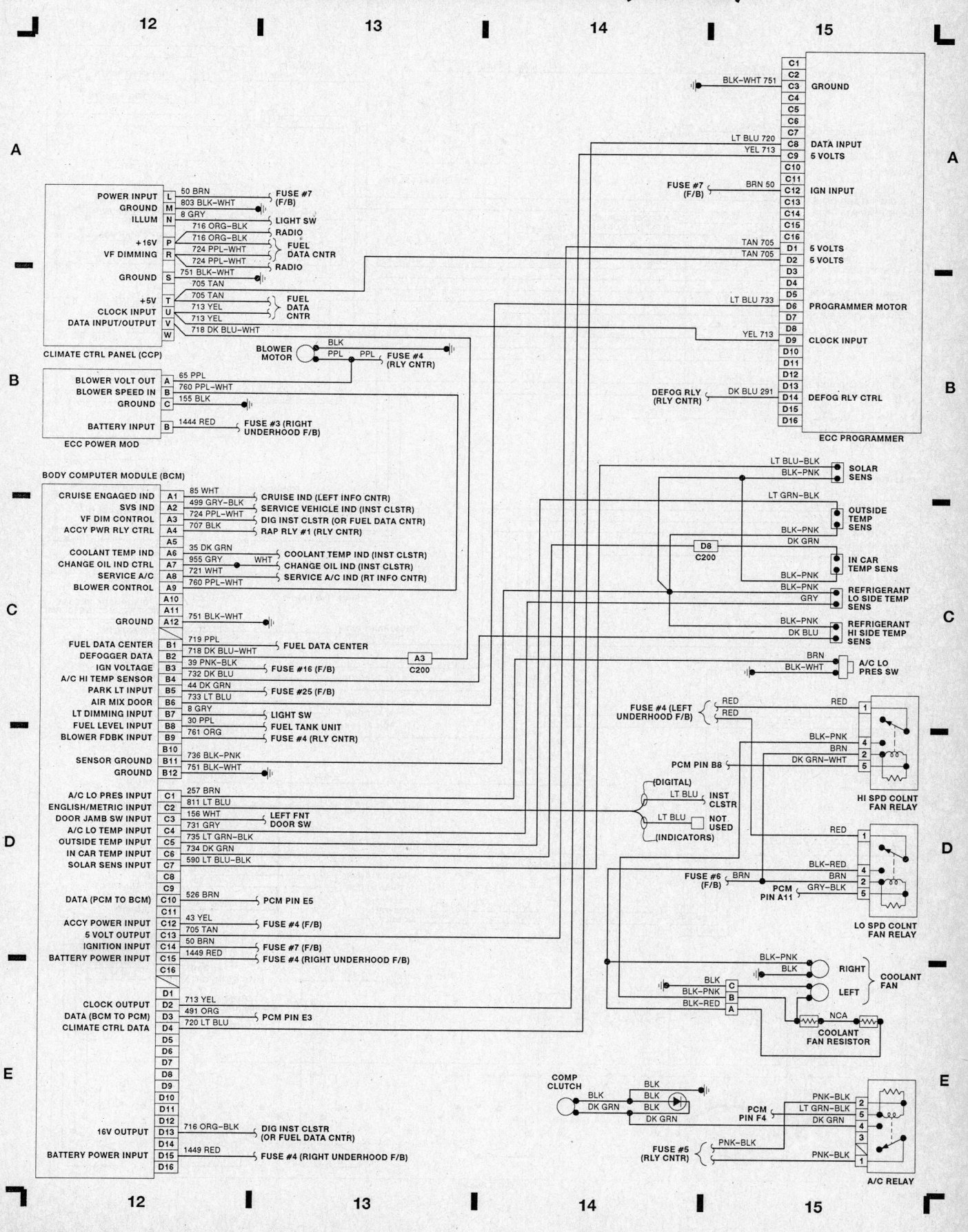

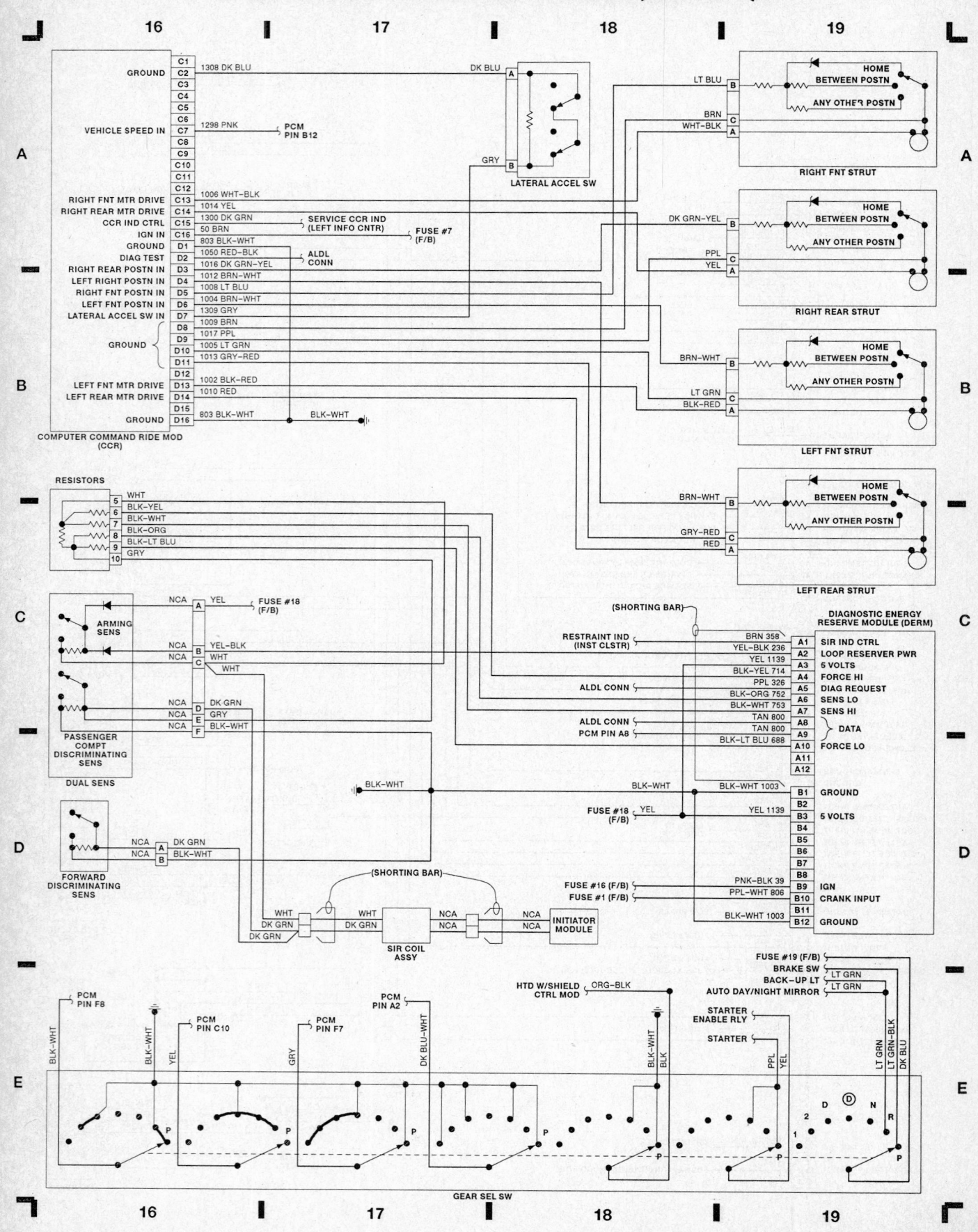

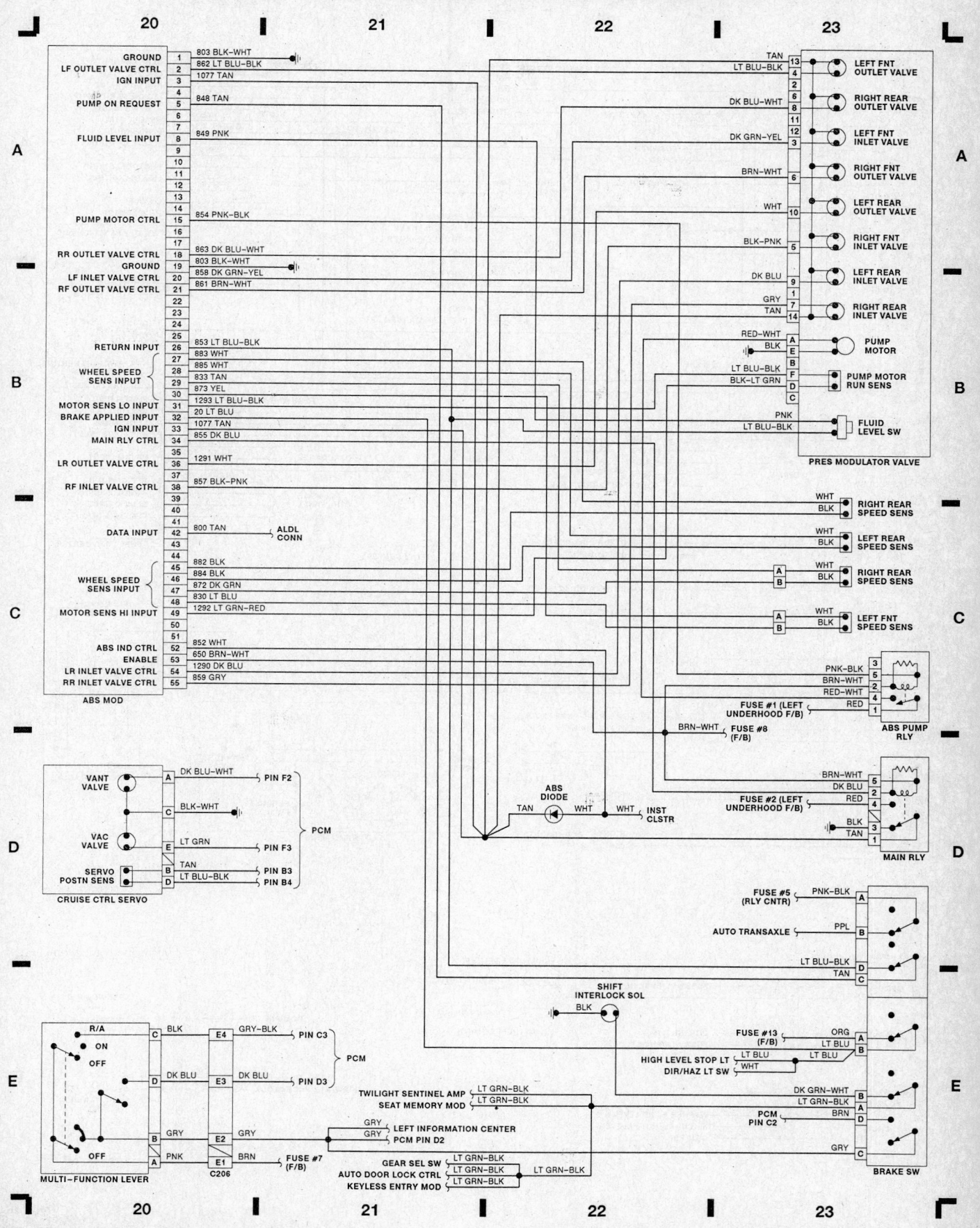

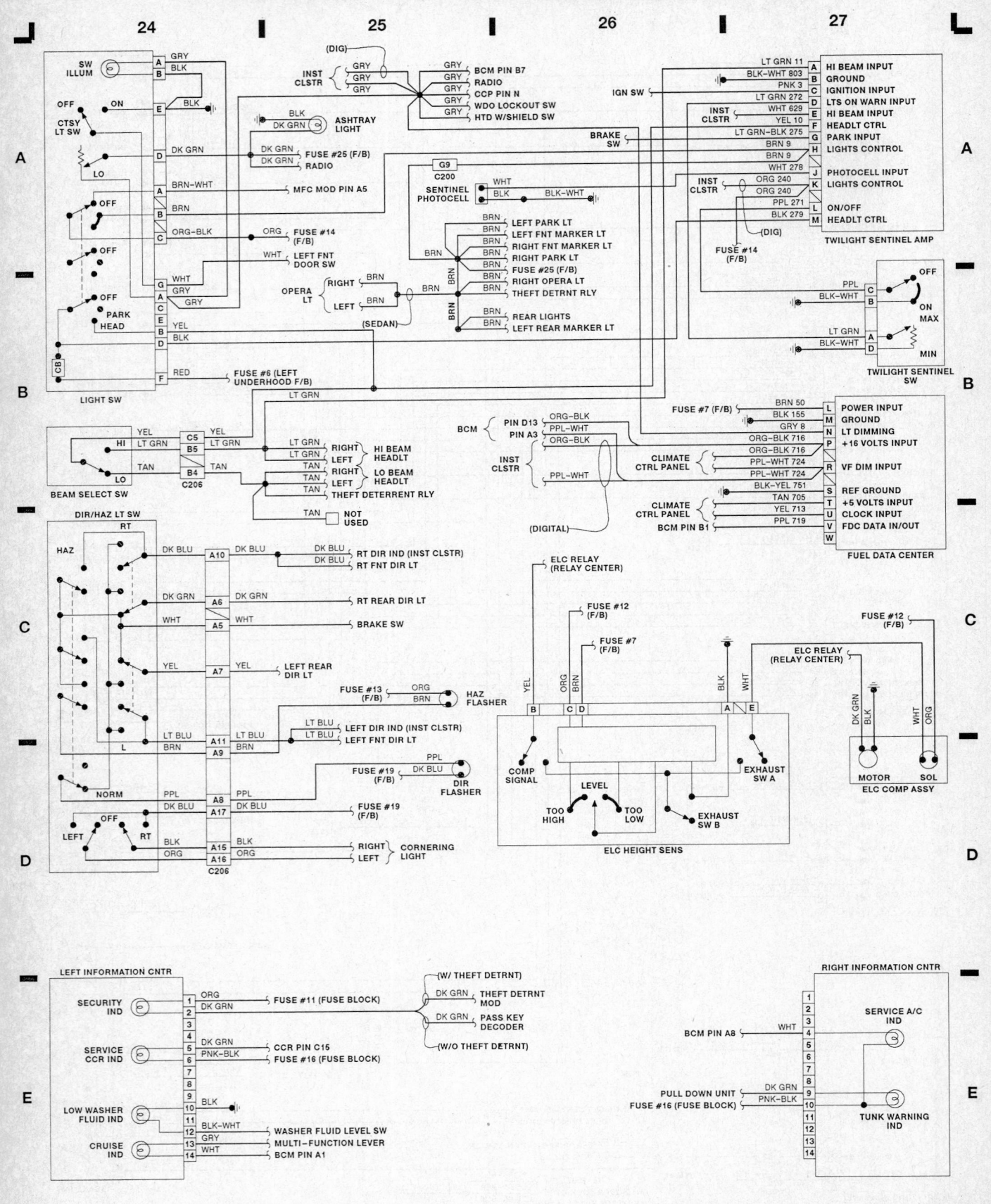

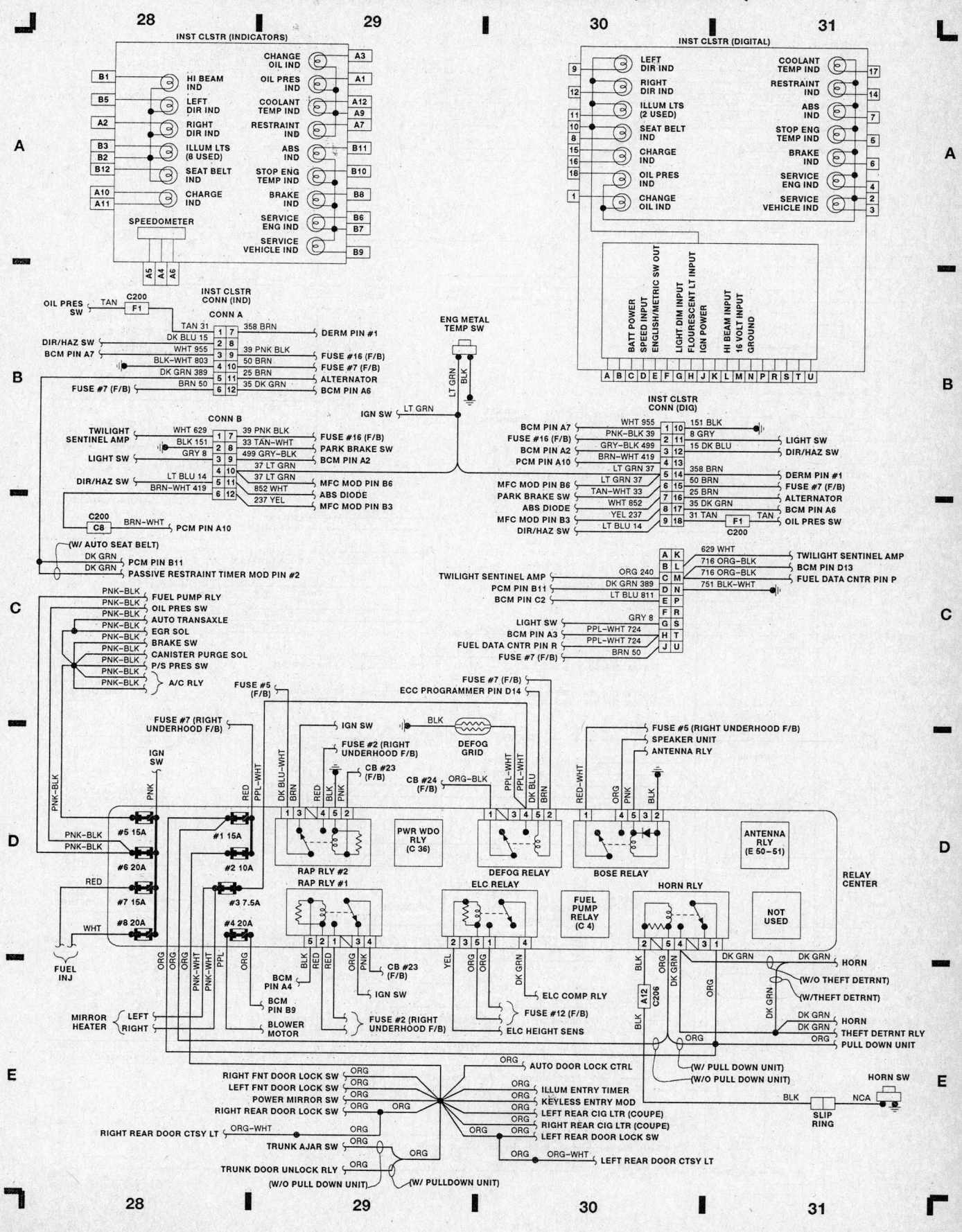

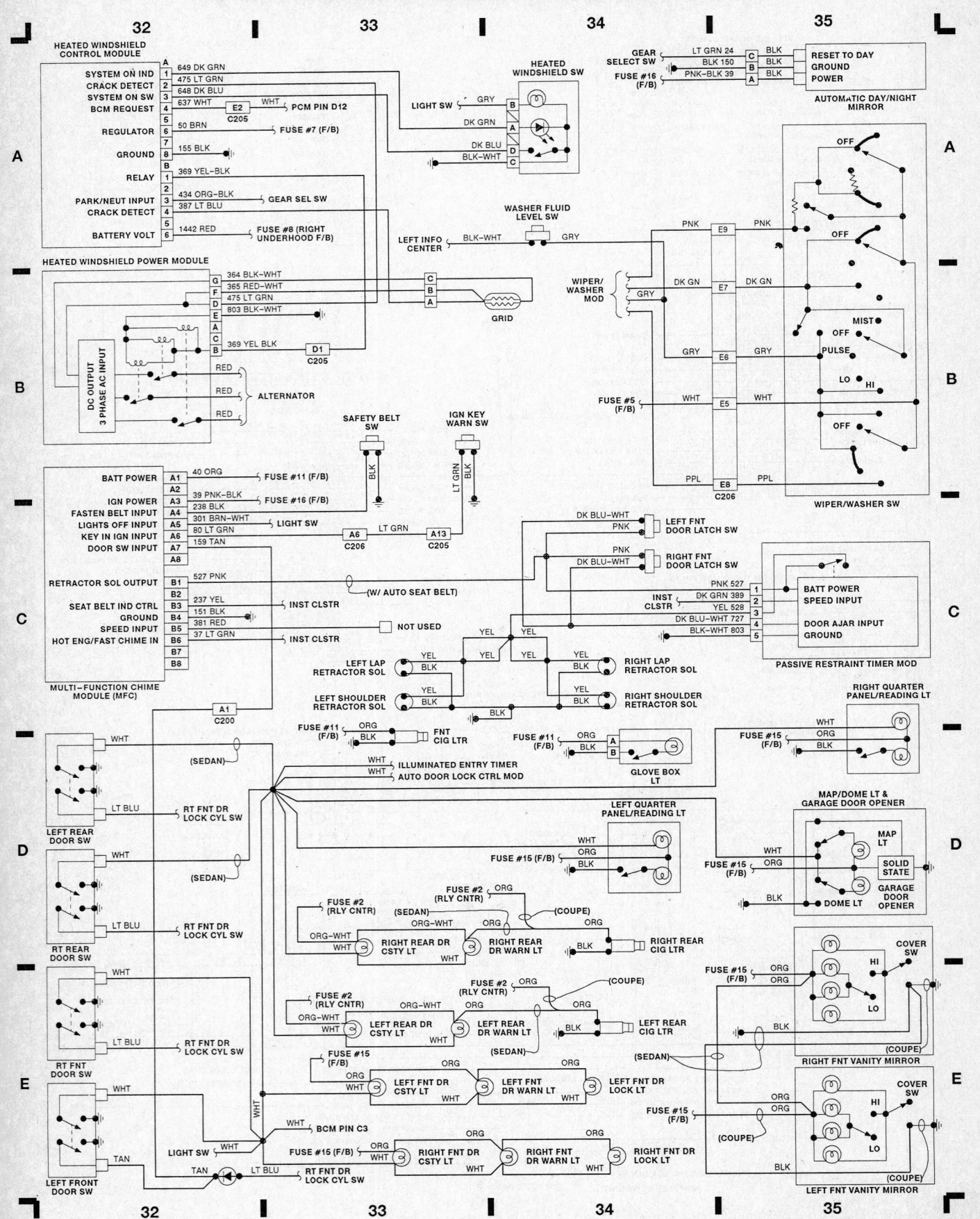

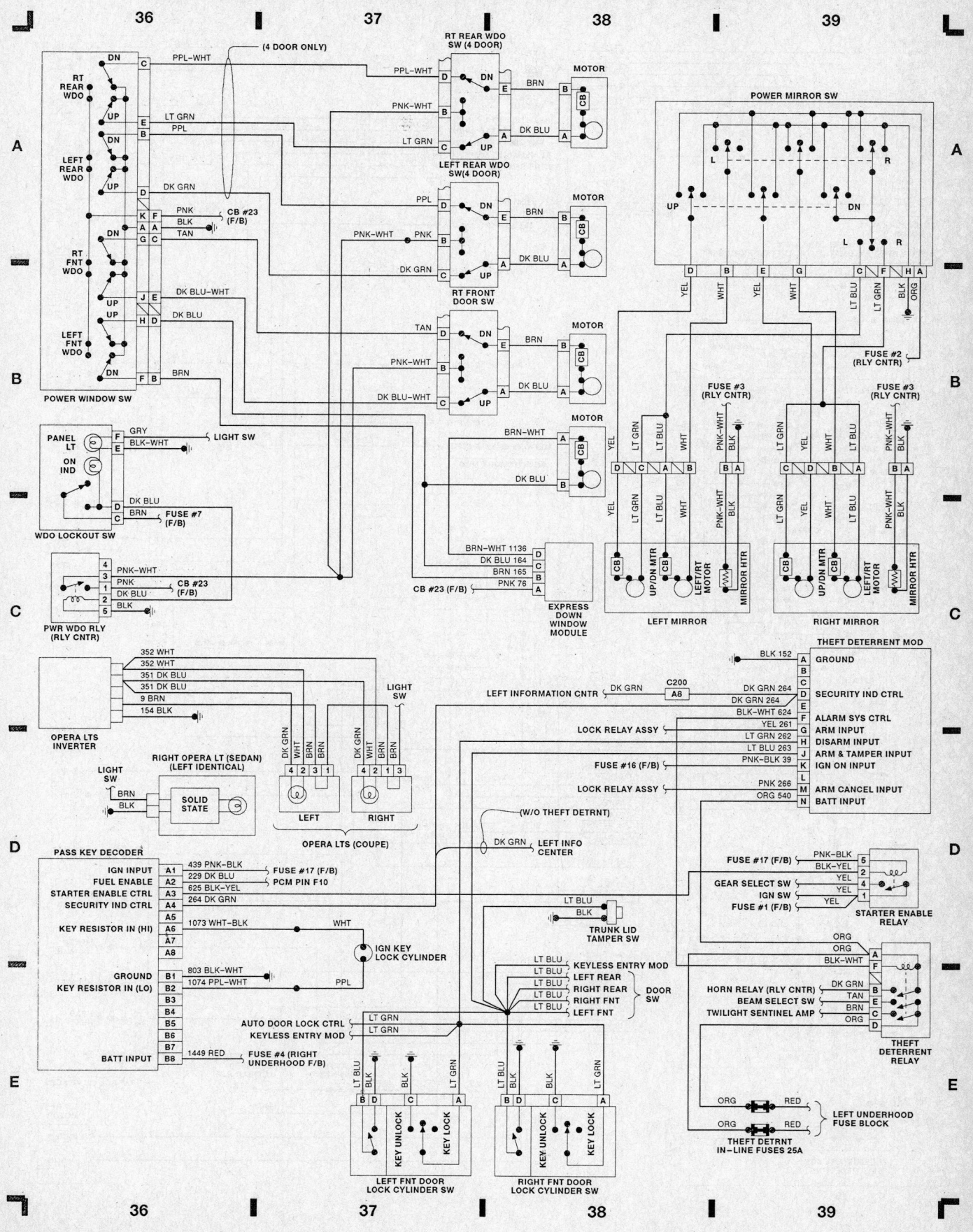

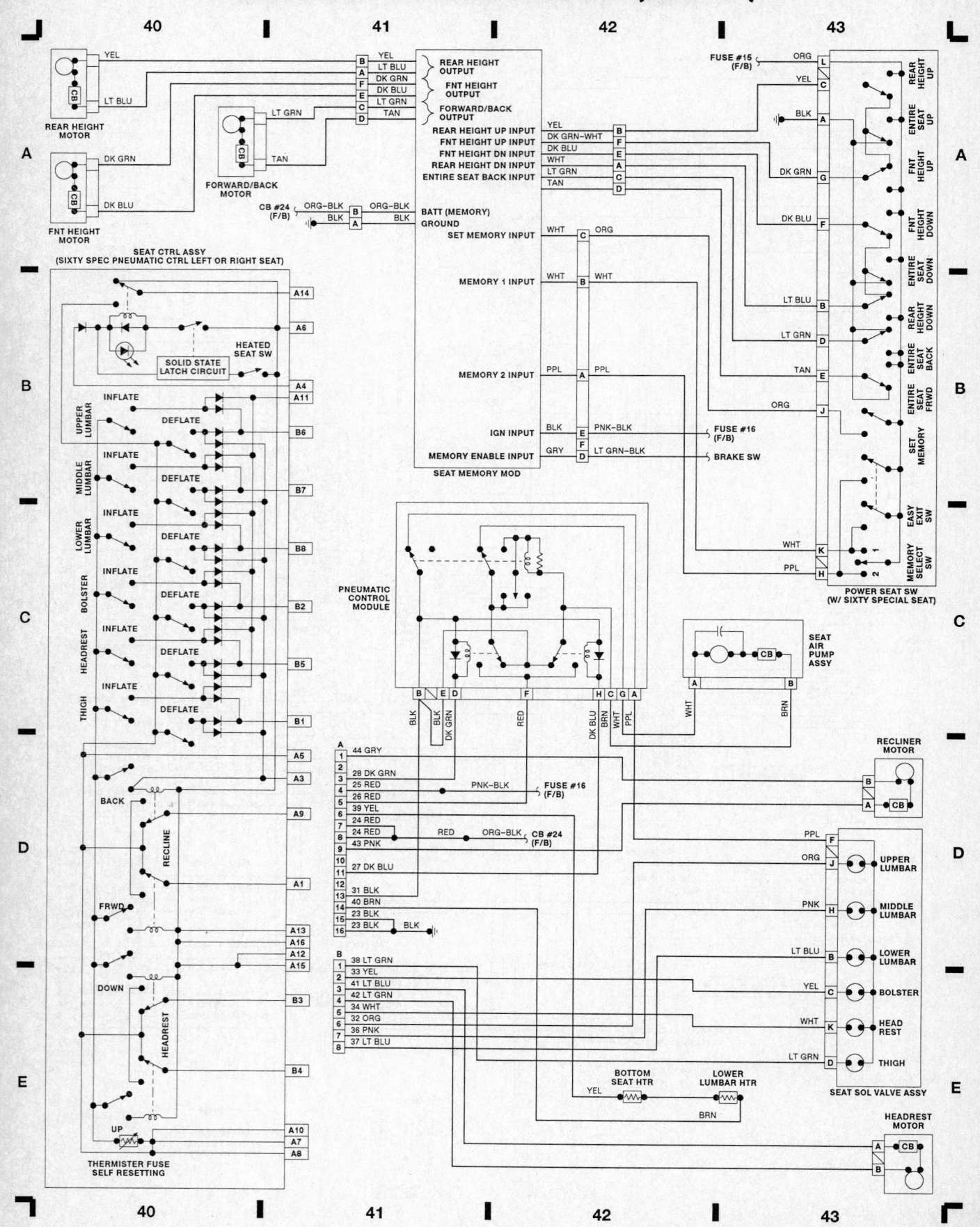

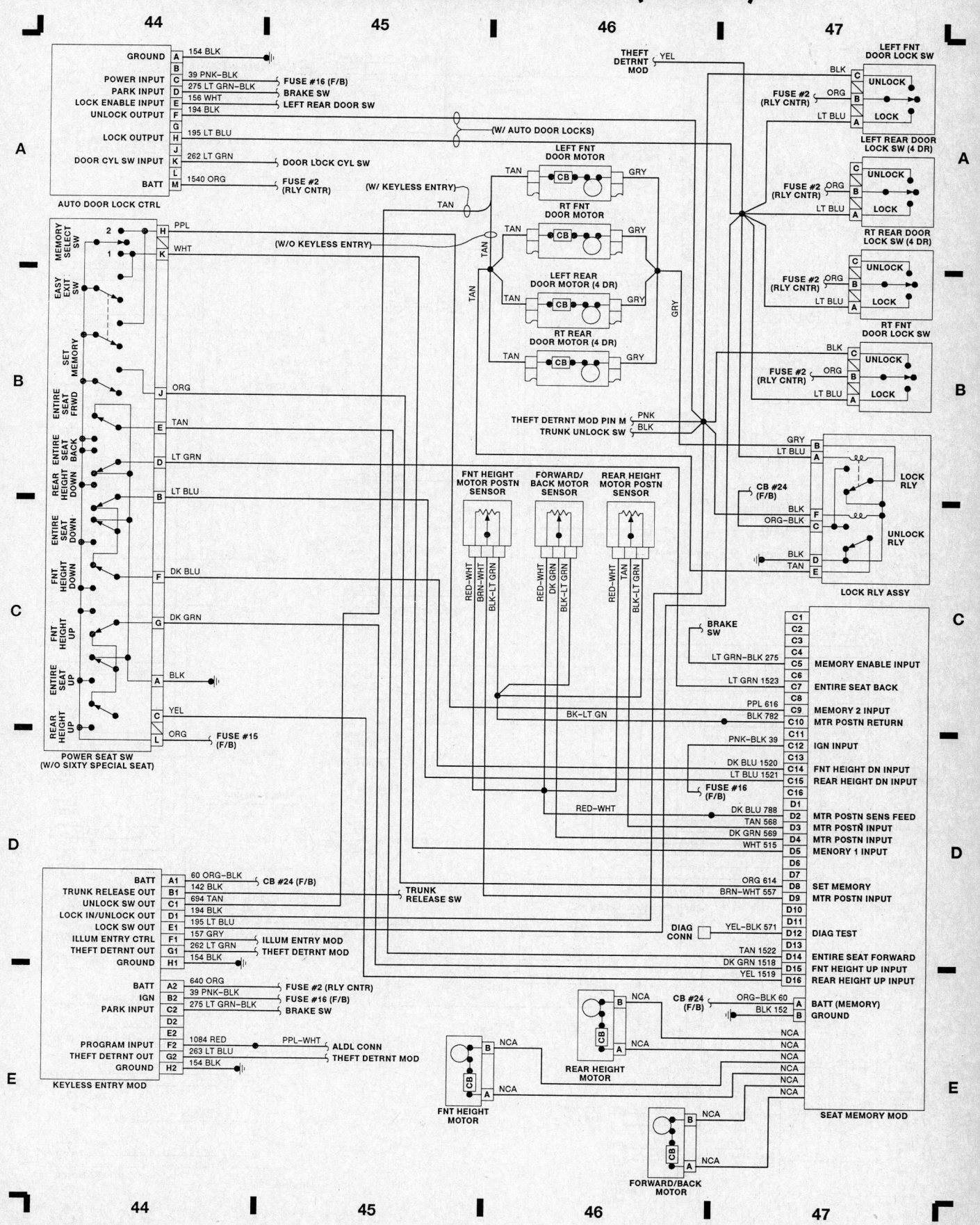

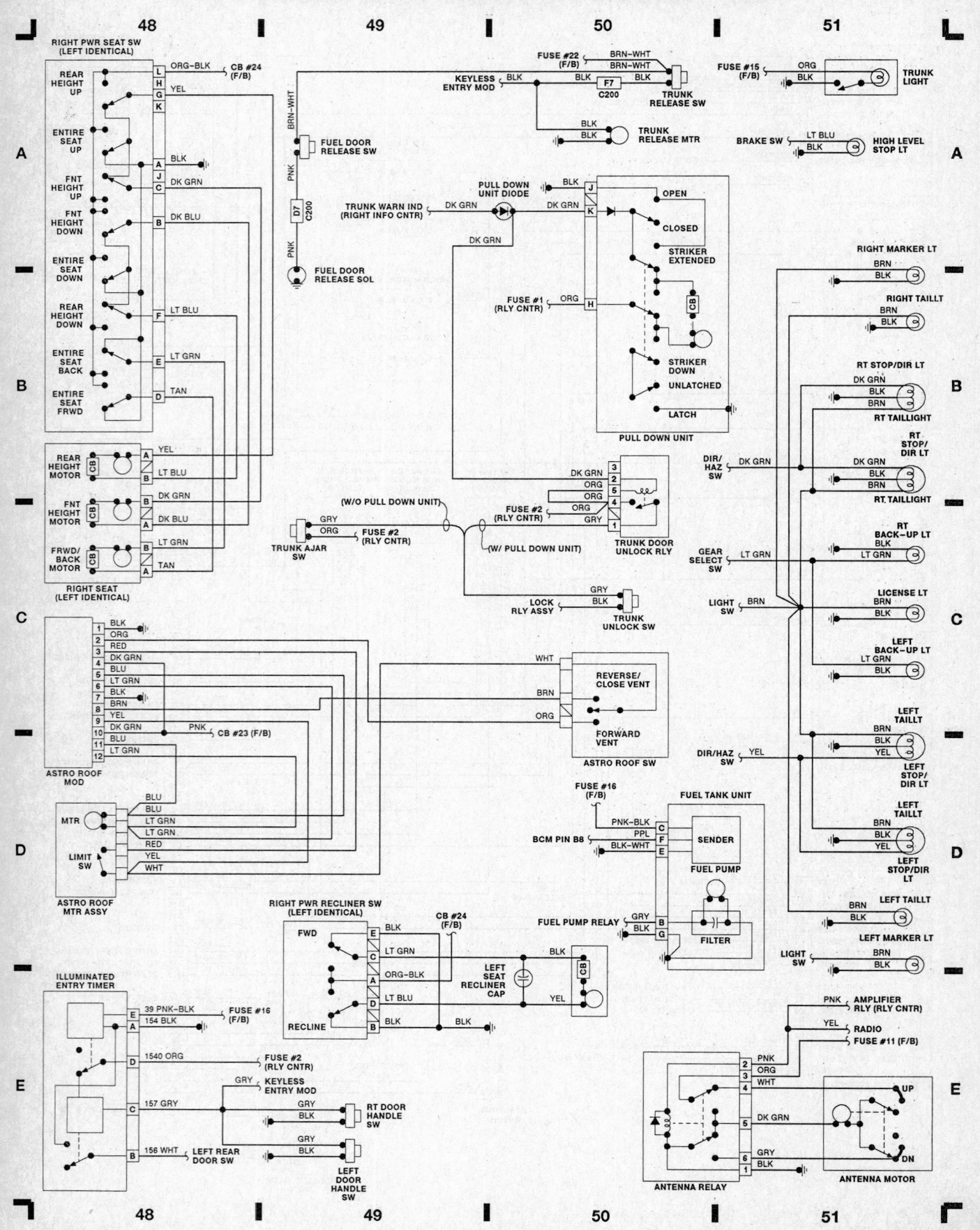

COMPONENT LOCATOR:

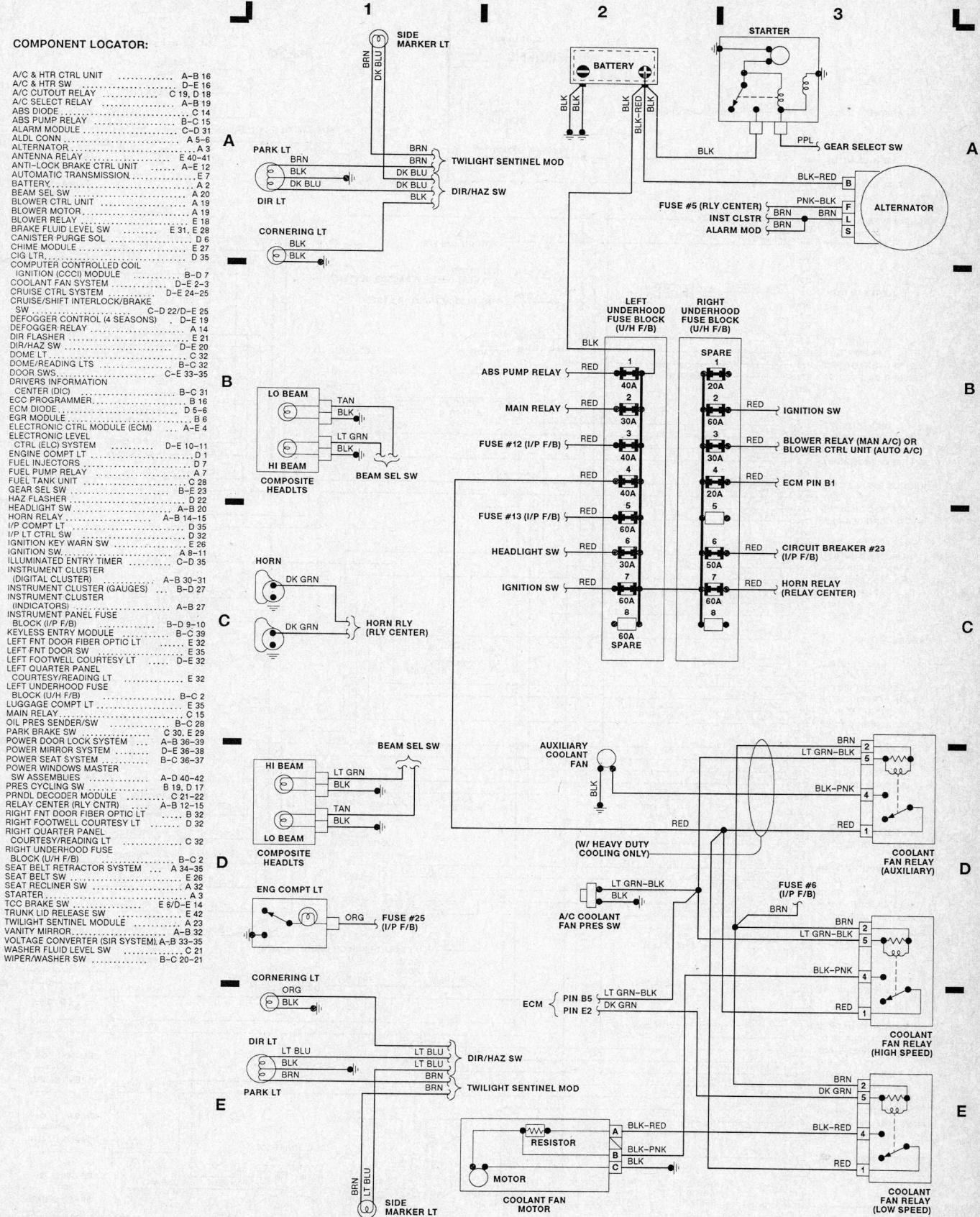

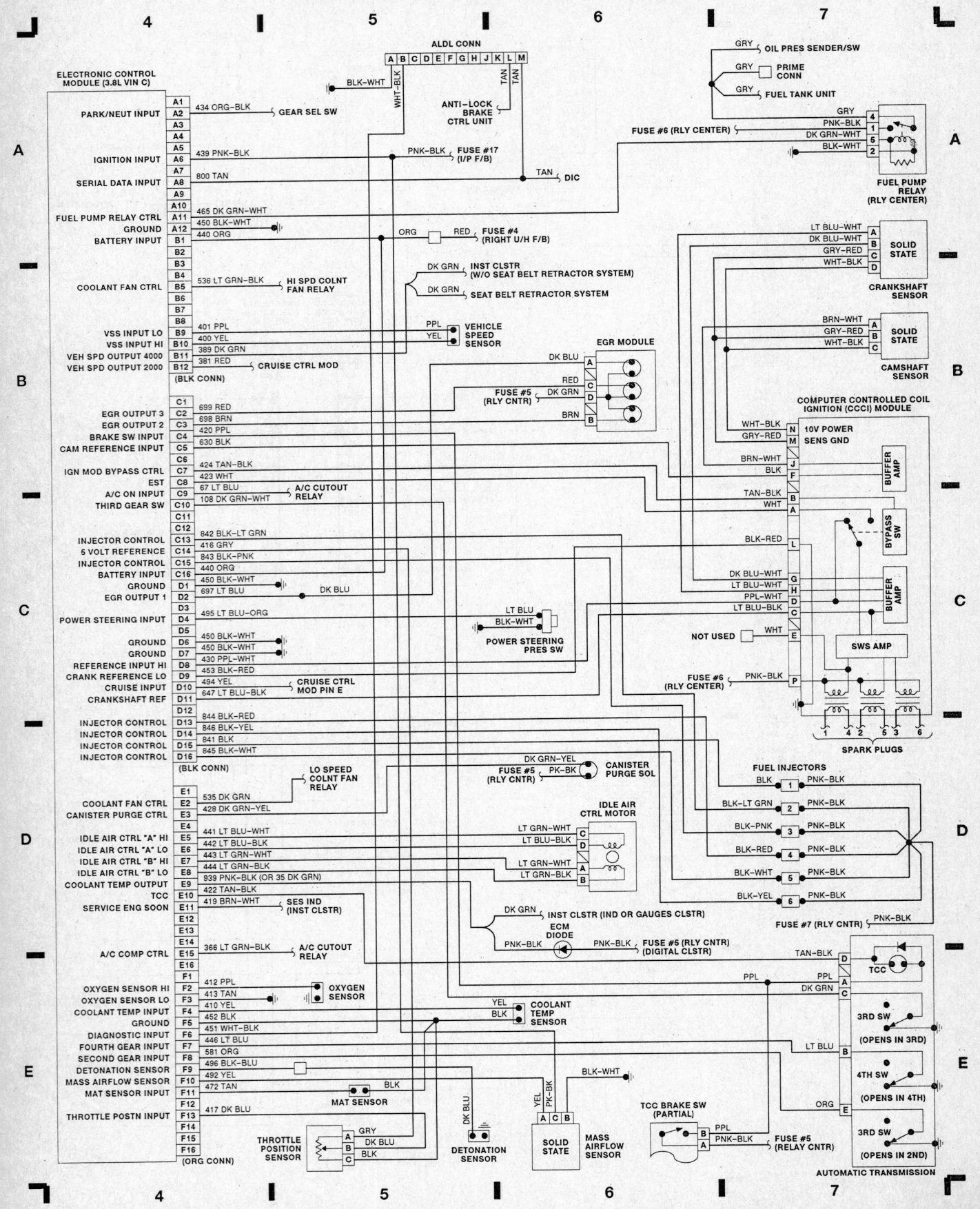

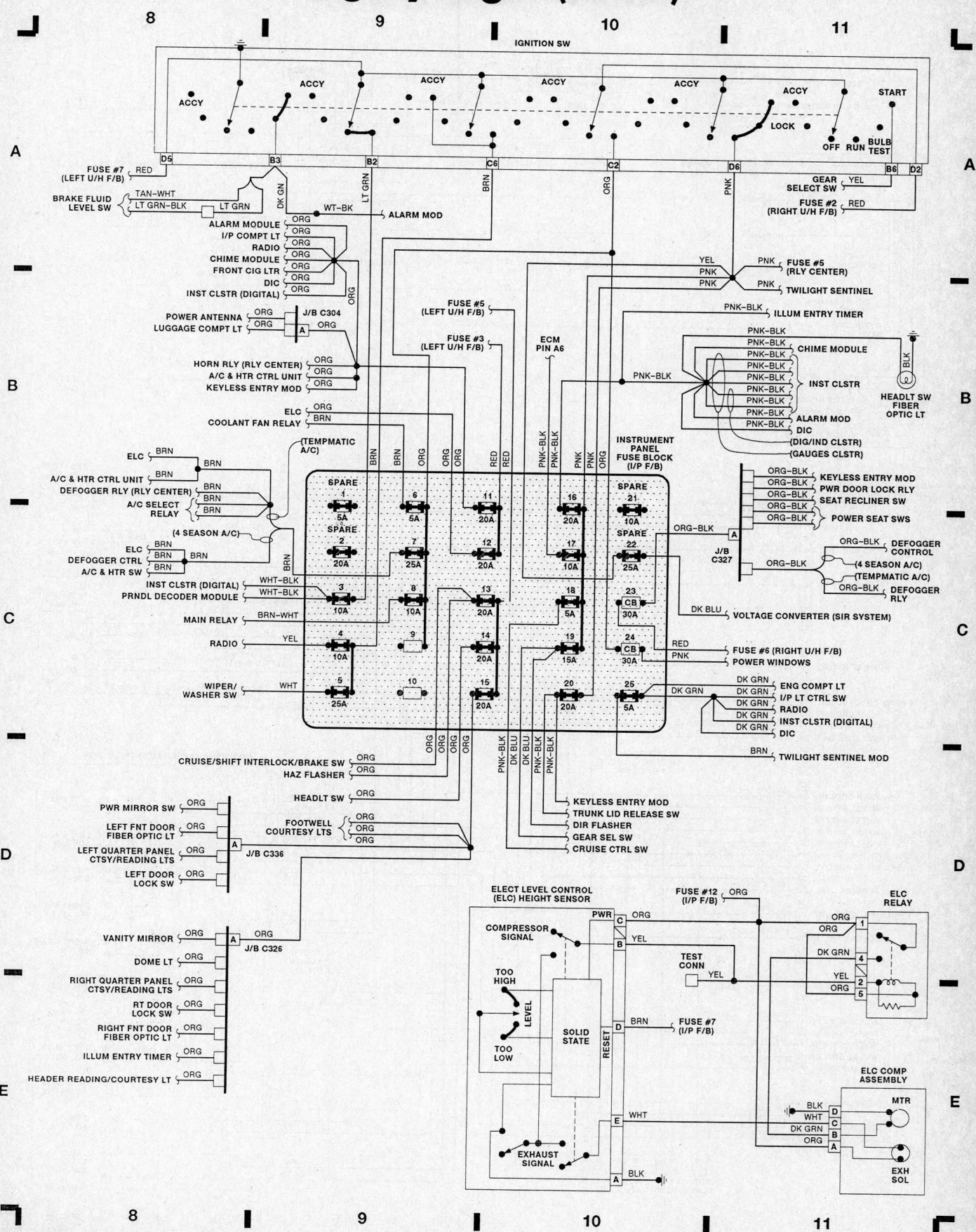

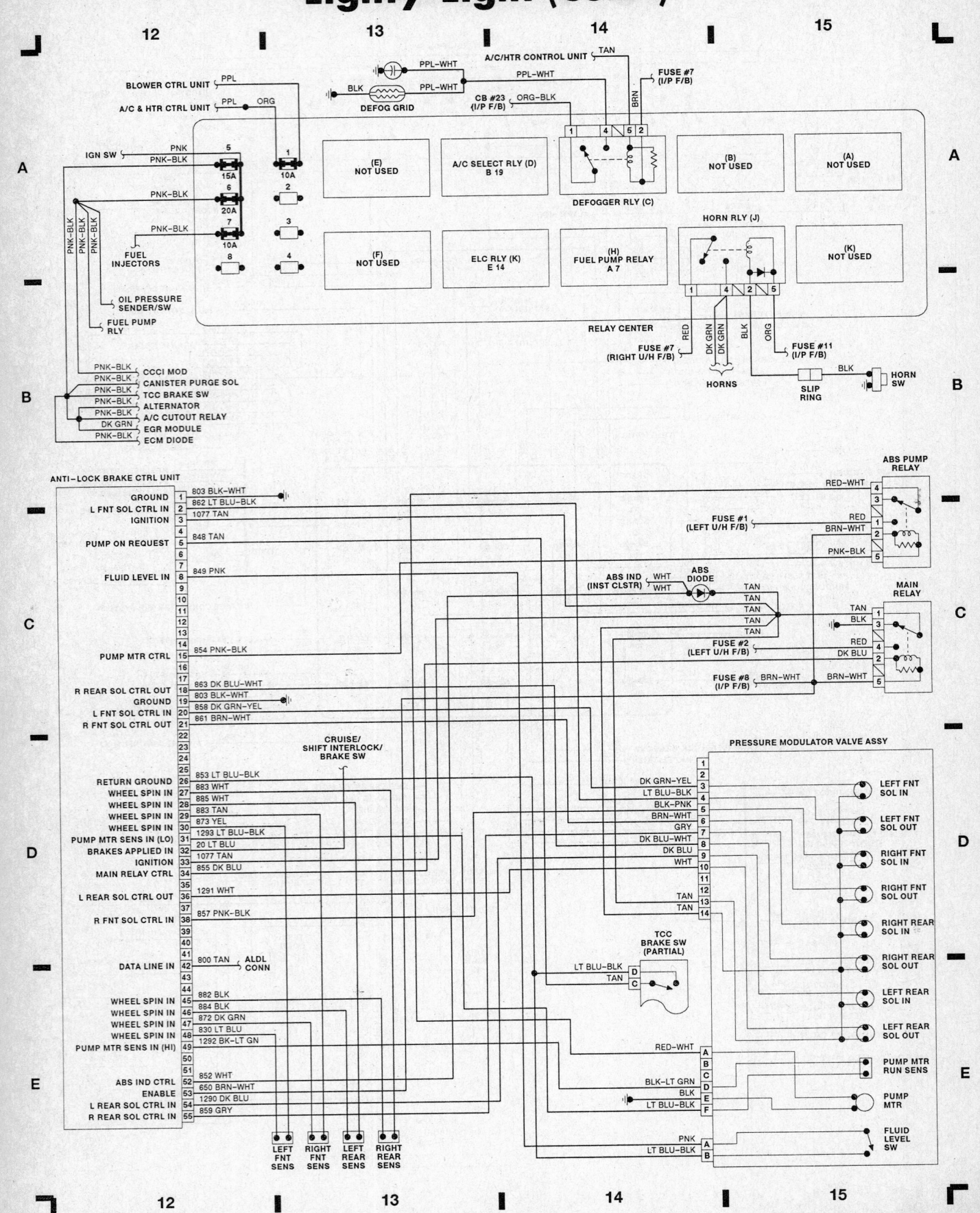

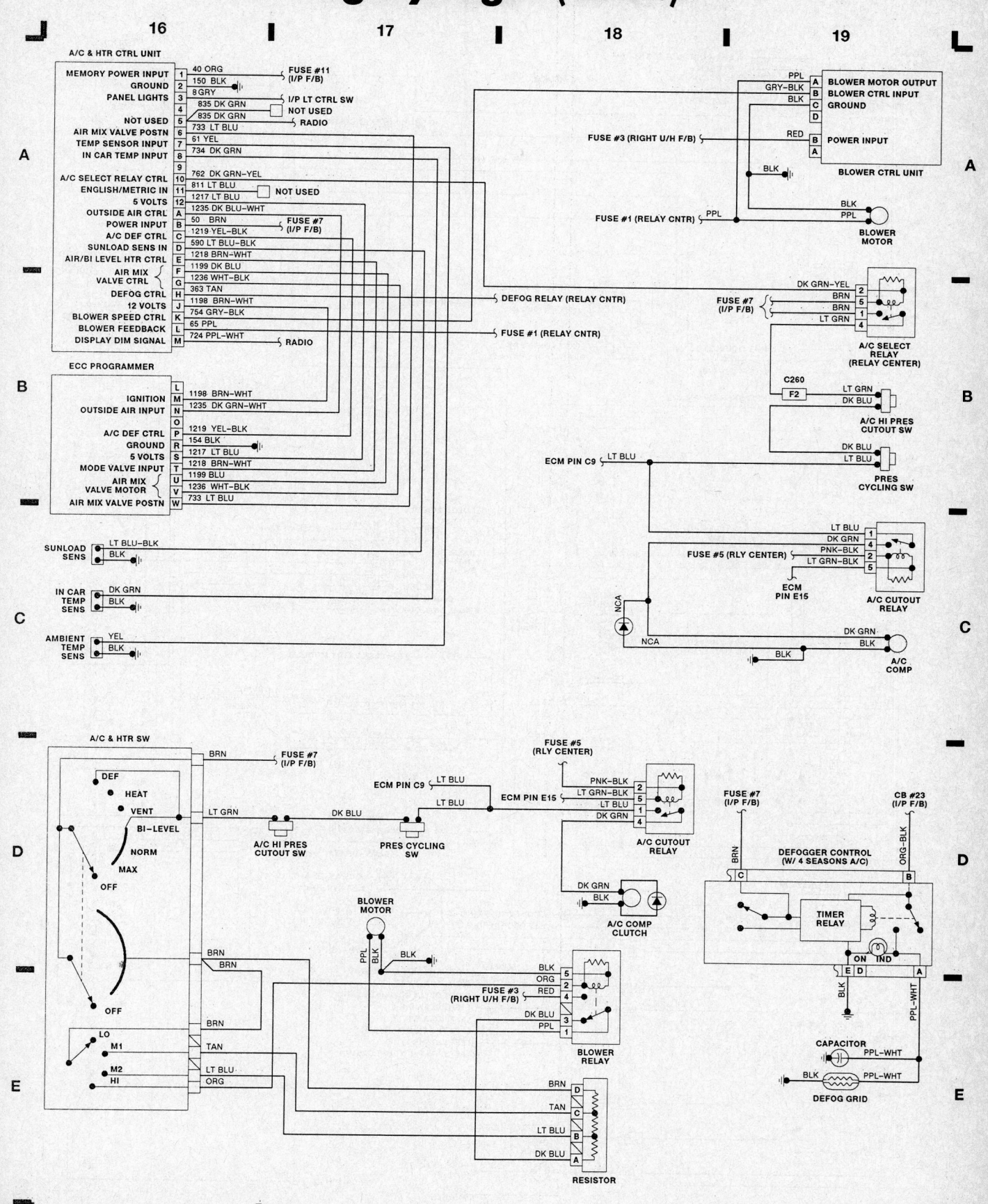

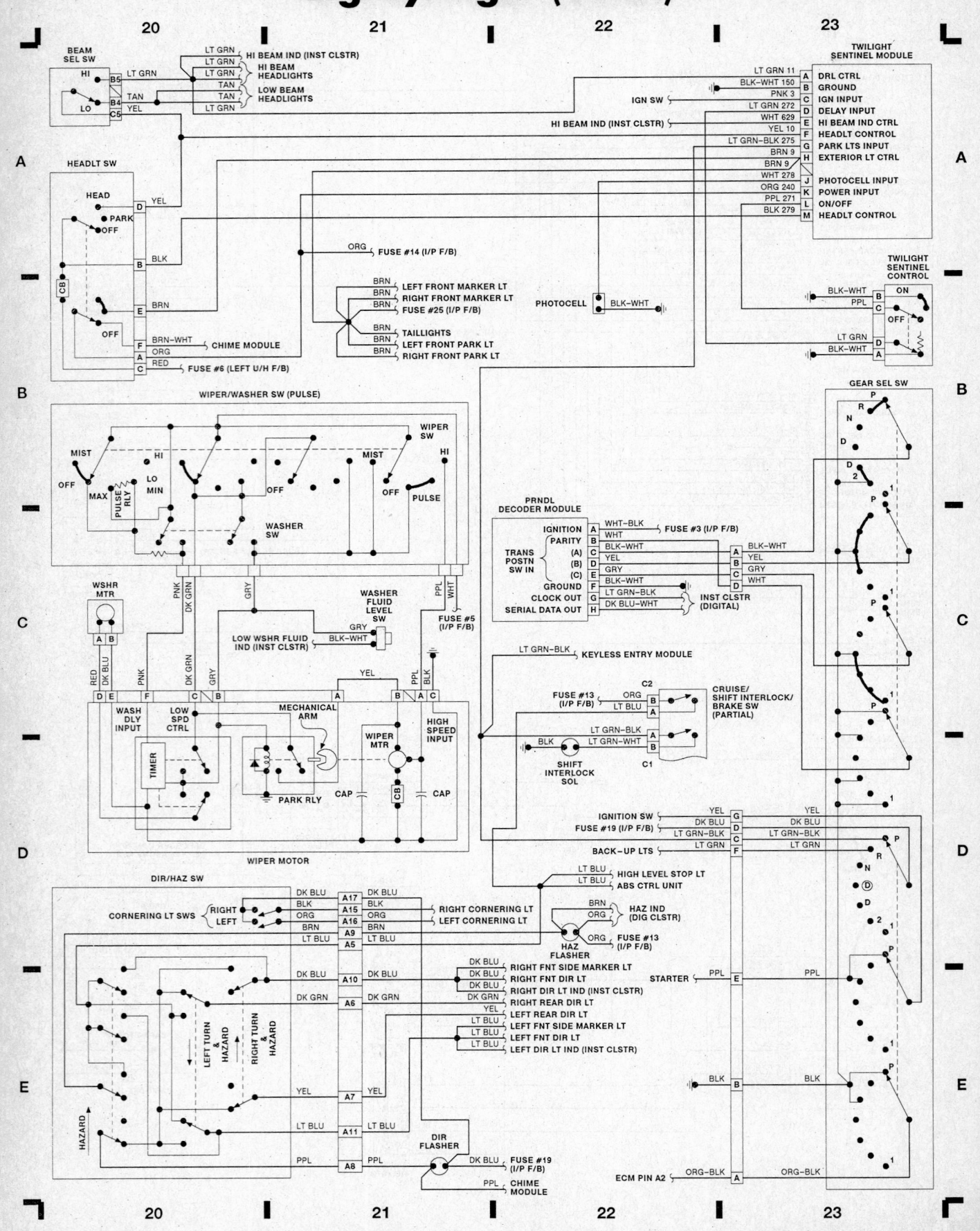

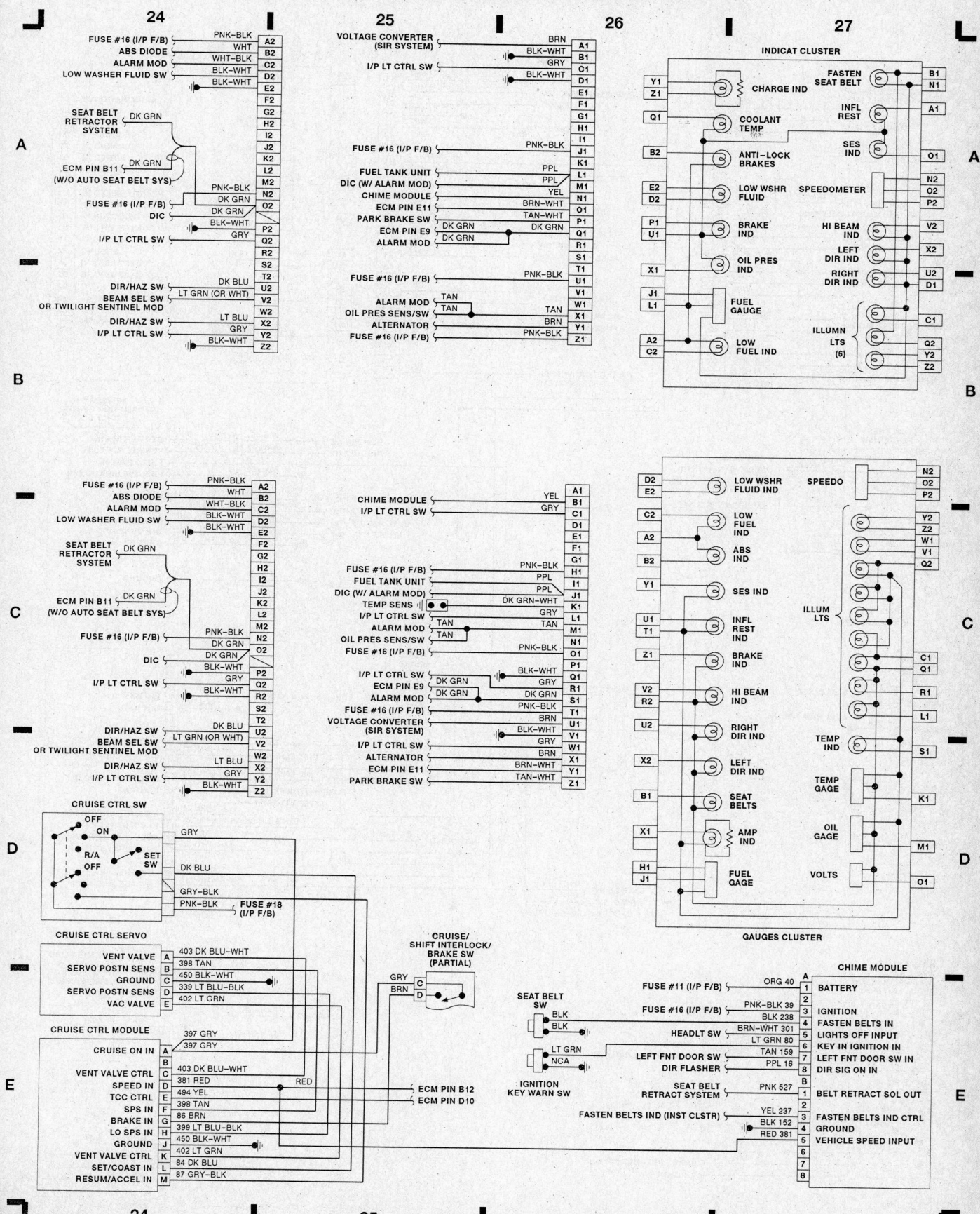

1991 WIRING DIAGRAMS
Eighty-Eight (Cont.)

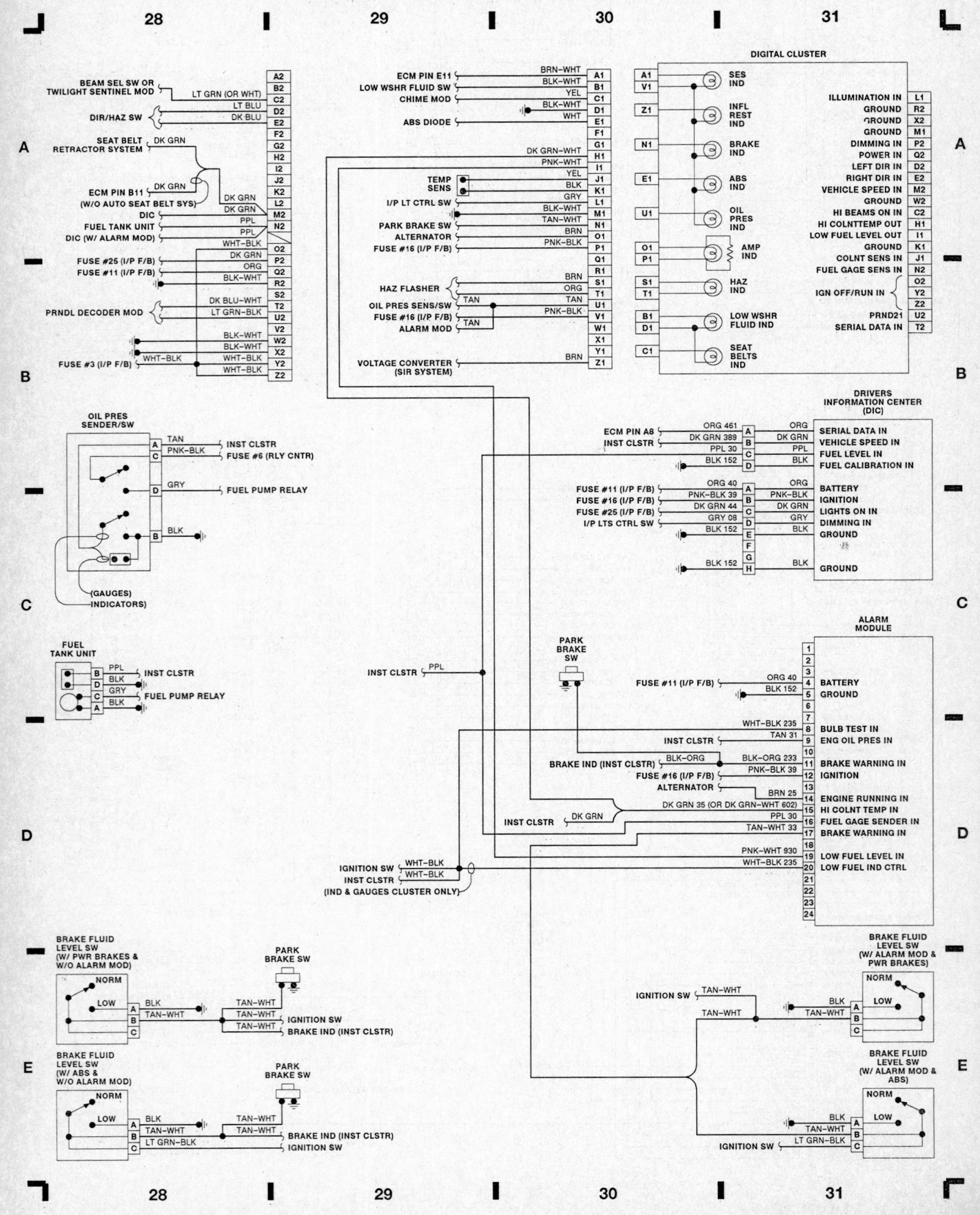

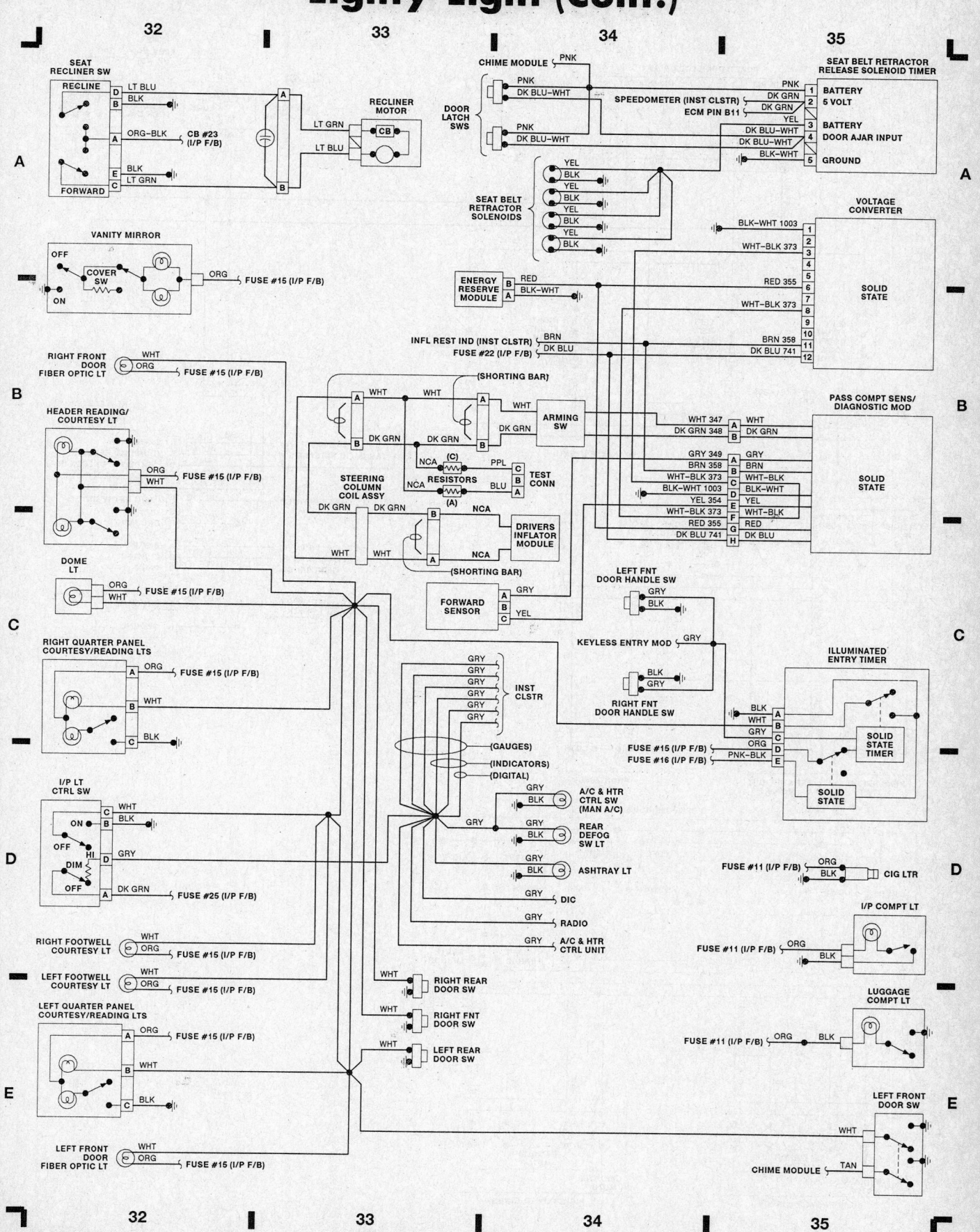

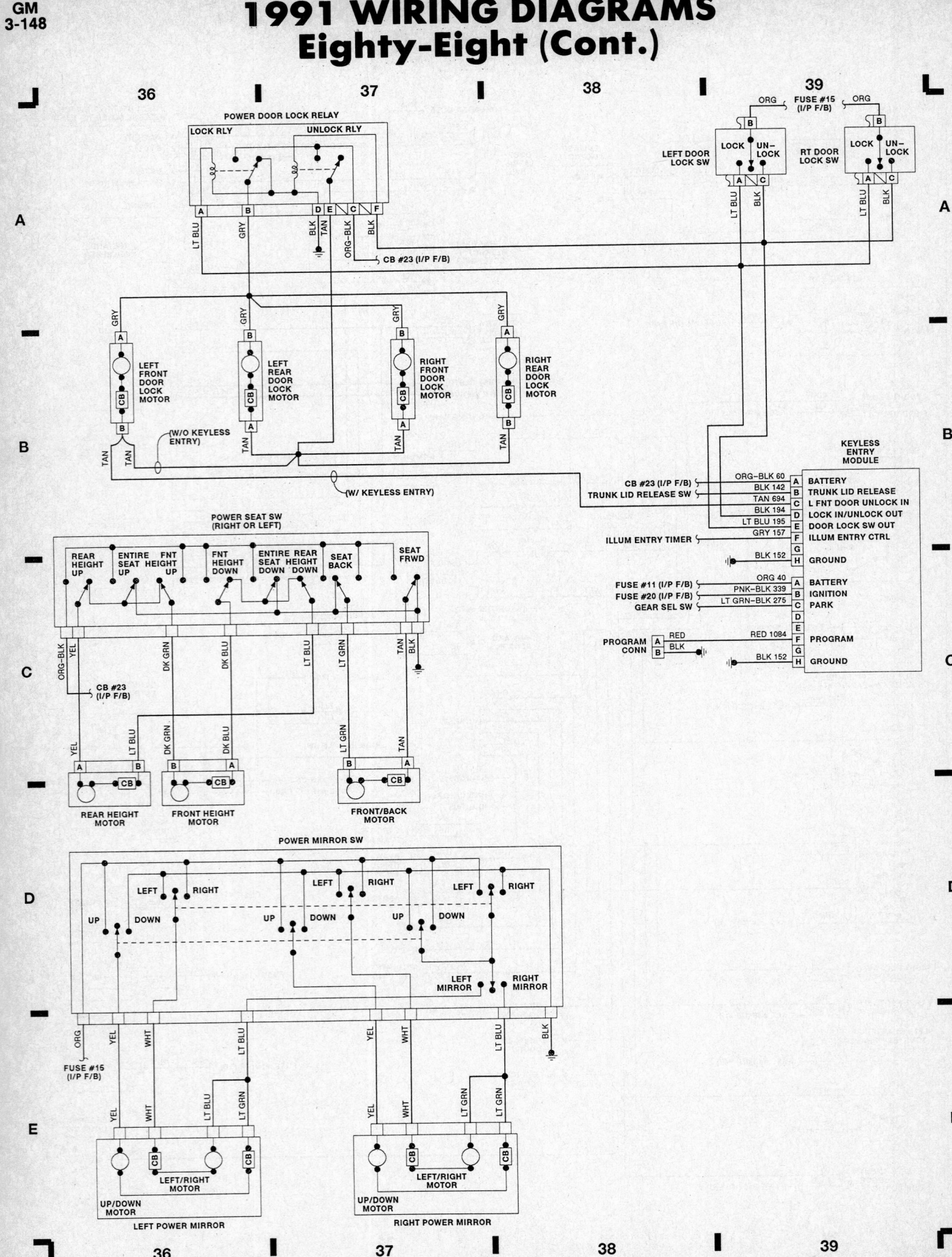

40   41   42   43

MASTER SW ASSY (4 DOOR)

LEFT REAR WDO   LEFT FRONT WDO   RIGHT FRONT WDO   RIGHT REAR WDO

UP   DN   UP   DN   UP   DN   UP   DN

SIDE MARKER LT
BRN
BLK

A

D   B   H   F   K   A   J   G   E   C

DK GRN   PPL   DK BLU   BRN   PNK   BLK   CB #24 (I/P F/B)   TAN   LT GRN   PPL–WHT

PNK

DK GRN   PNK   PPL   PNK BRN DK BLU BN–WT   DK BU–WT PNK TAN   LT GRN PNK PPL

E   A   B   A B C D   C   B   D   E   A   B

LEFT REAR WDO SW   **EXPRESS DOWN MODULE**   **RIGHT FNT WDO SW**   **RIGHT REAR WDO SW**

UP   DN   UP   DN   UP   DN

C   D   A   E   A   E   C   D

B

DK BLU   BRN   BN–WT   DK BLU   DK BLU   BRN   DK BLU   BRN

B   A   A   B   B   A   B   A

CB   CB   CB   CB

LEFT REAR WDO MOTOR   **LEFT FRONT WDO MOTOR**   **RIGHT FRONT WDO MOTOR**   **RIGHT REAR WDO MOTOR**

STOP/DIR LT
DK GRN
BLK
BRN
TAILLT

DIR/HAZ SW — STOP/DIR LT
DK GRN
BLK
BRN
BRN
TAILLT

DIR/HAZ SW — HIGH LEVEL STOP LT
LT BLU
BLK

BRN
BLK

C

TWILIGHT SENTINEL MOD — BRN   LICENSE LT
BRN
BLK

BRN   TAILLT
BRN
BLK
YEL
YEL

DIR/HAZ SW — STOP/DIR LT

BRN   TAILLT
BRN
BLK
YEL

STOP/DIR LT

MASTER SW ASSY (2 DOOR)

LEFT REAR WDO   LEFT FRONT WDO

UP   DN   UP   DN

D   B   F   A   E   C

DK BLU   BRN   PNK   BLK   DK BU–WT   TAN

PNK   PNK CB #24 (I/P F/B)

C   B   D

RIGHT WDO SW

UP   DN

A   E

D

GEAR SELECT SW — LT GRN
LT GRN
BLK

BACK–UP LTS
LT GRN
LT GRN
BLK

PNK BRN DK BLU BN–WT   DK BLU   BN–WT   DK BLU   BRN

A B C D   A   B   A   B

EXPRESS DOWN MODULE   CB   CB

LEFT WINDOW MOTOR   **LEFT REAR WDO MOTOR**

BLK   PNK   ORG
RADIO
FUSE #11 (I/P F/B)

COAX — RADIO

C B A   DN
1 2 3   4 — C — WHT   DN SW   UP
    5 — B — DK GRN   DN
    6 — A — GRY   UP SW   DN
UP

ANTENNA RELAY

ANTENNA MOTOR

TRUNK LID RELEASE SOL
BLK

BLK   BLK — KEYLESS ENTRY MOD

BLK
TRUNK LID RELEASE SW

PNK–BLK
FUSE #20 (I/P F/B)

E

BRN
BLK
SIDE MARKER LT

40   41   42   43

1991 WIRING DIAGRAMS
Eldorado & Seville

COMPONENT LOCATOR:

ABS MOD.	A–B 44
ALDL CONN	B–C 7
ALTERNATOR	A 3
ASTRO ROOF SW	B 52
AUTO DAY/NIGHT MIRROR	D 52
AUTO TRANSAXLE	A 7
BLOWER MTR	B 24
BODY COMPUTER MOD (BCM)	A–E 27
BRAKE MODULATOR	A–B 47
BRAKE SW	C 47
CANISTER PURGE SOL	E 6
CENTRAL POWER SUPPLY	C–D 23
CHIME MOD.	E 23
CLIMATE CONTROL DRIVER INFORMATION CENTER (CCDIC)	E 28
COMPUTER COMMAND RIDE (CCR) MOD	A–B 48
CONSOLE CIG LTR	C 28
COURTESY LIGHTS	A–B 43
COURTESY LTS RLY	C 40
CRUISE CTRL SERVO	C–D 44
DEFOG RLY	E 53
DERM	D–E 47
DIR. SW.	B 23
DIR/HAZ ALERT MOD	B–C 20
DIR/HAZ MOD	A 20
DOOR HANDLE SWS	E 41
DOOR LOCK CYL SWS	C–B 36
DOOR LOCK SYS	C–D 41–43
DOOR SWS.	D–E 40
DUAL SENSOR	E 44
EGR SOL	A 7
ELC HEIGHT SENS	E 32
ELC RLY	D–E 32
ELECT SPARK TIMING (EST) DISTR	D–E 7
ENG COMPT LT	D 3
EXPRESS DOWN MOD (2 DOOR)	B–C 37–38
EXPRESS DOWN MOD (4 DOOR)	E 36
FOOTWELL CTSY LT	A 40
FUEL DOOR RELEASE SW	C 42
FUEL INJ	A–B 7
FUEL PUMP RLY	C 7
FUEL TANK UNIT	C 55
FUS LINK	B–C 2
FUSE BLOCK	B–D 13–14
GEAR SELECT SW	E 8–11
HEATED W/SHIELD MOD	C 48
HEATED W/SHIELD POWER MOD	C–D 51
HORN SW	D 20
IGNITION SW	A 12–15
INFORMATION CENTER	A–C 31
INST CLSTR	C–E 31
INTERIOR RELAY CENTER	B–C 16–19
KEYLESS ENTRY MOD	D–E 48
LEFT REAR CIG LTR	C 38
LEFT SW ASSY	D–E 35
LOW REFRIGERANT SW	C 11
LUMBAR SYS	A–B 34–35
MULTI-FUNCTION SW	C 44
OIL PRES SW	C 7
OPERA LTS	B–C 54–55
OVERHEAD READING CTSY LTS	A–B 40–41
P/S PRES SW	C 6
PASS KEY DECODER MOD	D 36
POWER ANTENNA MTR	E 52
POWER MIRROR SW	B 53–54
POWER MOD	B 24
POWER SEAT RECLINER SW	B–C 32–33
POWER SEAT SYS	A 32–33
POWER WINDOW SYS (2 DOOR)	A–C 38–39
POWER WINDOW SYS (4 DOOR)	D–E 36–39
POWERTRAIN CONTROL MOD (PCM)	A–E 4
PROGRAMMER	A 24
QUARTER PANEL READING/CTSY LT	A–B 41
RIGHT REAR CIG LTR	C 38
RIGHT SW ASSY	A 28–30
STARTER ENABLE RLY	D 36
STARTER SOL	A 3
THEFT DETERRENT IN-LINE FUSE	B 36
THEFT DETERRENT MOD	A 36
THEFT DETERRENT RLY	B 36
TRUNK LT	A 42
TRUNK PULL DOWN UNIT	A 52–53
TRUNK RELEASE SOL	A 54
TRUNK RELEASE SW	A 54
UNDERHOOD FUSE BLOCK	A–B 8–11
VANITY MIRROR	B 40
VCC BRAKE SW	A 6
WIPER/WASHER MTR MOD	E 2–3

NOTE: B/H CONN

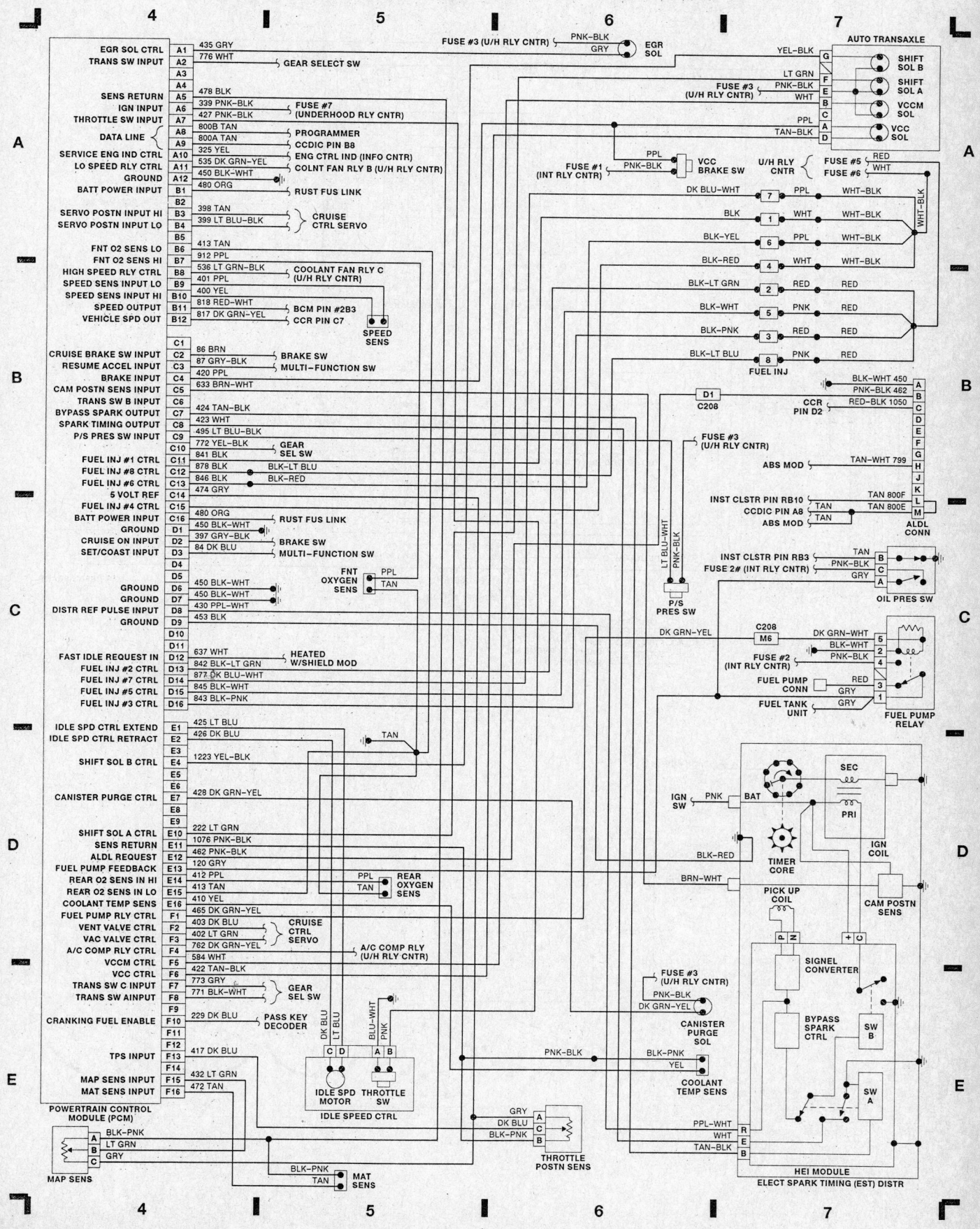

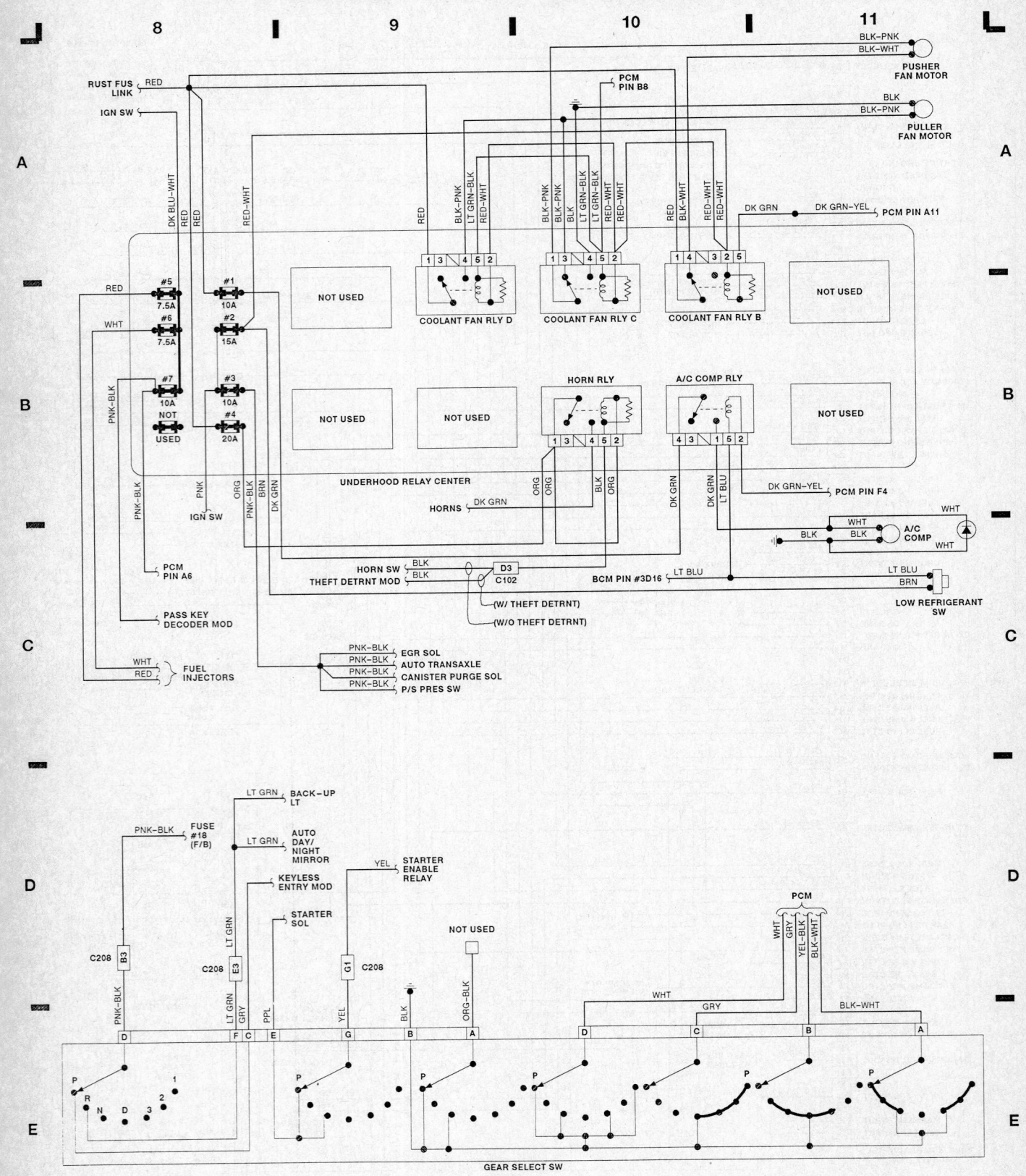

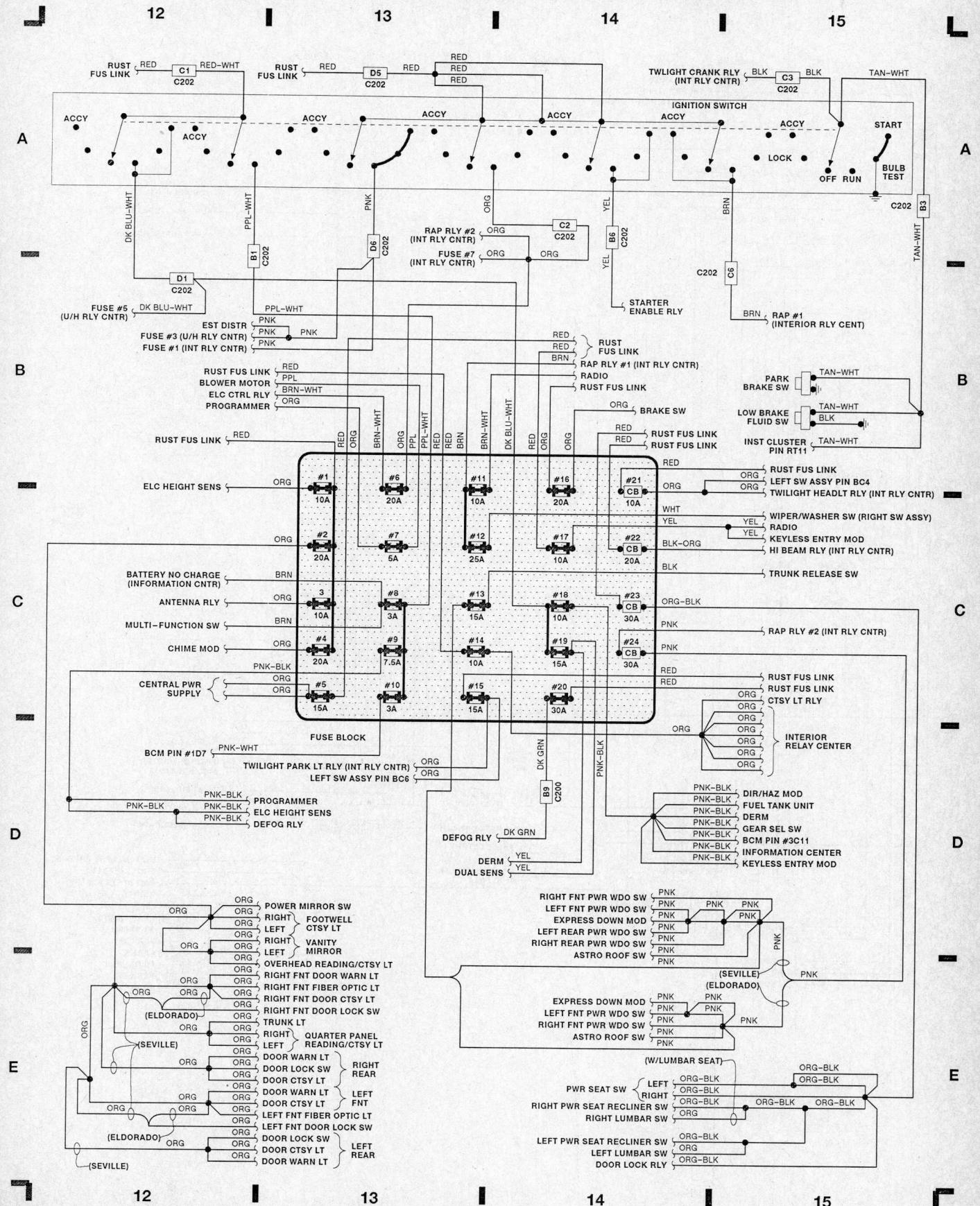

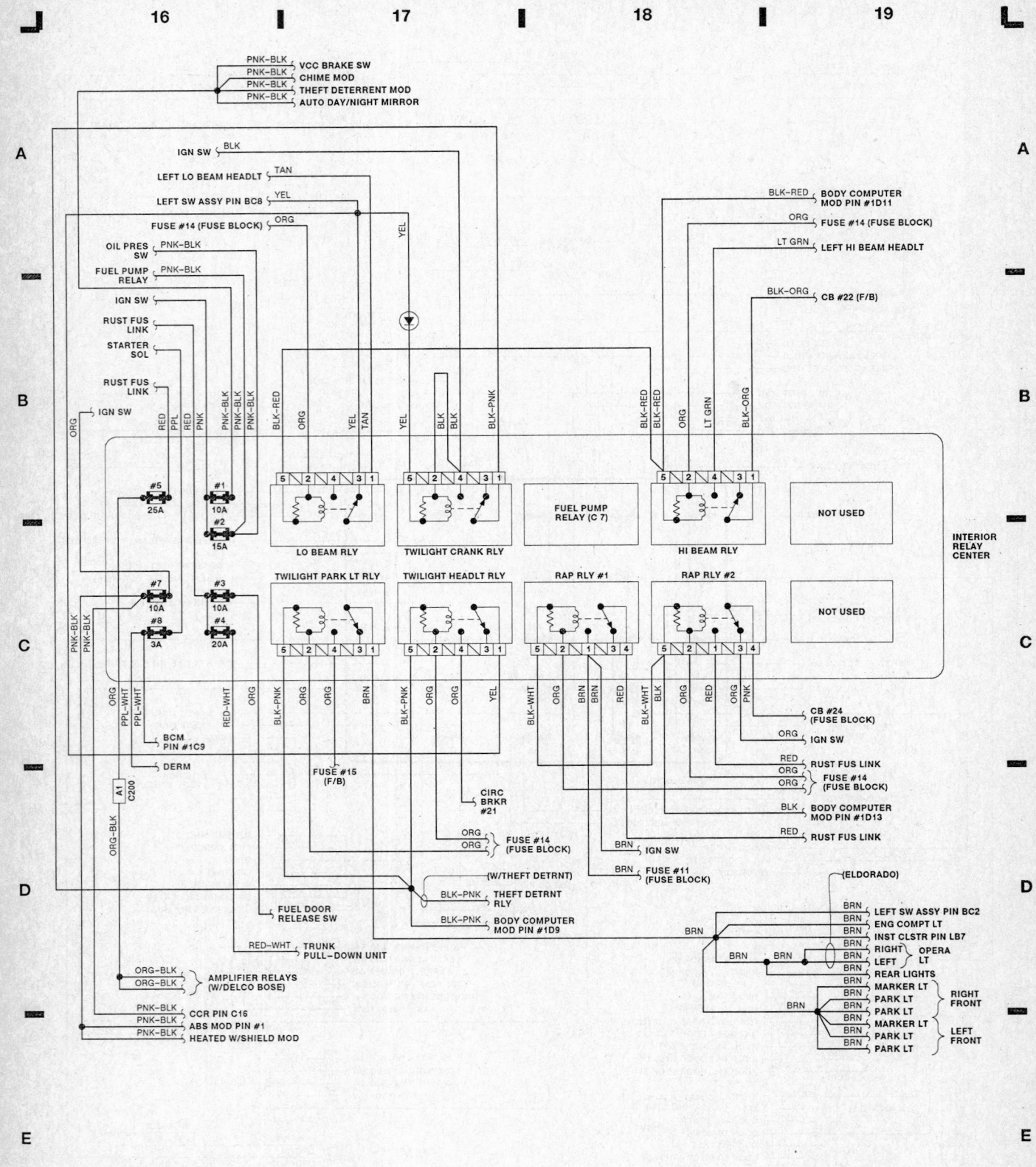

NOTE: B/H CONN

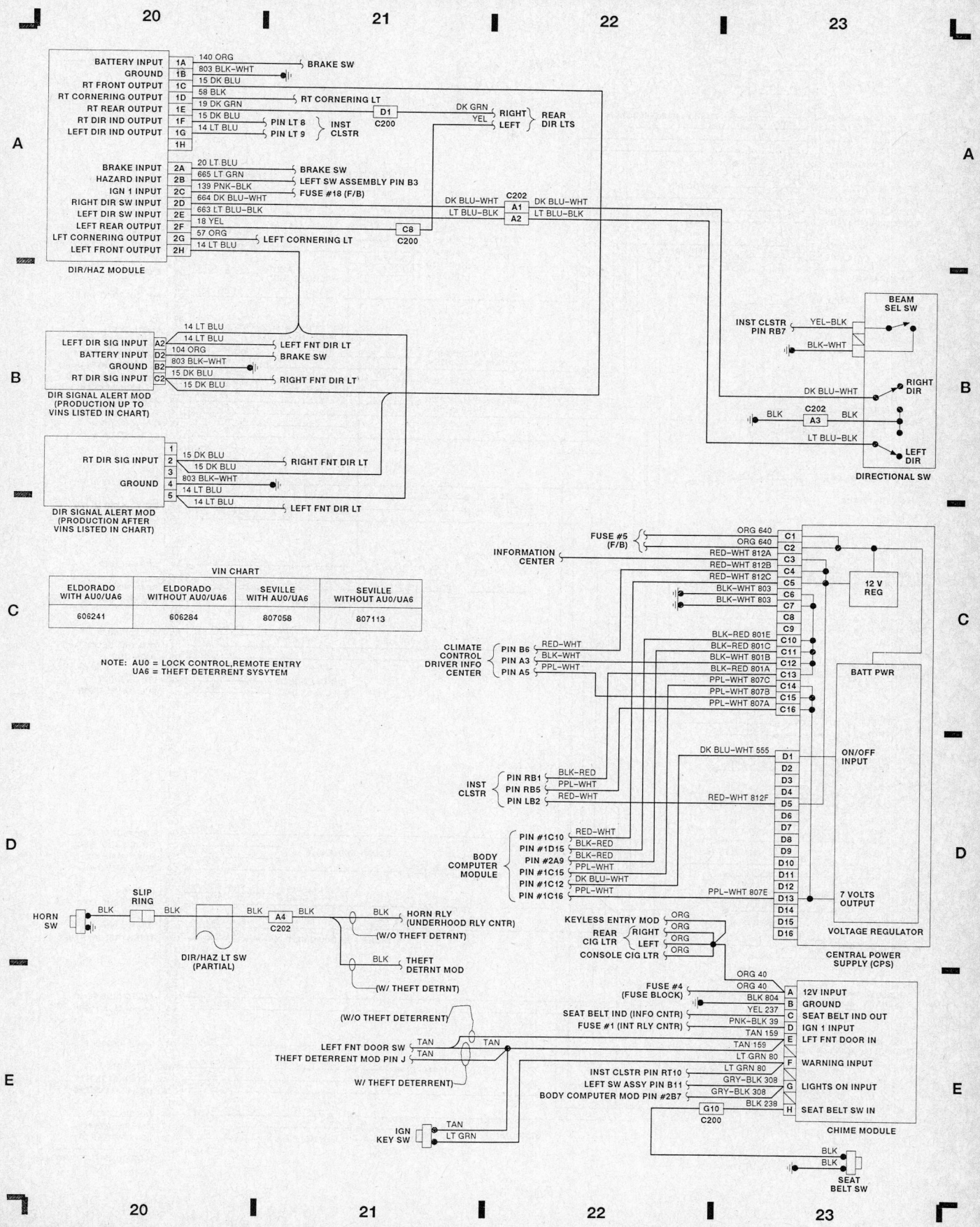

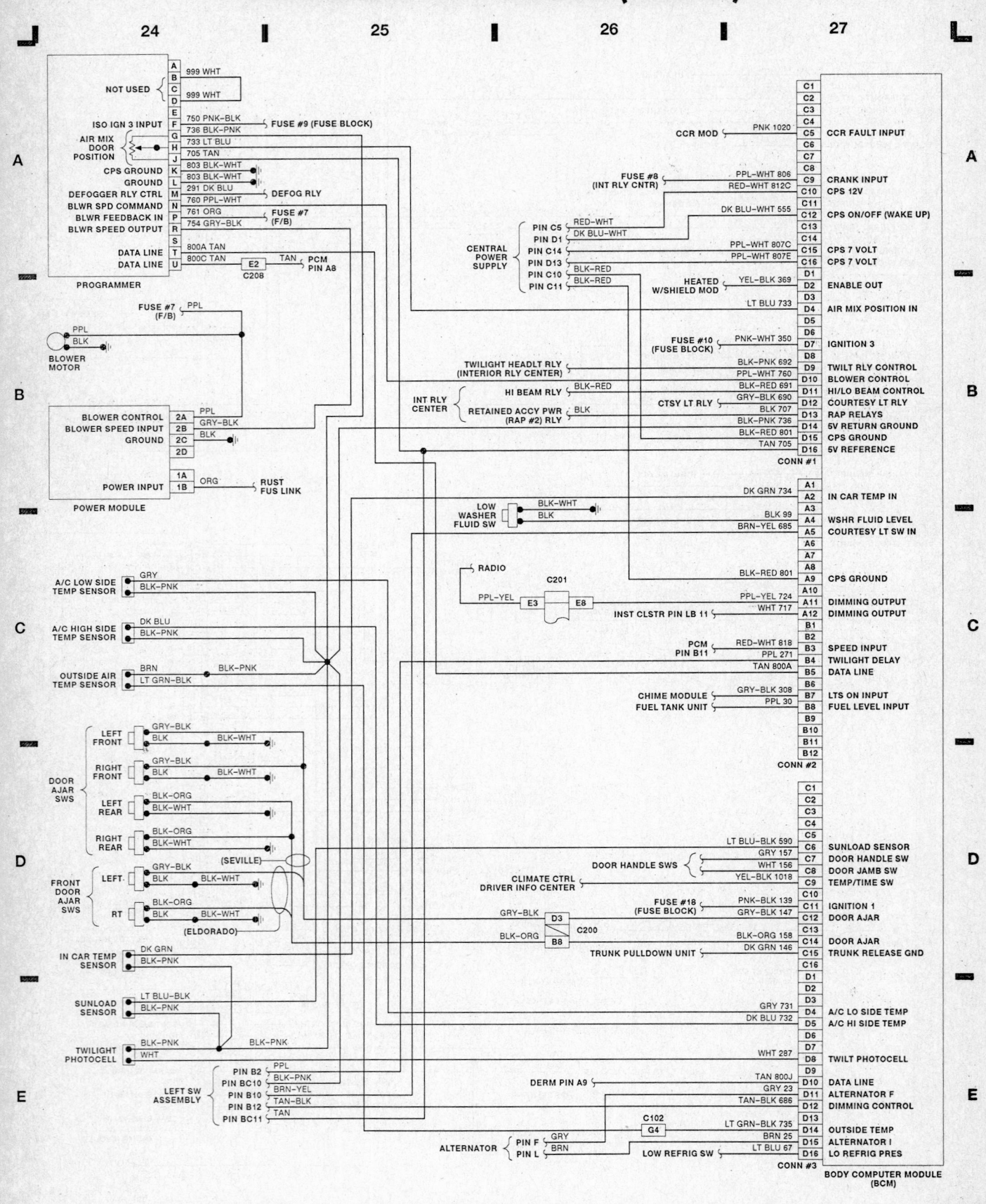

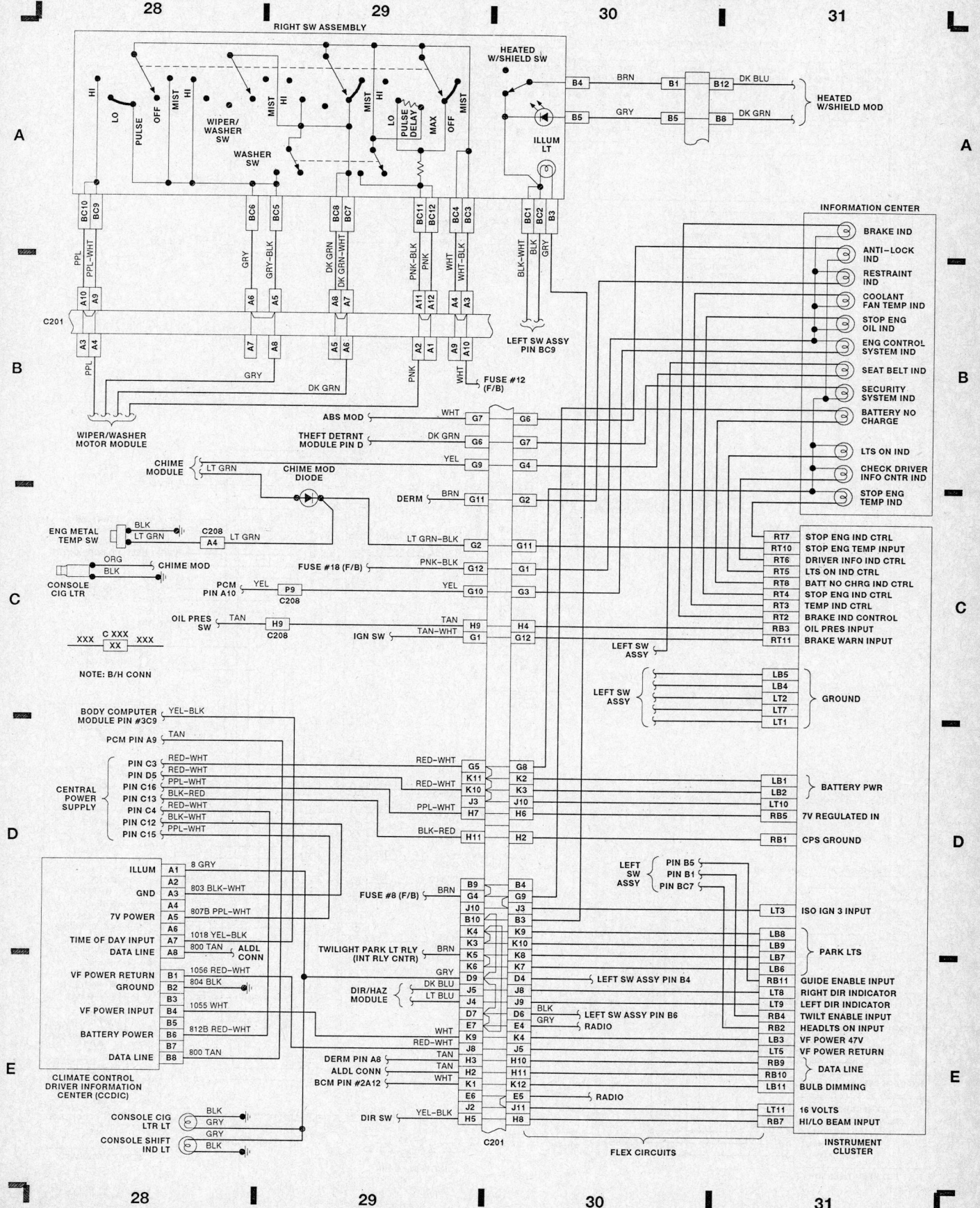

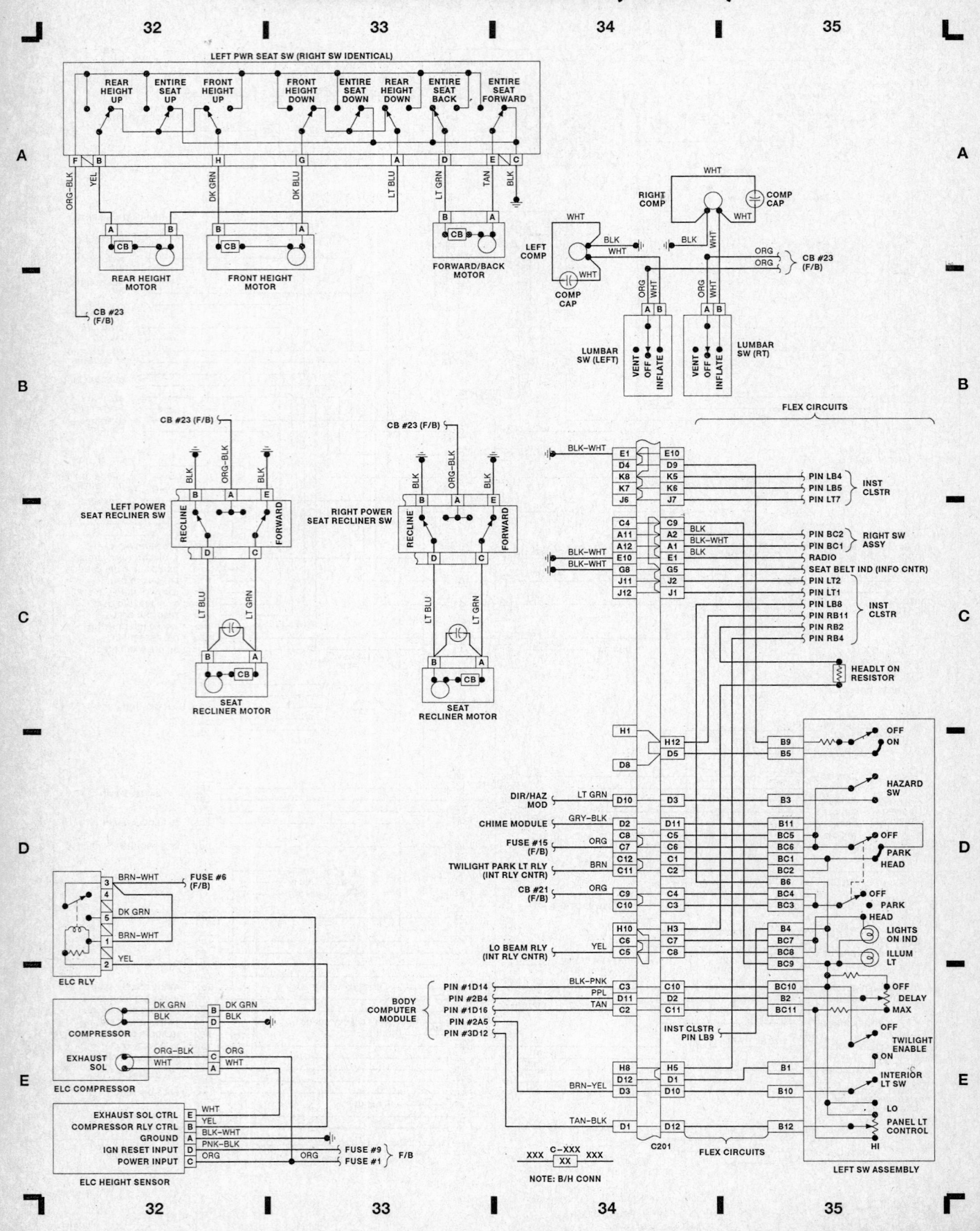

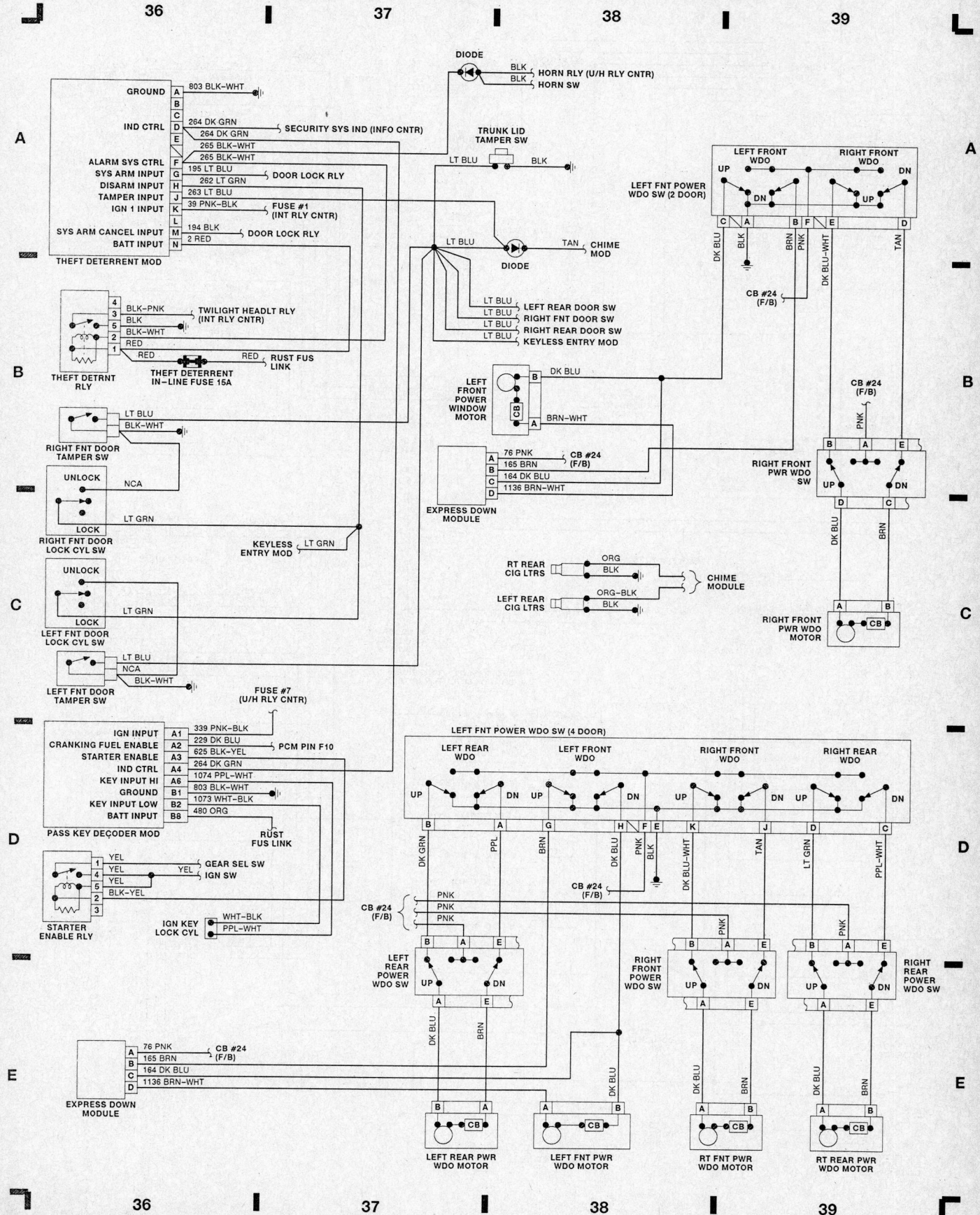

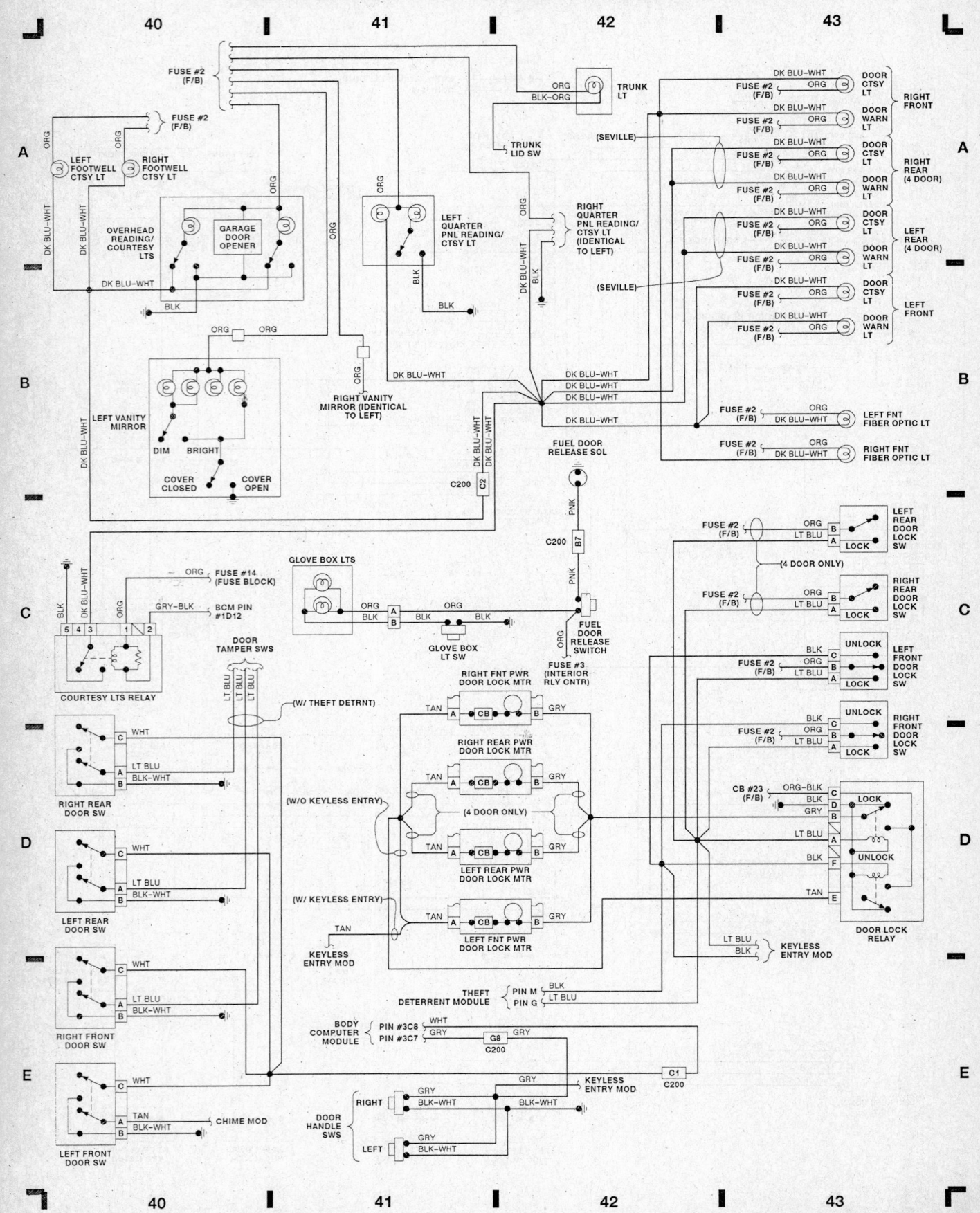

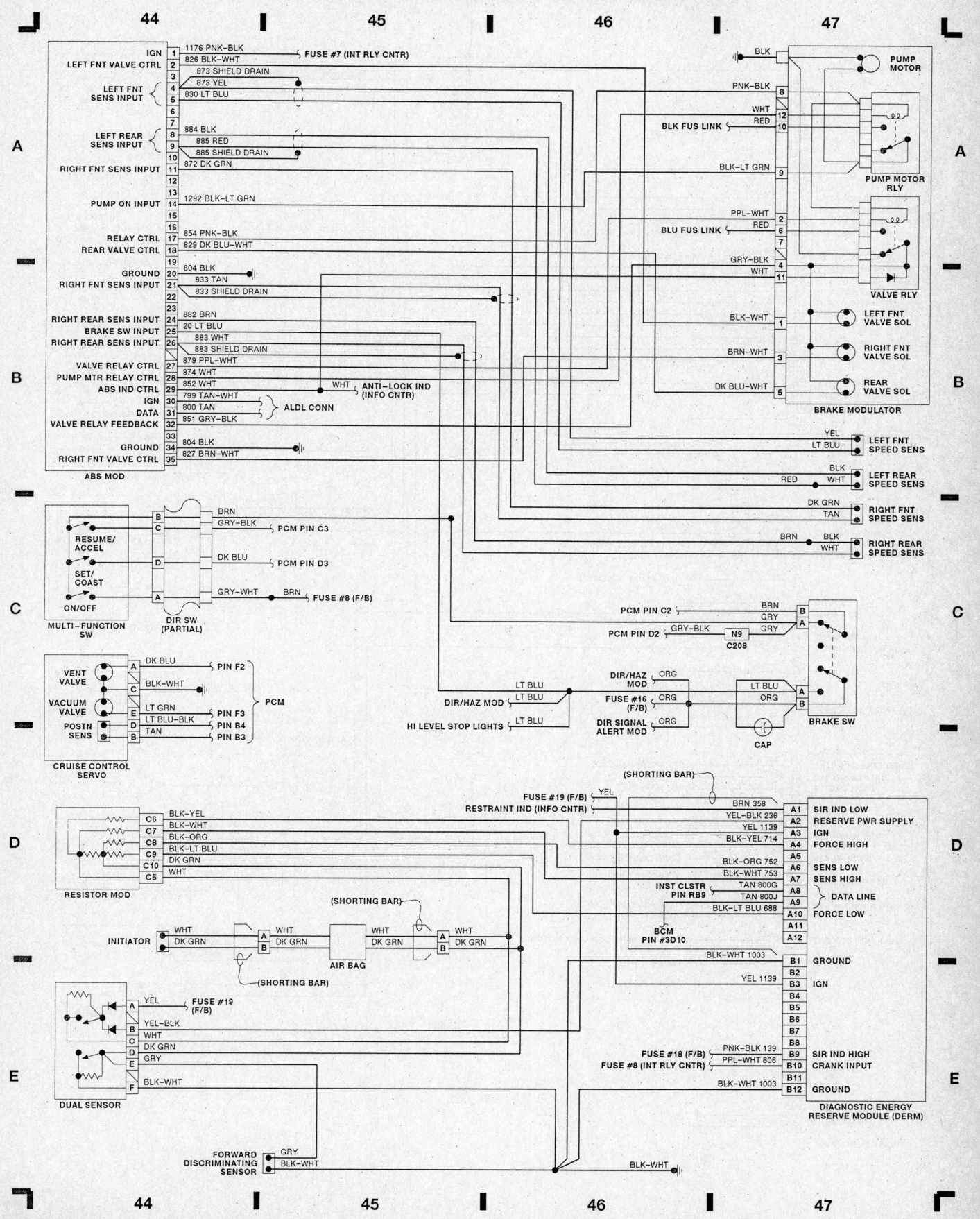

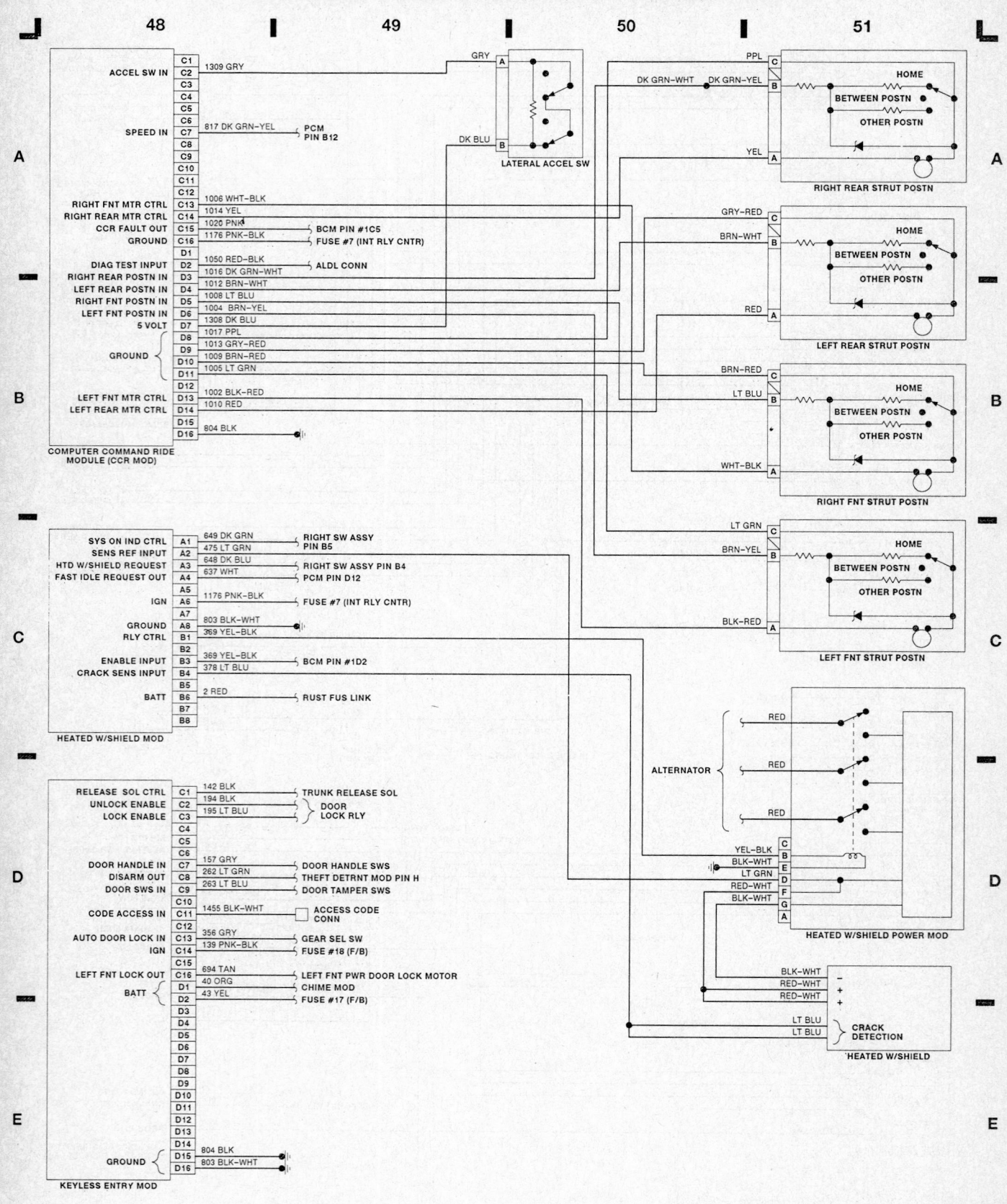

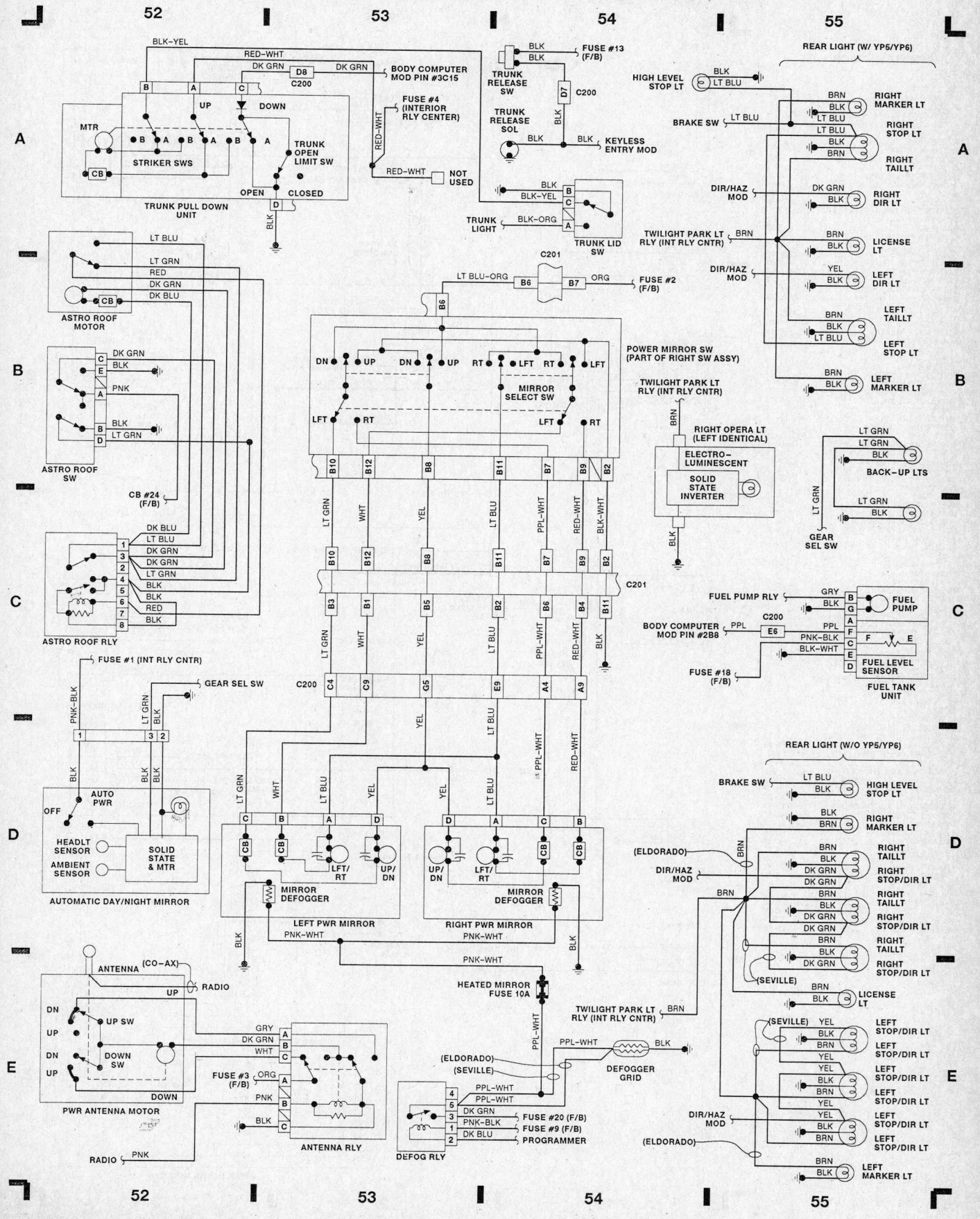

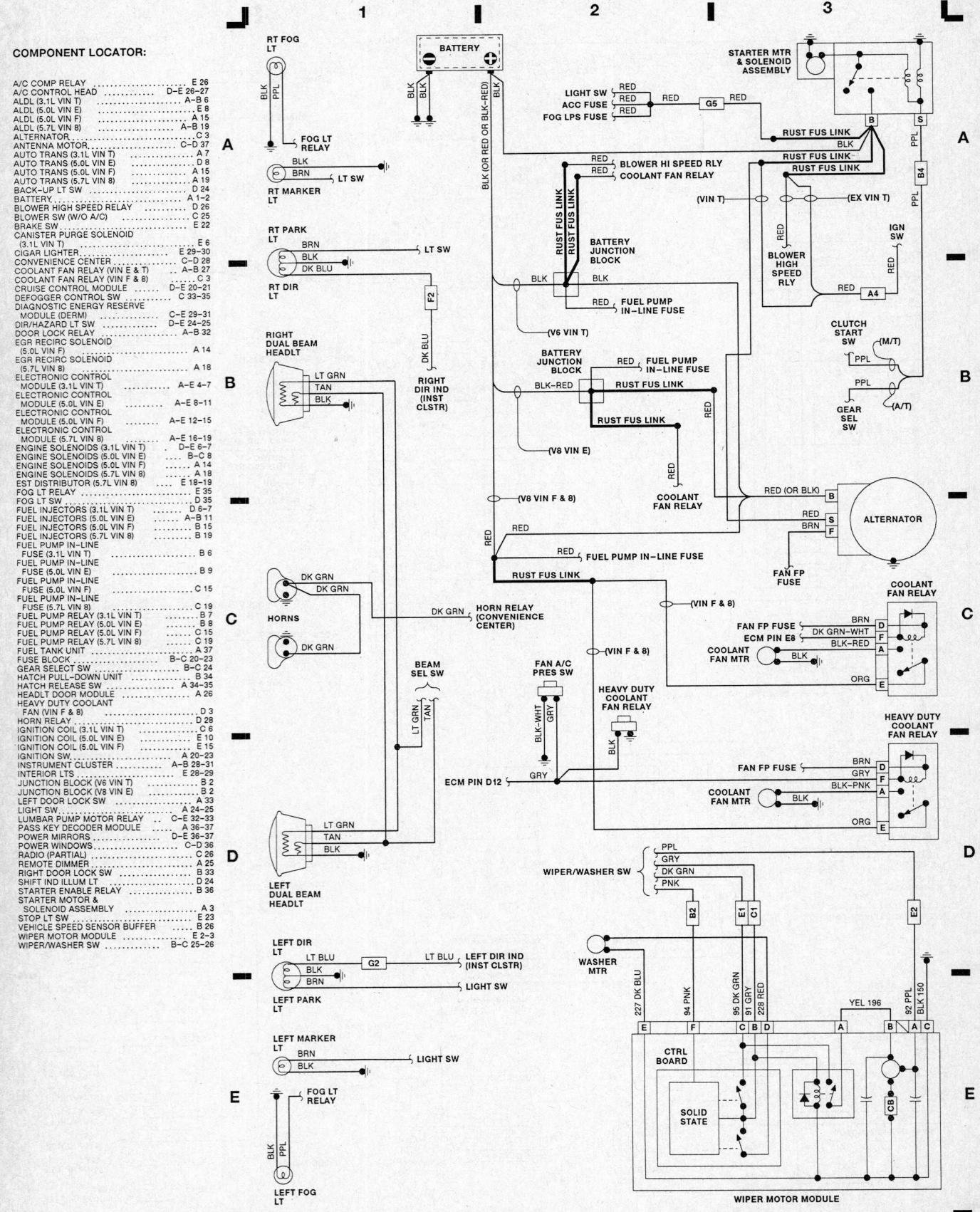

COMPONENT LOCATOR:

A/C COMP RELAY	E 26
A/C CONTROL HEAD	D–E 26–27
ALDL (3.1L VIN T)	A–B 6
ALDL (5.0L VIN E)	E 8
ALDL (5.0L VIN F)	A 15
ALDL (5.7L VIN 8)	A–B 19
ALTERNATOR	C 3
ANTENNA MOTOR	C–D 37
AUTO TRANS (3.1L VIN T)	A 7
AUTO TRANS (5.0L VIN E)	D 8
AUTO TRANS (5.0L VIN F)	A 15
AUTO TRANS (5.7L VIN 8)	A 19
BACK-UP LT SW	D 24
BATTERY	A 1–2
BLOWER HIGH SPEED RELAY	D 26
BLOWER SW (W/O A/C)	C 25
BRAKE SW	E 22
CANISTER PURGE SOLENOID (3.1L VIN T)	E 6
CIGAR LIGHTER	E 29–30
CONVENIENCE CENTER	C–D 28
COOLANT FAN RELAY (VIN E & T)	A–B 27
COOLANT FAN RELAY (VIN F & 8)	C 3
CRUISE CONTROL MODULE	D–E 20–21
DEFOGGER CONTROL SW	C 33–35
DIAGNOSTIC ENERGY RESERVE MODULE (DERM)	C–E 29–31
DIR/HAZARD LT SW	D–E 24–25
DOOR LOCK RELAY	A–B 32
EGR RECIRC SOLENOID (5.0L VIN F)	A 14
EGR RECIRC SOLENOID (5.7L VIN 8)	A 18
ELECTRONIC CONTROL MODULE (3.1L VIN T)	A–E 4–7
ELECTRONIC CONTROL MODULE (5.0L VIN E)	A–E 8–11
ELECTRONIC CONTROL MODULE (5.0L VIN F)	A–E 12–15
ELECTRONIC CONTROL MODULE (5.7L VIN 8)	A–E 16–19
ENGINE SOLENOIDS (3.1L VIN T)	D–E 6–7
ENGINE SOLENOIDS (5.0L VIN E)	B–C 8
ENGINE SOLENOIDS (5.0L VIN F)	A 14
ENGINE SOLENOIDS (5.7L VIN 8)	A 18
EST DISTRIBUTOR (5.7L VIN 8)	E 18–19
FOG LT RELAY	E 35
FOG LT SW	D 35
FUEL INJECTORS (3.1L VIN T)	D 6–7
FUEL INJECTORS (5.0L VIN E)	A–B 11
FUEL INJECTORS (5.0L VIN F)	B 15
FUEL INJECTORS (5.7L VIN 8)	B 19
FUEL PUMP IN–LINE FUSE (3.1L VIN T)	B 6
FUEL PUMP IN–LINE FUSE (5.0L VIN E)	B 9
FUEL PUMP IN–LINE FUSE (5.0L VIN F)	C 15
FUEL PUMP IN–LINE FUSE (5.7L VIN 8)	C 19
FUEL PUMP RELAY (3.1L VIN T)	B 7
FUEL PUMP RELAY (5.0L VIN E)	B 8
FUEL PUMP RELAY (5.0L VIN F)	C 15
FUEL PUMP RELAY (5.7L VIN 8)	C 19
FUEL TANK UNIT	A 37
FUSE BLOCK	B–C 20–23
GEAR SELECT SW	B–C 24
HATCH PULL-DOWN UNIT	B 34
HATCH RELEASE SW	A 34–35
HEADLT DOOR MODULE	A 26
HEAVY DUTY COOLANT FAN (VIN F & 8)	D 3
HORN RELAY	D 28
IGNITION COIL (3.1L VIN T)	C 6
IGNITION COIL (5.0L VIN E)	E 10
IGNITION COIL (5.0L VIN F)	E 15
IGNITION SW	A 20–23
INSTRUMENT CLUSTER	A–B 28–31
INTERIOR LTS	E 28–29
JUNCTION BLOCK (V6 VIN T)	B 2
JUNCTION BLOCK (V8 VIN E)	B 2
LEFT DOOR LOCK SW	A 33
LIGHT SW	A 24–25
LUMBAR PUMP MOTOR RELAY	C–E 32–33
PASS KEY DECODER MODULE	A 36–37
POWER MIRRORS	D–E 36–37
POWER WINDOWS	C–D 36
RADIO (PARTIAL)	C 26
REMOTE DIMMER	A 25
RIGHT DOOR LOCK SW	B 33
SHIFT IND ILLUM LT	D 24
STARTER ENABLE RELAY	B 36
STARTER MOTOR & SOLENOID ASSEMBLY	A 3
STOP LT SW	E 23
VEHICLE SPEED SENSOR BUFFER	B 26
WIPER MOTOR MODULE	E 2–3
WIPER/WASHER SW	B–C 25–26

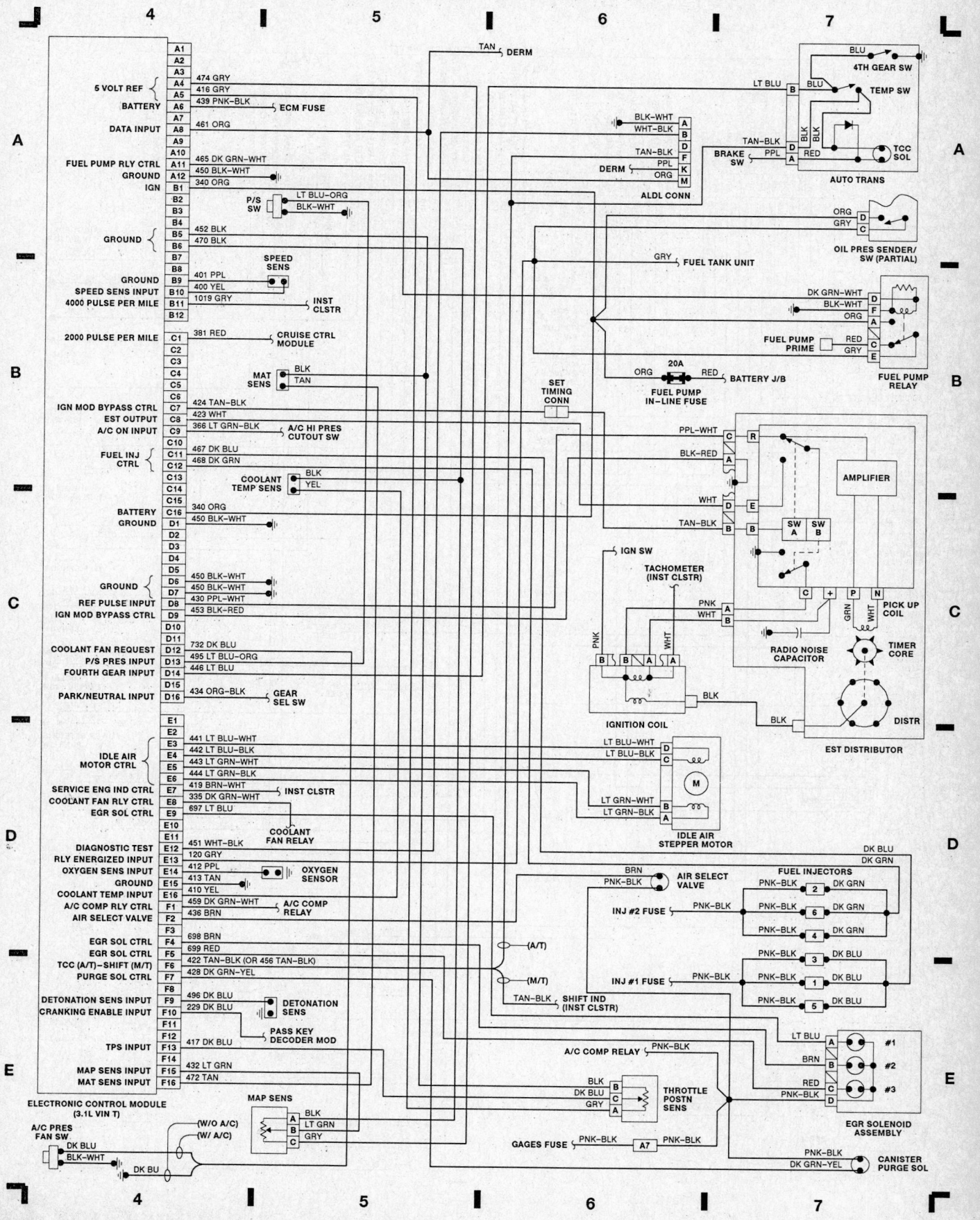

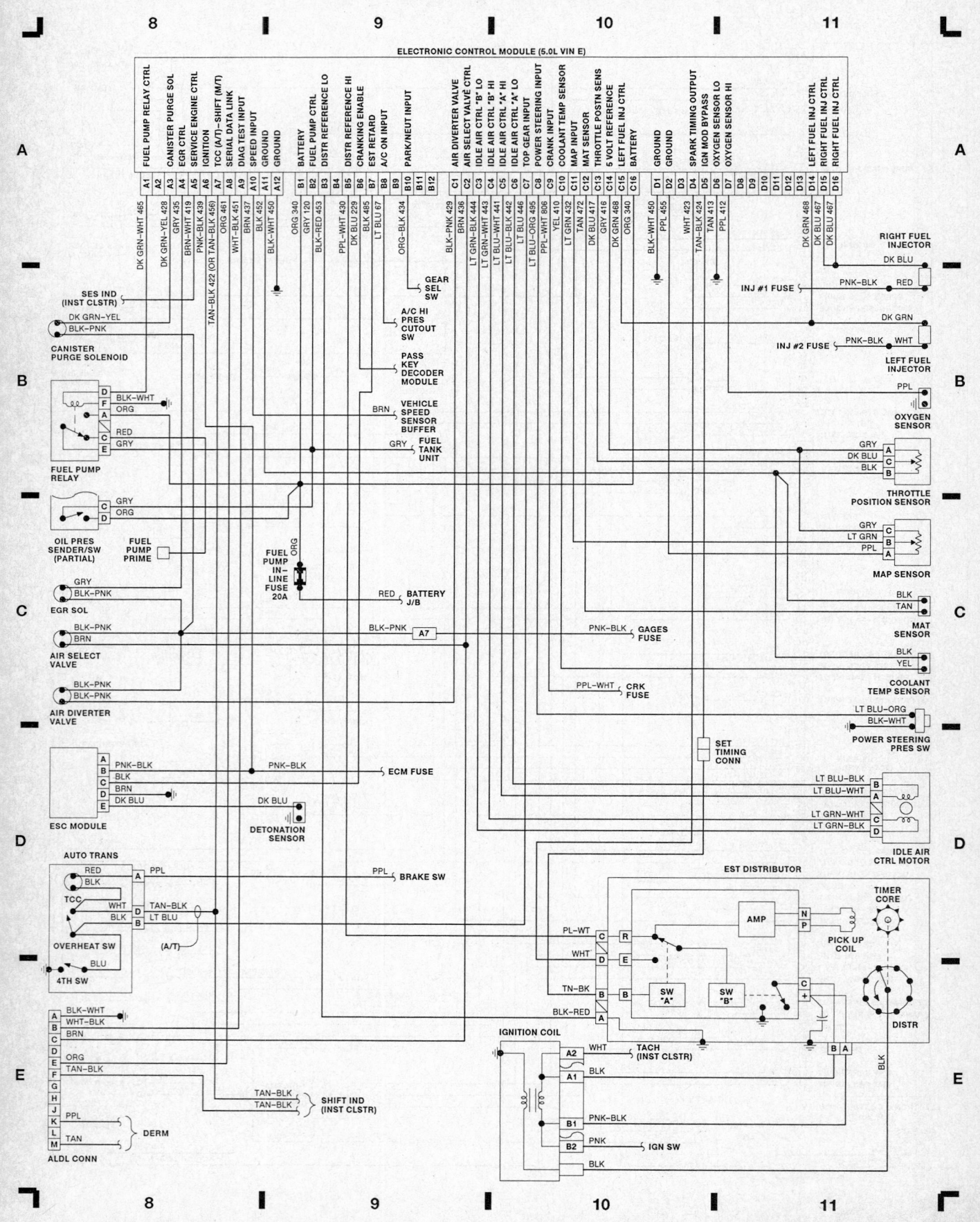

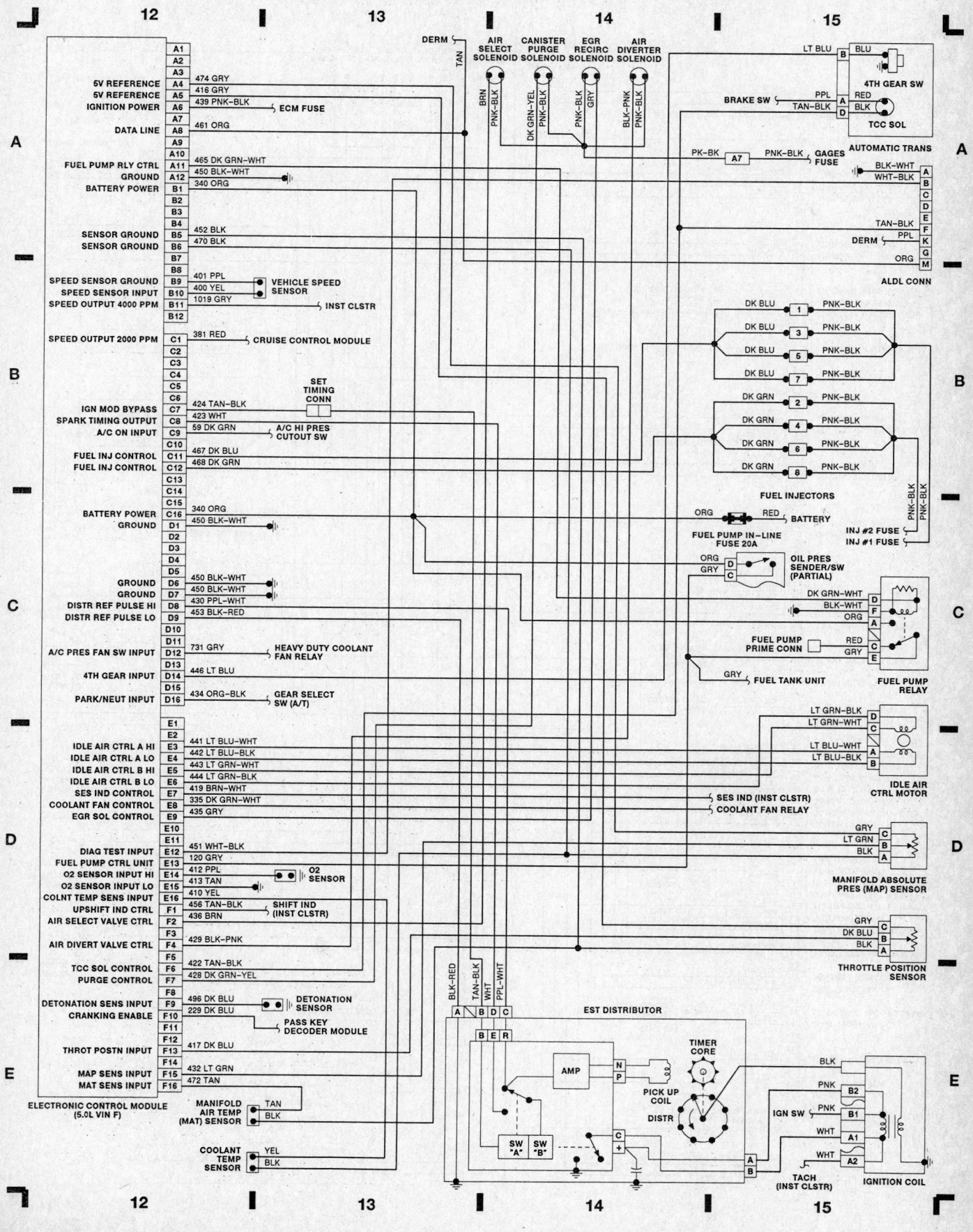

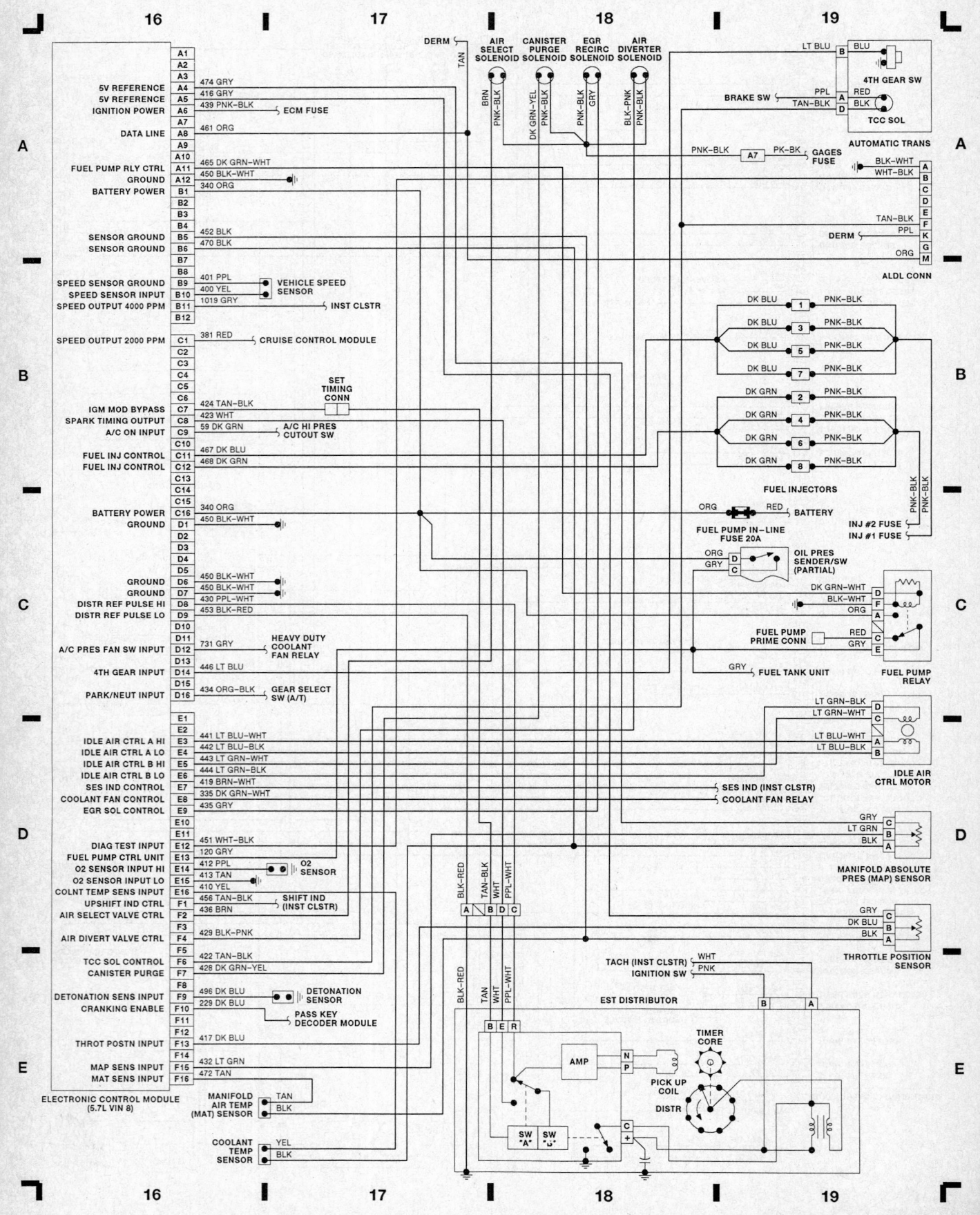

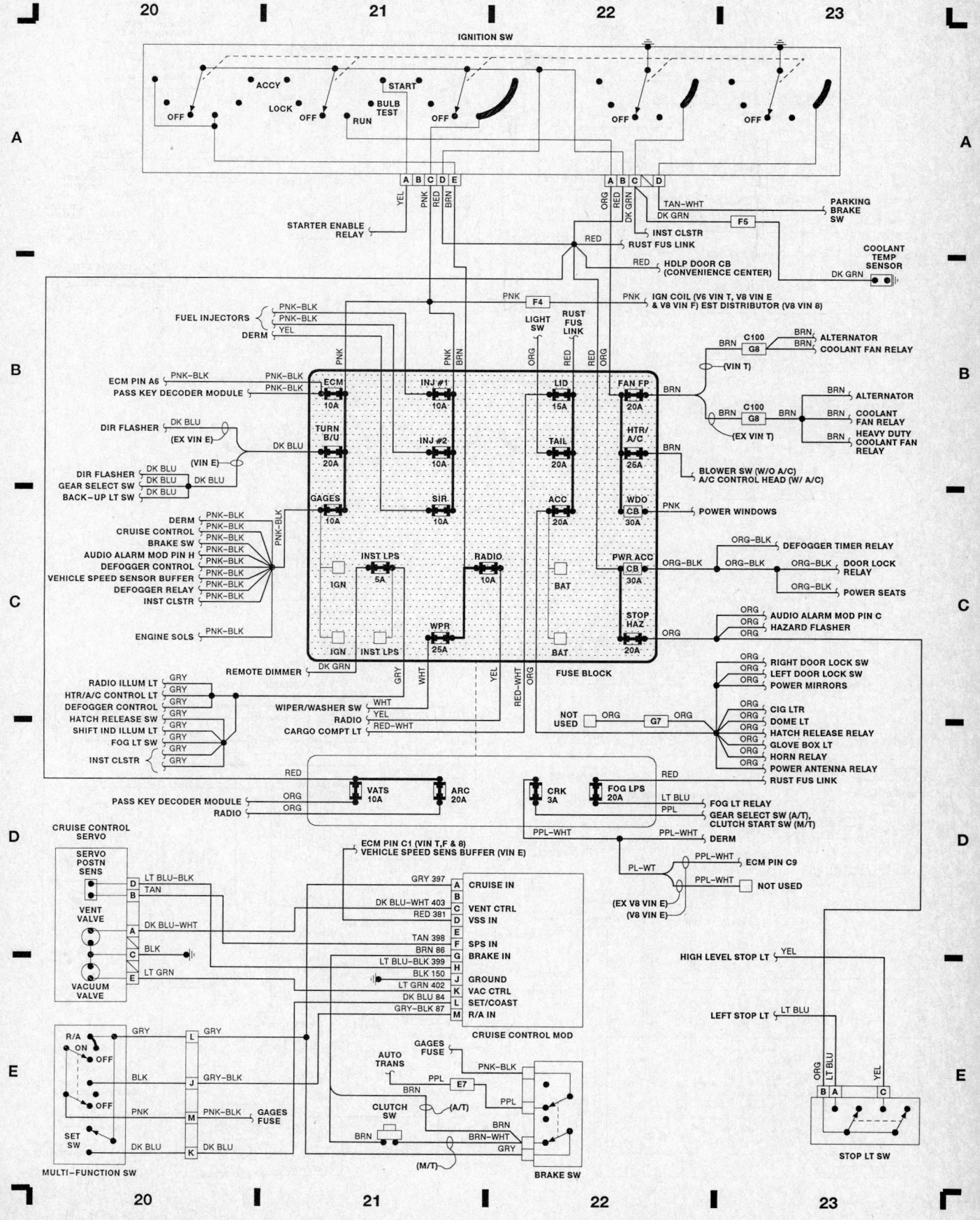

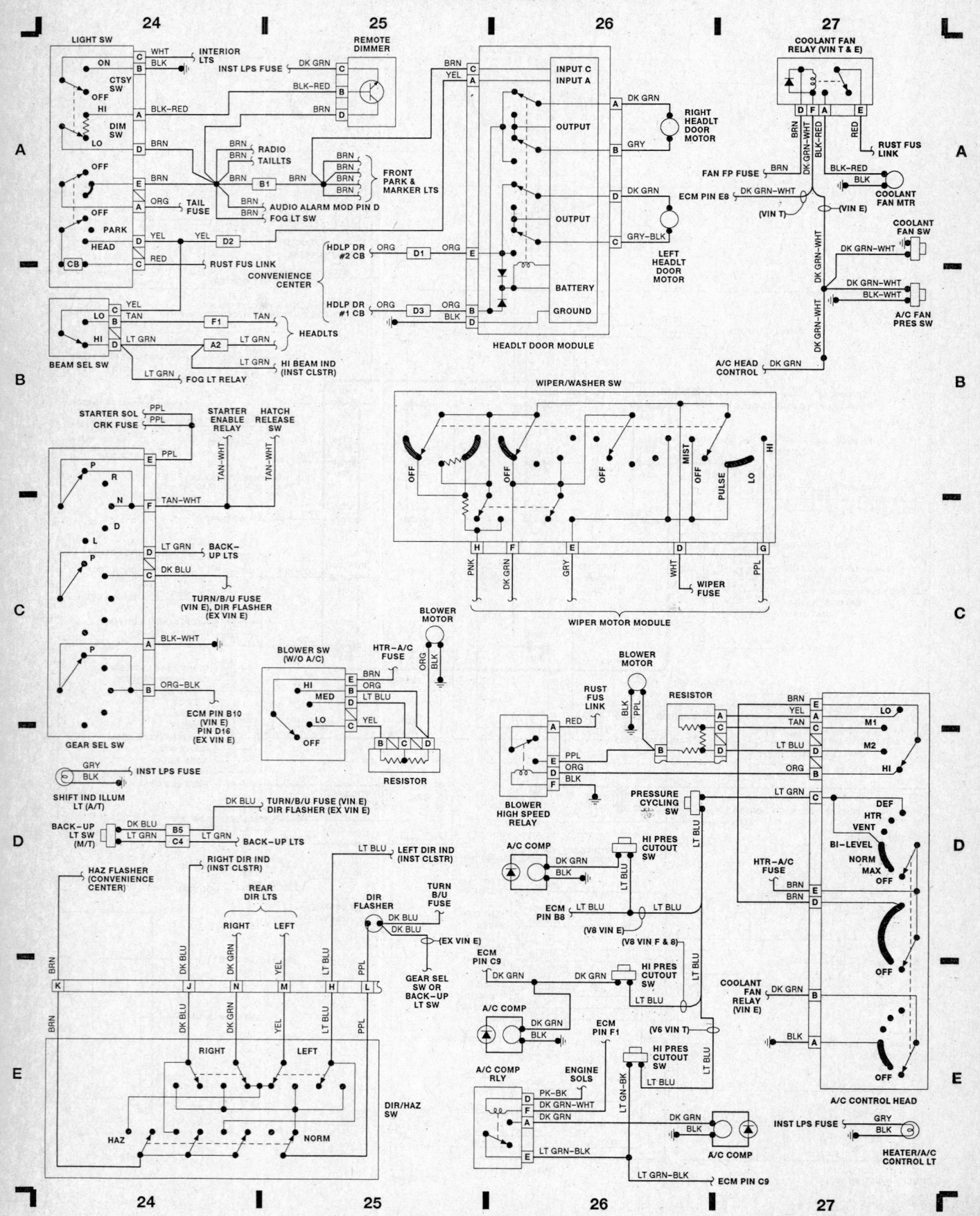

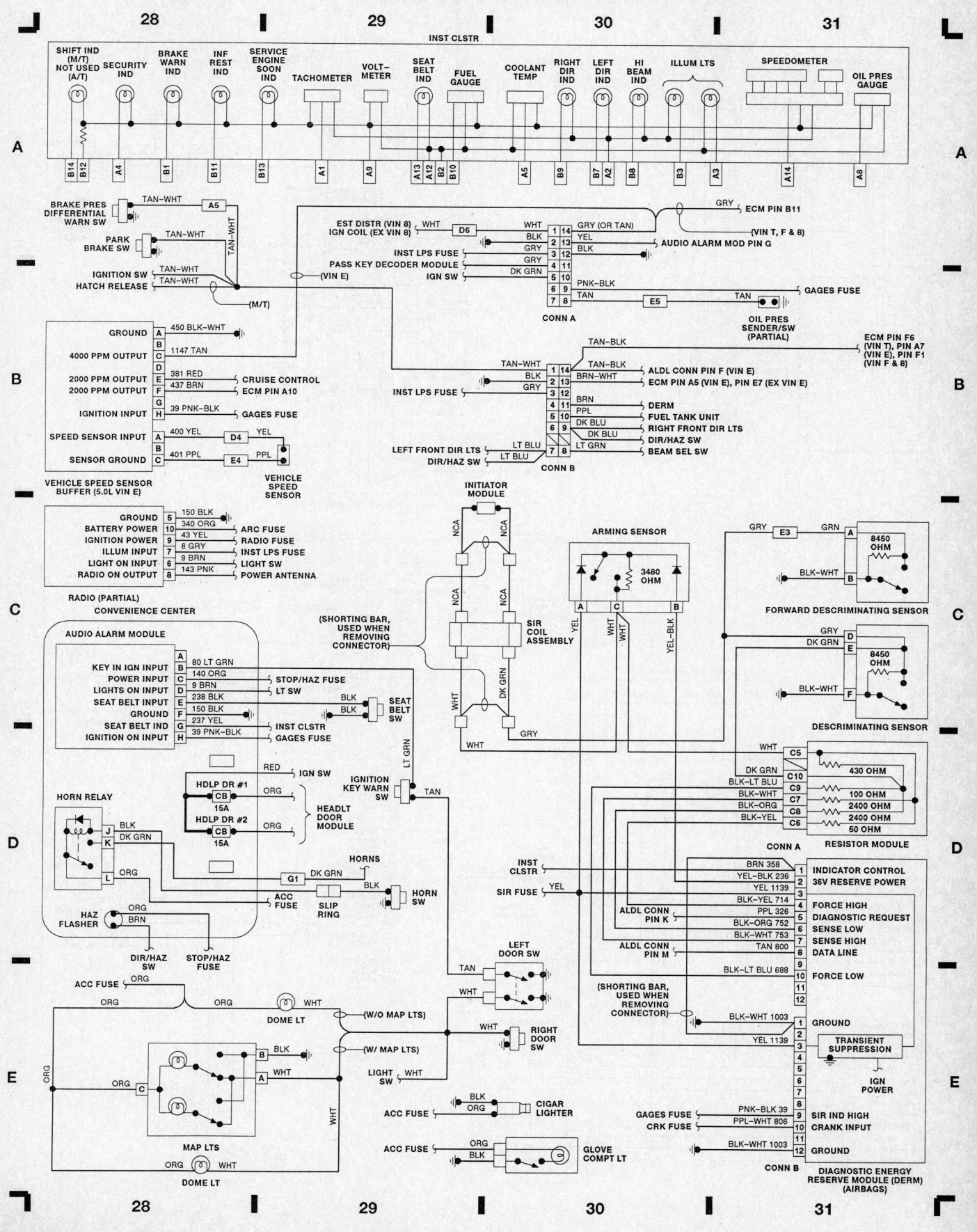

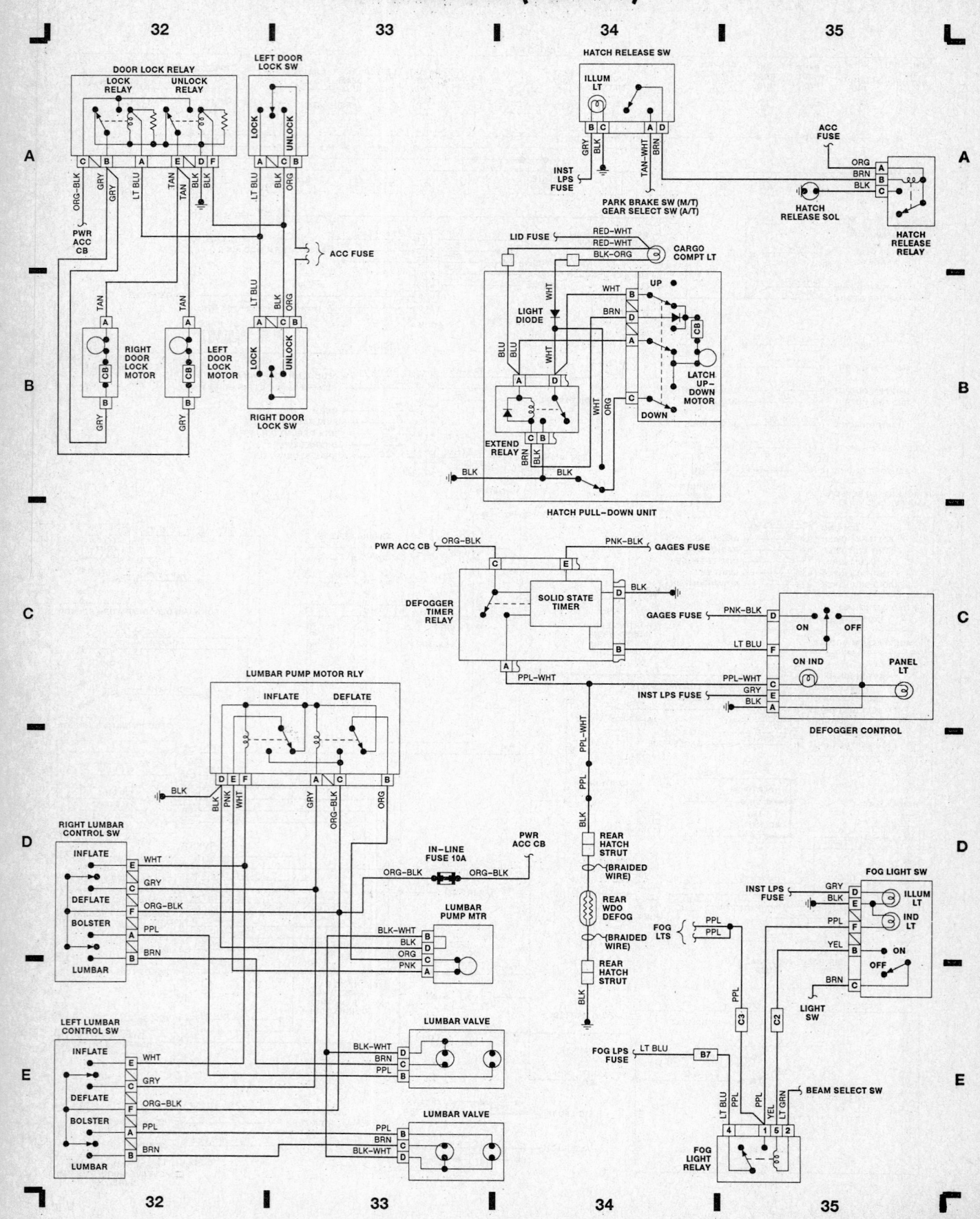

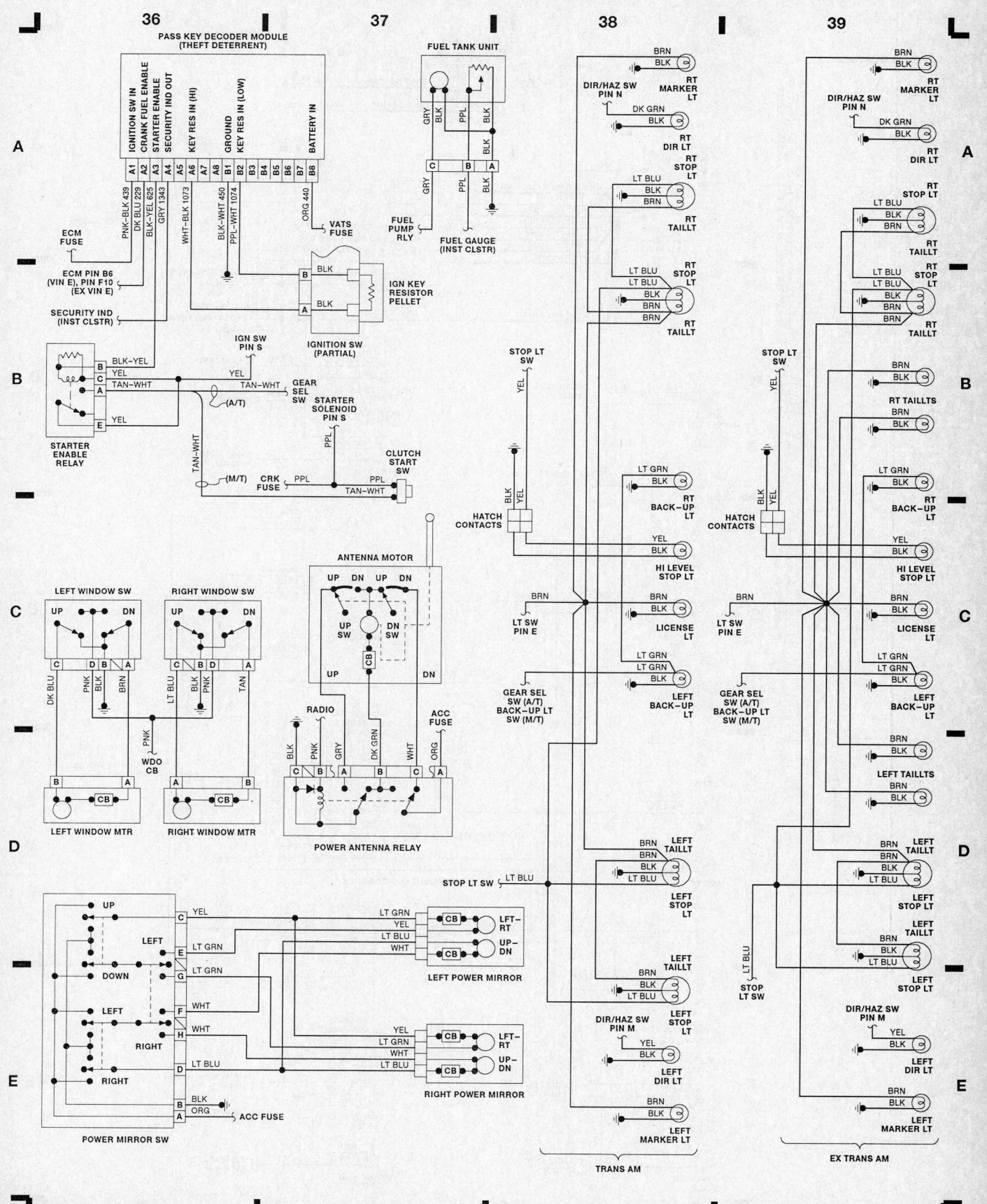

1991 WIRING DIAGRAMS
Grand Am

COMPONENT LOCATOR:

A/C COMP CTRL RLY	C 22
A/C PRES SWS	B 21–22
ABS ENABLE RLY	B 19
ABS MOD	A–B 16
ALDL CONN (2.3L)	D 7
ALTERNATOR	A 3
ASHTRAY LT	B 32
AUDIO ALARM MOD	D–E 32
AUTO TRANS (2.3L)	C–D 7
AUTO TRANS (2.5L)	E 8
BACK–UP LIGHT SW	D 12
BRAKE SW	C–D 23
CANISTER PURGE SOL (2.3L)	D–E 6
CIG LTR	B 32
CLUTCH START SW	A 14
COOLANT FAN RLY	C–D 19
COURTESY LTS	E 34
CRUISE CTRL SERVO	D 23
CRUISE CTRL CLUTCH SW	C 21
CRUISE CTRL MOD	E 23
DEFOG CTRL	A 39
DEFOG TIMER RLY	A–B 39
DIR FLASHER	B 26
DIR/HAZ SW	B–C 27
DIRECT IGN SYS (2.5L)	D–E 9–11
DOME LT	D 34
DOOR LOCK SWS	D 36–37
DRIVER INFORMATION CENTER	A 24
ELECTRONIC CONTROL MODULE (ECM) (2.3L)	A–E 4
ELECTRONIC CONTROL MODULE (ECM) (2.5L)	A 8–11
FOG LT RLY	C 3
FUEL PUMP RLY (2.3L)	A 5
FUEL PUMP RLY (2.5L)	B–C 11
FUEL TANK UNIT	A 37
FUSE BLOCK	C–D 13–14
GEAR SEL SW	B–C 20
GLOVE BOX SW	32
HEADER COURTESY/READING LTS ASSY	D–E 35
HEADLIGHT DIMMER SW	E 30
HEATER BLOWER SW	A 20
HEATER/A/C CTRL ASSY	A 21–23
HI SPEED BLOWER RLY	B 23
HORN RLY	C 2
IGN SW	A 12–15
ILLUM CTRL RLY	E 28
INST CLSTR	A–B 28–31
INTEGRATED DIRECT IGN SYS (2.3L)	A–B 7
J/B 200 CONN G	C 37–38
LAMP MOD	B–C 19
LEFT FNT WDO SW	E 38–39
LIGHT MONITOR MOD	D–E 27
LIGHT SW	D–E 24
MULTI–FUNCTION LEVER	E 20
OUTSIDE MIRROR SW	B–C 33–34
REMOTE DIMMER MOD	D–E 24
STARTER	A 1
STOP LIGHT SW	A–B 27
TRUNK RELEASE SW	A 36
WIPER/WASHER MOTOR ASSY	D–E 17–19
WIPER/WASHER SW	A 32–35

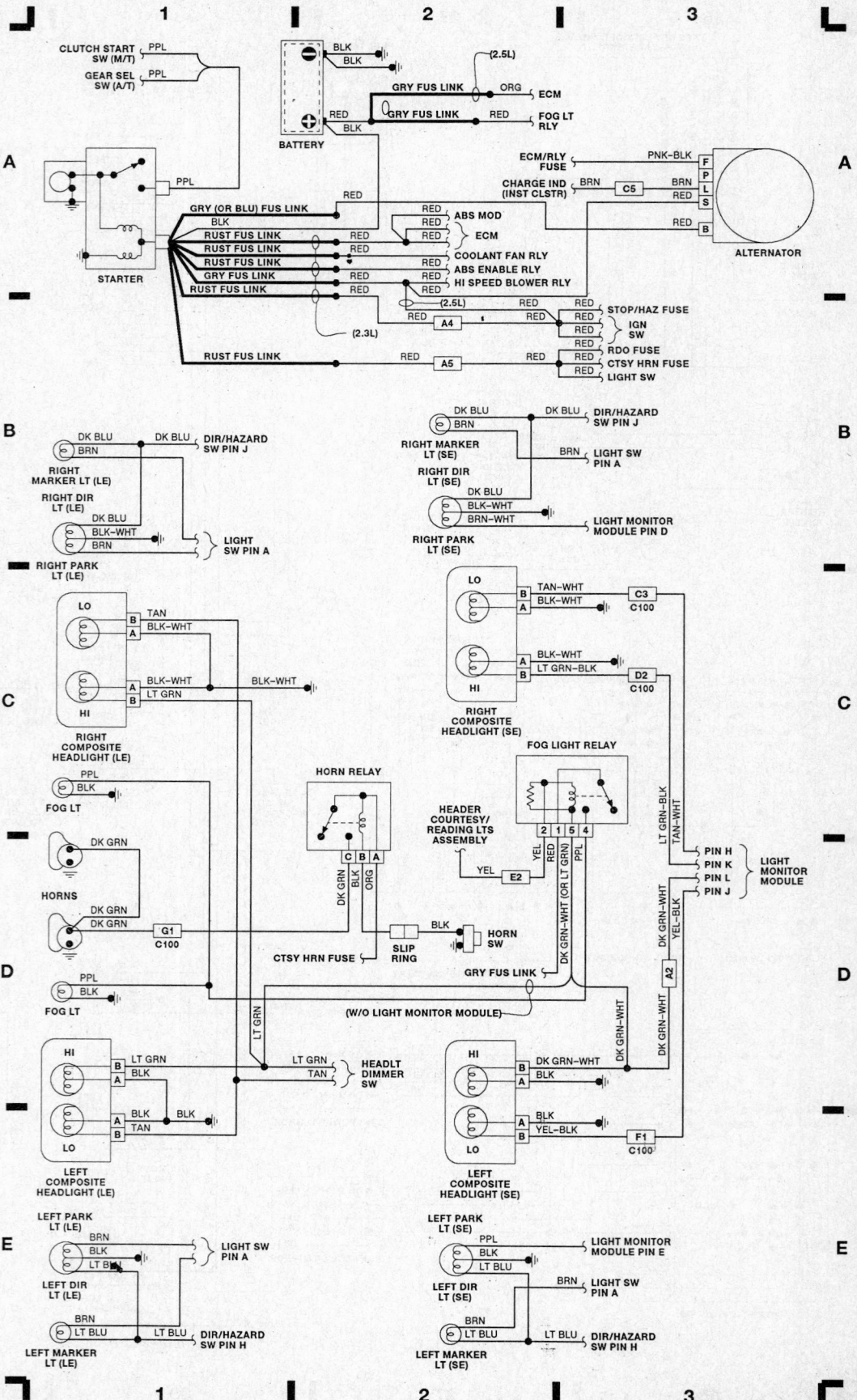

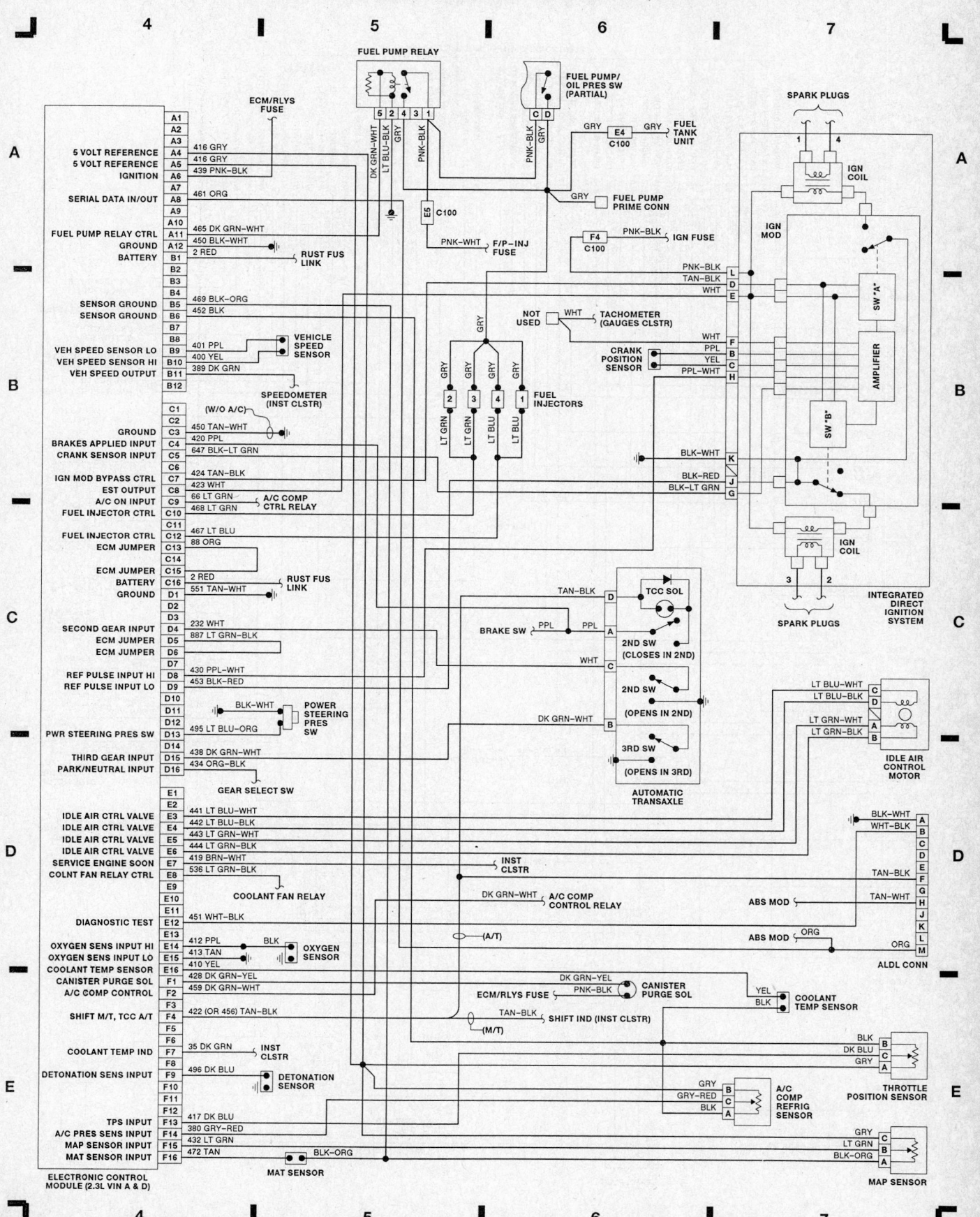

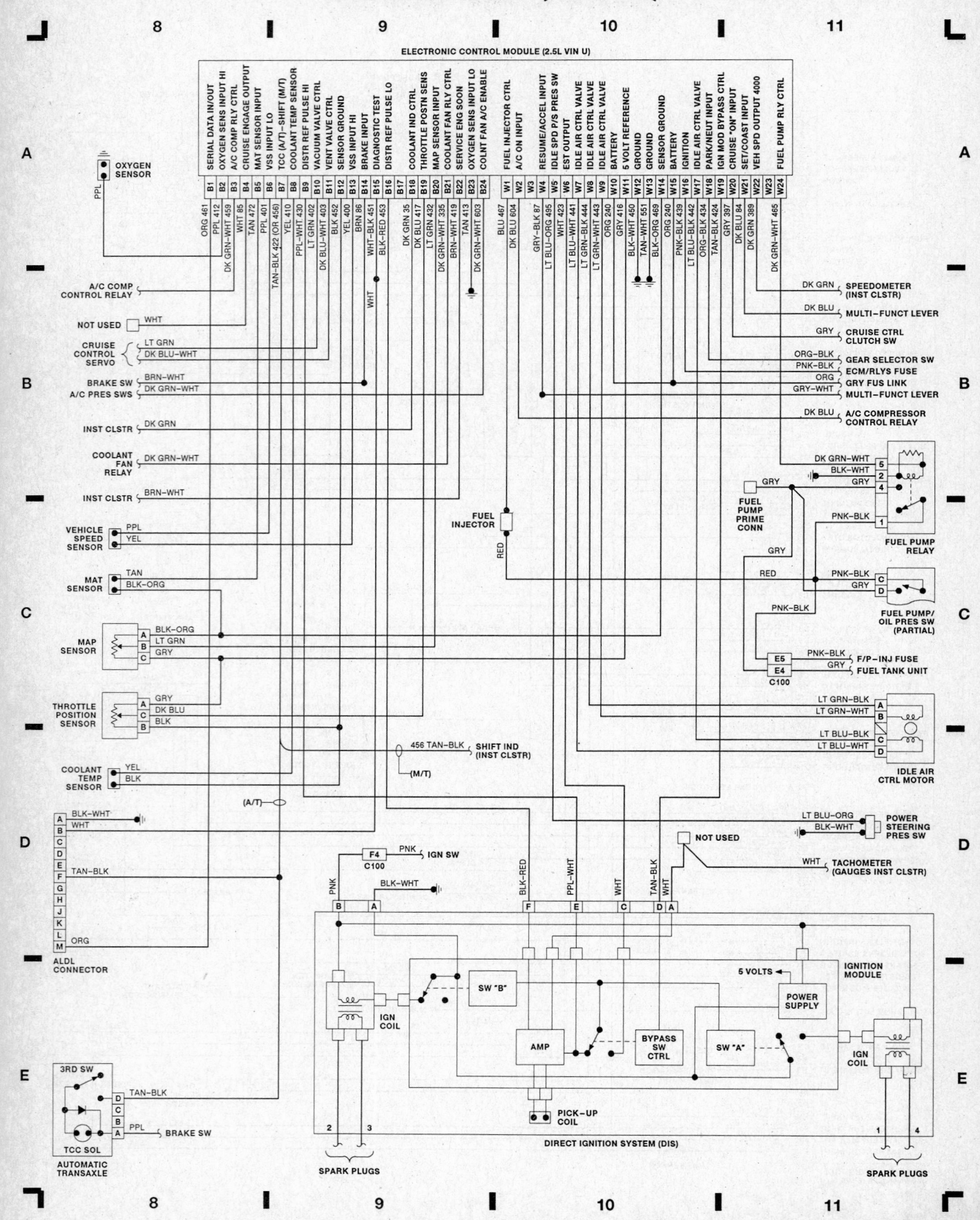

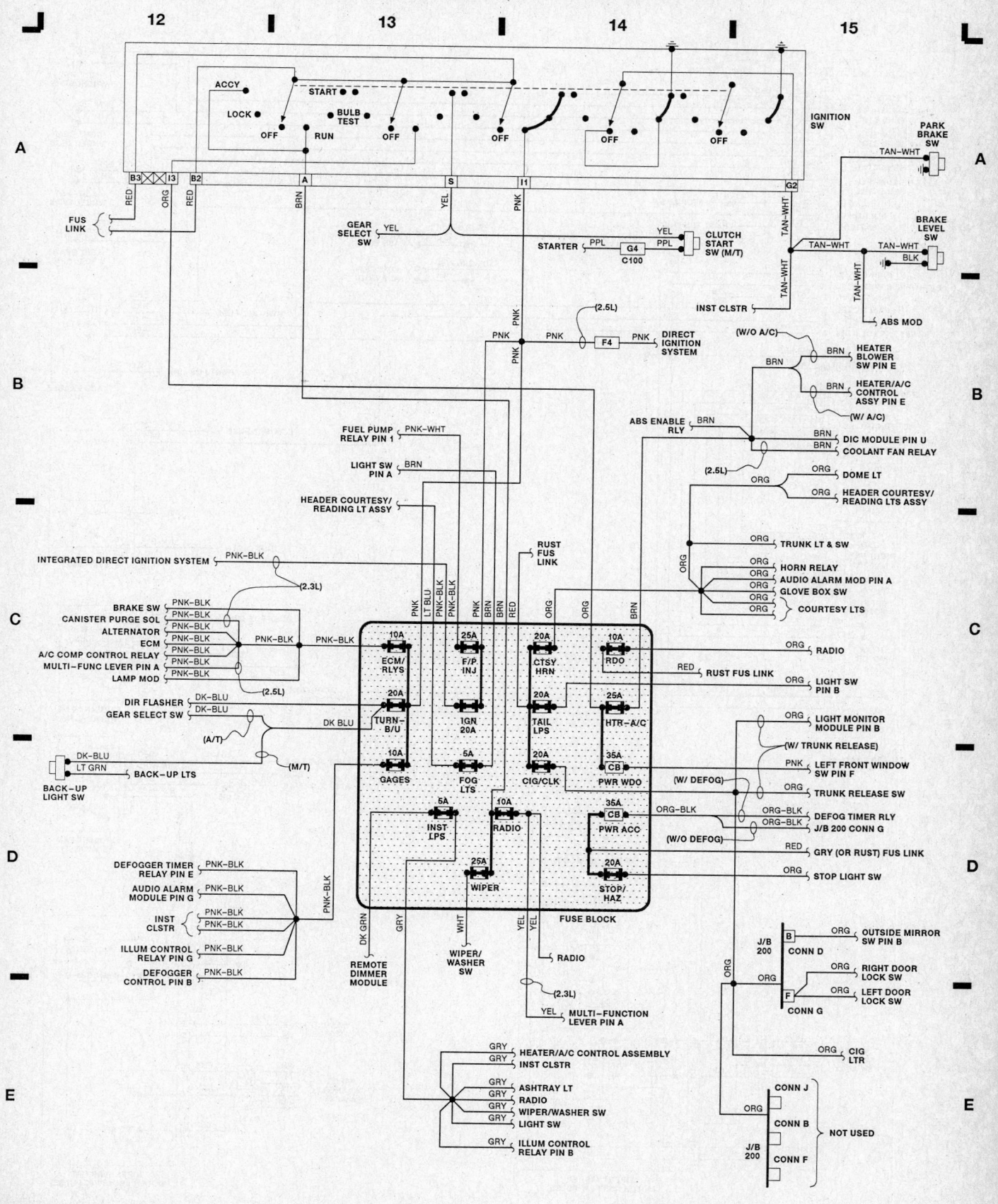

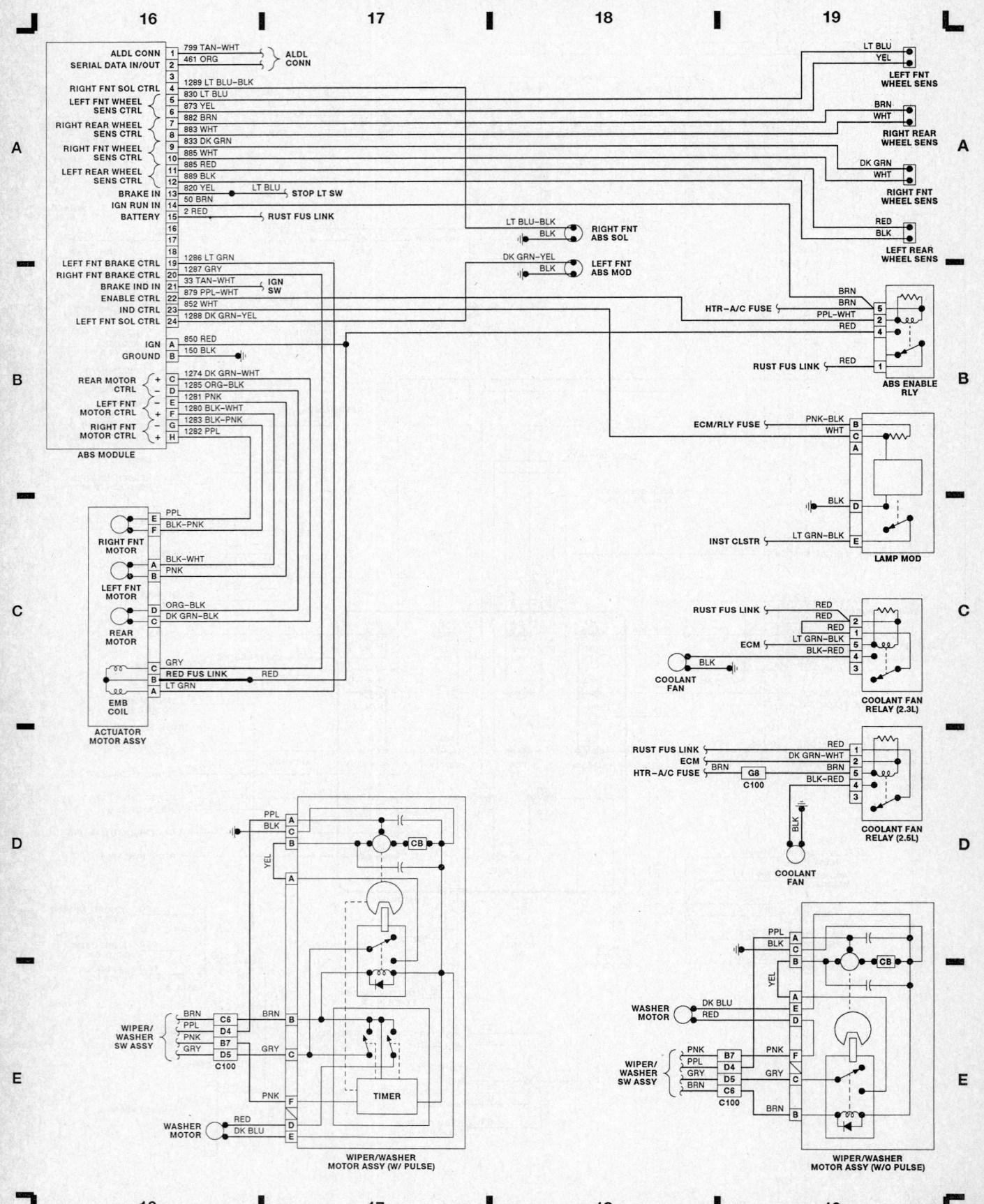

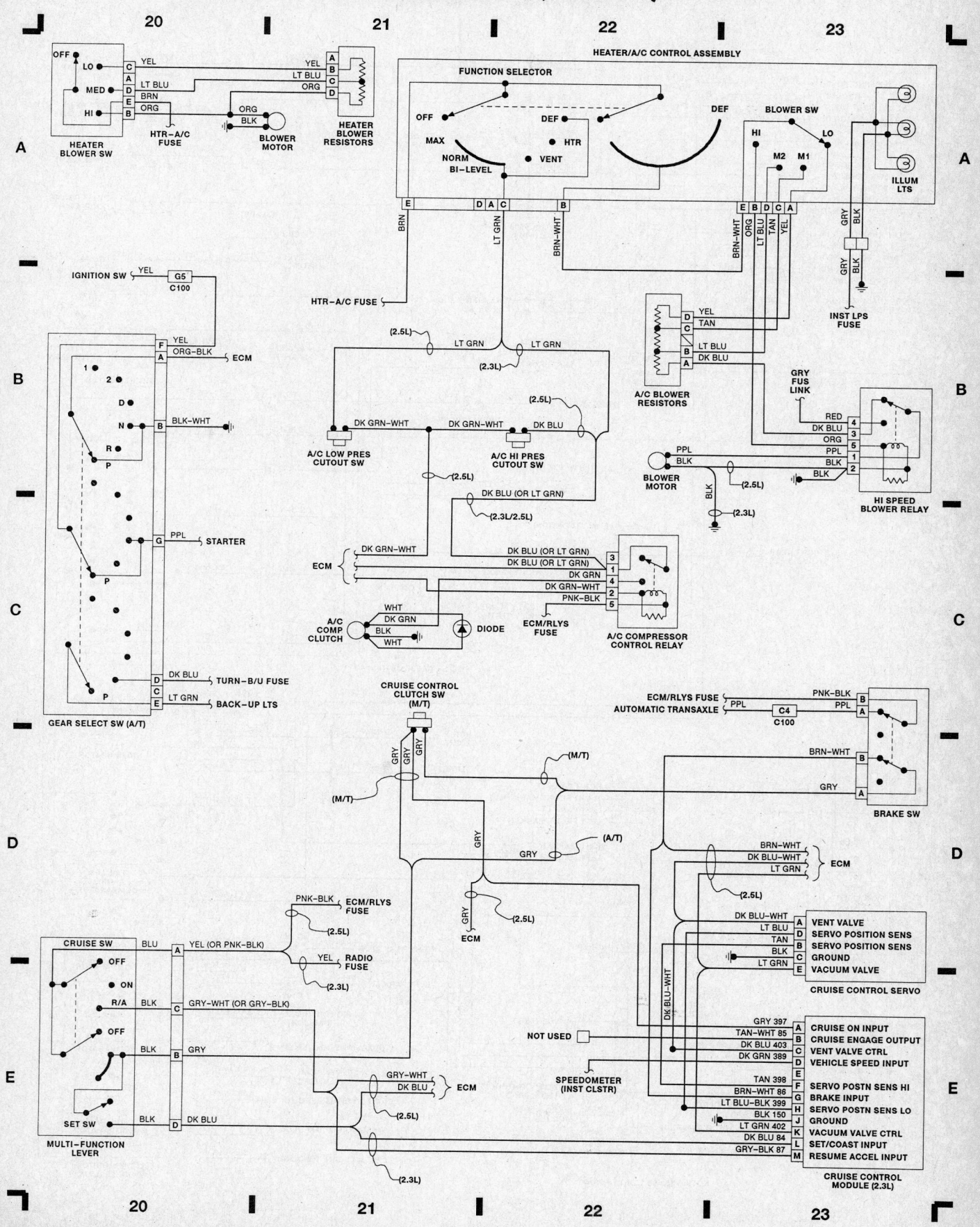

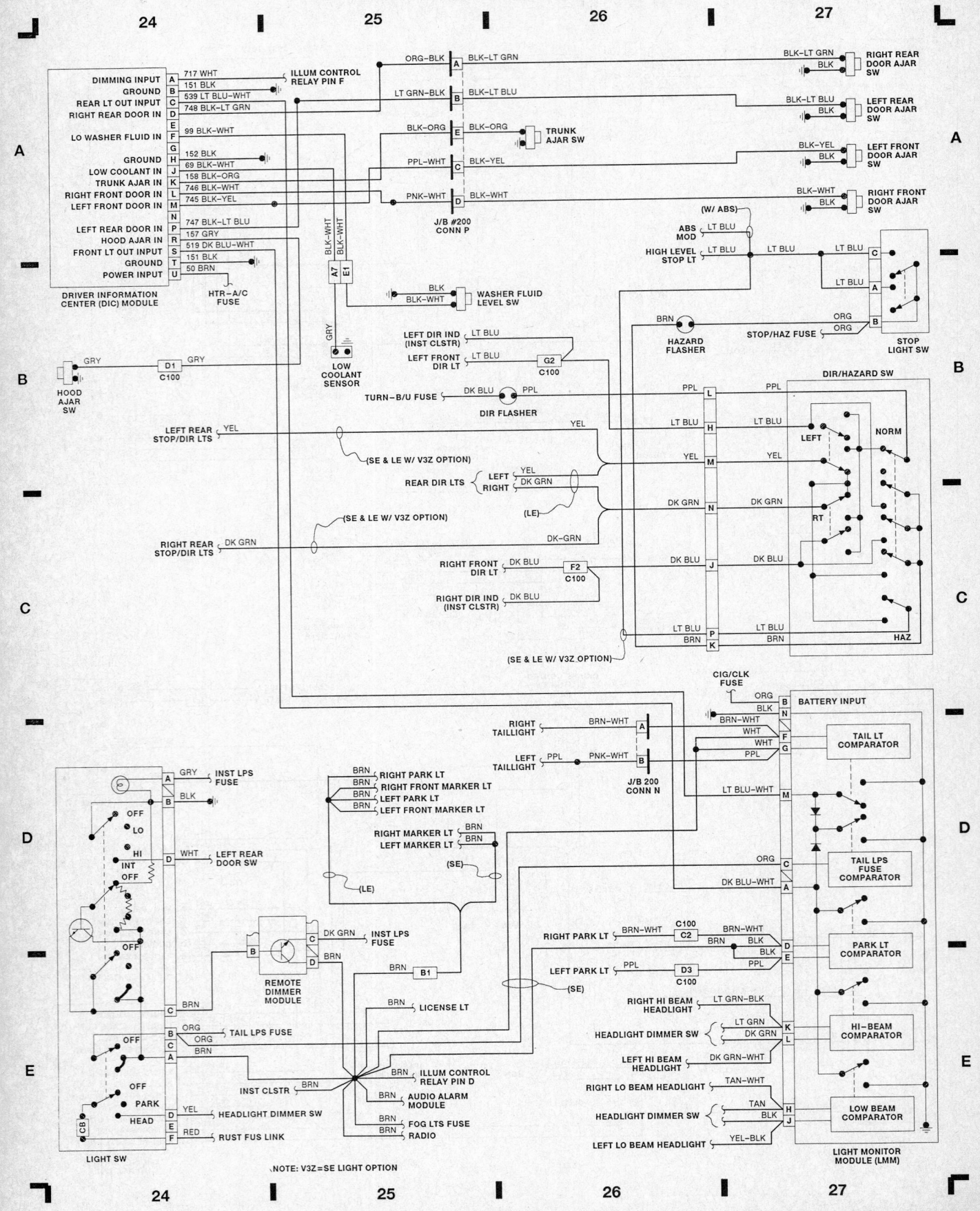

NOTE: V3Z=SE LIGHT OPTION

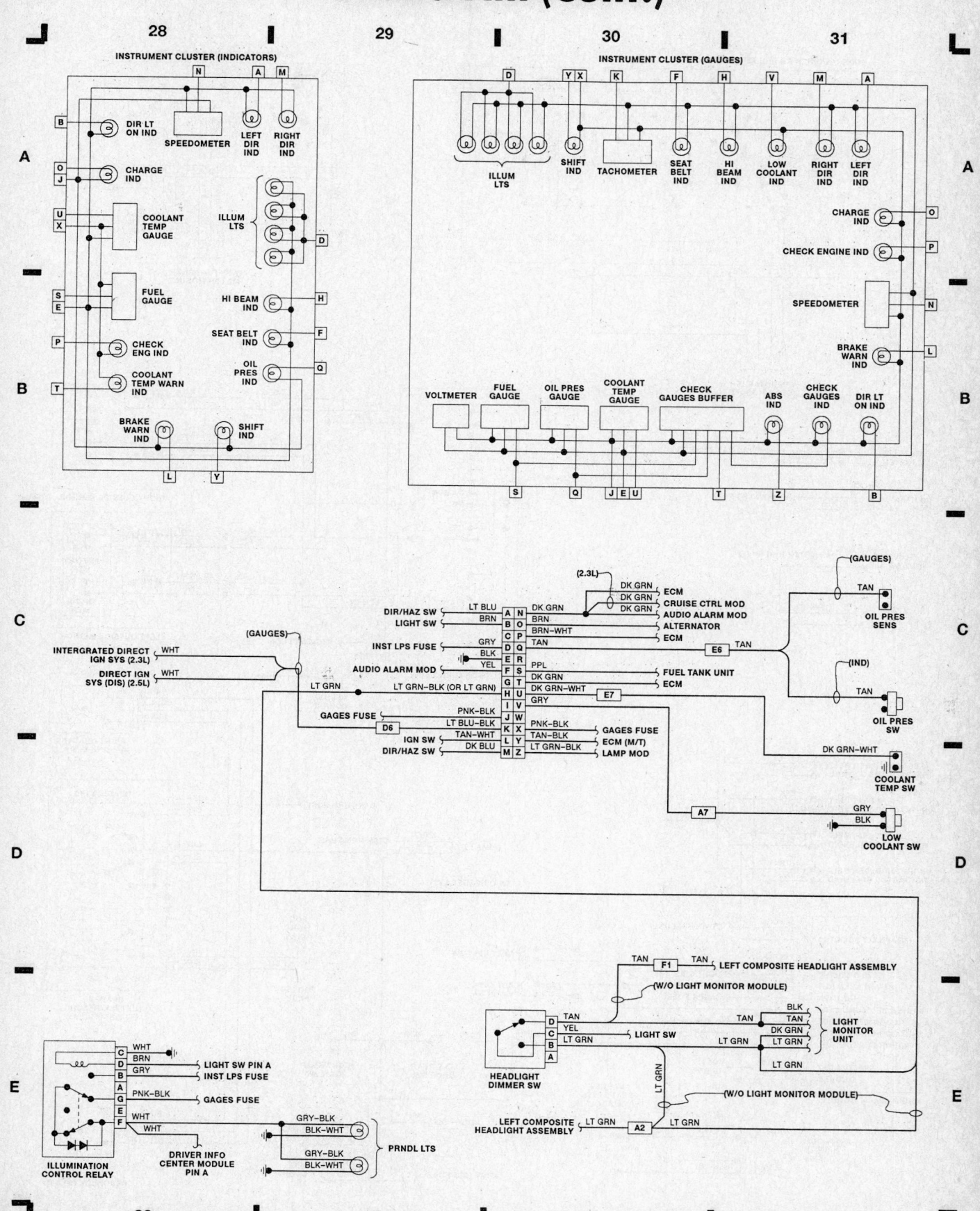

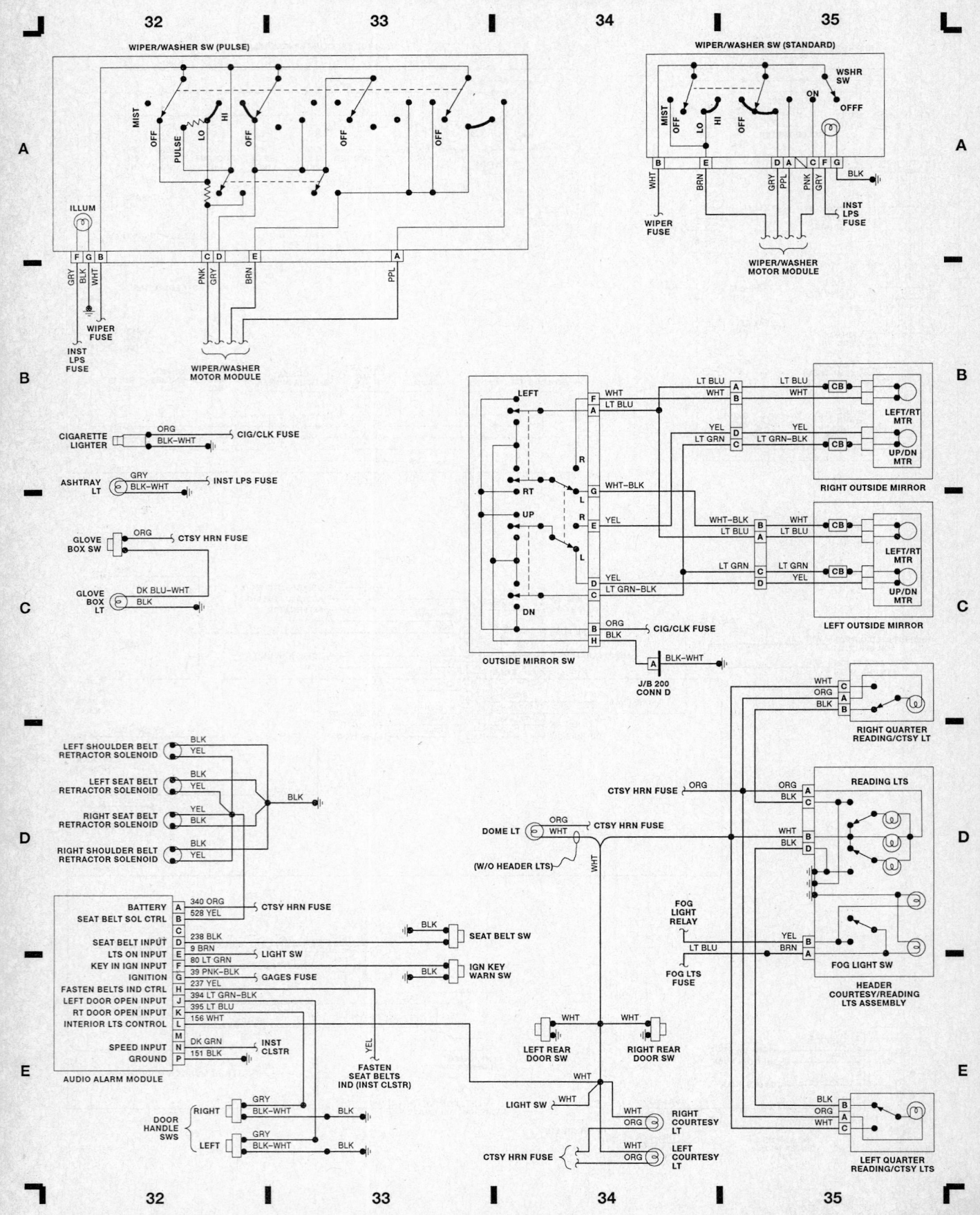

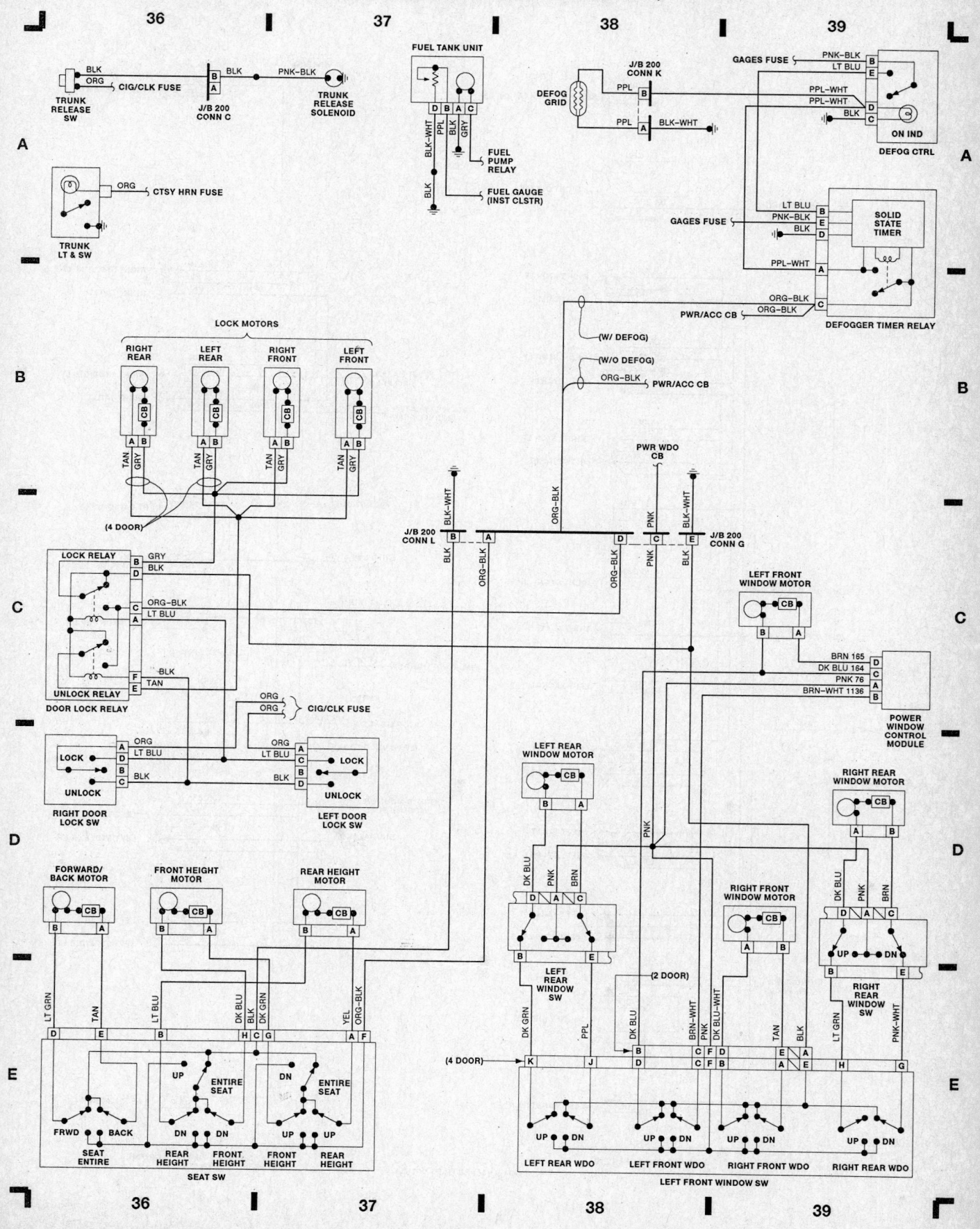

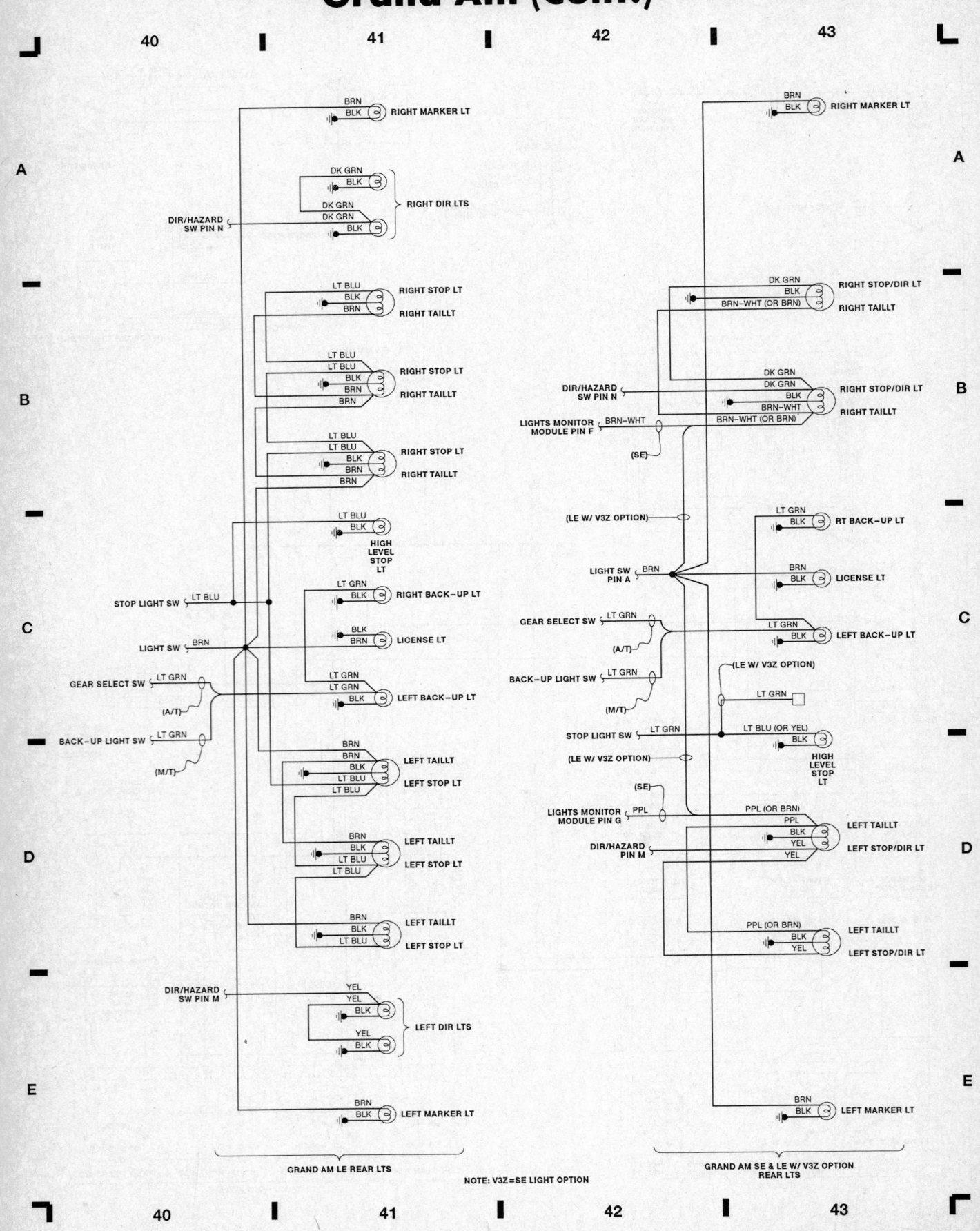

GRAND AM LE REAR LTS

NOTE: V3Z=SE LIGHT OPTION

GRAND AM SE & LE W/ V3Z OPTION
REAR LTS

COMPONENT LOCATOR:

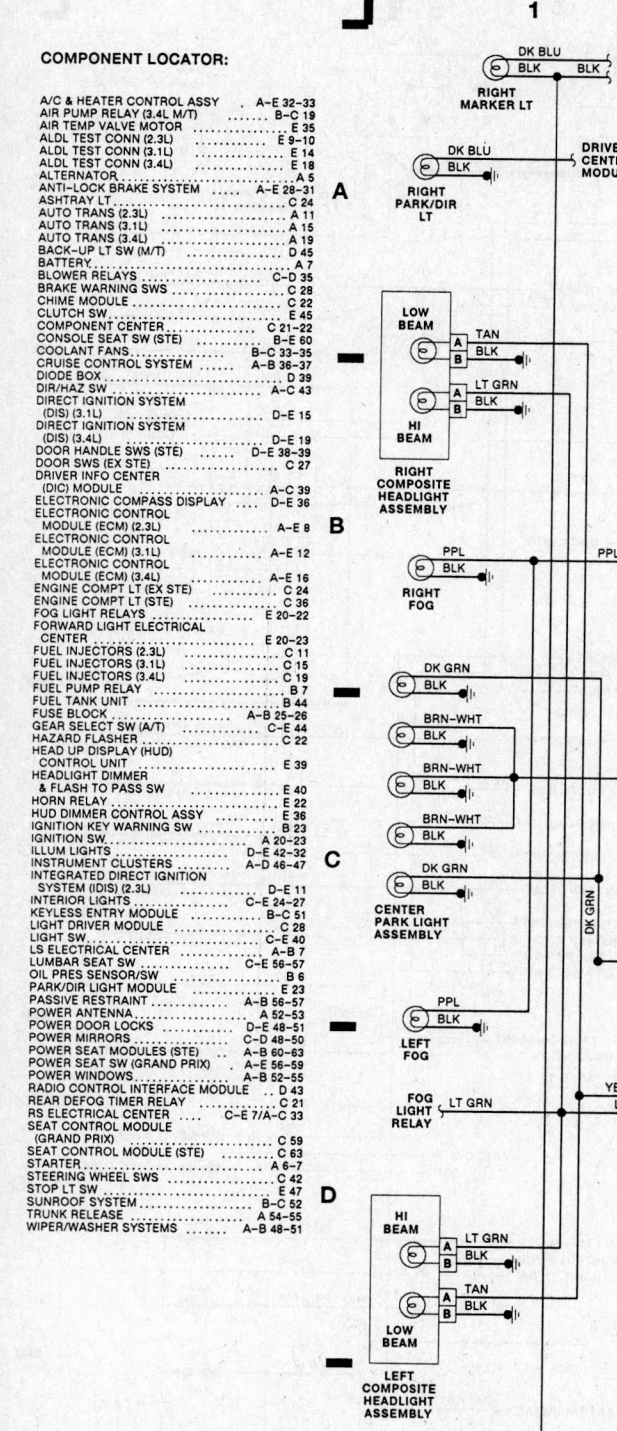

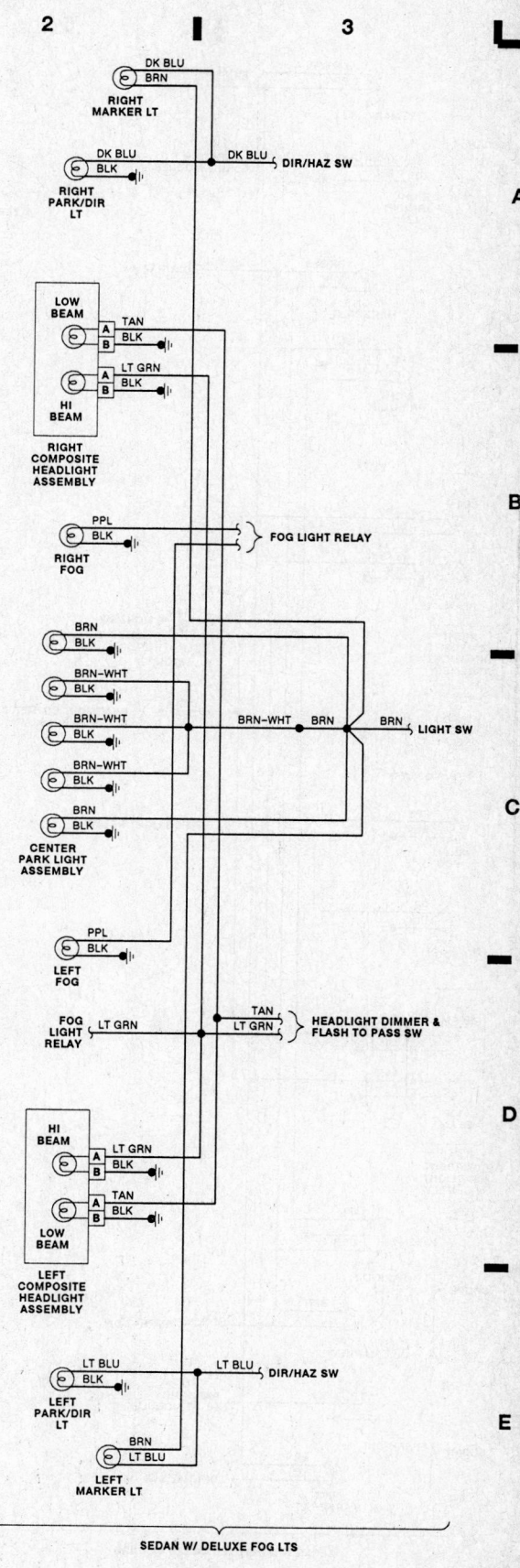

STE

SEDAN W/ DELUXE FOG LTS

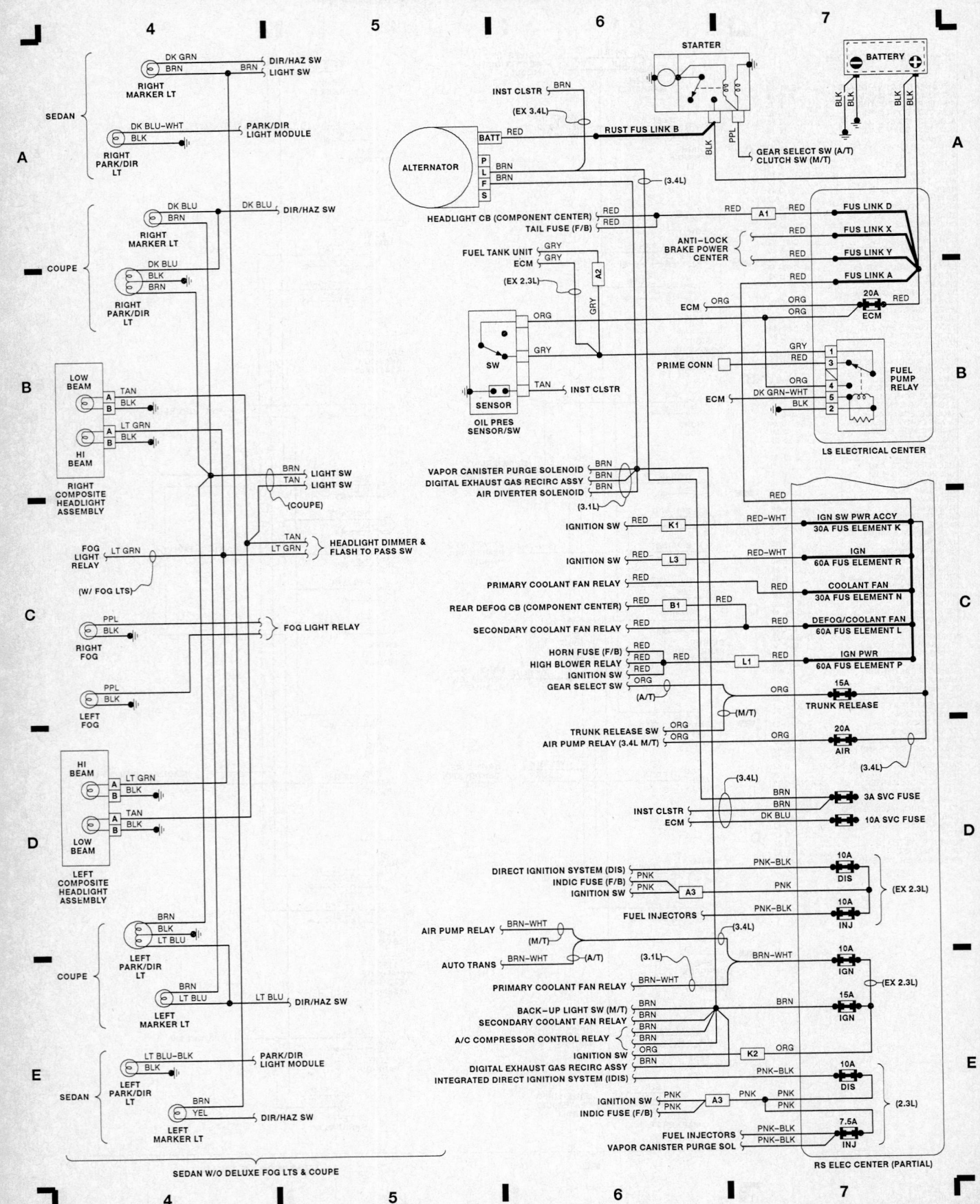

SEDAN W/O DELUXE FOG LTS & COUPE

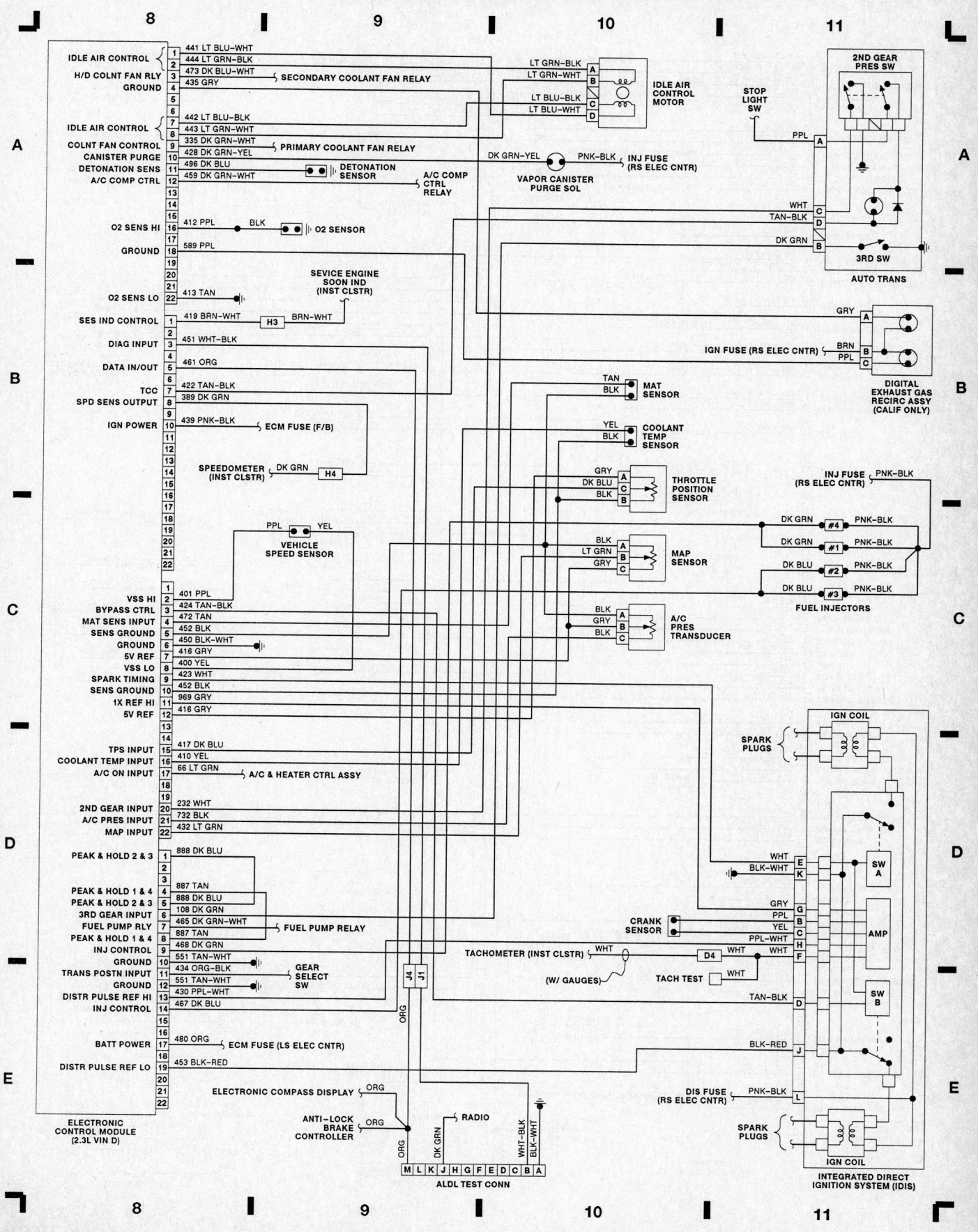

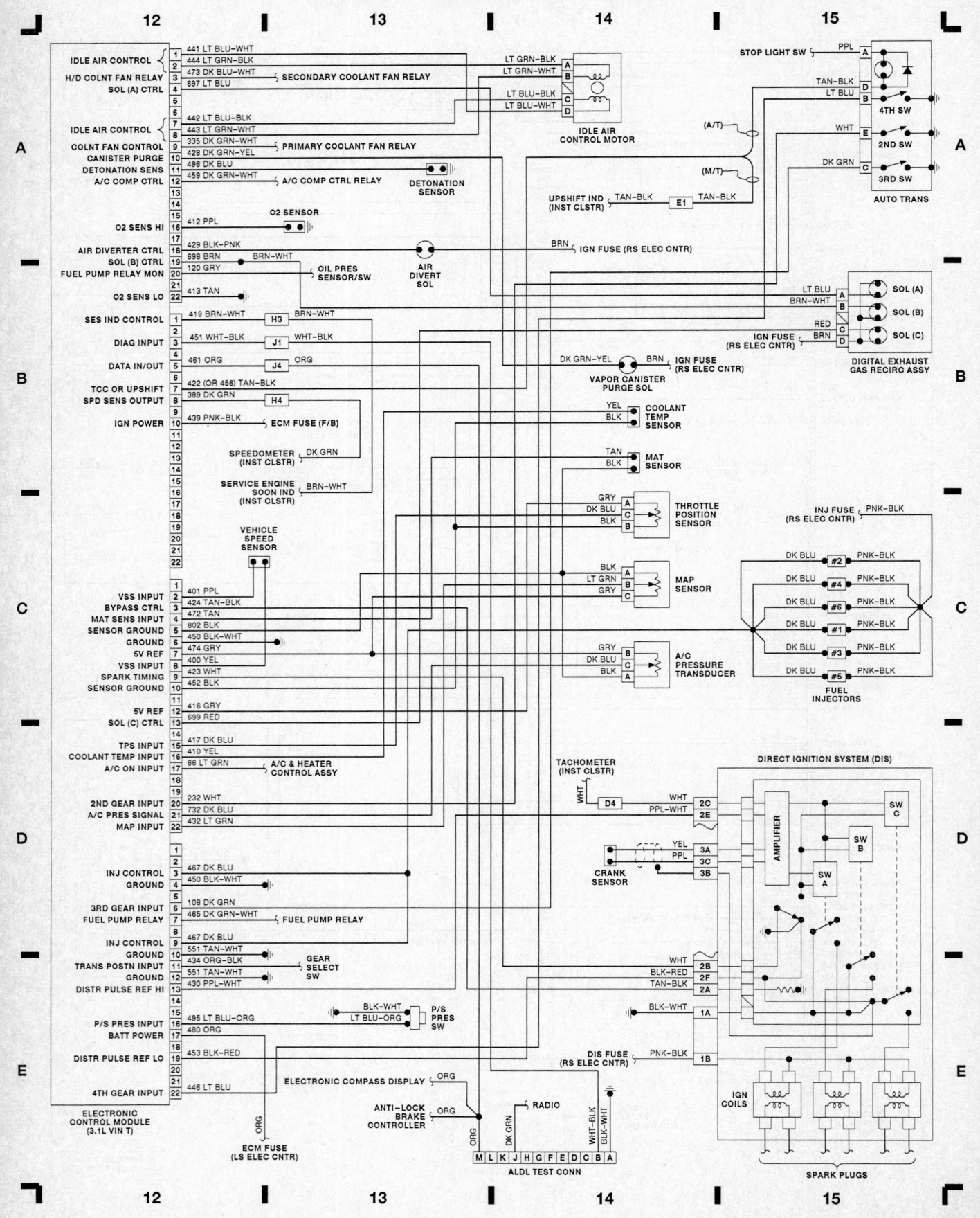

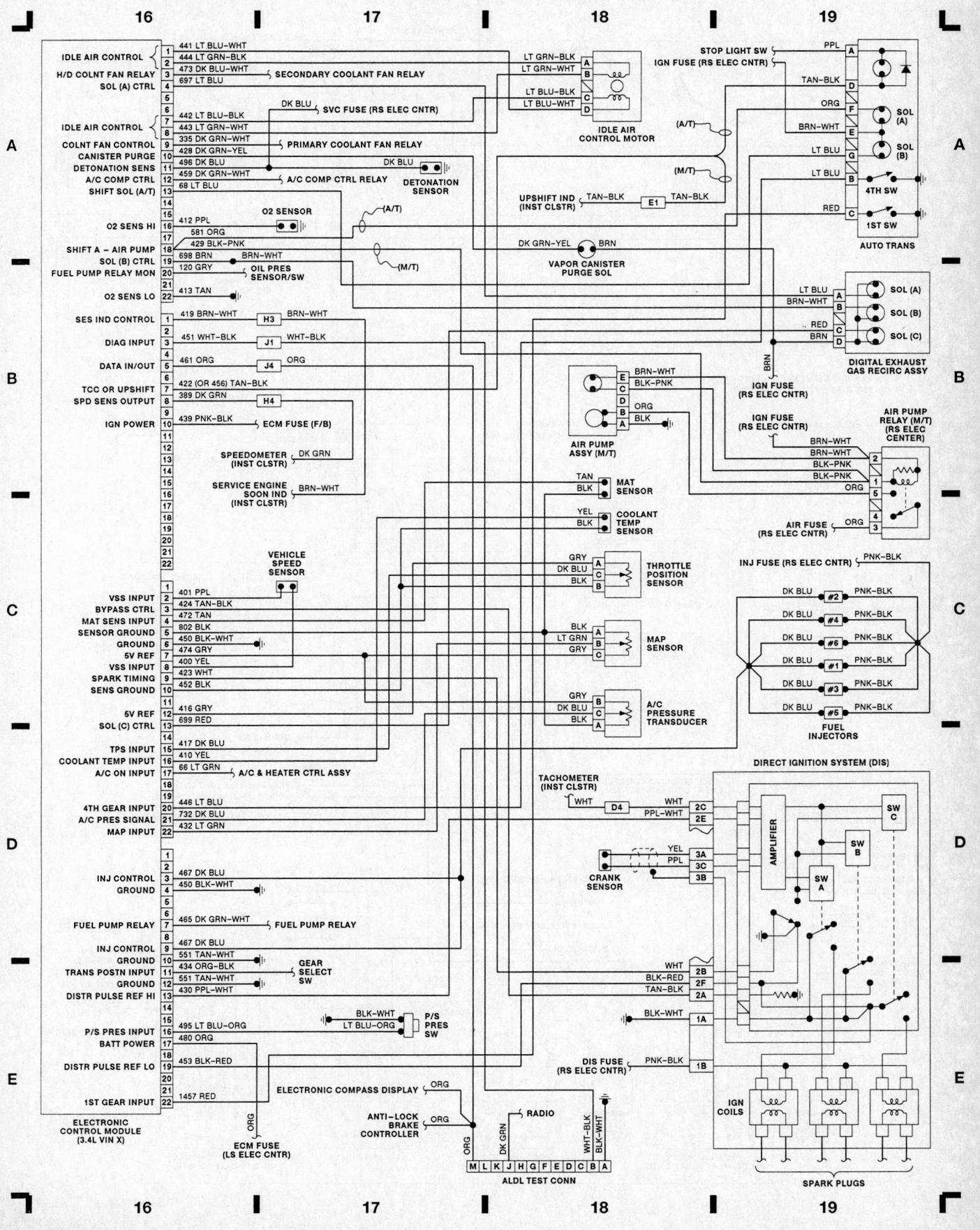

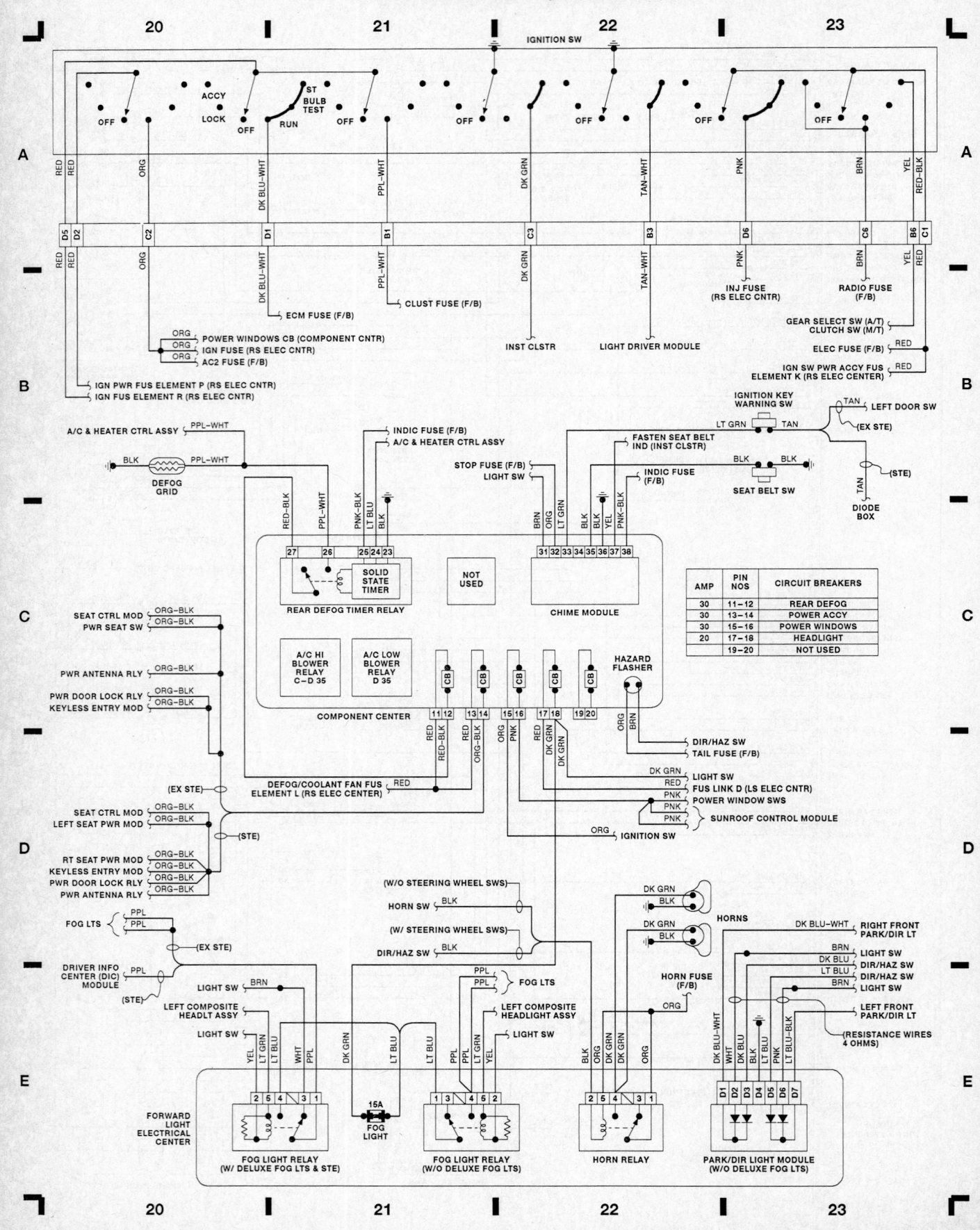

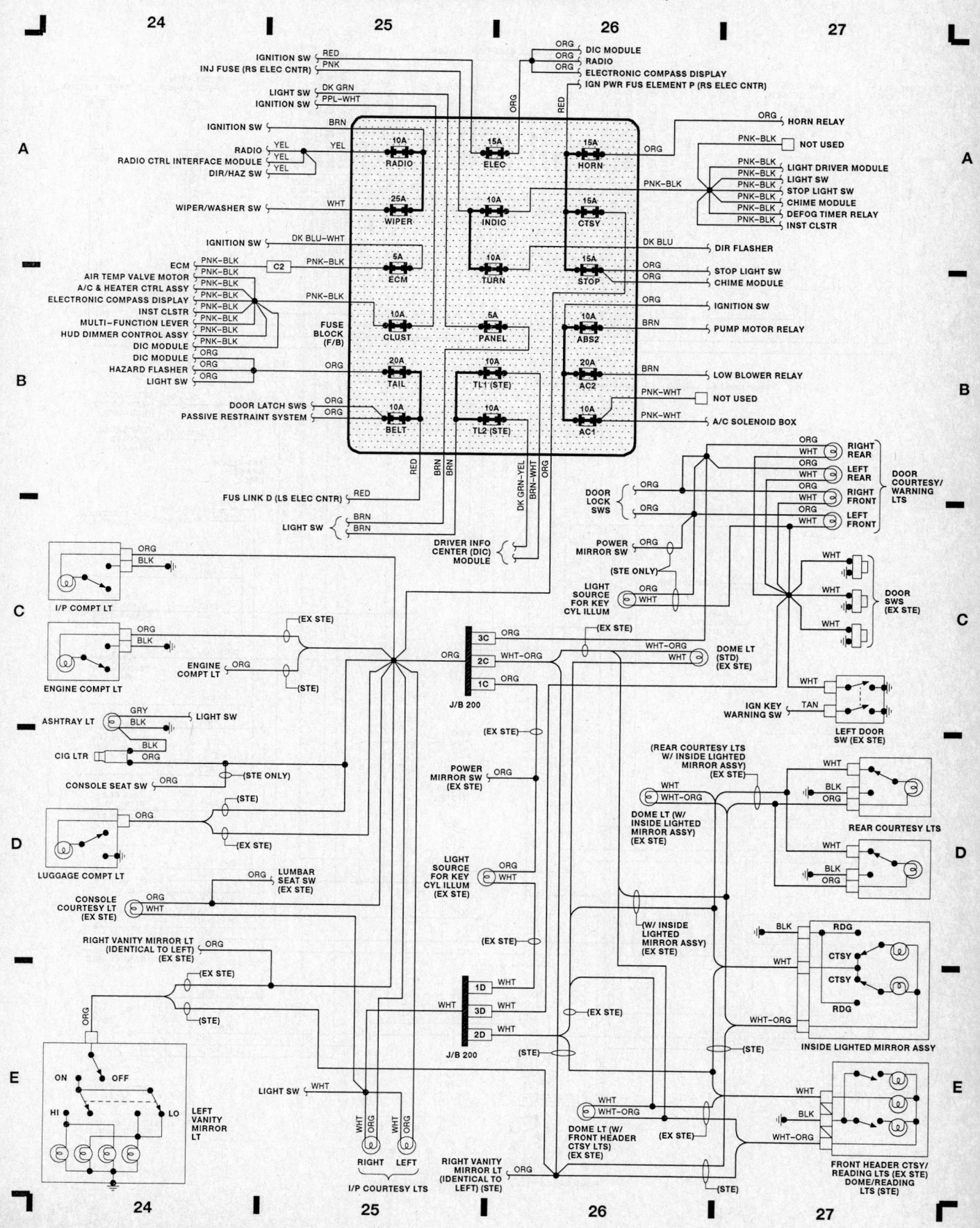

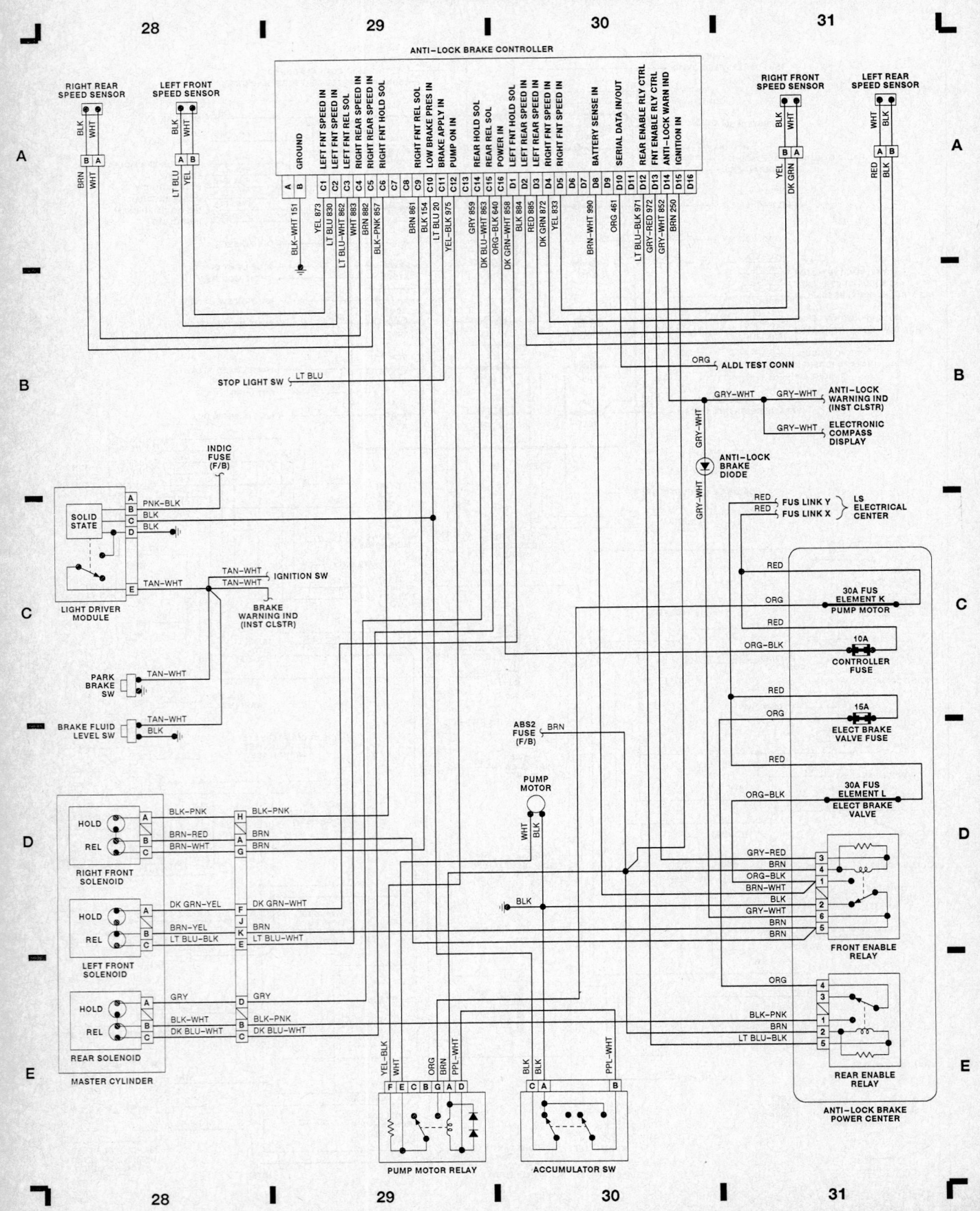

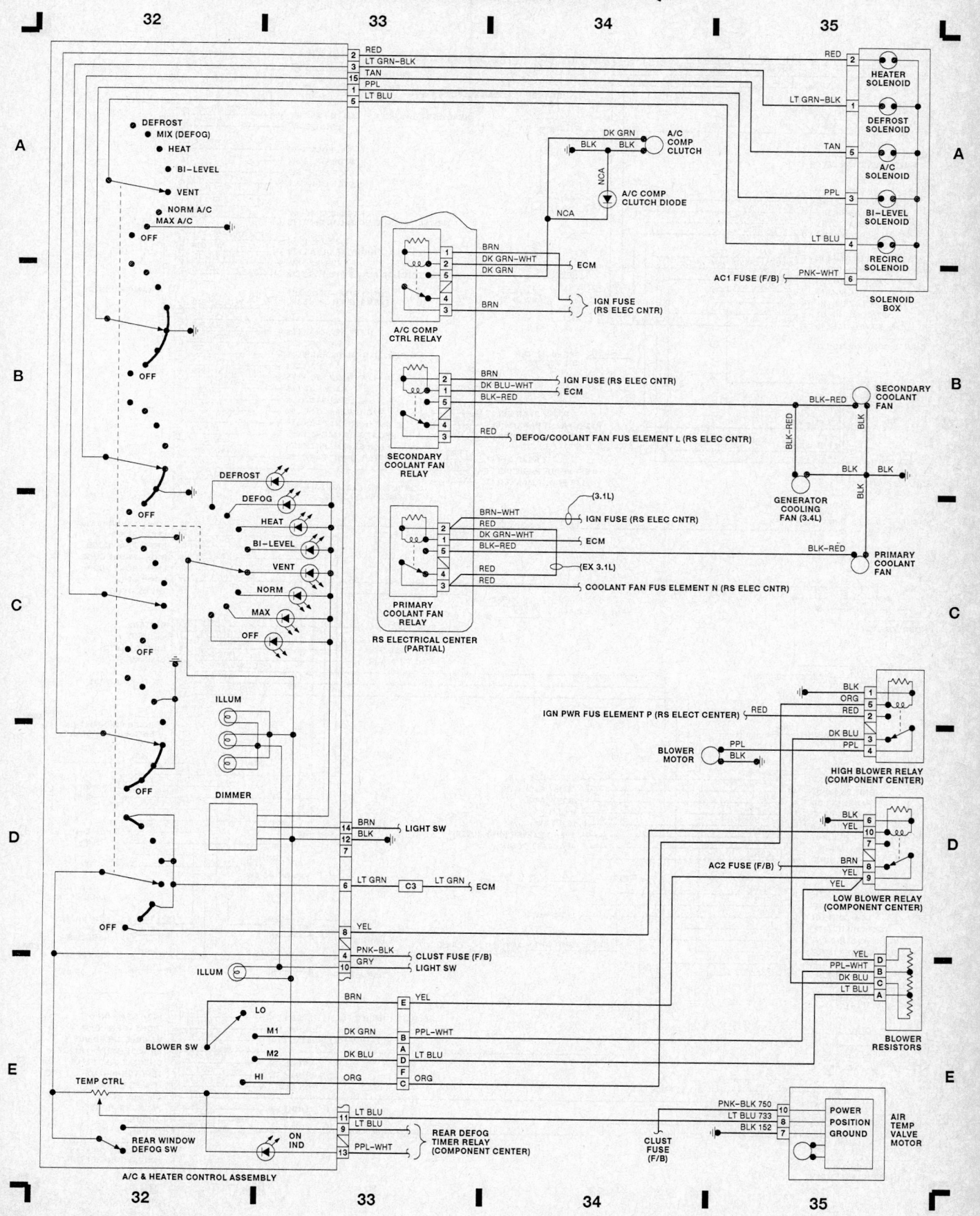

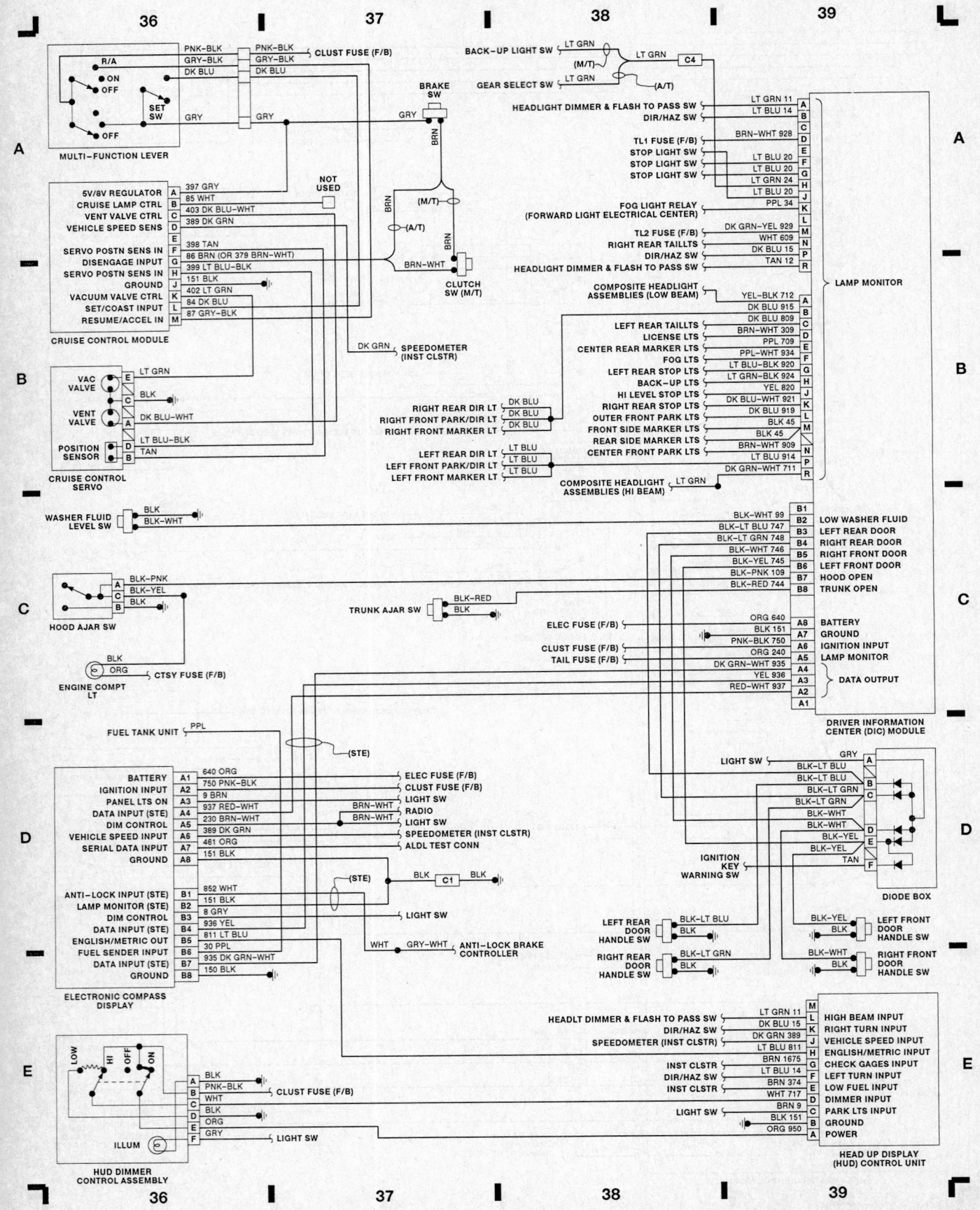

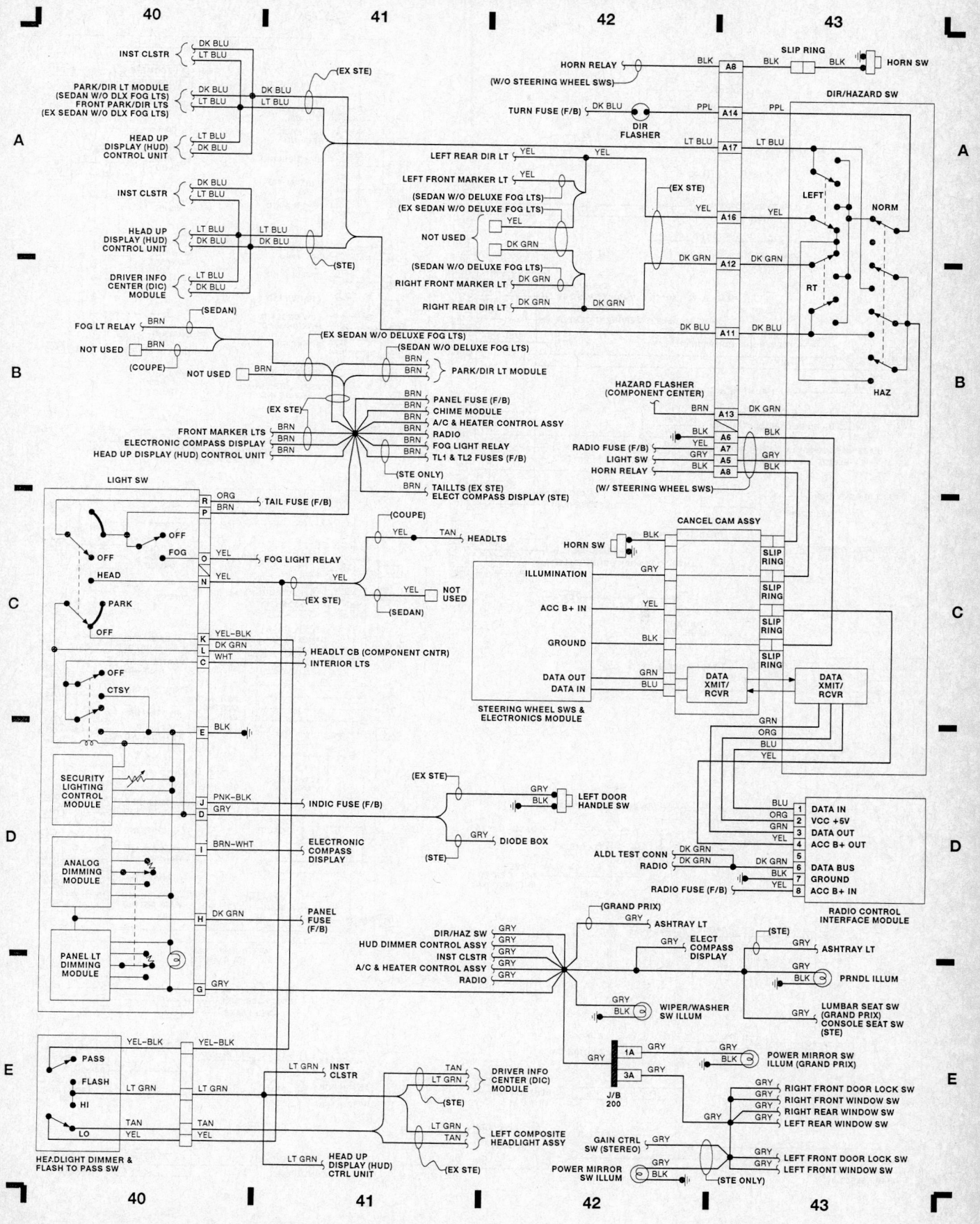

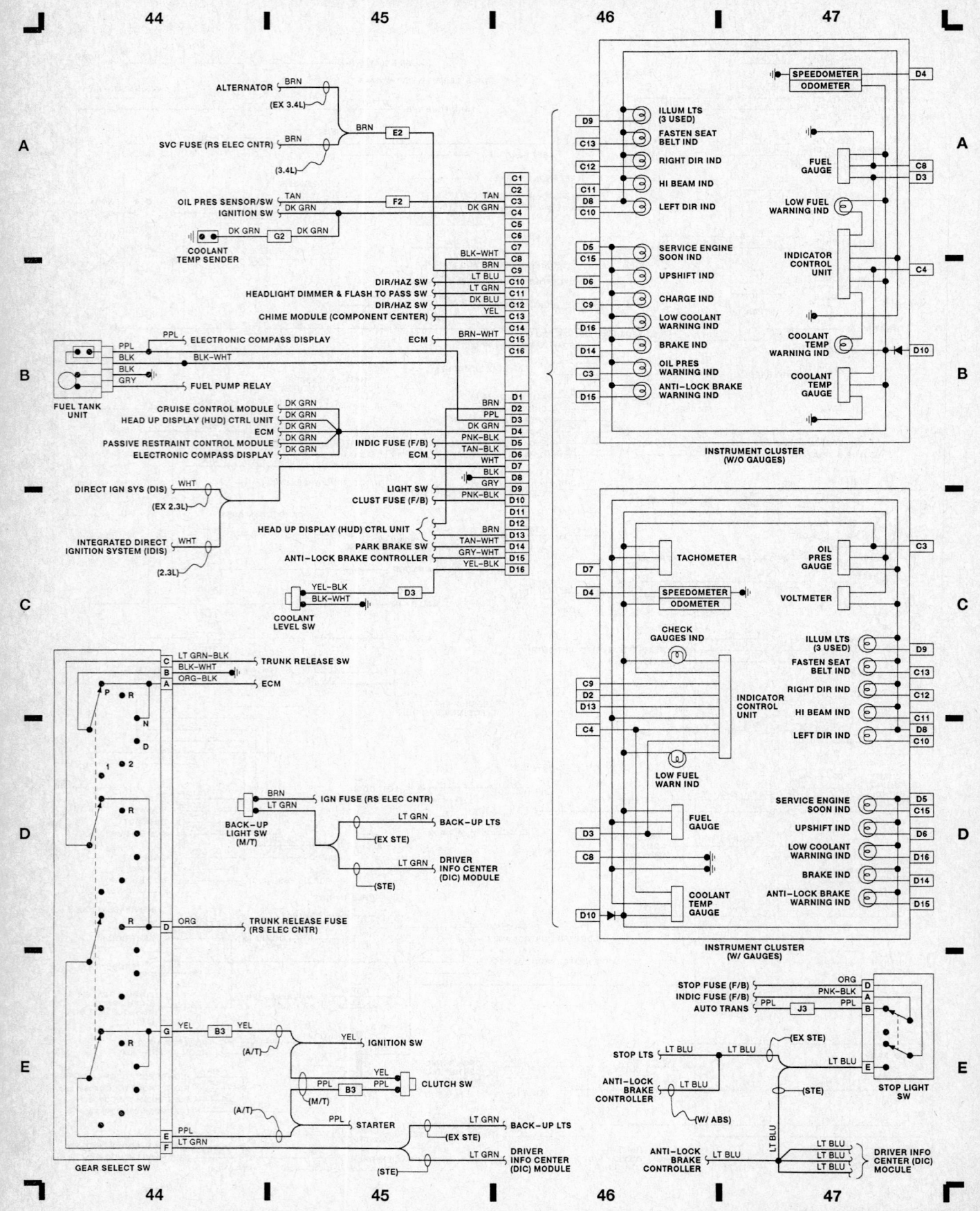

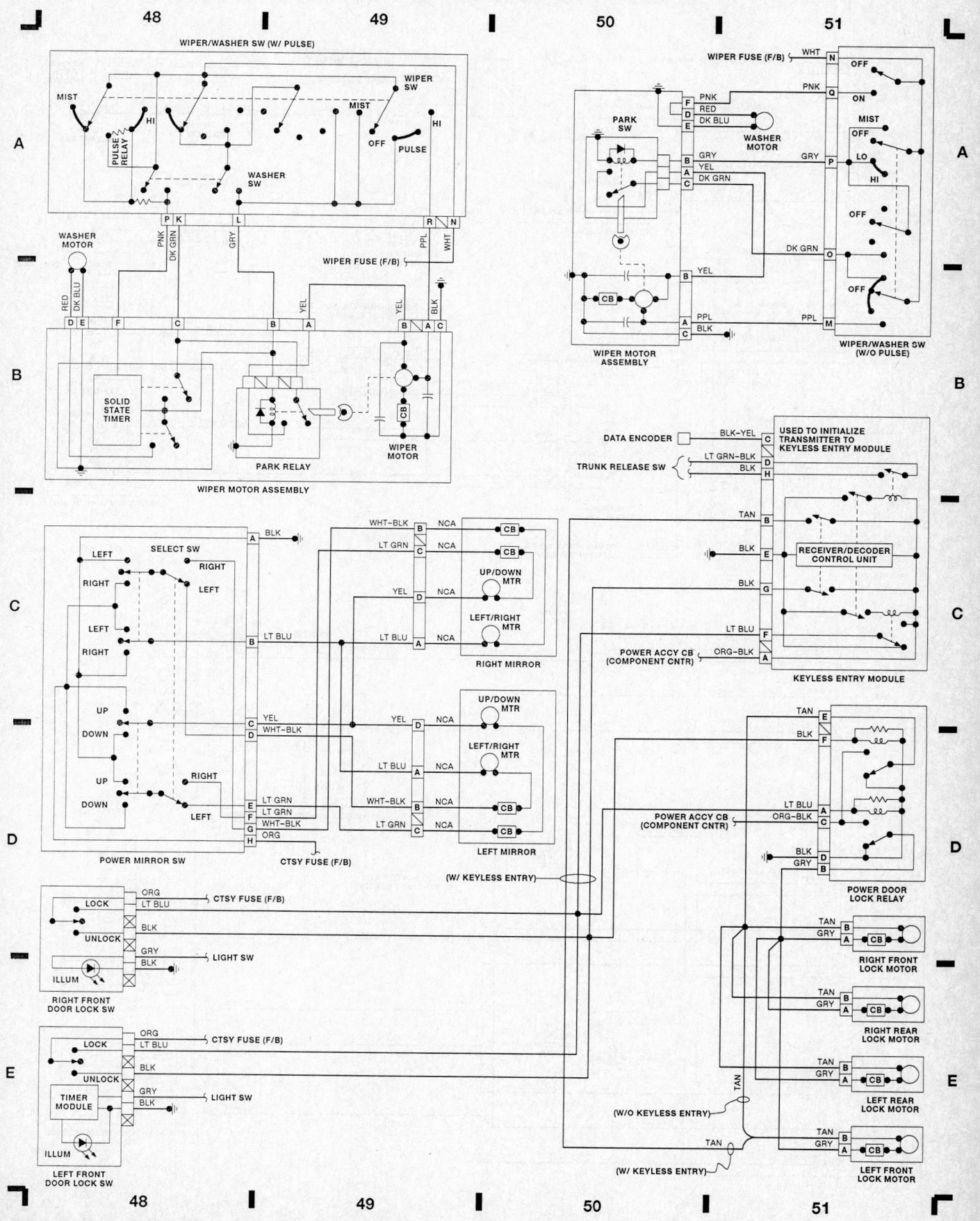

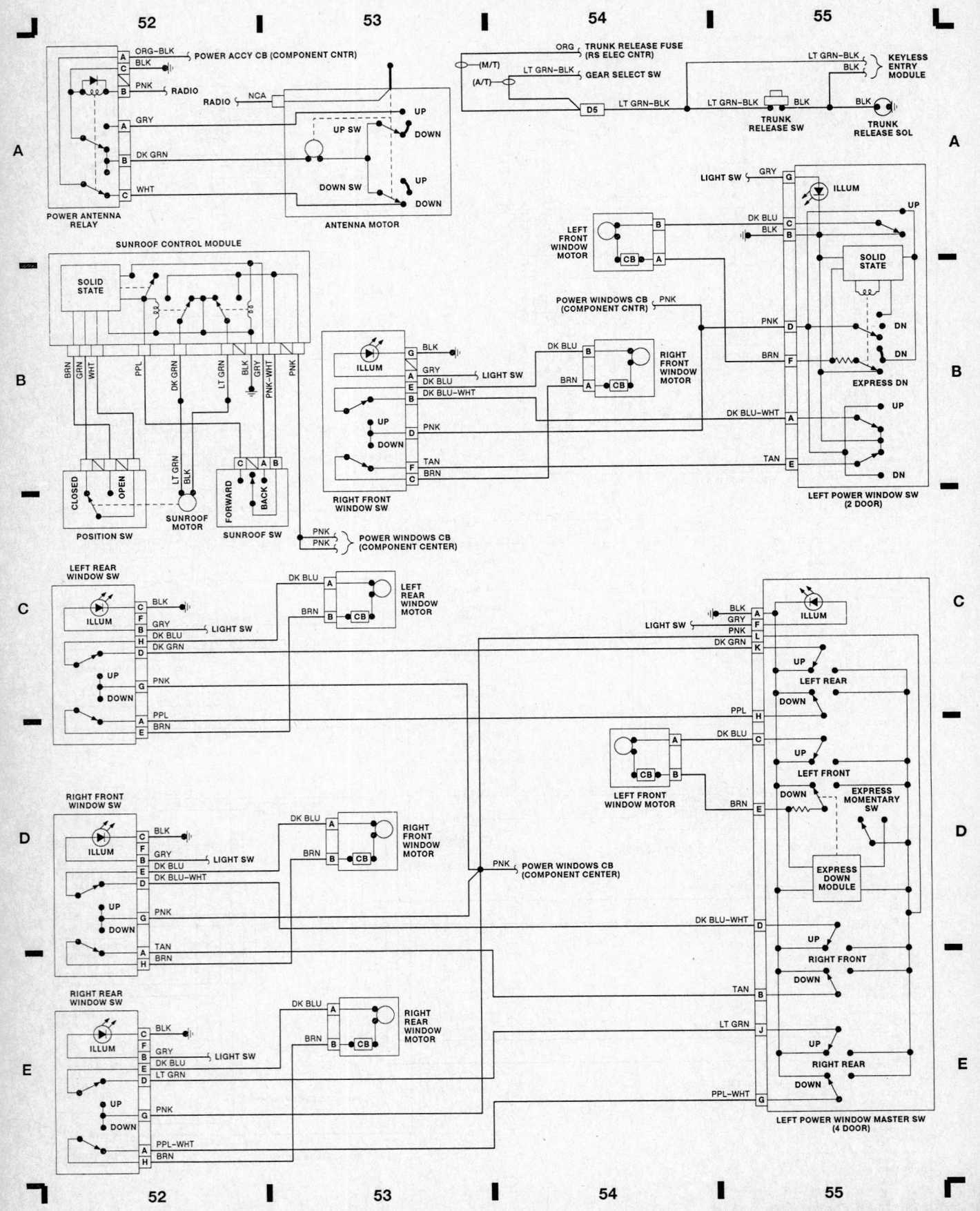

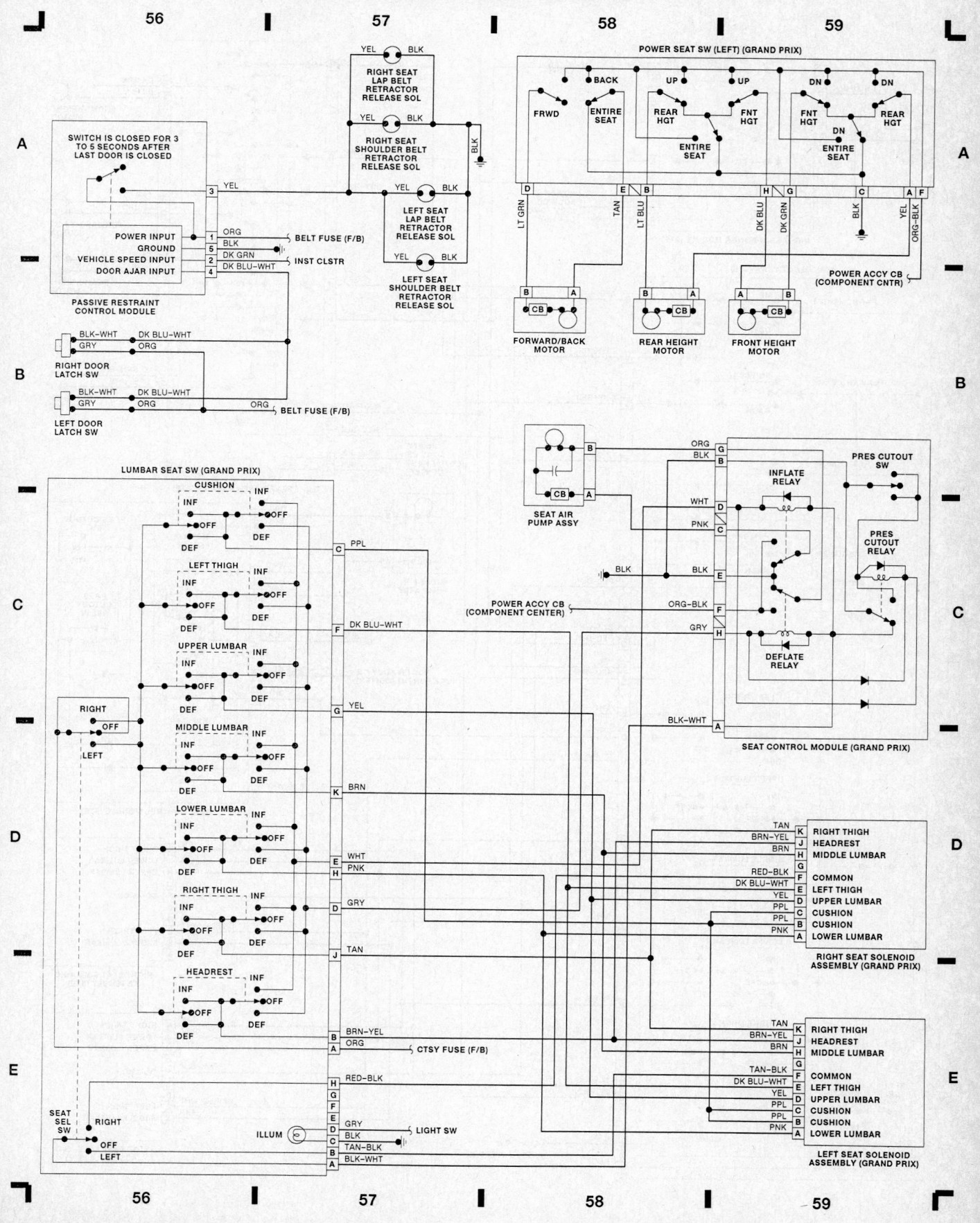

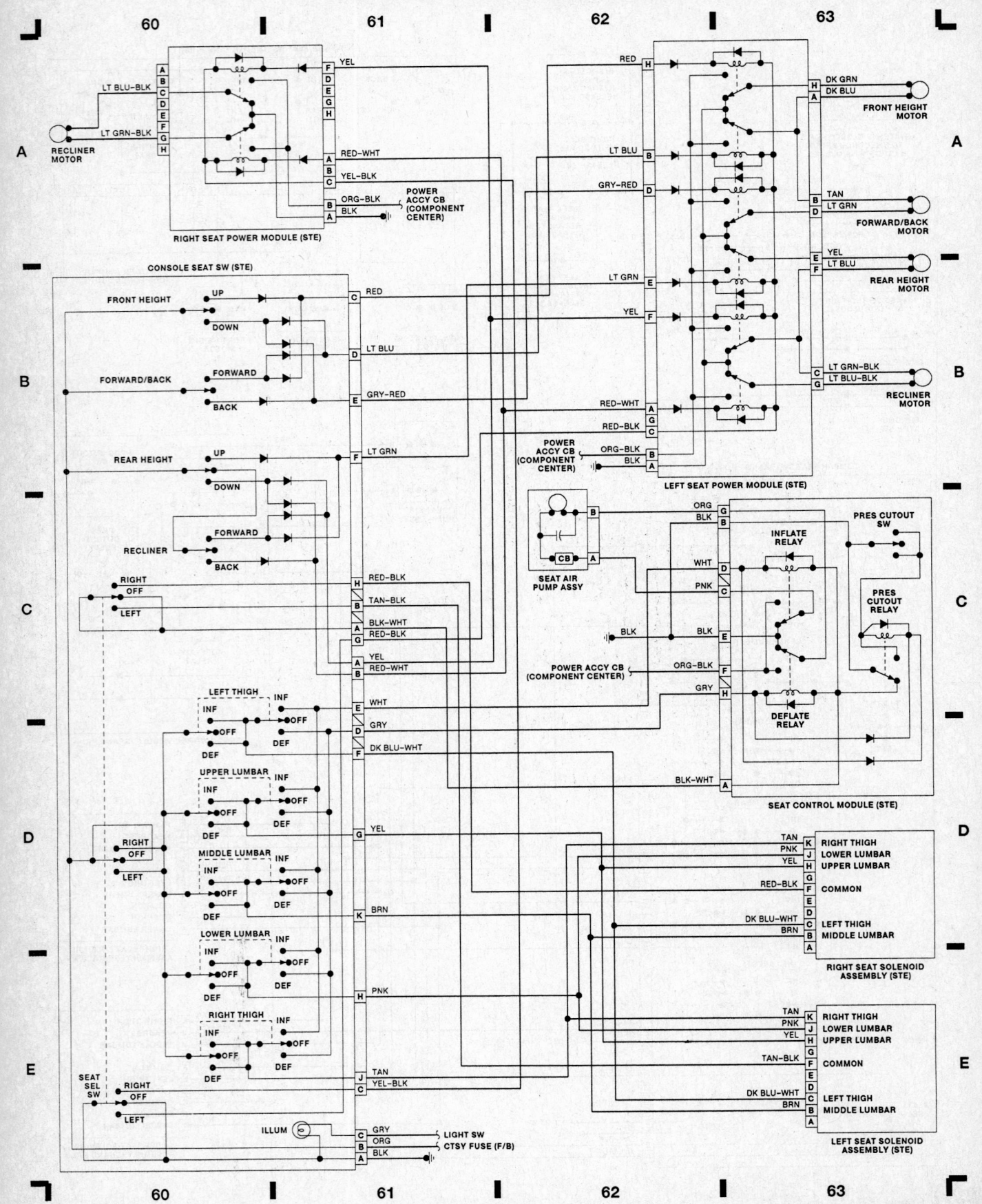

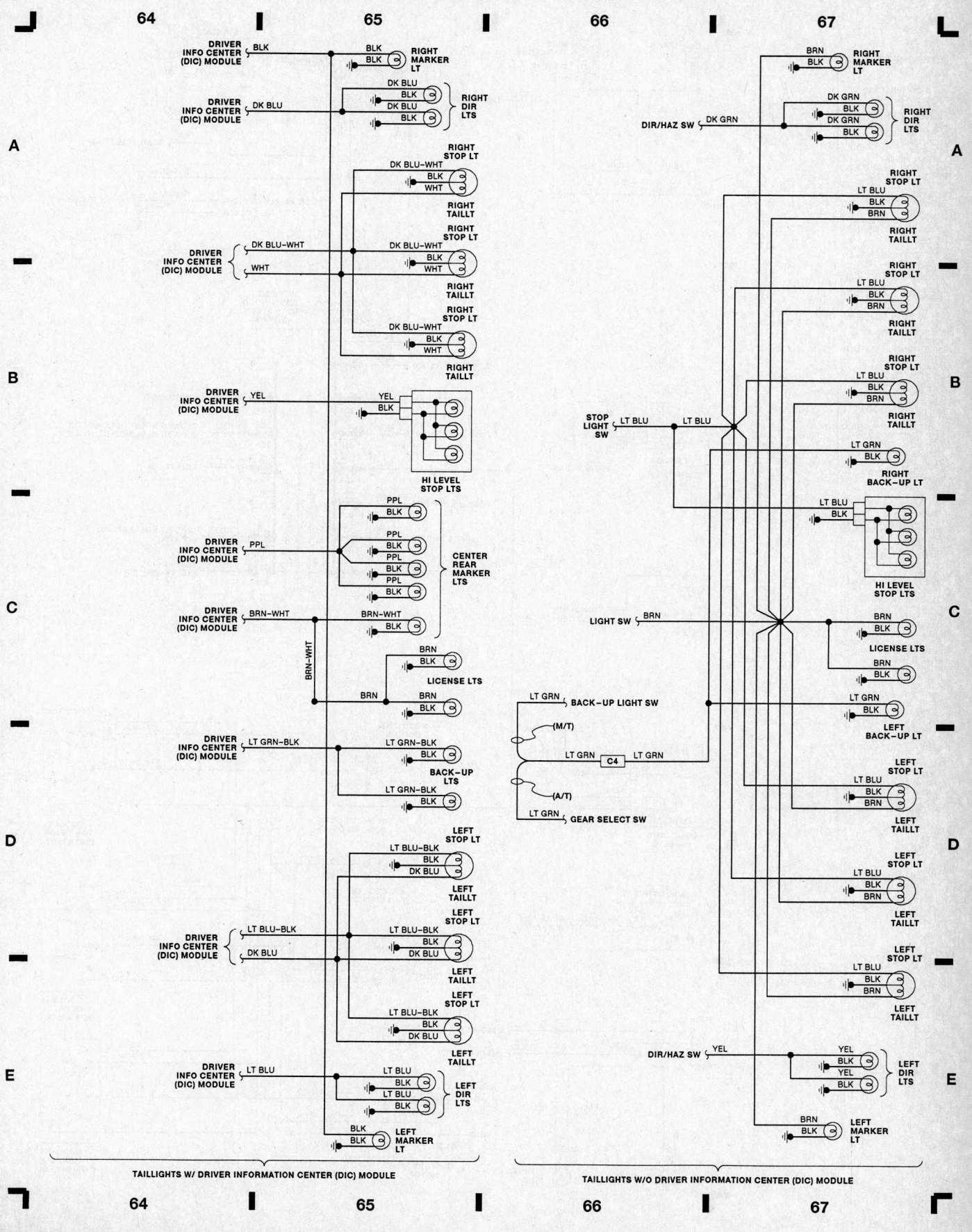

TAILLIGHTS W/ DRIVER INFORMATION CENTER (DIC) MODULE

TAILLIGHTS W/O DRIVER INFORMATION CENTER (DIC) MODULE

COMPONENT LOCATOR:

A/C & HEATER CTRL UNIT .... A 16
A/C & HEATER SW .... D-E 16
A/C CUTOUT RELAY .... C 19, D 18
A/C SELECT RELAY .... B 19
ABS DIODE .... C 14
ABS PUMP RELAY .... B-C 15
ALDL CONN .... A 5
ALTERNATOR .... A 3
ANTENNA RELAY .... E 36
ANTI-LOCK BRAKE CTRL UNIT .... B-E 12
AUTOMATIC TRANS .... E 7
BATTERY .... A 2
BEAM SELECT SW .... A 20
BLOWER CTRL UNIT .... A 19
BLOWER RELAY .... E 18
BRAKE FLUID LEVEL SW .... B 26
CANISTER PURGE SOLENOID .... D 6
CHIME MODULE .... E 27
CIG LTR .... D 31
COMPUTER CONTROLLED
  COIL IGNITION (CCCI) .... B-C 7
COOLANT FAN RELAYS .... D-E 3
COOLANT TEMP SENSOR .... E 6
CRUISE CTRL MODULE .... E 24
CRUISE CTRL SERVO .... D 24
CRUISE CTRL SW .... D 24
CRUISE/SHIFT INTERLOCK/BRAKE
  SW .... E 22/D-E 25
DEFOGGER CTRL UNIT .... D 19
DEFOGGER RELAY .... A 14
DIRECTIONAL/HAZARD SW .... D-E 20
DOME LT .... C 28
DOME/READING LT .... B 28
DOOR LATCH SWS .... A 30
DOOR LOCK SWS .... A 35
DOOR SWS .... E 31
EGR MODULE .... B 6
ELC HEIGHT SENSOR .... D-E 10
ELC RELAY .... D 11
ELECTRONIC CTRL MODULE (ECM) .... A-E 4
FUEL INJECTORS .... D 7
FUEL PUMP RELAY .... E 38
FUEL TANK UNIT .... E 38
GEAR SELECT SW .... D-E 23
HEADLIGHT SW .... A-B 20
HORN RELAY .... A 14-15
HORN SW .... B 15
I/P COMPT LT .... D 31
I/P LT CTRL SW .... D 20
IGNITION SW .... A 8-11
INSTRUMENT CLUSTERS .... A-D 24-27
INSTRUMENT PANEL FUSE
  BLOCK (I/P F/B) .... B-C 9-10
INTERIOR LTS .... B-E 28-31
LEFT FNT DOOR CTSY LT .... E 28
LEFT QUARTER PANEL
  CTSY/READING LTS .... E 28
LEFT UNDERHOOD FUSE
  BLOCK (U/H F/B) .... B-C 2
LUGGAGE COMPT LT .... D 31
MAIN RELAY .... C 15
OIL PRES SENDER/SW .... B 24
OXYGEN SENSOR .... E 5
PARK BRAKE SW .... C 26
POWER DOOR LOCK RELAY .... A 32-33
POWER MIRROR SW .... D 33
POWER SEAT SW .... B 35
POWER WINDOW SWS .... A-D 36-38
RELAY CENTER .... A-B 12-15
RIGHT & LEFT FOOTWELL LT .... D 28
RIGHT FNT DOOR CTSY LT .... B 28
RIGHT QUARTER PANEL
  CTSY/READING LTS .... C 28
RIGHT SEAT RECLINER SW .... A 28
RIGHT UNDERHOOD FUSE
  BLOCK (U/H F/B) .... B-C 2
SEAT BELT RETRACTOR SYSTEM .... A 31
STARTER .... A 3
TCC BRAKE SW .... E 6/D-E 14
TEMP SENS .... C 24
TRUNK LID RELEASE SW .... C-D 37-38
TWILIGHT SENTINEL MODULE .... A 23
VANITY MIRROR .... A 28
WIPER/WASHER SWS .... B-D 20-23

PARK LT
SIDE MARKER LT
BLK
BRN
BRN
DK BLU
DK BLU → DIR/HAZ SW
STARTER
BATTERY
BLK
BLK
BLK-RED
BLK
BLK
PPL → GEAR SELECT SW
PARK LT
BRN → BRN → HEADLT SW
BLK
DK BLU
TURN LT
BLK-RED — B
FUSE #5 (RLY CENTER) — PNK-BLK — F
INST CLSTR — BRN — L
S
ALTERNATOR

LO BEAM — TAN / BLK
HI BEAM — LT GRN / BLK
COMPOSITE HEADLTS
BEAM SEL SW

LEFT UNDERHOOD FUSE BLOCK (U/H F/B)
RIGHT UNDERHOOD FUSE BLOCK (U/H F/B)
BLK

ABS PUMP RELAY — RED — 1 — 40A
MAIN RELAY — RED — 2 — 30A — RED — IGNITION SW — 2 — 30A
FUSE #12 (I/P F/B) — RED — 3 — 40A — RED — BLOWER RELAY (MAN A/C) OR BLOWER CTRL MOD (AUTO A/C) — 3 — 40A
RED — 4 — 40A — RED — ECM PIN B1 — 4 — 40A
FUSE #13 (I/P F/B) — RED — 5 — 60A — 5
HEADLIGHT SW — RED — 6 — 30A — RED — CIRCUIT BREAKER #23 (I/P F/B) — 6 — 30A
IGNITION SW — RED — 7 — 60A — RED — HORN RELAY (RELAY CENTER) — 7 — 60A

DK GRN
DK GRN — HORN RLY (RLY CENTER)

HI BEAM — LT GRN / BLK
LO BEAM — TAN / BLK
COMPOSITE HEADLTS
BEAM SEL SW

ENG COMPT LT — ORG → FUSE #11 (I/P F/B)

AUXILIARY COOLANT FAN
BLK
BRN
LT GRN-BLK — 5
BLK-PNK — 4
RED — RED — 1
COOLANT FAN RELAY (AUXILIARY)

(W/ HEAVY DUTY COOLING ONLY)
RED

LT GRN-BLK
BLK
A/C COOLANT FAN PRES SW
FUSE #6 (I/P F/B)
BRN
BRN — 2
LT GRN-BLK
BLK-PNK — 4
RED — 1
COOLANT FAN RELAY (HIGH SPEED)

ECM { PIN B5 — LT GRN-BLK
      PIN E2 — DK GRN

TURN LT
BLK
BRN — BRN
LT BLU → DIR/HAZ SW
BRN → HEADLIGHT SW
PARK LT

BKL
BRN
PARK LT
BRN
LT BLU → MARKER LT SIDE

RESISTOR
A — BLK-RED
B — BLK-PNK
C — BLK
MOTOR
COOLANT FAN MOTOR

BRN
DK GRN — 5
BLK-RED — 4
RED — 1
COOLANT FAN RELAY (LOW SPEED)

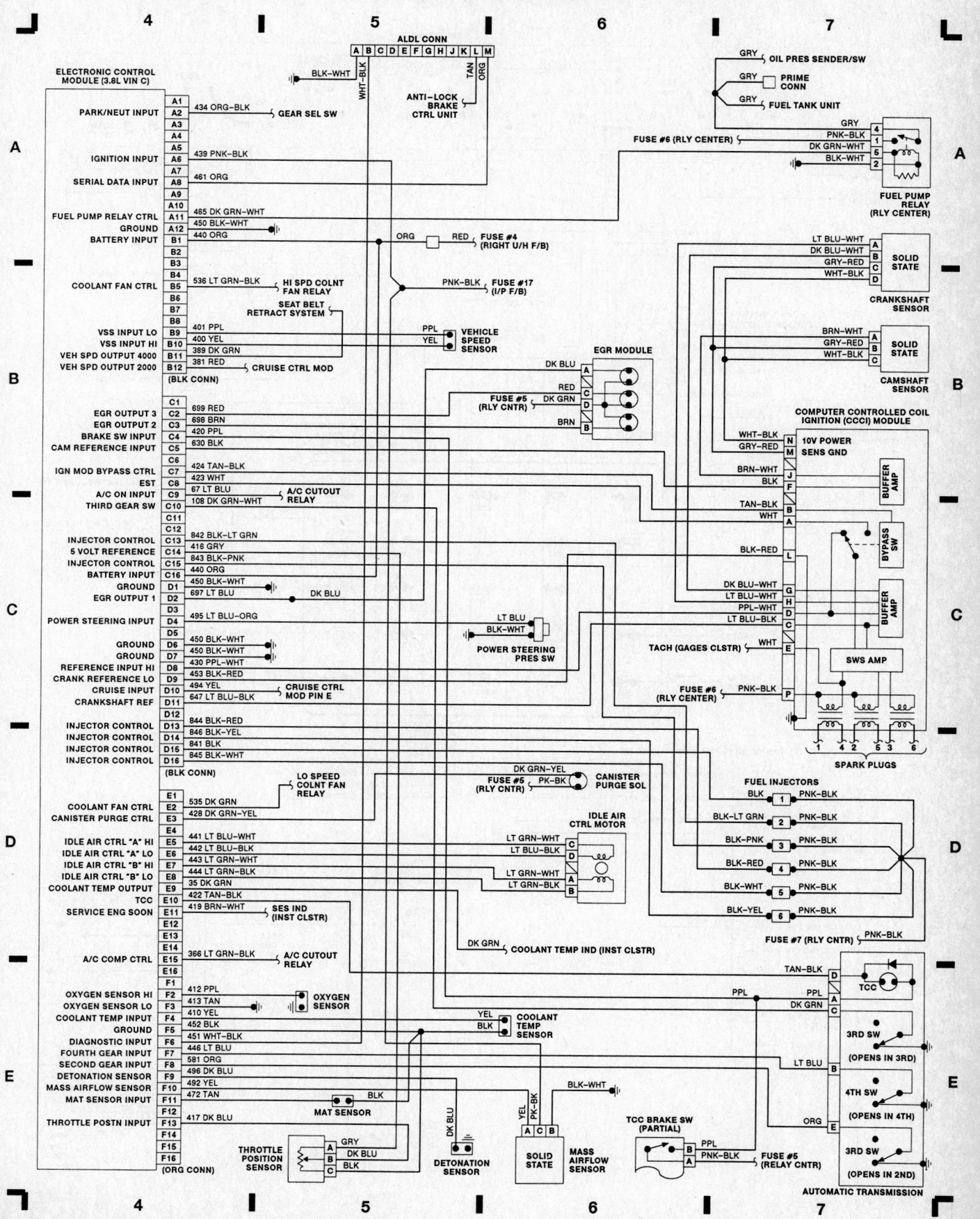

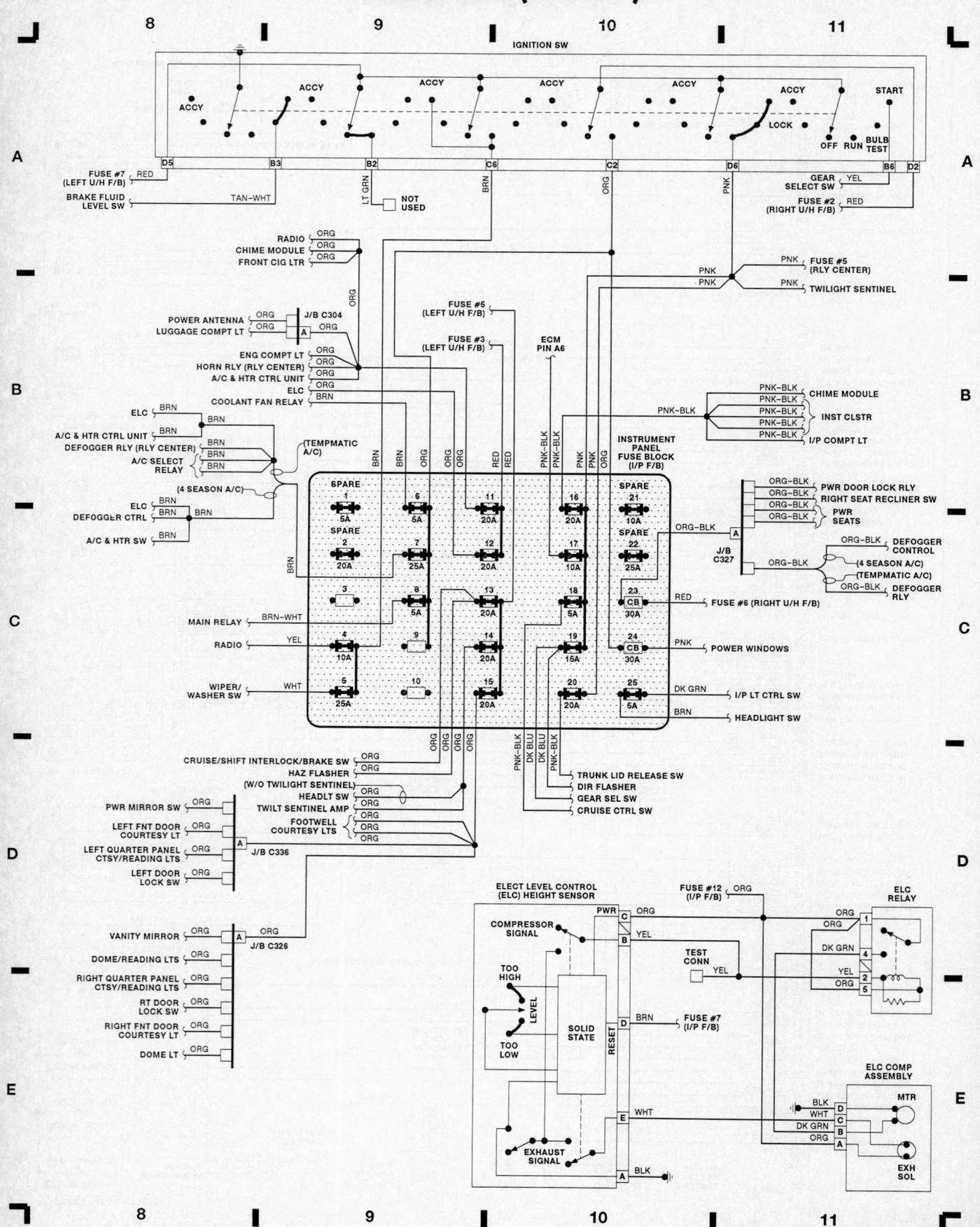

1991 WIRING DIAGRAMS
LeSabre (Cont.)

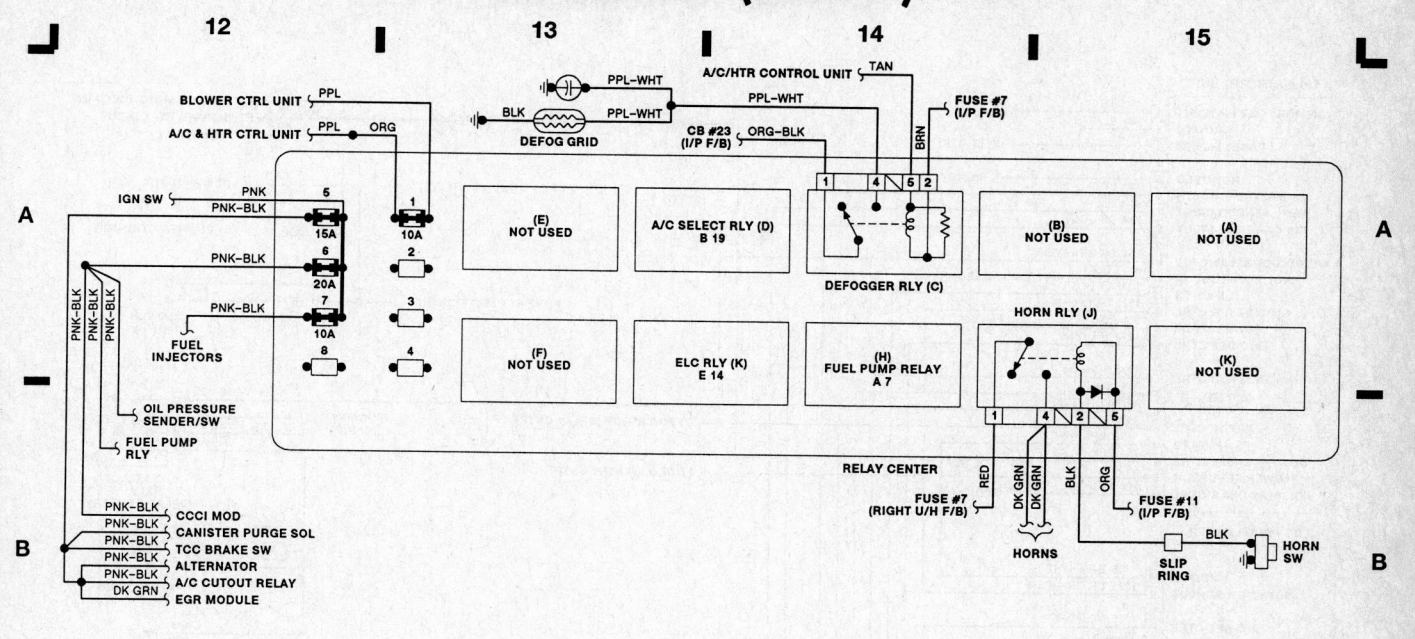

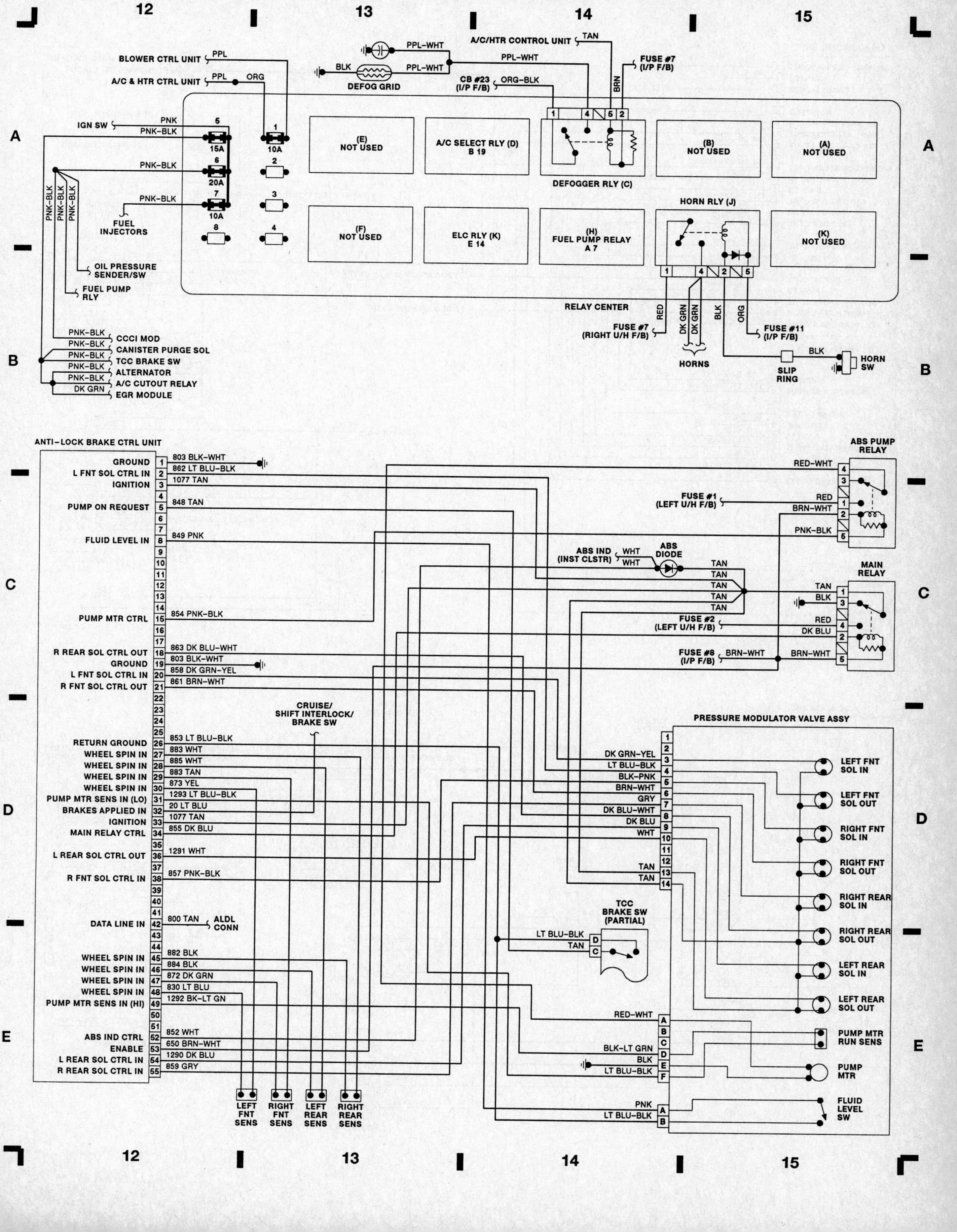

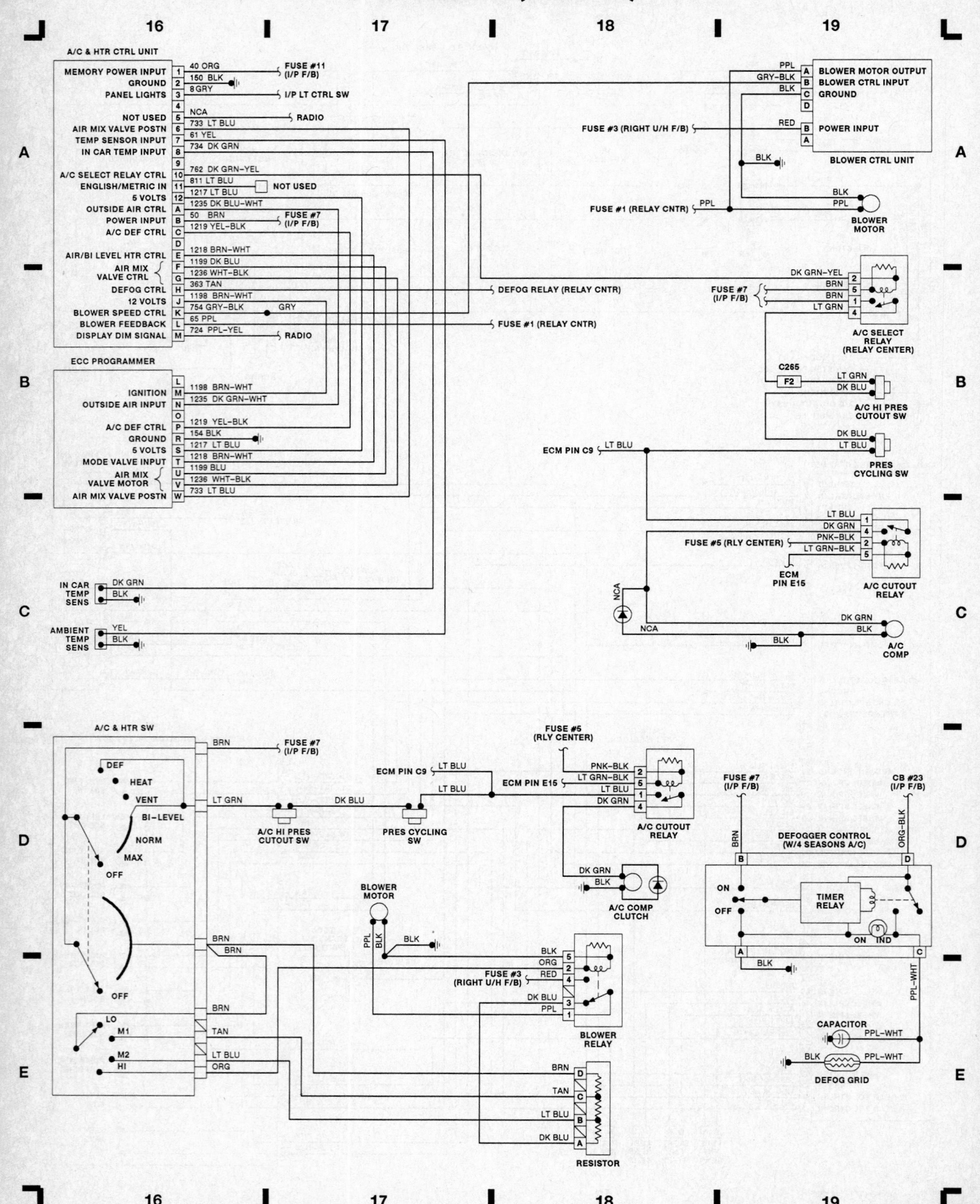

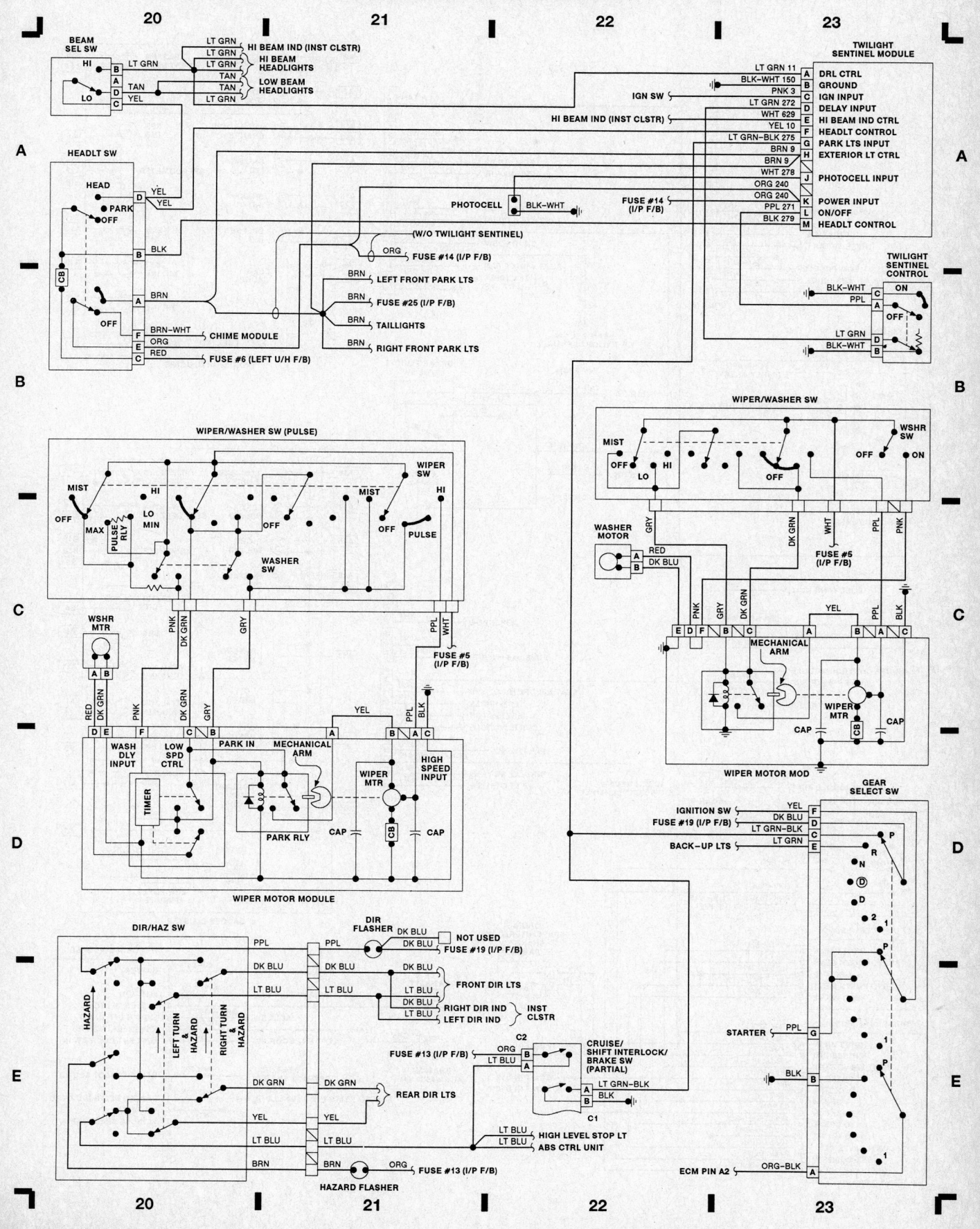

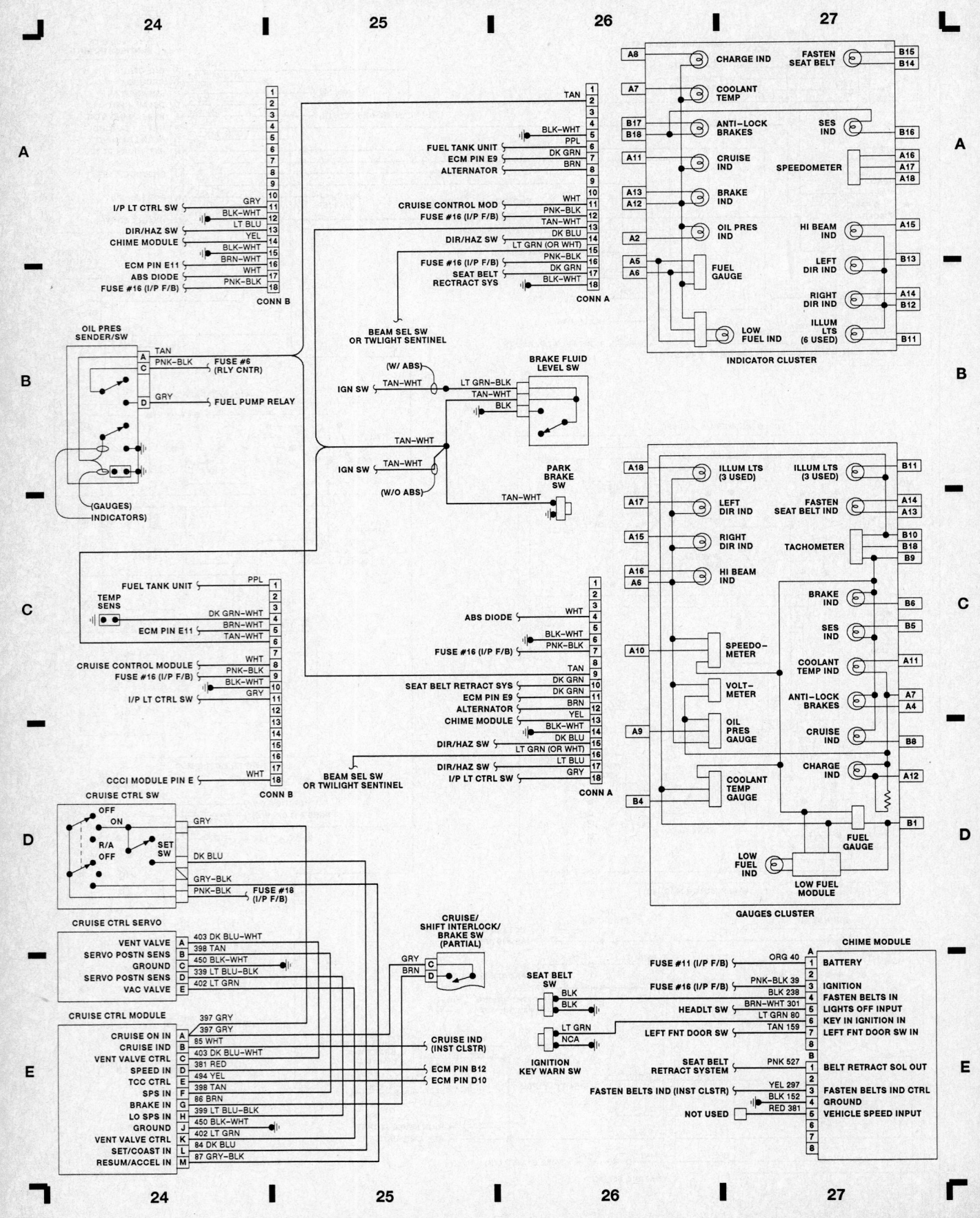

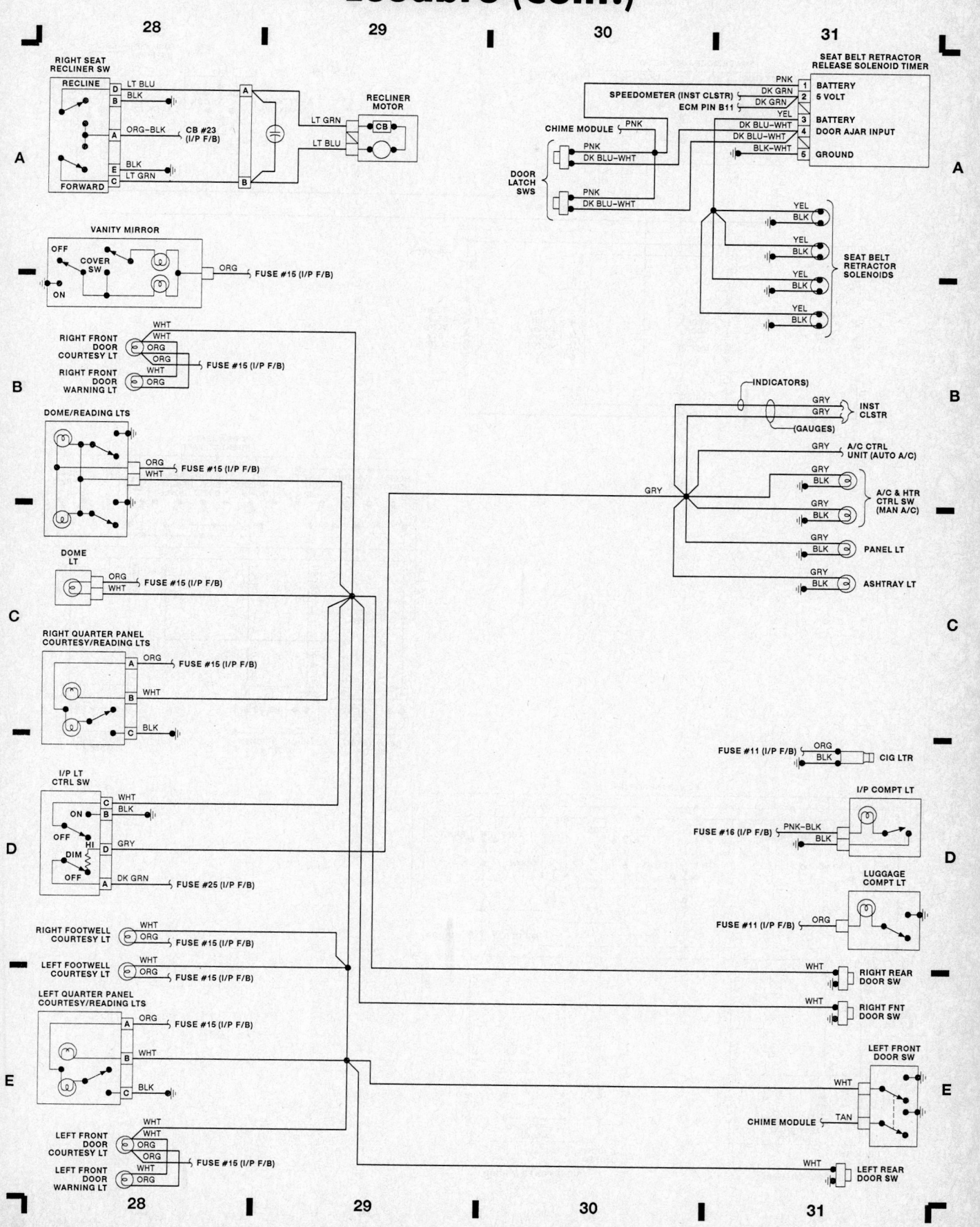

32   33   34   35

POWER DOOR LOCK RELAY

LOCK RLY   UNLOCK RLY

A   B   D E C F

LT BLU   GRY   BLK ORG-BLK BLK

CB #23 (I/P F/B)

35
FUSE #15
(I/P F/B)
ORG   ORG

B

LEFT DOOR   LOCK UN-   RT DOOR   LOCK UN-
LOCK SW   LOCK   LOCK SW   LOCK
A   C   A   C

LT BLU   BLK   LT BLU   BLK

GRY   GRY   GRY   GRY   (4 DOOR)

A   A   A   A

LEFT   LEFT   RIGHT   RIGHT
REAR   FRONT   FRONT   REAR
DOOR   DOOR   DOOR   DOOR
LOCK   LOCK   LOCK   LOCK
MOTOR   MOTOR   MOTOR   MOTOR

CB   CB   CB   CB

B   B   B   B

TAN   TAN   TAN   TAN

POWER SEAT SW
(RIGHT OR LEFT)

REAR   ENTIRE FNT   FNT   ENTIRE REAR   SEAT   SEAT
HEIGHT   SEAT   HEIGHT   HEIGHT   SEAT   HEIGHT BACK   FRWD
UP   UP   UP   DOWN   DOWN   DOWN

ORG-BLK YEL   DK GRN   DK BLU   LT BLU   LT GRN TAN BLK

CB #23
(I/P F/B)

YEL   LT BLU   DK GRN   DK BLU   LT GRN   TAN

A   B   B   A   B   A

REAR HEIGHT   FRONT HEIGHT   FRONT/BACK
MOTOR   MOTOR   MOTOR

POWER MIRROR SW

LEFT RIGHT   LEFT RIGHT   LEFT RIGHT

UP   DOWN   UP   DOWN   UP   DOWN

LEFT   RIGHT
MIRROR   MIRROR

ORG YEL WHT   LT BLU   YEL   WHT   LT BLU   BLK

FUSE #15
(I/P F/B)

YEL   WHT   LT BLU   LT GRN   YEL   WHT   LT GRN   LT GRN

LEFT/RIGHT   LEFT/RIGHT
CB   CB   MOTOR   CB   CB   MOTOR

UP/DOWN   UP/DOWN
MOTOR   MOTOR

LEFT POWER MIRROR   RIGHT POWER MIRROR

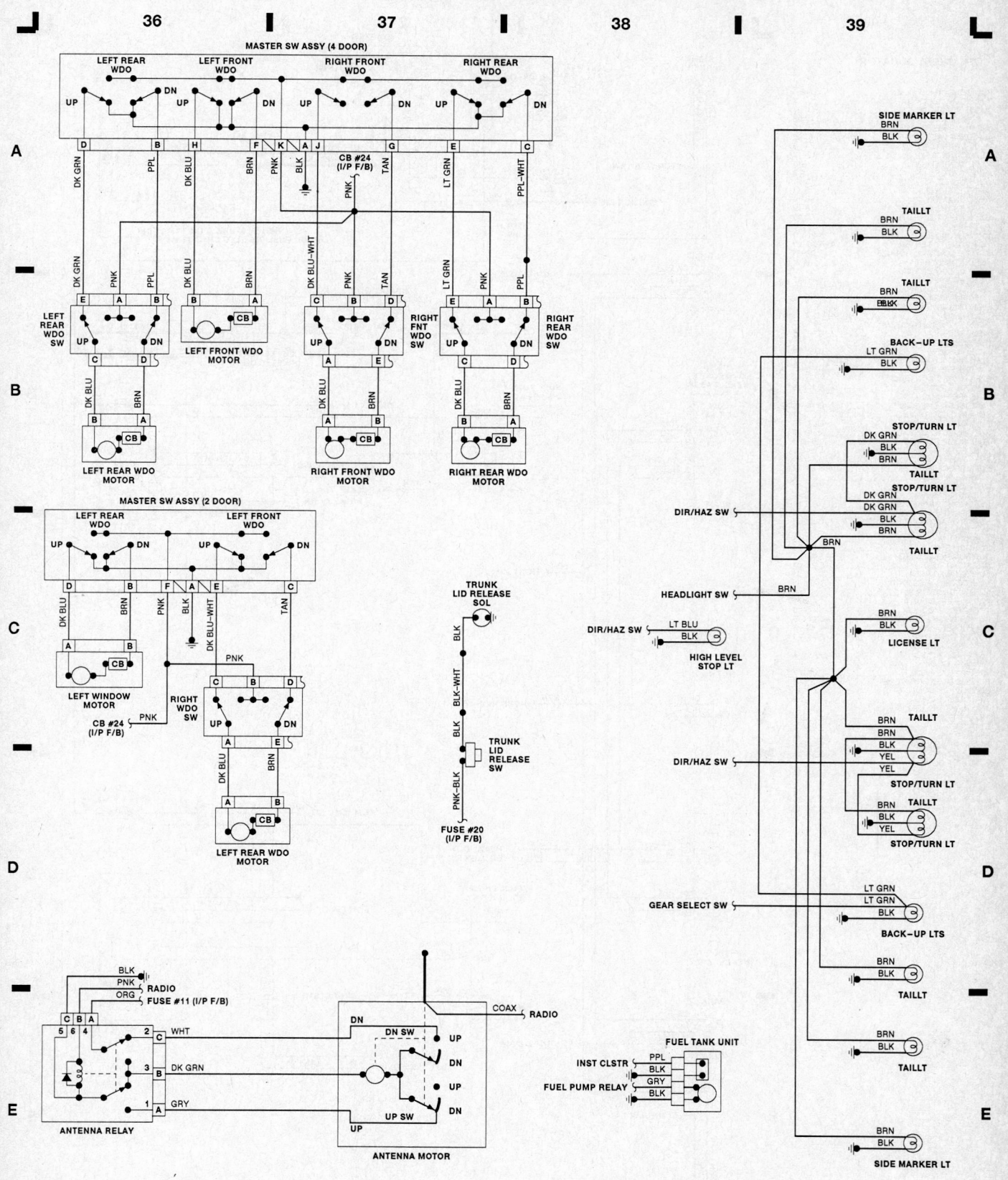

COMPONENT LOCATOR:

A/C COMP RELAY (2.5L) .... D–E 4
A/C COMP RELAY (3.1L & 3.4L) .... E 7
A/C HI PRESSURE SW .... C 31
A/C SOLENOID BOX .... B–C 28
AIR PUMP RELAY (M/T) (3.4L) .... B 19
AIR TEMP VALVE MOTOR .... B–C 29
ALDL CONN (2.5L) .... E 8–9
ALDL CONN (3.1L) .... E 12–13
ALDL CONN (3.4L) .... E 17–18
ALTERNATOR .... A 3
ASHTRAY LT .... C 24
AUTO TRANS (2.5L) .... B 11
AUTO TRANS (3.1L) .... A–B 15
AUTO TRANS (3.4L) .... A 19
BACK-UP LT SW (M/T) .... C 36
BATTERY .... A 2
CHIME MODULE .... A 22–23
COMPONENT CENTER .... A–B 20–23
CRUISE CONTROL MODULE .... E 28–31
DEFOG TIMER RELAY .... A 21
DIGITAL EXHAUST GAS
  RECIRC ASSY (3.1L) .... B–C 15
DIGITAL EXHAUST GAS
  RECIRC ASSY (3.4L) .... B 19
DIRECT IGNITION SYSTEM
  (DIS) (2.5L) .... D–E 11
DIRECT IGNITION SYSTEM
  (DIS) (3.1L) .... D–E 15
DIRECT IGNITION SYSTEM
  (DIS) (3.4L) .... D–E 19
ELECTRONIC CONTROL
  MODULE (ECM) (2.5L) .... A–E 8–11
ELECTRONIC CONTROL
  MODULE (ECM) (3.1L) .... A–E 12–15
ELECTRONIC CONTROL
  MODULE (ECM) (3.4L) .... A–E 16–19
FUEL INJECTORS (2.5L) .... B 11
FUEL INJECTORS (3.1L) .... C 15
FUEL INJECTORS (3.4L) .... C 19
FUEL PUMP RELAY (2.5L) .... B–C 3
FUEL PUMP RELAY (3.1L & 3.4L) ..... D 3
FUEL TANK UNIT .... D 39
FUSE BLOCK (F/B) .... A–B 24–27
FUSIBLE ELEMENTS .... A 4
GEAR SELECT SW .... B–C 39
HAZARD FLASHER .... B 22
HEADLIGHT DIMMER SW .... E 33
HEADLIGHT SW .... C–E 32–35
HEATER & A/C CONTROL ASSY ...... A–C 28–31
HI BLOWER RELAY .... D 31
HORN RELAY .... E 35
IGNITION SW .... D–E 20–23
INSTRUMENT CLUSTER .... A–E 36–39
INTERIOR LTS .... C–E 24–27
LOW BLOWER RELAY .... C 31
LS ELECTRICAL CENTER .... B–E 2–3
MULTI-FUNCTION SW .... D 29
PASSIVE RESTRAINT
  CONTROL MODULE .... D–E 44–45
POWER DOOR LOCK RELAY .... A–B 44–46
POWER SEAT SW .... A–C 40–41
POWER WINDOWS .... A–E 40–43
PRIMARY COOLING
  FAN RELAY (2.5L) .... C 4
PRIMARY COOLING FAN
  RELAY (3.1L & 3.4L) .... D 7
RS ELECTRICAL CENTER .... A–E 4–7
SECONDARY COOLING
  FAN RELAY (2.5L) .... D 4
SECONDARY COOLING FAN
  RELAY (3.1L & 3.4L) .... D 7
STARTER .... A 2
STOP LT SW .... C 35
TRUNK RELEASE SW .... E 44–45
TURN/HAZARD SW .... A–B 34–35
VAPOR CANISTER
  PURGE SOL (3.1L) .... A 14
VAPOR CANISTER
  PURGE SOL (3.4L) .... A–B 18
WIPER/WASHER MOTOR ASSY .... B–C 32–33
WIPER/WASHER SW (W/ PULSE) .... A 32–33

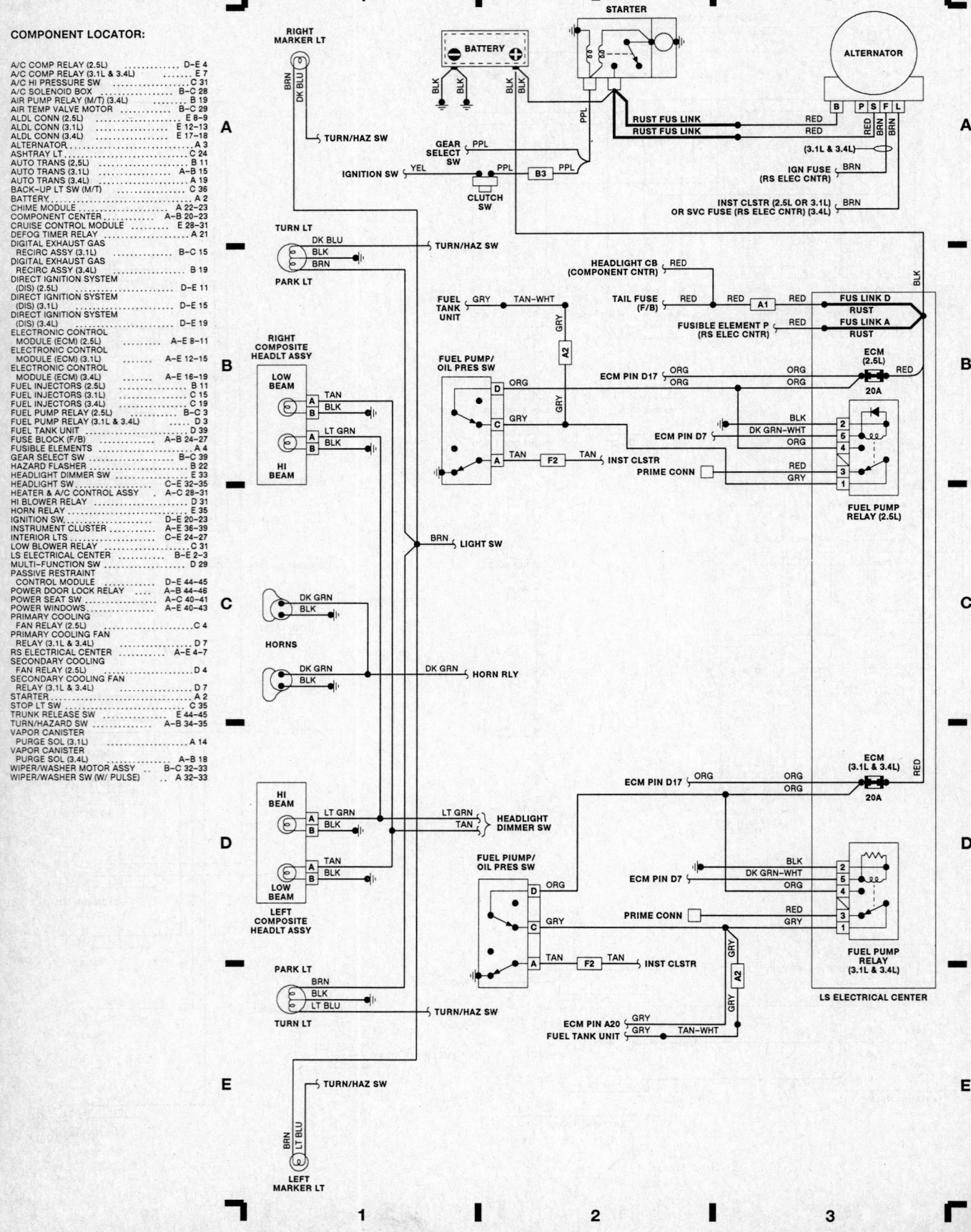

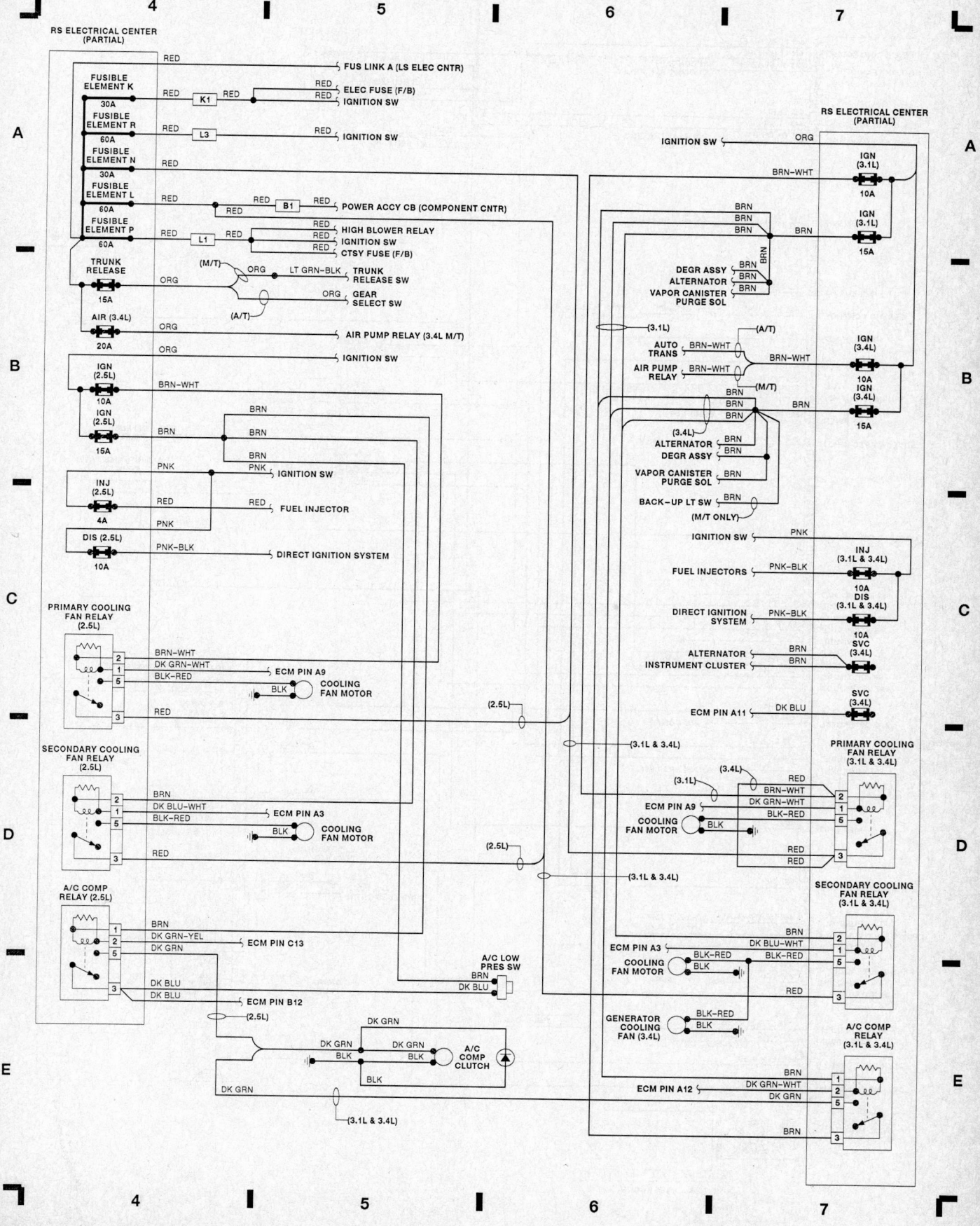

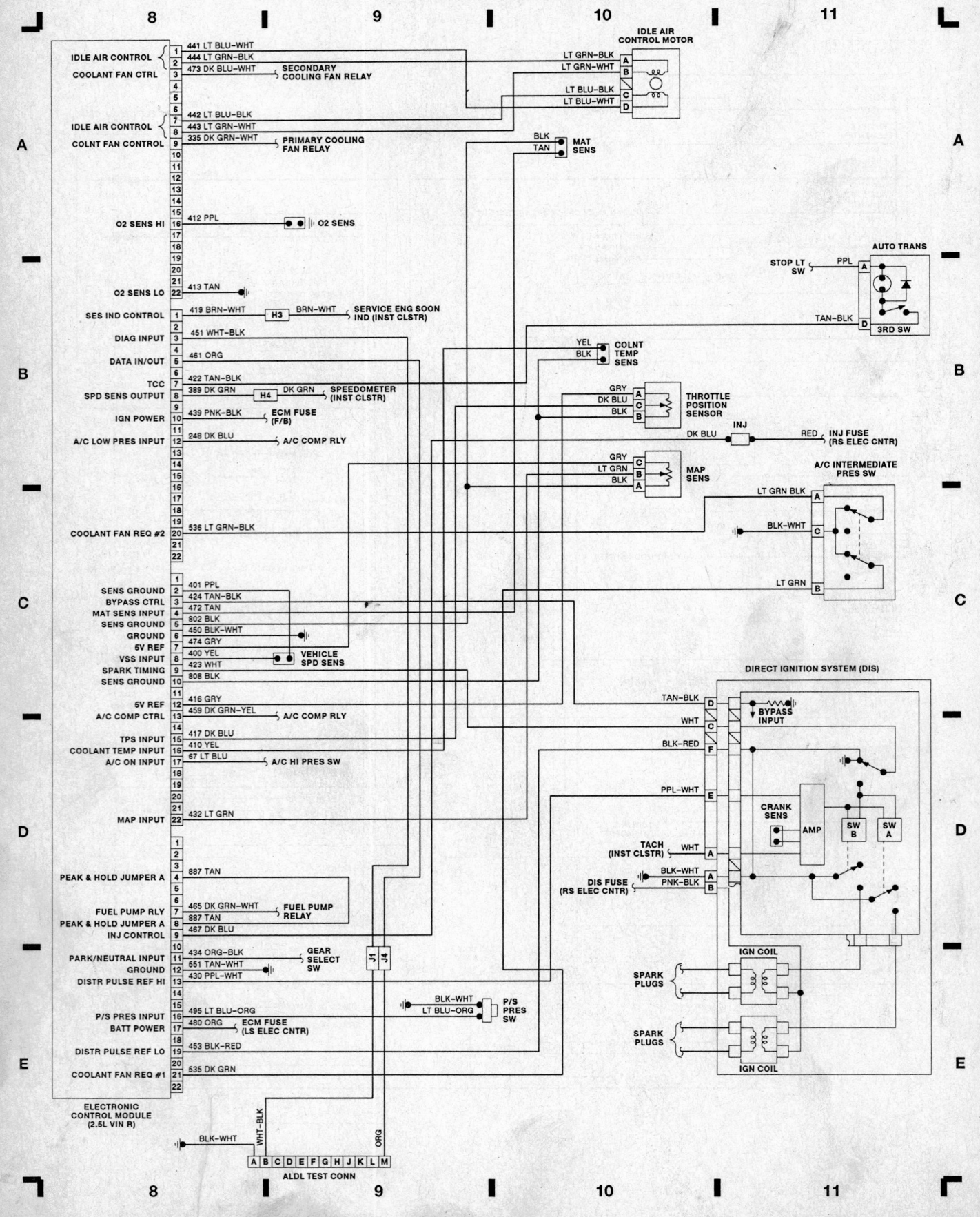

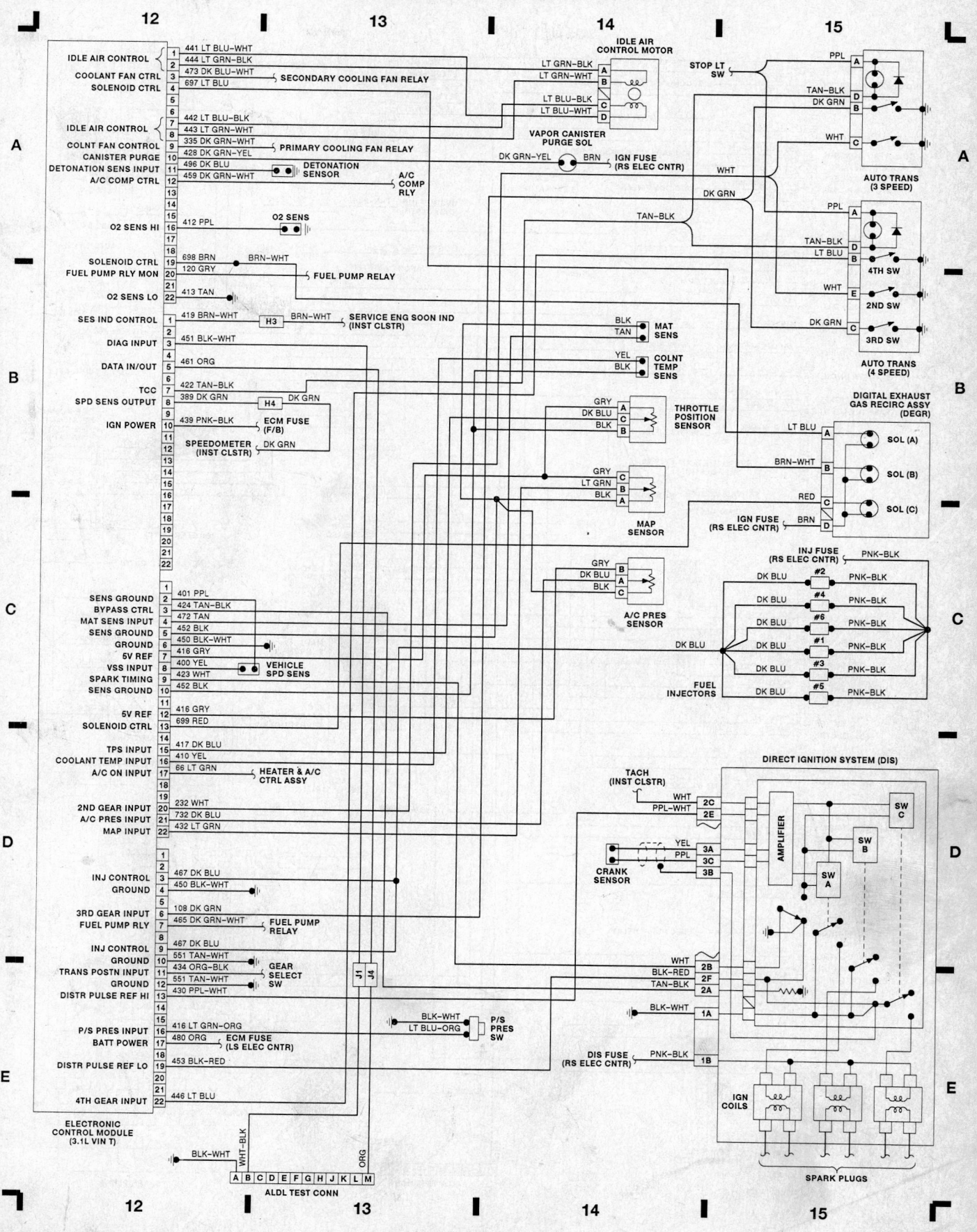

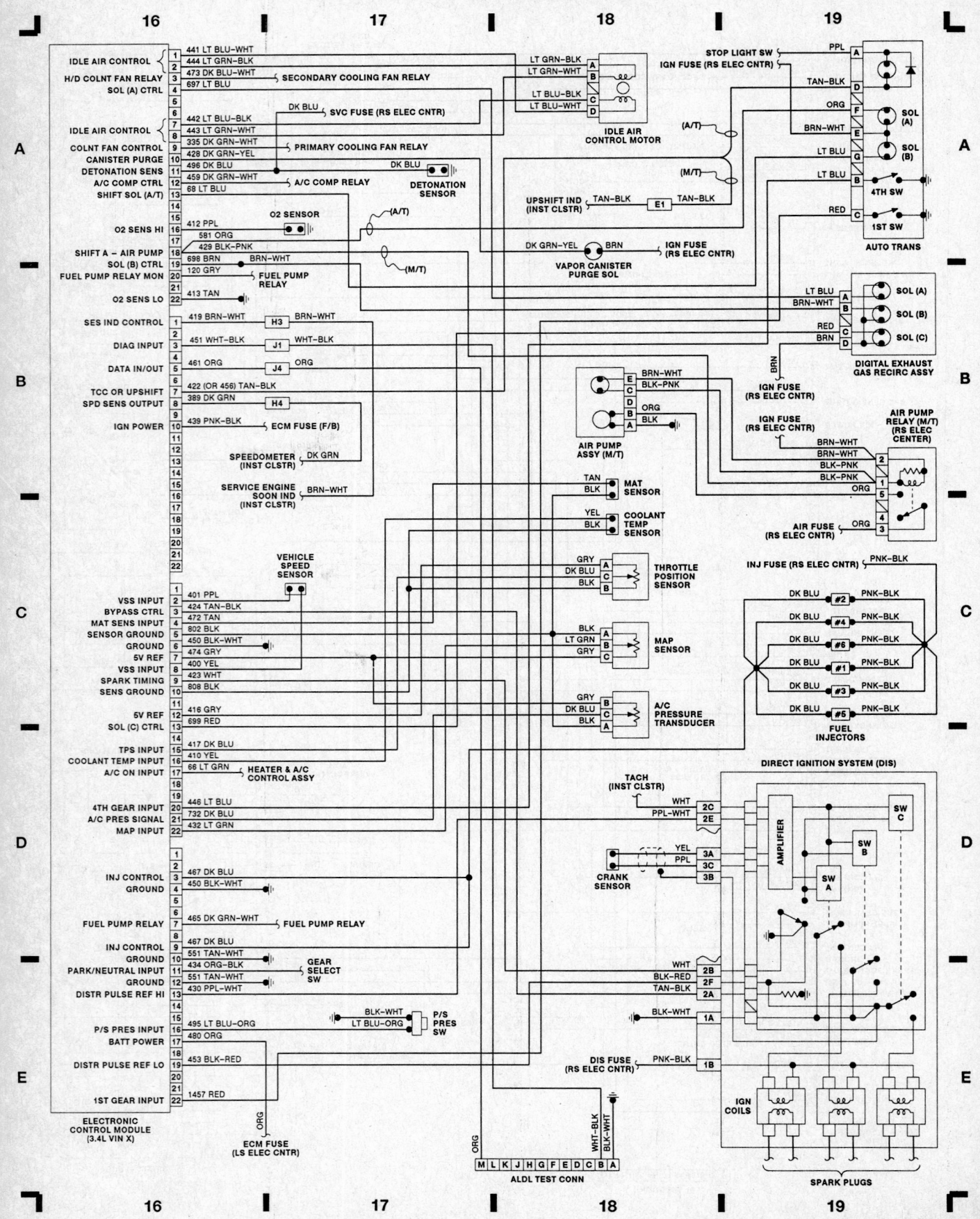

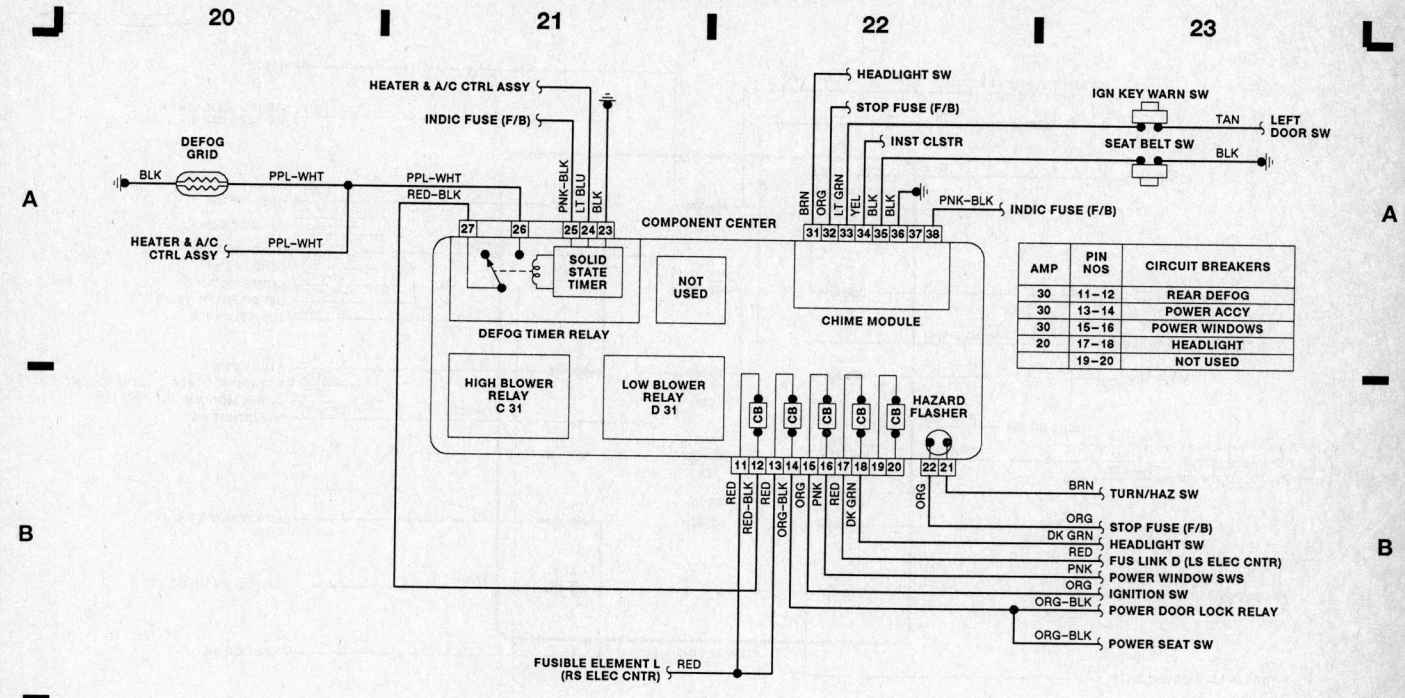

AMP	PIN NOS	CIRCUIT BREAKERS
30	11–12	REAR DEFOG
30	13–14	POWER ACCY
30	15–16	POWER WINDOWS
20	17–18	HEADLIGHT
	19–20	NOT USED

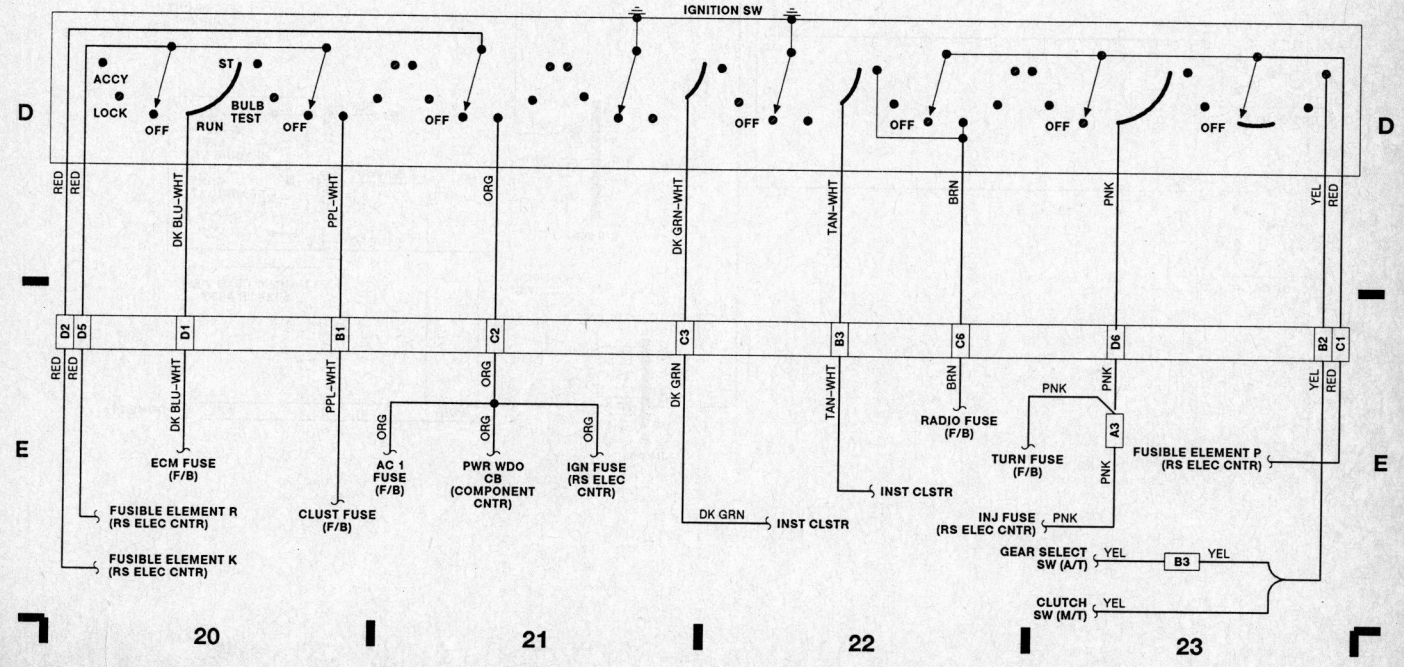

1991 WIRING DIAGRAMS
Lumina (Cont.)

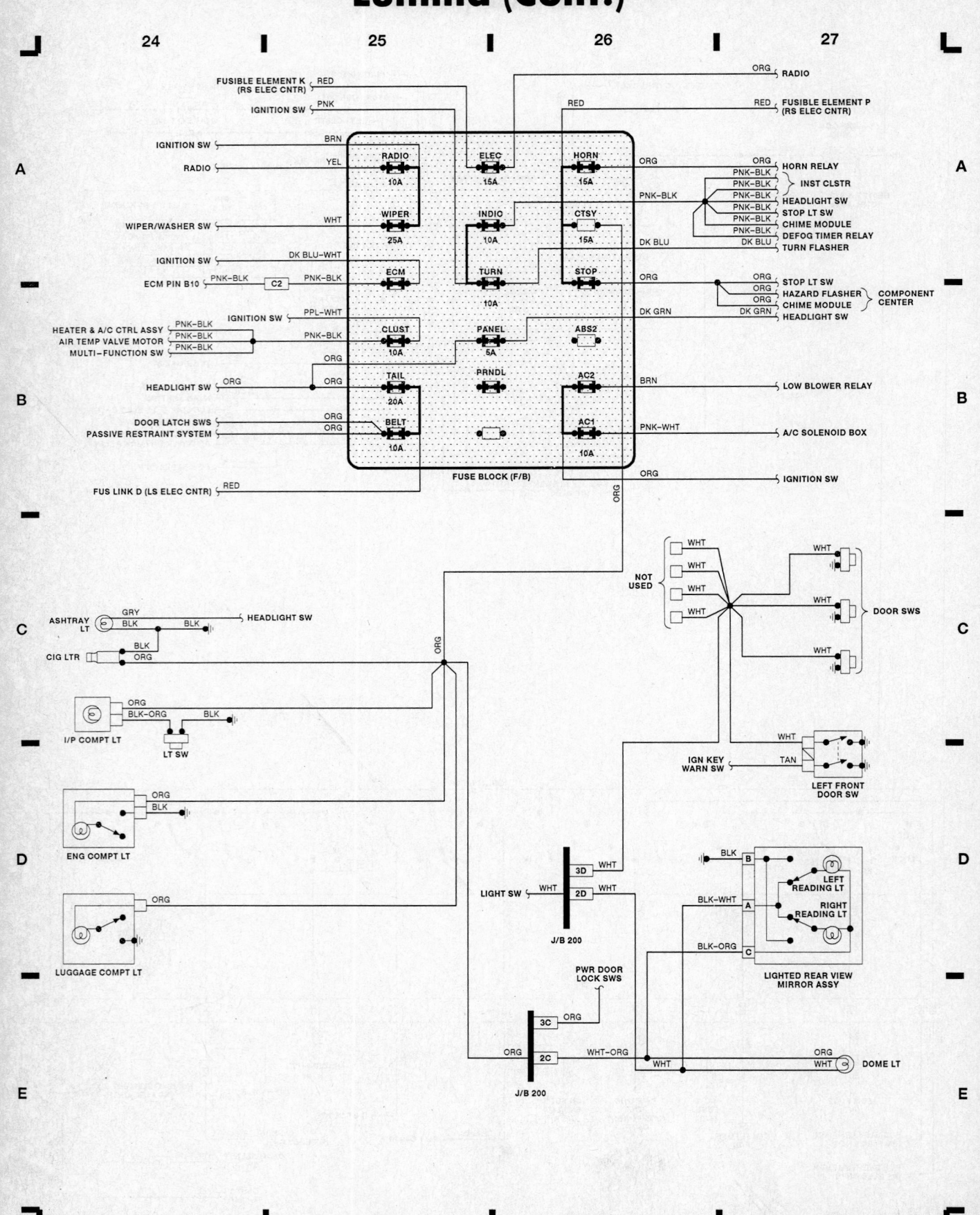

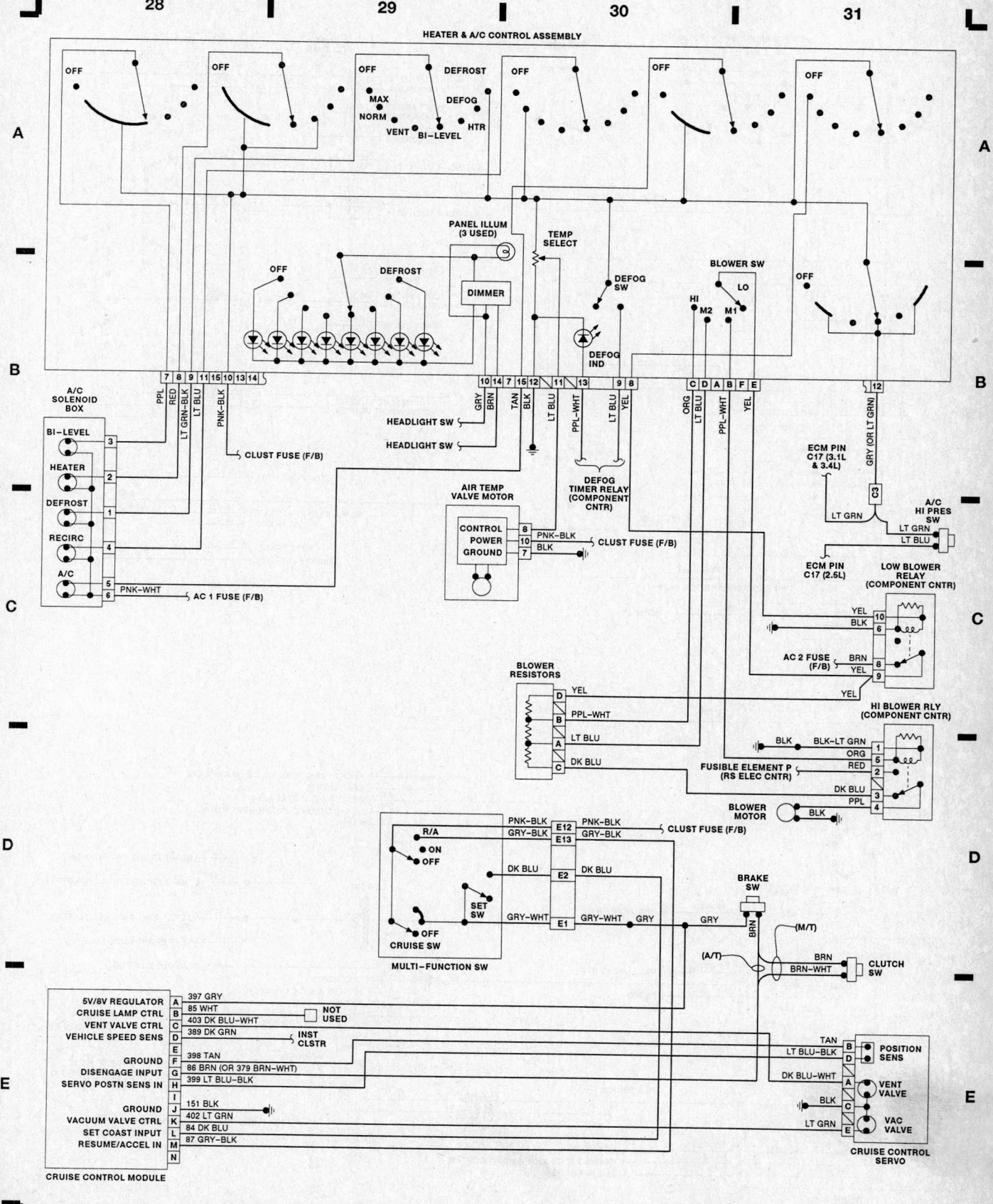

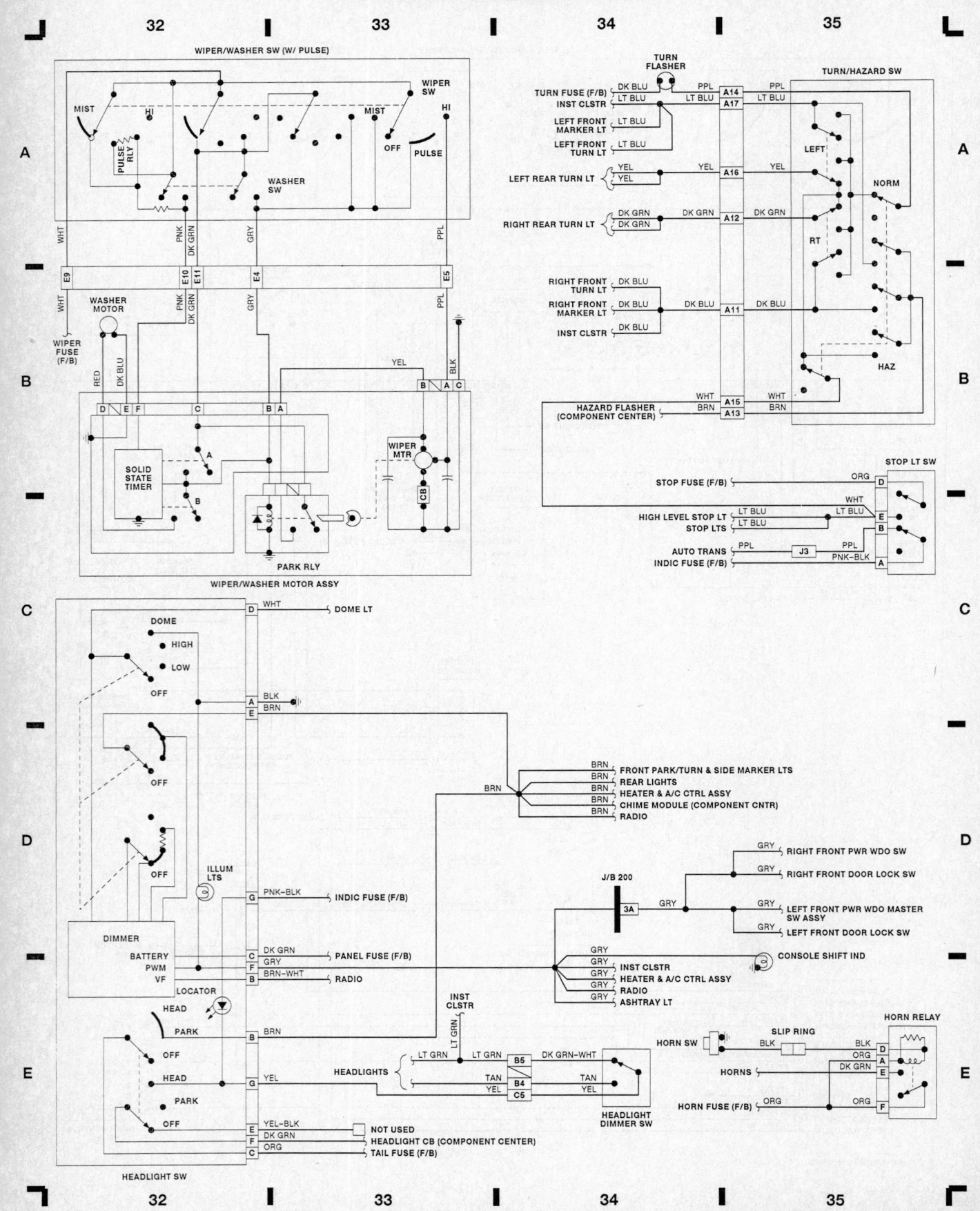

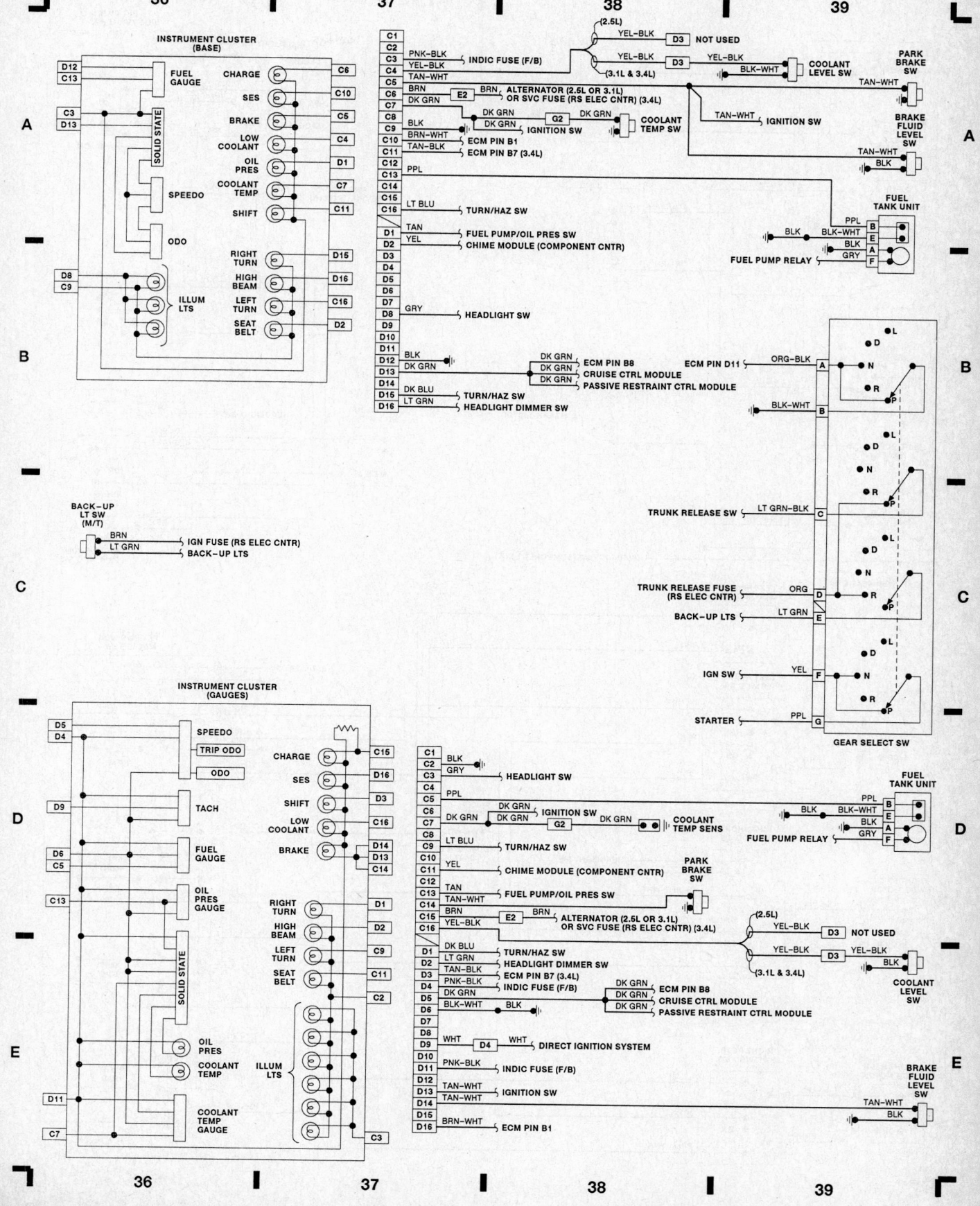

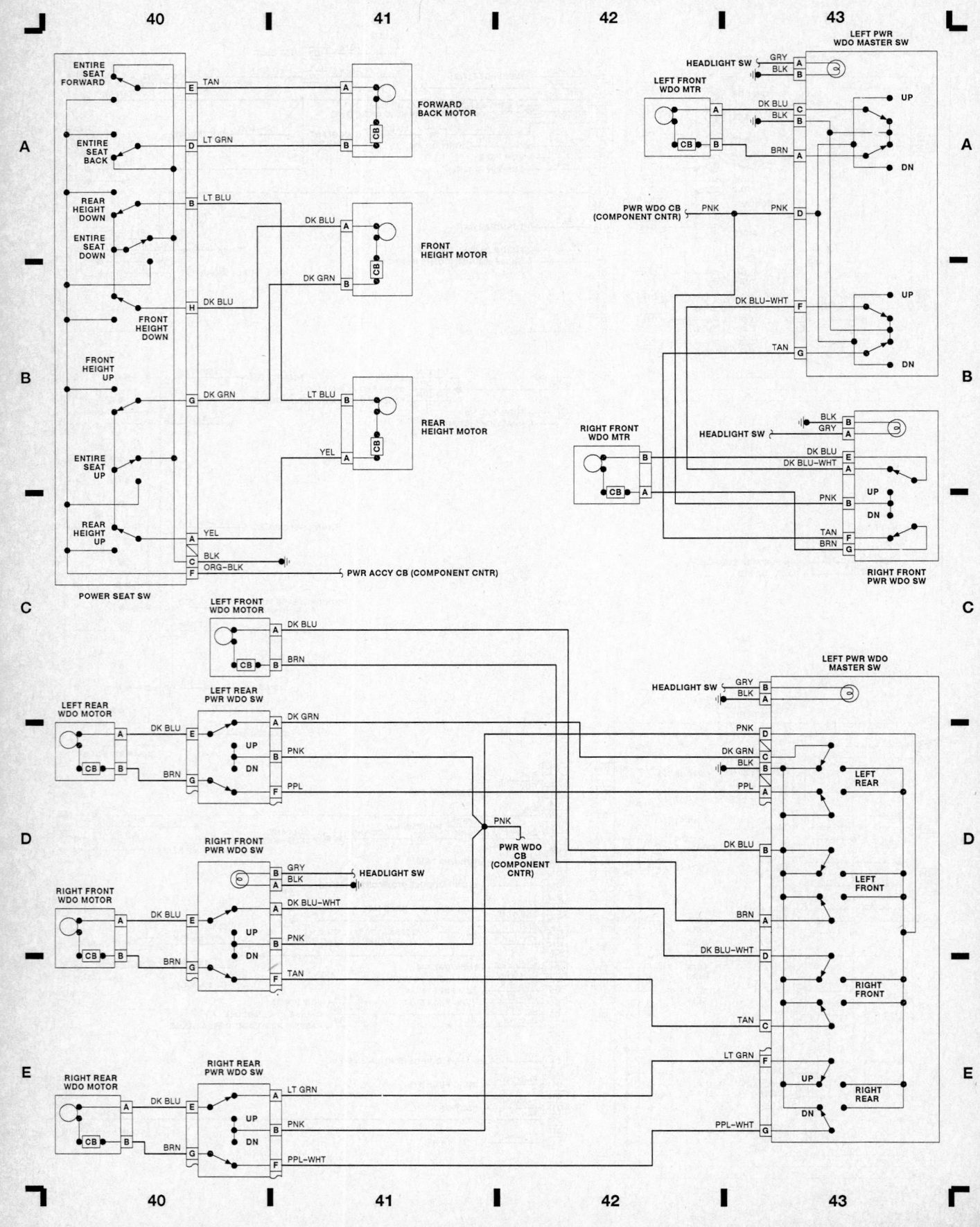

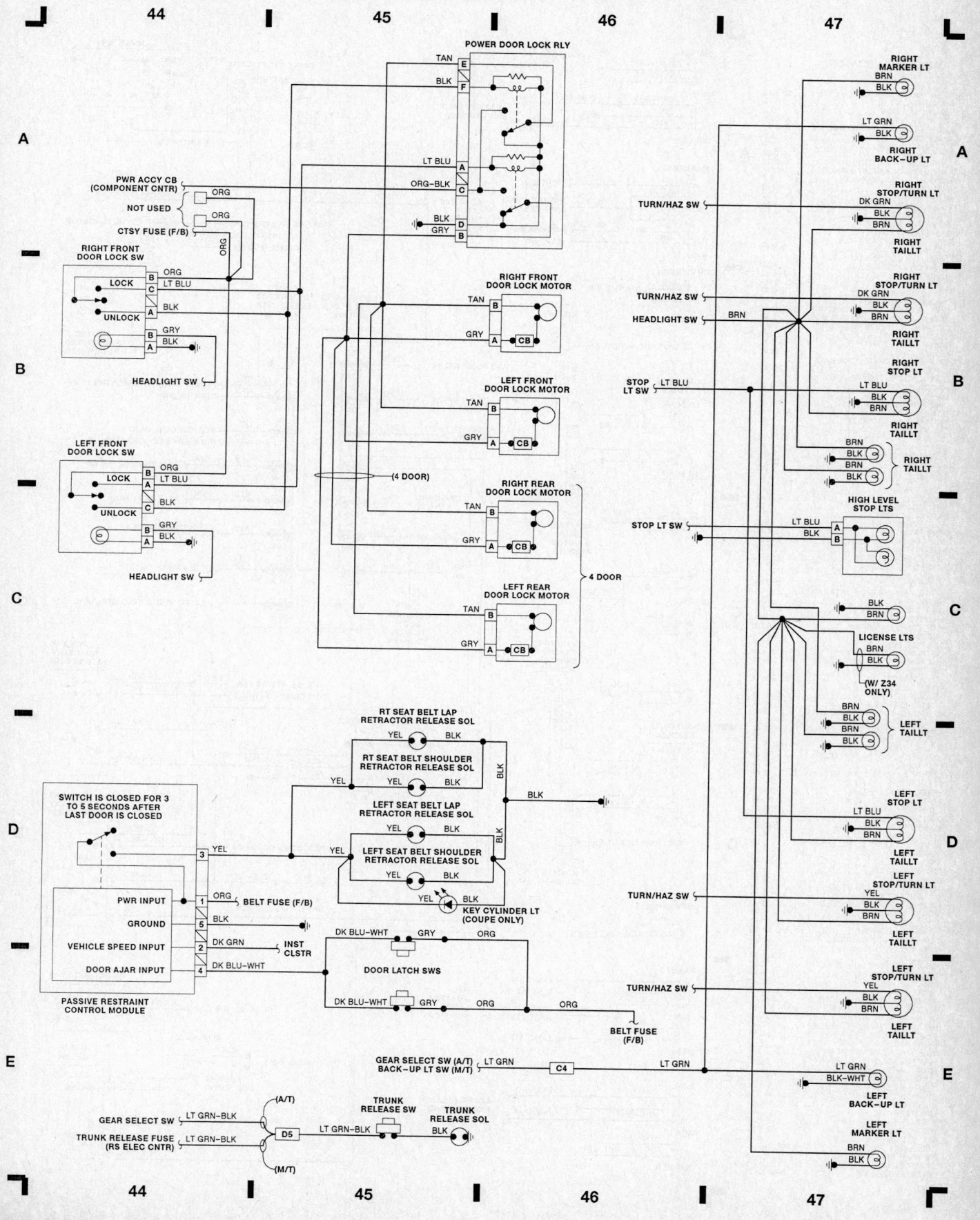

1991 WIRING DIAGRAMS
Ninety-Eight & Touring Sedan

Component Locator:

A/C & HEATER CTRL ASSY .... C-E 19
A/C COMP CTRL RLY .... B 19
A/C PRES FAN SW .... C 5
ABS PUMP RELAY .... B-C 15
ADAPTIVE LAMP MONITOR MODULE .. B-E 27
ALDL CONN .... E 5
ALTERNATOR .... E 52
ANTENNA RELAY .... E 3
ANTI-LOCK BRAKE CTRL UNIT ...... B-E 12
AUTOMATIC DAY/NIGHT MIRROR .. B-C 44
AUTOMATIC TRANSMISSION .... E 7
BATTERY .... A 2-3
BEAM SEL SW .... A 24, B 24
BLOWER CTRL UNIT .... A 19
BLOWER MOTOR .... A 19
BRAKE FLUID LEVEL SW .... A 28, E 31
CHIME MODULES .... C-E 28
COMPUTER COMMAND RIDE
   (CCR) CONTROLLER .... C-E 19
COMPUTER CONTROLLED COIL
   IGNITION (CCI) MODULE .... B-C 7
CONSOLE CIG LTRS .... D-E 44
CONSOLE SEAT SW .... A-C 48-49
CONSOLE SHIFT LT .... C 47
COOLANT FAN RELAYS .... C-D 3
COOLANT TEMP SENDER (DIGITAL) .. B 36
COOLANT TEMP SENDER (GAUGES) .. B 32
COOLANT TEMP SENDER (IND) .... B 8
COOLANT TEMP SENS .... A 6
CRUISE CTRL SERVO .... A-B 40
CRUISE CTRL SW .... A 40
CRUISE/SHIFT INTERLOCK/BRAKE
   SW .... E 22/A 40
DIAGNOSTIC ENERGY RESERVE
   MODULE (DERM) .... A-B 20
DIR FLASHER .... D 21
DIRECTIONAL/HAZARD SW .... D-E 20
DOOR HANDLE SWS .... C 41-42
DOOR LOCK RELAY ASSY .... A 41-42
DRIVERS INFORMATION
   CENTER (DIC) .... B-D 30-31
DUAL SENSOR .... A 23
ELC HEIGHT SENSOR .... D-E 8
ELC RELAY .... D-E 9
ENG COMPT LT .... E 3
FOG LT RELAY .... D 25
FOG LT SW .... D 24
FRONT CIG LTR .... D 44
FUEL DOOR RELEASE SW .... D 43
FUEL INJECTORS .... D 7
FUEL PUMP RELAY .... A 7
FUEL TANK UNIT .... B 28
GEAR SELECT SW .... B-E 23
HAZARD FLASHER .... E 21
HEATED SEAT MODULE .... D-E 51
HEATED SEAT SW .... E 51
HEATED WINDSHIELD
   CONTROL MODULE .... D-E 11
HEATED WINDSHIELD POWER MODULE .. E 9-10
HORN RELAY .... E 3
HVAC PROGRAMMER .... A-B 16
I/P COMPT LT .... D 44
IGNITION KEY WARN SW .... A-B 11
IGNITION SW .... A-B 11
INFLATOR MODULE .... A 23
INSTRUMENT CLUSTER (DIGITAL) .. A-E 38-39
INSTRUMENT CLUSTER (GAUGES) .. A-E 34-35
INSTRUMENT CLUSTER
   (INDICATORS) .... A-B 30-31
INSTRUMENT PANEL FUSE
   BLOCK (I/P F/B) .... B-C 9-10
INTERIOR LTS RELAY .... E 44
KEY RESISTOR SENSING TERMINAL .. E 42
LEFT FOOTWELL COURTESY LT .. D-E 47
LEFT FRONT DOOR COURTESY LT .. E 47
LEFT FRONT DOOR
   ISOLATION RELAY .... C 43
LEFT FRONT DOOR LOCK ASSY .. B 43
LEFT MIRROR .... A 46
LEFT REAR DOOR COURTESY LT .. E 47
LEFT UNDERHOOD FUSE
   BLOCK (LEFT U/H F/B) .... B-C 2
LEFT VANITY MIRROR .... E 45-46
LIGHT CTRL MODULE .... A-B 27
LIGHT SW .... A-B 24
LIGHT SW LT .... B-C 47
LOW COOLANT MODULE .... E 31
LUGGAGE COMPT LID RELEASE SW .. D 43
LUGGAGE COMPT LT .... D 44
MAIN RELAY .... C 15
OIL LEVEL MODULE .... E 28
OIL PRES SENS/SW .... A-B 28
PANEL/INTERIOR LTS CTRL ..... E 24
PARK BRAKE SW .... A 28, E 31
PASS KEY DECODER MODULE .. E 43
POWER MIRROR SW .... A-B 47
POWER SEAT SW .... A-B 52-53
POWER WINDOW SW .... B-D 52-53
POWERTRAIN CTRL MODULE (PCM) .. A-E 4
PRES CYCLING SW .... B 19
PULL DOWN UNIT .... A-B 44
REAR CONSOLE COURTESY LT .. C 47
REAR DEFOGGER RELAY .... E 48
RECLINER SW .... D 52
RELAY CENTER .... A-B 12-15
REMOTE ACCY CTRL MODULE .. B-C 40
REMOTE DIMMER MODULE ..... D-E 24
RETAINED ACCY POWER RLY #1 .. D 40
RETAINED ACCY POWER RLY #2 .. D 40
RIGHT FOOTWELL COURTESY LT .. C 47
RIGHT FRONT DOOR LOCK ASSY .. A 43
RIGHT FRONT DOOR WARN LT .. C 47
RIGHT REAR DOOR COURTESY LT .. D 47
RIGHT UNDERHOOD FUSE
   BLOCK (RIGHT U/H F/B) .... B-C 2
SEAT BELT SW .... B 28
SEAT CTRL MODULE .... A-B 51
SIR COIL ASSY .... B-C 16
STARTER .... A 3
STARTER ENABLE RELAY .... E 40
STEERING WHEEL CTRLS ..... C-E 16
SUNROOF CTRL MODULE .... A 44
TCC BRAKE SW .... E 6-7/D-E 14
TWILIGHT SENTINEL CTRL ..... C 24
VAPOR CANISTER PURGE SOL .. D 5
WIPER/WASHER SW .... B-D 20-21

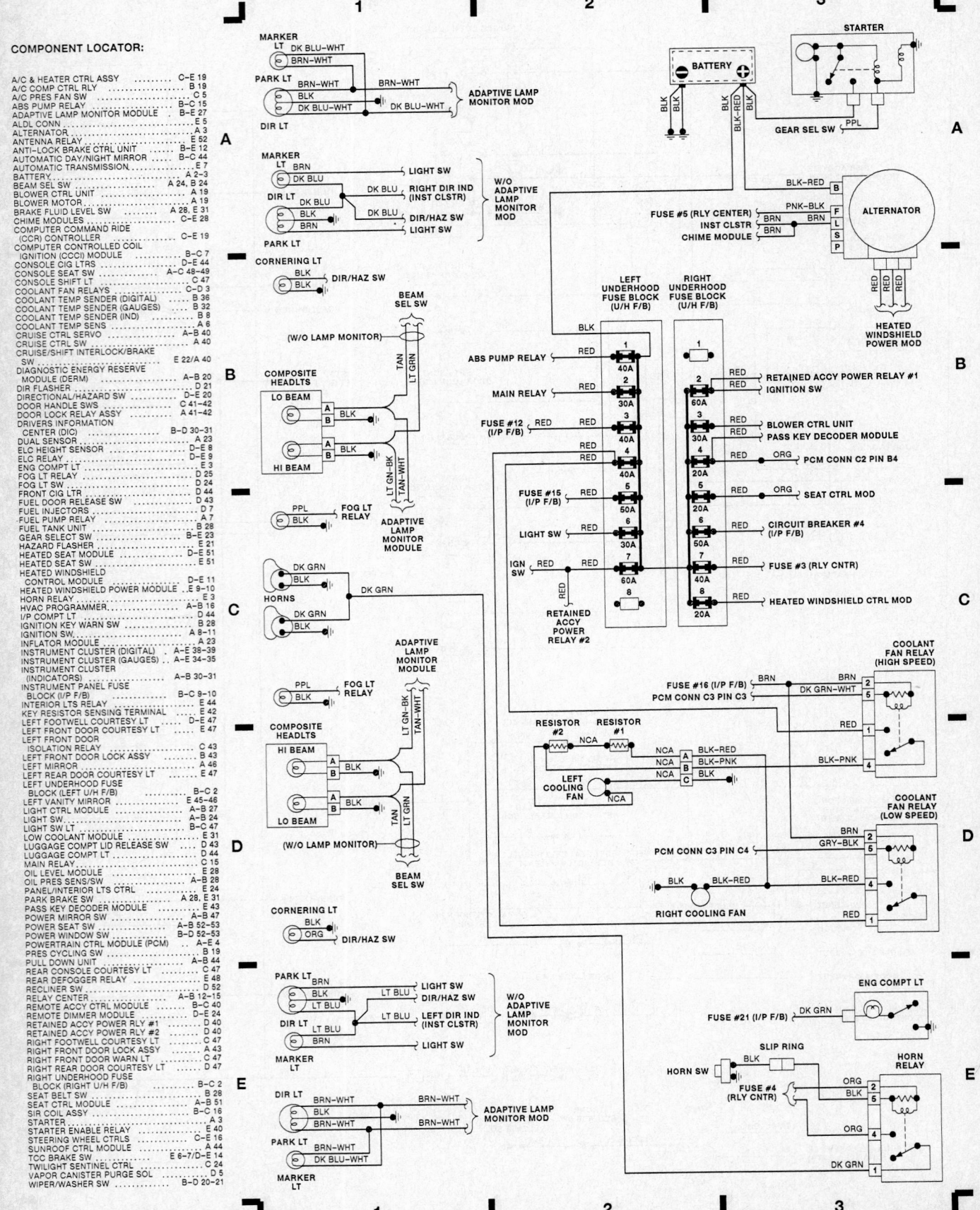

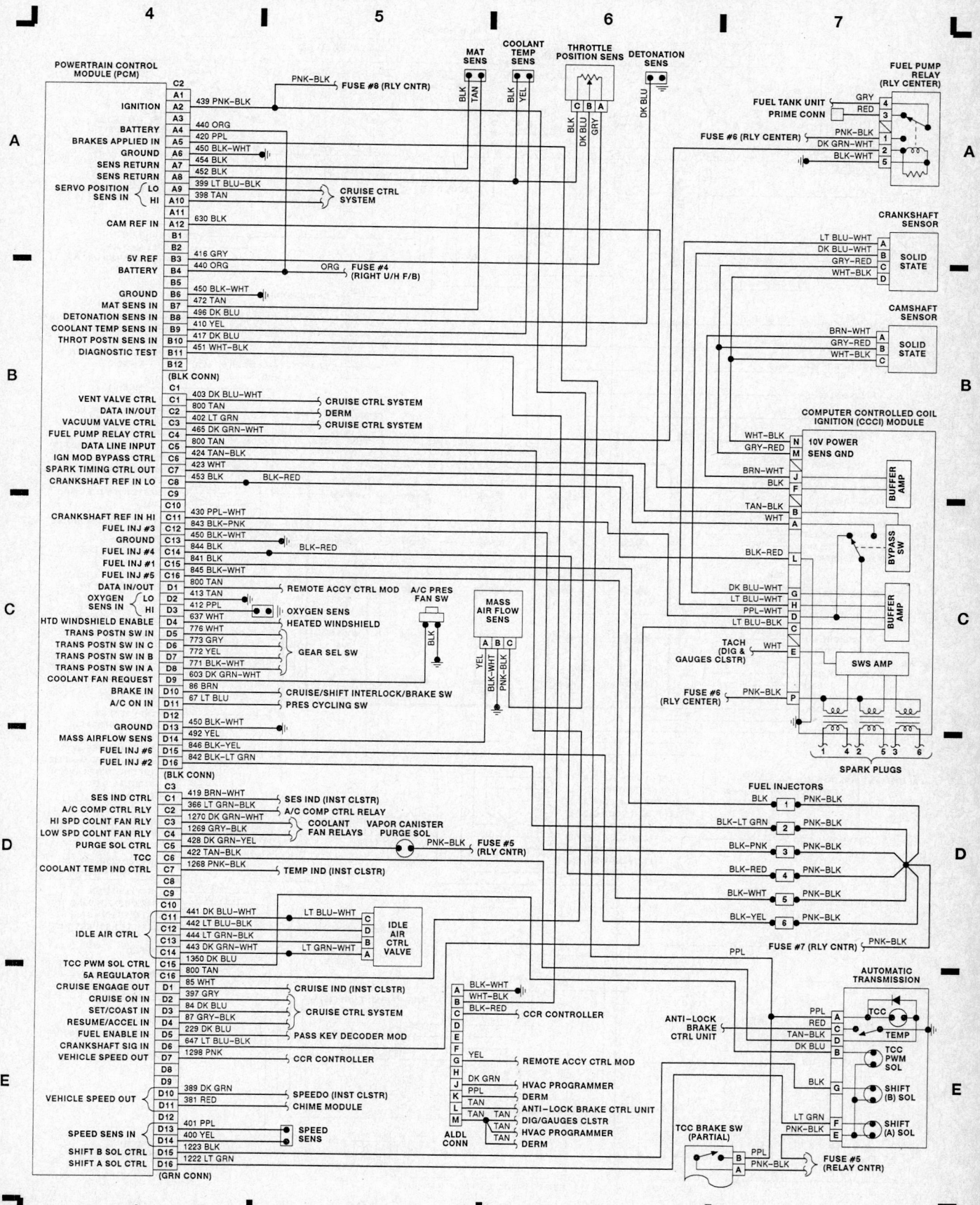

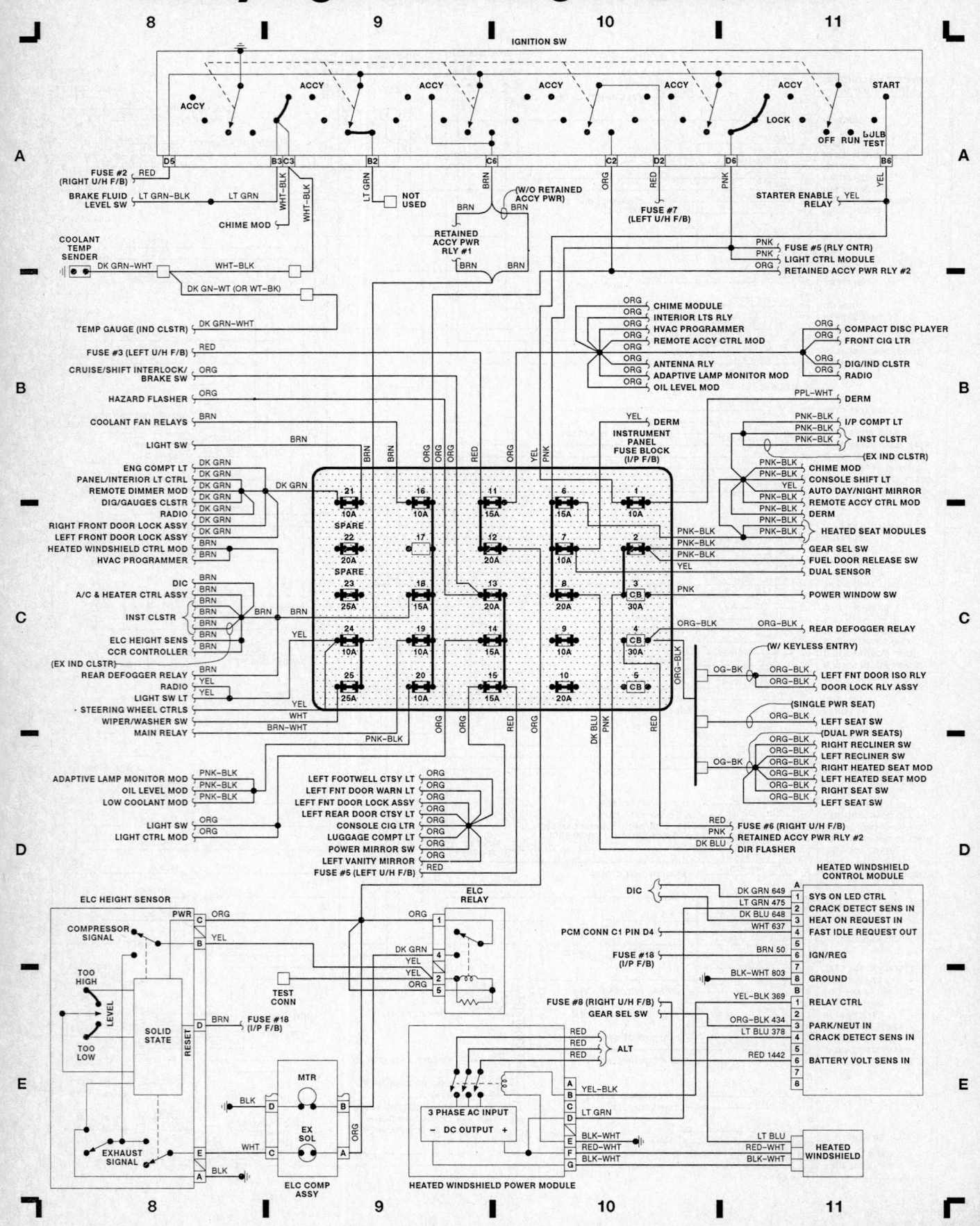

12   13   14   15

RED — FUSE #7 (RIGHT U/H F/B)
ORG — HVAC PROGRAMMER
PNK-WHT — LEFT MIRROR
PPL-WHT — REAR DEFOGGER RELAY

IGNITION SW — PNK

A

5 15A
6 20A
7 10A
8 10A

1 10A
2 10A
3 15A
4 25A

FUEL PUMP RLY — PNK-BLK
FUEL INJECTORS — PNK-BLK

(E) RETAINED ACCY PWR RELAY #1 (D 40)
(D) LUGGAGE COMPT LID RELEASE RELAY (C-D 43)
(C) FOG LT RELAY (D 25)
(B) LEFT FNT DOOR ISOLATION RELAY (C 43)
(A) NOT USED

RIGHT FNT DOOR WARN LT — ORG
RIGHT FNT DOOR LOCK ASSY — ORG
RIGHT FOOTWELL CTSY LT — ORG
RIGHT REAR DOOR CTSY LT — ORG
CONSOLE SEAT SW — ORG

(F) INTERIOR LTS RELAY (E 44)
(K) ELC RELAY (D-E 9)
(H) FUEL PUMP RELAY (A 7)
(J) RETAINED ACCY PWR RELAY #2 (D 40)
(K) NOT USED

B

REAR CONSOLE CTSY LT — ORG
CONSOLE CIG LTR — ORG

(TOURING SEDAN)

PPL — BLOWER CTRL UNIT
ORG — FOG LT RELAY   RELAY CENTER
ORG — HORN RELAY
ORG — PULL DOWN UNIT
ORG — LUGGAGE COMPT LID RELEASE RLY
PNK-BLK

ORG

PNK-BLK — PASS KEY DECODER MOD
PNK-BLK — STARTER ENABLE RLY
PNK-BLK — PCM CONN C2 PIN A2

PNK-BLK — PNK-BLK — OIL PRES SENS/SW
PNK-BLK — PNK-BLK — CCCI MOD

PNK-BLK — CRUISE CTRL SW
PNK-BLK — ALTERNATOR
PNK-BLK — TCC BRAKE SW
PNK-BLK — AUTO TRANS
PNK-BLK — VAPOR CANISTER PURGE SOL
PNK-BLK — A/C COMP CTRL RLY

ANTI-LOCK BRAKE CTRL UNIT

ABS PUMP RELAY

GROUND 1 — 803 BLK-WHT
L FNT SOL CTRL OUT 2 — 862 LT BLU-BLK
IGNITION 3 — 1077 TAN
4
PUMP ON REQUEST 5 — 848 TAN
6
TRACTION ENGAGE OUT 7 — 1656 LT GRN — GAUGES CLSTR
FLUID LEVEL IN 8 — 849 PNK
9
10
11
HI PRES IN 12
13 — 1659 LT BLU
14
PUMP MTR CTRL 15 — 854 PNK-BLK
16
17
R REAR SOL CTRL OUT 18 — 863 DK BLU-WHT
GROUND 19 — 803 BLK-WHT
L FNT SOL CTRL IN 20 — 858 DK GRN-YEL
R FNT SOL CTRL OUT 21 — 861 BRN-WHT
22
23
24
TRACTION CTRL ON IN 25 — 1571 BRN-WHT
RETURN GROUND 26 — 853 LT BLU-BLK
WHEEL SPIN IN 27 — 883 WHT
WHEEL SPIN IN 28 — 885 WHT
WHEEL SPIN IN 29 — 883 TAN
WHEEL SPIN IN 30 — 873 YEL
PUMP MTR SENS IN (LO) 31 — 1293 BLK
BRAKES APPLIED IN 32 — 20 LT BLU
IGNITION 33 — 1077 TAN
MAIN RELAY CTRL 34 — 855 DK BLU
35
L REAR SOL CTRL OUT 36 — 1291 WHT
LEFT ISOLATION SOL 37 — 1657 ORG
R FNT SOL CTRL IN 38 — 857 PNK-BLK
39
RIGHT ISOLATION SOL 40 — 1658 PPL
41
DATA LINE IN 42 — 800 TAN
TRANS TEMP IN 43 — 1660 RED
TRACTION CTRL IND 44 — PPL-WHT
WHEEL SPIN IN 45 — 882 BLK
WHEEL SPIN IN 46 — 884 BLK
WHEEL SPIN IN 47 — 872 DK GRN
WHEEL SPIN IN 48 — 830 LT BLU
PUMP MTR SENS IN (HI) 49 — 1292 LT GN-BK
50
51
ABS IND CTRL 52 — 852 WHT
ENABLE 53 — 650 BRN-WHT
L REAR SOL CTRL IN 54 — 1290 DK BLU
R REAR SOL CTRL IN 55 — 859 GRY

CRUISE/ SHIFT INTERLOCK/ BRAKE SW

ABS IND (INST CLSTR) — WHT / WHT — ABS DIODE

TAN
TAN
TAN
TAN

RED-WHT
4
3
2
1
FUSE #1 (LEFT U/H F/B) — RED
BRN-WHT
PNK-BLK
5

MAIN RELAY
TAN — 3
BLK
FUSE #2 (LEFT U/H F/B) — RED — 4
DK BLU — 2
FUSE #19 (I/P F/B) — BRN-WHT — BRN-WHT — 5

TRACTION CTRL SW — BLK

PRESSURE MODULATOR VALVE ASSY

ORG 1
PPL 2
DK GRN-YEL 3
LT BLU-BLK 4
BLK-PNK 5
BRN-WHT 6
GRY 7
DK BLU-WHT 8
DK BLU 9
WHT 10
LT BLU 11
LT BLU-BLK 12
TAN 13
TAN 14

RIGHT   LEFT

ISOLATION SOL

PRES SW

LEFT FNT SOL IN
LEFT FNT SOL OUT
RIGHT FNT SOL IN
RIGHT FNT SOL OUT
RIGHT REAR SOL IN
RIGHT REAR SOL OUT
LEFT REAR SOL IN
LEFT REAR SOL OUT

DATA LINE IN — ALDL CONN PIN L
AUTO TRANS

TCC BRAKE SW (PARTIAL)
LT BLU-BLK — D
TAN — C

RED-WHT — A
BLK-LT GRN — B
C
BLK — D
BLK — E
F

PUMP MTR RUN SENS

PUMP MTR

PNK — A
LT BLU-BLK — B

FLUID LEVEL SW

LEFT FNT SENS   RIGHT FNT SENS   LEFT REAR SENS   RIGHT REAR SENS

GAUGES CLSTR

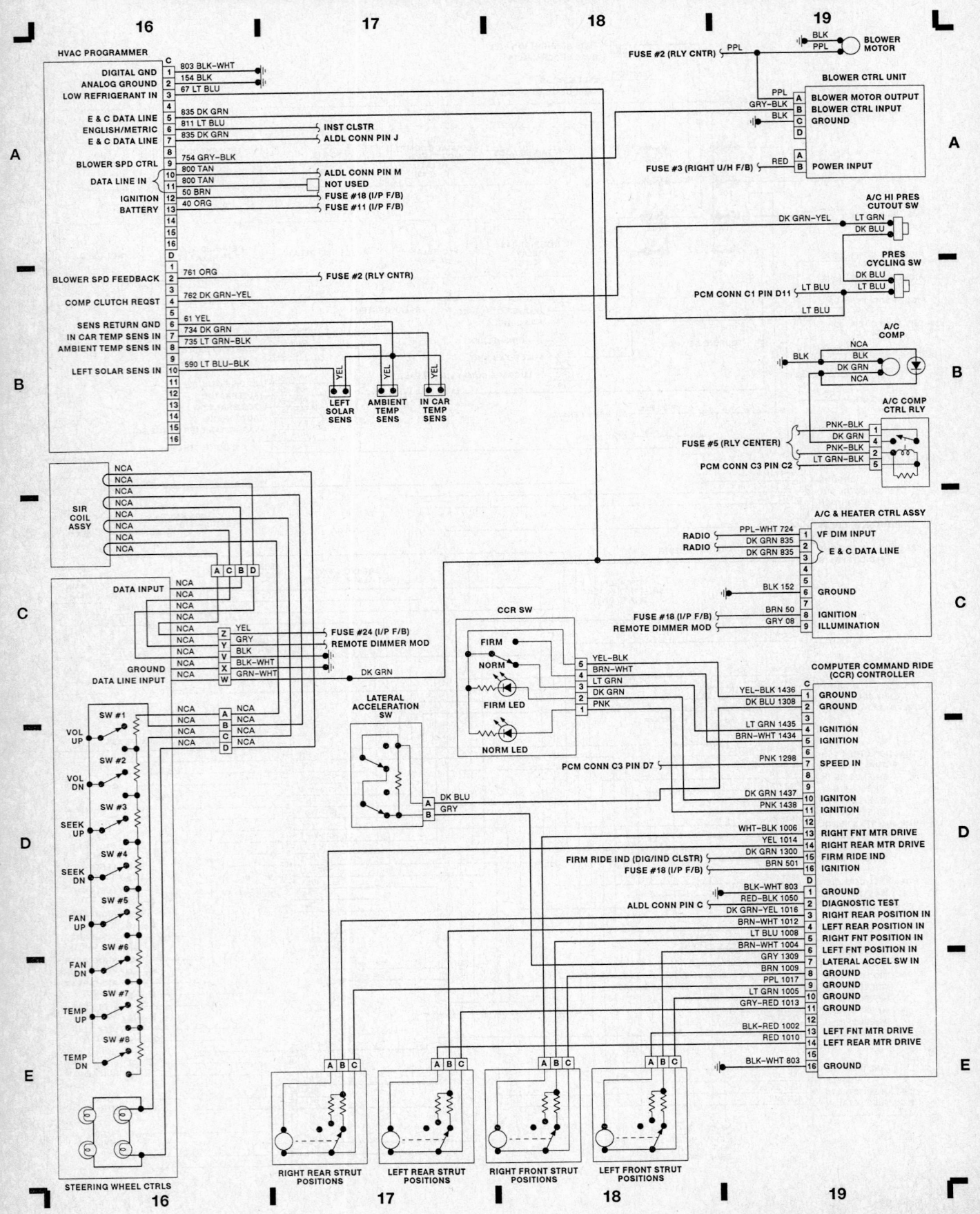

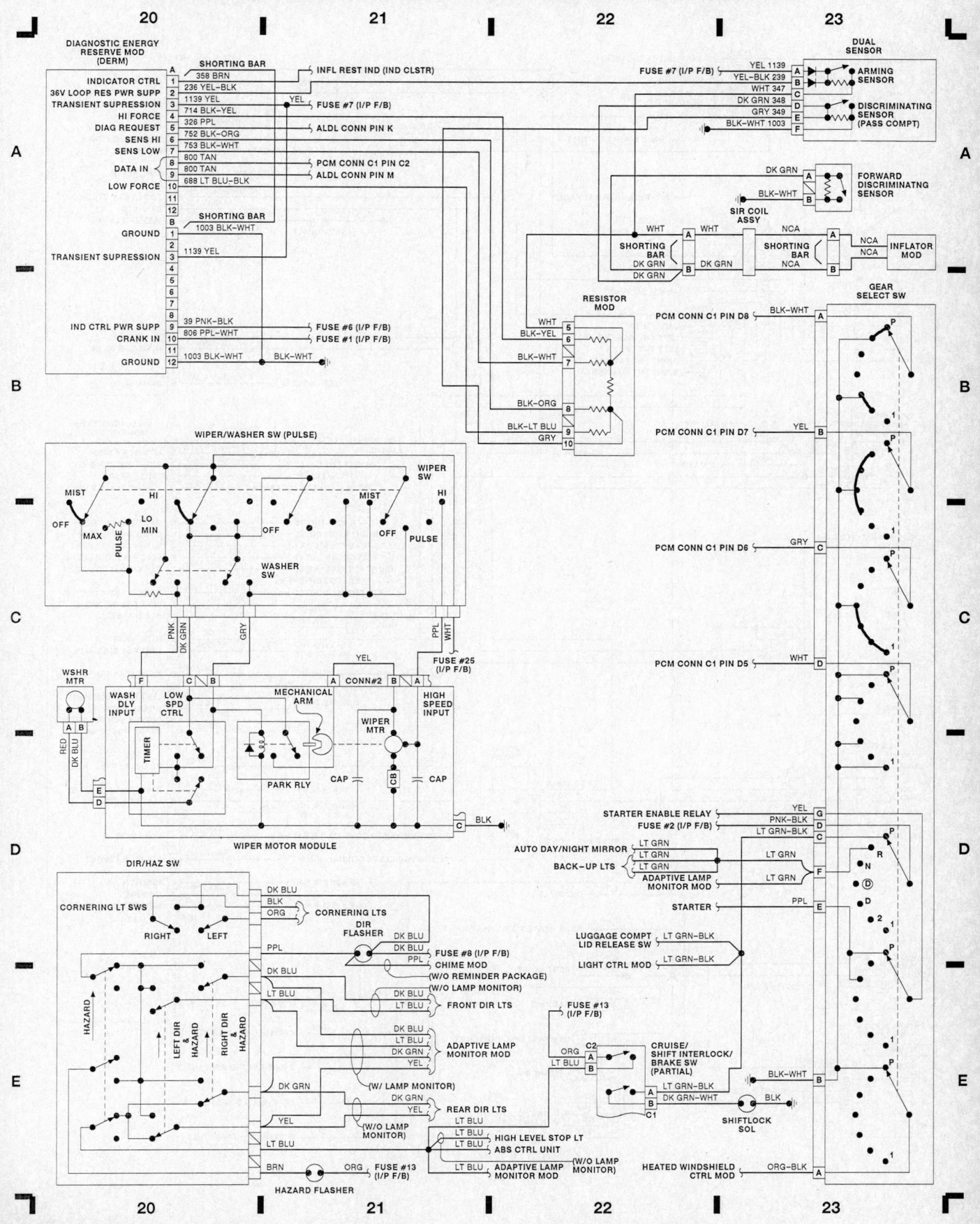

1991 WIRING DIAGRAMS
Ninety-Eight & Touring Sedan (Cont.)

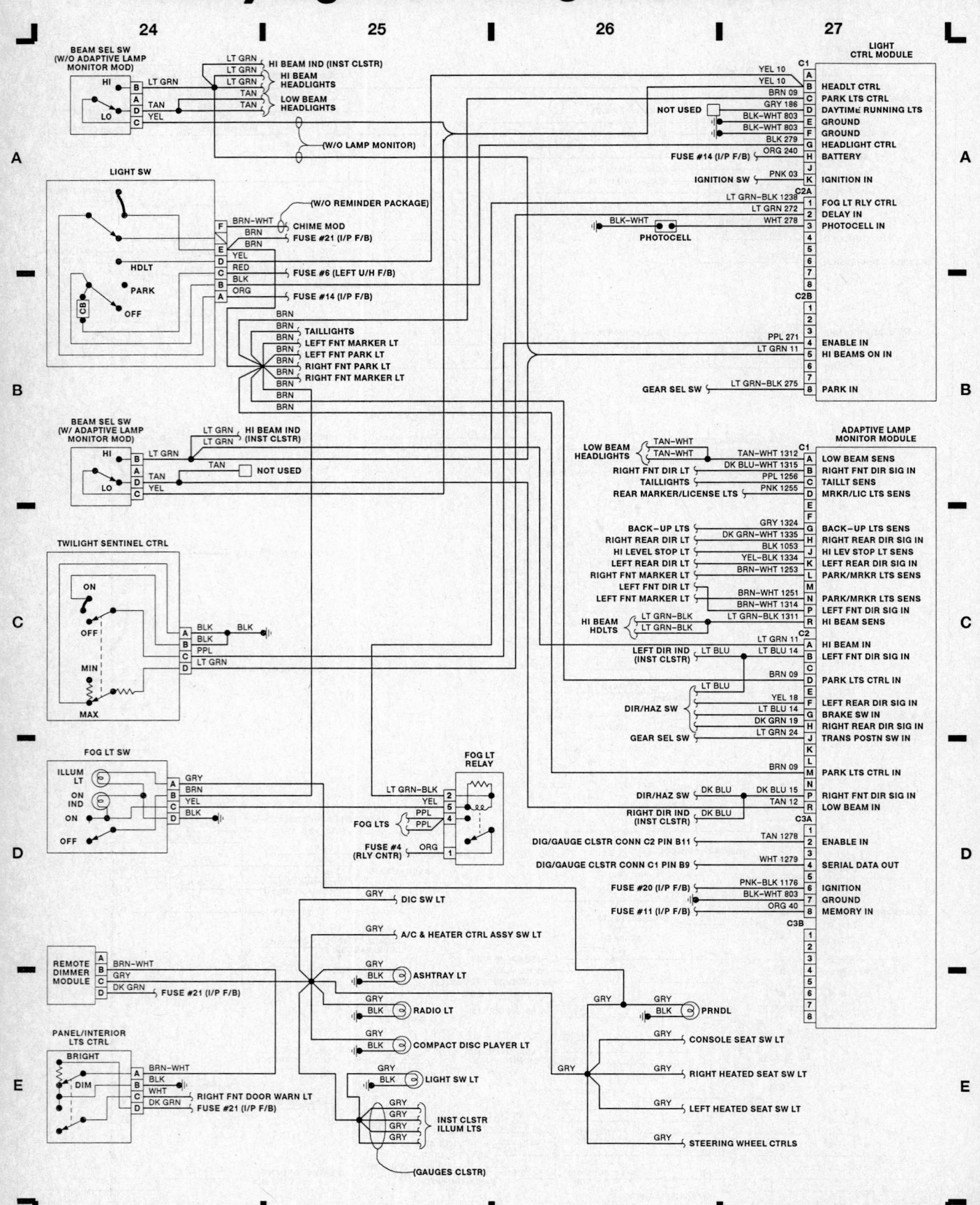

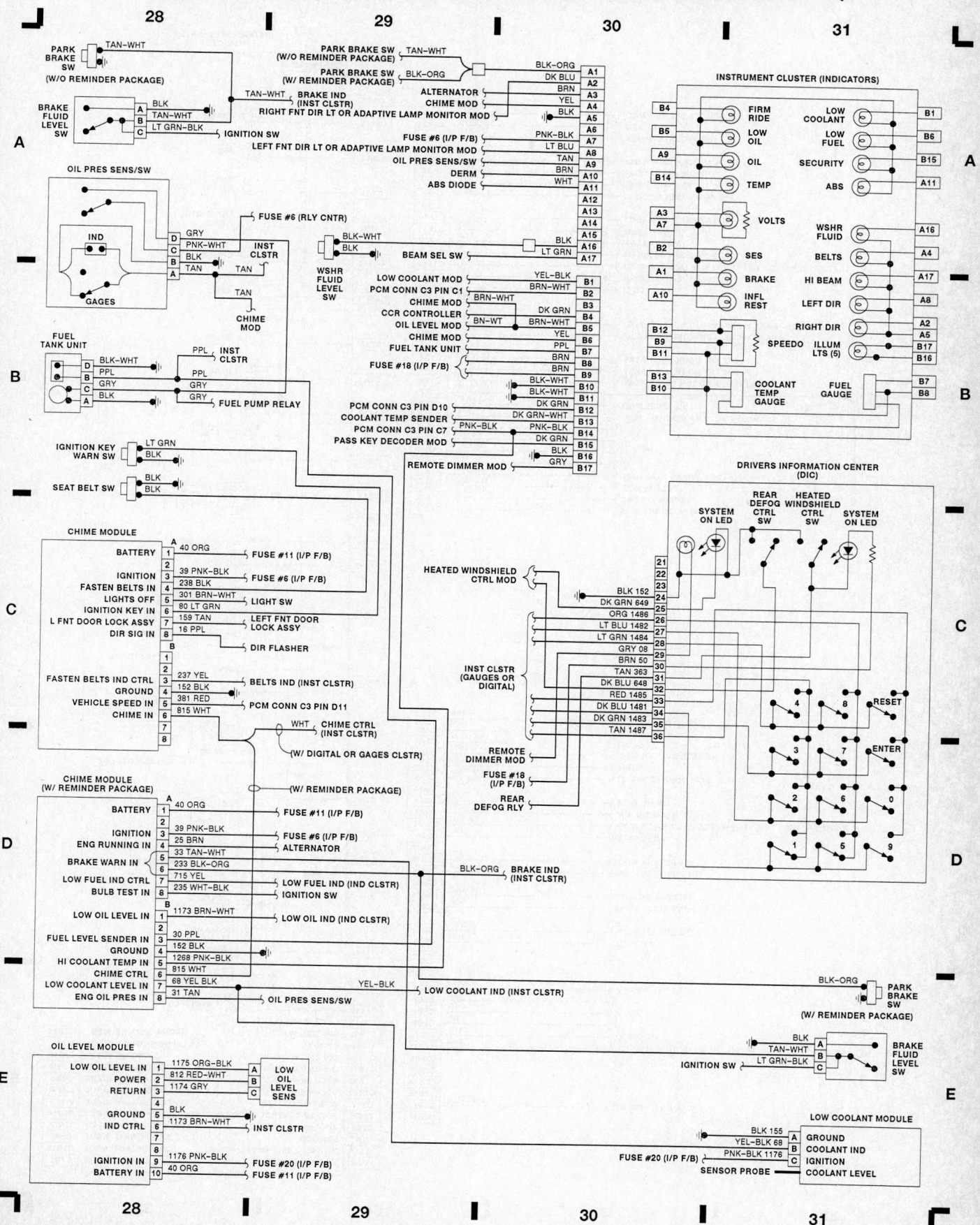

32   33   34   35

INSTRUMENT CLUSTER (GAUGES)

Source	Wire Color	Pin
REMOTE DIMMER MOD	GRY	C1A1
NOT USED	BLK-WHT	C1A2
HVAC PROGRAMMER	LT BLU	C1A3
		C1A4
PCM CONN C3 PIN D10	DK GRN	C1A5
FUSE #21 (I/P F/B)	DK GRN	C1A6
FUSE #18 (I/P F/B)	BRN	C1A7
REMOTE DIMMER MODULE	GRY	C1A8
		C1A9
ANTI-LOCK BRAKE CTRL UNIT	PPL-WHT	C1A10
NOT USED	DK GRN	C1A11
ALTERNATOR	BRN	C1A12
PCM CONN C3 PIN D1	WHT	C1A13
LEFT FNT DIR LT OR ADAPTIVE LAMP MONITOR MOD	LT BLU	C1A14
COOLANT TEMP SENDER	YEL	C1A15
CCCI	WHT	C1A16
	BLK	C1A17

Source	Wire Color	Pin
PARK BRAKE SW (W/O REMINDER PACKAGE)	TAN-WHT	C1B1
PARK BRAKE SW (W/ REMINDER PACKAGE)	BLK-ORG	C1B2
		C1B3
LEFT FNT DOOR LOCK ASSY	BLK-YEL	C1B4
RIGHT FNT DOOR LOCK ASSY	BLK-WHT	C1B5
RIGHT REAR DOOR LATCH ASSY	BLK-LT GRN	C1B6
	BLK-WHT	C1B7
OIL LEVEL MOD	BRN-WHT	C1B8
ADAPTIVE LAMP MONITOR MOD	WHT	C1B9
	DK BLU	C1B10
	LT BLU	C1B11
DIC	DK GRN	C1B12
	LT GRN	C1B13
ANTI-LOCK BRAKE CTRL UNIT	LT GRN	C1B14
LOW COOLANT MOD	YEL-BLK	C1B15
FUSE #6 (I/P F/B)	PNK-BLK	C1B16
ALDL CONN PIN M	TAN	C1B17

WSHR FLUID LEVEL SW — BLK

Source	Wire Color	Pin
FUSE #18 (I/P F/B)	BRN	C2A1
	BLK	C2A2
	BLK-WHT	C2A3
REMOTE DIMMER MOD	GRY	C2A4
DERM	BRN	C2A5
PCM CONN C3 PIN C1	BRN-WHT	C2A6
		C2A7
CHIME MOD	YEL	C2A8
BEAM SEL SW	LT GRN	C2A9
RIGHT FNT DIR LT OR ADAPTIVE LAMP MONITOR MOD	DK BLU	C2A10
ABS DIODE	WHT	C2A11
		C2A12
FUEL TANK UNIT	PPL	C2A13
OIL PRES SENS/SW — TAN	TAN-BLK	C2A14
	PNK-BLK	C2A15
FUSE #6 (I/P F/B)	PNK-BLK	C2A16
FUSE #18 (I/P F/B)	BRN	C2A17

Source	Wire Color	Pin
REMOTE DIMMER MOD	GRY	C2B1
NOT USED	BLK	C2B2
		C2B3
		C2B4
		C2B5
FUSE #11 (I/P F/B)	ORG	C2B6
	RED	C2B7
DIC	ORG	C2B8
	TAN	C2B9
CHIME MOD	WHT	C2B10
ADAPTIVE LAMP MONITOR MODULE	TAN	C2B11
		C2B12
		C2B13
		C2B14
		C2B15
PCM CONN C3 PIN C7	PNK-BLK	C2B16
		C2B17

Instrument cluster connections:

C1B1 — IGN IN
C1B2 — IGN IN
C2A16 — BRAKE
C2A6 — SES
C2A5 — INFLAT REST
C1A10 — TRACT CTRL FAULT
C1A13 — CRUISE
C2A11 — ABS
C2B16
C2A8 — BELTS
C2A9 — HI BEAM
C2A4 — ILLUM LTS
C2B1
C2A2 — SOLID STATE — 16 VOLT VF DISPLAY INPUT
C2A17
C1A8 — ILLUM LTS
C1A17
C2A13 — FUEL GAUGE
DIC FUEL INPUT
C2A3 — DIC
DIC OIL PRES INPUT
C2A14 — OIL PRES GAUGE
C1A16 — SOLID STATE — TACH
DIC AND GAUGES
C2A1 — DIC — SOLID STATE — SPEEDO
C2B6 — DIC MEM
C1A5 — ODOMETER
DIC VEH SPD IN
VOLTS
COOLANT TEMP GAUGE
C1A15
C1A14 — LEFT DIR
RIGHT DIR
C2A10

Pin	Signal	Signal	Pin
C1A12	GENERATOR INPUT		
C1B16	IGNITION INPUT	SERIAL DATA REQUEST	C2B11
C2A3	GROUND	ENGLISH/METRIC OUTPUT	C1A3
C1B10	COLUMN #1 INPUT	CHIME CONTROL	C2B10
C1B11	COLUMN #2 INPUT	DATA LINE IN/OUT	C1B17
C1B12	COLUMN #3 INPUT	RIGHT DOOR AJAR INPUT	C1B5
C1B13	COLUMN #4 INPUT	REAR DOOR AJAR INPUT	C1B6
C2B7	ROW #1 CONTROL	LEFT DOOR AJAR INPUT	C1B4
C2B8	ROW #2 CONTROL	DIC TRACTION CTRL ENGAGED INPUT	C1B14
C2B9	ROW #3 CONTROL	LOW WSHR FLUID INPUT	C1B7
C1A7	IGNITION	SERIAL DATA INPUT	C1B9
C1A1	VARIABLE VF DIMMING INPUT	LOW COOLANT INPUT	C1B15
C1A6	VF DIMMING INPUT	LOW OIL INPUT	C1B8

36   37   38   39

INSTRUMENT CLUSTER (DIGITAL)

Terminal	Wire	Description
REMOTE DIMMER MOD	GRY	C1A1
NOT USED	BLK–WHT	C1A2
HVAC PROGRAMMER	LT BLU	C1A3
NOT USED	GRY	C1A4
PCM CONN C3 PIN D10	DK GRN	C1A5
FUSE #21 (I/P F/B)	DK GRN	C1A6
FUSE #18 (I/P F/B)	BRN	C1A7
NOT USED	GRY	C1A8
		C1A9
		C1A10
PASS KEY DECODER MOD	DK GRN	C1A11
ALTERNATOR	BRN	C1A12
PCM CONN C3 PIN D1	WHT	C1A13
LEFT FNT DIR LT OR ADAPTIVE LAMP MONITOR MOD	LT BLU	C1A14
COOLANT TEMP SENDER	YEL	C1A15
CCCI	WHT	C1A16
	BLK	C1A17

Terminal	Wire	Description
PARK BRAKE SW (W/O REMINDER PACKAGE)	TAN–WHT	C1B1
PARK BRAKE SW (W/ REMINDER PACKAGE)	BLK–ORG	C1B2
LEFT FNT DOOR LOCK ASSY	BLK–YEL	C1B3
RIGHT FNT DOOR LOCK ASSY	BLK–WHT	C1B4
RIGHT REAR DOOR LATCH ASSY	BLK–LT GRN	C1B5
	BLK–WHT	C1B6
	BRN–WHT	C1B7
OIL LEVEL MOD	WHT	C1B8
ADAPTIVE LAMP MONITOR MOD	DK BLU	C1B9
DIC	LT BLU	C1B10
	DK GRN	C1B11
	LT GRN	C1B12
		C1B13
LOW COOLANT MOD	YEL–BLK	C1B14
FUSE #6 (I/P F/B)	PNK–BLK	C1B15
ALDL CONN PIN M	TAN	C1B16
		C1B17

WSHR FLUID LEVEL SW — BLK

Terminal	Wire	Description
FUSE #18 (I/P F/B)	BRN	C2A1
	BLK	C2A2
	BLK–WHT	C2A3
DERM	BRN	C2A4
PCM CONN C3 PIN C1	BRN–WHT	C2A5
		C2A6
		C2A7
CHIME MOD	YEL	C2A8
BEAM SEL SW	LT GRN	C2A9
RIGHT FNT DIR LT OR ADAPTIVE LAMP MONITOR MOD	DK BLU	C2A10
ABS DIODE	WHT	C2A11
CCR CONTROLLER	DK GRN	C2A12
FUEL TANK UNIT	PPL	C2A13
OIL PRES SENS/SW (TAN)	TAN–BLK	C2A14
		C2A15
FUSE #6 (I/P F/B)	PNK–BLK	C2A16
FUSE #18 (I/P F/B)	BRN	C2A17

Terminal	Wire	Description
	BLK	C2B1
		C2B2
		C2B3
		C2B4
		C2B5
FUSE #11 (I/P F/B)	ORG	C2B6
	RED	C2B7
DIC	ORG	C2B8
	TAN	C2B9
CHIME MOD	WHT	C2B10
ADAPTIVE LAMP MONITOR MODULE	TAN	C2B11
		C2B12
		C2B13
		C2B14
		C2B15
PCM CONN C3 PIN C7	PNK–BLK	C2B16
		C2B17

Cluster signal labels:
IGN IN, IGN IN, BRAKE, SES, INFLAT REST, CRUISE, ABS, BELTS, HI BEAM, LEFT DIR, RIGHT DIR, LIGHTS ON, VF DIM INPUT, OIL, IGNITION INPUT, AMP, SECURITY, FIRM RIDE, 16 VOLT VF DISPLAY INPUT, FUEL GAUGE, LOW FUEL INPUT, LOW FUEL PRES INPUT, TEMP GAUGE, SPEEDO, SOLID STATE, ODOMETER, DIC VEH SPD INPUT, MEMORY INPUT

Cluster pin labels:
C1B1, C1B2, C2A16, C2A6, C2A5, C1A13, C2A11, C2B16, C2A8, C2A9, C1A14, C2A10, C1A6, C1A17, C1A12, C1A11, C2A12, C2A2, C2A17, C2A13, C2A1, C2A14, C1A15, C1A5, C2B6

Pin	Description		Description	Pin
C1B16	IGNITION INPUT		SERIAL DATA REQUEST	C2B11
C2A3	GROUND		ENGLISH/METRIC OUTPUT	C1A3
C1B10	COLUMN #1 INPUT		CHIME CONTROL	C2B10
C1B11	COLUMN #2 INPUT		DATA LINE IN/OUT	C1B17
C1B12	COLUMN #3 INPUT		RIGHT DOOR AJAR INPUT	C1B5
C1B13	COLUMN #4 INPUT		REAR DOOR AJAR INPUT	C1B6
C2B7	ROW #1 CONTROL		LEFT DOOR AJAR INPUT	C1B4
C2B8	ROW #2 CONTROL		LOW WSHR FLUID INPUT	C1B7
C2B9	ROW #3 CONTROL		SERIAL DATA INPUT	C1B9
C1A7	IGNITION		LOW COOLANT INPUT	C1B15
C1A1	VARIABLE VF DIMMING INPUT		LOW OIL INPUT	C1B8
C2B2	SENSOR GROUND			

36   37   38   39

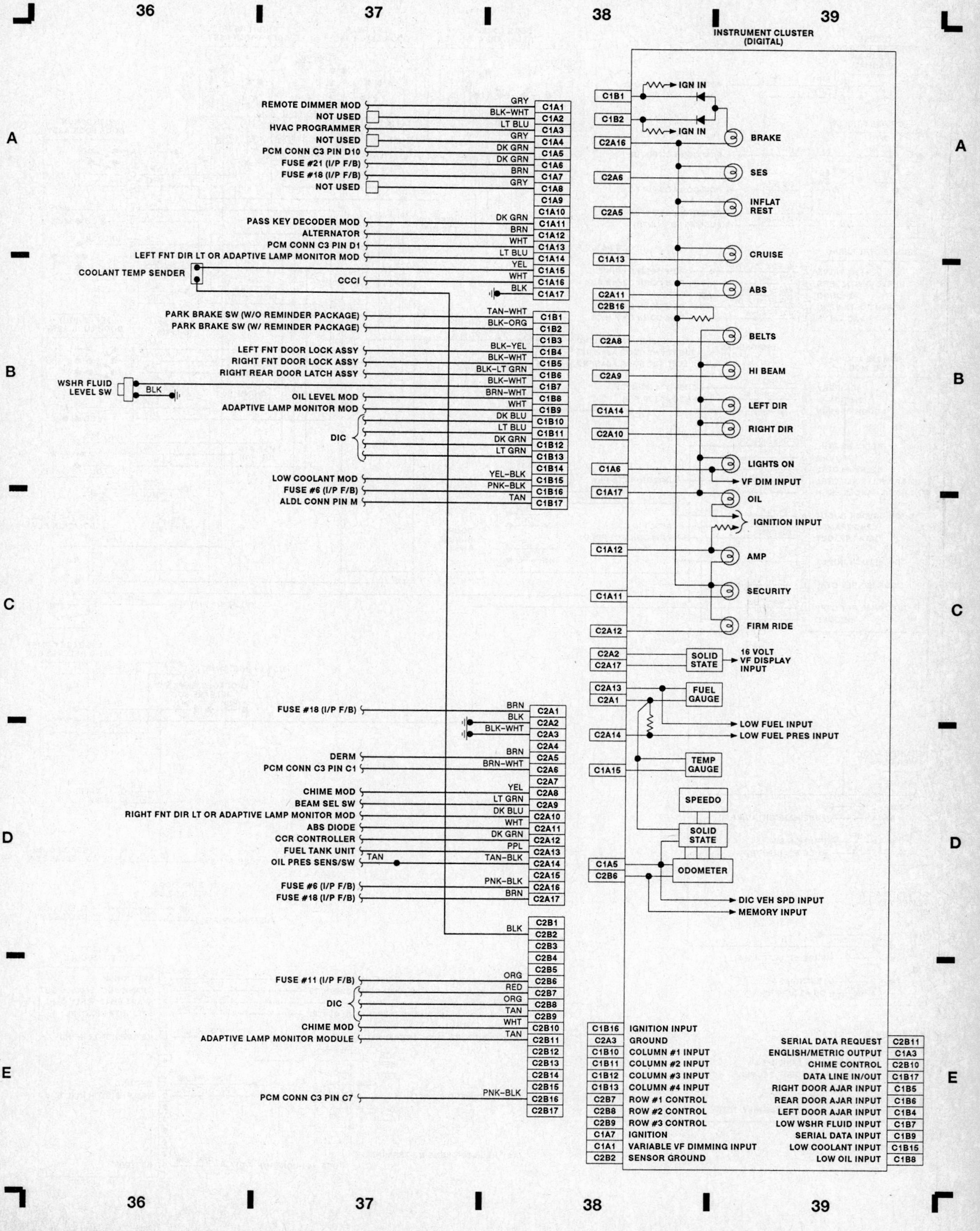

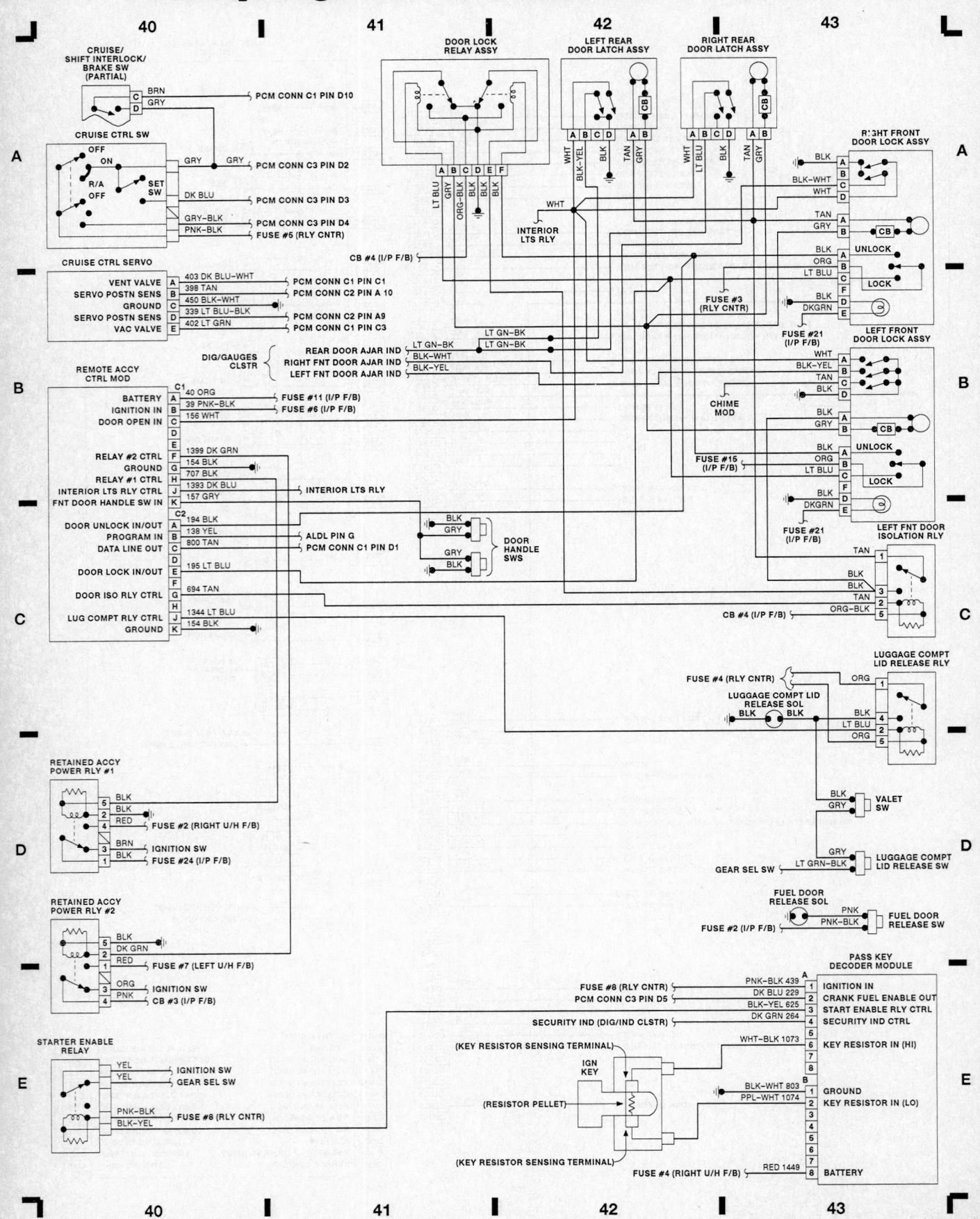

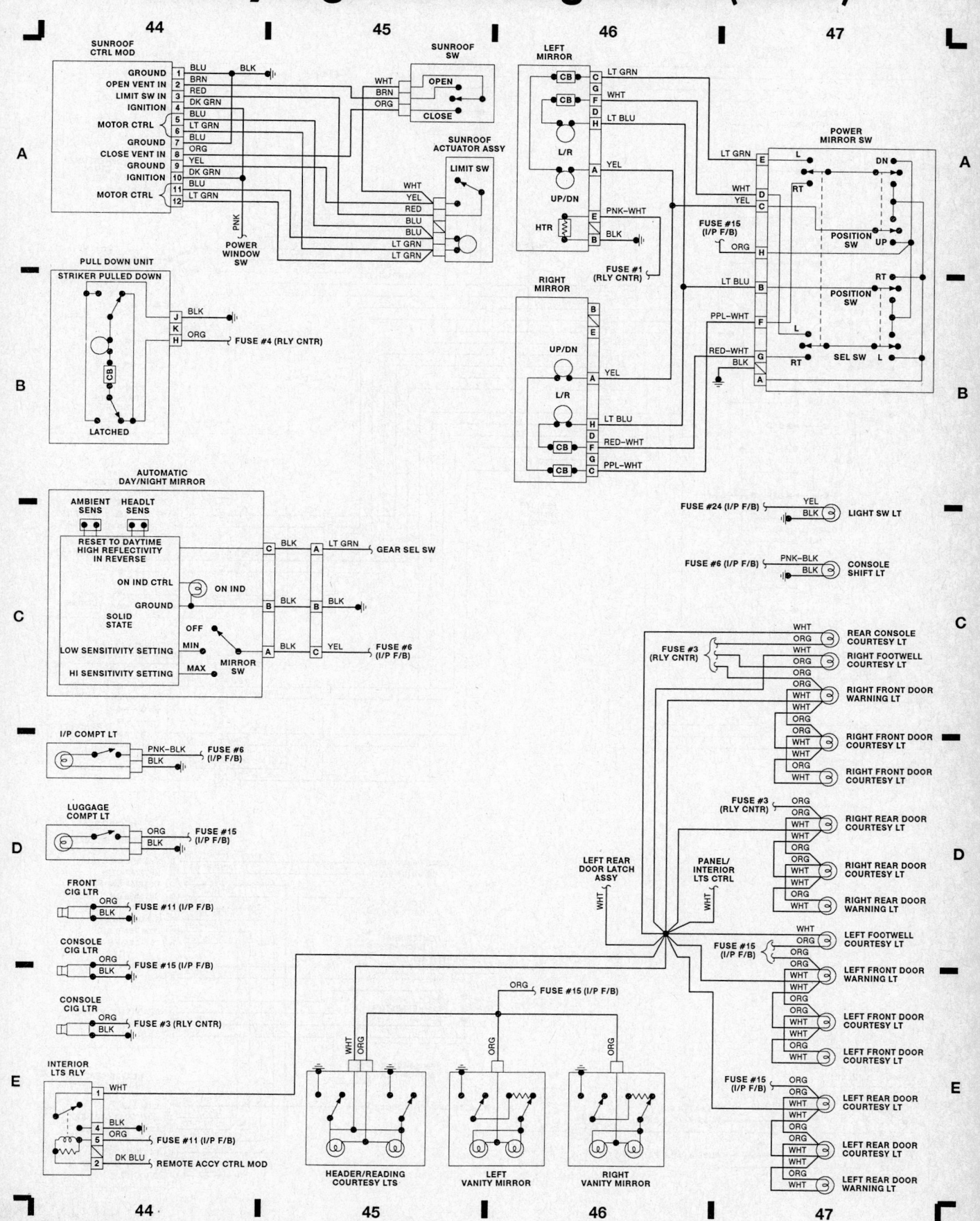

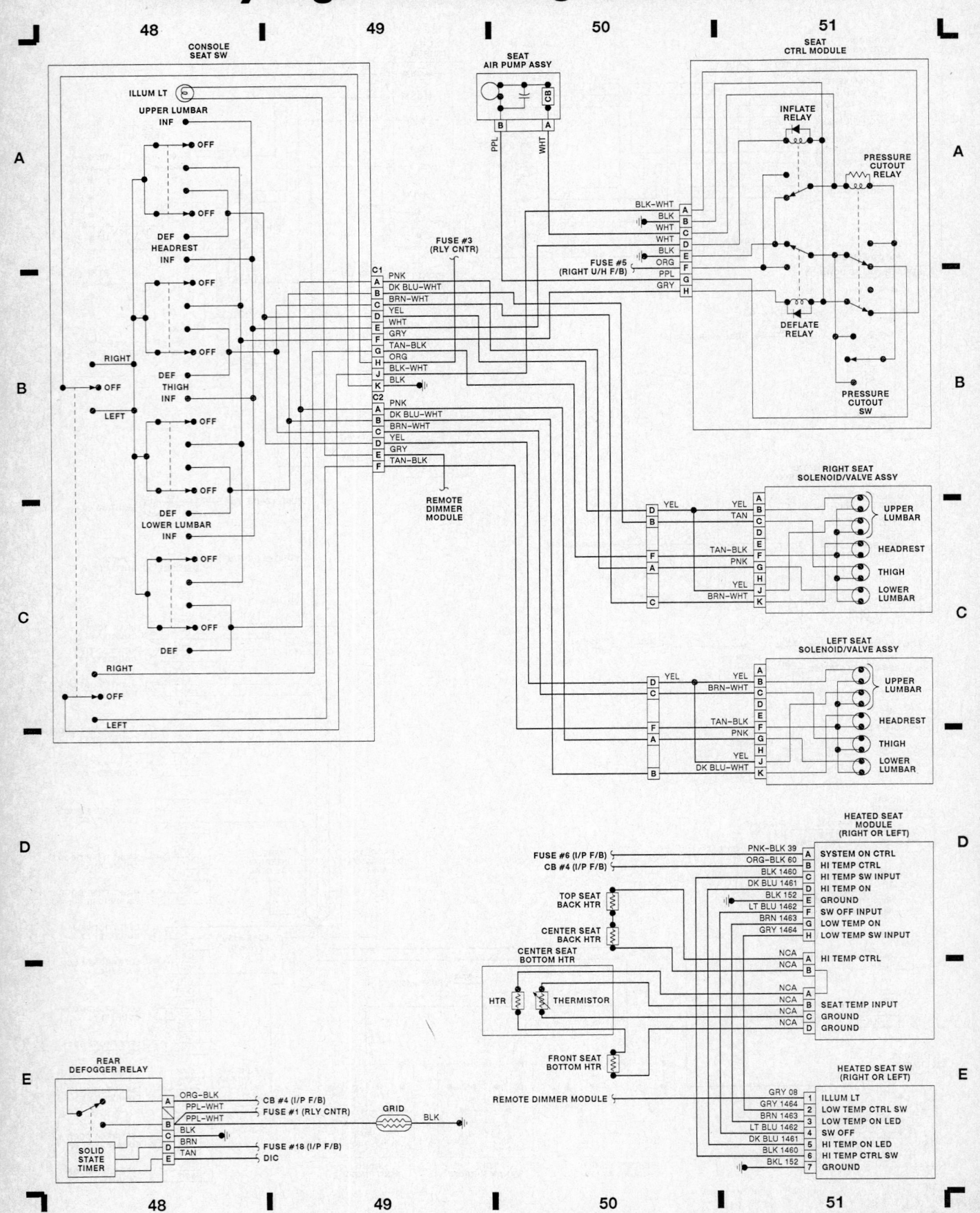

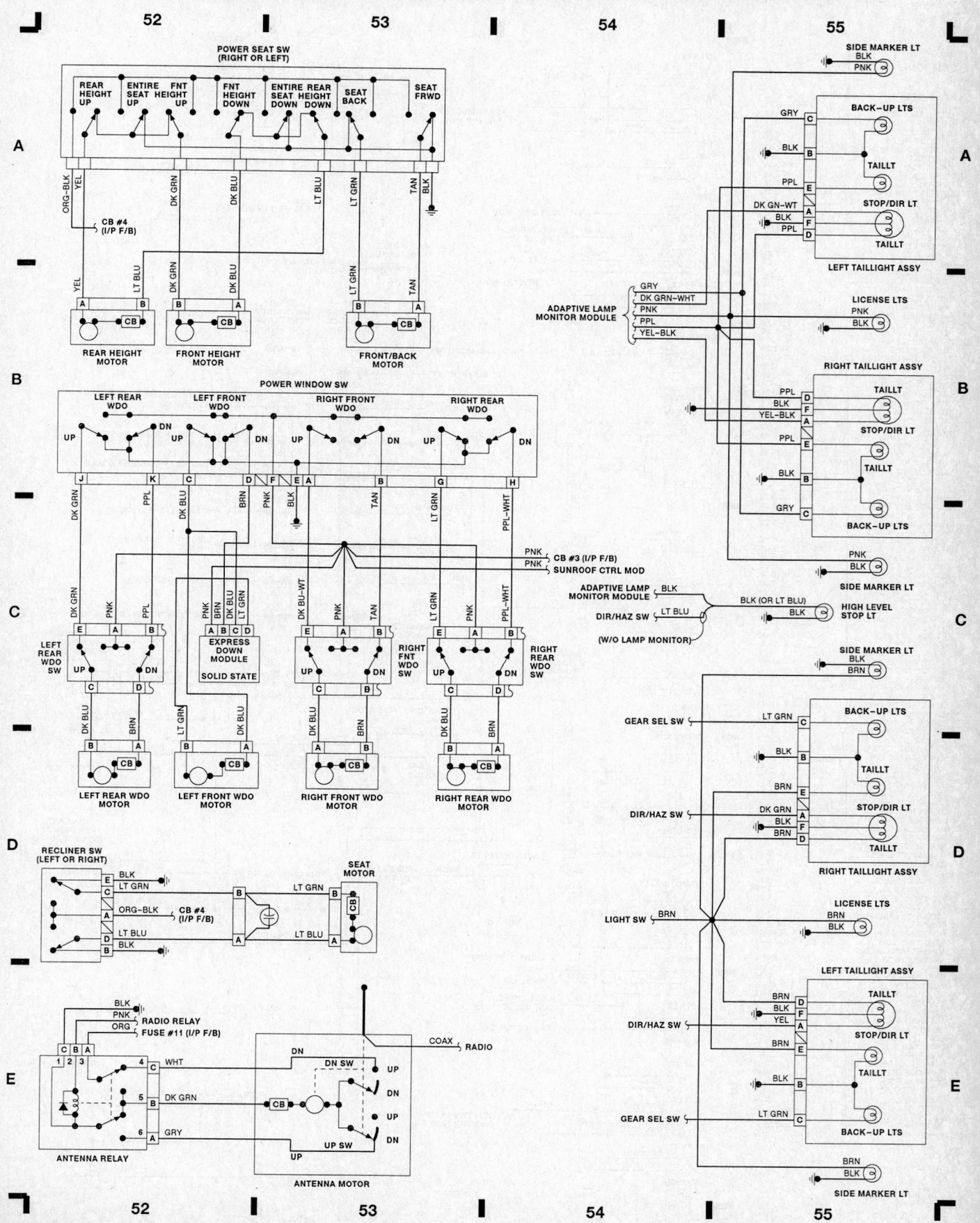

COMPONENT LOCATOR:

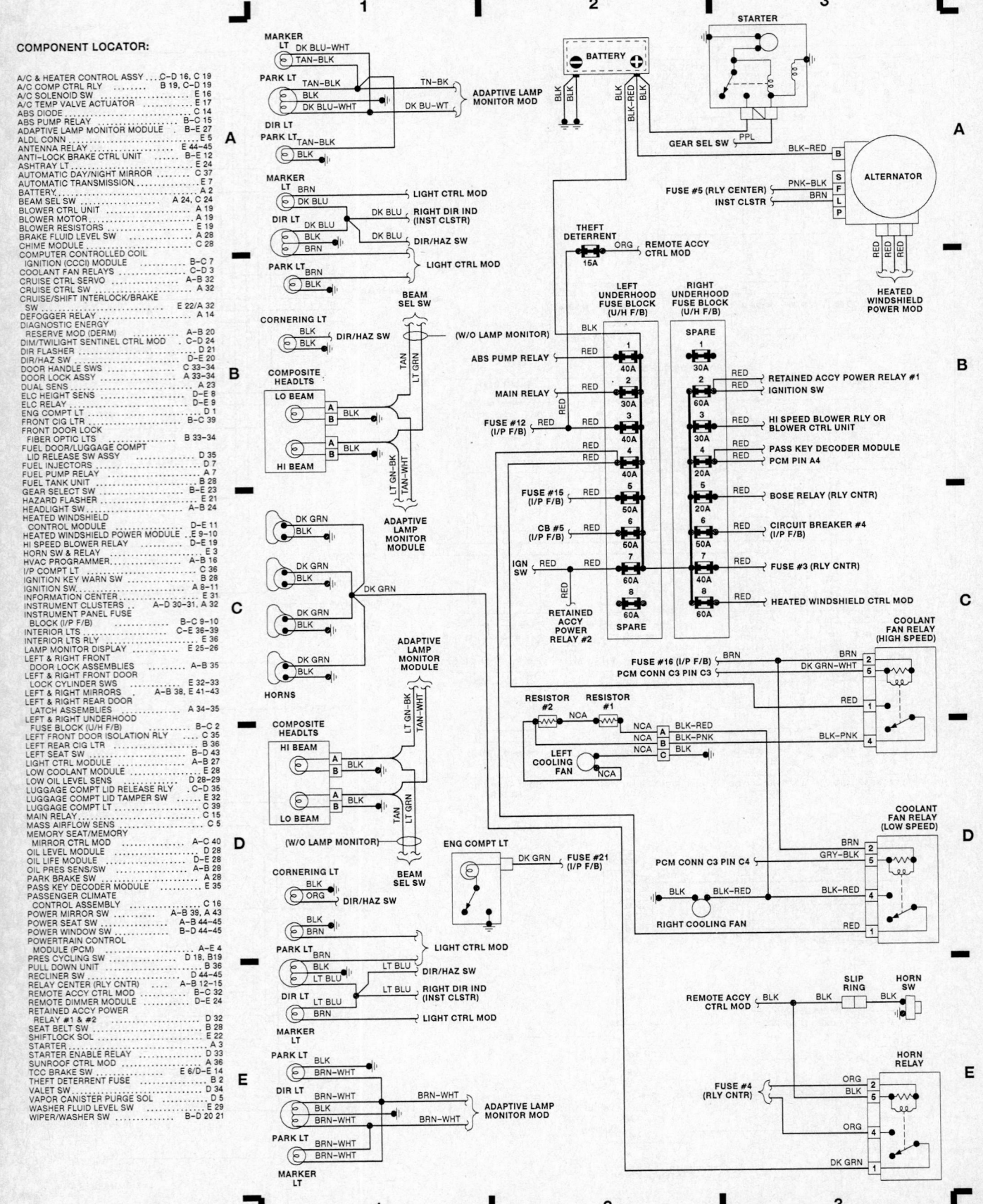

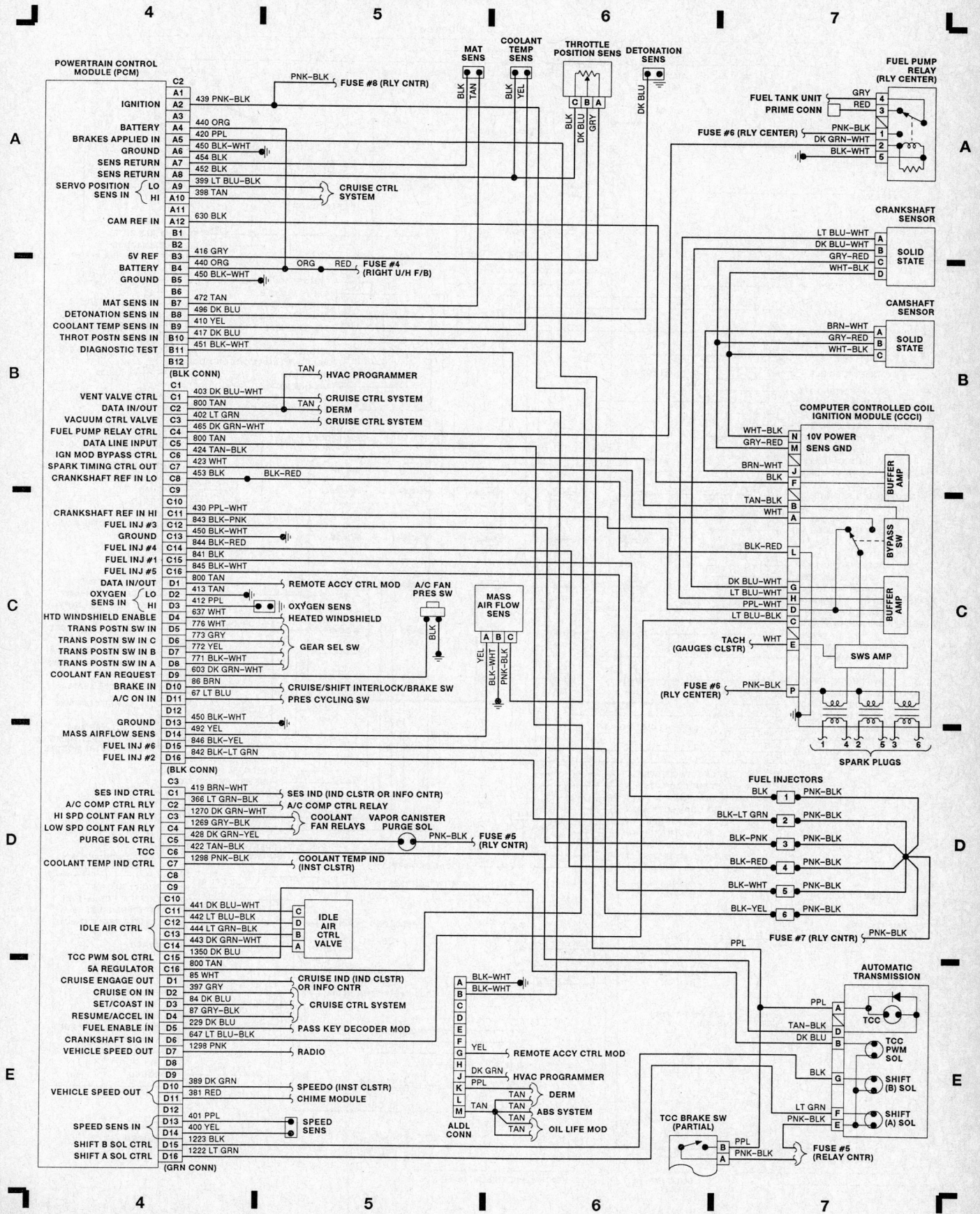

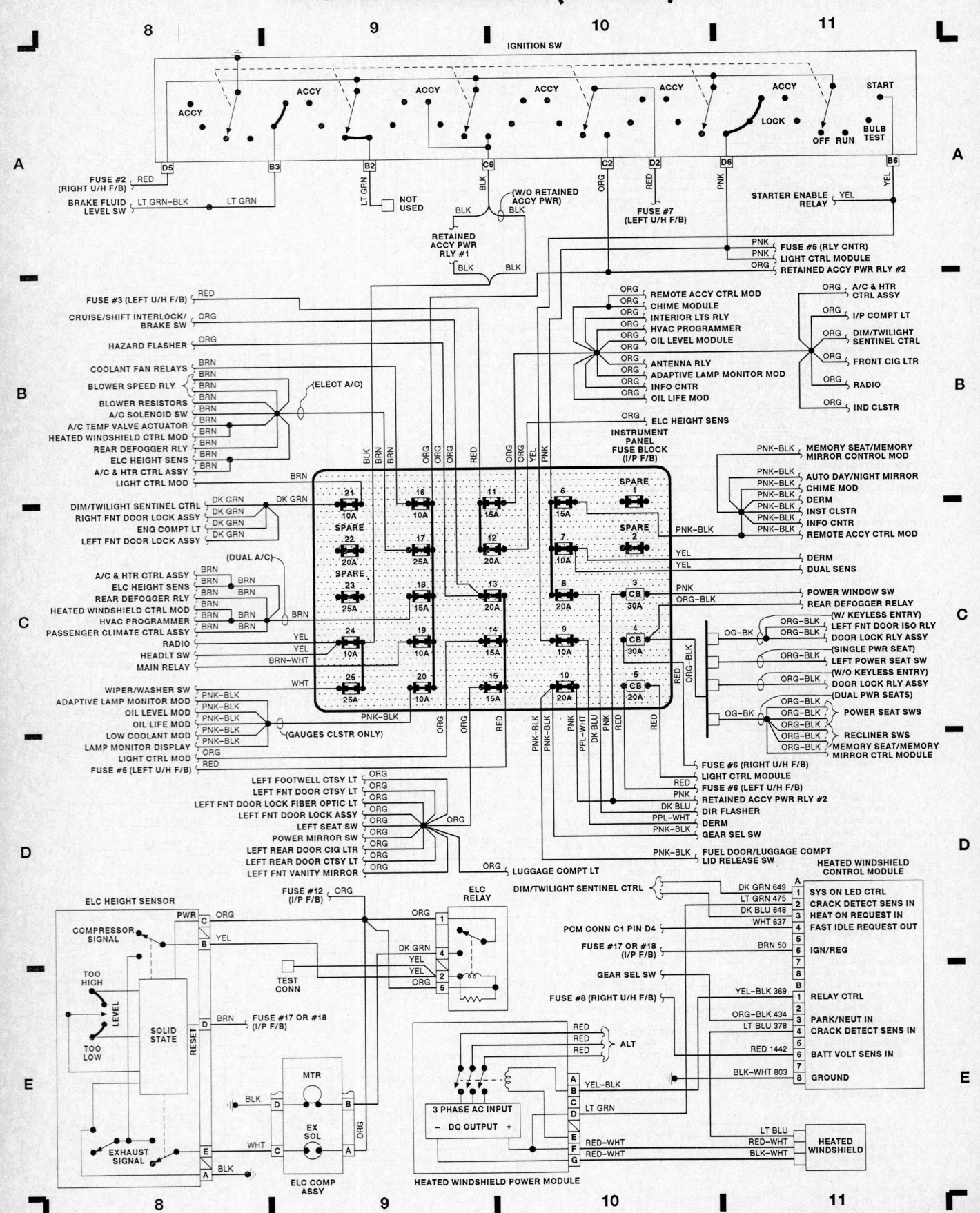

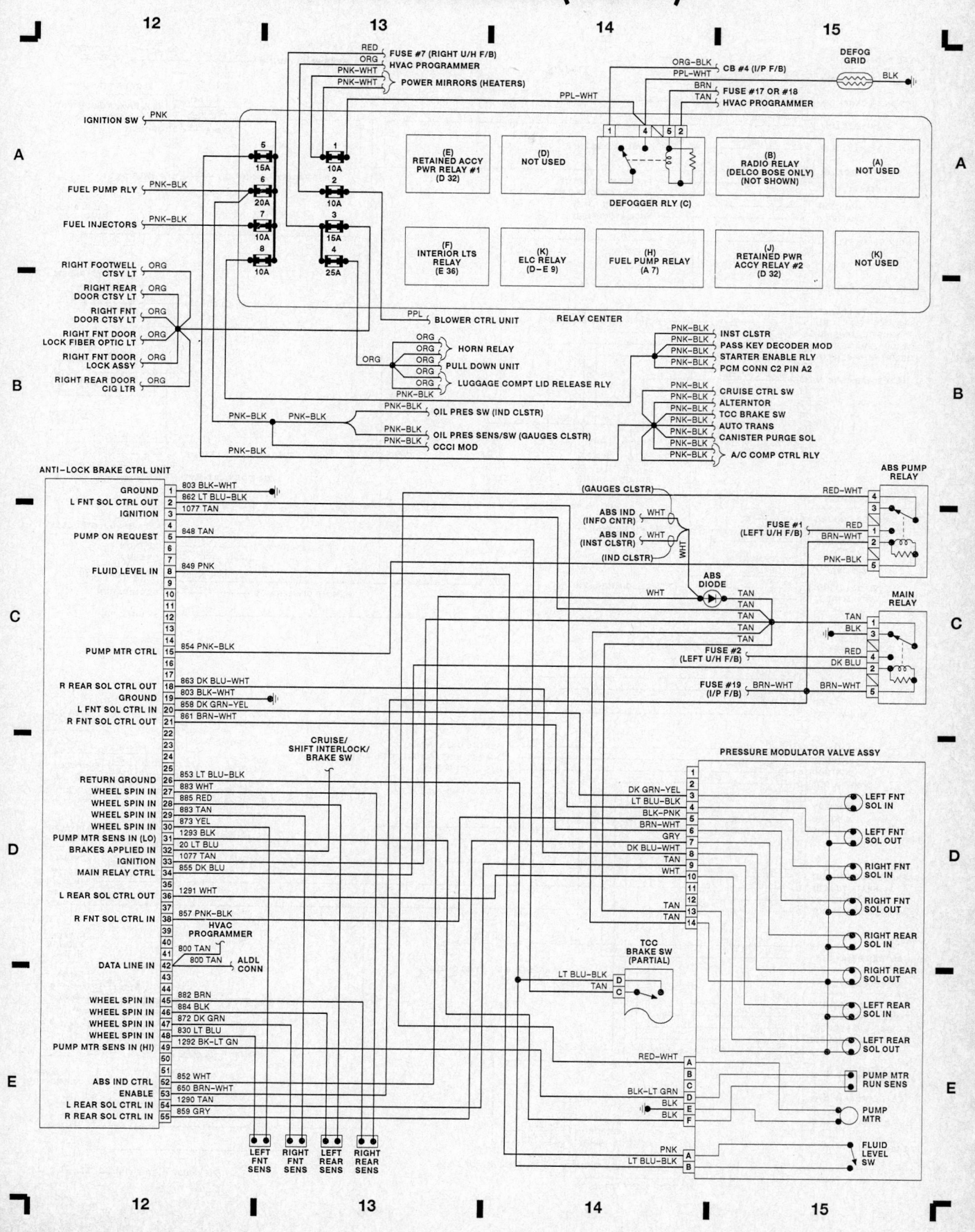

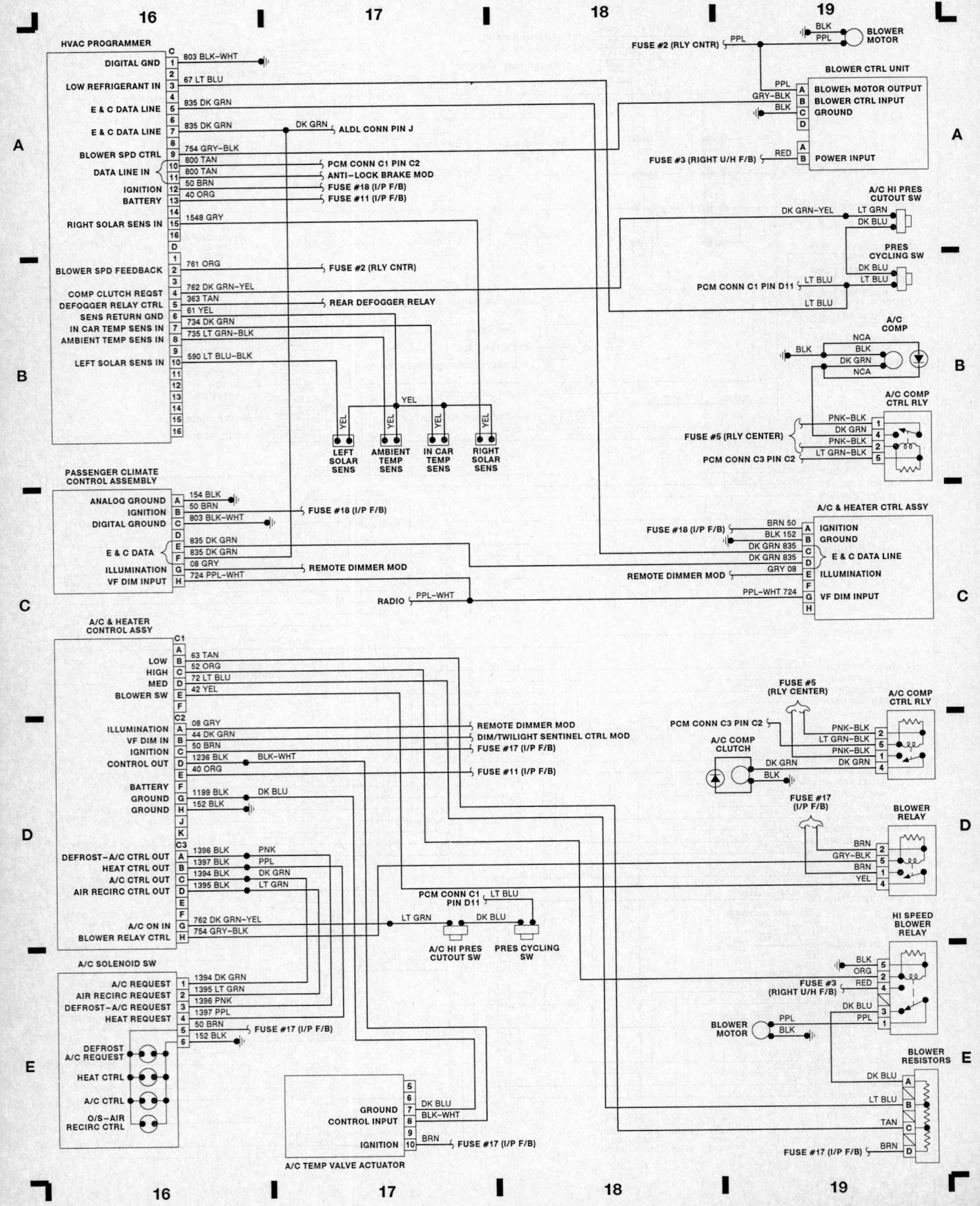

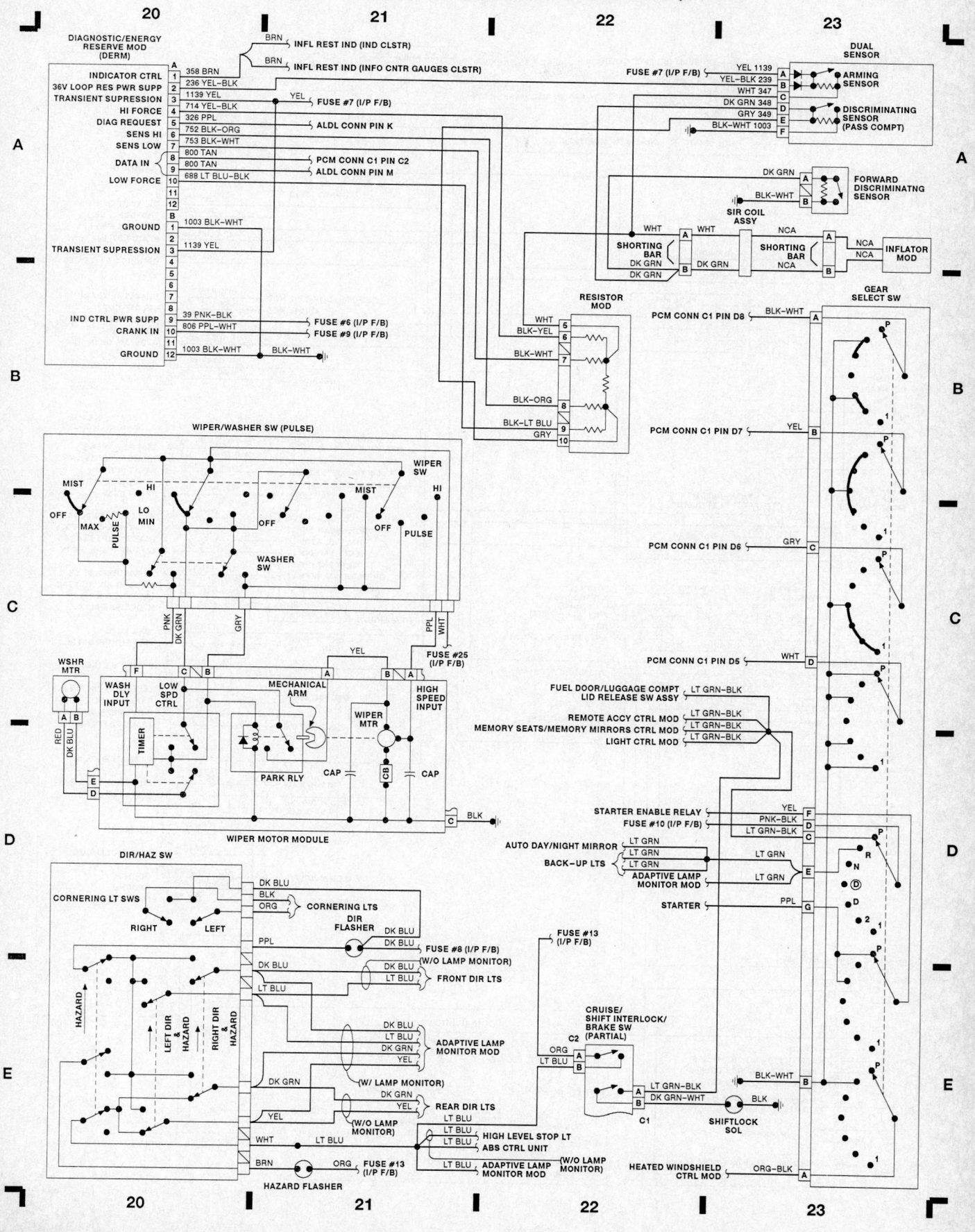

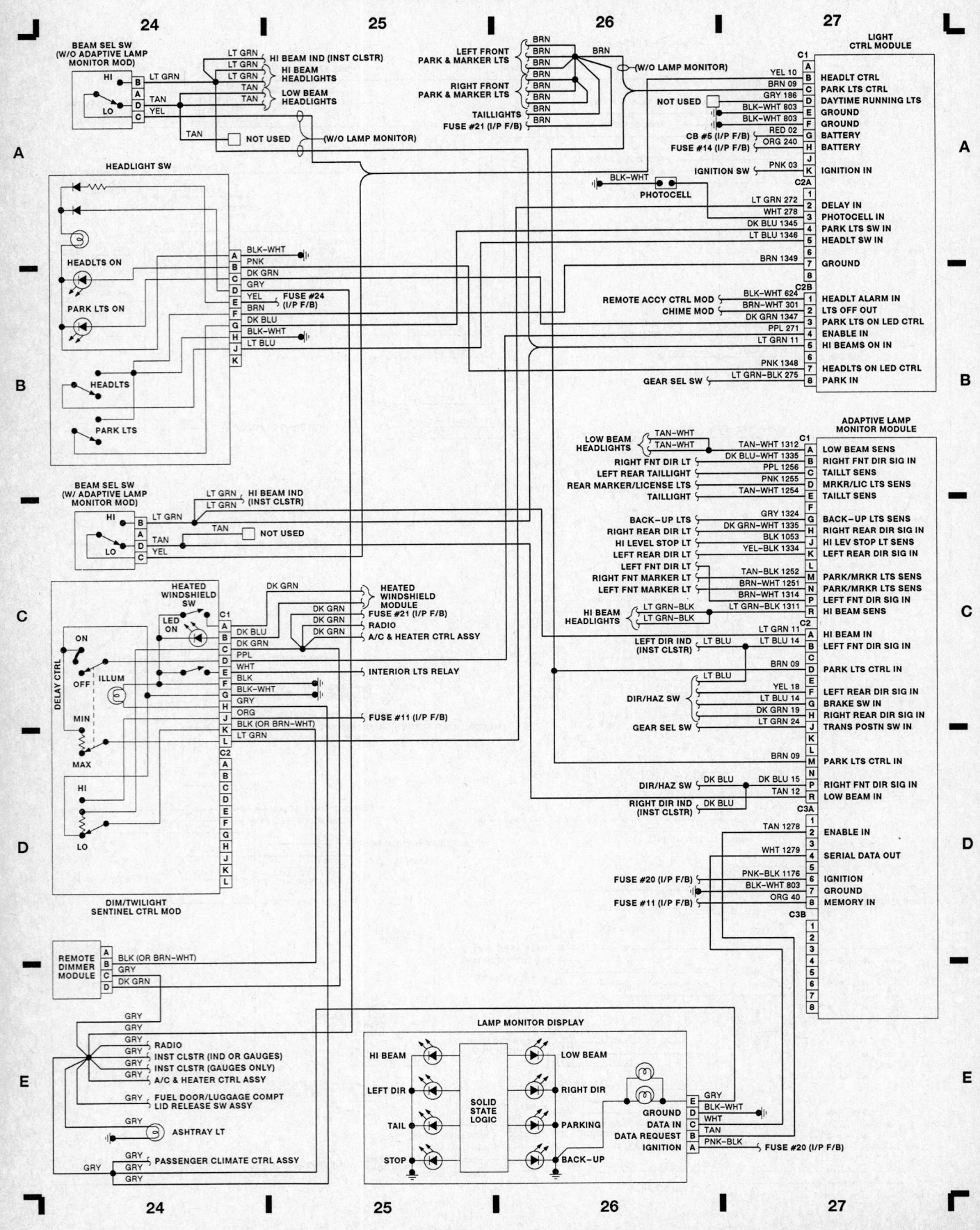

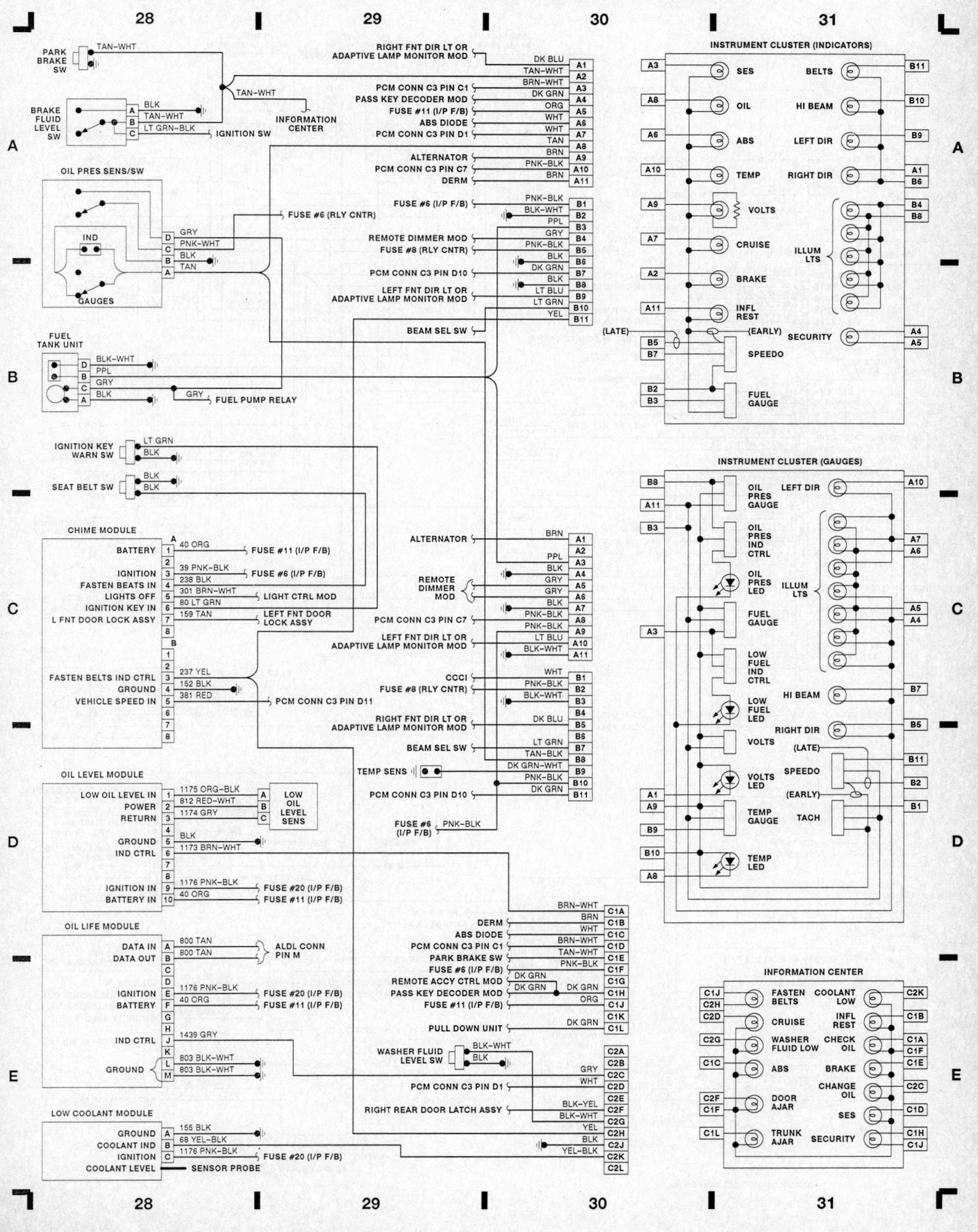

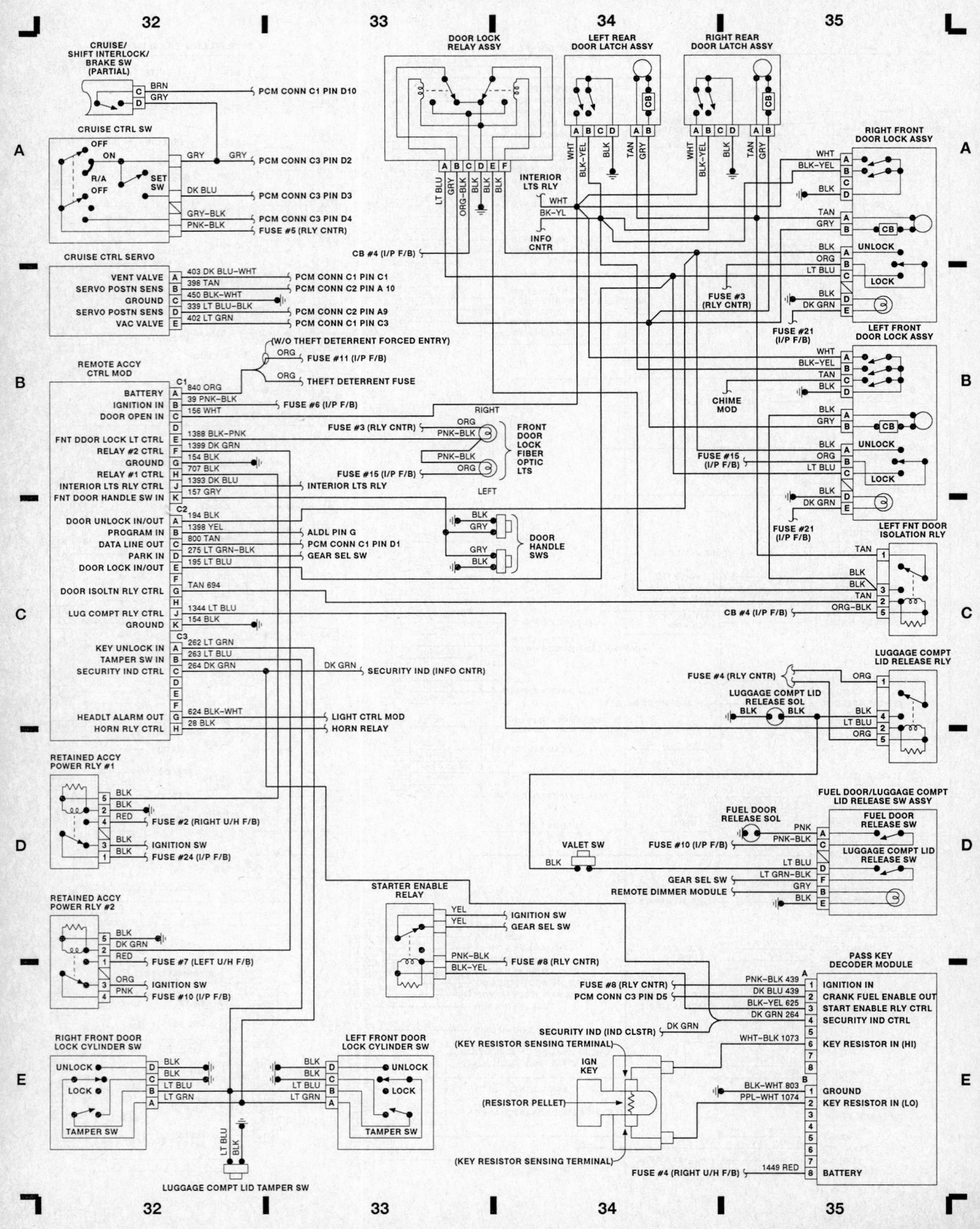

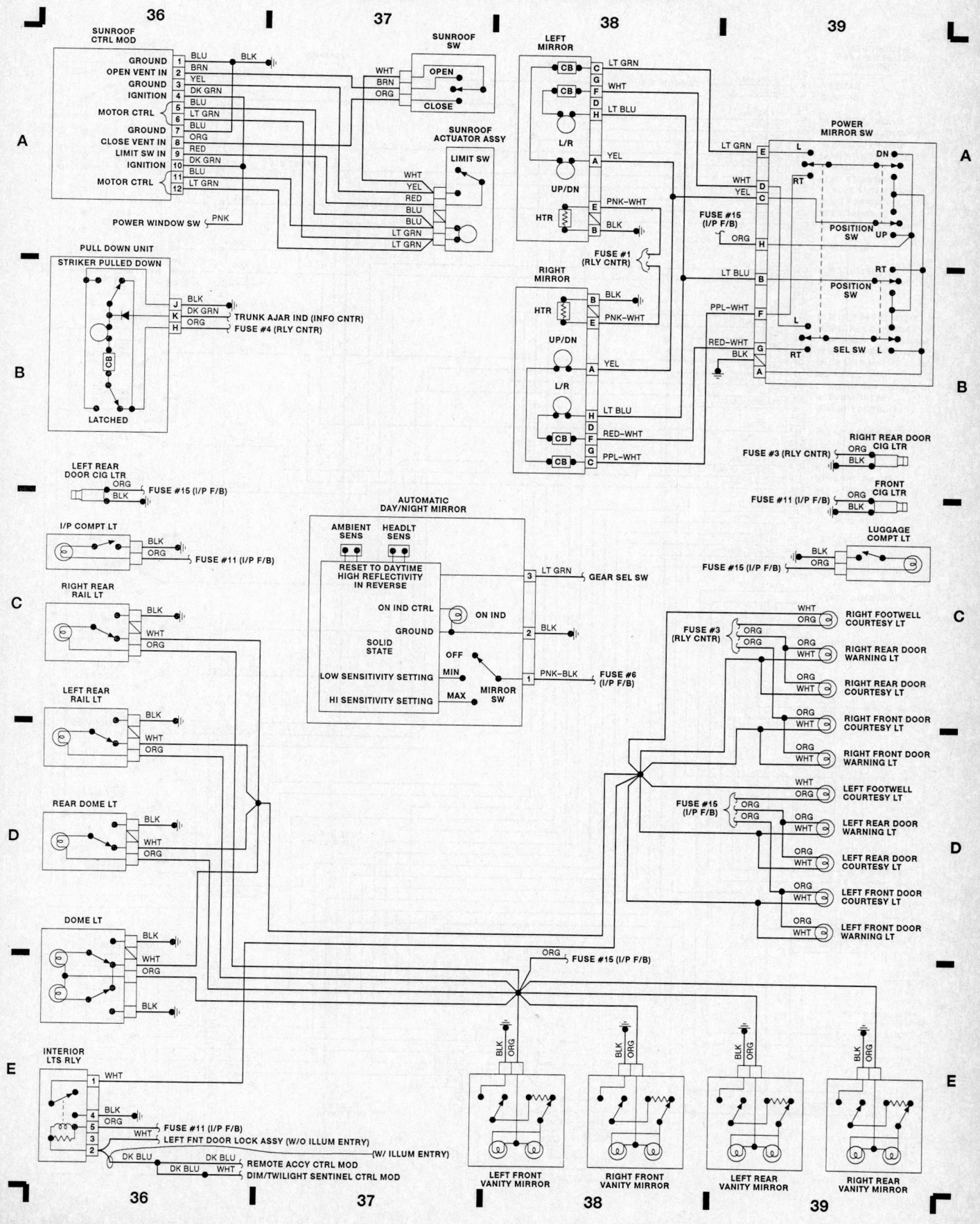

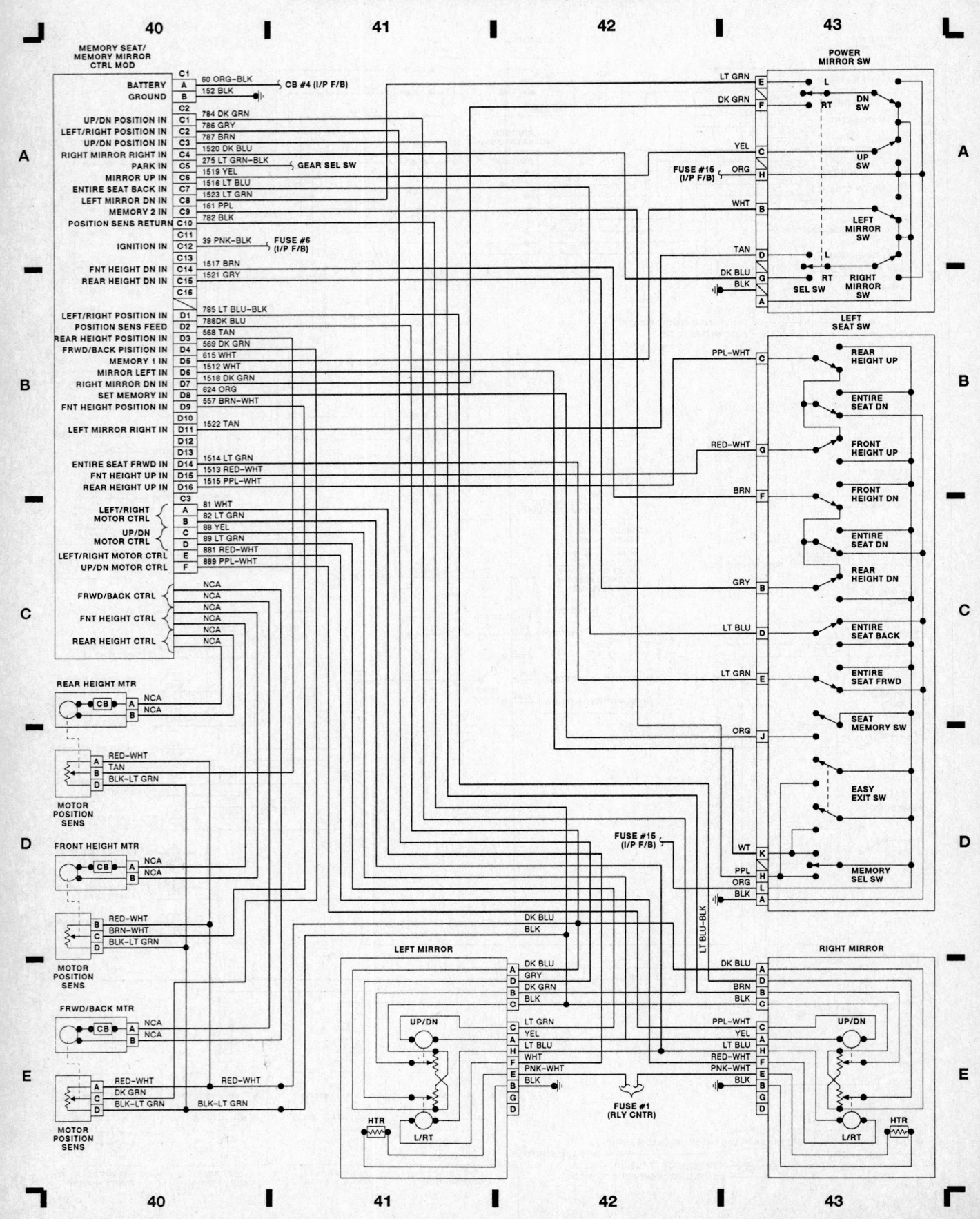

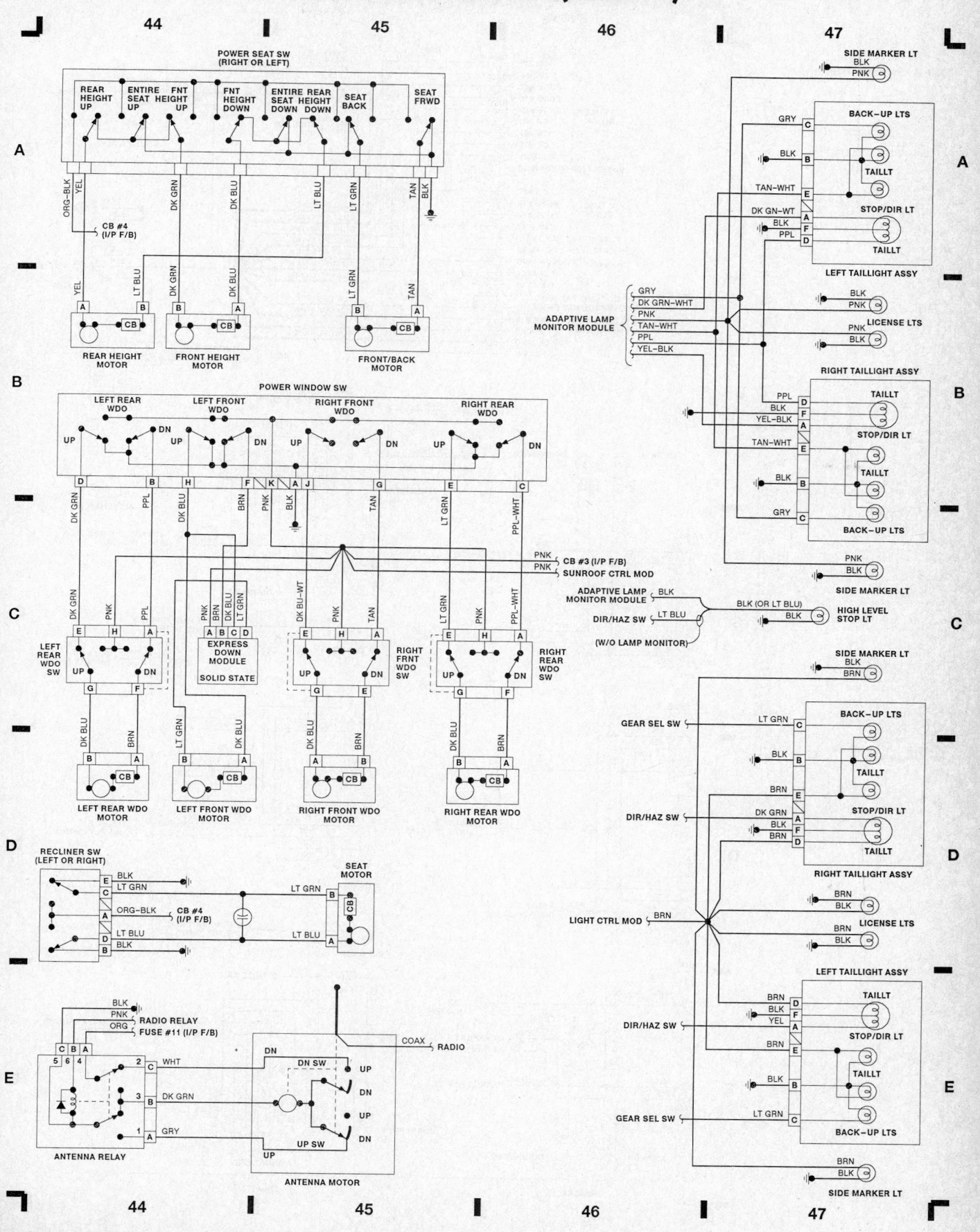

1991 WIRING DIAGRAMS
Reatta & Riviera

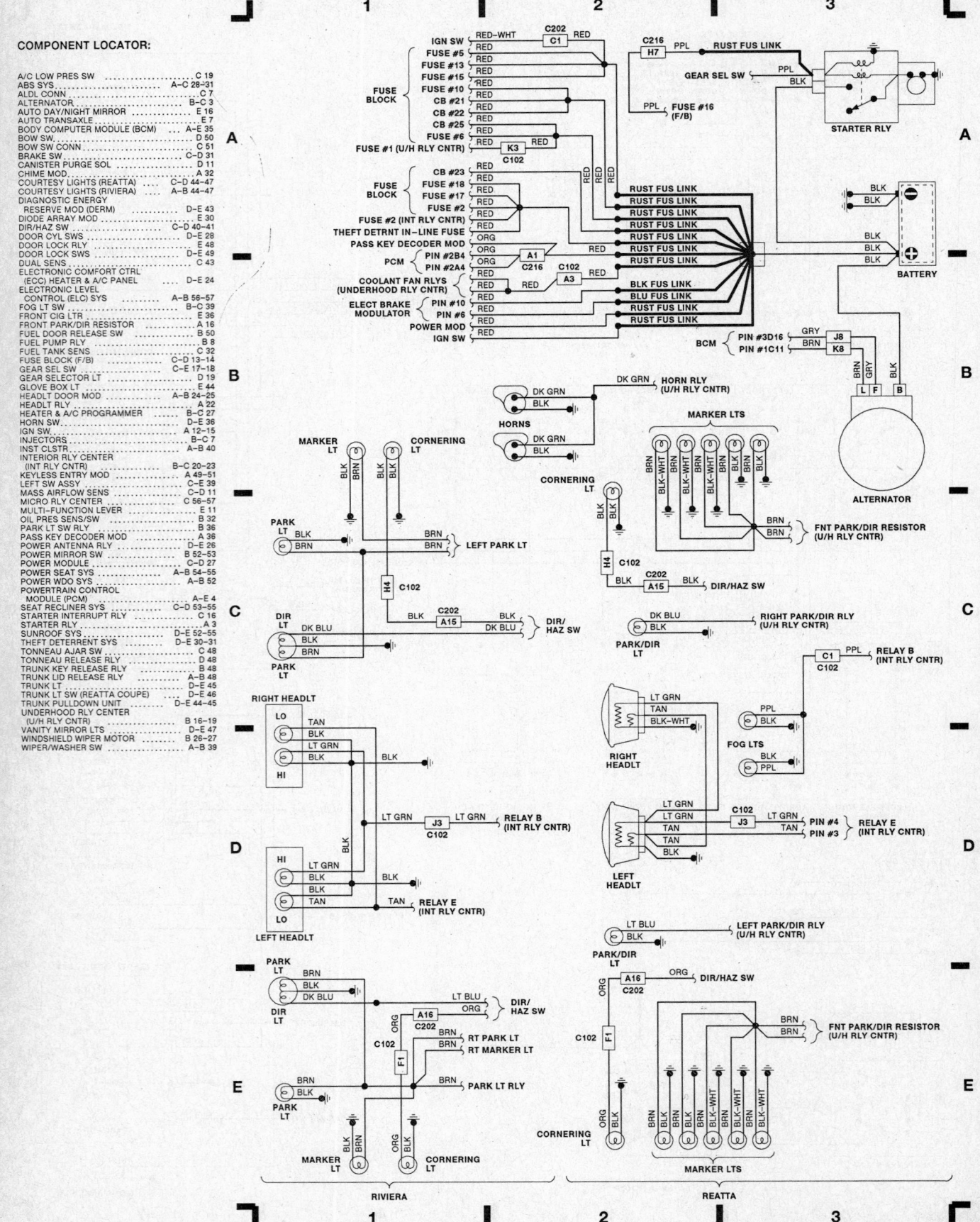

COMPONENT LOCATOR:

A/C LOW PRES SW .... C 19
ABS SYS .... A–C 28–31
ALDL CONN .... C 7
ALTERNATOR .... B–C 3
AUTO DAY/NIGHT MIRROR .... E 16
AUTO TRANSAXLE .... E 7
BODY COMPUTER MODULE (BCM) ..... A–E 35
BOW SW .... D 50
BOW SW CONN .... D 51
BRAKE SW .... C–D 31
CANISTER PURGE SOL .... D 11
CHIME MOD .... A 32
COURTESY LIGHTS (REATTA) .... C–D 44–47
COURTESY LIGHTS (RIVIERA) ...... A–B 44–47
DIAGNOSTIC ENERGY
  RESERVE MOD (DERM) .... D–E 43
DIODE ARRAY MOD .... E 30
DIR/HAZ SW .... C–D 40–41
DOOR CYL SWS .... D–E 28
DOOR LOCK RLY .... E 48
DOOR LOCK SWS .... D–E 49
DUAL SENS .... C 43
ELECTRONIC COMFORT CTRL
  (ECC) HEATER & A/C PANEL ..... D–E 24
ELECTRONIC LEVEL
  CONTROL (ELC) SYS .... A–B 56–57
FOG LT SW .... B–C 39
FRONT CIG LTR .... E 36
FRONT PARK/DIR RESISTOR .... A 16
FUEL DOOR RELEASE SW .... B 50
FUEL PUMP RLY .... B 8
FUEL TANK SENS .... C 32
FUSE BLOCK (F/B) .... C–D 13–14
GEAR SEL SW .... C–E 17–18
GEAR SELECTOR LT .... D 19
GLOVE BOX LT .... E 44
HEADLT DOOR MOD .... A–B 24–25
HEADLT RLY .... A 22
HEATER & A/C PROGRAMMER .... B–C 27
HORN SW .... D–E 36
IGN SW .... A 12–15
INJECTORS .... B–C 7
INST CLSTR .... A–B 40
INTERIOR RLY CENTER
  (INT RLY CNTR) .... B–C 20–23
KEYLESS ENTRY MOD .... A 49–51
LEFT SW ASSY .... C–E 39
MASS AIRFLOW SENS .... C–D 11
MICRO RLY CENTER .... C 56–57
MULTI–FUNCTION LEVER .... E 11
OIL PRES SENS/SW .... B 32
PARK LT SW RLY .... B 36
PASS KEY DECODER MOD .... A 36
POWER ANTENNA RLY .... D–E 26
POWER MIRROR SW .... B 52–53
POWER MODULE .... D 27
POWER SEAT SYS .... A–B 54–55
POWER WDO SYS .... A–B 52
POWERTRAIN CONTROL
  MODULE (PCM) .... A–E 4
SEAT RECLINER SYS .... C–D 53–55
STARTER INTERRUPT RLY .... C 16
STARTER RLY .... A 3
SUNROOF SYS .... D–E 52–55
THEFT DETERRENT SYS .... D–E 30–31
TONNEAU AJAR SW .... C 48
TONNEAU RELEASE RLY .... D 48
TRUNK KEY RELEASE RLY .... B 48
TRUNK LID RELEASE RLY .... A–B 48
TRUNK LT .... D–E 45
TRUNK LT SW (REATTA COUPE) ..... D–E 46
TRUNK PULLDOWN UNIT .... D–E 44–45
UNDERHOOD RLY CENTER
  (U/H RLY CNTR) .... B 16–19
VANITY MIRROR LTS .... D–E 47
WINDSHIELD WIPER MOTOR .... B 26–27
WIPER/WASHER SW .... A–B 39

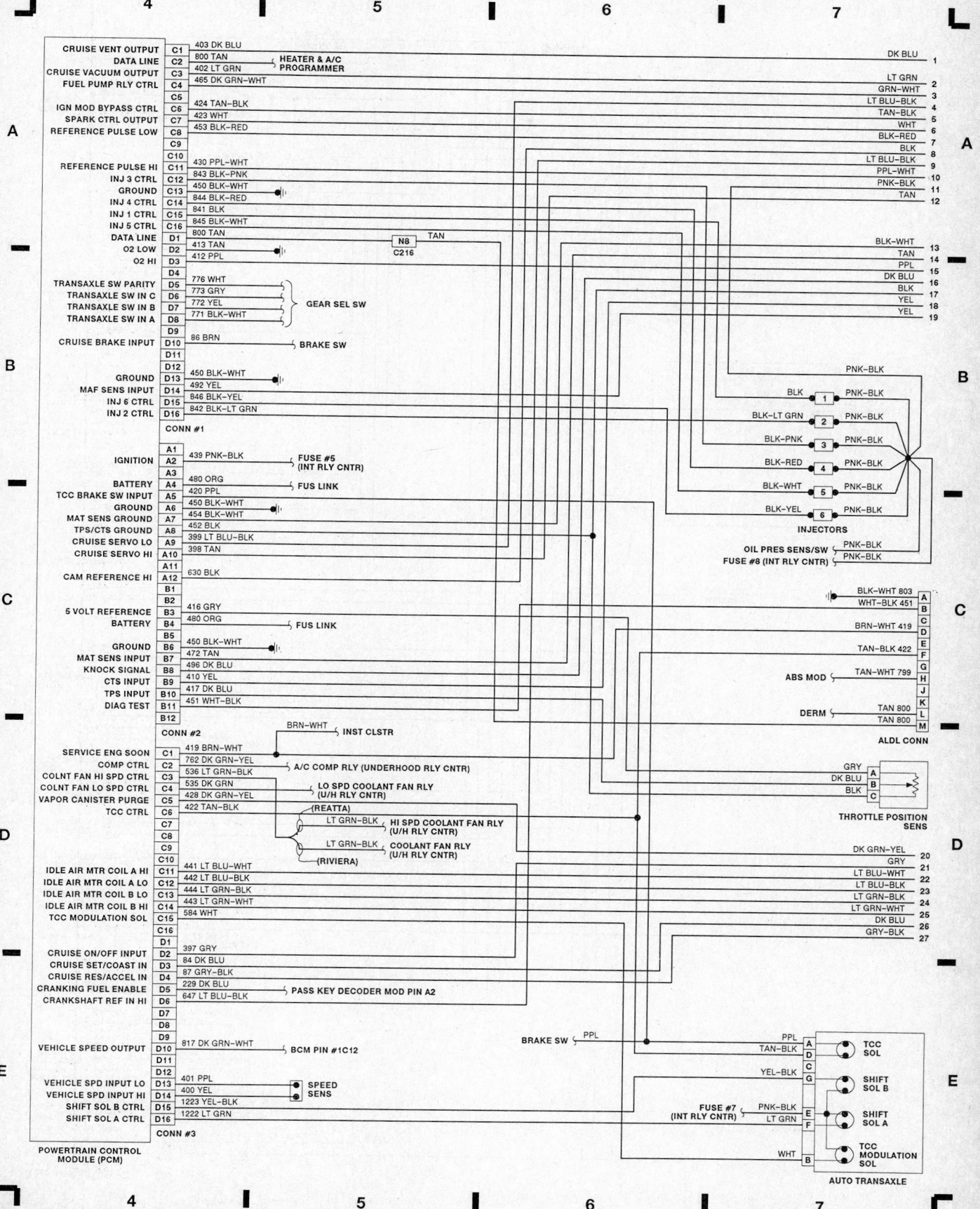

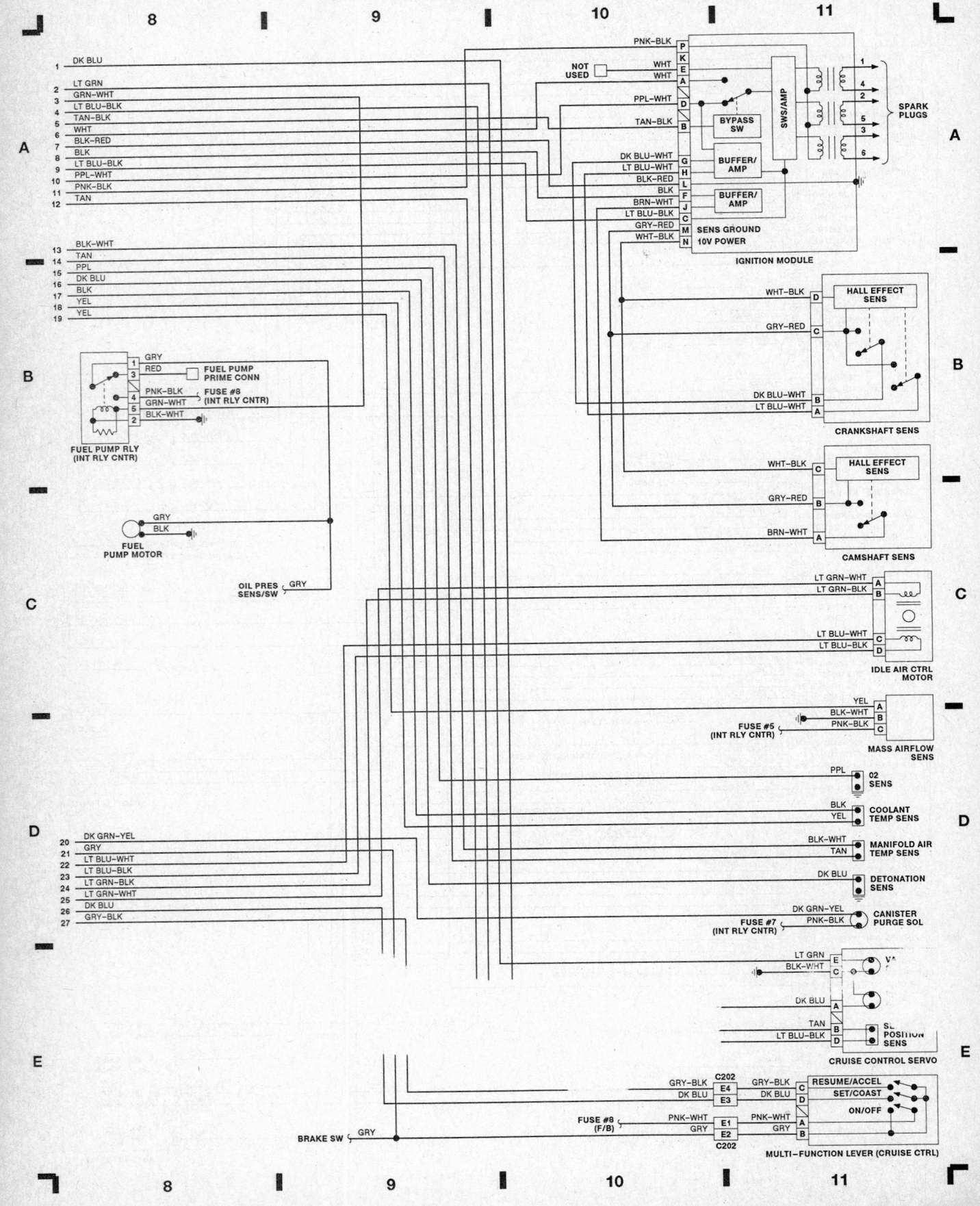

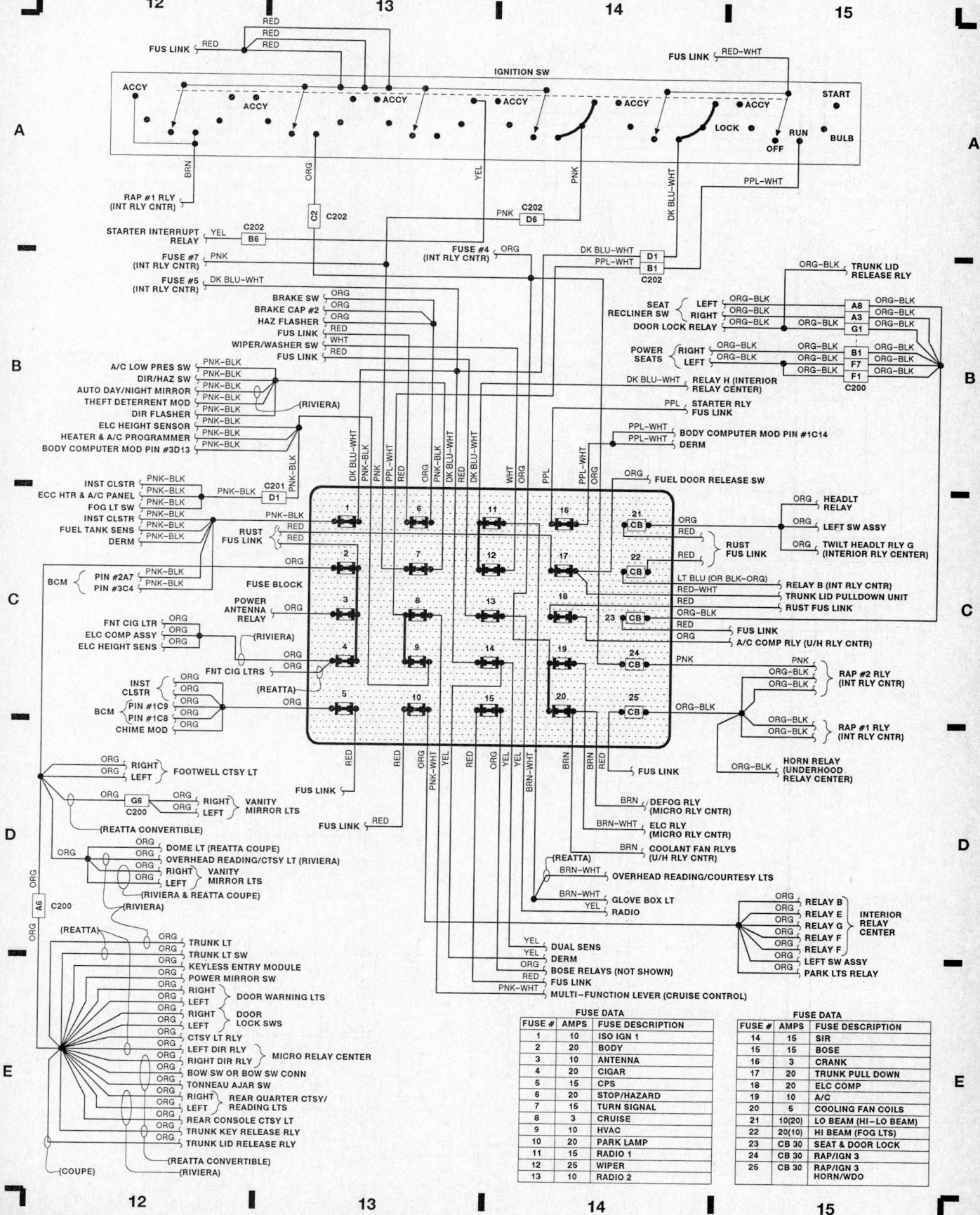

FUSE DATA		
FUSE #	AMPS	FUSE DESCRIPTION
1	10	ISO IGN 1
2	20	BODY
3	10	ANTENNA
4	20	CIGAR
5	15	CPS
6	20	STOP/HAZARD
7	15	TURN SIGNAL
8	5	CRUISE
9	10	HVAC
10	20	PARK LAMP
11	15	RADIO 1
12	25	WIPER
13	10	RADIO 2

FUSE DATA		
FUSE #	AMPS	FUSE DESCRIPTION
14	15	SIR
15	15	BOSE
16	3	CRANK
17	20	TRUNK PULL DOWN
18	20	ELC COMP
19	10	A/C
20	5	COOLING FAN COILS
21	10(20)	LO BEAM (HI-LO BEAM)
22	20(10)	HI BEAM (FOG LTS)
23	CB 30	SEAT & DOOR LOCK
24	CB 30	RAP/IGN 3
25	CB 30	RAP/IGN 3 HORN/WDO

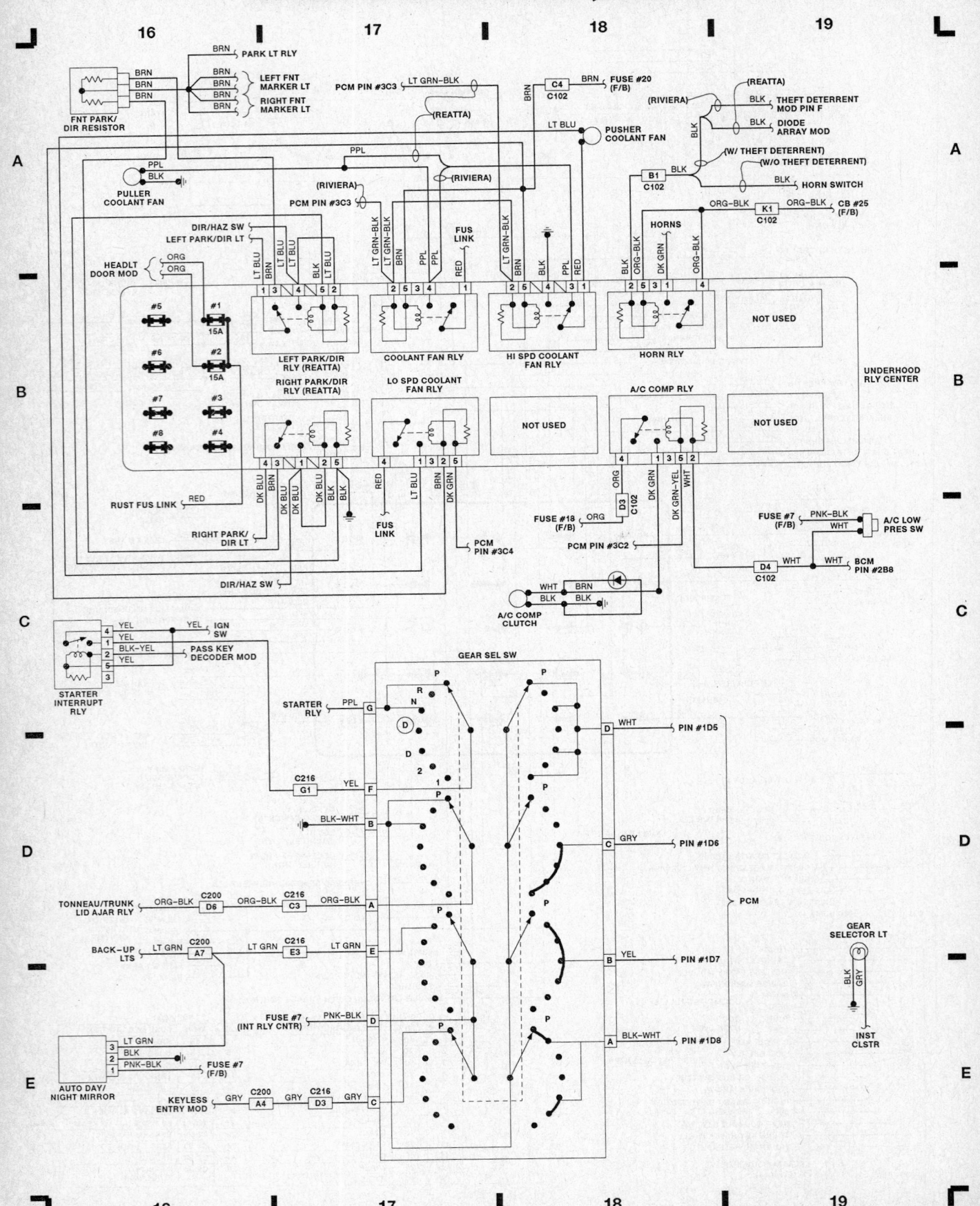

20   21   22   23

A

(REATTA)
HEADLT
DOOR MOD — YEL
YEL

(RIVIERA)

LEFT HEADLT — TAN — J2
C102

CB #21
(F/B)

YEL — 1
ORG — 4
LT BLU — 2
BLK — 5

LEFT SW
ASSEMBLY

HEADLT
RELAY

YEL PIN #1D1 BODY COMPUTER
BLK—RED PIN #2A10 MODULE

(RIVIERA)

YEL DIODE
ARRAY MOD

(REATTA)

LT GRN HI BEAM HEADLTS

(RIVIERA)

PPL FOG
LTS

(REATTA)

CIRC BRKR #22
(FUSE BLOCK)

PASS KEY
DECODER MOD

FUSE #10
(F/B)

ORG

MASS AIRFLOW
SENS

PNK—BLK

BODY
COMPUTER MOD
PIN #2A10

IGN
SW

PCM
PIN #2A2 PNK—BLK

BLK—RED

(RIVIERA)

FUSE #10
(F/B)

B

IGN
SW

C216 F2

DEFOGGER
RELAY (MICRO
RELAY CENTER)

LEFT
HEADLTS

(REATTA)

IGN
SW

DK BLU—WHT

PNK—BLK
PNK—BLK
PNK

RED—BLK

ORG
BLK—RED

LT GRN
TAN
YEL

ORG
BLK—RED (OR YEL)
BLK—RED (OR YEL)
LT GRN (OR PPL)
BLK—ORG (OR LT BLU)

FUS
LINK #5

RED

IGN
SW ORG

#2

#7

#8

#3

#4

5 2 4 3 1

E

5 2 3 4 1

FUEL PUMP RLY
(B 8)

B

NOT USED

A

INTERIOR
RELAY
CENTER

C

PNK—BLK

PNK—BLK

D F G H J K

4 1 3 5 2

F

4 1 3 2 5

G

4 1 2 5

H

4 3 1 2 5

J

NOT USED

C

PNK—BLK

ABS MOD
PIN #1 PNK—BLK

FUEL PUMP RELAY

FUEL INJECTORS C4
C200

KEYLESS
ENTRY MOD ORG

ORG
BRN
ORG
BLK—PNK

F ORG

YEL
BLK—PNK
ORG

DK BLU—WHT
BRN
ORG—BLK
ORG—BLK
BLK

PNK
PNK
ORG—BLK
ORG—BLK
BLK

ORG—BLK
ORG—BLK
ORG—BLK
ORG—BLK

CB #25
(F/B)

FUSE #10
(F/B) ORG
ORG
ORG
BRN

PARK LT RLY BLK—PNK
BCM PIN #1D4 BLK—PNK
DIODE ARRAY MOD

(REATTA)

CB #21
(F/B)

BODY
COMPUTER
MODULE
PIN #1C3

CB #24
(F/B)

D

PNK—BLK
PNK—BLK KEYLESS ENTRY MOD
BRAKE SW

PNK—BLK M7 PNK—BLK
C216

PNK—BLK CANISTER PURGE SOL
PNK—BLK AUTO TRANSAXLE
PNK—BLK GEAR SELECTOR SW

(RIVIERA)

(RIVIERA)

BODY COMPUTER
MOD PIN #1D4 BLK—PNK

BCM
PIN #2A11 BLK—PNK

(REATTA)

FUSE #11 DK BLU—WHT
(F/B)

C6 C202

BLK

BLK—PNK

THEFT
DETERRENT
RELAY

PNK TONNEAU RELEASE RELAY

PNK

(CONVERTIBLE)

PNK

PNK SUNROOF SW

(EX CONVERTIBLE)

A2 F2
C200

PNK
PNK

PNK
PNK

POWER
WDO SWS

IGN
SW

BRN

RLY DESIGN	RLY DESCRIPTION (RIVIERA)	RLY DESCRIPTION (REATTA)
A	NOT USED	NOT USED
B	HI BEAM	FOG LT
C	FUEL PUMP RLY	FUEL PUMP RLY
D	NOT USED	NOT USED
E	LO BEAM	HI-LO BEAM
F	TWILT PARK LT	PARK
G	TWILT HEADLT	NOT USED
H	RAP #1	RAP #1
J	RAP #2	RAP #2
K	NOT USED	NOT USED

FUSE DATA

FUSE #	AMP	DESCRIPTION
1		NOT USED
2	25	DEFOG
3	15	KEYLESS ENTRY
4	10	ANTI-LOCK
5	10	ECM/IGN
6		NOT USED
7	15	ECM SOL
8	15	CCCI

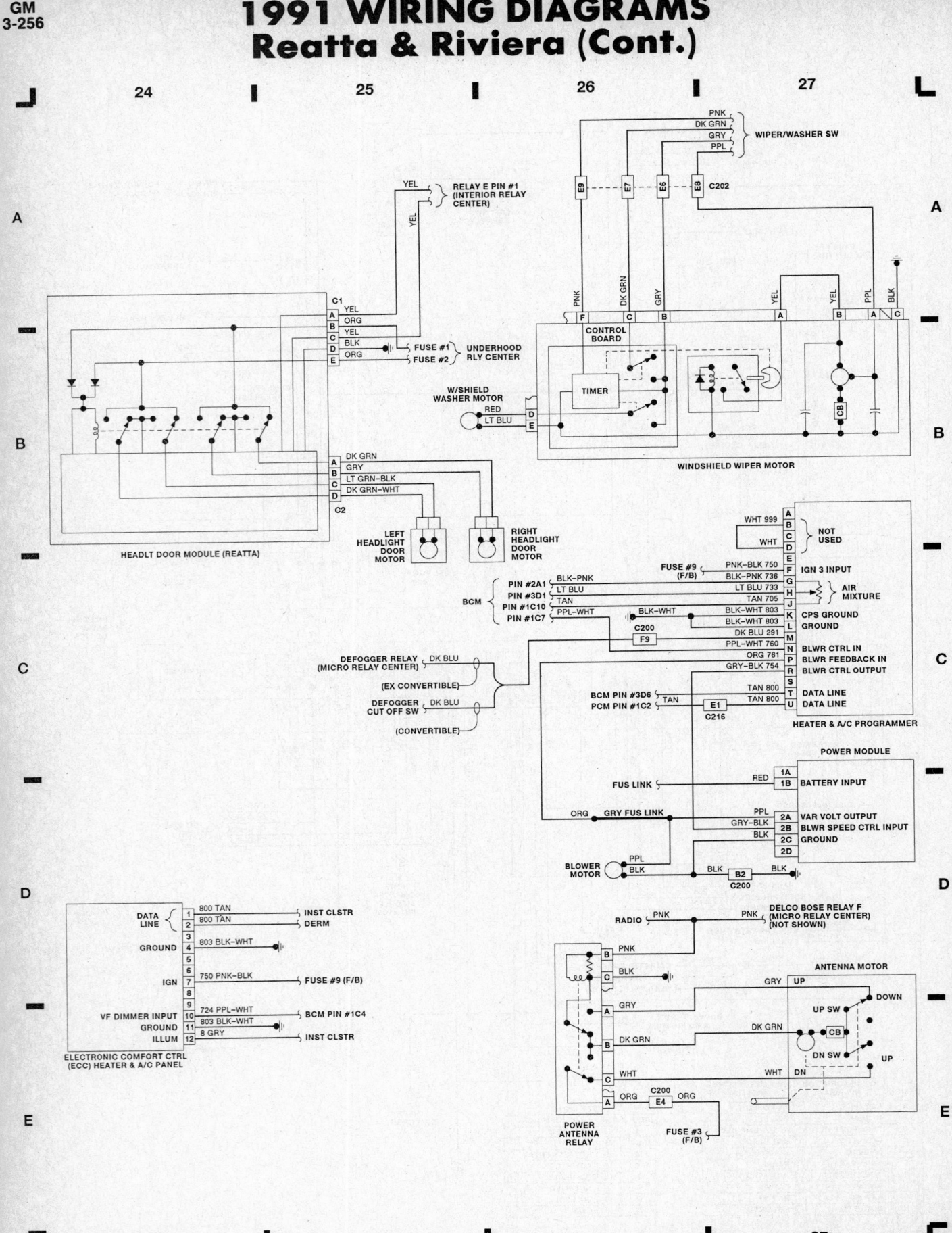

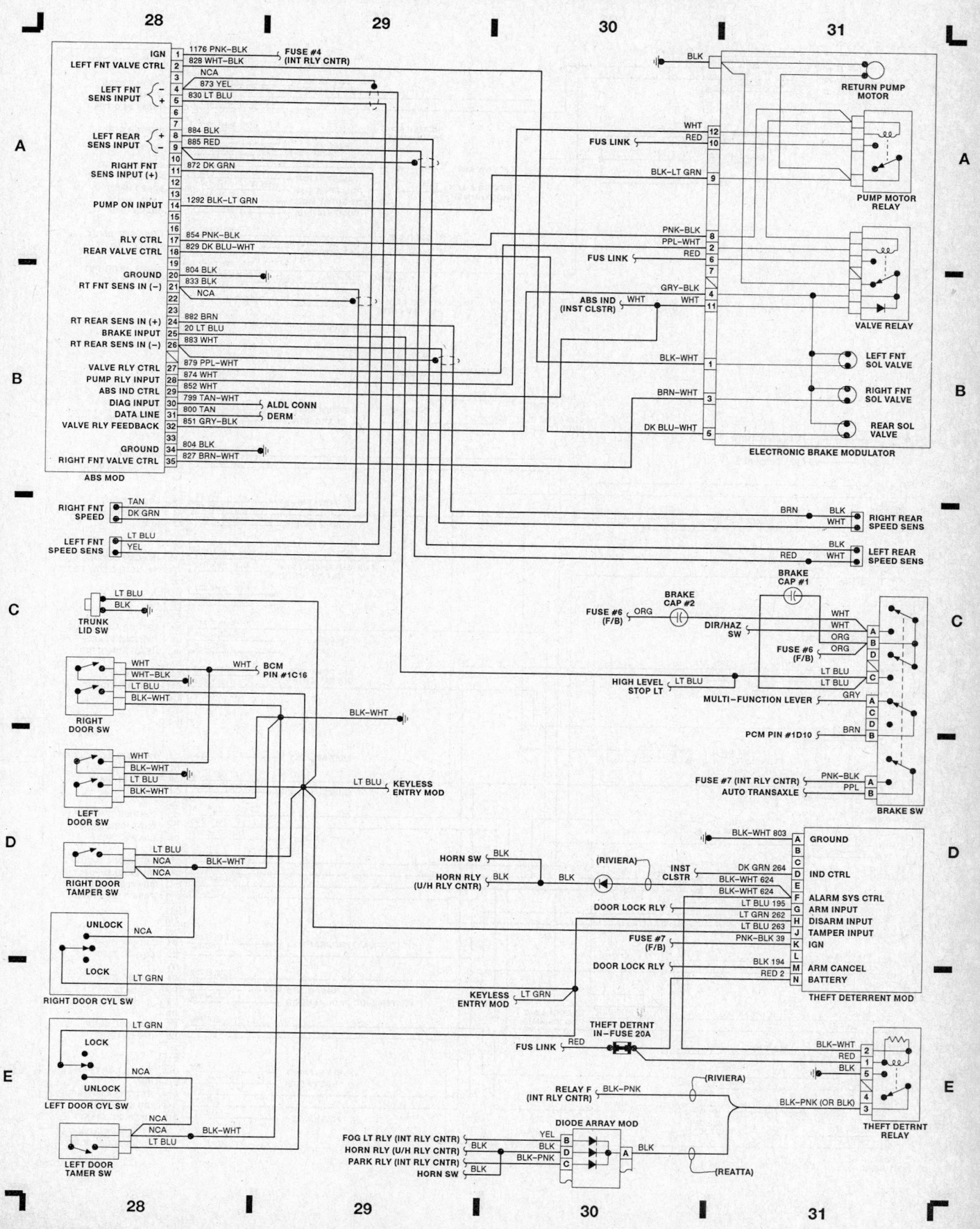

1991 WIRING DIAGRAMS
Reatta & Riviera (Cont.)

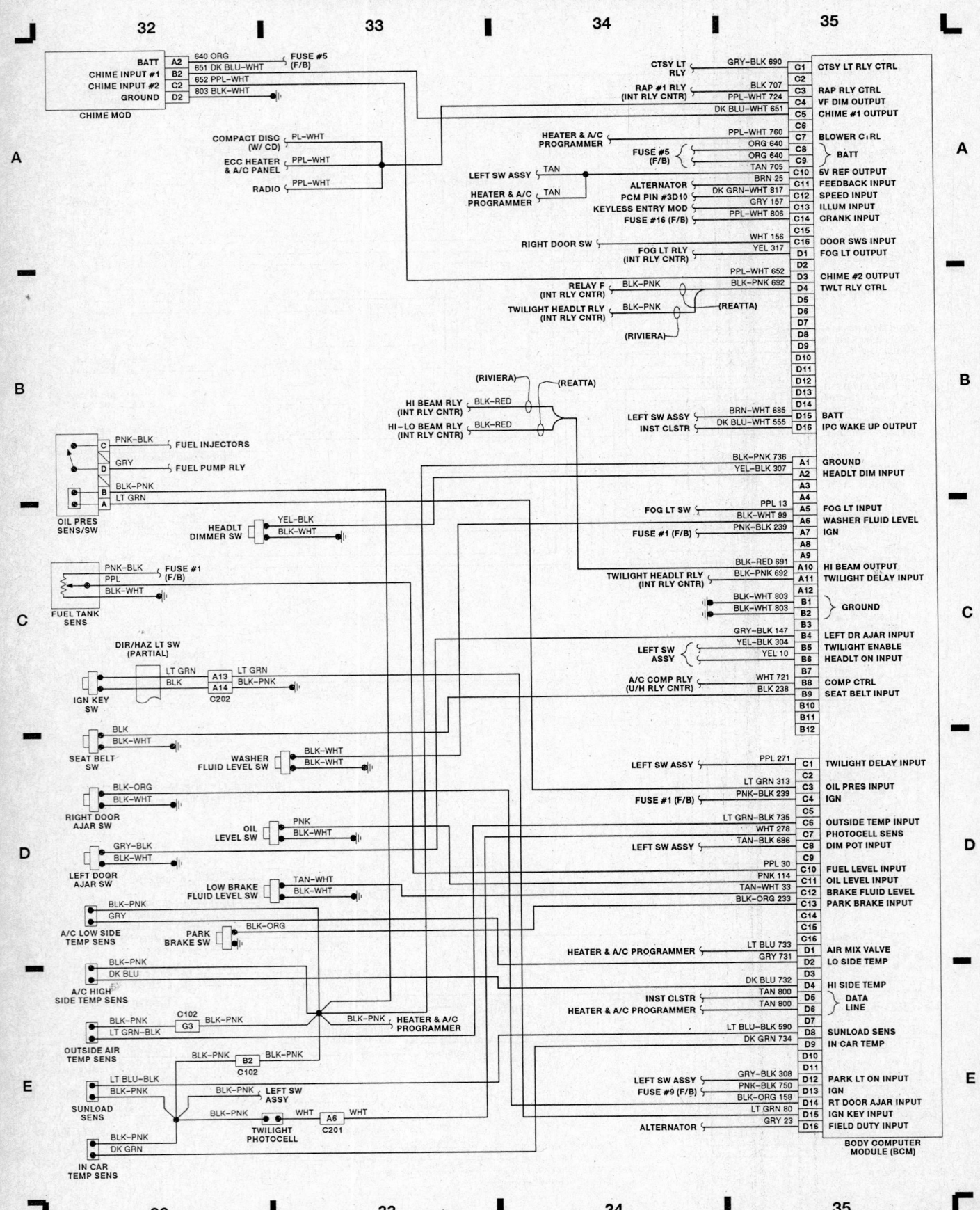

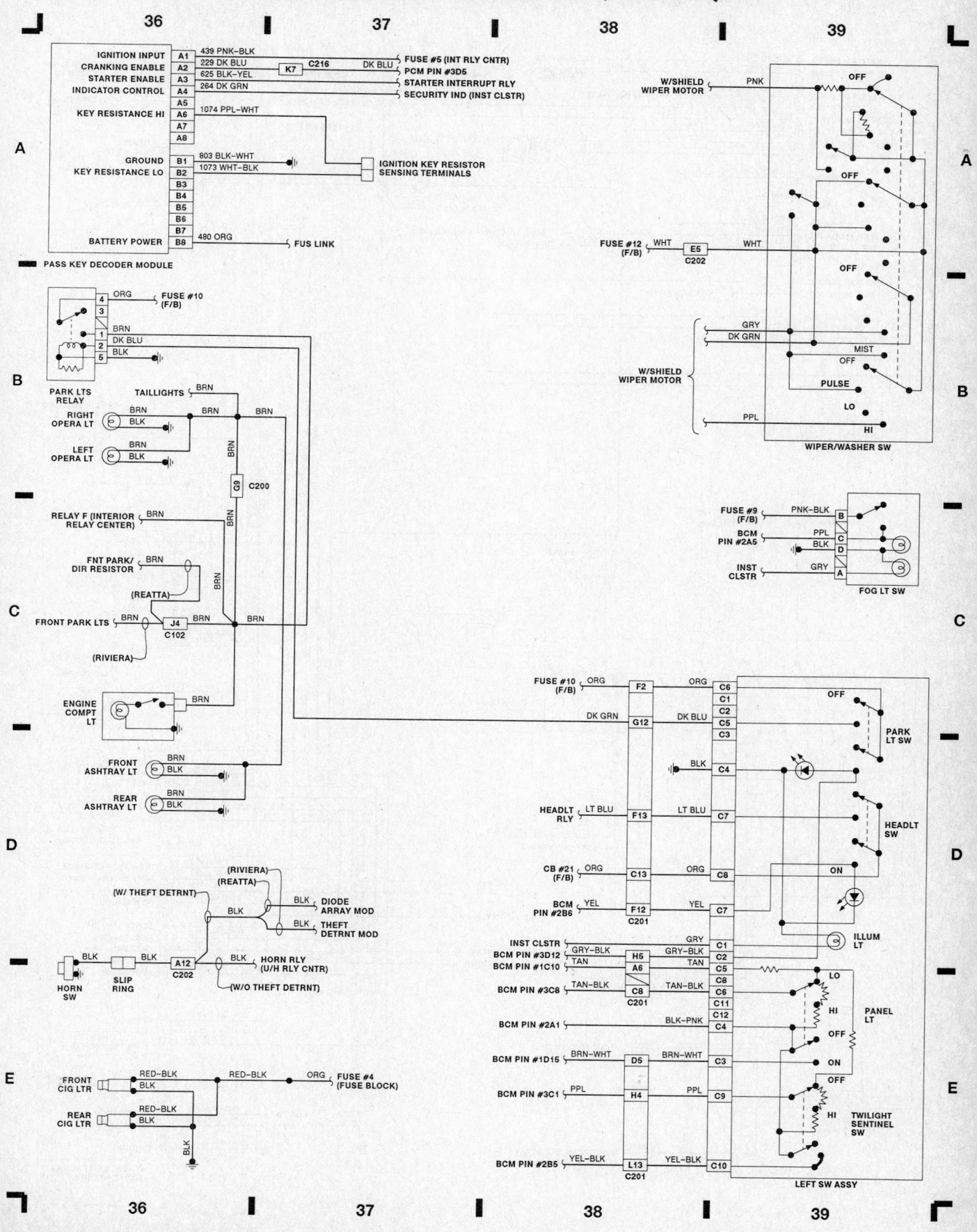

1991 WIRING DIAGRAMS
Reatta & Riviera (Cont.)

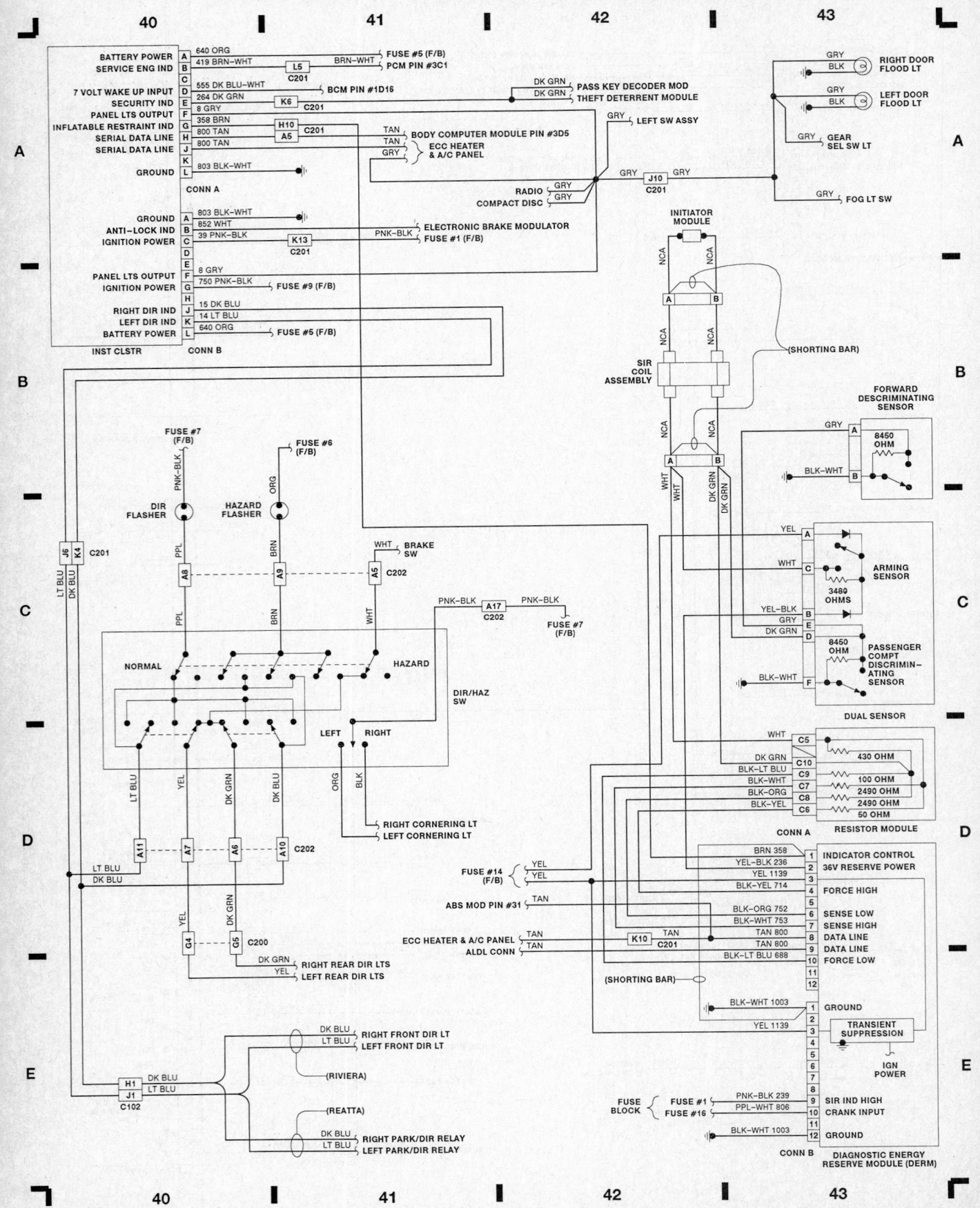

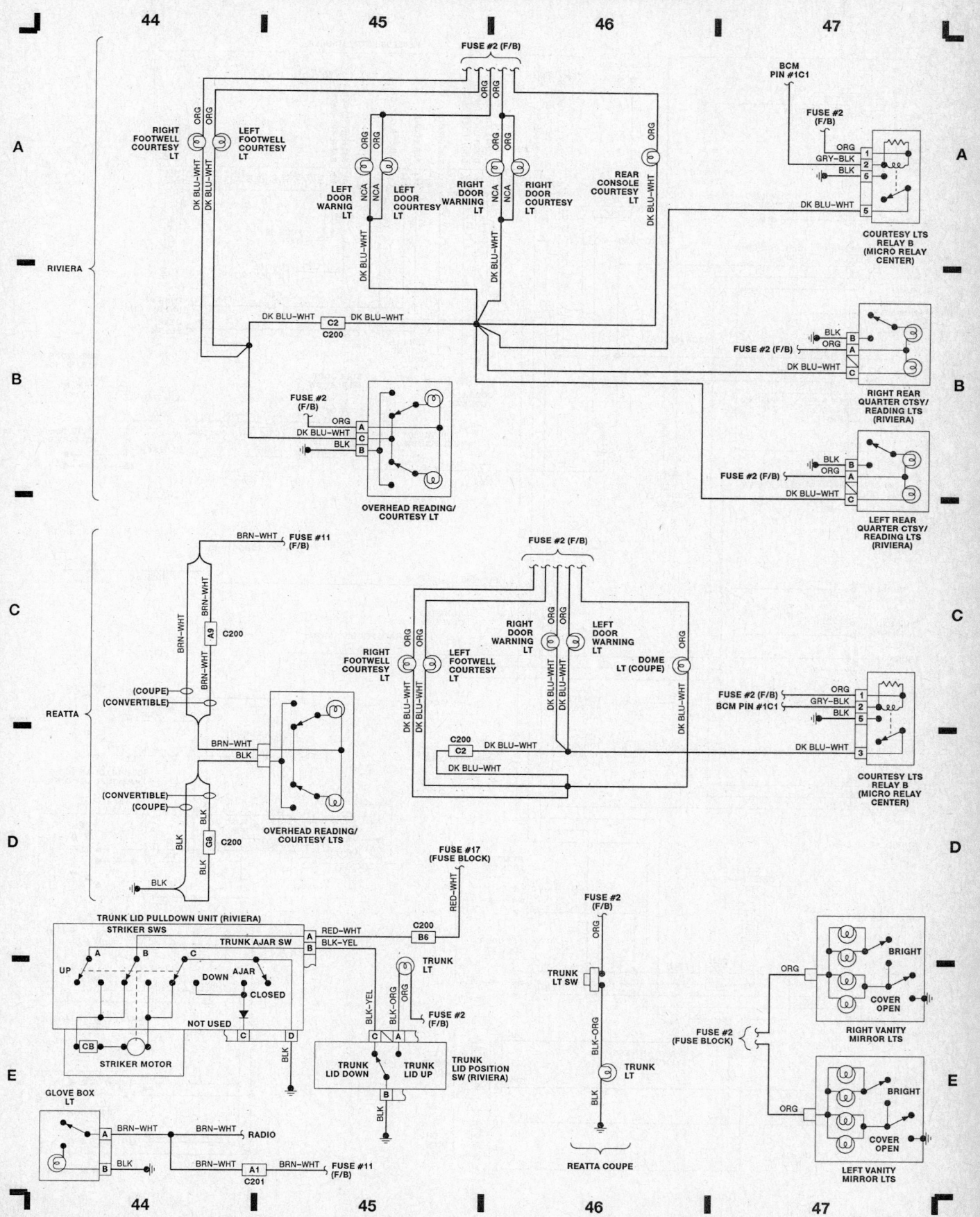

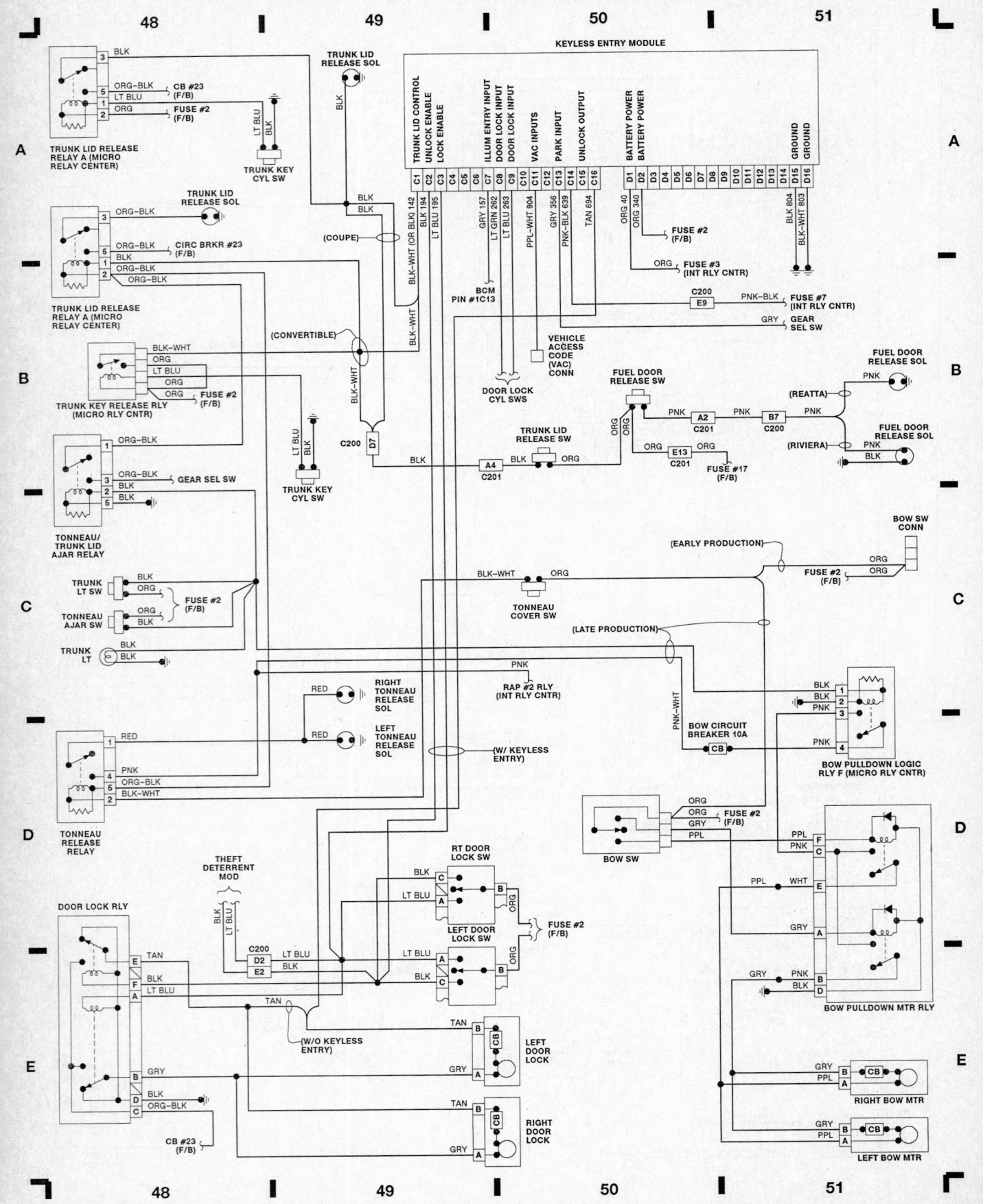

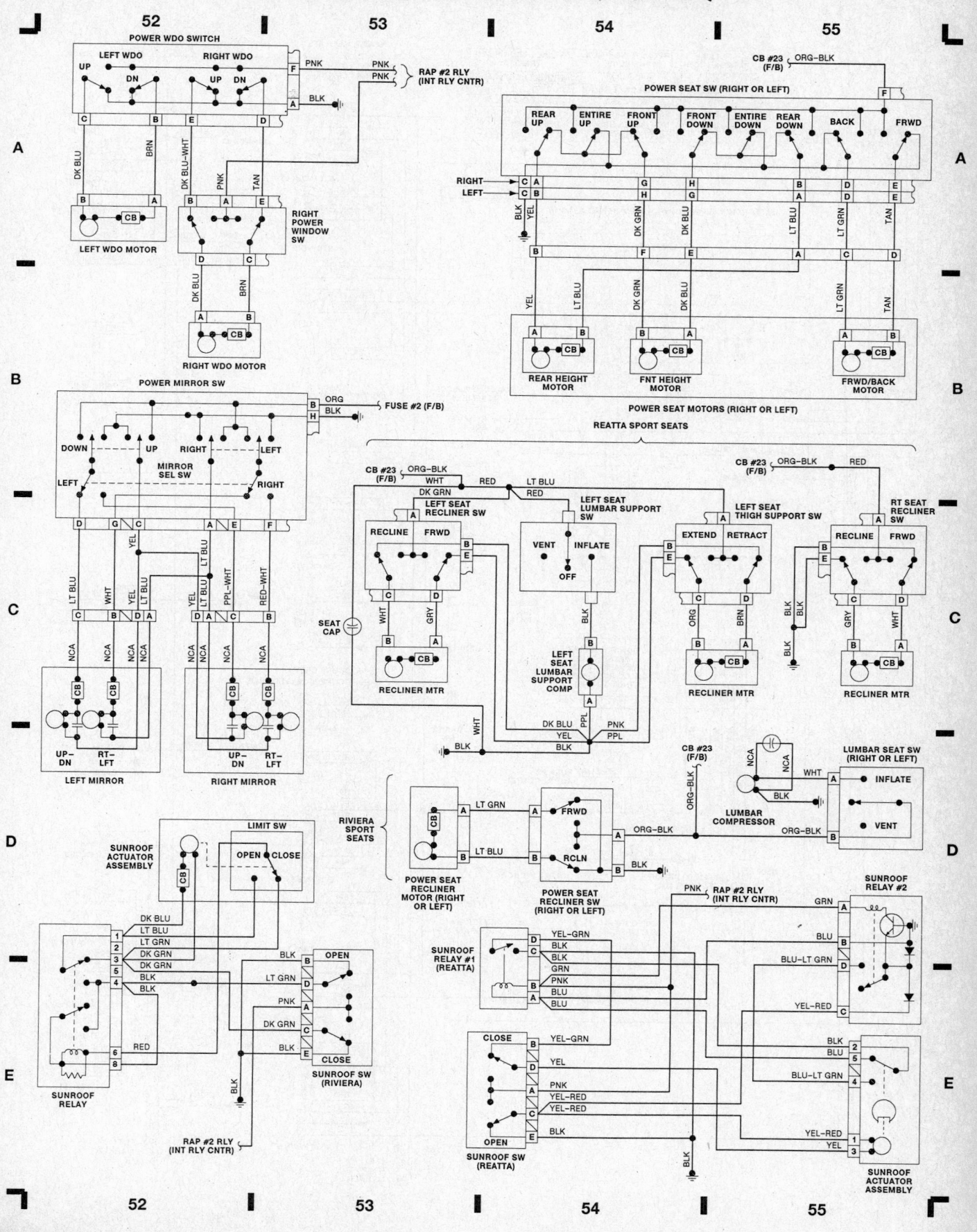

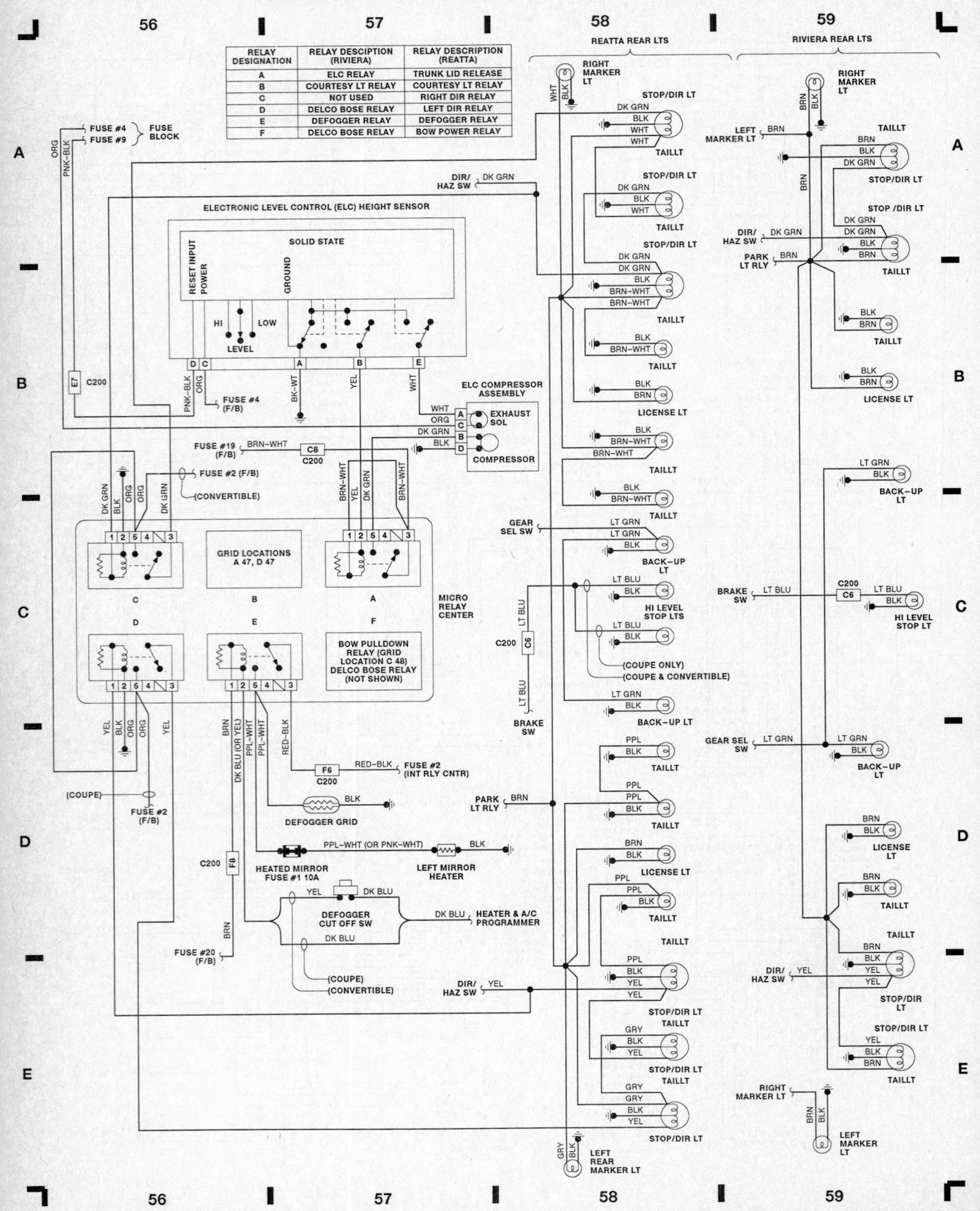

RELAY DESIGNATION	RELAY DESCIPTION (RIVIERA)	RELAY DESCRIPTION (REATTA)
A	ELC RELAY	TRUNK LID RELEASE
B	COURTESY LT RELAY	COURTESY LT RELAY
C	NOT USED	RIGHT DIR RELAY
D	DELCO BOSE RELAY	LEFT DIR RELAY
E	DEFOGGER RELAY	DEFOGGER RELAY
F	DELCO BOSE RELAY	BOW POWER RELAY

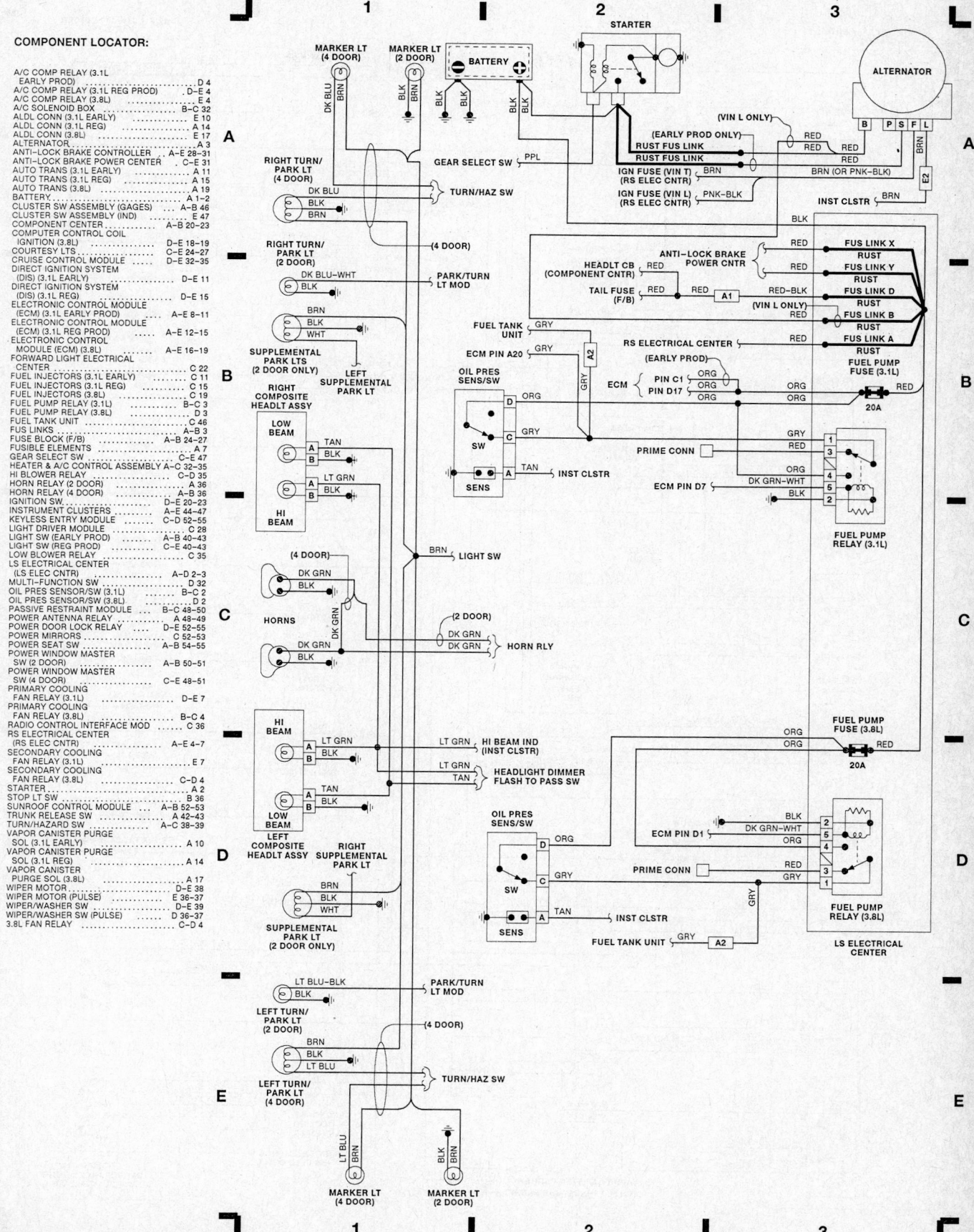

COMPONENT LOCATOR:

A/C COMP RELAY (3.1L EARLY PROD) .... D 4
A/C COMP RELAY (3.1L REG PROD) .. D-E 4
A/C COMP RELAY (3.8L) .... E 4
A/C SOLENOID BOX .... B-C 32
ALDL CONN (3.1L EARLY) .... E 10
ALDL CONN (3.1L REG) .... A 14
ALDL CONN (3.8L) .... E 17
ALTERNATOR .... A 3
ANTI-LOCK BRAKE CONTROLLER . A-E 28–31
ANTI-LOCK BRAKE POWER CENTER . C-E 31
AUTO TRANS (3.1L EARLY) .... A 11
AUTO TRANS (3.1L REG) .... A 15
AUTO TRANS (3.8L) .... A 19
BATTERY .... A 1–2
CLUSTER SW ASSEMBLY (GAGES) ... A-B 46
CLUSTER SW ASSEMBLY (IND) ...... E 47
COMPONENT CENTER .... A-B 20–23
COMPUTER CONTROL COIL
IGNITION (3.8L) .... D-E 18–19
COURTESY LTS .... C-E 24–27
CRUISE CONTROL MODULE ...... D-E 32–35
DIRECT IGNITION SYSTEM
(DIS) (3.1L EARLY) .... D-E 11
DIRECT IGNITION SYSTEM
(DIS) (3.1L REG) .... D-E 15
ELECTRONIC CONTROL MODULE
(ECM) (3.1L EARLY PROD) ...... A-E 8–11
ELECTRONIC CONTROL MODULE
(ECM) (3.1L REG PROD) ..... A-E 12–15
ELECTRONIC CONTROL
MODULE (ECM) (3.8L) .... A-E 16–19
FORWARD LIGHT ELECTRICAL
CENTER .... C 22
FUEL INJECTORS (3.1L EARLY) ..... C 11
FUEL INJECTORS (3.1L REG) .... C 15
FUEL INJECTORS (3.8L) .... C 19
FUEL PUMP RELAY (3.1L) .... B-C 3
FUEL PUMP RELAY (3.8L) .... D 3
FUEL TANK UNIT .... C 46
FUS LINKS .... A-B 3
FUSE BLOCK (F/B) .... A-B 24–27
FUSIBLE ELEMENTS .... A 7
GEAR SELECT SW .... C-E 47
HEATER & A/C CONTROL ASSEMBLY A-C 32–35
HI BLOWER RELAY .... C-D 35
HORN RELAY (2 DOOR) .... A 36
HORN RELAY (4 DOOR) .... A-B 36
IGNITION SW. .... D-E 20–23
INSTRUMENT CLUSTERS .... A-E 44–47
KEYLESS ENTRY MODULE .... C-D 52–55
LIGHT DRIVER MODULE .... C 28
LIGHT SW (EARLY PROD) .... A-B 40–43
LIGHT SW (REG PROD) .... C-E 40–43
LOW BLOWER RELAY .... C 35
LS ELECTRICAL CENTER
(LS ELEC CNTR) .... A-D 2–3
MULTI-FUNCTION SW .... D 32
OIL PRES SENSOR/SW (3.1L) ..... B-C 2
OIL PRES SENSOR/SW (3.8L) .... D 2
PASSIVE RESTRAINT MODULE ... B-C 48–50
POWER ANTENNA RELAY .... A 48–49
POWER DOOR LOCK RELAY .... D-E 52–55
POWER MIRRORS .... C 52–53
POWER SEAT SW .... A-B 54–55
POWER WINDOW MASTER
SW (2 DOOR) .... A-B 50–51
POWER WINDOW MASTER
SW (4 DOOR) .... C-E 48–51
PRIMARY COOLING
FAN RELAY (3.1L) .... D-E 7
PRIMARY COOLING
FAN RELAY (3.8L) .... B-C 4
RADIO CONTROL INTERFACE MOD ... C 36
RS ELECTRICAL CENTER
(RS ELEC CNTR) .... A-E 4–7
SECONDARY COOLING
FAN RELAY (3.1L) .... E 7
SECONDARY COOLING
FAN RELAY (3.8L) .... C-D 4
STARTER .... A 2
STOP LT SW .... B 36
SUNROOF CONTROL MODULE .... A-B 52–53
TRUNK RELEASE SW .... A 42–43
TURN/HAZARD SW .... A-C 38–39
VAPOR CANISTER PURGE
SOL (3.1L EARLY) .... A 10
VAPOR CANISTER PURGE
SOL (3.1L REG) .... A 14
VAPOR CANISTER
PURGE SOL (3.8L) .... A 17
WIPER MOTOR .... D-E 38
WIPER MOTOR (PULSE) .... E 36–37
WIPER/WASHER SW .... D-E 39
WIPER/WASHER SW (PULSE) .... D 36–37
3.8L FAN RELAY .... C-D 4

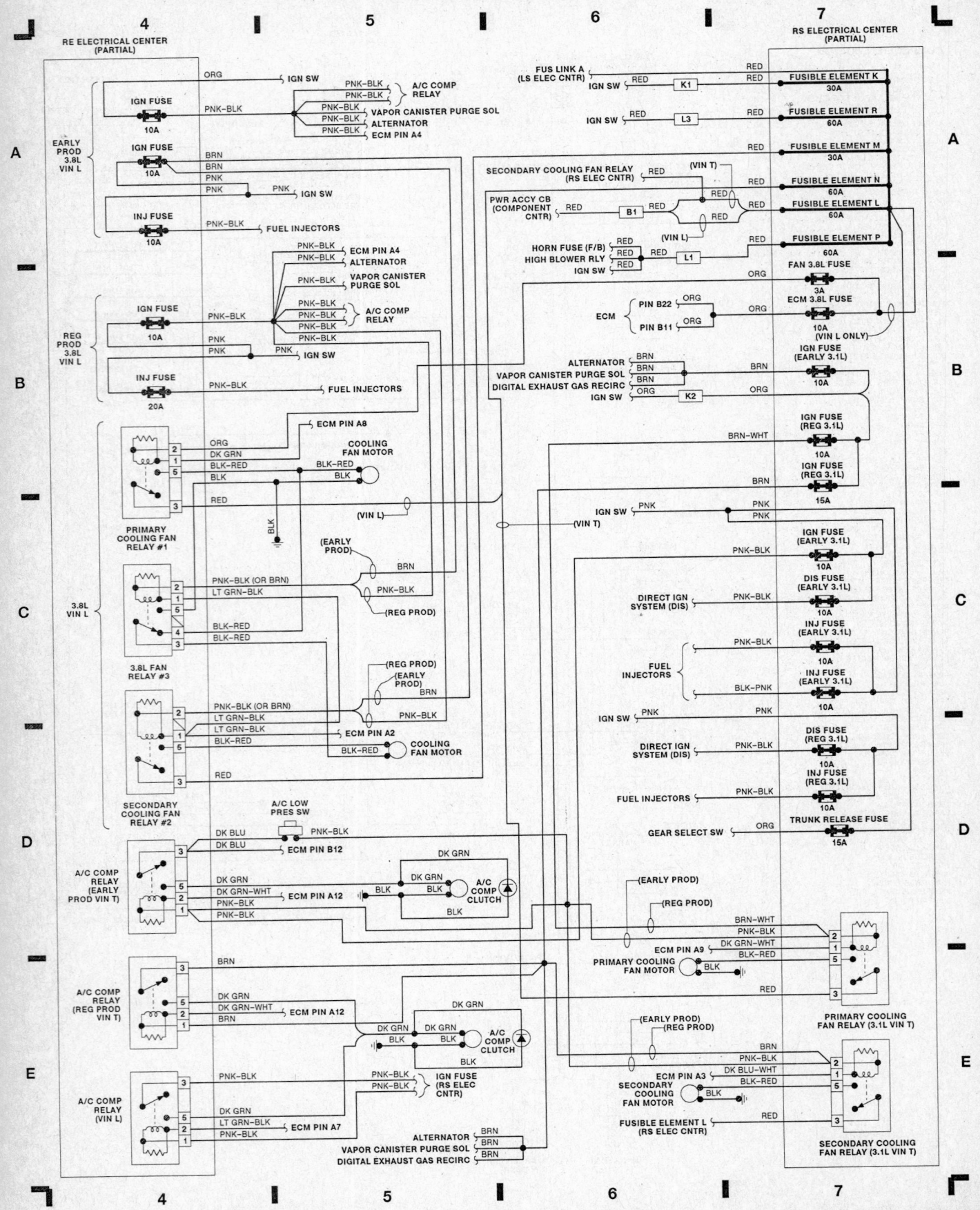

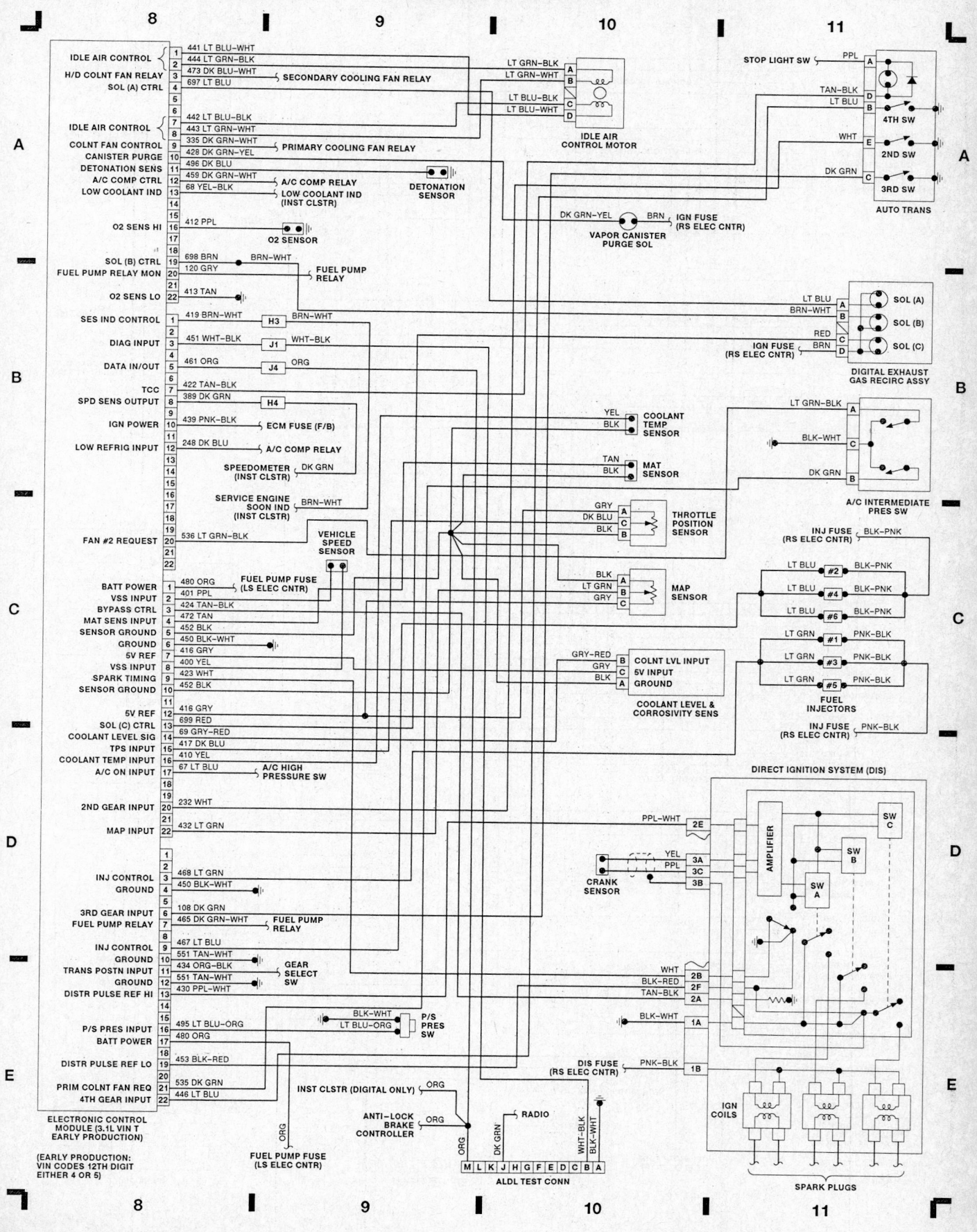

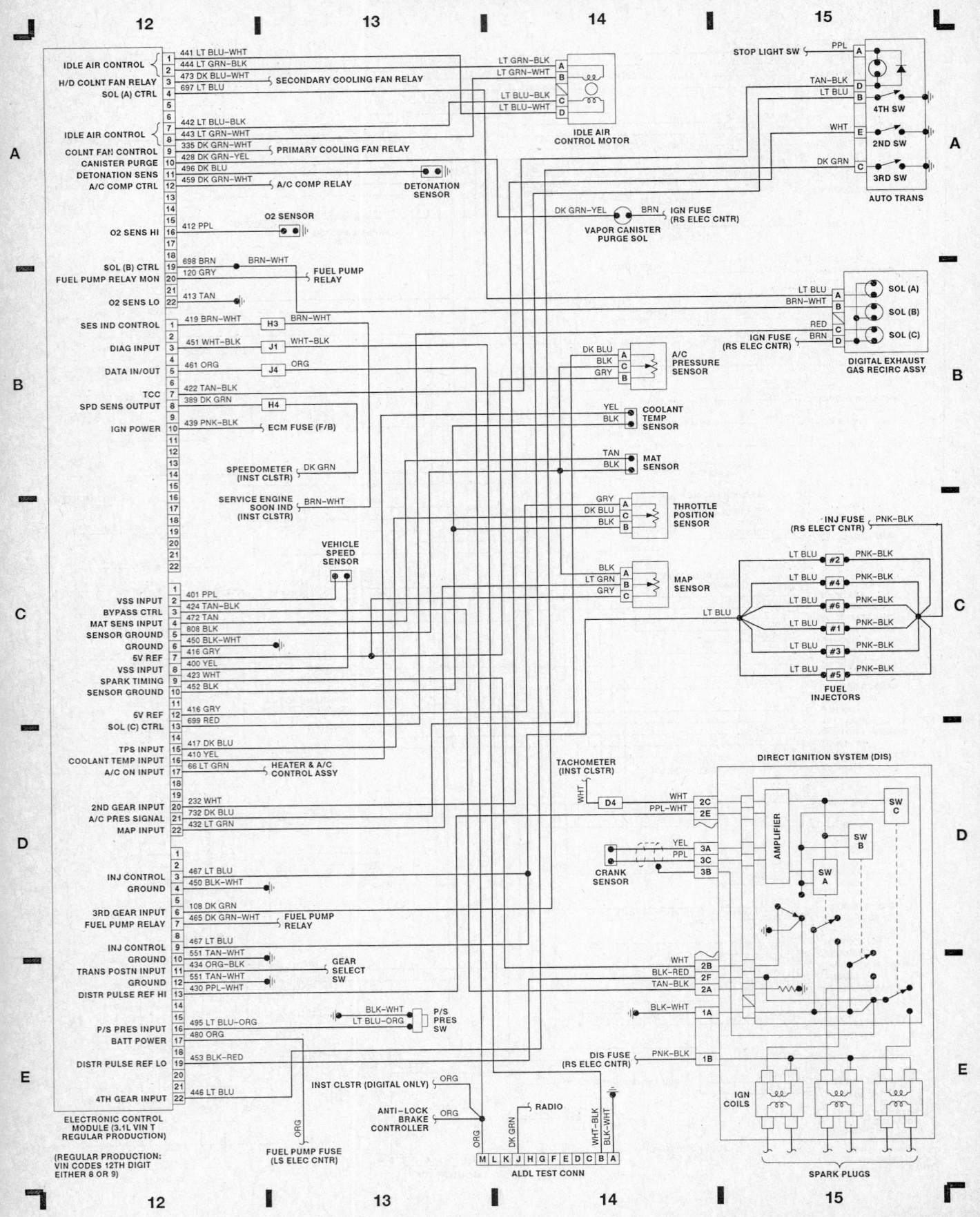

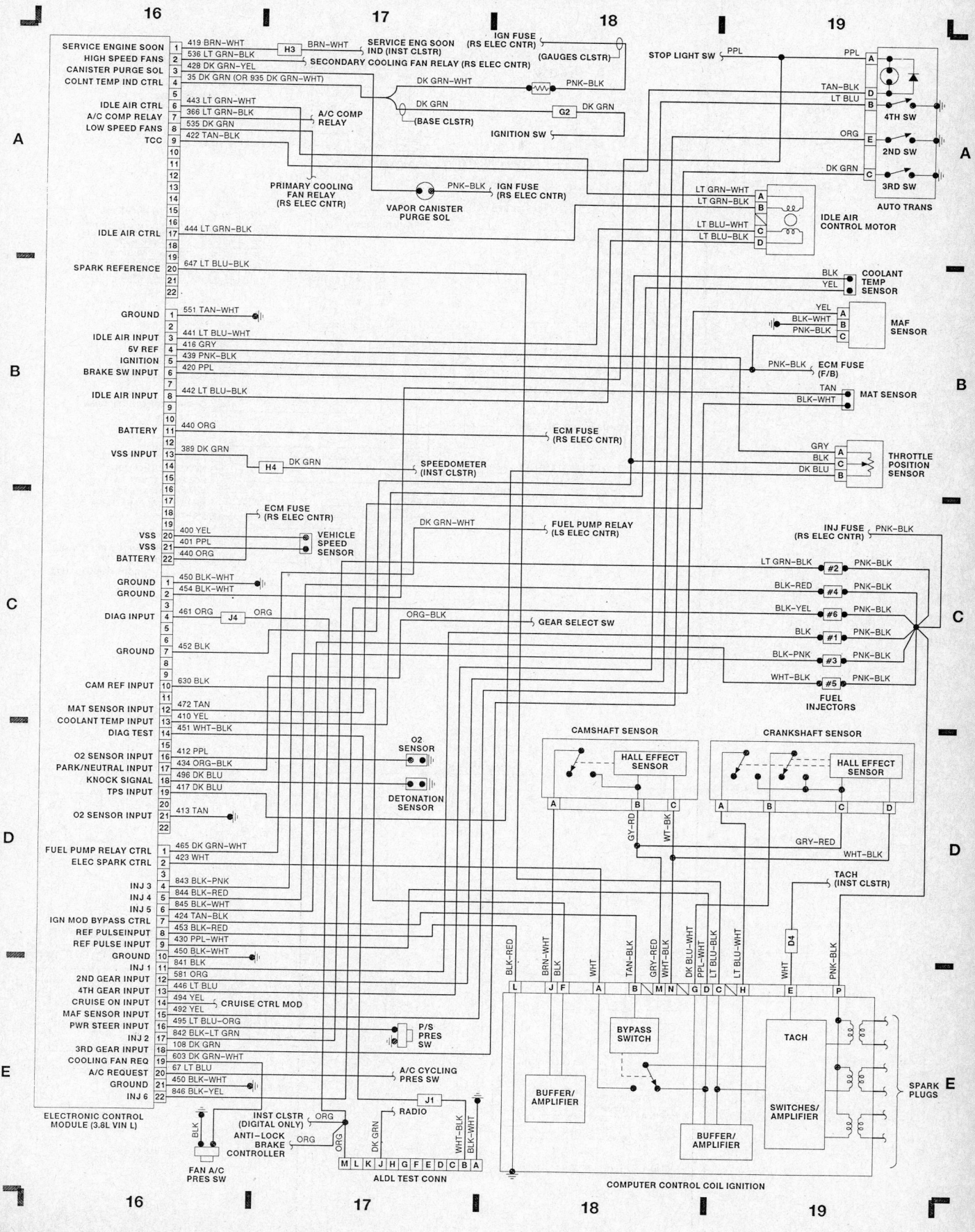

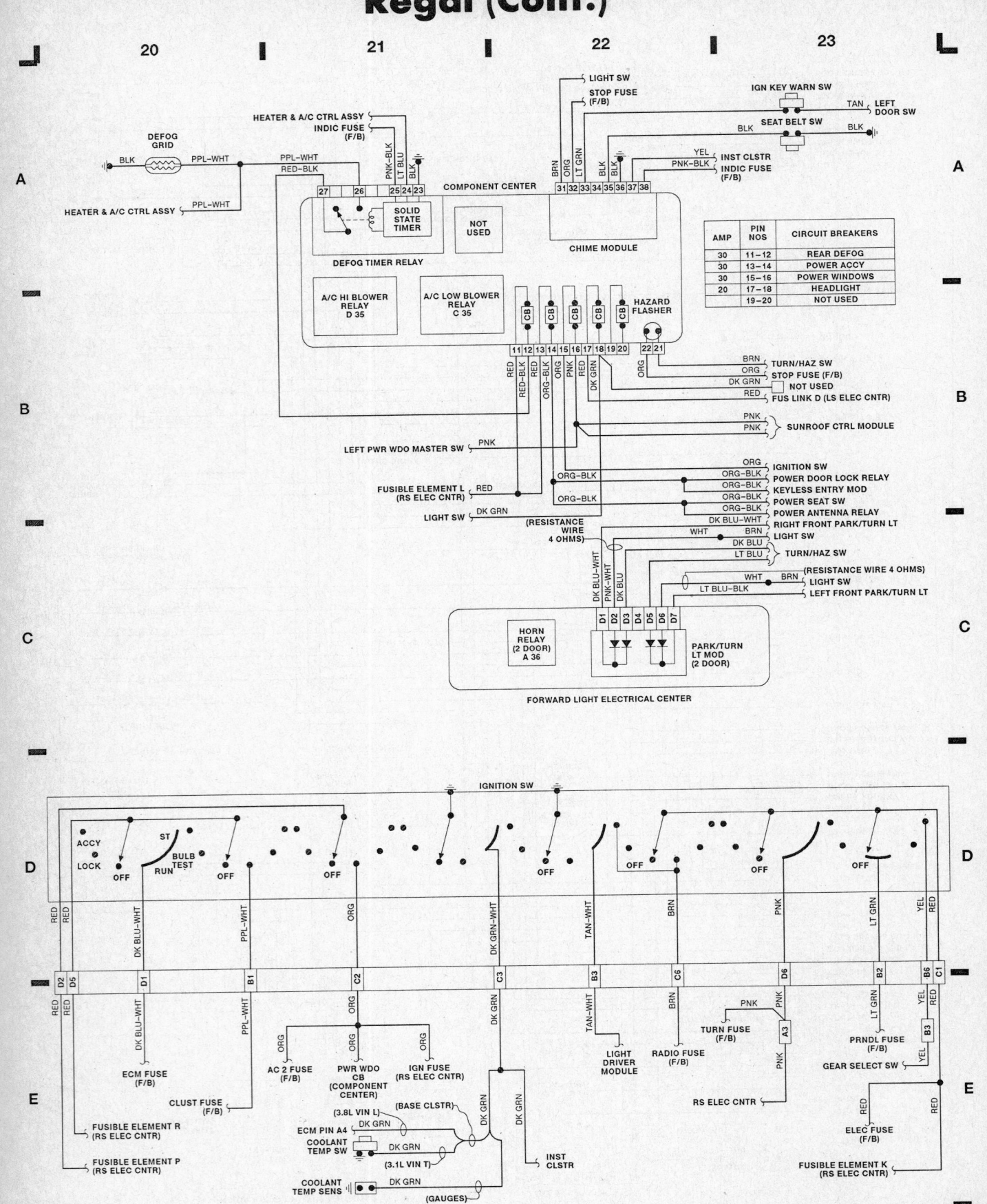

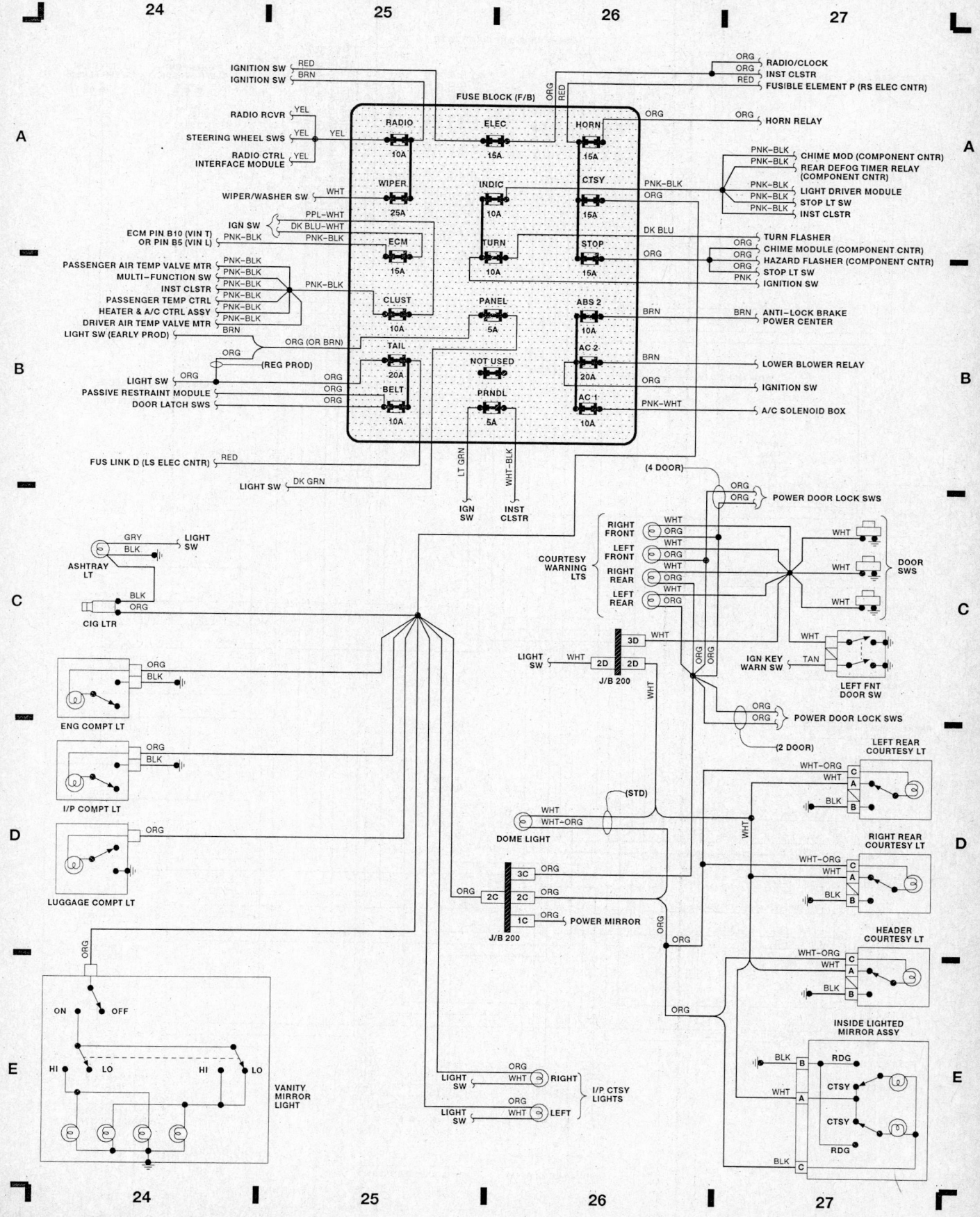

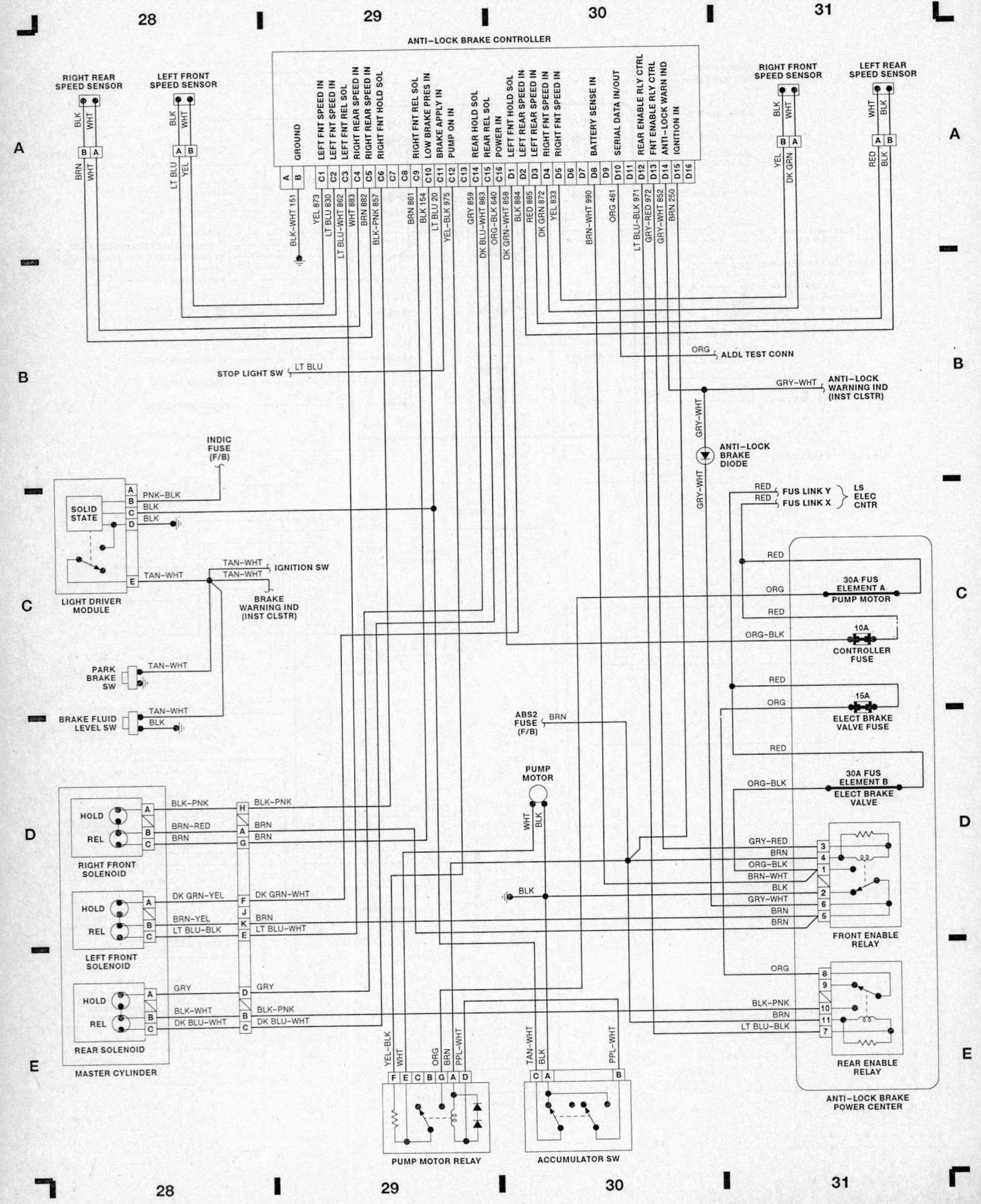

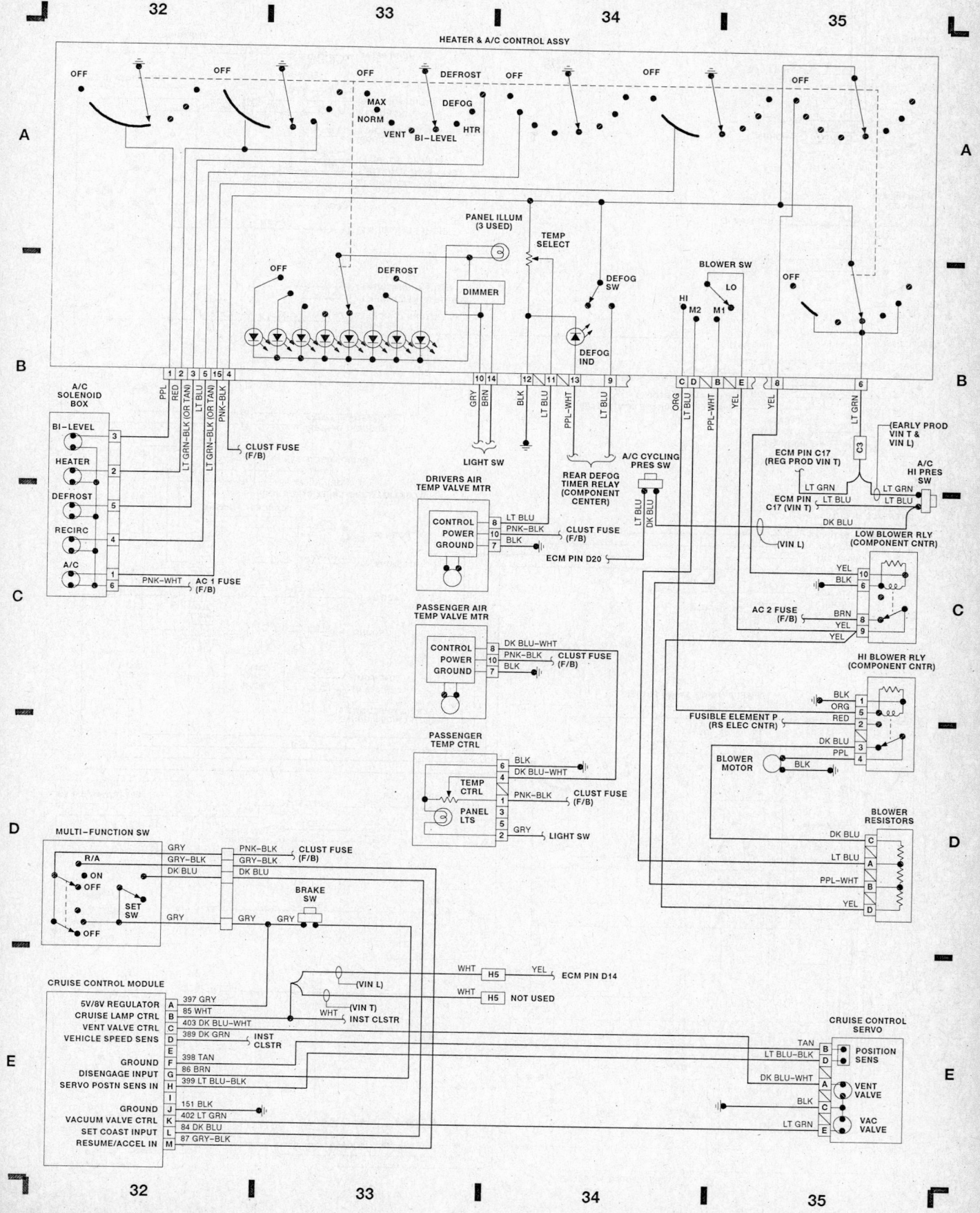

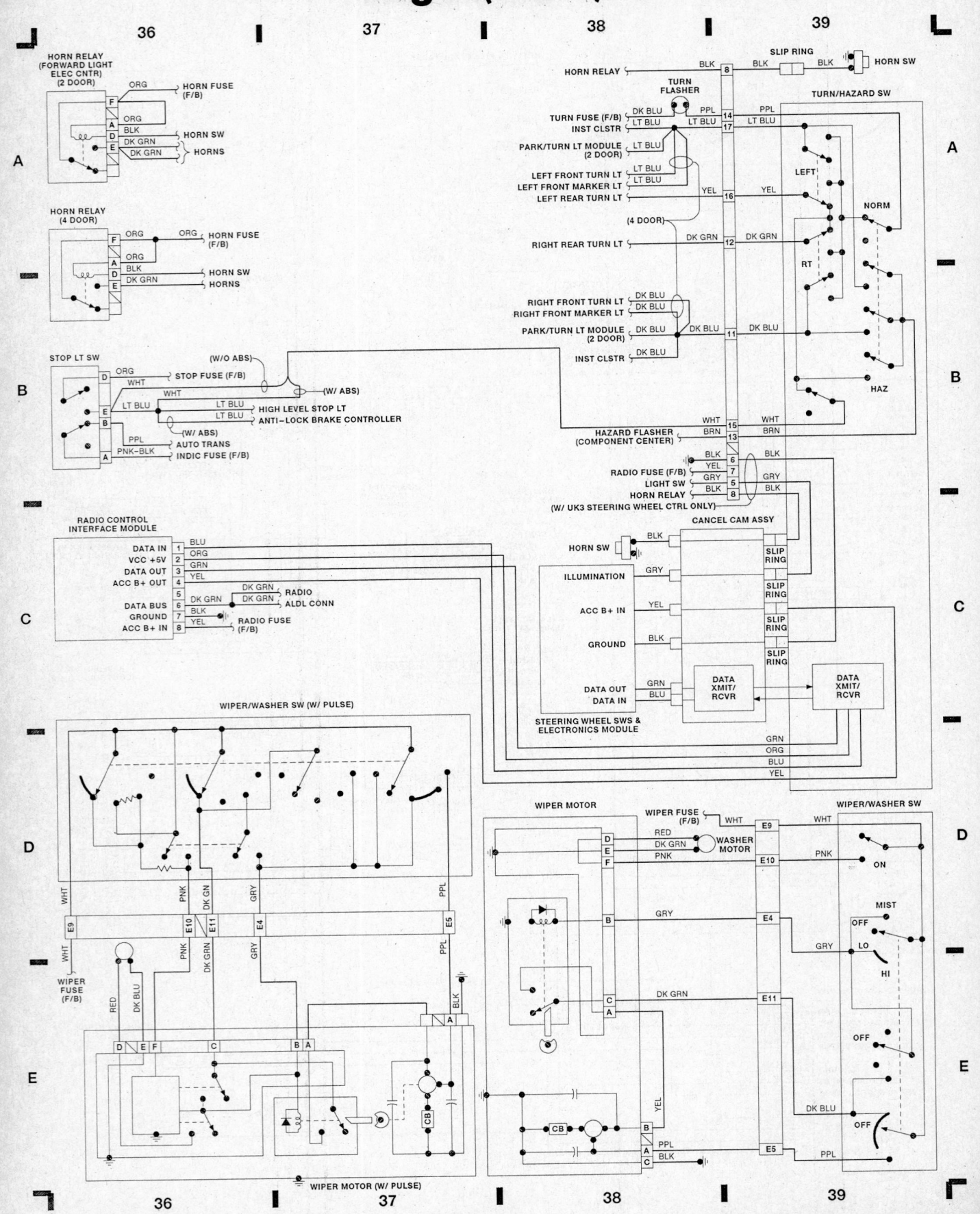

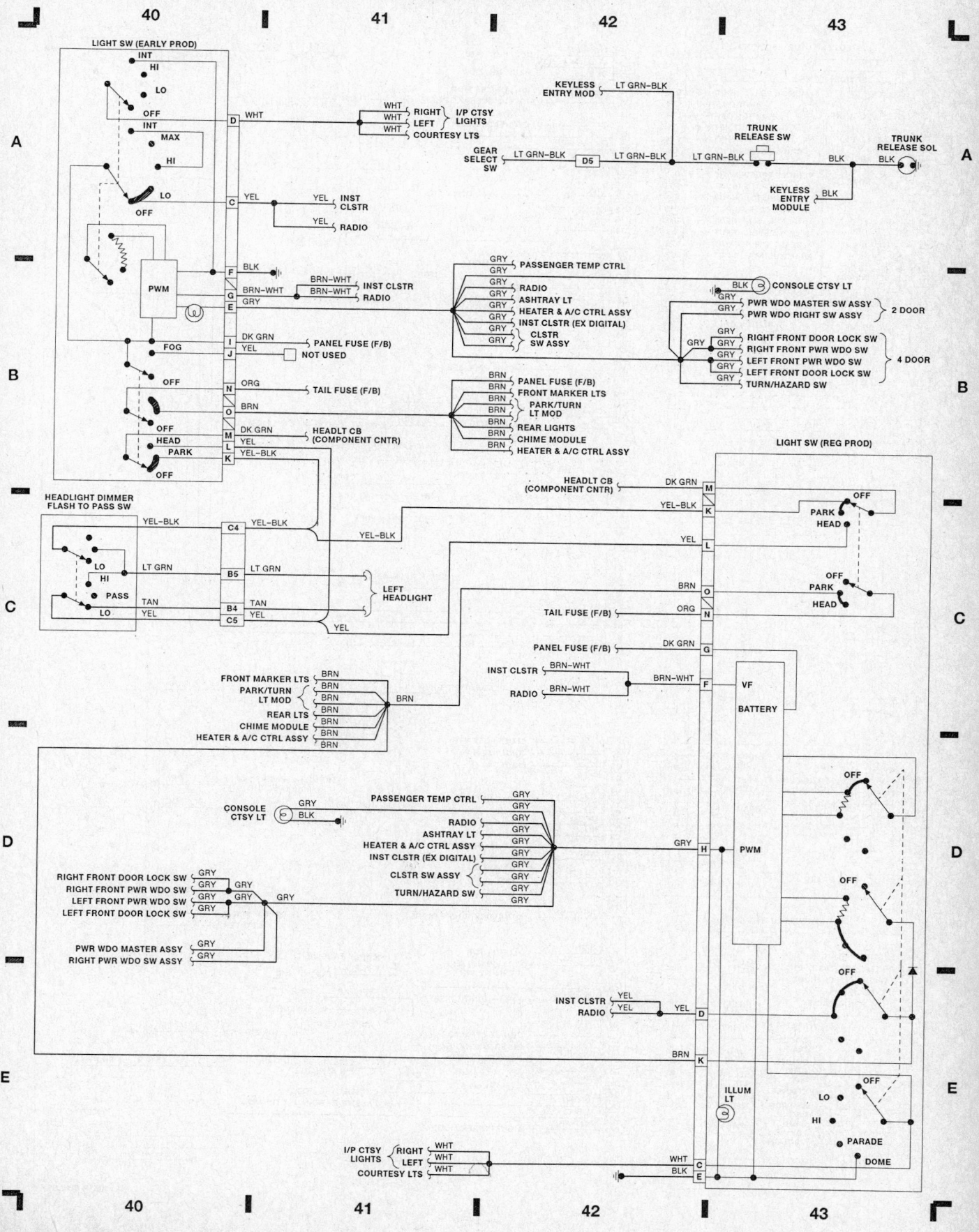

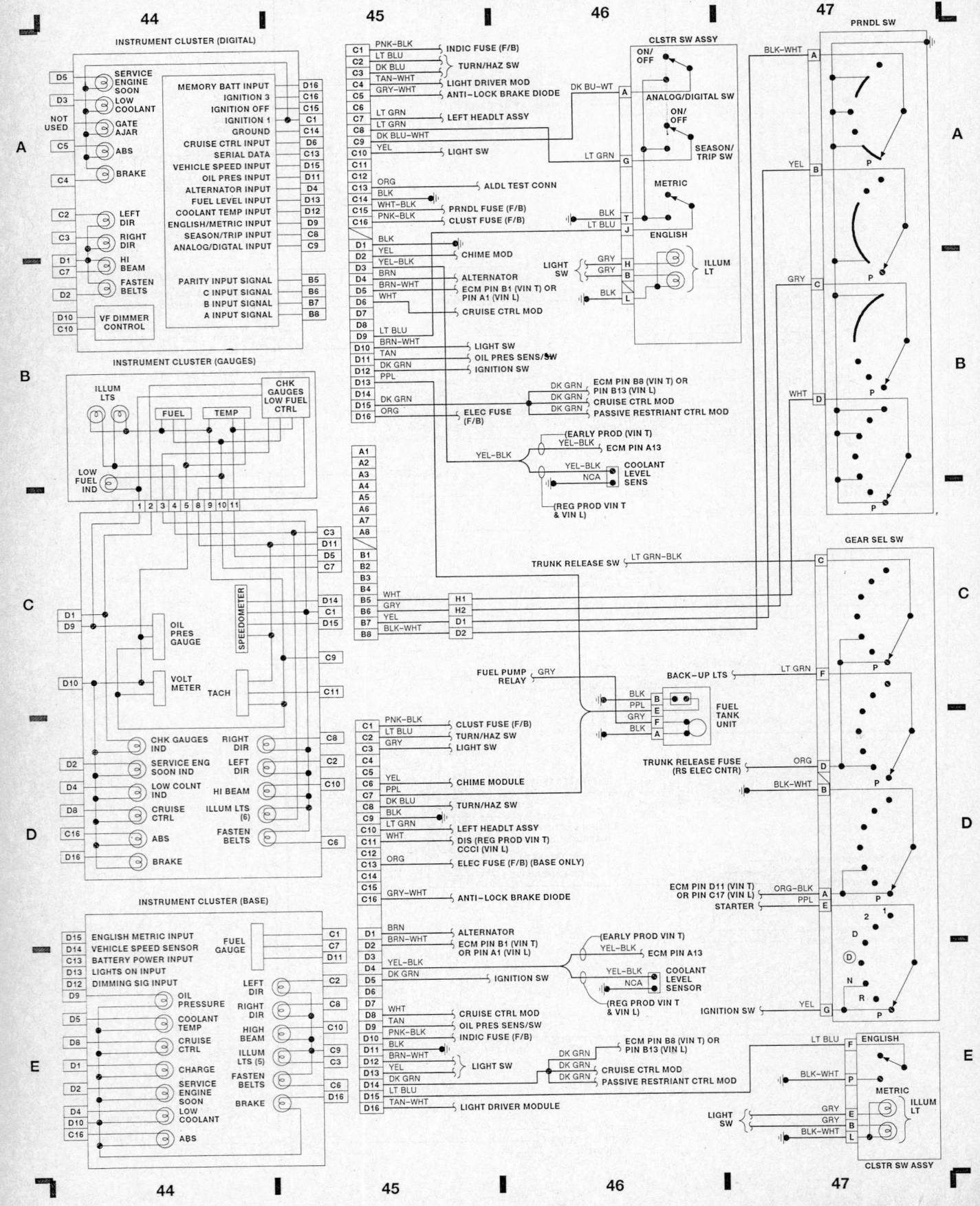

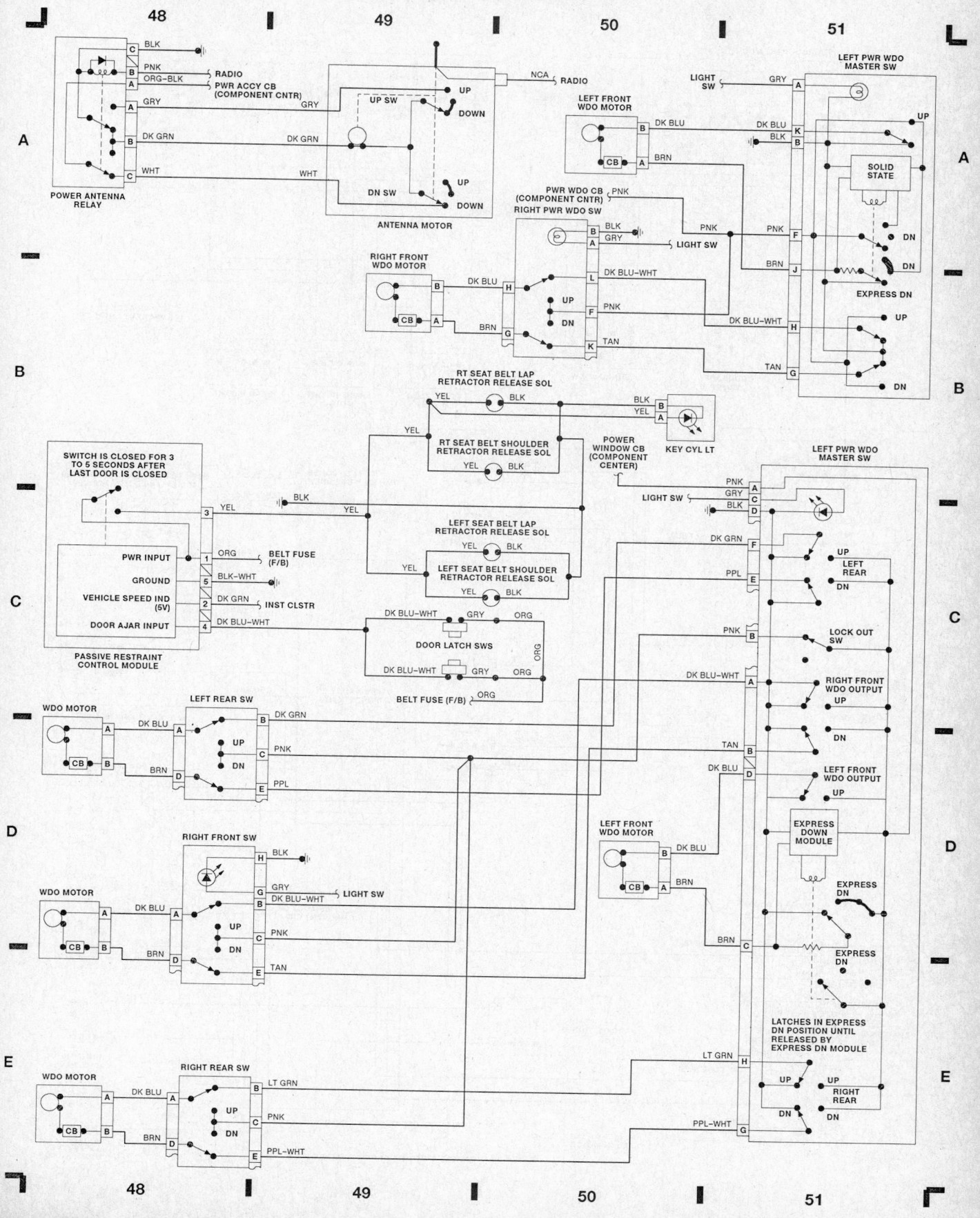

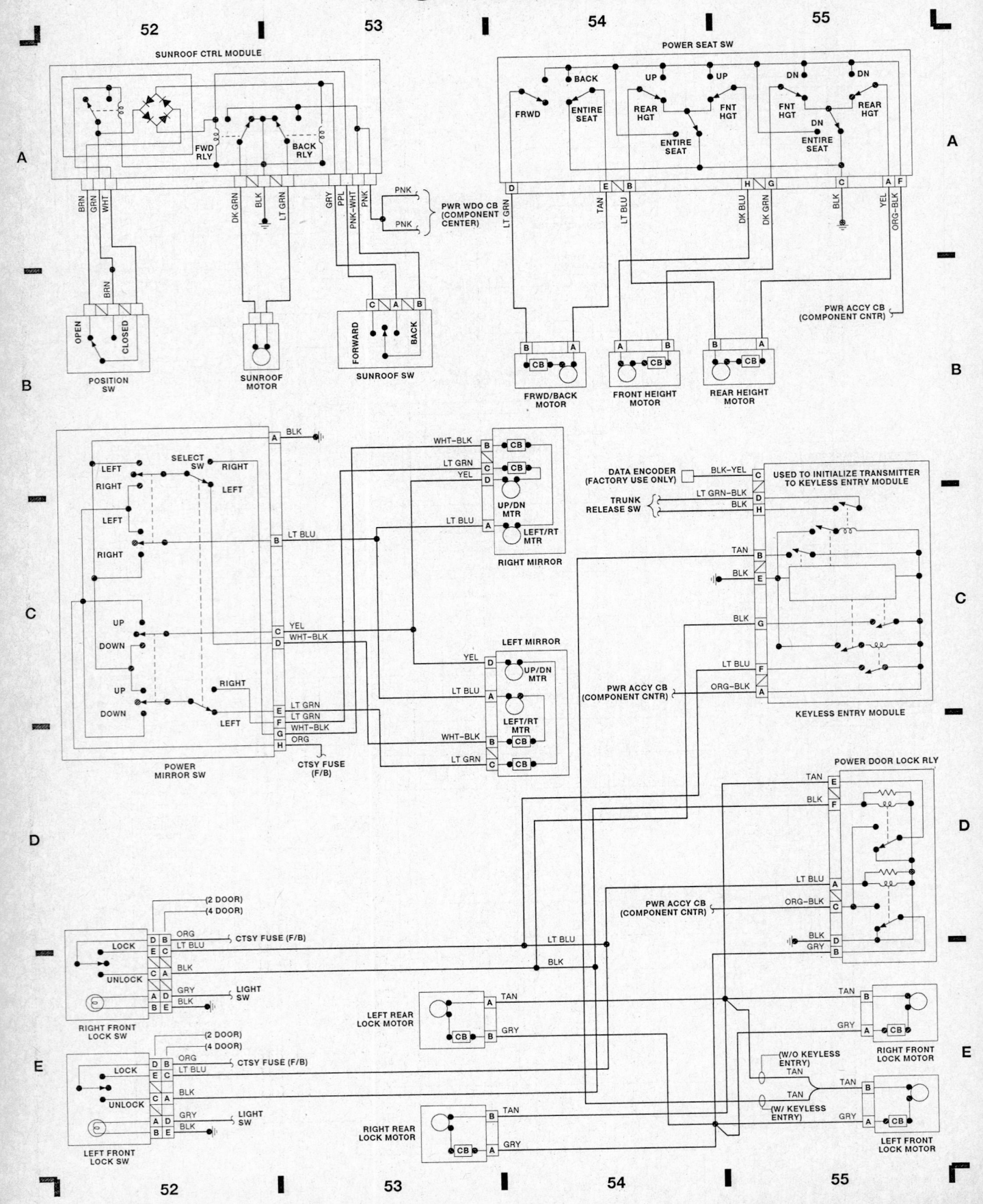

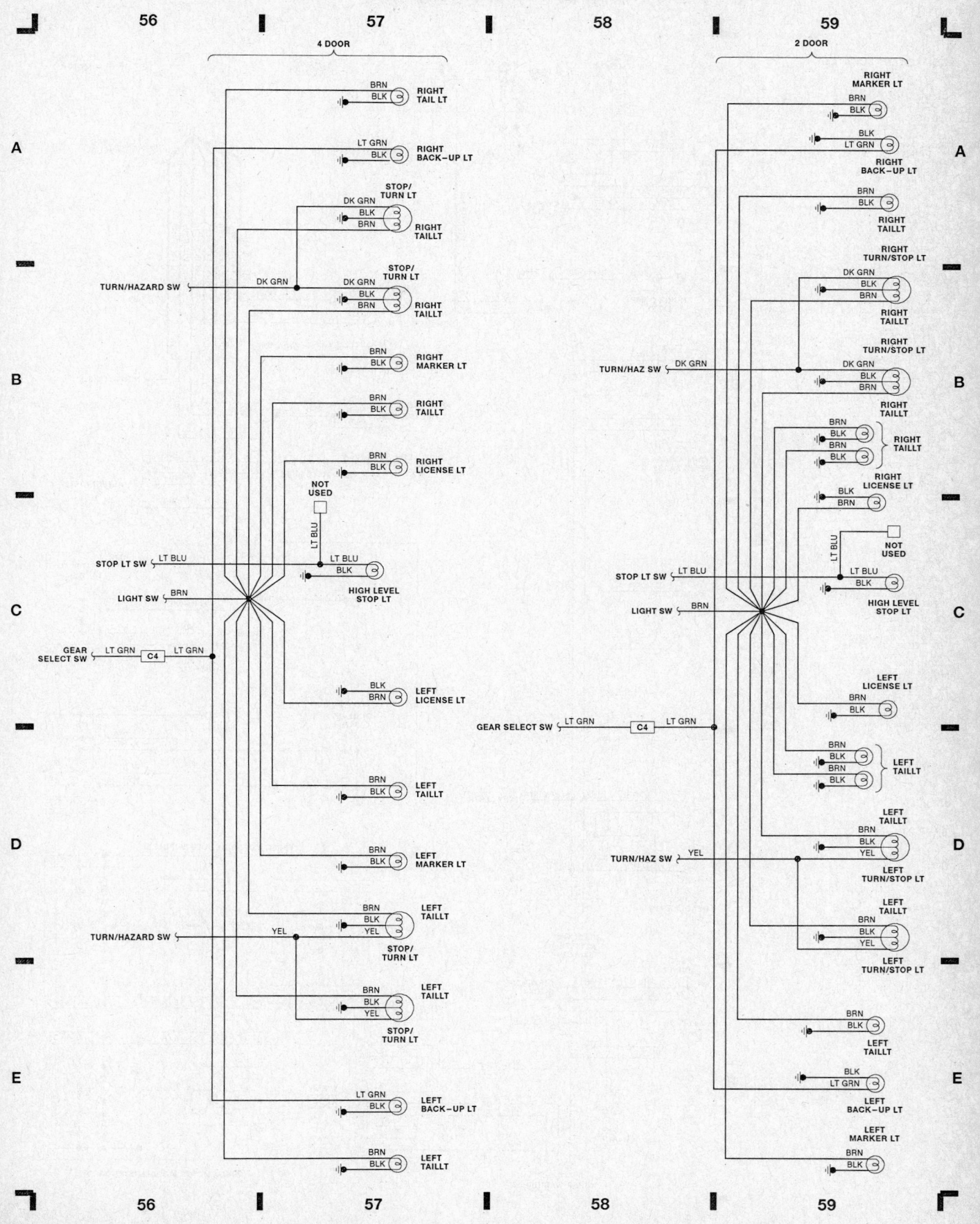

COMPONENT LOCATOR:

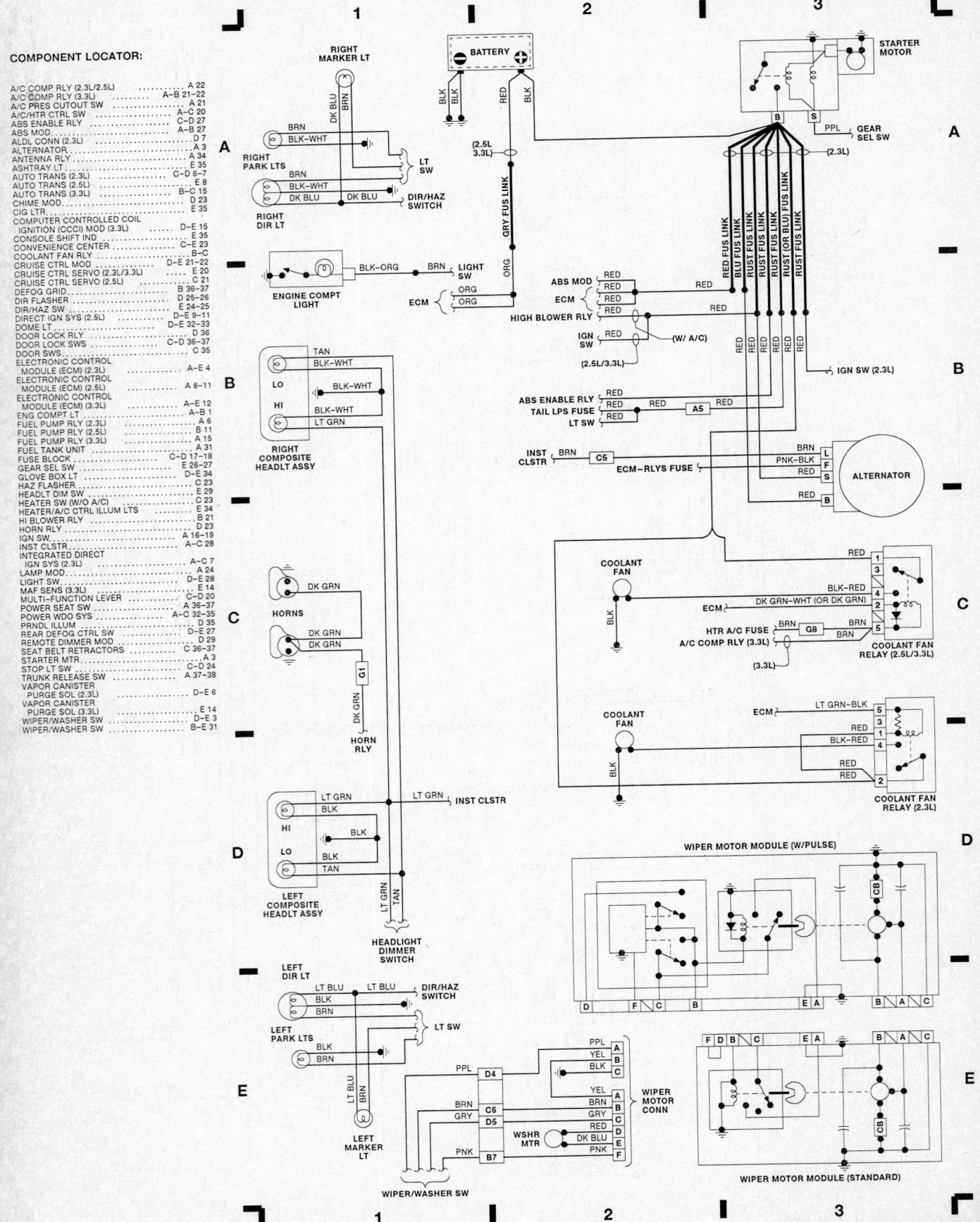

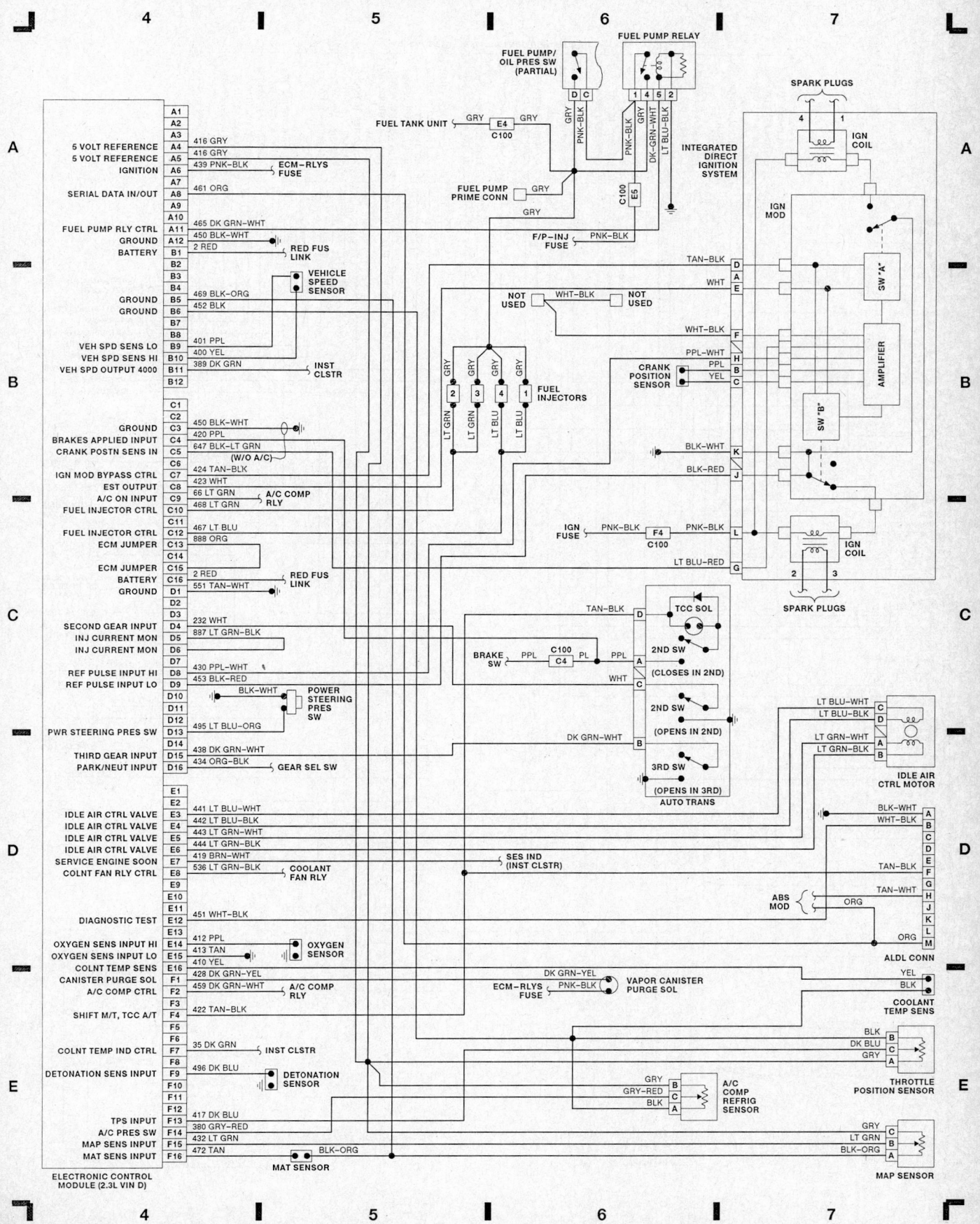

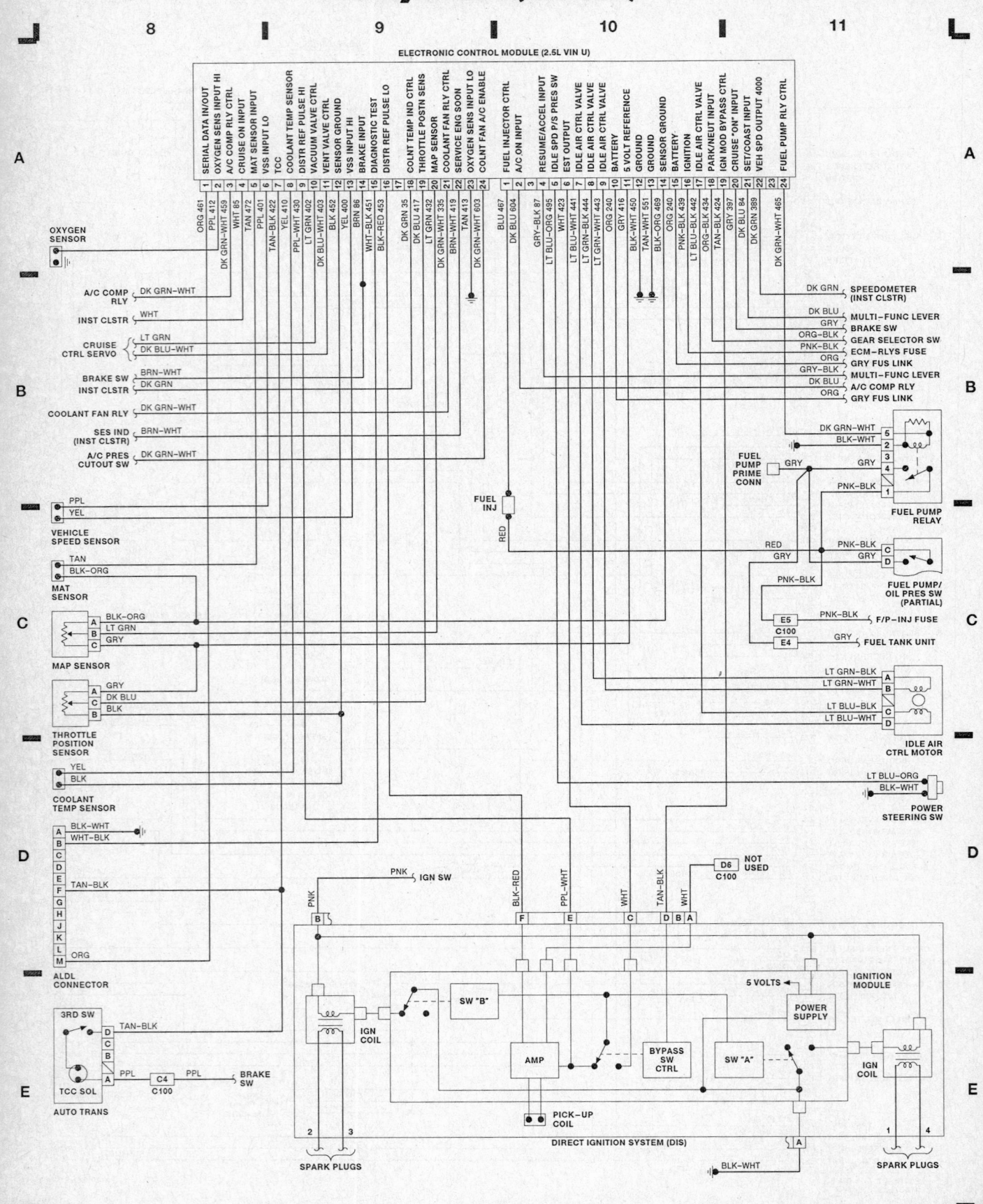

ELECTRONIC CONTROL MODULE (2.5L VIN U)

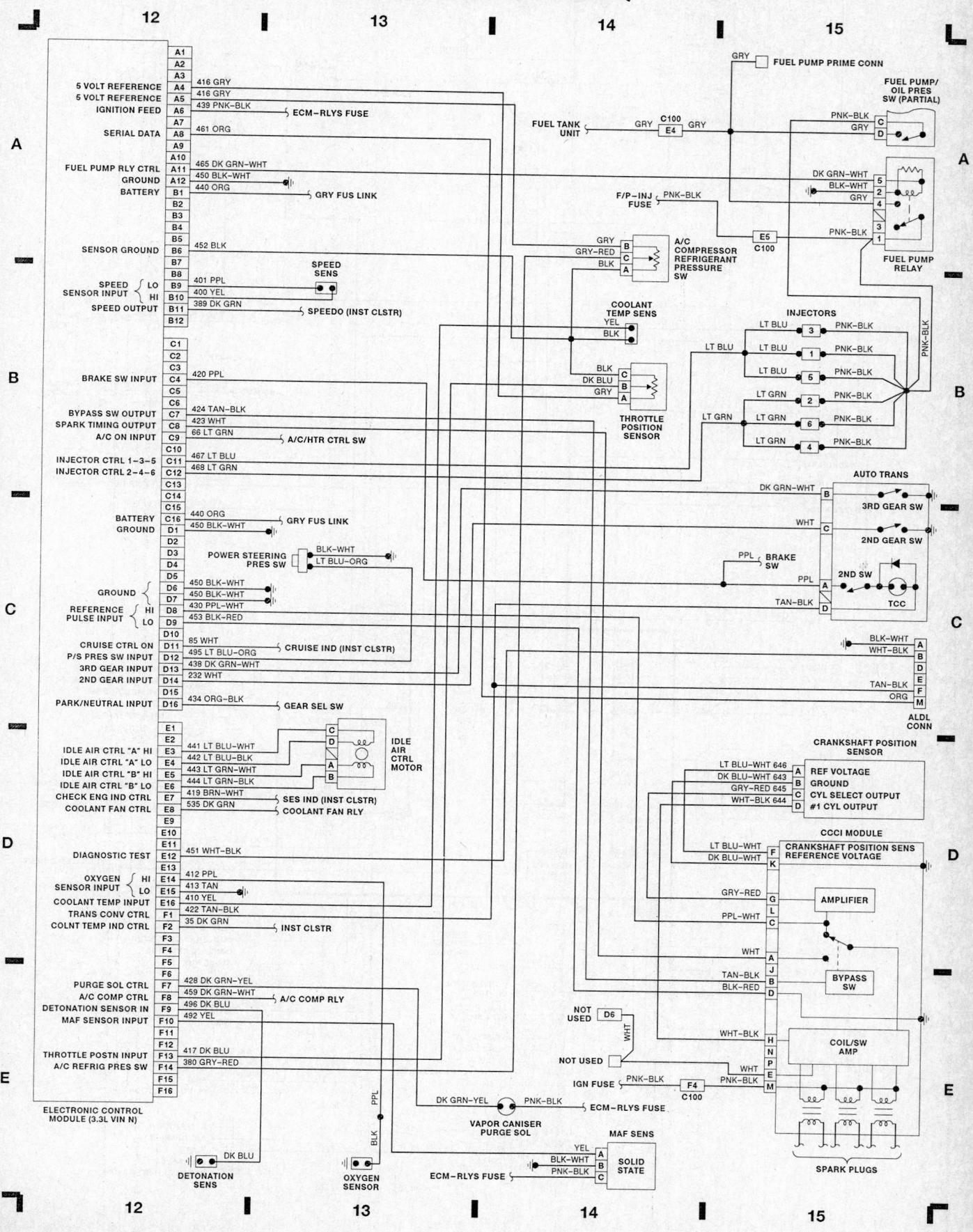

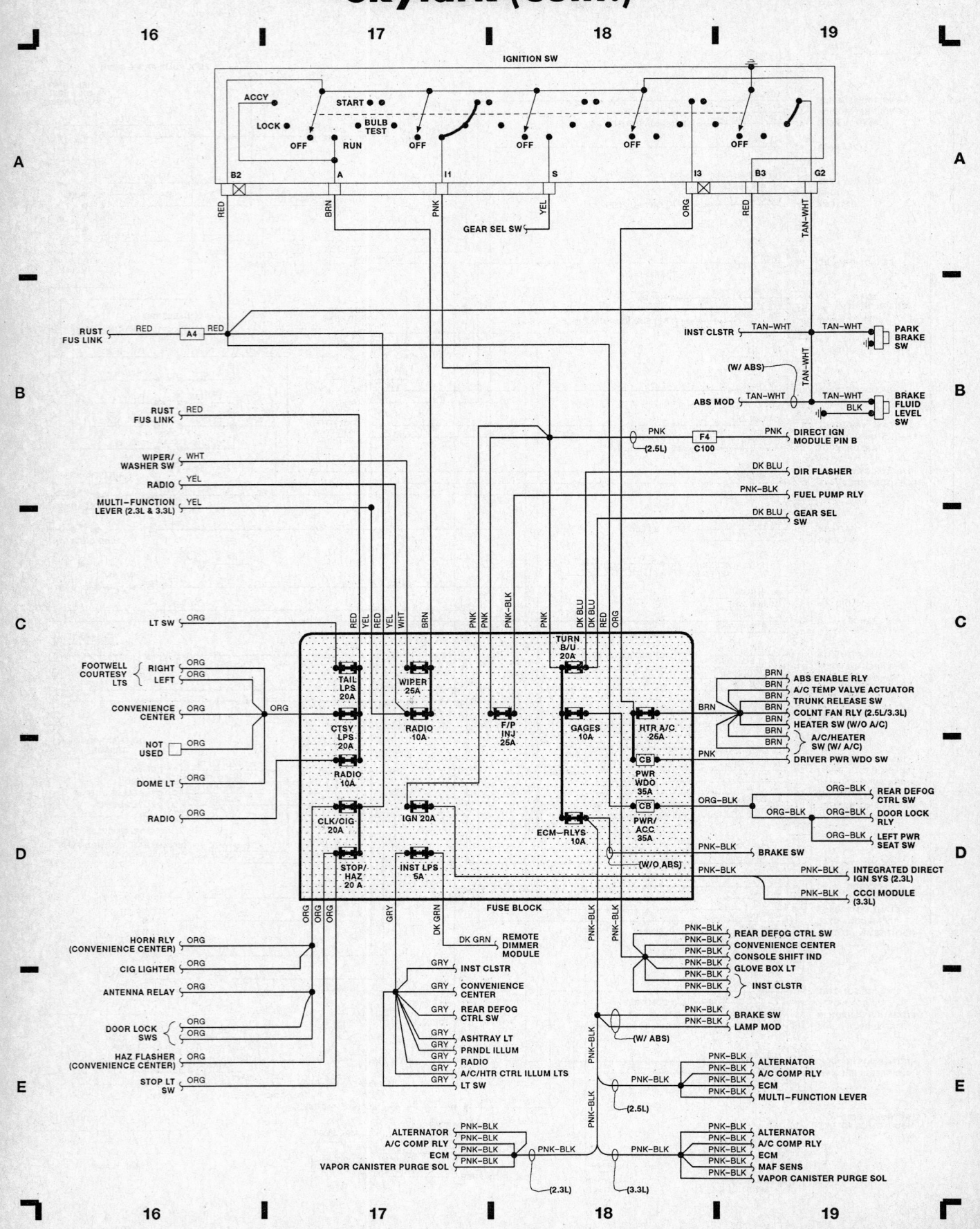

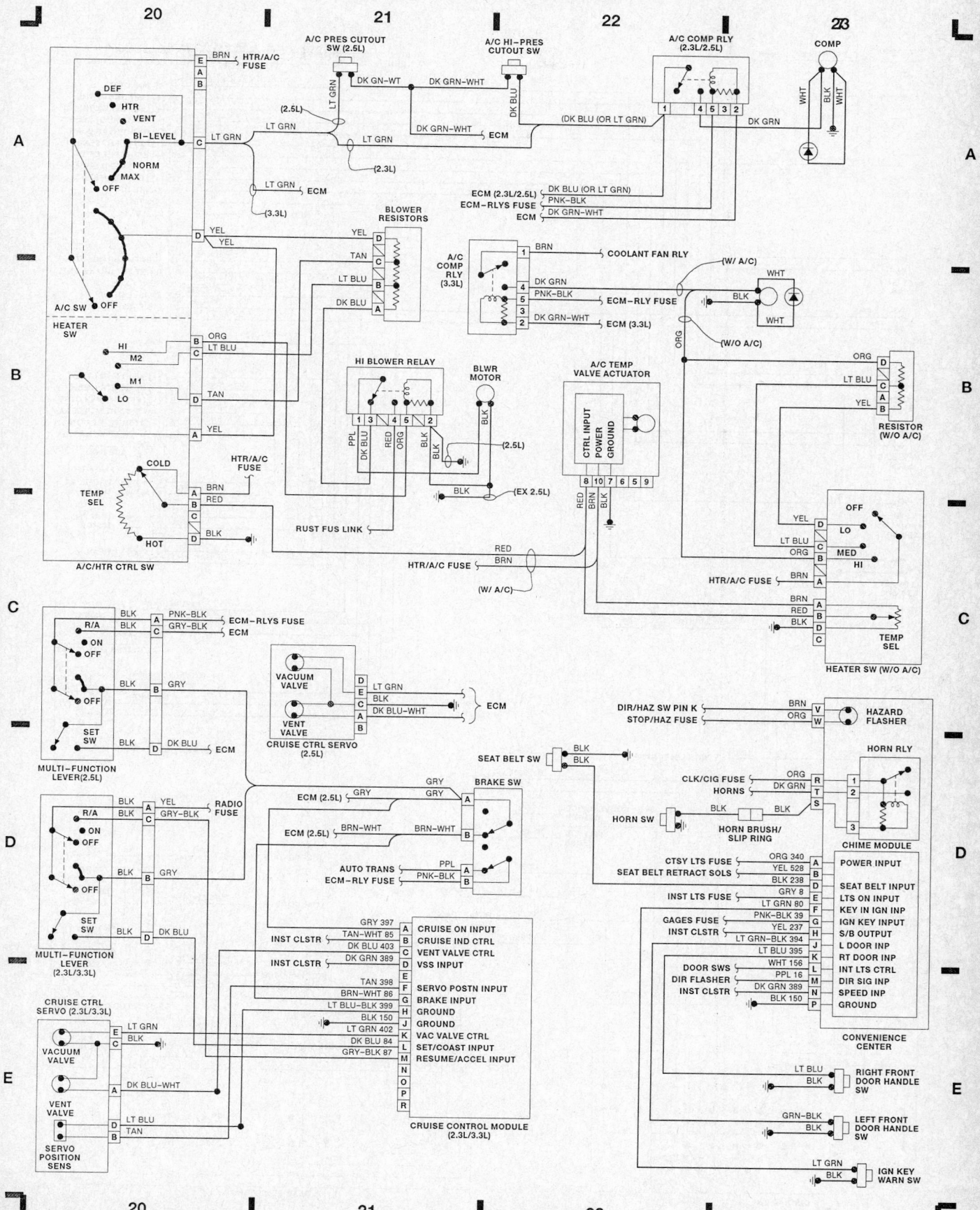

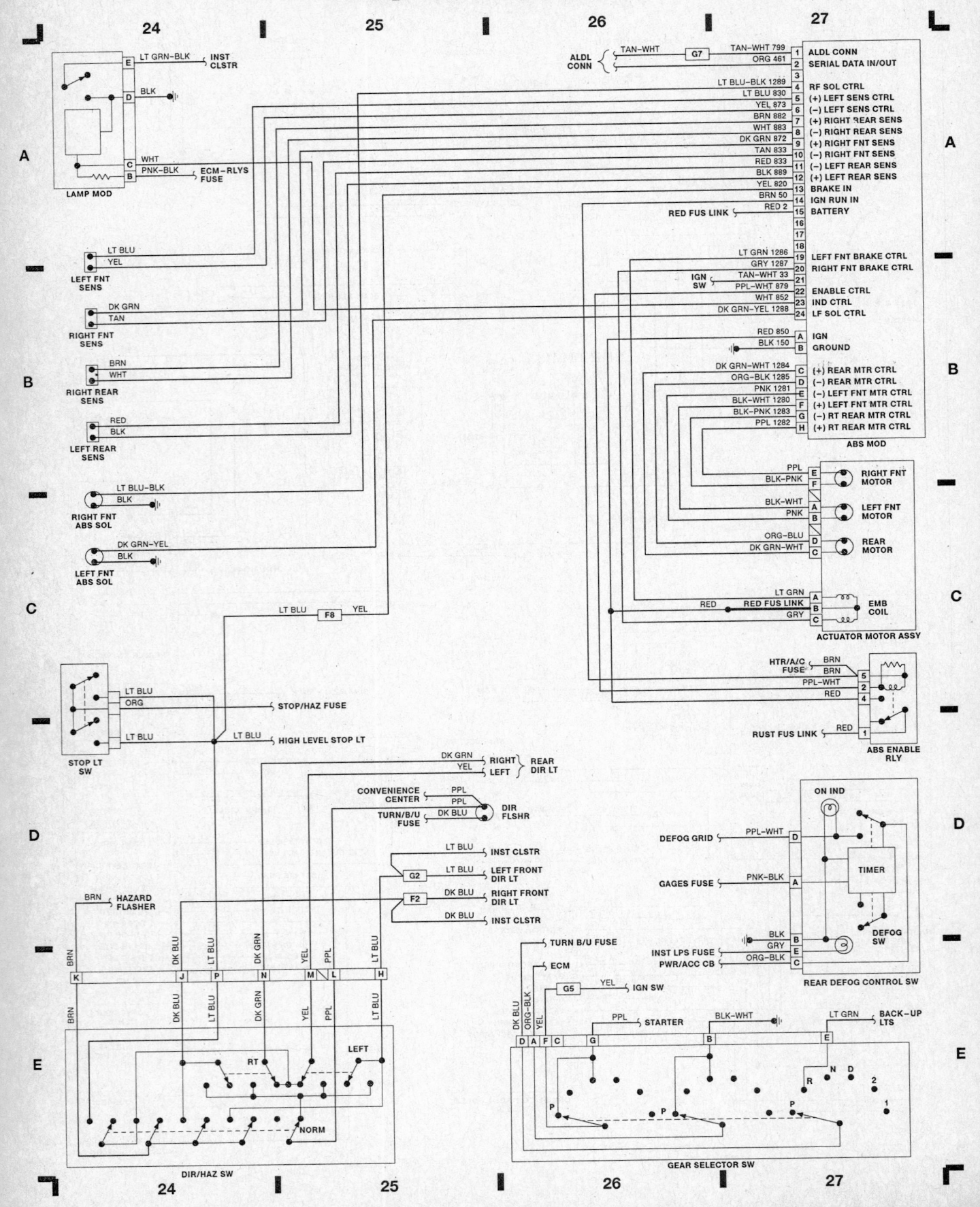

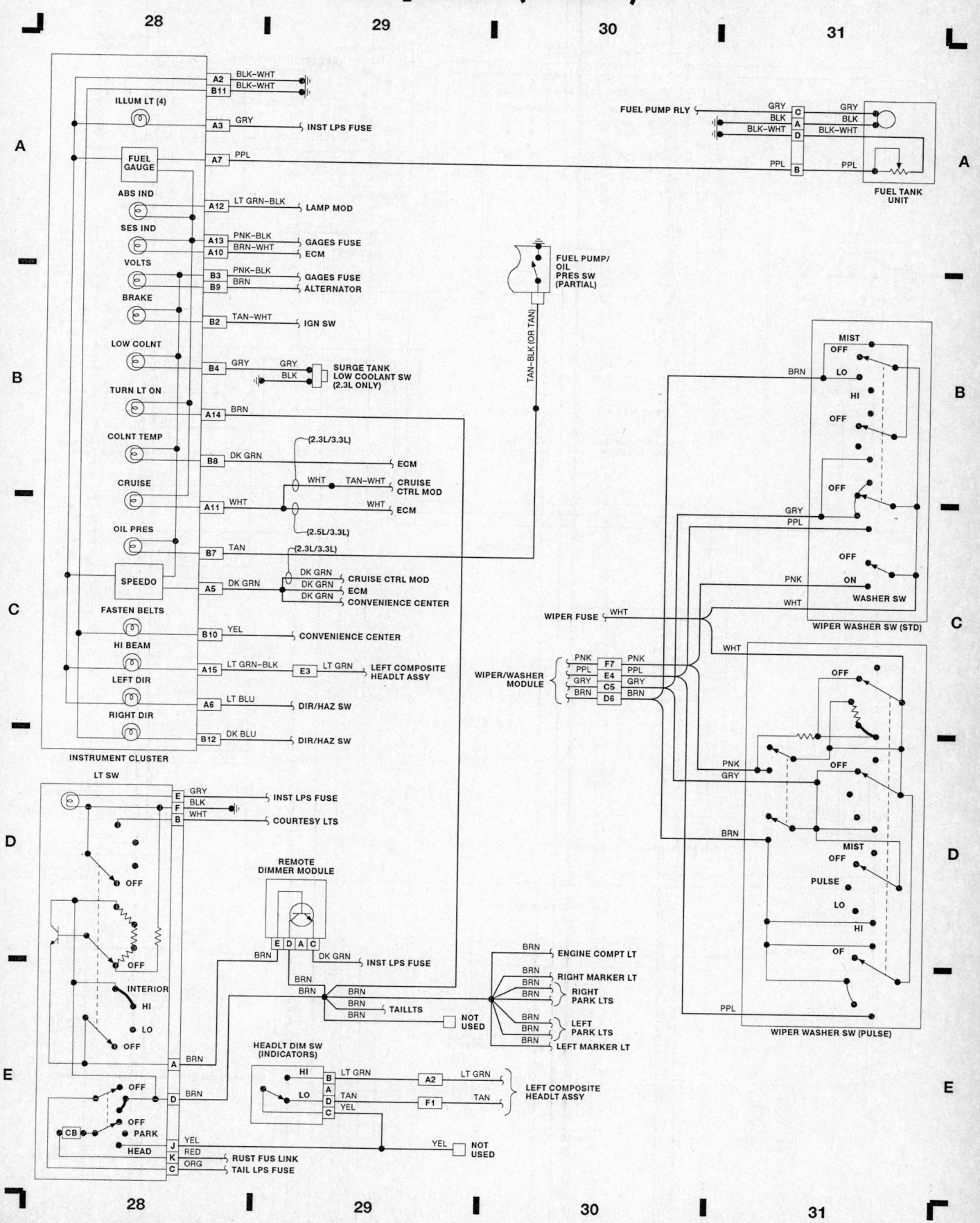

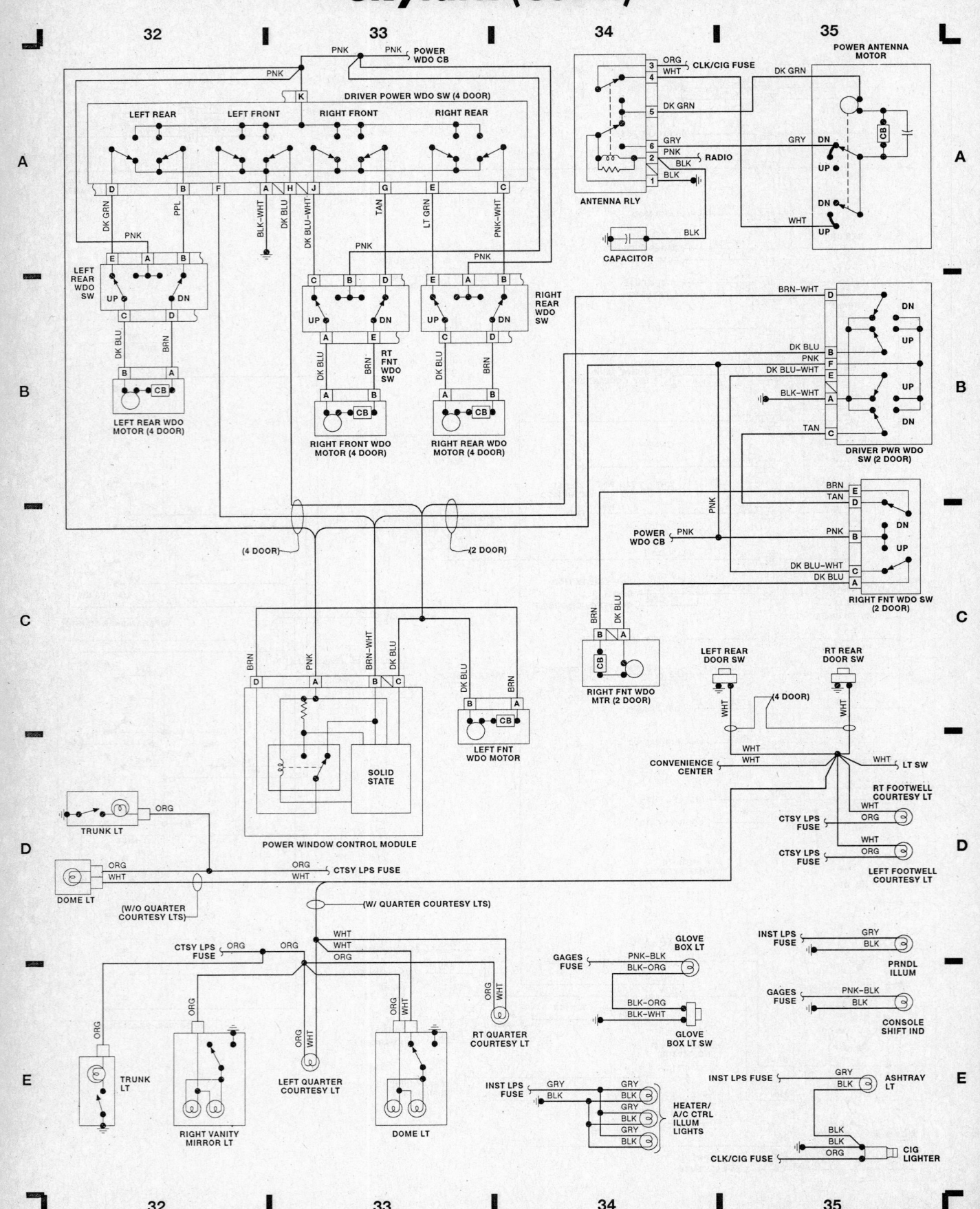

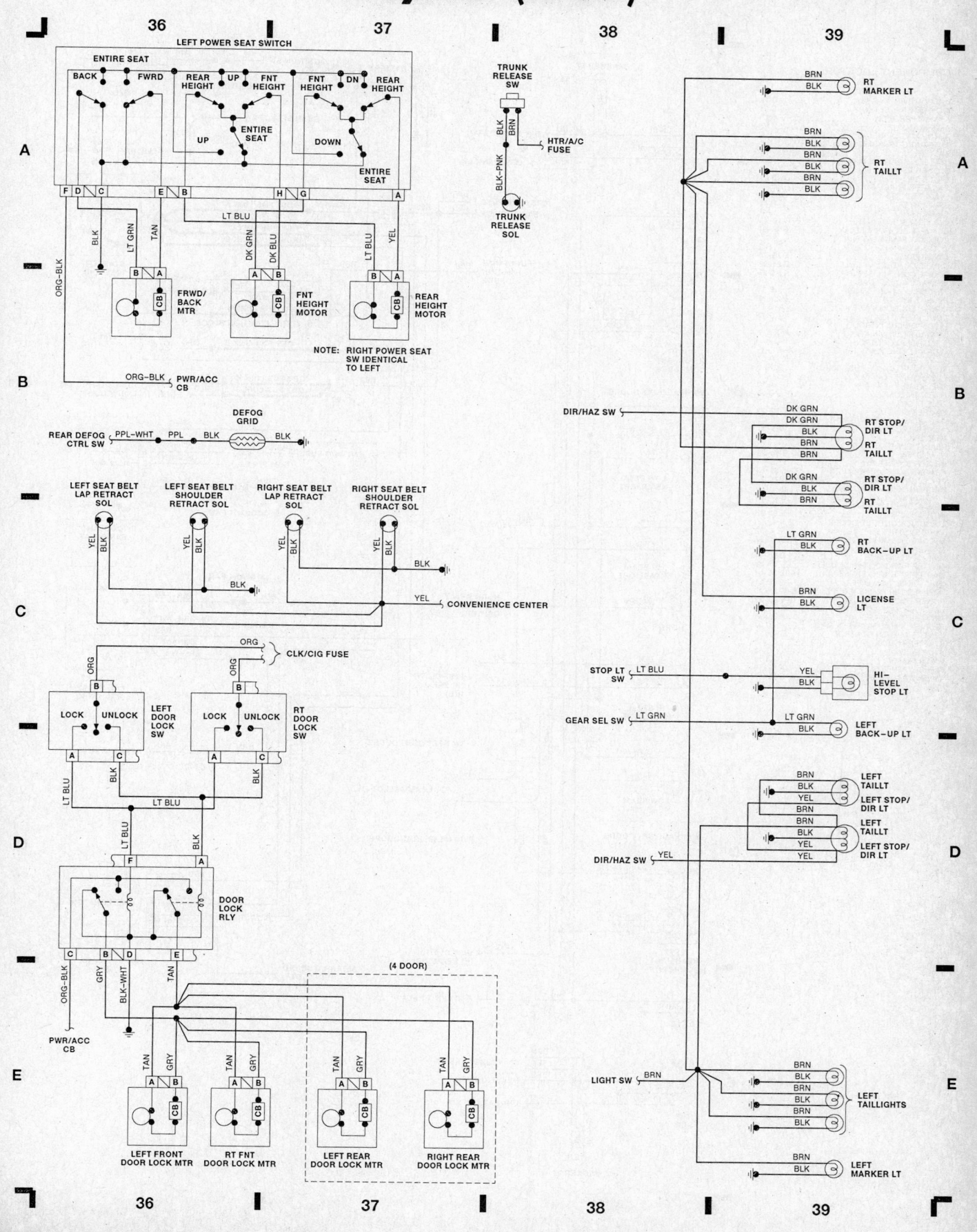

1991 WIRING DIAGRAMS
Sunbird

COMPONENT LOCATOR:

A/C COMP RELAY (VIN K) .... D 19
A/C COMP RELAY (VIN T) .... E 19
A/C HIGH PRES SW .... E 17
ALTERNATOR .... D 3
AUTOMATIC TRANSMISSION (VIN K) .... E 4
AUTOMATIC TRANSMISSION (VIN T) .... C-D 9
BATTERY .... A 2
BATTERY JUNCTION BLOCK .... B 2
BLOWER RELAY .... D 16
BRAKE SW .... D 24
CANISTER PURGE SOLENOID
  VALVE (VIN T) .... E 10
CIG LIGHTER .... B 32
CLUTCH START SW .... A 3
CONVENIENCE CENTER .... B-C 18-19
CONVERTIBLE ROOF RELAY .... E 30-31
COOLANT FAN RELAY (VIN K) .... C 3
COOLANT FAN RELAY (VIN T) .... B 3
COURTESY LTS .... E 25-26
CRUISE CONTROL MODULE .... C-D 24-27
CRUISE CONTROL SERVO .... D 27
DIGITAL EXHAUST GAS
  RECIRCULATION (DEGR) .... C 11
DIR/HAZARD SW .... D-E 22-23
DIRECT IGNITION SYSTEM .... A-B 11
DOME LT .... E 27
ELECTRONIC CONTROL
  MODULE (2.0L VIN K) .... A-E 4-7
ELECTRONIC CONTROL
  MODULE (3.1L VIN T) .... A-E 8-11
FOG LT RELAY .... A 27
FUEL PUMP IN-LINE FUSE (VIN T) .... C 9
FUEL PUMP RELAY (VIN K) .... C 7
FUEL PUMP RELAY (VIN T) .... A 10
FUEL TANK UNIT .... D 33
FUSE BLOCK .... B-E 12-15
GAUGES CLUSTER .... D-E 20-23
GAUGES CLUSTER (W/ TACH) .... A-B 20-23
GEAR SELECT SW .... B-C 23
HEADER LT .... E 24
HEADLT DOOR CONTROL .... E 21
HEADLT SW .... A-B 24-26
HEATER BLOWER SW .... E 18-19
HEATER-A/C CONTROL UNIT .... C-E 16-19
I/P COMPARTMENT LT .... B-C 32
IGNITION COIL (VIN K) .... D 5
IGNITION SW .... A 12-14
INDICATOR CLUSTER .... C 20-23
INTERIOR LTS .... E 24-27
LUGGAGE COMPT LT (COUPE
  & CONVERTIBLE) .... C 32
LUGGAGE COMPT LT (SEDAN) .... C 32
MASTER PWR WDO
  SW (CONVERTIBLE) .... C-D 30-31
MASTER PWR WDO SW (COUPE) .... A 28
MASTER PWR WDO SW (SEDAN) .... A-B 30-31
MULTI-FUNCTION LEVER .... C 24
POWER DOOR LOCKS (COUPE) .... B-C 28-29
POWER DOOR LOCKS (SEDAN) .... D-E 28-29
REAR DEFOGGER CONTROL SW .... A 33-34
REAR DEFOGGER RELAY .... A 32-33
RELEASE SW (LUGGAGE COMPT) .... D 33
REMOTE DIMMER CONTROL .... A 25
STARTER MOTOR .... A 3
STOP LT SW .... C 18
WIPER MOTOR .... A 18
WIPER/WASHER SW .... A 18-19
WIPER/WASHER SW (PULSE) .... A-B 16-17

MARKER LT

DIR LT
PARK LT
DK BLU — DK BLU — DIR/HAZARD SW
BLK
BRN — BRN
BRN — LEFT PARK LT

PPL
BLK
FOG LT

RIGHT HEADLIGHT (COMPOSITE)
LO — TAN
BLK
HI — BLK
LT GRN

W/ HEADLIGHT DOORS

LOW BEAM HEADLIGHT
BLK-WHT
TAN
BLK

HI BEAM HEADLIGHT
BLK — BLK
LT GRN

HORN
DK GRN — HORN RELAY (CONVENIENCE CENTER)

HI BEAM HEADLIGHT
BLK — BLK
LT GRN — LT GRN — INST CLSTR (HI BEAM IND)

LOW BEAM HEADLIGHT
BLK-WHT
TAN
BLK

TAN
LT GRN

(W/ HEADLIGHT DOORS)
LT GRN
TAN — BEAM SELECT SW
TAN
(W/O HEADLIGHT DOORS)

W/ HEADLIGHT DOORS

LEFT HEADLIGHT (COMPOSITE)
HI — LT GRN
BLK
LO — BLK
TAN
LT GRN — INST CLSTR (HI BEAM IND)

PPL
BLK — PPL — B2 — PPL — FOG LIGHT RELAY
FOG LT   C100

PARK LT
BRN
BRN — RIGHT PARK LT
BRN
BLK
LT BLU — HEADLIGHT SW
DIR LT
LT BLU — LT BLU — DIR/HAZARD SW

LT BLU
BRN
MARKER LT

BATTERY
BLK
BLK
RED
BLK

CTSY/CIG FUSE — RED — RED — C100 — RED — RED-WHT — RUST FUS LINK A
HEADLIGHT SW — RED — A5 — RED — GRY FUS LINK G
RED — GRY FUS LINK C
RED — RUST FUS LINK B

FUEL PUMP IN-LINE FUSE — RED — RED — RED
RED — C100 — RED — S/LP FUSE
A4 — RED — BLOWER RELAY
(W/ A/C)

GRY FUS LINK C
BATTERY JUNCTION BLOCK
(VIN K)
GRY FUS LINK F — ORG — ECM — (VIN T)

RED — A1 — GRY FUS LINK K — RED — PIN E — HEADLIGHT DOOR CONTROLLER
C100 — GRY FUS LINK J — RED — PIN B

RED
BRN-WHT — 1
HTR-A/C FUSE — BRN — C4 — BRN-WHT — 5
ECM PIN E8 — DK GRN-WHT — 2
BLK — BLK-RED — 4
COOLANT FAN
COOLANT FAN RELAY (3.1L VIN T)

COOLANT FAN
BLK — BLK-RED — 4
3
ECM PIN B21 — DK GRN-WHT — 2
RED — 1
BRN-WHT — 5
BRN-WHT
COOLANT FAN RELAY (2.0L VIN K)

BRN-WHT — C4 — BRN — HTR-A/C FUSE
C100

RED — BATT
BRN-WHT — F
RED — S — ALTERNATOR
BRN — L
ALTERNATOR IND (IND CLSTR)

IGNITION SW — YEL — PPL — G4 — PPL
CLUTCH START SW — C100 — (M/T)
GEAR SELECT SW — PPL
(A/T)

STARTER MOTOR
PPL
STARTER SOLENOID

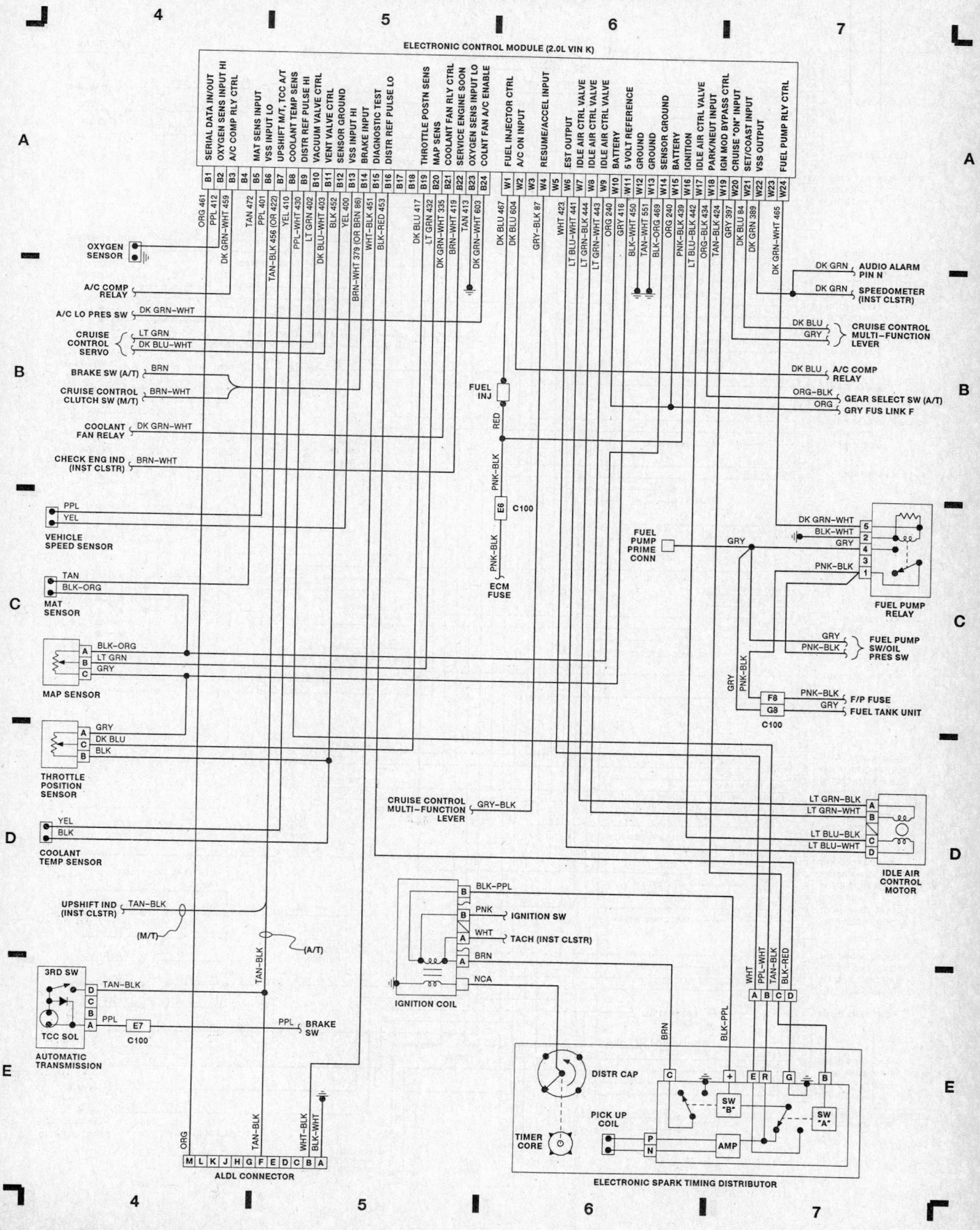

ELECTRONIC CONTROL MODULE (2.0L VIN K)

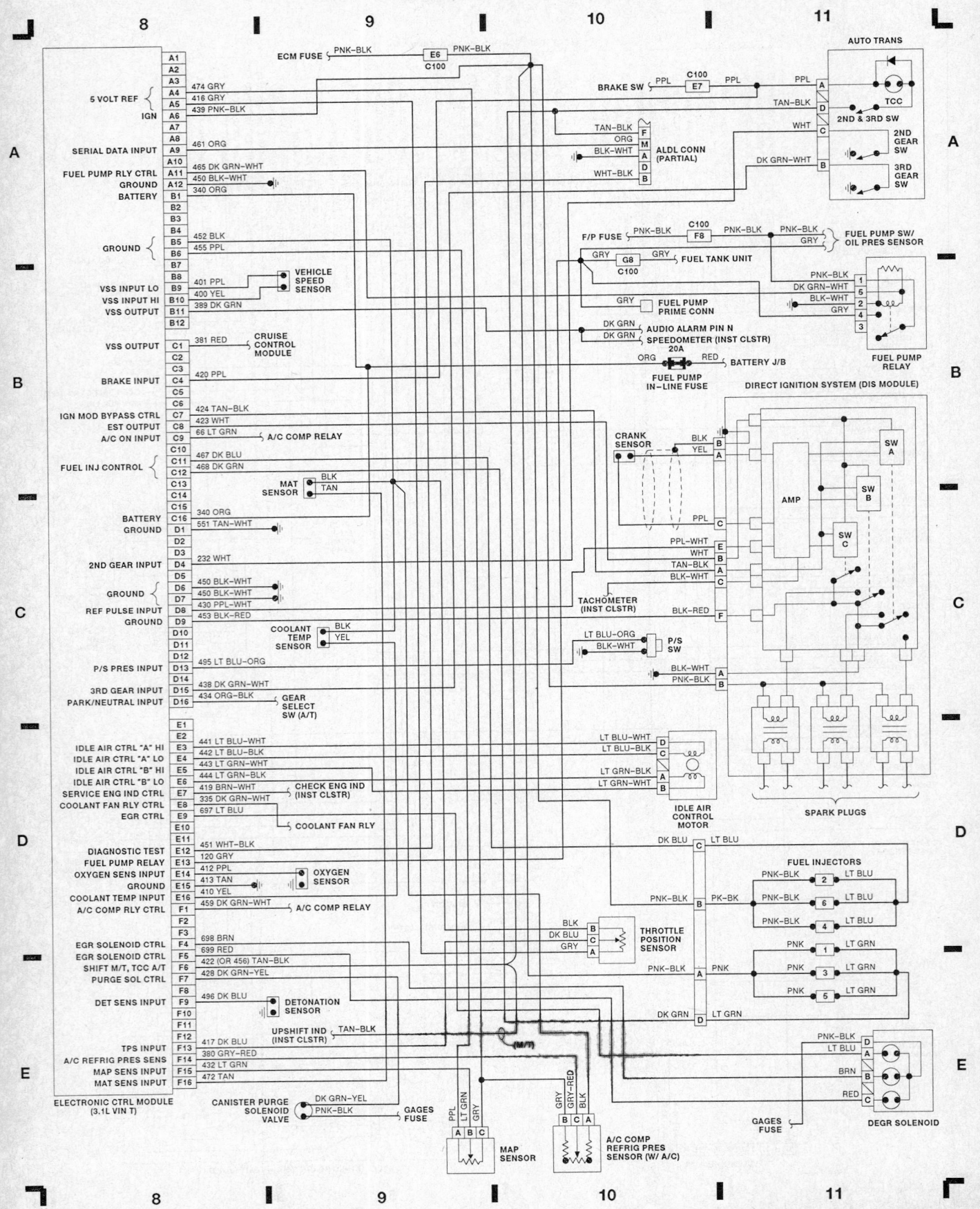

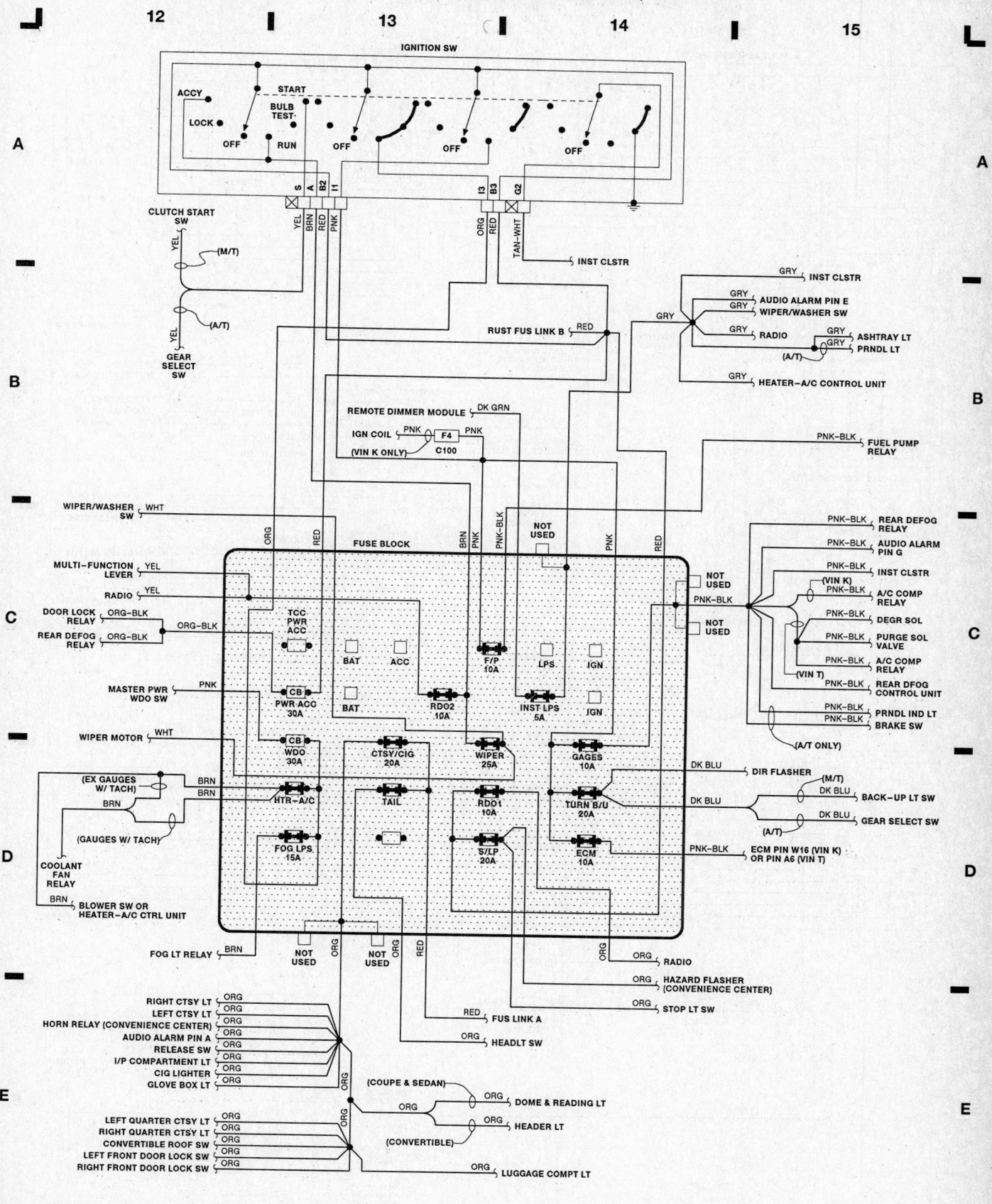

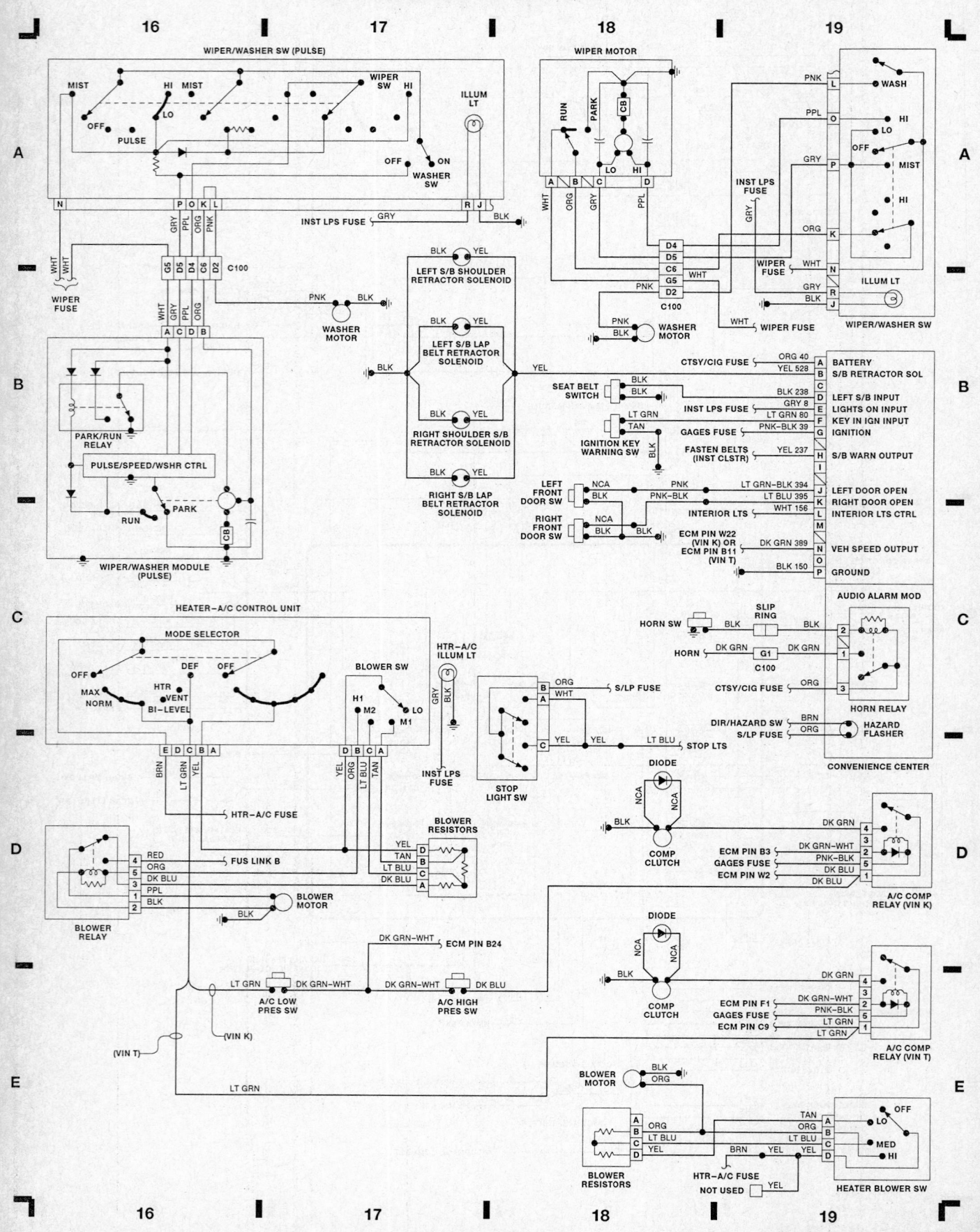

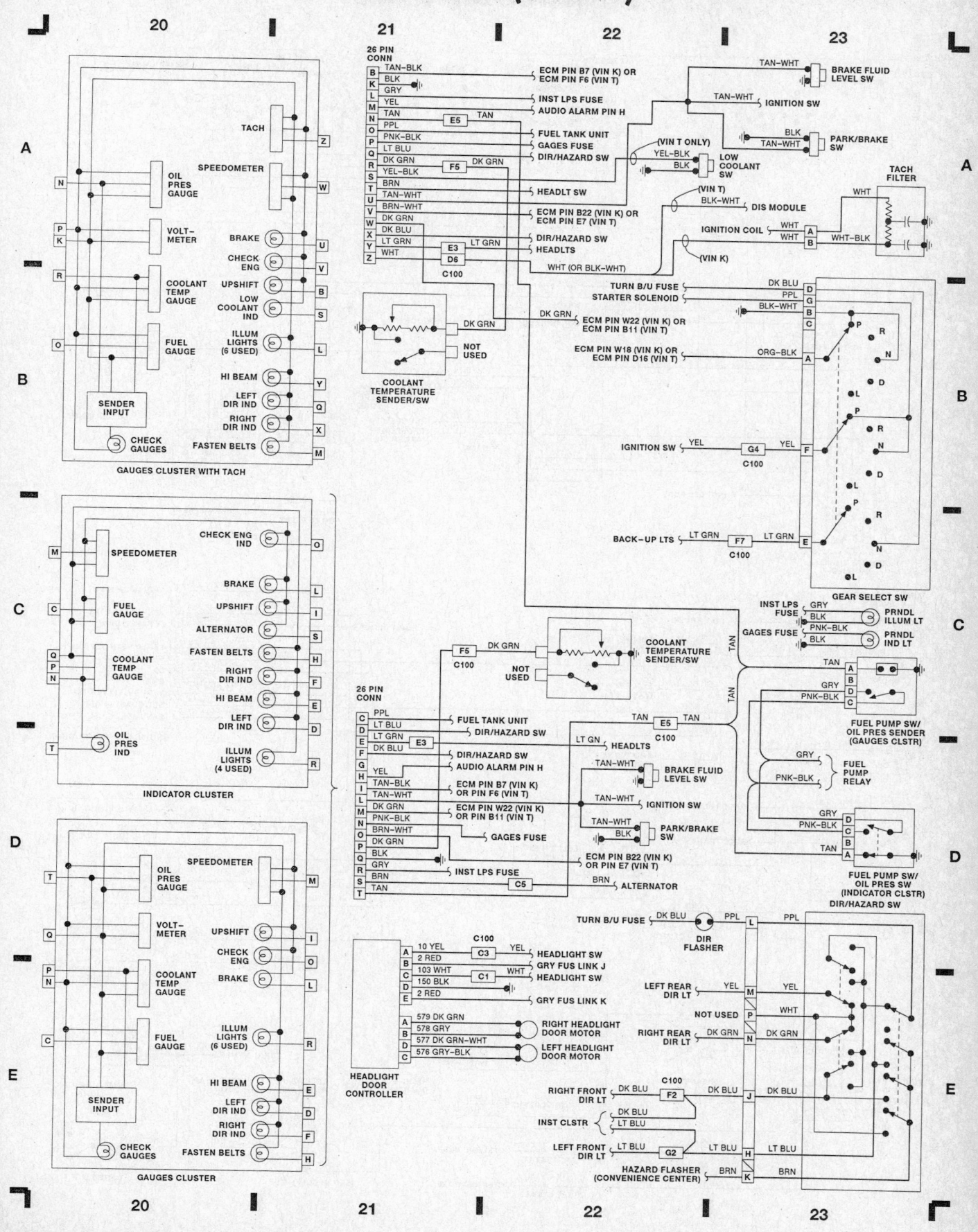

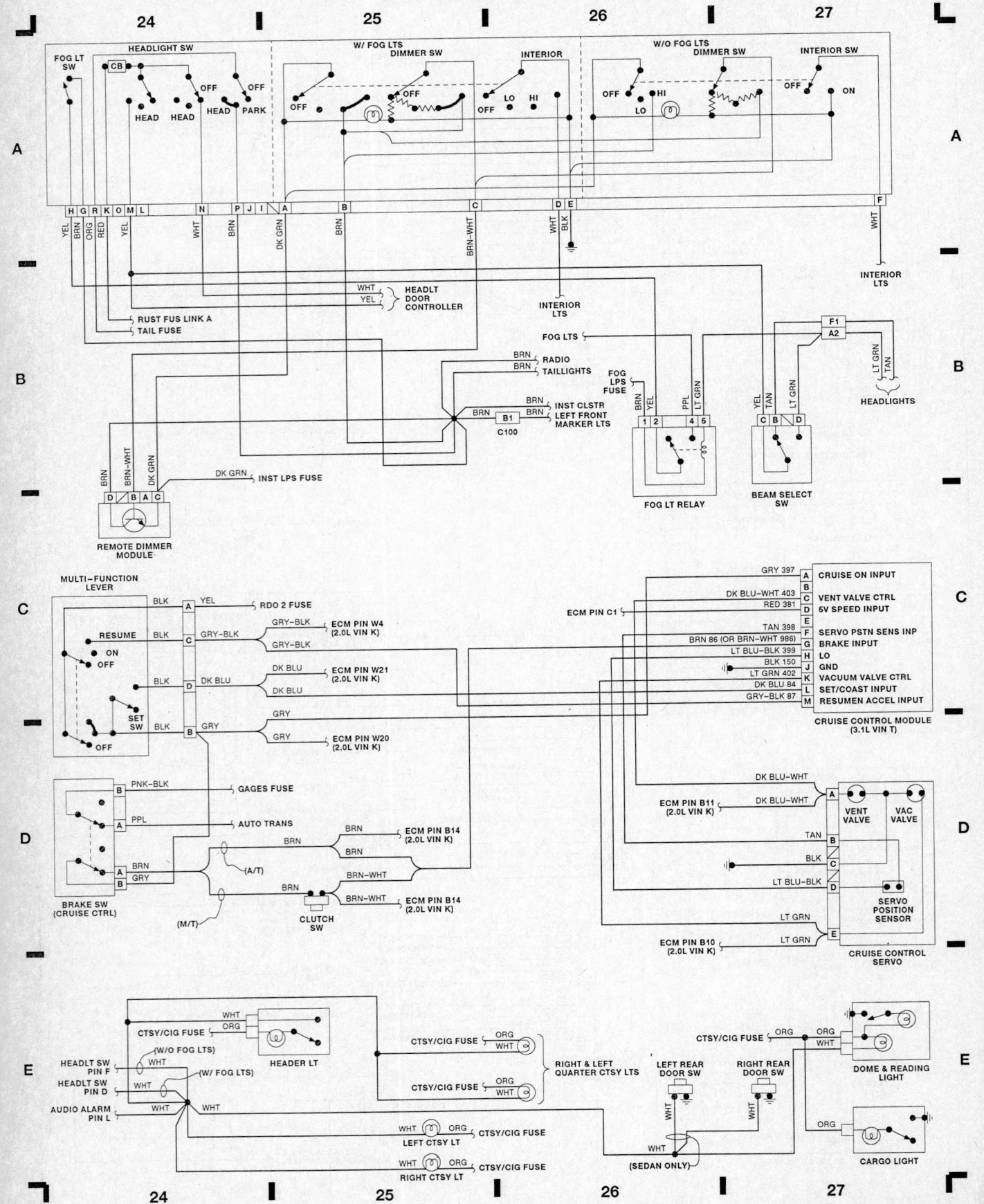

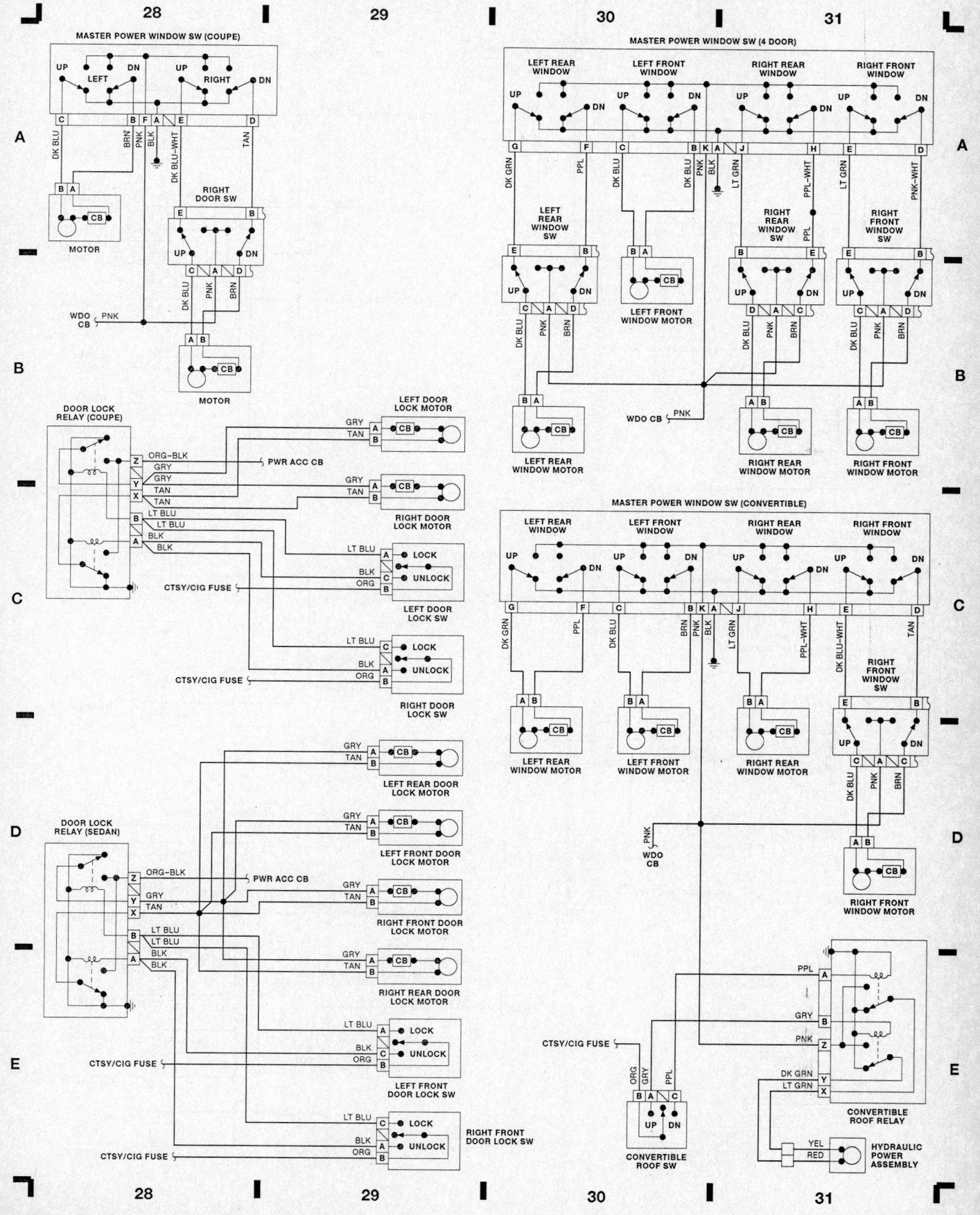

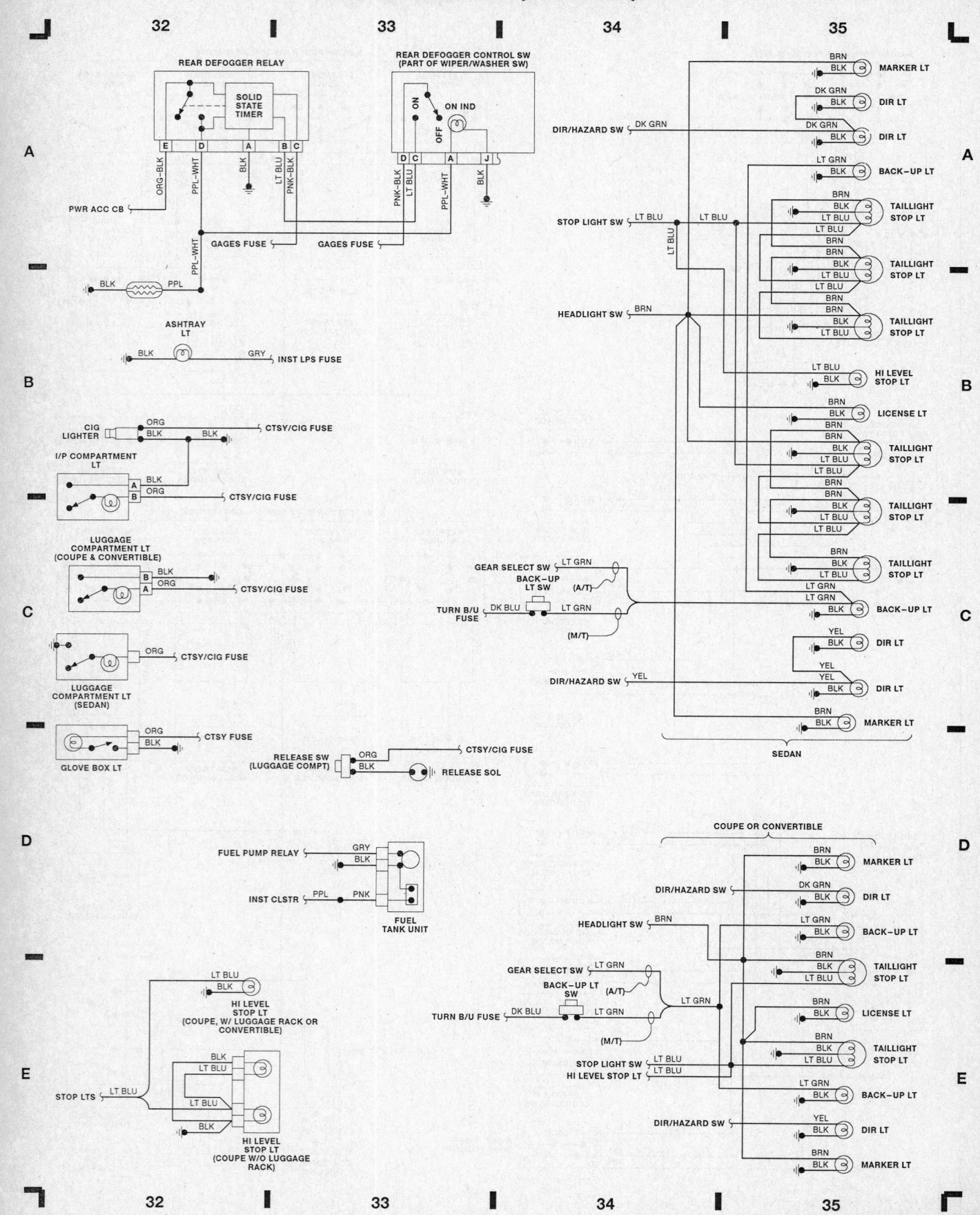

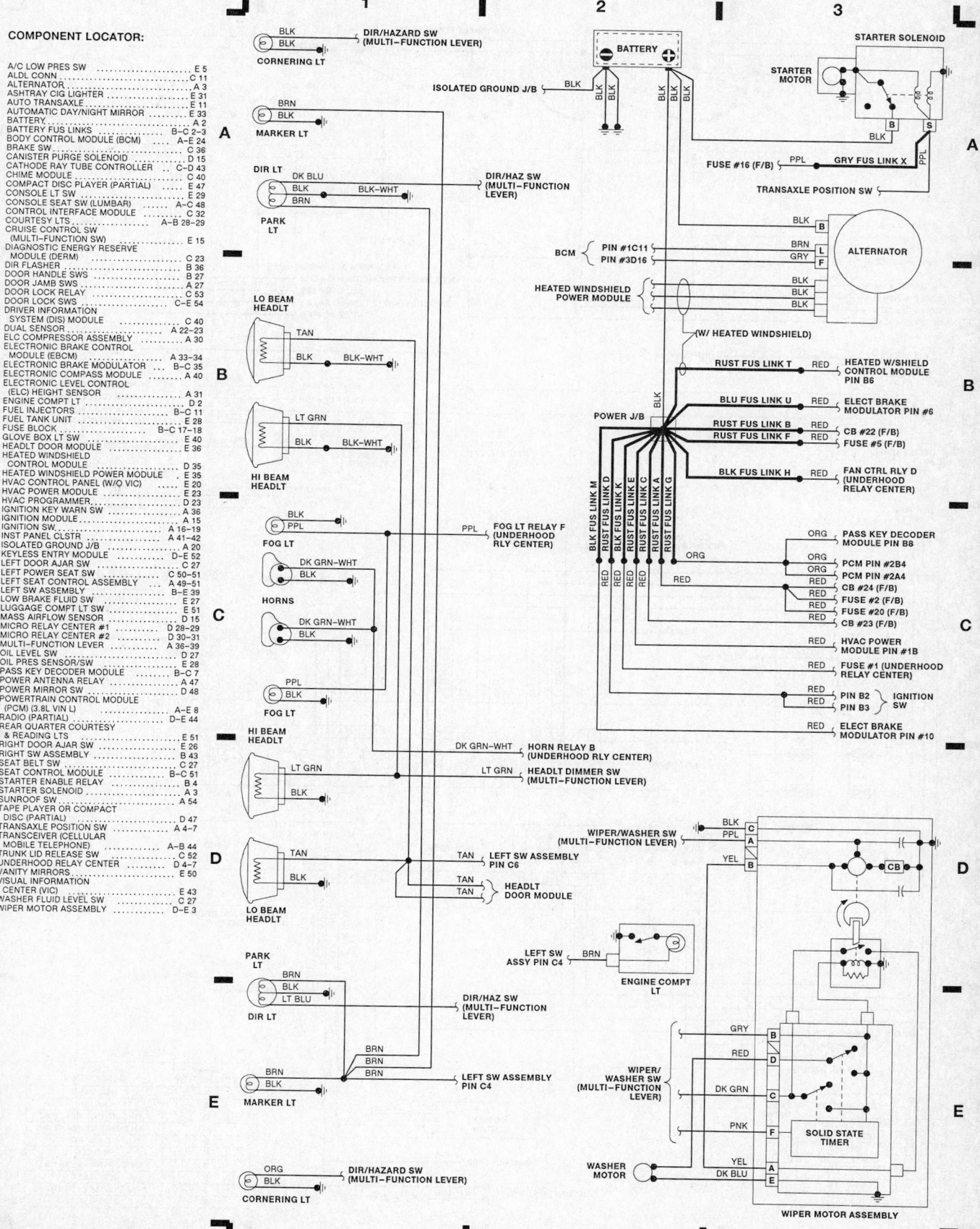

COMPONENT LOCATOR:

A/C LOW PRES SW .... E 5
ALDL CONN .... C 11
ALTERNATOR .... A 3
ASHTRAY CIG LIGHTER .... E 31
AUTO TRANSAXLE .... E 11
AUTOMATIC DAY/NIGHT MIRROR .... E 33
BATTERY .... A 2
BATTERY FUS LINKS .... B-C 2-3
BODY CONTROL MODULE (BCM) .... A-E 24
BRAKE SW .... C 36
CANISTER PURGE SOLENOID .... D 15
CATHODE RAY TUBE CONTROLLER ...... C-D 43
CHIME MODULE .... C 40
COMPACT DISC PLAYER (PARTIAL) .... E 47
CONSOLE LT SW .... E 29
CONSOLE SEAT SW (LUMBAR) .... A-C 48
CONTROL INTERFACE MODULE .... C 32
COURTESY LTS .... A-B 28-29
CRUISE CONTROL SW
(MULTI-FUNCTION SW) .... E 15
DIAGNOSTIC ENERGY RESERVE
MODULE (DERM) .... C 23
DIR FLASHER .... B 36
DOOR HANDLE SWS .... B 27
DOOR JAMB SWS .... A 27
DOOR LOCK RELAY .... C 53
DOOR LOCK SWS .... C-E 54
DRIVER INFORMATION
SYSTEM (DIS) MODULE .... C 40
DUAL SENSOR .... A 22-23
ELC COMPRESSOR ASSEMBLY .... A 30
ELECTRONIC BRAKE CONTROL
MODULE (EBCM) .... A 33-34
ELECTRONIC BRAKE MODULATOR .... B-C 35
ELECTRONIC COMPASS MODULE .... A 40
ELECTRONIC LEVEL CONTROL
(ELC) HEIGHT SENSOR .... A 31
ENGINE COMPT LT .... D 2
FUEL INJECTORS .... B-C 11
FUEL TANK UNIT .... E 28
FUSE BLOCK .... B-C 17-18
GLOVE BOX LT SW .... E 40
HEADLT DOOR MODULE .... E 36
HEATED WINDSHIELD
CONTROL MODULE .... D 35
HEATED WINDSHIELD POWER MODULE ... E 35
HVAC CONTROL PANEL (W/O VIC) ..... E 20
HVAC POWER MODULE .... E 23
HVAC PROGRAMMER .... D 23
IGNITION KEY WARN SW .... A 36
IGNITION MODULE .... A 15
IGNITION SW .... A 16-19
INST PANEL CLSTR .... A 41-42
ISOLATED GROUND J/B .... A 20
KEYLESS ENTRY MODULE .... D-E 52
LEFT DOOR AJAR SW .... C 27
LEFT POWER SEAT SW .... C 50-51
LEFT SEAT CONTROL ASSEMBLY .... A 49-51
LEFT SW ASSEMBLY .... B-E 39
LOW BRAKE FLUID SW .... E 27
LUGGAGE COMPT LT SW .... E 51
MASS AIRFLOW SENSOR .... D 15
MICRO RELAY CENTER #1 .... D 28-29
MICRO RELAY CENTER #2 .... D 30-31
MULTI-FUNCTION LEVER .... A 36-39
OIL LEVEL SW .... D 27
OIL PRES SENSOR/SW .... E 28
PASS KEY DECODER MODULE .... B-C 7
POWER ANTENNA RELAY .... A 47
POWER MIRROR SW .... A 47
POWERTRAIN CONTROL MODULE
(PCM) (3.8L VIN L) .... A-E 8
RADIO (PARTIAL) .... D-E 44
REAR QUARTER COURTESY
& READING LTS .... E 51
RIGHT DOOR AJAR SW .... E 26
RIGHT SW ASSEMBLY .... B 43
SEAT BELT SW .... C 27
SEAT CONTROL MODULE .... B-C 51
STARTER ENABLE RELAY .... B 4
STARTER SOLENOID .... A 3
SUNROOF SW .... A 54
TAPE PLAYER OR COMPACT
DISC (PARTIAL) .... D 47
TRANSAXLE POSITION SW .... A 4-7
TRANSCEIVER (CELLULAR
MOBILE TELEPHONE) .... A-B 44
TRUNK LID RELEASE SW .... C 52
UNDERHOOD RELAY CENTER .... D 4-7
VANITY MIRRORS .... E 50
VISUAL INFORMATION
CENTER (VIC) .... E 43
WASHER FLUID LEVEL SW .... C 27
WIPER MOTOR ASSEMBLY .... D-E 3

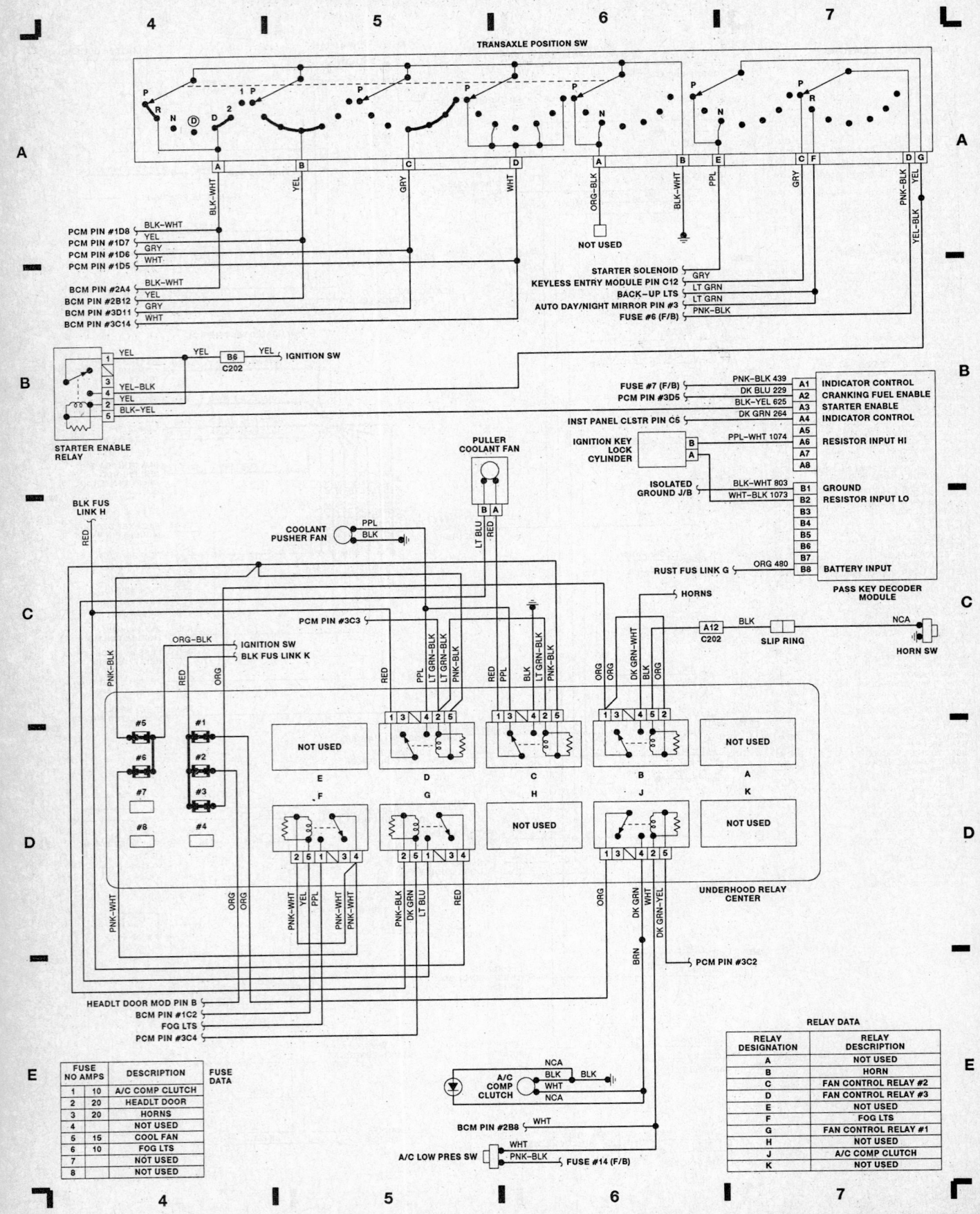

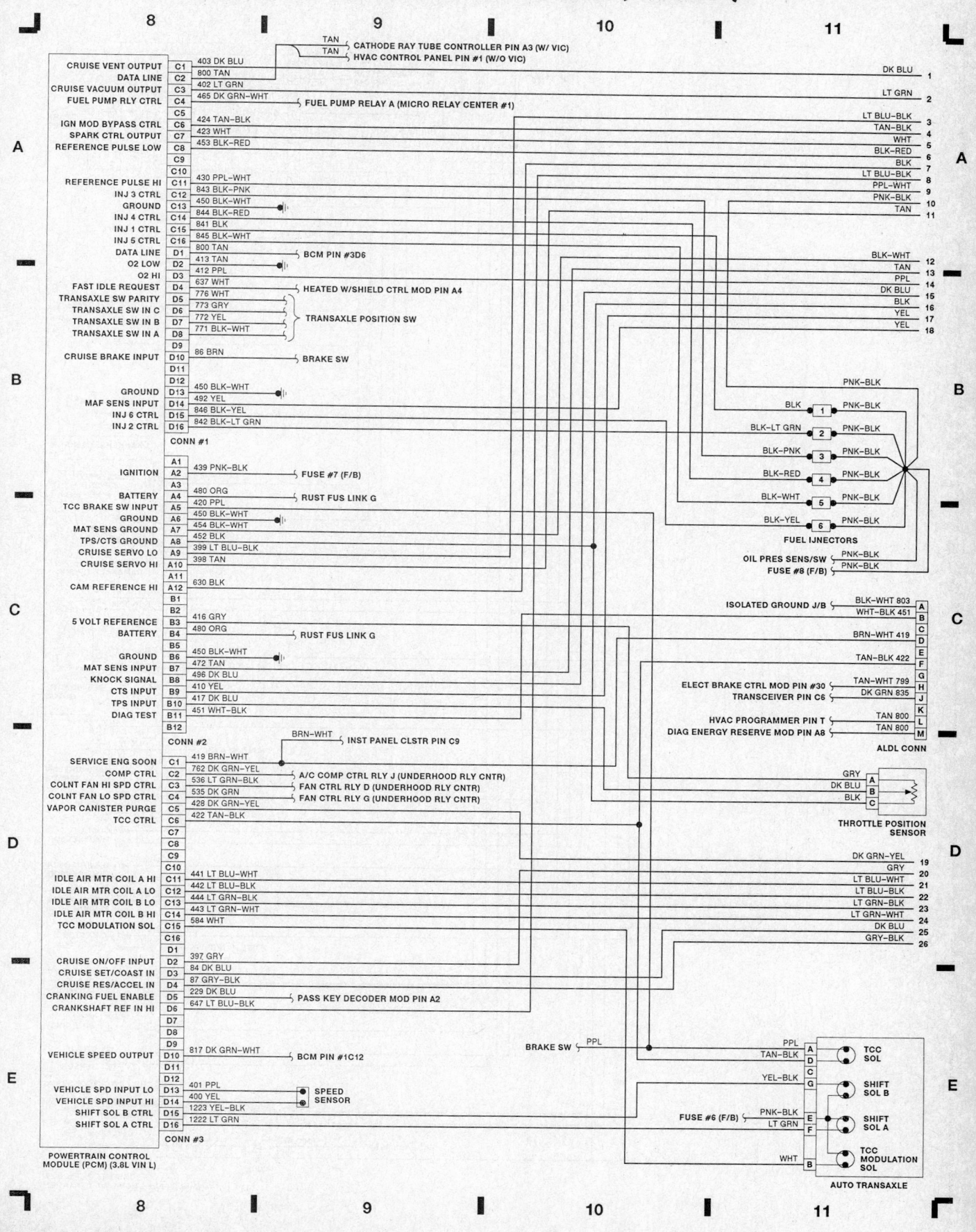

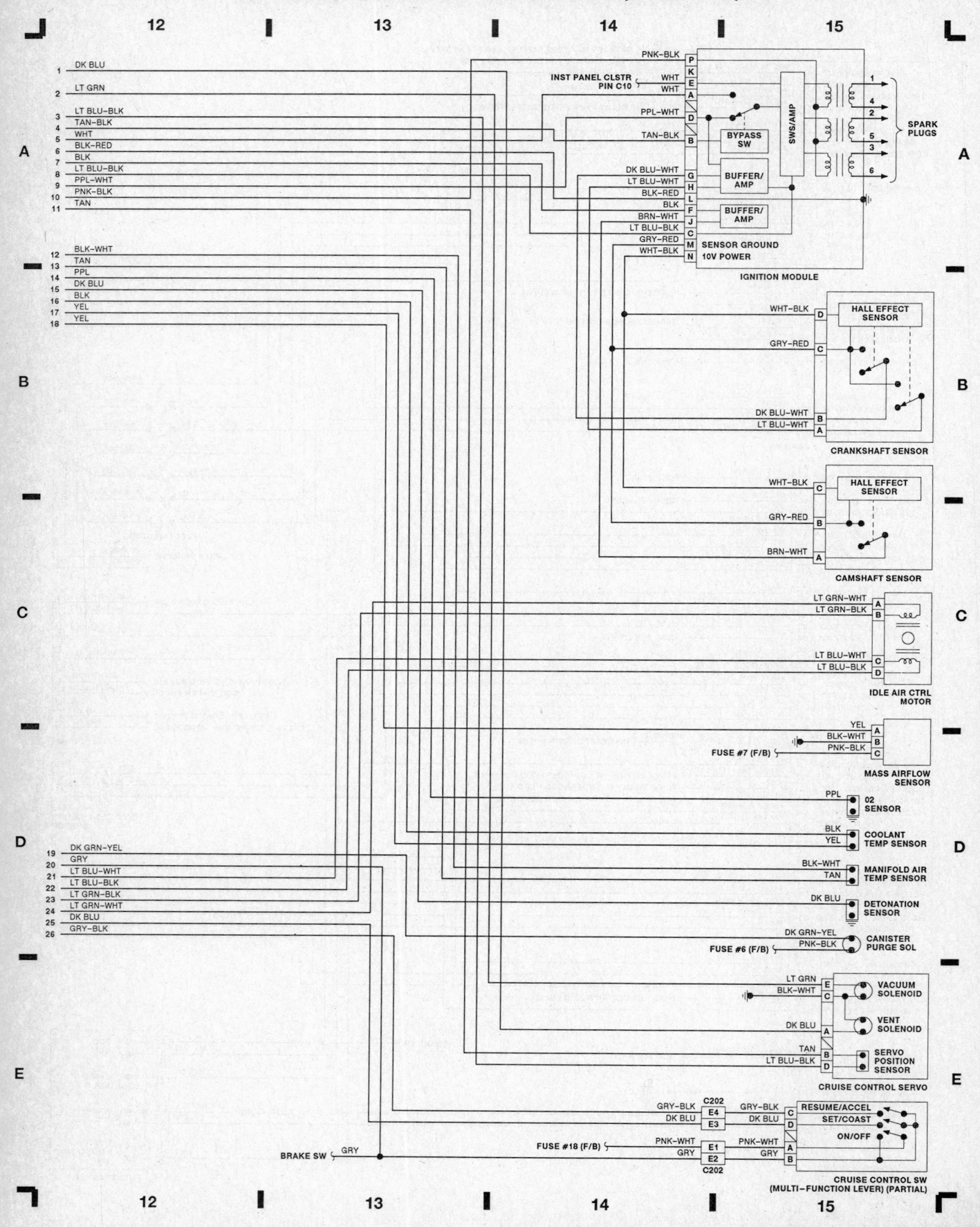

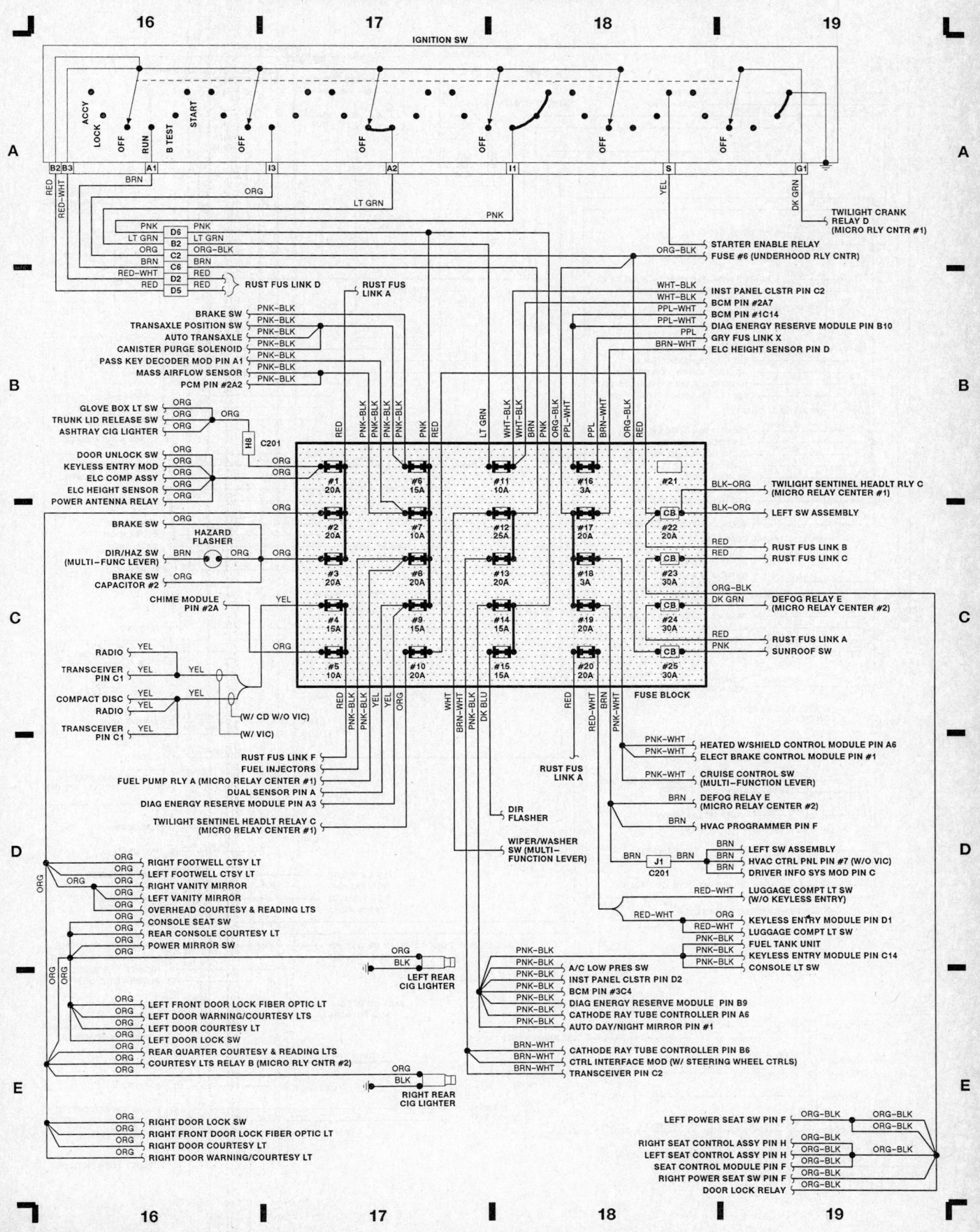

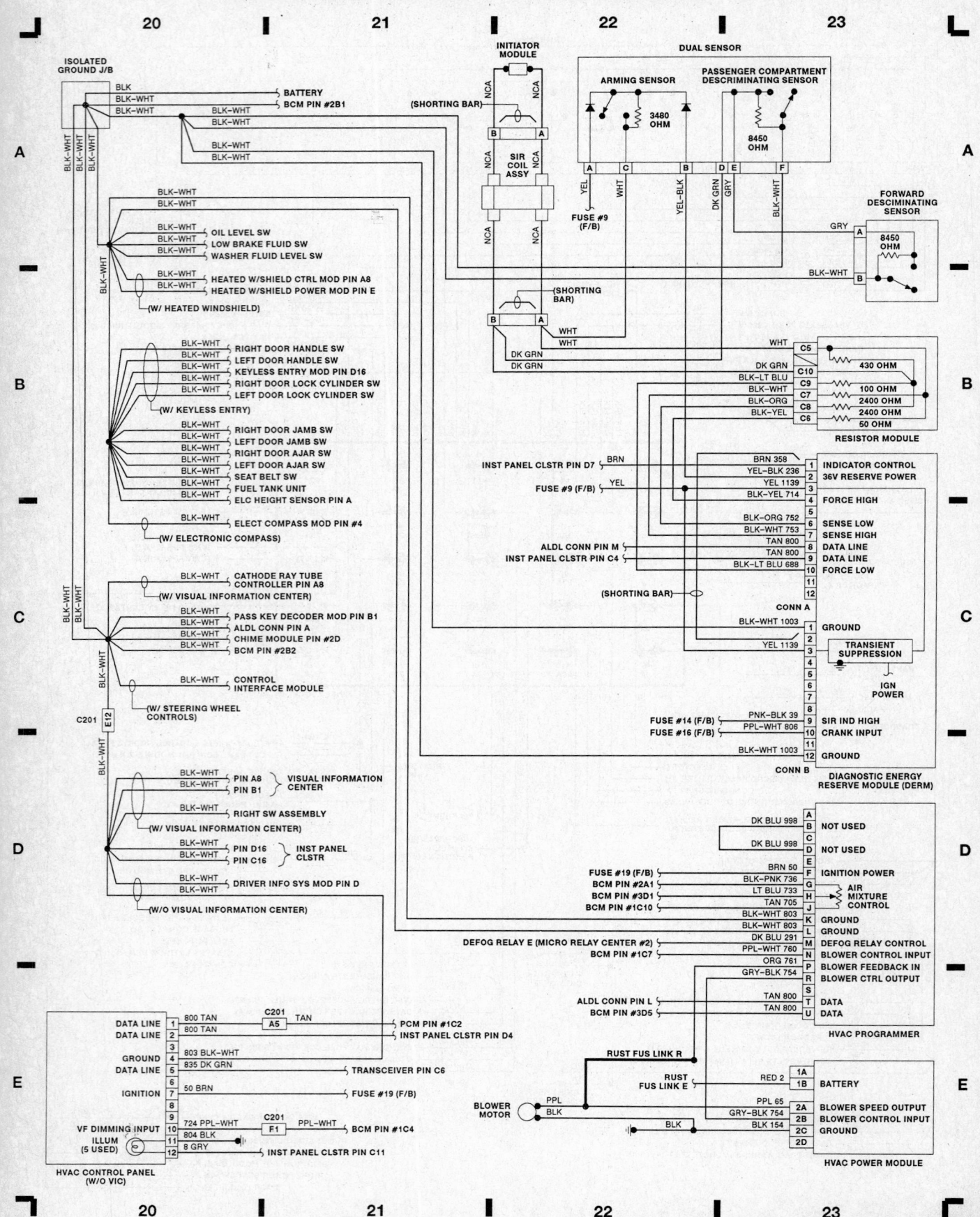

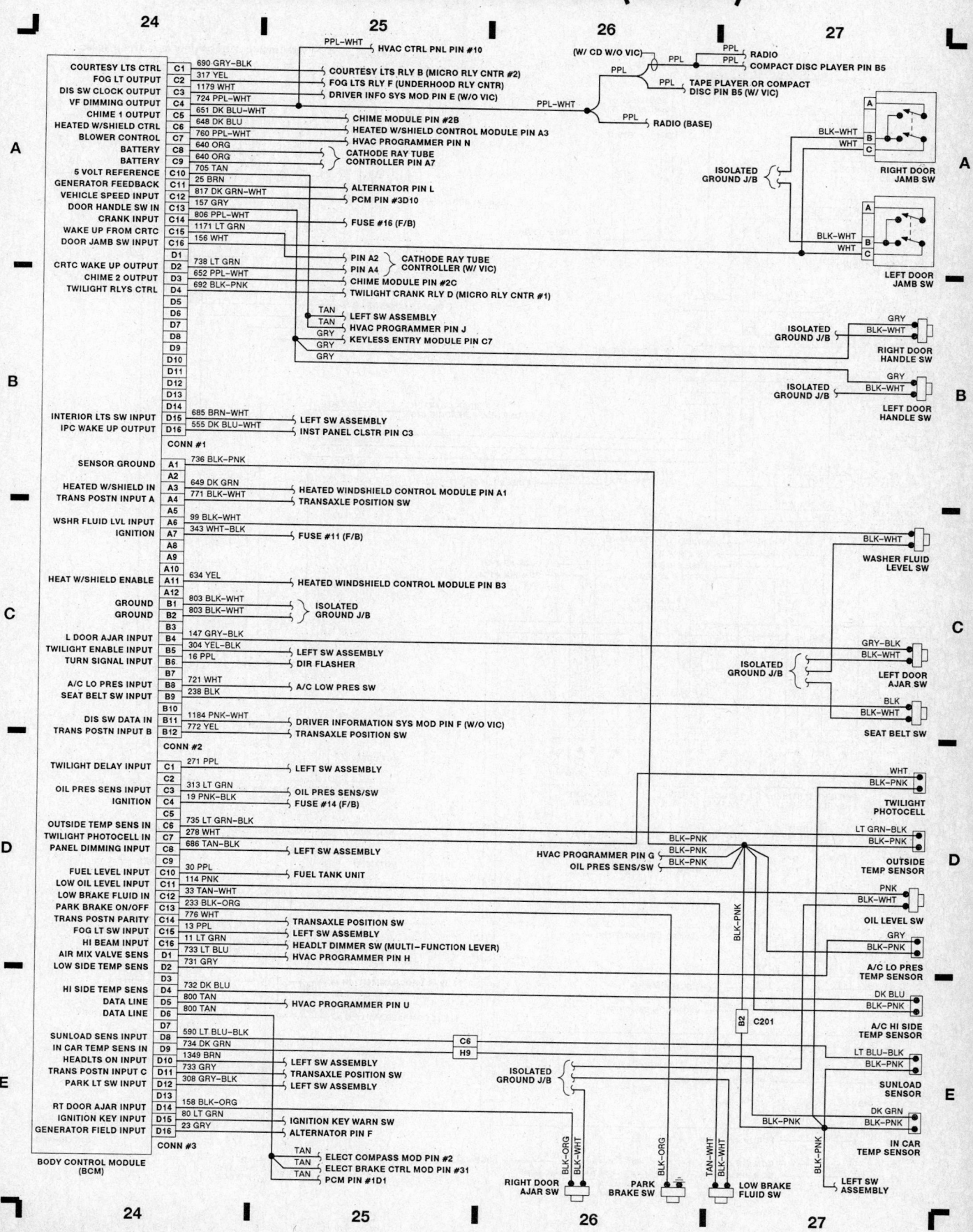

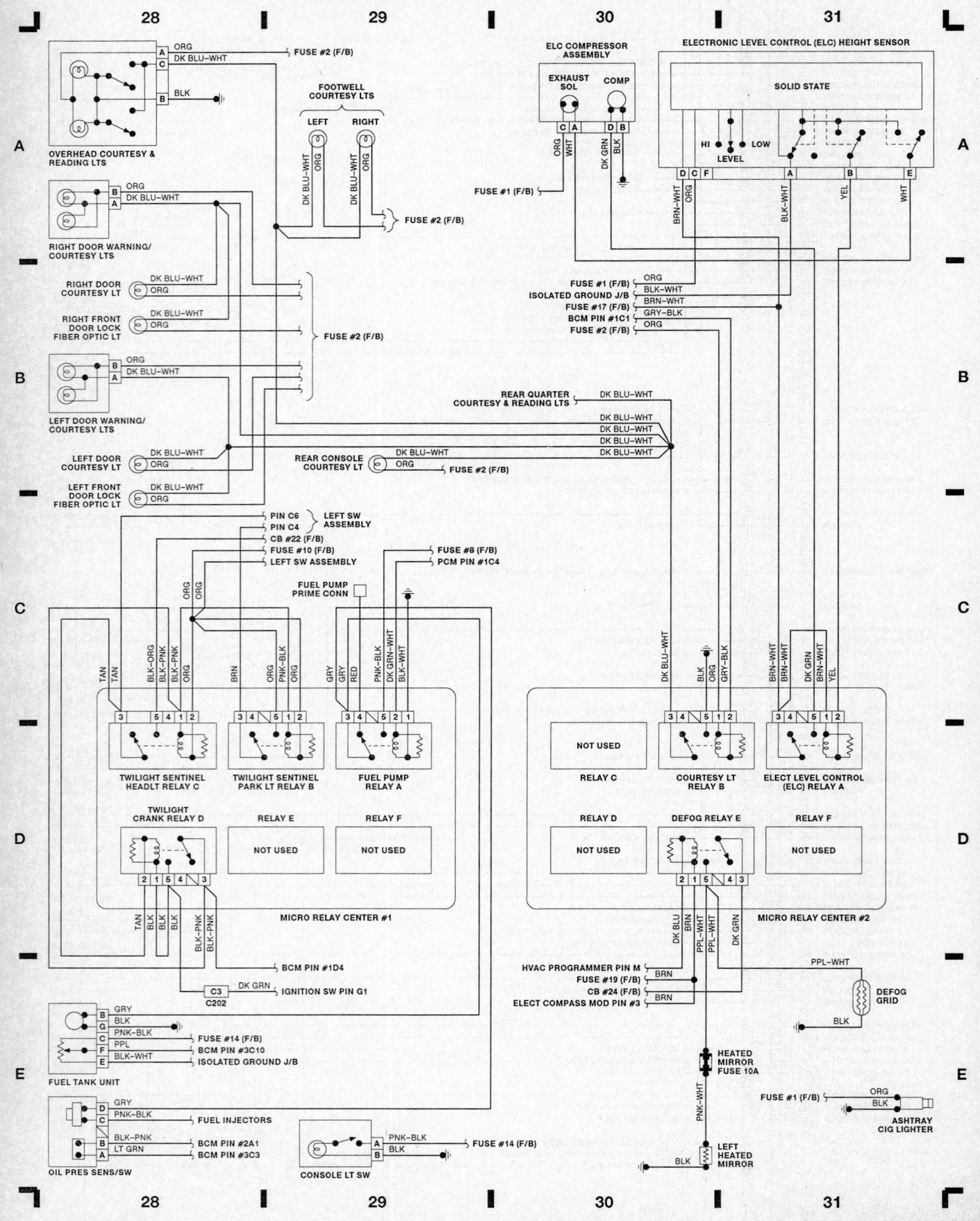

32   33   34   35

ELECTRONIC BRAKE CONTROL MODULE (EBCM)

A

Pin	Label
1	IGNITION
2	L FNT VALVE CTRL
3	L FNT SPD SENS
4	L FNT SPD SENS
5	
6	
7	L REAR SPD SENS
8	L REAR SPD SENS
9	
10	RT FNT SPD SENS
11	
12	
13	PUMP ON INPUT
14	
15	
16	RLY CTRL
17	REAR VALVE CTRL
18	
19	
20	GROUND
21	RT FNT SPD SENS
22	
23	
24	RT REAR SPD SENS
25	APPLIED BRAKE INPUT
26	RT REAR SPD SENS
27	VALVE RELAY CTRL
28	PUMP MOTOR RLY CTRL
29	ANTI-LOCK CTRL IND
30	IGNITION
31	BCM/PCM DATA LINE
32	VALVE RLY FEEDBACK
33	GROUND
34	RT FNT VALVE CTRL
35	RT FNT VALVE CTRL

Wire labels:
PNK-WHT 1176, BLK-WHT 826, SHIELD 837, YEL 837, DK BLU 830, BLK 884, RED 855, SHIELD 855, LT GRN 872, BLK-LT GRN 1292, PNK-BLK 854, DK BLU-WHT 829, BLK 804, TAN 833, SHIELD 833, BRN 882, LT BLU 20, SHIELD 883, PPL-WHT 879, WHT 874, WHT 852, TAN-WHT 799, TAN 800, GRY-BLK 851, BLK 804, BRN-WHT 827

FUSE #18 (F/B)
BCM PIN #3D6
ALDL CONN PIN H
BRAKE SW
BLK

RIGHT FRONT WHEEL SPEED SENSOR — LT GRN / LT GRN, TAN / TAN

RIGHT REAR WHEEL SPEED SENSOR — BLK A / BRN, WHT B / WHT

LEFT FRONT WHEEL SPEED SENSOR — YEL / YEL, DK BLU / DK BLU

LEFT REAR WHEEL SPEED SENSOR — BLK B / BLK, WHT A / RED

BRN-WHT 3 — RIGHT FRONT VALVE SOLENOID
BLK-WHT 1 — LEFT FRONT VALVE SOLENOID
DK BLU-WHT 5 — REAR VALVE SOLENOID

BLU FUS LINK U
PPL-WHT 2
RED 6

INST PANEL CLSTR PIN D6 — WHT
GRY-BLK 4
WHT 11
VALVE RELAY

WHT 12
PNK-BLK 7
BLK FUS LINK M — RED 8
BLK-LT GRN 10
9
PUMP MOTOR RELAY

BLK — PUMP MOTOR

ELECTRONIC BRAKE MODULATOR

GROUND — NCA
DATA LINE INPUT — NCA

X	BLK-WHT	A3	BLK-WHT	ISOLATED GROUND J/B
W	GRN-WHT	A4	DK GRN	TRANSCEIVER PIN C6
V	BLK	A14	BLK	
Y	GRY	A2	GRY	INST PANEL CLSTR PIN C11
Z	YEL	A1	BRN-WHT	FUSE #13 (F/B)

C202

DATA INPUT — A NCA, C NCA, D NCA, B NCA — NCA...

CONTROL INTERFACE MODULE

SIR COIL ASSEMBLY

STEERING WHEEL CONTROLS:
SW #1 — VOL UP
SW #2 — VOL DN
SW #3 — SEEK UP
SW #4 — SEEK DN
SW #5 — FAN UP
SW #6 — FAN DN
SW #7 — TEMP UP
SW #8 — TEMP DN
ILLUM

A B C D (NCA)

AUTOMATIC DAY/NIGHT MIRROR
RESET TO DAYTIME HI REFLECTIVITY IN REVERSE
HEADLT SENS (MIRROR SIDE)
AMBIENT SENS (W/SHIELD SIDE)
LO SENSITIVITY SETTING
HI SENSITIVITY SETTING
GROUND
OFF MIN MAX
ON IND
BLK BLK BLK
3 1 2

FUSE #14 (F/B)
TRANSAXLE POSITION SW
8 PIN CONN (PARTIAL) — A C B
LT GRN, PNK-BLK, BLK

HEATED WINDSHIELD
LT BLU, LT BLU, BLK-WHT, RED-WHT, RED-WHT

HEATED WINDSHIELD CONTROL MODULE

Pin	Label	Wire
A1	SYSTEM ON IND	DK GRN 649 — BCM PIN #2A3
A2	SENSING REF INPUT	LT GRN 475
A3	HEATED W/SHIELD ON	DK BLU 648 — BCM PIN #1C6
A4	FAST IDLE OUTPUT	WHT 637 — PCM PIN #1D4
A5		
A6	REGULATOR	PNK-WHT 350 — FUSE #18 (F/B)
A7		BLK-WHT 803 — ISOLATED GROUND J/B
A8	GROUND	YEL-BLK 369
B1	RELAY CONTROL	
B2		YEL 634 — BCM PIN #2A11
B3	ENABLE INPUT	LT BLU 378
B4	CRACK DETECTOR	
B5		RED 2 — RUST FUS LINK T
B6	BATTERY	
B7		
B8		

ALTERNATOR — BLK, BLK, BLK
YEL-BLK B, BLK-WHT A, E
ISOLATED GROUND J/B

3 PHASE A/C INPUT
DC OUTPUT (−) G, F
DC OUTPUT (+) D
BLK-WHT, RED-WHT, LT GRN

HEATED WINDSHIELD POWER MODULE

32   33   34   35

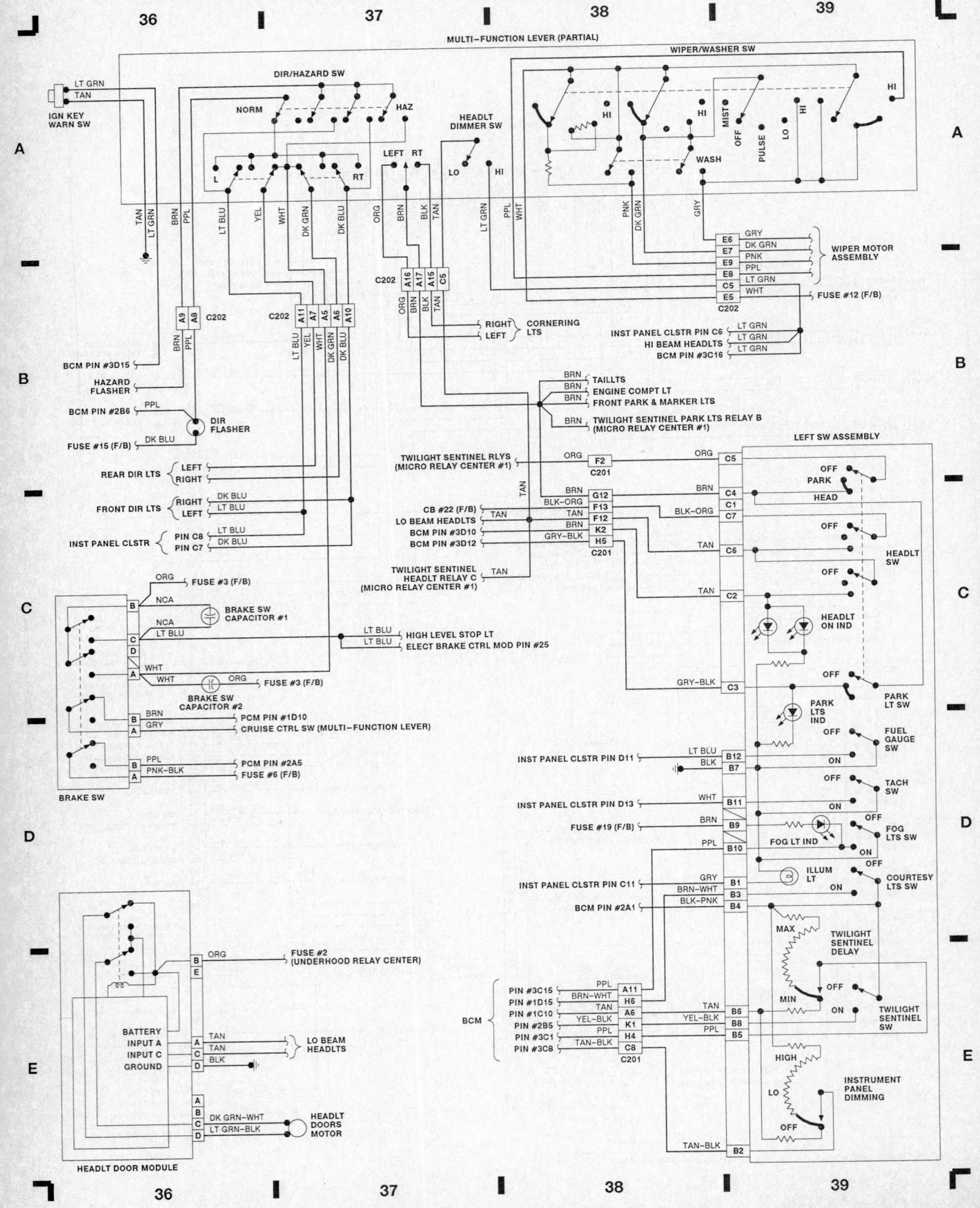

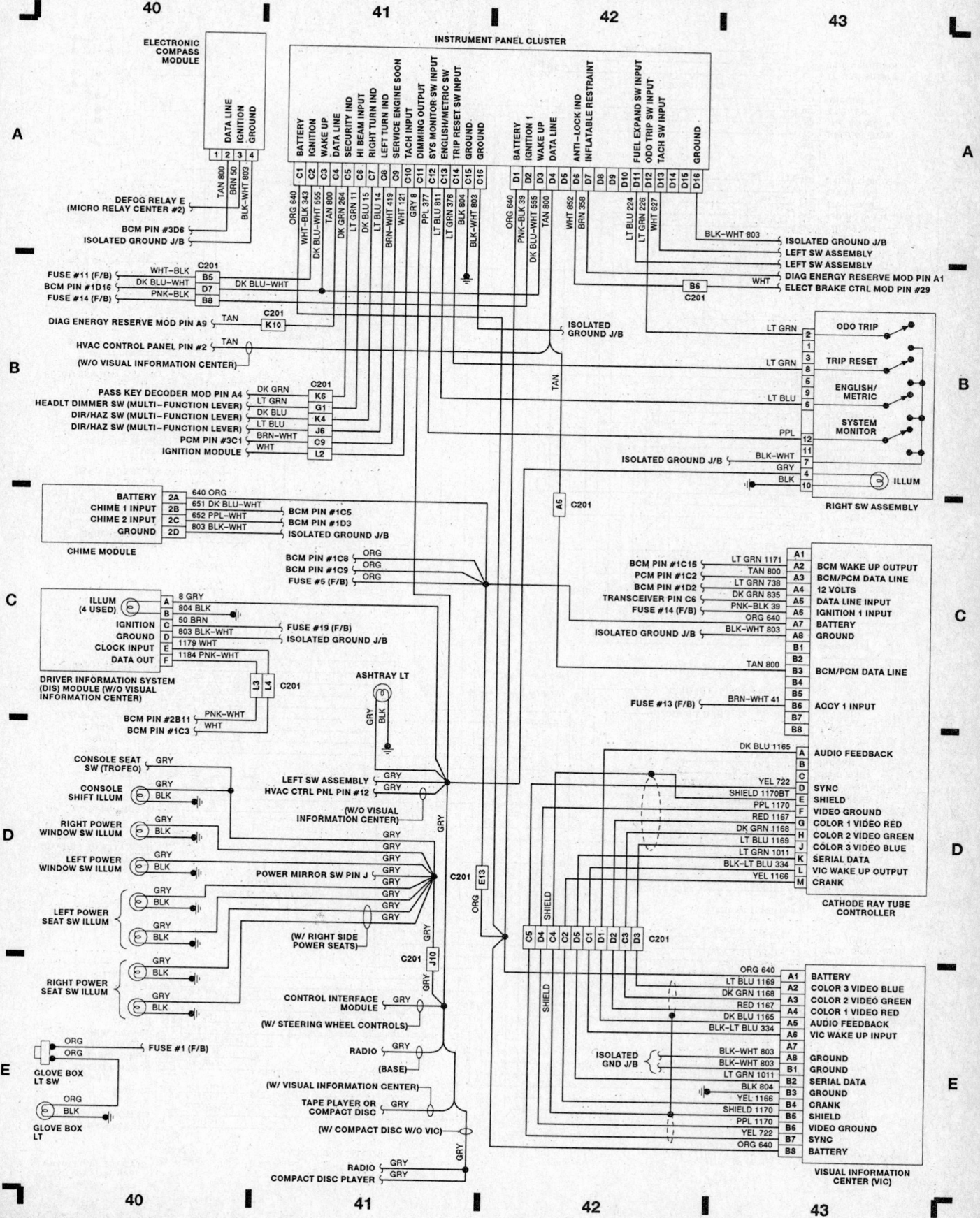

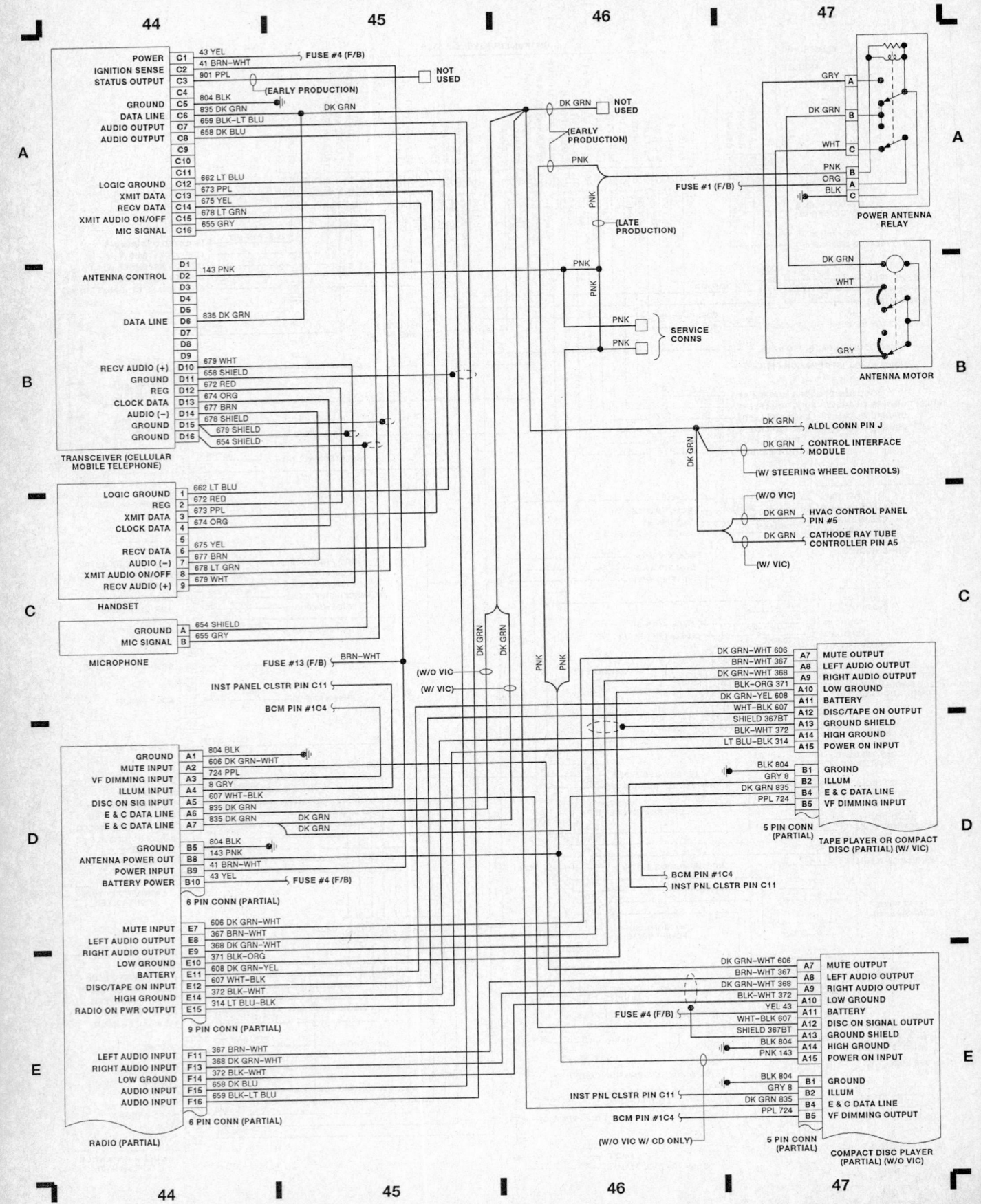

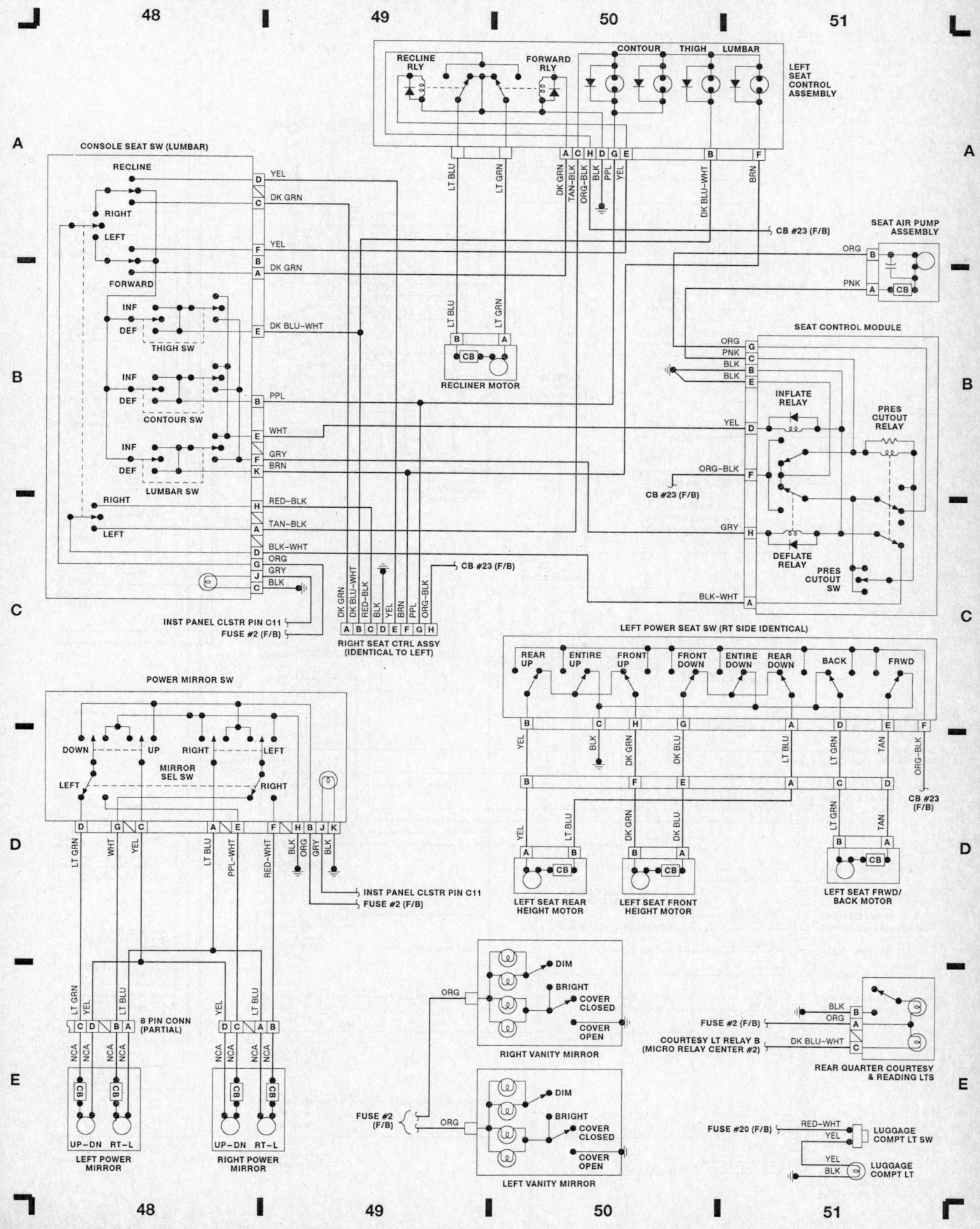

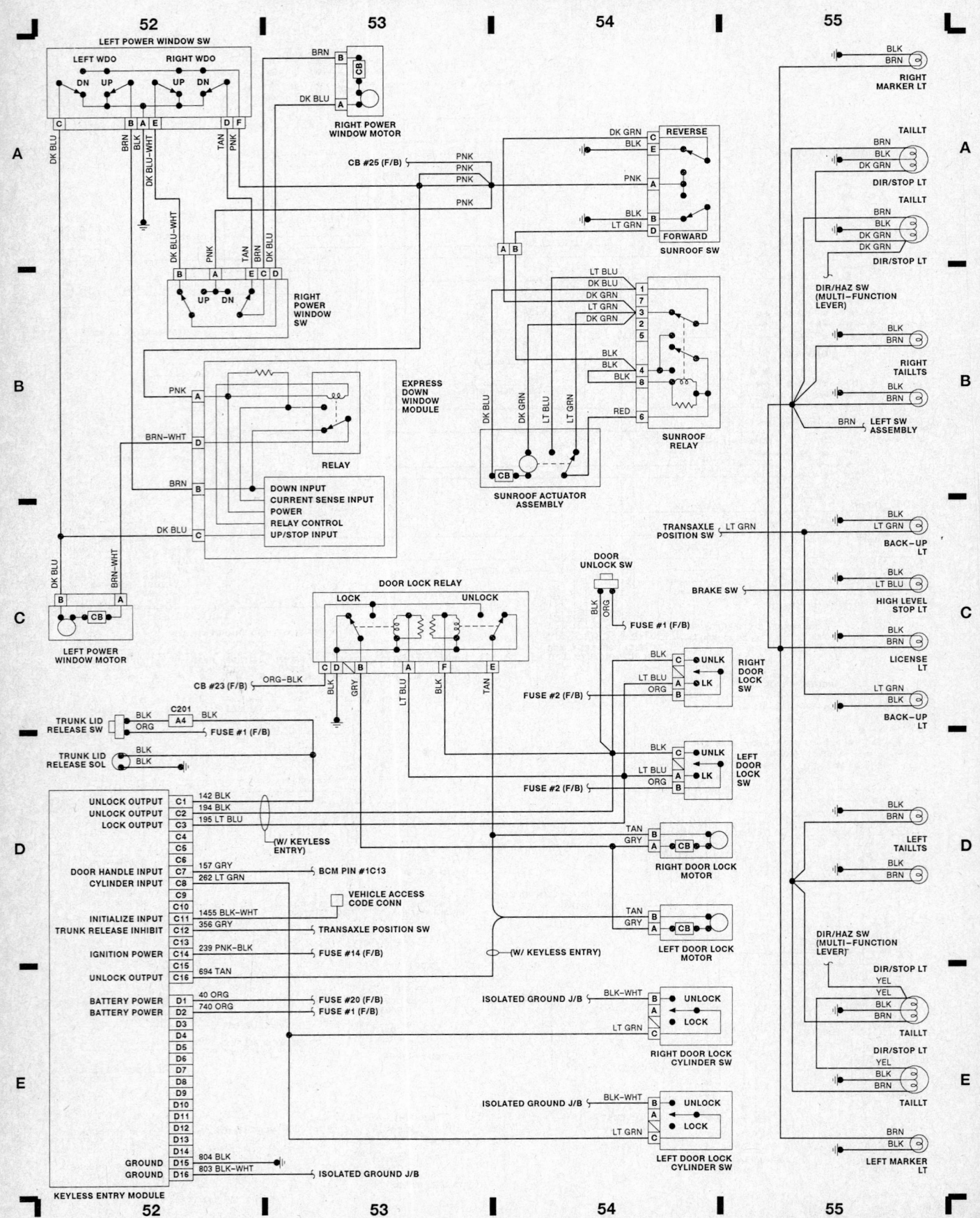

COMPONENT LOCATOR:

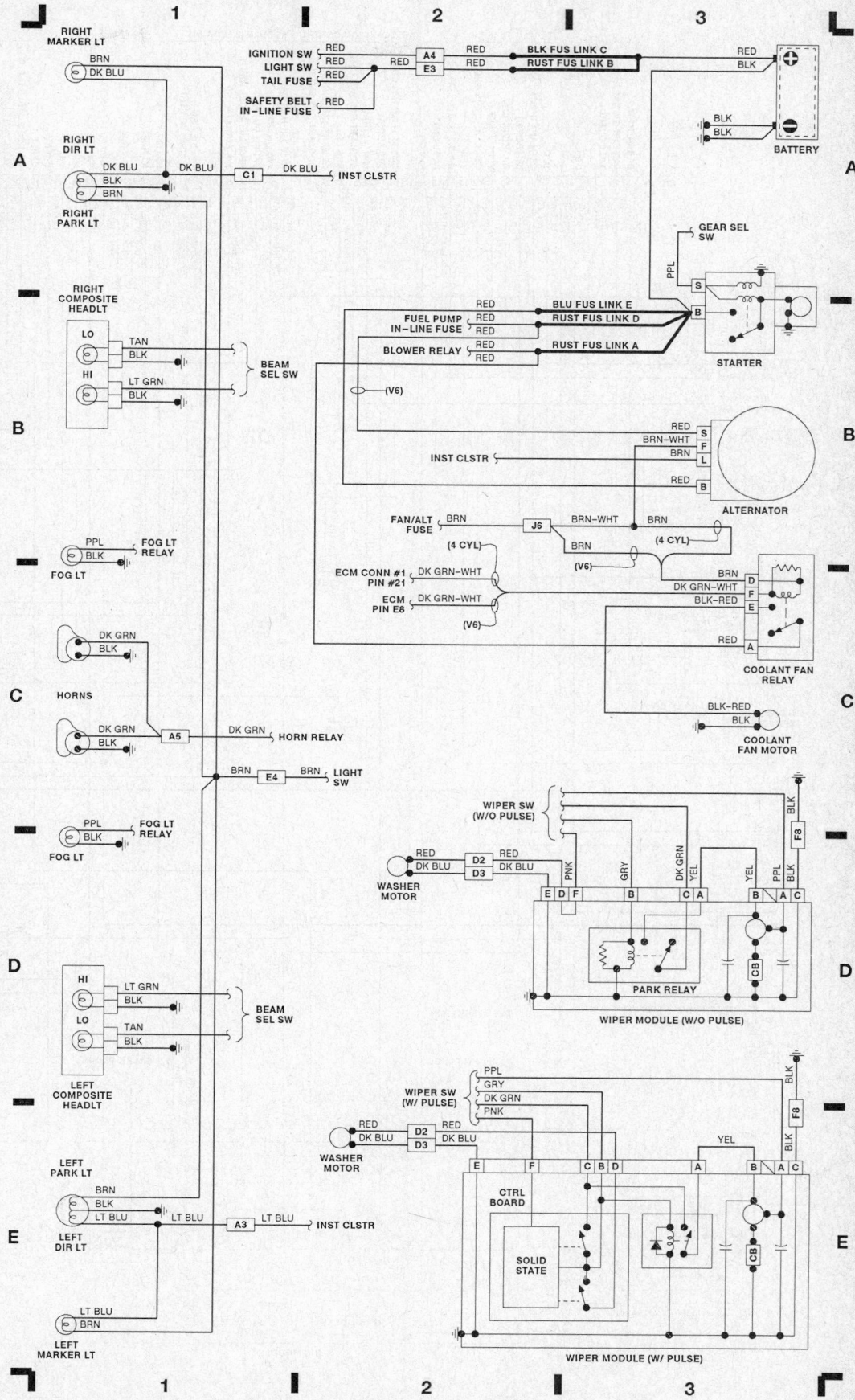

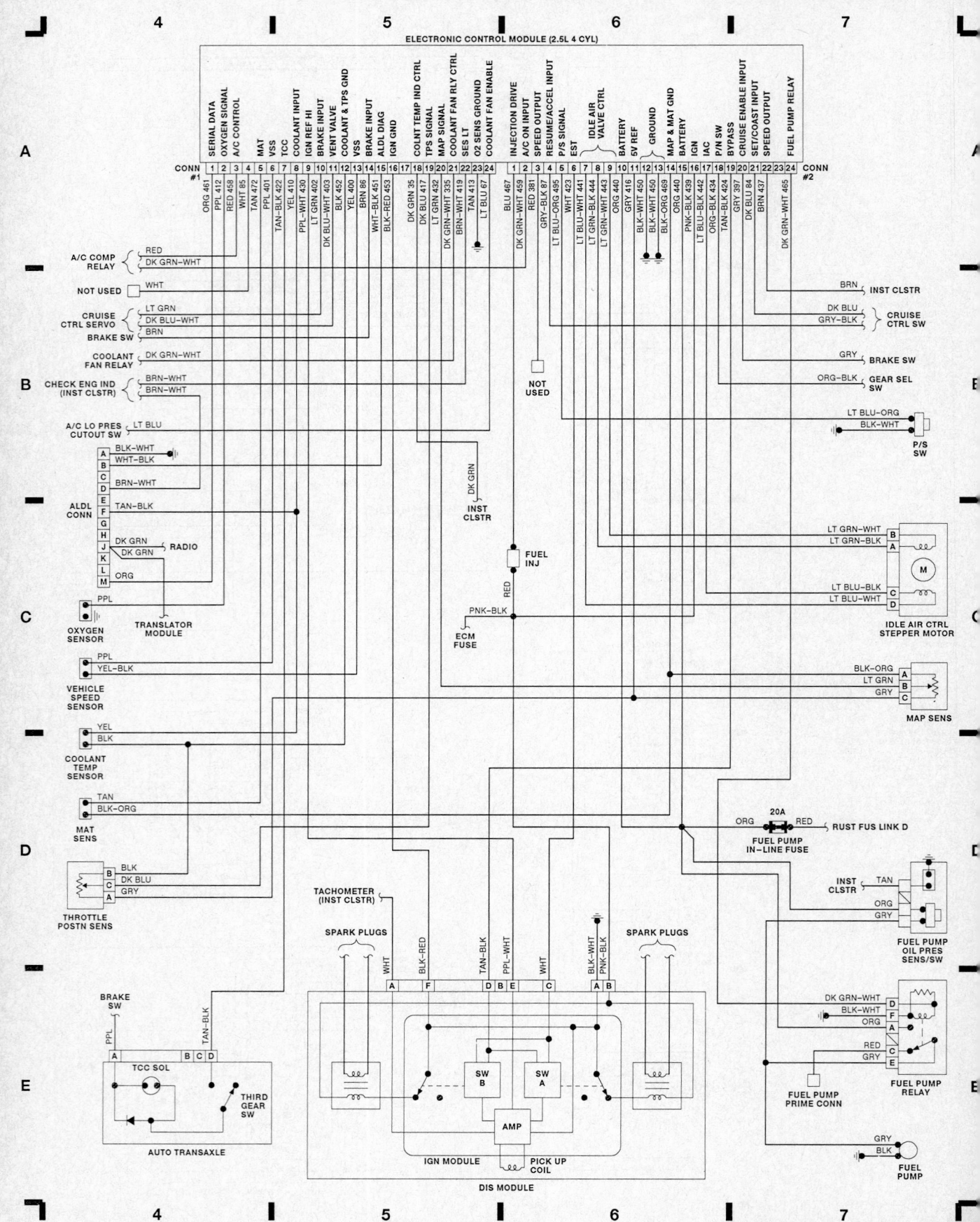

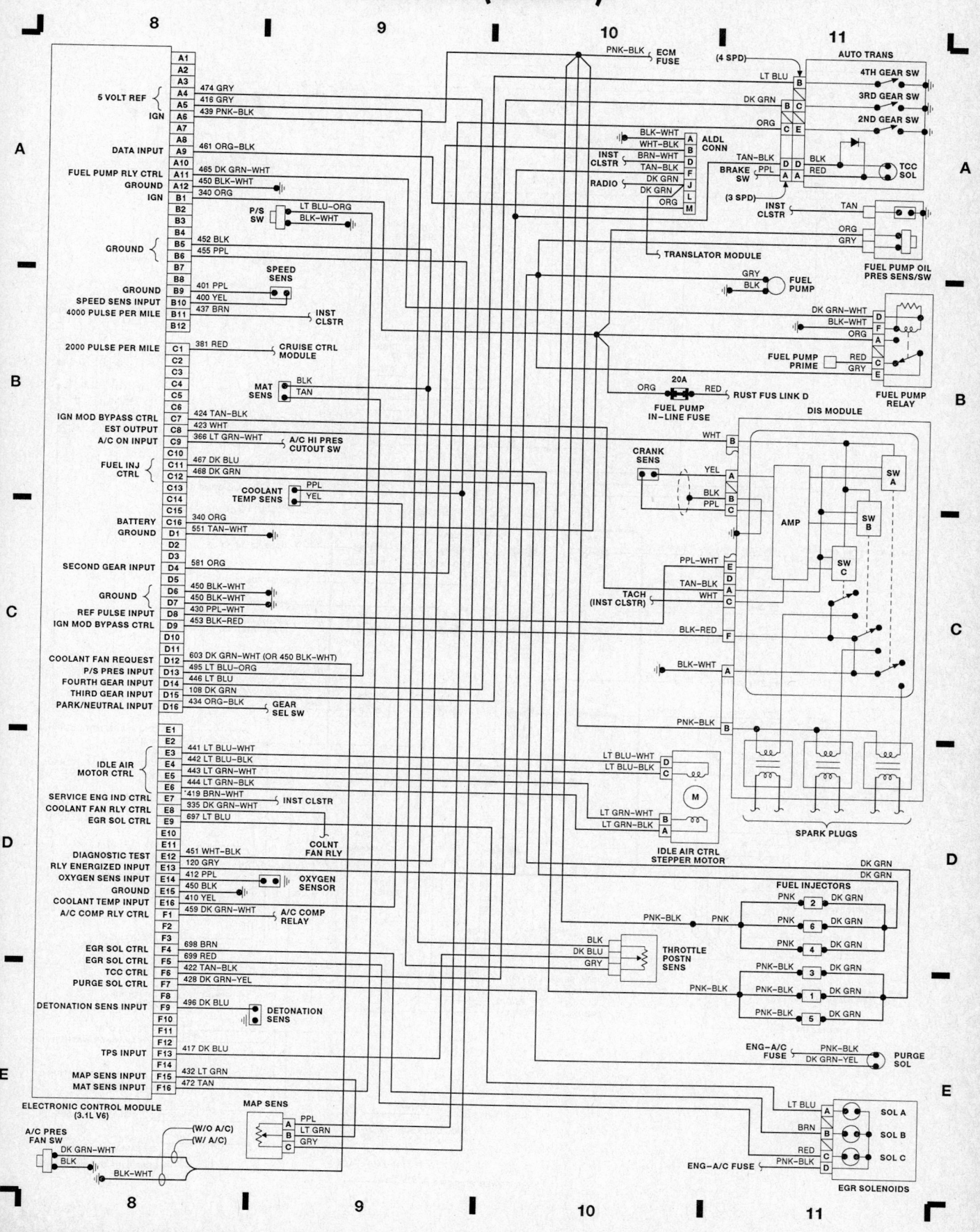

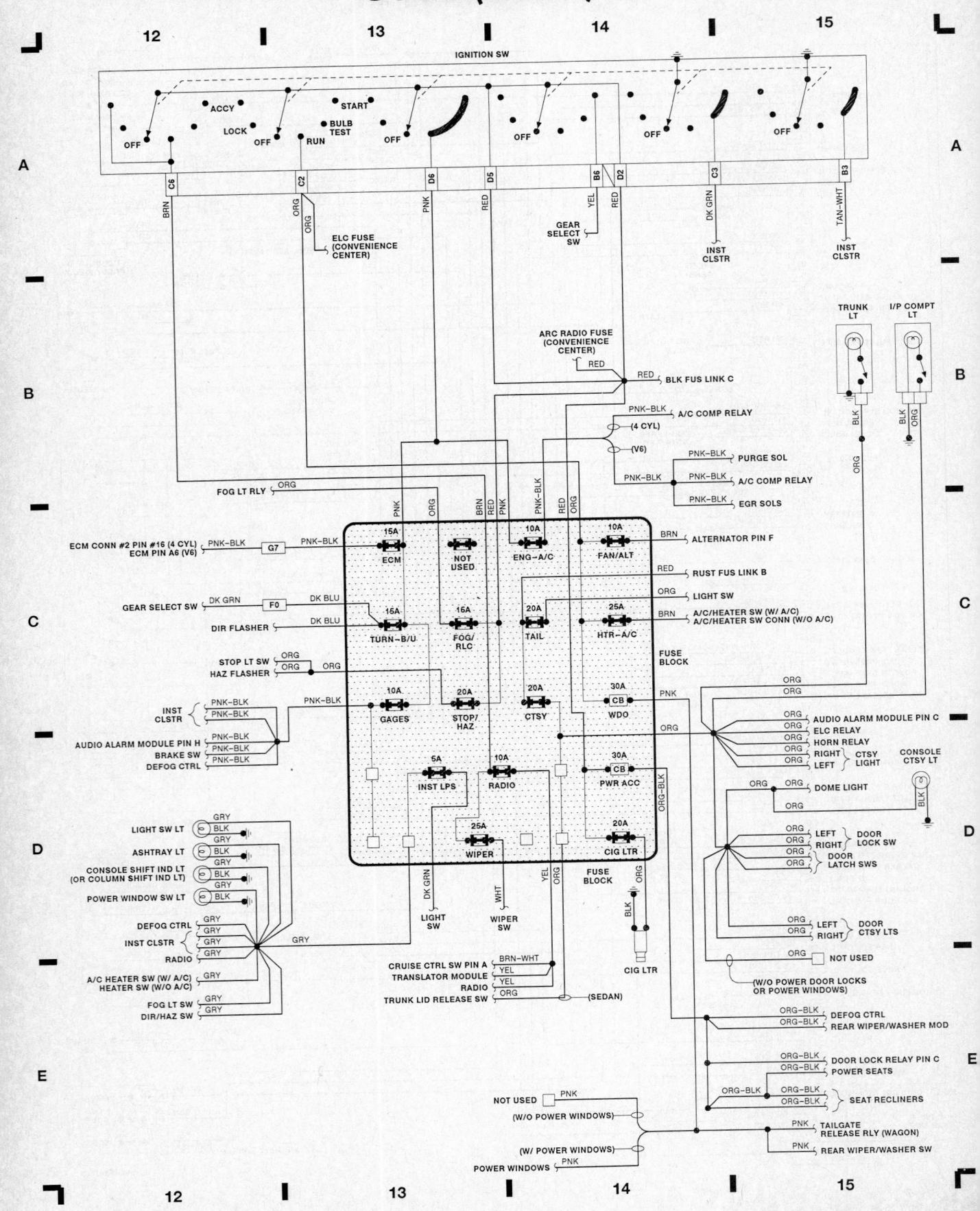

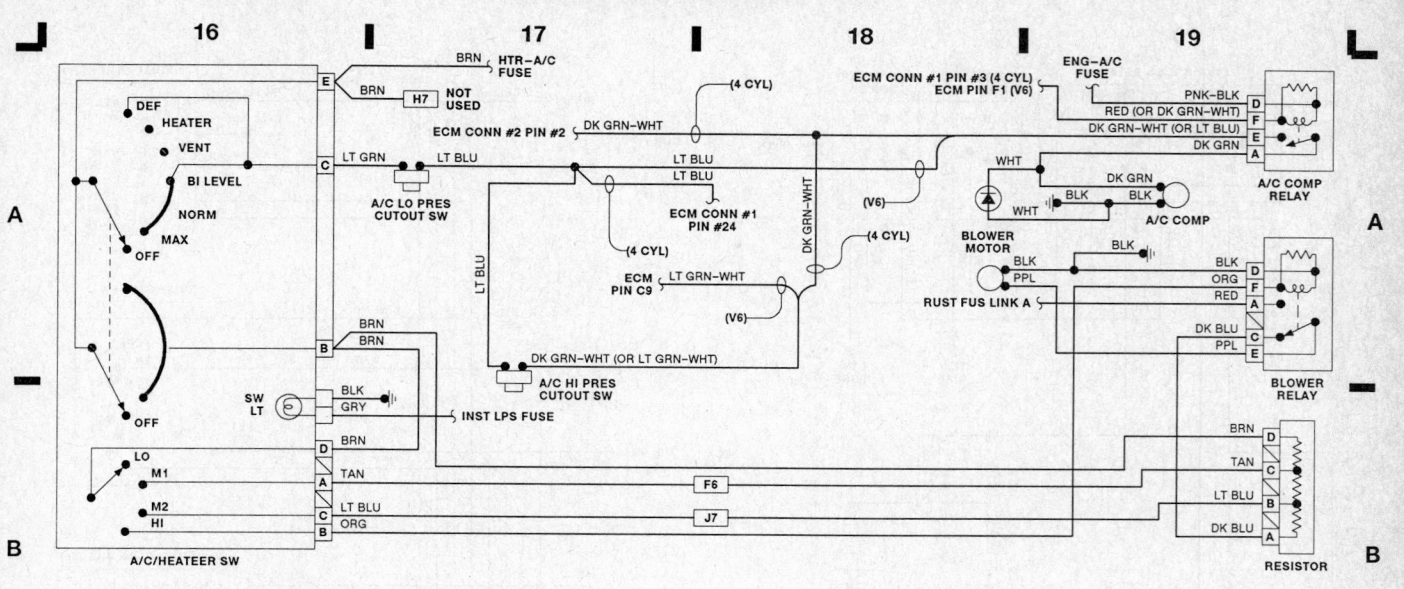

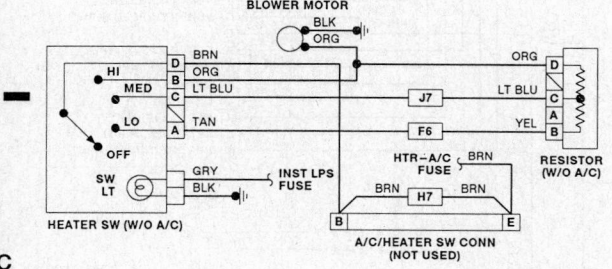

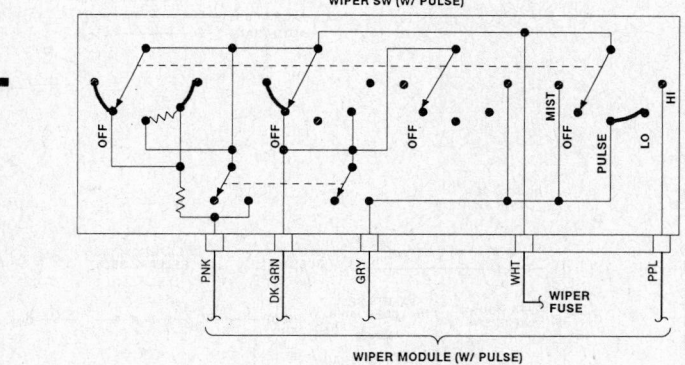

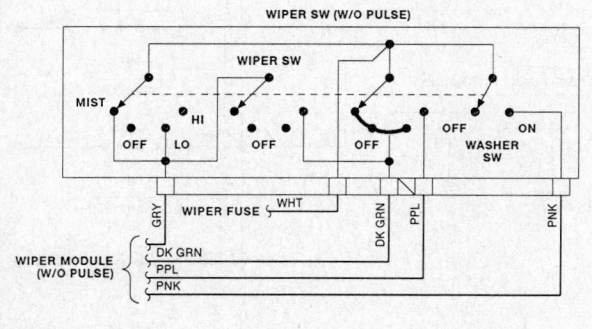

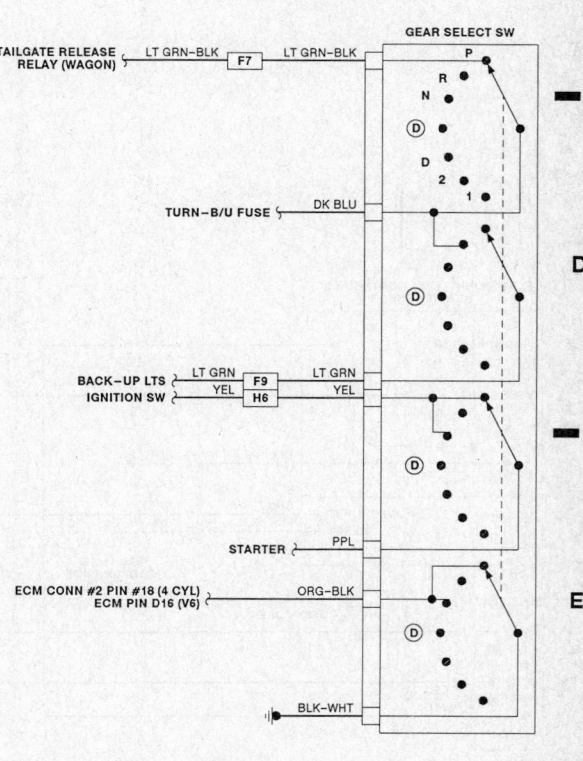

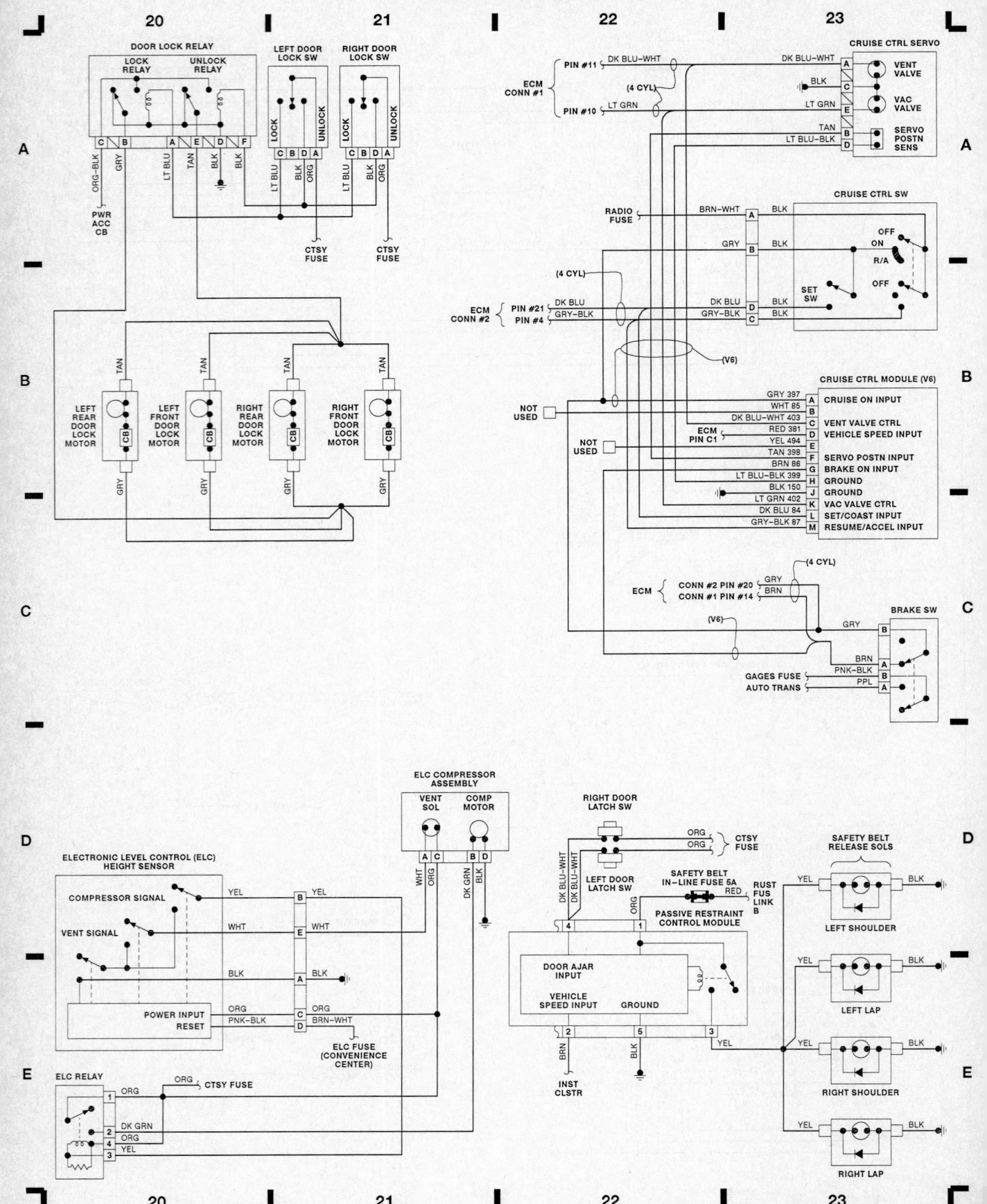

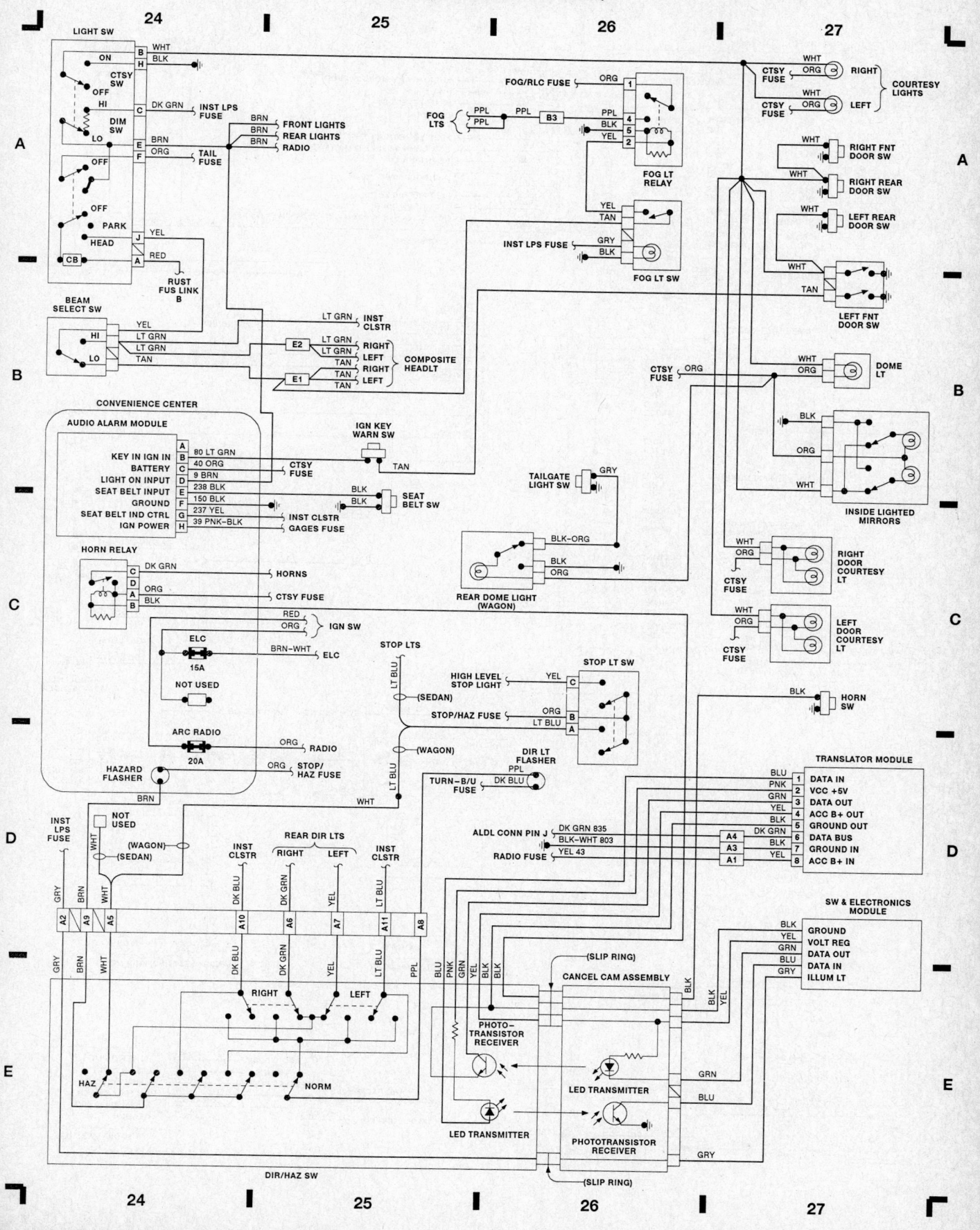

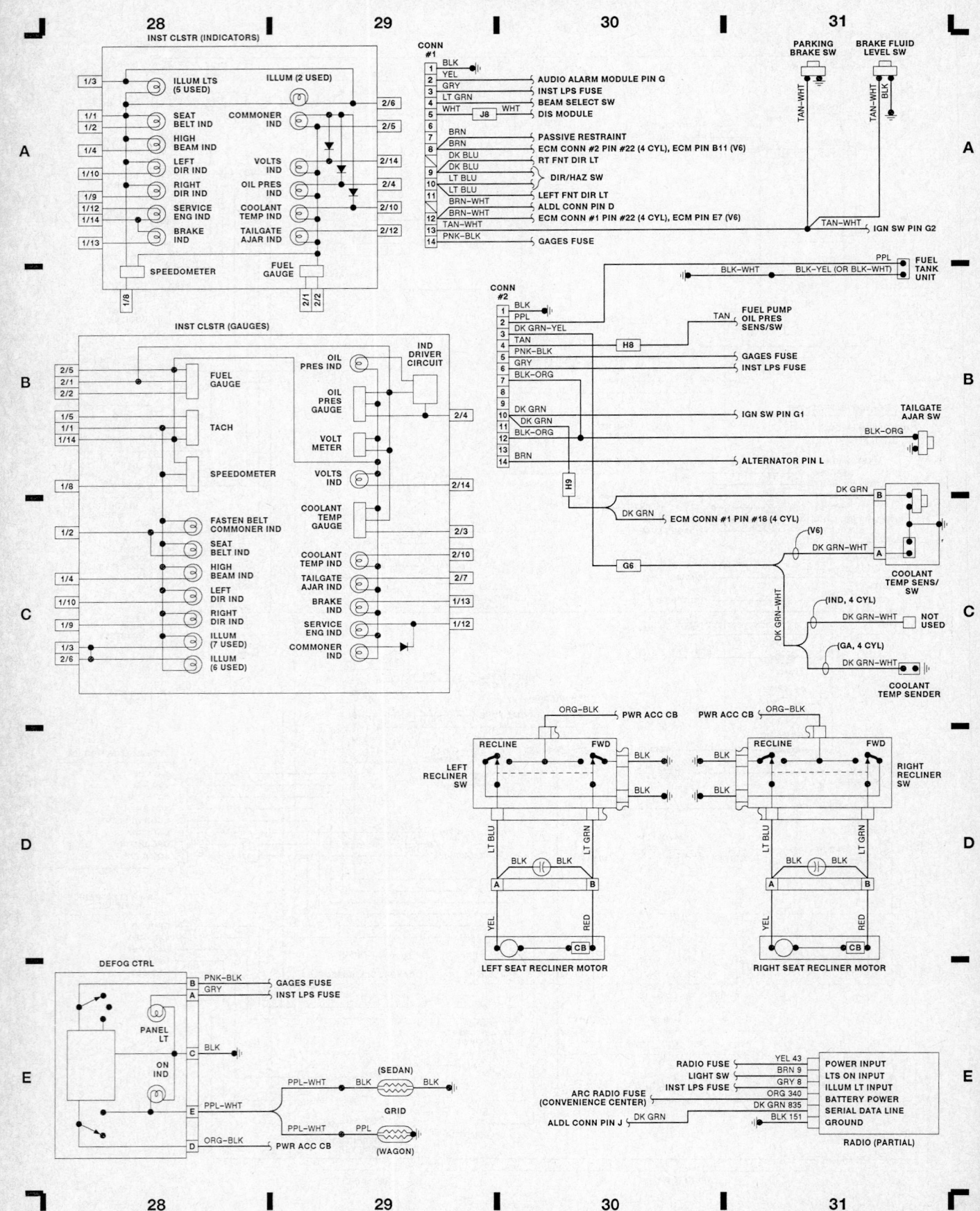

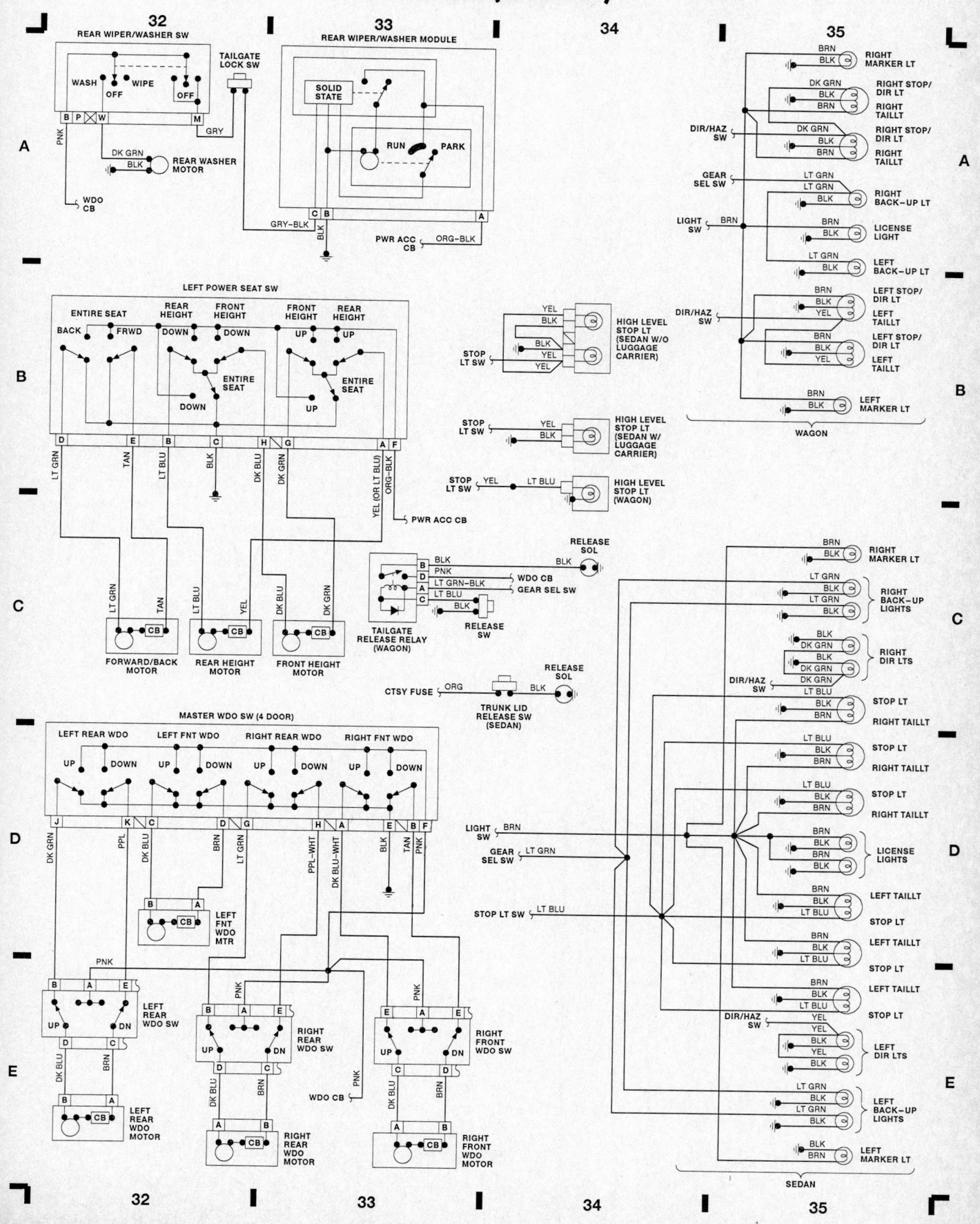

1991 SAFETY EQUIPMENT
Air Bag Restraint System – Except Eighty-Eight

Beretta, Camaro, Caprice, Corsica, Corvette, Custom Cruiser, DeVille, Eldorado, Firebird, Fleetwood, Ninety-Eight, Touring Sedan, Park Avenue, Reatta, Riviera, Roadmaster, Seville, Toronado, Trofeo

IDENTIFICATION

All General Motors models equipped with an air bag have the number "3" in the seventh position of the Vehicle Identification Number (VIN). Some vehicles have the words Supplemental Inflatable Restraint or SIR on the steering wheel hub, which is large in size (approximately 6" by 9") in order to accommodate the air bag.

DESCRIPTION & OPERATION

SUPPLEMENTAL INFLATABLE RESTRAINT (SIR) SYSTEM

The Supplemental Inflatable Restraint (SIR) system is designed to protect the driver in a frontal collision. The air bag will deploy only upon frontal or near frontal impact of no more than 30 degrees off the centerline of the vehicle. The system is not designed to deploy in rear impacts, side impacts or rollovers. A frontal impact of sufficient severity (comparable to a collision into a solid wall at approximately 14 MPH or more) will cause the sensors in the vehicle to detect this sudden deceleration. These sensors, in turn, trigger the inflator module.

DIAGNOSTIC ENERGY RESERVE MODULE (DERM)

The DERM maintains a 36-Volt Loop Reserve (36VLR) energy supply to provide deployment energy for approximately 10-14 minutes if the vehicle system voltage is low or is lost in an accident. In addition, the DERM performs diagnostic monitoring of all system components, stores both current and past SIR system fault code information, warns the driver of SIR system faults by controlling the INFLATABLE RESTRAINT indicator light, and records the SIR system status during a vehicle accident.

The DERM is connected to the SIR harness by a 24-pin connector. The harness connector uses gold-plated terminals and a gold-plated shorting bar in the terminal contact area. The DERM connector also has a gold-plated shorting bar that connects INFLATABLE RESTRAINT indicator input to ground when the DERM connector is disconnected. With the DERM disconnected, the INFLATABLE RESTRAINT indicator remains on when ignition switch is positioned at RUN, BULB TEST or START positions. The DERM is located under the instrument panel.

INFLATABLE RESTRAINT INDICATOR LIGHT

When ignition switch is in RUN, BULB TEST or START positions, battery voltage is applied to the INFLATABLE RESTRAINT indicator light. The DERM illuminates the light by providing a ground to a lamp driver. The INFLATABLE RESTRAINT indicator light verifies light and DERM operation by flashing 7-9 times when the ignition is first turned on, warning the driver of SIR electrical system faults that could potentially affect the operation of the SIR system. In addition, the light provides diagnostic information by flashing fault codes when the flash code diagnostic mode is entered. The INFLATABLE RESTRAINT indicator light is the key to driver notification of SIR system faults.

ARMING SENSOR

The arming sensor is a protective switch located in the power feed side (positive side) of the deployment loop. It is calibrated to close at low-level velocity changes (lower than discriminating sensors). This assures that the inflator module is connected directly to the 36VLR output of the DERM and ignition voltage when either of the discriminating sensors close.

The arming sensor consists of a sensing element, normally open switch contacts, a diagnostic resistor, and 2 diodes. The sensing element closes the normally open switch contacts when the velocity of the vehicle changes at a rate indicating potential need for deployment. The diagnostic resistor is connected in parallel with the normally open switch contacts and allows for a small amount of current flow through the deployment loop during normal nondeployment conditions. This small current flow results in voltage drops across each component within the loop.

The DERM monitors these voltage drops to detect circuit or component faults. The 2 diodes provide isolation between the 36VLR output of the DERM and ignition voltage. In some vehicles, the arming sensor is combined with the passenger compartment discriminating sensor. The arming sensor is located under the center of the instrument panel/console area of the vehicle.

DISCRIMINATING SENSORS

There are 2 discriminating sensors in the SIR system. Some vehicles have 2 forward discriminating sensors, while other vehicles have one forward discriminating sensor and a passenger compartment discriminating sensor. The forward discriminating sensor(s) is located on the radiator support brace. The passenger compartment discriminating is located under the center of the instrument panel/console area or under the front passenger seat. In some vehicles, the passenger compartment discriminating sensor is combined with the arming sensor. Discriminating sensors are wired in parallel on the ground side of the deployment loop. These sensors are calibrated to close when deceleration velocity changes are severe enough to warrant deployment.

The sensors consist of a sensing element, normally open switch contacts, and a diagnostic resistor. The sensing element closes the normally open switch contacts when the vehicle velocity changes are severe enough to warrant deployment.

A diagnostic resistor is connected in parallel with the normally open switch contacts within each of the sensors. These parallel resistors supply the ground path for the current passing through the deployment loop during normal nondeployment conditions. This small current flow results in a voltage drop across each component within the loop. The DERM monitors these voltage drops to detect circuit or component faults.

SIR COIL ASSEMBLY

The SIR coil assembly consists of 2 current-carrying coils. It is installed in the steering column and allows rotation of the steering wheel while maintaining continuous (directly wired) contact of the deployment loop through the inflator module. The SIR system does not utilize slip rings to transmit current from the column to the steering wheel.

Gold-plated terminals and a shorting bar are utilized on the coil assembly lower steering column Yellow connector. The shorting bar shorts the circuits to the main coil and inflator module when the lower steering column connector is disconnected. This shorts the circuit to the inflator module, preventing unwanted deployment of the air bag when servicing the steering column or other SIR components.

INFLATOR MODULE

When the vehicle is in an accident of sufficient force to simultaneously close the arming sensor and at least one discriminating sensor, nitrogen gas inflates the cloth bag packed inside the steering wheel hub. The bag inflates and deploys in less than 1/20 of a second. As the driver contacts the bag, the gas is vented through openings in the bag and deflates almost as soon as it is completely deployed.

RESISTOR MODULE

The resistor module is located in the SIR harness between the inflator module and the DERM. The resistor module allows the DERM to monitor the deployment loop for faults and also allows the DERM to detect when a deployment has occurred.

GM
4-2

1991 SAFETY EQUIPMENT
Air Bag Restraint System — Except Eighty-Eight (Cont.)

The resistors in the resistor module are balanced with the resistors on the arming and discriminating sensors to allow the DERM to monitor the voltage drops across the components of the deployment loop. Faults are detected during normal nondeployment conditions by monitoring these voltages. On some vehicles, the resistor module is mounted on the DERM.

SYSTEM OPERATION CHECK

If the system is functioning normally, the INFLATABLE RESTRAINT warning light will flash 7-9 times when the ignition switch is turned to ON position, then go off.

Four possible warning light conditions can indicate a system failure:
- Light does not illuminate at all.
- Light comes on while vehicle is driven.
- Light flashes 7-9 times and remains on.
- Light does not flash but remains lit when ignition is turned on.

SIR system faults are usually due to a disconnected/loose electrical connector caused by previous service on the vehicle. Always check the Yellow connector at the base of the steering column.

SPECIAL PRECAUTIONS

SYSTEM REPAIR

Before any repairs are performed, disconnect and shield battery ground. Because system has ability to retain voltage, remove SIR fuse and disconnect Yellow SIR connector at base of steering column. Wait 15 minutes before working on vehicle. All connectors used on SIR system use Connector Position Assurance (CPA) clips to ensure connector retention. Even if system is disconnected, always use caution when working near steering column.

SENSOR HANDLING

Use special care when handling a sensor. DO NOT strike or jar a sensor, as it could cause air bag deployment and result in personal injury or improper operation of the SIR system. A sensor must be replaced if it is dropped 2 feet or more. Sensors and mounting bracket bolts must be carefully torqued to ensure correct operation. Never power up the SIR system when any sensor is not rigidly attached to the vehicle, since sensor is easily activated when not attached and could cause air bag deployment.

LIVE INFLATOR MODULE HANDLING

Special care is necessary when handling and storing a live (undeployed) inflator module. The rapid gas generation produced during deployment of the air bag could cause the inflator module, or any object in front of the inflator module, to be thrown through the air in the event of an accidental deployment.

When carrying a live inflator module, ensure the bag and trim cover are pointed away from you. If an accidental deployment occurs, the bag will then deploy with minimal chance of injury. When placing a live inflator module on a bench or other surface, always face the bag and trim cover up and away from the surface so a free space is provided to allow the air bag to expand in case of deployment. In addition, never carry any SIR component by the wires or connector.

INFLATOR MODULE SHIPPING PROCEDURES

Transportation of undeployed inflator modules is regulated by the hazardous materials regulations of the U.S. Government Department of Transportation and most state governments. Special procedures are required, and it is recommended repair shops check with the hazardous material section of their respective state governments for applicable shipping requirements.

CAUTION: If SIR inflator is disposed of improperly, air bag deployment may result and cause personal injury. Undeployed inflator modules must not be disposed of at normal refuse locations. Undeployed inflator modules contain substances that can cause severe illness or personal injury if the sealed container is damaged during disposal. Disposal of the module in any manner inconsistent with proper procedures may be a violation of federal, state and/or local laws.

VEHICLE SCRAPPING PROCEDURES

Some vehicles that have to be scrapped may have undeployed SIR systems. Ensure the following procedures are followed when scrapping a vehicle with an undeployed module:

1) Turn the ignition switch to OFF position. Remove SIR fuse. Disconnect Yellow 2-pin connector at base of steering column. Cut harness side of SIR wiring approximately 3-6" from Yellow 2-pin connector.
2) Splice 2 wires at least 20 feet long to wiring that was cut from SIR harness. Connect the Yellow 2-pin connector.
3) Ensure inflator module is secured to steering wheel. Remove all loose objects from front seat and ensure no one is in vehicle. Stretch wires away from car as far as possible.
4) Connect the wires to a 12-volt battery. Air bag should deploy. DO NOT touch the inflator module area for 20 minutes due to heat generated during deployment. Wear gloves and safety glasses before handling deployed air bag. Wash hands with soap and water afterward.

DEPLOYED INFLATOR MODULES

Once an inflator module has been deployed, surface of air bag may contain a small amount of sodium hydroxide dust, combined with a White packing powder. The sodium hydroxide dust can be irritating to the skin if left on for an extended period of time. Always wear gloves and safety glasses when handling a deployed inflator module. Wash hands afterward.

INSPECTING SYSTEM AFTER ACCIDENT

All SIR components, including harness and brackets, must be inspected after an accident. If any components are damaged or bent they must be replaced, even if a deployment did not occur. Check steering column, knee bolster, instrument panel steering column reinforcement plate and lower brace for damage. DO NOT service the forward discriminating sensor, passenger compartment discriminating sensor, arming sensor, DERM, coil assembly or inflator module. System wiring harness can only be serviced with splice sleeves in Wire Repair Kit (J-38125-A).

CAUTION: Correct operation of the sensors and SIR system requires any repairs to the vehicle structure return it to its original production configuration. Deployment requires, at a minimum, replacement of discriminating/arming sensor, forward discriminating sensor and inflator module.

SPECIAL TOOLS

To avoid deployment when working on the SIR system, DO NOT use electrical test equipment such as test lights, battery or A/C-powered volt/ohmmeter, or any type of electrical equipment other than those specified by manufacturer. See SIR RECOMMENDED TOOL table.

SIR RECOMMENDED TOOL

Tool Name	Tool Number
Connector Test Adapter Kit	J-35616
Digital Volt/Ohmmeter	J-34029-A
Inflator Module & Steering Column Replacement Load	J-37808
Wire Repair Kit	J-38125-A

WIRING REPAIR

Because of the sensitive nature of the circuitry, special wiring repair procedures have been developed by the manufacturer. The Wire Repair Kit (J-38125-A) contains special sealed splices for use in repairing SIR wiring. The sealed splices are a heat shrink sleeve with sealing adhesive to produce a sealed splice and a cross-hatched core crimp to produce a positive contact for the low energy circuits.

1991 SAFETY EQUIPMENT
Air Bag Restraint System — Except Eighty-Eight (Cont.)

GM
4-3

If any terminal or connector in the SIR wire harness (except pigtails) is damaged, the component can be repaired using one of the connector repair assembly packs. The terminals in the SIR system are manufactured of a special metal to provide necessary contact for low energy circuits. These terminals are only available in the wiring kit and no other terminal should be substituted.

If an SIR wire pigtail is damaged, the entire component (including pigtail) should be replaced. Under no circumstances should wire, connector or terminal repair be attempted on the arming sensor, passenger compartment discriminating sensor, forward discriminating sensor, inflator module, or SIR coil assembly.

If any wire except a pigtail is damaged, wire can be repaired by splicing in a new section of wire of the same gauge. The sealed splices and crimping tool must be used for these splices. To open wiring harness, remove tape as necessary. To avoid wire insulation damage, manufacturer recommends the use of a sewing "seam ripper". Refer to instructions in kit for wire repair procedure.

REMOVAL & INSTALLATION

WARNING: Before any repairs are performed, disconnect and shield battery ground. Because system has ability to retain voltage, remove SIR fuse and disconnect Yellow SIR connector at base of steering column. Wait 10 minutes before beginning service. All connectors used on SIR system use Connector Position Assurance (CPA) clips to ensure connector retention. Even if system is disconnected, use caution when working near steering column.

DERM

Removal (Beretta & Corsica) – Remove right instrument panel sound insulator panel. Open glove box and loosen 2 nuts from side of DERM. Slide DERM from bracket. Remove DERM CPA clip and electrical connector. *See Fig. 1.*

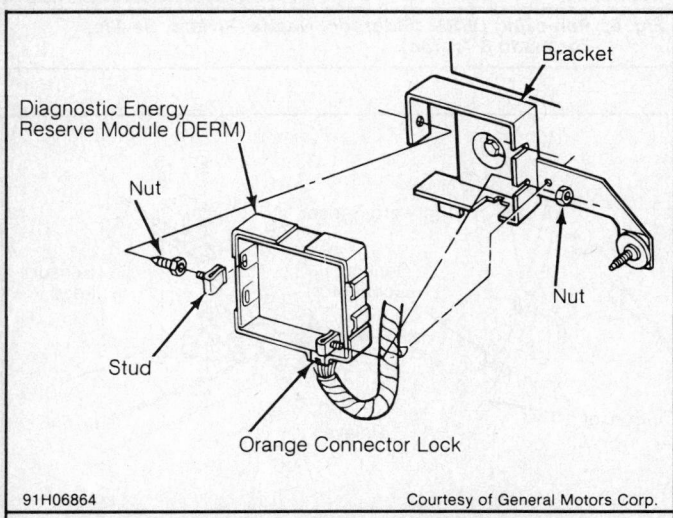

91H06864   Courtesy of General Motors Corp.

Fig. 1: Removing DERM From Bracket (Beretta & Corsica)

Installation – Remove DERM electrical connector and CPA clip. Slide DERM into bracket. Install DERM attaching nuts and torque to 12 INCH lbs. (1.4 N.m). To complete installation, reverse removal procedure.

Removal (Camaro) – Remove instrument panel pad. Remove windshield defogger duct and screws. Cut or break off the unused mounting screw tab from the front edge of the instrument panel, just above the DERM. *See Fig. 2.* Remove DERM attaching screw, DERM module, DERM electrical connector and CPA clip. *See Fig. 3.*

Installation – To install, reverse removal procedure. Turn ignition switch to RUN position and ensure the INFLATABLE RESTRAINT indicator flashes 7-9 times, then off.

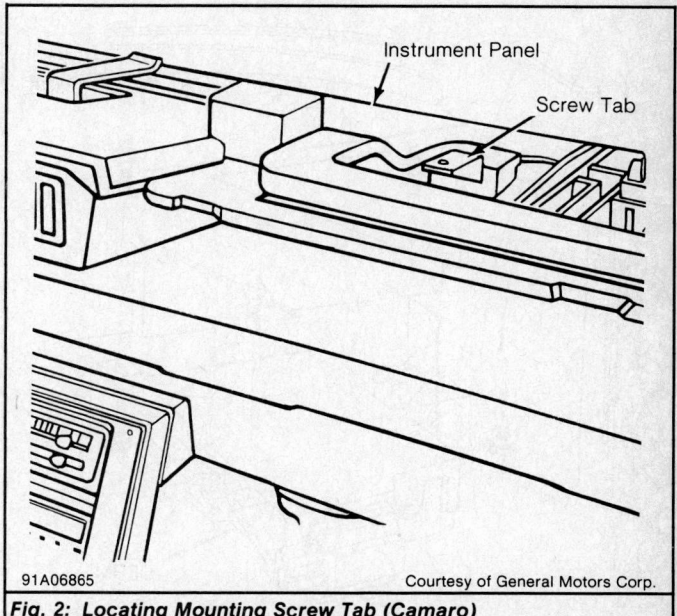

91A06865   Courtesy of General Motors Corp.

Fig. 2: Locating Mounting Screw Tab (Camaro)

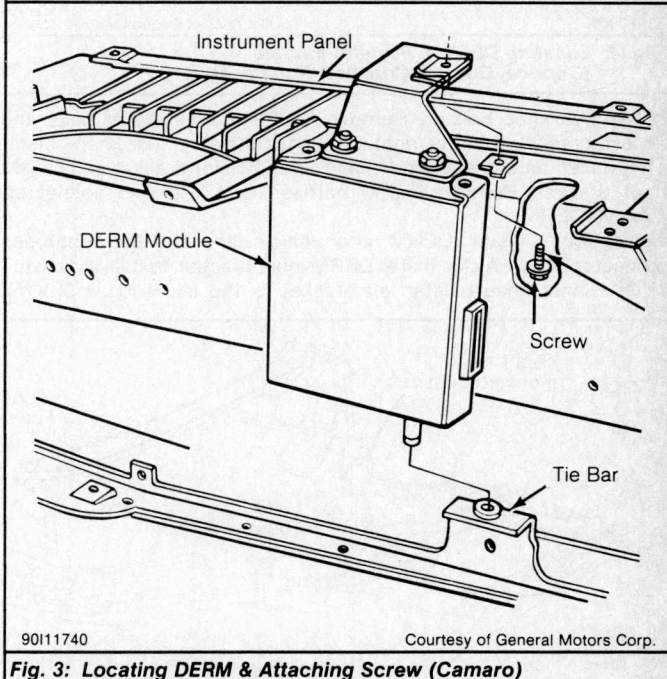

90I11740   Courtesy of General Motors Corp.

Fig. 3: Locating DERM & Attaching Screw (Camaro)

Removal (Caprice, Custom Cruiser & Roadmaster) – Remove resistor module from DERM by sliding it to the left on the DERM bracket. Disconnect DERM electrical connector. Remove 3 nuts from DERM bracket. Remove DERM and bracket. Loosen 3 bolts and remove DERM from bracket. *See Fig. 4.*

Installation – Install DERM onto bracket and torque 3 bolts to 17 INCH lbs. (2 N.m). Install DERM and bracket. Torque 3 nuts to 17 INCH lbs. (2 N.m). To complete installation, reverse removal procedure.

Removal (Corvette) – **1)** Remove console and accessory trim plates. Remove radio control head and upper 2 left side trim panel screws. Flip panel down to access DERM. *See Fig. 5.*

GM
4-4

1991 SAFETY EQUIPMENT
Air Bag Restraint System – Except Eighty-Eight (Cont.)

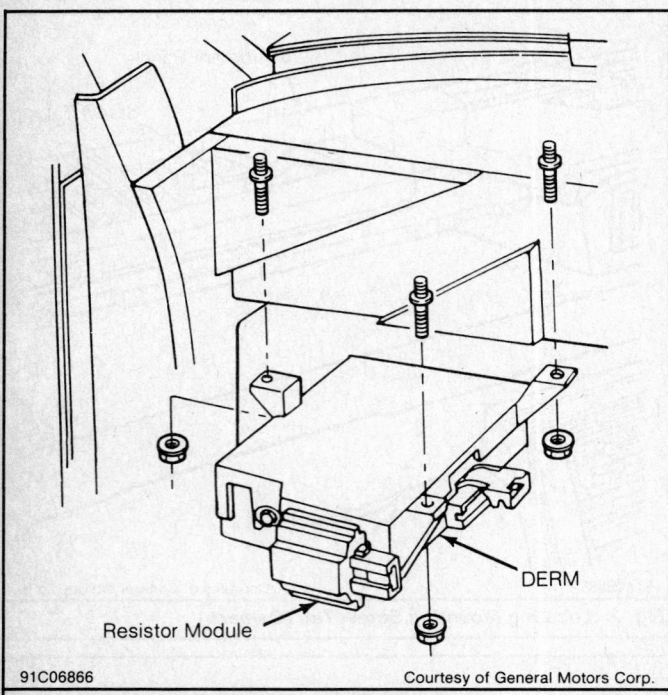

Fig. 4: Locating DERM & Resistor Module (Caprice, Custom Cruiser & Roadmaster)

91C06866   Courtesy of General Motors Corp.

2) Remove knee bolster. Remove 4 DERM left bracket bolts and remove bracket. Remove right trim panel, driver's inner knee bolster left bracket fasteners, driver's inner knee bolster bracket and DERM inner bracket. Remove DERM harness CPA clip and connector. Remove DERM.

Installation – Install DERM into vehicle. Install DERM harness connector and CPA clip. Install DERM inner bracket. Install and torque driver's inner knee bolster left bracket to 116 INCH lbs. (13 N.m).

Install right trim panel. Install DERM left bracket and torque retaining bolts to 116 INCH lbs. (13 N.m). To complete installation, reverse removal procedure.

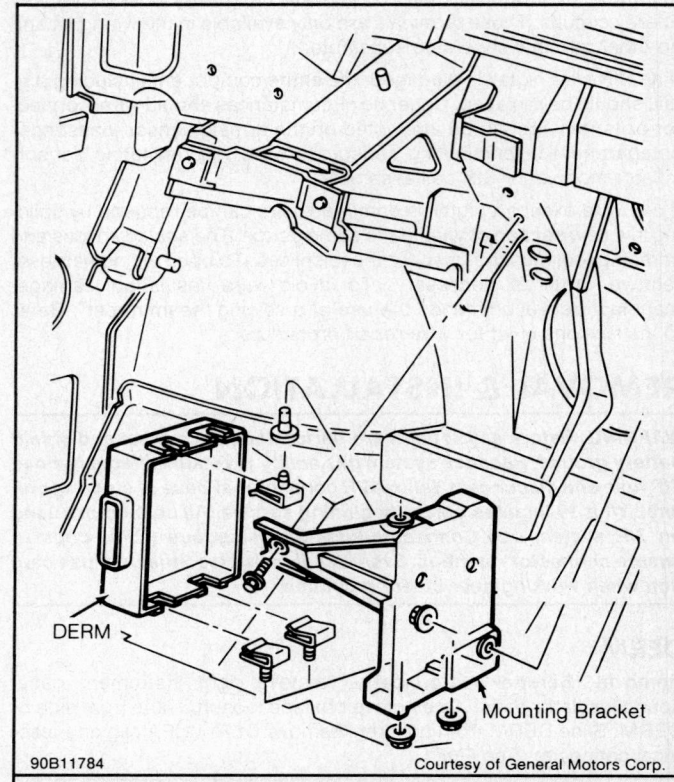

90B11784   Courtesy of General Motors Corp.

Fig. 6: Removing DERM (Eldorado, Reatta, Riviera, Seville, Toronado & Trofeo)

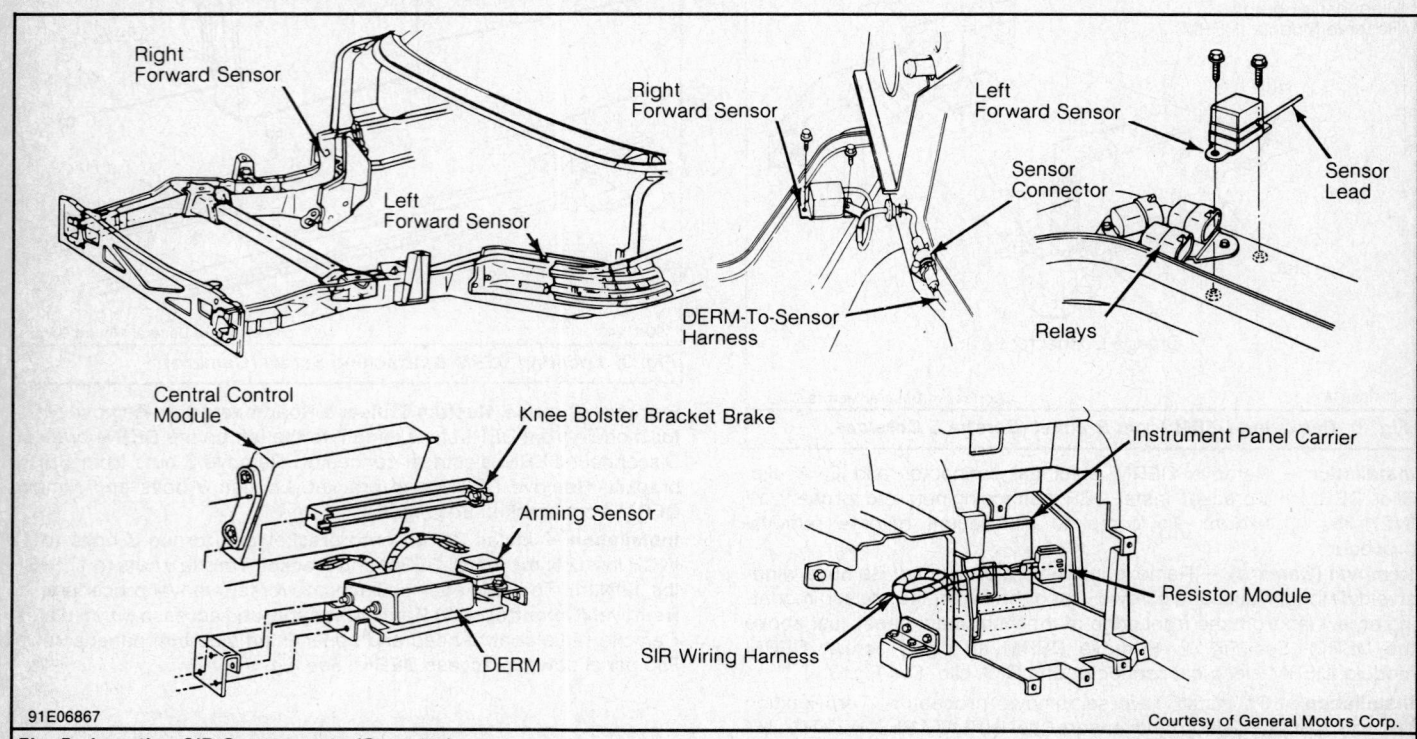

91E06867   Courtesy of General Motors Corp.

Fig. 5: Locating SIR Components (Corvette)

Removal & Installation (DeVille & Fleetwood) – Remove right and left instrument panel sound insulators. Remove glove box module. Loosen 3 nuts from DERM, unlatch Orange connector lock and disconnect electrical connector. Remove DERM. To install, reverse removal procedure. Tighten nuts to 35 INCH lbs. (4 N.m).

Removal & Installation (Eldorado, Reatta, Riviera, Seville, Toronado & Trofeo) – Remove electrical connector from DERM, located under left side of instrument panel, to right of steering column. Loosen 3 nuts and remove DERM from vehicle. *See Fig. 6.* To install, reverse removal procedure.

Removal & Installation (Firebird) – Remove instrument panel accessory hole cover. *See Fig. 7.* Remove DERM attaching nuts. Remove DERM by sliding down bracket. Remove DERM electrical connector and Orange CPA clip. To install, reverse removal procedure.

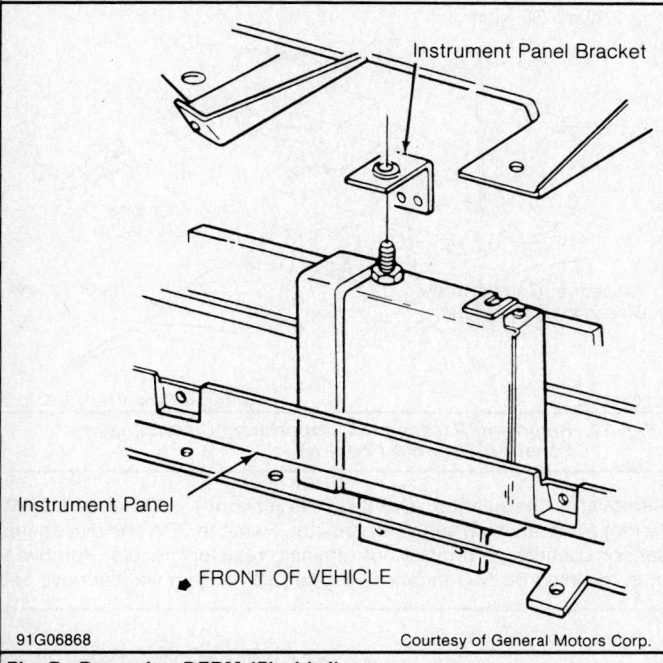

Fig. 7: Removing DERM (Firebird)

Removal & Installation (Ninety-Eight, Touring Sedan & Park Avenue) – Remove instrument panel right side sound insulator. Remove Remote Accessory Control (RAC) module from multi-use bracket and position aside. Remove bolt from DERM bracket and slide DERM from multi-use bracket. *See Fig. 8.* Remove DERM electrical connector. Remove nut attaching bracket to DERM and remove DERM. To install, reverse removal procedure. Torque attaching nuts to 35 INCH lbs. (4 N.m).

ARMING SENSOR

Removal & Installation (Beretta & Corsica) – Remove glove box, sensor CPA clip and electrical connection. Remove sensor mounting bolt and arming sensor. Install arming sensor with arrow pointing toward front of vehicle. Install sensor mounting bolt and tighten to 89 INCH lbs. (10 N.m). To complete installation, reverse removal procedure.

Removal (Camaro) – Turn ignition switch to OFF position. Disconnect and shield negative battery cable. Remove SIR fuse from fuse block. Remove left instrument panel sound insulator panel. Disconnect Yellow SIR connector at base of steering column. Remove knee bolster and upper console. Remove electrical connector, bolts and arming sensor.
Installation – Install arming sensor with arrow facing toward front of vehicle. Attach bolts and torque to 25 INCH lbs. (2.8 N.m). To complete installation, reverse removal procedure. Turn ignition switch to RUN

position and ensure the INFLATABLE RESTRAINT indicator flashes 7-9 times, then off.

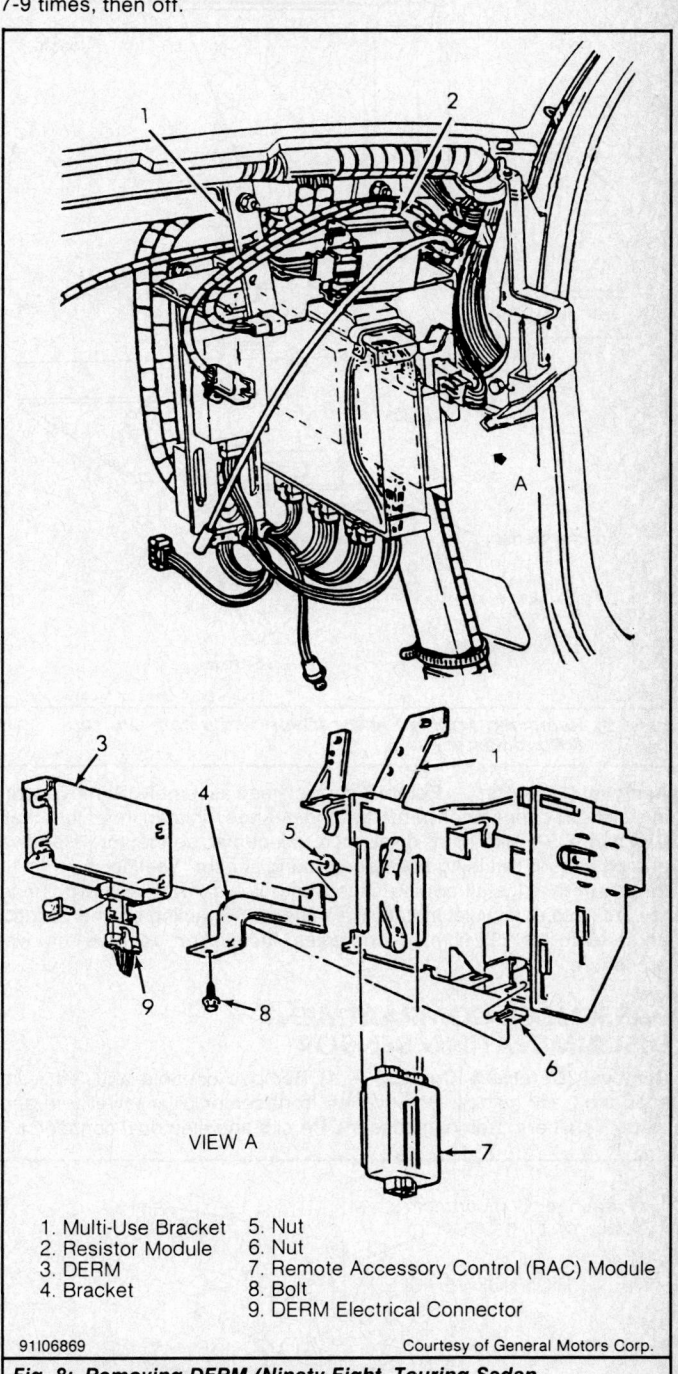

VIEW A

1. Multi-Use Bracket	5. Nut
2. Resistor Module	6. Nut
3. DERM	7. Remote Accessory Control (RAC) Module
4. Bracket	8. Bolt
	9. DERM Electrical Connector

91I06869   Courtesy of General Motors Corp.

Fig. 8: Removing DERM (Ninety-Eight, Touring Sedan & Park Avenue)

Removal (Caprice, Custom Cruiser & Roadmaster) – Remove twilight sentinel module from bracket (if equipped). Reposition dash mat for access to arming sensor. Remove CPA clip by moving it upward while holding electrical connector body. Remove arming sensor electrical connector from body harness connector near top of instrument panel. Remove arming sensor mounting screws and arming sensor. *See Fig. 9.*

Installation – Install arming sensor. Torque mounting screws to 25 INCH lbs. (2.8 N.m). To complete installation, reverse removal procedure.

GM
4-6

1991 SAFETY EQUIPMENT
Air Bag Restraint System – Except Eighty-Eight (Cont.)

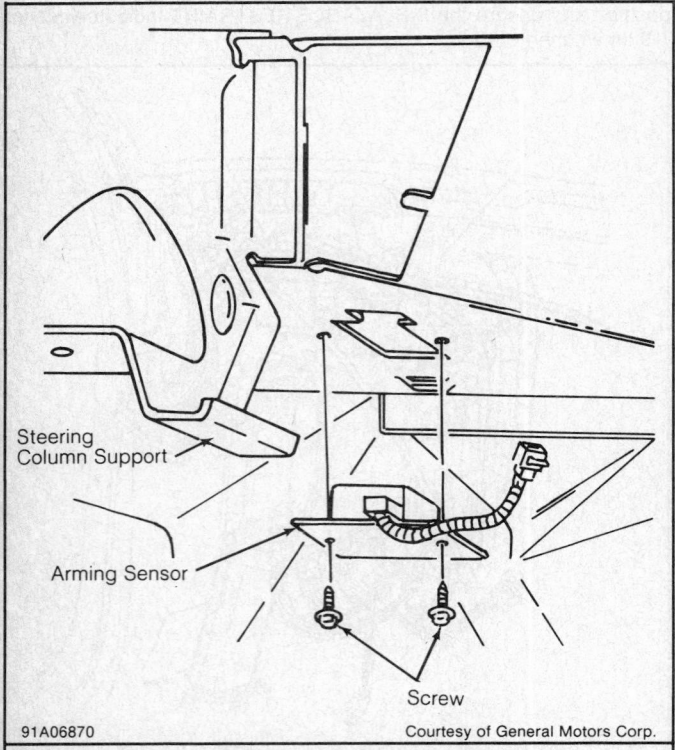

Fig. 9: Removing Arming Sensor (Caprice, Custom Cruiser & Roadmaster)

Removal (Corvette) – Remove control head assembly. Remove arming sensor connector from passenger knee bolster inner bracket. Remove CPA clip and disconnect electrical connector. Remove arming sensor retaining bolts and arming sensor. *See Fig. 5.*
Installation – Install arming sensor into vehicle with arrow pointing toward front of vehicle. Install arming sensor retaining bolts and tighten to 19 ft. lbs. (25 N.m). To complete installation, reverse removal procedure.

PASSENGER COMPARTMENT DISCRIMINATING SENSOR

Removal (Beretta & Corsica) – 1) Remove console and left front seat and track guides. Remove left front center pillar lower trim and carpet retainers. Remove sensor CPA clip and electrical connector.

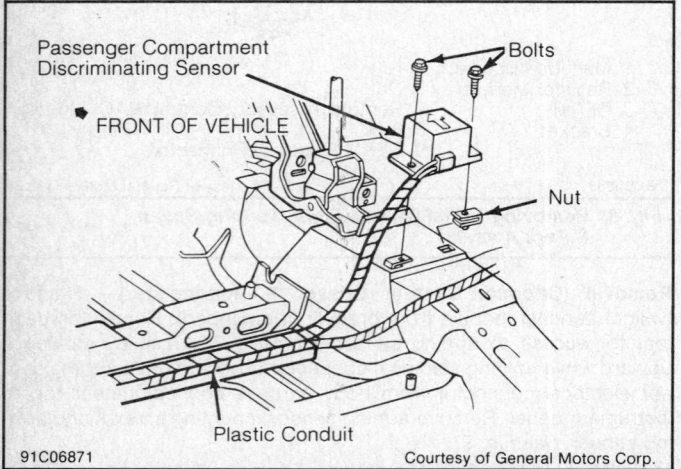

Fig. 10: Removing Passenger Compartment Discriminating Sensor (Beretta & Corsica)

2) Lift carpeting to access electrical harness routing conduits. Remove sensor mounting bolts. Snap conduits open to remove sensor wiring. Remove passenger compartment discriminating sensor. *See Fig. 10.*

Installation – Install passenger compartment discriminating sensor with arrow pointing toward front of vehicle. Install sensor mounting bolts and torque to 89 INCH lbs. (10 N.m). To complete installation, reverse removal procedure.
Removal & Installation (Camaro & Firebird) – Remove knee bolster and console. Remove heater air distribution duct and passenger compartment discriminating sensor. *See Fig. 11.* To install, ensure arrow on sensor faces forward and attaching screws are torqued to 25 INCH lbs. (2.8 N.m). To complete installation, reverse removal procedure.

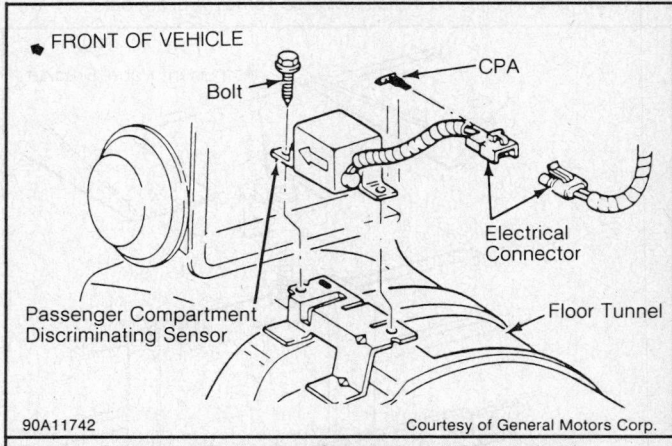

Fig. 11: Removing Passenger Compartment Discriminating Sensor (Camaro & Firebird)

Removal & Installation (DeVille & Fleetwood) – Remove DERM. Remove nut retaining sensor connector. Remove CPA and disconnect sensor connector. Remove nut retaining resistor module. Remove 2 nuts retaining Body Computer Module (BCM). Remove 3 screws and

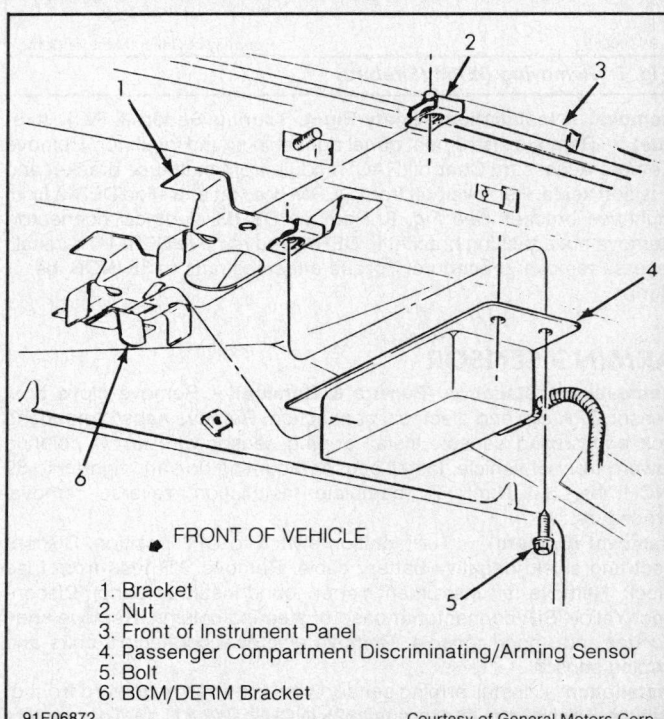

1. Bracket
2. Nut
3. Front of Instrument Panel
4. Passenger Compartment Discriminating/Arming Sensor
5. Bolt
6. BCM/DERM Bracket

Fig. 12: Removing Passenger Compartment Discriminating Sensor (DeVille & Fleetwood)

1991 SAFETY EQUIPMENT
Air Bag Restraint System – Except Eighty-Eight (Cont.)

**GM
4-7**

DERM/BCM bracket. Remove BCM. Remove 2 bolts from sensor and remove discriminating/arming sensor by rotating rear of sensor to disengage from mounting clip. *See Fig. 12.* To install, reverse removal procedure. Tighten all retaining nuts/bolts to 84 INCH lbs. (9.5 N.m).

Removal & Installation (Eldorado & Seville) – Remove 4 screws and glove box unit. Remove 2 nuts retaining Body Computer Module (BCM). Remove BCM electrical connectors and BCM from mounting bracket. Remove CPA and electrical connector from sensor. Remove 2 sensor retaining bolts and sensor. To install, reverse removal procedure. Tighten retaining bolts to 98 INCH lbs. (11 N.m).

Removal & Installation (Reatta, Riviera, Toronado & Trofeo) – Remove glove box. Remove right glass defroster hose. Remove body computer module. Move sound insulation from cowl, and disconnect sensor electrical connector. Remove 2 bolts retaining sensor to vehicle, and remove sensor. To install, reverse removal procedure. Tighten sensor retaining bolts to 98 INCH lbs. (11 N.m).

Removal & Installation (Ninety-Eight, Touring Sedan & Park Avenue) – Remove instrument panel assembly and air distributor assembly. Remove push-type fastener retaining sensor pigtail to theft deterrent control module bracket. Remove CPA and sensor electrical connector. Remove bolts attaching sensor to front of instrument panel. Remove sensor by rotating rear of sensor to disengage from mounting clip and pulling rearward. *See Fig. 13.* To install, reverse removal procedure. Tighten attaching bolts to 84 INCH lbs. (9.5 N.m).

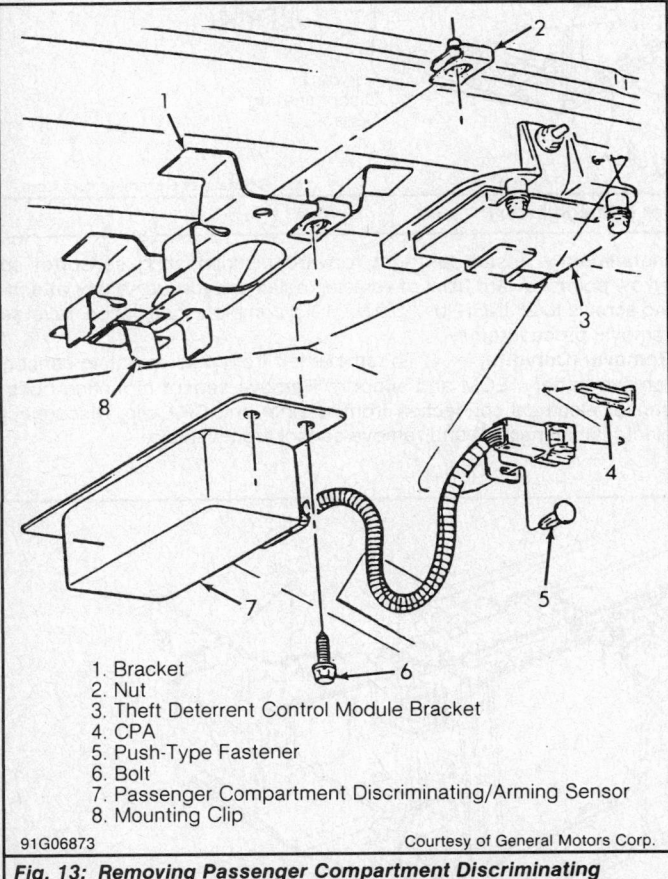

1. Bracket
2. Nut
3. Theft Deterrent Control Module Bracket
4. CPA
5. Push-Type Fastener
6. Bolt
7. Passenger Compartment Discriminating/Arming Sensor
8. Mounting Clip

91G06873   Courtesy of General Motors Corp.

Fig. 13: Removing Passenger Compartment Discriminating Sensor (Ninety-Eight, Touring Sedan & Park Avenue)

FORWARD DISCRIMINATING SENSOR(S)

Removal (Beretta & Corsica) – Remove right outer upper radiator air baffle. Remove forward discriminating sensor and CPA clip electrical connector. Remove electrical connection and wiring clips from upper radiator tie bar. Remove bolts securing bracket to upper radiator tie bar. Remove nuts securing sensor to bracket. Remove forward discriminating sensor. *See Fig. 14.*

Installation – Install forward discriminating sensor so arrow points toward front of vehicle. Install nuts securing sensor to bracket and torque to 89 INCH lbs. (10 N.m). Install bolts securing bracket to upper radiator tie bar and torque to 89 INCH lbs. (10 N.m). To complete installation, reverse removal procedure.

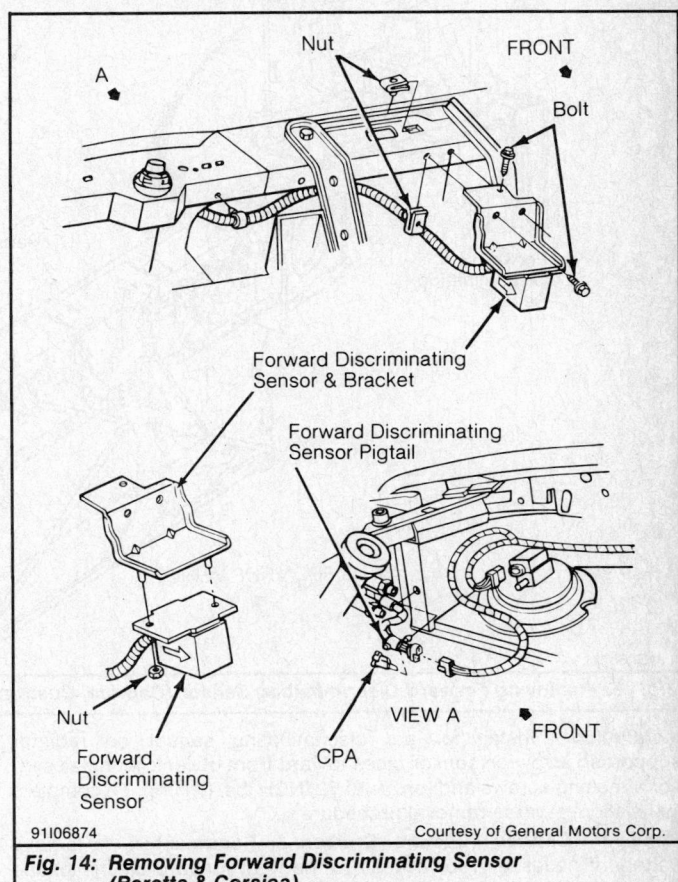

91I06874   Courtesy of General Motors Corp.

Fig. 14: Removing Forward Discriminating Sensor (Beretta & Corsica)

Removal (Camaro, Firebird, Ninety-Eight, Touring Sedan & Park Avenue) – Remove forward sensor electrical connector. Remove forward discriminating sensor attaching bolts and remove sensor from radiator support. *See Fig. 15.*

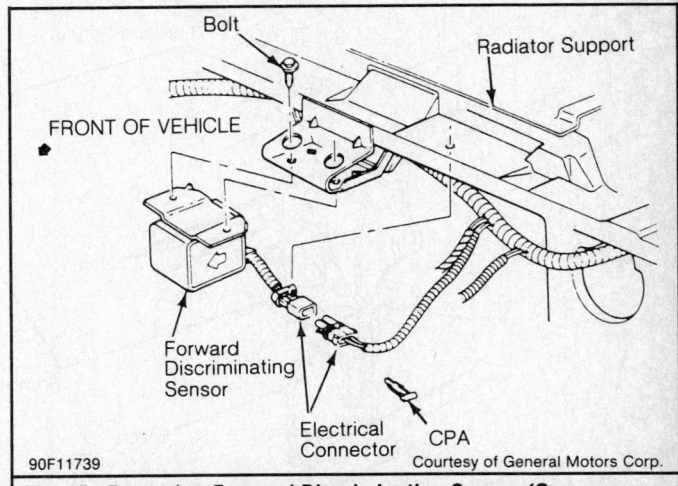

90F11739   Courtesy of General Motors Corp.

Fig. 15: Removing Forward Discriminating Sensor (Camaro, Firebird, Ninety-Eight, Touring Sedan & Park Avenue)

GM
4-8

1991 SAFETY EQUIPMENT
Air Bag Restraint System – Except Eighty-Eight (Cont.)

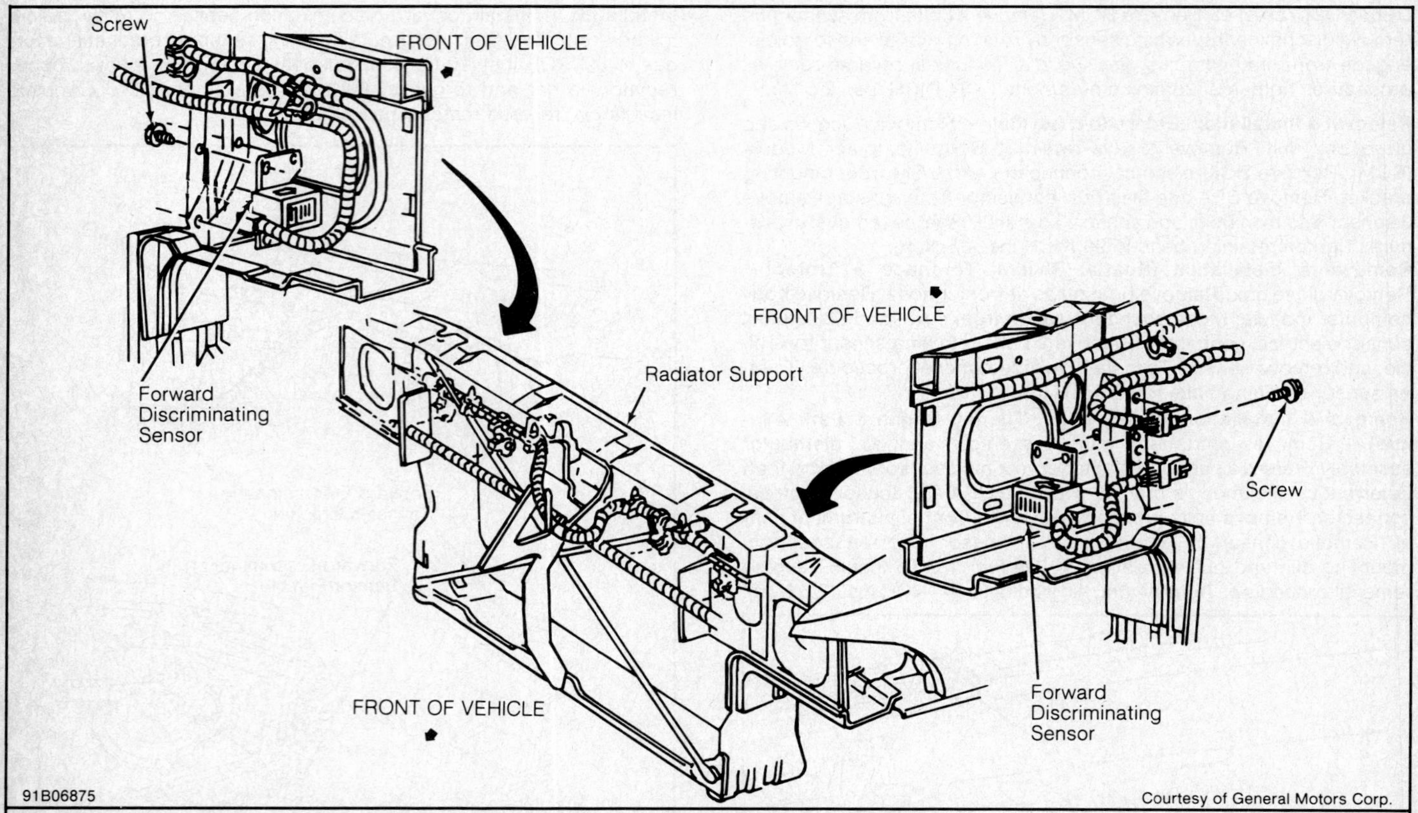

Screw

FRONT OF VEHICLE

FRONT OF VEHICLE

Forward
Discriminating
Sensor

Radiator Support

Screw

FRONT OF VEHICLE

Forward
Discriminating
Sensor

91B06875

Courtesy of General Motors Corp.

Fig. 16: Removing Forward Discriminating Sensor (Caprice, Custom Cruiser & Roadmaster)

Installation – Install forward discriminating sensor on radiator support so arrow on sensor faces toward front of vehicle. Install sensor attaching screws and torque to 62 INCH lbs. (7 N.m). To complete installation, reverse removal procedure.

Removal (Caprice, Custom Cruiser & Roadmaster) – Remove battery, if necessary, for access to the right forward discriminating sensor. Remove radiator support baffle from the radiator. Remove electrical connector and CPA clip from the radiator support. Remove screws and left/right discriminating sensor(s). *See Fig. 16.*

Installation – Install left/right forward discriminating sensor(s) so arrow points toward front of vehicle. Install and torque sensor attaching screws to 25 INCH lbs. (2.8 N.m). To complete installation, reverse removal procedure.

Removal (Corvette) – 1) To remove left front discriminating sensor, remove battery, ECM and support. Remove sensor mounting bolts, sensor electrical connection from retainer and CPA clip. Disconnect electrical connection and remove sensor from vehicle.

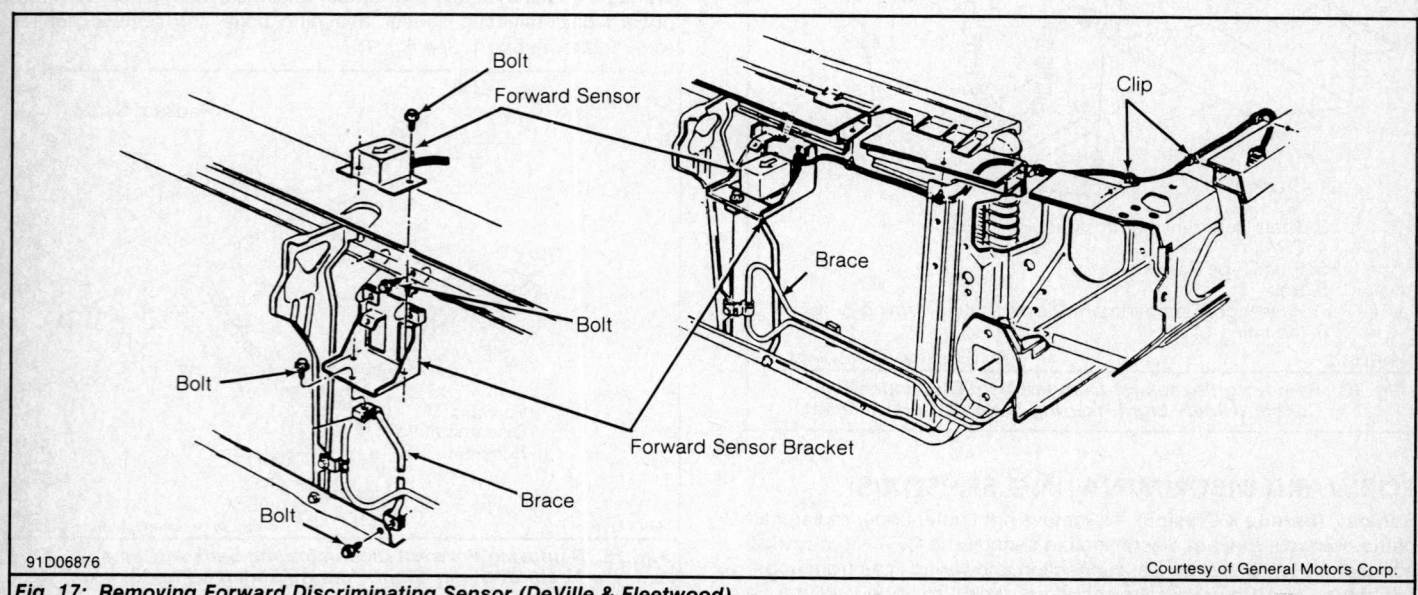

Bolt
Forward Sensor
Clip
Brace
Bolt
Bolt
Brace
Bolt
Forward Sensor Bracket

91D06876

Courtesy of General Motors Corp.

Fig. 17: Removing Forward Discriminating Sensor (DeVille & Fleetwood)

1991 SAFETY EQUIPMENT
Air Bag Restraint System — Except Eighty-Eight (Cont.)

GM
4-9

2) To remove right front discriminating sensor, remove 6 right front rocker panel retaining screws. Remove right front fender retaining bolts and remove fender. Peel back rear portion of wheelhouse-to-hood seal. Remove right lower wheelhouse retaining bolts and remove lower wheelhouse.

3) Remove 2 windshield washer reservoir retaining bolts. Loosen remaining washer reservoir bolt and rotate reservoir to access sensor. Remove sensor mounting bolts and electrical connector from retainer. Remove CPA clip and disconnect electrical connector. Remove sensor from vehicle. *See Fig. 5.*

Installation – Install left and right front discriminating sensors with arrow on sensor pointing toward front of vehicle. Install sensor attaching bolts and torque to 19 ft. lbs. (25 N.m). To complete installation, reverse removal procedure.

Removal & Installation (DeVille & Fleetwood) – Remove right and left instrument panel sound insulator. Remove grille. Remove CPA and sensor connector from left fender in engine compartment. Snap open 6 pigtail conduit clips and remove sensor pigtail. Remove 2 bolts retaining sensor and remove discriminating sensor. *See Fig. 17.* To install, reverse removal procedure. Torque sensor attaching bolts to 62 INCH lbs. (7 N.m).

Removal (Eldorado, Reatta, Riviera, Seville, Toronado & Trofeo) – Remove CPA clip and sensor electrical connector. Remove harness retaining clips and pull harness through radiator support brace. Raise and support vehicle. Remove 2 tamper-resistant retaining bolts with Insert Bit (J-38597). Remove sensor from vehicle. *See Fig. 18.*

Installation – Align sensor to vehicle bracket with arrow pointing toward front of vehicle. Install and tighten mounting bolts to 98 INCH lbs. (11 N.m). To complete installation, reverse removal procedure.

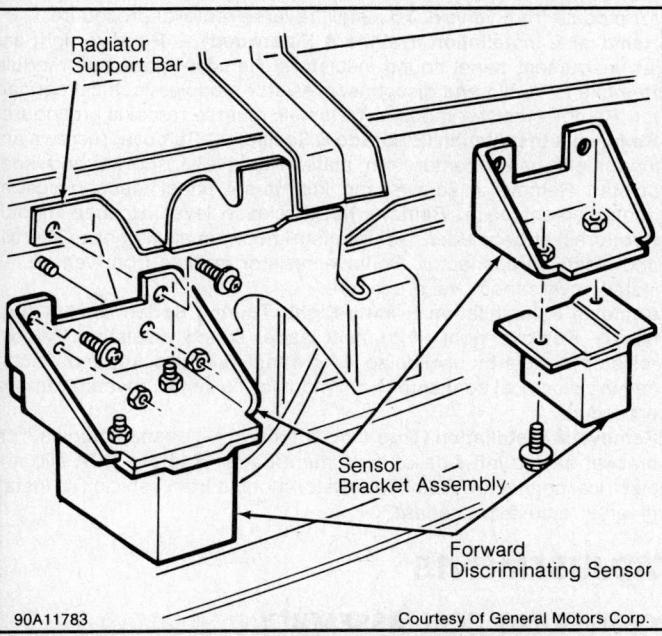

Radiator Support Bar

Sensor Bracket Assembly

Forward Discriminating Sensor

90A11783   Courtesy of General Motors Corp.

Fig. 18: Removing Forward Discriminating Sensor (Eldorado, Reatta, Riviera, Seville, Toronado & Trofeo)

SIR COIL ASSEMBLY

NOTE: Front wheels of vehicle must be turned to the straight-ahead position before beginning service. Failure to do so can result in the coil assembly being removed without being centered. Reinstalling the coil assembly under such circumstances will cause the ribbon in the coil assembly to break when the steering wheel is turned fully in one direction. Ensure the key is always in the LOCK position to prevent the wheel from turning and uncentering the coil assembly. To recenter coil assembly, see ADJUSTMENTS near end of this article.

Removal (Except Corvette) – **1)** Remove inflator module. See INFLATOR MODULE under REMOVAL & INSTALLATION. Remove horn contact wire from steering column. Remove steering wheel hexagon locking nut. Using a puller, remove steering wheel. DO NOT install puller bolts too far, as damage to coil assembly can result.

2) Remove coil assembly retaining ring from steering shaft. Grasp clear plastic wire protector shield on underside of steering column, and slide downward. Partially remove coil assembly from end of steering wheel shaft and allow coil to hang freely. Note orientation to steering column housing before removal.

3) Remove wave washer from steering shaft. Using Lock Plate Compressor (J-23653), depress shaft lock and remove shaft lock retaining ring. Remove shaft lock plate and upper bearing spring. Remove turn signal canceling cam.

4) Remove hazard knob and attaching screw. Remove turn signal switch arm. Remove 3 turn signal switch screws and partially withdraw switch. Attach mechanics wire to coil assembly lower connector at base of steering column and carefully pull wire through gear shift lever bowl, column housing and lock housing cover.

Installation – **1)** Carefully feed coil assembly wire and lower connector through lock housing cover, column housing and gear shift lever bowl and allow coil assembly to hang freely.

NOTE: Use care not to pinch wires when installing components. After wire is fed through, attach CAUTION tag to wire near connector at base of steering column. Tag is included in coil assembly repair kit.

2) Install turn signal switch and torque screws to 30 INCH lbs. (3.4 N.m). Install turn signal switch arm and torque attaching screw to 20 INCH lbs. (2.3 N.m).

3) Install hazard knob and attaching screw, turn signal canceling cam and shaft lock plate. Install shaft lock retaining ring. Using lock plate compressor, align block tooth on shaft and depress shaft lock plate. Install wave washer. Ensure coil assembly hub and steering shaft are centered. Coil assembly will become uncentered if column is separated from steering gear and is allowed to rotate, or centering spring is depressed, allowing hub to rotate while coil assembly is removed from column.

4) Install coil assembly, using horn tower on canceling cam to align hole on inner ring of coil and projections on steering column housing with projections on outer ring of coil. To complete installation, reverse removal procedure.

Removal (Corvette) – **1)** Remove inflator module. See INFLATOR MODULE under REMOVAL & INSTALLATION. Remove horn contact wire. Remove SIR coil assembly retaining ring. Remove SIR coil from shaft and allow to hang freely. Remove wave washer from steering shaft.

2) Using Shaft Lock Remover (J-23653), depress shaft lock plate and remove shaft lock retaining ring. Remove shaft lock plate, turn signal canceling cam, upper bearing spring, upper bearing inner race seat and inner race.

3) Position turn signal to right turn position. Remove multifunction lever. Remove column housing cover end cap by pulling rearward (toward front of vehicle). Remove electrical harness connector and grommet. Pull toward driver's door to release detent/multifunction lever. Remove screw and signal switch arm. Remove turn signal switch screws, hazard knob assembly and turn signal switch. Allow switch to hang freely.

4) Remove Yellow connector shroud from Black terminal connector. Remove wiring protector and carefully pull wire through housing shroud, column and lock housing cover.

Installation – **1)** Install coil assembly wire through lock housing cover, column housing and housing shroud. Allow coil to hang freely. Install connector shroud to terminal connector. Install turn signal switch and torque screws to 30 INCH lbs. (3.4 N.m). Install wiring protector, hazard knob assembly, multifunction lever, upper bearing spring, turn signal canceling cam assembly and shaft lock.

NOTE: If shaft lock retaining ring is damaged or deformed, replacement is necessary

GM
4-10

1991 SAFETY EQUIPMENT
Air Bag Restraint System – Except Eighty-Eight (Cont.)

2) Align shaft lock retaining ring to block tooth on shaft. Depress shaft lock and install shaft lock retaining ring. Ensure SIR coil hub is centered.

3) Set steering shaft so block teeth on upper steering shaft are at 12 o'clock and 6 o'clock positions. With wheels on vehicle straight ahead, set ignition switch to LOCK position to ensure no damage to coil assembly. The coil assembly will become uncentered if the column is separated from the steering gear and is allowed to rotate, or if centering spring is depressed, allowing hub to rotate while coil is removed from column.

4) Install wave washer. Using horn tower on canceling cam inner ring and projections on outer ring for alignment, install coil. Install coil retaining ring. Gently pull lower coil assembly wire to remove any wire kinks that may be inside column. To complete installation, reverse removal procedure.

INFLATOR MODULE

Removal – Remove screws and nuts from underside of steering wheel. Partially remove inflator module and disconnect steering wheel inflator module connector, CPA clip and horn contact from inflator. Remove inflator module.

Installation – Install horn contact and steering wheel inflator module connector and CPA clip. Install inflator module to steering wheel. On Corvette, secure with screws torqued to 87 INCH lbs. (9.7 N.m). On all other models, torque screws to 27 INCH lbs. (3 N.m). To complete installation, reverse removal procedure.

RESISTOR MODULE

Removal & Installation (Beretta & Corsica) – Remove tape securing resistor module to wiring harness under left side of instrument panel. Remove resistor module from vehicle. *See Fig. 19.* To install, reverse removal procedure.

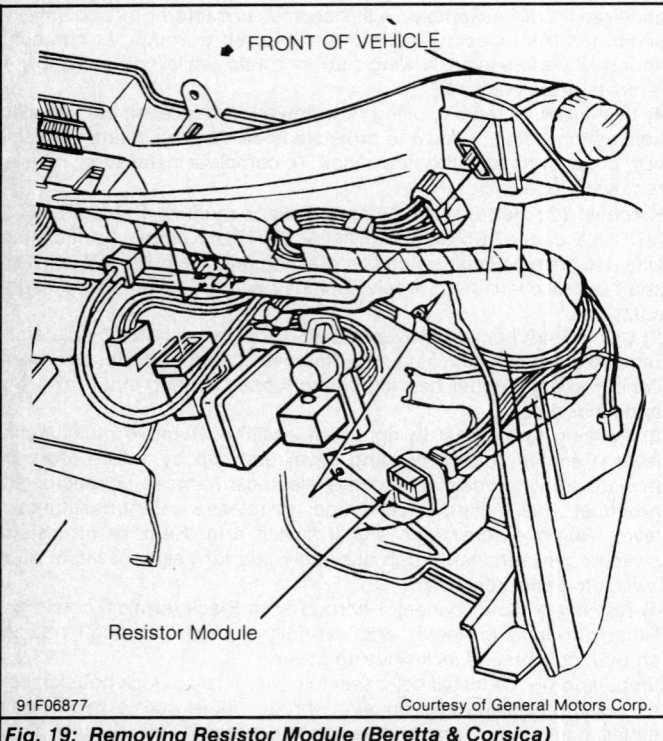

91F06877   Courtesy of General Motors Corp.

Fig. 19: Removing Resistor Module (Beretta & Corsica)

Removal & Installation (Camaro, Firebird, Reatta & Riviera) – Remove knee bolster. Remove resistor module by unsnapping it from bracket behind left side of instrument panel. Remove CPA clip and resistor module electrical connector. *See Fig. 20.* To install, reverse removal procedure.

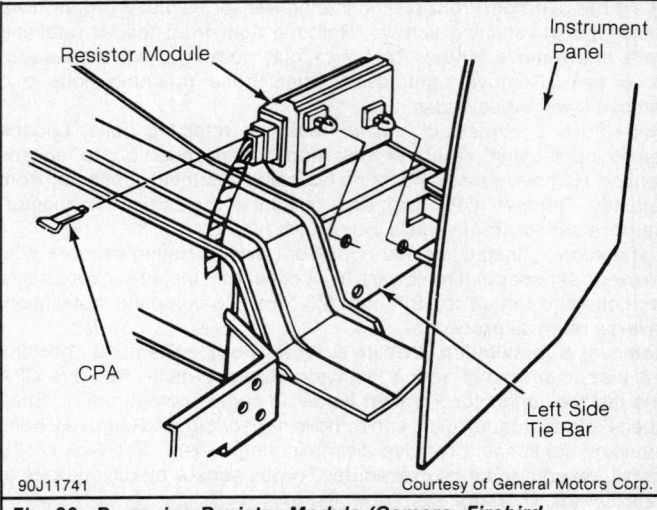

90J11741   Courtesy of General Motors Corp.

Fig. 20: Removing Resistor Module (Camaro, Firebird, Reatta & Riviera)

Removal & Installation (Caprice, Custom Cruiser & Roadmaster) – Resistor module is located on DERM bracket. *See Fig. 4.* To remove, disconnect CPA clip and electrical connector and slide module to the left. To install, reverse removal procedure.

Removal & Installation (Corvette) – Remove radio control head assembly. Unclip resistor module from instrument panel carrier. Remove CPA clip and disconnect electrical connector. Remove resistor module from vehicle. To install, reverse removal procedure.

Removal & Installation (DeVille & Fleetwood) – Remove right and left instrument panel sound insulators. Remove glove box module. Remove CPA clip and disconnect resistor module electrical connector. Remove resistor module. To install, reverse removal procedure.

Removal & Installation (Eldorado & Seville) – Remove 2 screws and instrument panel center trim plate. Remove 5 screws and knee bolster. Remove 4 screws and instrument panel steering column reinforcement plate. Remove hood release lever. Unsnap module from bracket behind left side of instrument panel. Remove CPA clip and electrical connector. Remove resistor module from vehicle. To install, reverse removal procedure.

Removal & Installation (Ninety-Eight, Touring Sedan & Park Avenue) – Remove right instrument panel sound insulator. Remove resistor module by unclipping it from multi-use bracket and disconnecting electrical connector from module. To install, reverse removal procedure.

Removal & Installation (Toronado & Trofeo) – Unsnap module from bracket behind left side of instrument panel. Remove CPA clip and electrical connector. Remove resistor module from vehicle. To install, reverse removal procedure.

ADJUSTMENTS

CENTERING COIL ASSEMBLY

1) If the coil assembly has been removed from the steering column and is being reinstalled, go to step **2)**. New coil assemblies are provided precentered and include a Blue plastic tab that is snapped off once the coil is installed. *See Fig. 21.*

2) Ensure the front wheels face straight-ahead when installing or removing a coil assembly. If coil is removed without the wheels in the straight-ahead position and the steering wheel has not been moved, the same coil can be reinstalled if the coil hub also has not been rotated.

3) Hold coil assembly with clear bottom upward to see coil ribbon. Note there are 2 different styles of coil assemblies; one rotates clockwise and the other rotates counterclockwise.

1991 SAFETY EQUIPMENT
Air Bag Restraint System — Except Eighty-Eight (Cont.)

GM
4-11

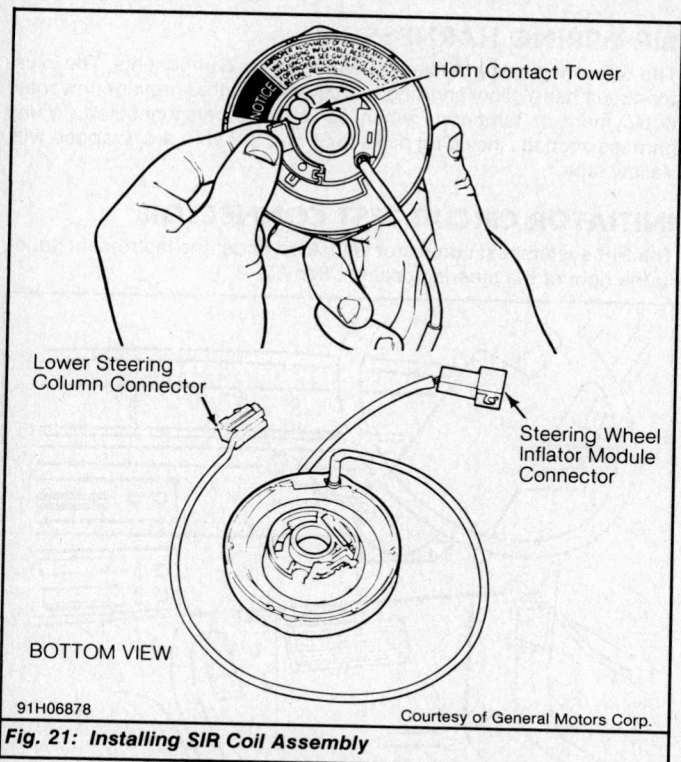

Horn Contact Tower

Lower Steering
Column Connector

Steering Wheel
Inflator Module
Connector

BOTTOM VIEW

91H06878

Courtesy of General Motors Corp.

Fig. 21: Installing SIR Coil Assembly

4) While holding coil assembly housing, depress spring lock and rotate hub in direction of arrow until it stops. The coil assembly should now be wound up snug against center hub. Rotate coil assembly hub in opposite direction approximately 2 1/2 turns. Release spring lock between locking tabs in front of arrow.

WIRING DIAGRAMS

See appropriate chassis wiring diagram in WIRING DIAGRAMS.

TORQUE SPECIFICATIONS

TORQUE SPECIFICATIONS

Application	Ft. Lbs. (N.m)
Arming Sensor	
Corvette	19 (25)

	INCH Lbs. (N.m)
Arming Sensor	
Beretta & Corsica	89 (10)
Camaro	25 (3)
Caprice, Custom Cruiser & Roadmaster	25 (3)
DERM	
Beretta & Corsica	12 (1.4)
Caprice, Custom Cruiser & Roadmaster	17 (2)
Corvette	116 (13)
DeVille & Fleetwood	35 (4)
Ninety-Eight, Touring Sedan & Park Avenue	35 (4)
Forward Discriminating Sensor	
Beretta & Corsica	89 (10)
Camaro, Firebird, Ninety-Eight	
Touring Sedan & Park Avenue	62 (7)
Caprice, Custom Cruiser & Roadmaster	25 (2.8)
Corvette	19 (25)
DeVille & Fleetwood	62 (7)
Eldorado, Reatta, Riviera,	
Seville, Toronado & Trofeo	98 (11)
Inflator Module	
Corvette	87 (9.7)
All Other Models	27 (3)
Inner Knee Bolster Left Bracket	
Corvette	16 (13)
Passenger Compartment Discriminating Sensor	
Beretta & Corsica	89 (10)
Camaro & Firebird	25 (2.8)
DeVille & Fleetwood	84 (9.5)
Eldorado & Seville	98 (11)
Reatta, Riviera, Toronado & Trofeo	98 (11)
Ninety-Eight, Touring Sedan & Park Avenue	84 (9.5)
Turn Signal Switch	27 (3.1)
Turn Signal Switch Arm	20 (2.2)

IDENTIFICATION

All Eighty-Eight models equipped with an air bag have the number "3" in the seventh position of the Vehicle Identification Number (VIN). The words Supplemental Inflatable Restraint or S.I.R. will be embossed on the steering wheel hub, which is larger (approximately 6" x 9") in order to accommodate the air bag.

DESCRIPTION & OPERATION

PASSENGER COMPARTMENT SENSOR/ DIAGNOSTIC MODULE (PCSDM)

Passenger Compartment Sensor/Diagnostic Module (PCSDM) contains the passenger compartment sensor and the Supplemental Inflatable Restraint (SIR) diagnostic module. The SIR diagnostic module monitors the integrity of the SIR sensing components and wiring harness, and controls the INFLATABLE RESTRAINT indicator.

The SIR diagnostic module processes the measured vehicle deceleration and the forward sensor signal to determine if deployment is needed. A deployment signal (electrical pulse) is sent to the steering wheel module when a forward sensor closure (or a signal from the passenger compartment sensor) and an arming sensor closure occur simultaneously.

FORWARD SENSOR

The forward sensor responds to vehicle deceleration and is mechanically actuated. A normally open switch distinguishes between deployment and non-deployment conditions. It uses a preset calibration, allowing sensor to close only during sufficient impact. In an accident, forward sensor contacts close, completing circuit. A forward sensor closure, combined with an arming sensor closure, will result in steering wheel (air bag) module deployment.

ARMING SENSOR

The arming sensor, a normally open mechanical switch, closes during rapid deceleration present in an accident. Sensor is wired in series with steering wheel (air bag) module and provides back-up for other sensors. A parallel resistor in arming sensor allows a small amount of current to flow through initiator circuit for diagnostic purposes.

POWER SUPPLY OR VOLTAGE CONVERTER

Power supply provides a boosted voltage to SIR system to ensure deployment for low voltage conditions, perform limited internal diagnostics and monitor integrity of SIR harness at 8-pin connector.

ENERGY RESERVE MODULE

Energy reserve module provides sufficient electrical energy to ensure deployment even if battery is damaged or disconnected in an accident.

STEERING COLUMN & COIL ASSEMBLY

The collapsible steering column uses a coil assembly to provide a continuous electrical connection between the SIR control module and steering wheel module.

STEERING WHEEL MODULE

The steering wheel (air bag) module consists of an inflatable bag, electrical initiator and inflator assembly. It is stored in steering wheel hub and covered by a vinyl trim cover. If a crash is sensed, inflatable bag is deployed by a gas-producing generator. As the air bag deploys, the trim cover ruptures at seams.

WARNING LIGHT

Instrument panel Red warning light displays INFLATABLE RESTRAINT. If INFLATABLE RESTRAINT light does not illuminate for a bulb check when ignition switch is turned to RUN or START position, or illuminates when car is being driven, system is malfunctioning.

SIR WIRING HARNESS

The SIR wiring harness interconnects system components. The initiator circuit has Yellow shorting bar connectors that prevent unwanted deployment or tampering when connector is disconnected. Wiring harness sections including more than one SIR wire are wrapped with Yellow tape.

INITIATOR CIRCUIT TEST CONNECTOR

The SIR system test connector is located under the instrument panel, to the right of the steering column. See Fig. 1.

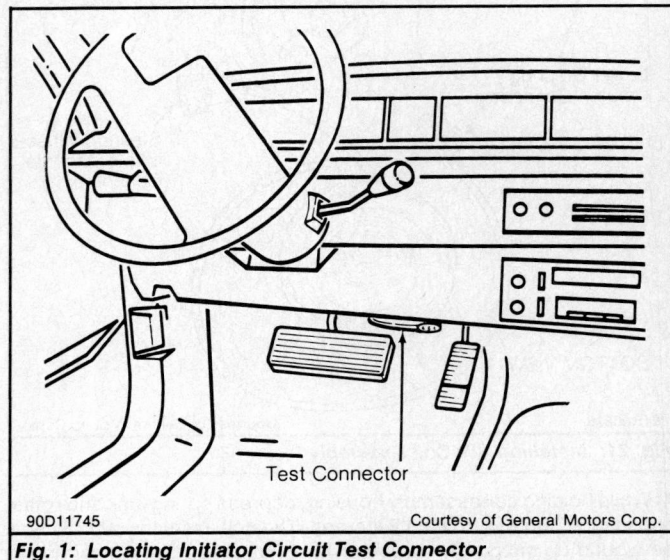

Test Connector

90D11745   Courtesy of General Motors Corp.

Fig. 1: Locating Initiator Circuit Test Connector

SYSTEM OPERATION CHECK

When ignition switch is at RUN, BULB TEST or START position, battery voltage is applied to INFLATABLE RESTRAINT indicator light. The INFLATABLE RESTRAINT indicator light should illuminate for 5-15 seconds, verifying indicator light and correct SIR operation. The INFLATABLE RESTRAINT indicator light is the key to driver notification of status of SIR system.

ON-VEHICLE SERVICE

SERVICE PRECAUTIONS

CAUTION: Wait 15 minutes after disconnecting battery before servicing SIR system. The energy reserve module will maintain SIR system voltage for 15 minutes after battery is disconnected. Servicing the SIR system during the 15-minute period may cause personal injury or deployment.

Disabling & Enabling System – To disable system, turn ignition switch to LOCK position. Remove AIR BAG (SIR) fuse. Remove negative battery cable and tape end. To activate system, install fuse and reconnect negative battery cable.

Sensors – Handle sensors carefully. DO NOT strike or jar sensors, especially while connected to wiring harness, as jarring could cause accidental deployment, personal injury or improper SIR system operation. Sensors and mounting brackets bolts must be carefully torqued to ensure correct operation. NEVER activate SIR system when a sensor is not mounted to the vehicle. Sensor is easily activated when not mounted and could deploy air bag.

1991 SAFETY EQUIPMENT
Air Bag Restraint System – Eighty-Eight (Cont.)

GM
4-13

Live (Undeployed) Steering Wheel (Air Bag) Module – Use extra care when handling or storing a live (undeployed) module. When carrying a live steering wheel (air bag) module, ensure module faces away from you to minimize injury if module accidentally deploys. DO NOT place a live module face down on work surface. Always store module facing upward. If steering wheel module accidently deploys, module's metal backing will not shoot upward.

Steering Wheel (Air Bag) Module Shipping Procedures – Transporting undeployed air bag modules is regulated by the hazardous materials regulations of the Department of Transportation (DOT) and most state governments. Special procedures are required. Repair shops should check with hazardous material section of their respective state governments for applicable shipping requirements. DO NOT expose the module to heat, open flame, impact, friction or electrical charge.

CAUTION: *Undeployed steering wheel (air bag) modules must NOT be disposed at normal refuse locations. Undeployed modules contain substances that can cause illness or injury. Disposal of the module in any manner inconsistent with proper procedures may be a violation of federal, state and/or local laws.*

Vehicle Scrapping Procedures – Perform the following procedures when scrapping a vehicle with an undeployed SIR module:
1) Turn the ignition switch to OFF position. Disconnect and tape negative battery cable.

CAUTION: *After disconnecting battery, wait 15 minutes before continuing SIR service. The energy reserve module maintains SIR system voltage after battery is disconnected. Servicing SIR system too soon can cause personal injury.*

2) Ensure steering wheel module is secured to steering wheel and there are no loose objects on front seat. Disconnect lower steering column connector and remove shorting clip from connector.
3) Splice 2 wires at least 20 feet long into steering wheel module circuit wiring at base of steering column. Stretch wires away from car as far as possible. Apply 12 volts across wires to deploy module. Due to heat generated during deployment, DO NOT touch module area for 20 minutes.

Deployed Steering Wheel Modules – Once a steering wheel module has been deployed, surface of air bag may contain a small amount of sodium hydroxide dust, combined with a white packing powder (corn starch). The sodium hydroxide dust can be irritating to the skin if left on for an extended period of time. Always wear gloves and safety glasses when handling a deployed steering wheel module. Wash hands afterward.

Inspecting System After Accident – All SIR components, including harness and brackets, must be inspected after an accident. If any components are damaged or bent, they must be replaced, even if a deployment did not occur. Check steering column, knee bolster, instrument panel steering column reinforcement plate and lower brace for damage. DO NOT service the forward sensor, steering column coil assembly, SIR control module, power supply, arming sensor, energy reserve module or steering wheel module. If these components are defective, replacement is necessary.

Special Tool Precaution – To avoid deployment when working on the SIR system, DO NOT use electrical test equipment such as test lights, battery or A/C-powered volt-ohmmeter, or any type of electrical equipment other than SIR Tester (J-36884-A).

REMOVAL & INSTALLATION

SERVICE PRECAUTIONS

CAUTION: *Before servicing SIR system, set ignition switch to LOCK position. Disconnect negative battery cable and tape end. Remove AIR BAG (SIR) fuse. Wait 15 minutes after disconnecting battery before servicing vehicle. Servicing SIR system too soon can result in personal injury.*

Use extreme care when handling modules or sensors. DO NOT strike or jar modules or sensors as accidental deployment can result. Ensure modules, sensors and mounting bracket bolts are carefully torqued to ensure correct operation. Never power up SIR system when any module or sensor is not rigidly attached to the vehicle.

PASSENGER COMPARTMENT SENSOR/ DIAGNOSTIC MODULE (PCSDM)

CAUTION: *Use care when handling SIR control module to avoid damaging passenger compartment sensor located inside.*

Removal – **1)** Disconnect negative battery cable. Remove AIR BAG (SIR) fuse and wait 15 minutes before proceeding. See SERVICE PRECAUTIONS under REMOVAL & INSTALLATION in this article. Remove front seat. If equipped with bucket seats, remove passenger seat only. Bend up carpet retention tabs and roll back carpeting to expose passenger compartment sensing system cover. See Fig. 2. Remove screws securing cover.
2) Remove sensor connector from harness assembly and arming sensor connector. Remove nuts securing module to bracket and remove module.
Installation – Install module with arrow toward front of vehicle. Install nuts securing sensor to bracket and tighten to 88 INCH lbs. (10 N.m). To install remaining components, reverse removal procedure.

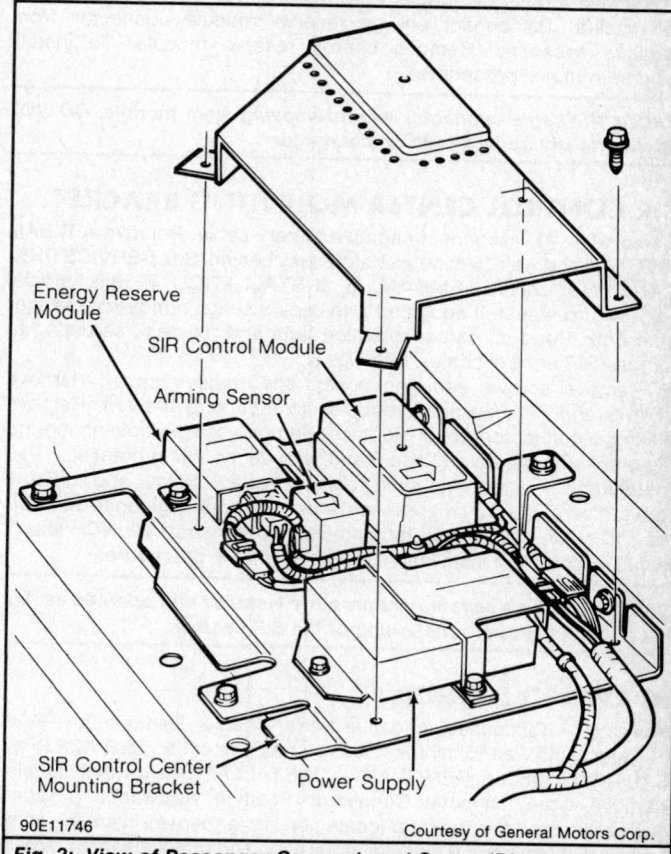

Energy Reserve Module
SIR Control Module
Arming Sensor
SIR Control Center Mounting Bracket
Power Supply

90E11746   Courtesy of General Motors Corp.

Fig. 2: View of Passenger Compartment Sensor/Diagnostic Module (PCSDM)

ARMING SENSOR

Removal & Installation – **1)** Disconnect negative battery cable. Remove AIR BAG (SIR) fuse and wait 15 minutes before proceeding. See SERVICE PRECAUTIONS under REMOVAL & INSTALLATION in this article. Remove front seat. If equipped with bucket seats, remove passenger seat only. Bend up carpet retention tabs and roll back carpeting to expose SIR control center. See Fig. 2.

GM
4-14

1991 SAFETY EQUIPMENT
Air Bag Restraint System – Eighty-Eight (Cont.)

2) Remove screws securing cover, and remove cover. Remove arming sensor connectors and retaining pins. Remove nuts securing arming sensor to mounting plate. Remove arming sensor. To install, reverse removal procedure.

POWER SUPPLY

Removal & Installation – 1) Disconnect negative battery cable. Remove AIR BAG (SIR) fuse and wait 15 minutes before proceeding. See SERVICE PRECAUTIONS under REMOVAL & INSTALLATION in this article. Remove front seat. If equipped with bucket seats, remove passenger seat only. Bend up carpet retention tabs and roll back carpeting to expose SIR control center. *See Fig. 2.*

2) Remove screws securing cover bracket. Remove 2 screws on side of power supply. Remove connector retainer bracket, power supply connector from harness assembly, screw securing power supply to bracket and power supply. To install, reverse removal procedure.

ENERGY RESERVE MODULE

Removal & Installation – 1) Disconnect negative battery cable. Remove AIR BAG (SIR) fuse and wait 15 minutes before proceeding. See SERVICE PRECAUTIONS under REMOVAL & INSTALLATION in this article. Remove front seat. If equipped with bucket seats, remove passenger seat only. Bend up carpet retention tabs and roll back carpeting to expose SIR control center. *See Fig. 2.*

2) Remove screws securing cover bracket and energy reserve module to bracket. Disconnect energy reserve module connector from harness assembly. Remove energy reserve module. To install, reverse removal procedure.

CAUTION: Wiggle connector when removing from module. DO NOT attempt to pry up lock tabs on connector.

SIR CONTROL CENTER MOUNTING BRACKET

Removal – 1) Disconnect negative battery cable. Remove AIR BAG (SIR) fuse and wait 15 minutes before proceeding. See SERVICE PRECAUTIONS under REMOVAL & INSTALLATION in this article. Remove front seat. If equipped with bucket seats, remove passenger seat only. Bend up carpet retention tabs and roll back carpeting to expose SIR control center. *See Fig. 2.*

2) Remove screws securing cover, and remove cover. Remove screws and nuts securing modules to mounting bracket. Remove electrical connectors to all modules. Remove screws holding mounting bracket to bars No. 2 and 3 and remove mounting bracket.

Installation – Align mounting bracket screw holes and drive 3 forward screws and right rear screw into "U" nuts. Tighten to 88 INCH lbs. (10 N.m). Tighten self-tapping left rear screw to 44 INCH lbs. (5 N.m). To complete installation, reverse removal procedure.

CAUTION: Ensure sensors are properly installed and oriented as this is critical for proper functioning of the SIR system.

FORWARD SENSOR

Removal – Disconnect negative battery cable. Remove AIR BAG (SIR) fuse and wait 15 minutes before proceeding. See SERVICE PRECAUTIONS under REMOVAL & INSTALLATION in this article. Remove grille. Remove Connector Position Assurance pin and disconnect sensor connector located on left fenderwell in engine compartment. Snap open 6 pigtail conduit clips and remove sensor pigtail. Remove 2 bolts retaining cover. Remove forward sensor. *See Fig. 3.*

Installation – Install forward sensor with arrow pointing toward front of vehicle. Install 2 sensor retaining bolts and tighten to 62 INCH lbs. (7 N.m). To complete installation, reverse removal procedure.

FORWARD SENSOR BRACKET ASSEMBLY

Removal – Disconnect negative battery cable. Remove AIR BAG (SIR) fuse and wait 15 minutes before proceeding. See SERVICE PRECAUTIONS under REMOVAL & INSTALLATION in this article.

Remove forward sensor. See FORWARD SENSOR under REMOVAL & INSTALLATION in this article. Remove bolts securing forward sensor bracket to upper radiator tie bar. *See Fig. 3.* Remove bolt securing brace to lower radiator tie bar. Remove bracket from brace.

Installation – Install bracket to brace and tighten bolts to 88 INCH lbs. (10 N.m). Install bracket to upper radiator tie bar and tighten bolts to 88 INCH lbs. (10 N.m). Install bracket to lower radiator tie bar and tighten bolts to 88 INCH lbs. (10 N.m). Install forward sensor. See FORWARD SENSOR under REMOVAL & INSTALLATION in this article.

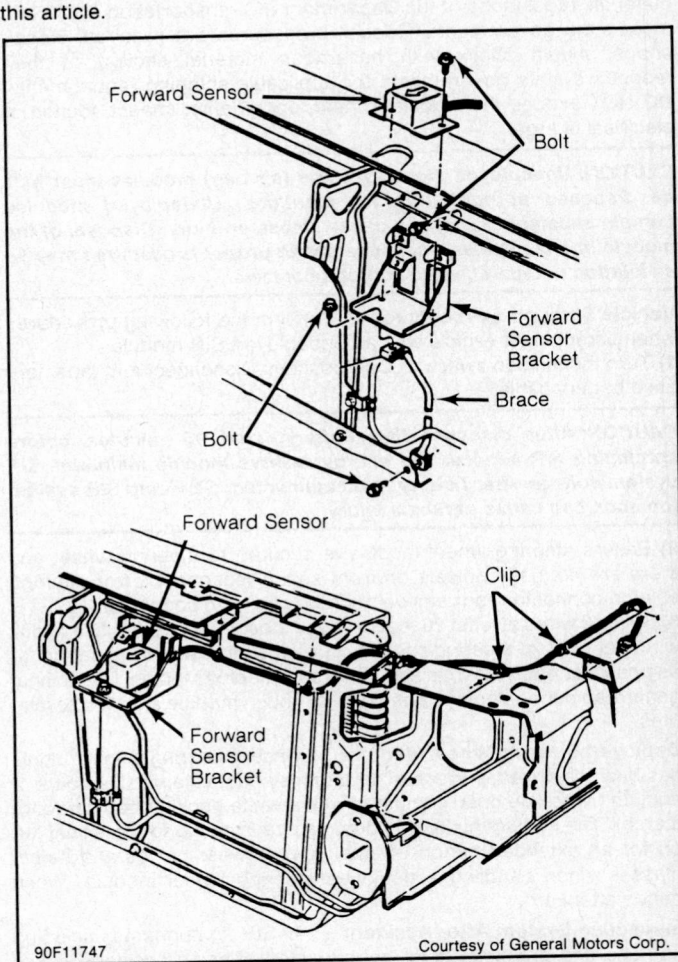

90F11747   Courtesy of General Motors Corp.

Fig. 3: Removing/Installing Forward Sensor & Bracket

STEERING WHEEL MODULE

Removal & Installation – Disconnect negative battery cable. Remove AIR BAG (SIR) fuse and wait 15 minutes before proceeding. See SERVICE PRECAUTIONS under REMOVAL & INSTALLATION in this article. From back of steering wheel remove 3 of 4 bolts securing module to steering wheel. *See Fig. 4.* Support module and carefully remove last bolt. Remove module connector and retainer pin. Protect connector with tape. To install, reverse removal procedure.

COIL ASSEMBLY

NOTE: Front wheels of vehicle must point straight ahead before beginning service. Failure to straighten wheels can result in coil assembly being removed uncentered. Reinstalling the coil assembly under such circumstances will cause the ribbon in coil assembly to break when the steering wheel is turned fully in one direction. Ensure ignition is always in LOCK position to prevent steering wheel from turning and uncentering the coil assembly. To recenter coil assembly, see ADJUSTMENTS in this article.

1991 SAFETY EQUIPMENT
Air Bag Restraint System – Eighty-Eight (Cont.)

GM
4-15

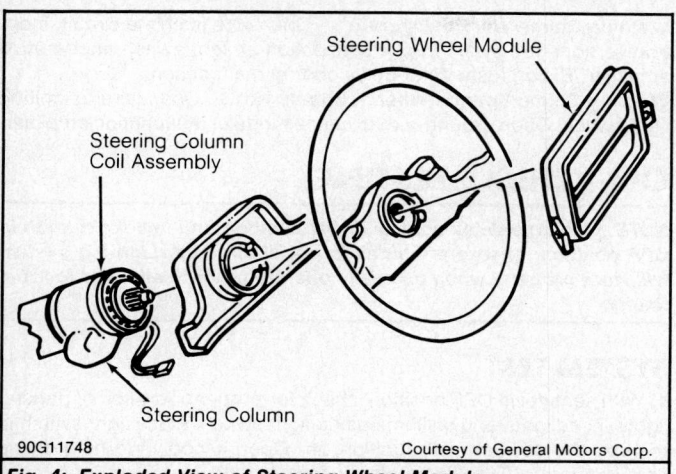

90G11748   Courtesy of General Motors Corp.

Fig. 4: Exploded View of Steering Wheel Module

Removal – 1) Remove steering wheel module. See STEERING WHEEL MODULE under REMOVAL & INSTALLATION in this article. Remove steering wheel hexagon locking nut. Using a puller, remove steering wheel. DO NOT install puller bolts too far, as damage to coil assembly can result.

2) Remove coil assembly retaining ring from steering shaft. Grasp clear plastic wire protector shield on underside of steering column and slide downward. Partially remove coil assembly from end of steering wheel shaft and allow coil to hang freely. Note orientation to steering column housing before removal.

3) Remove wave washer from steering shaft. Using Lock Plate Compressor (J-23653-C), depress shaft lock and remove shaft lock retaining ring. Remove shaft lock plate and upper bearing spring. Remove turn signal canceling cam.

4) Remove hazard knob and attaching screw. Remove turn signal switch arm. Remove 3 turn signal switch screws and partially withdraw switch. Attach mechanic's wire to coil assembly lower connector at base of steering column. Carefully pull wire through gear shift lever bowl, column housing and lock housing cover.

Installation – 1) Carefully feed coil assembly wire and lower connector through lock housing cover, column housing and gear shift lever bowl, and allow coil assembly to hang freely.

NOTE: Use care not to pinch wires when installing components. After wire is fed through, attach CAUTION tag to wire near connector at base of steering column. Tag is included in coil assembly repair kit.

2) Install turn signal switch and torque screws to 30 INCH lbs. (3.4 N.m). Install turn signal switch arm and torque attaching screw to 20 INCH lbs. (2.2 N.m).

3) Install hazard knob and attaching screw, turn signal canceling cam and shaft lock plate. Install shaft lock retaining ring. Using lock plate compressor, align block tooth on shaft and depress shaft lock plate. Install wave washer. Ensure coil assembly hub and steering shaft are centered. Coil assembly will become uncentered if column is separated from steering gear and is allowed to rotate. Coil assembly will become uncentered if centering spring is depressed, allowing hub to rotate while coil assembly is removed from column.

4) Install coil assembly, using horn tower on canceling cam to align hole on inner ring of coil and projections on steering column housing with projections on outer ring of coil. To complete installation, reverse removal procedure.

KNEE BOLSTER

Removal & Installation – Remove trim pad between instrument panel and lower trim panel. See Fig. 5. Remove screws along top of instrument panel lower trim panel. Remove screw from left end of lower trim

panel. Remove screws from bottom of lower trim panel. Remove electrical connectors, as necessary, to remove panel. To install, reverse removal procedure.

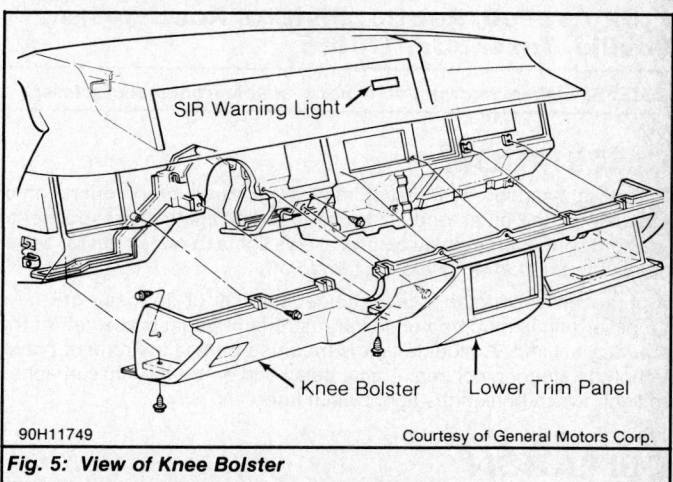

90H11749   Courtesy of General Motors Corp.

Fig. 5: View of Knee Bolster

ADJUSTMENTS

CENTERING COIL ASSEMBLY

1) If the coil assembly has been removed from the steering column and is being reinstalled, go to step **2)**. Replacement coil assemblies are provided precentered and include a Blue plastic tab that is snapped off once the coil is installed.

2) Ensure front wheels face straight ahead when installing or removing coil assembly. If coil is removed without the wheels straight ahead and the steering wheel has not been moved, the same coil can be reinstalled if the coil hub also has not been rotated.

3) Hold coil assembly with clear bottom upward to see coil ribbon. Note there are 2 different styles of coil assemblies; one rotates clockwise and the other rotates counterclockwise.

4) While holding coil assembly housing, depress spring lock and rotate hub in direction of arrow until it stops. The coil assembly should now be wound up snug against center hub. Rotate coil assembly hub in opposite direction approximately 2 1/2 turns. Release spring lock between locking tabs in front of arrow.

WIRING DIAGRAMS

See appropriate chassis wiring diagram in WIRING DIAGRAMS.

TORQUE SPECIFICATIONS

TORQUE SPECIFICATIONS

Application	INCH Lbs. (N.m)
Forward Sensor	62 (7)
Forward Sensor Bracket Assembly	
Bracket-To-Brace	88 (10)
Bracket-To-Upper Radiator Tie Bar	88 (10)
Bracket-To-Lower Radiator Tie Bar	88 (10)
Passenger Compartment Sensor/	
Diagnostic Module (PCSDM)	88 (10)
SIR Control Center	
Mounting Bracket	88 (10)
Self-Tapping Left Rear Screw	44 (5)
Turn Signal Switch	30 (4)
Turn Signal Switch Arm	20 (3)

Bonneville, Brougham, Caprice, Custom Cruiser, DeVille, Eighty-Eight, Eldorado, Fleetwood, LeSabre, Ninety-Eight, Park Avenue, Reatta, Riviera, Roadmaster, Seville, Toronado, Trofeo

NOTE: Brougham information is not available from manufacturer.

DESCRIPTION

The twilight sentinel system automatically controls on-off operation of headlights, taillights, and instrument panel lights in response to ambient light. A time-delay control allows lights to remain on for a pre-selected period after ignition is turned off.

A photocell is mounted face up, under speaker or defroster grille. An amplifier unit is mounted on lower instrument panel brace, left of the steering column. A module unit is mounted behind instrument panel, left of the steering column. A time delay and on-off switch is attached to light switch behind the light switch knob.

OPERATION

AUTOMATIC OPERATION

Twilight sentinel system operates automatically when ignition is in ON position, or headlight switch is in OFF position and the control ring pointer is turned on. System automatically activates lights at dusk.

At daybreak, system will turn lights off. There is a 30-second delay before the amplifier switches system on or off, preventing system to cycle under sudden lighting changes such as passing through tunnels or exposing to bright lights. The length of time delay is set in production and cannot be adjusted.

A variable time-delay switch control permits the driver to select a delay period before headlights turn off. This can be a few seconds to a maximum of 3 minutes after ignition is turned off. Additional lighting may be provided, during this period, by turning on cornering lights (if equipped). All lights will turn off automatically at end of time-delay period selected by driver.

MANUAL OPERATION

If lights are to be used during daylight hours, 2 methods may be used. The photocell assembly can be covered, causing lights to turn on. This allows lights to turn off automatically when ignition is turned off. Lights can also be turned on using regular light switch. In this position however, headlights will stay on when ignition switch is turned off. Some vehicles have a tone alarm which sounds as a reminder that lights are on.

TROUBLE SHOOTING

Headlights On Late Or Early In Evening/Morning – Defective photocell.

Lights Do Not Turn On In Darkness – Loose connection at light switch or amplifier connector. Open wiring between fusible link and light switch. Inoperative light switch (circuit breaker). Open ground path through on-off switch of time-delay control assembly. Inoperative photocell or amplifier.

Lights Do Not Turn Off In Daylight – Inoperative photocell or amplifier. Poor contact between photocell and socket, or socket disengaged from mounting hole. Obstructed photocell.

Lights Do Not Turn Off After Ignition Is Off – Ignition switch wire has power with key off. Fuse blown. Inoperative time-delay control. Open wiring in circuit. Inoperative amplifier. Malfunction photocell.

Lights Do Not Stay On Proper Time Span After Ignition Is Off – Inoperative time delay control assembly. Blown taillight fuse. Improper resistance at amplifier connector. Short in wiring circuit. Inoperative amplifier.

Warning Chime Will Not Operate – Open wire in chime circuit. Inoperative door jam switch. Poor connection at light switch. Inoperative amplifier. Blown fuse. Time-delay control malfunction.

Warning Chime Sounds When It Should Not – Open wire to ignition light switch. Open ground wire to chime module. Malfunction amplifier.

ON-VEHICLE TESTING

NOTE: With time-delay control in ON position and headlight knob in OFF position, ensure photocell is not obstructed. Lighting system will work properly when manually operated. Check all fuses for continuity.

SYSTEM TEST

1) With sentinel in OFF position, check for proper operation of parking lights, headlights and taillights using light switch. Place light switch in manual ON position with ignition off. Open a door. Warning chime should operate. Turn lights off.

2) Turn sentinel on after covering photocell. With ignition on, lights should come on automatically within 10-30 seconds. Remove cover and shine a bright light onto photocell.

3) Lights should turn off after a 30-second delay. Cover photocell and wait for lights to turn on. Wait 15 seconds and turn ignition off. Lights should turn off after a few seconds when control is in OFF position, and after 1 1/2 to 4 1/2 minutes when control is in MAX position.

4) Satisfactory performance of steps **1)** through **3)** indicates unit is operating properly.

INSTRUMENT PANEL CLUSTER TEST

Eldorado & Seville – 1) Enter Instrument Panel Cluster (IPC) diagnostics by turning ignition on, and pressing OFF and WARM controls on Climate Control/Driver Information Center (CCDIC) panel simultaneously until segment check appears on IPC and CCDIC. Select IPC input test 1I82. Turn twilight sentinel off. IPC should display HI. If reading is correct, proceed to TWILIGHT SENTINEL PHOTOCELL TEST. If IPC displays LO, disconnect left switch assembly. Check IPC display.

2) If display reads HI, replace left switch assembly. If display reads LO, reconnect left switch assembly. Remove IPC. Connect a self-powered test light at IPC terminal RB4, with twilight enable switch in OFF position. If test light glows, check wiring harness circuit No. 304 and connector C201 (behind instrument panel, right of steering column) for short to ground. If test light does not glow, check IPC terminal RB4 for good contact. If contact is good, replace IPC.

3) Turn twilight sentinel on. IPC should display LO. If reading is correct, proceed to TWILIGHT SENTINEL PHOTOCELL TEST. If IPC displays HI, disconnect left switch assembly, and connect a fused jumper between terminals B1 and BC10 of switch assembly. Check IPC display.

4) If display reads LO, replace left switch assembly. If display reads HI connect a fused jumper between left switch assembly connector terminal B1 and ground. If display reads LO, check wiring harness circuit, connector C201 and Black/Pink wire for open.

5) If display reads HI, reconnect left switch assembly. Remove IPC. Connect a self-powered test light at IPC terminal RB4 connector, with twilight enable switch in ON position. If test light does not glow, check wiring harness circuit and connector C201 for open. If test light glows, check IPC terminal RB4 for good contact. If contact is good, replace IPC.

TWILIGHT SENTINEL PHOTOCELL TEST

Eldorado & Seville – 1) Enter Body Control Module (BCM) diagnostics. See SELF DIAGNOSTICS – ELDORADO & SEVILLE ECM/BCM article in ENGINE PERFORMANCE. Select BCM data test BD44. Expose twilight photocell to bright sunlight or bright incandescent light. BCM should display 30 or less. If display is greater than 30, use a voltmeter to measure voltage between White wire and ground. Voltmeter should indicate 2 volts or less. If voltage is greater than 2 volts replace twilight photocell.

2) Cover twilight photocell with cardboard. BCM should display 75 or more. If display is less than 75, use a voltmeter to measure voltage between White wire and ground. Voltmeter should indicate 4 volts or more. If voltage is less than 4 volts, replace twilight photocell.

BODY CONTROL MODULE TEST

Eldorado & Seville – 1) Enter BCM diagnostics. See SELF DIAGNOSTICS – ELDORADO & SEVILLE PCM/BCM article in ENGINE PERFORMANCE. Select BCM output test BO05. If BCM displays LO, headlights and exterior lights should come on. If lights do not come on, go to TWILIGHT HEADLIGHT RELAY TEST or TWILIGHT PARK LIGHT RELAY test.

2) If BCM displays HI, headlights and exterior lights should be off. If lights are not off, go to TWILIGHT HEADLIGHT RELAY TEST or TWILIGHT PARK LIGHT RELAY test. If BCM display does not cycle from LO to HI, replace BCM.

Reatta, Riviera, Toronado & Trofeo – 1) Enter BCM diagnostics. See SELF DIAGNOSTICS – REATTA & RIVIERA PCM/BCM or SELF-DIAGNOSTICS – TORONADO & TROFEO PCM/BCM article in ENGINE PERFORMANCE. Select BCM data test BD43. Set twilight sentinel switch to MIN position. BCM should display 10. If display is NOT 10, replace left switch assembly. If display is 10, replace BCM.

2) Set twilight sentinel switch to MAX position. BCM should display 90. If display is NOT 90, replace left switch assembly. If display is 90, replace BCM.

3) Select BCM data test BD182. Set twilight sentinel switch to OFF position. BCM should display HI. If BCM does not display HI, replace left switch assembly. If display is as indicated, go to step **5)**.

4) Set twilight sentinel switch to ON position. BCM should display LO. If BCM does not display LO, replace left switch assembly. If display is as indicated, go to next step.

5) Select BCM output test BO13. With BCM displaying LO, headlights and exterior lights should turn on. With BCM displaying HI, headlights and exterior lights should turn off. If lights work properly, go to TWILIGHT HEADLIGHT RELAY TEST and PARK LIGHT RELAY TEST.

6) If headlights and exterior lights cycle on and off, go to step **7)**. If BCM display does not cycle from LO to HI, replace BCM.

7) Select BCM data test BD44. Expose photocell to bright sunlight or a very bright incandescent light. BCM should display 30 or less. If BCM display value is correct, replace BCM. If display value is not as specified, go to step **8)**.

8) Cover photocell with cardboard. BCM should display 90 or more. If BCM display value is correct, replace BCM. If display value is not as specified, go to step **9)**.

9) Turn ignition switch to RUN position. Expose photocell to bright sunlight or a very bright incandescent light. Connect voltmeter between BCM White wire connector and ground. Voltmeter should read 2 volts or less. If voltage is not as specified, replace photocell. If voltage is as indicated, replace BCM.

10) Cover photocell with cardboard. Connect voltmeter between BCM White wire connector and ground. Voltmeter should read 4 volts or greater. If voltage is not as indicated, replace photocell. If voltage is 4 volts or greater, replace BCM.

TWILIGHT SENTINEL TEST

Exterior Lights Do Not Turn Off (DeVille & Fleetwood) – 1) Disconnect twilight sentinel module connector (right of steering column). If exterior lights do not turn off after disconnecting module, go to step **3)**. If lights turn off, use a voltmeter to measure voltage from Pink wire terminal to ground at connector. If voltage is found, check Pink (3) wires for short to voltage. If wires are okay, replace ignition switch.

2) If voltage is not found from Pink wire terminal to ground, use an ohmmeter to measure resistance between Black/White wire terminal and ground. If resistance is greater than one ohm, check Black/White wire for open. If resistance is less than one ohm, replace twilight sentinel module.

3) Check Brown, Yellow, Light Green and Tan wires for short to voltage. If all wires are okay, replace headlight switch.

Exterior Lights Do Not Operate (DeVille & Fleetwood) – Check Orange/Black, Orange and Brown wires for open or short to ground.

Also check for blown fuse No. 14 or a faulty light switch.

Headlights Do Not Operate (DeVille & Fleetwood) – Check Red, Yellow, Light Green and Tan wires for open or short to ground. Also check for blown fuse at underhood fuse block (fuse No. 6) or a faulty light switch.

All Exterior Lights Are On During Daylight (Caprice, Custom Cruiser & Roadmaster) – 1) Set twilight sentinel switch to ON position. Turn ignition switch to RUN position. Remove photocell light sensor. See MODULE, AMPLIFIER & PHOTOCELL under REMOVAL & INSTALLATION. Use a digital voltmeter to measure voltage at photocell sensor connector, between Yellow/Black wire terminal and ground.

2) If voltage is not found, go to step **4)**. If voltage is found, connect a fused jumper to photocell sensor connector between Green/Black wire terminal and Yellow/Black wire terminal. If headlights do not come on, check for poor connection at photocell sensor. If connection is okay, replace photocell sensor.

3) If headlights come on, check for short to voltage at Green/Black wire or poor connection at twilight sentinel module Green/Black wire terminal. Also check for open in Yellow/Black wire. If wires and connections are okay, replace twilight sentinel module.

4) Check for open in Yellow/Black wire or poor connection of Yellow/Black wire at twilight sentinel module. If connection is okay, replace twilight sentinel module.

Headlights Only Operate With Twilight Sentinel (Caprice, Custom Cruiser & Roadmaster) – 1) Using test light, backprobe between twilight sentinel module Orange wire terminal and ground. If test light does not glow, check for open in Orange wire from twilight sentinel module to fuse block. If test light glows, go to next step.

2) Turn ignition switch to RUN position. Turn twilight sentinel switch to ON position. Cover photocell light sensor to turn headlights on. Backprobe between twilight sentinel module Brown wire terminal and ground. If test light glows, check for open in Brown wire circuit to twilight sentinel module. If test light does not glow, check for poor connection in Brown wire. If connection is okay, replace twilight sentinel module.

Headlights Do Not Operate With Twilight Sentinel (Caprice, Custom Cruiser & Roadmaster) – 1) Using test light, backprobe twilight sentinel module between Dark Green wire terminal and ground. If test light does not glow, go to step **5)**. If test light glows, put twilight sentinel switch in ON position, and turn ignition switch to RUN position. Backprobe twilight sentinel module between Pink/Black wire terminal and ground.

2) If test light does not glow, go to step **3)**. If test light glows, cover photocell, and backprobe twilight sentinel module between Yellow wire terminal and ground. If test light does not glow, go to step **4)**. If test light glows, check for open in Yellow wire circuit to twilight sentinel module.

3) Check for poor connection in Pink/Black wire circuit. If connection is okay, check for open in Pink/Black wire circuit between twilight sentinel module and fuse block.

4) Check for poor connections at twilight sentinel module. If connections are okay, replace twilight sentinel module.

5) Using test light, backprobe headlight switch between Dark Green wire terminal and ground. If test light glows, check for poor connections in Dark Green wire circuit; if connections are okay, check for open in Dark Green wire circuit between headlight switch and twilight sentinel switch. If test light does not glow, check for poor connection in Dark Green wire at headlight switch; if connection is okay, replace headlight switch.

Headlight Switch Operates, But Twilight Sentinel Does Not (Caprice, Custom & Roadmaster) – 1) Using test light, backprobe twilight sentinel module between Dark Green wire terminal and ground. If test light does not glow, go to step **3)**. If test light glows, turn ignition switch to RUN position. Backprobe twilight sentinel module between Pink/Black terminal and ground.

2) If test light does not glow, go to step **4)**. If test light glows, backprobe twilight sentinel module between Black wire terminal and Pink/Black wire terminal. If test light glows, go to step **5)**. If test light does not glow, check for open in Black wire circuit to twilight sentinel module.

3) Backprobe headlight switch between Dark Green terminal and ground. If test light does not glow, check for poor connection at headlight switch Dark Green wire terminal; if connection is okay, replace headlight switch. If test light glows, check for poor connection in Dark Green wire circuit; if connection is okay, check for open in Dark Green wire circuit between headlight switch and twilight sentinel module.

4) Check for poor connection in Pink/Black wire circuit. If connection is okay, check for open in Pink/Black wire circuit from twilight sentinel module and fuse block.

5) Turn twilight sentinel switch to OFF position. Use a digital voltmeter to measure voltage at twilight sentinel module between Light Green wire terminal and ground. If voltage is not found, go to step **7)**. If voltage is found, measure voltage at twilight sentinel switch between Light Green wire terminal and ground.

6) If voltage is not found, go to step **8)** If voltage is found, backprobe twilight sentinel switch between Black wire terminal and Light Green wire terminal. If test light does not glow, check for open in Black wire circuit to twilight sentinel switch. If test light glows, disconnect photocell sensor. If exterior lights go on, replace photocell sensor. If exterior lights do not turn on, go to step **9)**.

7) Check for poor connection at twilight sentinel module Light Green wire terminal. If connection is okay, replace twilight sentinel module.

8) Check for poor connection in Purple wire circuit. If connection is okay, check for open in Light Green wire circuit between twilight sentinel switch and twilight sentinel module.

9) Measure voltage at photocell sensor Yellow/Black wire terminal and ground. If voltage is not found, go to step **10)**. If voltage is found, measure voltage at photocell sensor from Green/Black wire terminal to Yellow/Black wire terminal. If voltage is not found, go to step **11)**. If voltage is found, check for poor connections at twilight sentinel switch. If connections are okay, replace switch.

10) Check for open in Yellow/Black wire circuit or poor connection at twilight sentinel module Yellow/Black wire terminal. Also check for short to ground in Yellow/Black wire circuit. If circuit is okay, replace twilight sentinel module.

11) Check for short to voltage in Green/Black wire circuit or open in Green/Black wire circuit. Also check for poor connection at twilight sentinel module Green/Black wire terminal. If circuit is okay, replace twilight sentinel module.

Headlights Delay Does Not Operate (Caprice, Custom Cruiser & Roadmaster) – 1) Turn ignition switch to RUN position. Set twilight sentinel switch in ON position. Set delay to MIN setting. Put headlight switch in OFF position. Using digital voltmeter, backprobe twilight sentinel switch between Purple wire terminal and Black wire terminal.

2) If voltage is not found, go to step **3)**. If voltage is found, with voltmeter still connected, move rheostat from MIN to MAX, and observe voltmeter readings. Voltage should increase at MAX setting, and decrease to approximately 4 volts at MIN setting. If readings are NOT as indicated, replace twilight sentinel switch. If readings are as indicated, check for poor connection at twilight sentinel module. If connection is okay, replace twilight sentinel module.

3) Using test light, backprobe between twilight sentinel switch Black wire terminal and Light Green wire terminal. If test light does not glow, check for open in Black wire circuit to twilight sentinel switch. If test light glows, check for poor connection at twilight sentinel switch. If connection is okay, replace switch.

Headlights-On Warning Does Not Operate (Caprice, Custom Cruiser & Roadmaster) – 1) Set headlight switch in ON position. Using a digital voltmeter, measure voltage at convenience center (left side of instrument panel, left of steering column) between Black/White wire terminal and ground. If voltage is not found, go to step **2)**. If voltage is found, check for poor connection at convenience center Black/White wire terminal. If connection is okay, replace audio alarm module (located at convenience center).

2) Using digital voltmeter, measure voltage at twilight sentinel module between Black/White wire terminal and ground. If voltage is not found, go to step **3)**. If voltage is found, check for poor connection in Black/White wire circuit. If connection is okay, check for open in Black/White wire circuit between convenience center and twilight sentinel module.

3) Measure voltage at twilight sentinel module Orange wire terminal to ground. If voltage is found, check for poor connection at twilight sentinel module Orange wire terminal. If connection is okay, replace twilight sentinel module. If voltage is not found, check for open or poor connection in Orange wire circuit to headlight switch terminal. If connection and wire are okay, replace headlight switch.

TWILIGHT HEADLIGHT RELAY TEST

Eldorado, Reatta, Riviera, Seville, Toronado & Trofeo – 1) Disconnect twilight headlight connector from interior relay center. Enter BCM diagnostics. See appropriate SELF DIAGNOSTICS PCM/BCM article in ENGINE PERFORMANCE. Select BCM output test BO05.

2) Connect test light between Orange/Dark Blue (Black/Orange on Toronado) wire and ground. Test light should glow and BCM should display HI or LO. If test light and BCM do not function as indicated, check low beam circuit breaker No. 21 and wires for open circuit.

3) On Eldorado and Seville, connect test light between Orange and Yellow wires. Test light should glow and BCM should display HI or LO. If test light and BCM do not function as indicated, check Yellow wire for open circuit.

4) On all models, connect test light between Orange wire and ground. Test light should glow and BCM should display HI or LO. If test light and BCM do not function as indicated, check BCM fuse and Orange wire for open circuit.

5) Connect test light between Orange and Black/Pink wires. Test light should glow when BCM displays LO, and should NOT glow when BCM displays HI. If test light does not glow and BCM displays LO, check Black/Pink wire for open circuit. If test light glows and BCM displays HI, check Black/Pink wire for short to ground.

6) On Toronado, connect a fused jumper between Black/Orange and Tan wires. Headlights should come on. If headlights do not come on, check and repair Tan wire as necessary.

7) On all models, if results from the previous steps are correct but system still does not operate properly, replace twilight headlight relay.

TWILIGHT PARK LIGHT RELAY TEST

Eldorado, Reatta, Riviera, Seville, Toronado & Trofeo – 1) Disconnect twilight park light connector from interior relay center. Enter BCM diagnostics. See appropriate SELF DIAGNOSTICS PCM/BCM article in ENGINE PERFORMANCE. Select BCM output test BO05.

2) Connect test light between Orange wire and ground. Test light should glow and BCM should display HI or LO. If test light and BCM do not function as indicated, check Orange wire for open and repair as necessary.

3) On Eldorado and Seville, connect test light between Orange wire and ground. Test light should glow and BCM displays HI or LO. If test light and BCM do not function as indicated, check taillights fuse No. 15 and Orange wire for open circuit.

4) On all models, connect test light between Orange and Black/Pink wires. Test light should glow when BCM displays LO, and should NOT glow when BCM displays HI. If test light does not glow and BCM displays LO, check Black/Pink wire for open circuit. If test light glows and BCM displays HI, check Black/Pink wire for short to ground.

5) On Toronado, connect a fused jumper between Orange and Brown wires. If park lights come on, check and repair Brown wire as necessary.

6) On all models, if results from previous steps are correct but system still does not operate properly, replace twilight park light relay.

TWILIGHT SHORT CIRCUIT TEST

Toronado & Trofeo – 1) Remove fuse No. 10 from fuse block, then reinsert. If headlights and exterior lights stay off, go to step **2)**. If headlights and exterior lights come back on, check Pink/Black wires for short to ground. If only headlights or only park lights are on, go to HEADLIGHT & PARK LIGHT SHORT TEST.

2) With ignition off, disconnect twilight crank relay (behind glove box). Connect a fused jumper from Black/Pink wire to Black wire of relay connector. If headlights and exterior lights come on, go to step **3)**. If headlights and exterior lights do not come on, disconnect fused jumper, and repeat step **1)**.

) With fused jumper still connected, disconnect 48-way connector located behind left hand side of instrument panel, left of steering column). If headlights and exterior lights go off, check ignition switch and Dark/Green wire in steering column for short to ground. If headlights and exterior lights stay on, check Black wires for short to ground.

HEADLIGHT & PARK LIGHT SHORT TEST

Headlight (Toronado & Trofeo) – Remove twilight sentinel headlight relay from micro relay center (located behind glove box). If headlights go out, replace relay. If headlights stay on, check Tan wire for a short to voltage. If wire is okay, replace left switch assembly.

Park Light (Toronado & Trofeo) – Remove twilight sentinel park light relay from micro relay. If exterior lights go out, replace park relay. If exterior lights stay on, check Brown wire for short to voltage. If wire is okay, replace left switch assembly.

POWER & GROUND TEST

Bonneville, DeVille, Eighty-Eight, Fleetwood, LeSabre, Ninety-Eight & Park Avenue – **1)** Disconnect twilight sentinel module connector. Turn ignition switch to RUN position. Set headlight switch to OFF position. Put dimmer switch in LO position. Put gear selector in Park position.

) Using a voltmeter, check voltage between Pink wire and ground. Voltage should be present. If voltage is not present, check Pink wire for open or short to ground.

) Check voltage between Orange wire and ground. Voltage should be present. If voltage is not present, check Orange wire for open or short to ground.

) Check voltage between Orange and Black/White wires. Voltage should be present. If voltage is not present, check Black/White wire for open.

) Check voltage between Black wire and ground. Voltage should be present. If voltage is not present, check Black wire for open. If wire is okay, replace headlight switch.

) Put headlight switch in HEAD position. Put dimmer switch in HI position. Check voltage between Yellow wire and ground. Voltage should be present. If voltage is not present, check Yellow wire for open.

) Check voltage between Brown wire and ground. Voltage should be present. If voltage is not present, check Brown wire for open.

) Check voltage between Light Green wire and ground. Voltage should be present. If voltage is not present, check Light Green wire for open.

) Check voltage between Light Green/Black wire and ground. Voltage should be present. If voltage is not present, check Light Green/Black wires for open. If wires are okay, check transaxle position switch for open or misalignment.

0) Place gear selector in Drive position. Check voltage between Light Green/Black wire and ground. Voltage should be present. If voltage is not present, check transaxle-position switch for short or misalignment. If switch is okay, check Light Green/Black wire for short to battery.

1) If voltage is present in each previous step, go to RESISTANCE TEST.

RESISTANCE TEST

Bonneville, DeVille, Eighty-Eight, Fleetwood, LeSabre, Ninety-Eight & Park Avenue – **1)** Disconnect twilight sentinel module connector. Turn ignition off. Turn twilight sentinel control off.

) Using an ohmmeter, measure resistance between Purple wire and Black/White wire. Ohmmeter should read infinite. If reading is as specified, go to step **3)**. If reading is not as indicated, check Purple wire for short to ground . If wire is okay, replace twilight sentinel control.

) Turn twilight sentinel control on. Measure resistance between Purple wire and Black/White wire terminals. Ohmmeter should read less than 0.5 ohm. If reading is as specified, go to step **5)**.

) If resistance is not as specified, measure resistance between Light Green wire and Black/White wire. If resistance is less than 0.5 ohm, check Purple and Black/White wires for open. If resistance is greater than 0.5 ohms, replace twilight sentinel control.

5) Vary twilight sentinel control between MIN and MAX settings while measuring resistance between Light Green and Black/White wires. Reading should vary between 1-260 k/ohms. If reading is as specified, go to step **7)**.

6) If reading is not as specified, measure resistance between Light Green wire and Pink wire terminals. If reading varies between 1-260 k/ohms, check Light Green wire for open or short to ground. Also check Black/White wire for open. If resistance does not vary between 1-260 k/ohms, replace twilight sentinel control.

7) Use a trouble light to expose twilight sentinel photocell to bright light; cover photocell with cardboard. DO NOT use fluorescent trouble light. Measure resistance between White and Black/White wires. Reading should vary between 15 k/ohms (bright light) and 20 megohms (covered). If reading is as specified but system still does not function properly, replace twilight sentinel.

8) If reading is not as specified, measure resistance at photocell. If resistance varies between 15 k/ohms (bright light) and 20 megohms (covered), check White wire for open or short to ground. Also check Black/White wire for open. If resistance does not vary between 15 k/ohms and 20 megohms, replace twilight sentinel photocell.

HIGH BEAM INPUT TEST

Ninety-Eight – **1)** Disconnect light control module wire connector (above fuse block). Turn fog light switch on. Put headlight switch in HEAD position. Put dimmer switch in HI position. Using a voltmeter, check voltage between Light Green wire and ground. If voltage is not found, check Light Green wire for open.
2) Check voltage between Light Green/Black wire and ground. If voltage is not found, check Light Green/Black wire for short to ground. If Light Green and Light Green/Black wires are okay, replace light control module.

HIGH BEAM INDICATOR TEST

Bonneville & Eighty-Eight – Disconnect twilight sentinel control module wire connector (above fuse block). Turn ignition switch to RUN position. Connect a fused jumper between Black and White wires. High beam indicator should come on.

If indicator does not come on, check White wire for open or short to ground; if wire is okay, refer to instrument panel wiring diagram. See appropriate chassis wiring diagram in WIRING DIAGRAMS. If indicator comes on, check Light Green wire for open. If wire is okay, replace twilight sentinel module.

REMOVAL & INSTALLATION

MODULE, AMPLIFIER & PHOTOCELL

Removal & Installation (Bonneville) – Disconnect negative battery terminal. Remove windshield defroster nozzle grille. Twist photocell socket 1/4 turn. To remove photocell from socket, turn photocell counterclockwise. To remove module, remove instrument panel trim plate, filler and reinforcement. Remove lower left and right sound absorbing panels. Remove module from underneath dashboard. To install, reverse removal procedure.

Removal & Installation (DeVille & Fleetwood) – Disconnect negative battery terminal. Remove instrument panel upper trim pad, photocell mounting bracket and electrical connector. Remove photocell. To remove amplifier, remove lower left sound absorbing panel. Remove screw securing left hand air conditioner duct. Remove screws securing lower instrument panel assembly. Remove electrical connectors. Remove amplifier. To install, reverse removal procedure.

Removal & Installation (Caprice, Custom Cruiser & Roadmaster) – Disconnect negative battery terminal. Remove windshield defroster nozzle grille from upper trim pad. Remove photocell and photo sensor harness connector from windshield defroster nozzle grille. Twist photocell counterclockwise. Remove photocell from sensor harness. To remove amplifier, remove harness connectors. Remove amplifier by sliding from bracket. To install, reverse removal procedure.

Removal & Installation (Eighty-Eight) – Disconnect negative battery terminal. Remove defroster grille by prying up on right side only. Twist socket 1/4 turn. Unplug photocell from socket. To remove control module, remove right sound absorbing panel. Remove glove box. Unplug electrical connector from module. Remove module retaining screw. To install, reverse removal procedure.

Removal & Installation (Ninety-Eight) – Disconnect negative battery terminal. Remove defroster grille by prying up on right side only. Twist socket 1/4 turn. Unplug photocell from socket. To remove control module, remove left sound absorbing panel. Remove glove box. Pry up on bracket and hold. Slide module forward. Pull down on module to release. Unplug connector and remove module. To install, reverse removal procedure.

Removal & Installation (LeSabre) – Remove instrument panel upper trim pad. Remove photocell from electrical connector. Remove module from underneath dashboard, on right side of steering column. To install, reverse removal procedure.

Removal & Installation (Park Avenue) – Remove instrument panel upper trim pad. Remove photocell from electrical connector. Remove module from underneath dashboard, right above fuse block. To install, reverse removal procedure.

Removal & Installation (Eldorado & Seville) – Disconnect negative battery terminal. Remove windshield defroster grille. Remove photocell and electrical connector. To install, reverse removal procedure.

Removal & Installation (Reatta & Riviera) – 1) Disconnect battery ground. To gain access to lower trim panel screws, remove glove box shell and lower right sound absorbing panel retaining screws. Remove center trim panel by pulling straight out.

2) Remove right trim panel. Disconnect electrical connector and remove amplifier retaining screws and bolts. Disconnect photocell electrical connector. Pop retainer up and rotate. Remove photocell. To install, reverse removal procedure.

Removal & Installation (Toronado & Trofeo) – Disconnect negative battery terminal. Remove windshield defroster grille. Remove photocell and electrical connector. To install, reverse removal procedure.

WIRING DIAGRAMS

See appropriate chassis wiring diagram in WIRING DIAGRAMS.

Corvette, Firebird, Reatta, Sunbird

DESCRIPTION & OPERATION

Headlight doors are actuated by reversible electric motors, mounted near each headlight door. Battery voltage is applied at all times to terminals "B" and "E" of Headlight Door Module (HDM) 5-pin connector. *See Fig. 1.* Module also has a 4-pin connector, supplying output voltage to door motors.

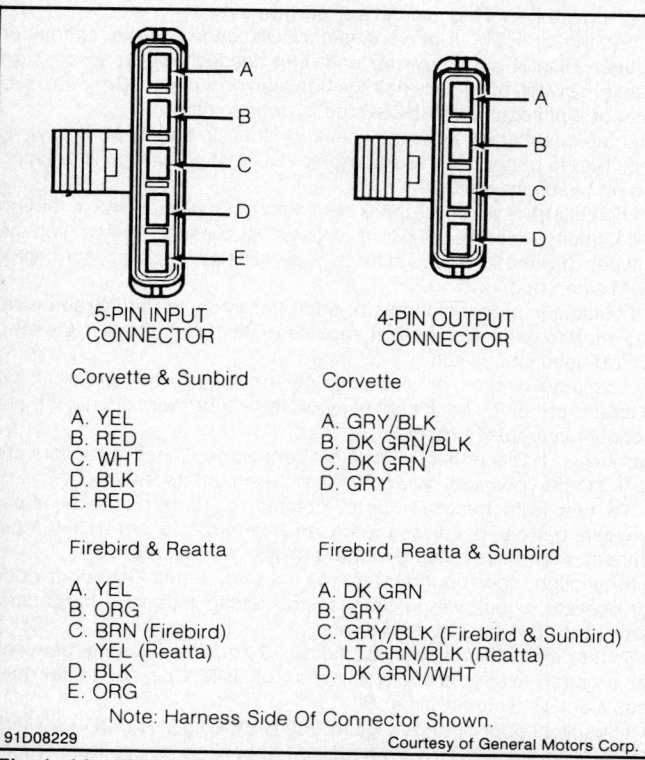

5-PIN INPUT CONNECTOR

4-PIN OUTPUT CONNECTOR

Corvette & Sunbird

A. YEL
B. RED
C. WHT
D. BLK
E. RED

Firebird & Reatta

A. YEL
B. ORG
C. BRN (Firebird)
   YEL (Reatta)
D. BLK
E. ORG

Corvette

A. GRY/BLK
B. DK GRN/BLK
C. DK GRN
D. GRY

Firebird, Reatta & Sunbird

A. DK GRN
B. GRY
C. GRY/BLK (Firebird & Sunbird)
   LT GRN/BLK (Reatta)
D. DK GRN/WHT

Note: Harness Side Of Connector Shown.

91D08229
Courtesy of General Motors Corp.

Fig. 1: Identifying Terminals of Headlight Door Module (HDM) Connectors

Depending on model and headlight switch position (or daytime running lights module, if equipped), battery voltage is applied to terminals "A" and "C" of HDM 5-pin connector to activate HDM. See appropriate chassis wiring diagram in WIRING DIAGRAMS.

Based on voltage inputs from headlight switch, HDM directs voltage through 4-pin connector to headlight door motors to actuate headlight doors. To reverse motor direction, HDM reverses circuit polarity. HDM determines when doors are fully open, closed or jammed and turns off power to motors to prevent overload.

ELECTRICAL COMPONENT LOCATIONS

Application	Location
Corvette	
Daytime Running Lights Module	Behind Instrument Panel, Above Driver Information Center.
Fusible Links "F" & "G"	In Left Rear Of Engine Compartment, At Jump-Start Junction Block
Headlight Door Module	In Left Front Of Engine Compartment, Near Air Injection Pump.
Firebird	
Convenience Center	Behind Instrument Panel, To Right Of Steering Column.
Daytime Running Lights Module	Behind Left Side Of Instrument Panel, Near Fuse Block.
Fuse Block	Behind Left Side Of Instrument Panel.
Headlight Door Module	Behind Left Side Of Instrument Panel.

ELECTRICAL COMPONENT LOCATIONS (Cont.)

Application	Location
Reatta	
Fuse Block	On Left Side Of Center Console, Near Floor.
Headlight Door Module	Below Underhood Relay Center.
Headlight Relay	Taped To Fuse Block Wiring Harness, Near Fuse Block.
Underhood Relay Center	In Left Front Of Engine Compartment.
Sunbird	
Fusible Links "J" & "K"	In Harness, Near Headlight Door Module.
Headlight Door Module	In Left Rear Of Engine Compartment, On Strut Tower.

TROUBLE SHOOTING

On Corvette, check fusible links "F" and "G". On Firebird and Reatta, check headlight door fuses No. 1 and 2. On Sunbird, check fusible links "J" and "K". On all models, check door linkage for mechanical binding before performing electrical tests, as high torque load may cause headlight door motors to stop operating before reaching end of travel. Check and repair headlights, if inoperative.

TESTING

CAUTION: HDM contains solid-state circuitry. DO NOT apply voltage (ohmmeter or other source) to HDM internal circuits.

NOTE: Before testing headlight door system, repair headlights if they remain on all the time or do not turn on at all.

BOTH HEADLIGHT DOORS INOPERATIVE

Corvette – 1) Disconnect HDM 5-pin connector. During this test procedure, use a test light to check for voltage at specified wire terminals of HDM 5-pin connector (harness side). *See Fig. 1.*

2) Check for voltage between terminals "D" and "E" and terminals "D" and "B". If voltage is present in both cases, go to next step. If no voltage is present, check for continuity of Black wire (terminal "D"). If continuity is present, check fusible link(s) and respective Red wire circuit(s).

3) Turn headlight switch to ON position. Check for voltage between terminals "A" and "D". If voltage is present, go to next step. If no voltage is present, repair open in Yellow wire.

4) Check for voltage between terminals "C" and "D" with headlight switch in ON, then OFF positions. If voltage is present only when headlight switch is in OFF position, perform appropriate test under ONE HEADLIGHT DOOR INOPERATIVE under TESTING.

5) If voltage is present with headlight switch in ON and OFF positions, check for short to battery voltage in White wire. If no short to battery voltage is present, replace headlight switch.

6) If no voltage is present with headlight switch in ON or OFF position, check continuity of White wire. If continuity is present, replace headlight switch.

Firebird – 1) Disconnect negative battery cable. Turn off headlights and parking lights. Disconnect HDM 5-pin connector. Using an ohmmeter, measure resistance between ground and terminal "C" of HDM 5-pin connector (harness side). *See Fig. 1.*

2) If resistance is more than one ohm, check Brown wire circuit. If resistance is less than one ohm, reconnect negative battery cable. For the remainder of this test procedure, use a test light to check for voltage at specified wire terminals of HDM 5-pin connector (harness side).

3) Check for voltage between ground and terminal "B". If voltage is present, go to next step. If no voltage is present, check headlight door fuse No. 1 and Orange wire.

4) Check for voltage between terminals "B" and "D". If voltage is present, go to next step. If no voltage is present, check Black wire.

5) Check for voltage between ground and terminal "E". If voltage is present, go to next step. If no voltage is present, check headlight door fuse No. 2 and Orange wire.

6) Check for voltage between ground and specified wire terminal with headlight and parking light switch in specified position. See FIREBIRD HEADLIGHT DOOR CIRCUIT VOLTAGE TEST table.

7) If voltage is not as specified, check wiring harness. If wiring harness is okay, replace HDM.

FIREBIRD HEADLIGHT DOOR CIRCUIT VOLTAGE TEST

Switch Position	Terminal	Voltage
Parking Lights ON, Headlights OFF C		Yes
A		No
Headlights ON C		Yes
A		Yes
Parking Lights & Headlights OFF C		No
A		No

Reatta – 1) Disconnect HDM 5-pin connector. During this test procedure, use a test light to check for voltage at specified wire terminals of HDM 5-pin connector (harness side). *See Fig. 1.*

2) Check for voltage between ground and terminal "E". If voltage is present, go to next step. If no voltage is present, check headlight door fuse No. 1 and Orange wire.

3) Check for voltage between ground and terminal "B". If voltage is present, go to next step. If no voltage is present, check headlight door fuse No. 2 and Orange wire.

4) Check for voltage between terminals "B" and "D". If voltage is present, go to next step. If no voltage is present, check Black wire.

5) Turn on headlight switch. Check for voltage between ground and terminal "A". If voltage is present, go to next step. If no voltage is present, check Yellow wire (terminal "A").

6) With headlight switch on, check for voltage between ground and terminal "C". If voltage is present, go to next step. If no voltage is present, check Yellow wire (terminal "C").

7) Turn off headlight switch. Check for voltage between ground and terminal "C". If no voltage is present, replace HDM. If voltage is present, repair short to battery in Yellow wire (terminal "A").

Sunbird – 1) Disconnect HDM 5-pin connector. Turn off headlight switch. Throughout this test, use a test light to check for voltage at specified wire terminals of HDM 5-pin connector (harness side). *See Fig. 1.*

2) Check for voltage between ground and terminal "B". If voltage is present, go to next step. If no voltage is present, check fusible link "J" and Red wire.

3) Check for voltage between ground and terminal "E". If voltage is present, go to next step. If no voltage is present, check fusible link "K" and Red wire.

4) Check for voltage between ground and terminal "C". If voltage is present, go to next step. If no voltage is present, check headlight switch and White wire.

5) Check for voltage between terminals "C" and "D". If voltage is present, go to next step. If no voltage is present, check Black wire.

6) Turn on headlight switch. Check for voltage between ground and terminal "A". If no voltage is present, check Yellow wire and headlight switch. If voltage is present, replace HDM.

ONE HEADLIGHT DOOR INOPERATIVE

Corvette (Left) – 1) Disconnect HDM 5-pin connector. Using a test light, check for voltage between HDM 5-pin terminals "D" and "E". *See Fig. 1.* If voltage is present, go to next step. If no voltage is present, repair open or short to ground in Red wire circuit.

2) Reconnect HDM 5-pin connector. Disconnect 2-pin connector between HDM 4-pin connector and left headlight door motor. Turn headlight switch off. Check voltage between ground and Gray/Black wire terminal of 2-pin connector (HDM side of connector).

3) If battery voltage is present, check for short to battery in Gray/Black wire. If no short to battery is present, replace HDM. If no voltage is present, turn on headlight switch.

4) If no voltage is present, check continuity of Gray/Black wire circuit. If there is continuity, replace HDM. If voltage is present, turn on headlight switch. Check voltage between ground and Dark Green/Black wire terminal of 2-pin connector (HDM side of connector).

5) If voltage is present, check for short to battery in Dark Green/Black wire. If no short to battery is present, replace HDM. If no voltage is present, turn off headlight switch.

6) If voltage is present, replace left headlight door motor. If no voltage is present, check continuity of Dark Green/Black wire circuit. If there is continuity, replace HDM.

Corvette (Right) – 1) Disconnect HDM 5-pin connector. Using a test light, check for voltage between HDM 5-pin terminals "D" and "B". *See Fig. 1.* If voltage is present, go to next step. If no voltage is present, repair open or short to ground in Red wire circuit.

2) Reconnect HDM 5-pin connector. Disconnect 2-pin connector between HDM 4-pin connector and right headlight door motor. Turn headlight switch off. Check voltage between ground and Gray wire terminal of 2-pin connector (HDM side of connector).

3) If battery voltage is present, check for short to battery in Gray wire. If no short to battery is present, replace HDM. If no voltage is present, turn on headlight switch.

4) If no voltage is present, check continuity of Gray wire circuit. If there is continuity, replace HDM. If voltage is present, check voltage between ground and Dark Green wire terminal of 2-pin connector (HDM side of connector).

5) If voltage is present, check for short to battery in Dark Green wire. If no short to battery is present, replace HDM. If no voltage is present, turn off headlight switch.

6) If voltage is present, replace right headlight door motor. If no voltage is present, check continuity of Dark Green wire circuit. If there is continuity, replace HDM.

Firebird – 1) Disconnect HDM 4-pin connector. If headlight doors are stuck in open position, manually close headlight doors.

2) To test right headlight door, connect a 15-amp fused jumper between battery positive source and terminal "B" of HDM 4-pin connector (harness side). Ground terminal "A". *See Fig. 1.*

3) If headlight door operates, go to next step. If headlight door does not operate, check wiring harness to headlight door. If harness is okay, replace headlight door motor.

4) To test left headlight door, connect a 15-amp fused jumper between battery positive source and terminal "C" of HDM 4-pin connector (harness side). Ground terminal "D".

5) If headlight door operates, go to BOTH HEADLIGHT DOORS INOPERATIVE under TESTING. If headlight door does not operate, check wiring harness to headlight door. If harness is okay, replace headlight door motor.

Reatta – 1) Disconnect HDM 4-pin connector. If headlight doors are stuck in open position, manually close headlight doors.

2) To test left headlight door motor, connect a 15-amp fused jumper between battery positive source and terminal "C" of HDM 4-pin connector (harness side). Ground terminal "D". *See Fig. 1.*

3) If headlight door opens, check for poor terminal connections at HDM. If terminal connections are okay, replace HDM. If headlight door does not open, check wiring harness to headlight door. If harness is okay, replace headlight door motor.

4) To test right headlight door motor, connect a 15-amp fused jumper between battery positive source and terminal "B" of HDM 4-pin connector (harness side). Ground terminal "A". *See Fig. 1.*

5) If headlight door opens, check for poor terminal connections at HDM. If terminal connections are okay, replace HDM. If headlight door does not open, check wiring harness to headlight door. If harness is okay, replace headlight door motor.

Sunbird (Left) – 1) Disconnect HDM 4-pin connector (all terminals referred to throughout this test procedure are at this connector). Connect a 15-amp fused jumper between terminal "D" (harness side) and terminal "A" (component side). *See Fig. 1.*

2) Connect a 15-amp fused jumper between terminal "C" (harness side) and terminal "B" (component side). Turn on headlight switch.

3) If headlight door operates, replace HDM. If headlight door does not operate, check Dark Green/White and Gray/Black wires. If wires are okay, replace headlight door motor.

Sunbird (Right) – 1) Disconnect HDM 4-pin connector. Connect a 15-amp fused jumper between terminal "A" (harness side) and terminal "D" (component side) of HDM 4-pin connector. *See Fig. 1.*

2) Connect a 15-amp fused jumper between terminal "B" (harness side) and terminal "C" (component side) of HDM 4-pin connector. Turn on headlight switch.

3) If headlight door operates, replace HDM. If headlight door does not operate, check Dark Green and Gray wires. If wires are okay, replace headlight door motor.

REMOVAL & INSTALLATION

NOTE: Headlight doors may be opened and closed manually by rotating knob on headlight door motor.

HEADLIGHT ASSEMBLY

Removal & Installation (Corvette) – 1) Open hood. Turn on headlights to open headlight doors. Disconnect headlight motor connector at outer side of headlamp. Turn off headlights.

2) Disconnect negative battery cable. Disconnect headlight assembly electrical connectors and release wiring harness from retainers. Remove 2 screws from front of assembly.

3) Remove assembly bracket from hood hinge fasteners. Remove 4 assembly-to-hood nuts and hood hinge bracket. Remove assembly. Remove 4 headlight bezel screws and remove bezel. Remove 4 closure/door screws and remove closure/door.

4) Release actuator motor harness from retaining clips. Remove actuator motor screws and remove actuator motor from assembly. To install, reverse removal procedure.

Removal & Installation (Firebird) – 1) Manually raise headlight by turning knob on top of door motor counterclockwise. Remove 4 screws and detach bezel. Remove retaining spring. Remove 4 screws from headlight retainer and detach retainer.

2) Remove headlight bulb from assembly. Disconnect electrical connector. Turn manual knob until headlight assembly is lowered halfway. Remove 2 lower headlight bolts and 2 upper headlight bolts. Disconnect electrical connector from headlight door motor. Remove headlight assembly.

3) Remove nut from headlight door motor arm. Remove 3 bolts attaching headlight door motor to assembly and detach headlight door motor. To install, reverse removal procedure.

Removal & Installation (Reatta) – 1) Disconnect negative battery cable. Remove 3 screws and 4 plastic retaining clips from radiator cover. Remove radiator cover.

2) Manually open headlight doors by turning knob on top of door motor counterclockwise. Remove 4 screws and headlight bezel. Remove 4 headlight assembly-to-body screws. Disconnect electrical harness. Remove headlight. To install, reverse removal procedure.

Removal & Installation (Sunbird) – 1) Disconnect negative battery cable. Remove radiator support filler. Manually open headlight doors by turning knob on top of door motor counterclockwise.

2) Remove headlight lower trim panel. Apply masking tape to horizontal surface of front fascia to prevent paint damage. Remove headlight/door actuator assembly screws.

3) Push down on fascia, pull headlight/door actuator assembly forward and disconnect 2 electrical connectors from assembly. Remove assembly. Remove shaft-to-actuator nut. Remove 3 mounting bolts and remove actuator from assembly. To install, reverse removal procedure.

WIRING DIAGRAMS

See appropriate chassis wiring diagram in WIRING DIAGRAMS.

DESCRIPTION

The Toronado concealed headlights are raised and lowered by a reversible electric motor. The headlight system consists of a fuse block, fusible links, headlight switch, headlight door motor, headlight door relays, headlight door module and twilight sentinel relays (if equipped).

OPERATION

OPENING SEQUENCE

When headlight switch is in HEAD position, or twilight sentinel is activated, battery voltage is applied to headlight door module. The headlight door module then applies voltage to headlight door motor to open headlight doors. The motor is controlled by module switching ground path. When headlight doors are fully open, module turns off motor.

CLOSING SEQUENCE

When headlight switch is in OFF position, or twilight sentinel is deactivated, battery voltage is removed from headlight door module. The module allows headlight doors to close when it senses a ground through low beam headlight filaments. Module de-energizes its relay, and battery voltage is applied to headlight door motor to close doors. Motor is controlled by module switching ground path. When headlight doors are fully closed, module turns off motor.

MANUALLY OPERATING HEADLIGHT DOORS

NOTE: The headlight doors cannot be manually opened if headlight motor is electrically active. Before using manual headlight opener, remove fuse No. 2 from engine compartment relay center.

To manually open headlight doors, remove fuse No. 2. Remove protective cover from manual control knob. Rotate control knob clockwise until headlight doors open. To manually close headlight doors, rotate control knob counterclockwise until headlight doors close. Install protective cover on manual control knob. Install fuse No. 2 in engine compartment relay center.

TROUBLE SHOOTING

Check fusible link "K" (at right front of engine compartment, at power junction block) and headlight doors fuse No. 2 (in under-hood relay center). Check for mechanical binding by manually operating headlight doors. Open hood. Turn on headlights, and check headlights operation. Repair any problems before continuing.

TESTING

NOTE: Measuring voltage at motor outputs of headlight door module is NOT a valid diagnostic procedure. Module rapidly pulses door motor on and off, thus voltage cannot be measured.

SYSTEM CHECK

Without Twilight Sentinel – Move headlight switch to HEAD position; headlight doors should open. Move headlight switch to PARK position; headlight doors should remain open. Move light switch to OFF position; headlight doors should close.

With Twilight Sentinel – 1) Turn ignition switch to RUN position. With light switch in OFF position and twilight sentinel control in ON position, cover twilight sentinel photocell. The headlights should come on, and headlight doors should open. With light switch and twilight sentinel control in OFF position, headlight doors should close.

2) With light switch in PARK position and twilight sentinel control in ON position, cover twilight sentinel photocell. The Body Computer Module (BCM) will open headlight doors. When photocell is uncovered, headlight doors will not close until light switch is in OFF position.

HEADLIGHT DOOR MODULE TEST

1) Disconnect headlight door module connector (module is in left front corner of engine compartment, behind headlights). If headlight doors are stuck open, manually close headlight doors. Use fused jumper wires to connect battery voltage to terminal "D" (Dark Green/White wire). Connect terminal "C" (Light Green/Black wire) to ground.

2) If headlight doors do not open, check wiring to headlight door motor. If wiring to headlight door motor is okay, replace motor. If headlight doors open, connect test light to Orange wire of headlight door module harness connector and ground. Test light should come on. If test light does not come on, check headlight door fuse No. 2, fusible link "K" (at right front of engine compartment, at power junction block), and Red and Orange wires for open or short to ground.

3) Connect test light between Orange and Black wires of module harness connector. Test light should light. If test light does not light, check Black wire for open and repair as necessary.

4) Turn headlight switch to ON position. Connect test light between one Tan wire and ground, then connect other Tan wire and ground. Test light should light in both cases. If test light does not light, check Tan wire(s) for open and repair as necessary.

5) Turn headlight switch to OFF position. Connect test light between Tan wire(s) and ground. Test light should not light. If test light lights, check Tan wire(s) for short to battery voltage and repair as necessary.

ADJUSTMENTS

HEADLIGHT DOOR STOP

Adjustment screw is located on inboard edge of headlight assembly, behind headlight door. Turn screw to increase or decrease door travel, and align horizontal bars of grille to bars of headlight door.

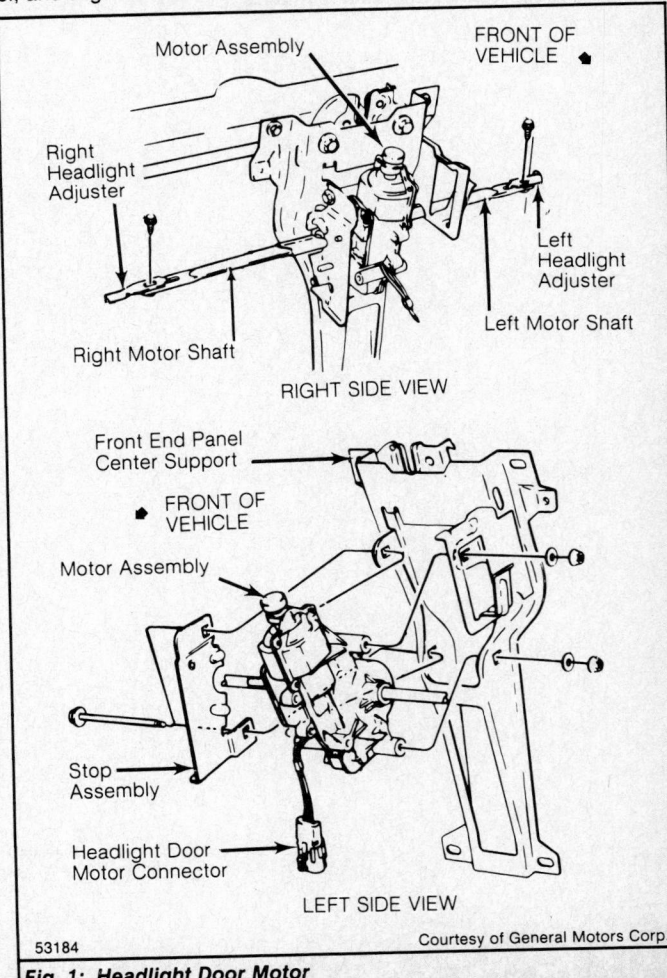

53184   Courtesy of General Motors Corp.

Fig. 1: Headlight Door Motor

REMOVAL & INSTALLATION

HEADLIGHT MOTOR

Removal – 1) Remove all retaining pins and radiator grille filler. Remove headlight door-to-motor assembly screws. Remove 2 retaining nuts and remove motor assembly from grille brace. *See Fig. 1.*
2) Remove electrical connector from motor assembly. Remove retaining bolt and remove motor assembly from radiator center support.

Installation – 1) Install motor assembly to radiator center support with retaining bolt. Install motor assembly to grille brace with 2 retaining nuts. Put both headlight doors in closed position and adjust motor assembly until linkage flats line up.
2) Install both headlight door linkages to motor assemblies. Connect electrical connector to motor. Install radiator grille opening filler.

WIRING DIAGRAMS

See appropriate chassis wiring diagram in WIRING DIAGRAMS.

**Century, LeSabre, Park Avenue
Regal, Roadmaster, Skylark**

DESCRIPTION & OPERATION

The instrument cluster uses an electric analog speedometer with stepper motor-driven season odometer and trip odometer, analog fuel gauge and indicator lights. The cluster is back lit for nighttime illumination.

BRAKE SYSTEM WARNING INDICATOR

The brake system warning indicator comes on when brake hydraulic pressure is lost. With ignition turned slowly past RUN position, brake indicator should come on before ignition reaches START position. With ignition in RUN position and parking brake engaged, brake indicator should come on.

BRIGHT HEADLIGHT INDICATOR

The BRIGHT headlight indicator illuminates when headlights are on and high beams are selected.

COOLANT TEMPERATURE INDICATOR

The TEMP indicator comes on when engine coolant temperature exceeds approximately 258°F (126°C). The indicator turned off when engine coolant temperature drops below 241°F (116°C). The TEMP

indicator comes on, as a bulb test, when ignition is in RUN or START position.

CRUISE INDICATOR

The CRUISE indicator comes on when cruise control system is turned on and system is active (controlling vehicle speed).

FASTEN SAFETY BELTS INDICATOR

The FASTEN SAFETY BELTS indicator comes on when ignition is in RUN position, with either front door open and/or front safety belts not fastened. The chime module will sound when ignition is turned to the RUN position, with the driver's safety belt not fastened. The chiming will stop after 6 seconds, or as soon as the driver's safety belt is fastened, whichever occurs first. The FASTEN SAFETY BELTS indicator will go out within 60-90 seconds, or as soon as the driver's safety belt is fastened, whichever occurs first.

LOW COOLANT INDICATOR

On vehicles with a low coolant switch in the coolant surge tank, the LOW COOLANT indicator comes on if coolant level in surge tank is low. Light will remain on until ignition switch is turned off, or coolant level in surge tank is restored to normal level.

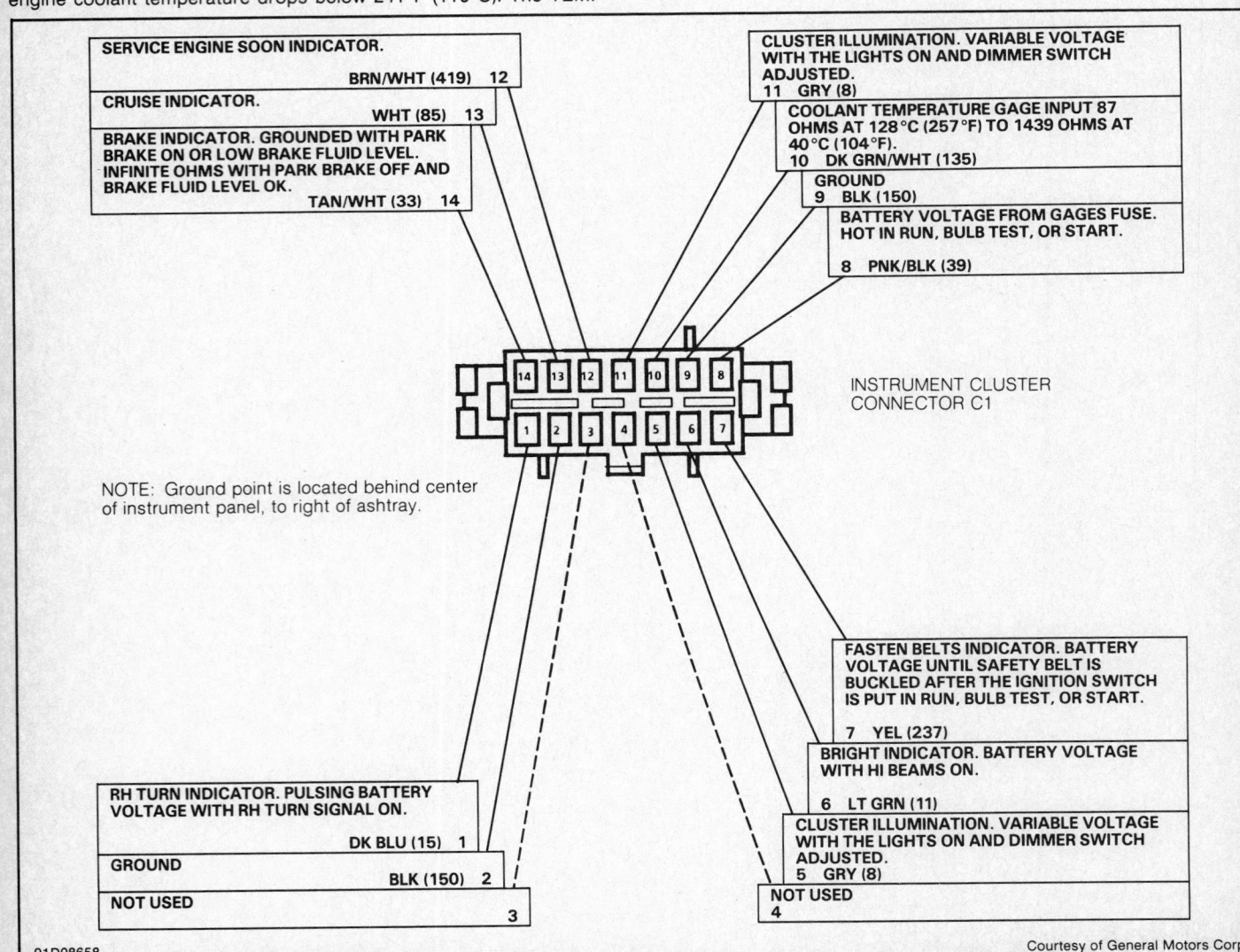

SERVICE ENGINE SOON INDICATOR.
BRN/WHT (419)   12

CRUISE INDICATOR.
WHT (85)   13

BRAKE INDICATOR. GROUNDED WITH PARK BRAKE ON OR LOW BRAKE FLUID LEVEL. INFINITE OHMS WITH PARK BRAKE OFF AND BRAKE FLUID LEVEL OK.
TAN/WHT (33)   14

CLUSTER ILLUMINATION. VARIABLE VOLTAGE WITH THE LIGHTS ON AND DIMMER SWITCH ADJUSTED.
11   GRY (8)

COOLANT TEMPERATURE GAGE INPUT 87 OHMS AT 128°C (257°F) TO 1439 OHMS AT 40°C (104°F).
10   DK GRN/WHT (135)

GROUND
9   BLK (150)

BATTERY VOLTAGE FROM GAGES FUSE. HOT IN RUN, BULB TEST, OR START.
8   PNK/BLK (39)

INSTRUMENT CLUSTER
CONNECTOR C1

NOTE: Ground point is located behind center of instrument panel, to right of ashtray.

FASTEN BELTS INDICATOR. BATTERY VOLTAGE UNTIL SAFETY BELT IS BUCKLED AFTER THE IGNITION SWITCH IS PUT IN RUN, BULB TEST, OR START.
7   YEL (237)

BRIGHT INDICATOR. BATTERY VOLTAGE WITH HI BEAMS ON.
6   LT GRN (11)

CLUSTER ILLUMINATION. VARIABLE VOLTAGE WITH THE LIGHTS ON AND DIMMER SWITCH ADJUSTED.
5   GRY (8)

NOT USED
4

RH TURN INDICATOR. PULSING BATTERY VOLTAGE WITH RH TURN SIGNAL ON.
DK BLU (15)   1

GROUND
BLK (150)   2

NOT USED
3

91D08658

Courtesy of General Motors Corp.

Fig. 1: Testing Instrument Cluster C1 Connector Pins (Century)

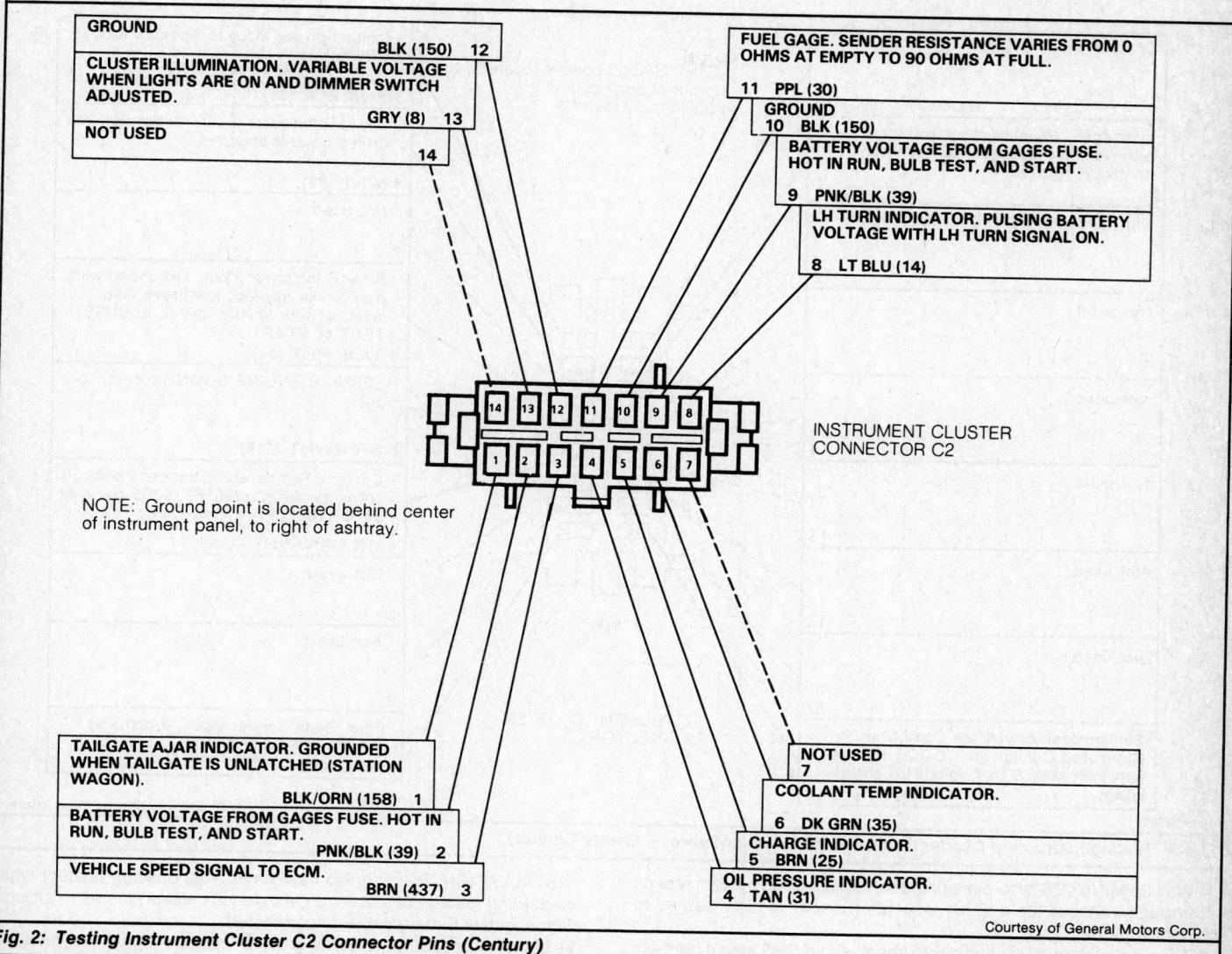

GROUND
BLK (150) 12

CLUSTER ILLUMINATION. VARIABLE VOLTAGE WHEN LIGHTS ARE ON AND DIMMER SWITCH ADJUSTED.
GRY (8) 13

NOT USED
14

FUEL GAGE. SENDER RESISTANCE VARIES FROM 0 OHMS AT EMPTY TO 90 OHMS AT FULL.
11 PPL (30)

GROUND
10 BLK (150)

BATTERY VOLTAGE FROM GAGES FUSE. HOT IN RUN, BULB TEST, AND START.
9 PNK/BLK (39)

LH TURN INDICATOR. PULSING BATTERY VOLTAGE WITH LH TURN SIGNAL ON.
8 LT BLU (14)

INSTRUMENT CLUSTER CONNECTOR C2

NOTE: Ground point is located behind center of instrument panel, to right of ashtray.

TAILGATE AJAR INDICATOR. GROUNDED WHEN TAILGATE IS UNLATCHED (STATION WAGON).
BLK/ORN (158) 1

BATTERY VOLTAGE FROM GAGES FUSE. HOT IN RUN, BULB TEST, AND START.
PNK/BLK (39) 2

VEHICLE SPEED SIGNAL TO ECM.
BRN (437) 3

NOT USED
7

COOLANT TEMP INDICATOR.
6 DK GRN (35)

CHARGE INDICATOR.
5 BRN (25)

OIL PRESSURE INDICATOR.
4 TAN (31)

Courtesy of General Motors Corp.

Fig. 2: Testing Instrument Cluster C2 Connector Pins (Century)

FUEL GAUGE

Circuit consists of an electrically operated indicator in instrument cluster and a fuel tank pick-up/sending unit. Gauge indicates quantity of fuel in tank when ignition is in RUN position. When ignition is in the OFF, START, LOCK or ACC position, pointer may come to rest at any position. A sending unit in the fuel tank changes resistance with fuel level. Resistance range of sending unit is approximately zero ohm (when tank is empty) to 90 ohms (when tank is full).

OIL PRESSURE INDICATOR

Warning light is controlled by a pressure-operated switch located on engine block. When ignition switch is turned to the RUN or START position, indicator should come on as a bulb test. After engine is started, indicator should go out when correct oil pressure is reached.

SERVICE ENGINE SOON LIGHT

The SERVICE ENGINE SOON light is mounted in the instrument cluster. The light comes on during engine starting and remains on a short time after engine is started. If light comes on while driving, the Engine Control Module (ECM) system may require service. The light is controlled by ECM.

VOLTS INDICATOR

The VOLTS indicator comes on when ignition is in the RUN position and engine is not running. The VOLTS indicator also comes on when engine is running, and an under- or overvoltage condition exists.

SHIFT INDICATOR

Some M/T models use a light to indicate when vehicle should be shifted into next higher gear. Battery voltage is applied to one side of bulb, and the opposite ground side is controlled by ECM.

TAILGATE AJAR INDICATOR

Some models are equipped with a light on dash that comes on when tailgate is ajar. Switch at tailgate supplies a ground to circuit when tailgate is ajar.

AIR BAG PRECAUTIONS

Observe the following precautions when working on vehicles equipped with Supplemental Inflatable Restraint (SIR) air bag systems.

- Before performing any instrument panel testing, diagnosis or repair, disable SRS system by disconnecting negative battery cable and Yellow 2-pin connector at base of steering column.

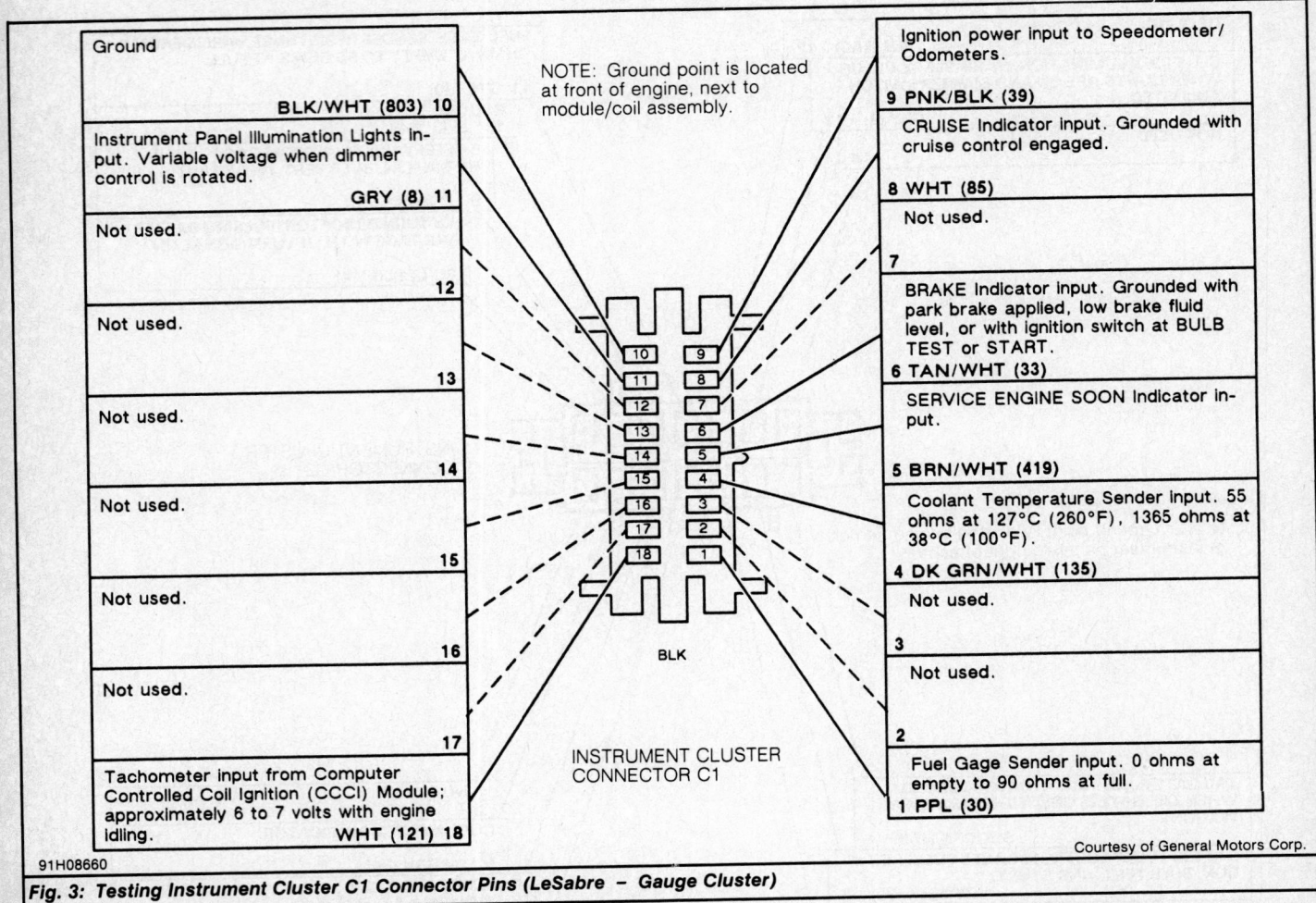

Fig. 3: Testing Instrument Cluster C1 Connector Pins (LeSabre — Gauge Cluster)

- Wait 20 MINUTES before making SRS repairs. SRS system retains enough voltage, for a short time after disconnecting power, to deploy air bag.
- To avoid accidental air bag deployment, avoid SRS wiring harness when trouble shooting instrument panel components. All SRS wires are color-coded Yellow.

TESTING

INSTRUMENT CLUSTER CONNECTOR PIN TEST
Century, LeSabre, Park Avenue, Regal & Skylark – 1) Remove instrument cluster. See INSTRUMENT CLUSTER under REMOVAL & INSTALLATION. Place ignition switch in RUN position (except when measuring resistance). Make all resistance measurements to ground, with negative battery cable disconnected.

2) Make all measurements to ground unless a specific terminal is given. See appropriate test under TESTING. If voltage or resistance readings at terminals being tested are correct, and the particular component using those terminals does not operate, check wires, bulbs and printed circuit. *See appropriate Figs. 1-11* for voltage and resistance specifications. If wires bulbs and printed circuit are okay, replace instrument cluster. If correct voltage or resistance is NOT found at a terminal, check circuit for malfunction.

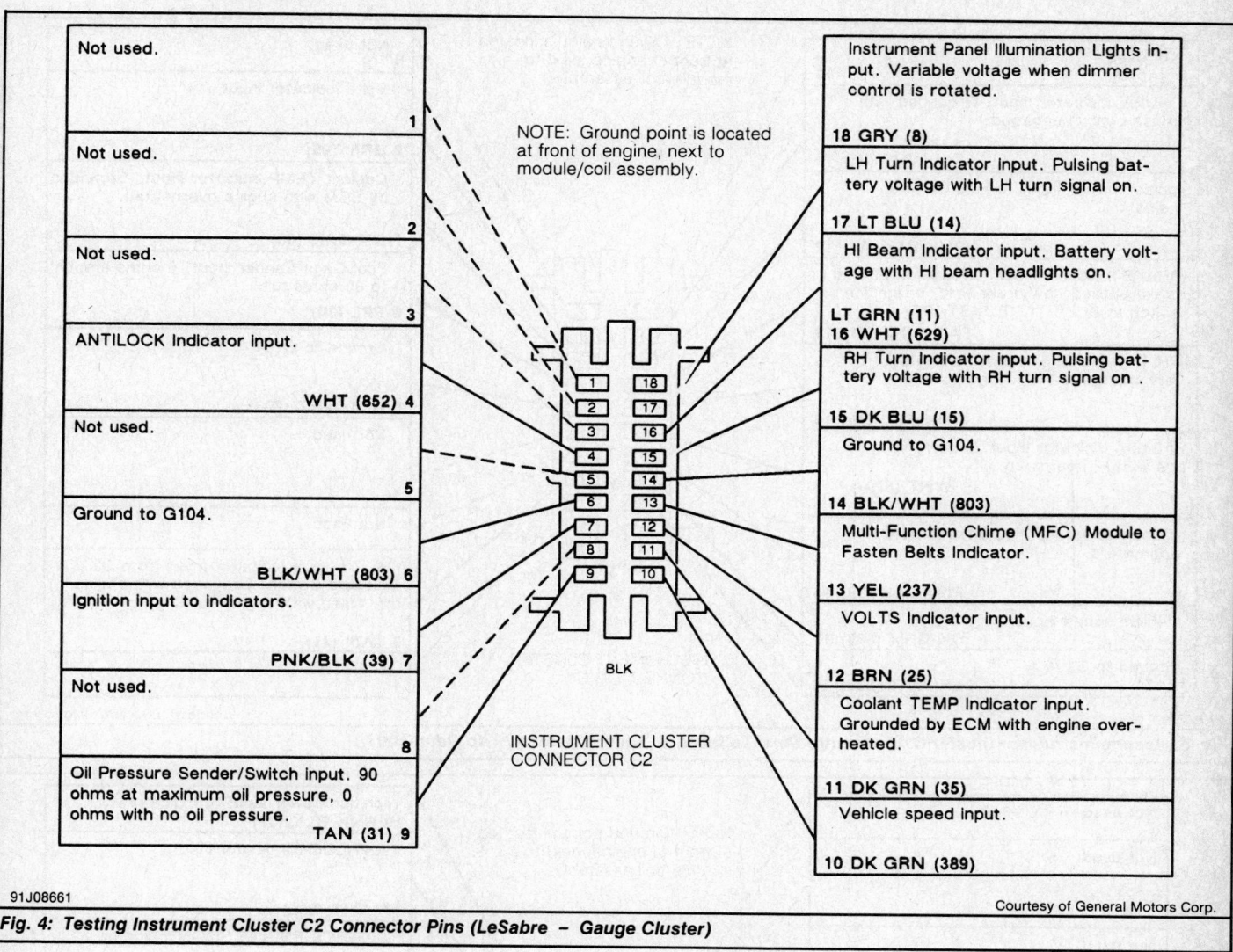

Not used.

1

Not used.

2

Not used.

3

ANTILOCK Indicator input.

WHT (852) 4

Not used.

5

Ground to G104.

BLK/WHT (803) 6

Ignition input to indicators.

PNK/BLK (39) 7

Not used.

8

Oil Pressure Sender/Switch input. 90 ohms at maximum oil pressure, 0 ohms with no oil pressure.

TAN (31) 9

NOTE: Ground point is located at front of engine, next to module/coil assembly.

BLK

INSTRUMENT CLUSTER CONNECTOR C2

Instrument Panel Illumination Lights input. Variable voltage when dimmer control is rotated.

18 GRY (8)

LH Turn Indicator Input. Pulsing battery voltage with LH turn signal on.

17 LT BLU (14)

HI Beam Indicator input. Battery voltage with HI beam headlights on.

LT GRN (11)
16 WHT (629)

RH Turn Indicator input. Pulsing battery voltage with RH turn signal on .

15 DK BLU (15)

Ground to G104.

14 BLK/WHT (803)

Multi-Function Chime (MFC) Module to Fasten Belts Indicator.

13 YEL (237)

VOLTS Indicator input.

12 BRN (25)

Coolant TEMP Indicator input. Grounded by ECM with engine over-heated.

11 DK GRN (35)

Vehicle speed input.

10 DK GRN (389)

91J08661

Courtesy of General Motors Corp.

Fig. 4: Testing Instrument Cluster C2 Connector Pins (LeSabre – Gauge Cluster)

1991 SAFETY EQUIPMENT
Analog Instrument Panels – Buick (Cont.)

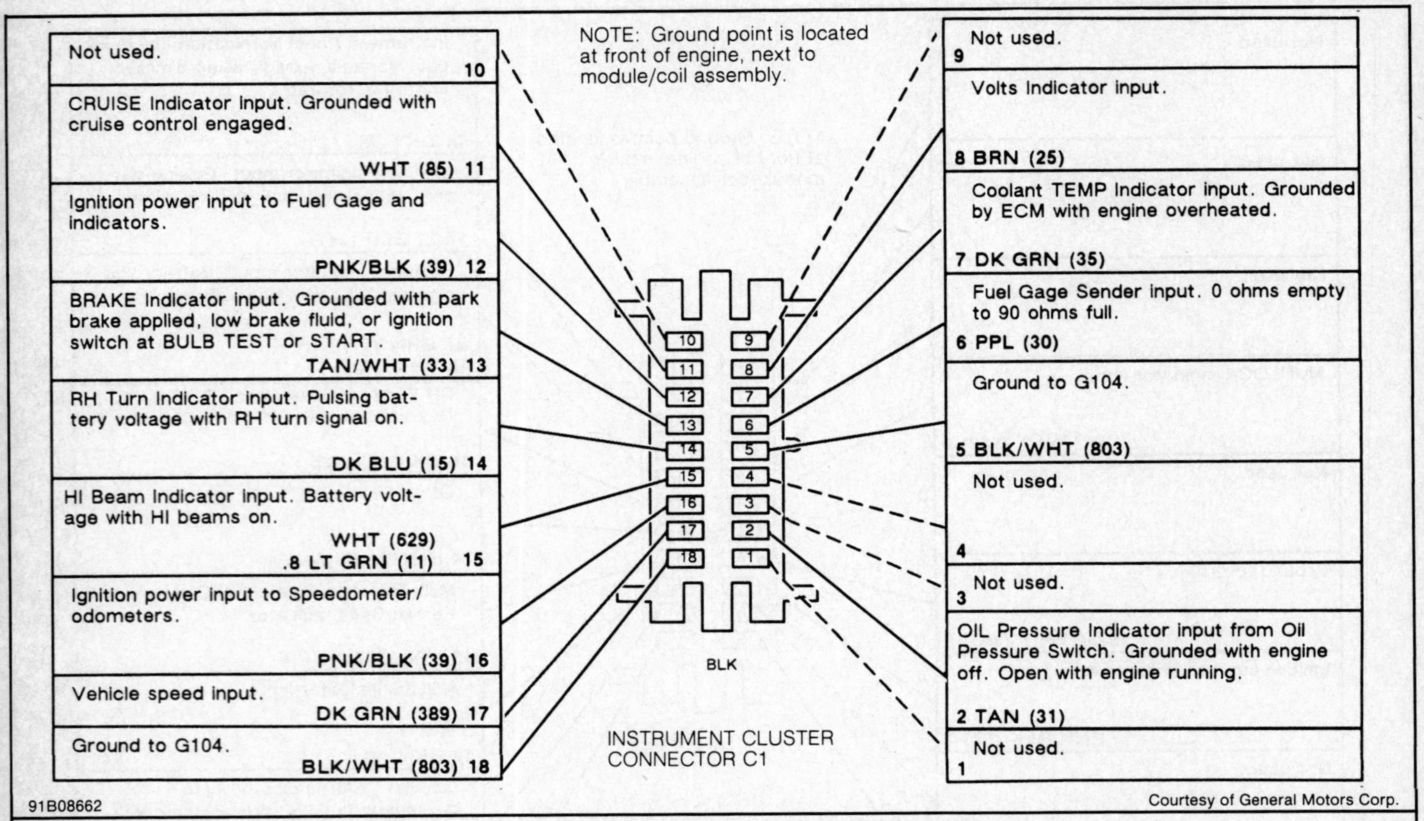
Not used. 10
CRUISE Indicator input. Grounded with cruise control engaged.
WHT (85) 11
Ignition power input to Fuel Gage and indicators.
PNK/BLK (39) 12
BRAKE Indicator input. Grounded with park brake applied, low brake fluid, or ignition switch at BULB TEST or START.
TAN/WHT (33) 13
RH Turn Indicator input. Pulsing battery voltage with RH turn signal on.
DK BLU (15) 14
HI Beam Indicator input. Battery voltage with HI beams on.
WHT (629)
.8 LT GRN (11) 15
Ignition power input to Speedometer/odometers.
PNK/BLK (39) 16
Vehicle speed input.
DK GRN (389) 17
Ground to G104.
BLK/WHT (803) 18
NOTE: Ground point is located at front of engine, next to module/coil assembly.
10 11 12 13 14 15 16 17 18
9 8 7 6 5 4 3 2 1
BLK
INSTRUMENT CLUSTER CONNECTOR C1
Not used.
9
Volts Indicator input.
8 BRN (25)
Coolant TEMP Indicator input. Grounded by ECM with engine overheated.
7 DK GRN (35)
Fuel Gage Sender input. 0 ohms empty to 90 ohms full.
6 PPL (30)
Ground to G104.
5 BLK/WHT (803)
Not used.
4
Not used.
3
OIL Pressure Indicator input from Oil Pressure Switch. Grounded with engine off. Open with engine running.
2 TAN (31)
Not used.
1
91B08662
Courtesy of General Motors Corp.

Fig. 5: Testing Instrument Cluster C1 Connector Pins (LeSabre – Speedometer w/ Trip Odometer)

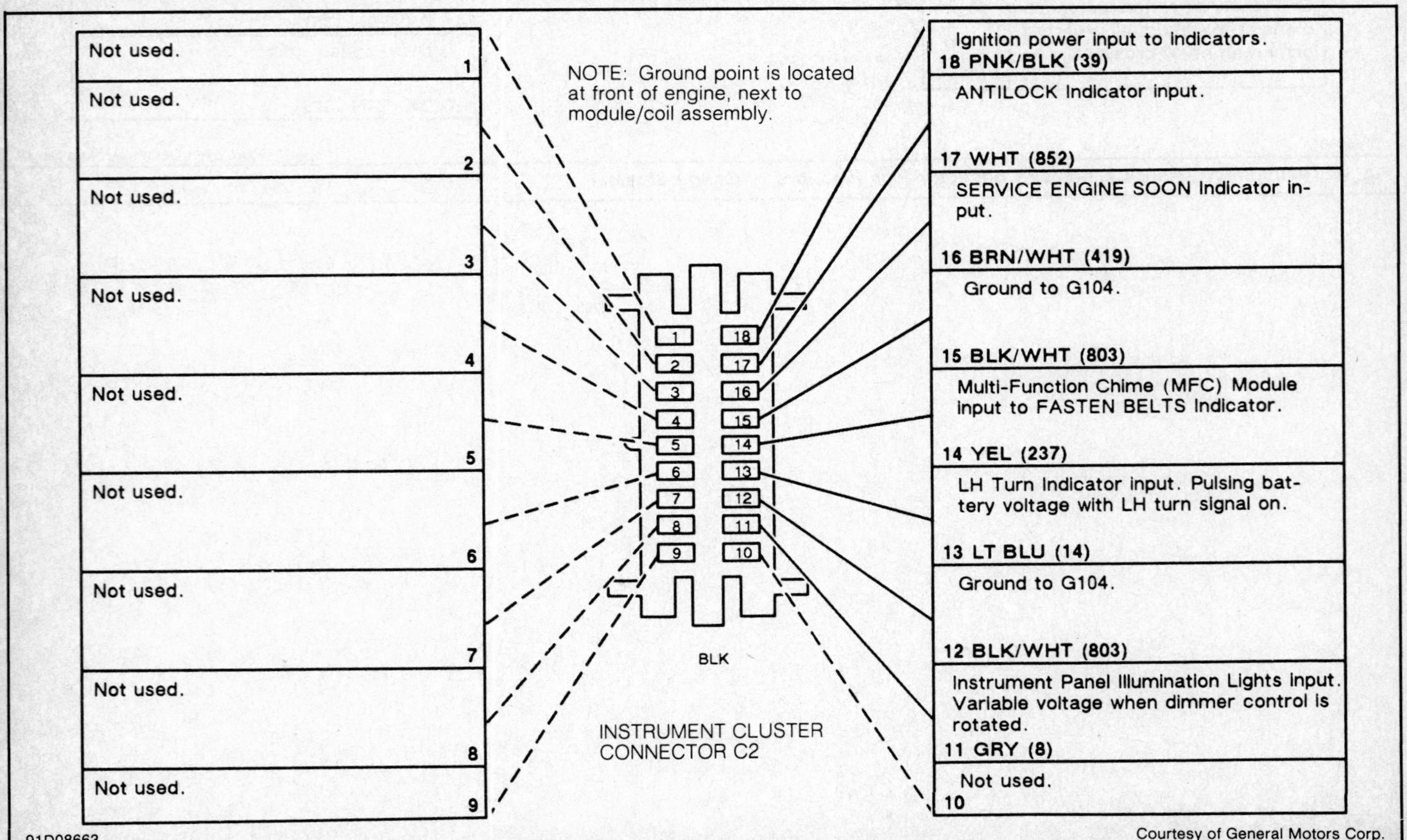
Not used. 1
Not used. 2
Not used. 3
Not used. 4
Not used. 5
Not used. 6
Not used. 7
Not used. 8
Not used. 9
NOTE: Ground point is located at front of engine, next to module/coil assembly.
1 2 3 4 5 6 7 8 9
18 17 16 15 14 13 12 11 10
BLK
INSTRUMENT CLUSTER CONNECTOR C2
Ignition power input to indicators.
18 PNK/BLK (39)
ANTILOCK Indicator input.
17 WHT (852)
SERVICE ENGINE SOON Indicator input.
16 BRN/WHT (419)
Ground to G104.
15 BLK/WHT (803)
Multi-Function Chime (MFC) Module input to FASTEN BELTS Indicator.
14 YEL (237)
LH Turn Indicator input. Pulsing battery voltage with LH turn signal on.
13 LT BLU (14)
Ground to G104.
12 BLK/WHT (803)
Instrument Panel Illumination Lights input. Variable voltage when dimmer control is rotated.
11 GRY (8)
Not used.
10
91D08663
Courtesy of General Motors Corp.

Fig. 6: Testing Instrument Cluster C2 Connector Pins (LeSabre – Speedometer w/ Trip Odometer)

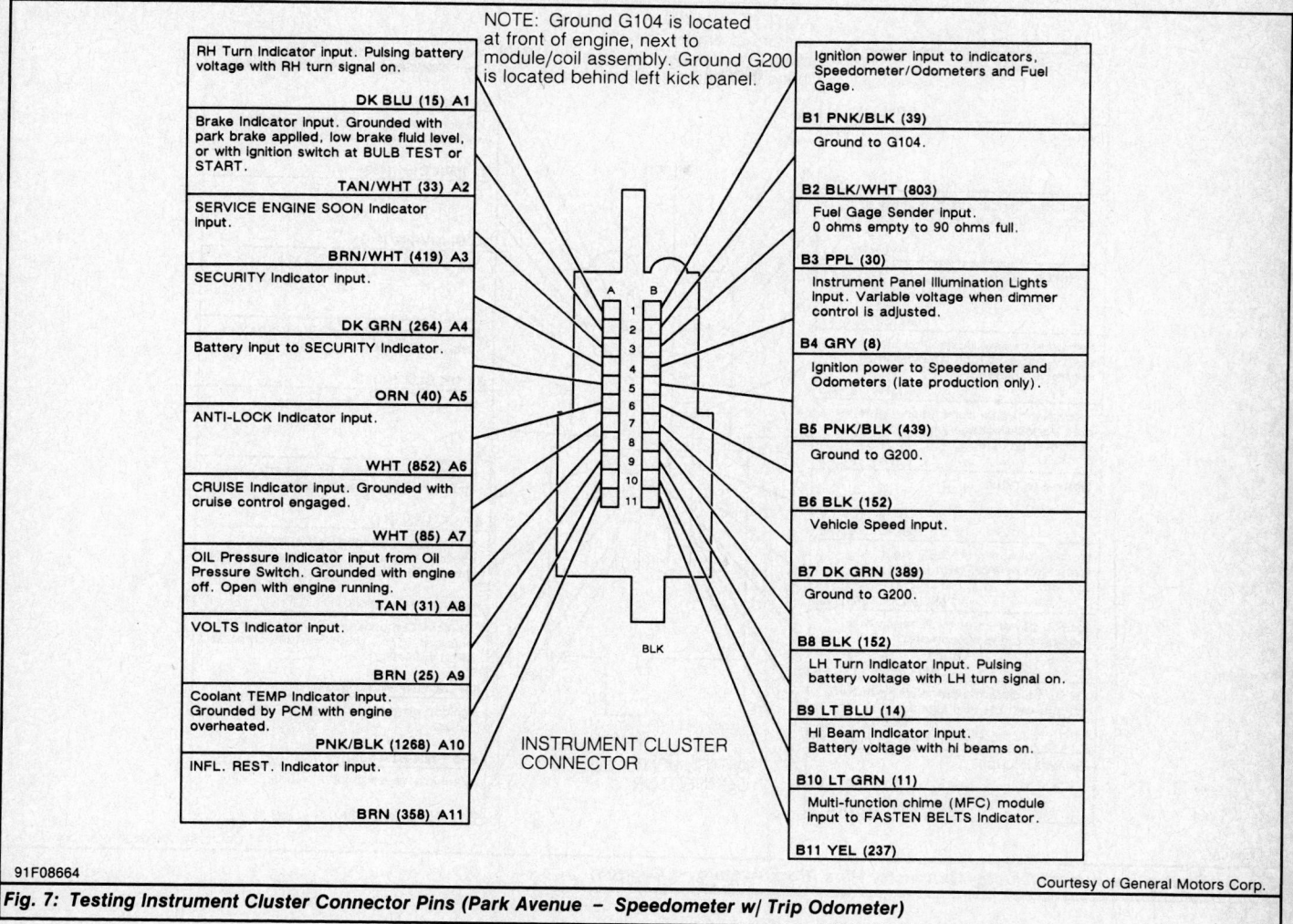

NOTE: Ground G104 is located at front of engine, next to module/coil assembly. Ground G200 is located behind left kick panel.

RH Turn Indicator input. Pulsing battery voltage with RH turn signal on.
DK BLU (15) A1

Brake Indicator input. Grounded with park brake applied, low brake fluid level, or with ignition switch at BULB TEST or START.
TAN/WHT (33) A2

SERVICE ENGINE SOON Indicator input.
BRN/WHT (419) A3

SECURITY Indicator input.
DK GRN (264) A4

Battery input to SECURITY Indicator.
ORN (40) A5

ANTI-LOCK Indicator input.
WHT (852) A6

CRUISE Indicator input. Grounded with cruise control engaged.
WHT (85) A7

OIL Pressure Indicator input from Oil Pressure Switch. Grounded with engine off. Open with engine running.
TAN (31) A8

VOLTS Indicator input.
BRN (25) A9

Coolant TEMP Indicator input. Grounded by PCM with engine overheated.
PNK/BLK (1268) A10

INFL. REST. Indicator input.
BRN (358) A11

Ignition power input to indicators, Speedometer/Odometers and Fuel Gage.
B1 PNK/BLK (39)

Ground to G104.
B2 BLK/WHT (803)

Fuel Gage Sender input. 0 ohms empty to 90 ohms full.
B3 PPL (30)

Instrument Panel Illumination Lights input. Variable voltage when dimmer control is adjusted.
B4 GRY (8)

Ignition power to Speedometer and Odometers (late production only).
B5 PNK/BLK (439)

Ground to G200.
B6 BLK (152)

Vehicle Speed input.
B7 DK GRN (389)

Ground to G200.
B8 BLK (152)

LH Turn Indicator input. Pulsing battery voltage with LH turn signal on.
B9 LT BLU (14)

Hi Beam Indicator input. Battery voltage with hi beams on.
B10 LT GRN (11)

Multi-function chime (MFC) module input to FASTEN BELTS Indicator.
B11 YEL (237)

A   B
1
2
3
4
5
6
7
8
9
10
11

BLK

INSTRUMENT CLUSTER CONNECTOR

91F08664

Courtesy of General Motors Corp.

Fig. 7: Testing Instrument Cluster Connector Pins (Park Avenue – Speedometer w/ Trip Odometer)

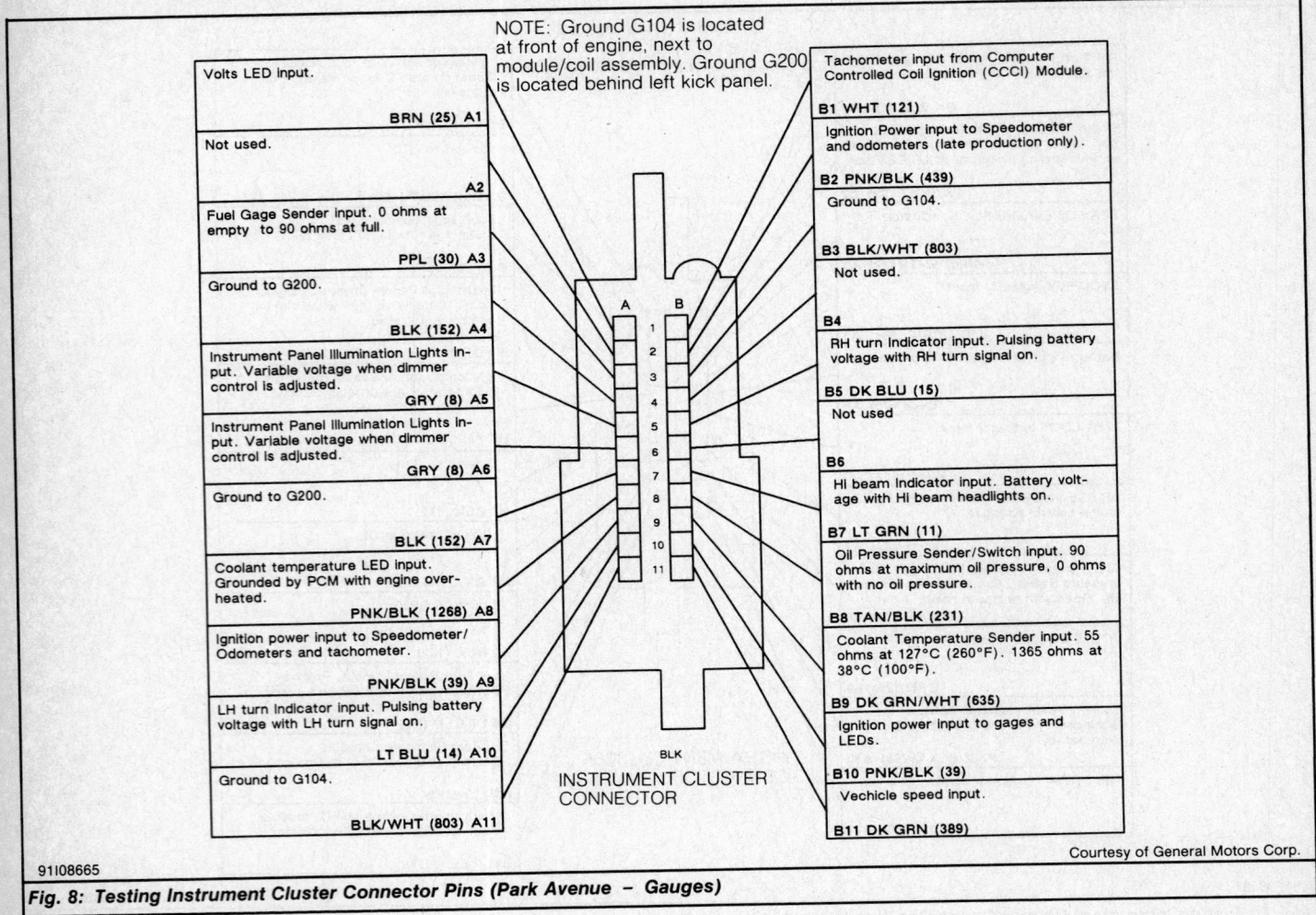

NOTE: Ground G104 is located at front of engine, next to module/coil assembly. Ground G200 is located behind left kick panel.

Volts LED input.

BRN (25) A1

Not used.

A2

Fuel Gage Sender input. 0 ohms at empty to 90 ohms at full.

PPL (30) A3

Ground to G200.

BLK (152) A4

Instrument Panel Illumination Lights input. Variable voltage when dimmer control is adjusted.

GRY (8) A5

Instrument Panel Illumination Lights input. Variable voltage when dimmer control is adjusted.

GRY (8) A6

Ground to G200.

BLK (152) A7

Coolant temperature LED input. Grounded by PCM with engine overheated.

PNK/BLK (1268) A8

Ignition power input to Speedometer/ Odometers and tachometer.

PNK/BLK (39) A9

LH turn Indicator input. Pulsing battery voltage with LH turn signal on.

LT BLU (14) A10

Ground to G104.

BLK/WHT (803) A11

A   B

1
2
3
4
5
6
7
8
9
10
11

BLK

INSTRUMENT CLUSTER CONNECTOR

Tachometer input from Computer Controlled Coil Ignition (CCCI) Module.

B1 WHT (121)

Ignition Power input to Speedometer and odometers (late production only).

B2 PNK/BLK (439)

Ground to G104.

B3 BLK/WHT (803)

Not used.

B4

RH turn Indicator input. Pulsing battery voltage with RH turn signal on.

B5 DK BLU (15)

Not used

B6

HI beam Indicator input. Battery voltage with HI beam headlights on.

B7 LT GRN (11)

Oil Pressure Sender/Switch input. 90 ohms at maximum oil pressure, 0 ohms with no oil pressure.

B8 TAN/BLK (231)

Coolant Temperature Sender input. 55 ohms at 127°C (260°F). 1365 ohms at 38°C (100°F).

B9 DK GRN/WHT (635)

Ignition power input to gages and LEDs.

B10 PNK/BLK (39)

Vechicle speed input.

B11 DK GRN (389)

Courtesy of General Motors Corp.

91I08665

Fig. 8: Testing Instrument Cluster Connector Pins (Park Avenue – Gauges)

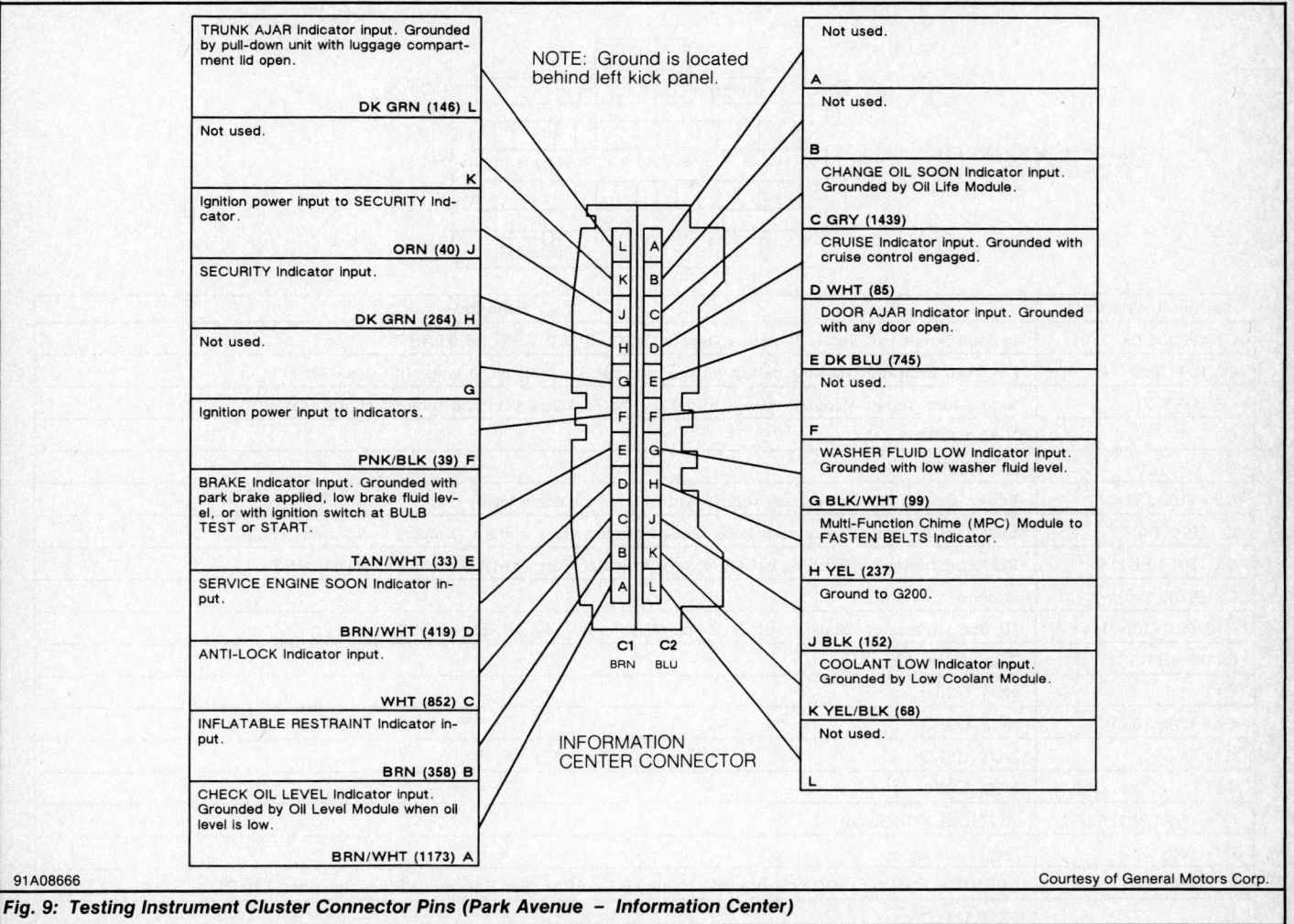

TRUNK AJAR Indicator input. Grounded by pull-down unit with luggage compartment lid open.

DK GRN (146) L

Not used.

K

Ignition power input to SECURITY Indicator.

ORN (40) J

SECURITY Indicator input.

DK GRN (264) H

Not used.

G

Ignition power input to indicators.

PNK/BLK (39) F

BRAKE Indicator Input. Grounded with park brake applied, low brake fluid level, or with ignition switch at BULB TEST or START.

TAN/WHT (33) E

SERVICE ENGINE SOON Indicator input.

BRN/WHT (419) D

ANTI-LOCK Indicator input.

WHT (852) C

INFLATABLE RESTRAINT Indicator input.

BRN (358) B

CHECK OIL LEVEL Indicator input. Grounded by Oil Level Module when oil level is low.

BRN/WHT (1173) A

NOTE: Ground is located behind left kick panel.

INFORMATION
CENTER CONNECTOR

Not used.

A

Not used.

B

CHANGE OIL SOON Indicator input. Grounded by Oil Life Module.

C GRY (1439)

CRUISE Indicator input. Grounded with cruise control engaged.

D WHT (85)

DOOR AJAR Indicator input. Grounded with any door open.

E DK BLU (745)

Not used.

F

WASHER FLUID LOW Indicator input. Grounded with low washer fluid level.

G BLK/WHT (99)

Multi-Function Chime (MPC) Module to FASTEN BELTS Indicator.

H YEL (237)

Ground to G200.

J BLK (152)

COOLANT LOW Indicator input. Grounded by Low Coolant Module.

K YEL/BLK (68)

Not used.

L

91A08666

Courtesy of General Motors Corp.

Fig. 9: Testing Instrument Cluster Connector Pins (Park Avenue – Information Center)

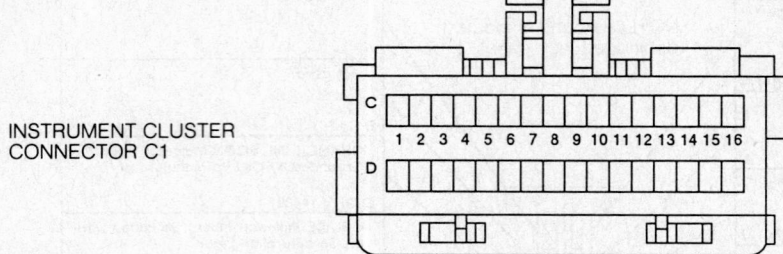

INSTRUMENT CLUSTER
CONNECTOR C1

Terminal-Wire Color	Function
C1 (PNK/BLK 750)	Ignition power to Cluster. Battery voltage in RUN, BULB TEST or START
C2 (LT BLU 14)	LH Turn Indicator, flashing battey voltage with LH Turn Signal, 0 volts with signal OFF
C3 (GRY 8)	Illumination Input. Variable voltage with Head or Park lights on and dimmer control varied
C4	NOT USED
C5	NOT USED
C6 (YEL 237)	Fasten Belts Indicator. Battery voltage with safety belt unbuckled
C7 (PPL 30)	Fuel Sensor Input. Sensor resistance varies from less than 2 ohms (Empty) to 90 ohms (Full)
C8 (DK BLU 15)	RH Turn Indicator. Flashing battery voltage with RH Turn Signal, 0 volts with signal OFF
C9 (BLK 150)	Ground
C10 (LT GRN 11)	Hi Beam Indicator. Battery with Hi Beam ON. 0 volts with Hi Beams OFF
C11 (WHT 121)	Tachometer Input.
C12	NOT USED
C13 (ORN 640)	NOT USED
C14	NOT USED
C15	NOT USED
C16 (GRY/WHT 852)	ANTILOCK Indicator
D1 (BRN 25)	Generator Input
D2 (BRN/WHT 419)	SERVICE ENGINE SOON Indicator. Grounded by ECM with Engine OFF and Ignition in RUN
D3	NOT USED
D4 (YEL/BLK 68)	LOW Coolant Indicator Input. Less than 2 ohms with coolant level low, open with coolant level OK
D5 (DK GRN 35)	Coolant Temperature Sender Input, 55 ohms at 260° F (125° C) to 1365 ohms at 100° F (37° C)
D6	NOT USED
D7	NOT USED
D8 (WHT 85)	CRUISE Indicator input
D9 (TAN 31)	Oil Pressure Sender Input Less than 2 ohms at 0 PSI, 0 kPa to 86 ohms at 80 PSI (550 kPa)
D10 (PNK/BLK 39)	Ignition power. Battery voltage in RUN, BULB TEST or START
D11 (BLK 151)	Ground.
D12 (BRN/WHT 230)	NOT USED
D13 (YEL 726)	NOT USED
D14 (DK GRN 389)	Vehicle Speed Input from ECM
D15 (LT BLU 811)	NOT USED
D16 (TAN/WHT 85)	BRAKE Indicator. Grounded with park brake set or low brake fluid

91C08672

Fig. 10: Testing C1 Connector Pins (Regal)

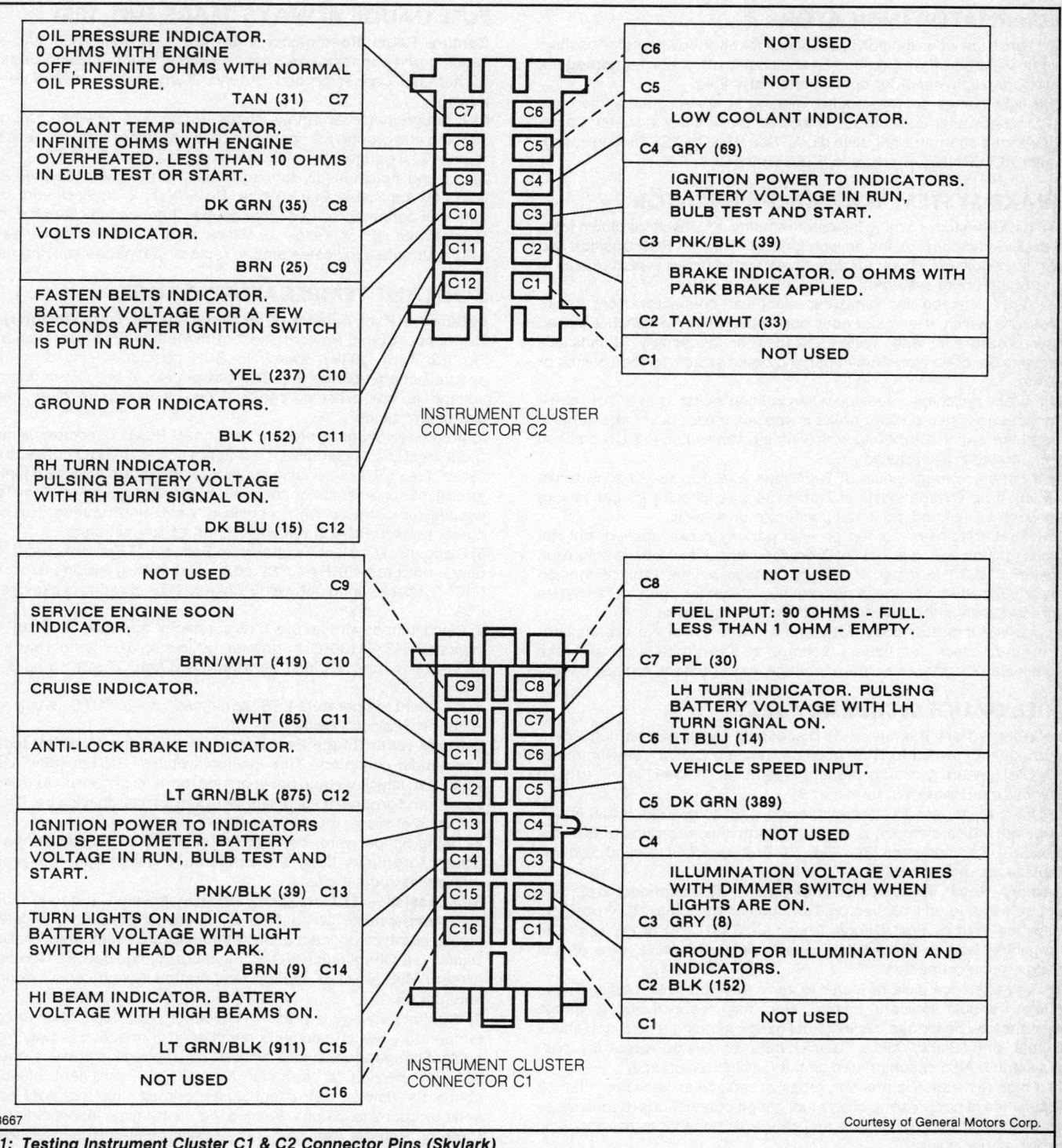

OIL PRESSURE INDICATOR.
0 OHMS WITH ENGINE OFF, INFINITE OHMS WITH NORMAL OIL PRESSURE.
TAN (31) C7

COOLANT TEMP INDICATOR.
INFINITE OHMS WITH ENGINE OVERHEATED. LESS THAN 10 OHMS IN BULB TEST OR START.
DK GRN (35) C8

VOLTS INDICATOR.
BRN (25) C9

FASTEN BELTS INDICATOR.
BATTERY VOLTAGE FOR A FEW SECONDS AFTER IGNITION SWITCH IS PUT IN RUN.
YEL (237) C10

GROUND FOR INDICATORS.
BLK (152) C11

RH TURN INDICATOR.
PULSING BATTERY VOLTAGE WITH RH TURN SIGNAL ON.
DK BLU (15) C12

C6 NOT USED

C5 NOT USED

LOW COOLANT INDICATOR.
C4 GRY (69)

IGNITION POWER TO INDICATORS.
BATTERY VOLTAGE IN RUN, BULB TEST AND START.
C3 PNK/BLK (39)

BRAKE INDICATOR. O OHMS WITH PARK BRAKE APPLIED.
C2 TAN/WHT (33)

C1 NOT USED

INSTRUMENT CLUSTER CONNECTOR C2

NOT USED C9

SERVICE ENGINE SOON INDICATOR.
BRN/WHT (419) C10

CRUISE INDICATOR.
WHT (85) C11

ANTI-LOCK BRAKE INDICATOR.
LT GRN/BLK (875) C12

IGNITION POWER TO INDICATORS AND SPEEDOMETER. BATTERY VOLTAGE IN RUN, BULB TEST AND START.
PNK/BLK (39) C13

TURN LIGHTS ON INDICATOR.
BATTERY VOLTAGE WITH LIGHT SWITCH IN HEAD OR PARK.
BRN (9) C14

HI BEAM INDICATOR. BATTERY VOLTAGE WITH HIGH BEAMS ON.
LT GRN/BLK (911) C15

NOT USED C16

C8 NOT USED

FUEL INPUT: 90 OHMS - FULL.
LESS THAN 1 OHM - EMPTY.
C7 PPL (30)

LH TURN INDICATOR. PULSING BATTERY VOLTAGE WITH LH TURN SIGNAL ON.
C6 LT BLU (14)

VEHICLE SPEED INPUT.
C5 DK GRN (389)

C4 NOT USED

ILLUMINATION VOLTAGE VARIES WITH DIMMER SWITCH WHEN LIGHTS ARE ON.
C3 GRY (8)

GROUND FOR ILLUMINATION AND INDICATORS.
C2 BLK (152)

C1 NOT USED

INSTRUMENT CLUSTER CONNECTOR C1

91C08667

Courtesy of General Motors Corp.

Fig. 11: Testing Instrument Cluster C1 & C2 Connector Pins (Skylark)

ALTERNATOR INDICATOR

1) If light is on when ignition is off, check for shorted alternator positive diode. If light is off with ignition on and engine off, check for burned out bulb, open light circuit or open in alternator field.

2) If light comes on with engine running at speed greater than idle RPM, check alternator output. Check for loose alternator belt. Check for shorted alternator negative diode. See BENCH TESTING in appropriate ALTERNATOR article in ELECTRICAL.

BRAKE SYSTEM WARNING INDICATOR

1) If brake system warning indicator remains off, check for blown fuse. If brake indicator remains on with ignition switch in RUN position and parking brake off, check for defective parking brake switch or leak in one of the brake systems.

2) Verify leakage by removing electrical connector from brake pressure switch. If indicator goes out, brake pressure switch is closed (low pressure in one system). Repair as necessary. If indicator remains on, check for short in parking brake switch, ignition switch or wiring.

3) If brake indicator comes on when ignition switch is in START position, but not when parking brake is applied, measure voltage at parking brake switch Tan/White wire (with ignition switch in RUN position and parking brake applied).

4) If battery voltage exists at Tan/White wire, replace parking brake switch. If no voltage exists at Tan/White wire, check for open in wire between switch and bulkhead connector on firewall.

5) If brake indicator comes on with parking brake applied, but not when ignition switch is in START position, check for voltage at ignition switch START terminal. If battery voltage exists, replace ignition switch. If battery voltage is not present, check for open in Tan/White wire between ignition switch and bulkhead connector.

6) If brake indicator does not come on with low brake accumulator pressure, check for battery voltage at Tan/White wire of brake accumulator pressure switch. If voltage is not present, replace switch.

FUEL GAUGE ACCURACY TEST

LeSabre & Park Avenue – **1)** Disconnect fuel tank unit connector. Turn ignition switch to RUN position. Using a Digital Volt-Ohmmeter (DVOM), ensure ground is present at terminal "D". *See Fig. 12.* Ensure 5 volts or more exist at terminal "B".

2) Using a jumper wire, connect terminal "B" to ground. If fuel gauge does not indicate empty, check instrument cluster ground at terminal No. 5 of C1 connector. *See Figs. 3, 5, 7 and 8.* If ground is okay, replace instrument cluster.

Century, Regal, Roadmaster & Skylark – **1)** Disconnect 2-pin fuel gauge sending unit connector. Turn ignition switch to RUN position. Clip one lead of Fuel Gauge Tester (J-33431) to Purple wire. Clip remaining lead to Black/White, Black/Yellow or Black wire of fuel sending unit connector.

2) Set resistance dials of tester to zero, then set to 90 ohms. Gauge pointer should indicate empty, then full, respectively. If gauge responds as described, replace fuel gauge sending unit. If not, check Purple and Black/Yellow, Black/White or Black wires for high resistance. Also check printed circuit for high resistance.

3) If high resistance is present, repair or replace as necessary. If high resistance is not present, check fuel gauge connections. If fuel gauge connections are okay, replace fuel gauge. If connections are not okay, repair as necessary.

FUEL GAUGE ALWAYS READS EMPTY TEST

Century, Regal, Roadmaster & Skylark – Disconnect fuel gauge sending unit connector. Turn ignition switch to RUN position. If gauge indicates full, repair or replace fuel gauge sending unit. If gauge does not indicate full, check Purple wire and printed circuit for short to ground. If short circuit is found, repair or replace as necessary. If Purple wire and printed circuit are okay, replace fuel gauge.

FUEL GAUGE ALWAYS READS FULL TEST

Century, Regal, Roadmaster & Skylark – **1)** Disconnect fuel gauge sending unit connector. Connect a jumper wire between Purple wire of harness connector and ground. Turn ignition switch to RUN position.

2) If gauge indicates empty, check Purple wire between fuel gauge sending and ground for open, and repair as necessary. If wire is okay, replace fuel gauge.

3) If gauge indicates full, connect a fused jumper wire between Purple wire and applicable Black/White, Black/Yellow or Black wire of fuel tank unit connector. Check fuel gauge. If gauge indicates full, check Black/White, Black/Yellow or Black wire for open; repair as necessary. If gauge indicates empty, replace fuel gauge sending unit.

COOLANT TEMPERATURE GAUGE

LeSabre & Park Avenue (With Speedometer/Trip Odometer) – **1)** Disconnect 32-pin Powertrain Control Module (PCM) connector. *See Fig. 12.* Turn ignition switch to RUN position. Using a voltmeter, ensure battery voltage is present at pin No. 7 of PCM connector. If voltage is not present, check wiring. If wiring is okay, replace instrument cluster.

2) If battery voltage is present, reconnect PCM connector. Connect a "Scan" tester at Assembly Line Diagnostic Link (ALDL) connector. Set "Scan" tester to read engine coolant temperature. Compare temperature of instrument cluster coolant temperature gauge to "Scan" tester coolant temperature while engine is warm and running. If readings agree, replace PCM. If readings differ, go to next step.

3) Disconnect Coolant Temperature Sensor (CTS) connector. If "Scan" tester indicates -40°F (-40°C), go to next step. If reading is not -40°F (-40°C), check wiring between PCM and CTS. If wiring is okay, replace PCM.

4) Place jumper wire across CTS connector terminals. If "Scan" tester indicates 266°F (130°C) or greater, go to step **5)**. If temperature is not as specified, check wiring between PCM and CTS. If wiring is okay, replace PCM.

5) If coolant temperature LED illuminates, replace CTS sensor. If LED is not on, replace PCM.

LeSabre (With Gauge Package) – **1)** Disconnect coolant temperature sender connector. Turn ignition switch to RUN position. Using a voltmeter, check voltage between ring terminal of coolant temperature sender and ground. If voltage is less than 5 volts, check wire. If voltage is 5 volts or more, replace instrument cluster.

2) Using jumper wire, connect ring terminal of coolant temperature sender to ground. If coolant temperature gauge does not read HOT, replace instrument cluster.

Roadmaster – **1)** Turn ignition to RUN position. If gauge indicates high temperature, go to step **3)**. If gauge does not indicate high temperature, disconnect coolant temperature switch/sender. Using a Digital Volt-Ohmmeter (DVOM), measure voltage between terminal "A" (Green/White wire) of coolant temperature switch/sender connector and ground.

2) If battery voltage is present, check for poor connection at coolant temperature switch/sender connection. If connection is okay, replace coolant temperature switch/sender. If no voltage is present, check for poor connection at terminal No. A1 of instrument cluster C1 connector, flaw on instrument cluster printed circuit, or poor connections or opens in circuits. *See Fig. 13* for terminal identification.

Century, Regal & Skylark – **1)** If coolant gauge is inaccurate, go to step **3)**. If coolant gauge always indicates COLD, go to step **5)**. If coolant gauge always indicates HOT, disconnect coolant temperature sender connector and turn ignition to RUN position. If coolant gauge reads COLD, replace coolant temperature sender.

2) On Century and Skylark, if coolant gauge does not read COLD, check Black wire at terminal No. 9 of C2 connector for open. On all models, check Dark Green/White and/or Dark Green wire to terminal No. 10 of C1 connector for short to ground. If circuits are okay, replace instrument cluster.

3) Disconnect coolant temperature sender connector. Connect Tester (J-33431) between Dark Green and/or Dark Green/White wire of har

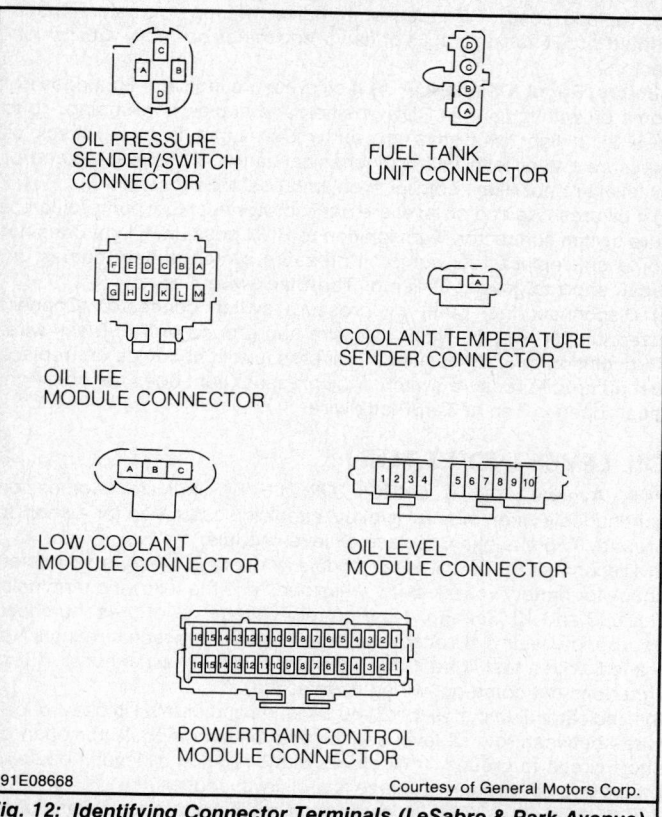

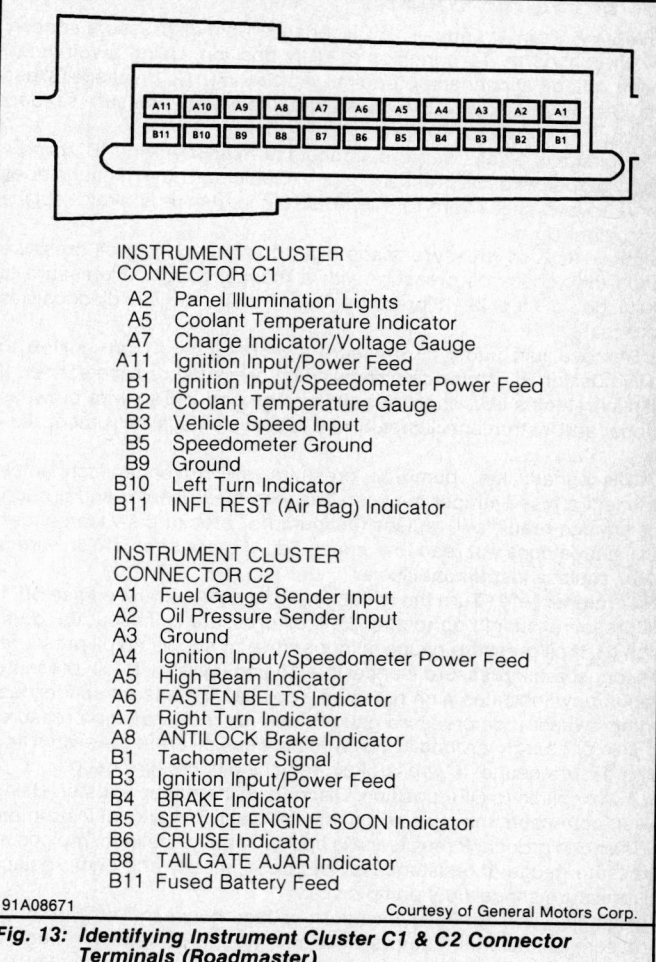

91E08668   Courtesy of General Motors Corp.

Fig. 12: Identifying Connector Terminals (LeSabre & Park Avenue)

INSTRUMENT CLUSTER
CONNECTOR C1

A2	Panel Illumination Lights
A5	Coolant Temperature Indicator
A7	Charge Indicator/Voltage Gauge
A11	Ignition Input/Power Feed
B1	Ignition Input/Speedometer Power Feed
B2	Coolant Temperature Gauge
B3	Vehicle Speed Input
B5	Speedometer Ground
B9	Ground
B10	Left Turn Indicator
B11	INFL REST (Air Bag) Indicator

INSTRUMENT CLUSTER
CONNECTOR C2

A1	Fuel Gauge Sender Input
A2	Oil Pressure Sender Input
A3	Ground
A4	Ignition Input/Speedometer Power Feed
A5	High Beam Indicator
A6	FASTEN BELTS Indicator
A7	Right Turn Indicator
A8	ANTILOCK Brake Indicator
B1	Tachometer Signal
B3	Ignition Input/Power Feed
B4	BRAKE Indicator
B5	SERVICE ENGINE SOON Indicator
B6	CRUISE Indicator
B8	TAILGATE AJAR Indicator
B11	Fused Battery Feed

91A08671   Courtesy of General Motors Corp.

Fig. 13: Identifying Instrument Cluster C1 & C2 Connector Terminals (Roadmaster)

ness connector and ground. Adjust resistance dials of tester to 1500 ohms, then adjust to 55 ohms.

4) Coolant temperature gauge should point to COLD, then to HOT (or vice versa). If gauge respond as described, replace coolant temperature sender. If gauge does not respond as described, check Dark Green and/or Dark Green/White wire for open. If circuit is okay, replace instrument cluster.

5) Disconnect coolant temperature sender. Ground Dark Green/White and/or Dark Green wire at coolant temperature sender connector. If coolant gauge reads HOT, replace coolant temperature sender.

6) If coolant gauge does not read HOT, check Dark Green/White and/or Dark Green wire for open. If circuit is okay, replace instrument cluster.

COOLANT INDICATOR

LeSabre (Speedometer & Trip Odometer Package) – 1) Ensure vehicle is not overheating. Verify cooling system is operating properly before testing coolant indicator. The coolant temperature sensor, in rare cases, may fail to set fault code (Code 14 or 15) even though system is malfunctioning. This could cause TEMP light to come on even though system is not overheating, or it could result in engine overheating without illuminating the TEMP light. Check coolant sensor resistance values against temperatures. See SENSOR OPERATING RANGE CHARTS article in ENGINE PERFORMANCE.

2) TEMP light is powered by the 20-amp fuse (No. 16). Light comes on when ECM provides a ground for circuit. If circuit ground is provided between light and ECM, light will illuminate every time ignition is turned on.

3) Turn ignition on with engine off (bulb test position). If TEMP light illuminates, go to step 5). If TEMP light does not illuminate, check 20-amp fuse (No. 16) and instrument cluster bulb. Check for open circuit between fuse and hot light.

4) Using test light, backprobe terminal No. E9 (Dark Green wire) of ECM TEMP light driver to battery voltage. Turn ignition on. If test light does not illuminate, ECM terminal connection is bad or ECM is faulty. If test light illuminates, turn ignition off. Disconnect ECM connectors. Jumper harness terminal of ECM TEMP light driver to ground. Turn

ignition on. If TEMP light does not illuminate, check for open circuit between TEMP light and ECM. If light does not illuminate and all circuits are intact, and power is available to light, replace instrument cluster.

5) Start engine. If test light goes off, no problem is evident. If test light remains on, turn ignition off. Disconnect ECM connector. Using test light, probe harness terminal of ECM TEMP light driver to battery voltage. If light is off, replace ECM. If light comes on, repair short to ground in TEMP light driver circuit. If short circuit is not present, replace instrument cluster.

Roadmaster – 1) If coolant temperature indicator comes on with engine running (not overheated), remove connector to coolant temperature switch/sender. If indicator goes off, replace coolant temperature switch/sender.

2) If indicator remains on, check Dark Green wire from coolant temperature switch/sender and ignition switch for short to ground. Ensure printed circuit has no cracks or flaws, and mates correctly with its connector.

3) If coolant temperature indicator does not come on while starting engine (and bulb is okay), ground Dark Green wire at terminal "C" of C1 connector at ignition switch. If indicator comes on, circuit is okay. Replace ignition switch. If indicator does not come on, check Dark Green wire and printed circuit for open circuit.

Century, Park Avenue, Regal & Skylark – 1) If HOT indicator fails to light when cranking engine, check for burned out bulb, open light circuit or defective ignition switch.

2) If indicator light remains on with engine running, check for excessively high coolant temperature, defective sending unit, or short to ground in wire between bulb and sending unit.

OIL PRESSURE GAUGE

LeSabre & Park Avenue – 1) Disconnect 4-pin oil pressure sender/switch connector. Turn ignition to RUN position. Using a voltmeter, check voltage at connector terminal "A". *See Fig. 12.* If voltage is less than 5 volts, check wire. If wire is okay, replace oil pressure sender/switch.

2) If voltage is 5 volts or more, connect terminals "A" and "B" using a fused jumper wire. Oil pressure gauge should read low. If gauge does not read low, check wire for high resistance. If wire is okay, replace instrument cluster.

Regal – 1) If oil pressure reads high, go to step **3)**. If oil pressure reads low, check oil pressure with a manual gauge. If pressure is okay, go to step **2)**. If pressure is not okay, engine diagnosis is necessary.

2) Remove fuel pump/oil pressure switch/sender. Turn ignition to RUN position. If display now shows high pressure, replace sender. If display remains low, check for short to ground in Tan wire between sender and instrument cluster. If wire is okay, replace instrument cluster.

3) Disconnect fuel pump/oil pressure switch/sender connector. Connect a fused jumper between Tan wire of connector and ground. If oil gauge reads low, replace fuel pump/oil pressure switch/sender. If oil gauge does not read low, check Tan wire for open. If Tan wire is okay, replace instrument cluster.

Roadmaster – 1) Turn the ignition to RUN position with engine off. If oil pressure is high, go to step **3)**. If oil pressure is inaccurate, go to step **2)**. If oil pressure gauge is inoperative or shows no oil pressure, disconnect oil pressure sender/fuel pump switch. If oil pressure gauge now indicates high pressure, replace oil pressure sender/fuel pump switch. If oil pressure gauge does not indicate high pressure, check for short to ground in Tan wire between oil pressure switch and oil pressure gauge. If wire is okay, replace oil pressure gauge.

2) Turn ignition to OFF position. Disconnect instrument cluster. Using a volt-ohmmeter, measure resistance between Tan wire of instrument cluster and ground. If resistance is approximately one ohm, replace oil pressure gauge. If resistance is not approximately one ohm, replace oil pressure sender/fuel pump switch.

3) Using a volt-ohmmeter, measure voltage between Tan wire of oil pressure sender/fuel pump switch and ground. If battery voltage is present, check for poor connection at oil pressure sender/fuel pump switch connector. If connection is okay, replace oil pressure sender/fuel pump switch.

4) If voltage is zero volt, check for poor connection or open in Tan wire between fuel pump switch/oil pressure sender and instrument cluster C2 connector. *See Fig. 13.* If connection and wire are okay, replace oil pressure gauge.

OIL INDICATOR LIGHT

LeSabre & Park Avenue – 1) Disconnect oil pressure switch connector. Turn ignition to RUN position. Using a voltmeter, check for battery voltage at terminal "A" of connector. *See Fig. 12.* If battery voltage is not present, check wire. If wire is okay, replace oil pressure switch.

2) If battery voltage is present, jump terminals "A" and "B" using a fused jumper wire. The oil pressure indicator should illuminate. If indicator does not illuminate, check ground wiring. If indicator comes on, check oil pressure with a mechanical gauge. If pressure is okay, replace oil pressure switch.

Roadmaster – 1) If oil pressure indicator remains on with engine running, disconnect fuel pump/oil pressure sender. If indicator goes off, replace sender. If indicator remains on, check Tan wire for short to voltage. Check printed circuit for short circuit. Ensure printed circuit mates correctly with its connectors.

2) If oil indicator does not come on before engine starts, and bulb is okay, measure resistance between fuel pump/oil pressure sender and ground. Resistance should be approximately one ohm. If resistance is NOT approximately one ohm, replace sender. If resistance is approximately one ohm, check Tan wire for open circuit.

3) Connect a fused jumper between terminal "A" (Tan wire) of fuel pump/oil pressure sender connector and ground. If indicator comes on, replace sender. If indicator remains off, repair cluster. Ensure printed circuit has no cracks or flaws, and mates correctly with its connector.

Century, Regal & Skylark – 1) If oil pressure indicator light does not come on with ignition in RUN position and engine not running, go to step **3)**. If light is always on, and oil pressure is okay, check oil pressure and oil level with a mechanical gauge. If oil pressure and/or oil level are not okay, correct problem(s) before proceeding.

2) If oil pressure and oil level are okay, disconnect fuel pump/oil pressure switch connector. Turn ignition to RUN position. If light does not come on, replace fuel pump/oil pressure switch. If light comes on, repair short to ground in Tan or Tan/Black wire.

3) Disconnect fuel pump/oil pressure switch connector. Connect fused jumper wire between Tan wire and ground or Tan/Black wire. Turn ignition to RUN position. If oil pressure light comes on, replace fuel pump/oil pressure switch. If oil pressure light does not come on, repair open in Tan or Tan/Black wire.

OIL LEVEL INDICATOR

Park Avenue – 1) If CHECK OIL LEVEL indicator comes on continuously when oil level is okay, check indicator lead for a short to ground. If wire is okay, replace oil level module.

2) Disconnect 10-pin oil level module connector. Using a voltmeter, check for battery voltage between ground and the following terminals: No. 6, 9 and 10. *See Fig. 12.* If battery voltage is not present, check appropriate wiring. If voltage is present, probe between terminals No. 5 and 6 with a test light. If test light comes on, go to next step. If test light does not come on, wiring is defective.

3) If indicator illuminates for 20-40 seconds and oil level is okay, check wires between low oil level sensor and oil level module for open or short circuit to ground. If wires are okay, replace oil level module. If problem is still present, replace low oil level sensor.

4) If CHECK OIL LEVEL indicator does not illuminate regardless of oil level, disconnect oil level sensor. Wait 8 minutes with ignition in OFF or LOCK position. If CHECK OIL LEVEL indicator illuminates for 20-40 seconds, replace low oil level sensor. If indicator does not come on as described, replace oil level module.

CHANGE OIL SOON INDICATOR

Park Avenue – 1) Disconnect 12-pin oil life module. *See Fig. 12.* Using ohmmeter, ensure continuity is present between oil life module pin "B" and Assembly Line Diagnostic Link (ALDL) connector pin "M".

2) Ensure battery voltage is present at pins "E" and "F" of module connector. Ensure ground is present at pins "L" and "M" of module connector. If continuity, battery voltage and ground are not present at the indicated terminals, check appropriate wiring. If continuity, battery voltage and ground are present as specified, ground pin "J" of module connector using a fused jumper. CHANGE OIL SOON light should illuminate. If light does not illuminate, check bulb and wiring. If bulb and wiring are okay, replace oil life module.

VOLTMETER

1) With ignition switch in RUN position, connect a test voltmeter between positive and negative terminals at battery. If voltage reading on test voltmeter is the same as vehicle's voltmeter, then vehicle's voltmeter is okay.

2) If voltage is not consistent with vehicle's voltmeter, check Pink/Black wire to terminal No. 9 and Black wire to terminal No. 10 of instrument cluster C2 connector for open circuit. If wires are okay, replace instrument cluster.

TACHOMETER

With engine running, measure voltage at tachometer input connector White wire. Voltmeter should indicate 1-10 volts and should vary with engine RPM. If voltmeter reading is not as specified, check White wire for open circuit. If White wire is okay, Computer Controlled Coil Ignition (C^3I) system is faulty. If voltage reading is correct, replace instrument cluster.

TAILGATE AJAR LIGHT

No Light – With ignition in RUN position, disconnect wire from tailgate switch and touch wire to known good ground. Light should glow. If light fails to glow, bulb is burned out, or circuit is open.

Light Stays On – Check circuit for short to ground. If short to ground is not present, replace switch.

REMOVAL & INSTALLATION

INSTRUMENT CLUSTER

Removal & Installation (Century) – **1)** Disconnect battery cable. Remove left trim plate. Remove shift indicator clip from steering column shift bowl. Remove 4 cluster attaching screws. On vehicles with column shift, shift transaxle to "1" position.

2) Place a clean shop towel over column to prevent steering column from getting scratched. On models with tilt wheel, lower steering wheel as far as possible and unscrew tilt lever. On all models, tip top of cluster down and work cluster out. To install, reverse removal procedure.

Removal & Installation (LeSabre) – **1)** Disconnect battery cable. Remove top cover. Use a coin to turn left trim plate retainers counterclockwise 1/4 turn. Retainers will pop out. Pull left side of trim plate to left.

2) Remove left trim plate. *See Fig. 14.* Remove cover plate by pulling out. Remove 4 screws behind cover plate and remove right trim plate. Remove 5 bolts holding filler panel. Remove shift indicator clip from steering column collar (note cable routing for installation).

3) Remove 5 bolts holding cluster in dash. Tilt steering wheel all the way down and place gear selector lever in "1" position. Pull cluster assembly straight out. This will disconnect electrical connectors from cluster. To install, reverse removal procedure.

Removal & Installation (Park Avenue) – Disconnect battery cable. Remove sound insulators and instrument panel lower trim pad. Remove rubber collar from steering column. *See Fig. 15.* Remove gear selector clip from steering column. Remove 4 bolts from instrument cluster and pull cluster straight out. To install, reverse removal procedure.

Removal & Installation (Regal) – Removal and installation procedure of instrument cluster is not available from manufacturer.

Removal & Installation (Roadmaster) – Disconnect battery cable. Remove left side trim plate. Remove 4 cluster-to-instrument panel carrier screws. Remove shift indicator cable from steering column and unclip cable. Remove cluster from instrument panel carrier. To install, reverse removal procedure. Tighten screws to 18 INCH lbs. (2 N.m).

Removal & Installation (Skylark) – **1)** Disconnect battery cable. Remove steering column cover. Remove left and right trim covers. Remove instrument cluster trim cover. Remove PRNDL cable clip from steering column shift collar. Remove 5 screws attaching lens and bezel to cluster carrier. *See Fig. 16.*

2) Loosen upper steering column attaching bolts, and lower column. Remove 4 cluster-to-cluster carrier screws. Remove cluster. To install, reverse removal procedure.

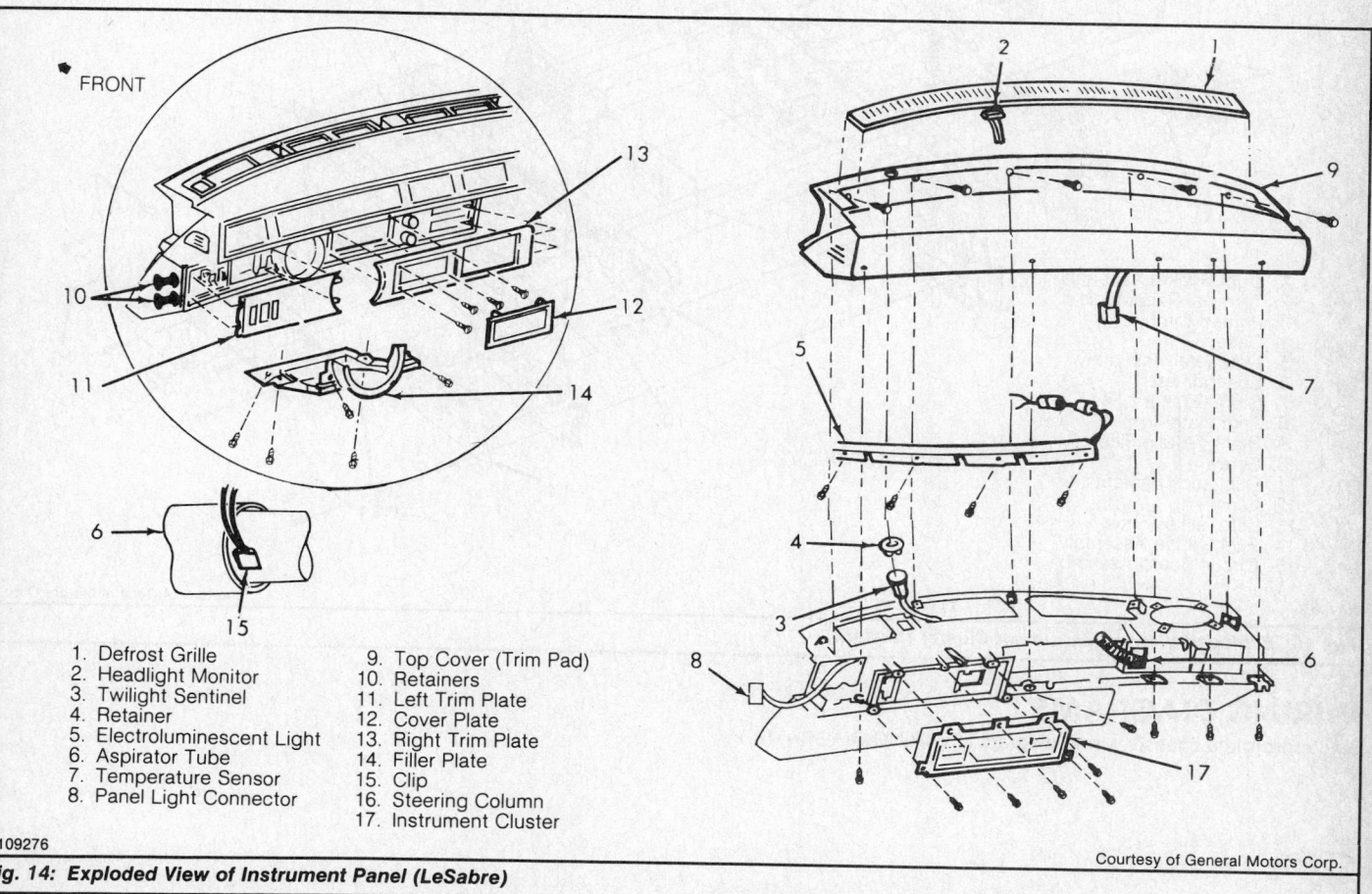

1. Defrost Grille
2. Headlight Monitor
3. Twilight Sentinel
4. Retainer
5. Electroluminescent Light
6. Aspirator Tube
7. Temperature Sensor
8. Panel Light Connector
9. Top Cover (Trim Pad)
10. Retainers
11. Left Trim Plate
12. Cover Plate
13. Right Trim Plate
14. Filler Plate
15. Clip
16. Steering Column
17. Instrument Cluster

109276

Courtesy of General Motors Corp.

Fig. 14: Exploded View of Instrument Panel (LeSabre)

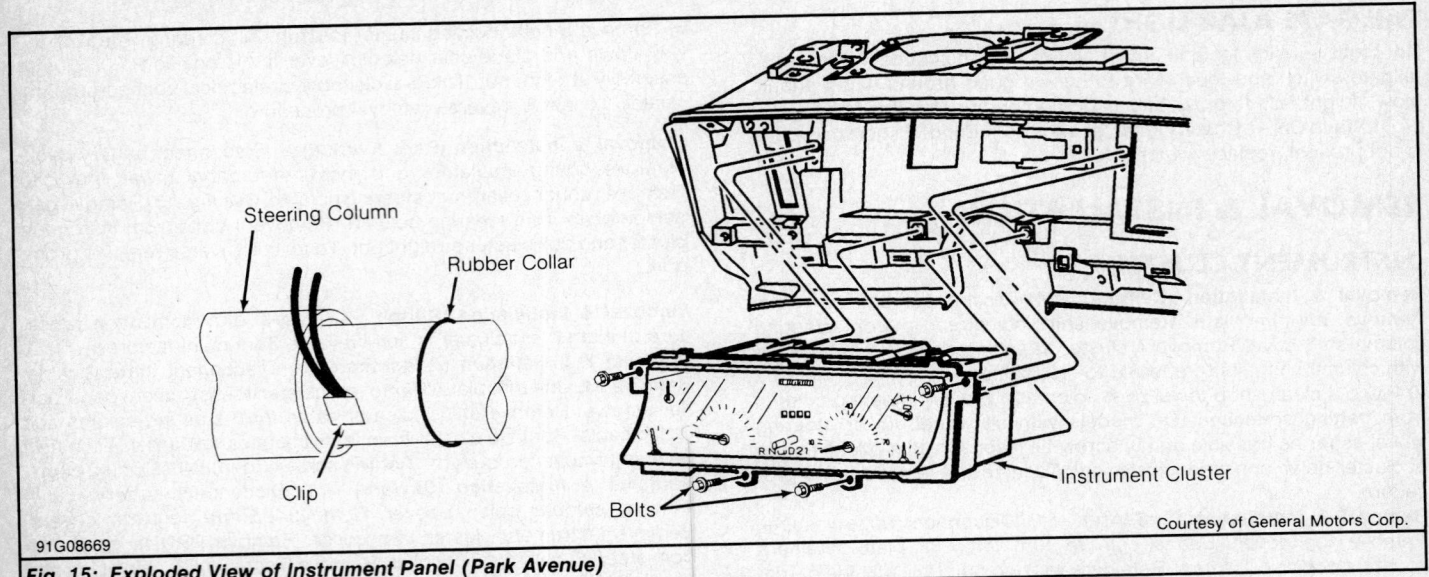

1991 SAFETY EQUIPMENT
Analog Instrument Panels – Buick (Cont.)

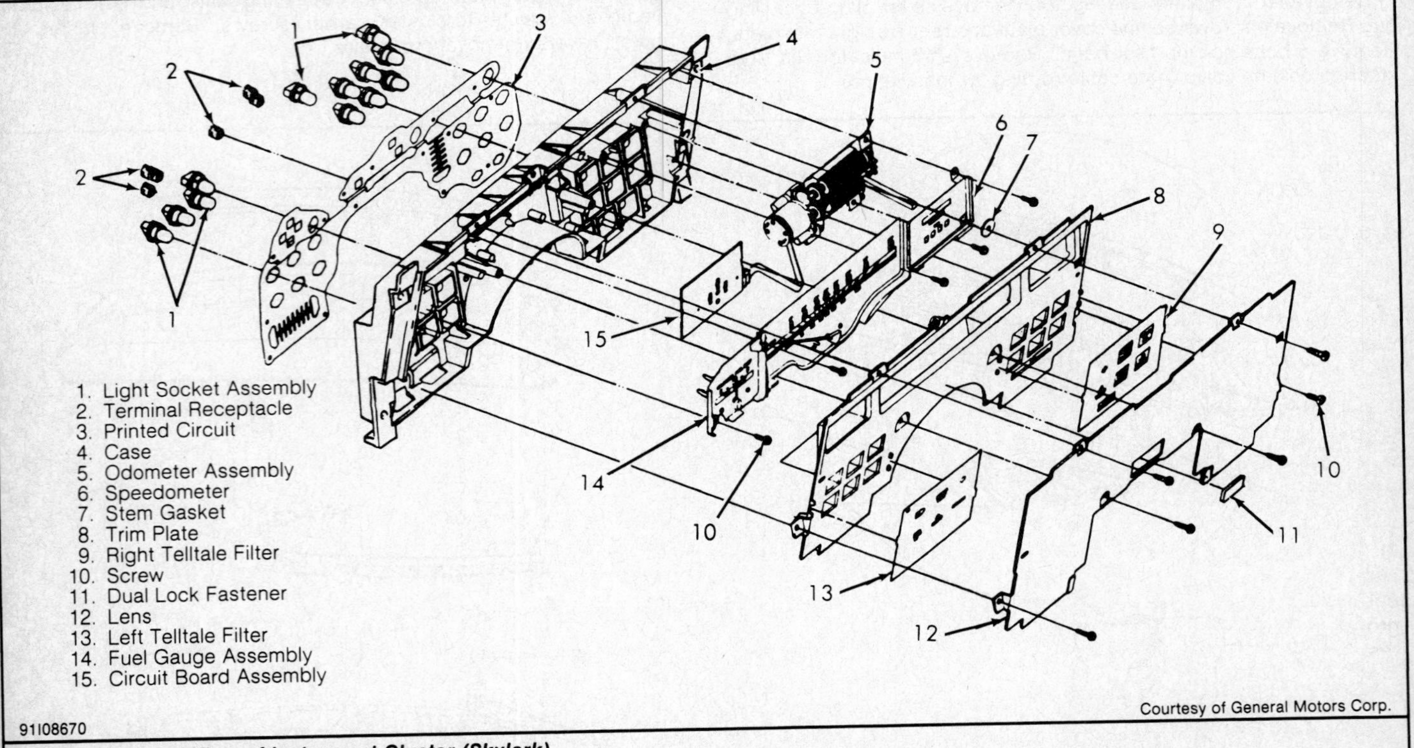

Steering Column
Rubber Collar
Clip
Bolts
Instrument Cluster
Courtesy of General Motors Corp.
91G08669

Fig. 15: Exploded View of Instrument Panel (Park Avenue)

1. Light Socket Assembly
2. Terminal Receptacle
3. Printed Circuit
4. Case
5. Odometer Assembly
6. Speedometer
7. Stem Gasket
8. Trim Plate
9. Right Telltale Filter
10. Screw
11. Dual Lock Fastener
12. Lens
13. Left Telltale Filter
14. Fuel Gauge Assembly
15. Circuit Board Assembly
Courtesy of General Motors Corp.
91I08670

Fig. 16: Exploded View of Instrument Cluster (Skylark)

WIRING DIAGRAMS

See appropriate chassis wiring diagram in WIRING DIAGRAMS.

Beretta, Camaro, Caprice, Cavalier, Corsica, Lumina

DESCRIPTION & OPERATION

Instrument cluster may be offered with indicator lights or various gauges. The instrument cluster consists of speedometer, odometer, trip odometer and fuel gauge. Indicators and gauges include voltage, oil pressure, seat belt, brake system, tailgate ajar, SERVICE ENGINE SOON, low coolant, turn signal, high beam indicator, supplemental restraint and anti-theft security light.

Some manual transaxle models may also be equipped with an upshift indicator light which indicates vehicle should be shifted for maximum fuel economy.

AIR BAG PRECAUTIONS

The following precautions should be taken when working with vehicles equipped with Supplemental Inflatable Restraint (SIR) air bag systems:

- Before performing any instrument panel testing, diagnosis or repair, disable SRS system by disconnecting negative battery cable and Yellow 2-pin connector at base of steering column.
- Wait 20 minutes before making SRS repairs. SRS system retains enough voltage to deploy air bag for a short time after disconnecting power.
- To avoid accidental air bag deployment, avoid the SRS wiring harness when trouble shooting instrument panel components. All SRS wires are color-coded Yellow.

TESTING & DIAGNOSIS

FUEL GAUGE

Fuel Gauge Accuracy Test – 1) Disconnect fuel gauge sending unit wiring connector. Connect Red lead of Gauge Tester (J-33431) to proper colored wire and remaining lead to proper wire color or ground. See FUEL GAUGE ACCURACY TEST CONNECTIONS table.

FUEL GAUGE ACCURACY TEST CONNECTIONS

Application	Terminal Or Location
Beretta & Corsica	Pink & Black Wire of Connector
Camaro & Lumina	Purple & Black Wire of Connector
Caprice	Purple Wire & Ground
Cavalier	Purple & Black/White Wire of Connector

2) Turn ignition on and adjust resistance dials of tester to zero ohms and then to 90 ohms. Note if gauge reads empty, then full. If gauge operates correctly, check ground wire from instrument cluster to ground, and ground wire from fuel gauge sending unit for excessive resistance. If wiring is okay, replace fuel gauge sending unit.

3) If gauge fails to operate correctly, check wire to instrument panel for excessive resistance and proper connection. If wiring and connection are okay, replace instrument cluster.

Fuel Gauge Always Reads Empty – Disconnect fuel gauge sending unit. Turn ignition on. If gauge indicates full, replace fuel gauge sending unit. If gauge still indicates empty, check wire from sending unit to instrument cluster for a short to ground or shorted instrument cluster. If wiring is okay, check fuel gauge connections or replace fuel gauge.

Fuel Gauge Always Reads Full (Caprice) – 1) Disconnect fuel gauge sending unit. Connect a test light between battery voltage and fuel gauge sending unit connector terminal "A" (Black wire). If test light does not illuminate, check for poor connections or open circuit(s).

2) If test light illuminates, connect a fused jumper wire between fuel gauge sending unit connector terminal "B" (Purple wire) and ground. If fuel gauge indicates empty, check for poor connections or open circuit(s) at fuel gauge sending unit connector. If wiring and connector are okay, replace fuel gauge sending unit.

3) If fuel gauge does not indicate empty, check for poor connections at instrument cluster connector terminal No. 15 (Purple wire), fuel gauge-to-fuse connector (Pink/Black wire), fuel gauge sending unit

ground, instrument cluster printed circuit, or open circuit in Purple wire.

Fuel Gauge Always Reads Full (Beretta, Camaro, Cavalier, Corsica & Lumina) – 1) Disconnect fuel gauge sending unit. Connect jumper wire between specified wire of harness half and ground. See FUEL GAUGE FULL TEST CONNECTIONS table, Step 1. Turn ignition on.

FUEL GAUGE FULL TEST CONNECTIONS

Application	Terminal Or Location
Step 1	
Beretta & Corsica	Pink & Ground
Camaro, Cavalier & Lumina	Purple & Ground
Step 2	
Beretta & Corsica	Pink & Black
Camaro & Cavalier	Purple & Black/White

2) If gauge indicates empty, check wiring between sending unit and dash for an open circuit or loose connections at instrument panel. If wiring is okay, replace fuel gauge sending unit.

3) On Lumina, if gauge still indicates full, check Purple wire for an open circuit. If Purple wire is okay, replace instrument cluster.

4) On Beretta, Camaro, Caprice, Cavalier and Corsica, connect jumper wire between specified wire of harness half and sending unit wire. See FUEL GAUGE FULL TEST CONNECTIONS table, Step 2. If gauge reads empty, check ground wire to sending unit for an open circuit. If fuel gauge operates correctly with jumper wire installed in both locations, replace sending unit.

OIL PRESSURE GAUGE

Oil Pressure Gauge Operation – Disconnect Tan wire from fuel pump/oil pressure switch. If oil pressure indicates low, install jumper wire from Tan wire to ground. Replace fuel pump/oil pressure switch if low reading is still indicated. If oil pressure indicates high, check Tan wire or instrument panel for shorted circuit.

Oil Pressure Gauge Accuracy Test (Beretta, Cavalier, Corsica & Lumina) – 1) Disconnect fuel pump switch/oil pressure sender connector. Connect one Red clip of Gauge Tester (J-33431) to terminal "A" (Tan or Tan/Black wire) of fuel pump switch/oil pressure sender connector and other Red clip lead to ground.

2) Turn ignition switch to RUN position. On Cavalier, set resistance dials on tester to one ohm, 44 ohms and then 86 ohms. If oil pressure indicates zero psi, 40 psi, and then 80 psi, replace fuel pump/oil pressure sender. If oil pressure shows no change, check Tan or Tan/Black wire for high resistance. If wire is okay, replace instrument cluster.

3) On Beretta, Corsica and Lumina, set resistance dials on tester to zero ohms, then to 90 ohms. Oil pressure gauge should indicate low pressure, then high pressure. If oil pressure gauge shows no change, check Tan wire for high resistance. If wire is okay, replace coolant temperature/oil pressure gauge assembly.

Oil Pressure Gauge Always Reads Low – Disconnect fuel pump switch/oil pressure sender connector. Turn ignition switch to RUN position. If gauge indicates high, replace fuel pump switch/oil pressure sender. If gauge still indicates low, check for a short to ground in Tan or Tan/Black wire. If wire is okay, replace instrument cluster.

Oil Pressure Gauge Always Reads High – 1) Disconnect fuel pump switch/oil pressure sender connector. Using a jumper wire, jump terminal "A" (Tan or Tan/Black wire) of fuel pump switch/oil pressure sender to ground. Turn ignition switch to RUN position.

2) If gauge indicates low oil pressure, replace fuel pump switch/oil pressure sender. If gauge indicates high oil pressure, check for an open circuit in Tan or Tan/Black wire. If wire is okay, replace instrument cluster.

COOLANT TEMPERATURE GAUGE

Coolant Temperature Gauge Accuracy Test – 1) Disconnect temperature gauge sending unit. Connect Red lead of Gauge Tester (J-33431) to Dark Green or Dark Green/White wire of temperature gauge electrical connector and remaining lead to ground.

2) Turn ignition on. Adjust gauge tester resistance dials to 1365 ohms (Beretta, Camaro and Corsica) or 1400 ohms (Caprice, Cavalier and

Lumina), and then to 42 ohms (Camaro) or 55 ohms (Beretta, Caprice, Cavalier, Corsica and Lumina). Temperature gauge should indicate cold and then hot.

3) If gauge operation is incorrect, check for excessive resistance in wiring to instrument cluster and proper connections at instrument cluster. Replace temperature gauge or instrument cluster if wiring and connections were okay. If gauge operation was correct, replace temperature sending unit.

Coolant Temperature Gauge Always Reads Hot (Beretta, Cavalier & Corsica) – Disconnect coolant temperature sender/switch. Turn ignition switch to RUN position. If gauge indicates cold, replace sender/switch. If gauge indicates hot, Dark Green or Dark Green/White wire is shorted to ground.

Coolant Temperature Gauge Always Reads Hot (Caprice) – Disconnect coolant temperature sender/switch. If gauge indicates cold, replace coolant temperature sender/switch. If gauge still indicates hot, check instrument cluster printed circuit and Dark Green/White wire for a short to ground. If wire is okay, repair coolant temperature gauge.

Coolant Temperature Gauge Always Reads Cold (Beretta, Cavalier & Corsica) – Disconnect coolant temperature sender/switch. Using a jumper wire, connect harness half of connector (Dark Green or Dark Green/White wire) to ground. If gauge does not indicate cold, replace coolant temperature sender/switch. If gauge indicates cold, check for an open circuit in Dark Green wire and repair as necessary. If wire is okay, replace instrument cluster.

Coolant Temperature Gauge Always Reads Cold (Caprice) – **1)** Disconnect coolant temperature switch/sender. Using a voltmeter, measure voltage from coolant temperature switch/sender connector terminal "B" (Green/White wire) and ground. If battery voltage is present, check for poor connection at coolant temperature switch/sender connector. If connector is okay, replace coolant temperature switch/sender.

2) If no voltage is present, check for poor connection or open circuit in Dark Green/White wire. If connector and wire are okay, repair coolant temperature gauge.

VOLTMETER

Turn ignition on. Install voltmeter between battery terminals and note reading. If voltmeter reading on vehicle varies with battery voltage reading, ensure wiring to voltmeter is okay and connections are tight. If connections and wiring are okay, replace voltmeter or instrument cluster.

OIL INDICATOR

1) If indicator does not illuminate with ignition on and engine not running, disconnect Tan wire from fuel pump/oil pressure switch. Connect jumper wire from Tan wire to ground. Oil indicator should illuminate with ignition on.

2) If indicator fails to illuminate, check for open circuit in Tan wire to instrument cluster or loose connections at instrument cluster. If wiring and connections are okay, replace instrument cluster. If indicator illuminates, replace fuel pump/oil pressure switch.

3) If indicator remains on when engine is running above idle speed, ensure oil pressure is correct. If oil pressure is correct, disconnect Tan wire at fuel pump/oil pressure switch. If indicator illuminates, check for grounded Tan wire between bulb and fuel pump/oil pressure switch. If indicator does not illuminate, replace fuel pump/oil pressure switch.

COOLANT TEMPERATURE INDICATOR

Coolant Temperature Indicator Accuracy Test (Beretta, Camaro, Caprice, Cavalier & Corsica) – **1)** If indicator does not illuminate when cranking engine, check for defective bulb, open light circuit, or defective ignition switch.

2) If indicator illuminates at all times with engine running, ensure engine is operating at proper temperature. With ignition on, disconnect electrical connector at temperature sending unit.

3) If indicator does not illuminate, replace sending unit. If indicator illuminates, check for ground in wire between bulb and sending unit, defective ignition switch, or defective instrument cluster.

Coolant Temperature Indicator Always On (Lumina) – If indicator illuminates at all times, disconnect coolant temperature switch. Turn ignition switch to RUN position. If indicator does not illuminate, replace coolant temperature switch. If indicator is still on, check Dark Green wire and ignition switch for a short to ground. If wires are okay, replace instrument cluster.

Coolant Temperature Indicator Does Not Illuminate With Ignition On (Lumina) – Install a fused jumper wire between Dark Green wire, at connector located between coolant temperature indicator and ignition switch, and ground.

2) After jumper wire is connected, turn ignition switch to RUN position. If coolant temperature indicator illuminates, replace ignition switch. If indicator does not illuminate, check Dark Green wire for an open circuit.

Coolant Temperature Indicator Does Not Illuminate When Engine Overheats – **1)** Disconnect coolant temperature switch. Using a jumper wire, jump Dark Green wire to ground. Move ignition switch to RUN position and check coolant temperature indicator.

2) If coolant temperature indicator illuminates, replace coolant temperature switch. If indicator does not illuminate, check Dark Green wire for an open circuit.

LOW COOLANT INDICATOR

Low Coolant Indicator Stays On (Beretta & Corsica) – **1)** Connect jumper wire between low coolant probe and ground. Turn ignition on. If indicator goes out, replace low coolant probe.

2) If indicator remains on, check Yellow or Yellow/Black wire to low coolant probe for an open circuit. If wiring is okay, test low coolant module. See LOW COOLANT MODULE in this article.

No Low Coolant Indicator With Low Coolant Level (Beretta & Corsica) – Disconnect low coolant probe or switch. Turn ignition on. If indicator illuminates, replace low coolant probe or switch. If indicator does not illuminate, check low coolant module. See LOW COOLANT MODULE in this article.

Low Coolant Indicator Stays On (Cavalier – 3.1L Engine) – Disconnect surge tank low coolant switch connector. Turn ignition switch to RUN position. If low coolant indicator illuminates, check Yellow/Black wire for a short to ground. If wire is okay, replace instrument cluster. If low coolant indicator does not illuminate, replace surge tank/low coolant switch.

No Low Coolant Indicator With Low Coolant Level (Cavalier & Lumina) – **1)** Disconnect low coolant switch connector. Install jumper wire between Yellow/Black wire of switch connector and ground. Turn ignition on. If indicator does not illuminate, check Yellow/Black wire to instrument cluster or instrument cluster printed circuit for an open circuit.

2) If indicator light illuminates, remove jumper wire and install jumper wire between Yellow/Black and Black wire of the low coolant switch connector. If light illuminates, replace low coolant switch. If light does not illuminate, check for an open circuit in Black wire to low coolant switch.

LOW COOLANT MODULE

Beretta & Corsica – **1)** Disconnect low coolant module connector. Low coolant module is located behind left side of instrument panel. Turn ignition on. Disconnect Yellow/Black wire from low coolant probe.

2) Measure voltage between module Pink/Black wire and ground. Battery voltage should exist. If battery voltage does not exist, check for an open circuit in Pink/Black wire.

3) Measure voltage between low coolant module Pink/Black wire and module Black (ground) wire. Battery voltage should exist. If battery voltage does not exist, check for an open circuit in Black wire.

4) Measure voltage at Gray/Black wire from low coolant module to ground. Battery voltage should exist. If no voltage exists, check for an open circuit in wire between low coolant module and instrument cluster and printed circuit for damage.

5) Measure voltage between Pink/Black wire and Yellow/Black wire. No voltage should exist. If voltage exists, check Yellow/Black wire for a short to ground. Yellow/Black wire goes to low coolant probe.

TAILGATE AJAR INDICATOR

Indicator Inoperative (Caprice) – 1) Using a voltmeter, measure voltage at tailgate ajar switch terminal "D" (Dark Green wire) to ground. If no voltage is present, check for poor connection at instrument cluster connector terminal No. 10 (Dark Green wire). If connectors and wire are okay, repair instrument cluster printed circuit.
2) If battery voltage is present, backprobe tailgate ajar switch connector terminal "D" (Dark Green wire) to tailgate ajar switch terminal "B" (Black wire). If no voltage is present, check tailgate ajar switch ground (Black wire).

Indicator Inoperative (Cavalier) – 1) Disconnect tailgate switch. Install jumper wire between Black/Orange wire of connector and ground. Turn ignition on.
2) If indicator light illuminates, replace tailgate switch. If indicator does not illuminate, check for open circuit in wire from switch to instrument cluster or for defective instrument cluster.

Tailgate Ajar Indicator On At All Times (Caprice) – Disconnect tailgate ajar switch. If tailgate ajar indicator is now off, replace tailgate ajar switch. If indicator remains on, repair short to ground in Dark Green wire.

Tailgate Ajar Indicator On At All Times (Cavalier) – Turn ignition on. Disconnect electrical connection at tailgate switch. Replace switch if indicator does not illuminate. If indicator illuminates, check for a short to ground in wiring from switch to instrument panel.

VOLTS/CHARGE INDICATOR

1) If indicator does not illuminate with ignition on, disconnect electrical connector at alternator. Install jumper wire between Brown wire of electrical connector and ground.
2) Turn ignition on. If indicator does not illuminate, check for voltage supply to indicator, open circuit in wire from alternator to indicator, or defective printed circuit in instrument cluster. If indicator illuminates, replace alternator.
3) If indicator illuminates with engine running, disconnect electrical connector from alternator with engine running. If indicator illuminates, check wire from alternator to indicator or instrument cluster for a short to ground. Replace alternator if indicator does not illuminate.

TACHOMETER

Tachometer Inaccurate (Beretta & Corsica) – 1) Disconnect electrical connector from instrument cluster. Turn ignition on. If battery voltage is present between Orange wire and ground at electrical connector, replace instrument cluster.
2) Measure voltage between Orange wire and Black wire of electrical connector. Battery voltage should be present. If battery voltage is not present, check for an open circuit in Black wire.
3) Measure voltage between White wire from tachometer and ground. Voltage should exceed 10 volts. If voltage is less than 10 volts, check for an open circuit in White wire. If no open circuit exists, check ignition system for tachometer signal.

Tachometer Inaccurate (Camaro) – 1) Remove cluster trim and remove instrument cluster. Unplug electrical connector at tachometer. Turn ignition switch on. Measure voltage between Pink/Black wire and ground at tachometer electrical connector. Battery voltage should exist. If battery voltage does not exist, check for an open circuit in Pink/Black wire.
2) Measure voltage between Pink/Black wire and Black wire of electrical connector. Battery voltage should exist. If voltage does not exist, check for an open circuit in Black wire.
3) Measure voltage between White wire and ground. Voltage should exceed 10 volts. If voltage is less than 10 volts, check wires for an open circuit. If no open circuit exists, check ignition system for tachometer signal.

UPSHIFT INDICATOR

Lumina – 1) Disconnect Electronic Control Module (ECM) connector "B". Turn ignition switch to RUN position. Using a voltmeter, measure voltage between ECM connector "B" (Tan/Black wire) and ground.
2) If battery voltage is present, see appropriate ENGINE PERFORMANCE article for ECM diagnosis. If battery voltage is not present, check bulb and Tan/Black wire for an open circuit or short to ground. If bulb and wire are okay, replace instrument cluster.

INDICATORS & GAUGES PINOUT TEST

Check voltage or resistance at instrument cluster connector to determine if proper readings are supplied to the instrument cluster. See Figs. 1-5.

HEADLIGHT SWITCH

Beretta & Corsica – With headlights on, battery voltage should be present at headlight switch terminal "K" (Yellow wire). If voltage is not present, check wiring and switch.
Camaro – Battery voltage should be present at headlight switch terminal "F" (Red wire). With headlights on, battery voltage should be present at headlight switch terminal "B" (Yellow wire). If voltage is not present, check wiring and switch.
Caprice – Battery voltage should be present at headlight switch terminals "E" (Orange wire) and "C" (Red wire). With headlights on, battery voltage should be present at terminals "A" (Brown wire) and "D" (Yellow wire). If voltage is not present, check wiring and switch.
Cavalier – Battery voltage should be present at headlight switch terminals "E" (Orange wire) and "A" (Orange wire). With headlights on, voltage should be present at terminal "C" (Tan wire). With high beams on, voltage should be present at terminal "B" (Light Green wire). If voltage is not present, check wiring and switch.
Lumina – Battery voltage should be present at headlight switch terminal "F" (Dark Green wire). With headlights on, voltage should be present at terminal "G" (Yellow wire). If voltage is not present, check wiring and switch.

REMOVAL & INSTALLATION

HEADLIGHT SWITCH

Removal & Installation (Beretta & Corsica) – Disconnect negative battery cable. Headlight switch is mounted in switch housing on left side of instrument cluster. Squeeze small knob at side and pull straight out. Insert a small flat blade into slots adjacent to center of inner knob to disengage knob from switch. Remove switch-to-bezel screws and remove switch. To install, reverse removal procedure.
Removal & Installation (Camaro) – 1) Disconnect negative battery cable. Remove knee bolster from underneath instrument panel. Pull headlight switch knob fully outward. Press release button located on headlight switch. Pull knob assembly from headlight switch.
2) Remove headlight switch trim plate. Remove headlight switch retaining nut. Disconnect headlight switch electrical connector and remove headlight switch. To install, reverse removal procedure.
Removal & Installation (Caprice) – Disconnect negative battery cable. Remove left side trim plate. Remove 3 screws attaching switch to instrument panel carrier. Remove switch, panel light dimmer switch connector, headlight switch connector and twilight sentinel switch connector. Remove headlight switch indicator light (if equipped). To install, reverse removal procedure.
Removal & Installation (Lumina) – Disconnect negative battery cable. Remove left instrument panel trim plate. Remove screws, switch assembly and connector. To install, reverse removal procedure.

INSTRUMENT CLUSTER

Removal & Installation (Beretta & Corsica) – Disconnect negative battery cable. Remove bezel-to-instrument panel screws. Pull bezel to rear to disengage clips. Unplug electrical connectors, headlight and windshield wiper switches. Remove instrument cluster bezel. To install, reverse removal procedure. See Fig. 6.

TESTING CONDITIONS

- Ignition switch in ON position except for resistance measurements.

- Make all resistance measurements to ground with the negative battery cable disconnected.

- Measure to ground unless another terminal is given.

- Cluster connector as seen from the driver's seat with the instrument cluster removed.

- If correct voltage or resistance exists at terminals, and cluster function for those terminals does not respond correctly to the measured inputs, replace bulb or instrument cluster.

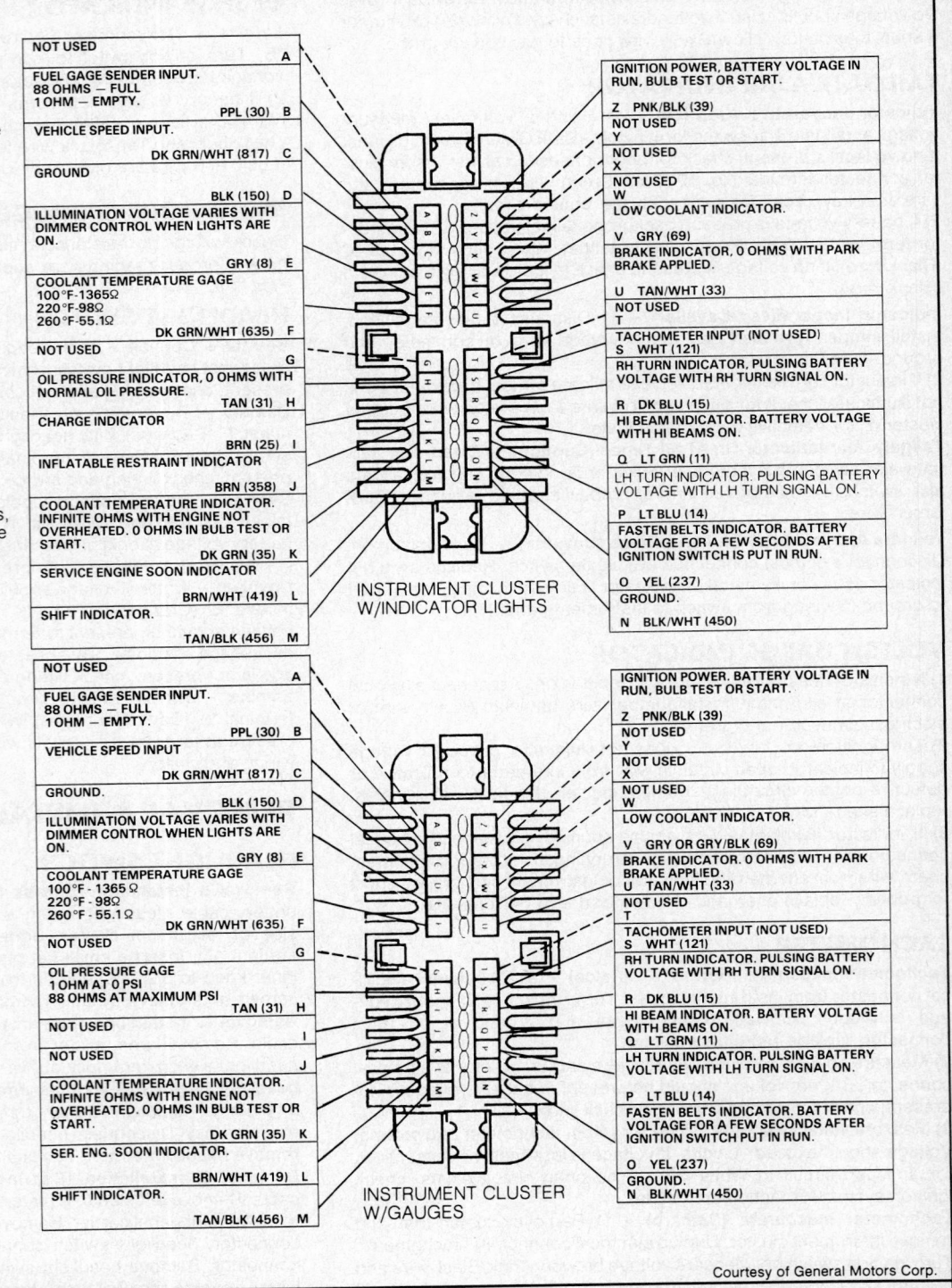

Top cluster (left connector):

NOT USED	A
FUEL GAGE SENDER INPUT. 88 OHMS — FULL 1 OHM — EMPTY. PPL (30)	B
VEHICLE SPEED INPUT. DK GRN/WHT (817)	C
GROUND BLK (150)	D
ILLUMINATION VOLTAGE VARIES WITH DIMMER CONTROL WHEN LIGHTS ARE ON. GRY (8)	E
COOLANT TEMPERATURE GAGE 100°F-1365Ω 220°F-98Ω 260°F-55.1Ω DK GRN/WHT (635)	F
NOT USED	G
OIL PRESSURE INDICATOR, 0 OHMS WITH NORMAL OIL PRESSURE. TAN (31)	H
CHARGE INDICATOR BRN (25)	I
INFLATABLE RESTRAINT INDICATOR BRN (358)	J
COOLANT TEMPERATURE INDICATOR. INFINITE OHMS WITH ENGINE NOT OVERHEATED. 0 OHMS IN BULB TEST OR START. DK GRN (35)	K
SERVICE ENGINE SOON INDICATOR BRN/WHT (419)	L
SHIFT INDICATOR. TAN/BLK (456)	M

Top cluster (right connector):

IGNITION POWER, BATTERY VOLTAGE IN RUN, BULB TEST OR START. Z PNK/BLK (39)	
NOT USED Y	
NOT USED X	
NOT USED W	
LOW COOLANT INDICATOR. V GRY (69)	
BRAKE INDICATOR, 0 OHMS WITH PARK BRAKE APPLIED. U TAN/WHT (33)	
NOT USED T	
TACHOMETER INPUT (NOT USED) S WHT (121)	
RH TURN INDICATOR, PULSING BATTERY VOLTAGE WITH RH TURN SIGNAL ON. R DK BLU (15)	
HI BEAM INDICATOR. BATTERY VOLTAGE WITH HI BEAMS ON. Q LT GRN (11)	
LH TURN INDICATOR. PULSING BATTERY VOLTAGE WITH LH TURN SIGNAL ON. P LT BLU (14)	
FASTEN BELTS INDICATOR. BATTERY VOLTAGE FOR A FEW SECONDS AFTER IGNITION SWITCH IS PUT IN RUN. O YEL (237)	
GROUND. N BLK/WHT (450)	

INSTRUMENT CLUSTER W/INDICATOR LIGHTS

Bottom cluster (left connector):

NOT USED	A
FUEL GAGE SENDER INPUT. 88 OHMS — FULL 1 OHM — EMPTY. PPL (30)	B
VEHICLE SPEED INPUT. DK GRN/WHT (817)	C
GROUND. BLK (150)	D
ILLUMINATION VOLTAGE VARIES WITH DIMMER CONTROL WHEN LIGHTS ARE ON. GRY (8)	E
COOLANT TEMPERATURE GAGE 100°F - 1365 Ω 220°F - 98Ω 260°F - 55.1Ω DK GRN/WHT (635)	F
NOT USED	G
OIL PRESSURE GAGE 1 OHM AT 0 PSI 88 OHMS AT MAXIMUM PSI TAN (31)	H
NOT USED	I
NOT USED	J
COOLANT TEMPERATURE INDICATOR. INFINITE OHMS WITH ENGNE NOT OVERHEATED. 0 OHMS IN BULB TEST OR START. DK GRN (35)	K
SER. ENG. SOON INDICATOR. BRN/WHT (419)	L
SHIFT INDICATOR. TAN/BLK (456)	M

Bottom cluster (right connector):

IGNITION POWER. BATTERY VOLTAGE IN RUN, BULB TEST OR START. Z PNK/BLK (39)	
NOT USED Y	
NOT USED X	
NOT USED W	
LOW COOLANT INDICATOR. V GRY OR GRY/BLK (69)	
BRAKE INDICATOR. 0 OHMS WITH PARK BRAKE APPLIED. U TAN/WHT (33)	
NOT USED T	
TACHOMETER INPUT (NOT USED) S WHT (121)	
RH TURN INDICATOR. PULSING BATTERY VOLTAGE WITH RH TURN SIGNAL ON. R DK BLU (15)	
HI BEAM INDICATOR. BATTERY VOLTAGE WITH BEAMS ON. Q LT GRN (11)	
LH TURN INDICATOR. PULSING BATTERY VOLTAGE WITH LH TURN SIGNAL ON. P LT BLU (14)	
FASTEN BELTS INDICATOR. BATTERY VOLTAGE FOR A FEW SECONDS AFTER IGNITION SWITCH PUT IN RUN. O YEL (237)	
GROUND. N BLK/WHT (450)	

INSTRUMENT CLUSTER W/GAUGES

91E08692   91G08693

Fig. 1: Instrument Cluster Pinout Test – Beretta & Corsica

TESTING CONDITIONS

- Ignition switch in ON position except for resistance measurements.

- Make all resistance measurements to ground with the negative battery cable disconnected.

- Measure to ground unless another terminal is given.

- Cluster connector No. 1 as seen from the driver's seat with the instrument cluster removed.

- Connector No. 1 is on the right side.

- If correct voltage or resistance exists at terminals, and cluster function for those terminals does not respond correctly to the measured inputs, replace bulb or instrument cluster.

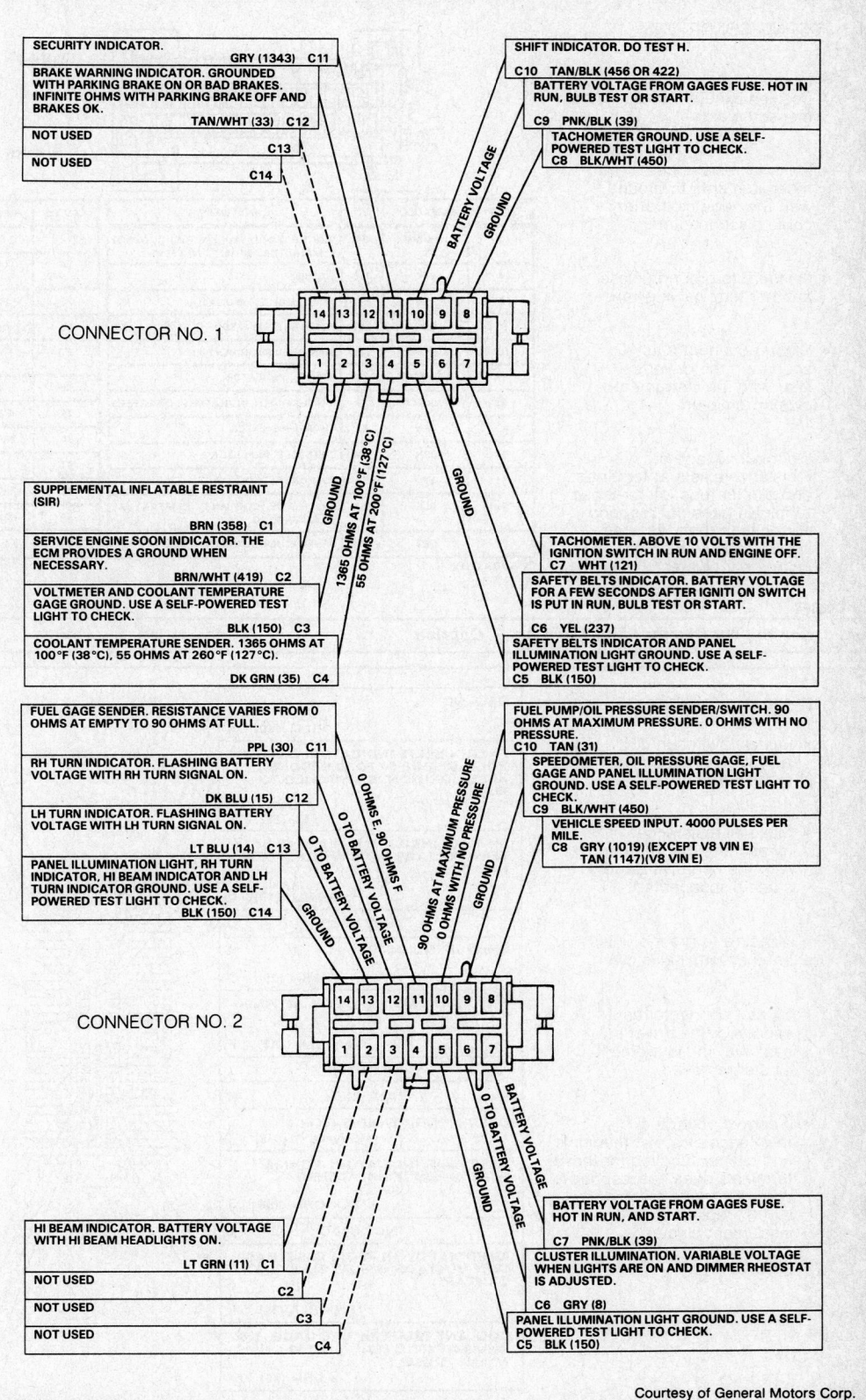

SECURITY INDICATOR.
GRY (1343) C11
BRAKE WARNING INDICATOR. GROUNDED WITH PARKING BRAKE ON OR BAD BRAKES. INFINITE OHMS WITH PARKING BRAKE OFF AND BRAKES OK.
TAN/WHT (33) C12
NOT USED C13
NOT USED C14

SHIFT INDICATOR. DO TEST H.
C10 TAN/BLK (456 OR 422)
BATTERY VOLTAGE FROM GAGES FUSE. HOT IN RUN, BULB TEST OR START.
C9 PNK/BLK (39)
TACHOMETER GROUND. USE A SELF-POWERED TEST LIGHT TO CHECK.
C8 BLK/WHT (450)

CONNECTOR NO. 1

SUPPLEMENTAL INFLATABLE RESTRAINT (SIR)
BRN (358) C1
SERVICE ENGINE SOON INDICATOR. THE ECM PROVIDES A GROUND WHEN NECESSARY.
BRN/WHT (419) C2
VOLTMETER AND COOLANT TEMPERATURE GAGE GROUND. USE A SELF-POWERED TEST LIGHT TO CHECK.
BLK (150) C3
COOLANT TEMPERATURE SENDER. 1365 OHMS AT 100°F (38°C), 55 OHMS AT 260°F (127°C).
DK GRN (35) C4

TACHOMETER. ABOVE 10 VOLTS WITH THE IGNITION SWITCH IN RUN AND ENGINE OFF.
C7 WHT (121)
SAFETY BELTS INDICATOR. BATTERY VOLTAGE FOR A FEW SECONDS AFTER SWITCH IS PUT IN RUN, BULB TEST OR START.
C6 YEL (237)
SAFETY BELTS INDICATOR AND PANEL ILLUMINATION LIGHT GROUND. USE A SELF-POWERED TEST LIGHT TO CHECK.
C5 BLK (150)

FUEL GAGE SENDER. RESISTANCE VARIES FROM 0 OHMS AT EMPTY TO 90 OHMS AT FULL.
PPL (30) C11
RH TURN INDICATOR. FLASHING BATTERY VOLTAGE WITH RH TURN SIGNAL ON.
DK BLU (15) C12
LH TURN INDICATOR. FLASHING BATTERY VOLTAGE WITH LH TURN SIGNAL ON.
LT BLU (14) C13
PANEL ILLUMINATION LIGHT, RH TURN INDICATOR, HI BEAM INDICATOR AND LH TURN INDICATOR GROUND. USE A SELF-POWERED TEST LIGHT TO CHECK.
BLK (150) C14

FUEL PUMP/OIL PRESSURE SENDER/SWITCH. 90 OHMS AT MAXIMUM PRESSURE. 0 OHMS WITH NO PRESSURE.
C10 TAN (31)
SPEEDOMETER, OIL PRESSURE GAGE, FUEL GAGE AND PANEL ILLUMINATION LIGHT GROUND. USE A SELF-POWERED TEST LIGHT TO CHECK.
C9 BLK/WHT (450)
VEHICLE SPEED INPUT. 4000 PULSES PER MILE.
C8 GRY (1019) (EXCEPT V8 VIN E)
TAN (1147)(V8 VIN E)

CONNECTOR NO. 2

HI BEAM INDICATOR. BATTERY VOLTAGE WITH HI BEAM HEADLIGHTS ON.
LT GRN (11) C1
NOT USED C2
NOT USED C3
NOT USED C4

BATTERY VOLTAGE FROM GAGES FUSE. HOT IN RUN, AND START.
C7 PNK/BLK (39)
CLUSTER ILLUMINATION. VARIABLE VOLTAGE WHEN LIGHTS ARE ON AND DIMMER RHEOSTAT IS ADJUSTED.
C6 GRY (8)
PANEL ILLUMINATION LIGHT GROUND. USE A SELF-POWERED TEST LIGHT TO CHECK.
C5 BLK (150)

91I08694 91B08695

Courtesy of General Motors Corp.

Fig. 2: Instrument Cluster Pinout Testing – Camaro

TESTING CONDITIONS

- Ignition switch in ON position except for resistance measurements.

- Make all resistance measurements to ground with the negative battery cable disconnected.

- Measure to ground unless another terminal is given.

- Cluster connector as seen from the driver's seat with the instrument cluster removed.

- If correct voltage or resistance exists at terminals, and cluster function for those terminals does not respond correctly to the measured inputs, replace bulb or instrument cluster.

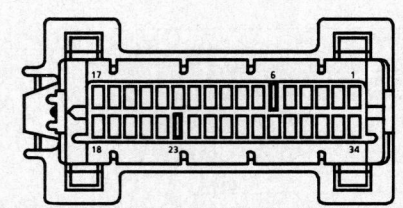

INSTRUMENT CLUSTER CONNECTOR

CAVITY	WIRE COLOR	CKT	DESCRIPTION
1	PNK/BLK	39	IGNITION INPUT, FUEL GAGE, COOLANT TEMPERATURE GAGE, POWER FEED
4	BLK	150	GROUND
8	YEL	237	"FASTEN BELTS" INDICATOR
9*	ORN	340	FUSED BATTERY FEED
10*	DK GRN	146	TAILGATE AJAR INDICATOR
11	TAN/WHT	33	"BRAKE" INDICATOR
12	PNK/BLK	39	IGNITION INPUT, INDICATORS POWER FEED
13	BRN	25	CHARGE INDICATOR
14	BRN	358	"INFL REST" INDICATOR
15	PPL	30	FUEL GAGE SENDER INPUT
16	BLK	150	FUEL GAGE, COOLANT TEMPERATURE GAGE, GROUND
21	GRY	8	PANEL ILLUMINATION LAMPS

CAVITY	WIRE COLOR	CKT	DESCRIPTION
22	BLK	150	INDICATOR AND PANEL LAMPS GROUND
24	LT BLU	14	LH TURN INDICATOR
25	LT GRN	11	HI BEAM INDICATOR
26	DK BLU	15	RH TURN INDICATOR
27	PNK/BLK	439	IGNITION INPUT, SPEEDOMETER POWER FEED
28	BRN	1147	VEHICLE SPEED INPUT
29	BLK/WHT	450	SPEEDOMETER GROUND
30	BRN/WHT	419	"SERVICE ENGINE SOON" INDICATOR
31	TAN	31	OIL PRESSURE INDICATOR
32	LT GRN/BLK	875	"ANTILOCK BRAKE" INDICATOR
33	DK GRN	35	COOLANT TEMPERATURE INDICATOR
34	DK GRN/WHT	135	COOLANT TEMPERATURE GAGE

*WAGON ONLY

91D08696

Courtesy of General Motors Corp.

Fig. 3: Instrument Cluster Pinout Testing – Caprice

TESTING CONDITIONS

- Ignition switch in ON position except for resistance measurements.

- Make all resistance measurements to ground with the negative battery cable disconnected.

- Measure to ground unless another terminal is given.

- Cluster connector as seen from the driver's seat with the instrument cluster removed.

- If correct voltage or resistance exists at terminals, and cluster function for those terminals does not respond correctly to the measured inputs, replace bulb or instrument cluster.

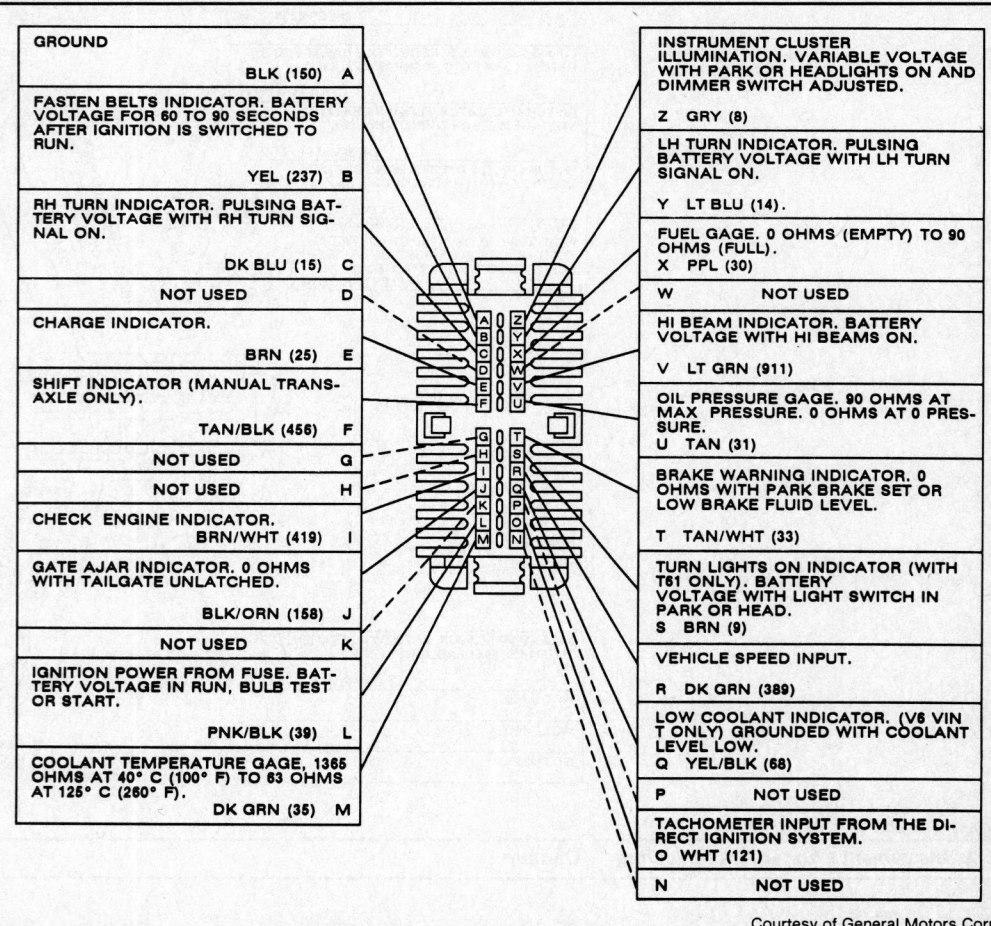

GROUND

BLK (150)   A

FASTEN BELTS INDICATOR. BATTERY VOLTAGE FOR 60 TO 90 SECONDS AFTER IGNITION IS SWITCHED TO RUN.

YEL (237)   B

RH TURN INDICATOR. PULSING BATTERY VOLTAGE WITH RH TURN SIGNAL ON.

DK BLU (15)   C

NOT USED   D

CHARGE INDICATOR.

BRN (25)   E

SHIFT INDICATOR (MANUAL TRANSAXLE ONLY).

TAN/BLK (456)   F

NOT USED   G

NOT USED   H

CHECK ENGINE INDICATOR.

BRN/WHT (419)   I

GATE AJAR INDICATOR. 0 OHMS WITH TAILGATE UNLATCHED.

BLK/ORN (158)   J

NOT USED   K

IGNITION POWER FROM FUSE. BATTERY VOLTAGE IN RUN, BULB TEST OR START.

PNK/BLK (39)   L

COOLANT TEMPERATURE GAGE, 1365 OHMS AT 40° C (100° F) TO 63 OHMS AT 125° C (260° F).

DK GRN (35)   M

INSTRUMENT CLUSTER ILLUMINATION. VARIABLE VOLTAGE WITH PARK OR HEADLIGHTS ON AND DIMMER SWITCH ADJUSTED.

Z   GRY (8)

LH TURN INDICATOR. PULSING BATTERY VOLTAGE WITH LH TURN SIGNAL ON.

Y   LT BLU (14).

FUEL GAGE. 0 OHMS (EMPTY) TO 90 OHMS (FULL).

X   PPL (30)

W   NOT USED

HI BEAM INDICATOR. BATTERY VOLTAGE WITH HI BEAMS ON.

V   LT GRN (911)

OIL PRESSURE GAGE. 90 OHMS AT MAX PRESSURE. 0 OHMS AT 0 PRESSURE.

U   TAN (31)

BRAKE WARNING INDICATOR. 0 OHMS WITH PARK BRAKE SET OR LOW BRAKE FLUID LEVEL.

T   TAN/WHT (33)

TURN LIGHTS ON INDICATOR (WITH T61 ONLY). BATTERY VOLTAGE WITH LIGHT SWITCH IN PARK OR HEAD.

S   BRN (9)

VEHICLE SPEED INPUT.

R   DK GRN (389)

LOW COOLANT INDICATOR. (V6 VIN T ONLY) GROUNDED WITH COOLANT LEVEL LOW.

Q   YEL/BLK (68)

P   NOT USED

TACHOMETER INPUT FROM THE DIRECT IGNITION SYSTEM.

O   WHT (121)

N   NOT USED

91F08697

Courtesy of General Motors Corp.

Fig. 4: Instrument Cluster Pinout Testing – Cavalier

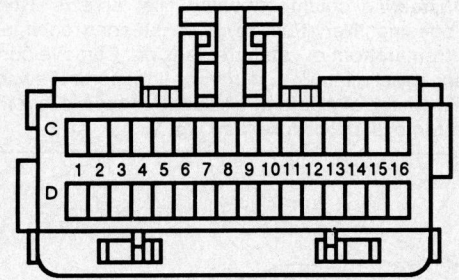

INSTRUMENT CLUSTER CONNECTOR

TESTING CONDITIONS

- Ignition switch in RUN position except for resistance measurements.

- Make all resistance measurements to ground with the negative battery cable disconnected.

- Measure to ground unless another terminal is given.

- Cluster connector as seen from the driver's seat with the instrument cluster removed.

- If correct voltage or resistance exists at terminals, and cluster function for those terminals does not respond correctly to the measured inputs, replace bulb or instrument cluster.

Terminal-Wire Color	Function
C1	NOT USED
C2 BLK (150)	Instrument Cluster ground
C3 GRY (8)	Illumination. Variable volts with lights on and dimmer control adjusted
C4	NOT USED
C5 PPL (30)	Fuel Gage input, 0 ohms empty, 90 ohms full.
C6	NOT USED
C7 DK GRN (35)	Coolant Temperature Gage input. 55 ohms at 260° F (125° C) to 1365 ohms at 100° F (37° C).
C8	NOT USED
C9 LT BLU (14)	LH Turn Indicator. Flashing battery voltage with LH turn signal on. 0 volts with signal off
C10	NOT USED
C11 YEL (237)	FASTEN BELTS Indicator. Battery voltage for about 5 seconds after ignition is switched to RUN
C12	NOT USED
C13 TAN (31)	Oil Gage input. 0 ohms 0 psi, 86 ohms 80 psi (550 kPa).
C14 TAN/WHT (33)	BRAKE Indicator. Ground with park brake set. Normally open
C15 BRN (25)	CHARGE INDICATOR
C16 YEL/BLK (68)	LOW COOLANT Indicator control line from Coolant Level Switch.
D1 DK BLU (15)	RH Turn Indicator. Battery voltage with RH turn signal on. 0 volts with signal off
D2 LT GRN (11)	HI Beam Indicator. Battery voltage with hi beams on. 0 volts with HI Beams off
D3 TAN/BLK (456)	SHIFT Indicator control line from Electronic Control Module (ECM). Do Test M
D4 PNK/BLK (39)	Ignition Power from INDIC Fuse. Battery voltage in RUN, BULB TEST and START
D5 DK GRN (389)	Speed input from ECM
D6 BLK (151)	Instrument Cluster ground
D7	NOT USED
D8	NOT USED
D9 WHT (121)	Tachometer input from Direct Ignition System.
D10	NOT USED
D11 PNK/BLK (39)	Ignition power from INDIC Fuse. Battery voltage in RUN, BULB TEST and START
D12	NOT USED
D13 TAN/WHT (33)	BRAKE Indicator. Grounded with Ignition Switch in BULB TEST or START. Normally open
D14 TAN/WHT (33)	BRAKE Indicator. Grounded with low brake fluid level. Normally open
D15	NOT USED
D16 BRN/WHT (419)	SERVICE ENGINE SOON Indicator

Terminal/ Wire	Function
C1	NOT USED
C2	NOT USED
C3 PNK/BLK (39)	Ignition power from INDC Fuse. Battery voltage in RUN, BULB TEST OR START
C4 YEL/BLK (68)	LOW COOLANT Indicator. Grounded by ECM with coolant level low.
C5 TAN/WHT (33)	BRAKE Indicator. Grounded with park brake set or low brake fluid level
C6 BRN (25)	Charge Indicator.
C7 DK GRN (35)	Coolant Temperature Indicator. Grounded in BULB TEST or with coolant level above 260° F (127°C).
C8	NOT USED
C9 BLK (150)	Ground
C10 BRN/WHT(419)	SERVICE ENGINE SOON Indicator
C11 TAN/BLK(456)	Shift Indicator.
C12	NOT USED
C13 PPL (30)	Fuel Gage. 90 ohms full, 0 ohms empty.
C14	NOT USED
C15	NOT USED
C16 LT BLU (14)	LH Turn Indicator. Flashing battery voltage with LH Turn Indicator on
D1 TAN (31)	Oil Pressure Indicator. Grounded with low oil pressure, open with Engine running and oil pressure OK
D2 YEL (237)	Fasten Belts Indicator
D3	NOT USED
D4	NOT USED
D5	NOT USED
D6	NOT USED
D7	NOT USED
D8 GRY (8)	Instrument Cluster Dimming. Variable voltage with lights on and dimmer control adjusted
D9	NOT USED
D10	NOT USED
D11	NOT USED
D12 BLK/WHT(151)	Ground
D13 DK GRN (389)	Vehicle Speed Sensor input
D14	NOT USED
D15 DK BLU (15)	RH Turn Indicator. Flashing battery voltage with RH Turn Signal on
D16 LT GRN (11)	Hi Beam Indicator. Battery voltage with HI Beams on

91H08698

Fig. 5: Instrument Cluster Pinout Testing – Lumina

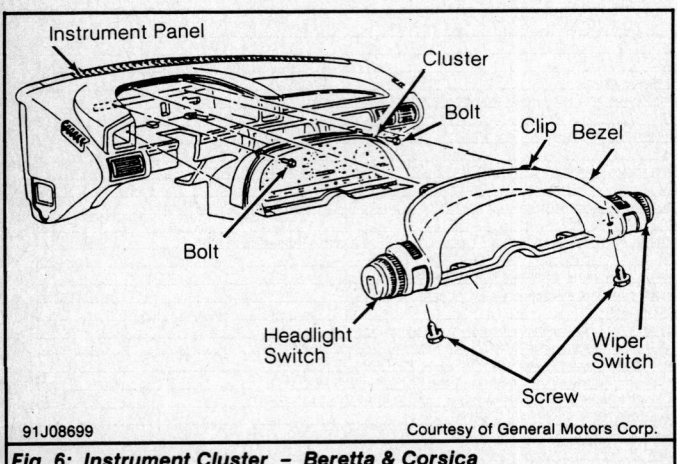

91J08699   Courtesy of General Motors Corp.

Fig. 6: Instrument Cluster – Beretta & Corsica

Removal & Installation (Camaro) – Disconnect negative battery cable. Place ignition switch in LOCK position. Remove instrument cluster trim plate. Remove cluster screws and remove cluster. Remove cluster lens attaching screws and remove cluster lens. *See Fig. 7.* To install, reverse removal procedure.

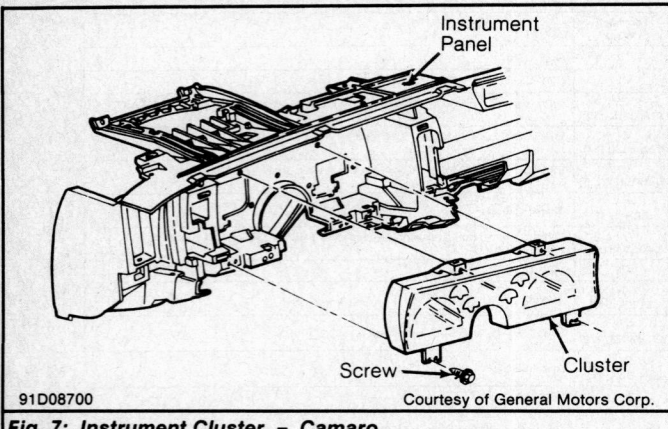

91D08700   Courtesy of General Motors Corp.

Fig. 7: Instrument Cluster – Camaro

Removal & Installation (Caprice) – Disconnect negative battery cable. Remove left side trim plate. Remove 5 screws attaching cluster to instrument panel carrier. Remove shift indicator cable from steering column. Remove cluster from instrument panel carrier. *See Fig. 8.* To install, reverse removal procedure.

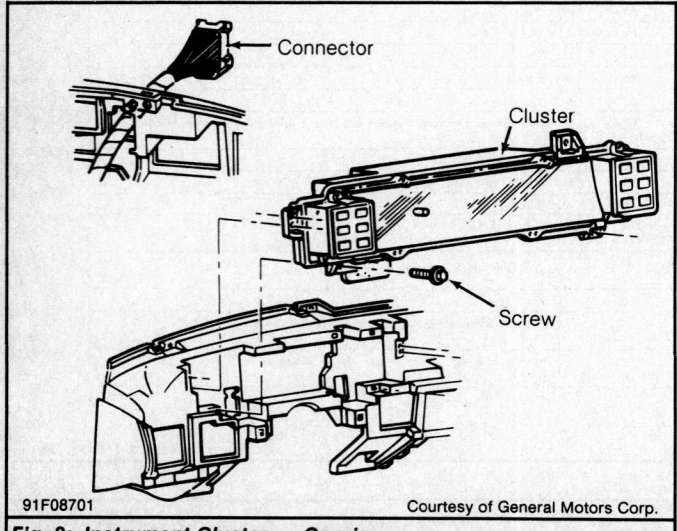

91F08701   Courtesy of General Motors Corp.

Fig. 8: Instrument Cluster – Caprice

Removal & Installation (Cavalier) – Disconnect negative batter‍y cable. Remove 4 steering column opening filler screws. Remov‍e steering column opening filler. Pull down on steering column an‍d remove 2 screws from bottom of cluster extension. Remove connec‍tor from instrument panel dimmer and interior light control switche‍s. Remove 2 screws from top of cluster. Pull cluster rearward to remov‍e. To install, reverse removal procedure. *See Fig. 9.*

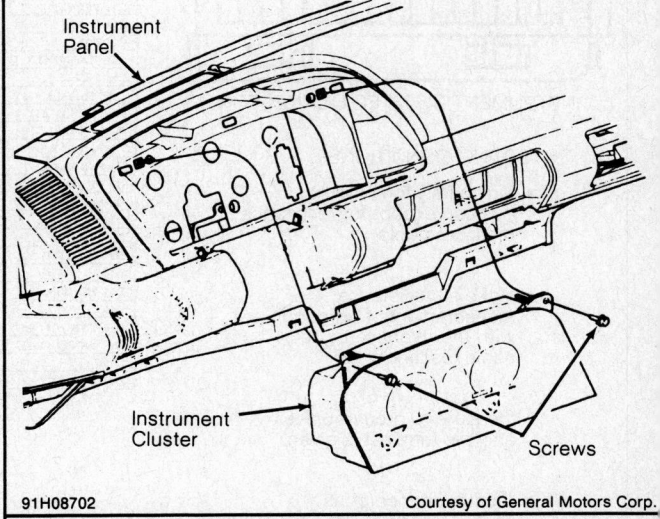

91H08702   Courtesy of General Motors Corp.

Fig. 9: Instrument Cluster – Cavalier

Removal & Installation (Lumina) – Disconnect negative batte‍ry cable. Remove instrument panel pad. Remove 4 cluster-to-dashboar‍d screws. Unplug electrical connectors and remove PRNDL shift indica‍tor cable (if equipped). Remove cluster. To install, reverse remova‍l procedure. *See Fig. 10.*

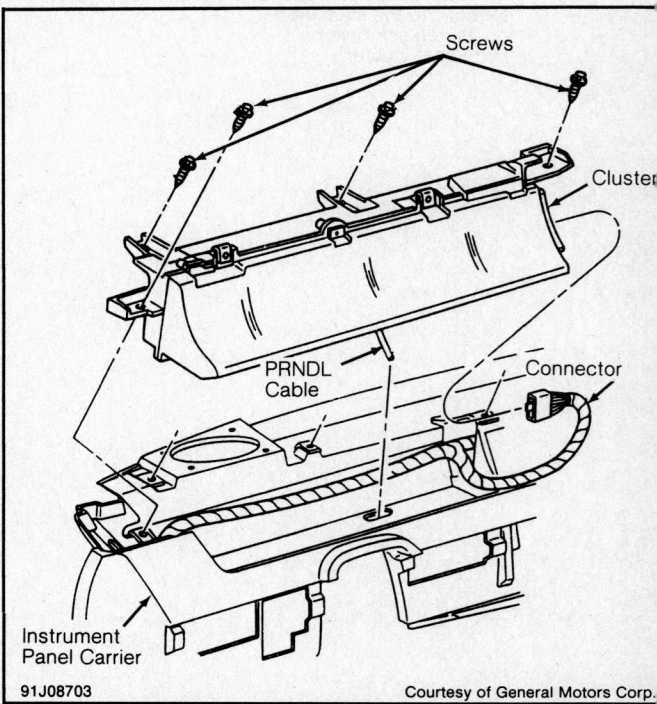

91J08703   Courtesy of General Motors Corp.

Fig. 10: Instrument Cluster – Lumina

WIRING DIAGRAMS
See appropriate chassis wiring diagram in WIRING DIAGRAMS.

Custom Cruiser, Cutlass Calais, Cutlass Ciera, Cutlass Cruiser, Eighty-Eight, Ninety-Eight, Toronado, Touring Sedan, Trofeo

DESCRIPTION & OPERATION

GAUGES & SENDERS

Current flows through coils in gauge, creating magnetic field that moves gauge needle. Resistance of sender determines current flow through gauge coils.

COOLANT TEMPERATURE & OIL PRESSURE SENDERS LOCATION

Application	[1] Location
Coolant Temperature Sender	
Custom Cruiser	Below Left Exhaust Manifold, Near Front Of Engine
Cutlass Calais	
2.3L	At Rear End Of Cylinder Head, Below Coolant Outlet
2.5L	At Rear End Of Cylinder Head, Near Exhaust Manifold
3.3L	Below Alternator
Cutlass Ciera & Cutlass Cruiser	
2.5L	Mounted Vertically To Rear End Of Cylinder Head
3.3L	On Front Of Engine, Above Water Pump Pulley
Eighty-Eight	On Rear End Of Intake Manifold
Ninety-Eight & Touring Sedan	On Intake Manifold, Near Rear End Of Right Cylinder Head
Toronado & Trofeo	Below Throttle Body Inlet
Oil Pressure Sender	
2.3L	Above Coolant Outlet
2.5L, 3.3L & 3.8L	On Right Side Of Cylinder Block
5.0L	On Left Side Of Cylinder Block

[1] – When determining component locations on vehicle with transverse-mounted engine, rear of engine refers to flywheel end of engine, not the side of engine facing firewall.

SPEEDOMETER

Speedometer is electrically operated. Current flows through coils in speedometer, creating magnetic field that moves speedometer needle. Vehicle speed sensor generates A/C voltage, which ECM converts to D/C voltage. This D/C voltage drives speedometer needle.

COOLANT TEMPERATURE INDICATOR

The coolant temperature indicator is actuated by a sending unit which grounds indicator circuit as engine coolant reaches approximately 260°F (127°C). It is also actuated when ignition switch is in ON position and engine is not running.

OIL PRESSURE INDICATOR

If oil pressure is less than 5 psi, a sending unit on the engine will close, completing indicator light ground circuit. Oil pressure light should come on when ignition is on and engine is not running.

ALTERNATOR INDICATOR

Indicator light should glow when engine is not running and ignition is on. Light should go off and stay off once engine has been started and accelerated above idle.

BRAKE SYSTEM WARNING INDICATOR

The brake system warning indicator will light when brake hydraulic pressure is lost or when parking brake is applied. With ignition switch turned slowly past RUN position, BRAKE indicator should come on before ignition switch reaches START position. With ignition switch in RUN position and parking brake on, BRAKE indicator should come on.

SHIFT INDICATOR

Some vehicles equipped with manual transaxle are equipped with a shift indicator lamp that indicates when vehicle should be shifted into next highest gear. Battery voltage is applied to one side of bulb and opposite side is controlled by ECM.

TESTING

PRELIMINARY CHECK

On Toronado, Touring Sedan and Trofeo, check for Power Train Control Module/Body Control Module (PCM/BCM) codes. See appropriate SELF-DIAGNOSTICS article in ENGINE PERFORMANCE. On all models, if more than one indicator or gauge is inoperative, check instrument cluster power and ground circuits, printed circuit (for cracks) and wiring harness connections on back of instrument cluster.

FUEL GAUGE & SENDER TEST (EXCEPT TORONADO, TOURING SEDAN & TROFEO)

Gauge Always Indicates Empty – 1) Disconnect fuel gauge sender connector near fuel tank. Turn ignition on. If gauge indicates full, replace sender.

2) If gauge still indicates empty, check for short to ground in Purple wire. If Purple wire is okay, replace fuel gauge.

Gauge Always Indicates Full – 1) Turn ignition on. Disconnect fuel gauge sender connector near fuel tank. Connect jumper between ground and Purple wire terminal of fuel gauge sender connector (harness side).

2) If fuel gauge no longer indicates full, go to next step. If fuel gauge still indicates full, check for open in Purple wire between instrument cluster and fuel gauge sender. If Purple wire is okay, replace fuel gauge.

3) Connect jumper wire between Purple and Black/White wire terminals of fuel gauge sender connector (harness side). If fuel gauge no longer indicates full, replace fuel gauge sender. If fuel gauge still indicates full, check for high resistance in Black/White wire between fuel gauge sender and ground.

Gauge Is Inaccurate – 1) Turn ignition on. Disconnect fuel gauge sender connector near fuel tank. Connect Gauge Tester (J-33431-B) between ground and Purple wire terminal of fuel gauge sender connector (harness side).

NOTE: If gauge tester is not available, use resistors of equal value to those specified in procedure.

2) Set gauge tester to 0 ohms. If fuel gauge indicates empty, go to next step. If fuel gauge does not indicate empty, check for open in instrument cluster printed circuit and wiring harness. Check for short to B+ in Purple wire between instrument cluster and fuel gauge sender. If instrument cluster printed circuit, wiring harness and Purple wire circuit are okay, repair or replace fuel gauge.

3) Set gauge tester to 90 ohms. If fuel gauge indicates full, go to next step. If fuel gauge does not indicate full, check for open in instrument cluster printed circuit, wiring harness and Purple wire between instrument cluster and fuel gauge sender. If instrument cluster printed circuit, wiring harness and Purple wire circuit are okay, repair or replace fuel gauge.

4) Observe fuel gauge while changing gauge tester resistance values from 0-90 ohms. If indicated fuel level does not match resistance values as specified in SIMULATED RESISTANCE TEST table, go to next step. If indicated fuel level matches resistance values, go to step 6).

5) Check for open in instrument cluster printed circuit and wiring harness and repair or replace as necessary. If printed circuit and wiring harness are okay, replace fuel gauge.

6) Ensure continuity is present in fuel gauge sender ground circuit, fuel gauge sender float does not contact tank interior and wiring harness is okay. If ground circuit, float clearance and wiring harness are okay, replace fuel gauge.

1991 SAFETY EQUIPMENT
Analog Instrument Panels – Oldsmobile (Cont.)

SIMULATED RESISTANCE TEST

Resistance (Ohms) [1]	Indicated Fuel Level
88	Full
60	3/4
50	1/2
26	1/4
1.0	Empty

[1] – Resistance values are approximate.

FUEL GAUGE & SENDER TEST (TORONADO, TOURING SEDAN & TROFEO)

Toronado & Trofeo – 1) Turn ignition on. Disconnect fuel gauge sender connector near fuel tank. In steps **2)**, **3)** and **4)**, check for battery voltage using voltmeter at harness side of fuel gauge sender connector.

2) Measure voltage between ground and Pink/Black wire terminal. If battery voltage is present, go to next step. If no voltage is present, check for open in Pink/Black wire.

3) Measure voltage between Pink/Black and Black/White wire terminals. If battery voltage is present, go to next step. If no voltage is present, check for open in Black/White wire.

4) Measure voltage between Pink/Black and Purple wire terminals. If battery voltage is present, go to next step. If no voltage is present, check for open or short to B+ in Purple wire. If Purple wire is okay, go to next step.

5) Leave fuel gauge sender connector disconnected. Enter diagnostics and select BCM Data Input BD40. See appropriate SELF-DIAGNOSTICS article in ENGINE PERFORMANCE. Connect fused jumper between Pink/Black and Purple wire terminals of fuel gauge sender connector.

6) If BCM Data Input BD40 displays approximately 25 and fuel gauge indicates full, replace sender. If BCM Data Input BD40 does not display approximately 25 and fuel gauge does not indicate full, check Purple wire for short to ground. If Purple wire is okay, replace Body Computer Module (BCM).

Touring Sedan – 1) Turn ignition on. If Driver's Information Center (DIC) displays FUEL SENDER PROB, go to next step. If DIC does not display FUEL SENDER PROB, go to step **4)**.

2) Disconnect fuel gauge sender connector near fuel tank. Connect jumper wire between ground and Purple wire terminal of sender connector (harness side).

3) If gauge indicates empty, check for open in Black/White wire circuit. If Black/White wire circuit is okay, replace sender. If fuel gauge does not indicate empty, check for open in Purple wire circuit. If Purple wire circuit is okay, replace instrument cluster.

4) To enter DIC diagnostic mode, turn ignition on. Press button No. 7 (DEST) on DIC panel. Press buttons No. 8, 1, 9 and 2 (ETA, ECON, E/T and FUEL). Press ENTER. DIC is now in diagnostic mode.

5) Observe percentage displayed in position EE of DIC display. *See Fig. 1.* If displayed percentage does not agree with fuel level indicated by gauge, replace instrument cluster. If percentage displayed agrees, disconnect fuel gauge sender connector near fuel tank.

6) Connect Gauge Tester (J-33431-B) between Purple and Black/White wire terminals of sender connector (harness side). Set gauge tester resistance to 0 ohms and then 90 ohms. Observe position EE of DIC display.

7) If DIC displays 00 with gauge tester set at 0 ohms, and 99 with gauge tester set at 90 ohms, replace sender. If DIC does not display as specified, check Purple wire for short to ground or high resistance (2 or more ohms), and check Black/White wire for high resistance (2

or more ohms). If Purple and Black/White wires are okay, replace instrument cluster.

TEMP GAUGE & SENDER TEST (EXCEPT TORONADO, TOURING SEDAN & TROFEO)

Gauge Always Indicates Cold – 1) Disconnect coolant temperature sender connector. Ground the Dark Green/White wire terminal. Turn ignition on.

2) If gauge indicates hot, replace sender. If gauge still indicates cold, check for open in Dark Green/White wire. If Dark Green/White wire is okay, replace gauge.

Gauge Always Indicates Hot – Disconnect coolant temperature sender connector. Turn ignition on. If gauge indicates cold, replace sender. If gauge does not indicate cold, check for short to ground in Dark Green/White wire. If Dark Green/White wire is okay, replace gauge.

Gauge Is Inaccurate – 1) Disconnect coolant temperature sender connector. Connect Red lead of Gauge Tester (J-33431) to ground and other lead to Dark Green/White wire terminal of coolant temperature sender connector (harness side).

NOTE: If gauge tester is not available, use resistors equal to resistances specified in procedure.

2) While observing temperature gauge, adjust gauge tester resistance values to 1400 ohms, 93 ohms and 55 ohms, respectively. If gauge indicates cold, mid-scale and hot, respectively, replace sender.

3) If gauge does not indicate as specified in step **2)**, check Dark Green/White wire. If Dark Green/White wire is okay, replace gauge.

TEMPERATURE GAUGE & SENDER TEST (TORONADO, TOURING SEDAN & TROFEO)

Toronado & Trofeo – 1) Ensure engine is not overheating. Enter diagnostics and ensure PCM codes E014 and E015 are not set. See appropriate SELF-DIAGNOSTICS article in ENGINE PERFORMANCE. Ensure BCM code B450 is not set. If any codes are set, perform necessary repairs and clear codes before continuing test procedure.

2) Measure actual coolant temperature. Select PCM Data Input ED04 and note data display. If PCM Data Input ED04 and data display are not approximately equal, replace coolant temperature sender.

Touring Sedan – 1) Disconnect coolant temperature sender connector. Connect Red lead of Gauge Tester (J-33431) to ground and other lead to Dark Green/White wire terminal of coolant temperature sender connector (harness side).

NOTE: If gauge tester is not available, use resistors equal to resistances specified in procedure.

2) While observing temperature gauge, adjust gauge tester resistance values to 1365 ohms and then 44 ohms. If gauge indicates cold at 1365 ohms and hot at 44 ohms, replace sender.

3) If gauge does not indicate as specified in step **2)**, check instrument cluster connections, Dark Green/White wire and Black wire for high resistance (2 or more ohms) or short to ground. If connections and wires are okay, replace gauge.

OIL PRESSURE GAUGE & SENDER TEST (EXCEPT TORONADO, TOURING SEDAN & TROFEO)

Gauge Always Indicates LOW – Turn ignition on. Disconnect oil pressure sender connector. If gauge indicates HIGH, replace sender. If gauge still indicates LOW, check Tan wire (Tan/Black on some models). If Tan wire is okay, replace gauge.

Gauge Always Indicates HIGH – Turn ignition on. Disconnect oil pressure sender connector. Connect fused jumper between ground and Tan wire terminal of oil pressure sender connector (Tan/Black on some models). If gauge indicates LOW, replace sender. If gauge still indicates HIGH, check Tan wire. If Tan wire is okay, replace gauge.

Gauge Is Inaccurate – 1) Disconnect oil pressure sender connector. Connect one lead of Gauge Tester (J-33431) to ground and other lead to Tan wire terminal of oil pressure sender connector (Tan/Black on

INFORMATION CENTER

_ A _ BB _ C _ DD _ EE _ FF _ G _ H

Position EE

91I08236   Courtesy of General Motors Corp.

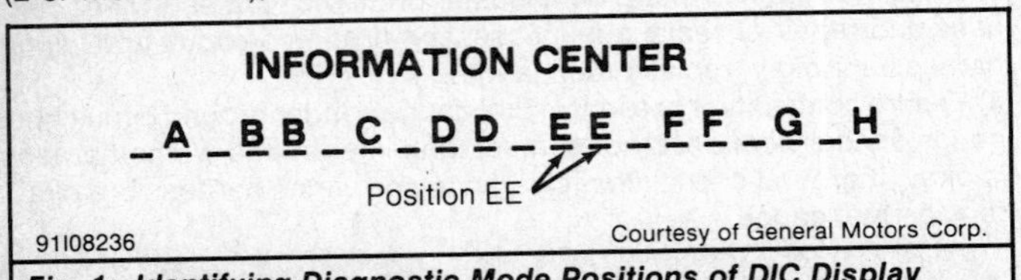

Fig. 1: Identifying Diagnostic Mode Positions of DIC Display (Touring Sedan)

some models). While observing oil pressure gauge, adjust gauge tester resistance values to 0 ohms and then 90 ohms.

NOTE: If gauge tester is not available, use resistors equal to resistances specified in procedure.

2) If gauge indicates LOW then HIGH, replace sender. If gauge does not indicate as specified, check Tan wire. If Tan wire is okay, replace gauge.

OIL PRESSURE GAUGE & SENDER TEST (TORONADO, TOURING SEDAN & TROFEO)

Toronado & Trofeo – 1) Enter diagnostics. See appropriate SELF-DIAGNOSTICS article in ENGINE PERFORMANCE. If BCM diagnostic code B132 is not set, go to next step. If code B132 is set, perform appropriate diagnostic procedure.

2) Measure oil pressure to determine if low or high oil pressure condition exists and repair as necessary. If oil pressure is okay, disconnect oil pressure sender connector.

3) Connect voltmeter between ground and Light Green wire terminal of oil pressure sender connector. Turn ignition on. If 5 volts are present, replace sender. If 5 volts are not present, connect voltmeter between ground and Light Green wire terminal of BCM 32-pin Red connector (connector connected).

4) If 5 volts are present, check for poor connections in Light Green wire circuit and repair as necessary. If 5 volts are not present, check for short to ground in Light Green wire circuit. If Light Green wire circuit is okay, replace BCM.

Touring Sedan – 1) Turn ignition on. If Driver's Information Center (DIC) displays OIL PRESSURE SENDER PROB, go to next step. If DIC does not display OIL PRESSURE SENDER PROB, go to step **4)**.

2) Disconnect oil pressure sender connector. Connect jumper wire between ground and Tan wire terminal of sender connector (harness side).

3) If gauge indicates low, check for open in Black wire circuit. If Black wire circuit is okay, replace sender. If oil pressure gauge does not indicate low, check for open in Tan wire circuit. If Tan wire circuit is okay, replace gauge.

4) Start engine. Press GAGE button on DIC panel until display shows oil pressure. If oil pressure displayed does not agree with oil pressure indicated by gauge, replace gauge.

5) If oil pressure displayed agrees with oil pressure indicated by gauge, disconnect oil pressure sender connector. Connect one lead of Gauge Tester (J-33431) to ground and other lead to Tan wire terminal of oil pressure sender connector.

6) Set gauge tester resistance to 0 ohms and then 86 ohms. If oil pressure gauge indicates 0 psi at 0 ohms and 120 psi at 86 ohms, replace sender.

7) If oil pressure gauge does not indicate as specified in step **6)**, check Tan wire for short to ground or high resistance (2 or more ohms), and check Black wire for high resistance (2 or more ohms). If Tan and Black wires are okay, replace gauge.

VOLTMETER TEST

Touring Sedan – Turn ignition on. Press GAGE button on DIC switch panel until DIC displays battery voltage. If DIC display voltage does not agree with voltmeter, replace instrument cluster.

Toronado & Trofeo – 1) Enter diagnostics and check for BCM codes B411 and B412. See appropriate SELF-DIAGNOSTICS article in ENGINE PERFORMANCE. If code(s) are not set, go to next step. If code(s) are set, perform appropriate diagnostic procedure.

2) Check instrument cluster connector terminal contact for poor connection and repair as necessary. If only one gauge does not operate, malfunctioning BCM/PCM or related sensor is probably the cause. If more than one gauge does not operate, replace instrument cluster.

All Others – Ensure charging system is operating, battery is fully charged and instrument panel wiring is okay. See appropriate ALTERNATORS & REGULATORS article in ELECTRICAL. If charging system is operating, battery is fully charged and instrument panel wiring is okay, repair or replace voltmeter.

HEADLIGHT SWITCH TEST

1) Check for battery voltage at Black/Orange wire terminal (Toronado and Trofeo) or Red wire terminal (all other models) of headlight switch connector. If no voltage is present, check fusible link and wire.

2) If battery voltage is present, turn on headlight switch. Check for battery voltage at Tan wire terminal (Toronado and Trofeo) or Yellow wire terminal (all other models) of headlight switch connector with connector intact.

3) If battery voltage is present, switch is okay. If battery voltage is not present, check for poor connection at headlight switch connector. If connections are okay, replace headlight switch.

WIPER SWITCH TEST

NOTE: For wiper switch testing information, see appropriate WIPER/WASHER SYSTEMS article.

REMOVAL & INSTALLATION

INSTRUMENT CLUSTER

Removal & Installation (Custom Cruiser) – 1) Turn ignition off. Remove 2 screws from lower steering column cover. Gently pull down lower steering column cover and remove. Loosen (DO NOT remove) steering column nuts, and partially lower the steering column.

2) Remove 8 left trim plate-to-instrument panel carrier screws. *See Fig. 2.* Carefully remove left trim plate by pulling rearward, unsnapping it from instrument panel carrier.

3) Remove 4 instrument cluster-to-instrument panel carrier screws. Disconnect shift indicator cable from steering column. Remove instrument cluster by carefully pulling rearward. To install, reverse removal procedure.

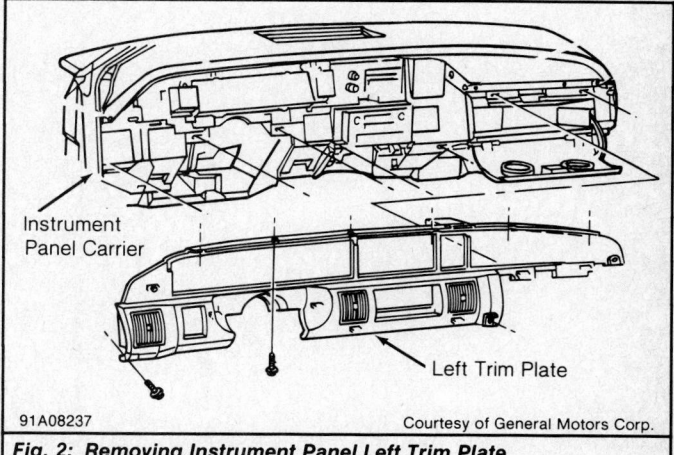

Instrument Panel Carrier

Left Trim Plate

91A08237 Courtesy of General Motors Corp.

Fig. 2: Removing Instrument Panel Left Trim Plate (Custom Cruiser)

Removal & Installation (Cutlass Calais) – Remove steering column collar. Remove 4 steering column trim plate screws. Remove 4 cluster trim plate screws. Remove 2 steering column support bolts and lower steering column. Remove 4 instrument cluster screws. Pull instrument cluster rearward and remove. To install, reverse removal procedure.

Removal & Installation (Cutlass Ciera & Cutlass Cruiser) – 1) Turn ignition off. Remove console upper trim plate (if equipped). Pry steering column collar rearward to release 5 clips.

2) Remove outer air deflectors (vents) by pulling rearward. Remove bolt and screw from each deflector opening. Remove bolt from steering column collar opening. On vehicles without console, open ashtray and remove 2 trim plate bolts.

3) On vehicles with console, remove 4 ashtray trim cover bolts and trim cover. Remove 2 center trim cover bolts. *See Fig. 3.* On vehicles with column shift, move shift lever to "1" position. On all vehicles, remove accessory trim cover by pulling rearward to release clips.

4) Remove instrument cluster trim cover screws. Remove instrument cluster trim cover by pulling top rearward then lifting up and out. Remove steering column trim cover.

5) Disconnect shift indicator clip from steering column shift bowl. Remove 4 cluster bolts and remove cluster. To install, reverse removal procedure.

Removal & Installation (Eighty-Eight) – **1)** Turn ignition off. Remove center trim cover. *See Fig. 3.* Remove instrument cluster trim plate screws and instrument cluster trim plate. Remove instrument cluster screws.

2) Disconnect shift indicator cable clip from shift bowl on steering column. Disconnect instrument cluster harness connectors from back of cluster, and remove instrument cluster. To install, reverse removal procedure.

Removal & Installation (Ninety-Eight & Touring Sedan) – **1)** Turn ignition off. Remove instrument cluster trim plate screws. Tilt instrument cluster trim plate rearward. Disconnect DIC and defogger/ heated windshield electrical connectors (if equipped). Remove instrument cluster trim plate.

2) Remove instrument cluster screws. Pull instrument cluster rearward. Disconnect instrument cluster connector and shift indicator cable. Remove instrument cluster. To install, reverse removal procedure.

Removal & Installation (Toronado & Trofeo) – **1)** Turn ignition off. Remove left sound insulator from below instrument panel. Remove outboard screw (above parking brake pedal) from knee bolster (below steering column).

2) Remove knee bolster by grasping top and bottom of knee bolster and pulling rearward to disengage clips (DO NOT pull downward). Remove instrument cluster trim plate. Remove instrument cluster screws. Remove instrument cluster by pulling outward, disengaging electrical connector. To install, reverse removal procedure.

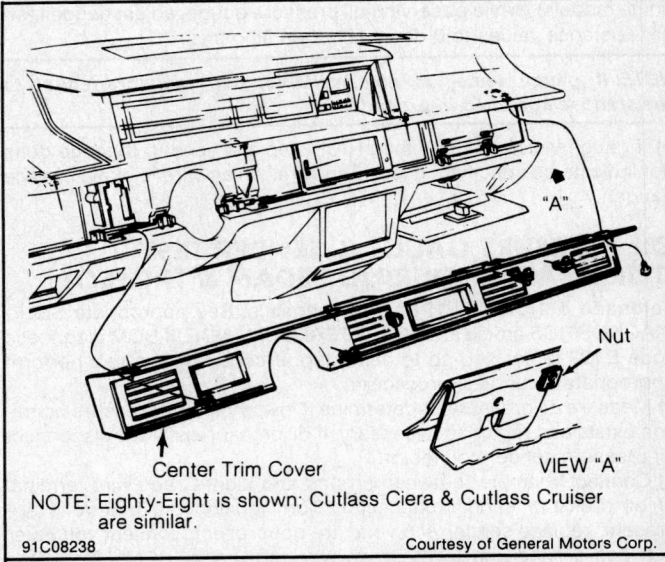

NOTE: Eighty-Eight is shown; Cutlass Ciera & Cutlass Cruiser are similar.

91C08238   Courtesy of General Motors Corp.

Fig. 3: Removing Instrument Panel Center Trim Cover

WIRING DIAGRAMS

See appropriate chassis wiring diagram in WIRING DIAGRAMS.

**Bonneville, Firebird, Grand Am,
Grand Prix, Sunbird, 6000**

DESCRIPTION & OPERATION

ALTERNATOR INDICATOR

Indicator on instrument panel should come on with ignition on and engine not running. Light will go off when engine is running and alternator voltage output is greater than battery voltage.

NOTE: Charging system malfunction may exist even if indicator light performs correctly.

COOLANT TEMPERATURE INDICATOR

The temperature indicator is controlled by a thermal switch that senses coolant temperature. With ignition switch in START position, temperature indicator should come on as a test of indicator bulb. When engine coolant temperature reaches about 258°F (126°C), engine sending unit will close and complete indicator ground circuit, allowing temperature indicator light to come on.

NOTE: If weak coolant or water is used in cooling system, indicator light may not come on when boiling point is reached.

FUEL GAUGE

Circuit consists of an electromagnetic gauge in instrument panel and a fuel tank sending unit. Fuel gauge sending unit consists of a float attached to a contact arm and a rheostat. As the float level changes with fuel level, contact arm moves over rheostat, which changes resistance to gauge circuit.

Gauge pointer moves in response to the magnetic field created by 2 coils in gauge located at right angles. Battery voltage is applied at the "E" coil. As the current leaves the circuit, it is divided into 2 directions: One path goes to ground through the "F" coil and the other path goes to ground through the variable resistor of fuel gauge sending unit. Gauge pointer may set at any position when ignition is off and should move to correct fuel level with ignition switch in ACC or ON position.

LOW COOLANT INDICATOR

The LOW COOLANT indicator is controlled by the low coolant module and low coolant probe. When the probe senses a low coolant condition, a signal is sent to the module where the circuit will close and complete indicator ground circuit allowing the indicator light to come on.

OIL PRESSURE INDICATOR

A pressure operated sending unit on V8 engines is located on top rear of block. On other engines, sending unit is located on oil filter bracket or side of block. Indicator light should come on when ignition is on and engine is not running. Indicator light will also illuminate when oil pressure drops below 5 psi (.35 kg/cm²). After engine has been started and oil pressure has reached predetermined value, light will go off.

SERVICE ENGINE SOON LIGHT

SERVICE ENGINE SOON light should come on when ignition is on and engine is not running. If light comes on while driving, the self-diagnostic system has detected a problem, and a trouble code will be stored in the Electronic Control Module (ECM).

TESTING

ALTERNATOR INDICATOR

If indicator light fails to come on with ignition on and engine not running, check bulb. If bulb is okay, or if indicator remains on after engine is started, test charging system.

CHECK GAUGES INDICATOR

Grand Am – 1) With ignition switch in RUN position, determine if CHECK GAUGES indicator illuminates. Go to step 2) if indicator illuminates. If indicator does not illuminate, check indicator bulb. If bulb is okay, replace instrument cluster.

2) If indicator illuminates with engine running, go to step 7). If not, determine whether CHECK GAUGES indicator illuminates with fuel gauge indicating "E". If not, go to step 3). If it does, disconnect fuel tank unit connector. Jumper terminal "B" (Purple wire) to ground. Start engine. If CHECK GAUGES indicator lights and fuel gauge indicates "E", system is operating okay. If not, replace instrument cluster.

3) If CHECK GAUGES indicator flashes when oil pressure gauge indicates low oil pressure, go to step 4). If not, disconnect fuel pump switch/oil pressure sender connector. Jumper terminal "A" (Tan wire) to ground. Start engine, ensuring oil pressure gauge indicates zero psi. If CHECK GAUGES indicator flashes, system is okay. If not, replace instrument cluster.

4) If CHECK GAUGES indicator flashes when engine overheats, system is operating properly. If not, disconnect ECM connector and jump terminal F7 (Dark Green wire) to ground and start engine. If CHECK GAUGES indicator flashes, go to next step. If not, check/repair Dark Green wire for an open circuit. If wire is okay, replace instrument cluster.

5) Reconnect ECM connector. Disconnect coolant temperature sensor connector. Jumper terminals "A" (Black wire) and "B" (Yellow wire) and start engine. If CHECK GAUGES indicator does not flash, CEC diagnosis is necessary. If light flashes, reconnect coolant temperature sensor connector. Connect a "Scan" tester to read coolant temperature. Start and warm engine while observing coolant temperature gauge and "Scan" tester coolant temperature.

6) If temperatures agree, system is okay. If not, allow engine to operate until coolant fan comes on. Observe coolant temperature gauge and "Scan" tester coolant temperature. If coolant temperature gauge shows engine temperature much higher than 195°F (91°C), replace coolant temperature sender. If "Scan" tester shows coolant temperature much lower than 195°F (91°C), replace coolant temperature sensor.

7) Determine whether CHECK GAUGES indicator flashes when engine is running. If not, replace instrument cluster. If gauge flashes when engine is running, determine whether oil pressure gauge operates correctly. If oil pressure gauge continues to operate incorrectly, see OIL PRESSURE GAUGE tests.

8) If oil pressure gauge operates correctly, turn engine off. Disconnect ECM connector. Turn ignition switch to RUN position. If CHECK GAUGES indicator flashes, ECM is grounding the coolant over temperature input. If indicator does not flash, check Dark Green wire for a short to ground and repair as necessary.

COOLANT TEMPERATURE INDICATOR

1) If light remains on when engine is not overheated, remove coolant temperature sensor connector. If light goes out, replace coolant temperature switch. If light does not go out, check Dark Green wire for short to ground. If wire is okay on Grand Prix only, replace instrument cluster. If wire is okay on all other models, replace ignition switch.

2) On Grand Prix, if light does not come on for bulb check test, disengage 48-pin connector located behind instrument panel near steering column. Jumper terminal C3 (Green/White wire) to ground. If light comes on, check Green/White wire for an open. If wire is okay, replace ignition switch.

3) On all other models, if light does not come on for bulb check test, check bulb and fuse. If bulb and fuse are okay, ground Dark Green wire at ignition switch connector, located behind instrument panel on steering column. If indicator light comes on, check wire for an open circuit. If wire is okay, replace ignition switch. If indicator light does not come on, check Dark Green wire for an open.

OIL PRESSURE INDICATOR

Bonneville – 1) If indicator light remains on, check oil level and oil pressure using a mechanical gauge. If oil level and pressure are okay, disconnect oil light relay (position "A" of relay center). Place ignition switch in RUN position.

2) If oil pressure indicator is now out, check Pink/Black, Tan/Black, Black and Gray wires (some models) and oil pressure sender/switch for an open circuit. If wire(s) is (are) okay, replace oil light relay. If oil pressure indicator is still illuminated, check Tan wire for a short to ground.

3) If oil pressure indicator does not illuminate with low oil pressure, jumper between terminal No. 5 and ground at relay center position "A". If indicator lights, replace oil light relay. If not, check/repair Tan wire for an open circuit.

4) Jumper between terminals No. 5 and 1 at relay center position "A". If indicator lights, replace oil light relay. If not, check/repair Black wire for an open circuit.

5) Jumper between terminals No. 5 and 3 at relay center position "A". If indicator does not light, replace oil light relay. If indicator lights, check/repair Tan/Black and Gray wires (some models) for a short to ground. If wire(s) is (are) okay, replace oil pressure sender/switch.

All Other Models – 1) If indicator light remains on, check oil level. If oil level is okay, check oil pressure with a gauge. If oil pressure is okay, remove oil pressure switch connector. If indicator light goes out, replace switch. If indicator light does not go out, inspect wiring and connectors for short to ground.

2) If light fails to come on, check bulb and fuse. If bulb and fuse are okay, remove oil pressure switch connector and jumper to ground. If indicator lights, replace switch. If indicator does not light, check circuit between oil pressure switch and instrument panel for an open circuit.

TAILGATE AJAR INDICATOR

1) If indicator light remains on with ignition switch in RUN position and tailgate closed, disconnect tailgate ajar switch. If TAILGATE AJAR indicator goes off, replace tailgate ajar switch. If TAILGATE AJAR indicator stays lit, check Black/Orange wire for a short to ground. If wire is okay, replace instrument cluster.

2) If indicator does not light when tailgate is open, jumper between tailgate switch connector Black/Orange wire and ground. If indicator lights, replace switch. If indicator does not light, check Black/Orange wire for an open circuit.

LOW COOLANT INDICATOR

Grand Am (VIN D) – 1) If LOW COOLANT indicator lights with coolant level okay, go to step **3)**. If LOW COOLANT indicator will not light with low coolant level, disconnect surge tank low coolant switch connector. Turn ignition switch to RUN position. Jumper terminal "A" (Gray wire) of surge tank low coolant switch connector to ground.

2) If LOW COOLANT indicator is not lit, check Gray wire for an open circuit. If wire is okay, replace instrument cluster. If LOW COOLANT indicator is lit, connect a jumper between terminals "A" (Gray wire) and "B" (Black wire) of surge tank low coolant switch connector. If LOW COOLANT indicator is lit, replace surge tank low coolant switch. If not, check Black wire for an open circuit.

3) Disconnect surge tank low coolant switch connector. Turn ignition switch to RUN position. If LOW COOLANT indicator lights, check Gray wire for a short to ground. If wire is okay, replace instrument cluster. If LOW COOLANT indicator does not light, replace surge tank low coolant switch.

Sunbird (VIN T) – 1) If LOW COOLANT indicator lights, but coolant level is okay, go to step **3)**. If LOW COOLANT indicator will not light and coolant level is low, disconnect surge tank low coolant switch connector. Turn ignition switch to RUN position. Jumper terminal "A" (Yellow/Black wire) of surge tank low coolant switch connector to ground.

2) If LOW COOLANT indicator is not lit, check Yellow/Black wire for an open circuit. If wire is okay, replace instrument cluster. If LOW COOLANT indicator is lit, connect a jumper between terminals "A" (Yellow/Black wire) and "B" (Black wire) of surge tank low coolant switch connector. If LOW COOLANT indicator is lit, replace surge tank low coolant switch. If not, check Black wire for an open circuit.

3) Disconnect surge tank low coolant switch connector. Turn ignition switch to RUN position. If LOW COOLANT indicator lights, check Yel-

low/Black wire for a short to ground. If wire is okay, replace instrument cluster. If low coolant indicator does not light, replace surge tank low coolant switch.

FUEL GAUGE ALWAYS READS FULL

Bonneville – 1) Unplug fuel gauge sending unit connector near fuel tank. Turn ignition on. Jumper between Purple wire and ground, and between Purple wire and Black/White wire. If fuel gauge indicates empty, repair or replace fuel gauge sender and wiring.

2) If fuel gauge does not indicate empty, check Purple and/or Black/White wires for an open circuit. Check for clean and tight fuel gauge connections. If wires and connectors are okay, replace instrument cluster.

Firebird – Unplug fuel gauge sending unit connector near fuel tank. Turn ignition on. If gauge pointer moves to FULL, replace fuel gauge sending unit. If gauge still reads EMPTY, check instrument cluster printed circuit and Pink wire from fuel gauge sending unit for short to ground. If printed circuit and wire are okay, replace fuel gauge sending unit.

Grand Am & Sunbird – 1) Unplug fuel gauge sending unit connector near fuel tank. Attach jumper wire between connector terminal "B" (Purple wire) and ground. Turn ignition on. If gauge pointer does not move to "E", check Purple wire or printed circuit board for open circuit. If printed circuit and wire are okay, replace fuel gauge.

2) If gauge pointer moves to "E", attach jumper wire between terminals "B" (Purple wire) and "D" (Black/White wire). If gauge pointer moves to "E", replace fuel gauge sending unit. If gauge pointer does not move to "E", check Black/White and Black wire for an open circuit.

Grand Prix – 1) Unplug fuel gauge sending unit connector near fuel tank. Attach terminal "B" (Purple) wire to ground. Turn ignition on. If gauge pointer moves to "E", check Black/White wire for an open circuit.

2) Replace fuel gauge sending unit. If gauge still reads "F", check instrument cluster printed circuit and fuel gauge connectors. If printed circuit and connections are okay, check Purple wire from fuel gauge sending unit to instrument cluster for open circuit. If wire is okay, replace instrument cluster.

6000 – Unplug fuel gauge sending unit connector near fuel tank. Attach Purple wire on wiring harness side of connector to ground. Turn ignition on. If gauge pointer moves to "E", check Black/Yellow, Black/White and Black wires for an open circuit. If wires are okay, replace fuel gauge sending unit. If fuel gauge still reads "F", check Purple wire for an open circuit. If wire is okay, replace fuel gauge.

FUEL GAUGE ALWAYS READS EMPTY

Bonneville – Unplug fuel gauge sending unit connector near fuel tank. Turn ignition on. If gauge pointer moves to "F", proceed to FUEL GAUGE INACCURATE test. If gauge still indicates empty, check Purple wire for short to ground. If wire is okay, replace instrument cluster.

Firebird – 1) Unplug fuel gauge sending unit connector near fuel tank. Turn ignition on. Attach terminal "B" (Pink wire) on wiring harness side of connector to ground. If gauge does not read empty, check instrument cluster printed circuit for flaws and fuel gauge connectors for good contact.

2) If printed circuit and connectors are okay, check Pink wire for an open circuit. If wire is okay, replace fuel gauge. Attach jumper wire between terminal "B" (Pink wire) and terminal "A" (Black wire). If fuel gauge reads empty, check Black wire for an open. If all results are okay, replace fuel gauge sending unit.

Grand Am & Sunbird – Unplug fuel gauge sending unit connector near fuel tank. Turn ignition on. If gauge pointer does not move to "E", replace fuel gauge sending unit. If gauge pointer does move to "E", check Purple wire or printed circuit board for short to ground. If wire and circuit board are okay, replace fuel gauge.

Grand Prix & 6000 – Unplug fuel gauge sending unit connector near fuel tank. Turn ignition on. If fuel gauge pointer moves to "F", replace fuel gauge sending unit. If gauge pointer moves to "E", check Purple wire for short to ground. If wire is okay, replace fuel gauge.

FUEL GAUGE INACCURATE

1) Unplug fuel gauge sending unit connector near fuel tank. Connect Tester (J-33431) between sending unit wire and ground. Turn ignition on. Set tester switch to correct resistance value. See FUEL GAUGE TESTING table. Fuel gauge pointer should read EMPTY, and then move to the FULL position. If gauge responds accurately only when tester is connected, check wiring to sending unit. If wiring is okay, replace sending unit.

2) If gauge readings are correct, check for loose wiring connections on rear of gauge. Check ground connection for good contact. If connections are okay, replace fuel gauge sending unit. If gauge does not respond correctly to tester, check wiring between tester and gauge for continuity. Check printed circuit board for defects. If wiring and printed circuit board are okay, replace fuel gauge.

FUEL GAUGE TESTING

Application	Resistance Ohms	Indicator Position
Bonneville	One	Empty
	88	Full
All Others	Zero	Empty
	90	Full

OIL PRESSURE GAUGE ALWAYS READS LOW

Remove connector from oil pressure sending unit. Turn ignition on. If oil pressure gauge reads high, replace oil pressure sending unit. If not, check sender wire to instrument cluster for short to ground. Check printed circuit board for defects. If wiring and printed circuit board are okay, replace oil pressure gauge.

OIL PRESSURE GAUGE ALWAYS READS HIGH

Remove connector from oil pressure sending unit. Attach Tan wire on wiring harness side of connector to ground. Turn ignition on. If gauge reads high, check sender wire to instrument cluster for short to ground. Check instrument cluster printed circuit for defects. If oil pressure gauge reads low, replace oil pressure sending unit.

OIL PRESSURE GAUGE INACCURATE

1) Unplug oil pressure gauge sender wire at instrument panel connector. Connect Tester (J-33431) between sender wire and ground. Turn ignition on. Set tester switch to zero, and then to 86 ohms. Gauge pointer should read low, and then move to high position.

2) If gauge readings are correct, replace oil gauge sending unit. If gauge readings are not correct, check for loose wiring connections on rear of gauge. Check ground connection for good contact. Check printed circuit board for defects and replace if necessary. Replace oil gauge if no other defects are found.

TEMPERATURE GAUGE ALWAYS READS HOT

Firebird, Grand Prix (Without Gauge Package) & Sunbird – Disconnect temperature gauge sending unit connector. Turn ignition on. If temperature gauge does not read cold, check Dark Green wire for short to ground. If wire is okay, replace temperature gauge.

Grand Am – 1) Disconnect temperature gauge sending unit connector. Turn ignition on. If temperature gauge reads cold, replace coolant temperature gauge sending unit.

2) If gauge reads hot, check Dark Green/White wire for short to ground. Check printed circuit board for defects. If printed circuit board and wire are okay, replace temperature gauge.

Grand Prix (With Gauge Package) – 1) Disconnect temperature gauge sending unit connector. Turn ignition on. If gauge reads cold, replace coolant temperature sender.

2) If gauge reads hot, check Dark Green/White wire, Dark Green wire and ignition switch for a short to ground. If wires and ignition switch are okay, replace instrument cluster.

6000 – 1) Disengage temperature gauge sending unit connector. Turn ignition on. If the temperature gauge reads cold, replace coolant temperature sender.

2) If gauge does not read cold, check Dark Green/White wire for short to ground. Check printed circuit board for defects. If wire and printed circuit board are okay, replace temperature gauge.

TEMPERATURE GAUGE ALWAYS READS COLD

Firebird, Grand Prix (Without Gauge Package) & Sunbird – Disconnect temperature gauge sending unit connector, and jumper Dark Green wire to ground. Turn ignition on. If temperature gauge reads hot, replace temperature gauge sending unit. If temperature gauge does not read hot, check Dark Green wire for an open circuit. If wire is okay, replace temperature gauge.

Grand Am – Disconnect temperature gauge sending unit connector and jumper terminal "A" (Dark Green/White wire) to ground. Turn ignition on. If the temperature gauge does not read cold, replace temperature gauge sending unit. If temperature gauge reads cold, check Dark Green/White wire for open circuit. Check printed circuit board for defects. If printed circuit board and wire are okay, replace temperature gauge.

6000 – 1) Disengage temperature gauge sending unit connector. Jumper Dark Green/White wire to ground. Turn ignition on. If temperature gauge reads "H", replace coolant temperature sending unit.

2) If gauge still reads "C", check Dark Green/White wire for an open circuit. If wire is okay, replace instrument cluster.

TEMPERATURE GAUGE INACCURATE

1) Unplug temperature gauge sender wire in engine compartment. Connect Tester (J-33431) between sender wire and ground. Set gauge to the correct resistance. See TEMPERATURE GAUGE TESTING table. Turn ignition on.

2) If gauge responds to tester accurately, replace sender. If gauge indicates beyond HOT end of scale, check for short to ground. If gauge does not respond or response is inaccurate, check for an open circuit. If circuit is okay, replace temperature gauge.

TEMPERATURE GAUGE TESTING

Application	Resistance Ohms	Indicator Position
Bonneville & Grand Prix	1365	100
	55	260
Firebird & Grand Am	1254	100
	54	260
Sunbird	1365	100
	63	260
6000	1365	C
	42	H

VOLTMETER

With ignition switch in RUN position, connect a voltmeter between positive and negative battery terminals. If voltage reading on test voltmeter is same as instrument cluster voltmeter, voltmeter is okay. If voltmeter reading on test voltmeter is different from cluster voltmeter, replace instrument cluster.

HEADLIGHT SWITCH

Bonneville, Firebird & Grand Am – With headlights on, battery voltage should be present at headlight switch terminal "D" (Yellow wire).

Grand Prix – Battery voltage should be present at headlight switch terminals "L" (Dark Green wire) and "R" (Orange wire). With headlights on, battery voltage should be present at headlight switch terminals "K" (Yellow/Black wire), "N" (Yellow wire) and "P" (Brown wire).

Sunbird – With headlights on, battery voltage should be present at headlight switch terminal "M" (Yellow wire).

6000 – With headlights on, battery voltage should be present at headlight switch terminal "J" (Yellow wire).

INSTRUMENT CLUSTER PINOUT TESTS

Preliminary Information – 1) Ignition switch should be in the RUN position except for resistance measurements. Make all resistance measurements to ground with negative battery cable disconnected.
2) Make all resistance measurements to ground unless a specific terminal number is given. If correct voltage or resistance is found at a terminal, check circuit for malfunction using appropriate test.
3) If correct voltage or resistance is found at terminals, but the function that uses those terminals is incorrect, check instrument cluster bulbs. If bulbs are okay, replace the instrument cluster.

NOTE: For the following PINOUT TESTS, see Figs. 1-5 for pin and connector identification

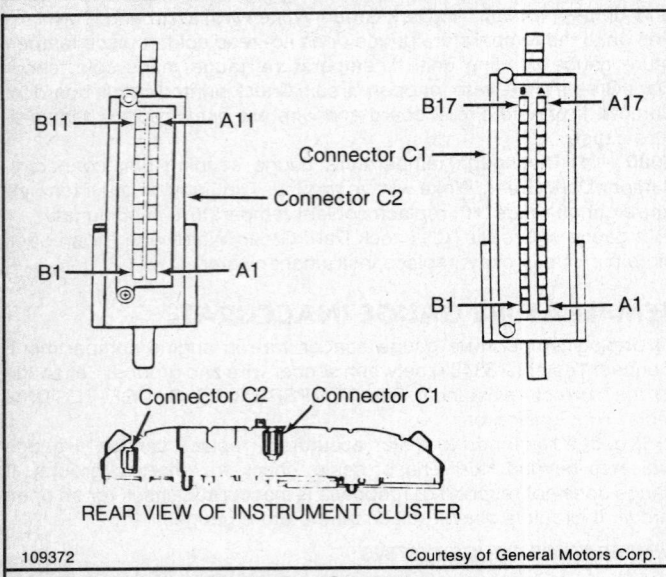

109372   Courtesy of General Motors Corp.

Fig. 1: Instrument Cluster Test Connectors Viewed with Cluster Removed (Bonneville)

BONNEVILLE INSTRUMENT CLUSTER CONNECTOR C1 PINOUT TEST
(Without Gauges)

Application	Wire Color	Pin
Right Turn Indicator	Dk. Blue	[1] A1
Fuel Gauge Input	Purple	A2
Not Used		A3 - A5
Ground	Black/White	A6
Panel Illumination	Gray	[2] A7
Service Engine	Brown/White	A8
Not Used		A9
Ignition Input To Fuel Gauge	Pink/Black	[3] A10
Brake Input	Tan/White	A11
Oil Pressure Input	Tan	A12
Coolant Temperature Indicator	Dk. Green	A13
Charge Indicator	Brown	A14
Fasten Safety Belts Indicator	Yellow	A15
Ground	Black/White	A16
Panel Illumination	Gray	[2] A17
Ground	Black/White	B1
Panel Illumination	Gray	[2] B2
Not Used		B3 - B6
Ground	Black/White	B7
High Beam	Lt. Green or White	[4] B8
Not Used		B9 - B11
Speedometer Ground	Black/White	B12
Vehicle Speed Input	Dk. Green	B13
Ignition Input To Speedometer	Brown/White	[3] B14
Input To Coolant Temperature Gauge	Pink/Black	B15

BONNEVILLE INSTRUMENT CLUSTER CONNECTOR C1 PINOUT TEST
(Without Gauges – Cont.)

Application	Wire Color	Pi
Coolant Temperature Input	Dk. Green/White	B1
Left Turn Indicator	Lt. Blue	[1] B1

[1] – Battery voltage pulses when flashing.
[2] – Voltage varies with rheostat adjustment.
[3] – Battery voltage with key on.
[4] – Battery voltage with high beams on.

BONNEVILLE INSTRUMENT CLUSTER CONNECTOR C1 PINOUT TES
(With Gauges & DIC, Except SSE Models)

Application	Wire Color	Pi
Not Used		A1 – A
Inst. Cluster Lights	Gray	[1] A
Ground	Gray	A
Power From Fuse No. 16	Pink/Black	[2] A
Service Engine	Brown/White	A
Not Used		A
Fuel Gauge Input	Purple	A
Not Used		A9 – A1
Park Brake Indicator	Tan/White	A1
Not Used		A12 – A1
Inst. Cluster Lights	Gray	[1] A1
Not Used		A1
Ground	Black/White	A1
Oil Pressure Sender	Tan/Black	A1
Not Used		B1 – B
Tachometer Input	White	B
Ground	Black/White	B
Power From Fuse No. 16	Pink/Black	[2] B
Ground	Black/White	B
Left Turn Indicator	Lt. Blue	[3] B
Not Used		B
Right Turn Indicator	Dk. Blue	[3] B1
High Beam Indicator	White or Lt. Green	[4] B1
Oil Pressure Sender	Tan/Black	B1
Ground	Black/White	B1
Speed Signal From ECM	Dk. Green	B1
Power From Fuse No. 10	Brown/White	[2] B1
Power From Fuse No. 16	Pink/Black	[2] B1
Coolant Temp. Sender	Dk. Green/White	B1

[1] – Voltage varies with rheostat adjustment.
[2] – Battery voltage with key on.
[3] – Battery voltage pulses when flashing.
[4] – Battery voltage with high beams on.

BONNEVILLE INSTRUMENT CLUSTER CONNECTOR C1 PINOUT TES
(With Gauges, Without DIC, Except SSE Models)

Application	Wire Color	Pi
Not Used		A1 – A
Inst. Cluster Lights	Gray	[1] A
Ground	Black/White	A
Power From Fuse No.16	Pink/Black	[2] A
Service Engine	Brown/White	A
Not Used		A
Fuel Gauge Input	Purple	A
Not Used		A
Power From Fuse No. 16	Pink/Black	[2] A1
Park Brake Indicator	Tan/White	A1
Oil Pressure Indicator	Tan	A1
Coolant Temp. Sender	Dk. Green	A1
Charge Indicator	Brown	A1
Safety Belt Indicator	Yellow	A1
Ground	Black/White	A1
Inst. Cluster Lights	Gray	[3] A1
Right Turn Indicator	Dk. Blue	[4] B

BONNEVILLE INSTRUMENT CLUSTER CONNECTOR C1 PINOUT TEST (With Gauges, Without DIC, Except SSE Models – Cont.)

Application	Wire Color	Pin
Ground	Black/White	B2
High Beam Indicator	White or Lt. Green	[1] B3
Tachometer Input	White	B4
Ground	Black/White	B5
Power From Fuse No. 16	Pink/Black	[2] B6
Not Used		B7
Left Turn Indicator	Lt. Blue	[4] B8
Not Used		B9 – B11
Oil Pressure Sender	Tan/Black	B12
Ground	Black/White	B13
Speed Signal From ECM	Dk. Green	B14
Power From Fuse No. 10	Brown/White	[2] B15
Power From Fuse No. 16	Pink/Black	[2] B16
Coolant Temp. Sender	Dk. Green/White	B17

[1] – Battery voltage with high beams on.
[2] – Battery voltage with key on.
[3] – Voltage varies with rheostat adjustment.
[4] – Battery voltage pulses when flashing.

BONNEVILLE INSTRUMENT CLUSTER CONNECTOR C1 PINOUT TEST (SSE Models)

Application	Wire Color	Pin
Not Used		A1 – A4
Inst. Cluster Lights	Gray	[1] A5
Ground	Black/White	A6
Fuel Gauge Input	Purple	A7
Safety Belt Indicator	Yellow	A8
Not Used		A9
Service Engine	Brown/White	A10
Power From Fuse No. 11	Orange	[2] A11
Security Indicator	Dk. Green	A12
Not Used		A13
Power From Fuse No. 16	Pink/Black	[2] A14
Park Brake Indicator	Tan/White	A15
Anti-Lock Indicator	White	A16
Inst. Cluster Lights	Gray	[1] A17
Not Used		B1
Charge Indicator	Brown	B2
Oil Light Relay	Tan	B3
Coolant Temp. Sender	Dk. Green/White	B4
Right Turn Indicator	Dk. Blue/White	[3] B5
Coolant Temp. Indicator	Dk. Green	B6
Oil Pressure Sender	Tan/Black	B7
High Beam Indicator	White	[4] B8
Not Used		B9
Left Turn Indicator	Lt. Blue/Black	[3] B10
Ground	Black/White	B11
Compass Dim Signal	Dk. Green	B12
Vehicle Speed Signal	Dk. Green	B13
Low Fuel Signal To DIC	Dk. Green/Yellow	B14
Tachometer Input	White	B15
Power From Fuse No. 25	Brown/White	[2] B16
Power From Fuse No. 16	Pink/Black	[2] B17

[1] – Voltage varies with rheostat adjustment.
[2] – Battery voltage with key on.
[3] – Battery voltage pulses when flashing.
[4] – Battery voltage with high beams on.

BONNEVILLE INSTRUMENT CLUSTER CONNECTOR C2 PINOUT TEST

Application	Wire Color	Pin
Power From Fuse No. 10	Brown/White	[1] A1
Hood Ajar Input To DIC	Black/Pink	A2
L/Rear Door Ajar Input To DIC	Black/Lt. Blue	A3

BONNEVILLE INSTRUMENT CLUSTER CONNECTOR C2 PINOUT TEST (Cont.)

Application	Wire Color	Pin
L/Front Door Ajar Input To DIC	Black/Yellow	A4
Trunk Ajar Input To DIC	Black/Red	A5
Coolant Temp. Indicator	Dk. Green	A6
R/Front Door Ajar Input To DIC	Black/White	A7
R/Rear Door Ajar Input To DIC	Black/Lt. Green	A8
Power From Fuse No. 10	Brown/White	[1] A9
Not Used		A10
Ground	Black/White	A11
Safety Belt Indicator	Yellow	B1
Charge Indicator	Brown	B2
Power From Fuse No. 16	Pink/Black	[1] B3
Ground	Black/White	B4
Not Used		B5 – B8
Rear Light Out Input To DIC	Dk. Blue/White	B9
Front Light Out Input To DIC	Lt. Blue/Black	B10
Low Washer Fluid Input To DIC	Black/White	B11

[1] – Battery voltage with key on.

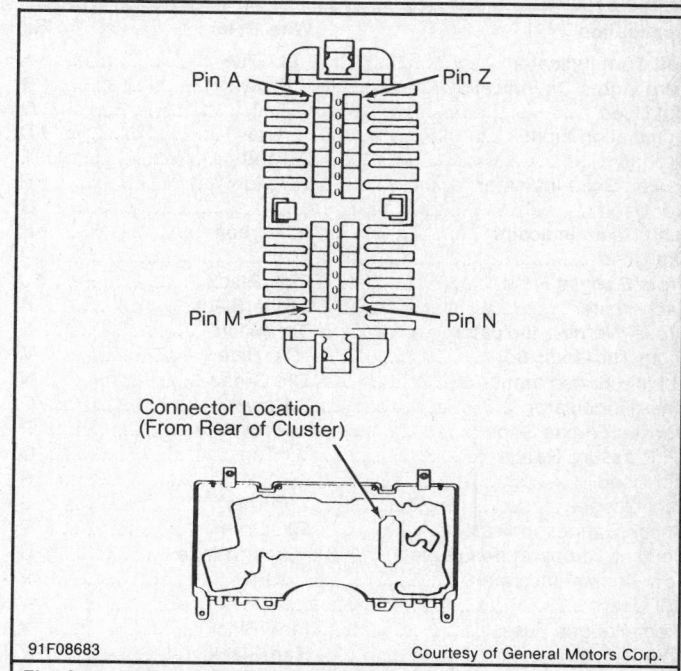

Fig. 2: Instrument Cluster Test Connector Viewed with Cluster Removed (Sunbird & Grand Am)

Pin A | Pin Z
Pin M | Pin N

Connector Location (From Rear of Cluster)

91F08683   Courtesy of General Motors Corp.

GRAND AM INSTRUMENT CLUSTER CONNECTOR PINOUT TEST (Standard Cluster)

Application	Wire Color	Pin
Left Turn Indicator	Lt. Blue	[1] A
Turn Lights On Indicator	Brown	[1] B
Not Used		C
Illumination Input	Gray	[2] D
Ground	Black	E
Fasten Belts Indicator	Yellow	F
Not Used		G
High Beam Indicator	Lt. Green/Black	[3] H
Not Used		I
From Gauges Fuse	Pink/Black	[4] J

GRAND AM INSTRUMENT CLUSTER CONNECTOR PINOUT TEST (Standard Cluster – Cont.)

Application	Wire Color	Pin
Not Used	.....	K
Brake Warning Indicator	Tan/White	L
Right Turn Indicator	Dk. Blue	[1] M
Vehicle Speed Input	Dk. Green	N
Charge Indicator	Brown	O
Service Engine Soon Indicator	Brown/White	P
Oil Pressure Warning Indicator	Tan	Q
Not Used		R
Fuel Gauge	Purple	S
Temperature Indicator	Dk. Green	T
Temperature Gauge	Dk. Green/White	[4] U
Not Used		V – W
From Gauges Fuse	Pink/Black	[4] X
Shift Indicator	Tan/Black	Y
Not Used		Z

[1] – Battery voltage pulses when flashing.
[2] – Voltage varies with rheostat adjustment.
[3] – Battery voltage with high beams on.
[4] – Battery voltage with key on.

GRAND AM INSTRUMENT CLUSTER CONNECTOR PINOUT TEST (Gauges Cluster)

Application	Wire Color	Pin
Left Turn Indicator	Lt. Blue	[1] A
Turn Lights On Indicator	Brown	B
Not Used		C
Illumination Input	Gray	[2] D
Ground	150	E
Fasten Belts Indicator	Yellow	F
Not Used		G
High Beam Indicator	Lt. Green	[3] H
Not Used		I
From Gauges Fuse	Pink/Black	[4] J
Tachometer	Lt. Blue/Black	K
Brake Warning Indicator	Tan/White	L
Right Turn Indicator	Dk. Blue	[1] M
Vehicle Speed Input	Dk. Green	N
Charge Indicator	Brown	O
Service Engine Soon	Brown/White	P
Oil Pressure Gauge	Tan	Q
Not Used		R
Fuel Gauge	Purple	S
Check Gauges Indicator	Dk. Green	T
Coolant Temperature Gauge	Dk. Green/White	U
Low Coolant Indicator	Gray	V
Not Used		W
From Gauges Fuse	Pink/Black	X
Shift Indicator	Tan/Black	Y
ABS Indicator	Lt. Green/Black	Z

[1] – Battery voltage pulses when flashing.
[2] – Voltage varies with rheostat adjustment.
[3] – Battery voltage with high beams on.
[4] – Battery voltage with key on.

SUNBIRD INSTRUMENT CLUSTER CONNECTOR PINOUT TEST (Standard Cluster)

Application	Wire Color	Pin
Not Used		A – B
Fuel Gauge Input	Brown	C
Left Turn Indicator	Lt. Blue	[1] D
High Beam Indicator	Lt. Green	[2] E
Right Turn Indicator	Dk. Blue	[1] F
Not Used		G
Fasten Belts Indicator	Yellow	H

SUNBIRD INSTRUMENT CLUSTER CONNECTOR PINOUT TEST (Standard Cluster – Cont.)

Application	Wire Color	Pin
Upshift Indicator	Tan/Black	I
Not Used		J – K
Brake Indicator	Tan/White	L
Speed Input From ECM	Dk. Green	M
From Gauges Fuse	Pink/Black	[3] N
Service Engine Indicator	Brown/White	O
Coolant Temp. Gauge	Dk. Green	P
Ground	Black	Q
Inst. Cluster Lights	Gray	[4] R
Volts Indicator	Brown	S
Oil Pressure Indicator	Tan	T
Not Used		U – Z

[1] – Battery voltage pulses when flashing.
[2] – Battery voltage with high beams on.
[3] – Battery voltage with key on.
[4] – Voltage varies with rheostat adjustment.

SUNBIRD INSTRUMENT CLUSTER CONNECTOR PINOUT TEST (Gauges Cluster)

Application	Wire Color	Pin
Not Used		A
Shift Indicator	Tan/Black	B
Not Used		C – J
Ground	Black	K
Cluster Illumination	Gray	[1] L
Fasten Belts Indicator	Yellow	M
Oil Pressure Gauge	Tan	N
Fuel Gauge Input	Purple	O
From Gauges	Pink/Black	[2] P
Left Turn Indicator	Lt. Blue	[3] Q
Coolant Gauge Input	Dk. Green	R
Low Coolant Indicator	Yellow/Black	S
Daytime Running Lights	Brown	T
Brake Indicator	Tan/White	U
Service Engine Soon Indicator	Brown/White	V
Speed Input From ECM	Dk. Green	W
Right Turn Indicator	Dk. Blue	[3] X
High Beam Indicator	Lt. Green	[4] Y
Tachometer Input	White	Z

[1] – Voltage varies with rheostat adjustment.
[2] – Battery voltage with key on.
[3] – Battery voltage pulses when flashing.
[4] – Battery voltage with high beams on.

SUNBIRD INSTRUMENT CLUSTER CONNECTOR PINOUT TEST (With Coolant Temperature Gauge)

Application	Wire Color	Pin
Not Used		A – B
Fuel Gauge Input	Purple	[1] C
Left Turn Indicator	Lt. Blue	[2] D
High Beam Indicator	Lt. Green	[3] E
Right Turn Indicator	Dk. Blue	[2] F
Not Used		G
Fasten Belts Indicator	Yellow	H
Upshift Indicator	Tan/Black	I
Not Used		J – K
Brake Indicator	Tan/White	L
Speed Input From ECM	Dk. Green	M
From Gauges Fuse	Pink/Black	[1] N
Check Engine Indicator	Brown/White	O
Temperature Gauge Input	Dk. Green	[1] P
Ground	Black	Q
Cluster Illumination	Gray	[4]

SUNBIRD INSTRUMENT CLUSTER CONNECTOR PINOUT TEST
(With Coolant Temperature Gauge – Cont.)

Application	Wire Color	Pin
Not Used		S
Oil Pressure Gauge Input	Tan	[1] T
Not Used		U – Z

- Battery voltage with key on.
- Battery voltage pulses when flashing.
- Battery voltage with high beams on.
- Voltage varies with rheostat adjustment.

FIREBIRD INSTRUMENT CLUSTER CONNECTOR PINOUT TEST

Application	Wire Color	Pin
Connector C1		
Tachometer	White	[1] 1
Instrument Cluster Ground	Black	2
Instrument Cluster Lights	Gray	[2] 3
Security Indicator	Gray	4
Coolant Temp. Gauge	Dk. Green	5
Not Used		6 – 7
Oil Pressure Indicator	Tan	8
From Gauges Fuse	Pink/Black	[3] 9
Not Used		10 – 11
Instrument Cluster Ground	Black	12
Fasten Belt Indicator	Yellow	13
Vehicle Speed Sensor	Gray or Tan	14
Connector C2		
Brake Indicator	Tan/White	1
Ground	Black	2
Instrument Cluster Lights	Gray	[2] 3
Not Used		4 – 6
Left Turn Indicator	Lt. Blue	[4] 7
High Beam Indicator	Lt. Green	[5] 8
Right Turn Indicator	Dk. Blue	[4] 9
Fuel Gauge Output	Purple	10
SIR Indicator	Brown	11
Not Used		12
Service Eng. Soon Indicator	Brown/White	13
Shift Indicator	Tan/Black	14

- Ten volts with key on.
- Voltage varies with rheostat adjustment.
- Battery voltage with key on.
- Battery voltage pulses when flashing.
- Battery voltage with high beams on.

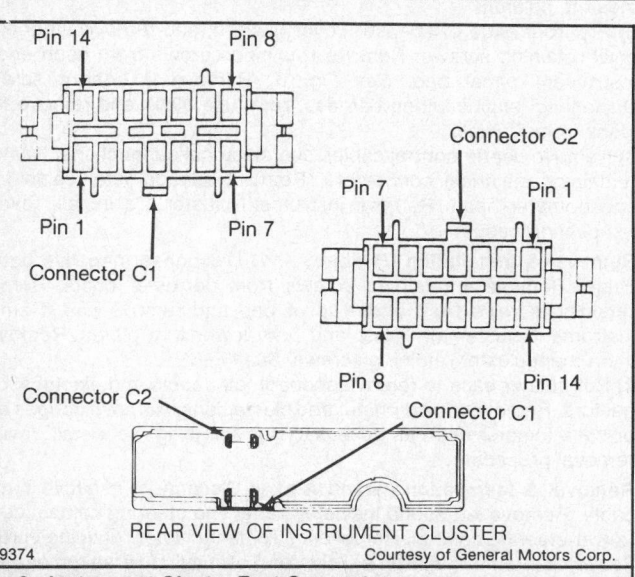

109374   Courtesy of General Motors Corp.

Fig. 3: Instrument Cluster Test Connector Viewed with Cluster Removed (Firebird)

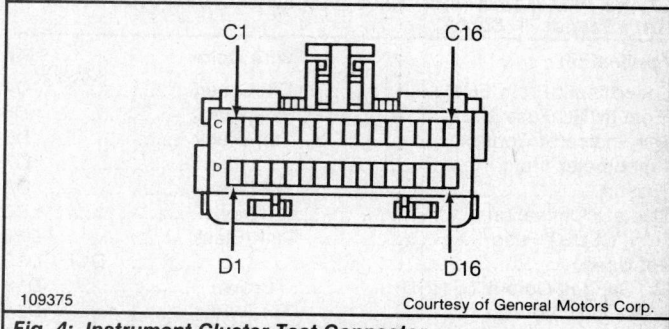

109375   Courtesy of General Motors Corp.

Fig. 4: Instrument Cluster Test Connector Viewed with Cluster Removed (Grand Prix)

GRAND PRIX INSTRUMENT CLUSTER CONNECTOR PINOUT TEST
(Standard Cluster)

Application	Wire Color	Pin
Not Used		C1 – C2
Oil Pressure Indicator	Tan	C3
Temperature Gauge Input	Dk. Green	C4
Not Used		C5 – C7
Fuel Gauge Sender Return	Black/White	C8
Charge Indicator	Brown	C9
Left Turn Indicator	Lt. Blue	[1] C10
High Beam Indicator	Lt. Green	C11
Right Turn Indicator	Dk. Blue	[1] C12
Fasten Belts Indicator	Yellow	C13
Not Used		C14
Service Eng. Indicator	Brown/White	C15
Not Used		C16
Not Used		D1 – D2
Fuel Gauge Input	Purple	D3
Speed Input From ECM	Dk. Green	D4
From INDIC Fuse	Pink/Black	[2] D5
Shift Indicator Control	Tan/Black	D6
Not Used	White	D7
Ground	Black	D8
Cluster Illumination	Gray	[3] D9
From CLUST Fuse	Pink/Black	[2] D10
Not Used		D11 – D13
Brake Indicator	Tan/White	D14
Anti-Lock Indicator	Gray/White	D15
Low Coolant Indicator	Yellow/Black	D16

[1] – Battery voltage pulses when flashing.
[2] – Battery voltage with key on.
[3] – Battery voltage with lights on.

GRAND PRIX INSTRUMENT CLUSTER CONNECTOR PINOUT TEST
(With Gauges)

Application	Wire Color	Pin
Not Used		C1 – C2
Oil Pressure Gauge	Tan	C3
Temperature Gauge Input	Dk. Green	C4
Not Used		C5 – C7
Fuel Gauge Sender Return	Black/White	C8
Charge Indicator	Brown	C9
Left Turn Indicator	Lt. Blue	[1] C10
High Beam Indicator	Lt. Green	C11
Right Turn Indicator	Dk. Blue	[1] C12
Fasten Belts Indicator	Yellow	C13
Not Used		C14
Service Engine Indicator	Brown/White	C15
Not Used		C16
Not Used		D1
Low Fuel Output To HUD	Brown	D2
Fuel Gauge Input	Purple	D3

GRAND PRIX INSTRUMENT CLUSTER CONNECTOR PINOUT TEST
(With Gauges – Cont.)

Application	Wire Color	Pin
Speed Input From ECM	Dk. Green	D4
From INDIC Fuse	Pink/Black	[2] D5
Shift Indicator Control	Tan/Black	D6
Tachometer Input		D7
Ground	Black	D8
Cluster Illumination	Gray	[3] D9
From CLUST Fuse	Pink/Black	[2] D10
Not Used		D11 – D12
Ck. Gauges Output To HUD	Brown	D13
Brake Indicator	Tan/White	D14
Anti-Lock Indicator	Gray/White	D15
Low Coolant Indicator	Yellow/Black	D16

[1] – Battery voltage pulses when flashing.
[2] – Battery voltage with key on.
[3] – Battery voltage with lights on.

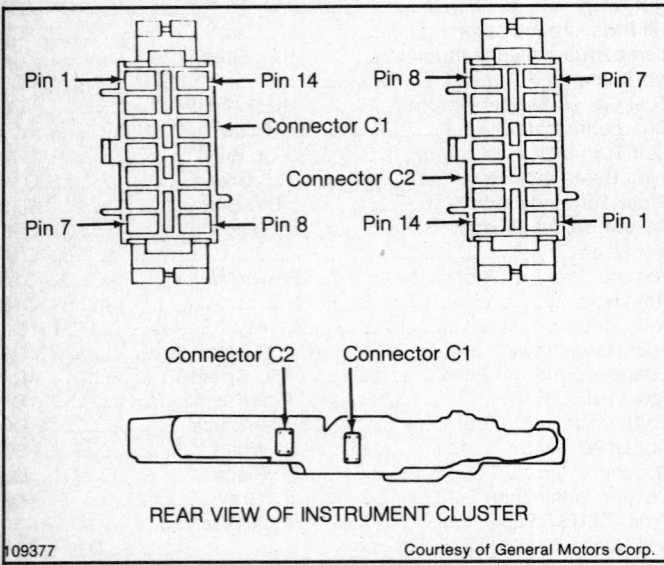

REAR VIEW OF INSTRUMENT CLUSTER

109377   Courtesy of General Motors Corp.

Fig. 5: Instrument Cluster Test Connector
Viewed with Cluster Removed (6000)

6000 INSTRUMENT CLUSTER CONNECTOR PINOUT TEST

Application	Wire Color	Pin
Connector C1		
Ground	Black	1
Fasten Belt Indicator	Yellow	2
Instrument Cluster Lights	Gray	[1] 3
High Beam Indicator	Lt. Green	[2] 4
Tachometer Input	White	5
Not Used		6 – 7
Speedom. Input From ECM	Brown	8
Right Turn Indicator	Dk. Blue	[3] 9
Left Turn Indicator	Lt. Blue	[3] 10
Not Used		11
Service Engine Indicator	Brown/White	12
Brake Indicator	Tan/White	13
Power to Gauges/Indicators	Pink/Black	[4] 14
Connector C2 (Base Cluster)		
Ground	Black	1
Fuel Gauge Input	Purple	2
Not Used	Dk. Green/White	3
Oil Pressure Indicator	Tan	4

6000 INSTRUMENT CLUSTER CONNECTOR PINOUT TEST (Cont.)

Application	Wire Color	Pin
Pwr. To Gauges & Ind.	Pink/Black	4
Instrument Cluster Lights	Gray	
Not Used	Black/Orange	
Not Used	Brown	
Not Used		
Coolant Temp. Indicator	Dk. Green	1
Not Used		1
Tailgate Ajar Indicator	Black/Orange	1
Not Used		1
Volts Indicator	Brown	1

Application	Wire Color	Pin
Connector C2 (Gauge Cluster)		
Ground	Black	
Fuel Gauge Input	Purple	
Temperature Gauge Input	Dk. Green/White	
Oil Pressure Gauge Input	Tan	
Power From Gauges Fuse	Pink/Black	4
Instrument Cluster Lights	Gray	
Tailgate Ajar Indicator	Black/Orange	
Not Used		
Not Used		
Coolant Temp. Indicator	Dk. Green	1
Not Used		1
Not Used	Black/Orange	1
Not Used		1
Volts Indicator	Brown	1

[1] – Voltage varies with rheostat adjustment.
[2] – Battery voltage with high beams on.
[3] – Battery voltage pulses when flashing.
[4] – Battery voltage with key on.

REMOVAL & INSTALLATION

INSTRUMENT CLUSTER

CAUTION: When handling electrostatic sensitive components, touch a known good ground frequently to avoid possible build-up o electrostatic charge and damage to electronic parts.

Removal & Installation (Bonneville) – 1) Disconnect negative bat tery cable. Remove sound insulation panels. Disconnect shift indicato cable at steering column. Remove steering column nuts and lowe steering column.
2) Pry front edge of speaker cover upward, and remove 2 panel-to cowl retaining screws. Remove retaining screws from each end o instrument panel pad. *See Fig. 6.* Remove 3 bottom screws Disconnect engine wiring harness from fuse block and remove fus block from firewall.
3) Remove heater control cables and electrical connections. Remove remaining electrical connectors. Remove speedometer cable fron speedometer head. Remove instrument cluster. To install, revers removal procedure.

Removal & Installation (Firebird) – 1) Disconnect negative batter cable. Remove 4 retaining screws from defroster ducts. Remov retaining screws from under lip of pad and remove pad. Remov instrument cluster trim plate and both lower trim plates. Remov instrument cluster retaining screws. *See Fig. 7.*
2) Pull cluster back to remove speedometer cable and electrical con nectors. Remove trip odometer and cluster lens. Remove gauges and or speedometer head as necessary for servicing. To install, revers removal procedure.

Removal & Installation (Grand Am) – Disconnect negative batter cable. Remove left sound insulator panel and steering column cove Lower steering column. Remove instrument cluster retaining screws *See Fig. 8.* Remove instrument cluster. To install, reverse removal pro cedure.

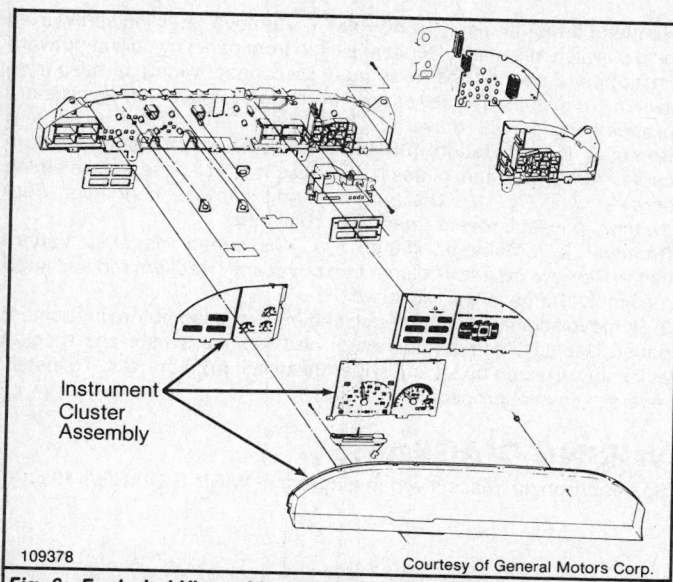

Fig. 6: Exploded View of Instrument Cluster (Bonneville)

Instrument Cluster Assembly

109378 — Courtesy of General Motors Corp.

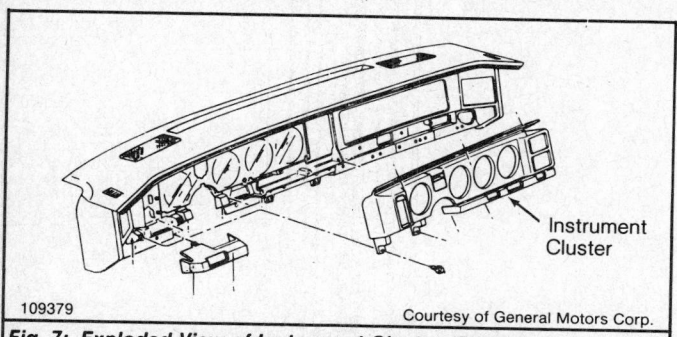

Fig. 7: Exploded View of Instrument Cluster (Firebird)

Instrument Cluster

109379 — Courtesy of General Motors Corp.

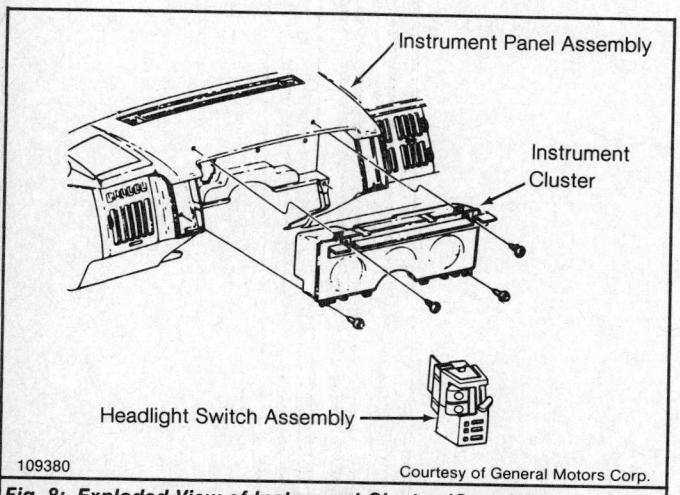

Fig. 8: Exploded View of Instrument Cluster (Grand Am)

Instrument Panel Assembly

Instrument Cluster

Headlight Switch Assembly

109380 — Courtesy of General Motors Corp.

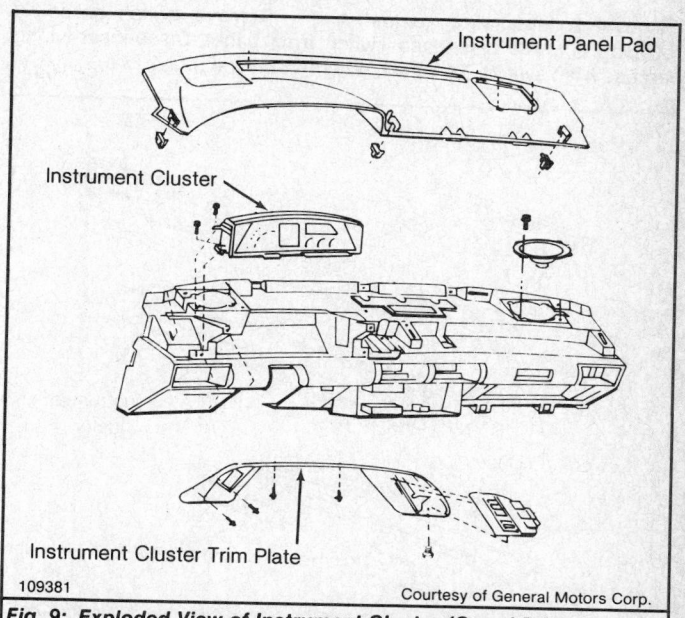

Fig. 9: Exploded View of Instrument Cluster (Grand Prix)

Instrument Panel Pad

Instrument Cluster

Instrument Cluster Trim Plate

109381 — Courtesy of General Motors Corp.

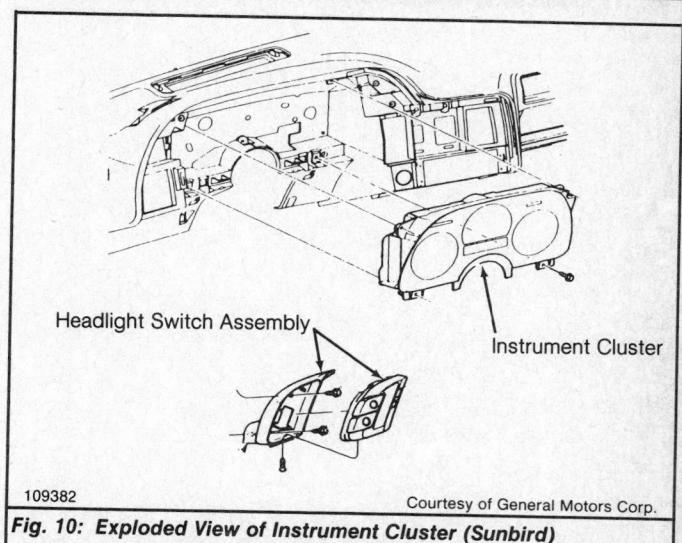

Fig. 10: Exploded View of Instrument Cluster (Sunbird)

Headlight Switch Assembly

Instrument Cluster

109382 — Courtesy of General Motors Corp.

Removal & Installation (Grand Prix) – Disconnect negative battery cable. Remove light switch and wiper/washer assemblies. Remove retaining screws from each switch opening. Remove upper trim plate retaining screws. *See Fig. 9.* Remove switch assembly connectors by pulling outward from holder. To install, reverse removal procedure.

Removal & Installation (Sunbird) – Disconnect negative battery cable. Remove speedometer cluster trim plate and 4 speedometer cluster attaching screws. *See Fig. 10.* Remove steering column trim cover, and lift instrument cluster away from instrument panel. To install, reverse removal procedure.

Removal & Installation (6000) – **1)** Call up and record maintenance reminder mileage on Driver Information Center (DIC). Disconnect negative battery cable. Remove center and lower left instrument panel trim plates.

2) Remove 8 screws holding cluster to instrument panel carrier. *See Fig. 11.* Pull cluster to rear and unplug connectors. Remove cluster. To install, reverse removal procedure. Reset maintenance reminder mileage.

HEADLIGHT SWITCH

Removal & Installation (Bonneville) – Pull switch knob to ON position. Press knob release button on headlight switch behind panel, and remove knob and shaft. Remove trim plate and retaining nut. Remove wiring connector and mounting screws. Remove switch. To install, reverse removal procedure.

Removal & Installation (Firebird) – Remove lower trim plates and instrument trim plate. Remove switch assembly retaining screws. Depress tangs and pull switch out of panel. Disconnect wiring harness from switch. To install, reverse removal procedure.

Removal & Installation (Grand Am) – Remove switch assembly retaining screws. Disengage switch from panel. Disconnect wiring harness from switch. To install, reverse removal procedure.

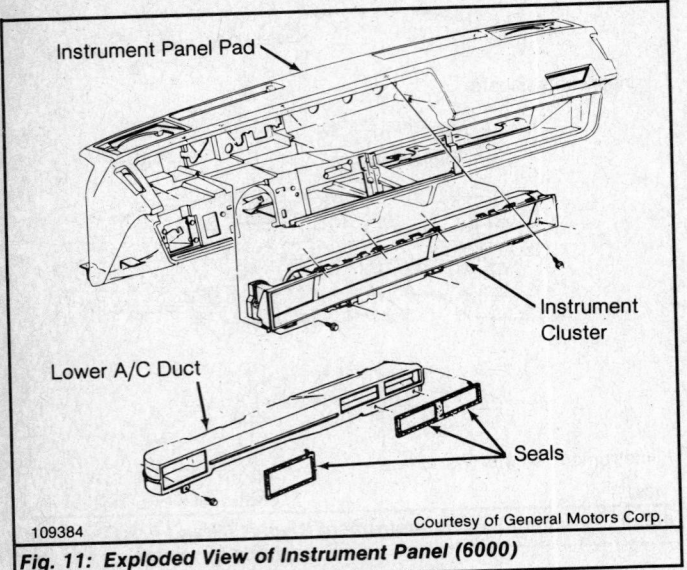

Instrument Panel Pad

Instrument Cluster

Lower A/C Duct

Seals

109384   Courtesy of General Motors Corp.

Fig. 11: Exploded View of Instrument Panel (6000)

Removal & Installation (Grand Prix) – Remove retaining screw from below switch assembly. Remove switch from panel by pulling outward until upper 2 spring clips disengage. Disconnect wiring harness from switch. To install, reverse removal procedure. Ensure spring clips are properly aligned with holes.

Removal & Installation (Sunbird) – Disconnect negative battery cable. Remove left trim plates and headlight switch assembly retaining screws. *See Fig. 10.* Disconnect wiring harness connector from switch. To install, reverse removal procedure.

Removal & Installation (6000) – 1) Disconnect negative battery cable. Remove steering column trim cover and headlight rod and knob assembly. Remove left trim plate.

2) Remove screws holding switch and bracket assembly to instrument panel. Unplug electrical connector and remove switch and bracket assembly. Loosen bezel and separate switch from bracket. To install, reverse removal procedure.

WIRING DIAGRAMS

See appropriate chassis wiring diagram in WIRING DIAGRAMS.

DeVille, Fleetwood

DESCRIPTION & OPERATION

Instrument panel components include the speedometer cluster, Electronic Climate Control (ECC) panel and indicator lights. Depending on option, the speedometer, odometer, trip odometer and fuel gauge are available as either digital or analog units. Both types of cluster receive vehicle speed information from the Vehicle Speed Sensor (VSS) mounted in the transaxle. *See Fig. 1.*

Indicator lights are used to alert driver of various vehicle conditions. Indicator warning lights illuminate during engine start to provide a bulb check.

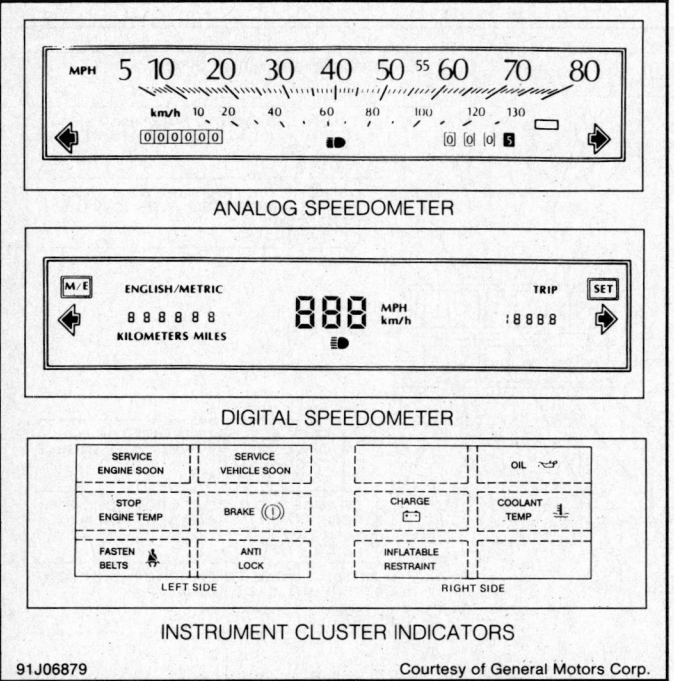

91J06879   Courtesy of General Motors Corp.

Fig. 1: Analog & Digital Instrument Clusters & Warning Indicators

AIR BAG PRECAUTIONS

Observe the following precautions when working with vehicles equipped with Supplemental Inflatable Restraint (SIR) air bag systems:

- Before performing any instrument panel testing, diagnosis or repair, disable SRS system by disconnecting negative battery cable and Yellow 2-pin connector at base of steering column.
- Wait 20 minutes before making SRS repairs. SRS system retains enough voltage to deploy air bag for a short time after disconnecting power.
- To avoid accidental air bag deployment, avoid the SRS wiring harness when trouble shooting instrument panel components. All SRS wires are color-coded Yellow.

TESTING

NOTE: For additional instrument panel testing and diagnosis, see SELF-DIAGNOSTICS – DEVILLE & FLEETWOOD PCM/BCM article in ENGINE PERFORMANCE.

INDICATORS & GAUGES PINOUT TEST

Check voltage or resistance at instrument cluster connector to determine if proper readings are supplied to the instrument cluster. See Figs. 2 and 3.

FUEL DATA CENTER CONNECTOR TEST

1) Disconnect fuel data center connector. Turn ignition switch to RUN position and turn parking lights or headlights on.
2) Using a voltmeter, measure voltage between terminal "L" (Brown wire) and ground. If battery voltage is present, go to next step. If battery voltage is not present, check Brown wire for an open circuit, and check instrument panel fuse No. 7.
3) Measure voltage between terminal "P" (Orange/Black wire) and ground. If 16 volts are present, go to next step. If 16 volts are not present, check Orange/Black wire for an open circuit. If wire is okay, Powertrain Control Module (PCM) and Body Control Module (BCM) diagnosis is necessary. See SELF-DIAGNOSTICS – DEVILLE & FLEETWOOD PCM/BCM article in ENGINE PERFORMANCE.
4) Measure voltage between terminal "T" (Tan wire) and ground. If 5 volts are present, go to next step. If 5 volts are not present, check Tan wire for an open circuit. If wire is okay, BCM/PCM diagnosis is necessary. See SELF-DIAGNOSTICS – DEVILLE & FLEETWOOD PCM/BCM article in ENGINE PERFORMANCE.
5) Measure voltage between terminals "L" (Brown wire) and "M" (Black/White wire). If battery voltage is present, go to next step. If battery voltage is not present, check Black/White wire for an open circuit. Ensure grounds are clean and tight.
6) Measure voltage between terminals "L" (Brown wire) and "S" (Black/White wire). If battery voltage is present and ECC display is normal, replace fuel data center. If battery voltage is not present, check Black/White wire for an open circuit.

FUEL DISPLAY SHOWS FLASHING "E" AT ALL TIMES

1) If diagnosis indicates no BCM Code F31, go to next step. If a Code F31 is present, see SELF-DIAGNOSTICS – DEVILLE & FLEETWOOD PCM/BCM article in ENGINE PERFORMANCE.
2) Check instrument panel fuse No. 16 and replace as necessary. If fuse is okay, ensure fuel tank is at least one-half full and disconnect fuel gauge sending unit. Turn ignition switch to RUN position and measure voltage at fuel gauge sending unit connector, terminal "C" (Pink/Black wire). If battery voltage is present, go to next step. If no voltage is present, check for an open circuit or short to ground in Pink/Black wire.
3) Connect a fused jumper wire between connector terminals "C" (Pink/Black wire) and "F" (Purple wire). Turn ignition switch to OFF, then RUN, and note fuel gauge. If fuel gauge reads full, replace fuel gauge sending unit. If fuel gauge reads a flashing "E", go to next step.
4) Using a voltmeter, backprobe BCM connector C1, terminal B8 (Purple wire). If zero voltage is present, check Purple wire for an open or short circuit and repair as necessary.
5) If battery voltage is present, backprobe BCM connector C1, terminal B3 (Pink/Black wire). If zero volts are present, check for an open circuit or short to ground in Pink/Black wire between instrument panel fuse block and BCM.
6) If battery voltage is present, check for loose connector pins, terminal and BCM grounds. If pins, terminal and BCM grounds are okay, replace BCM.

FUEL GAUGE SENDING UNIT TEST

Using an ohmmeter, check fuel gauge sender ground (Black/White wire) for high resistance and repair as necessary. If high resistance is not present, check Pink/Black and Purple wires for high resistance and repair as necessary. If high resistance is not present, replace fuel gauge sending unit.

OIL INDICATOR TEST

Indicator Does Not Illuminate With Ignition Switch In Run Position – **1)** Disconnect oil pressure switch connector. Turn ignition switch to RUN position. Connect a fused jumper between connector terminal "B" (Tan wire) and ground.
2) If oil indicator illuminates, replace engine oil pressure switch. If oil indicator does not illuminate, check Tan wire for an open circuit.

Indicator Does Not Go Out When Engine Is Running – 1) Ensure engine oil pressure is okay. If oil pressure is okay, turn ignition switch to RUN position. Disconnect engine oil pressure switch and check oil indicator.

2) If oil indicator is not illuminated, replace engine oil pressure switch. If oil indicator is still illuminated, check Tan wire for a short to ground.

SPEEDOMETER/ODOMETER TEST

1) If diagnosis indicates no Code 24, go to next step. If a Code 24 is present, see SELF-DIAGNOSTICS – DEVILLE & FLEETWOOD PCM/BCM article in ENGINE PERFORMANCE.

2) Turn ignition switch to RUN position. Using a voltmeter, measure voltage at Powertrain Control Module (PCM) connector C2, terminal B11 (Dark Green wire). If less than 5 volts (digital) or 12 volts (analog)

are present, go to step **5)**. If at least 5 volts (digital) or 12 volts (analog) are present, go to next step.

3) Reconnect PCM connector C2. Raise vehicle drive wheels and shift transaxle into Neutral. Place ignition switch in RUN position. Slowly turn drive wheels and measure voltage at PCM connector C2, terminal B11 (Dark Green wire).

4) If voltage changes, replace instrument cluster. If voltage does not change, replace PCM.

5) If less than 5 volts (digital) or 12 volts (analog) were present in step **2)**, check Dark Green wire for an open or short to ground and repair as necessary. If wire is okay, turn ignition switch to RUN position.

6) On digital cluster, measure voltage between instrument cluster connector C2, pin "J" (Brown wire) and ground. *See Fig. 3.* On analog clus-

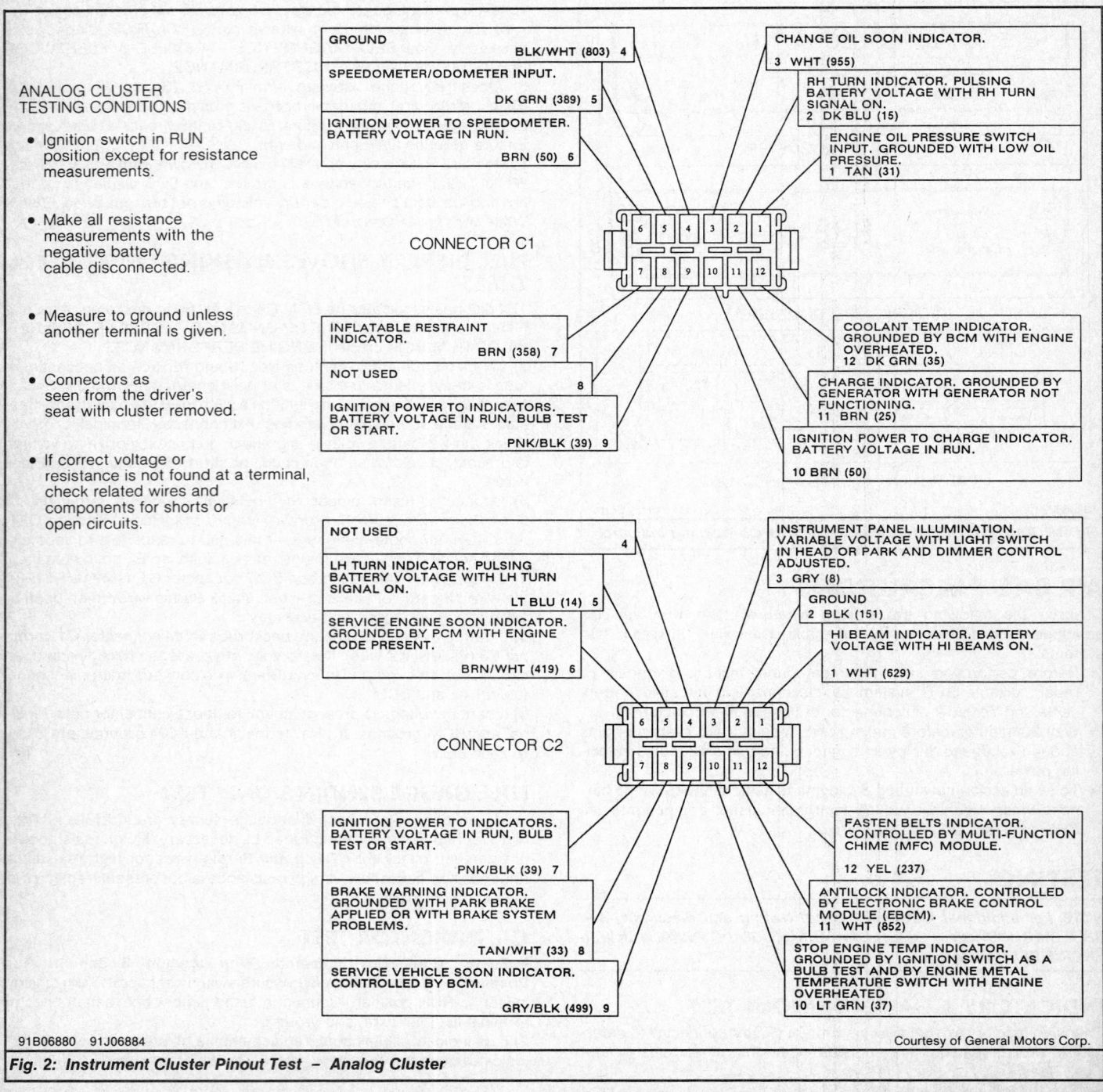

ANALOG CLUSTER TESTING CONDITIONS

- Ignition switch in RUN position except for resistance measurements.

- Make all resistance measurements with the negative battery cable disconnected.

- Measure to ground unless another terminal is given.

- Connectors as seen from the driver's seat with cluster removed.

- If correct voltage or resistance is not found at a terminal, check related wires and components for shorts or open circuits.

CONNECTOR C1

GROUND
BLK/WHT (803) 4

SPEEDOMETER/ODOMETER INPUT.
DK GRN (389) 5

IGNITION POWER TO SPEEDOMETER. BATTERY VOLTAGE IN RUN.
BRN (50) 6

CHANGE OIL SOON INDICATOR.
3 WHT (955)

RH TURN INDICATOR. PULSING BATTERY VOLTAGE WITH RH TURN SIGNAL ON.
2 DK BLU (15)

ENGINE OIL PRESSURE SWITCH INPUT. GROUNDED WITH LOW OIL PRESSURE.
1 TAN (31)

INFLATABLE RESTRAINT INDICATOR.
BRN (358) 7

NOT USED
8

IGNITION POWER TO INDICATORS. BATTERY VOLTAGE IN RUN, BULB TEST OR START.
PNK/BLK (39) 9

COOLANT TEMP INDICATOR. GROUNDED BY BCM WITH ENGINE OVERHEATED.
12 DK GRN (35)

CHARGE INDICATOR. GROUNDED BY GENERATOR WITH GENERATOR NOT FUNCTIONING.
11 BRN (25)

IGNITION POWER TO CHARGE INDICATOR. BATTERY VOLTAGE IN RUN.
10 BRN (50)

CONNECTOR C2

NOT USED
4

LH TURN INDICATOR. PULSING BATTERY VOLTAGE WITH LH TURN SIGNAL ON.
LT BLU (14) 5

SERVICE ENGINE SOON INDICATOR. GROUNDED BY PCM WITH ENGINE CODE PRESENT.
BRN/WHT (419) 6

INSTRUMENT PANEL ILLUMINATION. VARIABLE VOLTAGE WITH LIGHT SWITCH IN HEAD OR PARK AND DIMMER CONTROL ADJUSTED.
3 GRY (8)

GROUND
2 BLK (151)

HI BEAM INDICATOR. BATTERY VOLTAGE WITH HI BEAMS ON.
1 WHT (629)

IGNITION POWER TO INDICATORS. BATTERY VOLTAGE IN RUN, BULB TEST OR START.
PNK/BLK (39) 7

BRAKE WARNING INDICATOR. GROUNDED WITH PARK BRAKE APPLIED OR WITH BRAKE SYSTEM PROBLEMS.
TAN/WHT (33) 8

SERVICE VEHICLE SOON INDICATOR. CONTROLLED BY BCM.
GRY/BLK (499) 9

FASTEN BELTS INDICATOR. CONTROLLED BY MULTI-FUNCTION CHIME (MFC) MODULE.
12 YEL (237)

ANTILOCK INDICATOR. CONTROLLED BY ELECTRONIC BRAKE CONTROL MODULE (EBCM).
11 WHT (852)

STOP ENGINE TEMP INDICATOR. GROUNDED BY IGNITION SWITCH AS A BULB TEST AND BY ENGINE METAL TEMPERATURE SWITCH WITH ENGINE OVERHEATED
10 LT GRN (37)

91B06880 91J06884

Courtesy of General Motors Corp.

Fig. 2: Instrument Cluster Pinout Test – Analog Cluster

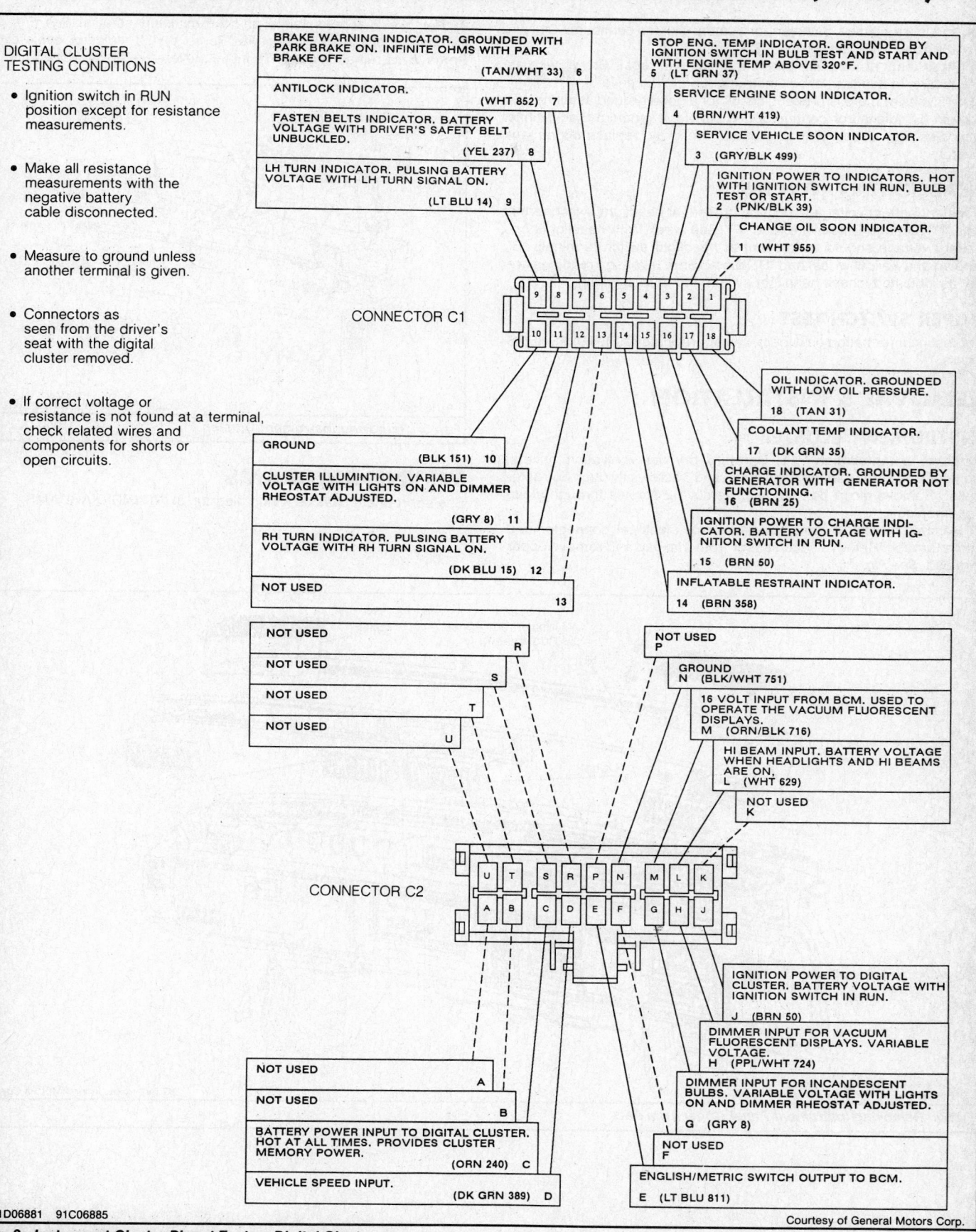

DIGITAL CLUSTER TESTING CONDITIONS

- Ignition switch in RUN position except for resistance measurements.

- Make all resistance measurements with the negative battery cable disconnected.

- Measure to ground unless another terminal is given.

- Connectors as seen from the driver's seat with the digital cluster removed.

- If correct voltage or resistance is not found at a terminal, check related wires and components for shorts or open circuits.

BRAKE WARNING INDICATOR. GROUNDED WITH PARK BRAKE ON. INFINITE OHMS WITH PARK BRAKE OFF.
(TAN/WHT 33) 6

ANTILOCK INDICATOR.
(WHT 852) 7

FASTEN BELTS INDICATOR. BATTERY VOLTAGE WITH DRIVER'S SAFETY BELT UNBUCKLED.
(YEL 237) 8

LH TURN INDICATOR. PULSING BATTERY VOLTAGE WITH LH TURN SIGNAL ON.
(LT BLU 14) 9

STOP ENG. TEMP INDICATOR. GROUNDED BY IGNITION SWITCH IN BULB TEST AND START AND WITH ENGINE TEMP ABOVE 320°F.
5 (LT GRN 37)

SERVICE ENGINE SOON INDICATOR.
4 (BRN/WHT 419)

SERVICE VEHICLE SOON INDICATOR.
3 (GRY/BLK 499)

IGNITION POWER TO INDICATORS. HOT WITH IGNITION SWITCH IN RUN, BULB TEST OR START.
2 (PNK/BLK 39)

CHANGE OIL SOON INDICATOR.
1 (WHT 955)

CONNECTOR C1

9 8 7 6 5 4 3 2 1
10 11 12 13 14 15 16 17 18

OIL INDICATOR. GROUNDED WITH LOW OIL PRESSURE.
18 (TAN 31)

COOLANT TEMP INDICATOR.
17 (DK GRN 35)

CHARGE INDICATOR. GROUNDED BY GENERATOR WITH GENERATOR NOT FUNCTIONING.
16 (BRN 25)

IGNITION POWER TO CHARGE INDICATOR. BATTERY VOLTAGE WITH IGNITION SWITCH IN RUN.
15 (BRN 50)

INFLATABLE RESTRAINT INDICATOR.
14 (BRN 358)

GROUND
(BLK 151) 10

CLUSTER ILLUMINTION. VARIABLE VOLTAGE WITH LIGHTS ON AND DIMMER RHEOSTAT ADJUSTED.
(GRY 8) 11

RH TURN INDICATOR. PULSING BATTERY VOLTAGE WITH RH TURN SIGNAL ON.
(DK BLU 15) 12

NOT USED
13

NOT USED
R

NOT USED
S

NOT USED
T

NOT USED
U

NOT USED
P

GROUND
N (BLK/WHT 751)

16 VOLT INPUT FROM BCM. USED TO OPERATE THE VACUUM FLUORESCENT DISPLAYS.
M (ORN/BLK 716)

HI BEAM INPUT. BATTERY VOLTAGE WHEN HEADLIGHTS AND HI BEAMS ARE ON.
L (WHT 629)

NOT USED
K

CONNECTOR C2

U T S R P N M L K
A B C D E F G H J

NOT USED
A

NOT USED
B

BATTERY POWER INPUT TO DIGITAL CLUSTER. HOT AT ALL TIMES. PROVIDES CLUSTER MEMORY POWER.
(ORN 240) C

VEHICLE SPEED INPUT.
(DK GRN 389) D

IGNITION POWER TO DIGITAL CLUSTER. BATTERY VOLTAGE WITH IGNITION SWITCH IN RUN.
J (BRN 50)

DIMMER INPUT FOR VACUUM FLUORESCENT DISPLAYS. VARIABLE VOLTAGE.
H (PPL/WHT 724)

DIMMER INPUT FOR INCANDESCENT BULBS. VARIABLE VOLTAGE WITH LIGHTS ON AND DIMMER RHEOSTAT ADJUSTED.
G (GRY 8)

NOT USED
F

ENGLISH/METRIC SWITCH OUTPUT TO BCM.
E (LT BLU 811)

91D06881   91C06885

Fig. 3: Instrument Cluster Pinout Test – Digital Cluster

ter, measure voltage between instrument cluster connector C1, pin No. 6 (Brown wire) and ground. *See Fig. 2.*

7) If less than 12 volts are present, check and repair Brown wire as necessary. In addition, check instrument panel fuse No. 7.

8) If 12 volts or more is present, check for a good ground at connector C2, pin "N" (digital) or connector C1, pin No. 4 (analog) Black/White wire. *See Figs. 2 and 3.* If all grounds are okay, replace instrument cluster.

HEADLIGHT SWITCH TEST

Constant battery voltage should be present at headlight switch terminals "C" (Orange/Black wire) and "F" (Red wire). With headlights on, battery voltage should be present at headlight switch terminals "B" (Brown and Yellow wires) and "D" (Black wire). If voltage readings are not as indicated, check headlight switch and related wiring.

WIPER SWITCH TEST

For testing information on wipers, see appropriate WIPER/WASHERS article.

REMOVAL & INSTALLATION

INSTRUMENT CLUSTER

Removal & Installation – 1) Carefully pry out ventilation outlets. Remove one screw behind each outlet and 3 screws through defroster outlet. Remove glove box module. Remove 2 screws through glove box opening.

2) Remove in-vehicle temperature sensor electrical connector and aspirator tube. Remove solar sensor from trim pad and remove upper trim pad. *See Fig. 4.*

3) Remove 2 screws, plate and 3 remaining screws. *See Fig. 5.* Disconnect electrical connectors. Remove shift indicator cable clip. Remove instrument cluster. To install, reverse removal procedure

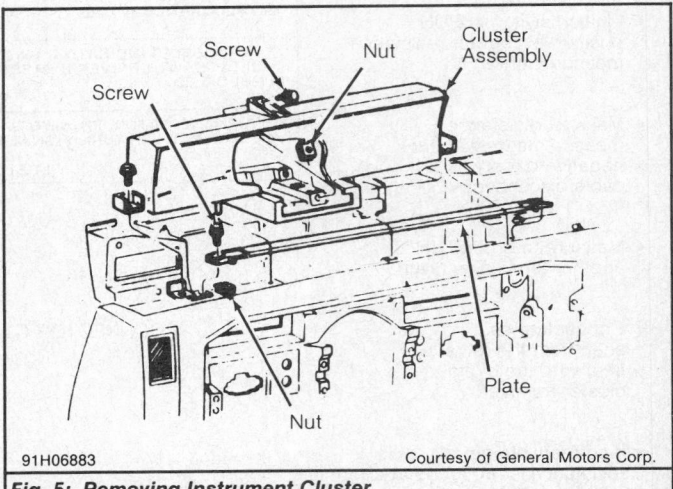

91H06883   Courtesy of General Motors Corp.

Fig. 5: Removing Instrument Cluster

WIRING DIAGRAMS

See appropriate chassis wiring diagram in WIRING DIAGRAMS.

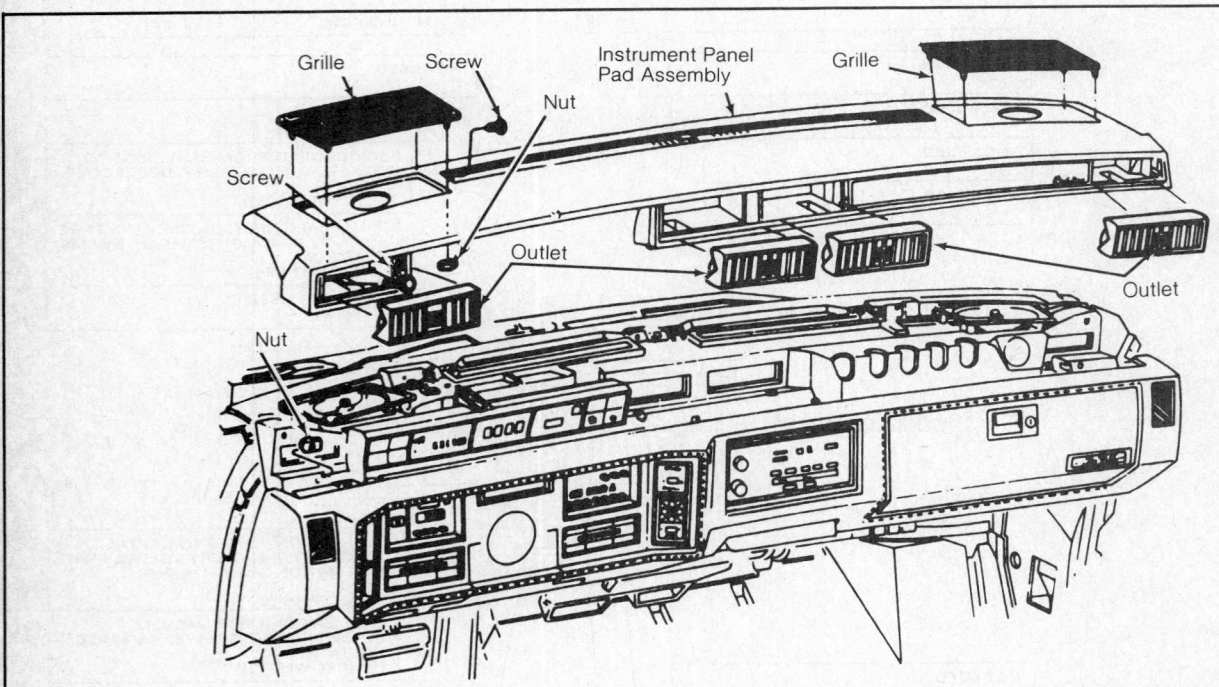

91F06882   Courtesy of General Motors Corp.

Fig. 4: Removing Instrument Panel Upper Trim Pad

DESCRIPTION

The instrument cluster is controlled by an electronic microprocessor unit called the Central Control Module (CCM). The CCM's self-diagnostic capabilities are referenced often in trouble code charts for quick and accurate diagnosis of non-code setting problems.

The instrument cluster utilizes a monitor system containing digital LCD displays, analog type gauges and telltale warning lights. A Red CHECK GAUGES warning light illuminates when any of the gauges operate within the gauges Red warning bands.

A Driver Information Center (DIC), switch pad and trip monitor are located to the right of the instrument cluster. DIC allows technician to select and display specific data for CCM diagnostic modes.

Central Control Module (CCM) uses the speedometer, odometer and trip computer to display codes. In diagnostic mode, speedometer displays malfunction codes, odometer displays data, and trip computer indicates system being tested and individual test number. Problems in the CCM-monitored systems are indicated by SYS flashing in the trip monitor display.

The accessory plug provides hot leads and a ground for electrical products such as a cellular phone. This 3-wire connector is located in center console under coin holder. The Orange wire is for constant battery voltage, Pink/Black wire is for battery voltage when ignition is in RUN position and Black wire is for ground.

OPERATION

DELAYED ACCESSORY BUS (DAB)

A Delayed Accessory Bus (DAB) is incorporated within electrical system to allow operation of power windows and radio for 15 minutes after ignition switch is turned off. Opening of driver's door will cancel DAB.

DRIVER INFORMATION CENTER (DIC) DISPLAY

Display panel is located to the right of DIC switch pad and above A/C-heater control head. DIC contains telltale warning indicators for ABS ACTIVE, CHARGING SYSTEM (battery symbol), FULL ENGINE POWER, INFL REST (inflatable restraint), LOW COOLANT, LOW OIL, LOW TIRE PRESSURE, SERVICE ABS (anti-lock brakes), SERVICE ENGINE SOON, SERVICE RIDE CONTROL, and SERVICE LTPWS (Low Tire Pressure Warning System).

An ambient light sensor (photocell) is located within the DIC switch pad. This sensor provides data to the instrument cluster circuitry to adjust panel illumination.

DRIVER INFORMATION CENTER (DIC) SWITCH PAD

By pressing following buttons, driver selects monitor display.

ENG/MET – Selects either English (ENG) or Metric (MET) units, shown in speedometer display.

TRIP/ODO – Selects either trip odometer (TRIP) or regular odometer (ODO).

INST/AVER – Selects either instant fuel economy (INST) or average fuel economy (AVER). Display reading appears to left of fuel gauge. When pressing INST button and INST is displayed, the instant fuel economy shown is fuel economy at time button was depressed. When AVER is displayed, figures shown are average fuel economy since system was last reset. It takes several miles at steady speed to get accurate average reading. Average reading is computed from miles driven divided by fuel used since system was last reset.

RANGE – Shows estimated distance you can expect to travel with fuel remaining in tank. Display appears to left of fuel gauge bar graph along with estimated AVER MPG. If RANGE is pressed when fuel gauge shows 2 bars or less or RESERVE light is illuminated, LO will appear on display. Range is determined from average fuel economy computed in last few miles driven.

FUEL RESET – Resets system when refueling to accurately compute fuel economy.

TRIP RESET – Resets trip odometer.

SPEEDOMETER DISPLAY

The speedometer digitally displays vehicle speed in either English (MPH) and Metric units (KM/H). The speedometer receives the vehicle speed data from the Central Control Module (CCM), which receives data from the ECM. The ECM receives signal pulses from the Vehicle Speed Sensor (VSS). The speedometer reacts slower to inputs in very cold weather due to ambient temperature of CCM. The range of display is from 0-220 MPH (0-354 KM/H).

TACHOMETER

The tachometer, an analog type gauge, receives its signal from the Direct Ignition System (DIS).

HANDLING PRECAUTIONS

CAUTION: When handling Electrostatic Discharge (ESD) sensitive electronic parts, technician should use following procedures to avoid damaging components.

1) Discharge personal static electricity by momentarily touching metal grounding point on vehicle before coming in contact with electronic components.

2) DO NOT touch terminals on components or connectors with fingers or metal tools. When disconnecting connectors, NEVER let metal tool contact any exposed terminal.

3) NEVER jumper, ground or use test probes on components or connectors unless specified in diagnosis. Always connect ground lead of test probe first.

4) DO NOT remove solid-state components from protective packaging until ready to install item. Touch packaging to ground before opening.

5) DO NOT bump or drop component. DO NOT lay component on metal work bench, electrical metal objects or other electrically operated components, such as radio, TV or oscilloscope.

Components Possibly Damaged By ESD:
- ABS Controller
- Central Control Module (CCM)
- Chime Module & Cruise Control Module
- Distributorless Ignition System (DIS) Module
- Electronic Instrument Clusters (digital)
- Electronic Control Module (ECM) (including PROM, CAL-PAK, or MEM-CAL)
- A/C-heater controllers and modules
- Low Tire Pressure Warning System Module (LTPWS)
- Radio & Theft Deterrent Modules

TROUBLE SHOOTING

INSTRUMENT CLUSTER & PANEL DISPLAYS

NOTE: Instrument cluster and instrument panel are 2 different components. Instrument Cluster (IC) fits into the instrument panel. Central Control Module (CCM) is located behind radio control head, in center of instrument panel. Access CCM wiring through door at front of center console left side trim panel. See Fig. 19.

Digital Display Inoperative – Check CCM malfunction codes. See CCM ON-BOARD DIAGNOSTICS.

All Instrument Cluster Indicators Are Inoperative – Check for open Supplemental Inflatable Restraint fuse (labeled either SIR or AIR BAG) and check for open in Pink/Black wire(s) from main fuse block to IC.

All DIC Indicators & All Gauges Are Inoperative – Check for open cluster (CLSTR) fuse or open in Pink/Black wire from main fuse block through wire junction to Instrument Cluster (IC).

All DIC Trip Computer Switches Inoperative – Check for CCM malfunction codes being set.

NOTE: To locate main fuse panel, open right side vehicle door to reveal main fuse panel door on instrument panel end.

DIAGNOSIS & TESTING

DIAGNOSIS

NOTE: TROUBLE SHOOTING must be performed before DIAGNOSIS. The Signal Generator and Instrument Panel Tester (J-33431-B) must be used on some of the following tests.

Oil Pressure Gauge Always Reads Low – Turn ignition on, with engine off. Disconnect oil pressure sensor connector. If oil pressure gauge starts reading high pressure, replace sensor unit. If no movement, check for short to ground in Tan wire from oil pressure sensor to instrument cluster. If circuit is okay, replace instrument cluster.

Oil Pressure Gauge Always Reads High – Turn ignition on, with engine off. Unplug oil pressure sensor connector. Connect jumper between terminal "C" of connector and ground. If gauge starts reading low pressure, replace sensor unit. If gauge remains high, check for poor connection or open in Tan wire between oil pressure sensor and instrument cluster. If circuit is okay, replace instrument cluster.

Oil Pressure Gauge Appears Inaccurate – 1) Check oil level. Check oil pressure with mechanical gauge before proceeding. Turn ignition on, with engine off.

2) Unplug oil pressure sensor connector. Using Signal Generator and Instrument Panel Tester (J-33431-B), connect Red clip lead to sensor connector terminal "A".

3) Oil pressure gauge should read correct pressure for specified resistance setting on tester. See OIL PRESSURE GAUGE TEST table.

4) If readings are as specified, replace sensor unit. If pressure readings are not as specified, check Tan wire from instrument cluster to oil pressure sensor for poor or corroded connections. If circuit is okay, replace instrument cluster.

OIL PRESSURE GAUGE TEST

Tester Setting	Pressure Reading
0 Ohms	Low
40 Ohms	About 30 psi
100 Ohms	High

Oil Temperature Gauge Always Indicates Cold – 1) Turn ignition on, with engine off. Disconnect oil temperature sensor connector. Connect test light between terminal "A" of connector and battery voltage.

2) If test light does not illuminate, check for poor connection or open in Black wire from oil temperature sensor through Black wire junction to ECM. If test light illuminates, install jumper from terminal "C" to ground at same connector.

3) If gauge moves to the right (HOT), replace sensor unit. If test light does not illuminate, check Dark Green/White wire from instrument cluster to oil temperature sensor for open or poor connection. If circuit is okay, replace instrument cluster.

Oil Temperature Gauge Always Indicates Hot – Turn ignition on, with engine off. Disconnect oil temperature sensor connector. If gauge moves back to left (COLD), replace sensor unit. If gauge does not move, check Dark Green/White wire from instrument cluster to oil temperature sensor for short to ground. If circuit is okay, replace Instrument Cluster (IC).

Oil Temperature Gauge Appears Inoperative – 1) Turn ignition on, with engine off. Disconnect oil temperature sensor connector. Connect test light between terminal "A" of connector and battery voltage.

2) If test light does not illuminate, check for poor connection or open in Black wire from oil temperature sensor through Black wire junction to ECM. If test light illuminates, at same connector install jumper from terminal "C" to ground.

3) If gauge moves to the right (HOT), replace sensor unit. If test light does not illuminate, check Dark Green/White wire from instrument cluster to oil temperature sensor for open or poor connection. If circuit is okay, replace instrument cluster.

Oil Temperature Gauge Always Indicates Hot – Turn ignition on, with engine off. Disconnect oil temperature sensor connector. If gauge moves back to left (COLD), replace sensor unit. If gauge does not move back to left, check Dark Green/White wire from instrument cluster to oil temperature sensor for short to ground. If circuit is okay, replace Instrument Cluster (IC).

Oil Temperature Gauge Appears Inaccurate – 1) Turn ignition on, with engine off. Unplug oil temperature sensor connector. Using Signal Generator and Instrument Panel Tester (J-33431-B), connect one Red clip lead to sensor connector terminal "C".

2) Connect other Red clip lead to ground. Adjust tester resistance dials to 1400 ohms, and then 55 ohms. If gauge reads COLD then HOT, replace sensor unit.

3) If gauge does not read as specified, check for poor connections, or high resistance in Dark Green/White wire from instrument cluster to oil temperature sensor. If circuit is okay, replace instrument cluster.

Coolant Temperature Gauge Always Indicates Cold – Turn ignition on, with engine off. Unplug coolant temperature sensor connector. Connect jumper wire between terminal "A" of connector and ground. If gauge moves all the way right (HOT), replace sensor unit. If gauge does not move to the right, check Dark Green wire from instrument cluster to coolant sensor for poor connections or open. If circuit is okay, replace instrument cluster.

Coolant Temperature Gauge Always Reads Hot – Turn ignition on, with engine off. Unplug temperature sensor connector. If gauge moves back to left (COLD), replace sensor unit. If gauge does not move back to left, check for short to ground in Dark Green wire from instrument cluster to sensor. If circuit is okay, replace instrument cluster.

Coolant Temperature Gauge Appears Inaccurate – 1) Turn ignition on, with engine off. Disconnect coolant temperature sensor connector. Using Signal Generator and Instrument Panel Tester (J-33431-B), connect one Red clip lead from tester to sensor connector terminal "A". Connect other Red clip lead to ground.

2) Adjust tester resistance dials to 1400 ohms, and then 55 ohms. If gauge reads cold, then goes to hot, replace sensor unit. If gauge does not read as specified, check for poor connections or high resistance in Dark Green wire from instrument cluster to sensor. If circuit is okay, replace instrument cluster.

Tachometer Does Not Operate Properly – 1) Check for moisture in firewall harness connector, located above battery and below cruise control servo unit. Repair as needed.

2) Turn ignition on, with engine off. Unplug connection C2 at Electronic Spark Timing (EST) distributor.

3) Connect Signal Generator and Instrument Panel Tester (J-33431-B) into 110V wall outlet. Connect Harness (J-33431-10) from tester to connection C2 and ground.

4) Set tester controls to on and to 54 MPH. If tachometer indicates near 900 RPM, problem is faulty Electronic Spark Timing (EST) distributor.

5) If tachometer does not indicate near 900 RPM, check for open or short to ground (or to battery voltage) in White wire from tachometer to EST, or to distributorless ignition module. For ZR1, check for open or short to ground to tachometer filter. If circuit is okay, replace instrument cluster.

Voltmeter Does Not Operate Properly – Turn ignition on, with engine off. Set digital voltmeter (DVOM) to DC scale, and connect to positive and negative battery terminals. If instrument cluster voltmeter closely matches voltage reading on DVOM, start engine and recheck DVOM voltage reading at battery. If instrument cluster voltmeter still closely matches DVOM reading, circuit is okay. If readings are different, replace voltmeter or Instrument Cluster (IC).

Fuel Gauge Always Reads EMPTY – 1) Check for fuel in tank before proceeding. Disconnect fuel tank unit wire connection at tank. Turn ignition on, with engine off.

2) If fuel gauge now reads FULL, replace fuel tank sending unit. If fuel gauge does not read as specified, connect test light between fuel tank sender unit connector (female) terminal "B" (Purple wire) and ground.

3) If test light illuminates, replace CCM. If test light does not illuminate, check for short to ground along Purple wire from fuel tank sender unit connector (female) terminal "B" to CCM. If circuit is okay, replace CCM.

Fuel Gauge Always Reads FULL – **1)** Unplug fuel tank connection at tank. Disconnect CCM Green connector. Turn ignition on, with engine off. Connect test light between fuel tank unit female connector terminal "B" (Purple wire) and ground. If test light illuminates, repair short to battery voltage along Purple wire from fuel tank sender to CCM.

2) If test light does not illuminate, LEAVE test light connected to terminal "B" and reconnect CCM Green connector. If test light does not illuminate, check for open in Purple wire. If circuit is okay, replace CCM.

3) If test light illuminates when CCM Green connector is plugged in, remove test light from terminal "B" and connect jumper wire between terminal "B" and ground. If fuel gauge reads empty, replace fuel tank sending unit. If gauge does not read as specified, replace CCM.

Fuel Gauge Appears Inaccurate – **1)** Unplug fuel tank connection at tank. Using Signal Generator and Instrument Panel Tester (J-33431-B), connect one Red clip lead to fuel tank unit female connector terminal "B" (Purple wire) and ground.

2) Turn ignition on, with engine off. Set tester resistance dials to 0 ohms, and then 50 ohms, and then 100 ohms. If fuel gauge in turn reads empty, then near half full, and then full, replace fuel tank sending unit. If gauge does not read as specified, check for poor or corroded connections in Purple wire from fuel tank sender to CCM. If circuit is okay, replace CCM.

All Gauges Inoperative – **1)** With ignition off, remove Instrument Cluster (IC). Connect test light between IC connector terminal A4 (Pink/Black wire) and ground. Turn ignition on, with engine off.

2) If test light does not illuminate, repair open or short to ground in Pink/Black wires from IC to DIC and to main fuse block. If shorted, replace cluster fuse after repairing wire. If test light illuminates, connect test light between terminals A1 (Black) and A4 (Pink/Black wire) of IC connector.

3) If test light does not illuminate, repair open in Black ground wiring from IC terminal A1 to ground location below left-hand side of instrument panel. If test light illuminates, check for poor connections at IC (bent terminal, etc.). If circuit is okay, replace Instrument Cluster (IC).

Digital Display Inoperative – **1)** Turn ignition on, with engine off. Using TECH 1 "Scan" Tester (94-00101-A), check for the following CCM malfunction codes 26, 27 and 31 through 37 in memory.

2) If any codes are set, See CCM ON-BOARD DIAGNOSTICS. If no codes are set, check for open in Black ground wire from terminal A7 of instrument cluster connector to ground location below left-hand side of instrument panel. If circuit is okay, replace Instrument Cluster (IC).

Speedometer Display Inoperative (Other Digital Displays Are Working) – **1)** Turn ignition on, with engine off. If SERVICE ENGINE SOON

light is on, check for related ECM diagnostic codes set. If light is not on, check cruise control for normal operation.

2) If no problem is found with cruise control, check for open in Dark Green/White wire from CCM Green connector, terminal E2, to splice connecting ECM, cruise control module, and radio control head. If circuit is okay, replace CCM.

3) If problem is found with cruise control, turn engine off. Disconnect ECM Red connector, radio control head connector C1, CCM Green connector, and cruise control module connector.

4) Connect test light between terminal No. 8 (Dark Green/White wire) of ECM Red connector and ground. Turn ignition on, with engine off.

5) If test light illuminates, check for and repair short to battery voltage in Dark Green/White wire from ECM terminal to one of following circuits: splice, CCM, cruise control module, or to radio control head.

6) If test light does not illuminate, reconnect test light between terminal No. 8 of ECM Red connector and battery voltage. If test light illuminates, check for and repair short to ground in Dark Green/White wire from ECM to one of following circuits: splice, CCM, cruise control module, or to radio control head.

7) If test light does not illuminate, check for continuity with DVOM (Digital Volt-Ohm Meter), between terminal No. 8 of ECM Red connector and terminal C2 of CCM Green connector.

8) If continuity does not exist in step **7)**, check for and repair open in Dark Green/White wire circuit from ECM to one of following circuits: splice, CCM, cruise control module, or radio control head. If continuity does exist in step **7)**, reconnect ECM Red and reconnect CCM Green connector.

9) Backprobe CCM Green connector with DVOM (set to AC voltage scale) between terminal C2 and ground. Raise vehicle off ground, ensure transmission is in Neutral, and turn rear wheels (by hand) while observing DVOM.

10) If voltage does not vary from less than one volt to more than 8.5 volts, reconnect radio control head connector C1 and disconnect CCM Green connector.

11) Backprobe radio control head connector C1 between terminal No. 5 and ground using DVOM (still set to AC voltage scale). If voltage varies when rear wheels are turned, replace CCM. If voltage does NOT vary, replace ECM.

12) If voltage does vary from less than one volt to more than 8.5 volts, plug in radio control head connector C1 and repeat step **9)**. If voltage still DOES NOT vary, repair/replace the radio control head. If voltage still varies, reconnect cruise control module connector and repeat step **11)** again.

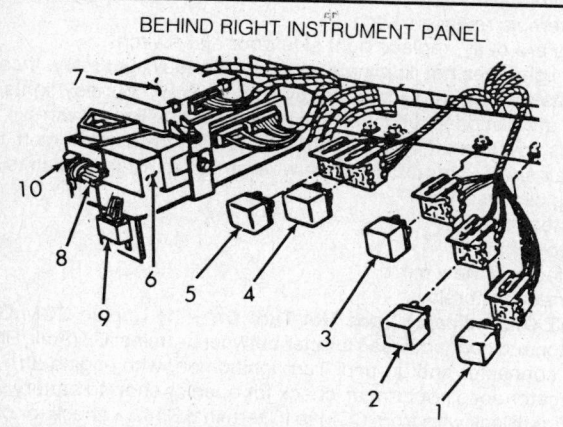

BEHIND RIGHT INSTRUMENT PANEL

1. Rear Window Defogger Relay
2. Horn Relay
3. Fuel Pump No. 1 Relay
4. Courtesy Light Relay
5. Fog Light Relay
6. Radio Receiver
7. Cruise Control Module
8. Hazard Flasher
9. Accessory Fuse Holder
10. Diode Module

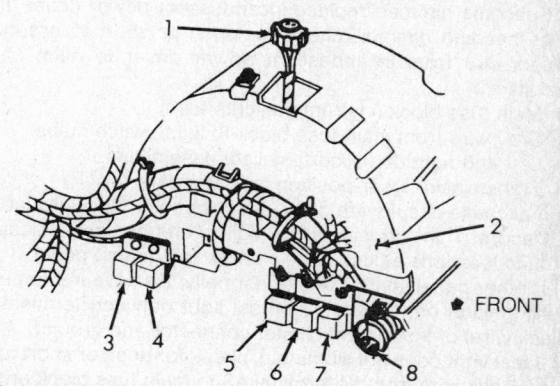

BEHIND LEFT INSTRUMENT PANEL

FRONT

1. DRL Sensor
2. Instrument Panel Carrier
3. Fuel Pump Relay No. 2 (If Equipped)
4. Radio Speaker Amplifier Relay
5. Starter Interrupt Relay
6. A/C Compressor Relay
7. Delayed Accessory Bus (DAB) Relay
8. Turn Signal Flasher

90G00782 91H08387

Fig. 1: Locating Relays Behind Instrument Panel

Courtesy of General Motors Corp.

13) If voltage still does not vary, replace cruise control module. If voltage still varies, check for an intermittent connection problem in Dark Green/White wiring circuit including ECM connectors, and connector between ECM and splice of Dark Green/White wires.

CAUTION: Ensure parking lights and taillights are operational before performing DIGITAL DISPLAY (LCD) BACKLIGHTS INOPERATIVE test. Display will NOT light up if ambient lighting is set too dark and parking lights are OFF or inoperative.

Digital Display (LCD) Backlights Inoperative – 1) If parking and taillights do not operate, see LIGHTING at end of DIAGNOSIS & TESTING. If display does not light up, shine bright light at ambient light sensor opening on DIC. If display still does not light, perform AMBIENT LIGHT SENSOR CHECK under LIGHTING.

2) With ignition off, remove Instrument Cluster (IC). Connect test light between terminal B5 (Orange wire) of IC connector and ground. If test light does not illuminate, check for open or short to ground in Orange wire from main fuse block to one of following circuits: splice, Orange wires to IC, CCM, tone generator, horn relay, courtesy light relay, and radio control head. See Fig. 1. Also check for open LCD fuse.

3) If test light illuminates, unplug CCM Gray connector. Connect jumper wire between terminal D8 (Gray/Red wire) of connector and ground. If display backlights turn on, replace CCM. If display backlights do not turn on, check for open in Gray/Red wire between CCM and IC, or check for faulty backlight bulbs. If all is okay, replace Instrument Cluster (IC).

IC Panel Lights Inoperative (Parking Lights & Taillights Operate Normally) – 1) If other panel lights operate normally, go to step **6)**. If other panel lights do not operate normally, check for blown instrument light, cluster, or CCM fuses. If fuses are okay, turn parking lights on, and dimmer switch to BRIGHT.

2) Backprobe incandescent power driver connector with test light between terminal "D" (Brown wire) and ground. Incandescent power driver is located behind far left corner of instrument panel, near starter enable relay. If test light does not illuminate, repair open in Brown wire between incandescent power driver and light switch. If test light illuminates, backprobe connector with test light between terminal "B" (Purple/White wire) and ground.

3) If test light does not illuminate, check for open in Purple/White wire from light switch to incandescent power driver. If circuit is okay, replace light switch. If test light illuminates, move dimmer switch slowly from BRIGHT to DIM. Test light should become dimmer. If test light does not become dimmer, replace light switch. If test light does become dimmer, backprobe incandescent power driver connector between terminal "C" (Light Green wire) and ground.

4) Move dimmer switch slowly from BRIGHT to DIM. If test light does not become dimmer, replace incandescent power driver. If test light does become dimmer, check for open or short to ground in Light Green wire from incandescent power driver to each of following circuits:

- Main fuse block (instrument lights fuse)
- Gray wire from main fuse block to light switch bulbs
- Left and right door courtesy light assemblies
- Transmission gear-position indicator light

5) If all these circuits are okay, repair open in Black ground wire from left and/or right door courtesy lights, and/or gear indicator light to ground locations at kick panels below instrument panel.

6) If other panel lights operate normally, Remove instrument cluster. Turn ignition on, and connect test light between terminal A3 (Pink/Black wire) of instrument cluster connector and ground.

7) If test light does not illuminate, check for open or short to ground in Pink/Black wire from IC terminal A3 to main fuse block and to DIC. If wire is shorted to ground, replace cluster fuse after repairing wire.

8) If test light illuminates, replace instrument cluster. Unplug CCM Green connector. Connect jumper between terminal E3 (Gray/Black wire) of CCM Green connector and ground. If panel lights do not illuminate, check for open or short to battery voltage in Gray/Black wire from CCM to IC terminal A2.

9) If circuit is okay, replace Instrument Cluster (IC). If panel lights do illuminate, check for open in Brown wire from CCM Gray connector

terminal D14 to splice of Brown wires. If wire is okay, replace the CCM.

IC Panel Lights Always On – Turn ignition on, with engine off. Unplug CCM Green connector. If lights do turn off normally, replace CCM. If panel lights do not turn off, check for short to ground in Gray/Black wire from IC terminal A2 to CCM Green connector terminal E3. If no short is present, replace Instrument Cluster (IC). If panel lights do not turn off normally, check exterior lights system for bad ground or power feed-back problem.

DOOR AJAR Indicator Will Not Turn On – 1) Cover ambient light sensor in DIC before proceeding. Unplug diode module connector. Diode module is located next to 4-way flasher under right side of dash, behind radio receiver in center of instrument panel. Turn ignition on, with engine off. Connect jumper wire between terminal "B" (Purple wire) of connector and ground.

2) If indicator is not on, check for open or short to ground in Purple wire from IC terminal B7 to diode module terminal "B", or check for open indicator bulb. If Purple wire circuit and bulb are okay, replace Instrument Cluster (IC). If indicator is on, and courtesy lights are on, replace diode module.

DOOR AJAR Indicator Always On – 1) Turn ignition on, with engine off. Unplug diode module connector. Diode module is located next to 4-way flasher under right side of dash, behind radio receiver in center of instrument panel. If indicator does not turn off, check for short to ground in Purple wire from IC terminal B7 to diode module connector. If Purple wire is not shorted, replace Instrument Cluster (IC).

2) If indicator does turn off when diode module connector is unplugged, first check for CCM code 25 to be set before proceeding and possible door key switch to be malfunctioning. If these 2 items are not causing problem, disconnect CCM Gray connector. Connect test light between terminal C12 (Black/Yellow wire) of CCM Gray connector and battery voltage. If test light illuminates, find short to ground in Black/Yellow wire circuit from CCM to each of following circuits:

- Left-hand door ajar switch
- Diode module
- Hatch release switch
- Convertible top release switch

If circuits are okay, replace left side door ajar switch.

3) If test light does not illuminate, connect test light between terminal D16 (Black/White wire) of CCM Gray connector and battery voltage.

4) If test light illuminates, find short to ground in Black/White wire circuit from CCM to each of following circuits:

- Right side door ajar switch
- Diode module
- Hatch release switch
- Convertible release switch

If circuits are okay, replace right side door ajar switch.

5) If test light does not illuminate, remove courtesy light relay. If courtesy lights turn off, replace courtesy light relay. If courtesy lights do not turn off, disconnect light switch connector C1 (Brown wire).

6) If lights now turn off, replace light switch. If lights do not turn off, find and repair short to ground in White wire circuit from light switch to the following circuits:

- Courtesy lights
- Cargo lights
- Lighted rear view mirror
- Courtesy light relay

CHANGE OIL Indicator Does Not Turn On – 1) Unplug CCM Gray connector and connect fused jumper between terminal C8 (Pink/Black wire) of connector and ground. Turn ignition on, with engine off.

2) If indicator does not turn on, check for open or short to battery voltage in Pink/Black wire from CCM to IC terminal B14, or check for open indicator bulb. If Pink/Black wire circuit is good, replace Instrument Cluster (IC).

3) If indicator does turn on, check for poor connections at CCM Gray connector, mainly terminal C8 (Pink/Black wire). If connections are okay, replace CCM.

CHANGE OIL Indicator Always On (No Oil Change Needed) – Unplug CCM Gray connector. Turn ignition on, with engine off. If indicator turns off, replace CCM. If not, check for short to ground in Pink/Black wire from CCM terminal C8 (Pink/Black wire) to IC terminal B14. If circuit is okay, replace Instrument Cluster (IC).

CHECK GAUGES Indicator Does Not Turn On – Unplug CCM Gray connector and connect fused jumper between terminal C9 (Light Blue wire) of connector and ground. Turn ignition on, with engine off. If indicator does not turn on, check for and repair open or short to battery voltage in Light Blue wire from CCM to each of following circuits:

- Instrument Cluster (IC)
- Oil pressure switch
- Open indicator bulb

If circuits are okay, replace Instrument Cluster (IC).

CHECK GAUGES Indicator Always On – **1)** Ensure no CCM or ECM codes are set. Unplug CCM Gray connector. Turn ignition on, engine running. If indicator is off, replace CCM. If indicator remains on, unplug oil pressure switch.

2) If indicator turns off when unplugging oil pressure switch, check oil level and check oil pressure with mechanical gauge. If oil pressure is within specifications, replace oil pressure switch.

3) If indicator remains on after unplugging oil pressure switch, check for short to ground in Light Blue wire circuit from CCM Gray connector terminal C9 to IC terminal A10 and to oil pressure switch connector. If circuit is okay, replace Instrument Cluster (IC).

LOW COOLANT Indicator Does Not Turn On – **1)** Unplug low coolant switch 2-way connector. Connect fused jumper between terminal "A" (Gray wire) of switch and ground. Turn ignition on, with engine off.

2) If indicator does not turn on, check for open or short to battery voltage in Gray wire circuit between DIC and low coolant switch, or check for open in bulb. If Gray wire circuit is okay, replace DIC flexible circuit board.

3) If indicator does turn on, check for open in ground wire to terminal "B" (Black wire) of low coolant connector. If ground wire circuit is not open, replace low coolant switch.

LOW COOLANT Indicator Always On (Coolant Capacity Correct) – Unplug low coolant switch 2-way connector. Turn ignition on, with engine off. If indicator turns off, replace low coolant switch. If indicator remains on, check for short to ground in Gray wire circuit from DIC to low coolant switch. If Gray wire circuit is not shorted, replace DIC flexible circuit board.

LOW OIL LEVEL Indicator Does Not Turn On – **1)** This condition can occur while engine is running. Allow engine to cool several hours before performing this diagnosis.

2) Enter CCM diagnostic mode. See CCM ON-BOARD DIAGNOSTICS. Select function mode "1.4" by pressing TRIP/ODO button. Next press ENG/MET button until parameter 11 (low oil indicator) is shown in first two digits of display. While output status item 11 is cycling on and off, low oil indicator should be illuminating on and off. Cycling status of output data being cycled will be displayed as "1" for ON position or "0" for OFF position. These two numbers will cycle in display every 3 seconds as status is changed.

3) If indicator does not illuminate after performing step **2)**. Check for open indicator bulb, check for open or short to battery voltage in Yellow wire circuit from DIC terminal "B" to CCM Gray connector terminal D13, check for open in DIC flexible circuit board.

4) If indicator illuminates after performing step **2)**, unplug low oil level sensor connector (Pink wire). Using DVOM, check for continuity between terminals "A" (Pink wire) and "B" (Black wire) of sensor connector. If continuity exists, check for short between two wires of sensor pigtail. If no problem exists with wires, replace sensor.

5) If continuity does not exist, connect DVOM (12-volt scale) between terminal "A" (Pink wire) of harness connector and ground. If reading is about 5 volts, replace CCM. If reading is not about 5 volts, check for open or short to ground in Pink wire circuit. If open or short does not exist, replace CCM.

LOW OIL LEVEL Indicator Always On (Oil Level Correct) – **1)** Enter CCM diagnostic mode. See CCM ON-BOARD DIAGNOSTICS. Select function mode "1.3" by pressing TRIP/ODO button. Next press ENG/MET button until input parameter 14 (low oil level switch) is shown in first two digits of display. The input status will be displayed as "1" for ON position or "0" for OFF position. These two numbers will display across screen as often as status is changed.

2) If display is showing "0", disconnect CCM Gray connector and check if LOW OIL LEVEL indicator turns off. If indicator does turn off, replace CCM. If indicator does not turn off, repair short to ground in Yellow wire circuit or short in DIC flexible circuit board.

3) If display is showing "1", unplug low oil level sensor connector. Check for continuity between sensor connector terminals "A" and "B" using DVOM. If continuity does not exist, replace sensor. If continuity does exist, Check for continuity between terminal "B" of harness connector and ground. If continuity does not exist, repair open in Black wire circuit to ground. If continuity does exist, repair open or short to voltage in Pink wire circuit.

LIGHTING

Parking Lights & Taillights Inoperative – **1)** Remove headlight switch. See HEADLIGHT SWITCH under REMOVAL & INSTALLATION. Using test light, backprobe between light switch connector C1 terminal "H" (Orange) and ground.

2) If test light does not illuminate, check for open or short to ground in Orange wire circuit between main fuse block and light switch. If Orange wire is shorted to ground, replace taillight fuse after repairing wire.

3) If test light illuminates, backprobe with test light between light switch connector C1 terminal "G" (Brown) and ground. Turn parking lights on. If test light does not illuminate now, replace light switch.

4) If test light illuminates in step **3)**, remove connector C1 from light switch and check for bent terminal pins at light switch. Also check for open in Brown wire circuits from light switch to front marker lights and to front parking/turn lights. Ensure ground wire circuits are good.

Ambient Light Sensor Check – **1)** Enter CCM on-board diagnostic mode. See CCM ON-BOARD DIAGNOSTICS. Select Display CCM data (trip monitor will display "1.2"). In this mode, go to parameter 03 (ambient light sensor) shown in left-side of odometer. Turn parking lights on.

2) While observing right-side 3 numbers (ambient/data count) in odometer display, shine bright light into ambient light sensor on DIC. The ambient/data count should go to "0". Cover ambient light sensor completely. Ambient/data count should go up to about 240. If ambient/data count responded as specified, no problem exists with ambient light sensor.

3) If ambient/data count did not respond as specified, disconnect DIC Blue connector. If ambient/data count does not go to about 255, check for short to ground in White wire circuit from CCM Green connector terminal E10 to DIC Blue connector terminal "L". If White wire circuit is okay, replace CCM.

4) If ambient/data count does go to about 255 after disconnecting DIC Blue connector, connect jumper between terminals "G" (Black-ground wire) and "L" (White wire) of DIC Blue connector. If ambient/data count now goes to "0", replace DIC.

5) If ambient/data count does not go to "0", check for open in White wire from CCM Green connector to DIC Blue connector. Also check for faulty connector terminal connections. If White wire circuit is okay, replace CCM.

CCM ON-BOARD DIAGNOSTICS

ENTERING DIAGNOSTICS

1) To enter diagnostic mode, locate ALDL connector under instrument cluster, to left of steering column. Using jumper wire, ground ALDL pin "G" (CCM) to pin "A" (ground). Turn ignition on, with engine off. If CCM will not enter diagnostic mode, A/C fuse is blown. This condition will set CCM code 16.

2) With CCM in diagnostic mode, speedometer displays malfunction codes and trip monitor displays particular module system number being investigated.

3) Code faults now present (current code) are indicated by a "C" following the code number, and an "H" indicates code fault has occurred (history code), but is not now present. All ECM codes will be displayed as history codes.

4) If Code C12 is displayed, no code problems exist, and no codes are stored.

5) Each malfunction code will be displayed for 3 seconds, followed by one second pause before next code is displayed. A 3 second pause occurs between each code display sequence for each separate module.

6) After all malfunction codes have been displayed for all modules, trip monitor will display function "1.0". At same time, speedometer will go blank, waiting further input instructions.

7) Manual mode can be entered at any time during any code display sequence by pressing any button on DIC. See Fig. 2.

8) When manual mode entered, speedometer will go blank and trip monitor will display function "1.0". This indicates system is ready for instructions.

The control systems are numbered as follows:

- 1.0 – Central Control Module (CCM)
- 4.0 – Engine Control Module (ECM – history codes only)
- 7.0 – Active Suspension (AS) Module (if equipped)

The system function modules (numerical display on trip monitor) are as follows:

- 1.0 – Waiting for further input instructions
- 1.1 – Display CCM malfunction codes
- 1.2 – Display CCM data
- 1.3 – Display CCM discrete inputs status
- 1.4 – Cycle CCM outputs
- 1.7 – Clear CCM malfunction codes
- 4.0 – Holding for further input
- 4.1 – Display ECM malfunction codes
- 4.7 – Clear ECM malfunction codes

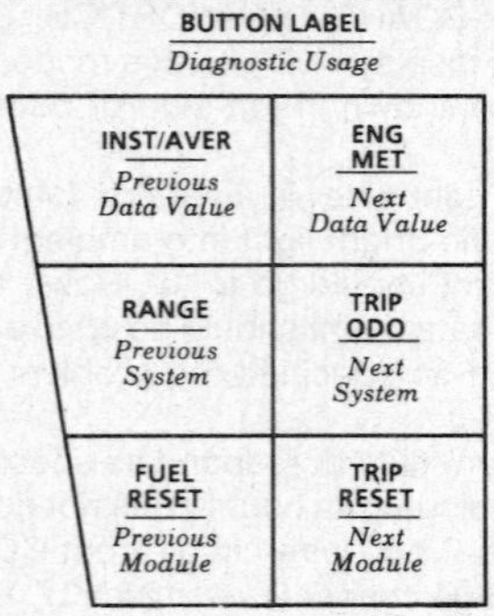

BUTTON LABEL
Diagnostic Usage

INST/AVER	ENG MET
Previous Data Value	*Next Data Value*
RANGE	TRIP ODO
Previous System	*Next System*
FUEL RESET	TRIP RESET
Previous Module	*Next Module*

90E00780   Courtesy of General Motors Corp.

Fig. 2: Driver Information Center Buttons/Functions

CCM Data – The data in CCM DATA table is displayed on trip computer when function "1.2" is selected. The data values are selected with the INST/AVER and ENG/MET buttons. The first 2 digits displayed on odometer are the data number, the last 3 digits displayed are the data value.

CCM DATA

Data Number	Data
01	Fuel Level (Gallons-Tenths)
02 [1]	Dimming Potentiometer (Ambient/Data Counts)
03	Ambient Light Sensor (Ambient/Data Counts)
04 [2]	Rear Defogger Timer (Seconds)
05	Vehicle Speed (MPH or KM/H)
06	PASS-Key Ambient/Data Counts
07	Ignition Voltage (Volts-Tenths)
08	Switched Battery Voltage (Volts-Tenths)
09	Cluster Incandescent Dimming PWM (0-100%)
10	Cluster LCD Backlight Dimming PWM (0-100%)
11	Radio & Climate Control LCD Dimming PWM (0-100%)
12	LED Dimming PWM (0-100%)
13	Oil Monitor Effective Revolution (0-200 counts) (100,000 revolutions per count)
14 [3]	CCM Software Version

[1] – Headlights or Parking lights must be on.
[2] – Engine running.
[3] – Note that data number 14 will not be displayed with version number.

CCM MALFUNCTION CODES

Code	Brief Definition
12	No Malfunction Codes Stored
13	DIC Switches Open Or Shorted To Battery Voltage
14	DIC Switches Shorted To Ground
16	Ignition 3 Fuse Circuit Open
21	Horn Relay Coil Shorted To Battery Voltage Or CCM Internal Open
22	Rear Defogger Relay Coil Shorted To Battery Voltage Or CCM Internal Open
24	Courtesy Light Relay Coil Shorted To Battery Voltage Or CCM Internal Open
25	Courtesy Light Relay Coil Circuit Open Or Shorted To Ground
26	LCD Blanking Control Circuit Shorted To Battery Voltage Or CCM Internal Open
27	LCD Blanking Control Circuit Open Or Shorted To Ground
31	LCD Data Circuit Shorted To Battery Voltage Or CCM Internal Open
32	LCD Data Circuit Open Or Shorted To Ground
33	Data Clock Circuit Shorted To Battery Voltage Or CCM Internal Open
34	Data Clock Circuit Open Or Shorted To Ground
35	Data Strobe Circuit Shorted To Battery Voltage Or CCM Internal Open
36	Data Strobe Circuit Open Or Shorted To Ground
37	M Clock Circuit Shorted To Battery Voltage Or CCM Internal Open
38	M Clock Circuit Open Or Shorted To Ground
41	Loss Of ECM Serial Data Communications
51	PASS-Key – Invalid Key Detection
52	PASS-Key – Key Detection Circuit Shorted
53	PASS-Key – Key Detection Circuit Open Or Shorted To Battery Voltage
54	PASS-Key – Fuel Enable Failure
61	PASS-Key – Key No. 1 Programming Resistance Out Of Range
62	PASS-Key – Key No. 2 Programming Resistance High
63	PASS-Key – Key No. 2 Programming Resistance Low
71	LCD Dimming Output Circuit Shorted To Battery Voltage Or CCM Internal Open
72	LCD Dimming Output Circuit Open Or Shorted to Ground
73	LED Display Dimming Output Circuit Shorted To Battery Voltage Or CCM Internal Open
74	LED Display Dimming Output Circuit Open Or Shorted to Ground

CCM DISCRETE INPUTS STATUS

Input Number	Input Definition	"1" Definition
01	PASS-KEY Fuel	Enabled
02 [1]	English/Metric Status	Metric
03	Door Key Switch	On
04	Right Door Ajar	Open
05	Left Door Ajar	Open
06 [2]	Key In Ignition	Closed
07	Hatch Ajar	Open
08	Power Door Unlock	Yes
09	Power Door Lock	Yes
10	Parking Lights	On
11 [3]	Rear Defogger Input	On
12 [4]	Seat Belt Switch	Buckled
13 [5]	High Beam Switch Input	On
14	Low Oil Level Switch	Low Oil

[1] – English or Metric status must be selected prior to grounding ALDL pin "G".

[2] – If input display does show a "1" for closed status, then key in ignition switch or its circuit is faulty. CCM only "sees" this switch closed when ignition key is in the OFF or ACC positions.

[3] – Engine must be running.

[4] – Driver's seat belt only.

[5] – Headlights must be ON.

CCM Discrete Inputs Status – 1) The input data is displayed on trip computer when the "1.3" function is selected by pressing TRIP/ODO button. The input data values are selected with the INST/AVER and ENG/MET buttons.

2) The first 2 digits displayed on odometer are the data number, the last 3 digits displayed are the input data value. The input status will be displayed as "1" for ON position or "0" for OFF position. These two numbers will display across screen as often as status is changed.

Cycle CCM Outputs – 1) The output data mode is displayed on trip computer when the "1.4" function is selected by pressing TRIP/ODO button. The individual output data items to be cycled are selected with the INST/AVER and ENG/MET buttons.

2) The first 2 digits displayed on odometer are the data item number. The status of the output data being cycled will be displayed as "1" for ON position or "0" for OFF position. These two numbers will cycle in display every 3 seconds as status is changed.

CYCLE CCM OUTPUTS

Output Number	Output
01	Change Oil Indicator
02 [1]	Check Gauges Indicator
03	Fasten Seat Belt Indicator
04	Security Lamp Indicator
05	High Beam Indicator
06	Chime 1
07	Chime 2
08	LCD Blanking Control
09	Rear Defogger Relay
10	Courtesy Lamp Relay
11	Low Oil Indicator
12 [2]	Starter Enable Relay
13	Delayed Accessory Bus Relay
14	Horn Relay

[1] – Engine must be running to cycle.
[2] – Starter enable relay output will cycle only if proper pass-key is in ignition switch.

CCM CODES DIAGNOSIS

NOTE: When diagnosing the following codes, this special test equipment is required:

- *Signal Generator and Instrument Panel Tester (J-33431-B)*
- *Terminal Adapter Kit (J-35616)*
- *TECH 1 "Scan" Tester (94-00101-A)*
- *Digital Volt-Ohmmeter (J-34029-A)*
- *Pass-Key Interrogator (J-35628)*

Code 13 (DIC Switches Open Or Shorted To Battery Voltage) – 1) If pressing DIC button causes different function to perform or no function at all, it indicates the DIC switches are internally open, or shorted. *See Fig. 3.*

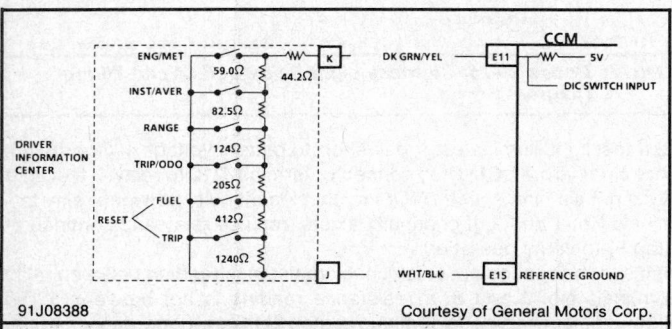

91J08388   Courtesy of General Motors Corp.

Fig. 3: Codes 13-14, DIC Switches Circuit Wiring Diagram

2) Remove DIC from instrument panel and unplug connector. See DRIVER INFORMATION CENTER (DIC) under REMOVAL & INSTALLATION. Connect DVOM (12-volt scale) between DIC Blue harness connector terminal "K" (Dark Green/Yellow wire) and ground. Turn ignition on and note voltage reading of DVOM.

3) If voltage reading is zero, backprobe DVOM between CCM Green connector terminal E11 and ground. If voltage reading is still zero, check terminal E11 connections. If connections are okay, replace CCM. If voltage reading is about 5 volts between CCM Green connector terminal E11 and ground, repair open in Dark Green/Yellow wire circuit or its connections to DIC from CCM.

4) If voltage reading in step **2)** is greater than 5.02 volts, turn ignition off and disconnect CCM Green connector. Connect DVOM between terminal E11 and ground. Turn ignition on. If there is no voltage reading, replace CCM. If there is voltage reading, repair short to battery voltage in Dark Green/Yellow wire.

5) If voltage reading in step **2)** is between 4.95-5.02 volts, connect DVOM between DIC Blue harness connector terminals "K" (Dark Green/Yellow wire) and "J" (White/Black wire). If voltage reading is now zero, check for open in White/Black wire circuit and its connections from CCM Green connector terminal E15 to DIC. If circuit is okay, replace CCM.

6) If voltage reading between terminals "K" and "J" is still between 4.95-5.02 volts, replace DIC switches. When repairs are completed, clear codes and verify operation.

Code 14 (DIC Switches Shorted To Ground) – 1) If pressing DIC button causes wrong function to perform, or no function at all, it indicates the DIC switches are internally shorted to ground. *See Fig. 3.*

2) Remove DIC from instrument panel and unplug connector. See DRIVER INFORMATION CENTER (DIC) under REMOVAL & INSTALLATION. Connect DVOM (12-volt scale) between DIC Blue harness connector terminal "K" (Dark Green/Yellow wire) and ground. Turn ignition on and note voltage reading of DVOM.

3) If voltage reading is 4.95-5.02 volts, check if H14 or C14 was displayed. If H14 (history) was displayed, check for poor DIC or CCM connections to cause this intermittent fault to set. If C14 (current) was displayed, replace DIC switches.

4) If voltage reading in step **2)** was less than 4.95 volts, turn ignition off and unplug CCM Green connector. Turn ignition on. Connect test light between battery voltage and CCM Green connector terminal E11 (Dark Green/Yellow wire).

5) If test light illuminates, repair short to ground in Dark Green/Yellow wire. If test light does not illuminate, connect DVOM (ohmmeter) between DIC terminals "K" and "J". Note DVOM reading. DO NOT push any DIC buttons.

6) If resistance reading is between 1950-2385 ohms, check for poor connection at CCM Green connector pin E11. If pin connection is okay, replace CCM. If resistance reading is not between 1950-2385 ohms, replace DIC switches. When repairs are completed, clear codes and verify operation.

Code 16 (Ignition 3 Fuse Circuit Open) – 1) This code will always appear as history code. If A/C fuse is blown, CCM will not receive Ignition 3 power and will not enter diagnostic mode. If for any reason CCM reads ignition 3 fuse circuit has low voltage for more than 3 seconds, Code 16 will set.

2) If A/C fuse is found to be blown, ensure ignition is off. Replace fuse and turn on ignition. If fuse blows when ignition turned on, repair short to ground in Brown wire circuit from CCM Green connector terminal E4 to A/C fuse in fuse block. *See Fig. 4.* If newly installed fuse did not blow, clear codes and re-enter diagnostic mode. If Code 16 is still set, proceed with following steps.

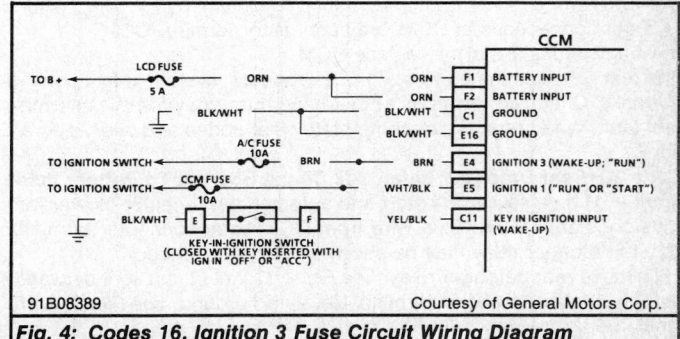

91B08389   Courtesy of General Motors Corp.

Fig. 4: Codes 16, Ignition 3 Fuse Circuit Wiring Diagram

3) If A/C fuse is not blown (or if Code 16 is still set), turn ignition off. Connect jumper between ALDL terminals "G" (CCM) and "A" (ground). Turn ignition on. If CCM does enter automatic display mode, no problem is present. Perform wiggle test of connections and wiring to locate intermittent fault source.

4) If CCM does not enter automatic display mode, backprobe using DVOM between CCM Green connector terminal E4 and ground. If voltage reading is not about 12 volts, repair open in Brown wire circuit from CCM Green connector terminal E4 to A/C fuse in fuse block.

5) If voltage reading is about 12 volts, turn ignition off. Disconnect CCM Green connector. Using Terminal Adapter Kit (J-35616), connect DVOM between CCM Green harness connector terminal E4 and ground. Turn ignition on. If voltage reading is about 12 volts, perform wiggle test of connnections and wiring to check for intermittent circuit faults. If no faults are found, replace CCM.

6) If voltage reading is about 12 volts using terminal adapter kit and DVOM, repair faulty connection at terminal E4. When repairs are completed, clear codes and verify operation.

Code 21 (Horn Relay Coil Circuit Shorted) – 1) If horn will not sound, not even through Universal Theft Deterrent (UTD) system, remove horn relay. *See Fig. 1.*

2) Connect test light between horn relay connector terminal No. 2 (Black wire) and ground. *See Fig. 5.* Turn ignition on. If test light illuminates, repair short to battery voltage in Black wire circuit from CCM Gray connector terminal C16 to horn switch.

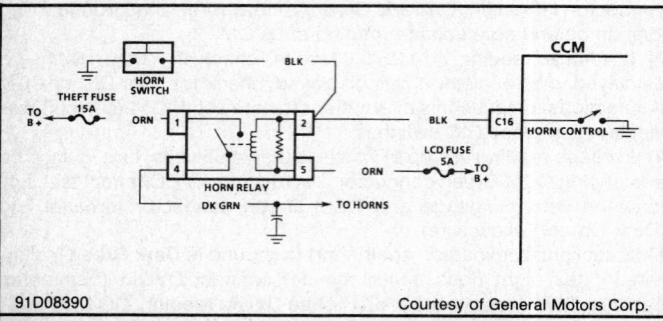

91D08390   Courtesy of General Motors Corp.

Fig. 5: Code 21, Horn Relay Coil Circuit Wiring Diagram

3) If test light does not illuminate, using a DVOM (ohmmeter) check for continuity between relay terminals No. 1 and 2. If continuity exists, replace relay and follow steps **5)** through **7)** for system verification.

4) If continuity does not exist, check resistance reading between relay terminals No. 5 and 2. If reading is not between 50-80 ohms, replace relay and follow next steps for system verification.

5) If reading is between 50-80 ohms, connect test light between battery voltage and relay connector terminal No. 2. Connect jumper between ALDL terminals "G" and "A". Turn ignition on. Press TRIP/ODO button until "1.4" appears in trip monitor, and then press ENG/MET button until "14...0" appears in odometer (cycling between "14...0" indicating OFF position, to "14...1" indicating ON position).

6) If test light does not illuminate when "14...1" appears, check for open in Black wire circuit from CCM to the following:
- Horn relay
- Horn switch
- Poor connections at CCM Gray connector terminal C16

If wiring circuits are okay, replace CCM

7) If test light illuminates when "14...1" appears, system is functioning normally. Check connections at CCM and horn relay for this intermittent fault. When repairs are completed, clear codes and verify operation.

Code 22 (Rear Defogger Relay Coil Circuit Shorted To Battery Voltage) – 1) If vehicle won't start and automatic A/C-heater blower fan runs constantly, Dark Blue wire from CCM Gray connector terminal D10 to defogger relay may be shorted to battery voltage.

2) Remove rear defogger relay. *See Fig. 1.* Connect test light between defogger relay connector terminal No. 2 and ground. *See Fig. 6.* Turn ignition on.

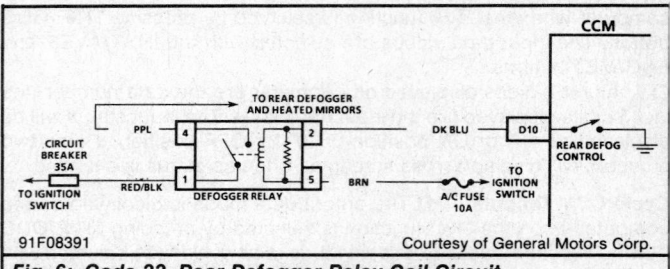

91F08391   Courtesy of General Motors Corp.

Fig. 6: Code 22, Rear Defogger Relay Coil Circuit Wiring Diagram

3) If test light illuminates, repair short to battery voltage in Dark Blue wire circuit. If test light does not illuminate, use DVOM to check for continuity between relay terminals No. 1 and 2. If continuity exists, replace relay and continue at step **5)** to verify operation.

4) If continuity does not exist, check resistance reading between relay terminals No. 2 and 5. If resistance reading is not between 50-80 ohms, replace relay and continue at step **5)** to verify operation. If resistance reading is between 50-80 ohms, follow next steps.

5) Connect test light between battery voltage and relay connector terminal No. 2. Connect jumper between ALDL terminals "G" and "A". Turn ignition on. Press TRIP/ODO button until "1.4" appears, and then press ENG/MET button until "9..0" appears in odometer (cycling between "9..0" for OFF position to "9..1" for ON position).

6) If test light does not illuminate when "9..1" appears, check for open in Dark Blue wire circuit or connections at CCM Gray connector terminal D10. If Dark Blue wire circuit is okay, replace CCM.

7) If test light illuminates when "9..1" appears, this is normal function. Perform wiggle test to connections and wiring at CCM and defogger relay for this intermittent fault. When repairs are completed, clear codes and verify operation.

Code 24 (Courtesy Light Relay Coil Shorted To Battery Voltage) –1) If courtesy and cargo lights do not come on, Gray/Black wire circuit may be shorted to battery voltage.

2) Cover ambient light sensor on DIC with dark tape. Remove courtesy light relay. *See Fig. 1.* Connect test light between relay connector terminal No. 2 and ground. *See Fig. 7.* Turn ignition on.

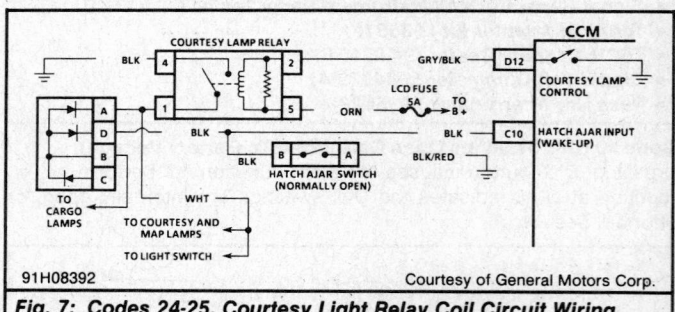

91H08392   Courtesy of General Motors Corp.

Fig. 7: Codes 24-25, Courtesy Light Relay Coil Circuit Wiring Diagram

3) If test light illuminates, repair short to battery voltage in Gray/Black wire circuit from CCM Gray connector terminal D12 to relay. If test light does not illuminate, use DVOM to check continuity between relay terminals No. 1 and 2. If continuity exists, replace relay and continue at step **5)** to verify operation.

4) If continuity does not exist, check resistance reading between relay terminals No. 2 and 5. If resistance reading is not between 50-80 ohms, replace relay and continue at step **5)** to verify operation. If resistance reading is between 50-80 ohms, proceed to step **5)**.

5) Connect test light between battery voltage and relay connector terminal No. 2. Connect jumper between ALDL terminals "G" and "A". Turn ignition on. Press TRIP/ODO button until "1.4" appears, and then press ENG/MET button until "10..0" appears in odometer (cycling between "10..0" for OFF position and "10..1" for ON position).

6) If test light does not illuminate when "10..1" appears, check for open in Gray/Black wire circuit or connections at CCM Gray connector terminal D12. If Gray/Black wire circuit is okay, replace CCM.

7) If test light illuminates when "10..1" appears, this is normal function. Perform wiggle test to connections at CCM and defogger relay for this intermittent fault. When repairs are completed, clear codes and verify operation.

Code 25 (Courtesy Light Relay Coil Circuit Open Or Grounded) – 1) If Gray/Black wire is shorted to ground, courtesy lights will stay on. If Gray/Black wire is open, courtesy lights will stay off.

2) Cover ambient light sensor on DIC with dark tape. Remove courtesy light relay. *See Fig. 1.* Connect test light between relay connector terminal No. 5 and ground. *See Fig. 7.* Turn ignition on.

3) If test light does not illuminate, check for blown LCD fuse and repair short to ground in Orange wire circuit from fuse block to relay. If LCD fuse is not blown, repair poor connections or open in Orange wire circuit.

4) If test light illuminates, use DVOM to check resistance between relay terminals No. 5 and 2. If resistance is not between 50-80 ohms, replace relay and follow next steps to verify operation.

5) If resistance is between 50-80 ohms, use DVOM to check continuity between relay connector terminals No. 2 and 4. If continuity exists, replace relay and follow next step. If continuity does not exist, follow next step.

6) Connect test light between relay connector terminal Nos. 2 and 5. Connect jumper between ALDL terminals "G" and "A". Turn ignition on. Press TRIP/ODO button until "1.4" appears in display. Press ENG/MET until "10..0" appears in odometer (cycling between "10..0" for OFF position and "10..1" for ON position).

7) If test light stays on continuously, repair short to ground in Gray/Black wire circuit from CCM Gray connector terminal D12 to relay. If test light illuminates when "10..1" appears, this is normal function. Perform wiggle test to connections at CCM and defogger relay to find intermittent fault setting this code.

8) If test light is off when "10..1" appears, connect test light to relay connector terminal No. 5 and backprobe CCM Gray connector terminal D12. Connect jumper between ALDL terminals "G" and "A". Turn ignition on. Press TRIP/ODO button until "1.4" appears in display. Press ENG/MET until "10..0" appears in odometer (cycling between "10..0" for OFF position and "10..1" for ON position).

9) If test light now illuminates when "10..1" appears, repair open in Gray/Black wire circuit or connections. If test light does not illuminate when "10..1" appears, check connections at CCM Gray connector terminal D12. If Gray/Black wire circuit is okay, replace CCM. When repairs are completed, clear codes and verify operation.

Code 26 (LCD Blanking Control Shorted To Battery Voltage) – 1) The LCD displays will be blank if this circuit is shorted to battery voltage or if CCM has open internal circuit.

2) Make note of all stored codes, and remove Instrument Cluster (IC).

3) Using Terminal Adapter Kit (J-35616), connect DVOM (12-volt scale) between IC connector terminal A13 and ground. *See Fig. 8.* Turn ignition on.

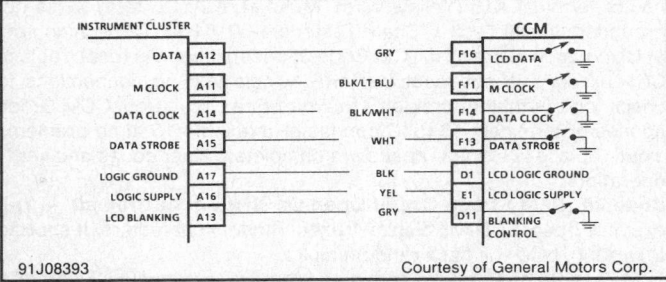

91J08393   Courtesy of General Motors Corp.

Fig. 8: Codes 26-38, CCM-To-Instrument Cluster Circuit Wiring Diagram

4) If voltage reading is 12 volts, repair short to battery voltage in Gray wire circuit from CCM Gray connector terminal D11 to IC connector terminal A13.

5) If voltage reading is zero volt and Code 27 was also set, repair open in Gray wire circuit from CCM Gray connector terminal D11 to IC connector terminal A13.

6) If voltage reading iš zero volt and Code 27 was not set, or if voltage reading is 2-5 volts; connect Red leads of Signal Generator and Instrument Panel Tester (J-33431-B) to DVOM. Using DVOM (ohmmeter) and ohm adjustment dials of tester, set tester resistance to 1150-1250 ohms. Turn ignition off, and disconnect DVOM from tester.

7) Using Terminal Adapter Kit (J-35616), connect one lead of Tester (J-33431-B) to IC connector terminal A13. Connect other lead to IC connector terminal A16. Make sure ALDL term "G" is not grounded. Install Tech 1 "Scan" Tester (94-00101-A). Turn ignition on.

8) Using Tech 1, check if CCM Code 26 reset. If code is reset, replace CCM. If code is not reset, perform "wiggle test" to connections to check for intermittent problems in Gray wire circuit from CCM Gray connector terminal D11 to IC connector terminal A13. If no problems exist, replace instrument cluster. When repairs are completed, clear codes and verify operation.

Code 27 (LCD Blanking Control Circuit Open Or Shorted To Ground) – 1) The LCD displays will be blank or frozen if there is an open or short to ground in Gray wire circuit.

2) Make note of all stored codes and remove Instrument Cluster (IC).

3) Using Terminal Adapter Kit (J-35616), connect DVOM (ohmmeter) between ground and IC harness connector terminal A13 (Gray wire). *See Fig. 8.* If continuity to ground exists, repair short to ground in Gray wire from CCM Gray connector terminal D11 to IC terminal A13. If continuity to ground does not exist, unplug CCM Gray connector.

4) Using Terminal Adapter Kit (J-35616), connect DVOM between CCM Gray connector terminal D11 and IC harness connector terminal A13. If continuity does not exist here, repair open in Gray wire or connections from CCM Gray terminal D11 to IC terminal A13.

5) If continuity does exist here, connect Red leads of Signal Generator and Instrument Panel Tester (J-33431-B) to DVOM. Using DVOM (ohmmeter) and ohm adjustment dials of tester, set tester resistance to 1150-1250 ohms. Turn ignition off and disconnect DVOM from tester.

6) Using Terminal Adapter Kit (J-35616), connect one lead of Tester (J-33431-B) to IC harness connector terminal A13. Connect other lead to terminal A16 (Yellow wire). Reconnect CCM Gray connector. Install Tech 1 "Scan" Tester (94-00101-A). Make sure ALDL terminal "G" is not grounded. Turn ignition on.

7) Using Tech 1, check if Code 27 is reset. If Code 27 is reset, replace CCM and ensure connections. If code is not reset, perform wiggle test to connections and wiring to check for intermittent problems in Gray wire circuit from CCM to IC. If no problems exist, replace IC. When repairs are completed, clear codes and verify operation.

Code 31 (LCD Data Circuit Shorted to Battery Voltage) – 1) The LCD will be blank if Gray wire circuit from CCM Green connector terminal F16 to IC connector terminal A12 is shorted to battery voltage or CCM has open internal circuit.

2) Make note of stored codes, and remove Instrument Cluster (IC).

3) Using Terminal Adapter Kit (J-35616), connect DVOM (12-volt scale) between IC connector terminal A12 and ground. *See Fig. 8.* Turn ignition on.

4) If voltage reading is 12 volts, repair short to battery voltage in Gray wire circuit from CCM Green connector terminal F16 to IC connector terminal A12.

5) If voltage reading is zero volt and Code 32 was also set, repair open in Gray wire circuit from CCM Green connector terminal F16 to IC connector terminal A12.

6) If voltage reading is zero volt and Code 32 was not set, OR if voltage reading is 2-5 volts; connect Red leads of Signal Generator and Instrument Panel Tester (J-33431-B) to DVOM. Using DVOM (ohmmeter) and ohm adjustment dials of tester, set tester resistance to 1150-1250 ohms. Turn ignition off, and disconnect DVOM from tester.

7) Using Terminal Adapter Kit (J-35616), connect one lead of Tester (J-33431-B) to IC connector terminal A12. Connect other lead to IC connector terminal A16 (Yellow wire). Make sure ALDL term "G" is not grounded. Install Tech 1 "Scan" Tester (94-00101-A). Turn ignition on.

8) Using Tech 1, check if CCM Code 31 reset. If code is reset, replace CCM. If code is not reset, perform wiggle test to connections and wir-

ing to check for intermittent problems in Gray wire circuit from CCM Green connector terminal F16 to IC connector terminal A12. If no problems exist, replace IC. When repairs are completed, clear codes and verify operation.

Code 32 (LCD Data Circuit Open Or Shorted To Ground) – **1)** The LCD will be blank if there is an open in circuit, or all of display will be on if there is short to ground in circuit.

2) Make note of all stored codes and remove Instrument Cluster (IC).

3) Using Terminal Adapter Kit (J-35616), connect DVOM (ohmmeter) between ground and IC harness connector terminal A13 (Gray wire). *See Fig. 8.* If continuity to ground exists, repair short to ground in Gray wire from CCM Green connector terminal F16 to IC terminal A12. If continuity to ground does not exist, unplug CCM Green connector.

4) Using Terminal Adapter Kit (J-35616), connect DVOM between CCM Green connector terminal F16 and IC harness connector terminal A12. If continuity does not exist here, repair open in Gray wire or connections from CCM Green terminal F16 to IC terminal A12.

5) If continuity exists here, connect Red leads of Signal Generator and Instrument Panel Tester (J-33431-B) to DVOM. Using DVOM (ohmmeter) and ohm adjustment dials of tester, set tester resistance to 1150-1250 ohms. Turn ignition off and disconnect DVOM from tester.

6) Using Terminal Adapter Kit (J-35616), connect one lead of Tester (J-33431-B) to IC harness connector terminal A12. Connect other lead to terminal A16 (Yellow wire). Reconnect CCM Green connector. Install Tech 1 "Scan" Tester (94-00101-A). Make sure ALDL terminal "G" is not grounded. Turn ignition on.

7) Using Tech 1, check if Code 32 is reset. If Code 32 is reset, ensure connections at terminal F16 and replace CCM. If code is not reset, perform wiggle test to connections and wiring to check for intermittent problems in Gray wire circuit from CCM Green connector to IC. If no problems exist, replace IC. When repairs are completed, clear codes and verify operation.

Code 33 (Data Clock Circuit Shorted To Battery Voltage) – **1)** The LCD will display random, frozen characters.

2) Make note of all stored codes and remove Instrument Cluster (IC).

3) Using Terminal Adapter Kit (J-35616), connect DVOM (12-volt scale) between IC connector terminal A14 and ground. *See Fig. 8.* Turn ignition on.

4) If voltage reading is 12 volts, repair short to battery voltage in Black/White wire circuit from CCM Green terminal F14 to IC connector terminal A14.

5) If voltage reading is zero volt and Code 34 was also set, repair open in Black/White wire circuit from CCM Green terminal F14 to IC connector terminal A14.

6) If voltage reading is zero volt and Code 34 was not set, if voltage reading is 2-5 volts; connect Red leads of Signal Generator and Instrument Panel Tester (J-33431-B) to DVOM. Using DVOM (ohmmeter) and ohm adjustment dials of tester, set tester resistance to 1150-1250 ohms. Turn ignition off, and disconnect DVOM from tester.

7) Using Terminal Adapter Kit (J-35616), connect one lead of Tester (J-33431-B) to IC connector terminal A14. Connect other lead to IC connector terminal A16 (Yellow wire). Make sure ALDL term "G" is not grounded. Install Tech 1 "Scan" Tester (94-00101-A). Turn ignition on.

8) Using Tech 1, check if CCM Code 33 reset. If code is reset, replace CCM. If code is not reset, perform wiggle test to connections and wiring to check for intermittent problems in Black/White wire circuit from CCM Green connector terminal F14 to IC connector terminal A14. If no problems exist, replace IC. When repairs are completed, clear codes and verify operation.

Code 34 (Data Clock Circuit Open Or Shorted To Ground) – **1)** If there is an open, LCD will be blank, or all segments will be on and frozen. If there is short to ground, LCD will have random segments on and display will not update.

2) Make note of all stored codes and remove Instrument Cluster (IC).

3) Using Terminal Adapter Kit (J-35616), connect DVOM (ohmmeter) between ground and IC harness connector terminal A14 (Black/White wire). *See Fig. 9.* If continuity to ground exists, repair short to ground in Black/White wire from CCM Green connector terminal F14 to IC connector terminal A14. If continuity to ground does not exist, unplug CCM Green connector.

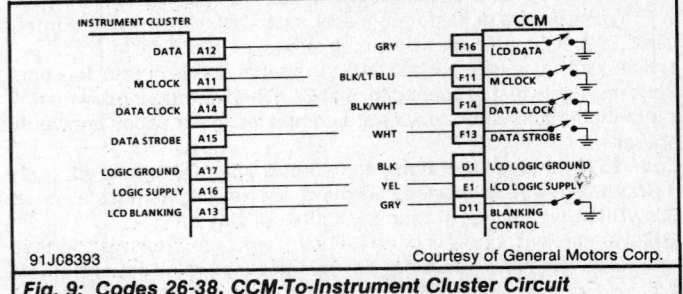

91J08393 — Courtesy of General Motors Corp.

Fig. 9: Codes 26-38, CCM-To-Instrument Cluster Circuit Wiring Diagram

4) Using Terminal Adapter Kit (J-35616), connect DVOM between CCM Green connector terminal F14 and IC harness connector terminal A14. If continuity does not exist here, repair open in Black/White wire or connections from CCM Green terminal F14 to IC terminal A14.

5) If continuity exists here, connect Red leads of Signal Generator and Instrument Panel Tester (J-33431-B) to DVOM. Using DVOM (ohmmeter) and ohm adjustment dials of tester, set tester resistance to 1150-1250 ohms. Turn ignition off and disconnect DVOM from tester.

6) Using Terminal Adapter Kit (J-35616), connect one lead of Tester (J-33431-B) to IC harness connector terminal A14. Connect other lead to terminal A16 (Yellow wire). Reconnect CCM Green connector. Install Tech 1 "Scan" Tester (94-00101-A). Make sure ALDL terminal "G" is not grounded. Turn ignition on.

7) Using Tech 1, check if Code 34 is reset. If Code 34 is reset, ensure connections at CCM terminal F14 and replace CCM. If code is not reset, perform wiggle test to connections and wiring to check for intermittent problems in Black/White wire circuit from CCM Green connector to IC. If no problems exist, replace IC. When repairs are completed, clear codes and verify operation.

Code 35 (Data Strobe Circuit Shorted To Battery Voltage) – **1)** The LCD cluster will display random, frozen characters.

2) Make note of all stored codes, and remove Instrument Cluster (IC).

3) Using Terminal Adapter Kit (J-35616), connect DVOM (12-volt scale) between IC connector terminal A15 (White wire) and ground. *See Fig. 9.* Turn ignition on.

4) If voltage reading is 12 volts, repair short to battery voltage in White wire circuit from CCM Green connector terminal F13 to IC connector terminal A15.

5) If voltage reading is zero volt and Code 36 was also set, repair open in White wire circuit from CCM Green connector terminal F13 to IC connector terminal A15.

6) If voltage reading is zero volt and Code 36 was not set, or if voltage reading is 2-5 volts; connect Red leads of Signal Generator and Instrument Panel Tester (J-33431-B) to DVOM. Using DVOM (ohmmeter) and ohm adjustment dials of tester, set tester resistance to 1150-1250 ohms. Turn ignition off, and disconnect DVOM from tester.

7) Using Terminal Adapter Kit (J-35616), connect one lead of Tester (J-33431-B) to IC connector terminal A15. Connect other lead to IC connector terminal A16 (Yellow wire). Make sure ALDL term "G" is not grounded. Install Tech 1 "Scan" Tester (94-00101-A). Turn ignition on.

8) Using Tech 1, check if CCM Code 35 reset. If code is reset, replace CCM. If code is not reset, perform "wiggle test" to connections to check for intermittent problems in White wire circuit from CCM Green connector terminal F13 to IC connector terminal A15. If no problems exist, replace IC. When repairs are completed, clear codes and verify operation.

Code 36 (Data Strobe Circuit Open Or Shorted To Ground) – **1)** If circuit is open, LCD will display frozen, random characters. If shorted to ground, LCD will flash random digits.

2) Make note of all stored codes, and remove Instrument Cluster (IC).

3) Using Terminal Adapter Kit (J-35616), connect DVOM (ohmmeter) between ground and IC harness connector terminal A15 (White wire). *See Fig. 9.* If continuity to ground exists, repair short to ground in White wire from CCM Green connector terminal F13 to IC terminal A15. If continuity to ground does not exist, unplug CCM Green connector.

4) Using Terminal Adapter Kit (J-35616), connect DVOM between CCM Green connector terminal F13 and IC harness connector terminal A15. If continuity does not exist here, repair open in White wire or connections from CCM Green terminal F13 to IC terminal A15.

5) If continuity exists here, connect Red leads of Signal Generator and Instrument Panel Tester (J-33431-B) to DVOM. Using DVOM (ohmmeter) and ohm adjustment dials of tester, set tester resistance to 1150-1250 ohms. Turn ignition off and disconnect DVOM from tester.

6) Using Terminal Adapter Kit (J-35616), connect one lead of Tester (J-33431-B) to IC harness connector terminal A15. Connect other lead to terminal A16 (Yellow wire). Reconnect CCM Green connector. Install Tech 1 "Scan" Tester (94-00101-A). Make sure ALDL terminal "G" is not grounded. Turn ignition on.

7) Using Tech 1, check if Code 36 is reset. If Code 36 is reset, ensure connections at terminal F13 are okay and replace CCM. If code is not reset, perform wiggle test to connections and wiring to check for intermittent problems in White wire circuit from CCM Green connector to IC. If no problems exist, replace IC. When repairs are completed, clear codes and verify operation.

Code 37 (M Clock Circuit Shorted To Battery Voltage) – 1) LCD will display some segments on and some off, some will be bright and others dim.

2) Make note of all stored codes, and remove Instrument Cluster (IC).

3) Using Terminal Adapter Kit (J-35616), connect DVOM (12-volt scale) between IC connector terminal A11 and ground. See Fig. 9. Turn ignition on.

4) If voltage reading is 12 volts, repair short to battery voltage in Black/Light Blue wire circuit from CCM Green connector terminal F11 to IC connector terminal A11.

5) If voltage reading is zero volt and Code 38 was also set, repair open in Black/Light Blue wire circuit from CCM Green connector terminal F11 to IC connector terminal A11.

6) If voltage reading is zero volt and Code 38 was not set, or if voltage reading is 2-5 volts; connect Red leads of Signal Generator and Instrument Panel Tester (J-33431-B) to DVOM. Using DVOM (ohmmeter) and ohm adjustment dials of tester, set tester resistance to 1150-1250 ohms. Turn ignition off, and disconnect DVOM from tester.

7) Using Terminal Adapter Kit (J-35616), connect one lead of Tester (J-33431-B) to IC connector terminal A11. Connect other lead to IC connector terminal A16 (Yellow wire). Make sure ALDL term "G" is not grounded. Install Tech 1 "Scan" Tester (94-00101-A). Turn ignition on.

8) Using Tech 1, check if CCM Code 37 reset. If code is reset, replace CCM. If code is not reset, perform wiggle test to connections and wiring to check for intermittent problems in Black/Light Blue wire circuit from CCM Green connector terminal F11 to IC connector terminal A11. If no problems exist, replace IC. When repairs are completed, clear codes and verify operation.

Code 38 (M Clock Circuit Opened Or Shorted To Ground) – 1) LCD will display some segments on and some off, some will be bright and others dim.

2) Make note of all stored codes and remove Instrument Cluster (IC).

3) Using Terminal Adapter Kit (J-35616), connect DVOM (ohmmeter) between ground and IC harness connector terminal A11 (Black/Light Blue wire). See Fig. 9. If continuity to ground exists, repair short to ground in Black/Light Blue wire from CCM Green connector terminal F11 to IC terminal A11. If continuity to ground does not exist, unplug CCM Green connector.

4) Using Terminal Adapter Kit (J-35616), connect DVOM between CCM Green connector terminal F11 and IC harness connector terminal A11. If continuity does not exist here, repair open in Black/Light Blue wire or connections from CCM Green terminal F11 to IC terminal A11.

5) If continuity exists here, connect Red leads of Signal Generator and Instrument Panel Tester (J-33431-B) to DVOM. Using DVOM (ohmmeter) and ohm adjustment dials of tester, set tester resistance to 1150-1250 ohms. Turn ignition off and disconnect DVOM from tester.

6) Using Terminal Adapter Kit (J-35616), connect one lead of Tester (J-33431-B) to IC harness connector terminal A11. Connect other lead to terminal A16 (Yellow wire). Reconnect CCM Green connector. Install Tech 1 "Scan" Tester (94-00101-A). Make sure ALDL terminal "G" is not grounded. Turn ignition on.

7) Using Tech 1, check if Code 38 is reset. If Code 38 is reset, ensure connections at terminal F11 and replace CCM. If code is not reset, perform wiggle test to connections and wiring to check for intermittent problems in Black/Light Blue wire circuit from CCM Green connector to IC. If no problems exist, replace IC. When repairs are completed, clear codes and verify operation.

Code 41 (ECM Serial Data Circuit – Loss Of Communications) – 1) If this fault is present, the trip computer will be inoperative, automatic A/C-heater control head display will flash OFF and CHECK GAUGES function will not work.

2) Connect jumper between ALDL terminals "G" and "A". Turn ignition on. Press TRIP RESET button until "4.1" appears in trip monitor.

3) If ERR does not display in speedometer, there is no problem. Recheck step **1)** again for telltale signs. Check for blown air bag fuse or ECM Code 51.

4) If ERR does display in speedometer, turn ignition off. Unplug ECM Red connector and Green CCM connector. Using Terminal Adapter Kit (J-35616), connect DVOM (ohmmeter) between CCM Green connector terminal E13 and ECM Red connector terminal B11. See Fig. 10.

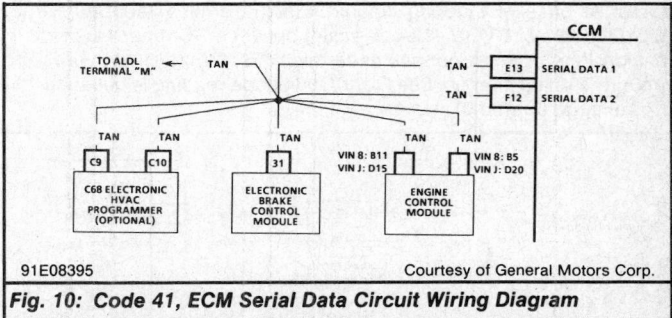

91E08395   Courtesy of General Motors Corp.

Fig. 10: Code 41, ECM Serial Data Circuit Wiring Diagram

5) If continuity does not exist, repair open in Tan wire circuit from ECM to CCM terminal E13. If continuity exists, use Terminal Adapter Kit (J-35616) to connect DVOM between CCM Green connector terminal F12 and ECM Red connector terminal B11.

6) If continuity does not exist here, repair open in Tan wire circuit from ECM to CCM Green terminal F12. If continuity does exist here, using Terminal Adapter Kit (J-35616), connect DVOM between CCM Green connector terminal E13 and ground.

7) If continuity exists, repair short to ground in Tan wire circuit from CCM terminal F12 to the following:

- Anti-lock brake controller
- ALDL terminal "M"
- Electronic Control Module (ECM)
- Automatic A/C-heater control head
- CCM terminal E13

8) If continuity does not exist between CCM Green connector terminal E13 and ground. Using Terminal Adapter Kit (J-35616), connect test light between CCM Green connector terminal E13 (Tan wire) and ground. Turn ignition on.

9) If test light illuminates, repair short to battery voltage in Tan wire circuit following step **7)** in reverse order. If test light does not illuminate, repeat steps **4)** through **8)**, except use ECM connector terminal B5 instead of B11. When repairs are completed, clear codes and verify operation.

Code 51 (Pass-Key Detection Circuit – Invalid Key Detection) – 1) Before proceeding, see PRECAUTIONS FOR CODES 51-54.

2) After determining key code number, connect jumper between ALDL terminals "G" and "A". Turn ignition on.

3) Press TRIP/ODO button until "1.2" appears in trip monitor. Press ENG/MET button until "06xxx" appears in odometer, with xxx being a number from 33 to 212. Note xxx number, and use it to find key code number. See KEY CODE IDENTIFICATION table.

4) If key code from table matches key code found using Pass-Key Interrogator, no problem exists with CCM system. For possible intermittent problems see PRECAUTIONS FOR CODES 51-54.

KEY CODE IDENTIFICATION

Number	Key Code
33-38	1
42-47	2
52-58	3
64-70	4
76-83	5
91-98	6
106-113	7
121-128	8
136-143	9
149-156	10
164-170	11
177-183	12
188-194	13
199-204	14
208-212	15

5) If key codes do not match, check for Code 52 and/or 53 to be set. If either of these other codes ARE set, repair these code problems first. Afterward, clear codes and check if Code 51 resets.

6) If Code 52 or 53 are not set. Disconnect ignition lock cylinder connector at base of steering column. Using Terminal Adapter Kit (J-35616), connect DVOM (12-volt scale) between CCM harness side of ignition lock cylinder connector terminal "B" (White/Black wire) and ground. Turn ignition on. *See Fig. 11.* If voltage reading is between 4.9-5.1 volts, go to step **9)**.

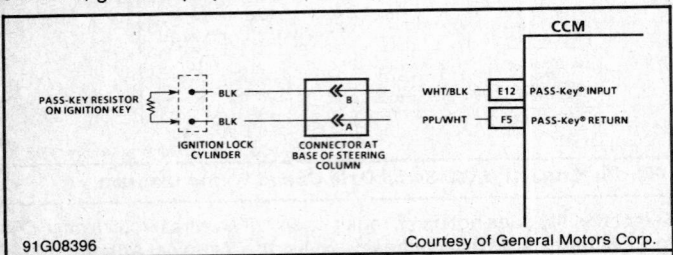

91G08396   Courtesy of General Motors Corp.

Fig. 11: Codes 51-53 & 61-63, Pass-Key Detection Circuit Wiring Diagram

7) If voltage reading is not between 4.9-5.1 volts. Using DVOM and Terminal Adapter Kit (J-35616), backprobe one lead to CCM Green connector terminal E12 (White/Black wire) and other lead to ground. If this voltage reading is not between 4.9-5.1 volts, repair poor connection at CCM Green terminal E12. If no problem exists with connection, replace CCM.

8) If voltage reading in step **7)** is between 4.9-5.1 volts, check White/Black wire circuit from CCM to ignition lock cylinder for damage or poor connections.

9) If voltage reading in step **6)** is between 4.9-5.1 volts, use DVOM (ohmmeter) and Terminal Adapter Kit (J-35616) to check for continuity by backprobing between ignition lock connector terminal "A" and CCM Green connector terminal F5 (Purple/White wire circuit). If continuity exists, no problem exists with CCM system. For possible intermittent problems see PRECAUTIONS FOR CODES 51-54.

10) If continuity does not exist, repair Purple/White wire circuit from CCM Green terminal F5 to ignition lock cylinder. If no problem exists, replace CCM. When repairs are completed, clear codes and verify operation.

Code 52 (Pass-Key Detection Circuit — Shorted To Ground) — 1) Before proceeding, see PRECAUTIONS FOR CODES 51-54. If vehicle owner's other keys do work, perform the following steps to determine if key or ignition lock cylinder is faulty.

2) After determining key code number, connect jumper wire between ALDL terminals "G" and "A". Turn ignition on. Press TRIP/ODO button until "1.2" appears in trip monitor, and press ENG/MET button until "06xxx" appears in odometer, with xxx being a number from 0 to 255. Make a note of xxx number.

3) If xxx number is not between 0-5, no problem exists with Pass-Key system. For possible intermittent problems see PRECAUTIONS FOR CODES 51-54.

4) If xxx number is between 0-5, perform following steps for lock cylinder and harness test. Remove hush panel under steering column. Unplug 2-way pass-key connector wires leading into steering column. The connector wires are Purple/White and White/Black, not the Yellow SIR 2-way connector. *See Fig. 11.* Connect the 2 wires to mating connector pigtails from Pass-Key Interrogator (J-35628).

5) Insert vehicle owner's key into steering column ignition lock cylinder. Turn on Pass-Key Interrogator. Notice Key Code Reader display. If it displays a key code number from 1 to 15, note this number while rotating key in ignition lock cylinder to ensure correct code number is read. If code is correct in all rotated positions, go to step **9)** to recheck keys.

6) If code is not correct in all positions, try another of owner's key. If code is correct in all positions with a different key, and then original key was defective and a new replacement key must be made.

7) If code is not correct in all positions with the different key, or an "E" appears in display, recheck keys by inserting them into key code reader ignition switch on Pass-Key Interrogator (J-35628). If the Reader displays an "E", the key is defective. If the Reader displays a key code (1-15), the ignition lock cylinder is defective.

8) Check by setting key code selector on the pass-key interrogator to the proper key code number found in step **6)**, and install ignition key into lock cylinder and start engine. If engine starts, this verifies proper key code number.

9) If problem was found in steps **2)** through **8)**, repair as needed. Clear codes and recheck to find if Code 52 resets. If Code 52 does reset, try tests again. If problem was not found in steps **2)** through **8)**, turn ignition off and proceed with following steps.

10) Ensure ignition is off. Unplug ignition lock cylinder connector. Using Terminal Adapter Kit (J-35616), connect DVOM (ohmmeter) between lock cylinder harness connector terminal "B" (White/Black wire) and ground. *See Fig. 11.* If continuity exists, repair short to ground in White/Black wire circuit from CCM Green connector terminal E12 to ignition lock cylinder.

11) If continuity does not exist, use Terminal Adapter Kit (J-35616) to connect DVOM between lock cylinder harness connector terminals "A" and "B". If continuity exists, repair short between Purple/White wire and White/Black wire circuits.

12) If continuity does not exist between terminals "A" and "B", repeat this test while wiggling key, wires, and connections to find intermittent problem. When repairs are completed, clear codes and verify operation. If code resets, and no problems are found, replace CCM.

Code 53 (Pass-Key Detection Circuit — Circuit Open Or Shorted To Battery Voltage) — 1) Before proceeding, see PRECAUTIONS FOR CODES 51-54. Other telltale signs of this code problem are inoperative or malfunctioning CCM-controlled circuits such as: fuel gauge, DIC, ambient light sensor, panel dimming control, etc.

2) After determining key code number, connect jumper between ALDL terminals "G" and "A". *See Fig. 11.* Turn ignition on. Press TRIP/ODO button until "1.2" appears in trip monitor display. Press ENG/MET button until "06xxx" appears in odometer display, with xxx being a number from 0 to 255. Make note of xxx number.

3) If number is not between 226 and 255, no problem exists with CCM system. For possible intermittent problems see PRECAUTIONS FOR CODES 51-54.

4) If xxx number is between 226 and 255, unplug ignition lock cylinder connector. Using Terminal Adapter Kit (J-35616), connect DVOM (12-volt scale) between connector terminal "B" and ground. Note voltage reading.

5) If voltage reading is zero volts, repair open in White/Black wire circuit from CCM Green connector terminal E12 to ignition lock cylinder. If voltage reading is greater than 5.1 volts, repair short to battery voltage in White/Black wire circuit from CCM Green connector terminal E12 to ignition lock cylinder.

6) If voltage reading is 4.9-5.1 volts, using Terminal Adapter Kit (J-35616), connect DVOM (12-volt scale) between lock cylinder connector terminal "A" and ground.

7) If voltage exists, repair short to battery voltage in Purple/White wire from CCM Green connector terminal F5 to ignition lock cylinder. If NO voltage is indicated, turn ignition off. Using Terminal Adapter Kit (J-35616) and DVOM (ohmmeter), check for continuity between lock cylinder connector terminal "A" and ground.

3) If continuity does not exist, repair open or poor connections in Purple/White wire circuit from CCM Green connector terminal F5 to ignition lock cylinder. If Purple/White wire circuit is okay, replace CCM. If continuity does exist, replace lock cylinder. When repairs are completed, clear codes and verify operation.

Code 54 (Pass-Key Fuel Enable Circuit, No Fuel Signal To Injectors) – 1) Check for poor connections at CCM, ECM and at White 10-way instrument panel harness-to-engine harness connector. A blown AIR BAG (SIR) fuse or unplugged SIR-DERM harness will set this code because the ECM receives power through the SIR system. Also ECM Code 46 will be set if Code 54 is set.

2) Unplug White 10-way instrument panel-to-engine harness connector located behind right instrument panel lower trim panel. *See Fig. 12.* Using Terminal Adapter Kit (J-35616), connect DVOM (12-volt scale) between White 10-way connector terminal "C" (Dark Blue wire) and ground. *See Fig. 12.* Turn ignition on.

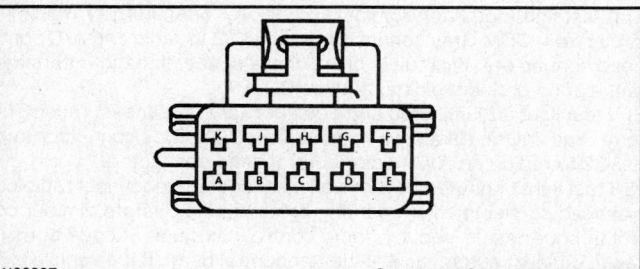

91I08397   Courtesy of General Motors Corp.

Fig. 12: Terminal View Of Instrument Panel-To-Engine Harness 10-Way Connector

3) If voltage reading is not 5 volts, check for open in Dark Blue wire circuit to ECM Brown connector terminal D6. *See Fig. 13.* If Dark Blue wire circuit is okay, replace ECM.

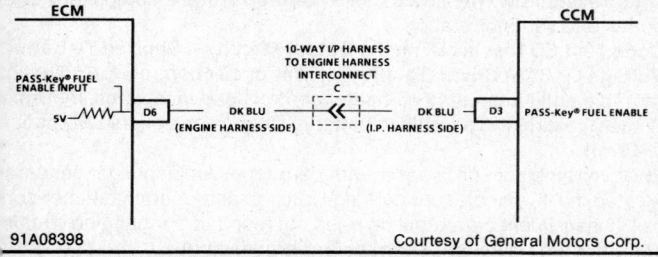

91A08398   Courtesy of General Motors Corp.

Fig. 13: Code 54, Pass-Key Fuel Enable Circuit Wiring Diagram

4) If voltage reading is about 5 volts, reconnect 10-way harness connection. Connect DVOM (12-volt scale) between ground and backprobe 10-way harness connector terminal "C".

5) Using Tech 1 "Scan" Tester (94-00101-A) plugged into the ALDL, check if fuel enable mode is DISABLED or ENABLED.

- If mode is DISABLED, DVOM voltage reading should be about 5 volts.
- If mode is ENABLED, DVOM voltage reading should be about 2.5 volts.

6) If either mode has correct voltage reading as indicated, no problem exists. Recheck connections and fuses for intermittent problems, and repeat step **1)**.

7) If either mode does not have correct voltage readings as indicated, connect DVOM between ground and backprobe CCM Gray connector terminal D3. Use Tech 1 to check fuel enable mode. Note DVOM voltage readings. If either mode now has correct voltage reading as previously indicated in step **5)** above, repair open in Dark Blue wire circuit from 10-way harness connector to CCM Gray connector terminal D3.

8) If voltage reading in either mode is not as indicated in step **5)**, check pass-key system Code 52, steps **5)** through **8)**. Repair pass-key as

needed and retest for codes. If pass-key system checks okay, recheck for poor connection at CCM Gray connector terminal D3. If circuit is okay, replace CCM. When repairs are completed, clear codes and verify operation.

Code 61 (Pass-Key No. 1 Programming Circuit – Resistance Out Of Range) – 1) Check for Code 52 or 53 before testing. If either or both of these codes are set, repair them first. Clear codes, and check if Code 61 resets. If Code 61 does reset, proceed with following steps.

2) Connect DVOM (ohmmeter) to pass-key ignition key resistor pellet contacts. Note if resistance is 394-12,036 ohms. If resistance is not as specified, replace key. If resistance is correct, insert key into ignition lock cylinder.

3) Unplug ignition lock cylinder connector at base of steering column. Using Terminal Adapter Kit (J-35616), connect DVOM (12-volt scale) between connector terminal "B" (White/Black wire) and ground. *See Fig. 14.* Note voltage reading.

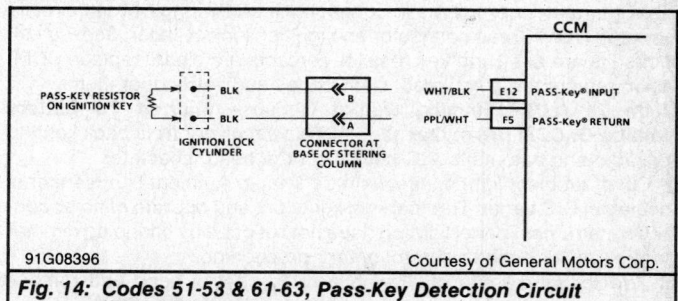

91G08396   Courtesy of General Motors Corp.

Fig. 14: Codes 51-53 & 61-63, Pass-Key Detection Circuit Wiring Diagram

4) If voltage reading is not 4.9-5.1 volts, connect DVOM to ground and backprobe CCM Green connector terminal E12 (White/Black wire). If this voltage reading is still not 4.9-5.1 volts, check poor connection at CCM Green connector terminal E12 (White/Black wire). If connection is okay, replace CCM. If this voltage reading is 4.9-5.1 volts, repair open in White/Black wire circuit.

5) If voltage reading in step **3)** is 4.9-5.1 volts, use Terminal Adapter Kit (J-35616) to connect test light between battery voltage and CCM harness side of lock cylinder connector terminal "A" (Purple/White wire). If test light does not illuminate, check for open circuit in Purple/White wire. If circuit is okay or intermittent problem is not found, replace CCM.

6) If test light illuminates, insert key into lock cylinder. Using Terminal Adapter Kit (J-35616) and DVOM, check continuity between lock cylinder connector terminals "A" and "B". If resistance is 394-12,036 ohms, problem is intermittent. For possible intermittent problems see PRECAUTIONS FOR CODES 51-54.

7) If resistance is not 394-12,036 ohms, perform following steps for the lock cylinder and harness test. Remove hush panel under steering column. Unplug 2-way pass-key connector wires leading into steering column. The connector wire colors are Purple/White and White/Black, not the Yellow SIR 2-way connector. *See Fig. 14.* Connect the two wires to mating connector pigtails from Pass-Key Interrogator (J-35628).

8) Insert vehicle owner's key into steering column ignition lock cylinder. Turn on Pass-Key Interrogator. Notice Key Code Reader display. If it displays key code number (1 to 15), note this number while rotating key in ignition lock cylinder to ensure correct code number is read. If code is correct in all rotated positions, go to step **12)** to recheck keys.

9) If code is not correct in all positions, try other owner's key. If code is correct in all positions with a different key, original key was defective and a new replacement key must be made.

10) If code is not correct in all positions with the different key, or an "E" appears in display, recheck keys by inserting them into key code reader ignition switch on Pass-Key Interrogator (J-35628). If the reader displays an "E", the key is defective. If the reader displays a key code (1-15), the ignition lock cylinder is defective.

11) Check by setting key code selector on the pass-key interrogator to the proper key code number found in step **8)**, and install ignition key into lock cylinder and start engine. If engine starts, this verifies proper key code number.

12) If problem was found in steps **7)** through **11)**, repair as needed. Clear codes, and recheck to find if Code 61 resets. If Code 61 does reset, replace CCM. When repairs are completed, clear codes and verify operation.

Codes 62-63 (Pass-Key Programming Circuit, Resistance Problems) – **1)** Check for Code 52 or 53 before testing. If either or both of these codes are set, repair their problem. Clear codes, and check if Code 62 or 63 resets. If either code does reset, proceed to next step.

2) Use Pass-Key Interrogator (J-35628) to determine key code number of keys No. 1 and 2. If the numbers are not the same, use Pass-Key Interrogator (J-35628) to determine key code number of key No. 3. Replace key that does not match other two. Begin CCM pass-key programming sequence again.

3) If key code numbers are the same, use wiggle test to check for possible intermittent problems in connections and wiring of both circuits between CCM Green connector and ignition lock cylinder. *See Fig. 14.* If circuits are okay and key resistor contacts are clean, replace CCM. When repairs are completed, clear codes and verify operation.

Code 71 (LCD Dimming Output Circuit – Shorted To Battery Voltage Or CCM Driver Open) – **1)** This circuit controls back lighting for radio and automatic A/C-heater control head faceplates.

2) Cover ambient light sensor with dark tape. Ambient light sensor is located in DIC panel. Turn parking lights on, and operate dimmer control. If instrument panel lighting does not respond by changing dimmer control, repair dimmer control before proceeding.

3) Turn parking lights off. Remove radio control head and remove automatic A/C-heater control head (if equipped). See RADIO CONTROL HEAD under REMOVAL & INSTALLATION. Unplug both units connectors.

4) Connect test light between ground and radio control head 7-way harness connector terminal No. 3 (Gray/Black wire). *See Fig. 15.*

5) Turn ignition on. If test light is illuminated, repair short to battery voltage in Gray/Black wiring circuit from CCM Gray connector terminal C2 to unit connector terminal No. 3.

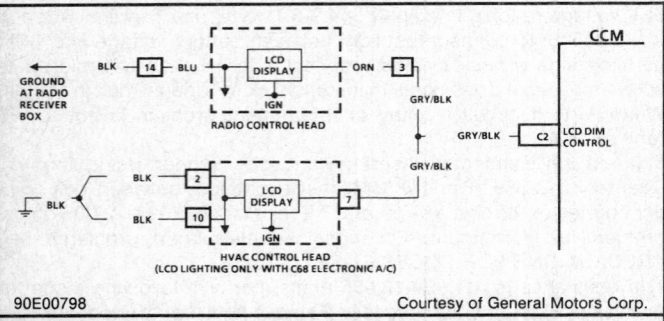

Fig. 15: Codes 71-72, LCD Dimming Circuit Wiring Diagram

6) If test light does not illuminate, turn ignition off. Connect test light between battery voltage and radio control head 7-way harness connector terminal No. 3 (Gray/Black wire). *See Fig. 15.* Turn parking lights on.

7) Put dimmer control to full bright position. Noting test light brightness, move dimmer control to low position and then back to high slowly. If test light brightness changes significantly, clear codes. Reconnect radio control head connector. Operate dimming control.

8) If code does not reset, reconnect A/C-heater control head connector and operate dimming control. If code does not reset now, no problem exists. Recheck connections for intermittent faults. If code resets with either control head, replace control head that caused code to reset.

9) If test light brightness does not change significantly, using test light, backprobe CCM Gray connector terminal C2 and battery voltage. Turn parking lights on. Noting test light brightness, move dimmer control to low position and back to high slowly. If test light brightness changes significantly, no problem exists, check for intermittents.

10) If test light brightness does not change significantly, check for poor connection at CCM Gray connector terminal C2. If connection is okay, replace CCM. When repairs are completed, clear codes and verify operation.

Code 72 (LCD Dimming Output Circuit – Shorted To Ground Or Circuit Open) – **1)** This circuit controls backlighting for radio and automatic A/C-heater control head faceplates.

2) Cover ambient light sensor with dark tape. Ambient light sensor is located in DIC panel. Turn parking lights on and operate dimmer control. If instrument panel lighting does not respond by changing dimmer control, repair dimmer control before proceeding.

3) Turn parking lights off. Remove radio control head and remove automatic A/C-heater control head (if equipped). See RADIO CONTROL HEAD under REMOVAL & INSTALLATION. *See Fig. 15.* Unplug both units connectors. Ensure ignition off.

4) Connect test light between battery voltage and radio control head 7-way connector terminal No. 3. Turn parking lights on. Operate dimmer control, moving dimmer from full bright to full dim position, slowly. Note test light brightness.

5) If test light does not illuminate, check for open in Gray/Black wire circuit from CCM Gray connector terminal C2 to radio and A/C control head connectors. If circuit is okay, check connections for intermittent faults. If no problem exists, replace CCM.

6) If test light is illuminated and does not vary brightness, repair short to ground in Gray/Black wire circuit from CCM Gray connector terminal C2 to radio and A/C-heater control head connectors.

7) If test light brightness does vary, clear codes. Reconnect radio control head connector. Turn parking lights on and operate dimmer control. If code resets, replace radio control head unit. If code does not reset, connect automatic A/C-heater control head. If the vehicle is not A/C equipped, go on to next step. Turn parking lights on and operate dimmer control. If code resets, replace automatic A/C-heater control head.

8) If code does not reset (for either head unit), check wiring and connections for intermittent faults. Clear codes, turn parking lights on and operate dimmer control. If code resets again, perform wiggle test to wiring and connections to locate intermittent faults. Clear codes. If code resets now, replace CCM. When repairs are completed, clear codes and verify operation.

Code 73 (LED Display Dimming Output Circuit – Shorted To Battery Voltage Or CCM Driver Open) – **1)** This circuit controls back lighting for radio and automatic A/C-heater control head faceplates. If Purple/White wire circuit is shorted to battery voltage, none of the LED panels will work.

2) Cover ambient light sensor with dark tape. Ambient light sensor is located in DIC panel. Turn parking lights on and operate dimmer control. If instrument panel lighting does not respond by changing dimmer control, repair dimmer control before proceeding.

3) Turn parking lights off. Remove radio control head and remove automatic A/C-heater control head (if equipped). See RADIO CONTROL HEAD under REMOVAL & INSTALLATION. *See Fig. 20.* Unplug both units connectors. Remove headlight switch and disconnect 4-way connector plug. See HEADLIGHT SWITCH under REMOVAL & INSTALLATION.

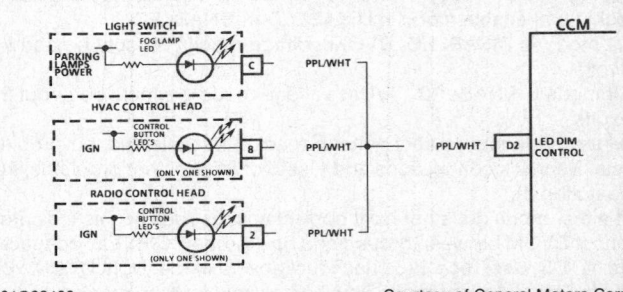

Fig. 16: Codes 73 & 74, LED Display Dimming Output Circuit Wiring Diagram

4) Using Terminal Adapter Kit (J-35616), connect test light between ground and backprobe radio control head 7-way connector terminal No. 2. *See Fig. 16.* Turn ignition on and observe test light. If test light comes on, repair short to battery voltage somewhere in Purple/White wire circuit from radio control head to the following:
- Automatic A/C-heater control head (if equipped)
- Headlight switch
- CCM

5) If test light does not come on, turn ignition off. Connect test light between battery voltage and radio harness connector terminal No. 2. Ensure ambient light sensor in DIC panel, is still covered. Turn parking lights on. Put dimmer control in full bright position. Noting test light brightness, move dimmer control from full bright to full dim position, slowly. If test light brightness does not change significantly, check for intermittents. If no problem is found, replace CCM.

6) If test light brightness changes significantly, clear codes. Reconnect radio control head and turn ignition on. Turn parking lights on and operate dimmer control. If code resets, replace radio control head. If code does not reset, clear codes and reconnect headlight switch 4-way connector. Turn ignition on. Turn parking lights on and operate dimmer control.

7) If code resets, replace headlight switch. If code does not reset, clear codes. Reconnect automatic A/C-heater control head connector and turn ignition on. Turn parking lights on and operate dimmer control. If codes resets, replace automatic A/C-heater control head.

8) If code does not reset again, no problem exists. Check for intermittent faults by performing wiggle test to wiring and connections. When repairs are completed, clear codes and verify operation.

Code 74 (LED Display Dimming Output Circuit — Shorted To Ground Or Circuit Open) — 1) This circuit controls back lighting for radio and/or automatic A/C-heater control head faceplates. If Purple/White wire circuit is shorted to ground, LED panels will stay at full brightness. If circuit is open, LED panels will remain off.

2) Cover ambient light sensor with dark tape. Ambient light sensor is located in DIC panel. Turn parking lights on and operate dimmer control. If instrument panel lighting does not respond by changing dimmer control, repair dimmer control before proceeding.

3) Turn parking lights on. Put dimmer control to middle position. Remove radio control head. See RADIO CONTROL HEAD under REMOVAL & INSTALLATION. DO NOT unplug connectors.

4) Using test light, backprobe between battery voltage and radio control head 7-way connector terminal No. 2. Turn ignition on. If test light does not illuminate, check for open in Purple/White wire circuit and repair as needed. *See Fig. 16.* If no open is found, check for intermittent faults by performing wiggle test to wiring and connections. Clear codes and operate dimmer control. If code resets again, replace CCM.

5) If test light illuminates, operate dimmer control. If test light brightness changes, clear codes. Operate dimmer control again. If code resets again, replace CCM. If test light does not change significantly, disconnect radio control head connector. See RADIO CONTROL HEAD under REMOVAL & INSTALLATION.

6) Using Terminal Adapter Kit (J-35616), connect test light between radio 7-way connector terminal No. 2 and battery voltage. Operate dimmer control. If test light brightness changes, replace radio control head unit.

7) If test light brightness does not change significantly, remove headlight switch and disconnect radio 4-way connector. See HEADLIGHT SWITCH and RADIO CONTROL HEAD under REMOVAL & INSTALLATION. Operate dimmer control. If test light brightness changes, replace headlight switch unit.

8) If test light brightness does not change, remove automatic A/C-heater control head and unplug harness connectors. See RADIO CONTROL HEAD under REMOVAL & INSTALLATION. Operate dimmer control. If test light brightness changes, replace automatic A/C-heater control head.

9) If test light brightness does not change, disconnect CCM Gray connector. Operate dimmer control. If test light brightness changes, reconnect CCM. Clear codes and operate dimmer control. If code resets, replace CCM. If test light brightness does not change, repair short to ground in Purple/White wire circuit and repair as needed. *See Fig. 16.*

PRECAUTIONS FOR CODES 51-54

1) Make sure pass-key ignition key resistor contacts are clean of grease, dirt or oil, etc. Check for poor connections at the CCM and ignition lock cylinder. Also check resistance of pass-key key resistor pellet for less than 50 ohms. If resistance is 50 ohms or more, replace key.

2) If key does not work, try another vehicle owner's key after you have waited 3 minutes for CCM pass-key system to reset timer. After vehicle owner key has been tried 4 separate times in ignition switch and still will not work, CCM pass-key timer will switch to 10-minute intervals before resetting.

3) If vehicle owner's other key does work, destroy faulty key and obtain new one. If none of the keys work, use Pass-Key Interrogator (J-35628) to determine key code number and make note of it.

CLEARING CCM CODES

1) With ignition off, ground pin "G" of ALDL connector. Turn ignition on. Ensure engine off.

2) Press TRIP/ODO button on DIC key pad until "1.7" appears in display on trip monitor. Next press the ENG/MET button and hold until "---" appears in speedometer. This will clear CCM codes. *See Fig. 2.*

3) Turn ignition off, then back on, and verify no CCM codes are present. Turn ignition off, and remove ground to pin "G" of ALDL connector.

RESETTING CHANGE OIL INDICATOR

1) Turn ignition on. Leave engine off. DO NOT ground pin "G" of ALDL connector.

2) Using DIC key pad, press ENG/MET button and release, then press it again. Within 5 seconds, press and hold in RANGE button. CHANGE OIL indicator will flash. *See Fig. 2.*

3) Continue holding RANGE button in until CHANGE OIL indicator stops flashing and goes out (after about 10 seconds). Reset cycle is complete.

CCM PASS-KEY PROGRAMMING PROCEDURE

A CCM is programmable in order to be matched to a set of 2 ignition keys having pass-key resistor pellets. When programming, be sure to use BOTH customer keys. Using same key twice will not work. The CCM will not accept the other key if its pellet resistance value is slightly different and key has not been programmed into CCM memory.

NOTE: DO NOT allow more than 10 seconds between any of the following steps or else programming sequence will stop. If this happens, procedure must be started over from step 1).

1) Insert first key into ignition lock cylinder and turn to RUN position. DO NOT start engine.

2) Turn key to LOCK position and remove key. CCM PASS-KEY programing mode has now been entered.

3) CCM will command technician to insert one of 2 keys by flashing the SECURITY light. This light will flash the number of times corresponding to the key number being programmed. Example: When CCM flashes SECURITY light once, insert key No. 1 into ignition lock cylinder, but DO NOT turn. The CCM is determining resistance value of key's resistor pellets and storing into memory.

4) If key No. 1 is a valid pass-key system key, CCM will command next key to be inserted by flashing SECURITY light twice. Quickly remove key No. 1 and insert key No. 2 into ignition lock cylinder, but DO NOT turn.

5) If key No. 2 is valid, CCM will finish programming sequence and will indicate this by the SECURITY light going out. If an invalid key is detected, CCM will stop programing mode and a trouble code will be set. Key is invalid if resistance values are too high or too low.

REMOVAL & INSTALLATION

WARNING: *Vehicle is equipped with Air Bag–Supplemental Inflatable Restraint (SIR) System. Before working on any part of instrument panel, console, or steering column, see SPECIAL PRECAUTIONS. Failure to follow precautions could result in air bag deployment, personal injury, and unneeded Air Bag (SIR) system repairs.*

NOTE: *Before proceeding, see HANDLING PRECAUTIONS at the beginning of DIAGNOSIS & TESTING.*

SPECIAL PRECAUTIONS

Supplemental Inflatable Restraint System (SIR) – The SIR wiring harness has Yellow covering for easy identification. The Diagnostic Energy Reserve Module (DERM) can maintain sufficient voltage to cause deployment of air bag for 10 minutes after ignition switch is turned off and/or battery is disconnected. Many repair procedures require removal of AIR BAG (SIR) fuse and disconnection of SIR 2-way connector near base of steering column.

Disabling SIR System – **1)** Turn ignition off. Remove AIR BAG (SIR) fuse from fuse panel located inside door, at right outside end of instrument panel.

2) Remove driver's side lower trim panel, beneath steering column. Disconnect Yellow 2-way SIR connector near base of steering column. See Fig. 17.

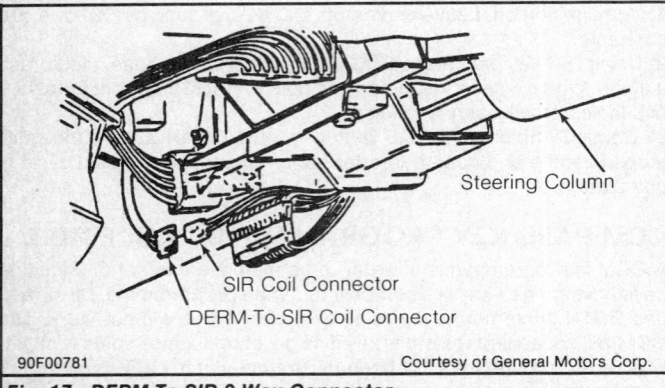

90F00781   Courtesy of General Motors Corp.
Fig. 17: DERM-To-SIR 2-Way Connector

3) When AIR BAG (SIR) fuse is removed and ignition is turned on, the INFL REST warning indicator light will be on. This is normal function and does not set a code or indicate a fault.

Enabling SIR System – **1)** Ensure ignition is off. Reconnect Yellow SIR connector near base of steering column.

2) Install AIR BAG (SIR) fuse and driver's side lower trim panel, beneath steering column. Turn ignition switch to RUN position and make sure INFL REST warning indicator light flashes 7-9 times and then goes off. SIR system is now reactivated. If light does not flash as described, SIR system is malfunctioning.

CENTRAL CONTROL MODULE (CCM)

Removal & Installation – **1)** Before replacing CCM due to pass-key Codes 51-65, be sure pass-key key resistor contacts are clean and free of any grease, oil, etc. These substances interfere with pass-key key detection circuit, possibly causing CCM to set faulty code. Using a clean key, clear all trouble codes, and check if code resets after using clean key.

2) Remove negative battery cable, driver's side lower trim panel and knee bolster. See Fig. 18. Remove center console left side trim panel. See Fig. 19. Remove driver's knee bolster right inner bracket (behind front of left side trim panel). See Fig. 18.

NOTE: *CCM connectors are not YELLOW harness connectors. Yellow harness connectors and coverings designate Air Bag (SIR) system circuits and connectors.*

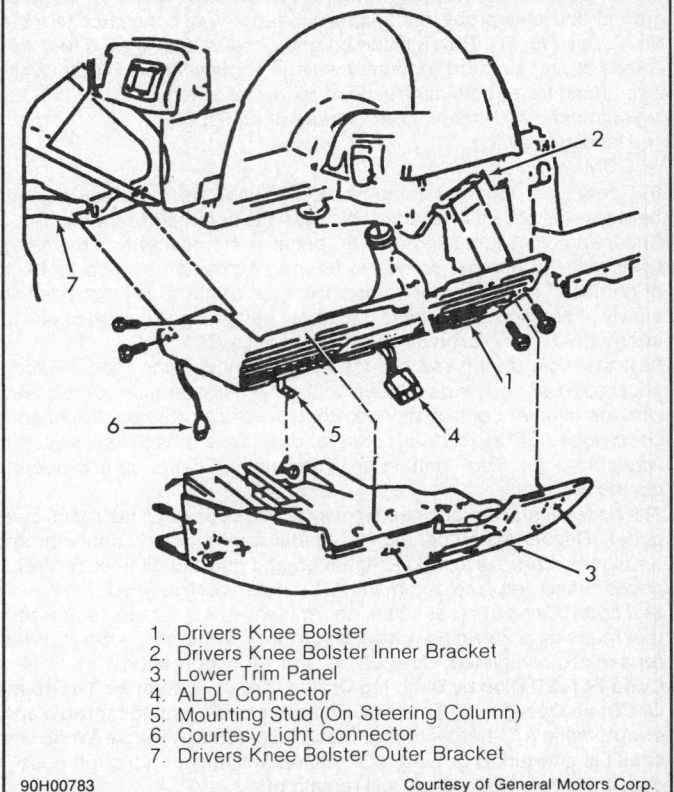

1. Drivers Knee Bolster
2. Drivers Knee Bolster Inner Bracket
3. Lower Trim Panel
4. ALDL Connector
5. Mounting Stud (On Steering Column)
6. Courtesy Light Connector
7. Drivers Knee Bolster Outer Bracket

90H00783   Courtesy of General Motors Corp.
Fig. 18: Exploded View of Driver's Side Knee Bolster & Lower Trim Panel

3) Remove CCM from left side of instrument panel center support system to access CCM harness connectors. Unplug connectors from CCM and from DIC light panel. To install, reverse removal procedure and program pass-key ignition keys into CCM.

4) The new CCM must be programmed for both pass-key system keys that came with the vehicle. See CCM PASS-KEY PROGRAMMING PROCEDURE. Perform pass-key programming procedure before completely installing new CCM in vehicle.

5) If new CCM will not enter programming mode for PASS-KEY, it is possible new CCM is faulty. Attempting PASS-KEY programming sequence before completely installing new CCM, could avoid additional work to remove a faulty new CCM.

DRIVER INFORMATION CENTER (DIC)

Removal – **1)** Remove negative battery cable. Pry up shifter top button. Remove snap ring or set screw in top of shift knob and remove shift knob.

2) Remove console's trim plate rear screws and screw under ashtray. Lift up console trim plate and unplug instrument panel harness connectors. Remove console trim plate. Remove 2 screws inside grille of center air outlet, located above DIC and remove outlet.

3) Remove screws from accessory (radio) trim plate. Pry and lift off trim plate and unplug connectors (note their locations). See Fig. 20.

4) Remove DIC panel screws from instrument panel. See Fig. 21. Remove DIC from instrument panel and remove DIC light sockets from rear of DIC panel. Unplug DIC harness connectors (note locations).

Installation – Connect light sockets and harness connectors to rear of DIC panel. Install DIC into instrument panel with panel screws. Align accessory trim plate spring clips to instrument panel and push plate into position. Install trim plate screws. To complete installation, reverse removal procedure.

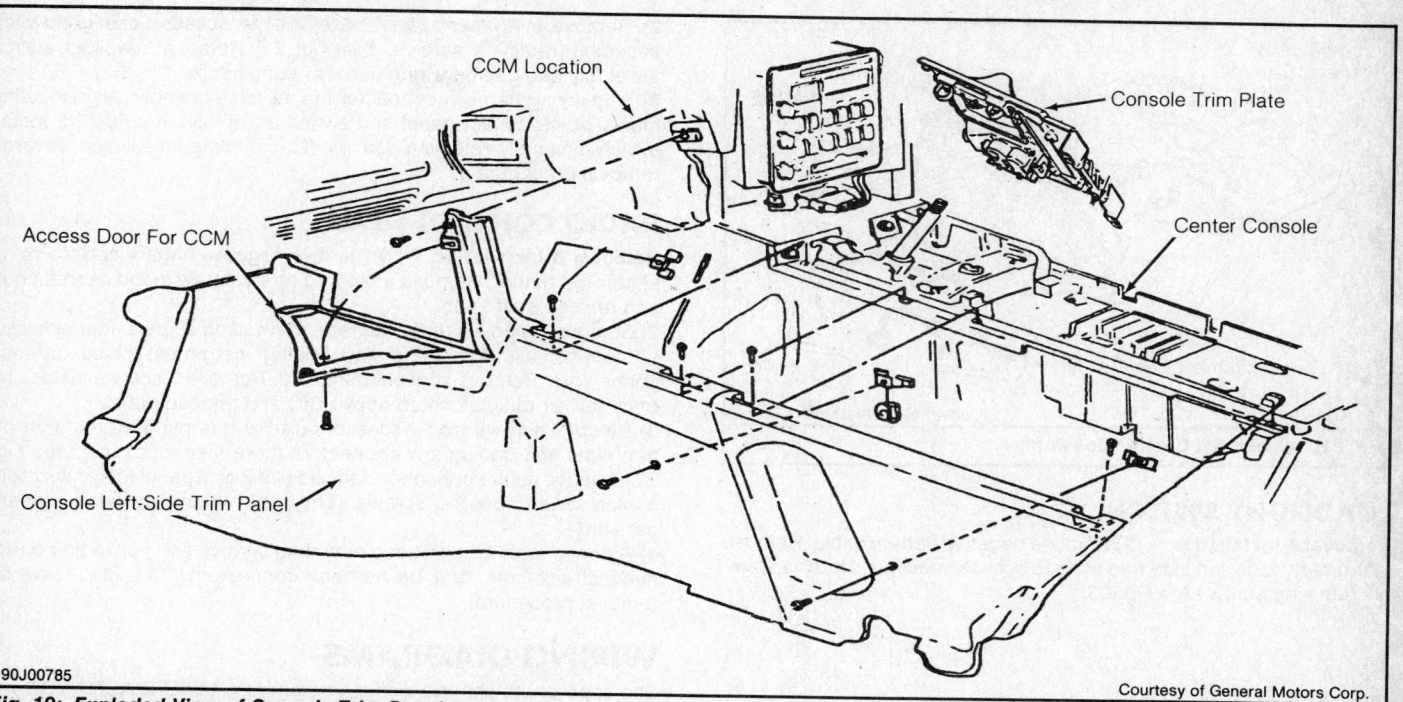

90J00785

Courtesy of General Motors Corp.

Fig. 19: Exploded View of Console Trim Panel

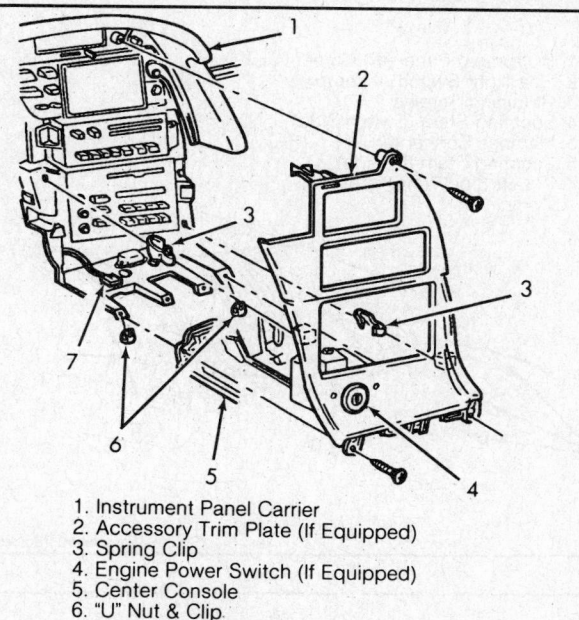

1. Instrument Panel Carrier
2. Accessory Trim Plate (If Equipped)
3. Spring Clip
4. Engine Power Switch (If Equipped)
5. Center Console
6. "U" Nut & Clip
7. Engine Power Switch Connector

91I08401

Courtesy of General Motors Corp.

Fig. 20: Removing Accessory Trim Plate

INSTRUMENT CLUSTER (IC)

NOTE: If IC is serviced, repaired, or replaced and odometer cannot register same mileage as before, odometer must be set to "0" and an odometer/Mileage/Date label attached to left front door frame.

Removal & Installation – 1) Remove negative battery cable. Pry up shifter top button. Remove snap ring or set screw in top of shift knob and remove shift knob.

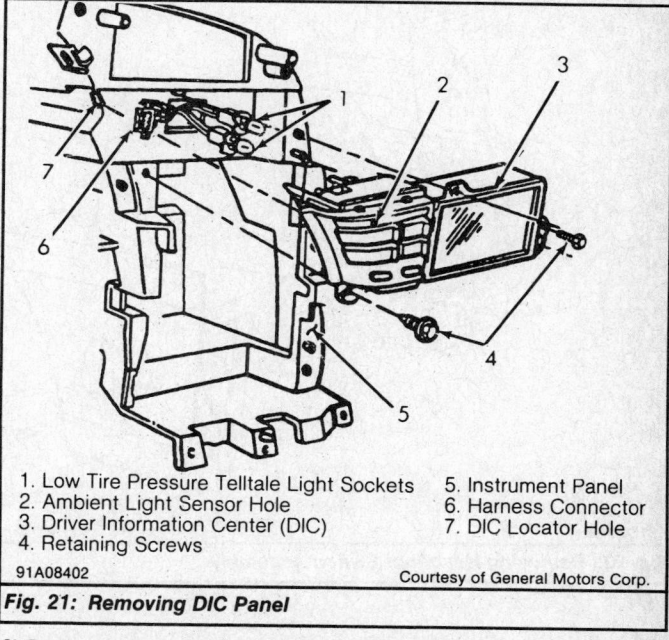

1. Low Tire Pressure Telltale Light Sockets
2. Ambient Light Sensor Hole
3. Driver Information Center (DIC)
4. Retaining Screws
5. Instrument Panel
6. Harness Connector
7. DIC Locator Hole

91A08402

Courtesy of General Motors Corp.

Fig. 21: Removing DIC Panel

2) Remove console's trim plate rear screws and screw under ashtray. Lift up console trim plate and unplug instrument panel harness connectors. Remove console trim plate. Remove 2 screws inside grille of center air outlet, located above DIC and remove outlet.

3) Remove screws from accessory (radio) trim plate. Pry and lift off trim plate and unplug any connectors (note their locations). See Fig. 20. Remove driver's lower trim pad assembly and disconnect courtesy light connector. See Fig. 18.

3) Remove ALDL connector screws, driver's knee bolster assembly screws, steering column lower cover and steering column support bolts. Remove instrument panel bezel assembly screws, and instrument cluster assembly screws. See Fig. 22.

4) Remove instrument cluster, noting location of light sockets and connectors. To install, reverse removal procedure.

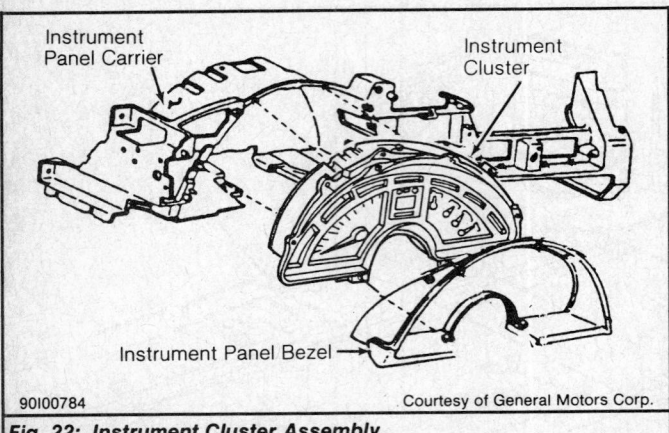

Instrument
Panel Carrier

Instrument
Cluster

Instrument Panel Bezel

90I00784

Courtesy of General Motors Corp.

Fig. 22: Instrument Cluster Assembly

HEADLIGHT SWITCH

Removal & Installation – 1) Remove negative battery cable. Remove instrument panel left side trim plate to access headlight switch assembly retaining screw. *See Fig. 23.*

2) Remove instrument panel bezel trim to access headlight switch assembly retaining screws. *See Fig. 21.* Remove headlight switch assembly and unplug wiring harness connectors.

3) Plug wiring harness connectors to switch assembly. Align locating stems of instrument panel and switch assembly. *See Fig. 23.* Install switch assembly retaining screws. To complete installation, reverse removal procedure.

RADIO CONTROL HEAD

Removal & Installation – 1) Remove negative battery cable. Pry up shifter top button. Remove snap ring or set screw in top of shift knob and remove shift knob.

2) Remove console's trim plate rear screws and screw under ash tray. Lift up console trim plate and unplug instrument panel harness connectors. Remove console trim plate. Remove 2 screws inside grill of center air outlet, located above DIC and remove outlet.

3) Remove screws from accessory (radio) trim plate. Pry and lift off trim plate and unplug any connectors (note their locations). *See Fig. 20.* Remove center console's right side long trim panel to access radio control lower mounting screws. (This may require removing passenger seat.)

4) Remove radio control head mounting screws and pull radio control head straight out. Unplug harness connectors. To install, reverse removal procedure.

WIRING DIAGRAMS

See appropriate chassis wiring diagram in WIRING DIAGRAMS.

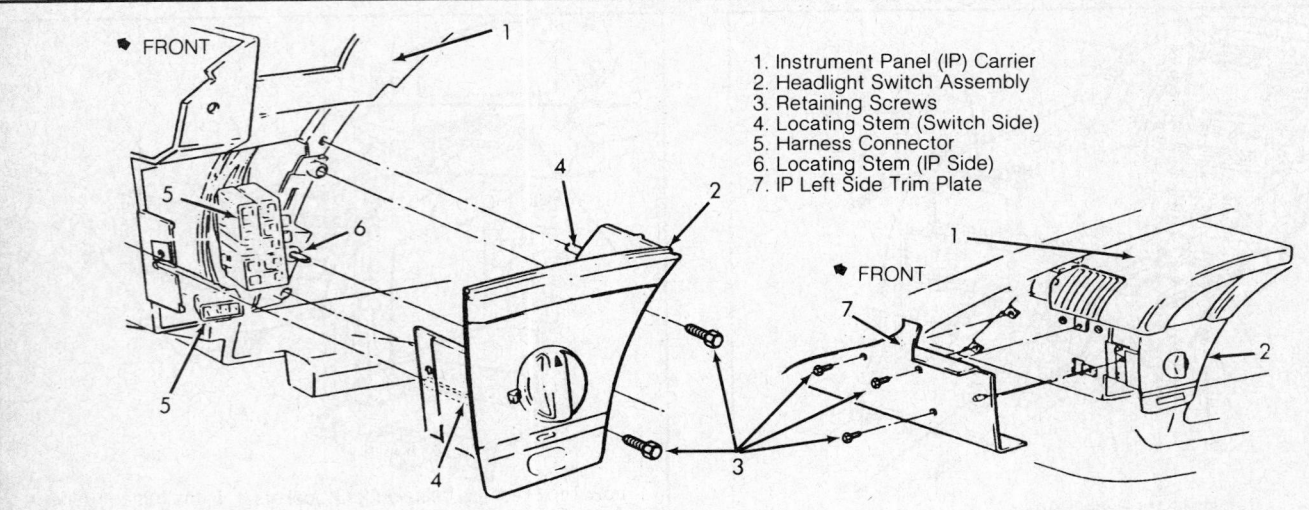

◆ FRONT

1. Instrument Panel (IP) Carrier
2. Headlight Switch Assembly
3. Retaining Screws
4. Locating Stem (Switch Side)
5. Harness Connector
6. Locating Stem (IP Side)
7. IP Left Side Trim Plate

◆ FRONT

91C08403

Courtesy of General Motors Corp.

Fig. 23: Removing Headlight Switch Assembly

DESCRIPTION & OPERATION

Standard and optional electronic instrument clusters are available for this vehicle. The standard cluster provides digital displays for speedometer and odometer and a bar graph for fuel display. The optional cluster has speedometer, odometer and fuel gauge, as well as gauges for volts, engine temperature and oil pressure. See Fig. 1. The odometer and speedometer on both clusters can display English or Metric units.

Both clusters contain warning indicator lights for low coolant, brake system condition, charging system, anti-lock brakes, etc. Electronically operated indicators are used for turn signals, headlight high beams and shift indicator display.

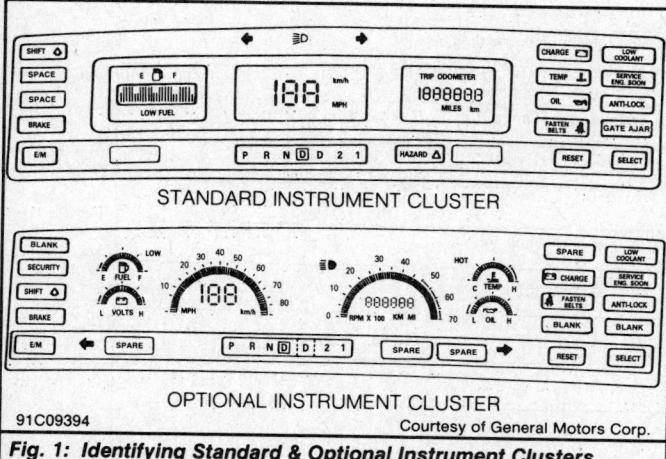

STANDARD INSTRUMENT CLUSTER

OPTIONAL INSTRUMENT CLUSTER

91C09394
Courtesy of General Motors Corp.

Fig. 1: Identifying Standard & Optional Instrument Clusters (Cutlass Supreme)

AIR BAG PRECAUTIONS

Follow precautions when working with vehicles equipped with Supplemental Inflatable Restraint (SIR) air bag systems:

- Before performing any instrument panel testing, diagnosis or repair, disable SIR system by disconnecting negative battery cable and Yellow 2-pin connector at base of steering column.
- Wait 20 minutes before making instrument panel repairs. SIR system retains enough voltage to deploy air bag for a short time after disconnecting power.
- To avoid accidental air bag deployment, avoid SIR wiring harness when trouble shooting instrument panel components. All SIR wires are color-coded Yellow.

TESTING

INDICATORS & GAUGES PINOUT TEST

Check voltage or resistance at instrument cluster connector to determine if proper readings are supplied to instrument cluster. See Figs. 2 and 3.

FUEL GAUGE TESTS

Gauge Indicates Empty Test – Disconnect Purple wire at fuel gauge sender. Turn ignition on. If fuel gauge indicates full, replace fuel gauge sender. If gauge still indicates empty, check Purple wire for a short to ground. If Purple wire is okay, replace instrument cluster.

Gauge Indicates Full Test (Standard Cluster) – 1) Disconnect Purple wire at fuel gauge sender. Connect a jumper wire between Purple wire connector at instrument cluster and ground. Turn ignition on. If fuel gauge indicates full, check Purple wire for an open circuit and instrument cluster connector terminals. If terminals and wire are okay, replace instrument cluster.

2) If fuel gauge indicates empty, check Black wire for an open circuit. If all wires are okay, replace fuel gauge sender.

Gauge Indicates Full Test (Optional Cluster) – 1) Disconnect Purple wire at fuel gauge sender. Connect a fused jumper wire between Purple wire and ground. Turn ignition switch to RUN position. If fuel gauge indicates empty, go to next step. If fuel gauge does not indicate empty, check Purple wire and connections for high resistance. If wire and connections are okay, replace instrument cluster.

2) Connect fused jumper wire between Purple and Black wires. If fuel gauge indicates empty, replace fuel gauge sender. If fuel gauge does not indicate empty, check Black wire and connections for high resistance. If wire and connections are okay, replace instrument cluster.

Gauge Accuracy Test – 1) Disconnect Purple and Black wires at fuel gauge sender. Connect one lead of Tester (J-33431) to Purple wire and other lead to Black/White wire.

2) Turn ignition on. On standard cluster, adjust resistance dial on tester to 11 ohms (one bar lit), 46 ohms (8 bars lit) and 86 ohms (16 bars lit). Turn ignition off after changing resistance settings.

3) On optional cluster, adjust resistance dial on tester to 18 ohms (one bar lit), 44 ohms (8 bars lit) and 88 ohms (16 bars lit). Turn ignition off after changing resistance settings.

4) If gauge operates correctly, install new fuel gauge sender. If gauge does not operate correctly, check Purple and Black wires for high resistance. If wires are okay, replace instrument cluster.

COOLANT TEMPERATURE INDICATOR TESTS

Engine Hot, No Indicator Light Test – 1) Disconnect coolant temperature switch connector. Connect a jumper wire between Dark Green wire and ground.

2) Turn ignition on, and observe indicator. If indicator lights, replace coolant temperature switch. If indicator does not light, check Dark Green wire for an open circuit. If wires are okay, replace instrument cluster.

Engine Normal, Indicator On Test – Disconnect coolant temperature switch connector. Turn ignition on, and observe indicator. If indicator does not light, replace coolant temperature switch. If indicator is still on, check Dark Green wire for a short to ground. If wires are okay, replace instrument cluster.

Ignition On/Engine Off, No Indicator Light Test – Leave ignition switch Dark Green wire connector connected. Connect a fused jumper wire between Dark Green wire and ground. Turn ignition on. If indicator lights, replace ignition switch. If indicator does not light, check Dark Green wire for an open circuit.

LOW COOLANT INDICATOR TESTS

Short Test – Disconnect coolant level switch. Put ignition switch in RUN position. If low coolant indicator illuminates, check Yellow/Black wire for a short to ground. If low coolant indicator does not illuminate, replace coolant level switch.

Does Not Light Test – 1) Turn switch to RUN position. Disconnect coolant level switch. Using a voltmeter, measure voltage between Yellow/Black wire and ground and between Black/White and Yellow/Black wires.

2) If battery voltage is present, replace coolant level switch. If battery voltage is not present, check Yellow/Black and/or Black/White wires for an open circuit. On optional cluster only, if Yellow/Black wire is okay, replace instrument cluster.

OIL PRESSURE INDICATOR TESTS

Indicator Always On Test – 1) Check oil level and pressure with a mechanical gauge. If oil level and pressure are not okay, make necessary mechanical repairs. If oil level and pressure are okay, turn ignition on.

2) Disconnect oil pressure switch connector. If indicator is off, replace oil pressure switch. If indicator is still on, check Tan wire for a short to ground. If Tan wire is okay, replace instrument cluster.

Ignition On/Engine Off, No Indicator Light Test – Disconnect oil pressure switch connector. Connect a fused jumper wire between Tan wire and ground. Turn ignition on. If indicator lights, replace oil pressure switch. If indicator does not light, check Tan wire for an open circuit. If Tan wire is okay, replace instrument cluster.

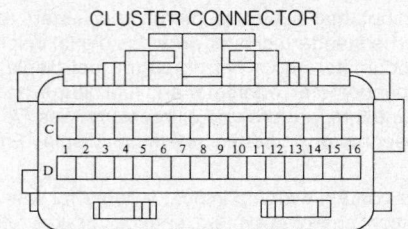

CLUSTER CONNECTOR

TESTING PROCEDURES

- Measure all voltages to ground with ignition switch in RUN position.
- Measure all resistances to ground with ignition switch in OFF position and negative battery cable disconnected.
- Check all ground terminals with a self-powered test light before making voltage or resistance measurements.
- If correct voltage or resistance is found at terminal and function which uses terminal does not operate, check appropriate incandescent bulbs. If bulbs are okay, replace instrument cluster.

INSTRUMENT CLUSTER CONNECTOR TERMINALS C1–D16

Terminal/Wire	Function
C1 (TAN/WHT 33)	To BRAKE Indicator. Indicator is grounded when Park Brake is on or brake fluid is low. Infinite ohms with Park Brake off
C2	NOT USED
C3 (GRY 8)	Illumination Bulbs Dimmer Input. Variable voltage with lights on and dimmer adjusted
C4 (PPL 30)	Fuel Gage Sender Input. 86 ohms, Full (16 bars lit); 11 ohms, Empty (1 bar lit); 8 ohms, Empty (0 bars lit)
C5 (DK GRN 389)	Vehicle Speed Input from ECM
C6 (YEL 726)	VF Dim Enable Input. Battery voltage when Park Lights or Headlights are on
C7 (BRN/WHT 230)	VF Dimmer Input. Variable voltage with Lights on and dimmer adjusted
C8 (ORN 640)	Battery Input. Battery voltage at all times
C9 (LT BLU 811)	English/Metric Switch output to Heater And A/C Control Assembly
C10 (BLK 151)	Ground
C11	NOT USED
C12	NOT USED
C13 (PNK/BLK 750)	Battery Power to VF Displays. Battery voltage in RUN
C14	NOT USED
C15 (PNK/BLK 39)	Ignition Power to the Indicators. Battery voltage in RUN, BULB TEST or START
C16 (DK GRN 35)	To Coolant TEMP Indicator. Grounded with engine overheated or with Ignition Switch in BULB TEST. Normally open
D1	NOT USED
D2	NOT USED
D3 (TAN/BLK 456)	To SHIFT Indicator. ECM provides a ground for the Indicator
D4 (LT BLU 14)	To Left Turn Indicator. Flashing battery voltage with Left Turn Signal
D5 (LT GRN 11)	To Hi Beam Indicator. Battery voltage with Hi Beams ON
D6 (DK BLU 15)	To Right Turn Indicator. Flashing battery voltage with Right Turn Signal
D7 (BLK 150)	Ground
D8 (YEL 237)	FASTEN BELTS Indicator. Battery voltage with safety belts unbuckled. Ignition is switched to RUN
D9	NOT USED
D10	NOT USED
D11 (TAN 31)	To OIL Pressure Indicator. Oil Pressure Switch grounds the Indicator with low oil pressure
D12	NOT USED
D13 (GRY/WHT 852)	To ANTI-LOCK Indicator
D14 (YEL/BLK 68)	To LOW COOLANT Indicator. Ground when the coolant level is low
D15 (BRN 25)	To CHARGE Indicator
D16 (BRN/WHT 419)	To SERVICE ENG. SOON Indicator. ECM provides a ground for the Indicator

91F09395

Fig. 2: Indicators & Gauges Pinout Test – Standard Cluster (Cutlass Supreme)

TESTING PROCEDURES

- Measure all voltages to ground with ignition switch in RUN position.
- Measure all resistances to ground with ignition switch in OFF position and negative battery cable disconnected.
- Check all ground terminals with a self-powered test light before making voltage or resistance measurements.
- If correct voltage or resistance is found at terminal and function which uses terminal does not operate, check appropriate incandescent bulbs. If bulbs are okay, replace instrument cluster.

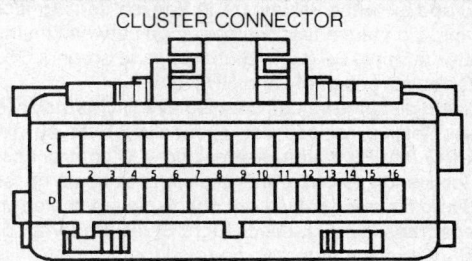

CLUSTER CONNECTOR

INSTRUMENT CLUSTER CONNECTOR – TERMINALS D1-D16

Terminal-Wire Color	Function
D1 (BLK 150)	Indicator bulbs ground
D2 (YEL 237)	Safety Belt input from Component Center. Battery voltage with Ignition in RUN until Driver's safety belt is buckled
D3 (YEL/BLK 68)	LOW COOLANT Indicator input
D4 (BRN 25)	CHARGE Indicator input
D5 (BRN/WHT 419)	SERVICE ENG. SOON input from ECM
D6	NOT USED
D7	NOT USED
D8	NOT USED
D9 (LT BLU 811)	English/Metric Switch output
D10 (BRN/WHT 230)	VF Dimmer input. Variable voltage with lights on and dimmer adjusted
D11 (TAN 31)	OIL Pressure input. Sender resistance varies from 15 ohms, low pressure, to 86 ohms, high pressure
D12 (DK GRN 35)	Coolant Temperature input. Sender resistance varies from 60 ohms, hot, to 1320 ohms, cold
D13 (PPL 30)	Fuel Level input. Sensor resistance varies from 18 ohms, empty, to 88 ohms, full
D14	NOT USED
D15 (DK GRN 389)	Vehicle Speed input from ECM
D16 (ORN 640)	Battery power (memory) to Cluster. Battery voltage at all times

91H09396

Courtesy of General Motors Corp.

Fig. 3: Indicators & Gauges Pinout Test – Optional Cluster (Cutlass Supreme)

COOLANT TEMPERATURE GAUGE TESTS

Always Indicates Cold Test – 1) Disconnect coolant temperature sender connector. Connect a fused jumper wire between Dark Green wire and ground. Turn ignition on.

2) If gauge reads maximum temperature, replace coolant temperature sender. If gauge does not read maximum temperature, check Dark/Green wire for an open circuit. If wire is okay, replace instrument cluster.

Always Indicates Hot Test – Disconnect coolant temperature sender connector. Turn ignition on, and observe gauge. If bars do not light, replace coolant temperature sender. If all bars are still illuminated, check Dark Green wire for a short to ground. If wires are okay, replace instrument cluster.

Gauge Inaccurate Test – 1) Disconnect coolant temperature sender. Connect one lead of Tester (J-33431) to Dark Green wire and other lead to ground. Adjust resistance of tester to 1320 ohms (one bar lit), 119 ohms (8 bars lit) and 60 ohms (16 bars lit).

2) If gauge reads correctly, replace coolant temperature sender. If gauge does not read correctly, check Dark Green wire for high resistance. If wire is okay, replace instrument cluster.

OIL PRESSURE GAUGE TESTS

Gauge Indicates Low Test – Check oil pressure manually with a gauge. If pressure is correct, remove connector from oil pressure sender. Turn ignition on. If display reads high, replace oil pressure sender. If display reads low, check Tan wire between sender and instrument cluster for a short to ground. If wire is okay, replace instrument cluster.

Gauge Indicates High Test – Disconnect oil pressure sender connector. Connect a jumper wire between Tan wire and ground. Turn ignition on. If gauge reads low, replace oil pressure sender. If gauge does not read low, check Tan wire for an open circuit. If wire is okay, replace instrument cluster.

Gauge Inaccurate Test – 1) Disconnect oil pressure sender. Connect one lead of Tester (J-33431) to Tan wire connector and other lead to ground. Adjust resistance of tester to 15 ohms (2 bars lit), 54 ohms (9 bars lit) and 91 ohms (16 bars lit).

2) If gauge reads correctly, replace oil pressure sender. If gauge does not read correctly, check Tan wire for high resistance. If wire is okay, replace instrument cluster.

ENGLISH/METRIC SWITCH TESTS

Standard Cluster Test – 1) Disconnect instrument cluster connector. Put ignition switch in RUN position, and check heater and A/C control assembly.

2) If values are in Metric, check Light Blue wire and heater and A/C control assembly for a short to ground. Repair or replace as necessary.

3) If values are in English, turn ignition switch to RUN position. Connect a fused jumper wire between instrument cluster connector terminal C9 (Light Blue wire) and ground. Check heater and A/C control assembly for a possible short to ground.

4) If fuse in jumper wire blows, check Light Blue wire and heater and A/C control assembly for a short to battery. Repair or replace as necessary.

5) If speed and distance values are not displayed in Metric, check Light Blue wire for an open circuit. Check heater and A/C control assembly for a short to battery. Repair or replace as necessary.

Optional Cluster Test – 1) Disconnect instrument cluster connector. Put ignition switch in RUN position. Observe Head Up Display (HUD) and heater and A/C control assembly.

2) If speed and distance values are in Metric or temperature is in degrees Celsius, check Light Blue wire, heater and A/C control assembly, and HUD unit for a short to ground. Repair and/or replace as necessary.

3) If speed and distance values are in English, turn ignition switch to RUN position. Connect a fused jumper wire between instrument cluster connector terminal D9 (Light Blue wire) and ground. Observe heater and A/C control assembly and HUD unit.

4) If speed and distance values are displayed in Metric or temperature is in degrees Celsius, replace instrument cluster. If fuse in jumper wire blows, check Light Blue wire, heater and A/C control assembly, and HUD unit for a short to battery. Repair or replace as necessary.

5) If speed and distance values are not displayed in Metric or temperature is in degrees Celsius, check Light Blue wire for an open circuit. If wire is okay, replace defective component.

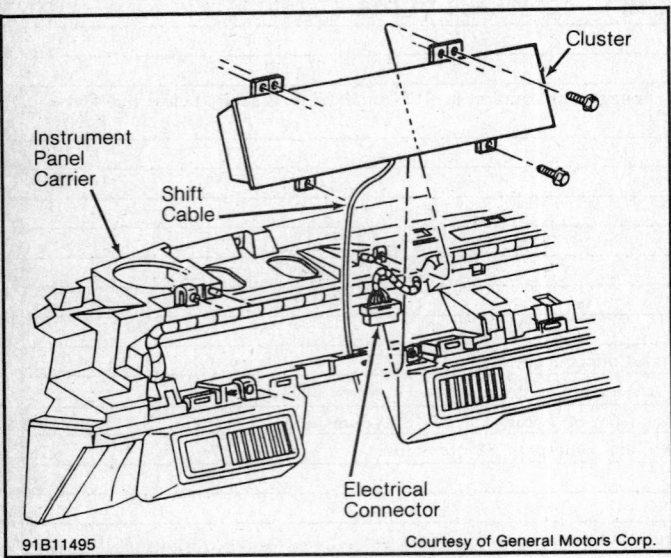

91B11495   Courtesy of General Motors Corp.

Fig. 4: Removing Instrument Cluster Assembly (Cutlass Supreme)

HEADLIGHT SWITCH TEST

Constant battery voltage should be present at headlight switch terminal "E" (Dark Green wire). With headlights on, battery voltage should be present at terminals "F" (Yellow wire) and "D" (Yellow/Black wire). If voltage is not present as indicated, repair or replace wire(s) and switch as necessary.

WIPER SWITCH TEST

For testing information on wipers, see appropriate WIPER/WASHER SYSTEMS article.

INSTRUMENT CLUSTER TROUBLE CODES

Instrument cluster contains circuitry which allows storage of 9 trouble codes. Codes cover fuel level, oil pressure, coolant temperature, speed sensor and serial data line circuits. Use Tech 1 "Scan" tester to access trouble codes. *See Figs. 5-13.*

REMOVAL & INSTALLATION

INSTRUMENT CLUSTER

Removal & Installation — Remove air cleaner assembly and negative battery cable. Remove instrument cluster trim plate. Remove cluster-to-carrier bolts and PRNDL shift indicator cable (if equipped). Pull cluster forward, and disconnect cluster connector. *See Fig. 4.* Remove cluster. To install, reverse removal procedure.

WIRING DIAGRAMS

See appropriate chassis wiring diagram in WIRING DIAGRAMS.

CODE I001 – FUEL PUMP/OIL PRESSURE SWITCH/SENDER ZERO BIAS

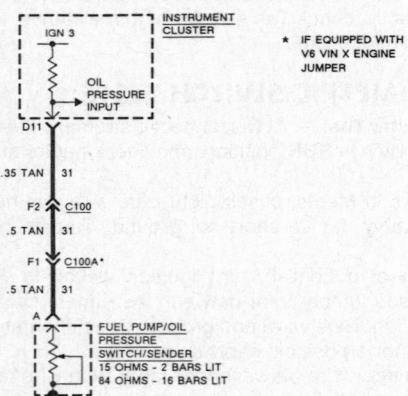

Code I001 sets if ignition is on, engine is not running and sensor resistance at instrument cluster was at or above 25 ohms for 5 successive readings within a 2.5-second period.

NOTE: Numbers refer to test numbers on diagnostic chart.

1) Checks if open is in fuel pump/oil pressure switch/sender or rest of circuit.
2) Checks if open is in circuit No. 31 or instrument cluster.

91J09397 91B09398

WHEN ALL DIAGNOSIS AND REPAIRS ARE COMPLETE, CLEAR CODES AND VERIFY OPERATION.

Courtesy of General Motors Corp.

Fig. 5: Code I001 – Fuel Pump/Oil Pressure Switch/Sender Zero Bias (Cutlass Supreme)

CODE I002 – FUEL PUMP/OIL PRESSURE SWITCH/SENDER OPEN CIRCUIT

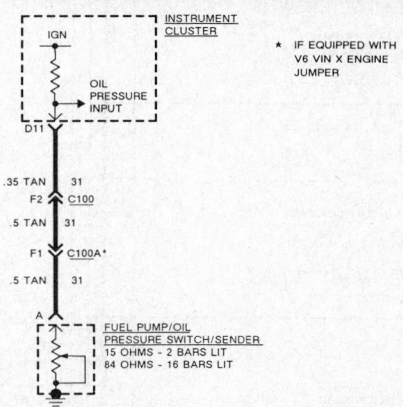

* IF EQUIPPED WITH V6 VIN X ENGINE JUMPER

Code I002 sets if ignition is on, engine is above 400 RPM and sender reading at instrument cluster was at or above 100 ohms for 5 successive readings within a 2.5-second period.

NOTE: Numbers refer to test numbers on diagnostic chart.

1) Checks if open is in fuel pump/oil pressure switch/sender or rest of circuit.
2) Checks if open is in circuit No. 31 or instrument cluster.

91D09399 91H09400

----

* KEY OFF
* DISCONNECT FUEL PUMP/OIL PRESSURE SWITCH/SENDER CONNECTOR
* CONNECT FUSED JUMPER BETWEEN TAN WIRE AND KNOWN GOOD GROUND
* KEY ON, ENGINE NOT RUNNING
* NOTE OIL PRESSURE DISPLAY ①

LOW PRESSURE
* CHECK FUEL PUMP/OIL PRESSURE SWITCH/SENDER CONNECTOR TERMINALS FOR A POOR CONNECTION
* REPLACE FUEL PUMP/OIL PRESSURE SWITCH/SENDER IF THE CONNECTOR TERMINALS ARE GOOD

HIGH PRESSURE
* CHECK FOR AN OPEN IN CKT 31 ②

CKT OK
* CHECK FOR POOR TERMINAL CONTACT AT INSTRUMENT CLUSTER CONNECTOR
* REPLACE INSTRUMENT CLUSTER IF TERMINAL CONTACT IS GOOD

CKT NOT OK
* REPAIR/ REPLACE AS NECESSARY

WHEN ALL DIAGNOSIS AND REPAIRS ARE COMPLETE, CLEAR CODES AND VERIFY OPERATION.

Courtesy of General Motors Corp.

Fig. 6: Code I002 – Fuel Pump/Oil Pressure Switch/Sender Open Circuit (Cutlass Supreme)

CODE I003 – FUEL LEVEL SENDER OPEN CIRCUIT

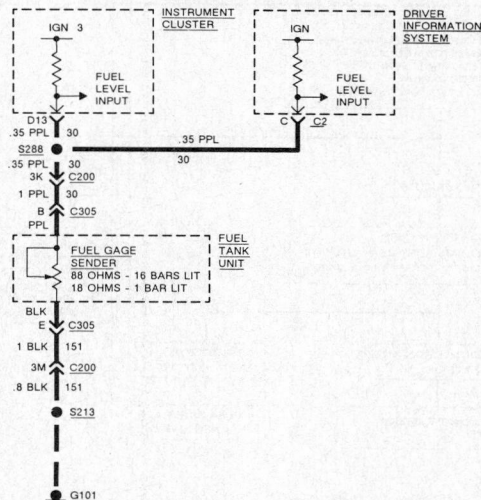

Code I003 sets if ignition is on and sender resistance at instrument cluster was at or above 100 ohms for 5 successive readings within a 2.5-second period.

NOTE: Numbers refer to test numbers on diagnostic chart.

1) Checks if circuits No. 30 and No. 151 are good.
2) Checks if open is in circuit No. 30 or No. 151.
3) Checks if problem is in instrument cluster.
4) Checks if open is in circuit No. 30, instrument cluster connector C1 or in instrument cluster.

91J09401 91B09402

----

* KEY ON, ENGINE NOT RUNNING
* DISCONNECT BODY TO FUEL SENDER CONNECTOR C305 (6 WAY)
* CONNECT A DVM BETWEEN TERMINALS B(PPL) & E (BLK) ON INSTRUMENT CLUSTER SIDE OF CONNECTOR
* NOTE VOLTAGE READING ①

O VOLTS
* MEASURE VOLTAGE FROM TERMINAL B (PPL) TO KNOWN GOOD GROUND ②

O VOLTS
* CHECK FOR OPEN IN CKT 30
* IF NOT OPEN, CHECK FOR POOR TERMINAL CONTACT AT INSTRUMENT CLUSTER CONNECTOR
* REPLACE INSTRUMENT CLUSTER IF TERMINAL CONTACT IS GOOD ④

BATTERY
* REPAIR OPEN IN CKT 151

BATTERY
* KEY OFF
* CONNECT FUSED JUMPER BETWEEN TERMINAL B (PPL) AND E (BLK) ON INSTRUMENT CLUSTER SIDE OF CONNECTOR C305 DISCONNECTED
* KEY ON, ENGINE NOT RUNNING
* NOTE FUEL DISPLAY ③

EMPTY
* CHECK FOR POOR CONNECTION ON FUEL GAGE SENDER SIDE OF CONNECTOR C305
* IF GOOD, REPLACE FUEL GAGE SENDER

NOT EMPTY
* REPLACE INSTRUMENT CLUSTER

WHEN ALL DIAGNOSIS AND REPAIRS ARE COMPLETE, CLEAR CODES AND VERIFY OPERATION.

Courtesy of General Motors Corp.

Fig. 7: Code I003 – Fuel Level Sender Open Circuit (Cutlass Supreme)

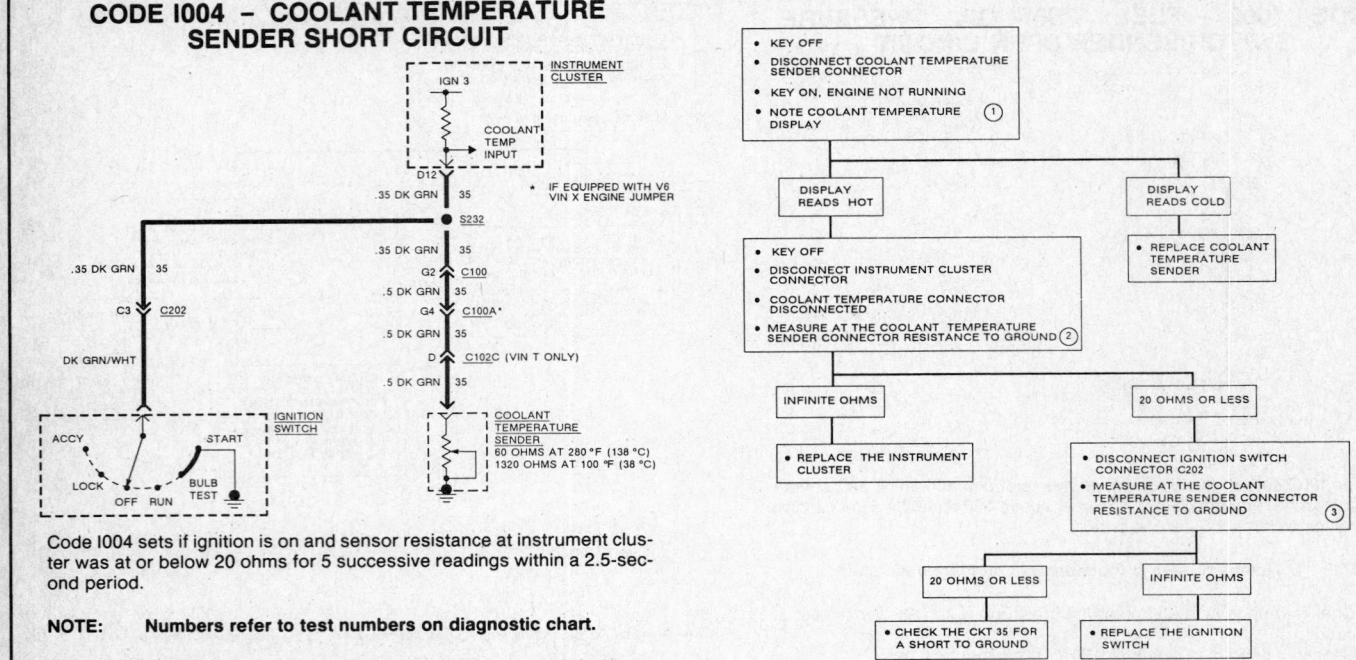

CODE I004 – COOLANT TEMPERATURE SENDER SHORT CIRCUIT

Code I004 sets if ignition is on and sensor resistance at instrument cluster was at or below 20 ohms for 5 successive readings within a 2.5-second period.

NOTE: Numbers refer to test numbers on diagnostic chart.

1) Checks if short is in coolant temperature sender or rest of circuit.
2) Narrows location of short between circuit No. 35 and ignition switch or instrument cluster.
3) Checks if short is in ignition switch or rest of circuit.

WHEN ALL DIAGNOSIS AND REPAIRS ARE COMPLETE, CLEAR CODES AND VERIFY OPERATION.

91D09403 91F09404

Courtesy of General Motors Corp.

Fig. 8: Code I004 – Coolant Temperature Sender Short Circuit (Cutlass Supreme)

CODE I005 – COOLANT TEMPERATURE SENDER OPEN CIRCUIT

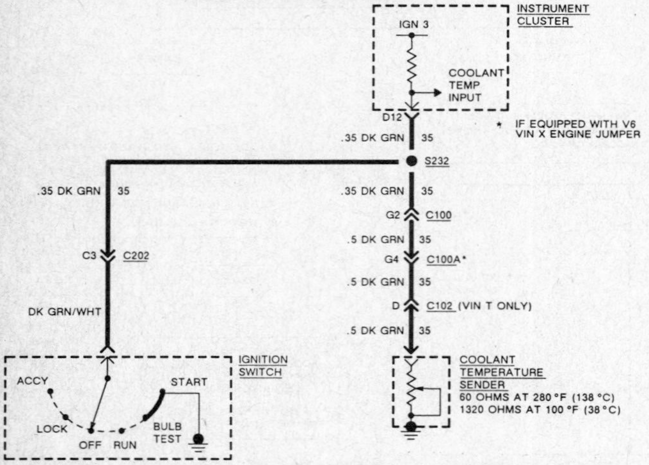

Code I005 sets if ignition is on, coolant temperature sender is greater than or equal to 100°F (38°C) and sensor resistance at instrument cluster was at or above 2000 ohms for 5 successive readings within a 2.5-second period.

NOTE: Numbers refer to test numbers on diagnostic chart.

1) Checks if open is between coolant temperature sensor and splice S232 or between splice S232 and instrument cluster. Splice S232 is located behind center of instrument panel.
2) Checks if open is in circuit No. 35 or instrument cluster.

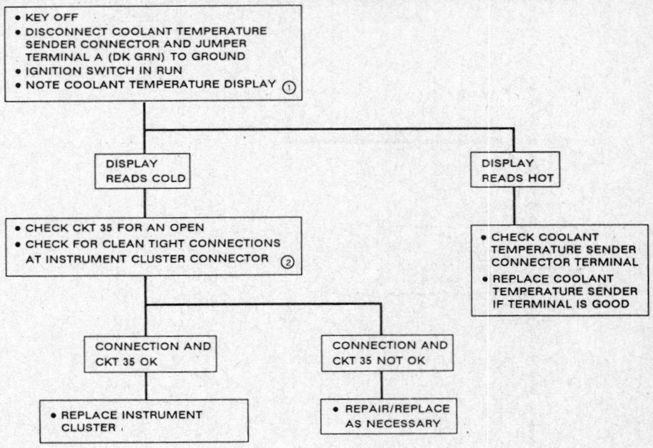

WHEN ALL DIAGNOSIS AND REPAIRS ARE COMPLETE, CLEAR CODES AND VERIFY OPERATION.

91I09405 91A09406

Courtesy of General Motors Corp.

Fig. 9: Code I005 – Coolant Temperature Sender Open Circuit (Cutlass Supreme)

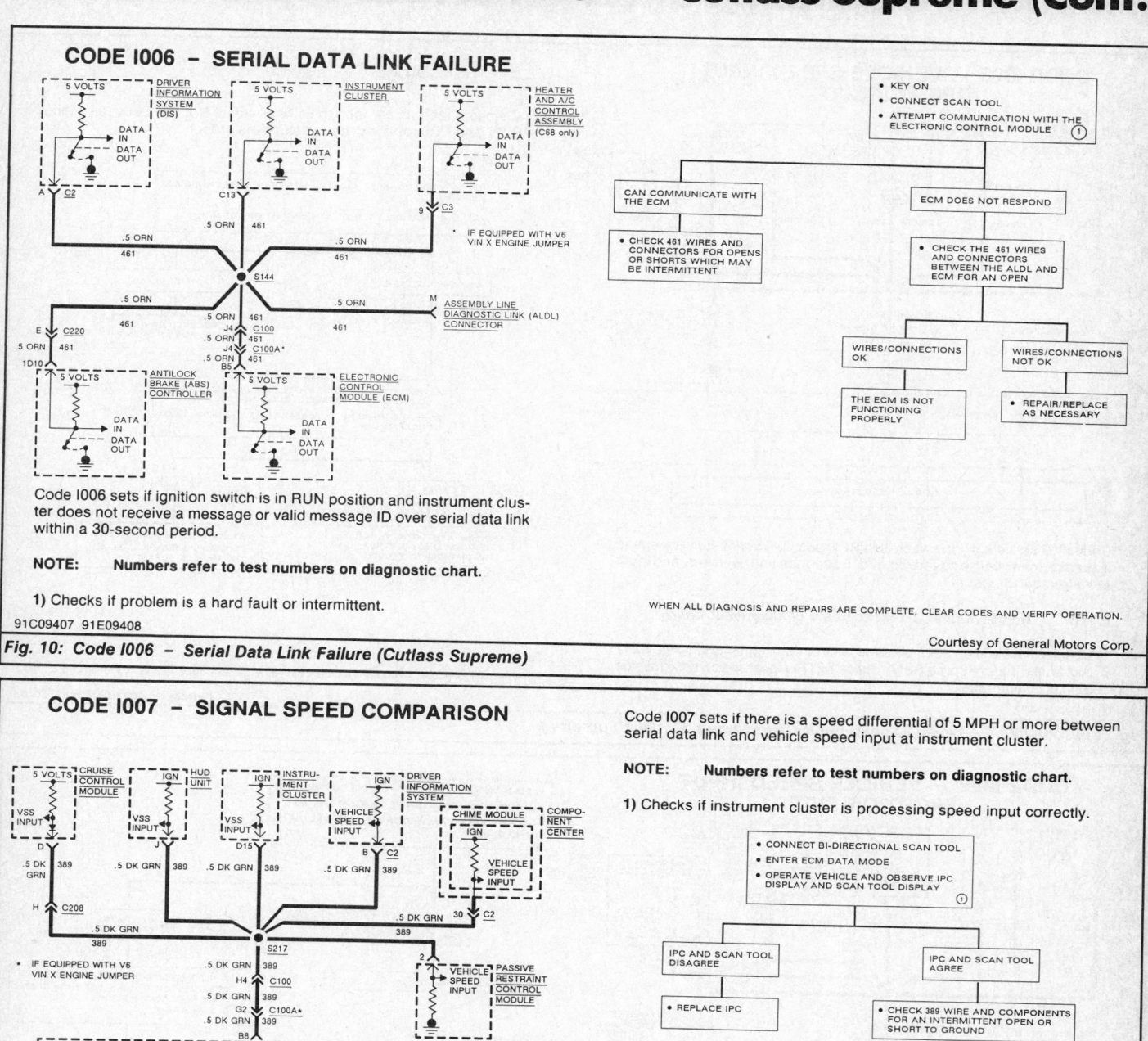

CODE I006 – SERIAL DATA LINK FAILURE

Code I006 sets if ignition switch is in RUN position and instrument cluster does not receive a message or valid message ID over serial data link within a 30-second period.

NOTE: Numbers refer to test numbers on diagnostic chart.

1) Checks if problem is a hard fault or intermittent.

91C09407 91E09408

WHEN ALL DIAGNOSIS AND REPAIRS ARE COMPLETE, CLEAR CODES AND VERIFY OPERATION.

Courtesy of General Motors Corp.

Fig. 10: Code I006 – Serial Data Link Failure (Cutlass Supreme)

CODE I007 – SIGNAL SPEED COMPARISON

Code I007 sets if there is a speed differential of 5 MPH or more between serial data link and vehicle speed input at instrument cluster.

NOTE: Numbers refer to test numbers on diagnostic chart.

1) Checks if instrument cluster is processing speed input correctly.

91G09409 91I09410

WHEN ALL DIAGNOSIS AND REPAIRS ARE COMPLETE, CLEAR CODES AND VERIFY OPERATION.

Courtesy of General Motors Corp.

Fig. 11: Code I007 – Signal Speed Comparison (Cutlass Supreme)

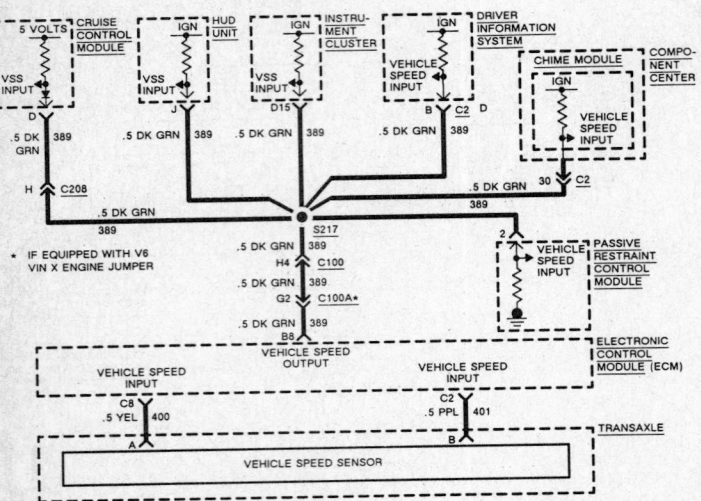

CODE I008 – VEHICLE SPEED INPUT OPEN CIRCUIT

Code I008 sets if ignition switch is in RUN position, serial data link speed is greater than vehicle speed input for 5 seconds and vehicle speed input at instrument cluster is HI.

NOTE: Numbers refer to test numbers on diagnostic chart.

1) Checks if there is an open between instrument cluster and splice S217 or if fault is before splice S217. Splice S217 is located behind right side of instrument panel.

91A09411 91I11492

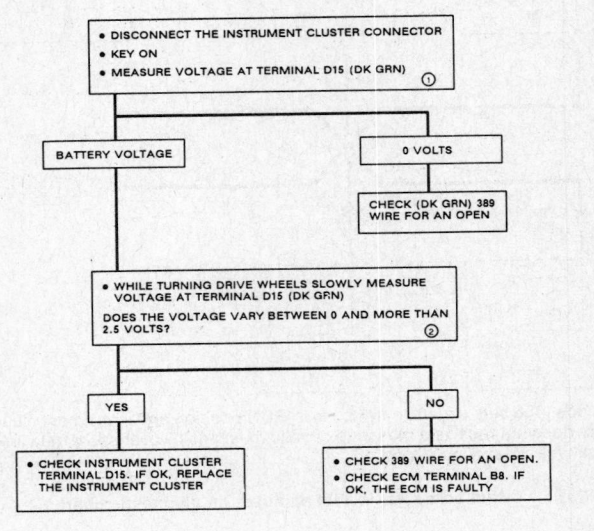

2) Checks if there is an open in ECM or circuit No. 389 between splice S217 and ECM or if instrument cluster is at fault.

WHEN ALL DIAGNOSIS AND REPAIRS ARE COMPLETE, CLEAR CODES AND VERIFY OPERATION.

Courtesy of General Motors Corp.

Fig. 12: Code I008 – Vehicle Speed Input Open Circuit (Cutlass Supreme)

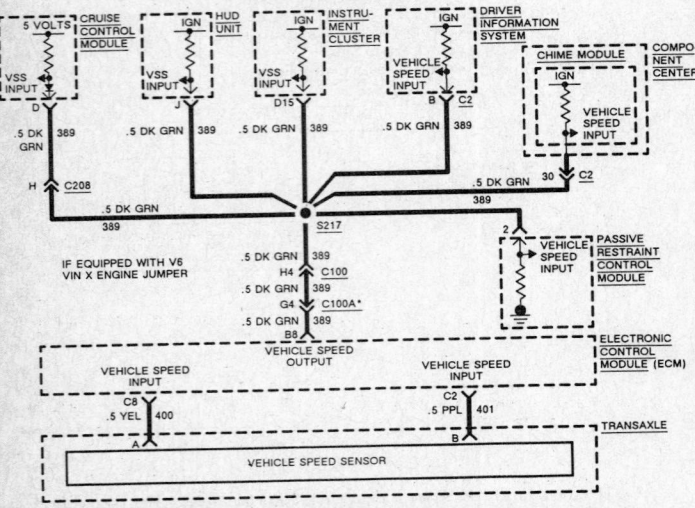

CODE I009 – VEHICLE SPEED INPUT SHORT CIRCUIT

Code I009 sets if ignition switch is in RUN position, serial data link speed is 5 MPH or greater than vehicle speed input for 5 seconds and vehicle speed input at instrument cluster is LO.

NOTE: Numbers refer to test numbers on diagnostic chart.

1) Checks if a short to ground exists in circuit No. 389 and if components sharing circuit No. 389 or electric instrument cluster are at fault.
2) Determines if short exists in circuit No. 389 or a component sharing circuit No. 389.

91J11493 91A11494

WHEN ALL DIAGNOSIS AND REPAIRS ARE COMPLETED, CLEAR CODES AND VERIFY OPERATION.

Courtesy of General Motors Corp.

Fig. 13: Code I009 – Vehicle Speed Input Short Circuit (Cutlass Supreme)

DESCRIPTION & OPERATION

The Instrument Panel Cluster (IPC) provides bar graph displays for speedometer, engine coolant temperature and fuel level. Digital displays are used for inside/outside temperature, odometer and trip odometer. Electronically operated indicators are used for turn signals, headlight high beams and shift indicator display. The odometer and speedometer can display English or Metric units.

AIR BAG PRECAUTIONS

Follow precautions when working with vehicles equipped with Supplemental Inflatable Restraint (SIR) air bag systems.

- Before performing any instrument panel testing, diagnosis or repair, disable SIR system by disconnecting negative battery cable and Yellow 2-pin connector at base of steering column.
- Wait 20 minutes before making instrument panel repairs. SIR system retains enough voltage to deploy air bag for a short time after disconnecting power.
- To avoid accidental air bag deployment, avoid SIR wiring harness when trouble shooting instrument panel components. All SIR wires are color-coded Yellow.

TESTING

INDICATORS & GAUGES PINOUT TEST

Check voltage or resistance at instrument cluster C1 and C2 connectors to determine if proper readings are supplied to instrument cluster. See Figs. 2 and 3.

FUEL GAUGE TESTS

Fuel Gauge Open Test – 1) Disconnect fuel tank sending unit connector located behind fuel tank. Connect a jumper wire between Purple and Black/White wires.

2) Turn ignition switch to RUN position, and observe fuel gauge. If fuel gauge indicates empty and low fuel indicator flashes, replace fuel tank sending unit. If fuel gauge is blank, check Purple and Black/White wires for an open circuit. If wires are okay, replace instrument cluster.

Fuel Gauge Short Test – 1) Disconnect fuel tank sending unit connector located behind fuel tank. Turn ignition switch to RUN position.

2) Observe fuel gauge. If fuel gauge is blank, replace fuel tank sending unit. If fuel gauge indicates empty, check Purple wire for short to ground. If wire is okay, replace instrument cluster.

Fuel Gauge Accuracy Test – 1) Disconnect fuel tank sending unit connector located behind fuel tank. Using Tester (J-33431-B), connect Red test lead to Purple wire and other lead to Black/White wire of harness. Set tester resistance dials to zero, and then 90 ohms.

2) Fuel gauge should indicate empty and full respectively. For faster fuel display response after setting resistance, turn ignition switch to OFF position, and then to RUN position. If display responds correctly, replace fuel tank sending unit.

3) If display does not respond correctly, use an ohmmeter to check resistance of Black/White and Purple wires of fuel tank sending unit connector. If resistance is less than 3 ohms, replace instrument cluster. If resistance is more than 3 ohms, replace wires showing high resistance.

ENGINE TEMPERATURE DISPLAY TESTS

Engine Temperature Display Not Working Test – 1) Disconnect coolant sensor connector. Coolant sensor connector is located on top left side of engine. Connect a jumper wire between Black and Yellow wires.

2) Turn ignition switch to RUN position, and observe engine temperature display. If engine temperature display indicates HOT, replace coolant sensor. If engine temperature display is still not working, check Yellow and Black wires for an open circuit. If okay, replace instrument cluster.

Engine Temperature Display Flashing HOT & "X" Test – 1) Disconnect coolant sensor connector. Coolant sensor connector is located on top left side of engine. Turn ignition switch to RUN position. Observe engine temperature display.

2) If engine temperature display is blank, replace coolant sensor. If engine temperature display still indicates HOT, check Yellow wire for short to ground.

Engine Temperature Display Inaccurate Test – 1) Disconnect coolant sensor connector. Coolant sensor connector is located on top left side of engine. Using Tester (J-33431-B), connect Red tester lead to Black wire and other lead to Yellow wire of harness.

2) Vary tester controls between 1365 ohms (COLD) and 40 ohms (HOT). For faster fuel display response after setting resistance, turn ignition switch to OFF position, and then to RUN position.

3) If display responds correctly, replace coolant sensor. If display does not respond correctly, use an ohmmeter to check resistance of Black and Yellow wires. If resistance is less than 3 ohms, replace instrument cluster. If resistance is more than 3 ohms, replace wires showing high resistance.

OIL PRESSURE GAUGE TESTS

Oil Pressure Indicator Constantly Illuminated Test – 1) Disconnect oil pressure sending unit switch connector. Turn ignition switch to RUN position, and observe oil pressure gauge.

2) If oil pressure indicator does not illuminate, replace oil pressure sending unit switch. If oil pressure indicator is still not illuminated, check Tan wire at oil pressure sending unit switch connector for short to ground.

Oil Pressure Indicator Does Not Illuminate Test – 1) Disconnect oil pressure sending unit switch connector. Connect jumper wire from oil pressure sending unit switch connector Tan wire to ground. Turn ignition switch to RUN position, and observe oil pressure gauge.

2) If oil pressure indicator lights, replace oil pressure sending unit switch. If oil pressure indicator does not light, check Tan wire for an open circuit.

SHIFT INDICATOR TEST

Shift Indicator Does Not Operate Correctly – 1) Disconnect shift indicator control module connector behind left side of instrument panel, left of steering column. Turn ignition switch to RUN position.

2) Using a voltmeter, measure voltage between terminal "A" (White/Black wire) and ground. If battery voltage is present, go to next step. If battery voltage is not present, repair open circuit in White/Black wire.

3) Measure voltage between terminals "A" (White/Black wire) and "F" (Black/White wire). If battery voltage is present, go to next step. If battery voltage is not present, repair open circuit in Black/White wire.

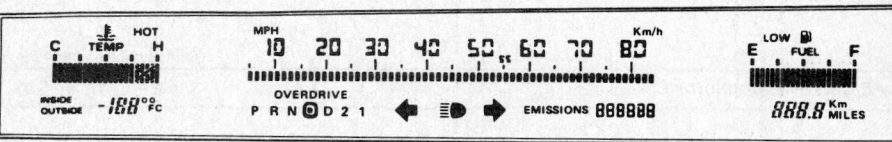
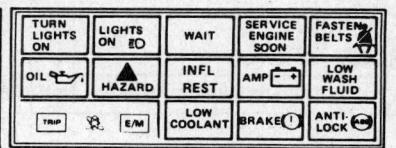

109363

Fig. 1: Identifying Electronic Instrument Cluster (Eighty-Eight)

4) Turn ignition off. Using ohmmeter, measure resistance at appropriate terminals. See PRNDL RESISTANCE CHECKS table. If any resistance readings are NOT correct, repair wiring. If resistance readings are okay, go to SHIFT DECODER MODULE TEST.

SHIFT DECODER MODULE TEST

Temporarily replace shift decoder module with a known good unit. If all circuits and displays operate correctly, replace shift decoder module. If all circuits and displays still do not operate correctly, install original shift decoder module, and replace instrument cluster.

HEADLIGHT SWITCH TEST

Constant voltage should be present at headlight switch terminal "C". With headlights on, 12 volts should be present at headlight switch terminal "D" (Yellow wire). If voltage is not as specified, check headlight switch and wiring.

WIPER SWITCH TEST

For testing information on wiper switches, see appropriate WIPER/WASHER SYSTEMS article.

TESTING CONDITIONS

- Ignition switch must be in RUN except for resistance measurements.
- Make all resistance measurements to ground with negative battery cable disconnected.
- Measure to ground unless another terminal is given.
- Cluster connector is shown as seen from driver's seat with the digital cluster removed.
- If correct voltage or resistance is found at terminals, and cluster function that uses those terminals does not operate, check bulbs. If okay, replace the instrument cluster.

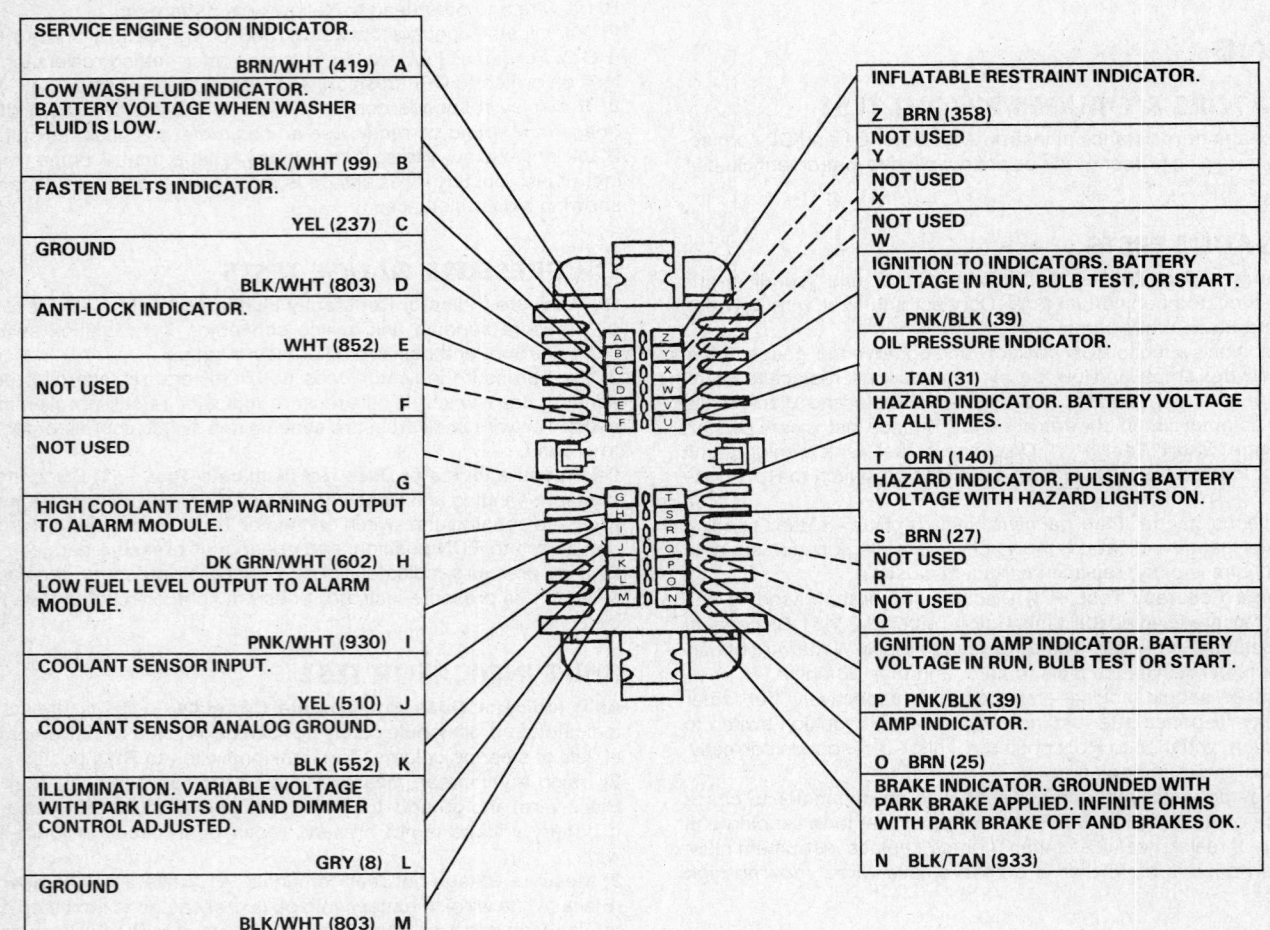

SERVICE ENGINE SOON INDICATOR.
BRN/WHT (419) A

LOW WASH FLUID INDICATOR. BATTERY VOLTAGE WHEN WASHER FLUID IS LOW.
BLK/WHT (99) B

FASTEN BELTS INDICATOR.
YEL (237) C

GROUND
BLK/WHT (803) D

ANTI-LOCK INDICATOR.
WHT (852) E

NOT USED
F

NOT USED
G

HIGH COOLANT TEMP WARNING OUTPUT TO ALARM MODULE.
DK GRN/WHT (602) H

LOW FUEL LEVEL OUTPUT TO ALARM MODULE.
PNK/WHT (930) I

COOLANT SENSOR INPUT.
YEL (510) J

COOLANT SENSOR ANALOG GROUND.
BLK (552) K

ILLUMINATION. VARIABLE VOLTAGE WITH PARK LIGHTS ON AND DIMMER CONTROL ADJUSTED.
GRY (8) L

GROUND
BLK/WHT (803) M

INFLATABLE RESTRAINT INDICATOR.
Z   BRN (358)

NOT USED
Y

NOT USED
X

NOT USED
W

IGNITION TO INDICATORS. BATTERY VOLTAGE IN RUN, BULB TEST, OR START.
V   PNK/BLK (39)

OIL PRESSURE INDICATOR.
U   TAN (31)

HAZARD INDICATOR. BATTERY VOLTAGE AT ALL TIMES.
T   ORN (140)

HAZARD INDICATOR. PULSING BATTERY VOLTAGE WITH HAZARD LIGHTS ON.
S   BRN (27)

NOT USED
R

NOT USED
Q

IGNITION TO AMP INDICATOR. BATTERY VOLTAGE IN RUN, BULB TEST OR START.
P   PNK/BLK (39)

AMP INDICATOR.
O   BRN (25)

BRAKE INDICATOR. GROUNDED WITH PARK BRAKE APPLIED. INFINITE OHMS WITH PARK BRAKE OFF AND BRAKES OK.
N   BLK/TAN (933)

NOTE: CONNECTOR C1 LOCATED BEHIND INSTRUMENT CLUSTER.

91G09386

Fig. 2: Instrument Cluster Pinpoint Test (Eight-Eight) – Connector C1

TESTING CONDITIONS

- Ignition switch must be in RUN except for resistance measurements.
- Make all resistance measurements to ground with negative battery cable disconnected.
- Measure to ground unless another terminal is given.
- Cluster connector is shown as seen from driver's seat with the digital cluster removed.
- If correct voltage or resistance is found at terminals, and cluster function that uses those terminals does not operate, check bulbs. If okay, replace the instrument cluster.

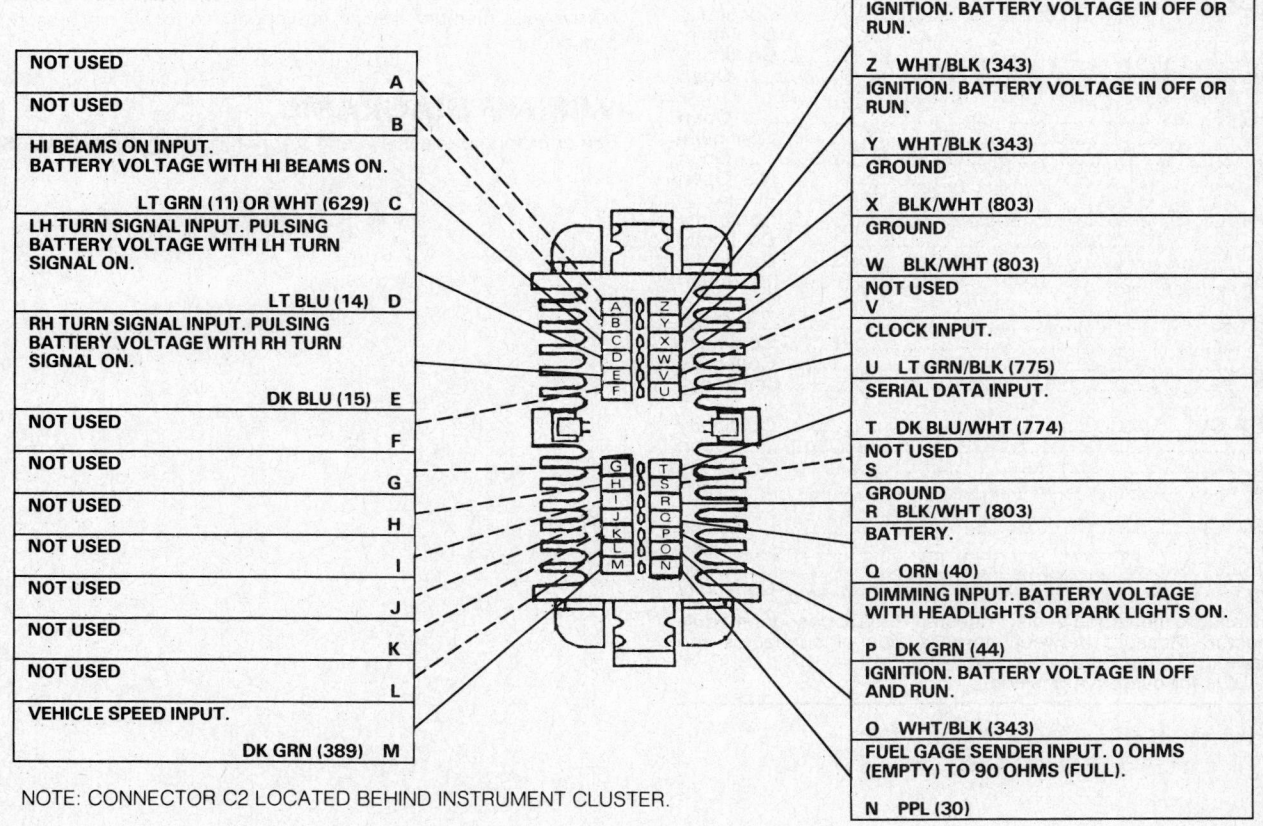

NOT USED	A
NOT USED	B
HI BEAMS ON INPUT. BATTERY VOLTAGE WITH HI BEAMS ON. LT GRN (11) OR WHT (629)	C
LH TURN SIGNAL INPUT. PULSING BATTERY VOLTAGE WITH LH TURN SIGNAL ON. LT BLU (14)	D
RH TURN SIGNAL INPUT. PULSING BATTERY VOLTAGE WITH RH TURN SIGNAL ON. DK BLU (15)	E
NOT USED	F
NOT USED	G
NOT USED	H
NOT USED	I
NOT USED	J
NOT USED	K
NOT USED	L
VEHICLE SPEED INPUT. DK GRN (389)	M

IGNITION. BATTERY VOLTAGE IN OFF OR RUN. Z WHT/BLK (343)	
IGNITION. BATTERY VOLTAGE IN OFF OR RUN. Y WHT/BLK (343)	
GROUND X BLK/WHT (803)	
GROUND W BLK/WHT (803)	
NOT USED V	
CLOCK INPUT. U LT GRN/BLK (775)	
SERIAL DATA INPUT. T DK BLU/WHT (774)	
NOT USED S	
GROUND R BLK/WHT (803)	
BATTERY. Q ORN (40)	
DIMMING INPUT. BATTERY VOLTAGE WITH HEADLIGHTS OR PARK LIGHTS ON. P DK GRN (44)	
IGNITION. BATTERY VOLTAGE IN OFF AND RUN. O WHT/BLK (343)	
FUEL GAGE SENDER INPUT. 0 OHMS (EMPTY) TO 90 OHMS (FULL). N PPL (30)	

NOTE: CONNECTOR C2 LOCATED BEHIND INSTRUMENT CLUSTER.

91I09387

Fig. 3: Instrument Cluster Pinout Test (Eighty-Eight) – Connector C2

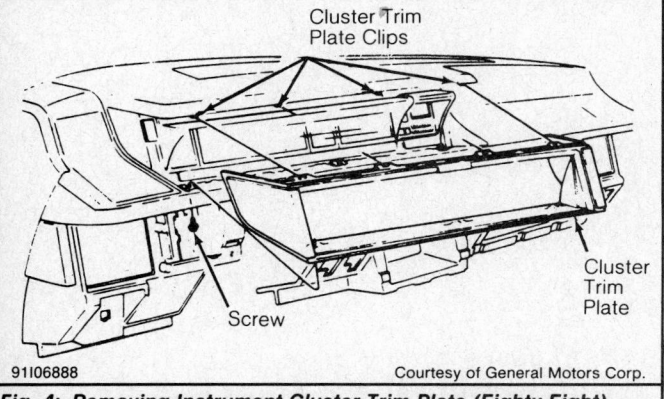

91I06888

Fig. 4: Removing Instrument Cluster Trim Plate (Eighty-Eight)

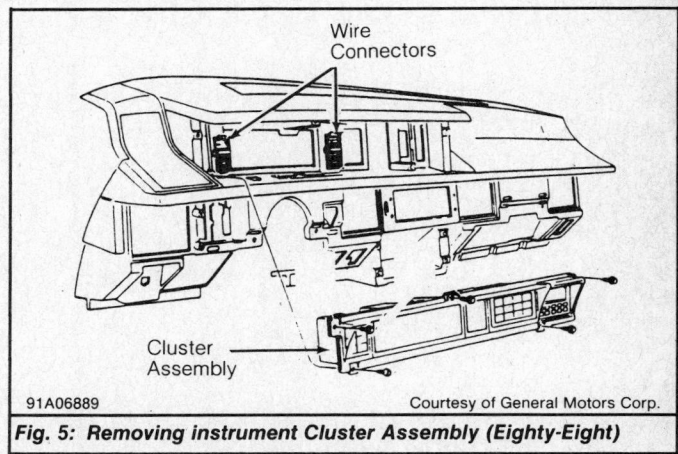

91A06889

Fig. 5: Removing instrument Cluster Assembly (Eighty-Eight)

PRNDL RESISTANCE CHECKS

Gear Position & Decoder Module Wire Color (Pin Letter)	[1] Ohmmeter Reading
"P"	
BLK/WHT (C)	Continuity
YEL (D)	Open
GRY (E)	Open
WHT (B)	Continuity
"R"	
BLK/WHT (C)	Continuity
YEL (D)	Continuity
GRY (E)	Continuity
WHT (B)	Open
"N"	
BLK/WHT (C)	Open
YEL (D)	Continuity
GRY (E)	Open
WHT (B)	Open
"D" [2]	
BLK/WHT (C)	Continuity
YEL (D)	Continuity
GRY (E)	Continuity
WHT (B)	Open
"D"	
BLK/WHT (C)	Open
YEL (D)	Continuity
GRY (E)	Continuity
WHT (B)	Conuinuity
"2"	
BLK/WHT (C)	Continuity
YEL (D)	Open
GRY (E)	Continuity
WHT (B)	Open
"1"	
BLK/WHT (C)	Open
YEL (D)	Open
GRY (E)	Open
WHT (B)	Continuity

[1] – Resistance is measured at disconnected PRNDL decoder module connector. Measure between harness side of connector and ground pin "F" (harness side).

[2] – This "D" is for overdrive position.

REMOVAL & INSTALLATION

INSTRUMENT CLUSTER

Removal & Installation – 1) Disconnect negative battery cable Loosen cluster trim plate, pulling rearward to remove. *See Fig. 4* Remove screws attaching cluster to instrument panel. Remove clip connecting shift indicator cable to shift bowl on steering column.
2) Remove wire connectors, lens and cover shield. *See Fig. 5.* Remove non-volatile memory chip (if equipped). To install, reverse removal procedure.

WIRING DIAGRAMS

See appropriate chassis wiring diagram in WIRING DIAGRAMS.

DESCRIPTION & OPERATION

Instrument cluster components include Climate Control and Driver Information Center (CCDIC), the speedometer cluster and warning indicator lights. *See Fig. 1.*

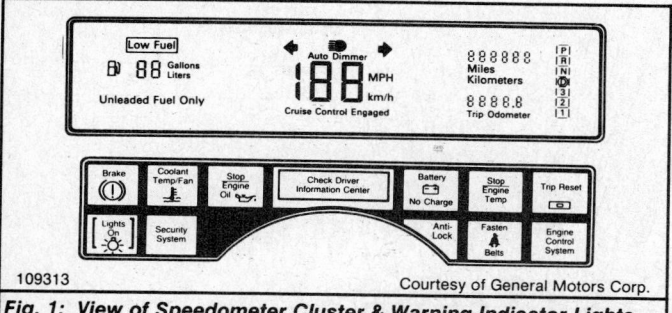

109313   Courtesy of General Motors Corp.

Fig. 1: View of Speedometer Cluster & Warning Indicator Lights

CLIMATE CONTROL & DRIVER INFORMATION CENTER

Climate Control and Driver Information Center (CCDIC) displays on-board diagnosis, fuel information, engine data, temperature, time and monitored system messages.

SPEEDOMETER CLUSTER

The speedometer cluster contains a digital speedometer, digital odometer, digital gear position indicator and digital fuel gauge. Digital speedometer uses a quartz mechanism to control display illumination. Speed and odometer displays are Blue/Green vacuum fluorescent indicators, and include MPH and mileage displays.

WARNING INDICATOR LIGHTS

Warning indicator lights alert driver of various vehicle conditions. All warning indicator lights illuminate during engine start to provide a bulb check.

AIR BAG PRECAUTIONS

Follow precautions when working with vehicles equipped with Supplemental Inflatable Restraint (SIR) air bag systems:

- Before performing any instrument panel testing, diagnosis or repair, disable SIR system by disconnecting negative battery cable and Yellow 2-pin connector at base of steering column.
- Wait 20 minutes before making SIR repairs. SIR system retains enough voltage to deploy air bag for a short time after disconnecting power.
- To avoid accidental air bag deployment, avoid SIR wiring harness when trouble shooting instrument cluster components. All SIR wires are color-coded Yellow.

TESTING

NOTE: For additional instrument panel testing and diagnosis, see SELF-DIAGNOSTICS – ELDORADO & SEVILLE PCM/BCM article in ENGINE PERFORMANCE.

WARNING INDICATOR LIGHTS & GAUGES PINOUT TEST

Check voltage or resistance at instrument cluster connector to determine if proper readings are supplied to instrument cluster. *See Fig. 2.*

TRIP RESET SWITCH TEST

1) Replace trip reset switch with a known good component. Turn ignition switch to RUN position. Press trip reset switch and check trip odometer.

2) If trip odometer now displays all zeros, replace trip reset switch. If trip odometer does not reset, replace instrument cluster.

FUEL TANK SENDING UNIT TEST

1) Disconnect fuel tank sending unit connector. Turn ignition switch to RUN position. Using a voltmeter, measure voltage between connector terminal "C" (Pink/Black wire) and ground. If battery voltage is present, go to next step. If battery voltage is not present, check Pink/Black wire for an open circuit.

2) Using a voltmeter, measure voltage between connector terminals "C" (Pink/Black wire) and "E" (Black/White wire). If battery voltage is present, go to next step. If battery voltage is not present, check Black/White wire for an open circuit.

3) Using a voltmeter, measure voltage between connector terminals "C" (Pink/Black wire) and "F" (Purple wire). If battery voltage is present, check Purple wire for a short to ground. If wire is okay, go to next step. If battery voltage is not present, check Purple wire for an open circuit or short to battery. If wire is okay, go to next step.

4) Connect a fused jumper wire between fuel tank sending unit connector terminals "C" (Pink/Black wire) and "F" (Purple wire). Enter diagnostics, and select BCM data test BD40.

5) To enter BCM diagnosis, turn ignition switch to ON position. Simultaneously depress OFF and WARM buttons on CCDIC.

6) Continue to depress OFF and WARM buttons until all segments and bulbs of instrument cluster and CCDIC illuminate. When all segments are lit, system has entered self-diagnostic mode. Release OFF and WARM buttons. Trouble code display can be by-passed at any time by depressing FAN DOWN button.

7) After trouble codes have been by-passed, SERVICE MODE system can be directed to perform specific system diagnostic tests. Display desired system (BCM) by depressing FAN DOWN button. Select desired system (BCM) by depressing FAN UP button.

8) After diagnostic system has been selected for testing, select DATA? test. To advance display, depress FAN DOWN button. When desired test type is displayed (BD40), depress FAN UP button. After test type selection, depress FAN DOWN or FAN UP button as necessary to access appropriate test.

9) If BCM displays approximately 25 and fuel display indicates a full tank, replace fuel tank sending unit. If BCM does not display correctly and fuel display does not indicate a full tank, check Purple wire for a short to ground. If Purple wire is okay, replace BCM.

OIL PRESSURE SWITCH TEST

1) Ensure oil pressure and level are correct. If oil pressure and level are okay, disconnect oil pressure switch. Turn ignition switch to RUN position, and observe STOP ENGINE OIL warning indicator light. If STOP ENGINE OIL warning indicator light is not illuminated, replace oil pressure switch.

2) If STOP ENGINE OIL warning indicator light is illuminated, check Tan wire and flexible circuit for a short to ground. If the flexible circuit is okay, replace instrument cluster.

ENGINE METAL TEMPERATURE INDICATOR TESTS

Switch Test – 1) Remove engine metal temperature switch connector. Turn ignition switch to RUN position, and observe STOP ENGINE TEMPERATURE warning indicator light.

2) If warning indicator light is not illuminated, replace engine metal temperature switch. If warning indicator light is illuminated, check Light Green wire and flexible circuit for a short to ground.

3) If wiring is okay, check for a shorted chime module diode. Chime module is located behind right side of instrument panel, above glove box. If chime module diode is okay, replace instrument cluster.

Open Wire Test – 1) Remove engine metal temperature switch connector. Connect a jumper wire between terminal "A" (Light Green wire) and ground. Turn ignition switch to RUN position, and observe STOP ENGINE TEMPERATURE warning indicator light.

2) If warning indicator light is illuminated, replace engine metal temperature switch. If warning indicator light is not illuminated, check Light Green wire and flexible circuit for an open circuit. If Light Green wire and flexible circuit are okay, use a voltmeter to check for battery voltage at right instrument panel connector terminal No. 7 (flexible circuit). *See Fig. 2.* If voltage is okay, replace instrument cluster.

TESTING CONDITIONS

- Ignition switch in RUN position except for resistance measurements.

- Make all resistance measurements with the negative battery cable disconnected.

- Measure to ground unless another terminal is given.

- Connectors as seen from the driver's seat with the digital cluster removed.

- If turn indicators do not operate correctly and correct voltage is found at terminals LT8 and LT9 (left connector), replace instrument cluster.

- If correct voltage or resistance is not found at a terminal, check related wires and components for shorts or open circuits.

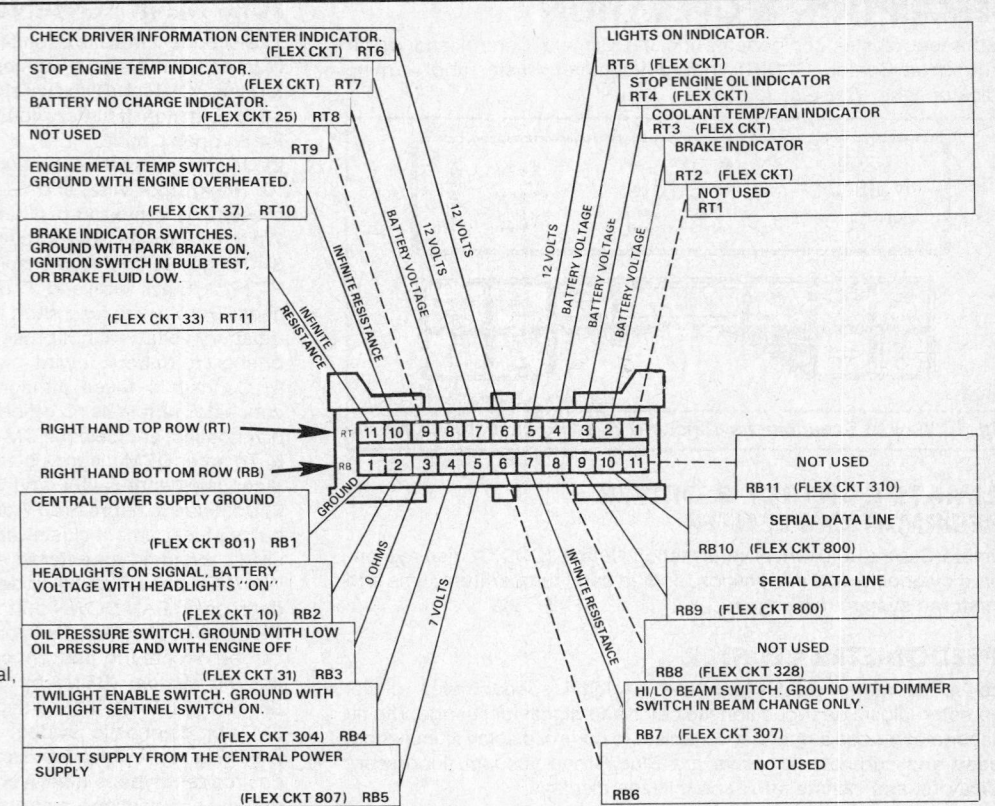

RIGHT INSTRUMENT CLUSTER CONNECTOR

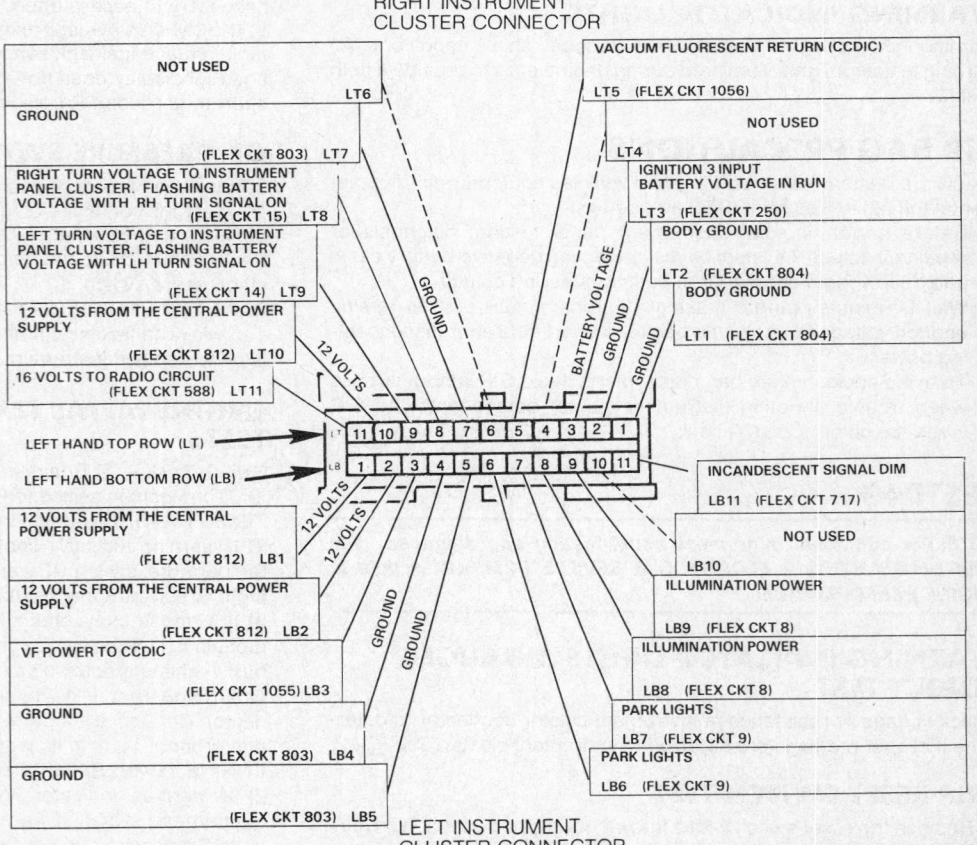

LEFT INSTRUMENT CLUSTER CONNECTOR

Courtesy of General Motors Corp.

91B08704   91E08705

Fig. 2: Testing Instrument Cluster Pinout – Left & Right Connectors

WARNING LIGHTS & ALARM CHIME TESTS

Chime Module Test – 1) Disconnect electrical connector at chime module located behind right side of instrument panel, behind glove box. Using a voltmeter, check for battery voltage between connector terminal "A" (Orange wire) and ground. If battery voltage is present, go to next step. If battery voltage is not present, repair open circuit in Orange wire.

2) Check for battery voltage between connector terminals "A" (Orange wire) and "B" (Black wire). If battery voltage is not present, repair open circuit in Black wire. If battery voltage is present, replace the chime module.

Key In Ignition Input Test – 1) Disconnect electrical connector at chime module located behind right side of instrument panel, behind glove box. Put ignition key in ignition switch. Leave ignition switch in LOCK position, and open driver's door. Using a voltmeter, check for battery voltage between connector terminals "A" (Orange wire) and "F" (Light Green wire).

2) If battery voltage is not present, check ignition key warning switch and driver's door jamb switch wiring for open circuit. If battery voltage is present, go to next step.

3) Remove key from ignition switch, and leave driver's door open. Using a voltmeter, check for battery voltage between connector terminals "A" (Orange wire) and "F" (Light Green wire). If voltage reading is zero, go to next step. If voltage is present, check Light Green wire for short to ground. Check ignition key warning switch. Warning switch should be open when key is removed.

4) With key in ignition and all doors closed, use voltmeter to check for battery voltage between connector terminals "A" (Orange wire) and "F" (Light Green wire). If voltage reading is zero, replace chime module. If voltage is present, check door jam switch and wiring for short to ground. Check door jamb switch. Switch should be open with doors closed.

Fasten Seat Belt Input Test – 1) Disconnect electrical connector at chime module located behind right side of instrument panel, behind glove box. Turn ignition switch to RUN position, and leave seat belt unbuckled. Using a voltmeter, check for battery voltage between connector terminal "D" (Pink/Black wire) and ground. If battery voltage is present, go to next step. If battery voltage is not present, repair open circuit in Pink/Black wire.

2) Check for battery voltage between connector terminals "D" (Pink/Black wire) and "H" (Black wire). If battery voltage is present, go to next step. If battery voltage is not present, check seat belt switch and Black wire for an open circuit.

3) Buckle left seat belt, and leave ignition switch in RUN position. Check for battery voltage between connector terminals "D" (Pink/Black wire) and "H" (Black wire). If voltage reading is zero, replace chime module. If voltage is present, check Black wire for short to ground. If wire is okay, replace seat belt switch.

Fasten Seat Belts Warning Indicator Light Test – 1) Disconnect electrical connector at chime module located behind right side of instrument panel, behind glove box. Turn ignition switch to OFF position. Connect a fused jumper wire between connector terminals "A" (Orange wire) and "C" (Yellow wire).

2) If indicator illuminates, go to next step. If indicator does not illuminate, check indicator bulb, Yellow wire, flexible circuit and connector for an open circuit.

3) Remove jumper wire. If indicator does not illuminate, replace chime module. If indicator illuminates, check CCDIC, Yellow wire and flexible circuit for a short to battery.

Stop Engine Temperature Warning Indicator Light Test – 1) Disconnect engine metal temperature switch electrical connector located at rear of cylinder head on firewall side. Turn ignition switch to RUN position. Connect a fused jumper wire between connector terminal "A" (Light Green wire) and ground. If STOP ENGINE TEMP indicator illuminates and alarm chime sounds, replace engine metal temperature switch.

2) If indicator light does not come on, check bulb, Light Green wire and flexible circuit for an open circuit. If alarm does not sound, check Light Green wire and chime module diode for an open circuit. Chime module is located behind right side of instrument panel, behind glove box.

HEADLIGHT SWITCH CHECK

Constant battery voltage should be present at headlight switch terminals BC3 and BC4 (flexible circuit). With headlights on, battery voltage should also be present at headlight switch terminals BC7, BC8 and BC9 (flexible circuit). If battery voltage is not present, check switch and wiring.

REMOVAL & INSTALLATION

INSTRUMENT CLUSTER

Removal & Installation – 1) Remove left A/C vent and radio trim plate by carefully pulling on vent and trim plate. See Fig. 3. Remove 7 instrument cluster trim plate attaching screws. Remove trim plate.

2) Remove 4 instrument cluster filter lens screws, and remove filter lens. Remove 2 screws and warning light lens. Remove trip reset switch.

3) Remove 2 screws retaining instrument cluster. Pull cluster out from electrical connectors. Use pliers to hold retaining tabs at each end of cluster board. To install, reverse removal procedure. Ensure electrical connectors are aligned with instrument cluster.

CLIMATE CONTROL & DRIVER INFORMATION CENTER

Removal & Installation – Remove 2 upper screws on center trim plate. Remove trim plate. Remove 3 CCDIC attaching screws. Pull CCDIC out of dash, and disconnect electrical connectors. To install, reverse removal procedure.

HEADLIGHT SWITCH

Removal & Installation – Remove 2 screws from left trim plate and air vent. Remove trim plate and headlight switch screws. Disconnect wiring, and remove switch. To install, reverse removal procedure.

WIRING DIAGRAMS

See appropriate chassis wiring diagram in WIRING DIAGRAMS.

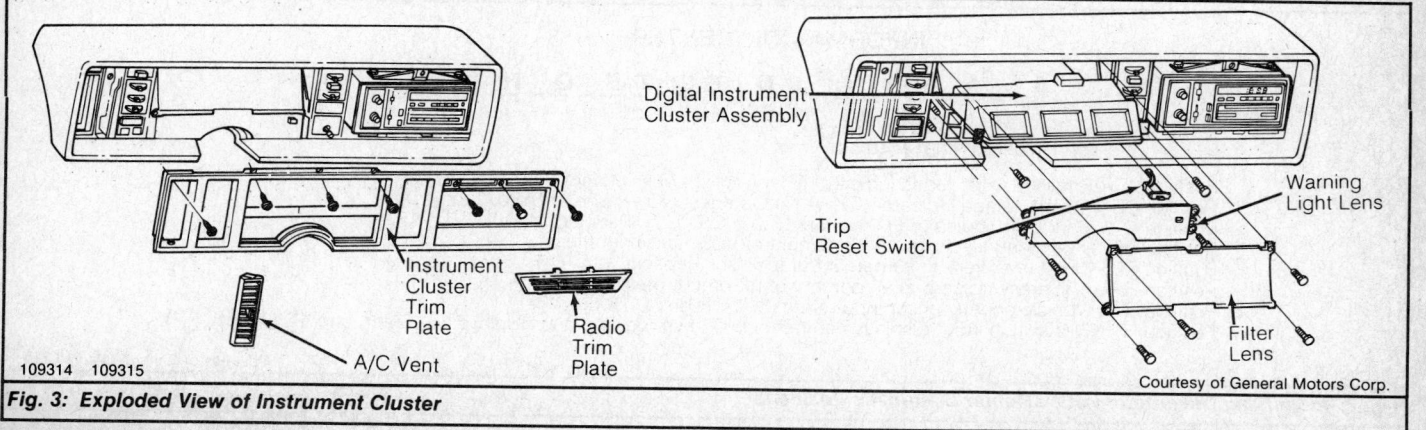

109314 109315

Fig. 3: Exploded View of Instrument Cluster

Digital Instrument Cluster Assembly

Warning Light Lens

Trip Reset Switch

Filter Lens

Instrument Cluster Trim Plate

Radio Trim Plate

A/C Vent

Courtesy of General Motors Corp.

1991 SAFETY EQUIPMENT
Electronic Instrument Panels – Ninety-Eight

DESCRIPTION & OPERATION

The Instrument Panel Cluster (IPC) provides digital displays for speedometer and odometer. Bar graph displays are used for engine coolant temperature and fuel display. *See Fig. 1.* Electronically operated indicators are used for warning lights, turn signals, headlight high beams and shift indicator display. The odometer and speedometer can display English or metric units. The Driver Information Center (DIC) provides travel, driver, and self-diagnostic information.

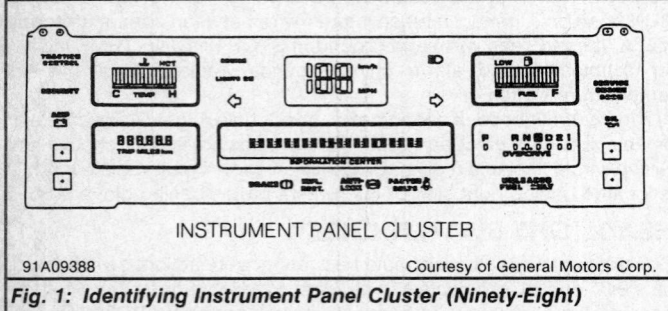

INSTRUMENT PANEL CLUSTER

91A09388   Courtesy of General Motors Corp.

Fig. 1: Identifying Instrument Panel Cluster (Ninety-Eight)

AIR BAG PRECAUTIONS

The following precautions should be taken when working with vehicles equipped with Supplemental Inflatable Restraint (SIR) air bag systems:

- Before performing any instrument panel testing, diagnosis or repair, disable SIR system by disconnecting negative battery cable and Yellow 2-pin connector at base of steering column.
- Wait 20 minutes before making SIR repairs. SIR system retains enough voltage to deploy air bag for a short time after disconnecting power.
- To avoid accidental air bag deployment, avoid the SRS wiring harness when trouble shooting instrument panel components. All SIR wires are color-coded Yellow.

TESTING

NOTE: For additional instrument panel testing and diagnosis, see SELF-DIAGNOSTICS – ECM/BCM EXCEPT CADILLAC article.

ENTERING DIC ON-BOARD DIAGNOSIS

The following procedure must be performed before the DIC on-board diagnosis can be used. To enter self-diagnostic mode, do the following:

- Turn ignition switch to RUN position and press DEST key.
- Press RESET key.
- Press 8192 (ETA, ECON, E/T, FUEL).
- Press ENTER.

The DIC display will now be in the diagnostic mode. Determine which display position to use when performing diagnostic tests. *See Fig. 2.*

INDICATORS & GAUGES PINOUT TEST

Check voltage or resistance at instrument cluster connector to determine if proper readings are supplied to the instrument cluster. *See Figs. 3 and 4.*

FUEL GAUGE TEST

1) Put ignition switch in RUN position. If DIC displays FUEL SENDER PROB, go to next step. If FUEL SENDER PROB is not displayed, go to step **5)**.

2) Disconnect fuel tank unit connector. Using a jumper wire, connect harness half of connector terminal "B" (Purple wire) to ground. Cycle ignition from OFF to RUN position.

3) If fuel gauge indicates empty, check Black/White wire at fuel tank unit for an open. If wire is okay, replace fuel tank unit.

4) If fuel gauge did not indicate empty, check Purple wire for an open circuit. If wire is okay, replace instrument cluster.

5) Enter DIC diagnostic mode. See ENTERING DIC ON-BOARD DIAGNOSIS in this article. Check position "EE" to determine whether percentage displayed agrees with fuel gauge. If percentage displayed does not agree with fuel gauge, replace instrument cluster.

6) If percentage displayed agrees with fuel gauge, disconnect fuel tank unit connector. Connect 2 Red leads from Tester (J-33431) to Purple wire and Black/White wire. Set tester resistance dials to zero ohms (empty), then to 90 ohms (full).

7) If DIC position "EE" displays "00" at zero ohms and "99" at 90 ohms, replace fuel tank unit sender. If DIC does not display as indicated, check Purple wire for a short to ground and high resistance (2 ohms or more). Check Black/White wire for high resistance (2 ohms or more). If wires are okay, replace instrument cluster.

OIL PRESSURE GAUGE TEST

1) Put ignition switch in RUN position. If DIC displays OIL PRESSURE SENDER PROB, go to next step. If OIL PRESSURE SENDER PROB is not displayed, go to step **4)**.

2) Disconnect oil pressure sender/switch connector. Using a jumper wire, connect terminal "A" to ground. Press GAGE button to display oil pressure on DIC.

3) If oil pressure display indicates zero psi, check Black wire for an open circuit. If Black wire is okay, replace oil pressure sender/switch. If oil pressure display does not indicate zero psi, check Tan wire for an open circuit. If Tan wire is okay, replace instrument cluster.

4) Start engine. Press GAGE button on DIC until DIC display shows oil pressure. If DIC display does not agree with oil pressure display, replace instrument cluster.

5) If DIC display agrees with oil pressure, disconnect oil pressure sender/switch connector. Connect 2 Red leads of Tester (J-33431) at terminals "A" (Tan wire) and "B" (Black wire). Set tester resistance dials to zero ohms, then to 86 ohms.

6) If oil pressure display shows zero psi at zero ohms and 120 psi at 86 ohms, replace oil pressure sender/switch. If oil pressure display does not show as indicated, check Tan wire for a short to ground or

---

INFORMATION CENTER

_ A _ BB _ C _ DD _ EE _ FF _ G _ H

↑
POSITION A

Position A – English/Metric mode indicator (E = English, M = Metric).
Position BB – Light outage indicator (OK = No Outages, NO = One or More Outages).
Position C – Park Light Indicator ("H" = Park Lights On, "L" = Park Lights Off).
Position DD – Dimming level zero to 99 percent of maximum brightness.
Position EE – Fuel level zero to 99 percent of fuel tank capacity.
Position FF – Oil pressure zero to 99 percent of maximum pressure.
Position G – Vehicle speed sensor input state ("H" = High, "L" = Low).
Position H – DIC switch input displays number of DIC keys pressed and displays "E" (Enter) and "R" (Reset).

91C09389   Courtesy of General Motors Corp.

Fig. 2: Identifying Driver Information Center Diagnostic Positions

high resistance (2 ohms or more) and Black wire for high resistance (2 ohms or more). If wires are okay, replace instrument cluster.

DIC OIL LEVEL MESSAGE DISPLAYED WITH OIL LEVEL OKAY

1) Disconnect oil level module connector located behind right side of instrument panel, to left of Powertrain Control Module (PCM). Start engine. If DIC CHECK OIL LEVEL message is displayed, check oil level module connector Brown/White wire for a short to ground.
2) If message is not displayed, turn ignition switch to LOCK position. Using a DVOM, measure resistance between terminals No. 3 (Gray wire) and 2 (Red/White wire). If resistance is not approximately 220 ohms, check Gray wire and Red/White wire for an open circuit. If wires are okay, replace low oil level sensor.
3) If resistance is approximately 220 ohms, set DVOM to diode check. Measure between terminals No. 1 (Orange/Black wire) and 2 (Red/White wire). If DVOM indicates an open circuit with meter probes reversed, check Orange/Black wire for an open circuit. If wires are okay, replace low oil level sensor.
4) If DVOM indicates continuity in one direction and an open circuit with meter probes reversed, measure resistance to ground at terminals No. 3 (Gray wire), 2 (Red/White wire) and 1 (Orange/Black wire).
5) If any wires have continuity to ground, check wire(s) for a short to ground. If no wires have continuity to ground, replace oil level module.

DIC CHECK OIL LEVEL MESSAGE IS NOT DISPLAYED WITH OIL LEVEL LOW

1) Disconnect oil level module connector located behind right side of instrument panel, to left of Powertrain Control Module (PCM). Turn ignition switch to RUN position. Measure voltage between connector terminal No. 10 (Orange wire) and ground. If battery voltage is present, go to next step. If battery voltage is not present, check Orange wire for an open circuit.
2) Measure voltage between terminal No. 9 (Pink/Black wire) and ground. If battery voltage is present, go to next step. If battery voltage is not present, check Pink/Black wire for an open.
3) Measure voltage between terminal No. 6 (Brown/White wire) and ground. If battery voltage is present, go to next step. If battery voltage is not present, check Brown/White wire for an open circuit. If wire is okay, replace instrument cluster.
4) Measure voltage between terminals No. 6 (Brown/White wire) and No. 5 (Black wire). If battery voltage is present, replace oil level module. If battery voltage is not present, check Pink wire for an open circuit.

COOLANT TEMPERATURE GAUGE TEST

1) Disconnect coolant sensor connector located on top left side of engine. Connect one Red clip of Tester (J-33431) to terminal "B" (Yellow wire) and other clip to terminal "A" (Black wire).
2) Adjust resistance dials of tester to 1365 ohms and then to 44 ohms. Coolant temperature gauge should indicate cold, then hot.
3) If gauge operates correctly, wiring and gauge are okay. Replace coolant sensor. If gauge does not operate correctly, check gauge connections and Yellow, Black and Dark Green wires for an open circuit,

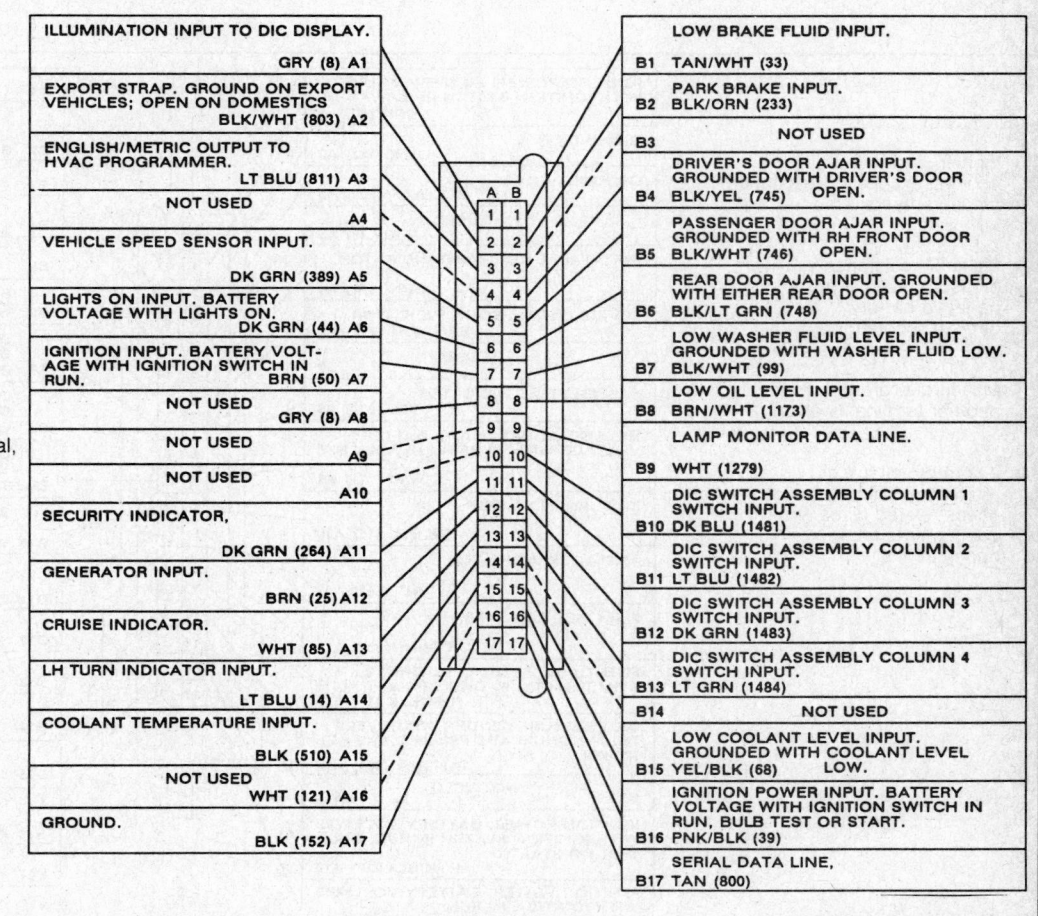

CONNECTOR C1 TEST

TESTING CONDITIONS

- Ignition switch in RUN position except for resistance measurements.

- Make all resistance measurements with the negative battery cable disconnected.

- Measure to ground unless another terminal is given.

- If correct voltage or resistance is not found at a terminal, check related wires and components for shorts or open circuits.

ILLUMINATION INPUT TO DIC DISPLAY. GRY (8) A1	LOW BRAKE FLUID INPUT. B1 TAN/WHT (33)
EXPORT STRAP. GROUND ON EXPORT VEHICLES; OPEN ON DOMESTICS BLK/WHT (803) A2	PARK BRAKE INPUT. B2 BLK/ORN (233)
ENGLISH/METRIC OUTPUT TO HVAC PROGRAMMER. LT BLU (811) A3	B3 NOT USED
NOT USED A4	DRIVER'S DOOR AJAR INPUT. GROUNDED WITH DRIVER'S DOOR OPEN. B4 BLK/YEL (745)
VEHICLE SPEED SENSOR INPUT. DK GRN (389) A5	PASSENGER DOOR AJAR INPUT. GROUNDED WITH RH FRONT DOOR OPEN. B5 BLK/WHT (746)
LIGHTS ON INPUT. BATTERY VOLTAGE WITH LIGHTS ON. DK GRN (44) A6	REAR DOOR AJAR INPUT. GROUNDED WITH EITHER REAR DOOR OPEN. B6 BLK/LT GRN (748)
IGNITION INPUT. BATTERY VOLTAGE WITH IGNITION SWITCH IN RUN. BRN (50) A7	LOW WASHER FLUID LEVEL INPUT. GROUNDED WITH WASHER FLUID LOW. B7 BLK/WHT (99)
NOT USED GRY (8) A8	LOW OIL LEVEL INPUT. B8 BRN/WHT (1173)
NOT USED A9	LAMP MONITOR DATA LINE. B9 WHT (1279)
NOT USED A10	DIC SWITCH ASSEMBLY COLUMN 1 SWITCH INPUT. B10 DK BLU (1481)
SECURITY INDICATOR. DK GRN (264) A11	DIC SWITCH ASSEMBLY COLUMN 2 SWITCH INPUT. B11 LT BLU (1482)
GENERATOR INPUT. BRN (25) A12	DIC SWITCH ASSEMBLY COLUMN 3 SWITCH INPUT. B12 DK GRN (1483)
CRUISE INDICATOR. WHT (85) A13	DIC SWITCH ASSEMBLY COLUMN 4 SWITCH INPUT. B13 LT GRN (1484)
LH TURN INDICATOR INPUT. LT BLU (14) A14	B14 NOT USED
COOLANT TEMPERATURE INPUT. BLK (510) A15	LOW COOLANT LEVEL INPUT. GROUNDED WITH COOLANT LEVEL LOW. B15 YEL/BLK (68)
NOT USED WHT (121) A16	IGNITION POWER INPUT. BATTERY VOLTAGE WITH IGNITION SWITCH IN RUN, BULB TEST OR START. B16 PNK/BLK (39)
GROUND. BLK (152) A17	SERIAL DATA LINE. B17 TAN (800)

Courtesy of General Motors Corp.

Fig. 3: Identifying Instrument Cluster Pinout Test (Connector C1)

high resistance (2 or more ohms), or a short to ground. If all wires are okay, replace instrument cluster.

LOW COOLANT LEVEL INPUT TEST

1) Disconnect low coolant module connector located in front of engine compartment, lower right rear of radiator. Using a jumper wire, connect terminal "B" (Yellow/Black wire) to ground. Start engine and check DIC display.

2) If COOLANT LEVEL LOW is not displayed, check Yellow/Black wire for an open circuit. If wire is okay, replace instrument cluster.

3) If COOLANT LEVEL LOW is displayed, turn ignition switch to RUN position (engine off). Connect a test light between terminal "C" (Pink/Black wire) and ground. If test light illuminates, go to next step. If test light does not illuminate, check Pink/Black wire for an open circuit.

4) Connect test light between terminals "C" (Pink/Black wire) and "A" (Black wire). If test light illuminates. replace low coolant module. If test light does not illuminate, check Black wire for an open circuit.

CLUSTER DISPLAY DOES NOT DIM OR GOES BLANK WITH HEAD/PARK LIGHT SWITCH IN HEAD OR PARK POSITION

1) Disconnect instrument cluster connector C1, located on rear of cluster. Position head/park light switch in PARK or HEAD position. Put dimmer control in "LO" position.

2) Using a voltmeter, measure voltage at connector C1, terminal A6 (Dark Green wire). If battery voltage is not present, repair or replace the Dark Green wire as necessary.

3) If battery voltage is present, measure voltage at connector C1, terminal A1 (Gray wire) while adjusting dimmer control. If voltage varies

with dimmer control, replace instrument cluster. If voltage does not vary, check Gray wire for an open or short to ground. If wire is okay, replace head/park light switch.

LEFT FRONT DOOR AJAR INPUT TEST

1) Disconnect left front door lock assembly connector. Turn ignition switch to RUN position. Using a voltmeter, measure voltage between terminal "B" (Black/Yellow wire) and ground. If battery voltage is present, go to next step. If battery voltage is not present, check Black/Yellow wire for an open or short to ground. If wire is okay, replace instrument cluster.

2) Measure voltage between terminals "B" (Black/Yellow wire) and "D" (Black wire). If battery voltage is present, check left front door lock assembly switch. If switch is okay, replace instrument cluster. If battery voltage is not present, check Black wire for an open circuit.

RIGHT FRONT DOOR AJAR INPUT TEST

1) Disconnect right front door lock assembly connector. Turn ignition switch to RUN position. Using a voltmeter, measure voltage between terminal "C" (Black/White wire) and ground. If battery voltage is present, go to next step. If battery voltage is not present, check Black/White wire for an open or short to ground. If wire is okay, replace instrument cluster.

2) Measure voltage between terminals "C" (Black/White wire) and "A" (Black wire). If battery voltage is present, check right front door lock assembly switch. If switch is okay, replace instrument cluster. If battery voltage is not present, check Black wire for an open circuit.

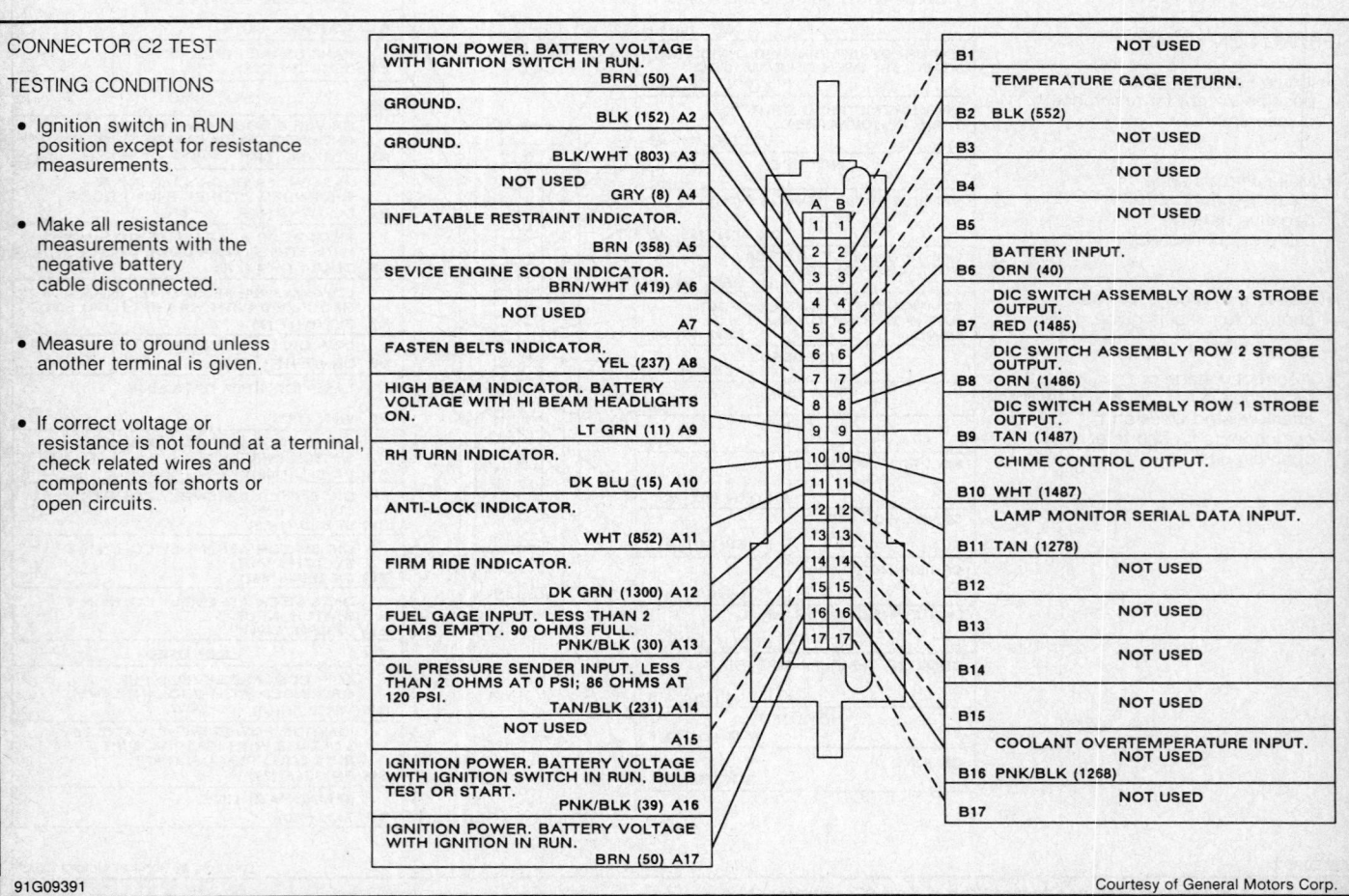

CONNECTOR C2 TEST

TESTING CONDITIONS

- Ignition switch in RUN position except for resistance measurements.

- Make all resistance measurements with the negative battery cable disconnected.

- Measure to ground unless another terminal is given.

- If correct voltage or resistance is not found at a terminal, check related wires and components for shorts or open circuits.

Terminal	Description
A1	IGNITION POWER. BATTERY VOLTAGE WITH IGNITION SWITCH IN RUN. BRN (50)
A2	GROUND. BLK (152)
A3	GROUND. BLK/WHT (803)
A4	NOT USED GRY (8)
A5	INFLATABLE RESTRAINT INDICATOR. BRN (358)
A6	SEVICE ENGINE SOON INDICATOR. BRN/WHT (419)
A7	NOT USED
A8	FASTEN BELTS INDICATOR. YEL (237)
A9	HIGH BEAM INDICATOR. BATTERY VOLTAGE WITH HI BEAM HEADLIGHTS ON. LT GRN (11)
A10	RH TURN INDICATOR. DK BLU (15)
A11	ANTI-LOCK INDICATOR. WHT (852)
A12	FIRM RIDE INDICATOR. DK GRN (1300)
A13	FUEL GAGE INPUT. LESS THAN 2 OHMS EMPTY. 90 OHMS FULL. PNK/BLK (30)
A14	OIL PRESSURE SENDER INPUT. LESS THAN 2 OHMS AT 0 PSI; 86 OHMS AT 120 PSI. TAN/BLK (231)
A15	NOT USED
A16	IGNITION POWER. BATTERY VOLTAGE WITH IGNITION SWITCH IN RUN, BULB TEST OR START. PNK/BLK (39)
A17	IGNITION POWER. BATTERY VOLTAGE WITH IGNITION IN RUN. BRN (50)

Terminal	Description
B1	NOT USED
B2	TEMPERATURE GAGE RETURN. BLK (552)
B3	NOT USED
B4	NOT USED
B5	NOT USED
B6	BATTERY INPUT. ORN (40)
B7	DIC SWITCH ASSEMBLY ROW 3 STROBE OUTPUT. RED (1485)
B8	DIC SWITCH ASSEMBLY ROW 2 STROBE OUTPUT. ORN (1486)
B9	DIC SWITCH ASSEMBLY ROW 1 STROBE OUTPUT. TAN (1487)
B10	CHIME CONTROL OUTPUT. WHT (1487)
B11	LAMP MONITOR SERIAL DATA INPUT. TAN (1278)
B12	NOT USED
B13	NOT USED
B14	NOT USED
B15	NOT USED
B16	COOLANT OVERTEMPERATURE INPUT. NOT USED PNK/BLK (1268)
B17	NOT USED

91G09391

Courtesy of General Motors Corp.

Fig. 4: Identifying Instrument Cluster Pinout Test (Connector C2)

REAR DOOR AJAR INPUT TEST

1) If REAR DOOR AJAR message does not appear with both doors open. check Black/Light Green wire for an open circuit. If wire is okay, replace instrument cluster.

2) If REAR DOOR AJAR message does not appear with one door only, check door latch assembly switch and wiring for an open circuit.

3) If REAR DOOR AJAR message is displayed with both rear doors closed, check Black/Light Green, Black/Yellow and Light Blue wires, and left and right rear door latch assembly switches for a short to ground. If no short to ground is found, replace instrument cluster.

WASHER FLUID LEVEL SWITCH TEST

1) Disconnect washer fluid level switch connector located near fluid reservoir. Turn ignition switch to RUN position. Using a voltmeter, measure voltage between terminal "B" (Black/White wire) and ground. If battery voltage is present, go to next step. If battery voltage is not present, check Black/White wire for an open or short to ground. If wire is okay, replace instrument panel cluster.

2) Measure voltage between terminals "B" (Black/White wire) and "A" (Black wire). If battery voltage is present, check washer fluid level switch. If switch is okay, replace instrument cluster. If battery voltage is not present, check Black wire for an open circuit.

ENGLISH/METRIC SWITCH OUTPUT TEST

1) Disconnect instrument cluster connector C1. Put ignition switch in RUN position. Turn on air conditioning and check temperature display.

2) If temperature is in degrees Celsius, check Light Blue wire for a short to ground. In addition, ensure the export ground (Black wire) has not been included at terminal C6 of Heating, Ventilation and Air Conditioning (HVAC) programmer behind center of instrument panel, to right of plenum. If Black wire is present it should be cut off.

3) If temperature is in degrees Fahrenheit, turn ignition switch to RUN position. Connect a fused jumper wire between instrument cluster connector C1 terminal A3 and ground. Check HVAC display.

4) If temperature is displayed in degrees Celsius, replace instrument cluster. If temperature is not displayed in degrees Celsius, check Light Blue wire for an open. If light blue wire is okay, replace HVAC programmer.

HEADLIGHT SWITCH TEST

Battery voltage should be present at headlight switch terminal "C". With headlights on, battery voltage should be present at headlight switch terminal "D" (Yellow wire). If voltage is not as indicated, check switch and related wiring.

WIPER SWITCH TEST

For testing information on wipers, see appropriate WIPER/WASHER SYSTEMS article in SAFETY EQUIPMENT.

REMOVAL & INSTALLATION

INSTRUMENT CLUSTER

Removal & Installation – 1) Remove instrument panel cluster trim plate-to-instrument panel screws. Tilt trim plate rearward. Unplug electrical connectors and remove trim plate. See Fig. 5..

2) Remove instrument cluster-to-instrument panel screws. Pull cluster rearward. Unplug cluster connector. Remove PRNDL cable and cluster assembly. See Fig. 6. To install, reverse removal procedure.

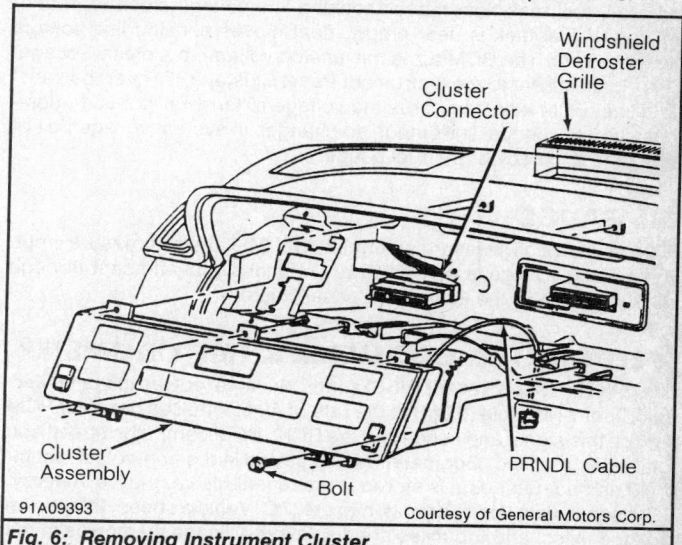

Fig. 6: Removing Instrument Cluster

Courtesy of General Motors Corp.

WIRING DIAGRAMS

See appropriate chassis wiring diagram in WIRING DIAGRAMS.

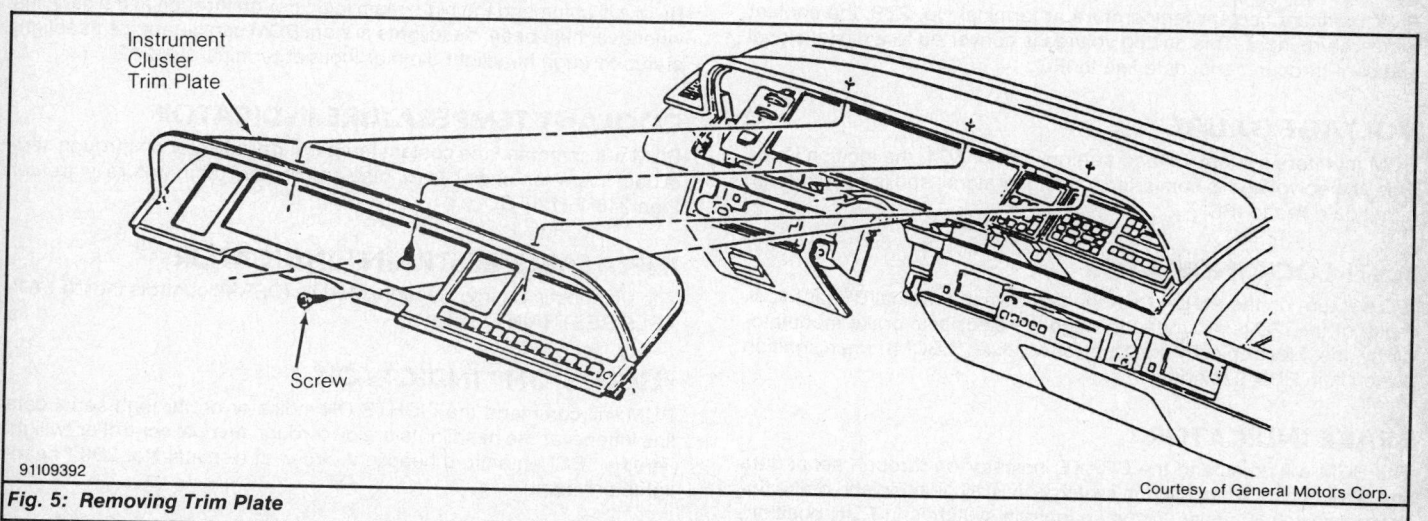

Fig. 5: Removing Trim Plate

Courtesy of General Motors Corp.

DESCRIPTION & OPERATION

The instrument cluster uses a vacuum florescent digital display for the speedometer and odometers. All gauges and indicators are shown by vacuum florescent bar graphs or displays. All functions within the cluster are controlled by a solid-state microprocessor.

The digital clusters used in these vehicles are interchangeable. If there is a malfunction in the cluster, the entire cluster must be replaced as a complete assembly.

FUEL GAUGE

Fuel gauge uses a 3-terminal fuel level sensor. One terminal is tied to ground, one terminal is tied to ignition voltage and third terminal is a sensing line, which is tied to Body Computer Module (BCM). With fuel tank full, fuel tank float moves sensing line voltage close to battery voltage. If fuel tank is near empty, float moves sensing line voltage closer to zero. The BCM turns this analog voltage to a digital voltage. This signal is sent to the Instrument Panel Cluster (IPC) over the serial data line. BCM also compares the voltage at terminal No. 3C11 (ignition 1 input) with fuel level input, so changes in system voltage do not affect the accuracy of the fuel gauge.

OIL GAUGE

BCM monitors oil pressure at terminal No. 3C3, the oil pressure input. This analog voltage is converted to a digital signal and sent through serial data line to the instrument panel cluster.

SPEEDOMETER, ODOMETER & TRIP ODOMETER

The Vehicle Speed Sensor (VSS) sends electrical pulses to the Powertrain Control Module (PCM) at the rate of 40,000 pulses per mile. PCM buffers this signal and sends it to the BCM. BCM computes speed and total miles traveled. Odometer data is stored in the non-volatile memory. Trip odometer data is stored in the resettable keep-alive memory. BCM sends data line information to the IPC. Vehicle speed, total accumulated miles, and trip miles are displayed. Mileage memory is in the BCM.

TACHOMETER

IPC receives data from PCM and BCM serial data communications for tachometer information.

TEMPERATURE GAUGE

PCM monitors coolant temperature at terminal No. 2B9, the coolant temperature input. This analog voltage is converted to a digital signal and sent through serial data line to IPC.

VOLTAGE GAUGE

BCM monitors system voltage at terminal No. 3C4, the ignition input. This analog voltage is converted to a digital signal and is sent through serial data line to IPC.

ANTI-LOCK INDICATOR

IPC will turn on the ANTI-LOCK indicator when terminal BB (anti-lock input) of the IPC is grounded through the electronic brake modulator or by the Electronic Brake Control Module (EBCM) when ignition switch is in RUN position.

BRAKE INDICATOR

The BCM will command the BRAKE indicator on through serial data line. This occurs when ignition switch is in RUN position and brake fluid level switch is closed, or when ignition switch is in RUN position, transmission is not in Park or Neutral and parking brake is set.

CRUISE & RESUME INDICATORS

The cruise indicator is controlled by BCM through serial data line. BCM will command the CRUISE indicator on when vehicle is cruising at a set speed greater than 25 MPH.

The RESUME indicator is also controlled by the BCM through the serial data line. BCM will command the RESUME indicator on when the brake pedal is depressed in the cruise mode. This is a reminder to push the RESUME switch to enter cruise mode again.

PCM receives all inputs from cruise control system, and communicates them through serial data line to BCM. BCM then controls the indicators through serial data line.

DOOR AJAR INDICATOR

BCM will command the DOOR AJAR indicator on through the serial data line when engine is running, transmission is not in Park or Neutral and driver's or passenger's door is ajar.

ELECTRICAL PROBLEM INDICATOR

The IPC will turn on the ELECTRICAL PROBLEM indicator when a serial data line failure is detected by the IPC. BCM will also command the IPC to flash the ELECTRICAL PROBLEM indicator when Code B333 (Diagnostic Energy Reserve Module serial data failure) is detected, or Code B410 (alternator malfunction) is detected.

FASTEN BELTS INDICATOR

BCM will command the FASTEN BELTS indicator on through serial data line when ignition switch is turned to RUN for 4-8 seconds regardless of seat belt status.

HAZARD INDICATOR

IPC will flash the hazard indicator when hazard switch is turned on and flashing battery voltage is applied to right and left turn inputs (terminals BK and BJ) of IPC.

HEADLIGHTS SUGGESTED INDICATOR

BCM will command the HEADLIGHTS SUGGESTED indicator on through serial data line when ignition switch is in RUN position, twilight photocell senses darkness, headlights are off and vehicle is moving.

HIGH BEAM INDICATOR

BCM will command the high beam indicator on through serial data line whenever high beam headlights are on. BCM can determine headlight status through headlight dimmer input at terminal No. 2A2.

COOLANT TEMPERATURE INDICATOR

BCM will command the coolant temperature indicator on through serial data line when engine is running and coolant temperature is greater than 248°F (120°C).

INFLATABLE RESTRAINT INDICATOR

The Diagnostic Energy Reserve Module (DERM) controls the INFLATABLE RESTRAINT indicator.

"LIGHTS ON" INDICATOR

BCM will command the LIGHTS ON indicator on through serial data line whenever the headlights are on through manual control or twilight sentinel. BCM monitors headlight circuit at terminal No. 2B6 ("headlights on" input).

LOW FUEL INDICATOR

IPC will light the LOW FUEL indicator when fuel level drops below 3.8 gallons.

LOW OIL LEVEL INDICATOR

BCM will command the low oil level indicator on through serial data line when ignition is in RUN, BULB TEST or START position and oil level input is high.

LOW OIL PRESSURE INDICATOR

BCM monitors oil pressure at terminal 3C3 (oil pressure input). BCM will command the low oil pressure indicator on when oil pressure is less than 7 psi for 3 seconds and engine is running.

LOW VOLTAGE INDICATOR

When ignition switch is in RUN and engine is not running, the LOW indicator on volts gauge will light as a bulb check. BCM will command the indicator on through serial data line when Code B411 (battery voltage too low) is set.

SECURITY INDICATOR

IPC provides battery voltage to the security indicator. The pass key decoder module and theft deterrent module control the indicator by providing a ground.

SERVICE A/C INDICATOR

BCM will command the SERVICE A/C indicator on through serial data line when a failure has been detected in the A/C system.

SERVICE ENGINE SOON INDICATOR

The SERVICE ENGINE SOON indicator warns that an engine problem needs service. With ignition switch in RUN position (engine not running), indicator will turn on as a bulb test. When engine is started, indicator should turn off. If PCM detects an engine problem, Brown/White wire to IPC is grounded and SERVICE ENGINE SOON light is illuminated. IPC provides battery voltage to the indicator and PCM controls indicator.

TURN INDICATORS

When turn signals are operated, flashing battery voltage is applied to left or right turn terminal. In response to voltage, IPC flashes corresponding turn indicator.

WASHER FLUID INDICATOR

BCM will command the WASHER FLUID indicator on through serial data line when ignition is in RUN position and washer fluid level switch input to BCM terminal is pulled to ground.

TESTING & DIAGNOSIS

NOTE: For additional instrument panel testing and diagnosis, see SELF-DIAGNOSTICS – REATTA & RIVIERA PCM/BCM article in ENGINE PERFORMANCE.

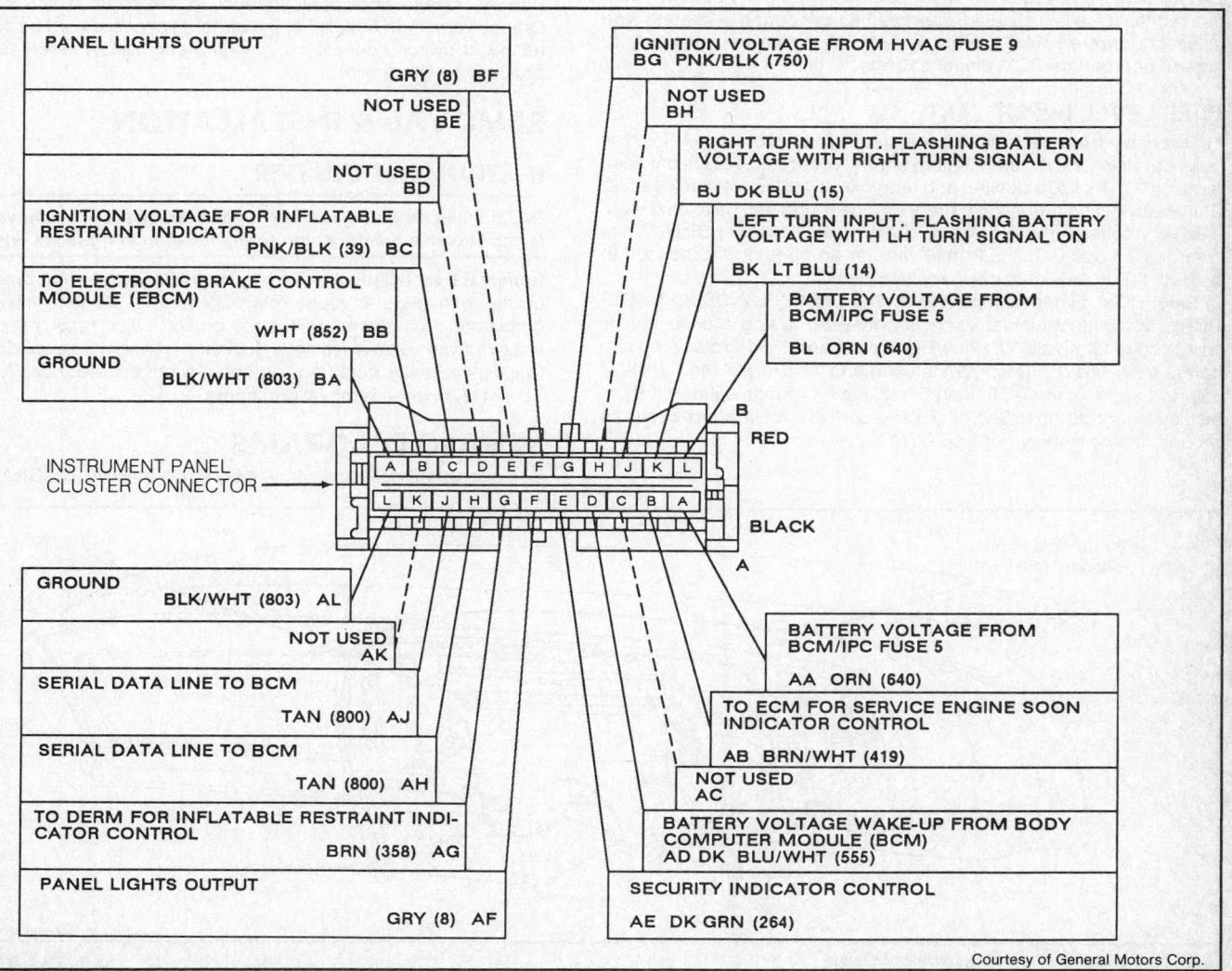

91B08681

Courtesy of General Motors Corp.

Fig. 1: Instrument Cluster Connector Pin Test

INSTRUMENT CLUSTER CONNECTOR PIN TEST

1) Remove instrument cluster. See INSTRUMENT CLUSTER under REMOVAL & INSTALLATION in this article. Place ignition switch in RUN position. *See Fig. 1.*
2) Make all measurements to ground unless a specific terminal number is given. If voltage is NOT correct at a terminal, check circuit for malfunction using appropriate test.
3) If correct voltage is found at terminals, and the function that uses those terminals is incorrect, check instrument cluster printed circuit and bulbs. If printed circuit and bulbs are okay, replace instrument cluster.

BCM DIAGNOSIS PROCEDURE

Entering BCM Diagnosis – 1) Turn ignition switch to ON position. Simultaneously depress OFF and WARM buttons on Electronic Climate Control Panel (ECCP).
2) Continue to depress OFF and WARM button until all segments and bulbs of the IPC, the Driver Information Center (DIC) and ECCP illuminate. When all segments are lit, system has entered self-diagnostic mode. Release OFF and WARM buttons. Trouble code display can be by-passed at any time by depressing FAN DOWN button on ECCP.
3) After trouble codes have been by-passed, the SERVICE MODE system can be directed to perform specific system diagnostic tests. Display the desired system (BCM) by depressing the FAN DOWN button. Select the desired system (BCM) by depressing the FAN UP button.
4) After diagnostic system has been selected for testing, select DATA? test. To advance display, depress FAN DOWN button. When desired test type is displayed, depress FAN UP button. After test type selection, depress FAN DOWN or FAN UP button as necessary to access appropriate BCM diagnostic test.

FUEL LEVEL INPUT TEST

1) Disconnect fuel tank unit connector. Turn ignition switch to RUN position. Using a voltmeter, ensure battery voltage is present between terminal "C" (Pink/Black wire) and terminals "E" (Black/White wire), "F" (Purple wire), and ground. If battery voltage is present, go to next step. If battery voltage is not present, check Pink/Black and Black/White wires for an open. Check Purple wire for an open or short circuit to battery. If Purple wire is okay, replace BCM.
2) Enter BCM diagnosis input BD40. See BCM DIAGNOSIS PROCEDURE. Disconnect fuel tank sender connector. Using a fused jumper wire, bridge terminals "C" (Pink/Black wire) and "F" (Purple wire), and bridge terminals "E" (Black/White wire) and "F" (Purple wire). If BCM displays approximately 25, then 0, replace fuel gauge sender. If BCM display is not as specified, check Purple wire for a short circuit to ground. If wire is okay, replace BCM.

HIGH BEAM INDICATOR TEST

1) Check high beam headlight operation. If high beams do not operate, headlight diagnosis is necessary. If high beams are okay, enter BCM diagnosis input BI79 and operate headlight dimmer switch. See BCM DIAGNOSIS PROCEDURE.
2) With headlight dimmer switch pulled toward steering wheel and held, display should indicate LO. With dimmer switch released, display should indicate HI.
3) If displays are correct and high beam indicator still does not operate, replace BCM. If the displays are incorrect, additional BCM diagnosis is necessary.

"LIGHTS ON" INDICATOR TEST

1) Check headlight operation. If headlights do not operate, headlight diagnosis is necessary. If headlights are okay, select BCM input BI78 and operate headlight switch. See BCM DIAGNOSIS PROCEDURE.
2) With headlight switch on, display should indicate HI. With headlight switch off, display should indicate LO.
3) If the displays are correct and the LIGHTS ON indicator still does not operate, replace BCM. If the display does not read HI with headlights on, check Yellow wire, left switch assembly and BCM terminal contact for an open. If items are okay, replace BCM.
4) If the display does not read LO with headlights off, check Yellow wire for a short to voltage. If Yellow wire is okay, replace BCM.

HEADLIGHT SWITCH TEST

Battery voltage should be present at headlight switch connector Orange wire. With headlights on, battery voltage should be present at headlight switch connector Light Blue and Yellow wires. Ground is provided by Black wire.

REMOVAL & INSTALLATION

INSTRUMENT CLUSTER

NOTE: When replacing instrument cluster, be sure to remove odometer non-volatile memory chip for installation in replacement cluster.

Removal & Installation – Turn ignition off. Remove instrument panel cluster trim plate 2 upper retaining screws, located in ventilation deflectors. Pull cluster trim plate out of lower retaining clips and remove from vehicle. Remove 4 cluster retaining screws. *See Fig. 2.* Pull cluster away from housing and disconnect electrical connector. To install, reverse removal procedure.

WIRING DIAGRAMS

See appropriate chassis wiring diagram in WIRING DIAGRAMS.

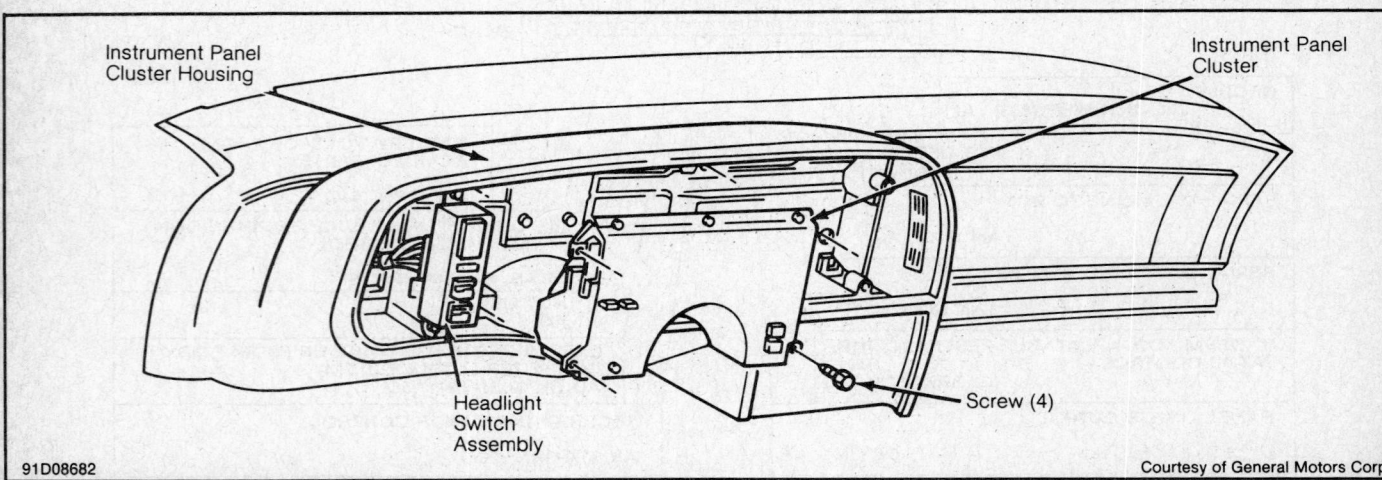

Instrument Panel Cluster Housing

Instrument Panel Cluster

Headlight Switch Assembly

Screw (4)

91D08682

Courtesy of General Motors Corp.

Fig. 2: Exploded View of Instrument Panel

DESCRIPTION

The electronic digital cluster uses a microcomputer to display data on instrument cluster. The warning indicators are on when ignition switch is in RUN, BULB TEST or START positions. They go out when engine starts.

With ignition switch in RUN, BULB TEST or START positions, the digital displays illuminate as a display test. The temperature and fuel display bar graph segments light sequentially from left to right. The display lasts less than 3 seconds.

The bar graphs then go off, from right to left, until current readings are displayed. The speedometer also displays current data. In operation, when the displays read at the extreme right or left side of their ranges, the underlined segments flash. The speedometer will flash at speeds greater than 85 MPH.

OPERATION

COOLANT TEMPERATURE DISPLAY

Coolant temperature display receives its signals through the instrument cluster, which is connected to coolant temperature sender. When engine is at 140°F (60°C), temperature sender resistance is 567 ohms and 2 light bars are illuminated. When engine reaches 260°F (127°C) resistance is 77 ohms and all 10 light bars will illuminate. Before 10th bar lights, coolant temperature indicator will light.

FUEL GAUGE DISPLAY

The resistance of fuel gauge sending unit changes with the amount of fuel in tank. With a full tank, the sending unit resistance is 90 ohms. With an empty tank, the sending unit resistance is less than one ohm. The instrument cluster electronics convert the analog signal from fuel gauge sender to a digital signal, which controls LCD fuel display. Changes in battery voltage do not affect fuel gauge reading.

INDICATORS

Low Coolant – Low coolant indicator warns driver of low coolant level in radiator. The ECM provides a switched path to ground.

Service Engine Soon – This indicator warns driver that a problem has occurred and vehicle should be serviced. The indicator receives battery voltage when ignition switch is in RUN, BULB TEST or START position. The ECM provides a switched path to ground.

OIL PRESSURE DISPLAY

The oil pressure display receives its signals through instrument cluster, which is connected to oil pressure sender. When engine oil is at 81 psi (5.7 kg/cm²), sender resistance is 90 ohms and all 10 light bars are illuminated. When bar graph changes from 3 to 2 segments, the oil pressure indicator lights.

PRNDL DISPLAY

Gear selection is shown by illumination of a rectangular box around appropriate letter. Indicator will not skip gear positions during gear selection but will light each box sequentially until selected gear position is shown.

SPEEDOMETER & ODOMETER DISPLAY

Vehicle Speed Sensor (VSS) generates a signal that is processed by ECM to supply inputs to cruise control module, speedometer and odometer. VSS is mounted in transaxle.

ECM takes voltage pulses from VSS and uses them to close a solid state output switch. Output terminal is switched to ground at a rate proportional to vehicle speed. The circuit board in cluster converts pulses received from ECM into a control signal for LCD displays.

TACHOMETER DISPLAY

Tachometer display contains both an analog and digital display. Digital display indicates 0 with engine off and ignition on. Digital display has a 10 RPM resolution below 1000 RPM and a 100 RPM resolution above 1000 RPM. First bar is always illuminated when cluster is on.

VOLTMETER DISPLAY

The instrument cluster receives battery voltage from incoming power leads. Instrument cluster converts this analog voltage to digital voltage where it is displayed. At 8 volts, first bar is illuminated. When 9th bar is turned on or 2nd bar is turned off, charge indicator will light.

AIR BAG PRECAUTIONS

Observe the following precautions when working with vehicles equipped with Supplemental Inflatable Restraint (SIR) air bag systems:

- Before performing any instrument panel testing, diagnosis or repair, disable SIR system by disconnecting negative battery cable and Yellow 2-pin connector at base of steering column.
- Wait at least 30 seconds after disconnecting battery. Some manufacturers recommend waiting up to 20 minutes before making SIR repairs. SIR system retains enough voltage to deploy air bag for a short time after disconnecting power.
- To avoid accidental air bag deployment, avoid SIR wiring harness when trouble shooting instrument panel components. All SIR wires are color-coded Yellow.

TESTING & DIAGNOSIS

NOTE: For complete diagnosis of instrument panel, a "Scan" tool (bidirectional) must be used.

FUEL GAUGE

Gauge Reads "E" – Disconnect Purple wire connector at fuel gauge sender. Turn ignition on. If fuel gauge indicates "F", replace fuel gauge sender. If gauge still indicates "E", check Purple wire for a short to ground. If Purple wire is okay, replace instrument cluster.

Gauge Reads "F" – 1) Disconnect Purple wire connector at fuel gauge sender. Connect a jumper wire between Purple wire connector from instrument panel and ground. Turn ignition on. If fuel gauge indicates "F", check Purple wire for an open and check instrument cluster connector terminals.

2) If fuel gauge indicates "E", check Black or Black/White wire for an open. If all wires are okay, replace fuel gauge sender.

Gauge Accuracy Test – 1) Disconnect Purple wire and Black wire connector at fuel gauge sender. Connect one lead of Tester (J-33431) to Purple wire. If tester is unavailable, go to step **4)**. Connect other lead of tester to Black/White wire connector.

2) Turn ignition on. Adjust resistance dial on tester to zero ohms. Fuel gauge should read "E". Adjust resistance dial on tester to 90 ohms. Fuel gauge should read "F". If fuel gauge responds correctly, replace fuel gauge sender. Gauge will not respond instantly due to anti-slosh device.

3) If fuel gauge does not respond correctly, check Purple and Black wires for high resistance. If wires are okay, replace instrument cluster. If vehicle is equipped with digital fuel gauge and does not respond properly, replace instrument cluster.

4) If Tester (J-33431) is unavailable, ensure electrical connections are clean and tight for fuel gauge sender circuit. Temporarily replace fuel gauge sender with a known good unit. Turn ignition off, and then turn ignition on. Move float to different positions. If fuel gauge responds correctly, replace fuel gauge sender. If fuel gauge does not respond correctly, replace instrument cluster. Reinstall original fuel gauge sender.

COOLANT TEMPERATURE INDICATOR

Engine Hot, No Indicator Light – Disconnect coolant temperature switch connector. Connect a jumper wire between Dark Green wire and ground. Turn ignition on and observe indicator. If indicator lights, replace coolant temperature switch. If indicator does not light, check Dark Green wire for an open.

Engine Normal, Indicator On – Disconnect coolant temperature switch connector. Turn ignition on and observe indicator. If indicator does not light, replace coolant temperature switch. If indicator is still on, check Dark Green wire for a short to ground. If wires are okay, replace ignition switch.

Ignition On/Engine Off, No Indicator Light – Disconnect ignition switch Dark Green wire connector. Connect a fused jumper wire between Dark Green wire and ground. Turn ignition on. If indicator lights, replace ignition switch. If indicator does not light, check Dark Green wire for an open.

LOW COOLANT INDICATOR

Short Test – 1) Disconnect ECM connector "A" (V6 VIN T early production only) or coolant level switch. Put ignition switch in RUN position.

2) If low coolant indicator illuminates, check Yellow/Black wire for a short to ground. If low coolant indicator does not illuminate, this condition is caused by the ECM (V6 VIN T early production only) or coolant level switch.

Does Not Light (V6 VIN T Early Production Only) – Turn ignition switch to RUN position. Using a voltmeter, measure voltage between ECM connector "A" terminal A13 (Yellow/Black) wire and ground. If battery voltage is present, ECM diagnosis is necessary. If battery voltage is not present, check Yellow/Black wire for an open.

Does Not Light (All Other Models) – Turn ignition switch to RUN position. Disconnect coolant level switch. Using a voltmeter, measure voltage between Yellow/Black wire and ground, and between Black/White wire and Yellow/Black wire. If battery voltage is present, replace coolant temperature switch. If battery voltage is not present, check Yellow/Black and/or Black/White wires for an open.

OIL PRESSURE INDICATOR

Indicator Always On – 1) Check oil level and pressure with a mechanical gauge. If oil level and pressure are not okay, make necessary mechanical repairs. If oil level and pressure are okay, turn ignition on.

2) Disconnect oil pressure switch connector. If indicator is off, replace oil pressure switch. If indicator is still on, check Tan wire for a short to ground. If Tan wire is okay, replace instrument cluster.

Ignition On/Engine Off, No Indicator Light – Disconnect oil pressure switch connector. Connect a fused jumper wire between Tan wire and ground. Turn ignition on. If indicator lights, replace oil pressure switch. If indicator does not light, check Tan wire for an open. If Tan wire is okay, replace instrument cluster.

COOLANT TEMPERATURE GAUGE

Always Reads Cold – Disconnect coolant temperature sender connector. Connect a jumper wire between Dark Green (VIN T) or Dark Green/White (VIN L) wire and ground. Turn ignition on. If gauge reads maximum temperature, replace coolant temperature sender. If gauge does not read maximum temperature, check Dark/Green or Dark Green/White wire for an open. If wires are okay, replace instrument cluster.

Always Reads Hot – Disconnect coolant temperature sender connector. Turn ignition on and observe gauge. If bars do not light, replace coolant temperature sender. If all bars are still illuminated, check Dark Green and Dark Green/White wires for a short to ground. If wires are okay, replace instrument cluster.

Gauge Inaccurate – 1) Disconnect coolant temperature sender. Connect one lead of Tester (J-33431) to Dark Green (VIN T) or Dark Green/White (VIN L) wire. If tester is unavailable, go to step **3)**. Connect other lead of tester to ground. Adjust resistance of tester to 567 ohms. Gauge should show a cold temperature. Adjust resistance of tester to 77 ohms. Gauge should show a hot temperature.

2) If gauge reads correctly, replace coolant temperature sender. If gauge is incorrect, check Dark Green or Dark Green/White wire for opens or shorts. If wires are okay, replace instrument cluster.

3) If Tester (J-33431) is unavailable, replace coolant temperature sender with a known good unit. Observe gauge with engine running. If display is accurate, replace coolant temperature sender. If display is still not accurate, replace instrument cluster. Reinstall original coolant temperature sender.

OIL PRESSURE GAUGE

Gauge Reads Low – Check oil pressure manually with a gauge. If pressure is correct, remove connector from oil pressure sender. Turn ignition on. If display reads high, replace oil pressure sender. If display reads low, check Tan wire between sender and instrument cluster for a short to ground. If wire is okay, replace instrument cluster.

Gauge Reads High – Disconnect oil pressure sender connector. Connect a jumper wire between Tan wire and ground. Turn ignition on. If gauge reads low, replace oil pressure sender. If gauge does not read low, check Tan wire for an open. If wire is okay, replace instrument cluster.

Gauge Inaccurate – 1) Disconnect oil pressure sender. Connect one lead of Tester (J-33431) to Tan wire connector. If tester is unavailable, go to step **3)**. Connect other tester lead to ground. Adjust resistance of tester to one ohm, then 90 ohms. Gauge should read low pressure, then show high pressure.

2) If gauge reads correctly, replace oil pressure sender. If gauge does not read correctly, check Tan wires for opens or shorts. If wires are okay, replace instrument cluster.

3) If Tester (J-33431) is unavailable, replace oil pressure sender with a known good unit. Run engine and observe oil pressure display. If display is now accurate, replace oil pressure sender. If display is not accurate, replace instrument cluster. Reinstall original oil pressure sender.

ENGLISH/METRIC SWITCH

1) If vehicle has instrument cluster with digital fuel gauge, go to next step. If vehicle has instrument cluster with analog fuel gauge, go to step **3)**.

2) Observe oil pressure, temperature, speedometer, total and trip odometer displays when E/M (English/Metric) switch is depressed. If only a partial number of displays change between English/Metric, replace instrument cluster. If none of the displays changed between English/Metric, go to next step.

3) Disconnect cluster switch assembly connector. Connect a fused jumper wire between Light Blue wire and ground. Turn ignition on. Display should read Metric. Disconnect jumper wire. Display should read English. If display reads properly, replace cluster switch assembly.

4) If display does not read properly, check for battery voltage at Light Blue wire. If battery voltage is present, replace instrument cluster. If battery voltage is not present, check Light Blue wire for an open. If Light Blue wire is okay, replace instrument cluster.

5) Connect a jumper wire between Light Blue and Black wires. Turn ignition on. Display should read Metric. If display reads properly, replace cluster switch assembly. If display does not read Metric, check Black wire for an open circuit to ground.

SEASON/TRIP SWITCH

1) Disconnect cluster switch assembly connector. Connect one end of fused jumper wire to Light Green wire. Turn ignition on. Connect other end of fused jumper wire to ground for one second.

2) If odometer changes between Season and Trip, check Black wire for an open. If Black wire is okay, replace cluster switch assembly. If odometer did not change between Season and Trip, repair Light Green wire. If Light Green wire is okay, replace instrument cluster.

3) With jumper wire connected to Light Green wire, ground other end of jumper wire for 2 seconds. If trip odometer does not reset to zero, replace instrument cluster. If trip odometer responds correctly, repair Black/White wire for an open. If Black/White wire is okay, replace cluster switch assembly.

ANALOG/DIGITAL SWITCH

1) Disconnect cluster switch assembly connector. Turn ignition switch to RUN position. Using voltmeter, check for battery voltage at Dark Blue/White wire. If battery voltage is not present, check Dark Blue/White wire for an open. If wire is okay, replace instrument cluster.

2) Connect voltmeter between Dark Blue/White and Black/White wire. Battery voltage should be present with ignition switch in RUN position. If battery voltage is not present, check Black wire for open.

3) If voltage in both tests is correct, check switch continuity. Continuity should exist between Dark Blue/White and Black/White switch terminals with switch held in. Continuity should not exist when switch is released. If switch tests okay, replace instrument cluster.

PRNDL SWITCH

Check White, Gray, Yellow and Black/White wires from PRNDL switch to instrument cluster for an open or short to ground. Ensure all connections are clean and tight. Check switch adjustment. If wires, connections and switch adjustment are good, replace PRNDL switch.

IGNITION SWITCH

Open Test – 1) Connect a fused jumper wire between coolant temperature sensor Dark Green wire and ground. Turn ignition on. Observe temperature display.

2) If display shows hot, check ignition switch and Dark Green and Dark Green/White wires for an open.

3) If display shows cold, check for an open in Dark Green/White and Dark Green wires to instrument cluster.

HEADLIGHT SWITCH

Early Production (12th Digit of VIN is 4 or 5) – 1) Using a voltmeter, battery voltage should be present at headlight switch terminals "M" (Dark Green), "N" (Orange), "I" (Dark Green), and "D" (White).

2) With park/headlights on, battery voltage should be present at terminal "K" (Yellow/Black), "L" (Yellow), and "O" (Brown). For additional information, see appropriate chassis wiring diagram in WIRING DIAGRAMS.

Regular Production (12th Digit of VIN is 8 or 9) – 1) Using a voltmeter, battery voltage should be present at headlight switch terminals "M" (Dark Green), "N" (Orange), and "G" (Dark Green).

2) With park/headlights on, battery voltage should be present at terminal "K" (Yellow/Black), "L" (Yellow), and "O" (Brown). For additional information, see appropriate chassis wiring diagram in WIRING DIAGRAMS.

WIPER SWITCH

For testing information on wiper switch, see appropriate WIPER/WASHERS article.

REMOVAL & INSTALLATION

ENGLISH/METRIC SWITCH

Removal & Installation – Remove cluster trim plate. Remove 2 bolts, then remove switch. To install, reverse removal procedure.

INSTRUMENT CLUSTER

Removal & Installation – 1) Remove speaker grilles by carefully prying. Remove one screw under each speaker grille. Remove 5 screws under lower edge of instrument panel pad. Remove instrument panel pad by lifting front, pulling rearward to release. Remove pad by lifting up and out. See Fig. 1.

2) Remove one bolt holding cluster trim plate. Remove trim plate. Disconnect electrical connector. Remove 6 bolts holding cluster, then remove cluster. To install, reverse removal procedure.

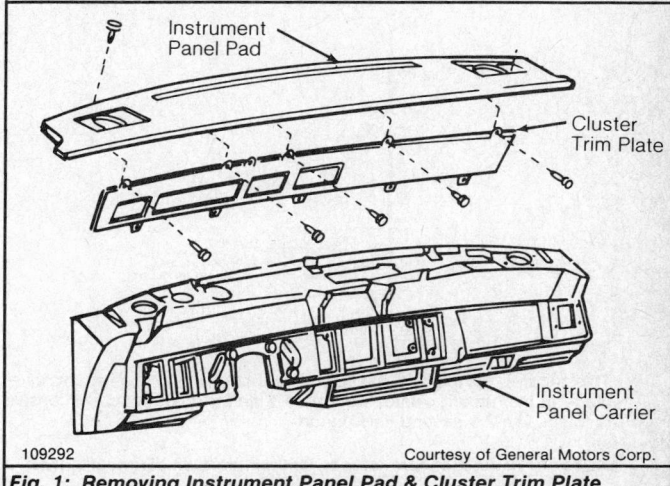

109292   Courtesy of General Motors Corp.

Fig. 1: Removing Instrument Panel Pad & Cluster Trim Plate

WIRING DIAGRAMS

See appropriate chassis wiring diagram in WIRING DIAGRAMS.

INSTRUMENT PANEL TROUBLE CODES

NOTE: For complete diagnosis of instrument panel, a "Scan" tool (bidirectional) must be used.

Note On Intermittents – The following diagnostic procedures may be helpful in determining the cause of intermittent problems in instrument panel or related electronic components.

In most cases the fault must be present to locate the problem effectively using the trouble charts. Most intermittent problems are caused by faulty wiring or electrical connections.

CODE I001,
OIL PRESSURE SENSOR ZERO BIAS

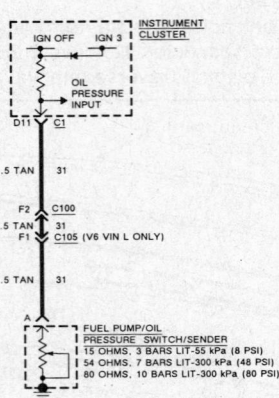

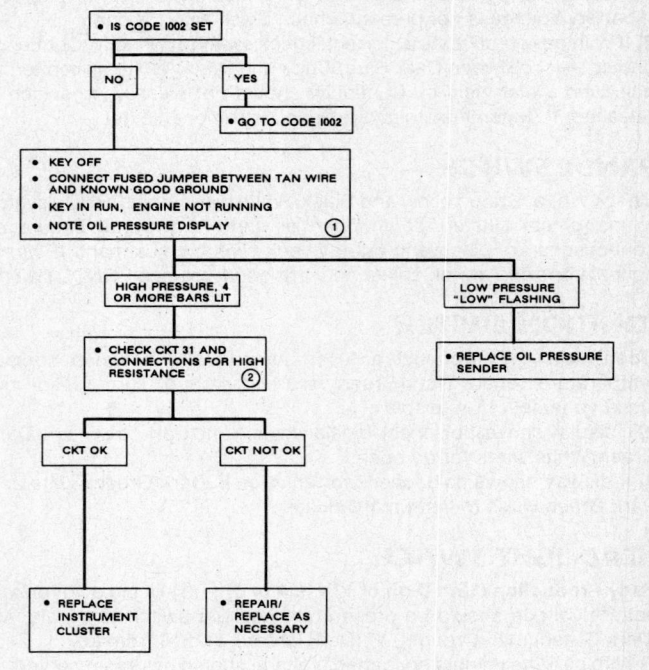

This code will set if ignition is on, engine is not running and sensor resistance at instrument cluster was more than 25 ohms for 5 successive readings in a 2.5-second time period.

NOTE: Test numbers refer to test numbers on diagnostic chart.

1) Checks if open is in fuel pump/oil pressure switch/sender or in rest of circuit.

2) Checks if open is in circuit No. 31 or instrument cluster.

When all diagnosis and repairs are complete, clear codes and verify operation.

91E08673   91A08690

Courtesy of General Motors Corp.

CODE I002,
OIL PRESSURE SENSOR OPEN CIRCUIT

NOTE: Test numbers refer to test numbers on diagnostic chart.

1) Checks if open is in fuel pump/oil pressure switch/sender or rest of circuit.

2) Checks if open is in circuit No. 31 or instrument cluster.

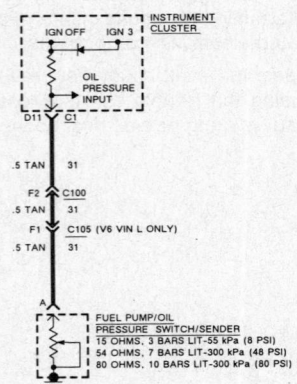

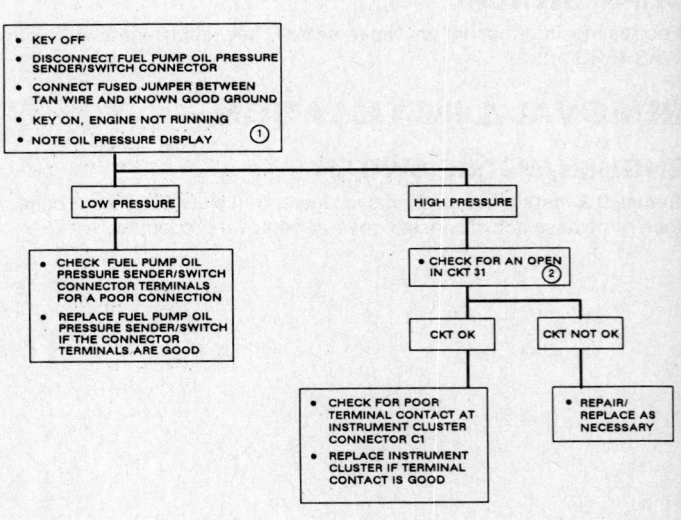

This code will set if ignition is on, engine speed is more than 400 RPM and sensor reading at instrument cluster was at least 100 ohms for 5 successive readings in a 2.5-second time period.

When all diagnosis and repairs are complete, clear codes and verify operation.

91G08674   91C08691

Courtesy of General Motors Corp.

CODE I003,
FUEL LEVEL SENDER OPEN CIRCUIT

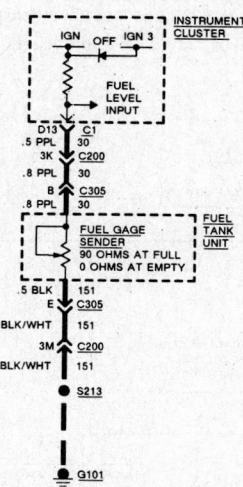

This code will set if ignition is on and sender resistance at instrument cluster was at least 100 ohms for 5 successive readings in a 2.5-second time period.

NOTE: Test numbers refer to test numbers on diagnostic chart.

1) Checks if circuits No. 30 and 151 are okay.

2) Checks if open is in circuit No. 30 or circuit No. 151.

3) Checks if problem is in instrument cluster.

4) Checks if open is in circuit No. 30, instrument cluster connector C1 or instrument cluster.

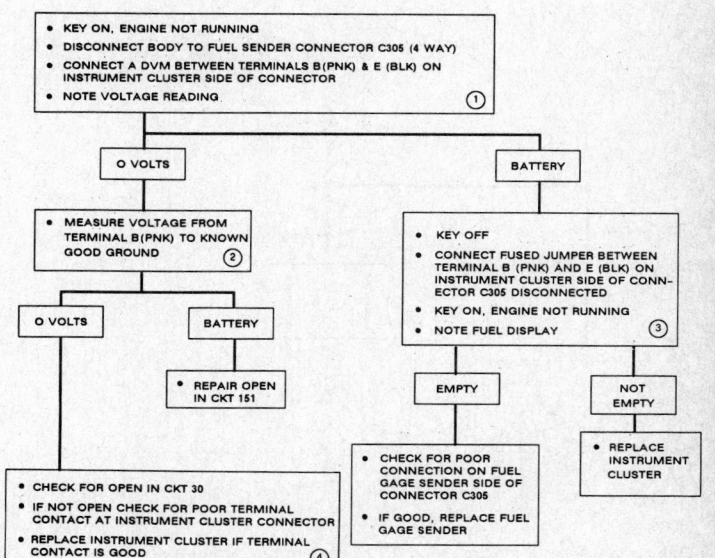

When all diagnosis and repairs are complete, clear codes and verify operation.

90C14441

Courtesy of General Motors Corp.

CODE I004,
COOLANT TEMPERATURE SENSOR
SHORT CIRCUIT

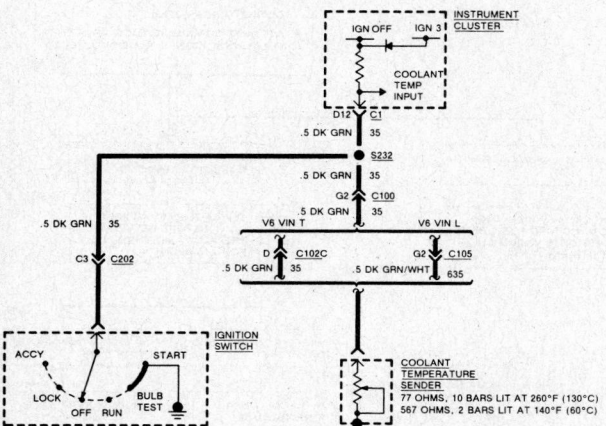

This code will set if ignition is on and sensor resistance at instrument cluster was at or below 20 ohms for 5 successive readings in a 2.5-second time period.

NOTE: Test numbers refer to test numbers on diagnostic chart.

1) Checks if short is in coolant temperature sensor or rest of circuit.

2) Determines location of short between circuit No. 35 and/or circuit No. 635 and the ignition switch or instrument cluster.

3) Checks if short is in ignition switch or rest of circuit.

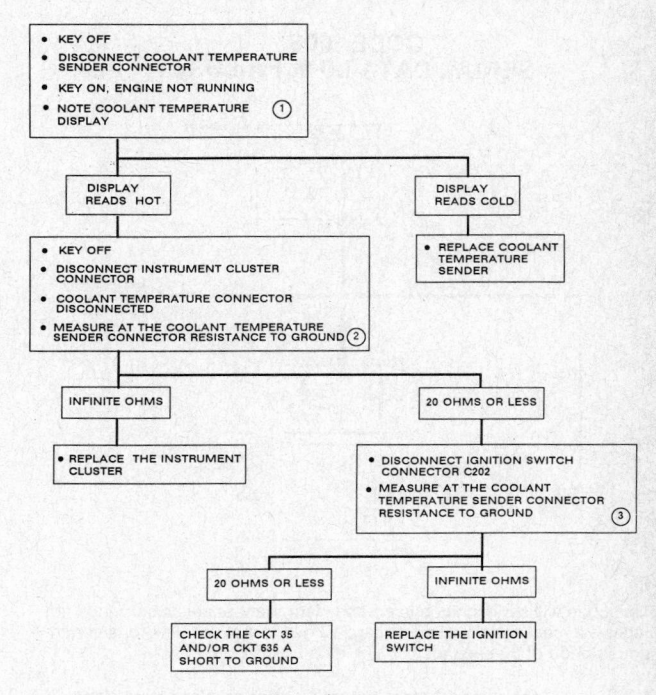

When all diagnosis and repairs are complete, clear codes and verify operation.

91J08675   91H08684

Courtesy of General Motors Corp.

CODE I005,
COOLANT TEMPERATURE SENSOR
OPEN CIRCUIT

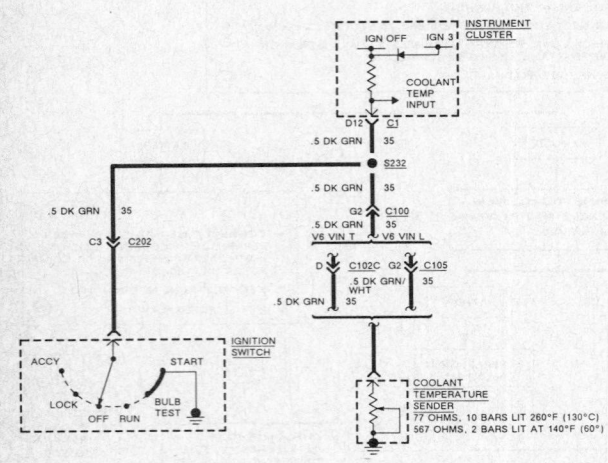

This code will set if ignition is on, ECM coolant temperature sender is more than or equal to 100°F (38°C) and sensor resistance at instrument cluster was at least 2000 ohms for 5 successive readings in a 2.5-second time period.

NOTE: Test numbers refer to test numbers on diagnostic chart.

1) Checks if open is between coolant temperature sensor and splice S232 or between splice S232 and instrument cluster.

2) Checks if open is in circuit No. 35 and/or circuit No. 635 or instrument cluster.

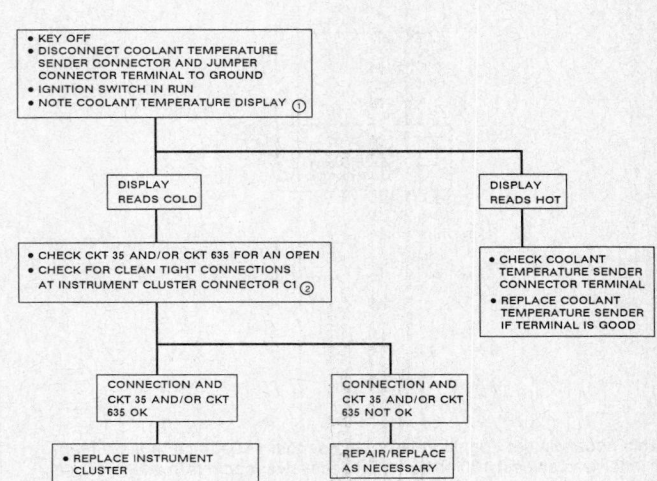

When all diagnosis and repairs are complete, clear codes and verify operation.

91B08676   91A08685

CODE I006,
SERIAL DATA LINK FAILURE

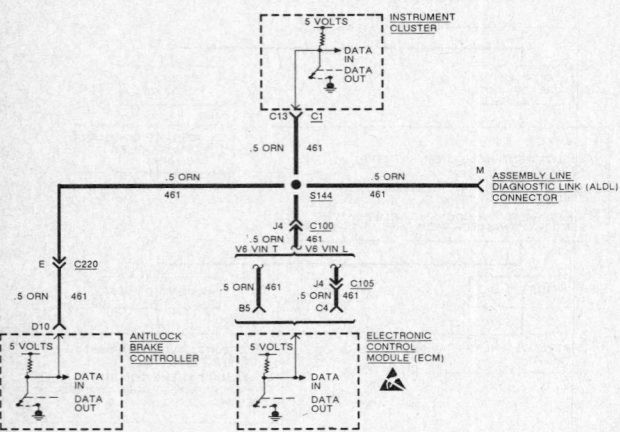

This code will set if ignition is on and instrument panel cluster does not receive a message or valid message ID over serial data link for a continuous period of 30 seconds.

NOTE: Test number refers to test number on diagnostic chart.

1) Checks if problem is hard fault or intermittent.

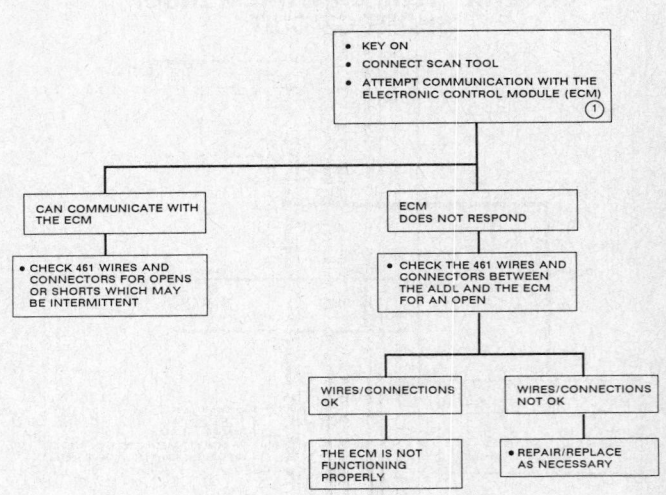

When all diagnosis and repairs are complete, clear codes and verify operation.

91D08677   91C08686

CODE I007,
SIGNAL SPEED COMPARISON

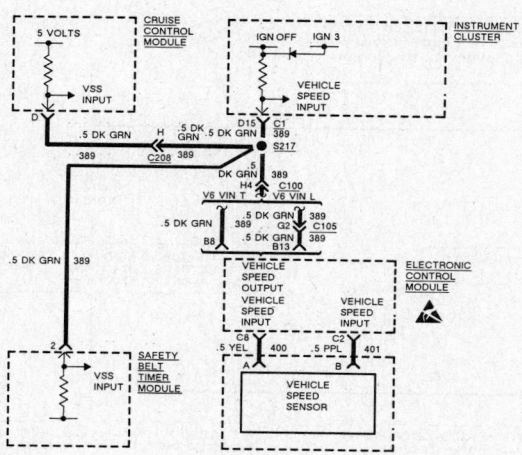

- CONNECT BI-DIRECTIONAL SCAN TOOL
- ENTER ECM DATA MODE
- OPERATE VEHICLE AND OBSERVE
  IPC DISPLAY AND SCAN TOOL DISPLAY ①

IPC AND SCAN TOOL DISAGREE	IPC AND SCAN TOOL AGREE
• REPLACE IPC	CHECK 389 WIRE FOR AN INTERMITTENT SHORT TO GROUND AND COMPONENTS SHORTING THE THE 389 WIRE FOR AN INTERMITTENT SHORT TO GROUND

When all diagnosis and repairs are complete, clear codes and verify operation.

This code will set if ignition is on and speed differential of 5 MPH or more exists for 5 seconds between serial data link and vehicle speed input at instrument cluster, with serial data link speed validity code equal to zero and a serial data link speed greater than 5 MPH.

NOTE: Test number refers to test number on diagnostic chart.

1) Checks if instrument cluster is processing speed input correctly.

91F08678   91E08687

CODE I008,
VEHICLE SPEED INPUT – OPEN CIRCUIT

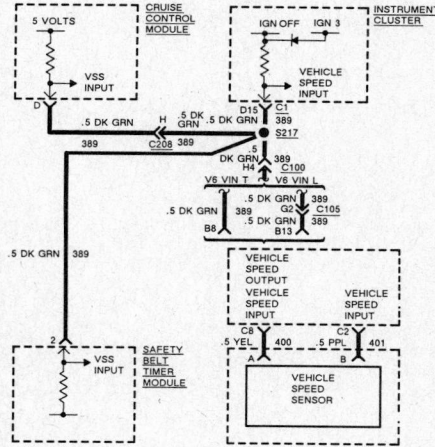

NOTE: Test number refers to test number on diagnostic chart.

1) Checks if there is an open between instrument cluster and splice S217, or if fault lies below splice S217.
2) Checks if there is an open in ECM or circuit No. 389 wire between splice S217 and ECM or if instrument cluster is at fault.

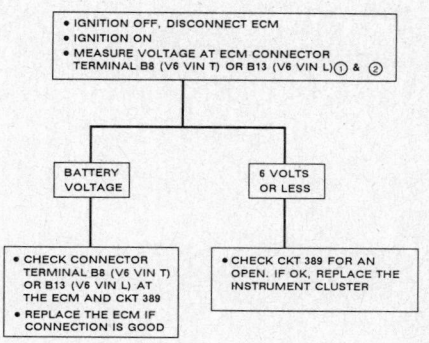

- IGNITION OFF, DISCONNECT ECM
- IGNITION ON
- MEASURE VOLTAGE AT ECM CONNECTOR TERMINAL B8 (V6 VIN T) OR B13 (V6 VIN L) ① & ②

BATTERY VOLTAGE	6 VOLTS OR LESS
• CHECK CONNECTOR TERMINAL B8 (V6 VIN T) OR B13 (V6 VIN L) AT THE ECM AND CKT 389 • REPLACE THE ECM IF CONNECTION IS GOOD	• CHECK CKT 389 FOR AN OPEN. IF OK, REPLACE THE INSTRUMENT CLUSTER

This code will set if ignition is on and serial data link speed is 5 MPH or more than vehicle speed input for 5 seconds and vehicle speed input at instrument cluster is high.

When all diagnosis and repairs are complete, clear codes and verify operation.

1H08679   91G08688

CODE I009,
VEHICLE SPEED INPUT – SHORT CIRCUIT

2) Determines if short exists in circuit No. 389 or a component sharing circuit No. 389.

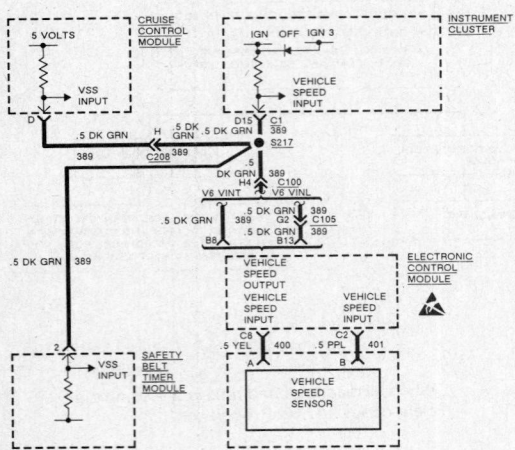

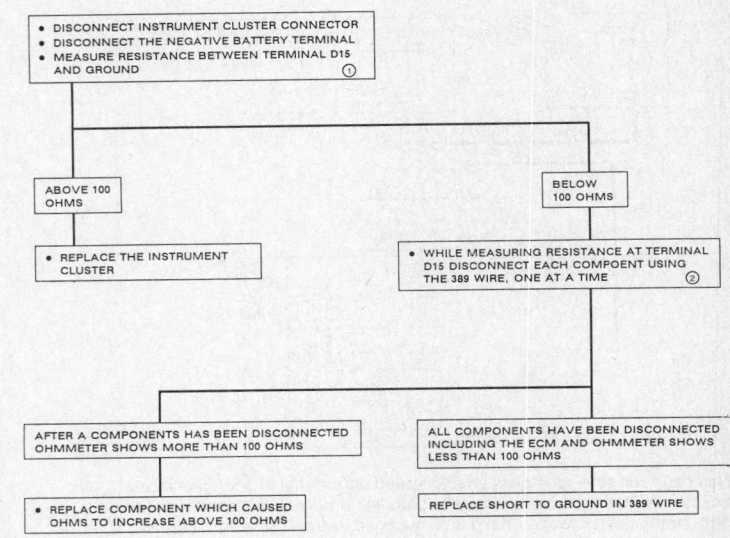

This code will set if ignition is on and serial data link speed is 5 MPH or more than vehicle speed input for 5 seconds and vehicle speed input at instrument cluster is low.

NOTE: **Test numbers refer to test numbers on diagnostic chart.**

1) Checks if a short to ground exists in circuit No. 389 and components sharing circuit No. 389 or instrument cluster is at fault.

When all diagnosis and repairs are complete, clear codes and verify operation.

Courtesy of General Motors Corp.

91J08680   91I08689

DESCRIPTION & OPERATION

The Instrument Panel Cluster (IPC) provides digital display for speedometer, odometer, engine RPM, trip odometer and transaxle range. See Fig. 1. An optional CRT/Driver Information Display (CRT/DID) provides warnings and reminders on performance and operation of vehicle. After a delay of one second when ignition is turned on, graphics illuminate, and gauges indicate engine condition.

NOTE: Electronic instrument cluster is not repairable.

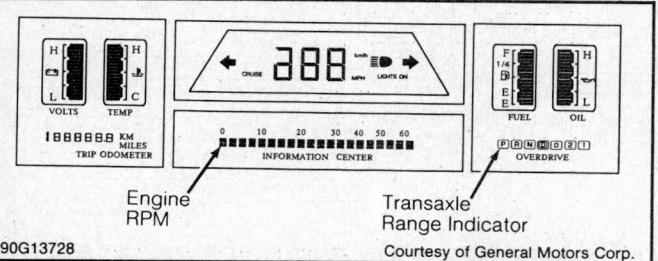

Fig. 1: Identifying Electronic Instrument Cluster (Toronado)

90G13728   Courtesy of General Motors Corp.

AIR BAG PRECAUTIONS

Follow precautions when working with vehicles equipped with Supplemental Inflatable Restraint (SIR) air bag systems:

- Before performing any instrument panel testing, diagnosis or repair, disable SIR system by disconnecting negative battery cable and Yellow 2-pin connector at base of steering column.
- Wait 20 minutes before making instrument panel repairs. SIR system retains enough voltage to deploy air bag for a short time after disconnecting power.
- To avoid accidental air bag deployment, avoid SIR wiring harness when trouble shooting instrument panel components. All SIR wires are color-coded Yellow.

ON-VEHICLE DIAGNOSIS

NOTE: For additional instrument panel testing and information on entering BCM, PCM and ECM diagnostics, see SELF-DIAGNOSTICS – TORONADO & TROFEO PCM/BCM article in ENGINE PERFORMANCE.

ENTERING IPC SELF-DIAGNOSIS

Electronic Comfort Control (ECC) panel or CRT/DID can access and control BCM self-diagnostic features. Self-diagnostic trouble codes are displayed on IPC Driver Information Center (DIC). See Fig. 1. When a malfunction is sensed by BCM, a driver warning message is displayed in this area.

To enter IPC self-diagnostics on non-CRT models, turn ignition on, and simultaneously press OFF and WARM controls on Electronic Climate Control Panel (ECCP) until all display segments light. Diagnostic code level will display Electronic Control Module (ECM), Body Control Module (BCM) and Supplemental Inflatable Restraint (SIR) codes. Proceed to IPC system by pressing FAN DOWN button. When IPC INPUTS? is displayed, press FAN UP button. IPC inputs will display, and diagnosis can begin. See IPC INPUTS under ON-VEHICLE DIAGNOSIS. To exit diagnosis, press BI-LEV button.

To enter IPC self-diagnosis on CRT/DID models, turn ignition on, and press OFF hard key and WARM soft key until all display segments light. Diagnostic code level will display Electronic Control Module (ECM), Body Control Module (BCM) and Supplemental Inflatable Restraint (SIR) codes. Proceed to IPC system by pressing NO button until IPC? is displayed. Once IPC? is displayed, press YES button. When IPC INPUTS? is displayed, press YES button again. IPC inputs will display, and diagnosis can begin. See IPC INPUTS under ON-VEHICLE DIAGNOSIS. To exit diagnosis, press RTN soft key or turn ignition off.

IPC INPUTS

INPUT? test types are displayed in numerical order. See IPC INPUT TEST TYPES table. DIC will then display voltage level (HI or LO) of selected input to system. In addition, DIC will display an "O" or an "X". An "O" indicates input has not cycled. An "X" indicates input has cycled since test was selected. Indicator is reset by selecting a new test, and then returning to present test.

IPC INPUT TEST TYPES

Input Number	Input
II05	¹ English/Metric Switch
II06	¹ System Monitor Switch
II07	¹ Trip/Odometer Switch
II08	Fuel Expand Switch
II09	Tachometer Switch
II10	¹ Trip Reset Switch

¹ – Vehicles with CRT/DID only.

TESTING

DISPLAY TEST

1) Check instrument panel terminal connections. Enter BCM self-diagnostics, and observe suspect display. See SELF-DIAGNOSTICS – TORONADO & TROFEO PCM/BCM article in ENGINE PERFORMANCE.

2) If all segments cycle and light correctly, problem is caused by PCM, BCM or associated sensor. If all segments do not cycle and light correctly, replace instrument panel cluster assembly. See INSTRUMENT CLUSTER under REMOVAL & INSTALLATION.

NO CLUSTER DISPLAY TEST

If no cluster display is present, refer to NO CLUSTER DISPLAY (CRT EQUIPPED) or NO CLUSTER DISPLAY (NON-CRT EQUIPPED) flow charts. See Figs. 2 and 3.

SYSTEM MONITOR TEST

With CRT/DID – 1) Enter system diagnosis. See ENTERING IPC SELF-DIAGNOSIS under ON-VEHICLE DIAGNOSIS. Select IPC input II06, and depress system monitor button. Display should indicate LO. With button released, display should indicate HI. If display indicates LO with system monitor switch released, go to next step. If display indicates HI with system monitor switch depressed, go to step 3).

2) Remove right switch assembly. If display indicates HI, replace right switch assembly. If display indicates LO, check Purple wire for a short to ground. If wire is okay, replace IPC. See INSTRUMENT CLUSTER under REMOVAL & INSTALLATION.

3) Remove right switch assembly, and connect a fused jumper wire between terminals No. 12 (Purple wire) and No. 7 (Black/White wire) of right switch assembly connector.

4) If display indicates HI, go to next step. If display indicates LO, check connections. If connections are okay, replace right switch assembly.

5) Connect a fused jumper wire between terminal No. 12 (Purple wire) of right switch assembly connector and ground. If display indicates HI, go to next step. If display indicates LO, check Black/White wire for an open circuit.

6) Remove IPC. See INSTRUMENT CLUSTER under REMOVAL & INSTALLATION. Connect an ohmmeter between IPC connector terminal No. C12 (Purple wire) and right switch assembly connector terminal No. 12 (Purple wire).

7) If zero ohms are present, replace IPC if terminal contact is okay. See INSTRUMENT CLUSTER under REMOVAL & INSTALLATION. If high resistance is present, check Purple wire for an open.

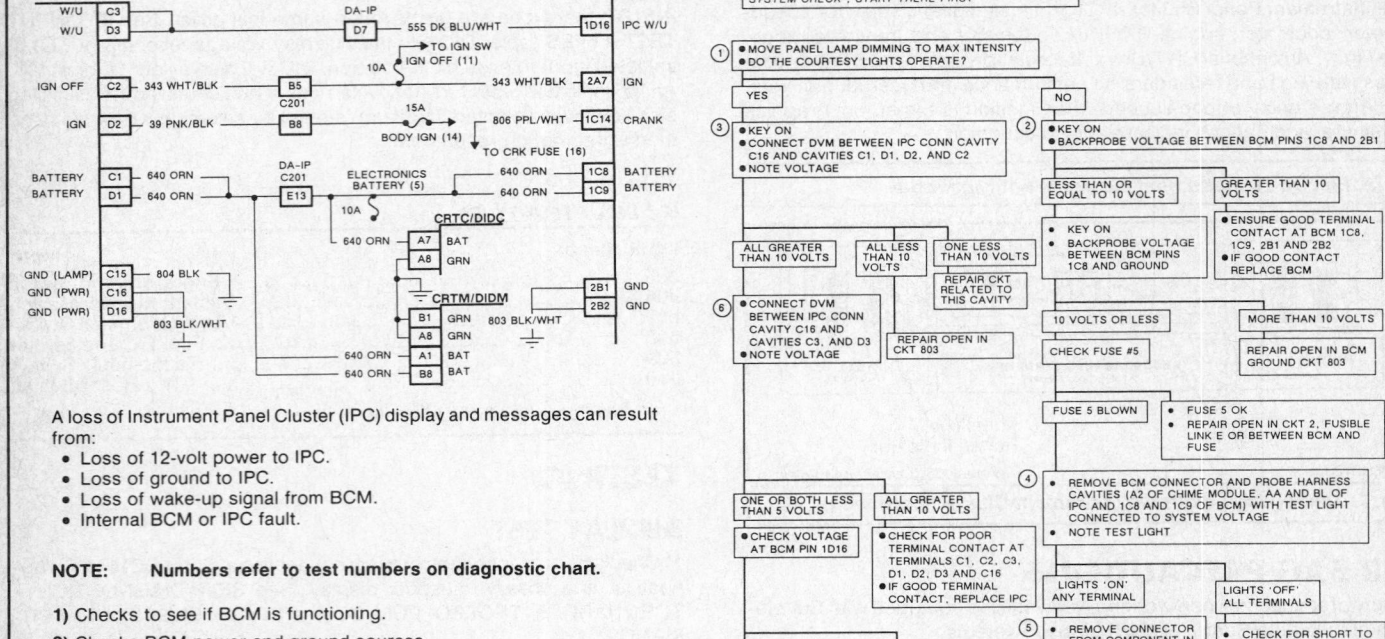

A loss of Instrument Panel Cluster (IPC) display and messages can result from:
- Loss of 12-volt power to IPC.
- Loss of ground to IPC.
- Loss of wake-up signal from BCM.
- Internal BCM or IPC fault.

NOTE: Numbers refer to test numbers on diagnostic chart.

1) Checks to see if BCM is functioning.

2) Checks BCM power and ground sources.

3) Checks to see if BCM has lost power or ground.

4) Checks for ignition source, power and ground to IPC. Normally with ignition switch ON, battery voltage should be present at listed terminals.

5) Checks for a short to ground in any No. 640 circuits.

6) Checks to see if short is inside a component or in circuit.

7) Checks to see if IPC is receiving wake-up signal from BCM.

WHEN ALL DIAGNOSIS AND REPAIRS ARE COMPLETE, CLEAR CODES AND VERIFY OPERATION

91G08706   91I08707   Courtesy of General Motors Corp.

Fig. 2: No Cluster Display Flow Chart – Toronado (CRT Equipped)

FUEL GAUGE TEST

1) Disconnect fuel tank sending unit connector, located under luggage compartment in front of fuel tank. With ignition switch in RUN position, connect voltmeter between terminal "C" (Pink/Black wire) and ground. If battery voltage is present, go to next step. If voltage is not present, check and repair Pink/Black wire.

2) Connect voltmeter between terminals "C" (Pink/Black wire) and "E" (Black/White wire). If voltage is present, go to next step. If voltage is not present, check and repair Black/White wire.

3) Connect voltmeter between terminals "C" (Pink/Black wire) and "F" (Purple wire). If voltage is present, go to next step. If voltage is not present, check Purple wire for open circuit.

4) With fuel tank sending unit connector unplugged and ignition switch in RUN position, enter BCM self-diagnostics. See SELF-DIAGNOSTICS – TORONADO & TROFEO PCM/BCM article in ENGINE PERFORMANCE. Select BCM data input BD40. Connect a fused jumper wire between fuel tank sending unit terminals "C" (Pink/Black wire) and "F" (Purple wire).

5) If BCM data input BD40 displays approximately 25 and fuel gauge indicates a full tank, replace fuel tank sending unit.

6) If BCM data input BD40 does not display approximately 25 and fuel gauge does not indicate a full tank, check Purple wire for a short to ground. If wire is okay, replace Body Control Module (BCM).

FUEL GAUGE SCALE TEST

1) With ignition switch in RUN position, enter self-diagnostics. See ENTERING IPC SELF-DIAGNOSIS under ON-VEHICLE DIAGNOSIS. Select IPC input I108, and operate gauge scale button.

2) With gauge scale button released, display should indicate HI. With gauge scale button depressed, display should indicate LO. If display indicates LO with gauge scale button released, go to next step. If display indicates HI with gauge scale button depressed, go to step 4).

3) Remove left switch assembly. If display indicates HI, replace left switch assembly. If display indicates LO, check Light Blue wire for short to ground. If wire is okay, replace IPC. See INSTRUMENT CLUSTER under REMOVAL & INSTALLATION.

4) Remove left switch assembly. Connect a fused jumper wire between left switch assembly connector terminals B12 (Light Blue wire) and B7 (Black wire). If display indicates LO, check connections. If connections are okay, replace left switch assembly.

5) If display indicates HI, connect fused jumper wire between left switch assembly connector terminal B12 (Light Blue wire) and ground. If display indicates LO, check Black wire for an open circuit. If display reads HI, remove IPC. See INSTRUMENT CLUSTER under REMOVAL & INSTALLATION.

6) Connect an ohmmeter between IPC connector terminal D11 (Light Blue wire) and left switch assembly connector terminal D11 (Light Blue wire).

7) If zero ohms are present, check terminal contact. If terminal contact is okay, replace IPC. See INSTRUMENT CLUSTER under REMOVAL & INSTALLATION. If high resistance is present, check Light Blue wire for an open circuit.

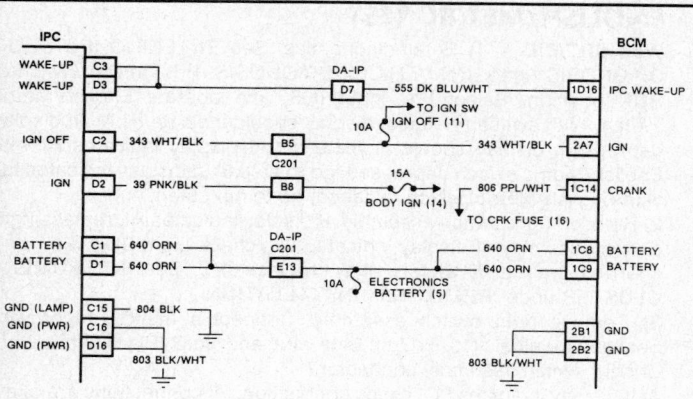

A loss of Instrument Panel Cluster (IPC) display and messages can result from:

- Loss of 12-volt power to IPC.
- Loss of ground to IPC.
- Loss of wake-up signal from BCM.
- Internal BCM or IPC fault.

NOTE: Numbers refer to test numbers on diagnostic chart.

1) Checks to see if BCM is functioning.

2) Checks BCM power and ground sources.

3) Checks for ignition source, power and ground to IPC. Normally with ignition switch ON, battery voltage should be present at listed terminals.

4) Checks for a short to ground in No. 640 circuits.

5) Checks to see if short to ground is inside a component or in circuit.

6) Checks to see if IPC is receiving wake-up signal from BCM.

WHEN ALL DIAGNOSIS AND REPAIRS ARE COMPLETE, CLEAR CODES AND VERIFY OPERATION

Courtesy of General Motors Corp.

91A08708   91C08709

Fig. 3: No Cluster Display Flow Chart – Toronado (Non-CRT Equipped)

TEMPERATURE GAUGE INCORRECT TEST

1) Ensure engine does not have an overheating condition. If engine is okay, check if PCM diagnostic code E014, E015 or BCM diagnostic code B450 is set. If ECM or BCM codes are set, repair as required. See SELF-DIAGNOSTICS – TORONADO & TROFEO PCM/BCM article in ENGINE PERFORMANCE. If no codes are set, go to next step.

2) Determine coolant temperature using an external gauge. Enter self-diagnostics. See SELF-DIAGNOSTIC – TORONADO & TROFEO PCM/BCM article in ENGINE PERFORMANCE. Select ECM data input ED04, and note data display.

3) If ECM data input ED04 and actual coolant temperature are not comparable, replace coolant temperature sensor. If ECM data input ED04 and actual coolant temperature are comparable, replace IPC. See INSTRUMENT CLUSTER under REMOVAL & INSTALLATION.

OIL PRESSURE GAUGE INCORRECT TEST

1) Enter self-diagnostics, and check if BCM diagnostic code B132 is set. If code B132 is set, repair as required. See SELF-DIAGNOSTICS – TORONADO & TROFEO PCM/BCM article in ENGINE PERFORMANCE. If no codes are present, go to next step.

2) Determine if engine has a high or low oil pressure condition by removing oil pressure sensor. Connect a known good mechanical oil pressure gauge to vehicle. If oil pressure is okay, go to next step.

3) Unplug oil pressure sensor. Oil pressure sensor is located on right side of engine, above drive axle. With ignition switch in RUN position, connect a voltmeter between terminal "A" (Light/Green wire) and ground. If voltmeter indicates 5 volts, replace oil pressure sensor. If 5 volts are not present, go to next step.

4) Using a voltmeter, backprobe terminal 3C3 (Light Green wire) of BCM to ground. BCM is located behind right side of instrument panel, behind left side of instrument panel compartment. If 5 volts are present, check and repair wiring connections as necessary. If 5 volts are not present, check Light Green wire for a short to ground. If wire is okay, replace BCM.

TACHOMETER DISPLAY MISSING/INTERMITTENT TEST

1) With ignition switch in RUN position, enter self-diagnostics. See ENTERING IPC SELF-DIAGNOSIS under ON-VEHICLE DIAGNOSIS. Select IPC input II09. Operate tachometer switch.

2) With tachometer switch released, display should indicate HI. With tachometer switch depressed, display should indicate LO. If display indicates LO with tachometer switch released, go to next step. If display indicates HI with tachometer switch depressed, go to step 4).

3) Remove left tachometer switch assembly. See LEFT TACHOMETER SWITCH under REMOVAL & INSTALLATION. If display now indicates HI, replace left tachometer switch assembly. If display indicates LO, check White wire from terminal B11 for a short to ground. If wire is okay, replace IPC. See INSTRUMENT CLUSTER under REMOVAL & INSTALLATION.

4) If display indicates HI with tachometer switch depressed, remove left tachometer switch assembly. See LEFT TACHOMETER SWITCH under REMOVAL & INSTALLATION. Connect a fused jumper wire between left tachometer switch assembly terminals B11 (White wire) and B7 (Black wire).

5) If display indicates HI, go to next step. If display indicates LO, check all connections. If connections are okay, replace left tachometer switch assembly.

6) Connect a fused jumper wire between left tachometer switch assembly terminal B11 (White wire) and ground. If display indicates HI,

go to next step. If display indicates LO, repair Black wire from terminal B7.

7) Remove IPC. See INSTRUMENT CLUSTER under REMOVAL & INSTALLATION. Connect an ohmmeter between IPC connector terminal D13 (White wire) and left switch assembly terminal B11 (White wire). If zero ohms are present, replace IPC after checking for good terminal contact. If high resistance is present, check and repair White wire between terminals B11 and D13 for an open circuit.

TRIP RESET TEST

With CRT/DID – 1) Enter diagnostics. See ENTERING IPC SELF-DIAGNOSIS under ON-VEHICLE DIAGNOSIS. Put ignition switch in RUN position. Select IPC input II10, and operate trip reset button. With trip button released, display should indicate HI. With trip button depressed, display should indicate LO. If IPC input II10 displays HI with trip reset switch depressed, go to step **3)**. If IPC input II10 displays LO with trip reset switch released, go to next step.

2) Remove right switch assembly. If display indicates HI, replace right switch assembly. If display indicates LO, check Light Green wire for a short to ground. If wire is okay, replace IPC. See INSTRUMENT CLUSTER under REMOVAL & INSTALLATION.

3) If IPC input II10 displays HI with trip reset switch depressed, remove right switch assembly. Connect a fused jumper wire between terminals No. 8 (Light Green wire) and No. 7 (Black/White wire) of right switch assembly connector.

4) If display indicates LO, check connections. If connections are okay, replace right switch assembly. If display indicates HI, connect fused jumper wire between terminal No. 8 (Light Green wire) of right switch assembly connector and ground.

5) If display now indicates LO, repair Black/White wire for an open. If display indicates HI, remove IPC. See INSTRUMENT CLUSTER under REMOVAL & INSTALLATION. Connect an ohmmeter between IPC connector terminal C14 (Light Green wire) and right switch assembly connector terminal No. 8 (Light Green wire).

6) If zero ohms are present, check terminal contact. If terminal contact is okay, replace IPC. See INSTRUMENT CLUSTER under REMOVAL & INSTALLATION. If high resistance is present, check Light Green wire for an open circuit.

ODOMETER/TRIP TEST

With CRT/DID – 1) Enter diagnostics. See ENTERING IPC SELF-DIAGNOSIS under ON-VEHICLE DIAGNOSIS. Put ignition switch in RUN position. Select IPC input II07, and operate ODO/TRIP button. With button released, display should indicate HI. With button depressed, display should indicate LO. If display indicates HI with trip switch depressed, go to step **3)**. If display indicates LO with trip switch released, go to next step.

2) Remove right switch assembly. If display indicates HI, replace right switch assembly. If display indicates LO, check Light Green wire for a short to ground. If wire is okay, replace IPC. See INSTRUMENT CLUSTER under REMOVAL & INSTALLATION.

3) Remove right switch assembly. Connect a fused jumper wire between terminals No. 2 (Light Green wire) and No. 7 (Black/White wire) of right switch assembly connector.

4) If display indicates LO, check connections. If connections are okay, replace right switch assembly. If display indicates HI, connect a fused jumper wire between terminal No. 2 (Light Green wire) of right switch assembly connector and ground.

5) If display reads LO, check Black/White wire for an open. If display reads HI, remove IPC. See INSTRUMENT CLUSTER under REMOVAL & INSTALLATION. Connect an ohmmeter between IPC connector terminal D12 (Light Green wire) and right switch assembly connector terminal No. 2 (Light Green wire).

6) If zero ohms are present, check terminal contact. If terminal contact is okay, replace IPC. See INSTRUMENT CLUSTER under REMOVAL & INSTALLATION. If high resistance is present, check Light Green wire for an open circuit.

ENGLISH/METRIC TEST

With CRT/DID – 1) Enter diagnostics. See ENTERING IPC SELF-DIAGNOSIS under ON-VEHICLE DIAGNOSIS. Put ignition switch in RUN position. Select IPC input II05, and operate English/Metric switch. With switch released, display should indicate HI. With display depressed, display should indicate LO. If display indicates HI with English/Metric switch depressed, go to step **3)**. If display indicates LO with English/Metric switch released, go to next step.

2) Remove right switch assembly. If display indicates HI, replace right switch assembly. If display indicates LO, check Light Blue wire for a short to ground. If wire is okay, replace IPC. See INSTRUMENT CLUSTER under REMOVAL & INSTALLATION.

3) Remove right switch assembly. Connect a fused jumper wire between terminals No. 6 (Light Blue wire) and No. 7 (Black/White wire) of right switch assembly connector.

4) If display indicates LO, check connections. If connections are okay, replace right switch assembly. If display indicates HI, connect fused jumper wire between terminal No. 6 of right switch assembly connector and ground.

5) If display indicates LO, repair Black/White wire for an open circuit. If display indicates HI, remove IPC. See INSTRUMENT CLUSTER under REMOVAL & INSTALLATION. Connect an ohmmeter between IPC connector terminal C13 (Light Blue wire) and right switch assembly connector terminal No. 6 (Light Blue wire).

6) If zero ohms are present, check terminal contact. If terminal contact is okay, replace IPC. See INSTRUMENT CLUSTER under REMOVAL & INSTALLATION. If high resistance is present, check Light Blue wire for an open circuit.

LEFT TURN INDICATOR TEST

1) Ensure left front park/turn light operates correctly. If light does not operate correctly, exterior light diagnosis is necessary. If light operates correctly, go to next step.

2) Remove IPC, and disconnect cluster connector. See INSTRUMENT CLUSTER under REMOVAL & INSTALLATION. Turn ignition switch to RUN position. Put multi-function lever in LEFT TURN position, and measure voltage between IPC terminal C8 (Light Blue wire) and ground.

3) If battery voltage pulses on and off, check terminal connections. If battery voltage does not pulse on and off, check Light Blue wire for an open circuit.

RIGHT TURN INDICATOR TEST

1) Ensure right front park/turn light operates correctly. If light does not operate correctly, exterior light diagnosis is necessary. If light operates correctly, go to next step.

2) Remove IPC, and disconnect cluster connector. See INSTRUMENT CLUSTER under REMOVAL & INSTALLATION. Turn ignition switch to RUN position. Put multi-function lever in RIGHT TURN position, and measure voltage between IPC terminal C7 (Dark Blue wire) and ground.

3) If battery voltage pulses on and off, check terminal connections. If battery voltage does not pulse on and off, check Dark Blue wire for an open circuit.

HIGH BEAM INDICATOR TEST

1) Ensure high beam headlights operate correctly. If high beams do not operate correctly, high beam diagnosis is necessary. If high beams operate correctly, go to next step.

2) Remove IPC, and disconnect cluster connector. See INSTRUMENT CLUSTER under REMOVAL & INSTALLATION. Turn high beam headlights on, and measure voltage between cluster connector terminal C6 (Light Green wire) and ground.

3) If battery voltage is present, check terminal connections. If battery voltage is not present, check Light Green wire for an open circuit.

HEADLIGHT SWITCH CHECK

Constant voltage should be present at headlight switch terminal C5. With headlights on, voltage should be present at headlight switch terminals C3 (Grey/Black wire), C4 (Brown wire) and B7 (Black wire). If voltages are not as indicated, check switch and wiring.

WIPER SWITCH TEST

For testing information on wiper switches, see appropriate WIPER/WASHERS article.

REMOVAL & INSTALLATION

LEFT TACHOMETER SWITCH

Removal & Installation – 1) Disconnect negative battery cable. Remove sound insulator, knee bolster and instrument panel trim plate. See INSTRUMENT CLUSTER under REMOVAL & INSTALLATION. *See Figs. 4-7.*
2) Remove screws retaining left tachometer switch assembly. Pull switch from electrical connector, and remove assembly. To install, reverse removal procedure.

INSTRUMENT CLUSTER

Removal & Installation – 1) Disconnect negative battery cable. Remove front retaining screws and nuts attaching left side sound insulator. Remove courtesy light from panel and sound insulator from vehicle. *See Fig. 4.*
2) Remove knee bolster retaining screws. Remove knee bolster. *See Fig. 5.* Remove instrument cluster trim plate retaining screws and trim plate. *See Fig. 6.*
3) Remove screws retaining cluster to instrument panel. *See Fig. 7.* Pull cluster out, and disconnect electrical connector. To install, reverse removal procedure.

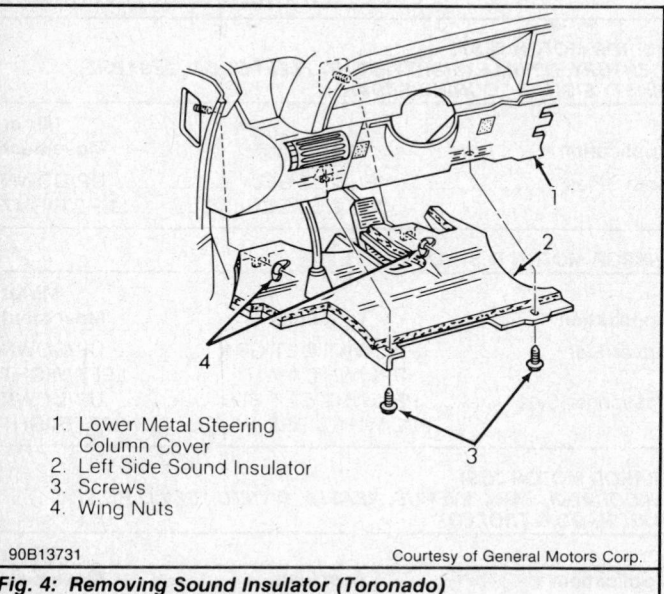

1. Lower Metal Steering Column Cover
2. Left Side Sound Insulator
3. Screws
4. Wing Nuts

90B13731   Courtesy of General Motors Corp.
Fig. 4: Removing Sound Insulator (Toronado)

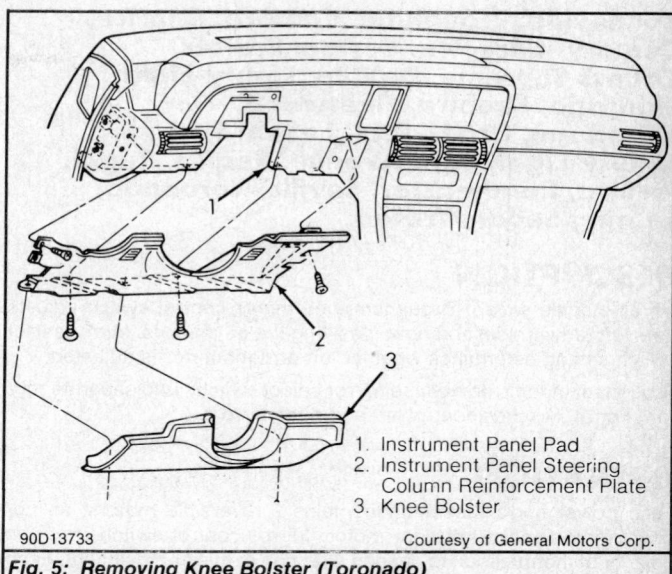

1. Instrument Panel Pad
2. Instrument Panel Steering Column Reinforcement Plate
3. Knee Bolster

90D13733   Courtesy of General Motors Corp.
Fig. 5: Removing Knee Bolster (Toronado)

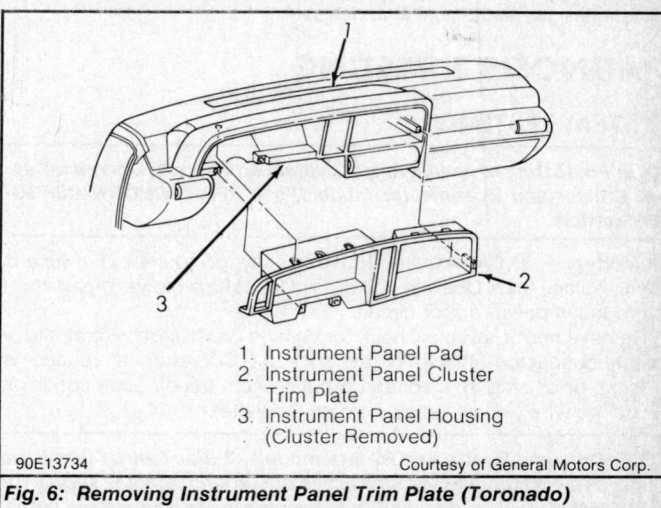

1. Instrument Panel Pad
2. Instrument Panel Cluster Trim Plate
3. Instrument Panel Housing (Cluster Removed)

90E13734   Courtesy of General Motors Corp.
Fig. 6: Removing Instrument Panel Trim Plate (Toronado)

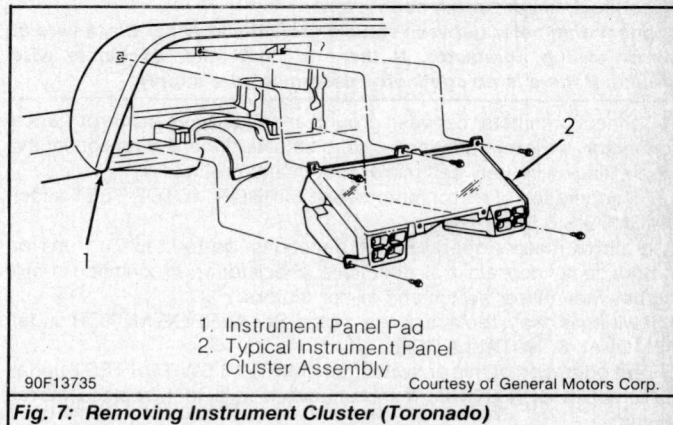

1. Instrument Panel Pad
2. Typical Instrument Panel Cluster Assembly

90F13735   Courtesy of General Motors Corp.
Fig. 7: Removing Instrument Cluster (Toronado)

WIRING DIAGRAMS

See appropriate chassis wiring diagram in WIRING DIAGRAMS.

Bonneville, Brougham, Camaro, Caprice, Century, Corvette, Custom Cruiser, Cutlass Supreme, DeVille, Eighty-Eight, Eldorado, Firebird, Fleetwood, Grand Am, Grand Prix, LeSabre, Ninety-Eight, Park Avenue, Reatta, Regal, Riviera, Roadmaster, Seville, Toronado, Touring Sedan, Trofeo

DESCRIPTION

On all models except Brougham, one mirror control switch adjusts both left (driver side) and right (passenger side) mirrors. Mirror select switch setting determines whether left or right mirror is adjusted.

Brougham models do not use mirror select switch. Two separate mirror control switches control left and right mirrors.

OPERATION

Each power mirror assembly contains 2 reversible motors: an up/down motor and a left/right motor. Mirror control switch reverses polarity of motor circuit to change direction of mirror movement. Each motor contains a self-resetting circuit breaker, which opens when mirror reaches its mechanical limit of travel.

DIAGNOSIS & TESTING

SYSTEM TESTING

NOTE: For testing of heated mirror system on Caprice, Corvette, Custom Cruiser and Roadmaster models, see REAR WINDOW DEFOGGERS article.

All Models – 1) Check fuse. If fuse is okay, go to step **2)**. If fuse is open, replace fuse. Operate power mirrors. If fuse blows, repair short to ground in power mirror circuit.
2) Remove mirror switch. Check for voltage on Orange wire at mirror switch connector (check Yellow wire on Corvette). If voltage is present, go to step **3)**. If voltage is not present, repair open condition in Orange wire (repair Yellow wire on Corvette).

NOTE: On some Reatta and Riviera models, 2 Black wires terminate at mirror switch connector. One is system ground; other is supply for UP/DOWN motor. To distinguish between ground and supply wires, disconnect mirror switch connector.
Connect ohmmeter between vehicle ground and either Black wire at mirror switch connector. If there is continuity, designate wire ground. If there is no continuity, designate wire supply.

3) Connect ohmmeter between ground and Black wire at mirror switch connector. If there is continuity, go to step **4)**. If there is no continuity, repair Black wire between mirror switch and ground.
4) Test operation of mirror motors. See MIRROR MOTOR TEST under DIAGNOSIS & TESTING.
5) If mirror motors operate in all directions, go to step **7)**. If mirror motors do not operate in all directions, check for open condition in wiring between mirror switch and mirror motors.
6) If wiring is okay, replace mirror motor. See MIRROR MOTOR under REMOVAL & INSTALLATION.
7) Test operation of mirror switch. See MIRROR SWITCH TEST under DIAGNOSIS & TESTING. If mirror switch fails test, replace mirror switch.

MIRROR MOTOR TEST

1) To perform mirror motor test, remove mirror switch. Disconnect electrical connector. Using a 12-volt source, connect positive and negative leads to specified wire terminals. See appropriate MIRROR MOTOR TEST table.

2) Reverse positive and negative leads on these wire terminals. Reverse leads again. Mirror motor should move up and down or left and right as specified.

NOTE: Most models with mirror select switch use duplicate wire colors in circuit between mirror switch and mirror motors: one set of wires leads to left mirror motors, other set leads to right mirror motors.
When testing mirror motors on models with duplicate wire colors, connect battery positive lead to one wire terminal and battery negative lead to other wire terminal as specified. If mirror motor does not operate, leave positive lead connected.
Disconnect negative lead and connect to other wire terminal of same color. If mirror motor does not operate, leave negative lead connected. Disconnect positive lead and connect to other wire terminal of same color.

MIRROR MOTOR TEST
(BONNEVILLE, BROUGHAM, CAPRICE, CUSTOM CRUISER, CUTLASS SUPREME, GRAND PRIX, REGAL & ROADMASTER)

Application	Terminals	Mirror Movement
Both Sides	YEL & [1] LT GRN	UP/DOWN
	LT BLU & [1] WHT	LEFT/RIGHT

[1] – WHT/BLK on Cutlass Supreme, Grand Prix and Regal.

MIRROR MOTOR TEST (CAMARO & FIREBIRD)

Application	Terminals	Mirror Movement
Driver Side	YEL & LT GRN	UP/DOWN
	LT BLU & WHT	LEFT/RIGHT
Passenger Side	YEL & LT GRN/BLK	UP/DOWN
	LT BLU & WHT/BLK	LEFT/RIGHT

MIRROR MOTOR TEST
(CENTURY, DEVILLE, EIGHTY-EIGHT, FLEETWOOD, LESABRE, NINETY-EIGHT & TOURING SEDAN)

Application	Terminals	Mirror Movement
Both Sides	YEL & LT BLU	UP/DOWN
	WHT & LT BLU	LEFT/RIGHT

MIRROR MOTOR TEST (CORVETTE)

Application	Terminals	Mirror Movement
Driver Side	PPL/WHT & LT GRN	UP/DOWN
	PPL/WHT & WHT	LEFT/RIGHT
Passenger Side	PPL/WHT & LT BLU	UP/DOWN
	PPL/WHT & RED/WHT	LEFT/RIGHT

MIRROR MOTOR TEST
(ELDORADO, PARK AVENUE, REATTA, RIVIERA, SEVILLE, TORONADO & TROFEO)

Application	Terminals	Mirror Movement
Driver Side	YEL & [1] LT GRN	UP/DOWN
	LT BLU & WHT	LEFT/RIGHT
Passenger Side	YEL & PPL/WHT	UP/DOWN
	LT BLU & RED/WHT	LEFT/RIGHT

[1] – BLK (Supply) on Reatta and Riviera. See NOTE in SYSTEM TESTING under DIAGNOSIS & TESTING.

MIRROR MOTOR TEST (GRAND AM)

Application	Terminals	Mirror Movement
Driver Side	YEL & LT GRN	UP/DOWN
	LT BLU & WHT	LEFT/RIGHT
Passenger Side	YEL & LT GRN/BLK	UP/DOWN
	LT BLU & WHT/BLK	LEFT/RIGHT

MIRROR SWITCH TEST

1) To perform mirror switch test, remove mirror switch. Leave electrical connector connected. Place mirror select switch in LEFT position. (On Brougham, test applies to both mirror switches).

2) Hold mirror directional switch in specified positions. See appropriate MIRROR SWITCH TEST table. Check voltage at specified terminals. Place mirror select switch in RIGHT position. Repeat voltage test.

3) Disconnect mirror switch connector. Place mirror select switch in LEFT position. Hold mirror directional switch in specified positions. Using an ohmmeter, check continuity of mirror switch by probing specified terminals. Place mirror select switch in RIGHT position. Repeat continuity test.

NOTE: Most models with mirror select switch use duplicate wire colors in circuit between mirror switch and mirror motors: one set of wires leads to left mirror motors, other set leads to right mirror motors.

When checking for voltage on models with duplicate wire colors, probe specified wire terminal. If voltage is not present, probe other wire terminal of same color.

When checking continuity, connect ohmmeter positive lead to one switch terminal and ohmmeter negative lead to other switch terminal as specified. If there is no continuity, leave positive lead connected. Disconnect negative lead and connect to other switch terminal of same color.

If there is no continuity, leave negative lead connected. Disconnect positive lead and connect to other switch terminal of same color.

MIRROR SWITCH TEST
(BONNEVILLE, BROUGHAM, CAPRICE, CUSTOM CRUISER, CUTLASS SUPREME, GRAND PRIX, REGAL & ROADMASTER)

Mirror Select Switch Position	Mirror Directional Switch Position	Voltage At This Terminal	Continuity Between These Terminals
Both Sides [1]	UP	YEL	LT GRN & BLK
	DOWN	LT GRN	YEL & BLK
	LEFT	LT BLU	[2] WHT & BLK
	RIGHT	[2] WHT	LT BLU & BLK

[1] – Same test for both switches on Brougham.
[2] – WHT/BLK on Cutlass Supreme, Grand Prix and Regal.

MIRROR SWITCH TEST (CAMARO & FIREBIRD)

Mirror Select Switch Position	Mirror Directional Switch Position	Voltage At This Terminal	Continuity Between These Terminals
LEFT	UP	YEL	LT GRN & BLK
	DOWN	LT GRN	YEL & BLK
	LEFT	WHT	LT BLU & BLK
	RIGHT	LT BLU	WHT & BLK
RIGHT	UP	YEL	LT GRN/BLK & BLK
	DOWN	LT GRN/BLK	YEL & BLK
	LEFT	WHT/BLK	LT BLU & BLK
	RIGHT	LT BLU	WHT/BLK & BLK

MIRROR SWITCH TEST
(CENTURY, DEVILLE, EIGHTY-EIGHT, FLEETWOOD, LESABRE, NINETY-EIGHT & TOURING SEDAN)

Mirror Select Switch Position	Mirror Directional Switch Position	Voltage At This Terminal	Continuity Between These Terminals
Both Sides	UP	YEL	LT BLU & BLK
	DOWN	LT BLU	YEL & BLK
	LEFT	LT BLU	WHT & BLK
	RIGHT	WHT	LT BLU & BLK

MIRROR SWITCH TEST (CORVETTE)

Mirror Select Switch Position	Mirror Directional Switch Position	Voltage At This Terminal	Continuity Between These Terminals
LEFT	UP	PPL/WHT	LT GRN & BLK
	DOWN	LT GRN	PPL/WHT & BLK
	LEFT	WHT	PPL/WHT & BLK
	RIGHT	PPL/WHT	WHT & BLK
RIGHT	UP	PPL/WHT	LT BLU & BLK
	DOWN	LT BLU	PPL/WHT & BLK
	LEFT	RED/WHT	PPL/WHT & BLK
	RIGHT	PPL/WHT	RED/WHT & BLK

MIRROR SWITCH TEST
(ELDORADO, PARK AVENUE, REATTA, RIVIERA, SEVILLE, TORONADO & TROFEO)

Mirror Select Switch Position	Mirror Directional Switch Position	Voltage At This Terminal	Continuity Between These Terminals
LEFT	UP	YEL	[1] LT GRN & [2] BLK
	DOWN	[1] LT GRN	YEL & [2] BLK
	LEFT	LT BLU	WHT & [2] BLK
	RIGHT	WHT	LT BLU & [2] BLK
RIGHT	UP	YEL	PPL/WHT & [2] BLK
	DOWN	PPL/WHT	YEL & [2] BLK
	LEFT	LT BLU	RED/WHT & [2] BLK
	RIGHT	RED/WHT	LT BLU & [2] BLK

[1] – BLK (Supply) on Reatta and Riviera. See NOTE in SYSTEM TESTING under DIAGNOSIS & TESTING.
[2] – BLK (Ground) on Reatta and Riviera.

MIRROR SWITCH TEST (GRAND AM)

Mirror Select Switch Position	Mirror Directional Switch Position	Voltage At This Terminal	Continuity Between These Terminals
LEFT	UP	YEL	LT GRN/BLK & BLK
	DOWN	LT GRN/BLK	YEL & BLK
	LEFT	LT BLU	WHT/BLK & BLK
	RIGHT	WHT/BLK	LT BLU & BLK
RIGHT	UP	YEL/BLK	LT GRN/BLK & BLK
	DOWN	LT GRN/BLK	YEL/BLK & BLK
	LEFT	LT BLU	WHT & BLK
	RIGHT	WHT	LT BLU & BLK

REMOVAL & INSTALLATION

CAUTION: On some models, momentary actuation of power window switch can cause window to move directly to fully open position. When working inside door, leave ignition off whenever possible.

MIRROR GLASS

Removal – Cover door to avoid damage to painted surface. Tape mirror, then break mirror glass. Remove broken glass and fiber pad from mirror frame. Wipe inside of mirror frame clean.

Installation – Remove paper backing from service mirror, and center mirror in frame. Firmly press mirror to ensure adhesion of mirror to mirror frame.

MIRROR MOTOR

Removal (Grand Am) – Pull mirror frame away from housing until it snaps free. Remove motor attaching screws, disconnect wiring harness and remove motor from housing. *See Fig. 1.*

Installation – Connect wiring harness to motor. Place motor in housing, and install attaching screws. Pull out stabilizer studs from motor, and install on mirror frame. Align mirror frame with stabilizer stud holes and pivot bar on motor. Install mirror frame.

Removal (All Others) – Cover door to avoid damage to painted surface. Remove mirror by taping mirror and breaking mirror glass. Remove broken glass, mirror frame attaching screw and mirror frame. Remove motor attaching screws. Lift motor out of housing, and disconnect wiring harness. *See Fig. 1.*

Installation – Connect wiring harness to motor, and install motor to housing using screws. Position new mirror frame to motor, and install attaching screw. Remove paper backing from service mirror, and center mirror in frame. Firmly press mirror to ensure adhesion of mirror to mirror frame.

MIRROR ASSEMBLY

Removal & Installation (Grand Am) – Remove inner belt sealing strip and trim panel. Remove escutcheon assembly screws and escutcheon. Remove mirror assembly screw, wiring harness, nuts, mirror and body filler. To install, reverse removal procedure.

Removal & Installation (All Others) – Remove door trim panel, and disconnect wiring harness at connector. Peel back insulator pad and water deflector enough to gain access to wire harness. Detach

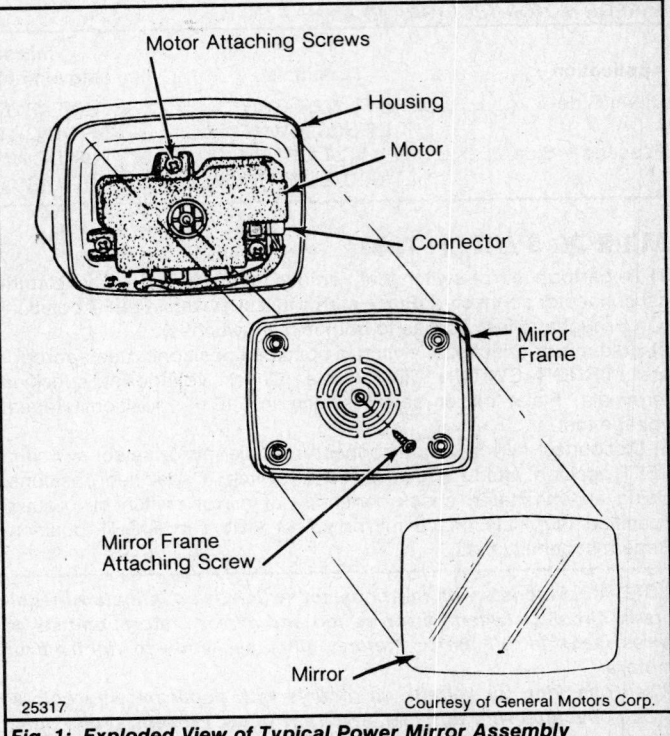

25317   Courtesy of General Motors Corp.

Fig. 1: Exploded View of Typical Power Mirror Assembly

harness from any retaining tabs in door. Remove attaching nuts from mirror frame, and remove mirror and harness from door. To install, reverse removal procedure.

WIRING DIAGRAMS

See appropriate chassis wiring diagram in WIRING DIAGRAMS.

"A" Body: **Century, Cutlass Ciera, Cutlass Cruiser, 6000**
"B" Body: **Caprice, Custom Cruiser, Roadmaster**
"C" Body: **DeVille, Fleetwood, Ninety-Eight, Park Avenue,Touring Sedan**
"E" Body: **Eldorado, Reatta, Riviera, Toronado, Trofeo**
"F" Body: **Camaro, Firebird**
"H" Body: **Bonneville, Eighty-Eight, LeSabre**
"J" Body: **Cavalier, Sunbird**
"K" Body: **Seville**
"L" Body: **Beretta, Corsica**
"N" Body: **Cutlass Calais, Grand Am, Skylark**
"W" Body: **Cutlass Supreme, Grand Prix, Lumina, Regal**
"Y" Body: **Corvette**

DESCRIPTION

Rear window defogger uses a heating grid on the inside of the rear window. Heat is controlled by a control switch and a timer/relay. The timer/relay is located in the accessory relay panel. When defogger is on, an indicator light illuminates. Current feed to defogger is through a circuit breaker, and power to control switch is through a fuse in the fuse block.

OPERATION

Voltage is applied to the rear defogger through the defogger relay. With the ignition switch in RUN position, voltage is applied to one side of defogger relay coil. When rear defogger switch is activated, a ground signal is sent from heater-A/C control to the Central Control Module (CCM). Upon receiving this ground signal, and only if the engine is running, the CCM energizes the defogger relay by grounding the other side of the defogger relay coil. When energized, the normally open contacts in the defogger relay close, applying voltage to heat the rear defogger. The CCM energizes the defogger relay 10 minutes during the first activation of the rear defogger after ignition on (engine running) and 5 minutes each additional activation. This timing process resets each ignition cycle.

TROUBLE SHOOTING

Before performing system test:
- Check seats circuit breaker by operating seats and power door locks.
- Check body fuse by operating courtesy lights.
- Check ignition fuse by operating back-up lights.
- Check fuse to gauges by observing fuel gauge operation. If components appear okay, proceed to TESTING.

TESTING

DEFOGGER GRID TEST

1) Start engine, and turn rear defogger control switch to ON position. Using a test light connected to ground, lightly touch each grid line. If test light shows full brilliance at both ends of all grid lines, check for loose ground wire. Test light brilliance should gradually change as test light probe is moved from left to right side of grid.
2) Contact each grid line a few inches on either side of glass center line to eliminate possibility of missing a break in grid line. If a problem on a grid line is detected, place test light probe on grid line at left bus bar and move probe toward right bus bar until light goes out, indicating a break in grid line continuity. See Fig. 1.

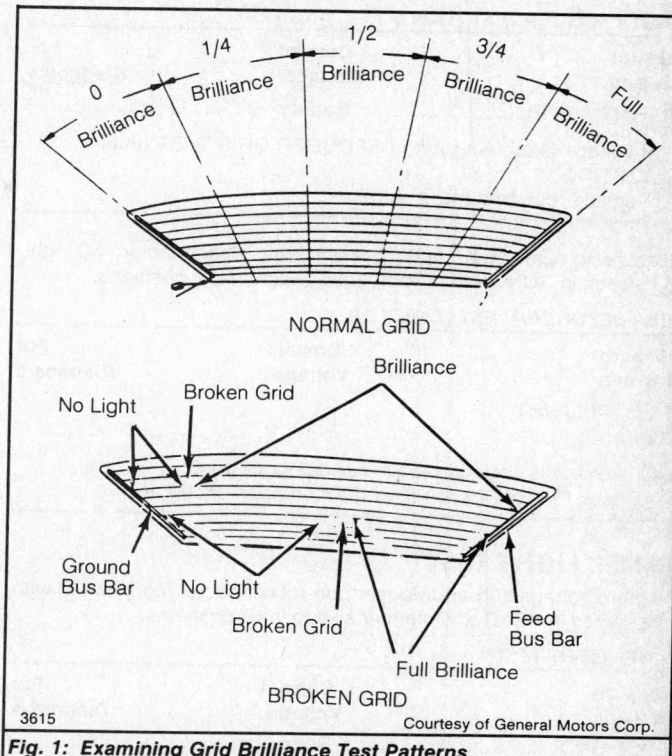

Fig. 1: Examining Grid Brilliance Test Patterns

"A" BODY TESTING

SYSTEM CHECK

1) With ignition on, turn rear defogger switch to ON position. If switch button does not return to rest position and ON indicator in center of rear defogger does not illuminate, go to REAR DEFOGGER CONTROL TEST. If rear window does not warm, go to REAR DEFOGGER TEST. If ON indicator and rear defogger do not turn off after approximately 10 minutes, replace rear defogger control.
2) Depress rear defogger switch again. If ON indicator and rear defogger do not operate for approximately 5 minutes, replace rear defogger control.
3) Turn light switch to HEAD or PARK. If panel light does not illuminate, go to PANEL LIGHT TEST.

REAR DEFOGGER CONTROL TEST

Measure voltage at rear defogger control connector (disconnected) with ignition switch in RUN position.

REAR DEFOGGER CONTROL TEST

Measure Between	Correct Voltage [1]	For Diagnosis
ORG/BLK & GND .... Battery		2
PNK/BLK & GND .... Battery		3
PNK/BLK & BLK .... Battery		4

[1] – If all results are correct, replace rear defogger control.
[2] – Check ORG/BLK wire for an open circuit.
[3] – Check PNK/BLK wire for an open circuit.
[4] – Check BLK wire for an open circuit.

REAR DEFOGGER TEST

Measure voltage at rear defogger control connector (connected) with ignition switch in RUN and rear defogger switch in ON positions.

REAR DEFOGGER TEST (TABLE 1)

Measure Between	Correct Voltage [1]	For Diagnosis
PPL/WHT & GND	Battery	[2]

[1] – If voltage is correct, go to DEFOGGER GRID TEST under TESTING.
[2] – Replace rear defogger control.

Measure voltage at rear defogger connector (disconnected) with ignition switch in RUN and rear defogger switch in ON positions.

REAR DEFOGGER TEST (TABLE 2)

Measure Between	Correct Voltage [1]	For Diagnosis
PPL or PPL/WHT & GND	Battery	[2]

[1] – If voltage is correct, repair rear defogger grid.
[2] – Check PPL or PPL/WHT wire for an open circuit.

PANEL LIGHT TEST

Measure voltage at rear defogger control connector (connected) with light switch in HEAD and dimmer switch in HI positions.

PANEL LIGHT TEST

Measure Between	Correct Voltage [1]	For Diagnosis
GRY & GND	Battery	[2]

[1] – If voltage is correct, check bulb. If okay, replace rear defogger control.
[2] – Check GRY wire for an open circuit.

"B" BODY TESTING

SYSTEM CHECK

NOTE: For appropriate "B" body wiring schematic, see Figs. 7 and 8.

With Manual A/C (Without Heated Mirrors) – 1) If rear defogger grid is inoperative, see Fig. 2. If indicator is inoperative but rear defogger is okay, replace rear defogger switch.
2) If rear defogger and indicator will not cycle on or off for 10 minutes on first use and 5 minutes for subsequent use or if rear defogger switch does not return to REST position, replace rear defogger switch.
With Manual A/C (With Heated Mirrors) – 1) If rear defogger and mirror defoggers are inoperative, see Fig. 3. If both mirror defoggers are inoperative and rear defogger is okay, see Fig. 4.
2) If one mirror defogger is inoperative and other mirror defogger is okay or if rear defogger is inoperative and mirror defoggers are okay, see Fig. 5. If indicator is inoperative but rear defogger and mirror defoggers are okay, replace rear defogger switch.
3) If rear defogger and indicator will not cycle on or off for 10 minutes on first use and 5 minutes for subsequent use or if rear defogger switch does not return to REST position, replace rear defogger switch.
With Automatic A/C – 1) If both mirror defoggers are inoperative but rear defogger is okay, see Fig. 4. If one mirror defogger is inoperative and other mirror defogger is operative or if rear defogger is inoperative and mirror defoggers are okay, see Fig. 5. If rear defogger and mirror defoggers (if equipped) are inoperative, see Fig. 6.
2) If indicator is inoperative but rear defogger grid and mirror defoggers are okay, replace electric A/C control head. If rear defogger grid and indicator will not cycle on or off for 10 minutes on first use and 5 minutes for subsequent use, replace electric A/C control head.

"C" BODY TESTING

SYSTEM CHECK

LeSabre – 1) If rear defogger and heated mirrors (if equipped) do not operate, go to REAR DEFOGGER RELAY TEST. If rear defogger operates correctly but heated mirrors do not operate, check defogger fuse located in relay center.
2) If fuse is okay, remove door trim panel. Check for power and ground at inoperable heated mirror. If power and ground are okay, replace mirror assembly. If heated mirrors operate correctly but defogger is inoperable or if some grid lines are inoperable, see DEFOGGER GRID TEST under TESTING.
3) On vehicles with automatic A/C, if rear defogger stays on for longer or shorter than 10 minutes during first cycle or longer or shorter than 5 minutes during second cycle, replace heater and A/C control assembly.
4) On vehicles with dual A/C, if rear defogger stays on for longer or shorter than 10 minutes during first cycle or longer or shorter than 5 minutes during second cycle, replace Heating, Air Conditioning and Ventilation (HVAC) programmer, located behind center of instrument panel.
5) On all vehicles, if defogger indicator does not illuminate with rear defogger on, replace heater and A/C control assembly.

Ninety-Eight & Touring Sedan – 1) Turn ignition switch to RUN position, and depress rear defogger switch. Switch button should return to rest position, and ON LED should illuminate in Driver Information Center (DIC). Rear window and left heated mirror should warm. ON LED and rear defogger should go off after approximately 10 minutes.
2) Depress rear defogger switch again. ON LED and rear defogger should go on. After approximately 5 minutes, defogger and LED should go off.
3) Depress rear defogger switch twice. ON LED and rear defogger should turn on and then off. If system does not operate as indicated, go to REAR DEFOGGER TIMER/RELAY TEST.

DeVille & Fleetwood – 1) If rear defogger and right and left mirrors do not operate, go to RELAY CENTER VOLTAGE TEST. If rear defogger does not operate but right and left heated mirrors operate normally, go to REAR DEFOGGER TEST.
2) If heated mirrors do not operate but rear defogger operates normally, go to HEATED MIRROR TEST. If rear defogger and right and left heated mirrors do not turn off, go to RELAY CENTER VOLTAGE TEST and ELECTRONIC CLIMATE CONTROL TEST.

REAR DEFOGGER RELAY TEST

LeSabre – 1) Remove rear defogger relay from relay center. Turn ignition switch to RUN position. Depress defogger button.
2) Using voltmeter, measure voltage between rear defogger relay terminal No. 5 (Brown wire) and ground. If battery voltage is present, go to next step. If battery voltage is not present, check fuse No. 17 (automatic A/C) or No. 18 (dual A/C).
3) Measure voltage between relay terminal No. 1 (Orange/Black wire) and ground. If battery voltage is present, go to next step. If battery voltage is not present, check instrument panel fuse block circuit breaker No. 4.
4) Measure voltage between relay terminals No. 2 (Tan wire) and 5 (Brown wire). If battery voltage is present, go to next step. If battery voltage is not present, check wiring. If wiring is okay, replace heater and A/C control assembly (automatic A/C) or Heating, Ventilation and Air Conditioning (HVAC) programmer (dual A/C), located behind right side of instrument panel.
5) Connect fused jumper wire between relay terminals No. 1 (Orange/Black wire) and No. 4 (Purple/White wire). Defogger should operate. If defogger does not operate, check defogger wiring. If wiring is okay, go to DEFOGGER GRID TEST under TESTING.

REAR DEFOGGER TIMER/RELAY TEST

Ninety-Eight & Touring Sedan – 1) Disconnect rear defogger Blue timer/relay connector. Turn ignition switch to RUN position. Using voltmeter, measure voltage between connector terminal "A" (Orange/

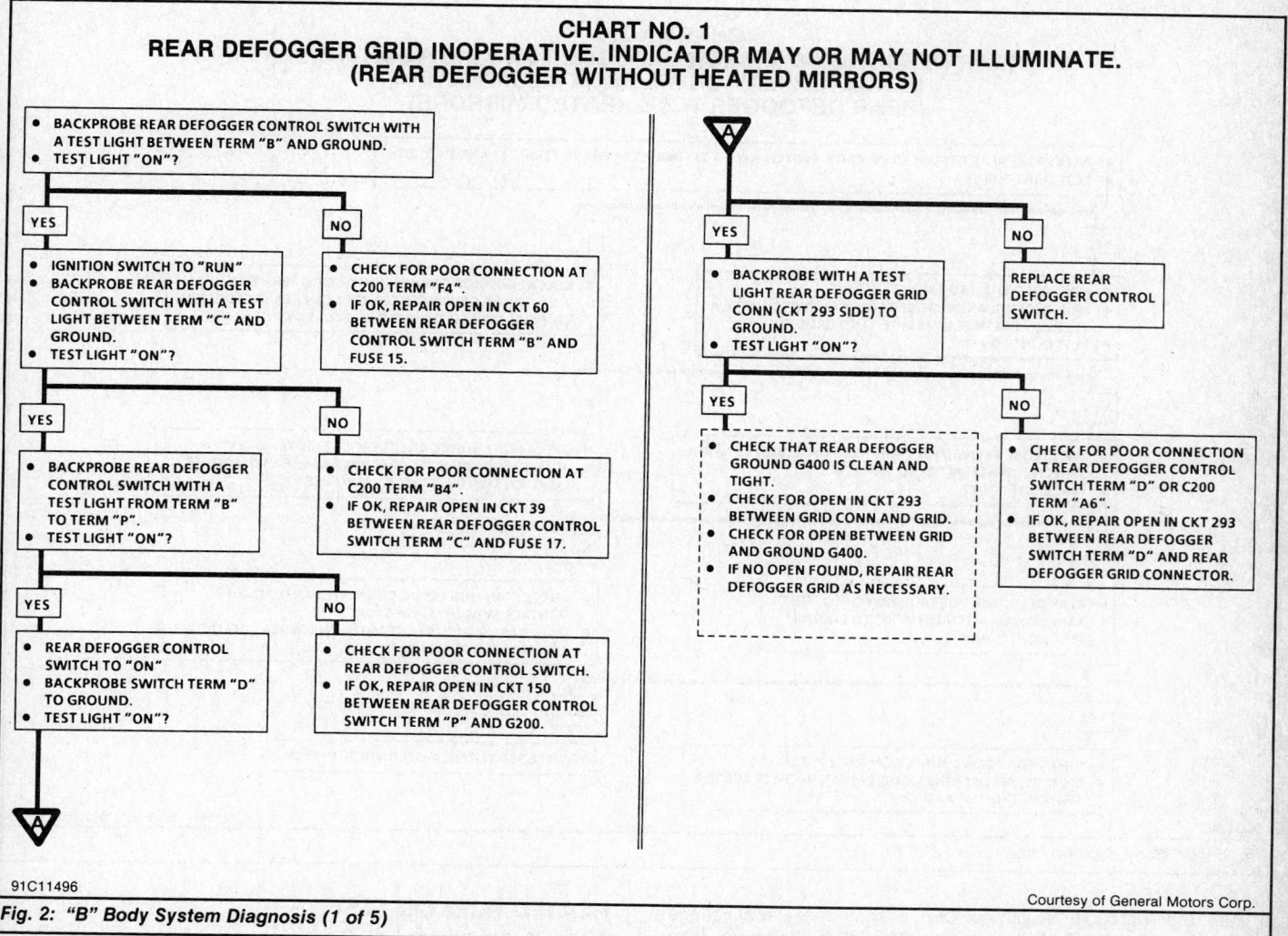

CHART NO. 1
REAR DEFOGGER GRID INOPERATIVE. INDICATOR MAY OR MAY NOT ILLUMINATE.
(REAR DEFOGGER WITHOUT HEATED MIRRORS)

- BACKPROBE REAR DEFOGGER CONTROL SWITCH WITH A TEST LIGHT BETWEEN TERM "B" AND GROUND.
- TEST LIGHT "ON"?

YES
- IGNITION SWITCH TO "RUN"
- BACKPROBE REAR DEFOGGER CONTROL SWITCH WITH A TEST LIGHT BETWEEN TERM "C" AND GROUND.
- TEST LIGHT "ON"?

NO
- CHECK FOR POOR CONNECTION AT C200 TERM "F4".
- IF OK, REPAIR OPEN IN CKT 60 BETWEEN REAR DEFOGGER CONTROL SWITCH TERM "B" AND FUSE 15.

YES
- BACKPROBE REAR DEFOGGER CONTROL SWITCH WITH A TEST LIGHT FROM TERM "B" TO TERM "P".
- TEST LIGHT "ON"?

NO
- CHECK FOR POOR CONNECTION AT C200 TERM "B4".
- IF OK, REPAIR OPEN IN CKT 39 BETWEEN REAR DEFOGGER CONTROL SWITCH TERM "C" AND FUSE 17.

YES
- REAR DEFOGGER CONTROL SWITCH TO "ON"
- BACKPROBE SWITCH TERM "D" TO GROUND.
- TEST LIGHT "ON"?

NO
- CHECK FOR POOR CONNECTION AT REAR DEFOGGER CONTROL SWITCH.
- IF OK, REPAIR OPEN IN CKT 150 BETWEEN REAR DEFOGGER CONTROL SWITCH TERM "P" AND G200.

A

A

YES
- BACKPROBE WITH A TEST LIGHT REAR DEFOGGER GRID CONN (CKT 293 SIDE) TO GROUND.
- TEST LIGHT "ON"?

NO
- REPLACE REAR DEFOGGER CONTROL SWITCH.

YES
- CHECK THAT REAR DEFOGGER GROUND G400 IS CLEAN AND TIGHT.
- CHECK FOR OPEN IN CKT 293 BETWEEN GRID CONN AND GRID.
- CHECK FOR OPEN BETWEEN GRID AND GROUND G400.
- IF NO OPEN FOUND, REPAIR REAR DEFOGGER GRID AS NECESSARY.

NO
- CHECK FOR POOR CONNECTION AT REAR DEFOGGER CONTROL SWITCH TERM "D" OR C200 TERM "A6".
- IF OK, REPAIR OPEN IN CKT 293 BETWEEN REAR DEFOGGER SWITCH TERM "D" AND REAR DEFOGGER GRID CONNECTOR.

91C11496

Courtesy of General Motors Corp.

Fig. 2: "B" Body System Diagnosis (1 of 5)

Black wire) and ground. If battery voltage is present, go to next step. If battery voltage is not present, check Orange/Black wire for an open circuit.

2) Measure voltage between connector terminal "D" (Brown wire) and ground. If battery voltage is present, go to next step. If battery voltage is not present, check Brown wire for an open circuit.

3) Measure voltage between connector terminals "C" (Black wire) and "D" (Brown wire). If battery voltage is present, go to next step. If battery voltage is not present, check Black wire for an open circuit.

4) Measure voltage between connector terminals "E" (Tan wire) and "D" (Brown wire). If battery voltage is present with rear defogger switch depressed and zero volts with switch released, go to next step. If voltage is not as indicated, check Tan wire for an open circuit or short to ground. If wire is okay, go to DIC SWITCH ASSEMBLY TEST.

5) Measure voltage between connector terminals "A" (Orange/Black wire) and "B" (Purple/White wire). If battery voltage is present, replace rear defogger timer/relay. If battery voltage is not present, rear defogger grid is defective.

DIC SWITCH ASSEMBLY TEST

Ninety-Eight & Touring Sedan – 1) Ensure rear defogger timer/relay is connected. Turn ignition switch to RUN position and rear defogger off. Measure voltage at DIC switch assembly connector (connected).

2) Using voltmeter, measure voltage between connector terminal No. 30 (Brown wire) and ground. If battery voltage is present, go to next step. If battery voltage is not present, check Brown wire for an open circuit.

3) Measure voltage between connector terminals No. 30 (Brown wire) and No. 24 (Black wire). If battery voltage is present, go to next step. If battery voltage is not present, check Black wire for an open circuit.

4) Measure voltage between terminals No. 30 (Brown wire) and No. 31 (Tan wire). If less than one volt is present, go to next step. If more than one volt is present, replace DIC switch assembly.

5) Depress and hold rear defogger switch. Measure voltage between terminals No. 30 (Brown wire) and No. 31 (Tan wire). If battery voltage is present, defogger grid is defective. If battery voltage is not present, replace DIC switch assembly.

RELAY CENTER VOLTAGE TEST

DeVille & Fleetwood – 1) Ensure defogger relay is disconnected. Turn ignition switch to RUN position and rear defogger on. Perform voltage checks at relay center, position "C".

2) Using voltmeter, measure voltage between terminal No. 2 (Brown wire) and ground. If battery voltage is present, go to next step. If battery voltage is not present, check Brown wire for an open circuit. If wire is okay, check instrument panel fuse block fuse No. 7.

3) Measure voltage between terminals No. 2 (Brown wire) and No. 5 (Dark Blue wire). If battery voltage is present, go to next step. If battery voltage is not present, go to ELECTRONIC CLIMATE CONTROL TEST.

4) Measure voltage between terminal No. 1 (Orange/Black wire) and ground. If battery voltage is present, go to next step. If battery voltage is not present, check Orange/Black wire for an open circuit. If wire is okay, check circuit breaker No. 24.

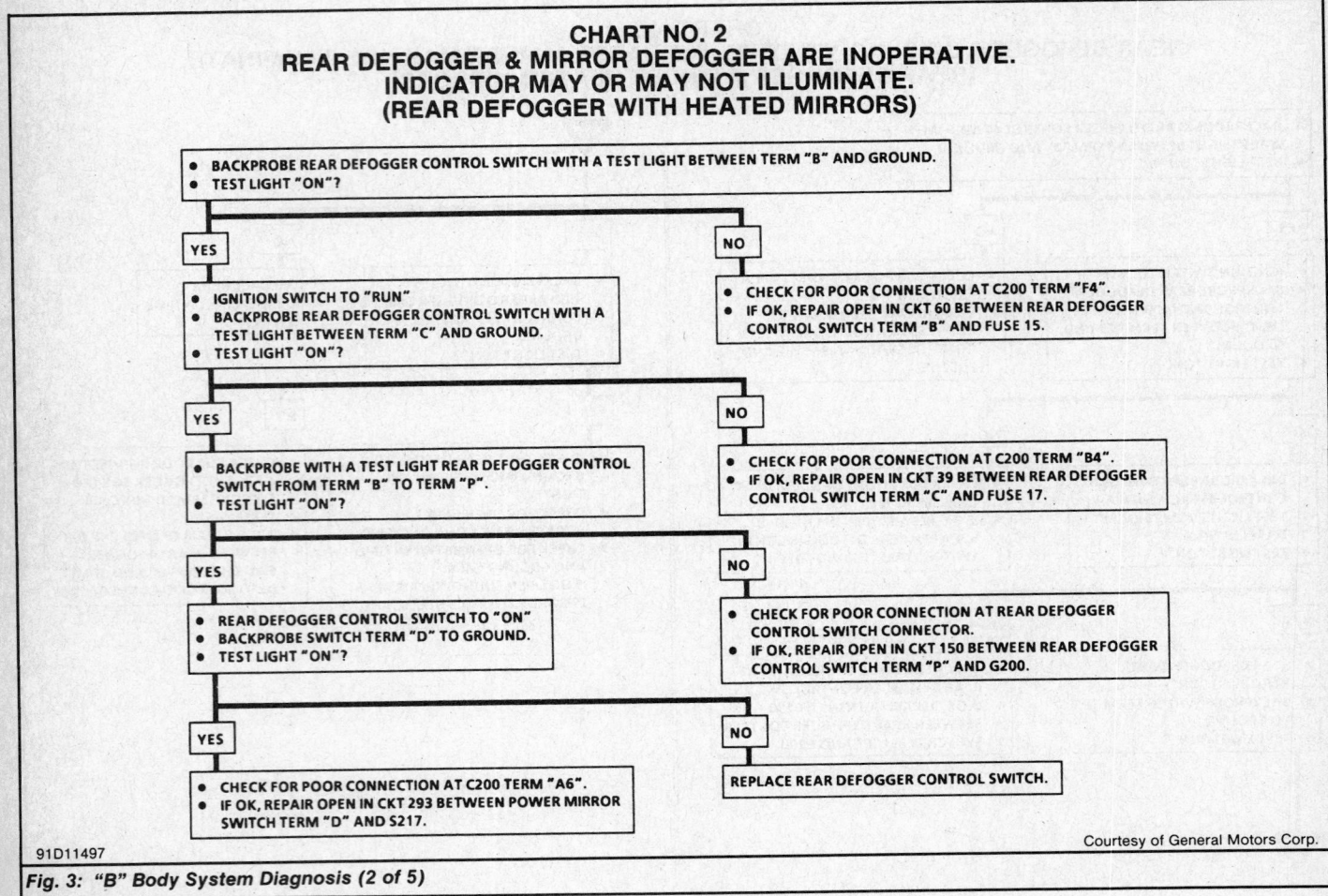

CHART NO. 2
REAR DEFOGGER & MIRROR DEFOGGER ARE INOPERATIVE.
INDICATOR MAY OR MAY NOT ILLUMINATE.
(REAR DEFOGGER WITH HEATED MIRRORS)

- BACKPROBE REAR DEFOGGER CONTROL SWITCH WITH A TEST LIGHT BETWEEN TERM "B" AND GROUND.
- TEST LIGHT "ON"?

YES
- IGNITION SWITCH TO "RUN"
- BACKPROBE REAR DEFOGGER CONTROL SWITCH WITH A TEST LIGHT BETWEEN TERM "C" AND GROUND.
- TEST LIGHT "ON"?

NO
- CHECK FOR POOR CONNECTION AT C200 TERM "F4".
- IF OK, REPAIR OPEN IN CKT 60 BETWEEN REAR DEFOGGER CONTROL SWITCH TERM "B" AND FUSE 15.

YES
- BACKPROBE WITH A TEST LIGHT REAR DEFOGGER CONTROL SWITCH FROM TERM "B" TO TERM "P".
- TEST LIGHT "ON"?

NO
- CHECK FOR POOR CONNECTION AT C200 TERM "B4".
- IF OK, REPAIR OPEN IN CKT 39 BETWEEN REAR DEFOGGER CONTROL SWITCH TERM "C" AND FUSE 17.

YES
- REAR DEFOGGER CONTROL SWITCH TO "ON"
- BACKPROBE SWITCH TERM "D" TO GROUND.
- TEST LIGHT "ON"?

NO
- CHECK FOR POOR CONNECTION AT REAR DEFOGGER CONTROL SWITCH CONNECTOR.
- IF OK, REPAIR OPEN IN CKT 150 BETWEEN REAR DEFOGGER CONTROL SWITCH TERM "P" AND G200.

YES
- CHECK FOR POOR CONNECTION AT C200 TERM "A6".
- IF OK, REPAIR OPEN IN CKT 293 BETWEEN POWER MIRROR SWITCH TERM "D" AND S217.

NO
- REPLACE REAR DEFOGGER CONTROL SWITCH.

91D11497

Courtesy of General Motors Corp.

Fig. 3: "B" Body System Diagnosis (2 of 5)

5) Turn rear defogger switch to OFF position. Measure voltage between terminals No. 2 (Brown wire) and No. 5 (Dark Blue wire). If no voltage is present, go to next step. If voltage is present, check Dark Blue wire for a short to ground. If wire is okay, replace Electronic Climate Control (ECC) programmer, located behind center of instrument panel on right side of A/C-heater plenum.

ELECTRONIC CLIMATE CONTROL TEST

DeVille & Fleetwood – 1) Disconnect ECC programmer connector, located behind center of instrument panel on right side of A/C-heater plenum. Ensure defogger relay is connected. Turn ignition switch to RUN position.
2) Using voltmeter, measure voltage between relay terminal D14 (Dark Blue wire) and ground. If battery voltage is present and air conditioning operates correctly, replace ECC programmer.
3) If battery voltage is not present, check Dark Blue wire for an open circuit. If wire is okay, replace defogger relay.

REAR DEFOGGER TEST

DeVille & Fleetwood – 1) Disconnect rear defogger connectors. Turn ignition switch to RUN and defogger switch to ON positions.
2) Connect voltmeter between Purple/White wire and ground. If battery voltage is present, go to next step. If battery voltage is not present, check Purple/White wire for an open circuit.
3) Connect voltmeter between Purple/White and Black wires. If battery voltage is present, rear defogger grid is defective. If battery voltage is not present, check Black wire for an open circuit.

HEATED MIRROR TEST

DeVille & Fleetwood – 1) Disconnect heated mirror connectors. Turn ignition switch to RUN and defogger switch to ON positions.
2) Using voltmeter, measure voltage between connector terminal "B" (Pink/White wire) and ground. If battery voltage is present, go to next step. If battery voltage is not present, check Pink/White wire for an open circuit. In addition, check relay center fuse No. 3.
3) Using voltmeter, measure voltage between connector terminals "B" (Pink/Black wire) and "A" (Black wire). If battery voltage is present, replace suspect heated mirror assembly. If battery voltage is not present, check Black wire for an open circuit.

"E" & "K" BODY TESTING

SYSTEM CHECK

Eldorado & Seville – 1) With engine running, depress and release rear defogger switch. Rear defogger switch should return to rest position, defogger indicator in Climate Control Driver Information Center (CCDIC) should illuminate and rear window and outside mirrors should warm. Defogger indicator, rear defogger and outside mirror defoggers turn off after approximately 10 minutes.
2) Depress rear defogger switch, and release. Defogger ON indicator, rear defogger and outside mirror defoggers should turn on. After approximately 5 minutes, they will turn off.
3) Depress rear defogger switch twice. Defogger ON indicator, rear defogger and outside mirror defoggers should turn on and then off.
4) If rear defogger and outside mirror defoggers do not operate or if rear defogger and outside mirror defoggers do not turn off, perform DEFOGGER RELAY TEST.

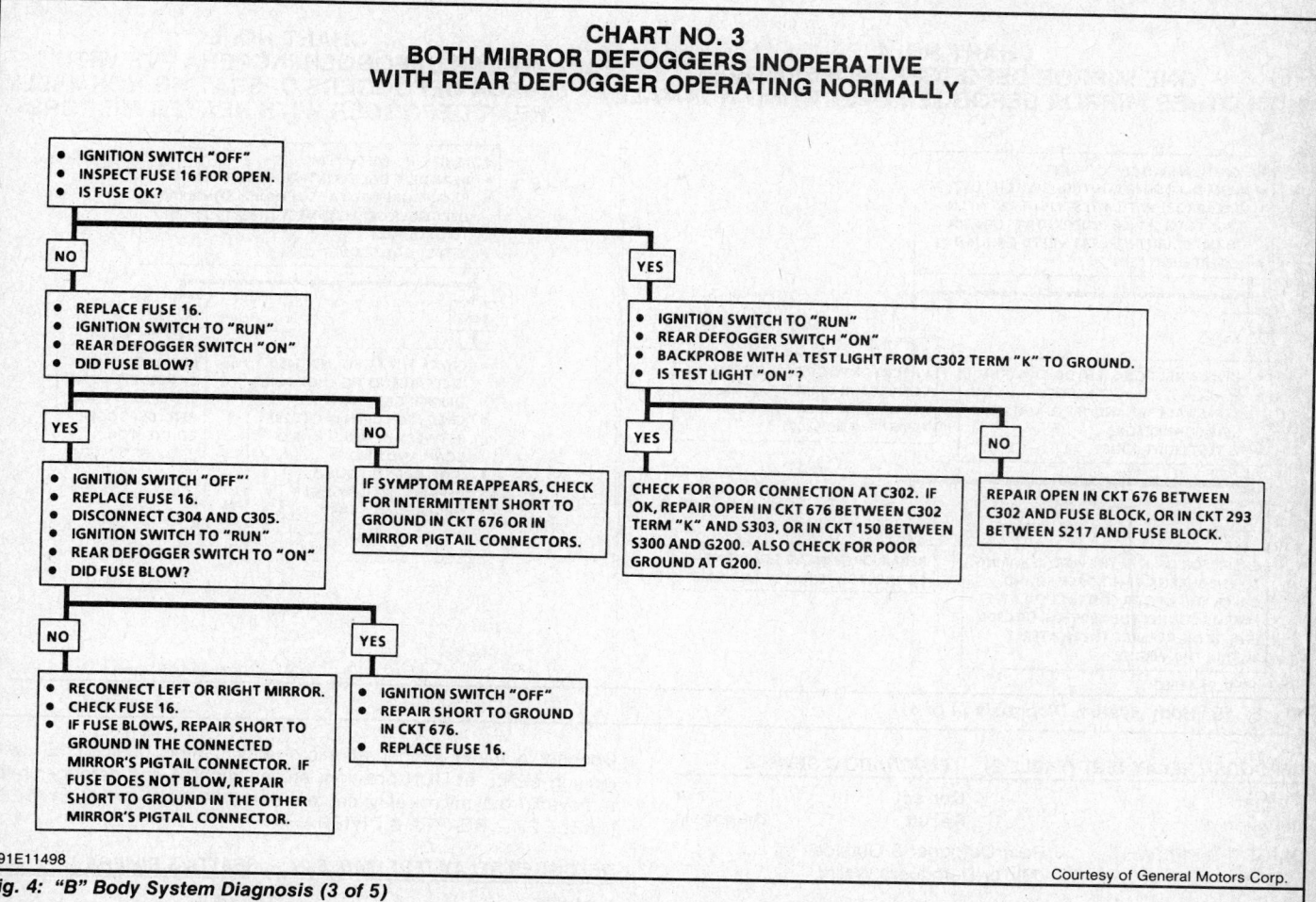

CHART NO. 3
BOTH MIRROR DEFOGGERS INOPERATIVE
WITH REAR DEFOGGER OPERATING NORMALLY

- IGNITION SWITCH "OFF"
- INSPECT FUSE 16 FOR OPEN.
- IS FUSE OK?

NO

- REPLACE FUSE 16.
- IGNITION SWITCH TO "RUN"
- REAR DEFOGGER SWITCH "ON"
- DID FUSE BLOW?

YES

- IGNITION SWITCH "OFF"
- REPLACE FUSE 16.
- DISCONNECT C304 AND C305.
- IGNITION SWITCH TO "RUN"
- REAR DEFOGGER SWITCH TO "ON"
- DID FUSE BLOW?

NO

- RECONNECT LEFT OR RIGHT MIRROR.
- CHECK FUSE 16.
- IF FUSE BLOWS, REPAIR SHORT TO GROUND IN THE CONNECTED MIRROR'S PIGTAIL CONNECTOR. IF FUSE DOES NOT BLOW, REPAIR SHORT TO GROUND IN THE OTHER MIRROR'S PIGTAIL CONNECTOR.

YES

- IGNITION SWITCH "OFF"
- REPAIR SHORT TO GROUND IN CKT 676.
- REPLACE FUSE 16.

NO

IF SYMPTOM REAPPEARS, CHECK FOR INTERMITTENT SHORT TO GROUND IN CKT 676 OR IN MIRROR PIGTAIL CONNECTORS.

YES

- IGNITION SWITCH TO "RUN"
- REAR DEFOGGER SWITCH "ON"
- BACKPROBE WITH A TEST LIGHT FROM C302 TERM "K" TO GROUND.
- IS TEST LIGHT "ON"?

YES

CHECK FOR POOR CONNECTION AT C302. IF OK, REPAIR OPEN IN CKT 676 BETWEEN C302 TERM "K" AND S303, OR IN CKT 150 BETWEEN S300 AND G200. ALSO CHECK FOR POOR GROUND AT G200.

NO

REPAIR OPEN IN CKT 676 BETWEEN C302 AND FUSE BLOCK, OR IN CKT 293 BETWEEN S217 AND FUSE BLOCK.

91E11498

Fig. 4: "B" Body System Diagnosis (3 of 5)

5) If rear defogger does not operate but outside mirror defoggers operate normally, perform REAR DEFOGGER TEST. If outside mirror defoggers will not operate but rear defogger operates normally, perform OUTSIDE MIRROR ASSEMBLY TEST.

Reatta, Riviera, Toronado & Trofeo – 1) With engine running, depress and release rear defogger switch. Defogger ON indicator should light, and defogger grid and left outside mirror (if equipped with defogger) should warm. Defogger ON indicator, rear defogger and left mirror defogger will turn off after approximately 10 minutes.

2) Depress rear defogger switch, and release. Defogger ON indicator, defogger and left mirror defogger should turn on. After approximately 5 minutes, they should turn off.

3) Depress rear defogger switch twice. Defogger ON indicator, rear defogger and left mirror defogger should turn on and then off. If rear defogger and left mirror defogger do not operate, perform DEFOGGER RELAY TEST.

4) If rear defogger does not operate but left mirror defogger operates normally, perform REAR DEFOGGER TEST. If left mirror defogger does not operate but rear defogger operates normally, check heated mirror fuse and wiring to left outside mirror.

5) If fuse and wiring are okay, repair left outside mirror. If rear defogger and left mirror defogger do not turn off, perform DEFOGGER RELAY TEST.

6) On Toronado and Trofeo vehicles, if left mirror defogger does not operate but rear defogger is okay, go to OUTSIDE MIRROR DEFOGGER TEST. If outside power mirror defogger and/or rear defogger remain on and do not turn off, go to DEFOGGER/MIRROR STAYS ON TEST.

DEFOGGER RELAY TEST

Eldorado & Seville – Connect test light at micro-relay center, position "E", with ignition on, engine running and defogger relay removed from micro-relay center.

DEFOGGER RELAY TEST (TABLE 1) – ELDORADO & SEVILLE

Connect Between	Correct Result [1]	For Diagnosis
DK GRN & GND	Light On	2
PNK/BLK & GND	Light On	3
PNK/BLK & DK BLU [4]	Light On	5
PNK/BLK & DK BLU [6]	Light Off	7

[1] – If all results are correct and defogger does not operate, go to DEFOGGER RELAY TEST (TABLE 2) – ELDORADO & SEVILLE. If all results are correct and defogger does not turn off, check for shorted rear defogger relay contacts and Purple/White wire for a short to battery voltage.

[2] – Check DK GRN wire for an open circuit or short to ground.

[3] – Check PNK/BLK wire for an open circuit.

[4] – Defogger switch in ON position.

[5] – Check DK BLU wire for an open circuit. If wire is okay, replace heater-A/C programmer.

[6] – Defogger switch in OFF position.

[7] – Check DK BLU wire for a short to ground. If okay, replace heater-A/C programmer.

Connect a fused jumper at micro-relay center, position "E", with ignition on, engine running, defogger relay removed from micro-relay center and defogger switch in ON position.

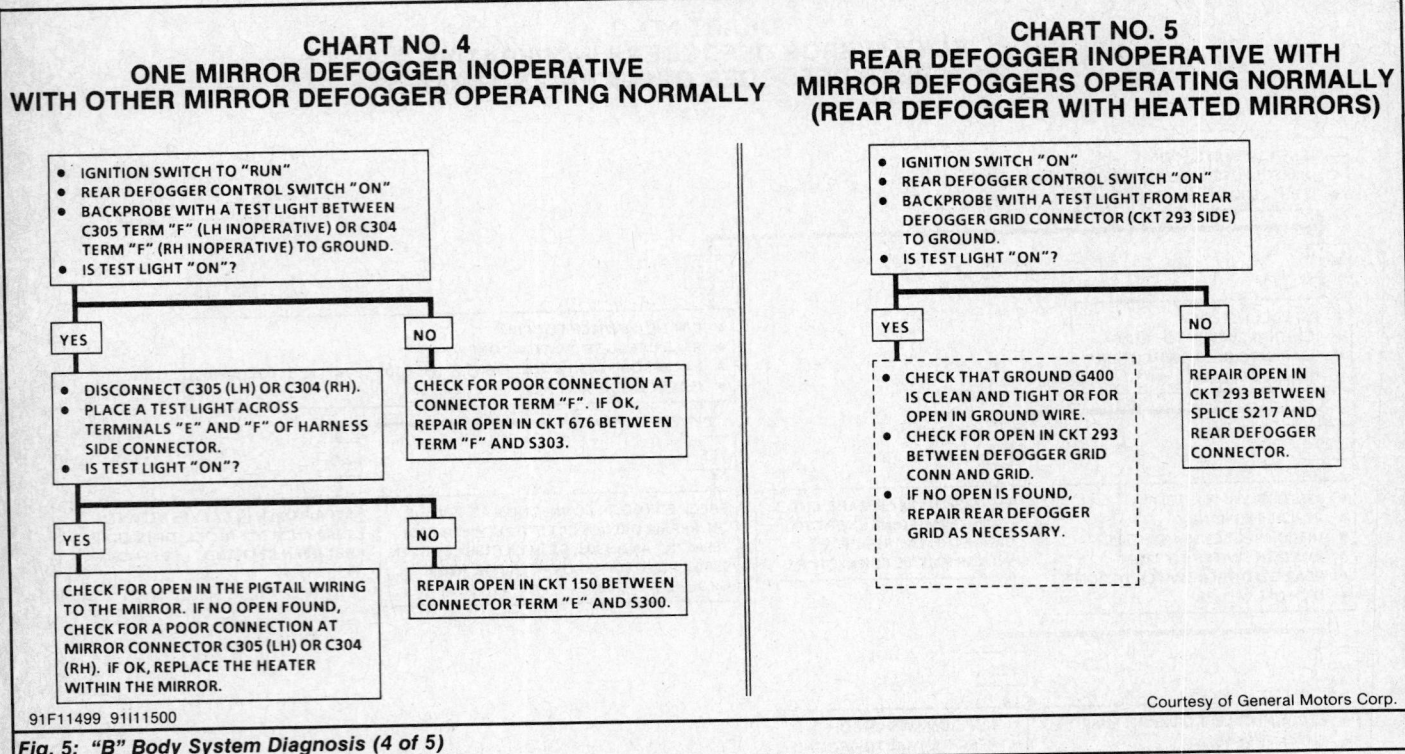

CHART NO. 4
ONE MIRROR DEFOGGER INOPERATIVE WITH OTHER MIRROR DEFOGGER OPERATING NORMALLY

- IGNITION SWITCH TO "RUN"
- REAR DEFOGGER CONTROL SWITCH "ON"
- BACKPROBE WITH A TEST LIGHT BETWEEN C305 TERM "F" (LH INOPERATIVE) OR C304 TERM "F" (RH INOPERATIVE) TO GROUND.
- IS TEST LIGHT "ON"?

YES
- DISCONNECT C305 (LH) OR C304 (RH).
- PLACE A TEST LIGHT ACROSS TERMINALS "E" AND "F" OF HARNESS SIDE CONNECTOR.
- IS TEST LIGHT "ON"?

NO
CHECK FOR POOR CONNECTION AT CONNECTOR TERM "F". IF OK, REPAIR OPEN IN CKT 676 BETWEEN TERM "F" AND S303.

YES
CHECK FOR OPEN IN THE PIGTAIL WIRING TO THE MIRROR. IF NO OPEN FOUND, CHECK FOR A POOR CONNECTION AT MIRROR CONNECTOR C305 (LH) OR C304 (RH). IF OK, REPLACE THE HEATER WITHIN THE MIRROR.

NO
REPAIR OPEN IN CKT 150 BETWEEN CONNECTOR TERM "E" AND S300.

CHART NO. 5
REAR DEFOGGER INOPERATIVE WITH MIRROR DEFOGGERS OPERATING NORMALLY (REAR DEFOGGER WITH HEATED MIRRORS)

- IGNITION SWITCH "ON"
- REAR DEFOGGER CONTROL SWITCH "ON"
- BACKPROBE WITH A TEST LIGHT FROM REAR DEFOGGER GRID CONNECTOR (CKT 293 SIDE) TO GROUND.
- IS TEST LIGHT "ON"?

YES
- CHECK THAT GROUND G400 IS CLEAN AND TIGHT OR FOR OPEN IN GROUND WIRE.
- CHECK FOR OPEN IN CKT 293 BETWEEN DEFOGGER GRID CONN AND GRID.
- IF NO OPEN IS FOUND, REPAIR REAR DEFOGGER GRID AS NECESSARY.

NO
REPAIR OPEN IN CKT 293 BETWEEN SPLICE S217 AND REAR DEFOGGER CONNECTOR.

Courtesy of General Motors Corp.

91F11499 91I11500

Fig. 5: "B" Body System Diagnosis (4 of 5)

DEFOGGER RELAY TEST (TABLE 2) – ELDORADO & SEVILLE

Jumper Between	Correct Result [1]	For Diagnosis
DK GRN & PPL/WHT	Rear Defogger & Outside Mirror Defoggers Warm	[2]

[1] – If result is correct, replace defogger relay.
[2] – Check PPL/WHT wire for an open circuit.

Reatta & Riviera – Connect test light at micro-relay center, position "E" (position "C" on Reatta convertible), with ignition on, engine running, convertible top closed (if equipped) and defogger relay removed from micro-relay center. See DEFOGGER RELAY TEST (TABLE 1) – REATTA & RIVIERA.

DEFOGGER RELAY TEST (TABLE 1) – REATTA & RIVIERA

Connect Between	Correct Result [1]	For Diagnosis
RED/BLK & GND	Light On	[2]
BRN & GND	Light On	[3]
BRN & DK BLU or YEL [4]	Light On	[5]
BRN & DK BLU or YEL [6]	Light Off	[7]

[1] – If all results are correct and defogger does not operate, go to DEFOGGER RELAY TEST (TABLE 2) – REATTA & RIVIERA. If all results are correct and defogger does not turn off, check PPL/WHT and PNK/WHT wires for a short to voltage. Replace defogger relay if wires are okay.
[2] – Check RED/BLK wire for an open circuit or short to ground. Check DEFOG fuse No. 2.
[3] – Check BRN wire for an open circuit. Check A/C fuse No. 19.
[4] – Defogger switch in ON position.
[5] – Check DK BLU wire for an open circuit. If wire is okay, replace heater-A/C programmer.
[6] – Defogger switch in OFF position.
[7] – Check DK BLU and YEL wires for a short to ground. If okay, replace heater-A/C programmer.

Connect a fused jumper at micro-relay center, position "E", with ignition switch at RUN position, engine running and defogger relay removed from micro-relay center. See DEFOGGER RELAY TEST (TABLE 2) – REATTA & RIVIERA.

DEFOGGER RELAY TEST (TABLE 2) – REATTA & RIVIERA

Jumper Between	Correct Result [1]	For Diagnosis
RED/BLK & PPL/WHT	Rear Defogger & Left Mirror Defogger Warm	[2]

[1] – If rear defogger and left mirror defogger operate, replace defogger relay.
[2] – Check PPL/WHT wire for an open circuit.

Toronado & Trofeo – 1) Perform test at micro-relay center, position "E". Turn ignition switch to RUN position. Remove defogger relay from micro-relay center.
2) Connect test light between terminal No. 3 (Dark Green wire) and ground. If test light illuminates, go to next step. If test light does not illuminate, check Dark Green wire for an open or short circuit to ground. Check circuit breaker No. 24.
3) Connect test light between terminal No. 1 (Brown wire) and ground. If test light illuminates, go to next step. If test light does not illuminate, check Brown wire for an open circuit.
4) Turn engine on, and depress defogger button. Connect a test light between terminals No. 1 (Brown wire) and No. 2 (Dark Blue wire). If test light illuminates, go to next step. If test light does not illuminate, check Dark Blue wire for an open circuit and good terminal contact. If wire is okay, replace heater and A/C programmer, located behind center of instrument panel on right side of plenum.
5) Connect a 30-amp fused jumper wire between terminals No. 3 (Dark Green wire) and No. 5 (Purple/White wire). If rear defogger and left mirror defogger operate, replace defogger relay.
6) If rear defogger and left mirror defogger do not operate, check and repair wiring to defoggers as necessary. If fused jumper blows, check wiring and defogger grids for a short to ground.

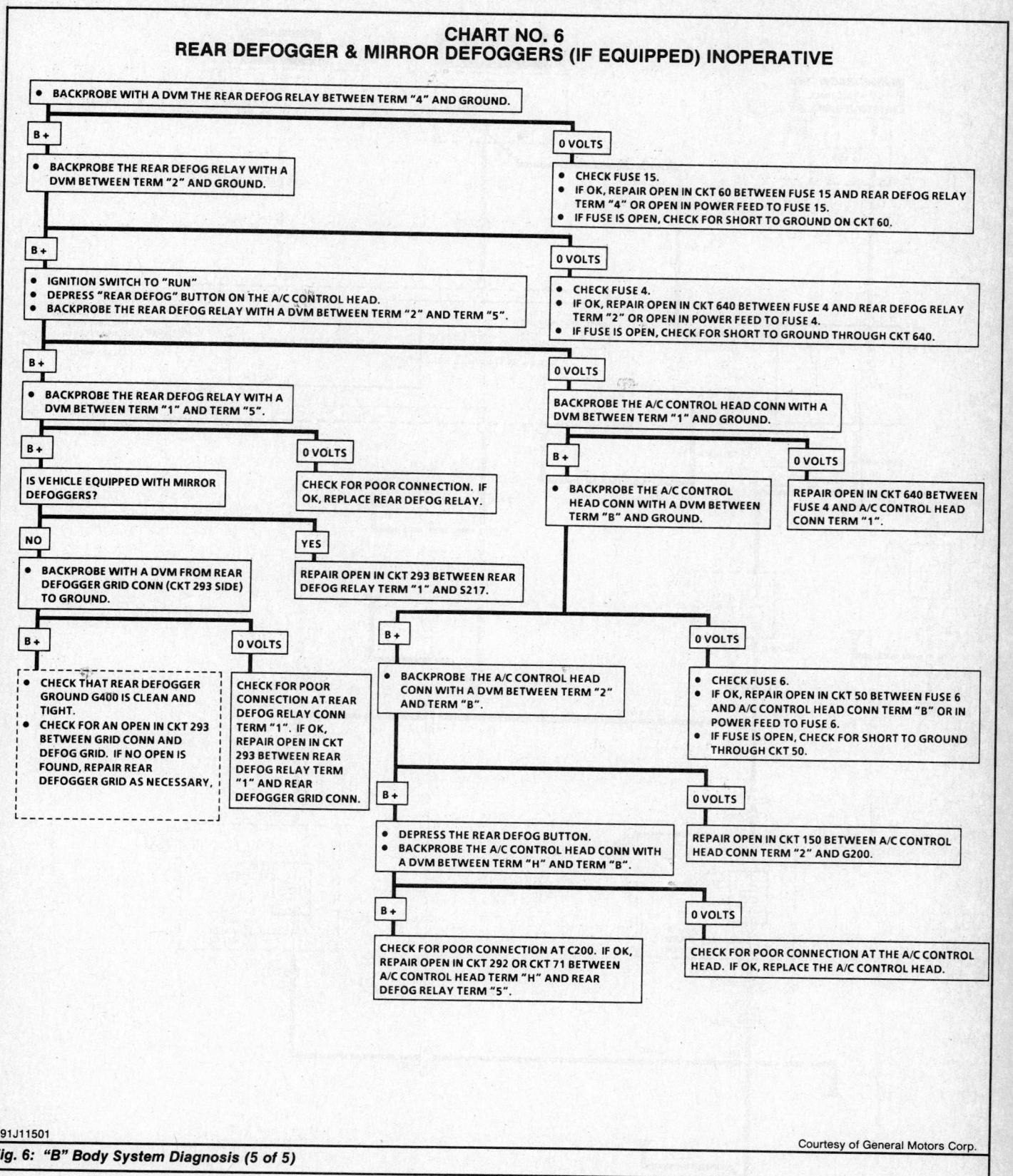

CHART NO. 6
REAR DEFOGGER & MIRROR DEFOGGERS (IF EQUIPPED) INOPERATIVE

- BACKPROBE WITH A DVM THE REAR DEFOG RELAY BETWEEN TERM "4" AND GROUND.

B +

- BACKPROBE THE REAR DEFOG RELAY WITH A DVM BETWEEN TERM "2" AND GROUND.

0 VOLTS
- CHECK FUSE 15.
- IF OK, REPAIR OPEN IN CKT 60 BETWEEN FUSE 15 AND REAR DEFOG RELAY TERM "4" OR OPEN IN POWER FEED TO FUSE 15.
- IF FUSE IS OPEN, CHECK FOR SHORT TO GROUND ON CKT 60.

B +

- IGNITION SWITCH TO "RUN"
- DEPRESS "REAR DEFOG" BUTTON ON THE A/C CONTROL HEAD.
- BACKPROBE THE REAR DEFOG RELAY WITH A DVM BETWEEN TERM "2" AND TERM "5".

0 VOLTS
- CHECK FUSE 4.
- IF OK, REPAIR OPEN IN CKT 640 BETWEEN FUSE 4 AND REAR DEFOG RELAY TERM "2" OR OPEN IN POWER FEED TO FUSE 4.
- IF FUSE IS OPEN, CHECK FOR SHORT TO GROUND THROUGH CKT 640.

B +

- BACKPROBE THE REAR DEFOG RELAY WITH A DVM BETWEEN TERM "1" AND TERM "5".

0 VOLTS
BACKPROBE THE A/C CONTROL HEAD CONN WITH A DVM BETWEEN TERM "1" AND GROUND.

B +

IS VEHICLE EQUIPPED WITH MIRROR DEFOGGERS?

0 VOLTS
CHECK FOR POOR CONNECTION. IF OK, REPLACE REAR DEFOG RELAY.

B +
- BACKPROBE THE A/C CONTROL HEAD CONN WITH A DVM BETWEEN TERM "B" AND GROUND.

0 VOLTS
REPAIR OPEN IN CKT 640 BETWEEN FUSE 4 AND A/C CONTROL HEAD CONN TERM "1".

NO
- BACKPROBE WITH A DVM FROM REAR DEFOGGER GRID CONN (CKT 293 SIDE) TO GROUND.

YES
REPAIR OPEN IN CKT 293 BETWEEN REAR DEFOG RELAY TERM "1" AND S217.

B +
- CHECK THAT REAR DEFOGGER GROUND G400 IS CLEAN AND TIGHT.
- CHECK FOR AN OPEN IN CKT 293 BETWEEN GRID CONN AND DEFOG GRID. IF NO OPEN IS FOUND, REPAIR REAR DEFOGGER GRID AS NECESSARY.

0 VOLTS
CHECK FOR POOR CONNECTION AT REAR DEFOG RELAY CONN TERM "1". IF OK, REPAIR OPEN IN CKT 293 BETWEEN REAR DEFOG RELAY TERM "1" AND REAR DEFOGGER GRID CONN.

B +
- BACKPROBE THE A/C CONTROL HEAD CONN WITH A DVM BETWEEN TERM "2" AND TERM "B".

0 VOLTS
- CHECK FUSE 6.
- IF OK, REPAIR OPEN IN CKT 50 BETWEEN FUSE 6 AND A/C CONTROL HEAD CONN TERM "B" OR IN POWER FEED TO FUSE 6.
- IF FUSE IS OPEN, CHECK FOR SHORT TO GROUND THROUGH CKT 50.

B +
- DEPRESS THE REAR DEFOG BUTTON.
- BACKPROBE THE A/C CONTROL HEAD CONN WITH A DVM BETWEEN TERM "H" AND TERM "B".

0 VOLTS
REPAIR OPEN IN CKT 150 BETWEEN A/C CONTROL HEAD CONN TERM "2" AND G200.

B +
CHECK FOR POOR CONNECTION AT C200. IF OK, REPAIR OPEN IN CKT 292 OR CKT 71 BETWEEN A/C CONTROL HEAD TERM "H" AND REAR DEFOG RELAY TERM "5".

0 VOLTS
CHECK FOR POOR CONNECTION AT THE A/C CONTROL HEAD. IF OK, REPLACE THE A/C CONTROL HEAD.

91J11501

Fig. 6: "B" Body System Diagnosis (5 of 5)

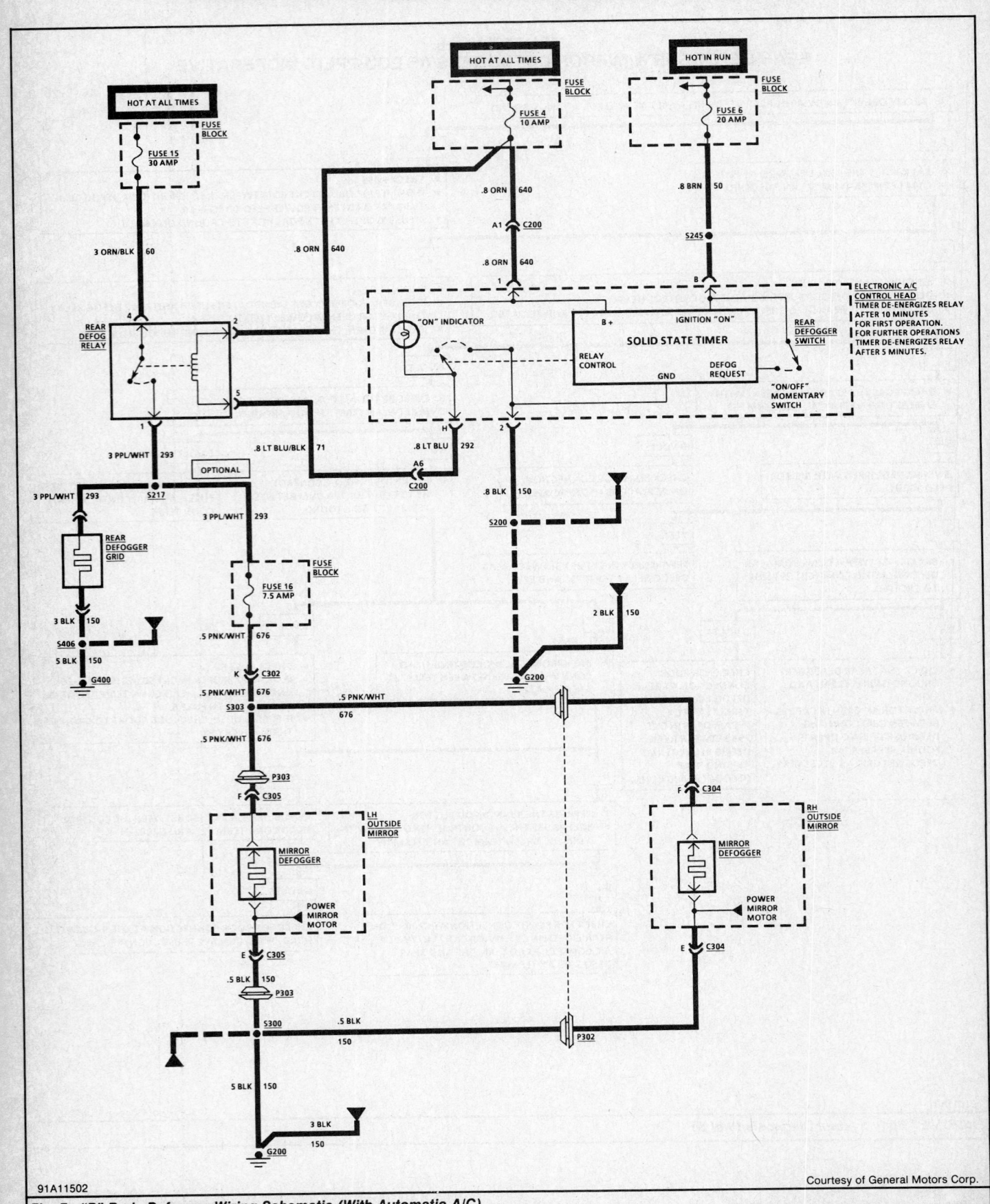

91A11502

Courtesy of General Motors Corp.

Fig. 7: "B" Body Defogger Wiring Schematic (With Automatic A/C)

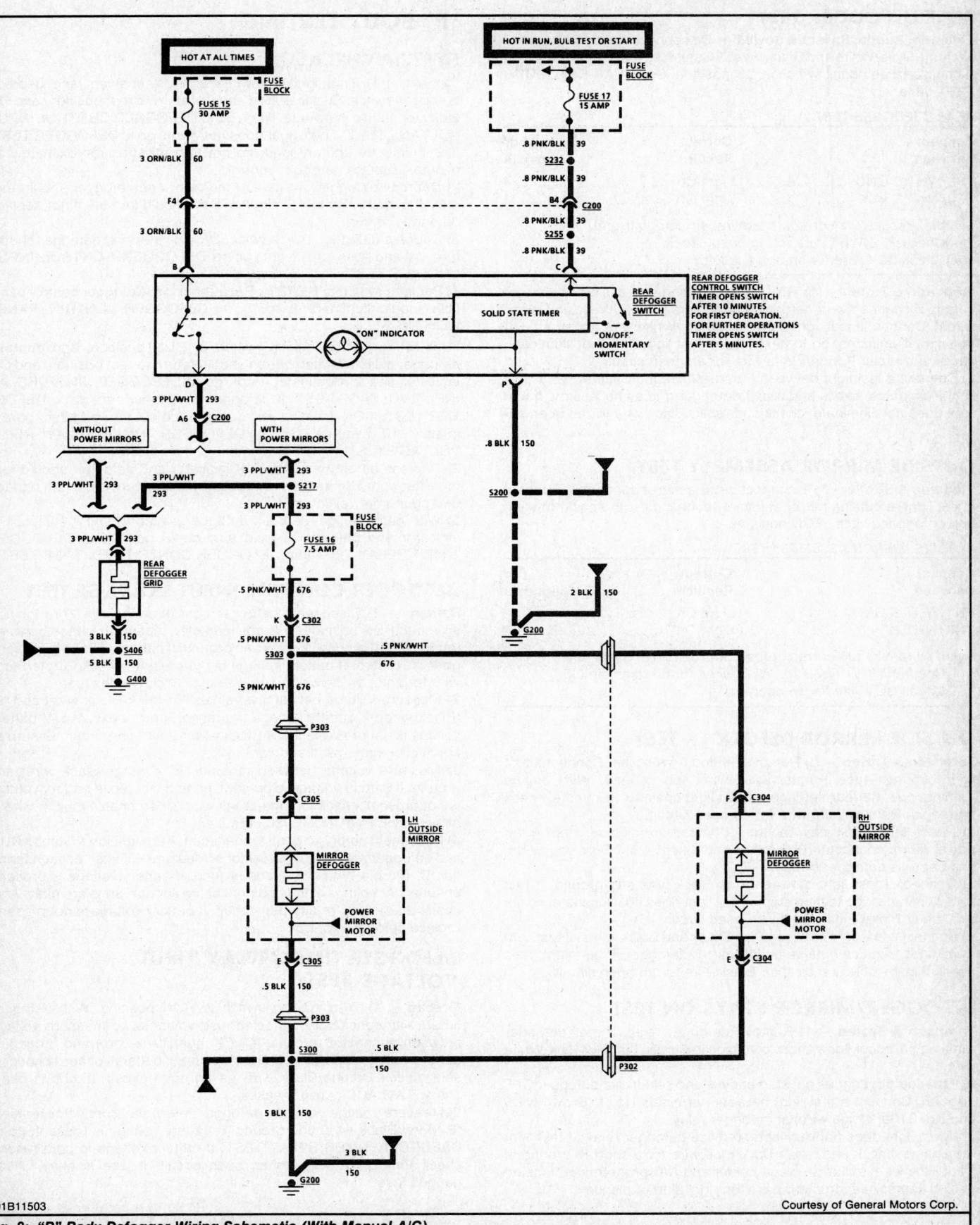

91B11503

Courtesy of General Motors Corp.

Fig. 8: "B" Body Defogger Wiring Schematic (With Manual A/C)

REAR DEFOGGER TEST

Eldorado, Reatta, Riviera & Seville – Disconnect rear defogger connector (Purple/White and Black wires). Connect a test light with engine running and defogger switch in ON position. See REAR DEFOGGER TEST table.

REAR DEFOGGER TEST

Connect Between	Correct Result [1]	For Diagnosis
PPL/WHT & GND	Light On	[2]
PPL/WHT & BLK	Light On	[3]

[1] – If all results are correct, check/repair defogger grid.
[2] – Check PPL/WHT wire for an open circuit.
[3] – Check BLK wire for an open circuit.

Toronado & Trofeo – 1) Turn engine on, and depress rear defogger button. Disconnect rear defogger connectors (Purple/White and Black wires). Connect a test light between Purple/White wire and ground. If test light illuminates, go to next step. If test light does not illuminate, check and repair Purple/White wire for an open circuit.
2) Connect a test light between Purple/White and Black wires. If test light illuminates, check and repair defogger grid as necessary. If test light does not illuminate, check and repair Black wire for an open circuit.

OUTSIDE MIRROR ASSEMBLY TEST

Eldorado & Seville – Disconnect outside mirror connector. Connect a test light at outside mirror assembly connector with engine running and defogger switch in ON position.

OUTSIDE MIRROR ASSEMBLY TEST

Connect Between	Correct Result [1]	For Diagnosis
PNK/WHT & GND	Light On	[2]
PNK/WHT & BLK	Light On	[3]

[1] – If all results are correct, repair outside mirror assembly.
[2] – Check PNK/WHT & PPL/WHT wires for an open circuit.
[3] – Check BLK wire for an open circuit.

OUTSIDE MIRROR DEFOGGER TEST

Toronado & Trofeo – 1) Remove heated mirror fuse. Connect a test light between fuse Purple/White wire and ground. With engine running, operate rear defogger. If test light does not illuminate, check and repair Purple/White wire for an open circuit.
2) If test light illuminates, reconnect heated mirror fuse. Unplug left power mirror connector (Pink/White and Black wires). Turn engine on, and depress defogger switch.
3) Connect a test light between Pink/Black wire and ground. If test light illuminates, go to next step. If test light does not illuminate, check and repair Pink/White wire for an open circuit.
4) Connect a test light between Pink/Black and Black wires. If test light illuminates, replace outside power mirror defogger. If test light does not illuminate, check and repair Black wire for an open circuit.

DEFOGGER/MIRROR STAYS ON TEST

Toronado & Trofeo – 1) Remove defogger relay. If rear defogger remains on, check for a short to voltage in Purple/White or Pink/White wire.
2) If rear defogger goes off, start engine, and select rear defogger OFF position. Connect a test light between terminals No. 1 (Brown wire) and No. 2 (Dark Blue wire) at defogger relay.
3) If test light does not illuminate, replace defogger relay. If test light illuminates, check and repair Dark Blue wire for a short to ground. If Dark Blue wire is okay, replace heater and A/C programmer, located behind center of instrument panel on right side of plenum.

"F" BODY TESTING

SYSTEM CHECK

Camaro – 1) Turn ignition switch to RUN position, and depress defogger switch. Switch button should return to rest position, and ON indicator should illuminate. If not, go to DEFOGGER CONTROL INPUT VOLTAGE TEST. If defogger does not warm, go to DEFOGGER TEST. If ON indicator and defogger do not turn off after approximately 10 minutes, replace defogger control.
2) Depress defogger switch. ON indicator and defogger should turn on. After approximately 5 minutes, they should turn off. If not, replace defogger control.
3) Depress defogger switch twice. ON indicator and defogger should turn on and then off. If not, go to DEFOGGER CONTROL INPUT VOLTAGE TEST.
4) Put light switch in HEAD or PARK position. Defogger control panel light should illuminate. If not, go to DEFOGGER CONTROL PANEL LIGHT TEST.

Firebird – 1) Turn ignition switch to RUN position, and depress defogger switch. Switch button should return to rest position, and ON indicator should illuminate. If not, go to DEFOGGER TIMER/RELAY INPUT VOLTAGE TEST. If defogger does not warm, go to DEFOGGER TEST. If ON indicator and defogger do not turn off after approximately 10 minutes, go to DEFOGGER TIMER/RELAY INPUT VOLTAGE TEST.
2) Depress defogger switch. ON indicator and defogger should turn on. After approximately 5 minutes, they should turn off. If not, replace defogger timer/relay.
3) With defogger on, depress defogger switch to OFF position. ON indicator and defogger should turn off. If not, go to DEFOGGER TIMER/RELAY TEST and DEFOGGER CONTROL VOLTAGE TEST.

DEFOGGER CONTROL INPUT VOLTAGE TEST

Camaro – 1) Disconnect defogger control connector. Turn ignition switch to RUN position. Using a voltmeter, measure voltage between terminal "C" (Pink/Black wire) and ground. If battery voltage is present, go to next step. If battery voltage is not present, check Purple/Black wire for an open circuit. If wire is okay, check gauges fuse.
2) Measure voltage between terminals "C" (Pink/Black wire) and "P" (Black wire). If battery voltage is present, go to next step. If battery voltage is not present, check Black wire for an open circuit. Ensure all connections are clean and tight.
3) Measure voltage between terminal "B" (Orange/Black wire) and ground. If battery voltage is present, go to next step. If battery voltage is not present, check Orange/Black wire for an open circuit. If wire is okay, check PWR ACC circuit breaker.
4) Reconnect defogger control connector. Turn ignition switch to RUN and defogger switch to ON positions. Measure voltage between terminal "D" (Purple/White wire) and ground. If battery voltage is present, ensure connections at left and right hatch support arms are okay. Also check Black wire for an open circuit. If battery voltage is not present, replace defogger control.

DEFOGGER TIMER/RELAY INPUT VOLTAGE TEST

Firebird – 1) Turn ignition switch to RUN position. With defogger timer/relay connector connected, use voltmeter to measure voltage between connector terminal "C" (Orange/Black wire) and ground. If battery voltage is present, go to next step. If battery voltage is not present, check Orange/Black wire for an open circuit. If wire is okay, check PWR ACC circuit breaker.
2) Measure voltage between defogger timer/relay connector terminal "E" (Pink/Black wire) and ground. If battery voltage is present, go to DEFOGGER TIMER/RELAY TEST. If battery voltage is not present, check Pink/Black wire for an open circuit. If wire is okay, check gauges fuse.

DEFOGGER TIMER/RELAY TEST

Firebird – 1) Turn ignition switch to RUN position and defogger on. With defogger timer/relay connector connected, use test light to check for voltage between connector terminal "B" (Light Blue wire) and ground. If test light illuminates, go to next step. If test light does not illuminate, check Light Blue wire for an open circuit. If wire is okay, go to DEFOGGER CONTROL VOLTAGE TEST.

2) Connect test light between terminals "D" (Black wire) and "B" (Light Blue wire). If test light illuminates, go to next step. If test light does not illuminate, check Black wire for an open circuit. Ensure ground is clean and tight.

3) Connect test light between terminal "A" (Purple/White wire) and ground. If test light illuminates, go to next step. If test light does not illuminate, replace defogger/timer relay.

4) Turn defogger off. Connect test light between terminals "B" (Light Blue wire) and "E" (Pink/Black wire). If test light illuminates, go to next step. If test light does not illuminate, go to DEFOGGER CONTROL VOLTAGE TEST.

5) Connect test light between terminal "A" (Purple/White wire) and ground. If test light does not illuminate, go to DEFOGGER TEST. If test light illuminates, replace defogger timer/relay.

DEFOGGER CONTROL VOLTAGE TEST

Firebird – 1) Turn ignition switch to RUN position and defogger on. Put headlight switch in PARK position. With defogger timer/relay connector connected, use voltmeter to check for voltage between terminal "D" (Pink/Black wire) and ground. If battery voltage is present, go to next step. If battery voltage is not present, check Pink/Black wire for an open circuit. If wire is okay, check gauges fuse.

2) Connect voltmeter between connector terminal "F" (Light Blue wire) and ground. If battery voltage is present, go to next step. If battery voltage is not present, replace defogger control.

3) Connect voltmeter between terminal "C" (Purple/White wire) and ground. If battery voltage is present, go to next step. If battery voltage is not present, check Purple/White wire for an open circuit. If wire is okay, go to DEFOGGER TIMER/RELAY TEST.

4) Connect voltmeter between terminal "E" (Gray wire) and ground. If battery voltage is present, go to next step. If battery voltage is not present, check INST LP fuse. Also check Gray wire for an open circuit.

5) Connect voltmeter between terminals "E" (Gray wire) and "A" (Black wire). If battery voltage is present, go to DEFOGGER TEST. If battery voltage is not present, check Black wire for an open circuit. Ensure ground connections are clean and tight. Replace panel light if wire and ground are okay. If battery voltage is present and defogger does not operate properly, go to DEFOGGER TEST.

DEFOGGER TEST

Camaro – 1) Turn ignition switch to RUN and defogger switch to ON positions. Connect one lead of test light to ground. From inside vehicle, lightly touch other lead to each grid line, and slowly move lead along length of grid. Test light brightness should increase as light is moved from left to right.

2) If test light does not illuminate along any grid lines, check Purple/White wire to defogger control for an open circuit. If wire is okay, go to DEFOGGER CONTROL INPUT VOLTAGE TEST.

3) If test light shows full brilliance at both ends of grid, check Black wire for an open circuit to ground. If test light suddenly illuminates as it is moved along grid, grid line is broken.

Firebird – 1) Turn ignition switch to RUN and defogger switch to ON positions. Connect one lead of test light to ground. From inside vehicle, lightly touch other lead to each grid line, and slowly move lead along length of grid. Test light brightness should increase as light is moved from left to right.

2) If test light does not illuminate along any grid lines, check Purple/White, Purple and Black wires to defogger control for an open circuit. If wires are okay, go to DEFOGGER LIGHT TEST. If test light shows full illumination at both sides of grid, check Black wire for an open circuit to ground. If test light suddenly illuminates as it is moved across grid, grid line is broken.

DEFOGGER CONTROL PANEL LIGHT TEST

Camaro – 1) Disconnect defogger control connector. Turn ignition switch to RUN and headlight switch to PARK positions. Connect one lead of voltmeter to terminal "A" (Gray wire) and other lead to ground. If battery voltage is present, go to next step. If battery voltage is not present, check Gray wire for an open circuit. If wire is okay, check INST fuse.

2) Connect voltmeter to terminals "A" (Gray wire) and "P" (Black wire). If battery voltage is present, repair/replace panel light as necessary. If battery voltage is not present, check Black wire for an open circuit. If wire is okay, ensure all grounds are clean and tight.

DEFOGGER LIGHT TEST

Firebird – 1) Turn ignition to RUN and defogger switch to ON positions. Connect a test light between left hatch support arm (braided wire) and ground. If test light does not illuminate, go to DEFOGGER/TIMER RELAY TEST. If test light does illuminate, go to next step.

2) Connect test light between left support arm (braided wire) and right support arm (braided wire). If test light illuminates, defogger grid line is defective. If test light does not illuminate, check Black wire for an open circuit. Ensure all grounds are clean and tight.

"H" BODY TESTING

SYSTEM CHECK

1) On Eighty-Eight and LeSabre, if rear defogger fails to operate properly, go to REAR DEFOGGER INOPERATIVE TEST. On Bonneville, turn ignition switch to RUN position. Turn and release rear defogger switch (manual A/C) or press rear defogger button (automatic A/C). Switch should return to rest position, and ON indicator should illuminate. If not, go to REAR DEFOGGER CONTROL VOLTAGE TEST (manual A/C) or REAR DEFOGGER RELAY VOLTAGE TEST (automatic A/C).

2) If defogger does not warm, go to REAR DEFOGGER TEST. If ON indicator and defogger do not turn off after approximately 10 minutes, replace rear defogger control (manual A/C) or go to HEATER & A/C CONTROL ASSEMBLY VOLTAGE TEST (automatic A/C).

3) Turn rear defogger switch (manual A/C) or press rear defogger button (automatic A/C), and then release. ON indicator and defogger should turn on. After approximately 5 minutes, they should turn off. If not, replace rear defogger control (manual A/C) or go to REAR DEFOGGER RELAY VOLTAGE TEST (automatic A/C).

REAR DEFOGGER INOPERATIVE TEST

Manual A/C (Eighty-Eight & LeSabre) – 1) Turn ignition switch to RUN position. With rear defogger control connector connected, use voltmeter to check for voltage between terminal "B" (Orange/Black wire) and ground. If battery voltage is present, go to next step. If not, check Orange/Black wire for an open circuit.

2) Connect voltmeter between terminal "C" (Brown wire) and ground. If battery voltage is present, go to next step. If battery voltage is not present, check Brown wire for an open circuit.

3) Turn rear defogger control to ON position. Connect voltmeter between terminals "A" (Purple/White wire) and "E" (Black wire). If battery voltage is present, go to REAR DEFOGGER TEST. If battery voltage is not present, check Purple/White wire for a short to ground. If wire is okay, replace rear defogger control.

Automatic A/C (Eighty-Eight & LeSabre) – 1) Turn ignition switch to RUN position and rear defogger on. Disconnect rear defogger relay. Using voltmeter, check for voltage between terminal No. 1 (Orange/Black wire) and ground. If battery voltage is present, go to next step. If battery voltage is not present, check Orange/Black wire for an open circuit.

2) Connect voltmeter between terminal No. 2 (Brown wire) and ground. If battery voltage is present, go to next step. If battery voltage is not present, check Brown wire for an open circuit.

3) Connect voltmeter between terminals No. 2 (Brown wire) and No. 5 (Tan wire). If battery voltage is present, go to next step. If battery volt-

age is not present, check terminal contact and Tan wire to heater-A/C control assembly for an open circuit. If wire is okay, replace heater-A/C control assembly.

4) Connect voltmeter between terminals No. 1 (Orange/Black wire) and No. 4 (Purple/White wire). If battery voltage is present, check Purple/White wire for a short to ground. If wire is okay, replace defogger relay. If battery voltage is not present, go to REAR DEFOGGER TEST.

REAR DEFOGGER CONTROL VOLTAGE TEST

Manual A/C (Bonneville) – 1) Turn ignition switch to RUN position. Disconnect rear defogger control connector. Using a voltmeter, measure voltage between connector terminal "E" (Brown wire) and ground. If battery voltage is present, go to next step. If battery voltage is not present, check Brown wire for an open circuit.

2) Measure voltage between terminals "E" (Brown wire) and "C" (Black wire). If battery voltage is present, go to next step. If battery voltage is not present, check Black wire for an open circuit.

3) Measure voltage between terminal "B" (Orange/Black wire) and ground. If battery voltage is present, go to next step. If battery voltage is not present, check Orange/Black wire for an open circuit. If wire is okay, check circuit breaker No. 23.

4) Reconnect rear defogger control connector. Turn rear defogger control to ON position. Using voltmeter, measure voltage between terminals "D" (Purple/White wire) and "C" (Black wire). If battery voltage is present, go to REAR DEFOGGER TEST. If battery voltage is not present, check Purple/White wire for a short to ground. If wire is okay, replace rear defogger control.

REAR DEFOGGER RELAY VOLTAGE TEST

Automatic A/C – 1) Turn ignition switch to RUN position. Remove rear defogger relay. Press rear defogger ON button. Using voltmeter, measure voltage between relay terminal No. 2 (Brown wire) and ground. If battery voltage is present, go to next step. If battery voltage is not present, check Brown wire for an open circuit.

2) Measure voltage between terminals No. 2 (Brown wire) and No. 5 (Tan wire). If battery voltage is present, go to next step. If battery voltage is not present, go to HEATER & A/C CONTROL ASSEMBLY VOLTAGE TEST.

3) Measure voltage between terminal No. 1 (Orange/Black wire) and ground. If battery voltage is present, check Purple/White wire for a short to ground. If wire is okay, replace rear defogger relay. If battery voltage is not present, check Orange/Black wire for an open circuit. If wire is okay, check circuit breaker No. 23.

HEATER & A/C CONTROL ASSEMBLY VOLTAGE TEST

Automatic A/C – 1) Disconnect heater and A/C control assembly connector. Ensure rear defogger relay is connected and ignition switch is in RUN position.

2) Using voltmeter, measure voltage between terminal "H" (Tan wire) and ground. If battery voltage is present, replace heater and A/C control assembly. If battery voltage is not present, check Tan wire for an open circuit or short to ground. If wire is okay, replace rear defogger relay.

REAR DEFOGGER TEST

1) Disconnect rear defogger connectors. Turn ignition switch to RUN position and defogger on. Connect voltmeter between Purple/White wire and ground. If battery voltage is present, go to next step. If battery voltage is not present, check Purple/White wire for an open circuit.

2) Connect voltmeter between Purple/White and Black wires. If battery voltage is present, rear defogger grid is defective. If battery voltage is not present, check Black wire for an open circuit.

"J" BODY TESTING

SYSTEM CHECK

Cavalier – 1) Turn ignition switch to RUN position, and depress rear defogger switch. Switch button should return to rest position, and ON indicator should illuminate. If not, go to HEATER-A/C & REAR DEFOGGER CONTROL ASSEMBLY POWER & GROUND TEST. If defogger does not warm, go to HEATER-A/C & REAR DEFOGGER CONTROL ASSEMBLY TEST. If ON indicator and defogger do not turn off after approximately 10 minutes, replace timing circuit located in heater-A/C and rear defogger control assembly.

2) After 10 minutes, depress rear defogger switch. ON indicator and rear defogger should turn on. After approximately 5 minutes, both should turn off. If not, replace timing circuit.

3) Depress rear defogger switch twice. ON indicator and defogger should turn on and then off. If not, go to HEATER-A/C & REAR DEFOGGER CONTROL ASSEMBLY POWER & GROUND TEST.

Sunbird – 1) Turn ignition switch to RUN position, and depress rear defogger switch. Switch button should return to rest position, and ON indicator should illuminate. If not, go to REAR DEFOGGER CONTROL TEST and REAR DEFOGGER TIMER/RELAY TEST. If defogger does not warm, go to REAR DEFOGGER TEST. If ON indicator and defogger do not turn off after approximately 10 minutes, replace rear defogger timer/relay.

2) Depress rear defogger switch. ON indicator and defogger should turn on. After approximately 5 minutes, they should turn off. If not, replace rear defogger timer/relay.

3) Depress rear defogger switch twice. ON indicator and defogger should turn on and then off. If not, go to REAR DEFOGGER CONTROL TEST.

HEATER-A/C & REAR DEFOGGER CONTROL ASSEMBLY POWER & GROUND TEST

Cavalier – 1) Disconnect heater-A/C and rear defogger control assembly connector. Control assembly connector is located behind center of instrument panel, on heater-A/C control assembly. Turn ignition switch to RUN position.

2) Connect a voltmeter between terminal "B" (Pink/Black wire) and ground. If battery voltage is present, go to next step. If battery voltage is not present, check Pink/Black wire for an open circuit.

3) Connect a voltmeter between terminals "B" (Pink/Black wire) and "A" (Black wire). If battery voltage is present, go to next step. If battery voltage is not present, check Black wire for an open circuit.

4) Connect a voltmeter between terminals "D" (Orange/Black wire) and ground. If battery voltage is present, go to HEATER-A/C & REAR DEFOGGER CONTROL ASSEMBLY TEST. If battery voltage is not present, check Orange/Black wire for an open circuit.

HEATER-A/C & REAR DEFOGGER CONTROL ASSEMBLY TEST

Cavalier – 1) Turn ignition switch to RUN and rear defogger switch to ON positions. With heater-A/C and rear defogger control assembly connector connected, use a voltmeter to check for voltage between connector terminal "H" (Purple/White wire) and ground. If battery voltage is present, go to next step. If battery voltage is not present, replace control assembly.

2) Disconnect rear defogger connector. Turn ignition switch to RUN and rear defogger switch to ON positions. Using a voltmeter, measure voltage between Purple wire and ground. If battery voltage is present, check grounds for tightness. If battery voltage is not present, check Purple and Purple/White wires for an open circuit.

REAR DEFOGGER CONTROL TEST

Sunbird – 1) Turn ignition switch to RUN position. With wiper switch assembly connector connected, use a test light to check for voltage between connector terminal "D" (Pink/Black wire) and ground. If test light illuminates, go to next step. If test light does not illuminate, check Pink/Black wire for an open circuit.

2) Connect test light between terminals "D" (Pink/Black wire) and "J" (Black wire). If test light illuminates, go to next step. If test light does not illuminate, check Black wire for an open circuit.

3) Turn rear defogger switch to ON position. Connect test light between terminal "C" (Light Blue wire) and ground. If test light illuminates and rear defogger still does not operate, go to REAR DEFOGGER TIMER/RELAY TEST. If test light does not illuminate, replace wiper switch assembly.

REAR DEFOGGER TIMER/RELAY TEST

Sunbird – 1) Turn ignition switch to RUN position. With rear defogger timer/relay connector connected, use a test light to check for voltage between connector terminal "E" (Orange/Black wire) and ground. If test light illuminates, go to next step. If test light does not illuminate, check Orange/Black wire for an open circuit.

2) Connect test light between terminals "E" (Orange/Black wire) and "A" (Black wire). If test light illuminates, go to next step. If test light does not illuminate, check Black wire for an open circuit.

3) Connect test light between terminal "C" (Pink/Black wire) and ground. If test light illuminates, go to next step. If test light does not illuminate, check Pink/Black wire for an open circuit.

4) Turn rear defogger switch to ON position. Connect test light between connector terminal "B" (Light Blue wire) and ground. If test light illuminates, go to next step. On all models, if test light does not illuminate, check Light Blue wire for an open circuit.

5) Connect test light between terminal "D" (Purple/White wire) and ground. If test light illuminates, go to REAR DEFOGGER TEST. If test light does not illuminate, replace rear defogger timer/relay.

REAR DEFOGGER TEST

Sunbird – Disconnect rear defogger connector. Turn ignition switch to RUN and defogger switch to ON positions. Connect voltmeter between Purple wire and ground. If battery voltage is present, rear defogger grid is defective. If battery voltage is not present, check Purple, Purple/White and Black wires for an open circuit.

"L" BODY TESTING

SYSTEM CHECK

1) Turn ignition switch to RUN position, and depress rear defogger switch. Switch button should return to rest position, and ON indicator should illuminate. If not, go to REAR DEFOGGER CONTROL VOLTAGE TEST.

2) If rear defogger does not warm, go to REAR DEFOGGER TEST. If ON indicator and defogger do not turn off after approximately 10 minutes, replace rear defogger control and wiper/washer switch.

3) Depress rear defogger switch. ON indicator and defogger should turn on. After approximately 5 minutes, they should turn off. If not, replace rear defogger control and wiper/washer switch.

4) Depress rear defogger switch twice. ON indicator and defogger should turn on and then off. If not, go to REAR DEFOGGER CONTROL VOLTAGE TEST.

REAR DEFOGGER CONTROL VOLTAGE TEST

1) Turn ignition switch to RUN position. With rear defogger control and wiper/washer switch connectors connected, use a voltmeter to check for voltage between connector terminal "A" (Orange/Black wire) and ground. If battery voltage is present, go to next step. If battery voltage is not present, check Orange/Black wire for an open circuit. If wire is okay, check circuit breaker No. 15.

2) Using a voltmeter, check for voltage between connector terminal "C" (Pink/Black wire) and ground. If battery voltage is present, go to next step. If battery voltage is not present, check Pink/Black wire for an open circuit. If wire is okay, check fuse No. 9.

3) Using a voltmeter, check for voltage between connector terminals "A" (Orange/Black wire) and "B" (Black wire). If battery voltage is present, go to REAR DEFOGGER CONTROL TEST. If battery voltage is not present, check Black wire for an open circuit.

REAR DEFOGGER CONTROL TEST

Turn ignition switch to RUN position. With rear defogger control and wiper/washer switch connectors connected, use a test light to check for voltage between connector terminal "B" (Purple/White wire) and ground. If test light illuminates, replace rear defogger control and wiper washer switch. If test light does not illuminate, go to REAR DEFOGGER TEST.

REAR DEFOGGER TEST

1) Turn ignition switch to RUN position and rear defogger on. With rear defogger connector connected, use a test light to check for voltage between Purple wire and ground. If test light illuminates, check wire for an open circuit.

2) If wire is okay and rear defogger still does not operate, defogger grid is defective. If test light does not illuminate, check Purple/White wire and hatchback contacts to rear defogger control for an open circuit.

"N" BODY TESTING

SYSTEM CHECK

1) Turn ignition switch to RUN position, and depress rear defogger switch. Switch button should return to rest position, and ON indicator should illuminate. If not, go to REAR DEFOGGER CONTROL TEST. If rear defogger does not warm, go to REAR DEFOGGER TEST. If ON indicator and defogger do not turn off after approximately 10 minutes, replace rear defogger timer/relay.

2) Depress rear defogger switch. ON indicator and defogger should turn off after approximately 5 minutes. If not, replace rear defogger timer/relay.

3) Depress rear defogger switch twice. ON indicator and defogger should turn on and then off. If not, go to REAR DEFOGGER CONTROL TEST.

REAR DEFOGGER CONTROL TEST

Cutlass Calais & Grand Am – 1) Turn ignition switch to RUN position. Connect a test light between rear defogger control connector terminal "B" (Pink/Black wire) and ground. If test light illuminates, go to next step. If test light does not illuminate, check Pink/Black wire for an open circuit.

2) Connect a test light between terminals "B" (Pink/Black wire) and "C" (Black wire). If test light illuminates, go to next step. If test light does not illuminate, check Black wire for an open circuit.

3) Turn rear defogger switch to ON position. Connect a test light between terminal "E" (Light Blue wire) and ground. If test light illuminates, go to REAR DEFOGGER TIMER/RELAY TEST. If test light does not illuminate, replace rear defogger control.

Skylark – 1) Turn ignition switch to RUN position. Disconnect rear defogger control switch connector. Using voltmeter, measure voltage between terminal "C" (Orange/Black wire) and ground. If battery voltage is present, go to next step. If battery voltage is not present, check Orange/Black wire for an open circuit.

2) Measure voltage between terminal "A" (Pink/Black wire) and ground. If battery voltage is present, go to next step. If battery voltage is not present, check Pink/Black wire for an open circuit.

3) Measure voltage between terminals "A" (Pink/Black wire) and "B" (Black wire). If battery voltage is present, go to next step. If battery voltage is not present, check Black wire for an open circuit.

4) Measure voltage between terminals "D" (Purple/White wire) and "B" (Black wire). If no voltage is present, go to next step. If voltage is present, check Purple/White and Purple wires for a short to voltage.

5) Turn rear defogger control switch to ON position. Reconnect rear defogger switch connector. Measure voltage between terminals "D" (Purple/White wire) and "B" (Black wire). If battery voltage is present, replace rear defogger switch. If battery voltage is not present, check Purple/White and Purple wires for an open circuit. If wires are okay, replace rear defogger switch.

REAR DEFOGGER TIMER/RELAY TEST

Cutlass Calais & Grand Am – 1) Turn ignition switch to RUN position. With rear defogger timer/relay connector connected, connect a test light between terminal "C" (Orange/Black wire) and ground. If test light illuminates, go to next step. If test light does not illuminate, check Orange/Black wire for an open circuit.

2) Connect test light between terminals "C" (Orange/Black wire) and "D" (Black wire). If test light illuminates, go to next step. If test light does not illuminate, check Black wire for an open circuit.

3) Connect test light between terminal "E" (Pink/Black wire) and ground. If test light illuminates, go to next step. If test light does not illuminate, check Pink/Black wire for an open circuit.

4) Turn rear defogger switch to ON position. Connect test light between terminal "B" (Light Blue wire) and ground. If test light illuminates, go to next step. If test light does not illuminate, check Light Blue wire for an open circuit.

5) Connect test light between terminal "A" (Purple/White wire) and ground. If test light illuminates, go to REAR DEFOGGER TEST. If test light does not illuminate, replace rear defogger timer/relay.

REAR DEFOGGER TEST

1) Disconnect rear defogger connectors. Using a voltmeter, measure voltage between Purple wire and ground. If battery voltage is present, go to next step. If battery voltage is not present, check Purple and Purple/White wires for an open circuit.

2) Connect voltmeter between Purple and Black wires. If battery voltage is present, defogger grid is defective. If battery voltage is not present, check Black wire for an open circuit.

"W" BODY TESTING

SYSTEM CHECK

1) Turn ignition switch to RUN position, and depress rear defogger switch. Switch button should return to rest position, and ON indicator should illuminate. If not, go to REAR DEFOGGER CONTROL TEST. If rear defogger does not warm, go to REAR DEFOGGER TEST. If ON indicator and defogger do not turn off after approximately 10 minutes, replace rear defogger timer/relay.

2) Depress rear defogger switch. ON indicator and defogger should turn off after approximately 5 minutes. If not, replace rear defogger timer/relay.

3) Depress rear defogger switch twice. ON indicator and defogger should turn on and then off. If not, replace rear defogger timer/relay.

REAR DEFOGGER CONTROL TEST

1) Turn ignition switch to RUN position. With heater and A/C control assembly connected, use a test light to check for voltage between connector terminal No . 4 (Pink/Black wire) and ground. If test light illuminates, go to next step. If test light does not illuminate, check Pink/Black wire for an open circuit. If wire is okay, check CLUST fuse.

2) Using test light, check voltage between terminals No. 4 (Pink/Black wire) and No. 12 (Black wire). If test light illuminates, go to next step. If test light does not illuminate, check Black wire for an open circuit. Ensure grounds are clean and tight.

3) Turn rear defogger switch to ON position. Connect test light between terminal No. 9 (Light Blue wire) and ground. If test light illuminates, go to next step. If test light does not illuminate, check Light Blue wire for a short to ground. If wire is okay, replace heater and A/C control assembly.

4) Connect test light between terminal No. 13 (Purple/White wire) and ground. If test light illuminates and rear defogger still does not operate properly, go to REAR DEFOGGER TIMER/RELAY TEST. If test light does not illuminate, check Purple/White wire for an open circuit or short to ground.

REAR DEFOGGER TIMER/RELAY TEST

1) Turn ignition switch to RUN position. Disconnect rear defogger timer/relay. Connect test light between relay terminal No. 27 (Red/Black wire) and ground. If test light illuminates, go to next step. If test light does not illuminate, check Red/Black wire for an open circuit. If wire is okay, check REAR DEFOG circuit breaker.

2) Connect test light between terminals No. 27 (Red/Black wire) and No. 23 (Black wire). If test light illuminates, go to next step. If test light does not illuminate, check Black wire for an open circuit. Ensure grounds are clean and tight.

3) Connect test light between terminal No. 25 (Pink/Black wire) and ground. If test light illuminates, go to next step. If test light does not illuminate, check Pink/Black wire for an open circuit. If wire is okay, check INDIC fuse.

4) Turn rear defogger switch to ON position. Connect test light between terminal No. 24 (Light Blue wire) and ground. If test light illuminates on Regal, go to REAR DEFOGGER TEST. If test light illuminates on all other models, go to next step. If test light does not illuminate, check Light Blue wire for an open circuit.

5) Connect test light between terminal No. 26 (Purple/White wire) and ground. If test light illuminates, go to REAR DEFOGGER TEST. If test light does not illuminate, replace rear defogger timer/relay.

REAR DEFOGGER TEST

1) Disconnect rear defogger connectors. Turn ignition switch to RUN and defogger switch to ON positions. Using a voltmeter, measure voltage between Purple/White wire and ground. If battery voltage is present, go to next step. If battery voltage is not present, check Purple/White wire for an open circuit. If wire is okay, replace rear defogger timer relay.

2) Connect voltmeter between Purple/White and Black wires. If battery voltage is present, defogger grid is defective. If battery voltage is not present, check Black wire for an open circuit.

"Y" BODY TESTING

NOTE: To test rear defogger, see Figs. 9-11. For appropriate wiring schematic, see Figs. 12 and 13.

Ensure engine is running when trying to activate rear defogger and heated mirrors. Check for open defogger circuit breaker or A/C fuse. If rear defogger works but heated mirrors do not, check for open heated mirror fuse. If some grid lines do not heat, see DEFOGGER GRID TEST under TESTING.

SYMPTOM TABLE

SYMPTOM	PROCEDURE
Rear Defogger, Heated Mirrors & Rear Defogger indicator inoperative: • Manual A/C • Electronic A/C	See Chart No. 1. See Chart No. 2.
One or both Heated Mirrors are inoperative. Rear Defogger okay.	See Chart No. 3.
Rear Defogger is inoperative. Heated Mirrors are okay.	See Chart No. 4.
Rear Defogger & Heated Mirrors always ON.	See Chart No. 5.

CHART NO. 1
REAR DEFOGGER, HEATED MIRRORS & REAR DEFOGGER INDICATOR INOPERATIVE
(MANUAL AIR CONDITIONING)

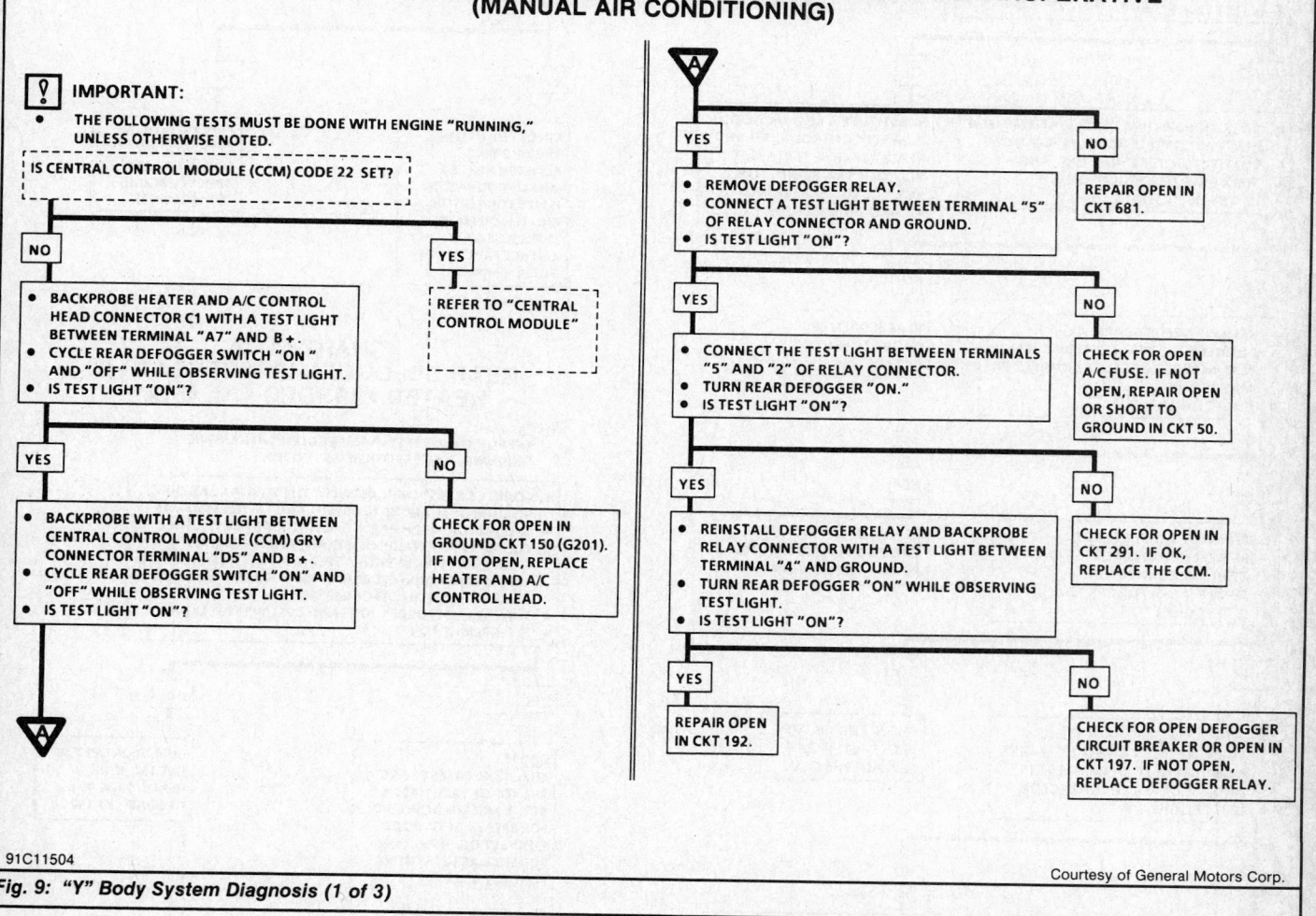

91C11504

Courtesy of General Motors Corp.

Fig. 9: "Y" Body System Diagnosis (1 of 3)

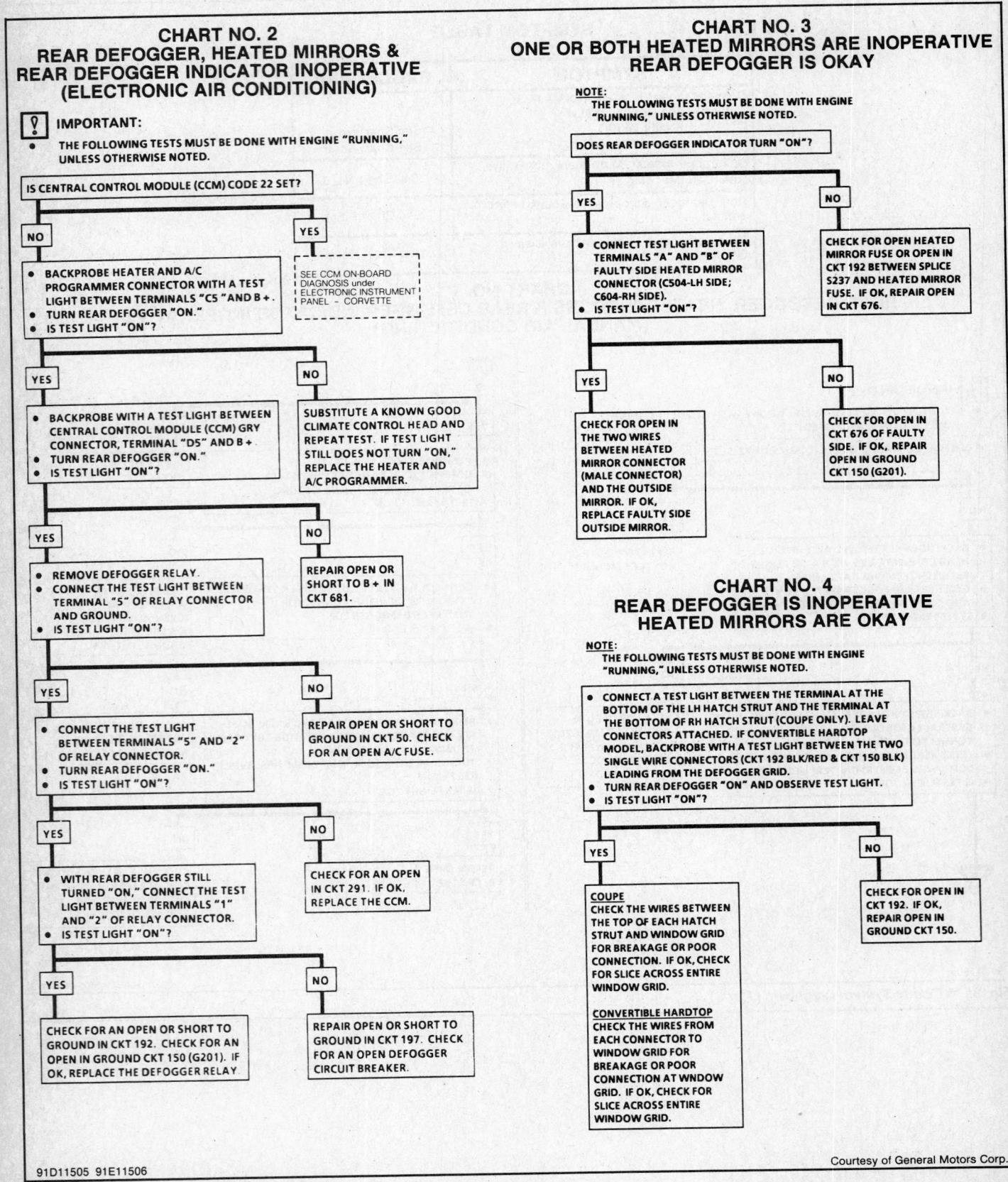

CHART NO. 2
REAR DEFOGGER, HEATED MIRRORS &
REAR DEFOGGER INDICATOR INOPERATIVE
(ELECTRONIC AIR CONDITIONING)

⚠ IMPORTANT:
- THE FOLLOWING TESTS MUST BE DONE WITH ENGINE "RUNNING," UNLESS OTHERWISE NOTED.

IS CENTRAL CONTROL MODULE (CCM) CODE 22 SET?

NO
- BACKPROBE HEATER AND A/C PROGRAMMER CONNECTOR WITH A TEST LIGHT BETWEEN TERMINALS "C5 "AND B +.
- TURN REAR DEFOGGER "ON."
- IS TEST LIGHT "ON"?

YES
SEE CCM ON-BOARD DIAGNOSIS under ELECTRONIC INSTRUMENT PANEL – CORVETTE

YES
- BACKPROBE WITH A TEST LIGHT BETWEEN CENTRAL CONTROL MODULE (CCM) GRY CONNECTOR, TERMINAL "D5" AND B +.
- TURN REAR DEFOGGER "ON."
- IS TEST LIGHT "ON"?

NO
SUBSTITUTE A KNOWN GOOD CLIMATE CONTROL HEAD AND REPEAT TEST. IF TEST LIGHT STILL DOES NOT TURN "ON," REPLACE THE HEATER AND A/C PROGRAMMER.

YES
- REMOVE DEFOGGER RELAY.
- CONNECT THE TEST LIGHT BETWEEN TERMINAL "5" OF RELAY CONNECTOR AND GROUND.
- IS TEST LIGHT "ON"?

NO
REPAIR OPEN OR SHORT TO B + IN CKT 681.

YES
- CONNECT THE TEST LIGHT BETWEEN TERMINALS "5" AND "2" OF RELAY CONNECTOR.
- TURN REAR DEFOGGER "ON."
- IS TEST LIGHT "ON"?

NO
REPAIR OPEN OR SHORT TO GROUND IN CKT 50. CHECK FOR AN OPEN A/C FUSE.

YES
- WITH REAR DEFOGGER STILL TURNED "ON," CONNECT THE TEST LIGHT BETWEEN TERMINALS "1" AND "2" OF RELAY CONNECTOR.
- IS TEST LIGHT "ON"?

NO
CHECK FOR AN OPEN IN CKT 291. IF OK, REPLACE THE CCM.

YES
CHECK FOR AN OPEN OR SHORT TO GROUND IN CKT 192. CHECK FOR AN OPEN IN GROUND CKT 150 (G201). IF OK, REPLACE THE DEFOGGER RELAY.

NO
REPAIR OPEN OR SHORT TO GROUND IN CKT 197. CHECK FOR AN OPEN DEFOGGER CIRCUIT BREAKER.

CHART NO. 3
ONE OR BOTH HEATED MIRRORS ARE INOPERATIVE
REAR DEFOGGER IS OKAY

NOTE:
THE FOLLOWING TESTS MUST BE DONE WITH ENGINE "RUNNING," UNLESS OTHERWISE NOTED.

DOES REAR DEFOGGER INDICATOR TURN "ON"?

YES
- CONNECT TEST LIGHT BETWEEN TERMINALS "A" AND "B" OF FAULTY SIDE HEATED MIRROR CONNECTOR (C504-LH SIDE; C604-RH SIDE).
- IS TEST LIGHT "ON"?

NO
CHECK FOR OPEN HEATED MIRROR FUSE OR OPEN IN CKT 192 BETWEEN SPLICE S237 AND HEATED MIRROR FUSE. IF OK, REPAIR OPEN IN CKT 676.

YES
CHECK FOR OPEN IN THE TWO WIRES BETWEEN HEATED MIRROR CONNECTOR (MALE CONNECTOR) AND THE OUTSIDE MIRROR. IF OK, REPLACE FAULTY SIDE OUTSIDE MIRROR.

NO
CHECK FOR OPEN IN CKT 676 OF FAULTY SIDE. IF OK, REPAIR OPEN IN GROUND CKT 150 (G201).

CHART NO. 4
REAR DEFOGGER IS INOPERATIVE
HEATED MIRRORS ARE OKAY

NOTE:
THE FOLLOWING TESTS MUST BE DONE WITH ENGINE "RUNNING," UNLESS OTHERWISE NOTED.

- CONNECT A TEST LIGHT BETWEEN THE TERMINAL AT THE BOTTOM OF THE LH HATCH STRUT AND THE TERMINAL AT THE BOTTOM OF RH HATCH STRUT (COUPE ONLY). LEAVE CONNECTORS ATTACHED. IF CONVERTIBLE HARDTOP MODEL, BACKPROBE WITH A TEST LIGHT BETWEEN THE TWO SINGLE WIRE CONNECTORS (CKT 192 BLK/RED & CKT 150 BLK) LEADING FROM THE DEFOGGER GRID.
- TURN REAR DEFOGGER "ON" AND OBSERVE TEST LIGHT.
- IS TEST LIGHT "ON"?

YES
COUPE
CHECK THE WIRES BETWEEN THE TOP OF EACH HATCH STRUT AND WINDOW GRID FOR BREAKAGE OR POOR CONNECTION. IF OK, CHECK FOR SLICE ACROSS ENTIRE WINDOW GRID.

CONVERTIBLE HARDTOP
CHECK THE WIRES FROM EACH CONNECTOR TO WINDOW GRID FOR BREAKAGE OR POOR CONNECTION AT WNDOW GRID. IF OK, CHECK FOR SLICE ACROSS ENTIRE WINDOW GRID.

NO
CHECK FOR OPEN IN CKT 192. IF OK, REPAIR OPEN IN GROUND CKT 150.

Courtesy of General Motors Corp.

91D11505 91E11506

Fig. 10: "Y" Body System Diagnosis (2 of 3)

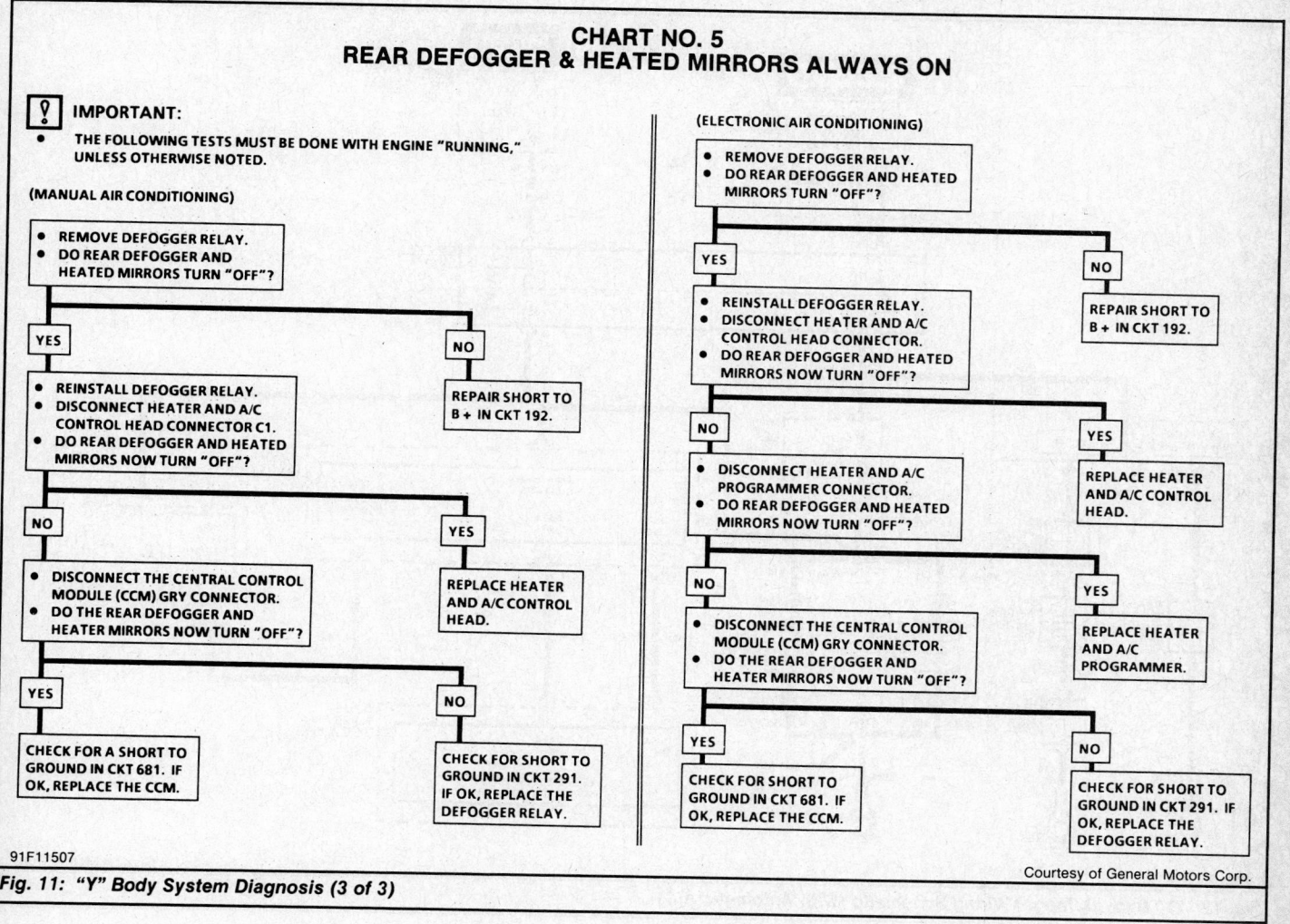

CHART NO. 5
REAR DEFOGGER & HEATED MIRRORS ALWAYS ON

IMPORTANT:
- THE FOLLOWING TESTS MUST BE DONE WITH ENGINE "RUNNING," UNLESS OTHERWISE NOTED.

(MANUAL AIR CONDITIONING)

- REMOVE DEFOGGER RELAY.
- DO REAR DEFOGGER AND HEATED MIRRORS TURN "OFF"?

YES

NO → REPAIR SHORT TO B + IN CKT 192.

- REINSTALL DEFOGGER RELAY.
- DISCONNECT HEATER AND A/C CONTROL HEAD CONNECTOR C1.
- DO REAR DEFOGGER AND HEATED MIRRORS NOW TURN "OFF"?

NO

YES → REPLACE HEATER AND A/C CONTROL HEAD.

- DISCONNECT THE CENTRAL CONTROL MODULE (CCM) GRY CONNECTOR.
- DO THE REAR DEFOGGER AND HEATER MIRRORS NOW TURN "OFF"?

YES → CHECK FOR A SHORT TO GROUND IN CKT 681. IF OK, REPLACE THE CCM.

NO → CHECK FOR SHORT TO GROUND IN CKT 291. IF OK, REPLACE THE DEFOGGER RELAY.

(ELECTRONIC AIR CONDITIONING)

- REMOVE DEFOGGER RELAY.
- DO REAR DEFOGGER AND HEATED MIRRORS TURN "OFF"?

YES

NO → REPAIR SHORT TO B + IN CKT 192.

- REINSTALL DEFOGGER RELAY.
- DISCONNECT HEATER AND A/C CONTROL HEAD CONNECTOR.
- DO REAR DEFOGGER AND HEATED MIRRORS NOW TURN "OFF"?

NO

YES → REPLACE HEATER AND A/C CONTROL HEAD.

- DISCONNECT HEATER AND A/C PROGRAMMER CONNECTOR.
- DO REAR DEFOGGER AND HEATED MIRRORS NOW TURN "OFF"?

NO

YES → REPLACE HEATER AND A/C PROGRAMMER.

- DISCONNECT THE CENTRAL CONTROL MODULE (CCM) GRY CONNECTOR.
- DO THE REAR DEFOGGER AND HEATER MIRRORS NOW TURN "OFF"?

YES → CHECK FOR SHORT TO GROUND IN CKT 681. IF OK, REPLACE THE CCM.

NO → CHECK FOR SHORT TO GROUND IN CKT 291. IF OK, REPLACE THE DEFOGGER RELAY.

91F11507

Courtesy of General Motors Corp.

Fig. 11: "Y" Body System Diagnosis (3 of 3)

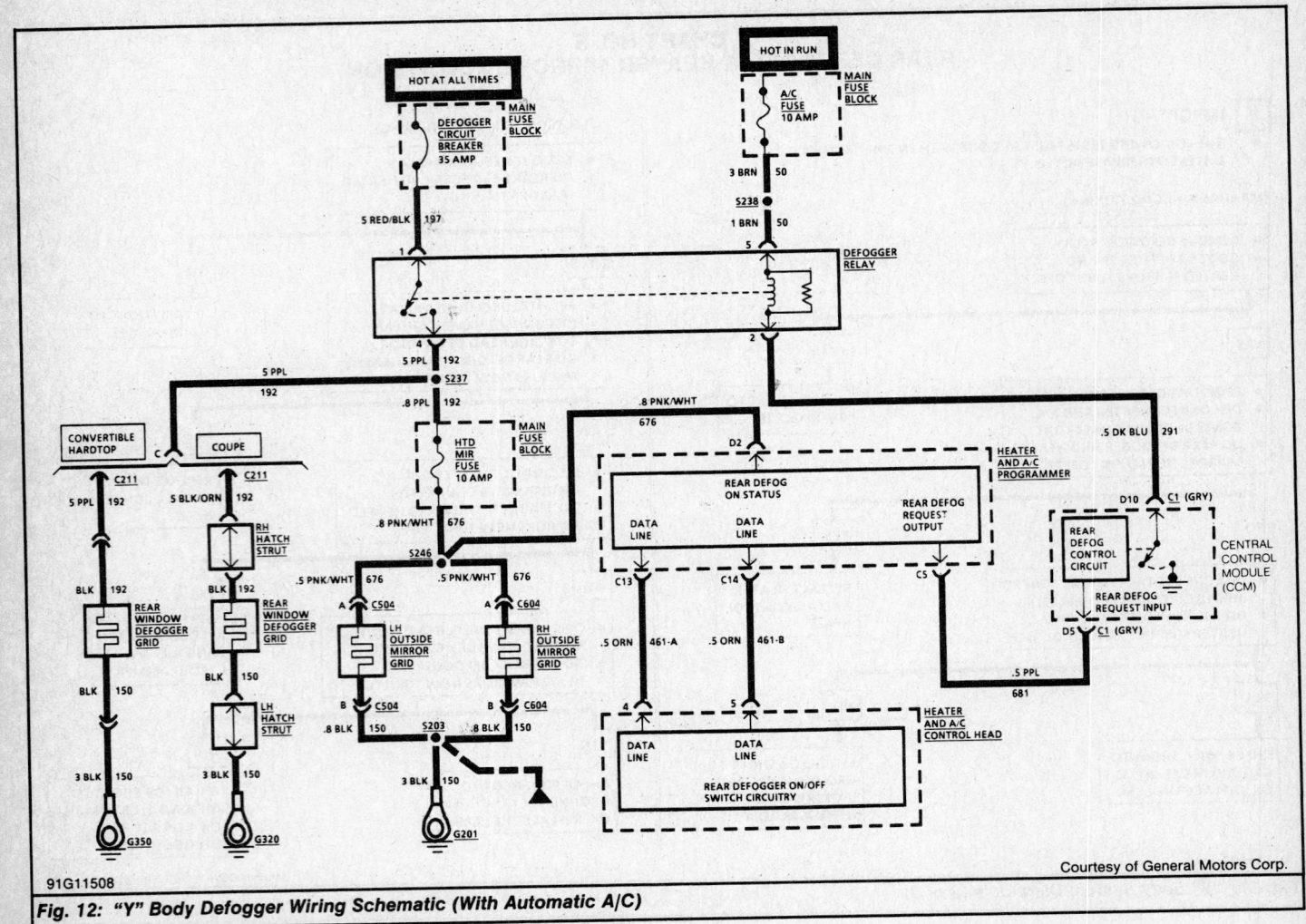

91G11508

Fig. 12: *"Y" Body Defogger Wiring Schematic (With Automatic A/C)*

Courtesy of General Motors Corp.

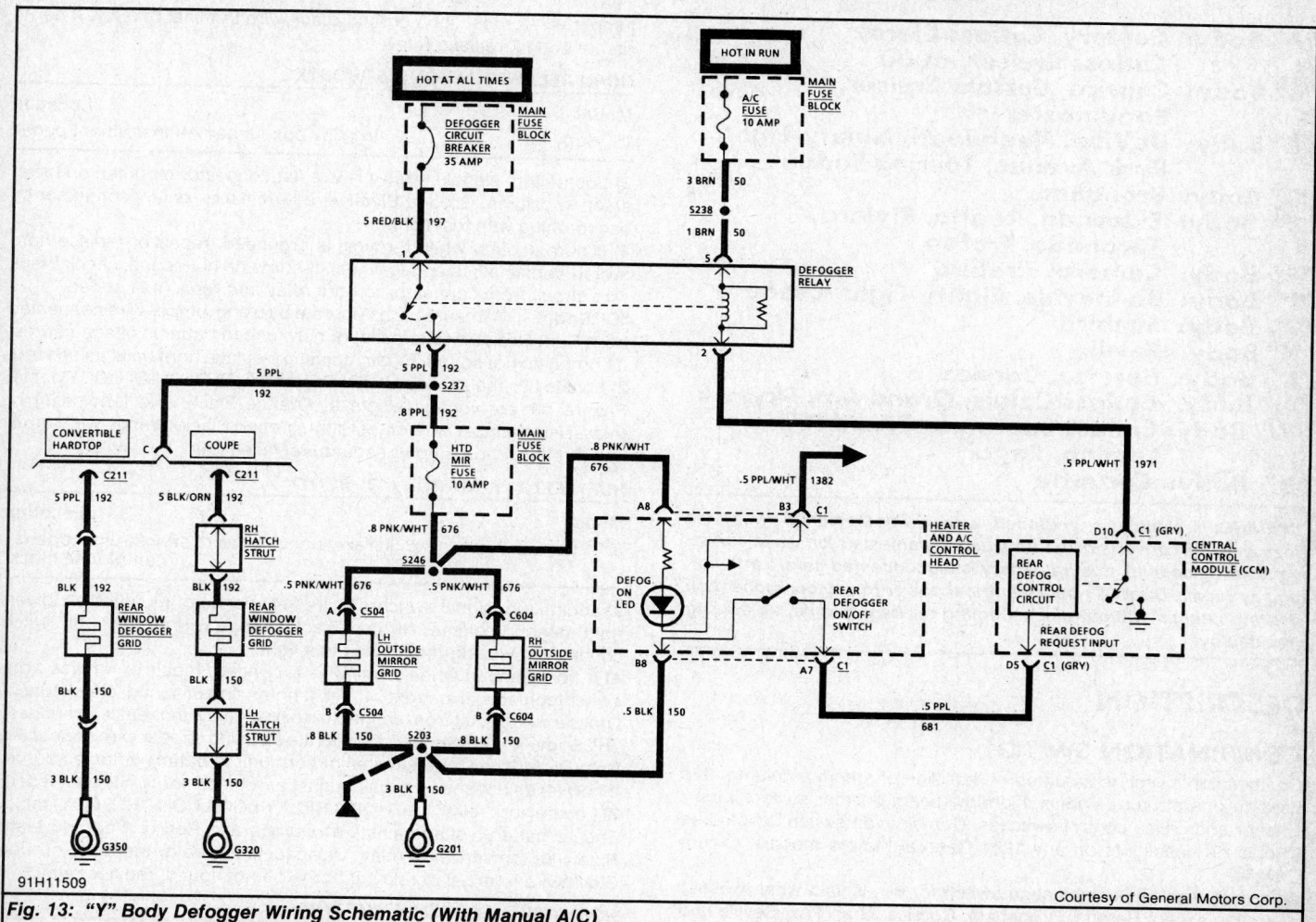

Fig. 13: "Y" Body Defogger Wiring Schematic (With Manual A/C)

91H11509

Courtesy of General Motors Corp.

WIRING DIAGRAMS

For additional information, see appropriate chassis wiring diagram in
WIRING DIAGRAMS.

"A" Body: Century, Cutlass Ciera, Cutlass Cruiser, 6000
"B" Body: Caprice, Custom Cruiser, Roadmaster
"C" Body: DeVille, Fleetwood, Ninety-Eight, Park Avenue, Touring Sedan
"D" Body: Brougham
"E" Body: Eldorado, Reatta, Riviera, Toronado, Trofeo
"F" Body: Camaro, Firebird
"H" Body: Bonneville, Eighty-Eight, LeSabre
"J" Body: Sunbird
"K" Body: Seville
"L" Body: Beretta, Corsica
"N" Body: Cutlass Calais, Grand Am, Skylark
"W" Body: Cutlass Supreme, Grand Prix, Lumina, Regal
"Y" Body: Corvette

WARNING: If vehicle is equipped with a Supplemental Inflatable Restraint (SIR) driver-side air bag, use extreme caution while servicing steering column. Ensure battery is disconnected before attempting any repair. DO NOT apply electrical power to any component on steering column without disconnecting air bag module, as air bag may deploy.

DESCRIPTION

COMBINATION SWITCH

Combination switch is mounted on left side of steering column. It is used to operate turn signals, high/low beam dimmer switch, wiper/washer and cruise control switches. Combination switch is not used to operate headlights on any 1991 General Motors models, except Cavalier.

All models use this combination switch for windshield wiper/washer operation except Beretta, Brougham, Corsica, Gran Prix, Seville and Sunbird. These vehicles have windshield wiper/washer switches mounted in or on instrument panel.

TESTING

HAZARD WARNING SWITCH

NOTE: All models use identical wire colors for electrical circuits, but different body styles use different terminal numbers for electrical circuit connectors.

1) Turn ignition on. Ensure battery voltage exists at stop-hazard fuse in fuse block and at Orange wire at hazard flasher unit. Turn hazard warning switch to ON position. Ensure battery voltage exists at Brown wire terminal of flasher unit and Brown wire terminal of turn signal switch 17-wire flat connector, on or near lower steering column. If voltage does not exist at Brown wire terminals, repair Brown wire wiring circuit.

2) Turn hazard warning switch to ON position. Check for battery voltage on Light Blue, Yellow, Dark Green and Dark Blue wire terminals of turn signal switch 17-wire flat connector, on or near lower steering column. If voltage does not exist on all terminals, replace turn signal switch.

HORN

"B" Body – 1) Ensure horns operate by using jumper wire connected from Dark Green wire terminal of horn unit to battery voltage source. If horns do not sound, repair, adjust or replace horn units as needed.
2) Locate horn relay. See HORN RELAY LOCATION ("B" BODY) table. Ensure battery voltage exists at White wire terminal(s) of relay. Using jumper wire or test light, ground Black wire terminal of relay. If horns do not sound, replace relay.

HORN RELAY LOCATION ("B" BODY)

Model	Location
"B" Body	In relay box, under left instrument panel.

3) Locate turn signal switch 17-wire flat connector mounted on lower steering column. Ground Black wire terminal of switch connector by backprobing with test light.
4) If horns sound when terminal is grounded, repair or replace horn switch/contacts in steering wheel. If horns do not sound, check Black wire circuit from connector to horn relay and repair as needed.
"D" Body – 1) Ensure horns operate by using jumper wire connected from Dark Green wire terminal of horn unit to battery voltage source. If horn(s) do not sound, repair, adjust or replace horn units as needed.
2) Locate horn relay. See HORN RELAY LOCATION ("D" BODY) table. Ensure battery voltage exists at Orange/Black wire terminal(s) of relay. Using jumper wire or test light, ground Black/Orange wire terminal of relay. If horns do not sound, replace relay.

HORN RELAY LOCATION ("D" BODY)

Model	Location
"D" Body	In relay panel, behind left instrument panel, left of fuse block.

3) Locate turn signal switch 17-wire flat connector mounted on lower, right steering column. Ground Black/Orange wire terminal of switch connector by backprobing with test light.
4) If horns sound when terminal is grounded, repair or replace horn switch/contacts in steering wheel. If horns do not sound, check Black/Orange wire circuit from connector to horn relay and repair as needed.
"H" Body – 1) Ensure horns operate by using jumper wire connected from Dark Green wire terminal of horn unit to battery voltage source. If horn(s) do not sound, repair, adjust or replace horn units as needed.
2) Locate horn relay. See HORN RELAY LOCATION ("H" BODY) table. Ensure battery voltage exists at Orange and Red or Red and Light Blue wire terminal(s) of relay. Using jumper wire or test light, ground Black wire terminal of relay. If horns do not sound, replace relay.

HORN RELAY LOCATION ("H" BODY)

Model	Location
"H" Body	In relay box, behind right dash, near kick panel.

3) Locate steering column switches main connector behind instrument panel near lower, left of steering column. Ground Black wire terminal (No. A12) of switches main connector by backprobing with test light.
4) If horns sound when terminal is grounded, repair or replace horn switch/contacts in steering wheel. If horns do not sound, check Black wire circuit from connector to horn relay and repair as needed.
Except "B", "D" & "H" Bodies – 1) Ensure horns operate by using jumper wire connected from Dark Green wire terminal of horn unit to battery voltage source. If horn(s) do not sound, repair, adjust or replace horn units as needed.
2) Locate horn relay. See HORN RELAY LOCATION (EXCEPT "B", "D" & "H" BODIES) table. Ensure battery voltage is at Orange wire terminal(s) of relay. Using jumper wire or test light, ground Black wire terminal of relay. If horns do not sound, replace relay.

HORN RELAY LOCATION (EXCEPT "B", "D" & "H" BODIES)

Model	Location
"A" Body	In relay box, at right rear of glove box.
"C" Body	In relay box, behind right dash near kick panel.
"E" & "K" Bodies	In relay box, behind left headlight
"F" Body	In relay box, at lower right of steering column
"J" Body	In relay box, near left kick panel.
"L" Body	In relay box, behind left instrument panel
"N" Body	In relay box, behind left instrument panel above fuse box
"W" Body	Behind right front grille, left of headlights
"Y" Body	On relay bracket, below right side dash panel

3) On "F" body, locate turn signal switch main harness flat connector mounted on lower steering column. On "A" and "W" bodies, locate steering column switches main connector behind instrument panel near lower, left of steering column.

4) Ground Black wire terminal of switch connector by backprobing with test light. If horns sound when terminal is grounded, repair or replace horn switch/contacts in steering wheel. If horns do not sound, check Black wire wiring circuit from connector to horn relay and repair as needed.

IGNITION SWITCH

"A", "C", "E", "H", "K" & "W" Bodies − **1)** Disconnect and shield negative battery cable. Remove left, lower instrument panel trim panel. Locate and disconnect steering column switches main connector (Black, 48-cavity) near lower, left steering column. See Fig. 1.

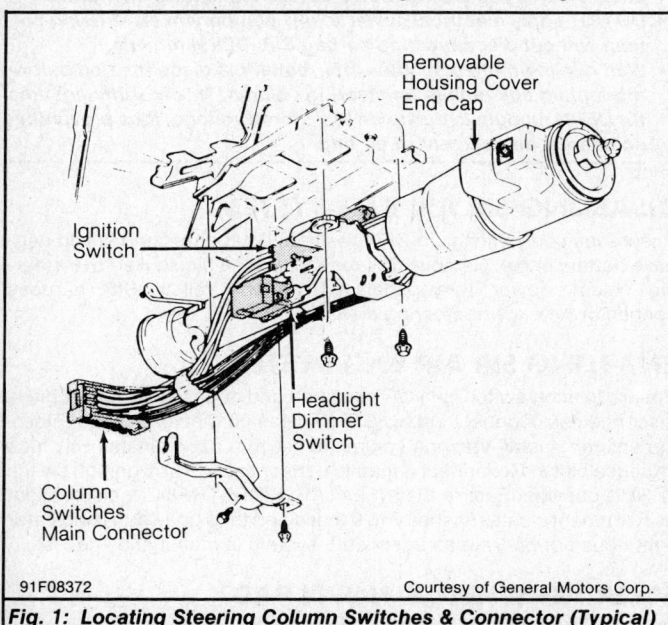

91F08372   Courtesy of General Motors Corp.

Fig. 1: Locating Steering Column Switches & Connector (Typical)

2) Using DVOM, check for continuity between wire terminals related to ignition switch/lock cylinder position. See TESTING IGNITION SWITCH CONTINUITY table. See Fig. 2.

"B", "F", "J", "L", "N" & "Y" Bodies − **1)** Disconnect and shield negative battery cable. Remove left lower instrument panel trim panel. Lower or remove steering column. Locate and disconnect ignition switch connectors on top of lower steering column. See Fig. 1.

2) Using DVOM, check for ignition switch continuity between wire terminals related to ignition switch/lock cylinder position. See TESTING IGNITION SWITCH CONTINUITY table. See Fig. 3.

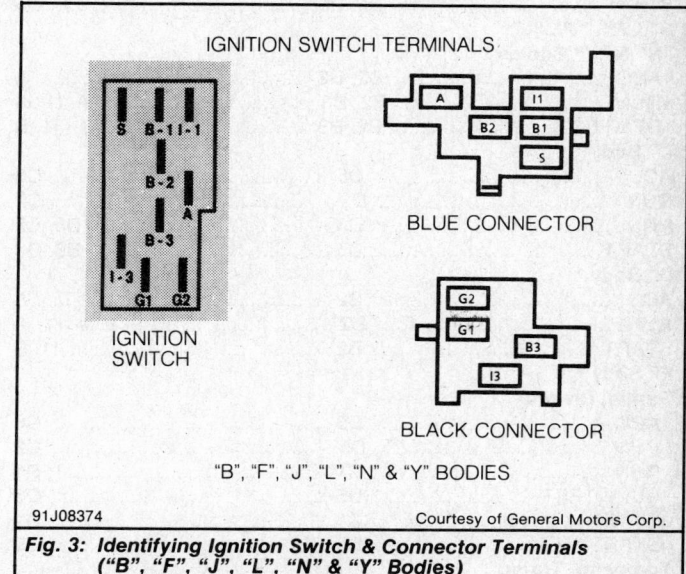

91J08374   Courtesy of General Motors Corp.

Fig. 3: Identifying Ignition Switch & Connector Terminals ("B", "F", "J", "L", "N" & "Y" Bodies)

TURN SIGNAL SWITCH

1) Turn ignition on. Ensure battery voltage exists at turn signal fuse in fuse block and on Purple wire at flasher unit. Ensure battery voltage exists at Purple wire terminal of turn signal switch connector.

2) Turn signal switch connector is a 17-terminal flat connector located near lower steering column, or connected to steering column switches main connector. See Fig. 1. If voltage does not exist at Purple wire terminal, repair wiring circuit.

3) Place turn signal switch in left turn position. Check for battery voltage on Light Blue and Yellow wire terminals of 17-terminal switch connector. If voltage does not exist, replace turn signal switch.

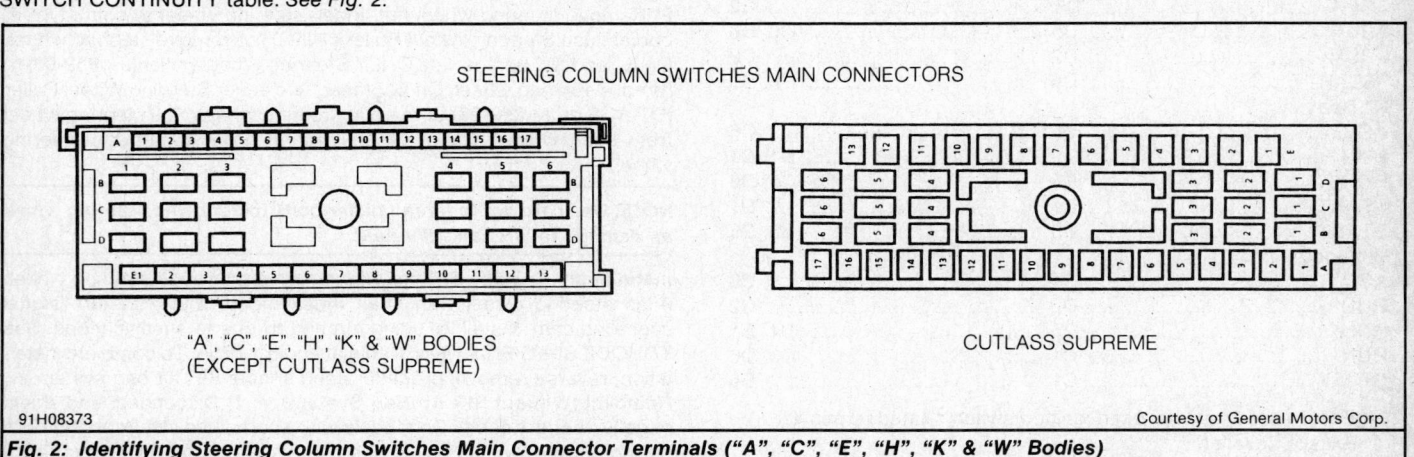

91H08373   Courtesy of General Motors Corp.

Fig. 2: Identifying Steering Column Switches Main Connector Terminals ("A", "C", "E", "H", "K" & "W" Bodies)

TESTING IGNITION SWITCH CONTINUITY

Switch Position	[1] Battery Terminal (s)	[1] Circuit Terminal (s)
"A" Body		
ACC	D2, D5	C6
RUN	D2, D5	C2, C6, D6
START	D2, D5	B6, D6
"B", "F", "J", "L", "N" & "Y" Bodies [2] [3]		
ACC	B2, B3	A
RUN	B2, B3	A, I1, I3
START	B2, B3	I1, S
"C" Body		
ACC	D5	C6
RUN	D2	C2
RUN	D5	D6, C6
START	D5	B6, D6
"D" Body [3]		
ACC	B2	A
RUN	B2	A, I1, I3
START	B2	I1, S
"E" Body [4]		
Reatta, Riviera		
ACC	D5	C6
RUN	D5	C2
RUN	C1	D1, B1
BULB TEST	D5	D6
START	C1	D1
START	D5	B6
Toronado, Trofeo		
ACC	D2, D5	C6
LOCK	D2, D5	NONE
OFF	D2, D5	B2
RUN	D2, D5	B2, C2, C6, D6
START	D2, D5	B6, D6
"H" Body		
Bonneville		
ACC	D5	C6
RUN	D5	C6, D6
RUN	D2	C2
START	D5	B6, D6
LeSabre		
ACC	D5	C6
OFF	D5	B2
RUN	D5	C6, D6
RUN	D2	C2
START	D5	B6, D6
"K" Body		
ACC	D5	C6
RUN	C1	B1, D1
RUN	D5	C2, C6, D6
START	C1	D1
START	D5	B6, D6
"W" Body		
ACC	C1	C6
RUN	D2	C2
RUN	D5	D1, B1
RUN	C1	C6, D6
START	C1	B6

[1] – Ensure continuity between ignition switch related terminals.
[2] – Except Cavalier.
[3] – Terminal numbers are marked on ignition switch.
[4] – For Eldorado, see "K" Body.

4) Place turn signal switch in right turn position. Check for battery voltage on Dark Blue and Dark Green wire terminals of 17-terminal switch connector. If voltage does not exist, replace turn signal switch.

5) To check brakelight circuit of turn signal switch, place switch in neutral position. While depressing brake pedal, ensure battery voltage exists at White wire terminal of brakelight switch.

6) With brake pedal depressed, check for battery voltage at White, Yellow and Dark Green wire terminals of 17-terminal switch connector. If voltage exists at White wire terminal and does not exist at Yellow and Dark Green wire terminals, replace turn signal switch.

WIPER SWITCH

For testing information on wiper switch, see appropriate WIPER/WASHER SYSTEMS article.

REMOVAL & INSTALLATION

WARNING: If vehicle is equipped with a Supplemental Inflatable Restraint (SIR) driver-side air bag, use extreme caution while servicing steering column.

- *Ensure battery is disconnected before attempting any repair.*
- *DO NOT apply electrical power to any component on steering column without disconnecting air bag SIR–DERM module.*
- *Wait minimum of 20 minutes after battery is disconnected before attempting any repairs on steering column. This is sufficient time for DERM module to dissipate any stored voltage, thus preventing accidental deployment of air bag.*

DISABLING SIR AIR BAG SYSTEM

Ensure ignition switch is in OFF position. Disconnect and shield negative battery cable. Remove SIR fuse from fuse block. Remove steering column lower trim panel. Disconnect Yellow SIR harness connector near lower steering column.

ENABLING SIR AIR BAG SYSTEM

Ensure ignition switch is in OFF position and negative battery cable is disconnected. Connect Yellow SIR harness connector at lower steering column. Install steering column lower trim panel. Install SIR fuse into fuse block. Reconnect negative battery cable. Turn ignition switch to RUN position. Ensure the INFLATABLE RESTRAINT indicator light in instrument cluster flashes 7 to 9 times and then goes out. If indicator light does not operate as described, system is malfunctioning.

STEERING WHEEL & HORN PAD

Removal (With SIR Air Bag System) – 1) Disconnect and shield negative battery cable. Disable SIR air bag system. Remove inflator module/center pad from steering wheel. Disconnect horn(s) wiring from slip ring connector. Remove horn contact(s) retaining screw(s).
2) Remove steering wheel nut. Index steering wheel to shaft. On "F" bodies, use Steering Wheel Puller (J-2927) to remove steering wheel. On "L" and "W" bodies, use ONLY Steering Wheel Puller (J-1859-03) to remove steering wheel. On all others, use either Steering Wheel Puller (BT-61-9 or J-1859-03) to remove steering wheel. Pull steering wheel from shaft while guiding SIR coil wiring harness through steering wheel.

NOTE: Use care not to thread puller bolts to deep into steering wheel as damage to SIR coil will result.

Installation – Guide SIR coil wiring harness through steering wheel. Align steering wheel with shaft index marks and with turn signal canceling cam. Install retaining nut and torque to specifications. See TORQUE SPECIFICATIONS table at end of article. To complete installation, reverse removal procedure and enable SIR air bag system.
Removal (Without SIR Air Bag System) – 1) Disconnect and shield negative battery cable. On models with sport wheel, lift or pry off horn button and/or switches pad. Remove 3 screws and take off contact, insulator eyelet and spring. On all other models, remove retaining screws from backside of wheel, partially lift off horn button. Unplug electrical connectors and remove horn pad.
2) On models equipped with tilt columns and telescoping columns, remove screws securing tilt or telescoping locking lever and flange to steering wheel hub. On all models, remove steering wheel nut. Index steering wheel to shaft for reassembly reference.

) On "F" bodies, use Steering Wheel Puller (J-2927) to remove steering wheel. On "L" and "W" bodies, use ONLY Steering Wheel Puller (J-1859-03) to remove steering wheel. On all others, use either Steering Wheel Puller (BT-61-9 or J-1859-03) to remove steering wheel.

Installation – Align steering wheel with shaft index marks and with turn signal canceling cam. Install retaining nut and torque to specifications. See TORQUE SPECIFICATIONS table at end of article. To complete installation, reverse removal procedure.

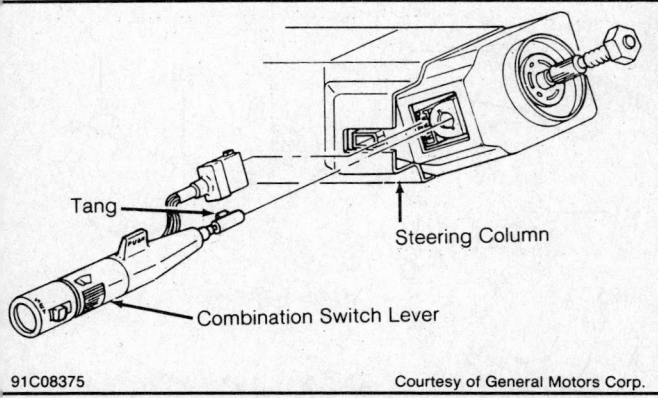

Fig. 4: Removing Combination Switch from Steering Column ("W" Body)

91C08375 — Courtesy of General Motors Corp.

COMBINATION SWITCH

Removal – **1)** If cruise control equipped, remove the following; wiper switch/dimmer pivot housing cover rear cap, or steering column left cover, or lower instrument panel trim panel. Disconnect cruise control wiring connector along left side of steering column or inside wiper switch/lock housing cover rear end cap. See Figs. 5 and 13.

2) For all combination switches, ensure switch lever is in OFF (center) position. Pull switch lever straight out from steering column. Pull cruise control wiring out of column along with lever. See Figs. 4 and 13.

Installation – Align tang on bottom of combination switch lever with slot in wiper switch or dimmer switch actuator pivot. Push lever straight in until bottomed. Connect cruise control wiring if required. Test lever functions.

DIMMER SWITCH

Removal & Installation ("W" Body) – Dimmer switch is mounted to ignition switch, on lower left side of steering column. See IGNITION SWITCH under REMOVAL & INSTALLATION. See Fig. 6.

Removal (Except "W" Body) – **1)** Disconnect negative battery cable. Remove lower steering column cover or lower instrument panel trim panel. Remove steering column support mounting bracket nuts. See Figs. 1 and 5.

2) Lower steering column. Remove dimmer switch by removing retaining nut and screw. Disconnect electrical connections. Remove switch.

Installation – **1)** Position switch on steering column and loosely install fasteners. Install electrical connectors. Insert 3/32" drill bit through locating hole securing dimmer switch to connector body. See Fig. 7.

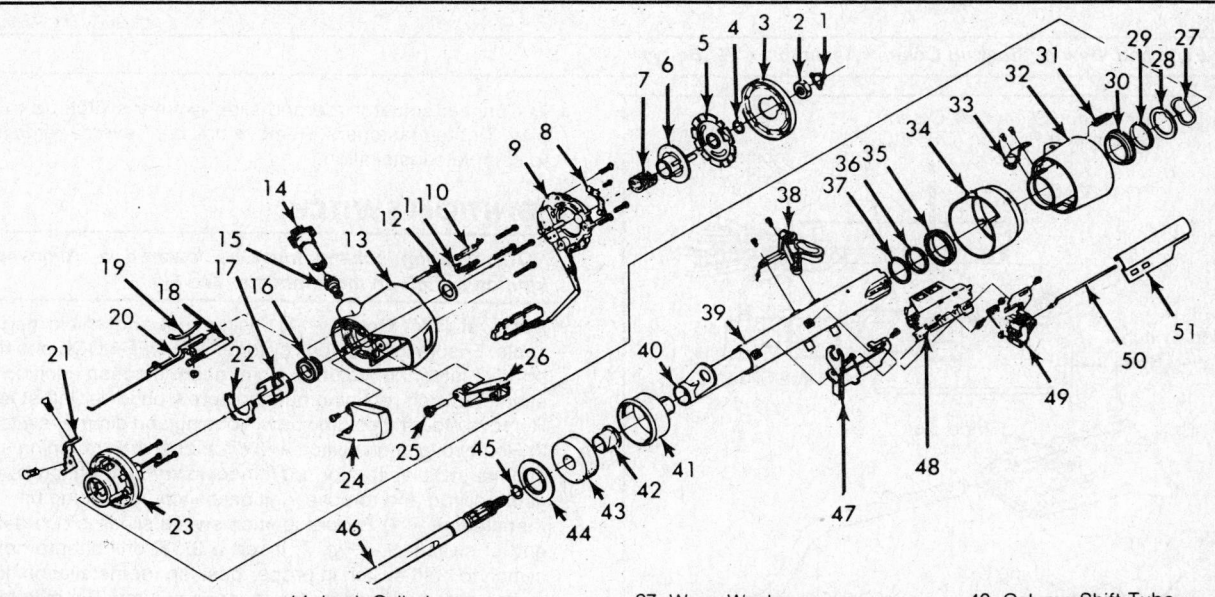

1. Retainer
2. Steering Wheel Nut
3. Shaft Lock Cover
4. Retaining Ring
5. Locking Ring
6. Turn Signal Canceling Cam
7. Upper Bearing Spring
8. Switch Actuator Arm
9. Turn Signal Switch
10. Buzzer Switch
11. Buzzer Switch Retaining Clip
12. Thrust Washer
13. Steering Column Lock Housing
14. Lock Cylinder
15. Switch Actuator Sector
16. Upper Bearing
17. Bearing Retaining Bushing
18. Spring & Bolt Assembly
19. Rack Preload Spring
20. Switch Actuator Rod & Rack
21. Shift Lever Gate
22. Upper Bearing Retainer
23. Housing Adapter
24. Lock Housing Cover End Cap
25. Switch Activator Pivot Pin
26. Switch Activator Pivot
27. Wave Washer
28. Bearing Retaining Washer
29. Bearing Seat
30. Gearshift Bowl Bearing
31. Shift Lever Spring
32. Gearshift Lever Bowl
33. Shift Lever Arm
34. Gearshift Bowl Shroud
35. Gearshift Bowl Bearing
36. Bearing Seat
37. Bearing Retaining Washer
38. Cable Shift Lever
39. Steering Column
40. Column Shift Tube
41. Column Bushing
42. Steering Shaft Bearing
43. Steering Shaft Seal
44. Seal Retaining Washer
45. Retaining Ring
46. Steering Shaft
47. Cable Mounting Bracket
48. Ignition Switch
49. Dimmer Switch
50. Dimmer Actuator Rod
51. Wiring Protector

56625 — Courtesy of General Motors Corp.

Fig. 5: Exploded View of Steering Column Assembly, Without Wiper Switch Assembly (Except "W" Body)

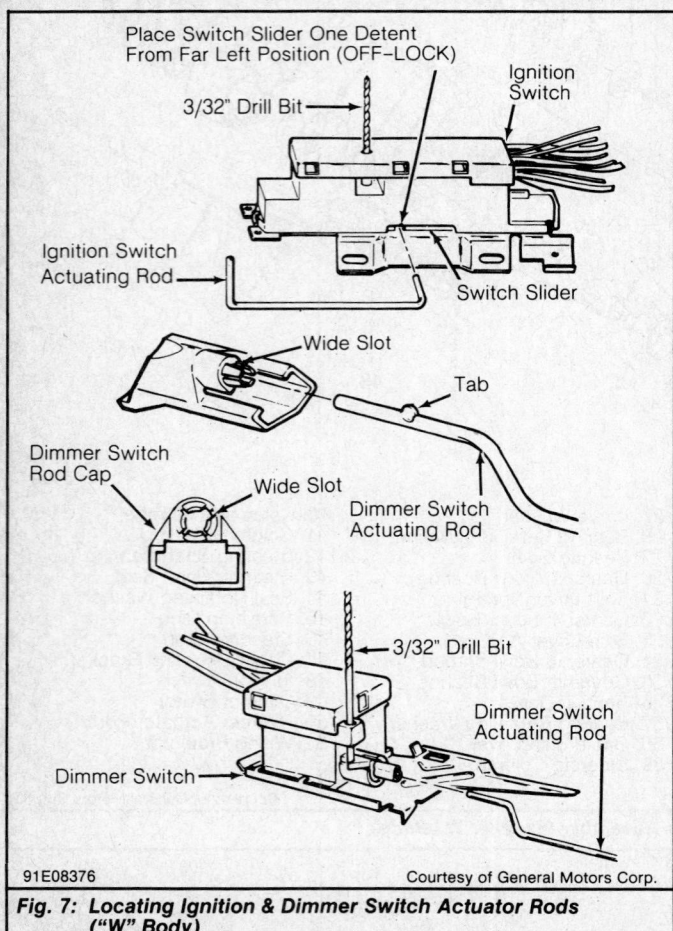

1. Steering Wheel Nut
2. Turn Signal Canceling Cam
3. Retaining Ring
4. Thrust Washer
5. Spring
6. Thrust Washer
7. Column Housing Cover
8. Hazard Warning Knob
9. Turn Signal Switch Assembly
10. Turn Signal Switch &
    Column Bearing Housing
11. Column Bearing
12. Spacer
13. Retaining Ring
14. Steering Shaft
15. Wiper Switch Assembly
16. Wiring Protector
17. Key Buzzer Switch Assembly
18. Lock Cylinder Retaining Screw
19. Lock Cylinder Set
20. Column Bowl & Lock Housing
21. Column Bowl Shield
22. Park Lock Cable Adjuster
23. Bearing Assembly Adapter
24. Lower Bearing Seat
25. Lower Bearing Spring
26. Lower Spring Retainer
27. Dimmer Switch Rod Cap
28. Dimmer Switch Actuator Rod
29. Dimmer Switch
30. Ignition Switch
31. Column Switches Main Connector

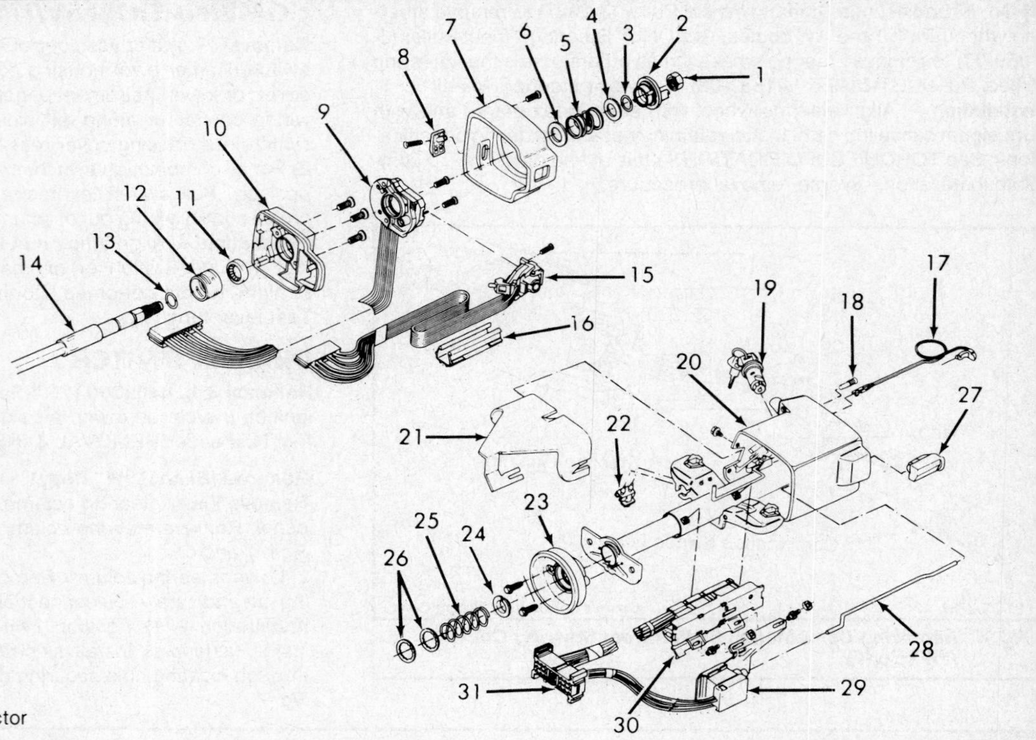

91I10007   Courtesy of General Motors Corp.

Fig. 6: Exploded View of Steering Column Assembly ("W" Body)

Place Switch Slider One Detent
From Far Left Position (OFF-LOCK)

Ignition
Switch

3/32" Drill Bit

Ignition Switch
Actuating Rod

Switch Slider

Wide Slot

Tab

Dimmer Switch
Rod Cap

Wide Slot

Dimmer Switch
Actuating Rod

3/32" Drill Bit

Dimmer Switch
Actuating Rod

Dimmer Switch

91E08376   Courtesy of General Motors Corp.

**Fig. 7: Locating Ignition & Dimmer Switch Actuator Rods
("W" Body)**

2) Connect actuator rod and slide dimmer switch up to remove fre
play. Tighten fasteners. Remove drill bit. Reverse removal procedur
to complete installation.

IGNITION SWITCH

*NOTE: Steering column must be lowered or removed to acces
ignition switch on most models. See Fig. 1.*

Removal ("W" Body) – 1) Disconnect and shield negative batter
cable. Ensure ignition lock cylinder is in OFF-LOCK position. Lower o
remove steering column from dash. Loosen ignition switch an
dimmer switch retaining nut and screw on lower left steering colum
Remove steering column bowl housing and dimmer switch. See Fig.
2) Remove ignition switch and dimmer switch retaining stud. Remov
dimmer switch actuator rod (if necessary). Lift off ignition switch fro
actuator rod and remove ignition switch from column.
Installation – 1) Ensure ignition switch slider is one detent from le
end of switch. See Fig. 7. Insert a 3/32" drill bit into hole on ignitio
switch to hold switch in proper position for installation. Install ignitio
switch onto actuator rod on steering column. Position ignition switc
on column to install lower retaining stud.
2) Torque lower retaining stud screw to 35 INCH lbs. (4.0 N.m
Remove drill bit from switch. Install dimmer switch actuator rod
removed) to dimmer switch rod cap. See Fig. 7. Dimmer switch rod ca
is located inside column lock housing and may be visible by removin
lock housing cover end cap. See Figs. 6 and 8.
3) Install dimmer switch to actuator rod and then to ignition switch low
er stud. Install upper stud, but do not tighten yet. Install 3/32" drill b
into dimmer switch adjustment hole. Push dimmer switch toward actu
ator rod to remove free play. Torque retaining stud screw and low
nut to 35 INCH lbs. (4.0 N.m). Remove drill bit. Install steering colum
bowl shield to steering column bowl housing and to dimmer switc
upper stud using retaining nut.
4) Turn lock cylinder alternately from ACC position to START positio
to check operation. Reconnect electrical connectors and install stee

1. Ignition Switch Actuator Rod
2. Steering Column
3. Actuator Rod Pack
4. Lock Bolt Retaining Plate
5. Lock Cylinder
6. Lock Bolt Spring
7. Steering Lock Bolt
8. Buzzer Switch Assembly
9. Dimmer Switch Rod Cap
10. Column Bowl & Lock Housing
11. Dimmer Switch Actuator Rod
12. Park Lock Cable Assembly
13. Dimmer Switch
14. Ignition/Dimmer Switch Stud
15. Ignition Switch
16. Steering Shaft
17. Spacer
18. Retaining Ring
19. Bearing
20. Turn Signal Switch &
    Column Bearing Housing
21. Thrust Washer
22. Spring
23. Thrust Washer
24. Retaining Ring
25. Turn Signal Switch
26. Turn Signal Canceling Cam
27. Hazard Warning Knob
28. Column Housing Cover
29. Steering Wheel Nut
30. Dimmer Switch Actuator Pivot
31. Wiring Protector

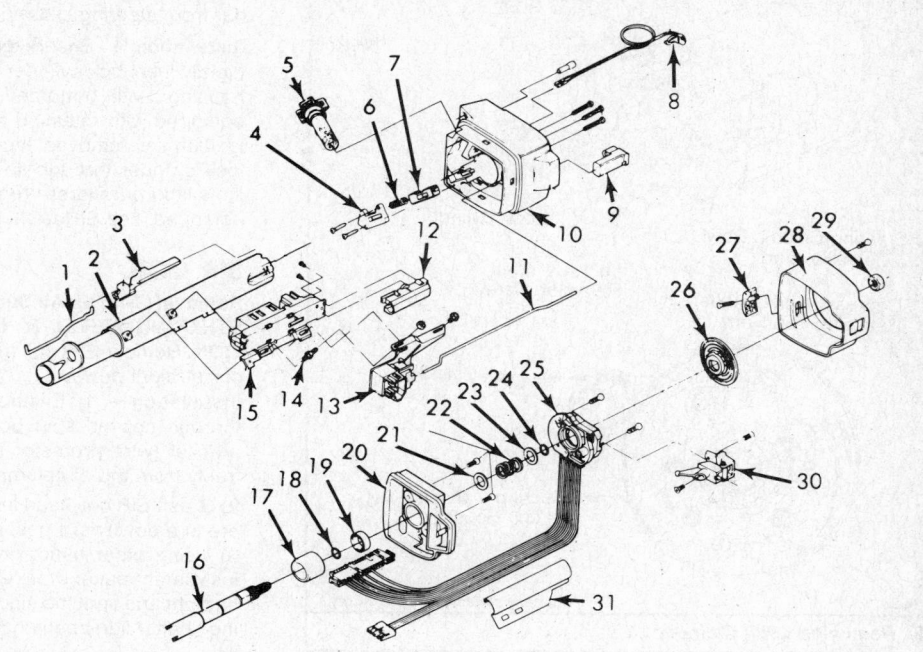

91G08377

Courtesy of General Motors Corp.

Fig. 8: Exploded View Of Non-Tilt Steering Column Assembly, Without Wiper Switch

ng column to dash. Torque all bolts to specifications. See TORQUE SPECIFICATIONS table at end of article.

Removal ("J", "L" & "N" Bodies) – 1) Disconnect and shield negative battery cable. Ensure ignition lock cylinder is in OFF-LOCK position. Lower or remove steering column from dash. On lower left side of steering column, remove park lock cable assembly from ignition switch. See Fig. 8.

2) Remove dimmer switch retaining nut and screw. Remove dimmer switch from actuator rod, leaving actuator rod connected to upper pivot point. Remove ignition switch lower retaining stud and lift ignition switch off actuator rod. Disconnect electrical connectors.

Installation – 1) Ensure ignition switch slider is one detent from left end of switch. Ensure ignition lock cylinder is in OFF-LOCK position. Install ignition switch onto actuator rod on steering column. Position ignition switch on column to install lower retaining stud.

2) Torque retaining stud screw to 35 INCH lbs. (4.0 N.m). Install dimmer switch actuator rod (if removed) to upper pivot point. Install dimmer switch to lower end of actuator rod. Install dimmer switch to ignition switch lower stud and install retaining nut. Install upper retaining stud, but do not tighten yet.

3) Install 3/32" drill bit into dimmer switch adjustment hole. Lightly push dimmer switch toward actuator rod to remove free play. Torque upper retaining stud screw and lower nut to 35 INCH lbs. (4.0 N.m). Remove drill bit. Place console shift lever in neutral and install park lock cable assembly to ignition switch. Reverse removal procedure to complete installation.

Removal (Except "J", "L", "N" & "W" Bodies) – 1) Disconnect and shield negative battery cable. Place ignition lock cylinder in OFF position. Steering column must be lowered (removed on some models) to gain access to ignition switch. Steering wheel removal is not required.

2) Remove ignition/dimmer switches retaining screws and studs. Lift ignition switch from column and actuator rod. Unplug electrical connectors.

Installation – 1) Ensure ignition lock cylinder is in OFF position. Install ignition switch slider hole onto actuator rod and position ignition switch onto steering column. See Fig. 7.

2) Lightly push ignition switch downward on steering column to take up free play in actuator rod. Install and torque lower retaining stud to

35 INCH lbs. (4 N.m). Connect ignition switch wiring harness connector.

3) Install and adjust dimmer switch. See DIMMER SWITCH under REMOVAL & INSTALLATION. Check operation of ignition switch using lock cylinder. Reconnect negative battery cable.

LOCK CYLINDER

For lock cylinder removal, remove steering wheel and turn signal switch to gain access to lock cylinder retaining screw or lock cylinder retaining tab.

Removal ("W" Body) – 1) Remove steering column housing cover and turn signal switch. See TURN SIGNAL & HAZARD WARNING SWITCH under REMOVAL & INSTALLATION. Remove retaining ring, thrust washers, spring and steering column bearing housing screws. See Fig. 6.

2) Remove steering column bearing housing from shaft and away from steering column bowl and lock housing. Ensure ignition lock cylinder is in OFF-LOCK position, and remove ignition key. Using a screwdriver to lift buzzer switch tab, carefully pull on buzzer switch wires to remove buzzer switch from lock cylinder and from steering column bowl and lock housing.

3) Remove lock cylinder retaining screw from steering column bowl and lock housing. See Fig. 9. Remove lock cylinder by pulling straight out from steering column bowl and lock housing.

Installation – 1) Ensure ignition lock cylinder is in OFF-LOCK position and remove ignition key. Install lock cylinder into steering column bowl and lock housing. Install and torque retaining screw to 27 INCH lbs. (3.0 N.m). See Fig. 9.

2) Push buzzer switch into retaining bore until it bottoms. Ensure plastic tab covers lock cylinder retaining screw. Install steering column housing to shaft and to steering column bowl and lock housing. Install and torque retaining screws to 88 INCH lbs. (10 N.m). To complete installation, reverse removal procedure. If SIR air bag system equipped, see SIR COIL under REMOVAL & INSTALLATION.

Removal (Except "W" Body) – Remove turn signal switch. See TURN SIGNAL & HAZARD WARNING SWITCH under REMOVAL & INSTALLATION. Ensure ignition lock cylinder is in OFF-LOCK position, and remove ignition key. Using a screwdriver to lift key buzz-

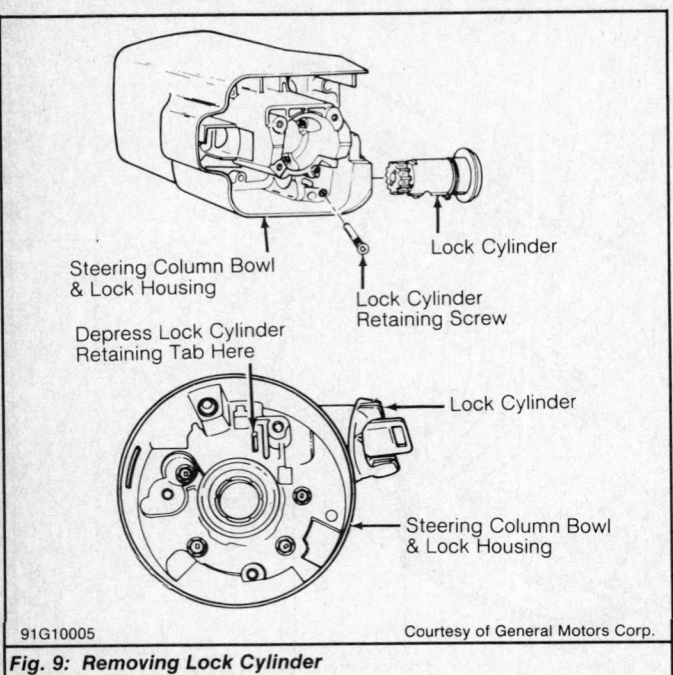

Fig. 9: Removing Lock Cylinder

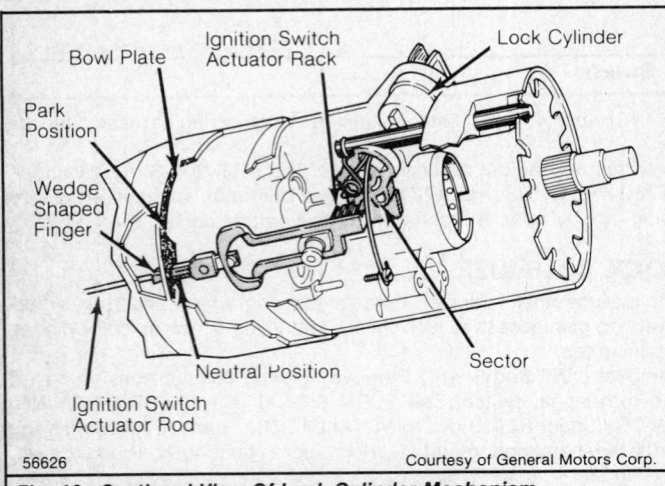

Fig. 10: Sectional View Of Lock Cylinder Mechanism For Tilt-Columns (Except "W" Body)

er switch tab, carefully pull on key buzzer switch to remove buzzer switch from lock cylinder and from steering column bowl and lock housing.

3) Remove lock cylinder retaining screw from steering column bowl housing, OR depress lock cylinder retaining tab with flat screwdriver

inserted into slot. See Fig. 9. Remove lock cylinder by pulling straight out from steering column bowl and lock housing. See Fig. 10.

Installation – Ensure ignition lock cylinder is in OFF-LOCK position. Lightly lube lock cylinder gear. Align and push lock cylinder into bowl housing until bottomed. Install lock cylinder retaining screw. If equipped with retaining tab, ensure tab locks into housing slot. With ignition key removed, install key buzzer switch tab into housing. Turn lock cylinder through its positions to check operation. To complete installation, reverse removal procedure. If SIR air bag system equipped, see SIR COIL under REMOVAL & INSTALLATION.

SIR COIL

Removal (With Sir Air Bag System) – **1)** Remove steering wheel. See STEERING WHEEL & HORN PAD under REMOVAL & INSTALLATION. Remove SIR coil from shaft and from column housing by pulling coil straight outward.

Installation – **1)** Ensure SIR coil wires are routed straight down through column shift bowl and exit at bottom of instrument panel bracket (wire protector removed). Ensure SIR coil head is hanging freely from top of column. See Fig. 11.

2) Grasp SIR coil head in one hand. Position SIR coil head so its wires are in a downward position as illustrated. See Fig. 11.

3) Using other hand, grasp ends of all lower SIR coil wires below instrument panel bracket. Carefully pull on lower wires to keep them straight and tight (no slack), while positioning SIR coil head onto steering shaft. Align opening in SIR coil head with canceling cam/horn tower.

4) Align SIR coil locating bumps between locating tabs in steering column cover. See Fig. 11. Continue to pull slack from lower wires while seating SIR coil head in cover. Install SIR coil retaining ring.

5) Holding lower wires straight and tight, install wire protector around wires and into instrument panel bracket. Install steering wheel.

TURN SIGNAL & HAZARD WARNING SWITCH

Removal ("W" Body) – **1)** Remove steering wheel. See STEERING WHEEL & HORN PAD under REMOVAL & INSTALLATION. Remove canceling cam. Remove hazard switch knob.

2) Position turn signal switch to remove steering column housing cover and turn signal switch screws. Steering column housing cover screws are long and Blue. Remove combination switch lever. See COMBINATION SWITCH under REMOVAL & INSTALLATION.

3) Remove steering column housing cover. Remove wiring protector from opening in instrument panel bracket on lower steering column. Disconnect wiper and turn signal switch connectors near lower steering column behind lower instrument panel. See Fig. 6.

4) Remove wiper switch pivot retaining screw from turn signal switch. Remove wiper switch from housing and allow to hang freely. Remove turn signal switch screws.

5) Align turn signal switch 17-wire flat connector to be parallel with wires and tape in this position. This will allow harness-connector assembly to be pulled through column when removing turn signal switch.

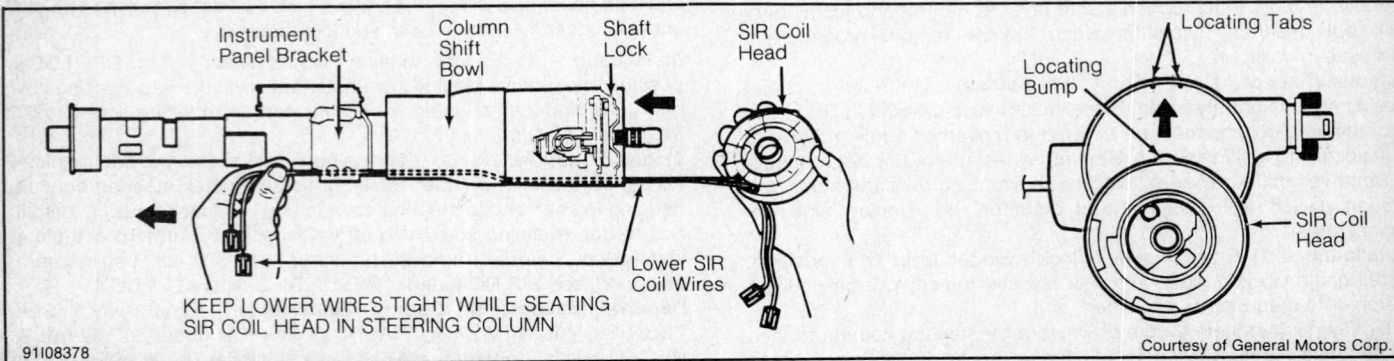

Fig. 11: Installing SIR Coil Head & Wiring Into Steering Column

) After removing turn signal switch and 17-wire flat connector, disconnect buzzer switch wire terminals No. 9 (Light Green wire) and No. 10 (Tan/Black wire) from connector using Terminal Remover (J-35689-A).

Installation – 1) Connect key buzzer wires to turn signal switch 17-wire connector. Install wire harness down through column. Install wiring protector around all wires, and close until interlocking grooves of protector engage.

) Slide wiring protector up into instrument panel bracket on lower steering column. To complete installation, reverse removal procedure. If SIR air bag system equipped, see SIR COIL under REMOVAL & INSTALLATION.

Removal (Except "W" Body) – 1) Remove steering wheel. See STEERING WHEEL & HORN PAD under REMOVAL & INSTALLATION. Remove hazard switch knob on outside of column housing. If SIR air bag system equipped, see SIR COIL under REMOVAL & INSTALLATION.

) Install Spring Compressor (J-23653) to steering shaft to compress shaft locking ring. See Fig. 12. Remove retaining snap ring from shaft. Slowly loosen spring compressor, and remove shaft locking ring, canceling cam and spring. See Fig. 5.

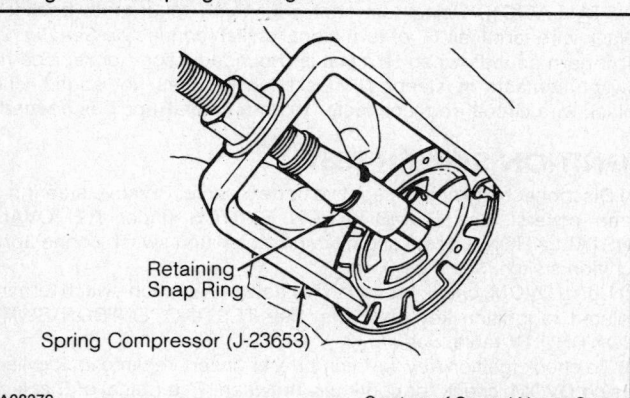

Retaining Snap Ring

Spring Compressor (J-23653)

91A08379   Courtesy of General Motors Corp.

Fig. 12: Removing Retainer Snap Ring

) Remove combination switch lever. See COMBINATION SWITCH under REMOVAL & INSTALLATION. Remove turn signal switch actuator arm screw, and remove arm. Remove wiring protector on lower steering column. Disconnect turn signal switch 17-wire flat connector located on lower column.

) Remove turn signal switch screws, and pull screws from switch using magnet. DO NOT allow screws to fall into column housing.

) Align turn signal switch 17-wire flat connector parallel with wires, and tape in this position. This allows harness-connector assembly to be pulled through column when removing turn signal switch.

) After removing turn signal switch and 17-wire flat connector, disconnect key buzzer switch wire terminals from connector using Terminal Remover (J-35689-A).

Installation – 1) Connect key buzzer switch wires to turn signal switch 17-wire connector. Install wire harness-connector down through column. Install wiring protector around all wires, and close until its interlocking grooves engage.

) To complete installation, reverse removal procedure. If SIR air bag system equipped, see SIR COIL under REMOVAL & INSTALLATION.

WINDSHIELD WIPER/WASHER SWITCH

Removal & Installation ("D", "K" & "L" Bodies, Gran Prix & Sunbird) – Windshield wiper/washer switch is located on instrument panel. See appropriate WIPER/WASHER SYSTEMS article.

Removal & Installation (Except "D", "K" & "L" Bodies, Gran Prix & Sunbird) – 1) Remove turn signal switch. See TURN SIGNAL & HAZARD WARNING SWITCH under REMOVAL & INSTALLATION. Remove lock cylinder. See LOCK CYLINDER under REMOVAL & INSTALLATION.

2) Remove housing cover end cap to expose wiper switch and disconnect cruise control plug-in, if equipped. See Fig. 13. Remove combination switch. See COMBINATION SWITCH under REMOVAL & INSTALLATION. Remove screws retaining lock housing cover to gearshift lever bowl.

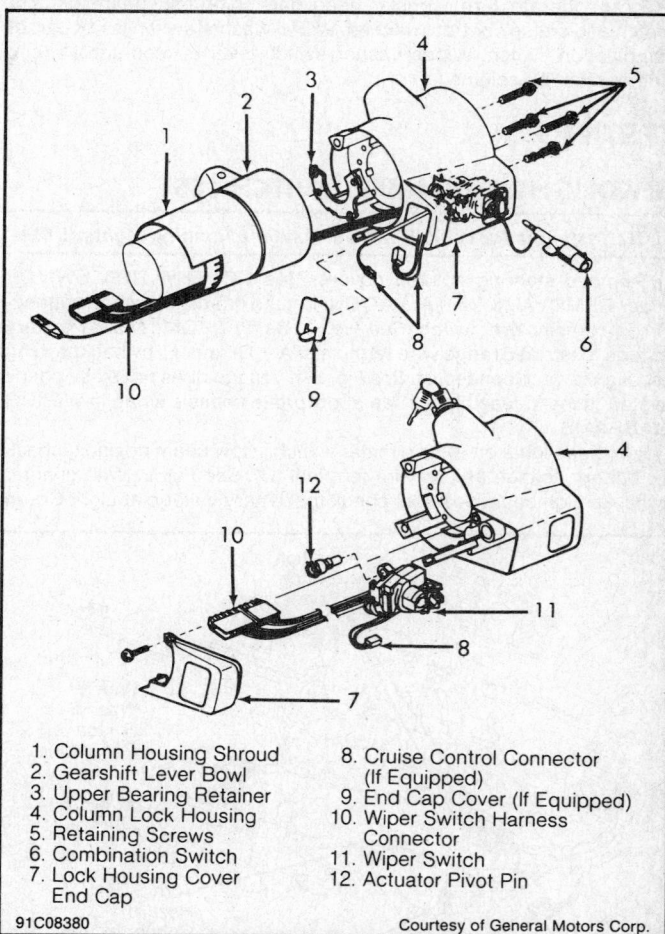

1. Column Housing Shroud
2. Gearshift Lever Bowl
3. Upper Bearing Retainer
4. Column Lock Housing
5. Retaining Screws
6. Combination Switch
7. Lock Housing Cover End Cap
8. Cruise Control Connector (If Equipped)
9. End Cap Cover (If Equipped)
10. Wiper Switch Harness Connector
11. Wiper Switch
12. Actuator Pivot Pin

91C08380   Courtesy of General Motors Corp.

Fig. 13: Removing Wiper Switch (Typical)

3) Disconnect wiper switch harness connector on lower steering column, and position connector parallel with wiring. Slowly remove housing cover, and pull wiper switch wiring harness through column housing shroud. Remove actuator pivot pin retaining wiper switch to lock housing cover. See Fig. 13. Remove wiper switch assembly.

4) To install, reverse removal procedure. If SIR air bag system equipped, see SIR COIL under REMOVAL & INSTALLATION.

TORQUE SPECIFICATIONS

TORQUE SPECIFICATIONS

Application	Ft. Lbs. (N.m)
Steering Wheel Retaining Nut (All)	30-35 (41-47)
Steering Column Support Bracket Bolt	
"L" Body	22 (30)
"N" Body	20 (26)
"W" Body	18 (24)
Pinch Bolt	
"N" Body	29 (40)
"W" Body	35 (47)
	INCH Lbs. (N.m)
Air Bag Module	13 (1.5)
Turn Signal Switch Screw	35 (4)
Lock Cylinder Retaining Screw	40 (4.5)

DESCRIPTION

COMBINATION & WIPER/WASHER SWITCHES

Combination switch is mounted on left side of steering column. It is used to operate turn signals, headlights, high/low beam dimmer switch and cruise control switches. Wiper/washer switch is not part of combination switch. Wiper/washer switch lever is mounted to right side of steering column.

TESTING

HEADLIGHT & DIMMER SWITCH TEST

NOTE: Testing is for vehicle without Daytime Running Lights (DRL).

1) Remove steering column covers. See COMBINATION SWITCH under REMOVAL & INSTALLATION. Locate headlight switch connector on combination switch. See Fig. 1. Using DVOM, ensure battery voltage exists at Orange wire terminals "A", "D" and "E" by backprobing headlight switch connector. See Fig. 2. If voltage does not exist, check related fuses in fuse block. See appropriate chassis wring in WIRING DIAGRAMS.
2) Turn headlights on. With dimmer switch in low beam position, check for battery voltage at Tan wire terminal "C". See Fig. 2. With dimmer switch in high beam position, check for battery voltage at Light Green

wire terminal "B". If voltage does not exist in either or both positions replace combination switch.
3) To check flash-to-pass switch, check for battery voltage at Ligh Green wire terminal "B" when engaging switch. See Fig. 2. If voltag does not exist, replace combination switch.
4) To check park lights, check for battery voltage at Brown wire termi nal "F" when switch is in park or headlight position. If voltage does no exist, replace combination switch. See Fig. 2.

HORN TEST

1) Ensure horn operates by using jumper wire connected from Dar Green wire terminal of horn unit (behind grille) to battery voltag source. If horn does not sound, repair, adjust or replace horn unit a needed.
2) Locate horn relay in fuse box. Fuse box is located near top of lef kick panel. Ensure battery voltage exists at Orange wire terminal c relay. Using jumper wire or test light, ground Black wire terminal c relay. If horn does not sound, replace relay.
3) Locate turn signal switch connector mounted to combinatio switch. See Fig. 1. See COMBINATION SWITCH under REMOVAL & INSTALLATION. Using test light connected to ground, backprob Black wire terminal "H" of turn signal switch connector. See Fig. 2.
4) If horn sounds when terminal is grounded, repair or replace hor switch/contacts in steering wheel. If horn does not sound, chec Black wire circuit from connector to horn relay. Repair as needed.

IGNITION SWITCH TEST

1) Disconnect and shield negative battery cable. Remove steering co umn covers. See COMBINATION SWITCH under REMOVAL & INSTALLATION. Locate and disconnect ignition switch connectors a ignition switch. See Figs. 1 and 4.
2) Using DVOM, check for continuity between ignition switch terminal related to ignition key positions. See TESTING IGNITION SWITCI CONTINUITY table. See Fig. 3.
3) To check ignition key warning buzzer, insert key into lock cylinde Using DVOM, check for continuity between "F" terminal of Black cor nector and "D" terminal of White connector. See Fig. 3. If continuit does not exist, replace lock cylinder assembly.

TESTING IGNITION SWITCH CONTINUITY

Switch Position	[1] Battery Terminal (s)	[1] Circu Terminal (s
ACC	[2] A, B	[2]
Bulb Test	[2] A, B	[2]
RUN	[2] A, B	[2] C, [3] A &
START	[2] A, B	[3] B &

[1] – Ensure continuity between ignition switch related terminals.
[2] – Terminals of Black connector.
[3] – Terminals of White connector.

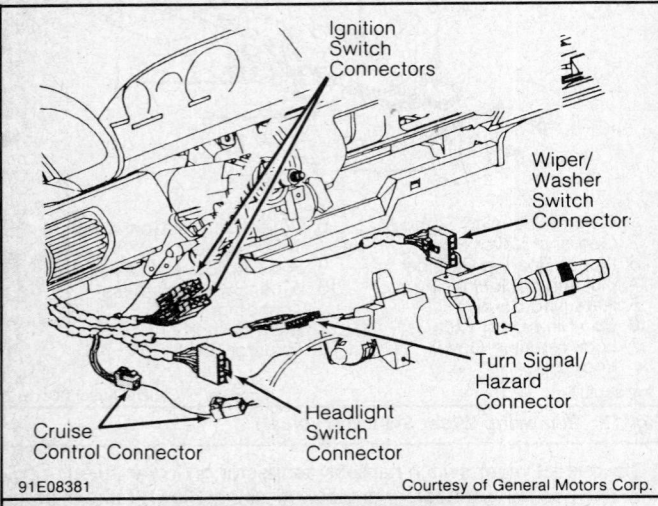

Fig. 1: Locating Steering Column Switch Connectors

HEADLIGHT SWITCH

TERMINAL WIRE COLORS

A Orange
B Light Green
C Tan
D Orange
E Orange
F Brown

BLUE CONNECTOR

TURN SIGNAL/HAZARD SWITCH

TERMINAL WIRE COLORS

A White (Brake)
B Dark Green
C Yellow
D Brown
E Purple
F Light Blue
G Dark Blue
H Black (Horn)

GRAY CONNECTOR

Fig. 2: Locating Steering Column Switch Connector Terminals

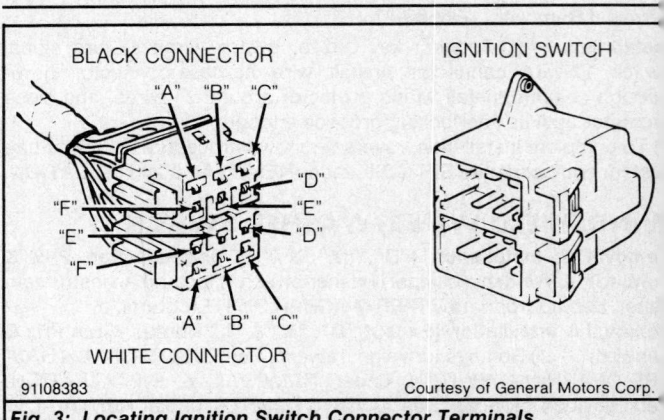

Fig. 3: Locating Ignition Switch Connector Terminals

TURN SIGNAL/HAZARD SWITCH TEST

1) Remove steering column covers. See COMBINATION SWITCH under REMOVAL & INSTALLATION. Locate turn signal/hazard switch connector on combination switch. *See Fig. 1.*

2) Turn ignition to on position. Using DVOM, check for battery voltage at Purple wire terminal "E" by backprobing switch connector. *See Fig. 2.* If battery voltage does not exist, check flasher unit and fuse.

3) Place turn signal lever in right turn position. Check for battery voltage at Dark Blue wire terminal "G" for front lighting circuit and check Dark Green wire terminal "B" for rear lighting circuit. *See Fig. 2.* If battery voltage does not exist at both terminals, replace combination switch.

4) Place turn signal lever in left turn position. Check for battery voltage at Light Blue wire terminal "F" for front lighting circuit and check Yellow wire terminal "C" for rear lighting circuit. If battery voltage does not exist at both terminals, replace combination switch.

5) To check hazard switch, ensure battery voltage at Brown wire terminal "D" by backprobing switch connector. If battery voltage does not exist, check hazard flasher unit and fuse.

6) Turn hazard switch to ON position. Check for battery voltage at the following terminals: Dark Blue wire terminal "G", Dark Green wire terminal "B", Light Blue wire terminal "F" and Yellow wire terminal "C". *See Fig. 2.* If battery voltage does not exist at any one of these terminals, replace combination switch.

7) To check brake light circuit through turn signal switch; ensure battery voltage at Orange wire terminal of brake light switch above brake pedal. Depress brake pedal. Ensure battery voltage exists at White wire terminal "A", Yellow wire terminal "C" and Dark Green wire terminal "B" by backprobing turn signal switch connector. If battery voltage does not exist at any one of these terminals, replace combination switch.

WIPER SWITCH TEST

For testing information on wiper switch, see appropriate WIPER/WASHER SYSTEMS article.

REMOVAL & INSTALLATION

STEERING WHEEL & HORN PAD

Removal – 1) On models with sport wheel, lift or pry off horn button and/or switches pad, remove 3 screws and take off contact, insulator eyelet and spring.

2) On all other models, remove retaining screws from backside of wheel; partially lift off horn button. Unplug electrical connectors and remove horn pad.

3) On all models, remove steering wheel nut. Index steering wheel to shaft for reassembly reference. Use Steering Wheel Puller (BT-61-9 or J-1859-03) to remove steering wheel.

Installation – Align steering wheel with shaft index marks and with turn signal cancelling cam tower. Install steering wheel nut and torque to specification. See TORQUE SPECIFICATIONS table at end of article. To complete installation, reverse removal procedure.

COMBINATION SWITCH

Removal – 1) Remove steering wheel. See STEERING WHEEL & HORN PAD under REMOVAL & INSTALLATION. Remove upper and lower column covers. *See Fig. 4.* On models equipped with tilt columns, it may be necessary to remove tilt lever to allow removal of covers.

2) Separate rosebud fastener of wiring harness from lower column jacket. Remove combination switch mounting screws from column housing. Remove all wiring harness connectors, and remove switch.

Installation – Install switch to column housing and torque mounting screws to 49 INCH lbs. (5.5 N.m). To complete installation, reverse removal procedure.

IGNITION SWITCH

Removal – 1) Remove steering wheel. See STEERING WHEEL & HORN PAD under REMOVAL & INSTALLATION. Remove upper and lower column covers. *See Fig. 4.* On models equipped with tilt columns, it may be necessary to remove tilt lever to allow removal of covers.

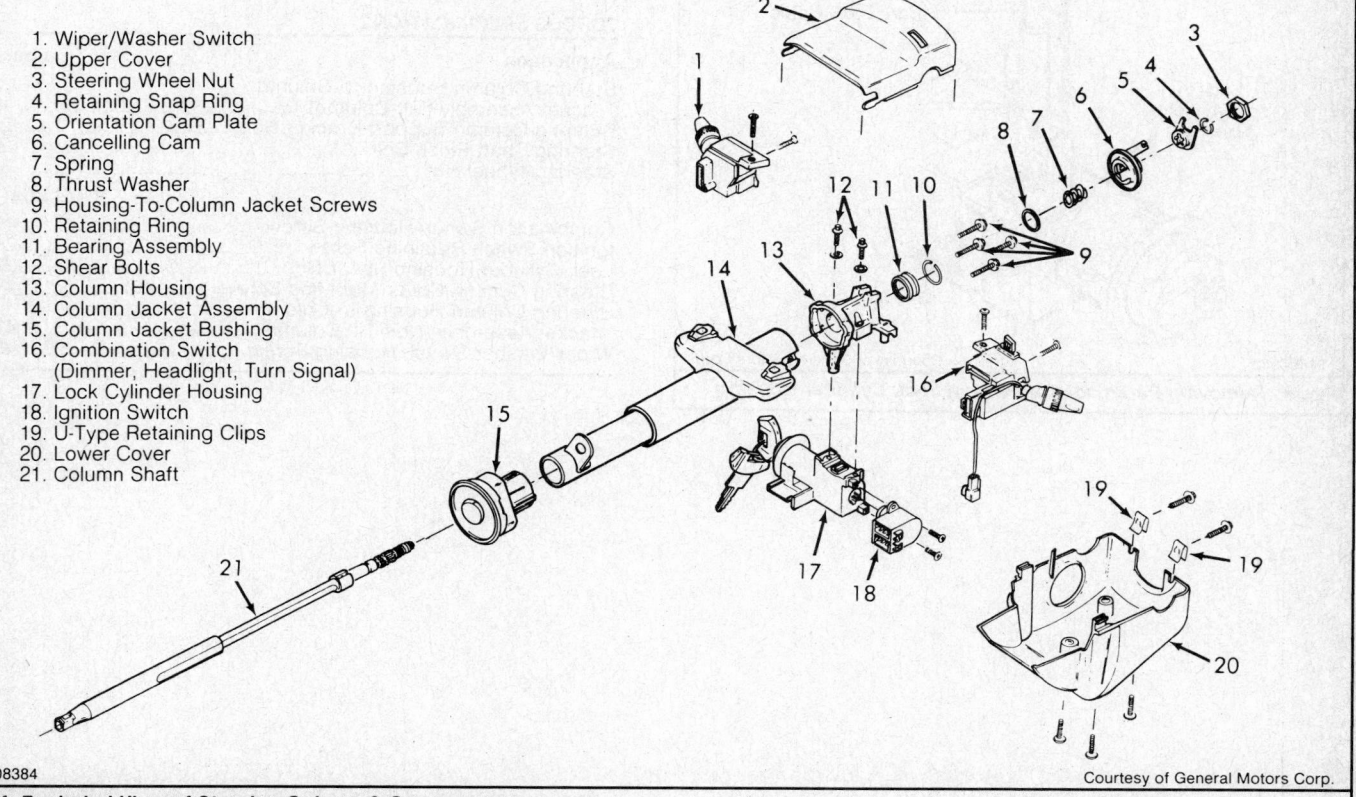

1. Wiper/Washer Switch
2. Upper Cover
3. Steering Wheel Nut
4. Retaining Snap Ring
5. Orientation Cam Plate
6. Cancelling Cam
7. Spring
8. Thrust Washer
9. Housing-To-Column Jacket Screws
10. Retaining Ring
11. Bearing Assembly
12. Shear Bolts
13. Column Housing
14. Column Jacket Assembly
15. Column Jacket Bushing
16. Combination Switch
   (Dimmer, Headlight, Turn Signal)
17. Lock Cylinder Housing
18. Ignition Switch
19. U-Type Retaining Clips
20. Lower Cover
21. Column Shaft

91A08384

Courtesy of General Motors Corp.

Fig. 4: Exploded View of Steering Column & Components

2) Separate rosebud fastener of wiring harness from lower column jacket. Remove combination switch to allow removal of ignition switch top screw. Disconnect and shield negative battery cable. Disconnect ignition switch harness connectors. Remove ignition switch from lock cylinder housing.

Installation – To connect ignition switch to lock cylinder housing, align tab on lock cylinder with slot in ignition switch. Install and torque switch retaining screws to 21 INCH lbs. (2.4 N.m). Install electrical connectors to ignition switch. Install combination switch and torque mounting screws to 49 INCH lbs. (5.5 N.m). Install rosebud fastener and column covers. Torque cover mounting screws to 49 INCH lbs. (5.5 N.m). To complete installation, reverse removal procedure.

LOCK CYLINDER

Removal – **1)** Remove steering wheel. See STEERING WHEEL & HORN PAD under REMOVAL & INSTALLATION. Remove upper and lower column covers. See Fig. 4. On models equipped with tilt columns, it may be necessary to remove tilt lever to allow removal of covers.

2) Separate rosebud fastener of wiring harness from lower column jacket. Remove all wiring harness connectors from column switches. See Fig. 1. Remove combination switch and wiper/washer switch from column housing.

3) Disconnect ignition switch harness connectors. Remove ignition switch from lock cylinder housing. Remove park lock cable by depressing locking tab with small screwdriver and then pulling cable out of lock cylinder housing. See Fig. 5.

4) Disconnect steering column wiring harness at bulkhead connector. Lower or remove steering column from vehicle. Carefully remove shear bolts by drilling off heads with 1/4" drill bit without damaging column housing or bolt washers. See Fig. 6. Remove lock cylinder housing from column housing.

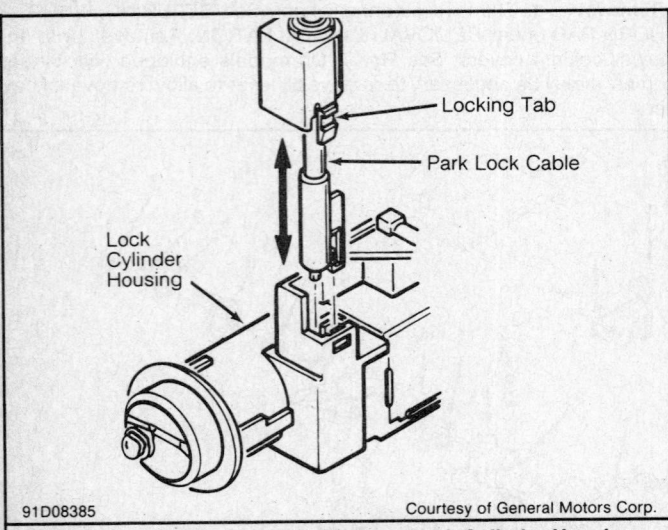

91D08385   Courtesy of General Motors Corp.

Fig. 5: Removing Park Lock Cable from Lock Cylinder Housing

Installation – Install lock cylinder housing to column housing. Ensure locking tab fits into column housing slot. Torque new shear bolts until heads break off. Check ignition key/column locking for proper operation. To complete installation, reverse removal procedure.

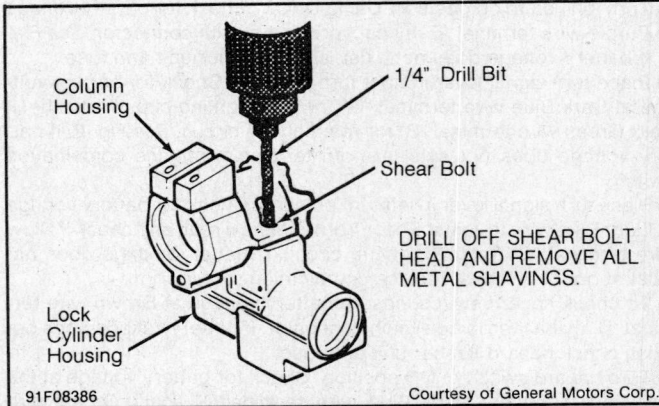

DRILL OFF SHEAR BOLT HEAD AND REMOVE ALL METAL SHAVINGS.

91F08386   Courtesy of General Motors Corp.

Fig. 6: Removing Shear Bolts from Lock Cylinder Housing

WIPER SWITCH

Removal – **1)** Remove steering wheel. See STEERING WHEEL & HORN PAD under REMOVAL & INSTALLATION. Remove upper and lower column covers. See Fig. 4. On models equipped with tilt columns, it may be necessary to remove tilt lever to allow removal of covers.

2) Separate rosebud fastener of wiring harness from lower column jacket. Remove wiper switch mounting screws from column housing. Remove all wiring harness connectors and remove switch.

Installation – Install switch to column housing and torque mounting screws to 49 INCH lbs. (5.5 N.m). To complete installation, reverse removal procedure.

TORQUE SPECIFICATIONS

TORQUE SPECIFICATIONS

Application	Ft. Lbs. (N.m)
Steering Column Housing-to-Column Jacket Assembly (Tilt-Column)	12 (16)
Steering Column Support Bracket Bolt	22 (30)
Steering Shaft Pinch Bolt	29 (40)
Steering Wheel Nut	30 (4)

	INCH Lbs. (N.m)
Combination Switch Housing Screw	49 (5.5)
Ignition Switch Retaining Screw	21 (2.4)
Lock Cylinder Housing Shear Bolt	97 (1)
Steering Column Cover Mounting Screw	49 (5.5)
Steering Column Housing-to-Column Jacket Assembly (Non-Tilt Column)	47 (5.)
Wiper/Washer Switch Housing Screw	49 (5.)

DESCRIPTION

The 2-speed wiper system may be equipped with either standard or pulse wipers. The standard system has 2 speeds for wiper operation with a single or steady wiping action.

On the pulse system, the pause time between the wiping action can be controlled. With wiper switch in DELAY mode, knob can be turned from MIN (minimum) to MAX (maximum) position to vary amount of delay time between wiping action.

Pulse and demand functions are controlled by a plug-in printed circuit board enclosed in wiper housing cover. System uses a washer system with a washer pump mounted in bottom of fluid reservoir.

ADJUSTMENTS

WIPER ARM

NOTE: Check wiper arm wiping pattern on wet windshield.

Wiper arm should be installed so wiping pattern at outer wipe position of wiper blade is 1 3/32" from tip of wiper blade to left windshield pillar molding. If adjustment is required, use Wiper Arm Remover (J-8966) to remove wiper arm from wiper transmission. Reposition wiper arm, and install. Recheck wiping pattern.

TESTING

Before performing tests, ensure wiring harness continuity has been checked, wiper motor and switch mountings are tight, fuses are okay and washer hoses are not restricted.

WIPER MOTOR

Motor Test – 1) Disconnect all wiring connections from wiper motor. Test wiper motor by connecting a power source to proper terminal and using a proper resistor. See Fig. 1.
2) Replace wiper motor if it fails to operate in all conditions. If wiper motor operates correctly, check wiper switch.

Motor Current Draw Test – 1) Remove wiper fuse. Connect an ammeter with 10-amp or greater range across fuse terminals. Apply water to windshield. Turn ignition switch to RUN and wiper switch to HI positions. If ammeter reading is less than 5 amps, check wiper linkage for binding. If linkage is okay, repair wiper motor assembly.
2) If ammeter reading is greater than 5 amps, replace wiper blades, and repeat test. If ammeter reading is now less than 5 amps, wiper blades were defective. If reading is still greater than 5 amps, disconnect linkage from motor crank, and repeat test.
3) If ammeter reading is less than 5 amps, linkage is binding. If ammeter reading is greater than 5 amps, repair wiper motor assembly.
Park Test (Standard Wipers) – 1) Disconnect wiper motor assembly connector. Turn ignition switch to ACCY position. Using a voltmeter, measure voltage between terminal "A" (White wire) and ground. If battery voltage is present, go to next step. If battery voltage is not present, repair White wire for an open circuit.
2) Turn ignition and wiper switches to OFF positions. Using an ohmmeter, check resistance between wiper motor assembly connector terminals "B" (Orange wire) and "C" (Gray wire). Continuity should be present. If no continuity is present, check Orange wire for an open circuit. If wire is okay, replace wiper switch assembly.

WIPER/WASHER SWITCH (STANDARD WIPERS)

Wiper Switch Input Test – Place ignition switch in ACCY position. Disconnect wiper switch assembly connector. Using a Dual Volt/Ohmmeter (DVOM), measure voltage between White wire and ground at wiper switch connector. Reading should be battery voltage. If voltage is not correct, check wiper fuse and White wire for open circuit. If voltage is correct, go to WIPER SWITCH OUTPUT TEST.
Wiper Switch Output Test – 1) Disconnect wiper motor assembly connector. Position wiper switch in LOW and MIST positions. Using a DVOM, voltage reading between Orange and ground should be zero volts. If voltage reading is correct, go to next step. If voltage reading is greater than zero volts, check Orange wire for short to voltage. If wire is okay, replace wiper switch assembly.
2) Measure voltage between Gray wire and ground. Reading should be battery voltage. If voltage reading is correct, go to next step. If voltage reading is incorrect, check Gray wire for an open circuit. If wire is okay, replace wiper switch assembly.

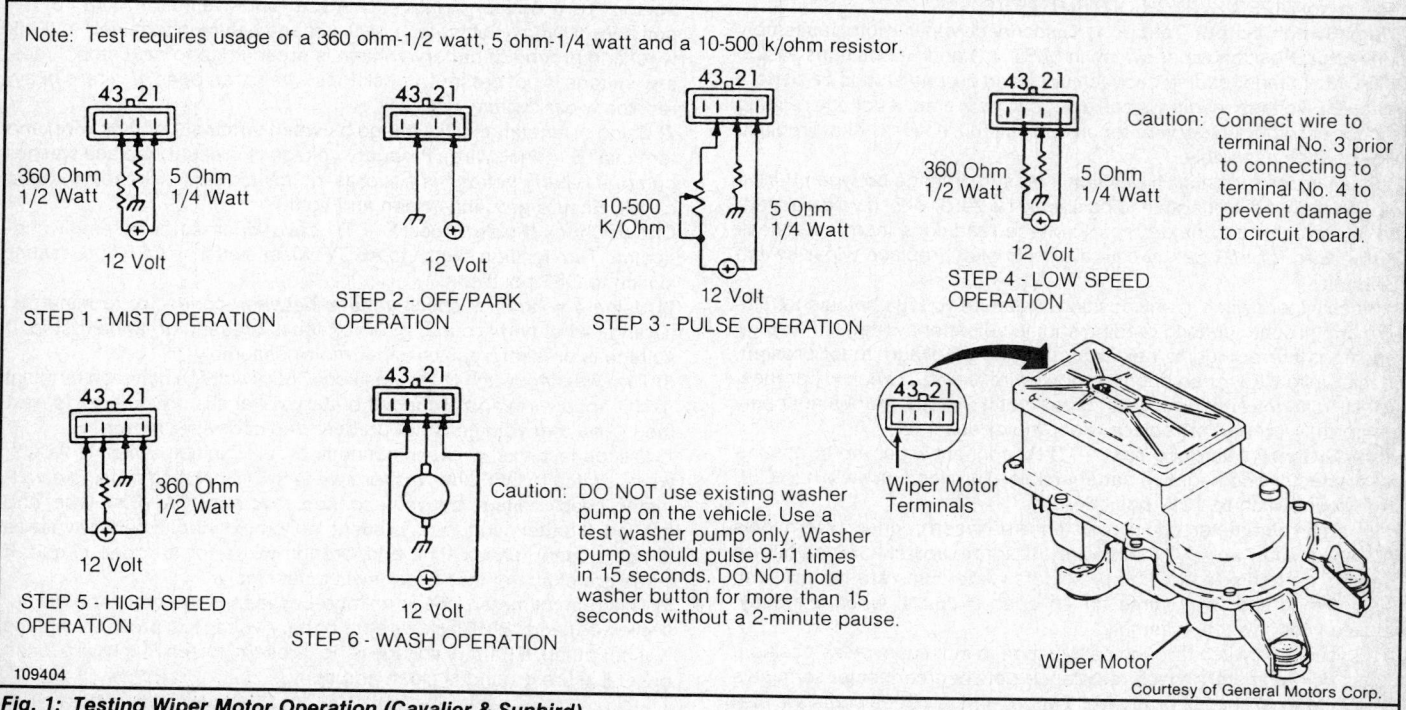

Note: Test requires usage of a 360 ohm-1/2 watt, 5 ohm-1/4 watt and a 10-500 k/ohm resistor.

STEP 1 - MIST OPERATION

STEP 2 - OFF/PARK OPERATION

STEP 3 - PULSE OPERATION

STEP 4 - LOW SPEED OPERATION

Caution: Connect wire to terminal No. 3 prior to connecting to terminal No. 4 to prevent damage to circuit board.

STEP 5 - HIGH SPEED OPERATION

STEP 6 - WASH OPERATION

Caution: DO NOT use existing washer pump on the vehicle. Use a test washer pump only. Washer pump should pulse 9-11 times in 15 seconds. DO NOT hold washer button for more than 15 seconds without a 2-minute pause.

Wiper Motor Terminals

Wiper Motor

Courtesy of General Motors Corp.

109404

Fig. 1: Testing Wiper Motor Operation (Cavalier & Sunbird)

3) Check voltage reading between Purple wire and ground. Voltage reading should be zero volts. If voltage reading is correct, go to next step. If voltage reading is incorrect, check Purple wire for short to voltage. If wire is okay, replace wiper switch assembly.

4) Place wiper switch in HI position. Check voltage reading between Orange wire and ground. Voltage reading should be zero volts. If voltage reading is correct, go to next step. If voltage reading is incorrect, check Orange wire for short to voltage. If wire is okay, replace wiper switch assembly.

5) Check voltage reading between Gray wire and ground. Voltage reading should be zero volts. If voltage reading is correct, go to next step. If voltage reading is incorrect, check Gray wire for short to voltage. If wire is okay, replace wiper switch assembly.

6) Check voltage reading between Purple wire and ground. Voltage reading should be battery voltage. If voltage reading is correct, go to next step. If voltage reading is incorrect, check Purple wire for an open circuit. If wire is okay, replace wiper switch assembly.

7) Place wiper switch in OFF position. Check voltage between Orange wire and ground. Voltage reading should be zero volts. If voltage reading is correct, go to next step. If voltage reading is incorrect, check Orange wire for short to voltage. If wire is okay, replace wiper switch assembly.

8) Check voltage reading between Gray wire and ground. Voltage reading should be zero volts. If voltage reading is correct, go to next step. If voltage reading is incorrect, check Gray wire for short to voltage. If wire is okay, replace wiper switch assembly.

9) Check voltage reading between Purple wire and ground. Voltage reading should be battery voltage. If voltage reading is correct, go to next step. If voltage reading is incorrect, check Purple wire for an open circuit. If wire is okay, replace wiper switch assembly.

10) If voltage readings are correct and wiper motor assembly does not operate normally, repair or replace wiper motor assembly.

WIPER/WASHER SWITCH (PULSE WIPERS)

Wiper Switch Input Test – Place ignition switch in ACCY position. Disconnect wiper switch assembly connector. Using a DVOM, measure voltage between White wire and ground at wiper switch connector. Reading should be battery voltage. If voltage is not correct, check wiper fuse and White wire for an open circuit. If voltage is correct, go to WIPER SWITCH OUTPUT TEST.

Wiper Switch Output Test – **1)** Disconnect wiper motor assembly connector. Position wiper switch in MIST, LO and HI positions. Using a DVOM, voltage reading between Gray and ground should be battery voltage. If voltage reading is correct, go to next step. If voltage reading is incorrect, check Gray wire for an open circuit. If wire is okay, replace wiper switch assembly.

2) Place wiper switch in HI position. Measure voltage between Purple wire and ground. Voltage reading should be zero volts. If voltage reading is correct, go to next step. If voltage reading is incorrect, check Purple wire for an open circuit. If wire is okay, replace wiper switch assembly.

3) Place wiper switch in any position. Measure voltage between White wire and ground. Voltage reading should be battery voltage. If voltage reading is correct, go to next step. If battery voltage is not present, check White wire for an open circuit. If wire is okay, check wiper fuse.

4) If all voltages are correct, but wiper motor assembly does not operate normally, repair or replace wiper motor assembly.

Wiper Switch Resistance Test – **1)** Disconnect wiper motor assembly connector and negative battery cable. Turn ignition switch to OFF and wiper switch to LOW positions.

2) Using an ohmmeter, check resistance between connector terminals "A" (White wire) and "C" (Gray wire). If approximately 350 ohms are present, go to next step. If approximately 350 ohms are not present, check White and Gray wires for an open circuit. If wires are okay, replace wiper switch assembly.

3) Move wiper switch through delay range to maximum delay position. Using an ohmmeter, check resistance between connector terminals "A" (White wire) and "C" gray wire. If approximately 5000 ohms are pre-

sent, but pulse mode does not operate, replace circuit board. If approximately 5000 ohms are not present, check White and Gray wires for an open circuit. If wires are okay, replace wiper switch assembly.

WASHER PUMP

Pump Motor Test – Remove wiring connector from washer pump. Using jumper wire, connect 12 volts to terminal No. 2. *See Fig. 2.* Replace washer pump if it fails to operate. If washer pump operates, check wiring. See CIRCUIT CHECK (STANDARD WIPERS) or CIRCUIT CHECK (PULSE WIPERS) under WASHER PUMP.

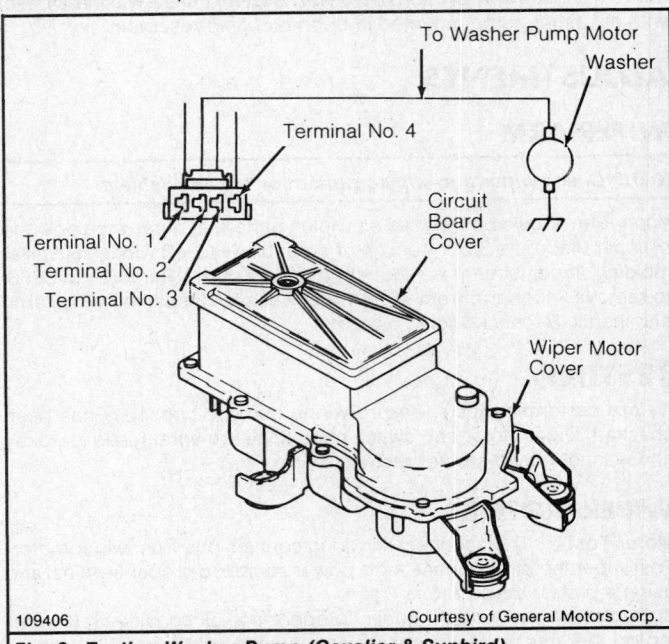

109406   Courtesy of General Motors Corp.

Fig. 2: Testing Washer Pump (Cavalier & Sunbird)

Circuit Check (Standard Wipers) – **1)** Disconnect washer pump connector. Turn ignition switch to ACCY and washer switch to ON positions. Using a voltmeter, check voltage between terminal "A" (Pink wire) and ground. If battery voltage is present, go to next step. If battery voltage is not present, check Pink wire for an open. If wire is okay, replace wiper switch assembly.

2) Using voltmeter, check voltage between terminal "A" (Pink wire) and terminal "B" (Black wire). If battery voltage is present, replace washer pump. If battery voltage is not present, check Black wire for an open circuit. Ensure ground is clean and tight.

Circuit Check (Pulse Wipers) – **1)** Leave wiper motor assembly connected. Turn ignition switch to ACCY, wiper switch to OFF and washer switch to OFF positions.

2) Using a voltmeter, check voltage between connector terminal "B" (Orange wire) and ground. If no voltage is present, go to next step. If voltage is present, replace wiper motor assembly.

3) Turn washer switch to ON position. Check voltage between terminal "B" (Orange wire) and ground. If battery voltage is present, go to next step. If battery voltage is not present, replace wiper motor.

4) Disconnect washer pump connector. Turn ignition switch to ACCY, wiper switch to OFF and washer switch to ON positions. Using a voltmeter, check voltage between connector terminal "A" (Pink wire) and ground. If battery voltage is present, go to next step. If battery voltage is not present, check Pink and Orange wires for an open circuit. If wires are okay, replace wiper switch assembly.

5) Using a voltmeter, check voltage between connector terminal "A" (Pink wire) and "B" (Black wire). If battery voltage is present, replace washer pump. If battery voltage is not present, check Black wire for an open. Ensure ground is clean and tight.

REMOVAL & INSTALLATION

WIPER MOTOR

NOTE: Repairs can only be made to wiper motor cover and circuit board.

Removal – 1) Loosen, but DO NOT remove, transmission drive link-to-crank arm nuts. Separate drive link from motor crank arm. Disconnect wiper motor electrical connections.

2) Remove wiper motor mounting bolts. Rotate wiper motor upward, and remove.

Installation – To install, reverse removal procedure. Tighten wiper motor attaching bolts to 48 INCH lbs. (5 N.m). Install wiper arms to obtain correct location. See WIPER ARM under ADJUSTMENTS.

WIPER MOTOR COVER

Removal – Remove wiper motor from vehicle. Using a 11/64" drill bit, drill off cover-to-housing rivets from housing side. Remove wiper motor cover. See Fig. 2.

Installation – Install wiper motor cover using 5/32" x 3/8" self-tapping screws. Install wiper motor.

CIRCUIT BOARD

Removal – Remove circuit board retaining screws. Remove circuit board cover. Lift circuit board at outer end so terminal clips are disengaged on inner end. Remove circuit board.

Installation – To install, reverse removal procedure. Ensure circuit board fully engages with all terminals. Tighten circuit board cover screws to 23 INCH lbs. (3 N.m).

CRANK ARM

Removal & Installation – With wiper motor removed from vehicle, place crank arm in soft-faced vice, and remove retaining nut. Note direction of crank arm installation. Remove crank arm. To install, reverse removal procedure. Tighten retaining nut to 31 ft. lbs. (42 N.m).

WASHER PUMP

Removal & Installation – To remove, drain washer fluid reservoir, and disconnect electrical connection and hose. Remove washer pump from washer fluid reservoir. To install, reverse removal procedure. Ensure washer pump is fully seated in gasket on washer fluid reservoir.

WIPER TRANSMISSION

Removal – Remove top vent grille and wiper arms. Loosen drive link-to-crank arm nuts. DO NOT remove nuts. Disengage drive link from crank arm. Remove wiper transmission retaining bolts and wiper transmission.

Installation – To install, reverse removal procedure. Tighten wiper transmission retaining bolts to 64 INCH lbs. (7 N.m). Install wiper arms to obtain correct location. See WIPER ARM under ADJUSTMENTS.

WIRING DIAGRAMS

See appropriate chassis wiring diagram in WIRING DIAGRAMS.

1991 SAFETY EQUIPMENT
Wiper/Washer Systems – All Others

Beretta, Bonneville, Brougham, Camaro, Caprice, Century, Corsica, Corvette, Custom Cruiser, Cutlass Calais, Cutlass Ciera, Cutlass Cruiser, Cutlass Supreme, DeVille, Eighty-Eight, Eldorado, Firebird, Fleetwood, Grand Am, Grand Prix, LeSabre, Lumina, Ninety-Eight, Park Avenue, Reatta, Regal, Riviera, Roadmaster, Seville, Skylark, Toronado, Touring Sedan, Trofeo, 6000

NOTE: Brougham information is not available from manufacturer.

DESCRIPTION

The permanent magnet windshield wiper/washer system uses a depressed park wiper motor with a remote windshield washer pump mounted on washer reservoir. The system is designed to deliver pulse timing and demand wash functions electronically.

Depending on control switch design and whether an integral electronic printed circuit board is used in the wiper cover, the system can function as either a pulse or standard wiper/washer system.

OPERATION

Electronic logic circuits on a pulse wiper system's printed circuit board create the timing and washer commands. Whenever the WASH switch is activated for less than one second, washer solvent is sprayed on the windshield for about 2.5 seconds, activating the wiper cycle for approximately 6 seconds.

If WASH switch is held for more than one second, a demand wash will be performed for as long as switch is held. This wash cycle is followed by the 6-second wiper cycle. When the control switch is in LO or HI speed position, the applicable brush circuit is completed to the power source, and the motor runs at set speed.

Switching the control to PULSE mode operates the wiper motor intermittently. The delay can be varied by adjusting the switch back and forth within the delay mode. An instant wipe is caused by positioning the switch in the MIST selection (if equipped). The wiping action continues until the switch is released.

TESTING

Before performing following tests, ensure wiper motor-to-dash mounting hardware is secure, washer hoses are not kinked, disconnected or broken, and circuit harness wiring and circuit fuses are okay.

WIPER MOTOR TEST

Except Corvette, Eldorado, Reatta, Riviera & Seville – 1) Check motor operation before removing wiper assembly from vehicle. Disconnect wiring harness from wiper assembly. Apply a 12-volt source to wiper connector pins. See Fig. 1.
2) If wiper motor runs in all operating modes (LO, HI, PARK and PULSE), perform voltage and continuity wiper switch tests. See Fig. 2. If wiper motor does not run in any or all operating modes, perform appropriate tests.

NOTE: For terminal and connector reference during wiper tests, see Fig. 3 or appropriate chassis wiring diagram in WIRING DIAGRAMS.

WIPER MOTOR INPUT VOLTAGE TEST

1) Disconnect wiper motor module connectors C1 and C2. Turn ignition switch to ACCESSORY position, and ensure wiper/washer switch is off. Use a voltmeter to measure voltage between C2 terminal "A" (Purple wire) and C1 terminal "B" (Gray wire) and ground.
2) If readings are zero volts, replace wiper motor module cover. If voltage is present, check associated wiring for short to voltage. If wiring

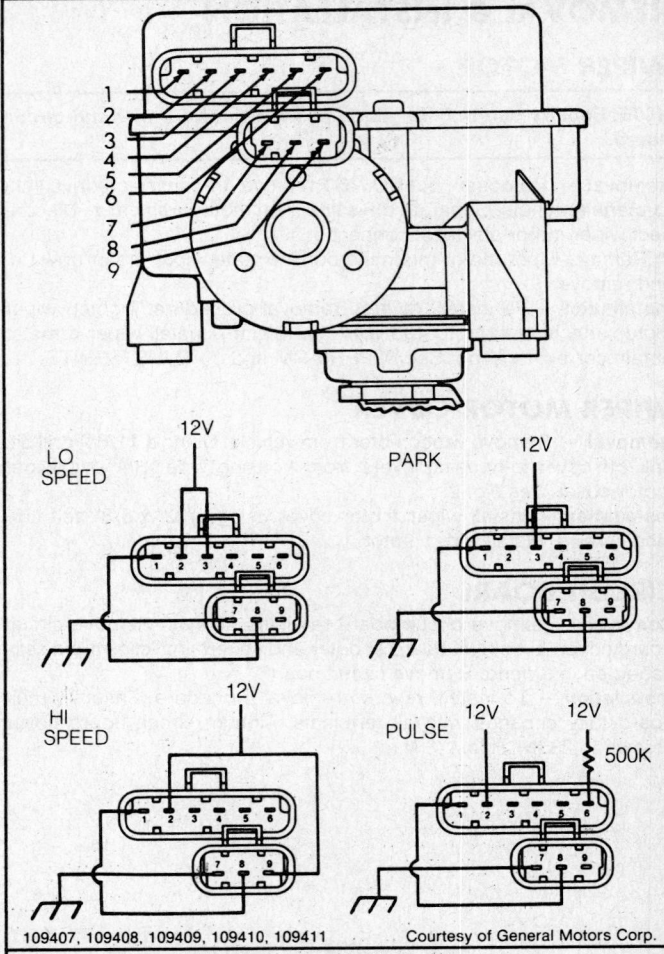

109407, 109408, 109409, 109410, 109411   Courtesy of General Motors Corp.

Fig. 1: Testing Wiper Motor Operating Modes

	SWITCH MODE	MIST	OFF	PULSE	LO	HI	WASH
	TERMINAL #						
PULSE	1	C	C	C	C	C	C
	2	B(+)	—	B(+)	B(+)	—	B(+)
	3	B(+)	B(+)	—	B(+)	—	B(+)
	4	—	—	—	—	—	—
	5	—	—	—	—	—	—
	6	10-12V	10-12V	10-12V	10-12V	10-12V	B(+)
	7	GROUND	GROUND	GROUND	GROUND	GROUND	GROUND
	8	C	C	C	C	C	C
	9	—	—	—	—	B(+)	—
STANDARD	1		C		C	C	C
	2		—		B(+)	—	B(+)
	3		B(+)		B(+)	—	B(+)
	4		—		—	—	—
	5		—		—	—	—
	6				—	—	B(+)
	7		GROUND		GROUND	GROUND	GROUND
	8		C		C	C	C
	9		—		—	B(+)	—

NOTE: C in chart indicates continuity with ohmmeter.
109413   Courtesy of General Motors Corp.

Fig. 2: Checking Switch & Harness (On-Vehicle)

is okay, replace wiper/washer switch. Measure voltage between C1 terminal "C" (Dark Green wire) and C1 terminal "F" (Pink wire) and ground.
3) If battery voltage is present, replace wiper motor module cover. If voltage is not present, check associated wiring to wiper/washer switch for open or short to ground. If wiring is okay, replace wiper/washer switch.

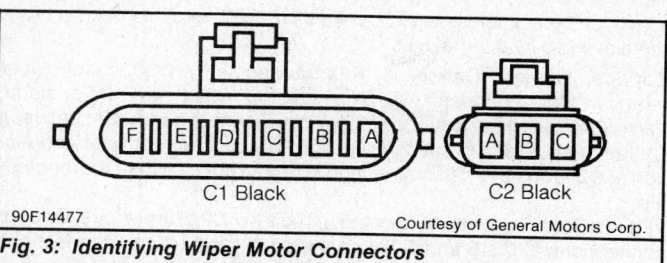

Fig. 3: Identifying Wiper Motor Connectors

90F14477 — Courtesy of General Motors Corp.

C1 Black   C2 Black

4) With wiper/washer switch in MIST position, measure voltage between C2 terminal "A" (Purple wire) and ground. If reading is zero volts, replace wiper motor module cover. If voltage is present, check wiring for short to voltage. If wiring is okay, replace wiper/washer switch.

5) Measure voltage between ground and C1 terminal "B" (Gray wire), C1 terminal "C" (Dark Green wire) and C1 terminal "F" (Pink wire). If battery voltage is present, replace wiper motor module cover. If battery voltage is not present, check wiring to wiper/washer switch for open or short to ground. If wiring is okay, replace wiper/washer switch.

6) With wiper/washer switch in PULSE position, measure voltage between C2 terminal "A" (Purple wire) and C1 terminal "C" (Dark Green wire) and ground. If reading is zero volts, replace wiper motor module cover. If voltage is present, check wiring for short to voltage. If wiring is okay, replace wiper/washer switch.

7) Measure voltage between C1 terminal "B" (Gray wire) and C1 terminal "F" (Pink wire) and ground. If battery voltage is present, replace wiper motor module cover. If battery voltage is not present, check wiring to wiper/washer switch for open or short to ground. If wiring is okay, replace wiper/washer switch.

8) With wiper/washer switch in LO position, measure voltage between C2 terminal "A" (Purple wire) and ground. If reading is zero volts, replace wiper motor module cover. If voltage is present, check wiring for short to voltage. If wiring is okay, replace wiper motor module cover.

9) Measure voltage between ground and C1 terminal "B" (Gray wire), C1 terminal "C" (Dark Green wire) and C1 terminal "F" (Pink wire). If battery voltage is present, replace wiper motor module cover. If battery voltage is not present, check wiring to wiper/washer switch for open or short to ground. If wiring is okay, replace wiper/washer switch.

10) With wiper/washer switch in HI position, measure voltage between C2 terminal "A" (Purple wire) and C1 terminal "F" (Pink wire) and ground. If battery voltage is present, replace wiper motor module cover. If battery voltage is not present, check wiring to wiper/washer switch for open or short to ground. If wiring is okay, replace wiper/washer switch.

11) Measure voltage between C1 terminal "B" (Gray wire) and C1 terminal "C" (Dark Green wire) and ground. If reading is zero volts, replace wiper motor module cover. If voltage is present, check wiring for short to voltage. If wiring is okay, replace wiper/washer switch.

12) With wiper/washer switch off and washer switch on, measure voltage between C2 terminal "A" (Purple wire) and ground. If reading is zero volts, replace wiper motor module cover. If voltage is present, check wiring for short to voltage. If wiring is okay, replace wiper/washer switch.

13) Measure voltage between ground and C1 terminal "B" (Gray wire), C1 terminal "C" (Dark Green wire) and C1 terminal "F" (Pink wire). If battery voltage is present, replace wiper motor module cover. If battery voltage is not present, check wiring to wiper/washer switch for open or short to ground. If wiring is okay, replace wiper/washer switch.

WIPER MOTOR MODULE RESISTANCE TEST

1) Disconnect wiper motor module connectors C1 and C2. Ensure ignition switch is in OFF position and wiper/washer switch is in HI position. Use an ohmmeter to measure resistance between C1 terminal "C" (Dark Green wire) and C1 terminal "B" (Gray wire). If resistance

is less than .5 ohms, check park switch latch arm and drive pawl for proper operation.

2) If resistance is more than .5 ohms, check circuits No. 95 (Dark Green wire) and No. 91 (Gray wire) for open or short to ground or each other. If wires are okay, replace wiper/washer switch. With ignition off and wiper/washer switch in PULSE position, check resistance between C1 terminal "C" (Dark Green wire) and C1 terminal "B" (Gray wire).

3) If ohmmeter reads infinite resistance, check park switch latch arm and drive pawl for proper operation. If reading shows measurable resistance, check circuits No. 95 (Dark Green wire) and No. 91 (Gray wire) for open or short to ground or each other. If wires are okay, replace wiper/washer switch.

4) Measure resistance between C1 terminal "A" (Yellow wire) and C2 terminal "B" (Yellow wire). If resistance is .5 ohms or less, check park switch latch arm and drive pawl for proper operation. If ohmmeter shows infinite resistance, check for open circuit No. 196 (Yellow wire).

5) Measure resistance between C1 terminal "A" (Yellow wire) and ground. If reading is infinite ohms, check park switch latch arm and drive pawl for proper operation. If reading is measurable resistance, check circuit No. 196 (Yellow wire) for short to ground.

WIPER PULSE CONTROL RESISTANCE TEST

1) Perform test with wiper motor module connector C1 and negative battery cable disconnected. Ensure ignition switch is in OFF position and wiper/washer switch is in LO position. Use an ohmmeter to measure resistance between C1 terminal "B" (Gray wire) and C1 terminal "F" (Pink wire). If resistance is approximately 24 k/ohms, replace wiper motor module cover.

2) If reading is infinite ohms, check for open circuits No. 94 (Pink wire) and No. 91 (Gray wire). If wires are okay, replace wiper/washer switch. Move wiper delay switch to maximum delay position. Check resistance between C1 terminal "B" (Gray wire) and C1 terminal "F" (Pink wire).

3) If reading is approximately 1.2 megohms, replace wiper motor module cover. If reading is infinite ohms, check for open circuits No. 94 (Pink wire) and No. 91 (Gray wire). If wires are okay, replace wiper/washer switch.

WIPER MOTOR MODULE CURRENT DRAW TEST

1) Remove wiper fuse. Connect an ammeter (30 amp range or higher) across fuse terminals. Turn ignition switch to RUN position and wiper/washer switch to HI position. Read ammeter, and record lowest reading. If reading is less than 3 amps or cycles between any number and zero, check:
- Motor ground
- Brush/Commutator condition
- Circuit Breaker (should be closed)
- Armature

2) If reading is greater than 6.5 amps, replace wiper blades, and repeat current measurement. If reading is less than 6.5 amps, wiper blades were problem. If reading is more than 6.5 amps, disconnect linkage from motor crank, and repeat current measurement.

3) If reading is less than 6.5 amps, linkage is binding. Repair as necessary. If reading is more than 6.5 amps, remove wiper motor module, and repair as necessary.

WIPERS DO NOT OPERATE IN ANY MODE TEST

Corvette – 1) Disconnect wiper/washer switch connector. Connect test light between terminal "B" and ground. Turn ignition switch to RUN position. If test light is on, reconnect wiper/washer connector, and disconnect all 3 connectors at wiper motor module. Go to step **3)**.

2) If test light is off, check for blown wiper fuse or open circuit No. 93 (White wire). If fuse and circuit are okay, check for open wiper fuse feed in circuit No. 4 (Brown wire).

3) Connect a test light between C2 terminal "C" and ground. If test light is off, check for open circuit No. 191 (Gray wire). If circuit is okay, replace wiper/washer switch.

4) If test light is on, connect test light between C2 terminal "B" and ground. Turn wiper/washer switch to LO position. If test light is on, go to step 5). If test light is off, check for open circuit No. 97 (Light Blue). If circuit is okay, replace wiper/washer switch.

5) Reconnect wiper motor module connectors C1 and C2. Leave 2-wire connector C3 disconnected. With wiper/washer switch still in LO position, connect test light between C3 terminal "B" and ground. If test light is on, go to step 6). If test light is off, check for open circuit No. 191 (Gray wire). If circuit is okay, repair or replace wiper motor module.

6) Connect test light between C3 terminal "A" and ground. Move wiper/washer switch to HI position. If test light is on, check for open or short to battery voltage in ground circuit No. 150 (Black wire). If okay, repair or replace wiper motor module. If test light is off, check for open circuit No. 92 (Purple wire). If circuit is okay, replace wiper/washer switch.

Caprice, Custom Cruiser & Roadmaster – 1) Disconnect wiper/washer switch connector. Turn ignition switch to RUN position. Connect a test light between C216 terminal "B" and ground. If test light is on, go to step 2). If test light is off, check for open in fuse 10 or circuit No. 93 (White wire). If circuit is okay, check for open power feed circuit No. 4 (Brown wire).

2) Disconnect wiper motor module connector C2. Connect a test light between C2 terminal "C" and battery voltage. If test light is on, go to test 3). If test light is off, check for open ground circuit No. 150 (Black wire).

3) Reconnect connector C216. Disconnect wiper motor module connector C1. Connect a test light between C1 terminal "C" and ground. If test light is on, go to step 4). If test light is off, check for poor connection at connector C216, and check connector C204 for an open circuit No. 95 (Dark Green wire). If connections and circuit are okay, replace wiper/washer switch.

4) Turn wiper/washer switch to LO position. Connect a test light between C1 terminal "B" and ground. If test light is on, go to step 5). If test light is off, check for poor connections at connectors C216 and C204. Also check for open circuit No. 91 (Gray wire). If connections and circuit are okay, replace wiper/washer switch.

5) Use an ohmmeter to check for continuity from wiper motor module C1 terminal "A" to C2 terminal "B". If continuity is found, check for poor connections at wiper motor module connectors. If connections are okay, replace wiper motor module. If no continuity is found, check for open circuit No. 196 (Yellow wire).

WIPERS RUN AT HIGH SPEED ONLY TEST

Corvette – 1) Disconnect wiper motor module connectors C2 and C3. Turn ignition switch to RUN or ACCESSORY position. Move wiper/washer switch to LO position. Connect test light between C2 terminal "C" and ground. If test light is off, check for open circuit No. 191 (Gray wire). If circuit is okay, replace wiper/washer switch.

2) If test light is on, connect test light between C2 terminal "B" and ground. If test light is on again, reconnect C2. If test light is off, check for open circuit No. 97 (Light Blue wire). If circuit is okay, replace wiper/washer switch.

3) Connect test light between C3 terminal "B" and ground. If test light is on, repair or replace wiper motor module. If test light is off, check for open circuit No. 191 (Gray wire). If circuit is okay, repair or replace wiper motor module.

Caprice, Custom Cruiser & Roadmaster – 1) Disconnect wiper motor module connector C1. Turn ignition switch to RUN position. Turn wiper/washer switch to LO position. Connect a test light between C1 terminal "B" and ground. If test light is on, go to step 2). If test light is off, check for open circuit No. 91 (Gray wire) or poor connections at connectors C216 and C204. If circuit and connections are okay, replace wiper/washer switch.

2) Check for poor connection at wiper motor module connector C1. If connection is okay, replace wiper motor module.

WIPERS RUN AT LOW SPEED ONLY TEST

Corvette – Disconnect wiper motor module connector C3. Turn ignition switch to RUN or ACCESSORY position. Move wiper/washer switch to HI position. Connect a test light between C3 terminal "A" and ground. If test light is on, repair or replace wiper motor module. If test

light is off, check for open circuit No. 92 (Purple wire). If circuit is okay, replace wiper/washer switch.

Caprice, Custom Cruiser & Roadmaster – 1) Disconnect wiper motor module connector C2. Turn ignition switch to RUN position. Turn wiper/washer switch to HI position. Connect a test light between C2 terminal "A" and ground. If test light is on, check for poor connection at C2 terminal "A." If connection is okay, replace wiper motor module.

2) If test light is off, check for open circuit No. 92 (Purple wire) or poor connections at C216 and C204 connectors. If circuit and connections are okay, replace wiper/washer switch.

WIPERS WILL NOT SHUT OFF TEST

Corvette – 1) Disconnect 3 wiper motor module connectors. Turn ignition switch to RUN or ACCESSORY position. Turn wiper/washer switch to OFF position. Connect a test light between C1 terminal "A" and ground. If test light is on, check for short to battery voltage in circuit No. 96 (Brown wire).

2) If circuit is okay, replace wiper/washer switch. If test light is off, connect test light between C2 terminal "B" and ground. If test light is on, check for short to battery voltage in circuit No. 97 (Light Blue wire). If circuit is okay, replace wiper/washer switch.

3) If test light is off, reconnect connectors C1 and C2. Connect test light between C3 terminal "B" and ground. If test light is on, check for short to battery voltage in circuit No. 191 (Gray wire). If circuit is okay, repair or replace wiper motor module. If test light is off, connect test light between C3 terminal "A" and ground.

4) If test light is on, check for short to battery voltage in circuit No. 92 (Purple wire). If circuit is okay, replace wiper/washer switch. If test light is off, repair or replace wiper motor module.

Caprice, Custom Cruiser & Roadmaster – 1) Disconnect wiper motor module connector C1. Turn ignition switch to RUN position. Turn wiper/washer switch to OFF position. Use a digital voltmeter to measure voltage between C1 terminal "B" and ground. If voltage is not present, go to step 2). If voltage is present, check for short to battery voltage in circuit No. 91 (Gray wire). If circuit is okay, replace wiper/washer switch.

2) Disconnect wiper motor module connector C2. Use a digital voltmeter to measure voltage between C2 terminal "A" and ground. If voltage is not present, repair/replace wiper motor module. If voltage is present, check for short to battery voltage in circuit No. 92 (Purple wire). If circuit is okay, replace wiper/washer switch.

PULSE DELAY INOPERATIVE OR INCORRECT TEST

Corvette – 1) Disconnect wiper motor module connectors C1 and C2. Turn ignition switch off. Move wiper/washer switch to LO position. Using a Digital Volt Ohmmeter (DVOM), measure resistance between C1 terminal "A" and C2 terminal "B".

2) If resistance reading shows open circuit, check for open circuit No. 96 (Brown wire). If circuit is okay, replace wiper/washer switch. If resistance is approximately 24 k/ohms with DVOM still across terminals, move wiper/washer switch through full pulse delay range.

3) If resistance increases to approximately 1224 k/ohms, repair or replace wiper motor module. If resistance does not increase to this value, replace wiper/washer switch.

Caprice, Custom Cruiser & Roadmaster – 1) Turn ignition switch to OFF position. Disconnect connector C216. Turn wiper/washer switch to PULSE position. Use an ohmmeter to measure resistance through wiper/washer switch at connector C216 from terminal "B" to terminal "F". Move wiper/washer switch through entire delay range.

2) If resistance varies from approximately 1224 k/ohms to 24 k/ohms, check circuit No. 94 (Pink wire) for open or poor connection. If circuit is okay, replace wiper motor module. If resistance does not vary to these values, replace wiper/washer switch.

WASHER MOTOR VOLTAGE TEST

1) Disconnect washer motor connector. Turn ignition switch to ACCESSORY position, and hold washer switch in ON position. Use a

voltmeter to measure voltage between terminal "A" (Red wire) and terminal "B" (Dark Blue wire). If reading is battery voltage, replace washer pump.

2) If no voltage is present, check for open circuits No. 228 (Red wire) and No. 227 (Dark Blue wire). If wires are okay, check terminal contact between park switch and cover assembly. If contact is good, replace cover assembly. With washer switch in OFF position, measure voltage between terminal "A" (Red wire) and terminal "B" (Dark Blue wire).

3) If reading is zero volts, replace washer motor. If voltage is present, check circuit No. 228 (Red wire) for short to battery. If wire is okay, replace cover assembly.

WASHER WILL NOT OPERATE TEST

Corvette – 1) Disconnect washer pump connector. Turn ignition switch to RUN or ACCESSORY position. Connect test light between terminals "A" and "B" of washer pump connector. Activate washer switch while observing test light. If test light comes on, replace washer pump. If test light stays off, connect test light between terminal "A" and ground. Activate washer switch.

2) If test light comes on, repair open ground circuit No. 150 (Black wire), terminal "B" of pump connector. If test light stays off, disconnect wiper motor module connectors C1 and C2. Connect test light between C1 terminal "C" and ground. Activate washer switch. If test light comes on, repair open circuit No. 94 (Pink wire).

3) If test light stays off, connect test light between C1 terminal "A" and ground. Activate washer switch. If test light stays off, check for open circuit No. 96 (Brown wire). If circuit is okay, replace wiper/washer switch. If test light comes on, connect test light between C2 terminal "B" and ground.

4) Activate washer switch. If test light comes on, repair or replace wiper motor module. If test light stays off, check for open circuit No. 97 (Light Blue wire). If circuit is okay, replace wiper/washer switch.

Caprice, Custom Cruiser & Roadmaster – 1) Disconnect washer pump connector. Turn ignition switch to RUN position. Connect test light between terminals "A" and "B" of washer pump connector. Activate washer switch while observing test light. If test light comes on, check for poor connection at washer motor connector. If connection is okay, replace washer pump. If test light stays off, connect test light between terminal "A" and ground. Activate washer switch.

2) If test light is on, check for open or poor connection in circuit No. 227 (Dark Blue wire). If connection is okay, replace wiper motor module. If test light is off, use a digital voltmeter to backprobe connector C216 between terminal "F" and ground with ignition switch in RUN position. Activate washer switch.

3) If voltage is present, check for poor connections at connectors C216 and C204 and wiper motor module. Also check for open circuit No. 94 (Pink wire). If okay, repair/replace wiper motor module. If voltage is not present, check for open or poor connection in circuit No. 94 (Pink wire). If circuit is okay, replace wiper/washer switch.

WIPER/WASHER SWITCH VOLTAGE TEST

Eldorado & Seville – 1) Disconnect right switch connector, and turn ignition switch to ACCESSORY position. Use a voltmeter to measure voltage between BC3 and ground. If battery voltage is present, ensure C2 terminal "C" is grounded. If grounded, reconnect right switch connector, and go to WIPER MOTOR INPUT VOLTAGE TEST.

2) If no voltage is present, check wiper fuse No. 12 and circuit No. 93 (White wire) for open or short to ground. Measure voltage between BC4 and ground.

3) If battery voltage is present, ensure C2 terminal "C" is grounded. If grounded, reconnect right switch connector, and go to WIPER MOTOR INPUT VOLTAGE TEST. If no voltage is present, check wiper fuse No. 12 and circuit No. 93 (White wire) for open or short to ground.

Except Eldorado & Seville – 1) Disconnect electrical connectors at wiper motor, and perform continuity, voltage and ground tests using a DVOM. Disconnect 8-wire wiper switch connector, located under dash on right side of brake pedal support. Turn ignition switch to ACCESSORY position.

2) Measure voltage between terminal "D" (White wire) and ground. If battery voltage is present, go to appropriate wiper motor test. If

battery voltage is not present, check for open wiper fuse or open circuit No. 93 (White wire).

REMOVAL & INSTALLATION

WIPER MOTOR MODULE

Removal & Installation (Eldorado & Seville) – Remove harness connectors. Remove wiper motor module screws. Remove wiper motor module. To install, reverse removal procedure.

Removal & Installation (Reatta & Riviera) – Remove A/C pipe shroud. Remove harness connectors, cover and wiper motor module screws. Remove wiper motor module. To install, reverse removal procedure.

WIPER MOTOR

Removal & Installation (Corvette) – Raise hood, and remove negative battery cable. Disconnect upper electrical harness connectors. Remove left plenum screen. Remove right and left transmission link nuts and sockets. Remove vacuum booster supply hose. Remove wiper motor mounting bolts. Remove wiper motor, and disconnect lower electrical connector. To install, reverse removal procedure.

Removal & Installation (Reatta & Riviera) – Remove A/C pipe shroud. Remove cowl cover and wiper arm drive link from crank arm. Disconnect harness connectors, and remove wiper motor mounting bolts. Remove wiper motor. To install, reverse removal procedure.

Removal & Installation (Caprice, Custom Cruiser & Roadmaster) – Remove right side wiper arm and hose. To prevent windshield damage, remove left side cowl vent first. Remove right side cowl vent. Remove linkage access hole cover screws and covers. Remove motor drive link from crank arm. Disconnect electrical connectors. Remove wiper motor mounting bolts and wiper motor. To install, reverse removal procedure.

Removal & Installation (All Others) – Remove wiper arms. Remove top vent screen shroud. Remove wiper arm drive link from crank arm. Remove electrical connectors. Remove wiper motor mounting bolts and wiper motor. Remove crank arm from motor. To install, reverse removal procedure.

WIPER MOTOR COVER

Removal & Installation – Remove wiper motor from vehicle (if necessary). See WIPER MOTOR under REMOVAL & INSTALLATION. Remove wiper motor cover screws. Remove cover. To install, reverse removal procedure.

WIPER PARK SWITCH

Removal & Installation (Eldorado, Reatta, Riviera & Seville) – Remove wiper motor module. See WIPER MOTOR MODULE under REMOVAL & ILLUSTRATION. If wiper motor is in PARK position, operate motor to remove lock pawl from relay slot. Remove park switch. To install, reverse removal procedure. *See Figs. 6 and 7.*

Removal & Installation (Except Eldorado, Reatta, Riviera & Seville) – Remove wiper motor cover. See WIPER MOTOR COVER under REMOVAL & ILLUSTRATION. If wiper motor is in PARK position, operate motor to remove lock pawl from relay slot. Remove park switch. To install, reverse removal procedure. *See Figs. 6 and 7.*

WASHER PUMP

Removal & Installation – Drain washer reservoir. Remove necessary braces to gain access to reservoir. Remove washer pump electrical connector. Remove pump retaining screws and pump. To install, reverse removal procedure.

OVERHAUL

GEAR BOX

Disassembly – 1) With wiper motor removed from vehicle, remove crank arm retaining nut. Disconnect crank arm. Remove rubber seal cap and thrust collar or retaining ring. *See Figs. 4 and 5.*

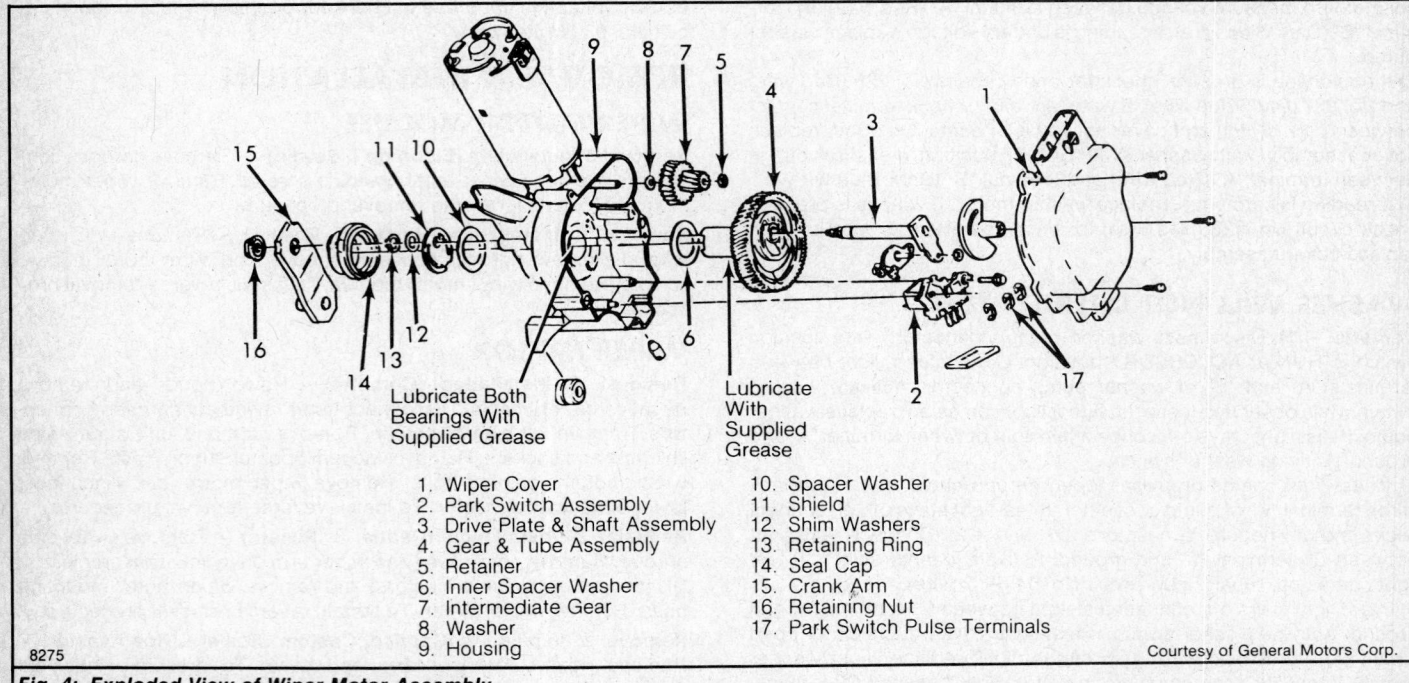

1. Wiper Cover
2. Park Switch Assembly
3. Drive Plate & Shaft Assembly
4. Gear & Tube Assembly
5. Retainer
6. Inner Spacer Washer
7. Intermediate Gear
8. Washer
9. Housing
10. Spacer Washer
11. Shield
12. Shim Washers
13. Retaining Ring
14. Seal Cap
15. Crank Arm
16. Retaining Nut
17. Park Switch Pulse Terminals

Lubricate Both Bearings With Supplied Grease

Lubricate With Supplied Grease

8275   Courtesy of General Motors Corp.

Fig. 4: Exploded View of Wiper Motor Assembly

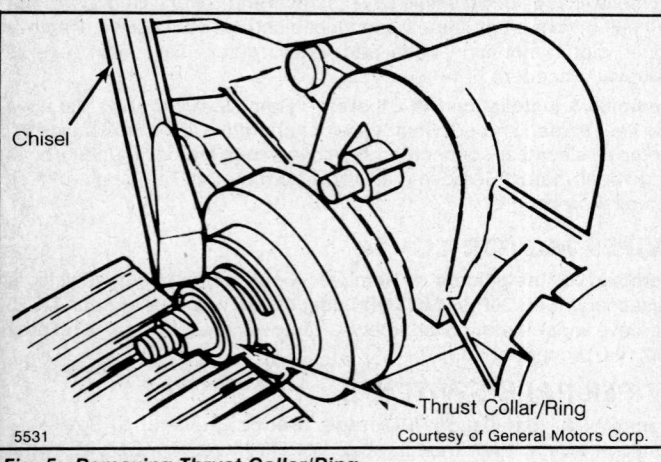

5531   Courtesy of General Motors Corp.

Fig. 5: Removing Thrust Collar/Ring

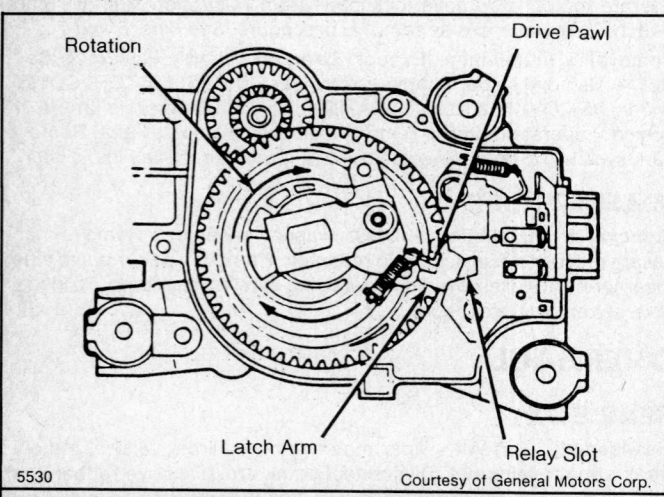

5530   Courtesy of General Motors Corp.

Fig. 6: Identifying Wiper Motor Gear Components

2) Remove shim washers, shield and spacer washer. Remove park switch assembly. Remove large gear, inner spacer washer, intermediate gear retainer and intermediate gear. When removing large gear, latch arm must be out of way. See Fig. 6. Disassemble drive plate and shaft assembly.

Reassembly – 1) Install intermediate gear and new intermediate gear retainer. Install inner spacer washer onto large gear tube. Install large gear, spacer washer and shield. Use shim washers to obtain .001-.010" (.03-.26 mm) end play.

NOTE: Move drive and lock pawls as required to fit respective pins in gear pockets. Ensure drive plate is firmly against gear.

2) Install retaining ring (in place of thrust collar on original motor). Install rubber seal cap. Install crank arm (check crank arm for proper position in park position). See Fig. 7. Tighten crank arm nut to 31 ft. lbs. (42 N.m).

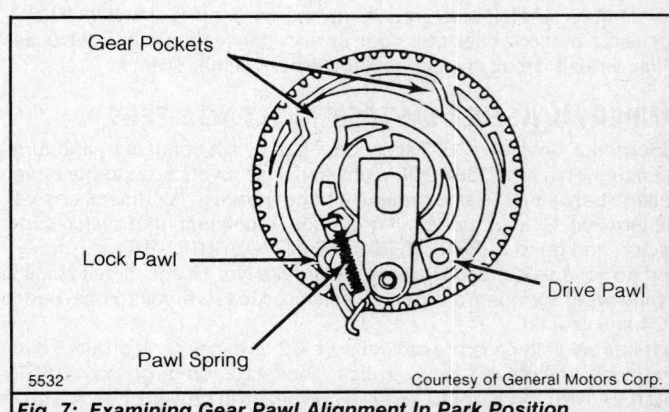

5532   Courtesy of General Motors Corp.

Fig. 7: Examining Gear Pawl Alignment In Park Position

WIRING DIAGRAMS

See appropriate chassis wiring diagram in WIRING DIAGRAMS.

Century, Roadmaster, Caprice, 6000

DESCRIPTION

Station wagon rear window wiper/washer systems use a one-speed permanent magnet motor. A gear box, attached to the motor, drives the wiper pivot to provide oscillating output to wiper arm. An autopark module is used to supply continued voltage to wiper motor after dash switch is turned off. This ensures wiper returns to park position. See Fig. 1.

The wiper motor is mounted to the vehicle with one or 2 screws, and one dowel pin, with dowel pin and screws going through grommets, depending on model. The washer pump is mounted with the washer reservoir in the engine compartment.

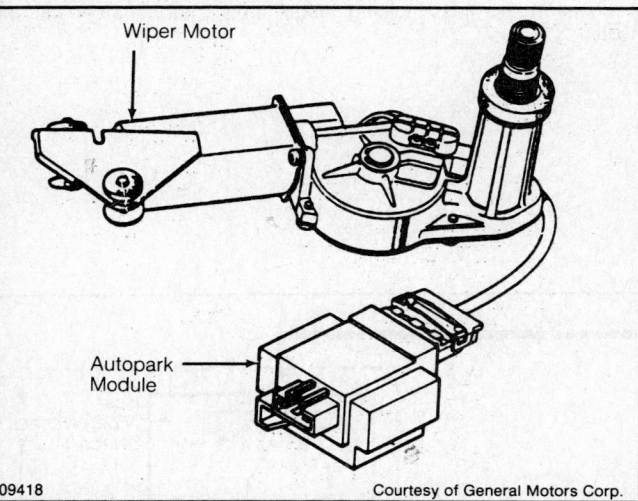

109418   Courtesy of General Motors Corp.

Fig. 1: Identifying Rear Window Wiper Motor

OPERATION

The wiper/washer can only be operated with ignition switch in the RUN or ACC position. Turning the dash-mounted switch to ON position will provide 12 volts to motor assembly. The circuit is completed to ground through terminal "B" to provide operation of the wiper motor. See Fig. 2.

Wiper will continue to operate until a cam, located in the transmission housing, opens the park switch contacts. The cam opens the park switch contacts when the wiper blade reaches the correct park position. Pushing the wash button completes washer motor circuit to ground and turns the washer motor on to operate the pump.

The washer pump allows direct control of amount of solution delivered to the back glass and shuts off as soon as washer button is released. Wiper will continue to operate until the dash wiper switch, or the ignition switch, is turned to the OFF position.

TESTING

TROUBLESHOOTING

Before going to SYMPTOM TABLE, check the following:
- Check WDO circuit breaker by operating power windows (if equipped).
- Check PWR ACC circuit breaker by operating power seats (if equipped).
- If rear washer does not operate, check washer fluid level. Check for kinked or incorrectly attached hoses, and check for clogging of nozzles.

SYMPTOM TABLE

SYMPTOM TABLE

Symptom	Perform Test
Rear Wiper Does Not Operate	A & B
Rear Washer Does Not Operate	A & C
Rear Wiper Does Not Park	B
Rear Wiper Does Not Turn Off	D

TEST A (REAR WIPER/WASHER SWITCH)

1) Gain access to connector on rear wiper/washer switch, but do not disconnect. Turn ignition switch to RUN position. On electrical connector to rear wiper/washer switch, measure voltage between Pink wire and ground. If battery voltage is present, go to step 2). If battery voltage is not present, check Pink wire (circuit No. 76) for open.

2) Push rear wiper/washer switch to WASH position and hold. Measure voltage between ground and Dark Green wire. If battery voltage is present, go to step 3). If battery voltage is not present, replace rear wiper/washer switch.

3) While still holding rear wiper/washer switch in WASH position, measure voltage between Gray wire and ground. If battery voltage is present, go to step 4). If battery voltage is not present, replace the rear wiper/washer switch.

4) Move rear wiper/washer switch to WIPE position. Measure voltage between Gray wire and ground. If battery voltage is present, go to SYMPTOM TABLE. If battery voltage is not present, replace rear wiper/washer switch.

TEST B (REAR WIPER MODULE)

1) Disconnect rear wiper module. Turn ignition switch to RUN position. Move rear wiper/washer switch to WIPER position. Ensure tailgate is closed. On electrical connector to wiper module, measure voltage between terminal "A" (Orange/Black wire) and ground. See Fig. 2. If battery voltage is present, go to step 2). If battery voltage is not present, check Orange/Black wire (circuit No. 60) for open.

2) Measure voltage between terminals "A" (Orange/Black) and "B" (Black) of electrical connector. If battery voltage is present, go to next step. If battery voltage is not present, check Black wire (circuit No. 150) and ground circuit for open.

3) Measure voltage between terminal "C" (Gray/Black) on electrical connector and ground. If battery voltage is present, go to step 4). If battery voltage is not present, check tailgate lock switch and Gray and Gray/Black wires for open(s).

4) Remove rear wiper module. See WIPER MOTOR under REMOVAL & INSTALLATION. Apply battery voltage to wiper module terminals "A" and "C". See Fig. 2. Ground terminal "B". Motor should run. If motor runs, go to step 5). If motor does not run, replace wiper motor.

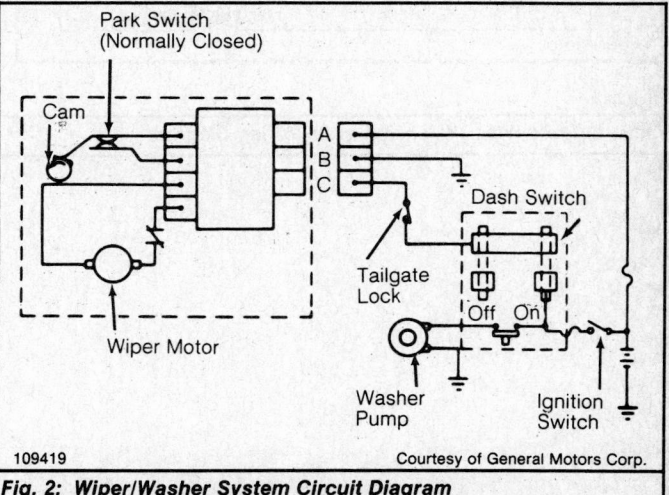

109419   Courtesy of General Motors Corp.

Fig. 2: Wiper/Washer System Circuit Diagram

5) Apply battery voltage to terminal "C". Ground terminal "B". Motor should park. If motor does not park, replace wiper motor.

TEST C (REAR WASHER PUMP)

1) Disconnect rear washer pump connector. Turn ignition switch to RUN position, and move or push rear wiper/washer switch to WASH position and hold. Measure voltage between terminal "A" (Dark Green) on electrical connector and ground. If battery voltage is present, go to step **2)**. If battery voltage is not present, check Dark Green wire (circuit No. 392) for open.

2) With rear wiper/washer switch still held in WASH position, measure voltage between terminals "A" (Dark Green) and "B" (Black) on electrical connector. If battery voltage is present, replace rear washer pump. If battery voltage is not present, check Black wire (circuit No. 151) and ground circuit for open.

TEST D (REAR WIPER MODULE – REAR WIPER/WASHER SWITCH)

1) Open rear window. If wiper turns off, check for short in wiring from rear window wiper/washer switch to rear window interlock switch. If no short is found, replace rear window wiper/washer switch. *See Fig. 3.*

2) If wiper does not turn off, check for short in wiring from interlock switch to wiper motor module. If no short is found, replace wiper motor module.

REMOVAL & INSTALLATION

WIPER MOTOR

Removal – Remove wiper arm and blade. Remove nut on motor shaft. Remove liftgate glass upper finishing molding. Disconnect electrical connector. Remove upper mounting screw. Rotate wiper motor to 12 o'clock position and pull motor off guide dowel.

Installation – Install motor at 12 o'clock position, guiding motor onto guide dowel. Install upper mounting screw. Connect electrical connector. Install liftgate glass molding. Install nut on motor shaft. Install wiper arm.

WIRING DIAGRAM

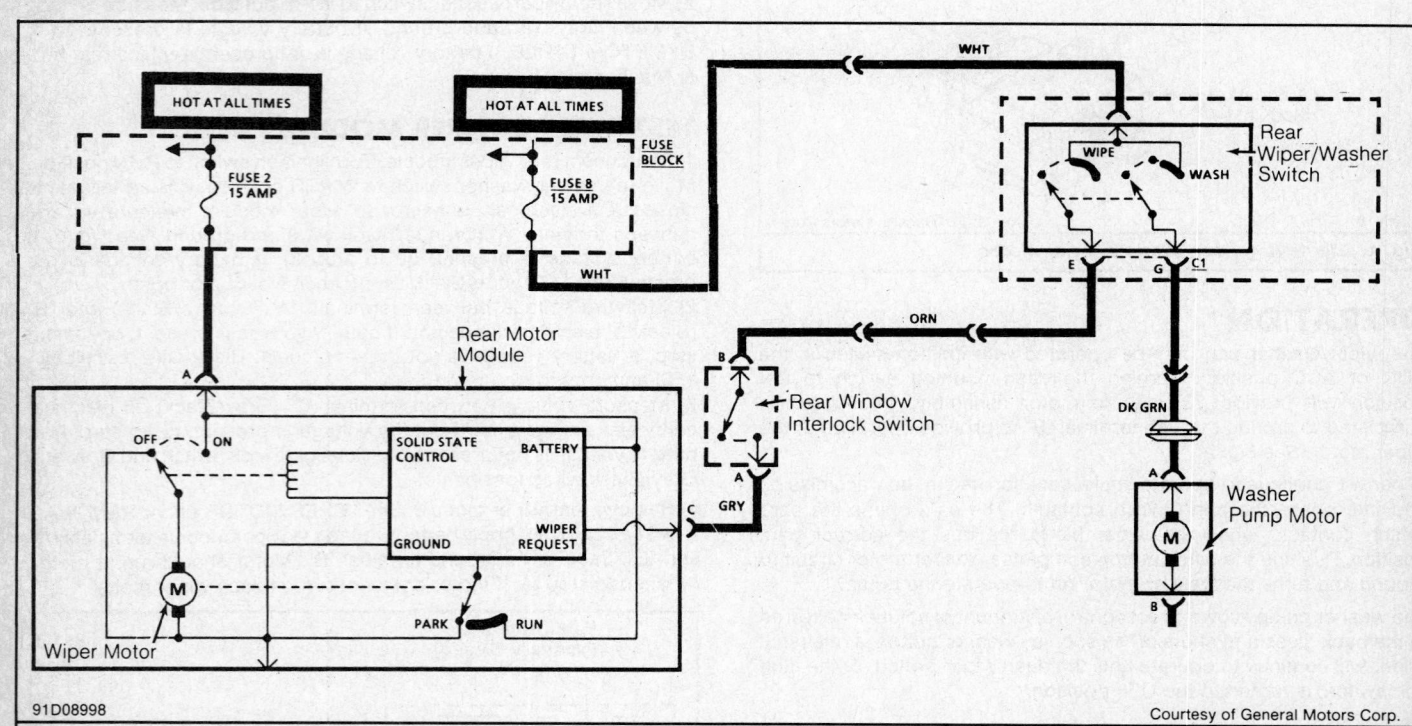

91D08998   Courtesy of General Motors Corp.

Fig. 3: Liftgate Wiper/Washer System Wiring Diagram

Sunbird

NOTE: For repair procedures not covered in this article, see ENGINE OVERHAUL PROCEDURES article in GENERAL INFORMATION.

ENGINE IDENTIFICATION

Engine may be identified by using Vehicle Identification Number (VIN) stamped on a metal pad, located near lower left corner of windshield. The eighth character identifies the engine model.

Engine code, located on cylinder block, may be required when ordering replacement parts (if needed). *See Fig. 1.*

ENGINE IDENTIFICATION CODE

Engine	Code
2.0L TBI	
8th Character On Dash VIN	K
Engine Code On Block ¹	LT2

¹ – See Fig. 1 for engine code location.

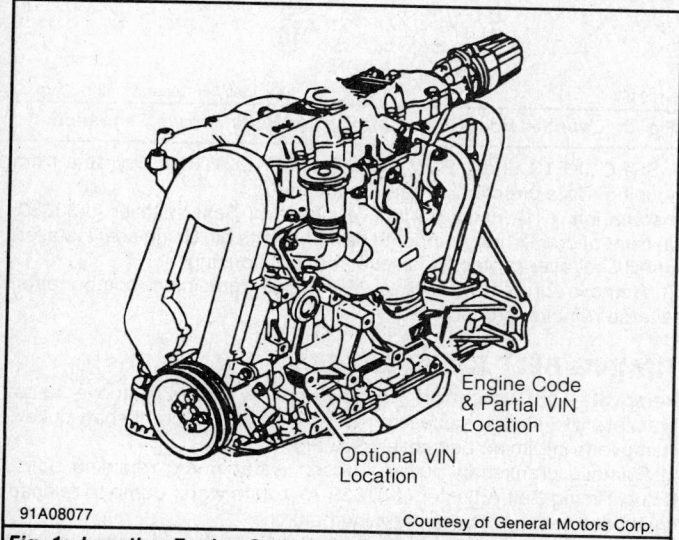

Engine Code & Partial VIN Location

Optional VIN Location

91A08077   Courtesy of General Motors Corp.

Fig. 1: Locating Engine Code On Cylinder Block

ADJUSTMENTS

VALVE CLEARANCE ADJUSTMENT

No valve adjustment is required, as hydraulic valve lifters are used.

REMOVAL & INSTALLATION

NOTE: For reassembly reference, label all electrical connectors, vacuum hoses and fuel lines before removal. Also place mating marks on engine hood and other major assemblies before removal.

FUEL PRESSURE RELEASE

1) Loosen fuel tank cap to release fuel tank pressure. Remove fuel pump fuse. Start engine and operate until engine stalls.

2) Crank engine for an additional 3 seconds to release residual line pressure. Disconnect negative battery cable and reinstall fuel pump fuse.

ENGINE

Removal – 1) Release fuel pressure. See FUEL PRESSURE RELEASE under REMOVAL & INSTALLATION in this article. Disconnect battery cables and engine ground wire. Remove battery and air cleaner. Drain coolant and remove cooling fan.

2) Disconnect all electrical connectors and vacuum hoses from engine. Disconnect throttle and shift cables. Disconnect power steering return hose at pump. Raise and support vehicle. Disconnect vehicle speed sensor at transaxle. Discard "O" ring.

3) Disconnect exhaust pipe at manifold and hangers, and swing pipe aside. Remove heater core hoses. On automatic transaxle vehicles, remove cooler lines. Remove front wheels and brake calipers. Support calipers out of the way.

4) Discharge A/C system. Disconnect wires at A/C compressor. Disconnect refrigerant lines from compressor. Remove 2 suspension support center bolts on each side. Remove one bolt and loosen remaining bolt at each end of suspension supports.

5) Support engine and transaxle. On automatic transaxle vehicles, remove transaxle lateral rear strut. On all vehicles, remove transaxle front strut. Support vehicle with jack stands under radiator core support.

6) Reposition jack at rear of cowl with 4" x 4" x 6' timber spanning vehicle width. Raise vehicle and remove jack stands. Position dolly under engine and transaxle with three 4" x 4" x 12" blocks as support.

7) Lower vehicle gently onto dolly. Remove remaining bolt at each end of right and left front suspension supports. Remove transaxle mount-to-bracket bolt and remove mount. Remove front and rear engine mounts.

8) Remove knuckle-to-strut bolts. Raise vehicle leaving engine, transaxle and suspension on dolly. Separate engine and transaxle.

Installation – 1) With assistance, assembly engine and transaxle assembly and position in chassis. Reverse removal procedure for remaining components.

2) Tighten all fasteners to specification. See TORQUE SPECIFICATIONS at end of this article. After installation, evacuate and charge A/C system. Check fluid levels.

INTAKE MANIFOLD

Removal – 1) Release fuel pressure. See FUEL PRESSURE RELEASE under REMOVAL & INSTALLATION in this article. Remove air cleaner and drain cooling system.

2) Remove power steering pump and bracket with hoses attached and lay aside. Remove alternator and bracket. Remove ignition coil. Disconnect throttle cable from TBI unit and intake manifold bracket.

3) Disconnect electrical connections, control cables and vacuum hoses at TBI. Disconnect brake vacuum hose at filter. Disconnect fuel lines and necessary coolant hoses.

4) Move ECM harness for access, and remove manifold retaining nuts, manifold and gasket.

Installation – 1) To install intake manifold, reverse removal procedure using new gasket. Tighten intake manifold retaining nuts to specification in proper sequence. *See Fig. 2.* See TORQUE SPECIFICATIONS table at end of article.

2) Reverse removal procedure for remaining components. Fill cooling system.

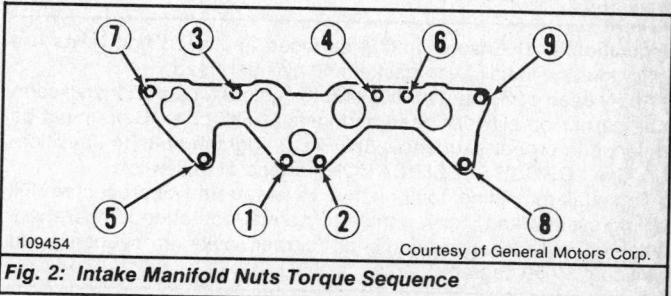

109454   Courtesy of General Motors Corp.

Fig. 2: Intake Manifold Nuts Torque Sequence

EXHAUST MANIFOLD

Removal – 1) Remove air cleaner, spark plug wires and retainers. Remove oil dipstick tube and breather assembly. Disconnect oxygen sensor.

2) Disconnect exhaust pipe at manifold. Remove exhaust manifold retaining nuts, manifold and gasket.

Installation – To install, reverse removal procedure using new gasket. Tighten nuts to specification, starting from the center and working outward. See TORQUE SPECIFICATIONS at end of this article.

CYLINDER HEAD

NOTE: Cylinder head gasket must be replaced whenever cylinder head/camshaft carrier bolts are loosened.

CAUTION: Cylinder head must be removed with engine cold to prevent cylinder head damage.

Removal – **1)** Release fuel pressure. See FUEL PRESSURE RELEASE under REMOVAL & INSTALLATION in this article. Remove air filter housing. Disconnect negative battery cable.
2) Drain cooling system and remove coolant reservoir tank. Remove fuel vapor pipe assembly and serpentine belt. Remove front timing belt cover upper bolts and nuts. Loosen serpentine belt tensioner and position aside.
3) Raise and support vehicle. Remove right side inner fender and lower splash shields. Remove A/C compressor belt and crankshaft pulley. Remove flywheel cover and timing belt front covers.
4) Align timing marks and, using Timing Belt Adjuster (J 33039-A), loosen water pump to release timing belt tension. Remove timing belt. Disconnect exhaust pipe from manifold. Lower vehicle.
5) Remove fuel vapor pipe and PCV hose. Remove rear timing belt cover. Disconnect electrical connections at intake manifold and cylinder head. Remove exhaust manifold bolts and manifold. Disconnect power steering pump hoses.
6) Remove alternator, bracket and power steering pump. Remove front and rear engine lift brackets and ignition coil assembly. Remove breather tube bracket and tube. Remove accelerator linkage and bracket.
7) Disconnect fuel lines, wires and hoses to cylinder head and intake manifold. Disconnect radiator hoses and coolant lines to cylinder head. Remove cylinder head bolts in sequence. *See Fig. 3.*

CAUTION: Cylinder head/camshaft carrier bolts must be loosened with engine cold and in proper sequence to prevent cylinder head damage.

8) Remove camshaft carrier, rocker arms, lash adjusters and thrust pieces. Remove cylinder head and intake manifold.
9) Clean all oil and foreign material from gasket surfaces of cylinder head and block. Ensure surfaces are free of nicks and scratches. Ensure cylinder block threads are clean and free of dirt.
Inspection – Inspect cylinder head for warpage. See CYLINDER HEAD under OVERHAUL in this article.

CAUTION: Replace all cylinder head/camshaft carrier bolts. NEVER reuse bolts.

Installation – **1)** Ensure mating surfaces and head bolt holes are clean and dry. Install head gasket and cylinder head.
2) Apply bead of Sealant (01052942) to camshaft carrier. Install camshaft carrier on cylinder head and install NEW bolts. Bolts must be tightened in proper sequence. *See Fig. 3.* Tighten bolts to specification. See TORQUE SPECIFICATIONS at end of this article.
3) To install remaining components, reverse removal procedure. Fill cooling system and warm engine to normal operating temperature. Retighten cylinder head/camshaft carrier bolts in sequence an additional 30-50 degrees.

CAUTION: Cylinder head/camshaft carrier bolts must be retightened in sequence an additional 30-50 degrees once engine has reached normal operating temperature.

FRONT CRANKSHAFT SEAL

Removal – Remove timing belt, crankshaft sprocket, Woodruff key and thrust washer. Remove rear timing belt cover. See TIMING BELT

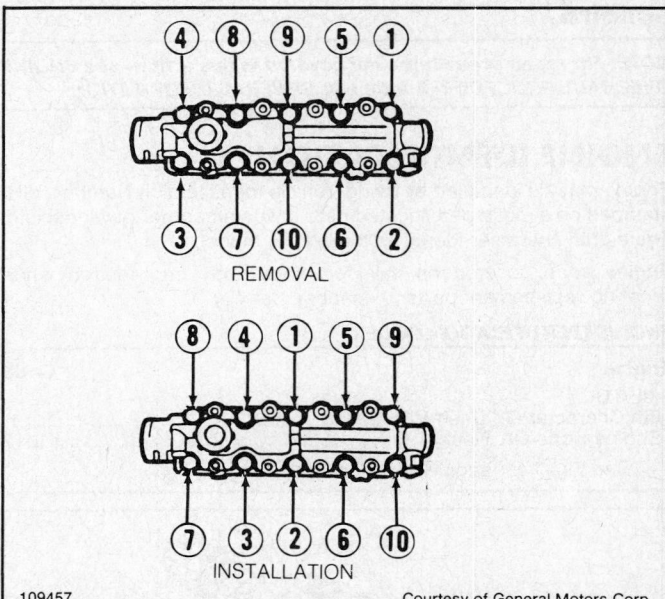

REMOVAL

INSTALLATION

109457   Courtesy of General Motors Corp.

Fig. 3: Cylinder Head/Camshaft Carrier Bolts Torque Sequence

& SPROCKETS under REMOVAL & INSTALLATION. Pry seal from housing. Note direction of seal installation.
Installation – **1)** Install protective sleeve of Seal Installer (J-33083) on front of crankshaft. Lubricate new seal with oil. Using seal installer, install seal over protective sleeve and into housing.
2) Remove protective sleeve. To install remaining components, reverse removal procedure.

TIMING BELT & SPROCKETS

Removal – **1)** Disconnect negative battery cable. Remove belts, brackets and shields necessary to gain access to crankshaft pulley. Remove front timing belt cover. *See Fig. 4.*
2) Remove crankshaft pulley. Loosen water pump retaining bolts. Using Timing Belt Adjuster (J-33039-A), rotate water pump to release timing belt tension. Remove timing belt.
3) If camshaft sprocket requires removal, remove camshaft carrier cover. Hold camshaft with open-end wrench. Remove sprocket retaining bolt, washer and sprocket.
4) If crankshaft sprocket requires removal, remove crankshaft pulley, sprocket bolt, washer and sprocket. Remove Woodruff key and thrust washer (if required). *See Fig. 4.* If removing rear timing belt cover, remove timing belt tensioner, rear cover retaining bolts and cover.
Installation – **1)** Install rear cover and timing belt tensioner, if removed. Start all rear cover bolts before tightening to specification. Ensure tensioner mating surfaces are clean prior to installation.
2) To install camshaft and crankshaft sprockets, reverse removal procedure. Tighten retaining bolts to specification. See TORQUE SPECIFICATIONS at end of this article.
3) Rotate crankshaft and camshaft clockwise to align timing marks on sprockets with marks on rear cover. Install new timing belt on sprockets. Ensure belt has tension on it between the camshaft sprocket and crankshaft sprocket.

NOTE: Adjust timing belt with engine coolant temperature at 68°F (20°C).

4) Using timing belt tension adjuster, rotate water pump clockwise until tensioner contacts the high torque stop. Slightly tighten water pump retaining bolts.
5) Using crankshaft sprocket bolt, rotate engine clockwise 2 revolutions to fully seat timing belt. Rotate water pump eccentric counterclockwise until hole in tensioner arm aligns with hole in base.
6) Tighten water pump bolts to specification. See TORQUE SPECIFICATIONS at end of this article. Ensure tensioner holes remain in alignment as stated in step **5)**. Ensure all timing marks are properly aligned.

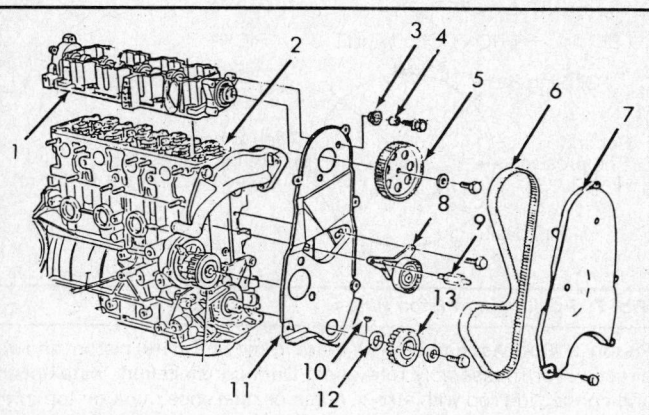

1. Camshaft Carrier & Camshaft
2. Cylinder Head
3. Grommet
4. Sleeve
5. Camshaft Sprocket
6. Timing Belt
7. Front Timing Belt Cover
8. Tensioner
9. Stud
10. Woodruff Key
11. Rear Timing Belt Cover
12. Thrust Washer
13. Crankshaft Sprocket

109455   Courtesy of General Motors Corp.

Fig. 4: Exploded View of Timing Belt & Components

7) To install remaining components, reverse removal procedure. Apply Loctite to crankshaft pulley retaining bolt prior to installation.

ROCKER ARMS & LASH ADJUSTERS

Removal – Remove camshaft carrier cover. Install Valve Compressor (J-33302-25) on camshaft carrier. See Fig. 5. Compress valve springs and remove rocker arm, thrust piece and lash adjuster. Mark component location for reassembly reference.

Installation – To install, reverse removal procedure. Ensure components are installed in original location.

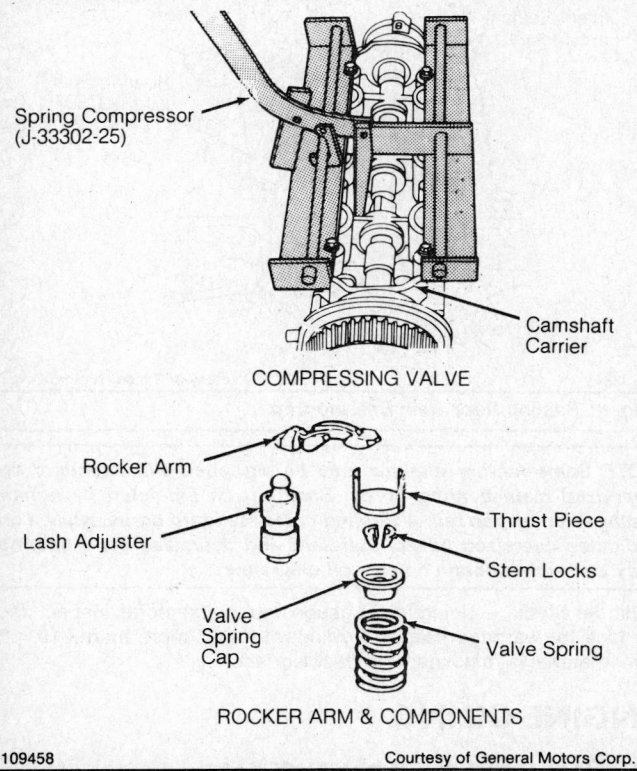

Spring Compressor
(J-33302-25)

Camshaft
Carrier

COMPRESSING VALVE

Rocker Arm

Lash Adjuster

Thrust Piece

Stem Locks

Valve
Spring
Cap

Valve Spring

ROCKER ARM & COMPONENTS

109458   Courtesy of General Motors Corp.

Fig. 5: Removing Rocker Arm & Components

CAMSHAFT

Removal – **1)** Remove rocker arms and lash adjusters. See ROCKER ARMS & LASH ADJUSTERS under REMOVAL & INSTALLATION. **2)** Remove timing belt and camshaft sprocket. See TIMING BELT & SPROCKETS under REMOVAL & INSTALLATION. Disconnect wiring at distributor. Mark location of distributor and remove. Remove thrust plate and camshaft from rear of camshaft carrier.

Inspection – Inspect camshaft journal diameter, lobe lift and oil clearance. Replace components if not within specification. See CAMSHAFT table in ENGINE SPECIFICATIONS at end of this article.

Installation – Install oil seal in camshaft carrier. Install camshaft and thrust plate bolts. Ensure camshaft end play is within specification. See CAMSHAFT table in ENGINE SPECIFICATIONS at end of article. To install remaining components, reverse removal procedure. Align reference mark on distributor.

CAMSHAFT CARRIER

NOTE: Cylinder head gasket must be replaced whenever cylinder head/camshaft carrier bolts are loosened.

For camshaft carrier removal and installation procedure, see CYLINDER HEAD under REMOVAL & INSTALLATION.

REAR CRANKSHAFT SEAL

Removal – **1)** Remove transaxle assembly. Place reference mark on clutch pressure plate (M/T) and flywheel for reassembly reference. **2)** Remove pressure plate and clutch disc (if equipped) and flywheel. Pry seal from housing. DO NOT damage crankshaft or seal surface. Note direction of seal installation.

CAUTION: DO NOT reuse flywheel bolts. Bolts must be replaced.

Installation – Coat outside seal surface with engine oil. Using Seal Installer (J-36227), install seal in housing. Install flywheel using NEW bolts. To install remaining components, reverse removal procedure. On M/T models, ensure reference marks are aligned on pressure plate and flywheel.

WATER PUMP

Removal – **1)** Disconnect negative battery cable. Remove timing belt and rear timing belt covers. See TIMING BELT & SPROCKETS under REMOVAL & INSTALLATION. Drain cooling system. **2)** Remove lower radiator hose from water pump. Remove water pump bolts, water pump and seal ring.

Installation – To install, reverse removal procedure using new seal ring. Install remaining components.

OIL PAN

Removal – **1)** Disconnect negative battery cable. Raise and support vehicle. Drain crankcase. Disconnect exhaust pipe from manifold. Remove flywheel cover and oil pan. **2)** Remove oil pump pick-up tube, oil scraper and gasket. Clean all sealing surfaces of components. Remove any remaining sealant from attaching holes.

Installation – Apply sealant to new gasket and install oil scraper. Install pick-up tube, drain plug, oil pan and bolts. Use Loctite 242 or equivalent on threads. Tighten bolts and drain plug to specification. See TORQUE SPECIFICATIONS at end of this article.

OVERHAUL

CYLINDER HEAD

Cylinder Head Inspection – Inspect cylinder head for warpage at deck surface and manifold surfaces. Resurface cylinder head if warpage exceeds specification. See CYLINDER HEAD table in ENGINE SPECIFICATIONS at end of article. Replace cylinder head if metal removed exceeds .010" (.25 mm).

Valve Seats – If valve seats require reconditioning, grind all valve seats to 45-degree angle using an oscillating type valve seat grinder.
Valve Guides – Valve guides must be reamed for an oversized valve if valve stem oil clearance is not within specification. See CYLINDER HEAD table in ENGINE SPECIFICATIONS at end of article.

Seat Correction Angles – If seat width is too wide, use 30-degree and 70-degree stone for seat adjustment. The 30-degree stone will lower the seat and the 70-degree will raise the seat.

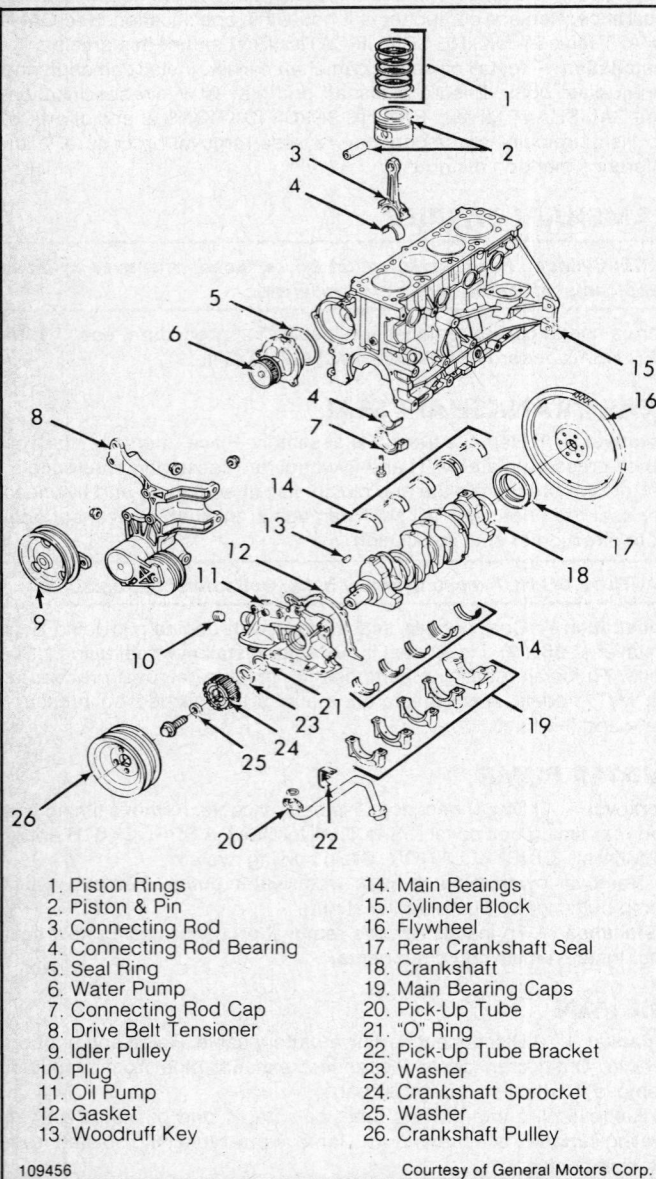

1. Piston Rings
2. Piston & Pin
3. Connecting Rod
4. Connecting Rod Bearing
5. Seal Ring
6. Water Pump
7. Connecting Rod Cap
8. Drive Belt Tensioner
9. Idler Pulley
10. Plug
11. Oil Pump
12. Gasket
13. Woodruff Key
14. Main Beaings
15. Cylinder Block
16. Flywheel
17. Rear Crankshaft Seal
18. Crankshaft
19. Main Bearing Caps
20. Pick-Up Tube
21. "O" Ring
22. Pick-Up Tube Bracket
23. Washer
24. Crankshaft Sprocket
25. Washer
26. Crankshaft Pulley

109456   Courtesy of General Motors Corp.

Fig. 6: Exploded View of Cylinder Block & Components

CYLINDER BLOCK ASSEMBLY

NOTE: Refer to Fig. 6 for identification and relationship of cylinder block components.

Piston Ring Installation – Install piston rings with identification mark toward top of piston and rings properly spaced. See Fig. 7.

CAUTION: Arrow or notch on top of piston must face toward front of engine. Place reference mark on piston to indicate piston position on connecting rod prior to removal. Connecting rod bolts must be replaced if rod cap is removed. DO NOT reuse bolts.

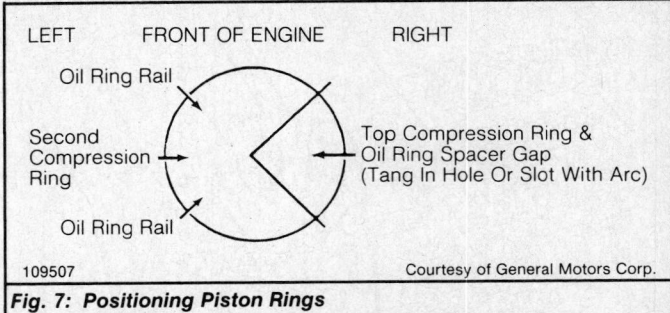

109507   Courtesy of General Motors Corp.

Fig. 7: Positioning Piston Rings

Piston & Rod Assembly – Prior to removal, mark piston and rod direction for reassembly reference. During installation, install piston and connecting rod with arrow, notch or reference mark on top of the piston toward the front of engine. Ensure connecting rod identification numbers are on the coolant pump side of the engine and NEW connecting rod bolts are installed.

Fitting Pistons – Oversized pistons must not be machined down or engine balance will be affected.

Crankshaft & Bearings – 1) To align crankshaft thrust surfaces, install all bearings and main caps with cap bolts loosely installed. Pry crankshaft toward rear of engine and then toward front of engine. Tighten main bearing cap bolts.

CAUTION: DO NOT reuse main bearing cap bolts. Bolts must always be replaced.

2) When installing rear main bearing cap, fill both areas of main bearing cap with sealing compound using Bearing Seal Kit (3997597). See Fig. 8.

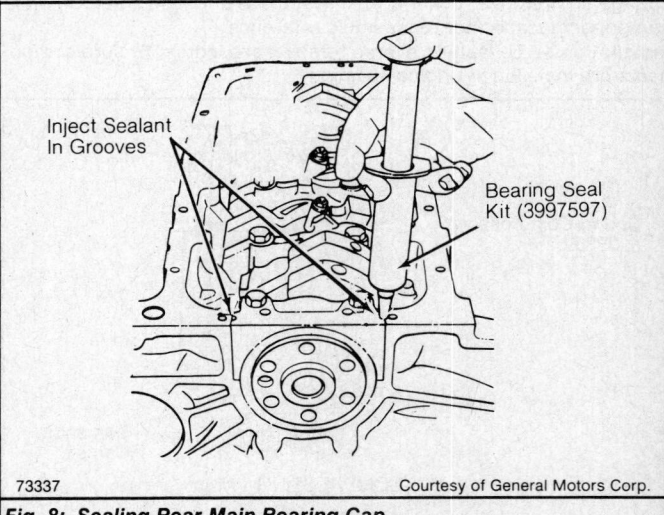

73337   Courtesy of General Motors Corp.

Fig. 8: Sealing Rear Main Bearing Cap

NOTE: Some factory engines may be equipped with standard and oversized main bearing bores. Bore size is indicated by number stamped on oil pan rail. A zero indicates standard bores, while a one indicates oversized bores. Standard and oversized main bearings may be used to obtain correct oil clearance.

Cylinder Block – Using feeler gauge and straightedge, inspect deck surface for warpage. Replace cylinder block if more than .010" (.25 mm) material is removed from deck surface.

ENGINE OILING

ENGINE LUBRICATION SYSTEM

The gear-type oil pump, driven by crankshaft, provides pressurized oil to main oil gallery on left side of block to feed crankshaft and main bearings. *See Fig. 9.* Passage in left side of cylinder head contains pressure relief valve to control maximum pressure in cylinder head.

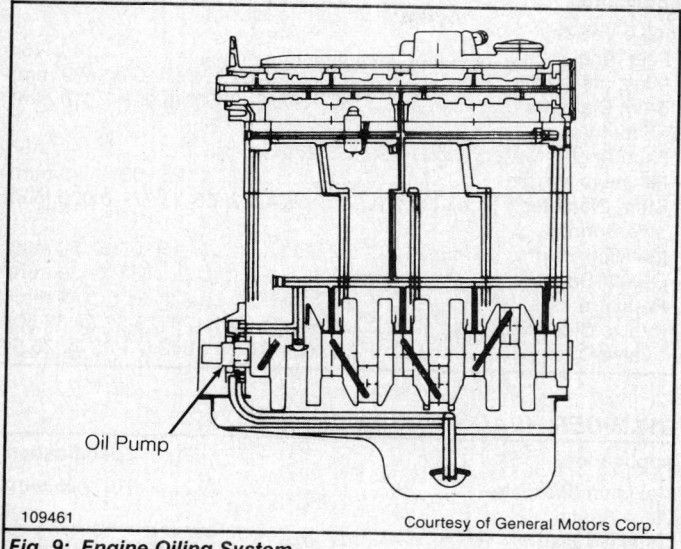

Oil Pump

109461   Courtesy of General Motors Corp.

Fig. 9: Engine Oiling System

Crankcase Capacity – Engine oil capacity is approximately 4 qts. (3.8L) with filter change. Recheck oil level after changing filter.

Normal Oil Pressure – Normal oil pressure is 65 psi (4.6 kg/cm²) at 2500 RPM.

OIL PUMP

Removal – **1)** Remove crankshaft sprocket, timing belt and rear timing belt cover. See TIMING BELT & SPROCKETS under REMOVAL & INSTALLATION. Disconnect electrical connector at pressure switch.
2) Remove oil pan. See OIL PAN under REMOVAL & INSTALLATION. Remove oil filter, pick-up tube and oil pump.

Disassembly & Inspection – **1)** Remove pump cover. Mark drive gear location and remove drive gears. Remove pressure regulator valve plug, spring and valve. Pry seal from housing.

CAUTION: *Pressure regulator valve plug is under spring pressure. Use caution during removal of plug to prevent personal injury.*

---

2) Inspect components for damage. Using straightedge and feeler gauge, measure gear end clearance. Measure housing gear pocket depth and diameter and gear diameter.
3) Measure clearance between outer gear and housing and clearance between inner and outer gears and crescent. Replace components or pump assembly if not within specification. See OIL PUMP SPECIFICATIONS table.

OIL PUMP SPECIFICATIONS

Application	In. (mm)
Gear Diameter	
Inner Gear	1.612-1.613 (40.94-40.97)
Outer Gear	3.2248-3.2269 (81.910-81.963)
Gear End Clearance	.001-.004 (.03-.10)
Gear To Crescent	
Inner Gear	.007-.010 (.18-.25)
Outer Gear	.004-.009 (.10-.23)
Housing Pocket	
Depth	.395-.397 (10.03-10.08)
Diameter	
Inner Gear	1.614-1.615 (40.99-41.02)
Outer Gear	3.231-3.234 (82.07-82.14)
Outer Gear To Housing	.004-.007 (.10-.18)

CAUTION: *Only original equipment gaskets should be used for oil pump service, as gasket thickness is critical. Ensure pump components are coated with engine oil prior to installation and all pump cavities are filled with petroleum jelly. Coat pressure regulator valve plug threads with thread sealant.*

Reassembly & Installation – **1)** To reassemble, reverse disassembly procedure. Coat all components with engine oil and fill pump cavities with petroleum jelly. Coat pressure regulator valve plug threads with thread sealant.
2) Ensure gears are installed in original location. Using Seal Installer (J-33083), install seal in housing. To install, reverse removal procedure using new gaskets and "O" rings. Tighten all fasteners to specification. See TORQUE SPECIFICATIONS at end of this article.

TORQUE SPECIFICATIONS

TORQUE SPECIFICATIONS

Application	Ft. Lbs. (N. m)
Camshaft Sprocket Bolt	33 (45)
Coolant Pipe-To-Block Bolt	20 (27)
Coolant Pump Bolt	18 (24)
Connecting Rod Nut	[1][2] 26 (35)
Crankshaft Pulley-To-Sprocket Bolt	[3] 20 (27)
Crankshaft Sprocket Bolt	114 (155)
Cylinder Head/Camshaft Carrier Bolt	
Step 1	[1][4] 18 (24)
Steps 2, 3 & 4	[5]
Step 5	[6]
Distributor Mounting Nut	12 (16)
Exhaust Manifold Nut	16 (22)
Exhaust Pipe-To-Manifold Nuts	19 (26)
Flywheel Bolt	[1][7] 48 (65)
Intake Manifold Nut	[8] 16 (22)
Main Bearing Cap Bolt	[1][9] 44 (60)
Oil Pan Drain Plug	34 (46)
Oil Pump Control Valve Plug	[3] 22 (30)
Serpentine Belt Tensioner Bolt	35 (47)
Timing Belt Tensioner Bolt	18 (24)

	INCH Lbs. (N.m)
Camshaft Carrier Cover Bolt	72 (8)
Camshaft Thrust Plate Bolt	72 (8)
Oil Pan Bolt	[3] 48 (5)
Oil Pick-Up Tube Bolt	72 (8)
Oil Pump Cover Bolt	72 (8)
Oil Pump Retaining Bolt	62 (7)
Timing Belt Cover Bolt	89 (10)

[1] – Bolts must be replaced. DO NOT reuse bolts.
[2] – Tighten an additional 40-45 degrees.
[3] – Apply thread sealant on threads.
[4] – Tighten in sequence. See Fig. 3.
[5] – Tighten an additional 180 degrees in 3 steps of 60 degrees each.
[6] – Warm engine to normal operating temperature and tighten bolts an additional 30-50 degrees in sequence. See Fig. 3.
[7] – On manual transaxle vehicles, tighten an additional 30 degrees.
[8] – Tighten in sequence. See Fig. 2.
[9] – Tighten an additional 40-50 degrees.

ENGINE SPECIFICATIONS

GENERAL SPECIFICATIONS

Application	Specification
Displacement	121 Cu. In. (2.0 L)
Bore	3.386" (86.00 mm)
Stroke	3.386" (86.00 mm)
Compression Ratio	8.8:1
Fuel System	TBI
Horsepower @ RPM	96 @ 4800
Torque Ft. Lbs. @ RPM	118 @ 3600

CRANKSHAFT, MAIN & CONNECTING ROD BEARINGS

Application	In. (mm)
Crankshaft End Play	.0028-.0118 (.071-.300)
Main Bearings	
Journal Diameter	2.2828-2.2833 (57.983-57.996)
Journal Out-Of-Round	.0002 (.005)
Journal Taper	.0002 (.005)
Oil Clearance	.0006-.0016 (.015-.041)
Connecting Rod Bearings	
Journal Diameter	1.9279-1.9287 (48.970-48.988)
Journal Out-Of-Round	.0002 (.005)
Journal Taper	.0002 (.005)
Oil Clearance	.0007-.0025 (.018-.063)

CONNECTING RODS

Application	In. (mm)
Maximum Bend	[1]
Maximum Twist	[1]
Side Play	.0028-.0095 (.071-.241)

[1] – Replace rod if any bend or twist exists.

PISTONS, PINS & RINGS

Application	In. (mm)
Pistons	
Clearance	.0004-.0012 (.010-.030)
Diameter	3.3844-3.3860 (85.964-86.005)
Pins	
Diameter	.8264-.8267 (20.9906-20.9982)
Piston Fit	.00045-.00055 (.0114-.0140)
Rod Fit	Press
Rings	
No. 1	
End Gap	.0098-.0177 (.249-.450)
Side Clearance	.0024-.0036 (.061-.091)
No. 2	
End Gap	.0118-.0197 (.300-.500)
Side Clearance	.0019-.0032 (.048-.081)

CYLINDER BLOCK

Application	In. (mm)
Cylinder Bore	
Standard Diameter	3.385-3.387 (85.98-86.03)
Maximum Taper	.0005 (.013)
Maximum Out-Of-Round	.0005 (.013)

VALVES & VALVE SPRINGS

Application	Specification
Intake Valves	
Face Angle	46°
Minimum Margin	.031" (.79 mm)
Stem Diameter	.2755-.2760" (6.998-7.010 mm)
Exhaust Valves	
Face Angle	46°
Minimum Margin	.031" (.79 mm)
Stem Diameter	.2747-.2753" (6.977-6.993 mm)
Valve Springs	
Installed Height	1.476" (37.50 mm)
Out-Of-Square	.063" (1.59 mm)
Pressure	Lbs. @ In. (kg @ mm)
Valve Closed	63-71 @ 1.476 (29-32 @ 37.50)
Valve Open	165-197 @ 1.043 (75-89 @ 26.5)

CYLINDER HEAD

Application	Specification
Maximum Warpage	.010" (.25 mm)
Valve Seats	
Intake Valve	
Seat Angle	45°
Seat Width	.050-.070" (1.27-1.78 mm)
Maximum Seat Runout	.002" (.05 mm)
Exhaust Valve	
Seat Angle	45°
Seat Width	.050-.070" (1.27-1.78 mm)
Maximum Seat Runout	.002" (.05 mm)
Valve Guides	
Intake Valve	
Valve Guide I.D.	.2766-.2772" (7.026-7.040 mm)
Valve Guide Oil Clearance	.0006-.0017" (.015-.043 mm)
Exhaust Valve	
Valve Guide I.D.	.2766-.2772" (7.026-7.040 mm)
Valve Guide Oil Clearance	.0012-.0024" (.030-.060 mm)

CAMSHAFT

Application	In. (mm)
End Play	.001-.006 (.03-.15)
Journal Diameter	
No. 1	1.6706-1.6712 (42.433-42.448)
No. 2	1.6812-1.6818 (42.703-42.718)
No. 3	1.6911-1.6917 (42.954-42.970)
No. 4	1.7009-1.7015 (43.203-43.218)
No. 5	1.7100-1.7106 (43.434-43.450)
Lobe Lift	
Intake	.2366 (6.010)
Exhaust	.2515 (6.389)
Oil Clearance	.0011-.0035 (.028-.089)

Beretta, Cavalier, Corsica

NOTE: For repair procedures not covered in this article, see ENGINE OVERHAUL PROCEDURES article in GENERAL INFORMATION.

ENGINE IDENTIFICATION

Engine may be identified by using Vehicle Identification Number (VIN), engine block code, and partial VIN.

VIN is stamped on a metal pad, located near lower left corner of windshield. Eighth character of VIN identifies engine model ("G" identifies 2.2L TBI engine). Tenth character of VIN identifies model year ("M" indicates 1991 model year).

Engine block code (3 characters) is stamped on left side of cylinder block at cylinder block-to-transaxle flange. *See Fig. 1.* "LM3" indicates 2.2L TBI engine.

Partial VIN (9 characters) is stamped on left side of cylinder block at cylinder block-to-transaxle flange. *See Fig. 1.* First character "1" of partial VIN, identifies manufacturer as Chevrolet. Second character "M" identifies model year as 1991.

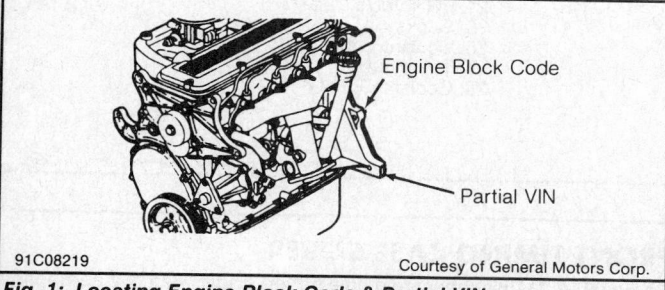

Engine Block Code

Partial VIN

91C08219   Courtesy of General Motors Corp.

Fig. 1: Locating Engine Block Code & Partial VIN

ADJUSTMENTS

VALVE CLEARANCE ADJUSTMENT

No valve clearance adjustment is required as engine is equipped with hydraulic valve lifters.

REMOVAL & INSTALLATION

NOTE: For reassembly reference, label all electrical connectors, vacuum hoses and fuel lines before removal. Also place mating marks on engine hood and other major assemblies before removal.

FUEL PRESSURE RELEASE

Disconnect negative battery cable. Loosen fuel tank filler cap to release tank vapor pressure. An internal constant bleed in the throttle body releases fuel system pressure when the engine is turned off; however, some residual line pressure may exist. Cover fuel lines with shop towel before disconnecting.

ENGINE

NOTE: Engine and transaxle are removed as an assembly from bottom of vehicle.

Removal & Installation – 1) Disconnect battery cables. Release fuel system pressure. See FUEL PRESSURE RELEASE under REMOVAL & INSTALLATION in this article. Drain cooling system. Disconnect hood light wiring and remove hood. Remove throttle body intake duct.
2) On Beretta GTZ, remove cover panels from firewall in engine compartment. On all models, remove battery and air cleaner housing. Remove upper radiator hose. Disconnect brake booster vacuum hose. Remove alternator top bracket. Disconnect alternator wiring.
3) Disconnect upper engine wiring harness. Discharge A/C system. Disconnect A/C refrigerant hoses from compressor. Plug hose and

compressor openings. Raise and support vehicle. Remove splash shield from below engine. Disconnect exhaust pipe from exhaust manifold. Remove exhaust system.
4) Disconnect lower wiring harness from engine. Remove flexplate/flywheel inspection cover. Remove front wheels and lower radiator hose. Disconnect heater hoses from heater core. Remove brake calipers and suspend with wire out of way. Separate outer tie rods from steering knuckles.
5) Lower vehicle. Remove clutch slave cylinder (M/T). Disconnect fuel lines as necessary. Disconnect shift cable (A/T) or linkage (M/T) from transaxle. Disconnect control cables from throttle body.
6) Disconnect transaxle fluid cooling lines from transaxle (A/T). Remove power steering pump (leave hoses connected and lay pump aside). Remove 4 center suspension support bolts (2 at center of each suspension support).
7) Position a 4-wheel dolly under suspension supports, engine and transaxle assembly. Lower vehicle onto dolly. Position supports under engine and rear of vehicle.
8) Remove upper transaxle mount and upper strut bolts and nuts. Remove front and rear engine mounts. Remove rear suspension support bolts. Remove front suspension support bolts and wire holes together to prevent axle separation.
9) Raise and support vehicle. Remove engine/transaxle assembly. To install, reverse removal procedure. Fill cooling system and crankcase.

INTAKE MANIFOLD

Removal – 1) Disconnect negative battery cable. Release fuel system pressure. See FUEL PRESSURE RELEASE under REMOVAL & INSTALLATION in this article. Remove air cleaner assembly. Drain cooling system. Disconnect necessary vacuum hoses, electrical connections and fuel lines.
2) Disconnect control cables from throttle body. Remove throttle body. Remove power steering pump (leave hoses connected and lay pump aside). Disconnect coolant hose from intake manifold. Remove intake manifold nuts. Remove intake manifold.
Installation – To install, reverse removal procedure using new gasket. Tighten nuts in sequence to 18 ft. lbs. (25 N.m). *See Fig. 2.* Fill cooling system.

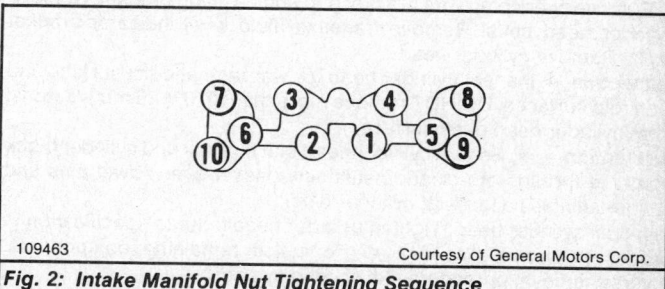

109463   Courtesy of General Motors Corp.

Fig. 2: Intake Manifold Nut Tightening Sequence

EXHAUST MANIFOLD

Removal – Disconnect negative battery cable. Disconnect oxygen sensor electrical connector. Remove serpentine drive belt and alternator. Raise and support vehicle. Disconnect exhaust pipe from exhaust manifold. Lower vehicle. Remove exhaust manifold nuts. Remove oil filler tube. Remove exhaust manifold.
Installation – To install, reverse removal procedure using new gasket. Tighten exhaust manifold nuts to 10 ft. lbs. (14 N.m). Tighten exhaust pipe nuts to 18 ft. lbs. (24 N.m).

CYLINDER HEAD

Removal – 1) Disconnect negative battery cable. Release fuel system pressure. See FUEL PRESSURE RELEASE under REMOVAL & INSTALLATION in this article.
2) Remove air cleaner assembly. Drain cooling system. Disconnect exhaust pipe from exhaust manifold. *See Fig. 3.* Disconnect vacuum hoses, electrical connectors and control cables from throttle body. Remove coolant reservoir, serpentine drive belt and alternator.

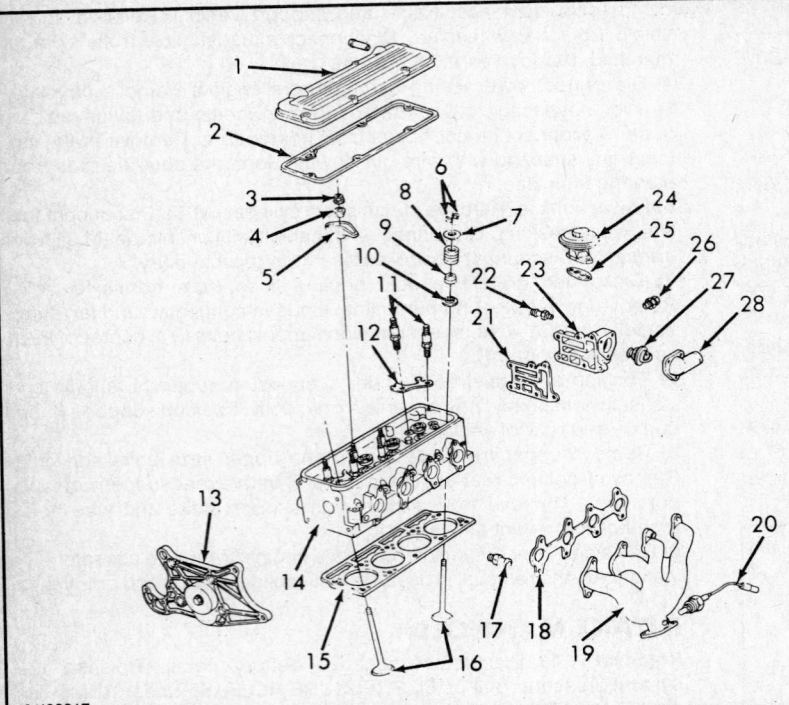

1. Valve Cover
2. Gasket
3. Nut
4. Rocker Arm Ball
5. Rocker Arm
6. Valve Keepers
7. Retainer
8. Spring
9. Valve Stem Seal
10. Valve Spring Seat
11. Rocker Arm Stud
12. Push Rod Guide
13. Drive Belt Tensioner Bracket
14. Cylinder Head
15. Cylinder Head Gasket
16. Valves
17. Coolant Hose Fitting
18. Exhaust Manifold Gasket
19. Exhaust Manifold
20. Oxygen Sensor
21. Gasket
22. Coolant Hose Fitting
23. Coolant Outlet Adapter
24. EGR Valve
25. Gasket
26. Coolant Sensor
27. Thermostat
28. Coolant Outlet

Courtesy of General Motors Corp.

91I08217

Fig. 3: Exploded View of Cylinder Head & Components

3) Remove power steering pump (leave hoses connected and lay pump aside). Remove serpentine drive belt tensioner and spark plug wires. Disconnect canister purge hose, upper radiator hose and heater hoses from intake manifold.

4) Remove intake manifold bracket from power steering bracket. Disconnect fuel lines as necessary. Remove valve cover. Loosen rocker arm nuts, rotate rocker arms to one side and remove push rods.

5) Remove spark plug wire bracket and engine lifting bracket. Remove cylinder head bolts. Remove transaxle fluid level indicator bracket (A/T). Remove cylinder head.

Inspection – Inspect cylinder head for warpage at deck surface and manifold surfaces. DO NOT remove more than .010" (.25 mm) material from cylinder head deck surface.

Installation – **1)** Ensure cylinder head bolt threads and cylinder block bolt hole threads are clean. Install new gasket over dowel pins and ensure all holes align with cylinder block.

2) Install cylinder head. Tighten cylinder head bolts to specification in proper sequence. See Fig. 4. To install remaining components, reverse removal procedure. Fill cooling system.

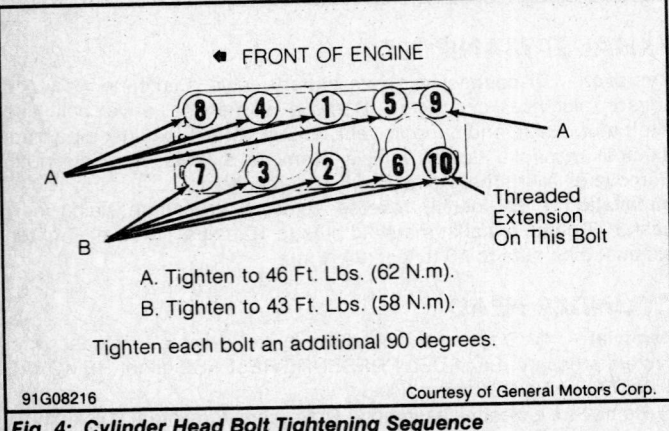

◀ FRONT OF ENGINE

A. Tighten to 46 Ft. Lbs. (62 N.m).
B. Tighten to 43 Ft. Lbs. (58 N.m).

Tighten each bolt an additional 90 degrees.

91G08216   Courtesy of General Motors Corp.

Fig. 4: Cylinder Head Bolt Tightening Sequence

FRONT TIMING CASE COVER

Removal – **1)** Disconnect negative battery cable. Remove serpentine drive belt and tensioner. Raise and support vehicle. Remove oil pan. See OIL PAN under REMOVAL & INSTALLATION in this article.

2) Remove right wheel. Remove engine splash shield. Remove 3 crankshaft pulley bolts. Remove crankshaft pulley hub bolt. Remove crankshaft pulley. See Fig. 5. Using Hub Puller (J-24420-B), remove crankshaft pulley hub. Remove front timing case cover bolts and remove cover.

Installation – **1)** Apply engine oil to front cover oil seal lip. Install cover using new gasket. Apply RTV sealant to crankshaft pulley hub keyway. Position crankshaft pulley hub onto crankshaft.

CAUTION: To prevent oil leakage, coat crankshaft pulley hub keyway with RTV sealant before installation.

2) Install crankshaft pulley hub using Hub Installer (J-29113), ensuring at least .24" (6.1 mm) of installer bolt thread is engaged into end of crankshaft.

3) To install remaining components, reverse removal procedure. Tighten nuts and bolts to specification. See TORQUE SPECIFICATIONS table at end of this article.

FRONT COVER OIL SEAL

Removal – **1)** Disconnect negative battery cable. Remove serpentine drive belt. Raise and support vehicle. Remove right wheel. Remove engine splash shield. Remove 3 crankshaft pulley bolts. Remove crankshaft center bolt. Remove crankshaft pulley.

2) Using Hub Puller (J-24420-B), remove crankshaft pulley hub. Using large screwdriver, pry out oil seal. Use care not to damage seal area of crankshaft or cover. Note direction of seal installation.

Installation – **1)** Apply engine oil to lip of new oil seal. Using Seal Installer (J-35468), drive seal into cover with seal lip toward engine. Ensure seal is fully seated. Apply RTV sealant to crankshaft pulley hub keyway. Position crankshaft pulley hub onto crankshaft.

CAUTION: To prevent oil leakage, coat crankshaft pulley hub keyway with RTV sealant before installation.

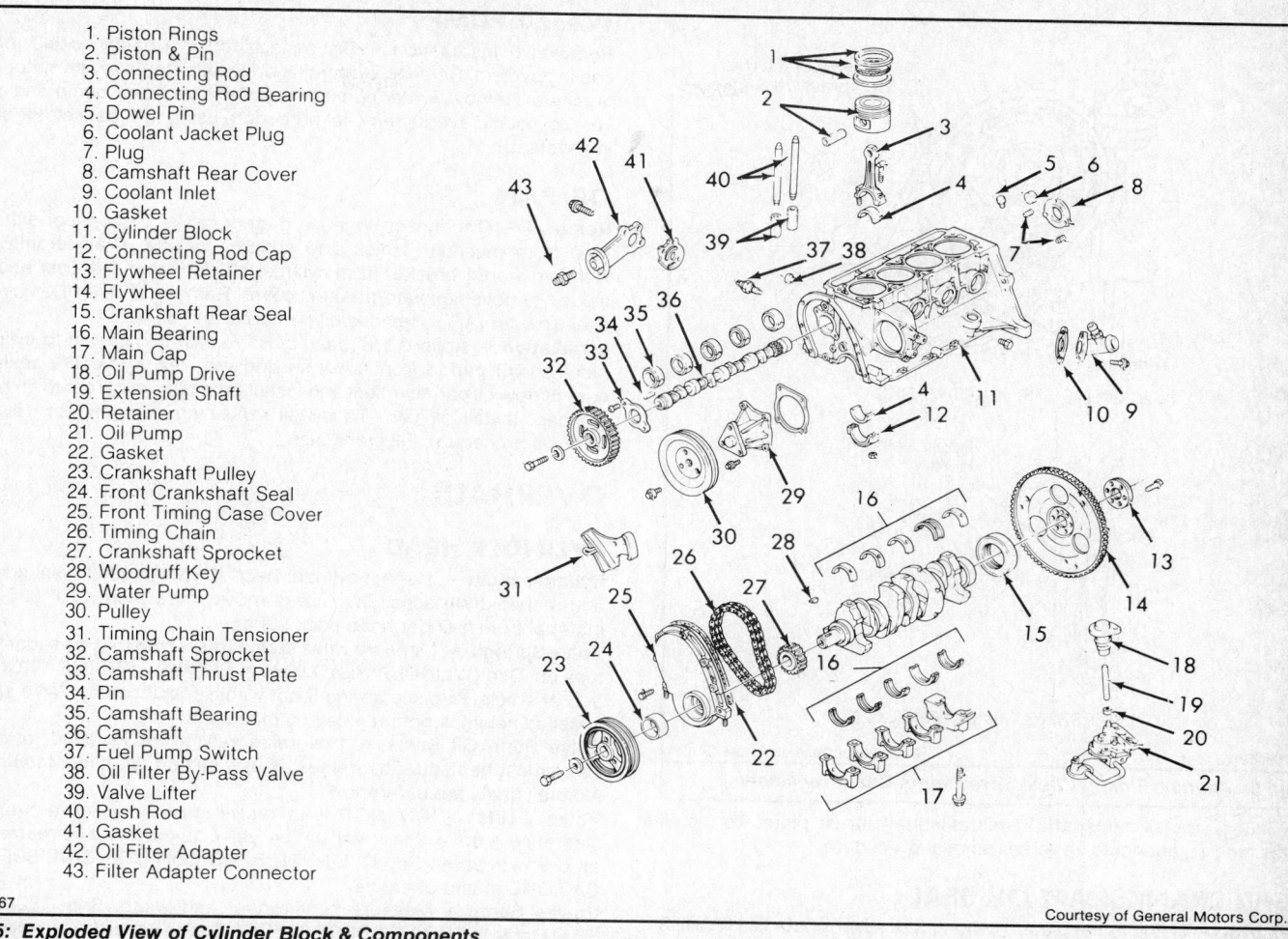

1. Piston Rings
2. Piston & Pin
3. Connecting Rod
4. Connecting Rod Bearing
5. Dowel Pin
6. Coolant Jacket Plug
7. Plug
8. Camshaft Rear Cover
9. Coolant Inlet
10. Gasket
11. Cylinder Block
12. Connecting Rod Cap
13. Flywheel Retainer
14. Flywheel
15. Crankshaft Rear Seal
16. Main Bearing
17. Main Cap
18. Oil Pump Drive
19. Extension Shaft
20. Retainer
21. Oil Pump
22. Gasket
23. Crankshaft Pulley
24. Front Crankshaft Seal
25. Front Timing Case Cover
26. Timing Chain
27. Crankshaft Sprocket
28. Woodruff Key
29. Water Pump
30. Pulley
31. Timing Chain Tensioner
32. Camshaft Sprocket
33. Camshaft Thrust Plate
34. Pin
35. Camshaft Bearing
36. Camshaft
37. Fuel Pump Switch
38. Oil Filter By-Pass Valve
39. Valve Lifter
40. Push Rod
41. Gasket
42. Oil Filter Adapter
43. Filter Adapter Connector

109467

Courtesy of General Motors Corp.

Fig. 5: Exploded View of Cylinder Block & Components

2) Install crankshaft pulley hub using Hub Installer (J-29113), ensuring at least .24" (6.1 mm) of thread is engaged into end of crankshaft. To install remaining components, reverse removal procedure.

TIMING CHAIN & SPROCKETS

Removal – 1) Remove front timing case cover. See FRONT TIMING CASE COVER under REMOVAL & INSTALLATION in this article. Align camshaft and crankshaft sprocket marks with tabs on chain tensioner. *See Fig. 6.* Remove upper bolt from timing chain tensioner.

2) Loosen timing chain tensioner Torx bolt as far as possible, but DO NOT remove bolt. Remove camshaft sprocket and timing chain. Using Sprocket Puller (J-22888), remove crankshaft sprocket.

Installation – 1) Install crankshaft sprocket using Sprocket Installer (J-5590). Ensure crankshaft sprocket is fully seated against crankshaft. Compress chain tensioner spring and install small cotter pin in hole of chain tensioner. *See Fig. 6.*

2) Install timing chain and camshaft sprocket, aligning sprocket marks with tabs on chain tensioner. Ensure hole in camshaft sprocket aligns with camshaft dowel pin. Install camshaft sprocket bolt and tighten to 77 ft. lbs. (104 N.m).

3) Lubricate timing chain with oil. Remove cotter pin from chain tensioner. To install remaining components, reverse removal procedure.

VALVE LIFTERS

Removal – Remove valve cover. Remove rocker arm nut and rocker arm. Remove push rod. Using flexible magnet, remove valve lifter from bore in cylinder block. Mark location of lifter for reassembly reference.

CAUTION: If installing new valve lifter, coat bottom of lifter with Camshaft Lubricant (1052365) before installation. Verify use of oversize lifters by mark on cylinder block near lifter bore.

Installation – Install valve lifter in original location. To install remaining components, reverse removal procedure.

CAMSHAFT

NOTE: To replace camshaft, engine must be removed from vehicle.

Removal – 1) Remove engine. See ENGINE under REMOVAL & INSTALLATION in this article. Remove valve lifters. See VALVE LIFTERS under REMOVAL & INSTALLATION in this article.

2) Remove timing chain and camshaft sprocket. See TIMING CHAIN & SPROCKETS under REMOVAL & INSTALLATION in this article. Remove oil pump drive from right side of cylinder block. *See Fig. 5.*

3) Remove camshaft thrust plate. Remove camshaft. Use Camshaft Bearing Remover (J-33049) to remove camshaft bearings.

Inspection – Inspect camshaft journal diameter, lobe lift and oil clearance. Replace components if not within specification. See CAMSHAFT table in ENGINE SPECIFICATIONS at end of this article.

CAUTION: If new camshaft is installed, all valve lifters must be replaced. Verify use of oversize valve lifters by mark on cylinder block near valve lifter bore. Add GM EP Lubricant (1051396) to engine oil if camshaft is replaced.

Installation – Install camshaft bearings (if removed), ensuring oil holes are aligned. Coat camshaft journals and bearings with Lubricant

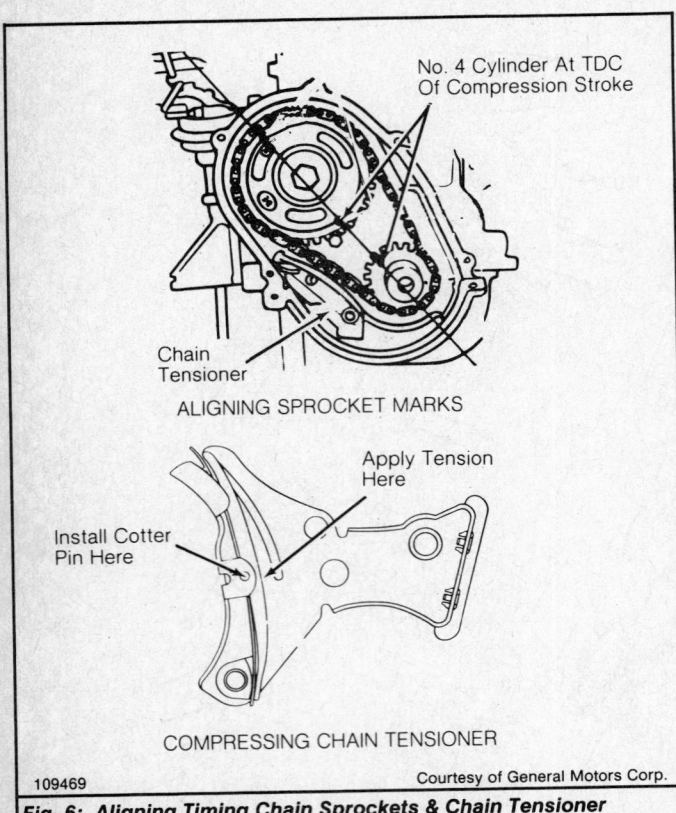

No. 4 Cylinder At TDC
Of Compression Stroke

Chain
Tensioner

ALIGNING SPROCKET MARKS

Apply Tension
Here

Install Cotter
Pin Here

COMPRESSING CHAIN TENSIONER

109469   Courtesy of General Motors Corp.

Fig. 6: Aligning Timing Chain Sprockets & Chain Tensioner

(1052365). Install camshaft. Install camshaft thrust plate. To install remaining components, reverse removal procedure.

REAR CRANKSHAFT OIL SEAL

Removal – Remove flexplate/flywheel. See appropriate CLUTCHES article (M/T) or TRANSMISSION SERVICING article (A/T). Pry seal from housing. Use care not to damage sealing surface of crankshaft. Note direction of seal installation.
Installation – 1) Coat inner and outer seal surfaces with engine oil. Install seal on mandrel of Seal Installer (J-34686) until dust lip bottoms against tool collar. *See Fig. 7.*

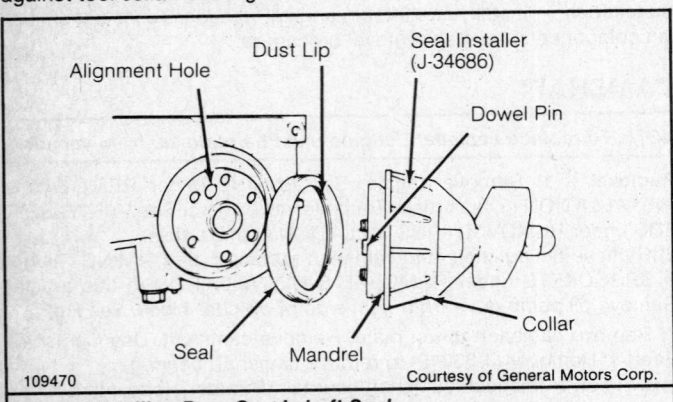

Alignment Hole

Dust Lip

Seal Installer
(J-34686)

Dowel Pin

Collar

Seal   Mandrel

109470   Courtesy of General Motors Corp.

Fig. 7: Installing Rear Crankshaft Seal

2) Align seal installer dowel pin with alignment hole of crankshaft. Install seal installer on crankshaft. Tighten seal installer bolts to 27-62 INCH lbs. (3-7 N.m).
3) Tighten seal installer handle until collar is even with cylinder block. Remove seal installer. To install remaining components, reverse removal procedure. Apply thread sealant to flexplate/flywheel bolts before installation.

WATER PUMP

Removal & Installation – Disconnect negative battery cable. Drain cooling system. Remove serpentine drive belt. Remove alternator and brackets. Remove water pump pulley. Remove water pump and gasket. To install, reverse removal procedure using new gasket. Fill cooling system.

OIL PAN

Removal – Disconnect negative battery cable. Disconnect exhaust pipe from manifold. Raise and support vehicle. Drain crankcase. Remove starter bracket from cylinder block. Remove starter and lay aside. Remove flexplate/flywheel cover. Remove oil filter. Remove oil filter adapter (A/T). Remove oil pan bolts and oil pan.
Installation – Apply a 1/8" bead of RTV sealant to oil pan-to-cylinder block and oil pan-to-front cover sealing surfaces. Apply RTV sealer to ears of new oil pan rear seal and install onto bottom of rear main bearing cap. Install oil pan. To install remaining components, reverse removal procedure. Fill crankcase.

OVERHAUL

CYLINDER HEAD

Cylinder Head – Inspect cylinder head for warpage at deck surface and manifold surfaces. DO NOT remove more than .010" (.25 mm) material from cylinder head deck surface.
Valve Springs – Measure valve spring free length, out-of-square and tension. See CYLINDER HEAD table in ENGINE SPECIFICATIONS at end of article. Replace spring if not within specification. Valve spring installed height is not provided by manufacturer.
Valve Stem Oil Seals – If oversize valves are installed, oversize seals must be used. Ensure seal is fully seated on guide. Intake and exhaust seals are different.
Valve Guides – DO NOT knurl valve guides. If valve stem oil clearance is not within specification, valve guides must be reamed for an oversize valve. See CYLINDER HEAD table in ENGINE SPECIFICATIONS at end of article.
Valves Seats – Measure seat runout and width. See CYLINDER HEAD table in ENGINE SPECIFICATIONS at end of article. If not within specification, machine or replace valve seat as necessary. Valve seat replacement procedure not provided by manufacturer.
Valves – Measure valve margin and valve stem-to-guide oil clearance. See VALVES & VALVE SPRINGS table in ENGINE SPECIFICATIONS at end of article. If valve margin is not within specification, machine or replace valve. If valve stem-to-guide oil clearance is not within specification, replace valve with an oversize valve.
Valve Seat Correction Angles – 1) If seat contact is too high (too close to margin), lower it using a 30-degree stone. If seat contact is too low (too close to stem), raise it using a 45-degree stone.
2) If seat is too narrow, widen it using a 45-degree stone. If seat is too wide, narrow it using a 60-degree stone.

CYLINDER BLOCK ASSEMBLY

CAUTION: If piston is to be separated from connecting rod, mark piston in relation to connecting rod before separation. Mark all parts before disassembly to ensure installation to original location.

Piston & Rod Assembly – Install piston with arrow on top of piston toward front of engine and connecting rod bearing tang slots facing camshaft side of engine.
Fitting Pistons – 1) Measure cylinder bore diameter at center of bore. Measure piston diameter at 90-degree angle to piston pin and .40" (10 mm) above bottom of piston skirt. Determine piston clearance.
2) If piston clearance is not within specification, machine cylinder bore and/or install oversize piston as necessary. See CYLINDER BLOCK table in ENGINE SPECIFICATIONS at end of article.
Piston Rings – 1) Measure piston ring end gap and side clearance. If end gap and side clearance are not within specification, replace piston rings and/or piston as necessary. See PISTONS, PINS & RINGS table in ENGINE SPECIFICATIONS at end of article.

2) Install piston rings with identification mark on ring land facing top of piston. Properly position ring end gaps around circumference of piston. *See Fig. 8.*

CAUTION: DO NOT shim, scrape or file bearing inserts. DO NOT touch bearing surface with fingers.

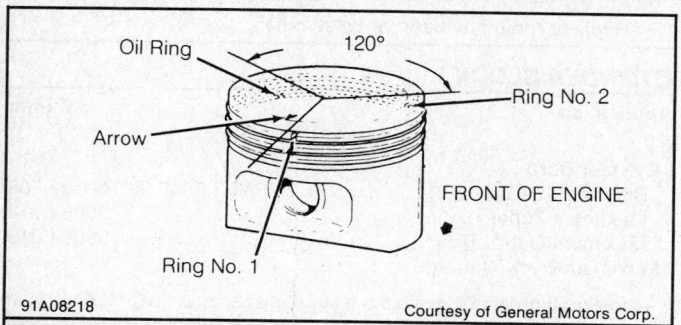

91A08218   Courtesy of General Motors Corp.

Fig. 8: Positioning Piston Rings

Rod Bearings – Measure rod bearing oil clearance. If oil clearance is not within specification, machine crankshaft rod bearing journals and install undersize bearings. See CRANKSHAFT, MAIN & CONNECTING ROD BEARINGS table in ENGINE SPECIFICATIONS at end of article. Install rod bearing cap onto piston rod with rod bearing tang slots facing camshaft side of engine.

Crankshaft & Main Bearings – Measure crankshaft main bearing oil clearance, out-of-round and taper. If not within specification, machine crankshaft main bearing journals and install undersize bearings. See CRANKSHAFT, MAIN & CONNECTING ROD BEARINGS table in ENGINE SPECIFICATIONS at end of article. Measure crankshaft end play (thrust bearing wear). See THRUST BEARING.

Thrust Bearing – No. 3 main bearing is the thrust bearing. Pry crankshaft toward rear of engine. Measure clearance between thrust bearing face and crankshaft. Clearance should be .002-.007" (.05-.18 mm).

Cylinder Block – Measure deck surface warpage. DO NOT remove more than .010" (.25 mm) material from deck surface.

Valve Lifter Bores – Oversize valve lifters are available. Oversize lifter should be indicated on cylinder block near lifter bore.

ENGINE OILING

ENGINE LUBRICATION SYSTEM

A camshaft-driven, gear-type oil pump is mounted to bottom of cylinder block and is accessible with oil pan removed. Oil pump supplies pressurized oil to internal passages of cylinder block. Internal passages intersect with hydraulic valve lifter bosses where oil flows to main and camshaft bearings and lifters. *See Fig. 9.*

Crankcase Capacity – Engine oil capacity is approximately 4 qts. (3.7L) without oil filter change. When changing oil filter, more oil may need to be added.

Oil Pressure – Normal oil pressure is 56 psi (3.9 kg/cm²) at 3000 RPM.

OIL PUMP

Removal & Disassembly – Remove oil pan. See OIL PAN under REMOVAL & INSTALLATION in this article. Remove oil pump-to-rear main bearing cap bolt. Remove oil pump and extension shaft. Remove extension shaft and retainer from oil pump. Disassemble oil pump. DO NOT remove pick-up tube unless loose or broken.

Inspection – **1)** Ensure retainer is not cracked. Inspect components for damage. Measure gear housing pocket depth and diameter, gear diameter and gear length.

2) Measure gear lash between the teeth of both gears and gear side clearance between tip of each gear tooth and housing pocket. Using straightedge and feeler gauge, measure gear end clearance.

3) Determine clearance between pressure regulator valve and bore. Replace components if not within specification. See OIL PUMP SPECIFICATIONS table.

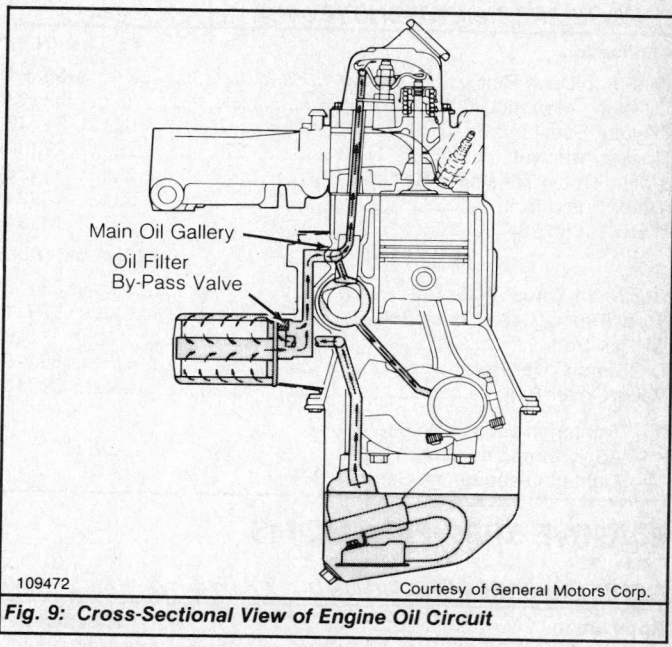

109472   Courtesy of General Motors Corp.

Fig. 9: Cross-Sectional View of Engine Oil Circuit

CAUTION: Use only original equipment gaskets when assembling oil pump as gasket thickness is critical. Pick-up tube MUST be replaced if removed.

Reassembly & Installation – To reassemble, reverse disassembly procedure. Replace pick-up tube if removed and apply Sealant (1050026) to new tube before installation. Install pick-up tube using Tube Installer (J-8369). To install, reverse removal procedure. Tighten oil pump mounting bolt to 32 ft. lbs. (43 N.m).

OIL PUMP SPECIFICATIONS

Application	In. (mm)
Gear	
Diameter	1.498-1.500 (38.05-38.10)
End Clearance	.002-.006 (.05-.15)
Lash	.004-.008 (.10-.20)
Length	1.199-1.200 (30.45-30.48)
Side Clearance	.0015-.0040 (.038-.102)
Gear Housing Pocket	
Depth	1.195-1.198 (30.35-30.43)
Diameter	1.503-1.506 (38.18-38.25)
Pressure Regulator Valve Clearance	.0015-.0035 (.038-.089)

TORQUE SPECIFICATIONS

TORQUE SPECIFICATIONS

Application	Ft. Lbs. (N.m)
Camshaft Sprocket Bolt	77 (104)
Connecting Rod Nut	38 (52)
Crankshaft Pulley-to-Hub Bolt	37 (50)
Crankshaft Pulley/Hub Bolt	77 (104)
Cylinder Head Bolt [1]	
Step 1	
Head Bolt A	46 (62)
Head Bolt B	43 (58)
Step 2	Tighten an additional 90°
Flexplate-to-Crankshaft Bolt (A/T) [2]	52 (70)
Flywheel-to-Crankshaft Bolt (M/T) [2]	55 (75)
Serpentine Belt Tensioner Pulley Bolt	37 (50)
Exhaust Manifold Bolt & Nut	10 (14)
Exhaust Pipe-to-Manifold Bolt	18 (24)
Intake Manifold Nut [3]	18 (24)
Main Bearing Cap Bolt	70 (95)
Oil Filter Adapter	18 (24)

TORQUE SPECIFICATIONS (Cont.)

Application	Ft. Lbs. (N.m)
Oil Pump Drive Bolt	18 (24)
Oil Pump Mounting Bolt	32 (43)
Oxygen Sensor	31 (42)
Rocker Arm Nut	22 (30)
Timing Chain Tensioner Bolt	18 (24)
Water Pump Bolt	18 (24)
Water Pump Inlet	18 (24)

Application	INCH Lbs. (N.m)
Camshaft Thrust Plate Bolt	106 (12)
Front Timing Case Cover Bolt	97 (11)
Oil Pan Bolt	71 (8)
Oil Pump Cover Bolt	89 (10)
Valve Cover Bolt	89 (10)

¹ – Tighten in sequence. See Fig. 4.
² – Apply thread sealant to bolts.
³ – Tighten in sequence. See Fig. 2.

ENGINE SPECIFICATIONS

GENERAL SPECIFICATIONS

Application	Specification
2.2L	
Displacement	134 Cu. In. (2.2L)
Bore	3.50" (89.0 mm)
Stroke	3.46" (88.0 mm)
Compression Ratio	9.0:1
Fuel System	TBI
Horsepower @ RPM	95 @ 5200
Torque Ft. Lbs. @ RPM	120 @ 3200

CRANKSHAFT, MAIN & CONNECTING ROD BEARINGS

Application	In. (mm)
2.2L	
Crankshaft End Play	.002-.007 (.05-.18)
Main Bearings	
Journal Diameter	2.4945-2.4954 (63.360-63.383)
Journal Out-of-Round	.0002 (.005)
Journal Taper	.0002 (.005)
Oil Clearance	.0006-.0019 (.015-.048)
Connecting Rod Bearings	
Journal Diameter	1.9983-1.9994 (50.757-50.785)
Journal Out-of-Round	.0002 (.005)
Journal Taper	.0002 (.005)
Oil Clearance	.0010-.0031 (.025-.079)

PISTONS, PINS & RINGS

Application	In. (mm)
2.2L	
Pistons	
Clearance	.0007-.0017 (.018-.043)
Pins	
Diameter	.8000-.8002 (20.320-20.325)
Piston Fit	.0004-.0009 (.010-.023)
Rod Fit	.0010-.0017 (.025-.043)
Rings	
No. 1	
End Gap	.010-.020 (.25-.50)
Side Clearance	.002-.003 (.05-.08)
No. 2	
End Gap	.010-.020 (.25-.50)
Side Clearance	.002-.003 (.05-.08)
No. 3 (Oil)	
End Gap	.010-.050 (.25-1.27)
Side Clearance	.002-.008 (.05-.20)

CONNECTING RODS

Application	In. (mm)
2.2L	
Maximum Bend	¹
Maximum Twist	¹
Side Play	.004-.015 (.10-.38)

¹ – Replace rod if any bend or twist exists.

CYLINDER BLOCK

Application	In. (mm)
2.2L	
Cylinder Bore	
Diameter	3.5036-3.5043 (88.991-89.009)
Maximum Taper	.0005 (.013)
Maximum Out-of-Round	.0005 (.013)
Maximum Deck Warpage	¹

¹ – Information is not available from manufacturer. DO NOT remove more than .010" (.25 mm) material from original surface of deck.

VALVES & VALVE SPRINGS

Application	Specification
2.2L	
Intake Valves	
Face Angle	45°
Minimum Margin	.031" (.79 mm)
Exhaust Valves	
Face Angle	45°
Minimum Margin	.031" (.79 mm)
Valve Springs	
Free Length	2.06" (52.3 mm)
Out-of-Square	.63" (1.6 mm)
Pressure	Lbs. @ In. (kg @ mm)
Valve Closed	100-110 @ 1.61 (45-50 @ 40.9)
Valve Open	208-222 @ 1.22 (94-101 @ 30.9)

CYLINDER HEAD

Application	Specification
2.2L	
Maximum Warpage	¹
Valve Seats	
Intake Valve	
Seat Angle	46°
Seat Width	.049-.059" (1.24-1.50 mm)
Maximum Seat Runout	.002" (.05 mm)
Exhaust Valve	
Seat Angle	46°
Seat Width	.063-.075" (1.60-1.91 mm)
Maximum Seat Runout	.002" (.05 mm)
Valve Guides	
Intake Valve	
Valve Guide Oil Clearance	.0011-.0026" (.028-.066 mm)
Exhaust Valve	
Valve Guide Oil Clearance	.0014-.0031" (.036-.079 mm)

¹ – Information is not available from manufacturer. DO NOT remove more than .010" (.25 mm) material from original surface of cylinder head.

CAMSHAFT

Application	In. (mm)
2.2L	
Journal Diameter	1.867-1.869 (47.42-47.47)
Lobe Lift	
Intake	.259 (6.58)
Exhaust	.259 (6.58)
Oil Clearance	.001-.004 (.03-.10)

**Beretta, Cutlass Calais, Cutlass Supreme
Grand Am, Grand Prix, Skylark**

NOTE: For repair procedures not covered in this article, see ENGINE OVERHAUL PROCEDURES article in GENERAL INFORMATION.

ENGINE IDENTIFICATION

Engine may be identified by the eighth character of the Vehicle Identification Number (VIN), stamped on metal tab located on top of left corner of instrument panel. The eighth character identifies the engine model.

Engine code, located on cylinder block, may be required when ordering replacement parts (if needed). *See Fig. 1.* A traceability and verification label is attached to the front housing. The 2.3L engine is offered in a standard (VIN D) and a high output (VIN A) version. See ENGINE IDENTIFICATION CODES table.

ENGINE IDENTIFICATION CODES

Engine	Code
2.3L (138") PFI (DOHC)	
Standard	
8th Character On Dash VIN	D
Engine Code On Block [1]	LD2
High Output [2]	
8th Character On Dash VIN	A
Engine Code On Block [1]	LGO

[1] – See Fig. 1 for engine code location.
[2] – High output is not offered in Cutlass Supreme, Grand Prix or Skylark models.

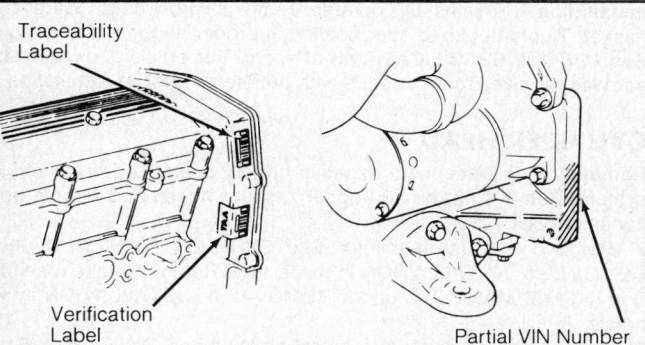

Traceability Label
Verification Label
Partial VIN Number

Note: First digit of partial VIN number indicates vehicle manufacturer. No. 1 indicates Chevrolet, No. 2 Pontiac, No. 3 Oldsmobile and No. 4 indicates Buick. Second digit "M" indicates 1991 model.

91A08082   Courtesy of General Motors Corp.

Fig. 1: Locating Engine Codes

ADJUSTMENTS

VALVE CLEARANCE ADJUSTMENT

Hydraulic valve lifters are used. No adjustment is required.

REMOVAL & INSTALLATION

NOTE: For reassembly reference, label all electrical connectors, vacuum hoses and fuel lines before removal. Also place mating marks on engine hood and other major assemblies before removal.

FUEL PRESSURE RELEASE

1) Loosen fuel tank cap to release fuel tank pressure. Remove fuel pump fuse. Start engine and operate until engine stalls.

2) Crank engine for an additional 3 seconds to release residual line pressure. Disconnect negative battery cable and reinstall fuel pump fuse.

ENGINE

Removal (Beretta, Cutlass Calais, Grand Am & Skylark) – 1) Release fuel pressure. See FUEL PRESSURE RELEASE under REMOVAL & INSTALLATION in this article. Disconnect negative battery cable and drain cooling system. Discharge A/C system (if equipped). Drain crankcase.

2) Remove heater hose at thermostat housing and radiator inlet hose. Remove air cleaner-to-throttle body duct. Remove upper radiator support and cooling fan. On A/C-equipped vehicles, remove compressor/condenser hose assembly at compressor, and discard "O" rings.

3) On all vehicles, disconnect 2 vacuum hoses from front of engine. Disconnect and place aside electrical connections for alternator, A/C compressor (if equipped), injector harness, IAC and TPS from throttle body, MAP sensor, MAT sensor, vacuum purge solenoid and starter solenoid.

4) Remove ground connections at front engine mount bracket and negative battery cable from transaxle. Disconnect electrical connections for ignition coil and module, coolant sensors, oil pressure sensor/switch, power steering switch, knock sensor, oxygen sensor, crankshaft position sensor and speed sensor.

5) On automatic transaxle vehicles, disconnect park/neutral/back-up light switch. On manual transaxle vehicles, disconnect backup light switch and position harness aside. On all vehicles, disconnect brake booster vacuum hose from throttle body.

6) Remove throttle cable and bracket. Remove power steering rear bracket along with brake booster vacuum tube. Check valve hose from vacuum tube. Replace if necessary. Remove power steering pivot bolt, pump and drive belt. Position pump aside with hoses attached. Disconnect fuel lines. Clean any spilled fuel.

7) On automatic transaxle vehicles, disconnect shift cables, T.V. cables and transaxle cooler pipes. On manual transaxle vehicles, disconnect shift cables and remove clutch actuator cylinder. On all vehicles, disconnect exhaust manifold and remove heat shield.

8) Remove radiator and heater outlet hoses from radiator. Remove front engine mount nut and install Engine Support (J 28467-A). Disconnect vacuum lines and pull vacuum harness back through front lift bracket. Raise and support vehicle. Remove front wheels.

9) Remove radiator air deflector and right lower splash shield. Separate ball joints from steering knuckles. Support suspension support, crossmember and stabilizer shaft with suitable holding fixture. Remove retaining bolts, and remove suspension supports, crossmember and stabilizer shaft as an assembly.

10) Install Drive Axle Boot Protector (J 34754) on drive axle boots, and remove axle shaft from transaxle and position aside. Remove nuts from transaxle mount, and remove rear engine mount through bolts. Remove rear engine mount body bracket. Support engine and transaxle assembly from below. Lower vehicle onto support.

11) Remove transaxle through bolt. Mark threads on engine upper support fixture hooks for installation reference. Remove engine upper support fixture. Raise vehicle slowly from engine and transaxle assembly. Separate engine from transaxle.

Installation – 1) Assemble engine to transaxle: Ensure bolts are in correct locations. On automatic transaxle vehicles, clean torque converter-to-flywheel bolt holes and apply sealant to bolts.

2) Position engine and transaxle assembly under engine compartment and lower vehicle until transaxle mount is indexed. Install transaxle bolt. Install engine support fixture and adjust to previous setting. Raise vehicle and remove lower engine and transaxle support.

3) Install rear mount to body bracket and tighten bolt to 55 ft. lbs. (75 N.m). Install rear mount nut and tighten nut to 46 ft. lbs. (62 N.m). See TORQUE SPECIFICATIONS at end of this article.

4) Install transaxle through bolt, washer and nut. Tighten to 40 ft. lbs. (54 N.m) while maintaining equal gaps within .008" (2 mm). If gaps are not equal to within .008" (2 mm), idle shake and harsh transaxle engagement will occur.

5) Reverse removal procedure for remaining components. Tighten all fasteners to specification. See TORQUE SPECIFICATIONS at end of this article. After installation, evacuate and charge A/C system. Check and fill all fluids.

Removal (Cutlass Supreme & Grand Prix) – 1) Release fuel pressure. See FUEL PRESSURE RELEASE under REMOVAL &

INSTALLATION in this article. Scribe alignment marks on hood hinge, and remove hood. Disconnect negative battery cable and drain cooling system.

2) Discharge A/C system (if equipped). Drain crankcase. Remove heater hose at thermostat housing and radiator inlet hose. Remove air cleaner to throttle body duct. Remove upper radiator support and cooling fan. On A/C-equipped vehicles, remove compressor/condenser hose assembly at compressor, and plug hose and compressor openings. Discard "O" rings.

3) On all vehicles, disconnect 2 vacuum hoses from front of engine. Disconnect and place aside electrical connections for alternator, A/C compressor (if equipped), injector harness, starter solenoid and IAC and TPS at throttle body.

4) Remove ground connections at front engine mount bracket and negative battery cable from transaxle. Disconnect electrical connections for ignition coil and module, coolant sensors, oil pressure sensor/switch, knock sensor and oxygen sensor.

5) Disconnect brake booster vacuum hose from throttle body. Remove throttle cable and bracket. Remove power steering pump, hydraulic lines and front and rear brackets. Remove power steering pivot bolt and drive belt. Disconnect fuel lines. Clean any spilled fuel.

6) Remove torque strut mounts and transaxle fill tube. Remove exhaust heat shield and serpentine belt. Remove transaxle-to-cylinder block bolts. Raise and support vehicle. Disconnect exhaust pipe from manifold and remove exhaust-to-transaxle brace. Remove remaining transaxle-to-cylinder block bolts.

7) Remove radiator lower outlet hose. Remove torque converter cover. Mark torque converter-to-flywheel position. Remove torque converter bolts. Remove transaxle-to-engine brace and lower engine mount.

8) Lower vehicle and support transaxle. Install engine lift fixture. Disconnect vacuum lines and pull vacuum harness back through front lift bracket. Remove engine assembly.

Installation – **1)** Assemble engine to transaxle. Ensure bolts are in correct locations. Clean torque converter-to-flywheel bolt holes and apply sealant to bolts. Raise vehicle. Install transaxle-to-engine brace.

2) Reverse removal procedure for remaining components. Tighten all fasteners to specification. See TORQUE SPECIFICATIONS at end of this article. After installation, evacuate and charge A/C system. Check and fill all fluids.

INTAKE MANIFOLD

Removal – **1)** Disconnect negative battery cable. Remove throttle body-to-air cleaner duct and vent tube to air cleaner duct. Remove throttle cable bracket and power brake booster hose. Disconnect electrical connector at MAP sensor. It may be necessary to remove coolant fan shroud for access.

2) Drain cooling system. Disconnect electrical connectors at MAT sensor, purge solenoid valve and fuel injector harness. Disconnect vacuum hoses at fuel pressure regulator and purge solenoid. Disconnect coolant lines from throttle body.

3) Remove throttle body from intake manifold with electrical connections and vacuum hoses attached. Remove oil/air separator with hoses attached at the separator.

4) Remove oil/air separator hoses at timing chain cover or housing and oil filler tube. Remove oil filler cap and oil dipstick. Remove oil filler tube retaining bolt (if equipped), and remove tube. Remove intake manifold support brace. Remove bolts and intake manifold and gasket.

Installation – **1)** To install, reverse removal procedure using a new gasket on intake manifold and throttle body. Install all bolts and nuts finger tight, then tighten bolts and nuts to specification in proper sequence. *See Fig. 2.* See TORQUE SPECIFICATIONS at end of this article.

NOTE: Install intake manifold gasket with numbered side toward the manifold surface.

---

2) Replace all "O" rings and lubricate with engine oil prior to installation. To install remaining components, reverse removal procedure. Fill cooling system (if required).

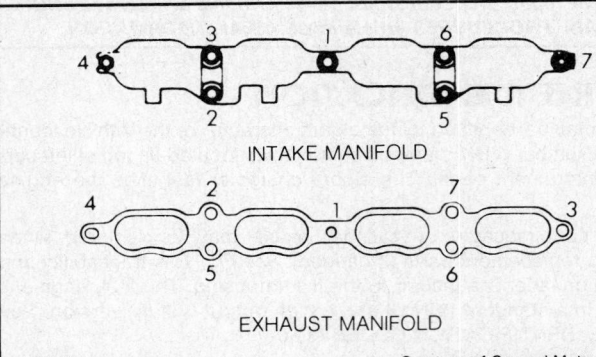

91C08078   Courtesy of General Motors Corp.

Fig. 2: Intake Manifold & Exhaust Manifold Tightening Sequence

EXHAUST MANIFOLD

Removal – **1)** Remove oxygen sensor connector. Remove hea shields and exhaust manifold brace bolt. Loosen exhaust pipe-to manifold spring-loaded nuts.

2) Raise and support vehicle. Disconnect exhaust pipe from exhaus manifold. Lower vehicle. Remove exhaust manifold-to-cylinder hea retaining nuts. Remove exhaust manifold, seals and gasket. If replacing exhaust manifold, transfer oxygen sensor, bolts, nuts, lower hea shield and exhaust manifold studs to new manifold.

Installation – To install, reverse removal procedure using nev gasket. Tighten bolts to specification in proper sequence. *See Fig. 2* See TORQUE SPECIFICATIONS at end of this article. If oxygen sen sor was removed, coat threads with anti-seize prior to installation.

CYLINDER HEAD

Removal – **1)** Disconnect negative battery cable, and drain coolin system. Remove heater and upper radiator hoses and throttle bod coolant hoses.

2) Remove exhaust manifold. See EXHAUST MANIFOLD unde REMOVAL & INSTALLATION in this article. Remove intake manifold See INTAKE MANIFOLD under REMOVAL & INSTALLATION in thi article.

3) Remove intake and exhaust camshaft housings. See INTAKE CAM SHAFT & HOUSING and EXHAUST CAMSHAFT & HOUSING unde REMOVAL & INSTALLATION in this article.

4) Disconnect MAT sensor and purge solenoid valve connector: Remove oil filler cap, oil dipstick and oil filler tube. Disconnect fue injector connector and coolant temperature sensor. Remove thrott body-to-air cleaner duct and throttle body cable bracket.

5) Remove throttle body from intake manifold with electrical harnes and throttle cable attached. Disconnect electrical and vacuum connec tions to MAP sensor. Remove cylinder head bolts in reverse order c tightening sequence. *See Fig. 5.* Remove cylinder head and gasket.

Inspection – Check cylinder head warpage. See CYLINDER HEA under OVERHAUL in this article.

Installation – **1)** Ensure cylinder head bolt threads and cylinder bloc holes are clean. Coat cylinder head bolt threads with engine oil an allow to drain.

2) Install gasket and ensure all holes align with cylinder block. Insta cylinder head. Tighten bolts to specification in proper sequence. Se TORQUE SPECIFICATIONS at end of article. *See Fig. 5.* To insta remaining components, reverse removal procedure.

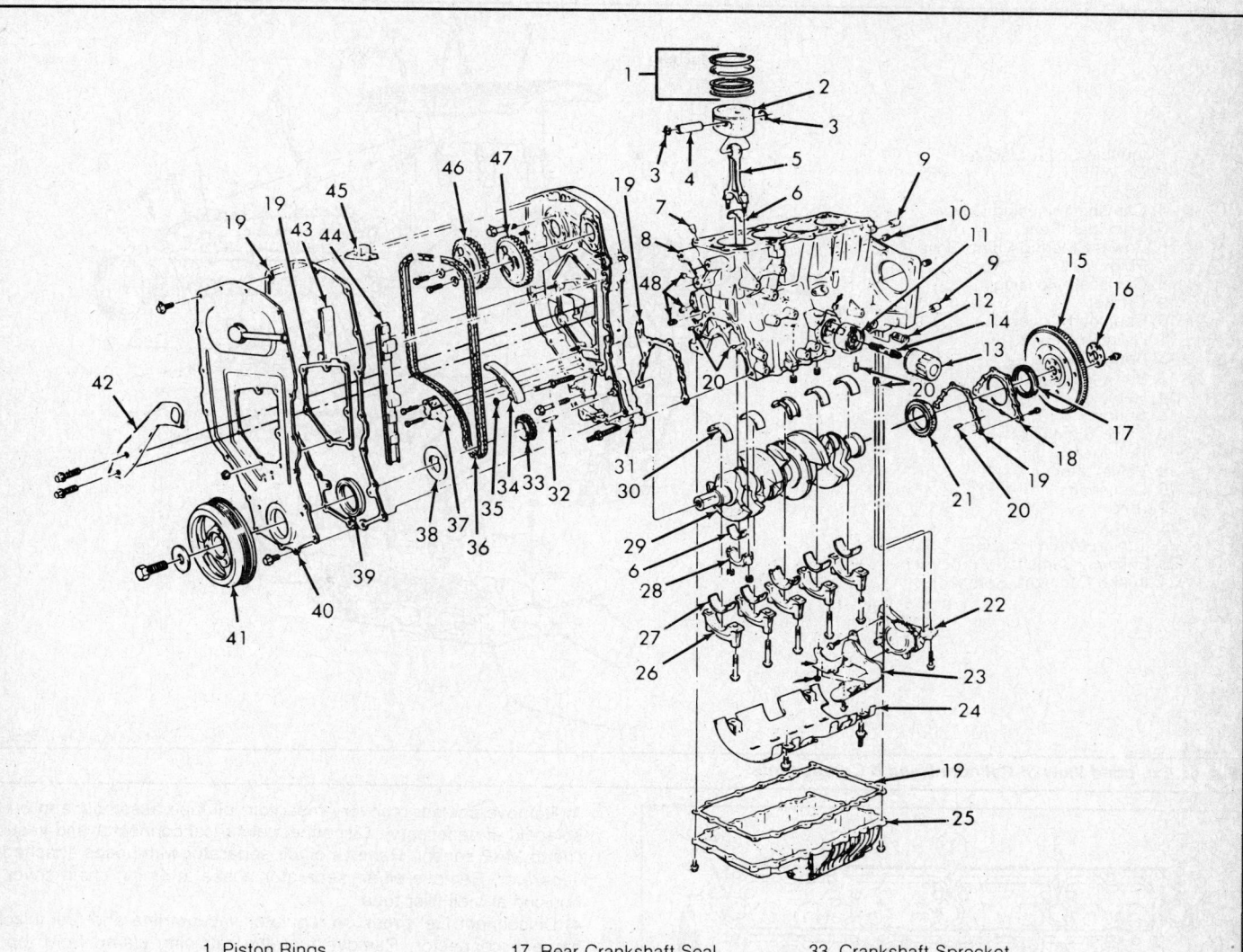

1. Piston Rings
2. Piston
3. Retainer
4. Piston Pin
5. Connecting Rod
6. Rod Bearing
7. Oil Flow Check Valve
8. Cylinder Block
9. Pin
10. Plug
11. Oil Cooler Adapter
12. Oil Filter By-Pass Valve
13. Oil Filter
14. Oil Cooler Connector
15. Flywheel
16. Flywheel Retainer

17. Rear Crankshaft Seal
18. Seal Housing
19. Gasket
20. Dowel Pin
21. Oil Pump Drive Gear
22. Oil Pump
23. Oil Pump Screen
24. Baffle
25. Oil Pan
26. Main Bearing Cap
27. Main Bearing
28. Connecting Rod Cap
29. Crankshaft
30. Main Bearing
31. Timing Chain Housing
32. Woodruff Key

33. Crankshaft Sprocket
34. Chain Tensioner Shoe
35. Retainer
36. Timing Chain
37. Tensioner
38. Slinger
39. Front Crankshaft Seal
40. Front Timing Case Cover
41. Crankshaft Pulley
42. Bracket
43. Right Chain Guide
44. Left Chain Guide
45. Upper Chain Guide
46. Exhaust Camshaft Sprocket
47. Intake Camshaft Sprocket
48. Plug

109475

Fig. 3: Exploded View of Cylinder Block & Components

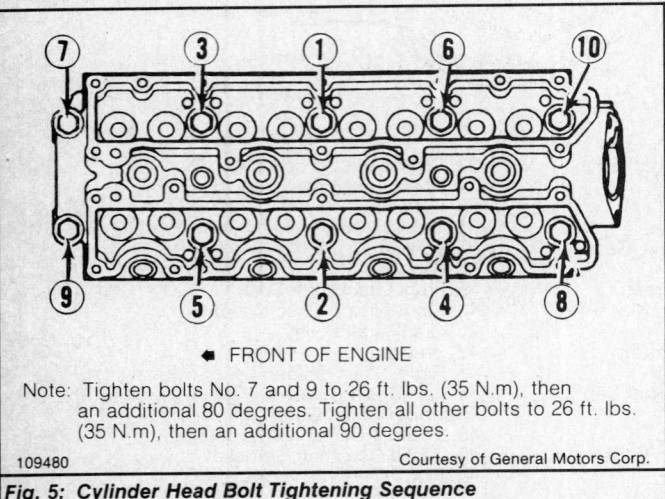

1. Ignition Coil & Module
2. Dowel Pin
3. Seal
4. Camshaft Housing Cover
5. Camshaft Seal
6. Power Steering Pump Drive Pulley
7. Plug
8. Camshaft Housing
9. Gasket
10. Camshaft Cover
11. Cylinder Head
12. Spark Plug
13. Valve Keepers
14. Retainer
15. Spring
16. Valve Stem Seal
17. Rotator
18. Valve Lifter
19. Camshaft
20. Stud
21. Valve
22. Timing Chain Housing
23. Exhaust Camshaft Sprocket
24. Intake Camshaft Sprocket

109476

Courtesy of General Motors Corp.

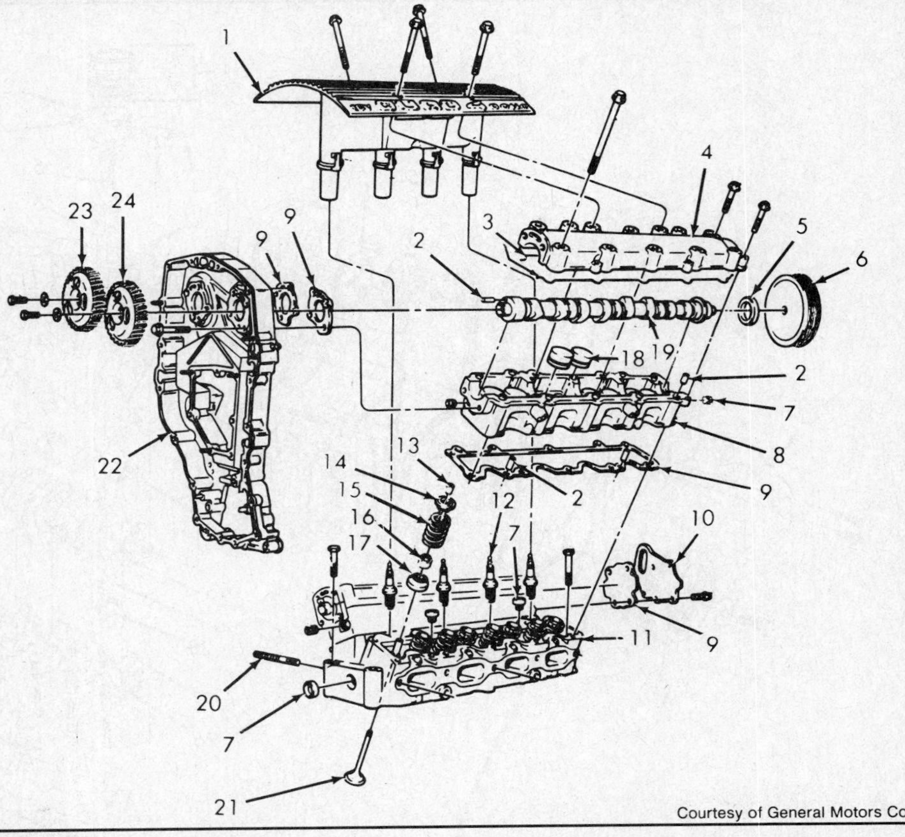

Fig. 4: Exploded View of Cylinder Head & Components

◄ FRONT OF ENGINE

Note: Tighten bolts No. 7 and 9 to 26 ft. lbs. (35 N.m), then an additional 80 degrees. Tighten all other bolts to 26 ft. lbs. (35 N.m), then an additional 90 degrees.

109480

Courtesy of General Motors Corp.

Fig. 5: Cylinder Head Bolt Tightening Sequence

INTAKE CAMSHAFT & HOUSING

NOTE: Camshaft housing-to-cylinder head gasket must be replaced whenever camshaft housing bolts are loosened or removed.

Removal – **1)** Disconnect negative battery cable. Disconnect ignition coil and module assembly electrical connector. Remove ignition coil and module-to-camshaft housing bolts. Remove assembly by pulling straight up. *See Fig. 4.*

2) Disconnect power steering pressure switch connector. Remove power steering pump and lay aside with hoses attached. Using Pulley Remover (J-38343-4) and Forcing Screw (J-36014-A), remove power steering pump drive pulley from intake camshaft. *See Fig. 4.*

3) Remove coolant recovery reservoir, oil tube assembly and purge solenoid (if necessary). Disconnect electrical connector and vacuum line to MAP sensor. Remove oil/air separator with hoses attached at separator. Remove oil/air separator hoses at timing chain cover or housing and oil filler tube.

4) Disconnect fuel pressure regulator vacuum line and fuel injector harness connector. Remove fuel line retaining clamp from top of intake camshaft housing. Remove fuel rail-to-camshaft housing retaining bolts, and remove fuel rail from cylinder head with fuel lines attached.

5) Cover cylinder head injector openings and injector nozzles. Disconnect, but do not remove, timing chain housing. See TIMING CHAIN HOUSING under REMOVAL & INSTALLATION in this article. DO NOT remove housing from vehicle.

6) Remove camshaft housing cover bolts. Remove camshaft housing-to-cylinder head bolts in reverse order of tightening sequence. See Fig. 6. Leave 2 bolts loosely in place to hold camshaft housing while separating camshaft housing cover from camshaft housing.

7) Install 4 bolts into tapped holes of camshaft housing cover. Evenly tighten bolts to remove camshaft housing cover. Remove 2 loosely installed camshaft housing-to-head bolts and remove housing cover. Note chain sprocket dowel pin position for reassembly. Remove camshaft and camshaft seal.

NOTE: If removing valve lifters, mark component location for reassembly reference. Store lifters upright in engine oil to prevent bleed-down.

Inspection – Inspect camshaft journal diameter, lobe lift and oil clearance. See CAMSHAFT table in ENGINE SPECIFICATIONS at end of article. Inspect lifter O.D. and lifter bore I.D. See CAMSHAFT HOUSING under OVERHAUL in this article. Replace components not within specification.

NOTE: Lifters must be replaced if new camshaft is installed. If camshaft or lifter is replaced, add Engine Oil Supplement (1052367) to oil.

Installation – 1) To install, reverse removal procedure. Ensure dowel pins are installed in cylinder head and lifters are installed in original location. Coat camshaft with Lubricant (12345501) prior to installation.

2) Install seal between camshaft housing and cover. Apply thread sealant to camshaft housing and cover retaining bolts. Tighten camshaft housing bolts in proper sequence. See Fig. 6. See TORQUE SPECIFICATIONS at end of this article.

3) Lubricate camshaft seal with oil and install using Seal Installer (J-36009). Apply thread sealant to ignition coil and module bolts.

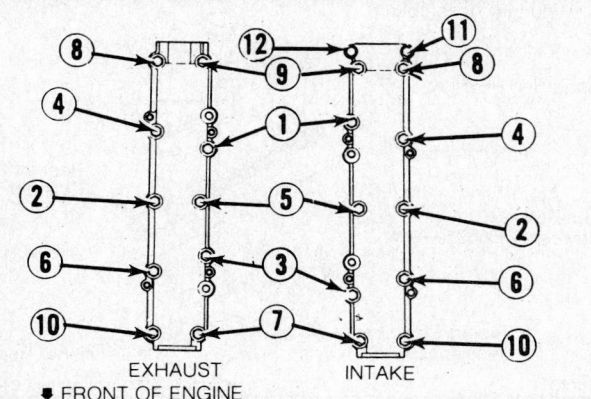

EXHAUST   INTAKE

↓ FRONT OF ENGINE

Note: Tighten bolts No. 11 and 12 to 11 ft. lbs. (15 N.m), then an additional 25 degrees. Tighten all other bolts to 11 ft. lbs. (15 N.m), then an additional 75 degrees.

55167   Courtesy of General Motors Corp.

Fig. 6: Camshaft Housing Bolt Tightening Sequence

EXHAUST CAMSHAFT & HOUSING

NOTE: Camshaft housing-to-cylinder head gasket must be replaced whenever camshaft housing bolts are loosened or removed.

Removal – 1) Disconnect negative battery cable and ignition coil and module assembly electrical connector. Remove ignition coil and module-to-camshaft housing bolts, and remove assembly by pulling straight up. See Fig. 4.

2) Disconnect oil pressure switch connector. On A/T models, remove transaxle fluid level tube from exhaust camshaft cover and move aside. On all models, remove camshaft cover bolts. Disconnect, but do not remove, timing chain housing. See TIMING CHAIN HOUSING under REMOVAL & INSTALLATION in this article. DO NOT remove housing from vehicle.

3) Remove camshaft housing-to-cylinder head bolts in reverse order of tightening sequence. See Fig. 6. Leave 2 bolts loosely in place to hold camshaft housing while separating camshaft housing cover from housing.

4) Install 4 bolts into tapped holes of camshaft housing cover. Evenly tighten bolts to remove camshaft housing cover. Remove the 2 loosely installed cam housing-to-head bolts and remove housing cover. Note the position of chain sprocket dowel pin for reassembly. Remove camshaft.

NOTE: If removing valve lifters, mark component location for reassembly reference. Store lifters upright in engine oil to prevent bleed-down.

Inspection – Inspect camshaft journal diameter, lobe lift and oil clearance. See CAMSHAFT table in ENGINE SPECIFICATIONS at end of article. Inspect lifter O.D. and lifter bore I.D. See CAMSHAFT HOUSING under OVERHAUL in this article. Replace components if not within specification.

NOTE: Lifters must be replaced if new camshaft is installed. If camshaft or lifter is replaced, add Engine Oil Supplement (1052367) to oil.

Installation – 1) To install, reverse removal procedure. Ensure dowel pins are installed in cylinder head and lifters are in original location. Coat camshaft with Lubricant (12345501) prior to installation.

2) Install seal between camshaft housing and cover. Apply thread sealant to camshaft housing and cover retaining bolts.

3) Tighten camshaft housing bolts to specification in proper sequence. See Fig. 6. See TORQUE SPECIFICATIONS at end of this article. Apply thread sealant to ignition coil and module bolts.

FRONT TIMING CASE COVER

Removal – 1) Drain cooling system enough to remove coolant surge tank. Remove coolant surge tank. Remove serpentine drive belt. Remove upper cover bolts and engine lift bracket. Disconnect vent hose from cover (if equipped).

2) Raise and support vehicle. Remove right front wheel and lower splash shield. Remove crankshaft balancer and lower cover bolts. Lower vehicle. Remove front timing case cover and gaskets.

Installation – To install, reverse removal procedure using new gasket. Lubricate front seal with grease prior to installing crankshaft balancer. Install remaining components and fill with coolant. Tighten all fasteners to specification. See TORQUE SPECIFICATIONS at end of this article.

FRONT CRANKSHAFT SEAL

Removal & Installation – Remove front timing case cover. See FRONT TIMING CASE COVER under REMOVAL & INSTALLATION in this article. Support cover and drive seal from rear of cover. Note direction of seal installation. Use Seal Installer (J-36010) to install seal. Edge of seal should be positioned .151" (3.84 mm) below front timing case cover mounting surface.

TIMING CHAIN & SPROCKETS

Removal – 1) Remove front timing case cover. See FRONT TIMING CASE COVER under REMOVAL & INSTALLATION in this article. Remove crankshaft oil slinger. Rotate crankshaft clockwise (viewed from front of engine) until camshaft sprocket timing pin alignment holes align with holes of timing chain housing See Fig. 7.

2) Ensure crankshaft sprocket timing marks align with mark on cylinder block. Crankshaft sprocket keyway should point upward and align with center line of cylinder bores. Timing chain is now in "timed" position. See Fig. 7.

CAUTION: Chain tensioner piston is under spring pressure. Use care to prevent components from coming out and causing injury.

3) Remove all timing chain guides. Raise and support vehicle. Remove timing chain tensioner shoe retainer. Ensure all timing chain slack is above chain tensioner, and remove chain tensioner shoe.

4) Timing chain must be disengaged from wear grooves in tensioner shoe to remove shoe. To disengage from grooves, slide screwdriver blade under timing chain while pulling shoe outward.

5) If timing chain tensioner shoe removal is difficult, lower vehicle. Using Camshaft Sprocket Wrench (J-36013), hold intake camshaft sprocket and remove sprocket bolt and washer.

NOTE: Camshaft sprocket must be removed using puller. DO NOT pry sprocket from camshaft or damage to sprocket and timing chain housing can occur.

6) Remove washer from sprocket bolt and reinstall into camshaft by hand. Using puller, remove intake cam sprocket by using sprocket relief holes. Remove chain tensioner retaining bolts and tensioner. Remove housing-to-block stud, pivot and timing chain.

CAUTION: Proper timing chain and sprockets installation procedure must be followed to prevent severe engine damage.

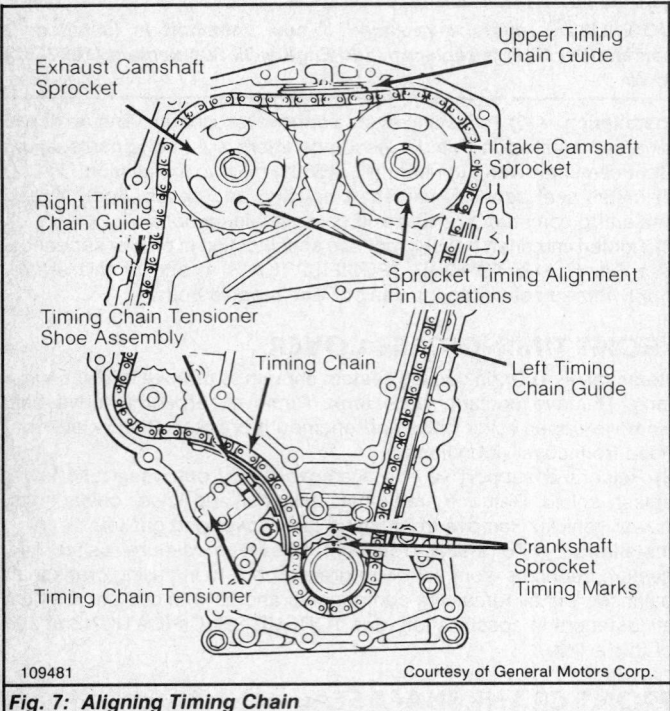

Fig. 7: Aligning Timing Chain

Installation – 1) Install camshaft sprocket (if removed). Apply Sealant (12345493) to camshaft sprocket retaining bolt. Install retaining bolt and washer. Using camshaft sprocket wrench, tighten retaining bolt to specification. See TORQUE SPECIFICATIONS at end of this article. Install Camshaft Alignment Pins (J-36008) in camshaft sprockets holes and timing chain housing for camshaft positioning.
2) If camshafts are out of position and must be rotated more than 1/8 turn for pin installation, crankshaft must be rotated 90 degrees clockwise from TDC to provide valve clearance.
3) Once camshafts are positioned and alignment pins are installed, rotate crankshaft counterclockwise back to TDC. DO NOT rotate crankshaft clockwise back to TDC.

CAUTION: If camshafts must be rotated more than 1/8 turn for pin installation, crankshaft must be rotated 90 degrees CLOCKWISE from TDC to provide valve clearance. Once camshafts are positioned and alignment pins are installed, rotate crankshaft COUNTERCLOCKWISE back to TDC. DO NOT rotate crankshaft clockwise to TDC or valve and piston damage can occur.

4) Install timing chain on exhaust camshaft, idler and crankshaft sprockets. Remove alignment pin from intake camshaft. Using camshaft sprocket wrench, rotate intake camshaft counterclockwise and install timing chain on camshaft sprocket. Release camshaft sprocket wrench. Timing chain will tighten between the camshaft sprockets.
5) Ensure alignment pin will fully engage and slides easily on intake camshaft. Ensure all timing marks are aligned. Repeat procedure if alignment pin fails to slide easily.
6) With alignment pin installed, raise vehicle on hoist. With slack removed from chain, ensure timing marks on crankshaft and cylinder block are aligned. If marks are not aligned, position chain one tooth forward or rearward, remove slack and recheck marks.
7) Install tensioner shoe pivot. To reposition the timing chain tensioner to the zero position, install restraint cylinder, spring and nylon plug into plunger. *See Fig. 8.*
8) Align restraint cylinder guide slot with peg in plunger. Rotate restraint cylinder clockwise and push restraint cylinder into plunger until it bottoms. Continue rotating restraint cylinder clockwise and allow spring to push it out of plunger.

9) Plunger pin will lock restraint cylinder in the loaded position. Install Timing Chain Tensioner Spacer (J-36589) onto plunger assembly. Install plunger into tensioner body with long end toward crankshaft.
10) Install tensioner to chain housing. Ensure long end is toward crankshaft. Install timing chain tensioner bolts and tighten to specification. See TORQUE SPECIFICATIONS at end of this article.
11) Install chain tensioner shoe and retainer. Remove timing chain tensioner spacer, and push plunger into tensioner body to release plunger. Lower vehicle and remove alignment pins.
12) Rotate crankshaft clockwise 2 full revolutions and align crankshaft timing mark with mark on cylinder block. Reinstall alignment dowel pins. If engine is timed correctly, dowel pins will slide in easily. Install timing chain guides and remaining components.

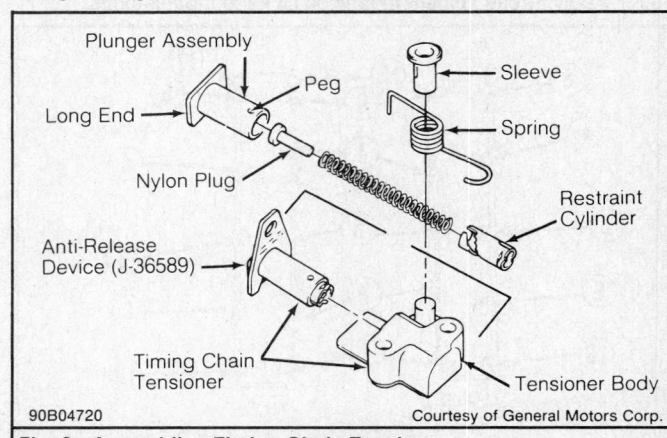

Fig. 8: Assembling Timing Chain Tensioner

TIMING CHAIN HOUSING

NOTE: Exhaust manifold may have to be removed during timing chain housing repairs. Water pump must be removed if replacing timing chain housing. Timing chain housing-to-cylinder block and camshaft housing gaskets can be removed without removing timing chain housing from vehicle.

Removal – 1) Remove front timing case cover. See FRONT TIMING CASE COVER under REMOVAL & INSTALLATION in this article. Remove timing chain and camshaft sprockets. See TIMING CHAIN & SPROCKETS under REMOVAL & INSTALLATION in this article.
2) If removing housing from vehicle, drain cooling system and remove lower front cover retaining stud. Remove rear engine mount nut. Remove oil/air separator hose from timing chain housing (except high output). Remove front engine mount nut. Reinstall nut approximately 3 turns.
3) Raise engine until front mount bracket contacts the nut. Remove water pump. See WATER PUMP under REMOVAL & INSTALLATION in this article.
4) For housing removal, remove timing chain housing-to-belt tensioner bracket brace. Remove oil pan-to-timing chain housing bolts. Remove water pump-to-timing chain housing bolts. Remove timing chain housing-to-cylinder block and camshaft housing bolts. Remove timing chain housing and gaskets.
Installation – 1) Inspect oil pan gasket. Replace gasket if damaged. Inspect silicone strips of oil pan gasket for damage. Slight damage can be repaired using silicone sealant.
2) Ensure dowel pins are installed in cylinder block. To install, reverse removal procedure using new gaskets. Install all housing retaining bolts finger tight before tightening to specification. See TORQUE SPECIFICATIONS at end of this article.
3) Coat coolant pipe "O" rings with anti-freeze prior to installation. If cooling system is drained, fill cooling system until coolant reaches heater hose outlet, and install hose.

TIMING CHAIN IDLER SPROCKETS & BEARING

NOTE: Replace bearing whenever idler sprocket is removed.

Removal – 1) Remove timing chain housing. See TIMING CHAIN HOUSING under REMOVAL & INSTALLATION in this article. Remove bearing snap ring. *See Fig. 9.* Install Remover/Installer Plate (J-36998-4) on front side of timing chain housing with 3 alignment pins engaged into front cover retaining bolt holes.

2) Using Handle (J-36998-2), press sprocket from bearing. Reposition remover/installer plate on rear of chain housing over water pump studs. Using Remover/Installer (J-36998-1) and Handle (J-36998-2), press bearing from timing chain housing.

Installation – 1) Clean all nylon from groove in timing chain housing. Coat new bearing-to-housing surfaces with Sealant (12345493). Install remover/installer plate on front side of chain housing with 3 alignment pins engaged into front cover retaining bolt holes.

2) Using remover/installer and handle, press bearing into timing chain housing. Reposition remover/installer plate on rear of chain housing over water pump studs.

3) Using remover/installer and handle, install idler sprocket. Install bearing snap ring. Install timing chain housing. See TIMING CHAIN HOUSING under REMOVAL & INSTALLATION in this article.

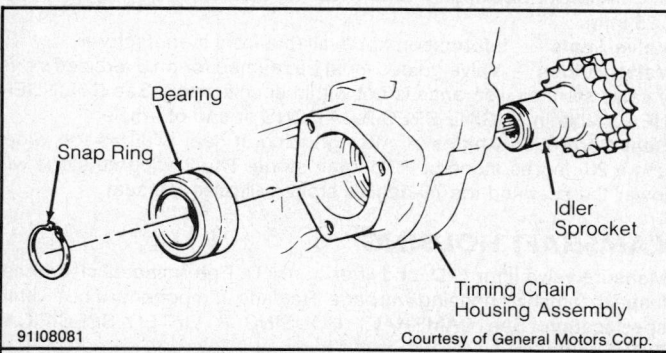

91I08081   Courtesy of General Motors Corp.

Fig. 9: Exploded View of Timing Chain Idler Sprocket Assembly

REAR CRANKSHAFT SEAL

Removal – 1) Remove transaxle assembly. Place reference mark on clutch pressure plate (M/T) and flywheel for reassembly reference. Remove pressure plate and clutch disc (if equipped) and flywheel or flexplate.

2) Remove oil pan-to-seal housing bolts. Remove seal housing-to-cylinder block bolts, and remove seal housing and gasket. *See Fig. 3.* Position seal housing on 2 wood blocks of equal thickness so transaxle side of seal housing is supported across dowel pin and center bolt holes on both sides of seal opening.

3) Using small chisel in seal relief grooves, drive seal evenly from seal housing. Note direction of seal installation.

Installation – 1) Replace oil pan gasket if cuts, deformation or separation from aluminum carrier in inner silicone bead exists. Inspect silicone strips at top of aluminum carrier at oil pan, cylinder block, and seal housing joint areas. Use silicone sealant to repair damaged silicone strips.

2) Using Rear Crankshaft Seal Installer (J-36005), install new seal into housing. Lubricate seal lip with engine oil. To install, reverse removal procedure using new gasket. Apply Sealant (12345493) to flywheel or flexplate bolts prior to installation.

3) On M/T models, ensure reference marks are aligned on pressure plate and flywheel. On all models, tighten fasteners to specification. See TORQUE SPECIFICATIONS at end of this article.

CYLINDER BLOCK OIL FLOW CHECK VALVE

Removal – 1) Oil flow check valve is located on front of cylinder block. *See Fig. 3.* Oil flow valve can be removed using Oil Flow Check Valve Tool (J-38123) or modified 3/16" x 5" stove bolt.

2) Bolt must be modified until bolt head can be installed past the indentations on check valve. Using slide hammer, install oil flow check valve tool or modified bolt into check valve.

3) Rotate check valve tool or bolt 90 degrees so it will lock into check valve indentations. Pull check valve from cylinder block.

CAUTION: Ensure check ball remains in cylinder block oil flow check valve during removal. If check ball is missing, ensure ball is located.

Installation – Use slide hammer and oil flow check valve tool or drift punch and hammer to seat new check valve into seat area.

VALVE LIFTERS

Removal & Installation – Valve lifters can only be removed once camshaft and camshaft housing are removed. See INTAKE CAMSHAFT & HOUSING and EXHAUST CAMSHAFT & HOUSING under REMOVAL & INSTALLATION in this article. New valve lifters must be installed if camshaft is replaced.

WATER PUMP

Removal – 1) Water pump is driven by idler sprocket and is mounted on rear of timing chain housing. *See Fig. 10.* Disconnect negative battery cable. Drain cooling system. Disconnect oxygen sensor and remove heat shields.

2) Remove exhaust manifold. See EXHAUST MANIFOLD under REMOVAL & INSTALLATION in this article. Disconnect outlet pipe from water pump cover, oil pan and transaxle. Remove water pump cover-to-cylinder block bolts.

3) Remove water pump-to-timing chain housing nuts. Remove water pump and cover assembly.

Installation – 1) Install water pump cover on water pump body with bolts finger tight. Lubricate water pump drive splines with grease. Install water pump and water pump cover on cylinder block.

2) Install retaining nuts on timing chain housing finger tight. Lubricate outlet pipe "O" ring with anti-freeze. Install "O" ring and outlet pipe with bolts finger tight.

3) Tighten bolts and nuts to specification in proper sequence, starting with pump-to-timing chain housing nuts, pump cover-to-pump body bolts, pump cover-to-cylinder block bolts and outlet pipe-to-cover bolts. See TORQUE SPECIFICATIONS at end of this article.

4) Install remaining components. Tighten all fasteners to specification. See TORQUE SPECIFICATIONS at end of this article. Fill cooling system until coolant reaches heater hose outlet, and install hose.

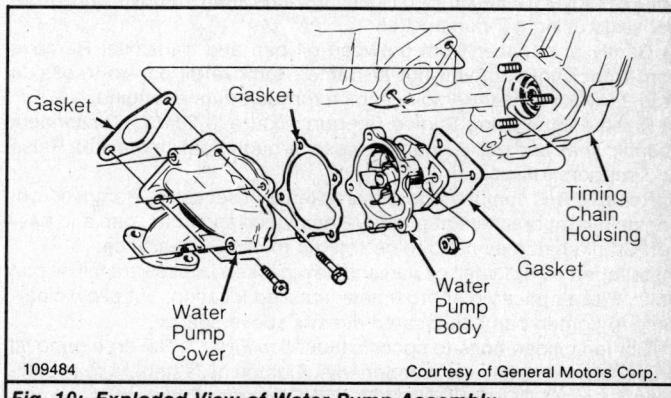

109484   Courtesy of General Motors Corp.

Fig. 10: Exploded View of Water Pump Assembly

OIL PAN

Removal (Beretta, Cutlass Calais, Grand Am & Skylark) – 1) Drain crankcase and remove flywheel cover. Remove splash shield-to-suspension support bolt. On manual transaxle vehicles, remove exhaust manifold brace. On all vehicles, remove radiator outlet pipe-to-oil pan bolt.

2) Remove transaxle-to-oil pan nut, and then remove stud from transaxle using a 7-mm socket. Gently pry spacer out from between oil pan and transaxle. Remove oil pan-to-transaxle stud. Remove oil pan bolts, pan and gasket. Crankshaft may need to be rotated to obtain clearance.

Installation – 1) Install oil pan and new gasket. Loosely install oil pan bolts. Place spacer in approximate installed location, but allow clearance to tighten pan bolt located directly above spacer.

2) Tighten oil pan bolts to specification. *See Fig. 11.* Reverse removal procedure for remaining components. Tighten all fasteners to specification. See TORQUE SPECIFICATIONS at end of this article.

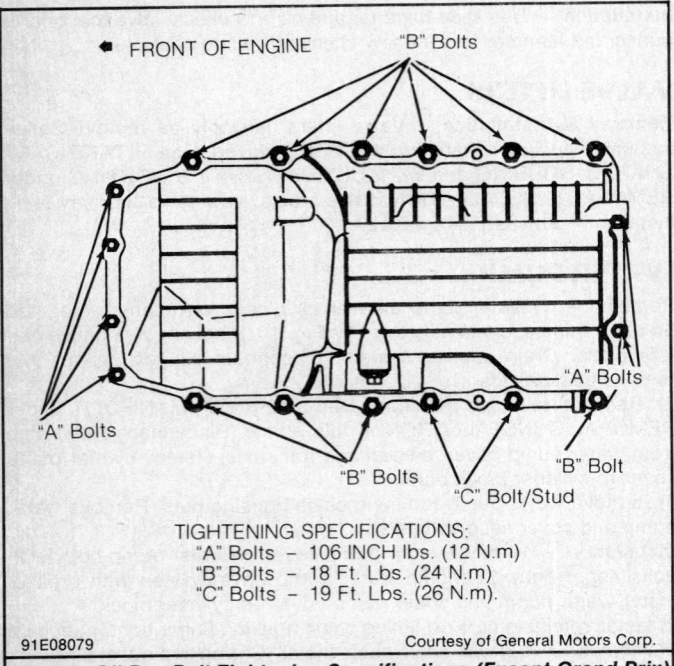

FRONT OF ENGINE   "B" Bolts

"A" Bolts   "A" Bolts

"B" Bolts   "B" Bolt
"C" Bolt/Stud

TIGHTENING SPECIFICATIONS:
"A" Bolts – 106 INCH lbs. (12 N.m)
"B" Bolts – 18 Ft. Lbs. (24 N.m)
"C" Bolts – 19 Ft. Lbs. (26 N.m)

91E08079   Courtesy of General Motors Corp.

Fig. 11: Oil Pan Bolt Tightening Specifications (Except Grand Prix)

Removal (Cutlass Supreme) – **1)** Drain cooling system and crankcase, and remove oil filter. Remove serpentine belt. Raise and support vehicle. Remove flywheel cover and exhaust manifold brace. Remove right front wheel and right splash shield.
2) Remove lower radiator hose. Disconnect electrical connector. Disconnect heater hose at water pump. Remove radiator pipe-to-oil pan bolt. Remove transaxle-to-oil pan nut, and then remove stud from transaxle using a 7-mm socket.
3) Gently pry spacer from between oil pan and transaxle. Remove right front engine mount nut at frame. Remove oil pan-to-transaxle stud. Lower vehicle. Remove engine torque struts at engine.
4) Raise engine using Engine Support Fixture (J 28467). Disconnect vacuum lines and pull vacuum harness through front lift bracket. Raise and support vehicle.
5) Remove A/C compressor and bracket, and set aside. Remove front engine mount brackets at engine. Remove oil pan bolts, pan and gasket. Crankshaft may need to be rotated to obtain clearance.
Installation – **1)** Install oil pan and new gasket. Loosely install oil pan bolts. Place spacer in approximate installed location, but allow clearance to tighten pan bolt located directly above spacer.
2) Tighten oil pan bolts to specification. *See Fig. 11.* Reverse removal procedure for remaining components. Tighten all fasteners to specification. See TORQUE SPECIFICATIONS at end of this article.
Removal (Grand Prix) – **1)** Drain crankcase. Remove air cleaner. Disconnect negative battery cable. Remove serpentine belt and belt tensioner.
2) Support engine using Engine Support (J 28467-A). Raise and support vehicle. Remove right front wheel and splash shield. Remove steering gear pinch bolt.

CAUTION: Ensure intermediate shaft is disconnected from rack and pinion stub shaft. Damage can result if shaft is not disconnected.

3) Remove transaxle mount retaining nuts and engine-to-frame mount retaining nuts. Remove front mount bracket from block. Remove outboard flywheel/starter plastic shield. Remove inboard flywheel metal shield.
4) Remove starter and hang from body. Place stand under front center crossmember. Loosen, but do not remove, rear frame bolts. Remove front frame bolts and lower front of frame.

5) Disconnect crankshaft sensor wire. Remove oil pan bolts and nuts, pan and gasket. Clean flanges, rail, front cover, main bearing cap and threaded holes.
Installation – **1)** Install oil pan and new gasket. Loosely install oil pan bolts. Tighten oil pan nuts to 89 INCH lbs. (10 N.m). Tighten oil pan rear bolts to 18 ft. lbs. (24 N.m) and then tighten remaining bolts to 89 INCH lbs. (10 N.m).
2) Reverse removal procedure for remaining components. Tighten all fasteners to specification. See TORQUE SPECIFICATIONS at end of this article. Ensure intermediate shaft is seated prior to pinch bolt installation.

OVERHAUL

CYLINDER HEAD

Inspection – Check cylinder head warpage at deck surface and manifold surfaces. Resurface cylinder head if warpage exceeds specification. See CYLINDER HEAD table in ENGINE SPECIFICATIONS at end of article. Replace cylinder head if metal removed exceeds .010" (.25 mm).
Valve Seats – Information not available from manufacturer.
Valve Guides – Valve guides must be reamed for an oversized valve if valve stem oil clearance is not within specification. See CYLINDER HEAD table in ENGINE SPECIFICATIONS at end of article.
Seat Correction Angles – After grinding, if seat width is too wide, use a 20-degree stone or 70-degree stone. The 20-degree stone will lower the seat and the 70-degree stone will raise the seat.

CAMSHAFT HOUSING

Measure valve lifter O.D. and lifter bore I.D. Determine oil clearance. Inspect camshaft housing warpage. Replace components if not within specification. See CAMSHAFT HOUSING & LIFTER SPECIFICATIONS table.

CAMSHAFT HOUSING & LIFTER SPECIFICATIONS

Application	In. (mm)
Housing Warpage	.002 (.05)
Lifter Bore I.D.	1.3775-1.3787 (34.989-35.019)
Lifter O.D.	1.3763-1.3770 (34.958-34.976)
Lifter Oil Clearance	.0006-.0024 (.015-.061)

VALVE TRAIN

Valve Installed Height – Measure valve installed height from top of valve stem to top of camshaft housing. Distance should be .984-1.004" (25.00-25.50 mm).

CYLINDER BLOCK ASSEMBLY

Piston Ring Installation – Install piston rings with identification mark toward top of piston and rings properly spaced. *See Fig. 12.*
Piston & Rod Assembly – Arrow on top of piston must be positioned toward front of engine and connecting rod oil hole positioned toward the exhaust manifold side of engine. *See Fig. 12.*
Crankshaft Oil Pump Drive Gear – **1)** Inspect crankshaft oil pump drive gear. If replacement is required, drill a hole between 2 teeth of drive gear. Using chisel, split gear and remove from crankshaft.
2) Ensure crankshaft is free of burrs. Preheat oven to 392°F (200°C) for one hour. Apply Tempilstik (J-24731-425) on replacement gear teeth. Heat gear in oven for 25-30 minutes. Ensure Tempilstik starts to melt.
3) Install gear on crankshaft. Ensure gear is fully seated against crankshaft counterweight.

CAUTION: Check oil pump drive gear backlash adjustment whenever drive gear is replaced. See OIL PUMP DRIVE GEAR BACKLASH ADJUSTMENT under ENGINE OILING in this article.

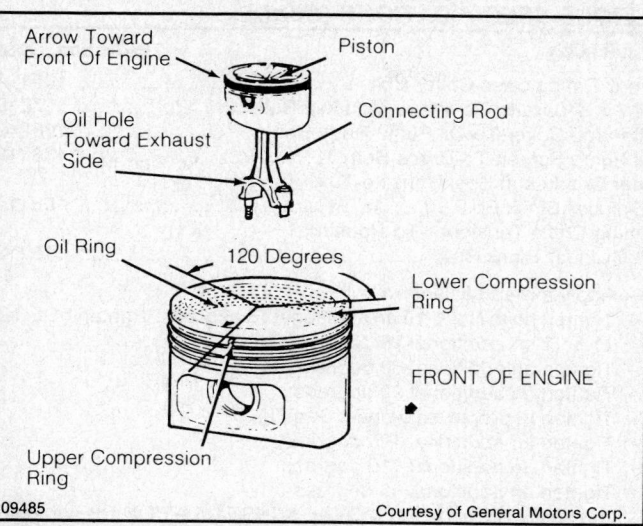

Arrow Toward Front Of Engine
Piston
Oil Hole Toward Exhaust Side
Connecting Rod
Oil Ring
120 Degrees
Lower Compression Ring
FRONT OF ENGINE
Upper Compression Ring

109485

Courtesy of General Motors Corp.

Fig. 12: Installing Piston & Rings

ENGINE OILING

LUBRICATION SYSTEM

Crankshaft-driven oil pump forces pressurized oil through oil filter to main gallery. A by-pass valve in engine block allows continuous oil flow in case oil filter is restricted. Oil is distributed from gallery to crankshaft and timing chain hydraulic tensioner. *See Fig. 13.*

Connecting rod bearings are oiled by passages through crankshaft. Piston cooling is provided through an oil cooling hole in connecting rod. Oil passes through oil flow check valve into cylinder head and then into each camshaft housing. Cast passages feed each valve lifter and drilled passages feed each camshaft bearing surface.

Crankcase Capacity – Oil capacity is 4 qts. (3.8L) without oil filter.

Normal Oil Pressure – Oil pressure should be at least 15 psi (1.05 kg/cm²) at 900 RPM or 30 psi (2.11 kg/cm²) at 2000 RPM with engine at normal operating temperature.

OIL PUMP

Removal – Remove oil pan. See OIL PAN under REMOVAL & INSTALLATION in this article. Remove oil pump and screen bolts and nut. Remove oil pump and shims (if required).

Disassembly & Inspection – 1) Remove oil pump screen and gerotor (oil pump) cover. Remove pressure regulator valve. Remove gerotor pump.

CAUTION: DO NOT remove drive gear and shaft from pump housing.

2) Inspect components for flaking or damage. Measure outer gerotor cavity depth. Measure outer gerotor diameter, thickness and tip clearance between both gerotors. Replace pump assembly if clearances are not within specification. See OIL PUMP SPECIFICATIONS table.

OIL PUMP SPECIFICATIONS

Application	In. (mm)
Cavity Depth	.6736-.6756 (17.109-17.160)
Cavity Diameter	2.1273-2.1292 (54.033-54.082)
Maximum Gerotor Tip Clearance	.006 (.15)
Outer Gerotor	
Outside Diameter Clearance	.0013-.0052 (.033-.132)
Thickness	.6727-.6731 (17.087-17.097)

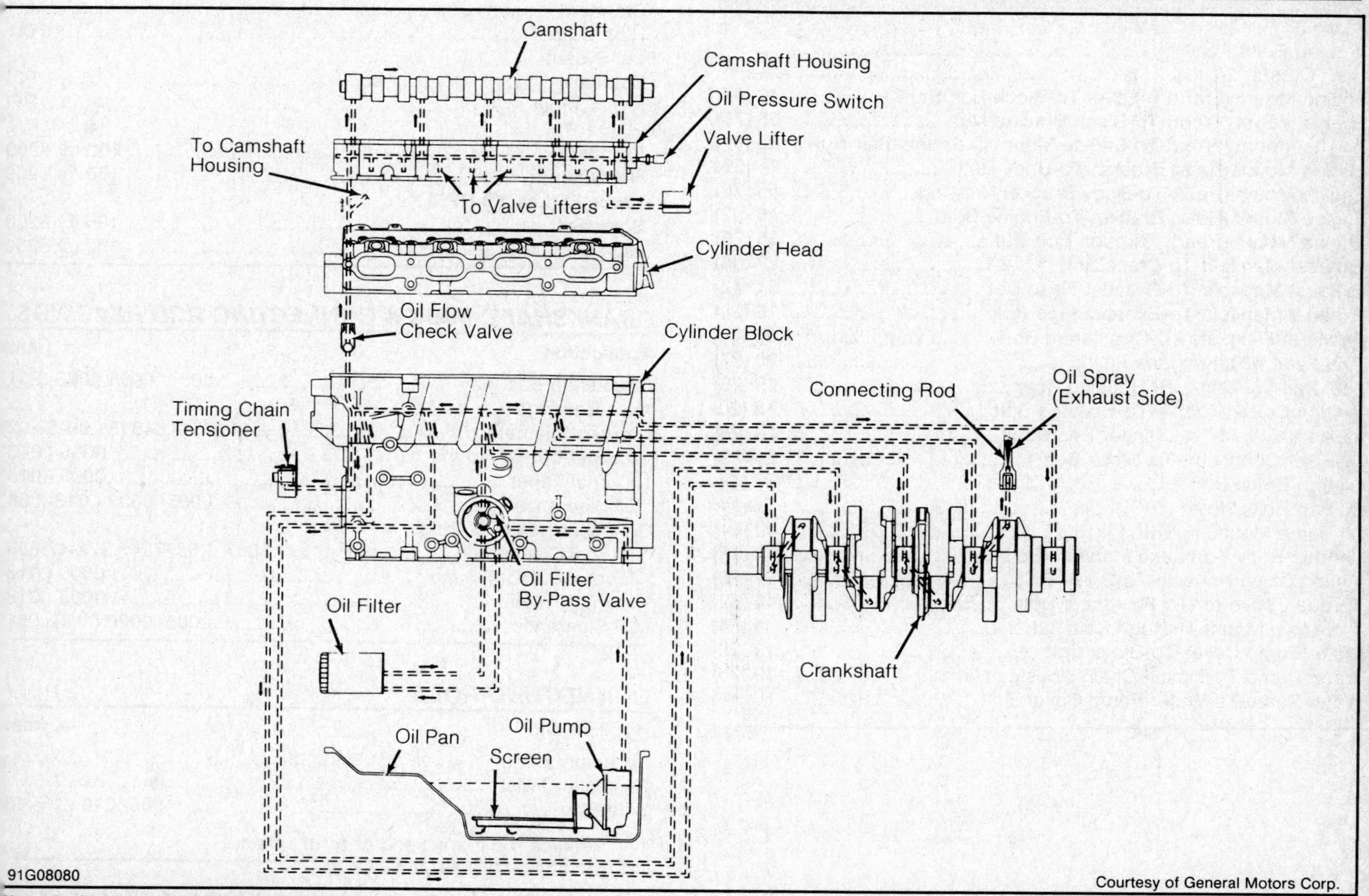

Camshaft
Camshaft Housing
Oil Pressure Switch
To Camshaft Housing
Valve Lifter
To Valve Lifters
Cylinder Head
Oil Flow Check Valve
Cylinder Block
Connecting Rod
Oil Spray (Exhaust Side)
Timing Chain Tensioner
Oil Filter By-Pass Valve
Oil Filter
Crankshaft
Oil Pan
Oil Pump Screen

91G08080

Courtesy of General Motors Corp.

Fig. 13: Engine Lubrication System

Reassembly & Installation – Coat components with oil prior to reassembly. To reassemble, reverse disassembly procedure. For installation procedure, see procedure under OIL PUMP DRIVE GEAR BACKLASH in this article.

OIL PUMP DRIVE GEAR BACKLASH

1) With oil pump removed from engine, remove driven gear cover and screen assembly from oil pump. Install oil pump on block. Tighten bolts to specification. See TORQUE SPECIFICATIONS at end of this article. Install dial indicator on cylinder block with stem resting against tooth on drive gear on oil pump.
2) Measure oil pump drive gear backlash. Ensure crankshaft does not rotate. Oil pump drive gear backlash should be .0091-.0201" (.231-.511 mm). Add or remove shims to obtain correct backlash.
3) Remove oil pump. Reinstall driven gear cover and screen assembly to pump. Install oil baffle (if removed). Reinstall oil pump assembly.

TORQUE SPECIFICATIONS

TORQUE SPECIFICATIONS

Application	Ft. Lbs. (N.m)
Camshaft Housing Bolt [1]	
Step 1	11 (15)
Step 2	
Bolts 1-10	[2]
Bolts 11 & 12	[2]
Camshaft Sprocket Bolt	[1] 40 (54)
Connecting Rod Nut	[3] 18 (24)
Crankshaft Balancer-To-Crankshaft Bolt	[4] 74 (100)
Crankshaft Bearing Cap Bolt	[4] 15 (20)
Cylinder Head Bolt [5]	
Step 1	26 (35)
Step 2	
Head Bolts 7 & 9	[6]
All Others	[7]
Engine Mount (Front) Bracket-To-Block Bolt/Stud	40 (54)
Engine Mount (Front)-To-Block Bracket Nut	55 (75)
Engine Mount (Front)-To-Engine Mount Crossmember Nut	30 (41)
Engine Mount (Rear) Bracket-To-Body Bolt	44 (59)
Engine Mount (Rear)-To-Body Bracket Nut	55 (75)
Engine Mount (Rear) Bracket-To-Engine Bolt	46 (62)
Engine Mount (Rear), Through Bolt Nut	55 (75)
Exhaust Manifold-To-Brace Bolt	22 (30)
Exhaust Manifold-To-Cylinder Head Bolt	31 (42)
Exhaust Manifold-To-Exhaust Pipe Bolt	18 (24)
Flywheel/Flexplate-To-Crankshaft Bolt	[1] [8] 22 (30)
Fuel Feed & Return Line Fitting	20 (27)
Fuel Rail-To-Camshaft Housing Bolt	19 (26)
Ignition Coil & Module-To-Housing Bolt	[1] 15 (20)
Intake Manifold-To-Cylinder Head Bolt	18 (24)
Oil Filter Connector-To-Block Bolt	21 (29)
Oil Pan Baffle Bolt	30 (41)
Oil Pan Bolts/Nuts	[9]
Oil Pump Mounting Bolt	40 (54)
Throttle Body-To-Intake Manifold Bolt	19 (26)
Timing Chain Housing-To-Block Bolt	19 (26)
Torque Converter-To-Flex Plate Bolt	46 (62)
Transaxle Mount Through Bolt/Nut	40 (54)
Water Pump Cover-To-Block Bolt	19 (26)
Water Pump-To-Timing Chain Housing Nut	19 (26)
Water Pump-To-Water Pump Cover Bolt	10 (14)

TORQUE SPECIFICATIONS (Cont.)

Application	INCH Lbs. (N.m)
Front Timing Case Cover Bolt	106 (12)
Oil/Air Separator-To-Intake Manifold Bolt	72 (8)
Oil Pump Cover-To-Oil Pump Body Bolt	106 (12)
Oil Pump Screen-To-Brace Bolt	106 (12)
Rear Crankshaft Seal Housing-To-Cylinder Block Bolt	106 (12)
Timing Chain Tensioner-To-Housing & Cylinder Block Bolt	115 (13)

[1] – Apply thread sealant on bolts.
[2] – Tighten bolts No. 1-10 an additional 75 degrees. Tighten bolts No. 11 & 12 an additional 25 degrees. See Fig. 5.
[3] – Tighten an additional 80 degrees.
[4] – Tighten an additional 90 degrees.
[5] – Tighten in proper sequence. See Fig. 6.
[6] – Tighten an additional 100 degrees.
[7] – Tighten an additional 110 degrees.
[8] – Tighten an additional 45 degrees.
[9] – See OIL PAN under REMOVAL & INSTALLATION for tightening specifications.

ENGINE SPECIFICATIONS

GENERAL SPECIFICATIONS

Application	Specification
Displacement	138 Cu. In. (2.3L)
Bore	3.62" (92.0 mm)
Stroke	3.35" (85.0 mm)
Compression Ratio	
Standard	9.5:1
High Output	10.0:1
Fuel System	
Standard	PFI
High Output	PFI
HP @ RPM	
Standard	160 @ 6200
High Output	180 @ 6200
Torque Ft. Lbs. @ RPM	
Standard	155 @ 5200
High Output	160 @ 5200

CRANKSHAFT, MAIN & CONNECTING ROD BEARINGS

Application	In. (mm)
Crankshaft End Play	.0034-.0095 (.086-.241)
Main Bearings	
Journal Diameter	2.047-2.048 (51.99-52.02)
Journal Out-Of-Round	.0005 (.013)
Journal Taper	.0005 (.013)
Oil Clearance	.0005-.0023 (.013-.058)
Connecting Rod Bearings	
Journal Diameter	1.8887-1.8897 (47.972-47.988)
Journal Out-Of-Round	.0005 (.013)
Journal Taper	.0005 (.013)
Oil Clearance	.0005-.0020 (.013-.051)

CONNECTING RODS

Application	In. (mm)
Maximum Bend	
Maximum Twist	
Side Play	.006-.018 (.15-.46)

[1] – Replace rod if any bend or twist exists.

PISTONS, PINS & RINGS

Application	In. (mm)
Pistons	
Clearance	.0007-.0020 (.019-.051)
Diameter	3.6203-3.6210 (91.957-91.973)
Pins	
Bore Diameter	
Standard	.8662-.8664 (22.002-22.006)
High Output	.8664-.8666 (22.008-22.012)
Piston Fit	
Standard	.00007-.00043 (.0018-.0109)
High Output	.0003-.0006 (.008-.015)
Rod Fit	.0003-.0012 (.007-.031)
Rings	
No. 1	
End Gap	.014-.024 (.35-.60)
Side Clearance	
Standard	.002-.004 (.05-.10)
High Output	.003-.005 (.07-.12)
No. 2	
End Gap	.016-.026 (.40-.65)
Side Clearance	.0016-.0032 (.040-.080)
No. 3 (Oil)	
End Gap	.016-.055 (.40-1.40)

CYLINDER BLOCK

Application	In. (mm)
Cylinder Bore	
Diameter	3.6217-3.6223 (91.992-92.008)
Maximum Taper [1]	.0003 (.008)
Maximum Out-Of-Round	.0004 (.010)

[1] – Measured 4.173" (106 mm) down from top of piston.

VALVES & VALVE SPRINGS

Application	Specification
Intake Valves	
Face Angle	44°
Head Diameter	1.418-1.442" (36.02-36.63 mm)
Minimum Margin	.010" (.25 mm)
Stem Diameter	.2751-.2744" (6.988-6.970 mm)
Exhaust Valves	
Face Angle	44.5°
Head Diameter	
Standard	1.1764-1.1866" (29.881-30.140 mm)
High Output	1.2350-1.2453" (31.369-31.631 mm)
Minimum Margin	.010" (.25 mm)
Stem Diameter	.2740-.2747" (6.959-6.977 mm)
Valve Springs	
Installed Height	1.437" (36.50 mm)
Pressure	Lbs. @ In. (Kg @ mm)
Valve Closed	71-79 @ 1.437 (32-36 @ 36.50)
Valve Open	193-207 @ 1.043 (88-94 @ 26.08)

CYLINDER HEAD

Application	Specification
Maximum Warpage	.008" (.20 mm)
Valve Seats	
Intake Valve	
Seat Angle	45°
Seat Width	.037-.075" (.94-1.90 mm)
Exhaust Valve	
Seat Angle	45°
Seat Width	.037-.075" (.94-1.90 mm)
Valve Guides	
Intake Valve	
Valve Guide Oil Clearance	.0010-.0027" (.025-.069 mm)
Exhaust Valve	
Valve Guide Oil Clearance	.0015-.0032" (.038-.081 mm)

CAMSHAFT

Application	In. (mm)
End Play	.0009-.0088 (.023-.224)
Journal Diameter	
No. 1	1.5720-1.5728 (39.93-39.95)
Nos. 2-5	1.3751-1.3760 (34.93-34.95)
Lobe Lift	
Standard	
Intake & Exhaust	.375 (9.525)
High Output	
Intake & Exhaust	.410 (10.414)
Oil Clearance	.0019-.0043 (.048-.109)

VALVE LIFTERS

Application	In. (mm)
Bore Diameter	1.3775-1.3787 (34.989-35.019)
Lifter Diameter	1.3763-1.3770 (34.959-34.975)
Oil Clearance	.0006-.0024 (.015-.061)

1991 ENGINES
2.5L 4-Cylinder

**Century, Cutlass Calais, Cutlass Ciera,
Cutlass Cruiser, Grand Am,
Lumina, Skylark, 6000**

NOTE: For repair procedures not covered in this article, see ENGINE OVERHAUL PROCEDURES article in GENERAL INFORMATION.

ENGINE IDENTIFICATION

Engine may be identified by using Vehicle Identification Number (VIN) stamped on a metal pad, located near lower left corner of windshield. The eighth character identifies the engine model.

Engine identification code, located on cylinder block, may be required when ordering replacement parts (if needed). *See Fig. 1.*

ENGINE IDENTIFICATION CODES

Engine	Code
2.5L (151") TBI	
8th Character of Dash VIN	R or U
Engine Code	
VIN R	LR8
VIN U	L68

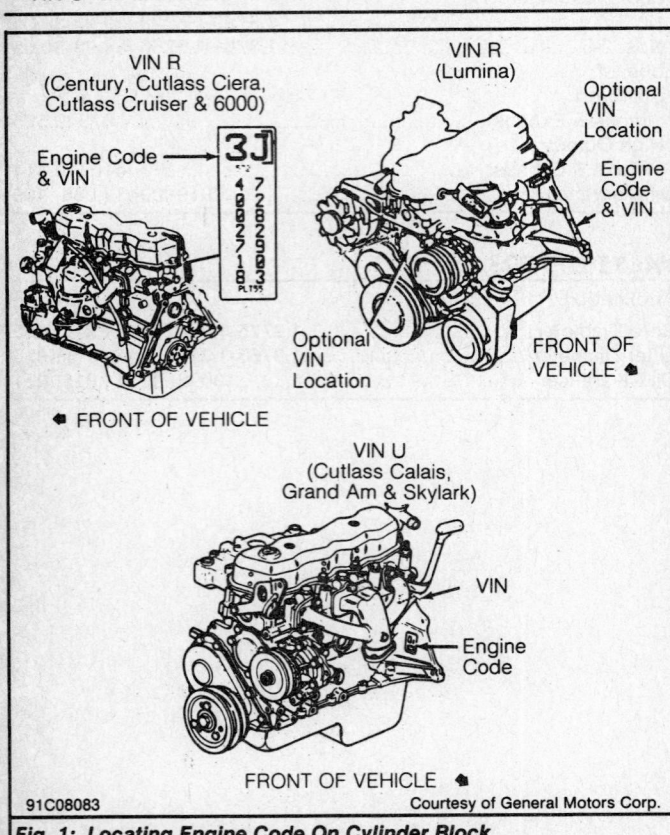

VIN R
(Century, Cutlass Ciera,
Cutlass Cruiser & 6000)

Engine Code & VIN

3J
4 7
0 0 2
8 2
2 5 0
7 1 8
0 3

◄ FRONT OF VEHICLE

VIN R
(Lumina)

Optional VIN Location

Engine Code & VIN

Optional VIN Location

FRONT OF VEHICLE ◄

VIN U
(Cutlass Calais,
Grand Am & Skylark)

VIN

Engine Code

FRONT OF VEHICLE ◄

91C08083   Courtesy of General Motors Corp.

Fig. 1: Locating Engine Code On Cylinder Block

ADJUSTMENTS

VALVE CLEARANCE ADJUSTMENT

No valve adjustment is required, as hydraulic valve lifters are used.

REMOVAL & INSTALLATION

NOTE: For reassembly reference, label all electrical connectors, vacuum hoses and fuel lines before removal. Also place mating marks on engine hood and other major assemblies before removal.

FUEL PRESSURE RELEASE

Loosen fuel tank filler cap to release tank pressure. Remove fuel pump fuse. Operate engine until it stalls. Crank engine for an additional 3 seconds to release residual line pressure. Reinstall fuel pump fuse with ignition off. Disconnect negative battery cable.

ENGINE

CAUTION: Relieve fuel pressure. See FUEL PRESSURE RELEASE under REMOVAL & INSTALLATION in this article.

Removal (Century, Cutlass Ciera, Cutlass Cruiser & 6000) – **1)** Disconnect battery cables. Remove hood. Drain cooling system and disconnect radiator hoses. Remove air cleaner. Disconnect engine wiring harness connector. Disconnect vacuum and heater hoses. Remove A/C compressor with hoses attached and place aside.

NOTE: On Century, Cutlass Ciera, Cutlass Cruiser and 6000 models, engine only is lifted from engine compartment. Transaxle is removed separately from below vehicle.

2) Remove engine torque strut. Disconnect throttle and transaxle linkage. Remove transaxle-to-engine bolts, except 2 upper bolts. Remove front mount-to-cradle nuts. Remove forward exhaust pipe. Remove converter housing cover or flywheel inspection cover. On A/T models, remove converter-to-flexplate bolts. On all models, remove starter motor.
3) Remove power steering pump (if equipped) with hoses attached and position aside. Remove rear transaxle support bracket bolts. Disconnect fuel line at fuel filter.
4) Position jack with wood block under transaxle, and raise engine and transaxle until front engine mount studs clear cradle. Support engine weight with lift equipment. Remove upper transaxle-to-engine bolts. Remove engine.
Installation – **1)** To install, reverse removal procedure. With engine off, fill radiator until level is even with filler neck. Run engine until upper radiator hose is hot. Add coolant as necessary.
2) After 5 minutes, add coolant to base of filler neck and install cap. Allow engine to cool, and then add coolant to recovery reservoir to ADD or FULL COLD mark. Install cap.
Removal (Cutlass Calais, Grand Am & Skylark) – **1)** Disconnect battery cables. Drain cooling system and disconnect radiator hoses. Remove air cleaner. Disconnect ECM connectors, route through firewall and lay harness across engine. Disconnect vacuum, radiator and heater hoses.

NOTE: On Cutlass Calais, Grand Am and Skylark models, engine and transaxle assembly are removed from below vehicle.

2) Recover refrigerant from A/C system. Hoist vehicle. Remove A/C compressor and brackets. Remove power steering pump with hoses attached, and wire out of way. Remove front and rear transaxle struts. Remove fuel lines.
3) Remove shift linkage. On A/T models, disconnect transaxle cooler lines and downshift cable. On all models, disconnect throttle cable at throttle body. Disconnect engine ground cable. Remove multiple relay bracket. Remove power steering line bracket. Remove tire and wheel assembly. Remove brake calipers and rotors.
4) Remove knuckle-to-strut bolts. Disconnect exhaust pipe from manifold and hangers, and wire out of way. Remove body-to-frame bolts at lower control arm and loosen remaining body-to-frame bolts. Remove bolts from frame, leaving one in each corner.
5) Support front of vehicle by placing 2 jack stands under front of body. Move hoist back to body pan and place a 6 foot long 4" x 4" block between hoist and vehicle. Raise hoist and remove jack stands.
6) Position 4-wheel dolly under transaxle assembly with 4" x 4" x 12" blocks as support. Lower vehicle and engine/transaxle to rest on dolly. Remove engine mount bolts and right front bracket. Remove remaining frame-to-body bolts. Raise vehicle from engine/transaxle assembly. Separate engine from transaxle.

Installation – 1) To install, reverse removal procedure. Check all fluid levels. With engine off, fill surge tank until level is even with base of filler neck. Run engine until upper radiator hose is hot.

2) Stop engine and observe coolant level in surge tank. If coolant level is not above FULL line, carefully remove pressure cap and add coolant as necessary. Install cap.

Removal (Lumina) – 1) Disconnect battery cables. Drain coolant. Remove air cleaner assembly. Remove hood. Disconnect engine harness connector. Disconnect vacuum, radiator and heater hoses. Remove A/C compressor with hoses attached, and position aside.

NOTE: On Lumina models, engine only is lifted from engine compartment. Transaxle is removed separately from below vehicle.

2) Remove alternator and bracket. Remove engine torque strut. Disconnect throttle and transaxle linkage. Remove engine-to-transaxle bolts, except 2 upper bolts.

3) Install Engine Support Fixture (J-28467-A) and Engine Support Adapter (J-36462). Raise vehicle. Remove engine mount-to-frame nuts. Disconnect exhaust pipe and position aside. Remove torque converter cover. Remove torque flexplate-to-torque converter bolts. Remove starter motor. Remove power steering pump with hoses attached, and position aside. Disconnect fuel line.

4) Support transaxle. Remove 2 remaining engine-to-transaxle bolts and rear support bracket. Remove transaxle from engine. Lower vehicle. Attach engine hoist and remove engine.

Installation – 1) To install, reverse removal procedure. With engine off, fill thermostat housing until level is even with base of radiator neck. Install radiator cap. Continue to fill thermostat housing until level is 1/2" below top of thermostat housing.

2) Install thermostat and thermostat housing cap. Fill coolant recovery reservoir to 1 1/4" above HOT mark. Run engine 5 minutes. Check coolant level in reservoir tank. Add coolant to HOT mark.

INTAKE MANIFOLD

Removal – 1) Release fuel pressure. See FUEL PRESSURE RELEASE under REMOVAL & INSTALLATION in this article. Disconnect negative battery cable. Remove air cleaner, PCV valve and hose. Drain cooling system.

2) On Lumina models, disconnect MAP sensor electrical connector. On all models, separate all electrical connections, fuel lines and vacuum lines from TBI assembly.

3) Disconnect throttle linkage, transaxle downshift linkage and cruise control linkage (if equipped). Remove throttle and T.V. cables. Remove heater hose at intake manifold. Remove intake manifold retaining bolts and manifold.

Installation – To install, reverse removal procedure using new gasket. Tighten bolts to specification in proper sequence. *Fig. 2.* See TORQUE SPECIFICATIONS at end of article.

EXHAUST MANIFOLD

Removal & Installation – 1) Remove air cleaner assembly. Remove torque rod bolts at radiator panel and cylinder head. Remove torque rod bracket at cylinder head.

2) Remove alternator (if necessary). Remove oil dipstick tube. Remove oxygen sensor connector. Disconnect exhaust pipe at exhaust manifold. Remove exhaust manifold retaining tabs, bolts and exhaust manifold.

3) To install, reverse removal procedure using new gasket. Tighten bolts to specification in proper sequence. *See Fig. 2.* See TORQUE SPECIFICATIONS at end of article. Bend over lock tabs.

CYLINDER HEAD

Removal – 1) Release fuel pressure. See FUEL PRESSURE RELEASE in this article. Disconnect negative battery cable. Remove air cleaner and drain cooling system. Disconnect heater hose from intake manifold. Disconnect electrical connections, throttle linkage and fuel lines from TBI assembly. Remove oil dipstick tube and disconnect oxygen sensor connector.

2) Disconnect exhaust pipe at manifold. Remove exhaust manifold (if necessary). See EXHAUST MANIFOLD under REMOVAL & INSTALLATION in this article. Remove electrical connections and vacuum hoses from intake manifold and cylinder head.

3) Remove engine strut rod from upper support (if necessary). Remove A/C compressor and position aside with hoses attached. Remove alternator and upper power steering pump brackets. Remove radiator hoses and valve cover.

4) Remove rocker arms and push rods. See ROCKER ARMS & PUSH RODS under REMOVAL & INSTALLATION in this article. Remove cylinder head bolts and cylinder head.

Inspection – Inspect cylinder head for warpage. See CYLINDER HEAD under OVERHAUL in this article.

Installation – 1) Ensure cylinder head bolt threads and cylinder block holes are clean. Install new gasket over dowel pins and ensure all holes align with cylinder block.

2) Install cylinder head with all bolts finger tight. Tighten all bolts in sequence to 18 ft. lbs. (24 N.m). *See Fig. 3.* Then tighten all bolts EXCEPT No. 9 to 26 ft. lbs. (35 N.m). Tighten bolt No. 9 to 18 ft. lbs. (24 N.m).

3) Repeat sequence, tightening all bolts an additional 1/4 turn (90 degrees). To install remaining components, reverse removal procedure.

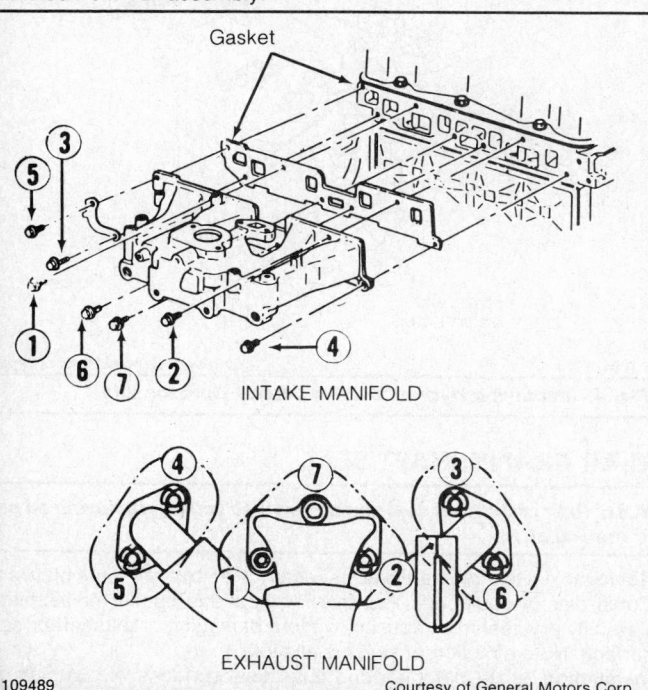

Fig. 2: Intake & Exhaust Manifold Bolt Torque Sequence

Courtesy of General Motors Corp.

109489

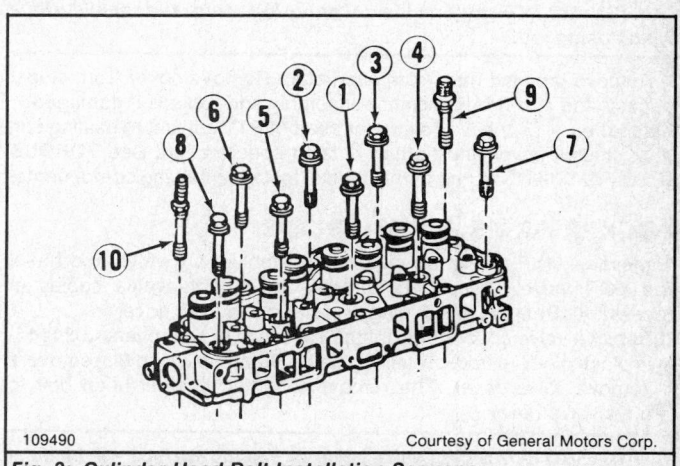

109490

Courtesy of General Motors Corp.

Fig. 3: Cylinder Head Bolt Installation Sequence

FRONT TIMING CASE COVER

Removal – 1) Disconnect negative battery cable. Remove accessory drive belts and belt tensioner. Remove right fender splash shield and right front wheel. Remove crankshaft pulley.

2) Remove alternator lower bracket, and front engine mount and bracket (if necessary). If front engine mount requires removal, remove engine mount-to-cradle nuts. Support engine with Support Fixture (J-28467) and remove front engine mount and bracket. Remove bolts and front timing case cover.

Installation – 1) Apply a 3/8" wide by 3/16" thick bead of RTV sealant at oil pan and cover sealing surface. Apply a 1/4" wide by 1/8" thick bead of RTV sealant at cylinder block and cover sealing surfaces.

2) Install Seal Installer (J-34995) in front timing case cover front seal. Install front cover on cylinder block. Install and partially tighten 2 opposing retaining bolts.

3) Install remaining front cover-to-block bolts. Starting with bottom bolt and moving counterclockwise, tighten all bolts to specification. See TORQUE SPECIFICATIONS at end of this article. Remove seal installer. To install remaining components, reverse removal procedure.

FRONT CRANKSHAFT SEAL

Removal & Installation – Remove front timing case cover. See FRONT TIMING CASE COVER under REMOVAL & INSTALLATION in this article. Pry seal from cover. Note direction of seal installation. To install, use Seal Installer (J-34995) and install seal. To complete installation, reverse removal procedure.

TIMING GEARS

Removal – Remove front timing case cover. See FRONT TIMING CASE COVER under REMOVAL & INSTALLATION in this article. Align timing marks. See Fig. 6. Remove cam sprocket bolt, timing chain and sprockets.

Installation – Install timing chain and sprockets. Align timing marks with engine at TDC. See Fig. 6. Install cam sprocket bolt and tighten to specification. See TORQUE SPECIFICATIONS at end of this article. To install remaining components, reverse removal procedure.

PUSH ROD SIDE COVER

NOTE: On some models, frame may need to be lowered away from body to allow access for side cover removal.

Removal – 1) Raise and support vehicle. Disconnect engine wiring harness clips (if equipped). Remove side cover nuts. Reinstall 2 nuts with washers facing outward on inner 2 studs.

2) Install 2 remaining nuts on same 2 inner studs with washers facing inward. Using a small wrench on inner nuts, jam 2 nuts tightly together. Unscrew studs with inner nut until cover breaks loose.

CAUTION: DO NOT pry on side cover during removal or seal surface will be damaged.

3) Remove jammed nuts from each stud. Remove cover from studs. Inspect stud and rubber washer assembly and replace if damaged.

Installation – Apply 3/16" diameter bead of RTV sealant to sealing surfaces. Install cover and tighten nuts to specification. See TORQUE SPECIFICATIONS at end of this article. Install remaining components.

ROCKER ARMS & PUSH RODS

Removal – 1) Remove air cleaner assembly, PCV valve and hose, and EGR valve. Disconnect throttle and throttle valve cables (if necessary). Remove spark plug wires and clip from cover.

2) Remove valve cover bolts. Install Valve Cover Removers (J-34144-A) in place of valve cover retaining bolts. Rotate valve cover removers to remove valve cover. The removers tighten against head bolt to remove valve cover.

CAUTION: DO NOT pry on valve cover or sealing surface will be damaged.

3) Remove rocker arm bolt and ball. Remove rocker arm, push rod and guide. Mark component location for reassembly reference.

CAUTION: Push rod guides are different style and must be installed in original locations.

Installation – 1) To install, reverse removal procedure. If installing new rocker arms or balls, coat components with Molykote prior to installation. Ensure push rods are seated in hydraulic lifters.

2) Install valve cover and gasket. Starting with center bolts and circling outward, tighten cover bolts to specification. See TORQUE SPECIFICATIONS at end of this article. To install remaining components, reverse removal procedure.

HYDRAULIC VALVE LIFTERS

Removal – 1) Remove valve cover bolts. Install Valve Cover Removers (J-34144-A) in place of valve cover retaining bolts. Rotate valve cover removers to remove valve cover. The removers tighten against head bolt to remove valve cover.

CAUTION: DO NOT pry on valve cover or seal surface will be damaged.

2) Remove intake manifold. See INTAKE MANIFOLD under REMOVAL & INSTALLATION in this article. Remove push rod side cover. See PUSH ROD SIDE COVER under REMOVAL & INSTALLATION in this article.

3) Loosen rocker arm and rotate for clearance from push rod. Remove push rod, lifter retainer, guide and lifter. See Fig. 4. Mark component location for reassembly reference.

Inspection – Measure lifter O.D. and determine lifter oil clearance. Replace components if not within specification. See VALVE LIFTERS table in ENGINE SPECIFICATIONS at end of article.

Installation – Lubricate lifter surfaces with oil and install in bore. To install, reverse removal procedure. Tighten rocker arm bolt to specification with lifter on base circle of camshaft. See TORQUE SPECIFICATIONS at end of this article. Install remaining components.

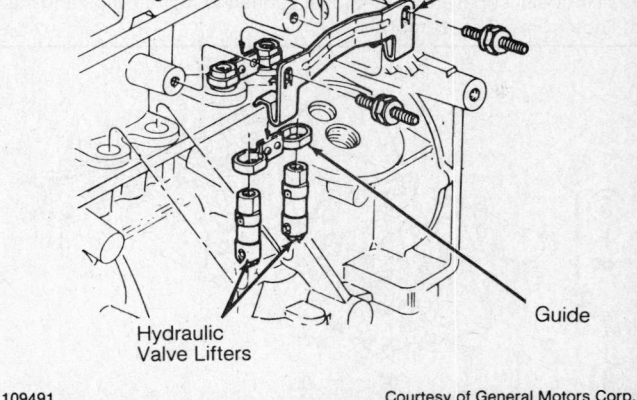

109491   Courtesy of General Motors Corp.

Fig. 4: Identifying Hydraulic Valve Lifter & Components

REAR CRANKSHAFT SEAL

NOTE: Rear crankshaft seal can be serviced without removing oil pan or crankshaft.

Removal – Remove transaxle assembly. Remove pressure plate and clutch disc (if equipped). Remove flywheel and spacer or flexplate. Carefully pry seal from housing without damaging crankshaft or seal surface. Note direction of seal installation.

Installation – 1) Coat inner and outer seal surfaces with engine oil. Using Seal Installer (J-34924-A), install seal.

2) To install remaining components, reverse removal procedure. Ensure flywheel or flexplate bolts and crankshaft threads are clean. Apply thread sealant to flywheel or flexplate bolts prior to installation.

CRANKSHAFT FORCE BALANCER ASSEMBLY

Removal – Remove oil pan. See OIL PAN under REMOVAL & INSTALLATION in this article. Remove balancer assembly bolts and balancer assembly. *See Fig. 5.*

Installation – **1)** Rotate crankshaft to TDC on No. 1 or No. 4 cylinders. Fourth crankshaft counterweight (from the front) should be at BDC. Install balancer assembly on crankshaft with fourth balancer weight at BDC (plus or minus one half gear tooth).

CAUTION: To provide correct gear contact, ensure end of balancer assembly housing without dowel pins remains in contact with cylinder block surface during installation. Crankshaft or balancer assembly gear damage will result if housing fails to remain in contact with cylinder block.

2) Install all retaining bolts. Tighten bolts in sequence to 108 INCH lbs. (12 N.m). *See Fig. 5.* Using proper sequence, tighten the short bolts to 11 ft. lbs. (15 N.m) plus an additional 75 degrees and the long bolts to 11 ft. lbs. (15 N.m) plus an additional 90 degrees. Install oil pan.

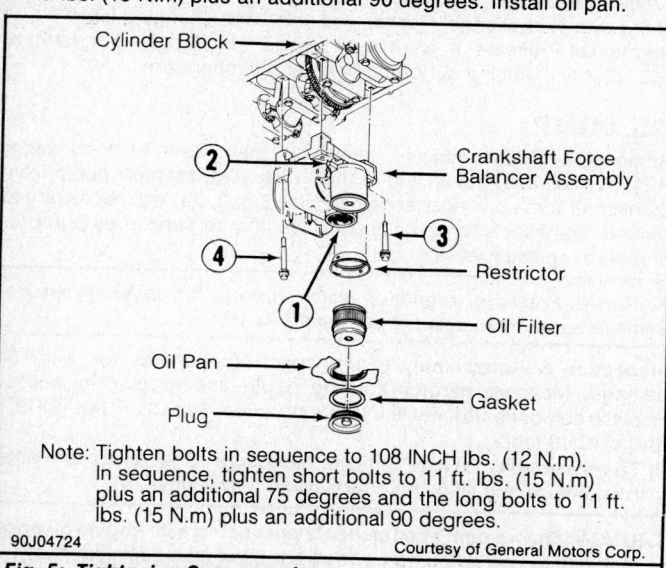

Note: Tighten bolts in sequence to 108 INCH lbs. (12 N.m). In sequence, tighten short bolts to 11 ft. lbs. (15 N.m) plus an additional 75 degrees and the long bolts to 11 ft. lbs. (15 N.m) plus an additional 90 degrees.

90J04724　　　　　Courtesy of General Motors Corp.

Fig. 5: Tightening Sequence for Crankshaft Force Balancer Assembly Bolts

CAMSHAFT

Removal – **1)** Remove engine from vehicle. See ENGINE under REMOVAL & INSTALLATION in this article. With engine removed, remove rocker arms and push rods. See ROCKER ARMS & PUSH RODS under REMOVAL & INSTALLATION in this article.

2) Remove hydraulic valve lifters. See HYDRAULIC VALVE LIFTERS under REMOVAL & INSTALLATION in this article. Remove front timing case cover. See FRONT TIMING CASE COVER under REMOVAL & INSTALLATION in this article.

3) Align timing marks. *See Fig. 6.* Remove timing chain, sprockets and thrust plate. Remove camshaft and bearings (if required).

CAUTION: All camshaft journals are the same diameter. Carefully remove camshaft to avoid damaging cam bearings.

Inspection – Inspect camshaft journal diameter, lobe lift and oil clearance. See CAMSHAFT table in ENGINE SPECIFICATIONS at end of article. Replace components if not within specification.

Installation – **1)** Install camshaft bearings (if removed). Ensure oil holes are aligned. Coat camshaft journals and bearings with Engine Oil Supplement (1052367) prior to installation.

2) Install camshaft and camshaft thrust plate. Install timing chain and sprockets. Align timing marks with engine at TDC. *See Fig. 6.* Install

cam sprocket bolt and tighten to 43 ft. lbs. (58 N.m). To install remaining components, reverse removal procedure.

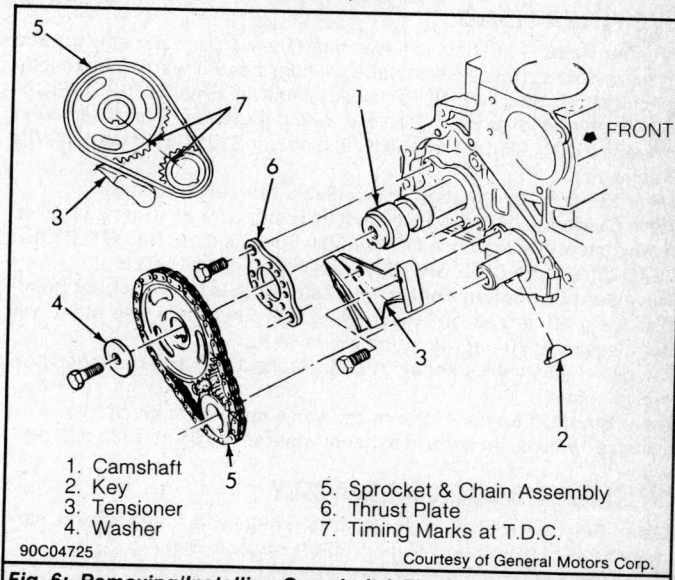

1. Camshaft
2. Key
3. Tensioner
4. Washer
5. Sprocket & Chain Assembly
6. Thrust Plate
7. Timing Marks at T.D.C.

90C04725　　　　　Courtesy of General Motors Corp.

Fig. 6: Removing/Installing Camshaft & Timing Chain Assembly

WATER PUMP

Removal – Disconnect negative battery cable. On VIN R (engine code LR8) engines, remove alternator. On all engines, drain cooling system. Remove drive belts. Remove water pump bolts and water pump.

Installation – **1)** If installing new pump with old pulley, remove pulley from old pump using Pulley Remover (J-25034-B). Install pulley on new pump using Pulley Installer (J-25033-B).

2) Apply 1/8" bead of RTV sealant to pump sealing surface. Apply RTV sealant to water pump bolts. Tighten bolts to specification. See TORQUE SPECIFICATIONS at end of this article. To install, reverse removal procedure.

OIL PAN

Removal (Century, Cutlass Ciera, Cutlass Cruiser, Lumina & 6000) – **1)** Disconnect negative battery cable. Remove coolant reservoir and engine torque strut. Remove drive belt, dipstick assembly, air cleaner and air inlet. Remove A/C compressor, and wire out of way. Install Engine Support Fixture (J-28467-A).

2) Raise and support vehicle. Drain crankcase. Remove flexplate covers, starter and bracket. Remove engine wiring harness under right and left sides of oil pan. Remove right side engine splash shield.

3) Remove front engine mount bracket bolts and engine mount nuts. Remove transaxle mount nuts. Using engine support fixture, raise engine approximately 2". Remove front engine mount and bracket. Loosen frame bolts. Remove oil pan bolts and oil pan.

Installation – Apply sealant to pan before installation. Install oil pan and bolts. Tighten bolts to specification. Reverse removal procedure for remaining components. See TORQUE SPECIFICATIONS at end of this article.

Removal (Cutlass Calais, Grand Am & Skylark) – Disconnect negative battery cable. Raise and support vehicle. Drain crankcase. Disconnect exhaust pipe at manifold and hanger, and wire out of way. Remove starter and flexplate access cover. Remove starter. Remove oil pan bolts and oil pan.

Installation – Apply sealant to pan before installation. Install oil pan and bolts. Tighten bolts to specification. Reverse removal procedure for remaining components. See TORQUE SPECIFICATIONS at end of this article.

OVERHAUL

CYLINDER HEAD

Cylinder Head – Inspect cylinder head for warpage at deck surface and manifold surfaces. Resurface cylinder head if warpage exceeds specification. See CYLINDER HEAD table in ENGINE SPECIFICATIONS at end of article. Replace cylinder head if metal removed exceeds .010" (.25 mm) on VIN R engines and .012" (.30 mm) on VIN U engines.

Valve Seats – Information not available from manufacturer.

Valve Guides – Valve guides must be reamed for an oversized valve, if valve stem oil clearance is not within specification. See CYLINDER HEAD table in ENGINE SPECIFICATIONS at end of article.

Valve Seat Correction Angles – If seat width is too wide after grinding, use a 20-degree or 70-degree stone. The 20-degree stone will lower seat and 70-degree stone will raise it.

Valves – New valves should NOT be lapped. Lapping damages protective coating.

Valve Stem Oil Seals – Oversized valve stem oil seals are used for oversized valves. Intake and exhaust valve stem oil seals are different.

CYLINDER BLOCK ASSEMBLY

Piston Ring Installation – Install piston rings with identification mark toward top of piston and rings properly spaced. *See Fig. 7.*

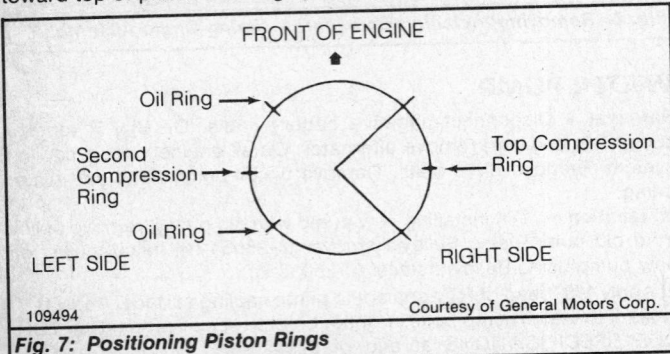

FRONT OF ENGINE

Oil Ring

Second Compression Ring

Oil Ring

Top Compression Ring

LEFT SIDE

RIGHT SIDE

109494

Courtesy of General Motors Corp.

Fig. 7: Positioning Piston Rings

NOTE: Mark piston position on connecting rod if removing piston from connecting rod. Information for connecting rod-to-piston positioning not available from manufacturer.

Piston & Rod Assembly – Piston must be installed in cylinder block with mark on top of the piston toward front of engine.

Fitting Pistons – Piston diameter should be measured 3/4" below center line of piston pin bore. Piston taper should be measured at the center and bottom of the piston skirt.

CAUTION: Manufacturer recommends seating bearing caps with leather or brass mallet BEFORE tightening bearing cap bolts.

Crankshaft & Bearings – Crankshaft thrust bearing thrust surface should be coated with Lubricant (1050169) prior to installation. With all bearings and caps installed and bolts loosely started, pry crankshaft toward rear of engine and then toward front of engine to align thrust bearing. Tighten main bearing cap bolts to specification. See TORQUE SPECIFICATIONS at end of this article.

CAUTION: Bearing inserts must not be shimmed, scraped or filed. DO NOT touch bearing surface with fingers.

Rod Bearings – 1) Ensure bearing cap bolt holes and mating surfaces are clean and dry. Use connecting rod stud protector on all rod cap bolts. Install inserts in connecting rod and cap.
2) Lubricate bearings and crank pin. Install bearing cap. Tighten rod bearing cap bolts to specification. See TORQUE SPECIFICATIONS at end of this article.

Crankshaft Flange Runout – 1) With engine removed and crankshaft installed, measure crankshaft flange runout. Mount dial indicator gauge plate flat against crankshaft flange. Place dial indicator stem on lower left transmission mounting bolt boss (flat area around bolt hole). Adjust indicator to zero.
2) Observe and record readings obtained on all mounting bolt hole bosses. Measurements should not vary more than .010" (.25 mm). If readings exceed specification, remount dial gauge plate and recheck flange runout. Replace crankshaft if runout exceeds specification.

Cylinder Block – Using feeler gauge and straightedge, inspect deck surface for warpage. Replace cylinder block if more than .010" (.25 mm) material is removed from deck surface.

ENGINE OILING

ENGINE LUBRICATION SYSTEM

The gerotor-type oil pump, driven by the crankshaft force balancer assembly, supplies pressurized oil to the internal passage on the right side of cylinder block. Internal passage intersects with the hydraulic lifter bosses, where oil flows to the main and camshaft bearings.

Oil is supplied to rocker arms and upper engine components through the drilled push rods. A by-pass valve is located in the oil filter mounting bracket. Oil pressure regulator valve is mounted in the oil pump body.

Crankcase Capacity – Engine oil capacity is approximately 4 qts. (3.8L) with filter change. Recheck oil level after changing filter.

Normal Oil Pressure – Normal oil pressure is 26 psi (1.8 kg/cm²) at 800 RPM with engine at normal operating temperature.

OIL PUMP

Removal & Disassembly – Remove oil pan. See OIL PAN under REMOVAL & INSTALLATION in this article. Disassemble pump from crankshaft force balancer assembly. *See Fig. 8.* It is not necessary to remove crankshaft force balancer assembly to service oil pump or pressure regulator valve.

WARNING: Pressure regulator valve spring is under pressure. Remove carefully to prevent personal injury.

Inspection & Reassembly – 1) Inspect components for wear or damage. Measure gerotor housing depth and gerotor thickness. Replace components if not within specification. See OIL PUMP SPECIFICATIONS table.
2) To reassemble, reverse removal procedure. Coat all components with engine oil and fill pump cavities with petroleum jelly.

CAUTION: Ensure pump components are coated with engine oil prior to installation and all pump cavities are filled with petroleum jelly.

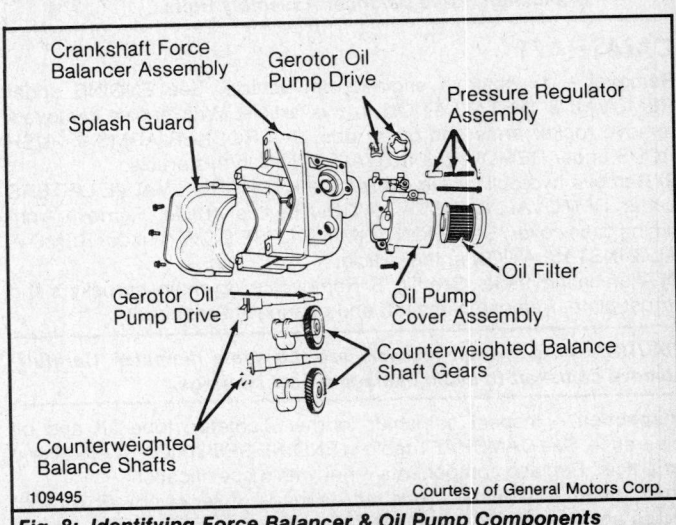

Crankshaft Force Balancer Assembly

Gerotor Oil Pump Drive

Pressure Regulator Assembly

Splash Guard

Oil Filter

Gerotor Oil Pump Drive

Oil Pump Cover Assembly

Counterweighted Balance Shaft Gears

Counterweighted Balance Shafts

109495

Courtesy of General Motors Corp.

Fig. 8: Identifying Force Balancer & Oil Pump Components

OIL PUMP SPECIFICATIONS

Application	In. (mm)
Gerotor Housing Depth	.514-.516 (13.05-13.11)
Gerotor Thickness	.511-.512 (12.97-13.00)

TORQUE SPECIFICATIONS

TORQUE SPECIFICATIONS

Application	Ft. Lbs. (N.m)
Camshaft Sprocket Bolt	43 (58)
Connecting Rod Nut	29 (40)
Crankshaft Pulley Bolt	162 (220)
Cylinder Head Bolt	[1]
Engine-To-Bracket Bolt	40 (54)
Engine Mount-To-Frame Nut	35 (47)
Engine Mount-To-Bracket Nut	35 (47)
Exhaust Manifold Bolt	[2]
Flywheel-To-Crankshaft Bolt	
A/T	[3] 55 (75)
M/T	[3] 69 (94)
Fuel Feed & Return Line Fitting	20 (27)
Intake Manifold Bolt	[4] 25 (34)
Main Bearing Cap Bolt	65 (88)
Rocker Arm Bolt	20 (27)
Thermostat Housing Bolt/Stud	20 (27)
Throttle Body-To-Manifold Bolt	18 (24)
Transaxle Mount-To-Frame Nut	33 (45)
Transaxle Mount-To-Bracket Nut	33 (45)
Water Pump-To-Block Bolt	[3] 25 (34)

Application	INCH Lbs. (N.m)
Camshaft Thrust Plate Bolt	90 (10)
Crankshaft Force Balancer-To-Block Bolt	[5]
Front Timing Case Cover Bolt	90 (10)
Oil Pan Bolt	90 (10)
Oil Pump Cover Bolt	90 (10)
Push Rod Side Cover Nut	90 (10)
Valve Cover Bolts	80 (9)
Valve Lifter Retainer-To-Block Bolt	90 (10)

[1] – Tighten all cylinder head bolts in sequence to 18 ft. lbs. (24 N.m). Then tighten all bolts except No. 9 to 26 ft. lbs. (35 N.m). See Fig. 3. Retighten bolt No. 9 to 18 ft. lbs. (24 N.m). Repeat sequence, tightening all bolts 1/4 turn (90 degrees).

[2] – Tighten bolts in sequence. See Fig. 2. Tighten 3 inner bolts to 37 ft. lbs. (51 N.m) and 4 outer bolts to 26 ft. lbs. (35 N.m).

[3] – Apply thread sealant to bolts.

[4] – Tighten bolts in sequence. See Fig. 2.

[5] – Tighten all bolts in sequence to 108 INCH lbs. (12 N.m). See Fig. 5. In sequence, tighten short bolts to 11 ft. lbs. (15 N.m) plus an additional 75 degrees. Tighten long bolts in sequence to 11 ft. lbs. (15 N.m) plus an additional 90 degrees.

ENGINE SPECIFICATIONS

GENERAL SPECIFICATIONS

Application	Specification
Displacement	2.5L (151 Cu. In.)
Bore	4.00" (101.6 mm)
Stroke	3.00" (76.2 mm)
Compression Ratio	8.3:1
Fuel System	TBI
Horsepower @ RPM	105 @ 4800
Torque Ft. Lbs. @ RPM	135 @ 5200

CRANKSHAFT, MAIN & CONNECTING ROD BEARINGS

Application	In. (mm)
Crankshaft End Play	
VIN R Engine	.0051-.0100 (.130-.254)
VIN U Engine	.0059-.0110 (.150-.279)
Main Bearings	
Journal Diameter	2.30 (58.4)
Journal Out-Of-Round	.0005 (.013)
Journal Taper	.0005 (.013)
Oil Clearance	.0005-.0022 (.013-.056)
Connecting Rod Bearings	
Journal Diameter	2.000 (50.80)
Journal Out-Of-Round	.0005 (.013)
Journal Taper	.0005 (.013)
Oil Clearance	.0005-.0030 (.013-.076)

CONNECTING RODS

Application	In. (mm)
Maximum Bend	[1] .010 (.25)
Maximum Twist	[2] .002 (.05)
Side Play	.0060-.0240 (.152-.610)

[1] – Bend per 3" of rod length.
[2] – Twist per inch of rod length.

PISTONS, PINS & RINGS

Application	In. (mm)
Pistons	
Clearance	.0014-.0022 (.036-.056)
Pins	
Diameter	.927-.928 (23.546-23.571)
Piston Fit	
VIN R Engine	.0003-.0005 (.008-.013)
VIN U Engine	.0004-.0006 (.010-.015)
Rod Fit	Press
Rings	
No. 1	
End Gap	.010-.020 (.25-.51)
Side Clearance	.002-.003 (.05-.08)
No. 2	
End Gap	.010-.020 (.25-.51)
Side Clearance	.001-.003 (.03-.08)
No. 3 (Oil)	
End Gap	.020-.060 (.51-1.52)
Side Clearance	.015-.055 (.38-1.40)

CYLINDER BLOCK

Application	In. (mm)
Cylinder Bore	
Diameter	4.00 (101.6)
Maximum Taper	.005 (.13)
Maximum Out-Of-Round	.001 (.03)

VALVES & VALVE SPRINGS

Application	Specification
Intake Valves	
Face Angle	45°
Exhaust Valves	
Face Angle	45°
Valve Springs	
Free Length	
VIN R Engine	2.01" (51.1 mm)
VIN U Engine	2.20" (55.9 mm)
Installed Height	1.68" (42.67 mm)
Pressure	Lbs. @ In. (Kg @ mm)
Valve Closed	75 @ 1.68 (34 @ 42.6)
Valve Open	173 @ 1.24 (79 @ 31.5)

1991 ENGINES
2.5L 4-Cylinder (Cont.)

CYLINDER HEAD

Application	Specification
Maximum Warpage	
VIN R Engine	.010" (.25 mm)
VIN U Engine	.012" (.30 mm)
Valve Seats	
Intake Valve	
Seat Angle	46°
Seat Width	.035-.075" (.89-1.91 mm)
Maximum Seat Runout	.002" (.05 mm)
Exhaust Valve	
Seat Angle	46°
Seat Width	.058-.105" (1.47-2.67 mm)
Maximum Seat Runout	.002" (.05 mm)
Valve Guides	
Intake Valve	
Valve Guide Oil Clearance	.0010-.0028" (.025-.071 mm)
Exhaust Valve	
Valve Guide Oil Clearance	.0013-.0041" (.030-.104 mm)

CAMSHAFT

Application	In. (mm)
End Play	
VIN R Engine	.0015-.0050 (.038-.127)
VIN U Engine	.0020-.0090 (.051-.229)
Journal Diameter	1.869 (47.47)
Lobe Lift	
Intake	.248 (6.30)
Exhaust	.248 (6.30)
Oil Clearance	.0007-.0027 (.018-.069)

VALVE LIFTERS

Application	In. (mm)
Bore Diameter	.844-.845 (21.44-21.46)
Lifter Diameter	.841-.843 (21.36-21.41)
Oil Clearance	.0006-.0020 (.015-.051)
Plunger Travel	.22 (5.6)

Beretta, Camaro, Cavalier, Corsica, Cutlass Supreme, Firebird, Grand Prix, Lumina, Regal, Sunbird, 6000

NOTE: For repair procedures not covered in this article, see ENGINE OVERHAUL PROCEDURES article in GENERAL INFORMATION.

ENGINE IDENTIFICATION

Engine may be identified by Vehicle Identification Number (VIN), engine block code or partial VIN.

VIN is stamped on a metal pad located near lower left corner of windshield. The eighth character of VIN identifies engine model ("T" indicates 3.1L PFI engine). The tenth character of VIN identifies model year ("M" indicates 1991 model year).

The engine block code (3 characters) is stamped on left side of cylinder block, at cylinder block-to-transaxle/transmission flange (LHO indicates 3.1L PFI engine). *See Fig. 1.*

The partial VIN (9-characters) is stamped on left side of cylinder block, at cylinder block-to-transaxle/transmission flange. *See Fig. 1.* First character of partial VIN identifies manufacturer. See PARTIAL VIN table. Second character identifies model year ("M" indicates 1991 model year).

PARTIAL VIN

First Character	Manufacturer
1	Chevrolet
2	Pontiac
3	Oldsmobile
4	Buick
6	Cadillac

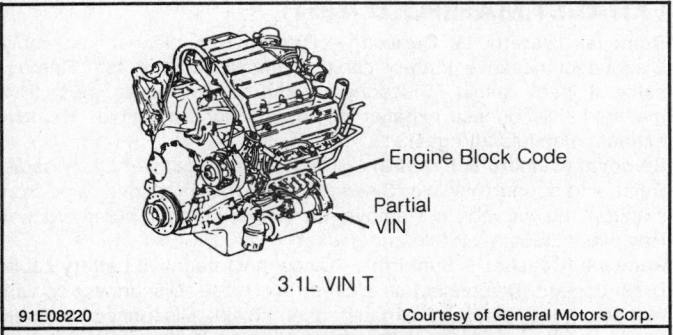

Engine Block Code

Partial VIN

3.1L VIN T

91E08220   Courtesy of General Motors Corp.

Fig. 1: Locating Engine Block Code & Partial VIN

ADJUSTMENTS

VALVE CLEARANCE ADJUSTMENT

Engine is equipped with hydraulic valve lifters. No valve clearance adjustment is required.

REMOVAL & INSTALLATION

NOTE: For reassembly reference, label all electrical connectors, vacuum hoses and fuel lines before removal. Also place mating marks on engine hood and other major assemblies before removal.

FUEL PRESSURE RELEASE

Disconnect negative battery cable. Loosen fuel tank filler cap. Connect Fuel Pressure Gauge (J 34730-1) to fuel line fitting (wrap shop towel around fitting to absorb leakage). Place gauge bleed hose into container. Open bleed valve to release pressure.

ENGINE

NOTE: On Beretta and Corsica, engine and transaxle are removed as an assembly from bottom of vehicle.

Removal & Installation (Beretta & Corsica) – **1)** Release fuel system pressure. See FUEL PRESSURE RELEASE under REMOVAL & INSTALLATION in this article. Remove air cleaner assembly and battery. Drain coolant.

2) Disconnect transaxle fluid cooler lines from radiator. Remove transaxle fluid level indicator. Disconnect upper and lower radiator hoses from engine. Disconnect heater outlet hose from water pump. Disconnect heater inlet hose from rear of engine.

3) Remove serpentine drive belt. Remove transaxle shift cable and linkage from mounting bracket. Disconnect accelerator cable and cruise control cable (if equipped) from throttle linkage. Disconnect A/C pressure switch connector. Remove vacuum check valve from brake booster, leaving hose attached to valve.

4) Disconnect canister purge vacuum line and upper wiring harness from engine. Disconnect vacuum hose from vacuum reservoir. Raise and support vehicle. Remove front wheels. Remove right splash shield and oil filter. Disconnect lower wiring harness from engine.

5) Remove A/C compressor, leaving refrigerant hoses and rear bracket attached to compressor; hang aside. Disconnect exhaust downpipe from manifold. Disconnect brake hose brackets from struts. Remove brake calipers.

6) Disconnect tie rods from struts. Position a 4-wheel dolly under suspension supports and transaxle assembly (assembly). Lower vehicle until dolly just touches assembly. Remove bolts from suspension supports. Lower assembly. To install, reverse removal procedure. Fill cooling system.

Removal & Installation (Camaro & Firebird) – **1)** Release fuel system pressure. See FUEL PRESSURE RELEASE under REMOVAL & INSTALLATION in this article. Remove hood. Remove air cleaner duct. Remove serpentine drive belt.

2) Remove A/C compressor with hoses attached and lay aside. Drain coolant. Remove upper and lower radiator hoses, and coolant recovery hose. Disconnect heater hoses. Disconnect throttle cable and cruise control cable (if equipped) from throttle body.

3) Disconnect vacuum brake booster hose. Remove distributor cap and lay aside with spark plug wires connected. Disconnect necessary electrical connectors and vacuum lines. Remove power steering pump with hoses attached and lay aside.

4) Raise and support vehicle. Disconnect transmission fluid cooler line clips from engine oil pan. Remove exhaust crossover pipe. Remove flexplate cover and torque converter bolts (A/T). Disconnect starter wires. Remove transmission-to-engine bolts.

5) Remove motor mount through bolts. Lower vehicle. Disconnect fuel lines. Support transmission. Connect engine hoist. Lift engine slightly and disconnect ground wire from bracket at left rear of engine. Remove engine. To install, reverse removal procedure. Fill cooling system.

Removal & Installation (Cavalier & Sunbird) – **1)** Release fuel system pressure. See FUEL PRESSURE RELEASE under REMOVAL & INSTALLATION in this article. Remove air cleaner and ducting. Disconnect battery cables. Drain coolant.

2) Remove exhaust manifold crossover pipe, serpentine drive belt and belt tensioner. Remove belt idler (if equipped). Remove upper and lower radiator hoses. Disconnect cables from bracket on upper intake manifold.

3) Remove alternator. Disconnect engine wiring harness and fuel lines. Disconnect coolant by-pass and overflow hoses. Support engine from top of vehicle using Engine Support (J 28467-A) or equivalent.

4) Raise and support vehicle. Remove right inner fender splash shield, flexplate/flywheel cover and starter. Remove A/C compressor. Disconnect exhaust downpipe from manifold. Remove torque converter bolts (A/T). Remove engine mounts.

5) Remove intermediate shaft (drive axle) bracket-to-cylinder block bolts (M/T). Disconnect shift control cable(s) and remove shift cable bracket from transaxle. Remove lower transaxle-to-engine bolts. Lower vehicle. Disconnect heater hoses from heater core.

6) Install engine hoist. Remove engine support from top of engine. Remove engine. Support transaxle. Remove remaining transaxle-to-engine bolts. To install, reverse removal procedure. Fill cooling system.

Removal & Installation (Cutlass Supreme, Grand Prix, Lumina, Regal & 6000) – 1) Release fuel system pressure. See FUEL PRESSURE RELEASE under REMOVAL & INSTALLATION in this article. Remove hood. Remove air cleaner and ducting. Disconnect battery cables. Drain coolant.

2) Disconnect necessary electrical connectors (except those on main engine harness) and fuel lines. Disconnect control cables from throttle body. Remove exhaust crossover pipe, serpentine drive belt and radiator hoses.

3) Remove bolts from A/C front mounting bracket. Remove power steering pump with hoses attached and set aside. Disconnect heater hoses from engine. Disconnect brake booster vacuum line. Remove EGR valve from exhaust manifold.

4) Raise and support vehicle. Remove A/C compressor, flexplate/flywheel cover and starter. Remove torque converter bolts (A/T). Remove transaxle bracket, engine front mount nuts and exhaust downpipe. Lower vehicle.

5) Remove engine torque struts. Disconnect bulkhead electrical connector. Support transaxle. Remove transaxle-to-engine bolts. Attach engine hoist and remove engine. To install, reverse removal procedure. Fill cooling system.

INTAKE MANIFOLD

Removal – 1) Release fuel system pressure. See FUEL PRESSURE RELEASE under REMOVAL & INSTALLATION in this article. Remove air cleaner assembly. Disconnect negative battery cable.

2) Disconnect control cables from throttle body. Disconnect brake booster vacuum pipe from upper intake manifold. Remove control cable bracket from upper intake manifold. Disconnect air intake duct from throttle body.

3) Remove throttle body from upper intake manifold. Remove EGR valve. Remove spark plug wire harness from upper intake manifold. Remove upper intake manifold and gaskets. *See Fig. 2.* Disconnect fuel lines from fuel rail. Remove serpentine drive belt and alternator.

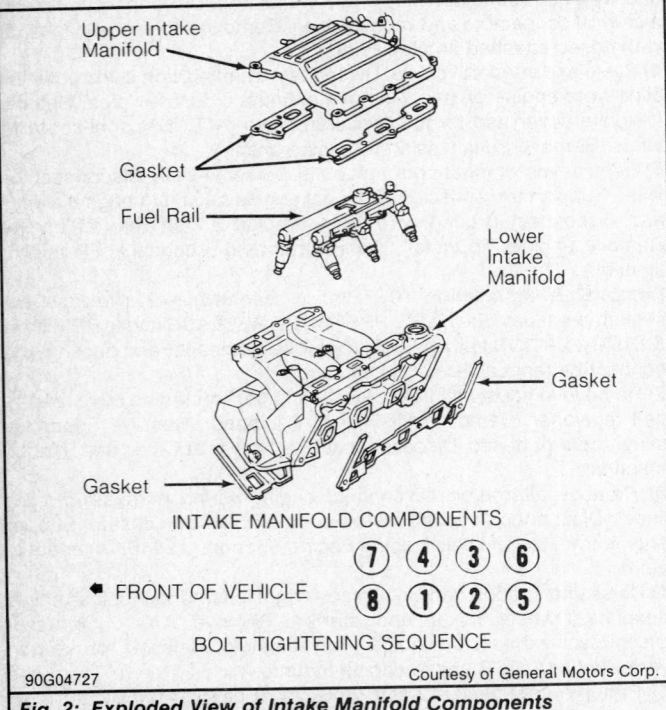

INTAKE MANIFOLD COMPONENTS

◄ FRONT OF VEHICLE

⑦ ④ ③ ⑥
⑧ ① ② ⑤

BOLT TIGHTENING SEQUENCE

90G04727   Courtesy of General Motors Corp.

Fig. 2: Exploded View of Intake Manifold Components & Bolt Tightening Sequence

4) Remove power steering hose bracket from alternator bracket. Remove power steering pump with hoses attached and lay aside. Disconnect fuel injector connectors. Remove fuel rail. Remove spark plug wire harness from lower intake manifold.

5) Drain cooling system. Disconnect heater hoses from water pump and cylinder head. Remove left valve cover. Remove PCV hose and alternator brackets. Remove right valve cover. Remove upper radiator hose. Disconnect necessary electrical connectors.

6) Remove coolant temperature sensor. Remove necessary fuel lines. Remove throttle body heater hose. Remove heater hose from lower intake manifold. Remove lower intake manifold bolts, maintaining Belleville washers in same orientation on 4 center bolts. Remove lower intake manifold.

7) Loosen rocker arm nuts. Rotate rocker arms to one side and remove push rods. Note push rod location for reassembly reference. Push rods are of different lengths. Intake push rods are shortest and Orange. Exhaust push rods are longest and Blue. Remove lower intake manifold gasket.

Installation – 1) Apply bead of RTV sealant to front and rear ridges of cylinder block sealing surfaces. Install new intake manifold gaskets on cylinder heads. Ensure all holes are aligned.

CAUTION: Ensure gaskets are properly installed. Gaskets may be marked for proper direction of installation.

---

2) Install push rods and rocker arms in original location. Tighten rocker arm nuts to 18 ft. lbs. (24 N.m). Install intake manifold. Tighten intake manifold bolts in sequence to 15 ft. lbs. (20 N.m). *See Fig. 2.* Tighten again in sequence to 24 ft. lbs. (33 N.m).

3) To install remaining components, reverse removal procedure; use new gaskets between lower and upper intake manifolds. Use new "O" rings for fuel system components. Fill cooling system.

EXHAUST MANIFOLD (LEFT)

Removal (Beretta & Corsica) – Remove air cleaner assembly. Disconnect negative battery cable. Remove radiator fan. Remove exhaust heat shield. Disconnect exhaust crossover pipe from manifold. Disconnect exhaust downpipe from manifold. Remove exhaust manifold and gasket.

Removal (Camaro & Firebird) – Disconnect negative battery cable. Raise and support vehicle. Disconnect exhaust crossover pipe from manifold. Lower vehicle. Remove rear power steering pump bracket. Remove exhaust manifold and gasket.

Removal (Cavalier & Sunbird) – Disconnect negative battery cable. Drain coolant. Disconnect air cleaner inlet hose. Disconnect coolant by-pass hose. Remove exhaust heat shield. Disconnect exhaust crossover pipe at manifold. Remove exhaust manifold and gasket.

Removal (Cutlass Supreme, Grand Prix, Lumina, Regal & 6000) – 1) Remove air cleaner assembly. Disconnect negative battery cable. Remove coolant recovery bottle. Remove serpentine drive belt. Remove A/C compressor with hoses attached and lay aside.

2) Remove right engine-to-body torque strut rod. Remove A/C and torque strut bracket from engine. Remove heat shield. Disconnect exhaust crossover pipe from manifold. Disconnect exhaust downpipe from manifold. Remove exhaust manifold.

Installation (All Models) – To install, reverse removal procedure; use new gasket. Tighten exhaust manifold bolts to 18 ft.lbs. (24 N.m)

EXHAUST MANIFOLD (RIGHT)

Removal (Beretta, Corsica, Cutlass Supreme, Grand Prix, Lumina, Regal & 6000) – 1) Remove air cleaner assembly. Disconnect negative battery cable. Raise and support vehicle. Disconnect exhaust crossover pipe from manifold. Lower vehicle.

2) On Cutlass Supreme, remove coolant reservoir. Remove engine-to-body torque strut rod. Rotate engine to allow working space. On all models, remove exhaust heat shield.

3) Disconnect exhaust crossover pipe from manifold. Disconnect control cables and bracket from throttle body and upper intake manifold. Disconnect oxygen sensor. Remove exhaust manifold and gasket.

Removal (Camaro & Firebird) – 1) Disconnect negative battery cable. Remove throttle body air duct. Disconnect EGR transfer tube from upper intake manifold. Remove EGR valve adapter, EGR valve and heat shield from exhaust manifold.

2) Remove serpentine drive belt, air pump pulley and air pump upper bracket. Disconnect air injection hose from check valve. Raise and support vehicle. Disconnect exhaust crossover pipe from manifold.

3) Disconnect vacuum hose and electrical connector from air injection diverter valve. Lower vehicle. Remove air pump. Remove air injection pipe from manifold. Remove alternator bracket. Remove exhaust manifold and gasket.

Removal (Cavalier & Sunbird) – 1) Disconnect negative battery cable. Raise and support vehicle. Remove exhaust heat shield. Disconnect exhaust downpipe from manifold. Lower vehicle.

2) Disconnect exhaust crossover pipe from manifold. Remove EGR pipe. Disconnect oxygen sensor wire. Remove exhaust manifold.

Installation (All Models) – To install, reverse removal procedure; use new gasket. Tighten exhaust manifold bolts to 18 ft. lbs. (24 N.m).

CYLINDER HEAD

Removal – 1) Release fuel system pressure. See FUEL PRESSURE RELEASE under REMOVAL & INSTALLATION in this article. Remove intake manifold. See INTAKE MANIFOLD under REMOVAL & INSTALLATION in this article.

2) Remove exhaust manifold. See EXHAUST MANIFOLD under REMOVAL & INSTALLATION in this article. Remove oil dipstick tube (if necessary). Remove cylinder head and gasket.

Inspection – Measure cylinder head surface warpage. Machine surface if warpage exceeds .005" (.13 mm). DO NOT remove more than .010" (.25 mm) of material from original surface.

Installation – 1) Clean cylinder head bolt threads and cylinder block holes. Install gasket on cylinder block with THIS SIDE UP mark upward (if equipped). Ensure all holes align with cylinder block.

2) Install cylinder head. Apply GM Sealant (1052080) to head bolt threads and install. Tighten cylinder head bolts in sequence to 33 ft. lbs. (45 N.m). *See Fig. 3.* Tighten in sequence an additional 90 degrees using Cylinder Head Bolt Wrench (J 36660).

3) To complete installation, reverse removal procedure. Tighten nuts and bolts to specification. See TORQUE SPECIFICATIONS table at end of article. Fill cooling system.

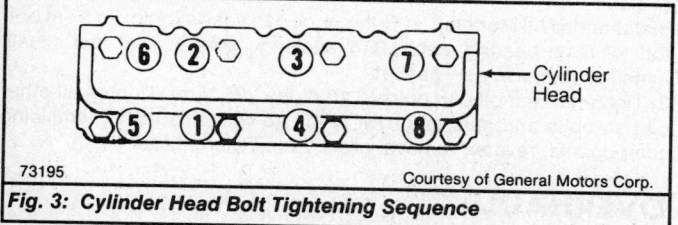

73195   Courtesy of General Motors Corp.

Fig. 3: Cylinder Head Bolt Tightening Sequence

FRONT COVER OIL SEAL

Removal (Camaro & Firebird) – 1) Disconnect negative battery cable. Remove serpentine drive belt and crankshaft pulley. Remove flexplate/flywheel cover.

2) Prevent crankshaft from turning and remove crankshaft damper bolt. Remove crankshaft damper using puller. Remove crankshaft damper key. Pry seal from front timing case cover.

Removal (Except Camaro & Firebird) – 1) Remove air cleaner. Disconnect negative battery cable. Remove serpentine drive belt. Raise and support vehicle. Remove right front wheel and inner fender splash shield. Remove drive belt pulley.

2) Remove flexplate/flywheel cover. Prevent crankshaft from turning and remove crankshaft damper bolt. Remove crankshaft damper using puller. Remove crankshaft damper key. Pry seal from front timing case cover.

Installation (All Models) – 1) Lubricate seal with engine oil. Install seal with open end of seal toward engine using Seal Installer (J 35468). Apply RTV sealant to keyway in crankshaft and crankshaft damper.

2) Install crankshaft damper using Damper Installer (J 29113). Ensure damper installer threads are at least .20" (5.1 mm) into crankshaft. To install remaining components, reverse removal procedure.

TIMING CHAIN

Removal (Camaro & Firebird) – 1) Remove oil pan. See OIL PAN under REMOVAL & INSTALLATION in this article. Remove serpentine drive belt. Remove power steering pump and bracket. Drain coolant. Remove intake duct.

2) Disconnect heater hose from water pump. Disconnect upper radiator hose from thermostat housing. Remove water pump. See WATER PUMP under REMOVAL & INSTALLATION in this article. Remove drive belt pulley from crankshaft damper.

3) Remove crankshaft damper bolt. Remove crankshaft damper using Damper Remover & Installer (J 23523-E). Remove front timing case cover.

4) Rotate crankshaft until crankshaft and camshaft sprocket timing marks are aligned. *See Fig. 4.* Remove camshaft sprocket bolts. Remove camshaft sprocket and timing chain. Remove crankshaft sprocket (if necessary).

Removal (Except Camaro & Firebird) – 1) Drain cooling system. Disconnect negative battery cable. Remove coolant reservoir. Remove serpentine drive belt and tensioner. Remove power steering pump with hoses attached and lay aside. Raise and support vehicle.

2) Remove right front wheel and inner splash shield. Remove crankshaft belt pulley. Remove flexplate/flywheel cover. Prevent crankshaft from turning and remove crankshaft damper bolt. Remove crankshaft damper using puller.

3) Remove serpentine drive belt idler pulley. Remove oil pan. See OIL PAN under REMOVAL & INSTALLATION in this article. Disconnect radiator hose and coolant by-pass pipe from water pump. Disconnect canister purge hose. Remove front timing case cover.

4) Rotate crankshaft, aligning timing marks on camshaft and crankshaft sprockets with No. 1 or No. 4 cylinder at TDC. *See Fig. 4.* Remove camshaft sprocket bolts. Remove camshaft sprocket and timing chain. Remove crankshaft sprocket (if necessary).

Installation (All Models) – 1) Install crankshaft sprocket (if removed). Apply assembly lube to camshaft sprocket thrust face. Install timing chain over camshaft sprocket. Hold sprocket vertically with chain hanging downward. Align timing marks. *See Fig. 4.*

2) Install timing chain and camshaft sprocket on camshaft. Ensure sprocket dowel pin hole aligns with camshaft dowel pin. Install camshaft sprocket. Ensure timing marks are aligned. Lubricate timing chain with engine oil.

3) Apply Sealant (1052917) or RTV sealant to sealing surfaces of front timing case cover. Install front timing case cover and new gasket. If crankshaft seal is removed, lubricate new seal with engine oil and install with open side of seal toward engine using Seal Installer (J 35468 A).

4) Apply sealant to crankshaft and crankshaft damper keyways. Install crankshaft damper using Damper Installer (J 29113). Ensure damper installer threads extend at least .20" (5.1 mm) into crankshaft.

5) To install remaining components, reverse removal procedure. Tighten nuts and bolts to specification. See TORQUE SPECIFICATIONS table at end of article.

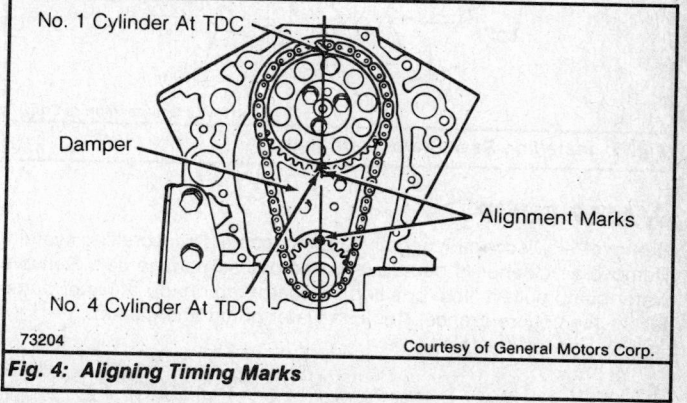

No. 1 Cylinder At TDC

Damper

Alignment Marks

No. 4 Cylinder At TDC

73204   Courtesy of General Motors Corp.

Fig. 4: Aligning Timing Marks

CAMSHAFT

NOTE: To remove and install camshaft, remove engine from vehicle.

Removal – 1) Remove engine. See ENGINE under REMOVAL & INSTALLATION in this article. Remove intake manifold. See INTAKE MANIFOLD under REMOVAL & INSTALLATION in this article.

NOTE: Mark location of rocker arm components, push rods and valve lifters for reassembly reference.

2) Remove rocker arms, push rods and valve lifters. Mark component locations for reassembly reference. Remove timing chain and camshaft sprocket. See TIMING CHAIN under REMOVAL & INSTALLATION in this article. Remove camshaft. Remove camshaft bearings if necessary.

Inspection – Inspect camshaft journal diameter, lobe lift and oil clearance. See CAMSHAFT table in ENGINE SPECIFICATIONS at end of article. Replace components if not within specification.

Installation – 1) Install camshaft bearings (if removed). Ensure oil holes are aligned. Lubricate camshaft bearings and lobes with engine oil. If camshaft is replaced, coat lobes with Engine Oil Supplement (10523675).

2) Install camshaft. To complete installation, reverse removal procedure. Ensure timing marks are aligned. Tighten nuts and bolts to specification. See TORQUE SPECIFICATIONS table at end of article.

CRANKSHAFT REAR OIL SEAL

Removal – 1) Remove transaxle or transmission. See appropriate TRANSMISSION REMOVAL & INSTALLATION article (A/T) or CLUTCHES article (M/T) in TRANSMISSION SERVICING.

2) On vehicles with M/T, place reference mark on clutch pressure plate and flywheel for reassembly reference. Remove pressure plate, clutch disc and flywheel.

3) On vehicles with A/T, remove flexplate. On all vehicles, pry seal from housing. Use care not to damage crankshaft at sealing surface. Note direction of seal installation.

Installation – 1) Coat inner and outer seal surfaces with engine oil. Install seal on mandrel of Seal Installer (J 34686) until dust lip bottoms against tool collar. *See Fig. 5*.

2) Align seal installer dowel pin with alignment hole of crankshaft. Install seal installer on crankshaft. To install seal in seal bore, tighten seal installer handle until seal installer collar is even with cylinder block.

3) To install remaining components, reverse removal procedure. On M/T models, ensure reference marks are aligned on pressure plate and flywheel.

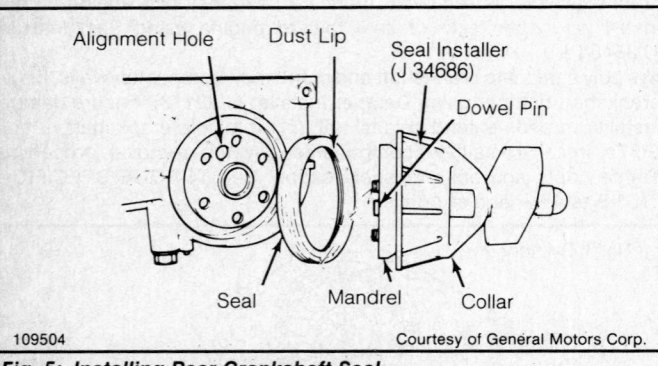

| 109504 | Courtesy of General Motors Corp. |

Fig. 5: Installing Rear Crankshaft Seal

WATER PUMP

Removal – Disconnect negative battery cable. Drain cooling system. Remove air cleaner (if necessary). Remove serpentine belt. Remove water pump pulley. Note position of locator tab on top of water pump for reassembly reference. Remove water pump and gasket.

Installation – Apply thread sealant to water pump bolts. Install water pump; use new gasket. Ensure locator tab on top of water pump housing is positioned vertically. To install remaining components, reverse removal procedure. Fill cooling system.

OIL PAN

Removal (Beretta & Corsica) – Raise and support vehicle. Drain crankcase. Remove oil filter, starter and flexplate/flywheel cover. Remove oil pan nuts and bolts. Remove oil pan.

Removal (Camaro & Firebird) – 1) Disconnect negative battery cable. Raise and support vehicle. Remove catalytic converter hanger bolts. Disconnect transmission fluid cooler lines from oil pan clips. Rotate crankshaft until timing mark on the crankshaft damper is at the 7 o'clock position as viewed from timing chain end of engine.

2) Drain crankcase. Remove torque converter dust cover (A/T). Disconnect exhaust crossover pipe from manifolds. Remove engine mount through bolts. Raise and support engine. Remove oil pan nuts and bolts. Remove oil pan.

Removal (Cavalier & Sunbird) – 1) Disconnect negative battery cable. Remove serpentine drive belt and tensioner. Raise and support vehicle. Drain crankcase. Remove plastic and metal shields from starter area. Remove starter with wires connected and hang aside.

2) Remove engine-to-frame mounting nuts. Lower vehicle. Support engine from top using Engine Support (J 28467-A). Raise and support vehicle. Remove right wheel and inner fender splash shield. Remove oil pan nuts and bolts. Remove oil pan.

Removal (Cutlass Supreme, Grand Prix, Lumina, Regal & 6000) – 1) Disconnect negative battery cable. Remove serpentine drive belt and tensioner. Support engine from top using Engine Support (J 28467-A) and Adapter Leg (J 36462) or equivalent.

2) Raise and support vehicle. Drain crankcase. Remove right wheel and splash shield. Remove steering gear pinch bolt. Remove transaxle mount nuts. Remove engine mount nuts. Remove front engine mount bracket from cylinder block.

3) Remove plastic and metal shields from starter area. Remove starter with wires connected and hang aside. Place support under center of front frame crossmember. Loosen rear crossmember frame bolts (DO NOT remove).

4) Remove front frame bolts. Lower front frame. Disconnect DIS crankshaft sensor connector. Remove oil pan nuts and bolts. Remove oil pan.

Installation (All Models) – 1) If rear oil pan seal is removed from bottom of main bearing, apply RTV sealer to tabs of seal and install. Install oil pan; use new gasket.

2) Tighten 2 rear oil pan bolts to 18 ft. lbs. (24 N.m). Tighten all other oil pan bolts and nuts to 71 INCH lbs. (8 N.m). To install remaining components, reverse removal procedure. Fill crankcase.

OVERHAUL

CYLINDER HEAD

Cylinder Head – Measure cylinder head warpage at deck surface. Resurface cylinder head if warpage exceeds .005" (.13 mm). DO NOT remove more than .010" (.25 mm) of material from original surface of cylinder head.

Valve Springs – Measure valve spring free length, out-of-square, tension and installed height (installed height measurement procedure is not available from manufacturer). See VALVES & VALVE SPRINGS table in ENGINE SPECIFICATIONS at end of article. Replace spring if not within specification.

Valve Stem Oil Seals – If oversize valves are installed, use oversize seals. Ensure seal is fully seated on guide. Intake and exhaust seals are different.

Valve Guides – DO NOT knurl valve guides. If valve stem oil clearance is not within specification, ream valve guides for oversize valve. See CYLINDER HEAD table in ENGINE SPECIFICATIONS at end of article.

Valve Seats – Measure seat runout and width. See CYLINDER HEAD table in ENGINE SPECIFICATIONS at end of article. If not within specification, machine or replace valve seat as necessary. Valve seat replacement procedure are not available from manufacturer.

Valves – Measure valve margin and valve stem-to-guide oil clearance. See VALVES & VALVE SPRINGS table in ENGINE SPECIFICATIONS at end of article. If valve margin is not within specification, machine or replace valve. If valve stem-to-guide oil clearance is not within specification, replace valve with oversize valve. New valves MUST NOT be lapped. Protective coating will be damaged if valve is lapped.

Valve Seat Correction Angles – If seat contact is too low (too close to stem), raise it using a 70-degree stone. If contact is too wide, use a 70-degree stone to narrow seat.

CYLINDER BLOCK ASSEMBLY

CAUTION: If removing piston from connecting rod, mark piston in relation to connecting rod. Information for connecting rod-to-piston positioning is not available from manufacturer.

Piston & Rod Assembly – Mark piston according to cylinder number for installation to original location. Replace rod if bend or twist exceeds specification. See CONNECTING ROD table in ENGINE SPECIFICATIONS at end of article. Install piston with arrow on top of piston toward front of engine.

Fitting Pistons – 1) Measure cylinder bore diameter at center of bore. Measure piston diameter at 90-degree angle to piston pin bore and 3/4" below center line of piston pin bore. Measure taper in 2 places: at center line of piston pin bore and near bottom of piston skirt (both at 90-degree angle to piston pin bore).
2) If piston clearance is not within specification, machine cylinder bore and install oversize piston as necessary. DO NOT machine oversize piston to fit cylinder bore, or engine balance will be affected. See PISTONS, PINS & RINGS table in ENGINE SPECIFICATIONS at end of article.

Piston Rings – 1) Measure piston ring end gap and side clearance. If end gap and side clearance are not within specification, replace piston rings and/or piston as necessary. See PISTONS, PINS & RINGS table in ENGINE SPECIFICATIONS at end of article.
2) Install piston rings, with identification mark on ring land facing top of piston. Properly position ring end gaps around circumference of piston. See Fig. 6.

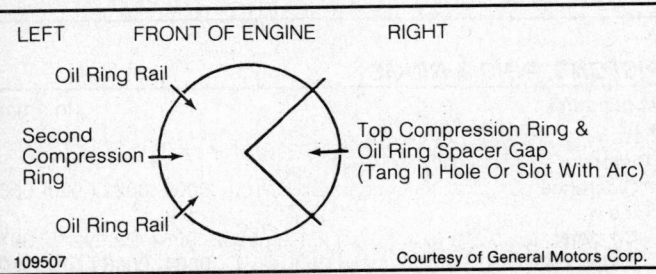

Fig. 6: Positioning Piston Rings

Rod Bearings – Measure rod bearing oil clearance. If oil clearance is not within specification, replace crankshaft. See CRANKSHAFT, MAIN & CONNECTING ROD BEARINGS table in ENGINE SPECIFICATIONS at end of article.

Crankshaft & Main Bearings – Measure crankshaft main bearing oil clearance, out-of-round and taper. If not within specification, replace crankshaft. See CRANKSHAFT, MAIN & CONNECTING ROD BEARINGS table in ENGINE SPECIFICATIONS at end of article.

Thrust Bearing – Manufacturer does not provide procedure for measuring thrust bearing clearance.

Cylinder Block – Measure deck surface warpage. Machine surface if warpage exceeds .005" (.13 mm). DO NOT remove more than .010" (.25 mm) of material from original deck surface.

Valve Lifter Bores – Oversize valve lifters are available. If oversize lifters are installed, stamp .025 O.S. on cylinder block near lifter bore to indicate .001" (.025 mm) oversize lifters have been installed.

ENGINE OILING

LUBRICATION SYSTEM

A camshaft-driven, gear-type oil pump provides pressurized lubrication through oil filter, to main gallery above left side of camshaft center line. This gallery provides lubrication to valve lifters on left bank, camshaft bearings, crankshaft and right gallery. *See Fig. 7.*

The right gallery supplies oil to valve lifters on right bank. Rocker arms are lubricated by passages in push rods. Slot in front camshaft bearing provides lubrication to camshaft thrust face. Pressure regulator valve is mounted in oil pump body.

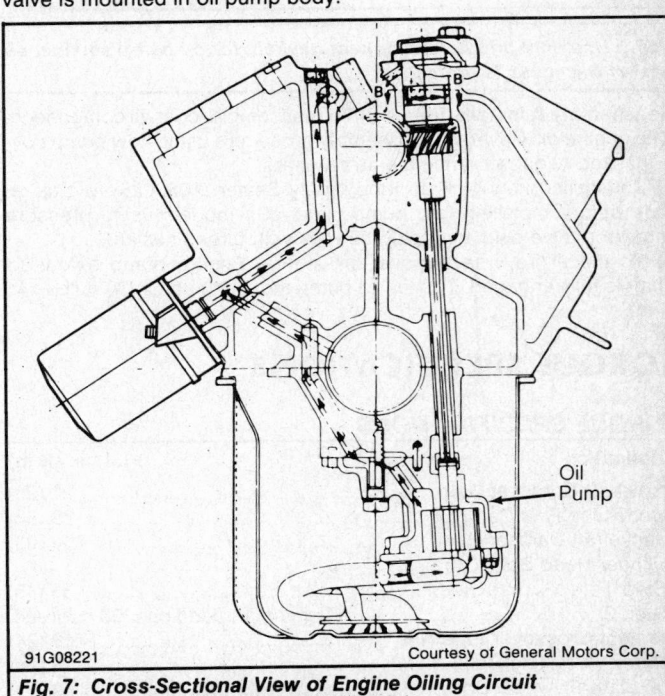

Fig. 7: Cross-Sectional View of Engine Oiling Circuit (Shown without Cylinder Heads)

Crankcase Capacity – Engine oil capacity is approximately 4 qts. (3.7L) without filter change. More oil may need to be added when replacing oil filter.

Oil Pressure – Normal oil pressure is 15 psi (1 kg/cm²) at 1100 RPM.

OIL PUMP

Removal & Disassembly – 1) Remove oil pan. See OIL PAN under REMOVAL & INSTALLATION in this article. Remove oil pump bolt, oil pump and extension shaft from rear main bearing cap.
2) To disassemble, remove pump cover. DO NOT remove pick-up tube from cover unless loose or broken. If pick-up tube is loose, bent or has been removed, replace pick-up tube and pump cover.

CAUTION: On some models, pressure regulator valve spring is under pressure. Use care when removing to prevent personal injury.

3) Mark idler gear in relation to drive gear for reassembly reference. Remove gears from pump body. Remove pressure regulator valve retaining plug (or cotter pin on some models). Remove valve and spring.
Inspection – 1) Inspect components for damage. Using straightedge and feeler gauge, measure gear end clearance. Measure housing gear pocket depth and diameter. Measure gear diameter and length (thickness).
2) Measure side clearance between gear tooth and housing. Measure gear lash clearance between gear teeth. Check clearance between pressure regulator valve and bore. Replace components or pump assembly if not within specification. See OIL PUMP SPECIFICATIONS table.

OIL PUMP SPECIFICATIONS

Application	In. (mm)
Gear	
Diameter	1.504-1.506 (38.20-38.25)
End Clearance	.002-.006 (.05-.15)
Lash	.0037-.0077 (.094-.196)
Length	1.199-1.200 (30.45-30.48)
Side Clearance	.003-.004 (.08-.10)
Housing Pocket	
Depth	1.202-1.205 (30.53-30.61)
Diameter	1.498-1.500 (38.05-38.10)
Pressure Regulator Valve-to-Bore	
Clearance	.0015-.0035 (.038-.089)

NOTE: Use only original equipment gaskets for oil pump service, as gasket thickness is critical.

Reassembly & Installation – 1) To reassemble, coat all components with engine oil. Reverse disassembly procedure using new pump cover gasket. Align reference marks on gears.
2) If installing new pick-up tube, apply Sealer (1050026) to pick-up tube before installing into pump cover. On models using pressure regulator valve plug, coat plug threads with thread sealant.
3) To install, reverse removal procedure. Ensure pump extension shaft is fully engaged. Tighten oil pump mounting bolt to 30 ft. lbs. (41 N.m).

TORQUE SPECIFICATIONS

TORQUE SPECIFICATIONS

Application	Ft. Lbs. (N.m)
Camshaft Sprocket Bolt	21 (28)
Connecting Rod Cap Nut	39 (53)
Crankshaft Damper Bolt	76 (103)
Cylinder Head Bolt [1]	
Step 1	[2] 33 (45)
Step 2	[2] Tighten an additional 90 degrees.
Exhaust Crossover Pipe Nut	18 (24)
Exhaust Manifold Bolt	18 (24)
Flexplate/Flywheel Bolt	52 (71)
Front Timing Case Cover Bolt	
8 mm	20 (27)
10 mm	28 (38)
Lower Intake Manifold Bolt	
Step 1	[3] 15 (20)
Step 2	[3] 24 (33)
Main Bearing Cap Bolt	73 (99)
Oil Filter Adapter Bolt	46 (62)
Oil Pan Rear Bolt (8 mm)	18 (24)
Oil Pump Bolt	30 (41)
Oil Pump Pressure Regulating Valve Plug	15 (20)
Rocker Arm Nut	18 (24)
Serpentine Drive Belt Tensioner Bolt	40 (54)
Throttle Body Bolt	18 (24)
Timing Chain Damper Bolt	15 (20)
Water Pump Pulley Bolt	18 (24)
	INCH Lbs. (N.m)
Exhaust Heat Shield Nut	89 (10)
Oil Pan Bolt & Nut (6 mm)	71 (8)
Upper Intake Manifold Bolt	88 (10)
Valve Cover Bolt	89 (10)

[1] – Apply Sealant (1052080) to cylinder head bolts.
[2] – Tighten cylinder head bolts in sequence. *See Fig. 3.*
[3] – Tighten lower intake manifold bolts in sequence. *See Fig. 2.*

ENGINE SPECIFICATIONS

GENERAL SPECIFICATIONS

Application	Specification
3.1L	
Displacement	192 Cu. In. (3.1L)
Bore	3.50" (89.0 mm)
Stroke	3.31" (84.0 mm)
Compression Ratio	8.8:1
Fuel System	PFI
Horsepower @ RPM	140 @ 4800
Torque Ft. Lbs. @ RPM	180 @ 3600

CRANKSHAFT, MAIN & CONNECTING ROD BEARINGS

Application	In. (mm)
3.1L	
Crankshaft	
End Play	.002-.008 (.05-.20)
Main Bearings	
Journal Diameter	2.6473-2.6483 (67.241-67.267)
Journal Out-Of-Round	.0002 (.005)
Journal Taper	.0002 (.005)
Oil Clearance	.0012-.0030 (.030-.076)
Connecting Rod Bearings	
Journal Diameter	1.9983-1.9994 (50.757-50.785)
Journal Out-Of-Round	.0002 (.005)
Journal Taper	.0002 (.005)
Oil Clearance	.0011-.0037 (.028-.094)

CONNECTING RODS

Application	In. (mm)
3.1L	
Maximum Bend	[1] .010 (.25)
Maximum Twist	[2] .002 (.05)
Side Play	.014-.027 (.36-.69)

[1] – Bend per 3" of rod length.
[2] – Twist per inch of rod length.

PISTONS, PINS & RINGS

Application	In. (mm)
3.1L	
Pistons	
Clearance	.0009-.0022 (.023-.056)
Pins	
Diameter	.9052-.9054 (22.992-22.997)
Piston Fit	.0004-.0008 (.010-.020)
Rod Fit	.0007-.0018 (.018-.046)
Rings	
No. 1	
End Gap	.010-.020 (.25-.51)
Side Clearance	.0020-.0035 (.051-.089)
No. 2	
End Gap	.020-.028 (.51-.71)
Side Clearance	.0020-.0035 (.051-.089)
No. 3 (Oil)	
End Gap	.010-.030 (.25-.76)
Side Clearance (Max.)	.008 (.20)

CYLINDER BLOCK

Application	In. (mm)
3.1L	
Cylinder Bore	
Standard Diameter	3.5046-3.5053 (89.02-89.03)
Maximum Taper	.0005 (.013)
Maximum Out-Of-Round	.0005 (.013)
Maximum Deck Warpage	[1] .005 (.13)

[1] – DO NOT remove more than .010" (.25 mm) material from original surface of cylinder block deck.

VALVES & VALVE SPRINGS

Application	Specification
3.1L	
Intake Valves	
Face Angle	45°
Exhaust Valves	
Face Angle	45°
Valve Springs	
Free Length	1.91" (48.5 mm)
Installed Height	1.57" (39.9 mm)
Out-Of-Square	.063" (1.6 mm)
Pressure	Lbs. @ In. (kg @ mm)
Valve Closed	90 @ 1.70 (41 @ 43.2)
Valve Open	215 @ 1.29 (98 @ 32.8)

CYLINDER HEAD

Application	Specification
3.1L	
Maximum Warpage	[1] .005" (.13 mm)
Valve Seats	
Intake Valve	
Seat Angle	46°
Seat Width	.061-.073" (1.55-1.85 mm)
Maximum Seat Runout	.001" (.025 mm)
Exhaust Valve	
Seat Angle	46°
Seat Width	.067-.079" (1.70-2.01 mm)
Maximum Seat Runout	.001" (.025 mm)
Valve Guides	
Intake Valve	
Valve Guide Oil Clearance	.001-.003" (.03-.08 mm)
Exhaust Valve	
Valve Guide Oil Clearance	.001-.003" (.03-.08 mm)

[1] – DO NOT remove more than .010" (.25 mm) material from original surface of cylinder head.

CAMSHAFT

Application	In. (mm)
3.1L	
Journal Diameter	1.868-1.882 (47.45-47.80)
Lobe Lift	
Intake	.263 (6.68)
Exhaust	.273 (6.93)
Oil Clearance	.001-.004 (.03-.10)

1991 ENGINES
3.3L & 3.8L V6

Bonneville, Century, Cutlass Calais, Cutlass Ciera, Cutlass Cruiser, Eighty-Eight, LeSabre, Ninety-Eight, Park Avenue, Reatta, Regal, Riviera, Skylark, Toronado, Touring Sedan, Trofeo

NOTE: For repair procedures not covered in this article, see ENGINE OVERHAUL PROCEDURES article in GENERAL INFORMATION.

ENGINE IDENTIFICATION

Engine may be identified by using Vehicle Identification Number (VIN) stamped on a metal pad, located near lower left corner of windshield. The eighth character identifies the engine model. See ENGINE IDENTIFICATION CODES table.

Engine code, located on cylinder block, may be required when ordering replacement parts. *See Fig. 1.* See ENGINE IDENTIFICATION CODES table.

ENGINE IDENTIFICATION CODES

Engine	Code
3.3L	
8th Character Of Dash VIN	N
Engine Code	LG7
3.8L	
8th Character Of Dash VIN	C
Engine Code	LN3
8th Character Of Dash VIN	L
Engine Code	L27

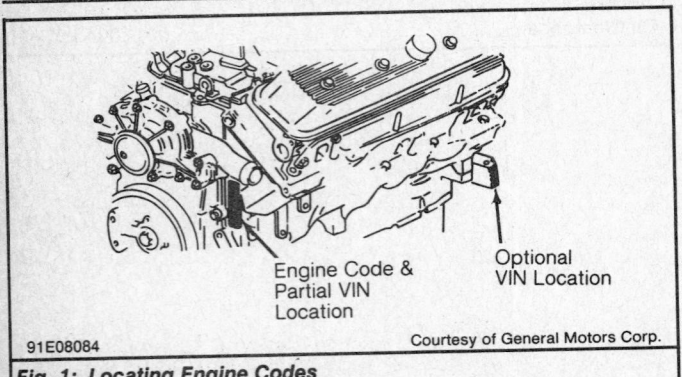

Engine Code & Partial VIN Location

Optional VIN Location

91E08084

Courtesy of General Motors Corp.

Fig. 1: Locating Engine Codes

ADJUSTMENTS

VALVE CLEARANCE ADJUSTMENT

No valve adjustment is required, as hydraulic valve lifters are used.

REMOVAL & INSTALLATION

NOTE: For reassembly reference, label all electrical connectors, vacuum hoses and fuel lines before removal. Also place mating marks on engine hood and other major assemblies before removal.

FUEL PRESSURE RELEASE

1) Loosen fuel tank cap to release fuel tank pressure. Remove fuel pump fuse. Start engine and operate until engine stalls.
2) Crank engine for an additional 3 seconds to release residual line pressure. Disconnect negative battery cable and reinstall fuel pump fuse.

ENGINE

Removal (3.3L) – **1)** Remove hood, and cover fenders. Depressurize fuel system. See FUEL PRESSURE RELEASE under REMOVAL & INSTALLATION in this article. Remove negative battery cable. Disconnect fuel lines from fuel rail. Disconnect air intake duct. Drain cooling system.

NOTE: Engine is lifted alone from engine compartment.

2) Disconnect radiator and heater hoses. Remove engine cooling fan. Raise and support vehicle. Disconnect electrical connections and vacuum hoses. Disconnect cables and bracket at throttle body. Remove drive belt. Remove power steering pump and set aside. Remove upper transaxle-to-engine bolts.
3) Raise vehicle on hoist. Disconnect A/C compressor (if equipped) and set aside. Remove rear engine mount-to-mount bracket bolts. Remove flexplate cover. Match mark flexplate to torque converter to ensure proper reassembly. Remove flexplate-to-torque converter bolts.
4) Remove lower transaxle-to-engine bolts. One bolt is located between transaxle case and engine block and is installed in opposite direction. Lower vehicle. Disconnect front engine mount to bracket bolts. Using engine lift, remove engine.
Installation – **1)** To install, reverse removal procedure. With engine off, fill surge tank until level is even with base of filler neck. Run engine until upper radiator hose is hot.
2) Stop engine and observe coolant level in surge tank. If coolant level is not above FULL line, carefully remove pressure cap and add coolant as necessary. Install cap.

Removal (3.8L) – **1)** Remove hood. Release fuel pressure. See FUEL PRESSURE RELEASE under REMOVAL & INSTALLATION in this article. Remove battery cables. Drain cooling system and crankcase oil. Remove windshield washer, radiator and heater supply hoses.

NOTE: Engine is lifted alone from engine compartment.

2) Disconnect all electrical harness connectors from engine. Remove drive belt. Remove power steering pump and set aside. Remove air-flow duct and air cleaner. Remove cables and hoses from throttle body. Remove ignition coil ground strap.
3) Disconnect fuel lines and vacuum hoses. Disconnect upper engine strut. Raise and support vehicle. Disconnect exhaust pipe. Disconnect engine mount bolts. Disconnect A/C compressor (if equipped) and set aside. Disconnect engine oil cooler lines (if equipped).
4) Remove lower transaxle-to-engine bolts. One bolt is located between transaxle case and engine block and is installed in opposite direction. Remove flexplate cover. Match mark flexplate to torque converter to ensure proper reassembly.
5) Remove flexplate-to-torque converter bolts. Disconnect engine support bracket at transaxle. Lower vehicle. Remove remaining transaxle-to-engine bolts. Remove engine.
Installation – **1)** To install, reverse removal procedure. Fill radiator to base of filler neck. Start engine. Place heater-A/C control in A/C mode and at highest temperature setting. Run engine to 3000 RPM and back to idle 5 times to expel any trapped air in system.
2) Refill radiator as necessary. Install radiator cap. Allow engine to cool. Check coolant level in reservoir. Add coolant as necessary to bring level to ADD or FULL COLD mark.

INTAKE MANIFOLD

Removal (3.3L) – **1)** Release fuel pressure. See FUEL PRESSURE RELEASE under REMOVAL & INSTALLATION in this article. Disconnect negative battery cable. Drain cooling system. Remove serpentine belt, alternator and brackets.
2) Remove power steering pump with hoses attached. Disconnect coolant by-pass hose, heater pipe and upper radiator hose. Disconnect control cables and air intake duct from throttle body. Disconnect necessary electrical connections, vacuum lines and fuel lines.
3) Disconnect spark plug wires. It may be necessary to remove fuel rail to gain access to intake manifold bolts. Remove intake manifold bolts, manifold, gaskets and seals.
Removal (3.8L) – **1)** Release fuel pressure. See FUEL PRESSURE RELEASE under REMOVAL & INSTALLATION in this article. Disconnect negative battery cable. Remove plastic engine cover and air intake duct.

2) Remove spark plug wires and fuel rail. Remove exhaust crossover heat shield and power steering pump bracket. Remove alternator and bracket. Remove cable bracket, heater pipes and by-pass hose. Remove intake manifold bolts, manifold, gaskets and seals.

Installation – 1) Ensure sealing surfaces and bolt threads and holes are clean. Apply GM Sealant (12345336) at the end of seals on cylinder block. Install manifold and gaskets. Coat bolt threads with thread sealant and install.

2) Tighten intake manifold bolts in sequence TWICE to 88 INCH lbs. (10 N.m). See Fig. 2. Lubricate coolant "O" rings with anti-freeze and fuel rail "O" rings with engine oil prior to installation. To install remaining components, reverse removal procedure. Fill cooling system.

NOTE: Apply thread sealant to intake manifold bolts prior to installation. Intake manifold bolts must be tightened in sequence TWICE to 88 INCH lbs. (10 N.m). See Fig. 2.

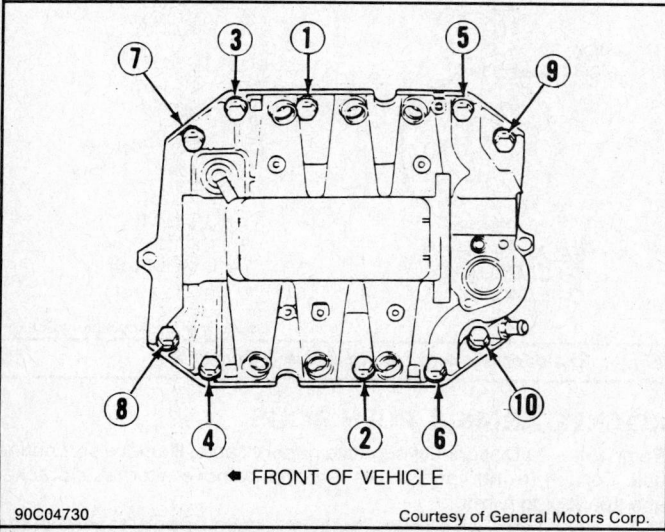

90C04730 Courtesy of General Motors Corp.

Fig. 2: Intake Manifold Bolt Tightening Sequence

EXHAUST MANIFOLD

Removal & Installation (Left/Front) – 1) Disconnect negative battery cable. It may be necessary to remove air inlet duct. Disconnect spark plug wires. Remove crossover pipe bolts from manifold.

2) Remove engine lift hook and manifold heat shield (if equipped). Remove oil dipstick and tube. Remove manifold bolts, manifold and gasket. To install, reverse removal procedure using new gasket.

Removal & Installation (Right/Rear) – 1) Disconnect negative battery cable. Disconnect spark plug wires and oxygen sensor. Remove EGR pipe (if equipped). It may be necessary to disconnect throttle cable from throttle body and brake booster hose. Disconnect crossover pipe and exhaust pipe from manifold.

2) Remove transaxle dipstick. Remove manifold heat shield (if equipped). Remove catalytic converter heat shield and pipe hanger. Remove exhaust pipe-to-manifold nuts. Remove engine lift bracket, manifold bolts, manifold and gasket. To install, reverse removal procedure using new gasket.

CYLINDER HEAD

Removal – 1) Remove intake manifold. See INTAKE MANIFOLD under REMOVAL & INSTALLATION in this article. Remove exhaust manifold. See EXHAUST MANIFOLD under REMOVAL & INSTALLATION in this article.

2) On front cylinder head applications, disconnect spark plug wires. Remove alternator, ignition coil and bracket. Remove A/C compressor bracket bolt.

3) On rear cylinder head applications, disconnect spark plug wires. Remove power steering pump with hoses attached and lay aside. Remove belt tensioner assembly and fuel line heat shield (if equipped).

4) Remove rocker arms, push rods and guide plates. See ROCKER ARMS & PUSH RODS under REMOVAL & INSTALLATION in this article. Remove cylinder head bolts, cylinder head and gasket.

Inspection – Inspect cylinder head warpage. See CYLINDER HEAD under OVERHAUL in this article.

Installation – 1) Ensure cylinder head bolt threads and cylinder block holes are clean. Ensure all holes align with cylinder block.

2) Install cylinder head. Apply GM Sealant (1052080) to head bolt threads and install. Tighten all bolts to 35 ft. lbs. (47 N.m) in proper sequence. See Fig. 3.

3) Tighten all bolts an additional 130 degrees in proper sequence. Tighten the center 4 bolts an additional 30 degrees in proper sequence.

4) To install remaining components, reverse removal procedure. Coat rocker arm bolts with GM Threadlock (12345493) prior to installation.

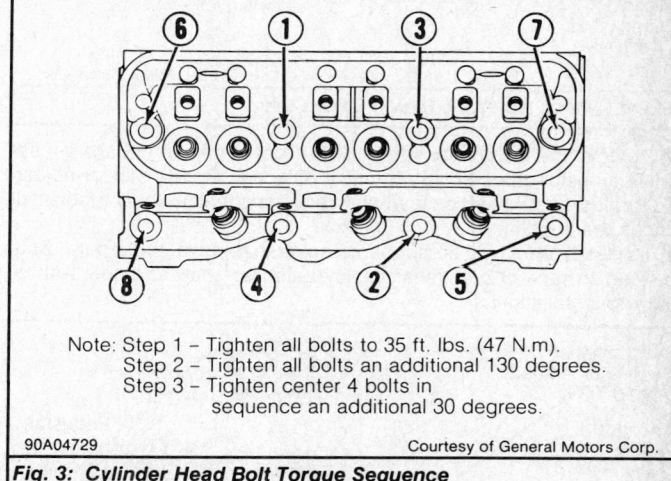

Note: Step 1 – Tighten all bolts to 35 ft. lbs. (47 N.m).
Step 2 – Tighten all bolts an additional 130 degrees.
Step 3 – Tighten center 4 bolts in sequence an additional 30 degrees.

90A04729 Courtesy of General Motors Corp.

Fig. 3: Cylinder Head Bolt Torque Sequence

FRONT CRANKSHAFT SEAL

Removal – Disconnect negative battery cable. Remove serpentine belt. Raise and support vehicle. Remove right front wheel and inner splash shield. Remove crankshaft pulley/balancer bolt and crankshaft pulley/balancer. Pry seal from front timing case cover.

Installation – Using Seal Installer (J-35354) and crankshaft pulley/balancer bolt, install seal. Remove seal installer. Coat outside surface of crankshaft pulley/balancer and seal with oil prior to installation. To install remaining components, reverse removal procedure.

FRONT TIMING CASE COVER

Removal – 1) Disconnect negative battery cable. Drain cooling system. Remove serpentine belt. Disconnect heater pipes. Disconnect coolant hoses at case cover.

2) Raise and support vehicle. Remove right front wheel and inner splash shield. Remove crankshaft pulley/balancer bolt and crankshaft pulley/balancer. Disconnect electrical connections at oil pressure sender, camshaft sensor and crankshaft sensor.

3) Remove oil pan-to-case cover bolts. Remove front timing case cover bolts, case cover and gasket. See Fig. 4.

Installation – 1) Inspect timing chain and sprockets for wear. Timing chain in and out movement should not exceed 1" (25.4 mm). Replace if necessary.

2) To install, reverse removal procedure using new gasket. Coat case cover bolts with thread sealant prior to installation. Crankshaft sensor must be adjusted.

3) With crankshaft sensor mounted loosely on mounting pedestal, install sensor and mounting pedestal on Crankshaft Sensor Adjuster (J-37089). See Fig. 5. Install crankshaft sensor adjuster and sensor assembly on crankshaft.

4) Install mounting pedestal-to-cylinder block bolts and tighten to 14-28 ft. lbs. (19-38 N.m). Install sensor-to-mounting pedestal bolts to 30-35 INCH lbs. (3.3-3.9 N.m).

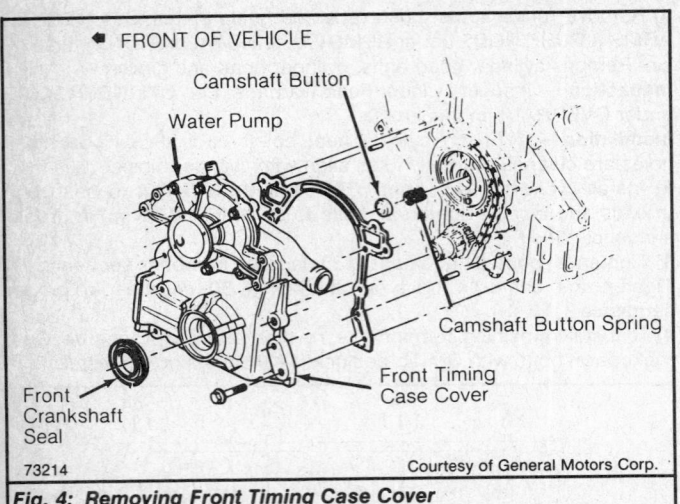

◀ FRONT OF VEHICLE

Camshaft Button

Water Pump

Camshaft Button Spring

Front Timing Case Cover

Front Crankshaft Seal

73214   Courtesy of General Motors Corp.

Fig. 4: Removing Front Timing Case Cover

5) Remove crankshaft sensor adjuster from crankshaft. Place sensor adjuster inside the crankshaft pulley/balancer. Rotate sensor adjuster. Replace crankshaft pulley/balancer if sensor adjuster contacts balancer at any point.
6) To install remaining components, reverse removal procedure. Coat outside surface of crankshaft pulley/balancer shaft and seal with oil prior to installation.

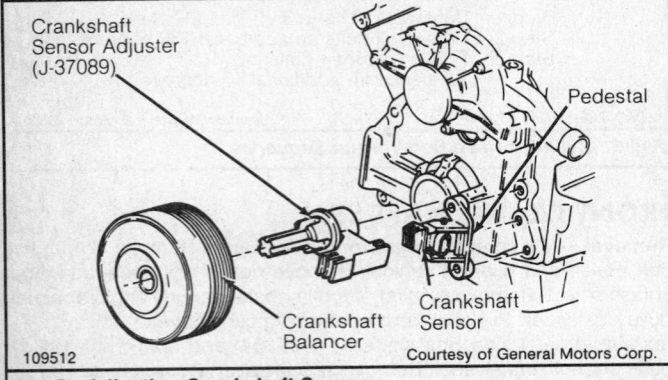

Crankshaft Sensor Adjuster (J-37089)

Pedestal

Crankshaft Sensor

Crankshaft Balancer

109512   Courtesy of General Motors Corp.

Fig. 5: Adjusting Crankshaft Sensor

TIMING CHAIN & SPROCKETS

Removal – 1) Remove front timing case cover. See FRONT TIMING CASE COVER under REMOVAL & INSTALLATION in this article. Remove camshaft button and camshaft button spring. *See Fig. 4.*
2) Inspect timing chain and sprockets for wear. Timing chain in and out movement should not exceed 1" (25.4 mm). Replace if necessary.
3) Rotate crankshaft and align timing marks on camshaft and crankshaft sprockets. *See Fig. 6.* Remove timing chain damper assembly.
4) Remove camshaft sprocket bolts. Remove camshaft sprocket and timing chain. Remove crankshaft sprocket (if necessary).

NOTE: On 3.8L models, if balance shaft has been moved, ensure alignment is correct. See BALANCE SHAFT under REMOVAL & INSTALLATION in this article.

Installation – 1) If engine has been rotated, rotate crankshaft so No. 1 cylinder is at TDC. Temporarily install camshaft sprocket. Rotate camshaft sprocket so timing mark is downward.
2) Remove camshaft sprocket and install timing chain on camshaft sprocket. Install timing chain and camshaft sprocket. Ensure timing marks are aligned. *See Fig. 6.* Install camshaft sprocket bolts. Install timing chain damper, camshaft button and camshaft button spring.
3) To install remaining components, reverse removal procedure. Ensure timing marks are aligned.

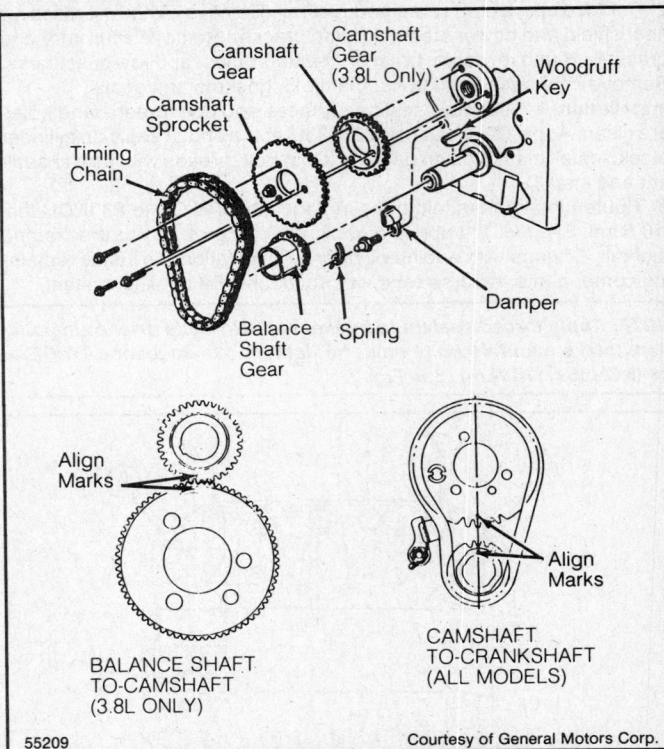

Camshaft Gear

Camshaft Gear (3.8L Only)

Woodruff Key

Camshaft Sprocket

Timing Chain

Damper

Balance Shaft Gear

Spring

Align Marks

Align Marks

BALANCE SHAFT TO-CAMSHAFT (3.8L ONLY)

CAMSHAFT TO-CRANKSHAFT (ALL MODELS)

55209   Courtesy of General Motors Corp.

Fig. 6: Exploded View of Timing Chain & Sprockets

ROCKER ARMS & PUSH RODS

Removal – 1) Disconnect negative battery cable. Remove serpentine belt. For left (front) valve cover removal, remove alternator bracket and spark plug wires.
2) For right (rear) valve cover removal, loosen power steering pump bolts and move pump forward with hoses still attached. Remove power steering pump brackets.
3) On 3.8L models, remove EGR pipe, EGR valve and adapter from throttle body adapter.
4) On all models, remove spark plug wires and valve cover. Remove rocker arm pivot bolts. Remove rocker arms and components. *See Fig. 7.* Mark component locations for reassembly reference.

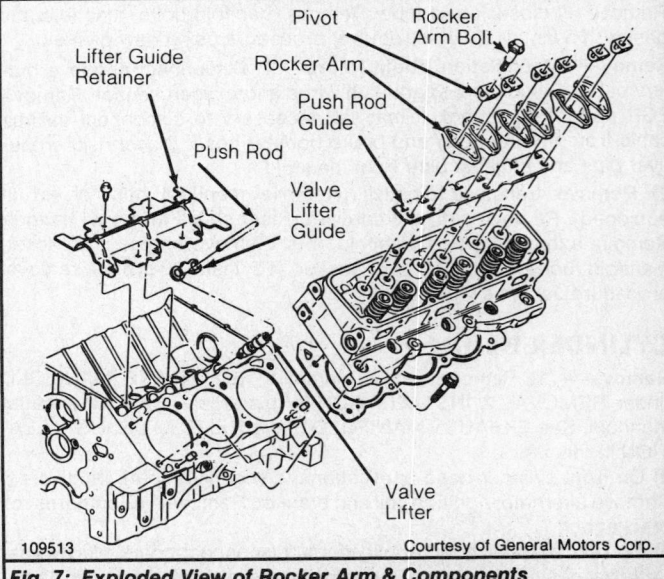

Pivot

Rocker Arm Bolt

Rocker Arm

Lifter Guide Retainer

Push Rod Guide

Push Rod

Valve Lifter Guide

Valve Lifter

109513   Courtesy of General Motors Corp.

Fig. 7: Exploded View of Rocker Arm & Components

NOTE: Mark location of all valve train components for reassembly reference. Components must be installed in original location.

Installation – To install, reverse removal procedure. Coat rocker arm bolts with GM Threadlock (12345493) prior to installation. Apply thread sealant to valve cover bolts prior to installation.

VALVE LIFTERS

Removal – **1)** Remove intake manifold. See INTAKE MANIFOLD under REMOVAL & INSTALLATION in this article. Remove rocker arms and push rods. See ROCKER ARMS & PUSH RODS under REMOVAL & INSTALLATION in this article.
2) Remove push rod guide bolts and push rod guide. *See Fig. 7.* Remove valve lifter guide and valve lifters. Mark component locations for reassembly reference.

Installation – To install, reverse removal procedure. Apply Engine Oil Supplement (1052367) to valve lifters prior to installation. Ensure components are installed in original location.

CAMSHAFT

Removal – **1)** Remove engine. See ENGINE REMOVAL & INSTALLATION article. Remove intake manifold. See INTAKE MANIFOLD under REMOVAL & INSTALLATION in this article.
2) Remove rocker arms and push rods. See ROCKER ARMS & PUSH RODS under REMOVAL & INSTALLATION in this article. Remove valve lifters. Remove timing chain and sprockets. See TIMING CHAIN & SPROCKETS under REMOVAL & INSTALLATION in this article. Remove camshaft and bearings (if required).

Inspection – Inspect camshaft journal diameter, lobe lift and oil clearance. See CAMSHAFT table in ENGINE SPECIFICATIONS at end of article. Replace components if not within specification.

NOTE: Lubricate camshaft bearings and camshaft lobes with GM Lubricant (1052365) prior to installation.

Installation – **1)** Install camshaft bearings (if removed). Ensure oil holes are aligned. Apply Sealant (1052914) to rear camshaft plug prior to installation. Lubricate camshaft bearings and camshaft lobes with GM Lubricant (1052365) prior to installation. Install camshaft.
2) To install remaining components, reverse removal procedure. Ensure components are installed in original location and all timing marks are aligned.

BALANCE SHAFT (3.8L)

Removal – **1)** Remove engine. See ENGINE REMOVAL & INSTALLATION article.
2) Remove flywheel. Remove intake manifold. See INTAKE MANIFOLD under REMOVAL & INSTALLATION in this article. Remove lifter guide retainer. *See Fig. 7.*
3) Remove front timing case cover. See FRONT TIMING CASE COVER under REMOVAL & INSTALLATION in this article. Remove balance shaft gear bolt. *See Fig. 8.* Remove camshaft sprocket and timing chain.
4) Remove bolts from balance shaft retainer. *See Fig. 8.* Remove balance shaft retainer and balance shaft gear. Install Slide Hammer (J-6125-B) in front of balance shaft and remove balance shaft. Remove balance shaft plug from rear of cylinder block.
5) Note direction of rear bearing installation. Using Rear Bearing Remover (J-36995-5), remove bearing from block. *See Fig. 9.*

NOTE: Balance shaft and bearings are serviced as complete assembly only. Proper installation tools must be used to prevent balance shaft damage.

Inspection – Inspect components for damage. Measure bearing bore I.D. Replace components if not within specification. See BALANCE SHAFT SPECIFICATIONS table.
Installation – **1)** Lubricate balance shaft bearings with engine oil. Install rear bearing with rolled edge facing inward, toward engine, and

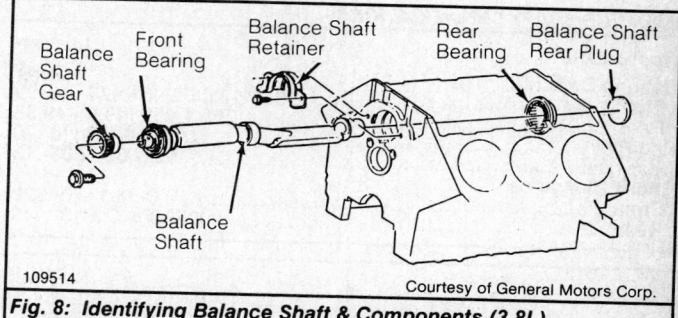

Fig. 8: Identifying Balance Shaft & Components (3.8L)

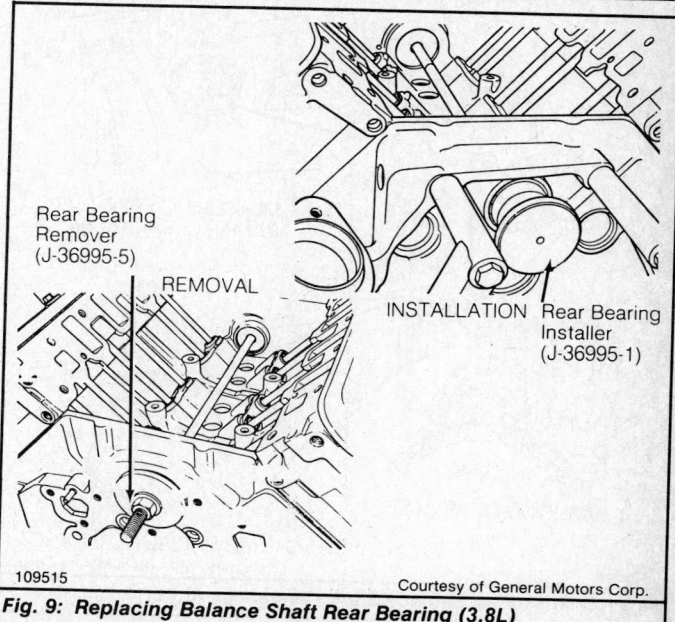

Fig. 9: Replacing Balance Shaft Rear Bearing (3.8L)

manufacturer's marking facing flywheel side of engine. Using Rear Bearing Installer (J-36995-1), install rear bearing. *See Fig. 9.*

NOTE: Install balance shaft rear bearing with rolled edge facing inward, toward engine, and manufacturer's marking facing flywheel side of engine.

2) Using Balance Shaft Installer (J-36996), install balance shaft. Temporarily install balance shaft retainer and bolts. Install balance shaft gear. Apply GM Threadlock (12345493) to gear retaining bolt, and install bolt. Tighten gear retaining bolt to specification. See TORQUE SPECIFICATIONS table at end of article.
3) Install balance shaft rear plug. Using dial indicator, measure balance shaft end play and radial clearance at front and rear of balance shaft. *See Fig. 10.* Replace components if not within specification. See BALANCE SHAFT SPECIFICATIONS table.
4) Rotate camshaft so timing mark is downward when sprocket is installed. With camshaft sprocket and gear removed, rotate balance shaft so timing mark on gear is downward.
5) Align timing marks on camshaft gear and balance shaft gear by rotating balance shaft, and install camshaft gear. *See Fig. 6.* Rotate crankshaft so No. 1 piston is at TDC. Install timing chain and sprocket. Ensure timing marks are aligned. *See Fig. 6.*
6) Using dial indicator, measure gear lash at 4 places. Gear lash should be within specification. See BALANCE SHAFT SPECIFICATIONS table. If all measurements are within specification, tighten balance shaft retainer bolts to specification. See TORQUE SPECIFICATIONS table at end of article. To install remaining components, reverse removal procedure.

BALANCE SHAFT SPECIFICATIONS

Application	In. (mm)
Bearing Bore I.D.	
Front	2.0462-2.0472 (51.973-51.999)
Rear	1.950-1.952 (49.53-49.58)
End Play	0-.008 (0-.20)
Gear Lash	.002-.005 (.05-.13)
Radial Clearance	
Front	0-.0011 (0-.028)
Rear	.0005-.0047 (.013-.119)

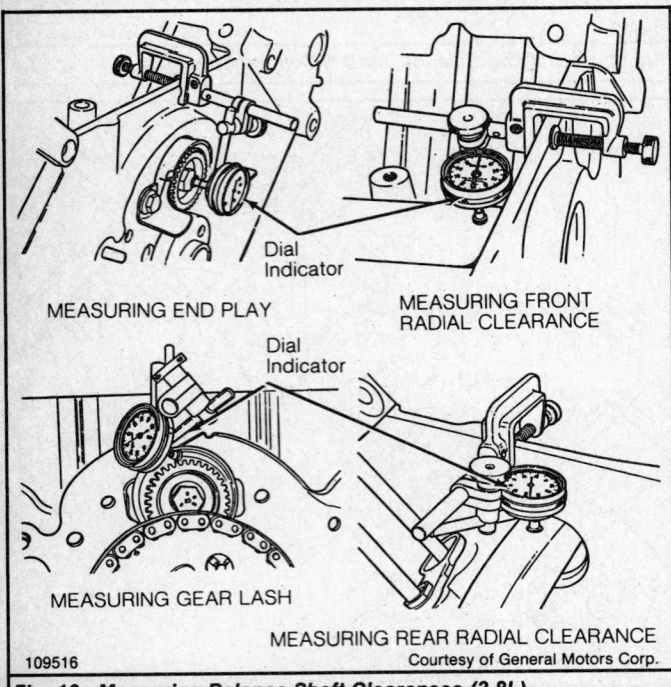

MEASURING END PLAY

MEASURING FRONT RADIAL CLEARANCE

MEASURING GEAR LASH

MEASURING REAR RADIAL CLEARANCE

Courtesy of General Motors Corp.

Fig. 10: Measuring Balance Shaft Clearances (3.8L)

REAR CRANKSHAFT OIL SEAL

Removal – 1) For seal replacement, engine must be removed. See ENGINE under REMOVAL & INSTALLATION in this article. Remove flywheel. Confirm rear seal leak.

2) To remove seal, pry around dust lip using a screwdriver or similar tool. DO NOT damage crankshaft O.D. surface or chamfer. Ensure seal areas are clean.

Installation – 1) Apply engine oil to new seal. Install seal using Seal Installer (J-38196). Align dowel pin of installer with dowel pin hole in crankshaft. Tighten installer attaching screws to 60 INCH lbs. (5 N.m).

2) Rotate handle of installer until collar is tight against case. Reverse removal procedure for remaining components.

WATER PUMP

Removal & Installation – 1) Disconnect negative battery cable. Drain cooling system. Remove water pump drive belt. Disconnect necessary coolant hoses.

2) Remove water pump pulley bolts and pulley (access hole in body side rail for long bolt). Remove water pump bolts, water pump and gasket. To install, reverse removal procedure using new gasket. Fill cooling system.

OIL PAN

Removal & Installation – 1) Disconnect negative battery cable. Raise and support vehicle. Drain crankcase and remove oil filter. Remove flexplate access cover and crossover pipe (if equipped).

2) Disconnect engine mounts. Raise and support engine. Remove oil pan bolts and oil pan. To install, reverse removal procedure. Tighten bolts to specification. See TORQUE SPECIFICATIONS at end of this article.

OVERHAUL

CYLINDER HEAD

Inspection – 1) Inspect cylinder head for warpage at deck surface and manifold surfaces. Resurface cylinder head if warpage exceeds specification. See CYLINDER HEAD table in ENGINE SPECIFICATIONS at end of article.

2) Check amount of metal removed from cylinder head to determine if head can be used. To determine amount removed, use depth micrometer and measure the distance from deck surface to the 3 cast pads. *See Fig. 11.*

3) Measurement should be .054-.066" (1.37-1.68 mm) on new cylinder heads. Minimum dimension is .044" (1.12 mm). Replace cylinder head if measurement is less than minimum dimension.

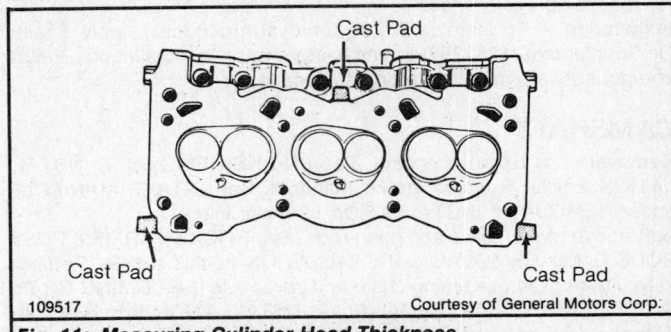

Cast Pad

Cast Pad

Cast Pad

109517

Courtesy of General Motors Corp.

Fig. 11: Measuring Cylinder Head Thickness

Valve Seats – No replacement procedure is given by manufacturer.

Valve Guides – Valve guides must be reamed for an oversized valve if valve stem oil clearance is not within specification. See CYLINDER HEAD table in ENGINE SPECIFICATIONS at end of article.

Seat Correction Angles – After grinding, if seat width is too wide, a 20-degree or 70-degree stone can be used to reduce seat width. The 20-degree stone will lower the seat, and the 70-degree stone will raise the seat.

Valve Spring Installed Height – 1) Install valve, valve retainer and keepers. Pull upward on valve and measure height from top of spring seat to spring side of the valve retainer. *See Fig. 12.*

2) Spring installed height must be within specification. See VALVES & VALVE SPRINGS table in ENGINE SPECIFICATIONS at end of article. If measurement exceeds specification, add shims under the valve spring to obtain correct height.

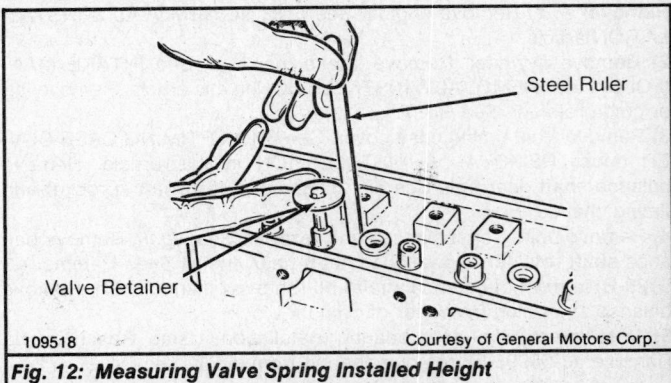

Steel Ruler

Valve Retainer

109518

Courtesy of General Motors Corp.

Fig. 12: Measuring Valve Spring Installed Height

Valve Stem Height – With valve installed in cylinder and in closed position, use steel ruler to measure distance from spring seat to the valve tip. Distance should be 1.935-1.975" (49.15-50.16 mm).

Valve Stem Oil Seals – Oversized valve stem oil seals are used for oversized valves. Intake and exhaust valve stem oil seals are different. Proper oil seal must be installed according to part number.

CYLINDER BLOCK ASSEMBLY

Cylinder Block – Using feeler gauge and straightedge, inspect deck surface for warpage. Replace cylinder block if more than .010" (.25 mm) material is removed from deck surface.

Piston Ring Installation – Install piston rings with identification mark toward top of piston and rings properly spaced. *See Fig. 13.*

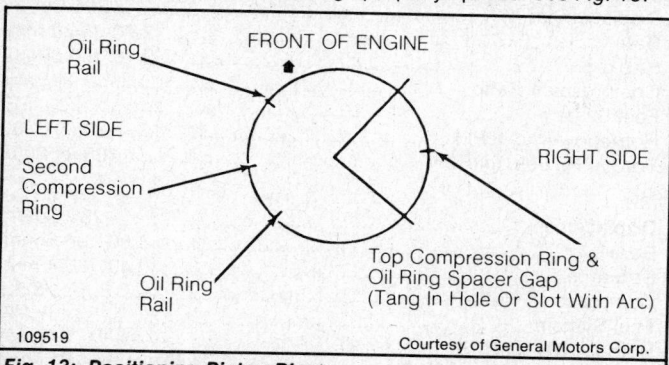

109519   Courtesy of General Motors Corp.

Fig. 13: Positioning Piston Rings

Piston & Rod Assembly – Piston can be installed on connecting rod in either direction. Piston and connecting rod must be installed with 2 parallel ridges on bottom of pin boss toward front of engine.

Fitting Pistons – **1)** On 3.3L models, piston diameter should be measured 1.65" (41.9 mm) from top of piston.

2) On 3.8L models, piston diameter should be measured 1.74" (44.2 mm) from top of piston.

NOTE: On all models, oversized pistons must not be machined down or engine balance will be affected.

Crankshaft & Main Bearings – **1)** Rear crankshaft oil seal must be installed prior to crankshaft installation. See REAR CRANKSHAFT OIL SEAL under REMOVAL & INSTALLATION in this article.

2) To align crankshaft thrust surfaces, install all bearings and main caps and tighten all bolts evenly. Loosen all bolts one turn.

3) Retighten all bolts to 90 ft. lbs. (122 N.m). Using wooden mallet, carefully tap crankshaft forward then backward to align thrust bearing.

CAUTION: Bearing inserts must not be shimmed, scraped or filed. Do not touch bearing surface with fingers.

CAUTION: Misalignment of main bearing cap toward transaxle can cause interference with the flywheel-to-converter bolt.

Rod Bearings – **1)** Ensure bearing cap bolt holes and mating surfaces are clean and dry. Use connecting rod stud protector on all rod cap bolts. Install inserts in connecting rod and cap. Lubricate bearings and crank pin.

2) Install bearing cap. Tighten rod bearing cap bolts to 20 ft. lbs. (27 N.m). Tighten bolts an additional 50 degrees using Torque Angle Meter (J-36660).

Crankshaft Flange Runout – **1)** With engine removed and crankshaft installed, measure crankshaft flange runout. Mount dial indicator gauge plate flat against crankshaft flange. Place dial indicator stem on lower left transmission mounting bolt boss (flat area around bolt hole). Adjust indicator to zero.

2) Observe and record readings obtained on all mounting bolt hole bosses. Measurements should not vary more than .010" (.25 mm). If readings exceed specification, remount dial gauge plate and recheck flange runout. Replace crankshaft if runout exceeds specification.

ENGINE OILING

LUBRICATION SYSTEM

The crankshaft driven gear-type oil pump provides pressurized lubrication to the main gallery. *See Fig. 14.* Oil pump and pressure regulator valve are located in the front timing case cover.

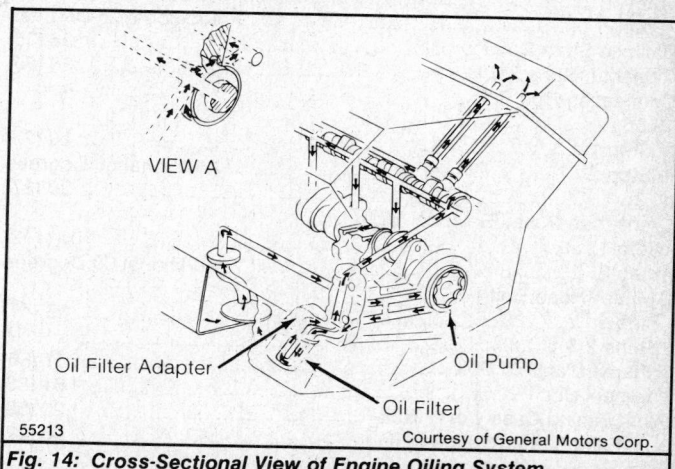

55213   Courtesy of General Motors Corp.

Fig. 14: Cross-Sectional View of Engine Oiling System

Crankcase Capacity – Engine oil capacity is approximately 4 qts. (3.7L) with filter change. Recheck oil level after changing filter.

Normal Oil Pressure – Normal oil pressure is 60 psi (4.2 kg/cm²) at 1850 RPM with 5W-30 engine oil and engine at normal operating temperature.

OIL PUMP

Removal – Remove front timing case cover. See FRONT TIMING CASE COVER under REMOVAL & INSTALLATION in this article. Remove oil filter adapter, gasket, pressure regulator and valve from front timing case cover. Remove pump cover and gears from case cover.

Inspection – **1)** Inspect components for damage. Measure gear end clearance. Measure housing gear pocket depth and diameter. Measure outer gear-to-housing clearance and tip clearance between gears.

2) Check clearance between pressure regulator valve and bore. Replace components or pump assembly if not within specification. See OIL PUMP SPECIFICATIONS table.

Reassembly & Installation – To reassemble, reverse disassembly procedure. Lubricate all gears and fill cavities with petroleum jelly. Install pump cover. To install, reverse removal procedure. Tighten cover screws to 97 INCH lbs. (11 N.m). Tighten oil filter adapter bolts to 24 ft. lbs. (33 N.m).

OIL PUMP SPECIFICATIONS

Application	In. (mm)
Gear End Clearance	.0010-.0035 (.025-.089)
Gear Tip Clearance	.006 (.15)
Housing Gear Pocket	
Depth	.4610-.4625 (11.709-11.748)
Diameter	3.508-3.512 (89.10-89.20)
Outer Gear-To-Housing	.008-.015 (.20-.38)
Pressure Regulator Valve-To-Bore	.0015-.0030 (.038-.076)

1991 ENGINES
3.3L & 3.8L V6 (Cont.)

TORQUE SPECIFICATIONS

TORQUE SPECIFICATIONS

Application	Ft. Lbs. (N.m)
Balance Shaft Gear Bolt [1]	
Step 1	14 (19)
Step 2	Additional 35 Degrees
Balance Shaft Retainer Bolt	26 (35)
Camshaft Sprocket Bolt	26 (35)
Connecting Rod Bolt	
3.3L	
Step 1	20 (27)
Step 2	Additional 50 Degrees
3.8L	20 (27)
Crankshaft Pulley/Balancer Bolt	
Step 1	105 (142)
Step 2	Additional 50 Degrees
Cylinder Head Bolt [1]	
Step 1	35 (47)
Steps 2 & 3	[2]
Exhaust Manifold Bolt	41 (56)
Flywheel Bolt	[1] 61 (83)
Front Timing Case Cover Bolt	[1] 22 (30)
Fuel Feed & Return Line Fitting	20 (27)
Main Bearing Cap Bolt	
Step 1	26 (35)
Step 2	Additional 50 Degrees
Oil Filter Adapter-To-Case Cover Bolt	24 (33)
Oil Pan Bolt	[1] 10 (14)
Rocker Arm Bolt	[1] 28 (38)
Throttle Body Adapter-To-Manifold Bolt	20 (27)
Throttle Body Bolt	20 (27)
Timing Chain Damper Bolt	14 (19)
Valve Lifter Guide Bolt	27 (37)
Water Pump Bolt	[3]

Application	INCH Lbs. (N.m)
Intake Manifold Bolt	[1][4] 88 (10)
Oil Pump Cover Bolt	97 (11)
Oil Screen-To-Block Bolt	115 (13)
Valve Cover Bolt	[1] 88 (10)

[1] – Apply thread sealant to bolt.
[2] – Step 2 – Tighten all bolts an additional 130 degrees.
Step 3 – Tighten center 4 bolts in sequence an additional 30 degrees. See Fig. 3.
[3] – Tighten water pump-to-timing case cover bolts to 97 INCH lbs. (11 N.m) and water pump-to-cylinder block bolts to 29 ft. lbs. (39 N.m).
[4] – Tighten bolts TWICE in sequence. See Fig. 2.

ENGINE SPECIFICATIONS

GENERAL SPECIFICATIONS

Application	Specification
3.3L	
Displacement	204 Cu. In.
Bore	3.70" (94.0 mm)
Stroke	3.16" (80.3 mm)
Compression Ratio	9.0:1
Fuel System	PFI
Horsepower @ RPM	160 @ 5200
Torque Ft. Lbs. @ RPM	185 @ 2000
3.8L	
Displacement	231 Cu. In.
Bore	3.80" (96.5 mm)
Stroke	3.40" (86.4 mm)
Compression Ratio	8.5:1
Fuel System	PFI
Horsepower @ RPM	
VIN C (Engine Code LN3)	165 @ 5200
VIN L (Engine Code L27)	170 @ 4800
Torque Ft. Lbs. @ RPM	
VIN C (Engine Code LN3)	210 @ 2000
VIN L (Engine Code L27)	220 @ 3200

CRANKSHAFT, MAIN & CONNECTING ROD BEARINGS

Application	In. (mm)
3.3L & 3.8L	
Crankshaft End Play	.003-.011 (.08-.28)
Main Bearings	
Journal Diameter	2.4988-2.4998 (63.469-63.495)
Journal Out-Of-Round	.0003 (.008)
Journal Taper	.0003 (.008)
Oil Clearance	.0003-.0018 (.008-.046)
Connecting Rod Bearings	
Journal Diameter	2.2487-2.2499 (57.117-57.147)
Journal Out-Of-Round	.0003 (.008)
Journal Taper	.0003 (.008)
Oil Clearance	.0003-.0026 (.008-.066)

CONNECTING RODS

Application	In. (mm)
3.3L & 3.8L	
Maximum Bend	[1] .005 (.13)
Maximum Twist	[1] .010 (.25)
Side Play	.003-.015 (.08-.38)

[1] – Bend or twist over total length.

VALVES & VALVE SPRINGS

Application	Specification
3.3L & 3.8L	
Intake & Exhaust Valves	
Face Angle	45°
Minimum Margin	.025" (.64 mm)
Valve Springs	
Installed Height	1.690-1.720" (42.93-43.69 mm)
Pressure	Lbs. @ In. (kg @ mm)
Valve Closed	80 @ 1.720 (36 @ 43.69)
Valve Open	210 @ 1.315 (95 @ 33.40)

PISTONS, PINS & RINGS

Application	In. (mm)
3.3L & 3.8L	
Pistons	
Clearance	.0004-.0022 (.010-.056)
Pins	
Diameter	.9053-.9055 (22.994-23.000)
Piston Fit	.0004-.0008 (.010-.020)
Rod Fit	.0007-.0017 (.018-.043)
Rings	
No. 1	
End Gap	.010-.025 (.25-.64)
Side Clearance	.0013-.0031 (.033-.079)
No. 2	
End Gap	.010-.025 (.25-.64)
Side Clearance	.0013-.0031 (.033-.079)
No. 3 (Oil)	
End Gap	
3.3L	.010-.040 (.25-1.02)
3.8L	.015-.055 (.38-1.40)
Side Clearance	.0011-.0081 (.028-.206)

CYLINDER BLOCK

Application	In. (mm)
3.3L & 3.8L	
Cylinder Bore	
Diameter	
3.3L	3.70 (93.9)
3.8L	3.80 (96.5)
Maximum Taper	.0005 (.013)
Maximum Out-Of-Round	.0004 (.010)

CYLINDER HEAD

Application	Specification
3.3L & 3.8L	
Maximum Warpage	.010" (.25 mm)
Valve Seats	
Intake Valve	
Seat Angle	45°
Seat Width	.060-.080" (1.53-2.03 mm)
Exhaust Valve	
Seat Angle	45°
Seat Width	.090-.110" (2.29-2.79 mm)
Valve Guides	
Intake Valve	
Valve Guide Oil Clearance	.0015-.0035" (.038-.089 mm)
Exhaust Valve	
Valve Guide Oil Clearance	.0015-.0032" (.038-.081 mm)

CAMSHAFT

Application	In. (mm)
3.3L & 3.8L	
Journal Diameter	1.785-1.786 (45.34-45.36)
Lobe Lift	
Intake	.250 (6.35)
Exhaust	.255 (6.48)
Oil Clearance	.0005-.0035 (.013-.089)

Cutlass Supreme, Grand Prix, Lumina

NOTE: For repair procedures not covered in this article, see ENGINE OVERHAUL PROCEDURES article in GENERAL INFORMATION.

ENGINE IDENTIFICATION

Engine may be identified by the eighth character of Vehicle Identification Number (VIN) located on top of instrument panel near lower left corner of windshield. See ENGINE IDENTIFICATION CODE table.

Partial VIN number and engine code or identification number can be found on engine block in either stampings, stick-on labels, or laser etchings. The first character indicates manufacturer, and second character indicates the year. *See Fig. 1.*

ENGINE IDENTIFICATION CODE

Engine	Code
3.4L DOHC V6	X

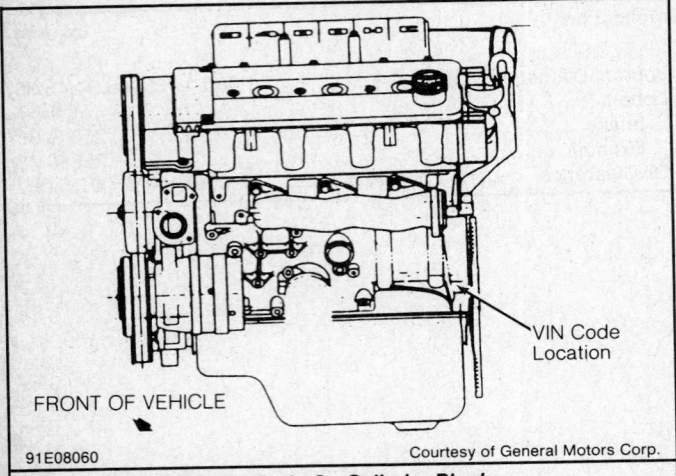

FRONT OF VEHICLE

VIN Code Location

91E08060   Courtesy of General Motors Corp.

Fig. 1: Locating Engine Code On Cylinder Block

ADJUSTMENTS

VALVE CLEARANCE ADJUSTMENT

No valve adjustment is required, as hydraulic valve lifters are used.

REMOVAL & INSTALLATION

NOTE: For reassembly reference, label all electrical connectors, vacuum hoses and fuel lines before removal. Also place mating marks on engine hood and other major assemblies before removal.

FUEL PRESSURE RELEASE

1) Remove fuel filler cap. Raise and support vehicle. Disconnect fuel pump electrical connector. Lower vehicle. Start engine and run until engine dies.
2) Crank starter for 3 seconds to ensure fuel pressure is depleted. Raise vehicle. Connect fuel pump electrical connector. Lower vehicle.
3) Disconnect negative battery cable to prevent accidental fuel pump engagement. Proceed with servicing.

ENGINE

NOTE: On automatic transaxle vehicles, remove engine from above. On manual transaxle vehicles, remove engine from below.

Removal (Automatic Transaxle) – 1) Release fuel pressure. See FUEL PRESSURE RELEASE under REMOVAL & INSTALLATION in this article. Remove air cleaner and duct assembly. Remove hood.

Drain cooling system. For proper drainage, open air bleed vents on thermostat housing and heater coolant inlet pipe.
2) Discharge A/C system. Remove coolant recovery tank. Disconnect heater hoses from engine. Remove engine torque strut mount and strut. Remove cooling fans. Disconnect and remove engine radiator hoses.
3) Disconnect control cables at throttle body. To disconnect accelerator control cable, remove lower instrument panel trim and disconnect accelerator cable at pedal. Push accelerator cable through bulkhead. Disconnect cable at throttle body.
4) Remove bulkhead connector from cowl. Disconnect fuel lines. Remove exhaust crossover pipe. Remove transaxle-to-engine bolts including ground wires. Disconnect power steering lines at pump and front cover. Disconnect EGR pipe from EGR valve. Raise and support vehicle.
5) Remove front wheels and right front splash shield. Remove A/C manifold from compressor. Remove flywheel inspection cover and starter. Remove front exhaust pipe and catalytic converter. Remove motor mount nuts from frame. Disconnect electrical connections from rear of engine.
6) Remove steel torque converter inspection cover and torque converter bolts. Disconnect electrical connections from front of engine. Remove right ball joint nut and separate from control arm. Disconnect right drive axle from transaxle and hub. Remove drive axle. Remove motor mount bracket-to-transaxle bolts and nuts.
7) Disconnect electrical connections from generator. Lower vehicle and support transaxle. Install engine lifting device. Disconnect quick connects near ECM. Remove remaining transaxle-to-engine bolt. Remove engine assembly out the top. Disconnect vacuum lines from rear of engine during removal.
Installation – 1) Install engine assembly. Connect vacuum lines to rear of engine during installation. Install two transaxle-to-engine bolts. Connect quick connects near ECM. Remove engine lifting device and transaxle support. Raise and support vehicle.
2) Connect electrical connectors to generator. Install motor mount bracket-to-transaxle nuts and bolts. Install drive axle to transaxle and hub. Install ball joint into control arm, and install nut. Connect electrical connections to front of engine.
3) Install torque converter bolts and steel torque converter inspection cover. Connect electrical connections to front of engine. Install motor mount nuts at frame. Install front exhaust pipe and catalytic converter. Install starter and flywheel inspection cover. Install A/C manifold to compressor.
4) Install right front splash shield and front wheels. Lower vehicle. Connect EGR pipe to EGR valve. Connect power steering lines at pump and front cover. Install remaining transaxle-to-engine bolts including all ground wires. Install exhaust crossover pipe and connect fuel lines. Install bulkhead connector to cowl.
5) Install control cables to bracket and throttle body. Install radiator and connect hoses to engine. Install cooling fans, engine torque strut bracket and strut. Connect heater hoses to engine.
6) Install coolant recovery tank and refill cooling system. Evacuate and charge A/C system. Fill and bleed power steering system. Install hood, air cleaner assembly and ducts. Add fluids as needed.
Removal (Manual Transaxle) – 1) Release fuel pressure. See FUEL PRESSURE RELEASE under REMOVAL & INSTALLATION in this article. Remove air cleaner and duct assembly. Drain cooling system. For proper drainage, open air bleed vents on thermostat housing and heater coolant inlet pipe.
2) Disconnect control cables at throttle body. To disconnect accelerator control cable, remove lower instrument panel trim and disconnect accelerator cable at pedal. Push accelerator cable through bulkhead. Disconnect cable at throttle body.
3) Remove serpentine belt. See SERPENTINE BELT & TENSIONER under REMOVAL & INSTALLATION in this article. Remove wiring harness cover. Disconnect upper engine wire connectors at right strut tower. Disconnect negative battery ground cable at body. Disconnect positive battery cable at battery and remote jumper terminal.
4) Disconnect engine ground near air cleaner bracket. Disconnect fuel lines from fuel rails. Disconnect heater hose quick connect at intake manifold and bracket. Remove engine torque strut.

5) Disconnect upper and lower radiator hoses at engine. Disconnect heater hoses near coolant pump. Remove engine torque strut bracket at frame. Remove right and left cooling fan retaining screws. Remove upper radiator support screws and support.

6) Remove both fan assemblies and disconnect electrical connectors. Disconnect electrical bulkhead connector at right-side firewall. Remove ECM and place on engine. Remove convenience center, wiring harness cover, harness clips and low coolant sensor electrical connector. Position entire harness assembly on top of engine.

7) Remove wiring harness clips near front of frame. Discharge A/C system. Disconnect A/C lines near accumulator. Disconnect shift control cable at lever and bracket. Disconnect necessary vacuum lines. Remove strut retaining nuts.

8) Raise and support vehicle. Remove front wheels. Remove flywheel covers. Drain engine crankcase and remove oil filter. Remove starter motor. Remove flywheel-to-drive plate bolts. Remove left and right engine splash shields.

9) Disconnect front brake ABS electrical connectors (if equipped). Remove front exhaust pipe and catalytic converter assembly. Remove front brake calipers, and wire calipers to body. Remove intermediate steering shaft pinch bolt and shaft from stub.

10) Support engine/transaxle. Disconnect transaxle cooler lines, and plug lines. Remove frame bolts. Remove engine/transaxle assembly. Disconnect electrical connectors and harness from left lower side of engine. Remove A/C compressor with lines still attached.

11) Disconnect electrical connectors and remove harness from rear of engine including generator, sensors, ground and clips. Remove exhaust crossover pipe. Disconnect right drive axle from transaxle. Remove engine mount bracket-to-transaxle bolts.

12) Remove power steering pump, lines and bracket from engine. Remove transaxle-to-engine bolts including all electrical grounds. Install engine lifting device. Lower engine assembly from transaxle and frame assembly.

Installation – 1) Install engine assembly to transaxle and frame assembly. Remove engine lifting device. Install transaxle-to-engine bolts including electrical grounds. Install power steering pump, lines and bracket.

2) Install engine mount nuts at frame. Install engine mount bracket to transaxle bolts. Install drive axle shields and retaining screws. Reconnect right drive axle to transaxle. Install exhaust crossover pipe.

3) Reconnect electrical connector and harness to rear of engine including generator, sensors, grounds and clips. Install A/C compressor with lines attached. Reconnect electrical connectors and harness to left lower side of engine. Install engine/transaxle assembly.

4) Install frame bolts. Reconnect transaxle cooler lines. Remove transmission table. Install intermediate steering shaft pinch bolt and shaft into stub. Install front brake calipers. Install front exhaust pipe and catalytic converter assembly.

5) Reconnect front brake ABS electrical connectors (if equipped). Install splash shields. Install flywheel-to-drive plate bolts. Install starter motor and new oil filter, and refill crankcase. Install flywheel covers and front wheels. Lower vehicle and install strut retaining nuts.

6) Connect all necessary vacuum lines. Connect shift control cable at lever and bracket. Connect A/C lines near accumulator. Evacuate and charge A/C system. Install wiring harness clips near front of frame. Install convenience center, wiring harness cover and harness clips, and connect low coolant sensor electrical connector.

7) Install ECM. Connect electrical bulkhead connector at right-side dash mat inside passenger compartment. Install both fan assemblies and reconnect electrical connectors. Install radiator support and screws. Install cooling fan retaining screws. Install engine torque strut bracket at frame.

8) Connect heater hose near coolant pump and upper and lower radiator hoses at engine. Install engine torque strut. Connect heater hose quick connect at intake manifold and bracket. Reconnect fuel lines at fuel rail. Reconnect positive battery cable and remote jump terminal.

9) Reconnect negative battery cable at battery and body. Install wiring harness cover and upper engine wire connectors at right strut tower. Install serpentine belt. See SERPENTINE BELT & TENSIONER under REMOVAL & INSTALLATION in this article.

10) Install coolant recovery tank (if removed) and refill cooling system. Reconnect control cables at throttle body. Fill and bleed power steering system. Install air cleaner and duct assembly. Adjust fluid levels as necessary. Adjust wheel alignment if necessary.

SERPENTINE BELT & TENSIONER

Removal & Installation – Remove coolant recovery tank. Rotate belt tensioner clockwise with a wrench. Remove belt. Remove tensioner bolt and tensioner. *See Fig. 2.* To install, reverse removal procedure. Ensure proper belt routing.

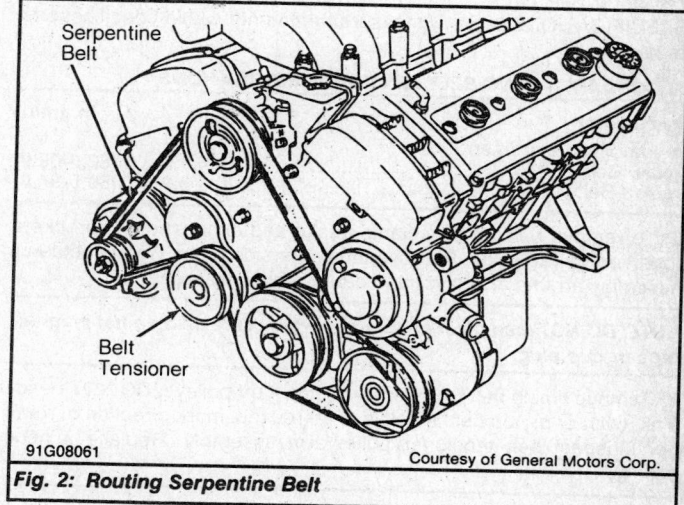

91G08061
Courtesy of General Motors Corp.

Fig. 2: Routing Serpentine Belt

ENGINE OIL COOLER ASSEMBLY

Removal – 1) Remove air cleaner. Disconnect negative battery cable. Drain cooling system. Raise and support vehicle. Place drain pan below engine to catch any fluids.

2) Remove oil filter. Disconnect outlet and inlet hoses, and position hoses aside. Remove connector, oil cooler and adapter. *See Fig. 3.*

Installation – Clean mating surface of engine block. Coat gasket with engine oil. To install, reverse removal procedure. *See Fig. 3.* Tighten connector to specification. See TORQUE SPECIFICATIONS at end of this article.

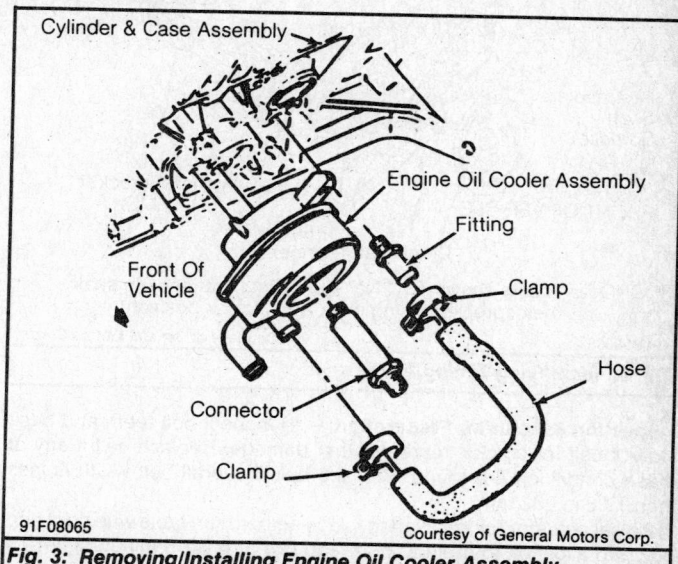

91F08065
Courtesy of General Motors Corp.

Fig. 3: Removing/Installing Engine Oil Cooler Assembly

SECONDARY TIMING BELT

Removal – 1) Remove air cleaner and duct assembly. Remove coolant recovery tank and serpentine belt. Siphon fluid from power steering pump. Remove power steering pump. Remove secondary timing belt covers.

2) Inspect drive and components for excessive wear or unusual conditions. Note any evidence of oil or other fluid intrusion.

3) Rotate engine clockwise to align timing marks (TDC No. 1 exhaust) on cam sprockets and intermediate shaft, if possible. See Fig. 4. If no timing marks are present, refer to CAM TIMING PROCEDURE under REMOVAL & INSTALLATION in this article.

4) Check tensioner pulley position to determine if length of belt is satisfactory. Measure actuator from center line of trunnion to end of rubber boot. See Fig. 5. See SECONDARY TIMING BELT TENSION SPECIFICATIONS table. If measurement is not within specifications, replace belt.

SECONDARY TIMING BELT TENSION SPECIFICATIONS

Application	In. (mm)
Actuator Measurement	
New Belt	3.2-3.5 (80.5-89.0)
Used Belt	3.2-3.7 (80.5-94.0)

5) To remove belt, loosely clamp intake and exhaust cam sprockets together on each side. Remove tensioner side plate. Rotate actuator assembly around arm pivot and out of mounting base.

NOTE: DO NOT lose pivot bushing. Hold in place using a flat magnet, tape or cup plug.

6) Remove timing belt by carefully sliding it off pulleys. DO NOT bend, kink, twist or pry on belt. If belt is to be reused, mark direction of rotation. Inspect belt tensioner pulley/arm assembly. Replace if necessary.

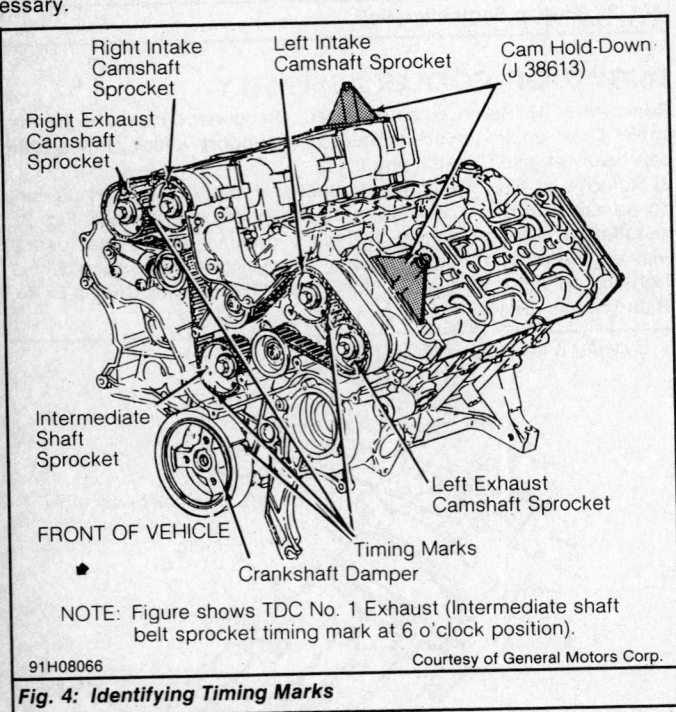

NOTE: Figure shows TDC No. 1 Exhaust (Intermediate shaft belt sprocket timing mark at 6 o'clock position).

91H08066   Courtesy of General Motors Corp.

Fig. 4: Identifying Timing Marks

Inspection & Actuator Preparation – 1) Inspect belt teeth and back side of belt for cracks, tears or other damage. Replace belt if any of these conditions are found. Replace belt if overall belt width is less than 1.26 in. (32 mm).

2) To set actuator for installation, place actuator on table with boot end down to allow oil to drain to boot end (for at least 5 minutes). When removing tensioner assembly, DO NOT lose or damage the tapered bushing between actuator and mounting base.

3) Hold actuator vertically and remove rubber end plug from rear of actuator. See Fig. 5. DO NOT remove vent plug.

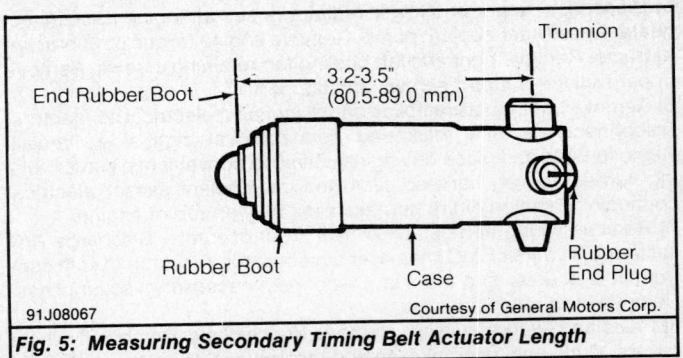

91J08067   Courtesy of General Motors Corp.

Fig. 5: Measuring Secondary Timing Belt Actuator Length

CAUTION: If securing actuator in a vise or other holding fixture, DO NOT damage actuator case or boot. Replace actuator if damaged.

4) Straighten a paper clip and push through center hole in vent plug and into pilot hole. Rotate actuator end screw with a small screwdriver in clockwise direction while pushing rod tip against table top until fully retracted.

5) Rotate screw slot to align with vent hole. Bend section of paper clip into screw slot to retain plunger in retracted position. If tensioner oil has been lost, fill tensioner with SAE 5W-30 engine oil through plug hole. Fill to bottom of plug hole only when plunger is fully retracted and pin is installed.

Installation – 1) Install rubber end plug in rear of actuator assembly until flush. Ensure plug is sealed against case. Install actuator bushing into side plate.

NOTE: Ensure bushings and appropriate holes are clean. DO NOT lubricate bushings.

2) Install actuator assembly into mounting base by inserting tapered trunnion of tensioner into matching hole of bushing in bracket and installing side plate and bolts. Tighten bolts to specification. See TORQUE SPECIFICATIONS at end of this article.

3) Ensure timing marks on sprockets are properly aligned. See Fig. 4. Install timing belt by routing around idlers and sprockets. DO NOT bend, kink, twist or pry on belt. Start at intermediate cam sprocket and work counterclockwise. Ensure belt is installed in direction of rotation.

4) Engage teeth into all sprockets, place rubber hose behind belt at intermediate sprocket and take up slack at tensioner.

5) Install tensioner pulley to mounting base (if removed). Use a flat magnet, tape or cup plug to hold pivot tube in pulley for installation. After starting pivot bolt, rotate arm counterclockwise to position square lug at 6 o'clock.

6) Tighten bolt to 37 ft. lbs. (50 N.m). DO NOT lubricate arm bushing and pivot. Inspect actuator assembly to assure it is free and rotates under its own weight.

7) Gently rotate tensioner pulley counterclockwise into belt using square lug in arm. Engage actuator shaft in arm socket. Remove and discard paper clip and allow pulley to move into belt.

8) Remove sprocket clamps. Gently rotate tensioner pulley counterclockwise into belt, and apply 12-15 ft. lbs. (16-20 N.m) of torque to tensioner pulley to set initial tension on belt.

9) Rotate engine clockwise (as viewed from front) three times to seat belt. DO NOT reverse rotation. Check sprocket reference marks to ensure correct timing. See Fig. 4. Inspect tensioner pulley position to confirm belt length. See step **4)** of removal procedure. Reverse removal procedure for remaining components.

CRANKSHAFT DAMPER, CRANKSHAFT PULLEY & FRONT COVER OIL SEAL

Removal & Installation – 1) Remove serpentine belt. See SERPENTINE BELT & TENSIONER under REMOVAL & INSTALLATION in this article. Raise and support vehicle. Remove right front wheel and engine splash shield.

2) Remove starter motor. Remove crankshaft damper bolt. *See Fig. 6.* Remove crankshaft pulley bolts and pulley. Install Damper Remover (J 24420-B) onto damper. Rotate puller screw and remove damper.

3) Pry out old front cover oil seal with large screwdriver. DO NOT damage crankshaft. Inspect crankshaft and front cover for scratches.

Installation – 1) Lubricate new seal with clean engine oil. Insert seal in front cover with lip facing engine. Drive seal into place using Oil Seal Installer (J 34995).

2) Coat front cover seal contact area on damper with engine oil. Apply Sealant (GM 9985059) to keyway of damper before installing damper. Place damper in position over key on crankshaft.

3) Push damper onto crankshaft using Damper Installer (J 29113). Install crankshaft pulley. Reverse removal procedure for remaining components. Tighten bolts to specification. See TORQUE SPECIFICATIONS at end of this article.

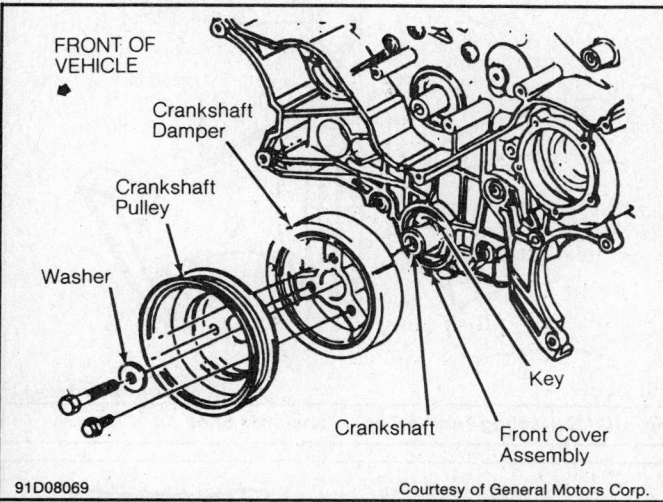

91D08069   Courtesy of General Motors Corp.

Fig. 6: Exploded View Of Crankshaft Pulley & Damper

INTERMEDIATE SHAFT BELT SPROCKET

Removal – 1) Mark position of sprocket to front cover. Raise and support vehicle. Remove starter motor. Position sprocket to factory alignment marks (TDC No. 1 exhaust). Install Flywheel Holding Tool (J 37096) and lower vehicle.

2) Remove attaching bolt and washer. Mark sprocket hub position to nose end of intermediate shaft. Remove secondary timing belt. See SECONDARY TIMING BELT under REMOVAL & INSTALLATION in this article. Remove mounting bolt and washer.

NOTE: Hitting nose of intermediate shaft and/or prying sprocket will cause thrust bearing damage.

3) Back out center bolt of Sprocket Puller (J 38616) and engage self-tapping screws of puller into 3 equally spaced holes on sprocket. Rotate center bolt of puller and remove sprocket. *See Fig. 7.*

NOTE: DO NOT damage intermediate shaft oil seal during installation.

Installation – 1) Lubricate seal or seal running surface of intermediate shaft sprocket. Install sprocket into position on intermediate shaft through oil seal. Engage locating tangs of sprocket into mating sockets of chain sprocket.

2) Verify engagement of tangs by measuring from front face of intermediate shaft belt sprocket to front cover. Measurement should not be more than 1.65 in. (42 mm). If measurement is more than specification, tangs are not engaged.

3) Ensure reference and timing marks are properly aligned. Lightly lubricate shaft seal ("O" ring) and place it into position at end of intermediate shaft. Install bolt and washer into intermediate shaft.

4) Lightly lubricate bolt threads and washer before installing. DO NOT over lubricate. Hold crankshaft in position and tighten bolt to specification. See TORQUE SPECIFICATIONS at end of article.

5) Raise vehicle. Remove flywheel holding tool and install starter. Lower vehicle. Install secondary timing belt. See SECONDARY TIMING BELT under REMOVAL & INSTALLATION in this article.

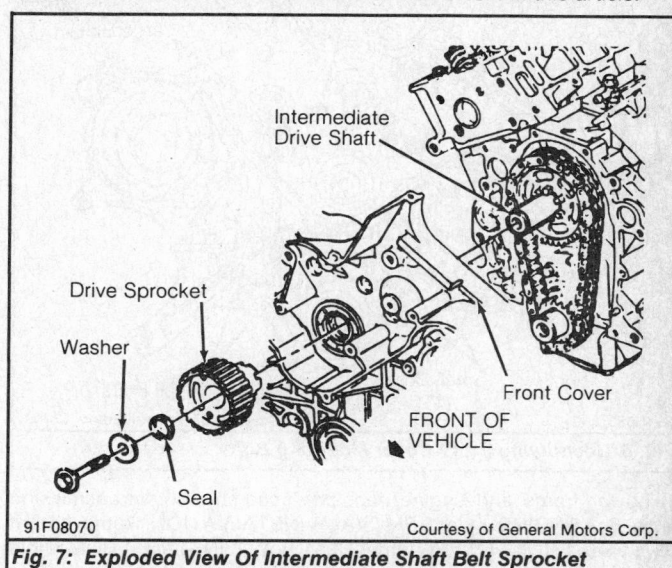

91F08070   Courtesy of General Motors Corp.

Fig. 7: Exploded View Of Intermediate Shaft Belt Sprocket

FRONT COVER

Removal – 1) Remove secondary tensioner pulley and arm assembly. See SECONDARY TIMING BELT under REMOVAL & INSTALLATION in this article. Remove mounting bracket Torx head bolts and mounting bracket.

2) Remove secondary timing belt idler pulleys. Remove front engine lift hook. Remove engine torque strut mount bracket-to-frame bolts and pull torque strut up and out of way. Remove cooling fan bolts and upper radiator support.

3) Remove right-side cooling fan heat shield. Remove right-side cooling fan. Disconnect lower radiator hose from coolant pump inlet pipe. On manual transaxle vehicles, disconnect front air hose at air pipe.

4) On all vehicles, disconnect heater hose at front cover. Remove heater pipe bracket retaining screws at frame. Raise and support vehicle. Remove right front wheel and right splash shield.

5) Remove crankshaft pulley and damper. See CRANKSHAFT DAMPER, CRANKSHAFT PULLEY & FRONT COVER OIL SEAL under REMOVAL & INSTALLATION in this article. Remove oil filter.

6) Remove A/C compressor mounting bolts. Remove lower front cover bolts. On automatic transaxle vehicles, disconnect drive axle. On all vehicles, remove rear alternator bracket and starter motor. Lower vehicle.

7) Remove camshaft drive belt sprocket bolt and sprocket using Sprocket Remover (J 38616). Remove upper alternator retaining bolts and forward light relay center screws. Position relay center aside. Disconnect oil cooler hose at front cover. Remove coolant pump pulley.

8) Remove upper front cover bolts and front cover with gasket. Clean all mating surfaces of front cover and cylinder block. Clean all sealing surfaces with degreaser.

Installation – 1) Install a new gasket. DO NOT damage sealing surfaces. Apply GM Sealer (1052080) or equivalent to lower edges of sealing surface of front cover.

2) Install front cover and upper mounting bolts. Apply thread sealant to large bolts. *See Fig. 8.* Tighten bolts sufficiently to pull front cover against block.

3) Reverse removal procedure for remaining components. Tighten all bolts to specification. See TORQUE SPECIFICATIONS at end of this article.

TIMING CHAIN & SPROCKETS

Removal – 1) Raise and support vehicle. Remove starter and flywheel cover. Remove necessary oil pan retaining bolts and nuts. See OIL PAN under REMOVAL & INSTALLATION in this article.

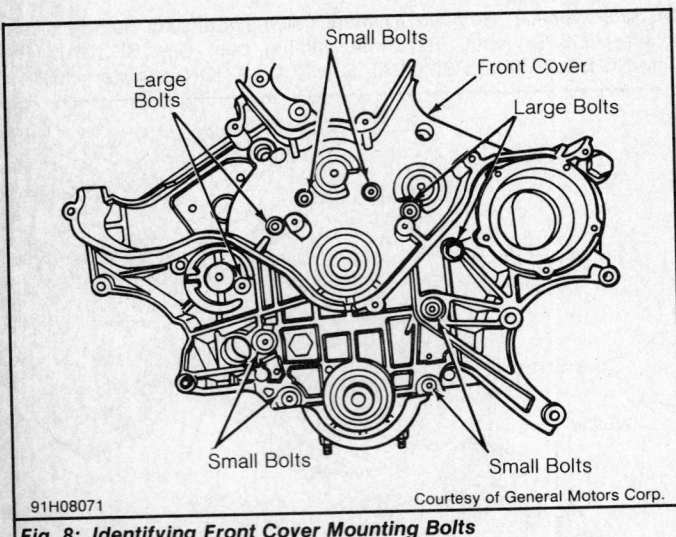

Fig. 8: Identifying Front Cover Mounting Bolts

2) Lower frame and engine/transaxle assembly onto transmission table. See ENGINE under REMOVAL & INSTALLATION. Remove front cover. See FRONT COVER under REMOVAL & INSTALLATION in this article.

3) Mark intermediate sprocket, chain link, front face of cylinder and crankshaft sprocket for reference. See Fig. 9. Retract timing chain tensioner shoe. Insert Tensioner Retractor (J 33875) on both sides of tensioner. See Fig. 10.

4) Pull pin in tensioner arm to retract tensioner arm spring. While compressing tensioner arm spring, insert a cotter pin or nail in hole of tensioner. See Fig. 10. Pin or nail should keep spring compressed.

5) Remove timing chain and crankshaft sprocket using Universal Puller Bridge (J 8433) and Legs and Protector (J 38611). If intermediate gear does not slide off easily with timing chain assembly, rotate crankshaft back and forth to help loosen the tight fit.

Inspection – Inspect crankshaft alignment key for burrs or marks that could affect assembly. Repair or replace as necessary.

Installation – **1)** Ensure crankshaft key is installed and fully seated. Using upper attaching hole as primary locator, install tensioner to engine block. Ensure chain tensioner is installed with blade retracted.

2) Tighten all tensioner bolts finger tight. Tighten slotted bolt, and then remaining bolts, to specification. See TORQUE SPECIFICATIONS at end of this article. Lightly oil or apply lithium grease to chain contact surfaces of nylon pad and blade.

3) Slip both sprockets and chain over proper shaft and engage slot in key. Intermediate shaft may move against rear cover. Slide sprocket

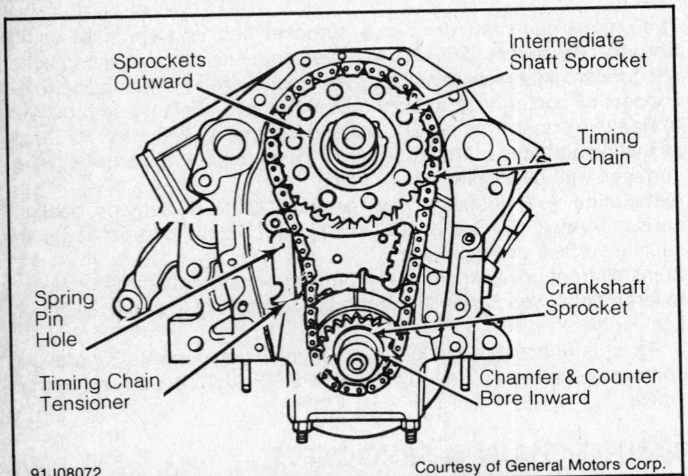

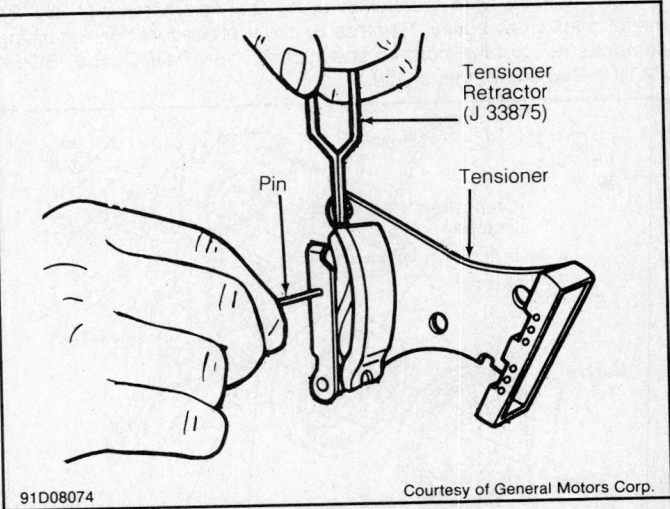

Fig. 9: Identifying Timing Chain, Crankshaft Sprocket & Intermediate Shaft Sprocket

and chain assembly on shafts maintaining parallel alignment of sprockets. See Fig. 11.

4) Ensure snubber and tension blade of tensioner do not become caught, misaligned or dislodged. Crankshaft sprocket is installed with large chamfer and counterbore towards crank. See Fig. 9. Intermediate sprocket is installed with spline sockets away from case.

5) Crankshaft sprocket must be pressed on for last .31" (8 mm) to seated position using Sprocket Installer (J 38612). Ensure correct timing is maintained. Pull retaining pin from tensioner. Install front cover. See FRONT COVER under REMOVAL & INSTALLATION in this article.

Fig. 10: Retracting Timing Chain Tensioner Shoe

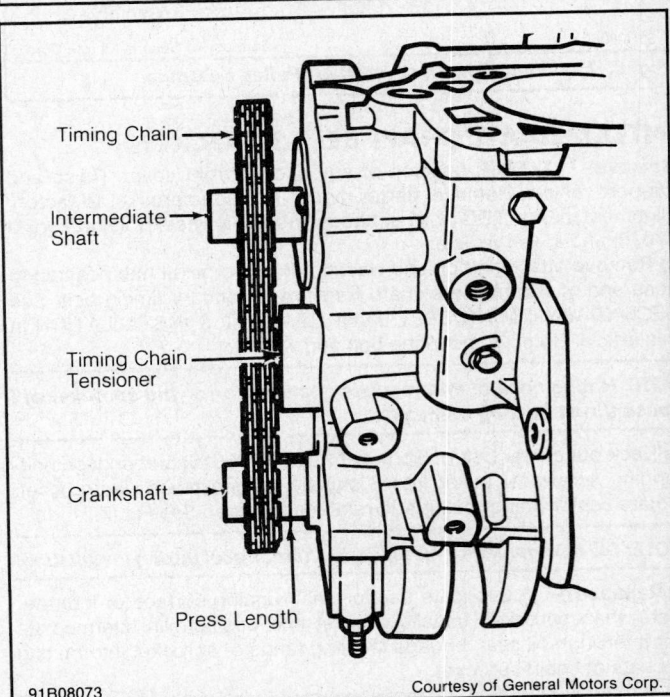

Fig. 11: Aligning Timing Chain Assembly

INTAKE MANIFOLD & PLENUM

Removal – **1)** Release fuel line pressure. See FUEL PRESSURE RELEASE under REMOVAL & INSTALLATION in this article. Remove air cleaner and drain cooling system. Disconnect control cables at throttle body.

2) Remove fuel rail cover bolts. Remove fuel rail cover and fuel rail. Disconnect heater hose at intake manifold. Remove PCV valve and vacuum line at throttle body. Disconnect electrical connectors for AIR solenoid, EGR valve and TPS.

3) Remove EGR valve and set aside. Remove fuel line bracket at throttle body. Loosen throttle body heater hose clamp at plenum. Disconnect electrical connectors for canister purge solenoid and MAP sensor.

4) Disconnect vacuum hoses at tee fitting on plenum. Remove wiring loom bracket for back rear spark plug wires. Remove nuts at plenum support bracket. Remove bolts, intake plenum and gasket.

5) Disconnect feed and return hoses from engine fuel pipes. Remove and discard "O" ring seals from feed and return pipes. Disconnect vacuum line at pressure regulator. Remove fuel rail retaining bolts.

6) Disconnect injector electrical connectors. Remove fuel rail assembly. Remove heater hose pipe bracket nut at thermostat housing. Remove temperature sensor from intake manifold.

7) Disconnect radiator hose from thermostat housing. Remove mounting bolts and intake manifold. Remove gaskets and clean mating surfaces of gasket material.

Installation – 1) Install gaskets and position intake manifold on engine. Install manifold mounting bolts; insert rubber isolators fully into manifold flange before tightening any fasteners. Tighten fasteners to specification. See TORQUE SPECIFICATIONS at end of this article.

NOTE: Draw manifold in place by tightening bolts gradually, starting with middle bolts and working in a circular pattern. DO NOT tighten one side or one end fully.

2) Connect radiator hose to thermostat housing. Install temperature sensor to intake manifold. Install heater hose pipe bracket nut at thermostat housing. Install fuel rail assembly. Reverse removal procedure for remaining components.

3) Use new "O" rings in feed and return pipes. Tighten all fasteners to specification. See TORQUE SPECIFICATIONS at end of this article.

OIL DISTRIBUTION COVER

Removal & Installation – 1) Remove intake manifold. See INTAKE MANIFOLD & PLENUM under REMOVAL & INSTALLATION in this article. Remove oil distribution cover mounting bolts. Remove cover and gasket.

2) Clean mating surfaces of gasket material. To install, reverse removal procedure. Tighten mounting bolts to specification. See TORQUE SPECIFICATIONS at the end of this article.

EXHAUST MANIFOLDS

Removal (Left Side) – 1) Remove air cleaner assembly. Remove exhaust crossover pipe. Remove engine torque strut bracket-to-frame bolts. Lift strut up and out of way. Remove upper radiator shroud.

2) Remove right-side cooling fan heat shield, and remove cooling fan. On manual transaxle vehicles, disconnect front hose from air pipe. Remove exhaust manifold retaining nuts, and remove manifolds and heat shield.

3) Remove gasket. If replacing manifold, transfer old air piping and heat shield to new manifold.

Installation – Install gasket, manifold and heat shield. Install manifold nuts and tighten to specification. See TORQUE SPECIFICATIONS at the end of this article. Reverse removal procedure for remaining components.

Removal (Right Side – Automatic Transaxle) – 1) Remove rear cam carrier. See CAM CARRIER & COVER under REMOVAL & INSTALLATION in this article. Remove exhaust manifold-to-crossover pipe nuts. Remove crossover pipe.

2) Raise and support vehicle. Disconnect front exhaust pipe at manifold. Lower vehicle. Disconnect oxygen sensor electrical connector. Remove manifold nuts and manifold.

3) Remove heat shield. Remove gasket and clean mating surfaces of gasket material. If replacing manifold, transfer old studs to new manifold.

Installation – Install gasket, manifold and heat shield. Install manifold nuts and tighten to specification. See TORQUE SPECIFICA-

TIONS at end of this article. Reverse removal procedure for remaining components.

Removal (Right Side – Manual Transaxle) – 1) Remove air cleaner assembly. Disconnect negative battery cable. Remove exhaust crossover pipe. Raise and support vehicle. Remove front exhaust pipe and catalytic converter assembly.

2) Disconnect and remove oxygen sensor. Remove manifold heat shield. Disconnect EGR pipe at exhaust manifold. Remove nuts and exhaust manifold. If replacing manifold, transfer old studs to new manifold.

Installation – To install, reverse removal procedure. Tighten fasteners to specification. See TORQUE SPECIFICATIONS at end of this article.

CAM CARRIER & COVER

Removal (Left Side) – 1) Remove oil/air breather hose from cover. Disconnect spark plug wires from plugs. Remove rear spark plug wires' cover.

2) Remove cam carrier cover bolts and cover. Remove cover gasket and "O" rings from cover. Remove secondary timing belt. See SECONDARY TIMING BELT under REMOVAL & INSTALLATION in this article.

NOTE: Install fuel line hoses under cam shaft and between lifters to hold lifters in carrier. Exhaust side uses 6 in. x 3/16 in. hose, and intake side uses 6 in. x 5/32 in. hose.

3) Remove exhaust crossover pipe. Remove engine torque strut. Remove engine torque strut bracket at engine. Remove cam carrier mounting bolts and nuts. Remove cam carrier and gasket.

Installation – 1) Remove oil from cam carrier-to-cylinder head bolt holes. Install gasket. Install Cam Hold-Down (J 38613). *See Fig. 4.* Install cam carrier and mounting bolts and nuts. Tighten fasteners to specification. See TORQUE SPECIFICATIONS at end of this article.

2) Remove lifter hold-down hoses and cam hold-down. Reverse removal procedure for remaining components. See TORQUE SPECIFICATIONS at end of this article.

Removal (Right Side) – 1) Remove intake manifold and plenum. See INTAKE MANIFOLD & PLENUM under REMOVAL & INSTALLATION in this article. Remove right timing belt cover. Disconnect right spark plug wires from plugs. Remove oil/air separator hose at cam carrier cover.

2) Remove cam carrier cover bolts and cover. Remove cover gasket and "O" rings from cover. Remove secondary timing belt. See SECONDARY TIMING BELT under REMOVAL & INSTALLATION in this article.

NOTE: Install fuel line hoses under cam shaft and between lifters to hold lifters in carrier. Exhaust side uses 6 in. x 3/16 in. hose, and intake side uses 6 in. x 5/32 in. hose.

3) Remove engine lift hook. Remove cam carrier mounting bolts and nuts. Remove cam carrier and gasket.

Installation – 1) Remove oil from cam carrier-to-cylinder head bolt holes. Install gasket. Install Cam Hold-Down (J 38613). *See Fig. 4.* Install cam carrier and mounting bolts and nuts. Tighten fasteners to specification. See TORQUE SPECIFICATIONS at end of this article.

2) Remove lifter hold-down hoses and cam hold-down. Reverse removal procedure for remaining components. See TORQUE SPECIFICATIONS at end of this article.

CAM SPROCKETS

Removal – 1) Remove front and rear cam carrier covers. See CAM CARRIER & COVER under REMOVAL & INSTALLATION in this article. Remove secondary timing belt. See SECONDARY TIMING BELT under REMOVAL & INSTALLATION in this article.

2) Remove clamping device from sprocket. Rotate camshafts so flats on cam to be serviced are face-up. *See Fig. 12.* Remove oil from hole and install Cam Hold-Down (J 38613). *See Fig. 4.* Tighten tool to 22 ft. lbs. (30 N.m) Remove sprocket using Sprocket Remover (J 38616).

Inspection – Inspect camshaft for wear or deformation. Replace if necessary. Inspect nose of camshaft for brinelling from lock ring. Pressure marks are acceptable. Replace camshaft if grooves are present.

Installation – **1)** Install new flat ring to large bore of sprocket. Wipe camshaft noses with light coat of oil. Install camshaft sprocket on nose of camshaft.

2) Lightly oil new lock ring, and insert ring far enough into sprocket to minimize tipping (flat edge into gap between flat ring and cam nose, up to bump).

3) Lightly oil camshaft sprocket bolt threads and washer before using. Thread a bolt and washer into camshaft and seat bolt finger tight. Back bolt off 1/4 - 1/2 turn.

4) Repeat steps **1)** through **3)** for each remaining camshaft sprocket. Check each sprocket for binding by rotating it around shaft. If binding is observed, check for foreign material or burrs.

5) Install secondary timing belt. See SECONDARY TIMING BELT under REMOVAL & INSTALLATION in this article. Set cam timing. See CAM TIMING PROCEDURE under REMOVAL & INSTALLATION in this article.

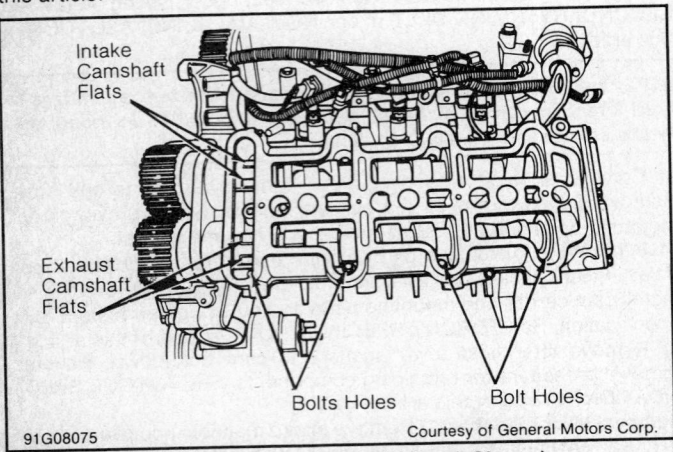

Intake
Camshaft
Flats

Exhaust
Camshaft
Flats

Bolts Holes   Bolt Holes

91G08075   Courtesy of General Motors Corp.

Fig. 12: Identifying Camshaft Flats (Left Bank Shown)

CAMSHAFT

Removal (Without Oil Seal) – **1)** Remove cam carrier. See CAM CARRIER & COVER under REMOVAL & INSTALLATION. Install Cam Hold-Down (J 38613) and remove lifters from cam carrier. *See Fig. 4.*

2) Remove cam sprockets. See CAM SPROCKETS under REMOVAL & INSTALLATION in this article. Remove cam carrier end cap bolts and end cap. Remove retaining plate bolts and plate. Remove cam hold-down. Carefully remove camshaft out the back of cam carrier.

NOTE: All camshaft journals are the same diameter. Carefully remove camshaft to avoid damaging bearings.

Installation – **1)** Coat camshaft lobes and journals with GM Lubricant (1052367) or equivalent. Install camshaft to cam carrier. DO NOT damage or distort oil seal.

2) Install retaining plate and bolts. Tighten bolts to specification. Install cam carrier end cap. Install cam sprocket. See CAM SPROCKETS under REMOVAL & INSTALLATION in this article.

3) Install cam hold-down. Coat lifter bores with petroleum jelly and install lifters. Adjust cam timing. See CAM TIMING PROCEDURE under REMOVAL & INSTALLATION in this article. Install cam carrier. See CAM CARRIER & COVER under REMOVAL & INSTALLATION in this article.

CAMSHAFT OIL SEAL

Removal & Installation – **1)** Remove camshaft. See CAMSHAFT under REMOVAL & INSTALLATION in this article. Carefully pry out oil seal using a large screwdriver.

2) DO NOT damage aluminum surfaces around seal. Inspect carrier for burrs or scratches. To install, reverse removal procedure. Use Seal Installer (J 38619).

CAM TIMING PROCEDURE

NOTE: If only timing one bank, ensure bank-to-bank cam timing relationship is one revolution apart. Timing flats should be 180 degrees opposite (right bank versus left bank) when finally timed.

Setting Cam Timing – **1)** Remove all spark plugs. Remove cam carrier covers (if necessary). See CAM CARRIER & COVER under REMOVAL & INSTALLATION in this article. Ensure right bank camshaft flats are facing up. *See Fig. 12.* Use Cam Sprocket Holder (J 38614) to rotate camshafts if necessary.

2) Install Cam Hold-Down (J 38613) on right bank. *See Fig. 4.* Remove oil from cam hold-down bolt hole, and tighten bolt to 22 ft. lbs. (30 N.m). Using sprocket holder, loosen sprocket bolt so sprocket spins freely on camshaft.

3) Install secondary timing belt and tensioner pulley arm assembly. See SECONDARY TIMING BELT under REMOVAL & INSTALLATION in this article. Ensure pulley rotates freely.

4) Rotate tensioner pulley counterclockwise into belt using cast square lug on body, and engage ball end of actuator into socket on pulley arm. Remove tensioner lock pin (paper clip) with needle-nose pliers. Ensure tensioner shaft extends and pulley moves into belt.

5) Remove sprocket holder and any belt holding devices. Applying 12-15 ft. lbs. (16-20 N.m) of torque, rotate tensioner pulley counterclockwise.

6) Rotate engine clockwise (as viewed from front) three times to seat belt. Align crankshaft reference marks during final rotation to TDC. DO NOT reverse rotation of engine. Use assistant to hold crankshaft from springing back.

7) Hold sprocket from turning with sprocket holder. Begin tightening sprocket bolt. Running torque of bolt (before seating) should be 44-66 ft. lbs. (60-90 N.m). Tighten bolt to 81 ft. lbs. (110 N.m). Repeat for other sprocket on right bank.

NOTE: If less than 44 ft. lbs. (60 N.m) of torque is required before seating, replace shim ring and lock ring, and inspect camshaft nose for brinelling. If torque required before seating is more than 66 ft. lbs. (90 N.m), replace shim ring and lock ring, and inspect attaching bolt threads for burrs or foreign material. Seating of lock ring is accomplished when edge is flush with sprocket hub.

8) Remove cam hold-down from right bank. Rotate engine (crankshaft) clockwise one revolution (or any number of odd revolutions) and realign balancer marks at TDC. DO NOT reverse engine rotation.

9) Ensure timing mark on damper lines up with front cover timing mark. Use assistant to hold crankshaft from springing back.

10) On left bank, use sprocket holder and loosen sprocket bolts so that sprockets spin freely on camshafts. Ensure left bank camshaft flats are facing up. *See Fig. 12.*

11) Install cam hold-down on left bank. Remove oil from hold-down hole, and tighten hold-down bolt to 22 ft. lbs. (30 N.m). Hold sprocket from turning with sprocket holder.

12) Begin tightening sprocket bolt. Running torque of bolt (before seating) should be 44-66 ft. lbs. (60-90 N.m). Tighten bolt to 81 ft. lbs. (110 N.m). Repeat for other sprocket on left bank.

NOTE: If less than 44 ft. lbs. (60 N.m) of torque is required before seating, replace shim ring and lock ring, and inspect camshaft nose for brinelling. If torque required before seating is more than 66 ft. lbs. (90 N.m), replace shim ring and lock ring, and inspect attaching bolt threads for burrs or foreign material. Seating of lock ring is accomplished when edge is flush with sprocket hub.

13) Remove cam hold-down from left bank. Remove old timing marks. Mark positions of each sprocket at TDC No. 1 exhaust position with permanent paint. *See Fig. 4.*

14) Install secondary timing belt cover. Install cam carrier covers. See CAM CARRIER & COVER under REMOVAL & INSTALLATION in this article.

NOTE: If a valve timing driveability problem is discovered, it is not always necessary to completely readjust valve train timing. Locate cause of problem. If problem is found to be a slipped belt, find reason for slipping and repair or replace belt as necessary. See SECONDARY TIMING BELT under REMOVAL & INSTALLATION in this article. If problem is caused by cam sprockets moving position in reference to camshafts, completely readjust timing.

CYLINDER HEAD

Removal (Left/Front Head) – 1) Remove intake manifold and plenum. See INTAKE MANIFOLD & PLENUM under REMOVAL & INSTALLATION in this article. Remove left cam carrier. See CAM CARRIER & COVER under REMOVAL & INSTALLATION in this article.

2) Remove right cooling fan. On manual transaxle vehicles, disconnect front air hose from air pipe. On all vehicles, remove exhaust manifold. See EXHAUST MANIFOLDS under REMOVAL & INSTALLATION in this article.

3) Remove oil dipstick tube bolt. Disconnect electrical connector from temperature sending unit. Remove cylinder head bolts and cylinder head. Remove gasket.

Removal (Right/Rear Head) – 1) Remove intake manifold and plenum. See INTAKE MANIFOLD & PLENUM under REMOVAL & INSTALLATION in this article. Remove right cam carrier. See CAM CARRIER & COVER under REMOVAL & INSTALLATION in this article.

2) Remove exhaust crossover pipe. Raise and support vehicle. Disconnect front exhaust pipe at manifold. On manual transaxle vehicles, disconnect rear air hose from air pipe. Lower vehicle.

3) Disconnect electrical connector from oxygen sensor. Remove rear timing belt tensioner bracket. Remove cylinder head bolts and cylinder head. Remove gasket.

Inspection – Inspect cylinder head gasket and mating surfaces for leaks, corrosion and blow-by. If gasket has failed, determine cause and repair. Inspect cylinder head for warpage. See CYLINDER HEAD under OVERHAUL in this article. If replacing cylinder head, transfer old exhaust manifold and studs to new cylinder head.

Installation – 1) Ensure cylinder head bolt threads and cylinder block holes are clean. Install gasket on cylinder block with metal tabs between cylinders facing up. Ensure all holes align with cylinder block.

2) Install cylinder head. Apply GM Sealant (1052080) to head bolt threads and install. Tighten bolts to specification in proper sequence. *See Fig. 13.* See TORQUE SPECIFICATIONS at end of this article. To complete installation, reverse removal procedure.

VALVE LIFTERS

NOTE: Keep valve lifters in order and marked for reassembly reference.

Removal – Remove cam carrier. See CAM CARRIER & COVER under REMOVAL & INSTALLATION in this article. Remove six lifter hold-down hoses. Remove valve lifters.

Installation – Lubricate lifters with GM Lubricant (1052367) or equivalent. Install valve lifters and hold-down hoses to cam carrier. Install cam carrier. See CAM CARRIER & COVER under REMOVAL & INSTALLATION in this article. Repeat for other bank.

OIL PUMP DRIVE ASSEMBLY

Removal – Remove right cylinder head. See CYLINDER HEAD under REMOVAL & INSTALLATION in this article. Remove mounting bolt and clamp. Remove oil pump drive assembly and "O" ring.

Installation – To install, reverse removal procedure. Lubricate "O" ring with engine oil and drive gear with grease. Tighten mounting bolt to specification. See TORQUE SPECIFICATIONS at end of this article.

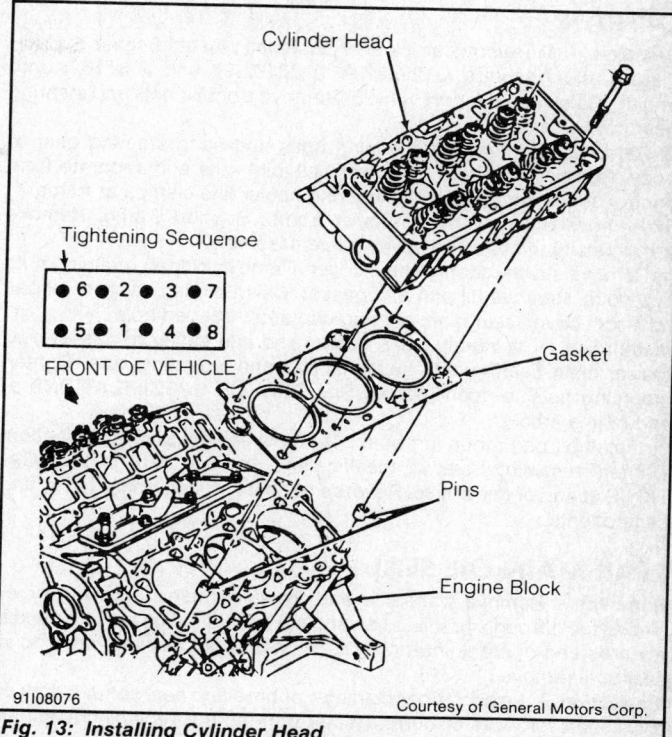

Tightening Sequence

```
● 6  ● 2  ● 3  ● 7
● 5  ● 1  ● 4  ● 8
```

FRONT OF VEHICLE

91I08076

Courtesy of General Motors Corp.

Fig. 13: Installing Cylinder Head

INTERMEDIATE SHAFT & BEARINGS

Removal – 1) Remove engine. See ENGINE under REMOVAL & INSTALLATION in this article. Remove oil pump drive assembly. See OIL PUMP DRIVE ASSEMBLY under REMOVAL & INSTALLATION in this article.

2) Remove timing chain assembly. See TIMING CHAIN & SPROCKETS under REMOVAL & INSTALLATION in this article. Remove thrust plate screws and plate.

3) Remove intermediate shaft. Using proper pilot, nut and thrust washer of Bearing Remover/Installer (J 33049), remove bearings.

NOTE: Carefully remove and install intermediate shaft to avoid damaging shaft journals.

Inspection – Inspect threads and bearing surfaces for wear, galling, gouges or overheating. If damaged, replace intermediate shaft. Measure bearing journal out-of-round. If out-of-round is more than .0002 in. (.005 mm), replace intermediate shaft. In a new intermediate shaft has been installed, add Lubricant (GM 1051396 EP) to engine oil.

Installation – 1) Assemble proper parts of remover/installer. Place bearing onto remover/installer, and index oil hole(s) of bearing with oil passage(s) in cylinder block. Pull bearing into place.

2) Install front bearing with oil feed holes at 4 o'clock and 7 o'clock positions (as viewed from front of engine block). For remaining bearing, install with oil feed holes at 4 o'clock position.

NOTE: Oil feed holes MUST be properly aligned. Serious engine damage could result from improper oil feed hole alignment.

3) Lubricate intermediate shaft journals and gear with engine oil. Install intermediate shaft, thrust plate and screws. Tighten screws to specification. See TORQUE SPECIFICATIONS at end of this article.

4) Replace "O" ring seal after sprocket installation. Install timing chain assembly. See TIMING CHAIN & SPROCKETS under REMOVAL & INSTALLATION in this article.

5) Install oil pump drive assembly. See OIL PUMP DRIVE ASSEMBLY under REMOVAL & INSTALLATION in this article.

6) Install engine. See ENGINE under REMOVAL & INSTALLATION in this article. Tighten fasteners to specification. See TORQUE SPECIFICATIONS at end of this article.

OIL PAN

Removal – 1) Remove air cleaner assembly. Install Engine Support Fixture and Adapters (J 28467-A, J 28467-90 and J 36462) onto engine. Raise and support vehicle. Remove front wheels and steering gear heat shield.

2) Remove steering gear retaining bolts and hang steering gear to body. Remove right and left lower ball joint nuts and separate from control arms. Remove power steering cooler line clamps at frame.

3) Remove engine mount nuts at frame. Support frame. Remove frame retaining bolts and lower frame assembly.

4) Remove starter and flywheel cover. Remove oil pan retaining nuts and bolts. Remove oil pan and gasket. Clean oil pan flanges, oil pan rail, front cover, rear main bearing cap and threaded holes.

Installation – 1) Install a new gasket and add sealer to gasket next to rear main bearing cap. Install oil pan and mounting nuts. Tighten mounting nuts to specification. See TORQUE SPECIFICATIONS at end of this article.

2) Install oil pan mounting bolts. Tighten rear bolts to specification. Tighten remaining bolts to specification. See TORQUE SPECIFICATIONS at end of this article. Reverse removal procedure for remaining components.

REAR MAIN OIL SEAL

Removal – Remove transaxle and flywheel. Insert screwdriver or similar tool through dust lip at an angle. Pry seal out by moving handle towards end of crankshaft pilot. Continue to pry as required around seal until removed.

Inspection – Inspect inner diameter of bore and seal contact area of crankshaft for nicks or burrs. Repair bore and/or replace crankshaft as required.

Installation – 1) Apply engine oil to inner and outer diameters of new seal. Slide new seal over mandrel until back of seal bottoms squarely against collar of Seal Installer (J 34686). See Fig. 14.

2) Align dowel pin of installer with dowel hole in crankshaft, and attach installer. Tighten attaching screws to 45 INCH lbs. (5 N.m). Turn handle of installer so collar pushes seal into bore.

3) Rotate handle until collar is tight against case. Loosen handle fully. Remove attaching screws. Ensure seal is seated squarely in bore. Install flywheel and transaxle.

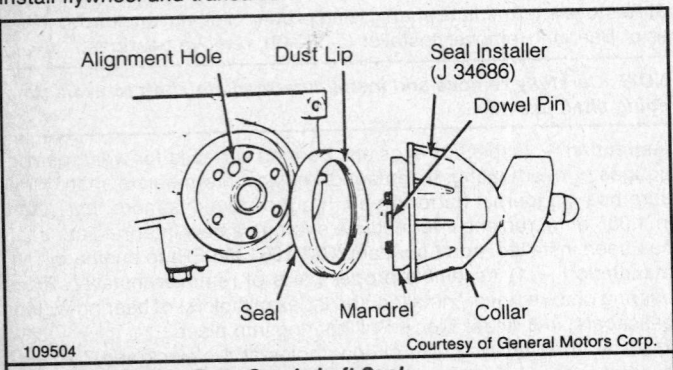

109504   Courtesy of General Motors Corp.

Fig. 14: Installing Rear Crankshaft Seal

WATER PUMP

Removal – Disconnect negative battery cable. Remove air cleaner assembly. Partially drain engine coolant. Remove serpentine belt. See SERPENTINE BELT & TENSIONER under REMOVAL & INSTALLATION in this article. Remove pulley. Remove water pump bolts, and remove pump. Clean mating surfaces.

Installation – To install, reverse removal procedure using new gasket. Tighten bolts to specification. See TORQUE SPECIFICATIONS at end of this article. Add coolant as needed.

OVERHAUL

CYLINDER HEAD

Inspection – Inspect cylinder head for warpage at deck surface and manifold surfaces. Resurface cylinder head if warpage exceeds specification. See CYLINDER HEAD table in ENGINE SPECIFICATIONS at end of article. Replace cylinder head if metal removed exceeds .010" (.25 mm).

Valve Seats – No replacement procedure given by manufacturer.

Valve Guides – Valve guides must be reamed for an oversized valve if valve stem oil clearance is not within specification. See CYLINDER HEAD table in ENGINE SPECIFICATIONS at end of article.

Seat Correction Angles – If seat width is too wide, use 20-degree and 70-degree stone for seat adjustment. The 20-degree stone will lower the seat, and the 70-degree stone will raise the seat.

VALVE TRAIN

Valves – New valves MUST NOT be lapped. Protective coating will be damaged if valve is lapped.

Valve Spring Installed Height – Measuring procedure is not available from manufacturer.

Valve Stem Oil Seals – Oversized valve stem oil seals are used for oversized valves. Intake and exhaust valve stem oil seals are different.

CYLINDER BLOCK ASSEMBLY

Piston Ring Installation – Piston rings must be installed with identification mark toward top of piston and ring gaps properly spaced. See Fig. 15.

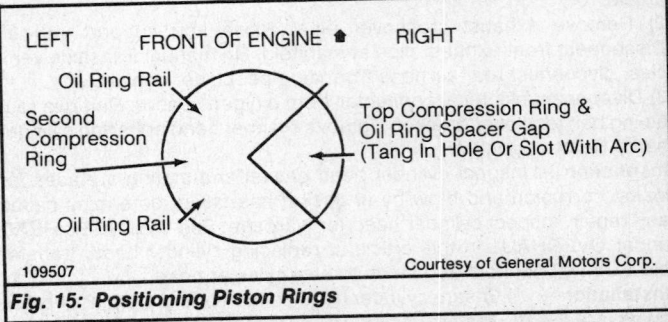

109507   Courtesy of General Motors Corp.

Fig. 15: Positioning Piston Rings

CAUTION: Mark piston position on connecting rod if removing piston from connecting rod. Information for connecting rod-to-piston positioning is not available from manufacturer.

Piston & Rod Assembly – Piston must be installed in cylinder block with arrow or notch on top of the piston toward the front of the engine.

Fitting Pistons – Piston diameter should be measured 7/16" (11 mm) below center line of piston pin bore. Piston taper should be measured at the center and bottom of the piston skirt. Oversized pistons must not be machined down or engine balance will be affected.

Crankshaft & Bearings – To align crankshaft thrust surfaces, install all bearings and main caps with cap bolts loosely installed. Pry crankshaft toward rear of engine and then toward front of engine. Tighten main bearing cap bolts to specification. See TORQUE SPECIFICATIONS at end of this article.

Crankshaft Flange Runout – 1) With engine removed and crankshaft installed, measure crankshaft flange runout. Mount dial indicator gauge plate flat against crankshaft flange. Place dial indicator stem on lower left transmission mounting bolt boss (flat area around bolt hole). Adjust indicator to zero.

2) Observe and record readings obtained on all mounting bolt hole bosses. Measurements should not vary more than .010" (.25 mm). If readings exceed specification, remount dial gauge plate and recheck flange runout. Replace crankshaft if runout exceeds specification.

Cylinder Block – Using feeler gauge and straightedge, inspect deck surface for warpage. Replace cylinder block if more than .010" (.30 mm) material is removed from deck surface.

ENGINE OILING

ENGINE LUBRICATION SYSTEM

The intermediate shaft-driven, gear-type oil pump provides pressurized lubrication through the oil filter to the main gallery. Crankshaft and intermediate shaft bearings are lubricated from main gallery. A passage above intermediate shaft bearing supplies oil to oil distribution cover assembly, which includes an anti-drainback valve. Oil distribution cover diverts oil supply to left and right back camshaft carriers. Passages in carriers supply oil to hydraulic lifters. Pressure oiling at root of thrust plate supplies lubrication to rear camshaft thrust plates.

Crankcase Capacity – Engine oil capacity is approximately 4 qts. (3.8L) with filter change. Check oil level after changing filter. Add oil if necessary.

Oil Pressure – Oil pressure is 15 psi (103 kPa) at 1100 RPM.

OIL PUMP & PAN BAFFLE

Removal – 1) Remove oil pan. See OIL PAN under REMOVAL & INSTALLATION in this article. Remove baffle mounting nuts. Rotate pick-up tube out of way. DO NOT remove pick-up tube assembly.

2) Remove baffle. REMOVE oil pump retaining bolt. Remove oil pump and drive shaft extension. Clean all parts with solvent. Dry with compressed air.

Inspection – 1) Inspect body an pump cover for cracks, scoring, casting imperfections and/or damaged threads. Replace oil pump if idler gear shaft is loose in pump body. Check pressure regulator valve for scoring or sticking.

2) Remove burrs with a fine oil stone. Check pressure regulator spring for loss of tension. Replace pick-up screen and pipe assembly if loose or damaged. Check gears for chipping, galling or wear. Check drive shaft and shaft extension for looseness or wear.

Installation – 1) Install drive shaft extension and oil pump, engage shaft extension into drive gear. Install oil pump retaining bolt and tighten to specification. See TORQUE SPECIFICATIONS at end of this article.

2) Install oil pan baffle and mounting nuts. Tighten nuts to specification. See TORQUE SPECIFICATIONS at end of this article. Install oil pan. See OIL PAN under REMOVAL & INSTALLATION in this article.

TORQUE SPECIFICATIONS

TORQUE SPECIFICATIONS

Application	Lbs. (N.m)
Cam Carrier Mounting Bolts/Nuts	18 (25)
Connecting Rod Nuts	39 (53)
Crankshaft Damper Bolt	78 (105)
Crankshaft Pulley Bolt	37 (50)
Cylinder Head Bolts	[1] 37 (50)
Engine Oil Cooler Assembly Connector	29 (39)
Front Cover Mounting Bolts	
Large Bolts	35 (47)
Small Bolts	18 (25)
Fuel Pipe Nuts	22 (30)
Intake Manifold Bolts/Nuts	18 (25)
Intermediate Shaft Belt Sprocket Bolt	96 (130)
Main Bearing Caps	
Step 1 (Bolts)	37 (50)
Step 2 (Bolts)	[2]
Step 3 (Nuts)	39 (53)
Oil Distribution Cover Bolts	18 (25)
Oil Pan Baffle Mounting Nuts	18 (25)
Oil Pan Rear Mounting Bolts	18 (25)
Oil Pump Drive Assembly Mounting Bolt	35 (47)
Oil Pump Retaining Nut	40 (54)
Power Train Mount Bracket Bolts	63 (85)
Power Train Mount Nuts	35 (47)
Rear Engine Mounting Bracket-To-Engine Bolt	61 (83)
Side Plate & Actuator Mounting Bolts	18 (25)

TORQUE SPECIFICATIONS (Cont.)

Application	Lbs. (N.m)
Tensioner Mounting Bolts	18 (25)
Timing Belt Pulley & Bracket Bolts	37 (50)
Trace Bracket-To-Rear Engine Mounting Bracket Bolt	61 (83)

Application	INCH Lbs. (N.m)
Cam Carrier Cover Bolts	89 (10)
Coolant Pump Mounting Bolts	89 (10)
Exhaust Manifold Nuts	115 (13)
Fuel Rail Attaching Bolts	89 (10)
Oil Pan Mounting Nuts	89 (10)
Oil Pan Non-Rear Mounting Bolts	89 (10)

[1] – Tighten in proper sequence. *See Fig. 13*. Tighten each bolt to specification, and then turn bolt an additional 90 degrees.

[2] – Tighten each bolt to specification, and then turn bolt an additional 75 degrees.

ENGINE SPECIFICATIONS

GENERAL SPECIFICATIONS

Application	Specification
Displacement	204 Cu. In. (3.4L)
Bore	3.62" (92.0 mm)
Stroke	3.31" (84.0 mm)
Compression Ratio	9.25-9.5:1
Fuel System	PFI
Horsepower @ RPM	
Automatic Transaxle	200 @ 5000
Manual Transaxle	210 @ 5200
Torque Ft. Lbs. @ RPM	215 @ 4000

CRANKSHAFT, MAIN & CONNECTING ROD BEARINGS

Application	In. (mm)
Crankshaft	
End Play	.0024 - .0083 (.060 - .210)
Main Bearings	
Journal Diameter	2.6473 - 2.6479 (67.241 - 67.257)
Journal Maximum Out-Of-Round	.0002 (.005)
Journal Maximum Taper	.0002 (.005)
Oil Clearance	.0013 - .0030 (.032 - .077)
Connecting Rod Bearings	
Journal Diameter	1.9987 - 1.9994 (50.768 - 50.784)
Journal Out-Of-Round	.0002 (.005)
Journal Taper	.0002 (.005)
Oil Clearance	.0011 - .0032 (.028 - .082)

CONNECTING RODS

Application	In. (mm)
Bore Diameter	
Center-To-Center Length	4.400 (111.76)
Maximum Bend	[1] .010 (.24)
Maximum Twist	[2] .002 (.05)
Side Play	.014 - .025 (.36 - .64)

[1] – Bend per 3" of rod length.

[2] – Twist per inch of rod length.

PISTONS, PINS & RINGS

Application	In. (mm)
Pistons	
Clearance	.0009 - .0023 (.022 - .058)
Diameter	3.6208 - 3.6215 (91.970 - 91.988)
Pins	
Diameter	.9052 - .9054 (22.992 - 22.997)
Piston Fit	.00046 - .00093 (.0116 - .0235)
Rod Fit	.0006 - .0018 (.0165 - .0464)
Rings	
No. 1	
End Gap	.012 - .022 (.30 - .56)
Side Clearance	.0016 - .0035 (.04 - .09)
No. 2	
End Gap	.019 - .029 (.48 - .74)
Side Clearance	.0016 - .0035 (.04 - .09)
No. 3 (Oil)	
End Gap	.010 - .030 (.25 - .76)
Side Clearance	.008 - .0019 (.203 - .048)

CYLINDER BLOCK

Application	In. (mm)
Cylinder Bore	
Diameter	3.6224 - 3.6231 (92.010 - 92.028)
Maximum Out-of-Round	.0003 (.007)
Maximum Deck Warpage	.004 (.10)

VALVES & VALVE SPRINGS

Application	Specification
Intake Valves	
Face Angle	45°
Exhaust Valves	
Face Angle	45°
Valve Springs	
Free Length	1.66" (42.0 mm)
Installed Height	1.40" (35.6 mm)
Pressure	Lbs. @ In. (kg @ mm)
Valve Closed	75 @ 1.40 (34.0 @ 35.6)
Valve Open	180 @ 1.03 (81.7 @ 26.2)

CYLINDER HEAD

Application	Specification
Maximum Warpage	.010" (.25 mm)
Valve Seats	
Intake Valve	
Seat Angle	46°
Seat Width	.049 - .059" (1.25 - 1.50 mm)
Maximum Seat Runout	.002" (.050 mm)
Exhaust Valve	
Seat Angle	46°
Seat Width	.063 - .075" (1.60 - 1.90 mm)
Maximum Seat Runout	.002" (.050 mm)
Valve Guides	
Intake Valve	
Valve Guide Oil Clearance	.0011 - .0026" (.028 - .066 mm)
Exhaust Valve	
Valve Guide Oil Clearance	.0014 - .0031" (.035 - .078 mm)

CAMSHAFT

Application	In. (mm)
Housing Bore	2.1643-2.1657 (55.050-55.075)
Journal Diameter	2.165-2.166 (54.99-55.01)
Lobe Lift	
Intake	.370 (9.40)
Exhaust	.370 (9.40)
Oil Clearance	.0015-.0035 (.037-.088)

DeVille, Eldorado, Fleetwood, Seville

NOTE: For repair procedures not covered in this article, see ENGINE OVERHAUL PROCEDURES article in GENERAL INFORMATION.

ENGINE IDENTIFICATION

Engine may be identified by the eighth character of Vehicle Identification Number (VIN), stamped on plate on top of instrument panel near lower left corner of windshield. If eighth character is B, vehicle is equipped with 4.9L V8 PFI engine. Vehicle model year may be identified by the tenth character of VIN. If tenth character is M, vehicle model year is 1991.

Engine model year may be identified by the second character of engine data number. Engine data number is stamped on plate on left side of cylinder block-to-transaxle flange. *See Fig. 1.* If second character of engine data number is M, engine model year is 1991. Fourth through ninth characters are the engine serial number, which may be needed when ordering parts.

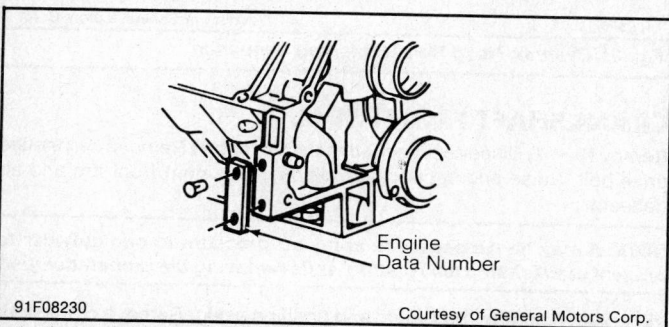

91F08230   Courtesy of General Motors Corp.

Fig. 1: Locating Engine Data Number On Cylinder Block

ADJUSTMENTS

VALVE CLEARANCE ADJUSTMENT

No valve clearance adjustment is required, as engine is equipped with hydraulic valve lifters.

REMOVAL & INSTALLATION

NOTE: For reassembly reference, label all electrical connectors, vacuum hoses and fuel lines before removal. Also place mating marks on engine hood and other major assemblies before removal.

FUEL PRESSURE RELEASE

Disconnect negative battery cable. Loosen fuel tank filler cap to relieve fuel tank pressure. Wrap shop towel around fuel gauge hose fitting, and connect fuel gauge hose to fuel pressure fitting on fuel line. Position a bleed hose into container. Open valve and bleed fuel pressure.

ENGINE

Removal & Installation – 1) Release fuel system pressure. See FUEL PRESSURE RELEASE under REMOVAL & INSTALLATION. Disconnect negative battery cable. Drain coolant. Remove air cleaner and hood. Remove left radiator fan. Remove serpentine drive belt. Disconnect upper radiator hose and heater hose from thermostat housing.

2) Disconnect the following electrical connectors: oil pressure switch, distributor, EGR solenoid, coolant temperature switch, idle speed control motor, throttle position sensor, coolant temperature sensor/fuel injectors harness (near fuel rail), manifold air temperature sensor, oxygen sensor, alternator and ground wire (at alternator bracket).

3) Disconnect throttle cable from throttle lever. Remove cruise control diaphragm and bracket. Remove exhaust crossover pipe. Disconnect

oil cooler and transmission fluid cooler lines from radiator. Remove radiator.

4) Disconnect oil cooler lines from oil filter adapter, and remove oil cooler lines. Remove oil cooler line bracket from transaxle, air cleaner mounting bracket and oil filter adapter.

5) On models with heated windshield, disconnect electrical connector from alternator. On all models, remove strut tower-to-body braces. Disconnect heater hose from heater pipe on engine. Remove P/S pump bracket from right cylinder head.

6) Leave hoses connected and remove P/S pump and tensioner assembly. Discharge A/C system. Disconnect refrigerant lines from accumulator and condenser. Disconnect fuel lines from fuel rail. Remove fuel line bracket from transaxle, and move fuel lines out of way.

7) Disconnect vacuum modulator line and power brake vacuum hose, and position out of way. Raise and support vehicle. Remove starter heat shield. Disconnect starter wiring and ground wires from cylinder block.

8) On DeVille and Fleetwood, disconnect exhaust pipe from right manifold. On Eldorado and Seville, disconnect exhaust pipe from left manifold, and move to one side. On all models, remove starter and 2 flexplate covers.

9) Remove 3 flexplate-to-torque converter bolts. Remove lower dust shield from A/C compressor. Remove right front wheel and plastic shield. Remove transaxle-to-engine support from right side of engine. Remove rear engine/transaxle assembly mount bolt (right side of engine).

10) Remove lower engine damper nut. Remove front engine mount nuts and right rear transaxle mount bolts. Disconnect oxygen sensor connector. Remove heater by-pass bracket from right side of engine compartment.

CAUTION: When connecting engine hoist, carefully attach right front lift hook to bracket to ensure clearance between lifting chain and A/C accumulator line.

11) Lower vehicle. Remove 5 engine-to-transaxle bolts. Connect engine hoist and remove engine. To install, reverse removal procedure. Fill cooling system. Evacuate and charge A/C system.

INTAKE MANIFOLD

Removal – 1) Release fuel system pressure. See FUEL PRESSURE RELEASE under REMOVAL & INSTALLATION. Disconnect negative battery cable. Remove air cleaner. Drain cooling system and disconnect necessary coolant hoses. Remove strut tower-to-body braces. Remove serpentine drive belt.

2) Remove P/S pump and tensioner bracket assembly with hoses attached. Remove alternator and bracket. Disconnect all electrical connections, vacuum hoses and control cables. Remove MAP sensor hoses.

3) Remove A/C hose bracket. Mark distributor location and remove distributor. DO NOT rotate crankshaft with distributor removed. Disconnect fuel lines at transaxle bracket. Remove fuel and vacuum lines from throttle body.

4) Loosen vacuum line clip at lift bracket. Disconnect vacuum supply line (at throttle body) and transaxle modulator line. Remove EGR solenoid and bracket assembly. Remove valve covers. Remove rocker arms and push rods. See ROCKER ARMS & PUSH RODS under REMOVAL & INSTALLATION.

CAUTION: Note intake manifold bolt length and location. Install bolts in proper location to prevent engine damage. See Fig. 2.

5) Remove brackets from right cylinder head. Remove oil filter and rear engine lift bracket. Remove intake manifold bolts. Note location and length of manifold bolts. Remove intake manifold, gaskets and seals.

Installation – 1) Install new front and rear manifold seals and side gaskets. Apply RTV sealant to corners of end seals where seals contact side gaskets. Ensure gasket holes align with cylinder head.

2) Install intake manifold. Install proper length bolt in specified location. *See Fig. 2.* Tighten bolts to specification. See TORQUE SPECIFICATIONS table at end of article.

3) To install remaining components, reverse removal procedure. Ensure rocker arm components are installed in original location and reference mark is aligned on distributor.

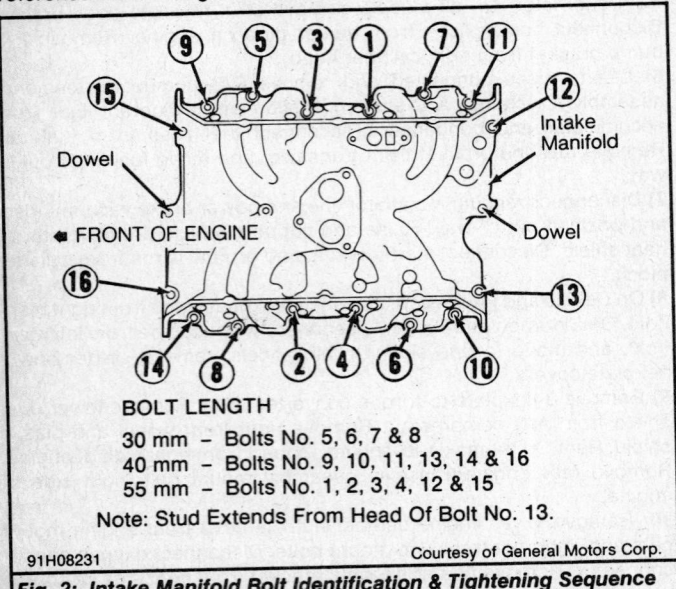

BOLT LENGTH

30 mm – Bolts No. 5, 6, 7 & 8
40 mm – Bolts No. 9, 10, 11, 13, 14 & 16
55 mm – Bolts No. 1, 2, 3, 4, 12 & 15
Note: Stud Extends From Head Of Bolt No. 13.

91H08231   Courtesy of General Motors Corp.

Fig. 2: Intake Manifold Bolt Identification & Tightening Sequence

EXHAUST MANIFOLD

Removal – Left Side (DeVille & Fleetwood) – Disconnect negative battery cable. Remove both cooling fans. Disconnect exhaust crossover pipe. Remove serpentine drive belt. Remove bracket from P/S pump and tensioner. Remove exhaust manifold bolts and manifold.

Removal – Left Side (Eldorado & Seville) – 1) Disconnect negative battery cable. Remove air cleaner, starter shield and serpentine belt. Remove bracket from P/S pump and tensioner. Remove A/C hose bracket and cooling fan.

2) Disconnect spark plug wires. Raise and support vehicle. Disconnect exhaust pipe. Remove A/C brace from manifold. Remove exhaust manifold bolts and exhaust manifold.

Removal – Right Side (DeVille & Fleetwood) – 1) Disconnect negative battery cable. Remove air cleaner. Disconnect exhaust crossover pipe. Disconnect oxygen sensor and coolant temperature sensor connectors.

2) Remove 2 upper forward exhaust manifold bolts. Raise and support vehicle. Disconnect exhaust pipe. Support engine cradle with jacks. Remove rear engine cradle bolts. Loosen front engine cradle bolts. Slightly lower the engine cradle. Remove remaining exhaust manifold bolts and manifold.

Removal – Right Side (Eldorado & Seville) – 1) Disconnect negative battery cable. Remove air cleaner and 2 heat shield screws. Raise and support vehicle. Disconnect exhaust pipe. Remove engine brace from manifold. Disconnect oxygen sensor wire.

2) Remove heat shield. Support engine cradle with jacks. Remove rear cradle bolts on both sides. Loosen front cradle bolts. Slightly lower engine cradle. Remove exhaust manifold bolts and manifold.

Installation (All Models) – Apply a thin layer of dry graphite on manifold sealing surfaces. Install manifold and tighten bolts to 16 ft. lbs. (22 N.m). To install remaining components, reverse appropriate removal procedure.

CYLINDER HEAD

Removal – 1) Remove intake manifold. See INTAKE MANIFOLD under REMOVAL & INSTALLATION. Remove exhaust manifold. See EXHAUST MANIFOLD under REMOVAL & INSTALLATION.

2) Remove engine lift bracket and dipstick tube. Remove cylinder head bolts, cylinder head and gasket.

CAUTION: Cylinder block is aluminum. Strictly follow cylinder head bolt tightening procedures to ensure proper gasket performance.

Installation – 1) Clean oil, coolant and debris from cylinder block bolt holes and cylinder head bolt threads. Apply GM Lubricant (1052356) to head bolts.

2) Install new gasket to cylinder head, aligning holes in gasket with dowels on cylinder block. Install cylinder head and tighten bolts to specification in proper sequence. See TORQUE SPECIFICATIONS table at end of article. *See Fig. 3.* To install remaining components, reverse removal procedure.

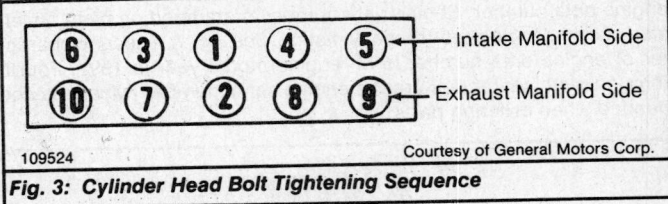

109524   Courtesy of General Motors Corp.

Fig. 3: Cylinder Head Bolt Tightening Sequence

CRANKSHAFT FRONT SEAL

Removal – 1) Disconnect negative battery cable. Remove serpentine drive belt. Raise and support vehicle. Remove right front tire and air deflector.

NOTE: It may be necessary to apply air pressure to one cylinder to prevent crankshaft from rotating while removing crankshaft damper.

2) Loosen heater by-pass line, and position aside. Remove crankshaft damper bolt and washer. Install Puller Pilot (J-21052-4) into crankshaft damper hole. Install Puller (J-38416) and remove crankshaft damper.

3) Install crankshaft damper bolt into crankshaft and finger tighten. Using Puller Arms (J-23129) and Puller (J-1859-03), remove seal from front timing case cover.

Installation – 1) Polish crankshaft damper hub seal surface with fine emery cloth. Lubricate new seal lip with engine oil. Install seal on crankshaft with garter spring toward engine. Using Seal Installer (J-29662) and hammer, install seal until it bottoms in front timing case cover.

NOTE: If limited space prevents seal installation using seal installer and hammer, install seal using seal installer with Crankshaft Damper Installer (J-29774). This presses seal into bore using threaded rod.

2) Lubricate crankshaft damper hub sealing surface with engine oil. Using crankshaft damper installer, install crankshaft damper until it seats on crankshaft. Remove crankshaft damper installer.

3) Install crankshaft damper washer and bolt, and tighten bolt to 70 ft. lbs. (95 N.m). To install remaining components, reverse removal procedure.

TIMING CHAIN

Removal – 1) Disconnect negative battery cable. Drain cooling system. Remove air cleaner, accessory drive belt and crankshaft pulley. Remove right strut tower-to-body brace and coolant reservoir.

2) Remove water pump. See WATER PUMP under REMOVAL & INSTALLATION. Raise and support vehicle. Remove right front tire and air deflector.

NOTE: It may be necessary to apply air pressure to one cylinder to prevent crankshaft from rotating while removing crankshaft damper.

3) Loosen heater by-pass line, and position aside. Remove crankshaft damper bolt and washer. Install Puller Pilot (J-21052-4) into crankshaft damper hole. Install Puller (J-38416) and remove crankshaft damper.

4) Remove oil pan-to-front cover bolts and front cover-to-cylinder block bolts. Remove front cover and gasket. Note oil slinger installation position and remove from crankshaft.

5) Rotate crankshaft until timing marks are aligned with No. 1 cylinder at TDC of compression stroke. *See Fig. 4.* Remove and discard thrust button (bearing) from end of camshaft. Remove camshaft sprocket bolt. Remove timing chain and sprockets from crankshaft and camshaft at same time.

Installation – 1) Install crankshaft sprocket. If necessary, rotate crankshaft until crankshaft sprocket timing mark is facing upward. *See Fig. 4.* Install timing chain and sprocket, ensuring camshaft dowel aligns with camshaft sprocket. Ensure timing marks are aligned.

2) Install camshaft sprocket retaining bolt and tighten to 36 ft. lbs. (49 N.m). Install new thrust button. Install oil slinger on crankshaft with smaller end toward crankshaft sprocket.

3) Ensure all sealing surfaces are clean. Apply bead of RTV sealant to oil pan-to-front cover sealing area, inward of the oil pan-to-front cover bolt holes. Apply RTV sealant to corners where oil pan, cylinder block and front cover join.

4) Install front cover using new gasket. Tighten front cover bolts to 15 ft. lbs. (20 N.m). Polish crankshaft damper hub sealing surface with fine emery cloth. If crankshaft seal has been removed, lubricate new seal lip with engine oil.

5) Install seal on crankshaft with garter spring toward engine. Using Seal Installer (J-29662) and hammer, install seal until it seats in front cover bore.

NOTE: If limited space prevents seal installation using seal installer and hammer, install seal using seal installer with Crankshaft Damper Installer (J-29774). This presses seal into bore using threaded rod.

6) Lubricate crankshaft damper hub sealing surface with engine oil. Using crankshaft damper installer, install crankshaft damper until it seats on crankshaft. Remove crankshaft damper installer.

7) Install crankshaft damper washer and bolt, and tighten bolt to 70 ft. lbs. (95 N.m). To install remaining components, reverse removal procedure.

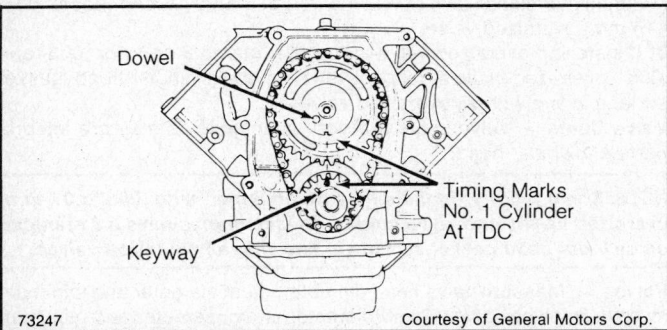

Fig. 4: Aligning Timing Marks

ROCKER ARMS & PUSH RODS

CAUTION: DO NOT remove pivot bolts from rocker arm support if rocker arm support is mounted to cylinder head. Valve spring pressure may damage pivot bolts and threads.

Removal – 1) Disconnect negative battery cable. Remove valve cover. Remove 4 rocker arm support bolts. *See Fig. 5.* Remove 5 rocker arm support nuts from cylinder head bolt studs. Remove rocker arm support with rocker arms and pivots attached.

2) Mark push rod location for reassembly reference and remove push rods. To remove rocker arms from support, place support in vise. Mark pivot and rocker arm locations for reassembly reference. Remove pivot bolts, pivots and rocker arms.

Installation – 1) Lubricate all components with Axle Lubricant (1052271). Install push rods in original location.

2) Install rocker arms, pivots and pivot bolts on rocker arm support. Tighten pivot bolts to 22 ft. lbs. (30 N.m). If new support is installed,

pivot holes do not require tapping, as pivot bolts are self-tapping.

3) Position support (with pivots and rocker arms attached) on cylinder head. Install 5 support nuts and loosely tighten. Install 4 support bolts and loosely tighten. Evenly tighten 5 support nuts until snug, occasionally inspecting push rods for alignment in rocker arm seats.

4) Evenly tighten 4 support bolts until snug. Tighten 5 support nuts to 37 ft. lbs. (50 N.m). Tighten 4 support bolts to 84 INCH lbs. (9 N.m). Apply a bead of RTV sealant to new triangular seal at intake manifold and cylinder head contact points. Install valve cover, and tighten bolts to 96 INCH lbs. (11 N.m).

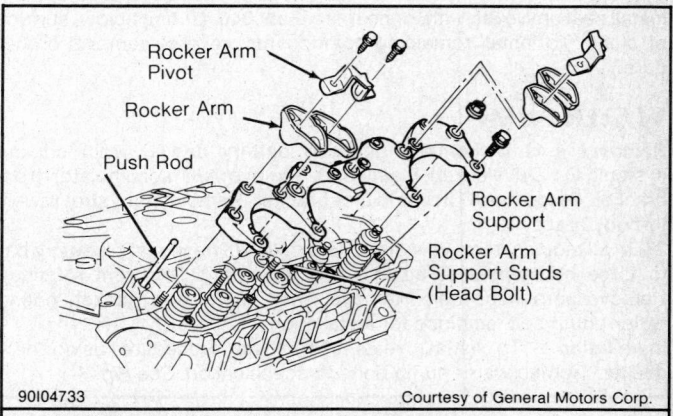

Fig. 5: Exploded View of Rocker Arm Assembly

VALVE LIFTERS

Removal – Remove intake manifold. See INTAKE MANIFOLD under REMOVAL & INSTALLATION. Remove valve guide retainer. *See Fig. 6.* Mark valve lifter location for reassembly reference. Remove valve lifters and guides, using Valve Lifter Remover (J-29834).

Installation – Apply GM Lubricant (1052365) to lifter roller. To install, reverse removal procedure, ensuring components are installed in original location.

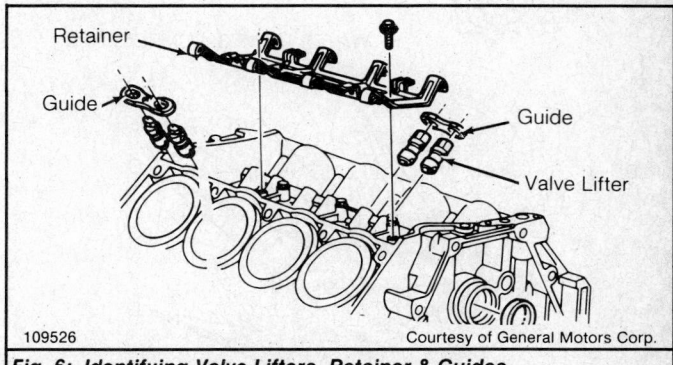

Fig. 6: Identifying Valve Lifters, Retainer & Guides

CAMSHAFT

CAUTION: Install new valve lifters and distributor drive gear when installing new camshaft.

Removal – 1) Remove engine. See ENGINE under REMOVAL & INSTALLATION. Remove timing chain. See TIMING CHAIN under REMOVAL & INSTALLATION.

2) Remove valve lifters. See VALVE LIFTERS under REMOVAL & INSTALLATION. Remove camshaft and bearings (if necessary).

Inspection – Inspect camshaft journal diameter, lobe lift and oil clearance. See CAMSHAFT table under ENGINE SPECIFICATIONS at end of article. Replace components if not within specifications.

Installation – Install camshaft bearings (if removed), ensuring oil holes are aligned. Lubricate camshaft bearings, camshaft lobes and distributor drive gear with GM Lubricant (1052365). Install camshaft. To install remaining components, reverse removal procedure.

REAR CRANKSHAFT SEAL

Removal – Remove transaxle and flexplate. See appropriate AUTOMATIC TRANSMISSIONS article in TRANSMISSION SERVICING. Note direction of seal installation. Carefully pry seal from housing using Seal Remover (J-26868). DO NOT damage crankshaft sealing surface.

Installation – Coat seal lip with wheel bearing grease. Install seal on crankshaft with spring facing engine. Using Seal Installer (J-34604), install seal until even with, or no more than .040" (1 mm) below, surface of block. To install remaining components, reverse removal procedure.

WATER PUMP

Removal – **1)** Disconnect negative battery cable. Drain cooling system. On DeVille and Fleetwood, remove A/C accumulator from bracket. Remove A/C accumulator bracket. Remove right strut tower-to-body brace.

2) On all models, remove water pump pulley (if necessary, use pry bar to force belt tensioner against belt to keep pulley from rotating). Remove serpentine belt. Remove water pump and gasket, noting water pump bolt locations for installation.

Installation – To install, reverse removal procedure using new gasket. Tighten water pump bolts to specification. *See Fig. 7.*

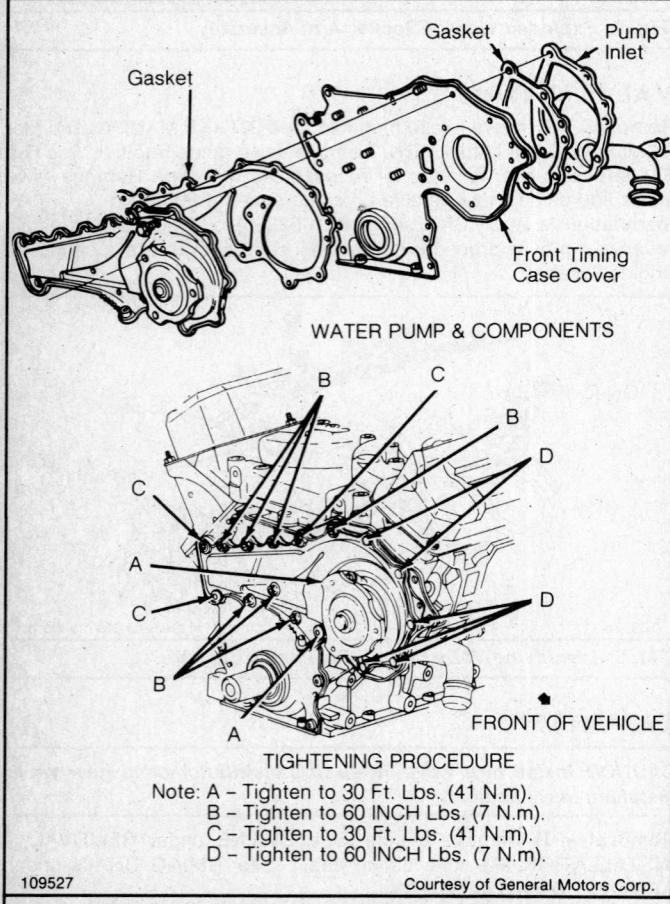

Note: A – Tighten to 30 Ft. Lbs. (41 N.m).
    B – Tighten to 60 INCH Lbs. (7 N.m).
    C – Tighten to 30 Ft. Lbs. (41 N.m).
    D – Tighten to 60 INCH Lbs. (7 N.m).

109527   Courtesy of General Motors Corp.

Fig. 7: Water Pump Components & Tightening Procedure

OIL PAN

Removal – Disconnect negative battery cable. Raise and support vehicle. Drain oil. Remove 2 flexplate covers. On Eldorado and Seville, disconnect exhaust pipe from left manifold, and move to one side. On all models, remove oil pan bolts and oil pan.

Installation – **1)** Clean cylinder block and oil pan sealing surfaces. Apply RTV sealant to corners of rear main bearing cap and front cover-to-cylinder block junctions. Install oil pan and new gasket. Tighten oil pan bolts to 14 ft. lbs. (19 N.m).

2) Install drain plug and tighten to 22 ft. lbs. (30 N.m). To install remaining components, reverse removal procedure. Fill crankcase.

OVERHAUL

CYLINDER HEAD

Cylinder Head – Cylinder head warpage information is not available from manufacturer.

Valve Springs – **1)** Measure valve spring free length and tension (pressure). Replace valve spring if free length and tension are not within specifications. See VALVES & VALVE SPRINGS table under ENGINE SPECIFICATIONS at end of article.

2) Intake valve spring is Yellow and exhaust valve spring is Black. Measure valve spring installed height between valve stem tip and spring seat. If installed height exceeds specification, replace cylinder head or valve.

Valve Stem Oil Seals – Pry seal off guide using small screwdriver. DO NOT reuse seal. Lubricate new seal with engine oil. Use Valve Stem Seal Installer (J-29790) to install seal until bottomed on valve guide.

NOTE: Some factory engines may be equipped with .003" (.07 mm) oversized valves and valve guides. These engines have a 3 stamped on cylinder head gasket surface in line with all oversized valves.

Valve Guides – **1)** Measure valve stem-to-guide oil clearance. If clearance exceeds specification, ream valve guide to accommodate an oversized valve and install oversized valve. See CYLINDER HEAD table under ENGINE SPECIFICATIONS at end of article. Valve guides are not replaceable as they are integral parts of cylinder head.

2) Oversized valves are available in .003" (.08 mm) and .006" (.15 mm) oversize. Ream guide using Reamer (J-5830-1) to accommodate .003" (.08 mm) oversized valve or Reamer (J-5830-6) to accommodate .006" (.15 mm) oversized valve.

3) If installing oversized valve and guide, stamp *3* or *6* (for .003" and .006" oversized valves respectively) on the cylinder head gasket surface in line with all oversized valves.

Valve Seats – Valve seats are not replaceable as they are integral parts of cylinder head.

NOTE: Some factory engines may be equipped with .003" (.07 mm) oversized valves and valve guides. These engines have a 3 stamped on cylinder head gasket surface in line with all oversized valves.

Valves – Measure valve head diameter, stem diameter and minimum margin. Replace valve if head diameter, stem diameter and minimum margin are not within specifications. See VALVES & VALVE SPRINGS table under ENGINE SPECIFICATIONS at end of article. DO NOT lap NEW valves, as protective coating will be damaged. If necessary, lightly lap used valves.

Valve Seat Correction Angles – After grinding, if seat width is too wide, use 20-degree and 70-degree stones to narrow the seat.

VALVE TRAIN

CAUTION: DO NOT remove pivot bolts from rocker arm support if mounted to cylinder head. Valve spring pressure may damage pivot bolts and threads.

Rocker Arm Assembly – Place rocker arm support in vise. Mark pivot and rocker arm locations for reassembly reference. Remove pivot bolts, pivots and rocker arms. Lubricate all components with Axle Lubricant (1052271) before reassembly.

CAUTION: Valve lifter plunger and body are fitted pair. DO NOT interchange with parts from other valve lifters.

Valve Lifters – 1) To disassemble, push down on push rod cup and remove lock ring using pointed tool. *See Fig. 8.* Remove push rod cup, metering disc and plunger.

2) If plunger is stuck in lifter body, place lifter (push rod end down) in Lifter Plunger Remover (J-4160). Hold remover in hand with thumb over lifter body. Strike tool sharply on block of wood to dislodge plunger. Remove ball, small spring, ball retainer and spring.

3) To reassemble, hold plunger upside-down. Insert ball, small spring and ball retainer. Snap the ball retainer into recess in plunger. Place ring over ball retainer. Slide lifter body over plunger at an angle to help seat spring.

4) Turn lifter upright. Fill plunger with clean engine oil. Jiggle ball with small piece of wire until oil drains out of plunger into body and trapped air is released from body. Refill plunger with oil.

5) Place metering disc and push rod cup on top of plunger. Position lock ring over push rod cup and press into groove using Valve Lifter Lock Ring Installer (J-2730). Apply Lubricant (1052365) to camshaft lobe contact on bottom of lifter.

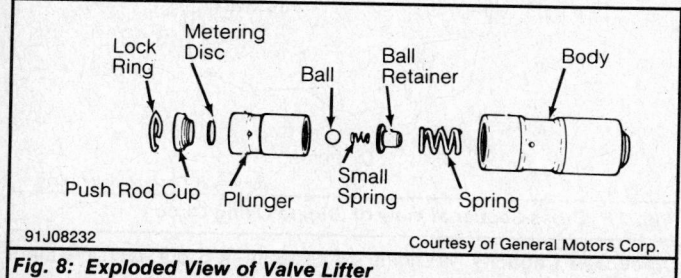

Fig. 8: **Exploded View of Valve Lifter**

CYLINDER LINER

CAUTION: Cylinder liner height must be checked when replacing cylinder block or cylinder liner. If reassembling original cylinder liner and cylinder block and no overheat condition exists, cylinder liner height does not require checking. DO NOT bore or hone cylinder liners.

Removal – 1) Remove cylinder head. See CYLINDER HEAD under REMOVAL & INSTALLATION. Remove oil pan. See OIL PAN under REMOVAL & INSTALLATION.

2) Install Cylinder Liner Holder (J-29775) on cylinder block. Note direction of piston installation. Remove piston and connecting rod. Using ink, place reference mark on cylinder liner and cylinder block for reassembly reference. DO NOT stamp the cylinder liner. Remove cylinder liner and "O" ring. Discard "O" ring.

CAUTION: Check cylinder liner height if engine overheated. See installation procedure for NEW cylinder liners.

Installation (Original Cylinder Liners) – 1) Ensure cylinder liner-to-cylinder block mating surfaces are clean. Remove burrs or nicks using

fine emery cloth. Lightly lubricate new "O" ring with oil, and install on bottom of cylinder liner. Install cylinder liner into cylinder block in original position, aligning reference marks made during disassembly.

2) Seat cylinder liners and install cylinder liner holder. Install pistons in corresponding cylinder liner with notch on top of piston toward front of engine. Install remaining components.

Installation (New Cylinder Liners) – 1) Install new cylinder liner in cylinder block without "O" ring. Position Cylinder Liner Gauge (J-29776) on a flat surface (cylinder block surface or piece of glass). *See Fig. 9.* Using moderate pressure, zero the gauge indicator. DO NOT apply excessive pressure on gauge or false reading will result.

2) Install spring-loaded pins on cylinder liner gauge in cylinder liner. Ensure machine pad on gauge rests on cylinder liner and indicator stem contacts block deck surface. *See Fig. 9.*

3) Apply slight pressure and note reading. If reading is on the (+) side, cylinder liner is higher than cylinder block deck. If reading is on the (–) side, cylinder liner is lower than cylinder block deck.

NOTE: Cylinder liner height gauge is graduated in millimeters.

4) Measure and record cylinder liner height at designated areas. *See Fig. 9.* Correct liner height is 0-.003" (0-.08 mm) above cylinder block deck. Cylinder liners may be rotated to obtain correct height. If cylinder liners are rotated, mark new position for reassembly reference. Replace cylinder liner if liner height is not within specifications.

5) After obtaining correct cylinder liner height, liner-to-liner height MUST be measured. To measure liner-to-liner height, install cylinder liners, without "O" rings, in original location adjacent to cylinder liner being measured.

6) Using cylinder liner gauge, measure cylinder liner height difference between cylinder liners while holding cylinder liners in position. *See Fig. 9.*

7) Liner-to-liner height difference must be within ±.002" (±.05 mm). After obtaining liner-to-liner height, mark liner location for reassembly reference. Repeat procedure on all cylinder liners.

8) After measurement is completed, remove cylinder liner. Install new, lightly lubricated "O" ring on cylinder liner, and install cylinder liner. Ensure reference marks are aligned. Seat cylinder liners, and install cylinder liner holder. Install pistons in corresponding cylinder liner with notch on top toward front of engine. Install remaining components.

CYLINDER BLOCK ASSEMBLY

CAUTION: Mark all components before removal and disassembly and install in original locations.

Piston & Rod Assembly – If connecting rod is bent, replace piston, rod and cylinder liner. Install piston and connecting rod assembly with notch on top of piston toward front of engine.

Fitting Pistons – Measure piston diameter 1.25" (32 mm) below top of piston at 90-degree angle to piston pin. Measure cylinder liner bore

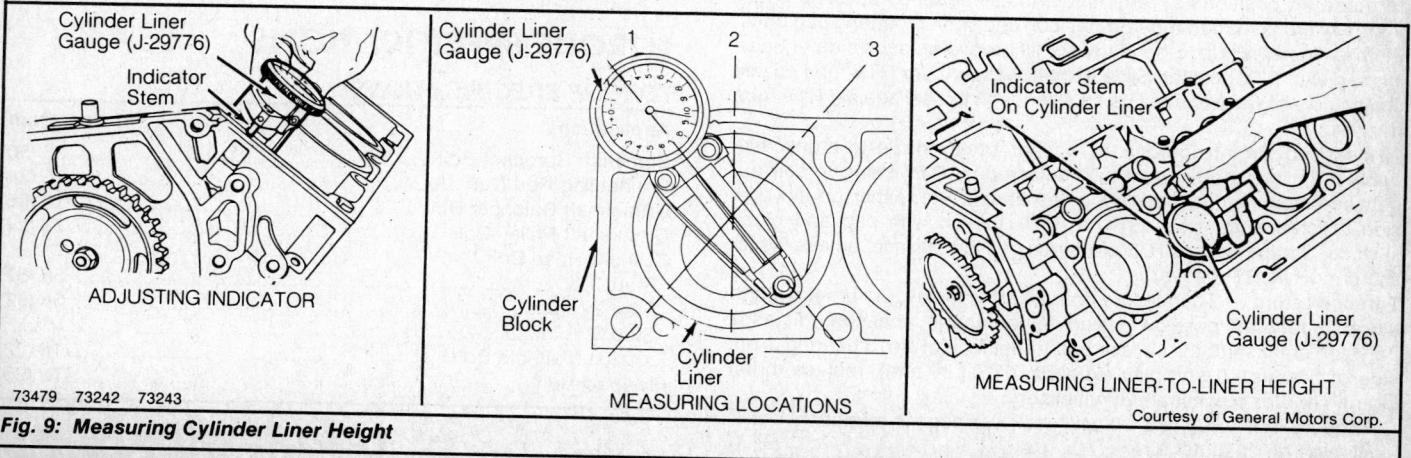

Fig. 9: **Measuring Cylinder Liner Height**

Courtesy of General Motors Corp.

2" (51 mm) below top of cylinder liner. If piston clearance is not .0010-.0018, replace piston and cylinder liner.

Piston Rings – Measure piston ring end gap and side clearance. If end gap and side clearance are not within specifications, replace rings and/or piston. See PISTONS, PINS & RINGS table under ENGINE SPECIFICATIONS at end of article. Install piston rings with identification mark (dimple) toward top of piston. Ensure ring end gaps are properly spaced around circumference of piston. See Fig. 10.

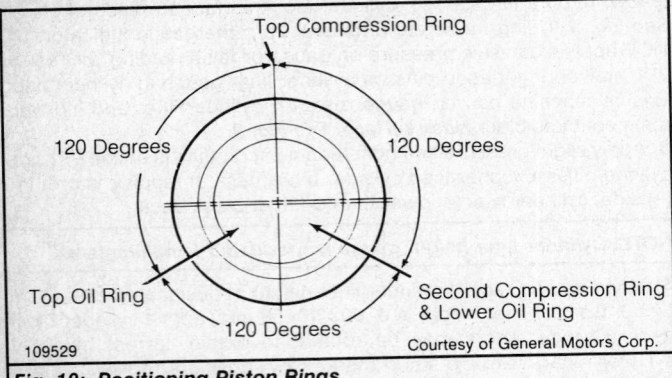

Fig. 10: Positioning Piston Rings

Rod Bearings – To prevent damage to bearings and cap, ensure tangs on bearings are positioned in notches on rod and cap before tightening cap nuts. Measure rod bearing oil clearance. Replace bearing if clearance exceeds .0035" (.089 mm).

Crankshaft & Main Bearings – **1)** Number of grooves on left side of bearing cap identifies bearing caps No. 1, 2 and 3. Bearing cap No. 4 has no grooves.

CAUTION: DO NOT shim, scrape or file bearing inserts. DO NOT touch bearing surface with fingers. DO NOT interchange main bearing No. 1 with bearings No. 2 or 4. If rear main bearing cap is removed, replace rear crankshaft seal and apply RTV sealant to rear main bearing cap as specified in steps 6 and 7.

2) Except for bearing No. 5 (rear bearing), upper and lower bearing halves are interchangeable (within same bearing). The No. 3 (center) bearing is thrust bearing. Oversized bearings are available for bearings No. 1 and 5 only.

3) If bearings are measured with engine in chassis, remove bearing caps adjacent to bearing being measured. Install a .005" (.13 mm) strip of brass shim stock between crankshaft and lower half of each adjacent bearing. Tighten adjacent bearing caps to specification. This supports crankshaft against upper bearing halves.

4) Measure bearing clearance. If clearance is not within specifications, replace main bearings. See CRANKSHAFT, MAIN & CONNECTING ROD BEARINGS table under ENGINE SPECIFICATIONS at end of article. Measure crankshaft end play. See THRUST BEARING.

5) To align No. 3 thrust bearing surfaces, pry crankshaft to extreme fore and aft positions several times. Install bearing cap bolts finger tight. Pry crankshaft to forward position and tighten bearing cap bolts.

6) When installing No. 5 bearing cap, fill groove on each side of bearing cap with RTV sealant. Slide a small washer over RTV tube nozzle (inside hole of washer must be small enough to seal against RTV tube nozzle).

7) Insert nozzle into groove so washer seals nozzle to crankcase. Force RTV into groove until full, indicated by RTV being forced out between block and main bearing cap at split line, either on flywheel side or crankshaft side. Ensure RTV is even with cap and block surface. Scrape excess RTV from pan sealing surface, unless installing pan while RTV is wet.

Thrust Bearing – To measure crankshaft end play, pry crankshaft to extreme forward position. Using feeler gauge, measure distance between crankshaft thrust face and thrust face of No. 3 bearing (front side of bearing). If end play exceeds .015" (.38 mm), replace thrust bearing and/or crankshaft as necessary.

Cylinder Block – Cylinder block deck warpage information is not available from manufacturer.

ENGINE OILING

ENGINE LUBRICATION SYSTEM

Positive displacement (gear-to-gear) oil pump, mounted to bottom of cylinder block, is driven by hexagonal shaft from distributor. Oil enters pump through screened pick-up tube, and is pumped through outlet tube to passage in cylinder block. This passage leads to oil filter adaptor on back of cylinder block. Adaptor contains 2 non-serviceable, integral by-pass valves. From the adaptor, oil is directed to the oil cooler, then back to filter. Oil then flows to main galleries. See Fig. 11.

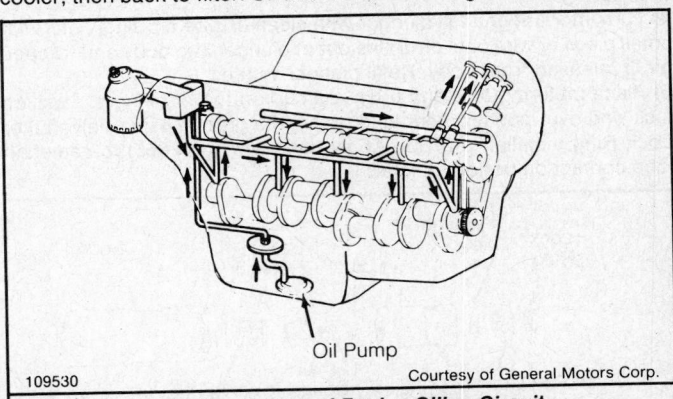

Oil Pump

Fig. 11: Cross-Sectional View of Engine Oiling Circuit

Crankcase Capacity – Engine oil capacity is 5 qts. (4.7L) without filter and 5.5 qts. (5.2L) with filter change.

Oil Pressure – Normal oil pressure is 11 psi (.77 kg/cm²) at idle and 53 psi (3.73 kg/cm²) at 2200 RPM with engine at normal operating temperature.

OIL PUMP

Removal & Disassembly – Remove oil pan. See OIL PAN under REMOVAL & INSTALLATION. Remove 2 bolts and one nut securing oil pump to engine. Remove oil pump, "O" ring and hexagon drive shaft from block. To disassemble, remove pump cover. Remove inlet tube from cover. Remove outlet tube from housing. Slide inner (drive) and outer (driven) rotors from housing.

NOTE: Pressure regulator valve is not serviceable.

Inspection – No oil pump specifications are available from manufacturer. Check all components for excessive wear, scoring and flatness. Fill pressure regulator valve cavity in housing with light-weight oil. Replace oil pump if cavity leaks.

Reassembly & Installation – To assemble, position outer rotor in rotor pocket with slots toward bottom of pump. Insert inner rotor into outer rotor with internal drive hex toward top of pump. Rotate gears to ensure no binding exists. To reassemble, reverse disassembly procedure. To install, reverse removal procedure using new "O" ring.

TORQUE SPECIFICATIONS

TORQUE SPECIFICATIONS

Application	Ft. Lbs. (N.m)
Camshaft Sprocket Bolt	36 (50)
Connecting Rod Nut	25 (34)
Crankshaft Balancer Bolt	70 (95)
Crankshaft Pulley Bolt	18 (24)
Cylinder Head Bolt [1]	
Step 1	38 (52)
Step 2	68 (92)
Step 3	[2]
Exhaust Manifold Bolt	16 (22)
Flywheel Bolt	70 (95)

TORQUE SPECIFICATIONS (Cont.)

Application	Ft. Lbs. (N.m)
Front Timing Case Cover Bolt	
Lower 4	17 (23)
Upper 4	30 (41)
Intake Manifold Bolt [3]	
Step 1	8 (11)
Step 2	12 (16)
Step 3	Repeat Step 2.
Lower Thermostat Housing-To-Intake Manifold Bolt	23 (31)
Main Bearing Cap Bolt	85 (115)
Oil Filter Adapter Bolt	14 (19)
Oil Pan Bolt	14 (19)
Oil Pump-To-Block Bolt	14 (19)
Oil Pump-To-Block Nut	22 (30)
Oxygen Sensor	30 (41)
Rocker Arm Pivot Bolt	22 (30)
Rocker Arm Support Retaining Nut	[4] 37 (50)
Upper Thermostat Housing-To-Lower Thermostat Housing Bolt	19 (26)
Valve Lifter Retainer Bolt	15 (20)
Water Pump	[5]

Application	INCH Lbs. (N.m)
Oil Pump Cover Bolt	84 (9)
Rocker Arm Support-To-Cylinder Head Bolt	[4] 84 (9)
Valve Cover Bolt	96 (11)

[1] – Apply GM Lubricant (1052356) to bolt threads. Tighten bolts in sequence. See Fig. 3.

[2] – Tighten bolts No. 1, 3 and 4 to 90 ft. lbs. (122 N.m).

[3] – Install proper length bolts and tighten in sequence. See Fig. 2. DO NOT EXCEED 12 ft. lbs. (16 N.m).

[4] – For proper installation of rocker arm support assembly, see ROCKER ARMS & PUSH RODS under REMOVAL & INSTALLATION.

[5] – See Fig. 7.

ENGINE SPECIFICATIONS

GENERAL SPECIFICATIONS

Application	Specification
4.9L	
Displacement	300 Cu. In. (4.9L)
Bore	3.62" (92 mm)
Stroke	3.62" (92 mm)
Compression Ratio	9.5:1
Fuel System	PFI
Horsepower @ RPM	200 @ 4400
Torque Ft. Lbs. @ RPM	275 @ 3000

CRANKSHAFT, MAIN & CONNECTING ROD BEARINGS

Application	In. (mm)
4.9L	
Crankshaft End Play	
Standard	.001-.008 (.03-.20)
Service Limit	.015 (.38)
Main Bearings	
Journal Diameter	2.6354-2.6364 (66.939-66.965)
Journal Length	
Journal No. 1	0.984 (24.99)
Journal No. 2	1.023 (25.98)
Journal No. 3	1.098 (27.89)
Journal No. 4	1.023 (25.98)
Journal No. 5	1.495 (37.97)
Journal Out-Of-Round	.0003 (.008)

CRANKSHAFT, MAIN & CONNECTING ROD BEARINGS (Cont.)

Application	In. (mm)
Oil Clearance [1]	
Journal No. 1	
Standard	.0008-.0031 (.020-.079)
Service Limit	.0031 (.079)
Journals No. 2, 3, 4 & 5	
Standard	.0016-.0039 (.041-.099)
Service Limit	.0045 (.114)
Connecting Rod Bearings	
Journal Diameter	1.927-1.928 (48.95-48.97)
Journal Out-Of-Round	.0003 (.008)
Oil Clearance	
Standard	.0005-.0028 (.013-.071)
Service Limit	.0035 (.089)

[1] – Oil clearances listed are with cylinder heads and intake manifold installed.

CONNECTING RODS

Application	In. (mm)
4.9L	
Crankpin Bore Diameter (Without Bearing)	2.052-2.053 (52.12-52.15)
Center-To-Center Length	5.700 (144.78)
Maximum Bend	[1]
Maximum Twist	[1]
Side Play	.008-.020 (.20-.51)

[1] – Replace rod if bent or twisted.

PISTONS, PINS & RINGS

Application	In. (mm)
4.9L	
Piston Clearance	.0004-.0020 (.010-.051)
Pins	
Diameter	.8659-.8661 (21.994-21.999)
Piston Fit	.0003-.0007 (.008-.018)
Rod Fit	Press Fit
Rings	
No. 1	
End Gap	.015-.025 (.38-.64)
Side Clearance	.0016-.0037 (.041-.094)
No. 2	
End Gap	.012-.022 (.30-.56)
Side Clearance	.0016-.0037 (.041-.094)
No. 3 (Oil)	
End Gap	.010-.050 (.25-1.27)
Side Clearance	None (Side Sealing)

CYLINDER BLOCK

Application	In. (mm)
4.9L	
Cylinder Bore Maximum Out-Of-Round	.0008 (.020)
Cylinder Liner Protrusion	0-.003 (0-.08)
Liner-To-Liner Maximum Height Difference	.002 (.05)

1991 ENGINES
4.9L V8 (Cont.)

VALVES & VALVE SPRINGS

Application	Specification
4.9L	
Intake Valves	
Face Angle	45°
Head Diameter	1.77" (45 mm)
Minimum Margin	.005" (.13 mm)
Stem Diameter	.3413-.3420" (8.669-8.687 mm)
Exhaust Valves	
Face Angle	45°
Head Diameter	1.50" (38.1 mm)
Minimum Margin	.030" (.76 mm)
Stem Diameter	.3401-.3408" (8.639-8.656 mm)
Valve Springs	
Free Length	1.95" (49.5 mm)
Installed Height	
Intake	
Standard	1.94" (49.2 mm)
Service Limit	1.977" (50.2 mm)
Exhaust	
Standard	1.83" (46.5 mm)
Service Limit	1.87" (47.5 mm)
Pressure	Lbs. @ In. (Kg @ mm)
Valve Closed	72 @ 1.73 (33 @ 43.9)
Valve Open	224 @ 1.35 (102 @ 34.3)

CYLINDER HEAD

Application	Specification
4.9L	
Valve Seats	
Intake Valve	
Seat Angle	45°
Seat Width	.063" (1.6 mm)
Maximum Seat Runout	.002" (.05 mm)
Exhaust Valve	
Seat Angle	45°
Seat Width	.094" (2.39 mm)
Maximum Seat Runout	.002" (.05 mm)
Valve Guides	
Intake Valve	
Valve Guide I.D. (Installed)	.343" (8.71 mm)
Valve Guide Oil Clearance	
Standard	.001-.003" (.03-.08 mm)
Service Limit	.005" (.13 mm)
Exhaust Valve	
Valve Guide I.D. (Installed)	.343" (8.71 mm)
Valve Guide Oil Clearance	
Standard	.002-.004" (.05-.10 mm)
Service Limit	.005" (.13 mm)

CAMSHAFT

Application	In. (mm)
4.9L	
Journal Runout	.0009 (.023)
Lobe Lift	
Intake	.384 (9.75)
Exhaust	.396 (10.06)
Oil Clearance	
Standard	.0018-.0037 (.046-.094)
Service Limit	.004 (.10)

VALVE LIFTERS

Application	In. (mm)
4.9L	
Oil Clearance	.0007-.0027 (.018-.069)

Brougham, Camaro, Caprice, Corvette, Custom Cruiser, Firebird, Roadmaster

NOTE: For repair procedures not covered in this article, see ENGINE OVERHAUL PROCEDURES article in GENERAL INFORMATION.

ENGINE IDENTIFICATION

Engine may be identified using Vehicle Identification Number (VIN) stamped on a metal pad, located near lower left corner of windshield. The eighth character identifies the engine model. See ENGINE IDENTIFICATION CODES table.

Engine identification code, located on cylinder block below cylinder head, may be required when ordering replacement parts. See ENGINE IDENTIFICATION CODES table.

ENGINE IDENTIFICATION CODES

Engine	Code
5.0L (305") TBI V8	
8th Character of Dash VIN	E
Engine Code	L03
5.0L (305") PFI V8	
8th Character of Dash VIN	F
Engine Code	LB9
5.7L (350") TBI V8	
8th Character of Dash VIN	7
Engine Code	L05
5.7L (350") PFI V8	
8th Character of Dash VIN	8
Engine Code	L98

ADJUSTMENTS

VALVE CLEARANCE ADJUSTMENT

NOTE: Hydraulic valve lifters are used. Under normal use, no valve adjustment is required.

REMOVAL & INSTALLATION

NOTE: For reassembly reference, label all electrical connectors, vacuum hoses and fuel lines before removal. Also place mating marks on engine hood and other major assemblies before removal.

FUEL PRESSURE RELEASE

Fuel Pressure Release (PFI) – Loosen fuel tank filler cap. Connect Fuel Gauge (J-34730-1) to fuel pressure connection mounted on fuel rail, on right side of fuel pressure regulator. Wrap shop towel around fitting during installation to avoid spillage. Install bleed hose. Turn gauge valve and drain fuel into an appropriate container.

Fuel Pressure Release (TBI) – All TBI engines are equipped with a constant bleed unit to relieve fuel pressure when ignition is turned off. To release fuel tank pressure, remove gas cap. No further procedure is necessary.

ENGINE

Removal (Except Corvette) – 1) Release fuel pressure. See FUEL PRESSURE RELEASE under REMOVAL & INSTALLATION in this article. Remove hood and air cleaner. Drain coolant from radiator. Disconnect radiator hoses and remove upper fan shroud. Remove fan assembly. Disconnect heater hoses at engine.

2) Remove serpentine belt. Remove power steering pump and set aside. Remove A/C compressor and set aside. Disconnect accelerator and throttle valve cable. Disconnect cooler lines at radiator (if equipped). Remove radiator.

3) Disconnect vacuum hoses. Disconnect Computer Command Control (CCC) wiring harness. Disconnect Air Injection Reaction (AIR) hose at pipe from converter. Remove MAP sensor (if equipped). Disconnect engine wiring harness at bulkhead. Disconnect necessary wires.

4) Remove distributor cap. Disconnect cruise control cable. Disconnect positive battery cable. Disconnect negative battery cable at A/C hose bracket and alternator bracket. Raise and support vehicle.

5) Remove crossover pipe and catalytic converter as an assembly. Remove flexplate cover. Remove torque converter bolts. Remove motor mount bolts. Disconnect fuel hose at in-line filter (TBI), or at fuel rail (PFI). Disconnect torque converter clutch wiring at transmission.

6) Disconnect transmission cooler lines at clip on engine pan. Remove transmission-to-engine bolts. Lower vehicle. Support transmission. Install lifting device and remove engine.

Installation – To install, reverse removal procedure. With engine off, fill radiator until level is even with base of filler neck. Fill coolant recovery reservoir to COLD FILL mark. Install coolant recovery reservoir cap. Run engine until radiator inlet hose is hot. With engine at idle, add coolant to radiator until level is even with base of filler neck. Install cap.

Removal (Corvette) – 1) Release fuel pressure. See FUEL PRESSURE RELEASE under REMOVAL & INSTALLATION in this article. Drain coolant from radiator. Remove air cleaner and serpentine belt. Remove brackets at back of A/C compressor. Disconnect wires at the A/C compressor.

2) Remove plenum extension (if equipped). Disconnect fuel lines at front fuel hose-to-fuel line connection. Remove A/C compressor mounting bracket nuts and bolts. Disconnect heater hoses. Disconnect upper radiator hose at thermostat outlet.

3) Remove A/C compressor-to-mounting bracket bolt and move compressor aside. Remove mounting bracket. Disconnect Port Fuel Injection (PFI) harness at engine. Disconnect cruise, detent and accelerator cables.

4) Remove distributor cap and wires from spark plugs, and remove as an assembly. Disconnect detent cable bracket at intake. Remove distributor. Remove cowl screen. Remove nut from wiper motor and remove wiper motor. Disconnect wires at oil pressure sending unit. Disconnect vacuum hoses.

5) Remove power steering pump, and wire aside. Remove crankshaft pulley. Disconnect bulkhead connector and necessary connectors. Disconnect Air Injection Reaction (AIR) hose at converter check valve. Move fuel lines aside.

6) Disconnect radiator hose at water pump. Disconnect upper radiator hose at power steering reservoir bracket. Raise and support vehicle. Drain engine oil and remove oil filter. Remove oil cooler adapter at engine. Disconnect AIR pipe at exhaust manifold. Remove AIR converter pipe.

7) Disconnect "Y" pipe hanger. Disconnect heat shields at "Y" pipe and converter. Disconnect oxygen sensor wire. Remove "Y" pipe. Remove flexplate/flywheel cover. On A/T models, remove torque converter bolts. On M/T models, remove transmission-to-bellhousing bolts.

8) On all models, loosen motor mount through bolts. Remove motor mount-to-engine block bolts. On A/T models, remove bellhousing bolts; lower vehicle. On all models, disconnect knock sensor wire. Disconnect ground cable at engine. Disconnect positive battery cable at battery and harness.

9) Lower vehicle. Support transmission with floor jack. Install engine lift. Carefully lift engine out of vehicle, disconnecting wire from bracket at left rear of engine.

Installation – 1) To install, reverse removal procedure. With engine off, fill radiator until level is even with base of filler neck. Fill coolant recovery reservoir to COLD mark. Add coolant to high-fill reservoir until level is at base of filler neck.

2) Install coolant recovery reservoir cap. Run engine until radiator inlet hose is hot. Add coolant to high-fill reservoir to maintain level at base of filler neck. Install cap. Fill coolant recovery reservoir to HOT mark.

INTAKE MANIFOLD

Removal (TBI Engines) – 1) Disconnect negative battery cable and drain cooling system. Remove air cleaner and throttle body assembly. Disconnect computer control harness and set aside. Remove upper radiator hose at thermostat, and heater hose at intake manifold.

2) Remove thermostat housing and gasket. Mark and remove necessary electrical connectors and vacuum hoses. Mark and remove necessary fuel line clips and lines. Remove throttle cable bracket.

Mark and remove spark plug wires at distributor cap. Remove EGR valve and solenoid. Remove distributor cap.

3) Mark distributor position for installation reference. Remove distributor. Remove ignition coil and coolant temperature sensor. Remove A/C compressor brace. Remove intake manifold bolts and studs. Remove intake manifold and gasket.

Installation – Clean all gasket surfaces. Apply 3/16" bead of RTV Sealer (1052289) on front and rear of cylinder block and apply 1/2" onto each cylinder head. *See Fig. 1.* Install gaskets and intake manifold. Tighten bolts and studs to specifications in sequence. *See Fig. 1.* See TORQUE SPECIFICATIONS table at end of article. To complete installation, reverse removal procedure.

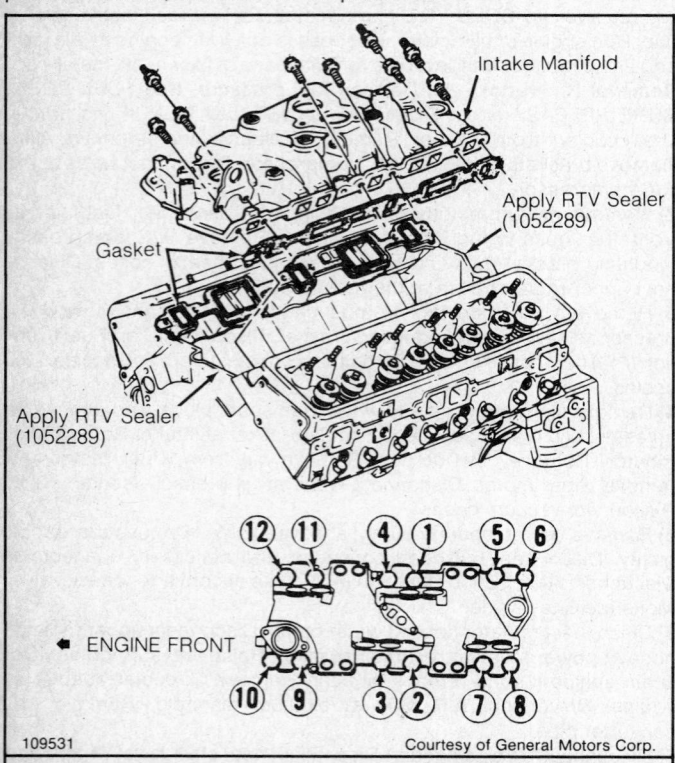

109531   Courtesy of General Motors Corp.

Fig. 1: Exploded View of Intake Manifold & Tightening Sequence (TBI Engines)

Removal (PFI Engines) – **1)** Disconnect negative battery cable and drain cooling system. Relieve fuel pressure. See FUEL PRESSURE RELEASE under REMOVAL & INSTALLATION in this article. Remove air intake duct assembly. Disconnect accelerator, throttle valve and cruise control cables (if equipped). Mark and disconnect necessary electrical connectors and vacuum hoses.

2) Remove heater hoses. Remove bolts attaching left runners to upper and lower intake manifold. *See Fig. 2.* Remove PCV valve and hose. Remove bolts attaching right runners to upper and lower intake manifold. Remove EGR valve, pipe and solenoid.

3) Remove lower manifold-to-runner bolts on each side. Right-side bolt is located near engine front, and left-side bolt is located near rear of engine. Remove upper intake manifold and runners. Remove and discard gaskets.

4) Disconnect injector harness and fuel lines. Remove fuel rail and injectors as an assembly. Mark and remove spark plug wires at distributor. Mark position of distributor for installation reference. Remove distributor assembly. Disconnect necessary cooling system hoses. Remove lower intake manifold bolts. Remove lower intake manifold and gaskets.

Installation – **1)** Clean all gasket surfaces. Apply 3/16" bead of RTV Sealer (1052289) on front and rear of cylinder block, and apply 1/2" onto each cylinder head. *See Fig. 2.* Install gaskets. Install lower intake manifold.

2) On Corvette, apply Loctite (1052624) to lower intake manifold bolts. On all models, tighten bolts to specifications in sequence. *See Fig. 2.* See TORQUE SPECIFICATIONS table at end of article. To complete installation, reverse removal procedure.

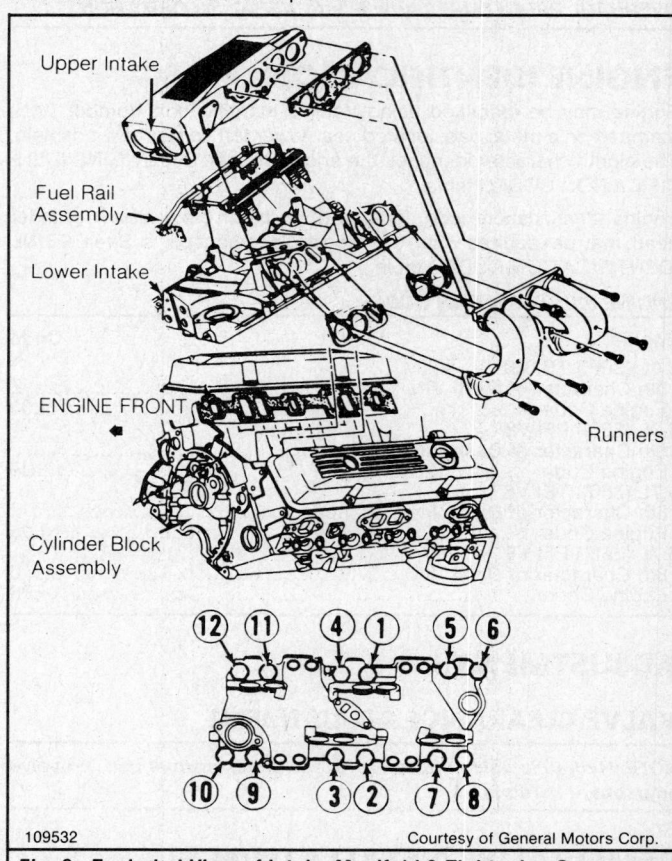

109532   Courtesy of General Motors Corp.

Fig. 2: Exploded View of Intake Manifold & Tightening Sequence (PFI Engines)

EXHAUST MANIFOLD

Removal & Installation – **1)** Disconnect negative battery cable. Remove air cleaner as necessary. Remove Air Injection Reaction (AIR) hoses and crossover pipe as necessary. Mark and disconnect spark plug wires at spark plugs.

2) Remove necessary accessory brackets. Separate inlet pipe from exhaust manifold. Remove exhaust manifold bolts. Remove exhaust manifold and gaskets (if equipped). To install, reverse removal procedure. Tighten bolts and nuts to specification. See TORQUE SPECIFICATIONS table at end of article.

VALVE COVERS

Removal & Installation – **1)** Disconnect negative battery cable. On Corvette, drain cooling system. Remove heater hose to upper intake manifold before removing right-side valve cover.

2) On all models, mark and disconnect spark plug wires at spark plugs. Remove necessary Air Injection Reaction (AIR) hoses and air cleaner. Mark and remove necessary electrical connectors.

3) Remove necessary accessories and brackets. Remove valve cover bolts. Use a block of wood and rubber mallet to loosen valve cover (if necessary). Remove valve cover and gasket. To install, reverse removal procedure.

ROCKER ARMS & PUSH RODS

Removal & Installation – **1)** Remove valve covers. See VALVE COVERS under REMOVAL & INSTALLATION in this article. Keep components in order for installation in original location and position.

2) Remove rocker arm nuts, balls, rocker arms and push rods. To install, reverse removal procedure. Apply Prelube (3755008) to rocker arm and ball mating surface.

ROCKER ARM STUD

Removal & Installation – 1) Remove rocker arm studs with Stud Remover (J 5802-01). Ream stud bore to replacement size of oversize stud. Oversize studs are available in .003" (.08 mm) and .013" (.33 mm). **2)** Coat press-fit area of stud with hypoid axle lubricant. Install rocker arm stud with Stud Installer (J 6880) until it bottoms out on cylinder head. To complete installation, reverse removal procedure.

CYLINDER HEAD

NOTE: Check and record compression before removing cylinder head. Remove cylinder head when engine is cold.

Removal – Remove intake manifold, exhaust manifold and valve covers. See INTAKE MANIFOLD, EXHAUST MANIFOLD and VALVE COVERS under REMOVAL & INSTALLATION in this article.
2) Drain cooling system. Ensure components are kept in order for installation reference. Remove cylinder head bolts in 3 steps, in reverse order of tightening sequence. *See Fig. 3.* Remove cylinder head and gasket.
Inspection – Clean all carbon and gasket material from mating surfaces. Check cylinder head for warpage or cracks. Clean and tap cylinder head bolt holes and threads.
Installation – 1) Coat steel-type head gaskets with sealer. DO NOT coat composition-type head gaskets with sealer. Install head gasket on cylinder block. Install cylinder head. Coat head bolts with Sealing Compound (1052080).
2) Install head bolts finger tight. Tighten head bolts to specifications in 3 steps, in proper sequence. *See Fig. 3.* To complete installation, reverse removal procedure.

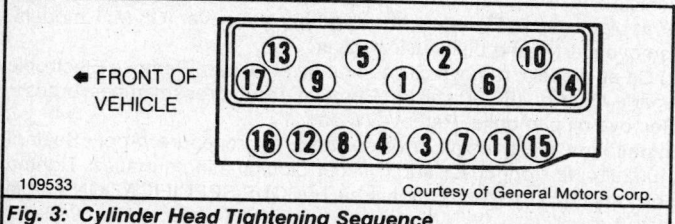

109533   Courtesy of General Motors Corp.

Fig. 3: Cylinder Head Tightening Sequence

FRONT COVER OIL SEAL

NOTE: It is not necessary to remove timing cover to replace timing cover seal.

Removal – 1) Remove negative battery cable and serpentine drive belt. Remove crankshaft pulley bolts and remove pulley. Remove harmonic balancer-to-crankshaft bolt. *See Fig. 4.* Remove harmonic balancer using Harmonic Balancer Remover/Installer (J 23523-E).
2) Remove oil pan. See OIL PAN under REMOVAL & INSTALLATION in this article. Remove water pump. See WATER PUMP under REMOVAL & INSTALLATION in this article.
3) On Corvette, remove Air Injection Reaction (AIR) assembly and A/C compressor mounting bracket; disconnect fuel lines. On all models, remove front cover-to-engine bolts. Remove cover and gasket. Carefully pry seal from timing cover using a large screwdriver.
Installation – 1) Install new oil seal in timing cover. Coat timing cover gasket with sealant and position on timing cover. Install timing cover and bolts. Tighten bolts finger tight.
2) Tighten bolts alternately and evenly to specifications. See TORQUE SPECIFICATIONS table at end of article. Apply sealant to area where oil pan, cylinder block and timing cover join. To complete installation, reverse removal procedure.

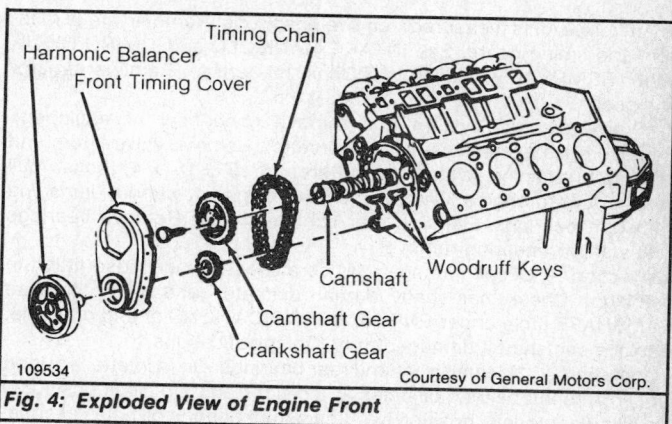

109534   Courtesy of General Motors Corp.

Fig. 4: Exploded View of Engine Front

TIMING CHAIN

Removal – 1) Remove front timing cover. See FRONT COVER OIL SEAL under REMOVAL & INSTALLATION in this article. Rotate crankshaft until camshaft gear and crankshaft gear timing marks align when No. 6 cylinder is at TDC of compression stroke. *See Fig. 5.*
2) Remove 3 camshaft gear retaining bolts. Remove camshaft gear and chain as an assembly. *See Fig. 4.* If replacing crankshaft gear, use Gear Remover (J 5825-A) to pull gear off crankshaft.
Installation – Drive crankshaft gear on crankshaft, with timing mark facing out. Align timing marks on camshaft gear and crankshaft gear. When timing marks are properly aligned, No. 6 cylinder should be on TDC of compression stroke. *See Fig. 5.* Install camshaft gear and chain as an assembly. To complete installation, reverse removal procedure.

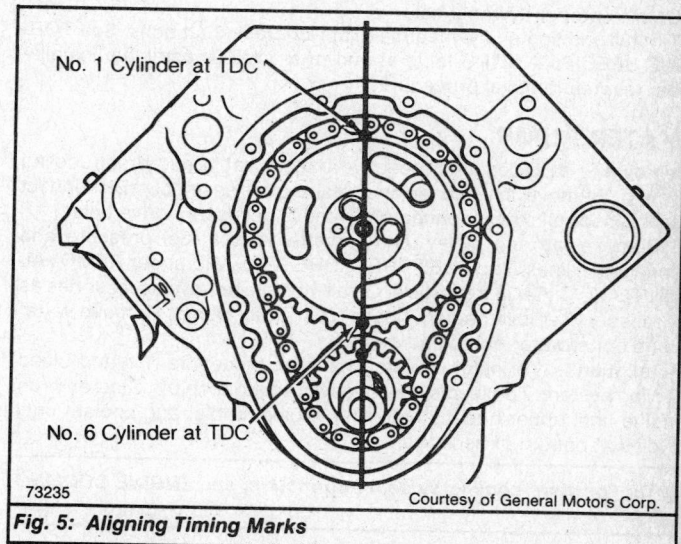

73235   Courtesy of General Motors Corp.

Fig. 5: Aligning Timing Marks

CAMSHAFT

NOTE: Rotate crankshaft in direction of normal operation only. Keep components in order for installation reference.

Removal – 1) Remove valve covers and rocker arms. DO NOT remove push rods. See VALVE COVERS and ROCKER ARMS & PUSH RODS under REMOVAL & INSTALLATION in this article. Measure lobe lift of camshaft with push rods installed.
2) To measure lobe lift, attach dial indicator to cylinder head. Position indicator pointer on tip of a push rod. Rotate crankshaft until push rod is at lowest point. Zero indicator and rotate crankshaft until push rod is at highest point. Record reading and repeat procedure for remaining lobes.

3) After lobe lift is measured, remove push rods. Remove intake manifold and timing gears. See INTAKE MANIFOLD and TIMING CHAIN under REMOVAL & INSTALLATION in this article. Remove radiator and hoses.

4) Discharge A/C system and remove condenser (if equipped). Remove grille assembly (except Corvette). Remove valve lifters and camshaft retaining plate. Using three 5/16" x 18" x 4" bolts, pull camshaft from engine. Carefully remove camshaft without damaging camshaft bearings. Remove rear camshaft plug. Remove bearings with standard bearing remover.

Inspection – Check camshaft for scratches, pits or loose fitting in bearings. Check camshaft journal diameter and lobe lift. See CAMSHAFT table under ENGINE SPECIFICATIONS at end of article. Replace camshaft if damaged or not to specifications.

Installation – **1)** Install front and rear bearings. On Corvette, position No. 1 camshaft bearing oil holes at 1 o'clock and 5 o'clock positions. On all other models, position No. 1 camshaft bearing oil holes at equal distance from 6-o'clock position.

2) On all models, position oil holes of bearings No. 2-4 at 5 o'clock position. Position oil hole of No. 5 bearing at 12 o'clock position. Install rear camshaft plug flush and .031" (.79 mm) deep in block. Use sealant on camshaft plug.

3) If replacing camshaft, replace lifters, engine oil and filter. Apply Camshaft Prelube (3755008) to camshaft lobes. Apply engine oil to bearings and camshaft bearing journals. To complete installation, reverse removal procedure.

REAR CRANKSHAFT OIL SEAL

Removal – Remove transmission. Remove flywheel/flexplate. Pry out seal with screwdriver, using notches in seal retainer. *See Fig. 6.*

Installation – **1)** Coat entire seal with engine oil. Install seal with Seal Installer (J 35621) until installer bottoms. *See Fig. 6.* Align crankshaft dowel to proper flywheel hole.

2) Install and tighten flywheel/flexplate-to-crankshaft bolts. See TORQUE SPECIFICATIONS table at end of article. To complete installation, reverse removal procedure.

WATER PUMP

Removal – **1)** Disconnect negative battery cable and drain cooling system. Remove air cleaner and intake duct assembly. Disconnect MAF sensor electrical connector. Remove accessory drive belt(s).

2) Remove fan and pulley. On Corvette, relieve fuel pressure and remove fuel lines. See FUEL PRESSURE RELEASE under REMOVAL & INSTALLATION in this article. On all models, remove accessories as necessary. Remove coolant hoses from water pump. Remove water pump bolts, water pump and gasket.

Installation – To install, reverse removal procedure. Fill and bleed cooling system. To bleed system, leave radiator cap off. Start and run engine until upper hose is hot. With engine at idle, add coolant until level is at bottom of neck.

NOTE: For more cooling system information, see ENGINE COOLING article.

OIL PAN

Removal (Except Corvette) – **1)** Disconnect negative battery cable. Remove air cleaner and fan shroud. On Camaro and Firebird, remove distributor cap. On all models, raise vehicle and drain crankcase. Remove cruise control servo bracket (if equipped).

2) Disconnect exhaust pipe at manifold, Air Injection Reaction (AIR) pipe clamp and catalytic converter hanger bolts. Remove exhaust crossover pipe at manifold and converter (if equipped).

3) Remove starter and flexplate access cover. On M/T models, it may be necessary to remove oil filter for access to flywheel cover bolts. Disconnect transmission line bracket at oil pan. Remove engine mount through bolts.

4) Remove oil pan bolts. Lower pan. Position front crankshaft throw and/or counterweight on horizontal plane so it does not interfere with oil pan removal. Raise engine, reinstall through bolts and remove oil pan.

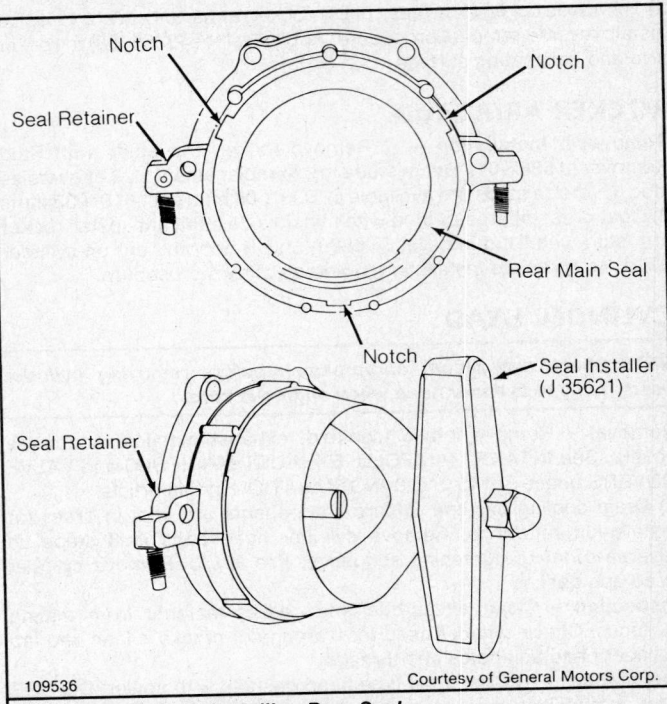

Fig. 6: Removing & Installing Rear Seal

Installation – To install, reverse removal procedure. Apply Sealant (1052914) to oil pan flange. Tighten bolts and nuts to specification. See TORQUE SPECIFICATIONS table at end of article.

Removal (Corvette) – **1)** Disconnect negative battery cable. Raise vehicle and drain crankcase. Remove oil filter. Remove oil filter adapter at block. On A/T models, remove flexplate cover. On M/T models, remove starter and bellhousing cover.

2) On all models, remove oil cooler pipe at oil pan. Remove Electronic Spark Control (ESC) shield. Remove front crossmember braces. Remove oil pan bolts. Remove oil pan.

Installation – To install, reverse removal procedure. Apply Sealant (1052914) to front cover and cylinder block mating surfaces. Tighten bolts and nuts to specification. See TORQUE SPECIFICATIONS table at end of article.

OVERHAUL

NOTE: Mark components and keep together for installation to original location and position. Components for 5.0L and 5.7L vary slightly.

CYLINDER HEAD

Valve Guides – Check and service guides before servicing valve and seat. Guide replacement information is not available from manufacturer. Valve guides may be reamed to .003" (.08 mm), .015" (.38 mm) or .030" (.76 mm) oversize for installation of oversize valve.

Valve Seat – Valve seat replacement information is not available from manufacturer. Follow instructions of tool manufacturer for servicing valve seats. If seats are serviced, valves must be serviced or replaced.

Valves – Check valves before servicing. Replace valves as necessary. See VALVES & VALVE SPRINGS table under ENGINE SPECIFICATIONS at end of article. Valves may be machined to specifications.

Valve Seat Correction Angles – If seat is too wide after grinding, use a 20-degree stone to lower, or a 70-degree stone to raise seat.

CYLINDER BLOCK ASSEMBLY

Piston & Rod Assembly – **1)** Mark rod and rod cap with matching cylinder number. Before disassembling, match mark piston to rod for reassembly reference. Notch or dot on piston top should face front of engine. Piston pin is a press fit.

2) When measuring, pin bore and piston pin must be free of varnish or scuffing. If piston-to-pin clearance exceeds .001" (.03 mm), replace piston and pin as an assembly.

Piston Rings – Rings are marked and must be installed properly. Marked side of ring must face toward top of piston. Top compression ring is chrome or molybdenum faced. Second compression ring has a tapered face. Oil ring is a 3-piece type. Ensure end gaps are positioned properly on piston. *See Fig. 7.*

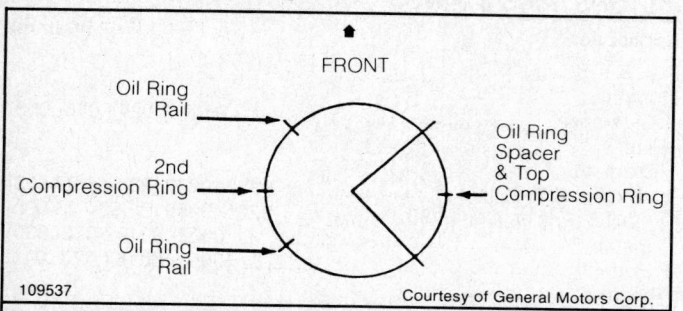

Fig. 7: Positioning Piston Ring End Gaps

Fitting Pistons – Ensure notch or dot on piston top faces front of engine. Check pistons for wear or damage. Replace pistons as necessary. Check piston-to-cylinder bore clearance. If one cylinder must be bored, all cylinders must be bored to same oversize.

Rod Bearings – Ensure bearing cap bolt holes and mating surfaces are clean and dry. Use connecting rod stud protectors on all rod cap bolts. Install inserts in connecting rod and cap. Lubricate bearings and crank pin. Install bearing cap. Tighten rod bearing cap bolts.

Crankshaft & Main Bearings – **1)** If bearing clearance is greater than specifications, replace upper and lower bearings. Service bearings are available in .001, .002, .009, .010 and .020" (.03, .05, .23, .25 and .51 mm) undersize. Ensure arrow on main bearing caps face engine front.

2) Tighten main bearing caps, except rear main cap, to 80 ft. lbs. (109 N.m). Tighten rear main cap to 12 ft. lbs. (15 N.m). Tap crankshaft rearward, then forward with lead hammer. This will align rear main bearing and crankshaft and thrust surfaces. Retighten all main bearing caps to 80 ft. lbs. (109 N.m).

Thrust Bearing – Check crankshaft end play by forcing crankshaft to extreme front position. Measure end play at front end of rear main bearing with a feeler gauge. If end play is not within specifications, replace thrust bearing. See CRANKSHAFT, MAIN & CONNECTING ROD BEARINGS table under ENGINE SPECIFICATIONS at end of article.

Cylinder Block – **1)** Check cylinder bore for wear, taper, out-of-round and piston fit. Cylinders with less than .005" (.13 mm) wear or taper may be honed.

2) Cylinders with greater than .005" (.13 mm) wear or taper must be bored to smallest oversize piston that will permit complete resurfacing of all cylinders. Machine cylinder or replace as necessary. See CYLINDER BLOCK table under ENGINE SPECIFICATIONS at end of article.

ENGINE OILING

ENGINE LUBRICATION SYSTEM

A gear-type oil pump provides full pressure lubrication through full-flow oil filter. Oil pump is bolted to bottom of cylinder block, inside oil pan. Intermediate (drive) shaft is splined into the distributor and oil pump. Distributor is camshaft driven.

Crankcase Capacity – Crankcase capacity is 4 qts. (3.8L) without oil filter, and 5 qts. (4.7L) with oil filter.

Minimum Oil Pressure – Oil pressure with engine at normal operating temperature should be 6 psi (0.4 kg/cm²) at 1000 RPM, 18 psi (1.3 kg/cm²) at 2000 RPM and 24 psi (1.7 kg/cm²) at 4000 RPM.

OIL PUMP

Removal & Disassembly – **1)** Remove oil pan. See OIL PAN under REMOVAL & INSTALLATION in this article. Remove oil pump retaining bolts and remove pick-up screen. Remove oil pump and intermediate shaft.

2) Remove oil pump cover screws and remove cover. Mark gear teeth for reassembly. Remove idler gear, drive gear and shaft. Remove pressure regulator pin, spring and valve from cover. Remove pick-up screen and pipe from cover only if replacing.

Inspection – Check oil pump body and gears for cracks, wear and damage. Check oil pump shaft for looseness in housing. Check inside of cover for wear which would permit oil leakage. Replace oil pump assembly as necessary. Oil pump specifications are not available from manufacturer.

Reassembly & Installation – Clean all parts in solvent and dry using compressed air. To reassemble, reverse disassembly procedure. See TORQUE SPECIFICATIONS table at end of article. To install, reverse removal procedure.

TORQUE SPECIFICATIONS

TORQUE SPECIFICATIONS

Application	Ft. Lbs. (N.m)
Camshaft Gear Bolt	21 (28)
Clutch Pressure Plate Bolts	30 (41)
Connecting Rod Cap Nuts	44 (60)
Crankshaft Pulley Bolts	
Center (Corvette)	70 (94)
Outer (Corvette)	32 (43)
Center & Outer (Except Corvette)	43 (58)
Cylinder Head Bolts [1]	
Step 1	22 (30)
Step 2	45 (61)
Step 3	67 (91)
Exhaust Manifold Bolts	
Corvette	19 (26)
Except Corvette	
Center Bolt/Studs	20 (27)
Outer Bolt/Studs	26 (35)
Flexplate-To-Crankshaft Bolts	[2] 74 (100)
Flywheel-To-Crankshaft Bolts	[2] 74 (100)
Harmonic Balancer (Damper) Bolt	
Corvette	60 (81)
Except Corvette	70 (94)
Intake Manifold [3]	
Lower Bolt	35 (47)
Runner-To-Upper Bolts	18 (25)
Runner-To-Lower Bolts	18 (25)
Main Bearing Cap Bolts	[4] 80 (109)
Oil Pan Bolts & Nuts (Except Corvette)	
5/16" Bolts & Nuts	14 (19)
Oil Pan Corner Stud/Nuts	16-17 (22-23)
Oil Pump Bolts	65 (88)
Spark Plugs	22 (30)
Torque Converter-To-Flexplate Bolts	46 (62)
Water Pump-To-Block Bolts	30 (41)
Water Pump Pulley Bolts	22 (30)
	INCH Lbs. (N.m)
Front Timing Cover Bolts	80 (9)
Oil Pan Bolts & Nuts	
1/4" Bolts & Nuts	80 (9)
Valve Cover Bolts	80 (9)

[1] – Coat threads with Sealing Compound (1052080). Tighten in 3 steps, evenly and in sequence. *See Fig. 3.*

[2] – Tighten flywheel bolts evenly, using a crisscross type sequence.

[3] – Tighten intake manifold-to-cylinder head bolts evenly and in sequence. *See appropriate Fig. 1 or 2.*

[4] – See CRANKSHAFT & MAIN BEARINGS in CYLINDER BLOCK ASSEMBLY under OVERHAUL.

1991 ENGINES
5.0L & 5.7L V8 (Cont.)

ENGINE SPECIFICATIONS

GENERAL SPECIFICATIONS

Application	Specification
5.0L	
Displacement	305 Cu. In. (5.0L)
Bore	3.74" (95.0 mm)
Stroke	3.48" (88.4 mm)
Compression Ratio	9.3:1
Fuel System	
VIN E (Engine Code L03)	TBI
VIN F (Engine Code LB9)	PFI
Horsepower @ RPM	
VIN E (Engine Code L03)	170 @ 4000
VIN F (Engine Code LB9)	205 @ 4200
Torque Ft. Lbs. @ RPM	
VIN E (Engine Code L03)	255 @ 2400
VIN F (Engine Code LB9)	285 @ 3200
5.7L	
Displacement	350 Cu. In. (5.7L)
Bore	4.00" (101.6 mm)
Stroke	3.48" (88.4 mm)
Compression Ratio	
VIN 7 (Engine Code L05)	9.75:1
VIN 8 (Engine Code L98)	10.25:1
Fuel System	
VIN 7 (Engine Code L05)	TBI
VIN 8 (Engine Code L98)	PFI
Horsepower @ RPM	
VIN 7 (Engine Code L05)	185 @ 3800
VIN 8 (Engine Code L98)	245 @ 4400
Torque Ft. Lbs. @ RPM	
VIN 7 (Engine Code L05)	290 @ 2400
VIN 8 (Engine Code L98)	345 @ 3200

CRANKSHAFT, MAIN & CONNECTING ROD BEARINGS

Application	In. (mm)
5.0L & 5.7L	
Crankshaft	
End Play	
Except VIN 8	.001-.007 (.03-.17)
VIN 8 (Engine Code L98)	.002-.006 (.05-.15)
Runout (Max.)	.001 (.03)
Main Bearings	
Journal Diameter	
Journal No. 1	2.4484-2.4493 (62.198-62.212)
Journals No. 2, 3 & 4	2.4481-2.4490 (62.182-62.205)
Journal No. 5	2.4479-2.4488 (62.120-62.177)
Journal Out-Of-Round (Max.)	.001 (.025)
Journal Taper (Max.)	.0002 (.005)
Oil Clearance	
Journal No. 1	.0010-.0015 (.025-.038)
Journals No. 2, 3 & 4	.0010-.0025 (.025-.064)
Journal No. 5	.0025-.0035 (.064-.089)
Connecting Rod Bearings	
Journal Diameter	
Except VIN 8	2.0893-2.0998 (53.068-53.334)
VIN 8 (Engine Code L98)	2.0988-2.0998 (53.309-53.334)
Journal Out-Of-Round (Max.)	.001 (.025)
Journal Taper (Max.)	.001 (.025)
Oil Clearance	
Except VIN 8	.0013-.0030 (.033-.076)
VIN 8	.0013-.0035 (.033-.089)

CONNECTING RODS

Application	In. (mm)
5.0L & 5.7L	
Maximum Bend	[1]
Maximum Twist	[1]
Side Play	.006-.014 (.16-.35)

[1] – Replace rod if any bend or twist exists.

PISTONS, PINS & RINGS

Application	In. (mm)
5.0L & 5.7L	
Pistons	
Clearance	.0007-.0027 (.018-.068)
Pins	
Diameter	
Except VIN 8	.9270-.9273 (23.546-23.553)
VIN 8 (Engine Code L98)	.9271-.9269 (22.994-23.000)
Piston Fit	.0003-.0010 (.076-.025)
Rod Fit	.0008-.0016 (.020-.041)
Rings	
No. 1	
End Gap	
Except VIN 8	.010-.035 (.25-.88)
VIN 8 (Engine Code L98)	.010-.030 (.25-.76)
Side Clearance	
Except VIN 8	.0012-.0032 (.030-.081)
VIN 8 (Engine Code L98)	.0012-.0039 (.030-.099)
No. 2	
End Gap	
Except VIN 8	.010-.025 (.25-.63)
VIN 8 (Engine Code L98)	.013-.027 (.33-.69)
Side Clearance	
Except VIN 8	.0012-.0032 (.030-.081)
VIN 8 (Engine Code L98)	.0012-.0039 (.030-.099)
No. 3 (Oil)	
End Gap	
Except VIN 8	.015-.055 (.38-1.39)
VIN 8 (Engine Code L98)	.010-.040 (.25-1.02)
Side Clearance	
Except VIN 8	.002-.008 (.05-.20)
VIN 8 (Engine Code L98)	.012-.039 (.30-.99)

CYLINDER BLOCK

Application	In. (mm)
5.0L & 5.7L	
Cylinder Bore	
Diameter	
5.0L	3.735-3.739 (94.87-94.96)
5.7L	4.000-4.002 (101.60-101.65)
Maximum Taper	.001 (.03)
Maximum Out-Of-Round	.002 (.05)

VALVES & VALVE SPRINGS

Application	Specification
5.0L & 5.7L	
Intake Valves	
Face Angle	45°
Minimum Margin	.031" (.80 mm)
Exhaust Valves	
Face Angle	45°
Minimum Margin	.031" (.80 mm)
Valve Springs	
Installed Height	1.689-1.768" (42.90-44.50 mm)
Pressure	Lbs. @ In. (kg @ mm)
Valve Closed	76-84 @ 1.72 (34-38 @ 43.7)
Valve Open	194-206 @ 1.25 (88-94 @ 32.0)

CYLINDER HEAD

Application	Specification
5.0L & 5.7L	
Valve Seats	
Intake Valve	
Seat Angle	46°
Seat Width	.031-.063" (.79-1.60 mm)
Exhaust Valve	
Seat Angle	46°
Seat Width	.063-.094" (1.60-2.40 mm)
Valve Guides	
Intake Valve	
Valve Guide Oil Clearance	
Except VIN 8	.0011-.0037" (.027-.094 mm)
VIN 8 (Engine Code L98)	.0010-.0037" (.025-.094 mm)
Exhaust Valve	
Valve Guide Oil Clearance	
Except VIN 8	.0011-.0047" (.027-.119 mm)
VIN 8 (Engine Code L98)	.0010-.0047" (.025-.119 mm)

CAMSHAFT

Application	In. (mm)
5.0L & 5.7L	
End Play	.004-.012 (.10-.30)
Journal Diameter	1.868-1.869 (47.45-47.48)
Lobe Lift	
5.0L	
VIN E (Engine Code L03)	
Intake	.232-.236 (5.89-5.99)
Exhaust	.255-.259 (6.48-6.58)
VIN F (Engine Code LB9)	
Intake	.273-.277 (6.93-7.04)
Exhaust	.283-.287 (7.19-7.29)
5.7L	
VIN 7 (Engine Code L05)	
Intake	.255-.259 (6.48-6.58)
Exhaust	.267-.271 (6.78-6.88)
VIN 8 (Engine Code L98)	
Intake	.273-.277 (6.93-7.04)
Exhaust	.283-.287 (7.19-7.29)

DeVille, Eldorado, Fleetwood & Seville

NOTE: Brougham information is not available from manufacturer.

SPECIFICATIONS

BELT ADJUSTMENT

Engine is equipped with automatic tensioner for serpentine belt. *See Fig. 1.* Measure belt tension using belt tension gauge. See BELT ADJUSTMENT table. If tension is not as specified, check belt length indicator marks on tensioner. Replace belt if indicator marks are not within operating range.

BELT ADJUSTMENT

Application	¹ Tension – Lbs. (kg)
DeVille & Fleetwood	70-110 (32-50)
Eldorado & Seville	120 (54)

¹ – Specification is for new belt.

COOLING SYSTEM SPECIFICATIONS

CAUTION: Use only engine coolant approved for use in aluminum engines and Engine Coolant Supplement (3634621) in cooling system or engine damage may result.

COOLING SYSTEM SPECIFICATIONS

Application	Specification
Coolant Replacement Interval	30,000 Miles
Coolant Capacity	
DeVille & Fleetwood	13.2 qts. (12.5 L)
Eldorado & Seville	12.1 qts. (11.5 L)
Pressure Cap	15 psi
Thermostat	
Starts To Open	192-199°F (89-93°C)
Fully Open	219°F (104°C)

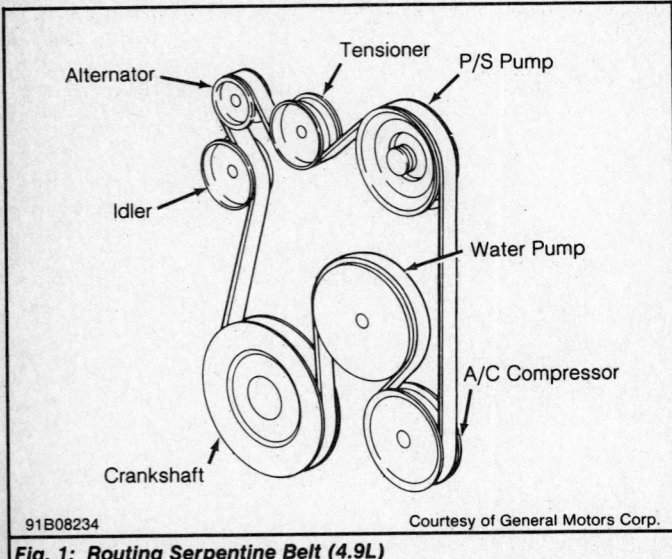

Fig. 1: Routing Serpentine Belt (4.9L)

91B08234   Courtesy of General Motors Corp.

ELECTRIC COOLING FAN

DESCRIPTION & OPERATION

DeVille & Fleetwood (Low Speed) – When coolant temperature reaches 208°F (98°C), Power Train Control Module (PCM) grounds low speed relay coils (PCM connector C2, terminal A11). This energizes low speed relay, completing circuit to left and right cooling fans. Under this condition, full battery voltage is applied to right cooling fan which operates at high speed. Left cooling fan operates at low speed because circuit runs through cooling fan resistors.

DeVille & Fleetwood (High Speed) – Full battery voltage continues to be applied to right cooling fan through low speed relay. See DEVILLE & FLEETWOOD (LOW SPEED) under DESCRIPTION & OPERATION. When coolant temperature reaches 226°F (106°C) or A/C high side temperature reaches 212°F (100°C), PCM grounds high speed relay coils (PCM connector C2, terminal B8). This energizes high speed relay. Full battery voltage is now applied to left cooling fan which now runs at high speed.

Eldorado & Seville (Low Speed) – Power Train Control Module (PCM) grounds coils of cooling fan relay "B" (at PCM terminal 2A11) under any of the following conditions:

- Coolant temperature exceeds 212°F (100°C).
- A/C high side temperature exceeds 140°F (60°C).
- Vehicle speed is less than 20 MPH, A/C compressor clutch engagement is possible and outside air temperature exceeds 113°F (45°C) or A/C high side temperature exceeds 122°F (50°C).

When cooling fan relay "B" is energized, circuit is completed through pusher fan, cooling fan relay "C" (terminals No. 1 and 3), puller fan and ground. Both motors operate at low speed due to circuit resistance of 2 motors (series circuit).

Eldorado & Seville (High Speed) – Power Train Control Module (PCM) grounds coils of cooling fan relays "B" and "C" (at PCM terminals 2A11 and 2B8) under any of the following conditions:

- Coolant temperature exceeds 226°F (108°C).
- Coolant temperature sensor failure is current (codes E014 and E015).
- A/C high side temperature exceeds 158°F (70°C).
- A/C high side temperature sensor failure is current (code B111).

When cooling fan relays "B" and "C" are energized, cooling fan relay "D" is energized. When all 3 relays are energized, full battery voltage is applied to both cooling fans, which now operate at high speed (parallel circuit).

DEVILLE & FLEETWOOD
COOLING FAN SYSTEM ELECTRICAL COMPONENT LOCATIONS

Component	Location
A/C High Side Temp. Sensor	Behind Right Headlight, On A/C Line.
Coolant Temp. Sensor	On Intake Manifold, Near Distributor.
Cooling Fan Relay	
Low Speed	In Left Underhood Fuse Block, Furthest Outboard.
High Speed	In Left Underhood Fuse Block, Next To Low Speed Relay.
Cooling Fan Resistors	On Left Cooling Fan Support.
Left Underhood Fuse Block	On Center Of Firewall.
Power Train Control Module (PCM)	Behind Top Right End Of Dashboard.

ELDORADO & SEVILLE
COOLING FAN SYSTEM ELECTRICAL COMPONENT LOCATIONS

Component	Location
A/C High Side Temp. Sensor	Left Center Of Firewall, On A/C Line.
Coolant Temp. Sensor	On Intake Manifold, Near Distributor.
Cooling Fan Relays	
"B", "C" & "D"	In Underhood Relay Center.
Fusible Link "L"	Forward Of Right Strut Tower, On Fusible Link Junction Block.
Power Train Control Module (PCM)	Behind Glove Box.
Underhood Relay Center	In Left Front Corner Of Engine Compartment

TROUBLE SHOOTING

NOTE: Electric cooling fan TROUBLE SHOOTING and TESTING procedures require entering self-diagnostics. For information on entering self-diagnostics, see SELF-DIAGNOSTICS – DEVILLE & FLEETWOOD PCM/BCM or SELF-DIAGNOSTICS – ELDORADO & SEVILLE PCM/BCM article in ENGINE PERFORMANCE.

Preliminary Check (DeVille & Fleetwood) – 1) Enter self-diagnostics and check for codes. If no codes are present, go to next step. If codes are present, repair system as necessary.

2) If only one fan operates, check wiring to inoperative fan. If wiring is okay, replace fan. If neither fan operates, perform appropriate test under TESTING (DEVILLE & FLEETWOOD) in this article.

Preliminary Check (Eldorado & Seville) – 1) If neither cooling fan operates, check fusible link "L" by operating horn. If horn operates, fusible link "L" is okay. If horn does not operate, check fusible link "L".

2) Check A/C clutch engagement. If A/C clutch does not engage, check COOLANT FAN fuse No. 2 in underhood relay center.

3) If both cooling fans operate in low speed with ignition off, check for short to battery (B+) in Black/White wire circuit between cooling fan relay "B" and pusher fan (front). If circuit is okay, replace cooling fan relay "B".

4) If both fans operate in high speed but not in low speed, check for open in Black/Pink wire circuit, and check continuity between terminals No. 1 and 3 (both are Black/Pink) of cooling fan relay "C".

NOTE: COOLING FAN SYSTEM OVERRIDE TEST overrides the normal operation of fan control system, allowing technician to manually operate cooling fans by pushing COOLER and WARMER buttons on A/C control panel.

Cooling Fan System Override Test (Eldorado & Seville) – 1) Enter self-diagnostics and check for codes. If codes are present, repair system before continuing procedures.

2) Select cooling fan mode (ES08) of PCM output overrides. Push COOLER and WARMER buttons on A/C control panel until "00", "01", "10" and "11" appear on diagnostic display. Observe cooling fan operation while each combination of numbers is displayed and compare with COOLING FAN SYSTEM OVERRIDE TEST table.

3) If results are abnormal, check cooling fans, relays and wiring. If results are normal, perform appropriate test under TESTING (ELDORADO & SEVILLE).

COOLING FAN SYSTEM OVERRIDE TEST

COOLER [1]	WARMER [1]	Normal Result
0	0	Both Fans Off
0	1	Puller Fan High, Pusher Fan Off
1	0	Both Fans Low
1	1	Both Fans High

[1] – Push this A/C panel button until number in this column is shown on diagnostic display.

NOTE: COOLING FAN SYSTEM OVERRIDE TEST overrides the normal operation of fan control system, allowing technician to manually operate cooling fans by pushing COOLER and WARMER buttons on A/C control panel.

Cooling Fan System Override Test (DeVille & Fleetwood) – 1) Enter self-diagnostics and check for codes. If codes are present, repair system before continuing procedures.

2) If no codes are present, select cooling fan mode of PCM output overrides (E.5.8). In this mode, "00" will appear on diagnostic display. No voltage is applied to cooling fan relays in this mode.

3) Push COOLER button on A/C control panel. Left digit of display will change to "1". Display now reads "10" and low speed cooling fan relay is energized. This supplies voltage to right cooling fan and low speed circuit of left cooling fan.

4) Push WARMER button. Right digit of display will change to "1". Display now reads "11" and low and high speed cooling fan relays are energized. This supplies voltage to right cooling fan and high speed circuit of left cooling fan.

TESTING (DEVILLE & FLEETWOOD)

Neither Cooling Fan Operates – 1) While in cooling fan system override test, turn on both cooling fans. See COOLING FAN SYSTEM OVERRIDE TEST (DEVILLE & FLEETWOOD) under TROUBLE SHOOTING.

2) If cooling fans do not operate as specified in test, go to step 5). If cooling fans operate as specified, start engine. Turn on A/C. Run engine at idle for a few minutes.

3) Enter self-diagnostics. Read PCM DATA – COOLANT TEMPERATURE SENSOR and BCM DATA – REFRIGERANT HIGH SIDE TEMPERATURE SENSOR. If both temperatures indicated on display are above ambient temperature and are increasing, replace PCM.

4) If one or both temperatures indicated on display remain at or below ambient temperature, check wiring to sensor. If wiring is okay, replace sensor.

5) Disconnect high speed cooling fan relay. Measure voltage between high speed cooling fan relay connector terminal No. 1 (Red wire) and ground. If battery voltage is present, go to next step. If no voltage is present, replace fuse No. 4 in left underhood fuse block or repair Red wire.

6) Turn ignition switch to RUN position. Measure voltage between high speed cooling fan relay connector terminal No. 2 (Brown wire) and ground.

7) If battery voltage is present, repair open in Black wires between cooling fans and ground. If no voltage is present, replace fuse No. 6 in instrument panel fuse block or repair Brown wire.

NOTE: When cooling fans are operated at low speed, left cooling fan should operate at low speed and right cooling fan should operate at high speed.

Left Cooling Fan Does Not Operate In Low Speed – 1) While in cooling fan system override test, turn on cooling fans at low speed. See COOLING FAN SYSTEM OVERRIDE TEST (DEVILLE & FLEETWOOD) under TROUBLE SHOOTING.

2) If cooling fans do not operate, go to step 5). If cooling fans operate, start engine. Turn on A/C. Run engine at idle for a few minutes.

3) Enter self-diagnostics. Read PCM DATA – COOLANT TEMPERATURE SENSOR and BCM DATA – REFRIGERANT HIGH SIDE TEMPERATURE SENSOR. If both temperatures indicated on display are above ambient temperature and are increasing, replace PCM.

4) If one or both temperatures indicated on display remain at or below ambient temperature, check wiring to sensor. If wiring is okay, replace sensor.

5) Turn ignition switch to RUN position. With PCM connectors intact, connect fused jumper wire between ground and PCM connector C2, terminal A11. If cooling fans operate, replace PCM. If cooling fans do not operate, leave jumper connected and go to next step.

6) Measure voltage between ground and low speed cooling fan relay connector terminal No. 1 (Red wire). If battery voltage is present, go to next step. If no voltage is present, check Red wire.

7) Measure voltage between low speed cooling fan relay connector terminals No. 1 and 5 (Red and Gray/Black wires). If battery voltage is present, go to next step. If no voltage is present, check Gray/Black wire.

8) Measure voltage between ground and low speed cooling fan relay connector terminal No. 2 (Brown wire). If battery voltage is present, go to next step. If no voltage is present, check Brown wire.

9) Connect fused jumper wire between low speed cooling fan relay connector terminals No. 2 and 4 (Brown and Black/Red wires). If cooling fans operate, replace low speed cooling fan relay. If cooling fans do not operate, check Black/Red wire. If wire is okay, check cooling fan resistors and wiring harness.

Both Cooling Fans Do Not Operate In High Speed – 1) While in cooling fan system override test, turn on cooling fans at high speed. See COOLING FAN SYSTEM OVERRIDE TEST (DEVILLE & FLEETWOOD) under TROUBLE SHOOTING.

2) If cooling fans do not operate, go to step 5). If cooling fans operate, start engine. Turn on A/C. Run engine at idle for a few minutes.

3) Enter self-diagnostics. Read PCM DATA – COOLANT TEMPERATURE SENSOR and BCM DATA – REFRIGERANT HIGH SIDE TEMPERATURE SENSOR. If both temperatures indicated on display are above ambient temperature and are increasing, replace PCM.

4) If one or both temperatures indicated on display remain at or below ambient temperature, check wiring to sensor. If wiring is okay, replace sensor.

5) Turn ignition switch to RUN position. With PCM connectors intact, connect fused jumper wire between ground and PCM connector C2, terminal B8. If cooling fans operate, replace PCM. If cooling fans do not operate, leave jumper connected and go to next step.

6) Measure voltage between ground and high speed cooling fan relay connector terminal No. 1 (Red wire). If battery voltage is present, go to next step. If no voltage is present, check Red wire.

7) Measure voltage between high speed cooling fan relay connector terminals No. 1 and 5 (Red and Dark Green/White wires). If battery voltage is present, go to next step. If no voltage is present, check Dark Green/White wire.

8) Measure voltage between ground and high speed cooling fan relay connector terminal No. 2 (Brown wire). If battery voltage is present, go to next step. If no voltage is present, check Brown wire.

9) Connect fused jumper wire between high speed cooling fan relay connector terminals No. 2 and 4 (Brown and Black/Pink wires). If cooling fans operate, replace high speed cooling fan relay. If cooling fans do not operate, check Black/Pink wire.

TESTING (ELDORADO & SEVILLE)

NOTE: Dark Green wire terminal of cooling fan relay "B" becomes Dark Green/Yellow at other end of circuit (at PCM).

No Low Speed (Both Fans), No High Speed (Both Fans) – 1) Check fusible link "L" (if horn operates, fusible link is okay). If fusible link is open, repair short in wiring. If fusible link is okay, check for battery voltage at Red wire terminals of cooling fan relays "B" and "D".

2) If no voltage is present at one or both terminals, repair open in Red wire circuit. If voltage is present at both terminals, remove cooling fan relay "B" from underhood relay center. Turn ignition to RUN position.

3) Measure voltage between ground and Red/White wire terminal of cooling fan relay "B". If no voltage is present, check COOLANT FAN FUSE No. 2 in underhood relay center and Red/White wire circuit. If battery voltage is present, check wiring between relays and cooling fans and repair as necessary.

4) If battery voltage is present, check for open in Dark Green/Yellow wire circuit between PCM and cooling fan relay "B" and Light Green/Black wire circuit between PCM and cooling fan relay "C". If both circuits are okay, perform PCM/BCM REPLACEMENT CHECK in appropriate SELF-DIAGNOSTICS article in ENGINE PERFORMANCE.

No Low Speed (Both Fans), No High Speed (Pusher Fan) – 1) Remove cooling fan relay "B" from underhood relay center. Turn ignition to RUN position. Measure voltage between ground and Red and Red/White wire terminals of cooling fan relay "B".

2) If battery voltage is present, go to next step. If no voltage is present, check COOLANT FAN FUSE No. 2 in underhood relay center, Red/White wire circuit, fusible link "L" and Red wire circuit.

3) Enter self-diagnostics and select PCM override ES08. See COOLING FAN SYSTEM OVERRIDE TEST (ELDORADO & SEVILLE) under TROUBLE SHOOTING. Set diagnostic display to "10". Connect test light between Red/White and Dark Green wire terminals of cooling fan relay "B".

4) If test light illuminates, go to next step. If test light does not illuminate, check for open or short to battery (B+) in Dark Green wire circuit between cooling fan relay "B" and PCM. If circuit is okay, perform PCM/BCM REPLACEMENT CHECK in appropriate SELF-DIAGNOSTICS article in ENGINE PERFORMANCE.

5) Connect a fused jumper wire between Red and Black/White wire terminals of cooling fan relay "B". If cooling fans do not run at low speed, leave jumper connected and go to next step. If cooling fans run at low speed, check for poor connections at relay. If relay connections are okay, replace cooling fan relay "B".

6) Remove cooling fan relay "C". Connect jumper wire between ground and Black/Pink wire terminal of cooling fan relay "C". If pusher fan runs at high speed, check/replace cooling fan relay "C".

7) If pusher fan does not run at high speed, check for open in Black/Pink wire between cooling fan relay "C" and pusher fan, and Black/White wire between cooling fan relay "B" and pusher fan. If wires are okay, replace pusher fan.

Low Speed OK (Both Fans), No High Speed (Pusher Fan) – 1) Remove cooling fan relay "C" from underhood relay center. Turn ignition to RUN position. Measure voltage between Red/White and Black wire terminals of cooling fan relay "B".

2) If no voltage is present, repair open in Black wire between cooling fan relay "C" and ground. If battery voltage is present, check for poor connection at cooling fan relay "C". If connection is okay, replace cooling fan relay "C".

Low Speed OK (Both Fans), No High Speed (Puller Fan) – 1) Remove cooling fan relay "D" from underhood relay center. Turn ignition to RUN position. Measure voltage between ground and Red and Red/White wire terminals of cooling fan relay "D".

2) If battery voltage is present, go to next step. If no voltage is present, check COOLANT FAN FUSE No. 2 in underhood relay center, Red/White wire circuit, fusible link "L" and Red wire circuit.

3) Enter self-diagnostics and select PCM override ES08. See COOLING FAN SYSTEM OVERRIDE TEST (ELDORADO & SEVILLE) under TROUBLE SHOOTING. Set diagnostic display to "01". Connect test light between Red/White and Light Green/Black wire terminals of cooling fan relay "D".

4) If test light illuminates, go to next step. If test light does not illuminate, repair for open in Light Green/Black wire circuit. Connect a fused jumper wire between Red and Black/Pink wire terminals of cooling fan relay "D".

5) If puller fan does not run at high speed, repair open in Black/Pink wire between cooling fan relay "D" and puller fan. If puller fan runs at high speed, check for poor connection at cooling fan relay "D". If connection is okay, check/replace cooling fan relay "D".

Low Speed OK (Both Fans), No High Speed (Both Fans) – 1) Remove cooling fan relays "C" and "D" from underhood relay center. Turn ignition to RUN position. Measure voltage between ground and Red/White wire terminal of cooling fan relay "C", and Red and Red/White wire terminals of cooling fan relay "D".

2) If battery voltage is present on all terminals, go to next step. If no voltage is present on one or more terminals, check for open wiring, fusible link "L" or COOLANT FAN FUSE No. 2.

3) Check for open in Light Green/Black wire circuit. If circuit is okay, perform PCM/BCM REPLACEMENT CHECK in appropriate SELF-DIAGNOSTICS article in ENGINE PERFORMANCE.

Continuous Low (Both Fans) With Ignition On Or Off – Perform step **3)** of PRELIMINARY CHECK under TROUBLE SHOOTING & TESTING.

Continuous Low (Both Fans) With Ignition In RUN Position – Check for short to ground in Dark Green wire circuit between cooling fan relay "B" and PCM. If circuit is okay, perform PCM/BCM REPLACEMENT CHECK in appropriate SELF-DIAGNOSTICS article in ENGINE PERFORMANCE.

No Low Speed (Both Fans), High OK (Both Fans) – Perform step **4)** of PRELIMINARY CHECK under TROUBLE SHOOTING.

Continuous High (Puller Fan) With Ignition On or Off – Check for short to battery (B+) in Black/Pink wire circuit. If circuit is okay, replace cooling fan relay "D".

Continuous High (Puller Fan) With Ignition In RUN Position – Check for short to ground in Light Green/Black wire circuit. If circuit is okay, perform PCM/BCM REPLACEMENT CHECK in appropriate SELF-DIAGNOSTICS article in ENGINE PERFORMANCE.

No Low Speed (Both Fans), No High Speed (Puller Fan) – Check for open condition in:

- Black/Pink wire between puller fan and wiring splice (splice between puller fan and cooling fan relay "D").
- Black wire between puller fan and wiring splice (splice between puller fan and ground.
- Puller fan and puller fan connector.

No Low Speed (Both Fans), No High Speed (Pusher Fan – Except During COOLING FAN SYSTEM OVERRIDE TEST With Display Reading "10") – Check for short to ground in Pink/Black wire between pusher fan and cooling fan relay "C". If circuit is okay, replace cooling fan relay "C".

WIRING DIAGRAMS

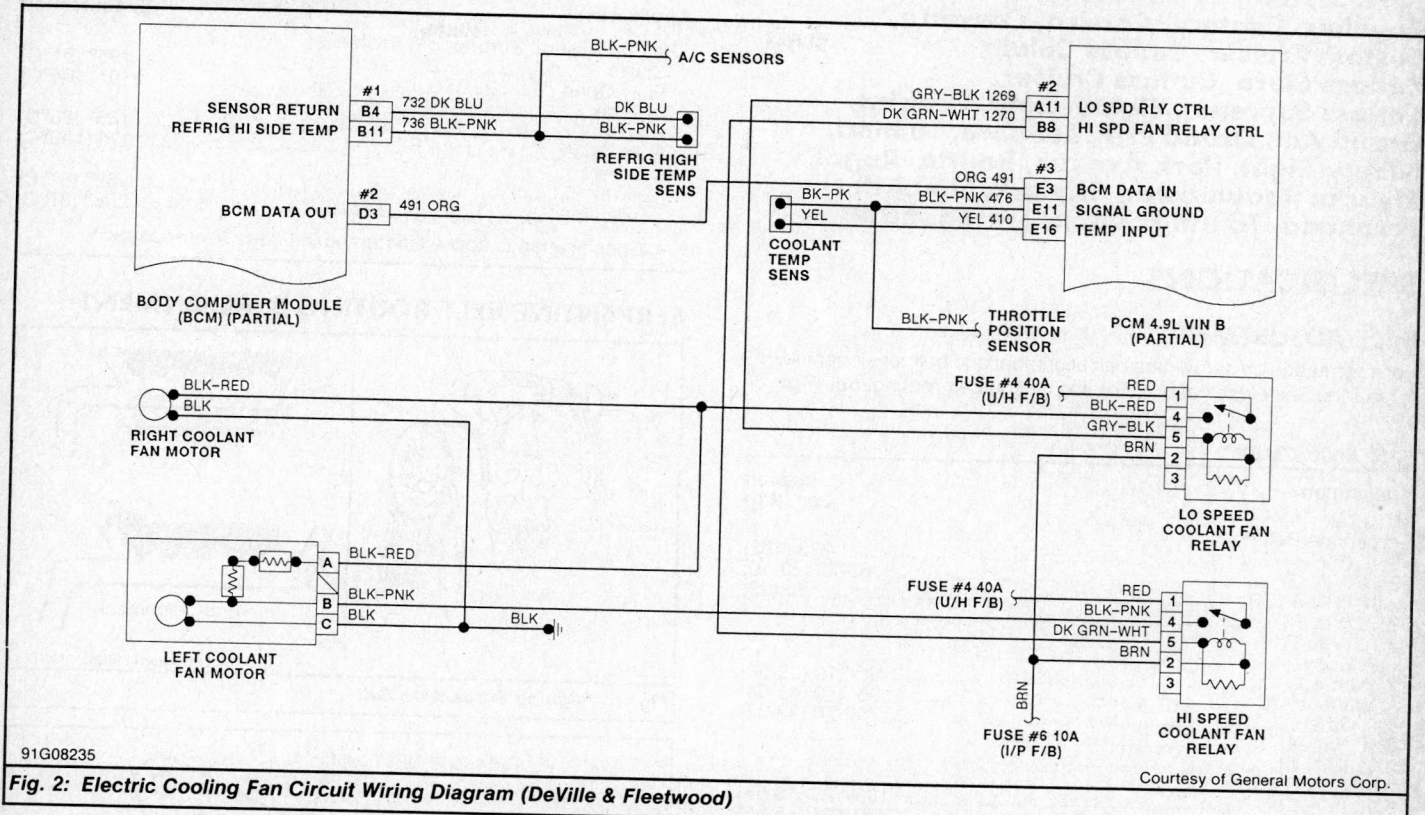

Fig. 2: Electric Cooling Fan Circuit Wiring Diagram (DeVille & Fleetwood)

Courtesy of General Motors Corp.

91G08235

Fig. 3: Electric Cooling Fan Circuit Wiring Diagram (Eldorado & Seville)

Courtesy of General Motors Corp.

91E05274

Beretta, Bonneville, Camaro, Caprice, Cavalier, Century, Corsica, Corvette, Custom Cruiser, Cutlass Calais, Cutlass Ciera, Cutlass Cruiser, Cutlass Supreme, Eighty-Eight, Firebird, Grand Am, Grand Prix, LeSabre, Lumina, Ninety-Eight, Park Avenue, Reatta, Regal, Riviera, Roadmaster, Skylark, Sunbird, Toronado, Touring Sedan, Trofeo, 6000

SPECIFICATIONS

BELT ADJUSTMENT

For information on serpentine belt alignment and belt tensioner indicator marks, *See Figs. 1 and 2.* For serpentine belt routing, *See Figs. 3-12.*

BELT ADJUSTMENT

Application	[1] Tension Lbs. (kg)
Serpentine Belt [2]	
2.0L (VIN K)	225 (102)
2.2L (VIN G)	63-77 (29-40)
2.3L (VIN A & D)	50 (23)
2.5L (VIN R)	[3]
3.1L (VIN T)	
"F" Body	
With A/C	85-110 (39-50)
Without A/C	95-140 (43-64)
All Others	50-70 (23-32)
3.4L (VIN X)	[3]
3.3L (VIN N)	[3]
3.8L (VIN C & L)	[3]
5.0L (VIN E)	105-125 (48-57)
5.0L (VIN F)	99-121 (45-55)
5.7L (VIN 7)	99-121 (45-55)
5.7L (VIN 8)	60-90 (27-41)
"V" Belt	
2.3L (VIN A)	
Power Steering	110 (50)
2.5L (VIN U)	
A/C Compressor	165 (75)
Alternator	165 (75)
Power Steering	180 (82)
Water Pump	180 (82)

[1] – Specifications are for new belts only. Measure tension with belt tension gauge.
[2] – Engines with serpentine belts have automatic tensioner. If tension reading is not as specified, check belt's operating length or tensioner's operating range. Replace belt as necessary.
[3] – Information is not available from manufacturer.

COOLING SYSTEM SPECIFICATIONS

COOLING SYSTEM SPECIFICATIONS

Application	Specification
Coolant Replacement Interval	30,000 Miles
Coolant Capacity [1]	
2.0L (VIN K)	11.7 qts. (11.1 L)
2.2L (VIN G)	11.7 qts. (11.1 L)
2.3L (VIN A & D)	9.2 qts. (8.7 L)
2.5L (VIN R)	9.9 qts. (9.4 L)
2.5L (VIN U)	7.8 qts. (7.4 L)
3.1L (VIN T)	14.0 qts. (13.2 L)
3.3L (VIN N)	13.0 qts. (12.3 L)
3.4L (VIN X)	13.0 qts. (12.3 L)
3.8L (VIN C & L)	13.0 qts. (12.3 L)
5.0L (VIN E & F)	18.0 qts. (17.0 L)
5.7L (VIN 7)	15.0 qts. (14.2 L)
5.7L (VIN 8)	17.0 qts. (16.0 L)
Pressure Cap	15 psi
Thermostat Opens	
Bonneville, Eighty-Eight, LeSabre, Ninety-Eight, Park Avenue, Touring Sedan	
Starts	195°F (91°C)
Fully Open	222° (106°C)

COOLING SYSTEM SPECIFICATIONS (Cont.)

Application	Specification
Reatta, Riviera, Toronado & Trofeo	
Starts	195° (91°C)
Fully Open	219° (104°C)
Corvette	
Starts	185° (85°C)
Fully Open	217° (103°C)
All Others	
Starts	188° (87°C)
Fully Open	206° (97°C)

[1] – Specification is approximate and includes heater capacity.

SERPENTINE BELT ROUTING & ALIGNMENT

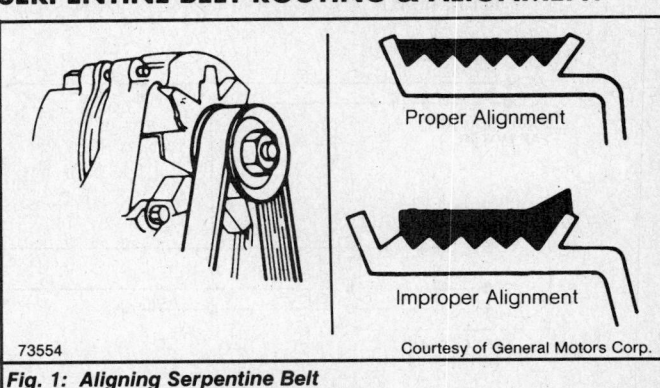

Proper Alignment

Improper Alignment

73554   Courtesy of General Motors Corp.

Fig. 1: Aligning Serpentine Belt

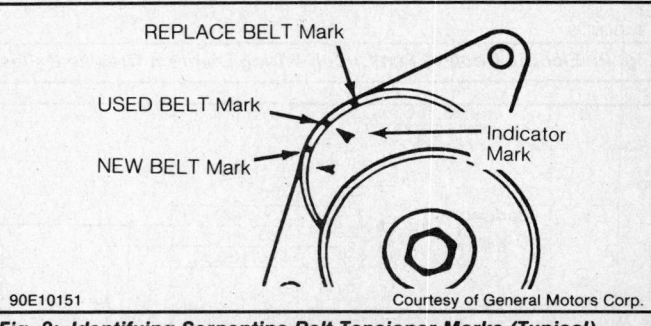

REPLACE BELT Mark
USED BELT Mark
NEW BELT Mark
Indicator Mark

90E10151   Courtesy of General Motors Corp.

Fig. 2: Identifying Serpentine Belt Tensioner Marks (Typical)

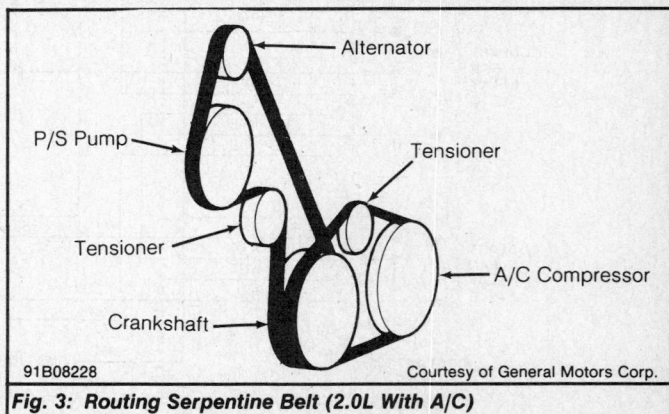

Alternator
P/S Pump
Tensioner
Tensioner
A/C Compressor
Crankshaft

91B08228   Courtesy of General Motors Corp.

Fig. 3: Routing Serpentine Belt (2.0L With A/C)

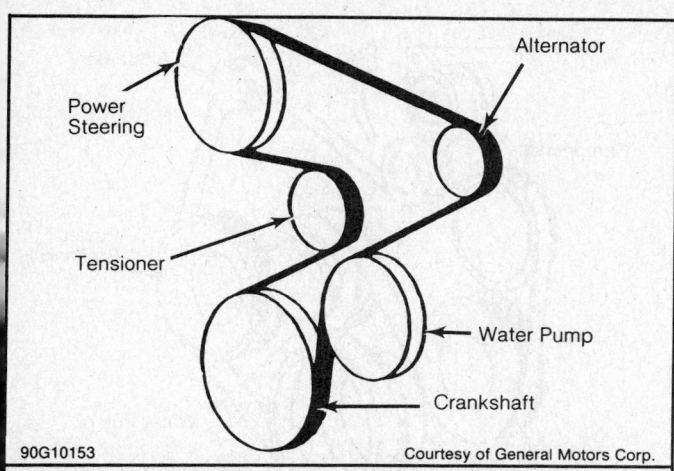

90G10153   Courtesy of General Motors Corp.

Fig. 4: Routing Serpentine Belt (2.2L & 2.5L Without A/C)

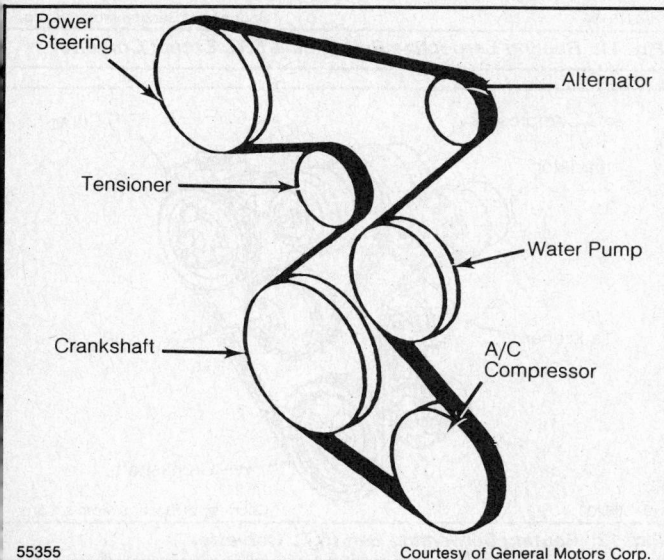

55355   Courtesy of General Motors Corp.

Fig. 5: Routing Serpentine Belt (2.2L & 2.5L With A/C)

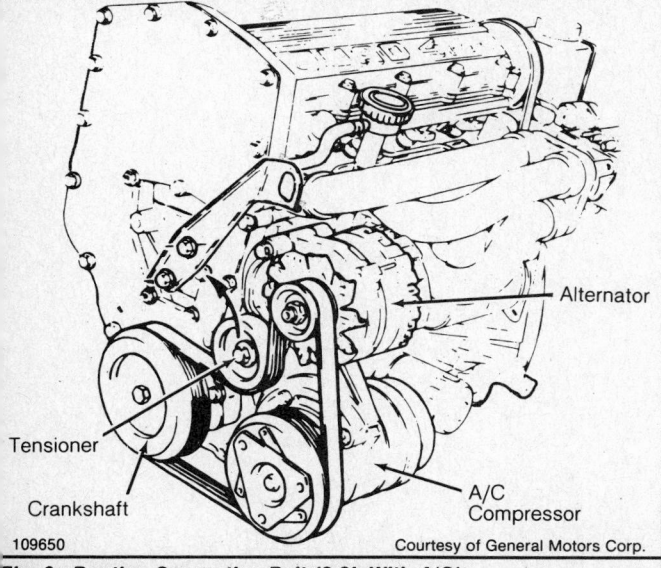

109650   Courtesy of General Motors Corp.

Fig. 6: Routing Serpentine Belt (2.3L With A/C)

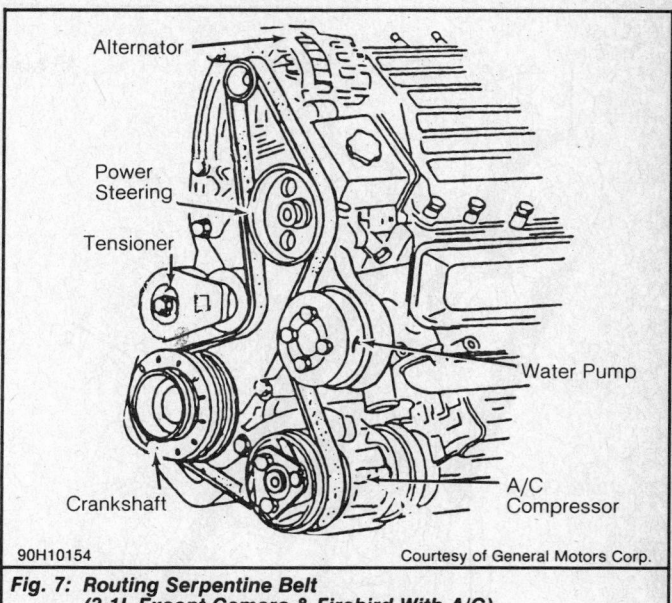

90H10154   Courtesy of General Motors Corp.

**Fig. 7: Routing Serpentine Belt
(3.1L Except Camaro & Firebird With A/C)**

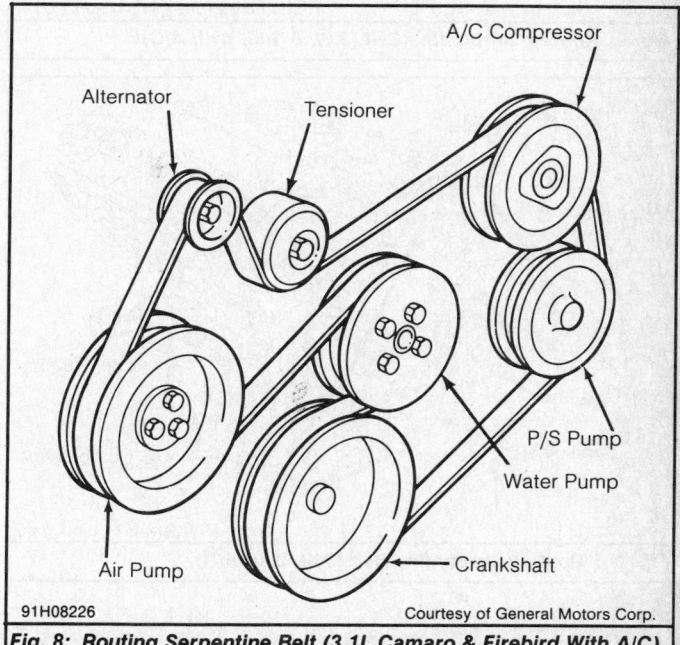

91H08226   Courtesy of General Motors Corp.

Fig. 8: Routing Serpentine Belt (3.1L Camaro & Firebird With A/C)

GM
5-78

1991 ENGINE COOLING
Specifications & Electric Cooling Fans – Exc. Cadillac (Cont.)

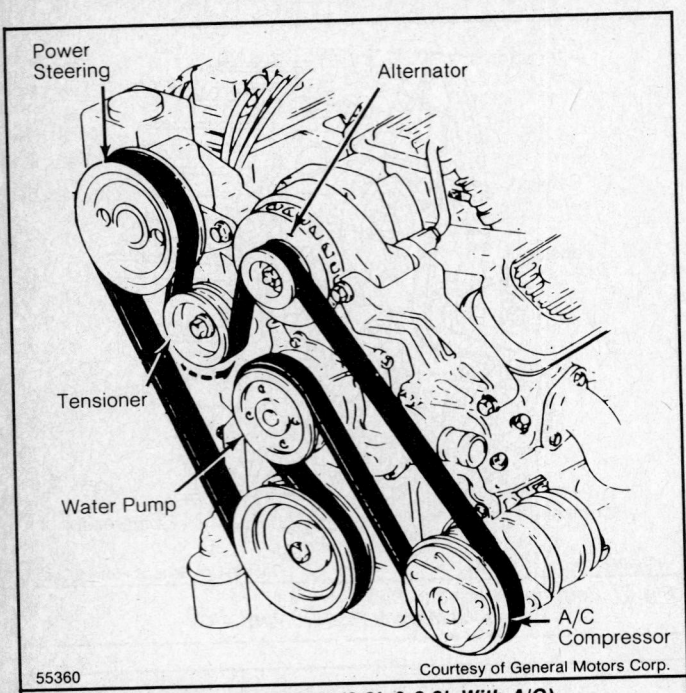

Fig. 9: Routing Serpentine Belt (3.3L & 3.8L With A/C)

Courtesy of General Motors Corp.

55360

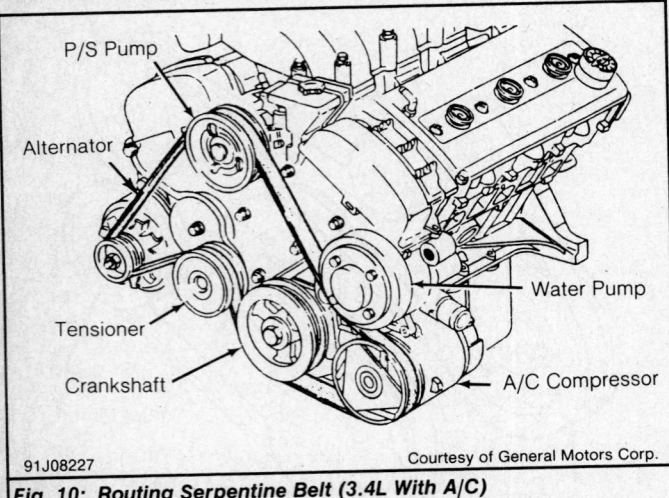

Fig. 10: Routing Serpentine Belt (3.4L With A/C)

Courtesy of General Motors Corp.

91J08227

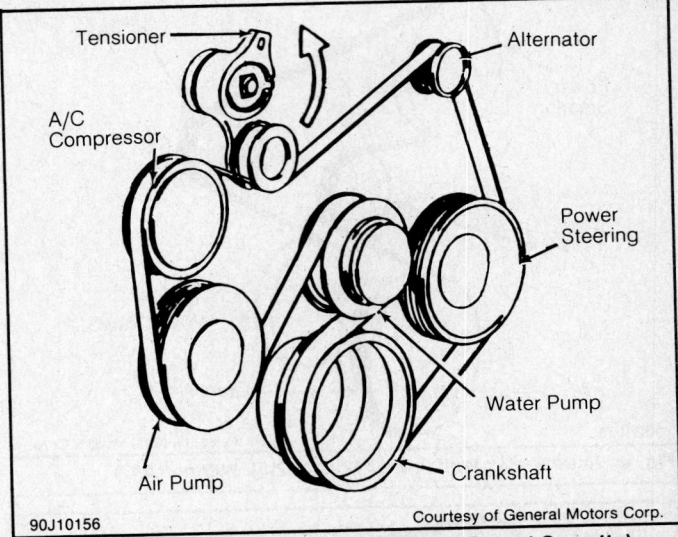

Fig. 11: Routing Serpentine Belt (5.0L & 5.7L Except Corvette)

Courtesy of General Motors Corp.

90J10156

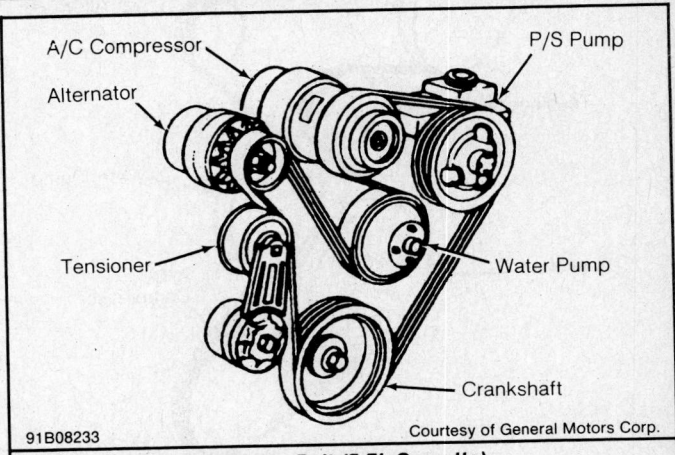

Fig. 12: Routing Serpentine Belt (5.7L Corvette)

Courtesy of General Motors Corp.

91B08233

1991 ENGINE COOLING
Specifications & Electric Cooling Fans – Exc. Cadillac (Cont.)

GM
5-79

ELECTRIC COOLING FAN

BODY CODE DESIGNATIONS

Body Designation [1]	Model
"A" Body	Century, Cutlass Ciera, Cutlass Cruiser & 6000
"B" Body	Caprice, Custom Cruiser & Roadmaster
"C" Body	Ninety-Eight, Park Avenue & Touring Sedan
"E" Body	Reatta, Riviera, Toronado & Trofeo
"F" Body	Camaro & Firebird
"H" Body	Bonneville, Eighty-Eight & LeSabre
"J" Body	Cavalier & Sunbird
"L" Body	Beretta & Corsica
"N" Body	Cutlass Calais, Grand Am & Skylark
"W" Body	Cutlass Supreme, Grand Prix, Lumina & Regal
"Y" Body	Corvette

[1] – Body designation is fourth character of VIN.

ELECTRIC COOLING FAN APPLICATION

Application	Engine
"A" Body	2.5L, 3.1L & 3.3L
"B" Body	5.0L & 5.7L
"C" Body	3.8L
"E" Body	3.8L
"F" Body	3.1L, 5.0L & 5.7L
"H" Body	3.8L
"J" Body	2.0L, 2.2L & 3.1L
"L" Body	2.2L, 2.3L & 3.1L
"N" Body	2.3L, 2.5L & 3.3L
"W" Body	2.3L, 2.5L, 3.1L, 3.4L & 3.8L
"Y" Body	5.7L

DESCRIPTION & OPERATION

All FWD and some RWD vehicles use an electric cooling fan. See ELECTRIC COOLING FAN APPLICATION table. Cooling fan is used for radiator and A/C condenser cooling and operates when A/C is on and/or when engine coolant exceeds a predetermined temperature. Electronic Control Module (ECM) or Power Train Control Module (PCM) completes ground path for the cooling fan relay circuit. Relay contacts close and complete circuit between fusible link and fan motor.

TROUBLE SHOOTING & TESTING

NOTE: TROUBLE SHOOTING & TESTING consists of General Motors Computerized Engine Control system test charts. Only those charts required to test electric cooling fans are included. Other diagnostic codes may appear in charts while performing electric cooling fan diagnosis. For complete information on General Motors Computerized Engine Control systems, see appropriate article in ENGINE PERFORMANCE.

NOTE: Although cooling fan charts contain wiring diagrams, additional wiring diagrams are provided in WIRING DIAGRAMS, located at end of TROUBLE SHOOTING & TESTING in this article.

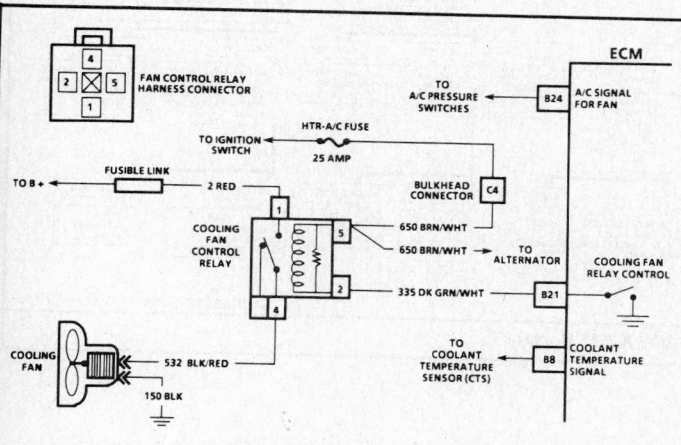

CHART C-12, COOLING FAN
2.0L – VIN K ("J" BODY)

Battery voltage for cooling fan motor is supplied through relay terminal No. 1. Ignition voltage to energize relay is supplied to relay terminal No. 5. Cooling fan is turned on when the ECM grounds circuit No. 335.

When engine is running, ECM will energize cooling fan relay if coolant temperature sensor Code 14 or 15 has been set or if A/C is turned on and vehicle speed is less than 70 MPH. Cooling fan is also energized when coolant temperature is greater than 223°F (106°C).

DIAGNOSTIC AIDS

If an overheating condition is suspected, verify if this is due to actual boil-over. If gauge or light indicates an overheat condition, and no boilover is in evidence, inspect the gauge/light circuit for malfunction.

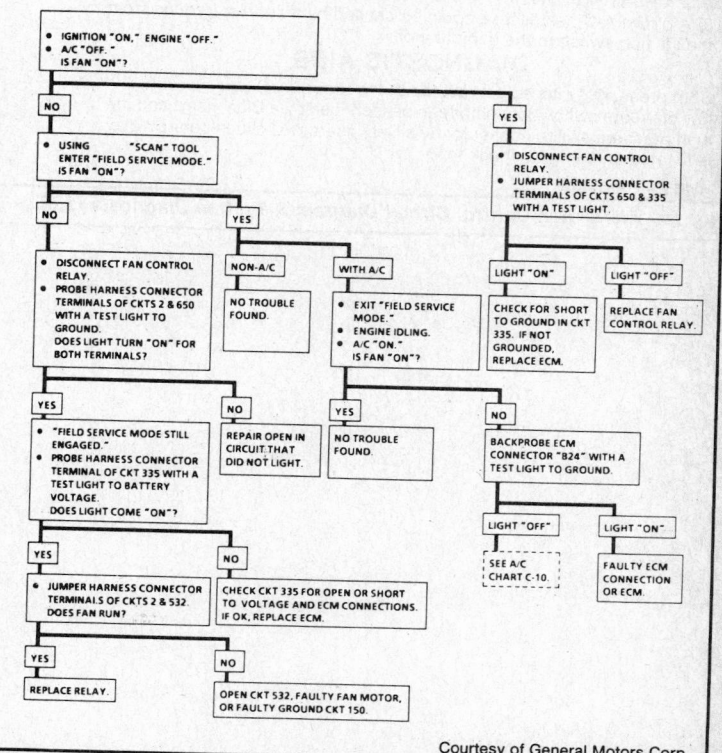

91F05552   91H05553

Fig. 13: Cooling Fan Circuit Diagram & System Diagnosis (2.0L – VIN K "J" Body)

Courtesy of General Motors Corp.

GM
5-80

1991 ENGINE COOLING
Specifications & Electric Cooling Fans – Exc. Cadillac (Cont.)

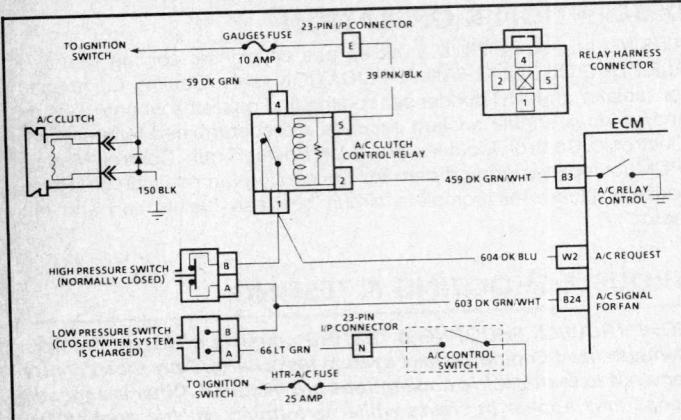

Low pressure switch closes at about 47 psi (3.3 kg/cm²) and opens at about 8 psi (.6 kg/cm²). High pressure switch opens at 430 psi (30 kg/cm²) and disengages compressor clutch to prevent system damage.

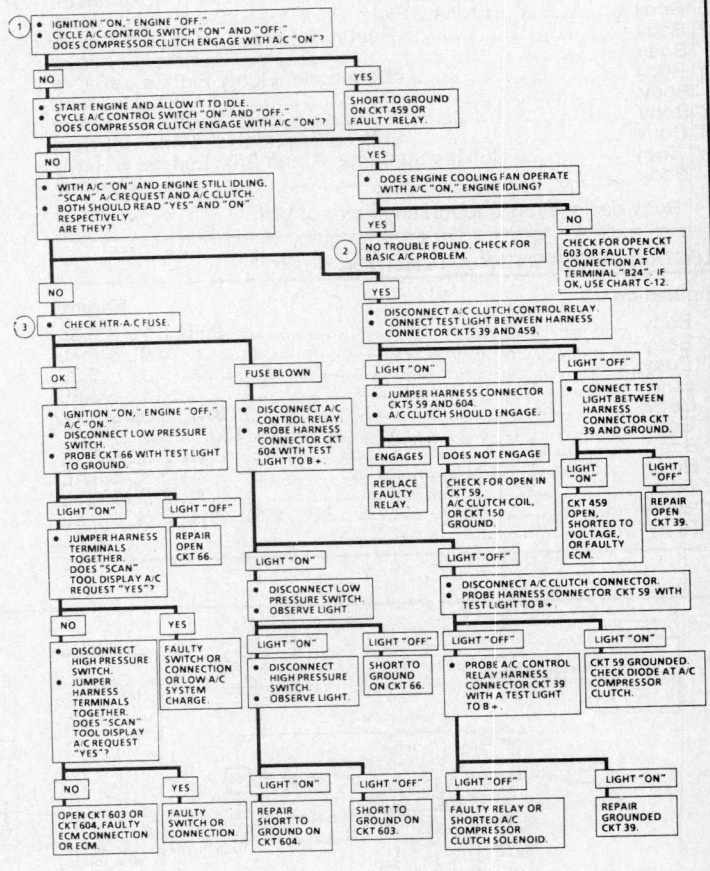

CHART C-10, A/C CLUTCH CONTROL 2.0L – VIN K ("J" BODY)

When A/C mode is selected, ignition battery voltage is supplied through the A/C request circuit to ECM. With sufficient A/C refrigerant charge, the low pressure switch will be closed and complete the circuit to the closed high pressure cut-off switch and to circuits No. 603 and No. 604. When an A/C request is sensed by ECM, ECM will ground circuit No. 359, energizing A/C clutch control relay, and voltage will be supplied from circuit No. 604 to circuit No. 59 and engages the A/C compressor clutch. A "Scan" tester will display the grounding of circuit No. 459 as A/C clutch on. Cooling fan will also be turned on when ECM senses voltage to circuit No. 603.

NOTE: Test numbers refer to test numbers on diagnostic charts.

1) The A/C compressor clutch should not engage until 3 seconds after engine is started.
2) Refer to appropriate article in MITCHELL domestic AIR CONDITIONING & HEATING SERVICE & REPAIR manual.
3) A blown A/C-heater fuse could be caused by a short to ground from the ignition switch to the compressor.

DIAGNOSTIC AIDS

Both pressure switches are located at the rear of A/C compressor. The low pressure switch connector can be identified by a Blue insert and the high pressure switch connector by a Red insert. A/C clutch control relay is located on the right shock tower.

Courtesy of General Motors Corp.

91J05554   91C05555

Fig. 14: A/C Clutch Control Circuit Diagram & System Diagnosis (2.0L – VIN K "J" Body)

1991 ENGINE COOLING
Specifications & Electric Cooling Fans – Exc. Cadillac (Cont.)

GM
5-81

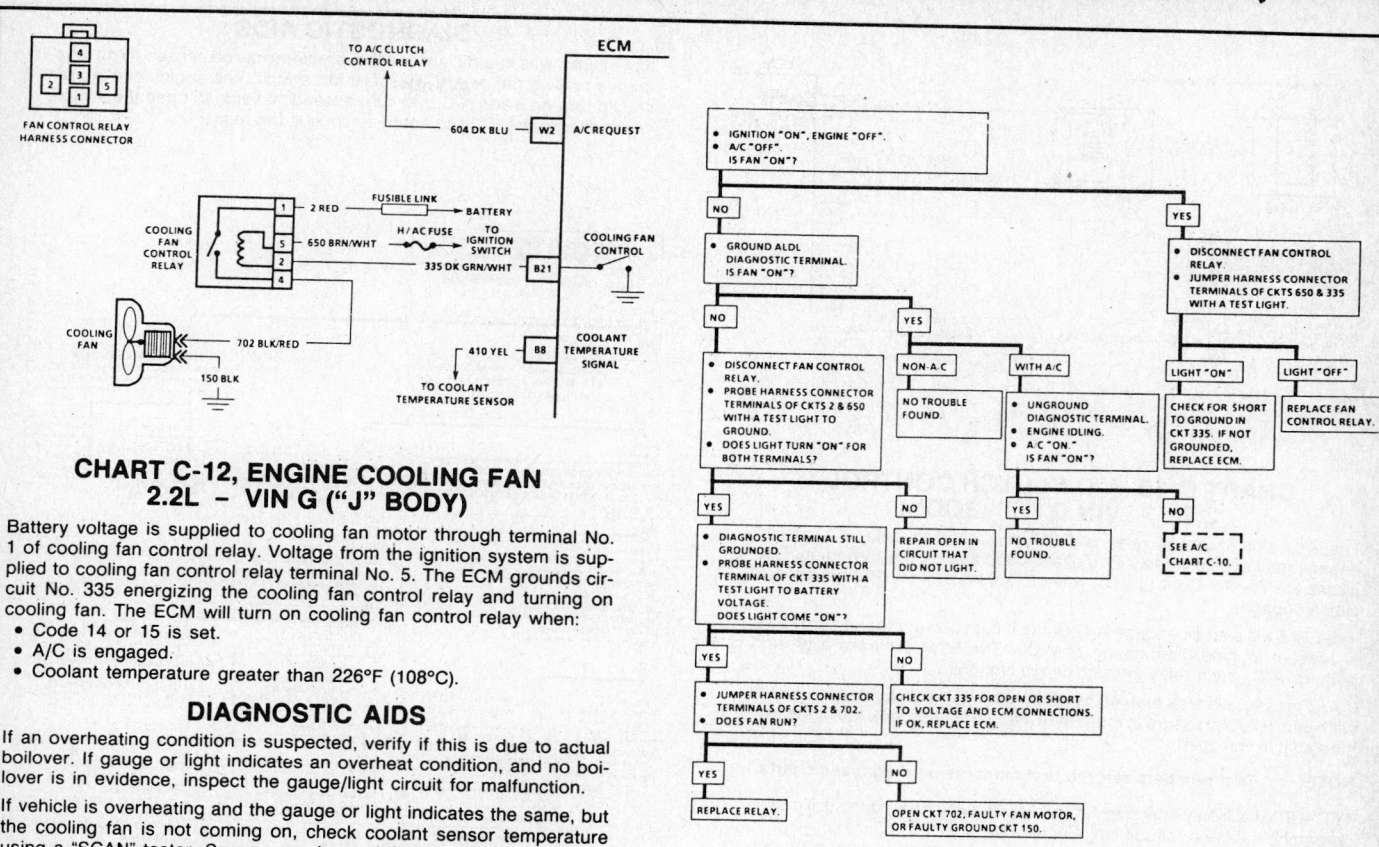

CHART C-12, ENGINE COOLING FAN 2.2L – VIN G ("J" BODY)

Battery voltage is supplied to cooling fan motor through terminal No. 1 of cooling fan control relay. Voltage from the ignition system is supplied to cooling fan control relay terminal No. 5. The ECM grounds circuit No. 335 energizing the cooling fan control relay and turning on cooling fan. The ECM will turn on cooling fan control relay when:
- Code 14 or 15 is set.
- A/C is engaged.
- Coolant temperature greater than 226°F (108°C).

DIAGNOSTIC AIDS

If an overheating condition is suspected, verify if this is due to actual boilover. If gauge or light indicates an overheat condition, and no boilover is in evidence, inspect the gauge/light circuit for malfunction.

If vehicle is overheating and the gauge or light indicates the same, but the cooling fan is not coming on, check coolant sensor temperature using a "SCAN" tester. Sensor may have shifted calibration. If engine is overheating and cooling fan is on, check cooling system.

90D10028   90A02122

Fig. 15: Cooling Fan Circuit Diagram & System Diagnosis (2.2L – VIN G "J" Body)

Courtesy of General Motors Corp.

GM
5-82

1991 ENGINE COOLING
Specifications & Electric Cooling Fans – Exc. Cadillac (Cont.

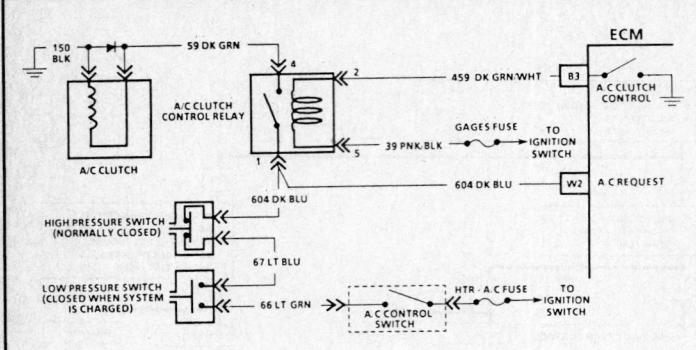

CHART C-10, A/C CLUTCH CONTROL
2.2L – VIN G ("J" BODY)

The A/C clutch control relay is ECM controlled to delay A/C clutch engagement approximately 4/10 of a second after A/C is turned on. This allows the Idle Air Control (IAC) valve to adjust engine RPM before A/C clutch engages.

The ECM will also disengage A/C clutch if high power steering pressure is present, engine overheating or WOT. The ECM provides a ground path for A/C clutch relay through circuit No. 459.

If A/C pressure is less than 40 psi (2.8 kg/cm²), the low pressure switch will open. If A/C pressure is more than 440 psi (31 kg/cm²), the high pressure switch will open.

NOTE: Test numbers refer to test numbers on diagnostic charts.

1) The ECM will only energize A/C relay when engine is running. This will determine if relay or circuit No. 459 is faulty.
2) For A/C clutch to engage, low pressure switch must be closed, providing 12 volts to relay. High pressure switch must be closed so A/C request (12 volts) will be present at ECM.
3) Determines if A/C control panel request signal is reaching the ECM on circuit No. 604. This signal should only be present when A/C or defrost is selected.
4) A blown fuse can be caused by a short to ground in circuits No. 604, No. 59, A/C request circuit or A/C clutch.
5) With A/C on and engine idling, ECM should be grounding circuit No. 459. This will cause test light to illuminate.

90E10029   90C02123

DIAGNOSTIC AIDS

If complaint was insufficient cooling, problem may be caused by an inoperative cooling fan or A/C pressure fan switch. The engine cooling fan should turn on when A/C pressure exceeds a value to open the switch, which causes the ECM to energize cooling fan relay.

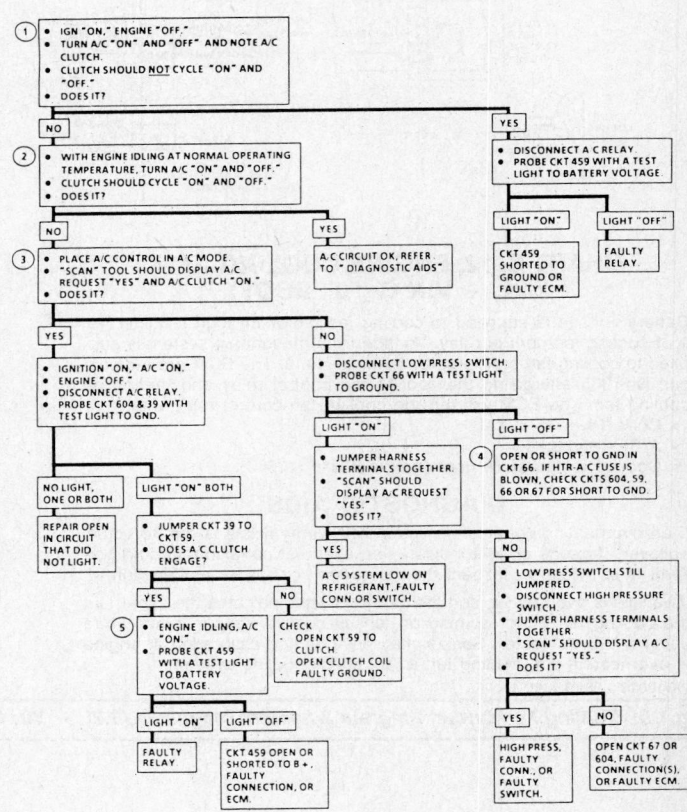

Courtesy of General Motors Corp.

Fig. 16: A/C Clutch Control Circuit Diagram & System Diagnosis (2.2L – VIN G "J" Body)

1991 ENGINE COOLING
Specifications & Electric Cooling Fans – Exc. Cadillac (Cont.)

GM
5-83

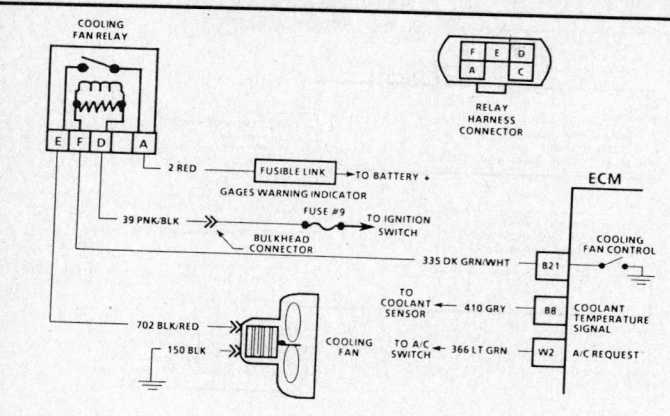

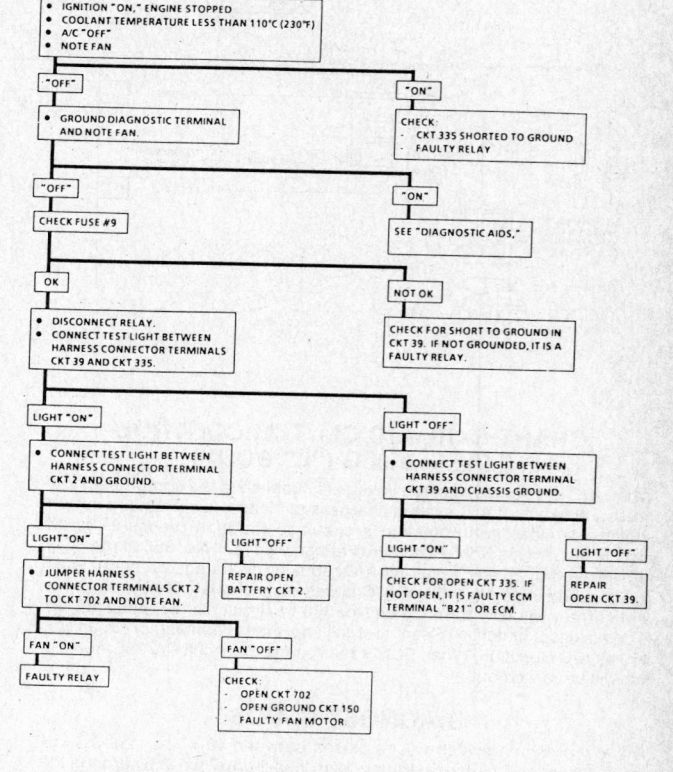

CHART C-12, COOLING FAN
2.2L – VIN G ("L" BODY)

Battery voltage is supplied on circuit No. 2 to operate cooling fan motor. Ignition voltage is supplied on circuit No. 39 to energize cooling fan relay. The cooling fan is energized when ECM grounds circuit No. 335. With engine running, ECM will energize cooling fan when:

- A/C is on.
- Coolant temperature is greater than 230°F (110°C).
- Code 14 or 15 is set.

DIAGNOSTIC AIDS

If an overheating condition is suspected, verify if this is due to actual boi-lover. If gauge or light indicates an overheat condition, and no boilover is in evidence, inspect the gauge/light circuit for malfunction.

If vehicle is overheating and the gauge or light indicates the same, but the cooling fan is not coming on, check coolant sensor temperature using a Scan tester. Sensor may have shifted calibration. If engine is overheating and cooling fan is on, check cooling system.

90H10030   90E02124

Fig. 17: Cooling Fan Circuit Diagram & System Diagnosis (2.2L – VIN G "L" Body)

GM
5-84

1991 ENGINE COOLING
Specifications & Electric Cooling Fans – Exc. Cadillac (Cont.)

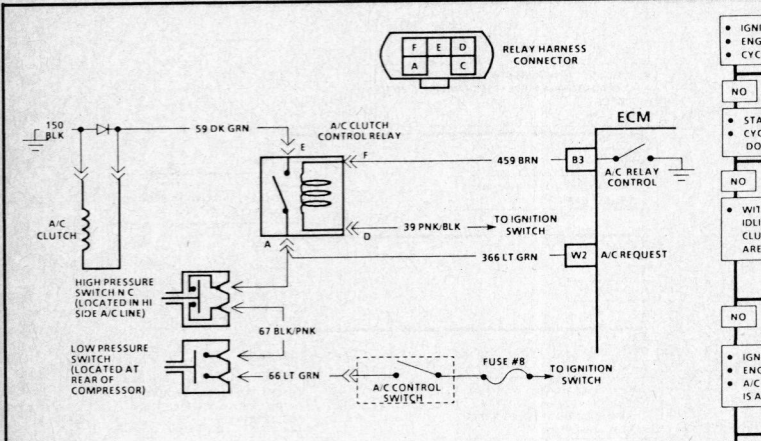

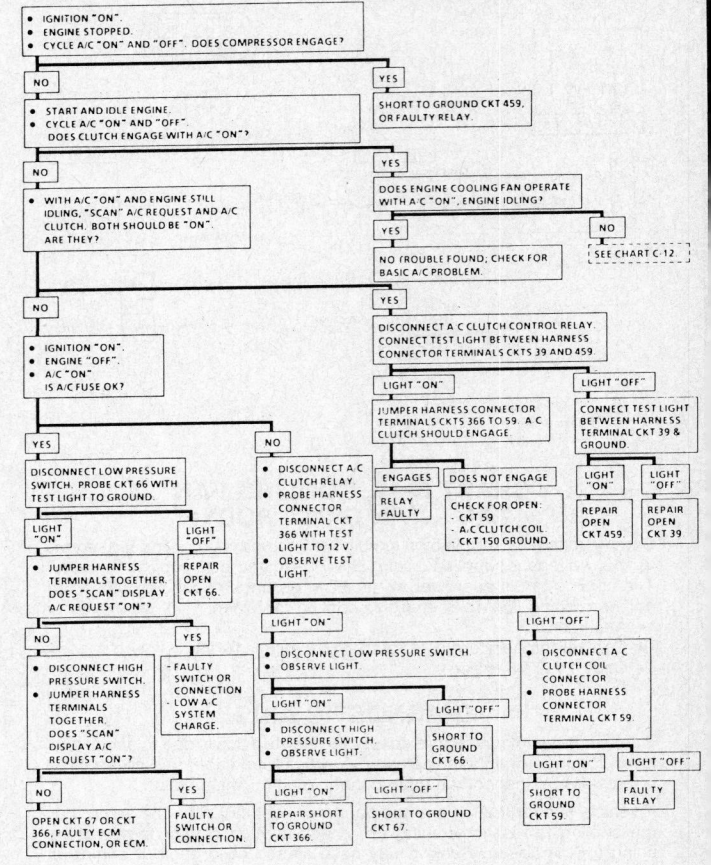

CHART C-10, A/C CLUTCH CONTROL
2.2L – VIN G ("L" BODY)

When A/C is selected, ignition voltage is supplied to the compressor low pressure switch. If A/C system charge is sufficient, low pressure cut-off switch will close and complete a circuit to the high pressure cut-off switch and circuits No. 67 and 366. Voltage on circuit No. 366 to the ECM is displayed by "Scan" tester as A/C request on (voltage present). ECM will ground circuit No. 459 of A/C clutch control relay. Relay will close and current will flow from circuit No. 366 to circuit No. 59, engaging A/C compressor clutch. A "Scan" tool will show the grounding of circuit No. 459 as A/C clutch on. When ECM sees voltage on circuit No. 366, cooling fan will be turned on.

DIAGNOSTIC AIDS

The low pressure switch will be closed between 40-47 psi (2.8-3.3 kg/cm²) allowing A/C clutch operation. With less than 37 psi (2.6 kg/cm²), the low pressure switch will open, stopping A/C clutch operation.

At approximately 430 psi (30 kg/cm²) the high pressure switch will open, disengaging A/C clutch operation. This will prevent system damage.

90H04285   90H02125

Courtesy of General Motors Corp.

Fig. 18: A/C Clutch Control Circuit Diagram & System Diagnosis (2.2L – VIN G "L" Body)

1991 ENGINE COOLING
Specifications & Electric Cooling Fans – Exc. Cadillac (Cont.)

GM
5-85

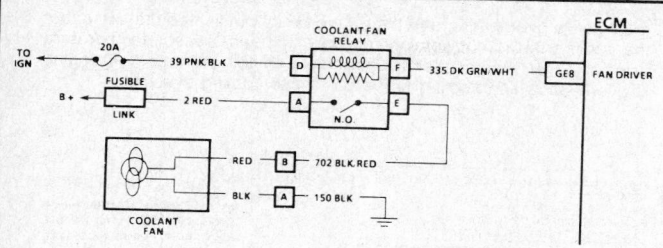

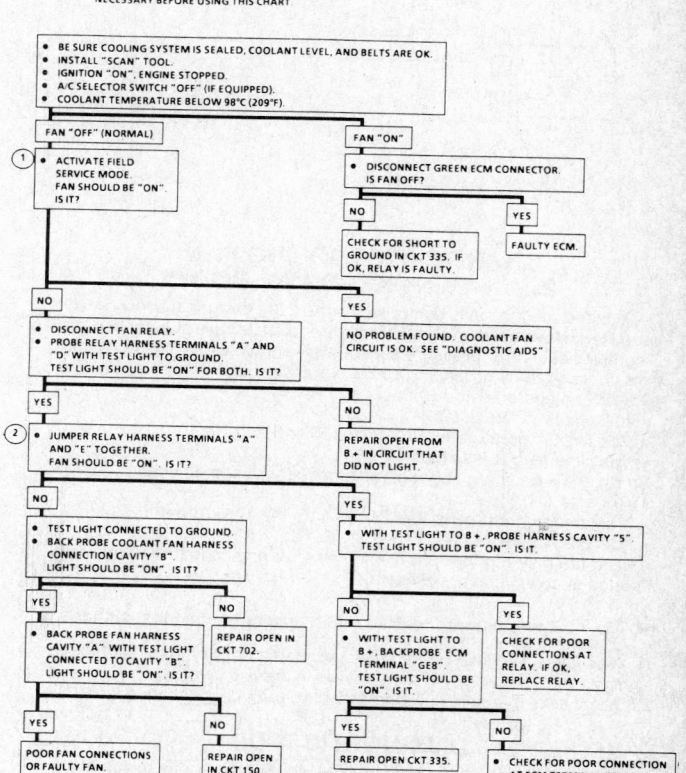

CHART C-12, COOLING FAN
2.3L – VIN A ("L" BODY)

The engine cooling fan is controlled by the ECM through a fan relay. The ECM controls fan relay with inputs from coolant temperature sensor, manifold air temperature sensor, A/C control switch, A/C pressure sensor and Vehicle Speed Sensor (VSS). ECM controls the cooling fan by grounding circuit No. 335, which energizes fan relay. The fan relay will be energized when:

- A/C clutch is requested.
- Coolant temperature is 217-222°F (103-106°C).
- Vehicle speed is less than 35 MPH.

Fan relay will be commanded on regardless of vehicle speed when:

- A/C pressure is high.
- Code 14 or 15 is set.
- Coolant temperature is 239-244°F (115-118°C).

NOTE: Test numbers refer to test numbers on diagnostic charts.

1) With field service mode activated, cooling fan control driver should close, energizing fan control relay.
2) This checks to see if fault is in wiring or fan connection.

DIAGNOSTIC AIDS

If an overheating condition is suspected, verify if this is due to actual boil-over. If gauge or light indicates an overheat condition, and no boilover is in evidence, inspect the gauge/light circuit for malfunction.

If vehicle is overheating and the gauge or light indicates the same, but the cooling fan is not coming on, check coolant sensor temperature using a "Scan" tester. Sensor may have shifted calibration. If engine is overheating and cooling fan is on, check cooling system.

91E05556 91G05557

Courtesy of General Motors Corp.

Fig. 19: Cooling Fan Circuit Diagram & System Diagnosis (2.3L – VIN A "L" Body)

GM
5-86

1991 ENGINE COOLING
Specifications & Electric Cooling Fans – Exc. Cadillac (Cont.)

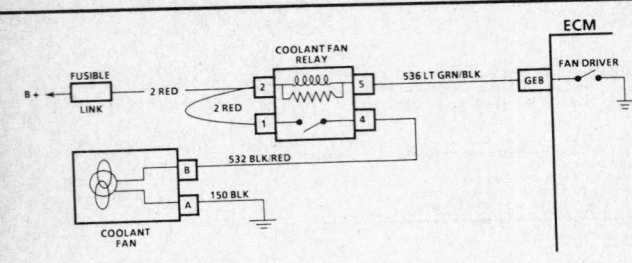

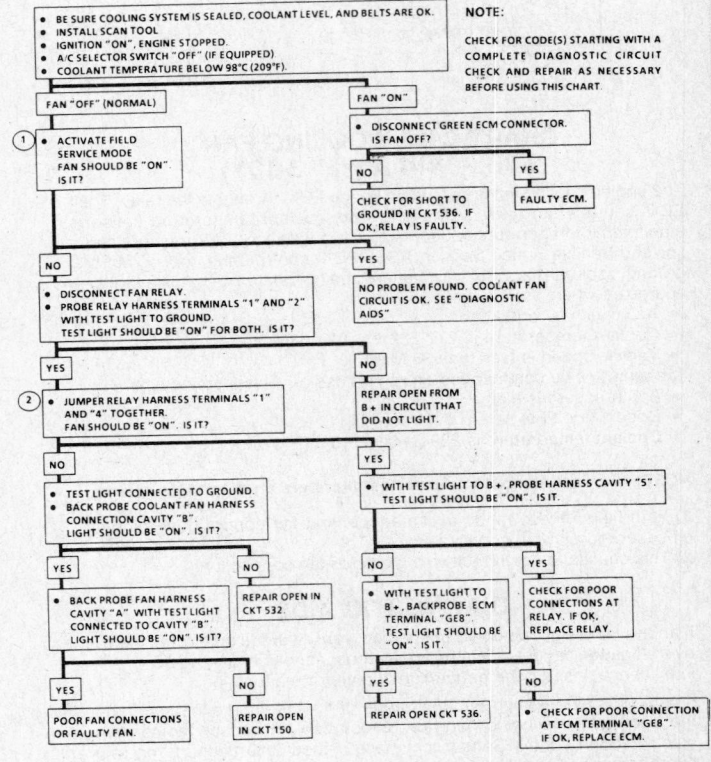

If vehicle is overheating and the gauge or light indicates the same, but the cooling fan is not coming on, check coolant sensor temperature using a "SCAN" tester. Sensor may have shifted calibration. If engine is overheating and cooling fan is on, check cooling system.

CHART C-12, COOLING FAN
2.3L – VINs A & D ("N" BODY)

The electric cooling fan is controlled by the ECM through the low or high speed fan relay based on inputs from the coolant temperature sensor, A/C control switch, A/C pressure sensor and vehicle speed. The ECM controls cooling fan by grounding circuit No. 536 which turns relay on. Fan relay will be energized on when:
- A/C clutch is requested.
- Coolant temperature is 217-222°F (103-106°C).
- Vehicle speed is less than 35 MPH.

Fan relay will be energized regardless of vehicle speed when:
- Code 14 or 15 is set.
- Coolant temperature is 239-244°F (115-118°C) or greater.
- A/C pressure is high.

Cooling fan may run for up to 7 minutes after engine is turned off when a series of conditions are present.

NOTE: Test numbers refer to test numbers on diagnostic charts.

1) With field service mode activated, fan control relay should be energized.
2) This checks if fault is in wiring to fan or if fan connection is faulty.

DIAGNOSTIC AIDS

If an overheating condition is suspected, verify if this is due to actual boilover. If gauge or light indicates an overheat condition, and no boilover is in evidence, inspect the gauge/light circuit for malfunction.

90G02120

Courtesy of General Motors Corp.

Fig. 20: Cooling Fan Circuit Diagram & System Diagnosis (2.3L – VINs A & D "N" Body)

1991 ENGINE COOLING
Specifications & Electric Cooling Fans – Exc. Cadillac (Cont.)

GM
5-87

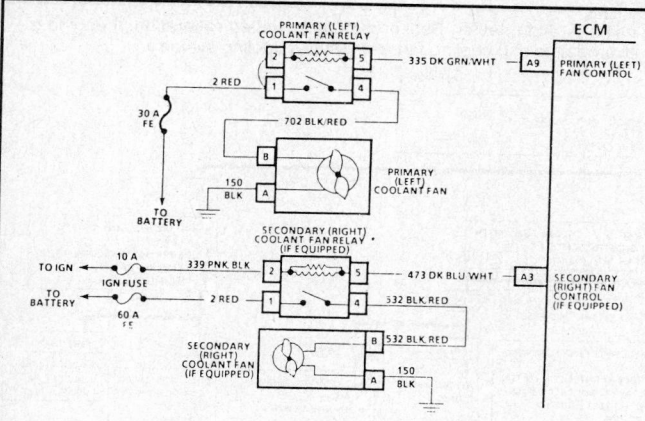

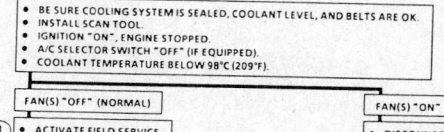

is suspected, verify if this is due to actual boilover. If gauge or light indicates an overheat condition, and no boilover is in evidence, inspect the gauge/light circuit for malfunction.

If vehicle is overheating and the gauge or light indicates the same, but the cooling fan is not coming on, check coolant sensor temperature using a "Scan" tester. Sensor may have shifted calibration. If engine is overheating and cooling fan is on, check cooling system.

NOTE: CHECK FOR CODE(S) STARTING WITH A COMPLETE DIAGNOSTIC CIRCUIT CHECK AND REPAIR AS NECESSARY BEFORE USING THIS CHART.

- BE SURE COOLING SYSTEM IS SEALED, COOLANT LEVEL, AND BELTS ARE OK.
- INSTALL SCAN TOOL.
- IGNITION "ON", ENGINE STOPPED.
- A/C SELECTOR SWITCH "OFF" (IF EQUIPPED).
- COOLANT TEMPERATURE BELOW 98°C (209°F).

FAN(S) "OFF" (NORMAL)
① ACTIVATE FIELD SERVICE MODE ON SCAN TOOL. FAN(S) SHOULD BE "ON".

FAN(S) "ON"
- DISCONNECT ECM "A" CONNECTOR. FAN(S) SHOULD BE "OFF".

FAN(S) "ON"
CHECK FOR SHORT TO GROUND IN DRIVER CKT (CKT 335 OR 473) FOR FAN WHICH REMAINED "ON". IF OK, RELAY IS FAULTY.

FAN(S) "OFF"
FAULTY ECM.

FAN(S) "OFF"
- DISCONNECT RELAY FOR FAN WHICH REMAINED "OFF".
- PROBE RELAY CENTER CAVITIES "1" AND "2" WITH TEST LIGHT TO GROUND. TEST LIGHT SHOULD BE "ON" FOR BOTH. IS IT?

FAN(S) "ON"
NO PROBLEM FOUND. COOLANT FAN CIRCUIT(S) OK. SEE "DIAGNOSTIC AIDS".

YES / **NO**

② JUMPER RELAY CENTER TERMINALS "1" AND "4" TOGETHER. FAN(S) SHOULD BE "ON".

NO
REPAIR OPEN FROM B+ IN CIRCUIT THAT DID NOT LIGHT.

FAN(S) "OFF"
- TEST LIGHT CONNECTED TO GROUND.
- BACK PROBE COOLANT FAN(S) RELAY CENTER CAVITY "B". LIGHT SHOULD BE "ON". IS IT?

FAN(S) "ON"
- WITH TEST LIGHT TO B+, PROBE FAN(S) RELAY CENTER CAVITY "5". TEST LIGHT SHOULD BE "ON". IS IT?

YES / **NO**
- BACK PROBE FAN(S) RELAY CENTER CAVITY "A" WITH TEST LIGHT CONNECTED TO CAVITY "B". LIGHT SHOULD BE "ON". IS IT?

NO
REPAIR OPEN IN CKT 702 OR 532

NO
- CHECK FOR OPEN RELAY DRIVER CKT (CKT 335 OR 535), OR FOR POOR CONNECTION AT ECM TERMINAL "A9" OR "A3". IF OK, REPLACE ECM.

YES
CHECK FOR POOR CONNECTIONS AT RELAY. IF OK, REPLACE RELAY.

YES
POOR FAN(S) CONNECTIONS OR FAULTY FAN(S).

NO
REPAIR OPEN IN CKT 150.

CHART C-12, COOLING FAN
2.3L – VINs A & D ("W" BODY)

The ECM controls engine cooling fan through a fan relay. ECM energizes fan relay with input from Manifold Air Temperature (MAT) sensor, A/C control switch, A/C pressure sensor and Vehicle Speed Sensor (VSS). The ECM grounds circuit No. 702 or circuit No. 532 to energize a fan relay. The primary fan relay will be energized when:
- A/C clutch is energized and VSS indicates less than 35 MPH.
- Any fault causing SERVICE ENGINE SOON light to illuminate.
- Coolant temperature is 217-223°F (103-106°C).

The secondary fan relay (if equipped) will be energized when:
- A/C pressure is high.
- Coolant temperature is 239-244°F (115-118°C).

The primary coolant fan may run for up to 7 minutes after engine is turned off when a series of conditions are present.

NOTE: Test numbers refer to test numbers on diagnostic charts.

1) With field service mode activated, cooling fan(s) control driver(s) should close, energizing coolant fan(s) control relay(s).

2) This checks if fault is in wiring to fan or fan connection.

DIAGNOSTIC AIDS

If vehicle is equipped with 2 fans and both are inoperative, check for open at circuit No. 2 or circuit No. 150 first. If an overheating condition

90C04283 90D02128

Fig. 21: Cooling Fan Circuit Diagram & System Diagnosis (2.3L – VINs A & D "W" Body)

GM
5-88

1991 ENGINE COOLING
Specifications & Electric Cooling Fans – Exc. Cadillac (Cont.)

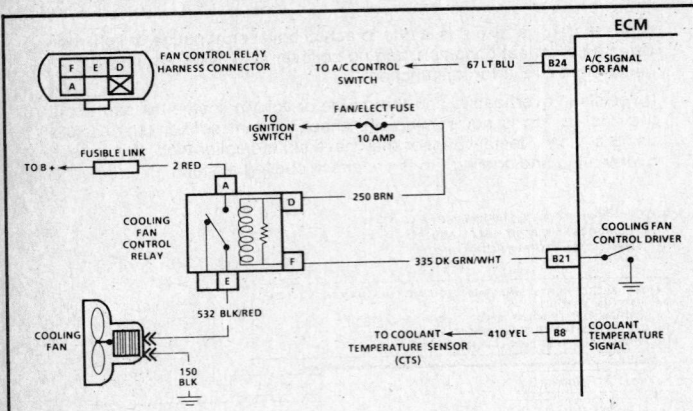

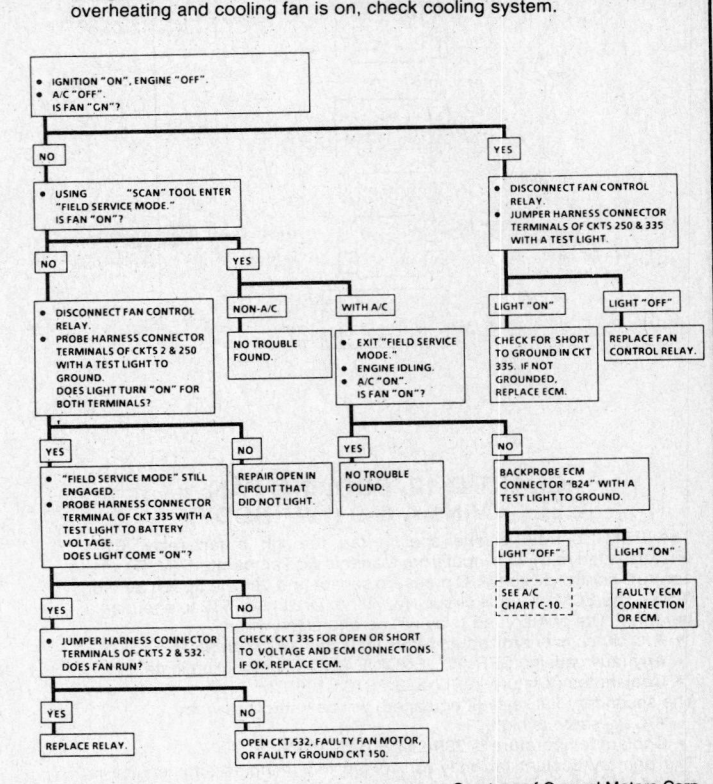

using a "Scan" tester. Sensor may have shifted calibration. If engine is overheating and cooling fan is on, check cooling system.

CHART C-12, COOLING FAN
2.5L – VIN R ("A" BODY)

Battery voltage is supplied to fan relay terminal "A". Ignition voltage to energize relay is supplied to relay terminal "D". When the ECM grounds circuit No. 335, relay is energized and cooling fan is turned on. When engine is running, ECM will turn on cooling fan if coolant temperature sensor Code 14 or 15 has been set. Fan is also energized when:

- A/C is on and vehicle speed is less than 70 MPH.
- Coolant temperature is greater than 223°F (106°C).

DIAGNOSTIC AIDS

If an overheating condition is suspected, verify if this is due to actual boil-over. If gauge or light indicates an overheat condition and no boilover is in evidence, inspect the gauge/light circuit for malfunction.

If vehicle is overheating and the gauge or light indicates the same, but the cooling fan is not coming on, check coolant sensor temperature

Courtesy of General Motors Corp.

91I05558   91A05559

Fig. 22: Cooling Fan Circuit Diagram & System Diagnosis (2.5L – VIN R "A" Body)

1991 ENGINE COOLING
Specifications & Electric Cooling Fans – Exc. Cadillac (Cont.)

GM 5-89

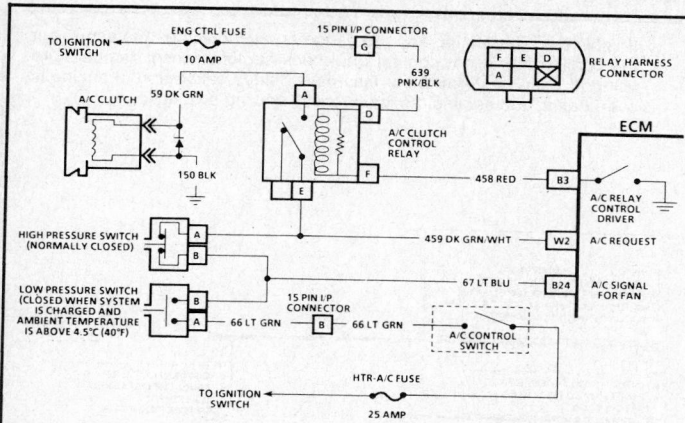

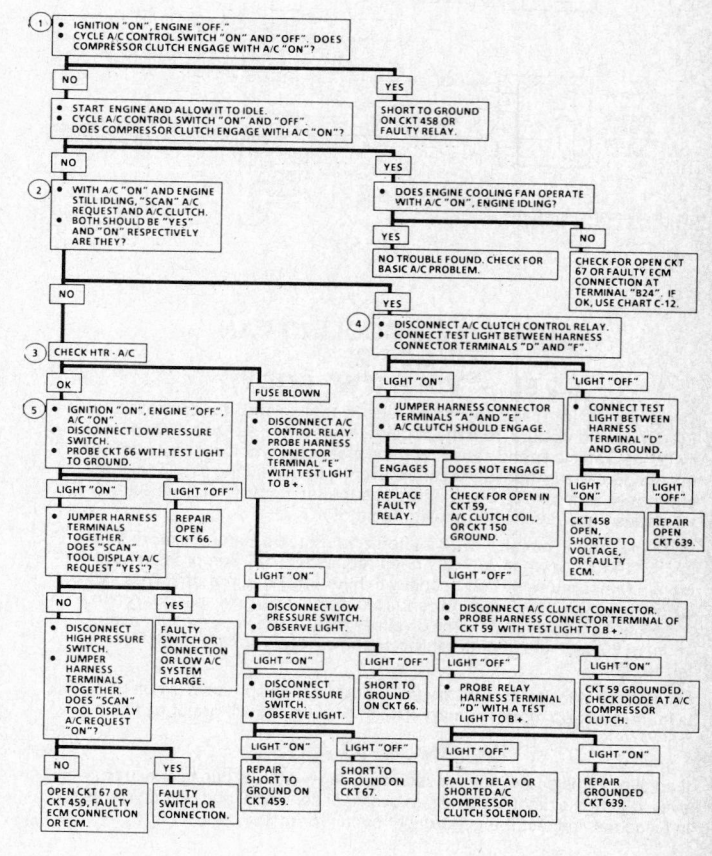

DIAGNOSTIC AIDS

If complaint was insufficient A/C cooling, problem may be caused by an inoperative cooling fan or A/C low or high pressure switches. Engine cooling fan should turn on when refrigerant pressure is high enough to close low pressure switch and energize cooling fan relay through ECM.

CHART C-10, A/C CLUTCH CONTROL 2.5L – VIN R ("A" BODY)

When A/C is selected, voltage is supplied to the A/C low pressure switch. If refrigerant pressure is high enough, the low pressure switch will close and complete circuits No. 67 and 459 to the normally closed high pressure cut-off switch. Voltage on circuit No. 459 to ECM is displayed by "Scan" tester as A/C request ON (voltage present), or OFF (no voltage present).

When a request for A/C is detected by ECM, ECM will ground circuit No. 458 of A/C clutch control relay. Relay contacts close, and current will flow from circuit No. 459 to circuit No. 59, engaging A/C compressor clutch. A "Scan" tester will display the grounding of circuit No. 458 as A/C clutch ON. When ECM detects voltage in circuit No. 67, cooling fan will also be turned on.

NOTE: Test numbers refer to test numbers on diagnostic charts.

1) ECM will energize A/C relay ONLY when engine is running. This test will determine if relay or circuit No. 458 is at fault.

2) The low pressure and high pressure switches must be closed for the A/C request signal (12 volts) to be present at ECM.

3) A short to ground in any part of A/C request or A/C clutch control circuits could fuse to blow.

4) With engine at idle and A/C on, ECM should be grounding circuit No. 458 causing test light illuminate.

5) This step determines if signal is reaching the low pressure switch on circuit No. 66 from A/C control panel. Signal should be present only when A/C or defrost mode is requested.

91C05560   91E05561

Courtesy of General Motors Corp.

Fig. 23: A/C Clutch Control Circuit Diagram & System Diagnosis (2.5L – VIN R "A" Body)

GM
5-90

1991 ENGINE COOLING
Specifications & Electric Cooling Fans – Exc. Cadillac (Cont.)

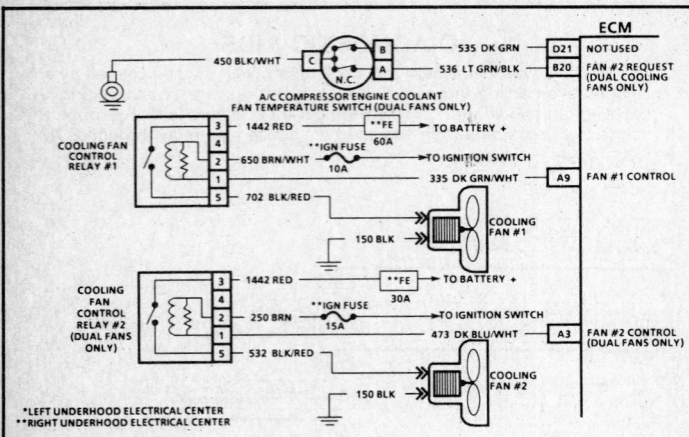

If vehicle is overheating and the gauge or light indicates the same, but the cooling fan is not coming on, check coolant sensor temperature using a "Scan" tester. Sensor may have shifted calibration. If engine is overheating and cooling fan is on, check cooling system.

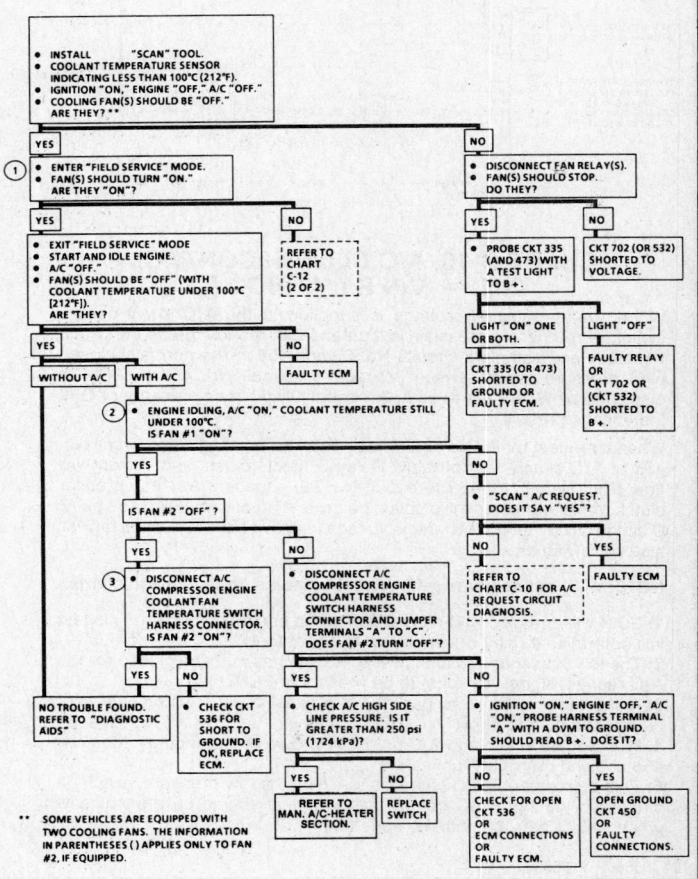

CHART C-12, COOLING FAN (1 OF 2)
2.5L – VIN R ("W" BODY)

The primary (No. 1) and secondary (No. 2) cooling fans are controlled by ECM, based on inputs from the coolant temperature sensor, A/C control switches, vehicle speed sensor and the state of A/C compressor cooling fan temperature switch. ECM controls fan(s) by grounding circuit No. 335 and/or circuit No. 473, which energizes the fan control relay(s). Battery voltage is then supplied to cooling fan motor.

ECM will ground circuit No. 335 when coolant temperature is more than 223°F (106°C) or when A/C has been requested. A/C compressor cooling fan temperature switch opens with high A/C pressure of 250 psi (18 kg/cm²). ECM will then ground circuit No. 473 to energize secondary (No. 2) cooling fan. Once ECM turns on either relay, it will keep it on for a minimum of 60 seconds or until vehicle speed exceeds 70 MPH (40 MPH for fan No. 2).

Cooling fan will also be activated if Code 14 or 15 is present. When ECM is in the back-up mode, primary (No. 1) cooling fan will run at all times.

DIAGNOSTIC AIDS

If an overheating condition is suspected, verify if this is due to actual boil-over. If gauge or light indicates an overheat condition, and no boilover is in evidence, inspect the gauge/light circuit for malfunction.

91G05562   91I05563

Courtesy of General Motors Corp.

Fig. 24: Cooling Fan Circuit Diagram & System Diagnosis (2.5L – VIN R "W" Body) (1 of 2)

1991 ENGINE COOLING
Specifications & Electric Cooling Fans – Exc. Cadillac (Cont.)

GM
5-91

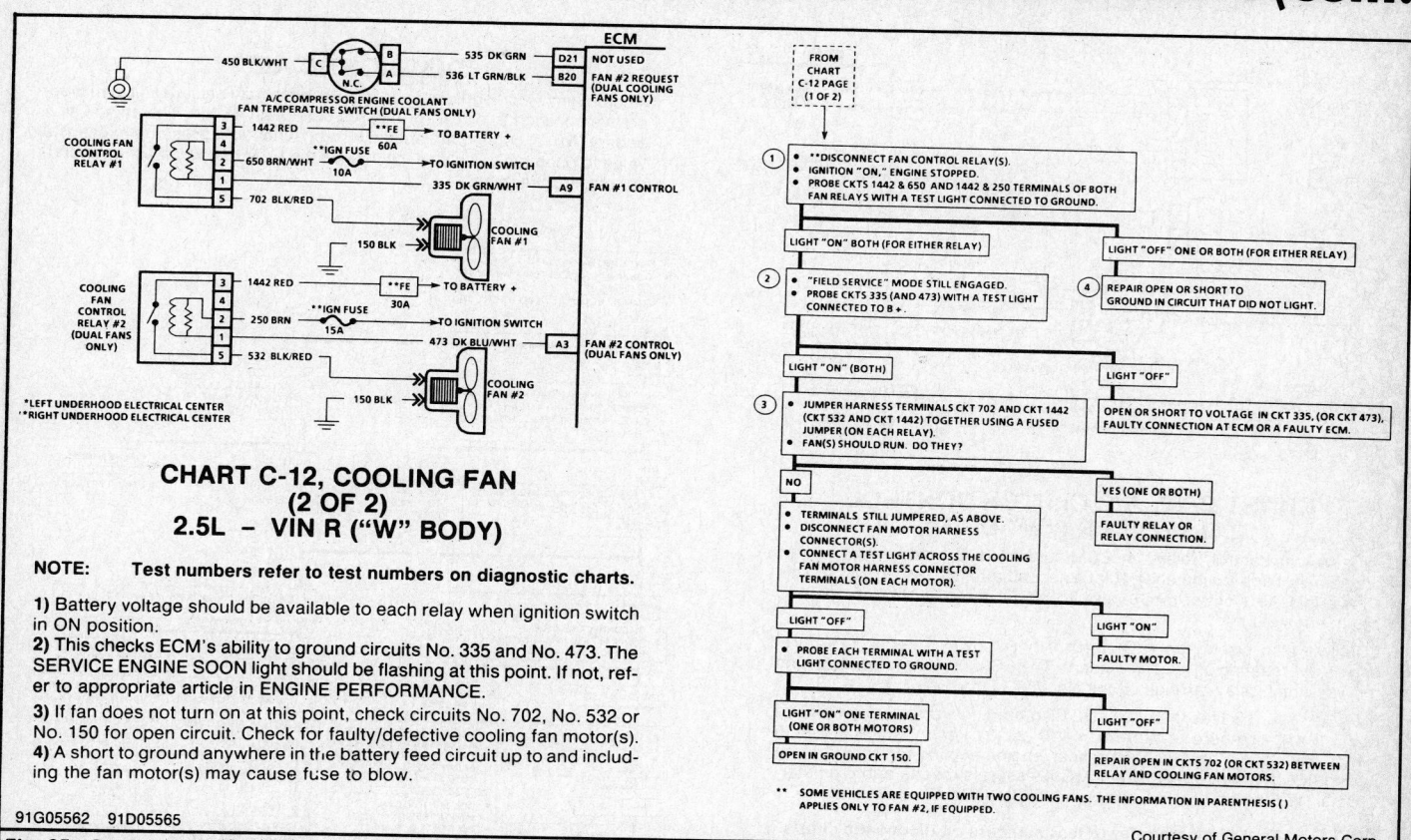

CHART C-12, COOLING FAN
(2 OF 2)
2.5L – VIN R ("W" BODY)

NOTE: Test numbers refer to test numbers on diagnostic charts.

1) Battery voltage should be available to each relay when ignition switch in ON position.

2) This checks ECM's ability to ground circuits No. 335 and No. 473. The SERVICE ENGINE SOON light should be flashing at this point. If not, refer to appropriate article in ENGINE PERFORMANCE.

3) If fan does not turn on at this point, check circuits No. 702, No. 532 or No. 150 for open circuit. Check for faulty/defective cooling fan motor(s).

4) A short to ground anywhere in the battery feed circuit up to and including the fan motor(s) may cause fuse to blow.

91G05562   91D05565

Courtesy of General Motors Corp.

Fig. 25: *Cooling Fan Circuit Diagram & System Diagnosis (2.5L – VIN R "W" Body) (2 of 2)*

GM
5-92

1991 ENGINE COOLING
Specifications & Electric Cooling Fans – Exc. Cadillac (Cont.)

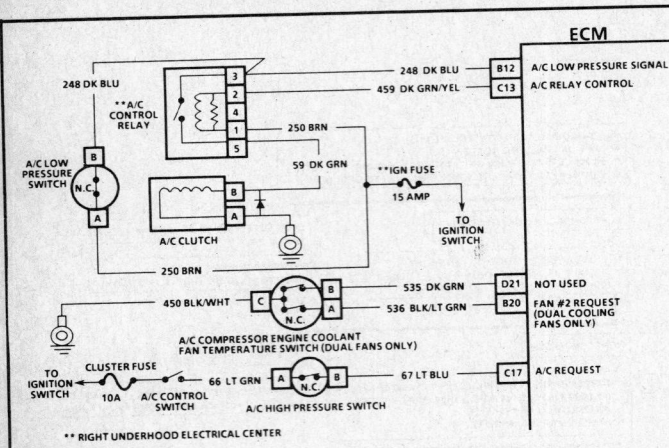

CHART C-10, A/C CLUTCH CONTROL
2.5L – VIN R ("W" BODY)

A/C clutch control relay is ECM-controlled to delay A/C clutch engagement approximately 4/10 of a second after A/C is turned on. This allows Idle Air Control (IAC) valve to adjust engine RPM before A/C clutch engages.

ECM will also disengage A/C clutch if high power steering pressure, engine overheating or WOT is present. The ECM provides a ground path for A/C clutch relay through circuit No. 459.

If A/C pressure is less than 40 psi (2.8 kg/cm²), low pressure switch will open. If A/C pressure is more than 440 psi (31 kg/cm²), high pressure switch will open. The A/C compressor/engine cooling fan temperature switch (if equipped) opens when A/C pressure exceeds approximately 250 psi (17.6 kg/cm²); this turns on secondary (No. 2) cooling fan.

NOTE: Test numbers refer to test numbers on diagnostic charts.

1) The ECM will only energize A/C relay when engine is running. This will determine if relay or circuit No. 459 is faulty.
2) For A/C clutch to engage, low pressure switch must be closed providing 12 volts to the relay. High pressure switch must be closed so A/C request (12 volts) will be present at ECM.
3) Determines if A/C control panel request signal is reaching the ECM on circuit No. 66. This signal should only be present when A/C or defrost is selected.
4) A short to ground in any part of the A/C request circuit will cause fuse to blow.
5) With A/C on and engine idling, ECM should be grounding circuit No. 459. This will cause test light to illuminate.

91F05566   91H05567

DIAGNOSTIC AIDS

If complaint was insufficient cooling, problem may be caused by an inoperative cooling fan or A/C pressure cooling fan switch. The engine secondary (No. 2) cooling fan should turn on when A/C pressure exceeds a value to open the switch, which causes the ECM to energize the secondary cooling fan relay.

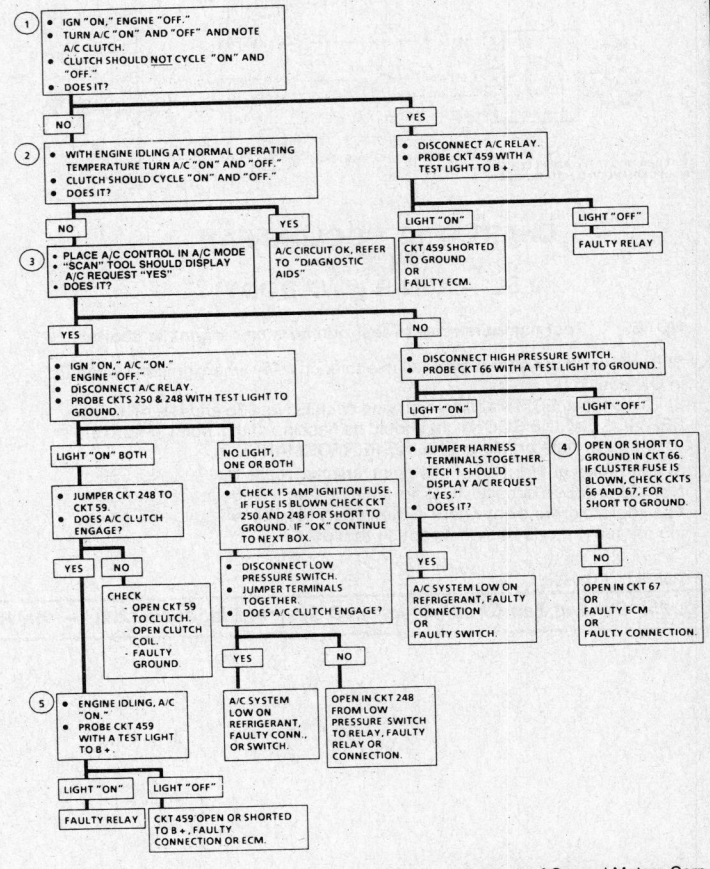

Courtesy of General Motors Corp.

Fig. 26: *A/C Clutch Control Circuit Diagram & System Diagnosis (2.5L – VIN R "W" Body)*

1991 ENGINE COOLING
Specifications & Electric Cooling Fans − Exc. Cadillac (Cont.)

GM
5-93

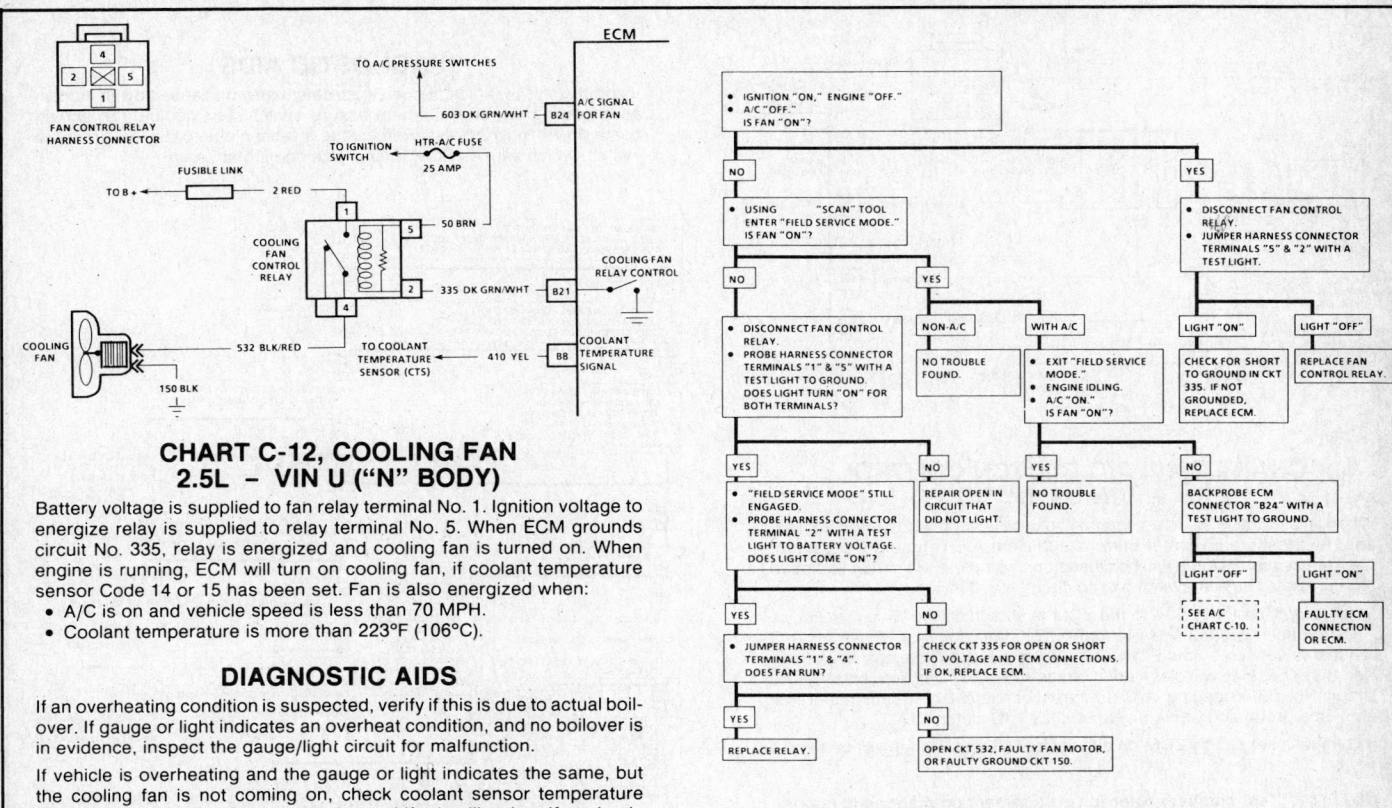

CHART C-12, COOLING FAN
2.5L − VIN U ("N" BODY)

Battery voltage is supplied to fan relay terminal No. 1. Ignition voltage to energize relay is supplied to relay terminal No. 5. When ECM grounds circuit No. 335, relay is energized and cooling fan is turned on. When engine is running, ECM will turn on cooling fan, if coolant temperature sensor Code 14 or 15 has been set. Fan is also energized when:
- A/C is on and vehicle speed is less than 70 MPH.
- Coolant temperature is more than 223°F (106°C).

DIAGNOSTIC AIDS

If an overheating condition is suspected, verify if this is due to actual boil-over. If gauge or light indicates an overheat condition, and no boilover is in evidence, inspect the gauge/light circuit for malfunction.

If vehicle is overheating and the gauge or light indicates the same, but the cooling fan is not coming on, check coolant sensor temperature using a "Scan" tester. Sensor may have shifted calibration. If engine is overheating and cooling fan is on, check cooling system.

91J05568   91B05569

Courtesy of General Motors Corp.

Fig. 27: Cooling Fan Circuit Diagram & System Diagnosis (2.5L − VIN U "N" Body)

GM
5-94

1991 ENGINE COOLING
Specifications & Electric Cooling Fans – Exc. Cadillac (Cont.)

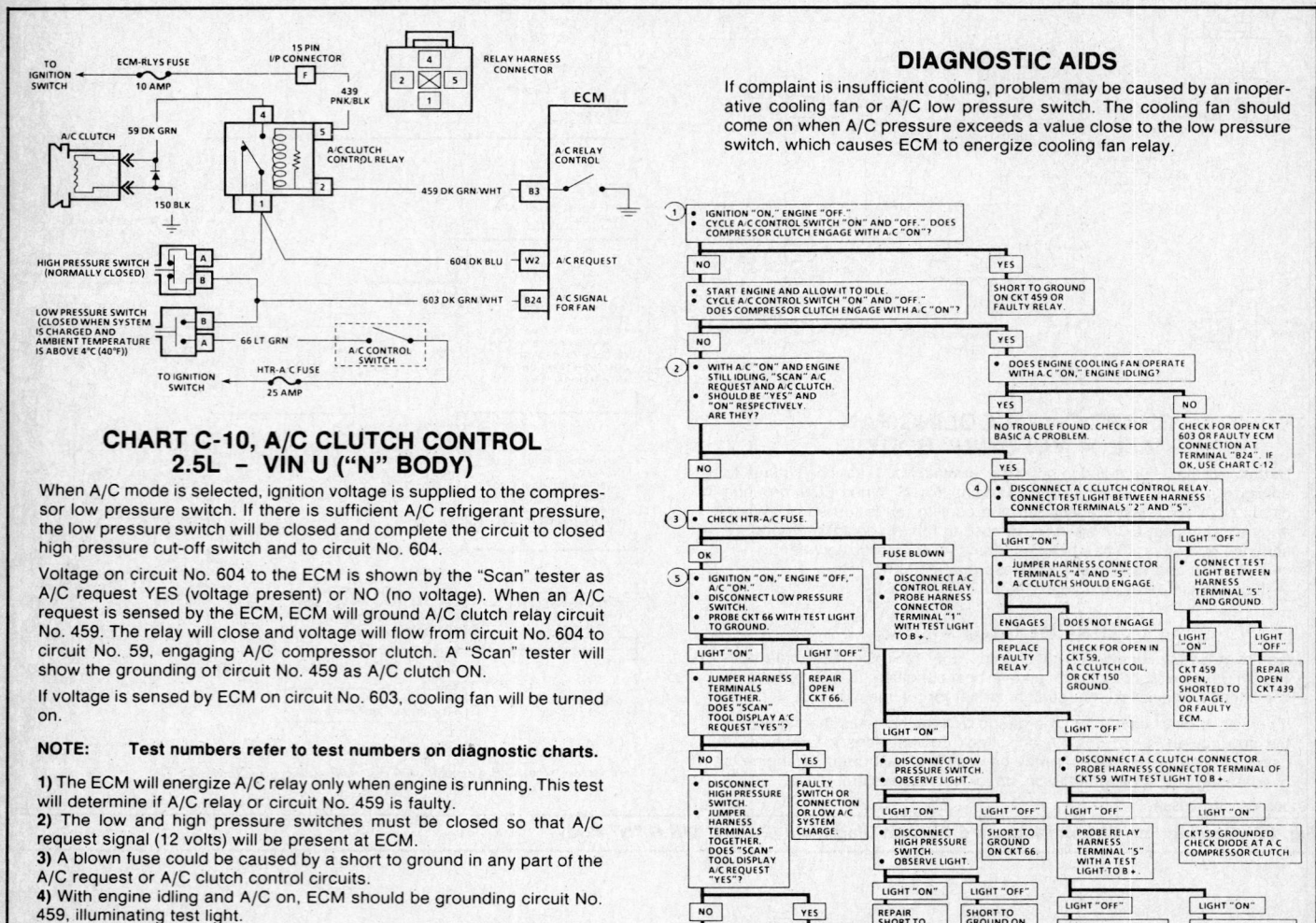

DIAGNOSTIC AIDS

If complaint is insufficient cooling, problem may be caused by an inoperative cooling fan or A/C low pressure switch. The cooling fan should come on when A/C pressure exceeds a value close to the low pressure switch, which causes ECM to energize cooling fan relay.

CHART C-10, A/C CLUTCH CONTROL
2.5L – VIN U ("N" BODY)

When A/C mode is selected, ignition voltage is supplied to the compressor low pressure switch. If there is sufficient A/C refrigerant pressure, the low pressure switch will be closed and complete the circuit to closed high pressure cut-off switch and to circuit No. 604.

Voltage on circuit No. 604 to the ECM is shown by the "Scan" tester as A/C request YES (voltage present) or NO (no voltage). When an A/C request is sensed by the ECM, ECM will ground A/C clutch relay circuit No. 459. The relay will close and voltage will flow from circuit No. 604 to circuit No. 59, engaging A/C compressor clutch. A "Scan" tester will show the grounding of circuit No. 459 as A/C clutch ON.

If voltage is sensed by ECM on circuit No. 603, cooling fan will be turned on.

NOTE: Test numbers refer to test numbers on diagnostic charts.

1) The ECM will energize A/C relay only when engine is running. This test will determine if A/C relay or circuit No. 459 is faulty.
2) The low and high pressure switches must be closed so that A/C request signal (12 volts) will be present at ECM.
3) A blown fuse could be caused by a short to ground in any part of the A/C request or A/C clutch control circuits.
4) With engine idling and A/C on, ECM should be grounding circuit No. 459, illuminating test light.
5) Test determines if signal is reaching the low pressure switch on circuit No. 66 from the A/C control panel. The signal should be present only when A/C mode or DEFROST mode has been selected.

91D05570   91F05571

Courtesy of General Motors Corp.

Fig. 28: A/C Clutch Control Circuit Diagram & System Diagnosis (2.5L – VIN U "N" Body)

1991 ENGINE COOLING
Specifications & Electric Cooling Fans – Exc. Cadillac (Cont.)

GM
5-95

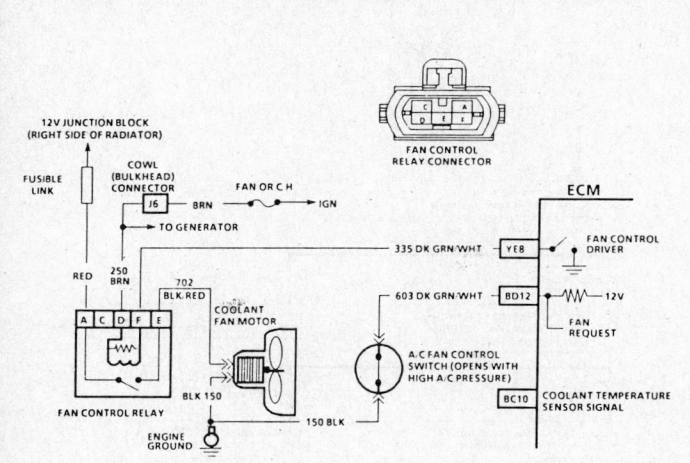

CHART C-12, COOLING FAN
(1 OF 2)
3.1L – VIN T ("A" BODY)

The ECM controls cooling fan with inputs A/C fan control switch, coolant temperature sensor and vehicle speed sensor. The ECM grounds circuit No. 335 to energizes the fan control relay. Battery voltage is then supplied to the fan motor.

The ECM grounds circuit No. 335 when A/C has been requested, coolant temperature is greater than 223°F (106°C) or fan control switch opens with high A/C pressure, approximately 200 psi (14 kg/cm²). When ECM energizes fan control relay, it will run for at least 30 seconds or until vehicle speed exceeds 70 MPH. If Code 14 or 15 is present, ECM will run fan continuously.

NOTE: Test numbers refer to test numbers on diagnostic charts.

1) With system in field service mode, the cooling fan control driver will close and energize fan control relay.
2) If A/C fan control switch or circuit is open, cooling fan will run continuously when A/C is requested.
3) With A/C clutch engaged, A/C fan control switch should open when A/C pressure exceeds 200 psi (14 kg/cm²). This will cause ECM to energize fan control relay.

90G10021   90I01616

DIAGNOSTIC AIDS

If an overheating condition is suspected, verify if this is due to actual boilover. If gauge or light indicates an overheat condition, and no boilover is in evidence, inspect the gauge/light circuit for malfunction.

If vehicle is overheating and the gauge or light indicates the same, but the cooling fan is not coming on, check coolant sensor temperature using a "Scan" tester. Sensor may have shifted calibration and should be replaced. If engine is overheating and cooling fan is on, check cooling system.

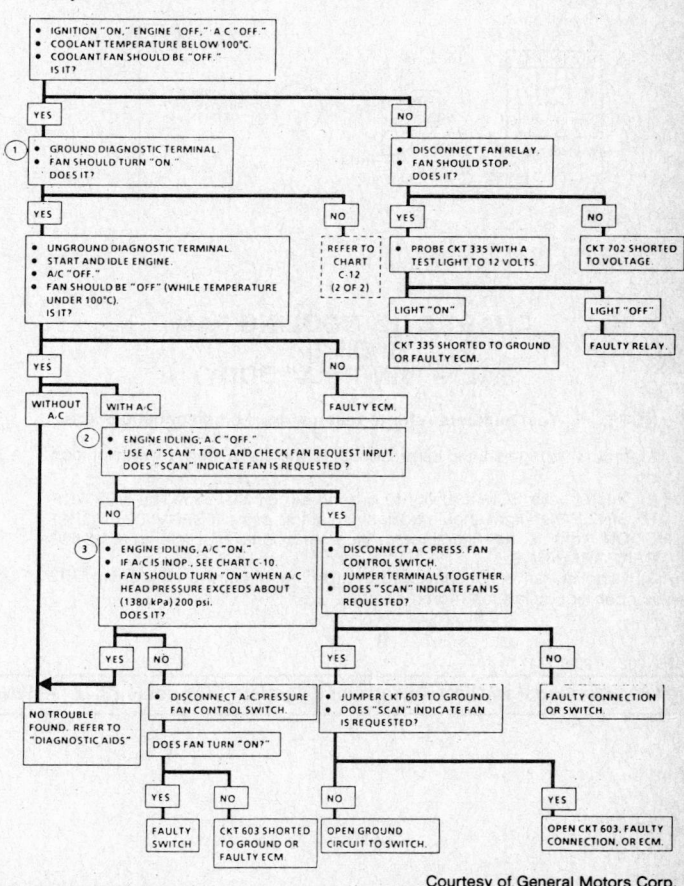

Courtesy of General Motors Corp.

Fig. 29: Cooling Fan Circuit Diagram & System Diagnosis (3.1L – VIN T "A" Body) (1 of 2)

GM
5-96

1991 ENGINE COOLING
Specifications & Electric Cooling Fans – Exc. Cadillac (Cont.)

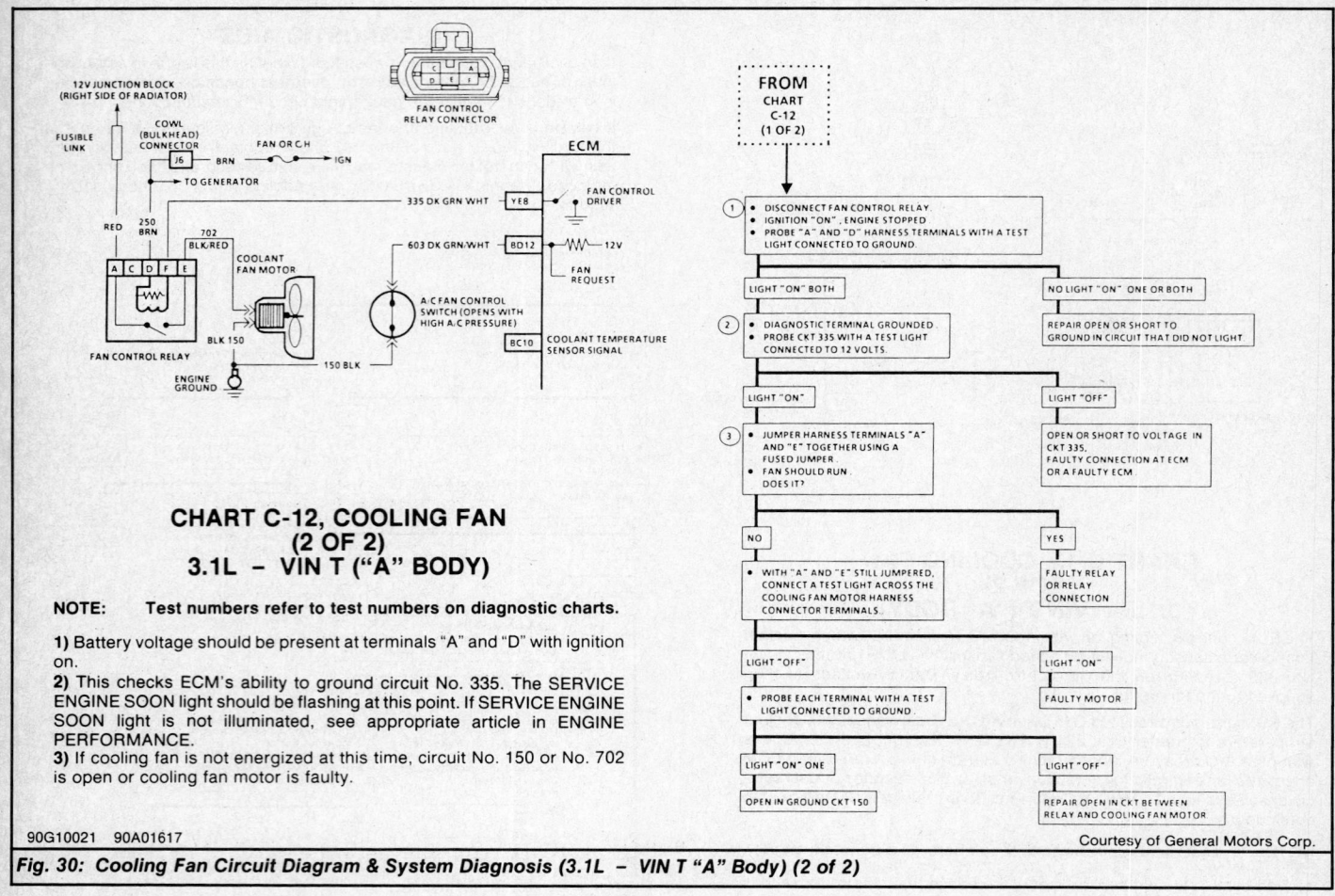

CHART C-12, COOLING FAN
(2 OF 2)
3.1L – VIN T ("A" BODY)

NOTE: Test numbers refer to test numbers on diagnostic charts.

1) Battery voltage should be present at terminals "A" and "D" with ignition on.

2) This checks ECM's ability to ground circuit No. 335. The SERVICE ENGINE SOON light should be flashing at this point. If SERVICE ENGINE SOON light is not illuminated, see appropriate article in ENGINE PERFORMANCE.

3) If cooling fan is not energized at this time, circuit No. 150 or No. 702 is open or cooling fan motor is faulty.

90G10021   90A01617

Courtesy of General Motors Corp.

Fig. 30: Cooling Fan Circuit Diagram & System Diagnosis (3.1L – VIN T "A" Body) (2 of 2)

1991 ENGINE COOLING
Specifications & Electric Cooling Fans – Exc. Cadillac (Cont.)

GM
5-97

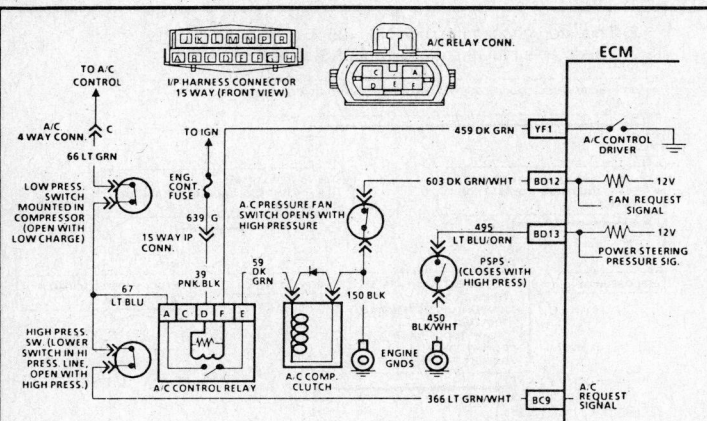

CHART C-10, A/C CLUTCH CONTROL 3.1L – VIN T ("A" BODY)

The A/C clutch control relay is ECM controlled to delay A/C clutch engagement approximately 4/10 of a second after A/C is turned on. This allows the Idle Air Control (IAC) valve to adjust engine RPM before A/C clutch engages.

The ECM will also disengage A/C clutch if high power steering pressure is present, engine is overheating or WOT. The ECM provides a ground path for A/C clutch relay through circuit No. 459.

If A/C pressure is less than 40 psi (2.8 kg/cm²), the low pressure switch will open. If A/C pressure is more than 440 psi (31 kg/cm²), the high pressure switch will open. The A/C pressure fan switch opens when A/C pressure exceeds 200 psi (14 kg/cm²).

NOTE: Test numbers refer to test numbers on diagnostic charts.

1) The ECM will only energize A/C relay when engine is running. This will determine if relay or circuit No. 459 is faulty.
2) For A/C clutch to engage, low pressure switch must be closed, providing 12 volts to the relay. High pressure switch must be closed so A/C request (12 volts) will be present at ECM.
3) Determines if A/C control panel request signal is reaching the ECM on circuit No. 366. This signal should only be present when A/C or defrost is selected.
4) A blown fuse can be caused by a short to ground in either circuit No. 59, circuit No. 67, A/C request circuit or A/C clutch.
5) If ECM sees high power steering pressure, A/C clutch will be disengaged by the ECM.
6) With engine idling and A/C on, ECM should ground circuit No. 459, which will cause test light to illuminate.

90C04278 90C01618

DIAGNOSTIC AIDS

If complaint was insufficient cooling, problem may be caused by an inoperative cooling fan or A/C pressure fan switch. The engine cooling fan should be turn on when A/C pressure exceeds a value to open the switch, which causes the ECM to energize the cooling fan relay.

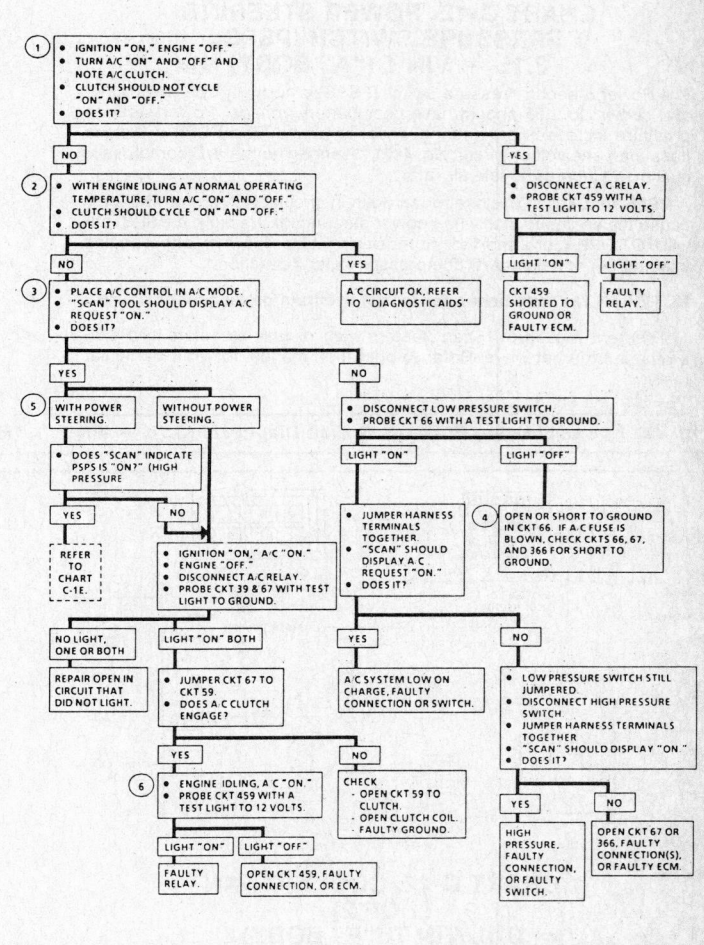

Courtesy of General Motors Corp.

Fig. 31: **A/C Clutch Control Circuit Diagram & System Diagnosis (3.1L – VIN T "A" Body)**

GM
5-98

1991 ENGINE COOLING
Specifications & Electric Cooling Fans – Exc. Cadillac (Cont.)

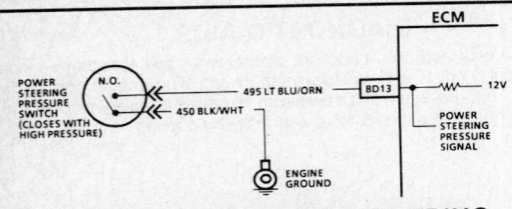

CHART C-1E, POWER STEERING PRESSURE SWITCH (PSPS) 3.1L – VIN T ("A" BODY)

The Power Steering Pressure Switch (PSPS) is normally open to ground, and circuit No. 495 should have near battery voltage. Power steering pressure increases as steering wheel is turned. The PSPS will close (less than one volt on circuit No. 495), disengaging the A/C compressor clutch and increasing idle air rate.

A PSPS that will NOT close, or an open in circuits No. 495 or 450, may cause the engine to stall when power steering load is high. A PSPS that will NOT OPEN, or a short to ground of circuit No. 495, may affect engine idle and will not allow A/C compressor clutch operation.

NOTE: Test numbers refer to test numbers on diagnostic charts.

1) Different makes of "Scan" testers may display the state of PSPS switch in different ways. Refer to operation manual for your particular tester.

91E05580   90E01619

2) This step checks if circuit No. 495 is shorted to ground.
3) This step simulates a closed PSPS switch.

Courtesy of General Motors Corp.

Fig. 32: *Power Steering Pressure Switch Diagnosis (3.1L – VIN T "A" Body)*

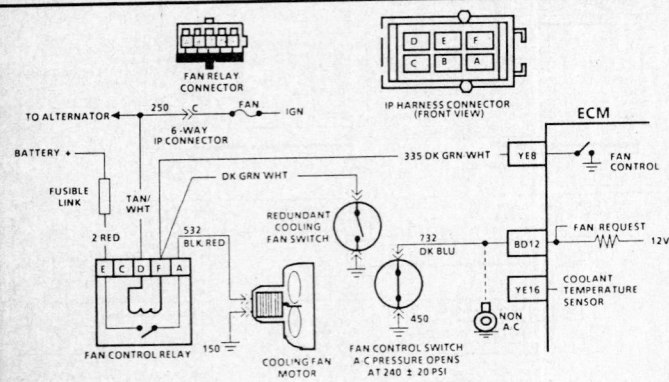

CHART C-12, COOLING FAN (1 OF 2) 3.1L VIN T ("F" BODY)

The ECM controls cooling fan inputs from A/C fan control switch, coolant temperature sensor and vehicle speed sensor. The ECM grounds circuit No. 335 to energize fan control relay. Battery voltage is then supplied to the fan motor.

The ECM grounds circuit No. 335 when A/C has been requested, coolant temperature is greater than 225°F (107°C) or fan control switch opens with high A/C pressure, approximately 240 psi (17 kg/cm²). When ECM energizes the fan control relay, it will run for at least 30 seconds or until vehicle speed exceeds 70 MPH. If Code 14 or 15 is present, ECM will run fan continuously. On vehicles without A/C, circuit No. 732 is jumpered to ground so that fan does not run continuously.

NOTE: Test numbers refer to test numbers on diagnostic charts.

1) With system in field service mode, the cooling fan control driver will close and energize the fan control relay.
2) If the A/C fan control switch or circuit is open, cooling fan would run when A/C is requested.
3) With A/C clutch engaged, A/C fan control switch should open when A/C pressure exceeds 200 psi (14 kg/cm²). This will cause ECM to energize fan control relay.

DIAGNOSTIC AIDS

If an overheating condition is suspected, verify if this is due to actual boilover. If gauge or light indicates an overheat condition, and no boilover is in evidence, inspect the gauge/light circuit for malfunction.

If vehicle is overheating and the gauge or light indicates the same, but the cooling fan is not coming on, check coolant sensor temperature using a "Scan" tester. Sensor may have shifted calibration and should be replaced. If engine is overheating and cooling fan is on, check cooling system.

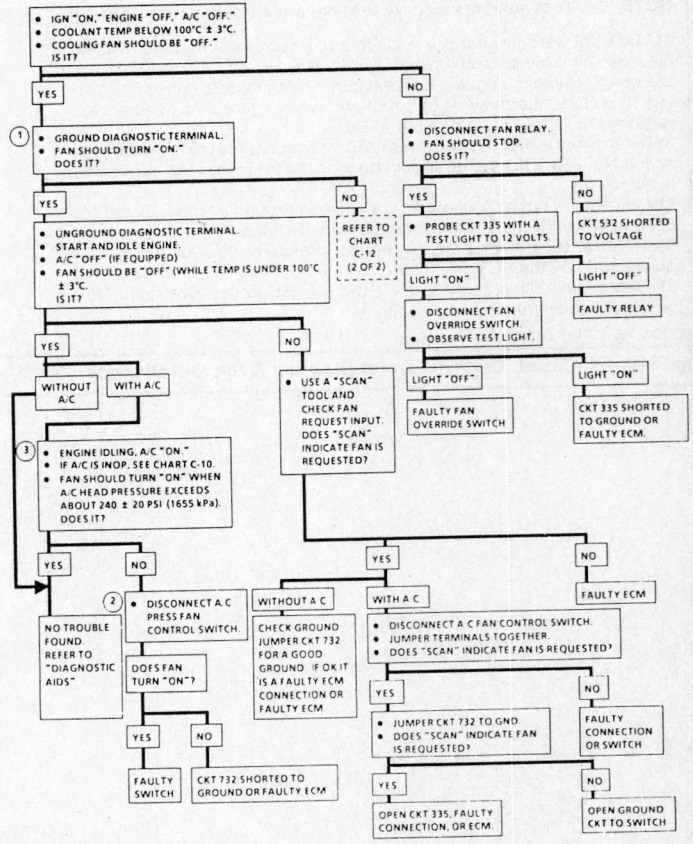

90A04277   90G01620

Courtesy of General Motors Corp.

Fig. 33: *Cooling Fan Circuit Diagram & System Diagnosis (3.1L – VIN T "F" Body) (1 of 2)*

1991 ENGINE COOLING
Specifications & Electric Cooling Fans – Exc. Cadillac (Cont.)

GM
5-99

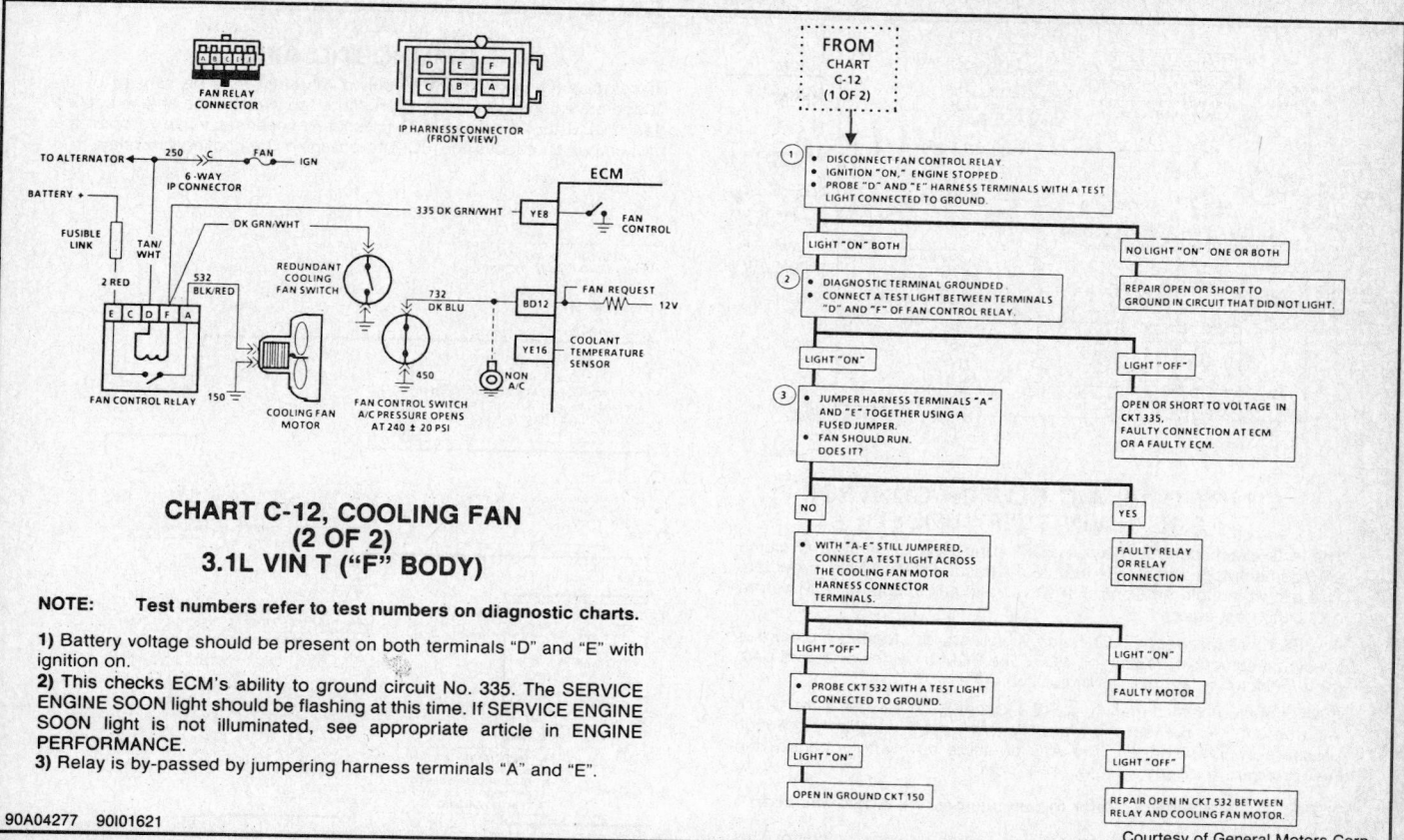

**CHART C-12, COOLING FAN
(2 OF 2)
3.1L VIN T ("F" BODY)**

NOTE: Test numbers refer to test numbers on diagnostic charts.

1) Battery voltage should be present on both terminals "D" and "E" with ignition on.
2) This checks ECM's ability to ground circuit No. 335. The SERVICE ENGINE SOON light should be flashing at this time. If SERVICE ENGINE SOON light is not illuminated, see appropriate article in ENGINE PERFORMANCE.
3) Relay is by-passed by jumpering harness terminals "A" and "E".

90A04277   90I01621

Courtesy of General Motors Corp.

Fig. 34: Cooling Fan Circuit Diagram & System Diagnosis (3.1L – VIN T "F" Body) (2 of 2)

GM
5-100

1991 ENGINE COOLING
Specifications & Electric Cooling Fans – Exc. Cadillac (Cont.)

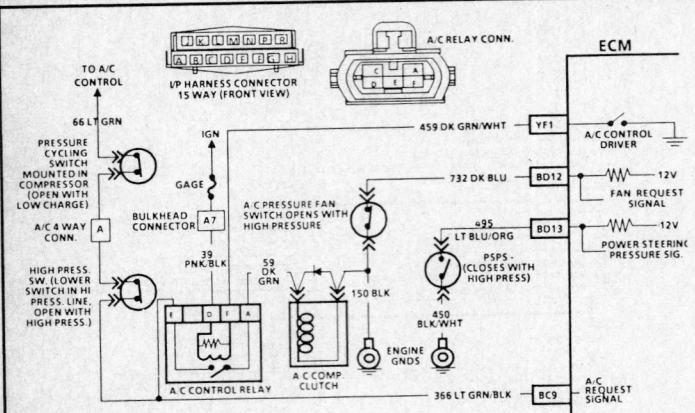

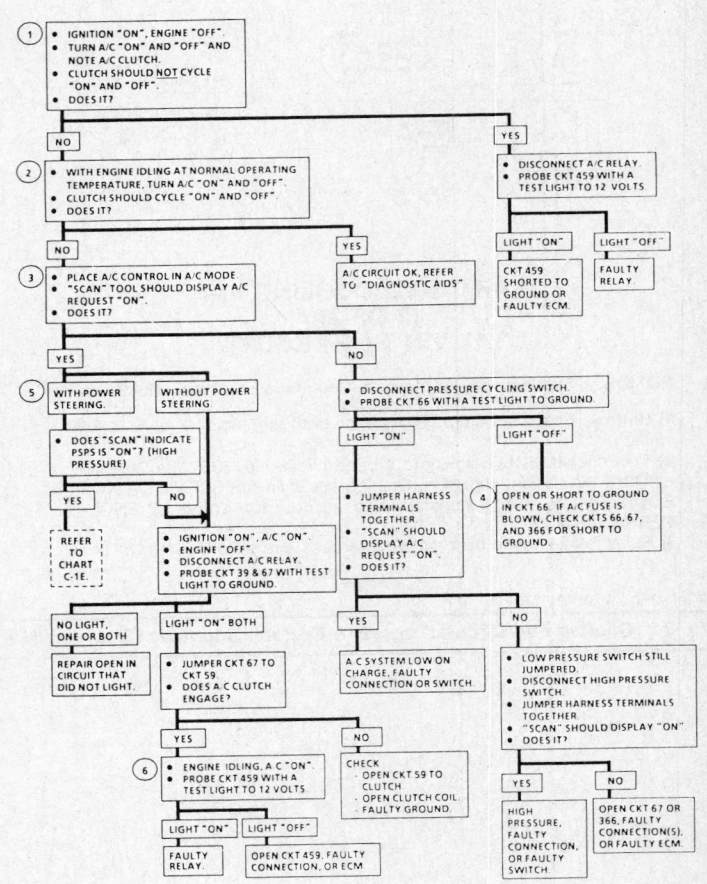

CHART C-10, A/C CLUTCH CONTROL 3.1L – VIN T ("F" BODY)

The A/C clutch control relay is ECM controlled to delay A/C clutch engagement approximately 4 tenths of a second after A/C is turned on. This allows the Idle Air Control (IAC) valve to adjust engine RPM before A/C clutch engages.

The ECM will disengage A/C clutch if high power steering pressure is present, engine overheating or WOT. The ECM provides a ground path for A/C clutch relay through circuit No. 459.

If A/C pressure is less than 40 psi (2.8 kg/cm²), the low pressure switch will open. If A/C pressure is more than 440 psi (31 kg/cm²), the high pressure switch will open. The A/C pressure fan switch opens when A/C pressure exceeds 200 psi (14 kg/cm²).

NOTE: Test numbers refer to test numbers on diagnostic charts.

1) The ECM will only energize A/C relay when engine is running. This will determine if relay or circuit No. 459 is faulty.
2) For A/C clutch to engage, low pressure switch must be closed providing 12 volts to the relay. High pressure switch must be closed so A/C request (12 volts) will be present at ECM.
3) Determines if A/C control panel request signal is reaching the ECM on circuit No. 366. This signal should only be present when A/C or defrost is selected.
4) A blown fuse can be caused by a short to ground in circuit No. 59, circuit No. 67, A/C request circuit or A/C clutch.
5) If ECM sees high power steering pressure, A/C clutch will be disengaged by the ECM.
6) With engine idling and A/C on, ECM should ground circuit No. 459, which will cause test light to illuminate.

DIAGNOSTIC AIDS

If complaint was insufficient cooling, problem may be caused by an inoperative cooling fan or A/C pressure fan switch. The engine cooling fan should turn on when A/C pressure exceeds a value to open the switch, which causes the ECM to energize the cooling fan relay.

90I04276   90J01626

Courtesy of General Motors Corp.

Fig. 35: A/C Clutch Control Circuit Diagram & System Diagnosis (3.1L – VIN T "F" Body)

1991 ENGINE COOLING
Specifications & Electric Cooling Fans – Exc. Cadillac (Cont.)

GM
5-101

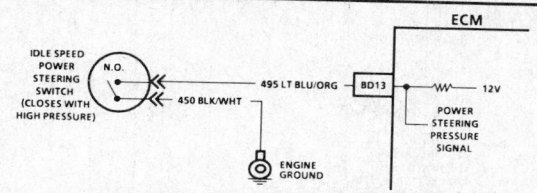

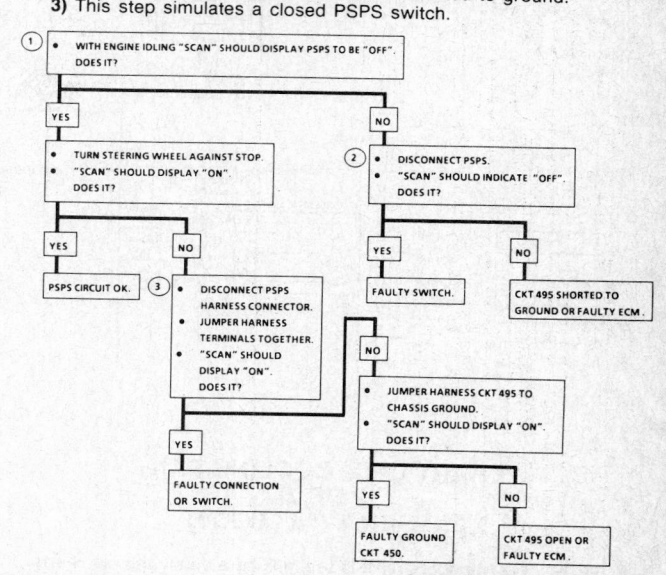

2) This step checks if circuit No. 495 is shorted to ground.
3) This step simulates a closed PSPS switch.

CHART C-1E, POWER STEERING PRESSURE SWITCH (PSPS) 3.1L – VIN T ("F" BODY)

The Power Steering Pressure Switch (PSPS) is normally open to ground, and circuit No. 495 should have near battery voltage. Power steering pressure increases as steering wheel is turned. The PSPS will close (less than one volt on circuit No. 495), disengaging the A/C compressor clutch and increasing the idle air rate.

A PSPS that will NOT close, or an open in circuits No. 495 or 450, may cause the engine to stall when power steering load is high. A PSPS that will NOT open, or a short to ground of circuit No. 495, may effect engine idle and will not allow for A/C compressor clutch operation.

NOTE: Test numbers refer to test numbers on diagnostic charts.

1) Different makes of "SCAN" testers may display the state of PSPS switch in different ways. Refer to operation manual for your particular tester.

91E05580   90B01627

Courtesy of General Motors Corp.

Fig. 36: Power Steering Pressure Switch Diagnosis (3.1L – VIN T "F" Body)

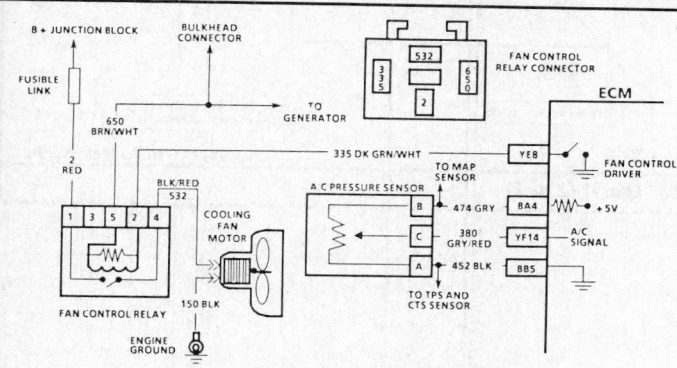

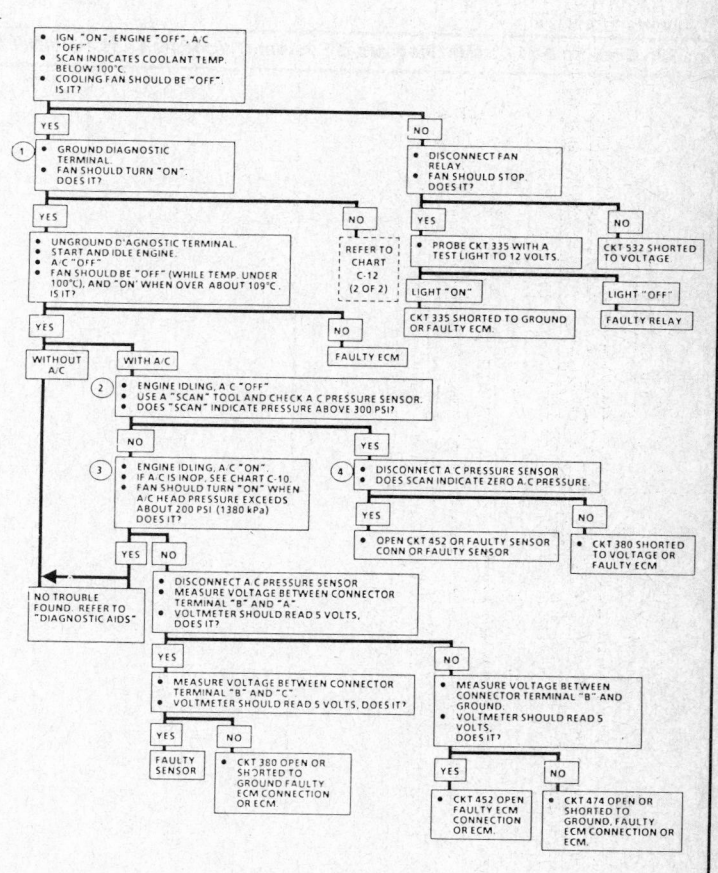

If vehicle is overheating and the gauge or light indicates the same, but the cooling fan is not coming on, check coolant sensor temperature using a "Scan" tester. Sensor may have shifted calibration and should be replaced. If engine is overheating and cooling fan is on, check cooling system.

CHART C-12, COOLING FAN (1 OF 2) 3.1L VIN T ("J" BODY)

The ECM controls cooling fan with inputs from A/C pressure sensor, coolant temperature sensor and vehicle speed. The ECM grounds circuit No. 335 to energize fan control relay. Battery voltage is then supplied to the fan motor.

The ECM grounds circuit No. 335 when A/C has been requested, coolant temperature is greater than 228°F (109°C) or when A/C pressure sensor indicates approximately 200 psi (14.1 kg/cm²). When ECM energizes the fan control relay, it will run for at least 30 seconds or until vehicle speed exceeds 70 MPH. If Code 14 or 15 is present, ECM will run fan continuously.

NOTE: Test numbers refer to test numbers on diagnostic charts.

1) With system in field service mode, cooling fan control driver will close and energize fan control relay.
2) If A/C fan control switch or circuit is open, cooling fan will run continuously when A/C is requested.
3) With A/C clutch engaged, A/C fan control switch should open when A/C high pressure exceeds 200 psi (14.1 kg/cm²). This will cause the ECM to energize fan control relay.
4) Code 66 will set when A/C pressure sensor is disconnected. After completing this step, clear codes.

DIAGNOSTIC AIDS

If an overheating condition is suspected, verify if this is due to actual boilover. If gauge or light indicates an overheat condition, and no boilover is in evidence, inspect the gauge/light circuit for malfunction.

90J10024   90A01622

Courtesy of General Motors Corp.

Fig. 37: Cooling Fan Circuit Diagram & System Diagnosis (3.1L – VIN T "J" Body) (1 of 2)

GM
5-102

1991 ENGINE COOLING
Specifications & Electric Cooling Fans – Exc. Cadillac (Cont.)

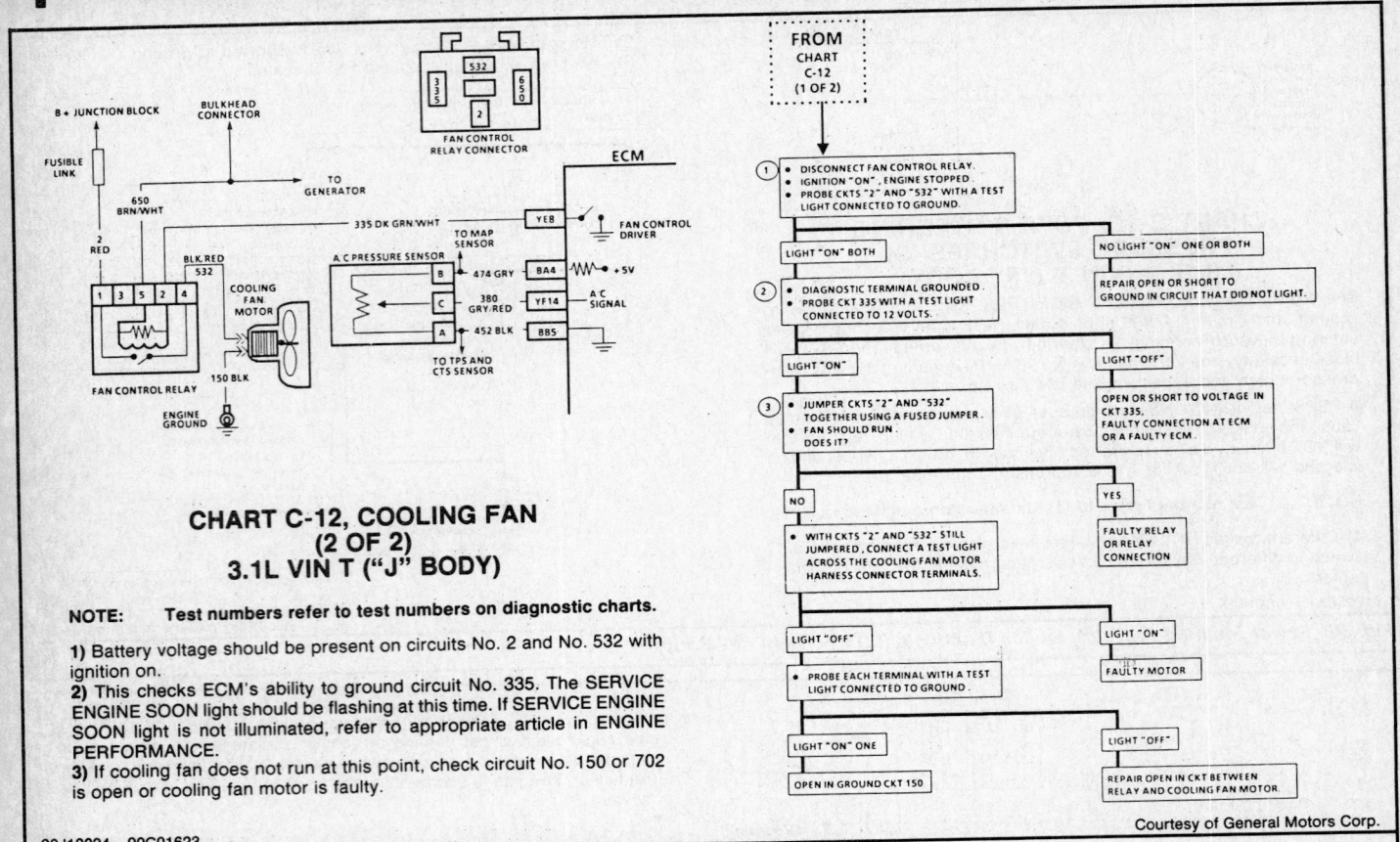

CHART C-12, COOLING FAN
(2 OF 2)
3.1L VIN T ("J" BODY)

NOTE: Test numbers refer to test numbers on diagnostic charts.

1) Battery voltage should be present on circuits No. 2 and No. 532 with ignition on.

2) This checks ECM's ability to ground circuit No. 335. The SERVICE ENGINE SOON light should be flashing at this time. If SERVICE ENGINE SOON light is not illuminated, refer to appropriate article in ENGINE PERFORMANCE.

3) If cooling fan does not run at this point, check circuit No. 150 or 702 is open or cooling fan motor is faulty.

90J10024   90C01623

Courtesy of General Motors Corp.

Fig. 38: Cooling Fan Circuit Diagram & System Diagnosis (3.1L – VIN T "J" Body) (2 of 2)

1991 ENGINE COOLING
Specifications & Electric Cooling Fans – Exc. Cadillac (Cont.)

GM
5-103

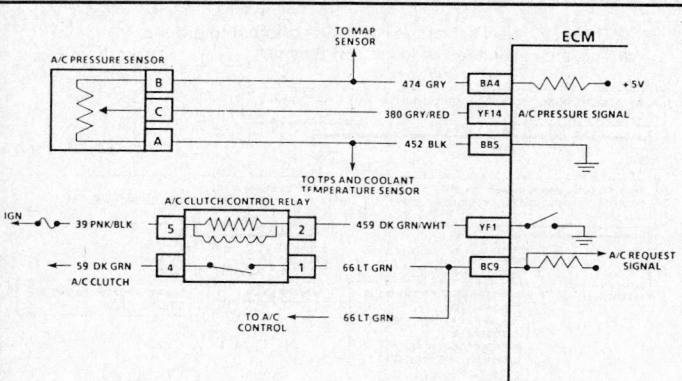

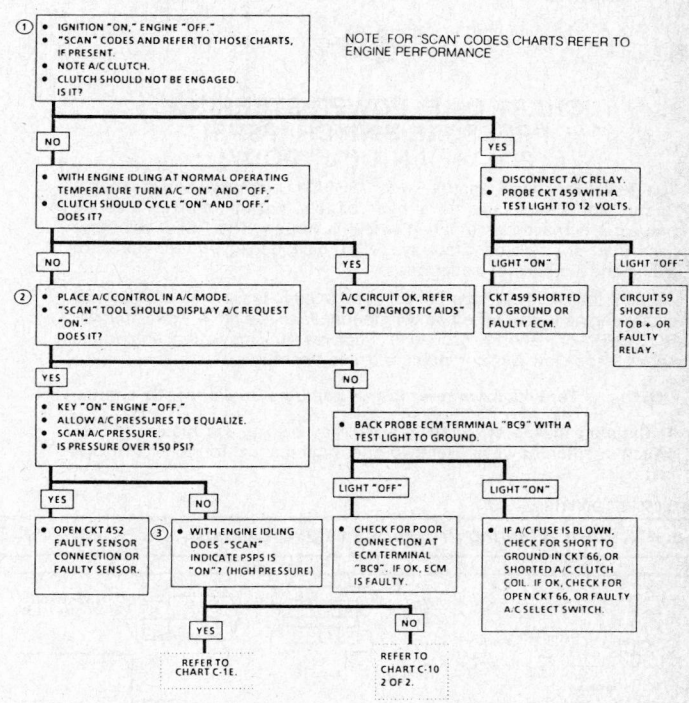

2) Determines if signal is reaching ECM through circuit No. 66 from the A/C control panel. Signal should only be present when A/C mode or defrost mode has been selected.

3) If ECM is receiving a high power steering pressure signal, A/C clutch will be disengaged by ECM.

CHART C-10, A/C CLUTCH CONTROL (1 OF 2)
3.1L – VIN T ("J" BODY)

The A/C clutch control relay is ECM controlled to delay A/C clutch engagement approximately 3/10 of a second after A/C is turned on. This allows the Idle Air Control (IAC) valve to adjust engine RPM before A/C clutch engages.

The ECM will disengage A/C clutch if high power steering pressure is present, engine overheating, WOT or IAC reset. The ECM provides a ground path for A/C clutch relay through circuit No. 459.

A/C clutch will remain disengaged if Code 66 is present. If A/C pressure is less than 44 psi (3.1 kg/cm²), the low pressure switch will open. If A/C pressure is greater than 430 psi (30 kg/cm²), the high pressure switch will open. If ECM sees high power steering pressure, A/C clutch will be disengaged by ECM.

NOTE: Test numbers refer to test numbers on diagnostic charts.

1) ECM will only energize A/C relay when engine is running. This test will determine if relay or circuit No. 459 is faulty.

90F10020 90D01628

Fig. 39: *A/C Clutch Control Circuit Diagram & System Diagnosis (3.1L – VIN T "J" Body) (1 of 2)*

Courtesy of General Motors Corp.

CHART C-10, A/C CLUTCH CONTROL (2 OF 2)
3.1L – VIN T ("J" BODY)

NOTE: Test numbers refer to test numbers on diagnostic charts.

1) This checks if pressure transducer is out of range causing A/C clutch to disengage.

2) With engine off and field service mode activated, ECM should ground circuit No. 459 causing test light to illuminate.

DIAGNOSTIC AIDS

If complaint was insufficient cooling, problem may be caused by an inoperative cooling fan or A/C pressure fan switch. The engine cooling fan should turn on when A/C pressure exceeds a value to open the switch, which causes the ECM to energize the cooling fan relay.

90F10020 90F01629

Courtesy of General Motors Corp.

Fig. 40: *A/C Clutch Control Circuit Diagram & System Diagnosis (3.1L – VIN T "J" Body) (2 of 2)*

GM
5-104

1991 ENGINE COOLING
Specifications & Electric Cooling Fans – Exc. Cadillac (Cont.)

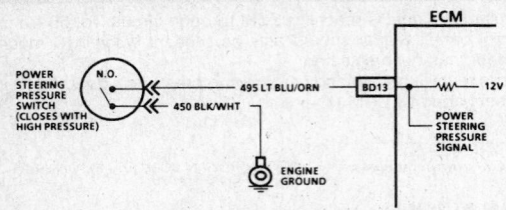

CHART C-1E, POWER STEERING PRESSURE SWITCH (PSPS) 3.1L – VIN T ("J" BODY)

The Power Steering Pressure Switch (PSPS) is normally open to ground. Circuit No. 495 should have near battery voltage. Power steering pressure increases as steering wheel is turned. The PSPS will close (less than one volt on circuit No. 495), disengaging A/C compressor clutch and increasing idle air rate.

A PSPS that will NOT close or an open in circuits No. 495 or 450, may cause engine to stall when power steering load is high. A PSPS that will NOT OPEN or a short to ground in circuit No. 495, may affect engine idle and will not allow A/C compressor clutch operation.

NOTE: Test numbers refer to test numbers on diagnostic charts.

1) Different makes of "Scan" testers may display the state of PSPS switch in different ways. Refer to operation manual for your particular tester.

91E05580 90H01630

2) This step checks if circuit No. 495 is shorted to ground.
3) This step simulates a closed PSPS switch.

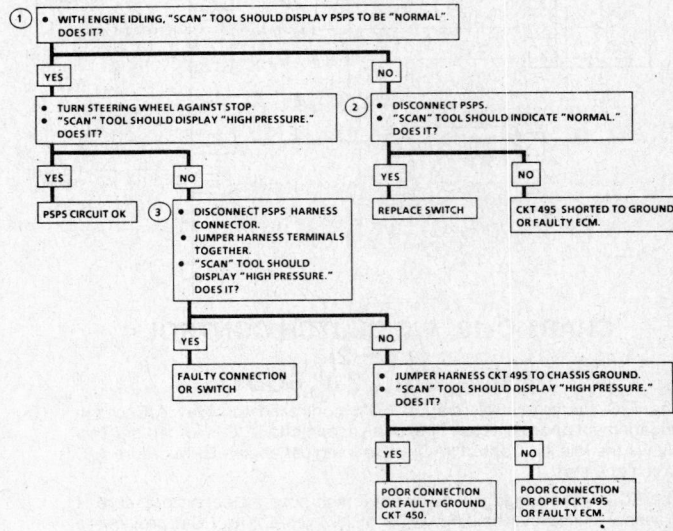

Courtesy of General Motors Corp.

Fig. 41: Power Steering Pressure Switch Diagnosis (3.1L – VIN T "J" Body)

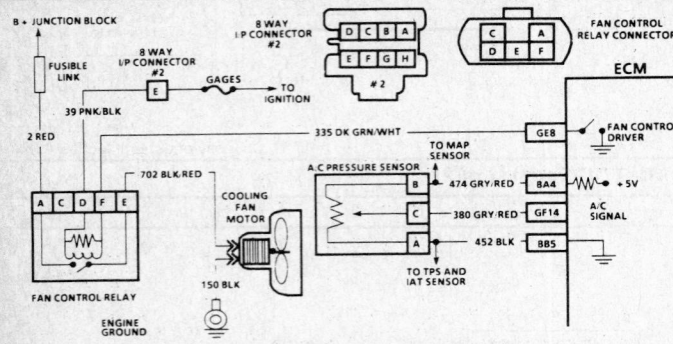

CHART C-12, COOLING FAN (1 OF 2) 3.1L VIN T ("L" BODY)

Electric cooling fan is controlled by ECM based on inputs from coolant temperature sensor, A/C fan control switch and vehicle speed. ECM controls cooling fan by grounding circuit No. 335, energizing fan control relay. Battery voltage is then supplied to fan motor.

ECM grounds circuit No. 335 when coolant temperature is more than 228°F (109°C) or when A/C has been requested and fan control switch opens with high A/C pressure of 200 psi (14 kg/cm²). Once ECM turns relay on, it will keep relay on for a minimum of 30 seconds or until vehicle speed exceeds 70 MPH. Cooling fan will also run constantly when Code 14 or 15 is present or if ECM in back-up mode.

NOTE: Test numbers refer to test numbers on diagnostic charts.

1) With diagnostic terminal grounded, the cooling fan control driver will close, energizing fan control relay.
2) If A/C fan control switch or circuit is open, cooling fan will run whenever A/C is requested.
3) With A/C clutch engaged, the A/C fan control switch should open when A/C high pressure exceeds 200 psi (14.1 kg/cm²). This signal should cause ECM to energize fan control relay.
4) Disconnecting A/C pressure sensor will set Code 66. After finishing this step, ensure codes are cleared.

DIAGNOSTIC AIDS

If an overheating condition is suspected, verify if this is due to actual boil-over. If gauge or light indicates an overheat condition, and no boilover is in evidence, inspect the gauge/light circuit for malfunction.

91H05572 91J05573

If vehicle is overheating and the gauge or light indicates the same, but cooling fan is not coming on, check coolant sensor temperature using a "Scan" tester. Sensor may have shifted calibration and should be replaced. If engine is overheating and cooling fan is on, check cooling system.

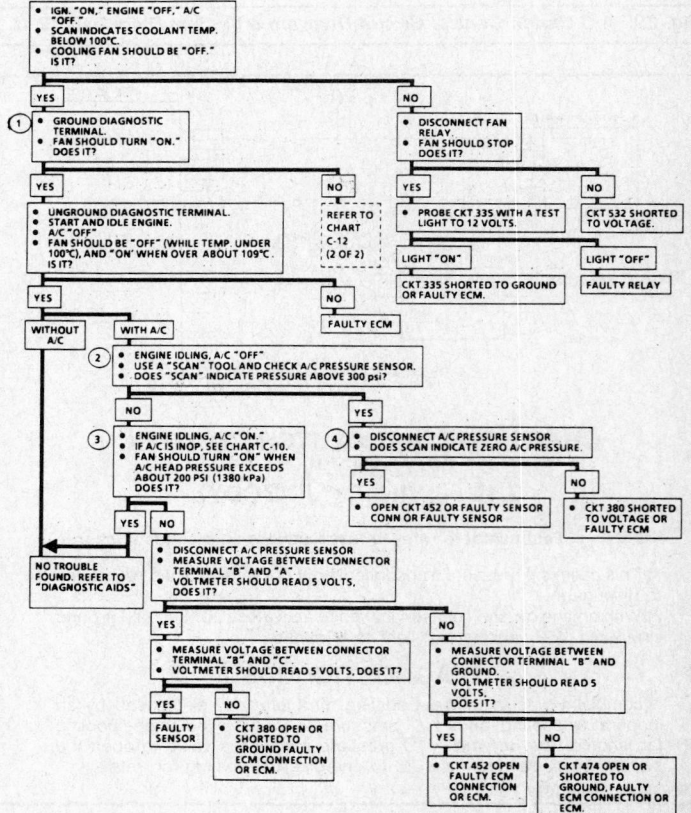

Courtesy of General Motors Corp.

Fig. 42: Cooling Fan Control Circuit Diagram & System Diagnosis (3.1T – VIN T "L" Body) (1 of 2)

1991 ENGINE COOLING
Specifications & Electric Cooling Fans – Exc. Cadillac (Cont.)

GM
5-105

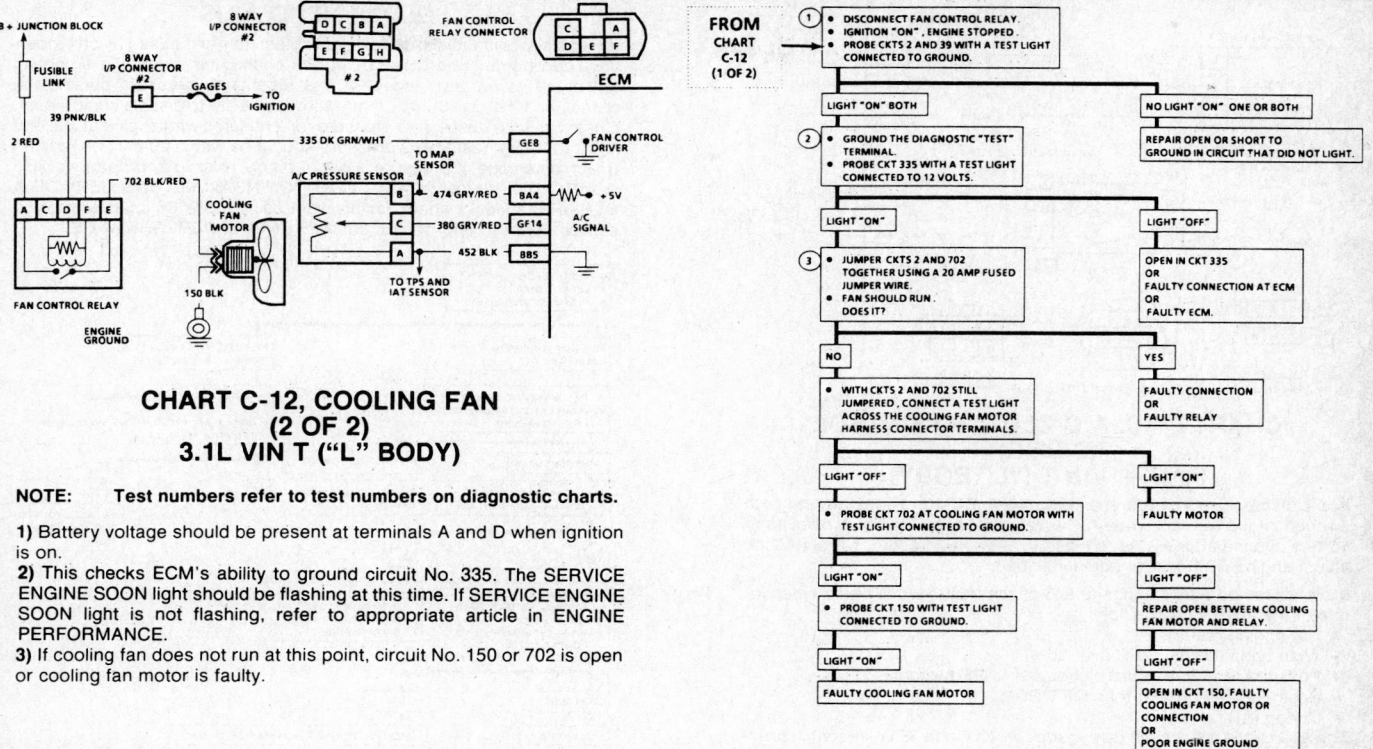

CHART C-12, COOLING FAN
(2 OF 2)
3.1L VIN T ("L" BODY)

NOTE: Test numbers refer to test numbers on diagnostic charts.

1) Battery voltage should be present at terminals A and D when ignition is on.

2) This checks ECM's ability to ground circuit No. 335. The SERVICE ENGINE SOON light should be flashing at this time. If SERVICE ENGINE SOON light is not flashing, refer to appropriate article in ENGINE PERFORMANCE.

3) If cooling fan does not run at this point, circuit No. 150 or 702 is open or cooling fan motor is faulty.

91H05572   91E05575

Courtesy of General Motors Corp.

Fig. 43: Cooling Fan Control Circuit Diagram & System Diagnosis (3.1L – VIN T "L" Body) (2 of 2)

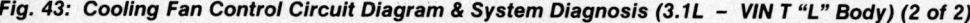

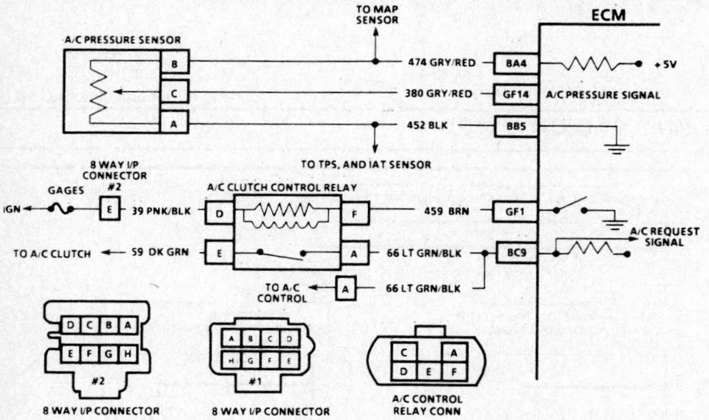

NOTE: Test numbers refer to test numbers on diagnostic charts.

1) ECM will only energize A/C relay when engine is running. This test will determine if relay or circuit No. 459 is faulty.

2) Test determines if signal is reaching the ECM through circuit No. 66 from the A/C control panel. Signal should only be present when A/C or defrost mode has been selected.

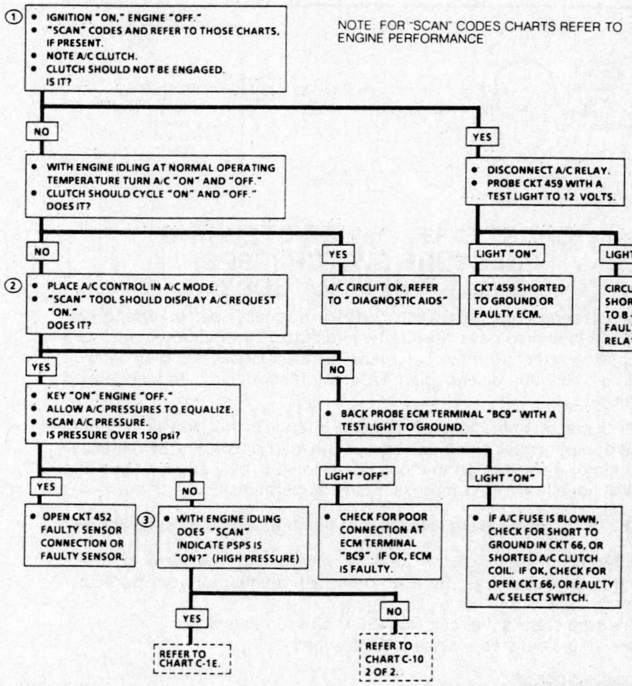

NOTE: FOR "SCAN" CODES CHARTS REFER TO ENGINE PERFORMANCE

CHART C-10, A/C CLUTCH CONTROL
(1 OF 2)
3.1L – VIN T ("L" BODY)

The A/C clutch control relay is energized when ECM provides ground path through circuit No. 459 when A/C is requested. A/C clutch is delayed 3/10 of a second after A/C is requested, allowing the Idle Air Control (IAC) to adjust engine RPM for the additional load.

ECM will temporarily disengage the A/C clutch relay for calibrated times for one of the following conditions:

- Hot engine restarts.
- Wide open throttle (TPS over 90%).
- Power steering pressure high (open PSPS switch).
- Engine speed greater than 6000 RPM.
- During IAC retest.

A/C clutch will remain disengaged when Code 66 is set, if pressure is out of range or there is no A/C request signal due to an open A/C select switch or circuit.

91G05576   91I05577

Courtesy of General Motors Corp.

Fig. 44: A/C Clutch Control Circuit Diagram & System Diagnosis (3.1L – VIN T "L" Body) (1 of 2)

GM
5-106

1991 ENGINE COOLING
Specifications & Electric Cooling Fans – Exc. Cadillac (Cont.)

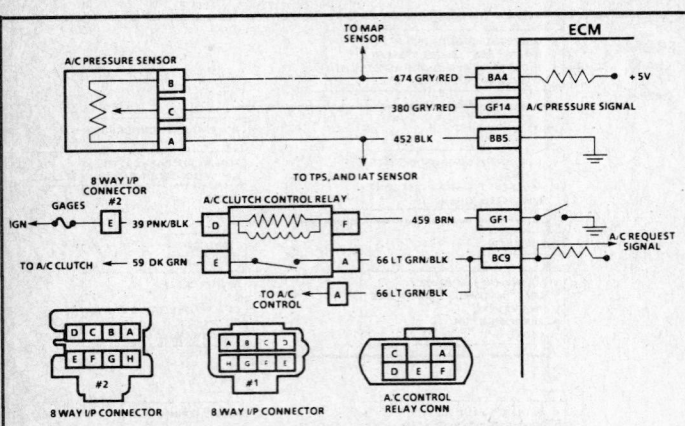

CHART C-10, A/C CLUTCH CONTROL
(2 OF 2)
3.1L – VIN T ("L" BODY)

A/C clutch control relay is energized when ECM provides ground path through circuit No. 459 when A/C is requested. A/C clutch is delayed 3/10 of a second after A/C is requested, allowing Idle Air Control (IAC) to adjust engine RPM for the additional load.

ECM will temporarily disengage A/C clutch relay for calibrated times for one of the following conditions:
- Hot engine restarts.
- Wide open throttle (TPS over 90%).
- Power steering pressure high (open PSPS switch).
- Engine speed greater than 6000 RPM.
- During IAC retest.

The A/C clutch will remain disengaged when Code 66 is present, if pressure is out of range or there is no A/C request signal due to an open A/C select switch or circuit.

NOTE: Test numbers refer to test numbers on diagnostic charts.

1) Determines if pressure transducer is out of range causing A/C compressor clutch to be disengaged.
2) With engine not running and field service mode activated, ECM should be grounding circuit No. 459, which should activate test light.

91G05576 91C05579

DIAGNOSTIC AIDS

If complaint is insufficient cooling, problem may be caused by an inoperative cooling fan. See CHART C-12 for cooling fan diagnosis. If cooling fan operates properly, check A/C system. A/C pressure outside the range of 43-428 psi (3-30 kg/cm²) will cause ECM to disable compressor. Observe "Scan" tester A/C pressure for 2 minutes with engine at idle and A/C on. "Scan" tester A/C pressure should be within 20 psi (1.4 kg/cm²) of actual reading. If pressure is out of range, refer to appropriate article in MITCHELL domestic AIR CONDITIONING & HEATING SERVICE & REPAIR manual or check for problem using Code 66 chart or replace sensor. Refer to appropriate article in ENGINE PERFORMANCE.

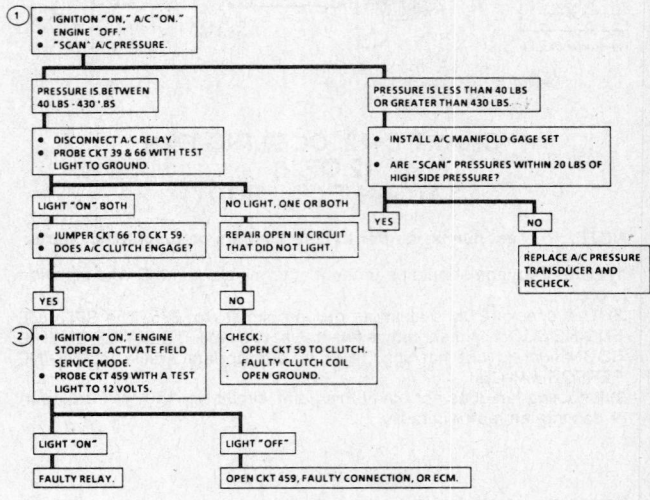

Courtesy of General Motors Corp.

Fig. 45: A/C Clutch Control Circuit Diagram & System Diagnosis (3.1L – VIN T "L" Body) (2 of 2)

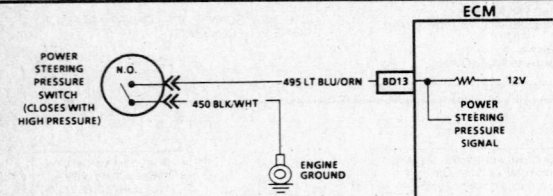

CHART C-1E, POWER STEERING
PRESSURE SWITCH (PSPS)
3.1L – VIN T ("L" BODY)

Power Steering Pressure Switch (PSPS) is normally open to ground. Circuit No. 495 should have near battery voltage. Power steering pressure increases as steering wheel is turned. PSPS will close (less than one volt on circuit No. 495), disengaging A/C compressor clutch and increasing idle air rate.

A PSPS that will not close or an open in circuits No. 495 or 450 may cause engine to stall when power steering load is high. A PSPS that will not open or a short to ground on circuit No. 495, may affect engine idle and will not allow A/C compressor clutch operation.

NOTE: Test numbers refer to test numbers on diagnostic charts.

1) Different makes of "Scan" testers may display the state of PSPS switch in different ways. Refer to operation manual for your particular tester.
2) This step checks if circuit No. 495 is shorted to ground.
3) This step simulates a closed PSPS switch.

91E05580 91G05581

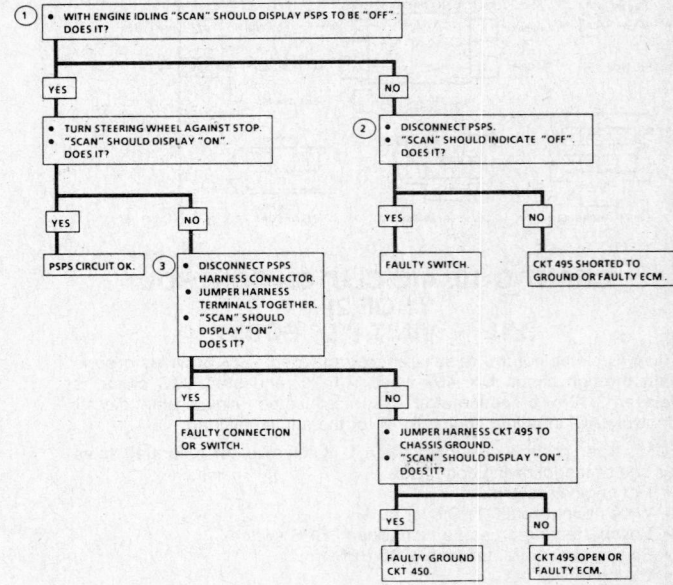

Courtesy of General Motors Corp.

Fig. 46: Power Steering Pressure Switch Diagnosis (3.1L – VIN T "L" Body)

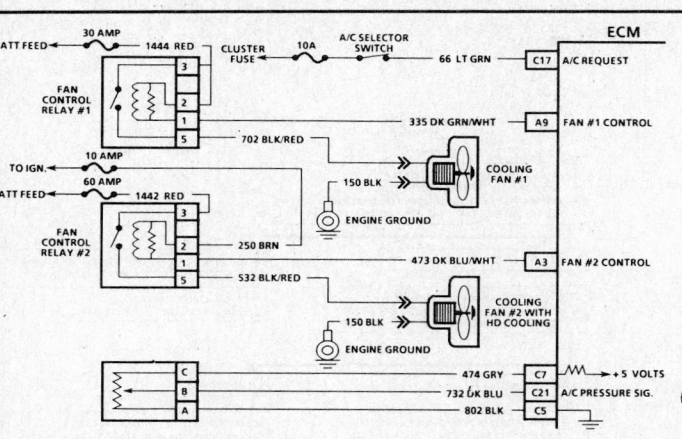

CHART C-12, COOLING FAN
(1 OF 2)
3.1L VIN T ("W" BODY)

The primary and secondary cooling fans are controlled by the ECM, based on inputs from the coolant temperature sensor, A/C control switches, vehicle speed and state of the A/C pressure sensor. ECM controls the fan(s) by grounding circuit No. 335 and/or circuit No. 473, which energizes the fan control relay. Battery voltage is then supplied to fan motor.

ECM grounds circuit No. 335 and/or circuit No. 473 when coolant temperature is above 223°F (106°C) or when A/C has been requested and A/C pressure is about 200 psi (14 kg/cm²). Once ECM turns the relay on, ECM will keep relay on for a minimum of 30 seconds or until vehicle speed exceeds 70 MPH (40 MPH for secondary fan). Cooling fan will run continuously if Code 14 or 15 is present or if ECM is in the back-up mode.

NOTE: Test numbers refer to test numbers on diagnostic charts.

1) With system in field service mode, cooling fan control driver(s) will close, energizing fan control relay(s).
2) If A/C pressure is more than 300 psi (21 kg/cm²) or if circuit is open, fan will run whenever A/C is requested.
3) With A/C clutch engaged and A/C pressure sensor functioning properly, cooling fan should turn on when pressure exceeds 200 psi (21 kg/cm²). This signal should cause ECM to energize the fan control relay(s).
4) This will determine if the A/C pressure sensor is faulty or if ECM or circuitry is faulty.

91I05582   91A05583

DIAGNOSTIC AIDS

If an overheating condition is suspected, verify if this is due to actual boil-over. If gauge or light indicates an overheat condition, and no boilover is in evidence, inspect the gauge/light circuit for malfunction.

If vehicle is overheating and the gauge or light indicates the same, but cooling fan is not coming on, check coolant sensor temperature using a "Scan" tester. Sensor may have shifted calibration and should be replaced. If engine is overheating and cooling fan is on, check cooling system.

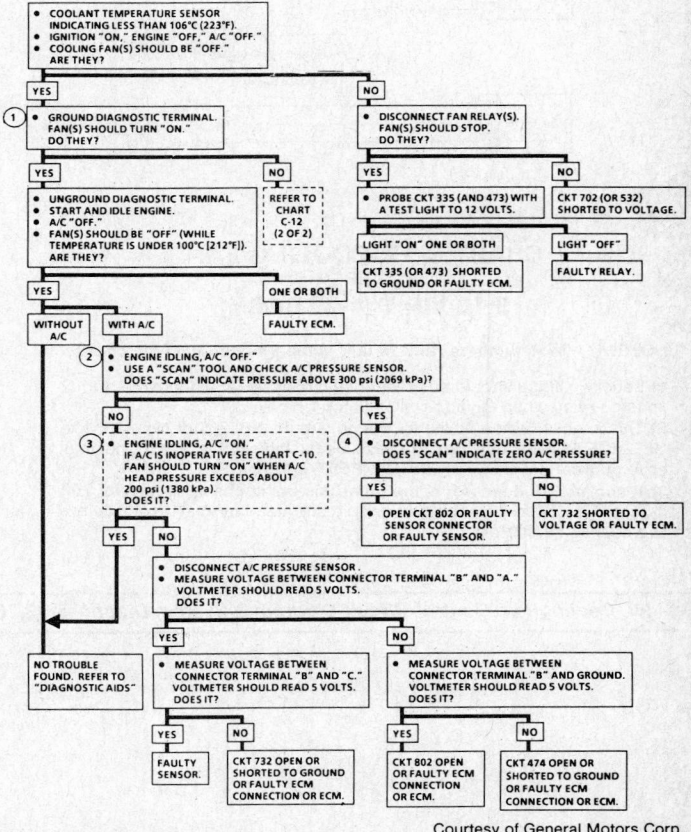

ig. 47: *Cooling Fan Control Circuit Diagram & System Diagnosis (3.1L – VIN T "W" Body) (1 of 2)*

GM
5-108

1991 ENGINE COOLING
Specifications & Electric Cooling Fans – Exc. Cadillac (Cont.)

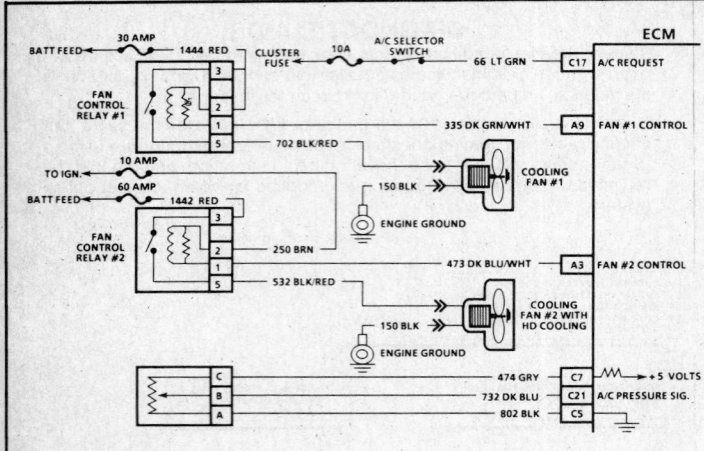

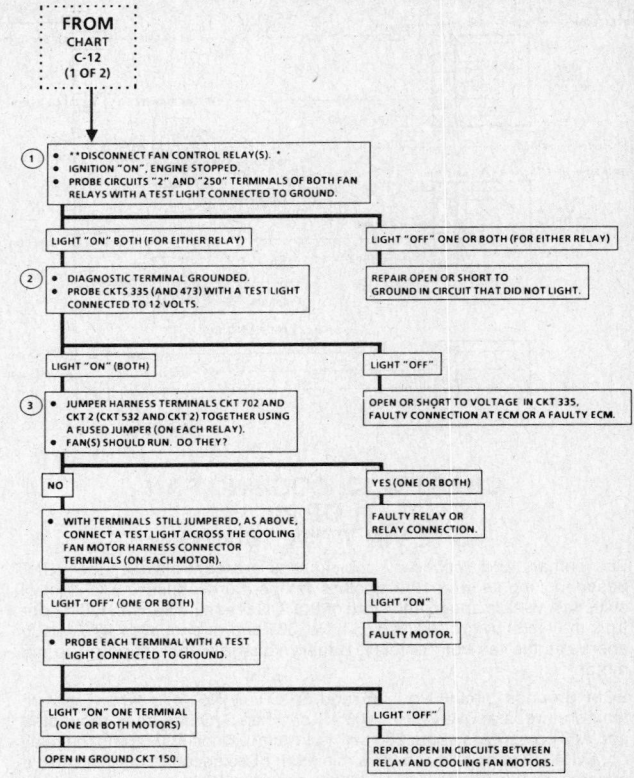

CHART C-12, COOLING FAN
(2 OF 2)
3.1L VIN T ("W" BODY)

NOTE: Test numbers refer to test numbers on diagnostic charts.

1) Battery voltage should be present on circuit No. 250 and circuit No. 2 on each relay when ignition switch is turned on.

2) This checks ECM's ability to ground circuits No. 335 or No. 473. The SERVICE ENGINE SOON light should be flashing at this point. If not, refer to appropriate article in ENGINE PERFORMANCE.

3) If cooling fan does not come on at this point, check circuit No. 702 (535) or No. 150 for an open circuit. If circuits are okay, check for a defective cooling fan motor.

** SOME VEHICLES ARE EQUIPPED WITH TWO COOLING FANS. THE INFORMATION IN PARENTHESIS ( ) APPLIES ONLY TO THE SECOND FAN, IF EQUIPPED.

91I05582   91F05585

Courtesy of General Motors Corp.

Fig. 48: *Cooling Fan Control Circuit Diagram & System Diagnosis (3.1L – VIN T "W" Body) (2 of 2)*

1991 ENGINE COOLING
Specifications & Electric Cooling Fans – Exc. Cadillac (Cont.)

GM
5-109

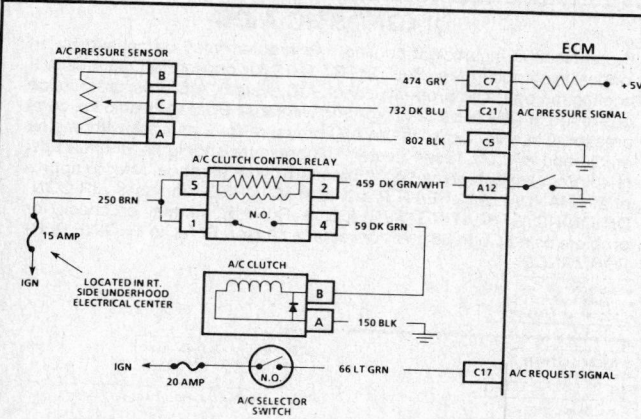

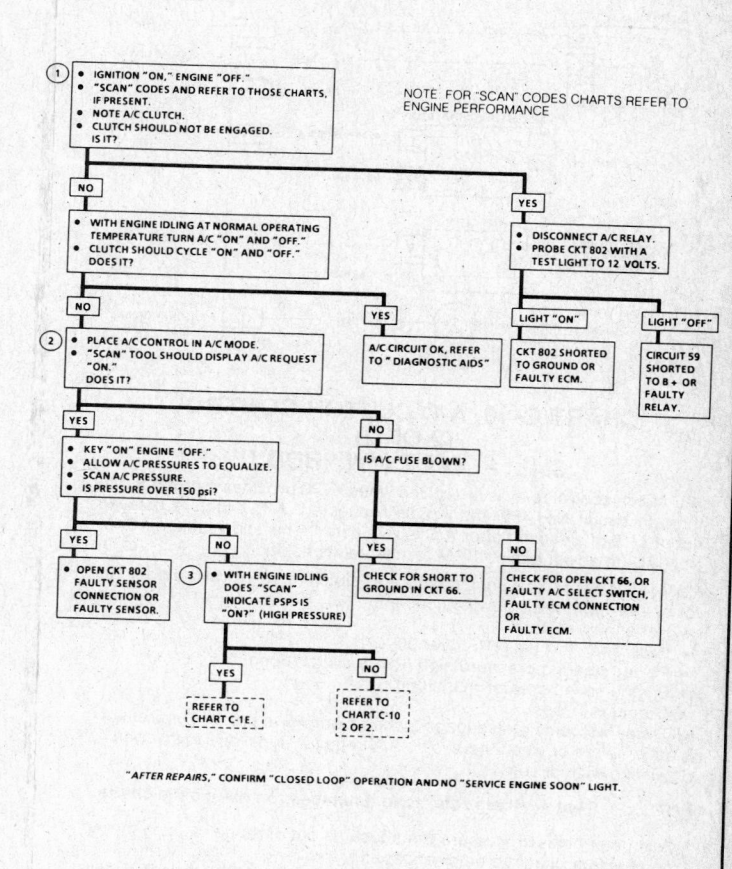

CHART C-10, A/C CLUTCH CONTROL
(1 OF 2)
3.1L – VIN T ("W" BODY)

A/C clutch control relay is ECM-controlled to delay A/C clutch engagement approximately 4/10 of a second after A/C is turned on. This allows Idle Air Control (IAC) valve to adjust engine RPM before A/C clutch engages.

ECM will disengage A/C clutch if high power steering pressure, engine overheating or WOT is present. ECM provides a ground path for A/C clutch relay through circuit No. 459. A/C pressure sensor is used to determine high and low pressure in system and also turns on cooling fan when needed.

NOTE: Test numbers refer to test numbers on diagnostic charts.

1) ECM will only energize A/C relay when engine is running. This test will determine if relay or circuit No. 459 is faulty.

2) This test determines if signal is reaching ECM through circuit No. 66 from A/C control panel. Signal should only be present when A/C mode or defrost mode has been selected.

3) If ECM is receiving a high power steering pressure signal, A/C clutch will be disengaged by ECM.

91H05586   91J05587

Fig. 49: A/C Clutch Control Circuit Diagram & System Diagnosis (3.1L – VIN T "W" Body) (1 of 2)   Courtesy of General Motors Corp.

GM
5-110

1991 ENGINE COOLING
Specifications & Electric Cooling Fans – Exc. Cadillac (Cont.

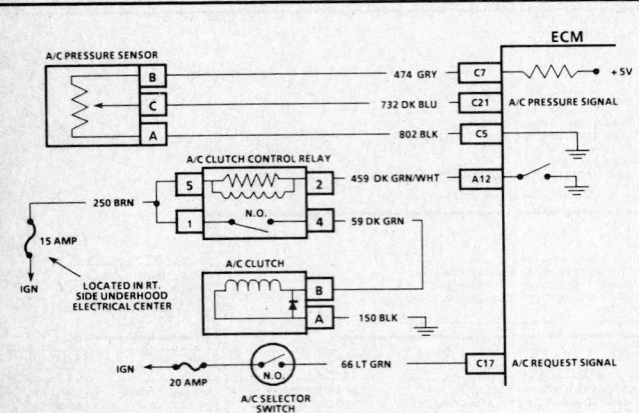

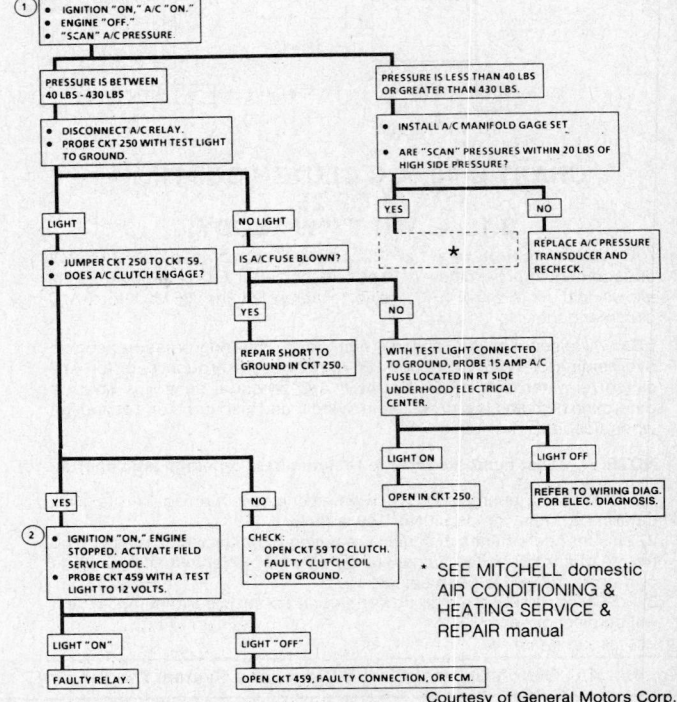

DIAGNOSTIC AIDS

If complaint is insufficient cooling, the problem may be caused by an inoperative cooling fan. See CHART C-12 for cooling fan diagnosis. If cooling fan operates properly, check A/C system. A/C pressure outside of a range of 43-428 psi (3-30 kg/cm²) will cause ECM to disable the compressor. Observe "Scan" tester A/C pressure for 2 minutes with engine at idle and A/C on. "Scan" tester A/C pressure should be within 20 psi (1.4 kg/cm²) of actual reading. If pressure is out of range, refer to appropriate MANUAL A/C-HEATER article in MITCHELL domestic AIR CONDITIONING & HEATING SERVICE & REPAIR manual or check for problem using Code 66 chart or replace sensor. Refer to ENGINE PERFORMANCE.

CHART C-10, A/C CLUTCH CONTROL (2 OF 2)
3.1L – VIN T ("W" BODY)

A/C clutch control relay is energized when ECM provides a ground path through circuit No. 459 and A/C is requested. A/C clutch is delayed about 3/10 of a second after A/C is requested. This allows Idle Air Control (IAC) to adjust engine RPM for the additional load.

ECM will temporarily disengage the A/C clutch relay for calibrated times for one or more the following condition:
• Hot engine restarts.
• Wide open throttle (TPS over 90%).
• Power steering pressure high (PSPS switch open).
• Engine speed greater than 6000 RPM.
• During IAC reset.
A/C relay will remain disengaged when Code 66 is present, if pressure is out of range or when there is no A/C request signal due to an open A/C select switch circuit.

NOTE: Test numbers refer to test numbers on diagnostic charts.

1) Test determines if pressure transducer is out of range causing the A/C compressor clutch to be disengaged.
2) With engine off and field service mode activated, ECM grounds circuit No. 459, which should activate test light.

91H05586 91D05589

* SEE MITCHELL domestic AIR CONDITIONING & HEATING SERVICE & REPAIR manual

Courtesy of General Motors Corp.

Fig. 50: A/C Clutch Control Circuit Diagram & System Diagnosis (3.1L – VIN T "W" Body) (2 of 2)

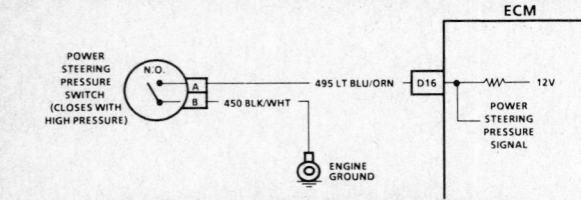

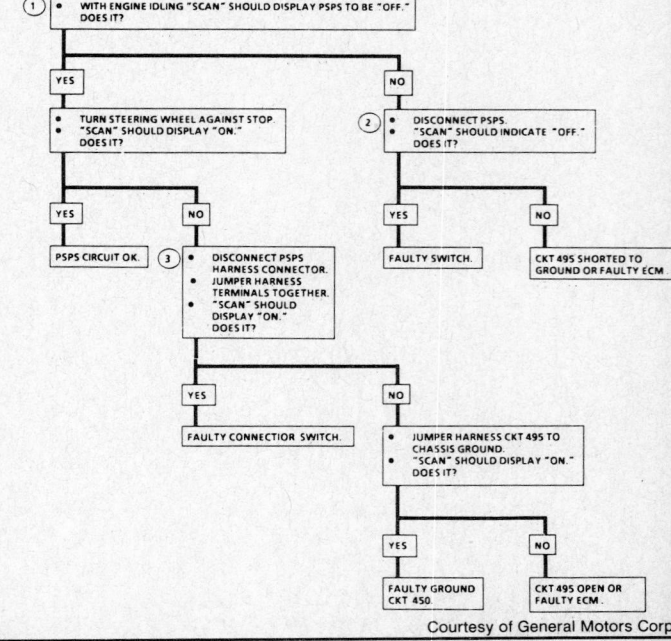

CHART C-1E, POWER STEERING PRESSURE SWITCH (PSPS) 3.1L VIN T ("W" BODY)

Power Steering Pressure Switch (PSPS) is normally open to ground. Circuit No. 495 should have near battery voltage. Power steering pressure increases as steering wheel is turned. PSPS will close (less than one volt on circuit No. 495), disengaging A/C compressor clutch and increasing idle air rate.

A PSPS that will NOT CLOSE or an open in circuit No. 495 or No. 450 may cause engine to stall when power steering load is high. A PSPS that will NOT OPEN or a short to ground in circuit No. 495, may affect engine idle and will not allow A/C compressor clutch operation.

NOTE: Test numbers refer to test numbers on diagnostic charts.

1) Different makes of "Scan" testers may display the state of PSPS switch in different ways. Refer to operation manual for your particular tester.
2) This step checks if circuit No. 495 is shorted to ground.
3) This step simulates a closed PSPS switch.

91F05590 91H05591

Courtesy of General Motors Corp.

Fig. 51: Power Steering Pressure Switch Diagnosis (3.1L – VIN T "W" Body)

1991 ENGINE COOLING
Specifications & Electric Cooling Fans — Exc. Cadillac (Cont.)

GM
5-111

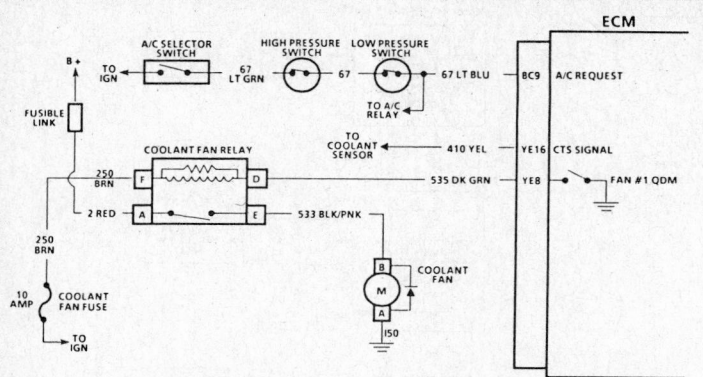

CHART C-12A, COOLING FAN FUNCTIONAL CHECK
3.3L – VIN N ("A" BODY)

Power for cooling fan motor is supplied through fusible link to terminal A on relay. The relay is energized when current flows to ground through Quad Driver Module (QDM) inside ECM.

ECM energizes cooling fan relay through ECM terminal YE8 when coolant temperature reaches 212°F (100°C). Cooling fan relay is also energized when A/C is requested.

NOTE: Test numbers refer to test numbers on diagnostic charts.

1) This output tests allows manual control of cooling fan.
2) Cooling fan should be on when A/C is requested at idle.
3) Test ensures that ECM is receiving an A/C request.

DIAGNOSTIC AIDS

If cooling fan operates normally but an overheating condition exists, check coolant temperature sensor resistance value. See Code 15 chart

91J05592   91B05593

in appropriate article in ENGINE PERFORMANCE. Replace coolant temperature sensor if resistance value is not as specified. If coolant temperature sensor resistance is okay, check cooling system.

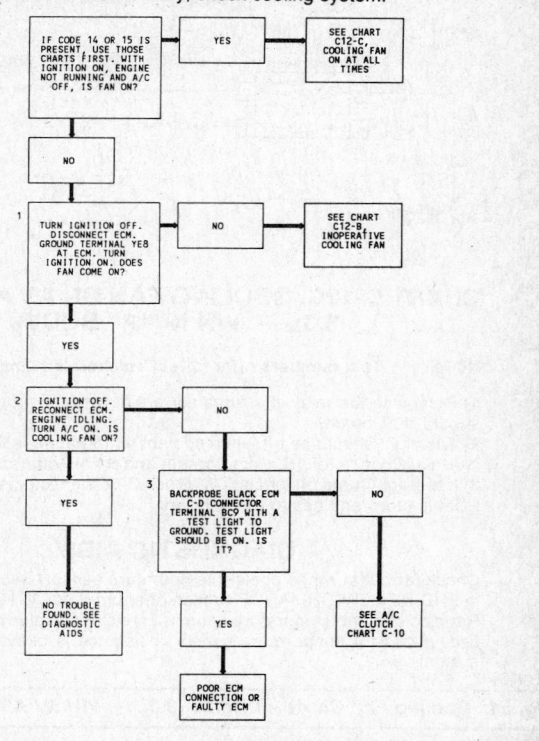

Schematic Courtesy of General Motors Corp.

Fig. 52: Cooling Fan System Functional Check (3.3L – VIN N "A" Body)

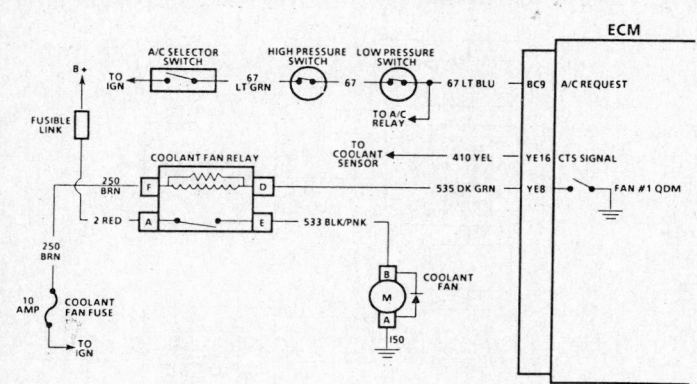

CHART C-12B, INOPERATIVE COOLING FAN
3.3L – VIN N ("A" BODY)

NOTE: Test numbers refer to test numbers on diagnostic charts.

1) Test light should be on. The F terminal is fed directly from the ignition switch.
2) This test function allows manual control of cooling fan relay. This test checks circuit No. 535.
3) Jumpering terminals A and E feeds the fan motor directly and fan should run.
4) Checks for battery voltage at cooling fan relay.

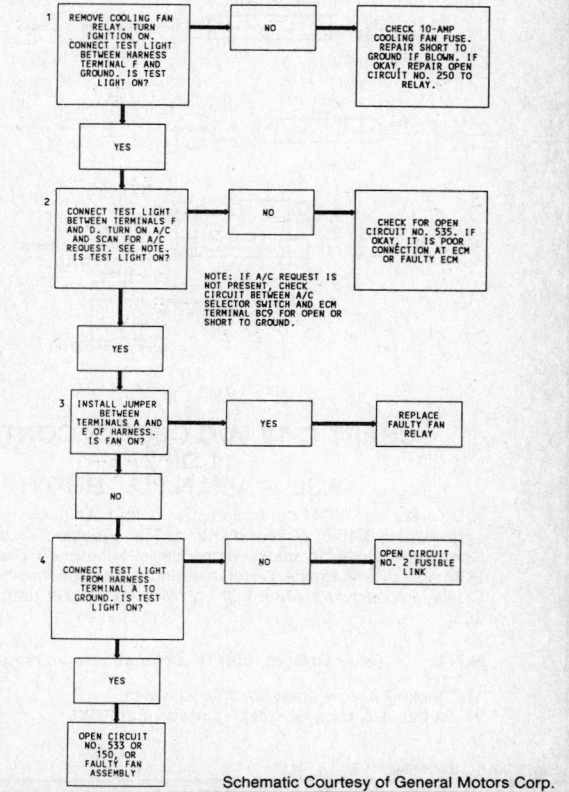

Schematic Courtesy of General Motors Corp.

91J05592   91D05594

Fig. 53: Inoperative Cooling Fan (3.3L – VIN N "A" Body)

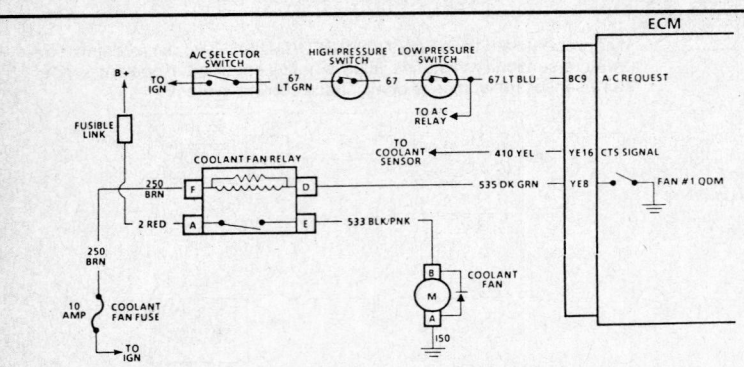

CHART C-12C, COOLING FAN ON AT ALL TIMES
3.3L – VIN N ("A" BODY)

NOTE: Test numbers refer to test numbers on diagnostic charts.

1) Removing the relay interrupts current flow to fan motor. Cooling fan should NOT be on.

2) Test light should be off when coolant temperature is less than 212°F (100°C), Code 14 or 15 is not present and A/C is off (no A/C request).

3) If test light turns off when ECM Black C-D connector is disconnected, ECM is faulty and has to be replaced.

DIAGNOSTIC AIDS

Check for out of range coolant temperature sensor. See Code 14 chart in ENGINE PERFORMANCE section of appropriate MITCHELL manual. Replace coolant temperature sensor if resistance value is not as specified. If coolant temperature sensor resistance is okay, check cooling system.

91J05592   91G05595

Schematic Courtesy of General Motors Corp.

Fig. 54: Cooling Fan On At All Times (3.3L – VIN N "A" Body)

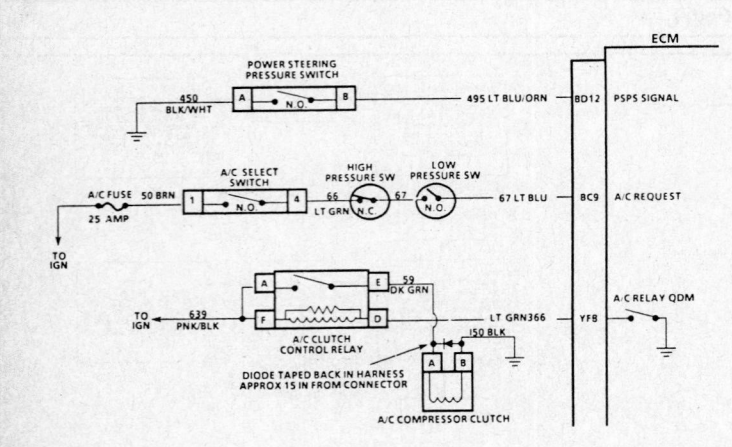

CHART C-10, A/C CLUTCH CONTROL
(1 OF 2)
3.3L – VIN N ("A" BODY)

A/C relay is ECM-controlled to delay A/C compressor clutch engagement 3/10 of a second after A/C is requested. This allows idle Air Control (IAC) valve to adjust engine idle RPM before A/C clutch engages. ECM also disengages A/C clutch during wide open throttle operation. A/C relay is energized when ECM provides a ground path for circuit No. 366.

NOTE: Test numbers refer to test numbers on diagnostic charts.

1) Checks A/C low pressure cutout switch.
2) Verifies A/C request signal is present at ECM.

90B10018   91I05596

Schematic Courtesy of General Motors Corp.

Fig. 55: A/C Clutch Control Circuit Diagram & System Diagnosis (3.3L – VIN N "A" Body) (1 of 2)

1991 ENGINE COOLING
Specifications & Electric Cooling Fans – Exc. Cadillac (Cont.)

GM
5-113

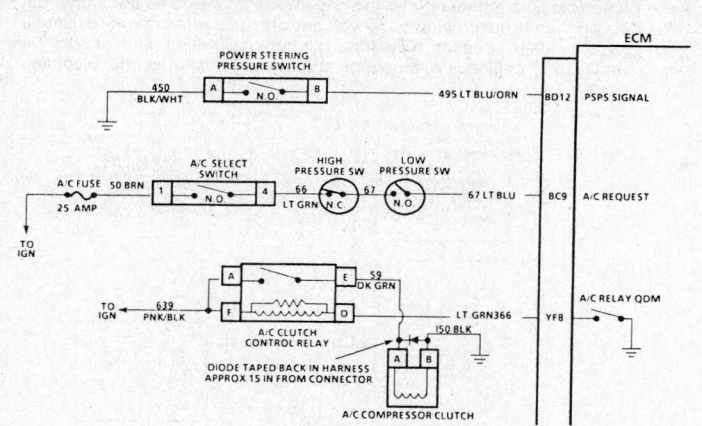

CHART C-10, A/C CLUTCH CONTROL
(2 OF 2)
3.3L – VIN N ("A" BODY)

NOTE: Test numbers refer to test numbers on diagnostic charts.

3) Test light illumination verifies integrity of circuits No. 366, No. 639 and QDM B in the ECM.

4) Test light illumination verifies integrity of circuit No. 639 to terminal A of A/C relay.

5) Test by-passes relay to determine whether relay, compressor clutch or clutch wiring is faulty.

90B10018   91A05597

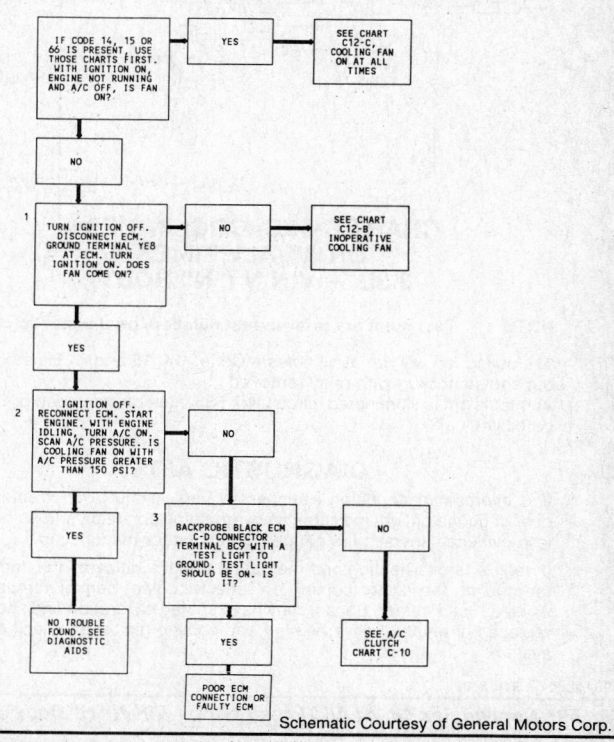

Schematic Courtesy of General Motors Corp.

Fig. 56: A/C Clutch Control Circuit Diagram & System Diagnosis (3.3L – VIN N "A" Body) (2 of 2)

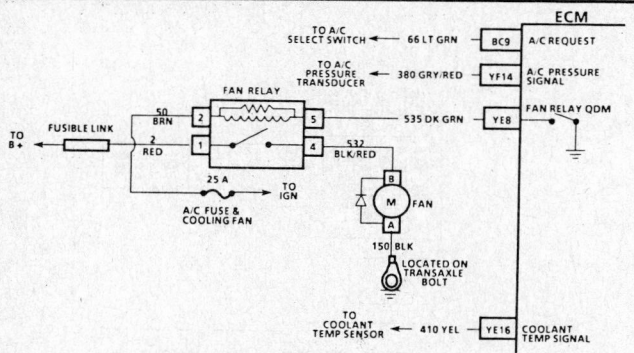

CHART C-12A, COOLING FAN
FUNCTIONAL CHECK
3.3L – VIN N ("N" BODY)

Voltage to cooling fan motor is supplied to relay terminal No. 1. Ignition voltage to energize relay is supplied to relay terminal No. 2. When ECM grounds circuit No. 535, relay is energized and cooling fan is turned on. When engine is running, ECM will energize cooling fan relay when Code 14 or 15 is present or when one of the following conditions are met:
- A/C is requested and A/C pressure is more than 150 psi (11 kg/cm²).
- Coolant temperature is greater than 212°F (100°C).

NOTE: Test numbers refer to test numbers on diagnostic charts.

1) This test manually energizes cooling fan, testing relay, fan motor and relative circuits.

2) The fan should be running when A/C is requested and A/C pressure is more than 150 psi (11 kg/cm²).

DIAGNOSTIC AIDS

Incorrect cooling fan operation or overheating may be caused by an out of calibration coolant temperature sensor or faulty A/C pressure sensor.

Compare coolant temperature displayed on "Scan" tester with actual coolant temperature. Check coolant temperature sensor resistance. Replace if resistance is not as specified.

Compare A/C pressure displayed on "Scan" tester with actual A/C system pressure. Replace A/C pressure sensor if found defective.

90A10017   91C05598

Schematic Courtesy of General Motors Corp.

Fig. 57: Cooling Fan System Functional Check (3.3L – VIN N "N" Body)

If vehicle is overheating and the gauge or light indicates the same, but cooling fan is not coming on, check coolant sensor temperature using a "Scan" tester. Sensor may have shifted calibration and should be replaced. If engine is overheating and cooling fan is on, check cooling system.

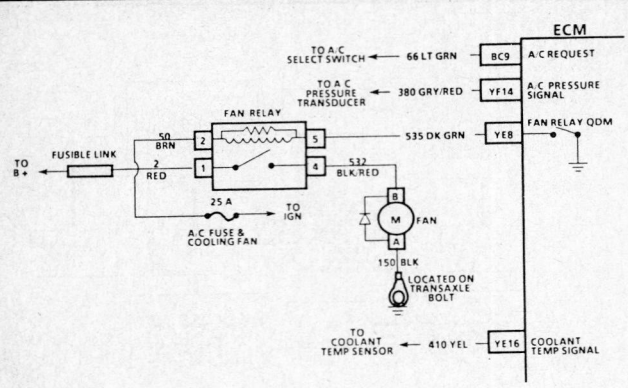

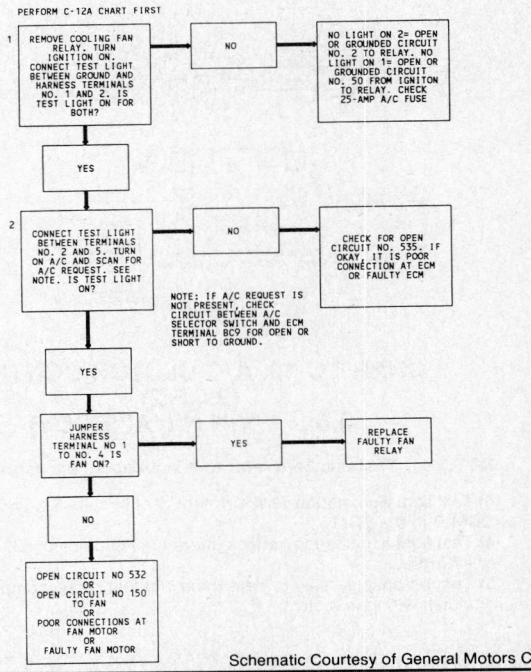

CHART C-12B, INOPERATIVE COOLING FAN
3.3L – VIN N ("N" BODY)

NOTE: **Test numbers refer to test numbers on diagnostic charts.**

1) Cooling fan relay terminal No. 2 should have battery voltage when ignition is on. Cooling fan relay terminal No. 1 is connected directly to battery voltage.

2) Test light should be on when A/C is requested. If light is not on, ECM may not be seeing A/C request, circuit No. 535 may be open or ECM maybe faulty.

DIAGNOSTIC AIDS

If an overheating condition is suspected, verify if this is due to actual boil-over. If gauge or light indicates an overheating condition and no boilover is in evidence, inspect the gauge/light circuit for malfunction.

90A10017   91E05599

Schematic Courtesy of General Motors Corp.

Fig. 58: Inoperative Cooling Fan (3.3L – VIN N "N" Body)

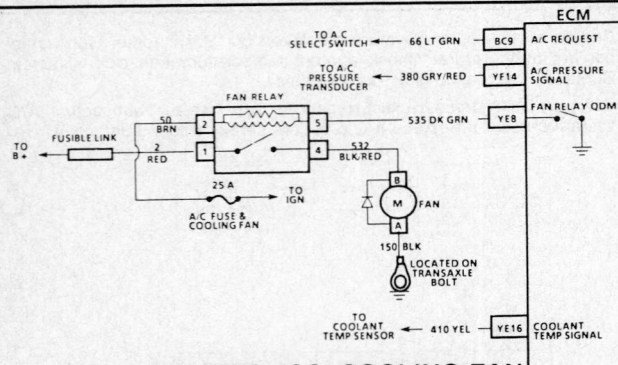

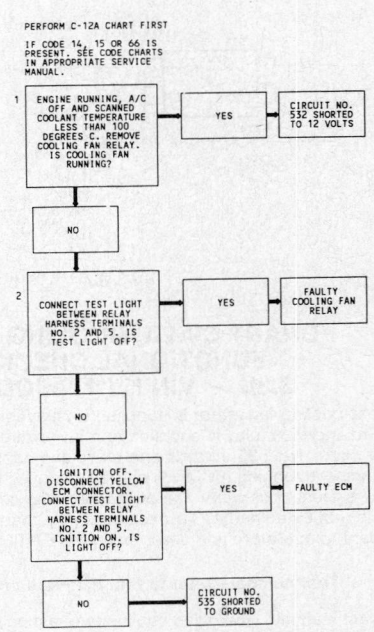

CHART C-12C, COOLING FAN
ON AT ALL TIMES
3.3L – VIN N ("N" BODY)

NOTE: **Test numbers refer to test numbers on diagnostic charts.**

1) Cooling fan will run at all times if Codes 14, 15 and/or 66 is present, but should not run with relay removed.

2) If test light is illuminated, circuit No. 535 must be grounded or ECM is defective.

DIAGNOSTIC AIDS

If an overheating condition is suspected, verify if this is due to actual boil-over. If gauge or light indicates an overheating condition and no boilover is in evidence, inspect the gauge/light circuit for malfunction.

If vehicle is overheating and the gauge or light indicates the same, but the cooling fan is not coming on, check coolant sensor temperature using a "Scan" tester. Sensor may have shifted calibration and should be replaced. If engine is overheating and cooling fan is on, check cooling system.

90A10017   91I05600

Schematic Courtesy of General Motors Corp.

Fig. 59: Cooling Fan On At All Times (3.3L – VIN N "N" Body)

1991 ENGINE COOLING
Specifications & Electric Cooling Fans – Exc. Cadillac (Cont.)

GM
5-115

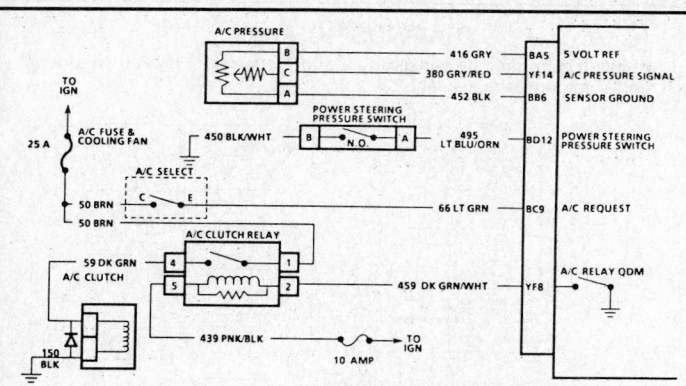

CHART C-10, A/C CLUTCH CONTROL
(1 OF 2)
3.3L – VIN N ("N" BODY)

The A/C clutch control relay is energized when ECM provides a ground path through circuit No. 459 and when A/C is requested. A/C compressor clutch engagement is delayed about 3/10 of a second after A/C is commanded. This allows Idle Air Control (IAC) valve to adjust engine idle RPM before A/C clutch engages.

ECM will temporarily disengage A/C clutch for a calibrated time for one or more of the following conditions:

- Hot engine restart.
- Wide open throttle (TPS over 90 percent).
- Power steering pressure high (PSPS closed).
- Engine RPM greater than 6000 RPM.
- During IAC valve reset.

A/C clutch relay will remain de-energized when a Code 66 is present, there is no A/C request signal or ECM detects high or low refrigerant pressure.

NOTE: Test numbers refer to test numbers on diagnostic charts.

1) This test determines whether or not ECM is receiving an A/C request from the control head.

2) This step determines if ECM is attempting to turn on A/C relay.

90J04267   91A05601

DIAGNOSTIC AIDS

If complaint was insufficient A/C cooling, problem may be caused by an inoperative cooling fan. See appropriate CHART C-12 in this article.

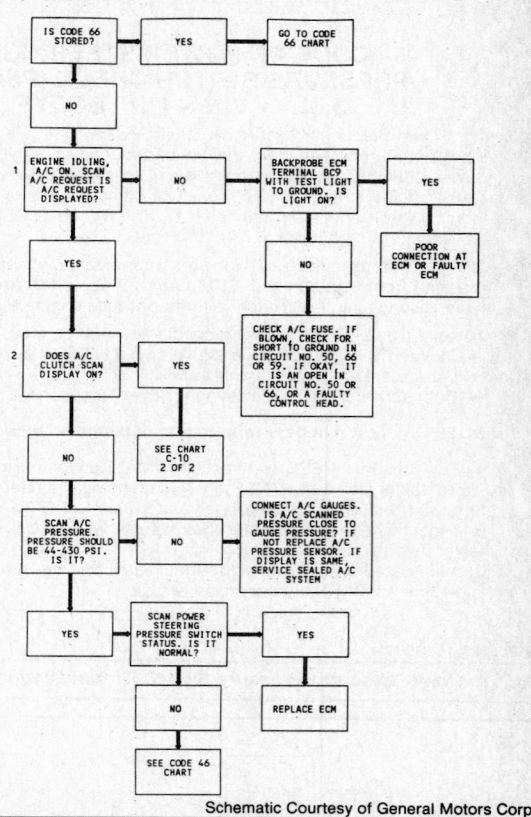

Schematic Courtesy of General Motors Corp.

Fig. 60: A/C Clutch Control Circuit Diagram & System Diagnosis (3.3L – VIN N "N" Body) (1 of 2)

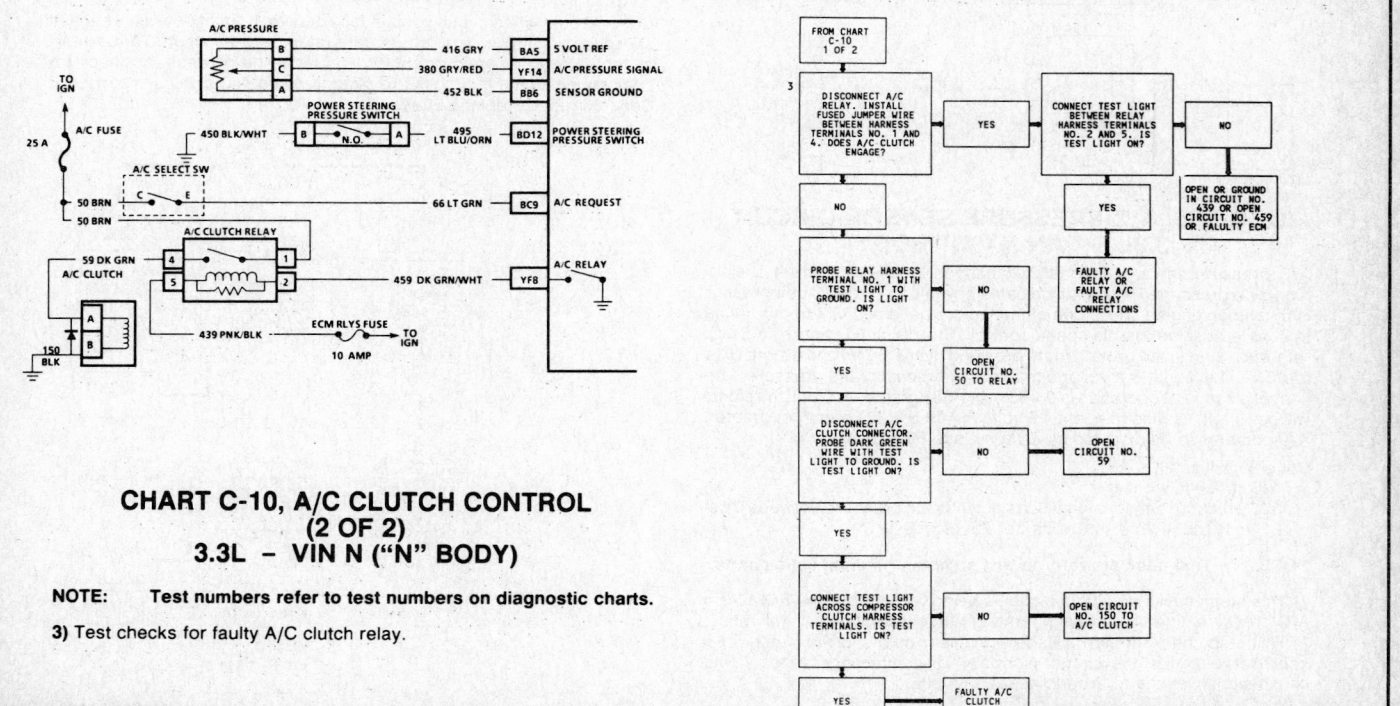

CHART C-10, A/C CLUTCH CONTROL
(2 OF 2)
3.3L – VIN N ("N" BODY)

NOTE: Test numbers refer to test numbers on diagnostic charts.

3) Test checks for faulty A/C clutch relay.

90J04267   91C05602

Schematic Courtesy of General Motors Corp.

Fig. 61: A/C Clutch Control Circuit Diagram & System Diagnosis (3.3L – VIN N "N" Body) (2 of 2)

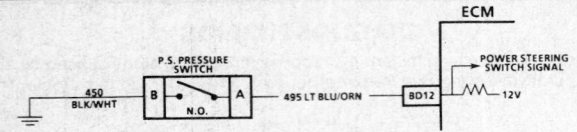

CODE 46, POWER STEERING PRESSURE SWITCH CHECK (PSPS) 3.3L – VIN N ("N" BODY)

The Power Steering Pressure Switch (PSPS) is incorporated as an ECM input signal, representing parasitic load placed on engine during high power steering demand periods such as parking. Heavy loads may cause engine to stall. Therefore, ECM compensates by automatically increasing idle speed through the IAC valve whenever PSPS closes and low voltage is monitored at ECM terminal BD12.

This low voltage indicates a high pressure within power steering system resulting from high demand. ECM turns voltage off to A/C compressor relay, disengaging A/C clutch to further reduce engine load.

To set a Code 46, the following conditions must be met:
- Closed PSPS. Low voltage signal on circuit No. 495.
- Vehicle speed greater than 40 MPH.
- Both above conditions existing for over 15 seconds.

NOTE: Test numbers refer to test numbers on diagnostic charts.

1) Test ensures PSPS is open (NORMAL) under normal conditions. "Scan" tester may display OFF or ON, depending on tester manufacturer.
2) If the PSPS is faulty, display should switch to NORMAL when PSPS is disconnected. "Scan" tester may display OFF or ON, depending on tester manufacturer.
3) A jumpered switch connector should indicate high pressure if circuit is okay. If so, PSPS or connection is faulty.

91E05603 91G05604

DIAGNOSTIC AIDS

An intermittent may be caused by a poor connection, broken wire or rubbed-through wire insulation.

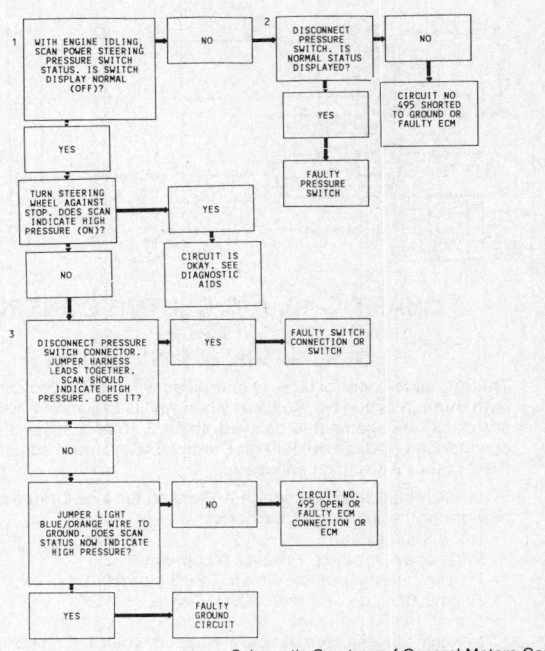

Schematic Courtesy of General Motors Corp.

Fig. 62: Power Steering Pressure Switch Circuit Diagnosis (3.3L – VIN N "N" Body)

CODE 66, A/C PRESSURE SENSOR CIRCUIT 3.3L – VIN N ("N" BODY)

A/C pressure sensor responds to changes in A/C refrigerant system high-side pressure. This input indicates how much load A/C compressor is putting on engine and is one of the factors used by ECM to determine IAC valve position for idle speed control. The circuit consists of a 5-volt reference signal and ground, both provided by the ECM, and a signal line to ECM. The signal is a voltage that is proportional to the pressure. The sensor's range of operation is 0-468 psi (0-33 kg/cm²). At 0 psi, the signal will be .1 volt, varying to about 4.9 volts at 449 psi (32 kg/cm²) or greater. A/C compressor is disabled by ECM if Code 66 is present.

Code 66 will set if:
- A/C request is on.
- A/C pressure sensor signal does not indicate pressure between 0 psi (.1 volt) and 449 psi (4.9 volts) for 25 seconds.

NOTE: Test numbers refer to test numbers on diagnostic charts.

1) This step checks if voltage signal is being received by the ECM from A/C pressure sensor. Normal operating range is between .1-4.9 volts.
2) This step checks if high voltage signal is from a shorted sensor or a short to voltage in the circuit. Normally, disconnecting sensor would cause signal voltage to drop to near zero volts.

3) This step checks if low voltage signal is from the sensor or circuit. Using a jumper wire between sensor signal circuit No. 380 and 5 volts checks the circuit, connections and the ECM.
4) This step checks if low voltage signal was due to an open in the sensor 5-volt reference circuit, since the prior step eliminated the pressure switch.

DIAGNOSTIC AIDS

Code 66 sets when signal voltage falls outside normal possible range of sensor and is not due to a refrigerant system problem. If problem is intermittent, check for open or shorted circuit in the harness, or check for poor connections. If circuits are okay, replace A/C pressure sensor. If Code 66 resets, replace ECM.

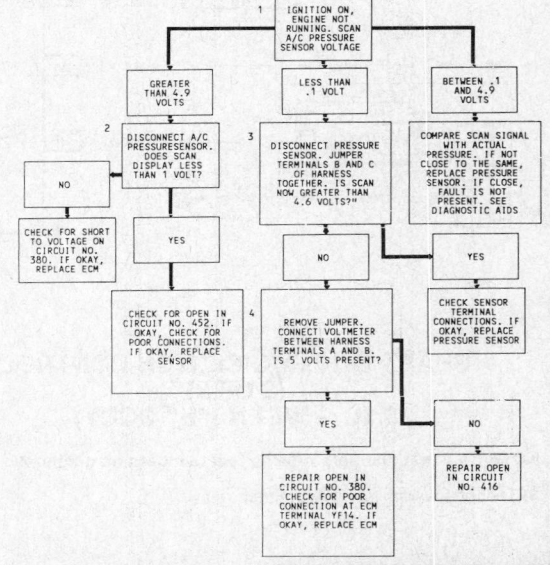

91J05605 91B05606

Schematic Courtesy of General Motors Corp.

Fig. 63: A/C Pressure Sensor Circuit Diagnosis (3.3L – VIN N "N" Body)

1991 ENGINE COOLING
Specifications & Electric Cooling Fans – Exc. Cadillac (Cont.)

GM
5-117

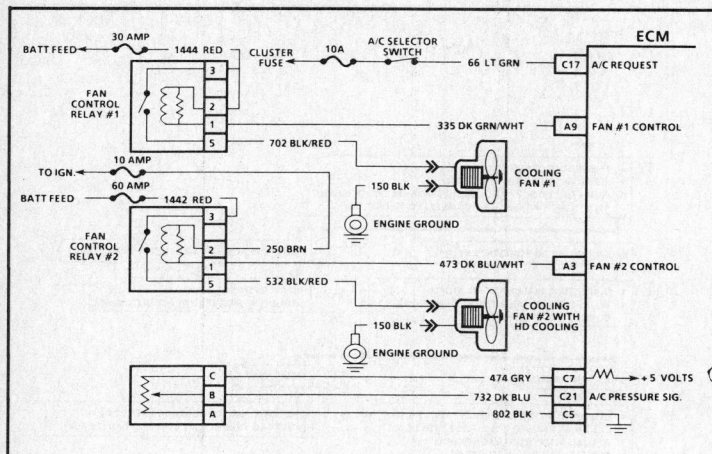

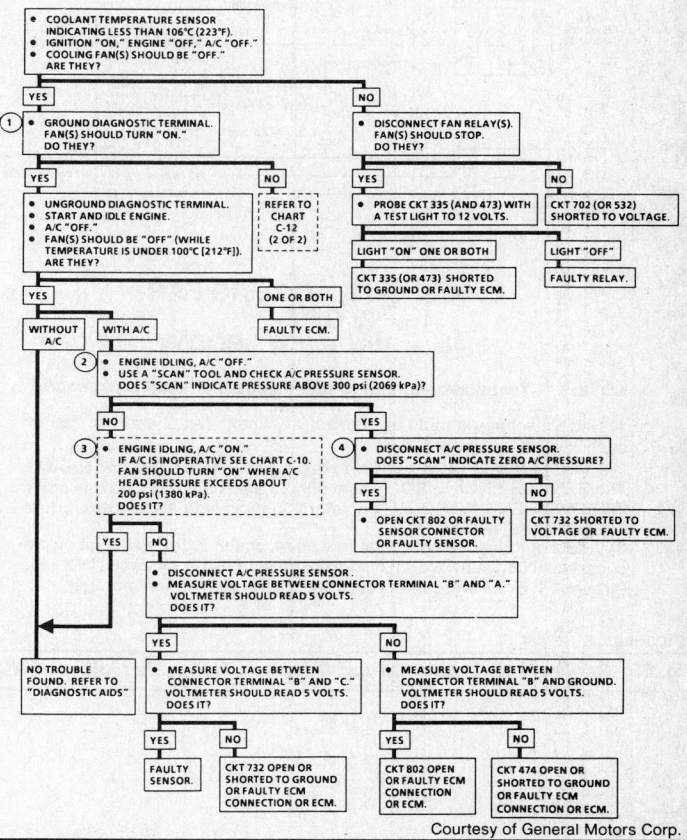

CHART C-12, COOLING FAN
(1 OF 2)
3.4L – VIN X ("W" Body)

The primary and secondary cooling fans are controlled by ECM based on inputs from coolant temperature sensor, A/C control switches, vehicle speed and the state of A/C pressure sensor. ECM controls the fan(s) by grounding circuit No. 335 and/or circuit No. 473, which energizes fan control relay(s). Battery voltage is then supplied to fan motor.

ECM grounds circuit No. 335 and/or circuit No. 473, when coolant temperature is more than 223°F (106°C), or when A/C has requested and A/C pressure is about 200 psi (14 kg/cm²). Once ECM turns relay on, ECM will keep it on for a minimum of 30 seconds or until vehicle speed exceeds 70 MPH (40 MPH secondary fan). If Code 14 or 15 is present or when ECM in the back-up mode, primary cooling fan will run all the time.

NOTE: Test numbers refer to test numbers on diagnostic charts.

1) With ALDL diagnostic terminal grounded, cooling fan control driver(s) will close, energizing fan control relay(s).
2) If A/C pressure is greater than 300 psi (21 kg/cm²) or when circuit is open, cooling fan would run whenever A/C is requested.
3) With A/C clutch engaged and A/C pressure sensor operating properly, cooling fan should run when pressure exceeds 200 psi (14 kg/cm²). This signal should cause ECM to energize fan control relay(s).
4) This test determines of A/C pressure sensor is faulty or if ECM or circuitry is faulty.

DIAGNOSTIC AIDS

If an overheating condition is suspected, verify if this is due to actual boilover. If gauge or light indicates an overheat condition, and no boilover is in evidence, inspect the gauge/light circuit for malfunction.

If vehicle is overheating and the gauge or light indicates the same, but the cooling fan is not coming on, check coolant sensor temperature using a "Scan" tester. Sensor may have shifted calibration and should be replaced. If engine is overheating and cooling fan is on, check cooling system.

Courtesy of General Motors Corp.

91D05607 91F05608

Fig. 64: *Cooling Fan Control Circuit Diagram & System Diagnosis (3.4L – VIN X "W" Body) (1 of 2)*

GM
5-118

1991 ENGINE COOLING
Specifications & Electric Cooling Fans – Exc. Cadillac (Cont.)

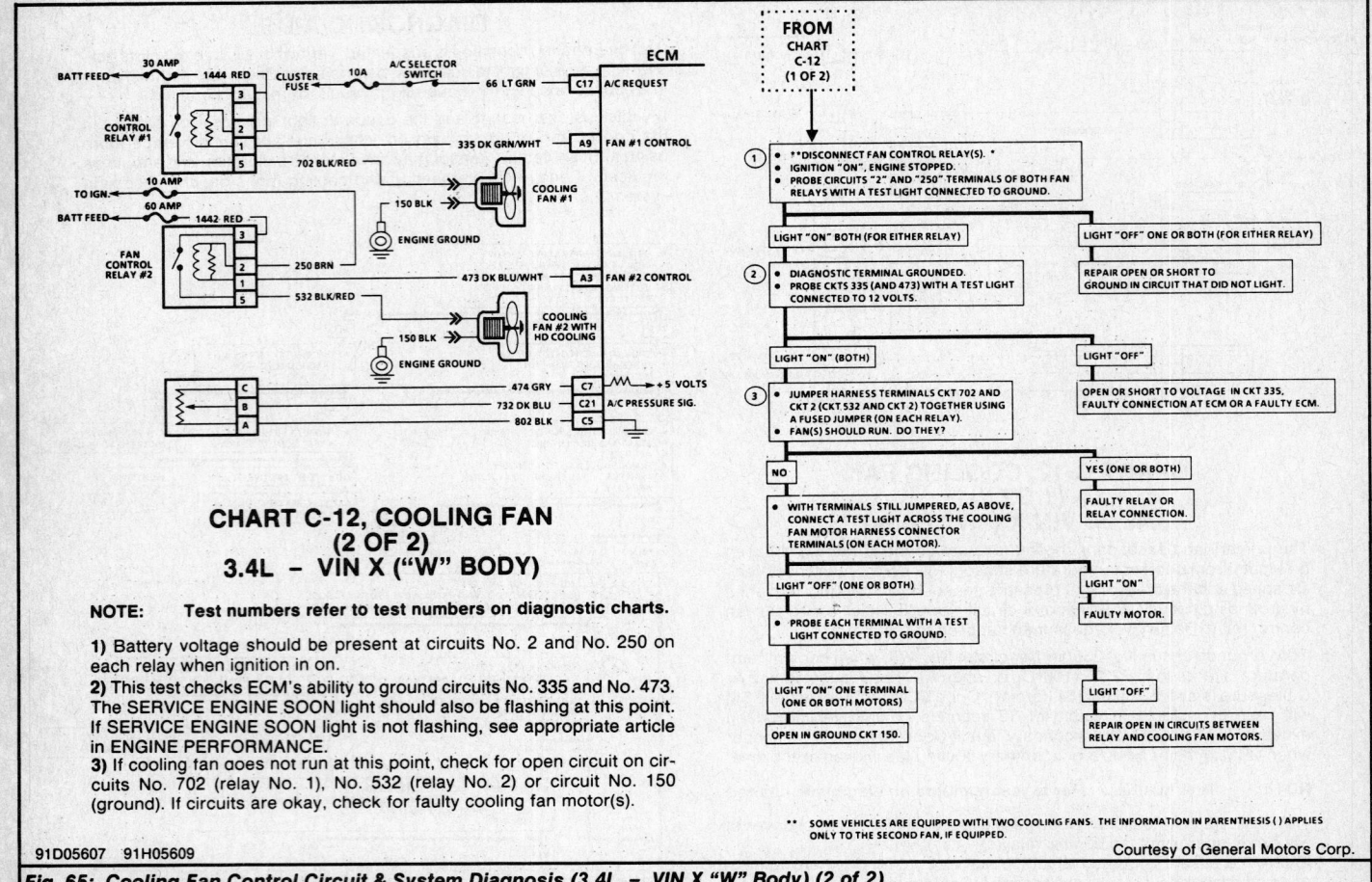

CHART C-12, COOLING FAN
(2 OF 2)
3.4L – VIN X ("W" BODY)

NOTE: Test numbers refer to test numbers on diagnostic charts.

1) Battery voltage should be present at circuits No. 2 and No. 250 on each relay when ignition in on.

2) This test checks ECM's ability to ground circuits No. 335 and No. 473. The SERVICE ENGINE SOON light should also be flashing at this point. If SERVICE ENGINE SOON light is not flashing, see appropriate article in ENGINE PERFORMANCE.

3) If cooling fan does not run at this point, check for open circuit on circuits No. 702 (relay No. 1), No. 532 (relay No. 2) or circuit No. 150 (ground). If circuits are okay, check for faulty cooling fan motor(s).

91D05607   91H05609

** SOME VEHICLES ARE EQUIPPED WITH TWO COOLING FANS. THE INFORMATION IN PARENTHESIS ( ) APPLIES ONLY TO THE SECOND FAN, IF EQUIPPED.

Courtesy of General Motors Corp.

Fig. 65: Cooling Fan Control Circuit & System Diagnosis (3.4L – VIN X "W" Body) (2 of 2)

1991 ENGINE COOLING
Specifications & Electric Cooling Fans – Exc. Cadillac (Cont.)

GM
5-119

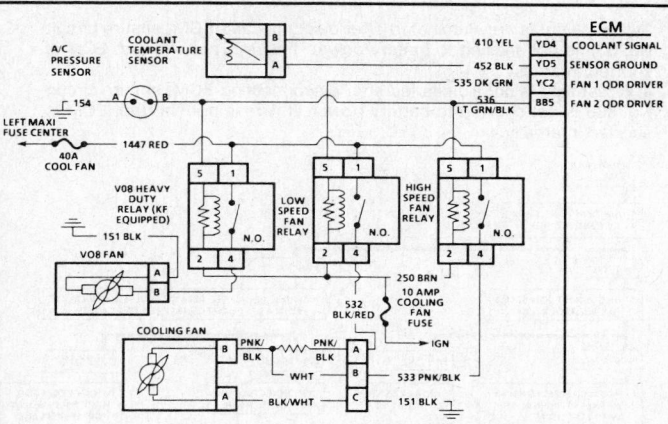

CHART C-12A, COOLING FAN FUNCTIONAL CHECK
3.8L – VIN C ("H" BODY)

Power for fan motor comes from 40A fuse to terminal No. 1 of low and high speed cooling fan relays. Relays are energized when current is grounded through the ECM quad-drivers.

Low speed relay is energized by ECM through ECM terminal YC2 when coolant temperature reaches 214°F (101°C). As long as ignition switch is on, cooling fan will continue to run.

High speed relay is energized by ECM or A/C pressure switch. If A/C refrigerant pressure reaches 275 psi (19 kg/cm²) or when coolant temperature reaches 226°F (108°C), high speed fan relay is energized.

NOTE: Test numbers refer to test numbers on diagnostic charts.

1) Grounding ALDL diagnostic test connector will cause ECM to ground circuit No. 536. Cooling fan should run at high speed.
2) Removing ground from ALDL diagnostic connector and disconnecting coolant temperature sensor connector will cause ECM to read coolant temperature of -38°F (-39°C). ECM will richen fuel mixture. "Scan" tester should display a coolant temperature of -38°F (-39°C). Cooling fan should run at low speed and "Scan" tester should display "Fan 1 On".
3) Jumper coolant temperature sensor wires together. "Scan" tester should display coolant temperature of 304°F (151°C). "Fan 1" should be displayed. "Fan 2" and high speed fan should come on momentarily when ignition switch is cycled from on to off.

4) Jumpering A/C pressure switch harness will cause cooling fan(s) to run at high speed.
5) This step checks if ECM monitors coolant temperature sensor signal properly. Anytime coolant temperature exceeds 214°F (101°C), ECM should turn on low speed fan by grounding circuit No. 535, unless vehicle speed exceeds 35 MPH. If engine temperature continues to rise above 226°F (108°C), high speed fan should come on when engine is running. A hot soak condition with key on, engine off will not activate cooling fan.

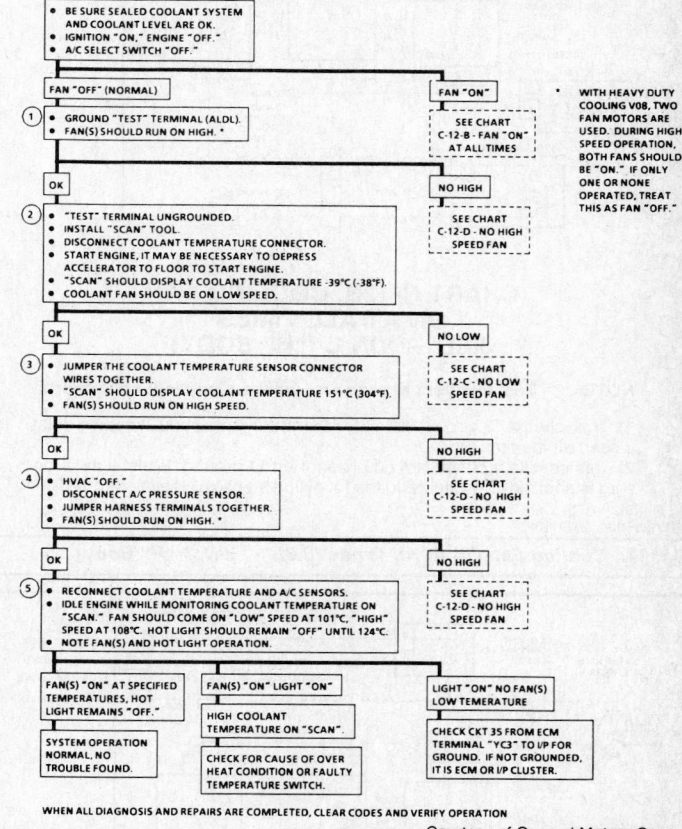

WHEN ALL DIAGNOSIS AND REPAIRS ARE COMPLETED, CLEAR CODES AND VERIFY OPERATION

Courtesy of General Motors Corp.

91A05620   91C05621

Fig. 66: *Cooling Fan System Functional Check (3.8L – VIN C "H" Body)*

GM
5-120

1991 ENGINE COOLING
Specifications & Electric Cooling Fans – Exc. Cadillac (Cont.)

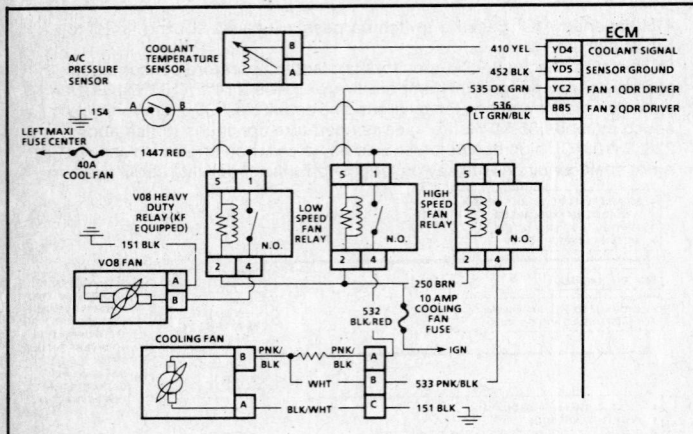

3) If test light is not illuminated after disconnecting ECM, ensure circuit No. 535 is not shorted to battery power. If wire is not shorted, ECM is shorted internally.

4) If test light is not illuminated after disconnecting ECM, ensure circuit No. 536 is not shorted to battery power. If wire is not shorted, ECM is shorted internally.

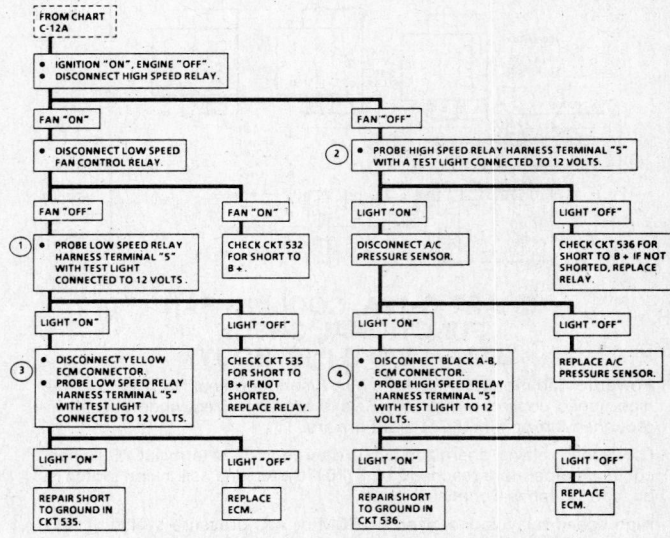

CHART C-12B, COOLING FAN ON AT ALL TIMES
3.8L – VIN C ("H" BODY)

NOTE: Test numbers refer to test numbers on diagnostic charts.

1) This checks if circuit No. 535 is shorted to ground, keeping relay closed all the time.

2) This checks if circuit No. 536 is shorted to ground. If test light is on, wire is shorted to ground and the following steps will isolate shorted circuit.

91A05620   91E05622

"AFTER REPAIRS," CONFIRM "CLOSED LOOP" OPERATION AND NO "SERVICE ENGINE SOON" LIGHT.

Courtesy of General Motors Corp.

Fig. 67: Cooling Fan On At All Times (3.8L – VIN C "H" Body)

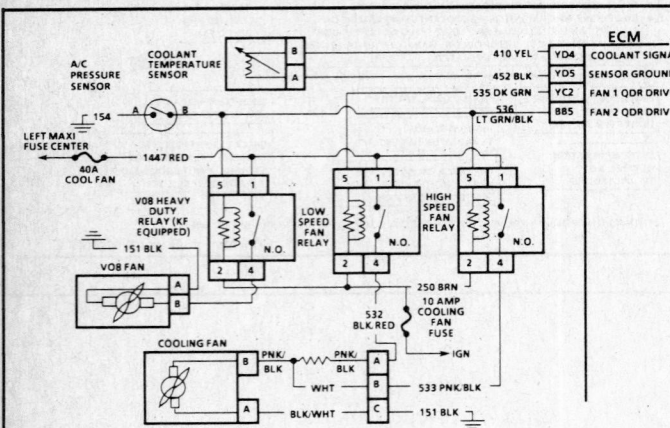

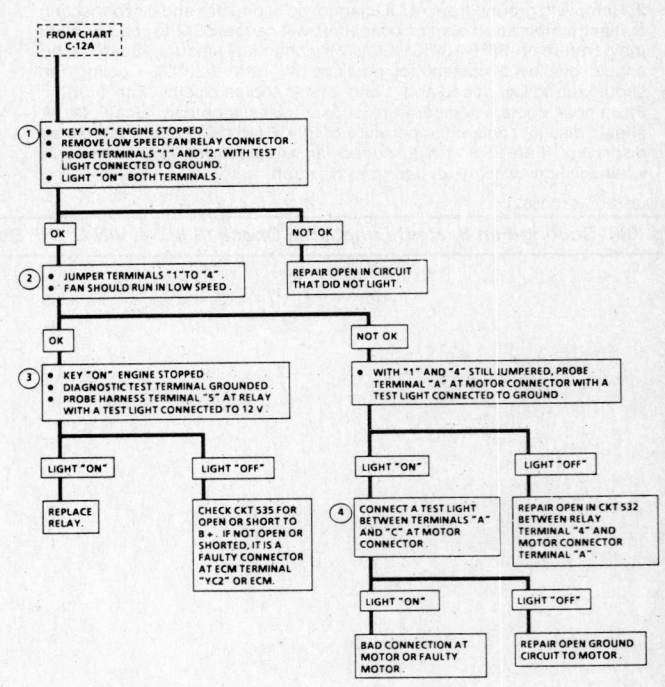

CHART C-12C, COOLING FAN NO LOW SPEED FAN
3.8L – VIN C ("H" BODY)

NOTE: Test numbers refer to test numbers on diagnostic charts.

1) Check for battery voltage at relay connector.

2) Using jumper wire to connect terminals No. 1 and No. 4 by-passes relay. Cooling fan should run if connectors and cooling fan motor are okay.

3) Grounding ALDL diagnostic connector should cause ECM to ground circuit No. 535. Test light should illuminate at this point, if ECM is good and circuit No. 535 is not open.

4) This checks for battery voltage and ground circuit to cooling fan motor. Test light illuminated at this point indicates a faulty cooling fan motor connection or a faulty cooling fan motor.

91A05620   91G05623

"AFTER REPAIRS," CONFIRM "CLOSED LOOP" OPERATION AND NO "SERVICE ENGINE SOON" LIGHT.

Courtesy of General Motors Corp.

Fig. 68: No Low Speed Cooling Fan (3.8L – VIN C "H" Body)

1991 ENGINE COOLING
Specifications & Electric Cooling Fans – Exc. Cadillac (Cont.)

GM
5-121

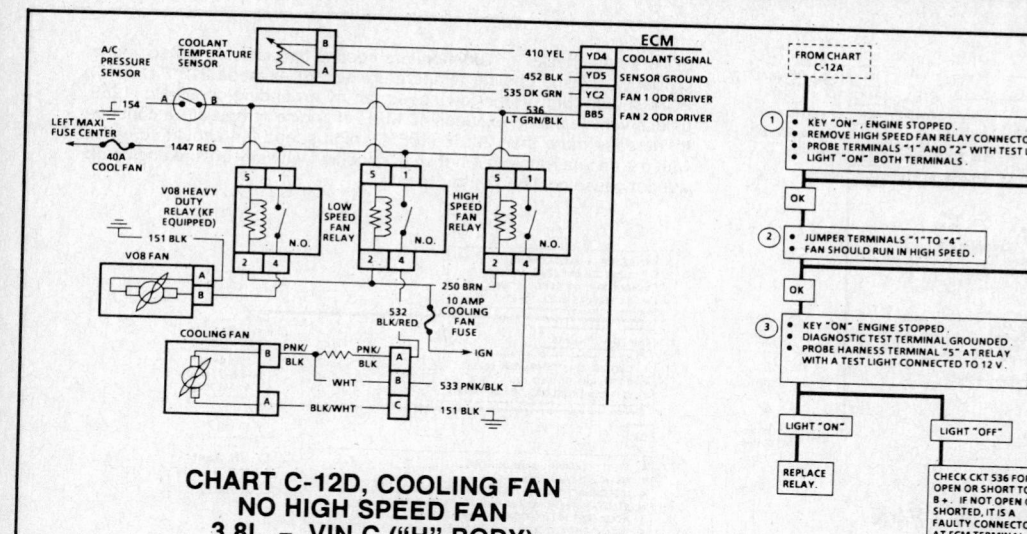

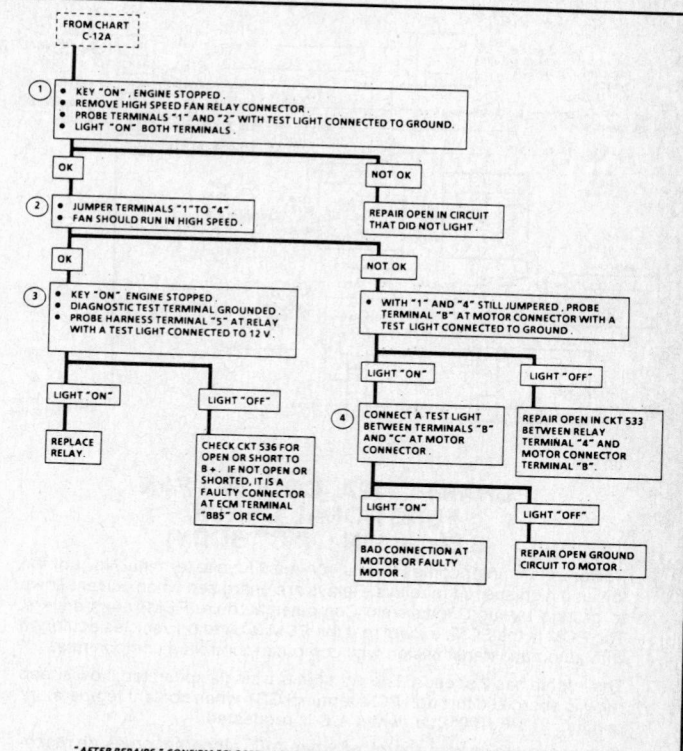

CHART C-12D, COOLING FAN
NO HIGH SPEED FAN
3.8L – VIN C ("H" BODY)

NOTE: Test numbers refer to test numbers on diagnostic charts.

1) With ignition switch on, battery voltage should be present at harness terminal No. 2. Test light should be on.
2) Using jumper wire to connect harness terminals No. 1 and No. 4 by-passes relay. If fan runs, relay is faulty.
3) Checks circuit No. 536 back to ECM. If circuit No. 536 is okay, relay is faulty.
4) Checks wiring to cooling fan motor. If wiring is okay, check connections and ground or check for a defective cooling fan motor.

91A05620   91I05624

Fig. 69: *No High Speed Cooling Fan (3.8L – VIN C "H" Body)*

"AFTER REPAIRS," CONFIRM "CLOSED LOOP" OPERATION AND NO "SERVICE ENGINE SOON" LIGHT.

Courtesy of General Motors Corp.

GM
5-122

1991 ENGINE COOLING
Specifications & Electric Cooling Fans – Exc. Cadillac (Cont.)

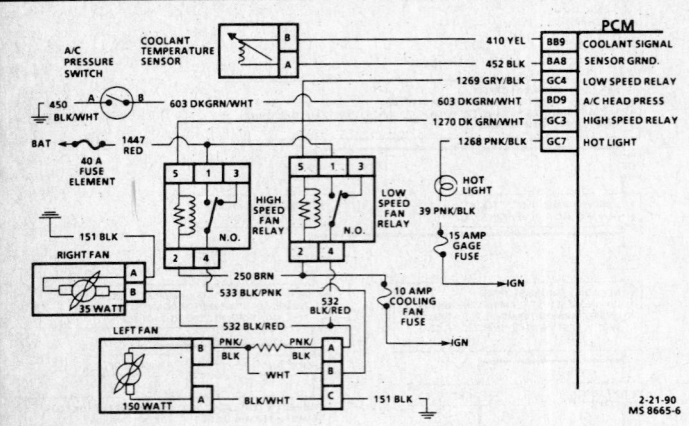

**CHART C-12A, COOLING FAN
FUNCTIONAL CHECK
3.8L – VIN L ("C" BODY)**

Power to fan motor comes from a 40A maxi fuse to terminal No. 1 of the low and high speed fan relays. Relays are energized when current flows to ground through Powertrain Computer Module (PCM) quad-drivers. The PCM is the ECM, except that the PCM is used on vehicles equipped with automatic transmission with computer-controlled components.

The left fan has 2 speeds. The right fan is a single speed fan. Low speed relay is energized through PCM terminal GC4 when coolant temperature reaches 212°F (100°C) or when A/C is requested.

High speed fan relay is energized when A/C refrigerant pressure reaches 210 psi (15 kg/cm²) or coolant temperature reaches 226°F (108°C).

NOTE: Test numbers refer to test numbers on diagnostic charts.

1) Grounding ALDL test connector will cause PCM to ground circuit No. 1270. Cooling fans should run at high speed.
2) Removing ground from ALDL test connector and disconnecting the coolant temperature sensor connector will cause PCM to read coolant temperature of -38°F (-39°C) and cause a rich fuel mixture. "Scan" tester should display coolant temperature of -38°F (-39°C), coolant fans should run at low speed and "Scan" tester should display "FAN 1 ON".
3) When using jumper to connect coolant temperature sensor wires together, "Scan" tester should display coolant temperature of 304°F (151°C). Both fans should be at high speed when ignition switch is cycled from off to on.
4) Jumpering A/C pressure switch harness will cause cooling fans to run at high speed.

5) This step checks if PCM monitors cooling temperature sensor signal properly. Anytime coolant temperature sensor exceeds 212°F (100°C), PCM should turn on the low speed fan by grounding circuit No. 1269, unless vehicle speed exceeds 40 MPH. If engine temperature continue to increase more than 226°F (108°C), high speed fan should come on with the engine running. A hot soak condition with key on and engine off will not cause cooling fan to operate.

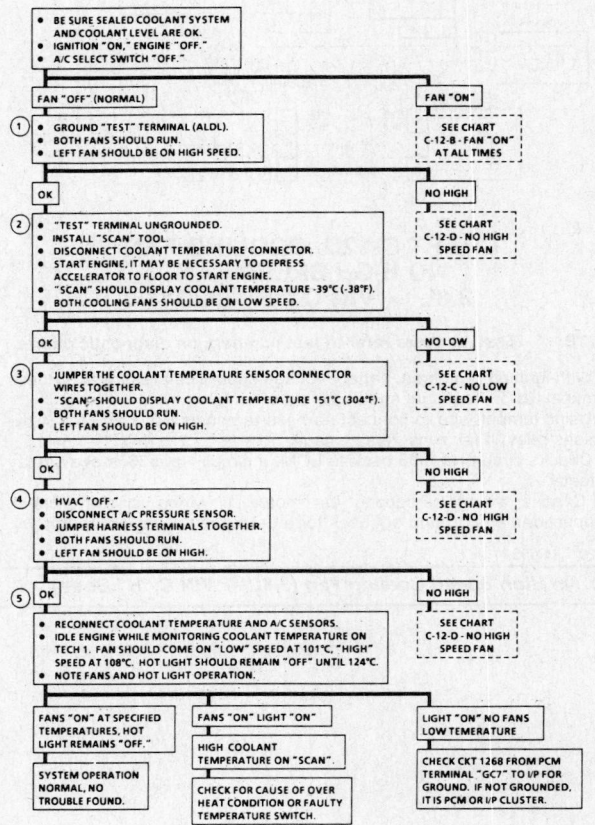

"AFTER REPAIRS," CONFIRM *"CLOSED LOOP"* OPERATION AND NO *"SERVICE ENGINE SOON"* LIGHT.

91B05625   91D05626

Courtesy of General Motors Corp.

Fig. 70: Cooling Fan System Functional Check (3.8L – VIN L "C" Body)

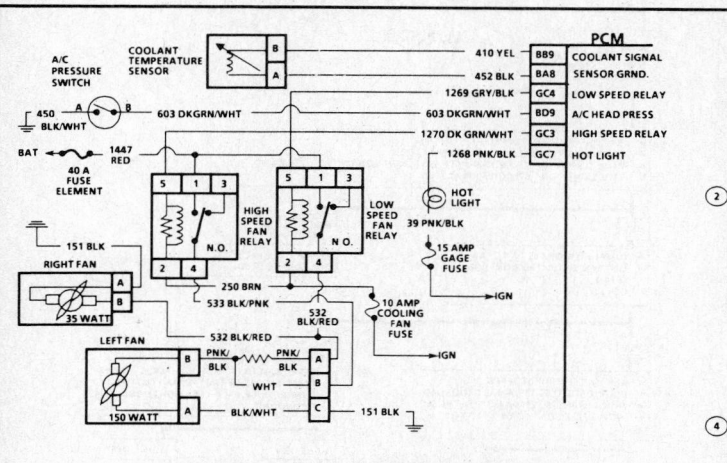

CHART C-12B, COOLING FAN ON AT ALL TIMES
3.8L – VIN L ("C" BODY)

NOTE: Test numbers refer to test numbers on diagnostic charts.

1) This checks if circuit No. 1269 is shorted to ground, keeping relay closed at all times.

2) This checks if circuit No. 1270 is shorted to ground. An illuminated test light indicates wire is shorted to ground, and the following steps will isolate shorted circuit.

3) If test light turns off after disconnecting PCM, ensure circuit No. 1269 is not shorted to battery voltage. If circuit is not shorted, PCM is internally shorted.

4) If test light turns off after disconnecting PCM, ensure circuit No. 1270 is not shorted to battery voltage. If circuit is not shorted, PCM is internally shorted.

91B05625   91F05627

"*AFTER REPAIRS*," CONFIRM "CLOSED LOOP" OPERATION AND NO "SERVICE ENGINE SOON" LIGHT.

Courtesy of General Motors Corp.

Fig. 71: Cooling Fan On At All Times (3.8L – VIN L "C" Body)

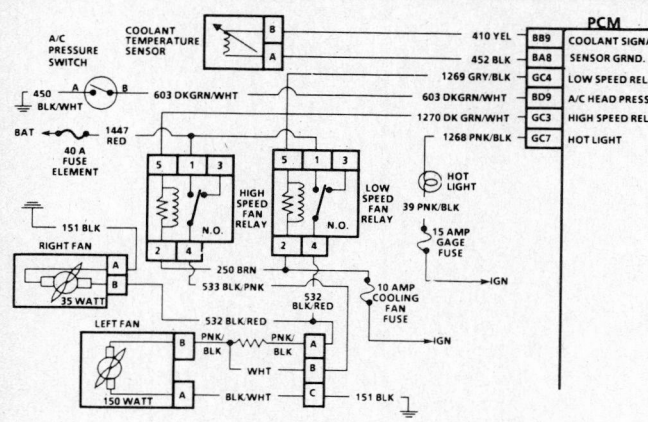

CHART C-12C, COOLING FAN NO LOW SPEED FAN
3.8L – VIN L ("C" BODY)

NOTE: Test numbers refer to test numbers on diagnostic charts.

1) Checks for battery voltage at relay harness connector.

2) Using jumper to connect low and high speed cooling fan relay terminals No. 1 and No. 4 by-passes the relay. Cooling fans should run if fan motors and wiring are okay.

3) Grounding ALDL test connector should cause PCM to ground circuit No. 1269. At this point, test light should illuminate if PCM is okay and circuit No. 1269 is not open.

4) This checks for battery voltage and ground to cooling fan motor. An illuminated test light at this point indicates a faulty fan motor connection or a faulty fan motor.

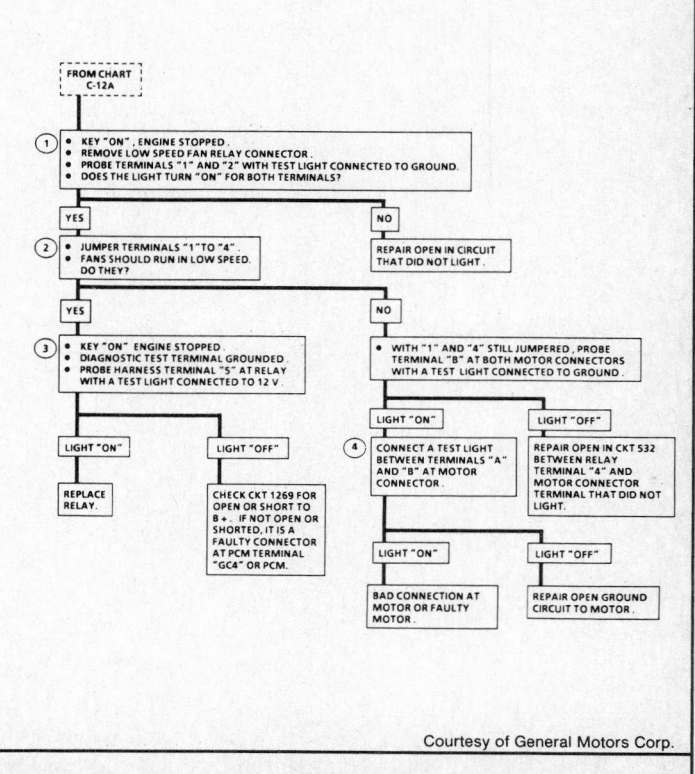

91B05625   91H05628

Courtesy of General Motors Corp.

Fig. 72: No Low Speed Cooling Fan (3.8L – VIN L "C" Body)

GM
5-124

1991 ENGINE COOLING
Specifications & Electric Cooling Fans – Exc. Cadillac (Cont.)

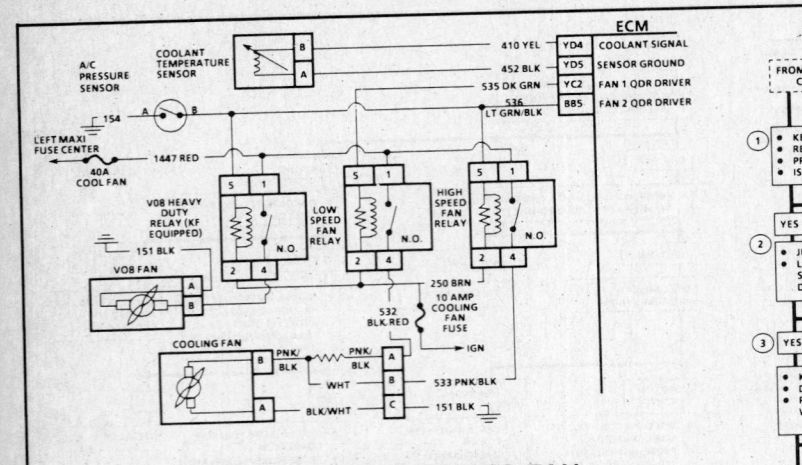

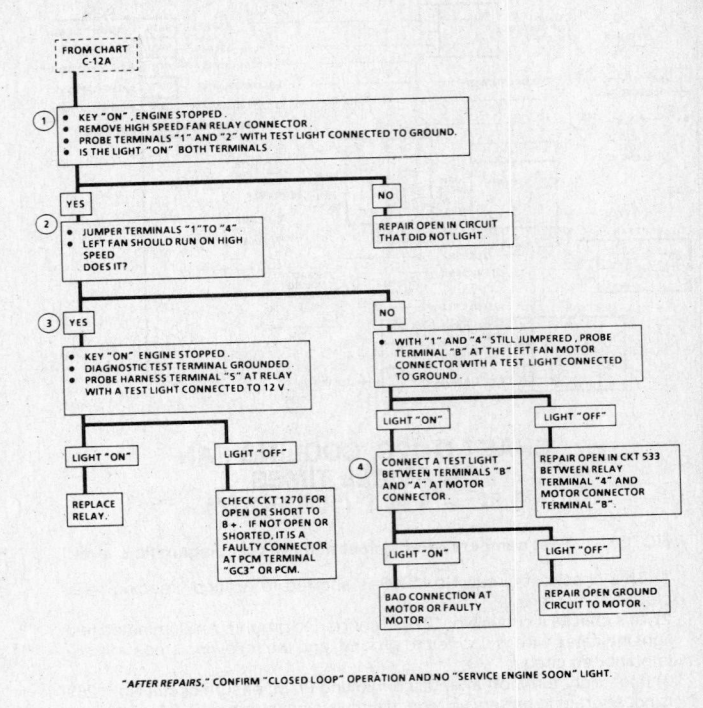

CHART C-12D, COOLING FAN
NO HIGH SPEED FAN
3.8L – VIN L ("C" BODY)

NOTE: Test numbers refer to test numbers on diagnostic charts.

1) With ignition switch on, test light should turn on when connected to harness terminal No. 2.

2) Using jumper to connect harness terminals No. 1 and No. 4 by-passes relay. If fan runs, relay is faulty.

3) This checks circuit No. 1270 back to the PCM. If circuit No. 1270 is okay, relay is faulty.

4) This checks wiring to cooling fan motor. If wiring is okay, check connectors and motor ground or check faulty cooling fan motor.

91B05625   91J05629

"AFTER REPAIRS," CONFIRM "CLOSED LOOP" OPERATION AND NO "SERVICE ENGINE SOON" LIGHT.

Courtesy of General Motors Corp.

Fig. 73: No High Speed Cooling Fan (3.8L – VIN L "C" Body)

1991 ENGINE COOLING
Specifications & Electric Cooling Fans – Exc. Cadillac (Cont.)

GM
5-125

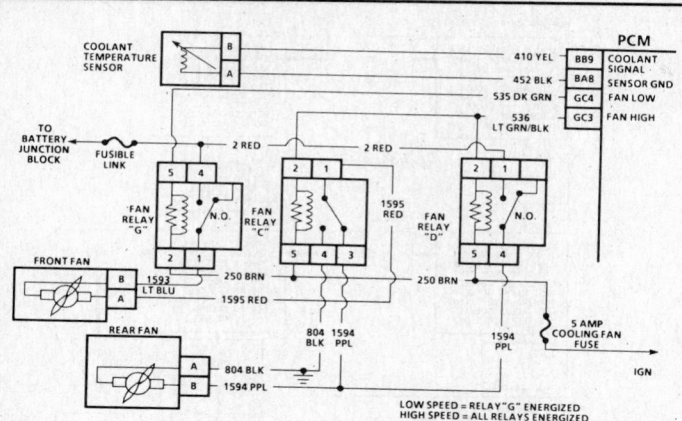

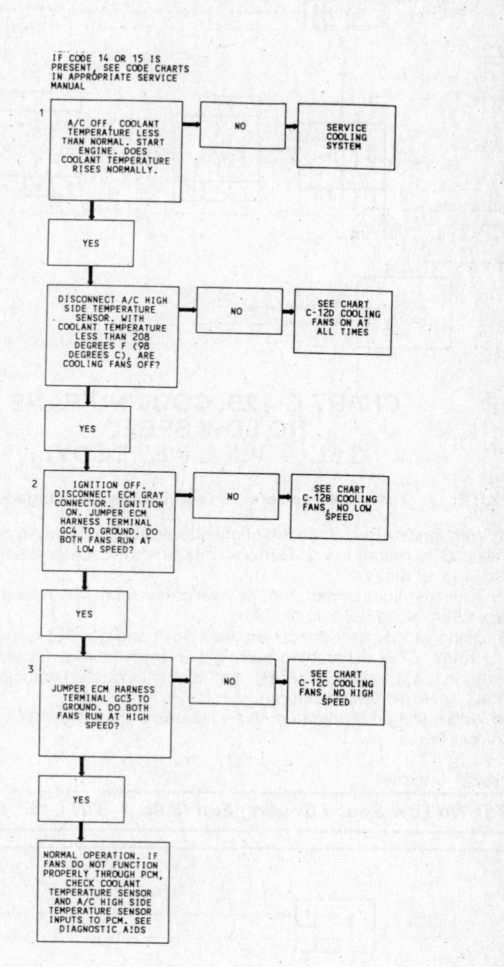

CHART C-12A, COOLING FANS FUNCTIONAL CHECK
3.8L – VIN L ("E" BODY)

Powertrain Control Module (PCM) and 3 relays are used to control the 2 cooling fans. The PCM is the ECM, except PCM is used on vehicles equipped with automatic transmission with computer controlled components.

On low speed fan operation, PCM energizes cooling fan relay "G" through terminal GC4 when coolant temperature exceeds 214°F (101°C) or when A/C high-side refrigerant temperature exceeds 122°F (50°C).

On high speed fan operation, PCM energizes all 3 relays when coolant temperature exceeds 226°F (108°C) or when A/C high-side refrigerant temperature exceeds 149°F (65°C).

Code 14 or 15 indicates cooling system or sensor operation is not normal. Cooling fan(s) operation cannot be checked correctly.

NOTE: **Test numbers refer to test numbers on diagnostic charts.**

1) Checks for normal cooling system operation.
2) Grounding cooling fan relay "G" through terminal GC4 will turn on cooling fans at low speed.
3) This test should energize cooling fan relays "C" and "D"; with GC4 terminal still grounded, both fans should run at high speed.

DIAGNOSTIC AIDS

An intermittent problem may be caused by a poor connection, rubbed through wire insulation or a broken wire.

Also check for the following:
- Poor connection or damaged PCM harness connector.
- Intermittent short or open circuit.
- Coolant temperature sensor resistance.
- Cooling system.

91J05610   91B05611

Fig. 74: Cooling Fan System Functional Check (3.8L – VIN L "E" Body)

GM
5-126

1991 ENGINE COOLING
Specifications & Electric Cooling Fans – Exc. Cadillac (Cont.)

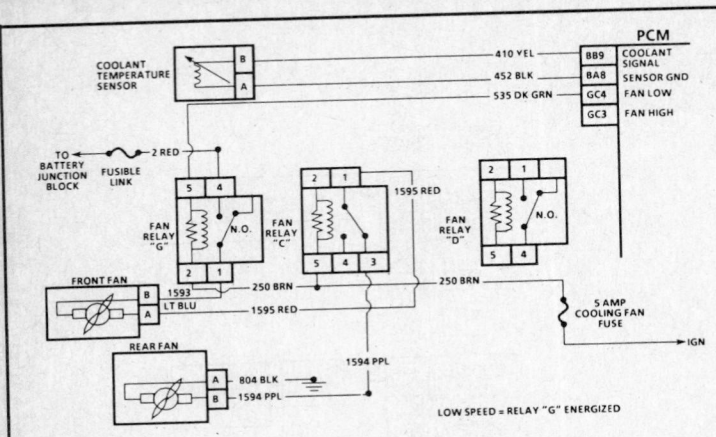

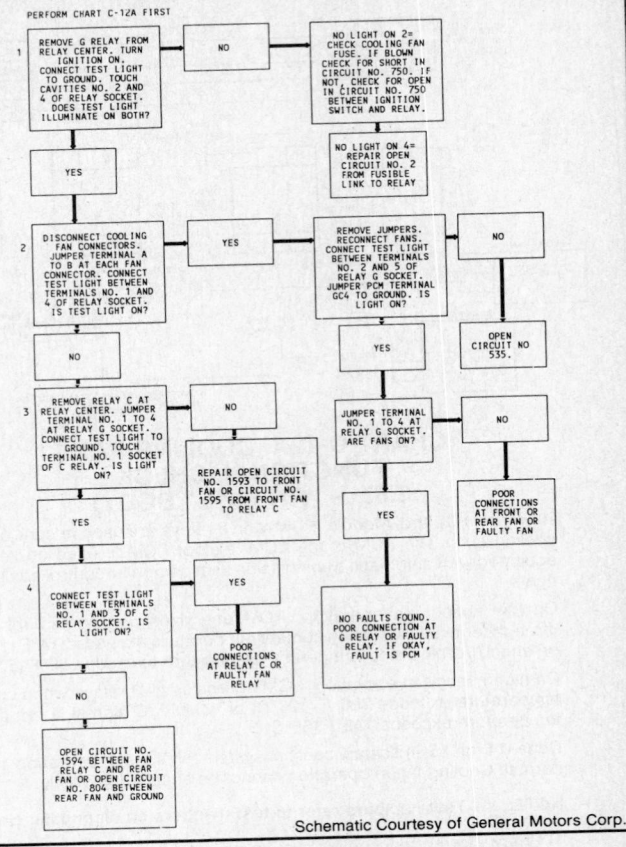

CHART C-12B, COOLING FANS
NO LOW SPEED
3.8L – VIN L ("E" BODY)

NOTE: Test numbers refer to test numbers on diagnostic charts.

1) With ignition switch on, test light should illuminate when connected to relay "G" terminal No. 2. Battery voltage should be present at terminal No. 4 at all times.

2) With test light illuminated, this validates relay "C", circuits No. 1593, No. 1594, No. 1595 and No. 804.

3) Using jumper to connect terminals No. 1 and No. 4 of relay "G", removing relay "C" and touching test light to terminal No. 1 validates circuit integrity up to relay "C". If test light is not illuminated, check circuits No. 1593 or No. 1595 to front fan.

4) With test light illuminated, this validates circuits No. 804 and No. 1594 to rear fan.

91D05612   91F05613

Fig. 75: No Low Speed Cooling Fan (3.8L – VIN L "E" Body)

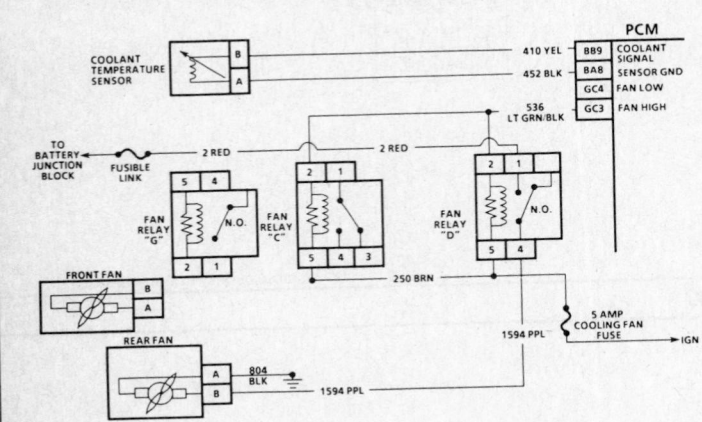

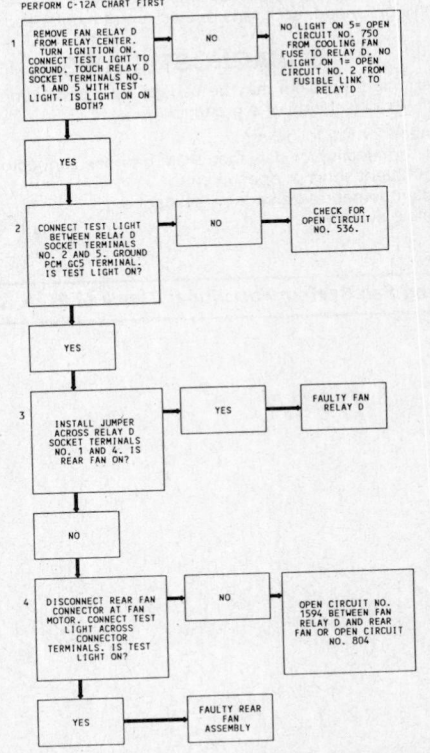

CHART C-12C-A, COOLING FANS
NO HIGH SPEED (REAR COOLING FAN)
3.8L – VIN L ("E" BODY)

NOTE: Test numbers refer to test numbers on diagnostic charts.

1) With ignition on, test light should illuminate when connected to cooling fan relay "D" terminal No. 5. Terminal No. 1 should have battery voltage at all times.

2) Test light should illuminate when connected to PCM terminal GC5.

3) Using jumper to connect harness terminals No. 1 and No. 4 by-passes the relay. If fan runs, relay is faulty.

4) If test light is illuminated, circuits No. 804 and No. 1594 are okay. Check for faulty fan motor.

91H05614   91A05615

Fig. 76: No High Speed Rear Cooling Fan (3.8L – VIN L "E" Body)

1991 ENGINE COOLING
Specifications & Electric Cooling Fans – Exc. Cadillac (Cont.)

GM
5-127

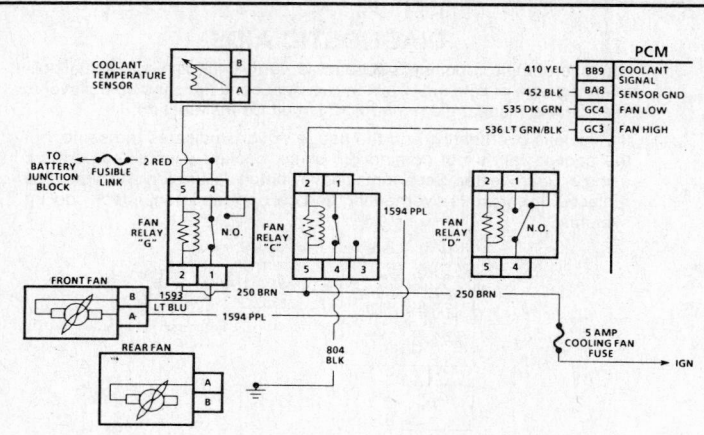

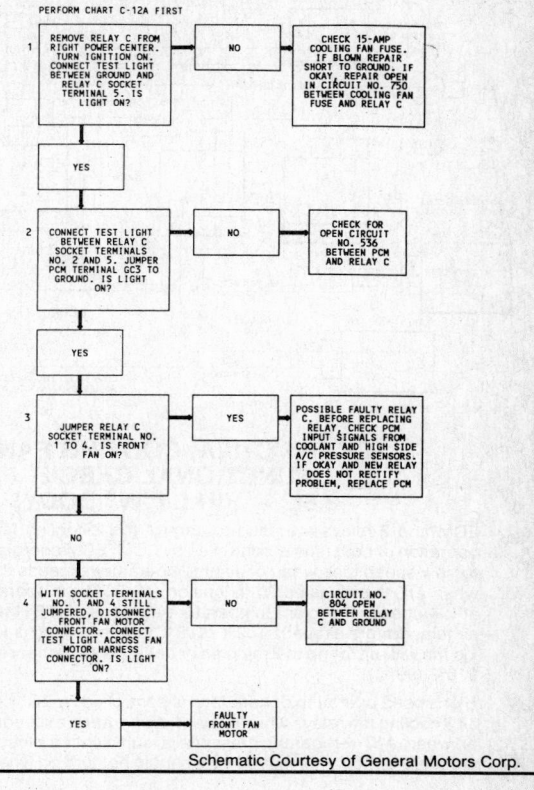

CHART C-12C-B, COOLING FANS
NO HIGH SPEED (FRONT COOLING FAN)
3.8L – VIN L ("E" BODY)

NOTE: Test numbers refer to test numbers on diagnostic charts.

1) With ignition on, test light should illuminate when connected to cooling fan relay "C" terminal 5.
2) Illuminated test light validates circuit No. 536 from PCM to relay "C".
3) Using jumper to connect relay "C" terminals No. 1 and No. 4 by-passes fan relay.
4) Illuminated test light validates all circuits. If test light is on, front cooling fan is faulty. If test light is off, check ground circuit No. 804.

91C05616   91E05617

Schematic Courtesy of General Motors Corp.

Fig. 77: No High Speed Front Cooling Fan (3.8L – VIN L "E" Body)

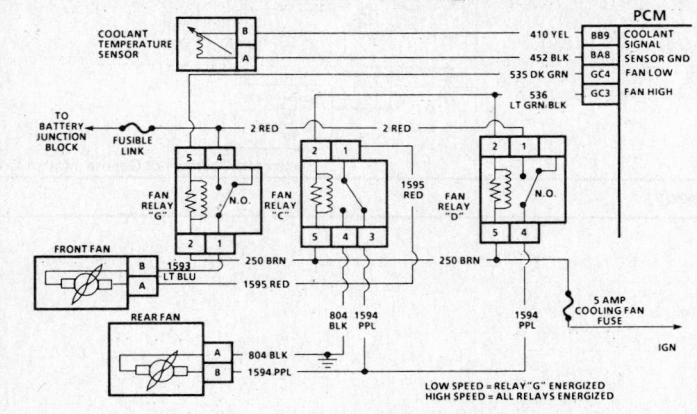

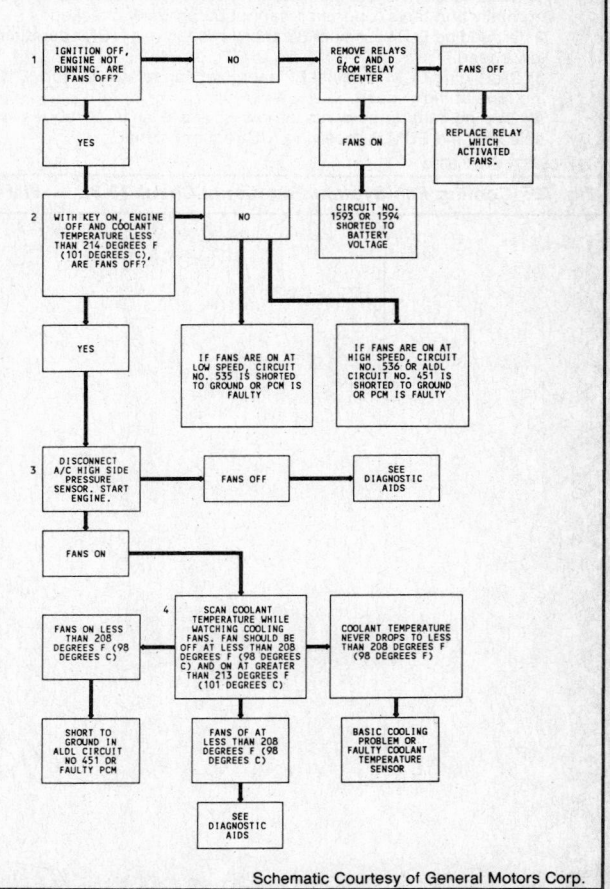

CHART C-12D, COOLING FANS
ON AT ALL TIMES
3.8L – VIN L ("E" BODY)

NOTE: Test numbers refer to test numbers on diagnostic charts.

1) Fans should not operate when ignition switch is in OFF position.
2) Fans should not operate when coolant temperature is less than 214°F (101°C).
3) Disconnecting A/C high side temperature sensor will disable BCM to PCM request due to A/C high-side temperature.
4) Defines fan operation based on coolant temperature only.

DIAGNOSTIC AIDS

Cooling fans should be off when coolant temperature is less than 208°F (98°C) and when A/C high side temperature is less than 122°F (50°C).

Normal cooling fan operation (low speed fan) occurs when engine is running and vehicle speed is more than 45 MPH, coolant temperature is more than 214°F (101°C) or A/C high-side temperature is more than 122°F (50°C).

91G05618   91I05619

Schematic Courtesy of General Motors Corp.

Fig. 78: Cooling Fans On At All Times (3.8L – VIN L "E" Body)

GM
5-128

1991 ENGINE COOLING
Specifications & Electric Cooling Fans – Exc. Cadillac (Cont.)

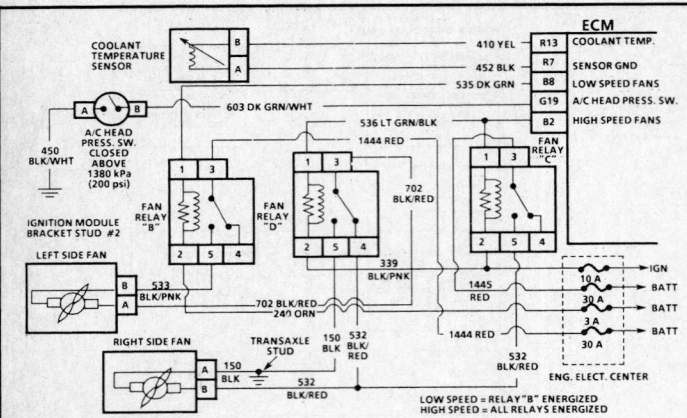

CHART C-12A, COOLING FANS FUNCTIONAL CHECK 3.8L – VIN L ("W" BODY)

ECM and 3 relays are used to control the 2 cooling fans. Low speed operation of both fans is controlled by ECM. ECM energizes fan relay "B" for low speed fans when coolant temperature exceeds 214°F (101°C) or when A/C is requested. With ignition off, ECM will operate cooling fans at low speeds if coolant temperature exceeds 230°F (110°C) and intake air temperature exceeds 102°F (108°C) when ignition is turned off. Cooling fan will run for up to 2 minutes or until coolant temperature falls below 210°F (99°C).

High speed operation of both fans is controlled by ECM. ECM energizes all 3 cooling fan relays when coolant temperature exceeds 226°F (108°C) or when A/C refrigerant pressure is sufficient to close the A/C head pressure switch. High speed fans should not turn on when ignition is off.

NOTE: Test numbers refer to test numbers on diagnostic charts.

1) Code 14 or 15 could mean cooling system or sensor is not operating normally and fan(s) operation cannot be properly checked.
2) Grounding ECM terminal B8 energizes fan relay "B", operating fans at low speed.
3) Grounding ECM terminal B2 energizes fan relays "C" and "D", operating fans at high speed.
4) Cooling fans should run at low speed if an A/C request mode is selected and ECM is receiving A/C request signal.

91F05632   91H05633

DIAGNOSTIC AIDS

If an overheating condition is suspected, verify if this is due to actual boil-over. If gauge or light indicates an overheat condition, and no boilover is in evidence, inspect the gauge/light circuit for malfunction.

If vehicle is overheating and the gauge or light indicates the same, but the cooling fan is not coming on, check coolant sensor temperature using a "Scan" tester. Sensor may have shifted calibration and should be replaced. If engine is overheating and cooling fan is on, check cooling system.

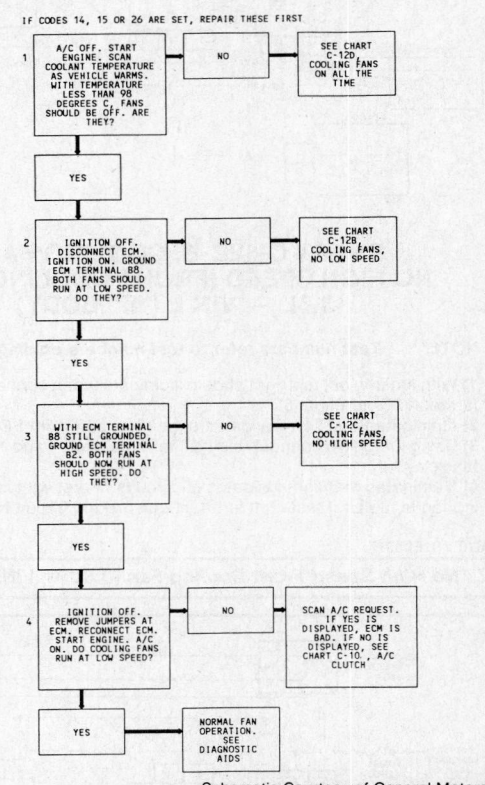

Fig. 79: Cooling Fan System Functional Check (3.8L – VIN L "W" Body)

1991 ENGINE COOLING
Specifications & Electric Cooling Fans – Exc. Cadillac (Cont.)

GM
5-129

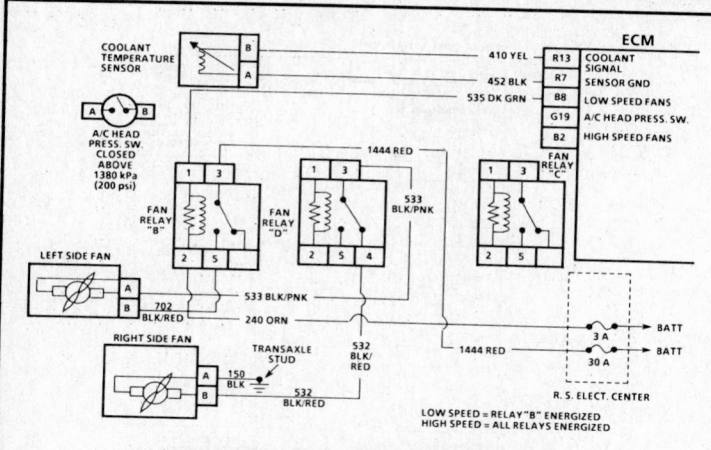

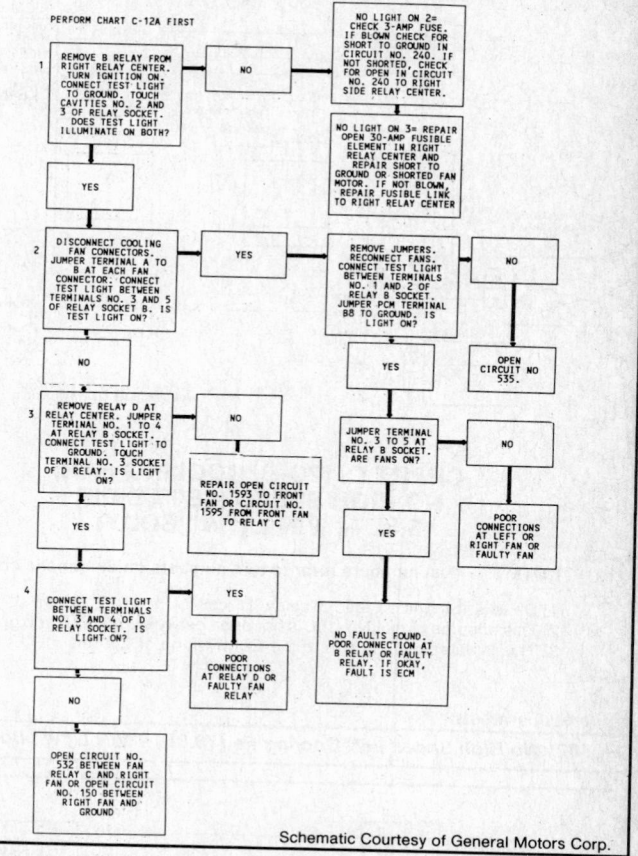

CHART C-12B, COOLING FANS
NO LOW SPEED
3.8L – VIN L ("W" BODY)

NOTE: Test numbers refer to test numbers on diagnostic charts.

1) With ignition on, an illuminated test light verifies battery voltage is present on harness terminals No. 2 and No. 3.

2) Illuminated test light verifies wiring for both fans.

3) Illuminated test light verifies circuit No. 702 between fan relay "B" and driver's side fan and circuit No. 533 between driver's side fan and fan relay "D".

4) Illuminated test light verifies circuit No. 532 between fan relay "D" and passenger's side fan and circuit No. 150 between passenger's side fan and ground.

91J05634   91C05635

Fig. 80: No Low Speed Cooling Fan (3.8L – VIN L "W" Body)

Schematic Courtesy of General Motors Corp.

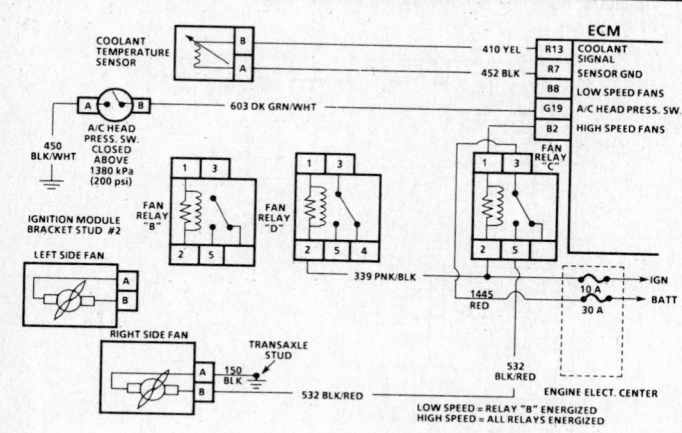

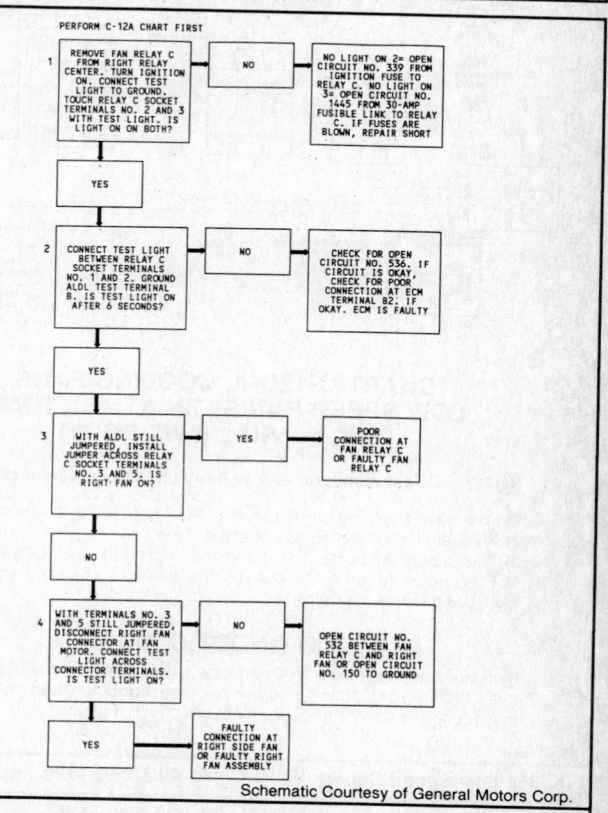

CHART C-12C-A, COOLING FANS
NO HIGH SPEED (RIGHT SIDE)
3.8L – VIN L ("W" BODY)

NOTE: Test numbers refer to test numbers on diagnostic charts.

1) Checks battery voltage and ignition at relay harness connector.

2) Illuminated test light verifies circuit No. 536 to cooling fan relay "C".

3) Using jumper to connect terminals No. 3 and No. 5 in relay "C" bypasses relay and should cause fan to run, if fan wiring and motor is operational.

4) This checks for battery voltage and ground at fan motor. An illuminated test light at this point indicates a faulty fan motor connection or fan motor.

91E05636   91G05637

Fig. 81: No High Speed Right Cooling Fan (3.8L – VIN L "W" Body)

Schematic Courtesy of General Motors Corp.

GM
5-130

1991 ENGINE COOLING
Specifications & Electric Cooling Fans – Exc. Cadillac (Cont.)

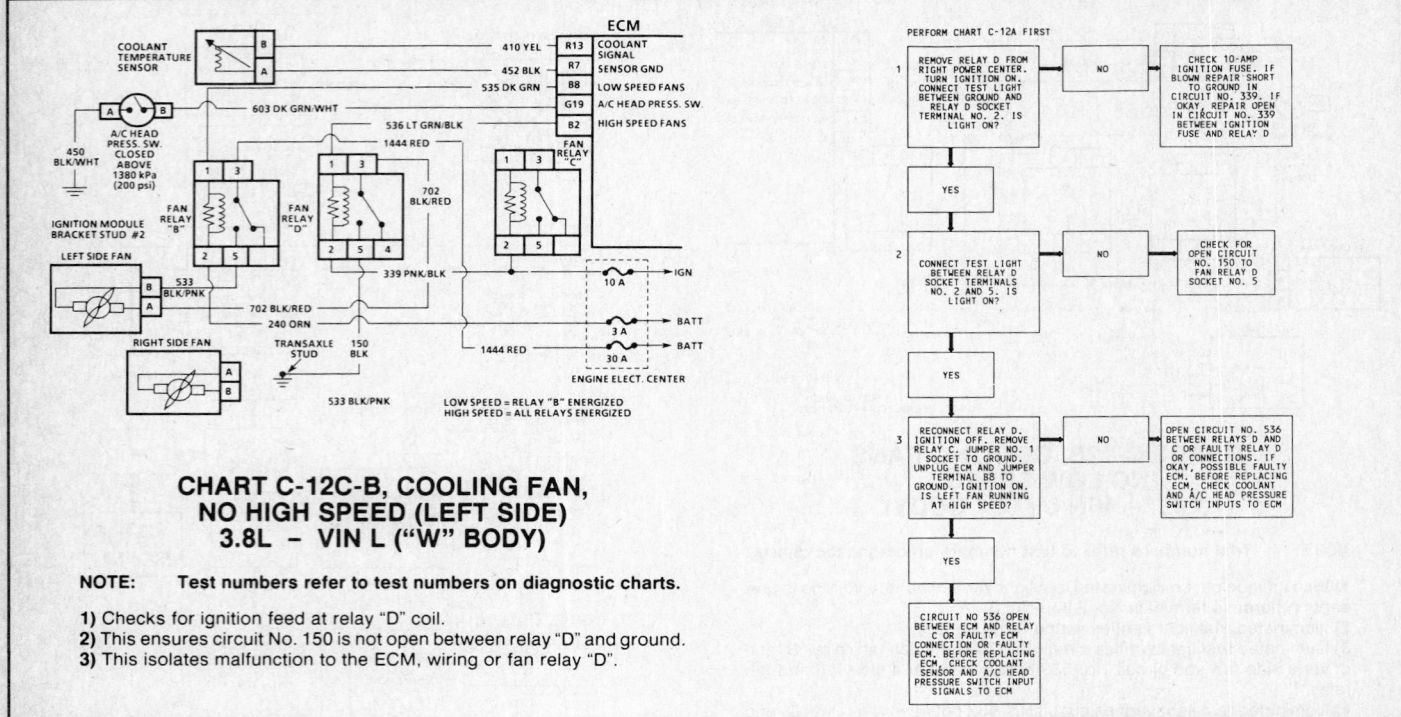

CHART C-12C-B, COOLING FAN, NO HIGH SPEED (LEFT SIDE)
3.8L – VIN L ("W" BODY)

NOTE: Test numbers refer to test numbers on diagnostic charts.

1) Checks for ignition feed at relay "D" coil.
2) This ensures circuit No. 150 is not open between relay "D" and ground.
3) This isolates malfunction to the ECM, wiring or fan relay "D".

91I05638   91A05639   Schematic Courtesy of General Motors Corp.

Fig. 82: No High Speed Left Cooling Fan (3.8L – VIN L "W" Body)

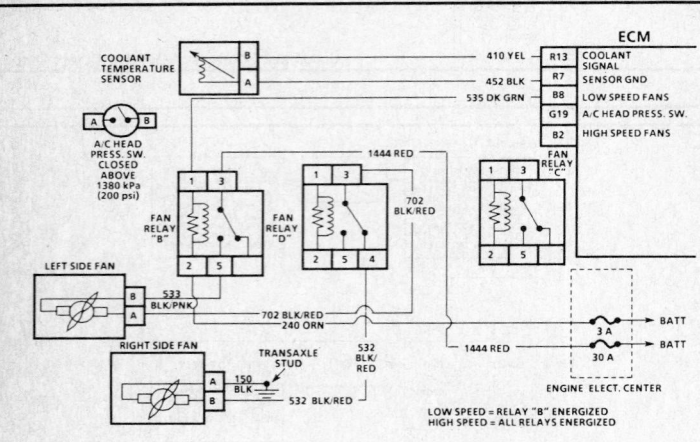

CHART C-12D-A, COOLING FANS, LOW SPEED FAN(S) ON AT ALL TIMES
3.8L – VIN L ("W" BODY)

NOTE: Test numbers refer to test numbers on diagnostic charts.

1) Low speed cooling fan may run up to 2 minutes with key off.
2) This verifies proper ECM control of fans.
3) This check circuit No. 535 if shorted to ground or a faulty fan relay.
4) This checks for an A/C request signal to the ECM, which would cause low speed fan(s) operation.

DIAGNOSTIC AIDS

If an overheating condition is suspected, verify if this is due to actual boil-over. If gauge or light indicates an overheat condition, and no boilover is in evidence, inspect the gauge/light circuit for malfunction.

If vehicle is overheating and the gauge or light indicates the same, but the cooling fan is not coming on, check coolant sensor temperature using a "Scan" tester. Sensor may have shifted calibration and should be replaced. If engine is overheating and cooling fan is on, check cooling system.

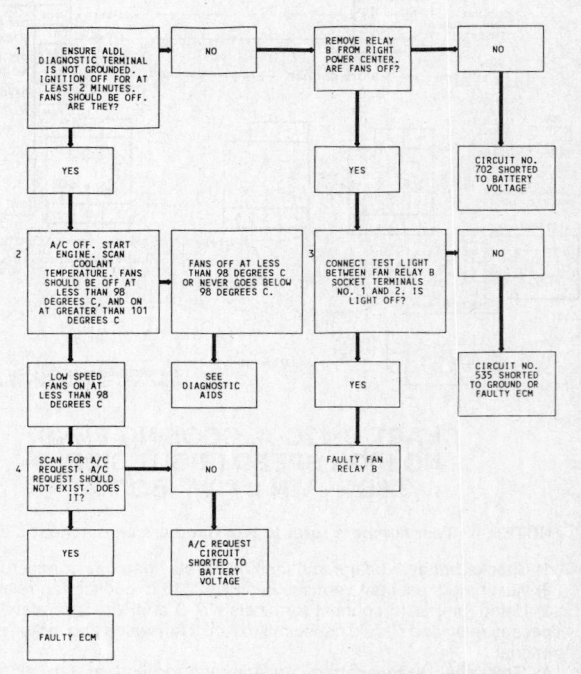

91C05640   91E05641   Schematic Courtesy of General Motors Corp.

Fig. 83: Low Speed Cooling Fans On At All Times (3.8L – VIN L "W" Body)

1991 ENGINE COOLING
Specifications & Electric Cooling Fans – Exc. Cadillac (Cont.)

GM
5-131

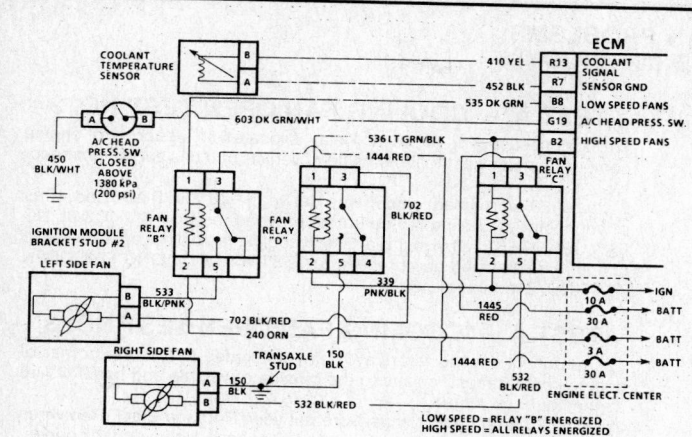

If vehicle is overheating and the gauge or light indicates the same, but the cooling fan is not coming on, check coolant sensor temperature using a "Scan" tester. Sensor may have shifted calibration and should be replaced. If engine is overheating and cooling fan is on, check cooling system.

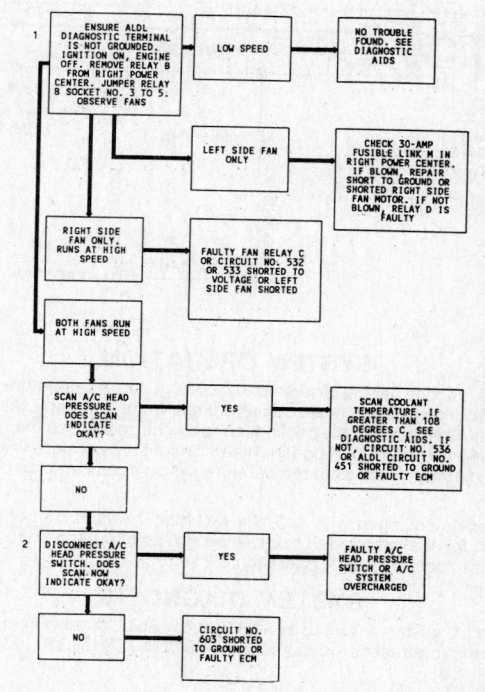

CHART C-12D-B, COOLING FAN, HIGH SPEED FAN(S) ON AT ALL TIMES 3.8L – VIN L ("W" BODY)

NOTE: Test numbers refer to test numbers on diagnostic charts.

1) This isolates problem to an ECM control fault, faulty fan or relay or a wiring problem.
2) This checks for proper operation of A/C head pressure switch.

DIAGNOSTIC AIDS

If an overheating condition is suspected, verify if this is due to actual boil-over. If gauge or light indicates an overheat condition, and no boilover is in evidence, inspect the gauge/light circuit for malfunction.

91G05642   91I05643

Schematic Courtesy of General Motors Corp.

Fig. 84: High Speed Cooling Fans On At All Times (3.8L – VIN L "W" Body)

GM
5-132

1991 ENGINE COOLING
Specifications & Electric Cooling Fans – Exc. Cadillac (Cont.)

COOLING FAN PROBLEMS
5.0L – VIN E ("F" BODY)

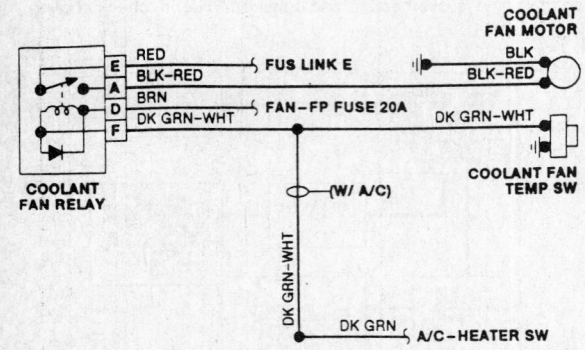

SYSTEM OPERATION

Electric cooling fan is activated by cooling fan temperature switch. Switch contacts close when coolant temperature is greater than 238°F (110°C). This grounds the cooling fan relay coil and closes the contacts, providing current to cooling fan. When coolant temperature is less than 214°F (101°C), cooling fan temperature switch opens and fan operation stops.

On models equipped with A/C, the A/C-heater switch control provides ground for the cooling fan relay when A/C is operating. This supplies current to cooling fan for operation.

SYSTEM DIAGNOSIS

Determine system failure. See SYSTEM DIAGNOSIS table in this article. Perform proper test procedure. See SYSTEM TESTING in this article.

SYSTEM DIAGNOSIS

Symptom	Diagnosis
Cooling Fan Inoperative	Do Test A
Cooling Fan Inoperative With High Engine Temperature	Do Test A
Cooling Fan Inoperative With A/C On	Do Test B
Cooling Fan Will Not Turn Off	Do Test C

SYSTEM TESTING

TEST A – COOLING FAN OPEN TEST NO. 1

1) Disconnect cooling fan relay. Relay is located at left rear corner of engine compartment. Relay is located closest to the outside of vehicle and has a 4-wire connector.
2) With ignition on, check for battery voltage at Red wire of connector and ground. If voltage exists, proceed to next step. If voltage did not exist, check for open circuit in Rust colored fusible link or wiring circuit. Fusible link is located at right front corner of engine compartment at the junction block.
3) Check for battery voltage at Brown wire of connector and ground. If voltage does not exist, check for defective FAN FP 20-amp fuse in fuse block or open in wiring circuit.

TEST A – COOLING FAN OPEN TEST NO. 2

1) Disconnect cooling fan relay. Relay is located at left corner of engine compartment, closest to the outside of vehicle and has a 4-wire connector.
2) Install 20-amp fused jumper wire between Red and Black/Red wires of connector. If cooling fan operates, proceed to TEST A – COOLING FAN OPEN TEST NO. 4 in this article. If cooling fan did not operate, leave jumper wire installed and proceed to TEST A – COOLING FAN OPEN TEST NO. 3 in this article.

TEST A – COOLING FAN OPEN TEST NO. 3

1) Disconnect cooling fan relay. Relay is located at left rear corner of engine compartment, closes to the outside of vehicle and has a 4-wire connector.
2) Install 20-amp fused jumper wire between Red and Black/Red wires of connector, it not previously installed. Disconnect cooling fan connector. Check for battery voltage at Black/Red wire of fan connector and ground. If no voltage exists, check for open in Red/Black wire. If voltage exist, proceed to next step.
3) Check for battery voltage between Black/Red and Black wire. If voltage does not exist, check for open in ground circuit.

TEST A – COOLING FAN OPEN TEST NO. 4

1) Ensure connector is installed on cooling fan relay. Install jumper wire from cooling fan temperature switch to ground. Cooling fan temperature switch is located at right rear corner of engine, above starter motor.
2) If cooling fan operates, replace cooling fan temperature switch. If cooling fan did not operate, check Dark Green/white wire from cooling fan temperature switch to cooling fan relay for open circuit. If wiring is okay, replace cooling fan relay.

TEST B – COOLING FAN A/C OPEN TEST

1) Disconnect A/C-heater switch control connector. Install fused jumper between Dark Green wire at connector and ground. Turn ignition on. If cooling fan operates, proceed to next step. If cooling fan did not operate, check Dark Green/White and Dark Green wire from A/C-heater switch to cooling fan relay for open circuit.
2) Install fused jumper wire between Dark Green and Black wires of A/C-heater switch control connector. If cooling fan operates, replace A/C-heater switch control. If cooling fan did not operate, check for open circuit in Black wire from A/C-heater switch control to cooling fan.

TEST C – COOLING FAN WILL NOT SHUT OFF

1) If cooling fan operates with ignition off, replace cooling fan relay.
2) If cooling fan operates all the time with ignition on and A/C off, disconnect cooling fan temperature switch. If fan quits, replace cooling fan temperature switch. If cooling fan continues to operate, check Dark Green/White and Dark Green wires and A/C-heater switch control for short to ground.

Fig. 85: Cooling Fan Control Circuit & System Diagnosis (5.0L – VIN E "F" Body)

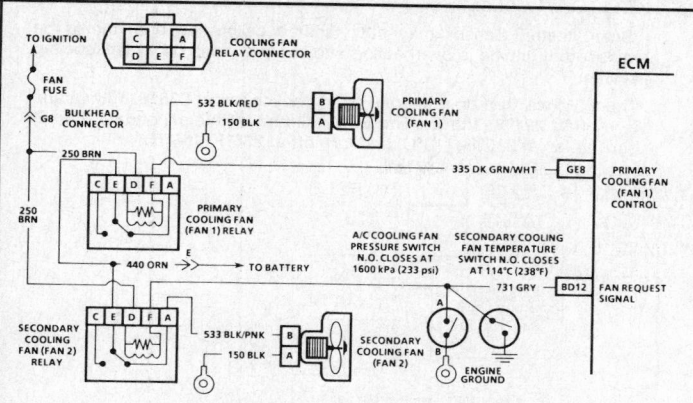

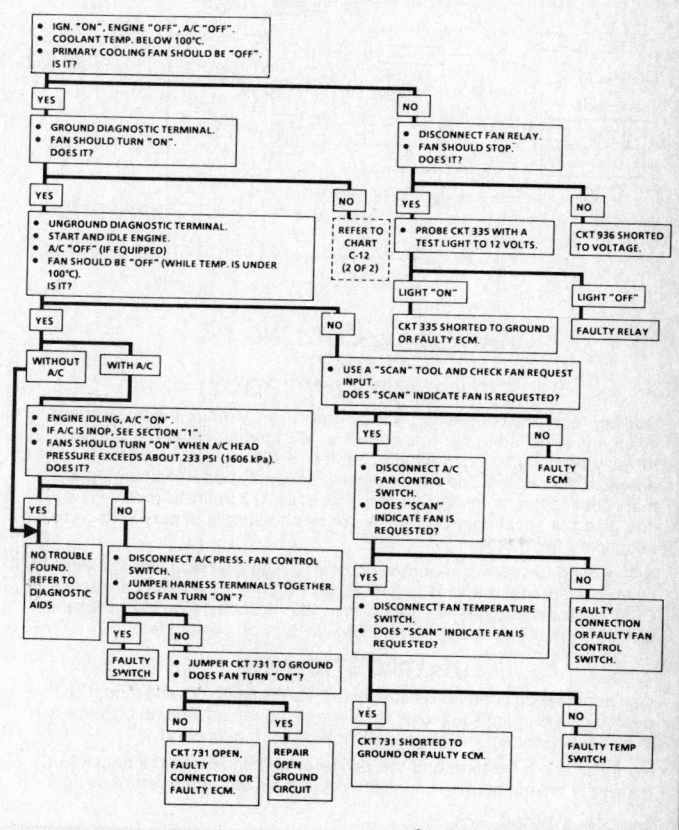

If vehicle is overheating and the gauge or light indicates the same, but the cooling fan is not coming on, check coolant sensor temperature using a "Scan" tester. Sensor may have shifted calibration and should be replaced. If engine is overheating and cooling fan is on, check cooling system.

CHART C-12, COOLING FAN
(1 OF 2)
5.0L – VIN F & 5.7L – VIN 8 ("F" BODY)

Cooling fans are controlled by the ECM based on inputs from the coolant temperature sensor and cooling fan control switch. Cooling fan(s) will run when coolant temperature is more than 223°F (106°C). Battery voltage is supplied to fan relay terminal "E". Ignition voltage is supplied to fan relay terminal "D".

ECM controls ground circuit through circuit No. 335 (relay terminal "F"). Grounding circuit No. 335 will energize relay and supply battery voltage to fan motor. Once fan relay is energized by ECM, cooling fan will remain on for 15 seconds. Cooling fan turns off when vehicle speed is more than 40 MPH, unless engine is overheating.

A/C cooling fan pressure switch, mounted in the A/C high pressure line, will close when head pressure exceeds 233 psi (16.4 kg/cm²), and this input will cause ECM to ground circuit No. 335, activating cooling fan(s).

Cooling fan(s) will also turn on when Code 14 or 15 is present or when ECM is in the back-up mode.

DIAGNOSTIC AIDS

If an overheating condition is suspected, verify if this is due to actual boil-over. If gauge or light indicates an overheat condition, and no boilover is in evidence, inspect the gauge/light circuit for malfunction.

90D10010   91B05630

Courtesy of General Motors Corp.

Fig. 86: Cooling Fan Control Circuit & System Diagnosis (5.0L – VIN F & 5.7L – VIN 8 "F" Body) (1 of 2)

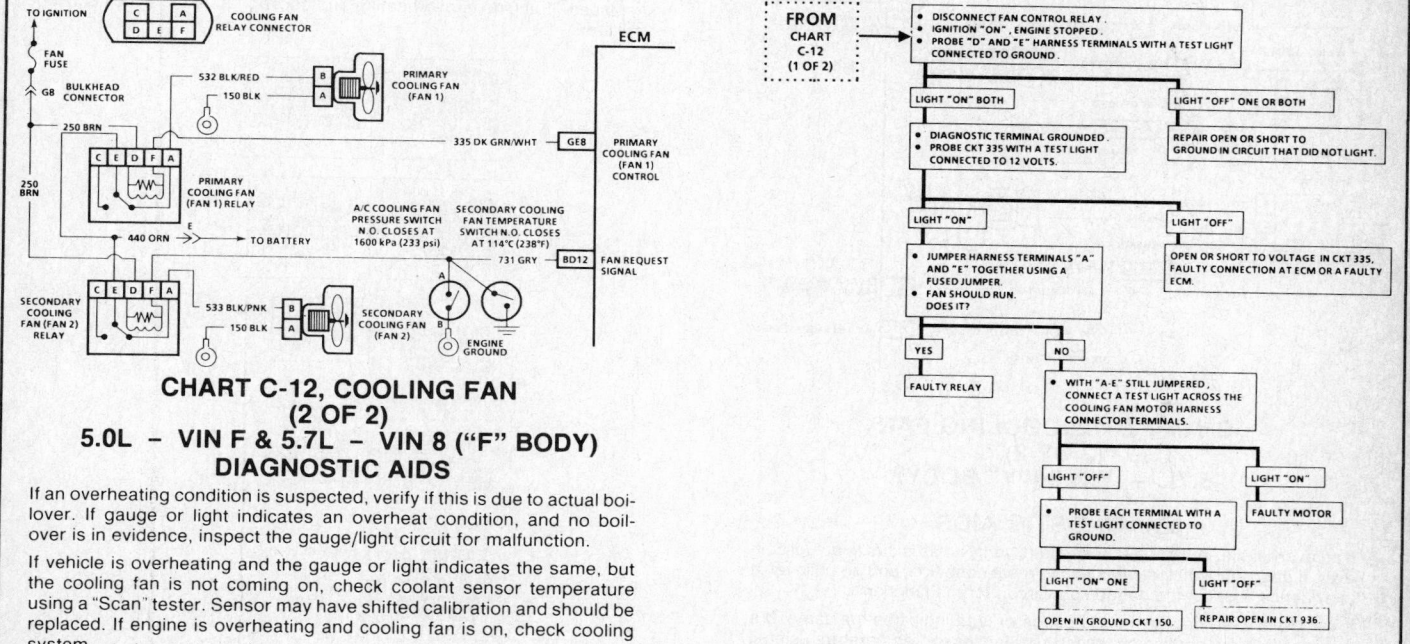

CHART C-12, COOLING FAN
(2 OF 2)
5.0L – VIN F & 5.7L – VIN 8 ("F" BODY)
DIAGNOSTIC AIDS

If an overheating condition is suspected, verify if this is due to actual boilover. If gauge or light indicates an overheat condition, and no boilover is in evidence, inspect the gauge/light circuit for malfunction.

If vehicle is overheating and the gauge or light indicates the same, but the cooling fan is not coming on, check coolant sensor temperature using a "Scan" tester. Sensor may have shifted calibration and should be replaced. If engine is overheating and cooling fan is on, check cooling system.

90D10010   91D05631

Courtesy of General Motors Corp.

Fig. 87: Cooling Fan Control Circuit & System Diagnosis (5.0L – VIN F & 5.7L – VIN 8 "F" Body) (2 of 2)

GM
5-134

1991 ENGINE COOLING
Specifications & Electric Cooling Fans – Exc. Cadillac (Cont.)

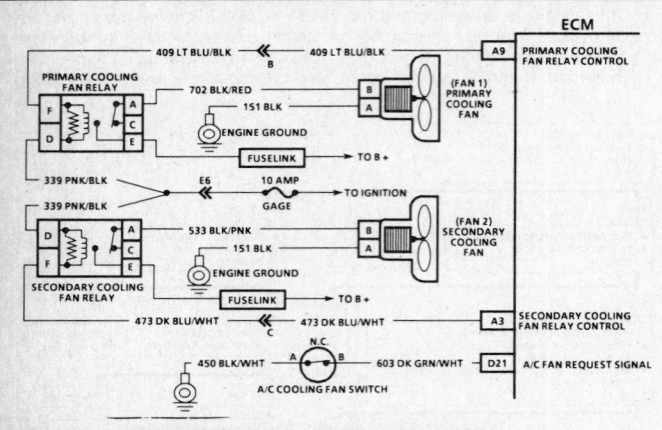

CHART C-12, COOLING FAN
(1 OF 2)
5.7L – VIN 8 ("Y" BODY)

Cooling fans are controlled by ECM based on various inputs. Battery voltage is supplied to fan relay terminal "E". Ignition voltage is supplied to relay terminal "D". Grounding circuit No. 409 (relay terminal "F") will energize the primary cooling fan relay and supply battery voltage to primary cooling fan motor. Grounding circuit No. 473 (relay terminal "F") will energize the secondary cooling fan relay and supply battery voltage to secondary fan motor.

A/C cooling fan switch, mounted in the A/C high pressure line, will open when head pressure exceeds 240 psi (17 kg/cm²). This input causes the ECM to ground circuits No. 473 or No. 409. If Code 14 or 15 is present or ECM is in the back-up mode, ECM will turn on cooling fan.

DIAGNOSTIC AIDS

If an overheating condition is suspected, verify if this is due to actual boilover. If gauge or light indicates an overheat condition, and no boilover is in evidence, inspect the gauge/light circuit for malfunction.

If vehicle is overheating and the gauge or light indicates the same, but cooling fan is not coming on, check coolant sensor temperature using a

"Scan" tester. Sensor may have shifted calibration and should be replaced. If engine is overheating and cooling fan is on, check cooling system.

The ECM will turn on primary (Fan 1) cooling fan at 226°F (108°C) and turn off at 221°F (108°C). The ECM will turn on the secondary (Fan 2) cooling fan at 235°F (113°C) and turn off at 226°F (108°C).

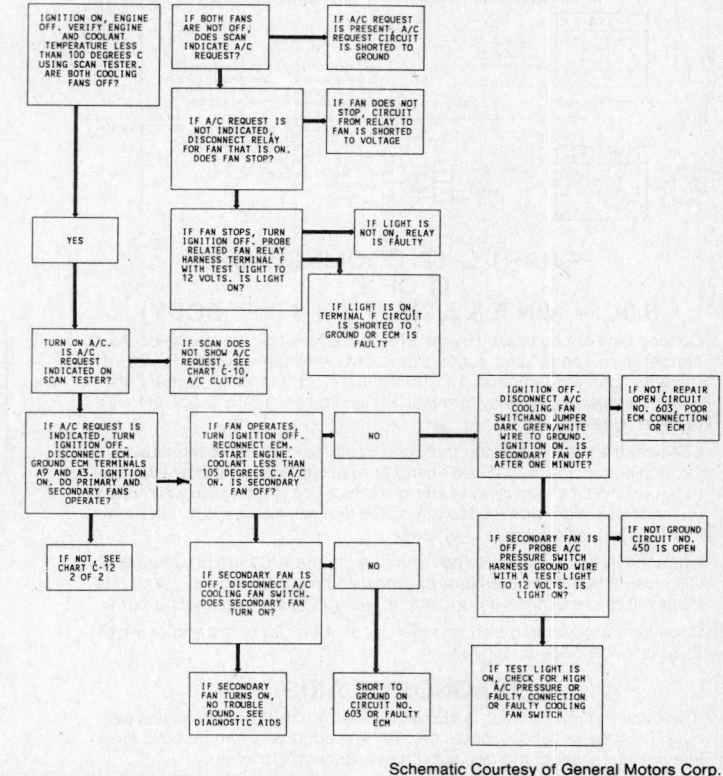

91A05644   91D05645

Schematic Courtesy of General Motors Corp.

Fig. 88: Cooling Fan Control Circuit & System Diagnosis (5.7L – VIN 8 "Y" Body) (1 of 2)

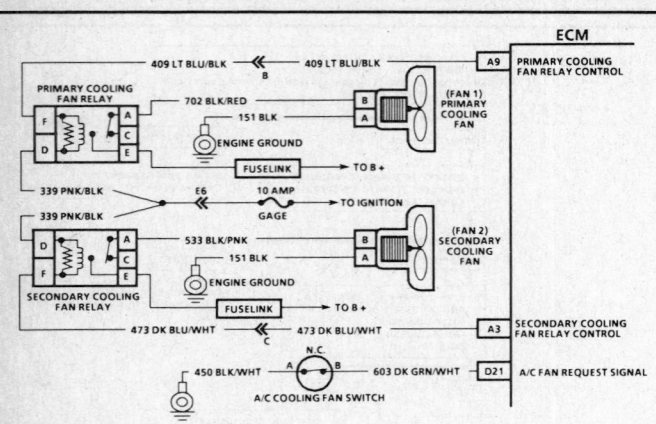

CHART C-12, COOLING FAN
(2 OF 2)
5.7L – VIN 8 ("Y" BODY)

DIAGNOSTIC AIDS

If an overheating condition is suspected, verify if this is due to actual boilover. If gauge or light indicates an overheat condition, and no boilover is in evidence, inspect the gauge/light circuit for malfunction.

If vehicle is overheating and the gauge or light indicates the same, but cooling fan is not coming on, check coolant sensor temperature using a

"Scan" tester. Sensor may have shifted calibration and should be replaced. If engine is overheating and cooling fan is on, check cooling system.

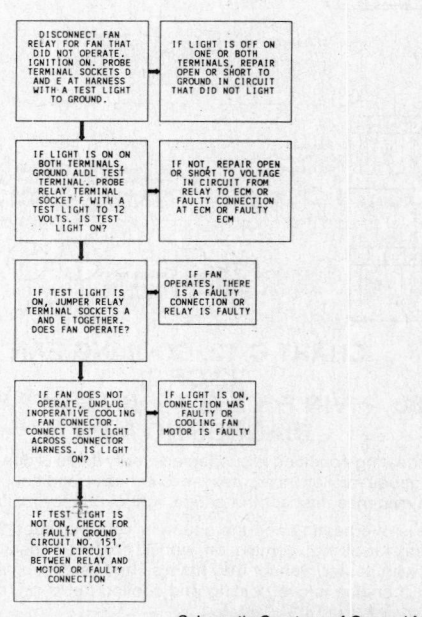

91A05644   91F05646

Schematic Courtesy of General Motors Corp.

Fig. 89: Cooling Fan Control Circuit & System Diagnosis (5.7L – VIN 8 "Y" Body) (2 of 2)

1991 ENGINE COOLING
Specifications & Electric Cooling Fans – Exc. Cadillac (Cont.)

GM
5-135

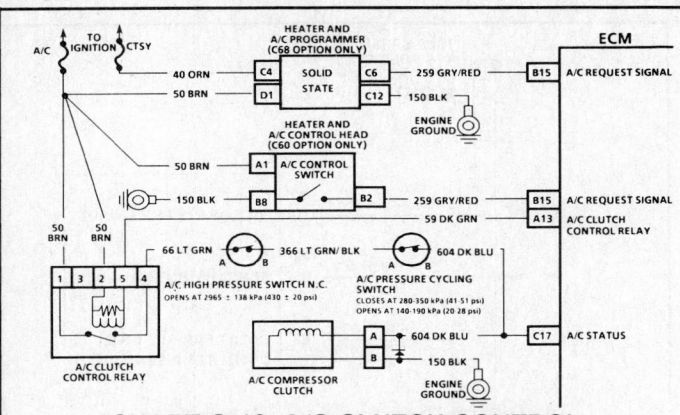

CHART C-10, A/C CLUTCH CONTROL
(1 OF 2)
5.7L – VIN 8 ("Y" BODY)

A/C clutch control is ECM-controlled to delay A/C clutch engagement after A/C is turned on, allowing ECM to adjust engine RPM before A/C clutch engages.

ECM will engage A/C clutch any time A/C has been requested unless any of the following conditions exist:

- High coolant temperature.
- Wide open throttle.
- High engine oil temperature.
- High engine RPM.

ECM can determine A/C request by sending a voltage signal to the A/C control head. When A/C control switch is closed, the A/C request voltage signal is grounded.

When an A/C request has been detected by ECM, ECM will ground A/C clutch control relay drive circuit, energizing compressor clutch portion of the circuit. If system is properly charged, circuit will be completed to A/C compressor clutch.

When A/C request has been detected by ECM, cooling fan(s) will be turned on unless vehicle speed is too high.

NOTE: Test numbers refer to test numbers on diagnostic charts.

1) Check A/C fuse and fuse circuit power distribution.
2) This checks ECM's ability to control A/C clutch control relay.
3) This determines if ECM is capable of detecting the A/C request signal being grounded.
4) Before replacing A/C control components, refer to appropriate AUTOMATIC A/C-HEATER SYSTEM article in this section for further A/C diagnostics.

91H05647   91J05648

Schematic Courtesy of General Motors Corp.

Fig. 90: A/C Clutch Control Circuit & System Diagnosis (5.7L – VIN 8 "Y" Body) (1 of 2)

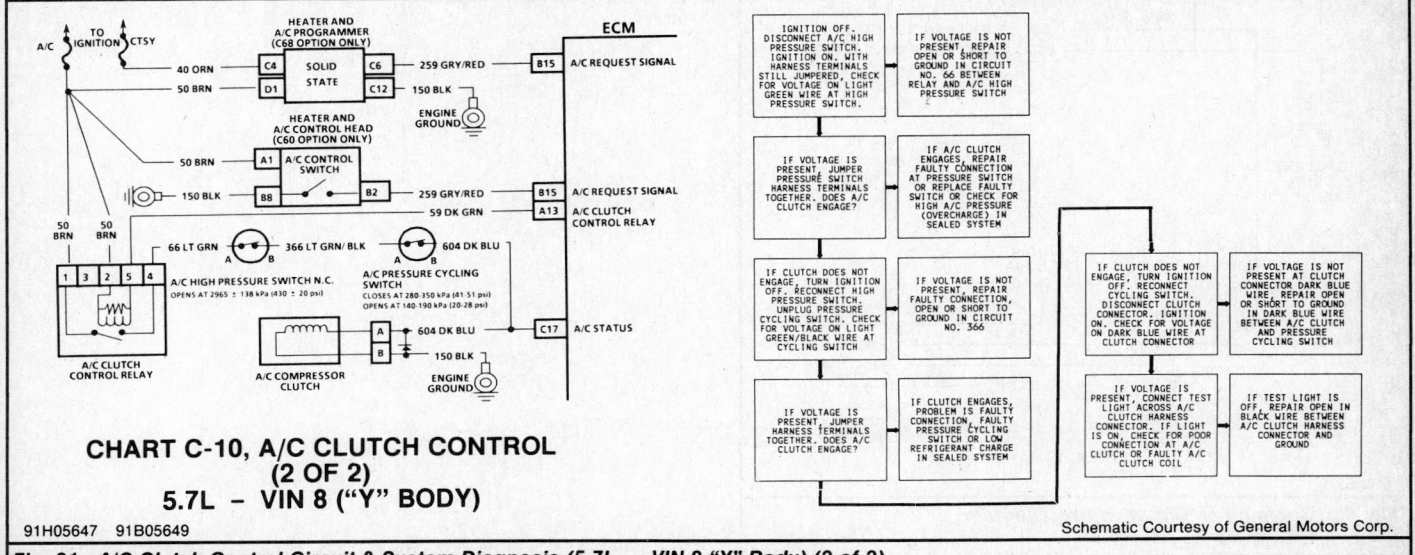

CHART C-10, A/C CLUTCH CONTROL
(2 OF 2)
5.7L – VIN 8 ("Y") BODY

91H05647   91B05649

Schematic Courtesy of General Motors Corp.

Fig. 91: A/C Clutch Control Circuit & System Diagnosis (5.7L – VIN 8 "Y" Body) (2 of 2)

GM
5-136

1991 ENGINE COOLING
Specifications & Electric Cooling Fans – Exc. Cadillac (Cont.)

WIRING DIAGRAMS

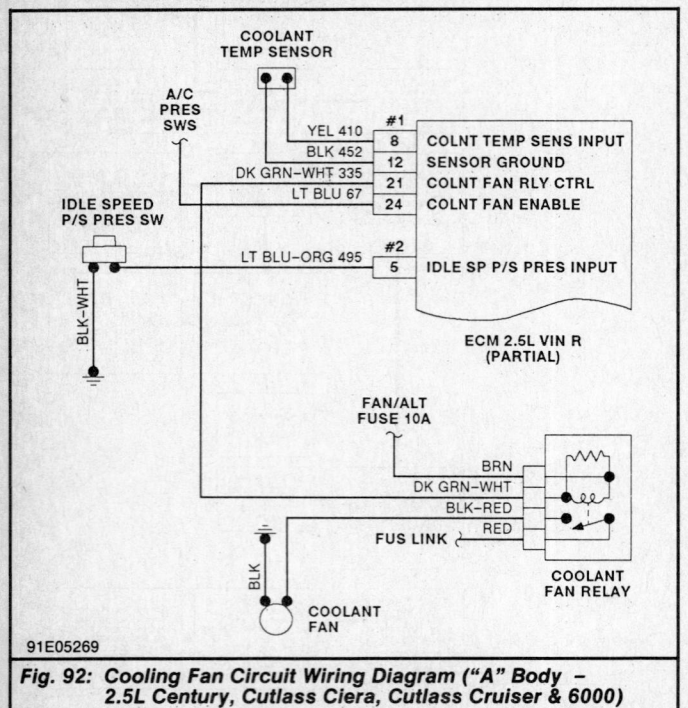

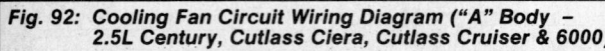

Fig. 92: Cooling Fan Circuit Wiring Diagram ("A" Body – 2.5L Century, Cutlass Ciera, Cutlass Cruiser & 6000)

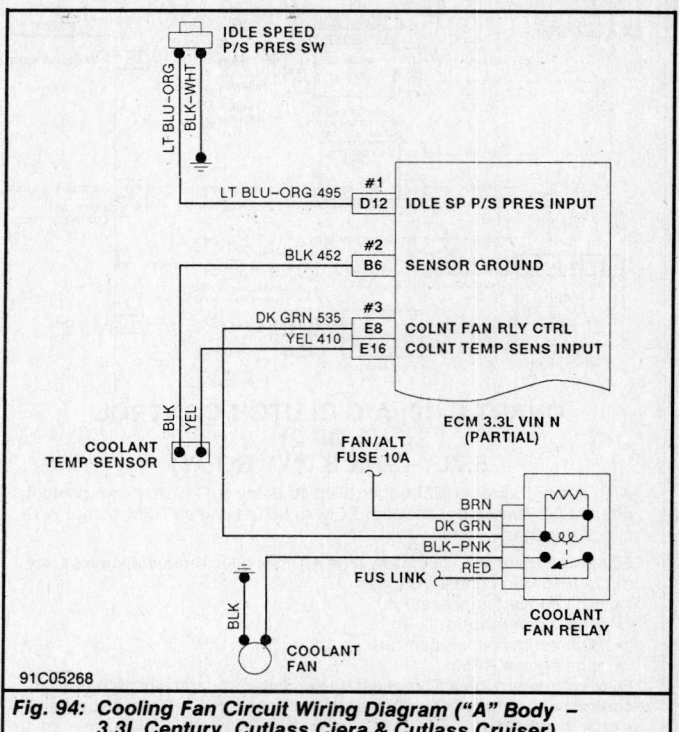

Fig. 94: Cooling Fan Circuit Wiring Diagram ("A" Body – 3.3L Century, Cutlass Ciera & Cutlass Cruiser)

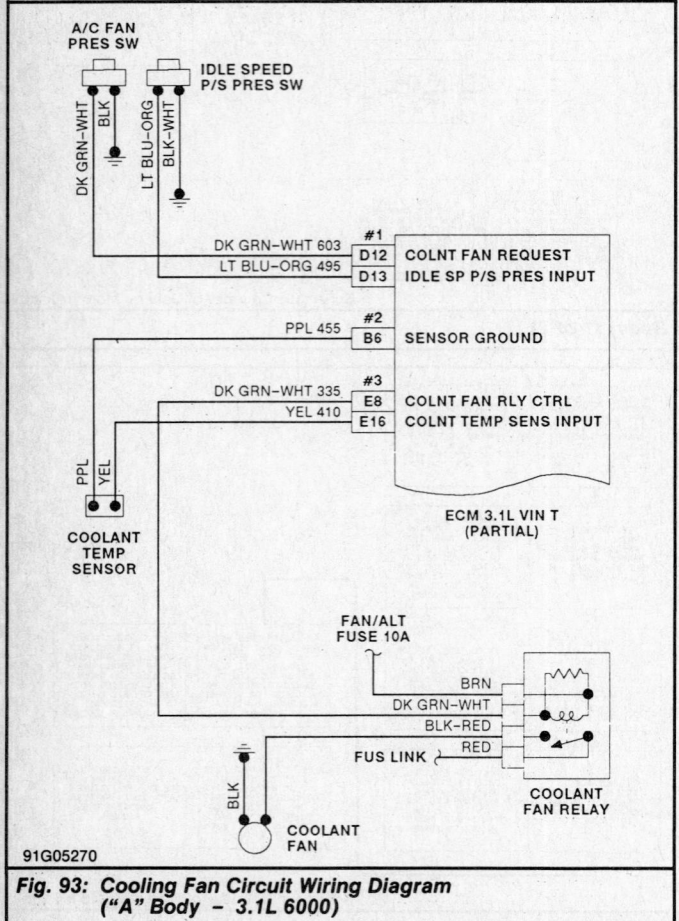

Fig. 93: Cooling Fan Circuit Wiring Diagram ("A" Body – 3.1L 6000)

1991 ENGINE COOLING
Specifications & Electric Cooling Fans – Exc. Cadillac (Cont.)

GM
5-137

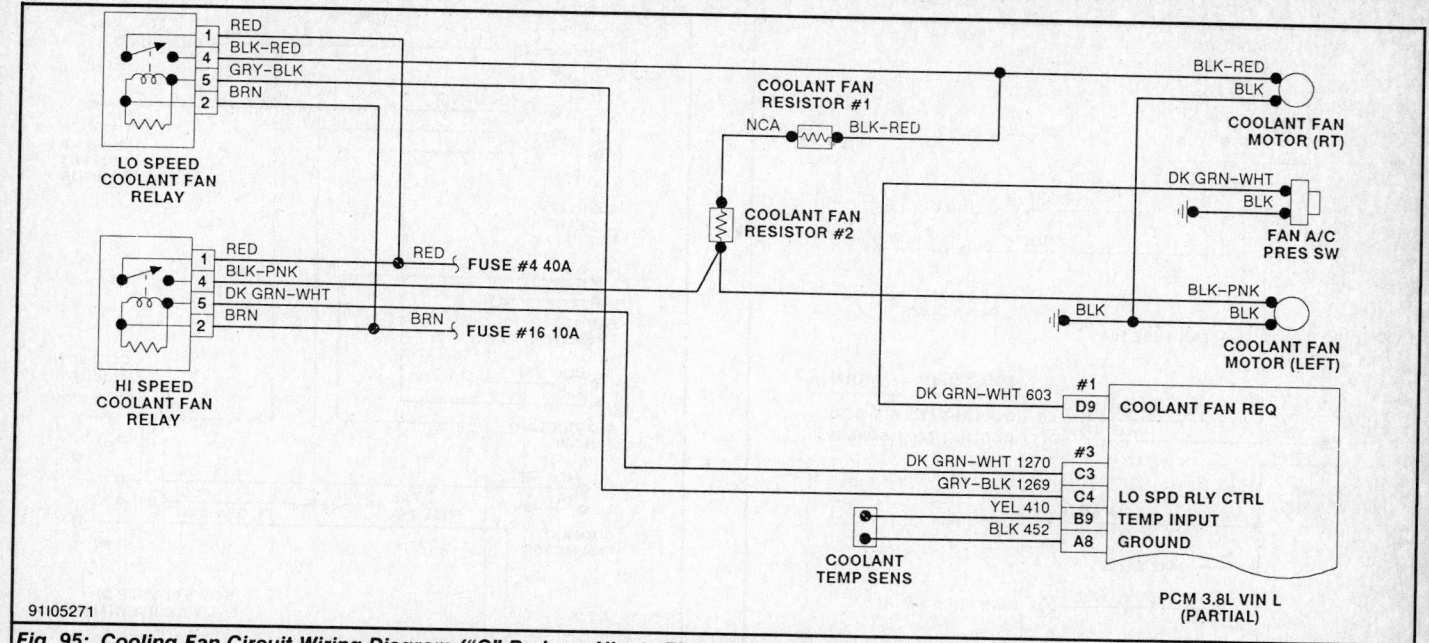

Fig. 95: Cooling Fan Circuit Wiring Diagram ("C" Body – Ninety-Eight, Park Avenue & Touring Sedan)

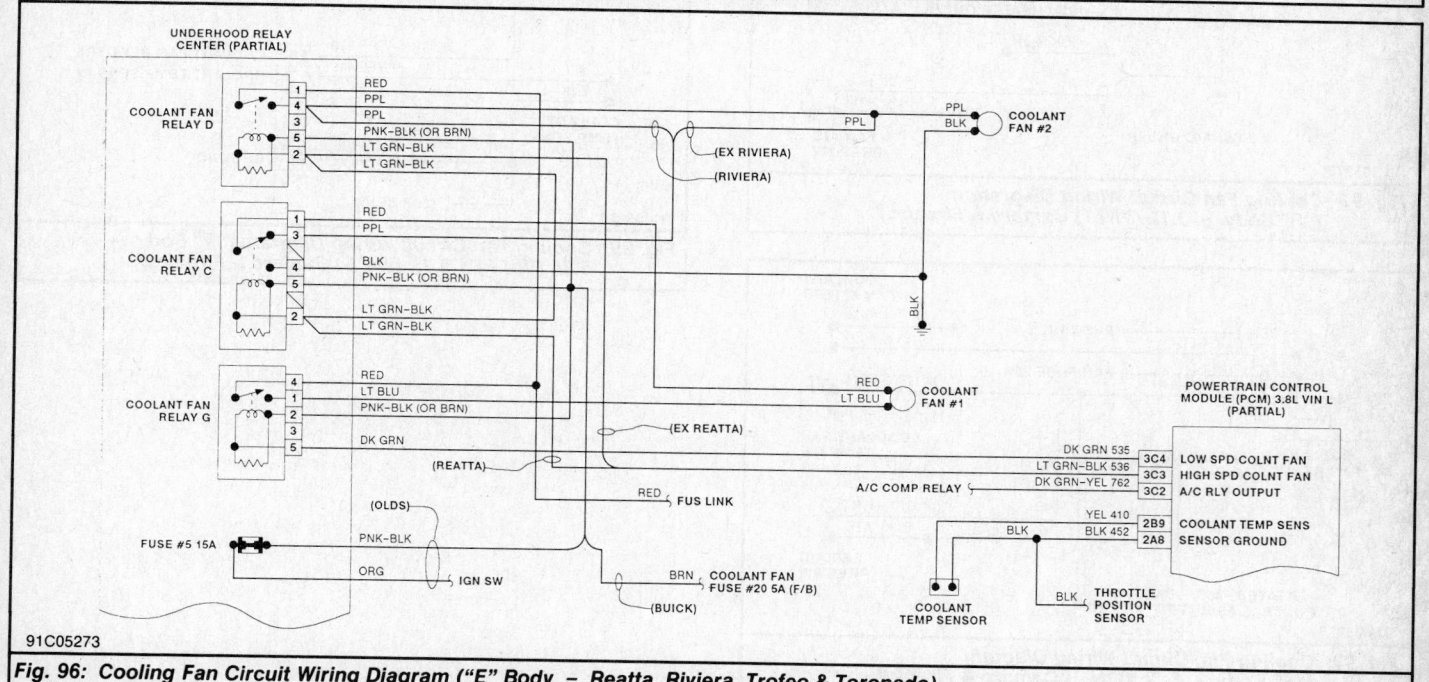

Fig. 96: Cooling Fan Circuit Wiring Diagram ("E" Body – Reatta, Riviera, Trofeo & Toronado)

GM
5-138

1991 ENGINE COOLING
Specifications & Electric Cooling Fans – Exc. Cadillac (Cont.)

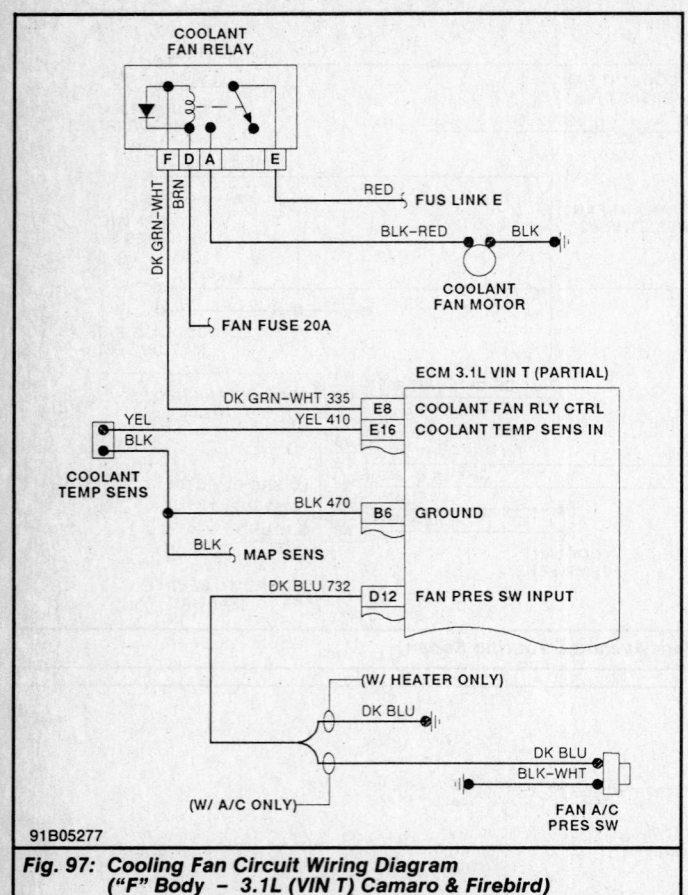

Fig. 97: Cooling Fan Circuit Wiring Diagram ("F" Body – 3.1L (VIN T) Camaro & Firebird)

91B05277

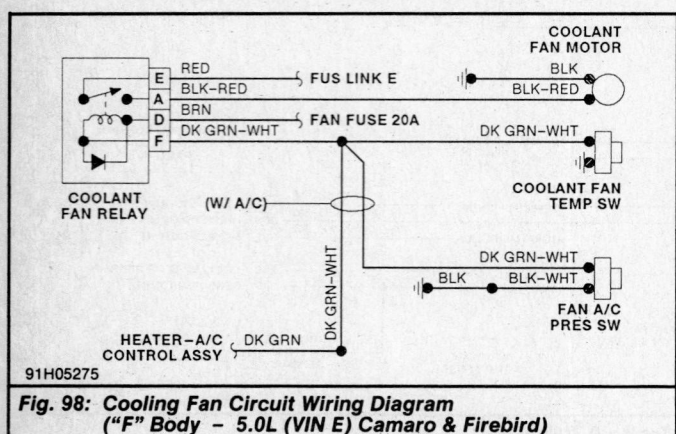

Fig. 98: Cooling Fan Circuit Wiring Diagram ("F" Body – 5.0L (VIN E) Camaro & Firebird)

91H05275

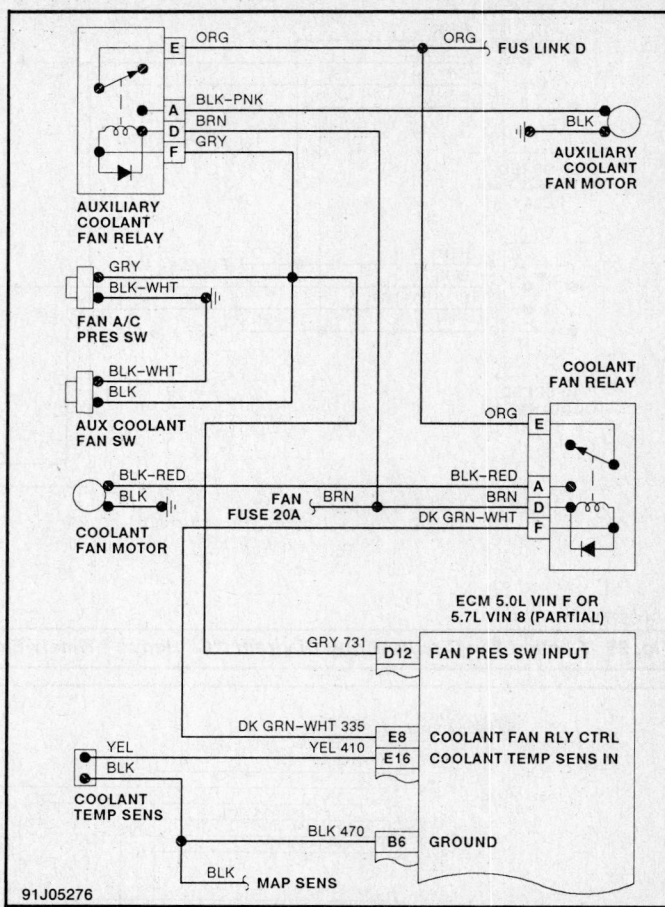

Fig. 99: Cooling Fan Circuit Wiring Diagram ("F" Body – 5.0L (VIN F) & 5.7L (VIN 8) Camaro & Firebird)

91J05276

1991 ENGINE COOLING
Specifications & Electric Cooling Fans – Exc. Cadillac (Cont.)

GM
5-139

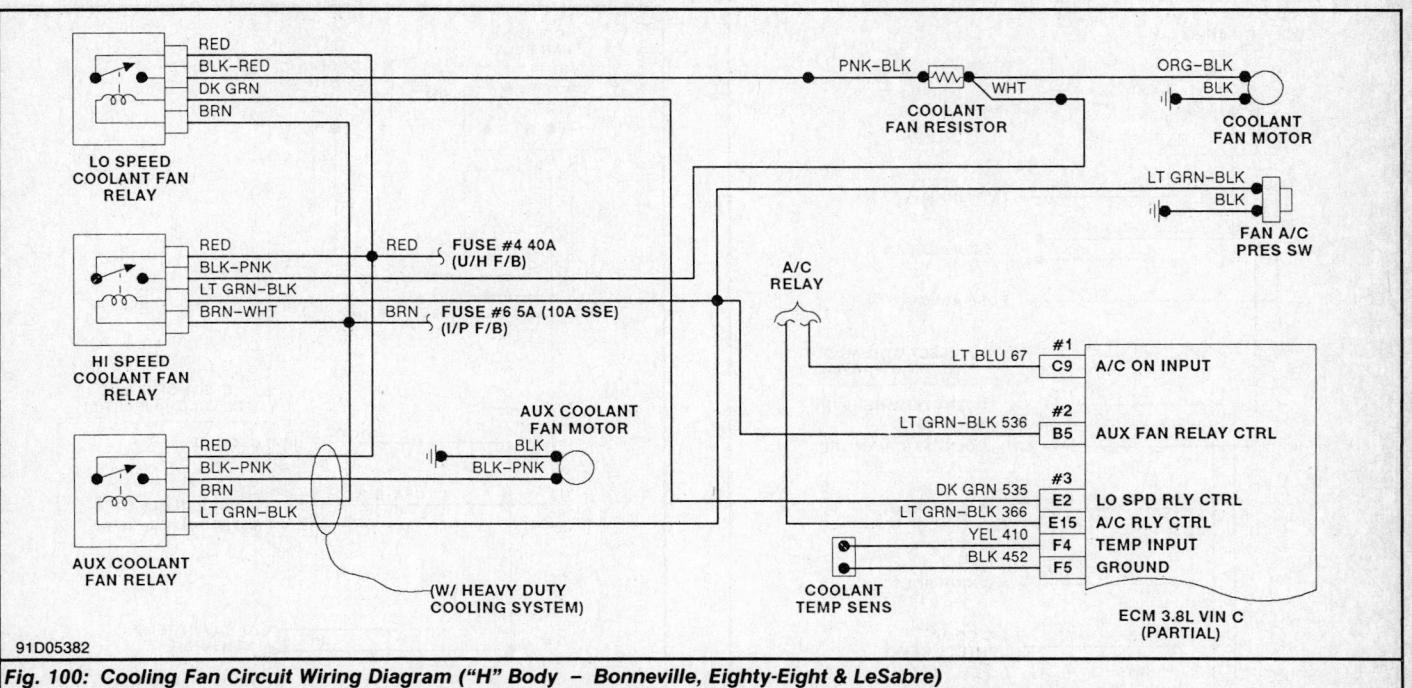

Fig. 100: Cooling Fan Circuit Wiring Diagram ("H" Body – Bonneville, Eighty-Eight & LeSabre)

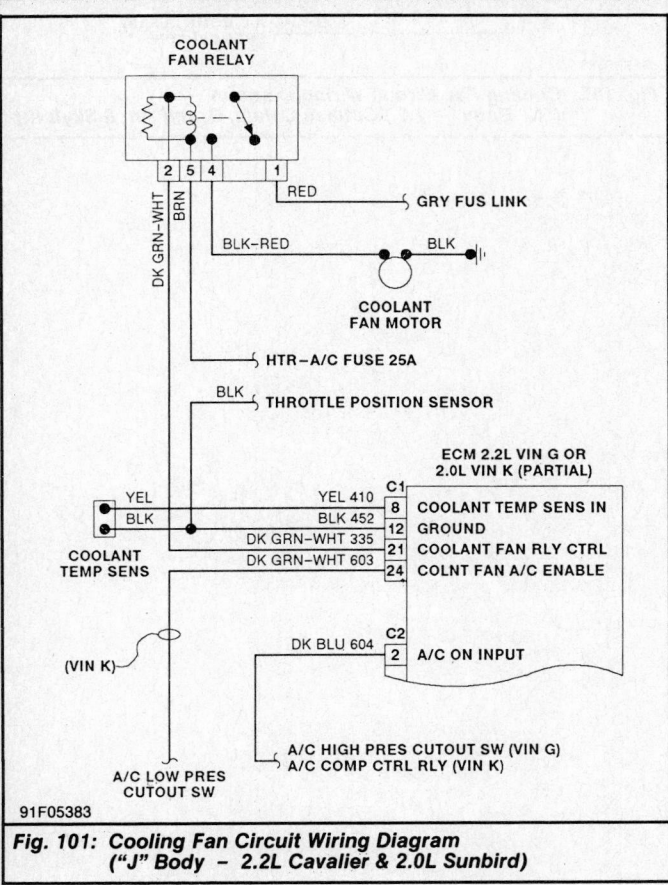

Fig. 101: Cooling Fan Circuit Wiring Diagram ("J" Body – 2.2L Cavalier & 2.0L Sunbird)

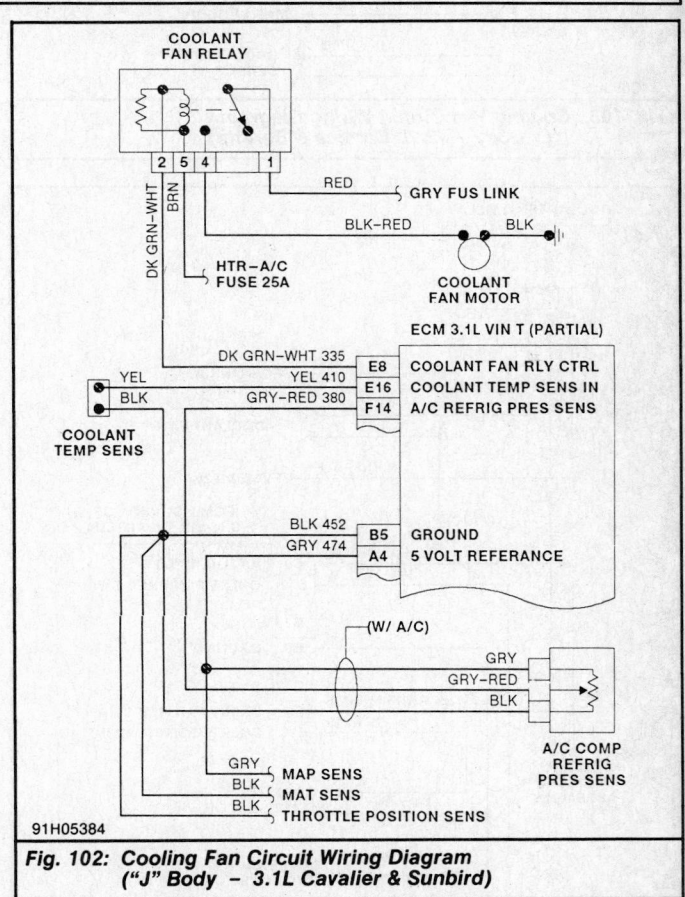

Fig. 102: Cooling Fan Circuit Wiring Diagram ("J" Body – 3.1L Cavalier & Sunbird)

GM
5-140

1991 ENGINE COOLING
Specifications & Electric Cooling Fans – Exc. Cadillac (Cont.)

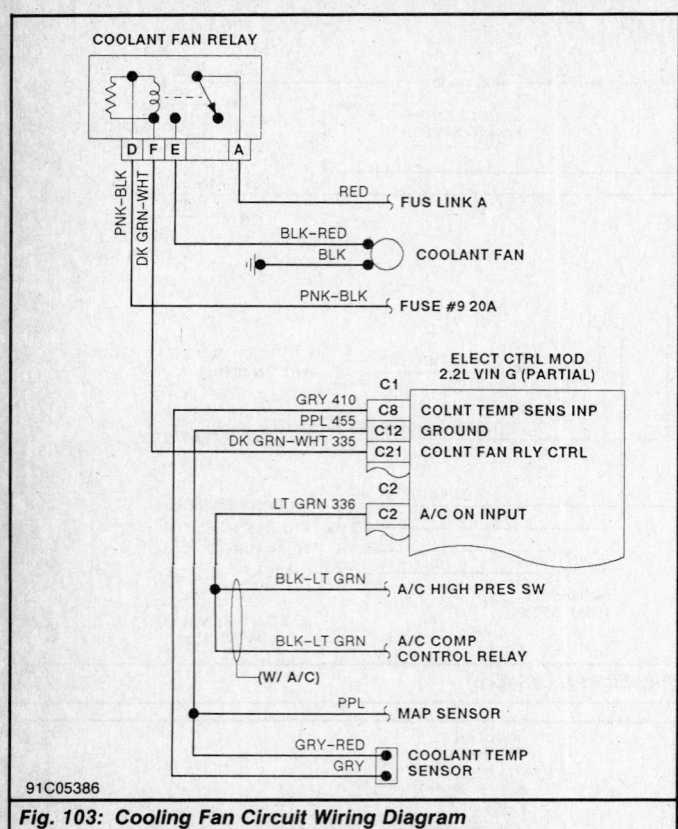

Fig. 103: **Cooling Fan Circuit Wiring Diagram**
("L" Body – 2.2L Corsica & Beretta)

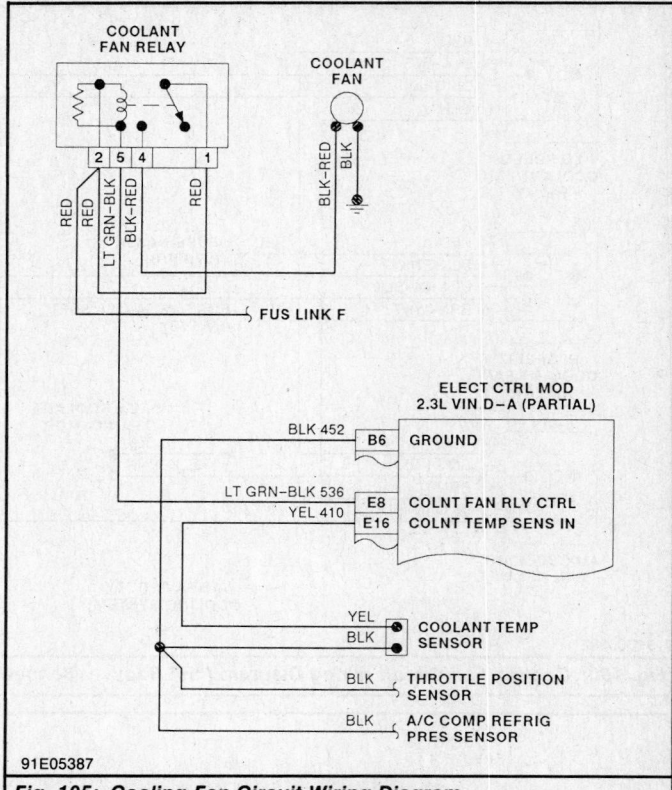

Fig. 105: **Cooling Fan Circuit Wiring Diagram**
("N" Body – 2.3L Cutlass Calais, Grand Am & Skylark)

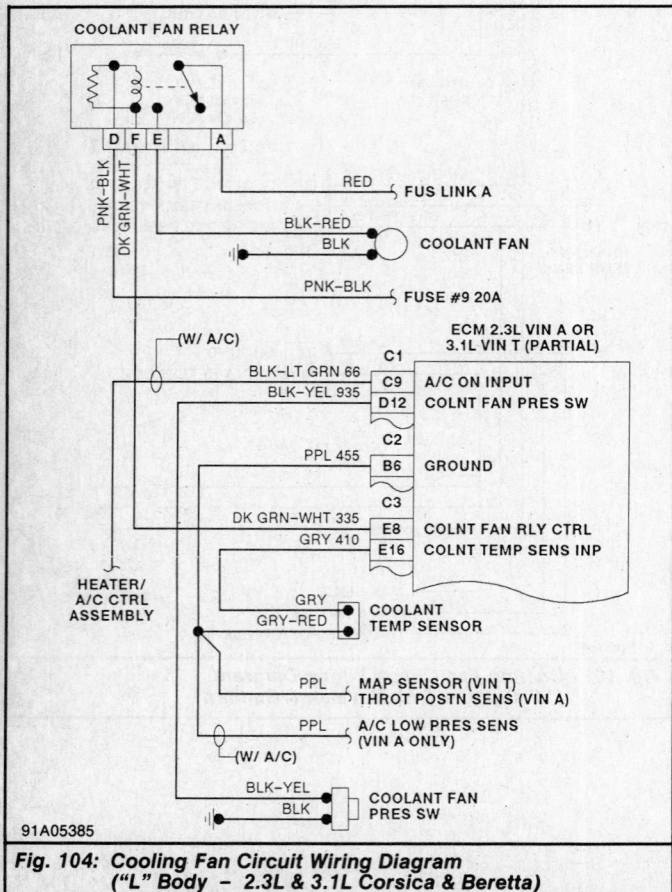

Fig. 104: **Cooling Fan Circuit Wiring Diagram**
("L" Body – 2.3L & 3.1L Corsica & Beretta)

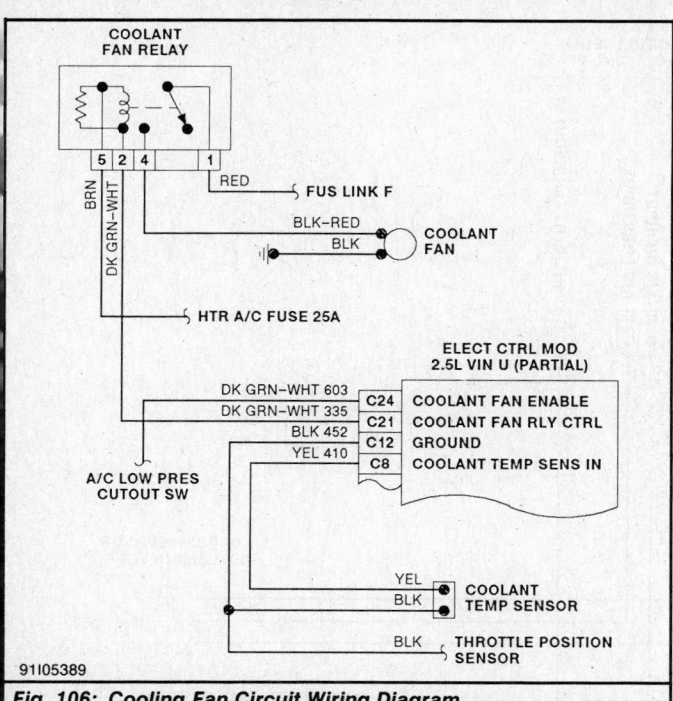

91I05389

Fig. 106: Cooling Fan Circuit Wiring Diagram
("N" Body – 2.5L Cutlass Calais, Grand Am & Skylark)

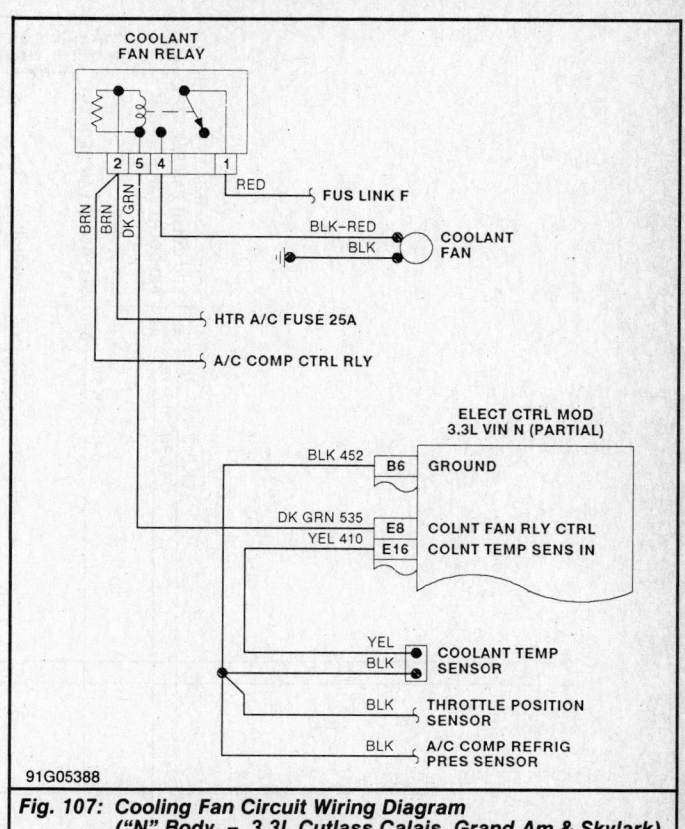

91G05388

Fig. 107: Cooling Fan Circuit Wiring Diagram
("N" Body – 3.3L Cutlass Calais, Grand Am & Skylark)

GM
5-142

1991 ENGINE COOLING
Specifications & Electric Cooling Fans – Exc. Cadillac (Cont.)

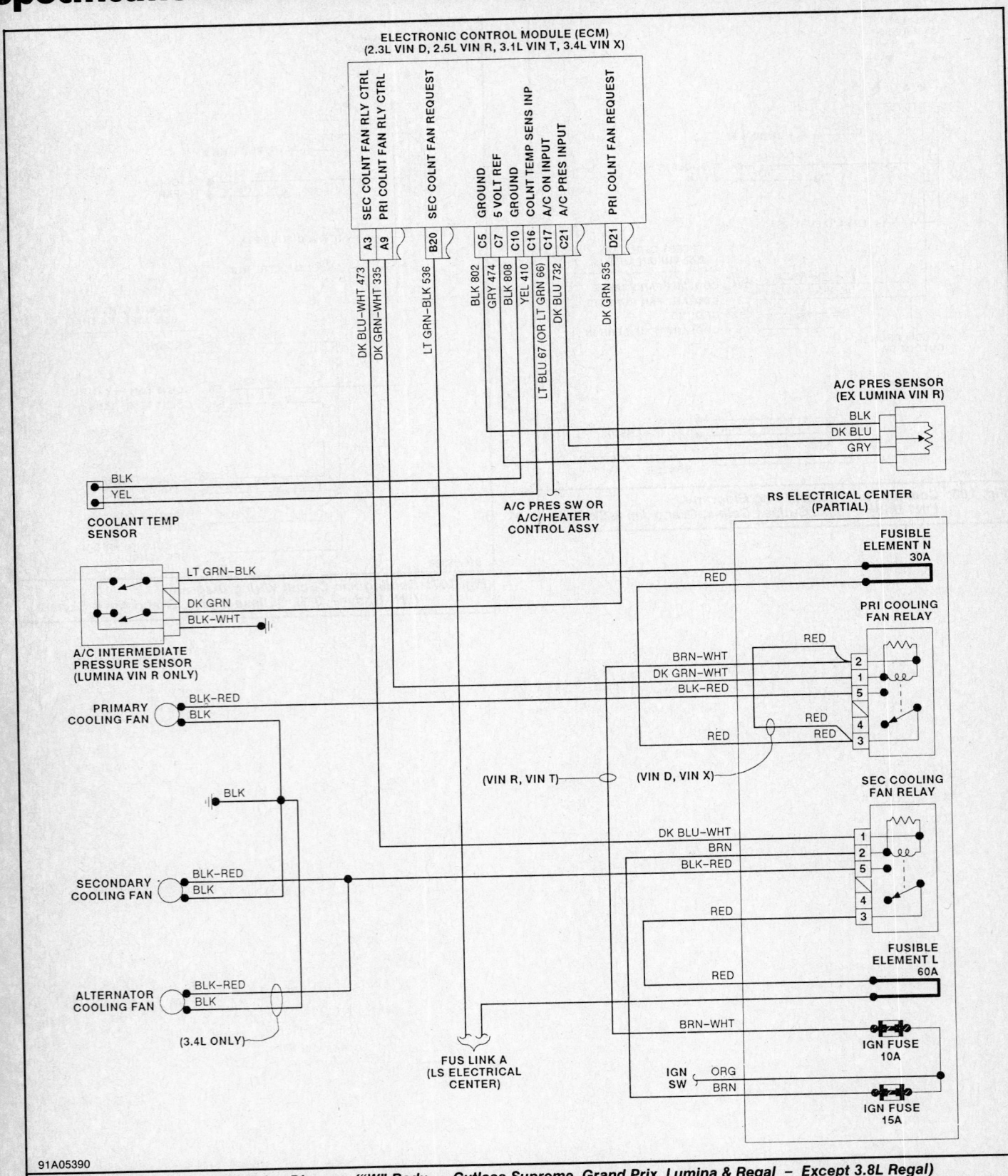

Fig. 108: Cooling Fan Circuit Wiring Diagram ("W" Body – Cutlass Supreme, Grand Prix, Lumina & Regal – Except 3.8L Regal)

91A05390

1991 ENGINE COOLING
Specifications & Electric Cooling Fans – Exc. Cadillac (Cont.)

GM
5-143

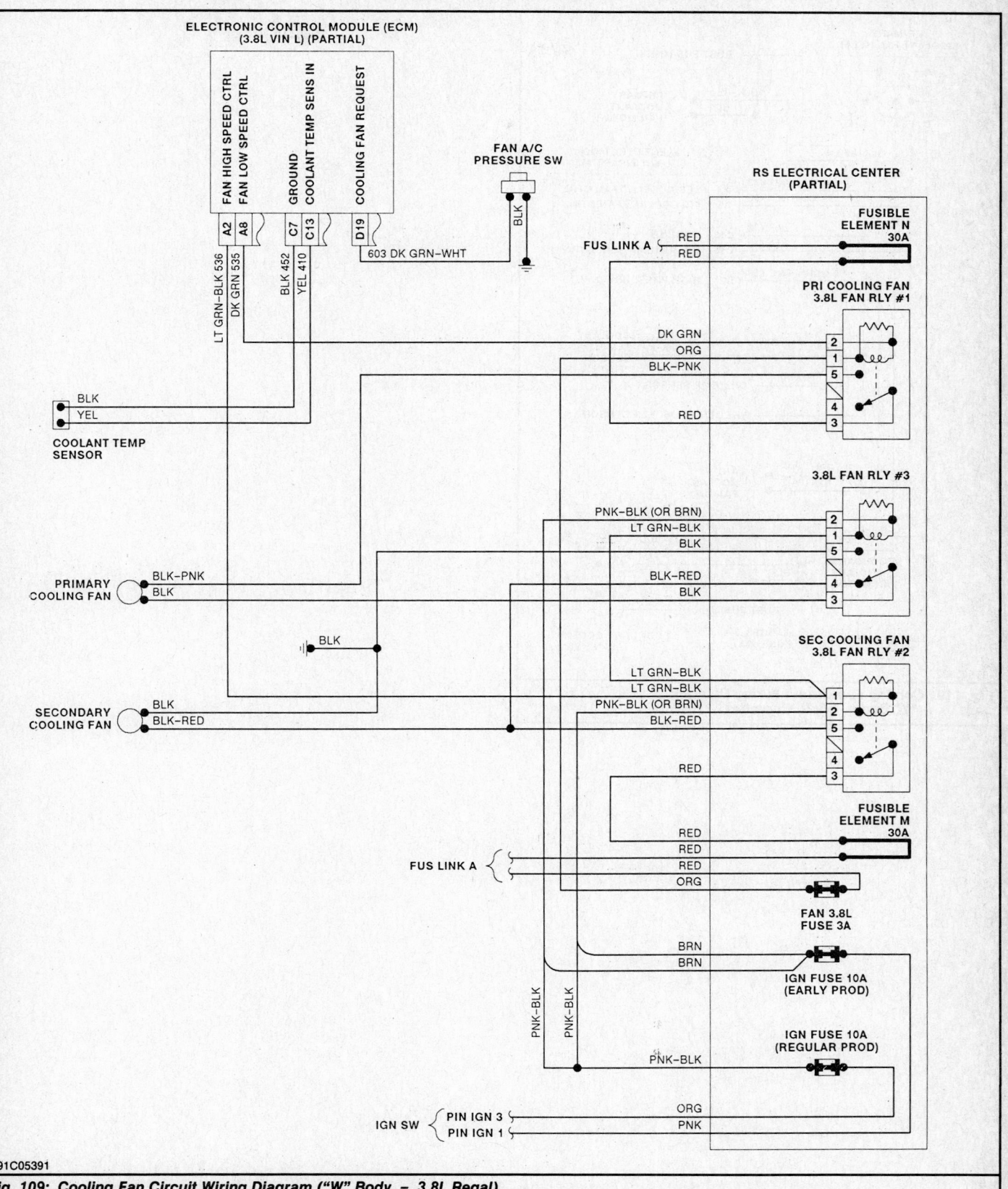

Fig. 109: Cooling Fan Circuit Wiring Diagram ("W" Body – 3.8L Regal)

91C05391

GM
5-144

1991 ENGINE COOLING
Specifications & Electric Cooling Fans – Exc. Cadillac (Cont.)

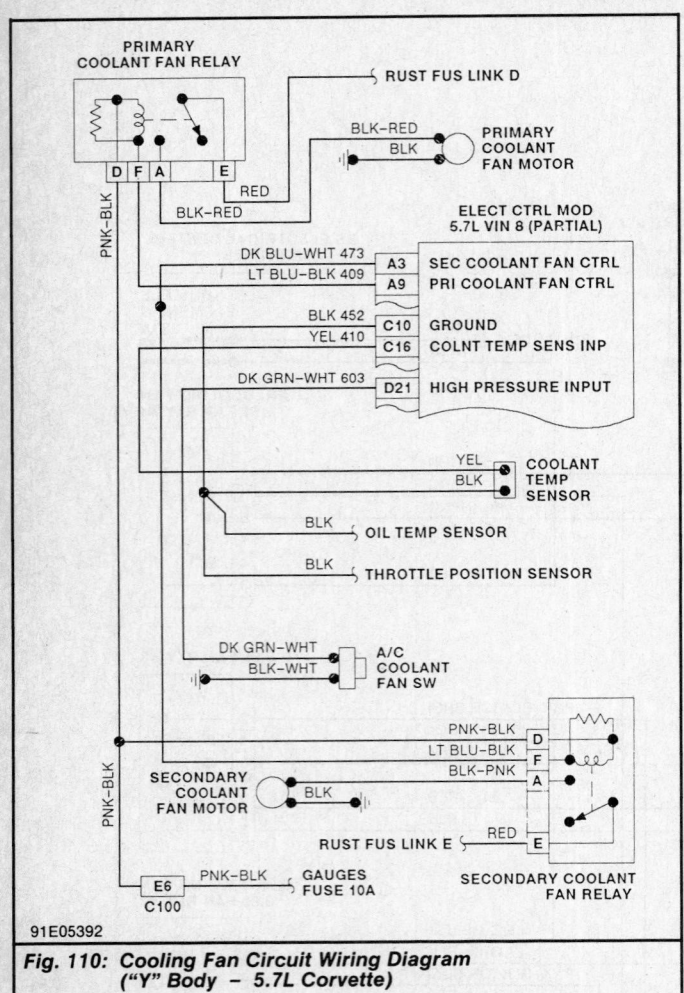

PRIMARY
COOLANT FAN RELAY

RUST FUS LINK D

BLK-RED
BLK

PRIMARY
COOLANT
FAN MOTOR

D F A E

RED

BLK-RED

PNK-BLK

ELECT CTRL MOD
5.7L VIN 8 (PARTIAL)

DK BLU-WHT 473 | A3 | SEC COOLANT FAN CTRL
LT BLU-BLK 409 | A9 | PRI COOLANT FAN CTRL

BLK 452 | C10 | GROUND
YEL 410 | C16 | COLNT TEMP SENS INP

DK GRN-WHT 603 | D21 | HIGH PRESSURE INPUT

YEL
BLK

COOLANT
TEMP
SENSOR

BLK — OIL TEMP SENSOR

BLK — THROTTLE POSITION SENSOR

DK GRN-WHT
BLK-WHT

A/C
COOLANT
FAN SW

PNK-BLK
LT BLU-BLK
BLK-PNK

D
F
A

SECONDARY
COOLANT
FAN MOTOR

BLK

PNK-BLK

RUST FUS LINK E

RED

E

SECONDARY COOLANT
FAN RELAY

E6 | PNK-BLK — GAUGES
C100 | FUSE 10A

91E05392

**Fig. 110: Cooling Fan Circuit Wiring Diagram
("Y" Body – 5.7L Corvette)**

Beretta, Camaro, Cavalier, Corsica, Corvette, Cutlass Calais, Cutlass Supreme, Firebird, Grand Am, Grand Prix, Lumina, Sunbird

DESCRIPTION

All models use a single plate clutch disc, a diaphragm spring-type pressure plate and a permanently lubricated clutch release bearing. Clutch release system is hydraulically operated, and consists of a clutch pedal, clutch master cylinder, clutch slave cylinder and clutch release fork.

The hydraulic clutch system provides automatic clutch release adjustment.

ADJUSTMENTS

CAUTION: DO NOT use mineral or paraffin base oil in clutch hydraulic system. These fluids will damage rubber parts in cylinders.

SLAVE CYLINDER PUSH ROD TRAVEL

1) Raise and support vehicle. Measure slave cylinder push rod travel as clutch pedal is depressed. See SLAVE CYLINDER PUSH ROD TRAVEL SPECIFICATIONS table for minimum travel allowed.

SLAVE CYLINDER PUSH ROD TRAVEL SPECIFICATIONS

Application	Minimum Travel In. (mm)
Camaro & Firebird	.57 (14.5)
Corvette	¹
All Other Models	.43 (10.9)

¹ – Information not available from manufacturer.

2) If push rod travel distance is incorrect, check master cylinder fluid reservoir level. If fluid level is low, check hydraulic system components for leakage.

NOTE: Manufacturers recommend replacing master cylinder and slave cylinder if excessive leakage is evident.

PEDAL FREE PLAY

No manual adjustment is required.

REMOVAL & INSTALLATION

CAUTION: Clutch master cylinder push rod must be removed from clutch pedal before any service requiring slave cylinder removal. If clutch pedal is depressed with slave cylinder removed, permanent slave cylinder damage will result.

CLUTCH

Removal (Beretta, Cavalier, Corsica & Sunbird) – 1) Disconnect negative battery cable. Drain cooling system. Disconnect heater core. Install Engine Support Fixture (J-28467-A) and raise engine enough to take weight off engine mounts. See Fig. 1.

2) Remove left sound insulator. Disconnect clutch master cylinder push rod from clutch pedal. Remove air cleaner and air intake duct assembly. Remove clutch slave cylinder from transaxle and support out of work area.

3) Remove transaxle mounting through bolt. Raise vehicle. Remove exhaust crossover bolts at right exhaust manifold. Lower vehicle. Disconnect left exhaust manifold.

4) Disconnect transaxle mount bracket and shift cables. Remove upper transaxle-to-engine bolts. See Fig. 2. Raise vehicle. Remove left front tire and wheel. Remove left front inner splash shield. Remove transaxle strut and bracket.

5) Drain transaxle. Remove clutch housing cover bolts. Disconnect vehicle speed sensor connector. Disconnect stabilizer shaft at left suspension support and control arm. Remove left suspension support attaching bolts and swing support aside. Remove left drive axle from transaxle.

Fig. 1: Installing Engine Holding Fixture

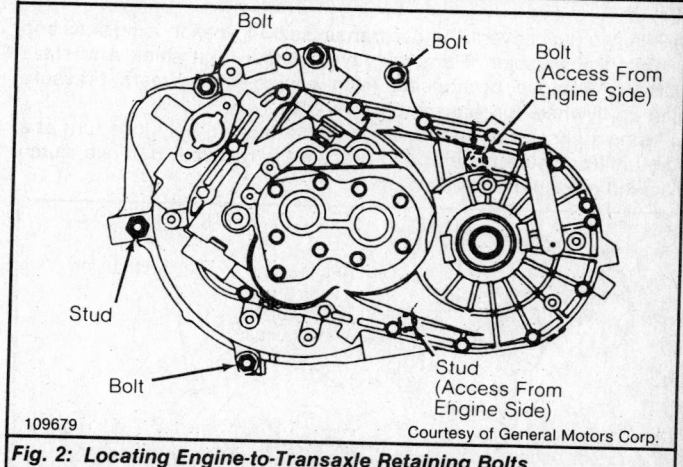

Fig. 2: Locating Engine-to-Transaxle Retaining Bolts

CAUTION: Drive Axle Boot Protector (J-34754) should be modified and installed on drive axle prior to service procedures on or near drive axle. Failure to observe this can result in boot damage and possible joint failure.

6) Remove intermediate shaft housing bolts. Slide intermediate shaft housing away from transaxle. Pry intermediate shaft from transaxle. Secure transaxle to a transmission jack.

7) Remove remaining transaxle-to-engine bolts. Remove transaxle by sliding it away from engine and carefully lowering jack while guiding intermediate shaft out of transaxle.

8) Index mark pressure plate to flywheel for reassembly reference. Using a crisscross sequence, loosen attaching bolts one turn at a time until pressure plate spring tension is relieved. Remove clutch disc and pressure plate. See Fig. 3.

Installation – 1) Position clutch disc and pressure plate on flywheel. Install clutch disc with damper springs toward transaxle. Stamped letters identify "Flywheel Side". Using clutch aligner, center clutch disc.

2) Using a crisscross sequence, install and tighten pressure plate-to-flywheel attaching bolts evenly and gradually. Lightly lubricate fork ends and pack I.D. recess of release bearing with grease.

3) Ensure bearing pads are located on fork ends and spring ends are in fork holes with spring completely seated in bearing groove.

CAUTION: Clutch lever must not move toward flywheel until transaxle is mounted to engine or damage to transaxle will occur.

4) To complete installation, reverse removal procedure. Tighten all bolts to specification. See TORQUE SPECIFICATIONS table at end of this article.

Removal (Camaro & Firebird) – 1) Disconnect negative battery cable. Remove shift lever boot attaching screws. Slide boot up lever and remove lever from transmission. Raise and support vehicle.

2) Remove rear suspension torque arm. Index mark and remove propeller shaft from vehicle. Disconnect speedometer cable and remove transmission mount attaching bolts. Remove catalytic converter hanger. Remove crossmember attaching bolts and remove crossmember.

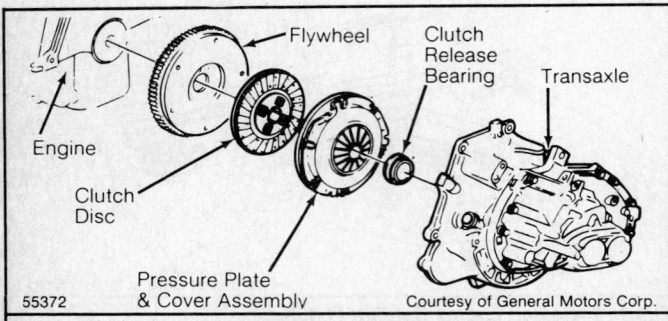

Fig. 3: Exploded View of FWD Clutch Assembly (Except Lumina)

3) Remove dust cover. Remove transmission-to-bellhousing bolts and remove transmission. Remove slave cylinder heat shield and slave cylinder. Remove bellhousing from engine. Index mark pressure plate-to-flywheel for reassembly reference.

4) Using a crisscross sequence, loosen attaching bolts one turn at a time until pressure plate spring pressure is relieved. Remove clutch disc and pressure plate. *See Fig. 4.*

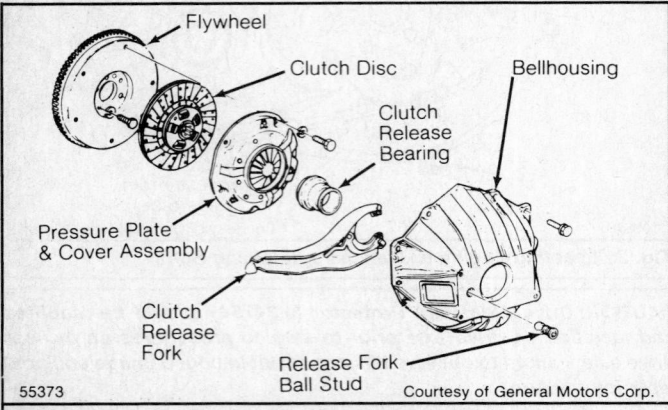

Fig. 4: Exploded View of RWD Clutch Assembly

Installation – 1) Using index marks, position clutch disc and pressure plate onto flywheel. Clutch disc stamped letters identify "Flywheel Side". Using clutch aligner, center clutch disc.

2) Using a crisscross sequence, tighten attaching bolts gradually and evenly. Remove clutch aligner and lubricate fork fingers, ball socket, inside of release bearing collar and clutch fork groove with graphite grease.

3) To complete installation, reverse removal procedure and torque all bolts to specification. See TORQUE SPECIFICATIONS table at end of this article. Check system for proper operation.

Removal (Corvette) – 1) Disconnect negative battery cable. Remove console and accessory trim plates. Remove shift knob and reverse lock-out collar. Raise vehicle. Remove complete exhaust system as an assembly. Remove exhaust hanger from transmission.

2) Support transmission with jack. Remove front crossover hanger from transmission. Mark propeller shaft-to-axle companion flange relationship. Remove propeller shaft. Remove driveline beam bolts and remove driveline beam.

3) Disconnect all electrical connections at transmission. Support engine and lower transmission. Remove transmission-to-bellhousing bolts. Remove transmission.

4) Remove slave cylinder attaching bolts and remove bellhousing. Mark pressure plate and flywheel for reassembly reference. Using a crisscross sequence, loosen pressure plate attaching bolts one turn at a time until spring pressure is released. Remove pressure plate and clutch disc. *See Fig. 4.*

NOTE: *If flywheel is damaged, replace it. DO NOT resurface it.*

Installation – 1) Position clutch disc with damper springs toward transmission and side marked "Flywheel Side" toward flywheel. Use clutch aligner to support and center clutch disc.

2) Position pressure plate on flywheel. Using a crisscross sequence, tighten pressure plate attaching bolts gradually and evenly to prevent distortion. Remove clutch aligner. Apply a light coat of graphite grease to ball socket, fork fingers at release bearing end, inside of release bearing collar and clutch fork groove.

3) To complete installation, reverse removal procedure. Torque all bolts to specification. See TORQUE SPECIFICATIONS table at end of this article. Check system for proper operation.

Removal (Cutlass Calais & Grand Am) – 1) Disconnect negative battery cable. Drain cooling system. Using Hose Clamp Tool (J-37097), disconnect heater core. Install Engine Support Fixture (J-28467-A) and raise engine to take pressure off engine mounts. *See Fig. 1.*

2) Remove left instrument panel sound insulator. Disconnect clutch slave cylinder and set aside. Remove power steering pump and brackets and set aside. Disconnect shift cables. Remove 2 transaxle mount bracket upper bolts from transaxle.

3) Remove upper transaxle-to-engine bolts. *See Fig. 2.* Raise vehicle. Remove front tire and wheel assemblies. Remove left inner splash shield. Drain transaxle. Disconnect speedometer connection at transaxle. Disconnect radiator outlet pipe (water pump inlet) from transaxle.

4) Remove engine mount crossmember retaining nuts from left suspension support. Disconnect stabilizer shaft from left suspension support attaching bolts. Swing stabilizer shaft aside and support with wire. Disconnect left drive axle from transaxle and position aside.

CAUTION: Drive Axle Boot Protector (J-34754) should be modified and installed on drive axle prior to service procedures on or near drive axle. Failure to observe this may result in boot damage and possible joint failure.

5) Remove lower transaxle mounting bracket bolt. Remove transaxle mount through bolt. Disconnect rear engine mounting bracket from engine block.

6) Disconnect stabilizer bar from right control arm. Separate ball joint from strut assembly. Disengage right drive axle from intermediate shaft and position aside. Disconnect remaining intermediate shaft-to-engine block retainer.

7) Remove intermediate shaft. Remove 2 flywheel housing covers. Install transmission jack. Disconnect transaxle ground strap. Remove remaining transaxle mounting spacer and stud. Remove transaxle.

8) Index mark pressure plate to flywheel for reassembly reference. Using a crisscross sequence, loosen attaching bolts one turn at a time until pressure plate spring tension is relieved. Remove clutch disc and pressure plate. *See Fig. 3.*

Installation – 1) Position clutch disc and pressure plate onto flywheel. Install clutch disc with damper springs toward transaxle. Stamped letters identify clutch disc "Flywheel Side". Using clutch aligner, center clutch disc.

2) Using a crisscross sequence, install and tighten pressure plate-to-flywheel attaching bolts evenly and gradually. Lightly lubricate fork ends and pack I.D. recess of release bearing with grease.

3) Ensure bearing pads are located on fork ends and spring ends are in fork holes with spring completely seated in bearing groove.

CAUTION: Clutch lever must not move toward flywheel until transaxle is mounted to engine or damage to transaxle will occur.

4) To complete installation, reverse removal procedure. Tighten all bolts to specification. See TORQUE SPECIFICATIONS table at end of this article.

Removal (Cutlass Supreme & Grand Prix) – 1) Disconnect negative battery cable. Install Engine Support Fixture (J-28467-A) and Support Adapter (J-36462). *See Fig. 1.* Remove air cleaner housing and intake tube. Remove slave cylinder from transaxle.

2) Disconnect electrical connector at speedometer signal assembly. Remove nut and retaining clamp securing shift cables-to-transaxle. Remove nuts from shift cable ball studs and transaxle levers.

3) Disconnect exhaust crossover pipe at left exhaust manifold. Remove EGR tube from crossover pipe. Remove crossover-to-exhaust pipe bolts. Loosen crossover-to-right exhaust manifold clamp.

4) Swing crossover pipe upward to gain clearance for top transaxle bolts. Remove upper transaxle mounting bolts and upper transaxle mounting studs. *See Fig. 2.* Leave one lower engine-to-transaxle mounting stud and one lower engine-to-transaxle mounting bolt attached.

5) Disconnect connection at back-up light switch. Raise vehicle. Drain transaxle. Remove 4 clutch housing cover retaining screws. Remove front wheel and tire assemblies. Remove right and left wheelwell splash shields.

6) Remove power steering cooler lines from frame. Remove power steering rack and pinion heat shield. Remove power steering rack and pinion from frame. Remove right and left ball joints at steering knuckle.

7) Remove transaxle mount upper retaining bolts. Remove engine mount lower retaining nuts. Remove frame retaining bolts. Remove crossmember from body frame. Remove right and left drive axles from transaxle and support to vehicle body.

8) Remove starter assembly and support to body. Securely attach transaxle case to transmission jack. Remove remaining engine-to-transaxle mounting bolt and stud. Remove transaxle assembly.

9) Index mark pressure plate to flywheel for reassembly reference. Using a crisscross sequence. Loosen attaching bolts one turn at a time until pressure plate spring tension is relieved. Remove clutch disc and pressure plate. *See Fig. 3.*

Installation – 1) Position clutch disc and pressure plate onto flywheel. Install clutch disc with damper springs toward transaxle. Stamped letters identify "Flywheel Side". Using clutch aligner, center clutch disc.

2) Using a crisscross sequence, install and tighten pressure plate-to-flywheel attaching bolts evenly and gradually. Lightly lubricate fork ends and pack I.D. recess of release bearing with grease.

3) Ensure bearing pads are located on fork ends and spring ends are in fork holes with spring completely seated in bearing groove.

4) To complete installation, reverse removal procedure. Tighten all bolts to specification. See TORQUE SPECIFICATIONS table at end of this article.

CAUTION: *DO NOT clean release bearing with degreasers as seal failure will result.*

Removal (Lumina) – 1) Remove air cleaner assembly. Disconnect negative battery cable. Install Engine Support Fixture (J-28467-A) and Support Adapter (J-36462). Remove left sound insulator. Disconnect clutch master cylinder pushrod from pedal. Remove 2 nuts holding slave cylinder to transaxle housing.

2) Remove slave cylinder. Disconnect harness at speedometer signal assembly. Remove clamp securing shift cables to transaxle. Disconnect exhaust pipe at left manifold. Loosen exhaust pipe at right manifold, and swing pipe upward for access to upper transaxle mounting bolts.

3) Remove 2 upper mounting bolts and studs, leave one lower mounting bolt and one lower stud in place. Disconnect harness from back-up lamp switch. Raise vehicle and drain transaxle. Remove 4 clutch cover housing bolts. Remove front wheel assemblies. Remove left and right splash shields.

4) Disconnect steering cooler lines from frame. Remove steering rack heat shield. Remove steering rack assembly from frame. Disconnect left and right lower ball joints at steering knuckle. Remove transaxle mount upper retaining bolts. Remove engine mount lower retaining nuts. Remove frame retaining bolts and remove frame.

5) Remove drive axles from transaxle and support by tying to underbody. Remove starter assembly and tie to underbody. Support transaxle using transaxle jack. Remove remaining transaxle mounting bolt and stud. Remove transaxle.

6) Using a flat-blade screwdriver, remove release bearing from clutch cover. *See Fig 5.* Index mark clutch cover to flywheel for proper reinstallation.

7) Loosen attaching bolts evenly until clutch tension is relieved. Remove clutch cover and carefully note "flywheel side" of disc. Inspect all components, paying particular attention to wedge collar fingers, and replace as necessary prior to installation. *See Fig. 6.*

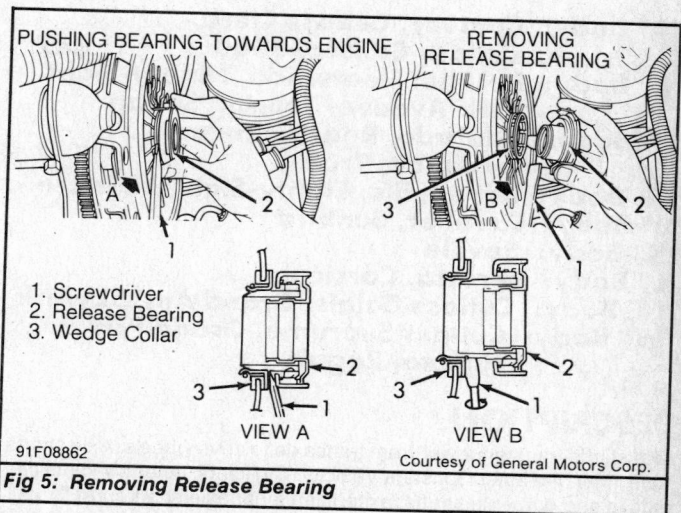

1. Screwdriver
2. Release Bearing
3. Wedge Collar

91F08862   Courtesy of General Motors Corp.

Fig 5: Removing Release Bearing

CAUTION: *DO NOT clean release bearing with degreasers as seal failure will result.*

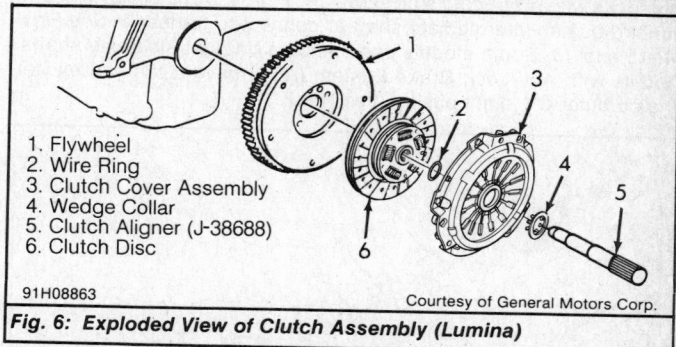

1. Flywheel
2. Wire Ring
3. Clutch Cover Assembly
4. Wedge Collar
5. Clutch Aligner (J-38688)
6. Clutch Disc

91H08863   Courtesy of General Motors Corp.

Fig. 6: Exploded View of Clutch Assembly (Lumina)

Installation – To install reverse removal procedure. Lightly lubricate all pivot points and clutch splines. Use Clutch Aligner (J-38688) to align clutch disc prior to tightening clutch cover attaching bolts.

TORQUE SPECIFICATIONS

TORQUE SPECIFICATIONS

Application	Ft. Lbs. (N.m)
Flywheel-to-Crankshaft Bolts	
Camaro & Firebird	
V6 Engine	50 (68)
V8 Engine	74 (100)
Corvette	74 (100)
All Other Models	52 (70)
Pressure Plate-to-Flywheel Bolts	
Camaro & Firebird	
V6 Engine	15 (20)
V8 Engine	30 (40)
Corvette	30 (40)
All Other Models	16 (21)
Transaxle-to-Engine Block	
Bolts or Nuts	55 (75)
Transmission-to-Bellhousing Bolts	
Camaro & Firebird	15 (20)
Corvette	37 (50)
Transmission-to-Engine Block Bolts	
Camaro & Firebird	
V6 Engine	55 (75)
V8 Engine	68 (92)
Corvette	37 (50)

1991 DRIVE AXLES
FWD Axle Shafts

"A" Body: Century, Cutlass Ciera, Cutlass Cruiser, 6000
"C" Body: DeVille, Fleetwood, Ninety-Eight, Park Avenue, Touring Sedan
"E" Body: Eldorado, Reatta, Riviera, Toronado, Trofeo
"H" Body: Bonneville, Eighty-Eight, LeSabre
"J" Body Cavalier, Sunbird
"K" Body: Seville
"L" Body: Beretta, Corsica
"N" Body: Cutlass Calais, Grand Am, Skylark
"W" Body: Cutlass Supreme, Grand Prix, Lumina, Regal

DESCRIPTION

Axle shafts transfer power from transaxle to drive wheels. Axle shafts have inner and outer Constant Velocity (CV) joints. Inner CV joints can slide in and out. Axle shafts, except left inner axle shaft on A/T models, use a male splined end and interlock with transaxle gears by a circlip.

Left inner axle shaft on A/T models uses a female splined end, and interlocks with protruding stub shaft. *See Figs. 1, 5 and 6.* Cavalier and Sunbird use an intermediate shaft to connect to transaxle. *See Figs. 14, 15 and 16.* Some models use dampers on right-side axle shafts. Models with Anti-Lock Brake System (ABS) have a toothed exciter ring on outer CV joint housing. *See Fig. 2.*

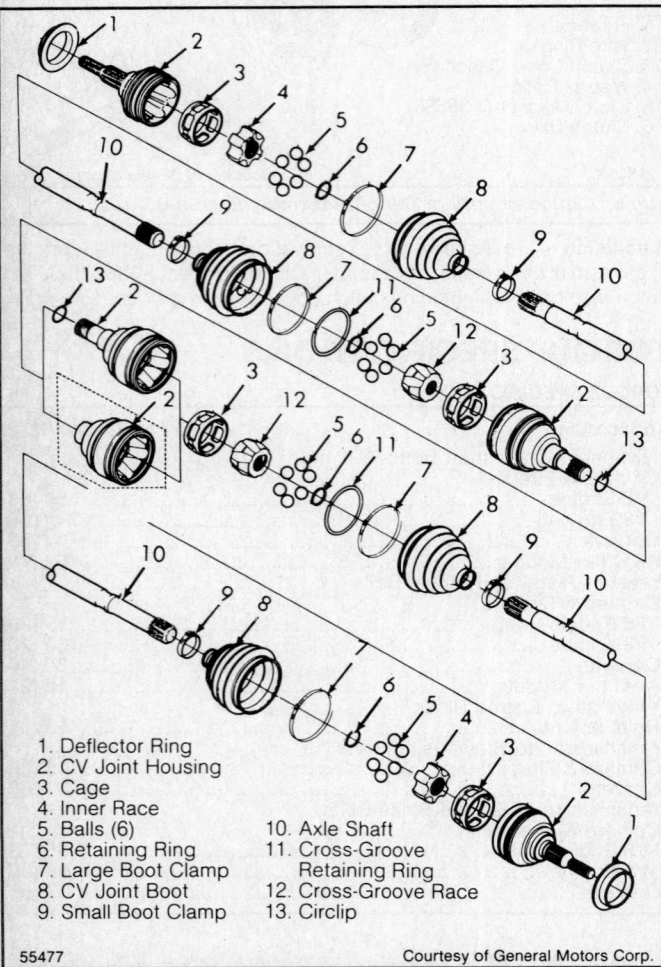

1. Deflector Ring
2. CV Joint Housing
3. Cage
4. Inner Race
5. Balls (6)
6. Retaining Ring
7. Large Boot Clamp
8. CV Joint Boot
9. Small Boot Clamp
10. Axle Shaft
11. Cross-Groove Retaining Ring
12. Cross-Groove Race
13. Circlip

55477   Courtesy of General Motors Corp.

Fig. 1: Exploded View of Axle Shaft (Cross-Groove Type)

CAUTION: On models with ABS, protect toothed exciter ring on outer CV joint, and wheel speed sensor on steering knuckle during disassembly and reassembly.

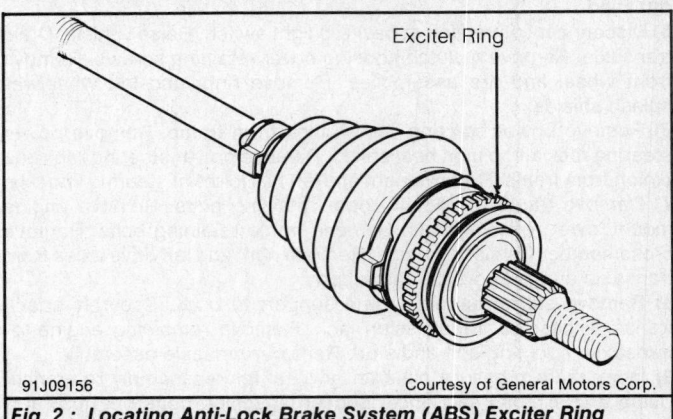

Exciter Ring

91J09156   Courtesy of General Motors Corp.

Fig. 2 : Locating Anti-Lock Brake System (ABS) Exciter Ring

REMOVAL & INSTALLATION

HUB & BEARING ASSEMBLY

NOTE: Hub and bearing must be replaced as an assembly.

Removal – 1) Loosen wheel lug nuts. Remove cotter pin and lock nut from axle shaft. Loosen hub nut. Raise and support vehicle. Remove wheel. Remove brake hose retaining clip from strut. Remove brake caliper and support aside. Remove rotor, hub nut and washer.
2) Remove bolts retaining hub and bearing assembly to steering knuckle. *See Fig. 3.* Install Hub Remover/Installer (J-28733) and remove hub and bearing assembly. *See Fig. 4.*

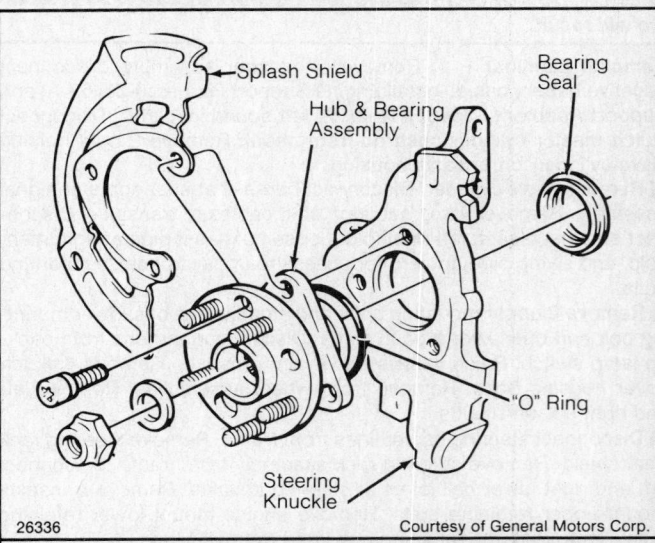

Splash Shield
Hub & Bearing Assembly
Bearing Seal
"O" Ring
Steering Knuckle

26336   Courtesy of General Motors Corp.

Fig. 3: Exploded View of Hub & Bearing Assembly (Typical)

Installation – 1) Install new "O" ring on hub and bearing assembly Using driver, install new seal in steering knuckle. Position hub and bearing assembly in steering knuckle bore. Install NEW hub nut and tighten until bearing and hub assembly is seated. Tighten to specification. See TORQUE SPECIFICATIONS table at end of article. Install hub-to-steering knuckle bolts and tighten evenly to specification.
2) To complete installation, reverse removal procedure. On models with bracket stops on upper and lower ends of brake calipers, check clearance. Clearance should be .005-.012" (.13-.31 mm) at each end. Replace or grind stops as necessary to ensure caliper slides freely.

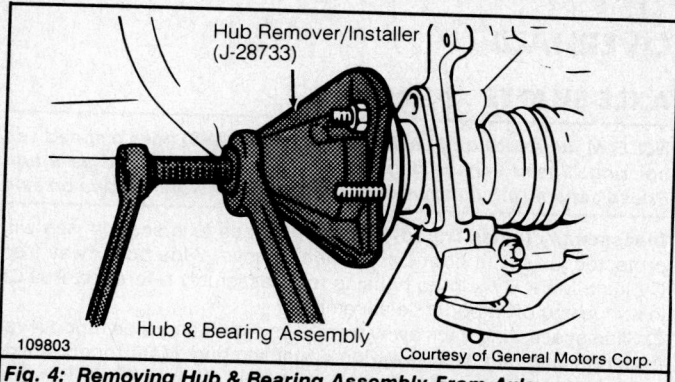

Fig. 4: Removing Hub & Bearing Assembly From Axle

109803 — Courtesy of General Motors Corp.

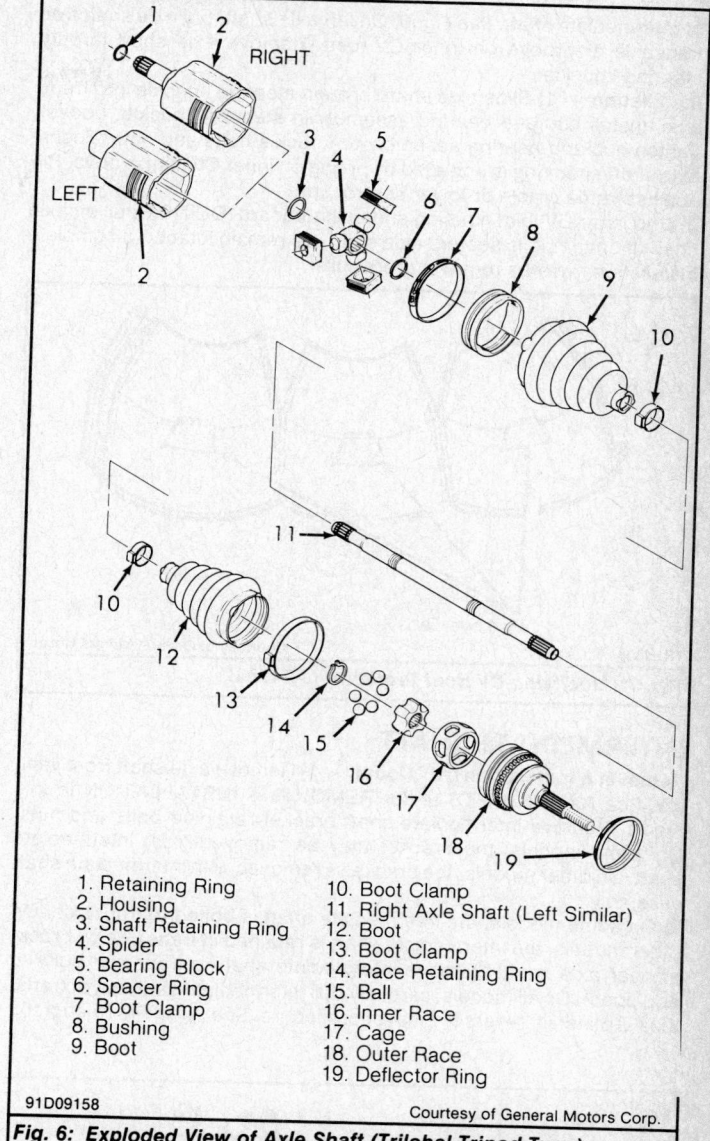

1. Retaining Ring
2. Housing
3. Shaft Retaining Ring
4. Spider
5. Bearing Block
6. Spacer Ring
7. Boot Clamp
8. Bushing
9. Boot
10. Boot Clamp
11. Right Axle Shaft (Left Similar)
12. Boot
13. Boot Clamp
14. Race Retaining Ring
15. Ball
16. Inner Race
17. Cage
18. Outer Race
19. Deflector Ring

91D09158 — Courtesy of General Motors Corp.

Fig. 6: Exploded View of Axle Shaft (Trilobal Tripod Type)

1. Retaining Ring
2. Housing
3. Shaft Retaining Ring
4. Joint Spider
5. Needle Retainer Ring
6. Needle Retainer
7. Ball
8. Needle Roller
9. Spacer Ring
10. Boot Clamp
11. Bushing
12. Boot
13. Boot Clamp
14. Axle Shaft
15. Boot
16. Boot Clamp
17. Race Retaining Ring
18. Ball
19. Inner Race
20. Cage
21. Outer Ring
22. Deflector Ring

91B09157 — Courtesy of General Motors Corp.

Fig. 5: Exploded View of Axle Shaft (Tripod Type)

AXLE SHAFTS

CAUTION: Protect CV joint boots to prevent damage. Keep axle shaft straight during removal and installation.

Removal & Installation (Except "W" Body) – **1)** Raise and support vehicle. Remove tire and wheel assembly. Install modified CV Boot Protector (J-34754). *See Fig. 7.* Insert drift in brake rotor to prevent turning. Remove axle shaft nut and washer.

2) Remove lower ball joint cotter pin and nut. Using Ball Joint Separator (J-29330), separate ball joint from knuckle by prying down on control arm. Pull out on lower knuckle area and strike end of axle shaft with soft-faced hammer to disengage axle hub.

3) Pull knuckle assembly away from axle shaft. Position knuckle assembly to rear. Using slide hammer and Axle Shaft Remover (J-33008), remove axle shaft from transaxle or intermediate shaft. *See Fig. 8.* To install, reverse removal procedure.

Removal ("W" Body) – Remove hub from steering knuckle. See HUB & BEARING ASSEMBLY under REMOVAL & INSTALLATION in this article. Install modified CV Boot Protector (J-34754). *See Fig. 7.* Place drain pan under transaxle. On right axle shaft, use slide hammer and Axle Shaft Remover (J-33008) to remove axle shaft from transaxle or intermediate shaft. *See Fig. 8.* On left axle shaft, pry axle shaft from transaxle at groove on inner CV joint. Remove axle shaft through steering knuckle.

Installation – 1) Slide axle shaft through steering knuckle into transaxle. Install hub and bearing assembly in steering knuckle. Loosely tighten hub and bearing assembly-to-knuckle bolts and nuts. Ensure axle shaft snap ring is engaged by prying on inner CV joint groove. Pry against frame cradle or lower control arm.

2) Grip inner CV joint housing and pull outboard. DO NOT pull on axle shaft. If snap ring is seated, axle shaft will remain intact. To complete installation, reverse removal procedure.

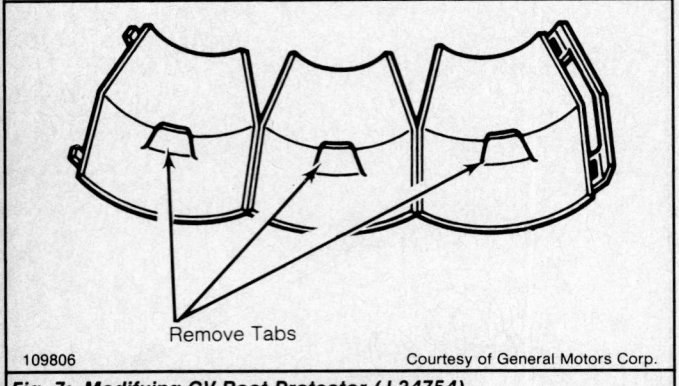

109806   Courtesy of General Motors Corp.

Fig. 7: Modifying CV Boot Protector (J-34754)

INTERMEDIATE SHAFT

Removal & Installation ("J" Body) – 1) Remove axle shaft from vehicle. See AXLE SHAFTS under REMOVAL & INSTALLATION in this article. Remove intermediate shaft bracket retaining bolts and nuts. On some models, the bracket may be removed from intermediate shaft. On other models, the bracket is removed with intermediate shaft assembly.

2) On some models, the intermediate shaft is bolted to transaxle. On other models, the intermediate shaft is retained in transaxle by bracket near axle shaft. Remove intermediate shaft-to-transaxle bolts (if equipped). On all models, carefully pull intermediate shaft out of transaxle. To install, reverse removal procedure. *See Figs. 14, 15 and 16.*

OVERHAUL

AXLE SHAFTS

NOTE: Models with Anti-Lock Brake System (ABS) have a speed sensor ring. Speed sensor ring and joint must be replaced as a unit. Speed sensor ring must be checked whenever work is done on axle.

Disassembly (Inner Tripod Type) – 1) Place axle shaft in vise with protected jaws. Cut boot clamps and remove. Slide boot away from CV joint. Mark CV joint to housing for reassembly reference. Pull CV joint housing off tripod/axle assembly.

2) Slide spacer ring back away from tripod joint, and slide tripod away from retaining ring. Remove tripod retaining ring. Mark tripod to axle shaft for installation reference. Slide tripod off axle shaft. Remove spacer ring. Remove boot (if replacing).

Inspection – Wash all parts (except boots) in solvent and dry with compressed air. Wash boots with soap and water. Inspect races for excessive wear and scoring. Inspect splined areas of shafts for wear, cracks and twists. Inspect balls for pitting, cracking or scoring. Check for cracks, chips or heavy dents on cage windows.

Reassembly – 1) Pack CV joint housing with approximately one-half amount of grease supplied in kit. Apply remaining grease in boot. Install small clamp and boot on axle shaft (if removed). Slide spacer ring on axle shaft past groove. Slide tripod on axle shaft. Install tripod in original location (marked during disassembly).

2) Install tripod retaining snap ring. Slide tripod against snap ring and install spacer ring in groove. Slide CV joint housing on tripod assembly. Position boot over housing. Remove trapped air; using a blunt screwdriver, lift large end of boot off sealed area. *See Fig. 8.*

3) Measure length of boot. *See Fig. 9.* Ensure length is 5.1" (130 mm) before clamping boot clamps. Move CV joint housing in or out as necessary. When length is within specification, position clamps on boot. Use Boot Clamp Installer (J-35910) and torque wrench to install boot clamps.

4) Large boot clamp should be tightened to 130 ft. lbs. (176 N.m). Small boot clamps should be tighten to 100 ft. lbs (136 N.m). Recheck boot length. To complete installation, reverse disassembly procedure.

NOTE: DO NOT disassemble inner CV joint on cross-groove-type axle shaft. Replace as a complete assembly.

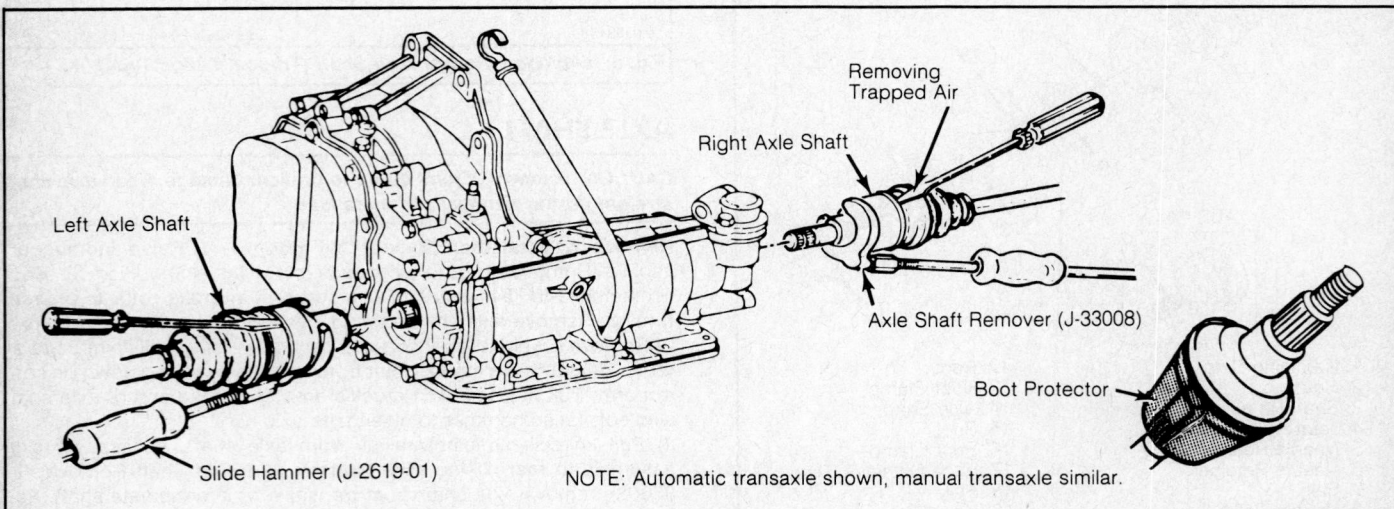

26472   Courtesy of General Motors Corp.

Fig. 8: Removing Axle Shaft from Transaxle

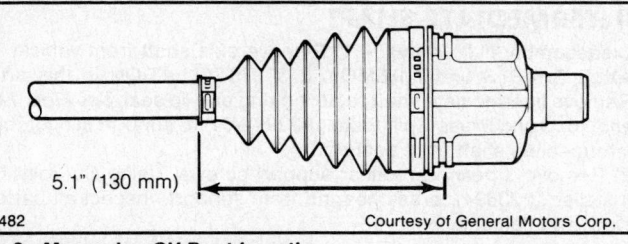

5.1" (130 mm)

55482   Courtesy of General Motors Corp.

Fig. 9: Measuring CV Boot Length

Disassembly (Cross-Groove-Type Outer CV Joints) – 1) Place axle shaft in vise with protected jaws. Cut boot clamps and remove clamps. Slide boot away from CV joint assembly.

2) Remove CV joint-to-axle shaft snap ring. *See Fig. 10.* Pull CV joint and housing assembly off axle shaft. Remove boot if replacing. Using a brass drift and hammer, gently tap on cage until tilted enough to remove first ball.

3) Repeat procedure for remaining balls. Pivot cage and inner race. Align cage windows with lands of outer race. *See Fig. 10.* Remove inner race and cage. Rotate inner race and align land with cage window. Remove inner race.

4) Remove steel deflector ring from end of stub shaft with hammer and brass drift. Remove rubber deflector ring by stretching ring out of its groove.

Reassembly – 1) Apply light coat of specified grease on all mating surfaces. Install small boot clamp and boot on axle shaft. To reassemble inner race, cage and balls, reverse disassembly procedure. *See Fig. 10.* Ensure retaining ring side of inner race faces axle shaft.

2) Pack CV joint with one-half amount of grease supplied in kit. Spread remaining grease evenly in boot. Install new retaining ring in CV joint. Slide CV joint assembly onto axle shaft. Ensure retaining ring seats in groove on axle shaft. Position large end of boot over housing and install boot clamp.

3) Use Boot Clamp Installer (J-34773) and torque wrench to install small boot clamp. Tighten small boot clamp to 100 ft. lbs. (136 N.m). Use boot clamp installer and torque wrench to tighten large boot clamp to 130 ft. lbs. (176 N.m).

4) Install new steel deflector ring with flange toward CV joint (if equipped). *See Fig. 11.* Install rubber deflector rings (flange toward hub assembly) by stretching ring over housing and seating in groove. To complete reassembly, reverse disassembly procedure.

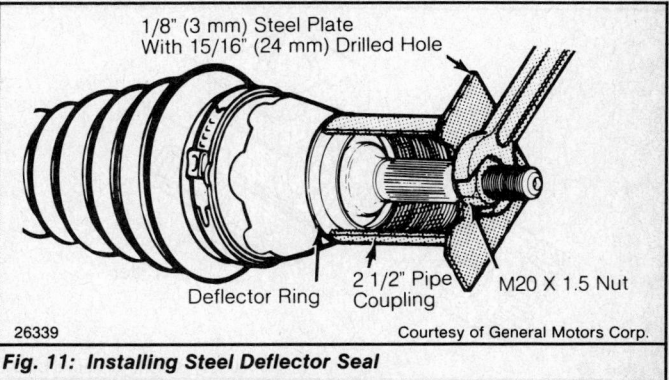

1/8" (3 mm) Steel Plate
With 15/16" (24 mm) Drilled Hole

2 1/2" Pipe Coupling

M20 X 1.5 Nut

Deflector Ring

26339   Courtesy of General Motors Corp.

Fig. 11: Installing Steel Deflector Seal

Disassembly (Trilobal Tripod Joint) – 1) Cut boot clamps and discard. Separate boot from trilobal tripod bushing and slide away from joint.

CAUTION: DO NOT cut through boot, as it may damage sealing surface of outer housing and trilobal tripod bushing.

2) Remove housing from spider and shaft. Spread spacer ring and slide spacer ring and spider back on axle shaft. Remove shaft retainer ring from groove at end of axle shaft. Slide spider assembly off shaft. Remove trilobal tripod bushing from housing. Remove spacer ring and boot from axle.

Inspection – Inspect boot, spider, housing, trilobal tripod bushing and bearing blocks for damage or wear.

Reassembly – 1) Install small boot clamp on neck of boot. DO NOT crimp. Slide boot onto shaft, and position neck of boot in seal groove on axle shaft. Crimp retaining clamp with Boot Clamp Installer (J-35910) to 100 ft. lbs. (136 N.m).

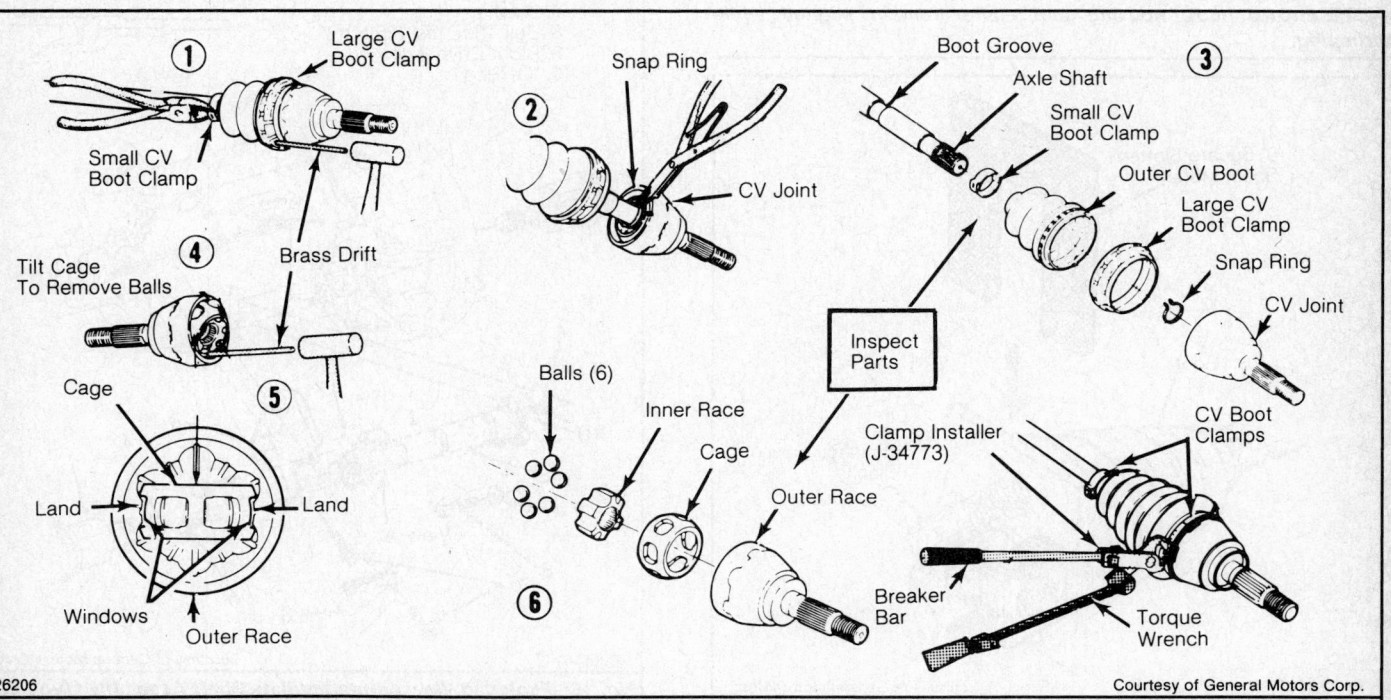

26206   Courtesy of General Motors Corp.

Fig. 10: Disassembling Outer CV Joint (Cross-Groove Type)

2) Install spacer ring past second groove on shaft. Apply small amount of grease to inside of bearing blocks before assembling. Align flats on opening in bearing block, with flats on spider trunnion. Rotate 90 degrees to secure block to spider. *See Fig. 12.*

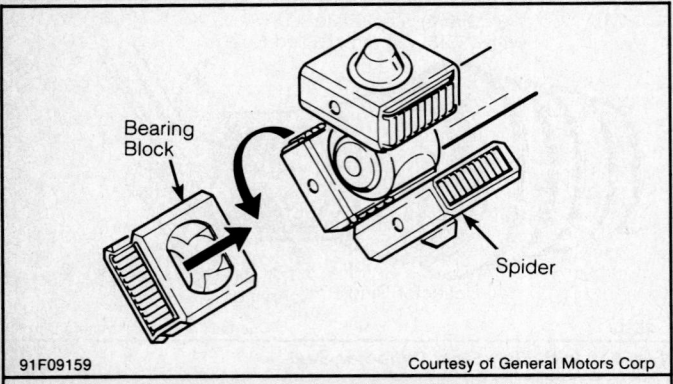

91F09159   Courtesy of General Motors Corp

Fig. 12: Installing Bearing Blocks (Trilobal Tripod Type)

3) Slide spider against spacer ring on shaft. Install shaft retaining ring in groove at end of shaft. Slide spider towards end of shaft and seat spacer ring in groove on shaft. Pack CV joint housing with approximately one-half amount of grease supplied in kit. Apply remaining grease in boot.

NOTE: Ensure counterbored face of spider faces end of shaft.

4) Place slotted, 6" square metal sheet between boot and bearing blocks to maintain proper bearing block alignment during reassembly. *See Fig. 13.* Install trilobal tripod bushing in housing. Position large clamp on boot. Slide housing over spider assembly and shaft; remove slotted metal sheet. Slide large end of boot, with clamp in place, over outside of trilobal tripod bushing and locate lip of boot in groove.

5) Position joint assembly at installed length. Ensuring boot is not dimpled, stretched or out of shape in any way, crimp large diameter retaining clamp with Boot Clamp Installer (J-35566) to 130 ft. lbs (176 N.m).

NOTE: Ensure boot, housing and clamp remain aligned while crimping.

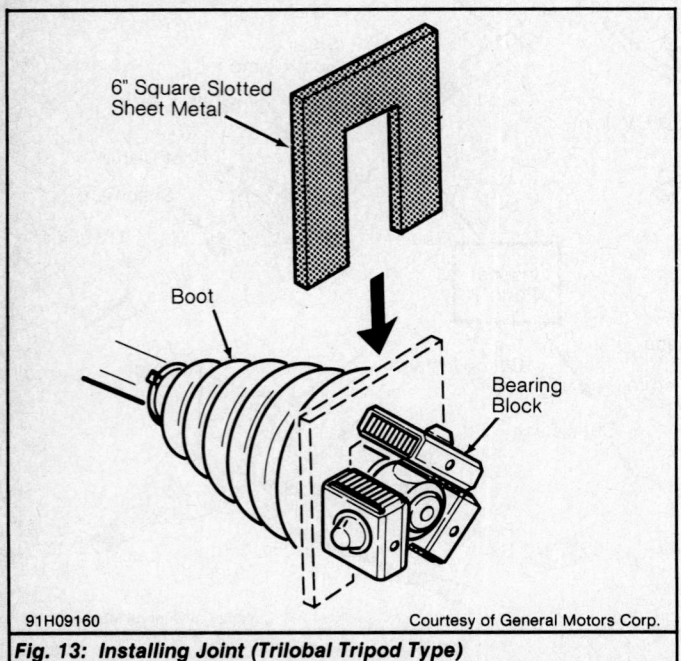

91H09160   Courtesy of General Motors Corp.

Fig. 13: Installing Joint (Trilobal Tripod Type)

INTERMEDIATE SHAFT

Disassembly ("J" Body) – 1) Remove axle shaft from vehicle. See AXLE SHAFTS under REMOVAL & INSTALLATION in this article. Remove intermediate shaft retaining ring and lip seal. *See Figs. 14, 15 and 16.* Using Press-Split Plate (J-22912-01) to support slinger, press intermediate shaft from bearing.

2) Remove 3 bearing retainer support screws. Using CV Joint Boot Installer (J-23694), press bearing from support. Inspect all parts for wear and damage.

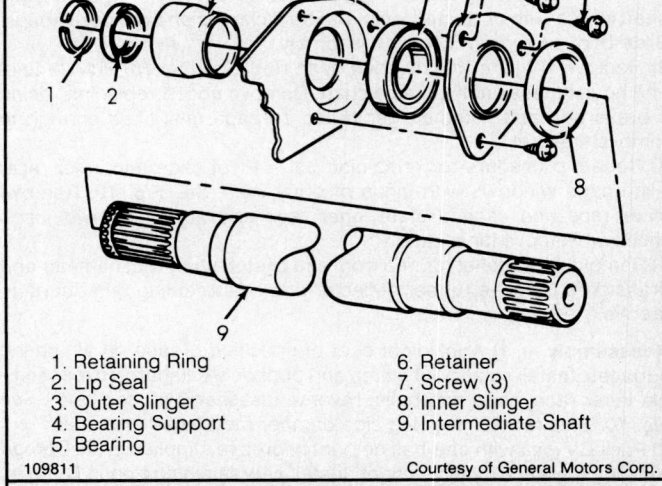

1. Retaining Ring
2. Lip Seal
3. Outer Slinger
4. Bearing Support
5. Bearing
6. Retainer
7. Screw (3)
8. Inner Slinger
9. Intermediate Shaft

109811   Courtesy of General Motors Corp.

Fig. 14: Exploded View of Intermediate Shaft Assembly (Type 1)

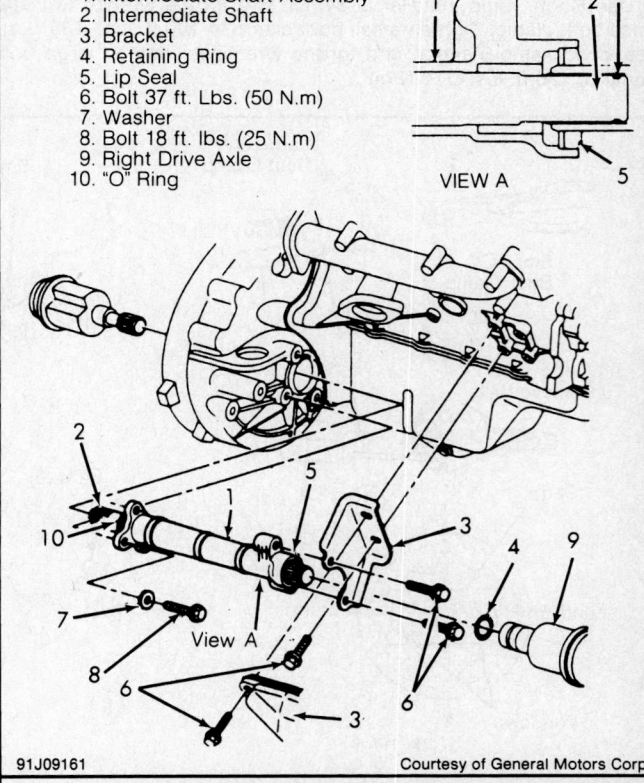

1. Intermediate Shaft Assembly
2. Intermediate Shaft
3. Bracket
4. Retaining Ring
5. Lip Seal
6. Bolt 37 ft. Lbs. (50 N.m)
7. Washer
8. Bolt 18 ft. lbs. (25 N.m)
9. Right Drive Axle
10. "O" Ring

VIEW A

91J09161   Courtesy of General Motors Corp.

Fig. 15: Exploded View of Intermediate Shaft Assembly (Type 2)

Reassembly – Press a new bearing into bearing support. Using press-split plate, press inner slinger on shaft. Install bearing retainer with 3 screws. To complete reassembly, reverse disassembly procedure.

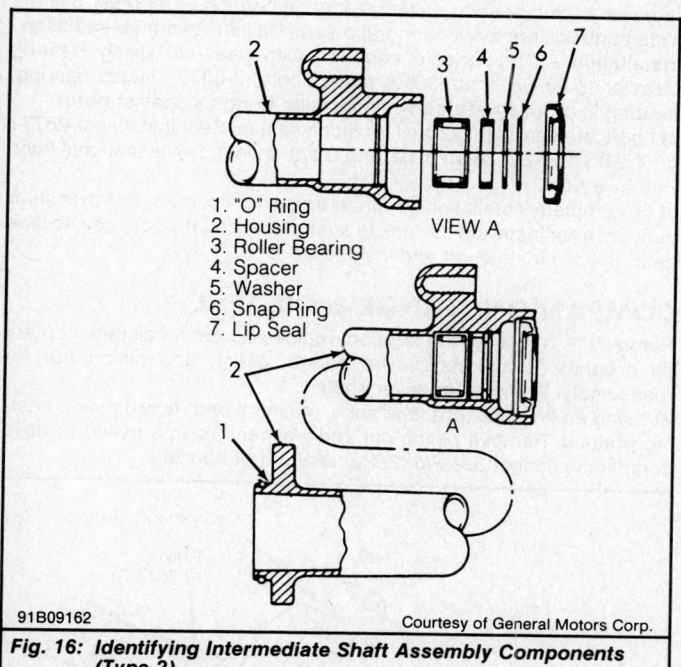

1. "O" Ring
2. Housing
3. Roller Bearing
4. Spacer
5. Washer
6. Snap Ring
7. Lip Seal

VIEW A

A

91B09162

Courtesy of General Motors Corp.

Fig. 16: Identifying Intermediate Shaft Assembly Components (Type 2)

TORQUE SPECIFICATIONS

TORQUE SPECIFICATIONS

Application	Ft. Lbs. (N.m)
Brake Hose-To-Strut Bolt	14-20 (19-27)
Caliper Bracket-To-Knuckle Bolt	
Except "E" Body	38 (51)
"E" Body	63 (85)
Hub & Bearing Assembly-To-Knuckle Bolt	
Except "A" Body	70 (95)
"A" Body	63 (85)
Hub Nut	
"A" Body	192 (260)
"C", "E", "H" & "K" Bodies	180 (244)
"J" & "L" Bodies	191 (259)
Step 1	74 (100)
Step 2	200 (271)
All Others	185 (251)
Intermediate Shaft Bracket-To-Engine Bolt	41 (56)
Lower Ball Joint-To-Control Arm Bolt	50 (68)
Lower Ball Joint-To-Steering Knuckle Nut	
"A" Body	33 (45)
"C", "E" & "H" Bodies	[1] [2]
"J" & "N" Bodies	42-45 (57-61)
"L" Body	55 (75)
Strut-To-Knuckle Bolt	
"A" Body	140 (190)
"C" & "H" Bodies	144 (195)
"E" Body	145 (197)
"J", "L" & "N" Bodies	129-133 (175-180)
Tie Rod End Nut	
"C" & "H" Bodies	[3] 35 (47)
"E" & "K" Bodies	[4]
All Others	35 (47)
Wheel Lug Nut	100 (136)

[1] – Tighten to 88 INCH lbs. (10 N.m), then turn nut an additional 120 degrees. Minimum torque of 37 ft. lbs. (50 N.m) must be obtained.

[2] – On replacement ball joint, tighten nut to 81 ft. lbs. (110 N.m) at initial installation only.

[3] – Maximum of 52 ft. lbs. (71 N.m) to align cotter key.

[4] – Tighten to 88 INCH lbs. (10 N.m), then turn nut an additional 1/3 turn. Minimum torque of 33 ft. lbs. (45 N.m) must be obtained.

Brougham, Camaro, Caprice, Custom Cruiser, Firebird, Roadmaster

DESCRIPTION & OPERATION

Drive axle is a semi-floating, hypoid-gear type with integral housing. Center line of pinion is set below center line of ring gear. A removable steel cover, bolted to rear of housing, permits servicing differential case without removing axle assembly from vehicle.

NOTE: Some models are equipped with positive traction differentials. For testing and overhaul procedures for these units, see appropriate DIFFERENTIALS – POSITIVE TRACTION article in DRIVE AXLES.

AXLE RATIO & IDENTIFICATION

Rear axle identification information is stamped on forward side of left or right axle tube on all models except Brougham. *See Fig. 1.* On Brougham, an identification code is stamped on rear of right axle tube 3" (76 mm) from differential housing or backside of right caliper support plate.

AXLE RATIO IDENTIFICATION

Application	Axle Code
7 5/8" Ring Gear	
2.73:1	2TM, 8HP, [1] 8HE & [1] 8HT
2.93:1	2TE
3.08:1	8HK, [1] 8HB, [1] 8HF
3.23:1	8HJ, [1] 2PM
3.42:1	8HL, [1] 2PN
8 1/2" Ring Gear	
2.56:1	4ZH, [1] 4ZL
2.73:1	4YL
3.08:1	2MG, 4LG, 4MF, [1] 4NC
3.23:1	4YE, [1] 4YM
3.42:1	4ZK, [1] 4ZJ
9 1/2" Ring Gear	
3.73:1	4ML

[1] – Positive traction differential.

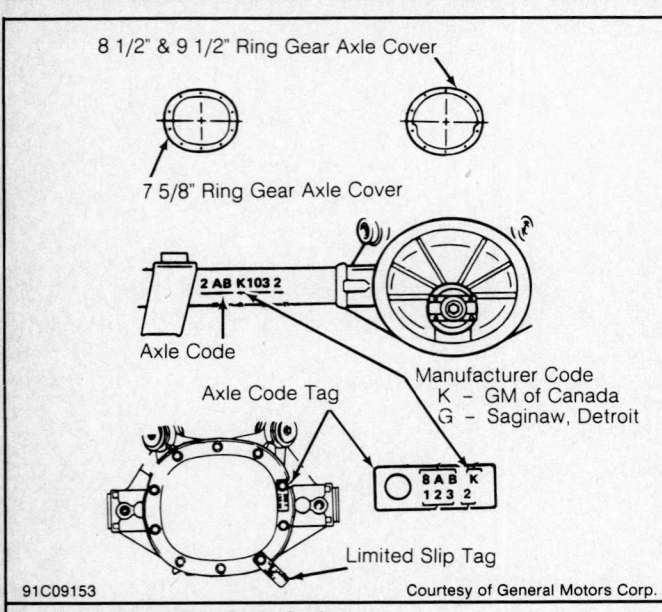

Fig. 1: Locating Axle Ratio Codes

REMOVAL & INSTALLATION

AXLE SHAFT & BEARING

Removal – 1) Raise and support vehicle. Remove rear wheels and brake drums (or disc calipers and rotors). Drain lubricant from differential by removing cover.

2) Remove pinion shaft lock screw and pinion shaft. Push axle shaft toward center of vehicle and remove "C" lock from inner end of shaft. Carefully remove axle shaft from housing.

3) Insert Bearing and Seal Remover (J-22813-01) into bore. Position remover behind bearing so tangs engage bearing outer race. Using a slide hammer, remove bearing and seal. Discard bearings and seals.

Installation – 1) Lubricate bearings with gear oil. Using Bearing Installer (J-23765 or J-23690) and Handle (J-8092), install bearing. Bearing is properly seated when installer bottoms against bore.

2) Lubricate seal with gear oil. Position seal on Seal Installer (J-23771 on 7 5/8", or J-21128 on 8 1/2 and 9 1/2" axles). Drive seal until flush with axle tube.

3) To complete installation, reverse removal procedure. Pull axle shaft outward after installing "C" lock to seat lock in counterbore of axle side gear. Install pinion shaft and lock screw.

COMPANION FLANGE & OIL SEAL

Removal – 1) Raise and support vehicle. Scribe an alignment mark on propeller shaft, companion flange, pinion and pinion nut for reassembly. Remove propeller shaft.

2) Using an INCH lb. torque wrench, measure and record pinion bearing preload. Remove pinion nut and washer. Using a puller, remove companion flange. *See Fig. 2.* Pry seal out of housing.

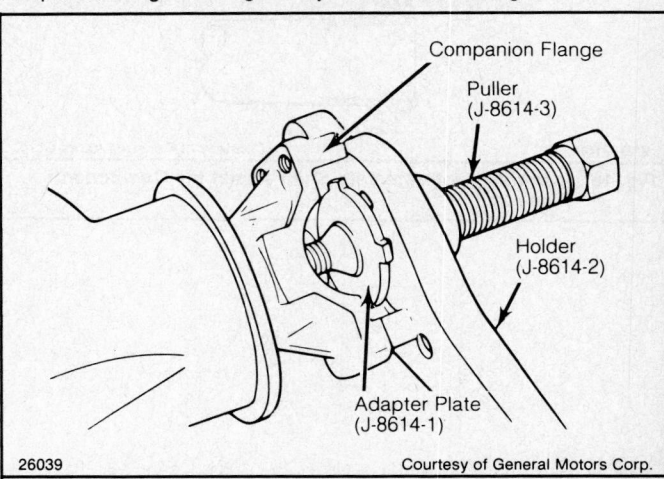

Fig. 2: Removing Companion Flange

Installation – 1) Pack seal lip of new seal with lithium-based, extreme-pressure grease. On Camaro and Firebird, drive seal flush, or recessed up to .010" (.25 mm) from edge of housing. On other models, drive seal into housing until seated against shoulder. On all models, install companion flange, washer and pinion nut.

2) Tighten pinion nut until all end play is removed. Continue tightening nut up to 1/16 turn beyond alignment mark made at disassembly, ensuring original preload is not exceeded by more than 3-5 INCH lbs. (.3-.6 N.m). Install propeller shaft.

NOTE: If preload specification is exceeded, a new collapsible spacer must be installed and nut retightened until correct preload is obtained.

REAR AXLE ASSEMBLY

Removal – 1) Raise vehicle and support at frame. Place supports under rear axle assembly. Disconnect shock absorbers from axle. Disconnect level control switch link (if equipped). On Camaro and Firebird, remove left track bar mounting bolt.

2) On all models, remove tires. Loosen parking brake cable adjuster nut. Remove parking brake cables from adjuster and body clips. Remove track bar and stabilizer bar links from axle and body.

3) Scribe alignment mark on companion flange and propeller shaft for installation reference. Remove propeller shaft and support out of way. Remove brake line junction block bolt from axle. Disconnect brake lines from junction block and wheel cylinders/calipers.

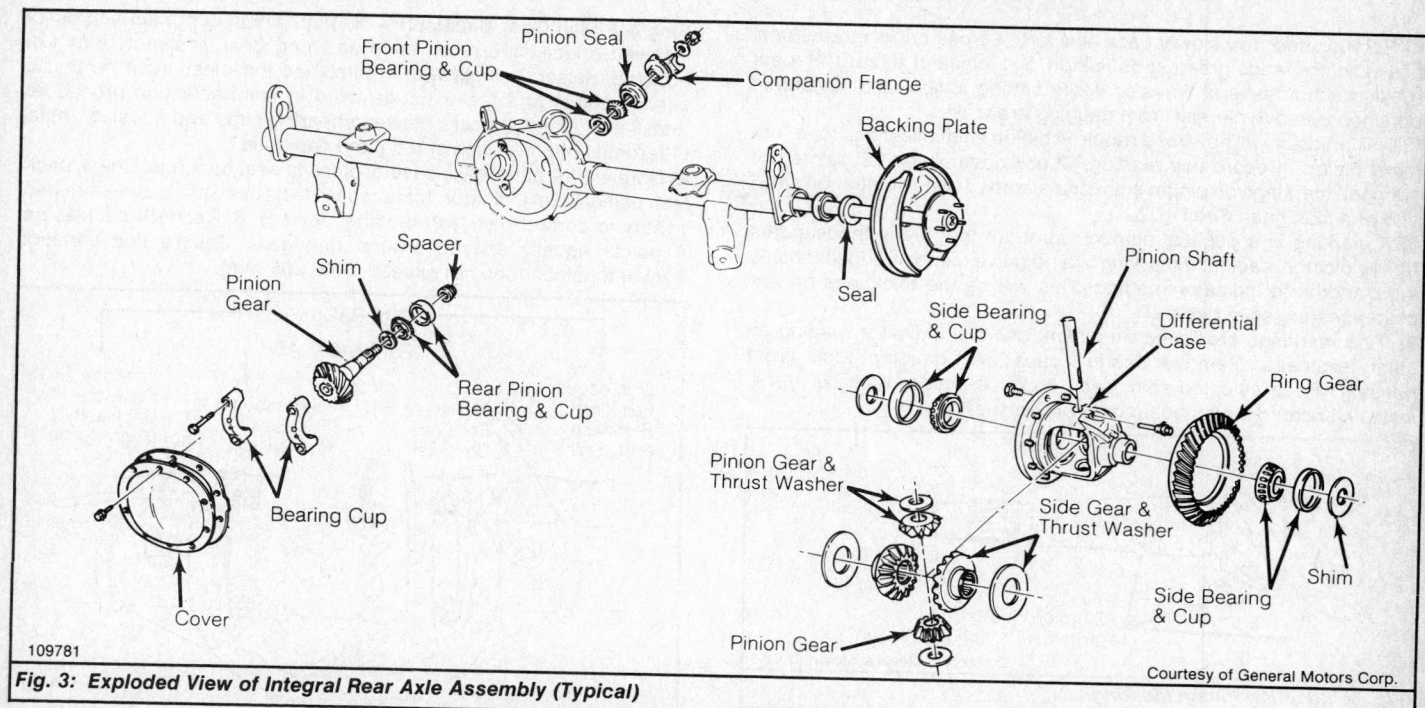

Fig. 3: Exploded View of Integral Rear Axle Assembly (Typical)

Courtesy of General Motors Corp.

WARNING: Use care when removing suspension springs. Uncontrolled expansion of coil springs could cause bodily injury or damage to vehicle.

4) Disconnect brake line from axle mounting clips. Remove or clear brake lines away from axle assembly. Disconnect upper control arms from axle assembly. Lower axle and remove springs.

5) Disconnect lower control arms and torque arm from axle (if equipped). Remove brake drums and backing plates, or calipers and rotors, and support out of way. Carefully lower axle and remove from vehicle.

Installation – To install, reverse removal procedure. Use a NEW cover gasket when installing cover. Refill axle housing with proper lubricant. Bleed and adjust brakes.

OVERHAUL

NOTE: For positive traction differential overhaul procedures, see DIFFERENTIALS – POSITIVE TRACTION article in DRIVE AXLES.

DISASSEMBLY

Differential – 1) Remove axle shafts. Check ring and pinion gear backlash and pinion bearing preload. This will indicate gear or bearing wear or an error in backlash or preload setting.

2) Mark differential bearing caps and housing for reassembly reference. Remove caps and pry differential case from housing. Remove bearing cups and shims. Keep each set with proper bearing cap for reassembly.

3) Remove differential pinion shaft, gears, and side gears with thrust washers. Keep components in order for reassembly. Remove ring gear bolts (left-hand threads) and tap gear from case using soft drift and hammer.

4) Remove pinion nut and companion flange. Remove pinion shaft and front bearing. If necessary, remove pinion bearing cups from housing using a brass drift. Press pinion shaft out of rear bearing and note thickness of pinion depth shim pack.

REASSEMBLY

Pinion Depth Adjustment – 1) Thickness of drive pinion rear bearing shim must be determined whenever a new axle housing, ring and pinion set, or pinion bearings and races are installed. Depth of mesh is determined using Pinion Setting Gauge Set (J-21777-B).

NOTE: Checking procedure for different axle sizes is the same, however, tool component combinations vary between axles.

2) If removed, lubricate and install pinion bearings into races. Install lubricated pinion bearings. Position gauge plate and rear pinion bearing pilot on preload stud. Install assembly through rear pinion bearing, front pinion bearing and front pinion bearing pilot. *See Fig. 4.*

3) Install hex nut until snug. Rotate bearings to ensure proper seating. Hold preload stud stationary with a wrench on flats. Tighten hex nut until 20 INCH lbs. (2.3 N.m) is required to rotate bearings.

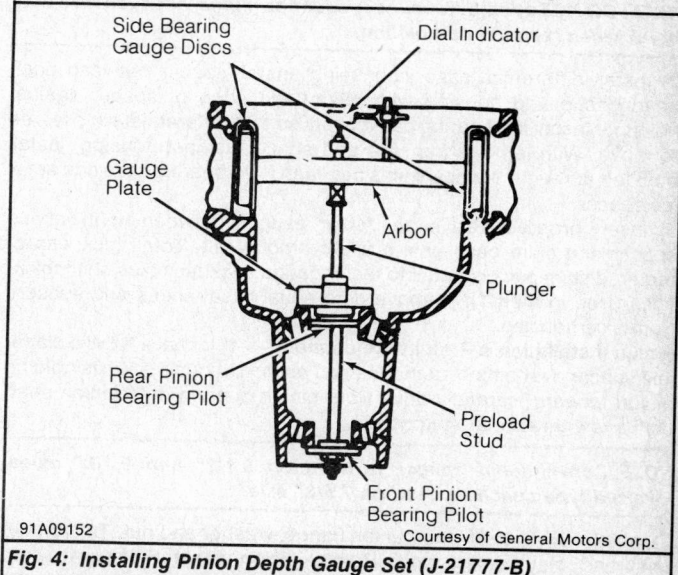

Fig. 4: Installing Pinion Depth Gauge Set (J-21777-B)

Courtesy of General Motors Corp.

4) Mount side bearing gauging discs on ends of arbor. Place arbor into carrier ensuring discs are properly seated. Install side bearing caps and bolts. Tighten bolts to avoid movement.

5) Position dial indicator on mounting post of arbor with contact button resting on top surface of plunger. Preload dial indicator one-half revolution and tighten. Place plunger onto gauging area of gauge plate.

6) Rock plunger rod slowly back and forth across gauging area until dial indicator reads greatest deflection. Set indicator to zero. Repeat rocking action several times to verify setting. Once zero reading is obtained, remove plunger from gauging area.

7) Dial indicator will now read required pinion shim thickness for a "nominal pinion". Record this reading. Check drive pinion for painted or stamped markings on pinion stem or a stamped code number on small end of pinion gear. See Fig. 5.

8) If marking is a positive number, subtract that many thousandths from indicator reading. If marking is a negative number, add that many thousandths to indicator reading. This will be the thickness of rear pinion bearing shim pack.

9) If no markings are found on pinion, use dial indicator reading as shim thickness. Remove bearing caps and gauging tools from housing. Place selected shim pack on drive pinion. Using a press, install lubricated pinion bearing on pinion shaft.

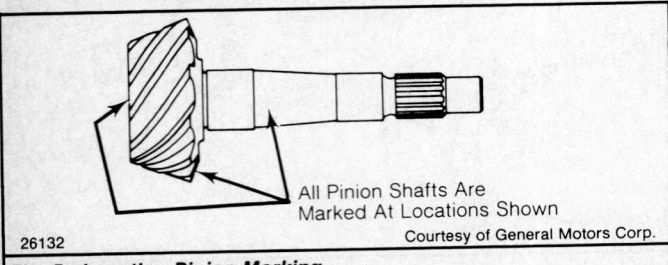

All Pinion Shafts Are Marked At Locations Shown

26132
Courtesy of General Motors Corp.

Fig. 5: Locating Pinion Marking

Case Reassembly – 1) Install ring gear on case with NEW bolts. Alternately tighten bolts to pull ring gear into position on case. Place side gear thrust washers over side gear hubs.

2) Install assemblies into case in their original positions. Install pinions and thrust washers into case. Install pinion shaft and lock bolt. Using bearing installer, install side bearings onto differential case.

Differential Shim Selection – 1) Measure thickness of original side bearing preload shims. Select a standard .17" (4.3 mm) service spacer and service shims with a total thickness slightly less than original shims. Standard service shims are steel and are available from .040-.082" (1.02-2.08 mm). Production shims are cast iron and available from .210-.272" (5.33-6.91 mm).

NOTE: DO NOT attempt to reuse production shims, because they may break when tapped into position.

2) Install differential case in housing. Install spacer between each bearing cup and housing with chamfered edge of spacer against housing. Install left bearing cap loosely so that differential case is free to move. With left bearing race and spacer against housing, install both left and right service shims between right bearing race and service spacer.

3) Insert progressively larger feeler gauges between right service spacer and shim pack until a slight drag is felt. Total thickness of required shim pack is equal to feeler gauge thickness plus shim thickness used in step 1). Remove differential case, shims and spacers from axle housing.

Pinion Installation & Preload Adjustment – 1) Install a NEW collapsible spacer over pinion stem. Position pinion in housing. While holding pinion forward, carefully drive front pinion bearing onto pinion shaft until a few threads are exposed.

NOTE: Conventional spacer is used on 8 1/2" and 9 1/2" axles. Inverted type spacer is used on 7 5/8" axle.

2) Install new oil seal, companion flange, washer and nut. Tighten nut until end play is removed. Rotate pinion several times to seat bearings.

3) Check preload using an INCH lb. torque wrench. Continue tightening nut and checking preload until correct preload is obtained. DO NOT overtighten. See AXLE ASSEMBLY SPECIFICATIONS table.

CAUTION: If preload is exceeded, a new collapsible spacer must be installed and nut retightened until proper preload is obtained.

Ring & Pinion Gear Backlash – 1) With pinion depth set and pinion installed, place differential case and ring gear assembly into axle housing. Select 2 shims with a combined thickness equal to that of service shims and feeler gauge used in shim selection procedure. Install shims and spacers between bearing cups and housing. Install differential bearing caps and tighten cap bolts.

2) Rotate differential case several times to seat bearings. Check backlash using a dial indicator. Increase or decrease shim size where necessary to correct backlash reading. See Fig. 6. Recheck backlash at 4 points equally spaced around ring gear. Ensure that variation between points does not exceed .002" (.05 mm).

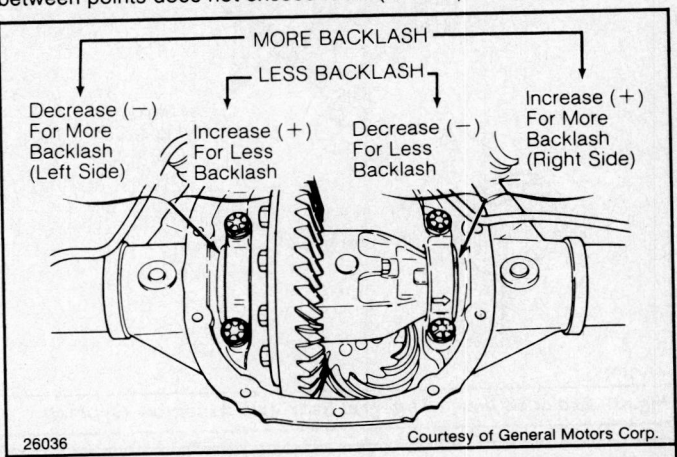

MORE BACKLASH
LESS BACKLASH

Decrease (−) For More Backlash (Left Side)
Increase (+) For Less Backlash
Decrease (−) For Less Backlash
Increase (+) For More Backlash (Right Side)

26036
Courtesy of General Motors Corp.

Fig. 6: Adjusting Backlash

Differential Bearing Preload – 1) Remove differential bearing caps and increase left and right shim sizes .004" (.10 mm). Gentle tapping may be necessary to install second shim. Ensure shims are seated and differential turns freely.

2) Using gear marking compound, check gear tooth contact pattern to verify proper assembly and adjustment. Complete necessary settings and install axle shafts. Install differential cover and fill with lubricant.

CAUTION: Avoid damaging seals when installing axle shafts.

DRIVE AXLE CAPACITIES

Application	Pts. (L)
7 5/8" Ring Gear	3.5 (1.7)
8 1/2" & 9 1/2" Ring Gear	4.25 (2.0)

AXLE ASSEMBLY SPECIFICATIONS

Application	Specification
Pinion Bearing Preload [1]	
Brougham	
New Bearings	20-25 INCH lbs. (2.3-2.8 N.m)
Used Bearings	10-15 INCH lbs. (1.1-1.7 N.m)
All Others	
New Bearings	24-32 INCH lbs. (2.7-3.6 N.m)
Used Bearings	9-12 INCH lbs. (1.0-1.4 N.m)
Ring Gear Backlash	.005-.009" (.13-.23 mm)
Side Bearing Preload [2]	Slip Fit Plus .008" (.20 mm)

[1] – Measured with new seal without ring gear installed.
[2] – Add .004" (.10 mm) to each side to preload bearings.

TORQUE SPECIFICATIONS

TORQUE SPECIFICATIONS

Application	Ft. Lbs. (N.m)
Bearing Cap Bolt	55 (75)
Housing Cover Bolts	20-27 (27-36)
Pinion Shaft Bolts	20 (27)
Rear Universal Joint Nuts	16 (22)
Ring Gear-To-Case Bolt	101 (137)
All Others	89 (127)

DESCRIPTION

Corvette uses Dana Model 36 (7 7/8" ring gear) and Dana Model 44 (8 1/2" ring gear) rear axle carriers. Model 36 is used in vehicles with automatic transmissions and Model 44 is used in vehicles with manual transmissions. Both differential carrier housings and cover beam are constructed of aluminum.

Internal carrier components incorporate hypoid gear set with a pinion supported on 2 preloaded, tapered roller bearing assemblies and a 2-pinion differential assembly supported on tapered roller bearings.

Pinion mounting distance, differential bearing preload and backlash adjustments are made with shims. Differential side gears drive 2 splined yokes which are retained laterally by snap rings, located on yoke splined end. Yokes are supported on caged needle bearings pressed into carrier.

AXLE RATIO & IDENTIFICATION

Axle identification number is stamped on back of carrier. *See Fig. 1.* See AXLE RATIO IDENTIFICATION table.

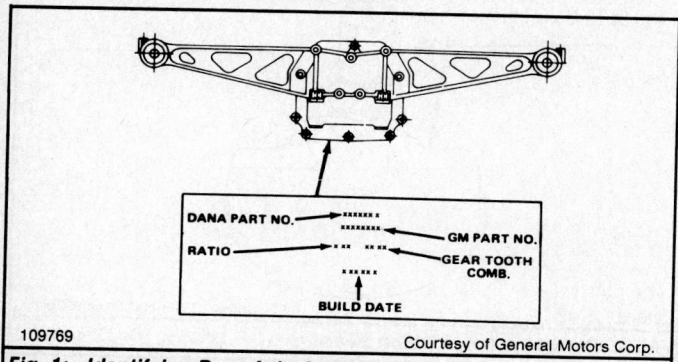

DANA PART NO. → xxxxxx x
xxxxxxx x
RATIO → x. xx = xx
GM PART NO.
GEAR TOOTH COMB.
BUILD DATE → xxxxx

109769
Courtesy of General Motors Corp.

Fig. 1: Identifying Rear Axle Assembly

AXLE RATIO IDENTIFICATION

Application	No. of Teeth Pinion/Ring Gear
Model 36 (7 7/8" Ring Gear)	
2.59:1	17/44
2.73:1	15/41
3.07:1	14/43
Model 44 (8 1/2" Ring Gear)	
3.33:1	12/40
3.45:1	11/38

REMOVAL & INSTALLATION

AXLE SHAFTS

Removal – 1) Raise and support vehicle. Disconnect leaf spring and tie rod end from knuckle. Scribe alignment mark on camber adjusting cam and mounting bracket. Remove cam bolt.
2) Separate spindle support rod from mounting bracket at carrier. Remove axle shaft trunnion straps at spindle and side gear yoke. Push out on wheel and tire assembly and remove axle shaft.
Installation – To install, reverse removal procedure. Align scribe mark on cam bolt with scribe mark on bracket. Check and adjust rear suspension alignment as necessary.

AXLE BEARINGS

Differential carrier assembly must be removed to remove axle bearings and seals. See OVERHAUL.

REAR AXLE ASSEMBLY

Removal – 1) Raise and support vehicle. Remove spare tire and spare tire cover. Remove upper and lower underbody braces. Remove exhaust system assembly.

NOTE: Only the rear crossover pipe needs to be removed for access to differential carrier and cover.

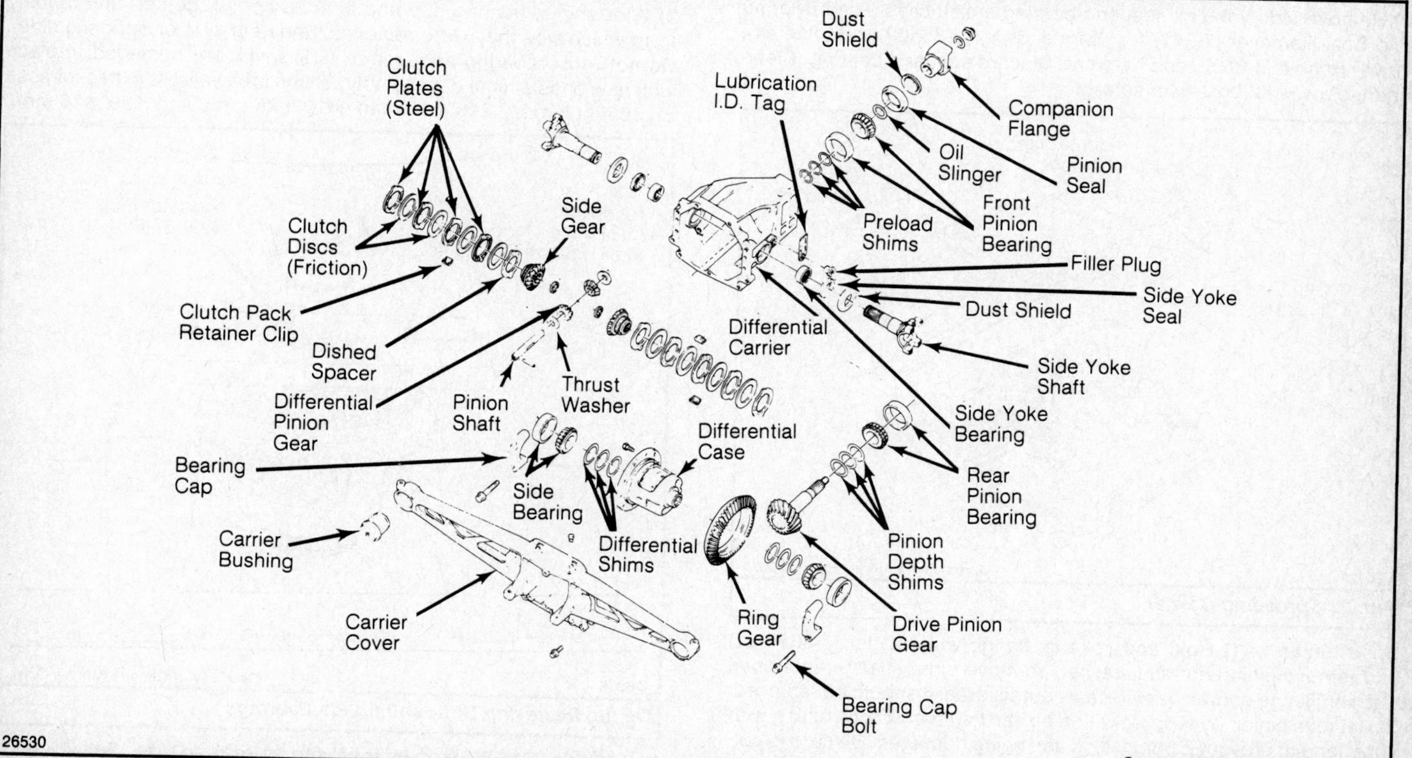

Clutch Plates (Steel)
Clutch Discs (Friction)
Clutch Pack Retainer Clip
Dished Spacer
Differential Pinion Gear
Bearing Cap
Carrier Bushing
Carrier Cover
Side Gear
Pinion Shaft
Side Bearing
Thrust Washer
Differential Shims
Ring Gear
Differential Carrier
Differential Case
Bearing Cap Bolt
Drive Pinion Gear
Pinion Depth Shims
Rear Pinion Bearing
Side Yoke Bearing
Side Yoke Shaft
Side Yoke Seal
Dust Shield
Filler Plug
Preload Shims
Front Pinion Bearing
Oil Slinger
Pinion Seal
Companion Flange
Dust Shield
Lubrication I.D. Tag

26530
Courtesy of General Motors Corp.

Fig. 2: Exploded View of Rear Axle Assembly

2) Disconnect leaf spring at knuckles and remove attaching bolts at cover. Remove leaf spring from vehicle. Scribe alignment mark on camber adjusting cam and mounting bracket. Remove cam bolts. Remove mounting bracket from carrier. Disconnect tie rod ends from knuckles.

3) Remove axle shaft trunnion straps from side yoke shaft. Push wheel and tire assemblies outward to disengage trunnions from side yoke shaft. Mark relationship of propeller shaft to companion flange. Remove propeller shaft trunnion straps at pinion flange.

4) Push propeller shaft forward into transmission and tie shaft to support beam. Support transmission. Remove differential support beam attaching bolts at frame brackets. Remove support beam attaching bolts at front of differential carrier. Remove differential carrier assembly from vehicle.

Installation – To install, reverse removal procedure. Apply GM Sealant (P/N 9639067) to support beam and differential carrier. Fill carrier with lubricant. Check and adjust rear suspension alignment.

OVERHAUL

DISASSEMBLY

Differential Assembly – 1) Drain lubricant. Remove differential carrier assembly. See REAR AXLE ASSEMBLY under REMOVAL & INSTALLATION. Bolt carrier to Holding Fixture (J-34162-A). Mount fixture to Base Plate (J-3389-20). Remove snap rings that retain yoke shafts in carrier. Remove yoke shafts. Remove bearing caps, noting assembly reference marks (matched letters on caps and carrier). Mark snap rings for reassembly reference.

NOTE: Snap rings control yoke shaft end play. There are 7 snap ring sizes available for Model 36 and 8 sizes for Model 44.

2) Mount Carrier Spreader (J-24385-01 and J-24385-20) onto carrier. Position a dial indicator onto spreader to measure carrier spread. *See Fig. 3.* Spread carrier a maximum of .010" (.25 mm). Remove dial indicator from spreader and pry differential from carrier. Note location of bearing cups for reassembly, and remove bearing cups.

3) Remove side yoke oil seal and bearing assemblies using Bearing and Seal Remover (J-34171 on Model 36, or J-35509 on Model 44), Driver Handle (J-8592) and hammer. Discard seal and bearing. Clean bearing and seal bore with solvent.

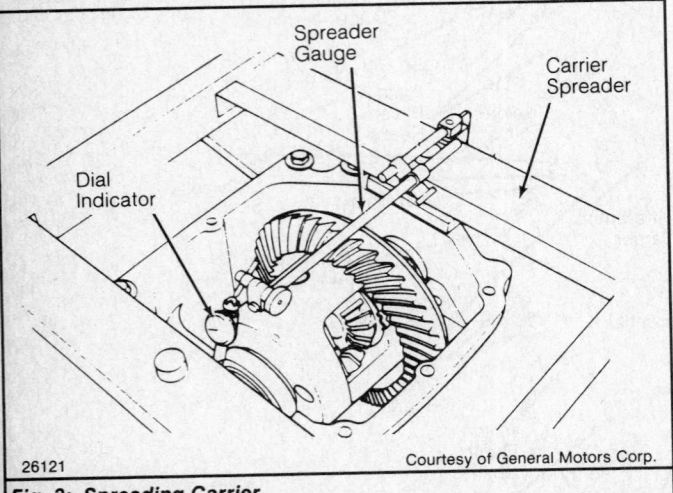

26121   Courtesy of General Motors Corp.

Fig. 3: Spreading Carrier

Drive Pinion – 1) Hold end yoke or flange with Holder (J-8614-01) and remove pinion nut and washer. Remove pinion flange and tools. If pinion flange shows wear in seal contact area, it should be replaced.

2) Remove pinion by tapping with a plastic hammer. Catch pinion with your hand to prevent it from falling and being damaged. Be sure to collect and keep together any shims from spline end of pinion that may stick to outer bearing and fall.

NOTE: Inspect shims and replace with new ones if damaged. Shims are available in thicknesses of .014-.030" (.36-.76 mm).

Pinion Bearings & Oil Seal – 1) Remove pinion oil seal with Puller (J-23129) and slide hammer. Discard seal and replace with new seal at time of reassembly. Remove outer pinion bearing and spacer. Remove inner pinion bearing cup with Remover (J-29358 on Model 36, or J-35501 on Model 44) and Driver (J-8592).

2) Turn nose of carrier down. Remove outer pinion bearing cup using Remover (J-29359 on Model 36, or J-35502 on Model 44) and Driver (J-8592). Remove inner pinion bearing with Remover (J-34165 on Model 36, or J-8612-B on Model 44). *See Fig. 4.*

CAUTION: DO NOT damage carrier bore.

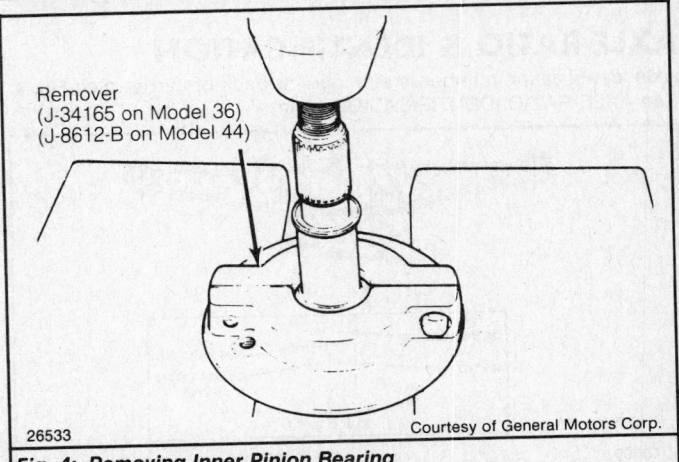

26533   Courtesy of General Motors Corp.

Fig. 4: Removing Inner Pinion Bearing

Differential Side Bearing – 1) Remove differential bearings with Remover (J-34108 on Model 36, or J-34108 on Model 44) and Adapter Plug (J-8107-2). *See Fig. 5.*

2) Wire shims, bearing cup and bearing cone together, and identify from which side they were removed (ring gear side or opposite side). Do not reuse bearing after removal. If shims are damaged, replace with new ones at time of assembly. Shims are available in thicknesses of .003" (.08 mm), .005" (.13 mm), .010" (.25 mm), and .030" (.76 mm).

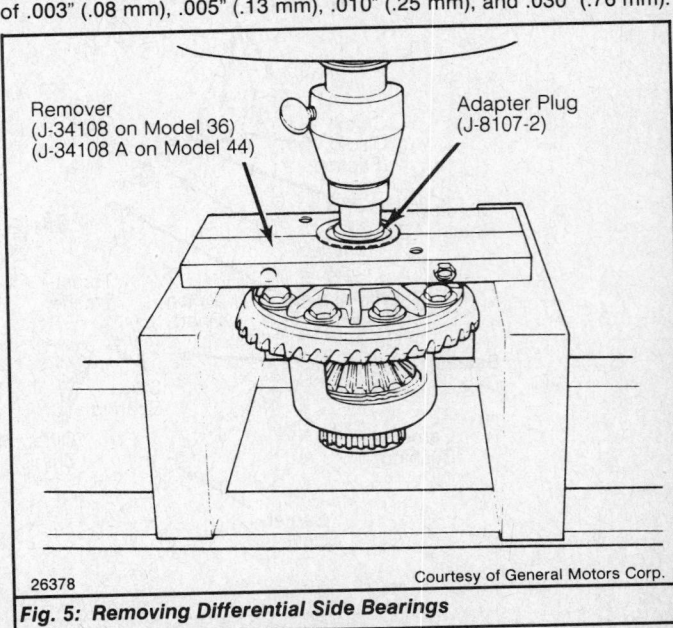

26378   Courtesy of General Motors Corp.

Fig. 5: Removing Differential Side Bearings

Ring Gear – 1) Place axle shaft into soft-jawed vise. Spline end of shaft is not to exceed 2.75" (69.85 mm) above top of vise. This will prevent shaft from fully entering into side gear and causing interference with step plate during disassembly of pinion gears. Ensure vise does not damage axle splines or machined surfaces.

2) Place shop towels over vise jaws to prevent any damage during removal of ring gear. Place differential on axle shaft with ring gear bolt heads up. Remove ring gear bolts. Remove ring gear by tapping with plastic hammer.

NOTE: DO NOT reuse ring gear bolts.

Differential Case – 1) Position differential case onto axle shaft. Using a punch, remove retaining pin from cross pin. Use hammer and punch to remove cross pin from case.

2) Assemble adapter plate into bottom side gear. Install Adapter Plate (J-34174) into top side gear. Thread forcing screw into threaded adapter until centered in bottom adapter plate.

3) Tighten forcing screw until slightly tight. This will collapse dished spacers and allow a loose condition between side gears and pinion gears. Remove both pinion gear spherical washers. Use .020" (.51 mm) thick shim to push out spherical washers.

4) Relieve tension of dished spacers by loosening forcing screw. Adjust forcing screw slightly to allow case to rotate. Assemble Turning Adapter (J-34501) onto Handle (J-8592). *See Fig. 6.* Insert small O.D. end of adapter into cross pin hole of case. Pull on handle and rotate case until pinion gears can be removed.

5) Remove gears. Hold top clutch pack with one hand and remove tools. Remove top side gear and clutch pack. Note location of plates for reassembly.

6) Remove case from axle shaft. Turn case with flange or ring gear side up and allow adapter plate, side gear and clutch pack to be removed from case. Remove retainer clips from both clutch packs to allow separation of plates and discs. Keep stack of plates and discs exactly as removed.

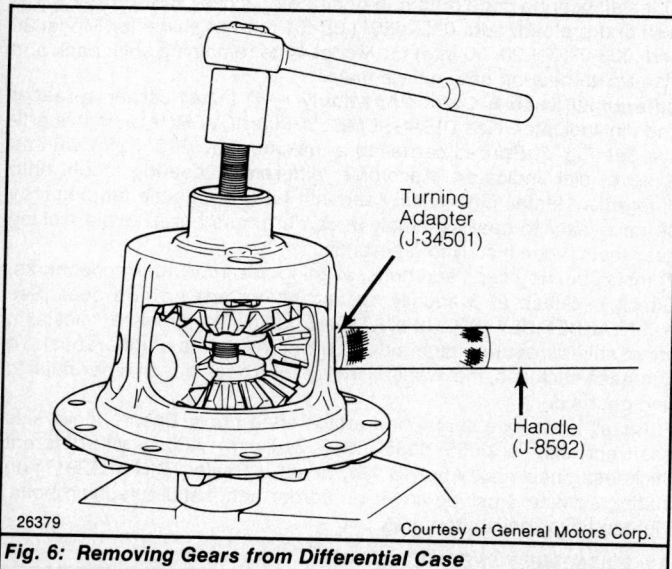

26379   Courtesy of General Motors Corp.

Fig. 6: Removing Gears from Differential Case

REASSEMBLY

Differential Case – 1) Lubricate thrust face of side gears, plates and discs with limited-slip rear axle lube. Assemble plates and discs in the same position as removed. Assemble retainer clips to ears of plates. Ensure both clips are completely assembled onto ears of plates.

2) Assemble clutch pack and side gear into top side gear bore. Ensure clutch pack stays assembled to side gear splines and retainer clips are completely seated in case pockets. To prevent pack from falling out of case, hold pack in place by hand while repositioning case on bench.

3) Position Adapter Plate (J-34174) onto side gear. Assemble other clutch pack and side gear. Hold clutch pack in position and insert Forcing Screw (J-34174). Tighten forcing screw into bottom adapter. This will hold both clutch packs in position. Position case onto axle shaft, aligning side gear and shaft splines.

4) Tighten forcing screw to compress clutch packs and provide clearance for pinion gears. Insert pinion gears. Hold gears in place and install Turning Adapter (J-34501) with Handle (J-8592) in cross pin hole of case. Pull handle and rotate case to turn gears.

5) Ensure pinion gear holes align with case. Adjust forcing screw tension to rotate case. Lubricate spherical washers and assemble into case. Use a small screwdriver to push washers into place. Remove tools.

6) Position cross pin shaft in case, and drive in shaft with a hammer. Ensure retaining pin hole of cross pin shaft is properly aligned, allowing retaining pin installation. Using a punch, install retaining pin to proper depth. Stake pin in place.

Differential Shim Selection – 1) Assemble Master Bearings (J-34170 on Model 36, or J-35505 on Model 44) onto differential case. Install differential case in carrier without pinion gear. Mount dial indicator on supporting fixture to read differential side play at ring gear flange. Force differential toward indicator. *See Fig. 7.*

2) With pressure applied, set dial indicator at zero. Force differential in opposite direction and check indicator reading. Repeat procedure until consistent reading is obtained. Record final reading. This is the shim thickness used in final assembly shim stacks and sets differential bearing preload and ring gear backlash. Remove dial indicator and differential case from carrier.

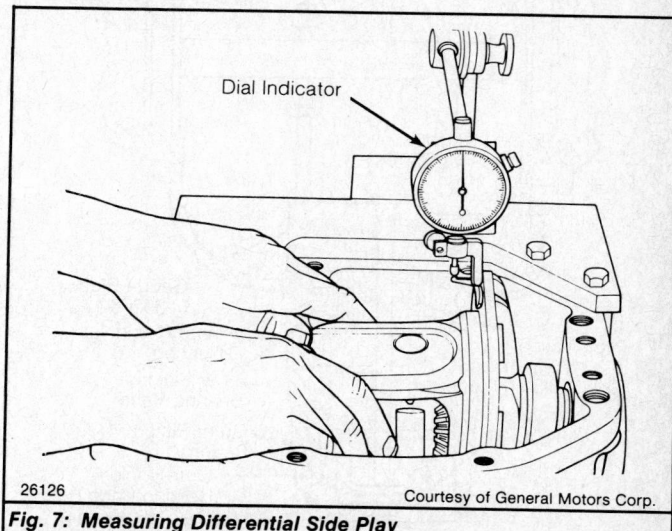

Dial Indicator

26126   Courtesy of General Motors Corp.

Fig. 7: Measuring Differential Side Play

Pinion Depth & Preload – 1) Observe and record pinion depth variance marked on end of pinion gear. This number shows how much to add or subtract (in thousandths) from nominal pinion depth setting. Install inner bearing cone onto pinion gear.

2) If installing new gear set, note difference between pinion depth variance markings on old and new gear sets. Change pinion depth shim pack thickness by amount of difference between old and new gear markings. See PINION VARIANCE PROCEDURE in this article.

3) Using Installer (J-7818 on Model 36, or J-8608 on Model 44), install inner pinion bearing cup in housing. Using Installer (J-7817 on Model 36, or J-8611-01 on Model 44), install outer pinion bearing cup in housing. Lubricate bearings and install pinion gauge assembly. Tighten nut on pinion gauge assembly until it requires 10 INCH lbs. (1.13 N.m) to rotate assembly. *See Fig. 8.*

4) Rotate assembly several times to seat bearing. Recheck torque required to rotate pinion gauge assembly. Install Discs (J-23597-8 on Model 36, or J-35506-2 on Model 44) onto Arbor (J-23597-1) and install assembly into carrier. Tap discs lightly with plastic hammer to seat.

5) Tighten side bearing caps onto discs until slight resistance is felt when rotating arbor. Position gauge plunger onto proper gauging step of gauge block for axle being serviced. Install dial indicator on arbor post.

6) Push dial indicator downward until needle rotates 3/4 turn clockwise. Tighten dial indicator in this position and recheck. Rotate gauge slowly back and forth until dial indicator reads greatest deflection. Set dial indicator to zero. Repeat rocking action of gauge shaft to verify gauge setting.

7) Rotate gauge shaft until dial indicator does not touch gauge block. Record dial indicator reading. Example: If pointer moved clockwise .067" to a dial reading of .033", this indicates a shim thickness of .033". This reading indicates shim thickness required for a pinion etched with a zero on pinion head.

8) If pinion has a plus or minus etching, adjustment of shim thickness is required. If pinion is etched with a "+3", then .003" less shim is required. Subtract .003" from indicator reading. Add shims for a negative number etched on pinion. Remove gauging tools.

9) Measure each shim separately with a micrometer and add together to get total required shim stack thickness. Assemble shims and inner pinion bearing on pinion. Place bearing installer over pinion shaft and drive bearing and shims on shaft until completely seated against pinion thrust face.

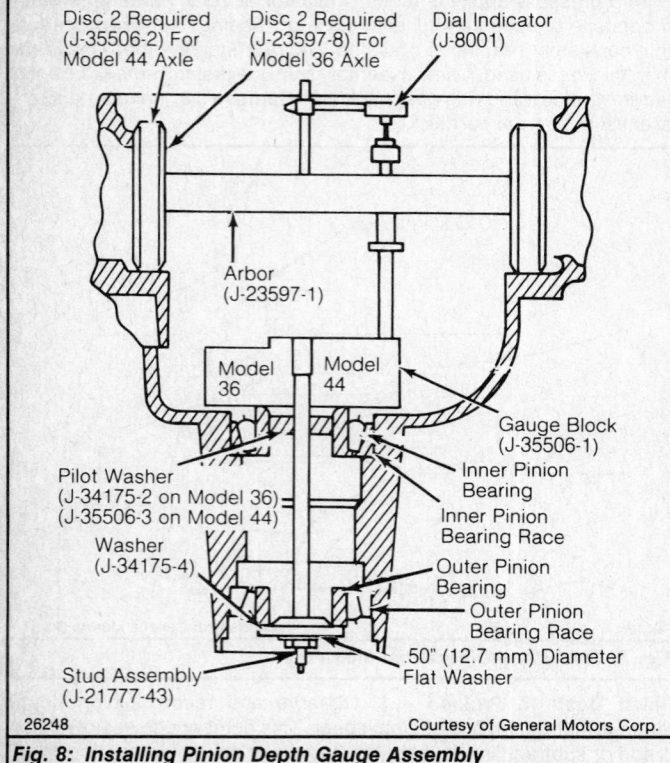

Disc 2 Required (J-35506-2) For Model 44 Axle

Disc 2 Required (J-23597-8) For Model 36 Axle

Dial Indicator (J-8001)

Arbor (J-23597-1)

Model 36

Model 44

Pilot Washer (J-34175-2 on Model 36) (J-35506-3 on Model 44)

Washer (J-34175-4)

Stud Assembly (J-21777-43)

Gauge Block (J-35506-1)

Inner Pinion Bearing

Inner Pinion Bearing Race

Outer Pinion Bearing

Outer Pinion Bearing Race

.50" (12.7 mm) Diameter Flat Washer

26248   Courtesy of General Motors Corp.

Fig. 8: Installing Pinion Depth Gauge Assembly

Drive Pinion – 1) Lubricate inner and outer bearings. Install outer bearing and spacer in carrier. Lubricate new pinion seal lip. Using Seal Installer (J-34163 on Model 36, or J-35503 on Model 44), install seal in carrier. Assemble original thickness of preload shims onto pinion. Insert pinion into carrier.

2) Assemble pinion flange, washer and NEW pinion nut on pinion. Hold flange with Holder (J-8614-01) and tighten pinion nut to specification. Using an INCH lb. torque wrench, rotate pinion. Pinion rotating torque with new bearings installed should be 25 INCH lbs. (3.0 N.m) on Model 36 or 30 INCH lbs. (3.4 N.m) on Model 44.

3) To increase preload, remove shims. To decrease preload, add shims. Preload pinion bearings and tighten to specifications. See TORQUE SPECIFICATIONS at end of article. Check pinion position. Install Disc (J-23597-8 on 7 7/8" Ring Gear, or J-35506-02 on 8 1/2" Ring Gear) and Arbor (J-23597-1) into carrier.

4) Tighten side bearing caps equally, using a torque wrench, onto discs until a slight resistance is felt when rotating arbor. Place Gauge Block (J-35506-4) on top of pinion button. Position gauge plunger onto proper gauging step of gauge plate for drive gear being serviced.

5) Install dial indicator to arbor post. Push dial indicator downward until needle rotates about 3/4 turn clockwise. Tighten dial indicator in

this position and recheck. While pushing gauge block down on top of pinion, rotate gauge shaft slowly back and forth until dial indicator reads greatest deflection. Set dial indicator to zero.

6) Repeat rocking action of gauge shaft to verify gauge setting. After zero setting is obtained, rotate gauge shaft until dial indicator plunger does not touch gauge block. Remove gauge block from top of pinion and place groove onto proper side of block (for ring gear being serviced) around indicator plunger between arbor and plunger head.

7) Read dial indicator. This reading indicates pinion position. An indicator reading within .002" (.06 mm) of etching on pinion is acceptable. If not within .002" (.06 mm), shim stack thickness is incorrect and must be adjusted. Add or subtract shims as necessary to correct adjustment.

Differential Preload & Backlash – 1) Install ring gear using new bolts. Install Master Bearings (J-34170 on Model 36, or J-35505 on Model 44) or original bearings, without shims, onto differential case. Place differential case in carrier and assemble bearing caps finger tight. Install dial indicator to read differential side play at back side of ring gear flange.

2) Force differential into pinion gear, rocking gear to ensure teeth are meshed. With force still applied to differential case, place dial indicator tip on flat machined surface of differential case, or on head of ring gear bolt.

3) Zero dial indicator. Apply force in opposite direction. Read dial indicator and repeat procedure to obtain a consistent reading. Ensure dial indicator reads zero each time differential is pressed away from pinion gear.

4) This reading, minus .006" (.15 mm), will be thickness of shims to be installed on ring gear side of differential. Remove dial indicator and differential case from carrier. Remove bearings from differential case. Install selected amount of shims.

5) Install bearing cone onto hub of differential case. For proper backlash and preload, add .015-.020" (.38-.51 mm) of shims for Model 36 and .008-.012" (.20-.30 mm) for Model 44 to remaining shim pack and install with bearing onto differential.

Differential Case & Carrier Assembly – 1) Install carrier spreader and dial indicator. See DISASSEMBLY under OVERHAUL in this article. See Fig. 3. Spread carrier to a maximum of .010" (.25 mm) and remove dial indicator. Assemble differential bearing cups onto differential. Install differential case into housing (gentle tapping may be necessary to seat assembly in carrier cross bore). Avoid nicking gear teeth when installing differential.

2) Install bearing caps and bolts, aligning assembly reference marks. Check backlash at 3 equally spaced points around ring gear. See AXLE ASSEMBLY SPECIFICATIONS table. To increase backlash, move shims from ring gear side to pinion gear side of differential. To decrease backlash, move shims from pinion gear side of differential to ring gear side.

3) Install inner axle shafts and attach snap rings. Ensure inner axle shaft end play is .0005-.0085" (.013-.216 mm). Adjust with different thickness snap ring. Apply a 1/4" bead of Sealer (P/N 1052917) on mating surface. Position cover on carrier and install attaching bolts. Tighten cover bolts alternately.

AXLE ASSEMBLY SPECIFICATIONS

Application	Specification
Pinion Bearing Preload	
Model 36	25 INCH lbs. (3.0 N.m)
Model 44	30 INCH lbs. (3.4 N.m)
Differential Bearing Preload	.006" (.15 mm)
Ring & Pinion Gear Backlash	.006-.009" (.15-.23 mm)
Maximum Backlash Variation	.0010-.0015" (.03-.04 mm)

PINION VARIANCE PROCEDURE

1) Ring gear and pinion drive gears are machined as a unit. If gears have been removed, it is important that numbers stamped on ring and pinion set be factored into shim selection process. See Fig. 9. The number stamped on pinion gear represents amount of adjustment necessary to obtain preferred position of gear set.

Old Pinion Marking	New Pinion Marking								
	−4	−3	−2	−1	0	+1	+2	+3	+4
+4	+0.008	+0.007	+0.006	+0.005	+0.004	+0.003	+0.002	+0.001	0
+3	+0.007	+0.006	+0.005	+0.004	+0.003	+0.002	+0.001	0	−0.001
+2	+0.006	+0.005	+0.004	+0.003	+0.002	+0.001	0	−0.001	−0.002
+1	+0.005	+0.004	+0.003	+0.002	+0.001	0	−0.001	−0.002	−0.003
0	+0.004	+0.003	+0.002	+0.001	0	−0.001	−0.002	−0.003	−0.004
−1	+0.003	+0.002	+0.001	0	−0.001	−0.002	−0.003	−0.004	−0.005
−2	+0.002	+0.001	0	−0.001	−0.002	−0.003	−0.004	−0.005	−0.006
−3	+0.001	0	−0.001	−0.002	−0.003	−0.004	−0.005	−0.006	−0.007
−4	0	−0.001	−0.002	−0.003	−0.004	−0.005	−0.006	−0.007	−0.008

74430   Courtesy of General Motors Corp.

Fig. 9: Pinion Variance Chart (Shim Variances Given in Inches)

● The ideal position of the gear set is 3.940" (100.08 mm) for Model 36 and 4.312" (109.52 mm) for Model 44 from back face of the drive pinion gear to centerline of the ring gear. This position is determined by thickness of shims placed between pinion bearing and pinion head.
● If "+2" is stamped on the drive pinion gear, the gear set will require .002" (.05 mm) less shimming than a drive pinion gear stamped zero. See Fig. 10. As shims are removed, the distance between the back face of the drive pinion gear to centerline of the ring gear is increased. See Fig. 11. If shims are added, distance between the back face of the drive pinion gear to the centerline of the ring gear is decreased.
● If ring gear and pinion drive gears are removed and are going to be reused, use a micrometer to measure shim(s) thickness and replace with shim(s) of equal thickness. If a new set of gears are used, locate old pinion marking and new pinion marking.
● Use these numbers and PINION VARIANCE CHART to determine correct shimming. See Fig. 9. If the old pinion has a "+2" stamp and the new pinion has a "-3" stamp, an additional .005" (.13 mm) of shims would be required.

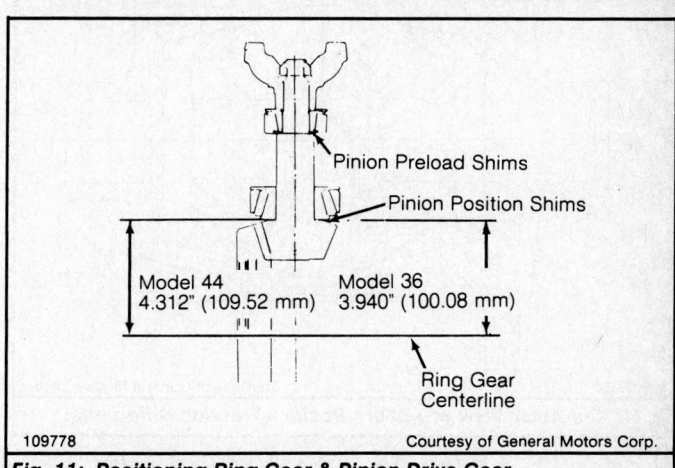

Model 44
4.312" (109.52 mm)

Model 36
3.940" (100.08 mm)

Ring Gear Centerline

109778   Courtesy of General Motors Corp.

Fig. 11: Positioning Ring Gear & Pinion Drive Gear

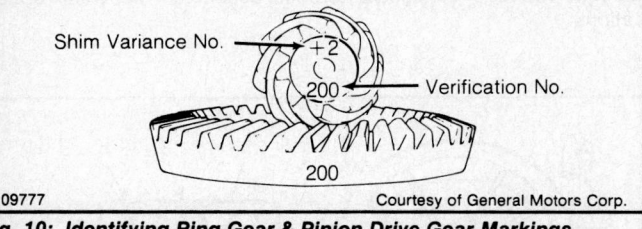

Shim Variance No. — +2
Verification No. — 200
200

109777   Courtesy of General Motors Corp.

Fig. 10: Identifying Ring Gear & Pinion Drive Gear Markings

TORQUE SPECIFICATIONS

TORQUE SPECIFICATIONS

Application	Ft. Lbs. (N.m)
Carrier Cover Beam-To-Carrier Bolts	
Model 36	19 (26)
Model 44	20 (27)
Carrier Cover Beam-To-Frame Bolts	89 (120)
Differential Bearing Cap Bolts	
Model 36	45 (61)
Model 44	63 (85)
Differential Carrier-to-Cover Beam Bolts	
Model 36	30 (41)
Model 44	35 (47)
Pinion Nut	200 (271)
Ring Gear Bolts	80 (108)
Support Beam-To-Carrier Bolts	60 (81)
Support Beam-To-Transmission Bolts	37 (50)
"U" Joint Retainer Bolts	18 (24)

1991 DRIVE AXLES
Differentials — Positive Traction

Camaro, Caprice, Custom Cruiser, Firebird, Roadmaster

DESCRIPTION

Positive traction differential directs a majority of driving force to the wheel with best traction. This is accomplished by 2 spring-loaded thrust plates pressing against differential side gears, seated in tapered brake cones.

Brake cones fit into a tapered recess in each end of differential case. Outward pressure of thrust plate assembly forces brake cones against recesses, providing resistance to normal differential action. Thrust plate spring load is calibrated to permit some slippage under variable torque conditions.

All models equipped with positive traction use Auburn-type differential units. The Auburn-type differential is not serviceable and must be replaced as a unit. *See Fig. 1.*

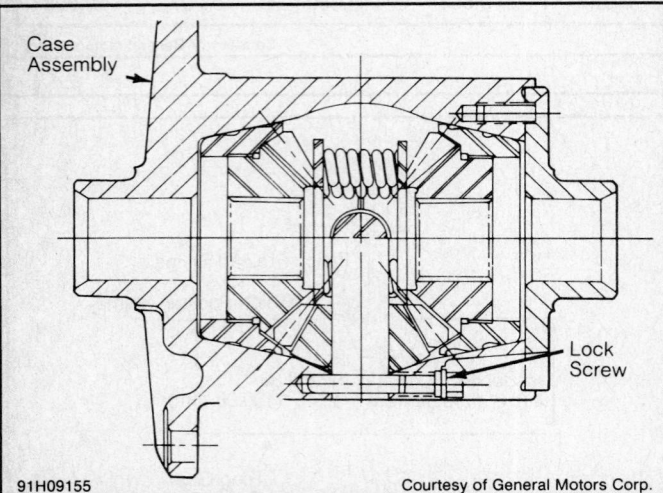

Case Assembly

Lock Screw

91H09155   Courtesy of General Motors Corp.

Fig. 1: Cut-Away View of Auburn Positive Traction Differential

IDENTIFICATION

The differential can be identified as a positive traction unit by raising vehicle and rotating one rear wheel. With transmission in Neutral, both rear wheels will rotate in same direction if vehicle is equipped with a positive traction differential.

The axle may also be identified by axle code. Axle code is stamped on front of right rear axle tube and on tag attached by ring gear cover bolt. *See Fig. 2.* Axle ratio, ring gear diameter and differential type is contained in axle code. See AXLE RATIO IDENTIFICATION table.

AXLE RATIO IDENTIFICATION

Application & Gear Ratio	Axle Code
7 5/8" Ring Gear	
2.73:1	8HE & 8HT
3.08:1	8HB & 8HF
3.23:1	2PM
3.42:1	2PN
8 1/2" Ring Gear	
2.56:1	4ZL
3.08:1	4NC
3.23:1	4YM
3.42:1	4ZJ

LUBRICATION

Fill differential with General Motors (1052271) 80W or 80W-90 GL-5 gear lubricant. See LUBRICATION CAPACITIES table for approximate capacity.

LUBRICATION CAPACITIES

Application	Pts. (L)
7 5/8" Ring Gear	3.50 (1.6)
8 1/2" Ring Gear	4.25 (2.0)

TESTING

1) Place transmission in Park. Raise rear of vehicle until both wheels are off ground. Remove rear wheel. Attach Adapter (J-2619-01) to axle shaft flange. Install 1/2" coarse-thread bolt into adapter. Attach torque wrench to adapter. *See Fig. 3.*

2) Measure torque required to rotate opposite wheel assembly. The reading should be 125-225 ft. lbs. (169-305 N.m). Lower vehicle so that one wheel is on ground. Place transmission in Neutral.

3) Check torque to rotate remaining wheel. Reading should be 45-110 ft. lbs. (61-149 N.m). Replace differential assembly if not within specifications.

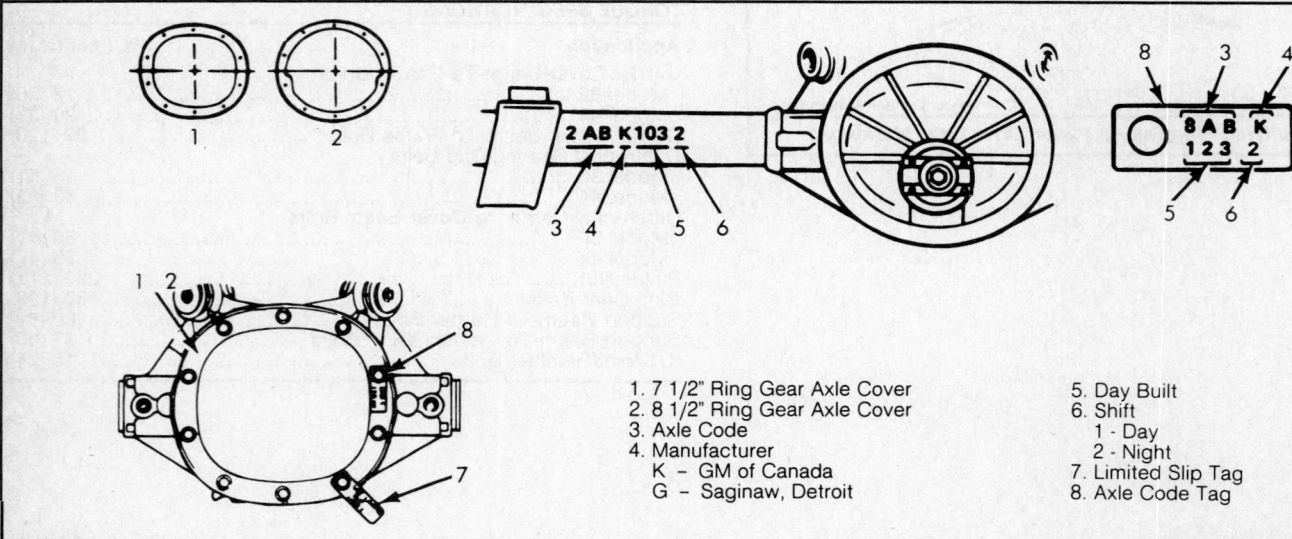

2 AB K103 2

8 AB K
1 2 3 2

1. 7 1/2" Ring Gear Axle Cover
2. 8 1/2" Ring Gear Axle Cover
3. Axle Code
4. Manufacturer
   K – GM of Canada
   G – Saginaw, Detroit
5. Day Built
6. Shift
   1 - Day
   2 - Night
7. Limited Slip Tag
8. Axle Code Tag

91E09154   Courtesy of General Motors Corp.

Fig. 2: Identifying Axle Codes

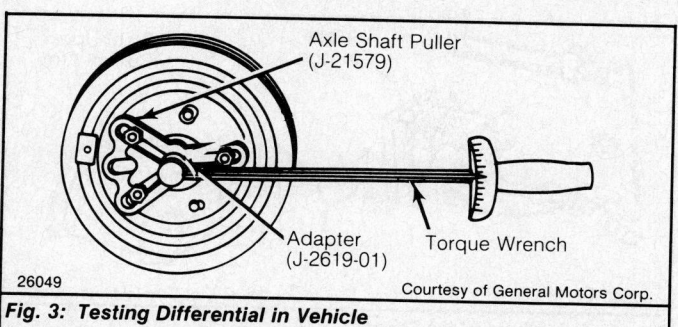

Axle Shaft Puller
(J-21579)

Adapter
(J-2619-01)

Torque Wrench

26049

Courtesy of General Motors Corp.

Fig. 3: Testing Differential in Vehicle

REMOVAL & INSTALLATION

DIFFERENTIAL ASSEMBLY

Removal – 1) Raise and support vehicle. Remove rear wheels and brake drums (or disc calipers and rotors). Drain lubricant from differential by removing cover.

2) Remove pinion shaft lock screw and pinion shaft. Push axle shafts toward center of vehicle and remove "C" lock from inner end of shafts. Carefully remove axle shafts from housing.

3) Check ring and pinion gear backlash and pinion bearing preload. This will indicate gear or bearing wear or an error in backlash or preload setting.

4) Mark differential bearing caps and housing for reassembly reference. Remove caps and pry differential case from housing. Remove bearing cups and shims. Keep each set with proper bearing cap for reassembly.

Installation – To install, reverse removal procedure. Use a NEW cover gasket when installing cover. Refill axle housing with proper lubricant. Bleed and adjust brakes.

NOTE: To prevent misalignment of splines in opposite cone and gear assembly, DO NOT rotate axle after differential and first axle shaft are installed in axle housing.

OVERHAUL

NOTE: Auburn differential units are serviced as a complete assembly only.

TORQUE SPECIFICATIONS

TORQUE SPECIFICATIONS

Application	Ft. Lbs. (N.m)
Axle Shaft Retainer Nuts	35 (47)
Bearing Cap Bolts	55 (75)
Differential Case Bolts	29 (39)
Pinion Shaft Lock Bolt	20 (27)
Rear Cover Bolts	21 (28)
Ring Gear Bolts (L/H Threads) [1]	89 (121)

[1] – Always use new ring gear bolts.

Propeller Shaft Alignment

Brougham, Camaro, Caprice, Custom Cruiser, Firebird, Roadmaster

DESCRIPTION

Use proper universal joint angle to provide smooth operation of propeller shaft. Check front and rear universal joint angles with vehicle at proper ride height and full gas tank. Adjust front universal joint by shimming transmission mount. Adjust rear universal joint angle by shimming transmission mount, or repositioning pinion nose.

NOTE: When both universal joints are not running at about the same angle, operation will be rough and an unwanted vibration is produced.

CHECKING & ADJUSTING

CHECKING

1) Ensure vehicle is at proper ride height with full tank of gasoline. Measure ride height from top of axle tube to bottom of frame. See Fig. 1. Bounce vehicle and allow to return to normal ride height before measuring. Ensure ride height is within specification. See RIDE HEIGHT & UNIVERSAL JOINT ANGLE SPECIFICATIONS table at end of article.

2) If ride height is not within specification on models with electronic suspension, adjust height sensor. See HEIGHT SENSOR under ADJUSTING in this article. On models without electronic suspension, add weight to trunk to obtain correct ride height.

3) With vehicle level and supported at axles, measure universal joint angles. Clean all bearing caps and install Inclinometer (J-23498 or J-23498-A) and Inclinometer Adapter (J-23498-20) on rear propeller shaft bearing cap. See Fig. 2. Bearing cap must be straight up and down. Center bubble in sight glass, and record reading.

4) Remove inclinometer, rotate propeller shaft 90 degrees and install inclinometer on drive yoke bearing cap. Measure angle and subtract smaller reading from larger reading to determine rear universal joint angle.

5) Attach Inclinometer Adapter (J-23498-20) to front propeller shaft bearing cap. See Fig. 3. Attach inclinometer to adapter and repeat procedure used on rear universal joint to obtain front universal joint angle.

ADJUSTING

CAUTION: Link must be attached to metal height sensor arm during adjustment.

Height Sensor (Brougham, Caprice, Custom Cruiser & Roadmaster) – With link attached to metal arm, loosen metal arm-to-height sensor plastic arm retaining nut. See Fig. 4. To increase ride height, move plastic arm upward. To decrease ride height, move plastic arm downward. Tighten retaining nut.

Transmission Shimming – Adding one shim at transmission mount decreases front universal joint angle 1/2 degree, and increases rear angle 1/4 degree. Removing one shim increases front angle 1/2 degree, and decreases rear angle 1/4 degree.

NOTE: Production transmission mount bolt is 10 mm x 35 mm (1.5-thread pitch). When using 2 or more shims, a longer bolt must be used.

Repositioning Pinion Nose – Suspension bracket bolt hole tolerances permit adjustment of rear universal joint angle. Loosen all rear suspension control arm bolts. Reposition pinion nose up or down, and tighten all bolts.

Control Arm Change (Caprice, Custom Cruiser & Roadmaster) – Rear universal joint angle, correct to within ±2 degrees, may be obtained using different length control arms. Front universal joint angle, correct to within ±1/3 degree, may be obtained using different length control arms.

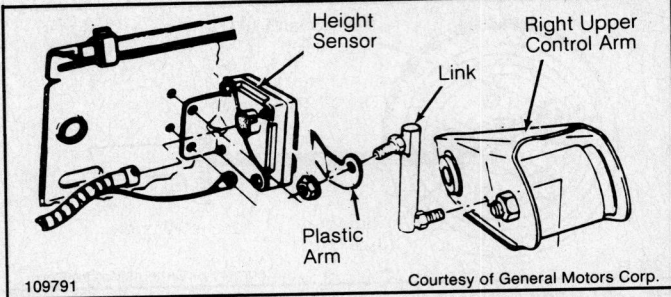

Fig. 4: Adjusting Height Sensor

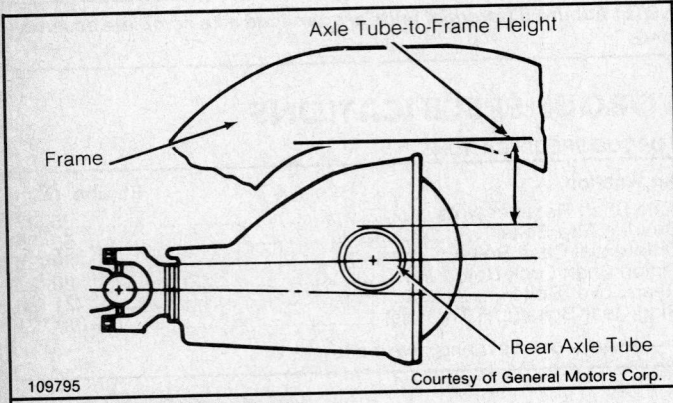

Fig. 1: Checking Ride Height

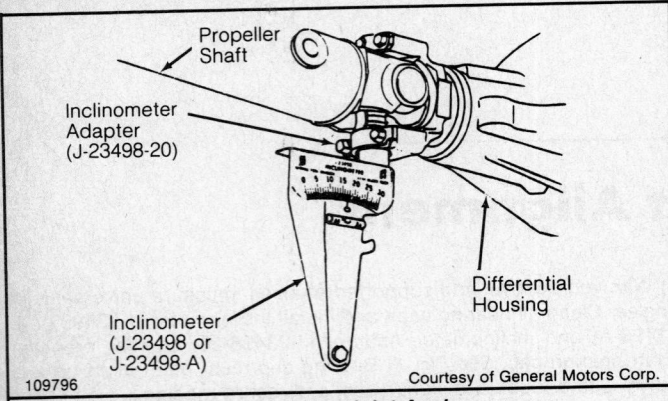

Fig. 2: Measuring Rear Universal Joint Angle

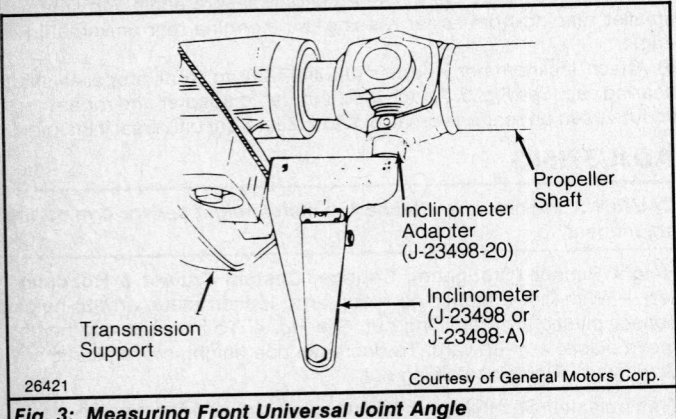

Fig. 3: Measuring Front Universal Joint Angle

RIDE HEIGHT & UNIVERSAL JOINT ANGLE SPECIFICATIONS

Application	Ride Height In. (mm)	[1] Front Joint (Degrees)	Rear Joint (Degrees)
Brougham	[2]	2.0	2.0
Camaro & Firebird	4.33 – 4.45 (110 – 113)	1.1	1.5
Caprice Sedan 7.5" Axle	6.14 [3] (156)	1.75	2.5
8.5" Axle	5.99 [3] (152)	1.75	2.5
Custom Cruiser 8.5" Axle	5.24 (133)	1.75	2.5
Custom Cruiser & Roadmaster 7.5" Axle	4.82 (122)	1.75	2

[1] – Angles may vary within ±1/2 degree.

[2] – Rear ride height is 4.80-5.59" (121.9-141.9 mm) on models with electronic suspension, or 5.15-5.98" (130.8-151.8 mm) on models without electronic suspension. Ride height must not vary more than .35" (8.9 mm) from each side.

[3] – Ride height may vary within ±1/4" (6 mm).

Caprice, Custom Cruiser, Roadmaster

DESCRIPTION

The Bosch 2U Anti-Lock Brake System (ABS) is designed to prevent wheel lockup during heavy braking. This provides improved driver control by reducing the distance required to stop vehicle.

Major component parts of system include the following: Electronic Brake Control Module (EBCM), 3 wheel speed sensors, 2 dash-mounted warning indicators, Overvoltage Protection (OVP) relay and hydraulic modulator assembly. The hydraulic modulator assembly, also known as a hydraulic unit, houses electric pump motor and solenoid valves.

NOTE: *For more information on brake system, see DISC & DRUM article.*

OPERATION

ANTI-LOCK BRAKE SYSTEM

During normal driving and braking operations, ABS acts like a conventional braking system. Each wheel sensor constantly sends an AC voltage signal to Electronic Brake Control Module (EBCM). This information is translated to wheel rotation speed. When the EBCM detects wheel lockup is about to occur, it activates the appropriate solenoid to pulse on and off rapidly, regulating hydraulic pressure to each wheel. A slight pulsation should be felt through brake pedal, indicating ABS is working.

Brake warning indicator will come on when ignition is turned to START position and should go off when ignition is turned to ON position. ANTI-LOCK warning indicator comes on when ignition is turned on and goes out after approximately 2 seconds. If either indicator stays on more than 30 seconds after vehicle is started, system malfunction is indicated. See DIAGNOSIS & TESTING.

Red warning indicator will activate if parking brake is applied or brake fluid is low. Amber ANTI-LOCK warning indicator is controlled by EBCM, and comes on if problem is detected with ABS. When indicator is on, ABS is disabled and braking is accomplished by conventional brake system. If both warning indicators are on, check conventional brake system for hydraulic system failure.

BLEEDING BRAKE SYSTEM

NOTE: *Brake system can be bled by either the manual or pressure method. Use DOT 3 brake fluid only.*

MANUAL BLEEDING PROCEDURE

1) With engine off, remove reserve vacuum by applying brakes several times. Fill master cylinder with brake fluid and keep reservoir one-half full during bleeding procedure.
2) Place proper size box end wrench over bleeder valve. Attach one end of clear tube over valve and submerge other end in container partially filled with clean brake fluid.
3) With aid of an assistant, slowly depress brake pedal and hold. Starting at right rear wheel, loosen bleeder valve to purge air from cylinder. Tighten bleeder valve and slowly release brake pedal. Repeat sequence until all air is removed.
4) Remove tube and wrench. Proceed to left rear, right front wheel and finish at left front wheel. Fill master cylinder reservoir and install cover.

PRESSURE BLEEDING PROCEDURE

1) Install Bleeder Adapter (J 29567) to brake master cylinder. Pressurize bleeder to 20-25 psi (1.41-1.76 kg/cm²). Connect bleeder hose to adapter and bleed air from adapter.
2) Raise and support vehicle. For rear drum brakes, manual override is required to permit fluid flow to front wheels when pressure bleeding. Use Proportioning Valve Depressor (J 35856) to hold valve stem of combination valve open during pressure bleeding.

3) Place proper size box end wrench over bleeder valve. Attach one end of clear tube over valve and submerge other end in container partially filled with clean brake fluid.
4) Starting at right rear wheel, loosen bleeder valve to purge air from cylinder. Tighten bleeder valve when air is no longer present in tube. Repeat sequence until all air is removed.
5) Remove tube and wrench. Proceed to left rear wheel, right front wheel and finish at left front wheel. Remove bleeder, fill master cylinder and replace cover.

ADJUSTMENTS

PARKING/EMERGENCY BRAKE

Depress parking brake lever 6 ratchet clicks. Raise and support vehicle. Tighten adjusting nut at parking brake equalizer rod until right rear wheel can be turned rearward but cannot be turned forward. Release parking brake. Both rear wheels should turn freely. If both wheels do not turn freely, repeat procedure. Lower vehicle.

BRAKELIGHT SWITCH

Hold brake pedal in depressed position. Insert brakelight switch into retainer until switch body seats on retainer. Pull brake pedal upward against internal pedal stop. Switch will be moved in retainer by brake pedal to provide proper adjustment.

REMOVAL & INSTALLATION

ELECTRONIC BRAKE CONTROL MODULE (EBCM)

CAUTION: *To prevent EBCM damage, never disconnect EBCM wiring harness connector with ignition on.*

Removal & Installation – 1) The EBCM is located behind trim panel at left rear quarter panel. Disconnect negative battery cable. On Caprice sedan, move rear compartment carpeting aside.
2) On all other models, remove left rear quarter trim panel. On all models, depress clip and remove EBCM connector. Remove retaining nuts and EBCM from bracket.
3) To install, reverse removal procedure. Ensure EBCM connector is fully seated and tight.

HYDRAULIC MODULATOR

Removal – 1) Disconnect negative battery cable. Remove air intake duct. Disconnect canister purge line at canister and position aside. Remove cover from hydraulic modulator. See Fig. 1.
2) Unlock tab and remove wiring harness connector from hydraulic modulator. Remove ground wire from hydraulic modulator. Note location of hydraulic modulator brake lines; remove lines. Remove nuts and hydraulic modulator from bracket.

Installation – To install, reverse removal procedure. Ensure brake lines are installed in original location. See Fig. 1. Tighten hydraulic modulator mounting nuts and brake lines to specification. See TORQUE SPECIFICATIONS table. Refill brake master cylinder, bleed brakes and check for leaks. See BLEEDING BRAKE SYSTEM.

OVERVOLTAGE PROTECTION (OVP) RELAY

Removal & Installation – 1) The OVP relay is located behind left rear quarter trim panel. Disconnect negative battery cable. On Caprice sedan, move rear compartment carpeting aside.
2) On all other models, remove left rear quarter trim panel. On all models, remove OVP relay from bracket and disconnect wiring harness connector. To install, reverse removal procedure.

WHEEL SPEED SENSOR

Removal (Front) – 1) Front wheel speed sensor is mounted in steering knuckle. Disconnect wheel speed sensor electrical connector at strut tower. Raise and support vehicle. Remove tire and wheel assembly.

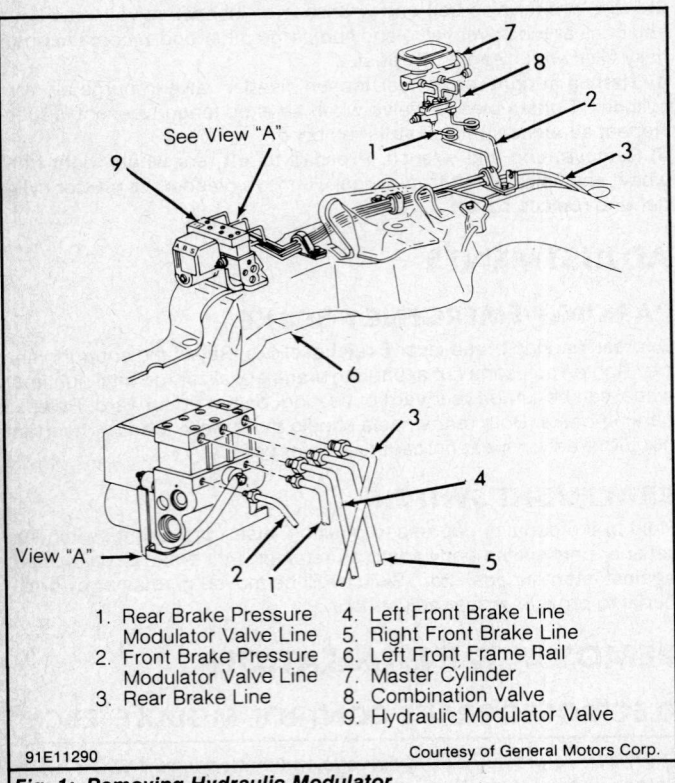

1. Rear Brake Pressure Modulator Valve Line
2. Front Brake Pressure Modulator Valve Line
3. Rear Brake Line
4. Left Front Brake Line
5. Right Front Brake Line
6. Left Front Frame Rail
7. Master Cylinder
8. Combination Valve
9. Hydraulic Modulator Valve

91E11290   Courtesy of General Motors Corp.

Fig. 1: Removing Hydraulic Modulator

2) Note wiring harness routing for installation reference. Disengage sensor wiring harness with grommets from brackets. Remove sensor mounting bolt and remove sensor from steering knuckle.

Installation – 1) To install, reverse removal procedure. Coat sensor with Anti-Corrosion Compound (1052856) before installing. Tighten sensor mounting bolt to specification. See TORQUE SPECIFICATIONS table.

2) Ensure wiring harness is routed in original location and properly installed in retainers. Sensor air gap is not adjustable.

Removal (Rear) – 1) Rear wheel speed sensor is also known as rear axle speed sensor. Sensor is mounted in rear axle differential. Raise and support vehicle. Disconnect sensor wiring harness connector.

2) Note wiring harness routing for installation reference. Disengage sensor wiring harness with grommets from brackets. Remove sensor mounting bolt and remove sensor from rear axle housing.

Installation – 1) To install, reverse removal procedure. Sensor fits tightly into rear axle housing. DO NOT use force to install sensor; use hand pressure only.

2) Tighten sensor mounting bolt to specification. See TORQUE SPECIFICATIONS table. Ensure wiring harness is routed in original location and properly installed in retainers. Sensor gap is not adjustable.

TOOTHED SENSOR RING

Removal (Front) – 1) Front toothed sensor ring is an integral part of front brake rotor. If sensor ring requires replacement, brake rotor must be replaced.

2) Raise and support vehicle. Remove tire and wheel assembly. Using a "C" clamp, bottom piston into caliper bore. Remove caliper mounting bolts and sleeves. Remove brake caliper and secure caliper aside. Remove brake rotor.

Installation – To install, reverse removal procedure. Tighten bolts to specification. See TORQUE SPECIFICATIONS table.

Removal & Installation (Rear) – 1) Rear toothed sensor ring is an integral part of rear axle differential pinion gear. To inspect sensor ring, remove rear wheel speed sensor. See WHEEL SPEED SENSOR under REMOVAL & INSTALLATION.

2) Using a flashlight and mirror, inspect sensor ring through sensor mounting hole. Check for missing or damaged teeth. If sensor ring

replacement is necessary, differential pinion gear must be removed. See appropriate differential article in DRIVE AXLES.

DIAGNOSIS & TESTING

NOTE: Manufacturer recommends using Tech 1 Diagnostic Computer with 88-91 Brake Cartridge and Bosch ABS ALDL adapter to diagnose ABS system. Some diagnostic procedures will require Pinout Box (J 35592).

PRE-DIAGNOSTIC INSPECTION

When checking potential ABS system faults, check the following before using DIAGNOSTIC CHARTS.

1) Check Overvoltage Protection (OVP) relay fuses (No. 3 and No. 17 in main fuse block). Check STOP/HAZ fuse (No. 19 in main fuse block).

2) Check fusible link to hydraulic modulator.

3) Ensure OVP relay connector and Electronic Brake Control Module (EBCM) connectors are fully seated and tight.

4) Ensure parking brake switch is functioning properly.

5) Check ground system for clean tight connections. Grounds for ABS system are located as follows:

- Behind left headlight support, in front of fuel vapor canister
- Near center of left "D" pillar (left rear quarter panel)
- Front of engine at thermostat housing
- Headlight wiring harness, near left headlight

6) Always perform ABS SYSTEM FUNCTION CHECK before using code charts under DIAGNOSTIC CHARTS. *See Fig. 3.*

ENTERING DIAGNOSTIC DISPLAY MODE

Flash Code Diagnostics – Ground pin "H" to pin "A" of ALDL connector. *See Fig. 2.* Connector is located under dash, near middle of instrument panel. Turn ignition on. Diagnostic display mode remains enabled as long as pin "H" is grounded, serial data link communications has not been initiated, and vehicle speed is less than 4 MPH.

About 3 seconds after ALDL pin "H" is grounded, EBCM will begin flashing ANTI-LOCK light in code sequence. Sequence will begin with Code 12, signaling beginning of fault code display. Each stored code will be displayed 3 times. After all codes have been displayed, sequence will repeat, starting with Code 12. If no code is present, go to SYMPTOM DIAGNOSIS.

NOTE: Certain codes can only be read through the ALDL connector using Tech 1 Diagnostic Computer.

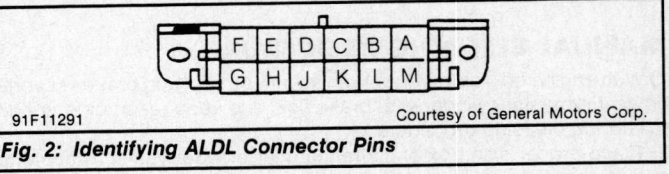

91F11291   Courtesy of General Motors Corp.

Fig. 2: Identifying ALDL Connector Pins

DIAGNOSTIC TROUBLE CODES

Code	[1] Definition
12	Diagnostic System Operational
21	Right Front Wheel Speed Sensor Fault
22	Right Front Toothed Wheel Frequency Error
25	Left Front Wheel Speed Sensor Fault
26	Left Front Toothed Wheel Frequency Error
35	Rear Axle Speed Sensor Fault
36	Rear Axle Toothed Wheel Frequency Error
41	Right Front Solenoid Valve Fault
45	Left Front Solenoid Valve Fault
55	Rear Solenoid Valve Fault
61	Pump Motor or Relay Fault
63	Solenoid Valve Relay Fault
71	EBCM Fault
72	Serial Data Link Fault (Tech 1 Error)

[1] – Always perform ABS SYSTEM FUNCTION CHECK before using code charts. *See Fig. 3.*

CLEARING CODES

The following 3 methods can be used to clear codes.

ALDL Diagnostic Request Line – 1) Turn ignition to RUN position. Ensure ANTI-LOCK indicator turns off after 3-4 seconds. If indicator remains on, a fault is still present and must be corrected.

2) Place a jumper between pin "A" and pin "H" of ALDL connector. *See Fig. 2.* Connector is located under dash, near middle of instrument panel. Disconnect jumper to pin "H" for approximately one second, then reconnect jumper to pin "H". Repeat this procedure 4 times within 10 seconds.

3) Leave jumper wire connected after the 4th time. Note ANTI-LOCK indicator. Code 12 should be displayed. If other codes are displayed, repeat code clearing process. After codes are cleared, wait a minimum of 15 seconds before turning ignition off.

Tech 1 CLEAR CODES Selection – 1) Connect Tech 1 Diagnostic Computer. See USING TECH 1. Before clearing codes, check and note history code data. Select appropriate menu and select CLEAR CODES function.

2) Verify codes are cleared. Code 12 should be only code displayed. If other codes are displayed, either codes were not cleared or ABS fault still exists. Correct fault and repeat procedure.

Ignition Cycle Default – If vehicle power is cycled 100 times without any particular fault reappearing, fault code will be erased from EBCM memory. Ignition cycle counter will reset to zero.

USING TECH 1

NOTE: Tech 1 Diagnostic Computer (94-00101-A) with Bosch ABS ALDL Adapter, Pinout Box (J 35592) and High-Impedance Multimeter will be needed to test parts of the ABS system.

1988-91 BRAKE cartridge must be inserted in Tech 1 to perform diagnostic procedures on anti-lock brake system. Plug Tech 1 into ALDL connector before turning ignition on. A Bosch ABS adapter is required when testing Bosch 2U anti-lock brake system.

Selecting Model Year – Turn ignition switch to RUN position. Select appropriate model year using function keys.

Selecting Vehicle – After selecting model year, enter type of vehicle being tested. Press NO until "B" is flashing. Pressing EXIT will return Tech 1 to previous screen.

Selecting Test Mode – Five test modes are available for diagnosing anti-lock brake system. Test modes are as follows:

Mode F0 (Data List) – Mode displays the actual reading that each wheel speed sensor is sending to EBCM. In this mode, vehicle can be driven and wheel speed information can be observed to determine if readings are comparable to actual vehicle speed. By pressing brake pedal, status of brakelight switch can be observed.

Mode F1 (Code History) – Mode displays trouble codes and description. Ignition cycle information is useful in determining reason vehicle is in for service. If display indicates zero ignition cycle since code was set, fault is currently present.

EBCM keeps track of ignition cycles since trouble code occurred. Vehicle speed information can be used to duplicate fault if an intermittent fault condition caused code to set.

Brakelight switch information can be used to duplicate fault if an intermittent fault condition caused code to set. ABS state information is useful in determining driving condition of vehicle when code was set.

Mode F2 (Trouble Codes) – Mode displays ABS trouble codes. Tech 1 will display any trouble codes and brief description of code displayed. If no code is stored, Tech 1 will display NO ABS CODES. Go to SYMPTOM DIAGNOSIS.

Tech 1 will respond to a clear codes command by indicating ABS CODES CLEARED or CODE CLEAR FAIL.

Mode F3 (ABS Snapshot) – Mode helps isolate intermittent problems by capturing data before and after condition.

By selecting Manual Trigger, Tech 1 will wait for ENTER to be pressed before storing speed sensor information. All stored information can be displayed and examined for conditions which might indicate a problem.

By selecting Automatic Trigger, Tech 1 will capture data which deviates from normal conditions, but alone may not set a code, such as driving over bumpy roads or over railroad tracks. Condition may be caused by loose connections or intermittent wiring problems. While Tech 1 is waiting for a trigger, the ENTER or F9 key may also be used to force a trigger.

Mode F4 (ABS Test) – This mode is used to perform the following tests:

- Solenoid Valve Pressure Hold Test
- Solenoid Valve Pressure Reduction
- Automatic Tests

By selecting appropriate test and observing results, error conditions and faults can be further identified.

Solenoid Valve Pressure Hold Test – 1) Raise vehicle on frame contact hoist so wheels to be tested are off ground. Spin wheel to be tested by hand. Using Tech 1, select PRESSURE HOLD mode.

2) Have assistant apply brakes. Try to spin wheel being tested. While in PRESSURE HOLD mode, even with brakes applied, wheel should spin. Repeat test if necessary to verify proper operation. Perform SOLENOID VALVE PRESSURE REDUCTION TEST.

Solenoid Valve Pressure Reduction Test – 1) Raise vehicle on frame contact hoist so wheels to be tested are off ground. Have assistant depress brake pedal. Using Tech 1, select PRESSURE REDUCE mode.

2) Try to spin wheel being tested. Wheel should spin freely. Repeat test if necessary to verify proper operation. Perform SOLENOID VALVE PRESSURE HOLD TEST if test has not yet been performed.

Automatic Tests – Select AUTO TEST. Press ENTER when ready. Valves can be heard and felt cycling from hydraulic control unit; have assistant verify that pump motor turned on. See DIAGNOSTIC CHARTS if codes are set.

SYMPTOM DIAGNOSIS

If no trouble codes are stored, it may be necessary to use SYMPTOM DIAGNOSTIC CHARTS at end of article. See SYMPTOM DIAGNOSTIC CHART INDEX table.

SYMPTOM DIAGNOSTIC CHART INDEX

Symptom	Refer To
Anti-Lock Light On, No Codes Set Or Tech 1 Unable To Receive Data	Chart "A"
Anti-Lock Light Inoperative Or Light Flashes Briefly With Ignition On	Chart "B"

INTERMITTENTS

Failures in anti-lock brakes may be difficult to diagnose accurately. If an ABS failure or fault occurs, ANTI-LOCK indicator will illuminate. If fault is an intermittent problem which has corrected itself (ANTI-LOCK indicator off), history trouble code will be stored.

Stored in history code will be history data of fault at time the fault occurred. FLASH CODE DIAGNOSTICS method can be used to identify stored history trouble codes, but Tech 1 must be used to read ABS history data. ABS self-diagnosis system can be used to help find suspected circuit.

- Record current codes and code history information. Record any descriptive driving circumstances during failure occurrence.
- Use Tech 1, mode F3 (ABS snapshot), while test driving vehicle. See USING TECH 1. Try to duplicate condition.
- If no trouble code is stored, it may be necessary to use SYMPTOM DIAGNOSTIC CHARTS.

Most intermittent problems are caused by faulty electrical connectors or wiring. When an intermittent failure is encountered, inspect suspected as follows:

- Check for poor mating of connector halves or terminals not fully seated in connector body (backed out).
- Check for improperly formed or damaged terminals. Carefully reform all connector terminals of problem circuit to increase contact tension.
- Check for poor terminal-to-wire connection. This requires removing terminal from connector body to inspect.

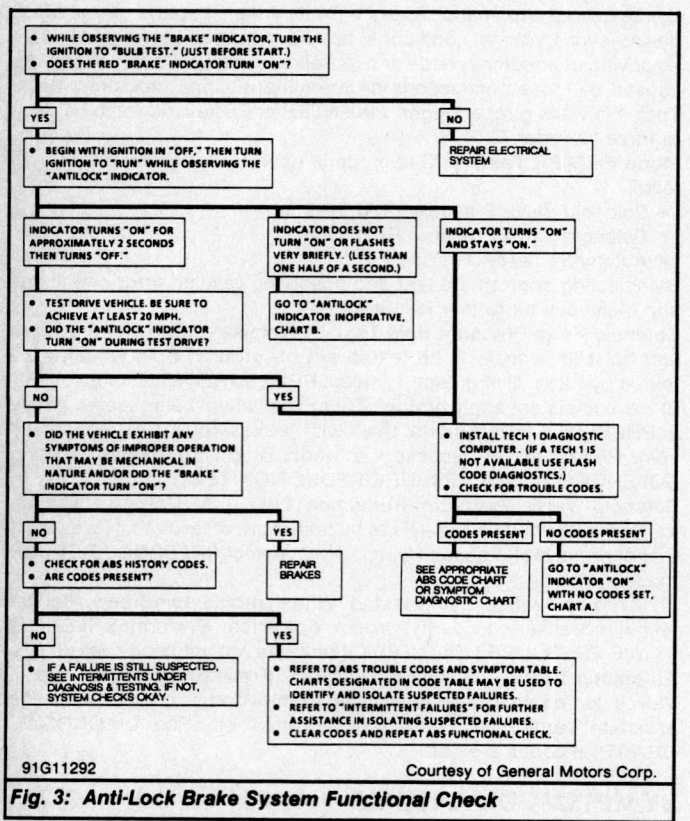

91G11292

Courtesy of General Motors Corp.

Fig. 3: Anti-Lock Brake System Functional Check

TORQUE SPECIFICATIONS

Application	Ft. Lbs. (N.m)
Brake Caliper Bolts	38 (51)
Wheel Lug Nuts	100 (140)
	INCH Lbs. (N.m)
Brake Lines	108 (12)
Hydraulic Modulator Nuts	95 (11)
Wheel Speed Sensor Bolt	71 (8)

WIRING DIAGRAM

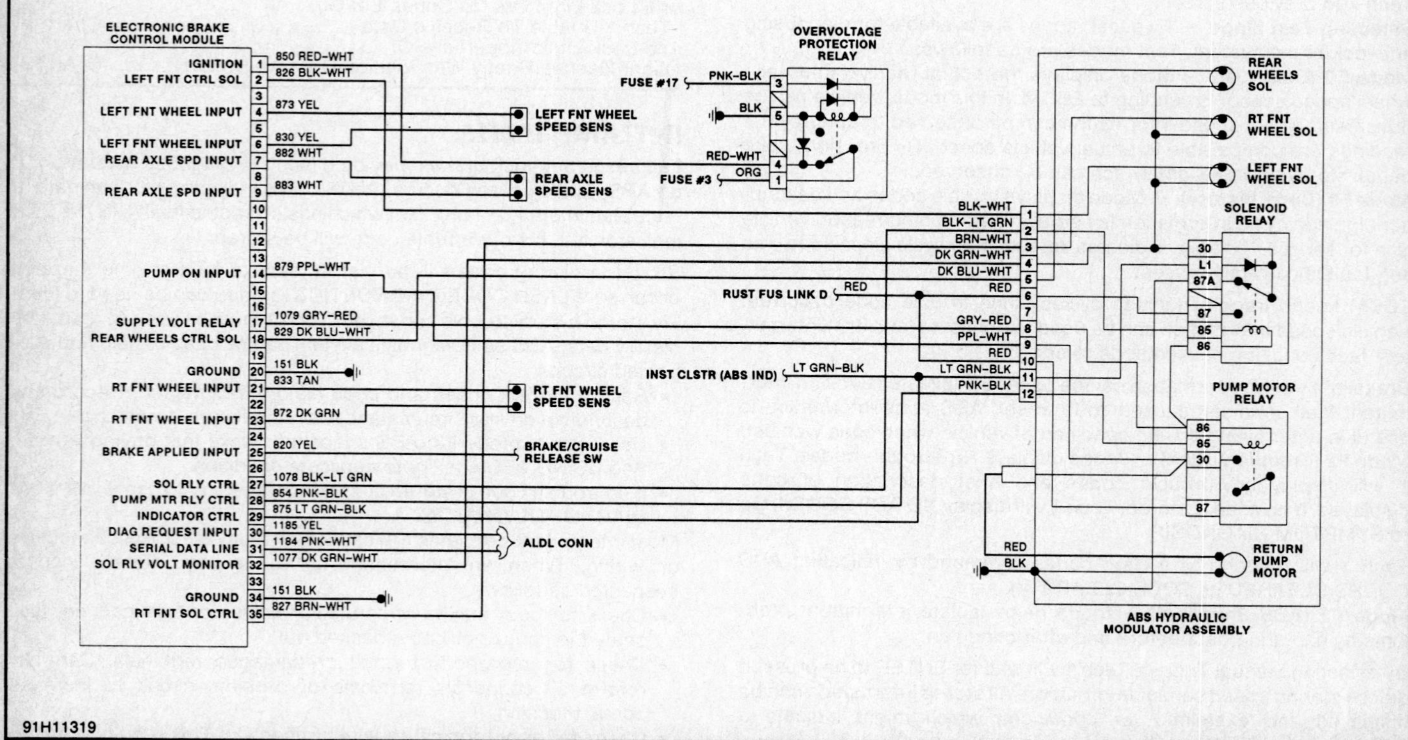

ELECTRONIC BRAKE CONTROL MODULE

Pin	Signal	Wire
1	IGNITION	850 RED-WHT
2	LEFT FNT CTRL SOL	826 BLK-WHT
4	LEFT FNT WHEEL INPUT	873 YEL
5		
6	LEFT FNT WHEEL INPUT	830 YEL
7	REAR AXLE SPD INPUT	882 WHT
8		
9	REAR AXLE SPD INPUT	883 WHT
14	PUMP ON INPUT	879 PPL-WHT
17	SUPPLY VOLT RELAY	1079 GRY-RED
18	REAR WHEELS CTRL SOL	829 DK BLU-WHT
20	GROUND	151 BLK
21	RT FNT WHEEL INPUT	833 TAN
23	RT FNT WHEEL INPUT	872 DK GRN
25	BRAKE APPLIED INPUT	820 YEL
26	SOL RLY CTRL	1078 BLK-LT GRN
28	PUMP MTR RLY CTRL	854 PNK-BLK
29	INDICATOR CTRL	875 LT GRN-BLK
30	DIAG REQUEST INPUT	1185 YEL
31	SERIAL DATA LINE	1184 PNK-WHT
32	SOL RLY VOLT MONITOR	1077 DK GRN-WHT
34	GROUND	151 BLK
35	RT FNT SOL CTRL	827 BRN-WHT

LEFT FNT WHEEL SPEED SENS

REAR AXLE SPEED SENS

RT FNT WHEEL SPEED SENS

BRAKE/CRUISE RELEASE SW

ALDL CONN

OVERVOLTAGE PROTECTION RELAY

FUSE #17 — PNK-BLK — 3
BLK — 5
RED-WHT
FUSE #3 — ORG — 1

RUST FUS LINK D — RED

INST CLSTR (ABS IND) — LT GRN-BLK

BLK-WHT — 1
BLK-LT GRN — 2
BRN-WHT — 3
DK GRN-WHT — 4
DK BLU-WHT — 5
RED — 6
GRY-RED — 7
PPL-WHT — 8
RED — 9
LT GRN-BLK — 11
PNK-BLK — 12

REAR WHEELS SOL

RT FNT WHEEL SOL

LEFT FNT WHEEL SOL

SOLENOID RELAY
30
L1
87A
87
85
86

PUMP MOTOR RELAY
86
85
30
87

RED
BLK

RETURN PUMP MOTOR

ABS HYDRAULIC MODULATOR ASSEMBLY

91H11319

Fig. 4: Anti-Lock Brake System Wiring Diagram (Caprice, Custom Cruiser & Roadmaster)

DIAGNOSTIC CHARTS

CODE 21
RIGHT FRONT WHEEL SPEED SENSOR FAULT

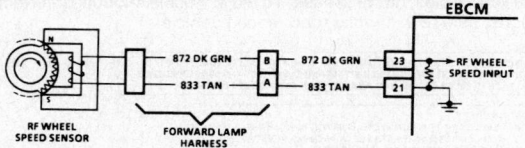

Circuit Description – Toothed wheel generates a voltage pulse as it moves past sensor. EBCM uses these pulses to determine wheel speed. The amount of voltage generated in each pulse depends on air gap between sensor and toothed wheel and wheel speed.

EBCM uses wheel speed sensor signal to calculate vehicle reference speeds and individual speed, acceleration and slip values for each wheel. These values are used to determine when anti-lock control is needed.

EBCM performs 2 basic types of checks on wheel speed sensors: sensor continuity and sensor output.

Code 21 will set if open or short exists in circuit No. 872, open exists in circuit No. 833, or an open exists across sensor coil.

Code 21 will also set if low output from wheel speed sensor is detected by EBCM. Conditions include shorted sensor coil and/or improperly installed wheel speed sensor.

Test Description – Numbers below refer to circled numbers in diagnostic chart.
1) Checks for correct resistance reading of wheel sensor.
2) Checks for short in wheel speed sensor wiring.
3) Checks for open, high resistance or short to voltage in wires between wheel speed sensor and EBCM.
4) Checks for short to ground in circuit No. 872.
5) Checks for intermittent in wheel sensor circuit. If no intermittent is found, wheel sensor may be faulty. Replace wheel sensor and road test vehicle. If code returns, replace EBCM.

DIAGNOSTIC AIDS

Intermittent setting of wheel speed sensor trouble codes may be caused by improperly mounted sensor or improper wire routing. Ensure sensor is mounted correctly and sensor face does not contain an accumulation of metallic particles, dirt or grease. To aid in trouble shooting intermittent conditions, use Tech 1 while road testing vehicle.

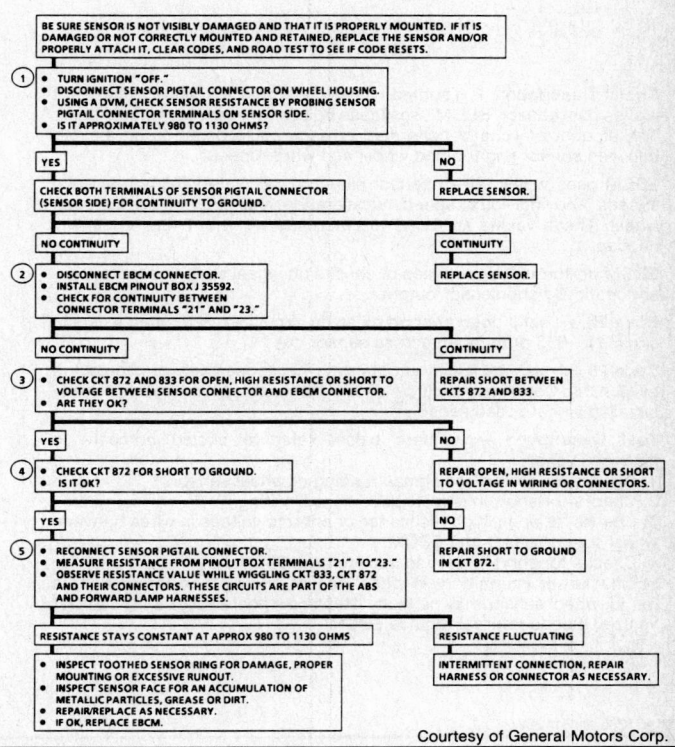

91H11293 91I11294

Courtesy of General Motors Corp.

CODE 22
RIGHT FRONT TOOTHED WHEEL
FREQUENCY ERROR

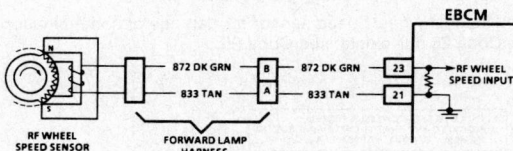

Circuit Description – Toothed wheel generates a voltage pulse as it moves past sensor. EBCM uses these pulses to determine wheel speed. The amount of voltage generated in each pulse depends on air gap between sensor and toothed wheel and wheel speed.

EBCM uses wheel speed sensor signal to calculate vehicle reference speeds and individual speed, acceleration and slip values for each wheel. These values are used to determine when anti-lock control is needed.

Code 22 will be set if improper speed signals are generated by toothed ring sensor. Possible causes are as follows: incorrect number of teeth on sensor ring, toothed sensor ring or sensor face covered with dirt, grease or metallic particles, or damaged toothed sensor ring.

Code 22 may set if mini-spare tire has been used or tire sizes on vehicle differ from each other.

Test Description – Numbers below refer to circled numbers in diagnostic chart.
1) Checks for properly mounted sensor and mounting torque.
2) Checks for faulty toothed sensor ring.
3) Checks for incorrect toothed sensor ring.

DIAGNOSTIC AIDS

Worn hub/bearing assembly may cause a Code 22 in extreme cases. Check for buildup of foreign material in gaps between teeth on toothed sensor ring. Check toothed sensor ring for large grooves, gouges or marks that may influence sensor ring's signal.

Remove and inspect wheel speed sensor for damage or contamination. If wheel speed sensor is okay and Code 22 still exists, see Code 21.

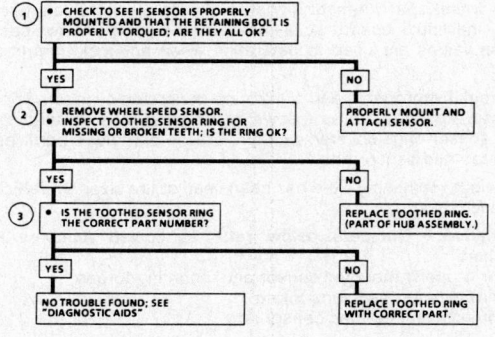

91H11293 91J11295

Courtesy of General Motors Corp.

CODE 25
LEFT FRONT WHEEL SPEED SENSOR FAULT

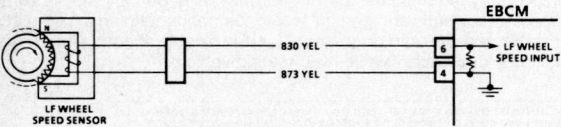

Circuit Description – Toothed wheel generates a voltage pulse as it moves past sensor. EBCM uses these pulses to determine wheel speed. The amount of voltage generated in each pulse depends on air gap between sensor and toothed wheel and wheel speed.

EBCM uses wheel speed sensor signal to calculate vehicle reference speeds and individual speed, acceleration and slip values for each wheel. These values are used to determine when anti-lock control is needed.

EBCM performs 2 basic types of checks on wheel speed sensors: sensor continuity and sensor output.

Code 25 will set if open or short exists in circuit No. 830, open exists in circuit No. 873 or an open across sensor coil.

Code 25 will also set if low output from wheel speed sensor is detected by EBCM. Conditions include shorted sensor coil or an improperly installed wheel speed sensor.

Test Description – Numbers below refer to circled numbers in diagnostic chart.
1) Checks for correct resistance reading of wheel sensor.
2) Checks for short in wheel speed sensor wiring.
3) Checks for open, high resistance or short to voltage in wires between wheel speed sensor and EBCM.
4) Checks for short to ground in circuit No. 830.
5) Checks for intermittent in wheel sensor circuit. If no intermittent is found, wheel sensor may be faulty. Replace wheel sensor and road test vehicle. If code returns, replace EBCM.

DIAGNOSTIC AIDS

Intermittent setting of wheel speed sensor trouble codes may be caused by improperly mounted sensor or improper wire routing. Ensure sensor is mounted correctly and sensor face does not contain an accumulation of metallic particles, dirt or grease. To aid in trouble shooting intermittent conditions, use Tech 1 while road testing vehicle.

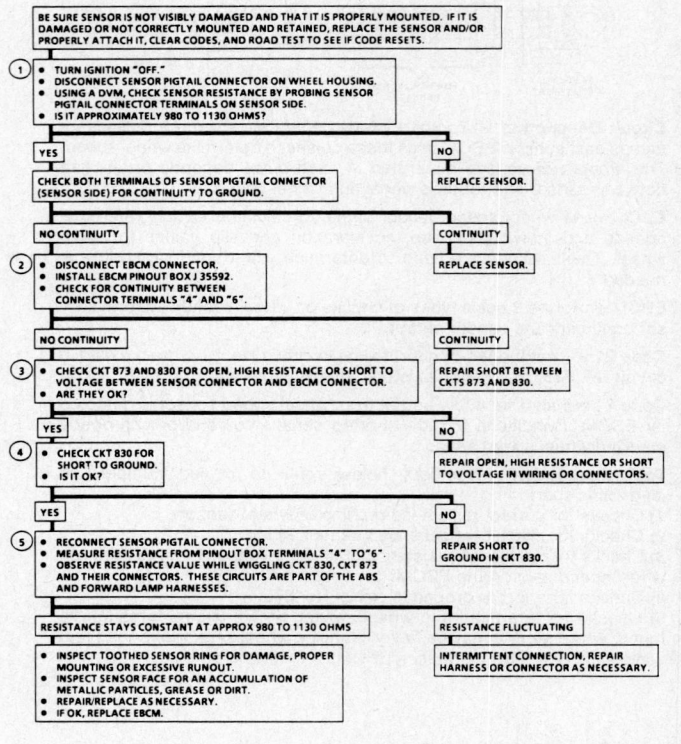

91A11296 91B11297

Courtesy of General Motors Corp.

CODE 26
LEFT FRONT TOOTHED WHEEL FREQUENCY ERROR

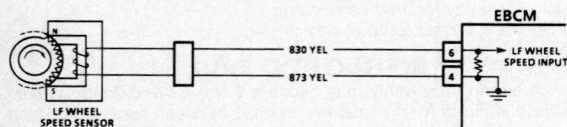

Circuit Description – Toothed wheel generates a voltage pulse as it moves past sensor. EBCM uses these pulses to determine wheel speed. The amount of voltage generated in each pulse depends on air gap between sensor and toothed wheel and wheel speed.

EBCM uses wheel speed sensor signal to calculate vehicle reference speeds and individual speed, acceleration and slip values for each wheel. These values are used to determine when anti-lock control is needed.

Code 26 will set if improper speed signals are generated by toothed ring sensor. Possible causes are as follows: incorrect number of teeth on sensor ring, sensor rings covered with dirt, grease or metallic particles, or damaged toothed sensor ring.

Code 26 may set if mini-spare tire has been used or tire sizes on vehicle differ from each other.

Test Description – Numbers below refer to circled numbers in diagnostic chart.
1) Checks for properly mounted sensor and mounting torque.
2) Checks for faulty toothed sensor ring.
3) Checks for incorrect toothed sensor ring.

DIAGNOSTIC AIDS

Worn hub/bearing assembly may cause a Code 26 in extreme cases. Check for buildup of foreign material in gaps between teeth on toothed sensor ring. Check toothed sensor ring for large grooves, gouges or marks that may influence sensor ring's signal.

Remove and inspect wheel speed sensor for damage or contamination. If okay and Code 26 still exists, see Code 25.

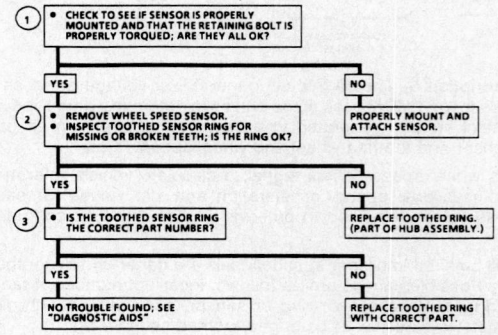

91A11296 91C11298

Courtesy of General Motors Corp.

CODE 35
REAR AXLES SPEED SENSOR FAULT

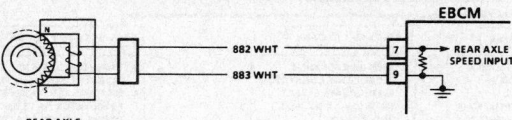

Circuit Description – Toothed wheel generates a voltage pulse as it moves past sensor. EBCM uses these pulses to determine wheel speed. The amount of voltage generated in each pulse depends on air gap between sensor and toothed wheel and wheel speed.

EBCM uses wheel speed sensor signal to calculate vehicle reference speeds and individual speed, acceleration and slip values for each wheel. These values are used to determine when anti-lock control is needed.

EBCM performs 2 basic types of checks on rear axle speed sensor: sensor continuity and sensor output.

Code 35 will set if open or short exists in circuit No. 882, open exists in circuit No. 883, or an open exists across sensor coil.

Code 35 will also set if low output from rear axle speed sensor is detected by EBCM. Conditions include shorted sensor coil or an improperly installed wheel speed sensor.

Test Description – Numbers below refer to circled numbers in diagnostic chart.
1) Checks for correct resistance reading of wheel sensor.
2) Checks for short in rear axle speed sensor wiring.
3) Checks for open, high resistance or short to voltage in wires between rear axle speed sensor and EBCM.
4) Checks for short to ground in circuit No. 882.
5) Checks for intermittent in rear axle speed sensor circuit. If no intermittent is found, wheel sensor may be faulty. Replace wheel sensor and road test vehicle. If code returns, replace EBCM.

DIAGNOSTIC AIDS

Intermittent setting of wheel speed sensor trouble codes may be caused by improperly mounted sensor or improper wire routing. Ensure sensor is mounted correctly and sensor face does not contain an accumulation of metallic particles, dirt or grease. To aid in trouble shooting intermittent conditions, use Tech 1 while road testing vehicle.

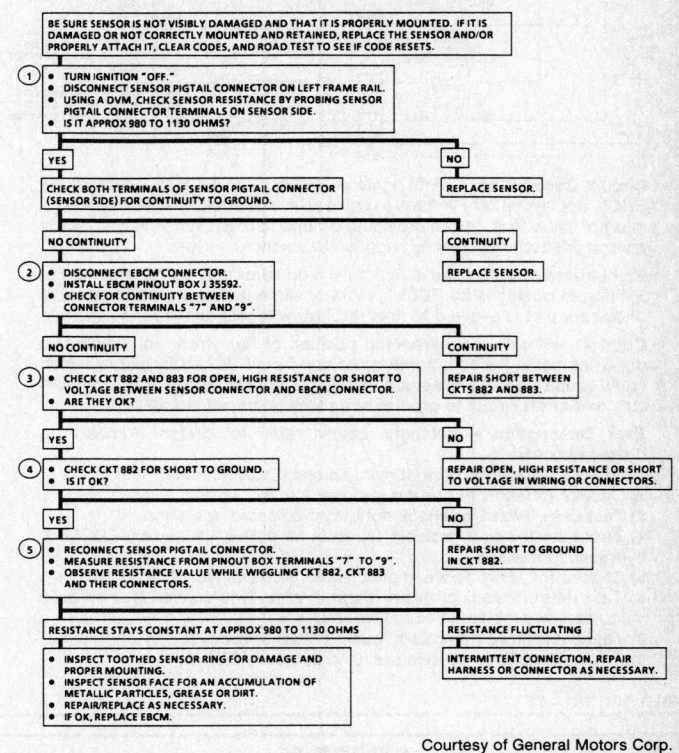

91D11299 91G11318

Courtesy of General Motors Corp.

CODE 36
RIGHT REAR TOOTHED WHEEL FREQUENCY ERROR

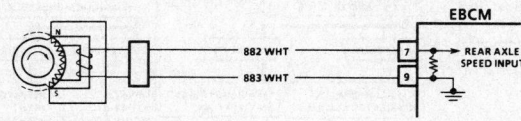

Circuit Description – Toothed wheel generates a voltage pulse as it moves past sensor. EBCM uses these pulses to determine wheel speed. The amount of voltage generated in each pulse depends on air gap between sensor and toothed wheel and wheel speed.

EBCM uses wheel speed sensor signal to calculate vehicle reference speeds and individual speed, acceleration and slip values for each wheel. These values are used to determine when anti-lock control is needed.

Code 36 will set if improper speed signals are generated by toothed ring sensor. Possible causes are as follows: incorrect number of teeth on sensor ring, sensor rings covered with dirt, grease or metallic particles, or damaged toothed sensor ring.

Code 36 may set if mini-spare tire has been used or tire sizes on vehicle differ from each other.

Test Description – Numbers below refer to circled numbers in diagnostic chart.
1) Checks for properly mounted sensor and mounting torque.
2) Checks for faulty toothed sensor ring.
3) Checks for incorrect toothed sensor ring.

DIAGNOSTIC AIDS

Check for buildup of foreign material in gaps between teeth on toothed sensor ring. Check toothed sensor ring for large grooves, gouges or marks that may influence sensor ring's signal.

Inspect wheel speed sensor for damage or contamination. If wheel speed sensor is okay and Code 36 still exists, see Code 35.

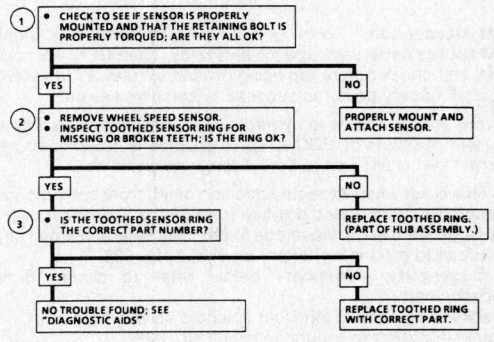

91D11299 91G11300

Courtesy of General Motors Corp.

CODE 41
RIGHT FRONT SOLENOID VALVE FAULT

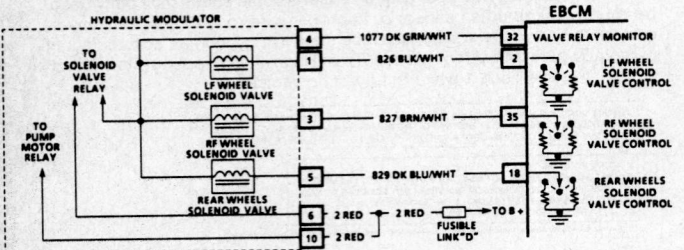

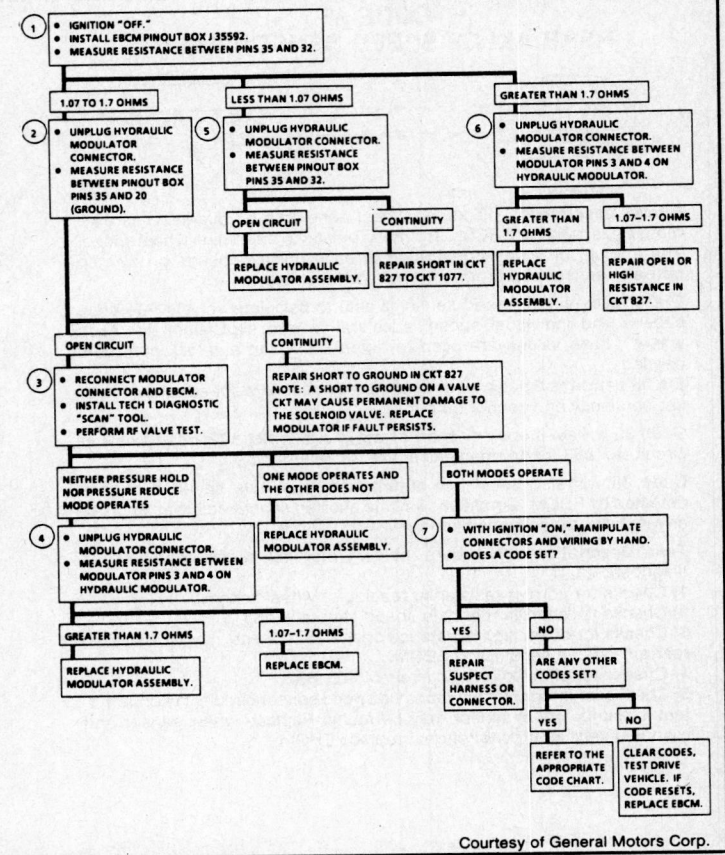

Circuit Description – With ignition in RUN or START position the EBCM applies battery voltage to valve relay. The EBCM will complete an internal self-check before providing ground to relay. When valve relay is energized, battery power is supplied to solenoid valves.

Right front solenoid valve in hydraulic modulator may be commanded to 3 different positions by EBCM. Valve position is determined by amount of current that is allowed to flow through solenoid coil.

Code 41 will set when expected position of right front solenoid valve does not match the commanded position from EBCM. Conditions which could cause Code 41 to set are damage to right front solenoid, open circuit, and short circuit to ground or battery on circuit No. 827.

Test Description – Numbers below refer to circled numbers in diagnostic chart.
1) Checks resistance of right front solenoid valve circuit.
2) Checks for short to ground in circuit No. 827.
3) Test uses Tech 1 to check right front solenoid operation.
4) Test determines if problem found in step 3) is caused by EBCM or hydraulic modulator.
5) Checks for short between circuits No. 827 and No. 1077.
6) Test determines if problem found in step 1) is caused by hydraulic modulator or problem in circuit No. 827.
7) Test determines if problem found in step 3) is caused by an intermittent in wiring and/or connectors, or a defective EBCM.

Courtesy of General Motors Corp.

91H11301 91I11302

CODE 45
LEFT FRONT SOLENOID VALVE FAULT

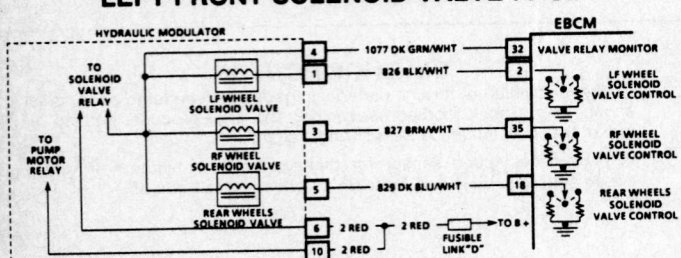

Circuit Description – With ignition in RUN or START position the EBCM applies battery voltage to valve relay. The EBCM will complete an internal self-check before providing ground to relay. When valve relay is energized, battery power is supplied to solenoid valves.

Left front solenoid valve in hydraulic modulator may be commanded to 3 different positions by EBCM. Valve position is determined by amount of current that is allowed to flow through solenoid coil.

Code 45 will set when expected position of left front solenoid valve does not match the commanded position from EBCM. Conditions which could cause Code 45 to set are damage to left front solenoid, open circuit, and short circuit to ground or battery on circuit No. 826.

Test Description – Numbers below refer to circled numbers in diagnostic chart.
1) Checks resistance of left front solenoid valve circuit.
2) Checks for short to ground in circuit No. 826.
3) Test uses Tech 1 to check left front solenoid operation.
4) Test determines if problem found in step 3) is caused by EBCM or hydraulic modulator.
5) Checks for short between circuits No. 826 and No. 1077.
6) Test determines if problem found in step 1) is caused by hydraulic modulator or problem in circuit No. 826.
7) Test determines if problem found in step 3) is caused by an intermittent in wiring and/or connectors, or a defective EBCM.

Courtesy of General Motors Corp.

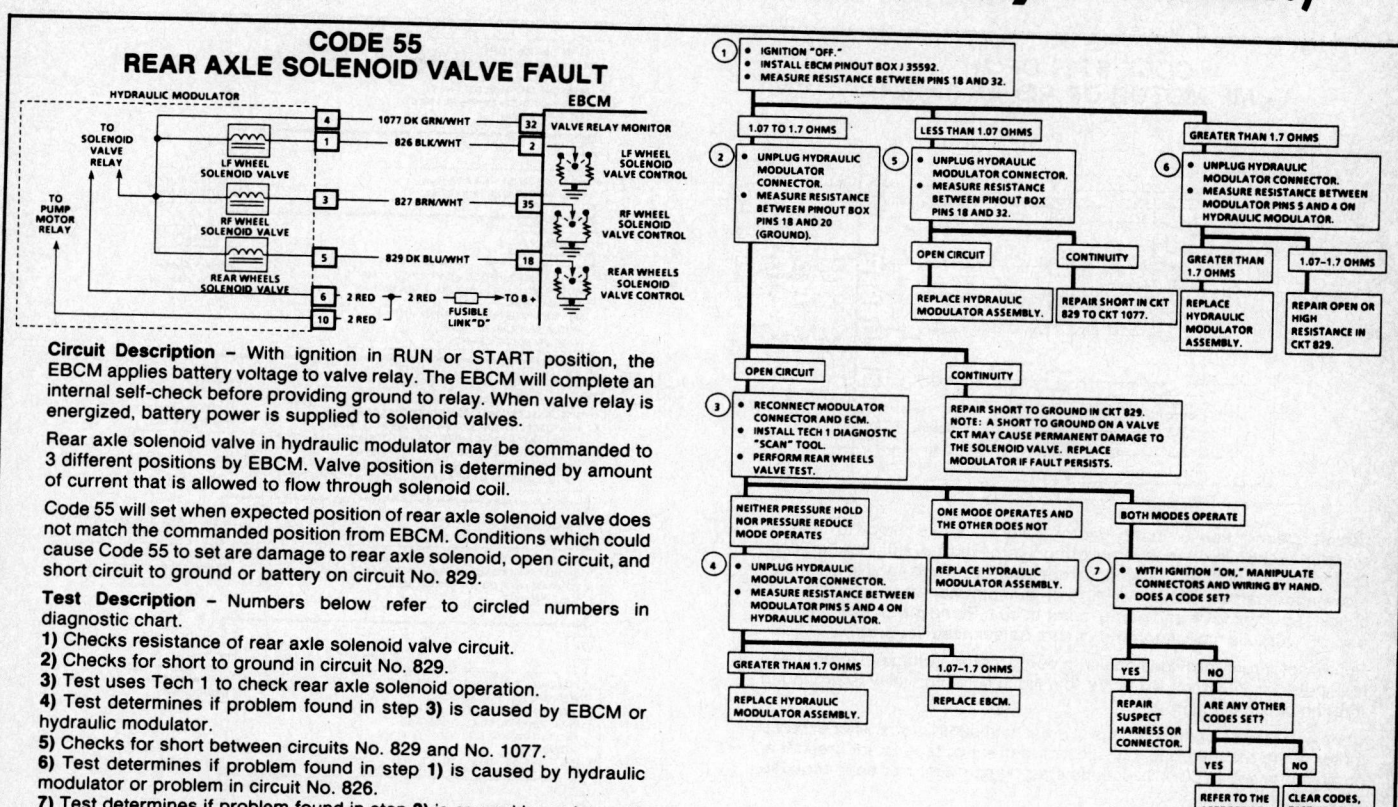

CODE 55
REAR AXLE SOLENOID VALVE FAULT

Circuit Description – With ignition in RUN or START position, the EBCM applies battery voltage to valve relay. The EBCM will complete an internal self-check before providing ground to relay. When valve relay is energized, battery power is supplied to solenoid valves.

Rear axle solenoid valve in hydraulic modulator may be commanded to 3 different positions by EBCM. Valve position is determined by amount of current that is allowed to flow through solenoid coil.

Code 55 will set when expected position of rear axle solenoid valve does not match the commanded position from EBCM. Conditions which could cause Code 55 to set are damage to rear axle solenoid, open circuit, and short circuit to ground or battery on circuit No. 829.

Test Description – Numbers below refer to circled numbers in diagnostic chart.
1) Checks resistance of rear axle solenoid valve circuit.
2) Checks for short to ground in circuit No. 829.
3) Test uses Tech 1 to check rear axle solenoid operation.
4) Test determines if problem found in step 3) is caused by EBCM or hydraulic modulator.
5) Checks for short between circuits No. 829 and No. 1077.
6) Test determines if problem found in step 1) is caused by hydraulic modulator or problem in circuit No. 826.
7) Test determines if problem found in step 3) is caused by an intermittent in wiring and/or connectors, or a defective EBCM.

91H11301 91A11304

Courtesy of General Motors Corp.

CODE 61 (1 OF 2)
PUMP MOTOR OR RELAY FAULT

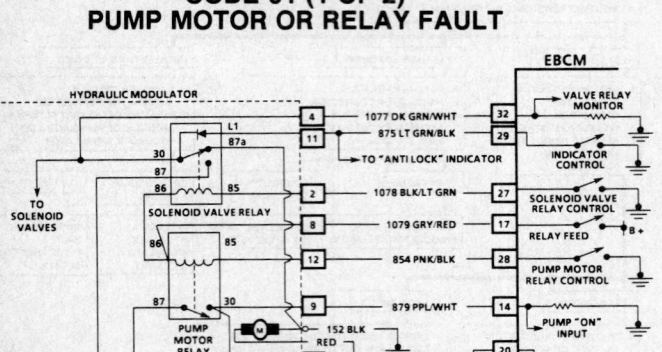

Circuit Description – Pump motor returns brake fluid to master cylinder brake circuit at hydraulic modulator during anti-lock braking. During normal braking, pump does not operate. When vehicle begins to move after start-up, EBCM will turn on pump motor and perform a self-check of pump motor and pump motor circuit. Pump motor is an integral part of hydraulic modulator and cannot be serviced separately.

Pump motor relay provides power to pump motor. Voltage to motor relay is supplied from circuit No. 1079 (pin No. 17). Motor relay is grounded through circuit No. 854.

Code 61 will set if battery voltage is present at pump motor without pump motor being requested to activate or if battery voltage is not present at pump motor within 60 milliseconds after pump motor has been requested to activate.

NOTE: To avoid misdiagnosis, ensure Red wire to hydraulic modulator is not damaged and is making a clean, tight connection.

Test Description – Numbers below refer to circled numbers in diagnostic chart.
1) Checks resistance of relay.
2) Checks if relay is stuck closed.
3) Checks for proper switching action in relay.
4) Checks for open in hydraulic modulator circuit.
5) Checks for good ground.
6) Checks resistance of pump motor.
7) Determines if battery voltage is available to pump motor relay.
8) Checks for open in circuit No. 854.
9) Determines if circuit No. 854 is shorted to ground.
10) Checks for short between circuits No. 854 and 1079.
11) Checks for open in circuit No. 879.

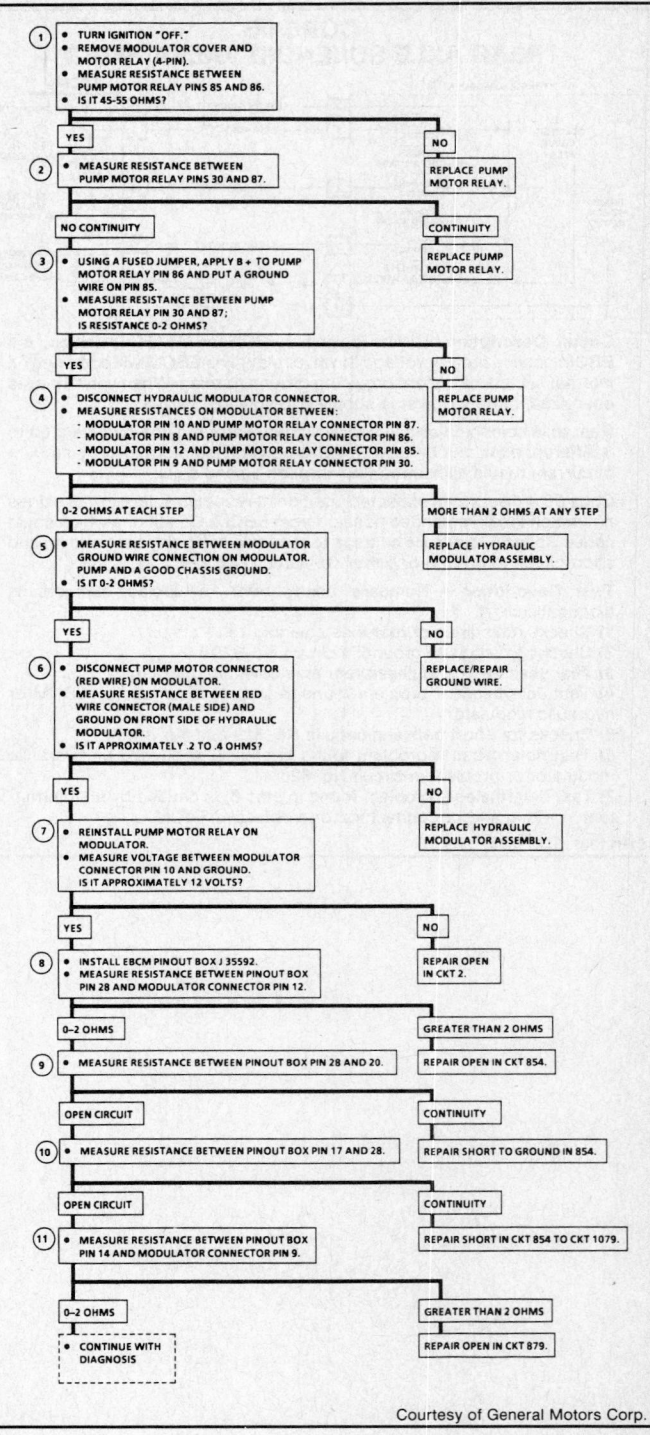

CODE 61 (2 OF 2)
PUMP MOTOR OR RELAY FAULT (CONT.)

Test Description – Numbers below refer to circled numbers in diagnostic chart.

12) Determines if circuit No. 879 is shorted to ground.

13) Checks for short to ground between circuits No. 879 and No. 1079.

14) Checks for short to voltage on circuit 854 or circuit No. 879.

15) Checks for internal short to ground within hydraulic modulator.

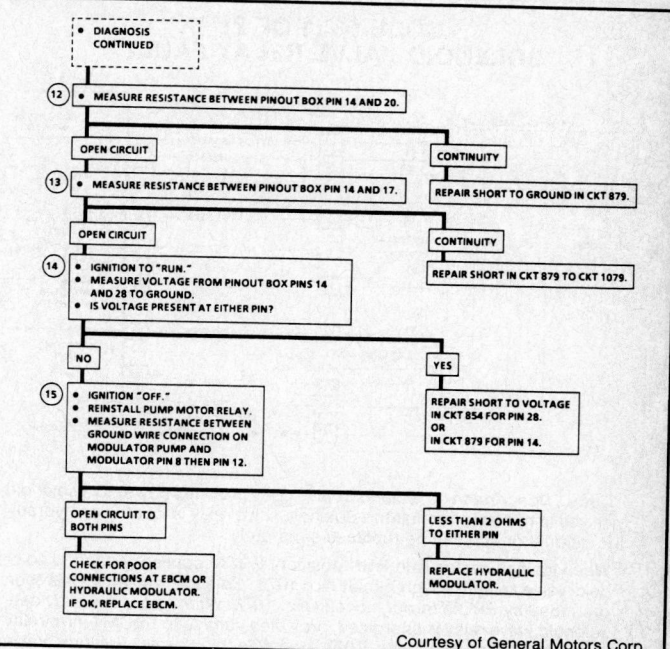

91E11308

Courtesy of General Motors Corp.

CODE 63 (1 OF 2)
SOLENOID VALVE RELAY FAULT

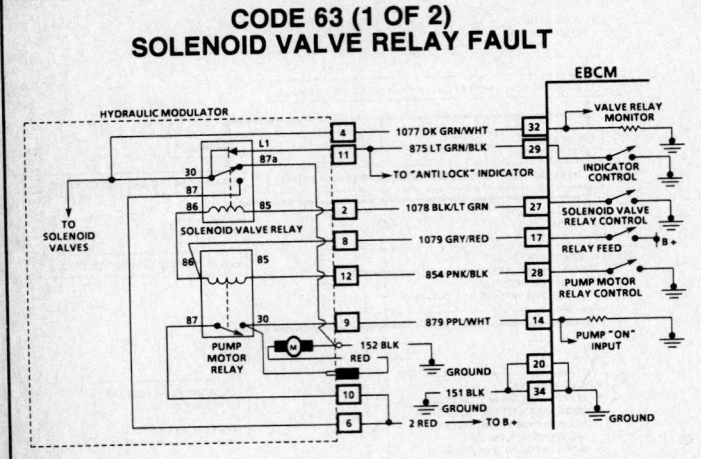

Circuit Description – Solenoid valve relay provides power to 3 solenoid valves in hydraulic modulator. Solenoid valve relay is located on hydraulic modulator and can be replaced separately.

When ignition switch is in RUN position, EBCM applies voltage to solenoid valve relay through circuit No. 1079. Solenoid valve relay is then grounded by EBCM through circuit No. 1078. When ground is provided, solenoid valve relay is energized, providing voltage to EBCM (valve relay monitor) through circuit No. 1077, and solenoid valves. Solenoid valve relay remains energized until ignition switch is turned off or a failure is detected.

Code 63 will set under the following conditions: valve relay monitor has battery voltage when not requested by EBCM, or valve relay monitor has less than 5 volts when EBCM has requested for the energizing of solenoid valve relay.

Test Description – Numbers below refer to circled numbers in diagnostic chart.
1) Checks resistance of relay.
2) Checks relay for a poor internal contact.
3) Checks relay for stuck internal contact.
4) Checks for proper switching action in relay.
5) Checks for faulty diode in relay.
6) Checks hydraulic modulator circuitry.
7) Checks for good ground.
8) Checks power feed to relay.
9) Checks for a potential open or short to ground in circuit No. 1079.
10) Checks for short to ground in circuit No. 1078.
11) Checks for open in circuit No. 1078.
12) Checks for short to battery voltage in circuit No. 1078.
13) Determines if fault is in circuit No. 1079 or EBCM.

① • IGNITION "OFF."
• REMOVE MODULATOR COVER AND SOLENOID VALVE RELAY (6-PIN).
• MEASURE RESISTANCE BETWEEN SOLENOID VALVE RELAY PINS 85 AND 86. IS IT 52-64 OHMS?

YES

② • MEASURE RESISTANCE BETWEEN SOLENOID VALVE RELAY PINS 30 AND 87A. IS IT BETWEEN 0-2 OHMS?

YES

③ • MEASURE RESISTANCE BETWEEN SOLENOID VALVE RELAY PINS 30 AND 87.

OPEN CIRCUIT

④ • USING A FUSED JUMPER, APPLY B+ TO SOLENOID VALVE RELAY PIN 86 AND PUT A GROUND WIRE ON PIN 85.
• MEASURE RESISTANCE BETWEEN SOLENOID VALVE RELAY PIN 30 AND 87. IS RESISTANCE 0-2 OHMS?

YES

⑤ • DISCONNECT FUSED JUMPERS.
• USING A DVM WITH DIODE TEST, CHECK SOLENOID VALVE RELAY INTERNAL DIODE. IS DIODE OK?

YES

⑥ • DISCONNECT HYDRAULIC MODULATOR CONNECTOR.
• MEASURE RESISTANCES ON MODULATOR BETWEEN:
  - MODULATOR PIN 6 AND VALVE RELAY CONNECTOR PIN 87.
  - MODULATOR PIN 2 AND VALVE RELAY CONNECTOR PIN 85.
  - MODULATOR PIN 11 AND VALVE RELAY CONNECTOR PIN L1.
  - MODULATOR PIN 4 AND VALVE RELAY CONNECTOR PIN 30.
  - MODULATOR PIN 8 AND VALVE RELAY CONNECTOR PIN 86.
  - VALVE RELAY CONNECTOR PIN 87A AND MODULATOR GROUND WIRE CONNECTION ON MODULATOR PUMP.

0-2 OHMS AT EACH STEP

⑦ • MEASURE RESISTANCE BETWEEN MODULATOR GROUND WIRE CONNECTION ON MODULATOR PUMP AND A GOOD CHASSIS GROUND. IS IT 0-2 OHMS?

YES

⑧ • MEASURE VOLTAGE BETWEEN MODULATOR CONNECTOR PIN 6 AND GROUND. IS IT APPROXIMATELY 12 VOLTS?

YES

⑨ • TURN IGNITION "ON."
• MEASURE VOLTAGE BETWEEN MODULATOR CONNECTOR PIN 8 AND GROUND. IS IT APPROXIMATELY 12 VOLTS?

YES

⑩ • TURN IGNITION "OFF."
• INSTALL EBCM PINOUT BOX J 35592.
• MEASURE RESISTANCE BETWEEN PINOUT BOX 27 AND 20.

OPEN CIRCUIT

⑪ • MEASURE RESISTANCE BETWEEN PINOUT BOX PIN 27 AND MODULATOR CONNECTOR PIN 2.

0-2 OHMS

⑫ • IGNITION SWITCH TO "RUN."
• MEASURE VOLTAGE BETWEEN PINOUT BOX PIN 27 AND GROUND. IS IT APPROXIMATELY 12 VOLTS?

YES — REPAIR SHORT TO VOLTAGE IN CKT 1078.

NO — • CONTINUE WITH DIAGNOSIS

NO → REPLACE SOLENOID VALVE RELAY.

NO → REPLACE SOLENOID VALVE RELAY.

CONTINUITY → REPLACE SOLENOID VALVE RELAY.

NO → REPLACE SOLENOID VALVE RELAY.

NO → REPLACE SOLENOID VALVE RELAY.

NO → REPLACE SOLENOID VALVE RELAY.

MORE THAN 2 OHMS AT ANY STEP → REPLACE HYDRAULIC MODULATOR ASSEMBLY.

NO → REPAIR GROUND WIRE.

NO → REPAIR OPEN IN CKT 2.

NO → ⑬ • IGNITION "OFF."
• INSTALL ECBM PINOUT BOX J 35592.
• MEASURE RESISTANCE BETWEEN PINOUT BOX PIN 17 AND MODULATOR CONNECTOR PIN 8.

GREATER THAN 2 OHMS → REPAIR OPEN IN CKT 1079.

0-2 OHMS → CHECK FOR POOR CONNECTION AT EBCM CONNECTOR PIN 17. IF OK, REPLACE EBCM.

CONTINUITY → REPAIR SHORT TO GROUND IN CKT 1078.

GREATER THAN 2 OHMS → REPAIR OPEN IN CKT 1078.

Courtesy of General Motors Corp.

CODE 63 (2 OF 2)
SOLENOID VALVE RELAY FAULT (CONT.)

Test Description – Numbers below refer to circled numbers in diagnostic chart.

14) Checks for short to ground in circuit No. 1077.
15) Checks for open in circuit No. 1077.
16) Checks for short to battery voltage in circuit No. 1077.
17) Determines is fault is in hydraulic modulator or EBCM.

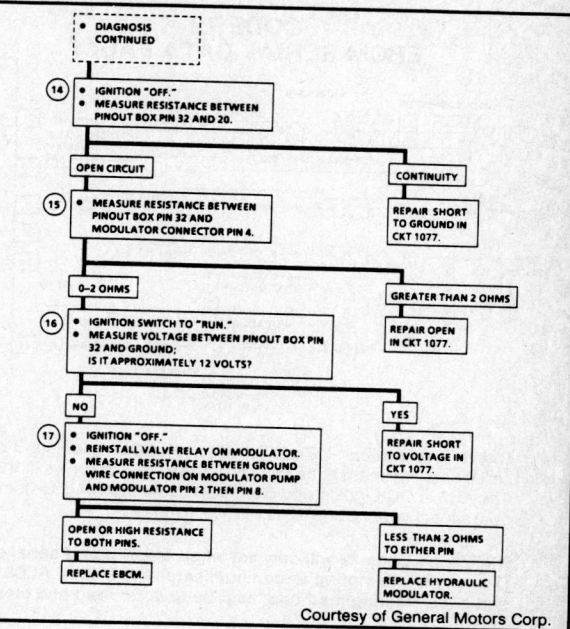

91J11311

Courtesy of General Motors Corp.

CODE 71
EBCM FAULT

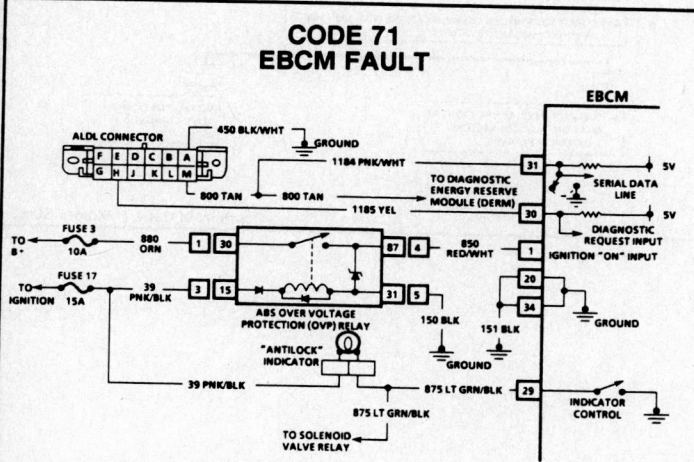

If failure is intermittent, EBCM will enable the system at next ignition cycle and a History Code 71 will be present.

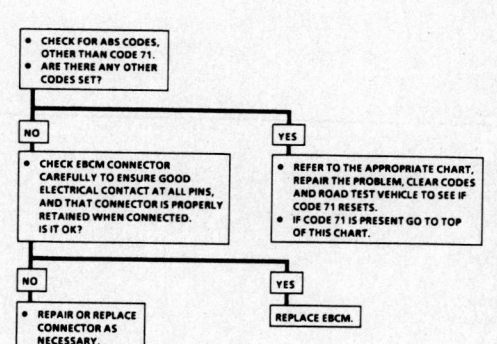

EBCM has self-diagnostics that can detect internal failure within the module. If a failure is detected and sets a Code 71, anti-lock braking is disabled and EBCM turns on ANTI-LOCK indicator for remainder of ignition cycle.

91A11312 91B11313

Courtesy of General Motors Corp.

CODE 72
EBCM SERIAL DATA FAULT

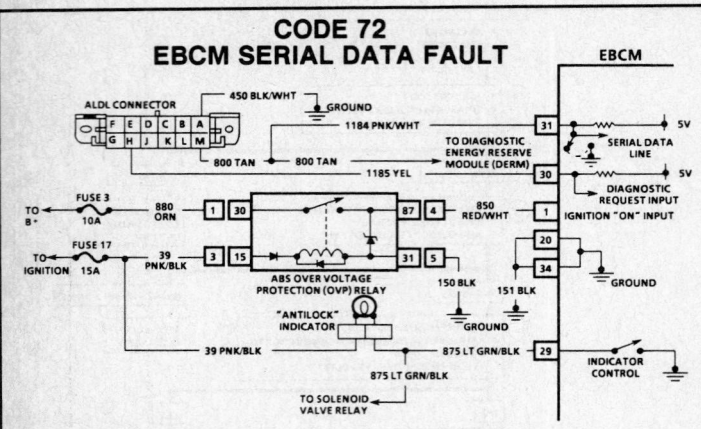

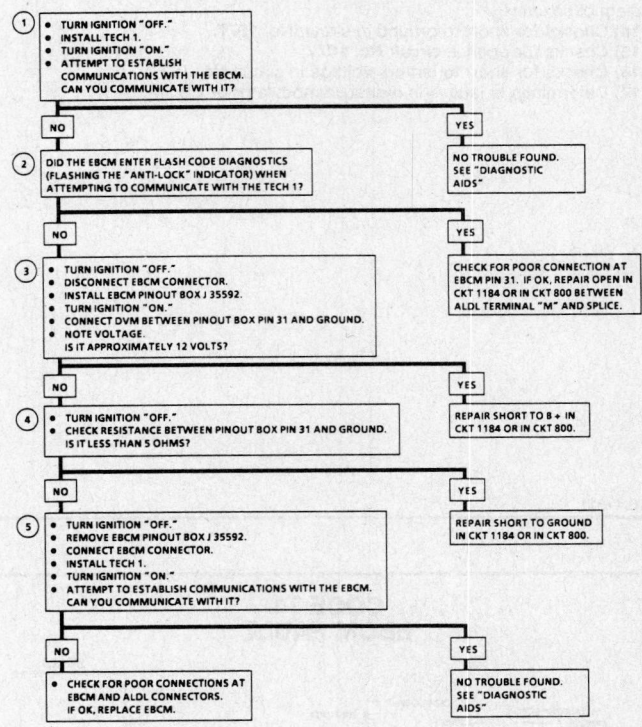

Circuit Description – Code 72 will set if EBCM detects 3 consecutive serial data line messages that are ignored due to errors in transmission. The ANTI-LOCK indicator will NOT be illuminated and system will remain operational when Code 72 is set.

NOTE: Code 72 will only set when an off-board serial data device (Tech 1) is attempting to communicate with EBCM. ALDL flash code and code clearing methods must be used to read and clear code.

Test Description – Numbers below refer to circled numbers in diagnostic chart.
1) Checks if Tech 1 can communicate with EBCM.
2) Determines if serial data circuit is open.
3) Checks for short to battery in serial data circuit.
4) Checks for short to ground in serial data circuit.
5) Checks if Tech 1 can communicate with EBCM.

DIAGNOSTIC AIDS

Problem may be intermittent. Perform test while wiggling wiring and connectors. Performing wiggle test may cause fault to appear.

① • TURN IGNITION "OFF."
   • INSTALL TECH 1.
   • TURN IGNITION "ON."
   • ATTEMPT TO ESTABLISH COMMUNICATIONS WITH THE EBCM. CAN YOU COMMUNICATE WITH IT?

NO → ② DID THE EBCM ENTER FLASH CODE DIAGNOSTICS (FLASHING THE "ANTI-LOCK" INDICATOR) WHEN ATTEMPTING TO COMMUNICATE WITH THE TECH 1?

YES → NO TROUBLE FOUND. SEE "DIAGNOSTIC AIDS"

NO → ③ • TURN IGNITION "OFF."
   • DISCONNECT EBCM CONNECTOR.
   • INSTALL EBCM PINOUT BOX J 35592.
   • TURN IGNITION "ON."
   • CONNECT DVM BETWEEN PINOUT BOX PIN 31 AND GROUND.
   • NOTE VOLTAGE. IS IT APPROXIMATELY 12 VOLTS?

YES → CHECK FOR POOR CONNECTION AT EBCM PIN 31. IF OK, REPAIR OPEN IN CKT 1184 OR IN CKT 800 BETWEEN ALDL TERMINAL "M" AND SPLICE.

NO → ④ • TURN IGNITION "OFF."
   • CHECK RESISTANCE BETWEEN PINOUT BOX PIN 31 AND GROUND. IS IT LESS THAN 5 OHMS?

YES → REPAIR SHORT TO B + IN CKT 1184 OR IN CKT 800.

NO → ⑤ • TURN IGNITION "OFF."
   • REMOVE EBCM PINOUT BOX J 35592.
   • CONNECT EBCM CONNECTOR.
   • INSTALL TECH 1.
   • TURN IGNITION "ON."
   • ATTEMPT TO ESTABLISH COMMUNICATIONS WITH THE EBCM. CAN YOU COMMUNICATE WITH IT?

YES → REPAIR SHORT TO GROUND IN CKT 1184 OR IN CKT 800.

NO → • CHECK FOR POOR CONNECTIONS AT EBCM AND ALDL CONNECTORS. IF OK, REPLACE EBCM.

YES → NO TROUBLE FOUND. SEE "DIAGNOSTIC AIDS"

91A11312 91C11314

Courtesy of General Motors Corp.

SYMPTOM DIAGNOSTIC CHARTS

SYMPTOM DIAGNOSTIC CHART "A"
ANTI-LOCK LIGHT ON, NO CODES SET OR
TECH 1 UNABLE TO RECEIVE DATA

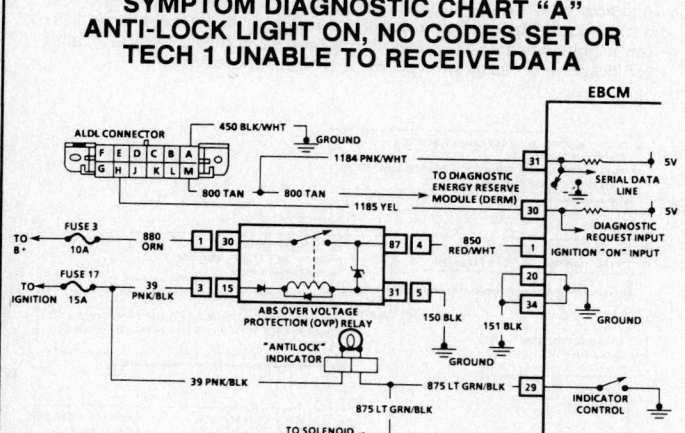

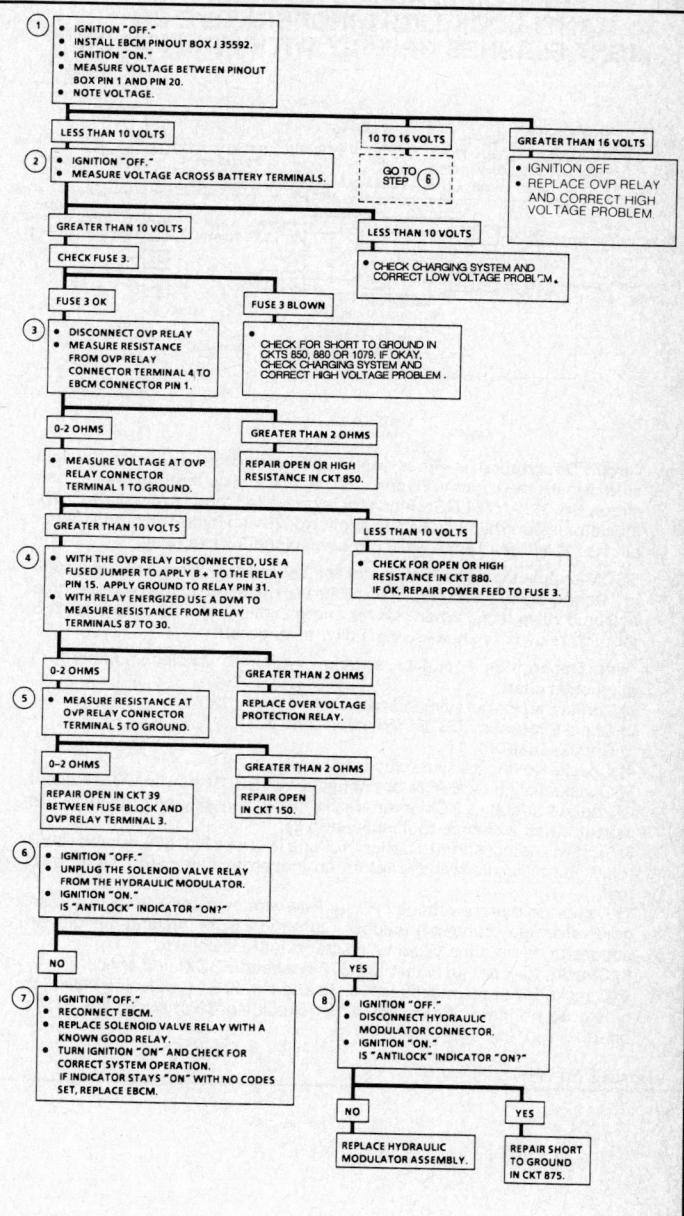

Circuit Description – Amber ANTI-LOCK indicator is located on right side of instrument panel. Battery voltage is supplied through fuse 17 and circuit No. 39. ANTI-LOCK indicator is grounded through circuit No. 875. Indicator is controlled by EBCM at pin No. 29 and hydraulic modulator at pin No. 11 (Green/Black wire) through solenoid valve relay.

EBCM supplies ground to indicator for 2 seconds when ignition is turned on. During those 2 seconds, if no faults are detected, EBCM will energize solenoid valve relay. When relay is energized, the ground circuit No. 875 through relay is open, allowing indicator to go off.

When ignition is turned to RUN position, OVP relay is energized by fuse No. 17. When OVP relay is energized, the normally open contacts are closed and voltage is supplied from fuse No. 3 through circuits No. 880 and 850, to EBCM at pin No. 1. If high voltages occur (16 volts or more), OVP relay will short circuit No. 880 to ground, causing fuse No. 3 to blow. This prevents damage to ABS.

CAUTION: DO NOT use quick charger for engine starting or battery charging if battery is still connected. Disconnect negative battery cable when charging battery. Failure to disconnect negative battery cable may cause fuse No. 3 to blow or cause damage to other electronic components.

Test Description – Numbers below refer to circled numbers in diagnostic chart.
1) Determines if EBCM has proper supply voltage.
2) Determines if fault is in charging system or power feed to OVP relay (fuse No. 3).
3) Checks for open or high resistance in circuit No. 850.
4) Determines if OVP relay is faulty.
5) Determines if open is in circuit No. 150 or circuit No. 39.
6) Checks for possible fault in solenoid valve relay or EBCM.
7) Determines if solenoid valve relay or EBCM is faulty.
8) Determines if fault is in hydraulic modulator or short to ground in circuit No. 875.

91A11312 91D11315 91E11316

Courtesy of General Motors Corp.

SYMPTOM DIAGNOSTIC CHART "B"
ANTI-LOCK LIGHT INOPERATIVE OR
LIGHT FLASHES BRIEFLY WITH IGNITION ON

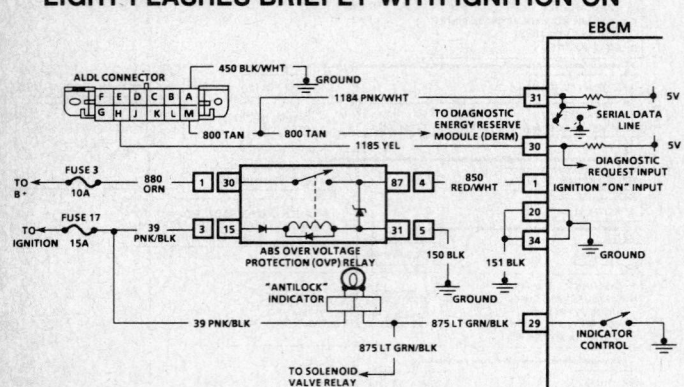

Circuit Description – Amber ANTI-LOCK indicator is located on right side of instrument panel. Battery voltage is supplied through fuse 17 and circuit No. 39. ANTI-LOCK indicator is grounded through circuit No. 875. Indicator is controlled by EBCM at pin No. 29 and hydraulic modulator at pin No. 11 (Green/Black wire) through solenoid valve relay.

EBCM supplies ground to indicator for 2 seconds when ignition is turned on. During those 2 seconds, if no faults are detected, EBCM will energize solenoid valve relay. When relay is energized, the ground circuit No. 875 through relay is open, allowing indicator to go off.

Test Description – Numbers below refer to circled numbers in diagnostic chart.
1) Verifies an inoperative indicator.
2) Checks for faulty EBCM indicator control.
3) Checks fuse No. 17.
4) Checks solenoid valve relay diode.
5) Checks for faulty EBCM or connection at EBCM pin No. 29. This test will detect a faulty EBCM even if solenoid valve relay energized before indicator had a chance to flash in step 2).
6) Test will detect short to battery voltage in circuit No. 850 or faulty OVP relay. Either failure will appear as an inoperative indicator during bulb test.
7) A short to battery voltage in Gray/Red wire between EBCM and solenoid valve relay causes a feedback through EBCM, making the ignition appear to be on, thus causing indicator not to illuminate.
8) Checks for open in circuit No. 875 between EBCM and splice.
9) Checks for open in circuits No. 39 and No. 875. If replacing indicator bulb does not correct problem, either circuit No. 39 or circuit No. 875 is open.

DIAGNOSTIC AIDS

If indicator failure is intermittent, install Tech 1 and select any ABS test mode so ANTI-LOCK indicator will be turned on. While observing indicator, wiggle wiring and connectors of ground and power circuits. Watch for flickering or failure of indicator to pin point problem area.

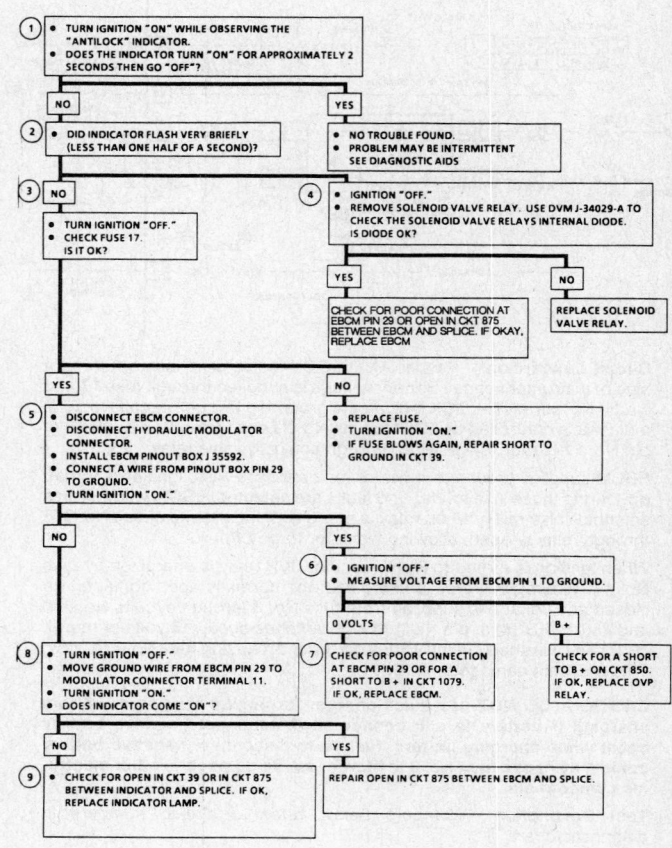

1991 BRAKES
Anti-Lock — Bosch 2U ("D", "E" & "K" Bodies)

DESCRIPTION

"D" Body: Brougham
"E" Body: Eldorado, Reatta, Riviera, Toronado, Trofeo
"K" Body: Seville

The Bosch 2U Anti-Lock Brake System (ABS) increases vehicle steerability, directional stability and optimum deceleration in severe braking conditions on most road surfaces. The ABS monitors wheel speed and controls brake line pressure to eliminate uncontrolled skidding.

The ABS consists of an Electronic Brake Control Module (EBCM), hydraulic modulator, solenoid valves, pump motor, ABS valve relay, pump relay and wheel speed sensors on front and rear wheels. See Fig. 1. ABS system utilizes a 4-way hydraulic circuit — one circuit for each front and rear wheel.

NOTE: *For more information on brake system, see DISC & DRUM article.*

OPERATION

The EBCM is located behind glove box. Wheel speed sensors relay information about wheel acceleration, deceleration and slip value to EBCM. The EBCM controls braking by activating and deactivating electromagnetic modulator valve.

The modulator valve consists of 3 rapidly switching solenoid valves, accumulator chamber and a return pump. The valves increase and decrease brake fluid pressure to each wheel (rear wheels are one circuit) to prevent wheel lock-up.

The modulator valve can supply only as much fluid pressure as applied by the driver through the master cylinder. The modulator valve alone CANNOT apply the brakes.

BLEEDING BRAKE SYSTEM

Brake system can be bled by either manual or pressure method. Use DOT 3 brake fluid only.

MANUAL BLEEDING PROCEDURE

1) With engine off, remove reserve vacuum by applying brakes several times. Fill master cylinder with brake fluid and keep one-half full during bleeding procedure.
2) Place proper size box end wrench over bleeder valve. Attach one end of clear tube over valve end and submerge other end in container partially filled with clean brake fluid.
3) Starting at left front wheel, slowly depress brake pedal and hold. Loosen bleeder valve to purge air from cylinder. Tighten bleeder valve and slowly release brake pedal. Repeat sequence until all air is removed.

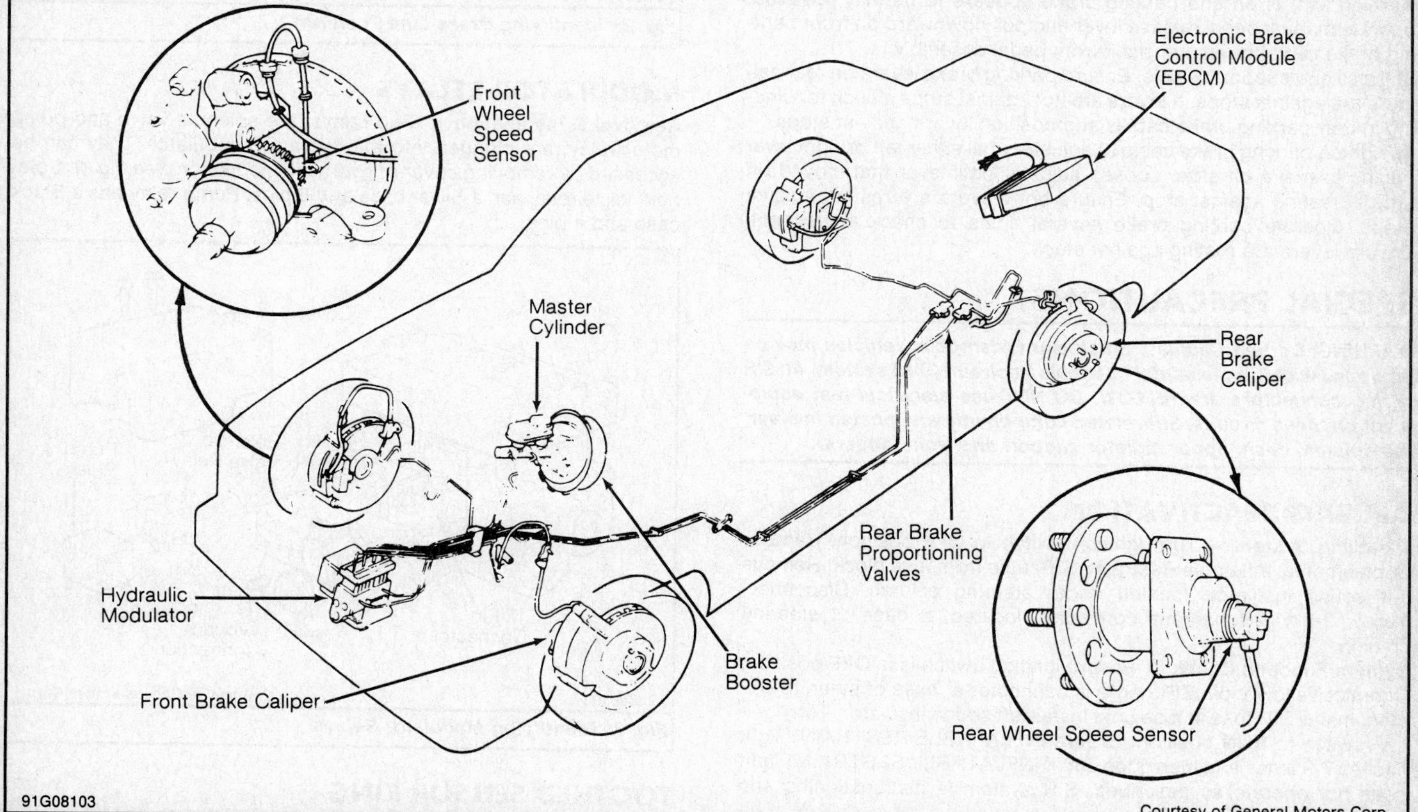

CAUTION: *See ANTI-LOCK BRAKE SAFETY PRECAUTIONS article in GENERAL INFORMATION in VOLUME 1.*

WARNING: *ABS systems are under high pressure under normal operating conditions. Before opening the fluid reservoir or before servicing any component of an ABS system, it is mandatory that system pressure be discharged. To discharge system, turn ignition off and pump brake pedal a minimum of 20-25 times using full pedal strokes. When a definite increase in pedal effort is felt, pump pedal 2 more times.*

As a quick system test: When ignition switch is turned to RUN position, Amber ANTI-LOCK warning light on instrument panel will illuminate. After engine is started, light goes out with battery warning light. If ABS warning light fails to go out or comes on while driving, a system fault is indicated.

Fig. 1: Anti-Lock Brake System Component Locations (Bosch 2U — "D", "E" & "K" Bodies)

Courtesy of General Motors Corp.

91G08103

GM
8-18

1991 BRAKES
Anti-Lock – Bosch 2U ("D", "E" & "K" Bodies – Cont.)

REMOVAL & INSTALLATION

HYDRAULIC MODULATOR

Removal – Drain or otherwise remove brake fluid from master cylinder. Remove left front radiator brace. Remove air cleaner intake hose. Remove hydraulic modulator relay cover and disconnect 12-pin electrical connector. Remove ground strap. Label brake lines for installation then remove brake lines from hydraulic modulator. See Fig.

2. Remove hydraulic modulator from mounting bracket.

Installation – To install, reverse removal procedure. Tighten hydraulic modulator mounting nuts to 95 INCH lbs. (11 N.m). Tighten brake lines to 108 INCH lbs. (12 N.m). Refill brake master cylinder, bleed brakes and check for leaks.

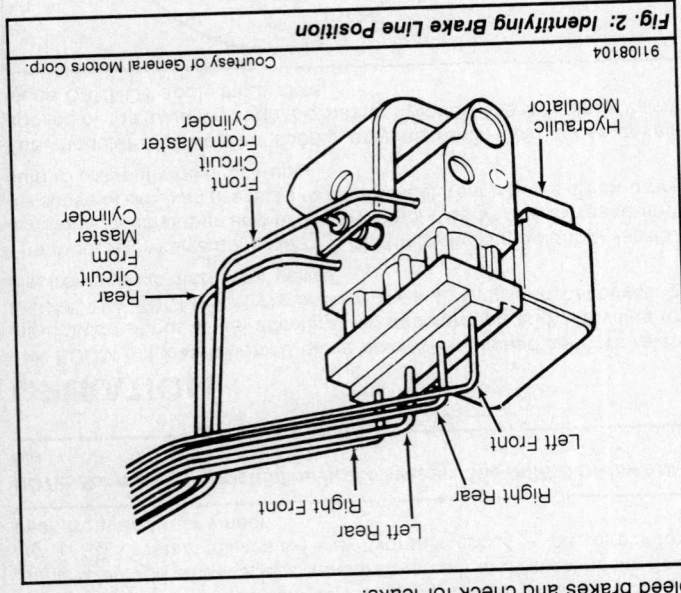

Courtesy of General Motors Corp.

Fig. 2: Identifying Brake Line Position

MODULATOR RELAYS

Removal & Installation – Two relays, the solenoid valve and pump motor relay, are plugged into the hydraulic modulator. They can be accessed by removing cover of hydraulic modulator. See Fig. 3. Solenoid valve relay has a Silver case and 6 pins. Pump relay has a Black case and 4 pins.

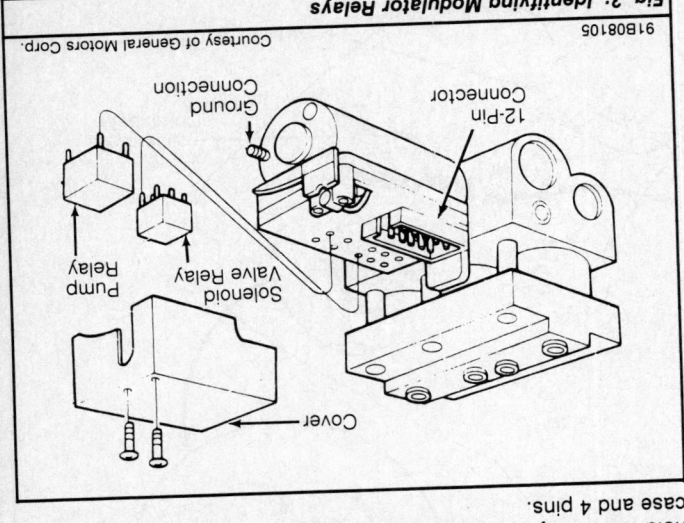

Courtesy of General Motors Corp.

Fig. 3: Identifying Modulator Relays

TOOTHED SENSOR RING

Removal & Installation (Front) – 1) Front toothed sensor ring is an integral part of outer Constant Velocity (CV) joint. Sensor ring is

---

PRESSURE BLEEDING PROCEDURE

1) Install Bleeder Adapter (J-33589) to brake master cylinder. Pressurize bleeder to 20-25 psi (1.41-1.76 kg/cm²). Connect bleeder hose to adapter and bleed air from adapter.

2) Place proper size over valve and wrench. Attach one end of clear tube over valve and submerge other end in container partially filled with clean brake fluid.

3) Starting at left front wheel, loosen bleeder valve to purge air from cylinder. Tighten bleeder valve when no more air is seen in tube. Repeat sequence until all air is removed.

4) Remove tube and wrench. Proceed to right front wheel, left rear wheel and finish at right rear wheel. Fill master cylinder and replace cover.

ADJUSTMENTS

STOPLIGHT SWITCH

Hold brake pedal in depressed position. Insert stoplight switch into retainer until switch body seats on tube clip. Pull brake pedal upward against internal pedal stop. Switch will be moved in retainer by brake pedal to provide proper adjustment.

PARKING BRAKE

1) Apply and release service brake several times. Fully apply and release parking brake several times (may require up to 4 pedal strokes) using approximately 125 lb. (57 kg) pedal force on final stroke.

2) Ensure parking brake is fully released by turning ignition switch on and observing BRAKE warning light. Light should be off. If BRAKE warning light is on and parking brake appears to be fully released, operate manual pedal release lever and pull downward on front parking brake cable to remove slack from pedal assembly.

3) Raise and support vehicle. Ensure parking brake levers on rear calipers are not against stops. If levers are against stops, check for binding in rear parking brake cables and position levers against stops.

4) Tighten parking brake cable at adjuster until either left or right lever begins to move off stop. Loosen adjuster until lever that moved off stop is resting against stop. Ensure both levers are resting against stops. Operate parking brake several times to check adjustment. Ensure levers are resting against stops.

SPECIAL PRECAUTIONS

WARNING: Certain Cadillac, Buick and Oldsmobile vehicles may be equipped with Supplemental Inflatable Restraint (SIR) system. All SIR wiring connectors are YELLOW. DO NOT use electrical test equipment on these circuits. SIR-related components are located in steering column, dash, upper radiator support and front fenders.

AIR BAG DEACTIVATION

Disabling System – Turn ignition switch to OFF position. Remove Supplemental Inflatable Restraint (SIR) fuse from fuse block. Remove left sound insulator, located under steering column. Disconnect Yellow 2-pin SIR harness connector, located at base of steering column.

System Function Check – Ensure ignition switch is in OFF position. Connect Yellow 2-pin SIR harness connector at base of steering column. Turn ignition switch to RUN position. Ensure INFLATABLE RESTRAINT light flashes 7-9 times and then goes out. If INFLATABLE RESTRAINT light does not operate as described, SIR system is malfunctioning and needs repair.

ment is necessary, outer CV joint must be replaced.

2) Raise and support vehicle. Remove tire and wheel assembly. Install modified CV Boot Protector (J-34754). Insert drift in brake rotor to prevent turning. Remove axle shaft nut and washer.

3) Remove lower ball joint cotter pin and nut. Using Ball Joint Separator (J-29330), separate ball joint from knuckle by prying down on control arm. Pull out on lower knuckle area and strike end of axle shaft with soft-faced hammer to disengage axle hub.

4) Pull knuckle assembly away from axle shaft. Position knuckle assembly to rear. Using slide hammer and Axle Shaft Remover (J-33008), remove axle shaft from transaxle or intermediate shaft. Place axle shaft in vise with protected jaws. Cut boot clamps and remove axle shaft away from CV joint assembly.

5) Remove CV joint-to-axle shaft snap ring. Pull CV joint and housing assembly off axle shaft. Remove boot if replacing. To install, reverse removal procedure.

Removal & Installation (Rear) – **1)** Rear toothed sensor ring is an integral part of the rear hub and bearing assembly and is not serviced separately. If sensor ring replacement is necessary, rear hub and bearing assembly must be replaced.

2) Raise vehicle on frame contact hoist. Remove wheel and tire assembly. Remove rear brake caliper and suspend out of way. Remove brake rotor retainers (if equipped) and remove brake rotors. Remove 4 hub and bearing assembly mounting bolts and remove hub and bearing assembly. To install, reverse removal procedure. Tighten hub and bearing assembly mounting bolts to 52 ft. lbs. (70 N.m).

SENSOR RING TOOTH SPECIFICATIONS

Position	Number Of Teeth
Front	47
Rear	47

WHEEL SPEED SENSOR

Removal & Installation (Front) – **1)** Disconnect wheel speed sensor electrical connector at strut tower. Raise and support vehicle. Remove tire and wheel assembly. Disengage sensor cable grommet from wheelwell pass-through hole and remove sensor cable from retainers. Remove sensor mounting bolt and remove sensor.

2) To install, reverse removal procedure. Coat sensor with Anti-Corrosion Compound (1052856) before installing. Tighten sensor mounting bolt to 106 INCH lbs. (12 N.m). Ensure cable is routed correctly and properly installed in retainers.

Removal & Installation (Rear) – Rear wheel speed sensor is an integral part of the rear hub and bearing assembly and is not serviced separately. If rear wheel speed sensor replacement is necessary, rear hub and bearing assembly must be replaced. See REMOVAL & INSTALLATION (REAR) under TOOTHED SENSOR RING.

DIAGNOSIS & TESTING

NOTE: *Manufacturer recommends using Tech 1 Diagnostic Computer with 88-91 Brake Cartridge and Bosch ABS adapter to diagnose ABS system. Some diagnostic procedures will require Pinout Box (J-35592).*

PRE-DIAGNOSTIC INSPECTION

When checking potential ABS system faults, check the following before using diagnostic code charts.

1) Check ABS, IGN 1-ISO and STOP/HAZ fuses.
2) Check fusible links on positive junction block.
3) Check ABS 6-way connector and electronic brake control module connectors are properly seated.
4) Ensure parking brake switch is functioning properly.
5) Check that ground system is clean and tight.

NOTE: *There are 2 grounds for the ABS system. One is located behind the right headlight. The other is located at left side of dash, near parking brake pedal.*

ENTERING DIAGNOSTIC DISPLAY MODE

Ground pin "H" to pin "A" of ALDL connector. Connector is located behind left side of instrument panel, to the right of parking brake. See *Fig. 4.* Turn ignition switch to RUN position (engine off). Diagnostic display mode will remain enabled as long as pin "H" is grounded, and vehicle speed is less than 5 MPH.

About 4 seconds after ALDL pin "H" is grounded, EBCM will begin flashing code sequence. Sequence will begin with Code 12, signaling beginning of fault code display. Each stored code will be displayed 3 times. After all codes have been displayed, sequence will repeat starting with Code 12.

Some codes can only be read through the ALDL connector using the Tech 1 Diagnostic Computer.

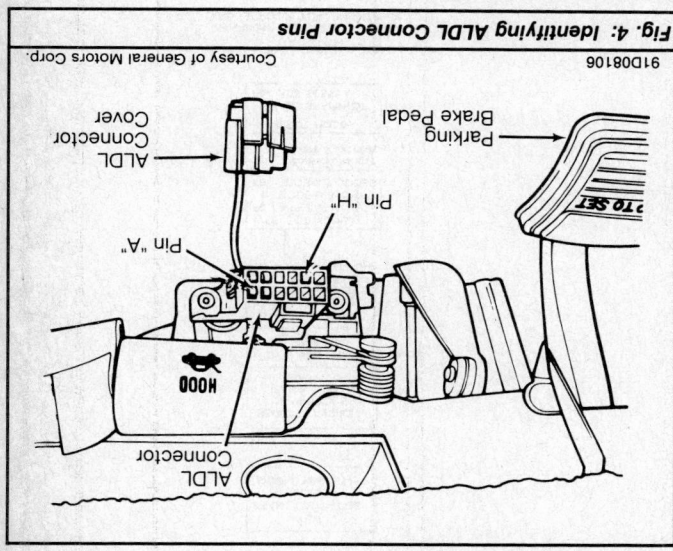

Fig. 4: Identifying ALDL Connector Pins
Courtesy of General Motors Corp.

DIAGNOSTIC TROUBLE CODES

Code	Definition
12	Diagnostic System Operational
21	RF Wheel Speed Sensor Fault
22	RF Toothed Wheel Frequency Error
25	LF Wheel Speed Sensor Fault
26	LF Toothed Wheel Frequency Error
31	RR Wheel Speed Sensor Fault
32	RR Toothed Wheel Frequency Error
35	LR Wheel Speed Sensor Fault
36	LR Toothed Wheel Frequency Error
41	RF Solenoid Valve Fault
45	LF Solenoid Valve Fault
55	Rear Solenoid Valve Fault
61	Pump Motor or Motor Relay Fault
63	Solenoid Valve Relay Fault
71	EBCM Fault
72	Serial Data Link Fault (Tech 1 Error)

CLEARING CODES

1) Turn ignition switch to RUN position. Ensure ANTI-LOCK light turns off after 3-4 seconds. If light remains on, a fault is still present and must be corrected. Place a jumper between pin "A" and pin "H" of ALDL connector. When ANTI-LOCK light turns on, remove jumper to pin "H".

2) When light turns off, replace jumper to pin "H". ANTI-LOCK light will turn on again. Remove jumper to pin "H". Repeat previous step. When light turns off, replace jumper to pin "H". ABS codes should now be cleared. Verify by checking codes. Code 12 should be displayed. If other codes are present, repeat code clearing process.

GM
8-20

1991 BRAKES
Anti-Lock — Bosch 2U ("D", "E" & "K" Bodies — Cont.)

USING TECH 1

NOTE: Tech 1 Diagnostic Computer (94-00101-A) with Bosch ABS ALDL Adapter, Pinout Box (J-35592) and High Impedance Multimeter will be needed to test parts of the ABS system.

1988-91 BRAKE cartridge must be inserted in TECH 1 to perform diagnostic procedures on anti-lock brake system. TECH 1 is plugged into ALDL connector before turning ignition on. A Bosch ABS adapter is required when testing Bosch 2U anti-lock brake system.

Selecting Model Year – Turn ignition switch to RUN position. Select appropriate model year using function keys.

Selecting Vehicle – After selecting model year, enter type of vehicle which is being tested. Press NO until "E" is flashing. Pressing EXIT will return TECH 1 to previous screen.

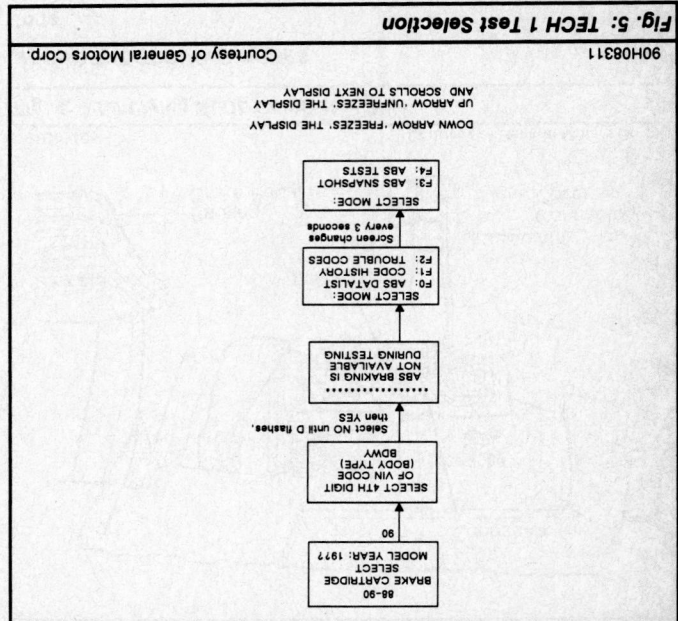

Fig. 5: TECH 1 Test Selection

Selecting Test Mode – Five test modes are available for diagnosing anti-lock brake system. Test modes are as follows:

Mode F0 – DATA LIST mode display is actual reading that each wheel speed sensor is sending to EBCM. In this mode, vehicle can be driven and wheel speed information can be observed to determine if readings are comparable to actual vehicle speed. By pressing brake pedal, status of brake light switch can be observed.

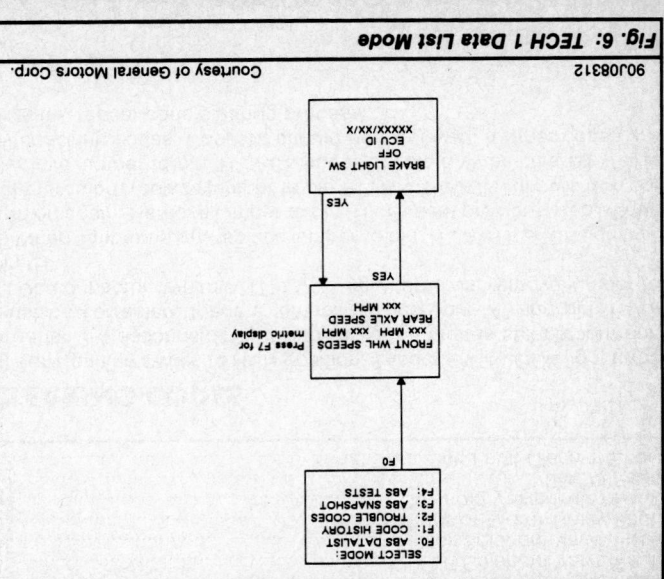

Fig. 6: TECH 1 Data List Mode

Mode F1 – CODE HISTORY Mode displays trouble codes and description. Ignition cycle information is useful in determining reason vehicle is in for service. If display indicates that it has been zero ignition cycles since code was set, fault is currently present.

EBCM keeps track of ignition cycles and will automatically erase any code information if no ABS faults are set in 50 cycles. This information is useful to determine if intermittent condition exists.

Vehicle speed information can be used to duplicate fault if an intermittent fault caused code to set.

Brake light switch information can be used to duplicate fault if an intermittent fault caused code to set.

ABS state information is useful in determining driving condition of vehicle when code was set.

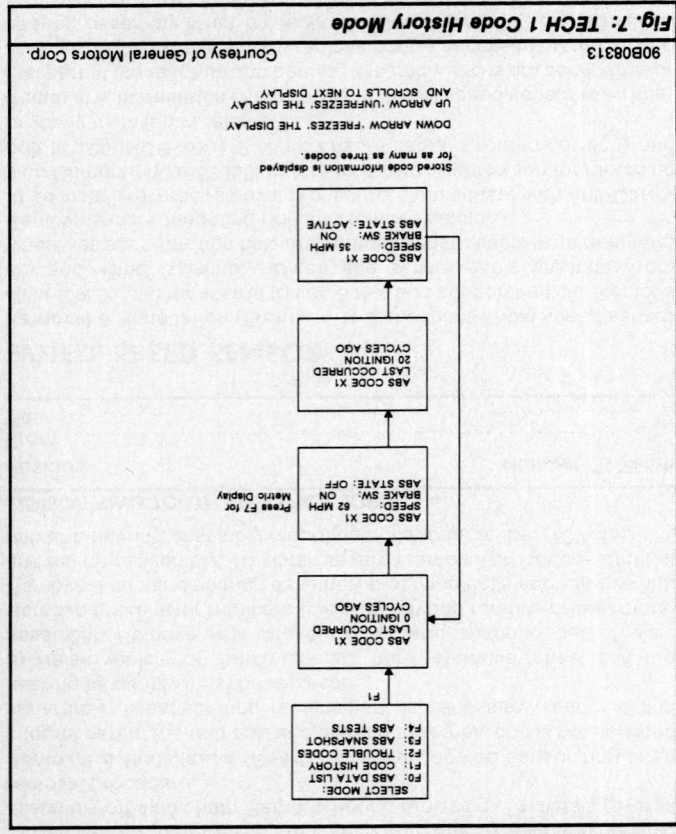

Fig. 7: TECH 1 Code History Mode

Mode F2 – TROUBLE CODES mode displays ABS malfunction codes. TECH 1 will display any error code and brief description of code number displayed. If no codes are stored, TECH 1 will display NO ABS CODES.

Mode F3 – ABS SNAPSHOT mode will help isolate intermittent problems by capturing data before and after condition.

By selecting Manual Trigger, TECH 1 will wait for ENTER to be pressed before storing speed sensor information. All stored information can be displayed and examined for conditions which might indicate a problem.

By selecting Automatic Trigger, TECH 1 will capture data which deviates from normal conditions but alone may not set a code, such as driving over bumpy roads or over railroad tracks. While TECH 1 is waiting for a trigger, the ENTER or F9 key may also be used to force a trigger.

TECH 1 will respond to a clear codes command by indicating ABS CODES CLEARED or CODE CLEAR FAIL.

1991 BRAKES
Anti-Lock — Bosch 2U ("D", "E" & "K" Bodies — Cont.)

GM
8-21

Mode F4 — ABS TEST mode is used to perform the following tests:
- Solenoid Valve Pressure Hold Test
- Solenoid Valve Pressure Release Test
- Automatic Tests

By selecting appropriate test and observing results, error conditions and faults can be further identified.

- **Solenoid Valve Pressure Hold — 1)** Raise vehicle on frame contact hoist so that wheels to be tested are off ground.
2) Select SOLENOID TEST. Select wheel circuit solenoid to be tested. If testing rear axle valve, ensure vehicle is in Neutral.
3) With foot off brake pedal, have assistant verify that wheel can be turned by hand. Press UP arrow, then apply and hold brake pedal. Verify that assistant can turn selected wheel by hand.
4) When UP arrow is pressed, display will change from OFF to ON. After 15 seconds, display will change back to OFF. Verify that selected wheel is now locked. Repeat test if necessary to verify proper operation. Perform SOLENOID VALVE PRESSURE RELEASE TEST.

- **Solenoid Valve Pressure Release Test — 1)** Raise vehicle on frame contact hoist so that wheels to be tested are off ground.
2) Select SOLENOID TEST. Select wheel circuit solenoid to be tested. If testing rear axle valve, ensure rear axle valve, ensure vehicle is in Neutral.
3) Apply brake and hold, have assistant verify that wheel cannot be turned by hand. Press DOWN arrow. Verify that assistant can turn selected wheel by hand. Display on TECH 1 should change from OFF to ON, indicating pressure release has been commanded properly.
4) After 15 seconds, display will change back to OFF. Verify that selected wheel is now locked. Repeat test if necessary to verify proper operation. Perform SOLENOID VALVE PRESSURE HOLD TEST if not completed.

- **Automatic Tests** - Select AUTO TEST. Press ENTER when ready. Valves can be heard and felt cycling from hydraulic control unit; have assistant verify that pump motor turned on. Go to diagnostic charts if codes are set.

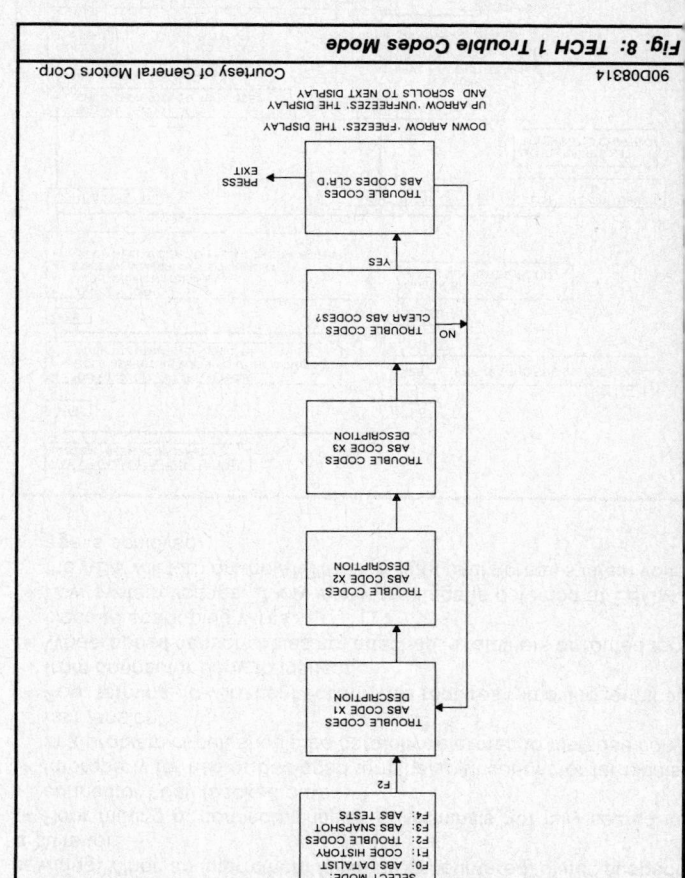

Fig. 8: TECH 1 Trouble Codes Mode

Courtesy of General Motors Corp.

90D08314

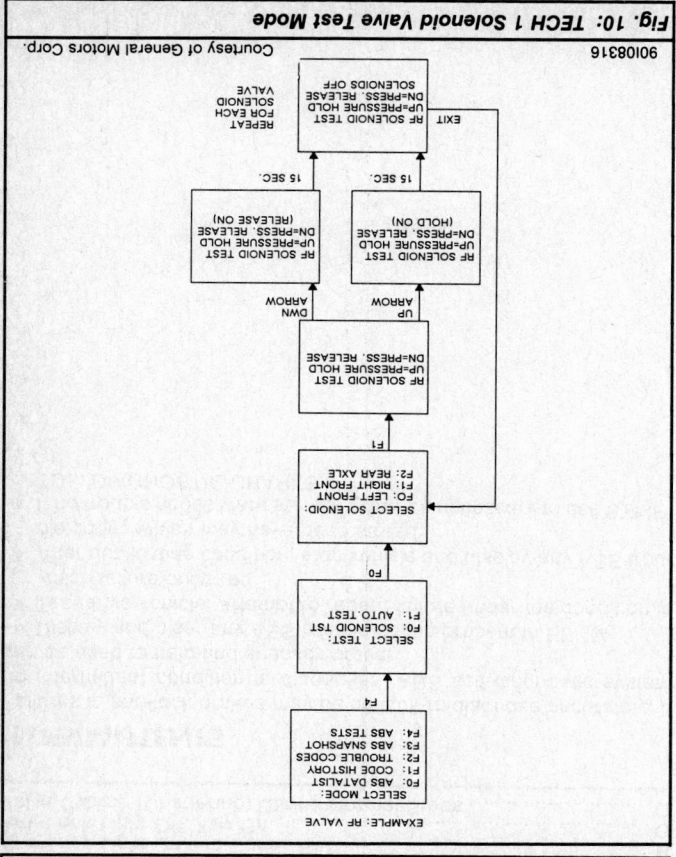

Fig. 9: TECH 1 ABS Snapshot Mode

Courtesy of General Motors Corp.

90G08315

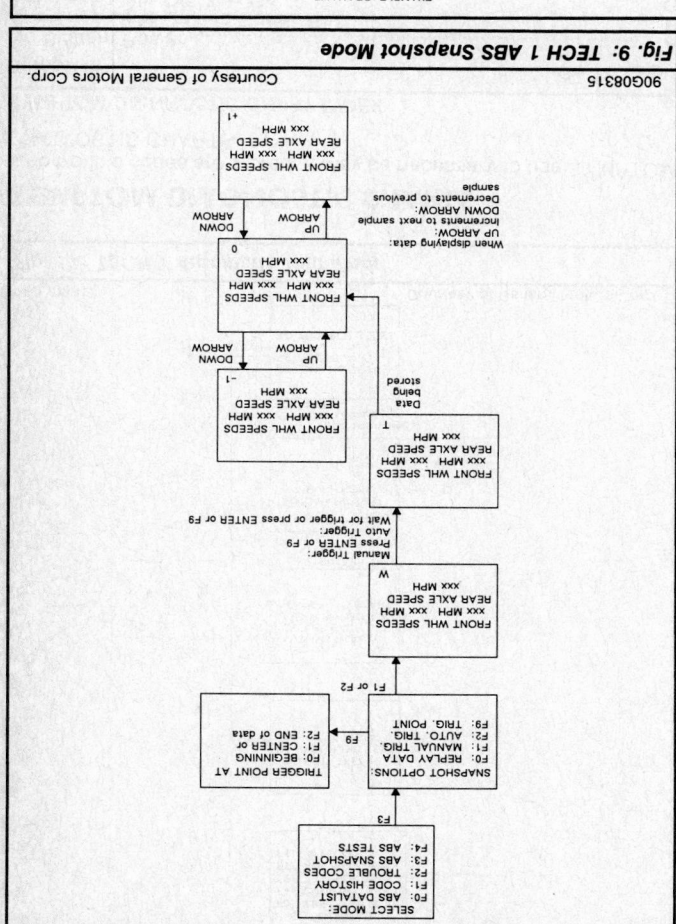

Fig. 10: TECH 1 Solenoid Valve Test Mode

Courtesy of General Motors Corp.

90I08316

1991 BRAKES
Anti-Lock — Bosch 2U ("D", "E" & "K" Bodies — Cont.)

GM
8-22

Most intermittent problems are caused by faulty electrical connectors or wiring. When an intermittent failure is encountered, check suspect circuits for:

• Poor mating of connector halves or terminals not fully seated in connector body (backed out).
• Improperly formed or damaged terminals. All connector terminals in a problem circuit should be carefully reformed to increase contact tension.
• Poor terminal-to-wire connection. This requires removing terminal from connector body to inspect.
• Wheel speed sensor cables not attached in retainers or routed too close to spark plug wires.
• Low system voltage. If low system voltage is detected at EBCM, the ABS will turn on the ANTI-LOCK light until normal system voltage is achieved.

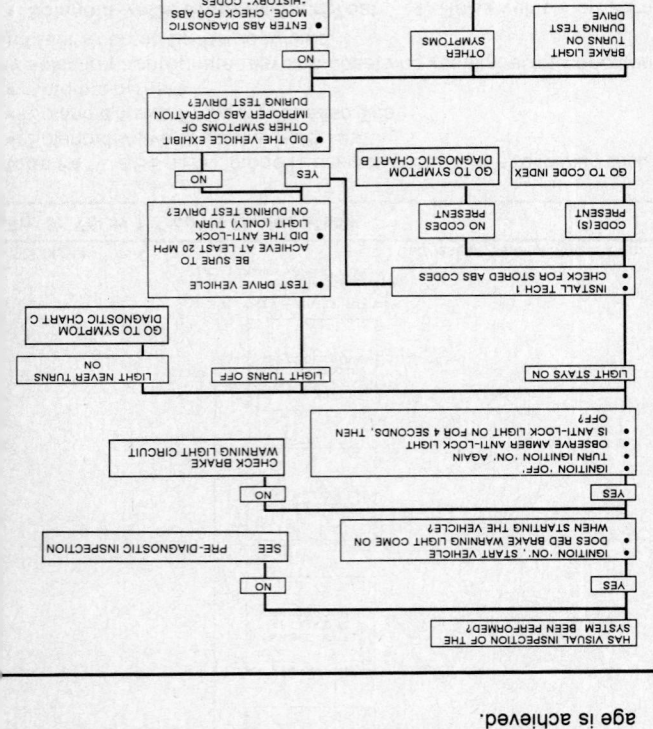

Fig. 12: Anti-Lock Brake System Functional Check

Courtesy of General Motors Corp.

90H08274

SYMPTOM DIAGNOSTIC CHARTS

If no trouble codes are stored, it may be necessary to use SYMPTOM DIAGNOSTIC CHARTS.

SYMPTOM DIAGNOSTIC CHART INDEX

Symptom	Go To Chart
No System Power	A
Anti-Lock Light On, No Codes Set	B
Anti-Lock Light Off, Key On	C
Valve Cycling (Chattering) During Normal Stops	D

INTERMITTENTS

Failures in anti-lock brakes may be difficult to diagnose accurately. If an intermittent condition is diagnosed, ABS self-diagnostic system can be used to help find suspect circuit.

• Display and clear any ABS trouble codes present in EBCM.
• Test drive vehicle. Attempt to repeat failure under the condition in which failure occurred.
• After duplicating condition, stop vehicle and display any ABS trouble codes which may have been stored.
• If no trouble codes were stored, it may be necessary to use SYMPTOM DIAGNOSTIC CHARTS.

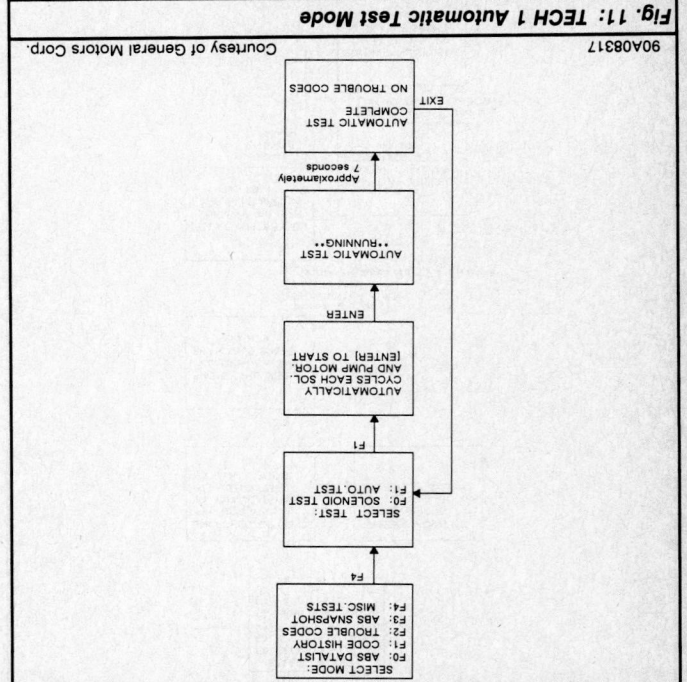

Fig. 11: TECH 1 Automatic Test Mode

Courtesy of General Motors Corp.

90A08317

Anti-Lock – Bosch 2U (“D”, “E” & “K” Bodies – Cont.)

WIRING DIAGRAMS

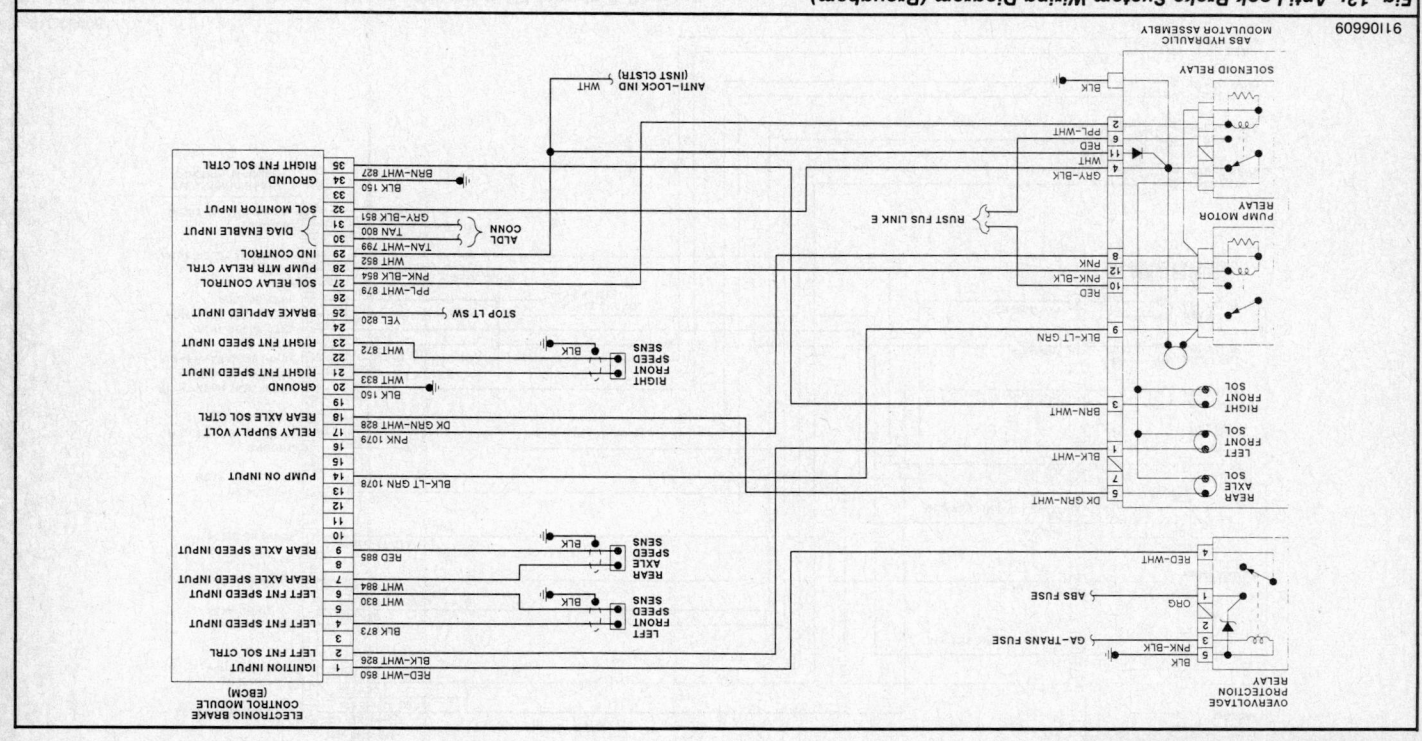

Fig. 13: Anti-Lock Brake System Wiring Diagram (Brougham)

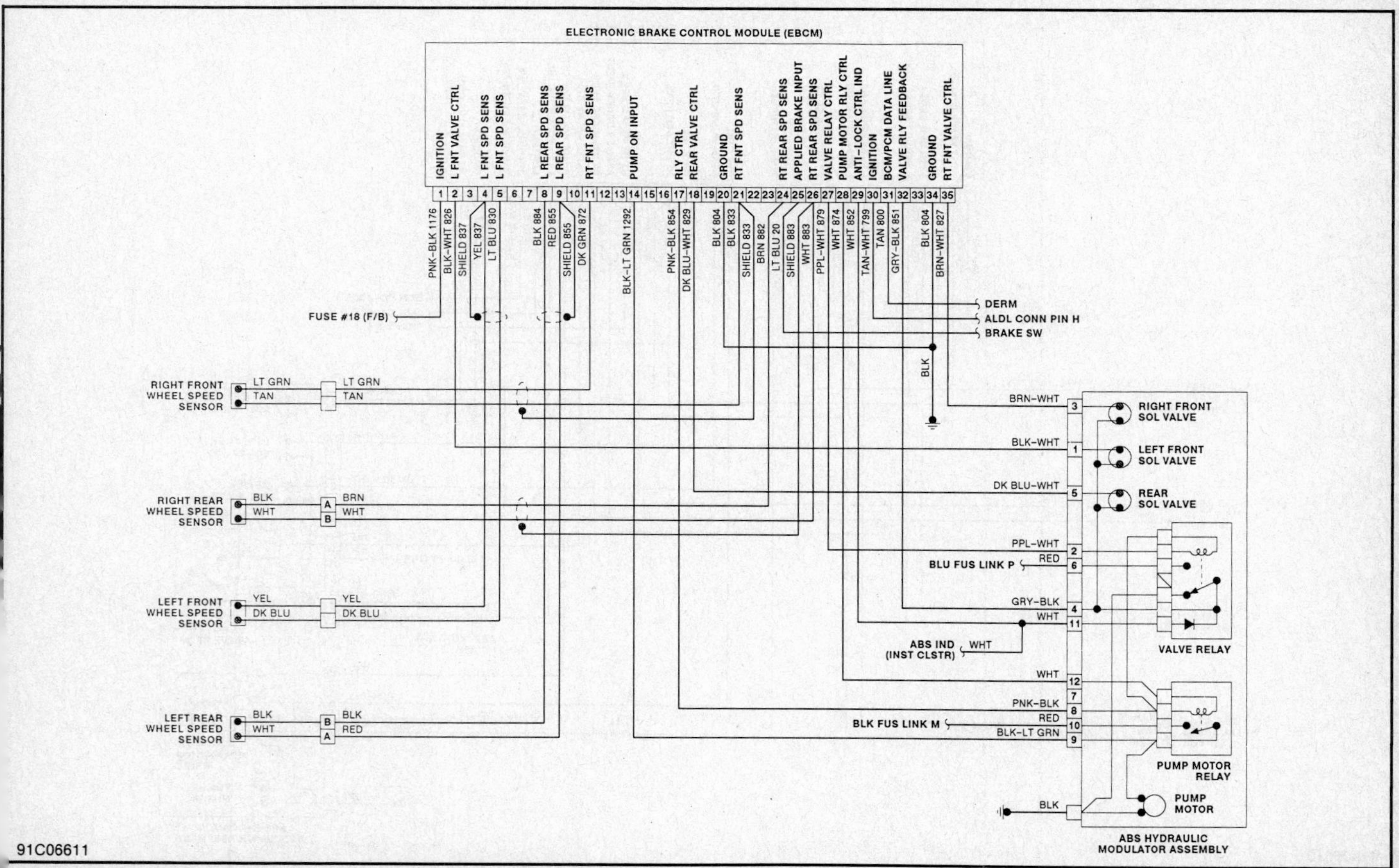

Fig. 14: Anti-Lock Brake System Wiring Diagram (Reatta & Riviera)

GM 8-24

1991 BRAKES
Anti-Lock – Bosch 2U ("D", "E" & "K" Bodies – Cont.)

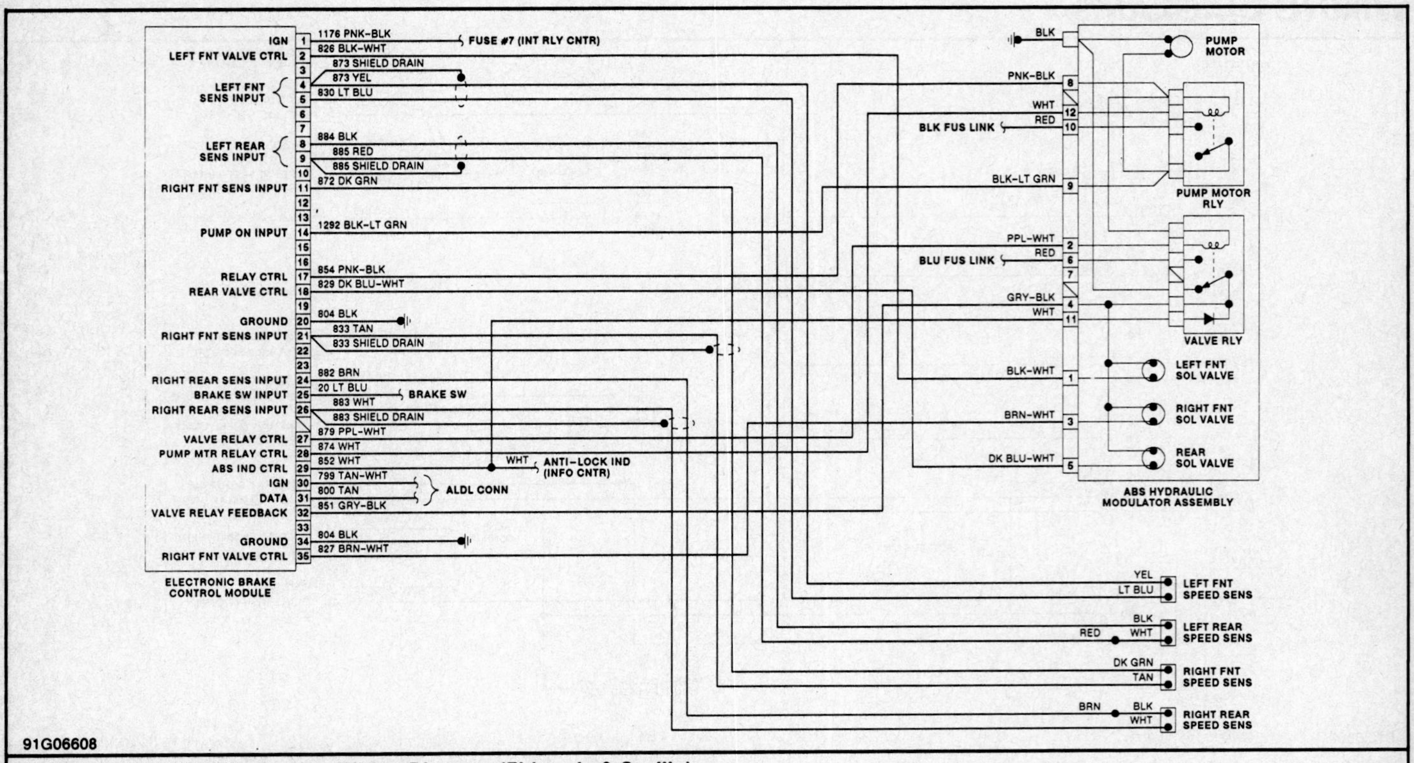

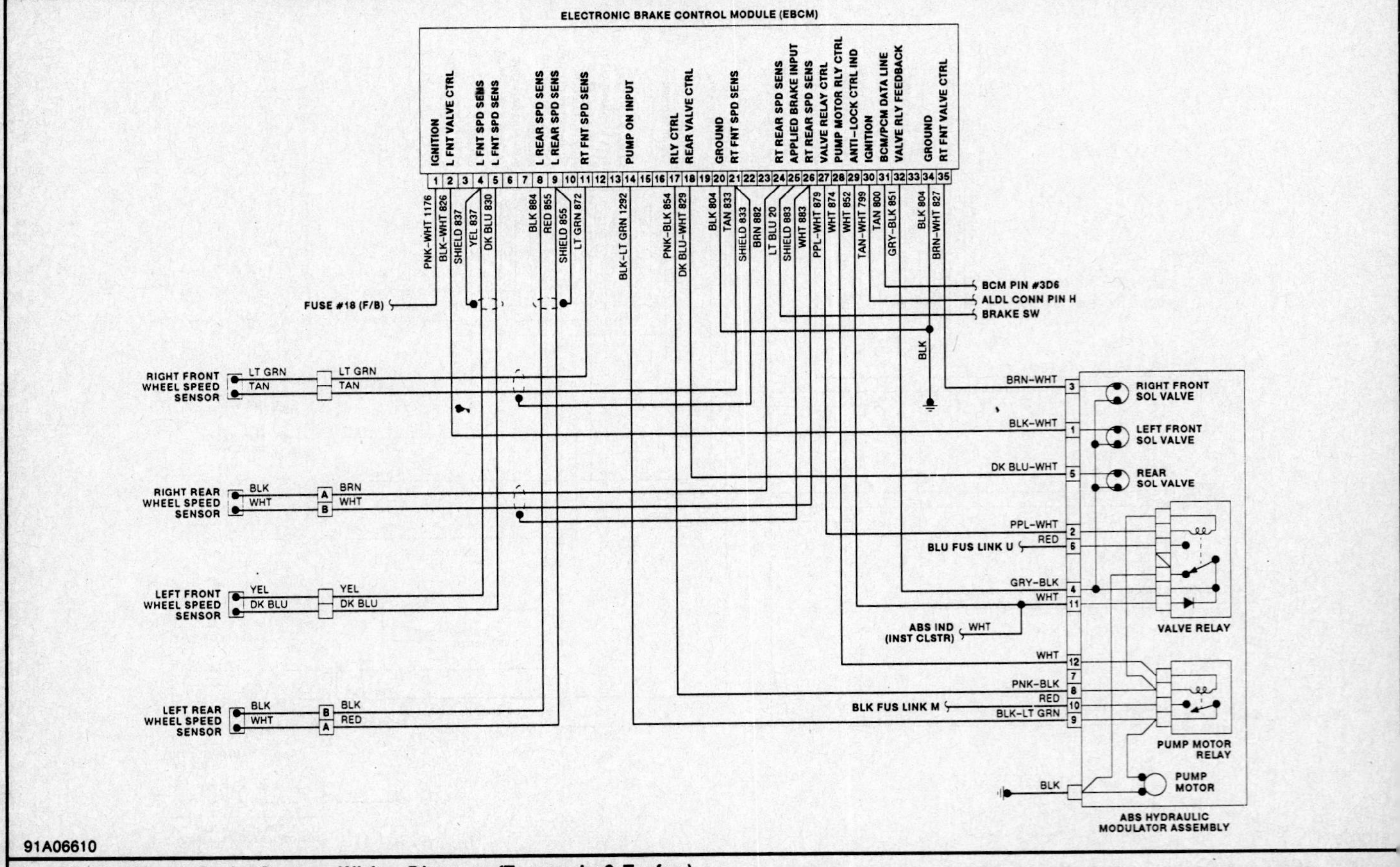

Fig. 16: Anti-Lock Brake System Wiring Diagram (Toronado & Trofeo)

91A06610

Fig. 15: Anti-Lock Brake System Wiring Diagram (Eldorado & Seville)

91G06608

1991 BRAKES
Anti-Lock – Bosch 2U ("D", "E" & "K" Bodies – Cont.)

GM
8-25

DIAGNOSTIC CHARTS

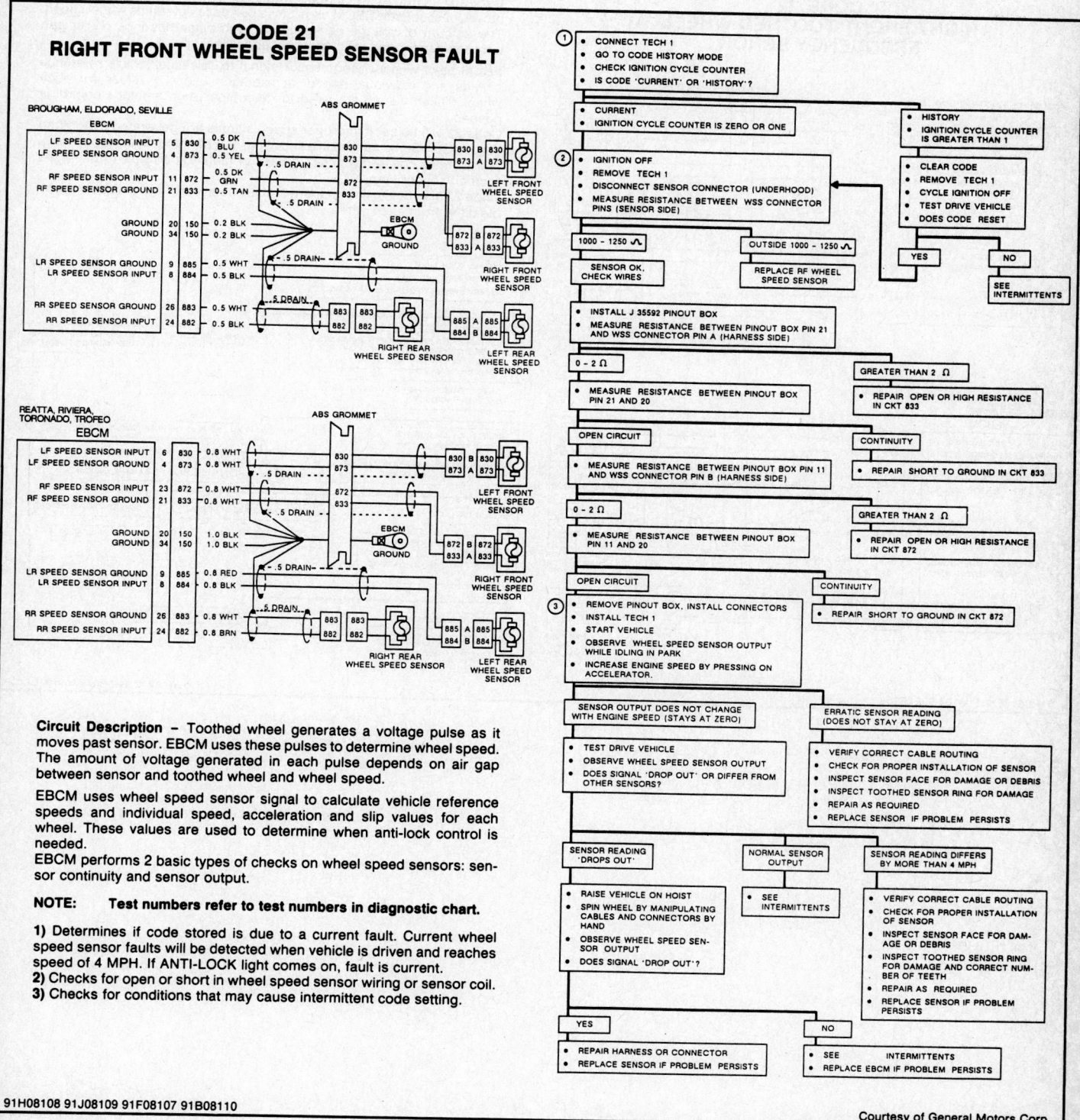

CODE 21
RIGHT FRONT WHEEL SPEED SENSOR FAULT

Circuit Description – Toothed wheel generates a voltage pulse as it moves past sensor. EBCM uses these pulses to determine wheel speed. The amount of voltage generated in each pulse depends on air gap between sensor and toothed wheel and wheel speed.

EBCM uses wheel speed sensor signal to calculate vehicle reference speeds and individual speed, acceleration and slip values for each wheel. These values are used to determine when anti-lock control is needed.

EBCM performs 2 basic types of checks on wheel speed sensors: sensor continuity and sensor output.

NOTE: Test numbers refer to test numbers in diagnostic chart.

1) Determines if code stored is due to a current fault. Current wheel speed sensor faults will be detected when vehicle is driven and reaches speed of 4 MPH. If ANTI-LOCK light comes on, fault is current.
2) Checks for open or short in wheel speed sensor wiring or sensor coil.
3) Checks for conditions that may cause intermittent code setting.

91H08108 91J08109 91F08107 91B08110

Courtesy of General Motors Corp.

GM
8-26

1991 BRAKES
Anti-Lock – Bosch 2U ("D", "E" & "K" Bodies – Cont.)

CODE 22
RIGHT FRONT TOOTHED WHEEL
FREQUENCY ERROR

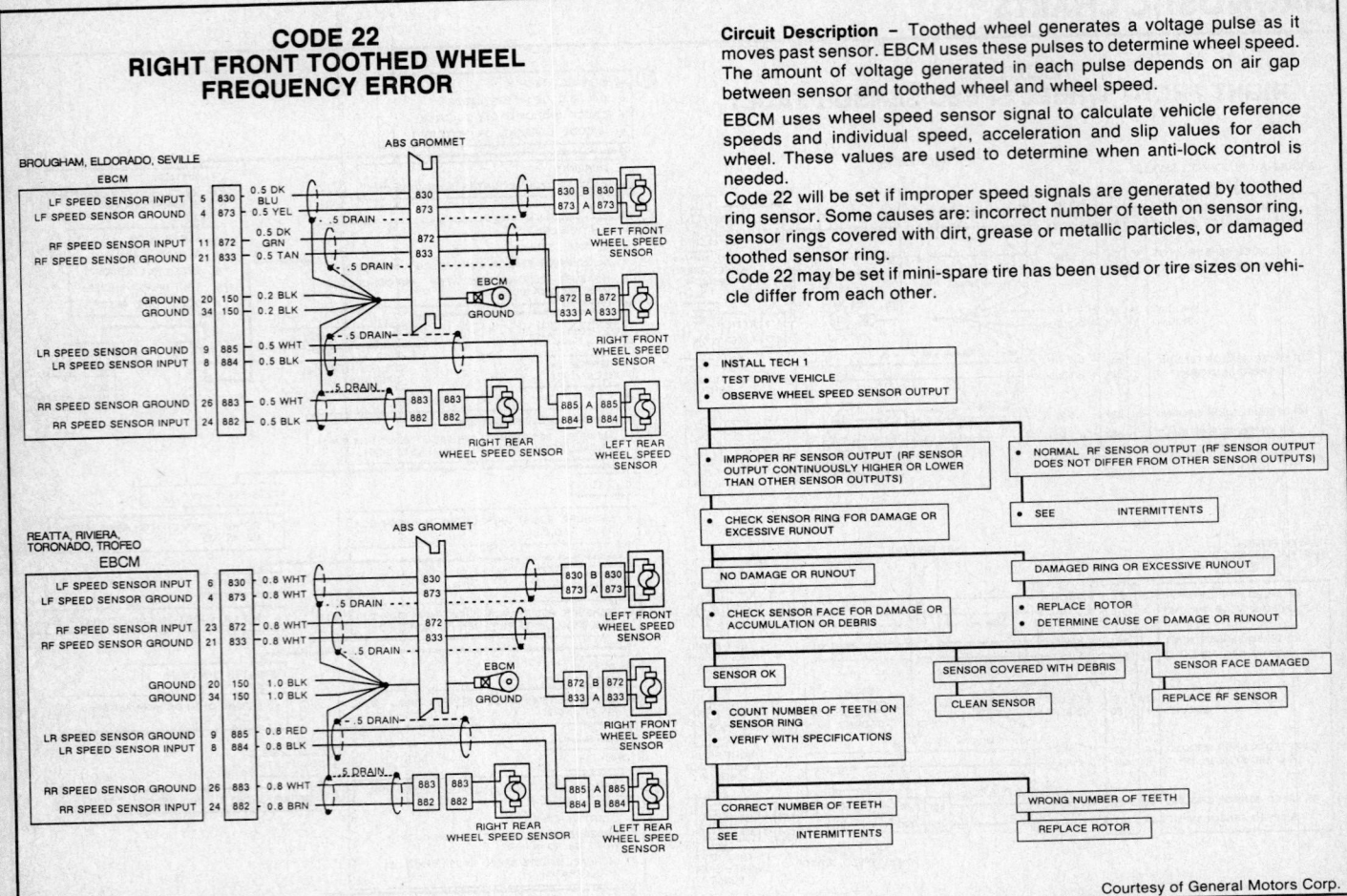

Circuit Description – Toothed wheel generates a voltage pulse as it moves past sensor. EBCM uses these pulses to determine wheel speed. The amount of voltage generated in each pulse depends on air gap between sensor and toothed wheel and wheel speed.

EBCM uses wheel speed sensor signal to calculate vehicle reference speeds and individual speed, acceleration and slip values for each wheel. These values are used to determine when anti-lock control is needed.

Code 22 will be set if improper speed signals are generated by toothed ring sensor. Some causes are: incorrect number of teeth on sensor ring, sensor rings covered with dirt, grease or metallic particles, or damaged toothed sensor ring.

Code 22 may be set if mini-spare tire has been used or tire sizes on vehicle differ from each other.

Courtesy of General Motors Corp.

91H08108 91F08107 90E08258

1991 BRAKES
Anti-Lock – Bosch 2U ("D", "E" & "K" Bodies – Cont.)

GM
8-27

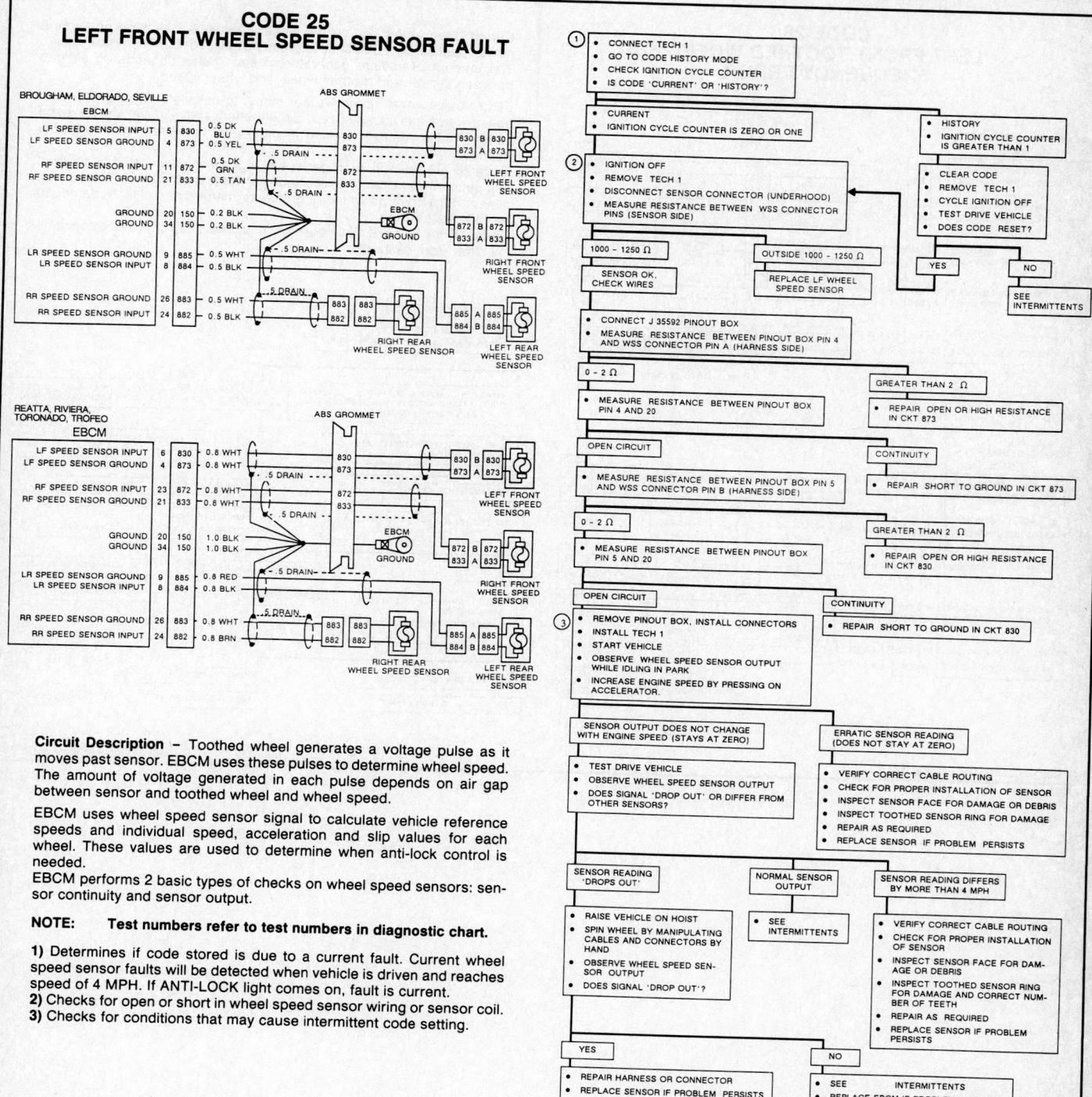

CODE 25
LEFT FRONT WHEEL SPEED SENSOR FAULT

Circuit Description – Toothed wheel generates a voltage pulse as it moves past sensor. EBCM uses these pulses to determine wheel speed. The amount of voltage generated in each pulse depends on air gap between sensor and toothed wheel and wheel speed.

EBCM uses wheel speed sensor signal to calculate vehicle reference speeds and individual speed, acceleration and slip values for each wheel. These values are used to determine when anti-lock control is needed.

EBCM performs 2 basic types of checks on wheel speed sensors: sensor continuity and sensor output.

NOTE: Test numbers refer to test numbers in diagnostic chart.

1) Determines if code stored is due to a current fault. Current wheel speed sensor faults will be detected when vehicle is driven and reaches speed of 4 MPH. If ANTI-LOCK light comes on, fault is current.
2) Checks for open or short in wheel speed sensor wiring or sensor coil.
3) Checks for conditions that may cause intermittent code setting.

91H08108 91D08111 91F08107 90A18820

Courtesy of General Motors Corp.

GM
8-28

1991 BRAKES
Anti-Lock – Bosch 2U ("D", "E" & "K" Bodies – Cont.)

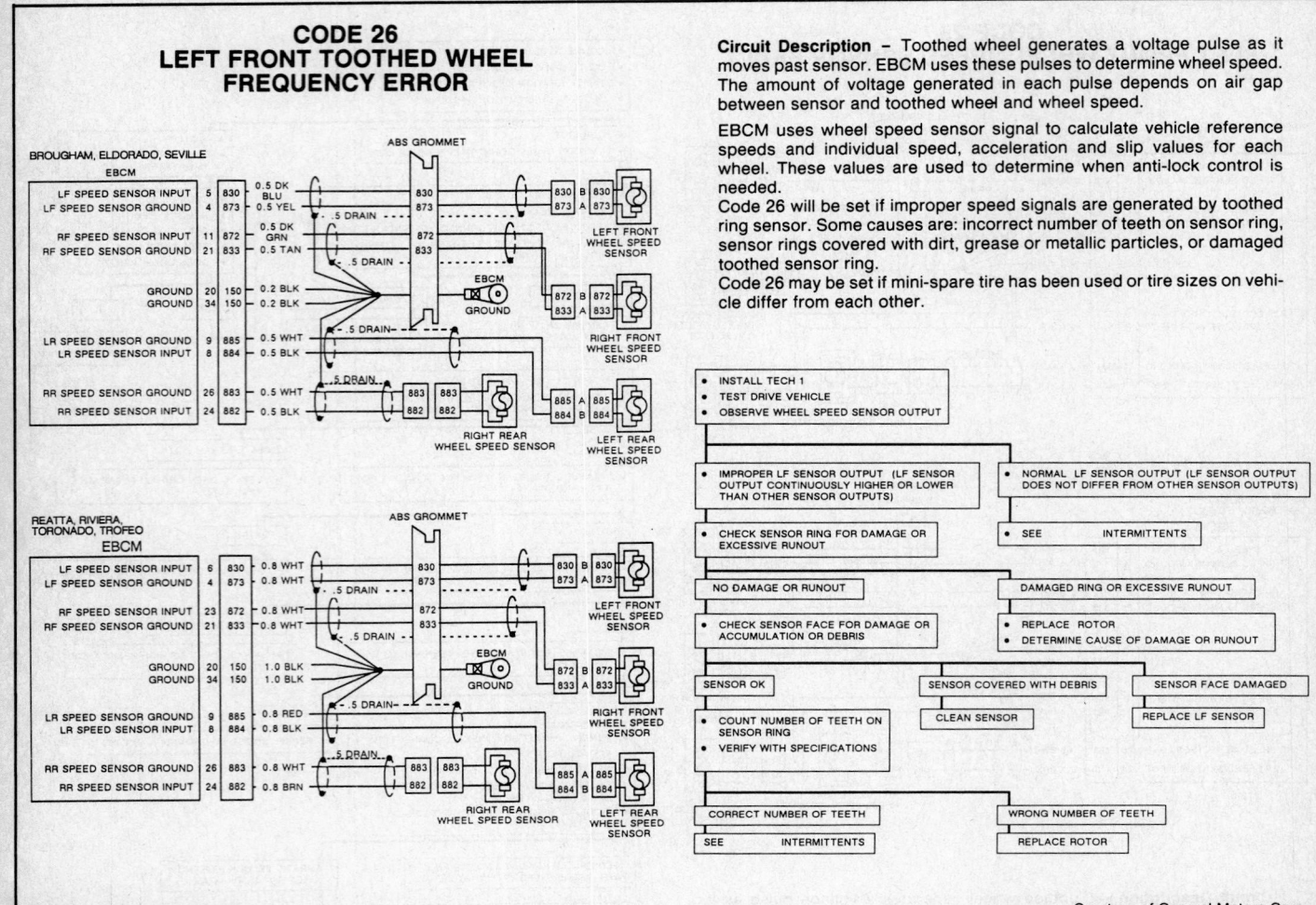

CODE 26
LEFT FRONT TOOTHED WHEEL
FREQUENCY ERROR

Circuit Description – Toothed wheel generates a voltage pulse as it moves past sensor. EBCM uses these pulses to determine wheel speed. The amount of voltage generated in each pulse depends on air gap between sensor and toothed wheel and wheel speed.

EBCM uses wheel speed sensor signal to calculate vehicle reference speeds and individual speed, acceleration and slip values for each wheel. These values are used to determine when anti-lock control is needed.

Code 26 will be set if improper speed signals are generated by toothed ring sensor. Some causes are: incorrect number of teeth on sensor ring, sensor rings covered with dirt, grease or metallic particles, or damaged toothed sensor ring.

Code 26 may be set if mini-spare tire has been used or tire sizes on vehicle differ from each other.

Courtesy of General Motors Corp.

1991 BRAKES
Anti-Lock — Bosch 2U ("D", "E" & "K" Bodies — Cont.)

GM
8-29

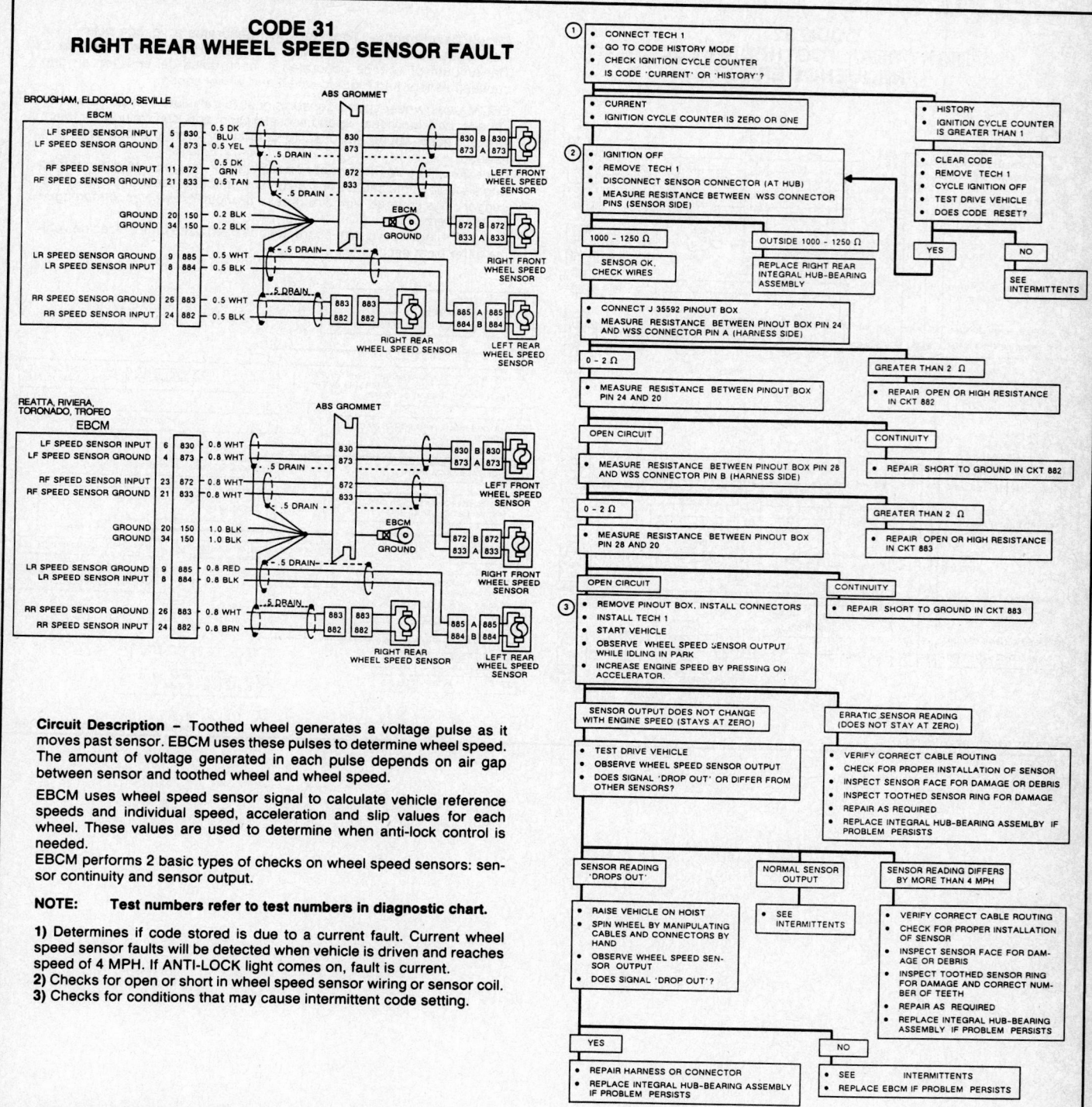

CODE 31
RIGHT REAR WHEEL SPEED SENSOR FAULT

Circuit Description – Toothed wheel generates a voltage pulse as it moves past sensor. EBCM uses these pulses to determine wheel speed. The amount of voltage generated in each pulse depends on air gap between sensor and toothed wheel and wheel speed.

EBCM uses wheel speed sensor signal to calculate vehicle reference speeds and individual speed, acceleration and slip values for each wheel. These values are used to determine when anti-lock control is needed.

EBCM performs 2 basic types of checks on wheel speed sensors: sensor continuity and sensor output.

NOTE: Test numbers refer to test numbers in diagnostic chart.

1) Determines if code stored is due to a current fault. Current wheel speed sensor faults will be detected when vehicle is driven and reaches speed of 4 MPH. If ANTI-LOCK light comes on, fault is current.
2) Checks for open or short in wheel speed sensor wiring or sensor coil.
3) Checks for conditions that may cause intermittent code setting.

91H08108 91F08112 91F08107 91H08113

Courtesy of General Motors Corp.

GM
8-30

1991 BRAKES
Anti-Lock – Bosch 2U ("D", "E" & "K" Bodies – Cont.)

CODE 32
RIGHT REAR TOOTHED WHEEL
FREQUENCY ERROR

Circuit Description – Toothed wheel generates a voltage pulse as it moves past sensor. EBCM uses these pulses to determine wheel speed. The amount of voltage generated in each pulse depends on air gap between sensor and toothed wheel and wheel speed.

EBCM uses wheel speed sensor signal to calculate vehicle reference speeds and individual speed, acceleration and slip values for each wheel. These values are used to determine when anti-lock control is needed.

Code 32 will be set if improper speed signals are generated by toothed ring sensor. Some causes are: incorrect number of teeth on sensor ring, sensor rings covered with dirt, grease or metallic particles, or damaged toothed sensor ring.

Code 32 may be set if mini-spare tire has been used or tire sizes on vehicle differ from each other.

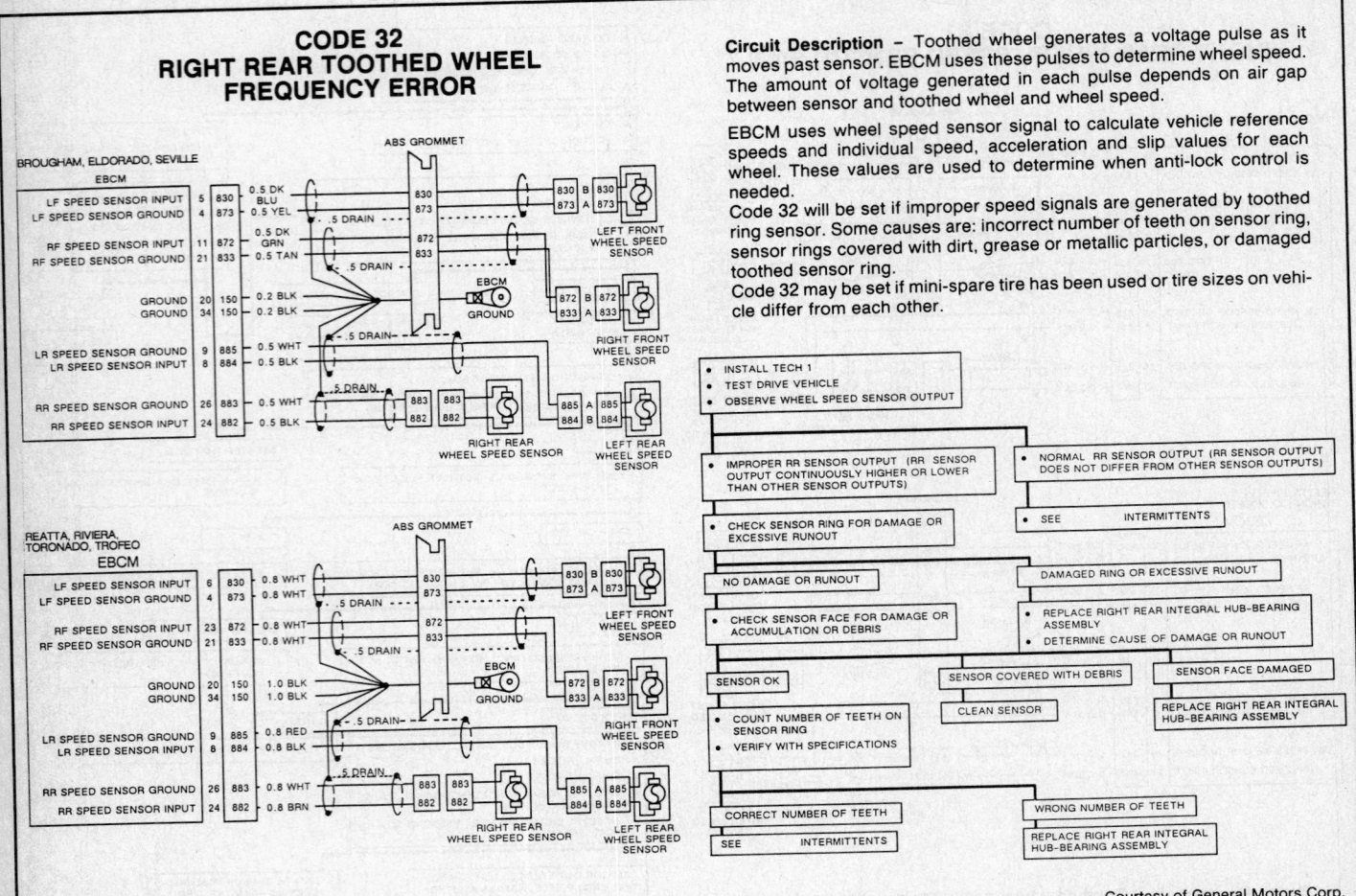

Courtesy of General Motors Corp.

91H08108 91F08107 91J08114

CODE 35
LEFT REAR WHEEL SPEED SENSOR FAULT

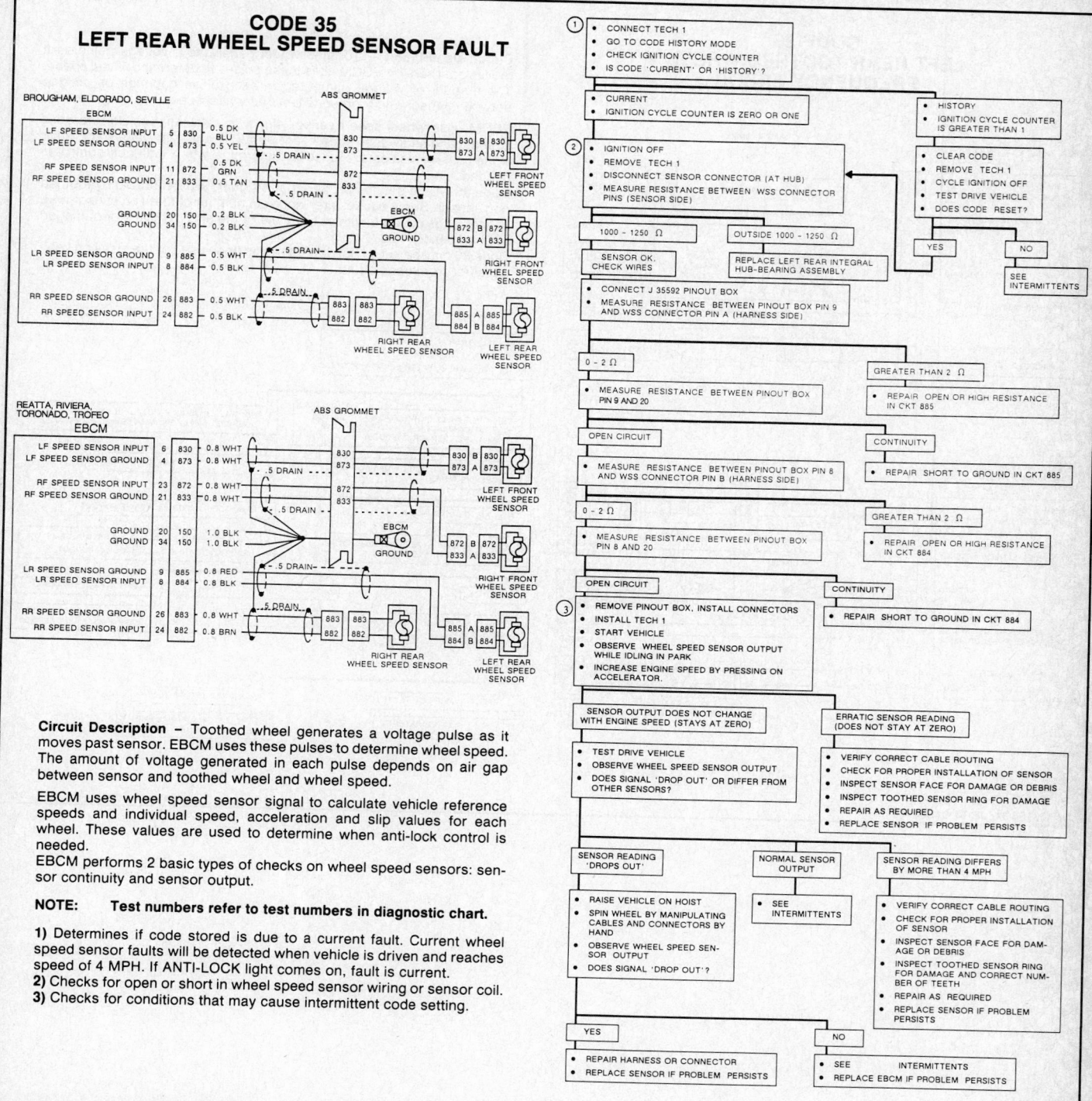

Circuit Description – Toothed wheel generates a voltage pulse as it moves past sensor. EBCM uses these pulses to determine wheel speed. The amount of voltage generated in each pulse depends on air gap between sensor and toothed wheel and wheel speed.

EBCM uses wheel speed sensor signal to calculate vehicle reference speeds and individual speed, acceleration and slip values for each wheel. These values are used to determine when anti-lock control is needed.

EBCM performs 2 basic types of checks on wheel speed sensors: sensor continuity and sensor output.

NOTE: Test numbers refer to test numbers in diagnostic chart.

1) Determines if code stored is due to a current fault. Current wheel speed sensor faults will be detected when vehicle is driven and reaches speed of 4 MPH. If ANTI-LOCK light comes on, fault is current.

2) Checks for open or short in wheel speed sensor wiring or sensor coil.

3) Checks for conditions that may cause intermittent code setting.

91H08108 91C08115 91F08107 90B18821

Courtesy of General Motors Corp.

GM
8-32

1991 BRAKES
Anti-Lock – Bosch 2U ("D", "E" & "K" Bodies – Cont.)

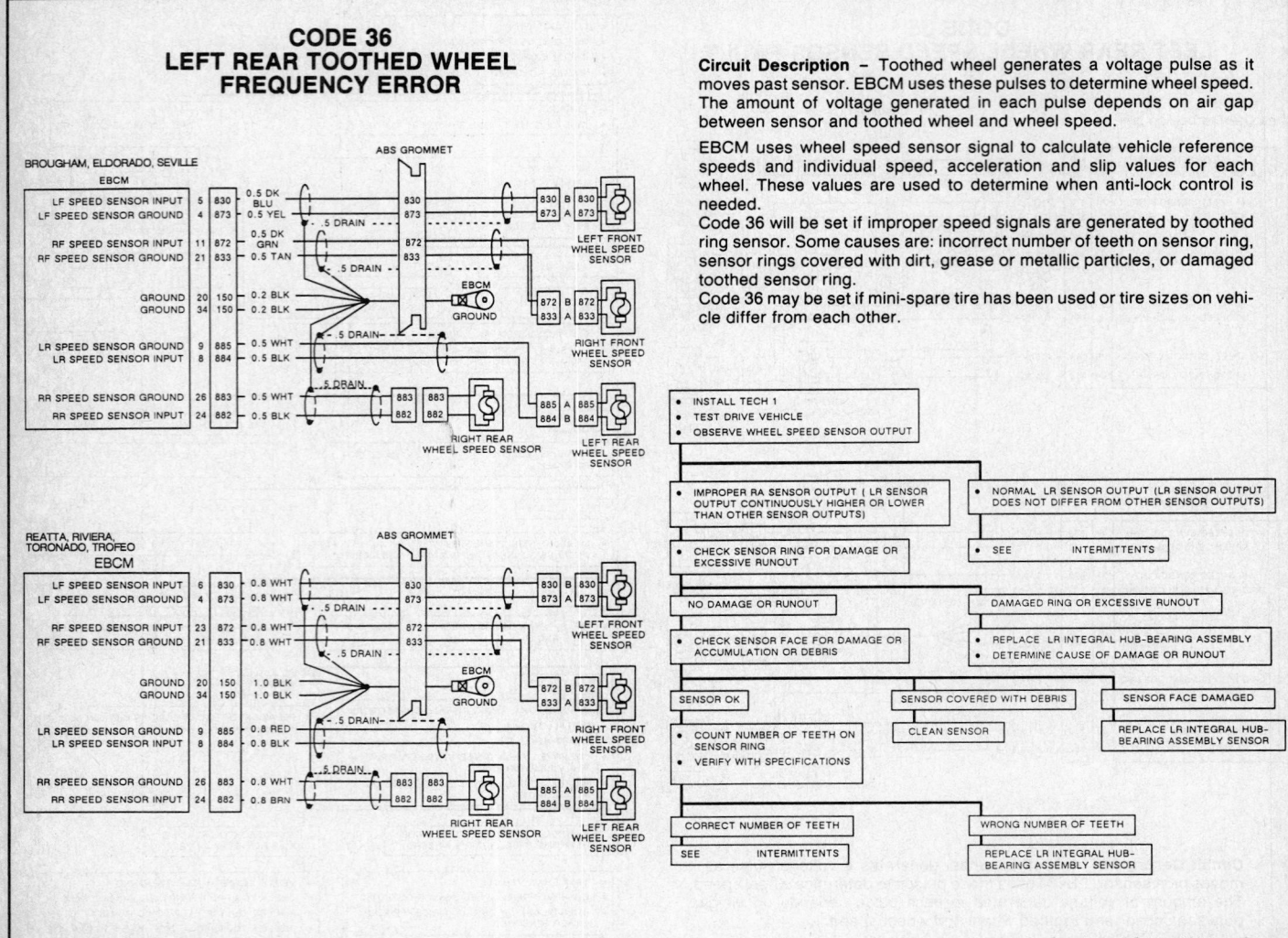

CODE 36
LEFT REAR TOOTHED WHEEL FREQUENCY ERROR

Circuit Description – Toothed wheel generates a voltage pulse as it moves past sensor. EBCM uses these pulses to determine wheel speed. The amount of voltage generated in each pulse depends on air gap between sensor and toothed wheel and wheel speed.

EBCM uses wheel speed sensor signal to calculate vehicle reference speeds and individual speed, acceleration and slip values for each wheel. These values are used to determine when anti-lock control is needed.

Code 36 will be set if improper speed signals are generated by toothed ring sensor. Some causes are: incorrect number of teeth on sensor ring, sensor rings covered with dirt, grease or metallic particles, or damaged toothed sensor ring.

Code 36 may be set if mini-spare tire has been used or tire sizes on vehicle differ from each other.

1991 BRAKES
Anti-Lock – Bosch 2U ("D", "E" & "K" Bodies – Cont.)

GM
8-33

CODE 41
RIGHT FRONT SOLENOID VALVE FAULT

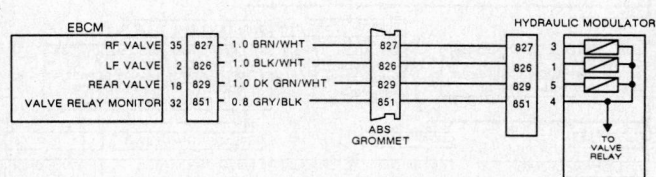

Circuit Description – Right front solenoid valve in hydraulic modulator may be commanded to 3 different positions by EBCM. Valve position is determined by amount of current that is allowed to flow through solenoid coil.

Solenoid valve circuits receive power through valve relay on hydraulic modulator. Valve relay is engaged at key-on and remains engaged throughout ignition cycle. Solenoid valve lines should have battery voltage available at all times.

When ignition switch is in RUN position, power is supplied to EBCM. EBCM will complete an internal self-check before providing ground to valve relay. When valve relay is energized, battery power is supplied to solenoid valves.

Code 41 will be set when expected position of right front solenoid valve does not match the commanded position from EBCM. Conditions which could cause code 41 to set are damage to right front solenoid, open circuit, or short circuit to ground or battery on circuit No. 827.

NOTE: This code is current if it cannot be flashed.

- IGNITION OFF
- INSTALL J-35592 PINOUT BOX
- MEASURE RESISTANCE BETWEEN PINS 35 AND 32

1.07 – 1.17 Ω
- UNPLUG HYDRAULIC MODULATOR CONNECTOR
- MEASURE RESISTANCE BETWEEN PINOUT BOX PINS 35 AND 20

LESS THAN 1.07 Ω
- REPLACE HYDRAULIC MODULATOR ASSEMBLY

GREATER THAN 1.17 Ω
- UNPLUG HYDRAULIC MODULATOR CONNECTOR
- MEASURE RESISTANCE BETWEEN MODULATOR PINS 3 AND 4 ON HYDRAULIC MODULATOR

OPEN CIRCUIT
- CONNECT MODULATOR CONNECTOR
- INSTALL TECH 1 DIAGNOSTIC SCAN TOOL
- PERFORM RF VALVE TEST

CONTINUITY
- REPAIR SHORT TO GROUND IN CKT 827 (BRN/WHT)
- NOTE: A SHORT TO GROUND ON A VALVE CIRCUIT MAY CAUSE PERMANENT DAMAGE TO THE SOLENOID VALVE. REPLACE MODULATOR IF FAULT PERSISTS.

GREATER THAN 1.17 Ω
- REPLACE HYDRAULIC MODULATOR ASSEMBLY

1.07 – 1.17 Ω
- REPAIR OPEN OR HIGH RESISTANCE IN CKT 827 (BRN/WHT)

NEITHER PRESSURE HOLD OR PRESSURE REDUCTION MODE OPERATES
- UNPLUG HYDRAULIC MODULATOR CONNECTOR MEASURE RESISTANCE BETWEEN MODULATOR PINS 3 AND 4 ON HYDRAULIC MODULATOR

ONE MODE OPERATES AND THE OTHER DOES NOT
- REPLACE HYDRAULIC MODULATOR ASSEMBLY

BOTH MODES OPERATE
- SEE INTERMITTENTS WITH IGNITION ON, MANIPULATE CONNECTORS AND WIRING BY HAND DOES A CODE SET?

OUTSIDE 1.07 – 1.17 Ω
REPLACE HYDRAULIC MODULATOR ASSEMBLY

1.07 – 1.17 Ω
REPLACE EBCM

YES
REPLACE SUSPECT HARNESS OR CONNECTOR

NO
REPLACE EBCM

91G08117 90E08263

Courtesy of General Motors Corp.

CODE 45
LEFT FRONT SOLENOID VALVE FAULT

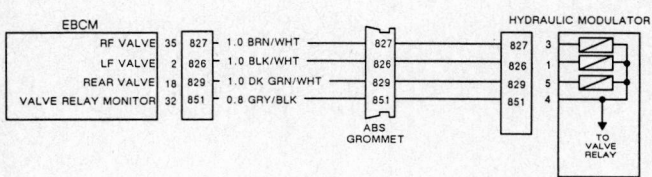

Circuit Description – Left front solenoid valve in hydraulic modulator may be commanded to 3 different positions by EBCM. Valve position is determined by amount of current that is allowed to flow through solenoid coil.

Solenoid valve circuits receive power through valve relay on hydraulic modulator. Valve relay is engaged at key-on and remains engaged throughout ignition cycle. Solenoid valve lines should have battery voltage available at all times.

When ignition switch is in RUN position, power is supplied to EBCM. EBCM will complete an internal self-check before providing ground to valve relay. When valve relay is energized, battery power is supplied to solenoid valves.

Code 45 will be set when expected position of left front solenoid valve does not match the commanded position from EBCM. Conditions which could cause code 45 to set are damage to left front solenoid, open circuit, or short circuit to ground or battery on circuit No. 826.

NOTE: This code is current if it cannot be flashed.

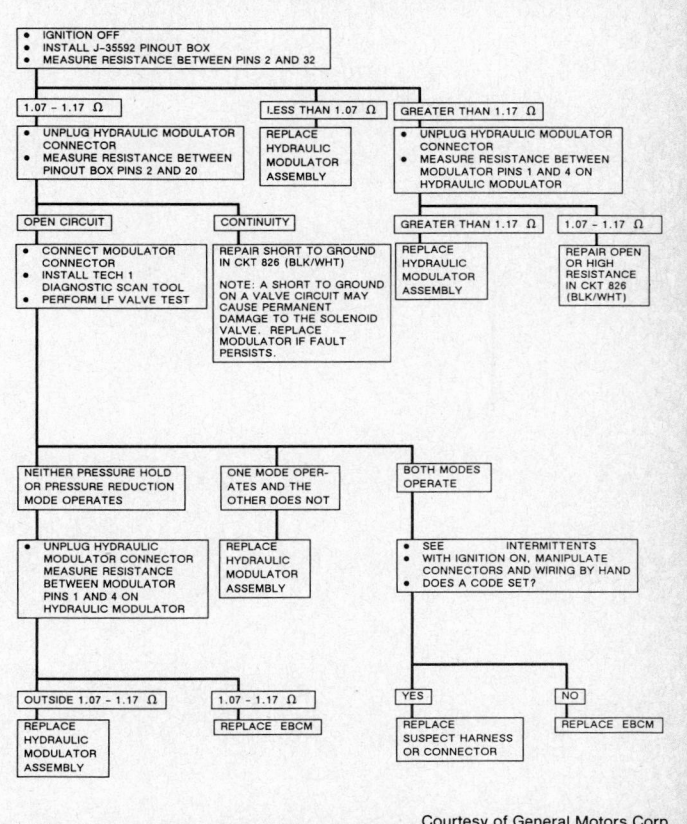

- IGNITION OFF
- INSTALL J-35592 PINOUT BOX
- MEASURE RESISTANCE BETWEEN PINS 2 AND 32

1.07 – 1.17 Ω
- UNPLUG HYDRAULIC MODULATOR CONNECTOR
- MEASURE RESISTANCE BETWEEN PINOUT BOX PINS 2 AND 20

LESS THAN 1.07 Ω
- REPLACE HYDRAULIC MODULATOR ASSEMBLY

GREATER THAN 1.17 Ω
- UNPLUG HYDRAULIC MODULATOR CONNECTOR
- MEASURE RESISTANCE BETWEEN MODULATOR PINS 1 AND 4 ON HYDRAULIC MODULATOR

OPEN CIRCUIT
- CONNECT MODULATOR CONNECTOR
- INSTALL TECH 1 DIAGNOSTIC SCAN TOOL
- PERFORM LF VALVE TEST

CONTINUITY
- REPAIR SHORT TO GROUND IN CKT 826 (BLK/WHT)
- NOTE: A SHORT TO GROUND ON A VALVE CIRCUIT MAY CAUSE PERMANENT DAMAGE TO THE SOLENOID VALVE. REPLACE MODULATOR IF FAULT PERSISTS.

GREATER THAN 1.17 Ω
- REPLACE HYDRAULIC MODULATOR ASSEMBLY

1.07 – 1.17 Ω
- REPAIR OPEN OR HIGH RESISTANCE IN CKT 826 (BLK/WHT)

NEITHER PRESSURE HOLD OR PRESSURE REDUCTION MODE OPERATES
- UNPLUG HYDRAULIC MODULATOR CONNECTOR MEASURE RESISTANCE BETWEEN MODULATOR PINS 1 AND 4 ON HYDRAULIC MODULATOR

ONE MODE OPERATES AND THE OTHER DOES NOT
- REPLACE HYDRAULIC MODULATOR ASSEMBLY

BOTH MODES OPERATE
- SEE INTERMITTENTS WITH IGNITION ON, MANIPULATE CONNECTORS AND WIRING BY HAND DOES A CODE SET?

OUTSIDE 1.07 – 1.17 Ω
REPLACE HYDRAULIC MODULATOR ASSEMBLY

1.07 – 1.17 Ω
REPLACE EBCM

YES
REPLACE SUSPECT HARNESS OR CONNECTOR

NO
REPLACE EBCM

91G08117 90G08264

Courtesy of General Motors Corp.

GM
8-34

1991 BRAKES
Anti-Lock — Bosch 2U ("D", "E" & "K" Bodies — Cont.)

CODE 55
REAR AXLE SOLENOID VALVE FAULT

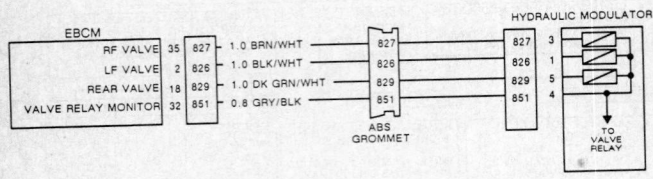

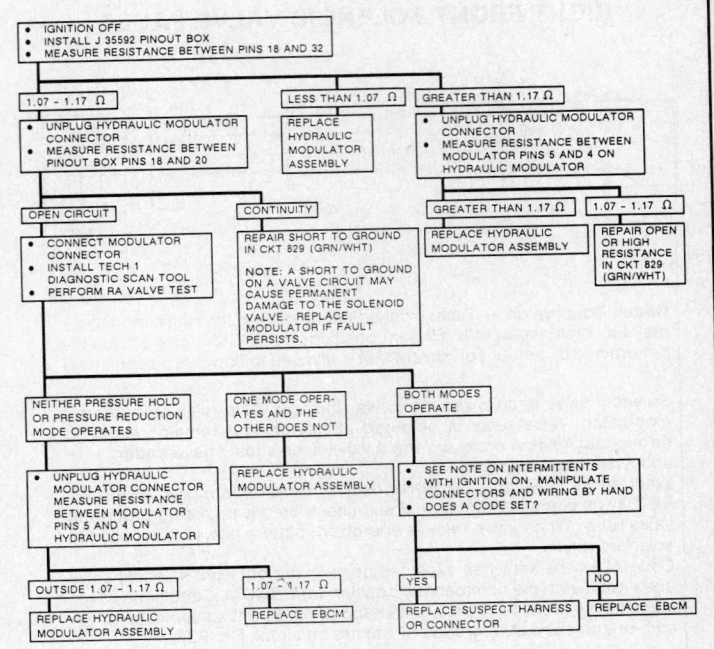

Circuit Description — Rear axle solenoid valve in hydraulic modulator may be commanded to 3 different positions by EBCM. Valve position is determined by amount of current that is allowed to flow through solenoid coil.

Solenoid valve circuits receive power through valve relay on hydraulic modulator. Valve relay is engaged at key-on and remains engaged throughout ignition cycle. Solenoid valve lines should have battery voltage available at all times.

When ignition switch is in RUN position, power is supplied to EBCM. EBCM will complete an internal self-check before providing ground to valve relay. When valve relay is energized, battery power is supplied to solenoid valves.

Code 55 will be set when expected position of rear axle solenoid valve does not match the commanded position from EBCM. Conditions which could cause code 55 to set are damage to rear axle solenoid, open circuit, or short circuit to ground or battery on circuit No. 829.

NOTE: This code is current if it cannot be flashed.

91G08117 91I08118

1991 BRAKES
Anti-Lock – Bosch 2U ("D", "E" & "K" Bodies – Cont.)

GM
8-35

CODE 61
PUMP MOTOR OR MOTOR RELAY FAULT

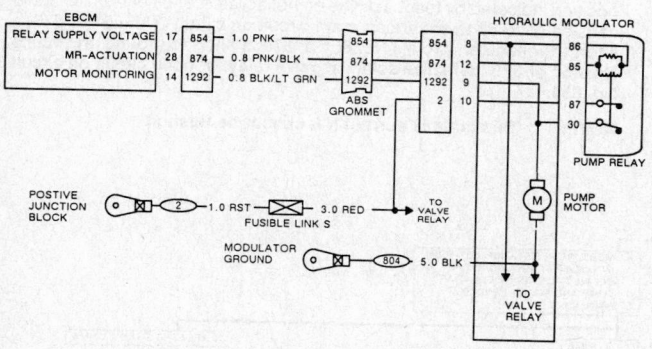

Circuit Description – Pump motor returns brake fluid to master cylinder brake circuit at hydraulic modulator during anti-lock braking. During normal braking, pump does not operate. When vehicle begins to move after start-up, EBCM will turn on pump motor and perform a self-check of pump motor and pump motor circuit. Pump motor is an integral part of hydraulic modulator and cannot be serviced separately.

Code 61 will be set if commanded position of pump motor relay and motor monitor do not agree. Conditions which could cause code 61 to set are an open in circuits No. 854 or 1292, short to voltage in circuits No. 854 or 1292, short to ground in circuits No. 854 or 1292, or a defective pump motor relay or pump motor.

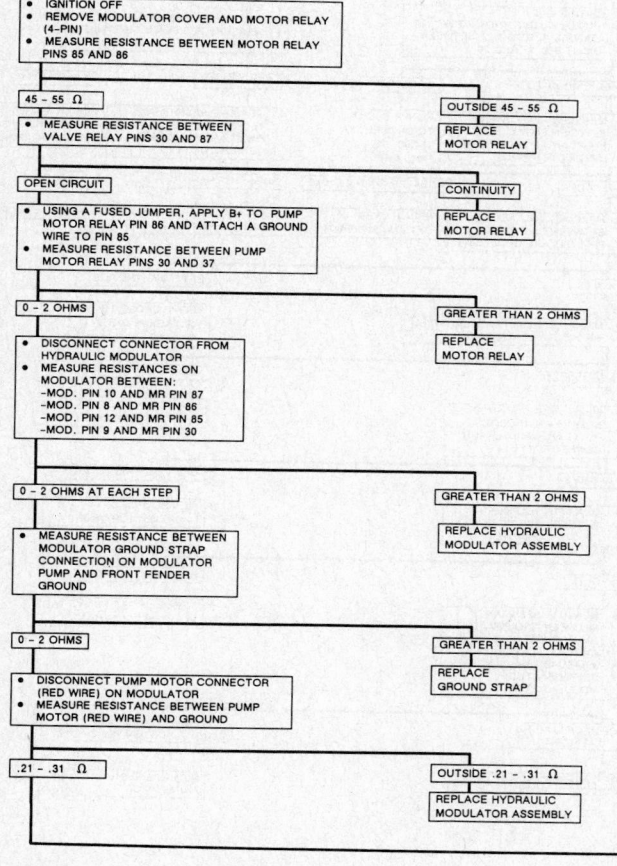

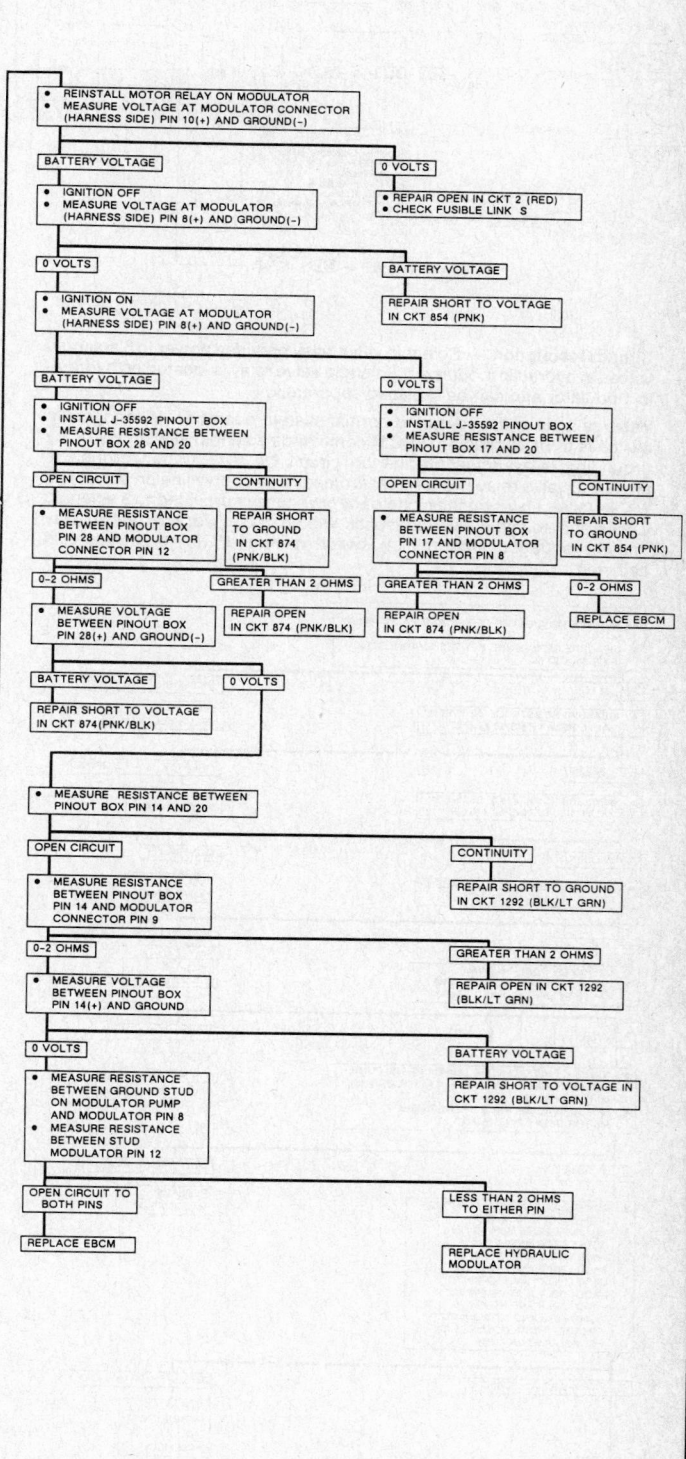

Courtesy of General Motors Corp.

GM
8-36

1991 BRAKES
Anti-Lock – Bosch 2U ("D", "E" & "K") Bodies – Cont.

CODE 63
SOLENOID VALVE RELAY FAULT

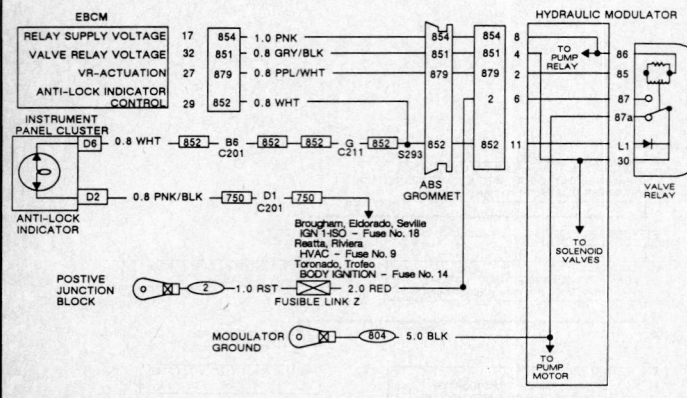

Code 63 will be set if commanded position of valve relay and valve relay position indicated by feedback line do not agree. Conditions which could cause a code 63 to set are an open circuit on circuits No. 851 or 879, a short to voltage on circuits No. 851 or 879, a short to ground on circuits No. 851 or 879, defective solenoid valve relay, or open circuit on circuit No. 854.

NOTE: This code is current if it cannot be flashed.

Circuit Description – Solenoid valve relay provides power to 3 solenoid valves in hydraulic modulator. Solenoid valve relay is located on hydraulic modulator and can be replaced separately.

Valve relay is engaged during normal system operation. When ignition switch is in RUN position, EBCM commands solenoid valve relay on by grounding relay actuation line on circuit No. 879. When ground is provided, valve relay is energized from voltage supply line on circuit No. 1079. Valve relay switches, and battery voltage is provided to 3 solenoid valves and solenoid valve feedback line on circuit No. 851. Valve relay remains engaged until ignition switch is turned OFF or a failure is detected.

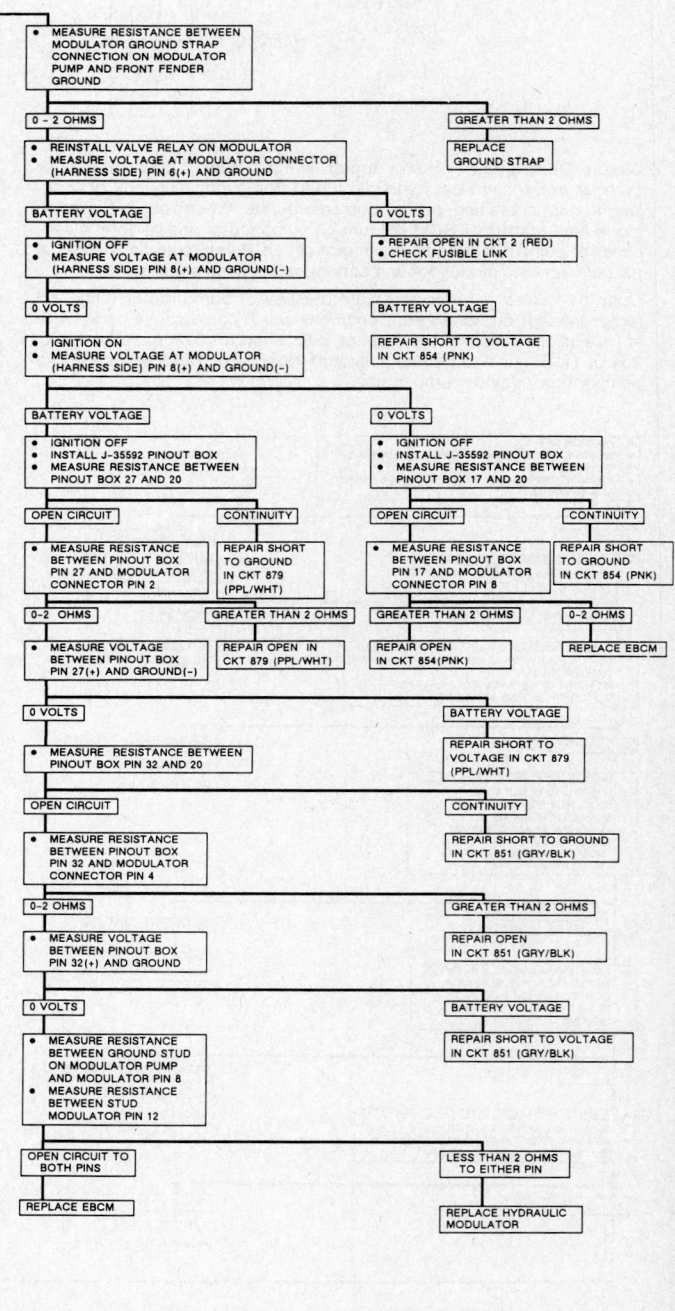

1991 BRAKES
Anti-Lock – Bosch 2U ("D", "E" & "K" Bodies – Cont.)

GM
8-37

CODE 71
EBCM FAULT

CODE 71 WILL SET IF CERTAIN INTERNAL EBCM FAILURES ARE DETECTED

- CLEAR CODES
- TEST DRIVE CAR AGAIN, ACCELERATING SLOWLY TO 25 MPH. REPEAT ACCELERATION AND STOP 2 TIMES
- DID AN ABS CODE SET?

NO

IS EBCM CONNECTED PROPERLY?

CODE 71

REPLACE EBCM

OTHER CODES

GO TO APPROPRIATE ABS CODE CHART

YES

- IGNITION OFF
- INSTALL J 35592 PINOUT BOX
- MEASURE RESISTANCE BETWEEN PINOUT BOX 20 AND GROUND
- MEASURE RESISTANCE BETWEEN PINOUT BOX 34 AND GROUND

NO

CONNECT EBCM

0–2 OHMS

- IGNITION ON
- MEASURE VOLTAGE BETWEEN PINOUT BOX 1 AND 20

GREATER THAN 2 OHMS

REPAIR OPEN OR HIGH RESISTANCE IN CKT 804

LOW VOLTAGE

REPAIR OPEN OR HIGH RESISTANCE IN CKT 804

SYSTEM VOLTAGE

SYSTEM OK, SEE ___ INTERMITTENTS

91A08124

Courtesy of General Motors Corp.

SYMPTOM DIAGNOSTIC CHART A
NO SYSTEM POWER

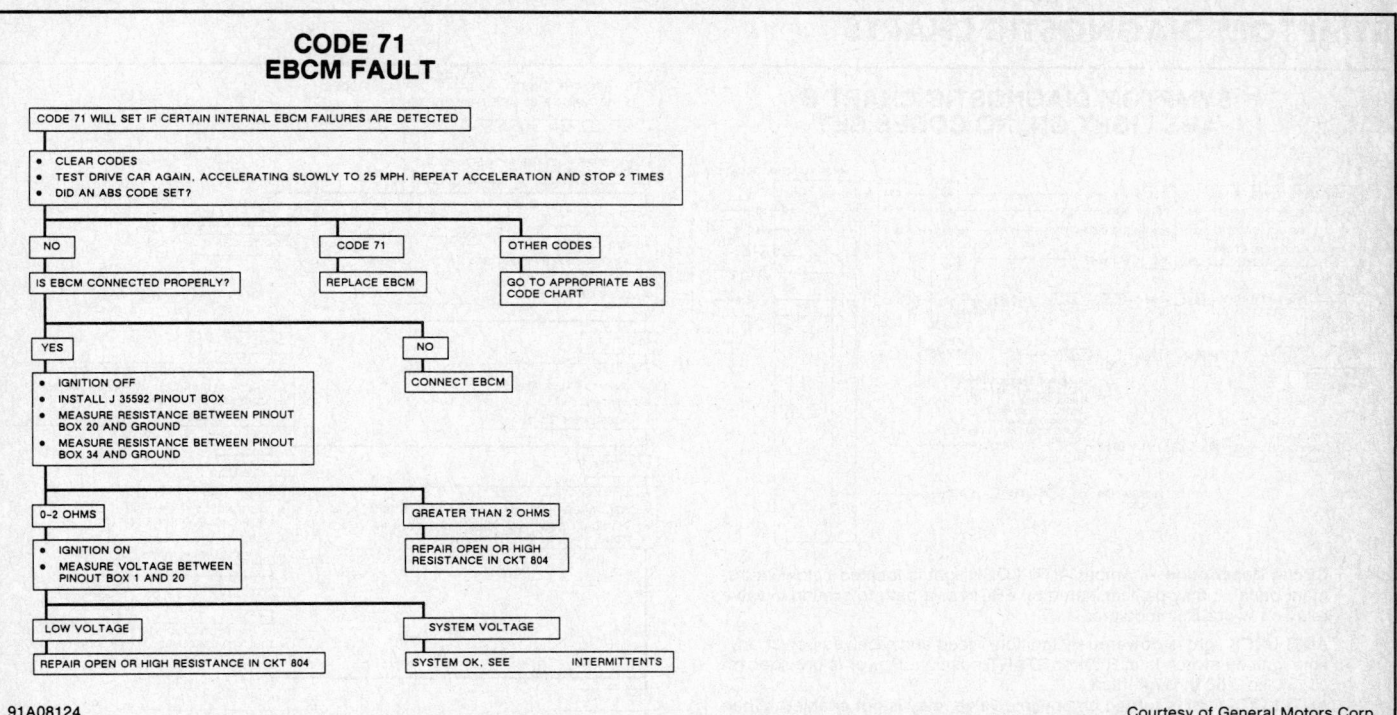

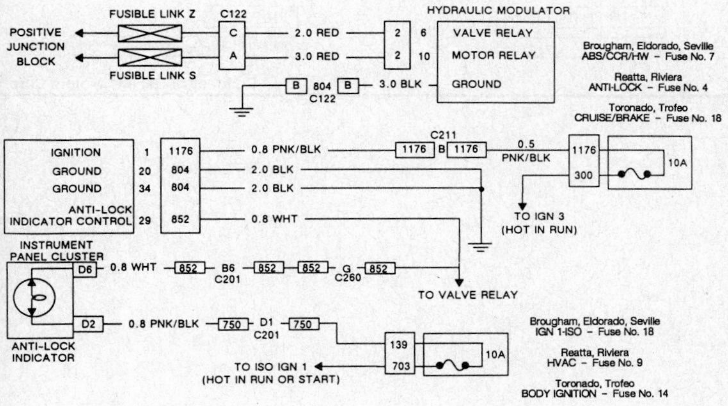

Circuit Description – EBCM receives power from ABS/CCR/HW – Fuse No. 7 (Brougham, Eldorado, Seville) or ANTI-LOCK – Fuse No. 4 (Reatta, Riviera) or CRUISE/BRAKE – Fuse No. 18 (Toronado, Trofeo) on circuit No. 1176. If high system voltages occur, the EBCM is internally protected by a network of diodes which directs excess voltage to ground.

Some conditions which may cause a lack of system power are improper electrical contact of EBCM connector, low system voltage, or improper electrical contact of vehicle power and ground connections.

- VERIFY THAT THE EBCM CONNECTOR IS SECURELY ATTACHED TO THE EBCM. IF DISCONNECTED, CONNECT AND VERIFY OPERATION.

- IF FUSES HAVE NOT ALREADY BEEN CHECKED, INSPECT 10A ANTI-LOCK FUSE IN THE INTERIOR RELAY CENTER.

FUSE OK

- INSTALL J 35592 PINOUT BOX
- MEASURE RESISTANCE BETWEEN PIN 20 AND BODY GROUND
- MEASURE RESISTANCE BETWEEN PIN 34 AND BODY GROUND

FUSE BLOWN

REPLACE FUSE AND VERIFY OPERATION

BOTH 0 – 1 Ω

- IGNITION SWITCH IN RUN
- MEASURE VOLTAGE FROM PIN 1 AND PIN 20

EITHER OR BOTH GREATER THAN 1 Ω

REPAIR OPEN OR HIGH RESISTANCE IN CKT 804 (BLK) BETWEEN EBCM AND NEGATIVE JUNCTION BLOCK

LOW VOLTAGE

- IGNITION SWITCH OFF
- ANTI-LOCK FUSE 4 REMOVED
- MEASURE RESISTANCE FROM GROUND SIDE OF FUSE TO PIN 1

BATTERY VOLTAGE

- CHECK TERMINAL 1 OF EBCM
- CHECK PIN 1 OF EBCM CONNECTOR FOR INTERMITTENT OPEN OR POOR CRIMP
- WIGGLE CKT 1176 FOR POSSIBLE INTERMITTENT OPEN

LESS THAN 1 Ω

- IGNITION SWITCH IN RUN
- MEASURE VOLTAGE ON POWER SIDE OF ANTI-LOCK FUSE 4 ●

● See circuit diagram for proper fuse identification

GREATER THAN 1 Ω

REPAIR OPEN OR PARTIAL OPEN IN CKT 1176 BETWEEN INTERIOR RELAY CENTER AND EBCM CONNECTOR

LOW VOLTAGE

- DISCONNECT NEGATIVE BATTERY CABLE
- INSPECT INTERIOR RELAY CENTER SPADE TERMINALS FOR POOR CRIMP
- INSPECT WIRING AT REAR OF INTERIOR RELAY CENTER FOR OPENS
- REPAIR OPEN IN CKT 300 BETWEEN IGNITION SWITCH AND FUSEBLOCK

BATTERY VOLTAGE

- DISCONNECT NEGATIVE BATTERY CABLE
- INSPECT INTERIOR RELAY CENTER SPADE TERMINALS FOR POOR CRIMP
- INSPECT WIRING AT REAR OF INTERIOR RELAY CENTER FOR OPENS
- REPLACE FUSE

91D08125 91F08126

Courtesy of General Motors Corp.

GM
8-38

1991 BRAKES
Anti-Lock – Bosch 2U ("D", "E" & "K" Bodies – Cont.)

SYMPTOM DIAGNOSTIC CHARTS

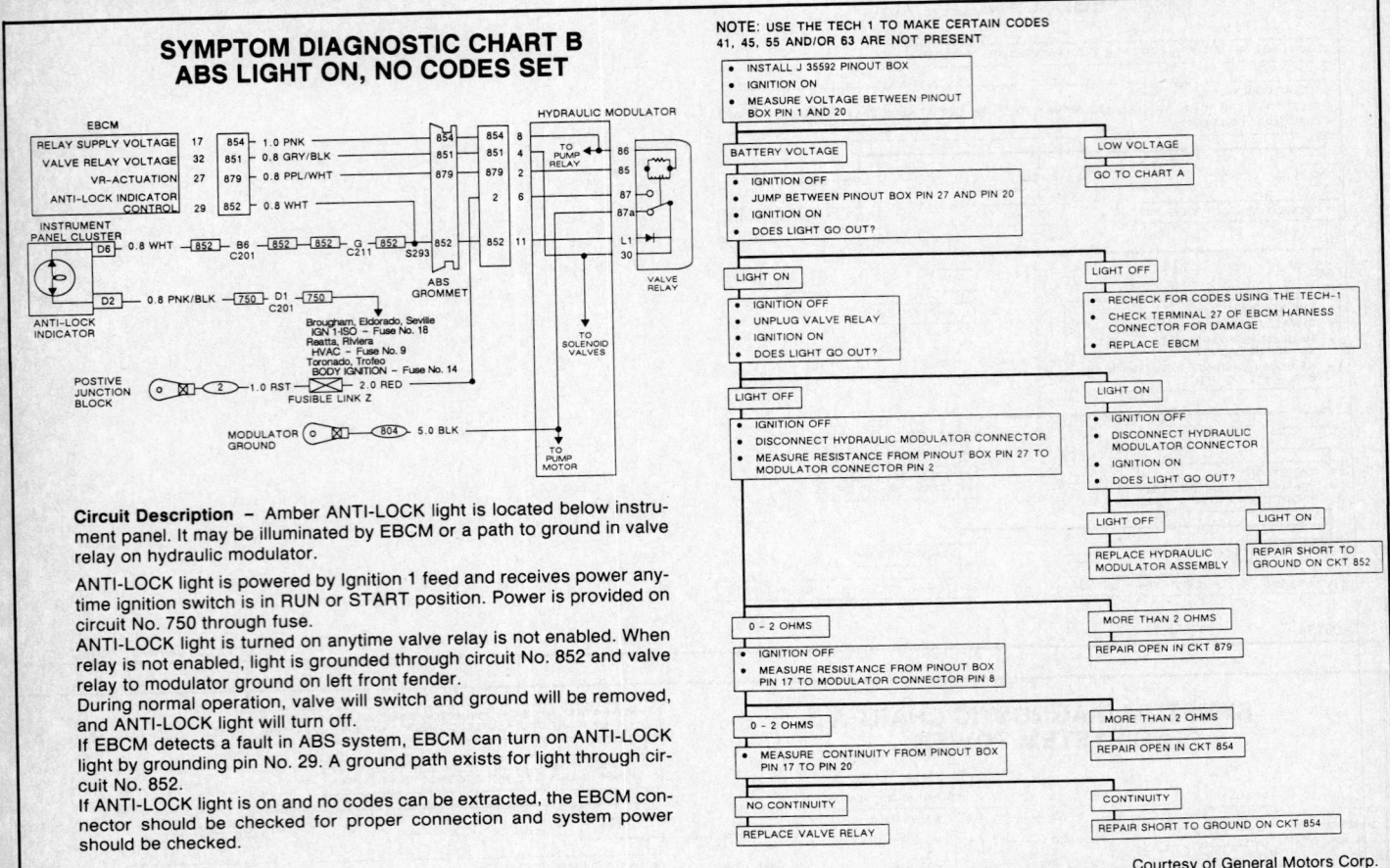

Circuit Description – Amber ANTI-LOCK light is located below instrument panel. It may be illuminated by EBCM or a path to ground in valve relay on hydraulic modulator.

ANTI-LOCK light is powered by Ignition 1 feed and receives power anytime ignition switch is in RUN or START position. Power is provided on circuit No. 750 through fuse.

ANTI-LOCK light is turned on anytime valve relay is not enabled. When relay is not enabled, light is grounded through circuit No. 852 and valve relay to modulator ground on left front fender.

During normal operation, valve will switch and ground will be removed, and ANTI-LOCK light will turn off.

If EBCM detects a fault in ABS system, EBCM can turn on ANTI-LOCK light by grounding pin No. 29. A ground path exists for light through circuit No. 852.

If ANTI-LOCK light is on and no codes can be extracted, the EBCM connector should be checked for proper connection and system power should be checked.

Courtesy of General Motors Corp.

91G08122 91H08127

1991 BRAKES
Anti-Lock – Bosch 2U ("D", "E" & "K" Bodies – Cont.)

GM
8-39

SYMPTOM DIAGNOSTIC CHART C
ANTI-LOCK LIGHT INOPERATIVE, KEY-ON

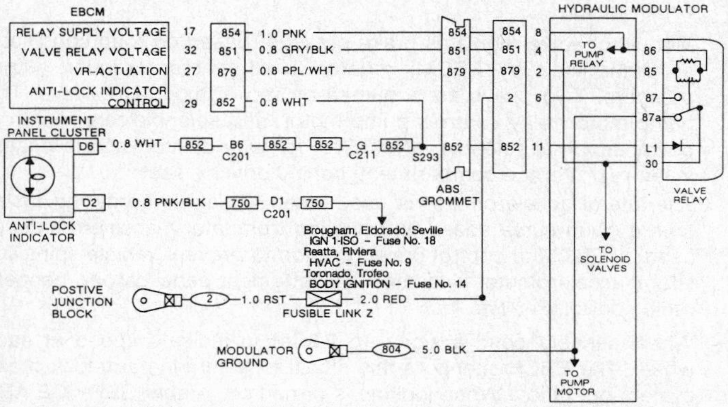

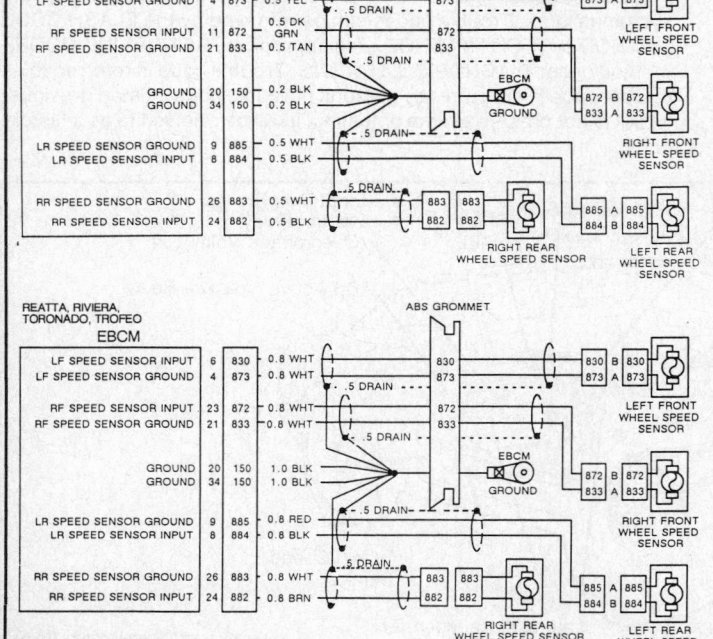

Circuit Description – Amber ANTI-LOCK light is located below instrument panel. It may be illuminated by EBCM or a path to ground in valve relay on hydraulic modulator.

ANTI-LOCK light is powered by Ignition 1 feed and receives power anytime ignition switch is in RUN or START position. Power is provided on circuit No. 750 through fuse.

ANTI-LOCK light is turned on anytime valve relay is not enabled. When relay is not enabled, light is grounded through circuit No. 852 and valve relay to modulator ground on left front fender.

During normal operation, valve will switch and ground will be removed, and ANTI-LOCK light will turn off.

If EBCM detects a fault in ABS system, EBCM can turn on ANTI-LOCK light by grounding pin No. 29. A ground path exists for light through circuit No. 852.

If ANTI-LOCK light does not turn on, a lack of power could exist and should be checked first.

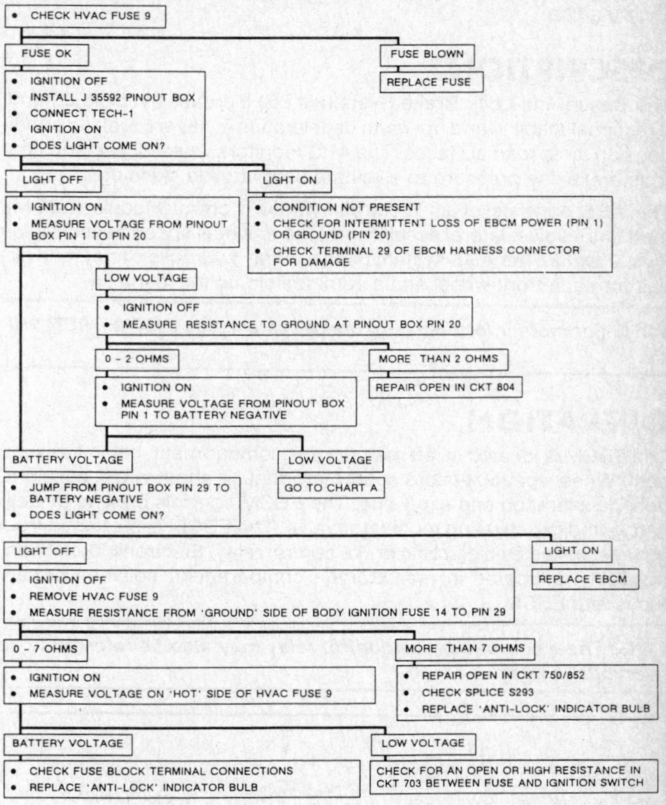

91G08122 91J08128

Courtesy of General Motors Corp.

SYMPTOM DIAGNOSTIC CHART D
VALVE CYCLING (CHATTERING) DURING NORMAL STOPS

Circuit Description – EBCM uses wheel speed sensor signal to calculate vehicle reference speeds and individual speed, acceleration and slip values for each wheel. These values are used to determine when anti-lock control is needed.

In order to prevent electromagnetic interference from disturbing wheel speed sensor signal, sensor cables are protected with grounded shielding. Shield surrounds 2 individual sensor wires. A Black conduit surrounds wires and shield. If shielding is disturbed, repair as required.

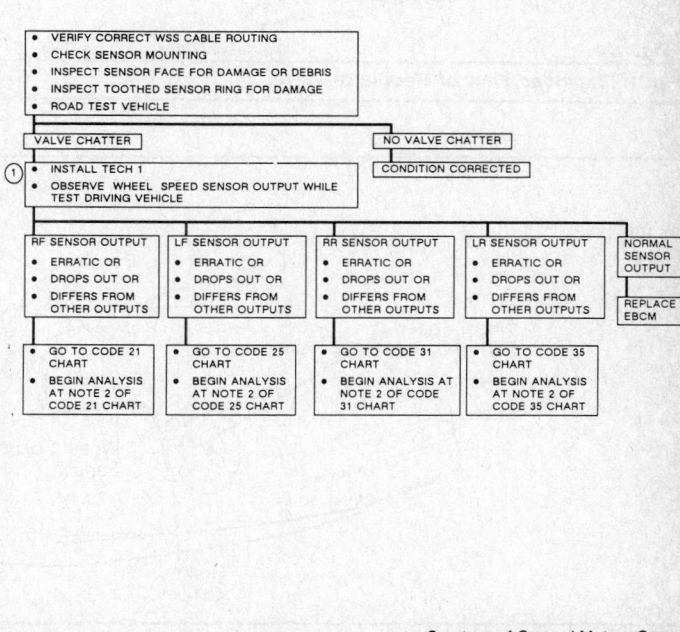

91H08108 91F08107 91B08129

Courtesy of General Motors Corp.

Corvette

DESCRIPTION

The Bosch Anti-Lock Brake System (ABS) increases vehicle control, directional stability and optimum deceleration in severe braking conditions on most road surfaces. The ABS monitors wheel speed and controls brake line pressure to eliminate uncontrolled skidding.

The ABS consists of an Electronic Brake Control Module (EBCM), modulator valve, lateral accelerometer and wheel speed sensors. *See Figs. 2 and 3.* The ABS system uses a 3-way hydraulic circuit; one circuit for each front wheel and a common circuit for rear axle.

NOTE: For more information on brake system, see DISC & DRUM article.

OPERATION

The EBCM is located in left rear storage compartment, behind driver's seat. Wheel speed sensors supply information about wheel acceleration, deceleration and slip value. The EBCM controls braking by activating and deactivating modulator valve. The EBCM is protected from voltage spikes by electronic brake control relay. Electronic brake control relay is located in rear storage compartment, between battery fuses and EBCM.

NOTE: The electronic brake control relay may also be referred to as overvoltage relay.

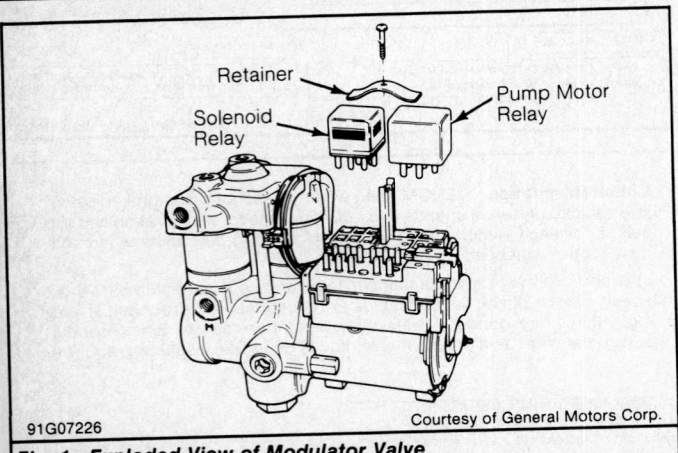

91G07226

Fig. 1: Exploded View of Modulator Valve

Courtesy of General Motors Corp.

Modulator valve consists of 3 switching solenoid valves, 2 accumulator chambers and a return pump. Valves increase and decrease brake fluid pressure to each wheel (rear wheels are on one circuit) to prevent wheel lockup.

Modulator valve regulates brake pressure based on road conditions as determined by EBCM, regardless of master cylinder output pressure. Two relays are mounted on top of modulator valve. The pump motor relay controls pump motor, and solenoid relay controls power supply to solenoid valves. *See Fig. 1.* Modulator valve is located in left rear storage compartment, behind driver's seat.

The lateral accelerometer is used when vehicle is cornering faster than a given curve speed. Information from lateral accelerometer is used by EBCM to control braking action to prevent vehicle spin. The lateral accelerometer is located on instrument panel carrier, beneath radio control. *See Fig. 4.*

Wheel sensors send a signal to EBCM to indicate speed at each wheel. The EBCM monitors this signal to determine anti-lock brake system operation. When ignition is turned on, Amber SERVICE ABS light on instrument panel will come on. After engine is started, light should go out. If light fails to go out or comes on during vehicle operation, a system malfunction exists and system must be checked.

If SERVICE ABS light is turned on by EBCM, ABS system will generally be turned off. System will remain off until vehicle is restarted. The SERVICE ABS light will also come on if supply voltage to EBCM drops below a specified value. The light will go off once voltage reaches specified value.

The Amber ABS ACTIVE light on instrument panel will activate when pump motor relay applies voltage to pump motor, and ABS ACTIVE indicator relay energizes to indicate ABS operation. When vehicle is first started and vehicle speed reaches approximately 4 MPH, modulator valve pump motor operation can be heard, and ABS ACTIVE light will come on while a system operating test is being performed. This is done to ensure all components are functioning properly.

If a system failure exists, a trouble code will be stored in EBCM memory and EBCM will turn on SERVICE ABS light. The ABS system will be turned off.

NOTE: The EBCM will not turn off ABS system if Code 71 exists.

The EBCM contains a self-diagnostic capability to detect and isolate system failures. Trouble codes can be retrieved by the FLASH CODE METHOD or TECH I METHOD. See appropriate RETRIEVING CODES method under DIAGNOSIS & TESTING. Trouble code is referred to as current code if it is currently present. If trouble code existed previously, but is not present at time of testing, it will be referred to as a history code.

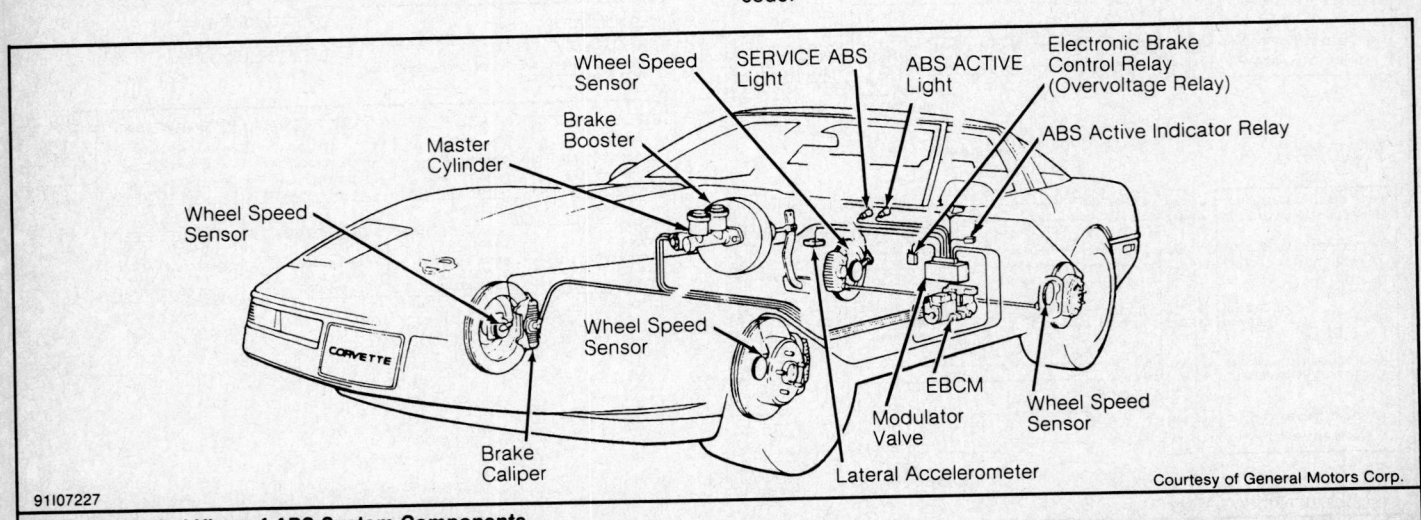

91I07227

Fig. 2: Exploded View of ABS System Components

Courtesy of General Motors Corp.

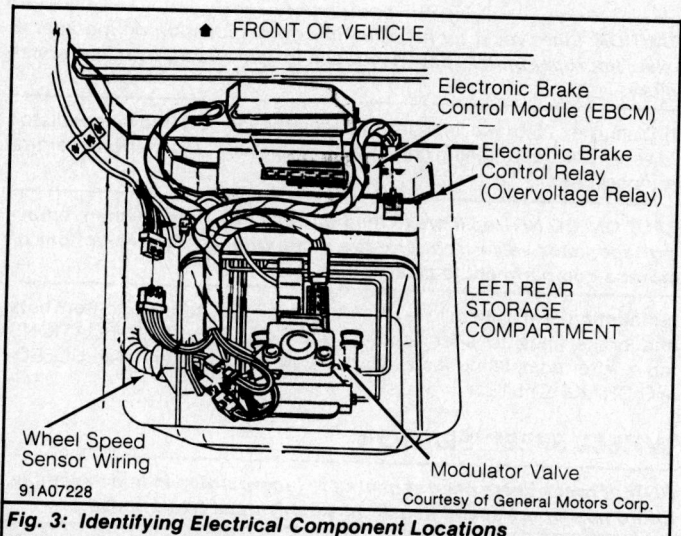

↑ FRONT OF VEHICLE

Electronic Brake Control Module (EBCM)

Electronic Brake Control Relay (Overvoltage Relay)

LEFT REAR STORAGE COMPARTMENT

Wheel Speed Sensor Wiring

Modulator Valve

91A07228

Courtesy of General Motors Corp.

Fig. 3: Identifying Electrical Component Locations

CAUTION: See ANTI-LOCK BRAKE SAFETY PRECAUTIONS article in GENERAL INFORMATION.

SERVICING PRECAUTIONS

SUPPLEMENTAL INFLATABLE RESTRAINT (SIR)

Disabling SIR – 1) Before performing any repairs near instrument panel or steering column, ensure ignition is off. Because system has ability to retain voltage, remove AIR BAG (SIR) fuse and disconnect Yellow SIR connector at base of steering column.
2) Wait 10 minutes before working on vehicle. All connectors used on AIR BAG (SIR) system use Connector Position Assurance (CPA) clips to ensure retention of connector. Even if system is disconnected, always use caution when working near steering column and instrument panel.
Enabling SIR – 1) Reconnect Yellow SIR connector at base of steering column. Install AIR BAG (SIR) fuse. Turn ignition on.
2) Observe INFL REST light. If light flashes 7 to 9 times and then goes off, SIR system is malfunctioning.

BLEEDING BRAKE SYSTEM

Brake system can be bled using MANUAL BLEEDING PROCEDURE or PRESSURE BLEEDING PROCEDURE. The Tech 1 Diagnostic Computer (94-00101-A) with Bosch ABS ALDL Adapter MUST be used to bleed modulator valve assembly.

CAUTION: Use ONLY DOT 3 brake fluid. DO NOT use DOT 5 silicone brake fluid. DO NOT allow brake fluid to contact skin or painted surfaces

MANUAL BLEEDING PROCEDURE

1) With engine off, release reserve vacuum by applying brakes several times. Fill master cylinder with brake fluid and keep reservoir half full during bleeding procedure.
2) If master cylinder is suspected to have air in it, disconnect forward brake line at master cylinder. Allow brake fluid to fill master cylinder bore until it flows from forward port of master cylinder. Install and tighten forward brake line at master cylinder.
3) Depress brake pedal one time and hold down. Loosen forward brake line at master cylinder to purge air from master cylinder. Tighten forward brake line. Release brake pedal.
4) Wait 15 seconds and repeat step 3) until no air exists in master cylinder. Tighten forward brake line to 13 ft. lbs. (18 N.m).
5) To bleed brake calipers, place box wrench over bleeder valve. Attach one end of clear tube over bleeder valve and submerge other end in container partially filled with clean brake fluid.

6) Slowly depress brake pedal and hold. Starting at right front wheel, loosen bleeder valve to purge air from cylinder. Tighten bleeder valve and slowly release brake pedal. Repeat procedure until all air is removed. Tighten bleeder valve to 80 INCH lbs. (9 N.m).
7) Repeat procedure on remaining brake calipers in following sequence: right rear wheel, left rear wheel and left front wheel. Fill master cylinder and replace cover.

PRESSURE BLEEDING PROCEDURE

1) Install Bleeder Adapters (J-29567 and J-34098) to brake master cylinder. Pressurize bleeder to 20-25 psi (1.4-1.8 kg/cm²). Connect bleeder hose to adapter and bleed air from adapter.
2) Place proper size box end wrench over bleeder valve. Attach one end of clear tube over valve and submerge other end in container partially filled with clean brake fluid.
3) Starting at right front wheel, loosen bleeder valve 3/4 turn to purge air from cylinder. Tighten bleeder valve when no more air exists. Remove tube and wrench. Tighten bleeder valve to 80 INCH lbs. (9 N.m).
4) Repeat procedure on remaining brake calipers in following sequence: right rear wheel, left rear wheel and left front wheel. Remove pressure bleeder and adapters. Ensure master cylinder is full. Install master cylinder cover.

ADJUSTMENTS

STOPLIGHT SWITCH

1) With brake pedal depressed, install stoplight switch into retainer until switch body seats on retainer in switch mounting bracket. Ensure a click is heard when stoplight switch is installed in retainer.
2) Pull brake pedal rearward against pedal stop with a force of 42 lbs. (19 kg) until no clicking sound can be heard. Stoplight switch will be positioned in retainer to obtain correct adjustment.

PARKING/EMERGENCY BRAKE

Cycle parking/emergency brake lever 3 times. This should obtain correct adjustment of 3 to 5 notches of brake lever movement before force will be applied.

REMOVAL & INSTALLATION

CAUTION: Vehicle is equipped with Supplemental Inflatable Restraint (SIR) system. Disable SIR system when working near steering column or instrument panel. See SUPPLEMENTAL INFLATABLE RESTRAINT (SIR) under SERVICING PRECAUTIONS.

CAUTION: Before removing any ABS component under high pressure, hydraulic pressure in system MUST be reduced to a manageable level. Turn ignition switch to OFF position. Pump brake pedal at least 25 times or until an increase in pedal force is clearly felt.

ABS ACTIVE INDICATOR RELAY

Removal & Installation – Disconnect negative battery cable. Remove storage tray and insulation from behind driver's seat. Disconnect ABS active indicator relay from wiring harness. To install, reverse removal procedure.

NOTE: The ABS active indicator relay contains a 4-pin connector with Light Green/Black, Dark Blue and 2 Black wires.

ELECTRONIC BRAKE CONTROL MODULE (EBCM)

Removal & Installation – 1) Disconnect negative battery cable. Remove storage tray and insulation from behind driver's seat. Disconnect control module connector by depressing spring clip on connector. Remove retaining screws and remove EBCM from bracket.
2) To install, reverse removal procedure. Tighten bolts to specification. See TORQUE SPECIFICATIONS table.

ELECTRONIC BRAKE CONTROL RELAY

NOTE: The electronic brake control relay may also be referred to as overvoltage relay.

Removal & Installation – Disconnect negative battery cable. Remove storage tray and insulation from behind driver's seat. Disconnect electronic brake control relay from bracket near EBCM. *See Fig. 3.* To install, reverse removal procedure.

LATERAL ACCELEROMETER

CAUTION: Vehicle is equipped with Supplemental Inflatable Restraint (SIR) system. Disable SIR system when working near steering column or instrument panel. See SUPPLEMENTAL INFLATABLE RESTRAINT (SIR) under SERVICING PRECAUTIONS.

Removal – **1)** Disconnect negative battery cable. On A/T vehicles, pry upward and remove gearshift button. Remove snap ring and shift knob.
2) On M/T vehicles, remove gearshift button, set screw and shift knob. On all models, remove screws from under ash tray and rear trim plate. Disconnect electrical connector from cigarette lighter, rear compartment lid release switch, and gear indicator light (A/T vehicles). Remove console trim plate.
3) Center trim plate around radio and driver information center must be removed. Remove center air outlet above driver information center. Remove retaining screws and center trim plate.
4) Remove radio assembly-to-instrument panel retaining screws. Pull radio assembly outward and disconnect wiring.
5) Depress spring retainer on lateral accelerometer wiring connector and remove. *See Fig. 4.* Remove retaining screws and remove lateral accelerometer.
Installation – Install lateral accelerometer. Tighten retaining screws to specification. See TORQUE SPECIFICATIONS table. To install remaining components, reverse removal procedure. Ensure all wiring connections are securely installed.

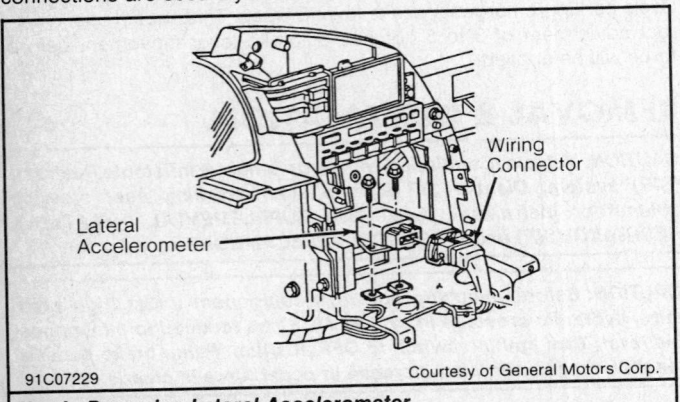

91C07229   Courtesy of General Motors Corp.

Fig. 4: Removing Lateral Accelerometer

MODULATOR VALVE

NOTE: The modulator valve may also be referred to as the hydraulic modulator assembly. The modulator valve MUST be removed through access hole in rear storage compartment. DO NOT attempt to remove bottom of rear storage compartment.

Removal – **1)** Disconnect negative battery cable. Remove storage tray and insulation from behind driver's seat. Disconnect and remove entire ABS wiring harness from storage compartment. See WIRING HARNESS under REMOVAL & INSTALLATION.
2) Disconnect modulator valve ground from body harness. Place shop rags under modulator valve fittings to catch brake fluid. Mark brake line location on modulator valve for reassembly reference.

CAUTION: Lines must be installed in original location on modulator valve. Improper installation may result in wheel lockup and personal injury.

3) Disconnect 5 brake lines from modulator valve. Remove modulator valve-to-bracket retaining nuts. Remove modulator valve from storage compartment.

CAUTION: DO NOT spill brake fluid on vehicle's interior when removing modulator valve from storage compartment. Ensure bottom of storage compartment is clean.

Installation – To install, reverse removal procedure. Tighten nuts and brake lines to specification. See TORQUE SPECIFICATIONS table. After completing installation, bleed brake system. See BLEEDING BRAKE SYSTEM.

WHEEL SPEED SENSOR

NOTE: Front wheel speed sensors are incorporated in hub assembly. Entire hub/wheel speed sensor assembly must be removed.

Removal (Front Wheel) – Raise and support vehicle. Remove wheel. Remove brake caliper and rotor. Disconnect electrical connector from wheel speed sensor. Remove retaining bolts and remove hub/wheel speed sensor assembly.
Installation – To install, reverse removal procedure. Tighten bolts to specification. See TORQUE SPECIFICATIONS table.

CAUTION: Ensure hub/wheel speed sensor assembly is installed with electrical connection toward rear of vehicle.

Removal (Rear Wheel) – **1)** Raise and support vehicle. Remove wheel. Remove wheel speed sensor connector from bracket and disconnect connector.
2) Remove bracket and bolt from knuckle. Remove wiring harness, with grommets attached, from remaining brackets. Remove retaining bolt and remove wheel speed sensor.

CAUTION: Ensure proper wheel speed sensor is installed on right and left sides. Sensors can be identified by a White tag near neck of sensor to indicate right or left application. Sensor must be coated with Anti-Corrosion Sealer (12345489) before installing. DO NOT take sensor out of package until ready to install.

Installation – **1)** To install, reverse removal procedure. Ensure all sealant is removed from wheel speed sensor and mounting area in knuckle.
2) Coat new sensor with Anti-Corrosion Sealer (12345489) before installing. DO NOT use chassis grease. DO NOT hammer on sensor during installation. Tighten bolts to specification. See TORQUE SPECIFICATIONS table.

PUMP MOTOR RELAY & SOLENOID RELAY

Removal & Installation – **1)** Disconnect negative battery cable. Remove storage tray and insulation behind driver's seat.
2) Remove screw, retainer and appropriate relay. *See Fig. 1.* Note alignment of relay electrical pins with modulator valve connector. To install, reverse removal procedure.

TOOTHED RING

Removal & Installation – The toothed ring on rear wheels is not serviceable. A new drive shaft spindle must be used.

WIRING HARNESS

CAUTION: DO NOT disconnect wiring harness from EBCM with ignition in ON position.

Removal – **1)** Disconnect negative battery cable. Remove storage tray and insulation from behind driver's seat.

2) Depress spring clip on connector and disconnect wiring connector from EBCM. Remove screws from harness retainer clip. Disconnect modulator valve connector.

3) Disconnect Red battery voltage supply wire connector. Disconnect wheel speed sensor wiring from wiring harness connector. *See Fig. 3.*

4) Disconnect electrical connector from electronic brake control relay. Remove wiring harness.

Installation – To install, reverse removal procedure. Ensure all connectors are securely fastened. Tighten retaining screws to specification. See TORQUE SPECIFICATIONS table.

TORQUE SPECIFICATIONS

TORQUE SPECIFICATIONS	
Application	**Ft. Lbs. (N.m)**
Brake Line-To-Master Cylinder	13 (18)
Brake Line-To-Modulator Valve	13 (18)
Hub Assembly Bolt	46 (62)
Wheel Lug Nut	100 (136)
	INCH Lbs. (N.m)
Bleeder Valve	80 (9)
EBCM-To-Bracket Bolt	22 (2)
Lateral Accelerometer Bolt	15 (1)
Modulator Valve Nut	86 (10)
Wheel Sensor Bolt	86 (10)
Wheel Sensor Bracket-To-Knuckle Bolt	86 (10)
Wiring Harness Bracket	86 (10)

DIAGNOSIS & TESTING

CAUTION: USE ONLY High-Impedance Digital Multimeter (J-34029-A), Pinout Box (J-35592), TECH 1 Diagnostic Computer (94-00101-A) and Bosch ABS ALDL Adapter for testing. The TECH 1 diagnostic computer is referred to as TECH 1. DO NOT use probe-type test light of any kind.

PRE-DIAGNOSTIC INSPECTION

Before diagnosing and testing ABS system, check the following to ensure components are okay:

1) Check STOP/HAZ, BRAKE and AIR BAG (SIR) fuses.

2) Check Rust-colored fusible link located near battery.

3) Check master cylinder fluid level.

4) If pump motor does not operate, check Black ground wire for pump motor.

5) Check EBCM and all ABS connectors for proper connection.

6) If SERVICE ABS or ABS ACTIVE light will not come on, check for defective CLUSTER fuse or open in Pink/Black wire between main fuse block and driver information center.

7) Perform ABS functional check. See ABS FUNCTIONAL CHECK chart under DIAGNOSTIC CHARTS.

RETRIEVING CODES USING ANTI-LOCK LIGHT

Flash Code Method – 1) With ignition off, install jumper wire between pin "H" (White/Tan wire) and pin "A" (Black/White wire) of Assembly Line Data Link (ALDL) connector. The ALDL connector is located below left side of instrument panel, near steering column. *See Fig. 5.*

2) Turn ignition on. Diagnostic display mode will remain active as long as pin "H" is grounded, serial data link communications has not been initiated, and vehicle speed is less than 4 MPH.

3) Approximately 3 seconds after ALDL pin "H" is grounded, EBCM will begin flashing SERVICE ABS light to indicate trouble codes in sequence. Sequence will start with Code 12 to signal the beginning of trouble code display.

4) Each stored trouble code will be displayed 3 times. After all trouble codes are displayed, sequence will be repeated.

NOTE: Codes 41, 45, 55, 61 and 63 can ONLY be read through ALDL using TECH 1 if trouble code is currently present (current code). The EBCM will not allow any trouble codes to be flashed if any of these codes is current. If trouble code existed previously (history code), but is not currently present, trouble code can be read using SERVICE ABS light.

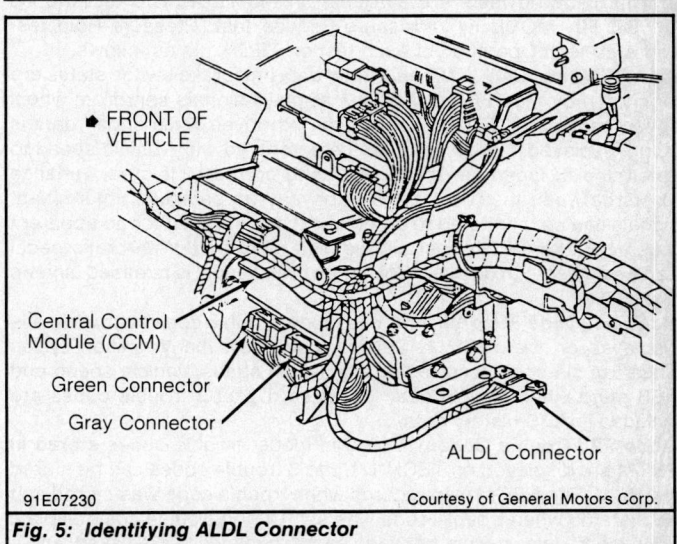

91E07230   Courtesy of General Motors Corp.

Fig. 5: Identifying ALDL Connector

TROUBLE CODES

Code	Definition
12	Diagnostic System Is Operational
21	Right Front Wheel Speed Sensor Fault
22	Right Front Toothed Wheel Frequency Error
25	Left Front Wheel Speed Sensor Fault
26	Left Front Toothed Wheel Frequency Error
31	Right Rear Wheel Speed Sensor Fault
32	Right Rear Toothed Wheel Frequency Error
35	Left Rear Wheel Speed Sensor Fault
36	Left Rear Toothed Wheel Frequency Error
41 [1]	Right Front Solenoid Valve Fault
45 [1]	Left Front Solenoid Valve Fault
55 [1]	Rear Wheel Solenoid Valve Fault
61 [1]	Pump Motor Or Motor Relay Fault
63 [1]	Solenoid Valve Relay Fault
71	EBCM Control Module Fault
72	EBCM Serial Data Link Fault
75	Lateral Accelerometer Fault (Short Or Open)
76	Lateral Accelerometer Fault (Signal)

[1] – Code can ONLY be read through ALDL using TECH 1 if trouble code is currently present (current code). The EBCM will not allow any trouble codes to be flashed if any of these trouble codes is current. If trouble code previously existed (history code), but is not currently present, trouble code can be read using SERVICE ABS light.

RETRIEVING CODES & TESTING ABS USING TECH 1

1) The TECH 1 and Bosch ABS ALDL Adapter are used to test ABS system. The TECH 1 is connected to Assembly Line Data Link (ALDL) connector. The ALDL connector is located below left side of instrument panel, near steering column. *See Fig. 5.*

2) The ABS system is disabled by EBCM when testing with TECH 1. The SERVICE ABS light will come on while performing tests when ignition is turned on. Ensure ignition is off before disconnecting or connecting TECH 1.

CAUTION: Once TECH 1 is disconnected, ensure ignition is off at least 10 seconds before road testing vehicle. This allows system to return to normal operation. When testing is completed, ignition must remain off for at least 10 seconds to return ABS system to normal operation.

3) The following tests are available on the TECH 1: 5 test modes (MODE F0 - MODE F4), Pressure-Reduce test, Pressure-Hold test and Auto test. Operation of each test on TECH 1 is as follows.

Mode F0 (Data List) – Wheel speed data and brake switch status are monitored by the TECH 1. TECH 1 displays signals sent from wheel speed sensors to EBCM. Vehicle can be driven while speed data is being displayed. Speed data can be compared with vehicle speed to determine if speed sensor is operating correctly. If great variance exists between the readings, sensor may be defective. Intermittent signals can be monitored to determine if signal varies for no apparent reason. Brake switch operation is also displayed. With brake pedal depressed, screen displays ON. When brake pedal is released, screen displays OFF.

Mode F1 (Code History) – In this mode, trouble code history data is displayed on the TECH 1. Data includes how many ignition cycles since trouble code occurred, brake switch status, vehicle speed and ABS state when trouble code occurred. Up to 3 trouble codes are included in ABS history data.

Mode F2 (Trouble Codes) – In this mode, trouble codes stored in EBCM are displayed on TECH 1. Up to 3 trouble codes can be stored in EBCM. The EBCM also records when trouble code was stored and ABS status when trouble code was set. During trouble code display, a 3-second delay occurs between each trouble code displayed, and a brief description of trouble code will be displayed. Trouble codes can also be cleared from EBCM memory. The TECH 1 will display either ABS CODES CLEARED or CODE CLEAR FAIL when trouble codes are cleared. The EBCM also stores other information about trouble code such as brakelight switch data, ABS state, vehicle speed and ignition cycles. This information can be displayed using the ENHANCED DIAGNOSTIC DATA function. This will indicate brake switch status to determine if brake switch was on or off when trouble code was set. The ABS state will indicate if anti-lock brake mode was active when trouble code was set. The vehicle speed at the time trouble code was set can be displayed. Ignition cycles will be displayed to indicate how many ignition cycles occurred since trouble code was set.

Mode F3 (ABS Snapshot) – In this mode, the ABS snapshot helps isolate problems of intermittent ABS operation caused by wheel speed sensor signals. Information is captured before and after a trigger condition. The manual and automatic trigger can be selected and operates as follows:

- **Manual Trigger** – When manual trigger is selected, TECH 1 will wait for the ENTER or F9 button to be pressed before taking a snapshot and displaying wheel speed sensor information. When TECH 1 is waiting for the ENTER or F9 button to be pressed, a W will appear in lower right corner. While waiting for the trigger, it continuously stores ABS speed sensor data. Up to 81 samples of ABS data can be stored before the trigger and 81 samples after the trigger. Oldest data will be discarded. When ENTER or F9 button is pressed, wheel speed sensor data will be stored and a T will be displayed. When data storage is full, the data point at the time ENTER button is pressed will be displayed by a ")". To view speed information stored, use UP ARROW and DOWN ARROW buttons. Numbers displayed will indicate a sample number relative to the trigger. If a "+1" is indicated, this is the first sample after ENTER button is pressed. If a "-1" is indicated, this is the first sample preceding the time when ENTER button is pressed. By pressing UP or DOWN buttons, all of stored data can be displayed to determine if problem exists. While displaying data, selecting the F7 button will convert English to Metric, and the ENTER button will convert number in lower right corner to time in seconds.

- **Automatic Trigger** – When automatic trigger is selected, TECH 1 captures data that may vary from normal operating conditions, but

when used alone, will not set a trouble code. For example, when driving over rough terrain, wheel speed sensor may change rapidly or drop out due to loose wire connections. Using automatic trigger, data will be stored when TECH 1 recognizes wheel speed sensor signal deviated from the normal range. While TECH 1 is waiting for trigger, the ENTER or F9 button may also be used to force a trigger display of stored information as explained under MANUAL TRIGGER. When displaying information, the cause of the trigger can be displayed using F3 button.

Mode F4 (ABS Tests) – In this mode, the ABS test mode performs function tests on ABS system used to verify proper system operation. Error conditions can be further identified by testing and observing test results. When in this mode, the following tests can be performed:

- **Solenoid Valve Pressure Reduction** – This test indicates if specific solenoid valves in modulator valve release pressure to specified wheel circuits.
- **Solenoid Valve Pressure Hold** – This test indicates if specific solenoid valves in modulator valve hold pressure at specified wheel circuits.
- **AUTO Test** – This test cycles each solenoid valve in modulator valve and operates pump motor briefly. The EBCM will store a trouble code if test conditions fail.

Pressure-Reduce Test – This test activates selected wheel circuit valves in the modulator valve by placing valve in pressure-reduce position. Valve action can be verified by checking appropriate wheel for braking action. The TECH 1 will indicate whether valve operated correctly. To perform pressure reduce test, raise and support vehicle. Depress brake pedal. Use TECH 1 to command the PRESSURE REDUCE mode. Try to spin the wheel being tested. Wheel should spin if solenoid valve reduces pressure.

Pressure-Hold Test – This test activates selected wheel circuit valves in the modulator valve by placing valve in pressure-hold position. Valve action can be verified by checking appropriate wheel for braking action. The TECH 1 will indicate whether valve operated correctly. To perform pressure hold test, raise and support vehicle. Spin wheel freely. Use TECH 1 to command the PRESSURE HOLD mode. Have assistant apply brakes. Try to spin the wheel being tested. Wheel should spin, even with brakes applied, due to the hold command.

Auto Test – The auto test is automatically performed once by EBCM during each ignition cycle, when vehicle reaches approximately 4 MPH. The TECH 1 will perform this test automatically during ABS TESTS mode. The auto test cycles each solenoid valve and pump motor to check component operation. If failure exists, EBCM will set a trouble code and activate SERVICE ABS light.

CLEARING CODES

NOTE: Trouble codes can be cleared using DIAGNOSTIC REQUEST LINE METHOD, IGNITION CYCLE DEFAULT METHOD or TECH 1 METHOD. Once repairs have been made and codes cleared, verify vehicle operation.

Diagnostic Request Line Method – **1)** With ignition off, install jumper wire between pin "H" (White/Tan wire) and pin "A" (Black/White wire) of Assembly Line Data Link (ALDL) connector.

2) The ALDL connector is located below left side of instrument panel, near steering column. *See Fig. 5.* Turn ignition on. SERVICE ABS light should begin flashing.

3) Disconnect jumper wire for approximately one second, then reconnect jumper wire for at least one second.

4) Repeat step **3)** 4 times within 10 seconds, leaving jumper wire connected after the fourth time. Ensure SERVICE ABS light indicates Code 12 only. If all trouble codes have not been cleared, repeat procedure.

CAUTION: Once all trouble codes are cleared, wait at least 15 seconds before turning ignition off. Once repairs have been made and codes cleared, verify vehicle operation.

Ignition Cycle Default Method – If ignition is cycled 100 times without a trouble code reappearing, trouble codes will be erased from EBCM memory. The ignition cycle counter in EBCM will reset to zero.

TECH 1 Method – 1) Before clearing trouble codes, check and note history code data, as this information will also be cleared.

2) Select appropriate menu. Select CLEAR CODES. Ensure all trouble codes are cleared by using TECH 1 to read trouble codes. If any trouble codes still exists, then either trouble codes were not cleared or fault still exists. Turn ignition off and disconnect TECH 1.

CAUTION: Once TECH 1 is disconnected, ensure ignition is off for at least 10 seconds before road testing vehicle. This allows system to return to normal operation.

INTERMITTENTS

If trouble code previously existed (history code), but is not currently present, fault may be intermittent. Trouble code history can only be obtained using TECH 1. If checking for intermittent fault, perform the following:

- Retrieve and record all trouble codes and trouble code history. Record any descriptive information during system failure.
- Using TECH 1 in MODE F3 (ABS Snapshot), test drive vehicle. Attempt to repeat failure condition. Obtain information when system failure exists.
- After duplicating condition, stop vehicle and access ABS trouble codes.
- If no trouble code is stored, it may be necessary to use CHART A – SERVICE ABS INDICATOR ON WITH NO CODES SET.

Most intermittent problems are caused by faulty electrical connectors or wiring. When intermittent failure exists, check wiring circuits for the following:

- Improper or poor connector or terminal mating
- Improperly formed or damaged terminals
- Poor terminal-to-wire connection

WIRING DIAGRAM

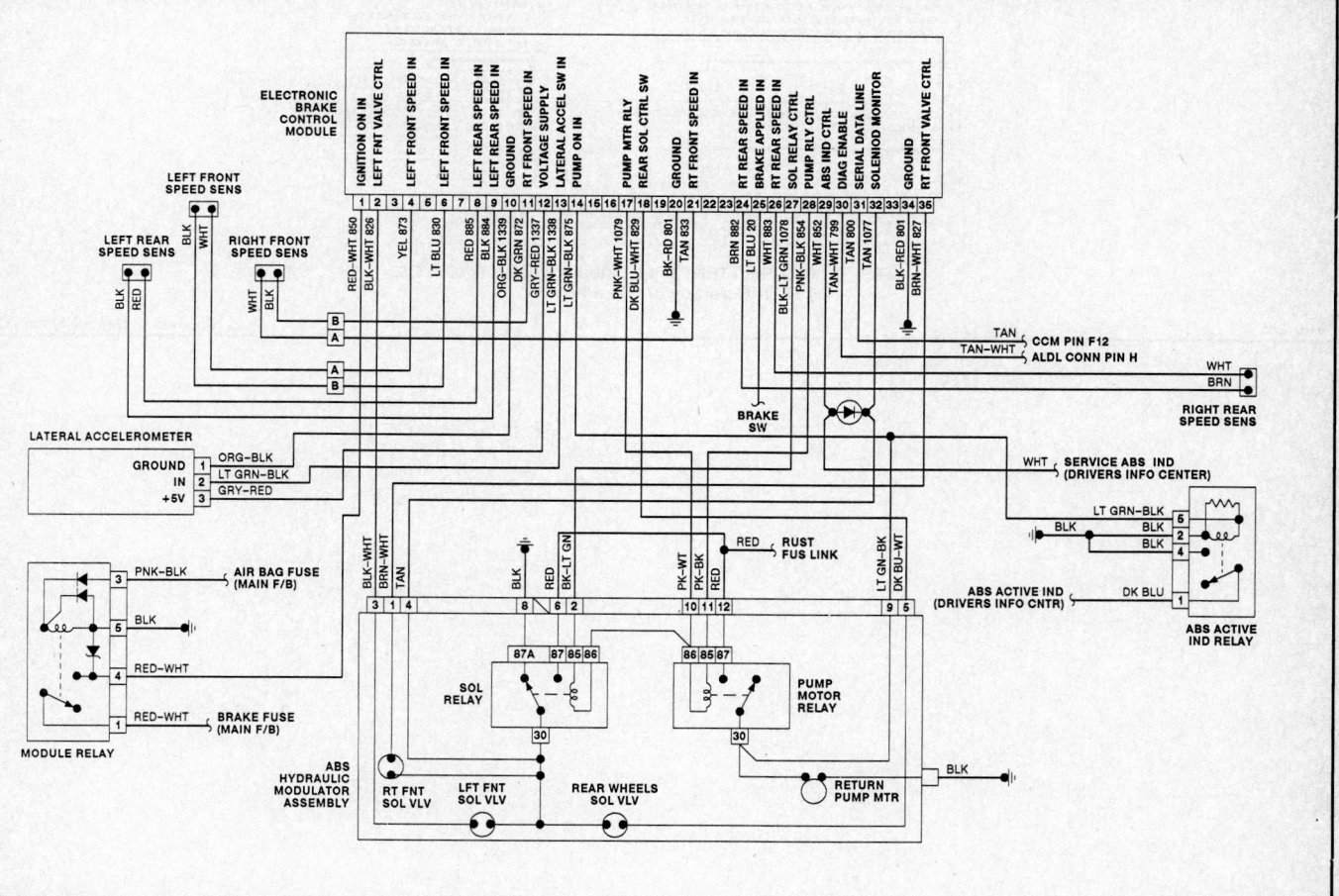

91G07231

Fig. 6: Anti-Lock Brake System Wiring Diagram (Corvette)

DIAGNOSTIC CHARTS

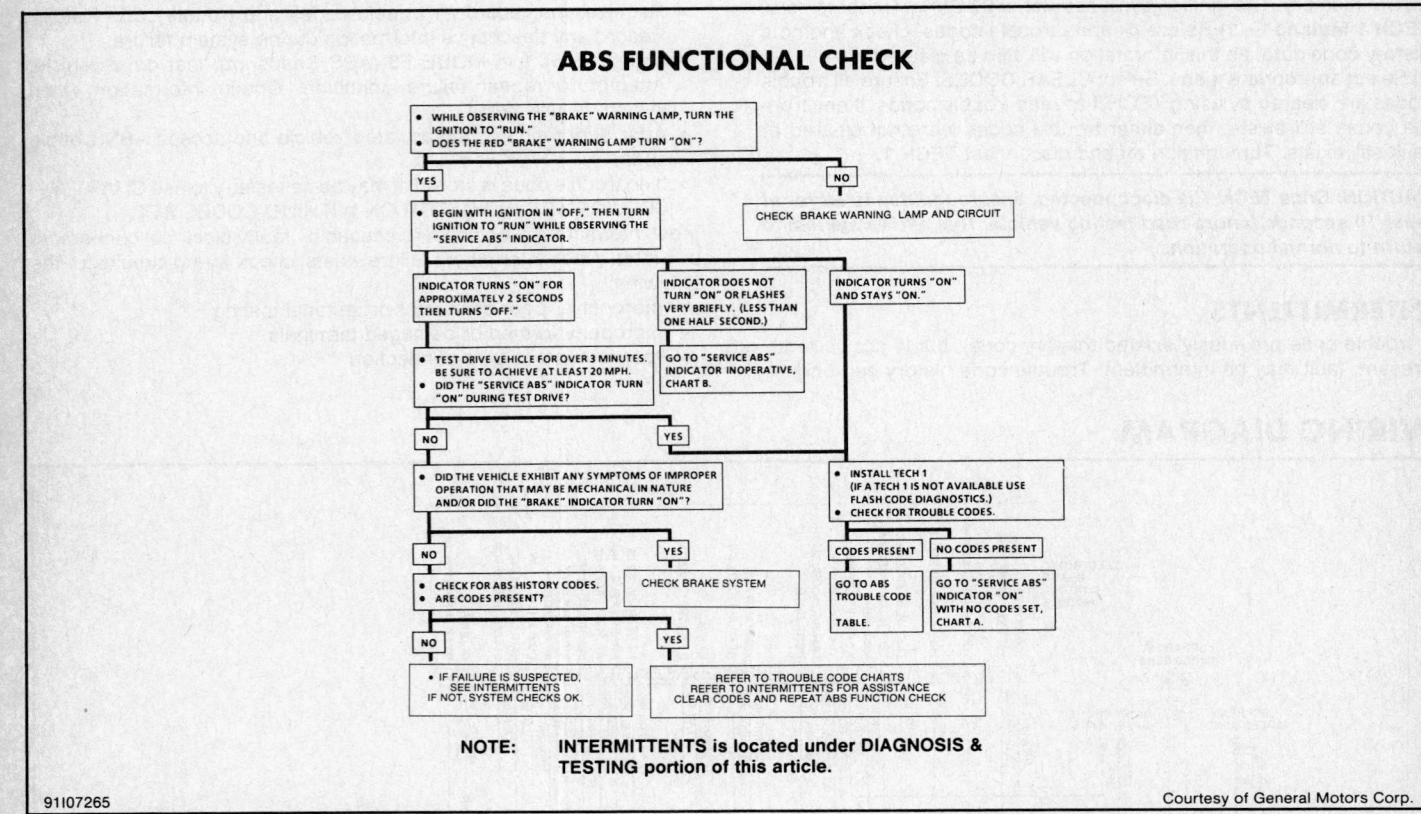

ABS FUNCTIONAL CHECK

- WHILE OBSERVING THE "BRAKE" WARNING LAMP, TURN THE IGNITION TO "RUN."
- DOES THE RED "BRAKE" WARNING LAMP TURN "ON"?

YES →
- BEGIN WITH IGNITION IN "OFF," THEN TURN IGNITION TO "RUN" WHILE OBSERVING THE "SERVICE ABS" INDICATOR.

NO → CHECK BRAKE WARNING LAMP AND CIRCUIT

INDICATOR TURNS "ON" FOR APPROXIMATELY 2 SECONDS THEN TURNS "OFF."

INDICATOR DOES NOT TURN "ON" OR FLASHES VERY BRIEFLY. (LESS THAN ONE HALF SECOND.)

INDICATOR TURNS "ON" AND STAYS "ON."

- TEST DRIVE VEHICLE FOR OVER 3 MINUTES. BE SURE TO ACHIEVE AT LEAST 20 MPH.
- DID THE "SERVICE ABS" INDICATOR TURN "ON" DURING TEST DRIVE?

GO TO "SERVICE ABS" INDICATOR INOPERATIVE, CHART B.

NO / **YES**

- DID THE VEHICLE EXHIBIT ANY SYMPTOMS OF IMPROPER OPERATION THAT MAY BE MECHANICAL IN NATURE AND/OR DID THE "BRAKE" INDICATOR TURN "ON"?

- INSTALL TECH 1 (IF A TECH 1 IS NOT AVAILABLE USE FLASH CODE DIAGNOSTICS.)
- CHECK FOR TROUBLE CODES.

NO / **YES**

- CHECK FOR ABS HISTORY CODES.
- ARE CODES PRESENT?

CHECK BRAKE SYSTEM

CODES PRESENT | NO CODES PRESENT

GO TO ABS TROUBLE CODE TABLE.

GO TO "SERVICE ABS" INDICATOR "ON" WITH NO CODES SET, CHART A.

NO / **YES**

- IF FAILURE IS SUSPECTED, SEE INTERMITTENTS IF NOT, SYSTEM CHECKS OK.

REFER TO TROUBLE CODE CHARTS
REFER TO INTERMITTENTS FOR ASSISTANCE
CLEAR CODES AND REPEAT ABS FUNCTION CHECK

NOTE: INTERMITTENTS is located under DIAGNOSIS & TESTING portion of this article.

91I07265

CHART A
SERVICE ABS INDICATOR ON
WITH NO CODES SET

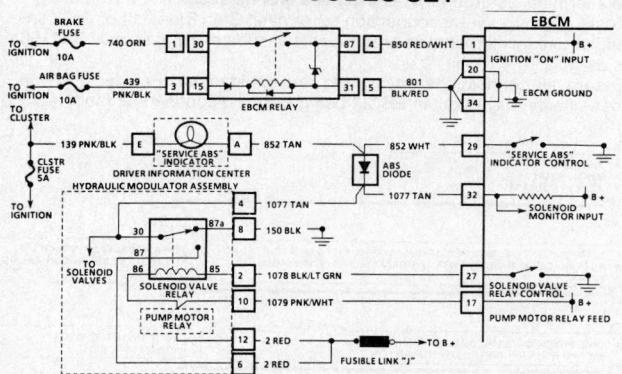

DIAGNOSTIC AIDS

Ensure all connections and wiring are okay. Failure to check may result in EBCM being falsely diagnosed as faulty.

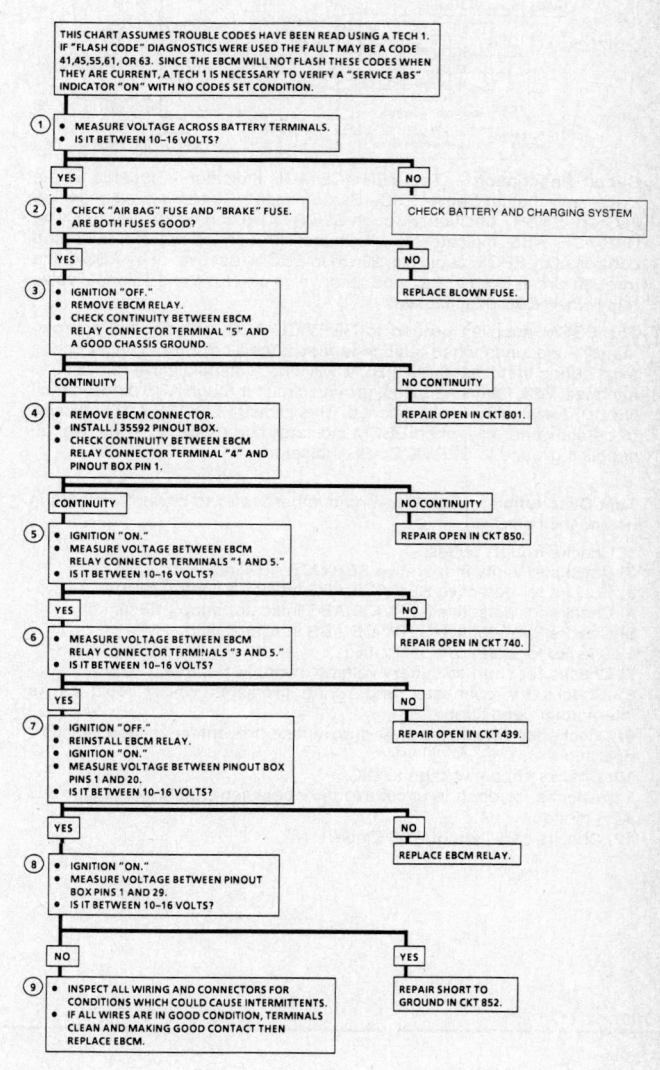

Circuit Description – The SERVICE ABS indicator is located in the Driver Information Center (DIC). Battery voltage is applied with ignition in ON or START position through CLSTR fuse and circuit No. 139. The SERVICE ABS indicator is grounded through circuit No. 852 and controlled by EBCM at pin No. 29 when EBCM is active, or by ABS diode through circuit No. 1077 to modulator valve pin No. 4 and solenoid valve relay when EBCM is inactive.

The EBCM supplies ground to SERVICE ABS indicator for approximately 2 seconds when ignition is first turned on. If no trouble codes exist during first 2 seconds, EBCM will allow solenoid valve relay coil to energize. With relay energized, ground circuit through ABS diode, circuit No. 1077 and relay will be opened. This allows SERVICE ABS indicator to be activated only when EBCM indicator control circuit at pin No. 29 supplies ground to SERVICE ABS indicator.

When ignition is in ON or START position, EBCM relay coil is energized through AIR BAG (SIR) fuse and circuit No. 439. When energized, EBCM relay contacts close, supplying power from BRAKE fuse through circuits No. 740 and 850 to EBCM pin No. 1. If high voltage (approximately 16 volts) exists, EBCM relay will short circuit No. 740 to ground through circuit No. 801, causing BRAKE fuse to blow to prevent EBCM damage.

Test Description – The following numbers refer to circled numbers in diagnostic chart.

1) Checks for proper system voltage.
2) Checks for defective fuses which could cause SERVICE ABS indicator to remain on.
3) Checks for open circuit No. 801.
4) Checks for open circuit No. 850.
5) Checks for supply voltage to EBCM relay contacts.
6) Checks for supply voltage to EBCM relay coil.
7) Checks EBCM relay operation.
8) Checks for short to ground in circuit No. 852.
9) Checks for connector or wiring problem which could cause intermittent condition.

91A07266 91C07267 91E07268

CHART B
SERVICE ABS INDICATOR INOPERATIVE

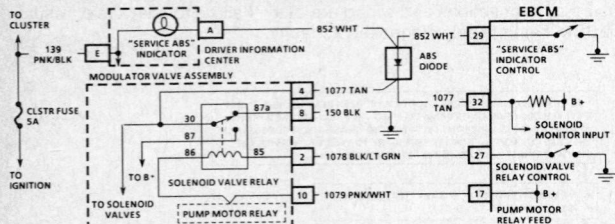

Circuit Description – The SERVICE ABS indicator is located in the Driver Information Center (DIC). Battery voltage is applied, with ignition in ON or START position, through CLSTR fuse and circuit No. 139. The SERVICE ABS indicator is grounded through circuit No. 852 and controlled by EBCM at pin No. 29 when EBCM is active, or by ABS diode through circuit No. 1077 to modulator valve pin No. 4 and solenoid valve relay when EBCM is inactive.

The EBCM supplies ground to SERVICE ABS indicator for approximately 2 seconds when ignition is first turned on. If no trouble codes exist during first 2 seconds, EBCM will allow solenoid valve relay coil to energize. With relay energized, ground circuit through ABS diode, circuit No. 1077 and relay will be opened. This allows SERVICE ABS indicator to be activated only when EBCM indicator control circuit at pin No. 29 supplies ground to SERVICE ABS indicator.

Test Description – The following numbers refer to circled numbers in diagnostic chart.

1) Checks trouble codes.
2) Checks to verify inoperative SERVICE ABS indicator.
3) Checks for defective SERVICE ABS indicator control circuit.
4) Checks for defective SERVICE ABS indicator supply circuit.
5) Checks for defective SERVICE ABS indicator bulb.
6) Checks for open circuit No. 852.
7) Checks for short to battery voltage in circuit No. 852.
8) Checks for connector and wiring problems which could cause intermittent condition.
9) Checks for defective power supply fuse preventing voltage indicator operation.
10) Checks supply voltage to DIC.
11) Checks for open in circuit No. 852 between EBCM connector and ABS diode.
12) Checks condition of ABS diode.

DIAGNOSTIC AIDS

Tests which require a connection at terminal No. 20 of Pinout box use this terminal as ground. This assumes ground circuit No. 801 is okay. Tests which require a connection to terminal G on Blue half of DIC connector use this terminal as ground. This assumes ground circuit No. 150 is okay.

Ensure all connections and wiring are satisfactory. Failure to check these items may result in EBCM being falsely diagnosed as faulty.

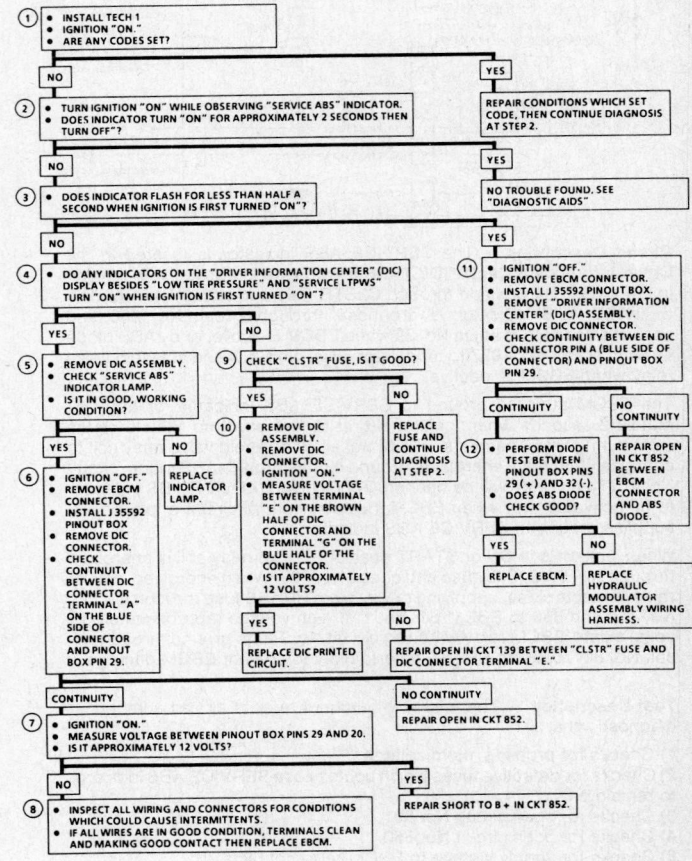

91I07232 91A07233

Courtesy of General Motors Corp.

CHART C
ABS ACTIVE INDICATOR INOPERATIVE

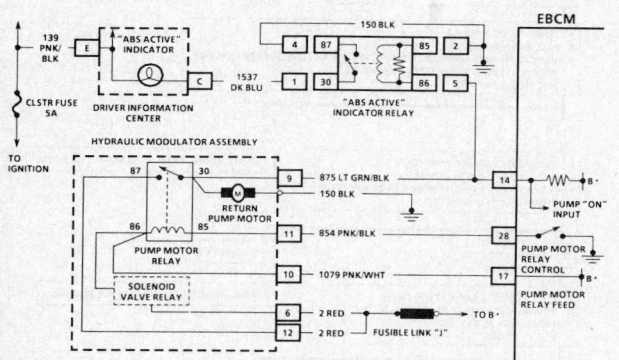

Circuit Description – The ABS ACTIVE indicator is located in the Driver Information Center (DIC). Battery voltage is applied, with ignition in ON or START position, through CLSTR fuse and circuit No. 139. When EBCM is active and receiving a pump-on input signal from pump motor relay contacts through circuit No. 2 and fusible link J, the ABS ACTIVE indicator is grounded through circuit No. 1537, through ABS active indicator relay contacts, to circuit No. 150. The ABS ACTIVE indicator will activate only when return pump motor is receiving power.

Test Description – The following numbers refer to circled numbers in diagnostic chart.

1) Checks trouble codes.
2) Checks to verify inoperative ABS ACTIVE indicator.
3) Checks for defective ABS ACTIVE power supply circuit.
4) Checks for defective ABS ACTIVE indicator bulb.
5) Checks condition of ABS active indicator relay coil.
6) Checks for stuck open contacts on active indicator relay.
7) Checks for open in circuit No. 1537.
8) Checks power supply fuse to prevent voltage indicator operation.
9) Checks supply voltage to DIC.
10) Determines if problem in step 3) is due to defective indicator light or faulty internal circuit of DIC.
11) Checks for short to battery voltage in circuit No. 1537.
12) Checks for open circuit No. 150 at ABS active relay contacts.
13) Checks for open circuit No. 150 at ABS active relay coil.
14) Checks for open circuit No. 875.
15) Checks for connector or wiring problem which could cause intermittent condition.

DIAGNOSTIC AIDS

Tests requiring a connection at Pinout box terminal No. 20 are using this terminal as ground. This assumes ground circuit No. 801 is okay.

Tests requiring a connection to terminal G on Blue half of DIC connector are using this terminal as ground. This assumes ground circuit No. 150 is okay.

Ensure all connections and wiring are satisfactory. Failure to check these items may result in EBCM being misdiagnosed as faulty.

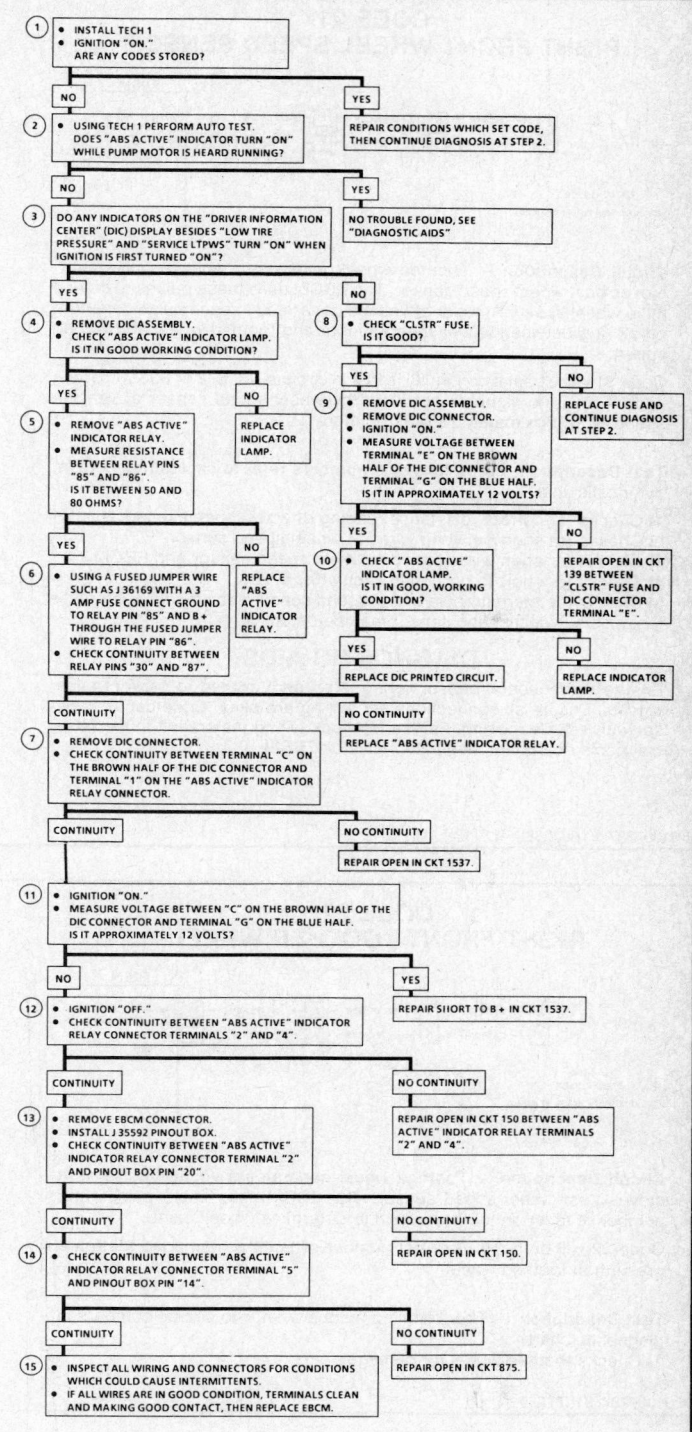

CODE 21
RIGHT FRONT WHEEL SPEED SENSOR

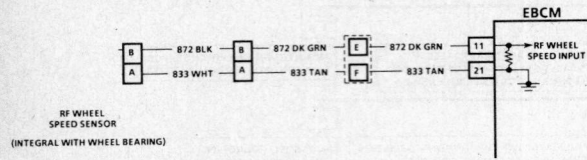

Circuit Description – Toothed wheel generates a voltage pulse as it moves past wheel speed sensor. The EBCM uses these pulses to determine wheel speed. Amount of voltage generated in each pulse depends on air gap between wheel speed sensor and toothed wheel and wheel speed.

Code 21 will be set if continuity is lost in circuits No. 872 or 833 with ignition on, or if no signal is produced by wheel speed sensor at vehicle speed of approximately 19 MPH or more.

Test Description – The following numbers refer to circled numbers in diagnostic chart.

1) Checks for correct resistance reading of wheel speed sensor.
2) Checks for short between wires of wheel speed sensor.
3) Checks for open wires between wheel speed sensor and EBCM.
4) Checks for short to ground in circuit No. 872.
5) Checks for intermittent in wheel speed sensor circuitry. If no intermittent exists, wheel speed sensor may be defective.

DIAGNOSTIC AIDS

Ensure wheel speed sensor wiring is properly routed to prevent false signals. Ensure all connections and wiring are okay. Code can only be set with vehicle moving. Failure to check wiring may result in the false diagnosis of a faulty modulator valve or EBCM.

91J07237 91B07238

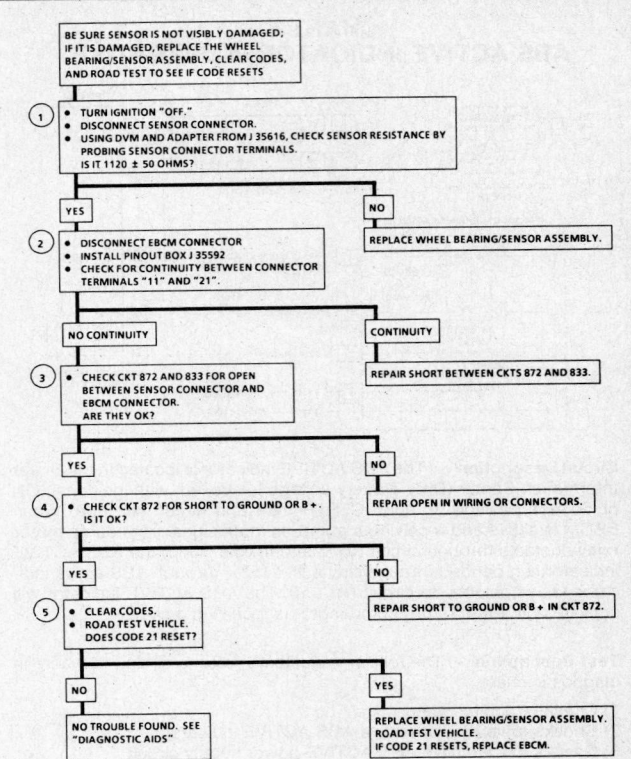

CODE 22
RIGHT FRONT TOOTHED WHEEL

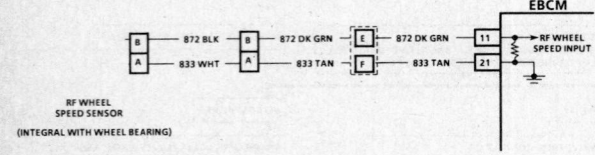

Circuit Description – Toothed wheel generates a voltage pulse as it moves past wheel speed sensor. The EBCM uses these pulses and number of teeth on toothed wheel to determine wheel speed.

Code 22 will be set if incorrect number of teeth or damaged teeth are present on toothed wheel.

Test Description – The following numbers refer to circled numbers in diagnostic chart.
1) Checks toothed wheel for damage.

91J07237 91D07239

DIAGNOSTIC AIDS

A worn hub/bearing assembly may cause fault in extreme cases, allowing wheel speed sensor-to-toothed ring gap to change excessively.

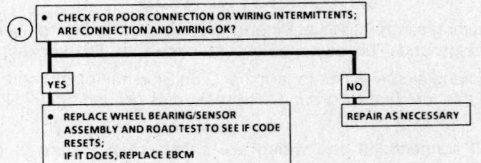

CODE 25
LEFT FRONT WHEEL SPEED SENSOR

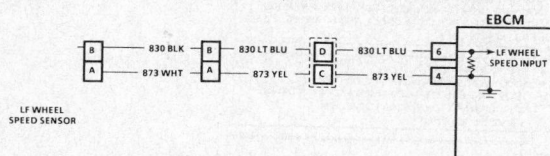

Circuit Description – Toothed wheel generates a voltage pulse as it moves past wheel speed sensor. The EBCM uses these pulses to determine wheel speed. Amount of voltage generated in each pulse depends on air gap between wheel speed sensor and toothed wheel and wheel speed.

Code 25 will be set if continuity is lost in circuits No. 830 or 873 with ignition on, or if no signal is produced by wheel speed sensor at vehicle speed of approximately 19 MPH or greater.

Test Description – The following numbers refer to circled numbers in diagnostic chart.
1) Checks for correct wheel speed sensor resistance.
2) Checks for short between wheel speed sensor wires.
3) Checks for open wires between wheel speed sensor and EBCM.
4) Checks for short to ground or battery voltage in circuit No. 830.
5) Checks for intermittent in wheel speed sensor circuitry. If no intermittent is found, wheel speed sensor may be faulty.

DIAGNOSTIC AIDS

Ensure wheel speed sensor wiring is properly routed to prevent false signals.

Ensure all connections and wiring are satisfactory. Code can only be set with vehicle moving. Failure to check wiring may result in false diagnosis of a faulty modulator valve or EBCM.

91F07240 91H07241

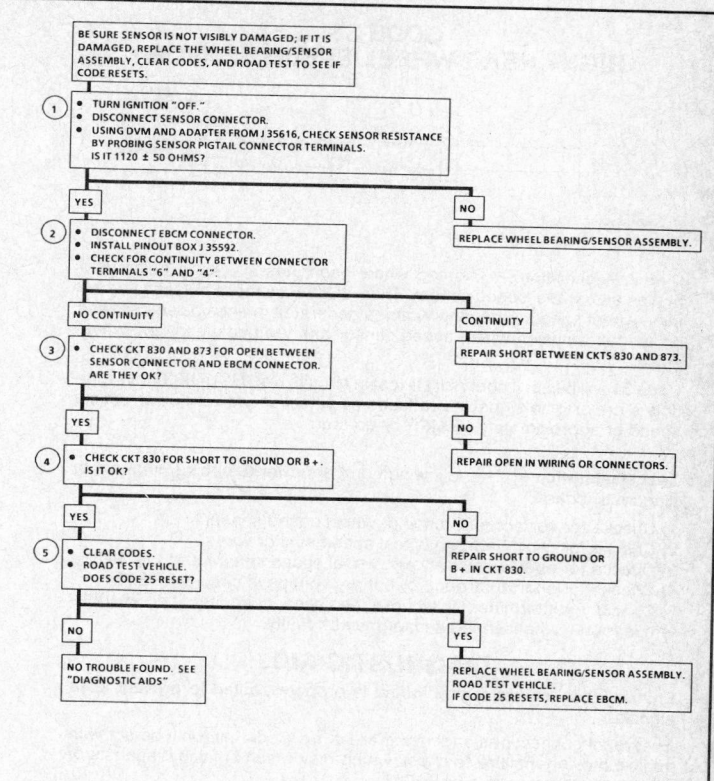

Courtesy of General Motors Corp.

CODE 26
LEFT FRONT TOOTHED WHEEL

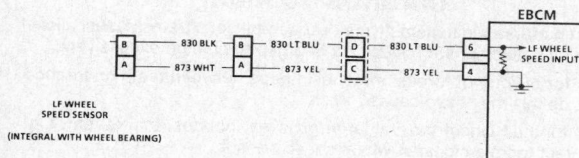

Circuit Description – Toothed wheel generates a voltage pulse as it moves past wheel speed sensor. The EBCM uses these pulses and number of teeth on toothed wheel to determine wheel speed.

Code 26 will be set if incorrect number of teeth or damaged teeth are present on toothed wheel.

Test Description – The following numbers refer to circled numbers in diagnostic chart.
1) Checks toothed wheel for damage.

DIAGNOSTIC AIDS

A worn hub/bearing assembly may cause fault in extreme cases, allowing wheel speed sensor-to-toothed ring gap to change excessively.

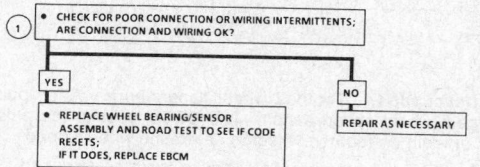

91F07240 91D07239

Courtesy of General Motors Corp.

CODE 31
RIGHT REAR WHEEL SPEED SENSOR

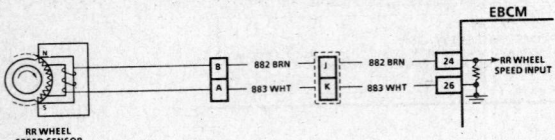

Circuit Description – Toothed wheel generates a voltage pulse as it moves past wheel speed sensor. The EBCM uses these pulses to determine wheel speed. Amount of voltage generated in each pulse depends on air gap between wheel speed sensor and toothed wheel and wheel speed.

Code 31 will be set if continuity is lost in circuits No. 882 or 883 while ignition is on, or if no signal is produced by wheel speed sensor at vehicle speed of approximately 19 MPH or greater.

Test Description – The following numbers refer to circled numbers in diagnostic chart.

1) Checks for correct resistance of wheel speed sensor.
2) Checks for short between wheel speed sensor wires.
3) Checks for open wires between wheel speed sensor and EBCM.
4) Checks for short to ground or battery voltage in circuit No. 882.
5) Checks for intermittent in wheel speed sensor circuitry. If no intermittent is found, wheel speed sensor may be faulty.

DIAGNOSTIC AIDS

Ensure wheel speed sensor wiring is properly routed to prevent false signals.

Ensure all connections and wiring are okay. Code can only be set with vehicle moving. Failure to check wiring may result in false diagnosis of a faulty modulator valve or EBCM.

91B07243 91D07244

BE SURE SENSOR IS NOT VISIBLY DAMAGED AND THAT IT IS PROPERLY MOUNTED; IF IT IS DAMAGED OR NOT CORRECTLY MOUNTED AND RETAINED, REPLACE THE SENSOR AND/OR PROPERLY ATTACH IT, CLEAR CODES, AND ROAD TEST TO SEE IF CODE RESETS.

(1)
- TURN IGNITION "OFF."
- DISCONNECT SENSOR PIGTAIL CONNECTOR.
- USING DVM, CHECK SENSOR RESISTANCE BY PROBING SENSOR PIGTAIL CONNECTOR TERMINALS. IS IT 1000 ± 100 OHMS?

YES | NO → REPLACE SENSOR.

(2)
- DISCONNECT EBCM CONNECTOR.
- INSTALL PINOUT BOX J 35592.
- CHECK FOR CONTINUITY BETWEEN CONNECTOR TERMINALS "24" AND "26".

NO CONTINUITY | CONTINUITY → REPAIR SHORT BETWEEN CKTS 882 AND 883.

(3)
- CHECK CKT 882 AND 883 FOR OPEN BETWEEN SENSOR CONNECTOR AND EBCM CONNECTOR. ARE THEY OK?

YES | NO → REPAIR OPEN IN WIRING OR CONNECTORS.

(4)
- CHECK CKT 882 FOR SHORT TO GROUND OR B +. IS IT OK?

YES | NO → REPAIR SHORT TO GROUND OR B + IN CKT 882.

(5)
- CLEAR CODES.
- ROAD TEST VEHICLE. DOES CODE 31 RESET?

NO → NO TROUBLE FOUND. SEE "DIAGNOSTIC AIDS"

YES → REPLACE SENSOR. ROAD TEST VEHICLE. IF CODE 31 RESETS, REPLACE EBCM.

Courtesy of General Motors Corp.

CODE 32
RIGHT REAR TOOTHED WHEEL

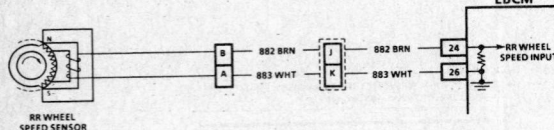

Circuit Description – Toothed wheel generates a voltage pulse as it moves past wheel speed sensor. The EBCM uses these pulses and number of teeth on toothed wheel to determine wheel speed.

Code 32 will be set if incorrect number of teeth or damaged teeth are present on toothed wheel. It may also set if wheel speed sensor-to-toothed wheel air gap is incorrect.

Test Description – The following numbers refer to circled numbers in diagnostic chart.
1) Checks toothed wheel for damage.
2) Checks for proper mounting, which includes "O" ring quality and position, and mounting torque.

DIAGNOSTIC AIDS

A worn hub/bearing assembly may cause fault in extreme cases, allowing wheel speed sensor-to-toothed ring gap to change excessively.

Check for buildup of foreign material in gaps between teeth on toothed wheel, as this may have caused fault.

Check toothed wheel for any large grooves, gouges, marks, etc. that may affect tooth's signal at wheel speed sensor.

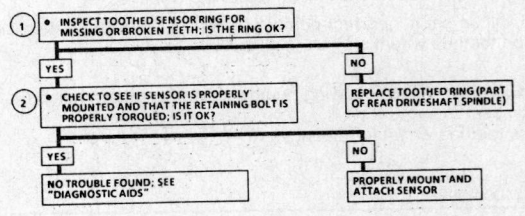

(1)
- INSPECT TOOTHED SENSOR RING FOR MISSING OR BROKEN TEETH; IS THE RING OK?

YES | NO → REPLACE TOOTHED RING (PART OF REAR DRIVESHAFT SPINDLE)

(2)
- CHECK TO SEE IF SENSOR IS PROPERLY MOUNTED AND THAT THE RETAINING BOLT IS PROPERLY TORQUED; IS IT OK?

YES → NO TROUBLE FOUND; SEE "DIAGNOSTIC AIDS"

NO → PROPERLY MOUNT AND ATTACH SENSOR

Courtesy of General Motors Corp.

91B07243 91G07245

CODE 35
LEFT REAR WHEEL SPEED SENSOR

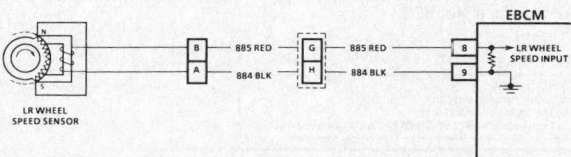

Circuit Description – Toothed wheel generates a voltage pulse as it moves past wheel speed sensor. The EBCM uses these pulses to determine wheel speed. Amount of voltage generated in each pulse depends on air gap between wheel speed sensor and toothed wheel and wheel speed.

Code 35 will be set if continuity is lost in circuits No. 885 or 884 with ignition on, or if no signal is produced by wheel speed sensor at vehicle speed of approximately 19 MPH or greater.

Test Description – The following numbers refer to circled numbers in diagnostic chart.

1) Checks for correct resistance reading of wheel speed sensor.
2) Checks for short between wheel speed sensor wires.
3) Checks for open wires between wheel speed sensor and EBCM.
4) Checks for short to ground or battery voltage in circuit No. 885.
5) Checks for intermittent in wheel speed sensor circuitry. If no intermittent is found, wheel speed sensor may be faulty.

DIAGNOSTIC AIDS

Ensure wheel speed sensor wiring is properly routed to prevent false signals.

Ensure all connections and wiring are okay. Code can only be set with vehicle moving. Failure to check wiring may result in false diagnosis of a faulty modulator valve or EBCM.

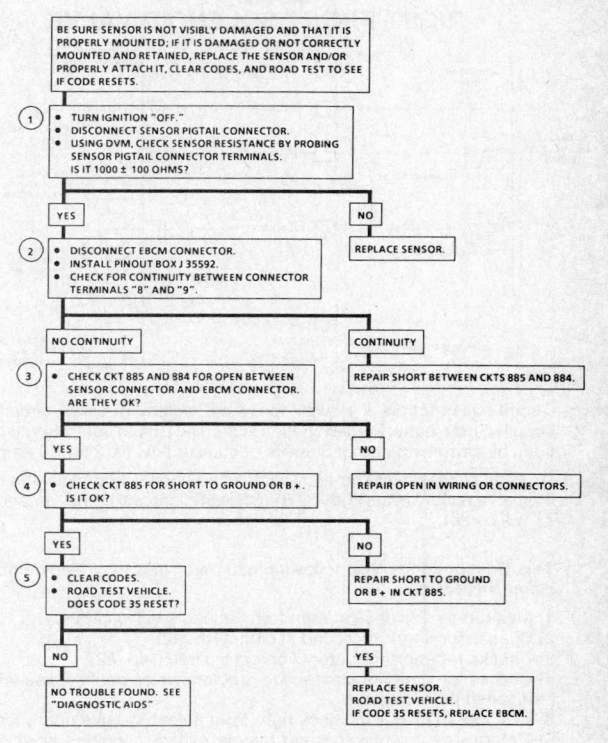

91I07246 91A07247

CODE 36
LEFT REAR TOOTHED WHEEL

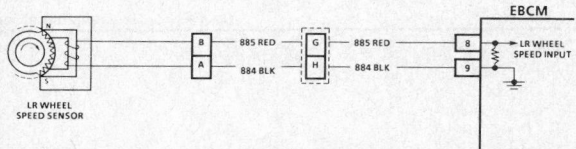

Circuit Description – Toothed wheel generates a voltage pulse as it moves past wheel speed sensor. The EBCM uses these pulses and number of teeth on toothed wheel to determine wheel speed.

Code 36 will be set if incorrect number of teeth or damaged teeth are present on toothed wheel. It may also set if wheel speed sensor-to-toothed wheel air gap is incorrect.

Test Description – The following numbers refer to circled numbers in diagnostic chart.

1) Checks toothed wheel for damage.
2) Checks for proper mounting, which includes "O" ring quality and position, and mounting torque.

DIAGNOSTIC AIDS

A worn hub/bearing assembly may cause fault in extreme cases, allowing wheel speed sensor-to-toothed ring gap to change excessively.

Check for buildup of foreign material in gaps between teeth on toothed wheel, as this may have caused error.

Check toothed wheel for any large grooves, gouges, marks, etc. that may influence tooth's signal at wheel speed sensor.

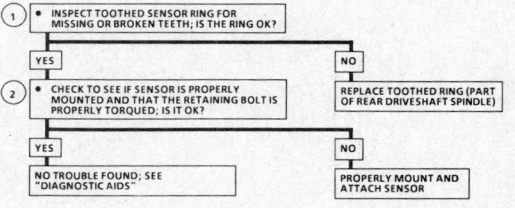

91I07246 91G07245

CODE 41
RIGHT FRONT SOLENOID VALVE

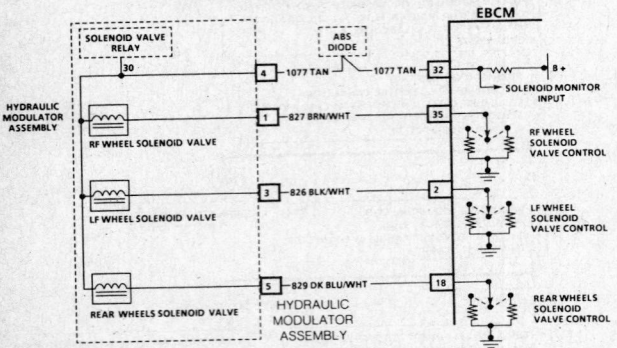

Circuit Description – Power to wheel solenoid valve circuits are supplied from battery when ignition is on. The EBCM controls valve functions by permitting one of 3 levels of current flow (0, 2.5 or 5 amps).

If EBCM senses a discrepancy such as an open or ground in the circuit, the valve relay will turn off, SERVICE ABS light will come on, and code 41 will be set.

Test Description – The following numbers refer to circled numbers in diagnostic chart.

1) Measures resistance in right front solenoid valve circuitry.
2) Checks for short to ground in circuit No. 827.
3) Checks for short to battery voltage in circuit No. 827.
4) Checks for wiring or connection problem which could cause intermittent condition.
5) Test uses TECH 1 to check right front solenoid valve operation.
6) Determines if problem is set by intermittent condition or an EBCM fault.
7) Determines if problem found in step **1)** is due to hydraulic modulator or an open in circuit No. 827.

DIAGNOSTIC AIDS

Tests requiring a connection at Pinout box terminal No. 20 are using this terminal as ground. This assumes ground circuit No. 801 is okay.

Ensure all connections and wiring are okay. Code can only be set with vehicle moving. Failure to check wiring may result in modulator valve or EBCM being falsely diagnosed as faulty.

91E07249 91G07250

If codes 41 and 45 are both set, fault is likely to be a short to battery voltage on circuit No. 827.

If codes 41 and 55 are both set, fault is likely to be a short to battery voltage on circuit No. 829.

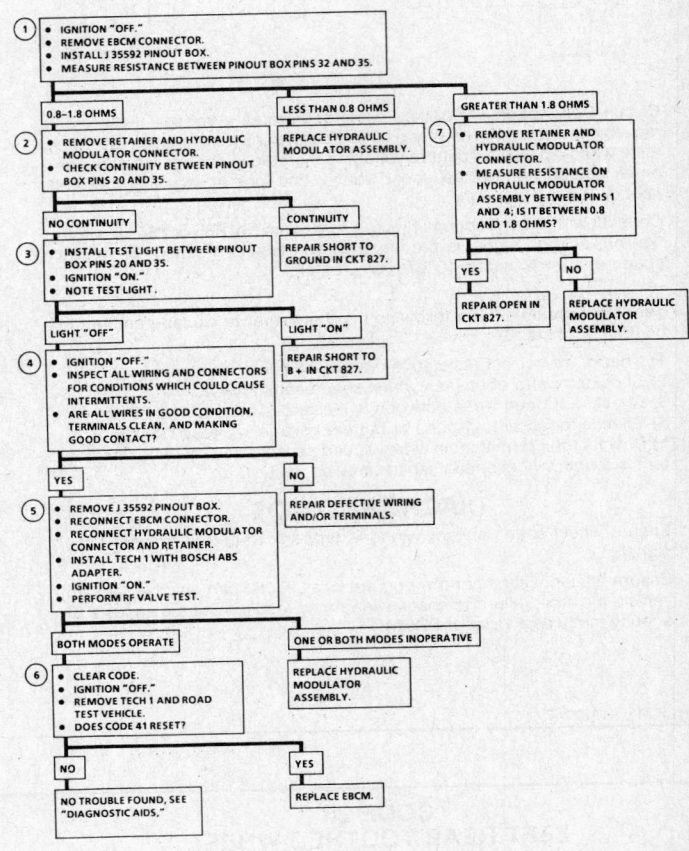

CODE 45
LEFT FRONT SOLENOID VALVE

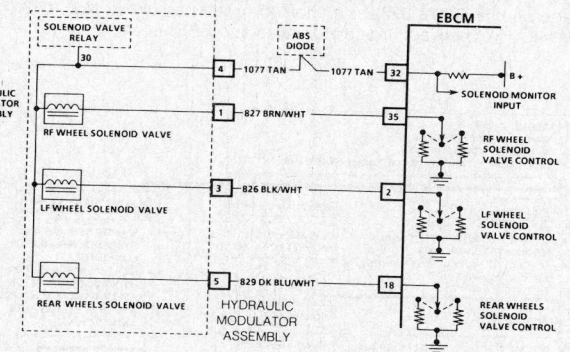

Circuit Description – Power to wheel solenoid valve circuits are supplied from battery when ignition is on. The EBCM controls valve functions by permitting one of 3 levels of current flow (0, 2.5 or 5 amps).

If EBCM senses a discrepancy such as an open or ground in the circuit, the valve relay will turn off, SERVICE ABS light will come on, and code 45 will be set.

Test Description – The following numbers refer to circled numbers in diagnostic chart.
1) Measures resistance in left front solenoid valve circuitry.
2) Checks for short to ground in circuit No. 826.
3) Checks for short to battery voltage in circuit No. 826.
4) Checks for wiring or connection problem which could cause intermittent condition.
5) Test uses TECH 1 to check left front solenoid valve operation.
6) Determines if problem is set by intermittent condition or an EBCM fault.
7) Determines if problem found in step 1) is due to hydraulic modulator or an open in circuit No. 826.

DIAGNOSTIC AIDS

Tests requiring a connection at Pinout box terminal No. 20 are using this terminal as ground. This assumes ground circuit No. 801 is okay.

Ensure all connections and wiring are okay. Code can only be set with vehicle moving. Failure to check wiring may result in modulator valve or EBCM being misdiagnosed as faulty.

If codes 41 and 45 are both set, fault is likely to be a short to battery voltage on circuit No. 826.

If codes 41 and 55 are both set, fault is likely to be a short to battery voltage on circuit No. 826, or a short to ground on circuit No. 1079 (Pink/White wire) between modulator valve and EBCM.

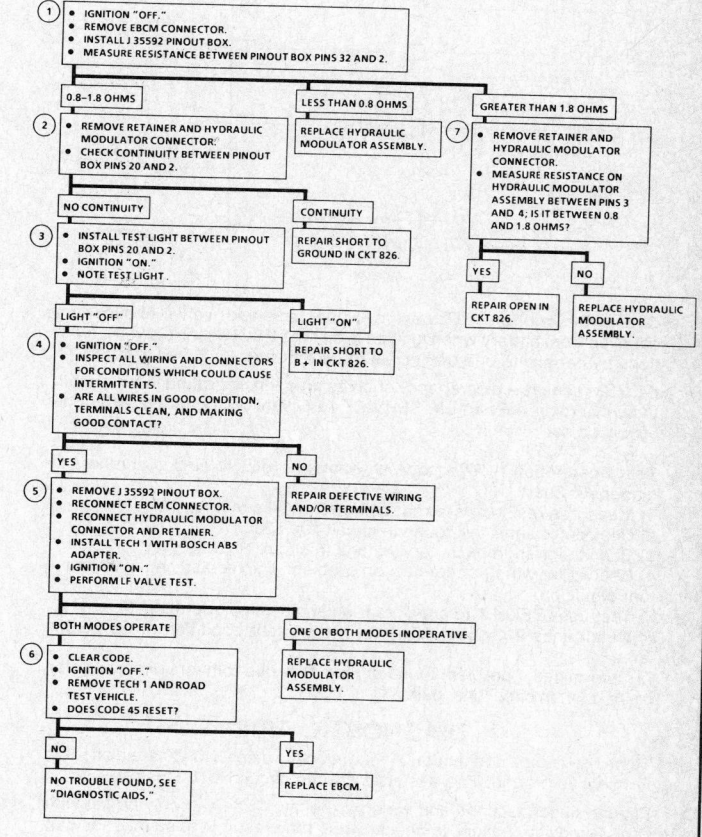

91E07249 91I07251

Courtesy of General Motors Corp.

CODE 55
REAR WHEEL SOLENOID VALVE

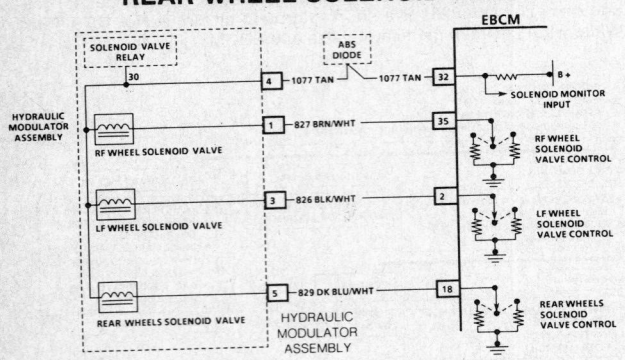

Circuit Description

Power to wheel solenoid valve circuits are supplied from battery when ignition is on. The EBCM controls valve functions by permitting one of 3 levels of current flow (0, 2.5 or 5 amps).

If EBCM senses a discrepancy such as an open or ground in the circuit, the valve relay will turn off, SERVICE ABS light will come on, and code 55 will be set.

Test Description

The following numbers refer to circled numbers in diagnostic chart.
1) Measures resistance in rear solenoid valve circuitry.
2) Checks for short to ground in circuit No. 829.
3) Checks for short to battery voltage in circuit No. 829.
4) Checks for wiring or connection problem which could cause intermittent condition.
5) Test uses TECH 1 to check rear solenoid valve operation.
6) Determines if problem is set by intermittent condition or an EBCM fault.
7) Determines if problem found in step 1) is due to hydraulic modulator or an open in circuit No. 829.

DIAGNOSTIC AIDS

Tests requiring a connection at Pinout box terminal No. 20 are using this terminal as ground. This assumes ground circuit No. 801 is okay.

Ensure all connections and wiring are okay. Code can only be set with vehicle moving. Failure to check wiring may result in false diagnosis of a faulty modulator valve or EBCM.

If codes 41 and 45 are both set, fault is likely to be a short to battery voltage on circuit No. 829.

If codes 41 and 55 are both set, fault is likely to be a short to battery voltage on circuit No. 826, or a short to ground on circuit No. 1079 (Pink/White wire) between modulator valve and EBCM.

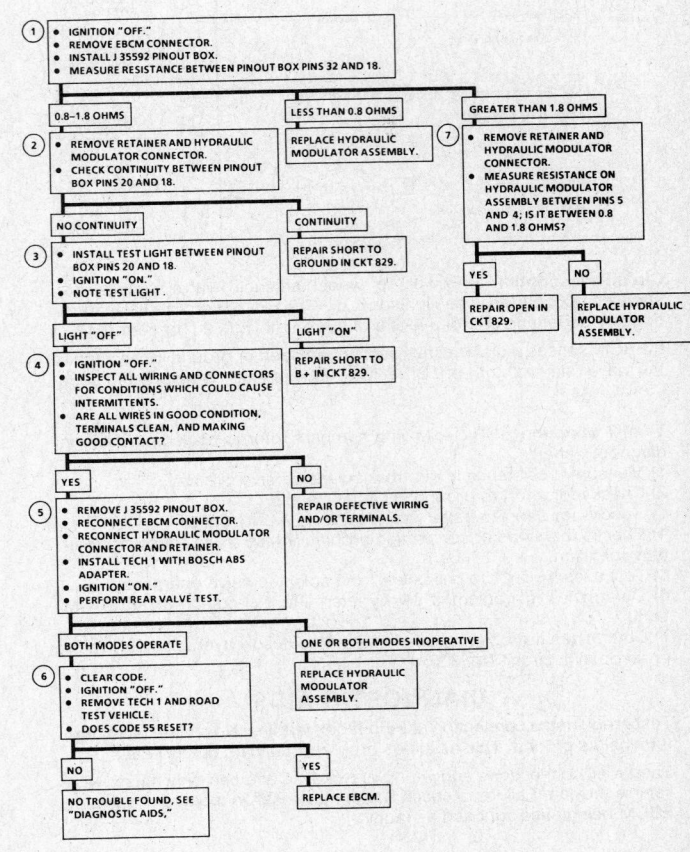

91E07249 91A07252

Courtesy of General Motors Corp.

CODE 61
PUMP MOTOR OR MOTOR RELAY

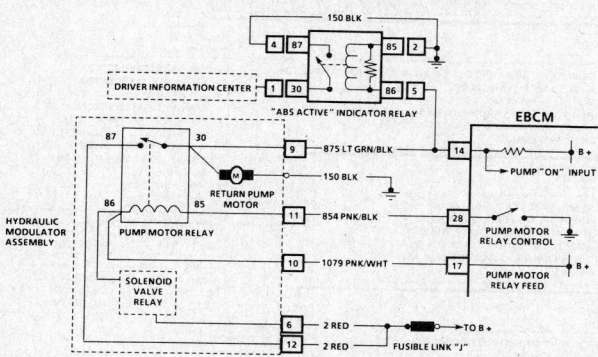

Circuit Description – When pump motor relay is grounded by EBCM, battery voltage it provided to operate pump motor. When pump motor circuit is energized, a pump-on signal is sent to EBCM to verify operation.

Code 61 will be set if 12 volts is present at pump motor with motor relay not activated, or if 12 volts is not present at pump motor within 60 milliseconds after pump motor relay is activated.

Test Description – The following numbers refer to circled numbers in diagnostic chart.
1) Checks relay for correct resistance.
2) Checks relay for contacts being stuck closed.
3) Checks relay for contacts being stuck open.
4) Checks condition of pump motor relay circuity in modulator valve.
5) Checks for open circuit No. 875.
6) Checks for short to ground in circuit No. 875.
7) Checks for short to battery voltage in circuit No. 875.
8) Determines if problem in step 6) is due to shorted coil in ABS active indicator relay or in circuit No. 875.
9) Checks for open circuit No. 854.
10) Checks for short to ground in circuit No. 854.
11) Checks for short to battery voltage in circuit No. 854.
12) Checks for connector or wiring problems which could cause an intermittent condition.
13) Test uses TECH 1 to check operation of pump motor and components.
14) Test determines if code is set by an intermittent or EBCM fault.
15) Determines if problem in step 13) is due to defective pump motor or fault in circuit No. 150.

DIAGNOSTIC AIDS

Tests requiring a connection at Pinout box terminal No. 20 are using this terminal as ground. This assumes ground circuit No. 801 is okay.

1
- IGNITION "OFF."
- REMOVE RELAY RETAINER AND PUMP MOTOR RELAY (4-PIN) FROM HYDRAULIC MODULATOR ASSEMBLY.
- MEASURE RESISTANCE BETWEEN PUMP MOTOR RELAY PINS 85 AND 86; IS IT WITHIN 45–55 OHMS?

YES → **2**
- CHECK CONTINUITY BETWEEN RELAY PINS 30 AND 87.

NO → REPLACE PUMP MOTOR RELAY.

NO CONTINUITY → **3**
- USING A FUSED JUMPER WIRE SUCH AS J 36169 WITH A 3 AMP FUSE, CONNECT GROUND TO RELAY PIN 85 AND B + THROUGH THE FUSED JUMPER WIRE TO PIN 86.
- CHECK CONTINUITY BETWEEN RELAY PINS 30 AND 87.

CONTINUITY → REPLACE PUMP MOTOR RELAY.

CONTINUITY → **4**
- REMOVE RETAINER AND HYDRAULIC MODULATOR CONNECTOR.
- CHECK CONTINUITY ON HYDRAULIC MODULATOR ASSEMBLY BETWEEN;
  - MODULATOR PIN 9 AND PUMP MOTOR RELAY CONNECTOR PIN 30.
  - MODULATOR PIN 10 AND PUMP MOTOR RELAY CONNECTOR PIN 86.
  - MODULATOR PIN 11 AND PUMP MOTOR RELAY CONNECTOR PIN 85.
  - MODULATOR PIN 12 AND PUMP MOTOR RELAY CONNECTOR PIN 87.

NO CONTINUITY → REPLACE PUMP MOTOR RELAY.

CONTINUITY AT EACH STEP → **5**
- REINSTALL PUMP MOTOR RELAY ON HYDRAULIC MODULATOR ASSEMBLY.
- REMOVE EBCM CONNECTOR.
- INSTALL J 35592 PINOUT BOX.
- CHECK CONTINUITY BETWEEN PINOUT BOX PIN 14 AND HYDRAULIC MODULATOR CONNECTOR PIN 9.

LACK OF CONTINUITY AT ANY STEP → REPLACE HYDRAULIC MODULATOR ASSEMBLY.

CONTINUITY → **6**
- CHECK CONTINUITY BETWEEN PINOUT BOX PINS 14 AND 20.

NO CONTINUITY → REPAIR OPEN IN CKT 875.

NO CONTINUITY → **7**
- INSTALL TEST LIGHT BETWEEN PINOUT BOX PINS 14 AND 20.
- IGNITION "ON."
- NOTE TEST LIGHT.

CONTINUITY → **8**
- REMOVE "ABS ACTIVE" INDICATOR RELAY.
- CHECK CONTINUITY BETWEEN PINOUT BOX PINS 14 AND 20.

LIGHT "OFF" → **9**

LIGHT "ON" → REPLACE SHORT TO B + IN CKT 875.

CONTINUITY → REPAIR SHORT TO GROUND IN CKT 875.

NO CONTINUITY → REPLACE "ABS ACTIVE" INDICATOR RELAY.

9
- IGNITION "OFF."
- CHECK CONTINUITY BETWEEN PINOUT BOX PIN 28 AND HYDRAULIC MODULATOR CONNECTOR PIN 11.

CONTINUITY → **10**
- CHECK CONTINUITY BETWEEN PINOUT BOX PINS 28 AND 20.

NO CONTINUITY → REPAIR OPEN IN CKT 854.

NO CONTINUITY → **11**
- INSTALL TEST LIGHT BETWEEN PINOUT BOX PINS 28 AND 20.
- IGNITION "ON."
- NOTE TEST LIGHT.

CONTINUITY → REPAIR SHORT TO GROUND IN CKT 854.

LIGHT "OFF." → **12**
- IGNITION "OFF."
- INSPECT ALL WIRING AND CONNECTORS FOR CONDITIONS WHICH COULD CAUSE INTERMITTENTS.
- ARE ALL WIRES IN GOOD CONDITION, TERMINALS CLEAN AND MAKING GOOD CONTACT?

LIGHT "ON." → REPAIR SHORT TO B + IN CKT 854.

YES → **13**
- REMOVE J 35592 PINOUT BOX.
- RECONNECT EBCM CONNECTOR.
- RECONNECT HYDRAULIC MODULATOR CONNECTOR AND RETAINER.
- INSTALL TECH 1 WITH BOSCH ABS ADAPTER.
- IGNITION "ON."
- PERFORM AUTO TEST.

NO → REPAIR FAULTY WIRING AND/OR CONNECTOR.

PUMP MOTOR RUNS → **14**
- CLEAR CODE.
- IGNITION "OFF."
- REMOVE TECH 1 AND ROAD TEST VEHICLE.
- DOES CODE 61 RESET?

PUMP MOTOR DOES NOT RUN → **15**
- CHECK CONTINUITY BETWEEN PUMP MOTOR GROUND AND A GOOD CHASSIS GROUND.

NO → NO TROUBLE FOUND, SEE "DIAGNOSTIC AIDS"

YES → REPLACE EBCM.

CONTINUITY → REPLACE HYDRAULIC MODULATOR ASSEMBLY.

NO CONTINUITY → REPAIR OPEN IN CKT 150.

91C07253 91E07254 91H07255

CODE 63
SOLENOID VALVE RELAY (1 OF 2)

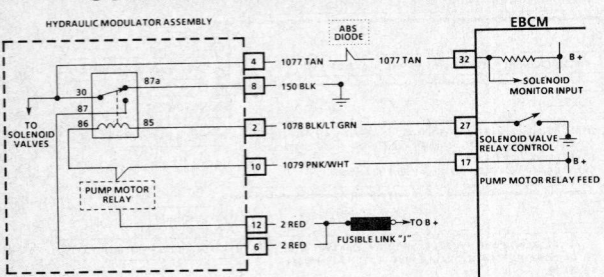

HYDRAULIC MODULATOR ASSEMBLY

ABS DIODE

EBCM

4 | 1077 TAN — 1077 TAN | 32 — B+
SOLENOID MONITOR INPUT

8 | 150 BLK

30 | 87a
87
86 | 85

2 | 1078 BLK/LT GRN | 27 — SOLENOID VALVE RELAY CONTROL

10 | 1079 PNK/WHT | 17 — B+ PUMP MOTOR RELAY FEED

TO SOLENOID VALVES

PUMP MOTOR RELAY

12 | 2 RED
6 | 2 RED — TO B+
FUSIBLE LINK "J"

Circuit Description – Solenoid valve relay circuit has 2 functions. When ABS is active, relay provides voltage to actuate 3 solenoid valves. Solenoid valves do not use this voltage unless EBCM provides grounds. The second function is to provide a ground path for illumination of SERVICE ABS light if solenoid relay loses power or ground.

Code 63 will be set if valve relay voltage drops to less than 5 volts, or if relay feed line is at 12 volts when EBCM is not requesting it to be, resulting in relay being on constantly.

Test Description – The following numbers refer to circled numbers in diagnostic chart.

1) Checks for battery voltage through solenoid valve relay and fusible link.
2) Checks for open circuit No. 2.
3) Checks relay coil resistance.
4) Checks for relay contacts on ground side to be stuck open.
5) Checks for relay contacts on battery voltage side to be stuck open.
6) Checks solenoid valve relay circuitry of modulator valve.
7) Checks for short to ground in circuit No. 2.
8) Check solenoid valve relay ground circuit No. 150.
9) Checks for open circuit No. 1077.
10) Checks for short to ground in circuit No. 1077.
11) Checks for short to battery voltage in circuit No. 1077.
12) Checks for open circuit No. 1079.
13) Checks for short to ground in circuit No. 1079.
14) Checks for open circuit No. 1078.
15) Checks for short to ground in circuit No. 1078.
16) Checks for short to battery voltage in circuit No. 1078.

DIAGNOSTIC AIDS

A disconnected or improperly seated modulator valve connector may set this code.

---

①
- IGNITION "OFF."
- USING ADAPTER FROM J 35616 TERMINAL TEST ADAPTER KIT, INSTALL TEST LIGHT BETWEEN FEMALE HALF OF C417 AND A GOOD CHASSIS GROUND.
- NOTE TEST LIGHT.

LIGHT "ON" → **②**

LIGHT "OFF." → **⑦**

②
- REMOVE RETAINER AND HYDRAULIC MODULATOR CONNECTOR.
- REMOVE EBCM CONNECTOR.
- INSTALL J 35592 PINOUT BOX.
- INSTALL TEST LIGHT BETWEEN HYDRAULIC MODULATOR CONNECTOR PIN 6 AND PINOUT BOX PIN 20.
- NOTE TEST LIGHT.

LIGHT "ON" → **③**

LIGHT "OFF" → REPAIR OPEN IN CKT 2.

③
- REMOVE RELAY RETAINER AND SOLENOID VALVE RELAY (5-PIN) FROM HYDRAULIC MODULATOR ASSEMBLY.
- MEASURE RESISTANCE BETWEEN RELAY PINS 85 AND 86; IS IT BETWEEN 54 AND 66 OHMS?

YES → **④**

NO → REPLACE SOLENOID VALVE RELAY.

④ CHECK CONTINUITY BETWEEN RELAY PINS 30 AND 87a.

CONTINUITY → **⑤**

NO CONTINUITY → REPLACE SOLENOID VALVE RELAY.

⑤
- USING A FUSED JUMPER WIRE, SUCH AS J 36169, WITH A 3 AMP FUSE, CONNECT GROUND TO RELAY PIN 85 AND B + THROUGH THE FUSED JUMPER WIRE TO RELAY PIN 86.
- CHECK CONTINUITY BETWEEN RELAY PINS 30 AND 87.

CONTINUITY → **⑥**

NO CONTINUITY → REPLACE SOLENOID VALVE RELAY.

⑥
- CHECK CONTINUITY ON HYDRAULIC MODULATOR ASSEMBLY BETWEEN:
  - MODULATOR PIN 2 AND SOLENOID VALVE RELAY CONNECTOR PIN 85.
  - MODULATOR PIN 4 AND SOLENOID VALVE RELAY CONNECTOR PIN 30.
  - MODULATOR PIN 6 AND SOLENOID VALVE RELAY CONNECTOR PIN 87.
  - MODULATOR PIN 8 AND SOLENOID VALVE RELAY CONNECTOR PIN 87a.
  - MODULATOR PIN 10 AND SOLENOID VALVE RELAY CONNECTOR PIN 86.

CONTINUITY AT EACH STEP

LACK OF CONTINUITY AT ANY STEP → REPLACE HYDRAULIC MODULATOR ASSEMBLY.

⑧
- CHECK CONTINUITY BETWEEN HYDRAULIC MODULATOR CONNECTOR PIN 8 AND PINOUT BOX PIN 20.

CONTINUITY

NO CONTINUITY → REPAIR OPEN IN CKT 150.

⑨
- REINSTALL SOLENOID VALVE RELAY AND RELAY RETAINER ON HYDRAULIC MODULATOR ASSEMBLY.
- CHECK CONTINUITY BETWEEN HYDRAULIC MODULATOR CONNECTOR PIN 4 AND PINOUT BOX PIN 32.

CONTINUITY

NO CONTINUITY → REPAIR OPEN IN CKT 1077.

⑩ CHECK CONTINUITY BETWEEN PINOUT BOX PINS 20 AND 32.

NO CONTINUITY

CONTINUITY → REPAIR SHORT TO GROUND IN CKT 1077.

⑪
- INSTALL TEST LIGHT BETWEEN PINOUT BOX PINS 20 AND 32.
- IGNITION "ON."
- NOTE TEST LIGHT.

LIGHT "OFF."

LIGHT "ON" → REPAIR SHORT TO B + IN CKT 1077.

⑫
- IGNITION "OFF."
- CHECK CONTINUITY BETWEEN HYDRAULIC MODULATOR CONNECTOR PIN 10 AND PINOUT BOX PIN 17.

CONTINUITY

NO CONTINUITY → REPAIR OPEN IN CKT 1079.

⑬ CHECK CONTINUITY BETWEEN PINOUT BOX PINS 17 AND 20.

NO CONTINUITY

CONTINUITY → REPAIR SHORT TO GROUND IN CKT 1079.

⑭ CHECK CONTINUITY BETWEEN HYDRAULIC MODULATOR CONNECTOR PIN 2 AND PINOUT BOX PIN 27.

CONTINUITY

NO CONTINUITY → REPAIR OPEN IN CKT 1078.

⑮ CHECK CONTINUITY BETWEEN PINOUT BOX PINS 20 AND 27.

NO CONTINUITY

CONTINUITY → REPAIR SHORT TO GROUND IN CKT 1078.

⑯
- INSTALL TEST LIGHT BETWEEN PINOUT BOX PINS 20 AND 27.
- IGNITION "ON."
- NOTE TEST LIGHT.

LIGHT "OFF" → CONTINUE WITH DIAGNOSIS ON NEXT PAGE.

LIGHT "ON" → REPAIR SHORT TO B + IN CKT 1078.

---

⑦
- REMOVE RETAINER AND HYDRAULIC MODULATOR CONNECTOR.
- REMOVE EBCM CONNECTOR.
- INSTALL J 35592 PINOUT BOX.
- INSTALL TEST LIGHT BETWEEN HYDRAULIC MODULATOR CONNECTOR PIN 6 AND PINOUT BOX PIN 1.
- IGNITION "ON."
- NOTE TEST LIGHT.

LIGHT "OFF." → REPAIR FUSIBLE LINK "J".

LIGHT "ON" → REPAIR SHORT TO GROUND IN CKT 2 AND FUSIBLE LINK "J".

Courtesy of General Motors Corp.

91J07256 91B07257 91D07258

CODE 63
SOLENOID VALVE RELAY (2 OF 2)

Note: See CODE 63 SOLENOID VALVE RELAY (1 OF 2) for wiring schematic.

Test Description – The following numbers refer to circled numbers in diagnostic chart.

17) Checks for connections or wiring which could cause an intermittent condition.

18) Determines if code is set by an intermittent condition or EBCM fault.

DIAGNOSTIC AIDS

A disconnected or improperly seated modulator valve connector may set this code.

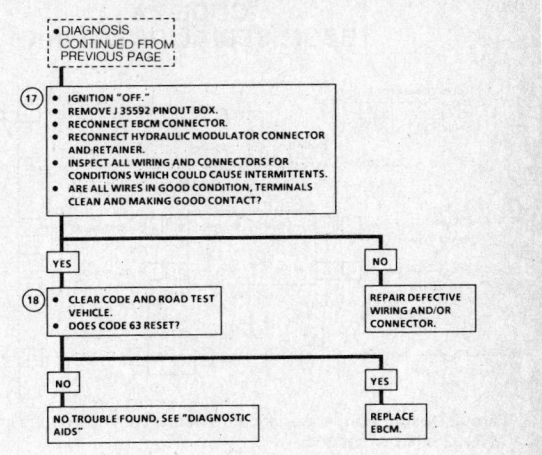

91F07259

Courtesy of General Motors Corp.

CODE 71
EBCM CONTROL MODULE

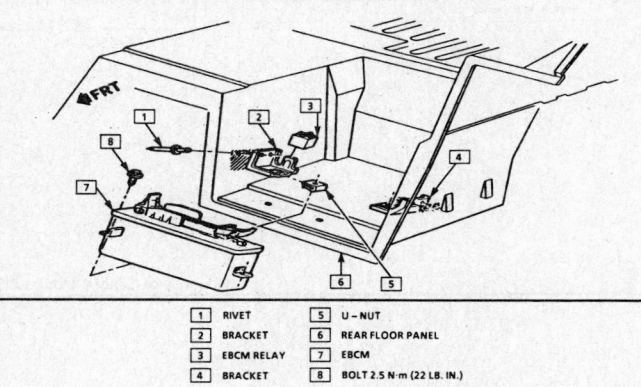

1 RIVET	5 U – NUT
2 BRACKET	6 REAR FLOOR PANEL
3 EBCM RELAY	7 EBCM
4 BRACKET	8 BOLT 2.5 N·m (22 LB. IN.)

Circuit Description – EBCM performs various diagnostic checks on itself. Code 71 will be set if a problem is detected.

Test Description – The following numbers refer to circled numbers in diagnostic chart.

1) Checks if minimum voltage is available to EBCM.

2) Checks for proper connections from harness to EBCM.

3) Checks if fault is false; if fault is not false, replace EBCM.

90H18827 91H07260

Courtesy of General Motors Corp.

CODE 72
EBCM SERIAL DATA LINK

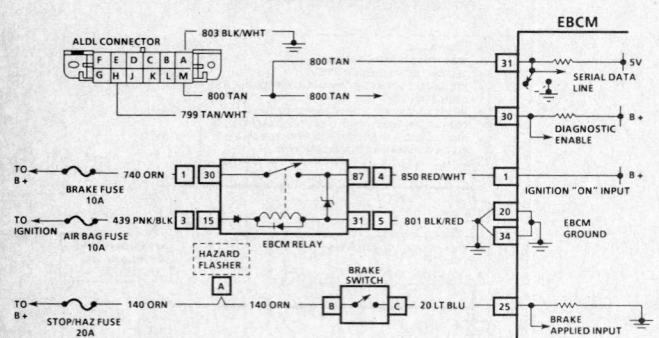

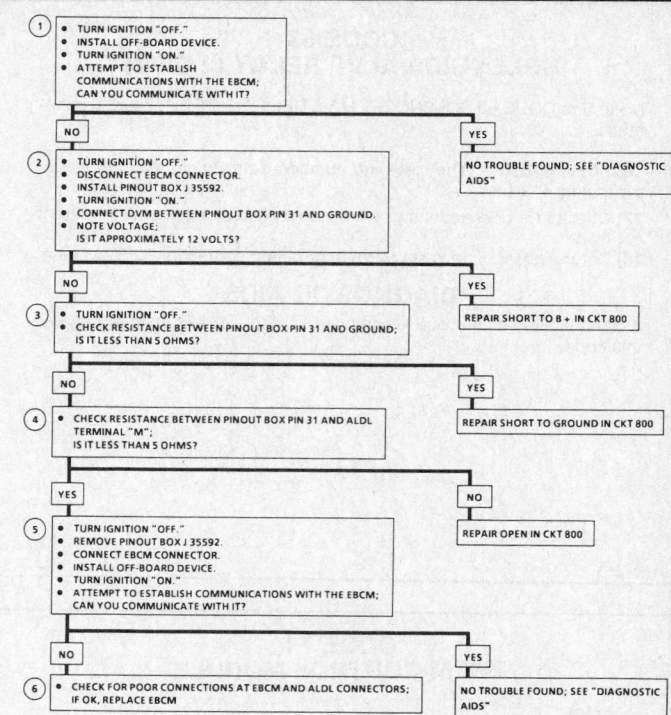

Circuit Description – Serial data link is an asynchronous link operating at 8192 bits per second.

Code 72 will be set if EBCM detects 3 consecutive serial data link messages being ignored due to errors in transmission. The SERVICE ABS light will not be illuminated for this fault.

Test Description – The following numbers refer to circled numbers in diagnostic chart.

1) Checks if off-board device can communicate with EBCM.
2) Checks for short to battery voltage in ABS serial data circuit.
3) Checks for short to ground in ABS serial data circuit.
4) Checks for open in ABS serial data circuit.
5) Checks if off-board device can communicate with EBCM.
6) If connections at EBCM and ALDL connector are okay, replace EBCM.

DIAGNOSTIC AIDS

Problem may be intermittent. While performing tests shown, move wiring and connectors, as this can often cause fault to appear.

91J07261 90H08250

Courtesy of General Motors Corp.

CODE 75
LATERAL ACCELEROMETER (SHORT OR OPEN)

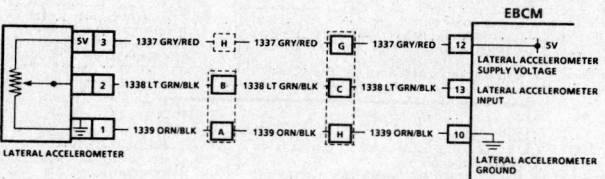

Circuit Description – Lateral accelerometer circuit provides signal reflecting severity of vehicle turn to EBCM. Information is used by EBCM to modify control of rear wheel brakes to help prevent loss of control in a turn due to light brake pedal pressure at speeds greater than 30 MPH.

Code 75 will be set if EBCM senses lateral accelerometer voltage is out of permissible range due to electrical wiring faults.

Test Description – The following numbers refer to circled numbers in diagnostic chart.

1) Checks for proper connections at lateral accelerometer and EBCM.

2) Checks for short to ground in power supply and signal circuits.

3) Checks for short to battery voltage in signal and ground circuits.

4) Checks for continuity in power supply circuit through accelerometer, and back to EBCM.

5) Checks for open in signal circuit wiring.

6) Checks for correct voltage supply to accelerometer from EBCM. If voltage is correct, EBCM is incorrectly setting code and should be replaced.

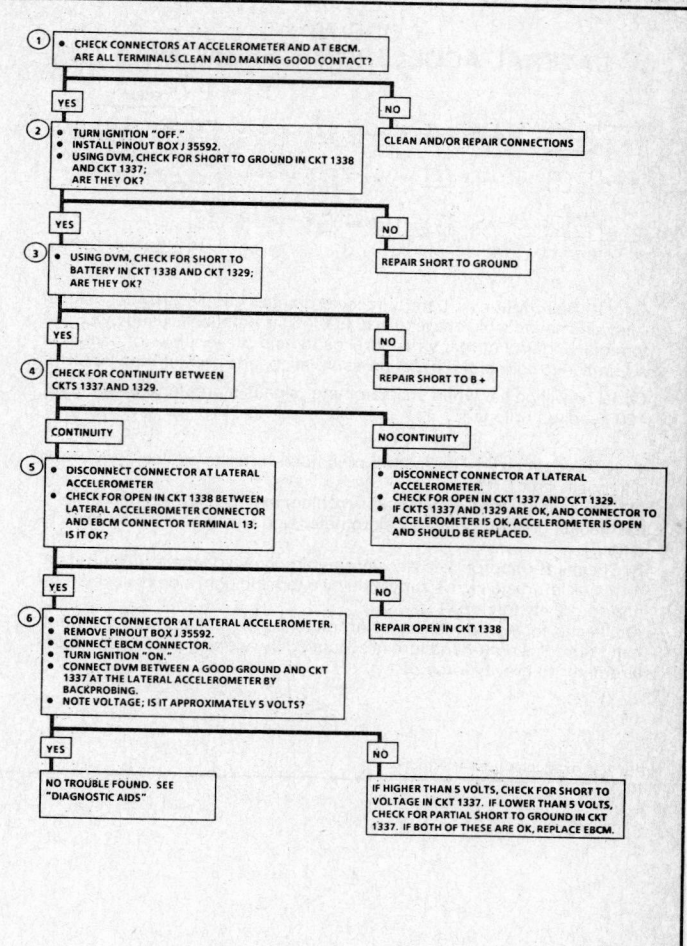

91B07262 91D07263

Courtesy of General Motors Corp.

CODE 76
LATERAL ACCELEROMETER (SIGNAL)

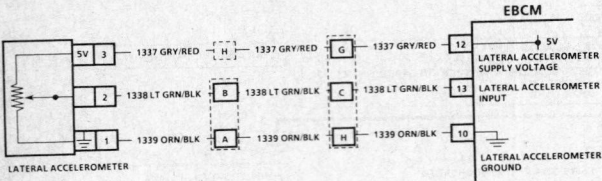

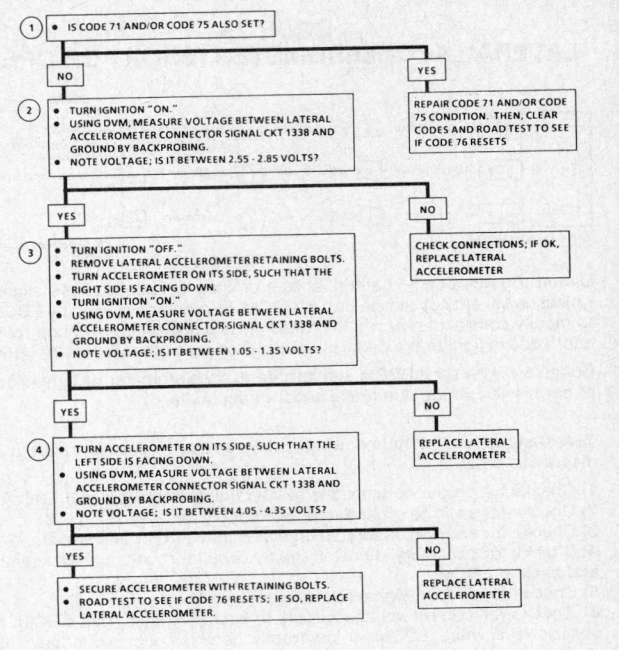

Circuit Description – Lateral accelerometer circuit provides signal reflecting severity of vehicle turn to EBCM. Information is used by EBCM to modify control of rear wheel brakes to help prevent loss of control in a turn due to light brake pedal pressure at speeds greater than 30 MPH.

Code 76 will be set when accelerometer signal is greater than 0.6 g for 120 seconds or longer.

Test Description – The following numbers refer to circled numbers in diagnostic chart.
1) Checks if another ABS system problem may be causing code 76.
2) Checks for appropriate accelerometer signal voltage in a no-turn condition.
3) Checks for appropriate accelerometer signal voltage at full left-hand turn. Full left-hand turn is simulated by exposing right side of accelerometer to gravity force of 1 g.
4) Checks for appropriate accelerometer signal voltage at a full right-hand turn. Full right-hand turn is simulated by exposing left side of accelerometer to gravity force of 1 g.

Courtesy of General Motors Corp.

91B07262 91F07264

Cutlass Supreme, Grand Prix, Regal

NOTE: *General Motors uses 5 different anti-lock brake systems. Use the appropriate ANTI-LOCK brake systems article.*

DESCRIPTION

The Delco Moraine Anti-Lock Brake System-III is designed to prevent wheel lockup during heavy braking. This provides improved driver control by reducing the distance required to stop vehicle.

Major component parts of system include the following: anti-lock brake controller, 4 wheel-speed sensors, 2 dash-mounted warning lights, front and rear enable relays and Powermaster-III booster/master cylinder assembly. The Powermaster-III, known as a hydraulic unit on other models, also houses hydraulic accumulator, electric pump motor, solenoids and pressure switch. *See Fig. 1.*

NOTE: *For more information on brake system, see DISC & DRUM article.*

OPERATION

ANTI-LOCK BRAKE SYSTEM

During normal driving and braking operations, ABS-III functions like a conventional brake system. Each wheel sensor constantly sends an AC voltage signal to anti-lock brake controller. This information is translated to wheel-rotation speed. When anti-lock brake controller detects wheel lock-up, it activates appropriate solenoid to pulse on and off rapidly, regulating hydraulic pressure to each wheel. A slight pulsation should be felt through brake pedal, indicating ABS-III is working.

Red and Amber warning lights should come on when ignition is turned on and vehicle is started. If either light stays on longer than 30 seconds after vehicle is started, system malfunction is indicated. See DIAGNOSIS & TESTING.

Red warning light is activated if parking brake is applied, brake fluid is low or accumulator pressure is low. Amber ANTI-LOCK warning light, controlled by anti-lock brake controller, comes on if problem is detected in system. When light is on, ABS-III can be partially or totally disabled.

CAUTION: *See ANTI-LOCK BRAKE SAFETY PRECAUTIONS article in GENERAL INFORMATION.*

BLEEDING BRAKE SYSTEM

NOTE: *Use only DOT 3 brake fluid from a sealed container.*

MANUAL BLEEDING

1) Discharge system pressure. With ignition off, pump brake pedal a MINIMUM of 40 times with complete pedal strokes. Verify reservoir is full. Raise and support vehicle. Attach a clear hose to right front bleeder valve and submerge other end of hose in container of clean brake fluid.

2) Open bleeder valve. Slowly depress brake pedal. Tap lightly on caliper housing to free trapped air. Close bleeder valve and release brake pedal. Repeat this step until no air is seen in hose. Repeat procedure for left front bleeder valve.

3) Before bleeding rear brakes, turn ignition on and allow pump motor to charge system. Pump motor should stop running within one minute. Verify reservoir is full. Attach a clear hose to right rear bleeder valve and submerge other end of hose in a container of clean brake fluid.

4) Open bleeder valve. Slowly depress brake pedal. Tap lightly on cylinder/caliper housing to free trapped air. Close bleeder valve and release brake pedal. Repeat this step until no air is seen in hose. Repeat procedure for left rear bleeder valve.

PRESSURE BLEEDING

1) Discharge system pressure. With ignition off, pump brake pedal a MINIMUM of 40 times with complete pedal strokes. Brake pedal will feel hard when accumulator is completely discharged.

CAUTION: *Once system is depressurized, DO NOT turn ignition on until all service operations have been completed.*

2) Remove reservoir cap. Attach Bleeder Adapter (J-37115) to reservoir. Attach bleeding equipment and pressurize system to 10 psi (.7 kg/cm²) for 30 seconds. Slowly increase pressure to 35 psi (2.5 kg/cm²).

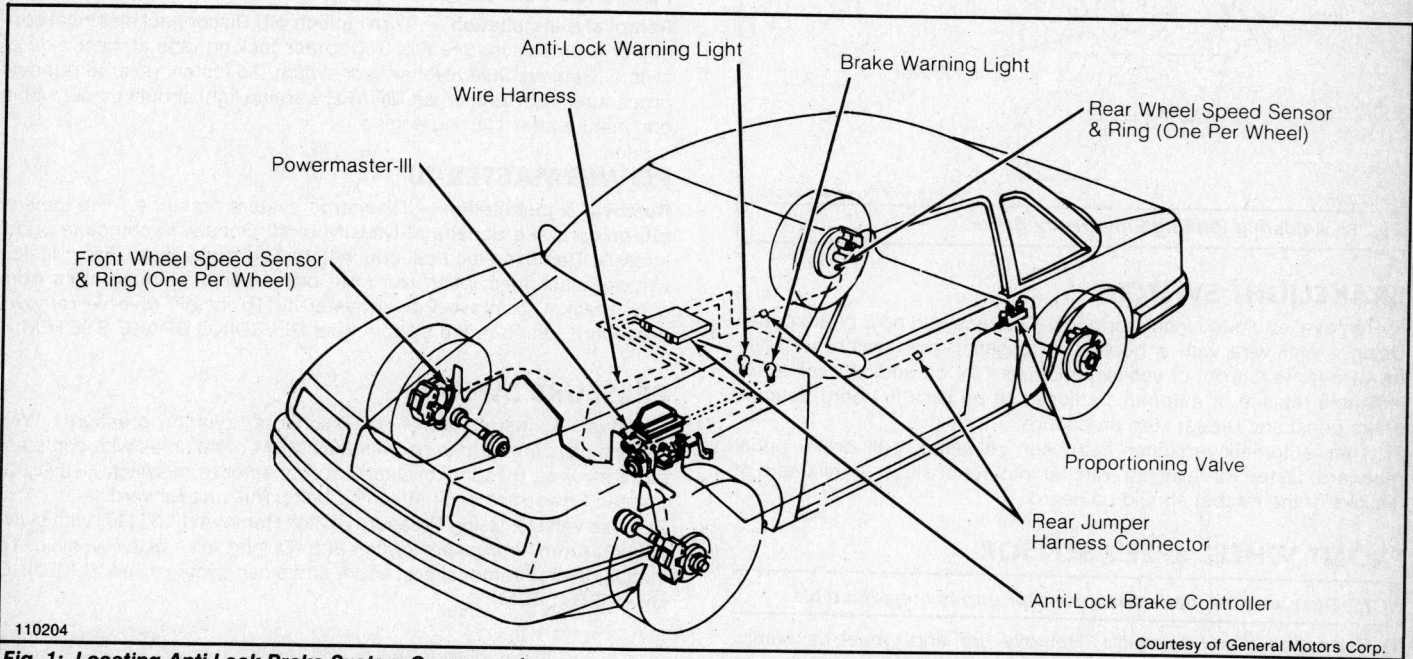

110204

Courtesy of General Motors Corp.

Fig. 1: Locating Anti-Lock Brake System Components

3) Attach a clear hose to bleeder valve and submerge other end of hose in a container of clean brake fluid. Bleeding sequence is as follows: right rear, left rear, right front and left front.

4) Starting at right rear, open bleeder valve. Allow fluid to flow until no air is seen in hose. Close bleeder valve. Repeat procedure for other bleeder valves. Fill fluid reservoir.

ADJUSTMENTS

PARKING/EMERGENCY BRAKE

1) Apply service brake 3 times using a pedal force of 175 lbs. (79.4 kg). Fully apply and release parking brake 3 times. It may require 2 pedal strokes to fully apply parking brake.

2) Turn ignition on. Brake warning light should be off. If warning light is on, operate manual brake release and pull downward on front parking brake cable to remove slack from pedal assembly. Lift and support vehicle. Mark wheel-to-hub relationship and remove wheels.

3) Parking brake levers (2) on both calipers should be against lever stops on caliper housings. If levers are not against stops, check for binding rear cables and/or loosen cables at adjuster until both levers are against their stops. Tighten parking brake cable at adjuster until clearance at either left or right lever is .02-.08" (.5-2.0 mm). *See Fig. 2.*

4) Apply parking brake several times to ensure proper operation. A firm brake pedal should be obtained by pumping pedal 2 full strokes. Ensure rear wheels do not rotate when parking brake is applied. If operation is not as specified, repeat step **3)**.

5) Align wheel-to-hub mark and install wheels. Lower vehicle.

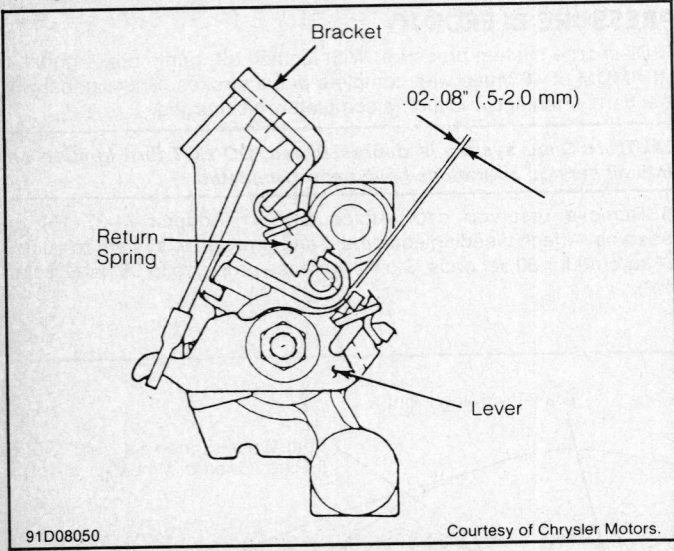

91D08050   Courtesy of Chrysler Motors.
Fig. 2: Adjusting Parking/Emergency Brake

BRAKELIGHT SWITCH

1) Remove left sound insulator panel. Depress and hold brake pedal. Using a stiff wire with a hooked end, gently pull switch set lever forward (toward front of vehicle) and listen for an audible click. Click indicates release of automatic adjuster. If no click is heard, release brake pedal and repeat step procedure.

2) After automatic adjuster has been released, pull brake pedal rearward. Listen for switch to ratchet into set position. A minimum of 3 clicks of the ratchet should be heard.

FRONT WHEEL SPEED SENSOR

NOTE: Rear wheel speed sensor-to-rotor gap is nonadjustable.

1) Raise and support vehicle. Remove tire and wheel assembly. Inspect sensor pole piece for damage. If damaged, replace as necessary. If sensor pole piece is okay, check wheel speed sensor-to-

rotor gap. Using a feeler gauge, check clearance between speed sensor pole and rotor tooth surface.

2) Clearance should be .019-.068" (.48-1.73 mm). If clearance is not within specification, loosen sensor mounting bolt. Adjust sensor position until clearance is within specification. Tighten sensor mounting bolt. Install tire and wheel assembly. Lower vehicle.

REMOVAL & INSTALLATION

CAUTION: Before servicing any component containing high pressure, DISCHARGE hydraulic pressure within system. With ignition off, pump brake pedal a MINIMUM of 40 times with complete pedal strokes.

ANTI-LOCK BRAKE CONTROLLER

Removal & Installation – Turn ignition off. Adjust front passenger seat forward. Remove bolts holding anti-lock brake controller. Remove anti-lock brake controller and disconnect wire connectors. *See Fig. 1.* To install, reverse removal procedure.

ABS-III FUSE/RELAY CENTER

Removal & Installation – Disconnect negative battery cable. Locate fuse panel behind glove box door. Pull large bracket side tab toward left fender. Position flat screwdriver between housing and bracket to disengage tab from bracket. Pull fuse/relay center upward. To install, reverse removal procedure.

ACCUMULATOR

Removal – Discharge brake system pressure. With ignition off, pump brake pedal a MINIMUM of 40 times with complete pedal strokes. Remove air cleaner and duct. Remove hydraulic accumulator and "O" ring by turning accumulator hex nut. *See Fig. 3.* Remove accumulator from below Powermaster-III toward left wheelwell. Remove "O" ring. Ensure dirt particles do not fall into open port.

Installation – Before installing accumulator, inspect "O" ring for damage and replace if necessary. Ensure "O" ring is in position on accumulator and is lubricated. Screw in accumulator and bleed system. See BLEEDING BRAKE SYSTEM.

FLUID LEVEL SENSOR SWITCH

Removal & Installation – Turn ignition off. Disconnect electrical connector from switch. *See Fig. 3.* Depress locking tabs at inner side of switch. Remove fluid level sensor switch. To install, reverse removal procedure. Turn ignition on. BRAKE warning light should go out within one minute after starting engine.

POWERMASTER-III

Removal & Installation – Discharge system pressure. With ignition off, pump brake pedal a MINIMUM of 40 times with complete pedal strokes. Remove electrical connectors and brake lines. From inside vehicle, disconnect push rod from brake pedal. Remove nuts from cowl bracket. Remove Powermaster-III. To install, reverse removal procedure. Bleed brake system. See BLEEDING BRAKE SYSTEM.

PRESSURE SWITCH

Removal & Installation – 1) Discharge system pressure. With ignition off, pump brake pedal a MINIMUM of 40 times with complete pedal strokes. Disconnect electrical connector from switch. *See Fig. 3.* Loosen Powermaster-III attaching bolts. Pull unit forward.

2) Raise vehicle. Using Pressure Switch Remover (J-37117) with swivel joint, remove pressure switch and "O" ring from below vehicle. To install, reverse removal procedure and bleed system. See BLEEDING BRAKE SYSTEM.

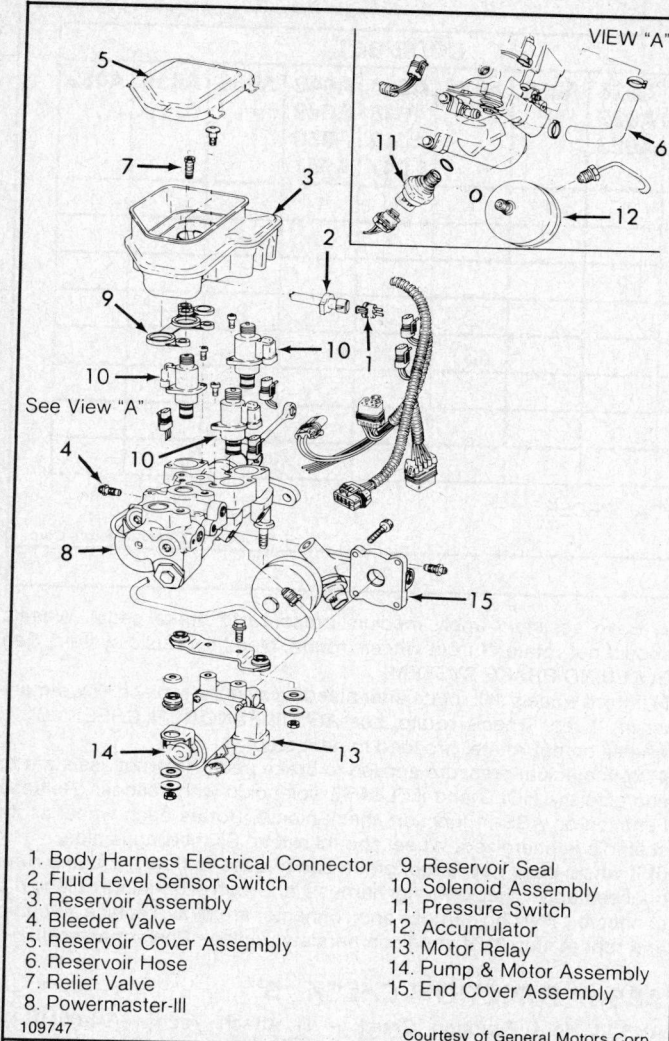

1. Body Harness Electrical Connector
2. Fluid Level Sensor Switch
3. Reservoir Assembly
4. Bleeder Valve
5. Reservoir Cover Assembly
6. Reservoir Hose
7. Relief Valve
8. Powermaster-III
9. Reservoir Seal
10. Solenoid Assembly
11. Pressure Switch
12. Accumulator
13. Motor Relay
14. Pump & Motor Assembly
15. End Cover Assembly

109747

Courtesy of General Motors Corp.

Fig. 3: Exploded View of Powermaster-III Assembly

SOLENOID ASSEMBLY

Removal & Installation – 1) Ensure reservoir area is clean. Discharge system pressure. With ignition off, pump brake pedal a MINIMUM of 40 times with complete pedal strokes. Remove reservoir assembly. See RESERVOIR ASSEMBLY under REMOVAL & INSTALLATION. *See Fig. 3.*

2) Remove solenoid wire harness connector. Remove solenoid attaching screws. Remove solenoid and "O" rings. To install, reverse removal procedure. Inspect "O" rings and replace if necessary. Bleed brake system. See BLEEDING BRAKE SYSTEM.

RESERVOIR ASSEMBLY

Removal & Installation – 1) Discharge system pressure. With ignition off, pump brake pedal a MINIMUM of 40 times with complete pedal strokes. Remove reservoir cover and fluid level sensor switch. *See Fig. 3.* Loosen Powermaster-III attaching bolts for accessibility. Pull unit forward. Drain reservoir.

2) Remove return hose. Remove reservoir mounting screws. Carefully lift reservoir and pull away, from below secondary dash. To install, reverse removal procedure. Inspect "O" rings and replace if necessary. Install new grommets. Bleed brake system. See BLEEDING BRAKE SYSTEM.

WHEEL SPEED SENSOR

Removal & Installation (Front) – 1) Raise and support vehicle. Disconnect sensor connector located near shock tower. Remove sensor and bracket retaining bolt. Remove sensor.

2) To install sensor, reverse removal procedure. Adjust sensor-to-rotor gap. See FRONT WHEEL SPEED SENSOR under ADJUSTMENTS. Ensure wiring harness is routed so it does not contact suspension components.

Removal & Installation (Rear) – 1) Rear wheel speed sensor is integral with hub/bearing assembly. To replace sensor, the hub/bearing assembly must be replaced.

2) Raise and support vehicle. Remove wheel. Remove brake caliper and support aside. Remove brake rotor. Remove hub/bearing retainer bolts. Remove hub and bearing assembly from knuckle.

3) Carefully remove wheel speed sensor connector using the following procedure. Using a pair of needle-nose pliers, squeeze Connector Position Assurance (CPA) locking pins and pull downward. *See Fig. 4.*

4) Using a slotted screwdriver, push in on retainer tab and remove sensor connector. To install, reverse removal procedure.

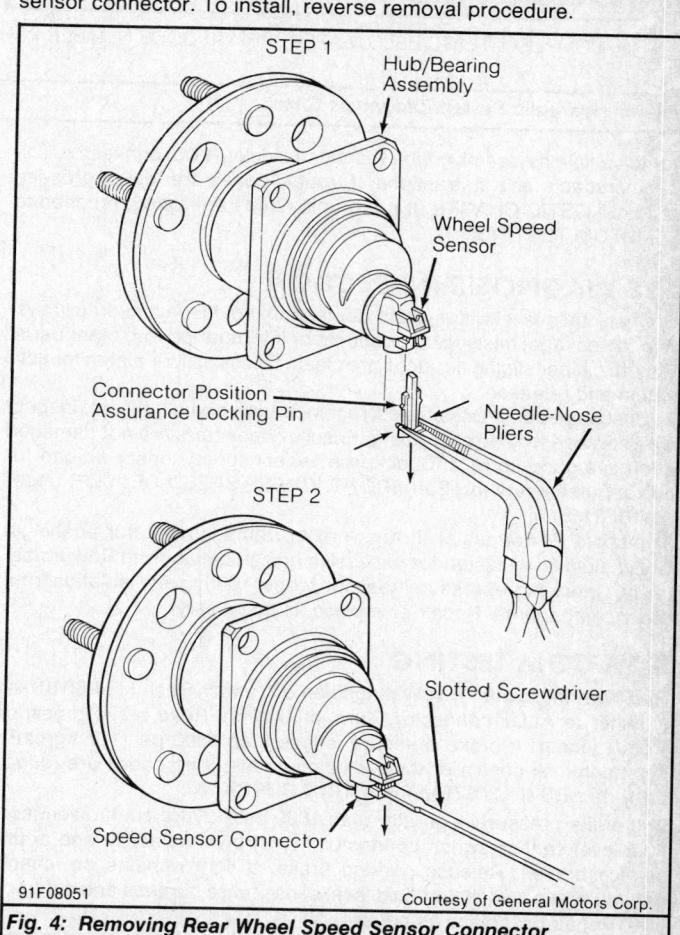

91F08051

Courtesy of General Motors Corp.

Fig. 4: Removing Rear Wheel Speed Sensor Connector

DIAGNOSIS & TESTING

NOTE: A Tech I (94-00101-A) scanner and Pressure Gauge (J-37118) are required to diagnose ABS-III.

Before attempting any diagnostic procedures, road test vehicle to verify complaint. Perform a pre-diagnosis visual inspection to detect any obvious problems. See PRE-DIAGNOSIS INSPECTION.

If no obvious problems are found, and road test verifies customer's complaint, anti-lock brake controller should be scanned for trouble codes. Retrieve trouble codes by attaching Tech I (94-00101-A) scan-

PERFORM TEST(S) ●	CODE SET								
	A023 A024 A025	A026 A027 A028	A031	A035	A044 A045 A046 A047	A048 A049 A050 A051	A056	A059	A062
PRE-DIAGNOSIS INSPECTION	1	1	1	1	1	1	1	1	1
ABS-III FUNCTION CHECK "A"	2						6		
ABS-III FUNCTION CHECK "B"		2					5		
ABS-III FUNCTION CHECK "C"				2			2	3	
ABS-III FUNCTION CHECK "D"				3				4	
ABS-III FUNCTION CHECK "E"							3		
ABS-III FUNCTION CHECK "F"							4	2	
ABS-III FUNCTION CHECK "G"									

● COMPLETE TESTS BELOW APPROPRIATE CODE NUMBER IN NUMERICAL ORDER.

Courtesy of General Motors Corp.

91F11325

Fig. 5: Hydraulic System Diagnosis Chart

ner to vehicle's Assembly Line Diagnostic Link (ALDL) connector. Follow manufacturer's instructions. If trouble codes are found, proceed to DIAGNOSTIC CHARTS. If no trouble codes are found, proceed to SYMPTOM TESTING.

PRE-DIAGNOSIS INSPECTION

1) Check fluid level with system depressurized. Inspect hydraulic system for leakage, missing components or interference with other parts. Ensure caliper sliding surfaces are clean. Check caliper piston for activation and release.
2) Check speed sensors for correct mounting and alignment. Inspect wire harness for correct routing. Ensure connectors are not damaged and have good contact. Check front wheel speed sensor air gap for correct measurement. See FRONT WHEEL SPEED SENSOR under ADJUSTMENT.
3) Inspect Powermaster-III for worn or damaged isolator bushings. Check fluid level. Listen for excessive noise coming from Powermaster-III. Check high-pressure hose for proper routing and isolation from other components. Repair or replace as necessary.

SYMPTOM TESTING

Red Warning Light – 1) With ignition off, attach Tech I (94-00101-A) scanner to ALDL connector. Turn ignition on. Read brake pressure from scanner. If brake pressure is less than 1800 psi (127 kg/cm²), scan anti-lock controller for additional codes. If no codes are found, perform ABS-III SYSTEM FUNCTION CHECK "A".
2) If brake pressure is greater than 1800 psi (127 kg/cm²), disengage fluid level sensor switch connector from Powermaster-III and apply service brakes. Release parking brake. If light remains on, check parking brake switch and fluid level sensor wire harness and connectors. Repair or replace as necessary.

NOTE: The following tests should only be used if a diagnostic chart has directed technician to these tests or if a problem exists but no codes have been set.

ABS-III FUNCTION CHECK "A"

NOTE: An assistant is required to perform ABS-III System Function Check.

ABS-III System Function Check – 1) Attach Tech I (94-00101-A) scanner. Raise vehicle with assistant in driver's seat. Turn ignition on and put transmission in Neutral. Rotate each wheel. All wheels should rotate.

2) Have assistant apply medium pressure to brake pedal. Wheels should not rotate. If front wheels rotate, bleed hydraulic system. See BLEEDING BRAKE SYSTEM.
3) If front wheels still rotate after bleeding system, replace Powermaster-III. If rear wheels rotate, see ABS-III FUNCTION CHECK "C". If wheels do not rotate, proceed to next step.
4) With medium pressure applied to brake pedal, instruct assistant to energize the HOLD and RELEASE solenoids with scanner (Release Function on ABS-III function check menu). Rotate each wheel as its solenoid is energized. Wheel should rotate. Slight drag is okay.
5) If wheel does not rotate, brake pedal fades to floor, or pump runs unacceptably, check wiring harness and corresponding solenoid's connector. If wiring harness and connector are okay, replace solenoid and repeat step 3). If condition persists, replace Powermaster-III.

ABS-III FUNCTION CHECK "B"

ABS-III Hold Function Check – 1) Attach Tech I (94-00101-A) scanner. Raise vehicle with assistant in driver's seat. Turn ignition on and put transmission in Neutral. Instruct assistant to energize the rear hold solenoids with scanner (Rear Hold Function on ABS-III function check menu). Apply medium pressure to service brake.
2) Note pedal travel and pump operational pattern while solenoid is energized. Rear wheel should turn freely for 6 seconds before brake begins application. If brake applies in 5 seconds or less, brake pedal fades to floor, or pump runs excessively, replace Powermaster-III rear solenoid. If problem persists, replace Powermaster-III. If okay, proceed to next step.
3) Instruct assistant to moderately apply brakes. Energize front HOLD solenoids with scanner (Front Hold Function on ABS-III function check menu). Brake fluid spraying within reservoir should not be heard. Apply medium pressure to service brake.
4) Wheel should turn freely for 6 seconds before brake begins application with only driveline resistance. If brake applies in 5 seconds or less, brake pedal fades to floor, or pump runs unacceptably, replace appropriate solenoid in Powermaster-III. If condition continues, replace Powermaster-III.

ABS-III FUNCTION CHECK "C"

Low Or No Boost Pressure Check – 1) Turn ignition off and depressurize system. With ignition off, pump brake pedal a MINIMUM of 40 times with complete pedal strokes. Attach Tech I (94-00101-A) scanner. Perform ABS-III PUMP POWER UP TEST according to Tech I (94-00101-A) scanner manufacturer's instructions. Record total pump run time. If pump run time is 40 seconds or more, perform ABS-III FUNCTION CHECK "D".

2) If pump run time is 40 seconds or less, apply moderate pressure on brake pedal and hold in the applied position. Measure time between brake application and pump start-up. Record total pump off time. If pump off time is 50 seconds or more, system is okay. If pump off time is 50 seconds or less, perform ABS-III FUNCTION CHECK "D".

ABS-III FUNCTION CHECK "D"

Pump-Run Time Excessive – 1) Turn ignition off. Disengage pump wire harness connector. Turn ignition on. Connect Digital Volt-Ohmmeter (DVOM) positive lead to pin "A" (White wire). Connect negative DVOM lead to ground and measure voltage. If voltage is less than 12 volts, check battery, charging system and related circuitry.

2) If voltage is greater than 12 volts, turn ignition off. Connect pump wire harness connector and depressurize system. With ignition off, pump brake pedal a MINIMUM of 40 times with complete pedal strokes. Remove accumulator and install Pressure Gauge (J-37118). Attach accumulator on pressure gauge. Bleed Powermaster-III at bleeder valves. Turn ignition on while observing pressure gauge.

3) System pressure should quickly rise from zero to 500 psi (35 kg/cm²). If system pressure does not rise quickly, replace accumulator. Turn ignition on to charge system. Observe maximum system pressure. If system pressure is more than 2900 psi (204 kg/cm²), replace pressure switch.

4) Observe pump activity with scanner while applying brake pedal 3 times. Record low-pressure reading when pump is turned on. Motor should come on at 2000 psi (141 kg/cm²) or higher. If motor does not come on at specified pressure, replace pressure switch.

CAUTION: DO NOT apply brakes with reservoir cover removed.

---

5) If pressure switch is okay, check pump inlet in reservoir assembly for restriction. Turn ignition on with engine off. If inlet is clear, place clear plastic hose over relief valve in reservoir. *See Fig. 7.*

6) Hold other end of tube (downward) in reservoir rear chamber. If fluid flows through tube into reservoir, replace relief valve. If fluid does not flow through tube, place one end of clear plastic tube over booster return port. *See Fig. 7.*

7) Place other end of tube (pointing downward) in rear reservoir. Turn ignition on. If fluid flows through tube, replace Powermaster-III unit. If no fluid flows, replace pump and motor.

ABS-III FUNCTION CHECK "E"

Pump Run Time Insufficient – 1) Depressurize system. With ignition off, pump brake pedal a MINIMUM of 40 times with complete pedal strokes. Remove accumulator and install Pressure Gauge (J-37118). Attach accumulator on gauge. *See Fig. 6.* Bleed Powermaster-III at bleeder valves. Bleed brake system. See BLEEDING BRAKE SYSTEM. Turn on ignition while observing pressure gauge.

2) System pressure should quickly rise from zero to 500 psi (35 kg/cm²). If pressure is not as specified, replace accumulator. If pressure is okay, allow system to pressurize until pump stops. Apply and hold brake pedal while observing time necessary to activate pump.

3) If pump off time is less than 50 seconds, check accumulator precharge. If precharge is less than 600 psi (42 kg/cm²), replace accumulator. If precharge exceeds 600 psi, pump off time must increase proportionately. See MINIMUM PUMP OFF TIME table. If pump off time does not increase proportionately, replace Powermaster-III unit.

MINIMUM PUMP-OFF TIME

Accumulator psi	Seconds
600	30
700	35
800	40
900	45
1000	50
1100	55
1200	60

ABS-III FUNCTION CHECK "F"

External Leak Inspection – 1) Depressurize Powermaster-III. With ignition off, pump brake pedal a MINIMUM of 40 times with complete

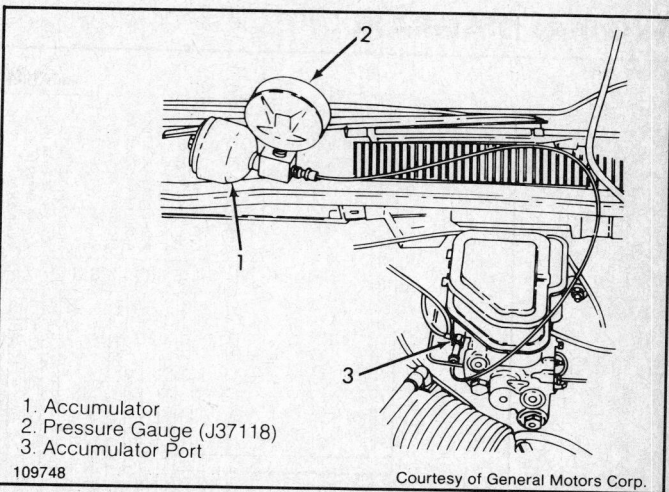

1. Accumulator
2. Pressure Gauge (J37118)
3. Accumulator Port

109748

Courtesy of General Motors Corp.

Fig. 6: Checking Pressure for ABS-III FUNCTION CHECK "E"

pedal strokes. Clean reservoir area and remove cover. If fluid level is high, remove excess fluid. Clean brake system components so source of leak can be isolated and located.

2) Install reservoir cover. Turn ignition on and pump brake pedal several times. Turn ignition off and inspect for leaks. If leakage is found, repair or replace as necessary. If no leakage occurs, proceed to next step.

3) Depressurize Powermaster-III. Inspect reservoir fluid level. If fluid level in FRONT chamber is high, proceed to ABS-III FUNCTION CHECK "G". If fluid level in REAR chamber is high, replace Powermaster-III.

ABS-III FUNCTION CHECK "G"

Internal Fluid Leak To Front Chamber – 1) Depressurize Powermaster-III. With ignition off, pump brake pedal a MINIMUM of 40 times with complete pedal strokes. Remove reservoir cover. Drain front chamber to below left/right divider. Replace reservoir cover. Turn ignition on to charge system and pump brake pedal several times.

2) Depressurize Powermaster-III again. Inspect reservoir fluid level. If fluid level has risen in either FRONT chamber, replace Powermaster-III. If fluid level has stabilized or dropped, replace reservoir and cover assembly.

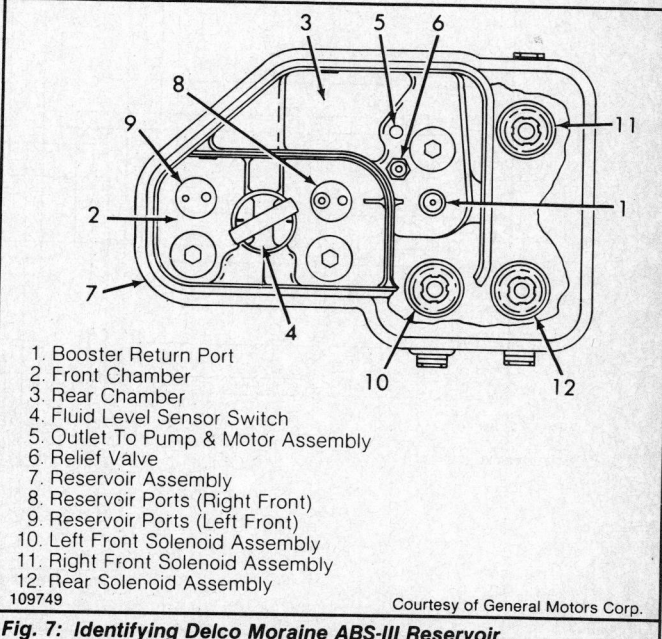

1. Booster Return Port
2. Front Chamber
3. Rear Chamber
4. Fluid Level Sensor Switch
5. Outlet To Pump & Motor Assembly
6. Relief Valve
7. Reservoir Assembly
8. Reservoir Ports (Right Front)
9. Reservoir Ports (Left Front)
10. Left Front Solenoid Assembly
11. Right Front Solenoid Assembly
12. Rear Solenoid Assembly

109749

Courtesy of General Motors Corp.

Fig. 7: Identifying Delco Moraine ABS-III Reservoir Assembly Components

WIRING DIAGRAM

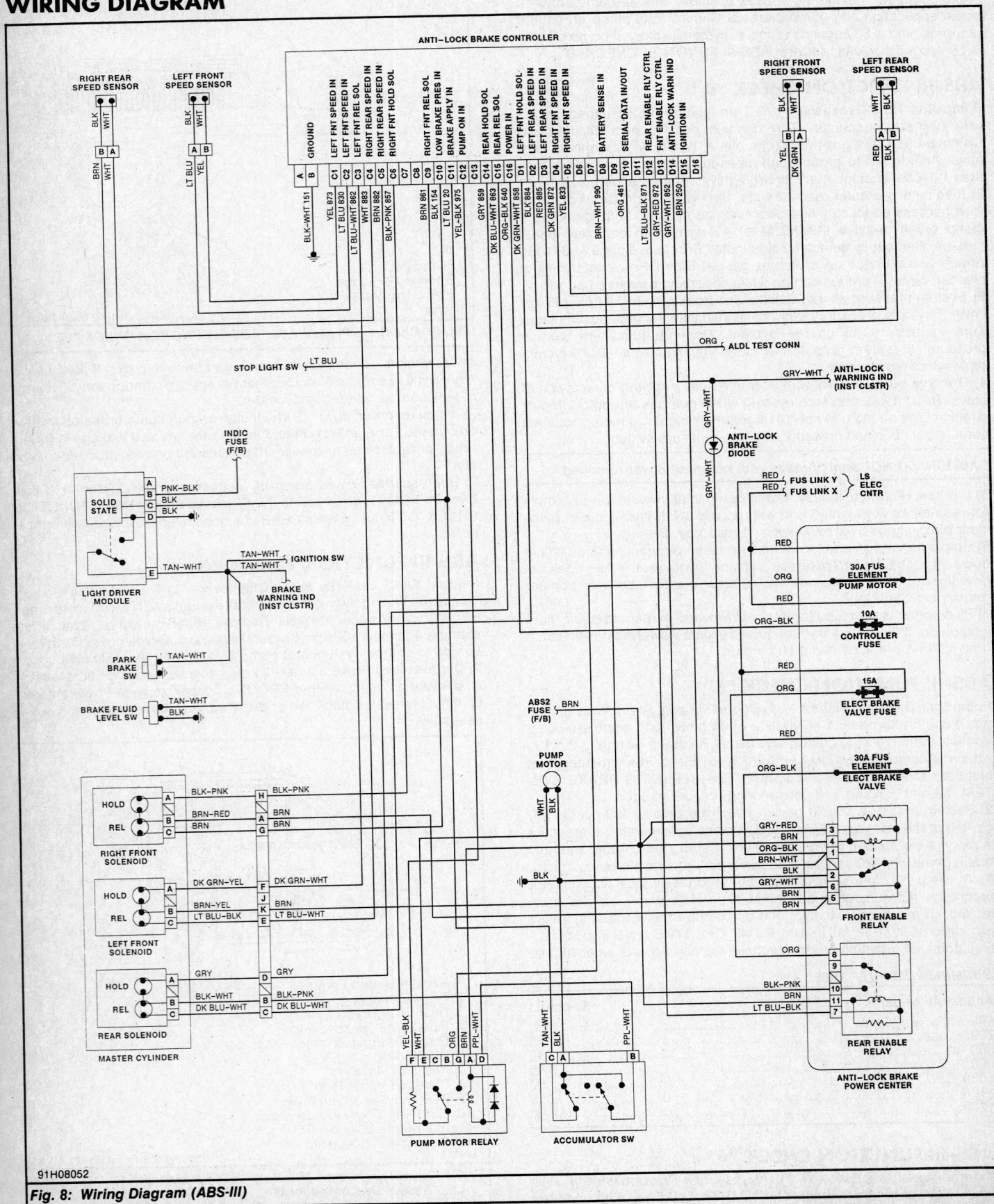

Fig. 8: Wiring Diagram (ABS-III)

91H08052

ABS-III SNAPSHOT

The ABS-III snapshot feature is used to locate variations in data that cause intermittent problems in anti-lock brake system components. This feature uses a trigger that can be set to take a snapshot of any ABS-III code. See Tech I (94-00101-A) scanner manufacturer's instructions for more information.

ENHANCED DIAGNOSTICS

The enhanced diagnostics feature is used to locate intermittent problems in anti-lock brake system components. This feature provides information regarding the frequency of intermittent fault and gives detail of order in which the last 5 trouble codes were set. See Tech I (94-00101-A) scanner manufacturer's instructions for more information.

INTERMITTENTS

To effectively locate fault(s) using charts, problem must currently be present. The diagnostic procedures may help determine the cause of intermittent problems in anti-lock brake system electrical components. Most intermittent problems are caused by faulty electrical connections or wiring.

When an intermittent failure is encountered, check for trouble codes stored in the anti-lock brake controller. If trouble codes are found,

inspect related components and circuitry for poor connections. If no trouble code is found, visually check suspected circuits.

- Check for Poor mating of connector halves or terminals not fully seated in connector body (backed out).
- Check for improperly formed or damaged terminals. All connector terminals in problem circuit should be carefully re-formed to increase contact tension.
- Check for poor terminal-to-wire connection. Remove terminal and wire from connector body to inspect.

If visual check does not identify cause of problem, use the ABS-III self-diagnostic system to help locate suspected circuit as follows.

- Display and then clear ABS-III trouble codes in anti-lock brake controller.
- Test drive vehicle, attempting to duplicate conditions that caused problem or complaint. Stop vehicle and record any codes set.

Intermittent operation of anti-lock light may be caused by the following circuits:

- Wheel speed sensor circuits – low or intermittent output
- Main relay – interruption in coil or switched battery power

Program ABS-III snapshot to identify intermittent fault. Use the enhanced diagnostic feature to recreate conditions causing trouble code to set. Determine how often and under what conditions fault occurs. See Tech I (94-00101-A) scanner manufacturer's instruction for more information. Analyze ABS-III snapshot data for unusual conditions.

DIAGNOSTIC CHARTS

ABS-III DIAGNOSTICS CANNOT BE ENTERED

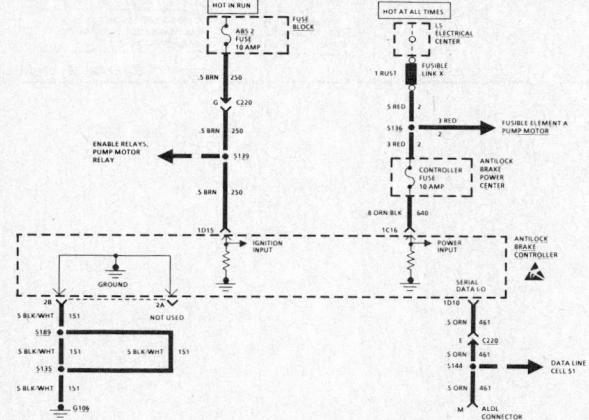

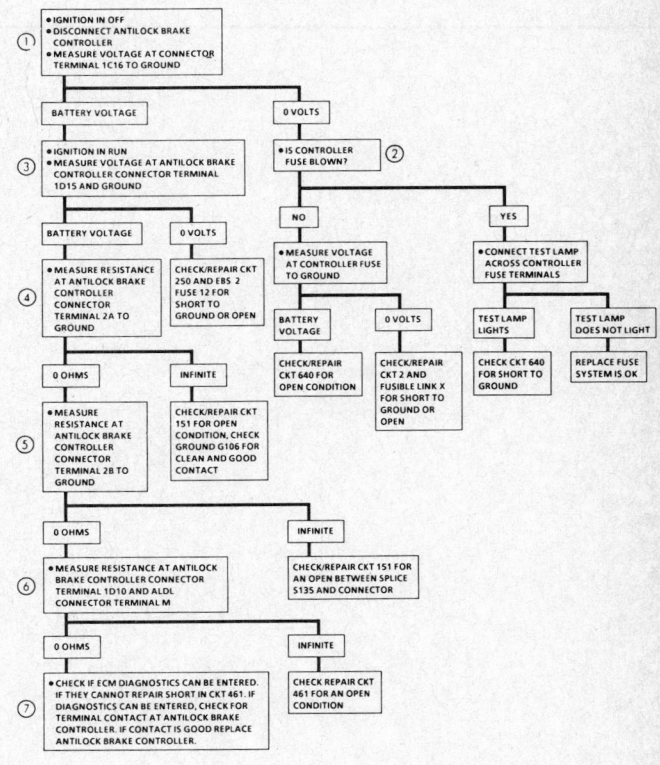

7) A short to ground has prevented communication between Anti-Lock Brake Controller and ECM. If connector has good contact and short cannot be found, replace Anti-Lock Brake Controller.

If power or ground supply to Anti-Lock Brake Controller is lost, the anti-lock brake system will be disabled and the Amber ANTI-LOCK warning light will come on.

NOTE: Test numbers refer to test numbers on diagnostic chart.

1) Determines if voltage is being applied to Anti-Lock Brake Controller at terminal 1C16.
2) Indicates whether fault is due to open condition or possible short to ground in circuit No. 640.
3) Determines if voltage is being applied to Anti-Lock Brake Controller at terminal 1D15.
4) If resistance is infinite, one or both of the Anti-Lock Brake Controller ground circuits are open.
5) If resistance is infinite, one or both of the Anti-Lock Brake Controller ground circuits are open.
6) If resistance is infinite, an open condition exists in data line circuit No. 461, preventing controller from communicating with scanner.

CODE A001, ANTI-LOCK WARNING INDICATOR OPEN OR SHORTED TO GROUND

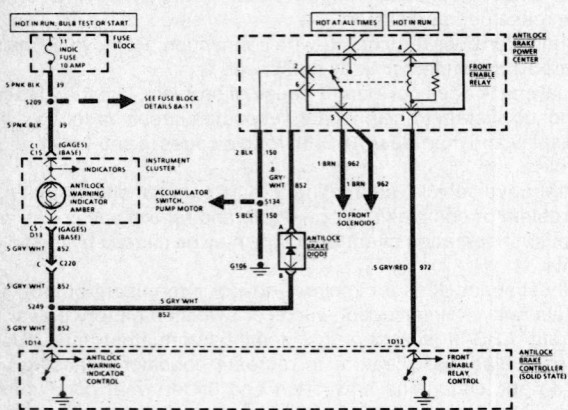

As the Front Enable Relay is energized, the contacts close and the ground path from the ANTI-LOCK warning indicator is opened. To set Code A001, the following conditions must occur.

- Front Enable Relay is energized.
- ANTI-LOCK warning indicator control is open.
- Anti-Lock Brake Controller senses no voltage at terminal 1D14.

NOTE: Test numbers refer to test numbers on diagnostic chart.

1) The G106 circuit from indicator to ground is good if the ANTI-LOCK warning indicator illuminates.
2) Energize Front Enable Relay to determine if circuit No. 852 to Anti-Lock Brake Controller is functional.
3) Voltage at 1D14 indicates circuit No. 852 is functional.
4) This establishes whether malfunction is open or short to ground.

111967   111968

5) Isolates ANTI-LOCK warning indicator to determine if short is in circuit No. 852 or Anti-Lock Brake Controller is defective.
6) Check for short to ground in circuit No. 39.
7) Determines whether open is in circuit No. 852 or circuit No. 39.

NOTE: To diagnose intermittent fault, see INTERMITTENTS under DIAGNOSIS & TESTING.

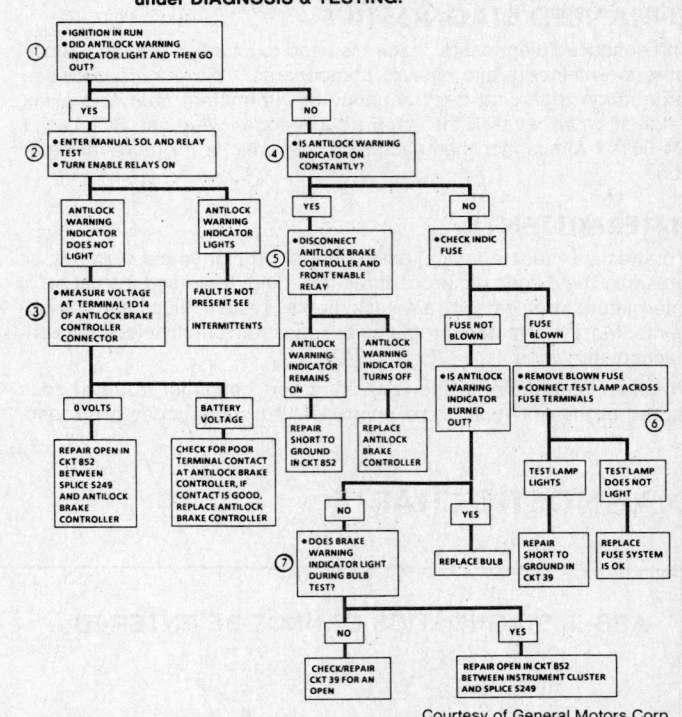

CODE A002, ANTI-LOCK WARNING INDICATOR SHORTED TO BATTERY OR DIODE SHORTED

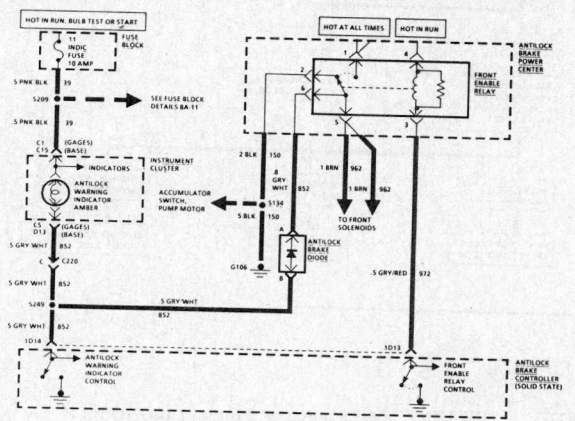

As the Front Enable Relay is energized, the Anti-Lock Brake Diode prevents voltage from being applied to the ANTI-LOCK warning indicator. If the Anti-Lock Brake Controller is inoperative, the Anti-Lock Brake Diode permits the ANTI-LOCK warning indicator to ground through de-energized Front Enable Relay. To set Code A002, the following conditions must occur.

- Front Enable Relay is energized.
- ANTI-LOCK warning indicator control is closed.
- Anti-Lock Brake Controller senses battery voltage at terminal 1D14.

NOTE: Test numbers refer to test numbers on diagnostic chart.

1) Isolates ANTI-LOCK warning indicator circuit to determine if another voltage source is shorted into the circuit or Anti-Lock Brake Controller is defective.
2) This establishes whether Anti-Lock Brake Diode is shorted, or short to battery exists in circuit No. 852.

NOTE: INTERMITTENTS is located under DIAGNOSIS & TESTING portion of this article.

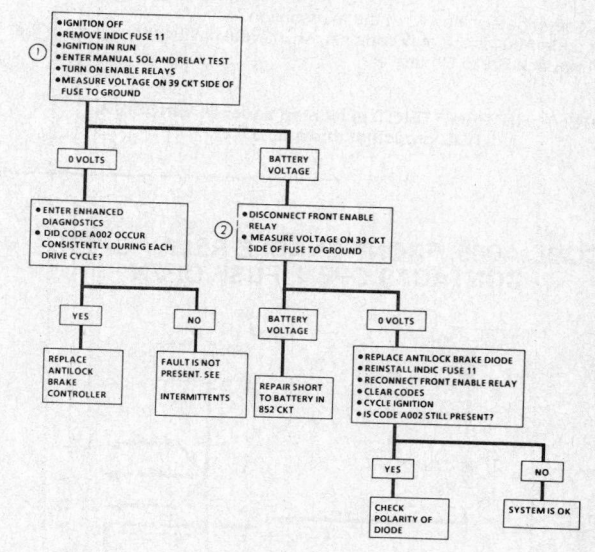

CODE A003, ANTI-LOCK BRAKE DIODE OPEN OR SHORTED TO GROUND

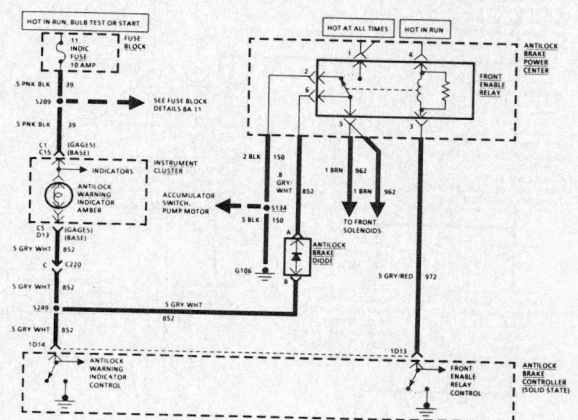

If the Anti-Lock Brake Controller loses power or ground, the ANTI-LOCK warning indicator is grounded through circuit No. 852, Anti-Lock Brake Diode, Front Enable Relay and circuit No. 150. The Anti-Lock Brake Diode prevents voltage from being applied to the ANTI-LOCK warning indicator when Front Enable Relay is energized. To set Code A003, the following conditions must occur.

- Front Enable Relay is not energized.
- ANTI-LOCK warning indicator control is open.
- Anti-Lock Brake Controller senses battery voltage at terminal 1D14.

NOTE: Test numbers refer to test numbers on diagnostic chart.

1) If Code 039 is set, circuit No. 150 is open.
2) This establishes whether an open or possible intermittent condition exists.
3) Determines if the condition is between splice S249 and Front Enable Relay.

4) Determines if the condition is in circuit No. 852 between splice S249 and Anti-Lock Brake Diode.
5) This establishes whether an open exists in circuit No. 852 to Front Enable Relay or in Anti-Lock Brake Diode.

NOTE: INTERMITTENTS is located under DIAGNOSIS & TESTING portion of this article.

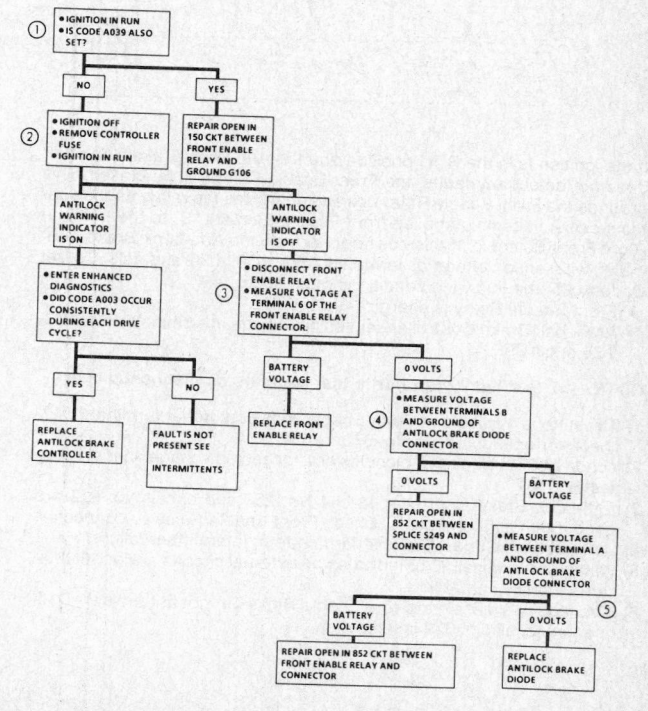

111967, 109754, 111967, 109756

CODE A004, ENABLE RELAY OR SOLENOID FAULT DETECTED

The Anti-Lock Brake Controller uses Code A004, as a pretest, to detect malfunction in solenoid or enable relay circuits. Code A004 should always be set with another code; this other code is the one identifying the malfunction.

NOTE: Test numbers refer to test numbers on diagnostic chart.

1) Code(s) determines what the malfunction is.
2) If code A004 is the only code set, an internal malfunction exists in the Anti-Lock Brake Controller.

NOTE: INTERMITTENTS is located under DIAGNOSIS & TESTING portion of this article.

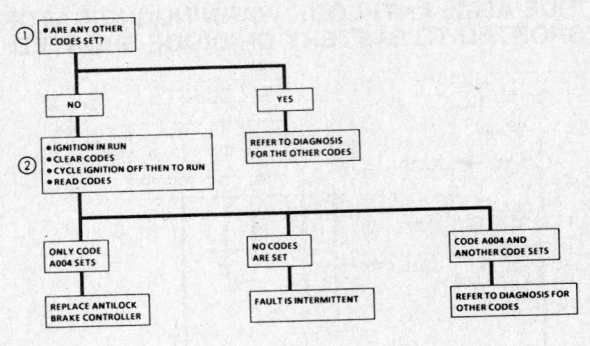

CODE A005, FRONT ENABLE RELAY OPEN, CONTACTS OPEN, FUSE OPEN

NOTE: INTERMITTENTS is located under DIAGNOSIS & TESTING portion of this article.

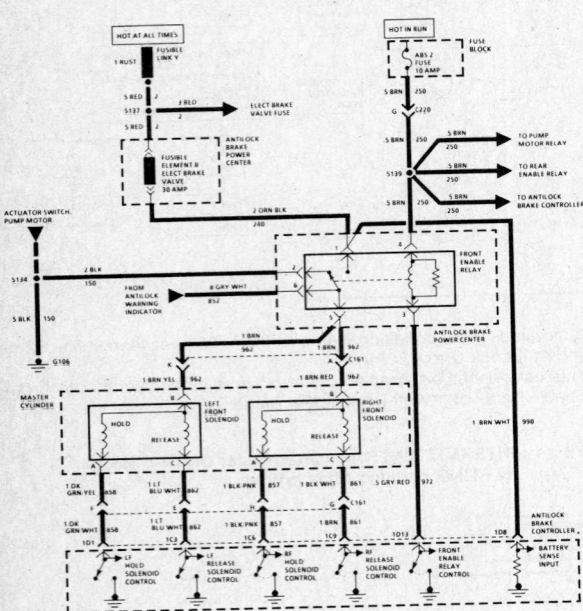

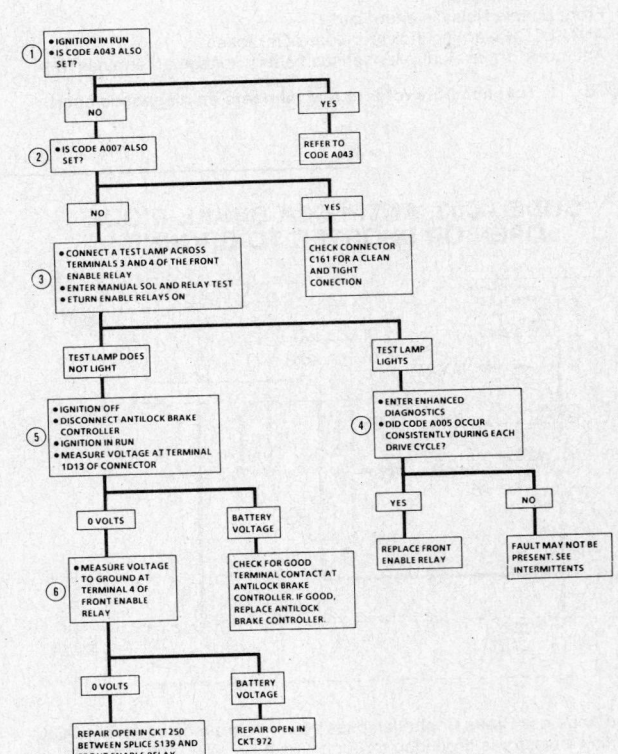

If the ignition is in the RUN position and the Anti-Lock Brake Controller does not detect any faults, the Front Enable Relay will be closed. This grounds the Front Enable Relay coil and energizes the relay. As the contacts close, voltage is applied from Fusible Element "B" to the Left and Right Front Solenoid. If this does not happen, the Anti-Lock Brake Controller will sense voltage at terminals 1D1, 1C3, 1C6 and 1C9. To set Code A005, the following conditions must occur.

- Front Enable Relay is energized (closed).
- Anti-Lock Brake Controller senses no voltage at terminals 1D1, 1C3, 1C6 and 1C9.

NOTE: Test numbers refer to test numbers on diagnostic chart.

1) If voltage is available at Front Enable Relay but not at terminal 1D13, check for open in circuit No. 972.
2) If code A007 is also set, solenoids are not getting voltage. Inspect connector C161.
3) Anti-Lock Brake Controller, circuit No. 250 and circuit No. 972 are good if test light energizes. Check Front Enable Relay or connector.
4) Determines if Code A005 is a hard code or intermittent failure.
5) Voltage at terminal 1D13 indicates all external circuits are good. Indicates a faulty controller.
6) If voltage is available at Front Enable Relay but not at terminal 1D13, open in circuit No. 972 is indicated.

CODE A006, FRONT ENABLE COIL SHORTED TO BATTERY

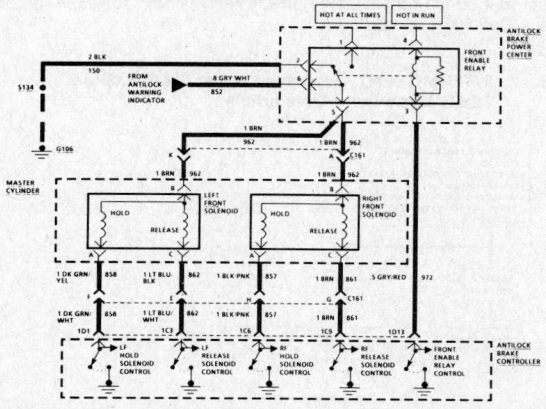

The Front Enable Relay receives voltage when the ignition is in the RUN position and Front Enable Relay Control is open. When Front Enable Relay Control is closed, Front Enable Relay terminal No. 3 and circuit No. 972 are grounded so terminal 1D13 of Anti-Lock Brake Controller will not have voltage. To set Code A006, the following conditions must occur.

- Front Enable Relay Control is energized (closed).
- Anti-Lock Brake Controller senses voltage at terminal 1D13.
- Anti-Lock Brake Controller senses no voltage at terminals 1D1, 1C3, 1C6 and 1C9.

NOTE: Test numbers refer to test numbers on diagnostic chart.

1) If both Enable Relay connectors are disconnected, Code A008 will be set.
2) Disconnect Front Enable Relay to determine if short to battery exists.
3) Test for short in Front Enable Relay.

4) Code A005 will set if open exists in relay coil.
5) Code A006 indicates Anti-Lock Brake Controller is defective.

NOTE: INTERMITTENTS is located under DIAGNOSIS & TESTING portion of this article.

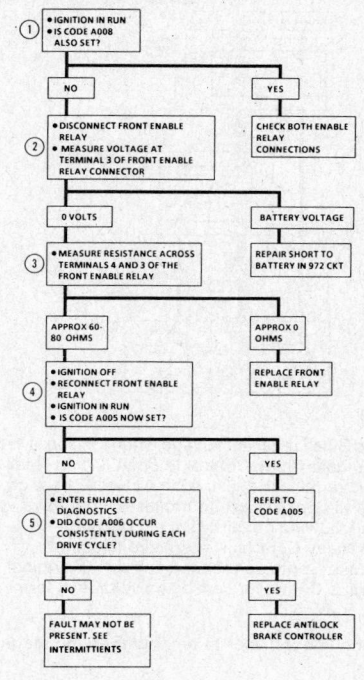

CODE A007, REAR ENABLE RELAY OPEN, CONTACTS OPEN, FUSE OPEN

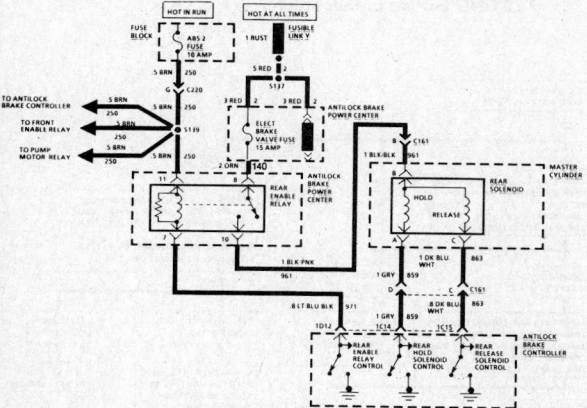

If ignition is in the RUN position and Anti-Lock Brake Controller does not detect any faults, Rear Enable Relay will be closed. This grounds Rear Enable Relay coil and energizes relay. As the contacts close, voltage is applied from ELECT BRAKE VALVE Fuse to the Rear Solenoid. If this does not happen, the Anti-Lock Brake Controller will sense voltage at terminals 1C14 and 1C15. To set Code A007, the following conditions must occur.

- Rear Enable Relay is energized (closed).
- Anti-Lock Brake Controller senses no voltage at terminals 1C14 and 1C15.

NOTE: Test numbers refer to test numbers on diagnostic chart.

1) If code A005 is also set, solenoids are not getting voltage. Inspect connector C161.
2) Code A054 will set if relay coil circuit is open.
3) Checks relay contact power feed.
4) Rear Solenoid and circuit No. 961 are good if battery voltage is present.

5) Check for open in Rear Solenoid and circuit No. 961.
6) Determines if Code A007 is hard or intermittent failure.
7) Check for short in Rear Solenoid and circuit No. 140.
8) If test light is on, check for short in circuit No. 961.
9) Checks power feed to ELECT BRAKE VALVE Fuse.

NOTE: INTERMITTENTS is located under DIAGNOSIS & TESTING portion of this article.

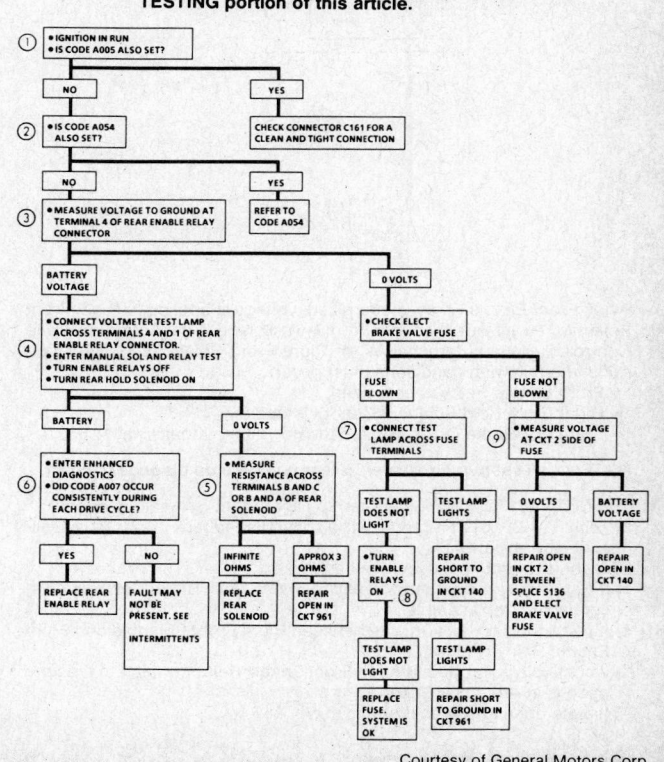

CODE A008, REAR ENABLE COIL SHORTED TO BATTERY

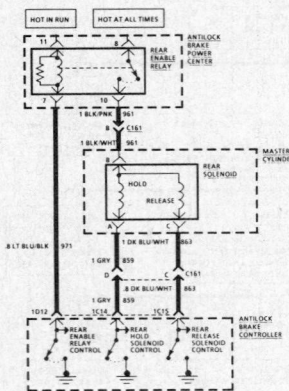

The Rear Enable Relay receives voltage when ignition is in the RUN position and Rear Enable Relay Control is open. When Rear Enable Relay Control is closed, terminal No. 7 and circuit No. 971 are grounded so terminal 1D12 of Anti-Lock Brake Controller will not have voltage. To set Code A008, the following conditions must occur.
- Rear Enable Relay Control is energized (closed).
- Anti-Lock Brake Controller senses voltage at terminal 1C12.
- Anti-Lock Brake Controller senses no voltage at terminals 1C14 and 1C15.

NOTE: Test numbers refer to test numbers on diagnostic chart.

1) With battery voltage at terminal No. 7, disconnect Rear Enable Relay to determine if short to battery exists in circuit No. 971.
2) Test for short in Front Enable Relay. If relay is not shorted, Anti-Lock Brake Controller is defective.

NOTE: INTERMITTENTS is located under DIAGNOSIS & TESTING portion of this article.

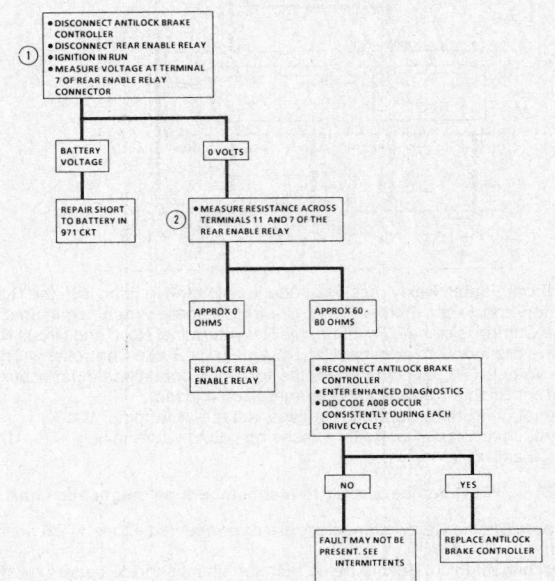

CODE A009, RIGHT FRONT HOLD SOLENOID OPEN OR SHORTED TO GROUND

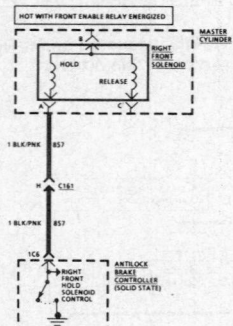

When Front Enable Relay is energized, voltage is applied to Right Front Solenoid. To activate the Right Front Hold Solenoid, the Anti-Lock Brake Controller grounds terminal "A" of Right Front Solenoid. To set Code A009, the following conditions must occur.
- Front Enable Relay is energized.
- Right Front Hold Solenoid Control is open.
- Anti-Lock Brake Controller senses no voltage at terminal 1C6.

NOTE: Test numbers refer to test numbers on diagnostic chart.

1) If Code A012 is set, power feed to Right Front Solenoid is open.
2) Tech I (94-00101-A) scanner will display HI feedback if voltage is available at terminal 1C6.
3) A short to ground exists if test light is on.
4) If a short to ground does not exist with Anti-Lock Brake Controller disconnected, replace unit.
5) If test light is on, Brown wire between Right Front Solenoid and Front Enable Relay is okay.
6) If continuity to ground through Front Enable Relay contacts is present, open is in Anti-Lock Brake Controller.
7) Isolate open in solenoid or circuit No. 857.

NOTE: INTERMITTENTS is located under DIAGNOSIS & TESTING portion of this article.

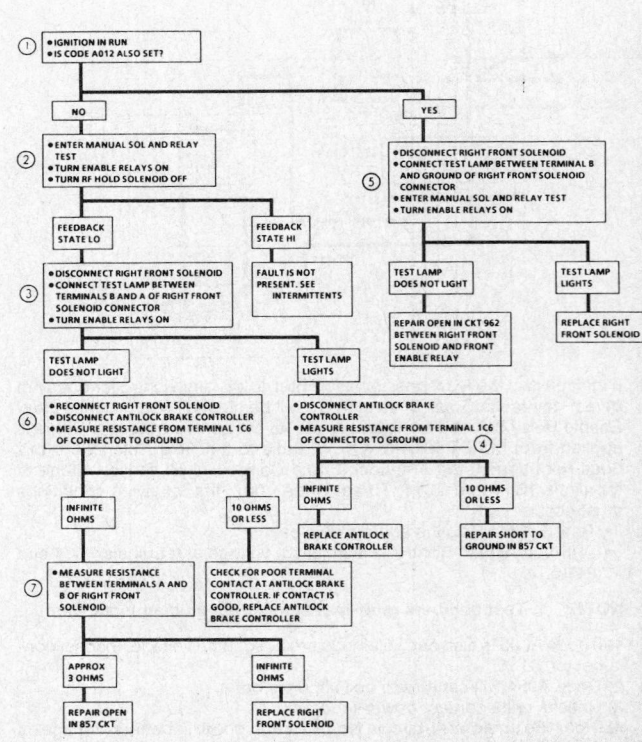

CODE A010, LEFT FRONT HOLD SOLENOID OPEN OR SHORTED TO GROUND

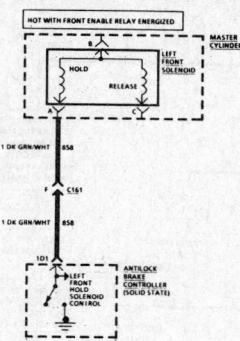

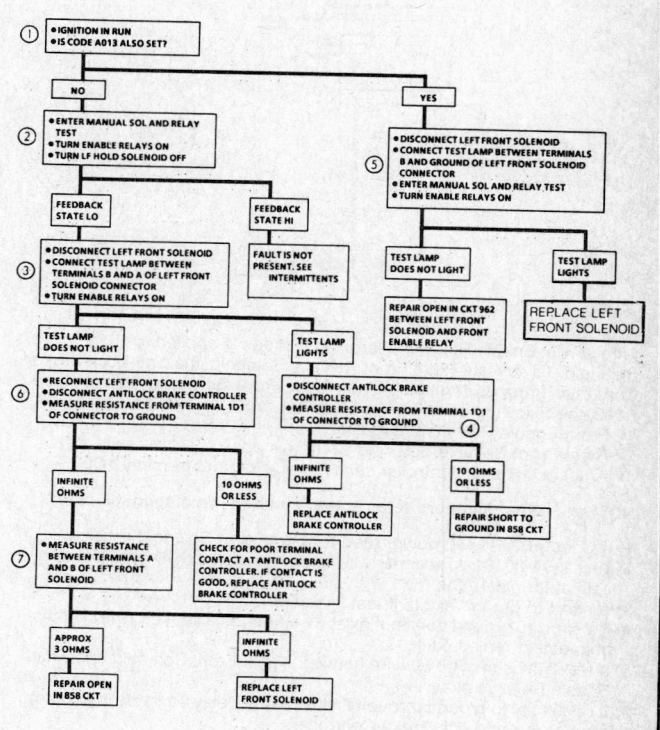

NOTE: INTERMITTENTS is located under DIAGNOSIS & TESTING portion of this article.

When Front Enable Relay is energized, voltage is applied to Left Front Solenoid. To activate Left Front Hold Solenoid, the Anti-Lock Brake Controller grounds terminal "A" of Left Front Solenoid. To set Code A010, the following conditions must occur.

- Front Enable Relay is energized.
- Left Front Hold Solenoid Control is open.
- Anti-Lock Brake Controller senses no voltage at terminal 1D1.

NOTE: Test numbers refer to test numbers on diagnostic chart.

1) If Code A013 is set, power feed to Left Front Solenoid is open.
2) Tech I (94-00101-A) scanner will display HI feedback if voltage is available at terminal 1D1.
3) A short to ground exists if test light is on.
4) If a short to ground does not exist with Anti-Lock Brake Controller disconnected, replace controller.
5) If test light is on, Brown wire between Left Front Solenoid and Front Enable Relay is okay.
6) If continuity to ground through Front Enable Relay contacts is present, open is in Anti-Lock Brake Controller.
7) Isolate open in solenoid or circuit No. 858.

CODE A011, REAR HOLD SOLENOID OPEN OR SHORTED TO GROUND

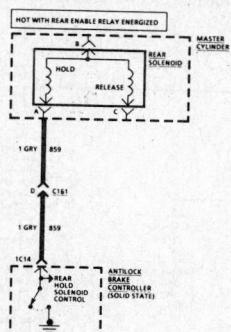

6) If test light is on, Rear Hold Solenoid and circuit No. 859 are okay.
7) Isolates open to solenoid or circuit No. 859.

NOTE: INTERMITTENTS is located under DIAGNOSIS & TESTING portion of this article.

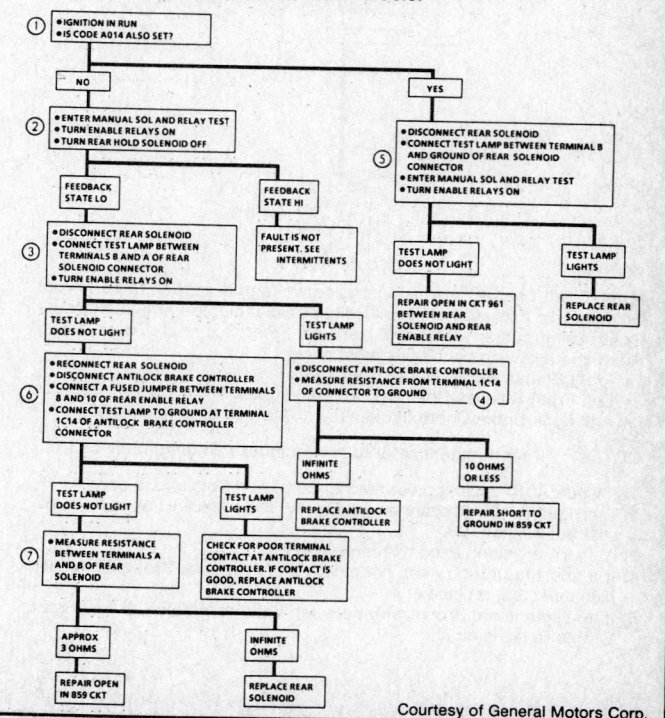

When Rear Enable Relay is energized, voltage is applied to Rear Solenoid. To activate Rear Hold Solenoid, the Anti-Lock Brake Controller grounds terminal "A" of Rear Solenoid. To set Code A011, the following conditions must occur.

- Rear Enable Relay Control is energized.
- Rear Hold Solenoid Control is open.
- Anti-Lock Brake Controller senses no voltage at terminal 1C14.

NOTE: Test numbers refer to test numbers on diagnostic chart.

1) If Code A014 is set, power feed to Rear Solenoid is open.
2) Tech I (94-00101-A) scanner will display HI feedback if voltage is available at terminal 1C14.
3) A short to ground exists if test light is on.
4) If a short to ground does not exist with Anti-Lock Brake Controller disconnected, replace unit.
5) If test light is on, Black wire between Rear Solenoid and Rear Enable Relay is okay.

109813   109814   109816   109815

CODE A012, RIGHT FRONT RELEASE SOLENOID OPEN OR SHORTED TO GROUND

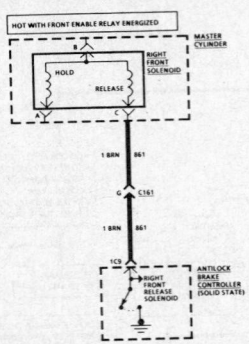

When Front Enable Relay is energized, voltage is applied to Right Front Solenoid. To activate Right Front Release Solenoid, the Anti-Lock Brake Controller grounds terminal "C" of Right Front Solenoid. To set Code A012, the following conditions must occur.

- Front Enable Relay is energized.
- Right Front Release Solenoid Control is open.
- Anti-Lock Brake Controller senses no voltage at terminal 1C9.

NOTE: Test numbers refer to test numbers on diagnostic chart.

1) If Code A009 is set, power feed to Right Front Solenoid is open.
2) Tech I (94-00101-A) scanner will display HI feedback if voltage is available at terminal 1C9.
3) A short to ground exists if test light is on.
4) If a short to ground does not exist with Anti-Lock Brake Controller disconnected, replace unit.
5) If test light is on, Brown wire between Right Front Solenoid and Front Enable Relay is okay.
6) If continuity to ground through Front Enable Relay contacts is present, open is in Anti-Lock Brake Controller.
7) Isolate open in solenoid or circuit No. 861.

NOTE: INTERMITTENTS is located under DIAGNOSIS & TESTING portion of this article.

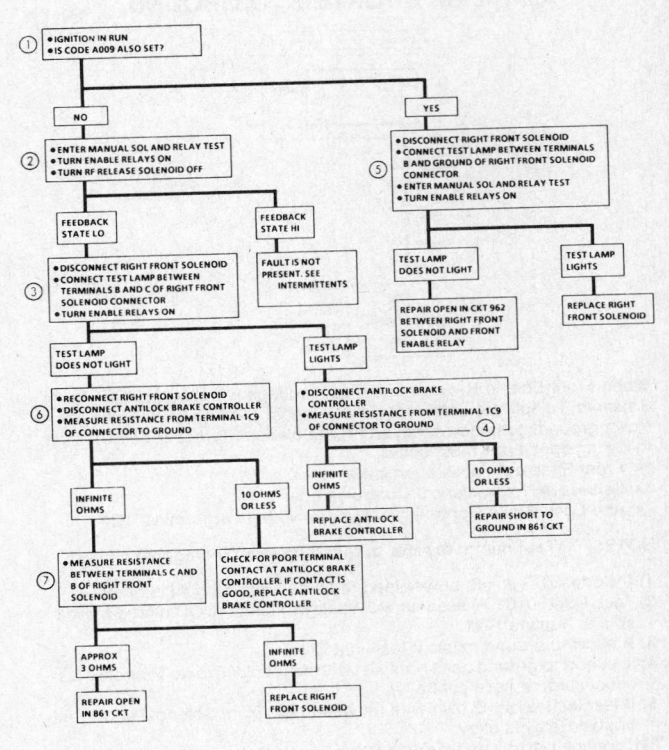

CODE A013, LEFT FRONT RELEASE SOLENOID OPEN OR SHORTED TO GROUND

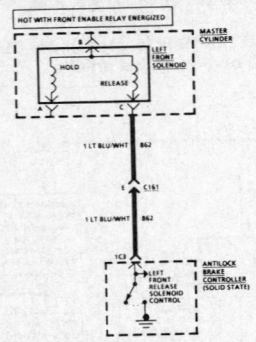

When Front Enable Relay is energized, voltage is applied to Left Front Solenoid. To activate Left Front Release Solenoid, the Anti-Lock Brake Controller grounds terminal "C" of Left Front Solenoid. To set Code A013, the following conditions must occur.

- Front Enable Relay is energized.
- Left Front Release Solenoid Control is open.
- Anti-Lock Brake Controller senses no voltage at terminal 1C3.

NOTE: Test numbers refer to test numbers on diagnostic chart.

1) If Code A010 is set, power feed to Left Front Solenoid is open.
2) Tech I (94-00101-A) scanner will display HI feedback if voltage is available at terminal 1C3.
3) A short to ground exists if test light is on.
4) If a short to ground does not exists with Anti-Lock Brake Controller disconnected, replace unit.
5) If test light is on, Brown wire between Left Front Solenoid and Front Enable Relay is okay.

6) If continuity to ground through Front Enable Relay contacts is present, open is in Anti-Lock Brake Controller.
7) Isolate open in solenoid or circuit No. 862.

NOTE: INTERMITTENTS is located under DIAGNOSIS & TESTING portion of this article.

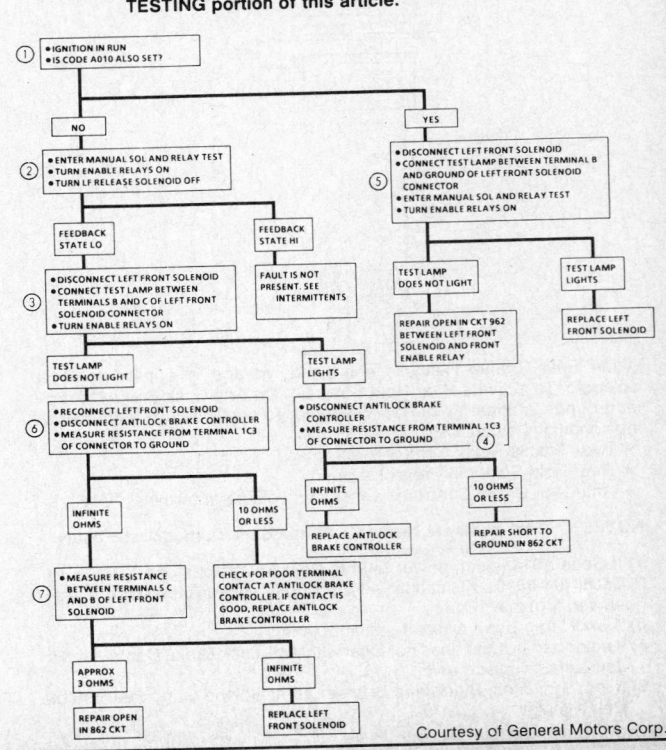

Courtesy of General Motors Corp.

CODE A014, REAR RELEASE SOLENOID OPEN OR SHORTED TO GROUND

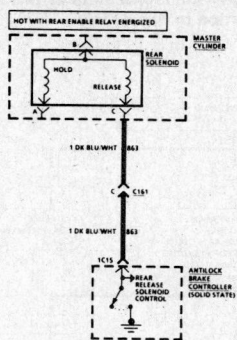

When Rear Enable Relay is energized, voltage is applied to Rear Solenoid. To activate Rear Release Solenoid, the Anti-Lock Brake Controller grounds terminal "C" of Rear Solenoid. To set Code A014, the following conditions must occur.

- Rear Enable Relay is energized.
- Rear Release Solenoid Control is open.
- Anti-Lock Brake Controller senses no voltage at terminal 1C15.

NOTE: Test numbers refer to test numbers on diagnostic chart.

1) If Code A011 is set, power feed to Rear Solenoid is open.
2) Tech I (94-00101-A) scanner will display HI feedback if voltage is available at terminal 1C15.
3) A short to ground exists if test light is on.
4) If a short to ground does not exists with Anti-Lock Brake Controller disconnected, replace unit.
5) If test light is on, Black wire between Rear Solenoid and Rear Enable Relay is okay.
6) If test light is on, Rear Hold Solenoid and circuit No. 863 are okay.
7) Isolate open in solenoid or circuit No. 863.

NOTE: INTERMITTENTS is located under DIAGNOSIS & TESTING portion of this article.

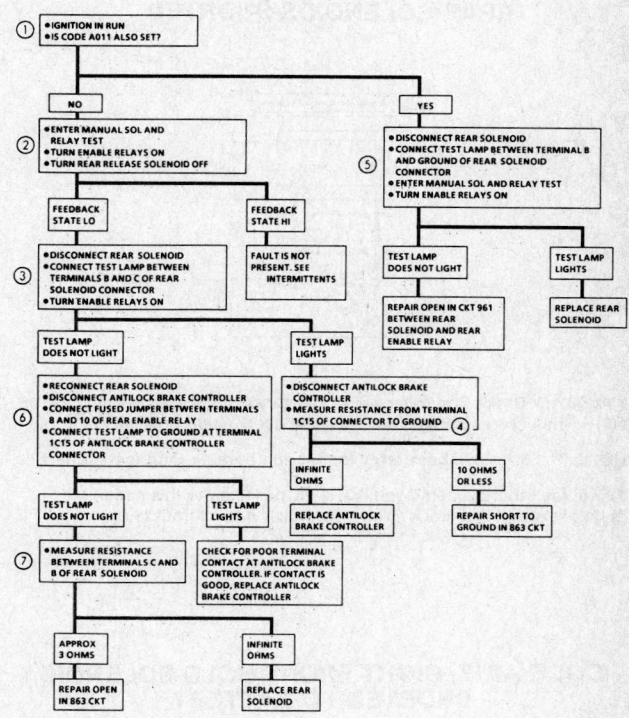

CODE A015, ONE OR MORE FRONT SOLENOIDS SHORTED

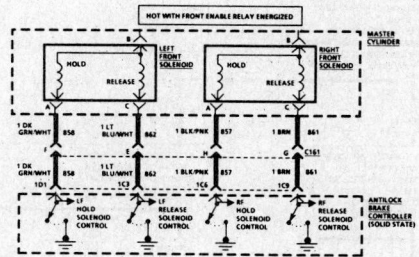

If Anti-Lock Brake Controller senses battery voltage at terminals 1D1, 1C3, 1C6 or 1C9 when corresponding solenoid is closed, Code A015 will set.

NOTE: Test numbers refer to test numbers on diagnostic chart.

1) The fault that caused Code A015 will be linked to this circuit.
2) If consistent, Anti-Lock Brake Controller has internal fault.

NOTE: INTERMITTENTS is located under DIAGNOSIS & TESTING portion of this article.

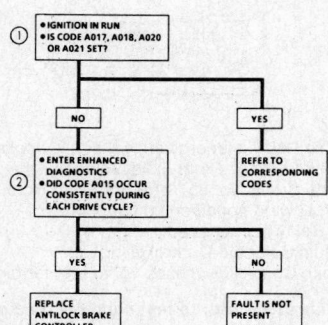

CODE A016, ONE OR MORE REAR SOLENOIDS SHORTED

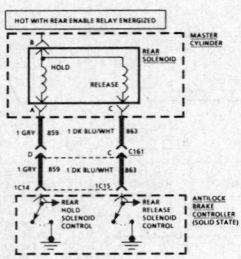

If Anti-Lock Brake Controller senses battery voltage at terminal 1C14, or 1C15 when corresponding solenoid is closed, Code A016 will set.

NOTE: Test numbers refer to test numbers on diagnostic chart.

1) The fault that caused Code A016 will be linked to this circuit.
2) If consistent, Anti-Lock Brake Controller has internal fault.

NOTE: INTERMITTENTS is located under DIAGNOSIS & TESTING portion of this article.

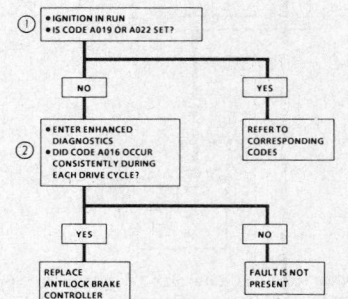

CODE A017, RIGHT FRONT HOLD SOLENOID SHORTED TO BATTERY

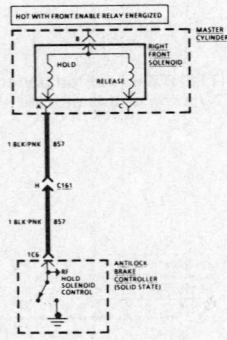

When Front Enable Relay is energized, voltage is applied to Right Front Solenoid. To activate Right Front Hold Solenoid, the Anti-Lock Brake Controller grounds circuit No. 857 of Right Front Hold Solenoid. To set Code A017, the following conditions must occur.

- Front Enable Relay is energized.
- Right Front Hold Solenoid Control is closed.
- Anti-Lock Brake Controller senses voltage at terminal 1C6.

NOTE: Test numbers refer to test numbers on diagnostic chart.

1) Verifies fault still exists.
2) Check for short to battery.
3) Isolate short in Anti-Lock Brake Controller or circuit No. 857.
4) If Right Front Solenoid is not shorted, Anti-Lock Brake Controller has internal defect.

NOTE: INTERMITTENTS is located under DIAGNOSIS & TESTING portion of this article.

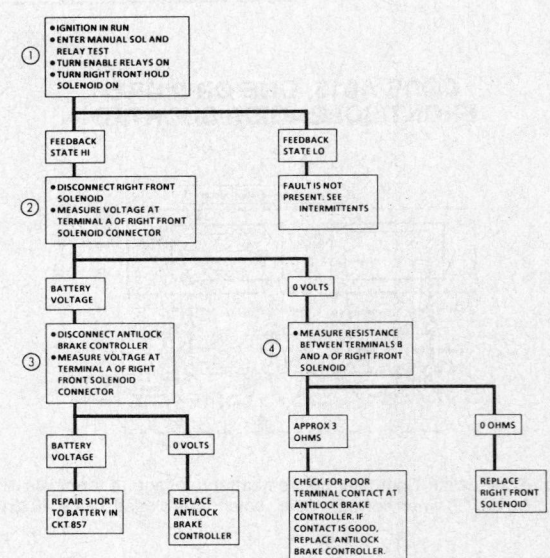

CODE A018, LEFT FRONT HOLD SOLENOID SHORTED TO BATTERY

NOTE: INTERMITTENTS is located under DIAGNOSIS & TESTING portion of this article.

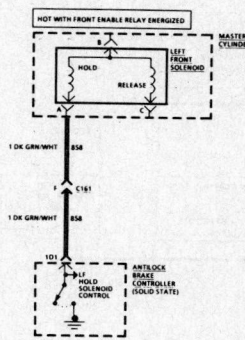

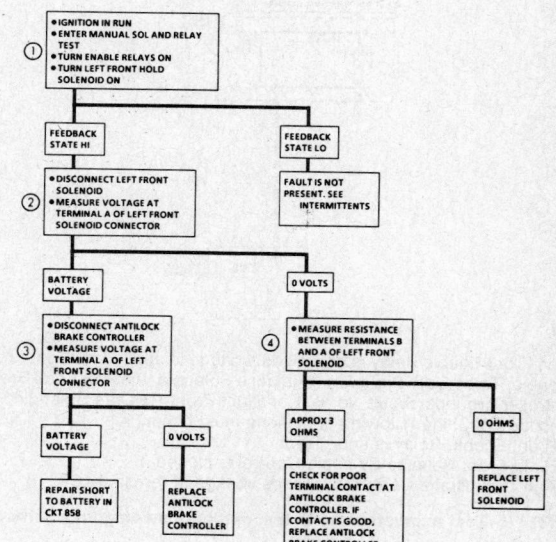

When Front Enable Relay is energized, voltage is applied to Left Front Solenoid. To activate Left Front Hold Solenoid, the Anti-Lock Brake Controller grounds circuit No. 858 of Left Front Hold Solenoid. To set Code A018, the following conditions must occur.

- Front Enable Relay is energized.
- Left Front Hold Solenoid Control is closed.
- Anti-Lock Brake Controller senses voltage at terminal 1D1.

NOTE: Test numbers refer to test numbers on diagnostic chart.

1) Verifies fault still exists.
2) Check for short to battery.
3) Isolate short in Anti-Lock Brake Controller or circuit No. 858.
4) If Left Front Solenoid is not shorted, Anti-Lock Brake Controller has internal defect.

CODE A019, REAR HOLD SOLENOID SHORTED TO BATTERY

NOTE: INTERMITTENTS is located in the DIAGNOSIS & TESTING portion of this article.

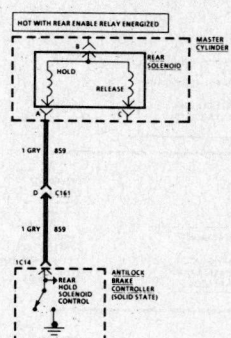

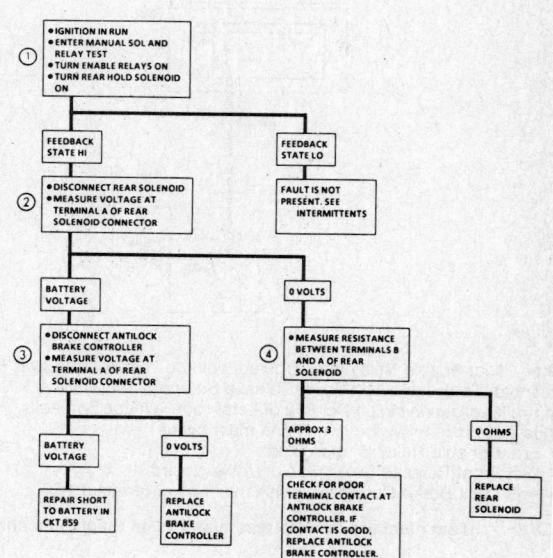

When Rear Enable Relay is energized, voltage is applied to Rear Solenoid. To activate Rear Hold Solenoid, the Anti-Lock Brake Controller grounds circuit No. 859 of Rear Hold Solenoid. To set Code A019, the following conditions must occur.

- Rear Enable Relay is energized.
- Rear Hold Solenoid Control is closed.
- Anti-Lock Brake Controller senses voltage at terminal 1C14.

NOTE: Test numbers refer to test numbers on diagnostic chart.

1) Verifies fault still exists.
2) Check for short to battery.
3) Isolate short in Anti-Lock Brake Controller or circuit No. 859.
4) If Rear Solenoid is not shorted, Anti-Lock Brake Controller has internal defect.

CODE A020, RIGHT FRONT RELEASE SOLENOID SHORTED TO BATTERY

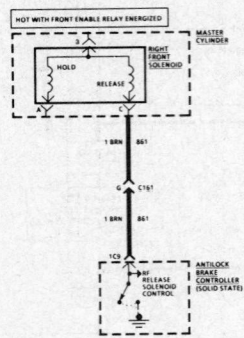

When Front Enable Relay is energized, voltage is applied to Right Front Solenoid. To activate Right Front Release Solenoid, the Anti-Lock Brake Controller grounds circuit No. 861 of Right Front Release Solenoid. To set Code A020, the following conditions must occur.

- Front Enable Relay is energized.
- Right Front Release Solenoid Control is closed.
- Anti-Lock Brake Controller senses voltage at terminal 1C9.

NOTE: Test numbers refer to test numbers on diagnostic chart.

1) Verifies fault still exists.
2) Check for short to battery.
3) Isolate short in Anti-Lock Brake Controller or circuit No. 861.
4) If Left Front Solenoid is not shorted, Anti-Lock Brake Controller has internal defect.

NOTE: INTERMITTENTS is located under DIAGNOSIS & TESTING portion of this article.

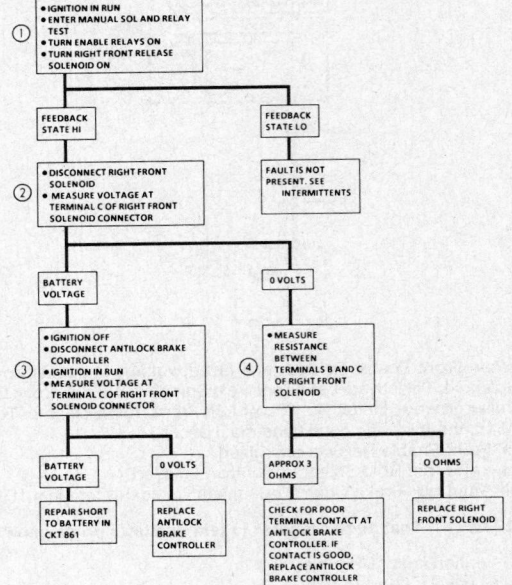

CODE A021, LEFT FRONT RELEASE SOLENOID SHORTED TO BATTERY

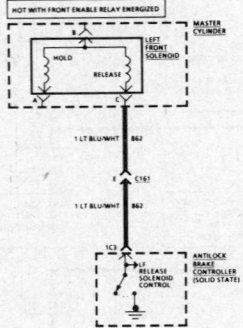

When Front Enable Relay is energized, voltage is applied to Left Front Solenoid. To activate Left Front Release Solenoid, the Anti-Lock Brake Controller grounds circuit No. 862 of Left Front Release Solenoid. To set Code A021, the following conditions must occur.

- Front Enable Relay is energized.
- Left Front Release Solenoid Control is closed.
- Anti-Lock Brake Controller senses voltage at terminal 1C3.

NOTE: Test numbers refer to test numbers on diagnostic chart.

1) Verifies fault still exists.
2) Check for short to battery.
3) Isolate short in Anti-Lock Brake Controller or circuit No. 862.
4) If Left Front Solenoid is not shorted, Anti-Lock Brake Controller has internal defect.

NOTE: INTERMITTENTS is located under DIAGNOSIS & TESTING portion of this article.

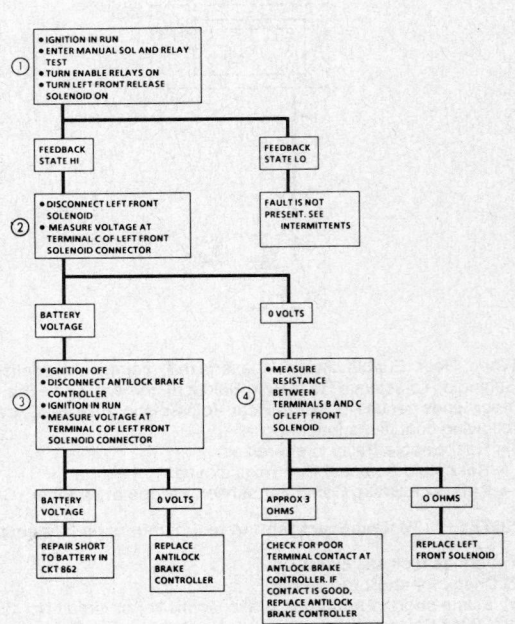

CODE A022, REAR RELEASE SOLENOID SHORTED TO BATTERY

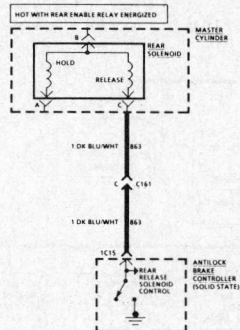

NOTE: INTERMITTENTS is located under DIAGNOSIS & TESTING portion of this article.

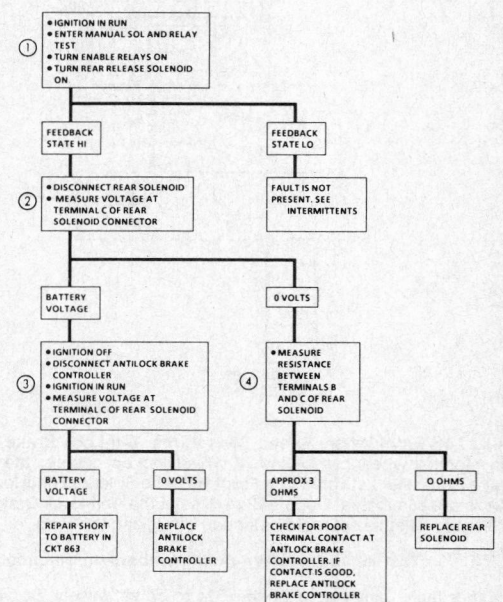

When Rear Enable Relay is energized, voltage is applied to Rear Solenoid. To activate Rear Release Solenoid, the Anti-Lock Brake Controller grounds circuit No. 863 of Rear Release Solenoid. To set Code A022, the following conditions must occur.

- Rear Enable Relay is energized.
- Rear Release Solenoid Control is closed.
- Anti-Lock Brake Controller senses voltage at terminal 1C15.

NOTE: Test numbers refer to test numbers on diagnostic chart.

1) Verifies fault still exists.
2) Check for short to battery.
3) Isolate short in Anti-Lock Brake Controller or circuit No. 863.
4) If Rear Solenoid is not shorted, Anti-Lock Brake Controller has internal defect.

CODE A023, RIGHT FRONT RELEASE SOLENOID ENERGIZED TOO LONG

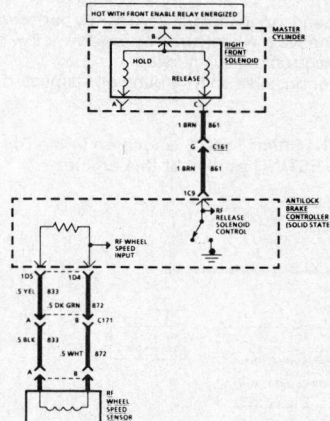

NOTE: INTERMITTENTS is located in the DIAGNOSIS & TESTING portion of this article.

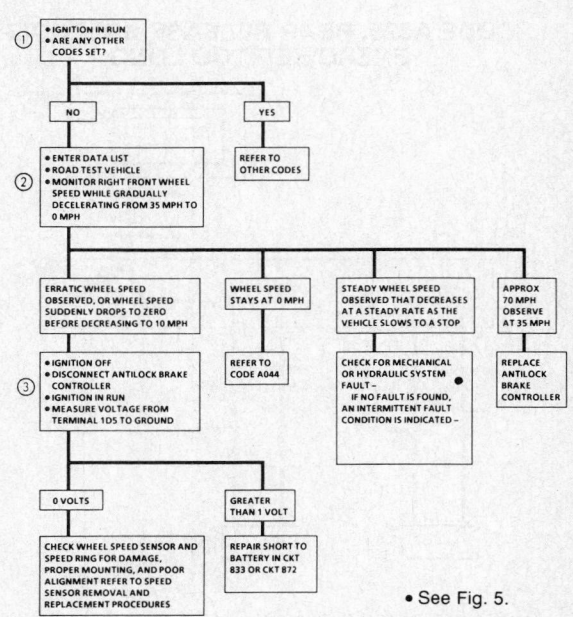

- See Fig. 5.

Using Right Front Wheel Speed Sensor, the Anti-Lock Brake Controller can monitor wheel for lockup. If wheel lockup occurs, the Anti-Lock Brake Controller activates Right Front Release Solenoid until lock-up conditions are eliminated. Code A023 will set if Anti-Lock Brake Controller senses release solenoid has been energized too long.

NOTE: Test numbers refer to test numbers on diagnostic chart.

1) Other faults may cause Code A023 to be set falsely. Servicing other codes first may eliminate need to perform diagnosis for Code A023.
2) If wheel speed input stays at zero MPH, perform Code A044 diagnosis. If wheel speed remains steadily at low speed, a mechanical or hydraulic problem is indicated.
3) Checks for possible short to voltage on circuit No. 833 and circuit No. 872.

CODE A024, LEFT FRONT RELEASE SOLENOID ENERGIZED TOO LONG

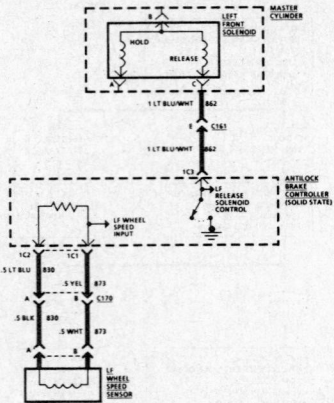

Using Left Front Wheel Speed Sensor, the Anti-Lock Brake Controller can monitor wheel for lockup. If wheel lockup occurs, the Anti-Lock Brake Controller activates Left Front Release Solenoid until lock-up conditions are eliminated. Code A024 will set if the Anti-Lock Brake Controller senses release solenoid has been energized too long.

NOTE: **Test numbers refer to test numbers on diagnostic chart.**

1) Other faults may cause Code A024 to be set falsely. Servicing other codes first may eliminate need to perform Code A024 diagnosis.
2) If wheel speed input stays at zero MPH, perform Code A045 diagnosis. If wheel speed remains steadily at low speed, a mechanical or hydraulic problem is indicated.
3) Checks for possible short to voltage on circuit No. 830 and circuit No. 873.

NOTE: INTERMITTENTS is located under DIAGNOSIS & TESTING portion of this article.

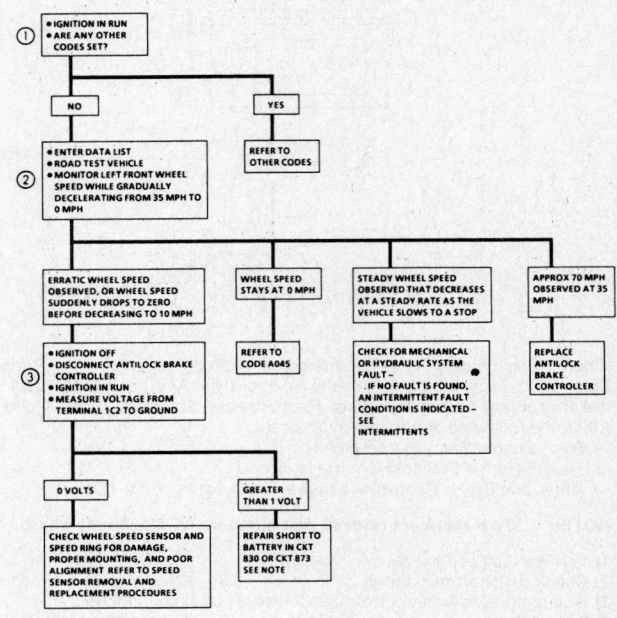

• See Fig. 5.

CODE A025, REAR RELEASE SOLENOID ENERGIZED TOO LONG

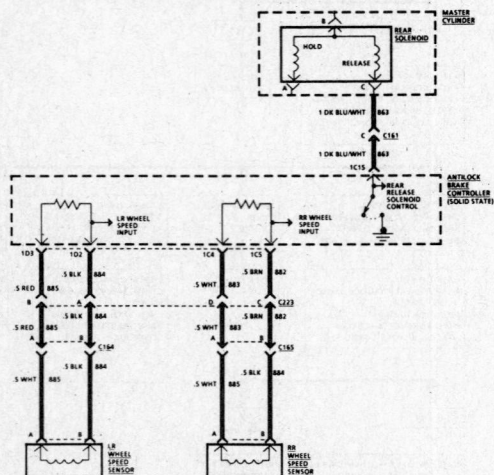

Using the Rear Wheel Speed Sensor, the Anti-Lock Brake Controller can monitor wheel for lockup. If lockup occurs, the Anti-Lock Brake Controller activates the Rear Release Solenoid until lockup conditions are eliminated. Code A025 will set if the Anti-Lock Brake Controller senses that the release solenoid has been energized too long.

NOTE: **Test numbers refer to test numbers on diagnostic chart.**

1) Other faults may cause Code A025 to set falsely. Servicing other codes first may eliminate need to perform Code A025 diagnosis.

2) If wheel speed input stays at zero MPH, perform Code A046 or Code A047 diagnosis. If wheel speed is steady at low speed, a mechanical or hydraulic problem is indicated.
3) To check for possible short ground on suspected wheel speed sensor circuit.

NOTE: INTERMITTENTS is located in the DIAGNOSIS & TESTING portion of this article.

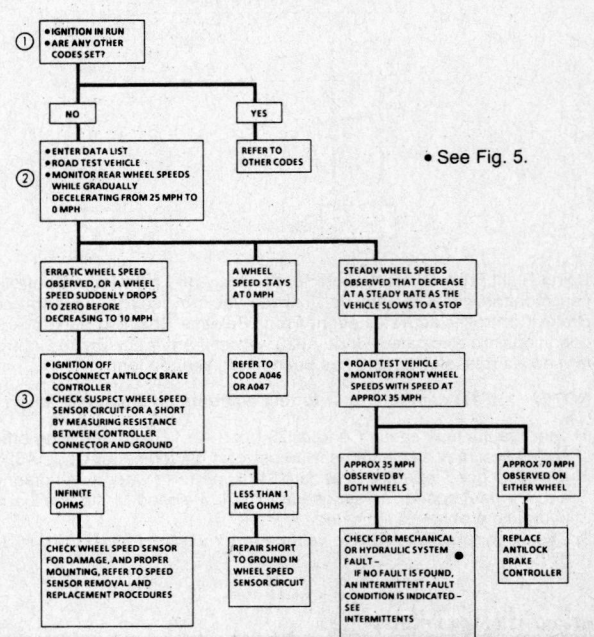

• See Fig. 5.

Courtesy of General Motors Corp.

CODE A026, RIGHT FRONT HOLD SOLENOID ENERGIZED TOO LONG

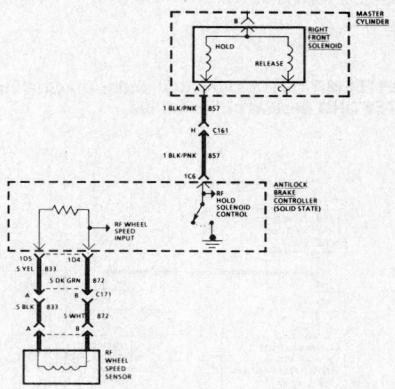

Using the Right Front Wheel Speed Sensor, the Anti-Lock Brake Controller can monitor wheel for incorrect deceleration during an ABS-III stop. If incorrect deceleration occurs, the Anti-Lock Brake Controller activates the Right Front Hold Solenoid by closing the Right Front Hold Solenoid Control. Normal operation of system will be restored when the Anti-Lock Brake Controller senses acceptable right front wheel speed. Code A026 will set if the Anti-Lock Brake Controller senses that the hold solenoid has been energized too long.

NOTE: Test numbers refer to test numbers on diagnostic chart.

1) Other faults may cause Code A026 to set falsely. Servicing other codes first may eliminate need to perform Code A026 diagnosis.
2) To determine if right front wheel speed input fault is based on erratic wheel speed inputs occurring at low speeds only. If wheel speed is steady at low speed, a mechanical or hydraulic problem is indicated.

NOTE: INTERMITTENTS is located under DIAGNOSIS & TESTING portion of this article.

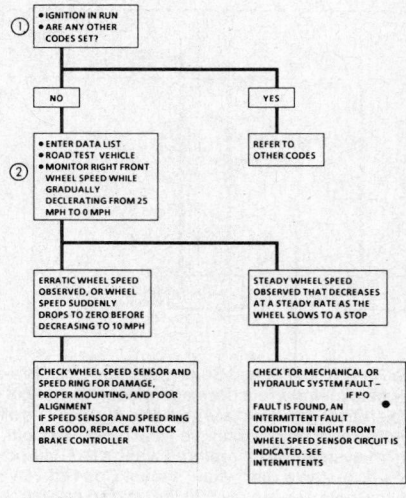

• See Fig. 5.

CODE A027, LEFT FRONT HOLD SOLENOID ENERGIZED TOO LONG

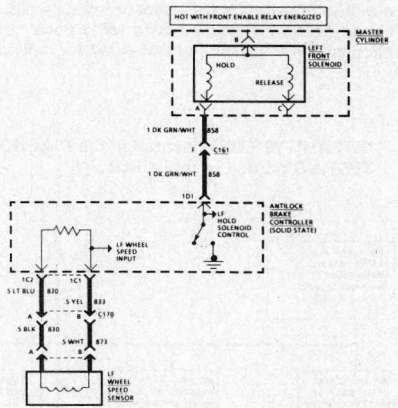

Using the Left Front Wheel Speed Sensor the Anti-Lock Brake Controller can monitor wheel for incorrect deceleration during an ABS-III stop. If incorrect deceleration occurs, the Anti-Lock Brake Controller activates the Left Front Hold Solenoid by closing the Left Front Hold Solenoid Control. Normal operation of system will be restored when the Anti-Lock Brake Controller senses acceptable left front wheel speed. Code A027 will set if the Anti-Lock Brake Controller senses that the hold solenoid has been energized too long.

NOTE: Test numbers refer to test numbers on diagnostic chart.

1) Other faults may cause Code A027 to set falsely. Servicing other codes first may eliminate need to perform Code A027 diagnosis.
2) To determine if left front wheel speed input fault is based on erratic wheel speed inputs occurring at low speeds only. If wheel speed is steady at low speed, a mechanical or hydraulic problem is indicated.

NOTE: INTERMITTENTS is located under DIAGNOSIS & TESTING portion of this article.

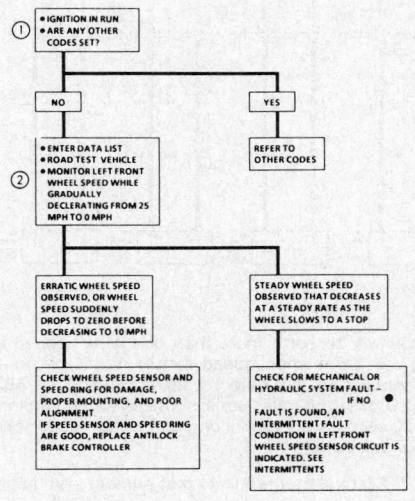

• See Fig. 5.

Courtesy of General Motors Corp.

CODE A028, REAR HOLD SOLENOID ENERGIZED TOO LONG

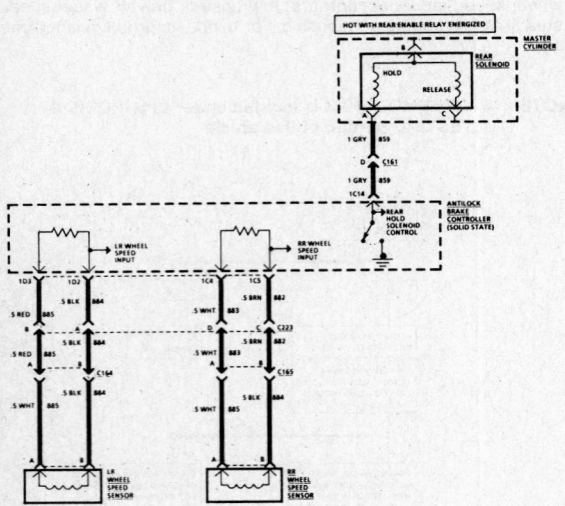

Using the Rear Wheel Speed Sensor the Anti-Lock Brake Controller can monitor wheel for incorrect deceleration during an ABS-III stop. If incorrect deceleration occurs, the Anti-Lock Brake Controller activates the Rear Hold Solenoid by closing the Rear Hold Solenoid Control. Normal operation of system will be restored when the Anti-Lock Brake Controller senses acceptable rear wheel speed. Code A028 will set if the Anti-Lock Brake Controller senses that the hold solenoid has been energized too long.

NOTE: Test numbers refer to test numbers on diagnostic chart.

1) Other faults may cause Code A028 to set falsely. Servicing other codes first may eliminate need to perform Code A028 diagnosis.
2) To determine if rear wheel speed input fault is based on erratic wheel speed inputs occurring at low speeds only. If wheel speed is steady at low speed, a mechanical or hydraulic problem is indicated.

NOTE: INTERMITTENTS is located under DIAGNOSIS & TESTING portion of this article.

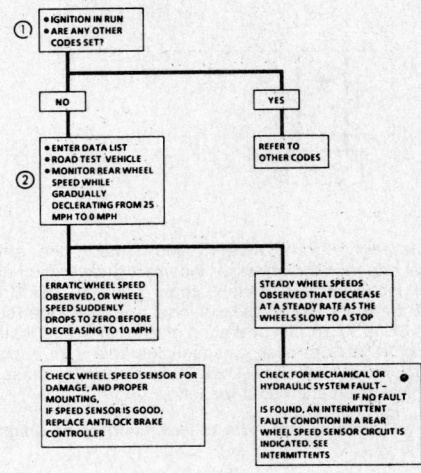

• See Fig. 5.

CODE A030, MORE THAN ONE SPEED SENSOR OPEN OR SHORTED TO GROUND

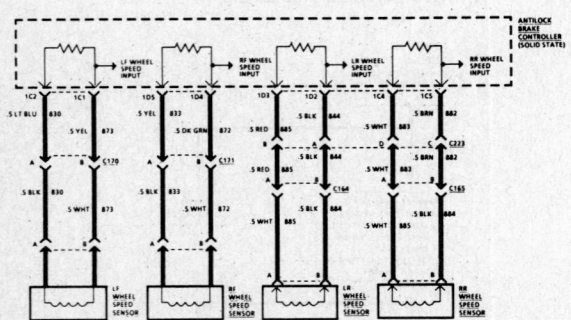

Code A030 will be set if more than one wheel speed inputs are not receiving data from wheel speed sensor. If this occurs, the Anti-Lock Brake Controller will not detect wheel lockup. Code A030 is set after Anti-Lock Brake Controller senses wheel speed sensor input at zero MPH for 20 seconds or more. If only one wheel speed sensor fails, Code A044-A047 will be set.

NOTE: Test number refers to test numbers on diagnostic chart.

1) Observe individual wheel speed sensor inputs while driving vehicle. Wheel speed sensors reporting zero MPH have defective sensors and/or circuits. Refer to Codes A044-A047 for individual component service.

NOTE: INTERMITTENTS is located in the DIAGNOSIS & TESTING portion of this article.

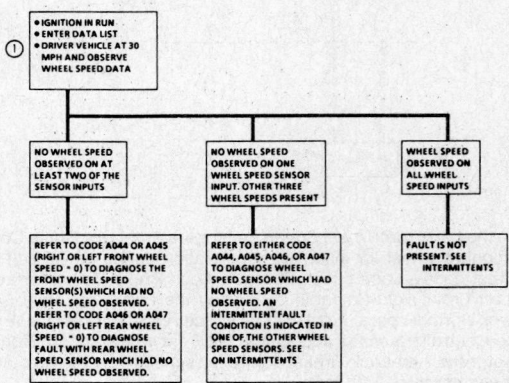

CODE A031, PUMP MOTOR FEEDBACK CIRCUIT OPEN

The pump on input is grounded through the pump motor relay and the pump motor when the pump motor relay contacts are open. When the pump motor relay contacts are closed, the pump on input and the pump motor will have voltage applied. If the pump on input does not sense these conditions, the Anti-Lock Brake Controller will set Code A031.

NOTE: Test numbers refer to test numbers on diagnostic chart. For location of CKT 975 and CKT 963, see CODE A035

1) If Code A036 is set, inspect for bad connection at pump motor relay or connector C160.
2) If Code A035 is set, inspect for open pump motor circuit.
3) To determine if Pump Motor Feedback Circuit is open.
4) If pump motor remains on, inspect for open in pump motor circuit that is preventing pump motor from activating.
5) To determine if open exists in circuit No. 150 between pump motor and ground G106.
6) Battery voltage indicates malfunction at Anti-Lock Brake Controller and/or connector.
7) Test of pump motor circuit to isolate defective pump motor.
8) If resistance between terminals "E" and "F" of the pump motor relay is infinite, open exists inside pump motor relay.

NOTE: INTERMITTENTS is located in the DIAGNOSIS & TESTING portion of this article.

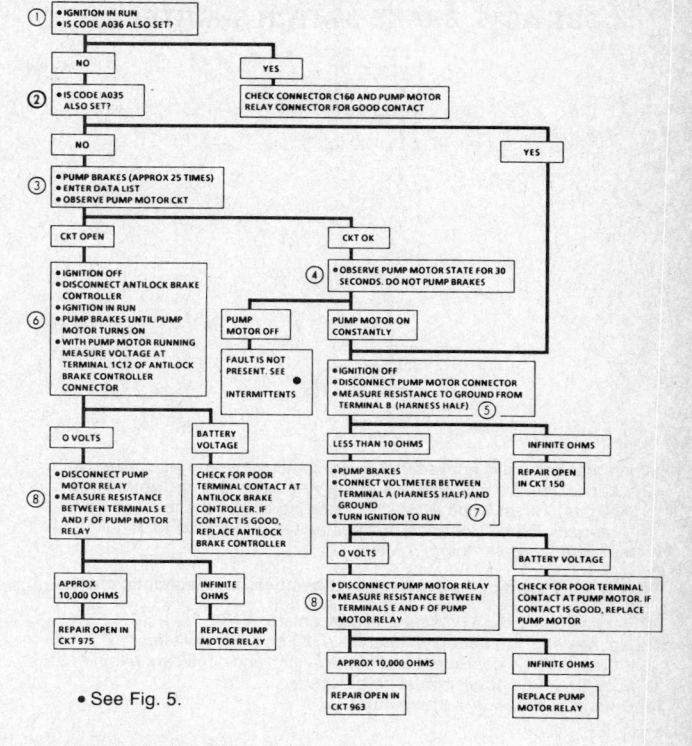

• See Fig. 5.

CODE A032, OPEN BRAKE SWITCH OR HYDRAULIC LEAK

Code A032 will be set if Anti-Lock Brake Controller receives 3 pump on inputs without receiving a brake switch on input. Brake switch fault will be detected without an Anti-Lock Brake situation occurring. Refer to Code A056 for testing.

NOTE: INTERMITTENTS is located under DIAGNOSIS & TESTING portion of this article.

CODE A033 — BRAKE SWITCH OPEN

Voltage is continuously applied to the brake switch. When brake switch is closed, voltage is applied to brakelights and terminal 1C11 (Light Blue wire) of Anti-Lock Brake Controller. The Anti-Lock Brake Controller can sense when brakes have been applied because voltage is received at the brake-apply input. To set Code A033, the following conditions must occur.

• Anti-Lock Brake Controller senses no voltage at terminal 1C11 (Light Blue wire).
• Anti-Lock Brake Controller senses two wheels are slowing at a rate that would be improbable without using the brakes.

NOTE: Test numbers refer to test numbers on diagnostic chart.

1) Checks for improperly adjusted or intermittent brake switch.
2) Checks for improperly adjusted or intermittent brake switch.

NOTE: INTERMITTENTS is located under DIAGNOSIS & TESTING portion of this article.

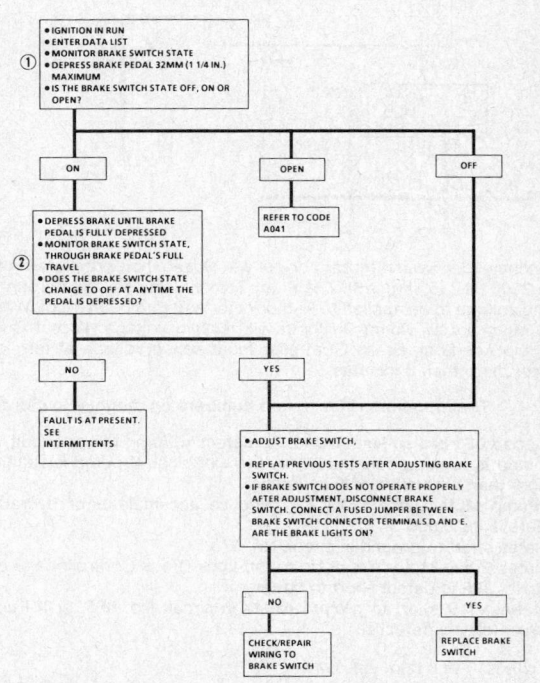

CODE A034, BRAKE SWITCH SHORTED

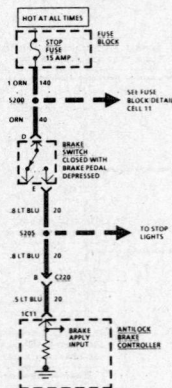

NOTE: INTERMITTENTS is located under DIAGNOSIS & TESTING portion of this article.

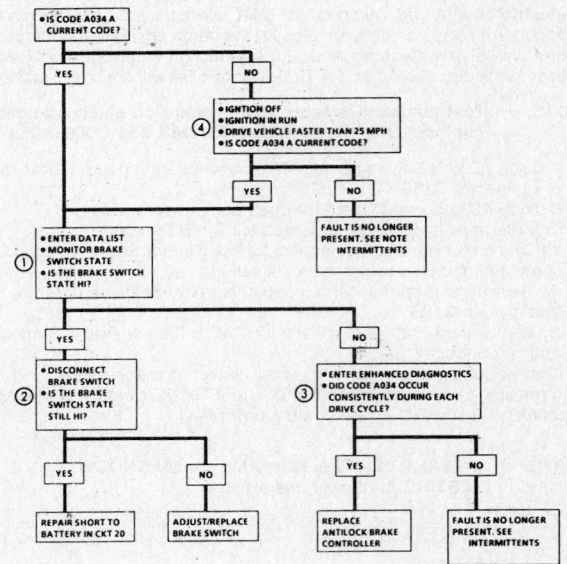

When brake pedal is applied, the brake switch closes. This causes voltage application from Stop Fuse to the Anti-Lock Brake Controller and brakelights. To set Code A034, the following conditions must occur.

- Anti-Lock Brake Controller senses battery voltage at terminal 1C11 at speeds greater than 25 MPH.

NOTE: Test numbers refer to test numbers on diagnostic chart.

1) Verifies short still exists (brakelights on).
2) Isolates short to battery in circuit No. 20 or brake switch.
3) If Code A034 is consistent and brake switch and circuit are okay, Anti-Lock Brake Controller must be defective.
4) Determines if code is intermittent.

CODE A035, PUMP MOTOR RUNS TOO LONG

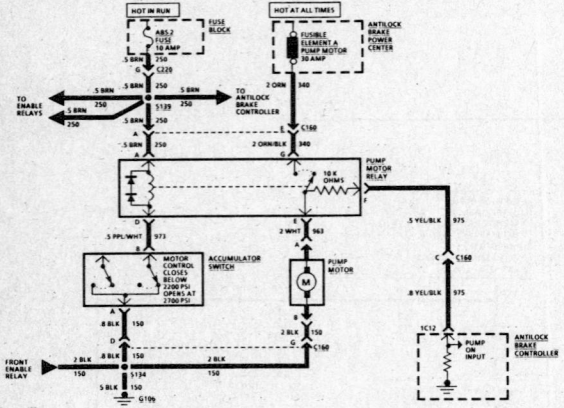

NOTE: INTERMITTENTS is located under DIAGNOSIS & TESTING portion of this article.

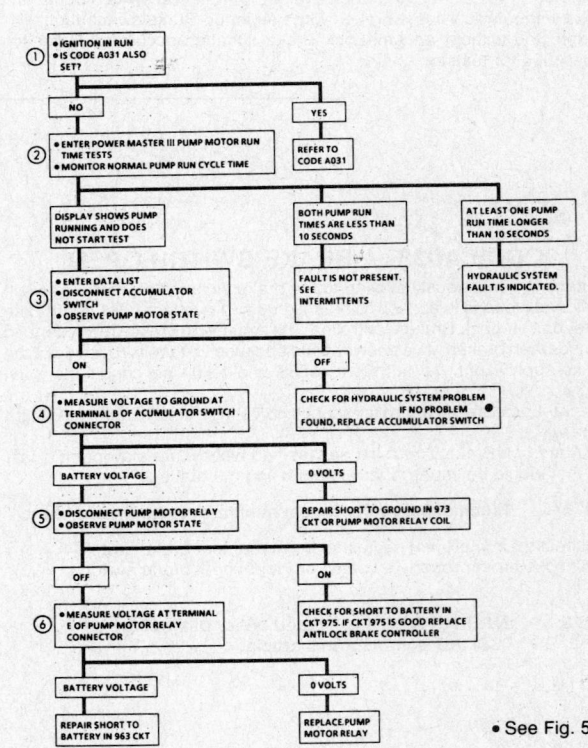

The accumulator switch motor control will close when pressure drops below 2200 psi (155 kg/cm²). The Pump Motor Relay coil then grounds, causing voltage to be applied to Pump Motor and Pump-On Input. When Pump Motor is on, Pump-On Input will receive voltage. To set Code A035, the Anti-Lock Brake Controller must sense voltage at terminal 1C12 for more than 3 minutes.

NOTE: Test numbers refer to test numbers on diagnostic chart.

1) If Code A031 is also set, inspect for defect in Pump Motor circuit.
2) If pump is running constantly, fault is electrical. If pump is running longer than normal, fault is hydraulic.
3) If Pump Motor remains off, a defective accumulator or hydraulic failure is indicated.
4) Isolates short to ground in circuit No. 973.
5) Isolates Pump Motor circuit from Anti-Lock Brake Controller and circuit No. 975 to detect short to battery.
6) Determines if short to ground exists in circuit No. 963, or if Pump Motor Relay is defective.

• See Fig. 5.

CODE A036, PUMP MOTOR WILL NOT RUN

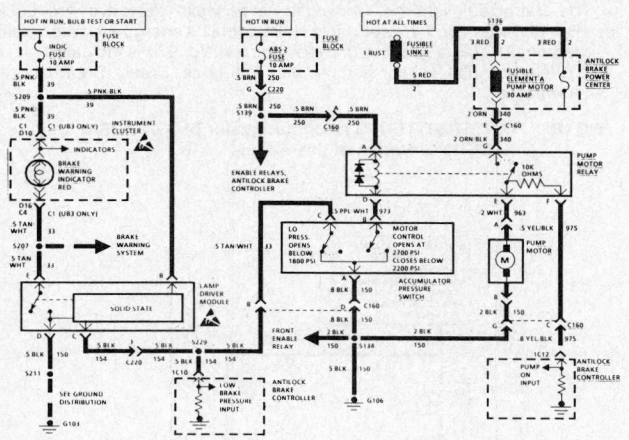

Voltage is applied to Pump-On Input when Pump Motor Relay contacts are closed. The accumulator switch opens when pressure drops below 1800 psi (127 kg/cm²), and ground to the Lamp Driver Module is removed. The Lamp Driver Module then closes the switch to activate the BRAKE Warning Indicator and apply voltage to Low Brake-Pressure Input of Anti-Lock Brake Controller. To set Code A036, the following conditions must occur.
- Anti-Lock Brake Controller senses no voltage at terminal 1C12.
- Anti-Lock Brake Controller senses voltage at terminal 1C10.

NOTE: Test numbers refer to test numbers on diagnostic chart.

1) If Code A031 set, inspect for bad connection at Pump Motor Relay or connector C160.
2) If Pump Motor operates, fault is in low-pressure circuit or Pump Motor Relay circuit.
3) Determines if fault is in accumulator switch circuit or Pump Motor Relay circuit.
4) Verifies fault still exists.
5) Battery voltage at terminal "A" indicates relay coil power feed is okay.
6) If Pump Motor operates, check accumulator switch or hydraulic system for malfunction.

7) Check for open ground circuit to accumulator switch.
8) Determines if circuit No. 973 is open.
9) A good power feed to relay contact indicates defective Pump Motor Relay.

NOTE: INTERMITTENTS is located under DIAGNOSIS & TESTING portion of this article.

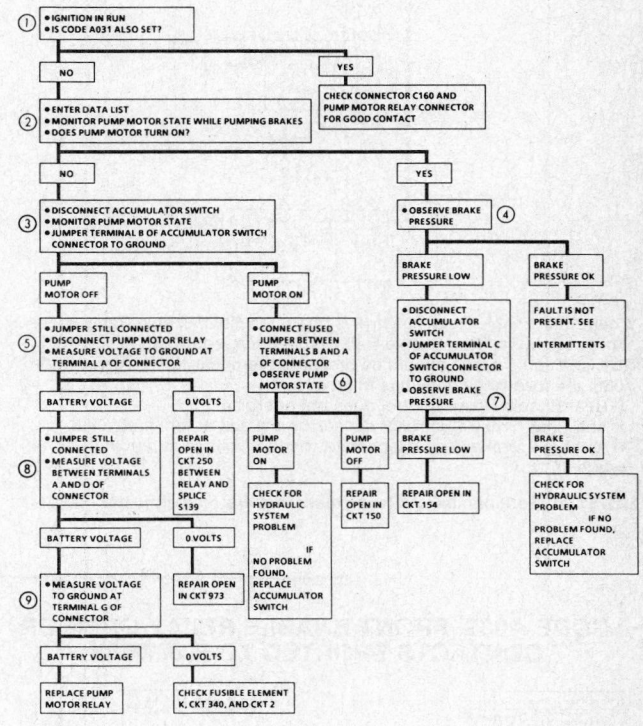

CODE A037, FRONT ENABLE RELAY COIL SHORTED TO GROUND

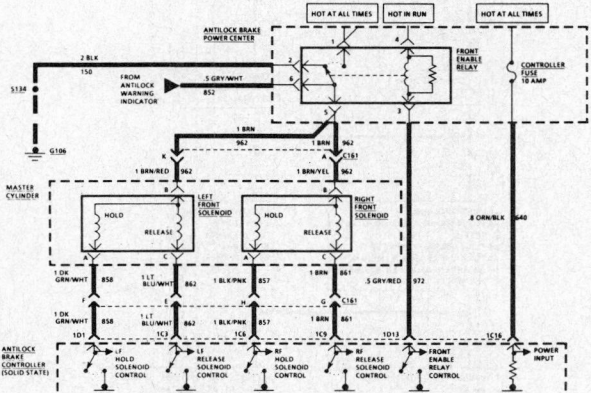

When Front Enable Relay Control is open, the Front Enable Relay is de-energized. If the Front Enable Relay is de-energized with ignition in the RUN position, voltage should be present at terminal 1D13. To set Code A037, the following conditions must occur.
- Front Enable Relay Control is open (relay de-energized).
- Anti-Lock Brake Controller senses no voltage at terminal 1D13.
- Anti-Lock Brake Controller senses battery voltage at terminals 1D1, 1C3, 1C6 and 1C9.

NOTE: Test numbers refer to test numbers on diagnostic chart.

1) Observe Anti-Lock Warning Indicator to determine whether Front Enable Relay has de-energized (light on), indicating a possible defective Anti-Lock Brake Controller. Otherwise, a short to ground in circuit No. 972 is indicated.
2) If Code A037 is consistent, the Anti-Lock Brake Controller is defective.

NOTE: INTERMITTENTS is located in the DIAGNOSIS & TESTING portion of this article.

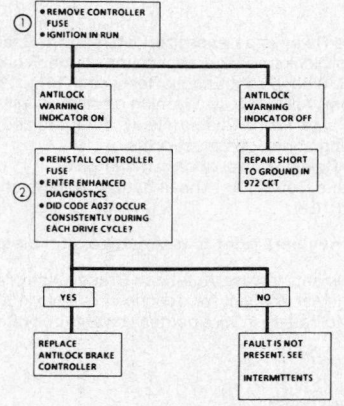

CODE A038, REAR ENABLE RELAY COIL SHORTED TO GROUND

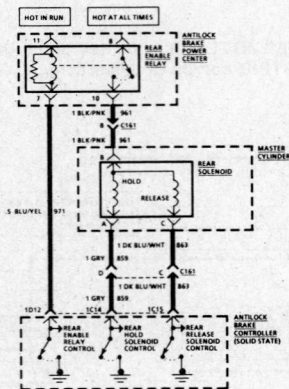

When Rear Enable Relay Control is open, the Rear Enable Relay is de-energized. If the Rear Enable Relay is de-energized with ignition in the RUN position, voltage should be present at terminal 1D12. To set Code A038, the following conditions must occur.

- Rear Enable Relay Control does not energize.
- Anti-Lock Brake Controller senses no voltage at terminal 1D12.
- Anti-Lock Brake Controller senses battery voltage at terminals 1C14 and 1C15.

NOTE: Test numbers refer to test numbers on diagnostic chart.

1) Observe Anti-Lock Warning Indicator to see if Rear Enable Relay has de-energized (light on), indicating a possible defective Anti-Lock Brake Controller. If Rear Enable Relay remains energized (zero volt at terminal 1D12), a short to ground in circuit No. 971 is indicated.
2) If Code A038 is consistent, the Anti-Lock Brake Controller is defective.

NOTE: INTERMITTENTS is located under DIAGNOSIS & TESTING portion of this article.

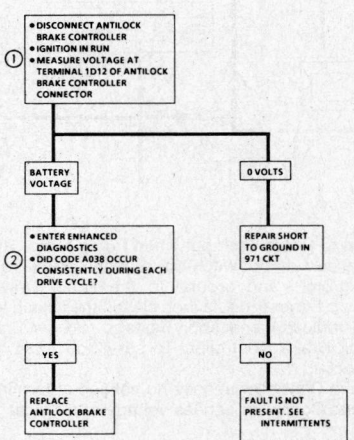

CODE A039, FRONT ENABLE RELAY OPEN OR CONTACTS SHORTED TO BATTERY

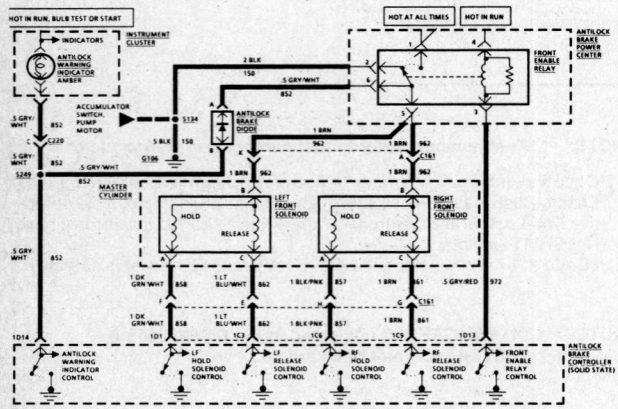

The Front Enable Relay is de-energized when Front Enable Relay Control is open. This blocks voltage application to the Front Solenoid and Solenoid Control. When Front Enable Relay circuit No. 150 is open, battery voltage from ANTI-LOCK Warning Indicator will be routed to solenoids, even with Front Enable Relay de-energized. To set Code A039, the following conditions must occur.

- Front Enable Relay Control does not energize.
- Anti-Lock Brake Controller senses battery voltage at terminals 1D1, 1C3, 1C6 and 1C9.

NOTE: Test numbers refer to test numbers on diagnostic chart.

1) If Code A040 is set, replace Anti-Lock Brake Controller.
2) If Code A003 is set, inspect for open in circuit No. 150.
3) Isolates short to battery in wire harness or Anti-Lock Brake Controller.

4) Isolates a short to battery in circuit No. 962, or a defective Front Enable Relay.
5) If Code A039 is consistent, the Anti-Lock Brake Controller has internal malfunction.

NOTE: INTERMITTENTS is located under DIAGNOSIS & TESTING portion of this article.

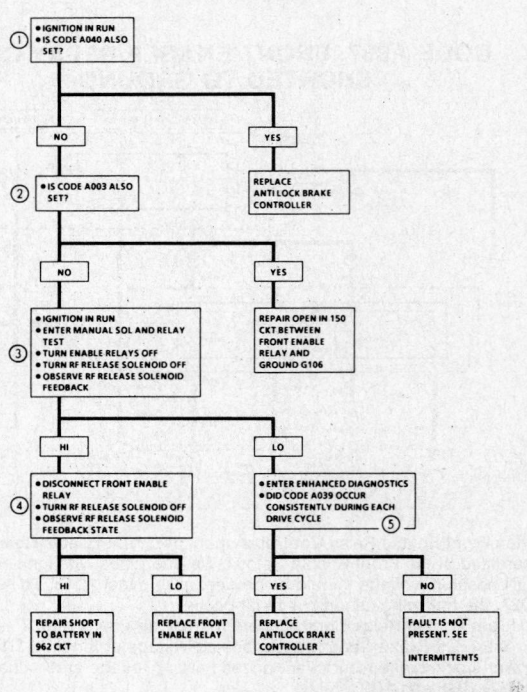

CODE A040, REAR ENABLE RELAY CONTACTS SHORTED TO BATTERY

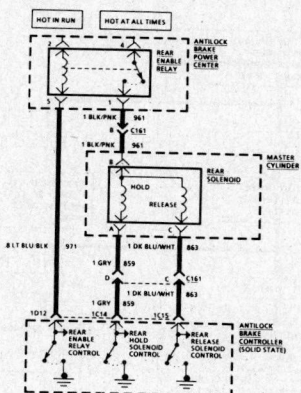

NOTE: INTERMITTENTS is located under DIAGNOSIS & TESTING portion of this article.

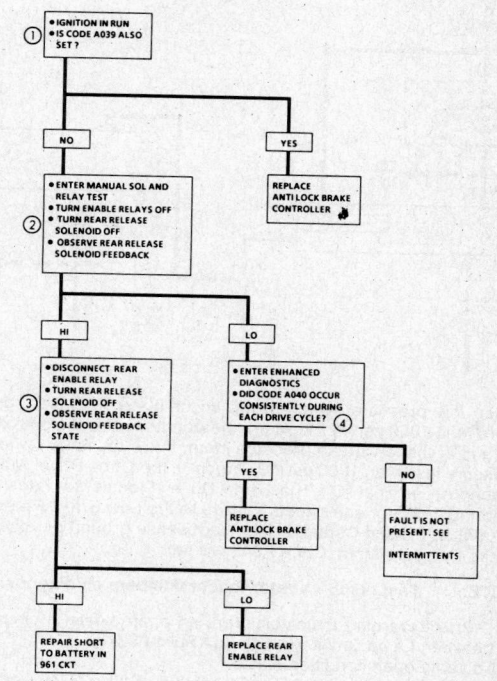

When Rear Enable Relay Control is open, the Rear Enable Relay is de-energized. This blocks voltage application to the Rear Solenoid and Solenoid Control. To set Code A040, the following conditions must occur.

- Rear Enable Relay Control does not energize.
- Anti-Lock Brake Controller senses voltage at terminal 1D12, or at both terminals 1C14 and 1C15.

NOTE: Test numbers refer to test numbers on diagnostic chart.

1) If Code A039 is set, replace Anti-Lock Brake Controller.
2) Isolates short to battery in wire harness or Anti-Lock Brake Controller.
3) Isolates a short to battery in circuit No. 961, or a defective Rear Enable Relay.
4) If Code A040 is consistent, the Anti-Lock Brake Controller has internal malfunction.

CODE A041, BRAKE SWITCH CIRCUIT OPEN

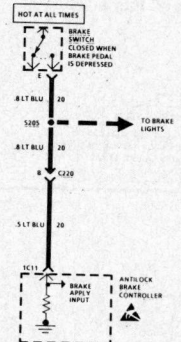

When the brake pedal is pressed, the Anti-Lock Brake Controller senses voltage at the Brake-Apply Input. If voltage is absent, Anti-Lock Brake Controller will ground through circuit No. 20 or the brakelights. Code A041 will also set if hazard lights are turned on and stoplight is non-functional. To set Code A041, the following conditions must occur.

- Battery voltage is not sensed at Brake-Apply Input (Brake Switch open).
- Anti-Lock Brake Controller does not sense ground through circuit No. 20 (Brake-Apply Input).

NOTE: Test numbers refer to test numbers on diagnostic chart.

1) Isolates open to circuit No. 20 between brake switch and BRAKE light (light off), or circuit No. 20 between brake switch and Anti-Lock Brake Controller (light on).
2) Observe state of brake switch. If brake switch is closed, Anti-Lock Brake Controller is sensing correct input.

3) Isolate open to circuit No. 20 between brake switch and Anti-Lock Brake Controller if zero volt is measured. If circuit No. 20 is okay, replace Anti-Lock Brake Controller.

NOTE: INTERMITTENTS is located under DIAGNOSIS & TESTING portion of this article.

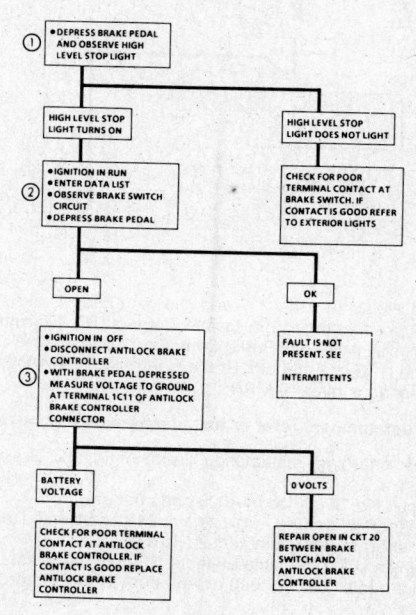

109866   109867   91B11263   109869

Courtesy of General Motors Corp.

CODE A042, LOW BRAKE PRESSURE CIRCUIT OPEN

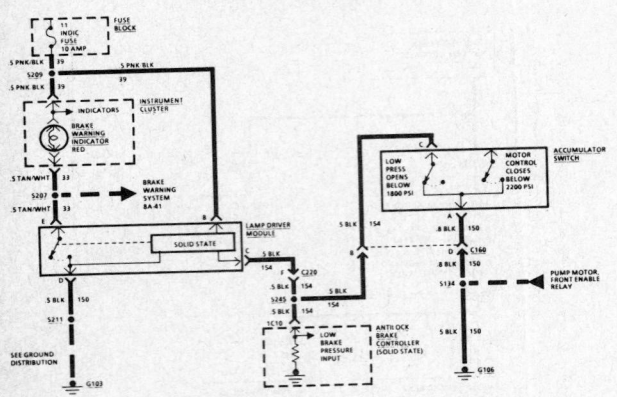

NOTE: INTERMITTENTS is located under DIAGNOSIS & TESTING portion of this article.

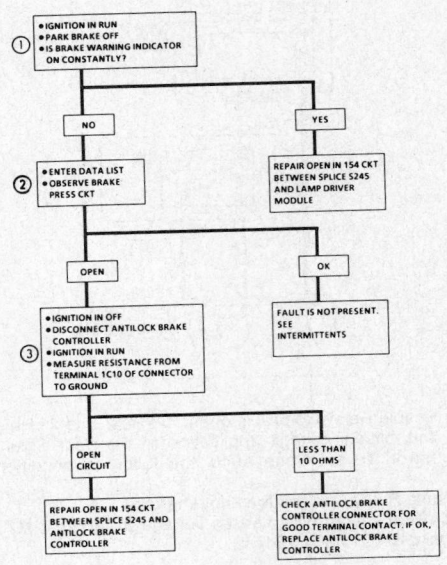

When low pressure switch in the accumulator is closed, pressure is more than 1800 psi (127 kg/cm²), the Anti-Lock Brake Controller senses ground at the low brake pressure input. If low pressure switch is open, pressure less than 1800 psi (127 kg/cm²), the Lamp Driver Module loses ground at terminal "C". The Lamp Driver Module activates the Brake Warning Indicator and directs voltage to the Low Brake Pressure Input. If Anti-Lock Brake Controller does not sense ground or voltage at Low Brake Pressure Input, Code A042 will set.

NOTE: Test numbers refer to test numbers on diagnostic chart.

1) If Brake Warning Indicator is on, an open exists in circuit No. 154 between Lamp Driver Module and Splice S245.
2) To verify open condition exists.
3) Isolate open in circuit No. 154 between Splice S245 and Anti-Lock Brake Controller.

CODE A043, SYSTEM VOLTAGE IS LOW

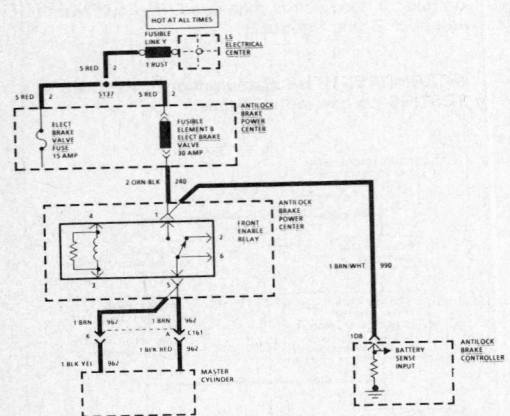

7) Determines if fault is constant or intermittent Anti-Lock Brake Controller failure.

NOTE: INTERMITTENTS is located under DIAGNOSIS & TESTING portion of this article.

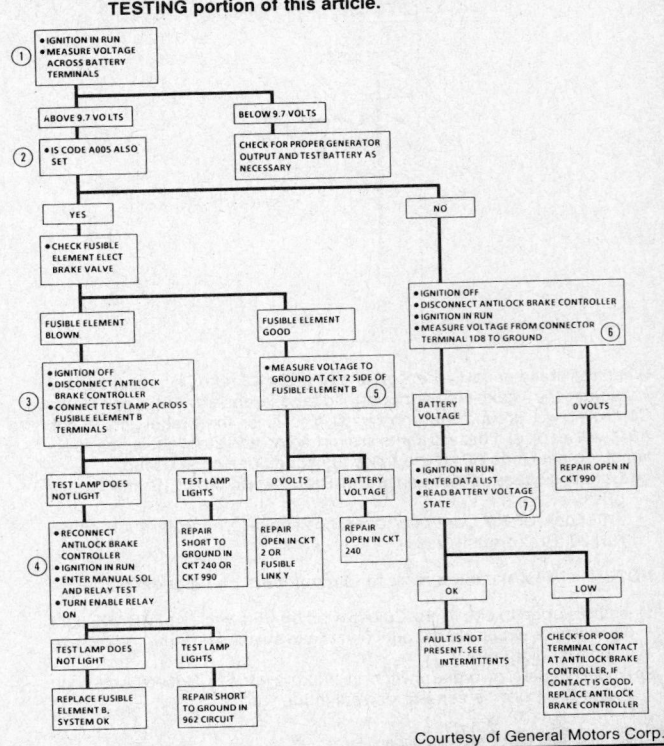

Front Enable Relay terminal "1" and the Anti-Lock Brake Controller receive continuous voltage from fusible Element "B". A minimum of 9.7 volts is required by Anti-Lock Brake Controller. Code A043 will set if voltage at terminal 1D8 of Anti-Lock Brake Controller is less than 9.7 volts and vehicle speed is over 10 MPH.

NOTE: Test numbers refer to test numbers on diagnostic chart.

1) Separates charging malfunction from Anti-Lock Brake System problem.
2) Check circuit No. 990 if Code A005 does not set.
3) Check for short to ground in circuit No. 240 and circuit No. 990.
4) Check for short to ground in circuit No. 962.
5) Isolates which side of Fusible Element "B" open condition exists.
6) Isolates open to circuit No. 990 or Anti-Lock Brake Controller.

Courtesy of General Motors Corp.

109870   109871   91C11264   91D11265

CODE A044, RIGHT FRONT WHEEL SPEED IS ZERO

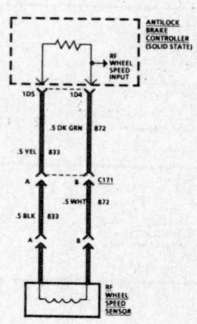

Wheel Sensors generate voltage pulses as their magnetic teeth pass a coil. The created AC voltage frequency enables the Anti-Lock Brake Controller to determine wheel RPM. The Anti-Lock Brake Controller compares individual wheel speed data to detect wheel lockup. To set Code A044, the following conditions must occur.

- Anti-Lock Brake Controller senses right front wheel speed is zero.
- Anti-Lock Brake Controller senses other wheel speeds are above 5 MPH and operating correctly.

NOTE: Test numbers refer to test numbers on diagnostic chart.

1) Observe right front wheel speed input to determine what type of input the Anti-Lock Brake Controller is sensing. Erratic or unsteady readings indicate a malfunction in Wheel Speed Sensor. Stable readings indicate problem is intermittent.

2) Indicates Wheel Speed Sensor has internal short to ground.

3) If infinite, Wheel Speed Sensor has internal open condition.

4) If voltage is present, a short to battery is present in circuit No. 833.

5) If voltage is present, a short to battery is present in circuit No. 872.

6) Circuit No. 833 is connected to ground. If infinite resistance is measured, an open condition is present in circuit No. 833.

7) With terminal "B" of circuit 872 grounded, resistance between terminal 1D5 and ground should be zero. If infinite resistance is measured, an open condition is present in circuit No. 872.

8) All systems that can be checked have tested good. Visually inspect speed sensor, speed ring wire harness and all connectors. Check component mounting and alignment. If problem persists but source cannot be found, replace Anti-Lock Brake Controller.

NOTE: INTERMITTENTS is located under DIAGNOSIS & TESTING portion of this article.

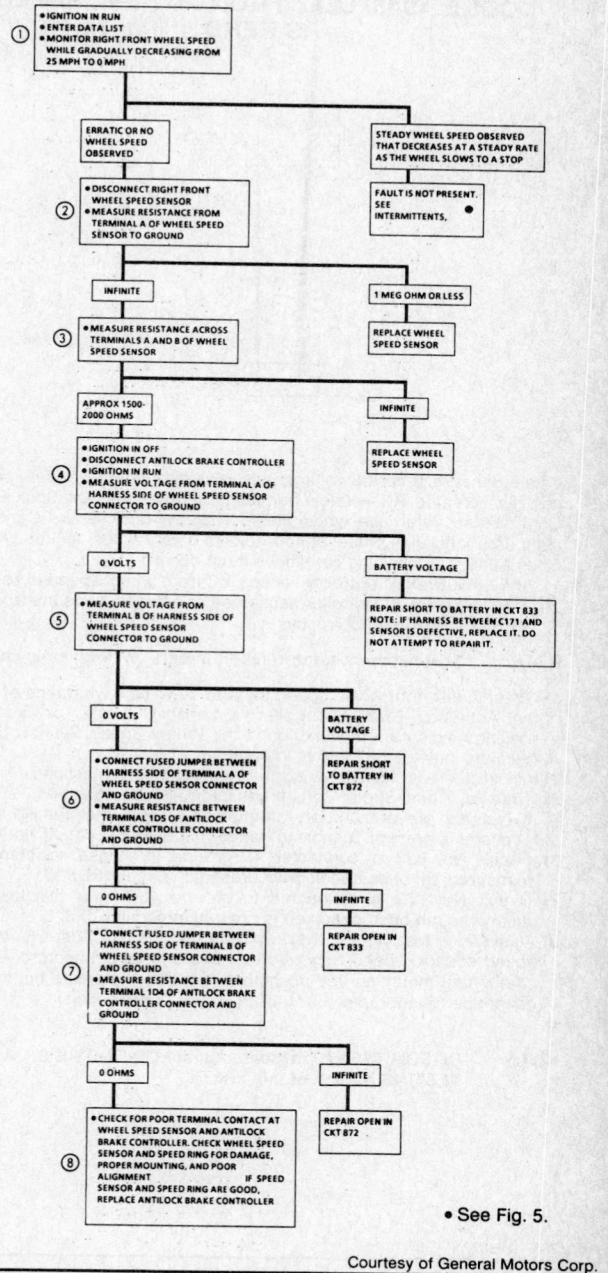

• See Fig. 5.

109874, 109875

CODE A045, LEFT FRONT WHEEL SPEED IS ZERO

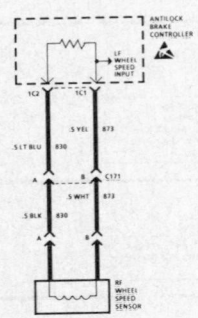

Wheel Sensors generate voltage pulses as their magnetic teeth pass a coil. The created AC voltage frequency enables the Anti-Lock Brake Controller to determine wheel RPM. The Anti-Lock Brake Controller compares individual wheel speed data to detect wheel lockup. To set Code A045, the following conditions must occur.
- Anti-Lock Brake Controller senses left front wheel speed is zero.
- Anti-Lock Brake Controller senses other wheel speeds are above 5 MPH and operating correctly.

NOTE: Test numbers refer to test numbers on diagnostic chart.

1) Observe left front wheel speed input to determine what type of input the Anti-Lock Brake Controller is sensing. Erratic or unsteady readings indicate a malfunction in the Wheel Speed Sensor. Stable readings indicate problem is intermittent.
2) Indicates Wheel Speed Sensor has internal short to ground.
3) If infinite, Wheel Speed Sensor has internal open condition.
4) If voltage is present, a short to battery is present in circuit No. 830.
5) If voltage is present, a short to battery is present in circuit No. 873.
6) Circuit No. 833 is connected to ground. If infinite resistance is measured, an open condition is present in circuit No. 830.
7) Circuit No. 873 is connected to ground. If infinite resistance is measured, an open condition is present in circuit No. 873.
8) All systems that can be checked have tested good. Visually inspect speed sensor, speed ring wire harness and all connectors. Check component mounting and alignment. If problem persists but source cannot be found, replace Anti-Lock Brake Controller.

NOTE: INTERMITTENTS is located under DIAGNOSIS & TESTING portion of this article.

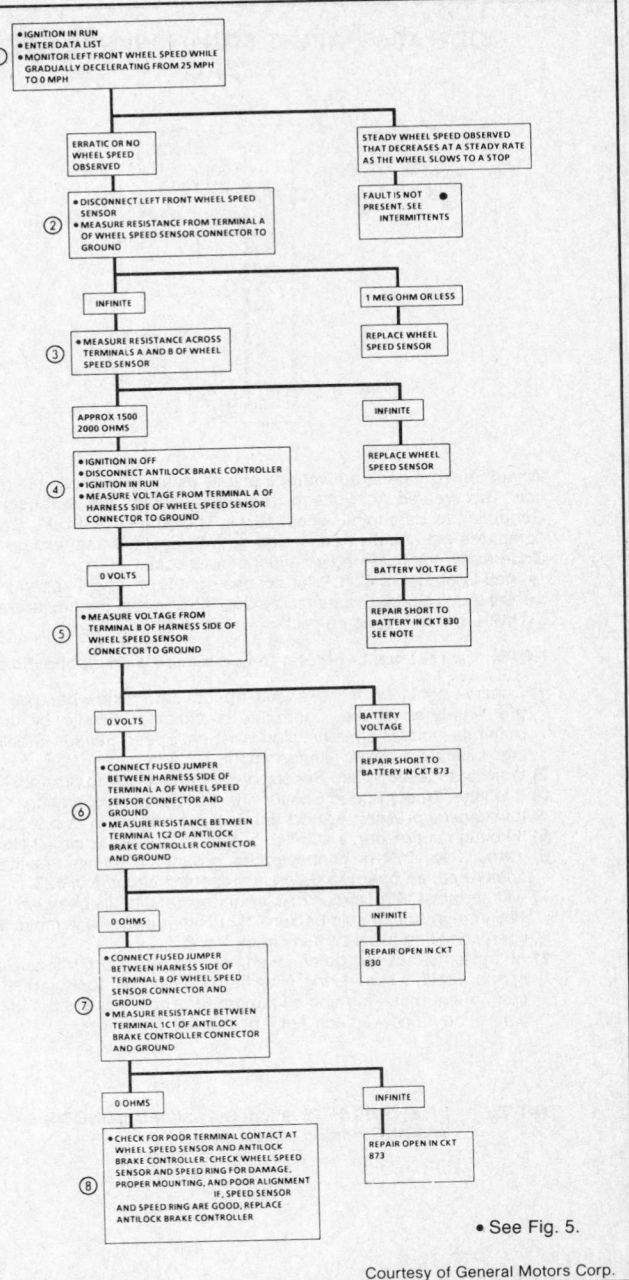

• See Fig. 5.

CODE A046, RIGHT REAR WHEEL SPEED IS ZERO

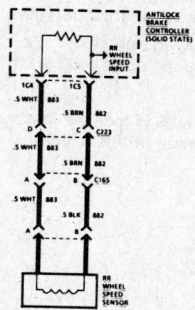

Wheel Sensors generate voltage pulses as their magnetic teeth pass a coil. The created AC voltage frequency enables the Anti-Lock Brake Controller to determine wheel RPM. The Anti-Lock Brake Controller compares individual wheel speed data to detect wheel lockup. To set Code A046, the following conditions must occur.

- Anti-Lock Brake Controller senses right rear wheel speed is zero.
- Anti-Lock Brake Controller senses other wheel speeds are above 5 MPH and operating correctly.

NOTE: Test numbers refer to test numbers on diagnostic chart.

1) Observe right rear wheel speed input to determine what type of input the Anti-Lock Brake Controller is sensing. Erratic or unsteady readings indicate a malfunction in Wheel Speed Sensor. Stable readings indicate problem is intermittent.
2) Indicates a short to battery.
3) If voltage is present, a short exists in Anti-Lock Brake Controller or wire harness.
4) If resistance is 9000-15,000 ohms, circuit between Anti-Lock Brake Controller and connector C165 is okay.
5) If resistance is 10 ohms or more, circuit between Anti-Lock Brake Controller and connector C165 is okay. Inspect for fault between Wheel Speed Sensor and connector C165.

6) If 1500-2500 ohms are measured, a short to ground exists. If over 2500 ohms are measured, an open condition exists. If under 1500 ohms are measured, a shorted sensor circuit is indicated.
7) Isolates fault to either wire harness or Wheel Speed Sensor. Harness must be replaced (not repaired) if defective.
8) Isolates fault to either wire harness or Wheel Speed Sensor. Harness must be replaced (not repaired) if defective.

NOTE: INTERMITTENTS is located under DIAGNOSIS & TESTING portion of this article.

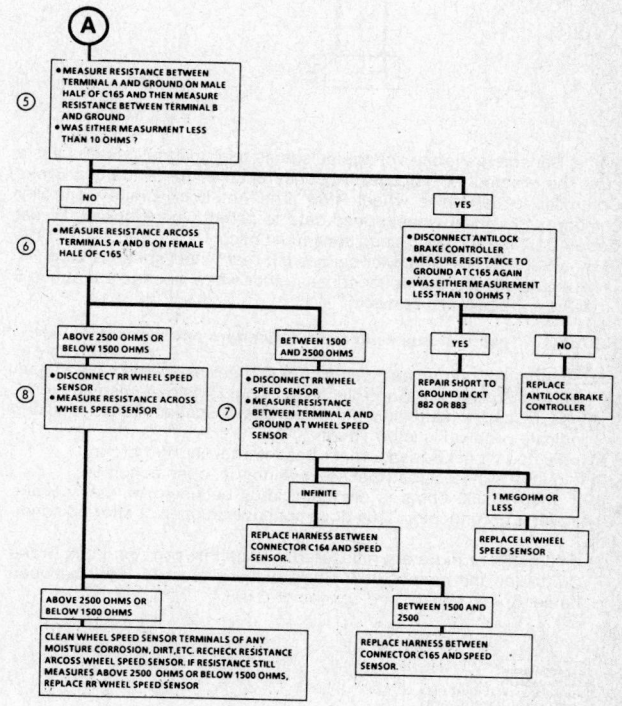

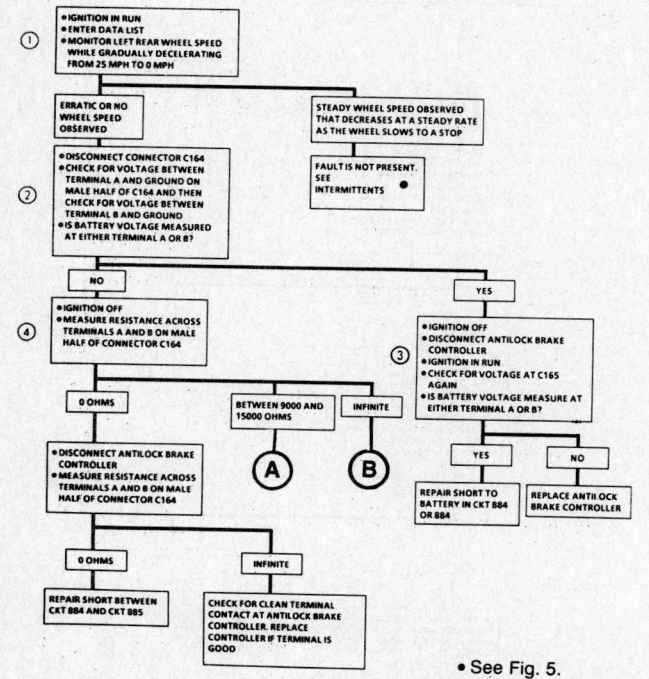

• See Fig. 5.

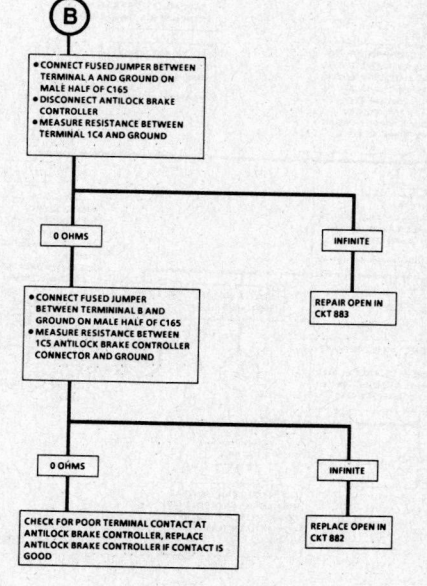

CODE A047, LEFT REAR WHEEL SPEED IS ZERO

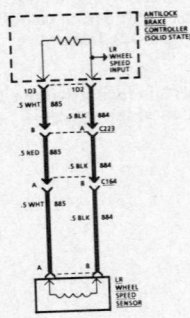

Wheel Sensors generate voltage pulses as their magnetic teeth pass a coil. The created AC voltage frequency enables the Anti-Lock Brake Controller to determine wheel RPM. The Anti-Lock Brake Controller compares individual wheel speed data to detect wheel lockup. To set Code A047, the following conditions must occur.

- Anti-Lock Brake Controller senses left rear wheel speed is zero.
- Anti-Lock Brake Controller senses other wheel speeds are above 5 MPH and operating correctly.

NOTE: **Test numbers refer to test numbers on diagnostic chart.**

1) Observe left rear wheel speed input to determine what type of input the Anti-Lock Brake Controller is sensing. Erratic or unsteady readings indicate a malfunction in wheel speed sensor. Stable readings indicate problem is intermittent.
2) Indicates Wheel Speed Sensor has internal short to ground.
3) If infinite, Wheel Speed Sensor has internal open condition.
4) If 9000-15,000 ohms is present, circuit between Anti-Lock Brake Controller and connector C164 does not have an open or shorted condition.
5) If 10 ohms or more are measured, circuit between Anti-Lock Brake Controller and connector C164 is okay. Inspect for fault between Wheel Speed sensor and connector C165.

6) If 1500-2500 ohms are measured, a short to ground exists. If over 2500 ohms are measured, an open condition exists. If under 1500 ohms are measured, a shorted sensor circuit is indicated.
7) Isolates fault to either wire harness or Wheel Speed Sensor. Harness must be replaced (not repaired) if defective.
8) Isolates fault to either harness or Wheel Speed Sensor. Harness must be replaced (not repaired) if defective.
9) If resistance is infinite, an open exist in circuit No. 884.
10) If resistance is infinite, an open exist in circuit No. 885.

NOTE: **INTERMITTENTS is located under DIAGNOSIS & TESTING portion of this article.**

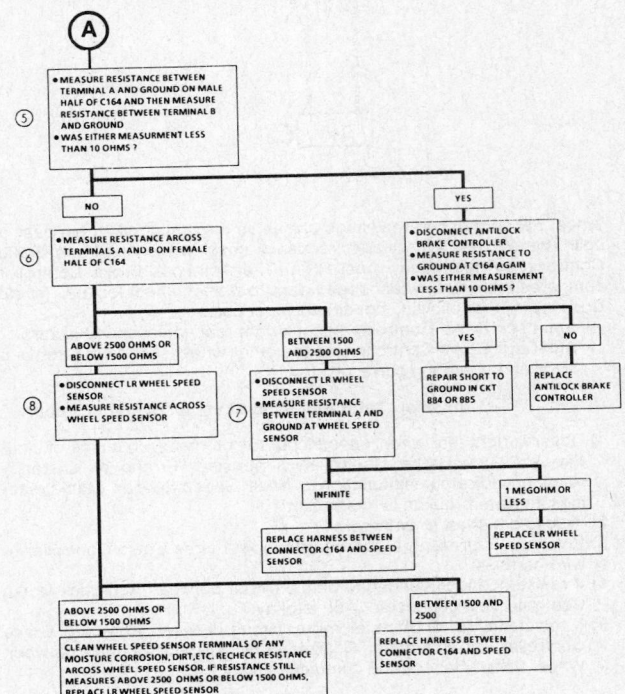

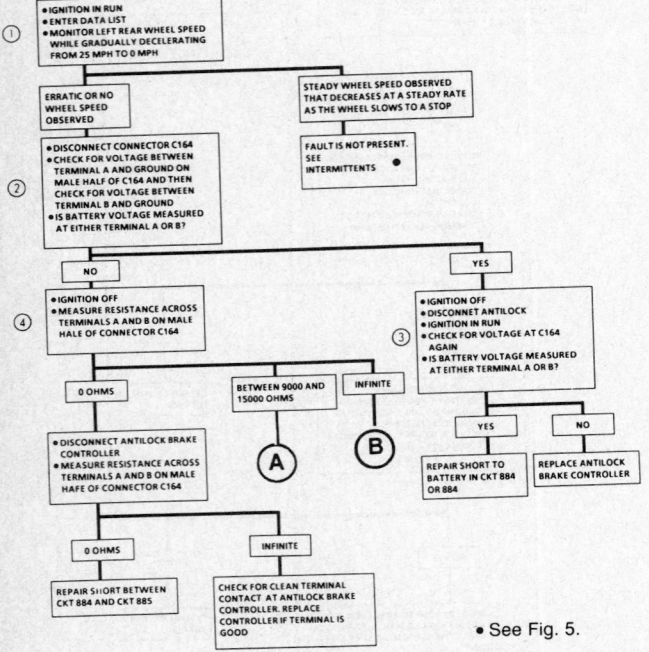

• See Fig. 5.

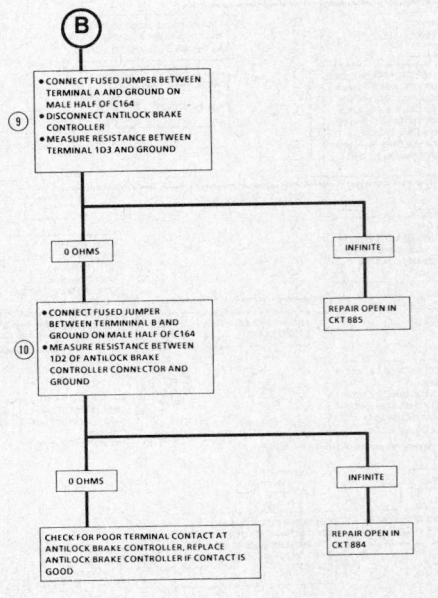

CODE A048, EXCESSIVE RIGHT FRONT WHEEL SPEED ACCELERATION

NOTE: INTERMITTENTS is located under DIAGNOSIS & TESTING portion of this article.

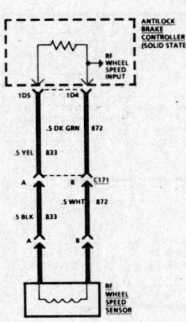

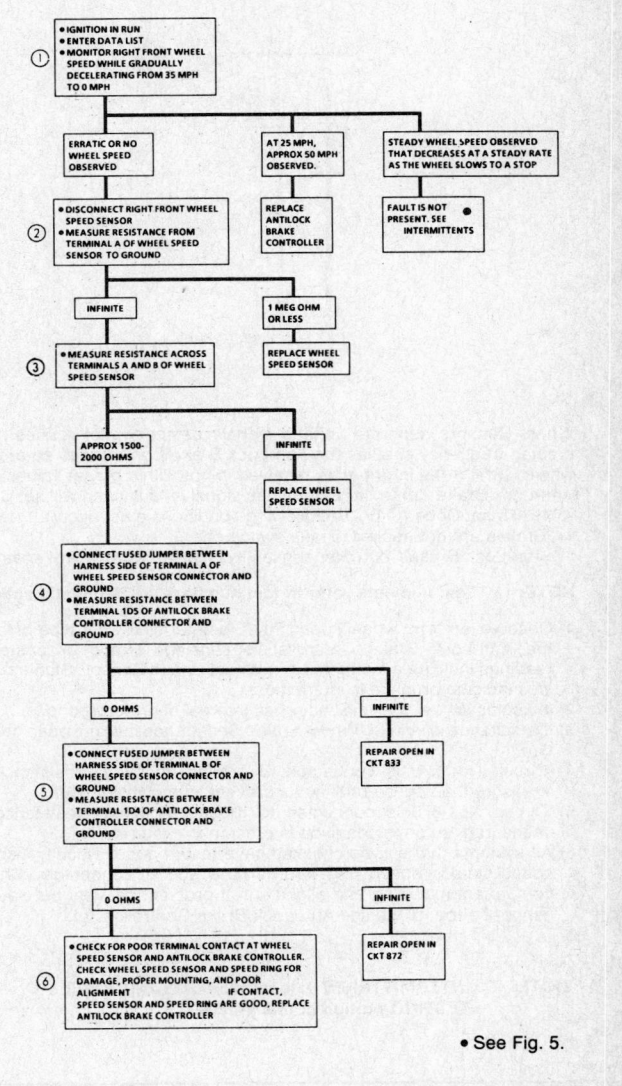

Wheel Sensors generate voltage signals as the wheel rotates. The created frequency enables the Anti-Lock Brake Controller to determine wheel RPM. If the information received is not within preset values, the Anti-Lock Brake Controller determines signal is faulty and set Code A048. To set Code A048, the following conditions must occur.

- Brakes are not applied (Brake switch off).
- Anti-Lock Brake Controller senses illogical right front wheel speeds.

NOTE: Test numbers refer to test numbers on diagnostic chart.

1) Observe right front wheel speed input to determine what type of input the Anti-Lock Brake Controller is sensing. Erratic or unsteady readings indicate a malfunction in Wheel Speed Sensor. Stable readings indicate problem is intermittent.
2) Indicates Wheel Speed Sensor has internal short to ground.
3) If resistance is infinite, Wheel Speed Sensor has internal open condition.
4) Circuit No. 833 is connected to ground. If infinite resistance is measured, an open condition is present in circuit No. 833.
5) Circuit No. 872 is connected to ground. If infinite resistance is measured, an open condition is present in circuit No. 872.
6) All systems that can be checked have tested good. Visually inspect speed sensor, speed ring wire harness and all connectors. Check component mounting and alignment. If problem persists but source cannot be found, replace Anti-Lock Brake Controller.

• See Fig. 5.

109886, 109887

Courtesy of General Motors Corp.

CODE A049, EXCESSIVE LEFT FRONT WHEEL SPEED ACCELERATION

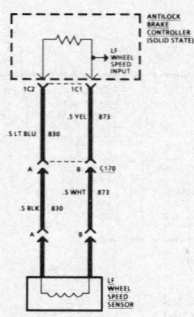

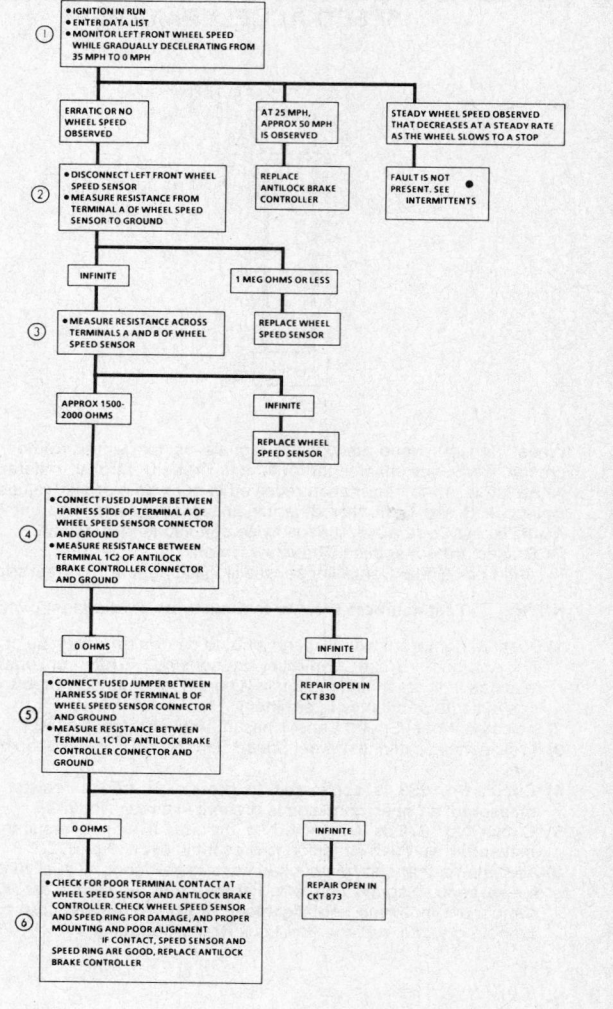

Wheel Sensors generate voltage signals as the wheel rotates. The created frequency enables the Anti-Lock Brake Controller to determine wheel RPM. If the information received is not within preset values, the Anti-Lock Brake Controller determines signal is faulty and will set Code A049. To set Code A049, the following conditions must occur.

- Brakes are not applied (Brake switch off).
- Anti-Lock Brake Controller senses illogical left front wheel speeds.

NOTE: Test numbers refer to test numbers on diagnostic chart.

1) Observe left front wheel speed input to determine what type of input the Anti-Lock Brake Controller is sensing. Erratic or unsteady readings indicate a malfunction in Wheel Speed Sensor. Stable readings indicate problem is intermittent.
2) Indicates Wheel Speed Sensor has internal short to ground.
3) If resistance is infinite, Wheel Speed Sensor has internal open condition.
4) Circuit No. 830 is connected to ground. If infinite resistance is measured, an open condition is present in circuit No. 830.
5) Circuit No. 873 is connected to ground. If infinite resistance is measured, an open condition is present in circuit No. 873.
6) All systems that can be checked have tested good. Visually inspect speed sensor, speed ring wire harness and all connectors. Check component mounting and alignment. If problem persists but source cannot be found, replace Anti-Lock Brake Controller.

NOTE: INTERMITTENTS is located under DIAGNOSIS & TESTING portion of this article.

• See Fig. 5.

CODE A050, EXCESSIVE RIGHT REAR WHEEL SPEED ACCELERATION

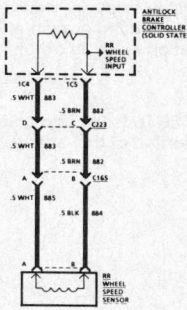

Wheel Sensors generate voltage signals as the wheel rotates. The created frequency enables the Anti-Lock Brake Controller to determine wheel RPM. If the information received is not within preset values, the Anti-Lock Brake Controller determines signal is faulty and will set Code A050. To set Code A050, the following conditions must occur.

- Brakes are not applied (Brake switch off).
- Anti-Lock Brake Controller senses illogical right rear wheel speeds.

NOTE: **Test numbers refer to test numbers on diagnostic chart.**

1) Observe right rear wheel speed input to determine what type of input the Anti-Lock Brake Controller is sensing. Erratic or unsteady readings indicate a continuous malfunction in Wheel Speed Sensor. Stable readings indicate problem is intermittent.
2) Indicates a short to battery.
3) If voltage is present, a short exists in the Anti-Lock Brake Controller or wire harness.
4) If 9000-15,000 ohms are measured, circuit between Anti-Lock Brake Controller and connector C165 is okay.
5) If 10 ohms or more are measured, circuit between Anti-Lock Brake Controller and connector C165 is okay. Inspect for fault between Wheel Speed Sensor and connector C165.

6) If 1500-2500 ohms are measured, a short to ground exists. If over 2500 ohms are measured, an open condition exists. If under 1500 ohms are measured, a shorted sensor circuit is indicated.
7) Isolates fault to either wire harness or Wheel Speed Sensor. Harness must be replaced (not repaired) if defective.
8) Isolates fault to either wire harness or Wheel Speed Sensor. Harness must be replaced (not repaired) if defective.
9) Circuit No. 883 is connected to ground. If infinite resistance is measured, an open condition is present in circuit No. 883.
10) Circuit No. 882 is connected to ground. If infinite resistance is measured, an open condition is present in circuit No. 882.

NOTE: **INTERMITTENTS is located under DIAGNOSIS & TESTING portion of this article.**

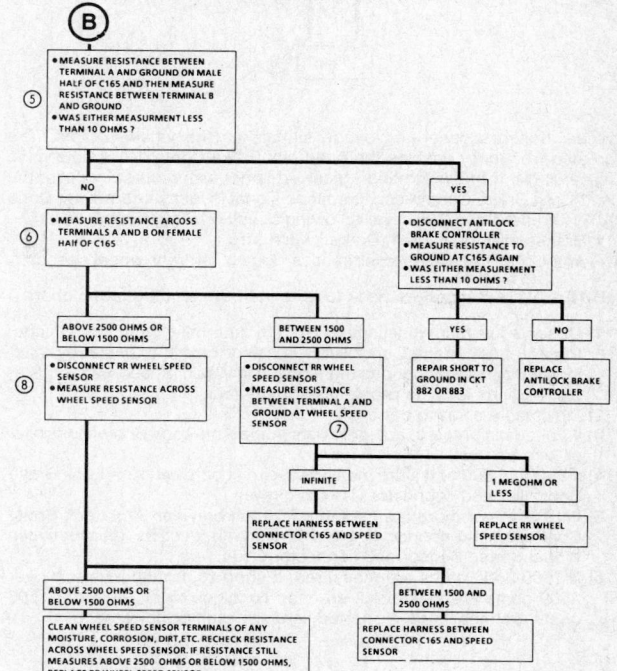

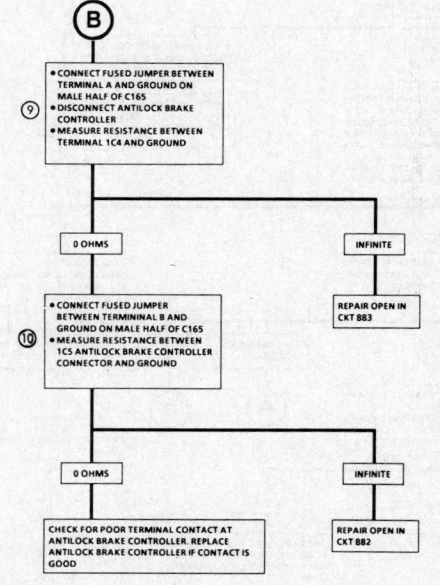

• See Fig. 5.

CODE A051, EXCESSIVE LEFT REAR WHEEL SPEED ACCELERATION

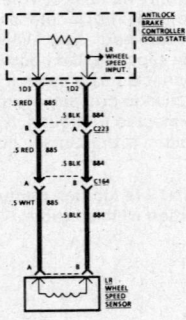

Wheel Sensors generate voltage signals as the wheel rotates. The created frequency enables the Anti-Lock Brake Controller to determine wheel RPM. If the information received is not within preset values, the Anti-Lock Brake Controller determines signal is faulty and will set Code A051. To set Code A051, the following conditions must occur.
- Brakes are not applied (Brake switch off).
- Anti-Lock Brake Controller senses illogical left rear wheel speeds.

NOTE: Test numbers refer to test numbers on diagnostic chart.

1) Observe left rear wheel speed input to determine what type of input the Anti-Lock Brake Controller is sensing. Erratic or unsteady readings indicate a continuous malfunction in Wheel Speed Sensor. Stable readings indicate problem is intermittent.
2) Indicates a short to battery.
3) If voltage is present, a short exists in the Anti-Lock Brake Controller or wire harness.
4) If 9000-15,000 ohms are measured, circuit between Anti-Lock Brake Controller and connector C164 is okay.
5) If 10 ohms or more are measured, circuit between Anti-Lock Brake Controller and connector C164 is okay. Inspect for fault between Wheel Speed Sensor and connector C164.
6) If 1500-2500 ohms are measured, a short to ground exists. If over 2500 ohms are measured, an open condition exists. If under 1500 ohms are measured, a shorted sensor circuit is indicated.

7) Isolates fault to either wire harness or Wheel Speed Sensor. Harness must be replaced (not repaired) if defective.
8) Isolates fault to either wire harness or Wheel Speed Sensor. Harness must be replaced (not repaired) if defective.
9) Circuit No. 884 is connected to ground. If infinite resistance is measured, an open condition exists in circuit No. 884.
10) Circuit No. 885 is connected to ground. If infinite resistance is measured, an open condition exists in circuit No. 885.

NOTE: INTERMITTENTS is located under DIAGNOSIS & TESTING portion of this article.

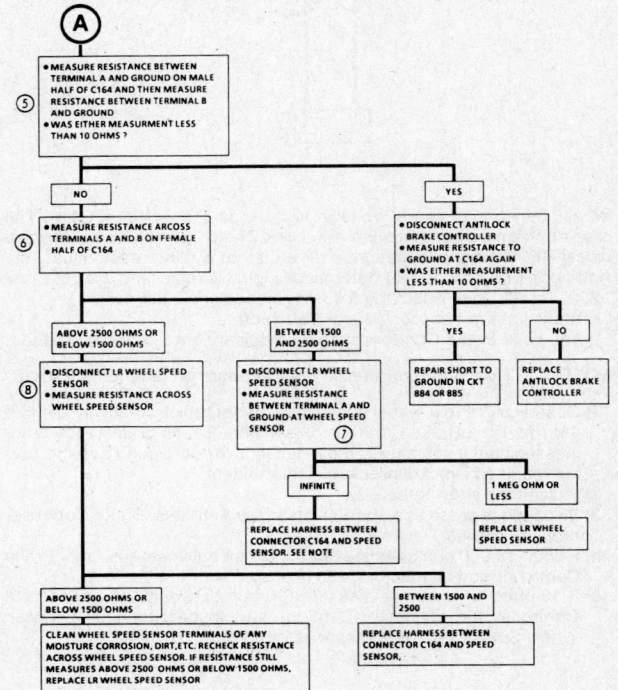

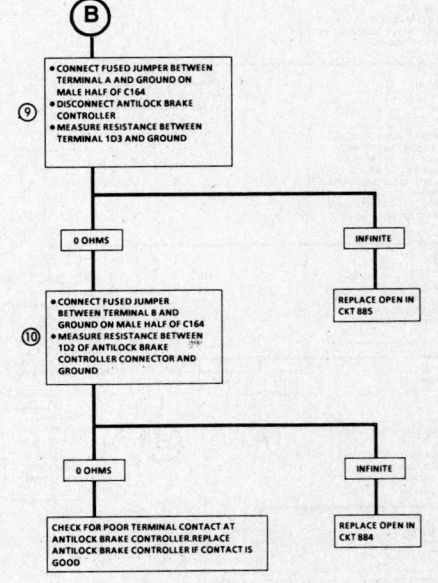

• See Fig. 5.

CODE A052, ANTI-LOCK BRAKE CONTROLLER CALIBRATION ERROR

This code will set if the Anti-Lock Brake Controller detects an internal defect. If code is present, verify code and replace Anti-Lock Brake Controller.

CODE A054 – REAR ENABLE RELAY CIRCUIT OPEN

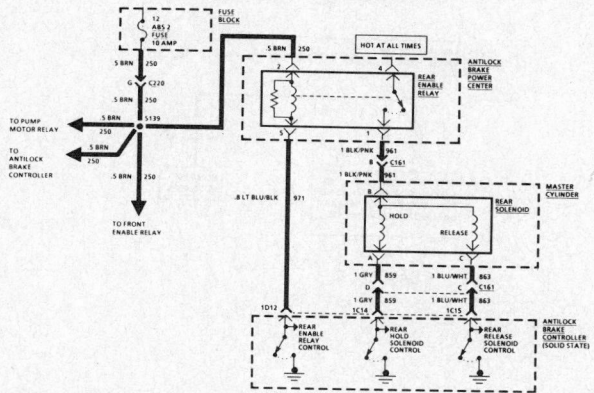

Voltage is applied to the Rear Enable Relay Coil from the ABS-III 2 fuse when the ignition is in the ON position. With Rear Enable Relay Control open, voltage should always be present at terminal 1D12 of Anti-Lock Brake Controller. To set Code A054, the following conditions must occur.

- Rear Enable Relay control is open (relay de-energized).
- Anti-Lock Brake Controller senses no voltage at terminals 1D12, 1D14 and 1D15.
- Codes A004 and A007 are current failures.

NOTE: Test numbers refer to test numbers on diagnostic chart.

1) Observe test light with enable relays on to see if power and ground circuits are good.

NOTE: INTERMITTENTS is located under DIAGNOSIS & TESTING portion of this article.

2) If test light is off, open exists between Rear Enable Relay and Splice S139.
3) If voltage is present, a circuit disruption is present in the Anti-Lock Brake Controller or wire harness connector.
4) Rear Enable Relay is defective.

NOTE: INTERMITTENTS is located under DIAGNOSIS & TESTING portion of this article.

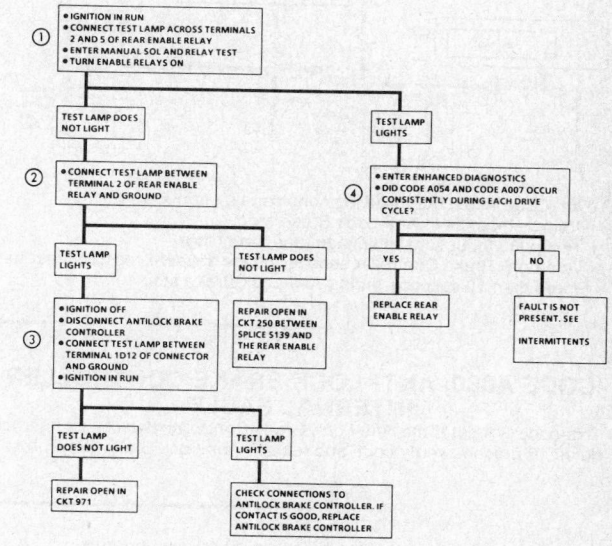

CODE A055 – ANTI-LOCK BRAKE CONTROLLER VOLTAGE FAULT

This code will set if the Anti-Lock Brake Controller detects an internal defect. If code is present, verify code and replace Anti-Lock Brake Controller.

CODE A056 – OPEN BRAKE SWITCH OR HYDRAULIC LEAK

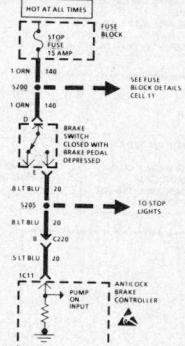

The brake switch receives continuous voltage. When brakes are applied, voltage is diverted to the brakelights and terminal 1C11 of Anti-Lock Brake Controller. The Anti-Lock Brake Controller determines brakes are being applied when Brake-Apply Input receives voltage. To set Code A056, the following condition must occur.

- Code A032 has been set during the previous ignition cycle.

NOTE: Test numbers refer to test numbers on diagnostic chart.

1) Checks for improperly adjusted brake switch.
2) Checks for improperly adjusted brake switch.

3) If Code 062 has also been set, service as necessary.

NOTE: INTERMITTENTS is located in the DIAGNOSIS & TESTING portion of this article.

NOTE: INTERMITTENTS is located under DIAGNOSIS & TESTING portion of this article.

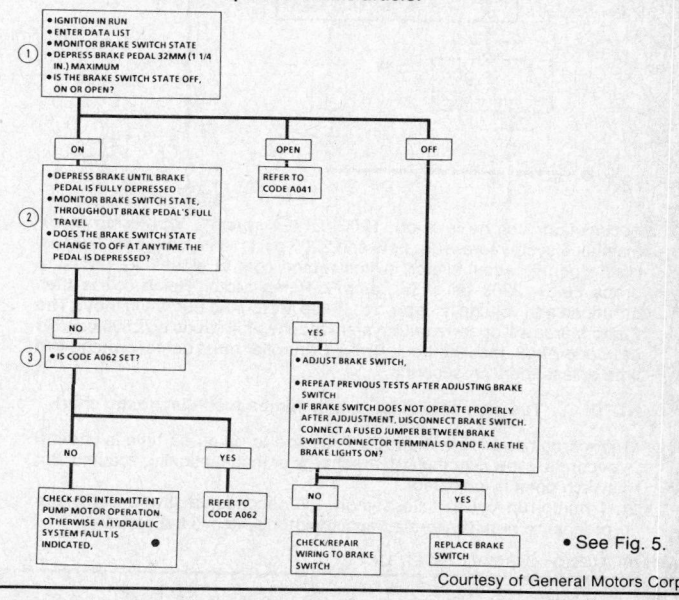

• See Fig. 5.

CODE A059, LOW BRAKE PRESSURE DURING ABS STOP

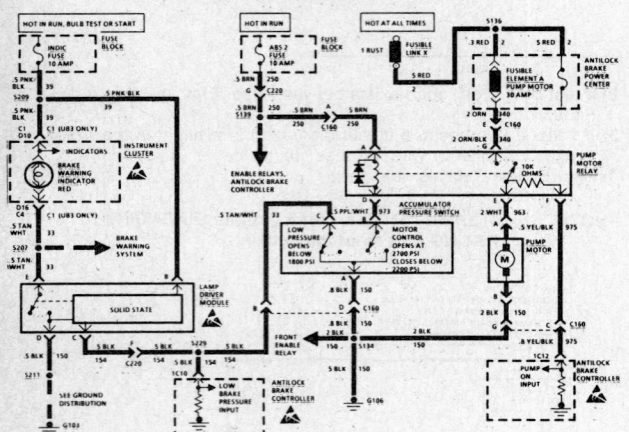

To set Code A059, the following conditions must occur.
- Vehicle must be in Anti-Lock Brake stop.
- Pump-On Input senses voltage (pump running).
- Anti-Lock Brake Controller senses voltage at Low-Pressure Input for more than 10 seconds during Anti-Lock Brake stop.

NOTE: Test number refers to test numbers on diagnostic chart.

1) If Code A035 has set, service this code before proceeding.
   If Code A059 is the only code set, problem is in the hydraulic system. Check for fluid leakage or pump failure.

NOTE: INTERMITTENTS is located in the DIAGNOSIS & TESTING portion of this article.

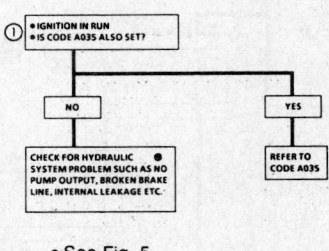

• See Fig. 5.

CODE A060, ANTI-LOCK BRAKE CONTROLLER INTERNAL FAULT

This code will set if the Anti-Lock Brake Controller detects an internal defect. If present, verify code and replace Anti-Lock Brake Controller.

NOTE: INTERMITTENTS is located under DIAGNOSIS & TESTING portion of this article.

CODE A062, LOW ACCUMULATOR PRE-CHARGE

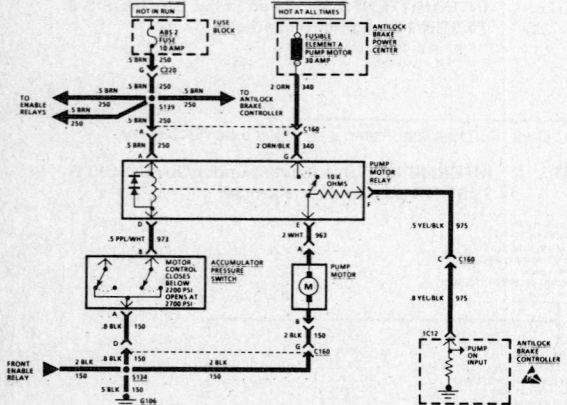

Accumulator charge is about 1200 psi (84 kg/cm²). The Pump Motor maintains system pressure between 2200 psi (155 kg/cm²) and 2700 psi (190 kg/cm²). Accumulator switch motor control closes as pressure drops below 2200 psi (155 kg/cm²). Pump Motor Relay coil is then grounded and voltage is applied to Pump Motor and Pump-On Input. The Pump Motor will operate until system reaches full capacity (2700 psi). To set Code A062, the Anti-Lock Brake Controller must detect a pump-run time of less than 1.4 seconds.

NOTE: Test numbers refer to test numbers on diagnostic chart.

1) When pump-run time from OK Pressure to pump-off time is under 6 seconds, a low accumulator precharge or malfunctioning accumulator switch point is indicated.
2) If pump-run cycle is less than 1.7 seconds, a low accumulator precharge or miscalibrated accumulator switch is indicated.

NOTE: INTERMITTENTS is located under DIAGNOSIS & TESTING portion of this article.

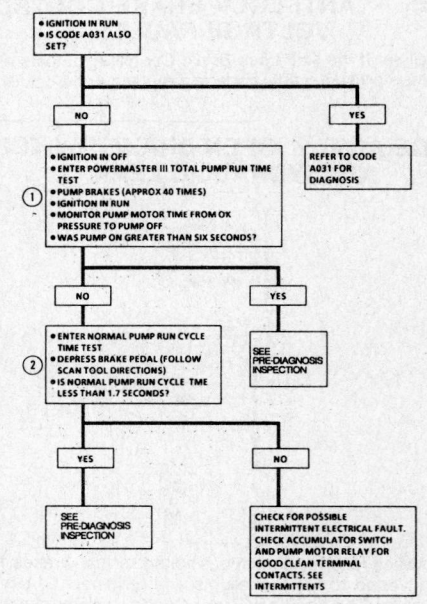

CODE A063, BOTH REAR WHEEL SPEED SENSORS OPEN

NOTE: INTERMITTENTS is located in the DIAGNOSIS & TESTING portion of this article.

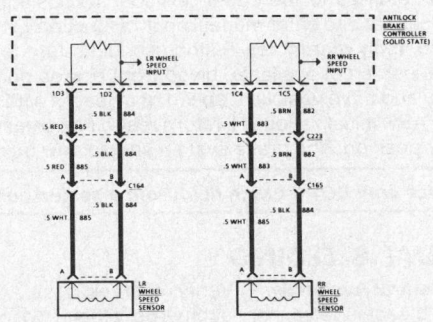

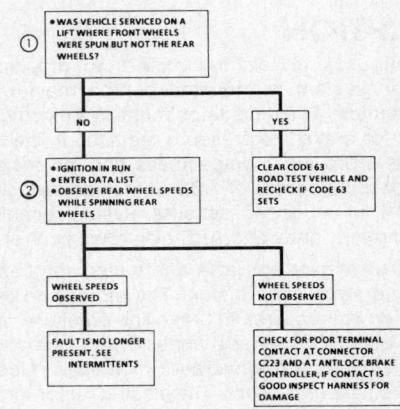

While monitoring Rear Wheel Speed Sensors, the Anti-Lock Brake Controller cannot detect wheel lockup if one or both rear speed sensors indicate zero MPH. Unlike Codes A046 and A047 which detect a single defective speed sensor, Code A063 records malfunction occurring in both rear wheels. To set Code A063, the following conditions must occur.

- Anti-Lock Brake Controller senses speeds of front wheels are greater than 10 MPH and functioning correctly.
- Anti-Lock Brake Controller senses speeds of both rear wheels are zero MPH for 20 seconds or longer.

NOTE: Test numbers refer to test numbers on diagnostic chart.

1) Code may have been falsely registered.
2) Establishes whether fault is a hard or intermittent failure.

109906, 109907

Courtesy of General Motors Corp.

Cutlass Calais, Grand Am, Skylark

NOTE: General Motors uses 5 different anti-lock brake systems. Be sure to use appropriate ANTI-LOCK article.

DESCRIPTION

The ABS-VI uses an electric motors to modulate displacement pistons. The system is mounted on the master cylinder/vacuum booster assembly. The modulator contains 3 electric motors that control pistons for brake line pressure regulation. The integrated design of this system provides compactness and fewer necessary components. Major components of ABS-VI include the following: hydraulic modulator, 4 wheel speed sensors, system enable relay, 2 dash-mounted warning lights, and ABS electronic control unit. *See Fig. 1.*

Each motor drive gear operates a threaded shaft assembly attached to a pressure modulating piston. The motor can drive piston up to increase or down to decrease brake line pressure. When the Electronic Control Unit (ECU) senses wheel lockup from the wheel sensors, a solenoid, located in the hydraulic modulator, closes the hydraulic path from the master cylinder. The electric motor for that brake circuit then cycles the piston up and down to modulate braking force to prevent wheel lockup.

NOTE: For more information on brake system, see DISC & DRUM article.

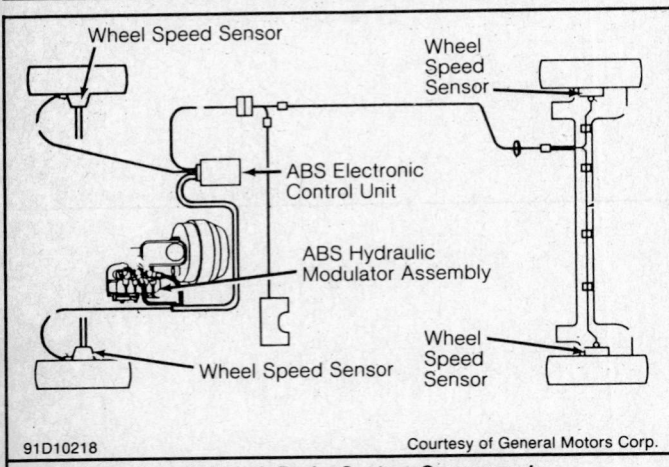

91D10218   Courtesy of General Motors Corp.

Fig. 1: Locating Anti-Lock Brake System Components

OPERATION

ANTI-LOCK BRAKE SYSTEM

During normal driving and braking operations, ABS-VI acts like a conventional braking system. Each wheel sensor constantly sends an AC voltage signal to the ECU. This information is translated to wheel rotation speed. When ECU detects wheel lockup is about to occur, it activates the appropriate solenoid to regulate hydraulic pressure to each wheel. The pedal pulsation normally felt with ABS application should be present.

Warning lights should come on when ignition is turned on and vehicle is started. If either light stays on more than 30 seconds after vehicle is started, system malfunction is indicated. See DIAGNOSIS & TESTING.

Red warning light comes on if parking brake is applied, brake fluid is low or accumulator pressure is low. Amber ANTI-LOCK warning light is controlled by anti-lock brake controller and comes on if problem is detected in system. When light is on, ABS operation can be partially or totally disabled.

WARNING: DO NOT tap into vehicle's brake system to operate trailer brake system.

BLEEDING BRAKE SYSTEM

BLEEDING PROCEDURE

1) Before servicing system, the rear displacement cylinder pistons must be returned to the upper position. To position piston, connect Tech I scanner and enter manual control function. Ensure enable relay is on and apply rear motor. Pistons should return to upper position.
2) If scanner is not available, bleed front brakes only. Ensure brakes are okay and drive vehicle at speed of at least 4 MPH to initialize ABS system. ABS initialization will return rear displacement cylinder piston to upper position. The brake system should now be ready for service.

NOTE: Use only DOT 3 brake fluid from a sealed container.

MANUAL BLEEDING

Brake Control Assembly – Verify reservoir is full. Attach a clear hose to rear bleeder valve and submerge other end of hose in clean container. Slowly open rear bleeder. Apply brake pedal until fluid begins to flow. Close valve and release brake pedal. Repeat procedure for front bleeder valve.
Brake Cylinder/Caliper – 1) Clean master cylinder reservoir cover and surrounding area. Ensure reservoir is full. Raise and support vehicle. Attach a clear hose to right rear bleeder valve and submerge other end of hose in container of brake fluid.
2) Open bleeder valve. Slowly depress brake pedal. Close bleeder valve and release brake pedal. Repeat this step until no air is seen in hose. Repeat procedure for left rear, right front and left front bleeder valves. Ensure reservoir is full.

PRESSURE BLEEDING

Brake Control Assembly – 1) Clean master cylinder reservoir cover and surrounding area. Remove reservoir cap. Ensure reservoir is full. Attach Bleeder Adapter (J-35589) to reservoir. Attach bleeding equipment and pressurize system to 10 psi (.7 kg/cm²) for 30 seconds to ensure there are no leaks.
2) Slowly increase pressure to 35 psi (2.5 kg/cm²). Attach a clear hose to rear bleeder valve and submerge other end of hose in clean container. Slowly open brake control assembly rear bleeder. Allow fluid to flow until no air is seen. Close valve and repeat procedure for front bleeder valve.
3) To bleed unit at brake pipe connections, position shop towel below brake pipes. Using flare wrench, slightly open front upper brake pipe fitting at brake control assembly. Allow air to escape and tighten fitting.
Brake Cylinder/Caliper – 1) Ensure master cylinder reservoir is full. Raise and support vehicle. Attach a clear hose to right rear bleeder valve and submerge other end of hose in container of brake fluid.
2) Open bleeder valve. Allow fluid to flow until no air is seen. Tap lightly on cylinder/caliper housing to free trapped air. Close valve and repeat procedure for remaining bleeder valves in following sequence: right rear, left rear, right front and left front.

ADJUSTMENTS

PARKING/EMERGENCY BRAKE

1) Ensure rear brakes are properly adjusted. See appropriate DISC & DRUM article. Lower vehicle. On vehicles with hand-operated parking brake, raise lever 5 ratchet clicks. On vehicles with foot-operated parking brake, apply pedal 2 ratchet clicks.
2) Raise and support vehicle. Tighten parking brake cable until rear wheels can be turned backward (with resistance) but lock when turned in forward direction. Release parking brake. Rear wheels should turn freely in either direction with no resistance.

STOPLIGHT SWITCH

Remove left sound insulator panel. Position stoplight switch into retainer, with body of switch seated on retainer. Pull brake pedal upward against internal pedal stop. Switch will self-position in retainer to complete adjustment. To verify correct adjustment, pull pedal upward. No clicks should be heard. Ensure brakelights are off.

WHEEL SPEED SENSORS

NOTE: Wheel speed sensor gaps are not adjustable.

Front Wheel Speed Sensor – The front wheel speed sensors are mounted to the steering knuckle. The gap between sensor and 47-tooth ring should be .020-.070" (.5-1.7 mm). Replace sensor and/or ring if gap is incorrect.

Rear Wheel Speed Sensor – The rear wheel speed sensor and ring are contained in the dust cap of the integral rear wheel bearing. If rear wheel speed sensor fails, replace integral bear/sensor as an assembly.

REMOVAL & INSTALLATION

ABS BRAKE ENABLE RELAY

Removal & Installation – Turn ignition off. Locate ABS enable relay on center of firewall. *See Fig. 2.* Remove relay attaching screws. Remove ABS enable relay from panel. To install, reverse removal procedure.

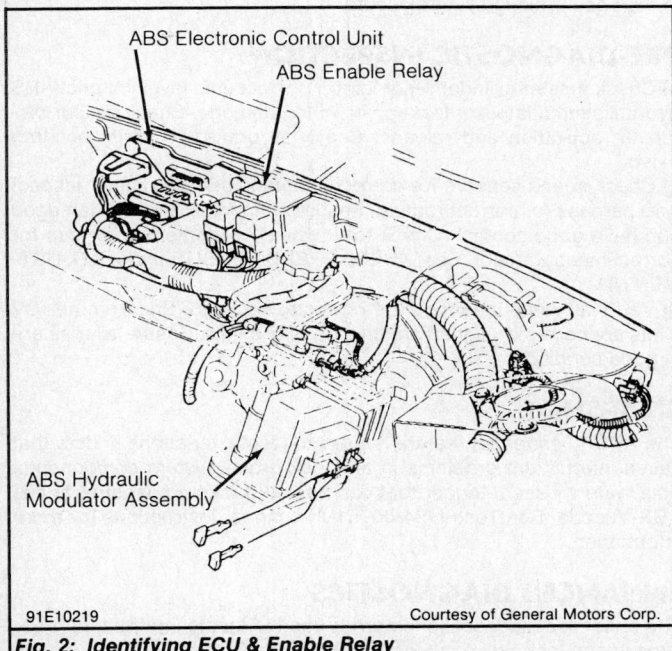

91E10219   Courtesy of General Motors Corp.

Fig. 2: Identifying ECU & Enable Relay

ABS LAMP DRIVER MODULE

Removal & Installation – Turn ignition off. Remove insulator panel below glove compartment. Disconnect ABS lamp driver module wiring harness connector. Remove ABS lamp driver module. *See Fig. 3.* To install, reverse removal procedure.

ELECTRONIC CONTROL UNIT (ECU)

Removal & Installation – Turn ignition off. Locate ECU on right side of firewall. *See Fig. 2.* Remove ECU connectors. Remove ECU attaching screws. Remove ECU from panel. To install, reverse removal procedure.

FLUID LEVEL SENSOR SWITCH

Removal & Installation – Turn ignition off. Disconnect electrical connector from switch. Depress locking tabs at inner side of switch and remove fluid level sensor switch. *See Fig. 4.* To install, reverse removal procedure.

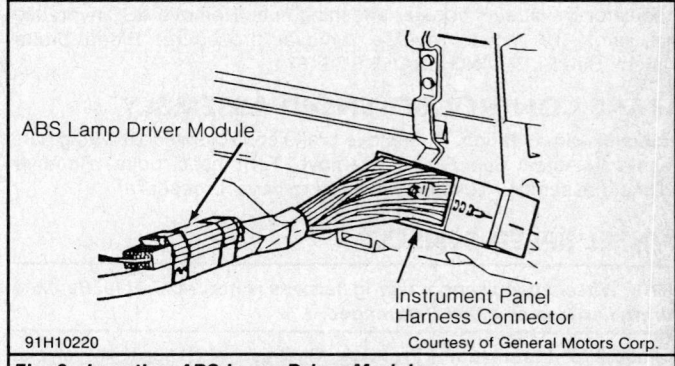

91H10220   Courtesy of General Motors Corp.

Fig. 3: Locating ABS Lamp Driver Module

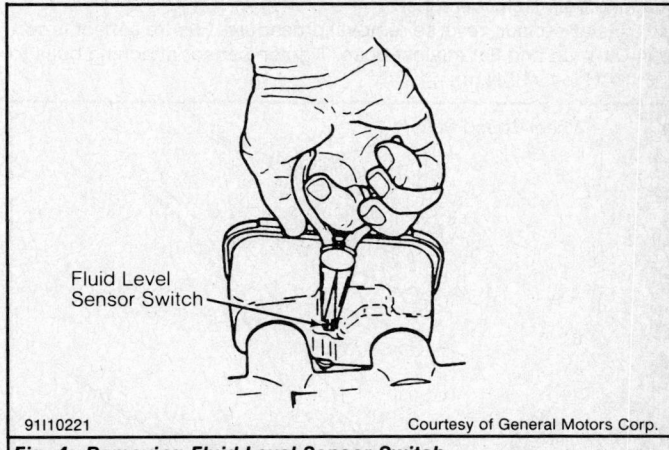

91I10221   Courtesy of General Motors Corp.

Fig. 4: Removing Fluid Level Sensor Switch

ABS HYDRAULIC MODULATOR ASSEMBLY

Removal & Installation – **1)** Using a Tech I scan tool, perform gear tension relief procedure. See Tech I scanner instructions for more information. Remove both wiring harness connectors of brake control solenoid. Remove fluid level sensor, 6-pin and 3-pin wiring harness connectors. *See Fig. 5.* Place shop towel on motor pack.

2) Remove brake line pipes. Plug pipes to prevent fluid loss. Remove vacuum check valve from vacuum booster. Remove ABS hydraulic

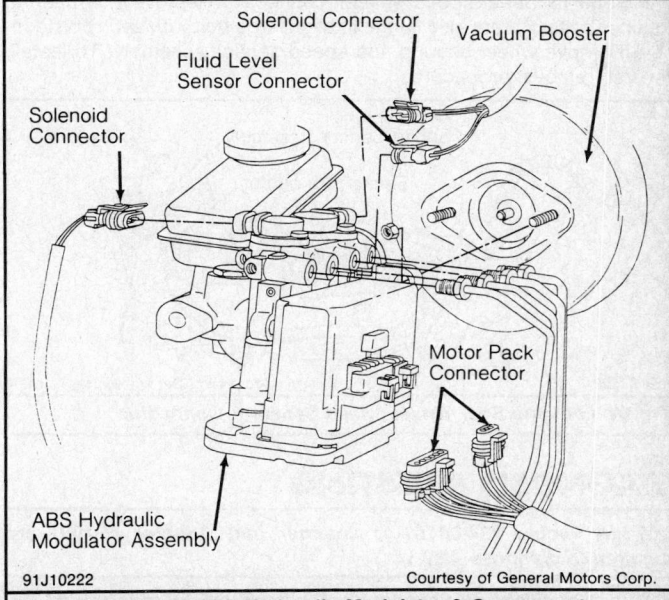

91J10222   Courtesy of General Motors Corp.

Fig. 5: Identifying ABS Hydraulic Modulator & Components

modulator-to-vacuum booster attaching nuts. Remove ABS hydraulic modulator. To install, reverse removal procedure. Bleed brake system. See BLEEDING BRAKE SYSTEM.

BRAKE CONTROL SOLENOID ASSEMBLY

Removal & Installation – Remove brake control solenoid wiring harness connector. *See Fig. 5*. Remove Torx head bolts. Remove solenoid assembly. To install, reverse removal procedure.

WHEEL SPEED SENSOR

NOTE: Wheel speed sensor wiring harness is not repairable. Replace wiring harness as a unit if damaged.

Removal & Installation (Front) – 1) Raise and support vehicle. Disconnect sensor connector. *See Fig. 6*. Remove sensor and bracket retaining bolt. Remove sensor.
2) To install sensor, reverse removal procedure. Ensure sensor is correctly aligned and flat against boss. Tighten sensor attaching bolts to 106 INCH lbs. (12 N.m).

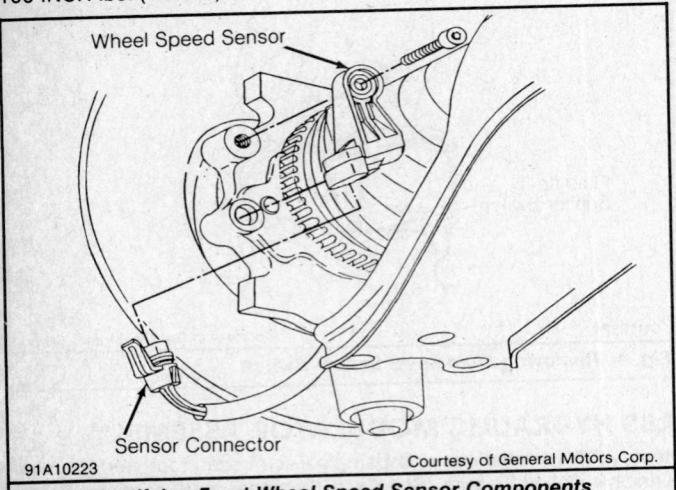

Wheel Speed Sensor

Sensor Connector

91A10223   Courtesy of General Motors Corp.

Fig. 6: Identifying Front Wheel Speed Sensor Components

Removal & Installation (Rear) – 1) Rear wheel speed sensor is integral with hub/bearing assembly. *See Fig. 7*. To replace sensor, the hub/bearing assembly must be replaced.
2) Raise and support vehicle. Remove wheel. Remove drum assembly. Remove wheel speed sensor connector. Remove hub/bearing retainer bolts. Rotate axle flange to align large bolt with each bolt location. Remove wheel bearing and speed sensor assembly. To install, reverse removal procedure.

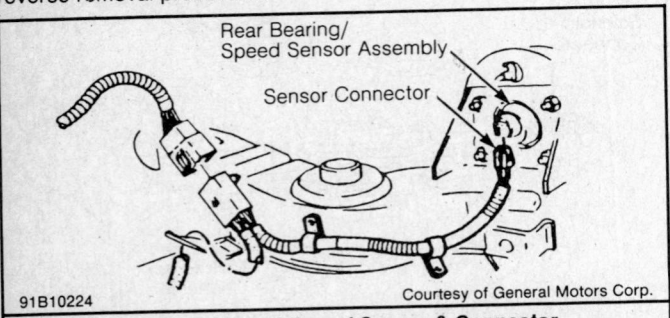

Rear Bearing/
Speed Sensor Assembly

Sensor Connector

91B10224   Courtesy of General Motors Corp.

Fig. 7: Locating Rear Wheel Speed Sensor & Connector

DIAGNOSIS & TESTING

NOTE: A Tech I (94-00101-A) scanner and Adapter (T-100) are required to diagnose ABS-VI.

Before attempting any diagnostic procedures, road test vehicle to verify complaint. Perform a pre-diagnostic visual inspection to detect obvious problems. See PRE-DIAGNOSTIC INSPECTION. Repair problems as necessary and retest vehicle.

If no obvious problems appear, scan ABS system for trouble codes. Attach Tech I (94-00101-A) scanner and Adapter (T-100) to the vehicle's ALDL connector and follow manufacturer's instructions to retrieve trouble codes. If trouble codes are found, proceed to diagnostic flow charts. See DIAGNOSTIC CHARTS at end of article.

If no problems are found, test drive vehicle while using automatic snapshot feature of Tech I scanner. See SNAPSHOT under DIAGNOSIS & TESTING. If failure(s) cannot be reproduced, use enhanced diagnostic information to reveal ABS fault history. See ENHANCED DIAGNOSTICS under DIAGNOSIS & TESTING.

WARNING LIGHTS

Amber Warning Light – With ignition on, a flashing Amber warning light indicates a problem exists in the ABS system, but system is still operational. If Amber light remains on steadily, it indicates problem has affected ABS operation and no anti-lock braking will be available.
Red Warning Light – With ignition on, Red warning light indicates the following possible problems: low fluid level in the master cylinder reservoir, parking brake switch closed or bulb test switch circuit of the ignition switch is closed. Red warning light also comes on if a problem in the base braking system occurs.

PRE-DIAGNOSTIC INSPECTION

1) Check master cylinder reservoir for correct fluid level. Inspect ABS hydraulic modulator for leakage or wiring damage. Check caliper piston for activation and release. Check all brakes to verify no drag exists.
2) Check speed sensors for correct mounting and alignment. Inspect wire harness for correct routing. Ensure connectors are not damaged and have good contact. Check front wheel speed sensor air gap for correct measurement. See WHEEL SPEED SENSOR under ADJUSTMENTS.
3) Verify all wheel bearings are correctly adjusted. Ensure outer CV joints are correctly aligned and that no play exists. Ensure all tires are in good condition.

SNAPSHOT

The ABS-VI snapshot feature is used to locate variations in data that cause intermittent problems in anti-lock brake system components. This feature uses a trigger that can be set to take a snapshot of any ABS-VI code. See Tech I (94-00101-A) scanner instructions for more information.

ENHANCED DIAGNOSTICS

The enhanced diagnostics feature is used to locate intermittent problems in anti-lock brake system components. This feature will provide information regarding the frequency of intermittent fault, and detail the order in which the last 5 trouble codes were set. See Tech I (94-00101-A) scanner manufacturer's instructions for more information.

INTERMITTENTS

To effectively locate fault(s) using charts, problem must be present currently. The diagnostic procedures may help determine cause of intermittent problems in anti-lock brake system electrical components. Most intermittent problems are caused by faulty electrical connections or wiring.

When an intermittent failure is encountered, check for trouble codes stored in the ABS Module. If trouble codes are found, inspect related components and circuitry for possible intermittent failure caused by poor connections. If no trouble codes are found, inspect suspected circuits as follows:
- Check for poor mating of connector halves, or terminals not fully seated in connector body (backed out).
- Check for improperly formed or damaged terminals. Carefully reform all connector terminals of problem circuit to increase contact tension.

- Check for poor terminal-to-wire connection. This requires removing terminal and wire from connector body for inspection.

If inspection of circuit does not disclose cause of problem, the ABS-VI self-diagnostic system can be useful in locating suspected circuit in the following manner:

- Display and then clear ABS-VI trouble codes in Anti-Lock Brake Controller.
- Test drive vehicle and attempt to duplicate conditions causing problem or complaint. Stop vehicle and record any codes set.

Circuits with poor connections could cause intermittent operation of anti-lock system.

Program ABS-VI snapshot to identify intermittent fault. Use the enhanced diagnostic feature to recreate the conditions causing the trouble code to set. Determine how often and under what conditions fault occurs. Analyze ABS-VI snapshot data for unusual conditions.

USING TECH 1

NOTE: *Tech 1 Diagnostic Scanner (94-00101-A) with Adapter (T-100) and high-impedance multimeter will be needed to test parts of the ABS system.*

Insert cartridge in Tech 1 to perform diagnostic procedures on anti-lock brake system. Plug Tech 1 and Adapter (T-100) into ALDL connector before turning ignition on.

Selecting Model Year – Turn ignition switch to RUN position. Select appropriate model year using function keys.

Selecting Vehicle – After selecting model year, enter type of vehicle being tested. Press NO until "B" is flashing. Pressing EXIT will return Tech 1 to previous screen.

Selecting Test Mode – Five test modes are available for diagnosing anti-lock brake system. Test modes are as follows:

Mode F0 (Data List) – Mode displays the actual reading that each wheel speed sensor is sending to EBCM. In this mode, vehicle can be driven and wheel speed information can be observed to determine if readings are comparable to actual vehicle speed. By pressing brake pedal, status of brakelight switch can be observed.

Mode F1 (Code History) – Mode displays trouble codes and description. This data includes how many ignition cycles since trouble code occurred. Up to 5 fault codes are included in the ABS history data.

Mode F2 (Trouble Codes) – Mode displays ABS trouble codes. Tech 1 will display any trouble codes and brief description of code displayed. If no codes are stored, Tech 1 will display NO ABS CODES.

Mode F3 (ABS Snapshot) – Mode helps isolate intermittent problems by capturing data before and after condition.

By selecting Manual Trigger, Tech 1 will wait for ENTER to be pressed before storing speed sensor information. All stored information can be displayed and examined for conditions which might indicate a problem.

Mode F4 (ABS Test) – Mode is used to perform hydraulic modulator assembly testing to assist in isolating problems during troubleshooting.

Scan Tool Parameters – Only the parameters used in SCAN DATA PARAMETERS table should be considered in ABS system diagnosing. If other data is received, it should not be considered reliable, and scan tool should be repaired or replaced.

SCAN DATA PARAMETERS

Scan Position	Unit Displayed
ABS Batt Voltage	Volts
ABS Warning Light	On-Off Flashing
Brakes Available	Anti-Lock/Base Brakes
Brake T-Tale CMD	On-Off
Brake Tell-Tale CMD	On-Off Circuit
Brake Switch	On-Off Circuit
Enable Relay CMD	On-Off
Front WHL Speeds	MPH-km/h
Left Front Solenoid	On-Off
Left Front EMB [1]	Release/Hold
Left Front Motor Command FWD/REV	Amps
Left Motor Feedback	Amps
Right Front Motor Command FWD/REV	Amps
Right Motor Feedback	Amps
Rear Motor Command FWD/REV	Amps
Rear Motor Feedback	Amps
Right Front Solenoid	On-Off
Right Front EMB [1]	Release/Hold

[1] – Electro-Mechanical Brake

CLEARING CODES

The following methods can be used to clear codes.

Tech 1 CLEAR CODES Selection – 1) Connect Tech 1 Diagnostic Computer. See USING TECH 1. Before clearing codes, check and note history code data. Select appropriate menu and select CLEAR CODES function.

2) Verify codes are cleared. Only Code 12 should be displayed. If other codes are displayed, either codes were not cleared or ABS fault still exists. Correct fault and repeat procedure.

Ignition Cycle Default – If vehicle power is cycled 100 times without a particular fault reappearing, fault code will be erased from EBCM memory. Ignition cycle counter will reset to zero.

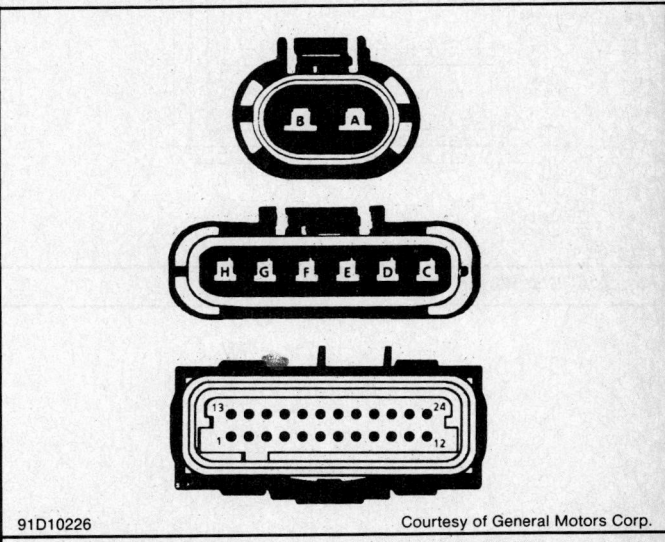

91D10226   Courtesy of General Motors Corp.

Fig. 8: Identifying ABS Electronic Control Unit (ECU) Connector Terminals

WIRING DIAGRAM

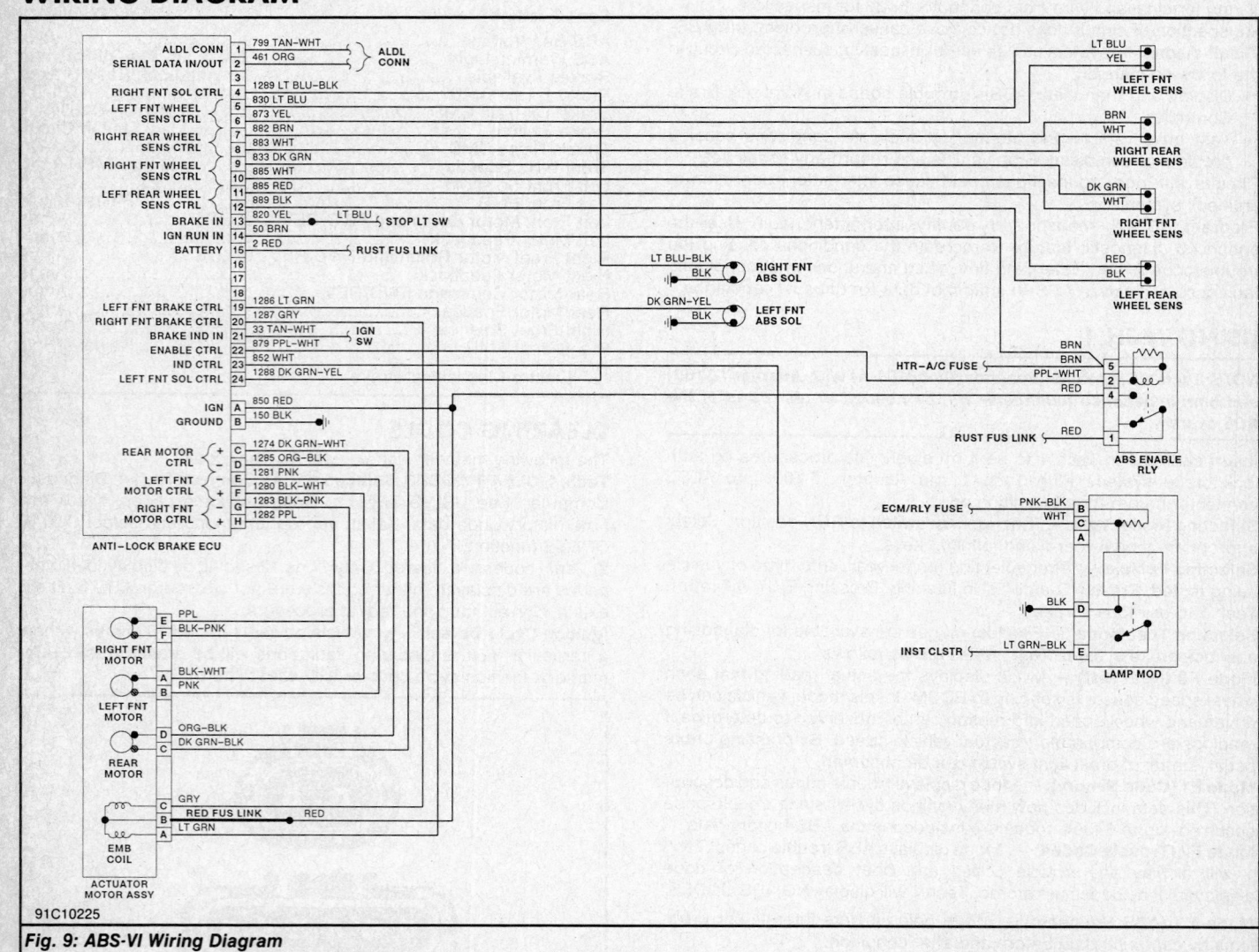

91C10225

Fig. 9: ABS-VI Wiring Diagram

DIAGNOSTIC TROUBLE CODES

Code	Definition
A011	ABS Warning Light Circuit Fault
A013	ABS Warning Light Circuit Fault
A014	Enable Relay Contacts Open, Fuse Open
A015	Enable Relay Contacts Shorted to Power
A016	Enable Relay Coil Circuit Open
A017	Enable Relay Coil Shorted to Ground
A018	Enable Relay Coil Shorted to Power
A021	Left Front Wheel Speed Zero
A022	Right Front Wheel Speed Zero
A023	Left Rear Wheel Speed Zero
A024	Right Rear Wheel Speed Zero
A025	Excessive Left Front Wheel Acceleration
A026	Excessive Right Front Wheel Acceleration
A027	Excessive Left Rear Wheel Acceleration
A028	Excessive Right Rear Wheel Acceleration
A031	2 Wheel Sensors Open
A036	System Voltage Low
A037	System Voltage High
A038	Left Front EMB Will Not Hold Motor
A041	Right Front EMB Will Not Hold Motor
A042	Rear Axle ESB Will Not Hold Motor
A044	Left Front EMB Will Not Release Motor
A045	Right Front EMB Will Not Release Motor
A046	Rear Axle ESB Will Not Release Motor
A047	Left Front Nut Failure
A048	Right Front Nut Failure
A051	Rear Axle Nut Failure
A052	Left Front Channel Release Too Long
A053	Right Front Channel Release Too Long
A054	Rear Axle Channel Release Too Long
A055	Motor Driver Interface Fault Detected

DIAGNOSTIC TROUBLE CODES (Cont.)

Code	Definition
A056	Left Front Motor Circuit Open
A057	Left Front Motor Shorted to Ground
A058	Left Front Motor Shorted to Battery
A061	Right Front Motor Circuit Open
A062	Right Front Motor Shorted to Ground
A063	Right Front Motor Shorted to Battery
A064	Rear Axle Motor Circuit Open
A065	Rear Axle Motor Circuit Shorted to Ground
A066	Rear Axle Motor Circuit Shorted to Battery
A067	Left Front EMB Release Circuit Open or Shorted to Ground
A068	Left Front EMB Release Circuit Shorted to Battery
A071	Right Front EMB Release Circuit Open or Shorted to Ground
A072	Right Front EMB Release Circuit Shorted to Battery
A076	Left Front Solenoid Circuit Open or Shorted to Battery
A077	Left Front Solenoid Circuit Shorted to Ground
A078	Right Front Solenoid Circuit Open or Shorted to Battery
A081	Right Front Solenoid Circuit Shorted to Ground
A082	Calibration Memory Failure
A086	ABS Enable Red Brake Telltale
A087	Red Brake Telltale Circuit Open
A088	ABS Red Brake Telltale Circuit Shorted to Battery
A091	Open Brake Switch Contacts (Deceleration Detection)
A092	Open Brake Switch Contacts
A093	Code 91 or 92 Failed Last or Current Ignition Cycle
A094	Brake Switch Contacts or Input Shorted to Battery
A095	Brake Switch Circuit Open
A096	Brake Light or 4-Way Flasher Circuit Failure

DIAGNOSTIC CHARTS

ABS-VI DIAGNOSTIC CIRCUIT CHECK

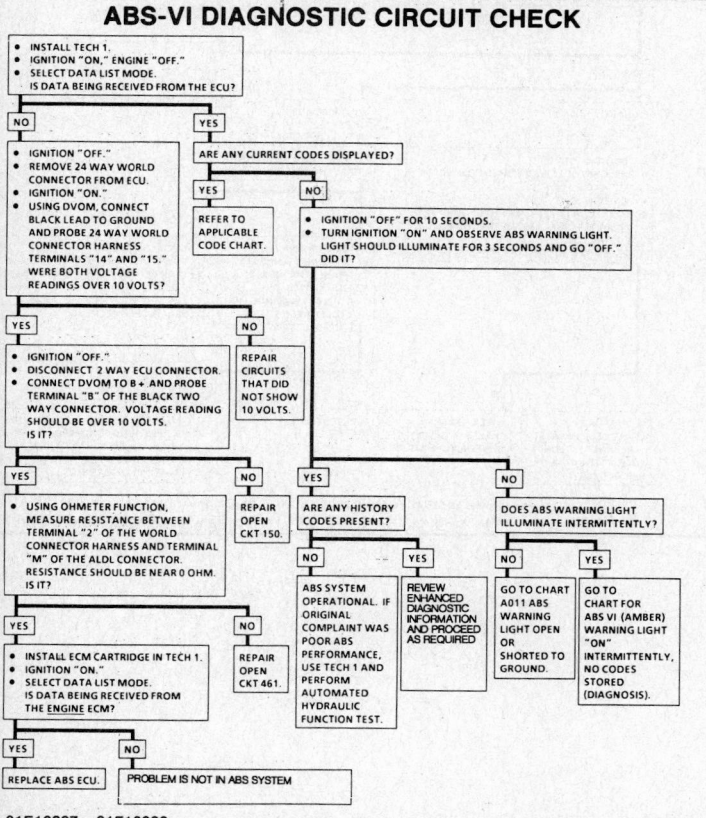

ABS AMBER WARNING LIGHT INTERMITTENTLY ON, NO CODES STORED

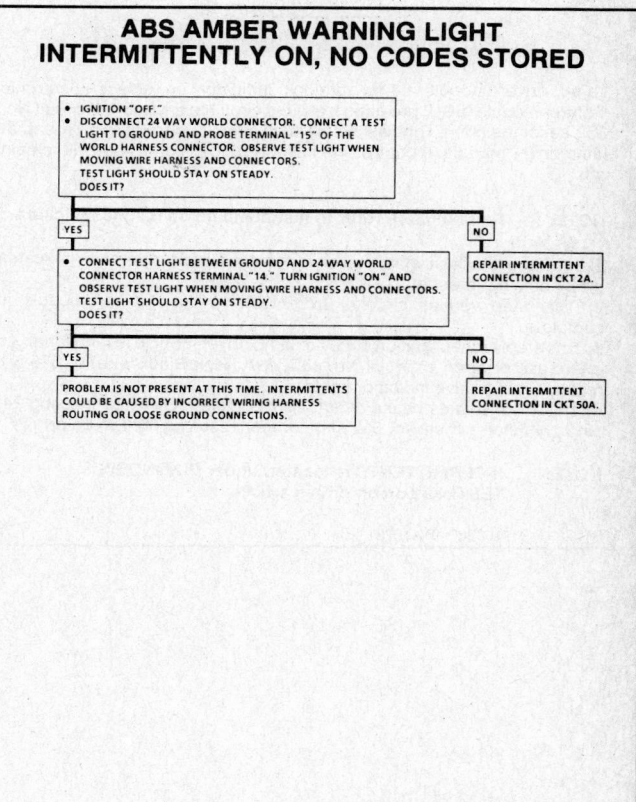

91E10227   91F10228

Courtesy of General Motors Corp.

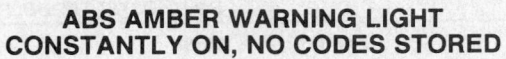

ABS AMBER WARNING LIGHT
CONSTANTLY ON, NO CODES STORED

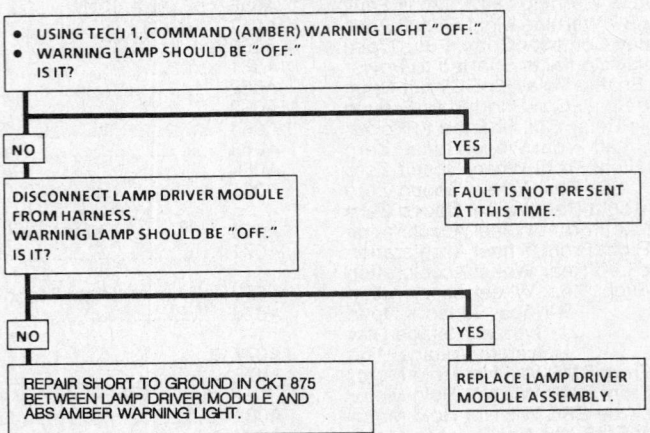

- USING TECH 1, COMMAND (AMBER) WARNING LIGHT "OFF."
- WARNING LAMP SHOULD BE "OFF."
  IS IT?

NO: DISCONNECT LAMP DRIVER MODULE FROM HARNESS. WARNING LAMP SHOULD BE "OFF." IS IT?

YES: FAULT IS NOT PRESENT AT THIS TIME.

NO: REPAIR SHORT TO GROUND IN CKT 875 BETWEEN LAMP DRIVER MODULE AND ABS AMBER WARNING LIGHT.

YES: REPLACE LAMP DRIVER MODULE ASSEMBLY.

CODE A011, ANTI-LOCK WARNING INDICATOR OPEN OR SHORTED TO GROUND

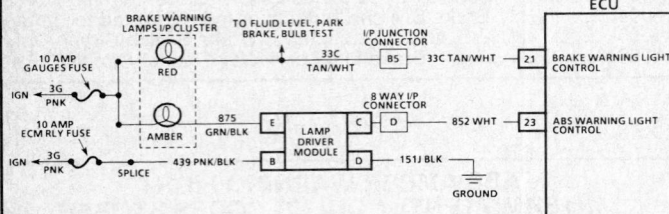

Lamp driver module turns anti-lock indicator on unless Electronic Control Module (ECU) provides a ground circuit to turn it off. If circuit No. 852 becomes open, light will be on at all times due to loss of ground at lamp driver module. If control line is shorted to ground, light will remain off.

NOTE: Test numbers refer to test numbers on diagnostic chart.

1) This step checks if light function is correct. Normal operation indicates problem is not present.
2) This step verifies circuitry from ECU to lamp driver module is complete.
3) This step verifies ignition circuit to lamp driver module is functional. An open fuse or open in circuit No. 33C, 39A (Pink/Black wire) or 875 will result in inoperative indicator lights.
4) This step isolates cause of light remaining off. By disconnecting 24-pin connector, circuit No. 852 should open, causing light to be on.

NOTE: INTERMITTENTS is located under DIAGNOSIS & TESTING portion of this article.

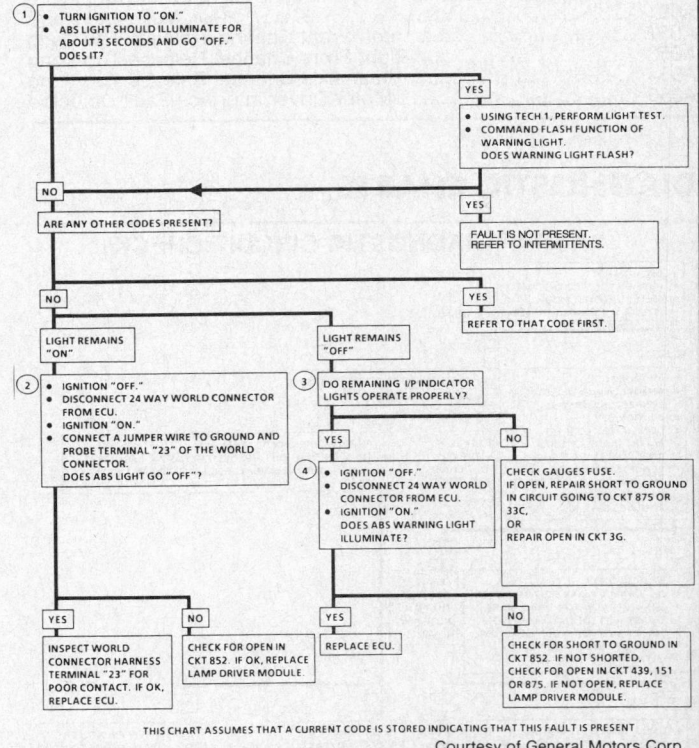

THIS CHART ASSUMES THAT A CURRENT CODE IS STORED INDICATING THAT THIS FAULT IS PRESENT

Courtesy of General Motors Corp.

CODE A013, ANTI-LOCK WARNING INDICATOR OPEN OR SHORTED TO BATTERY

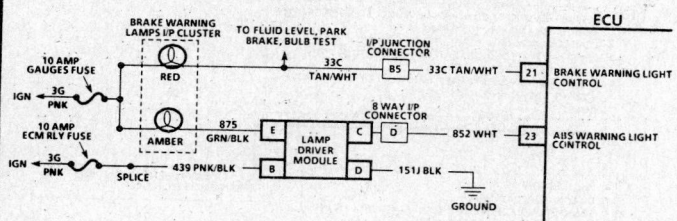

If light control line is shorted to battery or ECU control circuit is open, The ECU will not be able to turn ABS light off.

NOTE: Test numbers refer to test numbers on diagnostic chart.

1) This step checks if light function is correct. Normal operation indicates problem is not present.
2) When ignition is turned off, voltage to lamp driver module should be interrupted. If light remains on, a short to battery exists in circuit.
3) After removing fuse, voltage in circuit No. 852 should be eliminated. If voltage is still present, a short to battery between lamp driver module and ECU is indicated.

NOTE: INTERMITTENTS is located under DIAGNOSIS & TESTING portion of this article.

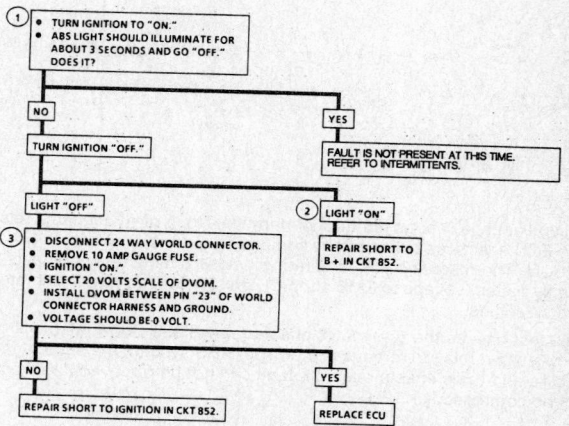

CODE A014, ENABLE RELAY CONTACTS OPEN, FUSE OPEN

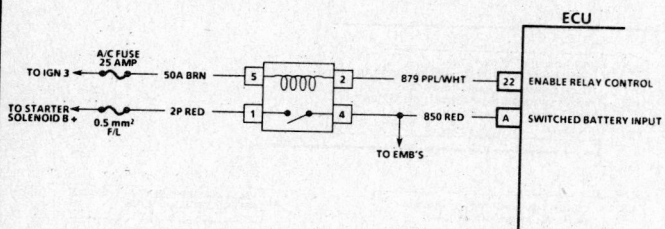

Ignition voltage is supplied through terminal No. 5 of ABS enable relay. The ECU energizes pull-in coil by completing ground circuit at pin No. 22 of ECU. The magnetic field created will close enable relay contacts to supply battery voltage to EMB and ECU, thus providing power to motors and solenoids.

This test checks availability of voltage to motors, solenoids and EMB's. Fault Code A014 indicates voltage is not available and ABS operation is not possible.

NOTE: Test numbers refer to test numbers on diagnostic chart.

1) This step determines if relay and circuitry are functional.
2) This step ensures voltage is available to relay terminals No. 1 and 5.
3) This step checks relay contact power feed.
4) This step checks ability of ECU to energize enable relay. An open circuit in ECU or circuit No. 879 would prevent enable relay from energizing.
5) This step checks for open in circuit No. 850 between enable relay and ECU.

NOTE: INTERMITTENTS is located under DIAGNOSIS & TESTING portion of this article.

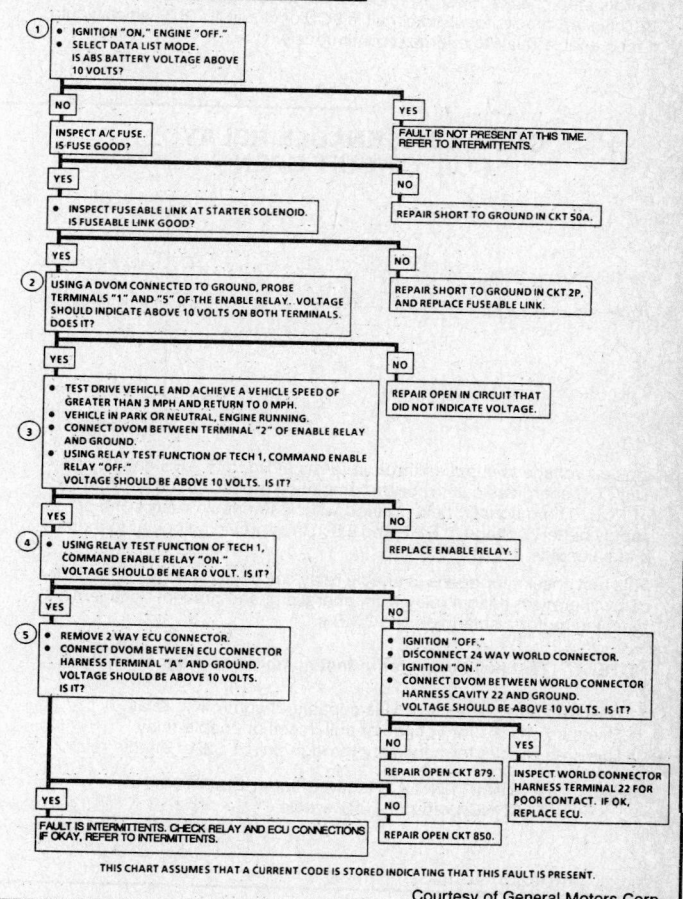

THIS CHART ASSUMES THAT A CURRENT CODE IS STORED INDICATING THAT THIS FAULT IS PRESENT.

91B10232   91C10233   91D10234   91E10235

Courtesy of General Motors Corp.

CODE A015, ENABLE RELAY CONTACTS SHORTED TO BATTERY

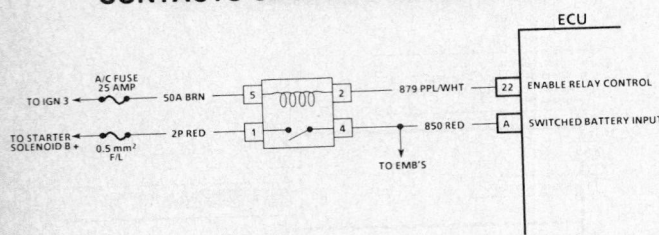

Ignition voltage is supplied through terminal No. 5 of ABS enable relay. The ECU energizes pull-in coil by completing ground circuit at pin No. 22 of ECU. The magnetic field created will close enable relay contacts to supply battery voltage to EMB and ECU, thus providing power to motors and solenoids.

This test checks the on time of enable relay. Fault Code A015 will not allow enable relay to remove power from ABS system. If a second fault occurs and turns enable relay off, fault can not be removed if relay can not be controlled.

NOTE: Test numbers refer to test numbers on diagnostic chart.

1) This step determines if ECU is capable of controlling relay.
2) This step checks for short to battery in circuit No. 850.
3) This step checks for short circuit in ECU or circuit No. 879 which would cause enable relay to energize continuously.

NOTE: INTERMITTENTS is located under DIAGNOSIS & TESTING portion of this article.

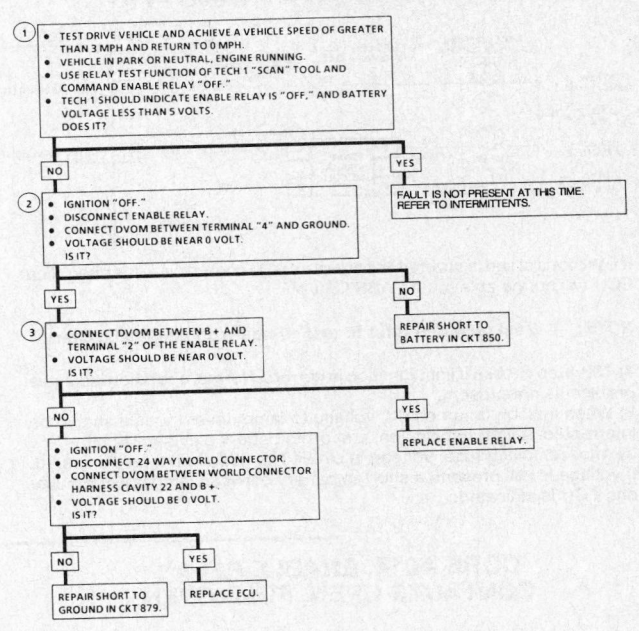

CODE A016, ENABLE RELAY COIL CIRCUIT OPEN

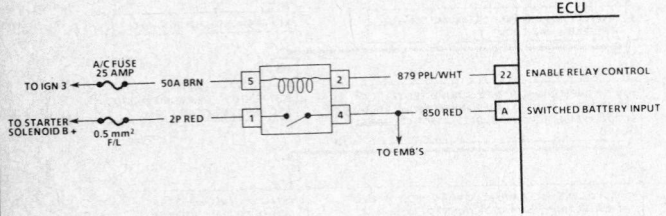

Ignition voltage is supplied through terminal No. 5 of ABS enable relay. The ECU energizes pull-in coil by completing ground circuit at pin No. 22 of ECU. The magnetic field created will close enable relay contacts to supply battery voltage to EMB and ECU, thus providing power to motors and solenoids.

This test checks for opens in enable relay coil circuit. An open in this circuit will prevent enable relay from energizing and prevent voltage from reaching motors, solenoids and EMB's.

NOTE: Test numbers refer to test numbers on diagnostic chart.

1) This step determines if ECU is capable of controlling relay.
2) This step checks for voltage at pull-in coil of enable relay.
3) This step checks for continuity through pull-in coil of enable relay.

NOTE: INTERMITTENTS is located under DIAGNOSIS & TESTING portion of this article.

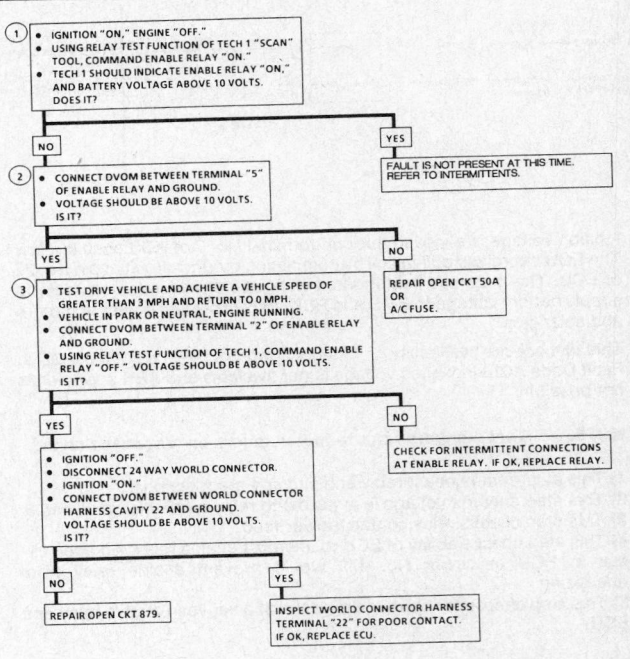

THIS CHART ASSUMES THAT A CURRENT CODE IS STORED INDICATING THAT THIS FAULT IS PRESENT

Courtesy of General Motors Corp.

91FI0236   91G10237   91H10238   91I10239

CODE A017, ENABLE RELAY
COIL CIRCUIT SHORTED TO GROUND

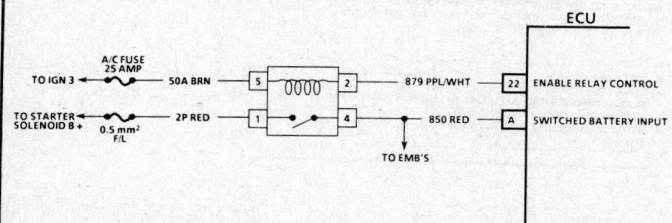

Ignition voltage is supplied through terminal No. 5 of ABS enable relay. The ECU energizes pull-in coil by completing ground circuit at pin No. 22 of ECU. The magnetic field created will close enable relay contacts to supply battery voltage to EMB and ECU, thus providing power to motors and solenoids.

This test checks the on time of enable relay. Fault Code A017 will not allow enable relay to remove power from ABS system. If a second fault occurs and turns enable relay off, fault can not be removed if relay can not be controlled.

NOTE: Test numbers refer to test numbers on diagnostic chart.

1) This step determines if ECU is capable of controlling relay.
2) This step checks for short to ground in enable relay or control circuit No. 879.

3) This step checks for short circuit in ECU or pin No. 22 which would cause enable relay to energize when ignition is on.

NOTE: INTERMITTENTS is located under DIAGNOSIS & TESTING portion of this article.

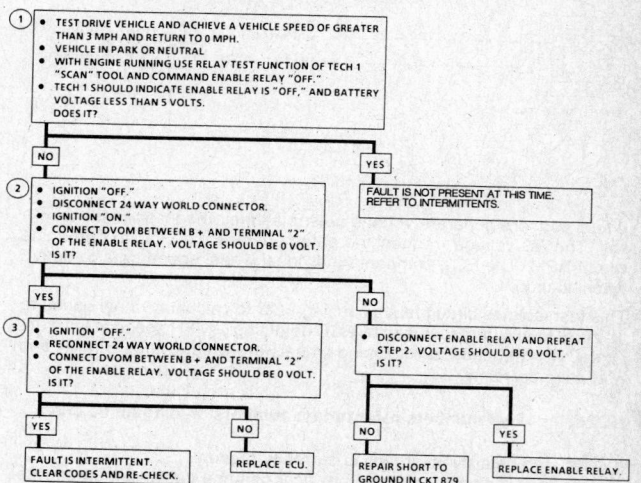

THIS CHART ASSUMES THAT A CURRENT CODE IS STORED INDICATING THAT THIS FAULT IS PRESENT.

CODE A018, ENABLE RELAY
COIL CIRCUIT SHORTED TO BATTERY
OR COIL HAS ZERO OHM

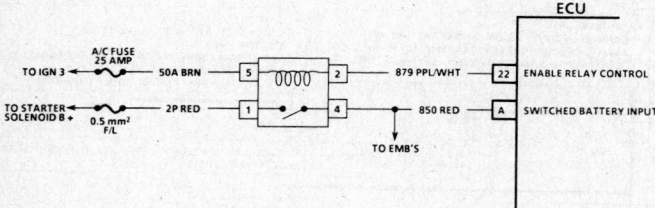

Ignition voltage is supplied through terminal No. 5 of ABS enable relay. The ECU energizes pull-in coil by completing ground circuit at pin No. 22 of ECU. The magnetic field created will close enable relay contacts to supply battery voltage to EMB and ECU, thus providing power to motors and solenoids.

This test checks availability of voltage to motors, solenoids and EMB's. Fault Code A018 will prevent ABS from being operational.

NOTE: Test numbers refer to test numbers on diagnostic chart.

1) This step determines if ECU is capable of controlling relay.
2) With enable relay removed, voltage should not be present at cavity No. 2. If any voltage is present, circuit No. 879 is shorted to battery.
3) This step checks for open circuit in ECU quad driver.

NOTE: INTERMITTENTS is located under DIAGNOSIS & TESTING portion of this article.

91B10240   91C10241   91D10242   91E10243

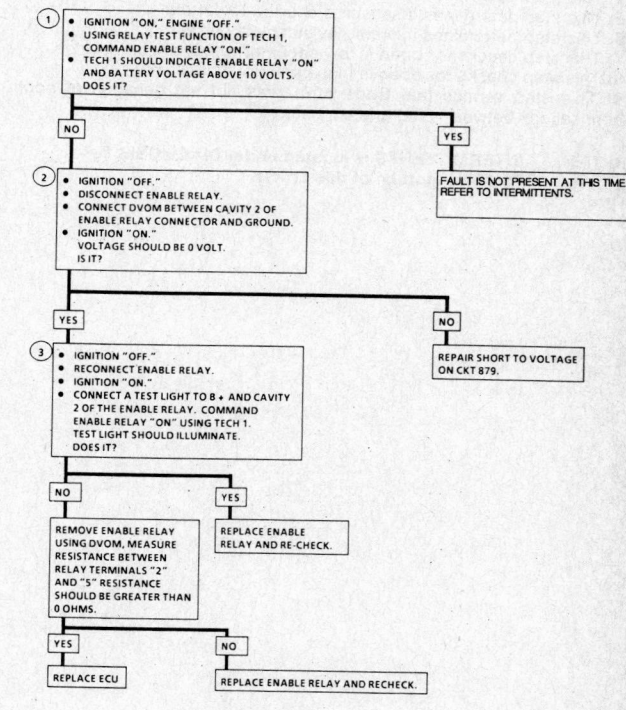

THIS CHART ASSUMES THAT A CURRENT CODE IS STORED INDICATING THAT THIS FAULT IS PRESENT.

Courtesy of General Motors Corp.

CODE A021
LEFT FRONT WHEEL SPEED IS ZERO

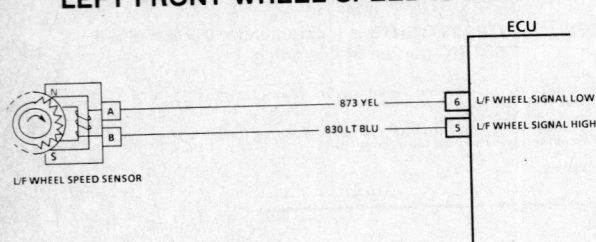

ECU

873 YEL — 6 — L/F WHEEL SIGNAL LOW
830 LT BLU — 5 — L/F WHEEL SIGNAL HIGH

L/F WHEEL SPEED SENSOR

Wheel sensors generate voltage pulses as their magnetic teeth pass a coil. The AC voltage frequency created enables the ECU to determine wheel RPM. The ECU compares individual wheel speed data to detect wheel lockup.

This test isolates circuit faults causing ECU to calculate wheel speed to be zero. Fault code is caused by ECU detecting 0-MPH speed at left front wheel, while speeds at remaining wheels are greater than 5 MPH and operating correctly.

NOTE: Test numbers refer to test numbers on diagnostic chart.

1) This step determines if fault is currently present.
2) This step indicates whether physical damage causing fault can be seen.
3) This step determines if sensor internal resistance is correct.
4) This step determines if sensor is shorted to ground.
5) This step determines if sensor is shorted to battery.
6) This step determines if circuit resistance is correct.
7) This step checks for open in low circuit of wheel circuit.
8) This step checks for open in high circuit of wheel circuit.
9) This step verifies that Code A021 was not set because of poor connections between ECU and connector.

NOTE: INTERMITTENTS is located under DIAGNOSIS & TESTING portion of this article.

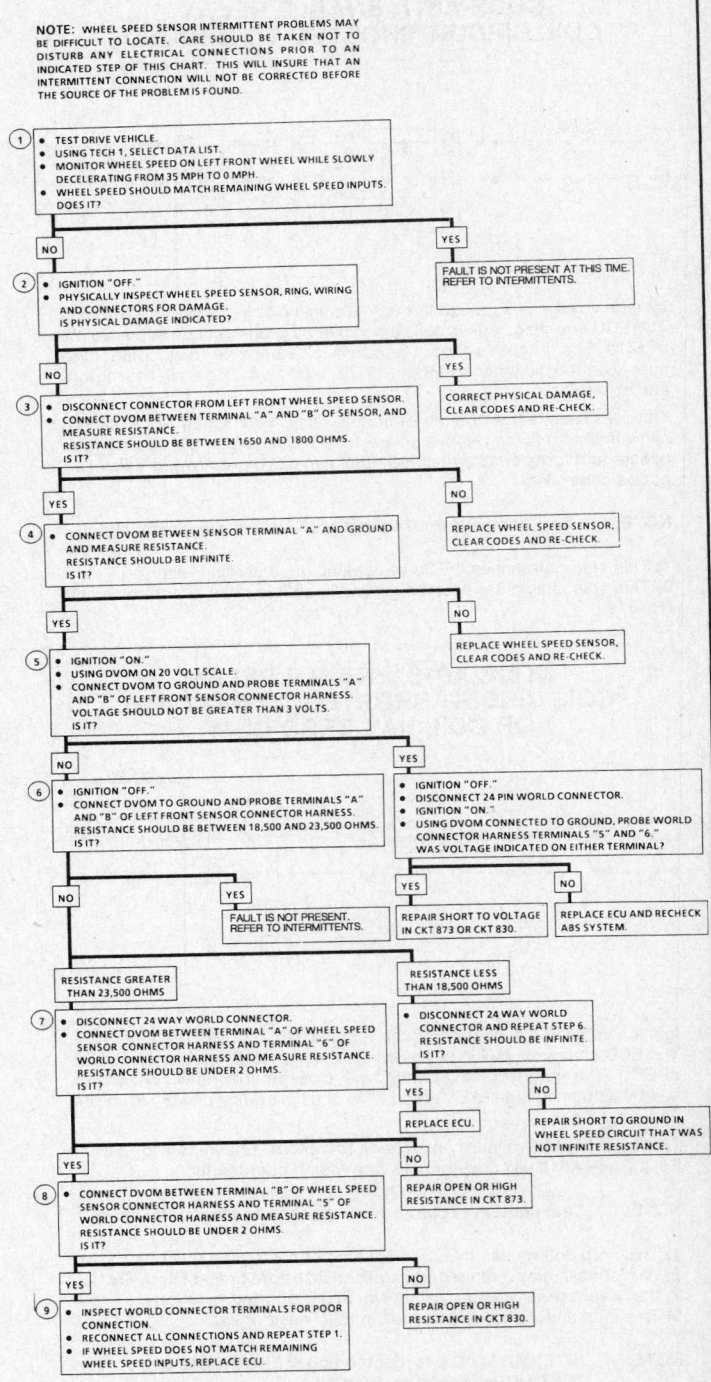

THIS CHART ASSUMES THAT A CURRENT CODE IS STORED INDICATING THAT THIS FAULT IS PRESENT.

91F10244   91G10245   91H10246

CODE A022
RIGHT FRONT WHEEL SPEED IS ZERO

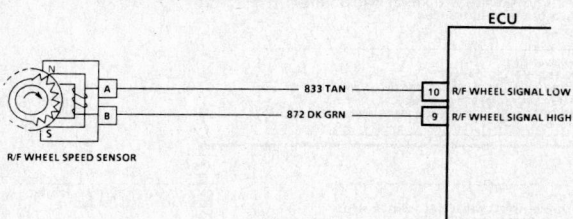

R/F WHEEL SPEED SENSOR

833 TAN — 10 R/F WHEEL SIGNAL LOW
872 DK GRN — 9 R/F WHEEL SIGNAL HIGH

ECU

Wheel sensors generate voltage pulses as their magnetic teeth pass a coil. The AC voltage frequency created enables ECU to determine wheel RPM. The ECU compares individual wheel speed data to detect wheel lockup.

This test isolates circuit faults causing ECU to calculate wheel speed to be zero MPH. Fault code is set if ECU detects 0-MPH speed at right front wheel, while speeds at remaining wheels are greater than 5 MPH and operating correctly.

NOTE: **Test numbers refer to test numbers on diagnostic chart.**

1) This step determines if fault is currently present.

2) This step indicates whether physical damage causing fault can be seen.

3) This step determines if sensor internal resistance is correct.

4) This step determines if sensor is shorted to ground.

5) This step determines if sensor is shorted to battery.

6) This step determines if circuit resistance is correct.

7) This step checks for open in low circuit of wheel circuit.

8) This step checks for open in high circuit of wheel circuit.

9) This step verifies that Code A022 was not set because of poor connections between ECU and connector.

NOTE: **INTERMITTENTS is located under DIAGNOSIS & TESTING portion of this article.**

NOTE: WHEEL SPEED SENSOR INTERMITTENT PROBLEMS MAY BE DIFFICULT TO LOCATE. CARE SHOULD BE TAKEN NOT TO DISTURB ANY ELECTRICAL CONNECTIONS PRIOR TO AN INDICATED STEP OF THIS CHART. THIS WILL INSURE THAT AN INTERMITTENT CONNECTION WILL NOT BE CORRECTED BEFORE THE SOURCE OF THE PROBLEM IS FOUND.

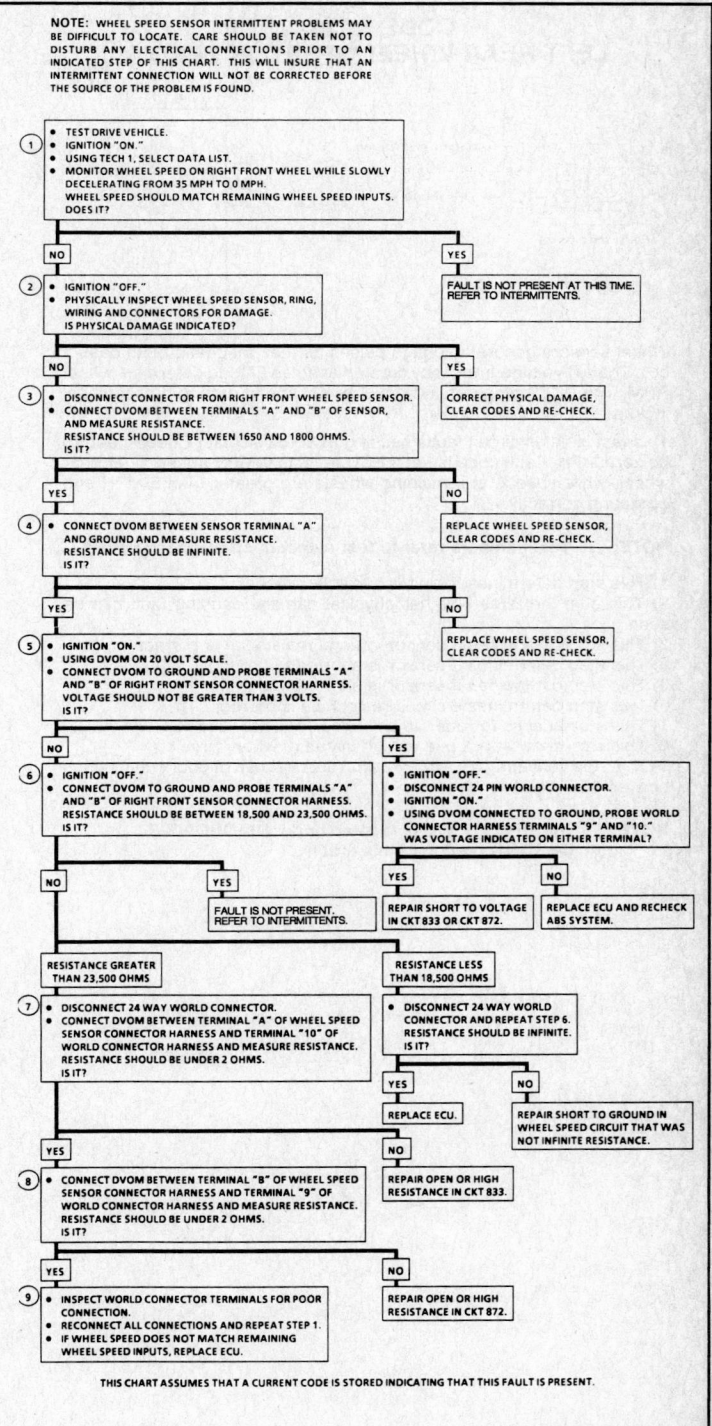

THIS CHART ASSUMES THAT A CURRENT CODE IS STORED INDICATING THAT THIS FAULT IS PRESENT.

91I10247   91J10248   91A10249

Courtesy of General Motors Corp.

CODE A023
LEFT REAR WHEEL SPEED IS ZERO

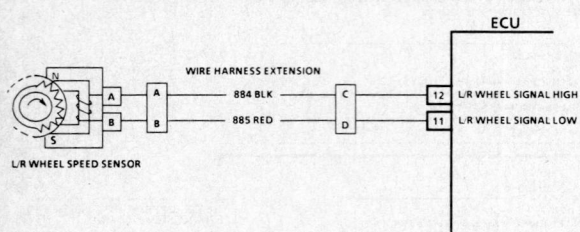

L/R WHEEL SPEED SENSOR

WIRE HARNESS EXTENSION

ECU

884 BLK — L/R WHEEL SIGNAL HIGH — 12

885 RED — L/R WHEEL SIGNAL LOW — 11

Wheel sensors generate voltage pulses as their magnetic teeth pass a coil. The AC voltage frequency created enables ECU to determine wheel RPM. The ECU compares individual wheel speed data to detect wheel lockup.

This test isolates circuit faults causing ECU to calculate wheel speed to be zero MPH. Fault code is set if ECU detects 0-MPH speed at left rear wheel, while speeds at remaining wheels are greater than 5 MPH and operating correctly.

NOTE: Test numbers refer to test numbers on diagnostic chart.

1) This step determines if fault is currently present.
2) This step indicates whether physical damage causing fault can be seen.
3) This step determines if sensor internal resistance is correct.
4) This step determines if sensor is shorted to ground.
5) This step determines if sensor is shorted to battery.
6) This step determines if circuit resistance is correct.
7) This step checks for open in low circuit of wheel circuit.
8) This step checks for open in high circuit of wheel circuit.
9) This step verifies Code A023 was not set because of poor connections between ECU and connector.

NOTE: INTERMITTENTS is located under DIAGNOSIS & TESTING portion of this article.

NOTE: WHEEL SPEED SENSOR INTERMITTENT PROBLEMS MAY BE DIFFICULT TO LOCATE. CARE SHOULD BE TAKEN NOT TO DISTURB ANY ELECTRICAL CONNECTIONS PRIOR TO AN INDICATED STEP OF THIS CHART. THIS WILL INSURE THAT AN INTERMITTENT CONNECTION WILL NOT BE CORRECTED BEFORE THE SOURCE OF THE PROBLEM IS FOUND.

1)
- TEST DRIVE VEHICLE.
- USING TECH 1, SELECT DATA LIST.
- MONITOR WHEEL SPEED ON LEFT REAR WHEEL WHILE SLOWLY DECELERATING FROM 35 MPH TO 0 MPH. WHEEL SPEED SHOULD MATCH REMAINING WHEEL SPEED INPUTS. DOES IT?

NO / YES

YES → FAULT IS NOT PRESENT AT THIS TIME. REFER TO INTERMITTENTS.

2)
- IGNITION "OFF."
- PHYSICALLY INSPECT WHEEL SPEED SENSOR, RING, WIRING AND CONNECTORS FOR DAMAGE. IS PHYSICAL DAMAGE INDICATED?

NO / YES

YES → CORRECT PHYSICAL DAMAGE, CLEAR CODES AND RE-CHECK.

3)
- DISCONNECT CONNECTOR FROM LEFT REAR WHEEL SPEED SENSOR.
- CONNECT DVOM BETWEEN TERMINALS "A" AND "B" OF SENSOR, AND MEASURE RESISTANCE. RESISTANCE SHOULD BE BETWEEN 2100 AND 2400 OHMS. IS IT?

YES / NO

NO → REPLACE WHEEL SPEED SENSOR, CLEAR CODES AND RE-CHECK.

4)
- CONNECT DVOM BETWEEN SENSOR TERMINAL "A" AND GROUND AND MEASURE RESISTANCE. RESISTANCE SHOULD BE INFINITE. IS IT?

YES / NO

NO → REPLACE WHEEL SPEED SENSOR, CLEAR CODES AND RE-CHECK.

5)
- IGNITION "ON."
- USING DVOM ON 20 VOLT SCALE.
- CONNECT DVOM TO GROUND AND PROBE TERMINALS "A" AND "B" OF LEFT REAR SENSOR CONNECTOR HARNESS. VOLTAGE SHOULD NOT BE GREATER THAN 3 VOLTS. IS IT?

NO / YES

6)
- IGNITION "OFF."
- CONNECT DVOM TO GROUND AND PROBE TERMINALS "A" AND "B" OF LEFT REAR SENSOR CONNECTOR HARNESS. RESISTANCE SHOULD BE BETWEEN 5,400 AND 6,750 OHMS. IS IT?

YES (right branch):
- IGNITION "OFF."
- DISCONNECT 24 PIN WORLD CONNECTOR.
- IGNITION "ON."
- USING DVOM CONNECTED TO GROUND, PROBE WORLD CONNECTOR HARNESS TERMINALS "11" AND "12." WAS VOLTAGE INDICATED ON EITHER TERMINAL?

YES → REPAIR SHORT TO VOLTAGE IN CKT 884 OR CKT 885.

NO → REPLACE ECU AND RECHECK ABS SYSTEM.

NO / YES

YES → FAULT IS NOT PRESENT. REFER TO INTERMITTENTS.

RESISTANCE GREATER THAN 6,750 OHMS

RESISTANCE LESS THAN 5,400 OHMS

7)
- DISCONNECT 24 WAY WORLD CONNECTOR.
- CONNECT DVOM BETWEEN TERMINAL "A" OF WHEEL SPEED SENSOR CONNECTOR HARNESS AND TERMINAL "12" OF WORLD CONNECTOR HARNESS, AND MEASURE RESISTANCE. RESISTANCE SHOULD BE UNDER 2 OHMS. IS IT?

(right branch):
- DISCONNECT 24 WAY WORLD CONNECTOR AND REPEAT STEP 6. RESISTANCE SHOULD BE INFINITE. IS IT?

YES → REPLACE ECU.

NO → REPAIR SHORT TO GROUND IN WHEEL SPEED CIRCUIT THAT WAS NOT INFINITE RESISTANCE.

YES / NO

NO → REPAIR OPEN OR HIGH RESISTANCE IN CKT 884.

8)
- CONNECT DVOM BETWEEN TERMINAL "B" OF WHEEL SPEED SENSOR CONNECTOR HARNESS AND TERMINAL "11" OF WORLD CONNECTOR HARNESS, AND MEASURE RESISTANCE. RESISTANCE SHOULD BE UNDER 2 OHMS.

YES / NO

NO → REPAIR OPEN OR HIGH RESISTANCE IN CKT 885.

9)
- INSPECT WORLD CONNECTOR TERMINALS FOR POOR CONNECTION.
- RECONNECT ALL CONNECTIONS AND REPEAT STEP 1.
- IF WHEEL SPEED DOES NOT MATCH REMAINING WHEEL SPEED INPUTS, REPLACE ECU.

THIS CHART ASSUMES THAT A CURRENT CODE IS STORED INDICATING THAT THIS FAULT IS PRESENT.

91E10250   91F10251   91G10252

CODE A024
RIGHT REAR WHEEL SPEED IS ZERO

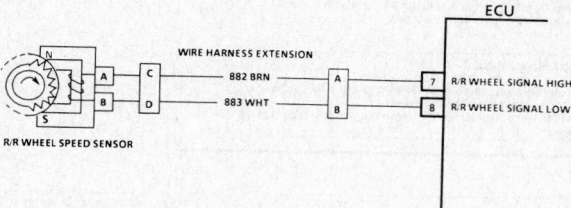

R/R WHEEL SPEED SENSOR

WIRE HARNESS EXTENSION

ECU

882 BRN — 7 R/R WHEEL SIGNAL HIGH

883 WHT — 8 R/R WHEEL SIGNAL LOW

Wheel sensors generate voltage pulses as their magnetic teeth pass a coil. The AC voltage frequency created enables ECU to determine wheel RPM. The ECU compares individual wheel speed data to detect wheel lockup.

This test isolates circuit faults causing ECU to calculate wheel speed to be zero MPH. Fault code is set if ECU detects 0-MPH speed at right rear wheel, while speeds at remaining wheels are greater than 5 MPH and operating correctly.

NOTE: Test numbers refer to test numbers on diagnostic chart.

1) This step determines if fault is currently present.
2) This step indicates whether physical damage causing fault can be seen.
3) This step determines if sensor internal resistance is correct.
4) This step determines if sensor is shorted to ground.
5) This step determines if sensor is shorted to battery.
6) This step determines if circuit resistance is correct.
7) This step checks for open in low circuit of wheel circuit.
8) This step checks for open in high circuit of wheel circuit.
9) This step verifies Code A024 was not set because of poor connections between ECU and connector.

NOTE: INTERMITTENTS is located under DIAGNOSIS & TESTING portion of this article.

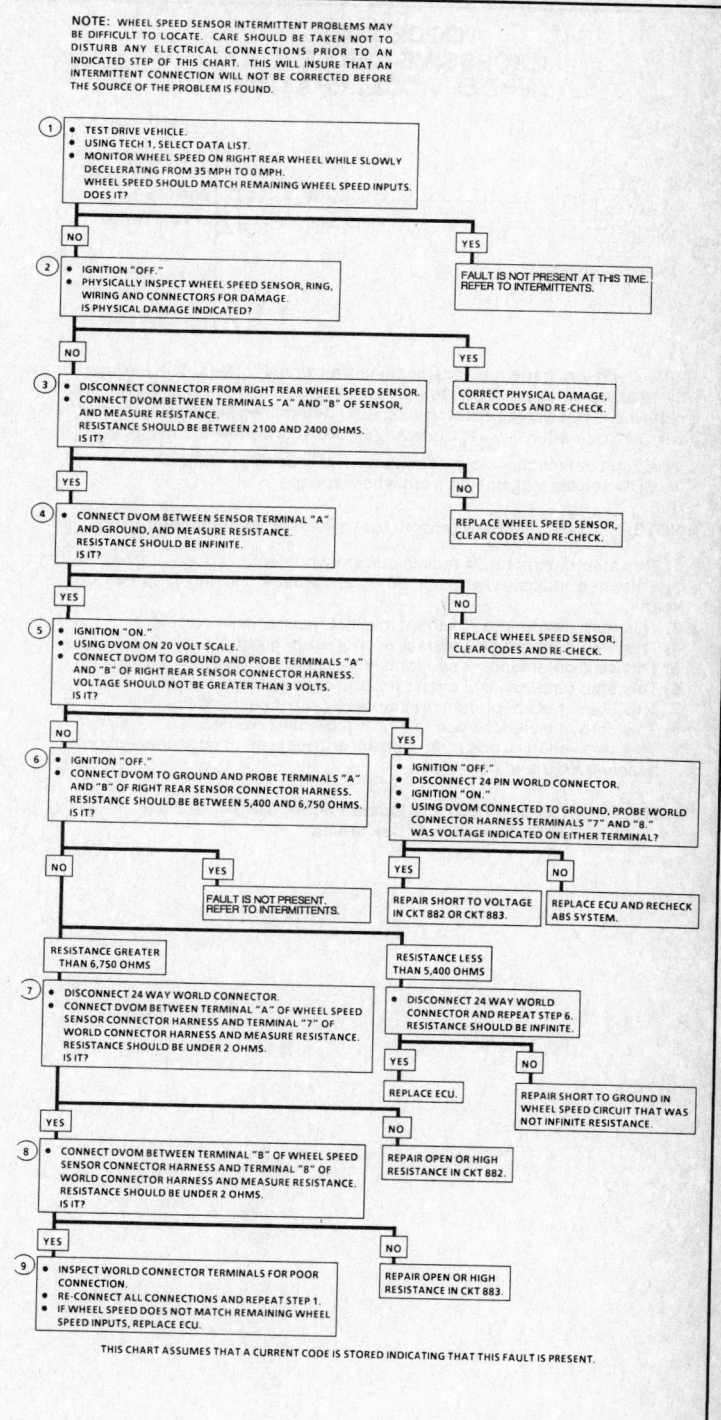

NOTE: WHEEL SPEED SENSOR INTERMITTENT PROBLEMS MAY BE DIFFICULT TO LOCATE. CARE SHOULD BE TAKEN NOT TO DISTURB ANY ELECTRICAL CONNECTIONS PRIOR TO AN INDICATED STEP OF THIS CHART. THIS WILL INSURE THAT AN INTERMITTENT CONNECTION WILL NOT BE CORRECTED BEFORE THE SOURCE OF THE PROBLEM IS FOUND.

THIS CHART ASSUMES THAT A CURRENT CODE IS STORED INDICATING THAT THIS FAULT IS PRESENT.

91H10253 91I10254 91J10255

CODE A025
EXCESSIVE LEFT FRONT
WHEEL ACCELERATION

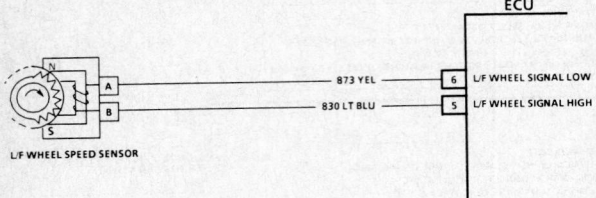

L/F WHEEL SPEED SENSOR

ECU

873 YEL — 6 — L/F WHEEL SIGNAL LOW

830 LT BLU — 5 — L/F WHEEL SIGNAL HIGH

Wheel sensors generate voltage signals as wheel rotates. The frequency created enables ECU to determine wheel RPM. If information received is not within preset values, ECU determines signal is faulty and will set Code A025. To set Code A025, following conditions must occur.

- Circuit defect causing intermittent wheel speed operation
- ECU senses illogical left front wheel speeds

NOTE: Test numbers refer to test numbers on diagnostic chart.

1) This step determines if fault is currently present.
2) This step indicates whether physical damage causing fault can be seen.
3) This step determines if sensor internal resistance is correct.
4) This step determines if sensor is shorted to ground.
5) This step determines if sensor is shorted to battery.
6) This step determines if circuit resistance is correct.
7) This step checks for open in low circuit of wheel circuit.
8) This step checks for open in high circuit of wheel circuit.
9) This step verifies Code A025 was not set because of poor connections between ECU and connector.

NOTE: INTERMITTENTS is located under DIAGNOSIS & TESTING portion of this article.

NOTE: WHEEL SPEED SENSOR INTERMITTENT PROBLEMS MAY BE DIFFICULT TO LOCATE. CARE SHOULD BE TAKEN NOT TO DISTURB ANY ELECTRICAL CONNECTIONS PRIOR TO AN INDICATED STEP OF THIS CHART. THIS WILL INSURE THAT AN INTERMITTENT CONNECTION WILL NOT BE CORRECTED BEFORE THE SOURCE OF THE PROBLEM IS FOUND.

1
- TEST DRIVE VEHICLE.
- USING TECH 1, SELECT DATA LIST.
- MONITOR WHEEL SPEED ON LEFT FRONT WHEEL WHILE SLOWLY DECELERATING FROM 35 MPH TO 0 MPH.
- WHEEL SPEED SHOULD MATCH REMAINING WHEEL SPEED INPUTS. DOES IT?

NO | YES

YES → FAULT IS NOT PRESENT AT THIS TIME. REFER TO INTERMITTENTS.

2
- IGNITION "OFF."
- PHYSICALLY INSPECT WHEEL SPEED SENSOR, RING, WIRING AND CONNECTORS FOR DAMAGE. IS PHYSICAL DAMAGE INDICATED?

NO | YES

YES → CORRECT PHYSICAL DAMAGE, CLEAR CODES AND RE-CHECK.

3
- DISCONNECT CONNECTOR FROM LEFT FRONT WHEEL SPEED SENSOR.
- CONNECT DVOM BETWEEN TERMINAL "A" AND "B" OF SENSOR, AND MEASURE RESISTANCE. RESISTANCE SHOULD BE BETWEEN 1650 AND 1800 OHMS. IS IT?

YES | NO

NO → REPLACE WHEEL SPEED SENSOR, CLEAR CODES AND RE-CHECK.

4
- CONNECT DVOM BETWEEN SENSOR TERMINAL "A" AND GROUND AND MEASURE RESISTANCE. RESISTANCE SHOULD BE INFINITE. IS IT?

YES | NO

NO → REPLACE WHEEL SPEED SENSOR, CLEAR CODES AND RE-CHECK.

5
- IGNITION "ON."
- USING DVOM ON 20 VOLT SCALE.
- CONNECT DVOM TO GROUND AND PROBE TERMINALS "A" AND "B" OF LEFT FRONT SENSOR CONNECTOR HARNESS. VOLTAGE SHOULD NOT BE GREATER THAN 3 VOLTS. IS IT?

NO | YES

YES →
- IGNITION "OFF."
- DISCONNECT 24 PIN WORLD CONNECTOR.
- IGNITION "ON."
- USING DVOM CONNECTED TO GROUND, PROBE WORLD CONNECTOR HARNESS TERMINALS "5" AND "6." WAS VOLTAGE INDICATED ON EITHER TERMINAL?

YES | NO

YES → REPAIR SHORT TO VOLTAGE IN CKT 873 OR CKT 830.

NO → REPLACE ECU AND RECHECK ABS SYSTEM.

6
- IGNITION "OFF."
- CONNECT DVOM TO GROUND AND PROBE TERMINALS "A" AND "B" OF LEFT FRONT SENSOR CONNECTOR HARNESS. RESISTANCE SHOULD BE BETWEEN 18,500 AND 23,500 OHMS. IS IT?

NO | YES

YES → FAULT IS NOT PRESENT. REFER TO INTERMITTENTS.

RESISTANCE GREATER THAN 23,500 OHMS

RESISTANCE LESS THAN 18,500 OHMS

7
- DISCONNECT 24 WAY WORLD CONNECTOR.
- CONNECT DVOM BETWEEN TERMINAL "A" OF WHEEL SPEED SENSOR CONNECTOR HARNESS AND TERMINAL "6" OF WORLD CONNECTOR HARNESS AND MEASURE RESISTANCE. RESISTANCE SHOULD BE UNDER 2 OHMS. IS IT?

- DISCONNECT 24 WAY WORLD CONNECTOR AND REPEAT STEP 6. RESISTANCE SHOULD BE INFINITE. IS IT?

YES | NO

YES → REPLACE ECU.

NO → REPAIR SHORT TO GROUND IN WHEEL SPEED CIRCUIT THAT WAS NOT INFINITE RESISTANCE.

YES | NO

NO → REPAIR OPEN OR HIGH RESISTANCE IN CKT 873.

8
- CONNECT DVOM BETWEEN TERMINAL "B" OF WHEEL SPEED SENSOR CONNECTOR HARNESS AND TERMINAL "5" OF WORLD CONNECTOR HARNESS AND MEASURE RESISTANCE. RESISTANCE SHOULD BE UNDER 2 OHMS. IS IT?

YES | NO

NO → REPAIR OPEN OR HIGH RESISTANCE IN CKT 830.

9
- INSPECT WORLD CONNECTOR TERMINALS FOR POOR CONNECTION.
- RECONNECT ALL CONNECTIONS AND REPEAT STEP 1.
- IF WHEEL SPEED DOES NOT MATCH REMAINING WHEEL SPEED INPUTS, REPLACE ECU.

THIS CHART ASSUMES THAT A CURRENT CODE IS STORED INDICATING THAT THIS FAULT IS PRESENT.

Courtesy of General Motors Corp.

CODE A026
EXCESSIVE RIGHT FRONT
WHEEL ACCELERATION

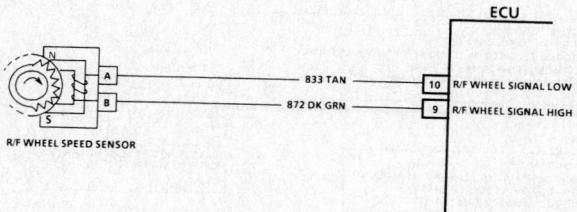

ECU

833 TAN — 10 R/F WHEEL SIGNAL LOW

872 DK GRN — 9 R/F WHEEL SIGNAL HIGH

R/F WHEEL SPEED SENSOR

Wheel sensors generate voltage signals as wheel rotates. The frequency created enables ECU to determine wheel RPM. If information received is not within preset values, ECU determines signal is faulty and will set Code A026. To set Code A026, following conditions must occur.

- Circuit defect causing intermittent wheel speed operation
- ECU senses illogical right front wheel speeds

NOTE: **Test numbers refer to test numbers on diagnostic chart.**

1) This step determines if fault is currently present.
2) This step indicates whether physical damage causing fault can be seen.
3) This step determines if sensor internal resistance is correct.
4) This step determines if sensor is shorted to ground.
5) This step determines if sensor is shorted to battery.
6) This step determines if circuit resistance is correct.
7) This step checks for open in low circuit of wheel circuit.
8) This step checks for open in high circuit of wheel circuit.
9) This step verifies Code A026 was not set because of poor connections between ECU and connector.

NOTE: **INTERMITTENTS is located under DIAGNOSIS & TESTING portion of this article.**

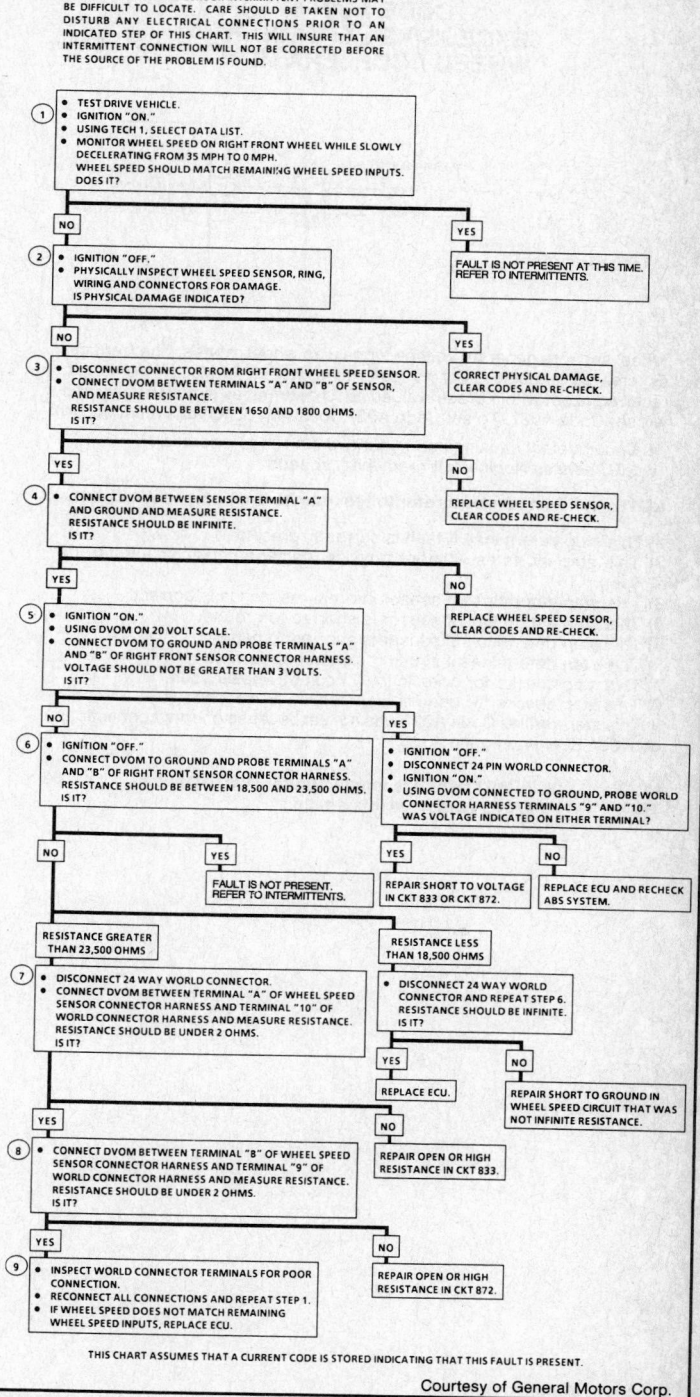

THIS CHART ASSUMES THAT A CURRENT CODE IS STORED INDICATING THAT THIS FAULT IS PRESENT.

91I10247 91G10260 91H10261

Courtesy of General Motors Corp.

CODE A027
EXCESSIVE LEFT REAR
WHEEL ACCELERATION

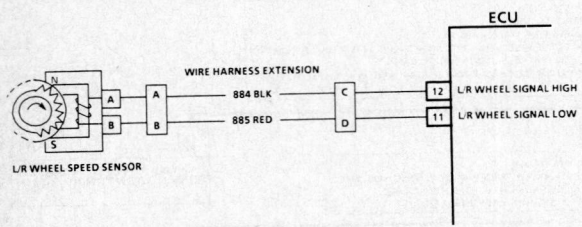

Wheel sensors generate voltage signals as wheel rotates. The frequency created enables ECU to determine wheel RPM. If information received is not within preset values, ECU determines signal is faulty and will set Code A027. To set Code A027, following conditions must occur.

- Circuit defect causing intermittent wheel speed operation
- ECU senses illogical left rear wheel speeds

NOTE: Test numbers refer to test numbers on diagnostic chart.

1) This step determines if fault is currently present.
2) This step indicates whether physical damage causing fault can be seen.
3) This step determines if sensor internal resistance is correct.
4) This step determines if sensor is shorted to ground.
5) This step determines if sensor is shorted to battery.
6) This step determines if circuit resistance is correct.
7) This step checks for open in low circuit of wheel circuit.
8) This step checks for open in high circuit of wheel circuit.
9) This step verifies Code A027 was not set because of poor connections between ECU and connector.

NOTE: INTERMITTENTS is located under DIAGNOSIS & TESTING portion of this article.

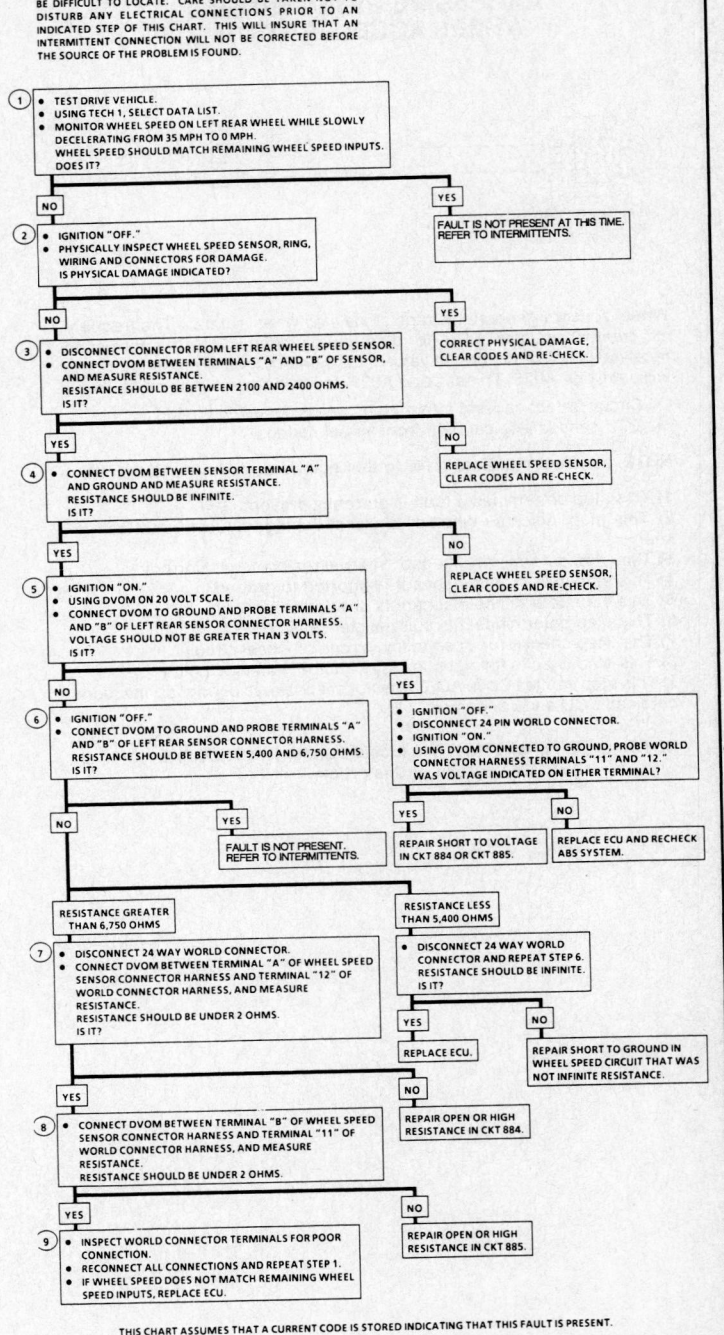

THIS CHART ASSUMES THAT A CURRENT CODE IS STORED INDICATING THAT THIS FAULT IS PRESENT.

Courtesy of General Motors Corp.

CODE A028
EXCESSIVE RIGHT REAR
WHEEL ACCELERATION

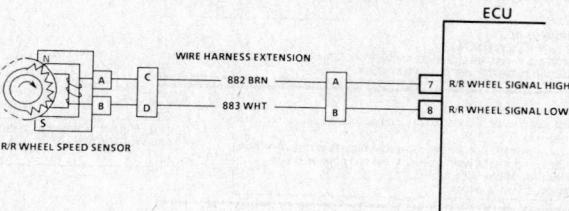

Wheel sensors generate voltage signals as wheel rotates. The frequency created enables ECU to determine wheel RPM. If information received is not within preset values, ECU determines signal is faulty and will set Code A028. To set Code A028, following conditions must occur.

- Circuit defect causing intermittent wheel speed operation
- ECU senses illogical right rear wheel speeds

NOTE: Test numbers refer to test numbers on diagnostic chart.

1) This step determines if fault is currently present.
2) This step indicates whether physical damage causing fault can be seen.
3) This step determines if sensor internal resistance is correct.
4) This step determines if sensor is shorted to ground.
5) This step determines if sensor is shorted to battery.
6) This step determines if circuit resistance is correct.
7) This step checks for open in low circuit of wheel circuit.
8) This step checks for open in high circuit of wheel circuit.
9) This step verifies Code A028 was not set because of poor connections between ECU and connector.

NOTE: INTERMITTENTS is located under DIAGNOSIS & TESTING portion of this article.

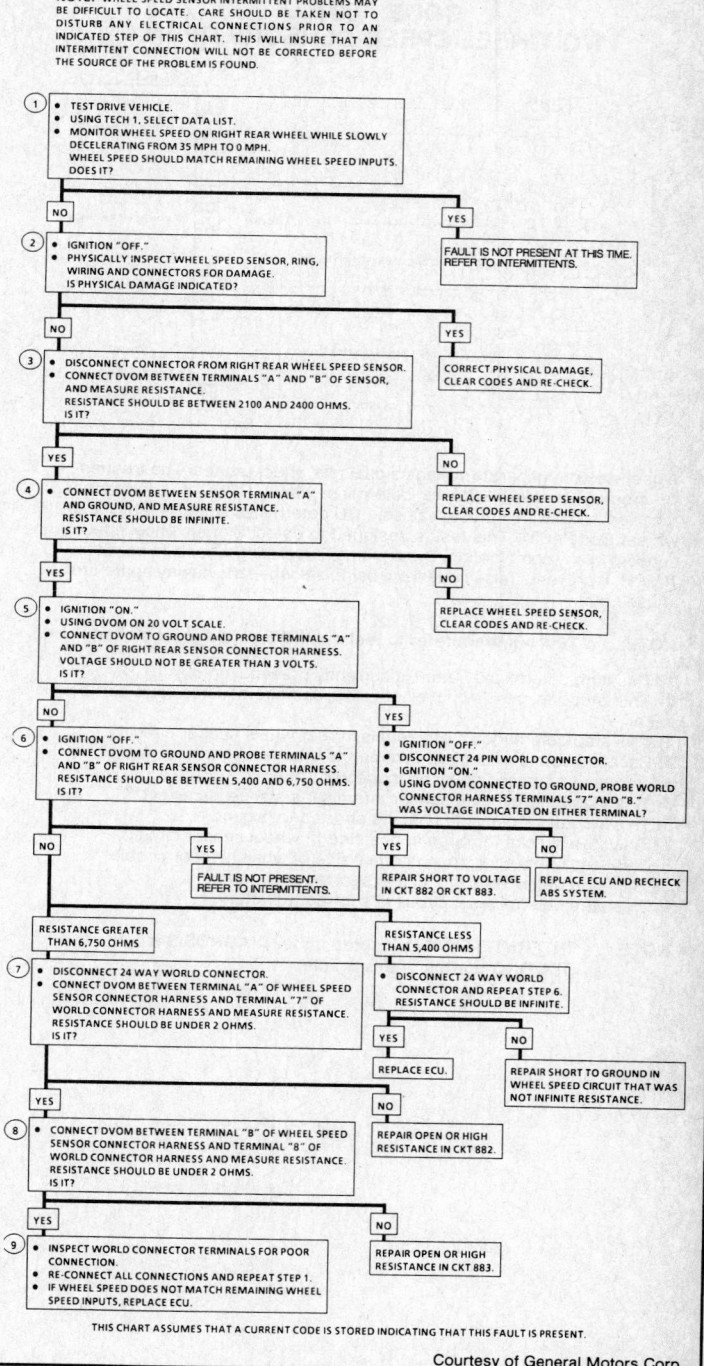

91H10253 91C10266 91D10267

Courtesy of General Motors Corp.

CODE A031
TWO WHEEL SPEED SENSORS OPEN

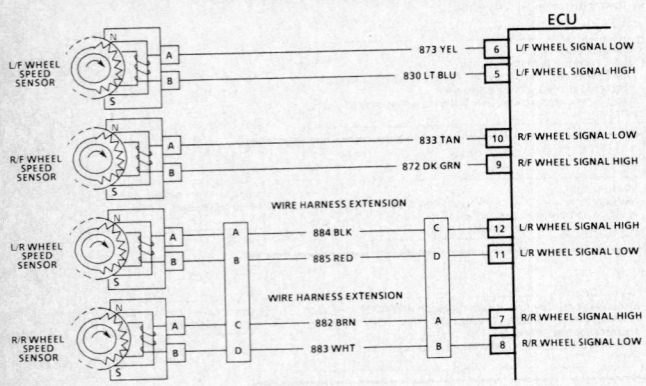

Wheel sensors generate voltage signals as wheel rotates. The frequency created enables ECU to determine wheel RPM. If information received is not within preset values, ECU determines signal is faulty and will set Code A031. This test is designed to detect 2 open wheel speed sensors in any combination. By requiring 2 operating wheels to be within 7 MPH, it prevents false code from being set when stowaway spare tire is used.

NOTE: **Test numbers refer to test numbers on diagnostic chart.**

1) This step determines if fault is currently present.
2) This step indicates whether physical damage causing fault can be seen.
3) This step determines if problem is in rear wheel sensor circuitry.
4) Because both sensors are common to extension harness, 4-pin connectors and harness should be inspected.
5) This step determines if sensor internal resistance is correct.
6) This step determines if sensor is shorted to ground.
7) This step checks for open in one side of wheel sensor circuit.
8) This step checks for open in other side of wheel sensor circuit.
9) This step determines if circuit is shorted to ground.
10) This step determines if circuit is shorted to battery.

NOTE: **INTERMITTENTS is located under DIAGNOSIS & TESTING portion of this article.**

NOTE: WHEEL SPEED SENSOR INTERMITTENT PROBLEMS MAY BE DIFFICULT TO LOCATE. CARE SHOULD BE TAKEN NOT TO DISTURB ANY ELECTRICAL CONNECTIONS PRIOR TO AN INDICATED STEP OF THIS CHART. THIS WILL INSURE THAT AN INTERMITTENT CONNECTION WILL NOT BE CORRECTED BEFORE THE SOURCE OF THE PROBLEM IS FOUND.

1
- TEST DRIVE VEHICLE.
- USING TECH 1, SELECT DATA LIST.
- MONITOR ALL WHEEL SPEEDS WHILE SLOWLY DECELERATING FROM 35 MPH TO 0 MPH. ARE ALL WHEEL SPEEDS APPROXIMATELY EQUAL?

— YES → FAULT IS NOT PRESENT AT THIS TIME. REFER TO INTERMITTENTS.

— NO ↓

2
- IGNITION "OFF."
- PHYSICALLY INSPECT WHEEL SPEED SENSOR CIRCUITS IN QUESTION FOR DAMAGE. ALSO, CHECK WIRE CONNECTIONS FOR CORROSION OR POOR MATING OF CONNECTORS. IS PHYSICAL DAMAGE INDICATED?

— YES → CORRECT PHYSICAL DAMAGE, CLEAR CODES AND RE-CHECK.

— NO ↓

3
- DID BOTH REAR WHEEL SPEED SENSORS INDICATE 0 MPH, OR ERRATIC WHEEL SPEEDS?

— NO → USING CHART BELOW, REFER TO SPEED SENSOR CODE CHART FOR AFFECTED WHEELS.

— YES ↓

4
- INSPECT 4 WAY REAR WHEEL EXTENSION HARNESS CONNECTORS FOR CORROSION, POOR MATING OR DAMAGE. IS DAMAGE INDICATED?

— YES → CORRECT DAMAGE, CLEAR CODES AND RE-CHECK.

— NO ↓

5
- DISCONNECT REAR WHEEL SPEED SENSORS.
- USING DVOM CONNECTED BETWEEN TERMINALS "A" & "B" OF THE REAR WHEEL SPEED SENSORS, MEASURE RESISTANCE. RESISTANCE SHOULD BE BETWEEN 2100 AND 2400 OHMS FOR REAR SENSORS. ARE RESISTANCE VALUES IN ACCEPTABLE RANGES?

— NO → REPLACE WHEEL SPEED SENSOR(S) THAT DID NOT INDICATE PROPER RESISTANCE, AND RE-CHECK.

— YES ↓

6
- USING DVOM CONNECTED BETWEEN TERMINAL "A" OF THE SUSPECTED WHEEL SENSOR AND GROUND, MEASURE RESISTANCE. DVOM SHOULD INDICATE INFINITE RESISTANCE. DOES IT?

— NO → REPLACE WHEEL SPEED SENSOR(S) THAT DID NOT INDICATE PROPER RESISTANCE, AND RE-CHECK.

— YES ↓

SENSOR	CODE
L/F SENSOR	A021
R/F SENSOR	A022
L/R SENSOR	A023
R/R SENSOR	A024

7
- CONNECT DVOM TO TERMINAL "A" OF WHEEL SPEED SENSOR HARNESS CONNECTOR IN QUESTION.
- DISCONNECT 24 WAY WORLD CONNECTOR.
- USING THE TABLE SUPPLIED AT THE BOTTOM OF THIS PAGE, CONNECT DVOM TO THE APPROPRIATE TERMINAL OF THE WORLD CONNECTOR AND MEASURE RESISTANCE. RESISTANCE SHOULD BE LESS THAN 2 OHMS. IS IT?

— NO → REPAIR CIRCUIT THAT SHOWED HIGH RESISTANCE OR OPEN.

— YES ↓

8
- USING DVOM, PROBE CONNECTOR TERMINAL "B" OF WHEEL SPEED SENSOR IN QUESTION.
- USING THE TABLE SUPPLIED, CONNECT DVOM TO THE APPROPRIATE TERMINAL OF THE WORLD CONNECTOR AND MEASURE RESISTANCE. RESISTANCE SHOULD BE LESS THAN 2 OHMS. IS IT?

— NO → REPAIR CIRCUIT THAT SHOWED HIGH RESISTANCE OR OPEN.

— YES ↓

9
- CONNECT DVOM BETWEEN WHEEL SPEED SENSOR CONNECTOR TERMINAL "A" AND GROUND THEN REPEAT PROCEDURE ON TERMINAL "B." RESISTANCE SHOULD BE INFINITE ON BOTH TERMINALS. IS IT?

— NO → REPAIR SHORT TO GROUND IN CIRCUIT THAT DID NOT SHOW INFINITE RESISTANCE.

— YES ↓

10
- DVOM STILL CONNECTED.
- SELECT THE 20 VOLT SCALE OF THE DVOM.
- IGNITION "ON."
- REPEAT STEP 8. VOLTAGE SHOULD BE 0. IS IT?

— NO → REPAIR SHORT TO VOLTAGE IN CIRCUIT THAT INDICATED VOLTAGE ABOVE 0 VOLTS.

— YES ↓

- INSPECT WORLD CONNECTOR TERMINALS FOR POOR CONNECTION.
- RE-CONNECT ALL CONNECTIONS AND REPEAT STEP 1.
- IF WHEEL SPEED DOES NOT MATCH REMAINING WHEEL SPEED INPUTS, REPLACE ECU.

SENSOR TERMINAL	WORLD CONNECTOR	CIRCUIT NUMBER
L/R WHEEL A	PIN 12	884
L/R WHEEL B	PIN 11	885
R/R WHEEL A	PIN 7	882
R/R WHEEL B	PIN 8	883

THIS CHART ASSUMES THAT A CURRENT CODE IS STORED INDICATING THAT THIS FAULT IS PRESENT.

Courtesy of General Motors Corp.

CODE A036, SYSTEM VOLTAGE IS LOW

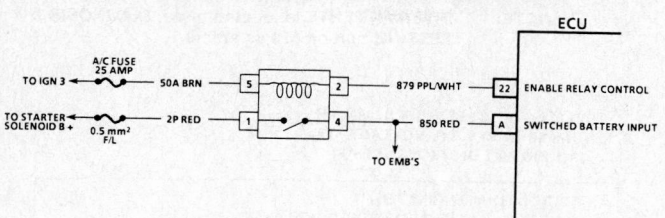

This test is used to check voltage available to ECU. If voltage drops below 11 volts, ABS performance may be affected. If voltage falls below a level that would provide full ABS capability, Code A036 will set.

NOTE: Test numbers refer to test numbers on diagnostic chart.

1) If voltage is acceptable, charging system is okay.
2) This step isolates ECU to check charging system performance.
3) This step isolates low voltage condition to high circuit resistance or incorrect charging system operation.

NOTE: INTERMITTENTS is located under DIAGNOSIS & TESTING portion of this article.

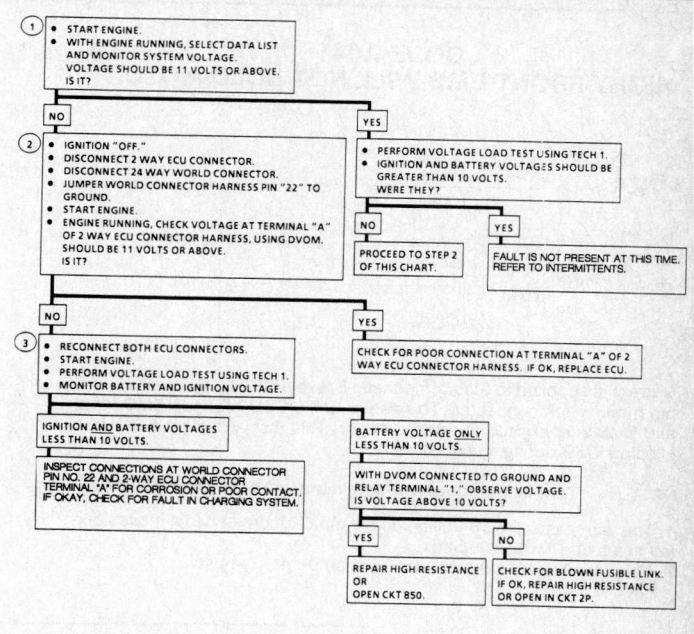

91J10271   91A10272

Courtesy of General Motors Corp.

CODE A037
SYSTEM VOLTAGE IS HIGH

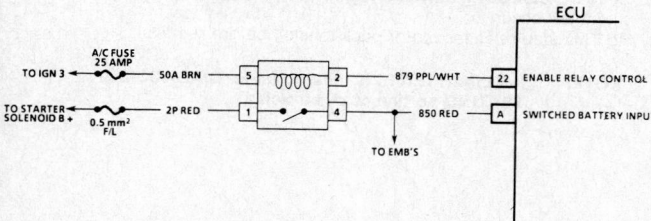

This test is used to check high ABS voltage. If voltage is excessive, demagnetization of motor magnets may occur.

NOTE: Test numbers refer to test numbers on diagnostic chart.

1) This step monitors voltage level being received by ECU. If high voltage is present, charging system malfunction is indicated.

NOTE: INTERMITTENTS is located under DIAGNOSIS & TESTING portion of this article.

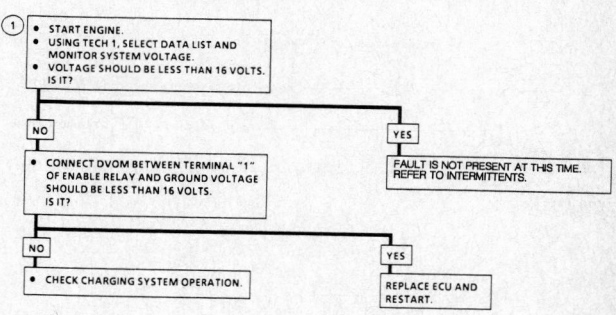

THIS CHART ASSUMES THAT A CURRENT CODE IS STORED INDICATING THAT THIS FAULT IS PRESENT.

CODE A038
LEFT FRONT EMB WILL NOT HOLD MOTOR

1) This step tests EMB's ability to hold motor. If brake pedal moves during this test, EMB is slipping.
2) This step releases motor pack tension before removal.

NOTE: INTERMITTENTS is located under DIAGNOSIS & TESTING portion of this article.

NOTE: TESTING EMB WITH JUMPER WIRES TO VOLTAGE OR GROUND WILL DESTROY THE EMB.

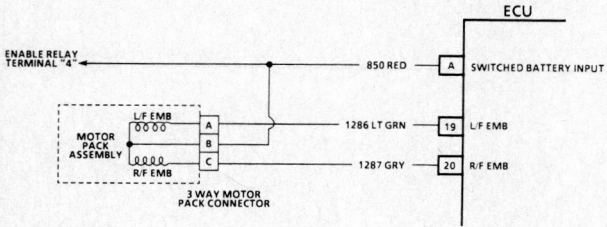

Current is supplied to Electromagnetic Brake (EMB) by terminal "B" of 3-pin motor pack connector. To release EMB, ECU grounds EMB input, and EMB is energized to release motor. This test is designed to detect slipping EMB during initialization.

NOTE: Test numbers refer to test numbers on diagnostic chart.

91E10276   91F10277   91G10278   91H10279

Courtesy of General Motors Corp.

CODE A041
RIGHT FRONT EMB WILL NOT HOLD MOTOR

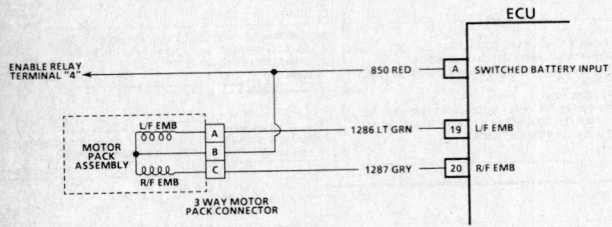

Current is supplied to Electromagnetic Brake (EMB) by terminal "B" of 3-pin motor pack connector. To release EMB, ECU grounds EMB input, and EMB is energized to release motor. This test is designed to detect slipping EMB during initialization.

NOTE: Test numbers refer to test numbers on diagnostic chart.

1) This step tests EMB's ability to hold motor. If brake pedal moves during this test, EMB is slipping.
2) This step releases motor pack tension before removal.

NOTE: INTERMITTENTS is located under DIAGNOSIS & TESTING portion of this article.

NOTE: TESTING END WITH JUMPER WIRES TO VOLTAGE OR GROUND WILL DESTROY THE EMB.

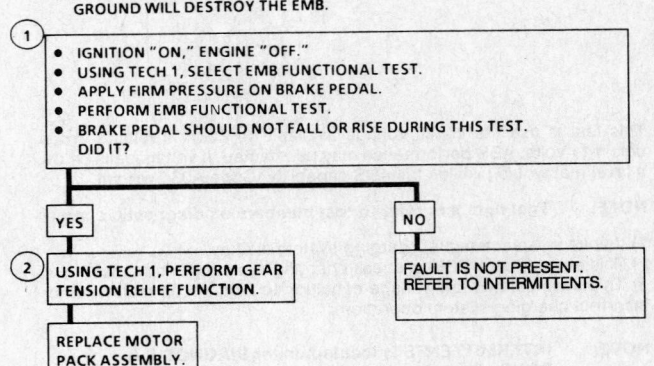

CODE A042
REAR AXLE ESB WILL NOT HOLD MOTOR

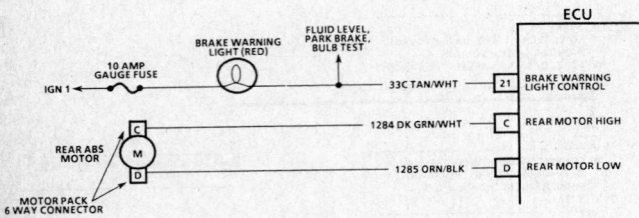

This test is designed to detect slipping rear axle Expansion Spring Brake (ESB) during initialization. If ESB slips, motor/piston moves.

NOTE: Test numbers refer to test numbers on diagnostic chart.

1) This step tests rear axle ESB. A broken or defective ESB would result in rear piston being back driven by hydraulic pressure, and wheel movement will occur.
2) This step releases motor pack tension before removal.

NOTE: INTERMITTENTS is located under DIAGNOSIS & TESTING portion of this article.

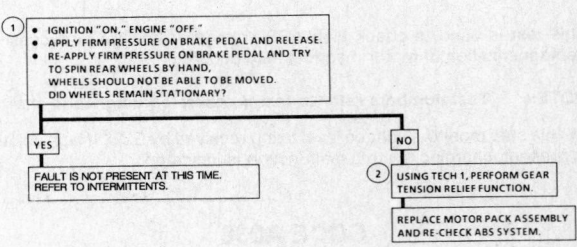

91G10278   91B10281   91C10282   91D10283

Courtesy of General Motors Corp.

CODE A044
LEFT FRONT EMB WILL
NOT RELEASE MOTOR, GEARS FROZEN

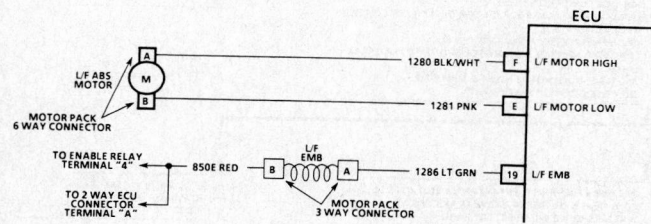

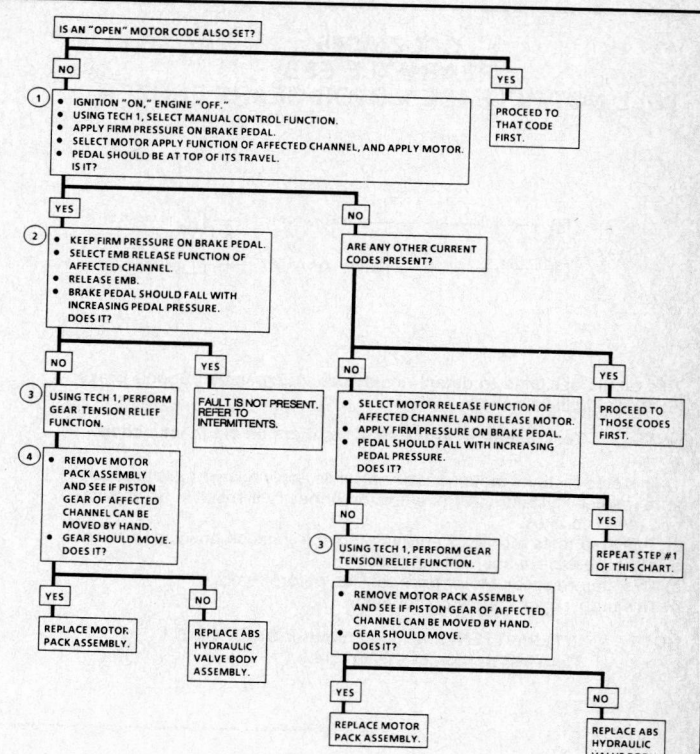

Current is supplied to Electromagnetic Brake (EMB) by terminal "B" of 3-pin motor pack connector. To release EMB, ECU grounds EMB input, and EMB is energized to release motor. This test is designed to detect non-actuating EMB during initialization.

NOTE: Test numbers refer to test numbers on diagnostic chart.

1) This step tests for motor movement while positioning brake pedal at top of travel.
2) This step tests for EMB release capability.
3) This step releases motor pack tension before removal.
4) This step isolates fault to either the motor pack or ABS hydraulic modulator.

NOTE: INTERMITTENTS is located under DIAGNOSIS & TESTING portion of this article.

CODE A045
RIGHT FRONT EMB
WILL NOT RELEASE MOTOR, GEARS FROZEN

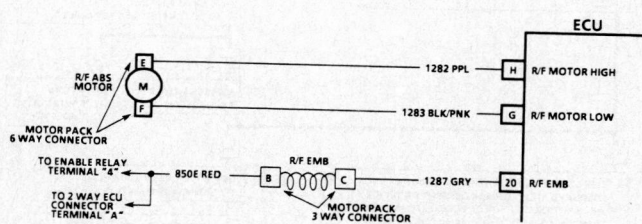

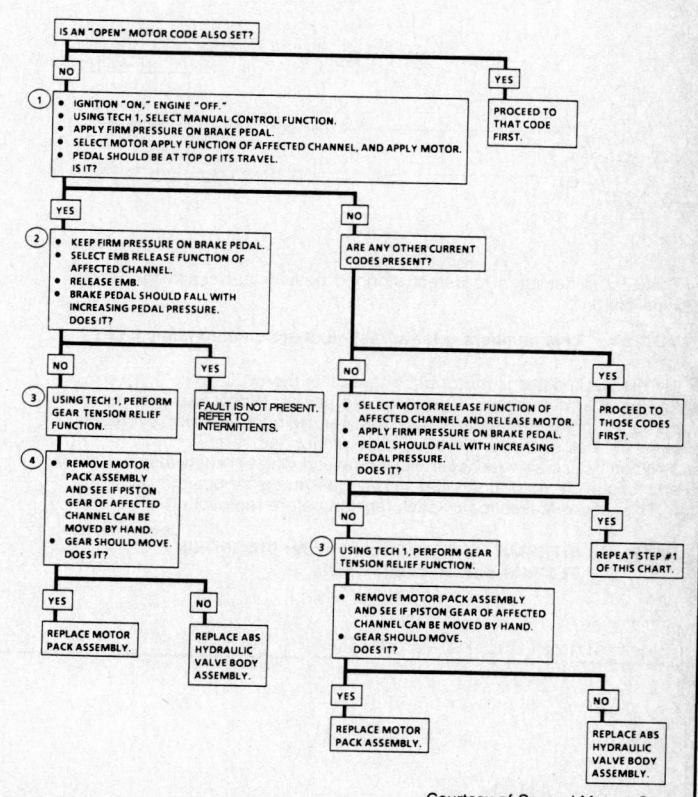

Current is supplied to Electromagnetic Brake (EMB) by terminal "B" of 3-pin motor pack connector. To release EMB, ECU grounds EMB input, and EMB is energized to release motor. This test is designed to detect non-actuating EMB during initialization.

NOTE: Test numbers refer to test numbers on diagnostic chart.

1) This step tests for motor movement while positioning brake pedal at top of travel.
2) This step tests for EMB release capability.
3) This step releases motor pack tension before removal.
4) This step isolates fault to either motor pack or ABS hydraulic modulator.

NOTE: INTERMITTENTS is located under DIAGNOSIS & TESTING portion of this article.

91E10284   91F10285   91G10286   91H10287

CODE A046
REAR AXLE ESB
WILL NOT RELEASE MOTOR GEARS FROZEN

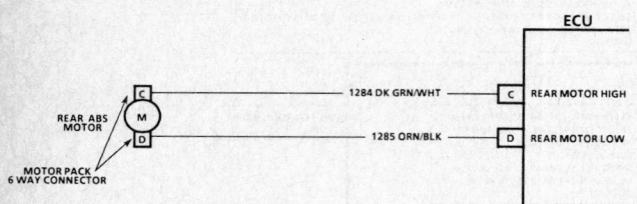

This test is designed to detect non-actuating Expansion Spring Brake (ESB) during initialization.

NOTE: Test numbers refer to test numbers on diagnostic chart.

1) This step tests for motor movement while applying hydraulic pressure to rear wheel cylinders. A frozen piston or gear will result in no application of rear brakes.
2) This step tests for motor ability to move to release position. If motor does not release, wheel will not turn.
3) This step releases motor pack tension before removal.
4) This step isolates faulty component.

NOTE: INTERMITTENTS is located under DIAGNOSIS & TESTING portion of this article.

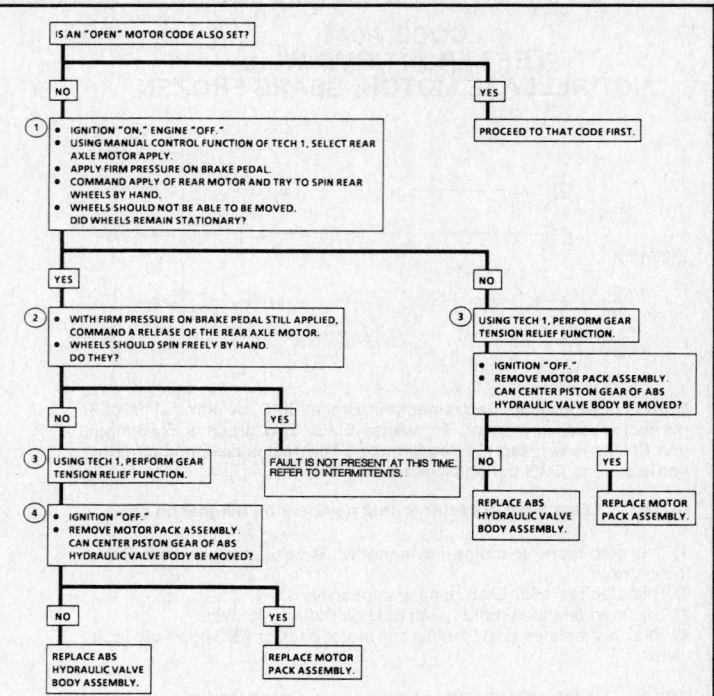

CODE A047
LEFT FRONT NUT FAILURE

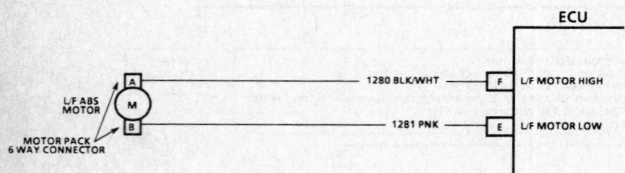

This test is designed to detect stripped gear or nut assembly during initialization.

NOTE: Test numbers refer to test numbers on diagnostic chart.

1) This step positions motor at bottom of its travel.
2) This step determines if gear/nut is stripped. If gear/nut is stripped, hydraulic pressure applied from master cylinder will not overcome hydraulic ball screw, and brake pedal will not rise.
3) When ball screw reaches top of its travel during full application, motor should stall. If motor continues to run, gear/nut is stripped.
4) This step releases motor pack tension before removal.

NOTE: INTERMITTENTS is located under DIAGNOSIS & TESTING portion of this article.

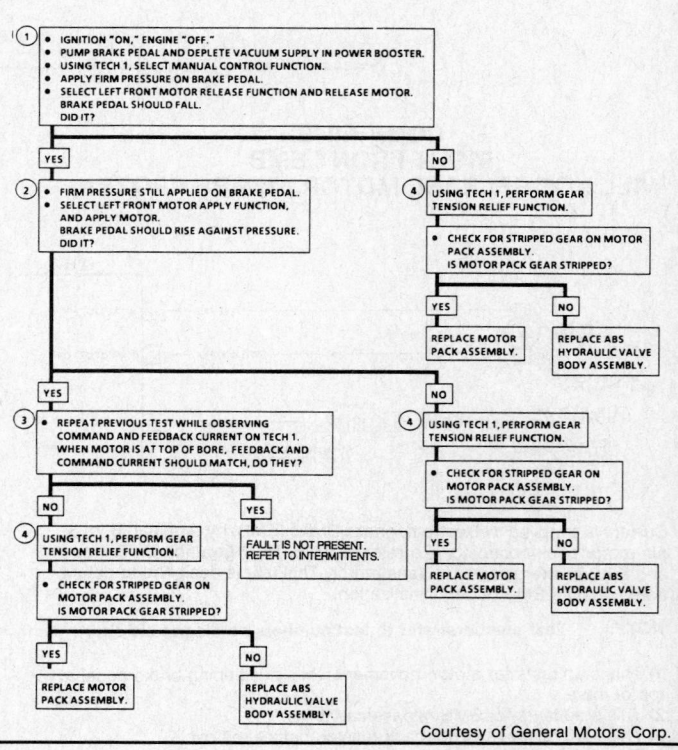

91I10288   91J10289   91C10290   91D10291

Courtesy of General Motors Corp.

CODE A048
RIGHT FRONT NUT FAILURE

This test is designed to detect stripped gear or nut assembly during initialization.

NOTE: Test numbers refer to test numbers on diagnostic chart.

1) This step positions motor at bottom of its travel.
2) This step determines if gear/nut is stripped. If gear/nut is stripped, hydraulic pressure applied from master cylinder will not overcome hydraulic ball screw, and brake pedal will not rise.
3) When ball screw reaches top of its travel during full application, motor should stall. If motor continues to run, gear/nut is stripped.
4) This step releases motor pack tension before removal.

NOTE: INTERMITTENTS is located under DIAGNOSIS & TESTING portion of this article.

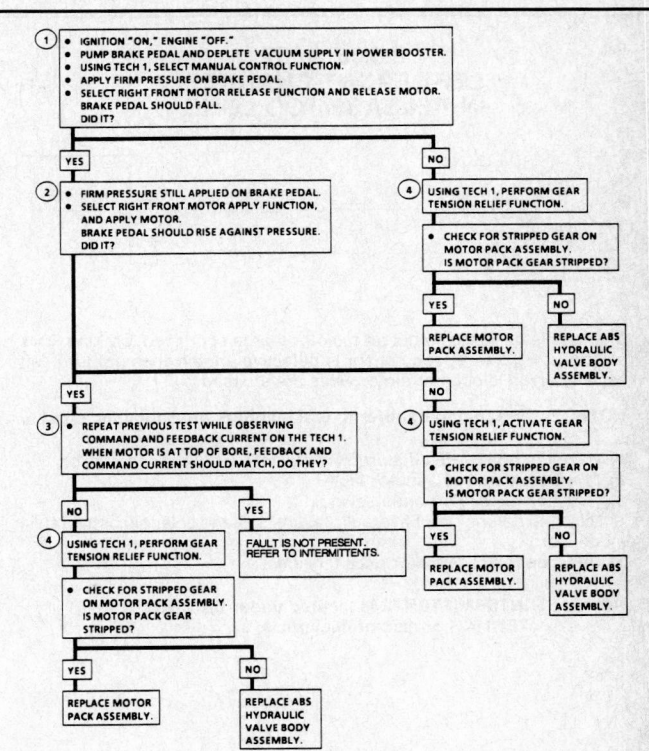

CODE A051
REAR AXLE NUT FAILURE

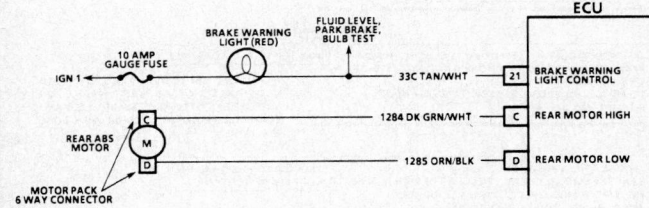

This test is designed to detect stripped gear or nut assembly during initialization.

NOTE: Test numbers refer to test numbers on diagnostic chart.

1) This step determines if gear/nut is stripped. If gear/nut is stripped, hydraulic pressure applied from master cylinder will not overcome hydraulic ball screw, and brake pedal will not rise.
2) When ball screw reaches top of its travel during full application, motor should stall. If motor continues to run, gear/nut is stripped.
3) This step releases motor pack tension prior to removal.

NOTE: INTERMITTENTS is located under DIAGNOSIS & TESTING portion of this article.

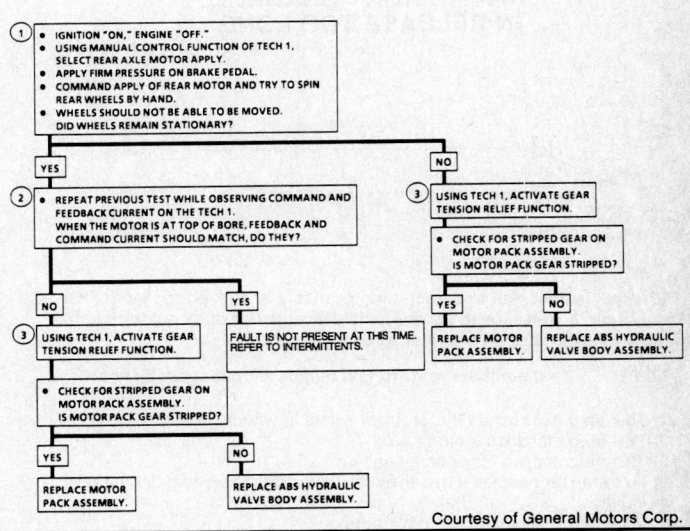

91E10292 91F10293 91C10282 91H10295

Courtesy of General Motors Corp.

CODE A052
LEFT FRONT CHANNEL
IN RELEASE TOO LONG

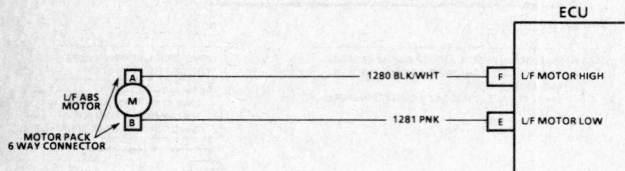

ECU

This test is designed to detect a motor that is energized too long. This will occur if wheel speed sensor is defective, motor does not turn, left front solenoid is open or motor wires are crossed.

NOTE: Test numbers refer to test numbers on diagnostic chart.

1) This step determines if a problem exists in wheel speed sensor.
2) This step identifies a motor fault.
3) This step checks for open solenoid.
4) This step determines if hydraulic failure is due to solenoid or hydraulic modulator.
5) This step releases motor pack tension.

NOTE: INTERMITTENTS is located under DIAGNOSIS & TESTING portion of this article.

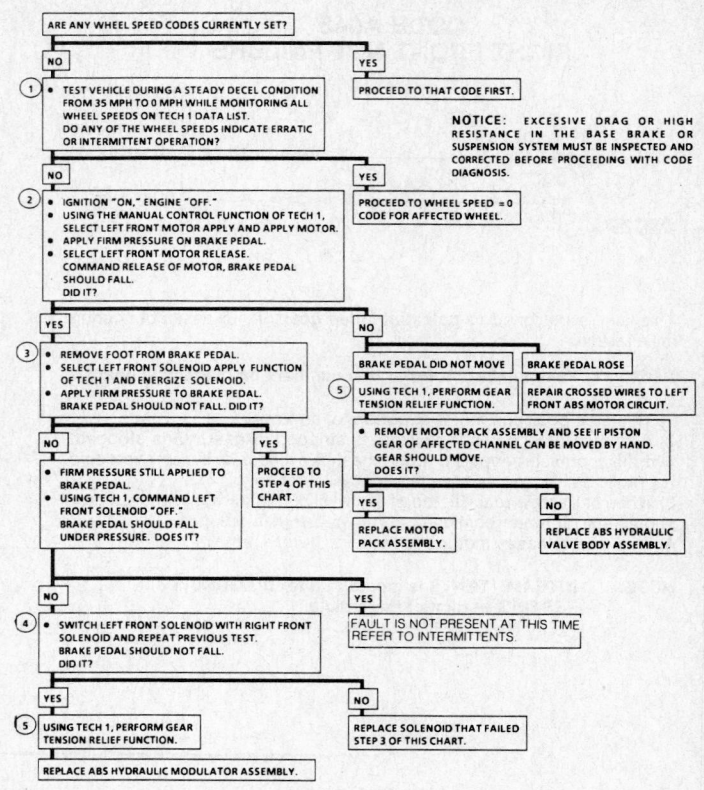

CODE A053
RIGHT FRONT CHANNEL
IN RELEASE TOO LONG

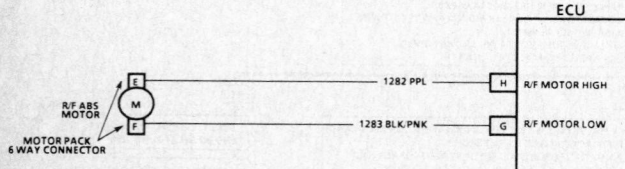

ECU

This test is designed to detect a motor that is energized too long. This will occur if wheel speed sensor is defective, motor does not turn, right front solenoid is open or motor wires are crossed.

NOTE: Test numbers refer to test numbers on diagnostic chart.

1) This step determines if a problem exists in wheel speed sensor.
2) This step identifies a motor fault.
3) This step checks for open solenoid.
4) This step determines if hydraulic failure is due to solenoid or hydraulic modulator.
5) This step releases motor pack tension.

NOTE: INTERMITTENTS is located under DIAGNOSIS & TESTING portion of this article.

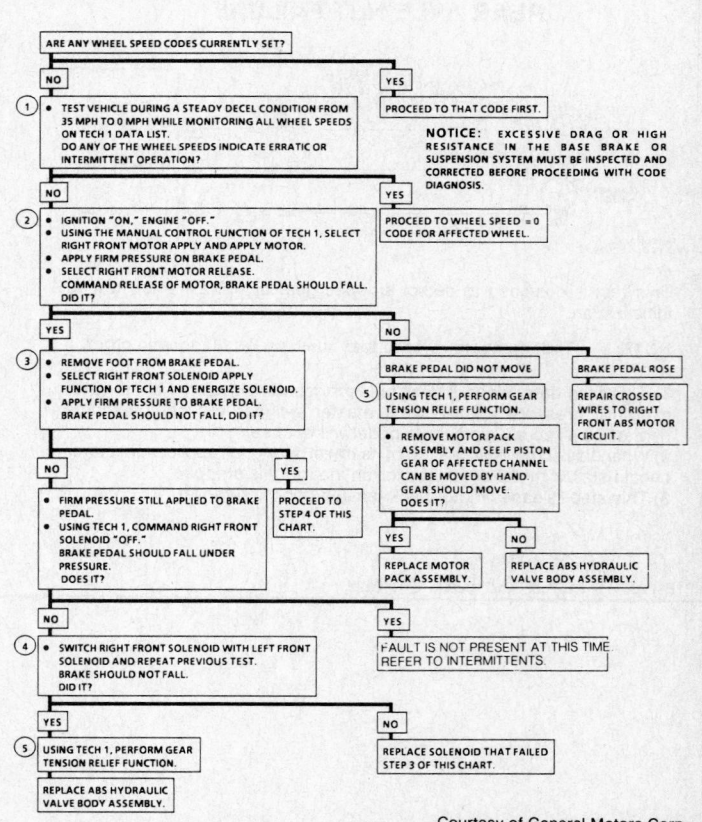

CODE A054
REAR AXLE IN RELEASE TOO LONG

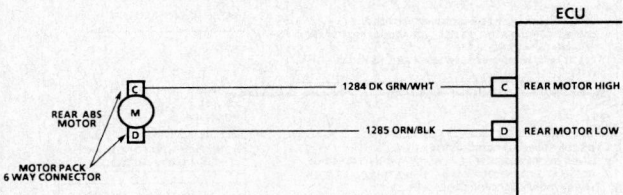

This test is designed to detect a motor that is energized too long. This will occur if wheel speed sensor is defective, motor does not turn, right front solenoid is open or motor wires are crossed.

NOTE: Test numbers refer to test numbers on diagnostic chart.

1) This step determines if a problem exists in wheel speed sensor.
2) This step identifies a wheel that drags due to mechanical fault.
3) This step determines if motor is capable of moving rear wheel hydraulic piston.
4) This step ensures motor wiring is not crossed.
5) This step releases motor pack tension before removal.
6) This step determines if no-brake application fault is due to motor pack or hydraulic modulator.

NOTE: INTERMITTENTS is located under DIAGNOSIS & TESTING portion of this article.

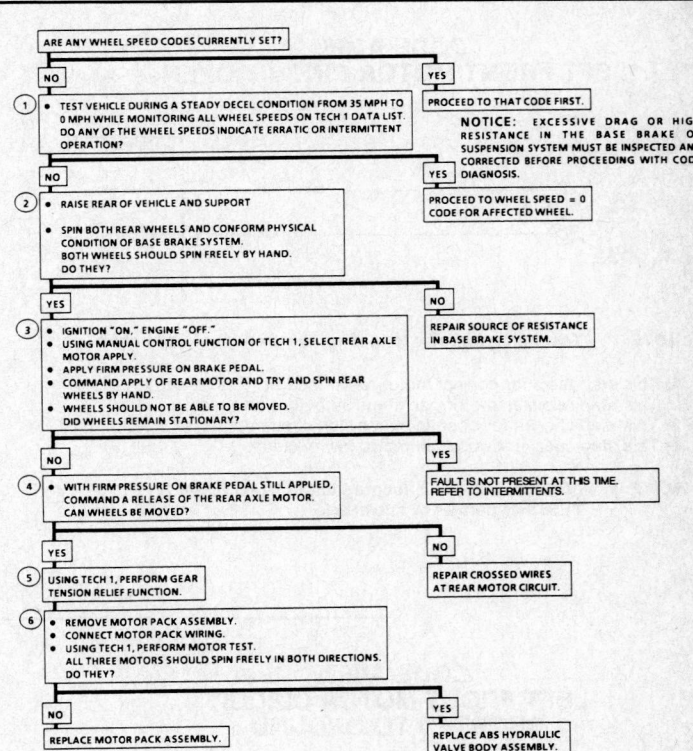

CODE A055
MOTOR DRIVER
INTERFACE FAULT DETECTED

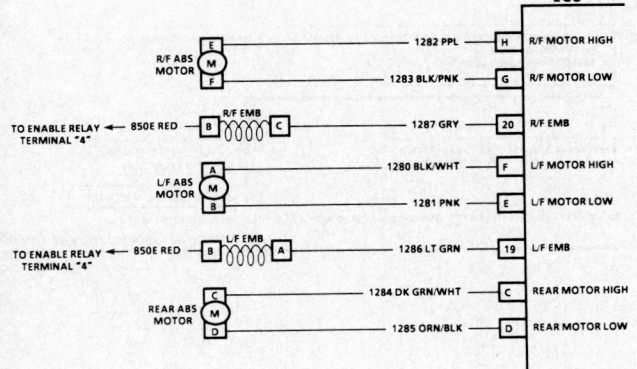

This test is designed identify which circuit has failed and may cause additional codes to set to pinpoint failed circuit.

NOTE: Test numbers refer to test numbers on diagnostic chart.

1) This step ensures fault was not set because of motor or EMB fault.
2) This step determines if fault is still present.
3) This step ensures fault was not set because of poor connector contact.

NOTE: INTERMITTENTS is located under DIAGNOSIS & TESTING portion of this article.

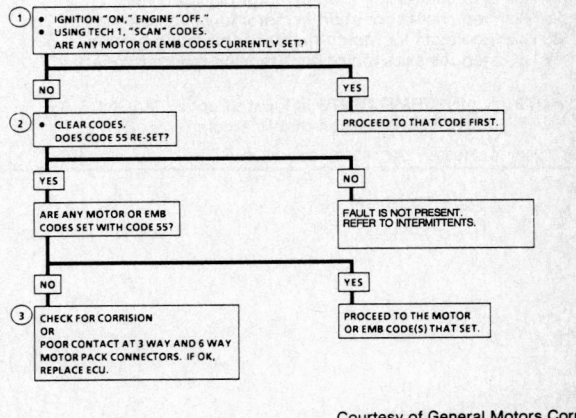

91I10288   91F10301   91G10302   91H10303

Courtesy of General Motors Corp.

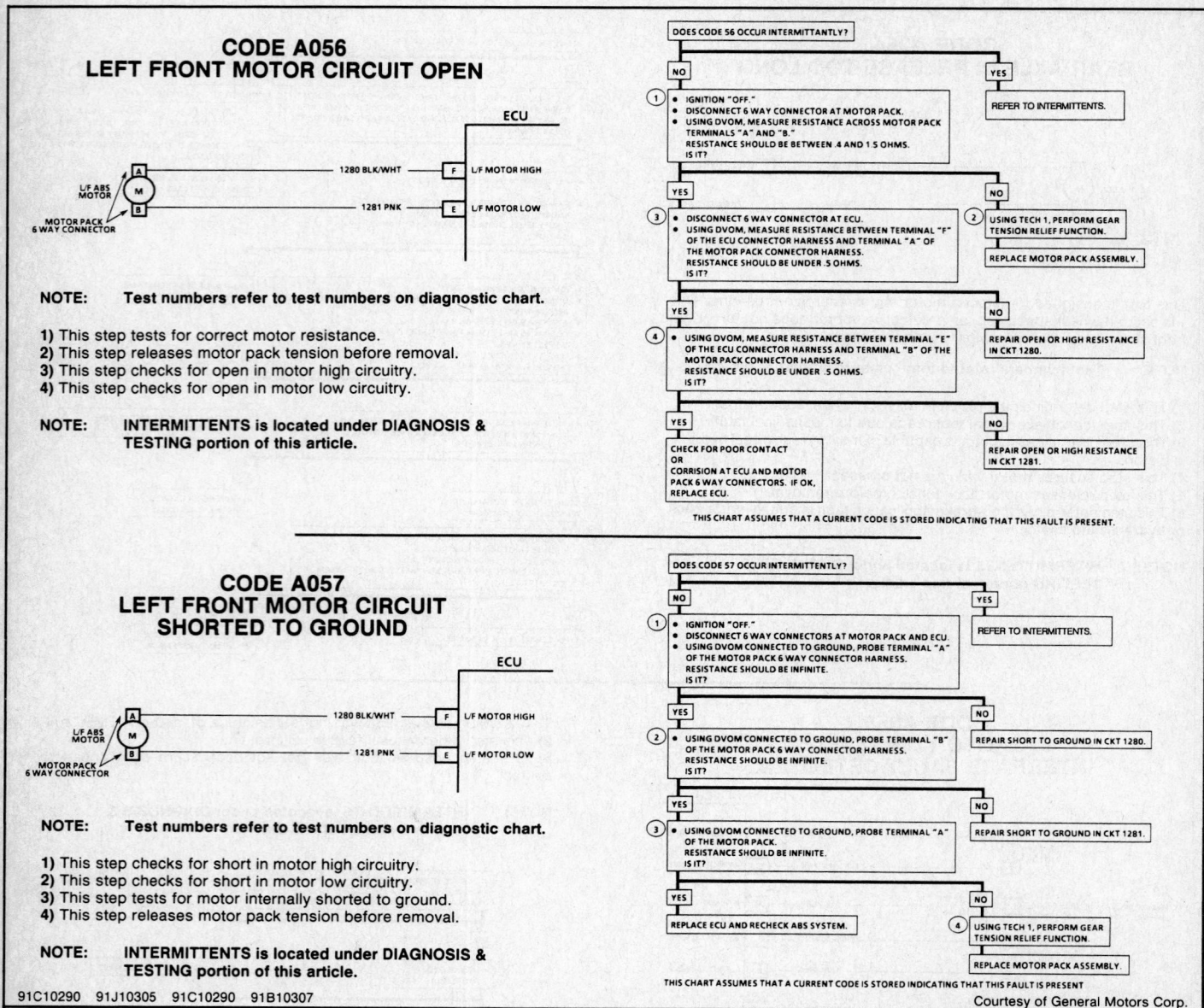

CODE A056
LEFT FRONT MOTOR CIRCUIT OPEN

ECU

L/F ABS MOTOR

A — 1280 BLK/WHT — F L/F MOTOR HIGH

B — 1281 PNK — E L/F MOTOR LOW

MOTOR PACK 6 WAY CONNECTOR

NOTE: Test numbers refer to test numbers on diagnostic chart.

1) This step tests for correct motor resistance.
2) This step releases motor pack tension before removal.
3) This step checks for open in motor high circuitry.
4) This step checks for open in motor low circuitry.

NOTE: INTERMITTENTS is located under DIAGNOSIS & TESTING portion of this article.

DOES CODE 56 OCCUR INTERMITTANTLY?

NO / YES

YES → REFER TO INTERMITTENTS.

1) • IGNITION "OFF."
• DISCONNECT 6 WAY CONNECTOR AT MOTOR PACK.
• USING DVOM, MEASURE RESISTANCE ACROSS MOTOR PACK TERMINALS "A" AND "B."
RESISTANCE SHOULD BE BETWEEN .4 AND 1.5 OHMS.
IS IT?

YES / NO

NO → 2) USING TECH 1, PERFORM GEAR TENSION RELIEF FUNCTION. → REPLACE MOTOR PACK ASSEMBLY.

3) • DISCONNECT 6 WAY CONNECTOR AT ECU.
• USING DVOM, MEASURE RESISTANCE BETWEEN TERMINAL "F" OF THE ECU CONNECTOR HARNESS AND TERMINAL "A" OF THE MOTOR PACK CONNECTOR HARNESS.
RESISTANCE SHOULD BE UNDER .5 OHMS.
IS IT?

YES / NO

NO → REPAIR OPEN OR HIGH RESISTANCE IN CKT 1280.

4) • USING DVOM, MEASURE RESISTANCE BETWEEN TERMINAL "E" OF THE ECU CONNECTOR HARNESS AND TERMINAL "B" OF THE MOTOR PACK CONNECTOR HARNESS.
RESISTANCE SHOULD BE UNDER .5 OHMS.
IS IT?

YES / NO

NO → REPAIR OPEN OR HIGH RESISTANCE IN CKT 1281.

YES → CHECK FOR POOR CONTACT OR CORRISION AT ECU AND MOTOR PACK 6 WAY CONNECTORS. IF OK, REPLACE ECU.

THIS CHART ASSUMES THAT A CURRENT CODE IS STORED INDICATING THAT THIS FAULT IS PRESENT.

CODE A057
LEFT FRONT MOTOR CIRCUIT SHORTED TO GROUND

ECU

L/F ABS MOTOR

A — 1280 BLK/WHT — F L/F MOTOR HIGH

B — 1281 PNK — E L/F MOTOR LOW

MOTOR PACK 6 WAY CONNECTOR

NOTE: Test numbers refer to test numbers on diagnostic chart.

1) This step checks for short in motor high circuitry.
2) This step checks for short in motor low circuitry.
3) This step tests for motor internally shorted to ground.
4) This step releases motor pack tension before removal.

NOTE: INTERMITTENTS is located under DIAGNOSIS & TESTING portion of this article.

DOES CODE 57 OCCUR INTERMITTENTLY?

NO / YES

YES → REFER TO INTERMITTENTS.

1) • IGNITION "OFF."
• DISCONNECT 6 WAY CONNECTORS AT MOTOR PACK AND ECU.
• USING DVOM CONNECTED TO GROUND, PROBE TERMINAL "A" OF THE MOTOR PACK 6 WAY CONNECTOR HARNESS.
RESISTANCE SHOULD BE INFINITE.
IS IT?

YES / NO

NO → REPAIR SHORT TO GROUND IN CKT 1280.

2) • USING DVOM CONNECTED TO GROUND, PROBE TERMINAL "B" OF THE MOTOR PACK 6 WAY CONNECTOR HARNESS.
RESISTANCE SHOULD BE INFINITE.
IS IT?

YES / NO

NO → REPAIR SHORT TO GROUND IN CKT 1281.

3) • USING DVOM CONNECTED TO GROUND, PROBE TERMINAL "A" OF THE MOTOR PACK.
RESISTANCE SHOULD BE INFINITE.
IS IT?

YES / NO

YES → REPLACE ECU AND RECHECK ABS SYSTEM.

NO → 4) USING TECH 1, PERFORM GEAR TENSION RELIEF FUNCTION. → REPLACE MOTOR PACK ASSEMBLY.

THIS CHART ASSUMES THAT A CURRENT CODE IS STORED INDICATING THAT THIS FAULT IS PRESENT

91C10290   91J10305   91C10290   91B10307

Courtesy of General Motors Corp.

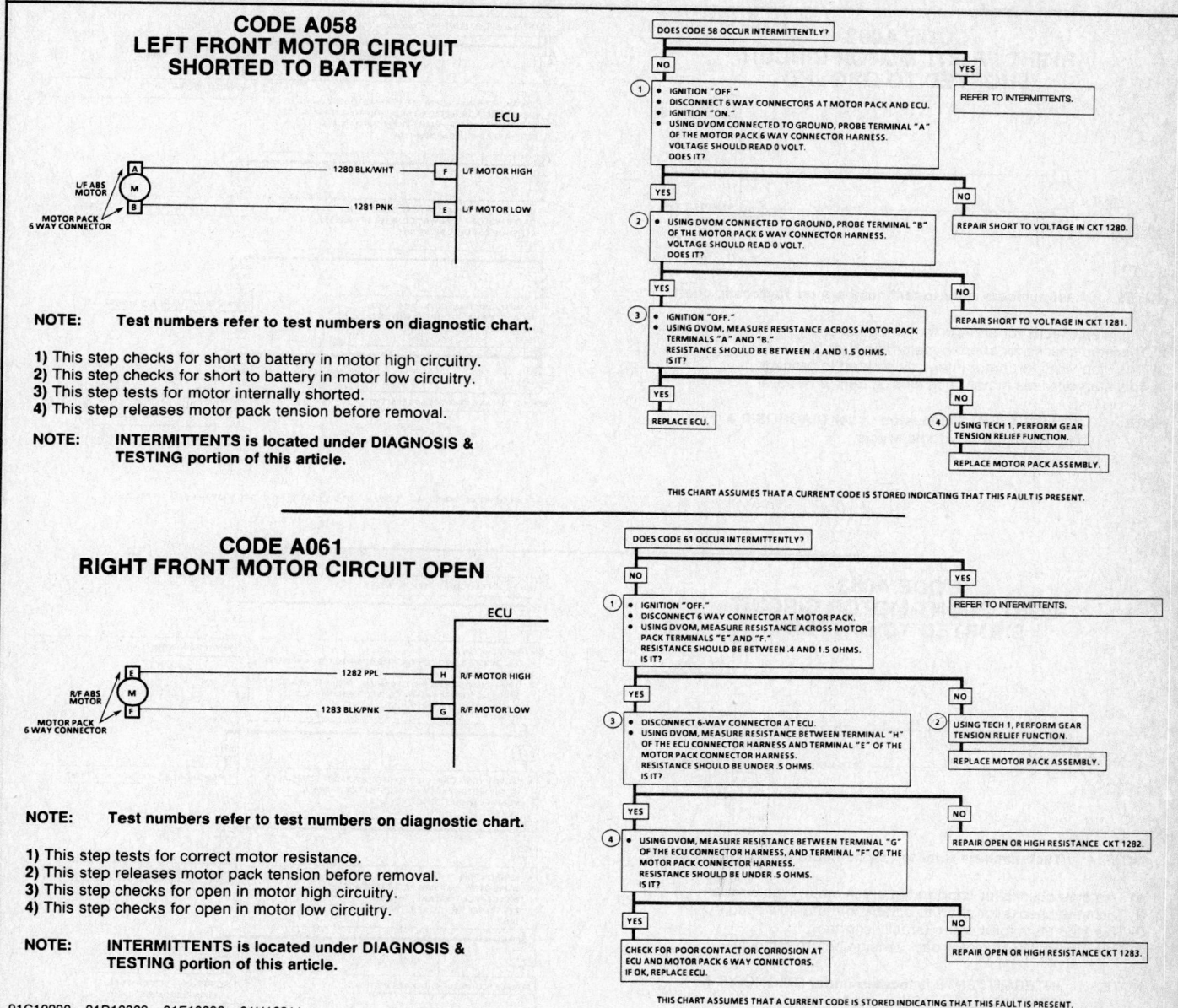

CODE A058
LEFT FRONT MOTOR CIRCUIT SHORTED TO BATTERY

NOTE: Test numbers refer to test numbers on diagnostic chart.

1) This step checks for short to battery in motor high circuitry.
2) This step checks for short to battery in motor low circuitry.
3) This step tests for motor internally shorted.
4) This step releases motor pack tension before removal.

NOTE: INTERMITTENTS is located under DIAGNOSIS & TESTING portion of this article.

CODE A061
RIGHT FRONT MOTOR CIRCUIT OPEN

NOTE: Test numbers refer to test numbers on diagnostic chart.

1) This step tests for correct motor resistance.
2) This step releases motor pack tension before removal.
3) This step checks for open in motor high circuitry.
4) This step checks for open in motor low circuitry.

NOTE: INTERMITTENTS is located under DIAGNOSIS & TESTING portion of this article.

91C10290 91D10309 91E10292 91H10311

Courtesy of General Motors Corp.

CODE A062
RIGHT FRONT MOTOR CIRCUIT
SHORTED TO GROUND

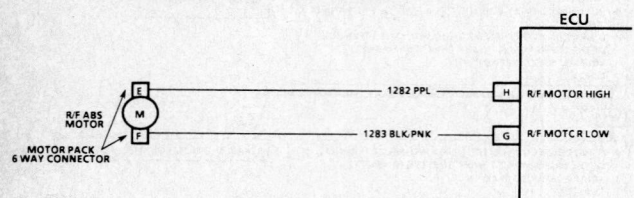

ECU

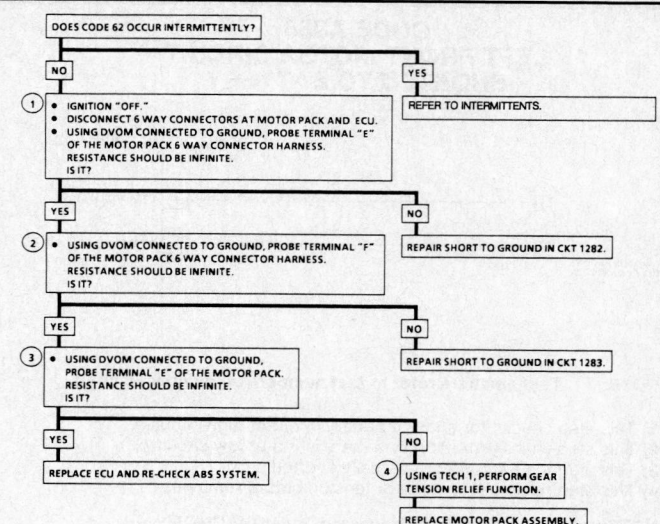

NOTE: Test numbers refer to test numbers on diagnostic chart.

1) This step checks for short in motor high circuitry.
2) This step checks for short in motor low circuitry.
3) This step tests for motor internally shorted to ground.
4) This step releases motor pack tension before removal.

NOTE: INTERMITTENTS is located under DIAGNOSIS &
TESTING portion of this article.

THIS CHART ASSUMES THAT A CURRENT CODE IS STORED INDICATING THAT THIS FAULT IS PRESENT.

CODE A063
RIGHT FRONT MOTOR CIRCUIT
SHORTED TO BATTERY

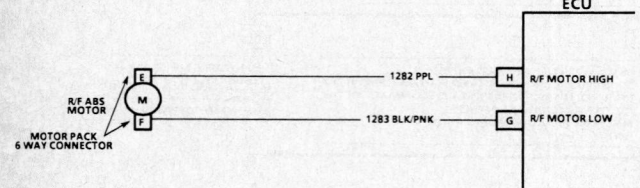

ECU

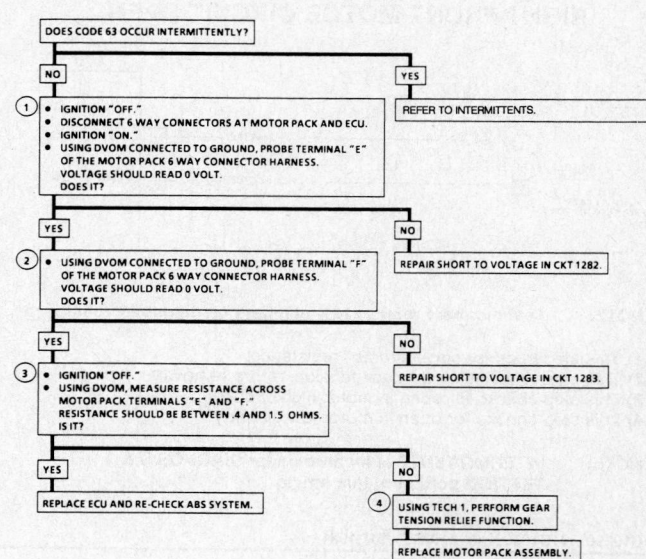

NOTE: Test numbers refer to test numbers on diagnostic chart.

1) This step checks for short to battery in motor high circuitry.
2) This step checks for short to battery in motor low circuitry.
3) This step tests for motor internally shorted.
4) This step releases motor pack tension before removal.

NOTE: INTERMITTENTS is located under DIAGNOSIS &
TESTING portion of this article.

THIS CHART ASSUMES THAT A CURRENT CODE IS STORED INDICATING THAT THIS FAULT IS PRESENT.

Courtesy of General Motors Corp.

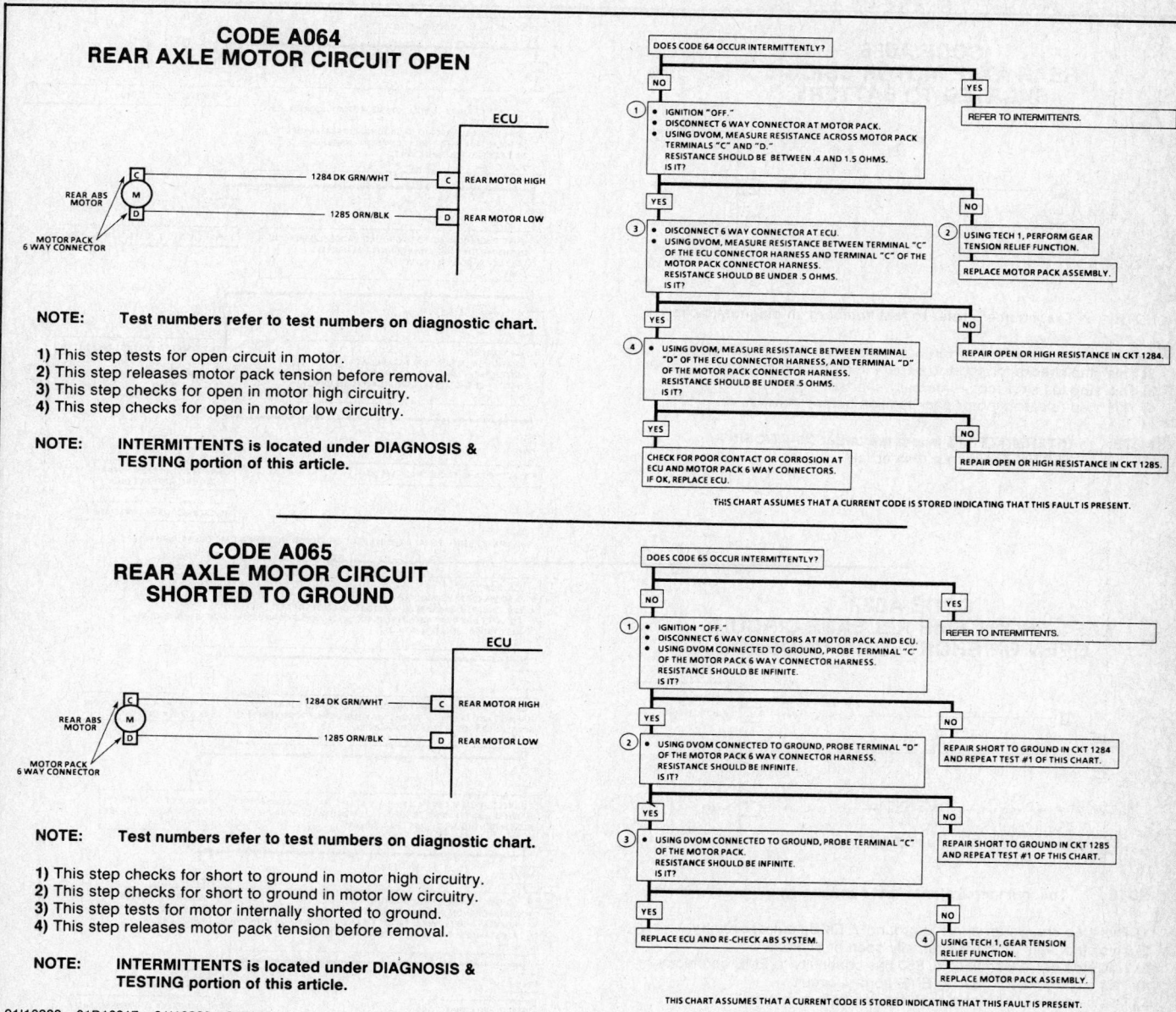

CODE A064
REAR AXLE MOTOR CIRCUIT OPEN

NOTE: Test numbers refer to test numbers on diagnostic chart.

1) This step tests for open circuit in motor.
2) This step releases motor pack tension before removal.
3) This step checks for open in motor high circuitry.
4) This step checks for open in motor low circuitry.

NOTE: INTERMITTENTS is located under DIAGNOSIS & TESTING portion of this article.

CODE A065
REAR AXLE MOTOR CIRCUIT SHORTED TO GROUND

NOTE: Test numbers refer to test numbers on diagnostic chart.

1) This step checks for short to ground in motor high circuitry.
2) This step checks for short to ground in motor low circuitry.
3) This step tests for motor internally shorted to ground.
4) This step releases motor pack tension before removal.

NOTE: INTERMITTENTS is located under DIAGNOSIS & TESTING portion of this article.

91I10288   91D10317   91I10288   91F10319

Courtesy of General Motors Corp.

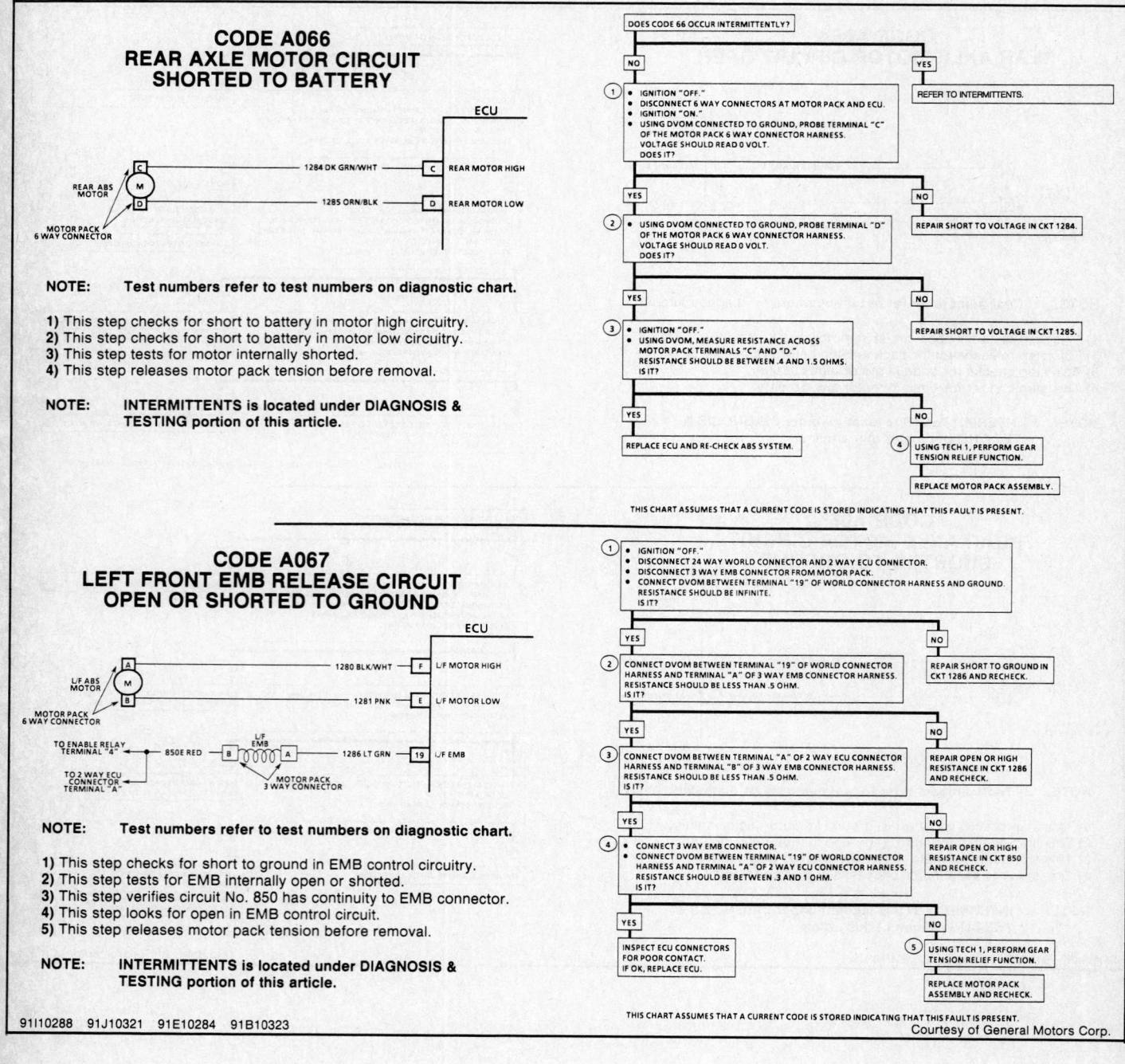

CODE A066
REAR AXLE MOTOR CIRCUIT
SHORTED TO BATTERY

NOTE: Test numbers refer to test numbers on diagnostic chart.

1) This step checks for short to battery in motor high circuitry.
2) This step checks for short to battery in motor low circuitry.
3) This step tests for motor internally shorted.
4) This step releases motor pack tension before removal.

NOTE: INTERMITTENTS is located under DIAGNOSIS & TESTING portion of this article.

DOES CODE 66 OCCUR INTERMITTENTLY?

NO

YES → REFER TO INTERMITTENTS.

1
- IGNITION "OFF."
- DISCONNECT 6 WAY CONNECTORS AT MOTOR PACK AND ECU.
- IGNITION "ON."
- USING DVOM CONNECTED TO GROUND, PROBE TERMINAL "C" OF THE MOTOR PACK 6 WAY CONNECTOR HARNESS. VOLTAGE SHOULD READ 0 VOLT. DOES IT?

YES

NO → REPAIR SHORT TO VOLTAGE IN CKT 1284.

2
- USING DVOM CONNECTED TO GROUND, PROBE TERMINAL "D" OF THE MOTOR PACK 6 WAY CONNECTOR HARNESS. VOLTAGE SHOULD READ 0 VOLT. DOES IT?

YES

NO → REPAIR SHORT TO VOLTAGE IN CKT 1285.

3
- IGNITION "OFF."
- USING DVOM, MEASURE RESISTANCE ACROSS MOTOR PACK TERMINALS "C" AND "D." RESISTANCE SHOULD BE BETWEEN .4 AND 1.5 OHMS. IS IT?

YES

NO

YES → REPLACE ECU AND RE-CHECK ABS SYSTEM.

NO → 4 USING TECH 1, PERFORM GEAR TENSION RELIEF FUNCTION.

REPLACE MOTOR PACK ASSEMBLY.

THIS CHART ASSUMES THAT A CURRENT CODE IS STORED INDICATING THAT THIS FAULT IS PRESENT.

CODE A067
LEFT FRONT EMB RELEASE CIRCUIT
OPEN OR SHORTED TO GROUND

NOTE: Test numbers refer to test numbers on diagnostic chart.

1) This step checks for short to ground in EMB control circuitry.
2) This step tests for EMB internally open or shorted.
3) This step verifies circuit No. 850 has continuity to EMB connector.
4) This step looks for open in EMB control circuit.
5) This step releases motor pack tension before removal.

NOTE: INTERMITTENTS is located under DIAGNOSIS & TESTING portion of this article.

1
- IGNITION "OFF."
- DISCONNECT 24 WAY WORLD CONNECTOR AND 2 WAY ECU CONNECTOR.
- DISCONNECT 3 WAY EMB CONNECTOR FROM MOTOR PACK.
- CONNECT DVOM BETWEEN TERMINAL "19" OF WORLD CONNECTOR HARNESS AND GROUND. RESISTANCE SHOULD BE INFINITE. IS IT?

YES

NO → REPAIR SHORT TO GROUND IN CKT 1286 AND RECHECK.

2
CONNECT DVOM BETWEEN TERMINAL "19" OF WORLD CONNECTOR HARNESS AND TERMINAL "A" OF 3 WAY EMB CONNECTOR HARNESS. RESISTANCE SHOULD BE LESS THAN .5 OHM. IS IT?

YES

NO → REPAIR OPEN OR HIGH RESISTANCE IN CKT 1286 AND RECHECK.

3
CONNECT DVOM BETWEEN TERMINAL "A" OF 2 WAY ECU CONNECTOR HARNESS AND TERMINAL "B" OF 3 WAY EMB CONNECTOR HARNESS. RESISTANCE SHOULD BE LESS THAN .5 OHM. IS IT?

YES

NO → REPAIR OPEN OR HIGH RESISTANCE IN CKT 850 AND RECHECK.

4
- CONNECT 3 WAY EMB CONNECTOR.
- CONNECT DVOM BETWEEN TERMINAL "19" OF WORLD CONNECTOR HARNESS AND TERMINAL "A" OF 2 WAY ECU CONNECTOR HARNESS. RESISTANCE SHOULD BE BETWEEN .3 AND 1 OHM. IS IT?

YES

NO

YES → INSPECT ECU CONNECTORS FOR POOR CONTACT. IF OK, REPLACE ECU.

NO → 5 USING TECH 1, PERFORM GEAR TENSION RELIEF FUNCTION.

REPLACE MOTOR PACK ASSEMBLY AND RECHECK.

THIS CHART ASSUMES THAT A CURRENT CODE IS STORED INDICATING THAT THIS FAULT IS PRESENT.

91I10288   91J10321   91E10284   91B10323

Courtesy of General Motors Corp.

CODE A068
LEFT FRONT EMB RELEASE CIRCUIT SHORTED TO BATTERY OR DRIVER OPEN

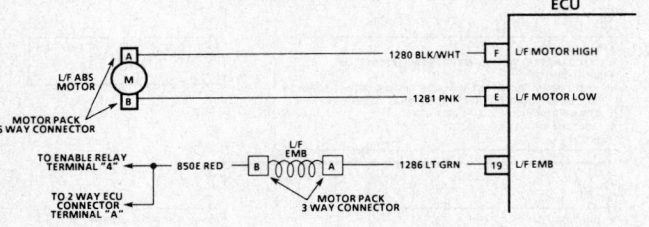

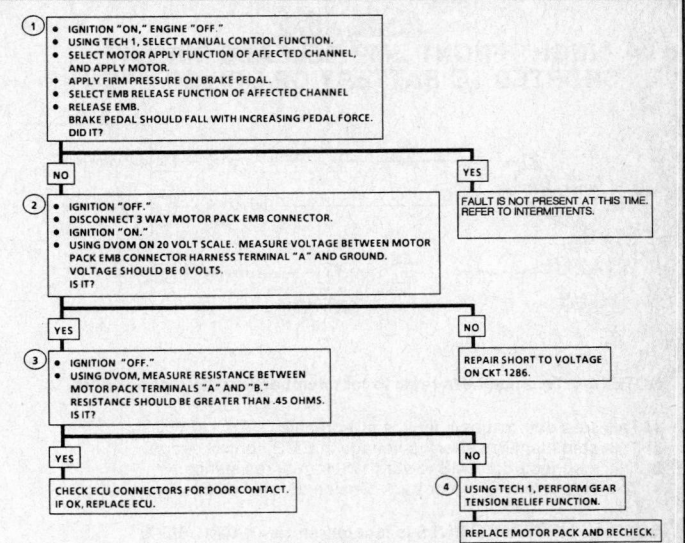

1. • IGNITION "ON," ENGINE "OFF."
   • USING TECH 1, SELECT MANUAL CONTROL FUNCTION.
   • SELECT MOTOR APPLY FUNCTION OF AFFECTED CHANNEL, AND APPLY MOTOR.
   • APPLY FIRM PRESSURE ON BRAKE PEDAL.
   • SELECT EMB RELEASE FUNCTION OF AFFECTED CHANNEL
   • RELEASE EMB.
   BRAKE PEDAL SHOULD FALL WITH INCREASING PEDAL FORCE. DID IT?

   YES → FAULT IS NOT PRESENT AT THIS TIME. REFER TO INTERMITTENTS.

2. **NO** • IGNITION "OFF."
   • DISCONNECT 3 WAY MOTOR PACK EMB CONNECTOR.
   • IGNITION "ON."
   • USING DVOM ON 20 VOLT SCALE. MEASURE VOLTAGE BETWEEN MOTOR PACK EMB CONNECTOR HARNESS TERMINAL "A" AND GROUND.
   VOLTAGE SHOULD BE 0 VOLTS.
   IS IT?

   NO → REPAIR SHORT TO VOLTAGE ON CKT 1286.

3. **YES** • IGNITION "OFF."
   • USING DVOM, MEASURE RESISTANCE BETWEEN MOTOR PACK TERMINALS "A" AND "B."
   RESISTANCE SHOULD BE GREATER THAN .45 OHMS.
   IS IT?

   YES → CHECK ECU CONNECTORS FOR POOR CONTACT. IF OK, REPLACE ECU.

   NO → 4. USING TECH 1, PERFORM GEAR TENSION RELIEF FUNCTION.
   → REPLACE MOTOR PACK AND RECHECK.

NOTE: Test numbers refer to test numbers on diagnostic chart.

1) This step determines if fault is still present.
2) This step identifies short to voltage in EMB control circuit.
3) This step tests for EMB lower than normal resistance.
4) This step releases motor pack tension before removal.

NOTE: INTERMITTENTS is located under DIAGNOSIS & TESTING portion of this article.

THIS CHART ASSUMES THAT A CURRENT CODE IS STORED INDICATING THAT THIS FAULT IS PRESENT.

CODE A071
RIGHT FRONT EMB RELEASE CIRCUIT OPEN OR SHORTED TO GROUND

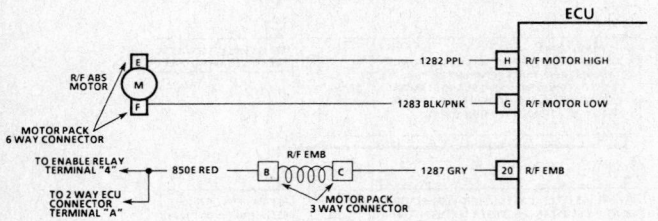

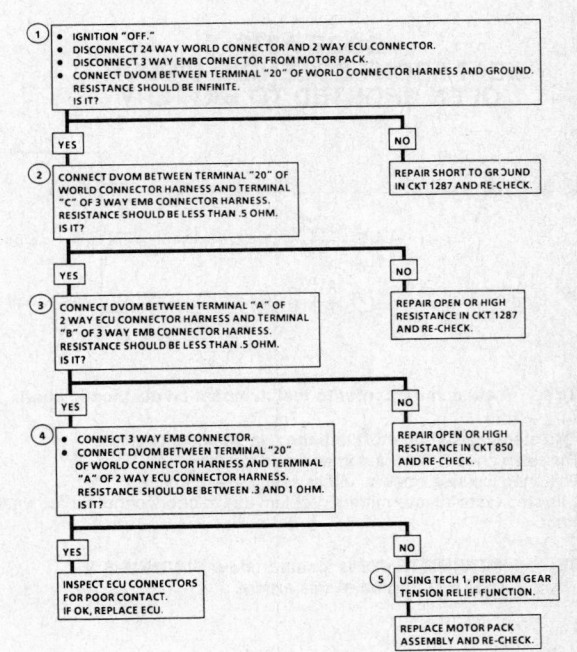

1. • IGNITION "OFF."
   • DISCONNECT 24 WAY WORLD CONNECTOR AND 2 WAY ECU CONNECTOR.
   • DISCONNECT 3 WAY EMB CONNECTOR FROM MOTOR PACK.
   • CONNECT DVOM BETWEEN TERMINAL "20" OF WORLD CONNECTOR HARNESS AND GROUND.
   RESISTANCE SHOULD BE INFINITE.
   IS IT?

2. **YES** CONNECT DVOM BETWEEN TERMINAL "20" OF WORLD CONNECTOR HARNESS AND TERMINAL "C" OF 3 WAY EMB CONNECTOR HARNESS.
   RESISTANCE SHOULD BE LESS THAN .5 OHM.
   IS IT?

   NO → REPAIR SHORT TO GROUND IN CKT 1287 AND RE-CHECK.

3. **YES** CONNECT DVOM BETWEEN TERMINAL "A" OF 2 WAY ECU CONNECTOR HARNESS AND TERMINAL "B" OF 3 WAY EMB CONNECTOR HARNESS.
   RESISTANCE SHOULD BE LESS THAN .5 OHM.
   IS IT?

   NO → REPAIR OPEN OR HIGH RESISTANCE IN CKT 1287 AND RE-CHECK.

4. **YES** • CONNECT 3 WAY EMB CONNECTOR.
   • CONNECT DVOM BETWEEN TERMINAL "20" OF WORLD CONNECTOR HARNESS AND TERMINAL "A" OF 2 WAY ECU CONNECTOR HARNESS.
   RESISTANCE SHOULD BE BETWEEN .3 AND 1 OHM.
   IS IT?

   NO → REPAIR OPEN OR HIGH RESISTANCE IN CKT 850 AND RE-CHECK.

   YES → INSPECT ECU CONNECTORS FOR POOR CONTACT. IF OK, REPLACE ECU.

5. **NO** USING TECH 1, PERFORM GEAR TENSION RELIEF FUNCTION.
   → REPLACE MOTOR PACK ASSEMBLY AND RE-CHECK.

NOTE: Test numbers refer to test numbers on diagnostic chart.

1) This step checks for short to ground in EMB control circuitry.
2) This step tests for EMB internally open or shorted.
3) This step verifies circuit No. 850 has continuity to EMB connector.
4) This step looks for open in EMB control circuit.
5) This step releases motor pack tension before removal.

NOTE: INTERMITTENTS is located under DIAGNOSIS & TESTING portion of this article.

THIS CHART ASSUMES THAT A CURRENT CODE IS STORED INDICATING THAT THIS FAULT IS PRESENT.

91E10284   91D10325   91G10286   91F10327

Courtesy of General Motors Corp.

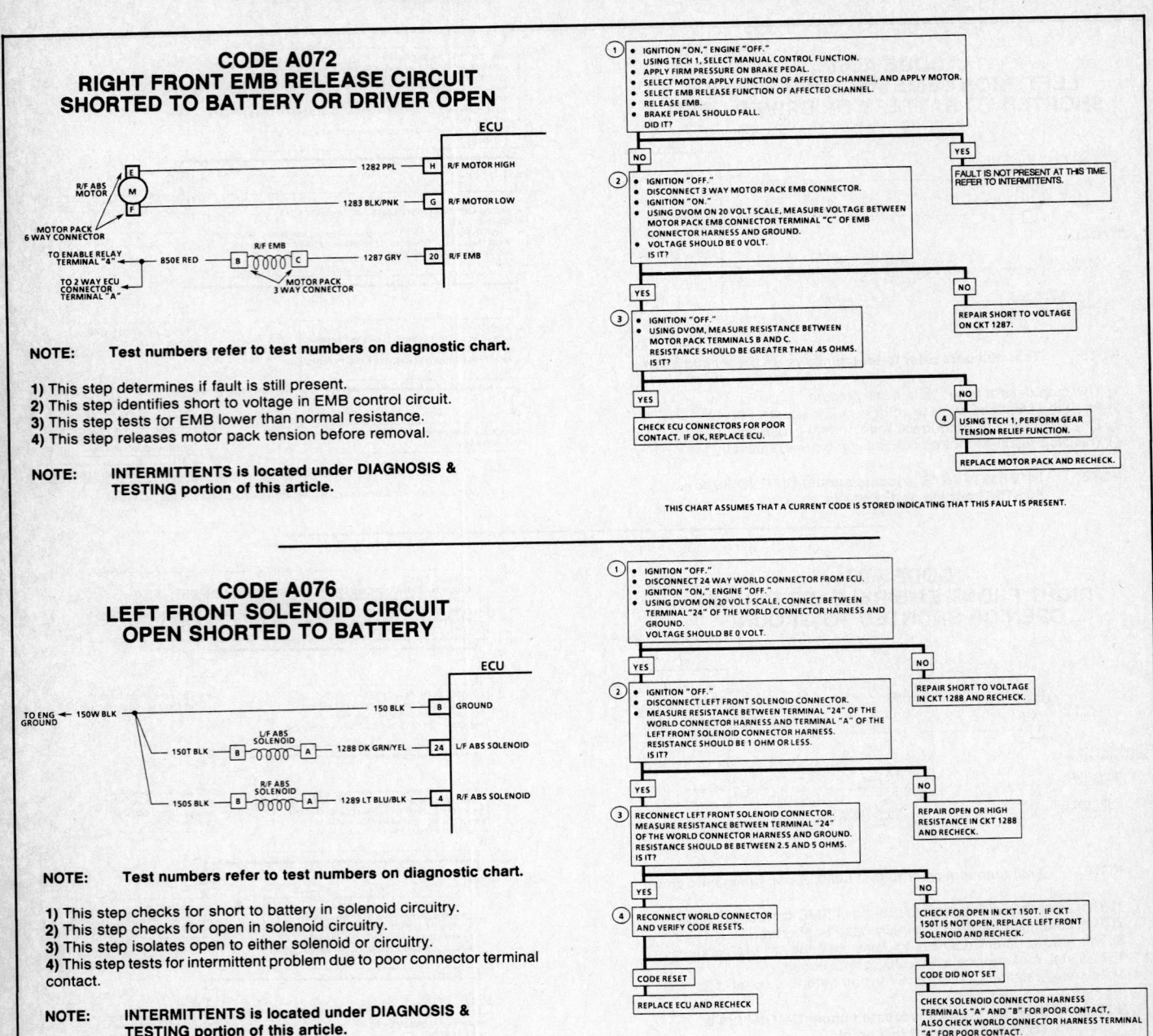

CODE A072
RIGHT FRONT EMB RELEASE CIRCUIT
SHORTED TO BATTERY OR DRIVER OPEN

NOTE: Test numbers refer to test numbers on diagnostic chart.

1) This step determines if fault is still present.
2) This step identifies short to voltage in EMB control circuit.
3) This step tests for EMB lower than normal resistance.
4) This step releases motor pack tension before removal.

NOTE: INTERMITTENTS is located under DIAGNOSIS & TESTING portion of this article.

THIS CHART ASSUMES THAT A CURRENT CODE IS STORED INDICATING THAT THIS FAULT IS PRESENT.

CODE A076
LEFT FRONT SOLENOID CIRCUIT
OPEN SHORTED TO BATTERY

NOTE: Test numbers refer to test numbers on diagnostic chart.

1) This step checks for short to battery in solenoid circuitry.
2) This step checks for open in solenoid circuitry.
3) This step isolates open to either solenoid or circuitry.
4) This step tests for intermittent problem due to poor connector terminal contact.

NOTE: INTERMITTENTS is located under DIAGNOSIS & TESTING portion of this article.

THIS CHART ASSUMES THAT A CURRENT CODE IS STORED INDICATING THAT THIS FAULT IS PRESENT.

Courtesy of General Motors Corp.

91G10286   91H10329   91A10330   91B10331

CODE A077
LEFT FRONT SOLENOID CIRCUIT
SHORTED TO GROUND OR DRIVER OPEN

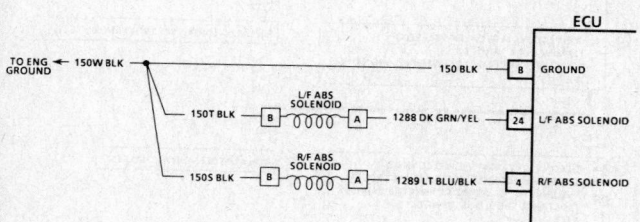

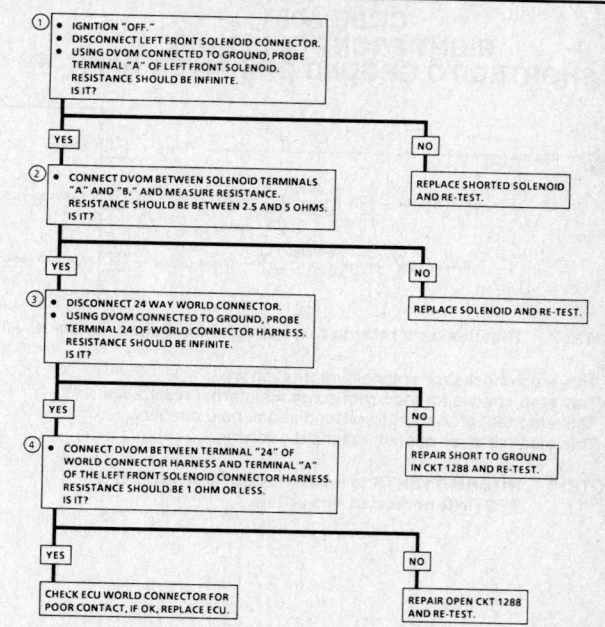

NOTE: Test numbers refer to test numbers on diagnostic chart.

1) This step checks for solenoid internal short.
2) This step checks for incorrect solenoid internal resistance.
3) This step tests for short to ground in solenoid circuitry.
4) This step tests for open in solenoid circuitry.

NOTE: INTERMITTENTS is located under DIAGNOSIS & TESTING portion of this article.

THIS CHART ASSUMES THAT A CURRENT CODE IS STORED INDICATING THAT THIS FAULT IS PRESENT.

CODE A078
RIGHT FRONT SOLENOID CIRCUIT
OPEN SHORTED TO BATTERY

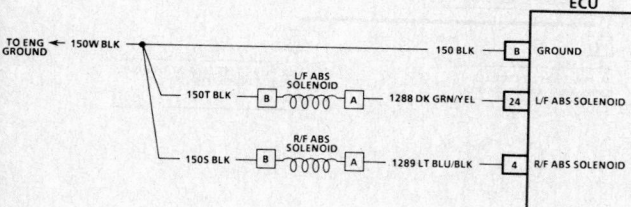

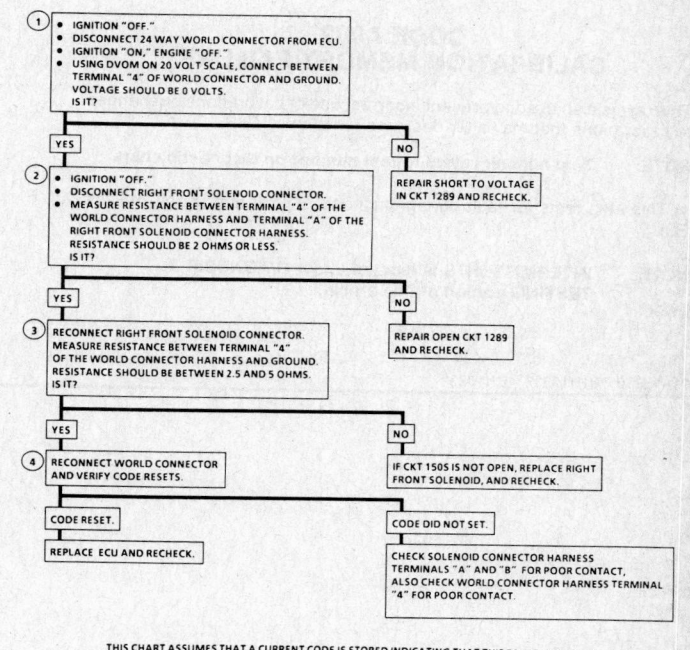

NOTE: Test numbers refer to test numbers on diagnostic chart.

1) This step checks for short to battery in solenoid circuitry.
2) This step checks for open in solenoid circuitry.
3) This step isolates open to either solenoid or circuitry.
4) This step tests for intermittent problem due to poor connector terminal contact.

NOTE: INTERMITTENTS is located under DIAGNOSIS & TESTING portion of this article.

THIS CHART ASSUMES THAT A CURRENT CODE IS STORED INDICATING THAT THIS FAULT IS PRESENT.

CODE A081
RIGHT FRONT SOLENOID
SHORTED TO GROUND OR DRIVER OPEN

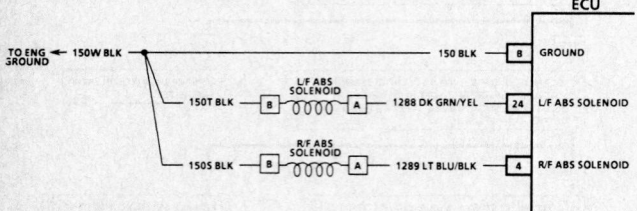

NOTE: Test numbers refer to test numbers on diagnostic chart.

1) This step checks for solenoid internal short.
2) This step checks for incorrect solenoid internal resistance.
3) This step tests for short to ground in solenoid circuitry.
4) This step tests for open in solenoid circuitry.

NOTE: INTERMITTENTS is located under DIAGNOSIS & TESTING portion of this article.

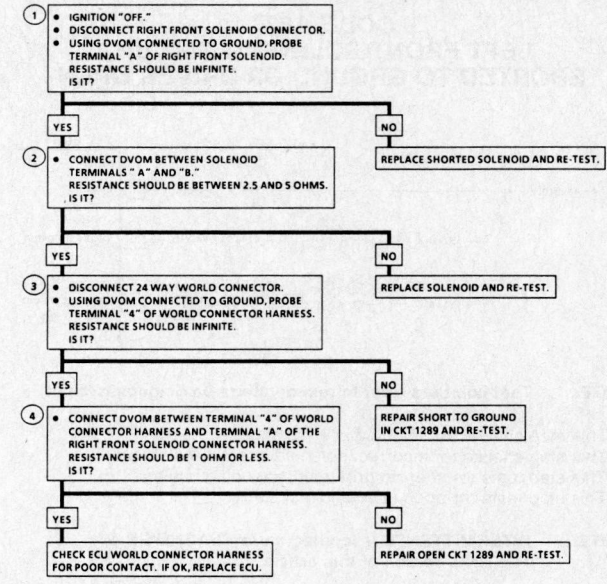

1
- IGNITION "OFF."
- DISCONNECT RIGHT FRONT SOLENOID CONNECTOR.
- USING DVOM CONNECTED TO GROUND, PROBE TERMINAL "A" OF RIGHT FRONT SOLENOID. RESISTANCE SHOULD BE INFINITE.
IS IT?

YES → 2
NO → REPLACE SHORTED SOLENOID AND RE-TEST.

2
- CONNECT DVOM BETWEEN SOLENOID TERMINALS " A" AND "B."
RESISTANCE SHOULD BE BETWEEN 2.5 AND 5 OHMS.
IS IT?

YES → 3
NO → REPLACE SOLENOID AND RE-TEST.

3
- DISCONNECT 24 WAY WORLD CONNECTOR.
- USING DVOM CONNECTED TO GROUND, PROBE TERMINAL "4" OF WORLD CONNECTOR HARNESS. RESISTANCE SHOULD BE INFINITE.
IS IT?

YES → 4
NO → REPAIR SHORT TO GROUND IN CKT 1289 AND RE-TEST.

4
- CONNECT DVOM BETWEEN TERMINAL "4" OF WORLD CONNECTOR HARNESS AND TERMINAL "A" OF THE RIGHT FRONT SOLENOID CONNECTOR HARNESS. RESISTANCE SHOULD BE 1 OHM OR LESS.
IS IT?

YES → CHECK ECU WORLD CONNECTOR HARNESS FOR POOR CONTACT. IF OK, REPLACE ECU.
NO → REPAIR OPEN CKT 1289 AND RE-TEST.

THIS CHART ASSUMES THAT A CURRENT CODE IS STORED INDICATING THAT THIS FAULT IS PRESENT.

CODE A082
CALIBRATION MEMORY FAILURE

This test is also used to prevent incorrect use of calibrations or changes to calibrations that may alter designed function of ABS.

NOTE: Test number refers to test number on diagnostic chart.

1) This step tests for fault during diagnosis. If fault is present, replace ECU.

NOTE: INTERMITTENTS is located under DIAGNOSIS & TESTING portion of this article.

1
- IGNITION "ON."
- USING TECH 1, CLEAR CODES. DOES CODE 82 RESET?

YES → REPLACE ABS CONTROLLER AND VERIFY ABS OPERATION.
NO → FAULT IS NOT PRESENT AT THIS TIME. REFER TO INTERMITTENTS.

91A10330   91H10337   91I10338

Courtesy of General Motors Corp.

CODE A086
ABS ENABLE RED BRAKE TELLTALE

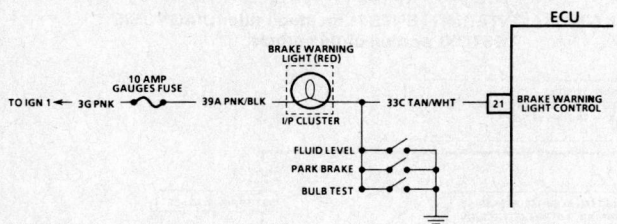

This test is used for information only. It reflects ability of ECU to illuminate Red BRAKE telltale light. If another test issues a command to illuminate light, a Code 86 will be stored as a history code.

NOTE: Test number refers to test number on diagnostic chart.

1) This step identifies if code other than Code 86 commanded illumination of Red telltale light

NOTE: INTERMITTENTS is located under DIAGNOSIS & TESTING portion of this article.

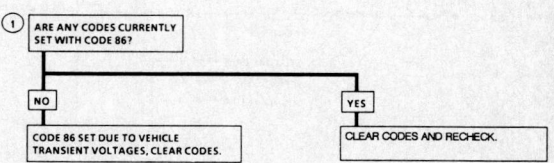

CODE A087
ABS RED BRAKE TELLTALE CIRCUIT OPEN

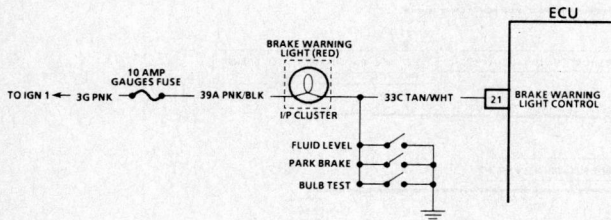

This test verifies ECU has continuity to Red BRAKE telltale light. Because other systems also use this circuit, a short to ground cannot be detected.

NOTE: Test number refers to test number on diagnostic chart.

1) This step determines if fault is still present.
2) This step tests ECU's ability to complete ground to Red BRAKE telltale light to illuminate it.
3) This step tests for circuit completion to instrument cluster.
4) This step isolates open circuit to either ECU of brake telltale.

NOTE: INTERMITTENTS is located under DIAGNOSIS & TESTING portion of this article.

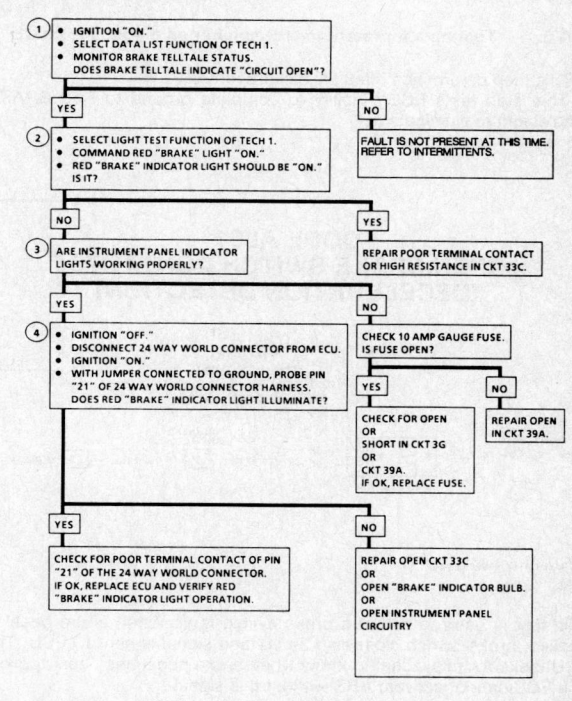

THIS CHART ASSUMES THAT A CURRENT CODE IS STORED INDICATING THAT THIS FAULT IS PRESENT.

91J10339   91C10340   91D10341   91E10342

Courtesy of General Motors Corp.

CODE A088
ABS RED BRAKE TELLTALE CIRCUIT
SHORTED TO BATTERY OR DRIVER OPEN

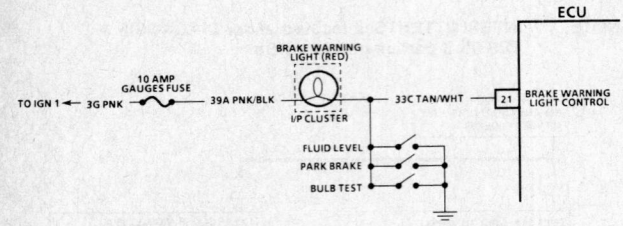

This test isolates a short to battery between ECU and Red BRAKE telltale light or an open driver that does not allow light to be illuminated by ECU.

NOTE: Test number refers to test number on diagnostic chart.

1) This step determines if fault is still present.
2) This step tests ECU's ability to complete ground to Red BRAKE telltale light to illuminate it.

3) This step tests for circuit completion to instrument cluster.
4) This step isolates open circuit to either ECU of brake telltale.

NOTE: INTERMITTENTS is located under DIAGNOSIS & TESTING portion of this article.

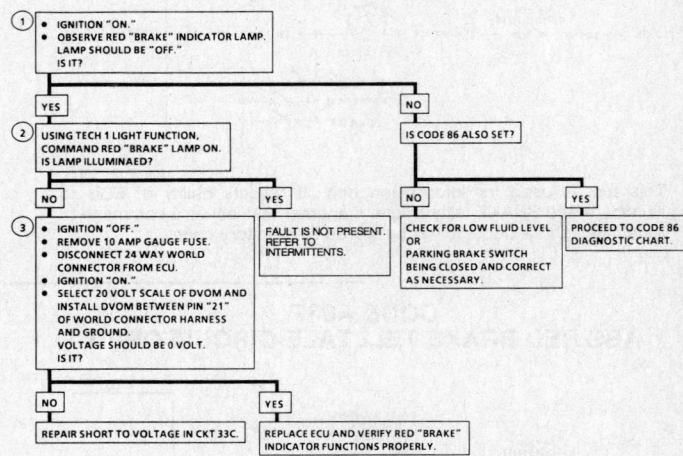

CODE A091
OPEN BRAKE SWITCH CONTACTS
(DECELERATION DETECTION)

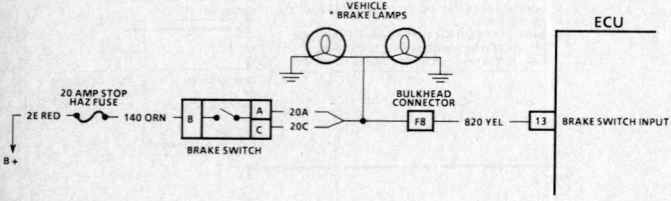

* NUMBER OF LAMPS MAY VARY

This test is used to detect a brake switch fault. When brake pedal is applied, brake switch closes and a voltage signal is sent to ECU. The ECU looks for this signal to know when brake pedal has been applied. The ECU cannot activate ABS without this signal.

NOTE: Test numbers refer to test numbers on diagnostic chart.

1) This step determines if brake switch signal is being received by ECU.
2) This step determines if fault is still present.
3) This test isolates open circuit to either brake switch input circuit or ECU.

NOTE: INTERMITTENTS is located under DIAGNOSIS & TESTING portion of this article.

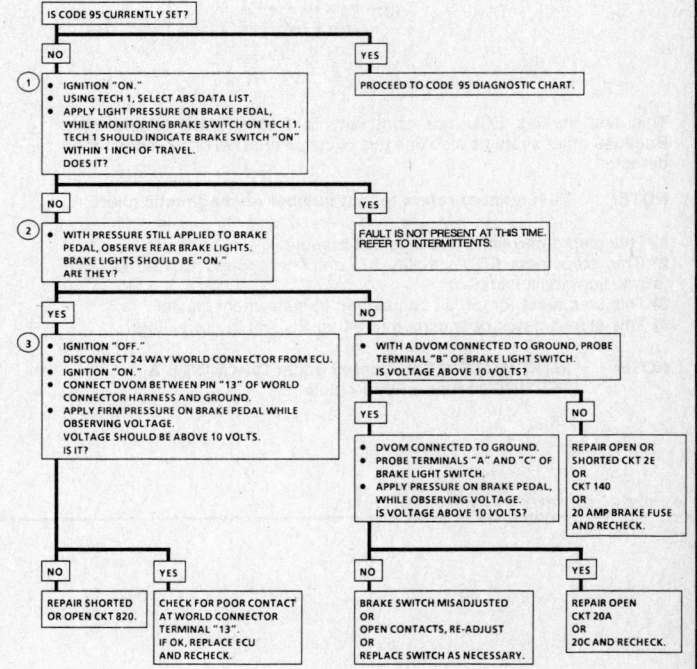

Courtesy of General Motors Corp.

CODE A092
OPEN BRAKE SWITCH CONTACTS

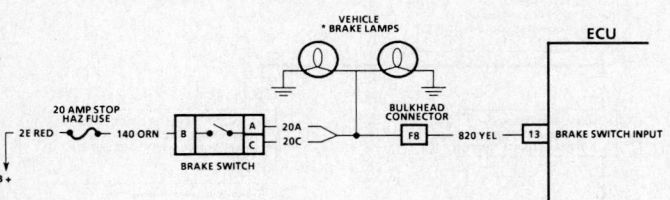

This test is used to detect a brake switch fault. When brake pedal is applied, brake switch closes and a voltage signal is sent to ECU. The ECU looks for this signal to know when brake pedal has been applied. The ECU cannot activate ABS without this signal. Code A092 will set only when conditions requiring ABS are present.

NOTE: **Test numbers refer to test numbers on diagnostic chart.**

1) This step determines if brake switch signal is being received by ECU.
2) This test isolates open circuit to either brake switch or brake light circuitry.
3) This test isolates open circuit to either brake switch input circuit or ECU.

NOTE: **INTERMITTENTS is located under DIAGNOSIS & TESTING portion of this article.**

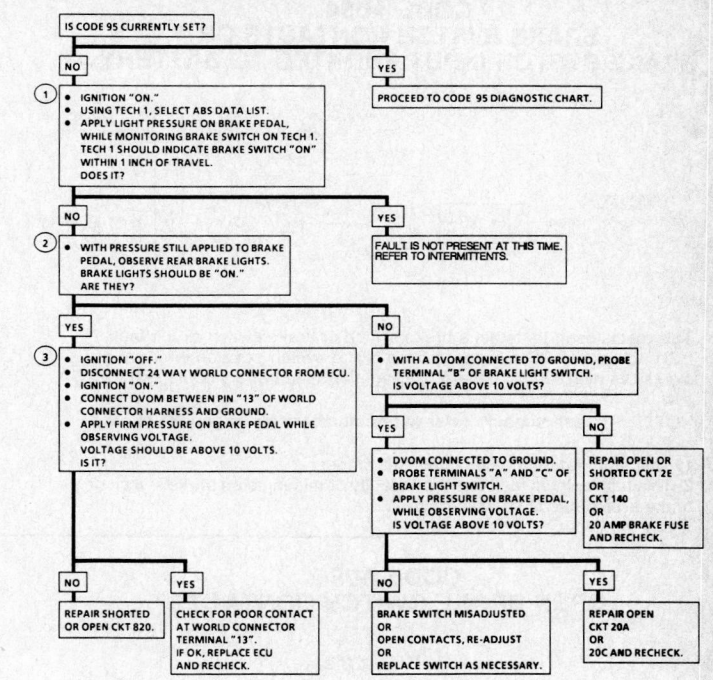

CODE A093
CODE 91 OR 92 FAILED IN
LAST OR CURRENT IGNITION CYCLE

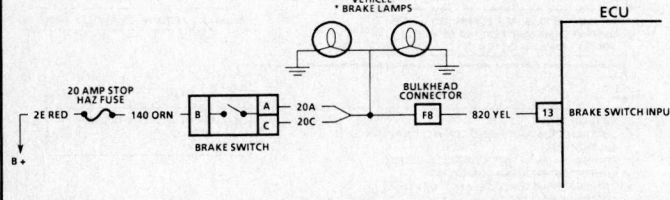

When Code A091 or A092 is set, Code A093 becomes a current failure and prevents ABS from activating.

NOTE: **Test numbers refer to test numbers on diagnostic chart.**

1) This test determines which code (A091 or A092) caused Code A093 to set.
2) Perform necessary repairs so that Code A093 can be cleared.

NOTE: **INTERMITTENTS is located under DIAGNOSIS & TESTING portion of this article.**

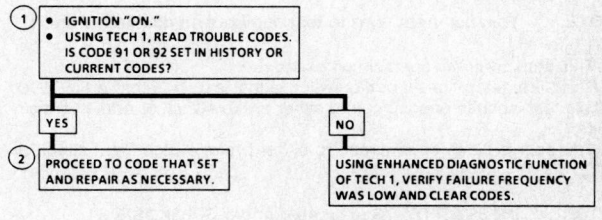

91H10345   91A10348   91H10345   91F10350

CODE A094
BRAKE SWITCH CONTACTS OR
BRAKE SWITCH INPUT SHORTED TO BATTERY

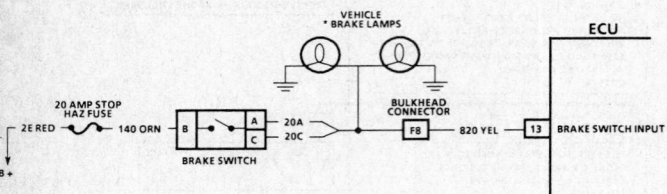

NOTE: INTERMITTENTS is located under DIAGNOSIS & TESTING portion of this article.

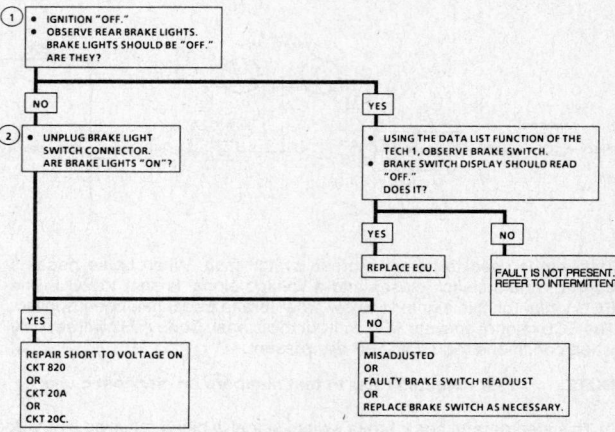

This test is used to detect a brake switch or brake switch circuit fault. If ECU activates ABS, based on false brake switch position information, excessive hydraulic modulator cycling and dead battery could result.

NOTE: Test numbers refer to test numbers on diagnostic chart.

1) This step determines if fault is still present.
2) This test isolates fault to either a faulty or misadjusted brake switch or brake switch circuit short to battery.

THIS CHART ASSUMES THAT A CURRENT CODE IS STORED INDICATING THAT THIS FAULT IS PRESENT.

CODE A095
OPEN BRAKE SWITCH CONTACTS

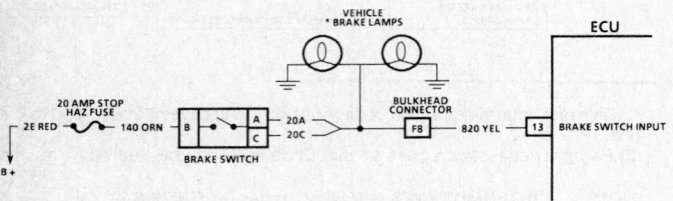

This test is used to identify open brake switch circuitry preventing brake switch input to ECU from changing when brakes are applied.

NOTE: Test numbers refer to test numbers on diagnostic chart.

1) This step confirms open circuit exists.
2) This step determines if brake switch signal is being received by ECU.
3 This test isolates open circuit to either brake switch or brake light circuitry.
4) This test isolates open circuit to either brake switch input circuit or ECU.

NOTE: INTERMITTENTS is located under DIAGNOSIS & TESTING portion of this article.

91H10345   91H10352   91H10345   91J10354

Courtesy of General Motors Corp.

CODE A096
BRAKE LIGHTS OPEN,
BRAKE LIGHT GROUNDS OPEN, CHMSL
OPEN WHEN 4-WAY FLASHER OPERATING

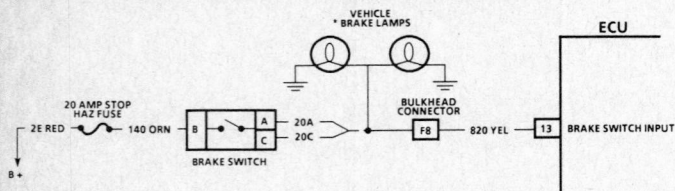

NOTE: Test numbers refer to test numbers on diagnostic chart.

1) A false Code A096 may set due to brake switch circuit malfunction. If any other codes are present, proceed to that code first.
2) This test confirms that fault is currently present.

NOTE: INTERMITTENTS is located under DIAGNOSIS & TESTING portion of this article.

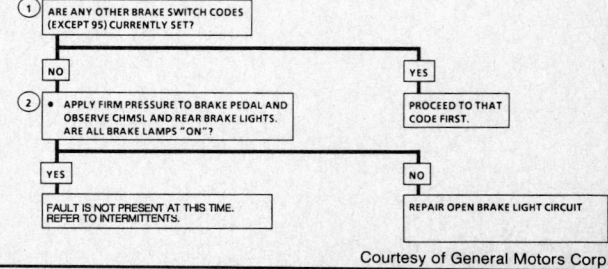

This test is used to identify cause of Code A095 failure. If Code A095 appears with Code A096, then either brakelights are open, brakelight ground is open, or Center High-Mounted Stoplight (CHMSL) is open during 4-way flasher operation.

91H10345   91B10356

Courtesy of General Motors Corp.

Bonneville, DeVille, Eighty-Eight, Fleetwood, LeSabre, Ninety-Eight, Park Avenue, Touring Sedan

DESCRIPTION

The Teves 4-wheel Anti-Lock Brake System (ABS) is designed to prevent wheel lock-up during heavy braking. This allows driver to maintain steering control while stopping vehicle in shortest distance possible. Major components include: pump motor and pressure modulator valve assembly, fluid reservoir with integral filter, wheel speed sensors (4), fluid level sensor, Electronic Brake Control Module (EBCM), booster/master cylinder assembly and BRAKE and ANTI-LOCK warning lights. *See Fig. 1.*

Some LeSabre, Ninety-Eight and Touring Sedan models may also be equipped with Traction Control System (TCS). This system uses ABS components to control wheel spin at speeds under 25 MPH (42 KM/H).

NOTE: For more information on brake system, see appropriate DISC & DRUM article.

OPERATION

ANTI-LOCK BRAKE SYSTEM

During normal driving and braking operations, ABS acts like a conventional braking system. Each wheel sensor constantly sends an AC VOLTAGE signal to EBCM. This information is translated into rotation or wheel speed.

When EBCM determines wheels are about to lock-up, it activates electromagnetic valves, located inside valve block, to increase or decrease hydraulic pressure to each wheel. A slight pulsation should be felt through brake pedal.

BRAKE, ANTI-LOCK and TRACTION (if equipped) warning lights should come on when key is turned and vehicle started. If any light stays on longer than approximately 5 seconds after vehicle is started, system malfunction is indicated. See DIAGNOSIS & TESTING.

BLEEDING BRAKE SYSTEM

WARNING: Under normal operating conditions, ABS system is under high pressure. Before servicing any component or opening fluid reservoir, system pressure must be discharged. With ignition off, pump brake pedal a minimum of 20-25 times using full pedal strokes. When a definite increase in pedal effort is felt, pump pedal twice more.

MANUAL BLEEDING

Master Cylinder – 1) With engine off, pump brake pedal several times to deplete vacuum reserve in brake booster. Remove brake fluid reservoir cap, and add fluid as necessary to fill to full mark. Replace reservoir cap.

2) Loosen forward (secondary) brake line fitting at master cylinder. Allow fluid to flow from fitting port while maintaining correct fluid level. Retighten forward brake line fitting. Slowly depress brake pedal once, and hold. Loosen forward fitting, and allow air to bleed out. Tighten fitting. Slowly release brake pedal.

3) Wait 15 seconds. Repeat step **2)** as necessary until all air is purged. Tighten brake line fitting to specification. See TORQUE SPECIFICATIONS. Follow same procedure at master cylinder rearward (primary) brake line fitting.

Brake Lines – 1) Raise and support vehicle. Remove bleeder cap from right rear wheel bleeder valve. Attach hose to bleeder valve. Submerge other end of hose in container of clean brake fluid.

2) Using Brake Bleeder Wrench (J-21472) or (J-28434), loosen bleeder valve while an assistant presses brake pedal down through its full travel. Hold brake pedal in depressed position, and close bleeder valve.

NOTE: Rapid pumping of brake pedal causes master cylinder secondary piston to move into a position that makes bleeding system difficult.

3) Slowly release brake pedal. Wait 15 seconds, and then repeat operation until no air bubbles emerge from submerged end of hose. Repeat procedure in sequence on left rear, right front and left front wheels. Tighten bleeder valves to specification. See TORQUE SPECIFICATIONS.

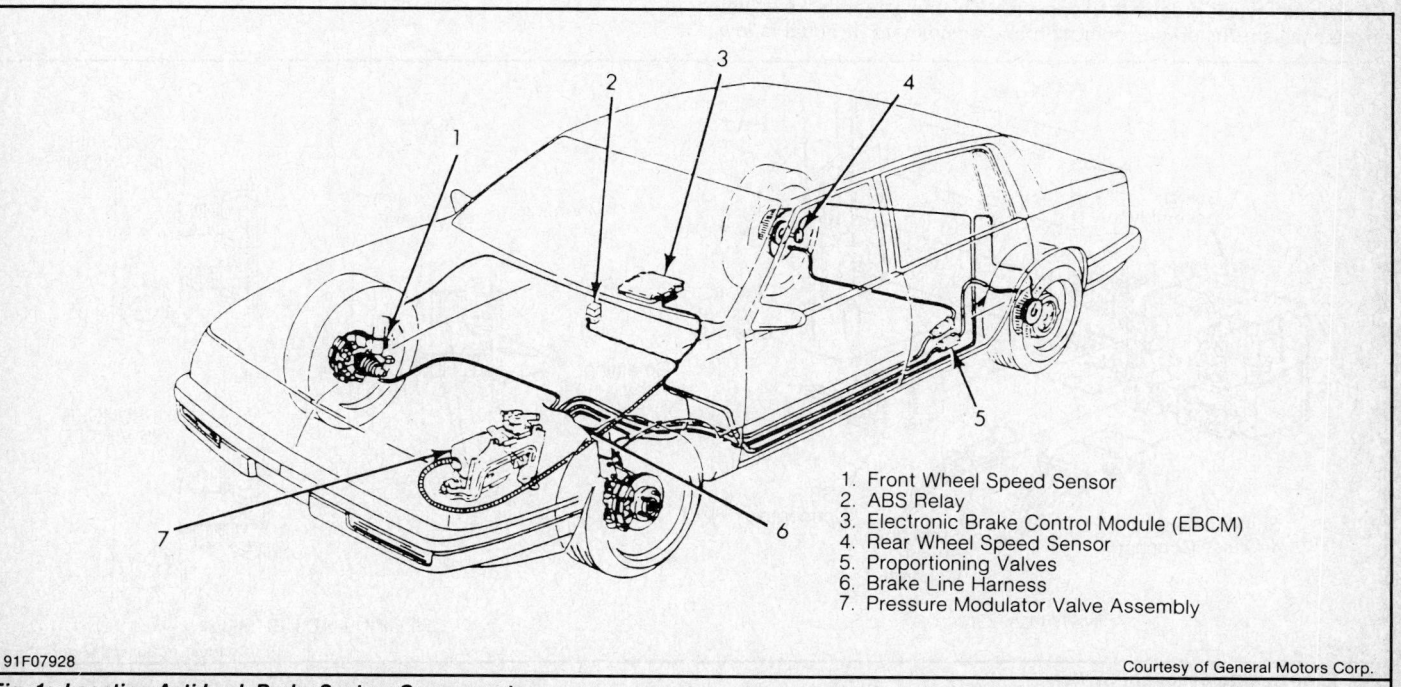

1. Front Wheel Speed Sensor
2. ABS Relay
3. Electronic Brake Control Module (EBCM)
4. Rear Wheel Speed Sensor
5. Proportioning Valves
6. Brake Line Harness
7. Pressure Modulator Valve Assembly

91F07928

Courtesy of General Motors Corp.

Fig. 1: Locating Anti-Lock Brake System Components

PRESSURE BLEEDING

NOTE: Pressure bleeding equipment must be diaphragm type with a rubber diaphragm between air supply and brake fluid to prevent contamination of brake system.

1) Clean reservoir cap area. Fill master cylinder to full mark. Install Brake Bleeder Adapter (J-35589) on master cylinder. Attach Pressure Bleeder (J-29532).

2) Raise and support vehicle. Remove dust cap from right rear wheel bleeder valve. Attach hose to right rear bleeder valve. Submerge other end of hose in container of clean brake fluid.

3) Open valve on bleeder tank to pressurize system. Maintain system pressure of 20-25 psi (1.4-1.8 kg/cm²). Using appropriate Brake Bleeder Wrench (J-21472 or J-28434), open bleeder valve until no air bubbles emerge from submerged end of hose.

4) Repeat procedure in sequence on left rear, right front and left front wheels. When complete, close pressure bleeder tank valve, remove adapter and adjust fluid level to full mark. Tighten bleeder valves to specification. See TORQUE SPECIFICATIONS.

ADJUSTMENTS

MASTER CYLINDER PUSH ROD

1) With master cylinder removed from brake booster, start engine, and let idle. Place Push Rod Height Gauge (J-37839) over master cylinder push rod, and check for minimum push rod length.

2) Reverse gauge, and check for maximum push rod length. If push rod does not meet maximum or minimum specification, replace or adjust push rod as necessary. Reinstall master cylinder. Tighten nuts to specification. See TORQUE SPECIFICATIONS.

BRAKE PEDAL TRAVEL

1) With engine off, pump brake pedal several times to deplete vacuum reserve in brake booster. Install Brake Pedal Effort Gauge (J-28662) on brake pedal. Hook end of tape measure over top edge of brake pedal, and measure distance to rim of steering wheel.

2) Apply service brake with 100 lbs. (45 kg.) of force, and remeasure distance to rim of steering wheel. Difference between 2 measurements is actual pedal travel. See BRAKE PEDAL TRAVEL SPECIFICATIONS table.

3) If pedal travel is greater than specification, check rear brake adjuster mechanism for proper operation and adjustment. If pedal is low,

soft or spongy, bleed brake system. Also check for hydraulic leak, parking brake adjustment, master cylinder push rod length and rear brake shoe wear.

BRAKE PEDAL TRAVEL SPECIFICATIONS

Application	In. (mm)
Bonneville, Eighty-Eight & LeSabre	2.24 (57.0)
DeVille, Fleetwood, Ninety-Eight, Park Avenue & Touring Sedan	2.00 (50.8)

STOPLIGHT SWITCH

CAUTION: When installing stoplight switch assembly into bracket, DO NOT apply more than 25 ft. lbs. (33.9 N.m) of side load pressure on electrical connector terminals.

1) Install electrical connectors and cruise vacuum line on stoplight switch. *See Fig. 2.* Fully depress brake pedal. Insert switch assembly into mounting bracket. Press switch assembly inward until no clicks are heard.

2) Pull brake pedal rearward until no clicks are heard. Release pedal, and then pull rearward again to ensure switch assembly is fully seated.

3) When properly installed, only notch in switch plunger should be visible. *See Fig. 2.* If not properly installed, repeat steps **1)** and **2)**.

PARKING BRAKE

1) Raise and support vehicle. Adjust rear brakes. See DISC & DRUM article. Apply parking brake 10 clicks. Release parking brake. Repeat 5 times. Ensure parking brake is fully released by turning ignition switch to ON position and observing BRAKE warning light. Warning light should be off.

2) If BRAKE warning light is on and parking brake appears to be released, operate brake release lever while pulling downward on front parking brake cable to remove slack from assembly. Apply parking brake 4 clicks.

3) Raise and support vehicle. Remove access hole plug from rear brake backing plate. Adjust cable until a 1/8" (3.18 mm) drill bit will fit space between parking brake shoe and parking brake lever. Release parking brake, and ensure wheel rotates freely. Replace access hole plug, and lower vehicle.

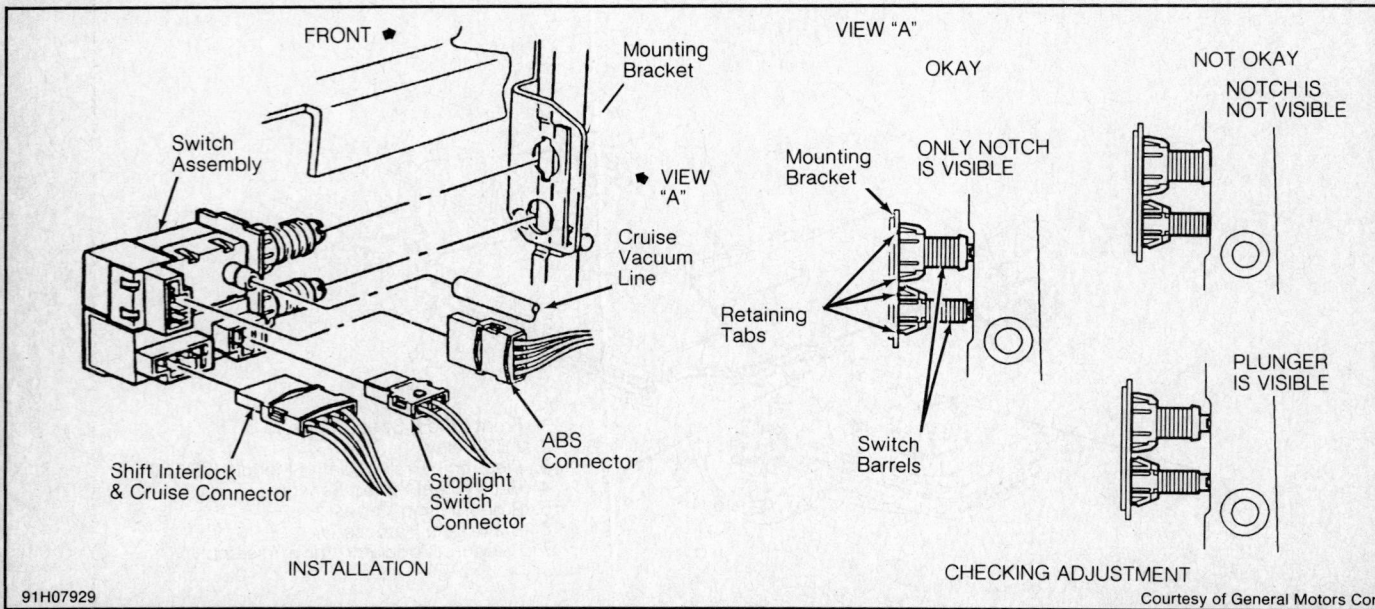

91H07929

Courtesy of General Motors Corp.

Fig. 2: Installing Stoplight Switch

TROUBLE SHOOTING

ANTI-LOCK WARNING LIGHT

ANTI-LOCK and TRACTION (if equipped) warning lights illuminate when vehicle is first started and when a malfunction in ABS or TCS system is detected. If either light remains on longer than approximately 5 seconds after vehicle is started or if they illuminate while driving, indicated system will be disabled, but normal braking will continue. See DIAGNOSIS & TESTING. If BRAKE warning light comes on, check parking brake and brake fluid level. Brake failure is indicated. See appropriate DISC & DRUM article.

DIAGNOSIS & TESTING

DIAGNOSTIC PROCEDURE

ABS and TCS (if equipped) malfunction diagnosis involves 3 basic steps which must be followed in order to isolate fault, accurately determine its cause and repair condition in least amount of time. Diagnostic procedure consists of following steps:

- **Pre-Diagnosis Inspection** – Perform a visual check of specific system components which could create an anti-lock system malfunction. Give special attention to electrical connectors, fluid level/leakage and system fuses.
- **ABS Functional Check** – Check warning light behavior, and check for ABS codes.
- **Symptom Diagnosis Charts** – SYMPTOM DIAGNOSIS CHARTS A-S and TROUBLE CODE INDEX are used after ABS FUNCTIONAL CHECK has indicated specific charts and/or codes needed to locate component failure.

NOTE: All diagnostic charts are located at end of article.

INTERMITTENTS

There are 2 types of codes set. Current codes are existing failures, while history codes indicate an intermittent failure. Diagnostic procedures can be helpful in solving intermittent problems in anti-lock brake system electrical components, but fault must be present during testing to locate problem correctly using charts.

Most intermittent problems are caused by faulty electrical connections or wiring. When an intermittent failure is encountered, visually inspect suspect circuits for:

- Poor mating of connector halves or terminals not fully seated in connector body (backed out).
- Improperly formed or damaged terminals. All connector terminals in a problem circuit should be carefully reformed to increase contact tension.
- Poor terminal-to-wire connection. Requires removing terminal and wire from connector body to inspect.

If visual inspection does not help locate intermittent problem, ABS self-diagnostic system can locate suspect circuit. Before using codes to diagnose intermittent failure:

- Display, and then clear, ABS trouble codes in Electronic Brake Computer Module (EBCM).
- Test drive vehicle, attempting to duplicate conditions causing problem or complaint. Stop vehicle, and record any codes set.

Conditions which could cause intermittent operation of ANTI-LOCK light include:

- Low or intermittent voltage at EBCM.
- Low brake fluid or low fluid pressure.
- Any condition causing interruption of power to EBCM or hydraulic pump motor. Circuits include main relay, pump motor relay, fuses and related wiring.

RETRIEVING & CLEARING CODES

Connect Tech 1 Scan Tool to Assembly Line Diagnostic Link (ALDL) connector, located below left side of instrument panel, right of steering column on all models except DeVille and Fleetwood. On DeVille and Fleetwood, ALDL connector is located in center of instrument panel, below ashtray. Follow Scan Tool manufacturer's instructions to retrieve and/or clear codes.

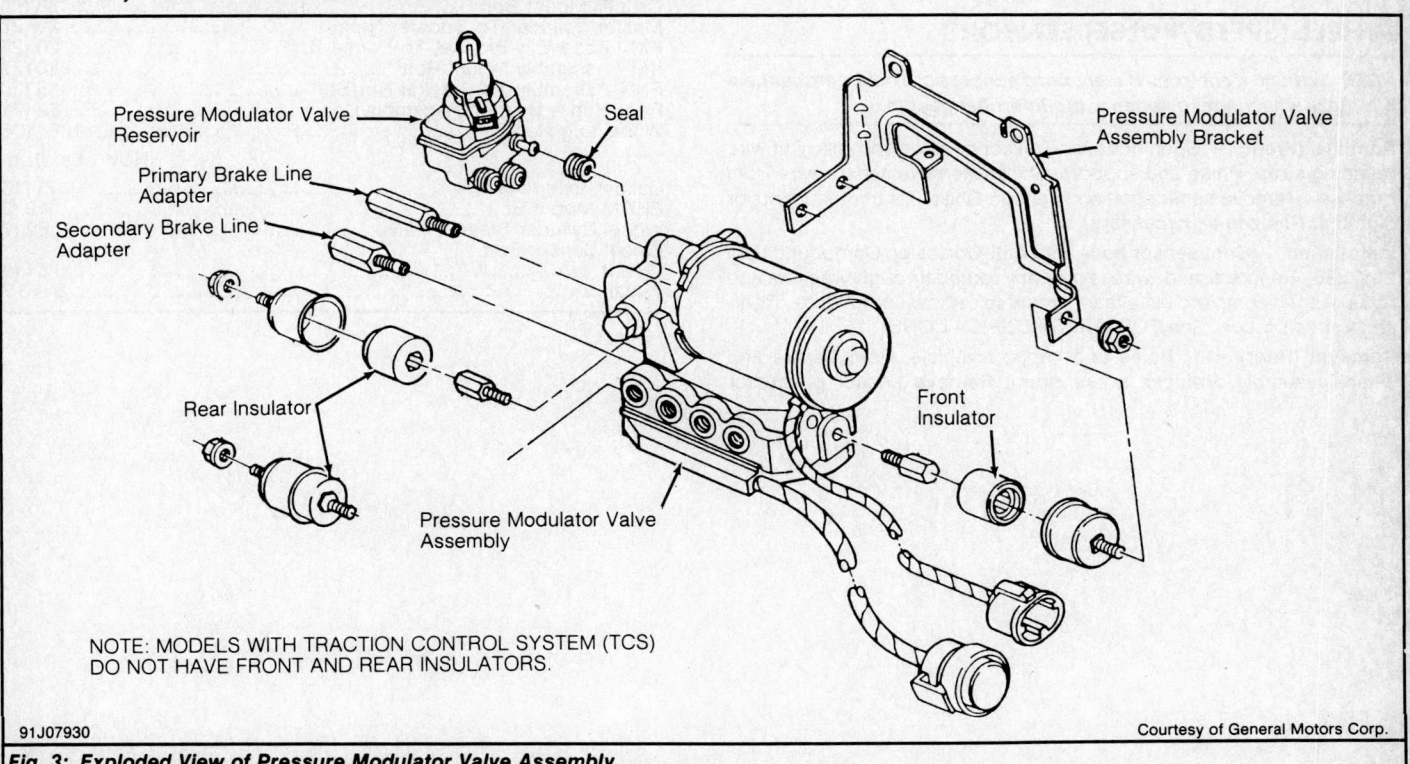

Pressure Modulator Valve Reservoir

Seal

Pressure Modulator Valve Assembly Bracket

Primary Brake Line Adapter

Secondary Brake Line Adapter

Rear Insulator

Front Insulator

Pressure Modulator Valve Assembly

NOTE: MODELS WITH TRACTION CONTROL SYSTEM (TCS) DO NOT HAVE FRONT AND REAR INSULATORS.

91J07930

Courtesy of General Motors Corp.

Fig. 3: Exploded View of Pressure Modulator Valve Assembly

REMOVAL & INSTALLATION

ELECTRONIC BRAKE CONTROL MODULE (EBCM)

Removal – **1)** Turn ignition switch to OFF position. On Bonneville and Eight-Eight models, remove right side underdash panel. On all other models, remove right and left side underdash panels and floor air distribution duct.

2) On Bonneville and Eight-Eight models, slide EBCM from bracket. On all other models, remove EBCM bolt, and slide EBCM toward accelerator pedal. On all models, disconnect electrical connector, and remove EBCM from vehicle.

Installation – To install, reverse removal procedure. Tighten EBCM mount bolt (if equipped) to specification. See TORQUE SPECIFICATIONS.

PRESSURE MODULATOR VALVE (PMV) ASSEMBLY

NOTE: Pump motor is an integral part of PMV assembly, and is not serviceable separately.

Removal – **1)** Disconnect negative battery cable. Remove air cleaner assembly. Disconnect electrical connectors from fluid level switch, pump motor and valve block.

2) Clamp off reservoir to PMV hose. Remove hose, and install a 5/8" (15.5 mm) plug to prevent brake fluid from leaking out of reservoir. Mark all hoses and brake lines for reassembly reference. Disconnect primary, secondary and 4 wheel brake lines at PMV assembly. *See Fig. 3.*

3) Raise and support vehicle. Remove lower PMV assembly mount bolt. Lower vehicle. Remove 2 upper PMV assembly bracket bolts. Remove PMV and bracket assembly. If replacing PMV assembly, transfer necessary parts to new unit.

Installation – To install, reverse removal procedure. Tighten bolts to specification. See TORQUE SPECIFICATIONS. Fill reservoir with fluid, and bleed system. See BLEEDING BRAKE SYSTEM.

WHEEL (SPEED/PULSE) SENSORS

NOTE: Left and right front wheel speed sensors are not interchangeable. Rear wheel speed sensors are interchangeable.

Removal (Front) – Open hood, and disconnect sensor wire. Cut wire retaining strap. Raise and support vehicle. Remove sensor wire from brackets. Remove sensor bolt and sensor. Check for contaminants or damage. Replace as necessary.

Installation – Coat sensor body with Anti-Corrosion Compound (GM 1052856). Ensure sensor wire is properly routed through brackets and retainers. To complete installation, reverse removal procedure. Tighten to specification. See TORQUE SPECIFICATIONS.

Removal (Rear) – **1)** Raise and support vehicle. Remove tire and wheel assembly. Remove brake drum. Remove sensor connector from sensor. Remove bolts from hub and bearing assembly. Use wire to support brake assembly.

2) Remove hub, bearing and sensor assembly. Clean area around sensor housing mount area. DO NOT allow dirt or contaminants to fall into sensor housing. Remove sensor from hub and bearing assembly. Check for contaminants or damage. Replace as necessary.

Installation – To install, reverse removal procedure. Tighten bolts to specification. See TORQUE SPECIFICATIONS.

NOTE: DO NOT remove grease from around toothed sensor ring. It does not effect sensor operation. DO NOT attempt to lubricate bearing.

ANTI-LOCK DIODE

Removal & Installation – **1)** Turn ignition switch to OFF position. On Bonneville and Eight-Eight models, remove right side underdash panel. On all other models, remove right and left side underdash panels and floor air distribution duct.

2) On all models, ABS anti-lock diode is taped to EBCM wire harness, near EBCM. Cut or remove tape as necessary. To install, reverse removal procedure.

LOAD-SENSING PROPORTIONING VALVES

Removal & Installation – Left and right proportioning valves are located on either side of fuel filter, at rear of vehicle. To remove, disconnect brake lines from proportioning valve, and remove proportioning valve from vehicle. To install, reverse removal procedure.

TORQUE SPECIFICATIONS

TORQUE SPECIFICATIONS

Application	Ft. Lbs. (N.m)
Brake Line-To-	
Master Cylinder	11 (15)
PMV Assembly	11 (15)
Proportioning Valve	11 (15)
Caliper Mount Bolt	38 (52)
Master Cylinder-To-Booster Nuts	20 (27)
PMV Assembly Bracket-To-Frame Bolt	20 (27)
PMV Assembly Mount Bolt	20 (27)
PMV Assembly-To-Bracket Nut/Bolt	15 (20)
Rear Hub & Bearing Assembly Bolt	52 (71)
Wheel Lug Nuts	100 (136)

	INCH Lbs. (N.m)
Caliper Bleeder Valve	115 (13)
EBCM Mount Bolt	19 (2)
Wheel Cylinder Bleeder Valve	62 (7)
Wheel Sensor Bolt	
Front	84 (9)
Rear	33 (3.7)

WIRING DIAGRAMS

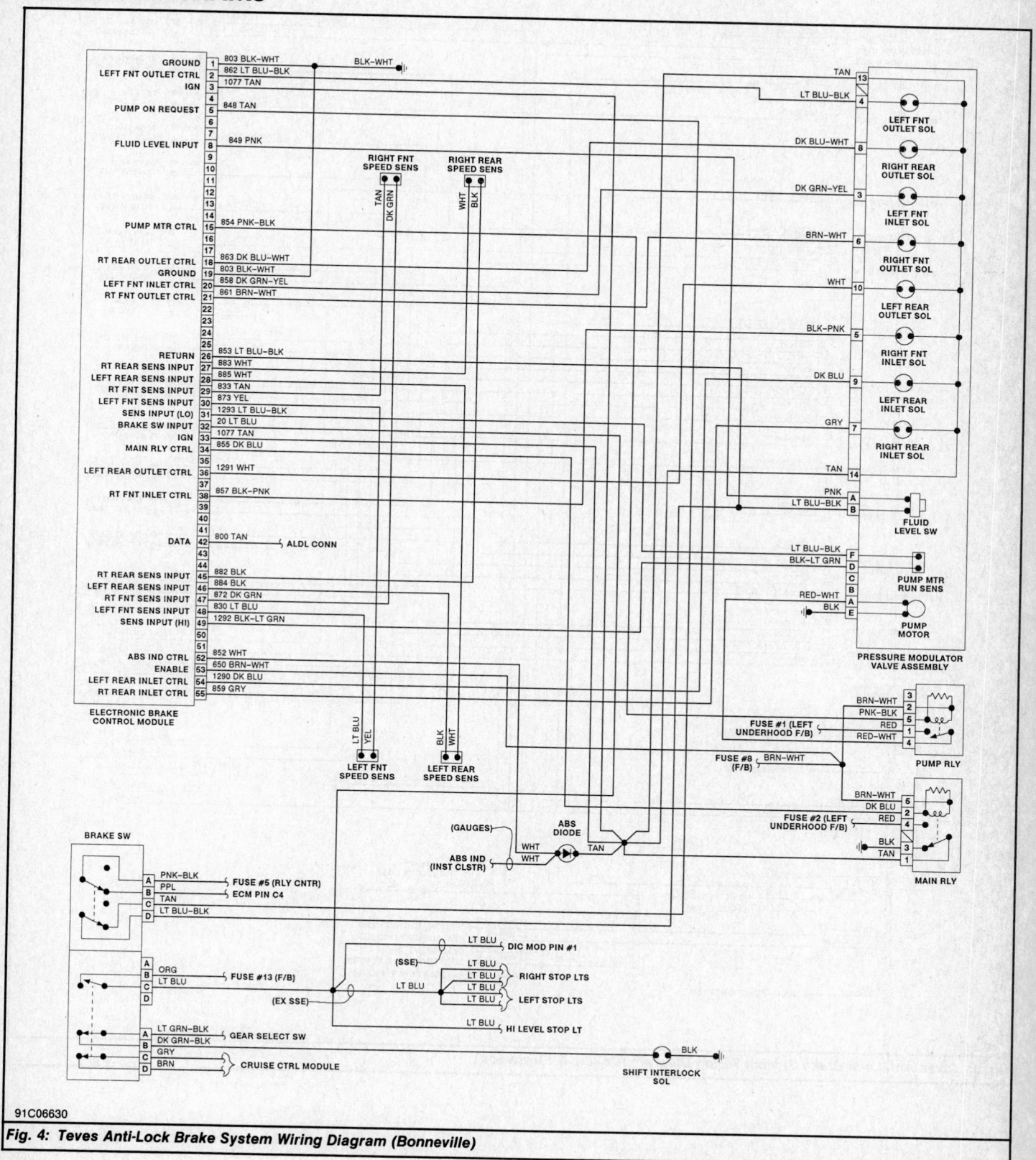

Fig. 4: Teves Anti-Lock Brake System Wiring Diagram (Bonneville)

91C06630

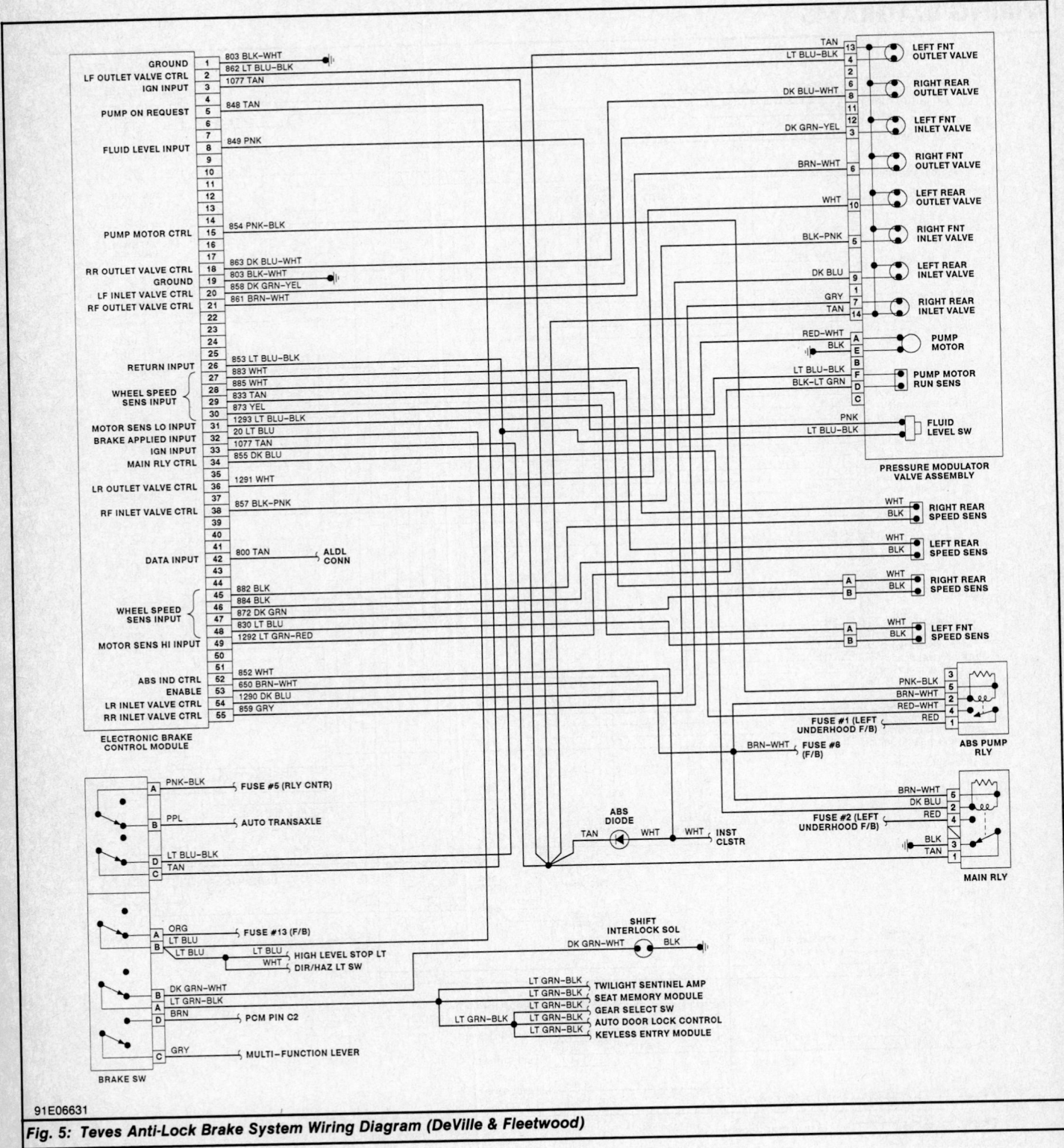

Fig. 5: *Teves Anti-Lock Brake System Wiring Diagram (DeVille & Fleetwood)*

91E06631

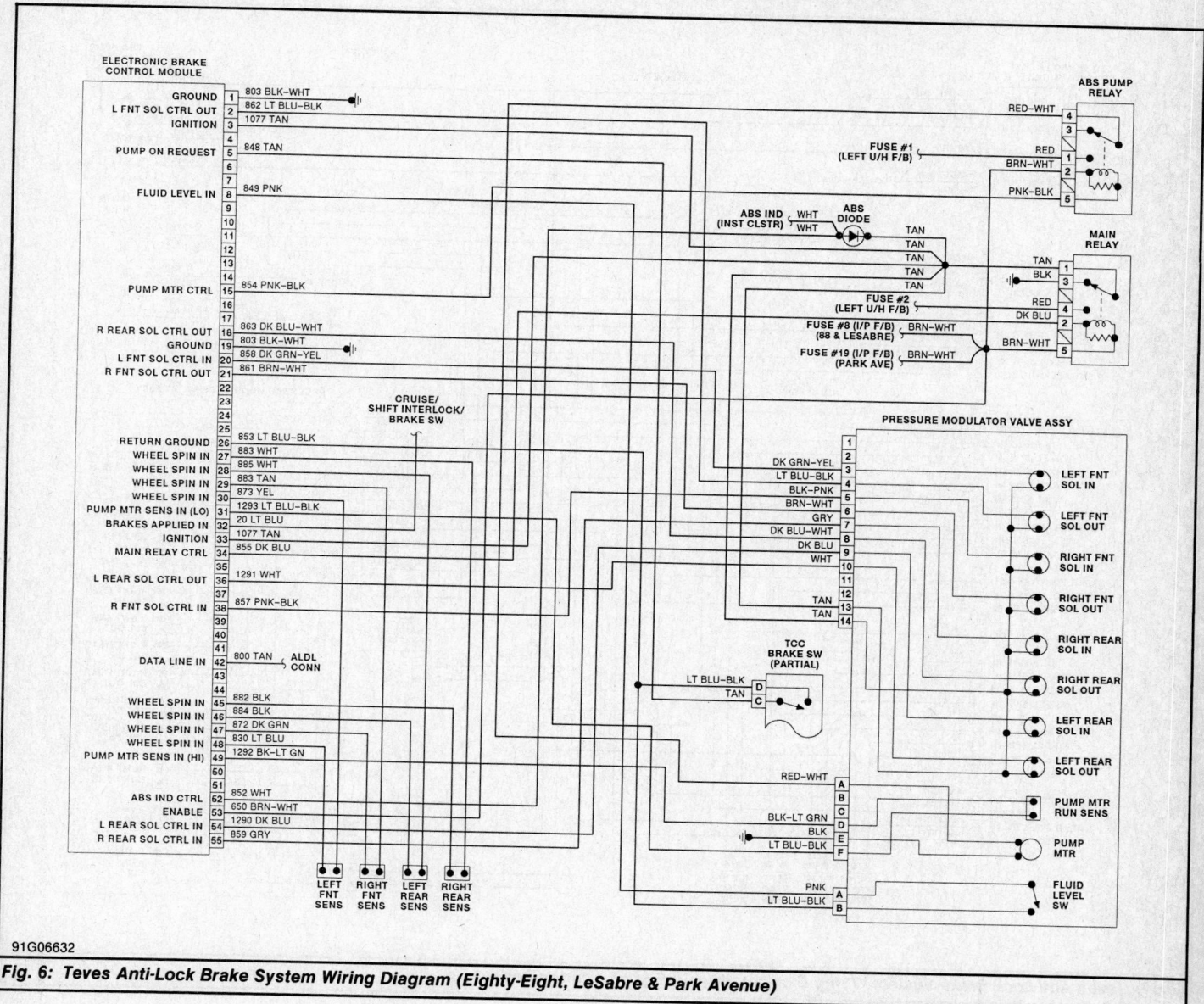

Fig. 6: Teves Anti-Lock Brake System Wiring Diagram (Eighty-Eight, LeSabre & Park Avenue)

91G06632

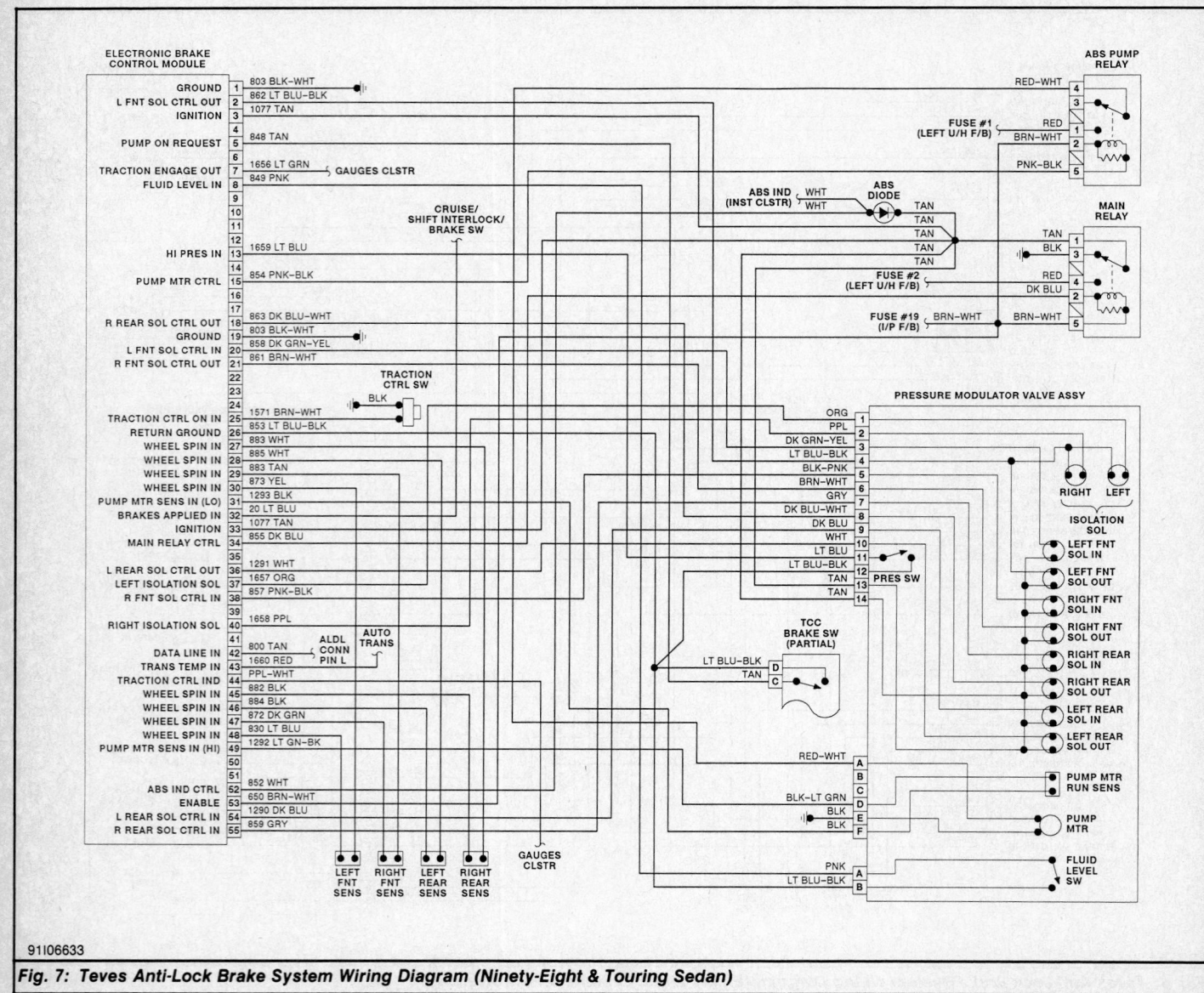

91I06633

Fig. 7: Teves Anti-Lock Brake System Wiring Diagram (Ninety-Eight & Touring Sedan)

DIAGNOSTIC CHARTS

ABS FUNCTIONAL CHECK

Bonneville, Eighty-Eight, LeSabre, Ninety-Eight, Park Avenue & Touring Sedan – After a visual inspection, next step in diagnosis of any antilock brake system condition is to perform ABS FUNCTIONAL CHECK. Procedures cover warning lamp behavior and setting ABS codes, and lead to third step in diagnosis of ABS condition. Always perform ABS FUNCTIONAL CHECK before beginning chart procedure.

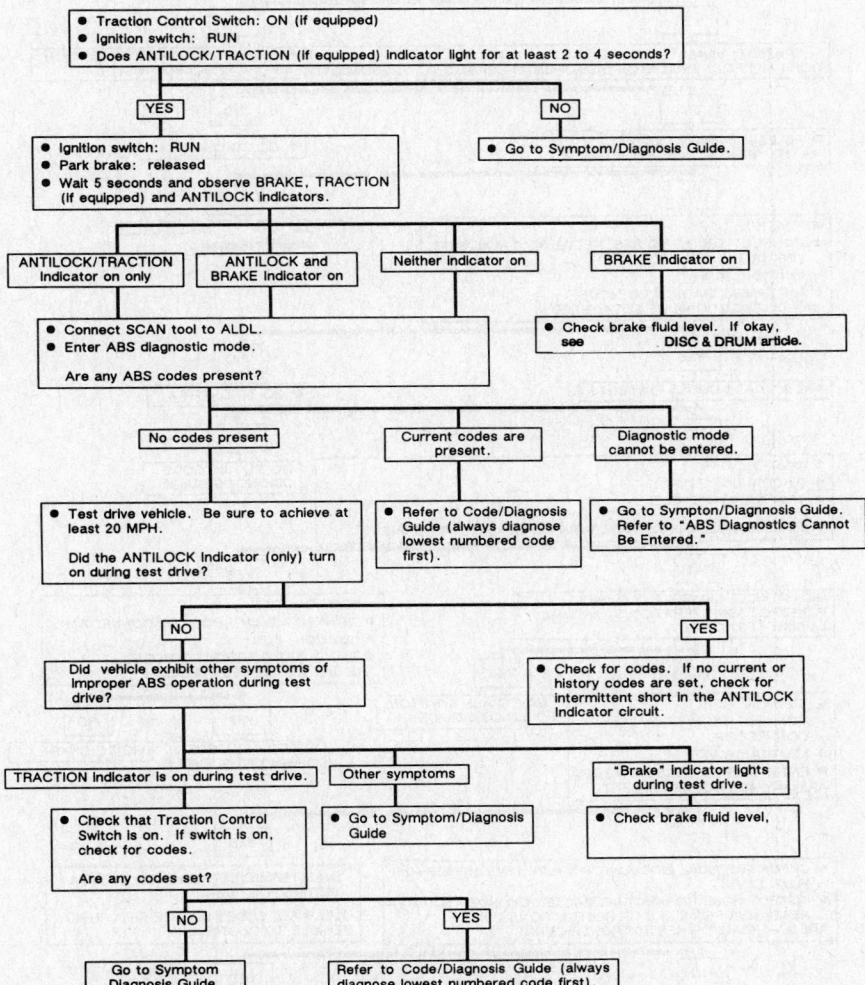

SYMPTOM DIAGNOSIS CHARTS

SYMPTOM DIAGNOSIS CHARTS A-S and TROUBLE CODE INDEX are used after ABS FUNCTIONAL CHECK has indicated specific charts and/or codes to be used in locating component failure. Always perform ABS FUNCTIONAL CHECK before beginning chart procedures.

After repairs are completed, clear codes with Tech 1 Scan Tool, and repeat ABS FUNCTIONAL TEST.

NOTE: No SYMPTOM DIAGNOSIS CHARTS are available from manufacturer for LeSabre and Park Avenue models.

91B07931

ABS FUNCTIONAL CHECK

DeVille & Fleetwood – After a visual inspection, next step in diagnosis of any anti-lock brake system condition is to perform ABS FUNCTIONAL CHECK. Procedures cover warning lamp behavior and setting ABS codes, and lead to third step in diagnosis of ABS condition. Always perform ABS FUNCTIONAL CHECK before beginning chart procedures.

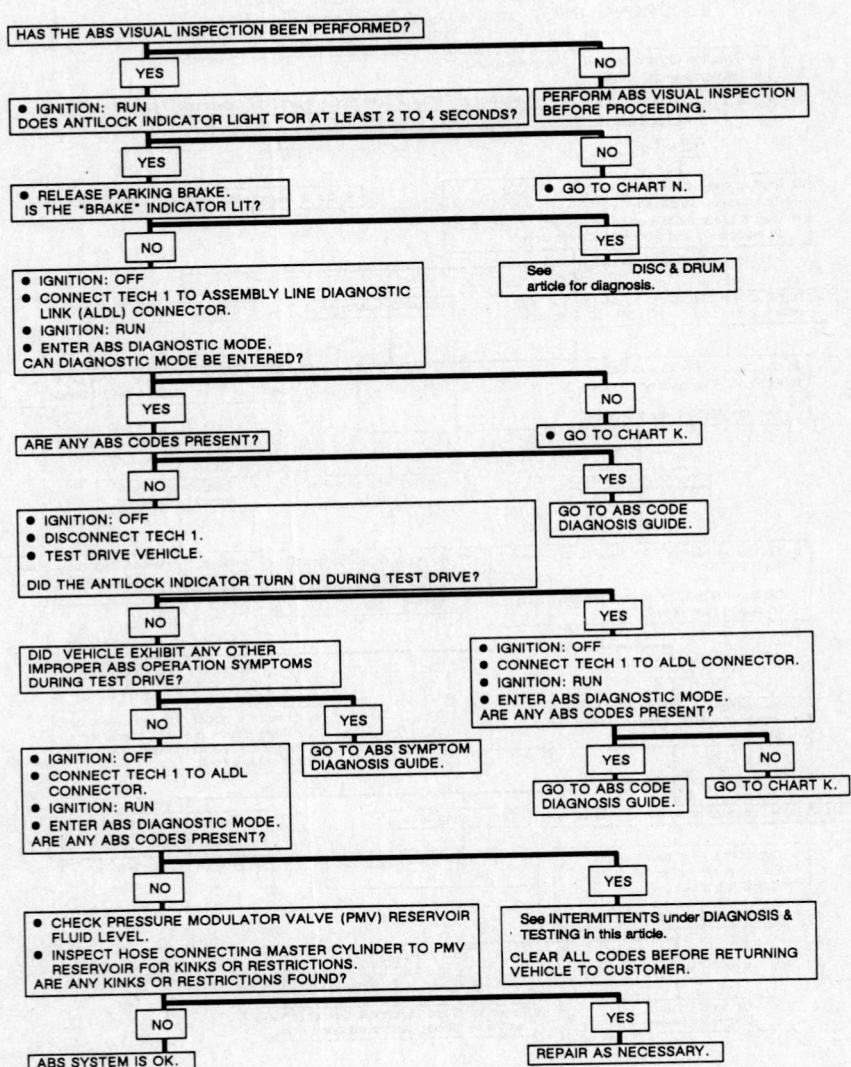

SYMPTOM DIAGNOSIS CHARTS

SYMPTOM DIAGNOSIS CHARTS A-S and TROUBLE CODE INDEX are used after ABS FUNCTIONAL CHECK has indicated specific charts and/or codes to be used in locating component failure. Always perform ABS FUNCTIONAL CHECK before beginning chart procedures.

After repairs are completed, clear codes with Tech 1 Scan Tool, and repeat ABS FUNCTIONAL TEST.

Courtesy of General Motors Corp.

91D07932

TROUBLE CODE INDEX
Bonneville, Eighty-Eight, LeSabre, Ninety-Eight, Park Avenue & Touring Sedan

CODE	DESCRIPTION	CAUSE	CHART
21	RF speed sensor circuit open	B	B
22	RF speed sensor signal erratic	C	D
23	RF wheel speed is 0 mph	D	B
25	LF speed sensor circuit open	B	B
26	LF speed sensor signal erratic	C	D
27	LF wheel speed is 0 mph	D	B
31	RR speed sensor circuit open	B	C
32	RR speed sensor signal is erratic	C	D
33	RR wheel speed is 0 mph	D	C
35	LR speed sensor circuit open	B	C
36	LR speed sensor signal erratic	C	D
37	LR wheel speed is 0 mph	D	C
41	RF inlet valve circuit	A	A
42	RF outlet valve circuit	A	A
43	RF speed sensor noisy	I	D
44	LF isolation valve circuit	A	O

CODE	DESCRIPTION	CAUSE	CHART
45	LF inlet valve circuit	A	A
46	LF outlet valve circuit	A	A
47	LF speed sensor noisy	I	D
48	RF isolation valve circuit malfunction	A	O
51	RR inlet valve circuit	A	A
52	RR outlet valve circuit	A	A
53	RR speed sensor noisy	I	D
55	LR inlet valve circuit	A	A
56	LR outlet valve circuit	A	A
57	LR speed sensor noisy	I	D
61	Pump motor test fault	G	F
62	Pump motor fault in ABS stop	H	I
71	EBCM problem	J	J
72	VCC/antilock brake switch sircuit	F	G
73	Fluid level switch circuit	E	H
74	Pressure switch circuit malfunction	K	P

CAUSE "A" • Circuit open or shorted to ground.
CAUSE "B" • Wheel speed sensor circuit open or shorted.
CAUSE "C" • Wheel speed sensor circuit open or shorted intermittently.
CAUSE "D" • Wheel speed sensor signal missing.
CAUSE "E" • Fluid level switch circuit.
CAUSE "F" • VCC/antilock brake switch circuit open.
CAUSE "G" • Malfunctioning pump motor, electrical or mechanical failure.
CAUSE "H" • Pump pressure is too low, defective pump motor or pump motor run sensor circuit, or air in hydraulic system.
CAUSE "I" • Electrical noise or excessive vibration detected in wheel speed sensor circuit above 40 km/h (25 mph).
CAUSE "J" • Internal electronic brake control module (EBCM) fault.

SYMPTOM DIAGNOSIS GUIDE

SYMPTOM	FOR DIAGNOSIS GO TO CHART
ABS diagnosis cannot be entered.	Chart K
ANTILOCK indicator is on all the time and no codes are set.	Chart K
ANTILOCK indicator does not light.	Chart N
Poor vehicle tracking during ABS stop (ABS engaged).	Chart L
Brake pedal rises or drops excessively during an ABS stop (ABS engaged).	Chart G
Pressure modulator valve (PMV) assembly pump motor runs continuously.	Chart M
Traction indicator does not light during bulb test or when system is turned off.	Chart Q
Traction indicator is on all the time and no codes are set.	Chart R
Traction control engaged message does not operate.	Chart S

91F07933 91H07934

TROUBLE CODE INDEX
DeVille & Fleetwood

CODE	DESCRIPTION	CHART
21	RF speed sensor circuit open	B
22	RF speed sensor signal erratic	D
23	RF wheel speed is 0 mph	D
25	LF speed sensor circuit open	B
26	LF speed sensor signal erratic	D
27	LF wheel speed is 0 mph	D
31	RR speed sensor circuit open	C
32	RR speed sensor signal is erratic	D
33	RR wheel speed is 0 mph	D
35	LR speed sensor circuit open	C
36	LR speed sensor signal erratic	D
37	LR wheel speed is 0 mph	D
41	RF inlet valve circuit	E
42	RF outlet valve circuit	E
43	RF speed sensor noisy	D

CODE	DESCRIPTION	CHART
45	LF inlet valve circuit	A
46	LF outlet valve circuit	E
47	LF speed sensor noisy	D
51	RR inlet valve circuit	E
52	RR outlet valve circuit	E
53	RR speed sensor noisy	D
55	LR inlet valve circuit	E
56	LR outlet valve circuit	E
57	LR speed sensor noisy	D
61	Pump motor test fault	F
62	Pump motor fault in ABS stop	I
71	EBCM problem	J
72	VCC/antilock brake switch circuit.	G
73	Fluid level switch circuit	H

SYMPTOM DIAGNOSIS GUIDE

SYMPTOM	FOR DIAGNOSIS GO TO CHART
ABS diagnosis cannot be entered.	Chart K
ANTILOCK indicator is on all the time and no codes are set.	Chart K
ANTILOCK indicator does not light.	Chart N
Poor vehicle tracking during ABS stop (ABS engaged).	Chart L
Brake pedal rises or drops excessively during an ABS stop (ABS engaged).	Chart G
Pressure modulator valve (PMV) assembly pump motor runs continuously.	Chart M

91A07935 91C07936

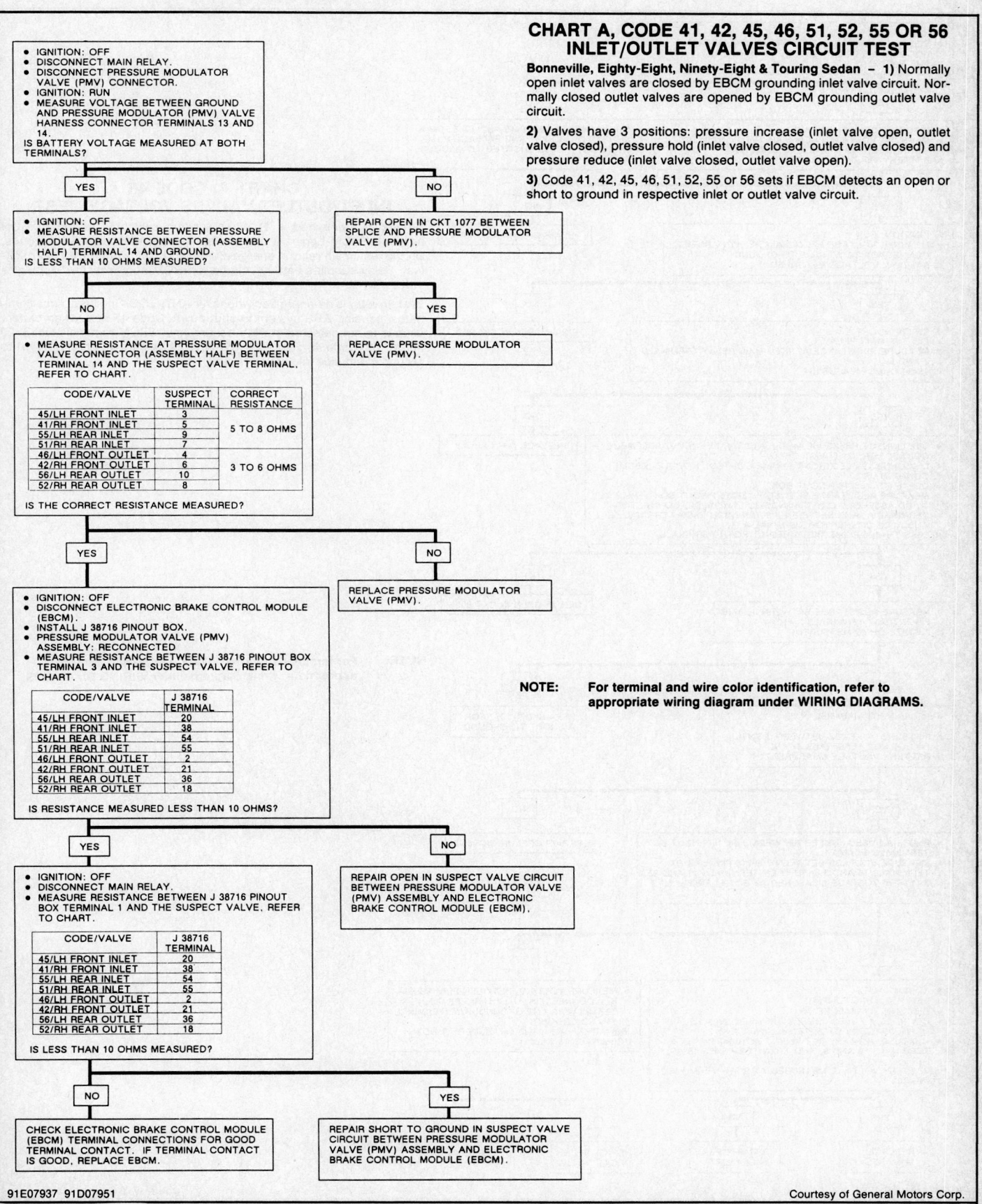

CHART A, CODE 41, 42, 45, 46, 51, 52, 55 OR 56 INLET/OUTLET VALVES CIRCUIT TEST

Bonneville, Eighty-Eight, Ninety-Eight & Touring Sedan – 1) Normally open inlet valves are closed by EBCM grounding inlet valve circuit. Normally closed outlet valves are opened by EBCM grounding outlet valve circuit.

2) Valves have 3 positions: pressure increase (inlet valve open, outlet valve closed), pressure hold (inlet valve closed, outlet valve closed) and pressure reduce (inlet valve closed, outlet valve open).

3) Code 41, 42, 45, 46, 51, 52, 55 or 56 sets if EBCM detects an open or short to ground in respective inlet or outlet valve circuit.

NOTE: For terminal and wire color identification, refer to appropriate wiring diagram under WIRING DIAGRAMS.

- IGNITION: OFF
- DISCONNECT MAIN RELAY.
- DISCONNECT PRESSURE MODULATOR VALVE (PMV) CONNECTOR.
- IGNITION: RUN
- MEASURE VOLTAGE BETWEEN GROUND AND PRESSURE MODULATOR (PMV) VALVE HARNESS CONNECTOR TERMINALS 13 AND 14.
IS BATTERY VOLTAGE MEASURED AT BOTH TERMINALS?

YES

NO → REPAIR OPEN IN CKT 1077 BETWEEN SPLICE AND PRESSURE MODULATOR VALVE (PMV).

- IGNITION: OFF
- MEASURE RESISTANCE BETWEEN PRESSURE MODULATOR VALVE CONNECTOR (ASSEMBLY HALF) TERMINAL 14 AND GROUND.
IS LESS THAN 10 OHMS MEASURED?

NO

YES → REPLACE PRESSURE MODULATOR VALVE (PMV).

- MEASURE RESISTANCE AT PRESSURE MODULATOR VALVE CONNECTOR (ASSEMBLY HALF) BETWEEN TERMINAL 14 AND THE SUSPECT VALVE TERMINAL. REFER TO CHART.

CODE/VALVE	SUSPECT TERMINAL	CORRECT RESISTANCE
45/LH FRONT INLET	3	
41/RH FRONT INLET	5	5 TO 8 OHMS
55/LH REAR INLET	9	
51/RH REAR INLET	7	
46/LH FRONT OUTLET	4	
42/RH FRONT OUTLET	6	3 TO 6 OHMS
56/LH REAR OUTLET	10	
52/RH REAR OUTLET	8	

IS THE CORRECT RESISTANCE MEASURED?

YES

NO → REPLACE PRESSURE MODULATOR VALVE (PMV).

- IGNITION: OFF
- DISCONNECT ELECTRONIC BRAKE CONTROL MODULE (EBCM).
- INSTALL J 38716 PINOUT BOX.
- PRESSURE MODULATOR VALVE (PMV) ASSEMBLY: RECONNECTED
- MEASURE RESISTANCE BETWEEN J 38716 PINOUT BOX TERMINAL 3 AND THE SUSPECT VALVE. REFER TO CHART.

CODE/VALVE	J 38716 TERMINAL
45/LH FRONT INLET	20
41/RH FRONT INLET	38
55/LH REAR INLET	54
51/RH REAR INLET	55
46/LH FRONT OUTLET	2
42/RH FRONT OUTLET	21
56/LH REAR OUTLET	36
52/RH REAR OUTLET	18

IS RESISTANCE MEASURED LESS THAN 10 OHMS?

YES

NO → REPAIR OPEN IN SUSPECT VALVE CIRCUIT BETWEEN PRESSURE MODULATOR VALVE (PMV) ASSEMBLY AND ELECTRONIC BRAKE CONTROL MODULE (EBCM).

- IGNITION: OFF
- DISCONNECT MAIN RELAY.
- MEASURE RESISTANCE BETWEEN J 38716 PINOUT BOX TERMINAL 1 AND THE SUSPECT VALVE. REFER TO CHART.

CODE/VALVE	J 38716 TERMINAL
45/LH FRONT INLET	20
41/RH FRONT INLET	38
55/LH REAR INLET	54
51/RH REAR INLET	55
46/LH FRONT OUTLET	2
42/RH FRONT OUTLET	21
56/LH REAR OUTLET	36
52/RH REAR OUTLET	18

IS LESS THAN 10 OHMS MEASURED?

NO → CHECK ELECTRONIC BRAKE CONTROL MODULE (EBCM) TERMINAL CONNECTIONS FOR GOOD TERMINAL CONTACT. IF TERMINAL CONTACT IS GOOD, REPLACE EBCM.

YES → REPAIR SHORT TO GROUND IN SUSPECT VALVE CIRCUIT BETWEEN PRESSURE MODULATOR VALVE (PMV) ASSEMBLY AND ELECTRONIC BRAKE CONTROL MODULE (EBCM).

91E07937 91D07951

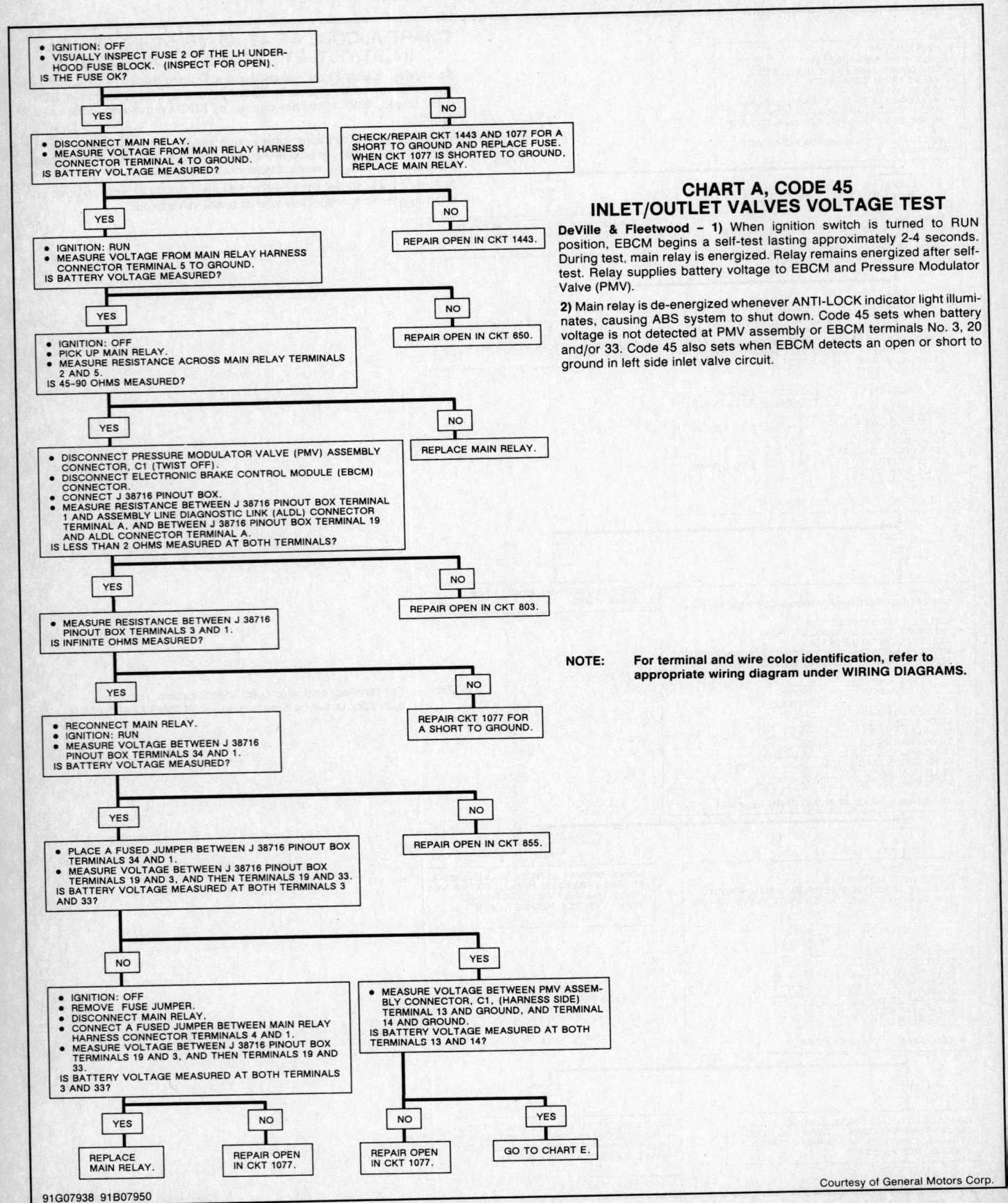

CHART A, CODE 45
INLET/OUTLET VALVES VOLTAGE TEST

DeVille & Fleetwood – 1) When ignition switch is turned to RUN position, EBCM begins a self-test lasting approximately 2-4 seconds. During test, main relay is energized. Relay remains energized after self-test. Relay supplies battery voltage to EBCM and Pressure Modulator Valve (PMV).

2) Main relay is de-energized whenever ANTI-LOCK indicator light illuminates, causing ABS system to shut down. Code 45 sets when battery voltage is not detected at PMV assembly or EBCM terminals No. 3, 20 and/or 33. Code 45 also sets when EBCM detects an open or short to ground in left side inlet valve circuit.

NOTE: For terminal and wire color identification, refer to appropriate wiring diagram under WIRING DIAGRAMS.

Courtesy of General Motors Corp.

91G07938 91B07950

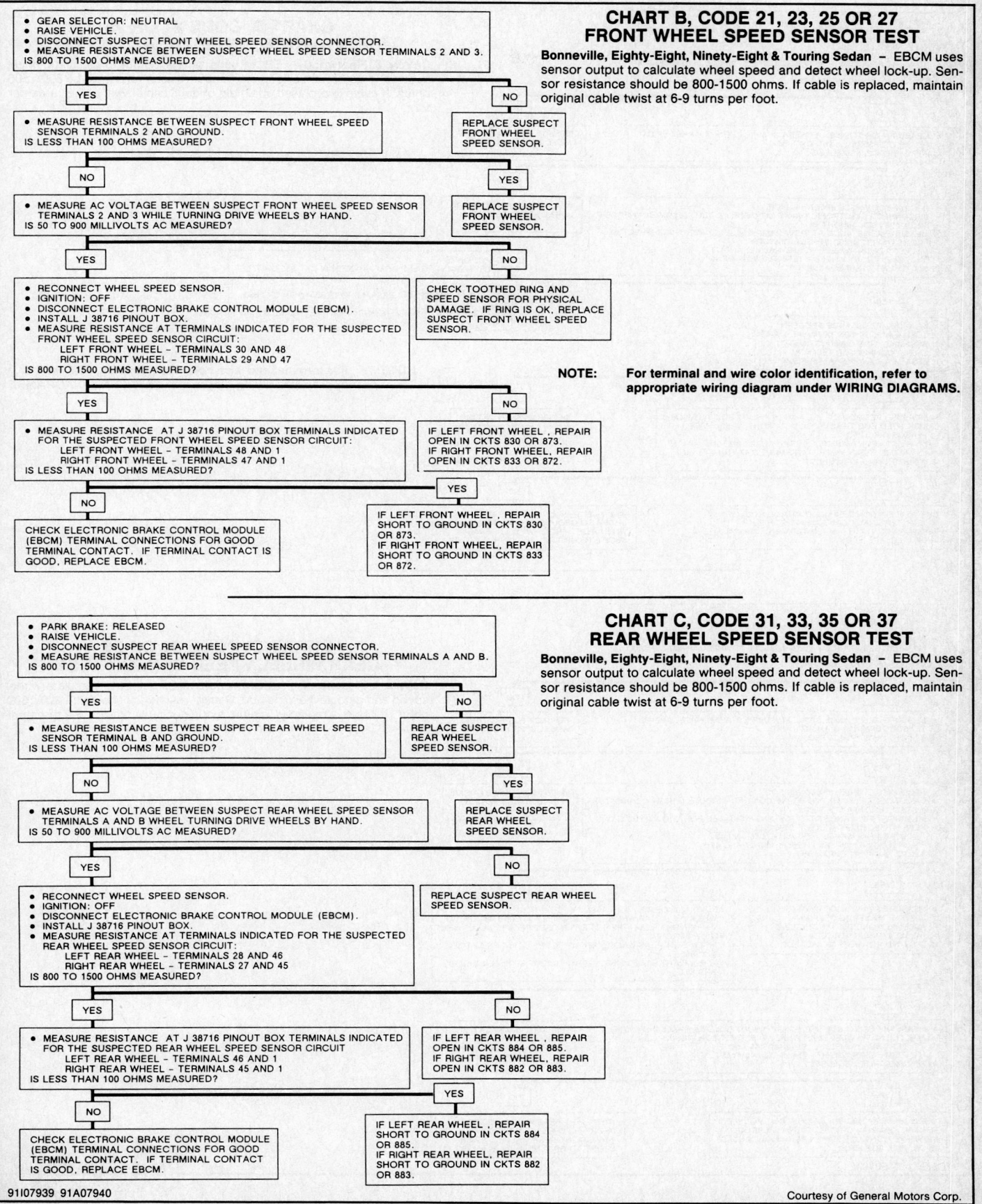

CHART B, CODE 21, 23, 25 OR 27
FRONT WHEEL SPEED SENSOR TEST

Bonneville, Eighty-Eight, Ninety-Eight & Touring Sedan – EBCM uses sensor output to calculate wheel speed and detect wheel lock-up. Sensor resistance should be 800-1500 ohms. If cable is replaced, maintain original cable twist at 6-9 turns per foot.

- GEAR SELECTOR: NEUTRAL
- RAISE VEHICLE.
- DISCONNECT SUSPECT FRONT WHEEL SPEED SENSOR CONNECTOR.
- MEASURE RESISTANCE BETWEEN SUSPECT WHEEL SPEED SENSOR TERMINALS 2 AND 3.
IS 800 TO 1500 OHMS MEASURED?

YES / **NO**

REPLACE SUSPECT FRONT WHEEL SPEED SENSOR.

- MEASURE RESISTANCE BETWEEN SUSPECT FRONT WHEEL SPEED SENSOR TERMINALS 2 AND GROUND.
IS LESS THAN 100 OHMS MEASURED?

NO / **YES**

REPLACE SUSPECT FRONT WHEEL SPEED SENSOR.

- MEASURE AC VOLTAGE BETWEEN SUSPECT FRONT WHEEL SPEED SENSOR TERMINALS 2 AND 3 WHILE TURNING DRIVE WHEELS BY HAND.
IS 50 TO 900 MILLIVOLTS AC MEASURED?

YES / **NO**

CHECK TOOTHED RING AND SPEED SENSOR FOR PHYSICAL DAMAGE. IF RING IS OK, REPLACE SUSPECT FRONT WHEEL SPEED SENSOR.

- RECONNECT WHEEL SPEED SENSOR.
- IGNITION: OFF
- DISCONNECT ELECTRONIC BRAKE CONTROL MODULE (EBCM).
- INSTALL J 38716 PINOUT BOX.
- MEASURE RESISTANCE AT TERMINALS INDICATED FOR THE SUSPECTED FRONT WHEEL SPEED SENSOR CIRCUIT:
  LEFT FRONT WHEEL – TERMINALS 30 AND 48
  RIGHT FRONT WHEEL – TERMINALS 29 AND 47
IS 800 TO 1500 OHMS MEASURED?

NOTE: For terminal and wire color identification, refer to appropriate wiring diagram under **WIRING DIAGRAMS.**

YES / **NO**

IF LEFT FRONT WHEEL, REPAIR OPEN IN CKTS 830 OR 873.
IF RIGHT FRONT WHEEL, REPAIR OPEN IN CKTS 833 OR 872.

- MEASURE RESISTANCE AT J 38716 PINOUT BOX TERMINALS INDICATED FOR THE SUSPECTED FRONT WHEEL SPEED SENSOR CIRCUIT:
  LEFT FRONT WHEEL – TERMINALS 48 AND 1
  RIGHT FRONT WHEEL – TERMINALS 47 AND 1
IS LESS THAN 100 OHMS MEASURED?

NO / **YES**

IF LEFT FRONT WHEEL, REPAIR SHORT TO GROUND IN CKTS 830 OR 873.
IF RIGHT FRONT WHEEL, REPAIR SHORT TO GROUND IN CKTS 833 OR 872.

CHECK ELECTRONIC BRAKE CONTROL MODULE (EBCM) TERMINAL CONNECTIONS FOR GOOD TERMINAL CONTACT. IF TERMINAL CONTACT IS GOOD, REPLACE EBCM.

CHART C, CODE 31, 33, 35 OR 37
REAR WHEEL SPEED SENSOR TEST

Bonneville, Eighty-Eight, Ninety-Eight & Touring Sedan – EBCM uses sensor output to calculate wheel speed and detect wheel lock-up. Sensor resistance should be 800-1500 ohms. If cable is replaced, maintain original cable twist at 6-9 turns per foot.

- PARK BRAKE: RELEASED
- RAISE VEHICLE.
- DISCONNECT SUSPECT REAR WHEEL SPEED SENSOR CONNECTOR.
- MEASURE RESISTANCE BETWEEN SUSPECT WHEEL SPEED SENSOR TERMINALS A AND B.
IS 800 TO 1500 OHMS MEASURED?

YES / **NO**

REPLACE SUSPECT REAR WHEEL SPEED SENSOR.

- MEASURE RESISTANCE BETWEEN SUSPECT REAR WHEEL SPEED SENSOR TERMINAL B AND GROUND.
IS LESS THAN 100 OHMS MEASURED?

NO / **YES**

REPLACE SUSPECT REAR WHEEL SPEED SENSOR.

- MEASURE AC VOLTAGE BETWEEN SUSPECT REAR WHEEL SPEED SENSOR TERMINALS A AND B WHEEL TURNING DRIVE WHEELS BY HAND.
IS 50 TO 900 MILLIVOLTS AC MEASURED?

YES / **NO**

REPLACE SUSPECT REAR WHEEL SPEED SENSOR.

- RECONNECT WHEEL SPEED SENSOR.
- IGNITION: OFF
- DISCONNECT ELECTRONIC BRAKE CONTROL MODULE (EBCM).
- INSTALL J 38716 PINOUT BOX.
- MEASURE RESISTANCE AT TERMINALS INDICATED FOR THE SUSPECTED REAR WHEEL SPEED SENSOR CIRCUIT:
  LEFT REAR WHEEL – TERMINALS 28 AND 46
  RIGHT REAR WHEEL – TERMINALS 27 AND 45
IS 800 TO 1500 OHMS MEASURED?

YES / **NO**

IF LEFT REAR WHEEL, REPAIR OPEN IN CKTS 884 OR 885.
IF RIGHT REAR WHEEL, REPAIR OPEN IN CKTS 882 OR 883.

- MEASURE RESISTANCE AT J 38716 PINOUT BOX TERMINALS INDICATED FOR THE SUSPECTED REAR WHEEL SPEED SENSOR CIRCUIT
  LEFT REAR WHEEL – TERMINALS 46 AND 1
  RIGHT REAR WHEEL – TERMINALS 45 AND 1
IS LESS THAN 100 OHMS MEASURED?

NO / **YES**

IF LEFT REAR WHEEL, REPAIR SHORT TO GROUND IN CKTS 884 OR 885.
IF RIGHT REAR WHEEL, REPAIR SHORT TO GROUND IN CKTS 882 OR 883.

CHECK ELECTRONIC BRAKE CONTROL MODULE (EBCM) TERMINAL CONNECTIONS FOR GOOD TERMINAL CONTACT. IF TERMINAL CONTACT IS GOOD, REPLACE EBCM.

91I07939 91A07940

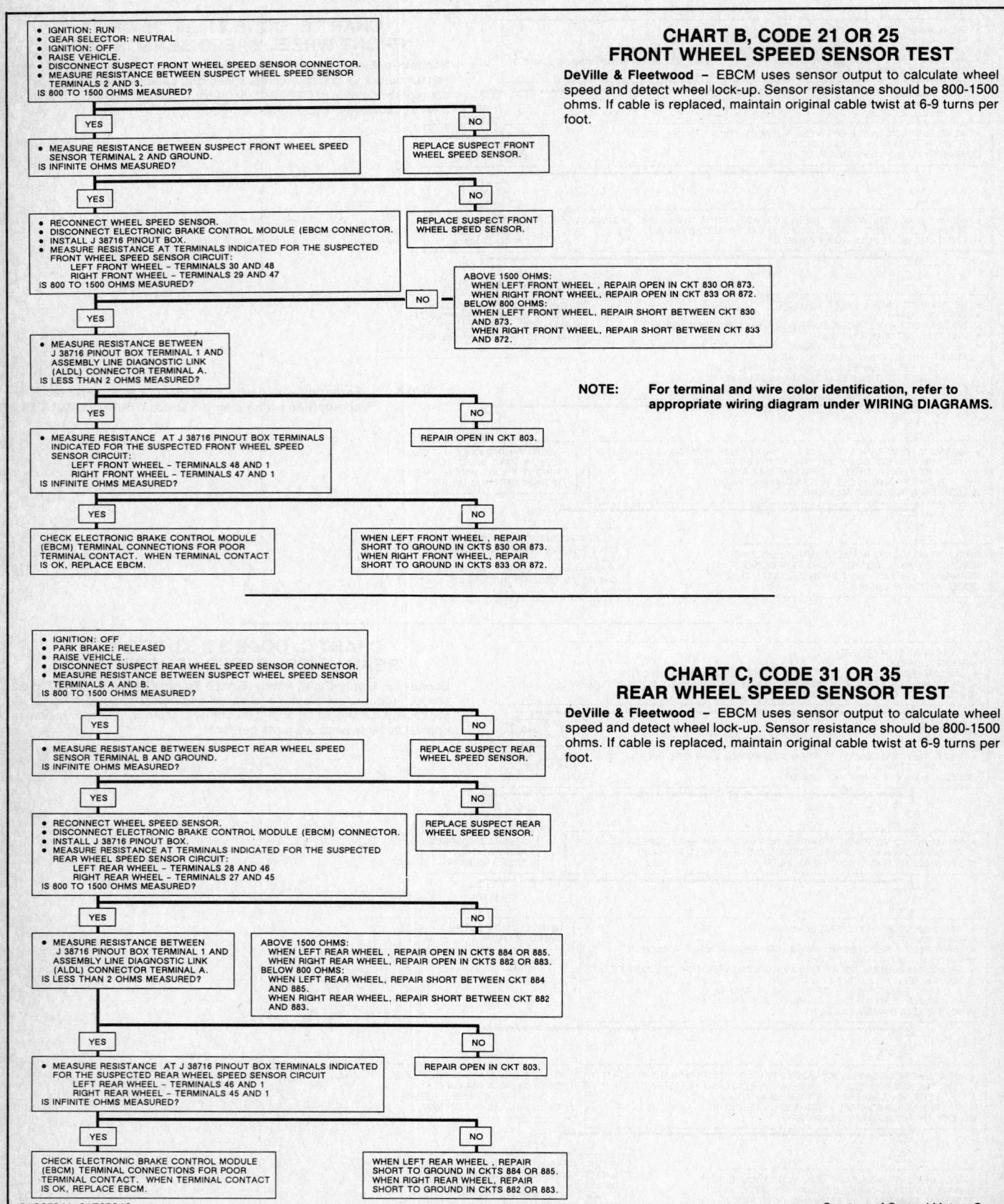

CHART B, CODE 21 OR 25
FRONT WHEEL SPEED SENSOR TEST

DeVille & Fleetwood – EBCM uses sensor output to calculate wheel speed and detect wheel lock-up. Sensor resistance should be 800-1500 ohms. If cable is replaced, maintain original cable twist at 6-9 turns per foot.

- IGNITION: RUN
- GEAR SELECTOR: NEUTRAL
- IGNITION: OFF
- RAISE VEHICLE.
- DISCONNECT SUSPECT FRONT WHEEL SPEED SENSOR CONNECTOR.
- MEASURE RESISTANCE BETWEEN SUSPECT WHEEL SPEED SENSOR TERMINALS 2 AND 3.
IS 800 TO 1500 OHMS MEASURED?

YES →
- MEASURE RESISTANCE BETWEEN SUSPECT FRONT WHEEL SPEED SENSOR TERMINAL 2 AND GROUND.
IS INFINITE OHMS MEASURED?

NO → REPLACE SUSPECT FRONT WHEEL SPEED SENSOR.

YES →
- RECONNECT WHEEL SPEED SENSOR.
- DISCONNECT ELECTRONIC BRAKE CONTROL MODULE (EBCM CONNECTOR.
- INSTALL J 38716 PINOUT BOX.
- MEASURE RESISTANCE AT TERMINALS INDICATED FOR THE SUSPECTED FRONT WHEEL SPEED SENSOR CIRCUIT:
  LEFT FRONT WHEEL – TERMINALS 30 AND 48
  RIGHT FRONT WHEEL – TERMINALS 29 AND 47
IS 800 TO 1500 OHMS MEASURED?

NO → REPLACE SUSPECT FRONT WHEEL SPEED SENSOR.

NO →
ABOVE 1500 OHMS:
  WHEN LEFT FRONT WHEEL , REPAIR OPEN IN CKT 830 OR 873.
  WHEN RIGHT FRONT WHEEL, REPAIR OPEN IN CKT 833 OR 872.
BELOW 800 OHMS:
  WHEN LEFT FRONT WHEEL, REPAIR SHORT BETWEEN CKT 830 AND 873.
  WHEN RIGHT FRONT WHEEL, REPAIR SHORT BETWEEN CKT 833 AND 872.

YES →
- MEASURE RESISTANCE BETWEEN J 38716 PINOUT BOX TERMINAL 1 AND ASSEMBLY LINE DIAGNOSTIC LINK (ALDL) CONNECTOR TERMINAL A.
IS LESS THAN 2 OHMS MEASURED?

NO → REPAIR OPEN IN CKT 803.

NOTE: For terminal and wire color identification, refer to appropriate wiring diagram under WIRING DIAGRAMS.

YES →
- MEASURE RESISTANCE AT J 38716 PINOUT BOX TERMINALS INDICATED FOR THE SUSPECTED FRONT WHEEL SPEED SENSOR CIRCUIT:
  LEFT FRONT WHEEL – TERMINALS 48 AND 1
  RIGHT FRONT WHEEL – TERMINALS 47 AND 1
IS INFINITE OHMS MEASURED?

YES → CHECK ELECTRONIC BRAKE CONTROL MODULE (EBCM) TERMINAL CONNECTIONS FOR POOR TERMINAL CONTACT. WHEN TERMINAL CONTACT IS OK, REPLACE EBCM.

NO → WHEN LEFT FRONT WHEEL , REPAIR SHORT TO GROUND IN CKTS 830 OR 873. WHEN RIGHT FRONT WHEEL, REPAIR SHORT TO GROUND IN CKTS 833 OR 872.

CHART C, CODE 31 OR 35
REAR WHEEL SPEED SENSOR TEST

DeVille & Fleetwood – EBCM uses sensor output to calculate wheel speed and detect wheel lock-up. Sensor resistance should be 800-1500 ohms. If cable is replaced, maintain original cable twist at 6-9 turns per foot.

- IGNITION: OFF
- PARK BRAKE: RELEASED
- RAISE VEHICLE.
- DISCONNECT SUSPECT REAR WHEEL SPEED SENSOR CONNECTOR.
- MEASURE RESISTANCE BETWEEN SUSPECT WHEEL SPEED SENSOR TERMINALS A AND B.
IS 800 TO 1500 OHMS MEASURED?

YES →
- MEASURE RESISTANCE BETWEEN SUSPECT REAR WHEEL SPEED SENSOR TERMINAL B AND GROUND.
IS INFINITE OHMS MEASURED?

NO → REPLACE SUSPECT REAR WHEEL SPEED SENSOR.

YES →
- RECONNECT WHEEL SPEED SENSOR.
- DISCONNECT ELECTRONIC BRAKE CONTROL MODULE (EBCM) CONNECTOR.
- INSTALL J 38716 PINOUT BOX.
- MEASURE RESISTANCE AT TERMINALS INDICATED FOR THE SUSPECTED REAR WHEEL SPEED SENSOR CIRCUIT:
  LEFT REAR WHEEL – TERMINALS 28 AND 46
  RIGHT REAR WHEEL – TERMINALS 27 AND 45
IS 800 TO 1500 OHMS MEASURED?

NO → REPLACE SUSPECT REAR WHEEL SPEED SENSOR.

YES →
- MEASURE RESISTANCE BETWEEN J 38716 PINOUT BOX TERMINAL 1 AND ASSEMBLY LINE DIAGNOSTIC LINK (ALDL) CONNECTOR TERMINAL A.
IS LESS THAN 2 OHMS MEASURED?

NO →
ABOVE 1500 OHMS:
  WHEN LEFT REAR WHEEL , REPAIR OPEN IN CKTS 884 OR 885.
  WHEN RIGHT REAR WHEEL, REPAIR OPEN IN CKTS 882 OR 883.
BELOW 800 OHMS:
  WHEN LEFT REAR WHEEL, REPAIR SHORT BETWEEN CKT 884 AND 885.
  WHEN RIGHT REAR WHEEL, REPAIR SHORT BETWEEN CKT 882 AND 883.

NO → REPAIR OPEN IN CKT 803.

YES →
- MEASURE RESISTANCE AT J 38716 PINOUT BOX TERMINALS INDICATED FOR THE SUSPECTED REAR WHEEL SPEED SENSOR CIRCUIT
  LEFT REAR WHEEL – TERMINALS 46 AND 1
  RIGHT REAR WHEEL – TERMINALS 45 AND 1
IS INFINITE OHMS MEASURED?

YES → CHECK ELECTRONIC BRAKE CONTROL MODULE (EBCM) TERMINAL CONNECTIONS FOR POOR TERMINAL CONTACT. WHEN TERMINAL CONTACT IS OK, REPLACE EBCM.

NO → WHEN LEFT REAR WHEEL , REPAIR SHORT TO GROUND IN CKTS 884 OR 885. WHEN RIGHT REAR WHEEL, REPAIR SHORT TO GROUND IN CKTS 882 OR 883.

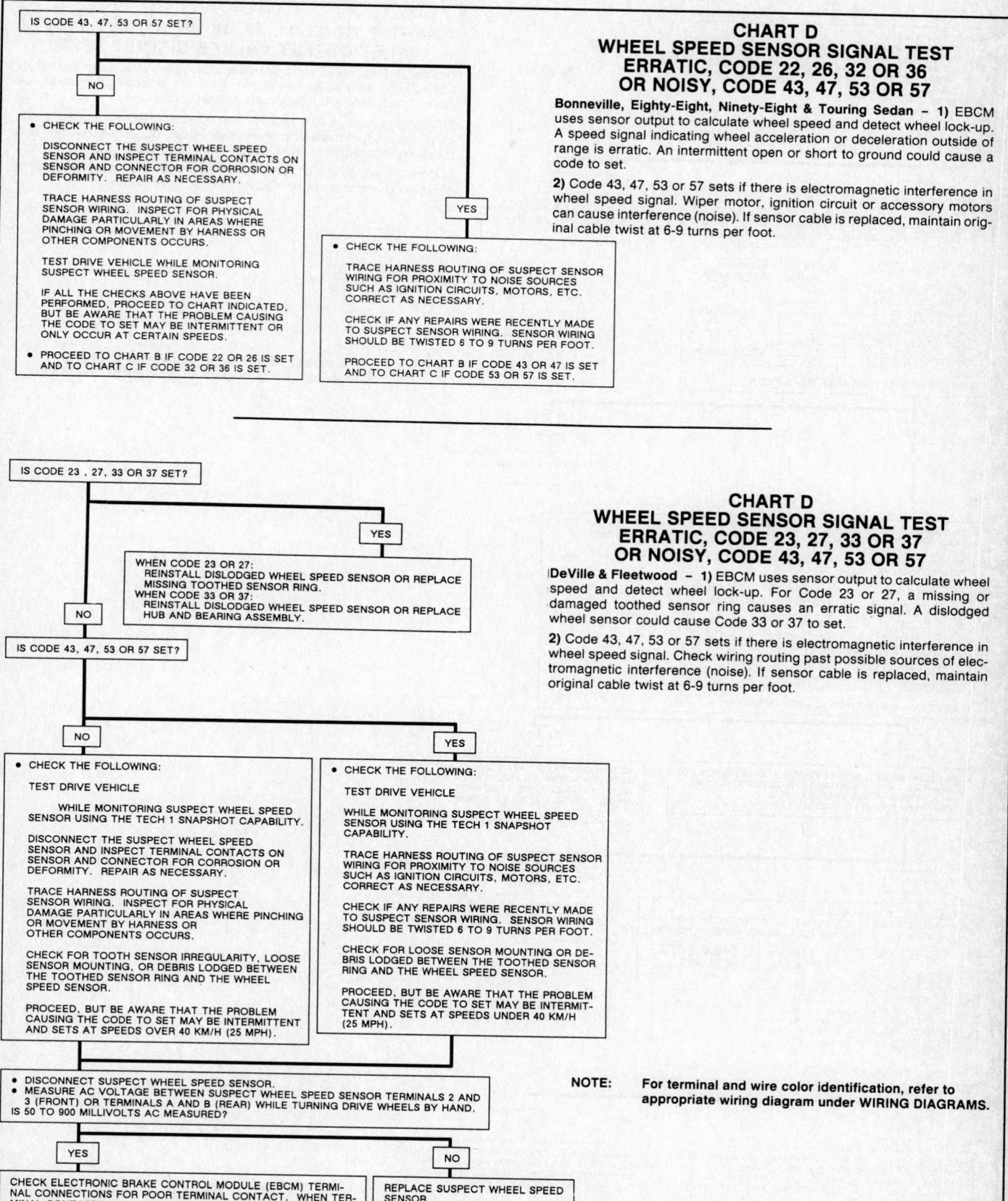

IS CODE 43, 47, 53 OR 57 SET?

NO

YES

- CHECK THE FOLLOWING:

  DISCONNECT THE SUSPECT WHEEL SPEED
  SENSOR AND INSPECT TERMINAL CONTACTS ON
  SENSOR AND CONNECTOR FOR CORROSION OR
  DEFORMITY. REPAIR AS NECESSARY.

  TRACE HARNESS ROUTING OF SUSPECT
  SENSOR WIRING. INSPECT FOR PHYSICAL
  DAMAGE PARTICULARLY IN AREAS WHERE
  PINCHING OR MOVEMENT BY HARNESS OR
  OTHER COMPONENTS OCCURS.

  TEST DRIVE VEHICLE WHILE MONITORING
  SUSPECT WHEEL SPEED SENSOR.

  IF ALL THE CHECKS ABOVE HAVE BEEN
  PERFORMED, PROCEED TO CHART INDICATED.
  BUT BE AWARE THAT THE PROBLEM CAUSING
  THE CODE TO SET MAY BE INTERMITTENT OR
  ONLY OCCUR AT CERTAIN SPEEDS.

- PROCEED TO CHART B IF CODE 22 OR 26 IS SET
  AND TO CHART C IF CODE 32 OR 36 IS SET.

- CHECK THE FOLLOWING:

  TRACE HARNESS ROUTING OF SUSPECT SENSOR
  WIRING FOR PROXIMITY TO NOISE SOURCES
  SUCH AS IGNITION CIRCUITS, MOTORS, ETC.
  CORRECT AS NECESSARY.

  CHECK IF ANY REPAIRS WERE RECENTLY MADE
  TO SUSPECT SENSOR WIRING. SENSOR WIRING
  SHOULD BE TWISTED 6 TO 9 TURNS PER FOOT.

  PROCEED TO CHART B IF CODE 43 OR 47 IS SET
  AND TO CHART C IF CODE 53 OR 57 IS SET.

CHART D
WHEEL SPEED SENSOR SIGNAL TEST
ERRATIC, CODE 22, 26, 32 OR 36
OR NOISY, CODE 43, 47, 53 OR 57

Bonneville, Eighty-Eight, Ninety-Eight & Touring Sedan – 1) EBCM uses sensor output to calculate wheel speed and detect wheel lock-up. A speed signal indicating wheel acceleration or deceleration outside of range is erratic. An intermittent open or short to ground could cause a code to set.

2) Code 43, 47, 53 or 57 sets if there is electromagnetic interference in wheel speed signal. Wiper motor, ignition circuit or accessory motors can cause interference (noise). If sensor cable is replaced, maintain original cable twist at 6-9 turns per foot.

IS CODE 23 , 27, 33 OR 37 SET?

YES

WHEN CODE 23 OR 27:
REINSTALL DISLODGED WHEEL SPEED SENSOR OR REPLACE
MISSING TOOTHED SENSOR RING.
WHEN CODE 33 OR 37:
REINSTALL DISLODGED WHEEL SPEED SENSOR OR REPLACE
HUB AND BEARING ASSEMBLY.

NO

IS CODE 43, 47, 53 OR 57 SET?

CHART D
WHEEL SPEED SENSOR SIGNAL TEST
ERRATIC, CODE 23, 27, 33 OR 37
OR NOISY, CODE 43, 47, 53 OR 57

DeVille & Fleetwood – 1) EBCM uses sensor output to calculate wheel speed and detect wheel lock-up. For Code 23 or 27, a missing or damaged toothed sensor ring causes an erratic signal. A dislodged wheel sensor could cause Code 33 or 37 to set.

2) Code 43, 47, 53 or 57 sets if there is electromagnetic interference in wheel speed signal. Check wiring routing past possible sources of electromagnetic interference (noise). If sensor cable is replaced, maintain original cable twist at 6-9 turns per foot.

NO

YES

- CHECK THE FOLLOWING:

  TEST DRIVE VEHICLE

  WHILE MONITORING SUSPECT WHEEL SPEED
  SENSOR USING THE TECH 1 SNAPSHOT CAPABILITY.

  DISCONNECT THE SUSPECT WHEEL SPEED
  SENSOR AND INSPECT TERMINAL CONTACTS ON
  SENSOR AND CONNECTOR FOR CORROSION OR
  DEFORMITY. REPAIR AS NECESSARY.

  TRACE HARNESS ROUTING OF SUSPECT
  SENSOR WIRING. INSPECT FOR PHYSICAL
  DAMAGE PARTICULARLY IN AREAS WHERE PINCHING
  OR MOVEMENT BY HARNESS OR
  OTHER COMPONENTS OCCURS.

  CHECK FOR TOOTH SENSOR IRREGULARITY, LOOSE
  SENSOR MOUNTING, OR DEBRIS LODGED BETWEEN
  THE TOOTHED SENSOR RING AND THE WHEEL
  SPEED SENSOR.

  PROCEED, BUT BE AWARE THAT THE PROBLEM
  CAUSING THE CODE TO SET MAY BE INTERMITTENT
  AND SETS AT SPEEDS OVER 40 KM/H (25 MPH).

- CHECK THE FOLLOWING:

  TEST DRIVE VEHICLE

  WHILE MONITORING SUSPECT WHEEL SPEED
  SENSOR USING THE TECH 1 SNAPSHOT
  CAPABILITY.

  TRACE HARNESS ROUTING OF SUSPECT SENSOR
  WIRING FOR PROXIMITY TO NOISE SOURCES
  SUCH AS IGNITION CIRCUITS, MOTORS, ETC.
  CORRECT AS NECESSARY.

  CHECK IF ANY REPAIRS WERE RECENTLY MADE
  TO SUSPECT SENSOR WIRING. SENSOR WIRING
  SHOULD BE TWISTED 6 TO 9 TURNS PER FOOT.

  CHECK FOR LOOSE SENSOR MOUNTING OR DE-
  BRIS LODGED BETWEEN THE TOOTHED SENSOR
  RING AND THE WHEEL SPEED SENSOR.

  PROCEED, BUT BE AWARE THAT THE PROBLEM
  CAUSING THE CODE TO SET MAY BE INTERMIT-
  TENT AND SETS AT SPEEDS UNDER 40 KM/H
  (25 MPH).

- DISCONNECT SUSPECT WHEEL SPEED SENSOR.
- MEASURE AC VOLTAGE BETWEEN SUSPECT WHEEL SPEED SENSOR TERMINALS 2 AND
  3 (FRONT) OR TERMINALS A AND B (REAR) WHILE TURNING DRIVE WHEELS BY HAND.
  IS 50 TO 900 MILLIVOLTS AC MEASURED?

YES

NO

CHECK ELECTRONIC BRAKE CONTROL MODULE (EBCM) TERMI-
NAL CONNECTIONS FOR POOR TERMINAL CONTACT. WHEN TER-
MINAL CONTACT IS OK, REPLACE EBCM.

REPLACE SUSPECT WHEEL SPEED
SENSOR.

NOTE: **For terminal and wire color identification, refer to appropriate wiring diagram under WIRING DIAGRAMS.**

91G07943 91I07944

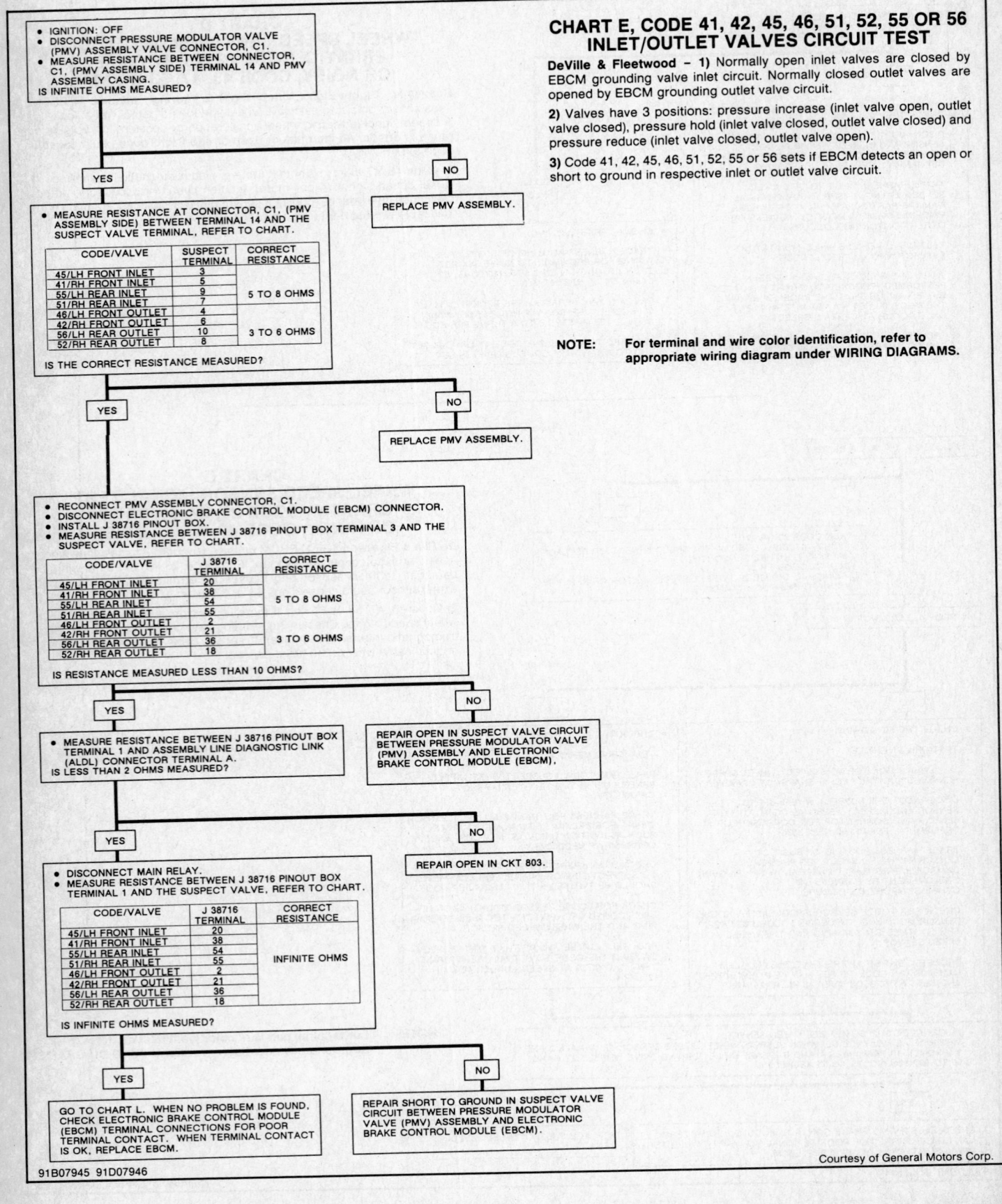

CHART E, CODE 41, 42, 45, 46, 51, 52, 55 OR 56 INLET/OUTLET VALVES CIRCUIT TEST

DeVille & Fleetwood – 1) Normally open inlet valves are closed by EBCM grounding valve inlet circuit. Normally closed outlet valves are opened by EBCM grounding outlet valve circuit.

2) Valves have 3 positions: pressure increase (inlet valve open, outlet valve closed), pressure hold (inlet valve closed, outlet valve closed) and pressure reduce (inlet valve closed, outlet valve open).

3) Code 41, 42, 45, 46, 51, 52, 55 or 56 sets if EBCM detects an open or short to ground in respective inlet or outlet valve circuit.

NOTE: For terminal and wire color identification, refer to appropriate wiring diagram under WIRING DIAGRAMS.

- IGNITION: OFF
- DISCONNECT PRESSURE MODULATOR VALVE (PMV) ASSEMBLY VALVE CONNECTOR, C1.
- MEASURE RESISTANCE BETWEEN CONNECTOR, C1, (PMV ASSEMBLY SIDE) TERMINAL 14 AND PMV ASSEMBLY CASING.
IS INFINITE OHMS MEASURED?

YES

NO — REPLACE PMV ASSEMBLY.

- MEASURE RESISTANCE AT CONNECTOR, C1, (PMV ASSEMBLY SIDE) BETWEEN TERMINAL 14 AND THE SUSPECT VALVE TERMINAL, REFER TO CHART.

CODE/VALVE	SUSPECT TERMINAL	CORRECT RESISTANCE
45/LH FRONT INLET	3	
41/RH FRONT INLET	5	
55/LH REAR INLET	9	5 TO 8 OHMS
51/RH REAR INLET	7	
46/LH FRONT OUTLET	4	
42/RH FRONT OUTLET	6	
56/LH REAR OUTLET	10	3 TO 6 OHMS
52/RH REAR OUTLET	8	

IS THE CORRECT RESISTANCE MEASURED?

YES

NO — REPLACE PMV ASSEMBLY.

- RECONNECT PMV ASSEMBLY CONNECTOR, C1.
- DISCONNECT ELECTRONIC BRAKE CONTROL MODULE (EBCM) CONNECTOR.
- INSTALL J 38716 PINOUT BOX.
- MEASURE RESISTANCE BETWEEN J 38716 PINOUT BOX TERMINAL 3 AND THE SUSPECT VALVE, REFER TO CHART.

CODE/VALVE	J 38716 TERMINAL	CORRECT RESISTANCE
45/LH FRONT INLET	20	
41/RH FRONT INLET	38	
55/LH REAR INLET	54	5 TO 8 OHMS
51/RH REAR INLET	55	
46/LH FRONT OUTLET	2	
42/RH FRONT OUTLET	21	
56/LH REAR OUTLET	36	3 TO 6 OHMS
52/RH REAR OUTLET	18	

IS RESISTANCE MEASURED LESS THAN 10 OHMS?

YES

NO — REPAIR OPEN IN SUSPECT VALVE CIRCUIT BETWEEN PRESSURE MODULATOR VALVE (PMV) ASSEMBLY AND ELECTRONIC BRAKE CONTROL MODULE (EBCM).

- MEASURE RESISTANCE BETWEEN J 38716 PINOUT BOX TERMINAL 1 AND ASSEMBLY LINE DIAGNOSTIC LINK (ALDL) CONNECTOR TERMINAL A.
IS LESS THAN 2 OHMS MEASURED?

YES

NO — REPAIR OPEN IN CKT 803.

- DISCONNECT MAIN RELAY.
- MEASURE RESISTANCE BETWEEN J 38716 PINOUT BOX TERMINAL 1 AND THE SUSPECT VALVE, REFER TO CHART.

CODE/VALVE	J 38716 TERMINAL	CORRECT RESISTANCE
45/LH FRONT INLET	20	
41/RH FRONT INLET	38	
55/LH REAR INLET	54	
51/RH REAR INLET	55	INFINITE OHMS
46/LH FRONT OUTLET	2	
42/RH FRONT OUTLET	21	
56/LH REAR OUTLET	36	
52/RH REAR OUTLET	18	

IS INFINITE OHMS MEASURED?

YES — GO TO CHART L. WHEN NO PROBLEM IS FOUND, CHECK ELECTRONIC BRAKE CONTROL MODULE (EBCM) TERMINAL CONNECTIONS FOR POOR TERMINAL CONTACT. WHEN TERMINAL CONTACT IS OK, REPLACE EBCM.

NO — REPAIR SHORT TO GROUND IN SUSPECT VALVE CIRCUIT BETWEEN PRESSURE MODULATOR VALVE (PMV) ASSEMBLY AND ELECTRONIC BRAKE CONTROL MODULE (EBCM).

Courtesy of General Motors Corp.

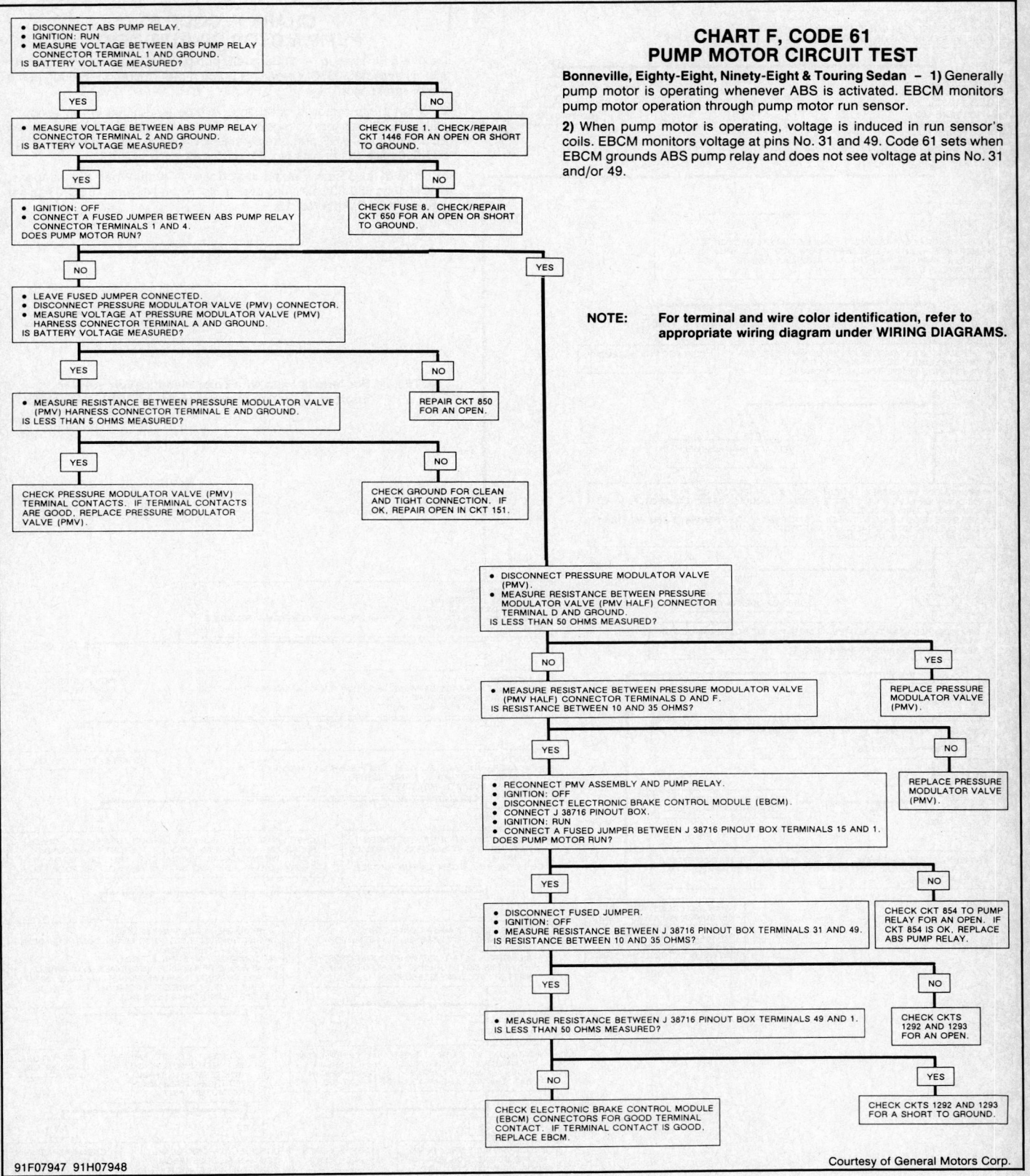

CHART F, CODE 61
PUMP MOTOR CIRCUIT TEST

Bonneville, Eighty-Eight, Ninety-Eight & Touring Sedan – 1) Generally pump motor is operating whenever ABS is activated. EBCM monitors pump motor operation through pump motor run sensor.

2) When pump motor is operating, voltage is induced in run sensor's coils. EBCM monitors voltage at pins No. 31 and 49. Code 61 sets when EBCM grounds ABS pump relay and does not see voltage at pins No. 31 and/or 49.

NOTE: For terminal and wire color identification, refer to appropriate wiring diagram under WIRING DIAGRAMS.

Flowchart boxes:

- DISCONNECT ABS PUMP RELAY.
- IGNITION: RUN
- MEASURE VOLTAGE BETWEEN ABS PUMP RELAY CONNECTOR TERMINAL 1 AND GROUND.
  IS BATTERY VOLTAGE MEASURED?

YES → (continues)
NO → CHECK FUSE 1. CHECK/REPAIR CKT 1446 FOR AN OPEN OR SHORT TO GROUND.

- MEASURE VOLTAGE BETWEEN ABS PUMP RELAY CONNECTOR TERMINAL 2 AND GROUND.
  IS BATTERY VOLTAGE MEASURED?

YES → (continues)
NO → CHECK FUSE 8. CHECK/REPAIR CKT 650 FOR AN OPEN OR SHORT TO GROUND.

- IGNITION: OFF
- CONNECT A FUSED JUMPER BETWEEN ABS PUMP RELAY CONNECTOR TERMINALS 1 AND 4.
  DOES PUMP MOTOR RUN?

NO → (continues)
YES → (continues to right side)

- LEAVE FUSED JUMPER CONNECTED.
- DISCONNECT PRESSURE MODULATOR VALVE (PMV) CONNECTOR.
- MEASURE VOLTAGE AT PRESSURE MODULATOR VALVE (PMV) HARNESS CONNECTOR TERMINAL A AND GROUND.
  IS BATTERY VOLTAGE MEASURED?

YES → (continues)
NO → REPAIR CKT 850 FOR AN OPEN.

- MEASURE RESISTANCE BETWEEN PRESSURE MODULATOR VALVE (PMV) HARNESS CONNECTOR TERMINAL E AND GROUND.
  IS LESS THAN 5 OHMS MEASURED?

YES → (continues)
NO → CHECK GROUND FOR CLEAN AND TIGHT CONNECTION. IF OK, REPAIR OPEN IN CKT 151.

CHECK PRESSURE MODULATOR VALVE (PMV) TERMINAL CONTACTS. IF TERMINAL CONTACTS ARE GOOD, REPLACE PRESSURE MODULATOR VALVE (PMV).

(Right side from YES):

- DISCONNECT PRESSURE MODULATOR VALVE (PMV).
- MEASURE RESISTANCE BETWEEN PRESSURE MODULATOR VALVE (PMV HALF) CONNECTOR TERMINAL D AND GROUND.
  IS LESS THAN 50 OHMS MEASURED?

NO → (continues)
YES → REPLACE PRESSURE MODULATOR VALVE (PMV).

- MEASURE RESISTANCE BETWEEN PRESSURE MODULATOR VALVE (PMV HALF) CONNECTOR TERMINALS D AND F.
  IS RESISTANCE BETWEEN 10 AND 35 OHMS?

YES → (continues)
NO → REPLACE PRESSURE MODULATOR VALVE (PMV).

- RECONNECT PMV ASSEMBLY AND PUMP RELAY.
- IGNITION: OFF
- DISCONNECT ELECTRONIC BRAKE CONTROL MODULE (EBCM).
- CONNECT J 38716 PINOUT BOX.
- IGNITION: RUN
- CONNECT A FUSED JUMPER BETWEEN J 38716 PINOUT BOX TERMINALS 15 AND 1.
  DOES PUMP MOTOR RUN?

YES → (continues)
NO → CHECK CKT 854 TO PUMP RELAY FOR AN OPEN. IF CKT 854 IS OK, REPLACE ABS PUMP RELAY.

- DISCONNECT FUSED JUMPER.
- IGNITION: OFF
- MEASURE RESISTANCE BETWEEN J 38716 PINOUT BOX TERMINALS 31 AND 49.
  IS RESISTANCE BETWEEN 10 AND 35 OHMS?

YES → (continues)
NO → CHECK CKTS 1292 AND 1293 FOR AN OPEN.

- MEASURE RESISTANCE BETWEEN J 38716 PINOUT BOX TERMINALS 49 AND 1.
  IS LESS THAN 50 OHMS MEASURED?

NO → CHECK ELECTRONIC BRAKE CONTROL MODULE (EBCM) CONNECTORS FOR GOOD TERMINAL CONTACT. IF TERMINAL CONTACT IS GOOD, REPLACE EBCM.
YES → CHECK CKTS 1292 AND 1293 FOR A SHORT TO GROUND.

Courtesy of General Motors Corp.

91F07947 91H07948

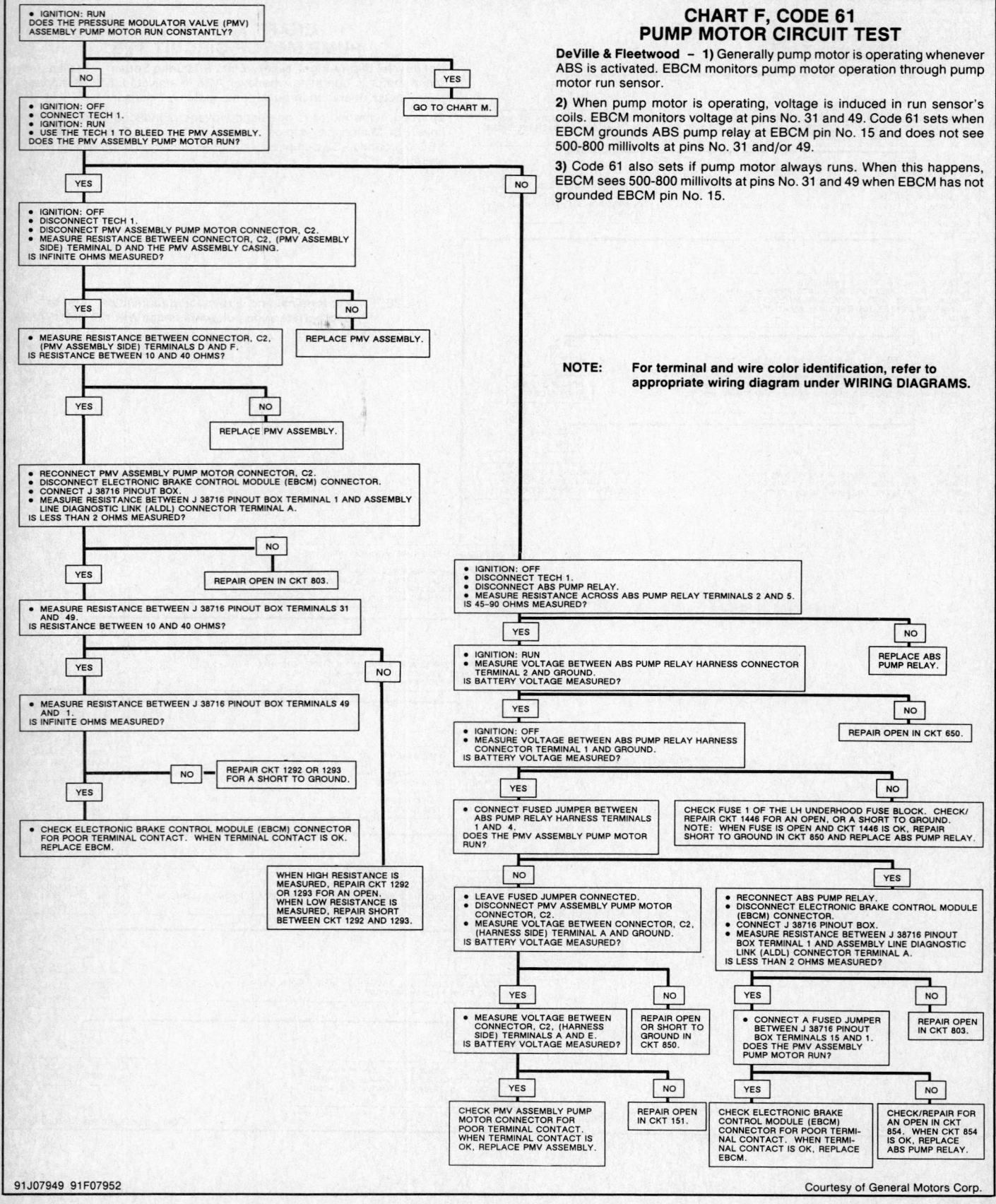

CHART F, CODE 61
PUMP MOTOR CIRCUIT TEST

DeVille & Fleetwood – 1) Generally pump motor is operating whenever ABS is activated. EBCM monitors pump motor operation through pump motor run sensor.

2) When pump motor is operating, voltage is induced in run sensor's coils. EBCM monitors voltage at pins No. 31 and 49. Code 61 sets when EBCM grounds ABS pump relay at EBCM pin No. 15 and does not see 500-800 millivolts at pins No. 31 and/or 49.

3) Code 61 also sets if pump motor always runs. When this happens, EBCM sees 500-800 millivolts at pins No. 31 and 49 when EBCM has not grounded EBCM pin No. 15.

NOTE: For terminal and wire color identification, refer to appropriate wiring diagram under WIRING DIAGRAMS.

Flowchart contents:

- IGNITION: RUN
  DOES THE PRESSURE MODULATOR VALVE (PMV) ASSEMBLY PUMP MOTOR RUN CONSTANTLY?
  - YES → GO TO CHART M.
  - NO →
    - IGNITION: OFF
    - CONNECT TECH 1.
    - IGNITION: RUN
    - USE THE TECH 1 TO BLEED THE PMV ASSEMBLY. DOES THE PMV ASSEMBLY PUMP MOTOR RUN?
    - YES →
      - IGNITION: OFF
      - DISCONNECT TECH 1.
      - DISCONNECT PMV ASSEMBLY PUMP MOTOR CONNECTOR, C2.
      - MEASURE RESISTANCE BETWEEN CONNECTOR, C2, (PMV ASSEMBLY SIDE) TERMINAL D AND THE PMV ASSEMBLY CASING. IS INFINITE OHMS MEASURED?
        - YES →
          - MEASURE RESISTANCE BETWEEN CONNECTOR, C2, (PMV ASSEMBLY SIDE) TERMINALS D AND F. IS RESISTANCE BETWEEN 10 AND 40 OHMS?
            - YES →
              - RECONNECT PMV ASSEMBLY PUMP MOTOR CONNECTOR, C2.
              - DISCONNECT ELECTRONIC BRAKE CONTROL MODULE (EBCM) CONNECTOR.
              - CONNECT J 38716 PINOUT BOX.
              - MEASURE RESISTANCE BETWEEN J 38716 PINOUT BOX TERMINAL 1 AND ASSEMBLY LINE DIAGNOSTIC LINK (ALDL) CONNECTOR TERMINAL A. IS LESS THAN 2 OHMS MEASURED?
                - YES →
                  - MEASURE RESISTANCE BETWEEN J 38716 PINOUT BOX TERMINALS 31 AND 49. IS RESISTANCE BETWEEN 10 AND 40 OHMS?
                    - YES →
                      - MEASURE RESISTANCE BETWEEN J 38716 PINOUT BOX TERMINALS 49 AND 1. IS INFINITE OHMS MEASURED?
                        - YES →
                          - CHECK ELECTRONIC BRAKE CONTROL MODULE (EBCM) CONNECTOR FOR POOR TERMINAL CONTACT. WHEN TERMINAL CONTACT IS OK. REPLACE EBCM.
                        - NO → REPAIR CKT 1292 OR 1293 FOR A SHORT TO GROUND.
                    - NO → WHEN HIGH RESISTANCE IS MEASURED, REPAIR CKT 1292 OR 1293 FOR AN OPEN. WHEN LOW RESISTANCE IS MEASURED, REPAIR SHORT BETWEEN CKT 1292 AND 1293.
                - NO → REPAIR OPEN IN CKT 803.
            - NO → REPLACE PMV ASSEMBLY.
        - NO → REPLACE PMV ASSEMBLY.

Right side branch:

- IGNITION: OFF
- DISCONNECT TECH 1.
- DISCONNECT ABS PUMP RELAY.
- MEASURE RESISTANCE ACROSS ABS PUMP RELAY TERMINALS 2 AND 5. IS 45-90 OHMS MEASURED?
  - YES →
    - IGNITION: RUN
    - MEASURE VOLTAGE BETWEEN ABS PUMP RELAY HARNESS CONNECTOR TERMINAL 2 AND GROUND. IS BATTERY VOLTAGE MEASURED?
      - YES →
        - IGNITION: OFF
        - MEASURE VOLTAGE BETWEEN ABS PUMP RELAY HARNESS CONNECTOR TERMINAL 1 AND GROUND. IS BATTERY VOLTAGE MEASURED?
          - YES →
            - CONNECT FUSED JUMPER BETWEEN ABS PUMP RELAY HARNESS TERMINALS 1 AND 4. DOES THE PMV ASSEMBLY PUMP MOTOR RUN?
              - NO →
                - LEAVE FUSED JUMPER CONNECTED.
                - DISCONNECT PMV ASSEMBLY PUMP MOTOR CONNECTOR, C2.
                - MEASURE VOLTAGE BETWEEN CONNECTOR, C2, (HARNESS SIDE) TERMINAL A AND GROUND. IS BATTERY VOLTAGE MEASURED?
                  - YES →
                    - MEASURE VOLTAGE BETWEEN CONNECTOR, C2, (HARNESS SIDE) TERMINALS A AND E. IS BATTERY VOLTAGE MEASURED?
                      - YES → CHECK PMV ASSEMBLY PUMP MOTOR CONNECTOR FOR POOR TERMINAL CONTACT. WHEN TERMINAL CONTACT IS OK, REPLACE PMV ASSEMBLY.
                      - NO → REPAIR OPEN IN CKT 151.
                  - NO → REPAIR OPEN OR SHORT TO GROUND IN CKT 850.
              - YES →
                - RECONNECT ABS PUMP RELAY.
                - DISCONNECT ELECTRONIC BRAKE CONTROL MODULE (EBCM) CONNECTOR.
                - CONNECT J 38716 PINOUT BOX.
                - MEASURE RESISTANCE BETWEEN J 38716 PINOUT BOX TERMINAL 1 AND ASSEMBLY LINE DIAGNOSTIC LINK (ALDL) CONNECTOR TERMINAL A. IS LESS THAN 2 OHMS MEASURED?
                  - YES →
                    - CONNECT A FUSED JUMPER BETWEEN J 38716 PINOUT BOX TERMINALS 15 AND 1. DOES THE PMV ASSEMBLY PUMP MOTOR RUN?
                      - YES → CHECK ELECTRONIC BRAKE CONTROL MODULE (EBCM) CONNECTOR FOR POOR TERMINAL CONTACT. WHEN TERMINAL CONTACT IS OK, REPLACE EBCM.
                      - NO → CHECK/REPAIR FOR AN OPEN IN CKT 854. WHEN CKT 854 IS OK, REPLACE ABS PUMP RELAY.
                  - NO → REPAIR OPEN IN CKT 803.
          - NO → REPAIR OPEN IN CKT 650.
      - NO → CHECK FUSE 1 OF THE LH UNDERHOOD FUSE BLOCK. CHECK/REPAIR CKT 1446 FOR AN OPEN, OR A SHORT TO GROUND. NOTE: WHEN FUSE IS OPEN AND CKT 1446 IS OK, REPAIR SHORT TO GROUND IN CKT 850 AND REPLACE ABS PUMP RELAY.
  - NO → REPLACE ABS PUMP RELAY.

1991 BRAKES
Anti-Lock – Teves (Cont.)

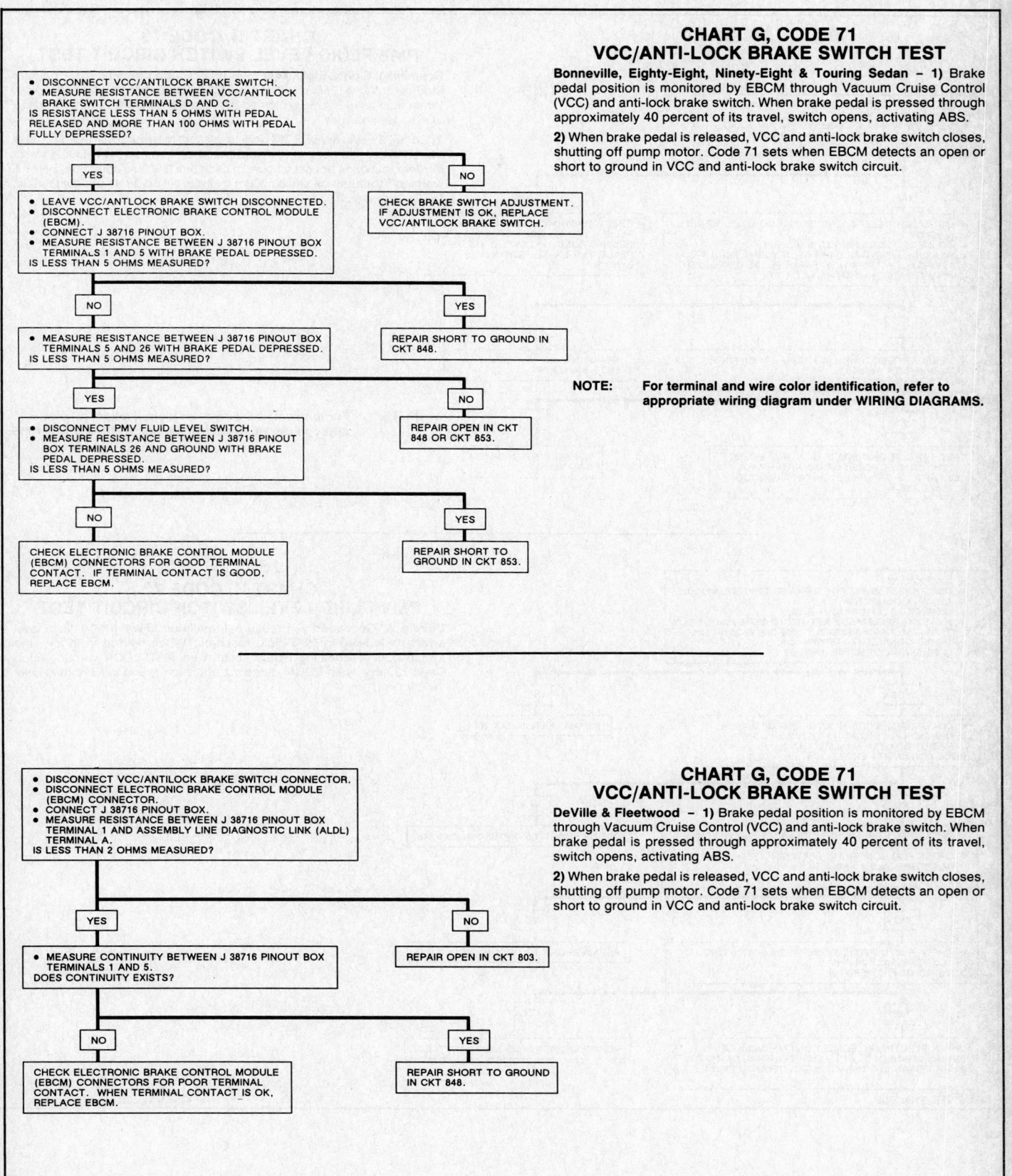

CHART G, CODE 71
VCC/ANTI-LOCK BRAKE SWITCH TEST

Bonneville, Eighty-Eight, Ninety-Eight & Touring Sedan – 1) Brake pedal position is monitored by EBCM through Vacuum Cruise Control (VCC) and anti-lock brake switch. When brake pedal is pressed through approximately 40 percent of its travel, switch opens, activating ABS.

2) When brake pedal is released, VCC and anti-lock brake switch closes, shutting off pump motor. Code 71 sets when EBCM detects an open or short to ground in VCC and anti-lock brake switch circuit.

NOTE: For terminal and wire color identification, refer to appropriate wiring diagram under WIRING DIAGRAMS.

CHART G, CODE 71
VCC/ANTI-LOCK BRAKE SWITCH TEST

DeVille & Fleetwood – 1) Brake pedal position is monitored by EBCM through Vacuum Cruise Control (VCC) and anti-lock brake switch. When brake pedal is pressed through approximately 40 percent of its travel, switch opens, activating ABS.

2) When brake pedal is released, VCC and anti-lock brake switch closes, shutting off pump motor. Code 71 sets when EBCM detects an open or short to ground in VCC and anti-lock brake switch circuit.

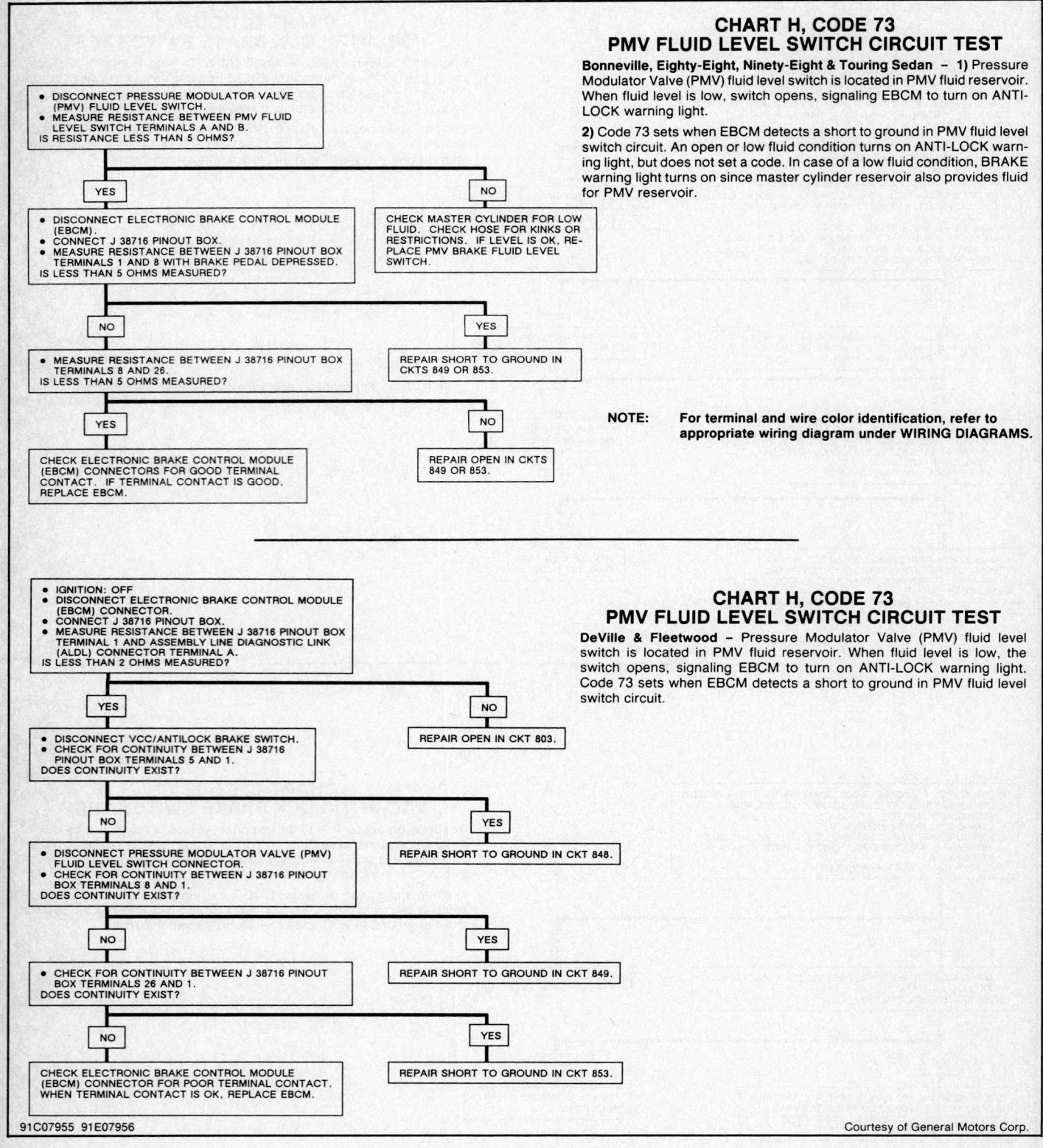

CHART H, CODE 73
PMV FLUID LEVEL SWITCH CIRCUIT TEST

Bonneville, Eighty-Eight, Ninety-Eight & Touring Sedan – 1) Pressure Modulator Valve (PMV) fluid level switch is located in PMV fluid reservoir. When fluid level is low, switch opens, signaling EBCM to turn on ANTI-LOCK warning light.

2) Code 73 sets when EBCM detects a short to ground in PMV fluid level switch circuit. An open or low fluid condition turns on ANTI-LOCK warning light, but does not set a code. In case of a low fluid condition, BRAKE warning light turns on since master cylinder reservoir also provides fluid for PMV reservoir.

- DISCONNECT PRESSURE MODULATOR VALVE (PMV) FLUID LEVEL SWITCH.
- MEASURE RESISTANCE BETWEEN PMV FLUID LEVEL SWITCH TERMINALS A AND B. IS RESISTANCE LESS THAN 5 OHMS?

YES

- DISCONNECT ELECTRONIC BRAKE CONTROL MODULE (EBCM).
- CONNECT J 38716 PINOUT BOX.
- MEASURE RESISTANCE BETWEEN J 38716 PINOUT BOX TERMINALS 1 AND 8 WITH BRAKE PEDAL DEPRESSED. IS LESS THAN 5 OHMS MEASURED?

NO

- MEASURE RESISTANCE BETWEEN J 38716 PINOUT BOX TERMINALS 8 AND 26. IS LESS THAN 5 OHMS MEASURED?

YES

CHECK ELECTRONIC BRAKE CONTROL MODULE (EBCM) CONNECTORS FOR GOOD TERMINAL CONTACT. IF TERMINAL CONTACT IS GOOD, REPLACE EBCM.

NO

CHECK MASTER CYLINDER FOR LOW FLUID. CHECK HOSE FOR KINKS OR RESTRICTIONS. IF LEVEL IS OK, RE-PLACE PMV BRAKE FLUID LEVEL SWITCH.

YES

REPAIR SHORT TO GROUND IN CKTS 849 OR 853.

NO

REPAIR OPEN IN CKTS 849 OR 853.

NOTE: For terminal and wire color identification, refer to appropriate wiring diagram under WIRING DIAGRAMS.

CHART H, CODE 73
PMV FLUID LEVEL SWITCH CIRCUIT TEST

DeVille & Fleetwood – Pressure Modulator Valve (PMV) fluid level switch is located in PMV fluid reservoir. When fluid level is low, the switch opens, signaling EBCM to turn on ANTI-LOCK warning light. Code 73 sets when EBCM detects a short to ground in PMV fluid level switch circuit.

- IGNITION: OFF
- DISCONNECT ELECTRONIC BRAKE CONTROL MODULE (EBCM) CONNECTOR.
- CONNECT J 38716 PINOUT BOX.
- MEASURE RESISTANCE BETWEEN J 38716 PINOUT BOX TERMINAL 1 AND ASSEMBLY LINE DIAGNOSTIC LINK (ALDL) CONNECTOR TERMINAL A. IS LESS THAN 2 OHMS MEASURED?

YES

- DISCONNECT VCC/ANTILOCK BRAKE SWITCH.
- CHECK FOR CONTINUITY BETWEEN J 38716 PINOUT BOX TERMINALS 5 AND 1. DOES CONTINUITY EXIST?

NO

- DISCONNECT PRESSURE MODULATOR VALVE (PMV) FLUID LEVEL SWITCH CONNECTOR.
- CHECK FOR CONTINUITY BETWEEN J 38716 PINOUT BOX TERMINALS 8 AND 1. DOES CONTINUITY EXIST?

NO

- CHECK FOR CONTINUITY BETWEEN J 38716 PINOUT BOX TERMINALS 26 AND 1. DOES CONTINUITY EXIST?

NO

CHECK ELECTRONIC BRAKE CONTROL MODULE (EBCM) CONNECTOR FOR POOR TERMINAL CONTACT. WHEN TERMINAL CONTACT IS OK, REPLACE EBCM.

NO

REPAIR OPEN IN CKT 803.

YES

REPAIR SHORT TO GROUND IN CKT 848.

YES

REPAIR SHORT TO GROUND IN CKT 849.

YES

REPAIR SHORT TO GROUND IN CKT 853.

91C07955 91E07956

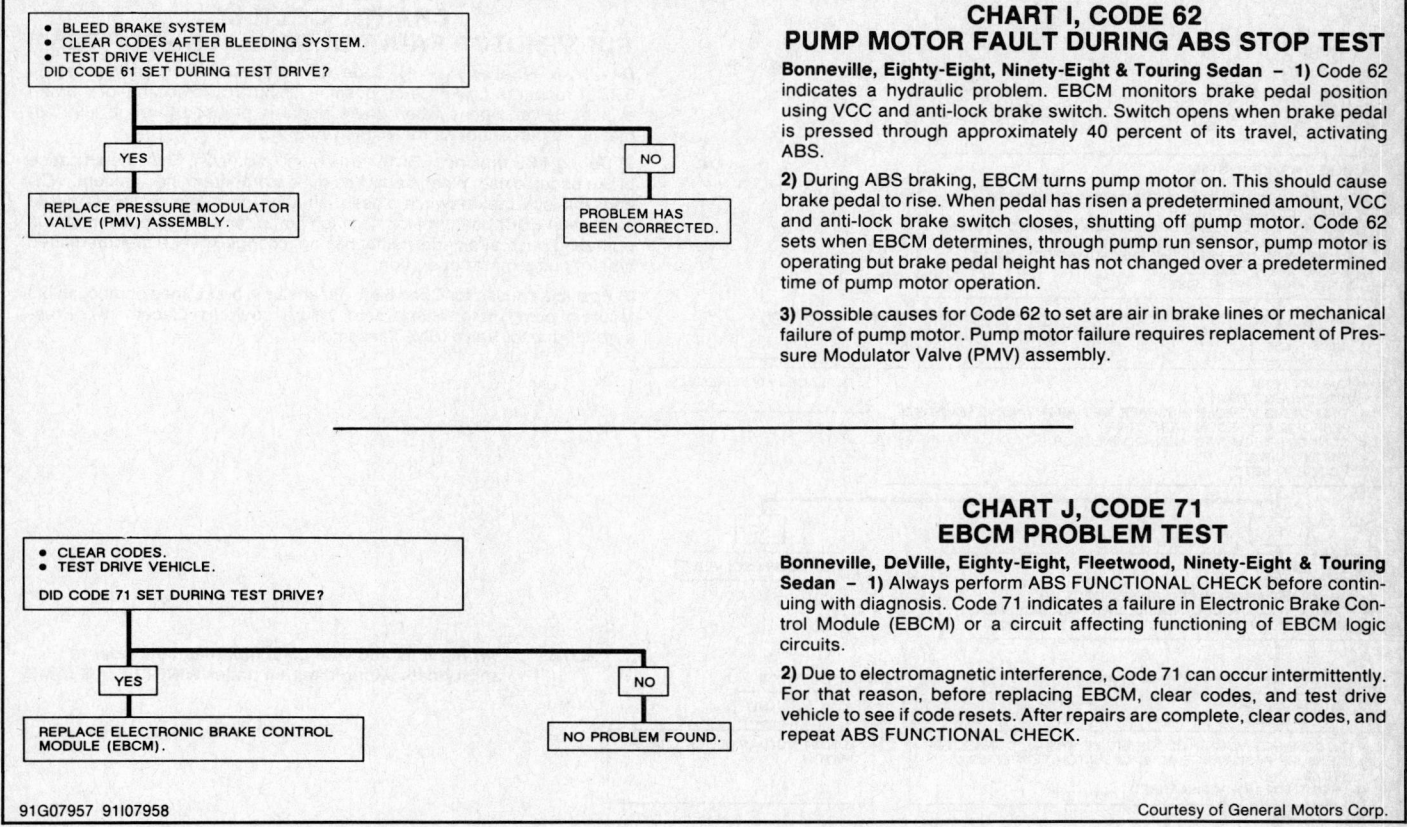

- BLEED BRAKE SYSTEM
- CLEAR CODES AFTER BLEEDING SYSTEM.
- TEST DRIVE VEHICLE
DID CODE 61 SET DURING TEST DRIVE?

YES → REPLACE PRESSURE MODULATOR VALVE (PMV) ASSEMBLY.

NO → PROBLEM HAS BEEN CORRECTED.

- CLEAR CODES.
- TEST DRIVE VEHICLE.
DID CODE 71 SET DURING TEST DRIVE?

YES → REPLACE ELECTRONIC BRAKE CONTROL MODULE (EBCM).

NO → NO PROBLEM FOUND.

CHART I, CODE 62
PUMP MOTOR FAULT DURING ABS STOP TEST

Bonneville, Eighty-Eight, Ninety-Eight & Touring Sedan – 1) Code 62 indicates a hydraulic problem. EBCM monitors brake pedal position using VCC and anti-lock brake switch. Switch opens when brake pedal is pressed through approximately 40 percent of its travel, activating ABS.

2) During ABS braking, EBCM turns pump motor on. This should cause brake pedal to rise. When pedal has risen a predetermined amount, VCC and anti-lock brake switch closes, shutting off pump motor. Code 62 sets when EBCM determines, through pump run sensor, pump motor is operating but brake pedal height has not changed over a predetermined time of pump motor operation.

3) Possible causes for Code 62 to set are air in brake lines or mechanical failure of pump motor. Pump motor failure requires replacement of Pressure Modulator Valve (PMV) assembly.

CHART J, CODE 71
EBCM PROBLEM TEST

Bonneville, DeVille, Eighty-Eight, Fleetwood, Ninety-Eight & Touring Sedan – 1) Always perform ABS FUNCTIONAL CHECK before continuing with diagnosis. Code 71 indicates a failure in Electronic Brake Control Module (EBCM) or a circuit affecting functioning of EBCM logic circuits.

2) Due to electromagnetic interference, Code 71 can occur intermittently. For that reason, before replacing EBCM, clear codes, and test drive vehicle to see if code resets. After repairs are complete, clear codes, and repeat ABS FUNCTIONAL CHECK.

91G07957 91I07958

CHART I, CODE 62
PUMP MOTOR FAULT DURING ABS STOP TEST

DeVille & Fleetwood – 1) Code 62 indicates a hydraulic problem. EBCM monitors brake pedal position using VCC and anti-lock brake switch. Switch opens when brake pedal is pressed through approximately 40 percent of its travel, activating ABS.

2) During ABS braking, EBCM turns pump motor on. This should cause brake pedal to rise. When pedal has risen a predetermined amount, VCC and anti-lock brake switch closes, shutting off pump motor. Code 62 sets when EBCM determines, through pump run sensor, pump motor is operating but brake pedal height has not changed over a predetermined time of pump motor operation.

3) Possible causes for Code 62 to set are air in brake lines or mechanical failure of pump motor. Pump motor failure requires replacement of Pressure Modulator Valve (PMV) assembly.

NOTE: For terminal and wire color identification, refer to appropriate wiring diagram under WIRING DIAGRAMS.

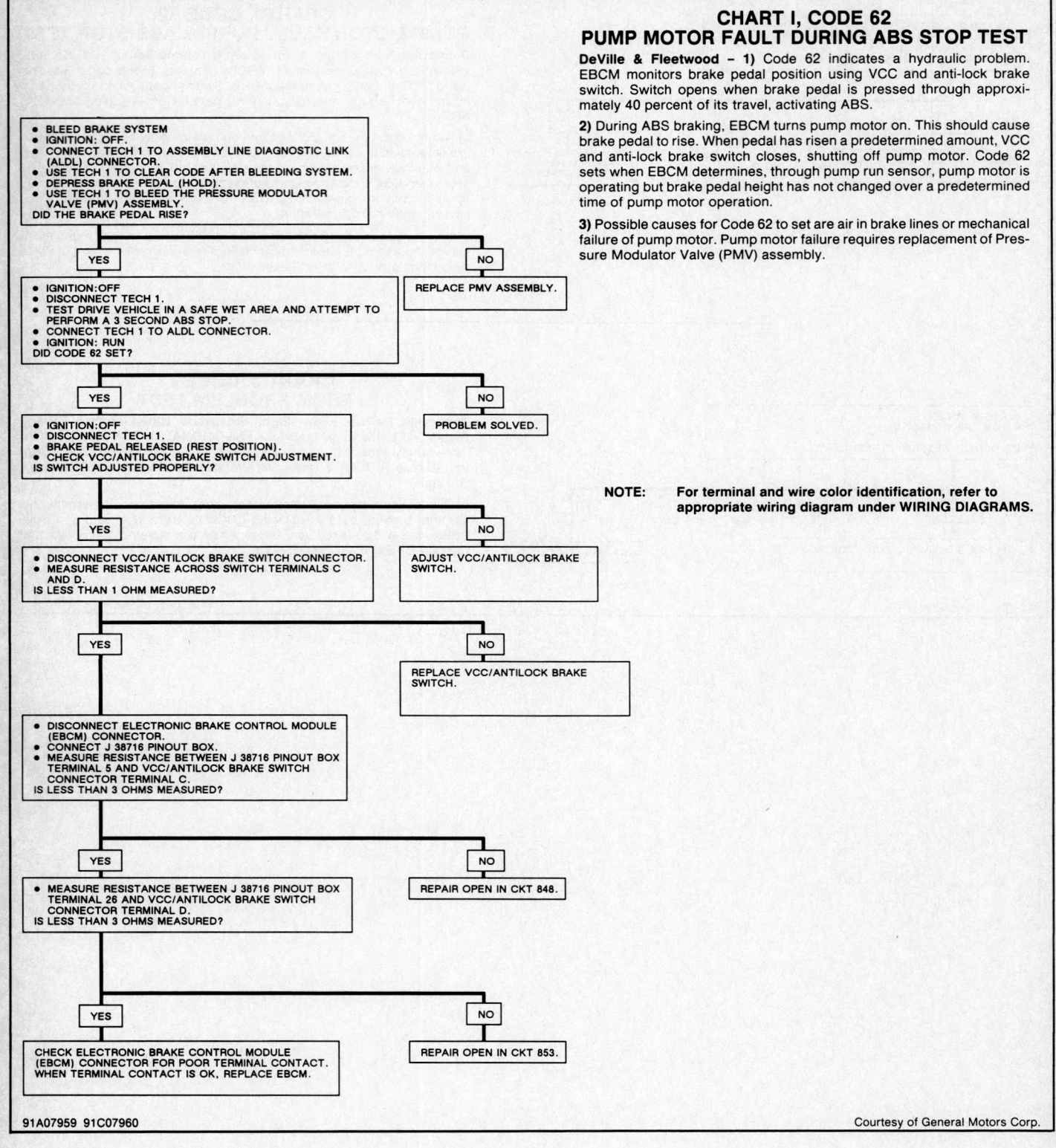

- BLEED BRAKE SYSTEM
- IGNITION: OFF.
- CONNECT TECH 1 TO ASSEMBLY LINE DIAGNOSTIC LINK (ALDL) CONNECTOR.
- USE TECH 1 TO CLEAR CODE AFTER BLEEDING SYSTEM.
- DEPRESS BRAKE PEDAL (HOLD).
- USE TECH 1 TO BLEED THE PRESSURE MODULATOR VALVE (PMV) ASSEMBLY.
DID THE BRAKE PEDAL RISE?

YES / NO → REPLACE PMV ASSEMBLY.

- IGNITION:OFF
- DISCONNECT TECH 1.
- TEST DRIVE VEHICLE IN A SAFE WET AREA AND ATTEMPT TO PERFORM A 3 SECOND ABS STOP.
- CONNECT TECH 1 TO ALDL CONNECTOR.
- IGNITION: RUN
DID CODE 62 SET?

YES / NO → PROBLEM SOLVED.

- IGNITION:OFF
- DISCONNECT TECH 1.
- BRAKE PEDAL RELEASED (REST POSITION).
- CHECK VCC/ANTILOCK BRAKE SWITCH ADJUSTMENT.
IS SWITCH ADJUSTED PROPERLY?

YES / NO → ADJUST VCC/ANTILOCK BRAKE SWITCH.

- DISCONNECT VCC/ANTILOCK BRAKE SWITCH CONNECTOR.
- MEASURE RESISTANCE ACROSS SWITCH TERMINALS C AND D.
IS LESS THAN 1 OHM MEASURED?

YES / NO → REPLACE VCC/ANTILOCK BRAKE SWITCH.

- DISCONNECT ELECTRONIC BRAKE CONTROL MODULE (EBCM) CONNECTOR.
- CONNECT J 38716 PINOUT BOX.
- MEASURE RESISTANCE BETWEEN J 38716 PINOUT BOX TERMINAL 5 AND VCC/ANTILOCK BRAKE SWITCH CONNECTOR TERMINAL C.
IS LESS THAN 3 OHMS MEASURED?

YES / NO → REPAIR OPEN IN CKT 848.

- MEASURE RESISTANCE BETWEEN J 38716 PINOUT BOX TERMINAL 26 AND VCC/ANTILOCK BRAKE SWITCH CONNECTOR TERMINAL D.
IS LESS THAN 3 OHMS MEASURED?

YES / NO → REPAIR OPEN IN CKT 853.

CHECK ELECTRONIC BRAKE CONTROL MODULE (EBCM) CONNECTOR FOR POOR TERMINAL CONTACT. WHEN TERMINAL CONTACT IS OK, REPLACE EBCM.

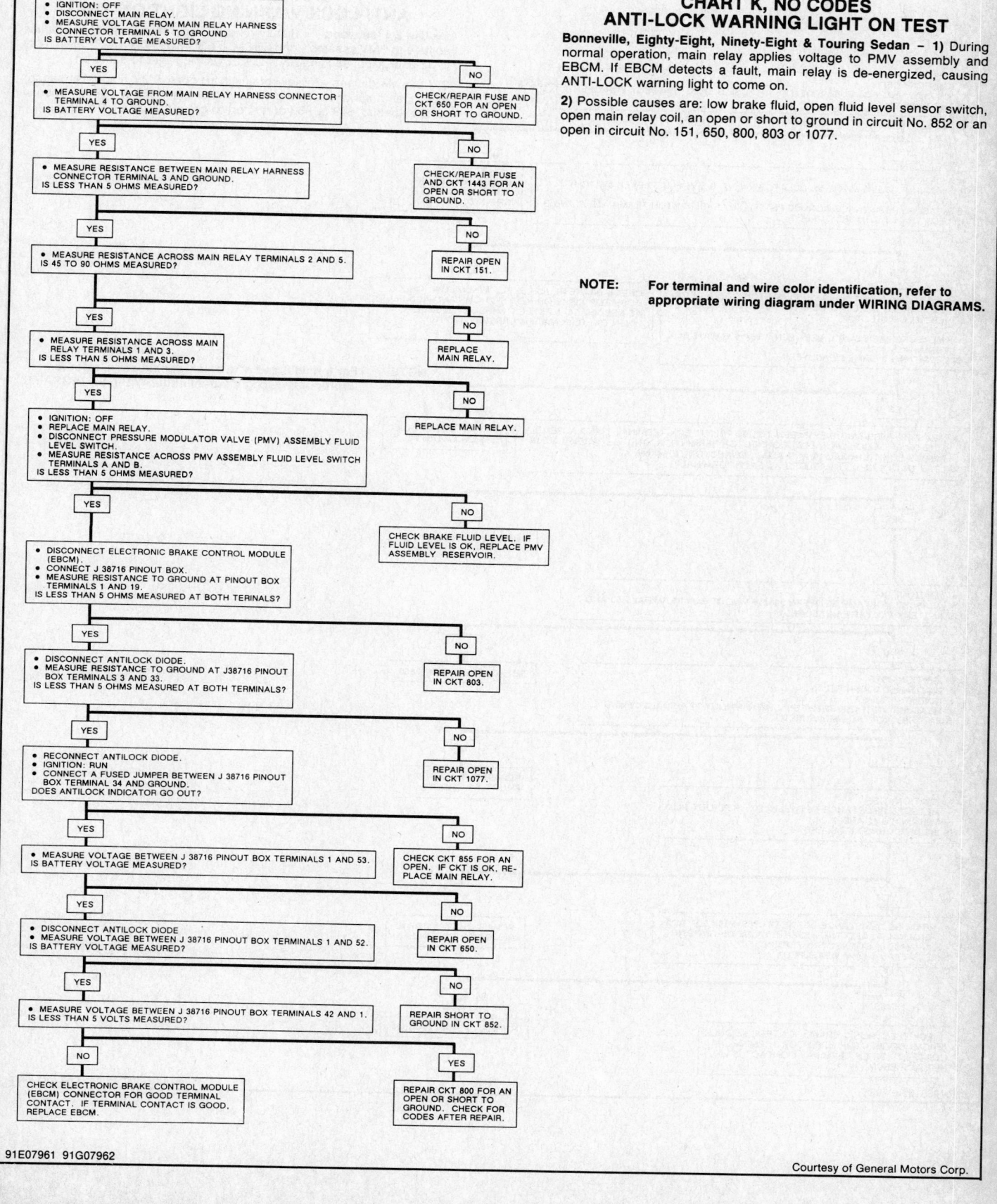

CHART K, NO CODES
ANTI-LOCK WARNING LIGHT ON TEST

Bonneville, Eighty-Eight, Ninety-Eight & Touring Sedan – 1) During normal operation, main relay applies voltage to PMV assembly and EBCM. If EBCM detects a fault, main relay is de-energized, causing ANTI-LOCK warning light to come on.

2) Possible causes are: low brake fluid, open fluid level sensor switch, open main relay coil, an open or short to ground in circuit No. 852 or an open in circuit No. 151, 650, 800, 803 or 1077.

NOTE: For terminal and wire color identification, refer to appropriate wiring diagram under **WIRING DIAGRAMS.**

Flowchart content:

- IGNITION: OFF
- DISCONNECT MAIN RELAY.
- MEASURE VOLTAGE FROM MAIN RELAY HARNESS CONNECTOR TERMINAL 5 TO GROUND
- IS BATTERY VOLTAGE MEASURED?

YES / NO → CHECK/REPAIR FUSE AND CKT 650 FOR AN OPEN OR SHORT TO GROUND.

- MEASURE VOLTAGE FROM MAIN RELAY HARNESS CONNECTOR TERMINAL 4 TO GROUND.
- IS BATTERY VOLTAGE MEASURED?

YES / NO → CHECK/REPAIR FUSE AND CKT 1443 FOR AN OPEN OR SHORT TO GROUND.

- MEASURE RESISTANCE BETWEEN MAIN RELAY HARNESS CONNECTOR TERMINAL 3 AND GROUND.
- IS LESS THAN 5 OHMS MEASURED?

YES / NO → REPAIR OPEN IN CKT 151.

- MEASURE RESISTANCE ACROSS MAIN RELAY TERMINALS 2 AND 5.
- IS 45 TO 90 OHMS MEASURED?

YES / NO → REPLACE MAIN RELAY.

- MEASURE RESISTANCE ACROSS MAIN RELAY TERMINALS 1 AND 3.
- IS LESS THAN 5 OHMS MEASURED?

YES / NO → REPLACE MAIN RELAY.

- IGNITION: OFF
- REPLACE MAIN RELAY.
- DISCONNECT PRESSURE MODULATOR VALVE (PMV) ASSEMBLY FLUID LEVEL SWITCH.
- MEASURE RESISTANCE ACROSS PMV ASSEMBLY FLUID LEVEL SWITCH TERMINALS A AND B.
- IS LESS THAN 5 OHMS MEASURED?

YES / NO → CHECK BRAKE FLUID LEVEL. IF FLUID LEVEL IS OK, REPLACE PMV ASSEMBLY RESERVOIR.

- DISCONNECT ELECTRONIC BRAKE CONTROL MODULE (EBCM).
- CONNECT J 38716 PINOUT BOX.
- MEASURE RESISTANCE TO GROUND AT PINOUT BOX TERMINALS 1 AND 19.
- IS LESS THAN 5 OHMS MEASURED AT BOTH TERINALS?

YES / NO → REPAIR OPEN IN CKT 803.

- DISCONNECT ANTILOCK DIODE.
- MEASURE RESISTANCE TO GROUND AT J38716 PINOUT BOX TERMINALS 3 AND 33.
- IS LESS THAN 5 OHMS MEASURED AT BOTH TERMINALS?

YES / NO → REPAIR OPEN IN CKT 1077.

- RECONNECT ANTILOCK DIODE.
- IGNITION: RUN
- CONNECT A FUSED JUMPER BETWEEN J 38716 PINOUT BOX TERMINAL 34 AND GROUND.
- DOES ANTILOCK INDICATOR GO OUT?

YES / NO → CHECK CKT 855 FOR AN OPEN. IF CKT IS OK, REPLACE MAIN RELAY.

- MEASURE VOLTAGE BETWEEN J 38716 PINOUT BOX TERMINALS 1 AND 53.
- IS BATTERY VOLTAGE MEASURED?

YES / NO → REPAIR OPEN IN CKT 650.

- DISCONNECT ANTILOCK DIODE
- MEASURE VOLTAGE BETWEEN J 38716 PINOUT BOX TERMINALS 1 AND 52.
- IS BATTERY VOLTAGE MEASURED?

YES / NO → REPAIR SHORT TO GROUND IN CKT 852.

- MEASURE VOLTAGE BETWEEN J 38716 PINOUT BOX TERMINALS 42 AND 1.
- IS LESS THAN 5 VOLTS MEASURED?

NO → CHECK ELECTRONIC BRAKE CONTROL MODULE (EBCM) CONNECTOR FOR GOOD TERMINAL CONTACT. IF TERMINAL CONTACT IS GOOD, REPLACE EBCM.

YES → REPAIR CKT 800 FOR AN OPEN OR SHORT TO GROUND. CHECK FOR CODES AFTER REPAIR.

91E07961 91G07962

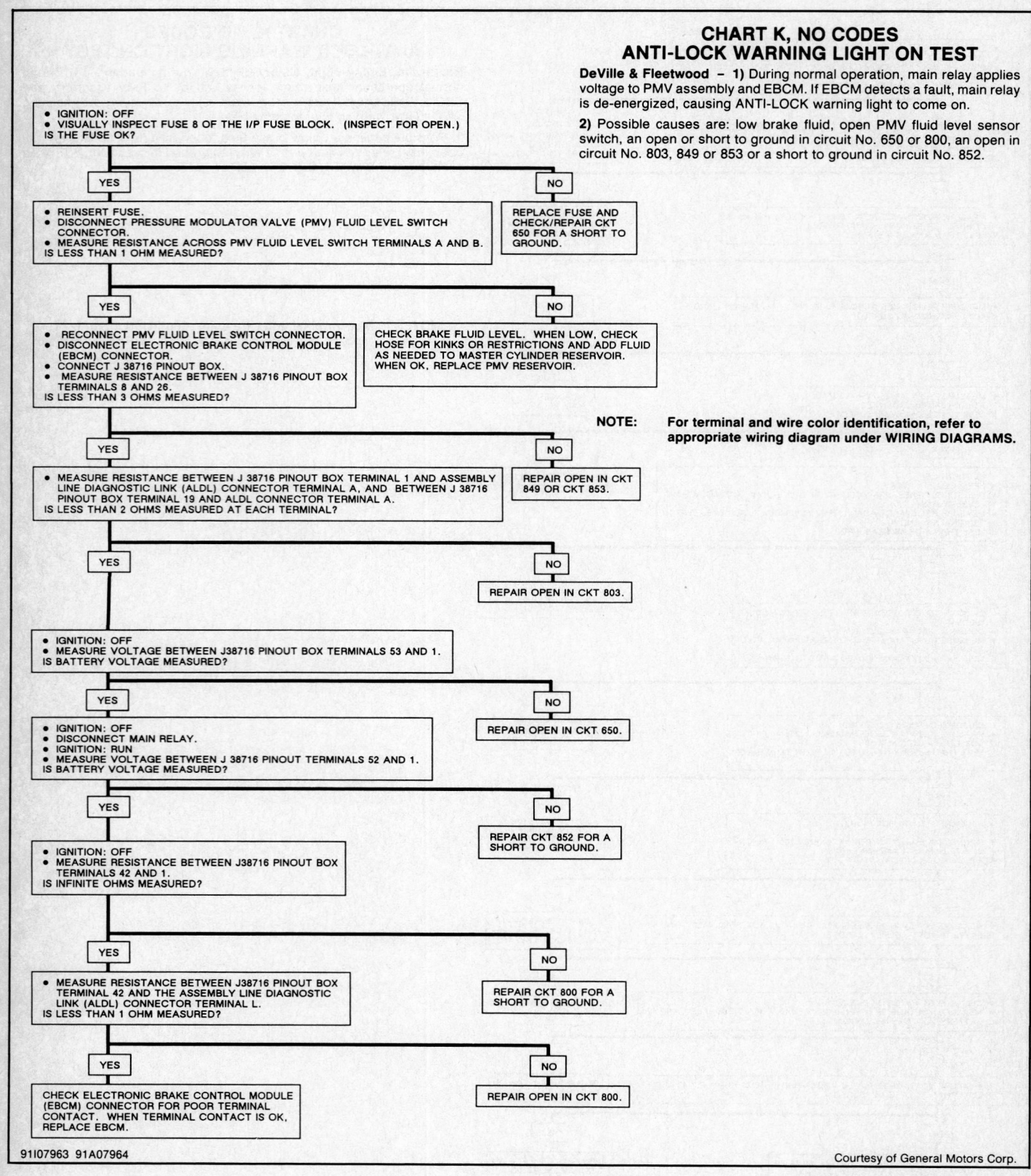

CHART K, NO CODES
ANTI-LOCK WARNING LIGHT ON TEST

DeVille & Fleetwood – 1) During normal operation, main relay applies voltage to PMV assembly and EBCM. If EBCM detects a fault, main relay is de-energized, causing ANTI-LOCK warning light to come on.

2) Possible causes are: low brake fluid, open PMV fluid level sensor switch, an open or short to ground in circuit No. 650 or 800, an open in circuit No. 803, 849 or 853 or a short to ground in circuit No. 852.

- IGNITION: OFF
- VISUALLY INSPECT FUSE 8 OF THE I/P FUSE BLOCK. (INSPECT FOR OPEN.) IS THE FUSE OK?

YES

NO → REPLACE FUSE AND CHECK/REPAIR CKT 650 FOR A SHORT TO GROUND.

- REINSERT FUSE.
- DISCONNECT PRESSURE MODULATOR VALVE (PMV) FLUID LEVEL SWITCH CONNECTOR.
- MEASURE RESISTANCE ACROSS PMV FLUID LEVEL SWITCH TERMINALS A AND B. IS LESS THAN 1 OHM MEASURED?

YES

NO → CHECK BRAKE FLUID LEVEL. WHEN LOW, CHECK HOSE FOR KINKS OR RESTRICTIONS AND ADD FLUID AS NEEDED TO MASTER CYLINDER RESERVOIR. WHEN OK, REPLACE PMV RESERVOIR.

- RECONNECT PMV FLUID LEVEL SWITCH CONNECTOR.
- DISCONNECT ELECTRONIC BRAKE CONTROL MODULE (EBCM) CONNECTOR.
- CONNECT J 38716 PINOUT BOX.
- MEASURE RESISTANCE BETWEEN J 38716 PINOUT BOX TERMINALS 8 AND 26. IS LESS THAN 3 OHMS MEASURED?

NOTE: For terminal and wire color identification, refer to appropriate wiring diagram under **WIRING DIAGRAMS**.

YES

NO → REPAIR OPEN IN CKT 849 OR CKT 853.

- MEASURE RESISTANCE BETWEEN J 38716 PINOUT BOX TERMINAL 1 AND ASSEMBLY LINE DIAGNOSTIC LINK (ALDL) CONNECTOR TERMINAL A, AND BETWEEN J 38716 PINOUT BOX TERMINAL 19 AND ALDL CONNECTOR TERMINAL A. IS LESS THAN 2 OHMS MEASURED AT EACH TERMINAL?

YES

NO → REPAIR OPEN IN CKT 803.

- IGNITION: OFF
- MEASURE VOLTAGE BETWEEN J38716 PINOUT BOX TERMINALS 53 AND 1. IS BATTERY VOLTAGE MEASURED?

YES

NO → REPAIR OPEN IN CKT 650.

- IGNITION: OFF
- DISCONNECT MAIN RELAY.
- IGNITION: RUN
- MEASURE VOLTAGE BETWEEN J 38716 PINOUT TERMINALS 52 AND 1. IS BATTERY VOLTAGE MEASURED?

YES

NO → REPAIR CKT 852 FOR A SHORT TO GROUND.

- IGNITION: OFF
- MEASURE RESISTANCE BETWEEN J38716 PINOUT BOX TERMINALS 42 AND 1. IS INFINITE OHMS MEASURED?

YES

NO → REPAIR CKT 800 FOR A SHORT TO GROUND.

- MEASURE RESISTANCE BETWEEN J38716 PINOUT BOX TERMINAL 42 AND THE ASSEMBLY LINE DIAGNOSTIC LINK (ALDL) CONNECTOR TERMINAL L. IS LESS THAN 1 OHM MEASURED?

YES

NO → REPAIR OPEN IN CKT 800.

CHECK ELECTRONIC BRAKE CONTROL MODULE (EBCM) CONNECTOR FOR POOR TERMINAL CONTACT. WHEN TERMINAL CONTACT IS OK, REPLACE EBCM.

91I07963 91A07964

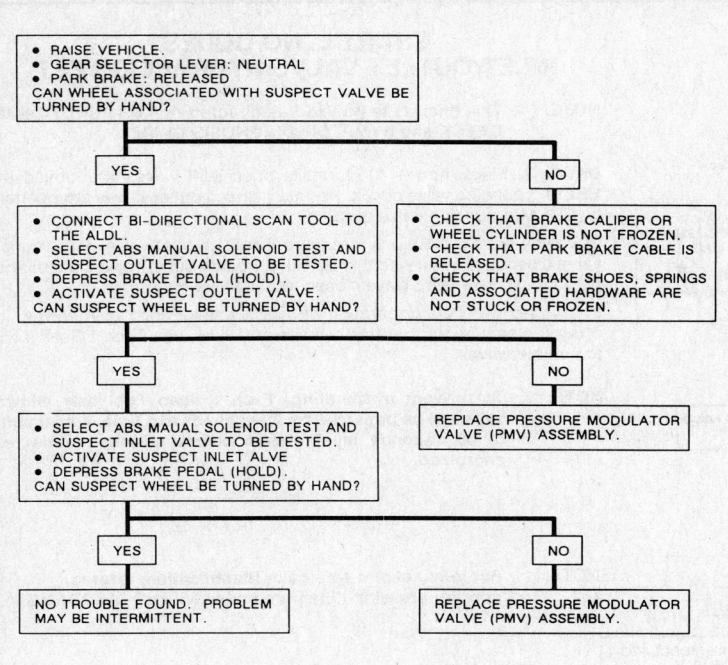

CHART L, NO CODES
INLET/OUTLET VALVE HYDRAULIC TEST

NOTE: This chart is to be used as directed by **ABS FUNCTIONAL CHECK** and **SYMPTOM DIAGNOSIS GUIDE.**

Bonneville, Eighty-Eight, Ninety-Eight & Touring Sedan – 1) Normally open inlet valves are closed by EBCM grounding valve circuit. Normally closed outlet valves are opened by EBCM grounding valve circuit.

2) Valves have 3 positions: pressure increase (inlet valve open, outlet valve closed), pressure hold (inlet valve closed, outlet valve closed) and pressure reduce (inlet valve closed, outlet valve open).

3) This test will verify operation of hydraulic inlet and outlet valves. In order to verify hydraulic effectiveness of valves, use Tech 1 Scan Tool to actuate valves.

NOTE: To prevent overheating, **Tech 1 Scan Tool** only allows valves to be activated for 20 seconds at a time. A minimum of 30 seconds must elapse before valves can be re-energized.

NOTE: For terminal and wire color identification, refer to appropriate wiring diagram under **WIRING DIAGRAMS.**

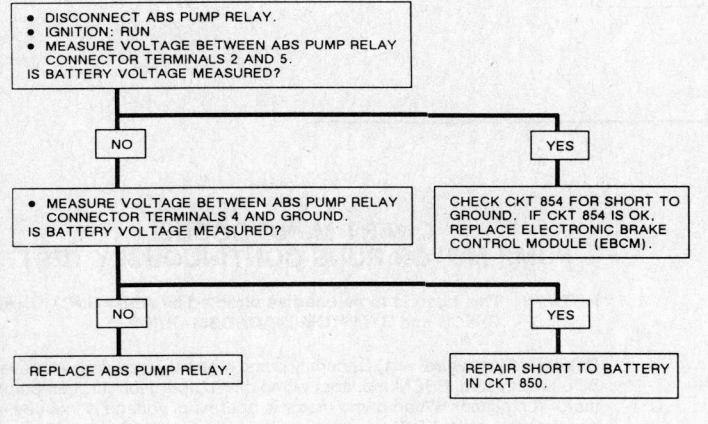

CHART M, NO CODES
PUMP MOTOR RUNS CONTINUOUSLY TEST

NOTE: This chart is to be used as directed by **ABS FUNCTIONAL CHECK** and **SYMPTOM DIAGNOSIS GUIDE.**

Bonneville, Eighty-Eight, Ninety-Eight & Touring Sedan – 1) Generally pump motor is operating whenever ABS is activated. EBCM monitors pump motor operation through pump motor run sensor. When pump motor is operating, voltage is induced in run sensor's coils. EBCM monitors voltage at pins No. 31 and 49.

2) Possible causes of pump motor running continuously are pump relay is shorted to ground or circuit No. 850 is shorted to battery voltage.

91D07965 91F07966

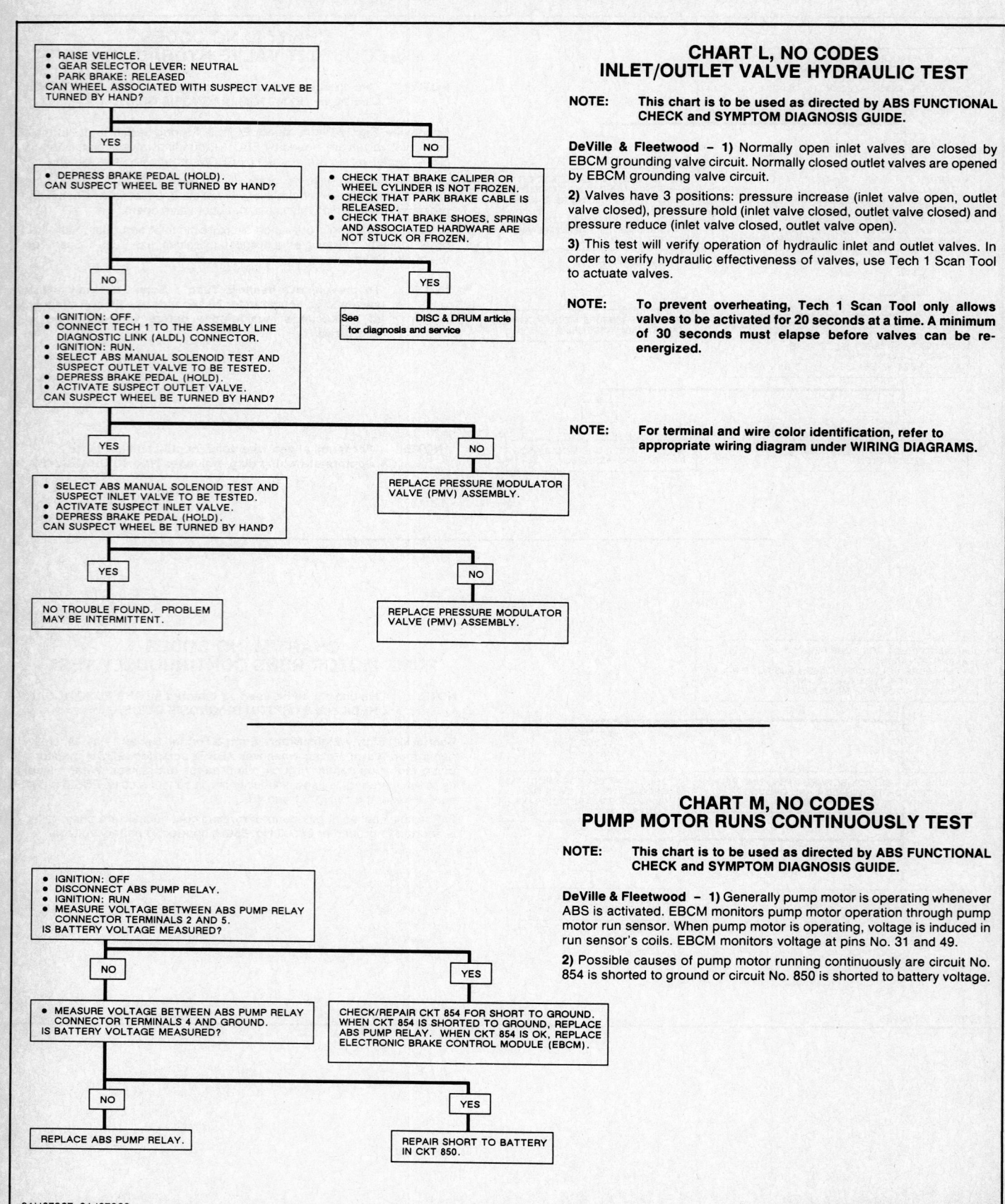

CHART L, NO CODES
INLET/OUTLET VALVE HYDRAULIC TEST

NOTE: This chart is to be used as directed by ABS FUNCTIONAL CHECK and SYMPTOM DIAGNOSIS GUIDE.

DeVille & Fleetwood – 1) Normally open inlet valves are closed by EBCM grounding valve circuit. Normally closed outlet valves are opened by EBCM grounding valve circuit.

2) Valves have 3 positions: pressure increase (inlet valve open, outlet valve closed), pressure hold (inlet valve closed, outlet valve closed) and pressure reduce (inlet valve closed, outlet valve open).

3) This test will verify operation of hydraulic inlet and outlet valves. In order to verify hydraulic effectiveness of valves, use Tech 1 Scan Tool to actuate valves.

NOTE: To prevent overheating, Tech 1 Scan Tool only allows valves to be activated for 20 seconds at a time. A minimum of 30 seconds must elapse before valves can be re-energized.

NOTE: For terminal and wire color identification, refer to appropriate wiring diagram under WIRING DIAGRAMS.

CHART M, NO CODES
PUMP MOTOR RUNS CONTINUOUSLY TEST

NOTE: This chart is to be used as directed by ABS FUNCTIONAL CHECK and SYMPTOM DIAGNOSIS GUIDE.

DeVille & Fleetwood – 1) Generally pump motor is operating whenever ABS is activated. EBCM monitors pump motor operation through pump motor run sensor. When pump motor is operating, voltage is induced in run sensor's coils. EBCM monitors voltage at pins No. 31 and 49.

2) Possible causes of pump motor running continuously are circuit No. 854 is shorted to ground or circuit No. 850 is shorted to battery voltage.

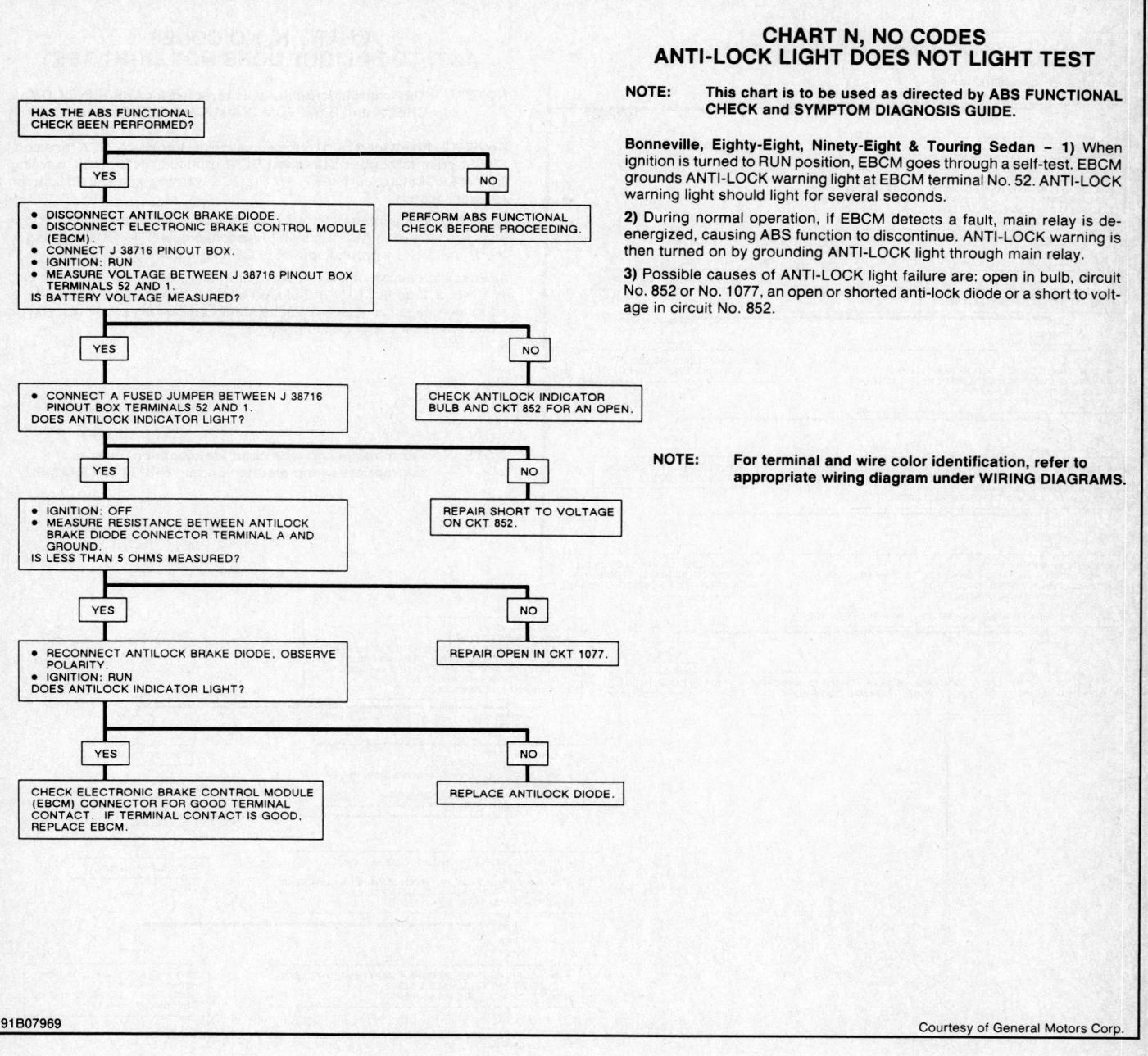

CHART N, NO CODES
ANTI-LOCK LIGHT DOES NOT LIGHT TEST

NOTE: This chart is to be used as directed by ABS FUNCTIONAL CHECK and SYMPTOM DIAGNOSIS GUIDE.

Bonneville, Eighty-Eight, Ninety-Eight & Touring Sedan – 1) When ignition is turned to RUN position, EBCM goes through a self-test. EBCM grounds ANTI-LOCK warning light at EBCM terminal No. 52. ANTI-LOCK warning light should light for several seconds.

2) During normal operation, if EBCM detects a fault, main relay is de-energized, causing ABS function to discontinue. ANTI-LOCK warning is then turned on by grounding ANTI-LOCK light through main relay.

3) Possible causes of ANTI-LOCK light failure are: open in bulb, circuit No. 852 or No. 1077, an open or shorted anti-lock diode or a short to voltage in circuit No. 852.

NOTE: For terminal and wire color identification, refer to appropriate wiring diagram under WIRING DIAGRAMS.

Flowchart content:

HAS THE ABS FUNCTIONAL CHECK BEEN PERFORMED?
- YES:
  - DISCONNECT ANTILOCK BRAKE DIODE.
  - DISCONNECT ELECTRONIC BRAKE CONTROL MODULE (EBCM).
  - CONNECT J 38716 PINOUT BOX.
  - IGNITION: RUN
  - MEASURE VOLTAGE BETWEEN J 38716 PINOUT BOX TERMINALS 52 AND 1.
  IS BATTERY VOLTAGE MEASURED?
- NO: PERFORM ABS FUNCTIONAL CHECK BEFORE PROCEEDING.

IS BATTERY VOLTAGE MEASURED?
- YES:
  - CONNECT A FUSED JUMPER BETWEEN J 38716 PINOUT BOX TERMINALS 52 AND 1.
  DOES ANTILOCK INDICATOR LIGHT?
- NO: CHECK ANTILOCK INDICATOR BULB AND CKT 852 FOR AN OPEN.

DOES ANTILOCK INDICATOR LIGHT?
- YES:
  - IGNITION: OFF
  - MEASURE RESISTANCE BETWEEN ANTILOCK BRAKE DIODE CONNECTOR TERMINAL A AND GROUND.
  IS LESS THAN 5 OHMS MEASURED?
- NO: REPAIR SHORT TO VOLTAGE ON CKT 852.

IS LESS THAN 5 OHMS MEASURED?
- YES:
  - RECONNECT ANTILOCK BRAKE DIODE. OBSERVE POLARITY.
  - IGNITION: RUN
  DOES ANTILOCK INDICATOR LIGHT?
- NO: REPAIR OPEN IN CKT 1077.

DOES ANTILOCK INDICATOR LIGHT?
- YES: CHECK ELECTRONIC BRAKE CONTROL MODULE (EBCM) CONNECTOR FOR GOOD TERMINAL CONTACT. IF TERMINAL CONTACT IS GOOD, REPLACE EBCM.
- NO: REPLACE ANTILOCK DIODE.

91B07969

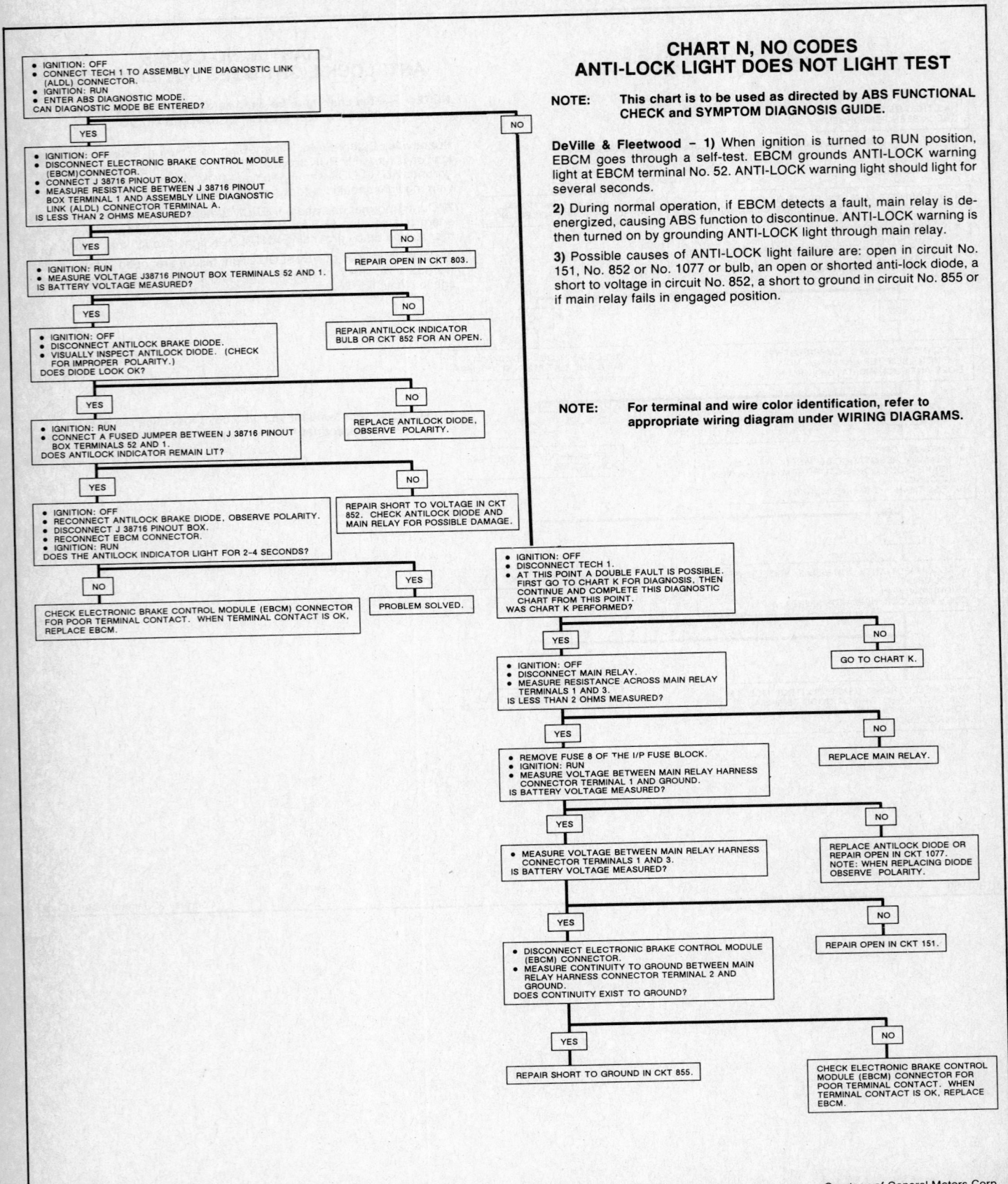

CHART N, NO CODES
ANTI-LOCK LIGHT DOES NOT LIGHT TEST

NOTE: This chart is to be used as directed by ABS FUNCTIONAL CHECK and SYMPTOM DIAGNOSIS GUIDE.

DeVille & Fleetwood – 1) When ignition is turned to RUN position, EBCM goes through a self-test. EBCM grounds ANTI-LOCK warning light at EBCM terminal No. 52. ANTI-LOCK warning light should light for several seconds.

2) During normal operation, if EBCM detects a fault, main relay is de-energized, causing ABS function to discontinue. ANTI-LOCK warning is then turned on by grounding ANTI-LOCK light through main relay.

3) Possible causes of ANTI-LOCK light failure are: open in circuit No. 151, No. 852 or No. 1077 or bulb, an open or shorted anti-lock diode, a short to voltage in circuit No. 852, a short to ground in circuit No. 855 or if main relay fails in engaged position.

NOTE: For terminal and wire color identification, refer to appropriate wiring diagram under WIRING DIAGRAMS.

The flowchart contains the following boxes:

- IGNITION: OFF
- CONNECT TECH 1 TO ASSEMBLY LINE DIAGNOSTIC LINK (ALDL) CONNECTOR.
- IGNITION: RUN
- ENTER ABS DIAGNOSTIC MODE.
CAN DIAGNOSTIC MODE BE ENTERED?

- IGNITION: OFF
- DISCONNECT ELECTRONIC BRAKE CONTROL MODULE (EBCM) CONNECTOR.
- CONNECT J 38716 PINOUT BOX.
- MEASURE RESISTANCE BETWEEN J 38716 PINOUT BOX TERMINAL 1 AND ASSEMBLY LINE DIAGNOSTIC LINK (ALDL) CONNECTOR TERMINAL A.
IS LESS THAN 2 OHMS MEASURED?

REPAIR OPEN IN CKT 803.

- IGNITION: RUN
- MEASURE VOLTAGE J38716 PINOUT BOX TERMINALS 52 AND 1.
IS BATTERY VOLTAGE MEASURED?

REPAIR ANTILOCK INDICATOR BULB OR CKT 852 FOR AN OPEN.

- IGNITION: OFF
- DISCONNECT ANTILOCK BRAKE DIODE.
- VISUALLY INSPECT ANTILOCK DIODE. (CHECK FOR IMPROPER POLARITY.)
DOES DIODE LOOK OK?

REPLACE ANTILOCK DIODE, OBSERVE POLARITY.

- IGNITION: RUN
- CONNECT A FUSED JUMPER BETWEEN J 38716 PINOUT BOX TERMINALS 52 AND 1.
DOES ANTILOCK INDICATOR REMAIN LIT?

REPAIR SHORT TO VOLTAGE IN CKT 852. CHECK ANTILOCK DIODE AND MAIN RELAY FOR POSSIBLE DAMAGE.

- IGNITION: OFF
- RECONNECT ANTILOCK BRAKE DIODE, OBSERVE POLARITY.
- DISCONNECT J 38716 PINOUT BOX.
- RECONNECT EBCM CONNECTOR.
- IGNITION: RUN
DOES THE ANTILOCK INDICATOR LIGHT FOR 2–4 SECONDS?

CHECK ELECTRONIC BRAKE CONTROL MODULE (EBCM) CONNECTOR FOR POOR TERMINAL CONTACT. WHEN TERMINAL CONTACT IS OK, REPLACE EBCM.

PROBLEM SOLVED.

- IGNITION: OFF
- DISCONNECT TECH 1.
- AT THIS POINT A DOUBLE FAULT IS POSSIBLE. FIRST GO TO CHART K FOR DIAGNOSIS, THEN CONTINUE AND COMPLETE THIS DIAGNOSTIC CHART FROM THIS POINT.
WAS CHART K PERFORMED?

GO TO CHART K.

- IGNITION: OFF
- DISCONNECT MAIN RELAY.
- MEASURE RESISTANCE ACROSS MAIN RELAY TERMINALS 1 AND 3.
IS LESS THAN 2 OHMS MEASURED?

REPLACE MAIN RELAY.

- REMOVE FUSE 8 OF THE I/P FUSE BLOCK.
- IGNITION: RUN
- MEASURE VOLTAGE BETWEEN MAIN RELAY HARNESS CONNECTOR TERMINAL 1 AND GROUND.
IS BATTERY VOLTAGE MEASURED?

REPLACE ANTILOCK DIODE OR REPAIR OPEN IN CKT 1077. NOTE: WHEN REPLACING DIODE OBSERVE POLARITY.

- MEASURE VOLTAGE BETWEEN MAIN RELAY HARNESS CONNECTOR TERMINALS 1 AND 3.
IS BATTERY VOLTAGE MEASURED?

REPAIR OPEN IN CKT 151.

- DISCONNECT ELECTRONIC BRAKE CONTROL MODULE (EBCM) CONNECTOR.
- MEASURE CONTINUITY TO GROUND BETWEEN MAIN RELAY HARNESS CONNECTOR TERMINAL 2 AND GROUND.
DOES CONTINUITY EXIST TO GROUND?

REPAIR SHORT TO GROUND IN CKT 855.

CHECK ELECTRONIC BRAKE CONTROL MODULE (EBCM) CONNECTOR FOR POOR TERMINAL CONTACT. WHEN TERMINAL CONTACT IS OK, REPLACE EBCM.

Courtesy of General Motors Corp.

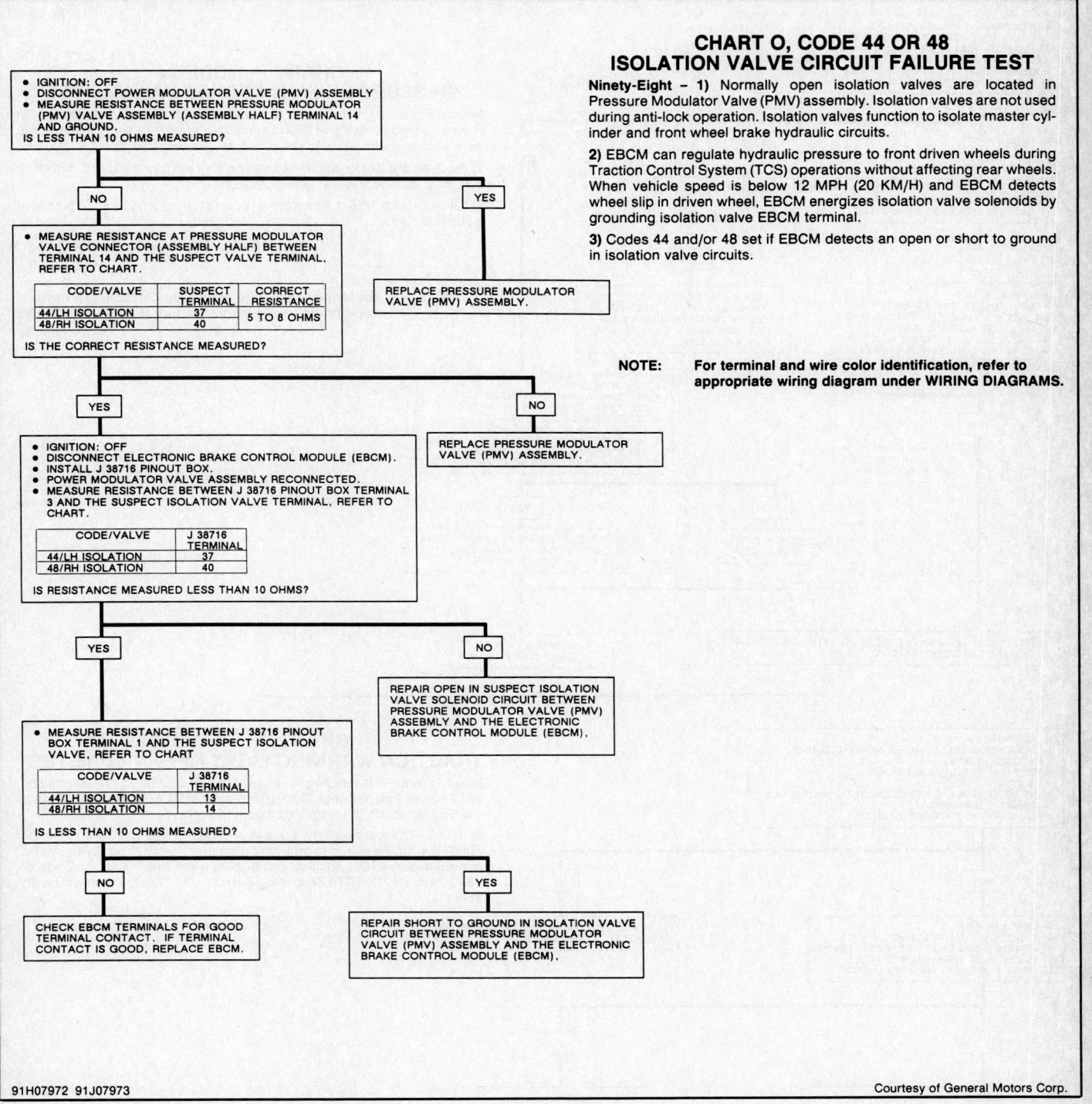

CHART O, CODE 44 OR 48
ISOLATION VALVE CIRCUIT FAILURE TEST

Ninety-Eight – 1) Normally open isolation valves are located in Pressure Modulator Valve (PMV) assembly. Isolation valves are not used during anti-lock operation. Isolation valves function to isolate master cylinder and front wheel brake hydraulic circuits.

2) EBCM can regulate hydraulic pressure to front driven wheels during Traction Control System (TCS) operations without affecting rear wheels. When vehicle speed is below 12 MPH (20 KM/H) and EBCM detects wheel slip in driven wheel, EBCM energizes isolation valve solenoids by grounding isolation valve EBCM terminal.

3) Codes 44 and/or 48 set if EBCM detects an open or short to ground in isolation valve circuits.

NOTE: For terminal and wire color identification, refer to appropriate wiring diagram under WIRING DIAGRAMS.

Content of flowchart:

- IGNITION: OFF
- DISCONNECT POWER MODULATOR VALVE (PMV) ASSEMBLY
- MEASURE RESISTANCE BETWEEN PRESSURE MODULATOR (PMV) VALVE ASSEMBLY (ASSEMBLY HALF) TERMINAL 14 AND GROUND.
IS LESS THAN 10 OHMS MEASURED?

NO / YES

YES → REPLACE PRESSURE MODULATOR VALVE (PMV) ASSEMBLY.

- MEASURE RESISTANCE AT PRESSURE MODULATOR VALVE CONNECTOR (ASSEMBLY HALF) BETWEEN TERMINAL 14 AND THE SUSPECT VALVE TERMINAL, REFER TO CHART.

CODE/VALVE	SUSPECT TERMINAL	CORRECT RESISTANCE
44/LH ISOLATION	37	5 TO 8 OHMS
48/RH ISOLATION	40	

IS THE CORRECT RESISTANCE MEASURED?

YES / NO

NO → REPLACE PRESSURE MODULATOR VALVE (PMV) ASSEMBLY.

- IGNITION: OFF
- DISCONNECT ELECTRONIC BRAKE CONTROL MODULE (EBCM).
- INSTALL J 38716 PINOUT BOX.
- POWER MODULATOR VALVE ASSEMBLY RECONNECTED.
- MEASURE RESISTANCE BETWEEN J 38716 PINOUT BOX TERMINAL 3 AND THE SUSPECT ISOLATION VALVE TERMINAL, REFER TO CHART.

CODE/VALVE	J 38716 TERMINAL
44/LH ISOLATION	37
48/RH ISOLATION	40

IS RESISTANCE MEASURED LESS THAN 10 OHMS?

YES / NO

NO → REPAIR OPEN IN SUSPECT ISOLATION VALVE SOLENOID CIRCUIT BETWEEN PRESSURE MODULATOR VALVE (PMV) ASSEBMLY AND THE ELECTRONIC BRAKE CONTROL MODULE (EBCM).

- MEASURE RESISTANCE BETWEEN J 38716 PINOUT BOX TERMINAL 1 AND THE SUSPECT ISOLATION VALVE, REFER TO CHART

CODE/VALVE	J 38716 TERMINAL
44/LH ISOLATION	13
48/RH ISOLATION	14

IS LESS THAN 10 OHMS MEASURED?

NO / YES

NO → CHECK EBCM TERMINALS FOR GOOD TERMINAL CONTACT. IF TERMINAL CONTACT IS GOOD, REPLACE EBCM.

YES → REPAIR SHORT TO GROUND IN ISOLATION VALVE CIRCUIT BETWEEN PRESSURE MODULATOR VALVE (PMV) ASSEMBLY AND THE ELECTRONIC BRAKE CONTROL MODULE (EBCM).

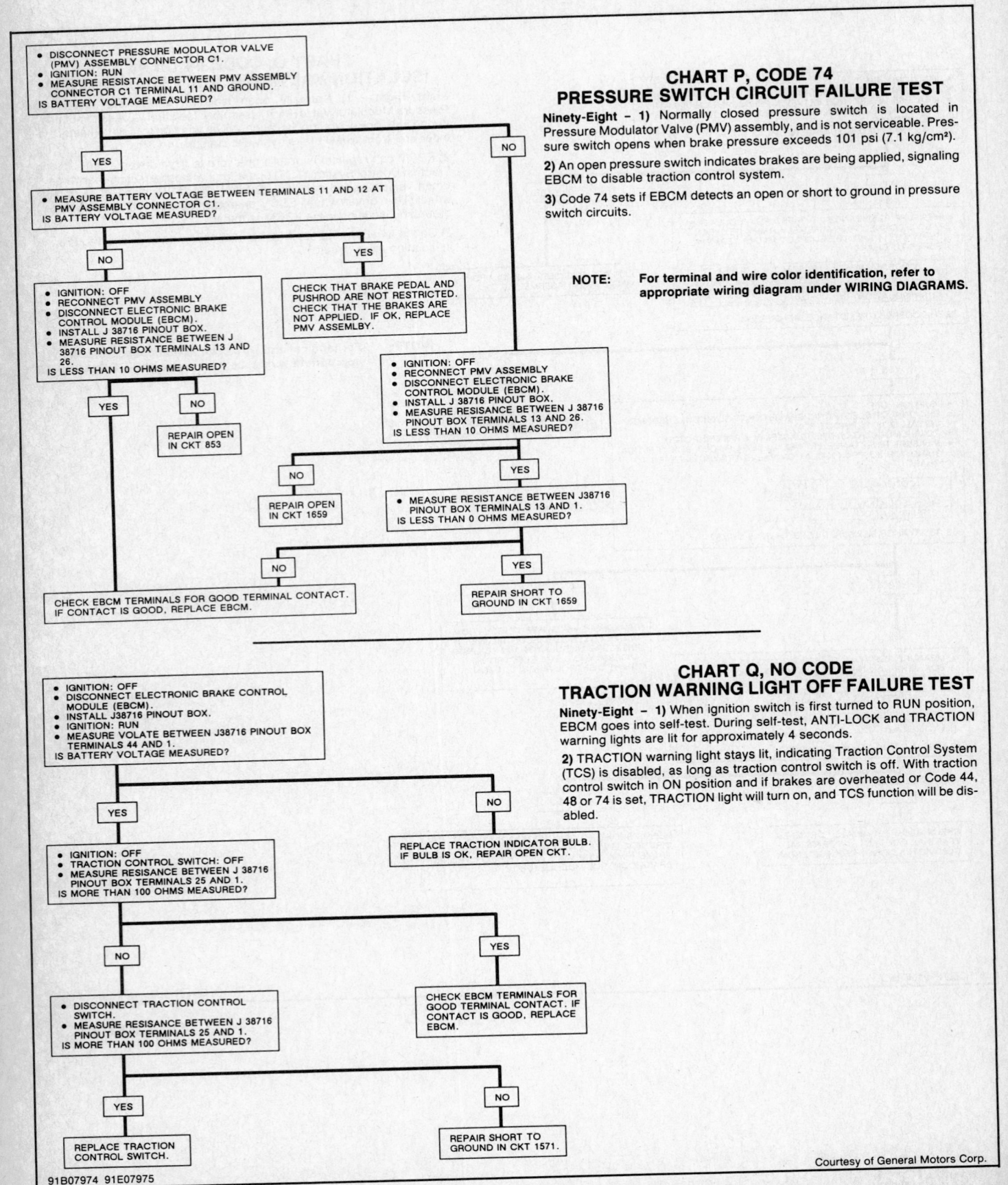

CHART P, CODE 74
PRESSURE SWITCH CIRCUIT FAILURE TEST

Ninety-Eight – 1) Normally closed pressure switch is located in Pressure Modulator Valve (PMV) assembly, and is not serviceable. Pressure switch opens when brake pressure exceeds 101 psi (7.1 kg/cm²).

2) An open pressure switch indicates brakes are being applied, signaling EBCM to disable traction control system.

3) Code 74 sets if EBCM detects an open or short to ground in pressure switch circuits.

NOTE: For terminal and wire color identification, refer to appropriate wiring diagram under WIRING DIAGRAMS.

Flowchart boxes:

- DISCONNECT PRESSURE MODULATOR VALVE (PMV) ASSEMBLY CONNECTOR C1.
- IGNITION: RUN
- MEASURE RESISTANCE BETWEEN PMV ASSEMBLY CONNECTOR C1 TERMINAL 11 AND GROUND.
IS BATTERY VOLTAGE MEASURED?

YES / NO

- MEASURE BATTERY VOLTAGE BETWEEN TERMINALS 11 AND 12 AT PMV ASSEMBLY CONNECTOR C1.
IS BATTERY VOLTAGE MEASURED?

NO / YES

- IGNITION: OFF
- RECONNECT PMV ASSEMBLY
- DISCONNECT ELECTRONIC BRAKE CONTROL MODULE (EBCM).
- INSTALL J 38716 PINOUT BOX.
- MEASURE RESISTANCE BETWEEN J 38716 PINOUT BOX TERMINALS 13 AND 26.
IS LESS THAN 10 OHMS MEASURED?

CHECK THAT BRAKE PEDAL AND PUSHROD ARE NOT RESTRICTED. CHECK THAT THE BRAKES ARE NOT APPLIED. IF OK, REPLACE PMV ASSEMLBY.

YES / NO

REPAIR OPEN IN CKT 853

- IGNITION: OFF
- RECONNECT PMV ASSEMBLY
- DISCONNECT ELECTRONIC BRAKE CONTROL MODULE (EBCM).
- INSTALL J 38716 PINOUT BOX.
- MEASURE RESISANCE BETWEEN J 38716 PINOUT BOX TERMINALS 13 AND 26.
IS LESS THAN 10 OHMS MEASURED?

NO / YES

REPAIR OPEN IN CKT 1659

- MEASURE RESISTANCE BETWEEN J38716 PINOUT BOX TERMINALS 13 AND 1.
IS LESS THAN 0 OHMS MEASURED?

NO / YES

CHECK EBCM TERMINALS FOR GOOD TERMINAL CONTACT. IF CONTACT IS GOOD, REPLACE EBCM.

REPAIR SHORT TO GROUND IN CKT 1659

CHART Q, NO CODE
TRACTION WARNING LIGHT OFF FAILURE TEST

Ninety-Eight – 1) When ignition switch is first turned to RUN position, EBCM goes into self-test. During self-test, ANTI-LOCK and TRACTION warning lights are lit for approximately 4 seconds.

2) TRACTION warning light stays lit, indicating Traction Control System (TCS) is disabled, as long as traction control switch is off. With traction control switch in ON position and if brakes are overheated or Code 44, 48 or 74 is set, TRACTION light will turn on, and TCS function will be disabled.

Flowchart boxes:

- IGNITION: OFF
- DISCONNECT ELECTRONIC BRAKE CONTROL MODULE (EBCM).
- INSTALL J38716 PINOUT BOX.
- IGNITION: RUN
- MEASURE VOLATE BETWEEN J38716 PINOUT BOX TERMINALS 44 AND 1.
IS BATTERY VOLTAGE MEASURED?

YES / NO

REPLACE TRACTION INDICATOR BULB. IF BULB IS OK, REPAIR OPEN CKT.

- IGNITION: OFF
- TRACTION CONTROL SWITCH: OFF
- MEASURE RESISANCE BETWEEN J 38716 PINOUT BOX TERMINALS 25 AND 1.
IS MORE THAN 100 OHMS MEASURED?

NO / YES

CHECK EBCM TERMINALS FOR GOOD TERMINAL CONTACT. IF CONTACT IS GOOD, REPLACE EBCM.

- DISCONNECT TRACTION CONTROL SWITCH.
- MEASURE RESISANCE BETWEEN J 38716 PINOUT BOX TERMINALS 25 AND 1.
IS MORE THAN 100 OHMS MEASURED?

YES / NO

REPLACE TRACTION CONTROL SWITCH.

REPAIR SHORT TO GROUND IN CKT 1571.

Courtesy of General Motors Corp.

CHART R, NO CODE
TRACTION WARNING LIGHT ON FAILURE TEST

Ninety-Eight – 1) When ignition switch is first turned to RUN position, EBCM goes into self-test. During self-test, ANTI-LOCK and TRACTION warning lights are lit for approximately 4 seconds.

2) TRACTION warning light stays lit, indicating Traction Control System (TCS) is disabled, as long as traction control switch is off. With traction control switch in ON position and if brakes are overheated or code 44, 48 or 74 is set, TRACTION light will turn on, and TCS function will be disabled.

NOTE: For terminal and wire color identification, refer to appropriate wiring diagram under WIRING DIAGRAMS.

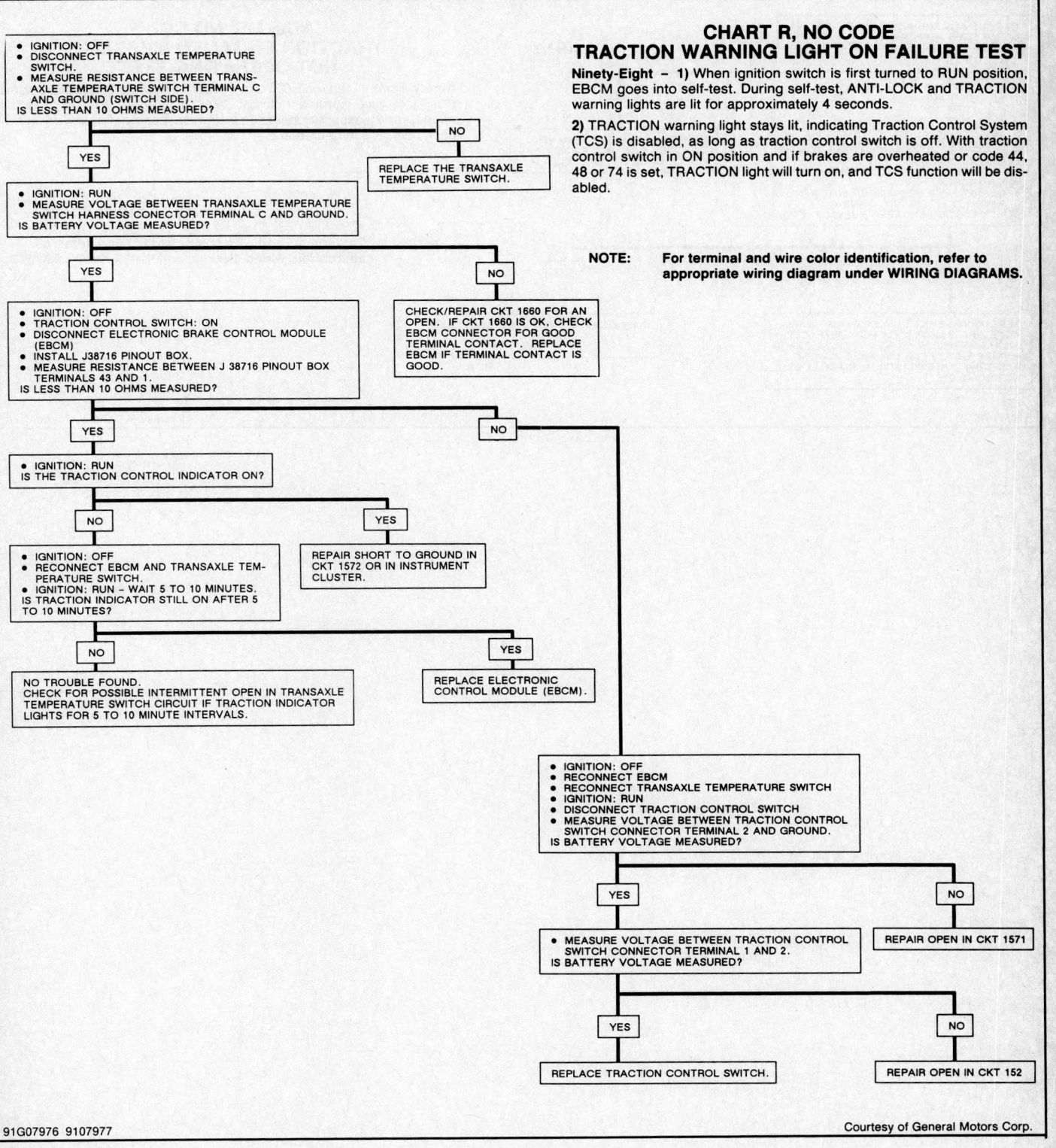

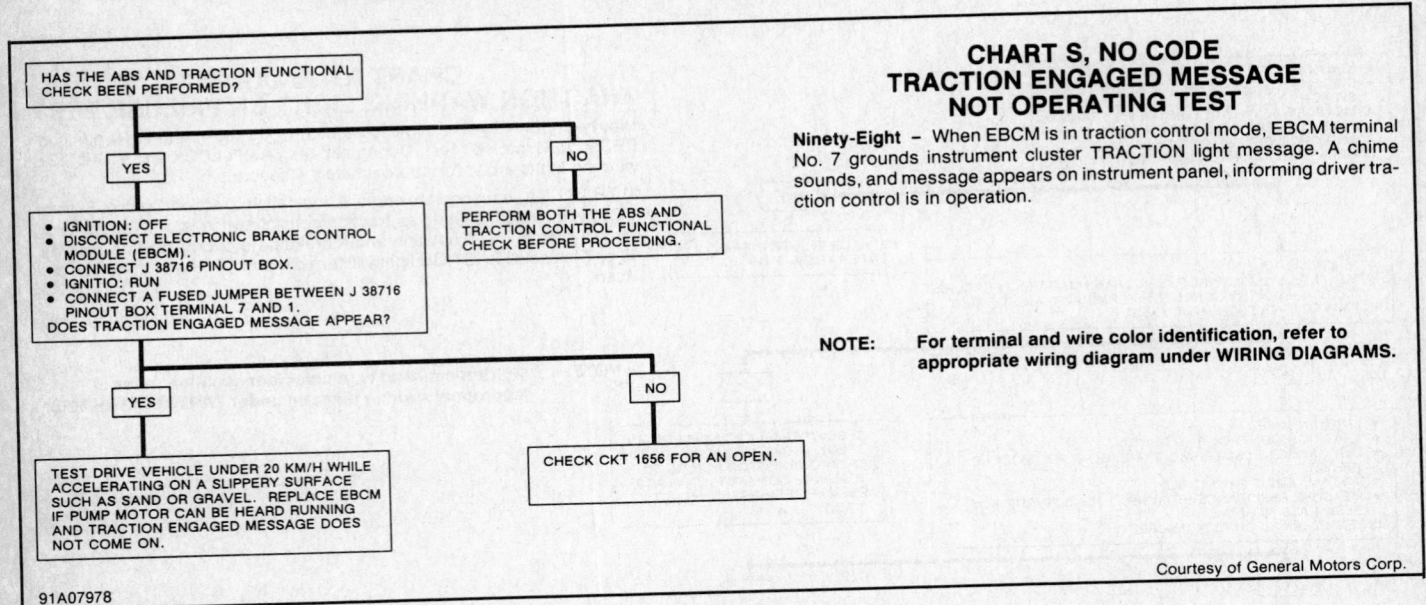

CHART S, NO CODE
TRACTION ENGAGED MESSAGE
NOT OPERATING TEST

Ninety-Eight – When EBCM is in traction control mode, EBCM terminal No. 7 grounds instrument cluster TRACTION light message. A chime sounds, and message appears on instrument panel, informing driver traction control is in operation.

NOTE: For terminal and wire color identification, refer to appropriate wiring diagram under WIRING DIAGRAMS.

Flowchart content:

HAS THE ABS AND TRACTION FUNCTIONAL CHECK BEEN PERFORMED?

→ YES:
- IGNITION: OFF
- DISCONECT ELECTRONIC BRAKE CONTROL MODULE (EBCM).
- CONNECT J 38716 PINOUT BOX.
- IGNITIO: RUN
- CONNECT A FUSED JUMPER BETWEEN J 38716 PINOUT BOX TERMINAL 7 AND 1.
DOES TRACTION ENGAGED MESSAGE APPEAR?

→ NO: PERFORM BOTH THE ABS AND TRACTION CONTROL FUNCTIONAL CHECK BEFORE PROCEEDING.

DOES TRACTION ENGAGED MESSAGE APPEAR?

→ YES: TEST DRIVE VEHICLE UNDER 20 KM/H WHILE ACCELERATING ON A SLIPPERY SURFACE SUCH AS SAND OR GRAVEL. REPLACE EBCM IF PUMP MOTOR CAN BE HEARD RUNNING AND TRACTION ENGAGED MESSAGE DOES NOT COME ON.

→ NO: CHECK CKT 1656 FOR AN OPEN.

Courtesy of General Motors Corp.

91A07978

A" Body: **Century, Cutlass Ciera, Cutlass Cruiser, 6000**
B" Body: **Caprice, Custom Cruiser, Roadmaster**
C" Body: **DeVille, Fleetwood, Ninety-Eight, Park Avenue, Touring Sedan**
D" Body: **Brougham**
E" Body: **Eldorado, Reatta, Riviera, Toronado, Trofeo**
F" Body: **Camaro, Firebird**
H" Body: **Bonneville, Eighty-Eight, LeSabre**
J" Body: **Cavalier, Sunbird**
K" Body: **Seville**
L" Body: **Beretta, Corsica**
N" Body: **Cutlass Calais, Grand Am, Skylark**
W" Body: **Cutlass Supreme, Grand Prix, Lumina, Regal**
Y" Body: **Corvette**

DESCRIPTION & OPERATION

The dual hydraulic brake system is a conventional pedal-actuated system with a master cylinder, pressure control valve, brake calipers or wheel cylinders and brake hoses and tubes. Hydraulic brake line routing is diagonally split front to rear for safety reasons.

BLEEDING BRAKE SYSTEM

BLEEDING PROCEDURES

WARNING: ABS systems are under high pressure under normal operating conditions. Before opening the fluid reservoir or before servicing any component of an ABS system, it is mandatory that system pressure be discharged. To discharge system, turn ignition off and pump brake pedal a minimum of 20-25 times using full pedal strokes. When a definite increase in pedal effort is felt, pump pedal 2 more times.

Use only new, clean DOT 3 brake fluid. Never reuse contaminated brake fluid. DO NOT use DOT 5 silicone brake fluid such as Delco Supreme No. 24. If necessary to bleed all calipers, follow sequence in BRAKE LINE BLEEDING SEQUENCE table.
Manual Bleeding – 1) Exhaust vacuum from power unit by depressing brake pedal several times. Fill master cylinder. Install clear vinyl bleeder hose onto first bleeder valve to be serviced. See BRAKE LINE BLEEDING SEQUENCE table. Place other end of hose in clean transparent container.
2) Partially fill container with clean brake fluid so end of hose is submerged in fluid. Open bleeder valve 1-2 turns. Slowly depress brake pedal through its full travel.
3) Close bleeder valve and release pedal. Pump pedal several times to push air toward wheel cylinders. Repeat procedure until flow of brake fluid is clear and shows no signs of air bubbles. Proceed to next bleeder valve.

NOTE: Check fluid level in master cylinder frequently during the bleeding sequence.

Pressure Bleeding – 1) Exhaust all vacuum from power unit by depressing brake pedal several times. Clean master cylinder cap and surrounding area, and remove cap. With pressure tank at least 1/2 full of brake fluid and charged with 10-30 psi (.70-2.10 kg/cm²) air pressure, connect tank to master cylinder using proper adapter(s).
2) Attach bleeder hose to first bleeder valve to be serviced. See BRAKE LINE BLEEDING SEQUENCE table. Place other end of hose in clean transparent container. Partially fill container with clean brake fluid until end of hose is submerged in fluid.
3) Open release valve on pressure bleeder. Open bleeder valve 1-2 turns, while noting fluid flow. When fluid flowing into container is clear and free of bubbles, close bleeder valve securely.

4) Finish bleeding system in the same manner using correct sequence. Remove pressure tank from master cylinder and check fluid level of master cylinder reservoir.

BRAKE LINE BLEEDING SEQUENCE

Application	Sequence
"F" & "Y" Bodies	RF, RR, LR, LF
"A" Body	RR, LF, LR, RF
All Others	RR, LR, RF, LF

ADJUSTMENTS

BRAKE SHOE ADJUSTMENT (REAR)

NOTE: Adjustment should only be required after relining or replacing shoes, or if length of adjusting screw is changed.

1) Raise vehicle and remove wheels and drums. Ensure parking brake cable and linkage, including levers on rear secondary shoes, have free movement. Measure brake drum inside diameter using inside caliper portion of Brake Drum Gauge (J-21177).
2) Adjust brake shoes, through slotted hole in backing plate, to dimension obtained on outside caliper portion of brake drum gauge. *See Fig. 1.* Check brake fluid level in both master cylinder reservoirs. Add fluid (if necessary). Adjust parking brake.

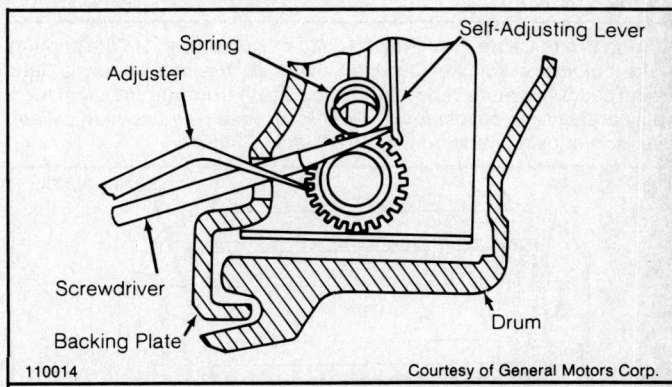

Fig. 1: Adjusting Brake Shoes Through Backing Plate

110014   Courtesy of General Motors Corp.

3) Install drums and wheels, and lug nuts. Torque lug nuts to specification. See TORQUE SPECIFICATIONS table at end of this article. Lower vehicle. Drive car alternately, forward and backward, applying brakes firmly in each direction until pedal travel is satisfactory.

HYDRAULIC SYSTEM SWITCHES

Hydraulic system switches and valves are not adjustable. If switches and valves are defective, entire unit must be replaced.

MASTER CYLINDER PUSH ROD

NOTE: Push rod is nonadjustable, and if out of limits, must be replaced with adjustable service rod.

1) Gauge push rod with booster holding 25 in. Hg (85 kPa) vacuum. The booster can be gauged without being installed on the vehicle by using either a suitable vacuum source or the MAXIMUM vacuum available from the engine.
2) Position Push Rod Height Gauge (J-37839) over piston rod. *See Fig. 2.* If piston rod length does not fall between the maximum and minimum dimensions, use an adjustable service piston rod (with self-locking screw) to make adjustments.

PARKING BRAKE (DISC)

Disabling Automatic Parking Brake Adjuster ("F" & "Y" Bodies) – 1) Remove driver's seat cushion, parking brake lever cover and screws. Fabricate a hook on end of a solid wire.

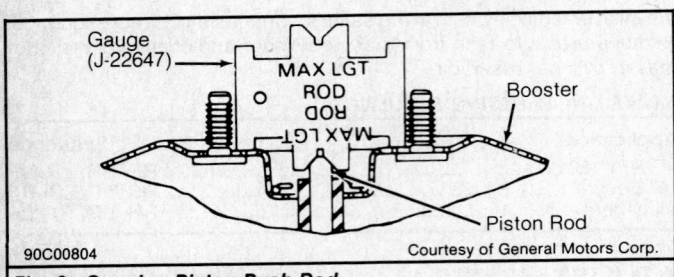

Fig. 2: Gauging Piston Push Rod

2) Using wire hook, hold drive pawl so it disengages from drive sector notches. Insert a nail through hole in anchor plate to retain drive pawl in disengaged position.

3) Move lever until it aligns with lock pawl. Depress button on lever and move lever to down position. Visually inspect to see that anchor plate is against stud. If anchor plate is not against stud, repeat procedure as needed.

NOTE: Brake pads must be new or parallel to within .006" (0.15 mm) thickness of each other. Parking brake adjustment will not be accurate with heavily tapered pads. Parking brake free play adjustment should only be made if caliper has been disassembled. Free play adjustment will not correct a condition such as levers not returning to their stops.

Parking Brake Cable Free Play ("F" & "Y" Bodies) – 1) With parking brake automatic adjuster disabled, have an assistant apply a light brake pedal pressure (enough to stop rotor from turning by hand). Apply pressure to caliper lever. *See Fig. 3.* Free play between caliper lever and housing must be .024-.028" (.60 -.70 mm).

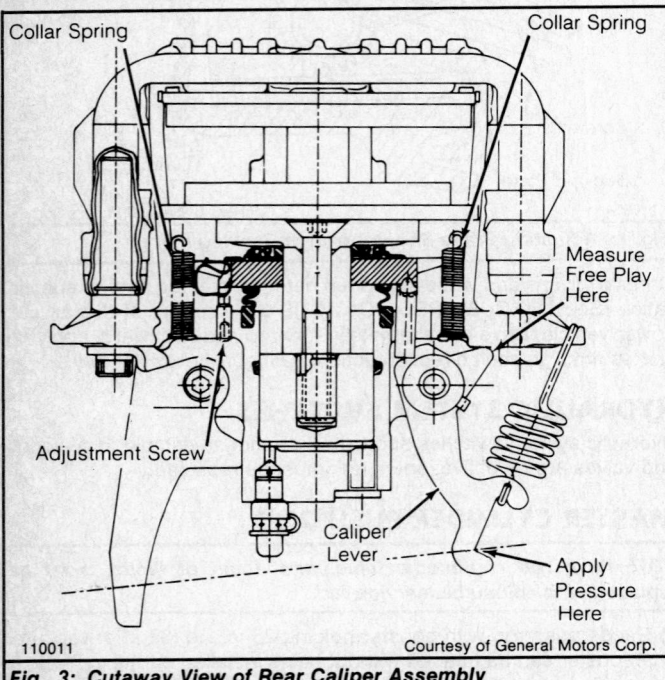

Fig. 3: Cutaway View of Rear Caliper Assembly

2) If free play is incorrect, remove adjustment screw and clean threads. Coat threads with adhesive. Screw in adjustment screw far enough to obtain proper free play between caliper lever and caliper housing. Have assistant release brake pedal, apply brake pedal firmly 3 times. Recheck free play and readjust (if necessary).

(Except "F" & "Y" Bodies) – 1) Depress brake pedal 3 times with a force of about 175 lbs. (79 kg). Apply and release parking brake 3 times. Raise and support vehicle. Inspect parking brake assembly for full release.

2) Turn ignition on. Brake warning light should be off. If light is on, operate manual brake release and pull down on front parking brake cable to remove slack from pedal assembly.

3) The 2 parking brake levers should be against lever stops on caliper housings. If not, check for binding in rear cables and/or loosen cables at adjuster until both left and right levers are against stops.

4) Tighten parking brake cable at adjuster until either left or right lever begins to move off stop. Loosen adjustment until lever moves back, slightly touching stop.

5) Operate parking brake to ensure adjustment is correct. Rear wheels should not rotate when parking brake is applied. Lower vehicle.

PARKING BRAKE (DRUM)

NOTE: When drum brakes are serviced, parking brake linkage cable at equalizer must always be readjusted to prevent possible burn out of drum brakes.

"H" Body – 1) Raise and support vehicle. Remove rear wheels and drums. Make sure stops on parking brake levers are against edge of brake shoe web. If parking brake cable is holding stops off edge of shoe web, loosen cable adjustment.

2) Measure drum inside diameter. Turn adjuster nut and adjust shoe and lining diameter to .05" (1.3 mm) less than drum inside diameter for each rear wheel. Install drums and wheels.

3) Apply and release service brake pedal 30-35 times until clicking noise from self adjusters stops on both sides of vehicle. Apply firmly and release parking brake 6 times.

4) Check parking brake pedal assembly for full release by turning ignition on and observing brake warning light. Light should be off. If brake light is on and parking brake appears to be fully released, operate pedal release lever and pull downward on front parking brake cable to remove slack.

5) Raise car and support. Remove access hole plug in backing plate. Adjust parking brake cable until a 1/8" drill can be inserted through hole into space between shoe web and parking brake lever.

6) Satisfactory adjustment is achieved when a 1/8" drill will fit into notch but a 1/4" drill will not. Install access plug and lower car. Check operation of parking brake.

(Except "H" Body) – 1) Lubricate parking brake linkage at cable equalizer bar and stud. Ensure free movement of cables inside housings.

2) Slowly depress parking brake pedal or pull parking brake lever up from fully released position and listen for proper number of clicks, and maintain at this position. See PEDAL/LEVER ADJUSTMENT table. Raise rear wheels.

PEDAL/LEVER ADJUSTMENT

Body Code	Ratchet Clicks
"A", "B", "C", "D" & "L"	3
"F"	2
"J" & "N"	5

3) To adjust cable free play, hold parking brake cable from turning and tighten equalizer bar nut one turn at a time.

4) Check for brake drag, after each turn of nut, by rotating wheel forward. When light drag is felt on both wheels, release parking brake. No drag should be present at either wheel.

SERVICE BRAKES

Disc brakes are continually self-adjusting. Caliper piston seals are designed to retract pistons enough to allow brake lining to lightly brush rotor. Sliding caliper design compensates for lining wear.

STOPLIGHT SWITCH

1) With brake pedal depressed, insert switch assembly into tubular clip until switch body seats on tube clip. Ensure clicks can be heard as threaded portion of switch and valve are pushed through clip toward brake pedal.

2) Pull brake pedal fully against pedal stop, until click can no longer be heard. Switch assembly will be moved in tubular clip providing proper adjustment. Release brake pedal and ensure no click can be heard remain.

CAUTION: Power booster may be damaged if excessive force is used while adjusting stoplight switch.

TESTING

WARNING LIGHT SWITCH TEST

1) Attach one end of bleeder hose to either rear brake bleeder screw. Immerse the other end of bleeder hose in brake fluid container.

2) Turn ignition switch to ON position and open bleeder screw. Apply brake pedal pressure. Warning lamp should light. Close bleeder screw before releasing brake pedal pressure.

3) Reapply moderate-to-heavy brake pedal pressure. Light should go out. Repeat test on front system. Results should be same. Turn ignition off. If lamp does not light on either system, but electrical system checked good, warning light switch part of valve is defective. Replace valve and retest.

REMOVAL & INSTALLATION

WARNING: ABS systems are under high pressure under normal operating conditions. Before opening the fluid reservoir or before servicing any component of an ABS system, it is mandatory that system pressure be discharged. To discharge system, turn ignition off and pump brake pedal a minimum of 20-25 times using full pedal strokes. When a definite increase in pedal effort is felt, pump pedal 2 more times.

FRONT BRAKE CALIPER

Removal & Installation ("F" & "Y" Bodies) – Remove and plug brake hose attached to caliper. Remove retaining pin circlips, retaining pins and pull off caliper. To install, reverse removal procedure and bleed brakes.

Removal (Except "F" & "Y" Bodies) – **1)** Remove and discard 2/3 of brake fluid in master cylinder reservoir to prevent overflow during servicing.

2) Raise vehicle. Mark relationship of wheel to hub. Remove front wheels. Position "C" clamp over inner brake shoe tab and inner caliper housing.

3) Tighten "C" clamp until caliper moves away from vehicle, pushing piston to bottom of its bore. This will provide clearance between disc pads and rotor surface. Remove "C" clamp. If caliper is being removed from vehicle, disconnect brake line at caliper. Plug opening in inlet brake line and caliper housing to prevent fluid loss or contamination.

4) On "B", "D", "E", "F" and "K" bodies, unbolt caliper mounting bolts to support bracket.

5) On "A", "C", "H", "J", "L" and "N" bodies, remove caliper mounting bolt boots and remove caliper mounting bolts to support bracket.

6) On all models, lift caliper off support bracket. If caliper is not being removed from vehicle, tie caliper with wire so brake hose will not be damaged.

Installation ("E" & "K" Bodies) – **1)** Position caliper over rotor on support bracket. Install caliper mounting bolts and tighten to specification. See TORQUE SPECIFICATIONS table at end of this article. Connect brake line to caliper. Install brake hose, using a new copper gasket.

CAUTION: On "E" and "K" bodies, mounting bracket bolts to steering knuckle must be replaced any time they become loose or removed. Failure to replace bracket mounting bolts, may result in loosening of caliper to steering knuckle.

2) Bleed hydraulic system. See BLEEDING BRAKE SYSTEM. If hydraulic brake line was not removed, apply brake pedal 2 or 3 times

to seat disc pads. Install tire and align with previous marks. Check brake fluid level and road test.

Installation (Except "E" & "K" Bodies) – **1)** Install caliper over rotor and onto mounting bracket.

2) On "D", "B" and "F" bodies, install mounting bolts and tighten to specification. See TORQUE SPECIFICATIONS table at end of this article. Connect brake line to caliper. Bleed hydraulic system. See BLEEDING BRAKE SYSTEM. Install tire and align with previous marks. If hydraulic brake line was not removed, apply brake pedal 2 or 3 times to seat disc pads. Check brake fluid level and road test.

3) On "C" and "H" bodies, install mounting bolts and sleeve assembly. Tighten to specification. See TORQUE SPECIFICATIONS table at end of this article. Install caliper mounting bolt boots. Ensure boots are mounted securely. Connect brake line to caliper. Install brake hose, using a new copper gasket.

4) Bleed hydraulic system. See BLEEDING BRAKE SYSTEM. Install tire and align with previous marks. Check brake fluid level and road test. If hydraulic brake line was not removed, apply brake pedal 2 or 3 times to seat disc pads.

FRONT BRAKE ROTOR

Removal & Installation ("F" & "Y" Bodies) – Remove caliper and caliper mounting bracket. Remove spindle nut, bearing washer and outer wheel bearing. Slide rotor from spindle. To install, reverse removal procedure. Bleed brakes if brake line was removed from caliper.

Removal (RWD Models Except "F" & "Y" Bodies) – Raise and support vehicle. Remove wheel. Remove and support caliper. See FRONT BRAKE CALIPER under REMOVAL & INSTALLATION. Remove grease cup, cotter pin and nut. Remove rotor.

Installation – **1)** To install, reverse removal procedure. Adjust wheel bearings. Tighten spindle nut to 12 ft. lbs. (16 N.m), while spinning wheel forward by hand. Back off nut until just loose, then hand tighten.

2) Tighten nut until either hole in spindle lines up with a slot in the nut. DO NOT move nut more than 1/2 flat. Install new cotter pin. Tighten all bolts to specification. See TORQUE SPECIFICATIONS table at end of this article.

Removal (FWD Models) – Raise and support vehicle. Remove front wheel and reinstall one wheel nut to retain rotor during caliper removal. Remove caliper and wire up out of way. See FRONT BRAKE CALIPER under REMOVAL & INSTALLATION. Mark rotor and hub for reassembly and remove rotor.

Installation – To install, reverse removal procedure. Tighten all bolts to specification. See TORQUE SPECIFICATIONS table at end of this article.

REAR BRAKE CALIPER

Removal & Installation ("F" & "Y" Bodies) – **1)** Remove and plug brake hose attached to caliper. Disable automatic parking brake adjuster. Remove caliper lever return spring. Replace return spring if damaged.

2) Disconnect parking brake cable from caliper lever and caliper bracket. Remove caliper guide pin bolts and caliper. To install, reverse removal procedure and bleed brakes.

Removal ("E" Body) – **1)** Remove and discard 2/3 of brake fluid from master cylinder reservoir. Raise vehicle, mark relationship of wheel to axle and remove wheel. Replace 2 lug nuts (flat side toward rotor) to hold rotor when caliper is removed.

2) Loosen tension on parking brake cable at equalizer. Disconnect cable and return spring from parking brake lever. Hold lever and remove lock nut. Remove lever, lever seal and anti-friction washer. Using a large "C" clamp, compress caliper piston until it bottoms in bore. Remove "C" clamp.

NOTE: DO NOT position "C" clamp on actuator screw.

3) Remove brake line from caliper. Plug opening to prevent fluid loss and keep dirt out of system. Remove caliper mounting bolts. Remove caliper and brake pads. Inspect caliper for damage. Replace or repair as needed. Remove and discard 2 caliper mounting sleeves and 4 bushings. Remove and discard piston check valve.

Installation – 1) Clean and lubricate caliper housing surface under lever seal with silicone brake lubricant. Install new anti-friction washer. Lubricate new lever seal with silicone, and install with sealing bead against housing. Install lever on actuator screw with lever pointing down.

2) Install new piston check valve. Using silicone grease, install new bushings and sleeves. Place new inner lining on piston with "D" shaped tab fitting into piston notch. If tab does not line up with notch, turn piston with a Spanner Wrench (J-7624). Install outer lining.

3) Slide caliper over rotor, and install mounting bolts under inner lining ears. Using new washers, install brake line. Pump brake pedal to seat lining against caliper. Using adjustable lock pliers, clinch upper ears of outer lining against caliper. Ensure all ears are flat against caliper with no clearance.

4) Rotate lever toward front of vehicle, and tighten nut. Rotate lever back against caliper stop, and install spring. Connect and adjust parking brake cable. See PARKING BRAKE (DISC) under ADJUSTMENTS. Bleed brake system. Remove 2 lug nuts used to retain rotor, and install wheel.

Removal ("W" Body) – 1) Remove and discard 2/3 of brake fluid from master cylinder reservoir. Raise vehicle, mark relationship of wheel to axle and remove wheel. Replace 2 lug nuts (flat side toward rotor) to retain rotor when caliper is removed.

2) Loosen tension on parking brake cable at equalizer. Disconnect cable and return spring from parking brake lever. Hold lever and remove lock nut. Remove lever and lever seal. Using 2 pairs of water-pump pliers, compress caliper piston until it bottoms in bore. Position pliers over inboard shoe tabs and flanges on caliper housing.

3) Clean and lubricate caliper housing surface under lever seal with silicone brake lubricant. Lubricate new lever seal with silicone, and install with sealing bead against housing. Install lever on actuator screw with lever pointing down.

4) Remove brake line from caliper. Plug opening to prevent fluid loss and keep dirt out of system. Remove caliper mounting bolts using Rear Caliper Torque Wrench Adapter (J-36581). Remove caliper and brake pads. Inspect caliper for damage. Replace or repair as needed. Remove and discard caliper mounting bolts and sleeves if corroded. Remove and discard piston check valve.

Installation – 1) Install new piston check valve. Using silicone grease, install new sleeves. Replace inner and outer brake lining.

2) Slide caliper over rotor, and install mounting bolts under inner lining ears. Using new washers, install brake line. Pump brake pedal to seat lining against caliper. Using Rear Caliper Torque Wrench Adapter (J-36581), torque mounting bolts to 92 ft. lbs. (125 N.m).

3) Hold parking brake lever against stop on caliper, and tighten nut. Rotate lever back against caliper stop, and install spring. Connect and adjust parking brake cable. Bleed brake system. Remove 2 lug nuts used to retain rotor, and install wheel.

REAR BRAKE ROTOR

Removal & Installation ("F" & "Y" Bodies) – Remove caliper and caliper mounting bracket. Remove rotor. To install, reverse removal procedure.

Removal & Installation (Except "F" & "Y" Bodies) – With caliper removed, remove lug nuts attaching rotor. Remove rotor. To install, place rotor on axle and hold in place with 2 lug nuts. To complete installation, reverse removal procedure.

MASTER CYLINDER

Removal – 1) On power brake systems, disconnect brake fluid level indicator and brake warning switch leads (if equipped). Disconnect hydraulic brake lines. Remove master cylinder attaching nuts, and remove master cylinder.

2) On manual brake systems, disconnect negative battery cable and warning switch lead (if equipped). Disconnect hydraulic brake lines.

Remove push rod at brake pedal, and remove stoplight switch. Remove master cylinder attaching nuts, and remove master cylinder.

Installation – 1) Bench bleed master cylinder. To complete installation, reverse removal procedure. Bleed hydraulic brake system. See BLEEDING BRAKE SYSTEM.

2) Check master cylinder compensating ports. Remove master cylinder cover, and observe brake fluid. Upon brake application, a small spurt should appear in one or both reservoirs. If no spurt appears, push rod may be improperly adjusted.

3) On manual brakes, adjust push rod at brake pedal. Push rod should have a slight amount of play when brake pedal is released. On power brakes, see MASTER CYLINDER PUSH ROD under ADJUSTMENTS.

POWER BRAKE UNIT

Removal ("Y" Body) – 1) Remove negative battery cable, ECM and ECM housing bracket bolt.

2) Disconnect cruise control cable from servo and bracket. Disconnect pressure sensor connector and vacuum hose. Remove master cylinder from power booster (with lines connected), and relocate.

3) Remove vacuum check valve from power booster. From inside driver compartment, remove instrument panel sound insulator. Remove master cylinder push rod valve assembly retaining ring and washer. Remove nuts and washers from booster tie rods.

4) Remove power booster, ECM brackets and seal as assembly. Remove assembly from brake pedal bracket and brake pedal. Inspect seals and mounting-sealing surfaces for damage. Repair/replace as needed.

Installation – 1) Attach seals to brackets. Install complete power booster and bracket assembly to brake pedal bracket and brake pedal.

2) Install booster tie rod nuts, and tighten to 15 ft. lbs. (21 N.m). To complete installation, reverse removal procedure. Tighten master cylinder nuts to 13 ft. lbs. (18 N.m). Tighten ECM housing bracket mounting bolt to 18 ft. lbs. (25 N.m).

3) Clear ALL ECM and CCM codes, unlock radio Delco-Loc II security function (If equipped) and check VATS (PASS-KEY) program for proper operation.

Removal (Except "Y" Body) – 1) Without disconnecting hydraulic lines, remove master cylinder from power booster unit, and position aside.

CAUTION: DO NOT bend or kink hydraulic lines. DO NOT force master cylinder push rod to side when disconnecting master cylinder.

2) Disconnect check valve from front of power booster unit. Disconnect push rod from brake pedal. Remove nuts under instrument panel, mounting power booster unit to firewall. Remove power booster unit.

Installation – To install, reverse removal procedure. Tighten booster to inside firewall nuts to 15 ft. lbs. (21 N.m). Tighten master cylinder to booster nuts to 20 ft. lbs. (27 N.m). Check stoplight and cruise control (if equipped) switch adjustments.

REAR BRAKE SHOES

NOTE: Mark position of springs and star adjusters for reassembly reference. Note lengths of brake linings and their shoe locations.

Removal – 1) Release parking brake, and loosen parking brake cable at equalizer. If necessary, back off brake adjustment before removing brake drums. Unhook return springs from anchor plate and brake shoes. Remove return springs. Remove actuating lever return spring, lever and actuating link.

2) Separate brake shoes from wheel cylinders and connecting links. Remove parking brake strut and spring. Remove brake shoe hold-down springs and cups. Remove brake shoes, adjusting screw (noting position) and spring from backing plate. Disconnect parking brake lever and cable from shoe by removing circlip. If applicable, remove parking brake lever pin from secondary shoe.

Installation – 1) Lubricate fulcrum end of parking brake lever, and attach to secondary shoe. Connect adjusting screw spring. Place adjusting screw in position. Ensure star is aligned with adjusting hole. Lubricate where shoes and parking brake cable contacts backing plate. Position and insert shoes into wheel cylinders or links.

2) Install parking brake strut and spring between parking brake lever and primary shoe. Install actuating lever, pawl, actuator return spring and actuating link. Adjust brake shoes to drums, and adjust parking brake. See PARKING BRAKE (DRUM) under ADJUSTMENTS. Install wheels, and torque lug nuts to specification. See TORQUE SPECIFICATIONS table at end of article. Check for proper operation of brakes before moving vehicle.

OVERHAUL

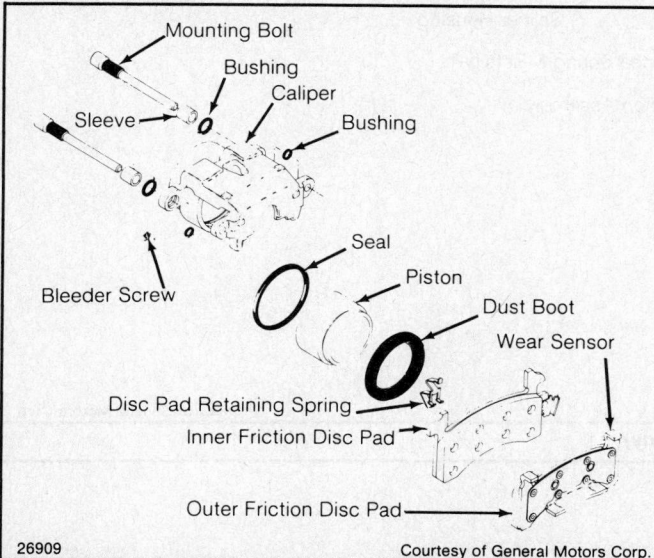

26909   Courtesy of General Motors Corp.

Fig. 4: Exploded View of Front Brake Caliper Assembly ("B", "D" & "F" Bodies)

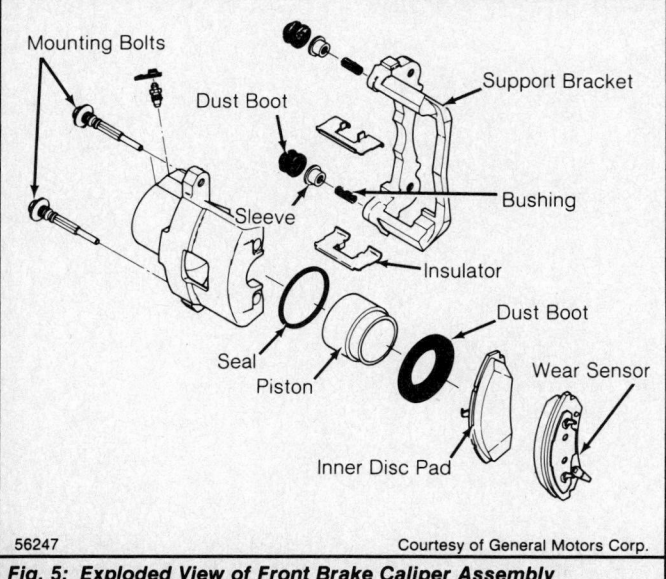

56247   Courtesy of General Motors Corp.

Fig. 5: Exploded View of Front Brake Caliper Assembly ("E" & "K" Bodies)

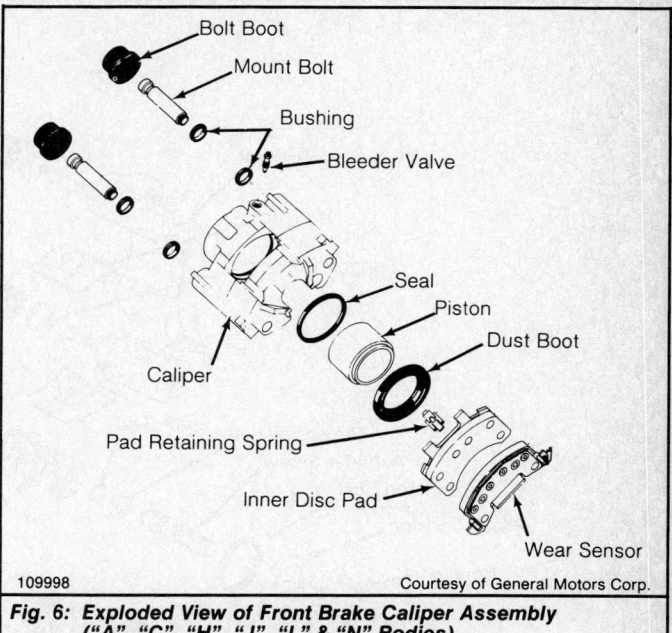

109998   Courtesy of General Motors Corp.

Fig. 6: Exploded View of Front Brake Caliper Assembly ("A", "C", "H", "J", "L" & "N" Bodies)

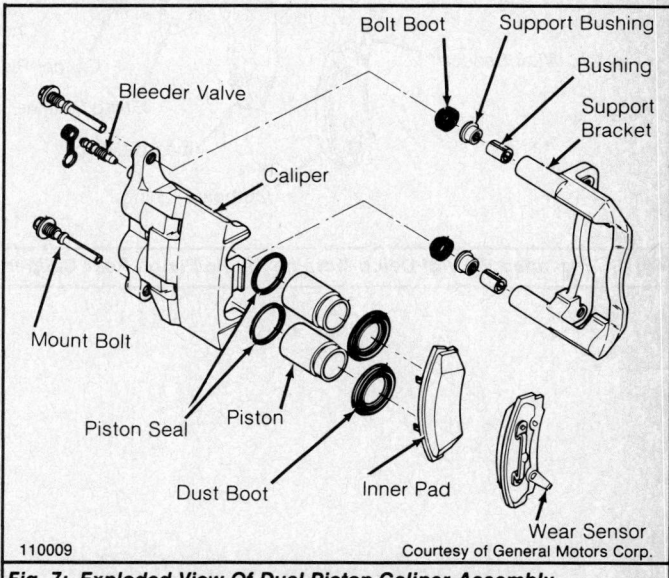

110009   Courtesy of General Motors Corp.

Fig. 7: Exploded View Of Dual Piston Caliper Assembly

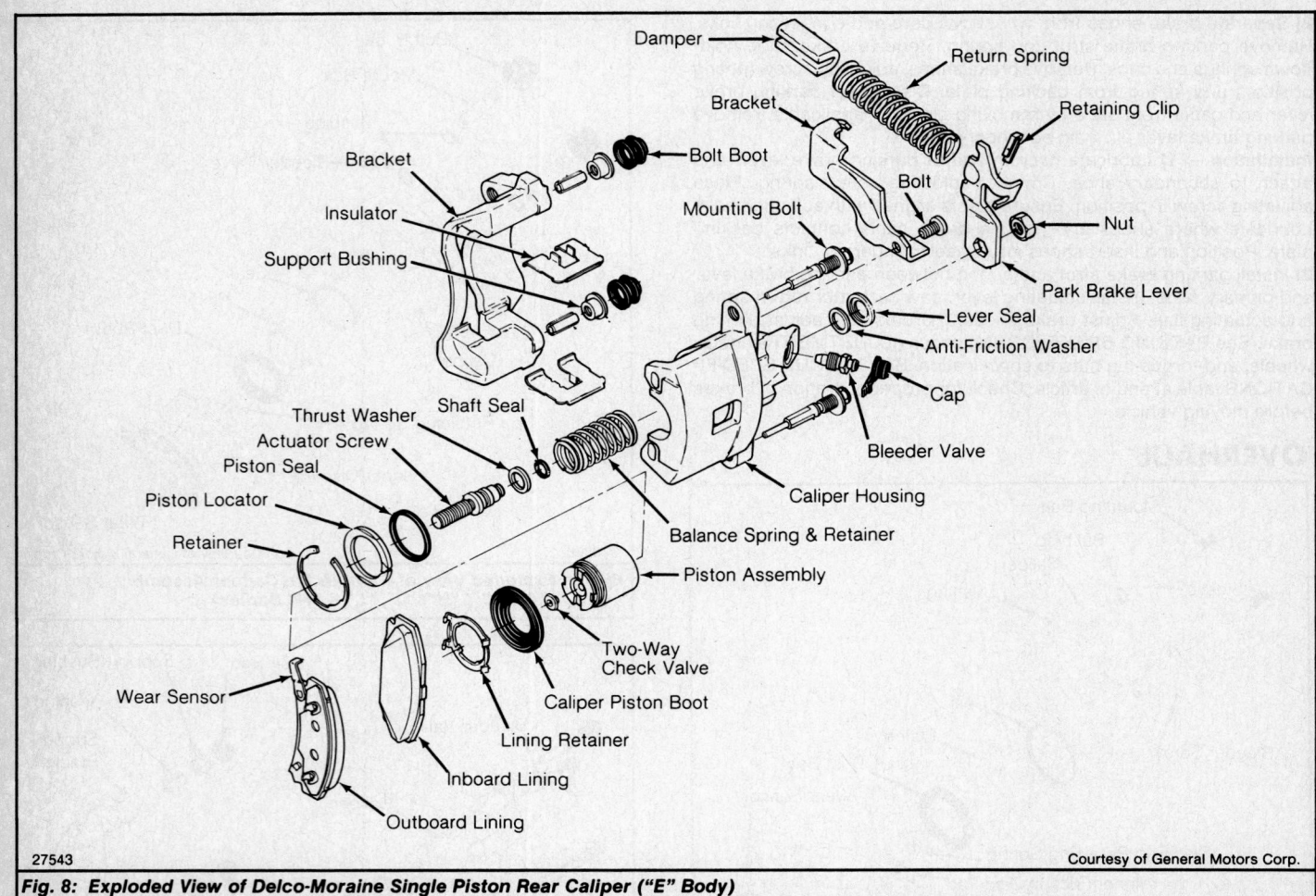

27543

Courtesy of General Motors Corp.

Fig. 8: Exploded View of Delco-Moraine Single Piston Rear Caliper ("E" Body)

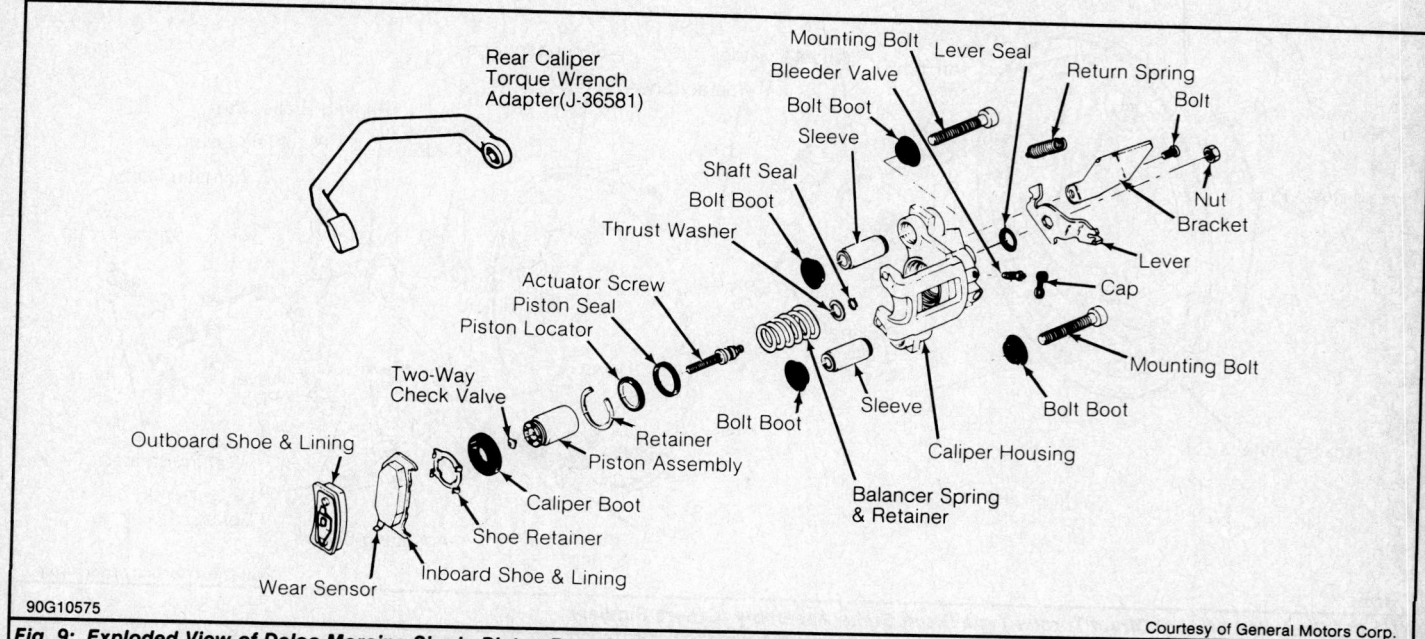

Rear Caliper
Torque Wrench
Adapter(J-36581)

Mounting Bolt — Lever Seal — Return Spring — Bolt
Bleeder Valve
Bolt Boot
Sleeve
Shaft Seal
Bolt Boot
Thrust Washer
Nut
Bracket
Lever
Actuator Screw
Piston Seal
Piston Locator
Cap
Two-Way
Check Valve
Mounting Bolt
Retainer
Bolt Boot
Outboard Shoe & Lining
Piston Assembly
Sleeve
Bolt Boot
Caliper Boot
Shoe Retainer
Caliper Housing
Balancer Spring
& Retainer
Wear Sensor
Inboard Shoe & Lining

90G10575

Courtesy of General Motors Corp.

Fig. 9: Exploded View of Delco-Moraine Single Piston Rear Caliper ("W" Body)

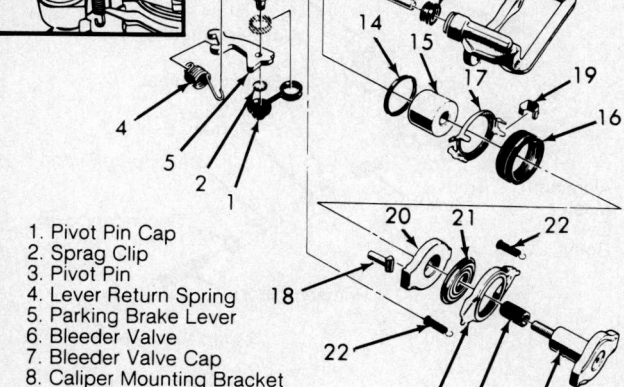

1. Pivot Pin Cap
2. Sprag Clip
3. Pivot Pin
4. Lever Return Spring
5. Parking Brake Lever
6. Bleeder Valve
7. Bleeder Valve Cap
8. Caliper Mounting Bracket
9. Adjustment Screw
10. Caliper Housing
11. Guide Pin
12. Boot
13. Caliper Mounting Bracket
14. Piston Seal
15. Piston
16. Boot
17. Retainer
18. Push Rod

19. Preload Spring
20. Actuating Collar
21. Boot
22. Collar Return Spring
23. Compliance Bushing
24. Clamp Rod
25. Retainer

110013

Courtesy of General Motors Corp.

Fig. 10: Exploded View of Rear Caliper Assembly (All Others)

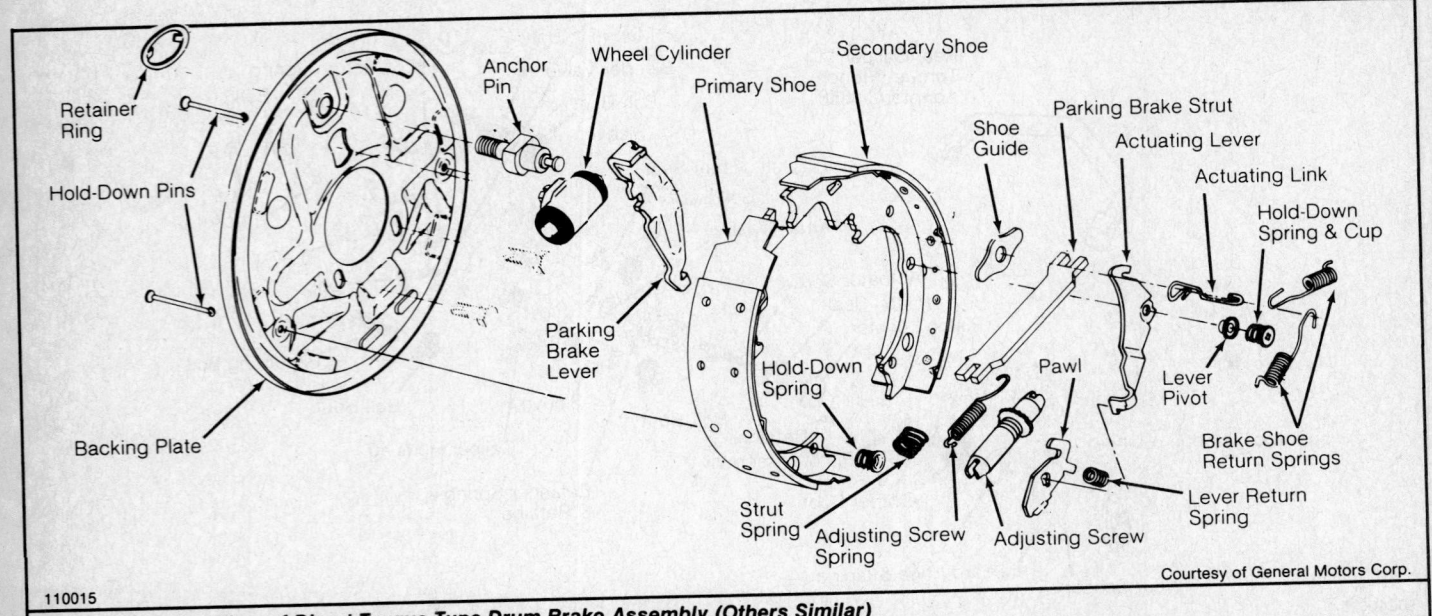

Fig. 11: Exploded View of Direct Torque Type Drum Brake Assembly (Others Similar)

Retainer Ring — Hold-Down Pins — Backing Plate — Anchor Pin — Wheel Cylinder — Primary Shoe — Parking Brake Lever — Secondary Shoe — Hold-Down Spring — Strut Spring — Adjusting Screw Spring — Shoe Guide — Adjusting Screw — Pawl — Parking Brake Strut — Actuating Lever — Actuating Link — Hold-Down Spring & Cup — Lever Pivot — Lever Return Spring — Brake Shoe Return Springs

110015

Courtesy of General Motors Corp.

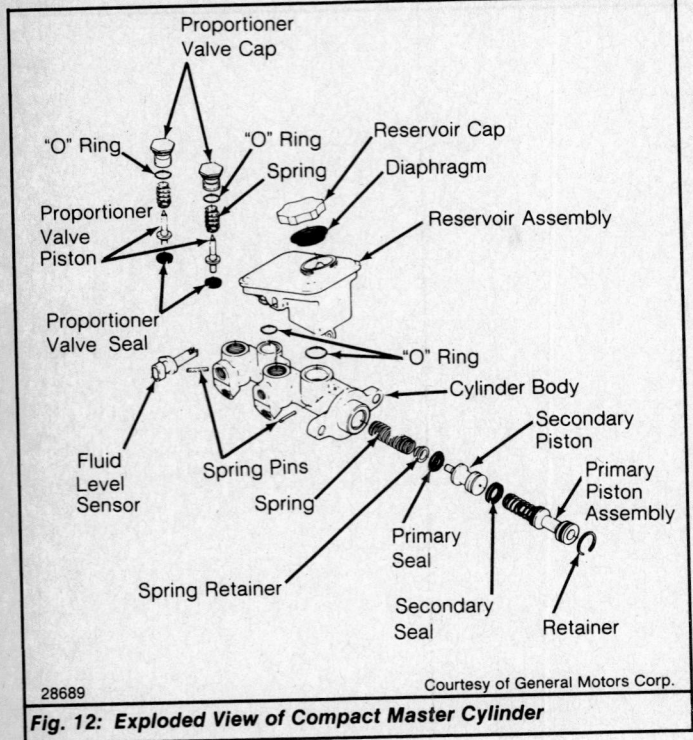

Fig. 12: Exploded View of Compact Master Cylinder

Proportioner Valve Cap — "O" Ring — "O" Ring — Proportioner Valve Piston — Proportioner Valve Seal — Reservoir Cap — Spring — Diaphragm — Reservoir Assembly — "O" Ring — Cylinder Body — Secondary Piston — Primary Piston Assembly — Fluid Level Sensor — Spring Pins — Spring — Primary Seal — Secondary Seal — Retainer — Spring Retainer

28689

Courtesy of General Motors Corp.

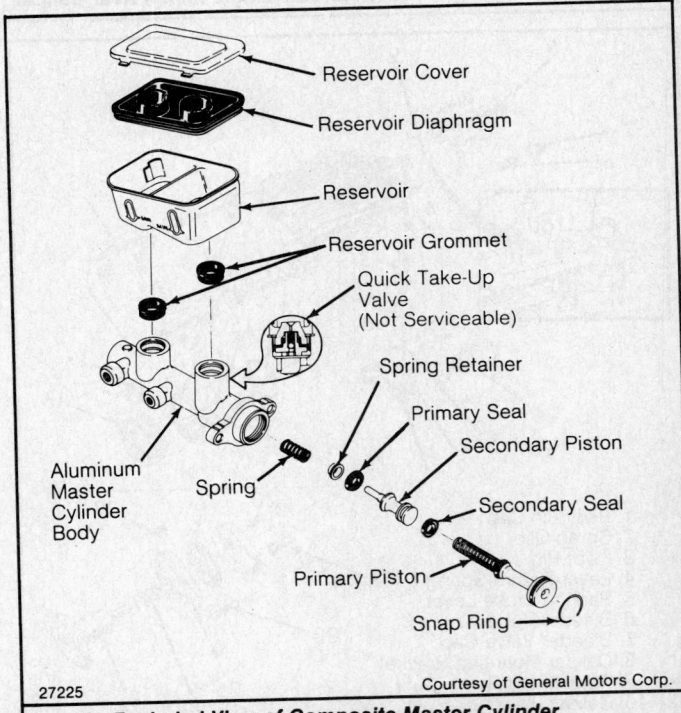

Fig. 13: Exploded View of Composite Master Cylinder

Reservoir Cover — Reservoir Diaphragm — Reservoir — Reservoir Grommet — Quick Take-Up Valve (Not Serviceable) — Spring Retainer — Primary Seal — Secondary Piston — Secondary Seal — Aluminum Master Cylinder Body — Spring — Primary Piston — Snap Ring

27225

Courtesy of General Motors Corp.

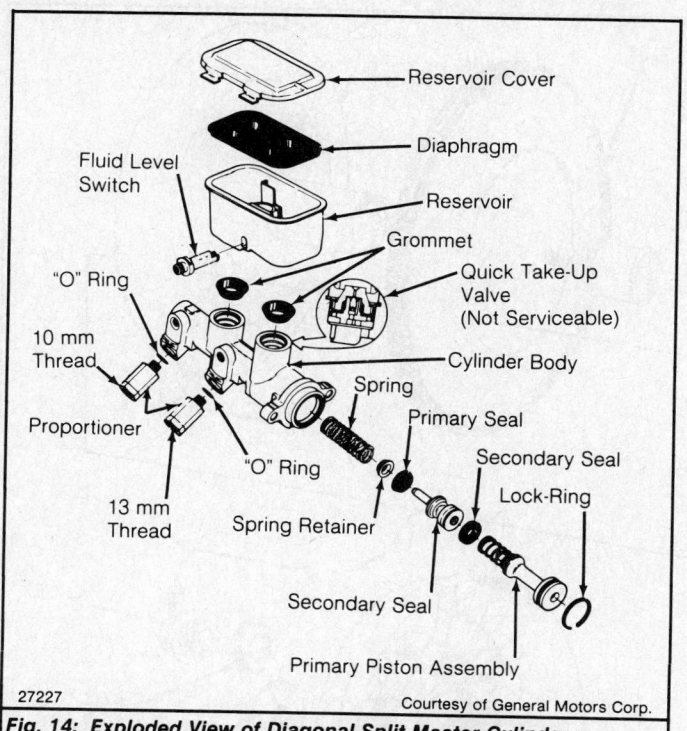

Reservoir Cover

Diaphragm

Reservoir

Fluid Level Switch

Grommet

Quick Take-Up Valve (Not Serviceable)

"O" Ring

Cylinder Body

10 mm Thread

Spring

Proportioner

Primary Seal

Secondary Seal

"O" Ring

Lock-Ring

13 mm Thread

Spring Retainer

Secondary Seal

Primary Piston Assembly

27227

Courtesy of General Motors Corp.

Fig. 14: Exploded View of Diagonal Split Master Cylinder

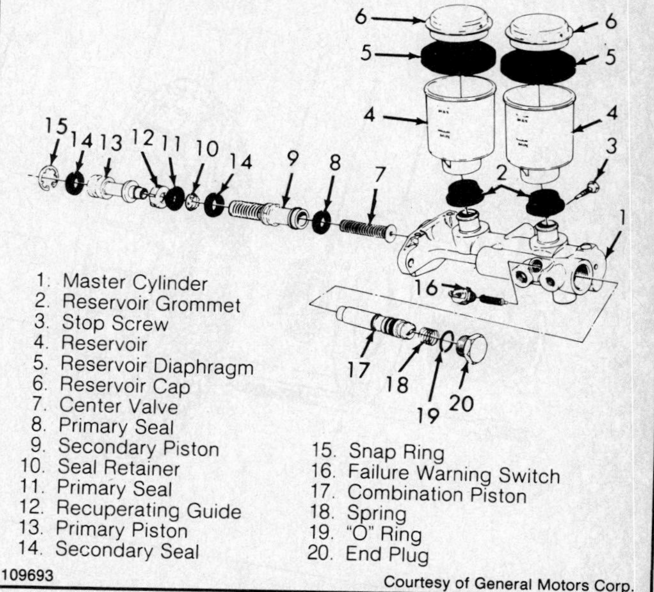

1. Master Cylinder
2. Reservoir Grommet
3. Stop Screw
4. Reservoir
5. Reservoir Diaphragm
6. Reservoir Cap
7. Center Valve
8. Primary Seal
9. Secondary Piston
10. Seal Retainer
11. Primary Seal
12. Recuperating Guide
13. Primary Piston
14. Secondary Seal
15. Snap Ring
16. Failure Warning Switch
17. Combination Piston
18. Spring
19. "O" Ring
20. End Plug

109693

Courtesy of General Motors Corp.

Fig. 16: Exploded View of Corvette Master Cylinder

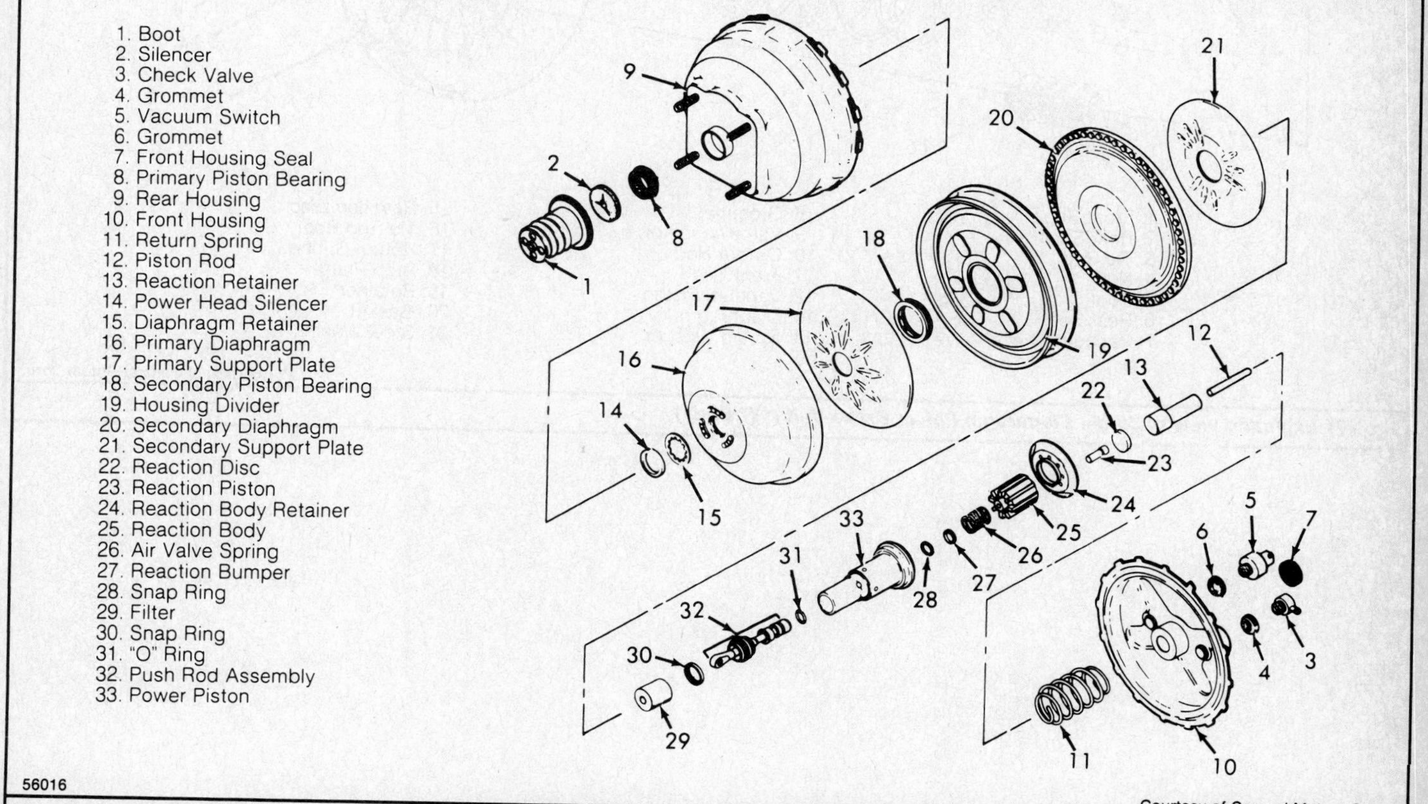

1. Boot
2. Silencer
3. Check Valve
4. Grommet
5. Vacuum Switch
6. Grommet
7. Front Housing Seal
8. Primary Piston Bearing
9. Rear Housing
10. Front Housing
11. Return Spring
12. Piston Rod
13. Reaction Retainer
14. Power Head Silencer
15. Diaphragm Retainer
16. Primary Diaphragm
17. Primary Support Plate
18. Secondary Piston Bearing
19. Housing Divider
20. Secondary Diaphragm
21. Secondary Support Plate
22. Reaction Disc
23. Reaction Piston
24. Reaction Body Retainer
25. Reaction Body
26. Air Valve Spring
27. Reaction Bumper
28. Snap Ring
29. Filter
30. Snap Ring
31. "O" Ring
32. Push Rod Assembly
33. Power Piston

56016

Courtesy of General Motors Corp.

Fig. 15: Exploded View of Delco-Moraine Tandem Diaphragm Power Brake Unit (Except "Y" Body)

1991 BRAKES
Disc & Drum (Cont.)

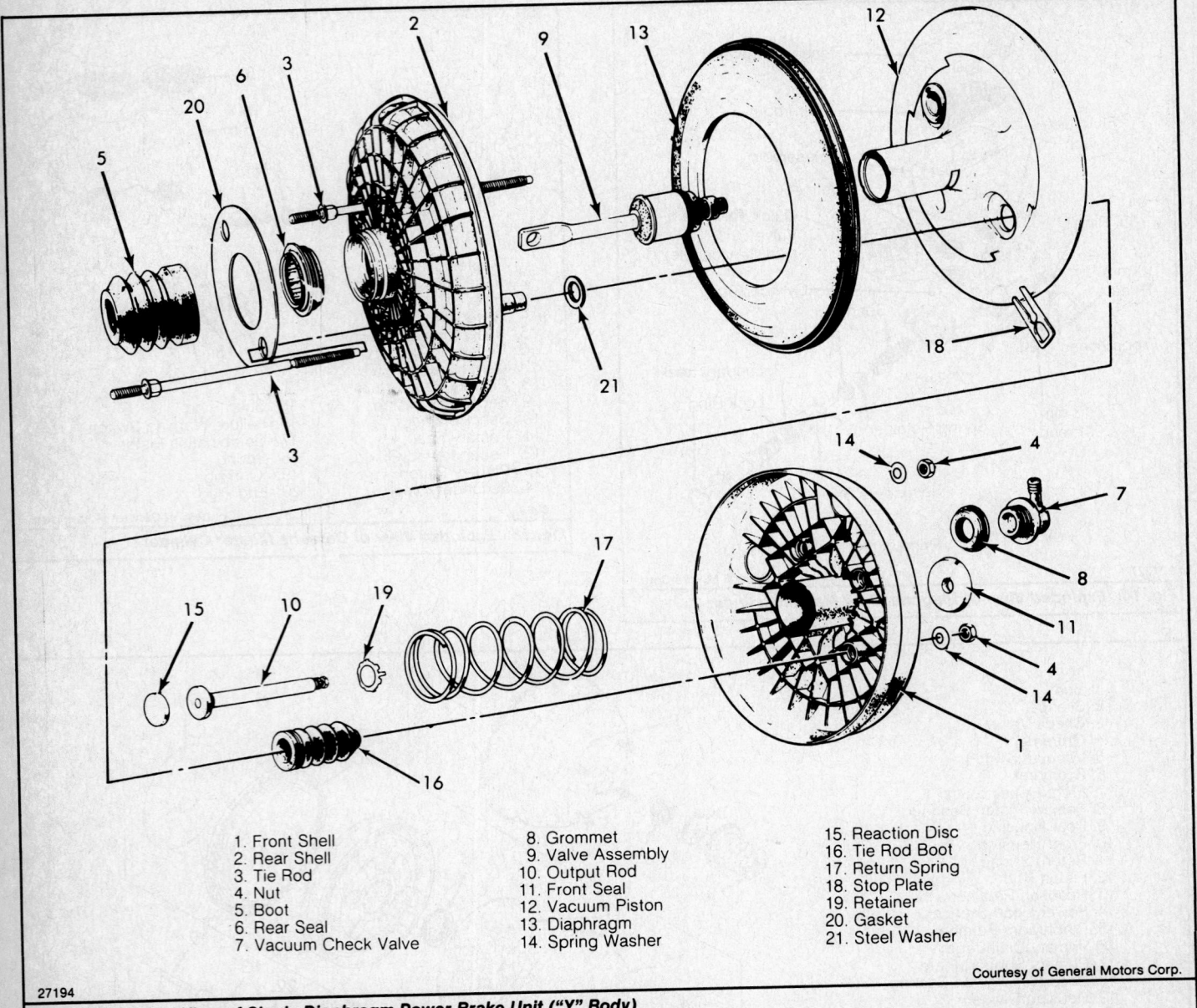

1. Front Shell	8. Grommet	15. Reaction Disc
2. Rear Shell	9. Valve Assembly	16. Tie Rod Boot
3. Tie Rod	10. Output Rod	17. Return Spring
4. Nut	11. Front Seal	18. Stop Plate
5. Boot	12. Vacuum Piston	19. Retainer
6. Rear Seal	13. Diaphragm	20. Gasket
7. Vacuum Check Valve	14. Spring Washer	21. Steel Washer

Courtesy of General Motors Corp.

27194

Fig. 17: Exploded View of Single Diaphragm Power Brake Unit ("Y" Body)

TORQUE SPECIFICATIONS

TORQUE SPECIFICATIONS

Application	Ft. Lbs. (N.m)
Backing Plate-to-Axle Bolt	35 (48)
Booster Mounting Nut	
"A" Body	25 (34)
"E" & "L" Bodies	20 (27)
All Others	15 (21)
Caliper Inlet Fitting	33 (45)
Caliper Bracket Bolts	
"F" Body Heavy Duty	137 (185)
"F" Body Rear	70 (95)
"W" Body	148 (200)
"Y" Body Front	166 (225)
"Y" Body Rear	70 (95)
All Others	83 (112)
Caliper Mounting Bolt	
"E" Body	63 (85)
"F" Body Rear Hex Head	26 (35)
"F" Body Rear Allen Head	16 (22)
"W" Body Front	79 (107)
"W" Body Rear	92 (125)
All Others	38 (51)
Caliper Pivot Pin Nut	16 (22)
Front Brake Hose-to-Caliper Bolt	32 (44)
Master Cylinder Lines	13 (17)
Master Cylinder Mounting Nut	
"B" & "N" Bodies	15 (21)
"F" Body	18 (25)
"W" Body	28 (38)
All Others	20 (27)
Wheel Cylinder Mounting Bolt	
"A" & "J" Bodies	15 (20)
"C" & "H" Bodies	9 (12)
All Others	13 (18)

	INCH lbs. (N.m)
Brake Hose Bracket	97 (11)
Brake Shield Bolts	89 (10)
Caliper Bleeder Screw	115 (13)
Wheel Cylinder Bleeder Screw	62 (7)
Wheel Cylinder Fitting	133 (15)

DISC BRAKE SPECIFICATIONS

DISC BRAKE SPECIFICATIONS

Application	In. (mm)
Disc Diameter	
"A" Body	
Front	9.724 (247)
Front (Heavy Duty)	10.236 (260)
"B" & "D" Bodies	
Front	12.00 (305)
"C" Body	
Front	10.945 (278)
"E" & "K" Bodies	
Front	10.24 (260)
Rear	10.00 (254.5)
"F" Body	
Front	10.50 (267)
Front (Heavy Duty)	12.00 (305)
Rear	11.50 (296)
"H" Body	
Front	10.24 (260)
"J" & "L" Bodies	
Front	9.72 (247)
"N" Body	
Front	10.197 (259)
"W" Body	
Front	10.50 (267)
Rear	10.10 (256.5)
"Y" Body	
Front & Rear	12.00 (305)
Front (Heavy Duty)	13.00 (330)
Lateral Runout	
"A", "B", "C", "D", "H", "J" & "L" Bodies	
Front	.004 (.10)
"E" & "K" Bodies	
Front	.004 (.10)
Rear	.003 (.08)
"F" Body	
Front & Rear	.005 (.13)
"N" Body	
Front	.003 (.08)
"W" Body	
Front & Rear	.004 (.10)
"Y" Body	
Front & Rear	.006 (.15)
Front (Heavy Duty)	.006 (.15)
Parallelism	
All Models	.0005 (.013)
Original Thickness	
"A" Body	
Front	.885 (22.48)
Front (Heavy Duty)	1.043 (26.50)
"B" & "H" Bodies	
Front	1.043 (26.50)
"C" Body	
Front	1.276 (32.40)
"D" Body	
Front	1.032 (26.20)
"E" & "K" Bodies	
Front	1.035 (26.30)
Rear	.494 (12.55)
"F" Body	
Front	1.043 (26.50)
Front (Heavy Duty)	1.043 (26.50)
Rear	.795 (20.20)
"J" & "L" Bodies	
Front	.885 (22.48)
"N" Body	
Front	.806 (20.48)
"W" Body	
Front	1.04 (26.30)
Rear	.492 (12.50)
"Y" Body	
Front & Rear	.795 (20.20)
Front (Heavy Duty)	1.11 (28.20)

DISC BRAKE SPECIFICATIONS (Cont.)

Application	In. (mm)
Minimum Refinish Thickness	
"A" Body	
Front	.830 (21.08)
Front (Heavy Duty)	.972 (24.68)
"B" Body	
Front	.980 (24.89)
"C" Body	
Front	1.204 (30.58)
"D" & "H" Bodies	
Front	.972 (24.68)
"E" & "K" Bodies	
Front	.971 (24.66)
Rear	.444 (11.28)
"F" Body	
Front	.980 (24.89)
Front (Heavy Duty)	.980 (24.89)
Rear	.744 (18.90)
"J" & "L" Bodies	
Front	.830 (21.08)
"N" Body	
Front	.786 (19.96)
"W" Body	
Front	.984 (25.00)
Rear	.441 (11.20)
"Y" Body	
Front & Rear	.744 (18.90)
Front (Heavy Duty)	1.059 (26.90)
Discard Thickness	
"A" Body	
Front	.815 (20.7)
Front (Heavy Duty)	.957 (24.30)
"B" & "D" Bodies	
Front	.965 (24.50)
"C" Body	
Front	1.209 (30.70)
"E" & "K" Bodies	
Front	.956 (24.28)
Rear	.429 (10.90)
"F" Body	
Front	.965 (24.50)
Front (Heavy Duty)	.965 (24.50)
Rear	.724 (18.40)
"H" Body	
Front	.957 (24.30)
"J" & "L" Bodies	
Front	.815 (20.70)
"N" Body	
Front	.736 (18.70)
"W" Body	
Front	.972 (24.70)
Rear	.429 (10.90)
"Y" Body	
Front & Rear	.724 (18.40)
Front (Heavy Duty)	1.039 (26.50)

DRUM BRAKE SPECIFICATIONS

DRUM BRAKE SPECIFICATIONS

Application	In. (mm)
Drum Diameter	
"A" Body	8.863 (225.12)
"B" & "D" Bodies	11.00 (279.00)
"C" & "H" Bodies	8.860 (225.12)
"F" Body	9.50 (241.00)
"J", "L" & "N" Bodies	7.879 (200.12)
Maximum Refinish Diameter [1]	
"A" Body	
Coupe & Sedan	8.920 (226.57)
Wagon	8.877 (225.50)
"B" & "D" Bodies	11.060 (280.92)
"C" & "H" Bodies	8.880 (225.50)
"F" Body	9.560 (242.81)
"J", "L" & "N" Bodies	7.899 (200.64)
Discard Diameter [2]	
"A" Body	
Coupe & Sedan	8.946 (227.25)
Wagon	8.909 (226.30)
"B" & "D" Bodies	11.090 (281.70)
"C" & "H" Bodies	8.909 (226.30)
"F" Body	9.590 (243.59)
"J", "L" & "N" Bodies	7.929 (201.40)
Wheel Cylinder Diameters	
"A" Body	
Standard	11/16 (17.5)
Heavy Duty	3/4 (19.0)
Wagon (Standard)	3/4 (19.0)
Wagon (Heavy Duty)	13/16 (20.6)
"B" Body	3/4 (19.0)
Wagon	1 (25.4)
"C" & "H" Bodies	15/16 (23.8)
"D" Body	1 (25.4)
"F" Body	3/4 (19.0)
"J" Body	5/8 (16.0)
"L" Body	
Sedan	5/8 (16.0)
Coupe	3/4 (19.0)
"N" Body	11/16 (17.5)

[1] – Maximum runout is .006" (.15 mm)
[2] – Specification stamped on drum should always be used.

"A" Body: Century, Cutlass Ciera, Cutlass Cruiser, 6000

"B" Body: Caprice, Custom Cruiser, Roadmaster

"C" Body: DeVille, Fleetwood, Ninety-Eight, Park Avenue, Touring Sedan

"D"Body: Brougham

"E" Body: Eldorado, Reatta, Riviera, Toronado, Trofeo

"F" Body: Camaro, Firebird

"H" Body: Bonneville, Eighty-Eight, LeSabre

"J" Body: Cavalier, Sunbird

"K" Body: Seville

"L" Body: Beretta, Corsica

"N" Body: Cutlass Calais, Grand Am, Skylark

"W" Body: Cutlass Supreme, Grand Prix, Lumina, Regal

"Y" Body: Corvette

RIDING HEIGHT ADJUSTMENT

NOTE: On vehicles with electronic chassis controls, ensure all systems are functional before adjusting riding height or wheel alignment.

Before adjusting alignment, check riding height. Riding height must be checked with vehicle on level floor and tires properly inflated. Tire inflation specifications can be found on door pillar, side wall of tire, sun visor or glove box. Bounce vehicle several times and allow suspension to settle.

Visually inspect vehicle for signs of abnormal height from front to rear or side to side. Remove extra heavy items from passenger and luggage compartments. If riding height is not within specifications, check, repair or replace suspension components. See RIDING HEIGHT SPECIFICATIONS table. *See Fig. 1.*

NOTE: For vehicles not listed, riding height between left and right side of vehicle should vary less than 1" (25.4 mm).

RIDING HEIGHT SPECIFICATIONS

Application	Front "A" In. (mm)	Rear "B" In. (mm)
"A" Body		
Century		
Coupe	[1] 8.1 (206)	[2] 8.2 (208)
Sedan	[1] 8.3 (211)	[2] 8.5 (216)
Wagon	[1] 8.6 (218)	[2] 8.9 (226)
Cutlass Ciera		
Coupe, Sedan	[1] 8.4 (213)	[2] 8.4 (213)
Wagon	[1] 8.6 (218)	[2] 8.8 (224)
Cutlass Cruiser	[1] 9.6 (244)	[2] 9.9 (251)
6000		
P185/75R14	[1] 9.0 (229)	[2] 9.2 (234)
P195/75R14, P195/75R15	[1] 9.4 (239)	[2] 9.6 (244)
"B" Body	[3] 9.9 (251)	[4] 10.4 (264)
"C" Body	[5] 9.0-9.7 (229-246)	[5] 9.1-9.8 (231-249)
"D" Body	[6]	[6]

[1] – Location "A" measured 20.0" (508 mm) from center of front axle.
[2] – Location "B" measured 18.0" (457 mm) from center of rear axle.
[3] – Location "A" measured 32.0" (813) from center of front axle.
[4] – Location "B" measured 24.0" (610 mm) from center of rear axle.
[5] – Locations "A" and "B" measured 23.5" (597 mm) from center of nearest axle.
[6] – Information is not available from manufacturer.

RIDING HEIGHT SPECIFICATIONS (Cont.)

Application	Front "A" In. (mm)	Rear "B" In. (mm)
"E" Body		
Eldorado	[7] 28.3 (719)	[7] 28.0 (711)
Reatta	[7] 28.9 (734)	[7] 29.3 (744)
Riviera	[7] 27.4 (696)	[7] 27.8 (706)
Toronado	[6]	[6]
Trofeo	[6]	[6]
"F" Body		
Camaro		
P215/65R15	[8] 8.3 (211)	[9] 8.3 (211)
P245-50ZR16	[8] 8.0 (203)	[9] 8.1 (206)
Firebird	[8] 8.2 (208)	[9] 8.3 (211)
"H" Body		
Bonneville	[7] 27.9-28.7 (709-729)	[7] 27.9-28.7 (709-729)
Eighty-Eight	[7] 27.7-28.5 (704-724)	[7] 28.0-28.7 (711-729)
LeSabre	[7] 27.5-28.3 (704-719)	[7] 27.5-28.3 (704-719)
"J" Body		
Cavalier		
Coupe, Sedan	[10] 9.2 (234)	[10] 9.1 (231)
Station Wagon	[10] 9.5 (241)	[10] 9.6 (244)
Sunbird	[10] 9.2 (234)	[10] 9.1 (231)
"K" Body	[7] 28.3 (719)	[7] 28.0 (711)
"L" Body		
Beretta	[11] 8.7 (221)	[12] 8.8 (224)
P195/70R14	[11] 9.4 (239)	[12] 9.8 (249)
P205/60R15	[11] 9.0 (229)	[12] 9.3 (236)
P205/55R16	[11] 9.0 (229)	[12] 9.4 (239)
P205/55VR16	[11] 9.0 (229)	[12] 9.6 (244)
Corsica		
P185/75R14, P195/70R14	[11] 9.5 (241)	[12] 9.9 (251)
P205/60R15	[11] 9.0 (229)	[12] 9.4 (239)
"N" Body		
Cutlass Calais	[10] 9.4 (239)	[10] 9.3 (236)
Grand Am	[10] 9.6 (244)	[10] 9.6 (244)
Skylark	[10] 9.4 (239)	[10] 9.2 (234)
"W" Body		
Cutlass Supreme	[13] 9.8 (249)	[14] 9.8 (249)
Grand Prix	[13] 9.9 (251)	[14] 10.1 (257)
Regal	[13] 9.8 (249)	[14] 9.8 (249)
Lumina	[13] 9.8 (249)	[14] 9.8 (249)
"Y" Body	[15] 7.5 (191)	[16] 7.7 (196)

[1] – Location "A" measured 20.0" (508 mm) from center of front axle.
[2] – Location "B" measured 18.0" (457 mm) from center of rear axle.
[3] – Location "A" measured 32.0" (813) from center of front axle.
[4] – Location "B" measured 24.0" (610 mm) from center of rear axle.
[5] – Locations "A" and "B" measured 23.5" (597 mm) from center of nearest axle.
[6] – Information is not available from manufacturer.
[7] – Measured at center of fender well outer lip.
[8] – Location "A" measured 32.5" (825 mm) from center of front axle.
[9] – Location "B" measured 17.2" (437 mm) from center of rear axle.
[10] – Locations "A" and "B" measured 21.9" (556 mm) from center of nearest axle.
[11] – Location "A" measured 24.3" (617 mm) from center of front axle.
[12] – Location "B" measured 22.0" (558 mm) from center of rear axle.
[13] – Location "A" measured 23.8" (605 mm) from center of front axle.
[14] – Location "B" measured 20.7" (525 mm) from center of rear axle.
[15] – Location "A" measured 25.7" (653 mm) from center of front axle.
[16] – Location "B" measured 19.1" (485 mm) from center of rear axle.

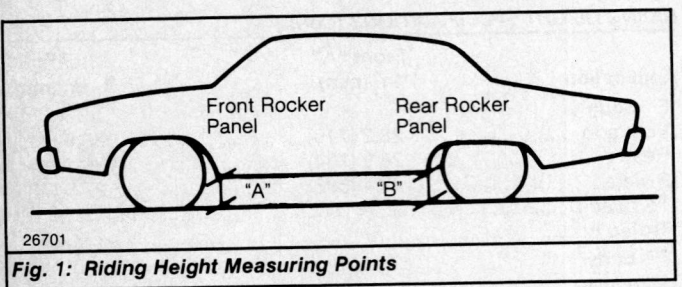

Fig. 1: Riding Height Measuring Points

JACKING & HOISTING

FLOOR JACK

FWD Vehicles – When supporting vehicle with floor jack, place support at suspension lift points or frame lift points. Floor jacks may be placed under front crossmember on most models. *See Figs. 2-7.*

RWD Vehicles – Floor jack may be used under rear axle or front suspension lower control arms. Observe the following precautions:

- NEVER use jack on any part of underbody.
- DO NOT raise entire vehicle at side rail with jack midway between front and rear wheels, or permanent body damage may result.
- DO NOT allow lifting plate fingers to contact axle cover plate when lifting at rear axle housing.
- If vehicle is equipped with a stabilizer bar, DO NOT lift at rear axle housing. *See Figs. 2-7.*

BUMPER JACK

Bumper jack should only be used if supplied as original equipment with vehicle. If vehicle is not supplied with a bumper jack, DO NOT lift vehicle by the bumper at any time. Bumper jack should only be used to change flat tire.

NOTE: *Always follow hoist manufacturer's instructions. DO NOT allow hoist or adapters to contact suspension, exhaust or steering components. Frame contact must be made. Use adapters if necessary. Lift vehicle as shown in illustrations. Illustration is not available for Corvette.*

AXLE CONTACT HOIST

Hoist should contact lower control arms or front crossmember, and rear axle as shown in illustrations. *See Figs. 2-7.*

FRAME CONTACT HOIST

Hoist adapters must contact vehicle in specified areas. *See Figs. 2-7.* Adapters must be positioned to distribute load and support vehicle in a stable manner. DO NOT allow lift pads to contact exhaust system components. On Corvette, position frame contact hoist on frame rails, forward of rear wheels and rearward of front wheels.

CAUTION: *If removing rear axle, fuel tank, spare tire or liftgate, and single-post hoist is used, anchor vehicle to hoist. Place jack stands under vehicle or add weight on rear end of vehicle to prevent tipping when center of gravity changes.*

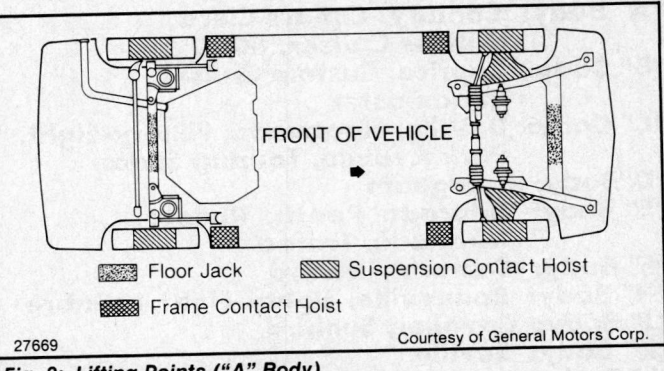

Fig. 2: Lifting Points ("A" Body)

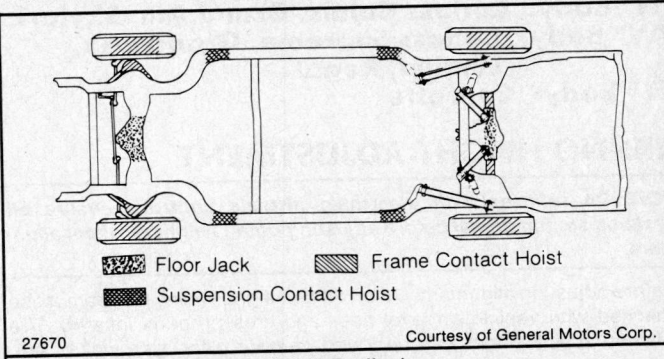

Fig. 3: Lifting Points ("B" & "D" Bodies)

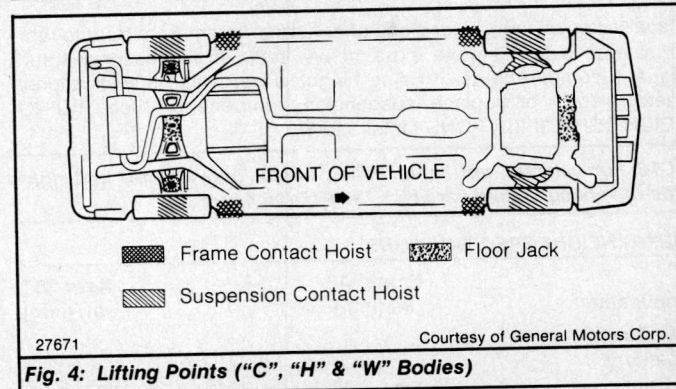

Fig. 4: Lifting Points ("C", "H" & "W" Bodies)

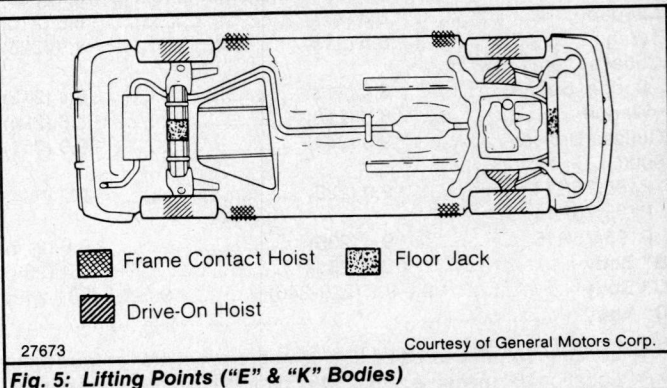

Fig. 5: Lifting Points ("E" & "K" Bodies)

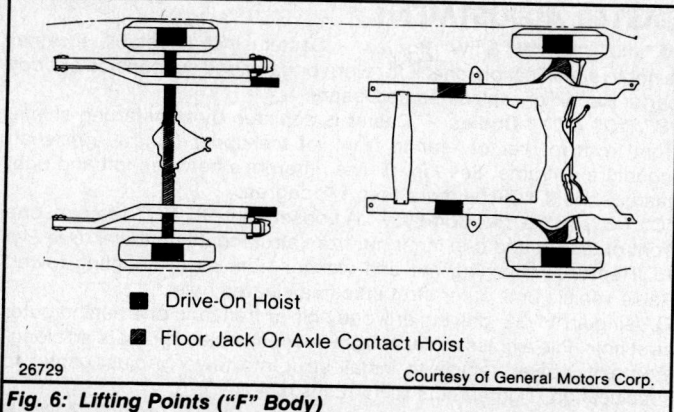

■ Drive-On Hoist

■ Floor Jack Or Axle Contact Hoist

26729   Courtesy of General Motors Corp.

Fig. 6: Lifting Points ("F" Body)

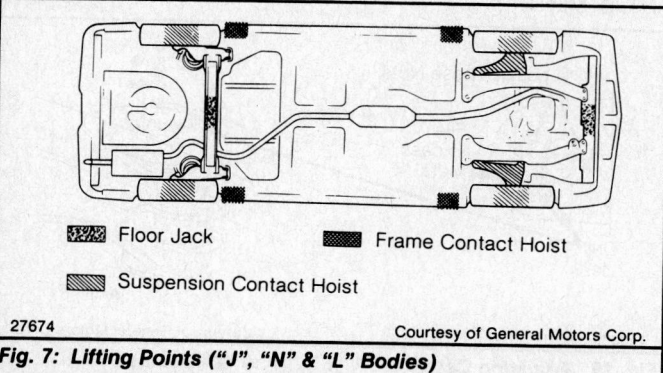

▨ Floor Jack   ■ Frame Contact Hoist

▨ Suspension Contact Hoist

27674   Courtesy of General Motors Corp.

Fig. 7: Lifting Points ("J", "N" & "L" Bodies)

ALIGNMENT PROCEDURES

NOTE: Refer to RIDING HEIGHT SPECIFICATIONS table for body code applications.

CAMBER ADJUSTMENT

"A", "J", "L" & "N" Bodies – To adjust front camber, loosen 2 strut-to-steering knuckle bolts. See Fig. 8. Move top of wheel in or out to obtain correct camber specification. While holding wheel in position, tighten 2 strut-to-steering knuckle bolts. Rear camber is not adjustable. If rear camber is not to specification, repair or replace damaged or worn suspension or body parts.

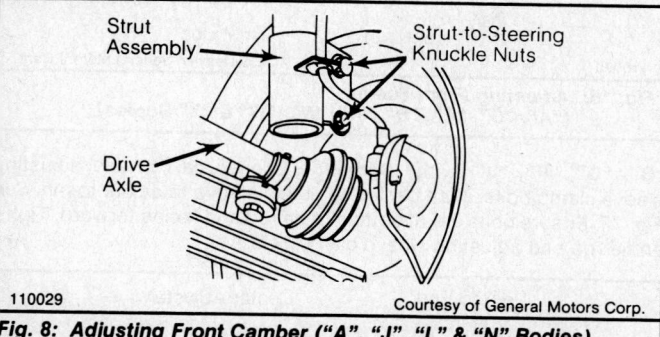

110029   Courtesy of General Motors Corp.

Fig. 8: Adjusting Front Camber ("A", "J", "L" & "N" Bodies)

"B", "D" & "Y" Bodies – Adjust front camber by adding or subtracting equal number of shims between both ends of upper control arm shaft and frame. See Fig. 9. To adjust rear camber on Corvette, loosen lower spindle rod adjusting cam lock nut and bolt. Turn cam to obtain correct camber. See Fig. 10. Tighten adjusting cam lock nut and bolt.

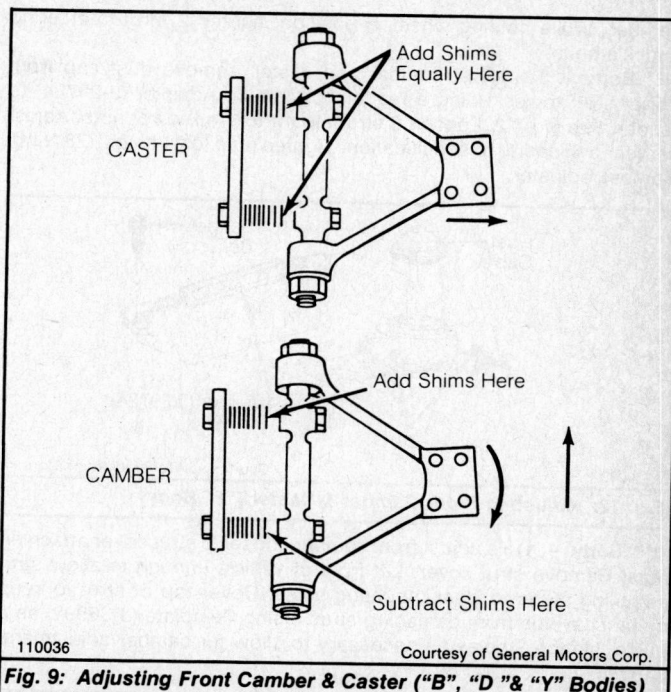

110036   Courtesy of General Motors Corp.

Fig. 9: Adjusting Front Camber & Caster ("B", "D" & "Y" Bodies)

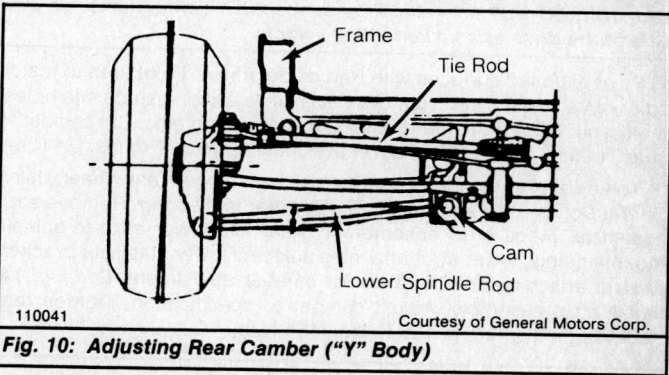

110041   Courtesy of General Motors Corp.

Fig. 10: Adjusting Rear Camber ("Y" Body)

"C" & "H" Bodies – To adjust front or rear camber, loosen 2 strut-to-steering knuckle bolts. Install Camber Adjuster (J-29862). See Fig. 11. Tighten or loosen camber adjuster as necessary to obtain correct camber. While holding wheel in position, tighten 2 strut-to-steering knuckle bolts.

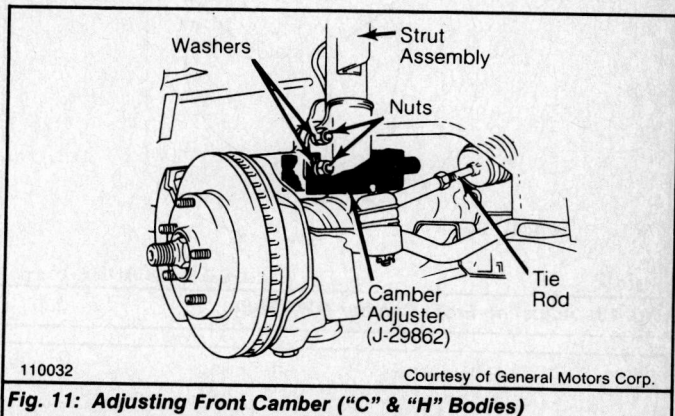

110032   Courtesy of General Motors Corp.

Fig. 11: Adjusting Front Camber ("C" & "H" Bodies)

"E" & "K" Bodies – To adjust camber, loosen 2 strut-to-steering knuckle bolts. Tighten or loosen camber adjusting bolt, located above spindle next to upper strut-to-steering knuckle bolt, to obtain correct camber. While holding wheel in position, tighten 2 strut-to-steering knuckle bolts.

"F" Body – To adjust camber and caster, remove dust cap from upper strut tower. Using a fender bolt, attach Adjuster (J-29724) to fender. See Fig. 12. Loosen 3 strut mount-to-strut tower nuts. Adjust camber and caster to specification. Tighten nuts to 21 ft. lbs. (28 N.m). Remove adjuster.

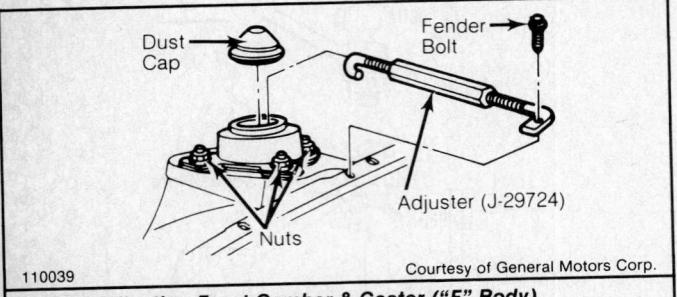

110039

Fig. 12: Adjusting Front Camber & Caster ("F" Body)

"W" Body – 1) To adjust front camber, loosen 3 strut cover attaching nuts. Remove strut cover. Lift front of vehicle enough to allow strut attaching studs to clear mounting holes. Cover top of strut to keep metal shavings from damaging strut. Using Template (J-36892) as a guide, file the 3 holes as necessary to allow for camber adjustment. See Fig. 13.

CAUTION: DO NOT lift vehicle by suspension components, or over extend the drive axles when lifting vehicle.

2) Paint exposed surfaces with Red oxide primer. Paint area to match color of vehicle. Lower front of vehicle while aligning studs into holes. Install, but DO NOT tighten 3 strut cover attaching nuts. Set camber to specification. Tighten strut cover attaching nuts to 17 ft. lbs. (24 N.m).

3) To adjust rear camber, raise vehicle and remove rear wheel. Using Spring Compressor (J-35778), remove rear leaf spring. Remove strut assembly. Place strut assembly in vise. File lower strut-to-spindle mounting hole, lower strut attaching hole and lower stabilizer bracket-to-strut attaching hole to allow for camber adjustment. See Fig. 14. Install strut assembly. Adjust camber to specification. Tighten rear strut-to-spindle nuts to 136 ft. lbs. (184 N.m).

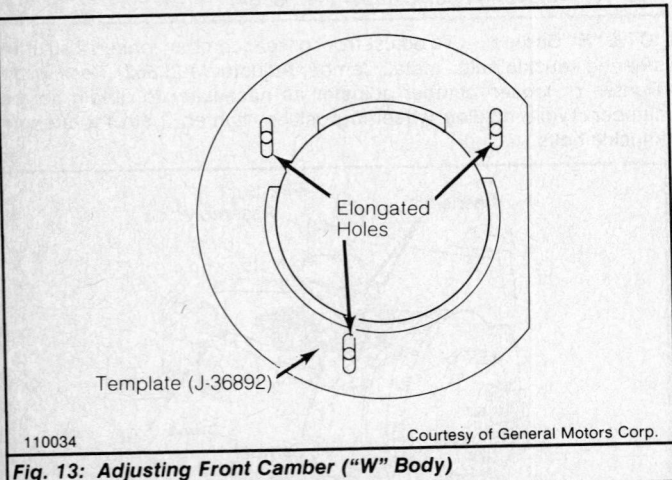

110034

Fig. 13: Adjusting Front Camber ("W" Body)

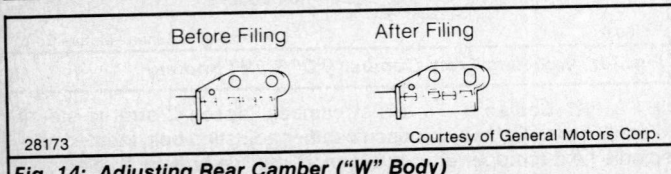

28173

Fig. 14: Adjusting Rear Camber ("W" Body)

CASTER ADJUSTMENT

"A", "J", "L", "N" & "W" Bodies – Caster is not adjustable. If caster is not to specification, check for worn or damaged suspension or body parts. Repair or replace as necessary.

"B", "D" & "Y" Bodies – Caster is adjusted by transferring shims, from front to rear or rear to front, of the upper control arm shaft mounts and frame. See Fig. 9. The difference between left and right caster should NOT be more than 1/2 degree.

"C", "E", "H" & "K" Bodies – 1) Loosen, but DO NOT remove, one front outer nut and one inner nut from strut mounting tower. See Fig. 15. Remove remaining nut and washer from strut mounting tower. Raise vehicle until outer strut stud has cleared hole.

2) Using an 11/32" drill bit, drill one hole in front and one behind outer strut hole. File excess material from between holes to create an elongated slot. Lower vehicle to install strut into tower. Adjust caster to specification. Tighten nuts to 17 ft. lbs. (24 N.m).

"F" Body – To adjust caster, see "F" BODY under CAMBER ADJUSTMENT.

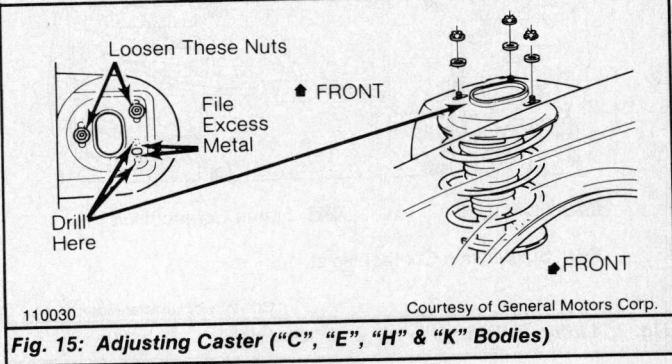

110030

Fig. 15: Adjusting Caster ("C", "E", "H" & "K" Bodies)

TOE-IN ADJUSTMENT (FRONT)

"A", "C", "E", "H", "K", "N", "W" & "Y" Bodies – Loosen tie rod end lock nut. See Fig. 16. Loosen steering gear dust boot clamp(s) at tie rod end. Turn tie rod end to obtain correct toe-in. Tighten lock nut to specification. See TORQUE SPECIFICATIONS table at end of article. Ensure steering gear dust boot is straight after adjustment. Tighten dust boot clamp.

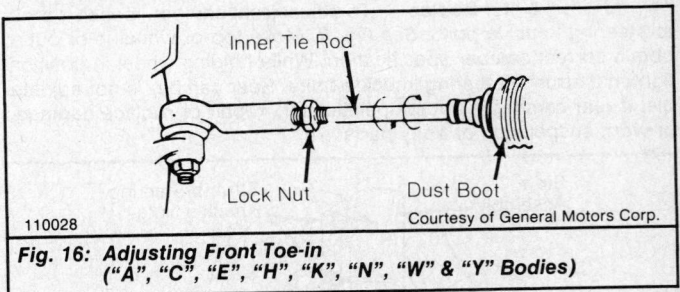

110028

Fig. 16: Adjusting Front Toe-in ("A", "C", "E", "H", "K", "N", "W" & "Y" Bodies)

"B", "D", "F", "J" & "L" Bodies – Loosen tie rod end adjusting sleeve clamp bolts. Turn center adjusting sleeve to adjust toe-in. See Fig. 17. Ensure bolts are at bottom of tie rod and facing forward. Tighten tie rod end adjusting sleeve clamp bolts.

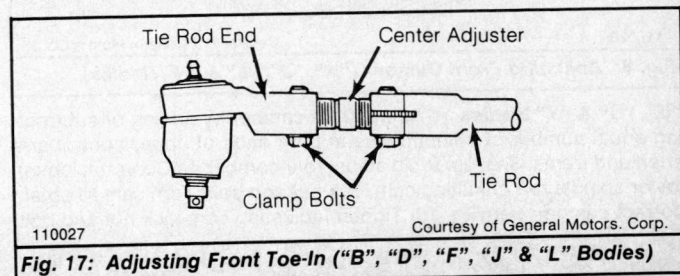

110027

Fig. 17: Adjusting Front Toe-In ("B", "D", "F", "J" & "L" Bodies)

TOE−IN ADJUSTMENT (REAR)

"A" & "N" Bodies – Rear toe-in is not adjustable. If rear toe-in is not to specification, repair or replace worn or damaged components.

"E" & "K" Bodies – Loosen front and rear inside control arm mounting bolts. Pry between rear control arm mounting bolts and rear support assembly until proper toe-in is obtained. *See Fig. 18.* Tighten control arm mounting bolts to 66 ft. lbs. (90 N.m).

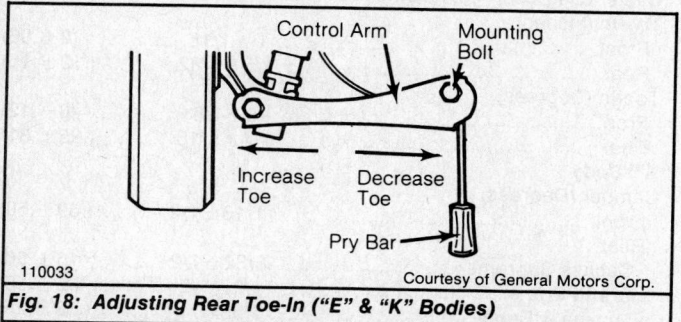

Courtesy of General Motors Corp.

110033

Fig. 18: Adjusting Rear Toe-In ("E" & "K" Bodies)

"Y" Body – Loosen rear tie rod adjusting lock nut. Turn tie rod end to obtain correct toe-in. Tighten lock nut to specification. See TORQUE SPECIFICATIONS table.

"W" Body – 1) Using holes in rear suspension rod and jack stand pad, hook Turnbuckle Adjuster (J-38118) between rear suspension rod and jack stand pad. Hand tighten turnbuckle adjuster.

2) Loosen rear rod-to-crossmember nut at crossmember a minimum of 4 turns. Tighten or loosen turnbuckle adjuster as necessary to obtain correct rear toe-in. Tighten rear rod-to-crossmember nut to 81 ft. lbs. (110 N.m), plus an additional 1/6 turn (60 degrees).

TORQUE SPECIFICATIONS

TORQUE SPECIFICATIONS

Application	Ft. Lbs. (N.m)
Front Inside Control Arm Mounting Bolt	66 (90)
Front Suspension-To-Frame Bolt	37 (50)
Lateral Link Cam Nut	140 (190)
Rear Inside Control Arm Mounting Bolt	66 (90)
Rear Rod-To-Crossmember Nut	[1] 81 (110)
Rear Strut-To-Spindle Attaching Nut	136 (184)
Rear Tie Rod Lock Nut	46 (62)
Strut Cover Attaching Nut	17 (24)
Strut Mount-To-Strut Tower Nut	21 (28)
Strut-to-Steering Knuckle Nut	
"A" & "N" Bodies	140 (190)
"C" Body	144 (195)
"E", "K" & "W" Bodies	136 (185)
"J" & "L" Bodies	133 (180)
"H" Body	180 (244)
Tie Rod End Lock Nut	46 (62)
Tie Rod End Clamp Bolt	14 (19)
Upper Control Arm-To-Frame	72 (98)
Upper Strut-To-Body Bolt	34 (46)
Spindle Rod Adjusting Cam Nut	187 (253)

[1] – Tighten to specification plus 1/6 turn (60 degrees).

ALIGNMENT SPECIFICATIONS

WHEEL ALIGNMENT SPECIFICATIONS

Application	Fraction	Decimal
"A" Body		
Camber (Degrees)		
Front	0 ± 1/2	(0 ± .50)
Rear	0 ± 5/16	(0 ± .31)
Caster (Degrees) [1]	1 11/16 ± 1	(1.69 ± 1)
Toe-In (Inches)		
Front	0 ± 3/32	(0 ± .09)
Rear	0 ± 5/32	(0 ± .15)

[1] – Left-to-right caster differential must not exceed 1 1/2° (1.5°).

WHEEL ALIGNMENT SPECIFICATIONS (Cont.)

Application	Fraction	Decimal
Toe-In (Degrees)		
Front	0 ± 3/16	(0 ± .18)
Rear	0 ± 5/16	(0 ± .31)
"B" Body		
Camber (Degrees)	13/16 ± 13/16	(.81 ± .81)
Caster (Degrees) [1]	2 13/16 ± 1/2	(2.81 ± .50)
Toe-In (Inches)	3/32 ± 3/32	(.09 ± .09)
Toe-In (Degrees)	5/32 ± 3/16	(.15 ± .18)
"C" Body		
Camber (Degrees)		
Front		
DeVille & Fleetwood	[2]	[2]
Ninety-Eight, Park Avenue & Touring Sedan	3/16 ± 1/2	(.18 ± .50)
Rear		
DeVille & Fleetwood	3/16 ± 1/2	(.18 ± .50)
Ninety-Eight, Park Avenue & Touring Sedan	−5/16 ± 1/2	(−.31 ± .50)
Caster (Degrees) [1]	3 ± 1/2	(3 ± .50)
Toe-In (Inches)		
Front	0 ± 5/32	(0 ± .15)
Rear		
DeVille & Fleetwood	3/32 ± 3/32	(.15 ± .15)
Ninety-Eight, Park Avenue & Touring Sedan	1/16 ± 3/32	(.06 ± .15)
Toe-In (Degrees)		
Front	0 ± 5/16	(0 ± .31)
Rear		
DeVille & Fleetwood	3/16 ± 3/16	(.18 ± .18)
Ninety Eight, Park Avenue & Touring Sedan	3/32 ± 3/16	(.09 ± .18)
"D" Body		
Camber (Degrees)	0 ± 1/2	(0 ± .50)
Caster (Degrees) [1]	3 ± 1/2	(3 ± .50)
Toe-In (Inches)		
Front	0 ± 3/32	(0 ± .09)
Toe-In (Degrees)		
Front	0 ± 3/16	(0 ± .18)
"E" Body		
Camber (Degrees)		
Front	0 ± 13/16	(0 ± .81)
Rear		
Eldorado	−3/32 ± 5/16	(−.09 ± .31)
Reatta	3/16 ± 5/16	(.18 ± .31)
Riviera	−11/16 ± 5/16	(−.68 ± .31)
Toronado & Trofeo	−13/32 ± 5/16	(−.40 ± .31)
Caster (Degrees) [1]	2 5/16 ± 1	(2.31 ± 1)
Toe-In (Inches)		
Front		
Eldorado	0 ± 3/32	(0 ± .09)
Except Eldorado	3/32 ± 3/32	(.09 ± .09)
Rear	3/32 ± 3/32	(.09 ± .09)
Toe-In (Degrees)		
Front		
Eldorado	0 ± 3/16	(0 ± .18)
Except Eldorado	3/16 ± 3/16	(.18 ± .18)
Rear	3/16 ± 3/16	(.18 ± .18)
"F" Body		
Camber (Degrees)		
Front	5/16 ± 1/2	(.31 ± .50)
Rear	3/32 ± 13/32	(.09 ± .40)
Caster (Degrees) [1]	4 13/16 ± 1/2	(4.81 ± .50)
Toe-In (Inches)		
Front	0 ± 3/32	(0 ± .09)
Rear	0 ± 5/16	(0 ± .31)

[1] – Left-to-right caster differential must not exceed 1 1/2° (1.5°).

[2] – Left: −1/2° ± 1/2°, Right: 1/2° ± 1/2°. Cross camber = 0° ± 1/2°.

WHEEL ALIGNMENT SPECIFICATIONS (Cont.)

Application	Fraction	Decimal
Toe-In (Degrees)		
Front	0 ± 3/16	(0 ± .18)
Rear	0 ± 5/16	(0 ± .31)
"H" Body		
Camber (Degrees)		
Front	3/16 ± 1/2	(.18 ± .50)
Rear	−5/16 ± 1/2	(−.31 ± .50)
Caster (Degrees) [1]	3 ± 1/2	(3 ± .50)
Toe-In (Inches)		
Front	0 ± 3/32	(0 ± .09)
Rear	1/16 ± 1/16	(.06 ± .06)
Toe-In (Degrees)	0 ± 3/16	(0 ± .18)
"J" Body		
Camber (Degrees)		
Front	5/8 ± 5/16	(.62 ± .31)
Rear	−1/4 ± 1/2	(−.25 ± .50)
Caster (Degrees) [1]	1 11/16 ± 1	(1.69 ± 1)
Toe-In (Inches)		
Front		
Z24	1/16 ± 3/32	(.06 ± .09)
Except Z24	0 ± 3/32	(0 ± .09)
Rear (All)	1/8 ± 3/32	(.12 ± .09)
Toe-In (Degrees)		
Front		
Z24	1/8 ± 3/16	(.12 ± .18)
Except Z24	0 ± 3/16	(0 ± .18)
Rear (All)	1/4 ± 3/16	(.25 ± .18)
"K" Body		
Camber (Degrees)	0 ± 13/16	(0 ± .81)
Caster (Degrees) [1]	2 5/16 ± 1	(2.31 ± 1)
Toe-In (Inches)		
Front	0 ± 3/32	(0 ± .09)
Rear	3/32 ± 3/32	(.09 ± .09)
Toe-In (Degrees)		
Front	0 ± 3/16	(0 ± .18)
Rear	3/16 ± 3/16	(.18 ± .18)
"L" Body		
Camber (Degrees)	9/16 ± 9/16	(.56 ± .56)
Caster (Degrees) [1]	1 5/32 ± 3/4	(1.15 ± .75)
Toe-In (Inches)		
Front	0 ± 3/32	(0 ± .09)
Rear	5/32 ± 1/8	(.15 ± .12)
Toe-In (Degrees)		
Front	0 ± 3/16	(0 ± .18)
Rear	5/16 ± 1/4	(.31 ± .25)

[1] – Left-to-right caster differential must not exceed 1 1/2° (1.5°).
[2] – Left: −1/2° ± 1/2°, Right: 1/2° ± 1/2°. Cross camber = 0° ± 1/2°.

WHEEL ALIGNMENT SPECIFICATIONS (Cont.)

Application	Fraction	Decimal
"N" Body		
Camber (Degrees)		
Front	0 ± 1 1/16	(0 ± 1.06)
Rear	−1/4 ± 9/16	(−.25 ± .56)
Caster (Degrees) [1]	1 11/16 ± 1	(1.68 ± 1)
Toe-In (Inches)		
Front	0 ± 1/16	(0 ± .06)
Rear	1/8 ± 5/32	(.12 ± .15)
Toe-In (Degrees)		
Front	0 ± 1/8	(0 ± .12)
Rear	1/4 ± 5/16	(.25 ± .31)
"W" Body		
Camber (Degrees)		
Front	11/16 ± 1/2	(.69 ± .50)
Rear		
Cutlass Supreme	−5/32 ± 1/2	(−.15 ± .50)
Grand Prix	1/2 ± 1/2	(.5 ± .50)
Lumina & Regal	3/8 ± 1/4	(.38 ± .25)
Caster (Degrees) [1]		
Cutlass Supreme &		
Grand Prix	1 13/16 ± 1/2	(1.81 ± .50)
Lumina	2 ± 1/2	(2 ± .50)
Regal	1 11/16 ± 1	(1.69 ± 1.0)
Toe-In (Inches)		
Front	0 ± 3/32	(0 ± .09)
Rear	0 ± 5/32	(0 ± .15)
Toe-In (Degrees)		
Front	0 ± 3/16	(0 ± .18)
Rear	0 ± 5/16	(0 ± .31)
"Y" Body		
Camber (Degrees)		
Front	1/2 ± 1/2	(.50 ± .50)
Rear	0 ± 1/2	(0 ± .50)
Caster (Degrees) [1]	6 ± 1/2	(6 ± .50)
Toe-In (Inches)		
Front	0 ± 3/32	(0 ± .09)
Rear	0 ± 3/16	(0 ± .18)
Toe-In (Degrees)		
Front	0 ± 3/16	(0 ± .18)
Rear	0 ± 3/8	(0 ± .38)

[1] – Left-to-right caster differential must not exceed 1 1/2° (1.5°).
[2] – Left: −1/2° ± 1/2°, Right: 1/2° ± 1/2°. Cross camber = 0° ± 1/2°.

"A" Body: Century, Cutlass Ciera, Cutlass Cruiser, 6000
"C" Body: DeVille, Fleetwood, Ninety-Eight, Park Avenue, Touring Sedan
"H" Body: Bonneville, Eighty-Eight, LeSabre
"J" Body: Cavalier, Sunbird
"L" Body: Beretta, Corsica
"N" Body: Cutlass Calais, Grand Am, Skylark

DESCRIPTION

The MacPherson strut design front suspension uses lower control arms which pivot from engine cradle on "A", "C" and "H" bodies and from lower side rails on "J", "L" and "N" bodies. The cradle has isolation mounts securing it to the unibody. Lower control arms contain rubber pivot bushings.

The strut upper end is isolated by a rubber mount, containing a bearing for strut turning to steer vehicle. Lower end of steering knuckle pivots on the lower control arm mounted ball joint. On "A" body, the steering knuckle is a pinch bolt, clamped to the ball joint stud. On all except "A" body, the ball joint fits through a tapered bore in the steering knuckle. Tie rod ends are connected to steering knuckle or to steering arms located on the struts.

ADJUSTMENTS & INSPECTION

WHEEL ALIGNMENT SPECIFICATIONS & PROCEDURES

NOTE: See SPECIFICATIONS & PROCEDURES article in WHEEL ALIGNMENT.

WHEEL BEARING INSPECTION

Bearing Looseness Check – 1) Move pads away from disc or remove caliper assembly. Use 2 wheel lug nuts to secure disc to hub. Mount dial indicator support to lower steering knuckle ball joint or to lower "A" arm assembly.
2) Position dial indicator plunger onto outer lip of hub (not onto disc surface). Grasp disc outer edges and using a push-pull movement, note dial indicator readings. If looseness exceeds .005" (.1270 mm), replace complete hub assembly.

NOTE: Hub and bearing assemblies are pre-adjusted and lubricated, and require no routine maintenance or adjustment. Replace as a complete assembly.

RIDING HEIGHT

NOTE: See SPECIFICATIONS & PROCEDURES article in WHEEL ALIGNMENT.

BALL JOINT INSPECTION

1) Raise and support vehicle. Allow suspension to hang freely. Inspect ball joint seals for cracks or tears. Replace ball joint if seal is damaged. Grasp tire at top and bottom. Moving tire inward and outward, note horizontal movement of ball joint. Replace ball joint if any horizontal movement exists.
2) Ball joint stud tightness in steering knuckle boss should be checked by shaking wheel and looking for looseness at stud end or castellated nut. When ball joint is disconnected from steering knuckle, check ball joint free play by using finger pressure to spin ball joint stud in its socket. If stud spins in socket, replace ball joint.

REMOVAL & INSTALLATION

BALL JOINT

CAUTION: When servicing suspension, on inner Tri-Pod axle joint with Gray silicone boot, use Drive Axle Boot Protector (J-33162). Boots made of Black thermo-plastic material require Boot Protector (J-34754). For outer double-offset joint, modify Boot Protector (J-34754) by removing 3 tabs on inside surface. DO NOT over-extend inner Tri-Pod joint, internal parts may separate.

Removal – 1) Raise front of vehicle. Using jack stands for support and depending on vehicle model; position stands under subframe rails, near front wheels or position stands under engine cradle. Allow suspension to hang freely. Remove front wheel(s). Place drive axle boot protector on outer joint.
2) Remove cotter pin and castle nut from ball joint stud. Using Ball Joint Separator (J-36226) for "C" and "H" bodies and (J-29330) for all others, separate ball joint stud from steering knuckle.
3) On pinch bolt/clamp type ball joint studs, remove pinch bolt from steering knuckle securing ball joint stud. Separate ball joint from steering knuckle. It may be necessary to pry lower control arm from steering knuckle or to tap steering knuckle with mallet to loosen ball joint stud.
4) Drill out ball joint retaining rivets. Disconnect stabilizer bar from lower control arm. See STABILIZER BAR & BUSHING ASSEMBLY under REMOVAL & INSTALLATION. Lower the control arm. Remove ball joint from control arm.

NOTE: If insufficient clearance exists for ball joint removal, remove drive axle hub nut and install Front Hub Spindle Remover (J-28733). Tighten front hub spindle remover until enough CV joint clearance is obtained to remove ball joint.

Installation – 1) Install ball joint to lower control arm. On "J" and "L" bodies, install ball joint retaining bolts facing upward. On all other bodies, install retaining bolts facing downward.
2) Tighten ball joint retaining bolts to specification. See TORQUE SPECIFICATIONS table at end of this article. Position steering knuckle over ball joint stud and install castle nut. Tighten to specification. Install new cotter pin.

CAUTION: Always install new pinch bolt and nut on "A" bodies whenever ball joint is separated from steering knuckle.

3) On pinch bolt/clamp type ball joint stud, align notch in stud to allow pinch bolt to be installed. Install new pinch bolt and nut. Install stabilizer bar assembly. Tighten bolts to specification. See TORQUE SPECIFICATIONS table at end of this article.
4) Remove drive axle boot protector(s). If drive axle was removed, slide drive axle into hub assembly and install nut. Install wheel and lower vehicle. Tighten drive axle hub nut to specification. Check wheel alignment. See SPECIFICATIONS & PROCEDURES article in WHEEL ALIGNMENT.

HUB & BEARING ASSEMBLY

Removal – 1) Raise vehicle and remove wheels. Allow suspension to hang freely. Install drive axle boot protector (J-34754).
2) Remove drive axle hub nut and washer. See Figs. 1-4. Remove disc brake caliper. DO NOT disconnect brake line. Wire caliper up out of the way, to prevent brake hose damage.
3) Remove rotor. Using Front Hub Spindle Remover (J-28733-A), separate drive axle shaft from hub splines.
4) Mark hub and bearing assembly-to-steering knuckle location for reassembly reference. Remove 3 hub and bearing assembly Torx head retaining bolts. See Fig. 4. Remove splash shield. Remove hub and bearing assembly.
5) To replace inner grease seal, disconnect stabilizer bar from lower control arm. Separate ball joint. See BALL JOINT under REMOVAL & INSTALLATION. Remove drive axle shaft from steering knuckle and support axle shaft. Remove grease seal from steering knuckle.

GM
10-2

1991 SUSPENSION
Front – "A", "C", "H", "J", "L" & "N" Bodies (Cont.)

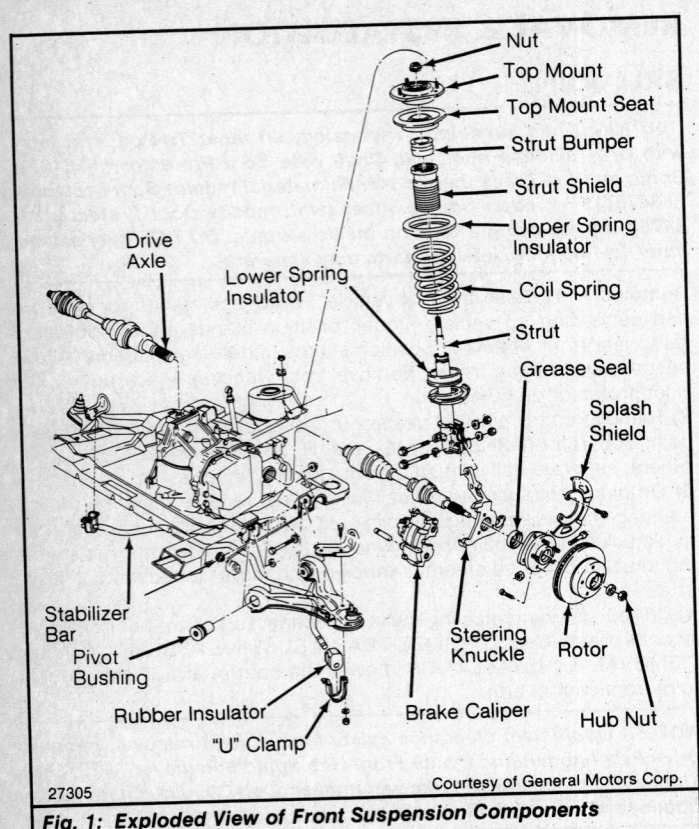

Fig. 1: Exploded View of Front Suspension Components ("A" Body)

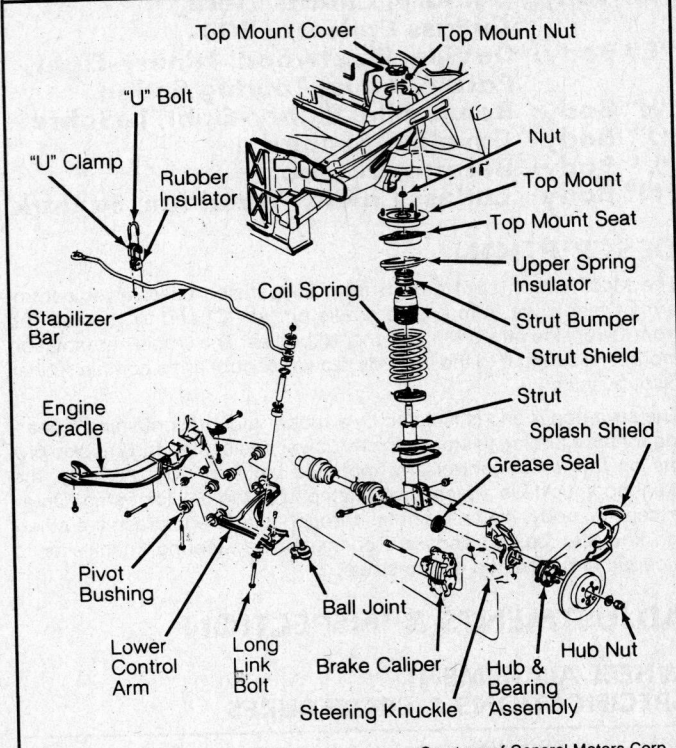

Fig. 3: Exploded View of Front Suspension Components ("J", "L" & "N" Bodies)

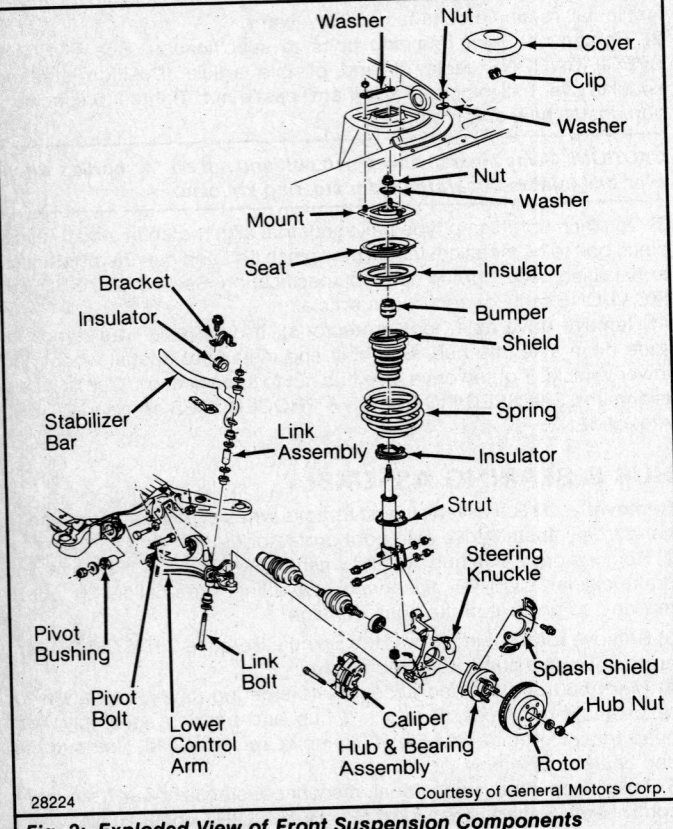

Fig. 2: Exploded View of Front Suspension Components ("C" & "H" Bodies)

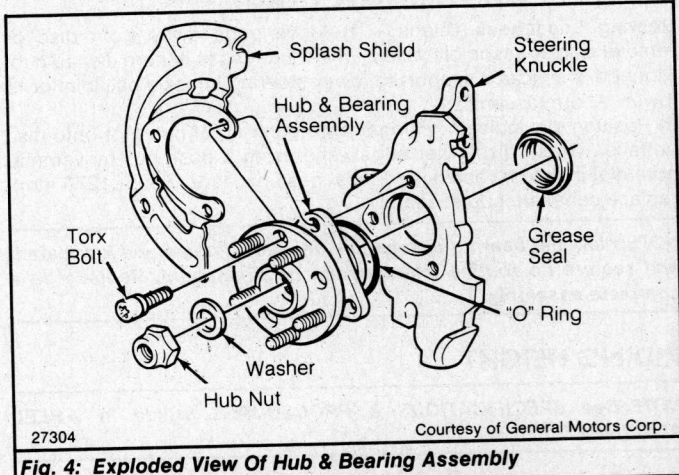

Fig. 4: Exploded View Of Hub & Bearing Assembly

NOTE: Factory seal is installed from engine side of steering knuckle on "A", "C" and "H" bodies. Service replacement seal is installed from wheel side of steering knuckle.

Installation – 1) When installing new replacement grease seal in steering knuckle, lubricate seal lip with grease. Install "O" ring on hub and bearing assembly. *See Fig. 4.* Hub and bearing are replaced as one assembly. Use care not to damage grease seal during axle shaft, and hub and bearing assembly installation.

2) Align reference mark on hub and bearing assembly to steering knuckle and install. Install splash shield and Torx head retaining bolts. Tighten Torx head bolts to specification. Align reference mark of rotor to hub and bearing assembly. Install new hub-to-drive axle nut. Initially tighten nut to 74 ft. lbs. (100 N.m). Install wheel and tighten lug nuts to specification. Lower vehicle and tighten hub-to-drive axle nut to specification. See TORQUE SPECIFICATIONS table at end of this article.

1991 SUSPENSION
Front – "A", "C", "H", "J", "L" & "N" Bodies (Cont.)

GM
10-3

LOWER CONTROL ARM

Removal – 1) Raise and support vehicle. Allow suspension to hang freely. Remove wheel. Install boot protectors on inner and outer drive axle joints. Remove stabilizer bar from control arm. See STABILIZER BAR & BUSHING ASSEMBLY under REMOVAL & INSTALLATION.
2) Separate ball joint from lower control arm. See BALL JOINT under REMOVAL & INSTALLATION. Remove lower control arm bolts and lower control arm.

Installation – To install, reverse removal procedure. On pinch bolt/clamp type ball joints install new bolt and nut. Tighten lower control arm-to-engine cradle bolts with vehicle weight on lower control arms. Check alignment.

NOTE: Lower control arm mounting bolts must be tightened to specification with vehicle weight on control arms. See TORQUE SPECIFICATIONS table at end of this article.

LOWER CONTROL ARM BUSHINGS

Removal & Installation ("A" Body) – Remove lower control arm. See LOWER CONTROL ARM under REMOVAL & INSTALLATION. Use Control Arm Bushing Service Set (J-21474-01) along with Bushing Remover (J-21058-12) and Bushing Installer (J-35561-3) to change bushings in control arm. See Fig. 5.

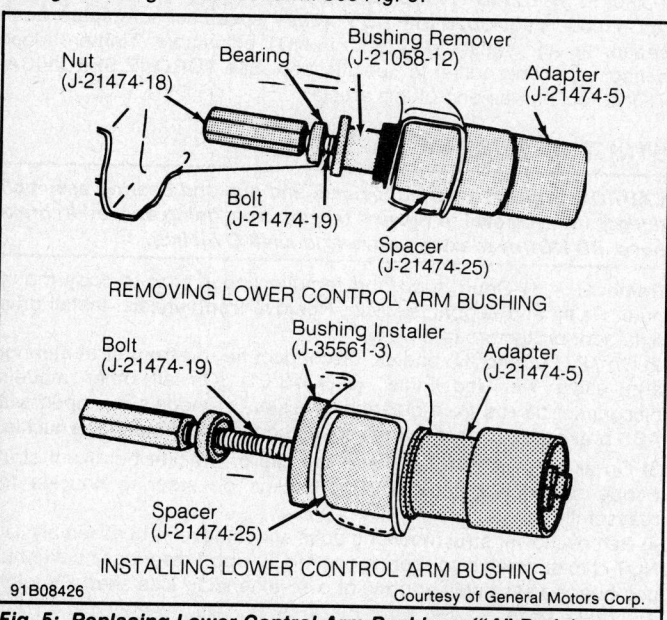

REMOVING LOWER CONTROL ARM BUSHING

INSTALLING LOWER CONTROL ARM BUSHING

91B08426   Courtesy of General Motors Corp.

Fig. 5: Replacing Lower Control Arm Bushings ("A" Body)

Removal & Installation ("C" & "H" Bodies) – 1) Remove lower control arm. See LOWER CONTROL ARM under REMOVAL & INSTALLATION. To enable lower control arm bushing removal, tap down flare on lip of bushing using a hammer and punch.
2) Using Bushing Service Set (J-21474-01), press out bushing. To install, lubricate new bushing and use Bushing Service Set (J-21474-01) to press bushing into control arm. Using Flare Tool (J-23915) and Bushing Service Set (J-21474-01), tighten nut on flare tool to obtain a 45-degree flare on bushing. See Fig. 6.
3) When replacing lower control arm cradle bushing, use Bushing Service Set (J-21474-01) to press out bushing. Lubricate bushing prior to installation. Using Bushing Service Set (J-21474-01), install cradle bushing. Ensure bushing is fully seated in cradle. See Fig. 7.

Removal & Installation ("J", "L" & "N" Bodies) – Remove lower control arm. See LOWER CONTROL ARM under REMOVAL & INSTALLATION. Use Control Arm Bushing Service Set (J-29792) to press bushing from control arm. See Fig. 8. Lubricate bushing prior to press installation. Install bushing, using Control Arm Bushing Service Set (J-29792).

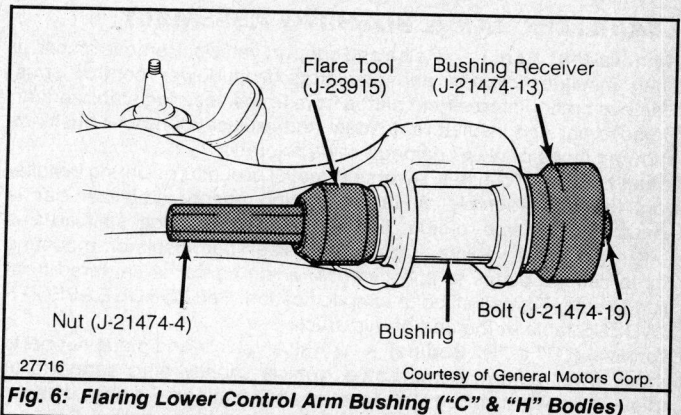

27716   Courtesy of General Motors Corp.

Fig. 6: Flaring Lower Control Arm Bushing ("C" & "H" Bodies)

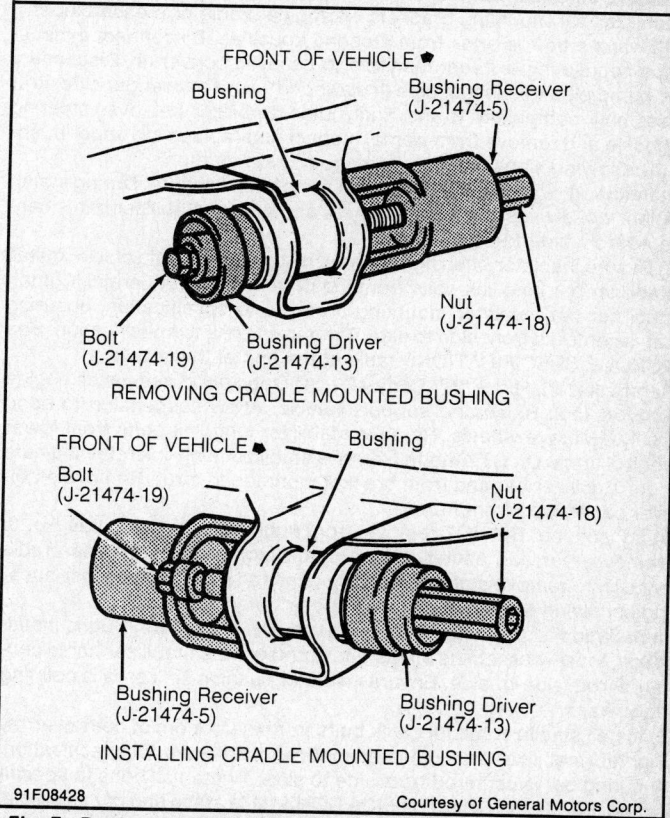

REMOVING CRADLE MOUNTED BUSHING

INSTALLING CRADLE MOUNTED BUSHING

91F08428   Courtesy of General Motors Corp.

Fig. 7: Replacing Cradle Mounted Lower Control Arm Bushings ("C" & "H" Bodies)

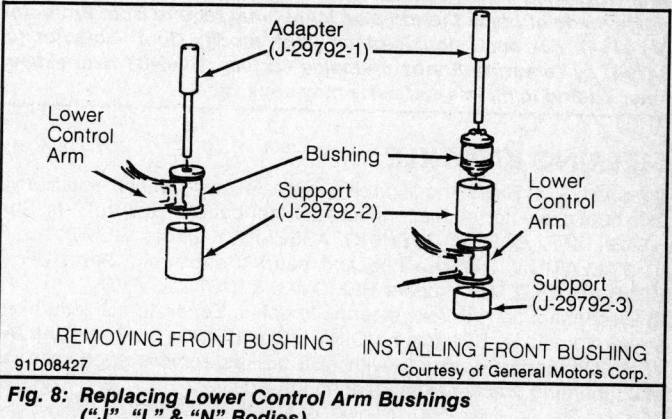

REMOVING FRONT BUSHING   INSTALLING FRONT BUSHING

91D08427   Courtesy of General Motors Corp.

Fig. 8: Replacing Lower Control Arm Bushings ("J", "L" & "N" Bodies)

GM
10-4

1991 SUSPENSION
Front — "A", "C", "H", "J", "L" & "N" Bodies (Cont.)

STABILIZER BAR & BUSHING ASSEMBLY

Removal ("A" Body) – Raise and support vehicle. Remove stabilizer shaft insulator clamps and insulators from lower control arms. Remove both reinforcement plates from frame securing stabilizer bar. Remove bar and insulators. Inspect and replace all rubber bushings showing signs of wear, damage or deterioration.

Installation – To install, reverse removal procedure. During installation, loosely assemble all fasteners and ensure stabilizer bar is centered from side-to-side. Ensure insulator bushing split area is toward front of vehicle. Tighten stabilizer bar insulator mounting reinforcement plates to specification, ensuring bar is centered from side to side. Tighten all bolts to specification. See TORQUE SPECIFICATIONS table at the end of this article.

Removal ("C" & "H" Bodies) – 1) Raise vehicle and place supports under lower control arms. Lower vehicle slightly onto supports to relieve downward pull on stabilizer bar and bushings. Remove wheels. Remove stabilizer bar long link bolts from lower control arms. Remove stabilizer bar mounting brackets on engine cradle or crossmember.

2) Remove tie rod ends from steering knuckles. Disconnect exhaust pipe connecting exhaust manifold to catalytic converter. Disconnect air pump pipe to exhaust pipe (if equipped). Turn passenger side strut assembly completely to the right. Slide stabilizer bar over steering knuckle and remove from frame. Inspect and replace all rubber bushings showing signs of wear, damage or deterioration.

Installation – 1) To install, reverse removal procedure. During installation, loosely assemble all fasteners and ensure stabilizer bar is centered from side-to-side.

2) Ensure insulator bushing split area is toward front of vehicle. Install stabilizer bar long link bolts from the bottom of control arms. Tighten stabilizer bar insulator mounting brackets to specification, ensuring bar is centered from side to side. Tighten all bolts to specification. See TORQUE SPECIFICATIONS table at the end of this article.

Removal ("J", "L" & "N" Bodies) – 1) Open hood and install engine support tool. Raise and support vehicle. Allow suspension to hang freely. Remove wheels. Remove stabilizer long link bolts from lower control arms. On GTZ model, remove stabilizer long link retaining nuts from stabilizer bar and from bracket mounted to strut. Remove stabilizer bar clamps from frame.

2) Loosen, but DO NOT remove, front engine cradle bolts. See Fig. 3. Remove rear and center engine cradle bolts. Lower engine cradle enough to remove stabilizer bar. Inspect and replace all rubber bushings showing signs of wear, damage or deterioration.

Installation – 1) To install, reverse removal procedure. During installation, loosely assemble all fasteners and ensure stabilizer bar is centered from side-to-side. Ensure insulator bushing split area is pointing downward.

2) Install stabilizer bar long link bolts from the bottom of control arms. Tighten stabilizer bar insulator mounting brackets to specification, ensuring bar is centered from side to side. Tighten all bolts to specification. See TORQUE SPECIFICATIONS table at the end of this article.

CAUTION: When servicing suspension, on inner Tri-Pod axle joint with Gray silicone boot, use Drive Axle Boot Protector (J-33162). Boots made of Black thermo-plastic material require Boot Protector (J-34754). For outer double-offset joint, modify Boot Protector (J-34754) by removing 3 tabs on inside surface. DO NOT over-extend inner Tri-Pod joint, internal parts may separate.

STEERING KNUCKLE

Removal – 1) Raise and support vehicle. Remove wheel. Install drive axle boot protector(s). Disconnect stabilizer bar from control arm. See STABILIZER BAR & BUSHING ASSEMBLY under REMOVAL & INSTALLATION. Remove hub and bearing assembly. See HUB & BEARING ASSEMBLY under REMOVAL & INSTALLATION.

2) Disconnect tie rod from steering knuckle. Separate ball joint from steering knuckle. See BALL JOINT under REMOVAL & INSTALLATION. On models equipped with ABS brakes, remove speed sensor and mounting bracket from steering knuckle.

CAUTION: DO NOT over-extend drive axle CV joints, internal parts may separate.

---

3) Scribe reassembly reference marks on steering knuckle as follows:
- Along lower outboard strut radius.
- On inboard side of strut along curve of steering knuckle.
- On strut lower mount clamp and steering knuckle.

4) Remove strut-to-steering knuckle retaining bolts. Remove steering knuckle. See Fig. 1, 2 or 3.

Installation – 1) Install new bearing seal (if removed) into steering knuckle and lubricate seal lips. Slide drive axle shaft through bearing and hub assembly. Install steering knuckle onto ball joint stud. Tighten ball joint retaining castle nut or pinch bolt to specification. Always install NEW pinch bolt and nut. See TORQUE SPECIFICATIONS table at the end of this article.

2) Ensure drive axle boot protectors are in proper position. Raise steering knuckle assembly to align steering knuckle and strut bolt holes. Align reference marks on strut and steering knuckle. Install strut-to-steering knuckle retaining bolts. Tighten to specification.

3) Install tie rod and hub assembly to steering knuckle and tighten to specification. Initially tighten hub-to-drive axle nut to 74 ft. lbs. (100 N.m). Install rotor, caliper, wheel and lug nuts. Tighten to specification. Lower vehicle and tighten hub-to-drive axle nut to specification. See TORQUE SPECIFICATIONS table at the end of this article.

4) On models equipped with ABS brakes, speed sensor gap between sensor tip and sensor ring tooth is NOT adjustable. Tighten speed sensor mounting bolt(s) to specification. See TORQUE SPECIFICATIONS table at the end of this article.

STRUT ASSEMBLY

CAUTION: Support steering knuckle and hub and bearing assembly during strut removal to prevent tension from being applied to brake hose. DO NOT over-extend drive axle shaft CV joints.

Removal – 1) Open hood and remove upper strut-to-body mount nuts. Raise and support vehicle. Remove front wheels. Install drive axle boot protectors (J-34754).

2) On "J", "L" and "N" bodies, disconnect tie rod from strut steering arm using Tie Rod Puller (J-24319-01). On all other models, disconnect tie rod from steering knuckle. On models equipped with ABS brakes, disconnect wheel speed sensor from steering knuckle.

3) On all models, remove brake line clip or bracket bolt from strut. Scribe strut lower mount clamp outline on steering knuckle for reassembly reference.

4) Remove lower strut mounting bolts and remove strut assembly. DO NOT chip or scratch coil spring coating. Support steering knuckle-hub and bearing assembly to prevent over-extending axle shaft CV joints and brake hose.

Disassembly – 1) Mount strut assembly in strut-spring compressor. Use eye protection while performing this operation. Compress strut-spring to approximately 1/2 its height. DO NOT bottom spring or strut rod. Hold strut rod stationary while removing nut from top of shaft.

2) Install Guide Rod (J-34013-27) on strut stud threads to guide shaft down through bearing cap of top mount assembly. Loosen strut-spring compressor while guiding strut shaft from top mount assembly. Continue to loosen compressor until spring tension is removed. Remove strut and spring from compressor.

CAUTION: DO NOT chip or crack coil spring coating. Coil spring damage may occur if coating is damaged.

Reassembly – Upper spring seat flat must be aligned with lower strut-to-steering knuckle mounting flange. To reassemble, reverse disassembly procedure. Torque strut top nut to specification. See TORQUE SPECIFICATIONS table at the end of this article.

NOTE: Alignment must be checked after strut installation. See SPECIFICATIONS & PROCEDURES article in WHEEL ALIGNMENT.

1991 SUSPENSION
Front – "A", "C", "H", "J", "L" & "N" Bodies (Cont.)

GM 10-5

Installation – 1) Before installation on "J", "L" and "N" bodies, strut may be modified to allow for camber adjustment during wheel alignment. File bottom mounting holes on strut outer flanges to enlarge holes until they match slots on inner flanges. *See Fig. 9.*

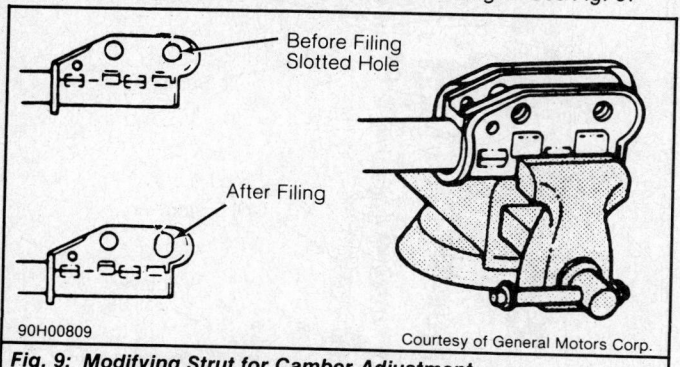

Before Filing
Slotted Hole

After Filing

90H00809

Courtesy of General Motors Corp.

Fig. 9: Modifying Strut for Camber Adjustment ("J", "L" & "N" Bodies)

2) On all models, to install, reverse removal procedure. When installing strut assembly in steering knuckle, ensure scribe marks on steering knuckle are aligned with strut for proper lower adjusting cam bolt position.

3) On "J", "L" and "N" bodies, strut-to-steering knuckle lower mounting bolts must be installed with the machined flats on bolt heads in horizontal position. Tighten bolts to specification. See TORQUE SPECIFICATIONS tables at end of article. Check wheel alignment. See SPECIFICATIONS & PROCEDURES article in WHEEL ALIGNMENT.

TORQUE SPECIFICATIONS

TORQUE SPECIFICATIONS

Application	Ft. Lbs. (N.m)
"A" Body	
Ball Joint-To-Control Arm Mount Bolt/Nut	[1]
Ball Joint-To-Steering Knuckle Pinch Bolt	33 (45)
Brake Caliper Bolt	38 (52)
Control Arm-To-Crossmember Pivot Bolt	61 (83)
Hub & Bearing Retainer Bolt	
With Heavy Duty Power Brakes	70 (95)
All Others	63 (85)
Hub-To-Axle Shaft Nut	[2] 192 (260)
Stabilizer Bar	
Bar-To-Control Arm Clamp Nut	32 (43)
Reinforcement Plate-To-Crossmember Mount Bolt	40 (54)
Strut Assembly	
Top Nut	65 (88)
Strut-To-Steering Knuckle Bolt	140 (190)
Strut-To-Upper Body Mount Nut	18 (24)
Tie Rod End-To-Steering Knuckle Nut	[3] 35 (47)
Wheel Nut	92 (125)
"C" & "H" Bodies	
Ball Joint-To-Control Arm Bolt	[1]
Ball Joint-To-Steering Knuckle Nut	[4] 37 (50)
Brake Caliper Bolt	38 (52)
Exhaust Pipe-To-Manifold Bolt	15 (20)
Hub & Bearing Retainer Bolt	70 (95)
Hub-To Axle Shaft Nut	[2] 192 (260)
Control Arm-To-Crossmember Pivot Bolt	
Front	140 (190)
Rear	90 (122)
Stabilizer Bar	
Bar-To-Control Arm Link Bolt Nut	13 (18)
Bar-To-Crossmember Bolt	37 (50)
Strut Assembly	
Top Nut	55 (75)
Strut-To-Steering Knuckle Bolt	180 (244)
Strut-To-Upper Body Mount Nut	18 (24)
Tie Rod End-To-Steering Knuckle Nut	[3] 35 (47)
Wheel Nut	100 (136)
"J", "L" & "N" Bodies	
Ball Joint-To-Control Arm Bolt	[1]
Ball Joint-To-Steering Knuckle Nut	
Beretta, Cavalier, Corsica	[5]
All Others	41-50 (56-68)
Brake Caliper Bolt	38 (52)
Hub & Bearing Retainer Bolt	70 (95)
Hub-To-Axle Shaft Nut	
"N" Body	[2] 185 (251)
All Others	[2] 192 (260)
Control Arm-To-Crossmember Pivot Bolt	61 (83)
Stabilizer Bar	
Bar-To-Control Arm Link Bolt Nut	
Except Beretta GTZ	13 (17)
Beretta GTZ Link Nut	70 (95)
Bar-To-Crossmember Clamp Nut	17 (23)
Strut Assembly Top Nut	65 (88)
Strut-To-Steering Knuckle Bolt	133 (180)
Strut-To-Upper Body Mounting Nut	18 (24)
Tie Rod End-To-Strut	[3] 37 (50)
Wheel Nut	100 (136)

	INCH Lbs. (N.m)
"C" & "H" Bodies	
ABS Speed Sensor Bolt	84 (9.5)
"J", "L" & "N" Bodies	
ABS Speed Sensor Bolt	106 (12)

[1] – Tighten to specification shown on instruction sheet that came with ball joint kit.

[2] – Tighten to 74 ft. lbs. (100 N.m) during initial assembly. After installing wheels and lowering to ground, tighten nut to final torque.

[3] – May be tightened to 52 ft. lbs. (71 N.m) to align cotter pin hole.

[4] – Tighten to 88 INCH lbs. (10 N.m). Then turn additional 120 degrees during which time final torque must be obtained.

[5] – Tighten to 26 ft. lbs. (35 N.m), then turn additional 60 degrees.

1991 SUSPENSION
Front – "B" & "F" Bodies

"B" Body: Caprice, Custom Cruiser, Roadmaster
"F" Body: Camaro, Firebird

DESCRIPTION

Caprice, Custom Cruiser and Roadmaster models use independent front suspension. Each wheel is attached to the frame by a steering knuckle, upper and lower control arm and ball joint assembly.

Lower control arm inner ends connect to the frame with rubber pivot bushings and outer ends connect to steering knuckle at ball joints. Upper control arm inner ends attach to a pivot shaft bolted to the frame. Upper control arm outer ends attach to steering knuckle with a ball joint.

The stabilizer bar controls suspension side roll. Coil springs, around shock absorbers, mount between each frame side rail or crossmember and lower control arm.

Camaro and Firebird models use a steering knuckle, strut assembly, lower ball joint and lower control arm. Steering knuckles on Camaro and Firebird connect to the bottom strut.

ADJUSTMENTS & INSPECTION

WHEEL ALIGNMENT SPECIFICATIONS & PROCEDURES

NOTE: See SPECIFICATIONS & PROCEDURES article in WHEEL ALIGNMENT.

WHEEL BEARINGS

1) Raise and support vehicle at lower control arms. Remove dust cap and cotter pin. Tighten spindle nut to 12 ft. lbs. (16 N.m), while spinning wheel forward by hand. Back off nut until just loose, then hand tighten.
2) Tighten nut until either hole in spindle lines up with a slot in the nut. DO NOT move nut more than one-half hex. Install new cotter pin.
3) Adjustment should provide .001-.005" (.03-.13 mm) wheel hub end play. Install dust cap and lower vehicle.

RIDING HEIGHT

NOTE: See SPECIFICATIONS & PROCEDURES article in WHEEL ALIGNMENT.

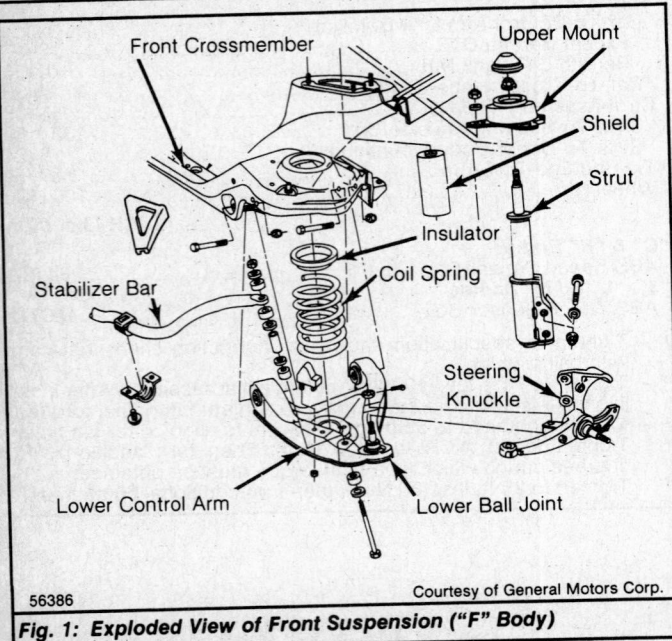

56386   Courtesy of General Motors Corp.

Fig. 1: Exploded View of Front Suspension ("F" Body)

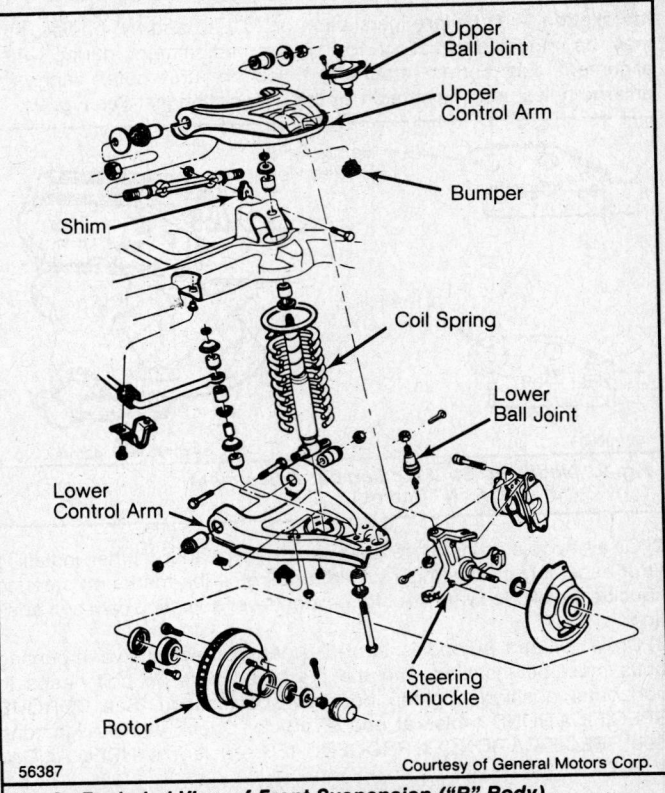

56387   Courtesy of General Motors Corp.

Fig. 2: Exploded View of Front Suspension ("B" Body)

BALL JOINT CHECKING

Upper Ball Joint ("B" Body) – 1) Raise vehicle, and position jack stands under lower control arms near each ball joint. Upper control arm bumpers must not contact frame. Ensure wheel bearings are properly adjusted.
2) Position dial indicator against lowest point of rim. Grasp wheel at top and bottom and move in and out. If gauge reads more than .125" (3.18 mm), replace ball joint.

Lower Ball Joint – Wheels must support vehicle to load ball joint. Ensure ball joint grease fitting shoulder protrudes from ball joint cover. If grease fitting shoulder is flush or inside cover, replace ball joint. *See Fig. 3.* If boot is torn, replace ball joint.

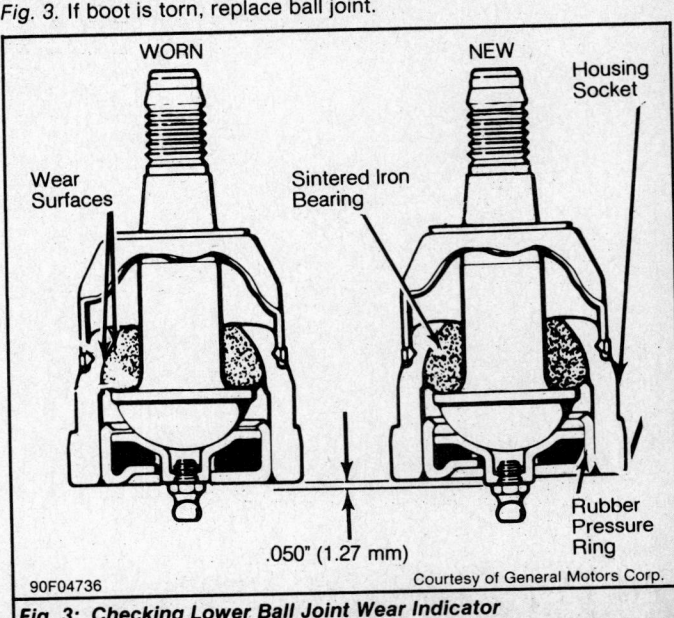

90F04736   Courtesy of General Motors Corp.

Fig. 3: Checking Lower Ball Joint Wear Indicator

REMOVAL & INSTALLATION

COIL SPRING

Removal – 1) Raise vehicle support at frame side rails. Remove wheel. Remove shock absorber. Remove stabilizer linkage and retainers. Remove cotter pin and nut from tie rod end.

2) Remove tie rod ball joint from steering knuckle, using Tie Rod Puller (J-6627-A) on "B" bodies or Ball Joint Remover (J-24292-B) on "F" bodies.

3) Install universal spring compressor and compress spring. Remove frame-to-lower control arm bolts. Pivot control arm rearward and remove spring and spring compressor.

NOTE: DO NOT apply force on lower control arm and ball joint to remove spring. Proper maneuvering of spring will allow easy removal.

Installation – To install, reverse removal procedure. *See Fig. 4.* Ensure insulators are in place on "F" bodies. When replacing front pivot bolt on lower control arm, bolt head MUST face forward. Rear pivot bolt may be installed in either direction.

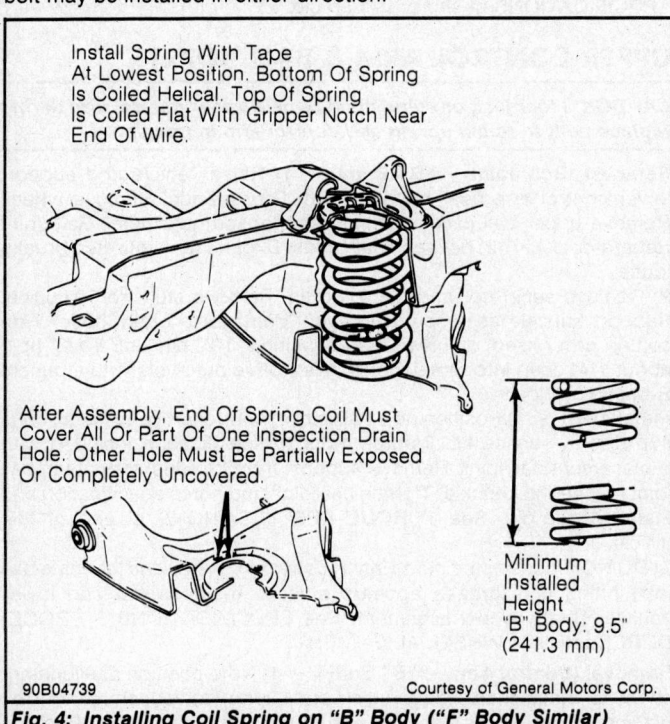

Install Spring With Tape At Lowest Position. Bottom Of Spring Is Coiled Helical. Top Of Spring Is Coiled Flat With Gripper Notch Near End Of Wire.

After Assembly, End Of Spring Coil Must Cover All Or Part Of One Inspection Drain Hole. Other Hole Must Be Partially Exposed Or Completely Uncovered.

Minimum Installed Height "B" Body: 9.5" (241.3 mm)

90B04739

Courtesy of General Motors Corp.

Fig. 4: Installing Coil Spring on "B" Body ("F" Body Similar)

STEERING KNUCKLE

Removal ("B" Body) – 1) Raise and support vehicle at front lift points. DO NOT support lower control arm. Remove wheel, caliper, hub and rotor. Remove splash shield. Remove tie rod end from steering knuckle using Tie Rod Puller (J-6627-A).

2) Remove knuckle seal if knuckle is being replaced. Remove lower ball joint cotter pin and nut. Using Ball Joint Separator (J-23742), break stud loose from knuckle. Place floor jack under lower control arm to keep coil spring in place.

3) Remove upper ball joint cotter pin and nut. Using Ball Joint Separator (J-23742), break stud loose from knuckle. Raise upper control arm to remove stud from knuckle. Raise knuckle from lower ball joint stud and remove knuckle.

Installation – To install knuckle, reverse removal procedure. Tighten ball stud nut, but DO NOT loosen to insert cotter pin. Adjust front wheel bearings.

Removal & Installation ("F" Body) – 1) Raise vehicle and remove wheel. Remove brake hose from strut. Remove caliper and support out of the way. Remove hub and rotor assembly.

2) Remove splash shield. Disconnect tie rod end from knuckle. Support lower control arm. Disconnect ball joint from knuckle using Ball Joint Separator (J-24292-B). Remove 2 strut-to-knuckle bolts and remove knuckle. To install knuckle, reverse removal procedure. Adjust wheel bearings.

LOWER CONTROL ARM & BALL JOINT

Removal (Ball Joint – "B" Body) – 1) Raise and support vehicle under frame. Remove wheel. Place floor jack under lower control arm spring seat. Remove cotter pin and nut from ball joint stud.

2) Using Ball Joint Separator (J-23742), remove stud from steering knuckle. Guide end of lower control arm past opening in brake splash shield. If needed, block knuckle assembly out of way by placing wooden block between frame and upper control arm.

3) Remove grease fittings. Assemble Ball Joint Installer (J-9519-16) and Control Arm Bushing Installer (J-21474-13) on Ball Joint Fixture (J-9519-30). *See Fig. 5.* Mount assembled tool over lower control arm ball joint. Turn pressing screw until ball joint comes loose.

Installation – Assemble Ball Joint Fixture (J-9519-30) and Large Installer (J-9519-9). *See Fig. 5.* Mount assembled tool over lower control and arm ball joint. Turn pressing screw until ball joint is fully seated. To complete installation, reverse removal procedure. Grease purge on seal must face inward. Tighten ball joint stud nut to specification. Check wheel alignment. See SPECIFICATIONS & PROCEDURES article in WHEEL ALIGNMENT.

Removal (Ball Joint – "F" Body) – 1) Raise and support vehicle under frame. Remove wheel. Place floor jack under lower control arm spring seat. Remove cotter pin and nut from ball joint stud.

2) Using Ball Joint Separator (J-24292-B), remove stud from steering knuckle. Guide end of lower control arm past opening in brake splash

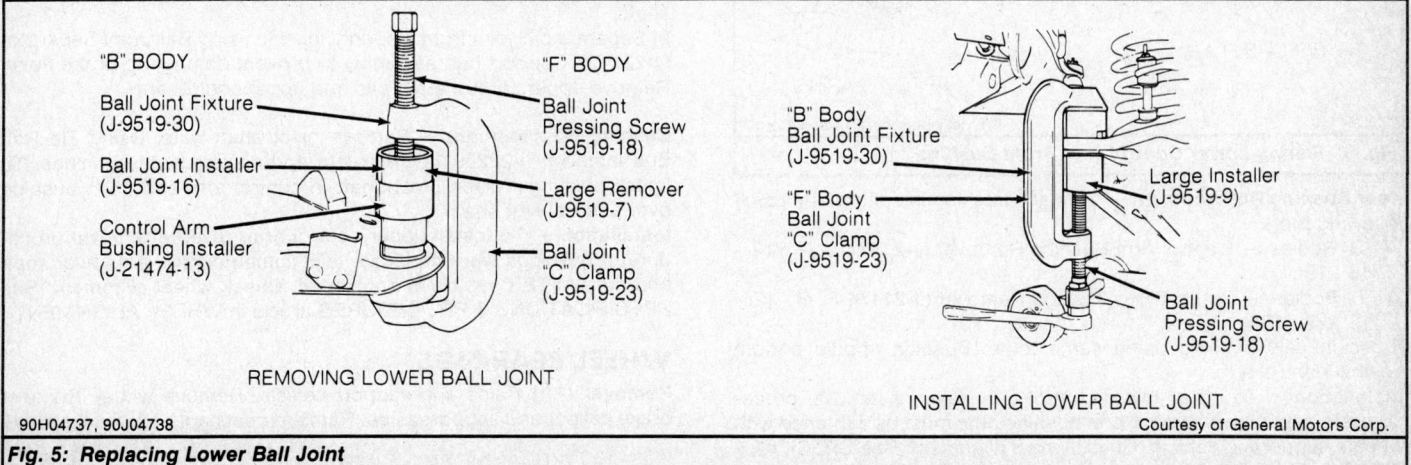

"B" BODY

Ball Joint Fixture (J-9519-30)

Ball Joint Installer (J-9519-16)

Control Arm Bushing Installer (J-21474-13)

"F" BODY

Ball Joint Pressing Screw (J-9519-18)

Large Remover (J-9519-7)

Ball Joint "C" Clamp (J-9519-23)

REMOVING LOWER BALL JOINT

"B" Body Ball Joint Fixture (J-9519-30)

"F" Body Ball Joint "C" Clamp (J-9519-23)

Large Installer (J-9519-9)

Ball Joint Pressing Screw (J-9519-18)

INSTALLING LOWER BALL JOINT

Courtesy of General Motors Corp.

90H04737, 90J04738

Fig. 5: Replacing Lower Ball Joint

shield. If needed, block knuckle assembly out of way by placing wooden block between frame and upper control arm.

3) Assemble Ball Joint Pressing Screw (J-9519-18) and Large Remover (J-9519-7) on Ball Joint "C" Clamp (J-9519-23). See Fig. 5. Mount assembled tool over lower control arm ball joint. Turn pressing screw until ball joint comes loose.

Installation — 1) Assemble Ball Joint Pressing Screw (J-9519-18) and Ball Joint "C" Clamp (J-9519-23) and Large Installer (J-9519-9). See Fig. 5.

2) Mount assembled tool over lower control and arm ball joint. Turn pressing screw until ball joint is fully seated. To complete installation, reverse removal procedure. Grease purge on seal must face inward. Tighten ball joint stud nut to specification. Check wheel alignment. See SPECIFICATIONS & PROCEDURES article in WHEEL ALIGNMENT.

LOWER CONTROL ARM BUSHINGS

Removal — Remove coil spring. See COIL SPRING. Separate ball joint from steering knuckle using Ball Joint Separator (J-23742 for "B" bodies, or J-24292-B for "F" bodies). Support and remove lower control arm. Guide lower control arm past opening in splash shield.

Front Bushing Replacement — 1) Using a blunt chisel, drive bushing flare down flush with bushing rubber. Press out bushing using following tools:

- "B" Bodies — Control Arm Bushing Remover (J-21474-5, -8, -19; J-22323-1).
- "F" Bodies — Control Arm Bushing Remover (J-21474-5, -18, -19, -23; J-22899).

2) Using same tools, press new bushing into place. Front bushing must be flared after installation. See Fig. 6.

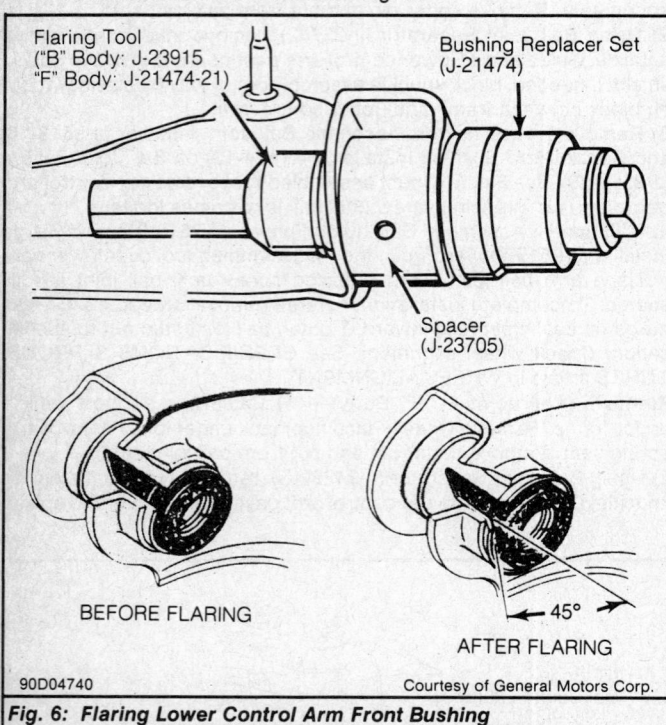

Flaring Tool
("B" Body: J-23915
"F" Body: J-21474-21)

Bushing Replacer Set
(J-21474)

Spacer
(J-23705)

BEFORE FLARING

AFTER FLARING

45°

90D04740   Courtesy of General Motors Corp.

Fig. 6: Flaring Lower Control Arm Front Bushing

Rear Bushing Replacement — Replace bushing in control arm using following tools:

- "B" Bodies — Control Arm Bushing Remover (J-21474-5, -8, -12, -18, -19).
- "F" Bodies — Control Arm Bushing Remover (J-21474-5, -8, -12, -13, -18, -19).

Press in new bushing using same tools. Bushing should bottom against control arm.

Installation — To install lower control arm, reverse removal procedure. Note that lower control arm bushing nuts must be tightened with wheels supporting vehicle. Check wheel alignment. See SPECIFICATIONS & PROCEDURES article in WHEEL ALIGNMENT.

STABILIZER BAR

Removal — Raise vehicle and support with safety stands. Disconnect each stabilizer bar end linkage. Pull bolt from linkage and remove retainers, grommets and spacers. Remove bracket-to-body bolts. Remove stabilizer bar, bushings and brackets.

Installation — 1) To install stabilizer bar, reverse removal procedure. Install with stabilizer bar identification mark on right side of vehicle. On all vehicles, rubber bushings should be installed with slits facing forward.

2) Stabilizer bar attaching bolts should be installed with bolt head facing down. On "F" bodies, hold end of stabilizer bar about 2" from bottom of side rail when tightening rubber bushings. Tighten bracket bolts to specification.

STRUT ASSEMBLY

Removal & Installation ("F" Body) — Raise vehicle and support lower control arm with jack stand. Remove wheel and brake hose bracket. Remove strut to steering knuckle bolts. Remove cover from upper mount assembly. Remove nut from upper end of strut. Remove strut and shield. To install, reverse removal procedure. See TORQUE SPECIFICATIONS at end of this article.

UPPER CONTROL ARM & BALL JOINT

CAUTION: Floor jack or stand must remain under control arm during replacement to retain spring and control arm in position.

Removal (Ball Joint — "B" Body) — 1) Raise vehicle and support lower control arm near ball joint with floor stands. Remove wheel. Remove upper ball joint cotter pin and loosen nut. Install Ball Joint Separator (J-23742) between ball studs. Expand tool until stud breaks loose.

2) Remove separator and ball joint nut. Remove stud from knuckle. Support knuckle assembly to prevent damage to brake hose. With control arm raised, drill rivet heads, using a 1/2" bit. Drill a 1/8" hole about 1/4" deep into remainder of rivet. Drive out rivets with a punch. Remove ball joint.

Installation — 1) Position new ball joint in control arm and install bolts supplied in service kit. Tighten bolts to specification included with replacement ball joint. Remove support from knuckle and attach ball joint to steering knuckle. Tighten ball joint stud nut to specification and install cotter pin. See TORQUE SPECIFICATIONS at end of this article.

2) DO NOT loosen stud nut to insert cotter pin. Install and lubricate ball joint fitting until grease appears at seal. Install wheel and lower vehicle. Check wheel alignment. See SPECIFICATIONS & PROCEDURES article in WHEEL ALIGNMENT.

Removal (Control Arm — "B" Body) — 1) Note position of alignment shims for installation. Raise vehicle and support lower control arms by placing safety stands between spring seats and ball joints. Remove wheel and tire assembly. Remove nuts from upper control arm pivot shaft.

2) Separate ball joint from steering knuckle using Ball Joint Separator (J-23742). Support hub assembly to prevent damage to brake hose. Remove upper control arm bolts and upper control arm.

Bushing Replacement — Remove pivot shaft nuts. Using Tie Rod End Installer (J-22269-1), press out and discard both bushings. To install bushings, place pivot shaft in control arm and push bushing over end of pivot shaft.

Installation — To install upper control arm, reverse removal procedure. If bushings were replaced, fully tighten control arm pivot shaft end nuts AFTER vehicle is on ground. Check wheel alignment. See SPECIFICATIONS & PROCEDURES article in WHEEL ALIGNMENT.

WHEEL BEARINGS

Removal — 1) Raise and support vehicle. Remove wheel. Remove brake caliper and support aside. Remove dust cap, cotter pin, spindle nut and washer. Remove hub and bearing. DO NOT let outer bearing fall from hub.

2) Pry out inner grease seal and remove inner bearing. Discard seal. Drive races from hub using a drift or Race Remover (J-29117-A). Wash parts thoroughly in cleaning solvent and blow dry with compressed air.

Installation – 1) Press races into hub. Apply thin coat of high temperature grease to spindle at inner and outer bearing seats, shoulder and seal seat. Lightly grease inboard of each bearing race in hub.

2) Pack bearing cone and roller with grease. Place inner bearing cone and roller in hub. Using finger, put some grease outboard of bearing. Using a flat plate, install new grease seal until flush with hub. Lubricate seal lip with grease.

3) Install hub and rotor assembly. Place outer bearing cone and roller in outer bearing race. Install washer and nut. Install brake caliper. Adjust bearing preload. See WHEEL BEARINGS under ADJUSTMENTS & INSPECTION.

TORQUE SPECIFICATIONS

TORQUE SPECIFICATIONS

Application	Ft. Lbs. (N.m)
Ball Joint Stud Nut [1]	
Lower	83 (113)
Upper ("B" Body)	60 (81)
Lower Control Arm-To-Frame Bolts	
"B" Body	92 (125)
"F" Body	66 (90)
Strut-To-Steering Knuckle Bolts ("F" Body)	203 (275)
Strut Upper Mounting Bolts ("F" Body)	18 (24)
Stabilizer Shaft Bracket-To-Frame Nuts	
"F" Body	39 (53)
"B" Body	24 (33)
Stabilizer Shaft Link Nut	13 (18)
Upper Control Arm-To-Frame Bolts ("B" Body)	72 (98)
Upper Control Arm Bushing Nuts ("B" Body) [2]	85 (115)
	INCH Lbs. (N.m)
Upper Ball Joint-To-Control Arm Bolts	[3]

[1] – Always advance nut to line up cotter pin slot; never loosen.
[2] – Tighten after wheels are on ground.
[3] – See specification included with replacement ball joint.

DESCRIPTION

System is an independent coil-spring suspension with upper and lower control arms and ball joints, shock absorbers, steering knuckles and a stabilizer bar.

ADJUSTMENTS & INSPECTION

WHEEL ALIGNMENT
SPECIFICATIONS & PROCEDURES

NOTE: See SPECIFICATIONS & PROCEDURES article in WHEEL ALIGNMENT.

WHEEL BEARINGS

Raise vehicle and support at lower control arm. Remove wheel, dust cap and cotter pin. Tighten steering knuckle nut to 12 ft. lbs. (16 N.m) while rotating wheel by hand. Back off nut until barely loose, then hand tighten until snug. Back off about one-half hex, so cotter pin may be inserted. Adjustment should provide .001-.005 (.03-.13 mm) end play. Install new cotter pin and dust cap. Lower vehicle.

RIDING HEIGHT

NOTE: See SPECIFICATIONS & PROCEDURES article in WHEEL ALIGNMENT.

BALL JOINT CHECKING

Lower Ball Joint – 1) Vehicle must be supported by wheels to properly load ball joints. Lower ball joint has a visual wear indicator. Wear is indicated by the protrusion length of nipple into which grease fitting is threaded. See Fig. 1.

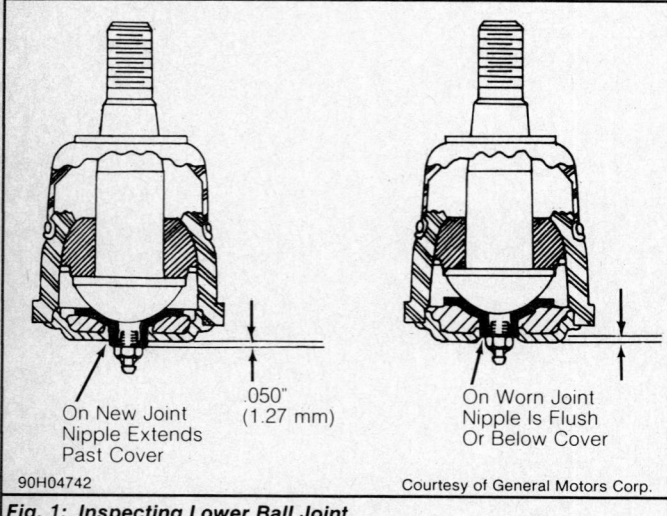

Fig. 1: Inspecting Lower Ball Joint

2) On new ball joints, this round nipple projects .050" (1.27 mm) beyond the surface of ball joint cover. If fitting is flush or recessed, replace ball joint.

Upper Ball Joint – 1) Ensure wheel bearings are properly adjusted. Raise vehicle. Position floor stands under lower control arms as near as possible to ball joint. Upper control arm bumpers must NOT contact frame.

2) Position dial indicator against lowest point of wheel rim. Grasp wheel at top and bottom, moving it in and out. Check indicator reading. If measurement is more than .13" (3.2 mm), replace ball joint.

REMOVAL & INSTALLATION

COIL SPRING

Removal – 1) Raise vehicle. Remove shock absorber lower mounting bolts. Push shock absorber through control arm and into spring. Support vehicle so control arm hangs free.

2) Place floor jack, with Adapter (J-23028-01) attached, into position so it cradles inner bushings of lower control arm. Adapter must be secured to jack. Remove stabilizer bar-to-lower control arm attaching bolts.

3) Raise jack to remove tension on lower control arm pivot bolts. Install a safety chain around spring and through lower control arm. Remove rear pivot bolt first, then remaining bolts and nuts.

4) Lower control arm by slowly lowering jack. When all compression is removed from spring, remove chain and spring. DO NOT use force to remove spring. Proper maneuvering of spring will allow it to be removed easily.

Installation – Position spring into frame so lower end of coil covers all or part of one inspection hole in lower control arm. Second hole must be partially or completely uncovered. See Fig. 2. To install remaining components, reverse removal procedure. Check wheel alignment. See SPECIFICATIONS & PROCEDURES article in WHEEL ALIGNMENT.

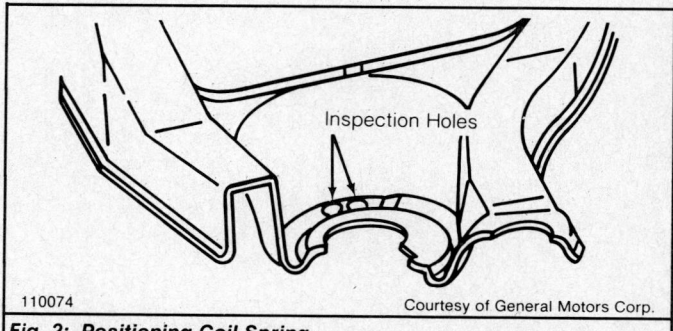

Fig. 2: Positioning Coil Spring

STEERING KNUCKLE

Removal – 1) If a frame hoist rather than twin post hoist is used to raise vehicle, support lower control arm so coil spring will remain compressed at its curb height position.

2) Raise vehicle and support lower control arm. Remove wheel assembly. Remove tie rod end from steering knuckle. Remove caliper, rotor and hub assembly. Support caliper out of way.

3) Remove splash shield and ball joint studs from steering knuckle. Remove steering knuckle.

Installation – 1) Place steering knuckle in position and install upper and lower ball joint studs in bosses. Install stud nuts, splash shield, hub and rotor assembly.

2) Install outer bearing, spindle washer and nut. Adjust wheel bearings. See WHEEL BEARINGS under ADJUSTMENTS & INSPECTION. Install caliper and wheel assembly. Check wheel alignment. See SPECIFICATIONS & PROCEDURES article in WHEEL ALIGNMENT.

LOWER BALL JOINT

Removal – 1) Raise vehicle and remove wheel assembly. Loosen stud nut one turn but DO NOT remove. Using Ball Joint Separator (J-23742) between studs, turn threaded end of ball joint separator until stud is free of steering knuckle.

NOTE: Lower control arm must be supported so coil spring cannot force arm down.

2) Remove lower stud nut. Pull outward on bottom of tire and at same time push wheel assembly upward to free knuckle from ball joint stud. Lift upper control arm, with steering knuckle and hub assembly attached, and place a wood block between frame and upper control arm.

3) Remove tie rod end from steering knuckle (if necessary). Place Ball Joint Remover/Installer (J-9519-03 and J-9519-7) over ball joint. Turn hex nut bolt until lower ball joint is pushed out of control arm.
Installation – 1) Position ball joint in lower control arm with bleed vent in boot facing inward. Using ball joint remover/installer, turn down hex head bolt until joint is seated. Remove ball joint remover/installer. Cotter pin hole in stud should run parallel with wheel.
2) Remove wood support from upper control arm. Clean and inspect tapered hole in steering knuckle and clean. Connect lower joint stud to steering knuckle and install stud nut. Install new cotter pin.

NOTE: DO NOT back off nut for cotter pin installation. Turn nut 1/6 turn maximum to install cotter pin.

3) Lubricate ball joint. Install tie rod end (if removed). Install wheel assembly. Check wheel alignment. See SPECIFICATIONS & PROCEDURES article in WHEEL ALIGNMENT.

LOWER CONTROL ARM

Removal – 1) Raise vehicle. Remove shock absorber lower mounting bolts. Push shock absorber through control arm and into spring. Support vehicle so control arm hangs free.
2) Place floor jack, with Adapter (J-23028-01) attached, into position so it cradles inner bushings of lower control arm. Adapter must be secured to jack. Remove stabilizer bar-to-lower control arm attaching bolts.
3) Raise jack to remove tension on lower control arm pivot bolts. Install a safety chain around spring and through lower control arm. Remove rear pivot bolt first, then remaining bolts and nuts.
4) Lower control arm by slowly lowering jack. When all compression is removed from spring, remove chain and spring. DO NOT use force to remove spring. Proper maneuvering of spring will allow it to be removed easily.
5) To remove lower control arm from steering knuckle, use Ball Joint Separator (J-23742). Remove lower control arm from vehicle.
Installation – Position spring into frame so lower end of coil covers all or part of one inspection hole in lower control arm. Second hole must be partially or completely uncovered. *See Fig. 2.* To install remaining components, reverse removal procedure. Check wheel alignment. See SPECIFICATIONS & PROCEDURES article in WHEEL ALIGNMENT.

LOWER CONTROL ARM BUSHINGS

Removal (Rear Bushing) – Remove lower control arm. See LOWER CONTROL ARM under REMOVAL & INSTALLATION. Assemble Hex Nut (J-21474-4), Adapter (J-21474-5), Adapter (J-21474-8) and Spacer (J-21474-12) onto lower control arm. *See Fig. 3.* Turn hex bolt and nut until bushing is removed.

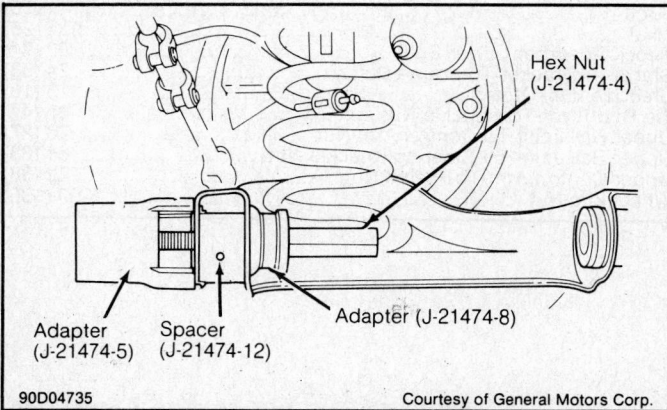

Fig. 3: *Removing Lower Control Arm Bushing*

Installation – Assemble Hex Nut (J-21474-4), Lower Control Arm Bushing Flarer (J-23915), Adapter (J-21474-5), Bolt (J-21474-3) and Spacer (J-21474-12) onto lower control arm. *See Fig. 4.* Position new

bushing and install. Turn hex bolt and nut until new bushing is seated. To complete installation, reverse removal procedure.

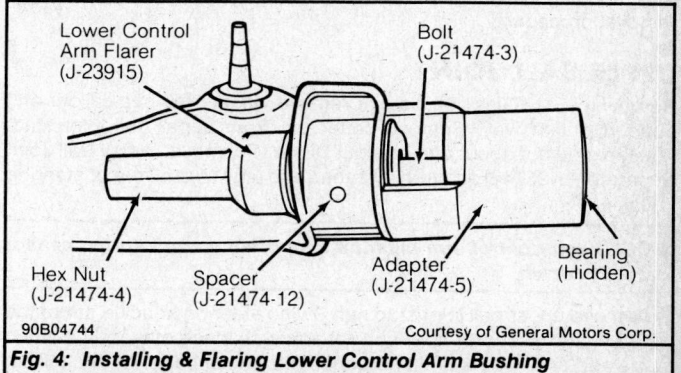

Fig. 4: *Installing & Flaring Lower Control Arm Bushing*

Removal (Front Bushing) – 1) Remove lower control arm. See LOWER CONTROL ARM under REMOVAL & INSTALLATION. Remove bushing flare by tapping on edge with hammer.
2) Assemble Hex Nut (J-21474-4), Adapter (J-21474-5), Adapter (J-21474-8) and Spacer (J-21474-12) onto lower control arm. *See Fig. 3.* Turn hex bolt and nut until bushing is removed.
Installation – 1) Assemble Hex Nut (J-21474-4), Lower Control Arm Bushing Flarer (J-23915), Adapter (J-21474-5), Bolt (J-21474-3) with NEW control arm bushing, and Spacer (J-21474-12) onto lower control arm. Position new bushing and install. Turn hex bolt and nut until new bushing is seated. To complete installation, reverse removal procedure.
2) Remove installation adapters and install Lower Control Arm Bushing Flarer (J-23915). Turn tool until bushing is flared. *See Fig. 5.* To complete installation, reverse removal procedure.

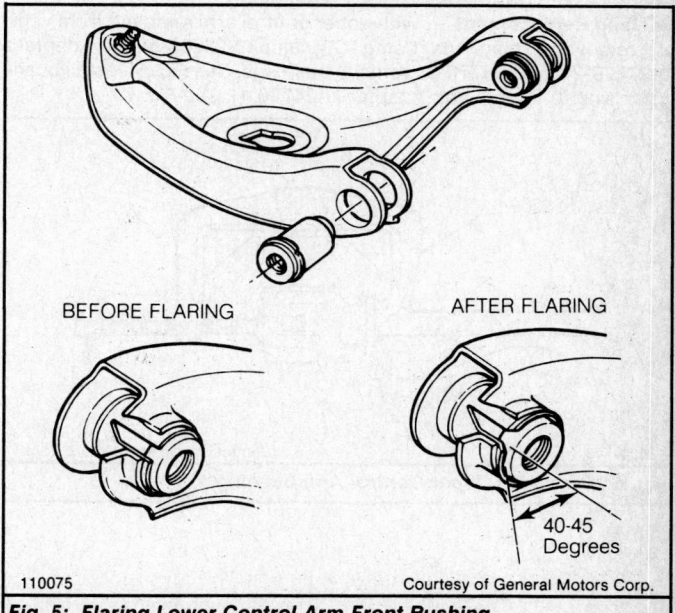

Fig. 5: *Flaring Lower Control Arm Front Bushing*

STABILIZER BAR

Removal – 1) Remove nuts, retainer and grommet from bottom of stabilizer links. Remove stabilizer bar mounting brackets from frame.
2) Remove rubber bushing from bar. Remove grommets, retainers, spacers, and links from stabilizer bar ends. Keep grommets and spacers in correct order for reassembly. Turn wheels to full stop and work stabilizer bar from vehicle.

NOTE: Stabilizer bar grommets and retainers are larger than those used on shock absorbers. Ensure replacement parts are correct size.

Installation – Position stabilizer bar under front frame side rails. Slide bushings into place with slit forward. Install mounting brackets over bushings and tighten bolts. To complete installation, reverse removal procedure.

UPPER BALL JOINT

Removal – **1)** Raise vehicle and remove wheel. Remove caliper and support out of way. Remove cotter pin from upper ball joint stud. Loosen stud nut about one turn but DO NOT remove. Install Ball Joint Separator (J-23742) and turn threaded end until stud is free of steering knuckle.

NOTE: Lower control arm must be supported so coil spring cannot force arm down.

2) Remove upper ball joint stud nut. Swing steering knuckle out of the way. Lift and support upper control arm with block of wood between frame and arm. Use a drill and punch to remove ball joint rivets from control arm.
Installation – **1)** Install new ball joint in arm and attach with bolts (supplied in kit). Insert bolts from bottom of control arm. Cotter pin hole in stud should run parallel with wheel.
2) Remove wood support from upper control arm and clean and inspect tapered hole in steering knuckle. Attach ball joint to steering knuckle. Install caliper. Lubricate ball joint and install wheel assembly. Lower vehicle and check alignment. See SPECIFICATIONS & PROCEDURES article in WHEEL ALIGNMENT.

UPPER CONTROL ARM

Removal – **1)** Raise vehicle and support at lower control arm. Remove wheel assembly. Separate upper arm ball joint stud from steering knuckle.
2) Remove nuts securing control arm shaft to frame bracket and remove assembly. Mark shims for reassembly.
Bushing Replacement – With upper control arm removed from vehicle, remove bushing nuts. Using "C" Clamp (J-22269-5) and Adapters (J-24770-2 and J-24770-3), remove bushings. See Fig. 6. Install bushings using "C" clamp and Adapter (J-24770-1). See Fig. 7.

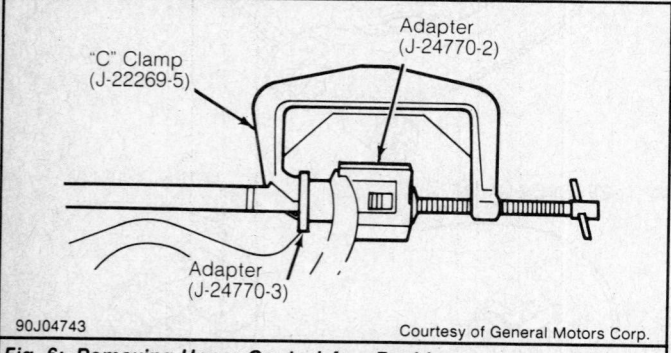

Fig. 6: Removing Upper Control Arm Bushing
90J04743   Courtesy of General Motors Corp.

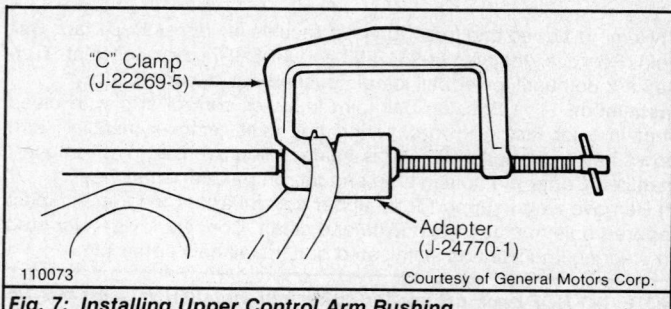

110073   Courtesy of General Motors Corp.
Fig. 7: Installing Upper Control Arm Bushing

Installation – **1)** Position new upper control arm attaching bolts loosely in frame. Install control arm cross shaft on attaching bolts. Using a free running nut, instead of lock nut, tighten both nuts until serrated bolts seat.
2) Remove free running nuts. Install lock nuts. Install same number of shims to each bolt as removed. Tighten mounting nuts. Tighten nut on thinner shim pack first for proper clamping force. Install wheel assembly and lower vehicle. Check alignment. See SPECIFICATIONS & PROCEDURES article in WHEEL ALIGNMENT.

WHEEL BEARINGS

Removal – Raise and support vehicle. Remove wheel assembly. Remove caliper and support out of way. Remove dust cap, cotter pin, spindle nut, washer and outboard bearing assembly. Remove hub and rotor from steering knuckle. Remove inner bearing and grease seal. Discard seal. Use a long punch and hammer to remove inner and outer bearing races.
Installation – **1)** Apply a small amount of grease to spindle at bearing seat and at inner seat, shoulder, and seal seat. Install inner and outer bearing races. Thoroughly grease both bearings. Place inner bearing into hub.
2) Install a new grease seal with flat plate. Seal should be flush with hub surface. Lubricate seal lip with thin coating of grease. Install hub and rotor assembly. Place outer bearing in outer bearing race.
3) Install washer and nut finger tight. Install caliper and wheel assembly. Install lug nuts finger tight. Adjust wheel bearings. See WHEEL BEARINGS under ADJUSTMENTS & INSPECTION. Install dust cap. Tighten lug nuts, and lower vehicle.

TORQUE SPECIFICATIONS

TORQUE SPECIFICATIONS

Application	Ft. Lbs. (N.m)
Lower Ball Joint-To-Steering Knuckle Nut	83 (113)
Lower Control Arm Bushing	
Bolt	114 (155)
Nut	92 (125)
Shock Absorber Lower Bolt	20 (27)
Stabilizer Bracket-To-Frame Bolt	24 (33)
Stabilizer Link Nut	13 (18)
Tie Rod Pivot-To-Knuckle Nut	35 (47)
Upper Ball Joint-To-Control Arm Nut	20 (27)
Upper Ball Joint-To-Steering Knuckle Nut	61 (83)
Upper Control Arm-To-Frame Nut	72 (98)
Wheel Lug Nut	100 (136)

DESCRIPTION

The major suspension components are made of high strength, lightweight, forged, aluminum alloy. A fiberglass monoleaf spring is mounted transversely below the lower control arms. Pressurized gas (nitrogen) shock absorbers are mounted between frame shock absorber towers and lower control arms.

Upper control arms have alignment shims for caster and camber adjustments. Tubular steel stabilizer bar is standard with the option of a solid spring steel stabilizer bar. The hub and bearing assembly are a sealed unit, eliminating wheel bearing maintenance. An electronic Selective Ride Control (SRC) suspension system is optional.

NOTE: *Following procedures DO NOT apply to vehicles with electronic suspension systems. For information on electronic suspension systems, see ELECTRONIC – SELECTIVE RIDE CONTROL article in SUSPENSION.*

ADJUSTMENTS & INSPECTION

WHEEL ALIGNMENT SPECIFICATIONS & PROCEDURES

NOTE: *See SPECIFICATIONS & PROCEDURES article in WHEEL ALIGNMENT.*

WHEEL BEARINGS

1) Wheel bearings are permanently sealed inside hub assembly and require no service or adjustment. Raise and support vehicle. Remove front wheels.
2) Move brake pads away from rotor or remove caliper. Install 2 wheel lug nuts to secure rotor to hub. Mount dial indicator to bottom of steering knuckle. Position dial indicator plunger rod against outside of wheel bearing, inside hub bore.
3) Grasp rotor at top and bottom, and by pushing and pulling, check for looseness. If looseness exceeds .005" (.13 mm), replace hub and bearing assembly.

RIDING HEIGHT

Riding height is nonadjustable. For correct original riding height specifications, see SPECIFICATIONS & PROCEDURES article in WHEEL ALIGNMENT. If riding height of vehicle is incorrect after allowing for tire wear, check frame and suspension components for wear, bending or metal fatigue. Riding Height is NOT the same as Trim Height measurement.

BALL JOINT CHECKING

NOTE: *Ensure wheel bearings DO NOT have excessive looseness. See WHEEL BEARINGS under ADJUSTMENTS & INSPECTION.*

Upper Ball Joint – 1) Raise vehicle and position jackstands under lower control arms, near each ball joint. Lower vehicle so weight is on jackstands. Ensure upper control arm bumpers DO NOT contact frame.
2) Mount a dial indicator on shock tower and position plunger rod against the inside of wheel upper rim. Zero dial indicator. Grasp tire at top and bottom and move in and out. If dial reads more than .125" (3.18 mm), replace ball joint.
3) Check ball joint free play with ball joint disconnected from steering knuckle. If ball joint stud spins in socket using finger pressure, replace ball joint.
Lower Ball Joint – Wheels must support vehicle to load ball joint. Verify ball joint grease fitting shoulder protrudes from ball joint cover. If grease fitting shoulder is flush or up inside cover, replace ball joint. See Fig. 1.

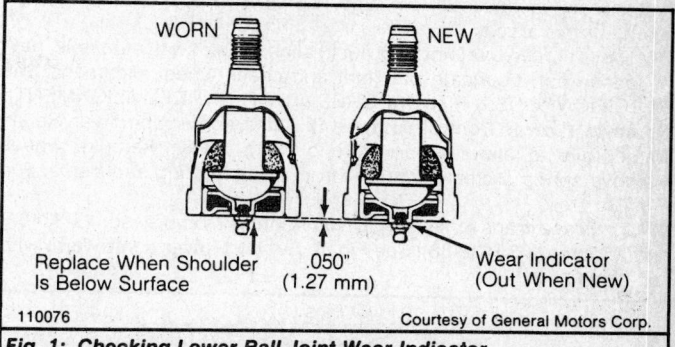

Fig. 1: *Checking Lower Ball Joint Wear Indicator*

REMOVAL & INSTALLATION

HUB & BEARING ASSEMBLY

NOTE: *Wheel bearings are sealed and require no servicing.*

Removal – Raise and support vehicle. Remove wheel, brake caliper and rotor. Disconnect speed sensor wire harness connector and harness bracket assembly from steering knuckle. Mark harness position for reassembly reference. Remove speed sensor retaining bolt, and pull sensor from steering knuckle. Remove hub and bearing assembly by removing retaining bolts.
Installation – 1) To install, reverse removal procedure. Install new hub assembly "O" ring seal in steering knuckle. Install hub and bearing assembly.
2) Clean speed sensor and reapply Sealer (12345106) before reinstalling speed sensor into steering knuckle. DO NOT install sensor without sealer and "O" ring or damage to anti-lock brake system will result. Speed sensor does not require gap adjustment. Tighten bolts to specification. See TORQUE SPECIFICATIONS table at end of this article.

LOWER CONTROL ARM & BALL JOINT

Removal (Lower Ball Joint) – 1) Raise and support vehicle at lower control arms. Remove wheel. Remove ball joint stud cotter pin and nut. Install Ball Joint Separator (J-33436) between upper and lower ball joints with large end of separator upward.
2) Expand separator to loosen ball joint stud from steering knuckle. Support steering knuckle and remove separator. Using Ball Joint Press (J-9519-E), remove lower ball joint from control arm.
Installation – 1) Using ball joint press, install new ball joint in control arm. Install ball joint stud into steering knuckle so that cotter pin can be installed from rear to front of vehicle. Tighten ball joint nut to spec-

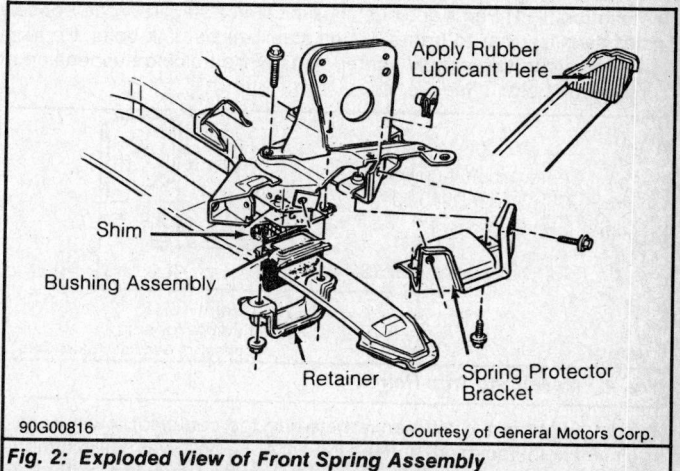

Fig. 2: *Exploded View of Front Spring Assembly*

ification and install cotter pin. See TORQUE SPECIFICATIONS table at end of this article.

2) Always tighten ball joint stud nut to align nut slot with stud hole, never loosen nut. Lubricate ball joint and check wheel alignment. See SPECIFICATIONS & PROCEDURES article in WHEEL ALIGNMENT.

Removal (Lower Control Arm) – 1) Raise and support vehicle on frame rails to allow suspension to hang freely. Remove wheel. Remove spring protector bracket from end of spring and frame. See Fig. 2.

2) Compress transverse spring with Spring Compressor (J-33432) and Adapter (J-33432-88). See Fig. 3. Support lower control arm with jackstand.

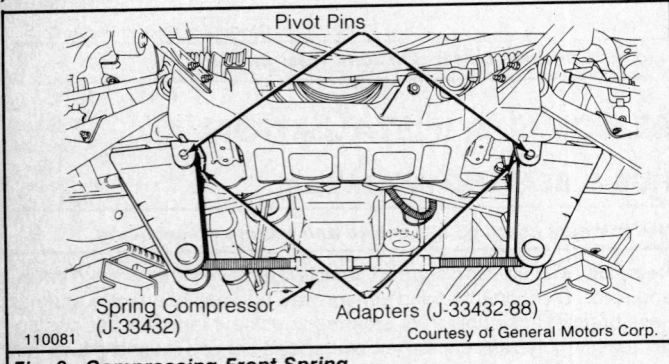

Fig. 3: Compressing Front Spring

3) Unbolt shock absorber and stabilizer link from lower control arm. Remove speed sensor wire harness bracket from steering knuckle. Disconnect lower ball from steering knuckle with Ball Joint Separator (J-33436). Remove lower control arm bushing bolts, jackstand and lower control arm.

Installation – 1) To install, reverse removal procedure. See TORQUE SPECIFICATIONS table at end of this article. Always tighten ball joint stud nut to align nut slot with stud hole, never loosen nut. Install new cotter pin. Cotter pin must be installed from rear towards front of vehicle.

2) Maintain proper suspension trim height while tightening lower control arm bushing bolts and stabilizer link bolts. For proper trim height measuring, see STABILIZER BAR under REMOVAL & INSTALLATION. Check wheel alignment. See SPECIFICATIONS & PROCEDURES article in WHEEL ALIGNMENT.

STABILIZER BAR

Removal – Raise and support vehicle. Remove front wheel assemblies. Support lower control arms with jackstands. Disconnect stabilizer bar links at lower control arms. Disconnect stabilizer bar insulator brackets at frame. Remove stabilizer bar. If necessary, remove upper insulators using Puller (J-24319-01).

Installation – 1) Press end bushings in service stabilizer bar. Loosely install stabilizer bar to frame. Install stabilizer bar link bolts. Perform following steps to properly tighten bolts while holding suspension at correct trim height. See Fig. 4.

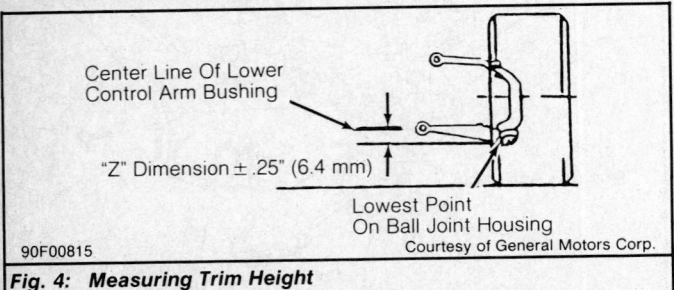

Fig. 4: Measuring Trim Height

2) Trim height is the difference between the center of lower control arm pivot point (bushing) and the lowest point on lower ball joint housing (not the grease fitting). Trim height must be adjusted to within .25" (6.4 mm) of specification.

3) Proper "Z" Dimension is the average of the high and low measurements. Proper "Z" Dimension is obtained by lifting front bumper about 1.5" (38.0 mm), gently remove hands and let suspension settle on its own. Repeat this step 2 more times. Take "Z" measurement. See Fig. 4.

4) Next, push down on front bumper about 1.5" (38.0 mm), gently remove hands and let suspension rise on its own. Repeat this step 2 more times. Take "Z" measurement. Proper "Z" Dimension is the average of the high and low measurements. Trim height must be within specification. See TRIM HEIGHT SPECIFICATIONS table. Check wheel alignment. See SPECIFICATIONS & PROCEDURES article in WHEEL ALIGNMENT.

TRIM HEIGHT SPECIFICATIONS

Digits 4, 5 & 6 [1] of VIN Code	[2] "Z" Dimension In. (mm)
Soft Ride Suspension – FE1	
1YY07	2.25 (57.2)
1YY67	2.60 (66.2)
Heavy Duty Suspension – FE7	
1YY07	2.13 (54.2)

[1] – Digit 4 denotes "Y" body. Digit 5 denotes "Y" for standard series and "Z" for special performance series coupe. Digit 6 denotes "2" for liftback style (07) or "3" for convertible style (67).

[2] – Above dimensions are at curb weight with full gasoline tank.

UPPER CONTROL ARM & BALL JOINT

CAUTION: Carefully note routing, position, mounting and location of ABS components and wiring. Components are extremely sensitive to EMI (Electro-Magnetic Interference).

Removal (Upper Ball Joint) – 1) Raise and support vehicle at lower control arms. Remove wheel. Remove ball joint stud cotter pin and nut. Install Ball Joint Separator (J-33436) between upper and lower ball joints with large end downward.

2) Expand ball joint separator to loosen ball joint stud from steering knuckle. Support steering knuckle and remove separator. Drill out rivet heads and remove rivets. Remove ball joint.

Installation – 1) Install ball joint in upper control arm. Install and tighten retaining bolts with nuts above ball joint. Install ball joint stud into steering knuckle with cotter pin installed from rear. Tighten ball joint nut to specification and install cotter pin. See TORQUE SPECIFICATIONS table at end of this article.

2) Always tighten ball joint stud nut to align nut slot with stud hole, never loosen nut. Lubricate ball joint and check wheel alignment. See SPECIFICATIONS & PROCEDURES article in WHEEL ALIGNMENT.

Removal (Upper Control Arm) – 1) Raise and support vehicle at lower control arm. Remove wheel. Remove wheelwell panel seal and center panel. Remove shock absorber electrical actuator (if equipped).

2) Separate upper ball joint stud from steering knuckle using Ball Joint Separator (J-33436). Loosen upper control arm retaining bolts. Note

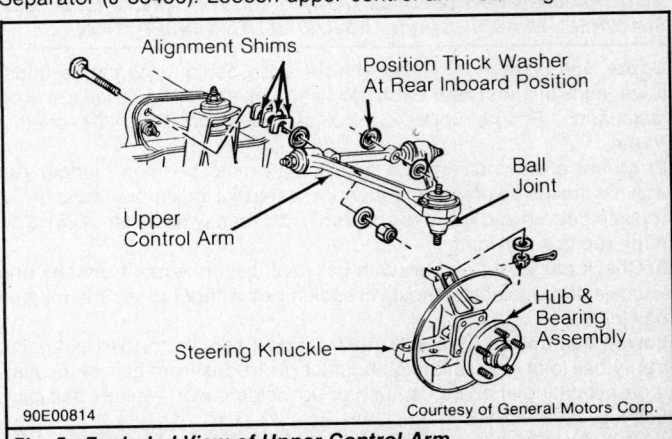

Fig. 5: Exploded View of Upper Control Arm

number of alignment shims on each retaining bolt between upper control arm shaft and frame.

3) Remove alignment shims and retain shims for reassembly. Remove upper control arm retaining bolts. Note location of thick washers on retaining bolts. *See Fig. 5*. Remove upper control arm.

Installation – **1)** To install, reverse removal procedure. Ensure thick washers are properly positioned on retaining bolts. *See Fig. 5*. Ensure alignment shims are in original locations. Tighten bolts to specification.

2) Install ball joint into steering knuckle. Install cotter pin from rear. Tighten ball joint nut to specification and install cotter pin. See TORQUE SPECIFICATIONS table at end of this article.

3) Always tighten ball joint stud nut to align nut slot with stud hole. Never loosen nut. Lubricate ball joint and check wheel alignment. See SPECIFICATIONS & PROCEDURES article in WHEEL ALIGNMENT.

STEERING KNUCKLE

CAUTION: Carefully note routing, position, mounting and location of ABS components and wiring. Components are extremely sensitive to EMI (Electro-Magnetic Interference).

Removal – **1)** Raise and support vehicle. Remove wheel, brake caliper and rotor. Disconnect speed sensor wire harness connector and harness bracket assembly from steering knuckle. Note position of harness for reassembly reference.

2) Remove hub and bearing assembly. See HUB & BEARING ASSEMBLY under REMOVAL & INSTALLATION. Disconnect tie rod from steering knuckle using Tie Rod Puller (J-6627-A). Disconnect upper and lower ball joints from steering knuckle, using Ball Joint Separator (J-33436). Remove steering knuckle.

Installation – **1)** To install, reverse removal procedure. Clean speed sensor, if removed, and apply Sealer (Part No. 12345489) before pushing assembly into steering knuckle. DO NOT install sensor without sealer or damage to anti-lock brake system will result. There is no speed sensor gap adjustment. Install ball joint studs into steering knuckle so cotter pins can be installed from rear vehicle.

2) Tighten ball joint nuts to specification and install cotter pins. Always tighten ball joint stud nut to align nut slot with stud hole, never loosen nut. Tighten all bolts to specification. See TORQUE SPECIFICATIONS table at end of this article. Check wheel alignment. See SPECIFICATIONS & PROCEDURES article in WHEEL ALIGNMENT.

TRANSVERSE SPRING

CAUTION: DO NOT scratch or use corrosive cleaners, engine degreasers, solvents, etc. on or near fiberglass front leaf spring. Extensive damage can result.

Removal – **1)** Raise and support vehicle on frame rails. Remove wheels. Disconnect shock absorbers and stabilizer bar links from lower control arms. Remove speed sensor wire harness brackets from steering knuckles. Remove speed sensor electrical connector. Remove both spring protector brackets. Install and compress spring using Spring Compressor (J-33432) and Adapters (J-33432-88). *See Fig. 3*.

2) Using Ball Joint Separator (J-33436), disconnect lower ball joints from steering knuckles. Remove spring retainers. *See Fig. 2*. Release and remove spring compressor. With the help of an assistant, pull lower control arms downward and carefully remove spring. Note and record the position and number of spring shims for reassembly reference. Do not scratch spring during removal.

Installation – **1)** To install, reverse removal procedure. Apply Rubber Lubricant (1051717) to spring pads. *See Fig. 2*. Ensure spring shims are installed in previous position. See SPRING SHIM REQUIREMENT table.

SPRING SHIM REQUIREMENT

Spring Color Code	Shims Required
Blue	0
Green	2
Yellow	1

2) With help from an assistant, pull down on lower control arms while seating spring. Use spring compressor to compress spring. Install spring retainers, and temporarily hand-tighten nuts.

3) Install ball joints into steering knuckles so cotter pins can be installed from rear to front of vehicle. Tighten ball joint nuts to specification, and install cotter pins. Always tighten ball joint stud nut to align nut slot with stud hole; never loosen nut. See TORQUE SPECIFICATIONS table at end of article.

4) Remove spring compressor, and install both spring protector brackets to frame rail. Tighten nuts to specification. Install speed sensor connector and wire harness bracket to steering knuckle. Install stabilizer bar links and shock absorbers to lower control arms. Install wheels.

5) Slowly lower vehicle, stopping when suspension is about proper trim height. To set trim height, see STABILIZER BAR under REMOVAL & INSTALLATION. Tighten all bolts to specification, starting with leaf spring retainer bolts.

TORQUE SPECIFICATIONS

TORQUE SPECIFICATIONS

Application	Ft. Lbs. (N.m)
Ball Joint Stud Nut	
Lower	50 (68)
Upper	33 (45)
Ball Joint-to-Upper Control Arm Bolt	19 (26)
Hub & Bearing Assembly Mounting Bolt	46 (62)
Lower Control Arm Bushing Bolt	[1] 82 (111)
Shock Absorber Mounting Bolt	19 (26)
Spindle Rod Bearing Nut	187 (253)
Spring Protector Bracket Nut	18 (24)
Spring Retaining Nut	[1] 48 (65)
Stabilizer Bar	
Insulator Bracket Bolt	[1] 40 (54)
Link Bolt	[1] 35 (47)
Tie Rod-to-Steering Knuckle Nut	33 (45)
Upper Control Arm Retaining Bolt	37 (51)
Wheel Lug Nut	100 (136)

	INCH Lbs. (N.m)
Speed Sensor Harness Bracket Bolt	86 (9.7)
Speed Sensor-To-Hub Bolt	86 (9.7)

[1] – Tighten with vehicle at proper trim height.

1991 SUSPENSION
Front – "E" & "K" Bodies

"E" Body: Eldorado, Reatta, Riviera,
Toronado, Trofeo
"K" Body: Seville

DESCRIPTION

All models use MacPherson strut-type front suspension. The frame has isolation mounts connecting it to the unibody. Rubber bushings are used at control arm pivots. The upper end of the strut is isolated by a rubber mount, containing a bearing which allows wheel turning. The lower end of strut is bolted to the top of steering knuckle.

The lower end of the steering knuckle pivots on a ball joint, riveted to the control arm. Control arm is the anchoring point for a stabilizer bar and tension strut.

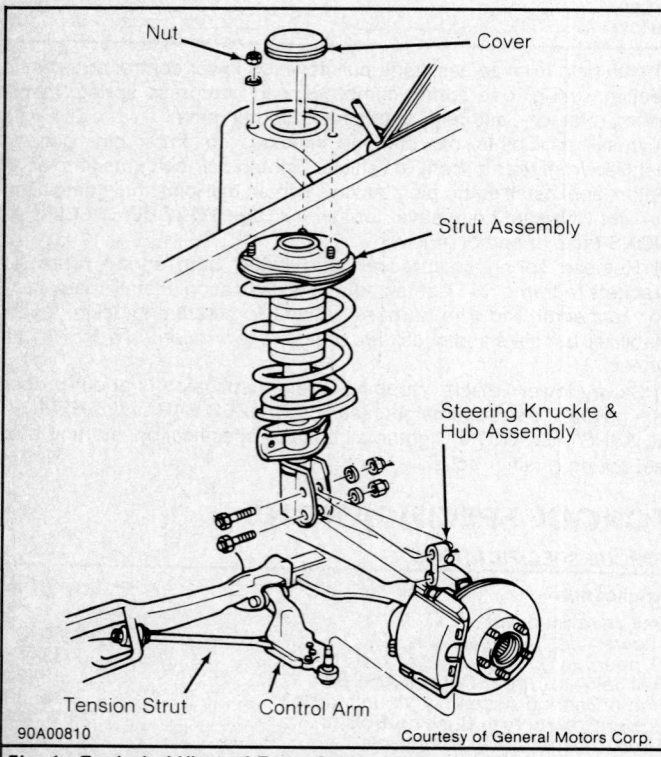

Fig. 1: Exploded View of Front Suspension

ADJUSTMENTS & INSPECTION

WHEEL ALIGNMENT
SPECIFICATIONS & PROCEDURES

NOTE: See SPECIFICATIONS & PROCEDURES article in WHEEL ALIGNMENT.

RIDING HEIGHT

NOTE: See SPECIFICATIONS & PROCEDURES article in WHEEL ALIGNMENT.

BALL JOINT CHECKING

Raise and support vehicle. Allow suspension to hang freely. Inspect ball joint seals for cracks or tears. Replace ball joint if seal is damaged. Grasp tire at top and bottom. Note horizontal movement of steering knuckle at ball joint, while moving tire inward and outward. Replace ball joint if any movement exists.

Ball stud tightness in steering knuckle tapered boss should be checked by shaking wheel and looking for looseness at ball stud end

or castellated nut. When ball joint is disconnected from steering knuckle, check ball joint for free play. If stud can be turned in socket with finger pressure, replace ball joint.

REMOVAL & INSTALLATION

STEERING KNUCKLE

NOTE: For reassembly reference, match mark steering knuckle-to-strut relationship before removing steering knuckle from strut.

Removal – 1) Raise and support vehicle. Allow control arms to hang freely. Remove wheels. Modify Boot Protector (J-34754) by cutting off 3 tabs on inside surface. Install boot protector on outer CV joint.
2) Separate tie rod end at steering knuckle. Remove hub and bearing assembly. See HUB & BEARING ASSEMBLY under REMOVAL & INSTALLATION. On models with anti-lock brake system, remove speed sensor bracket from steering knuckle. On all models, remove lower ball joint from steering knuckle using ball joint separator. Remove strut-to-steering knuckle bolts. Remove steering knuckle.

NOTE: If speed sensor is removed from mounting bracket, coat all surfaces with Anti-Corrosive Compound (1052856) where sensor contacts mounting bracket.

Installation – 1) To install, reverse removal procedure. Tighten ball joint-to-steering knuckle castellated nut. If necessary, tighten nut an additional 60 degrees to allow for cotter pin installation. See TORQUE SPECIFICATIONS table at end of this article.
2) Reinstall speed sensor bracket, if applicable. Front wheel speed sensor gap is set at factory and is nonadjustable. Verify setting of .020" (.51 mm).

HUB & BEARING ASSEMBLY

Removal – 1) Raise and support vehicle. Allow control arms to hang freely. Remove front wheels. Remove hub-to-axle nut and washer.
2) Remove disc brake caliper and support bracket from steering knuckle and wire aside without disconnecting brake line. Remove brake disc. Using Front Hub Spindle Remover (J-28733), separate drive axle shaft from hub. *See Fig. 2.*

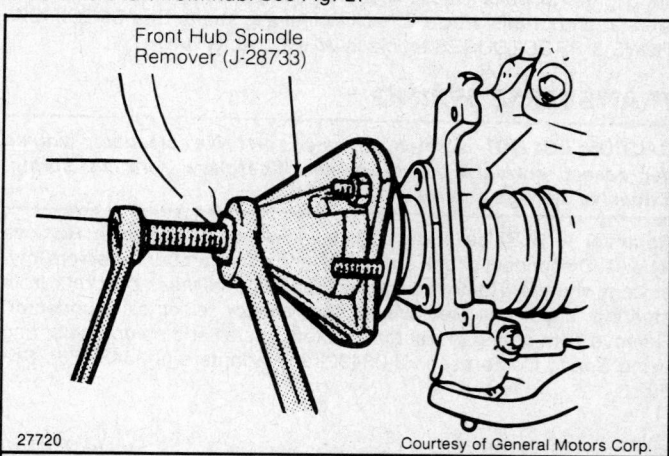

Fig. 2: Removing Drive Axle Shaft From Front Hub

3) Match mark steering knuckle and hub and bearing assembly for reassembly reference. Remove hub and bearing assembly retaining bolts. Remove hub and bearing assembly from vehicle.
4) If replacing hub and bearing seal, drive seal towards engine then cut seal off drive axle. *See Fig. 3.*

CAUTION: Always use NEW mounting bolts when installing brake caliper support bracket and caliper.

Installation – 1) If hub and bearing seal was removed, lubricate lip of new seal with wheel bearing grease. Using Seal Installer (J-34657-A),

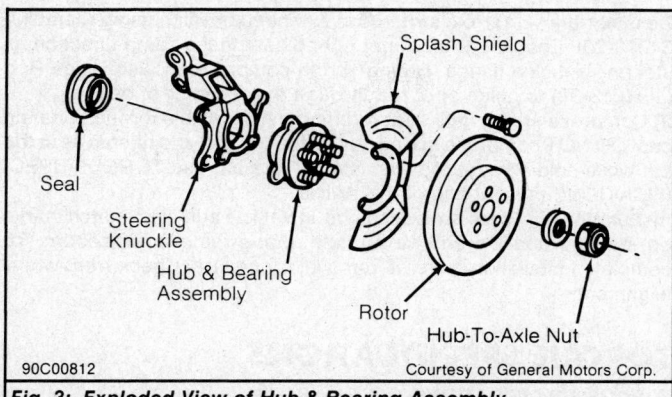

Fig. 3: Exploded View of Hub & Bearing Assembly

install seal. Install new "O" ring. Fill cavity between seal and bearing with wheel bearing grease.

2) Install hub and bearing assembly using match mark(s) made during removal procedure. Install hub and bearing retaining bolts and tighten to specification. See TORQUE SPECIFICATIONS table at end of this article.

3) Install drive axle shaft into hub and bearing assembly. Install brake disc. Loosely install hub-to-axle washer and nut. Install caliper support bracket and caliper using NEW mounting bolts and tighten to specification. Tighten caliper bolts to specification.

4) Tighten hub-to-axle nut to 75 ft. lbs. (102 N.m). Install wheels. Lower vehicle to ground. Tighten hub-to-axle nut to specification. See TORQUE SPECIFICATIONS table at end of this article.

LOWER CONTROL ARM & BALL JOINT

Removal (Ball Joint) – 1) Raise and support vehicle. Allow control arms to hang freely. Remove front wheels. Modify Boot Protector (J-34754) by cutting off 3 tabs on inside surface. Install boot protector on outer CV joint.

2) Disconnect ball joint from steering knuckle using ball joint separator. Using a drill and starting with a 1/4" bit and finishing with a 1/2" bit, drill out ball joint retaining rivets. Remove ball joint from control arm.

Installation – To install, reverse removal procedure. New ball joint mounting bolts are installed from bottom of lower control arm. Tighten ball joint-to-steering knuckle castellated nut. If necessary, tighten nut an additional 60 degrees to allow for cotter pin installation.

Removal (Lower Control Arm) – 1) Raise and support vehicle. Allow control arms to hang freely. Remove front wheels. Modify Boot Protector (J-34754) by cutting off 3 tabs on inside surface. Install boot protector on outer CV joint.

CAUTION: DO NOT overextend tripod CV joints on drive axle shafts or separation of internal components may occur.

2) Disconnect ball joint from steering knuckle using ball joint separator. Remove control arm bushing bolt, tension strut rod nut, retainers and insulators. *See Fig. 4.* Remove control arm.

Bushing Replacement – Using a hydraulic press and Bushing Remover/Installer Adapters (J-35561-1 and J-35561-3), remove bushing from lower control arm. Lubricate new bushing with rubber lube. Position new bushing in control arm. Using hydraulic press and Bushing Remover/Installer Adapters (J-35561-1 and J-35561-2), install new bushing.

Installation – 1) Install control arm on frame. DO NOT fully tighten bushing pivot bolt. Install control arm tension strut retainers, insulators and nut. DO NOT tighten nut.

2) Place ball joint in steering knuckle boss. Tighten ball joint-to-steering knuckle castellated nut. See TORQUE SPECIFICATIONS table at end of this article. If necessary, tighten nut an additional 60 degrees to allow for cotter pin installation.

3) Install wheels. Lower vehicle so weight of vehicle is supported by control arms. Tighten control arm bushing bolt and tension strut nut. See TORQUE SPECIFICATIONS table at end of this article.

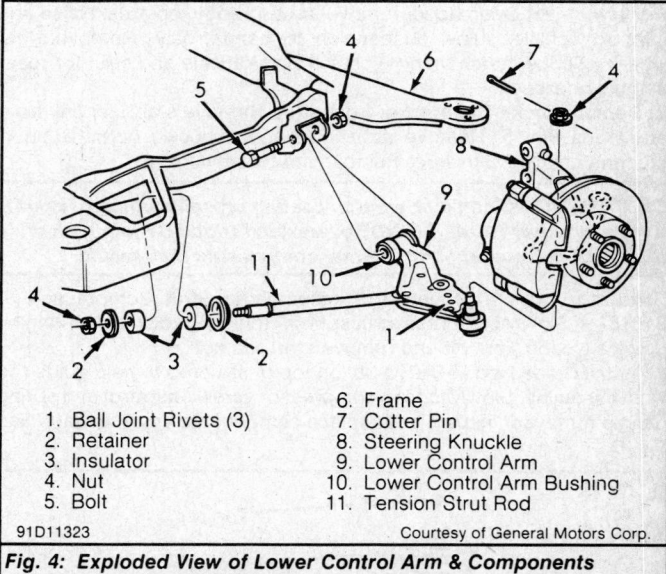

1. Ball Joint Rivets (3)	6. Frame
2. Retainer	7. Cotter Pin
3. Insulator	8. Steering Knuckle
4. Nut	9. Lower Control Arm
5. Bolt	10. Lower Control Arm Bushing
	11. Tension Strut Rod

Fig. 4: Exploded View of Lower Control Arm & Components

STABILIZER BAR & BUSHINGS

Removal & Installation – 1) Raise and support vehicle. Allow control arms to hang freely. Remove front wheels.

2) Remove left and right stabilizer links, spacers, bolts, brackets and insulators. *See Fig. 5.* It may be necessary to hold stabilizer link ball stud from turning while loosening nut. Remove exhaust pipe from rear manifold and move pipe upward. Slide, turn and lift out stabilizer bar.

3) To install, reverse removal procedure. Ensure stabilizer bar bracket insulator is installed with slit toward rear of vehicle. Tighten bolts to specification. See TORQUE SPECIFICATIONS table at end of this article.

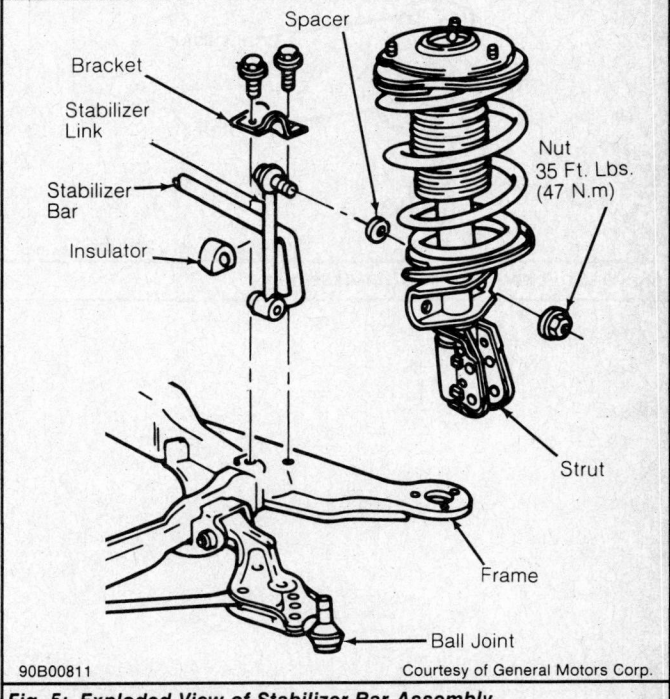

Fig. 5: Exploded View of Stabilizer Bar Assembly

STRUT ASSEMBLY

NOTE: For reassembly reference, match mark steering knuckle-to-strut relationship before removing strut from steering knuckle.

Removal – 1) Open hood, remove strut-to-body top nuts. Raise and support vehicle. Allow suspension to hang freely. Remove front wheels. Scribe match mark(s) on steering knuckle and strut for reassembly reference.

2) Remove brake line bracket from strut. Remove stabilizer link from strut. *See Fig. 5.* Remove strut-to-steering knuckle bolts. Support steering knuckle with wire. Remove strut from vehicle.

CAUTION: DO NOT chip or scratch coating on coil springs or premature failure may result. DO NOT overextend tripod CV joints on drive axle shaft or separation of internal components may result.

Disassembly – 1) Mount strut assembly in Strut Compressor (J-34013-A). Slowly compress strut spring. Hold strut rod from turning by using a No. 50 Torx bit and remove strut top nut.

2) Install Guide Rod (J-34013-38) on top of strut rod to help guide rod from assembly. Slowly loosen compressor screw until strut and spring can be removed. Inspect and replace components as necessary. *See Fig. 6.*

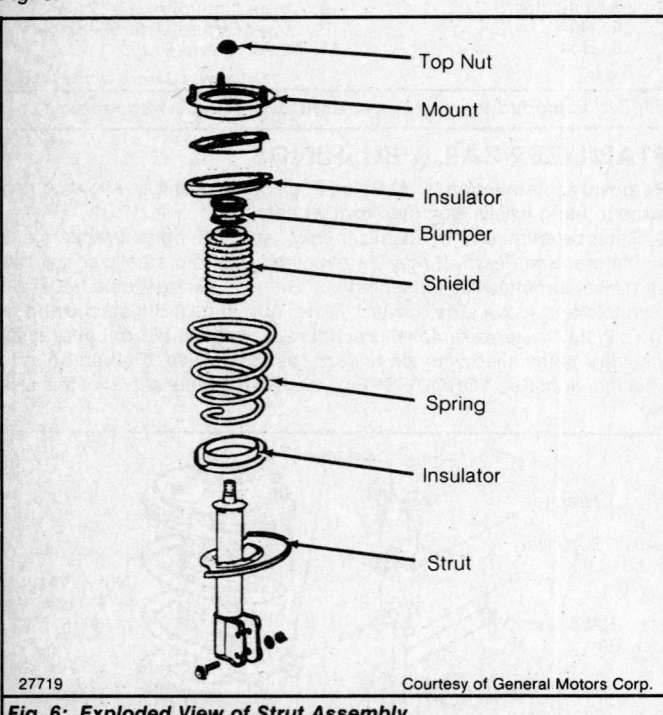

27719   Courtesy of General Motors Corp.

Fig. 6: Exploded View of Strut Assembly

Top Nut
Mount
Insulator
Bumper
Shield
Spring
Insulator
Strut

Reassembly – 1) Hold strut rod in extended position using Clamp (J-34013-20). Ensure flat on upper spring seat faces same direction as steering knuckle flange. During spring compression, use Guide Rod (J-34013-38) to guide strut rod through exact center of bearing.

2) Compress spring until strut rod threads are visible through bearing cap. DO NOT compress spring any further. Install and tighten strut top nut while holding strut rod with No. 50 Torx bit. See TORQUE SPECIFICATIONS table at end of this article.

Installation – Place strut assembly in vehicle and align match marks on steering knuckle and strut made during removal procedure. To complete installation, reverse removal procedure. Check front wheel alignment.

TORQUE SPECIFICATIONS

TORQUE SPECIFICATIONS

Application	Ft. Lbs. (N.m)
Ball Joint-To-Control Arm Bolts	50 (68)
Ball Joint Nut	[1] 37 (51)
Brake Caliper	
Mounting Bracket Bolt	63 (85)
Mounting Bracket-To-Steering Knuckle Bolt	83 (113)
Control Arm [2]	
Pivot Bolt	100 (136)
Pivot Nut	91 (124)
Front Hub-To-Axle Nut [2]	180 (244)
Hub and Bearing Retaining Bolt	70 (95)
Speed Sensor	
Sensor Bracket Bolt	19 (26)
Sensor Mounting Bolt	10 (14)
Stabilizer Bar Bracket Bolt	35 (47)
Stabilizer Link Nuts	35 (47)
Strut Mount-To-Body Nut	18 (24)
Strut-to-Steering Knuckle Bolt	136 (184)
Strut Top Nut	55 (75)
Tension Strut Nut	52 (71)
Tie Rod Nut	33 (45)
Wheel Lug Nut	100 (136)

[1] – Specification is minimum allowable. Tighten nut an additional 60 degrees for cotter pin installation.

[2] – With weight of vehicle supported by control arms.

"W" Body: Cutlass Supreme, Grand Prix, Lumina, Regal

DESCRIPTION

The front suspension is a MacPherson strut type with stabilizer bar. The strut tube is welded to a stamped steel knuckle. Lower ball joints are riveted to the knuckles. The steering pivot bearing is located in lower spring seat. Replacement strut cartridges can be installed from under the hood without removing strut.

ADJUSTMENTS & INSPECTION

WHEEL ALIGNMENT
SPECIFICATIONS & PROCEDURES

NOTE: See SPECIFICATIONS & PROCEDURES article in WHEEL ALIGNMENT.

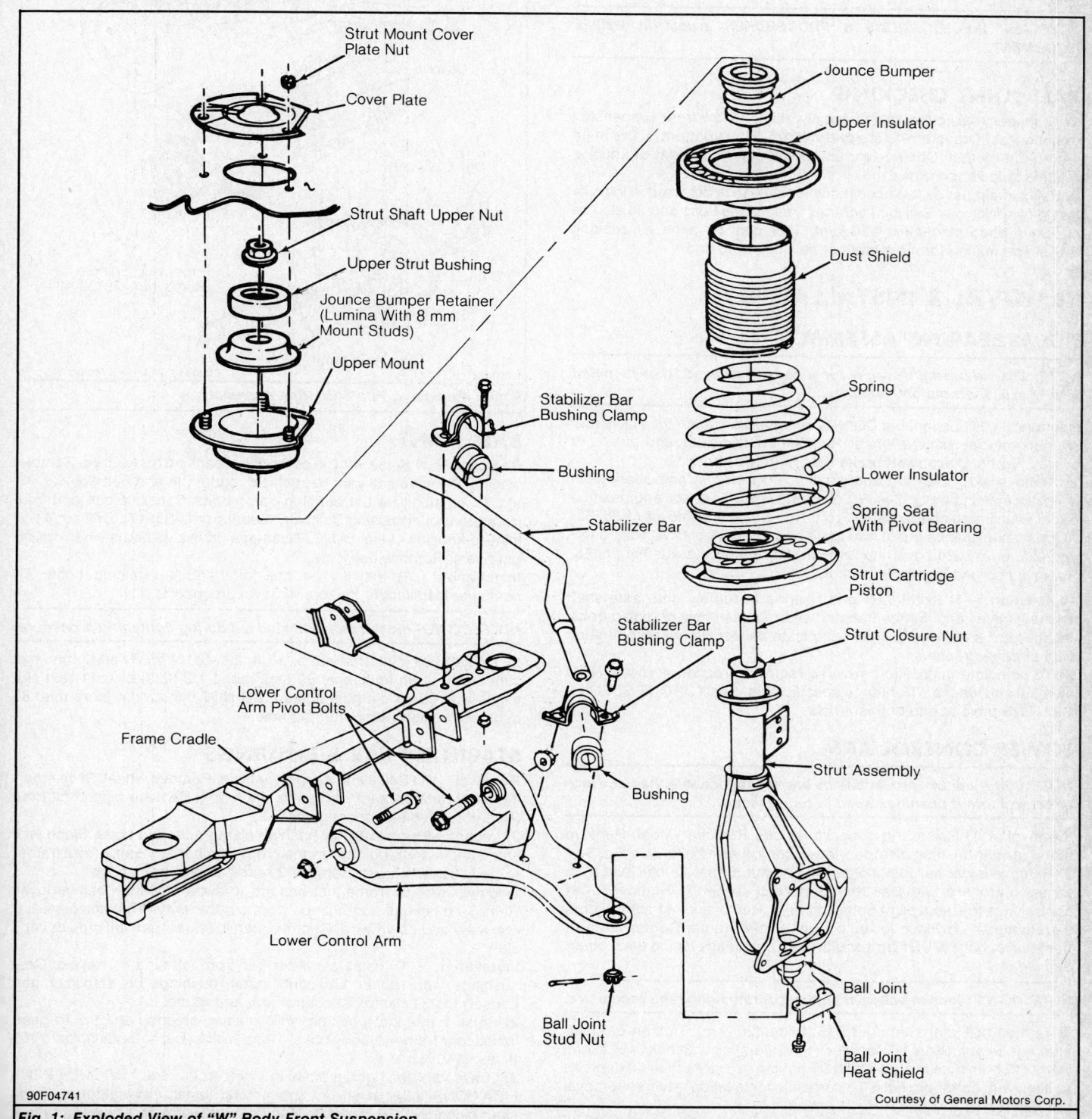

90F04741

Courtesy of General Motors Corp.

Fig. 1: Exploded View of "W" Body Front Suspension

WHEEL BEARING

Inspection – Wheel bearing is worn if end play is more than .005" (.13 mm). To check end play, remove wheel. Remove disc brake caliper. Install one wheel lug nut to hold rotor in place. Mount dial indicator with stem against hub shoulder. Pull rotor in and out to measure end play. If end play exceeds specification, disassemble, inspect and replace parts as required.

RIDING HEIGHT

NOTE: See SPECIFICATIONS & PROCEDURES article in WHEEL ALIGNMENT.

BALL JOINT CHECKING

1) To inspect ball joints, raise front of vehicle. Allow front suspension to hang free. Grasp tire at top and bottom. Move bottom of tire in an in-and-out motion. Observe for any horizontal movement of knuckle relative to lower control arm.

2) Ball joints must be replaced if any looseness is detected in joint, or ball joint seal is cut. Ball joint tightness in knuckle boss should also be checked when inspecting ball joint. This may be done by shaking wheel and feeling for movement of ball joint stud end.

REMOVAL & INSTALLATION

HUB & BEARING ASSEMBLY

NOTE: Whenever original nut is loosened or removed, always install a NEW axle shaft nut and washer.

Removal – **1)** Loosen, but DO NOT remove axle shaft nut. Raise and support vehicle. Remove wheel. Remove brake caliper, and wire it out of way. Do not disconnect brake line. Remove rotor.

2) Remove axle shaft nut and washer. Loosen hub and bearing-to-knuckle retaining bolts. *See Fig. 2.* Remove ABS sensor and position out of way (if equipped). Using Front Hub Spindle Remover (J-28733-A), push axle splines out of hub and bearing assembly. DO NOT damage axle boots. Remove hub and bearing-to-knuckle retaining bolts. Remove hub and bearing assembly.

Installation – **1)** Install hub and bearing assembly onto axle shaft splines. Install and tighten hub and bearing assembly retaining bolts. Install rotor and brake caliper. Lubricate caliper mounting bolt shaft with silicone grease.

2) To complete installation, reverse removal procedure. Install NEW axle nut and washer. Tighten to specification. See TORQUE SPECIFICATIONS table at end of this article.

LOWER CONTROL ARM

NOTE: Lower control arm bushings are not serviceable. Replace lower control arm if bushings need to be replaced.

Removal – **1)** Raise and support vehicle. Remove wheel. Remove stabilizer bar bushing clamp-to-lower control arm bolts. *See Fig. 1.*

2) Remove lower ball joint cotter pin and nut. Separate ball joint from lower control arm with Ball Joint Separator (J-39517). Remove lower control arm-to-frame pivot bolts and nuts. Remove lower control arm.

Installation – **1)** Place lower control arm in frame. Control arm-to-frame pivot bolts MUST be installed with bolt heads facing each other. *See Fig. 1.*

NOTE: DO NOT loosen ball joint stud nut during tightening procedure.

2) Tighten ball joint stud nut to 15 ft. lbs. (20 N.m). Tighten ball joint stud nut an additional 90 degrees (1 1/2 flats) or until next slot aligns with cotter pin hole in stud. DO NOT tighten nut more than 60 degrees to align with cotter pin hole. To complete installation, reverse removal procedure.

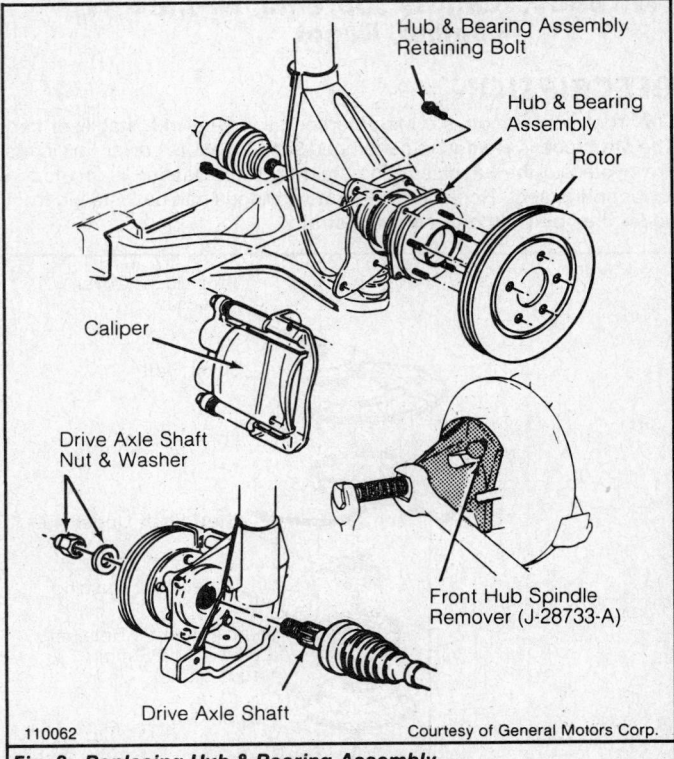

Fig. 2: Replacing Hub & Bearing Assembly

BALL JOINT

Removal – **1)** Raise vehicle so front suspension hangs free. Remove wheels. Remove ball joint heat shield, cotter pin and nut. *See Fig. 1.*

2) Loosen stabilizer bar bushing clamp bolts. Separate ball joint from lower control arm using Ball Joint Separator (J-35917). Drill out 4 ball joint-to-knuckle rivets. DO NOT damage drive axle boots when drilling out rivets. Remove ball joint.

Installation – **1)** Install new ball joint and 4 retaining bolts. To complete installation, reverse removal procedure.

NOTE: DO NOT loosen ball joint stud nut during tightening procedure.

2) Tighten ball joint stud nut to 15 ft. lbs. (20 N.m). Then tighten ball joint stud nut an additional 90 degrees (1 1/2 flats) or until next slot aligns with cotter pin hole in stud. DO NOT tighten nut more than 60 degrees to align with cotter pin hole.

STABILIZER BAR & BUSHINGS

Removal – **1)** Raise and support vehicle. Remove wheel. Slide steering shaft dust boot for access to pinch bolt. Remove pinch bolt from lower intermediate steering shaft.

2) Loosen all stabilizer bar bushing clamp nuts and bolts. Place jack stand under center of rear frame crossmember. Loosen 2 front frame-to-body bolts, 4 turns. Remove 2 rear frame-to-body bolts.

3) Lower rear of frame just enough to allow stabilizer bar removal. Remove bushings and clamps from control arms. Pull stabilizer bar rearward and downward. Remove stabilizer bar from left side of vehicle.

Installation – **1)** Install stabilizer bar from left side of vehicle. Coat bushings with rubber lubricant. Install bushings on stabilizer bar. Loosely install clamps at control arm and frame.

2) Raise frame into position while guiding steering shaft onto gear. Install rear frame-to-body bolts. Tighten all frame-to-body bolts to 103 ft. lbs. (140 N.m).

3) Lower vehicle. Tighten bushing clamp bolts. See TORQUE SPECIFICATIONS table at end of this article. Install and tighten steering shaft pinch bolt. To complete installation, reverse removal procedure.

STRUT CARTRIDGE

WARNING: To avoid personal injury, DO NOT remove cartridge unless weight of vehicle is on suspension. Weight of vehicle keeps coil spring compressed.

Removal – 1) Mark strut mount cover plate-to-body position for installation reference. *See Fig. 1.* Using No. 50 Torx bit and Strut Shaft Nut Remover (J-35669), remove upper strut nut. Pry out upper strut bushing.

2) On Lumina models with 8 mm strut-to-body studs, remove jounce bumper retainer using Spanner Wrench (J-35670). On all models, place Strut Extension Rod (J-35668) on strut shaft. Compress shaft into cartridge. Remove rod and pull out jounce bumper.

3) Install strut extension rod and extend strut piston shaft. Remove strut extension rod. Remove strut closure nut with Strut Cap Nut Wrench (J-35671). Lift out strut cartridge. Suction out oil from strut tube.

Inspection – Clamp strut dampener upside down in vise. Stroke strut. If lag is noticed, gas filled cell has ruptured and cartridge should be replaced.

Installation – To install strut cartridge, reverse removal procedure. To ease installation, use soap solution to lubricate strut mount bushing. If necessary, install Strut Extension Rod (J-35668) on strut shaft after strut mount bushing is partially installed and position strut shaft as required. Tighten all fasteners to specification. See TORQUE SPECIFICATIONS table at end of this article.

STRUT & KNUCKLE ASSEMBLY

Removal – 1) Disconnect negative battery cable. Loosen, but DO NOT remove axle shaft nut. Scribe strut cover plate for installation reference. Loosen 3 cover plate nuts. Raise and support vehicle. Remove wheels. Remove caliper from knuckle and hang out of way. Remove rotor.

2) Remove axle shaft nut and washer. Loosen hub and bearing-to-knuckle retaining bolts. Remove ABS sensor and position out of way (if equipped). Using Front Hub Spindle Remover (J-28733-A), push axle splines out of hub and bearing assembly. *See Fig. 2.* DO NOT damage axle boots.

3) Remove hub and bearing-to-knuckle retaining bolts. Remove hub and bearing assembly. Place drain pan below transaxle. Separate drive axle shaft from transaxle using a slide hammer and Axle Shaft Remover (J-33008). Lower drive axle shaft out of vehicle.

4) Remove tie rod-to-knuckle nut. Separate tie rod from knuckle using Tie Rod Remover (J-35917). Remove ball joint cotter pin and nut. Separate ball joint from lower control arm using Ball Joint Separator (J-35917). Remove ball joint heat shield. Lower strut assembly out of vehicle.

WARNING: Springs are under high tension. To avoid injury, DO NOT remove strut shaft nut without compressing spring.

Disassembly – 1) Using spring compressor, compress spring enough to remove strut piston shaft nut with Strut Shaft Nut Remover (J-35669) and Torx bit.

2) On Lumina models with 8-mm strut-to-body studs, use Spanner Wrench (J-35670) to remove jounce bumper retainer. On all models, relieve spring tension and lift out spring and other strut components. *See Fig. 1.* Use Strut Cap Nut Wrench (J-35671) to remove closure nut if cartridge is to be replaced.

Reassembly – 1) To reassemble strut, reverse disassembly procedure. Lower spring coil end must be visible between step and first retention tab of lower insulator.

2) Upper spring coil end must be between step and location mark on upper insulator. Install jounce bumper retainer (if equipped). Align strut piston shaft using Strut Extension Rod (J-35668). Tighten strut shaft upper nut.

Installation – 1) Install strut mount cover plate and upper strut mount-to-body nuts. Tighten nuts after vehicle is lowered to ground. Install ball joint heat shield. Place lower ball joint into lower control arm.

NOTE: DO NOT loosen ball joint stud nut during tightening procedure.

2) Tighten ball joint stud nut to 15 ft. lbs. (20 N.m). Tighten ball joint stud nut an additional 90 degrees (1 1/2 flats). Tighten to align next slot with cotter pin hole in stud. DO NOT tighten nut more than 60 degrees to align with cotter pin hole.

3) Install tie rod into steering knuckle. Tighten tie rod nut and install cotter pin. Install drive axle shaft into opening in steering knuckle and into transaxle. Using frame cradle or lower control arm for leverage, seat drive axle shaft into transaxle. Use pry bar in groove provided on inner joint.

4) Ensure axle snap ring is seated by tapping on inner groove. Grasp inner housing, NOT axle shaft, and pull outward. Axle will remain seated if snap ring is properly seated.

5) Install hub and bearing assembly into knuckle. Install and tighten hub and bearing retaining bolts. Install rotor and brake caliper. Coat shaft of caliper mounting bolts with silicone grease. Install wheel.

NOTE: Install new axle shaft nut and washer whenever original nut is removed.

6) Lower vehicle. Install new axle shaft nut and washer. Tighten to specification. See TORQUE SPECIFICATIONS table. Align scribe marks and tighten cover plate nuts. Connect negative battery cable.

TORQUE SPECIFICATIONS

TORQUE SPECIFICATIONS

Application	Ft. Lbs. (N.m)
Axle Shaft Nut	[1] 184 (250)
Ball Joint Stud Nut	[2]
Brake Caliper Mounting Bolt	79 (107)
Frame-To-Body Bolts	103 (140)
Hub and Bearing Retaining Bolts	52 (70)
Lower Control Arm Pivot Bolts	52 (70)
Stabilizer Bar Bushing	
Clamp Bolts (Frame & Control Arms)	35 (47)
Steering Shaft Pinch Bolt	34 (46)
Strut Closure Nut	82 (110)
Strut Mount Cover Plate Nut	17 (24)
Strut Shaft Upper Nut	72 (98)
Tie Rod Nut	40 (54)
Wheel Lug Nuts	
Except Lumina	103 (140)
Lumina	92 (125)

[1] – Always use NEW nut and washer whenever old nut is loosened or removed.

[2] – Tighten ball joint stud nut to 15 ft. lbs. (20 N.m). Tighten ball joint stud nut an additional 90 degrees (1 1/2 flats) or until next slot aligns with cotter pin hole in stud. DO NOT tighten nut more than 60 degrees to align with cotter pin hole.

1991 SUSPENSION
Rear – "A", "J", "L" & "N" Bodies

"A" Body: Century, Cutlass Ciera,
Cutlass Cruiser, 6000
"J" Body: Cavalier, Sunbird
"L" Body: Beretta, Corsica
"N" Body: Cutlass Calais, Grand Am,
Skylark

NOTE: Following procedures DO NOT apply to vehicles equipped with electronic suspension systems. See appropriate article in SUSPENSION.

DESCRIPTION

The "A" body rear suspension consists of a rear axle assembly, 2 coil springs, 2 shock absorbers and a track bar. The track bar controls the side movement of the axle assembly. On some models, the track bar may contain an additional track bar brace. Control arms, welded to the axle housing, provide axle-to-body mounting. Control arms, with track bar and shock absorber maintain proper body to axle relation and provide for best handling.

The track bar is a single unit with non-replaceable bushings. A non-serviceable stabilizer shaft, welded inside the axle housing, is an integral part of the rear axle assembly. Coil springs are retained between an underbody seat and a welded rear axle seat. *See Fig. 1.*

The "J", "L" and "N" body suspension consists of an axle with control arms and twisting crossbeam, 2 coil springs, 2 shock absorbers, 2 upper spring insulators, and 2 spring compression bumpers.

The axle assembly is mounted to the body through rubber control arm bushings. A serviceable stabilizer shaft is attached to the axle beam and lower control arms (optional on "L" body). Hub and bearing assembly is a sealed unit and cannot be serviced. *See Fig. 3.*

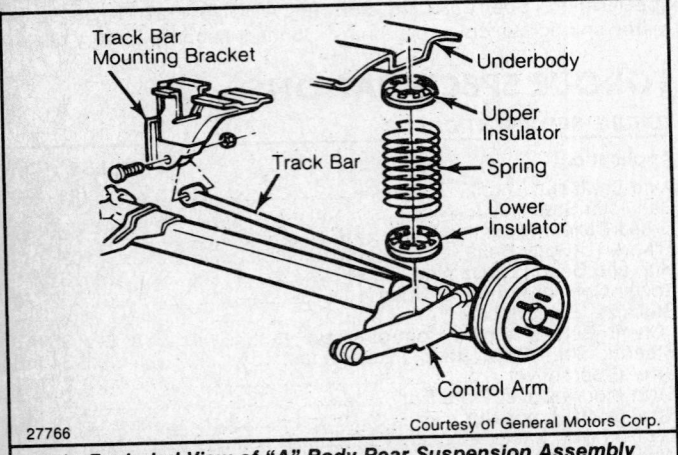

Fig. 1: Exploded View of "A" Body Rear Suspension Assembly

Labels: Track Bar Mounting Bracket; Underbody; Upper Insulator; Track Bar; Spring; Lower Insulator; Control Arm

27766   Courtesy of General Motors Corp.

ADJUSTMENTS & INSPECTION

WHEEL ALIGNMENT SPECIFICATIONS & PROCEDURES

NOTE: See SPECIFICATIONS & PROCEDURES article in WHEEL ALIGNMENT.

WHEEL BEARINGS

1) Raise and support vehicle. Remove wheel. Remove brake drum. Free disc brake pads away from rotor or remove caliper (if equipped). Install 2 wheel nuts to secure rotor (if equipped).
2) Mount dial indicator with stem resting against hub. Push inward on rotor or hub. Adjust indicator to zero. Pull outward and note reading. Replace hub and bearing assembly if movement exceeds .005" (.12 mm).

REMOVAL & INSTALLATION

SHOCK ABSORBERS

NOTE: DO NOT remove both shock absorbers at one time. Suspending rear axle at full length may damage brake lines and hoses.

Removal – Open deck lid and remove trim cover. Remove upper shock retaining nut. Raise vehicle and support rear axle assembly. Remove lower retaining bolt and nut. Remove shock absorber.
Installation – **1)** Install shock absorber lower mounting bolt. Install nut finger tight. Lower vehicle while guiding upper stud into body opening.
2) Install upper nut finger tight only. Tighten lower mounting to specification. See TORQUE SPECIFICATIONS tables at end of this article. Lower vehicle. Tighten upper nut to specification. Install trim cover.

COIL SPRINGS & INSULATORS

CAUTION: When removing coil springs, DO NOT use twin-post type hoist. Swing arc tendency of axle, caused when certain fasteners are removed, may cause vehicle to slip from hoist.

Removal – **1)** Raise and support vehicle at rear axle or control arms. Remove rear wheels. Remove brake line bracket retaining bolts.
2) On "A" body, remove track bar-to-axle nut and bolt.
3) On all models, remove lower shock absorber mounting bolts. Lower rear axle assembly. Carefully remove coil springs and insulators.
Installation – **1)** Before installing coil spring on "J", "L" and "N" bodies, it may be necessary to install upper insulators to the body using adhesive. This retains insulator in correct location during installation.
2) On "J" & "N" bodies, install coil springs with upper spring end positioned within 9/16" (15 mm) of spring stop located in spring seat. *See Fig. 2.* On all models, raise axle and install shock absorbers. Loosely install retaining bolts.

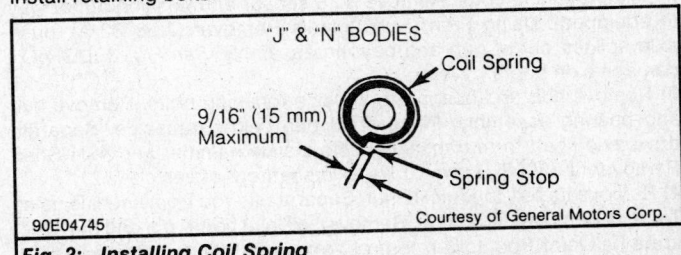

Fig. 2: Installing Coil Spring

Labels: "J" & "N" BODIES; Coil Spring; 9/16" (15 mm) Maximum; Spring Stop

90E04745   Courtesy of General Motors Corp.

NOTE: Vehicle must be at normal operating height before tightening shock absorber retaining bolts.

3) Install brake line brackets and wheels. Lower vehicle. Tighten shock absorber retaining bolts to specification. See TORQUE SPECIFICATIONS tables at end of this article.

TRACK BAR ("A" BODY)

Removal – Raise vehicle and support rear axle. Remove bolts from brace to track bar (if equipped). Remove track bar bolts at body and axle assembly. Remove track bar.
Installation – Replace track bar if bushings are damaged. Install track bar on axle mount. DO NOT tighten bolt at this time. Install track bar on body mount. Install track bar brace (if equipped). Tighten bolts to specification. See TORQUE SPECIFICATIONS tables at end of this article.

STABILIZER BAR ("J", "L" & "N" BODIES)

Removal – Raise and support vehicle. Remove stabilizer bar retaining bolts at axle and control arms. Remove brackets, insulators and stabilizer bar.

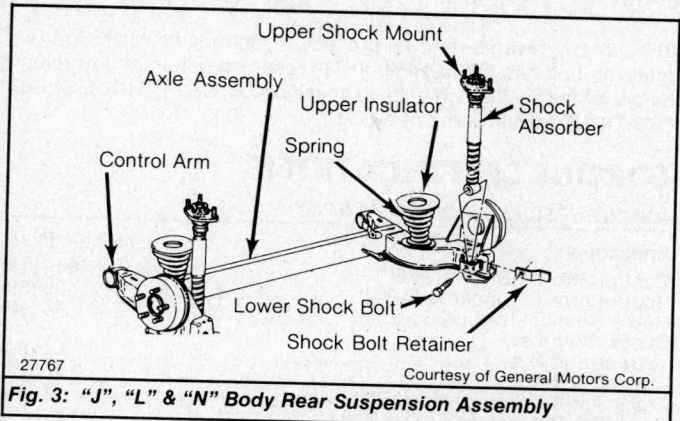

27767   Courtesy of General Motors Corp.

Fig. 3: "J", "L" & "N" Body Rear Suspension Assembly

Installation – 1) Replace damaged insulators. Install upper clamps, spacers and insulators on axle assembly. Install stabilizer bar in insulators. Loosely install lower clamps and nuts.
2) Install retaining bolts at control arms. Tighten to specification. Tighten remaining bolts on axle assembly to specification. See TORQUE SPECIFICATIONS tables at end of this article.

CONTROL ARM

Control arm is an integral part of axle assembly and cannot be replaced separately.

CONTROL ARM BUSHINGS

Removal ("A" Body) – 1) Raise vehicle and support axle in front of coil spring seat. Remove wheels. When removing right control arm bushing, disconnect parking brake cable from hook guide. Remove parking brake cables from bracket for access to control arm bushing.
2) On all bushings, remove brake line brackets. Remove shock absorber lower mounting bolt. Remove spring for access to control arm. Only one control arm bushing should be replaced at a time.
3) Remove control arm-to-body mounting nut. Rotate control arm downward. Mark bracket location on control arm. Remove bracket from control arm.
4) Assemble Control Arm Bushing Remover/Installer (J-28685) and "C" Clamp (J-9519-23). Install bushing remover/installer assembly on control arm bushing. See Fig. 4. Ensure components are aligned before tightening removal tool bolt. Tighten bolt until bushing is removed.

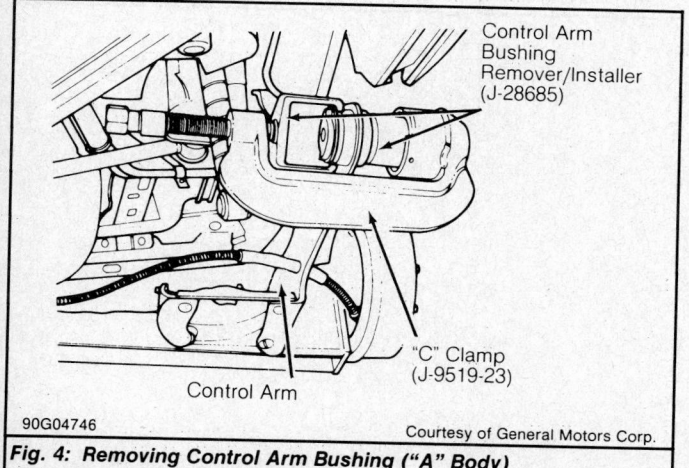

Control Arm Bushing Remover/Installer (J-28685)

"C" Clamp (J-9519-23)

Control Arm

90G04746   Courtesy of General Motors Corp.

Fig. 4: Removing Control Arm Bushing ("A" Body)

Installation – 1) Ensure bushing areas are clean. Invert Control Arm Bushing Remover/Installer (J-28685) in bushing remover/installer assembly. Install control arm bushing. Use bolt to align bushing installer and control arm bushing.
2) Control arm bushing cutouts must face front and rear. Press bushing into control arm by tightening bolt of installer. Proper location of

control arm bushing may be identified by the alignment of scribe mark through the gauge hole on installer.
3) Install bracket on control arm. Align reference marks made during removal. Bracket should be located at 40-44 degree angle. Once angle is correct, tighten bolts. Clean control arm-to-body mounting bolts.
4) Raise control arm and align control arm-to-body mounting bolt holes. Install bolts and tighten to specification. See TORQUE SPECIFICATIONS tables at end of this article. Install coil spring. Ensure coil spring is correctly installed. See COIL SPRINGS & INSULATORS under REMOVAL & INSTALLATION.
5) Install shock absorber, brake line bracket and parking brake cable. Adjust parking brake cable.

Removal ("J", "L" & "N" Bodies) – 1) Raise vehicle and support body. Remove wheels. If removing right bushing, disconnect brake lines from body. If left bushing is being removed, disconnect brake line bracket from body and parking brake cable from hook guide on body. Replace only one bushing at a time.
2) Remove control arm-to-body mounting bolt. Note direction of bolt installation. Rotate control arm downward.
3) Control Arm Bushing Kit (J-29376) is used for bushing replacement. Install Receiver (J-29376-1) on control arm. Install bolt through Plate (J-29376-7) and receiver.
4) Install Bushing Remover (J-29376-6) and Nut (J-21474-18) on bolt. See Fig. 5. Ensure components are aligned. Tighten nut until control arm bushing is removed.

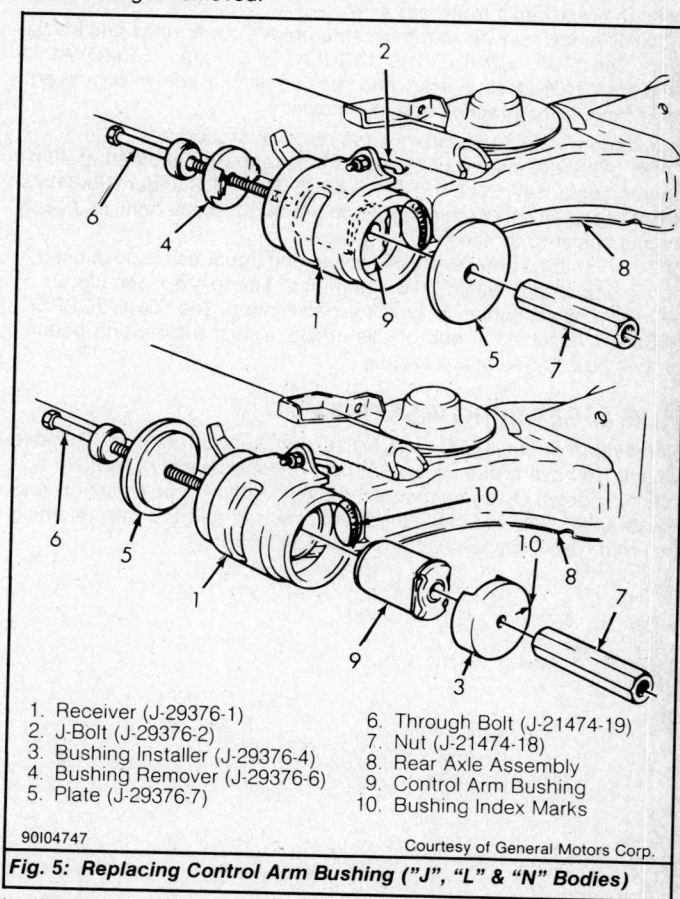

1. Receiver (J-29376-1)	6. Through Bolt (J-21474-19)
2. J-Bolt (J-29376-2)	7. Nut (J-21474-18)
3. Bushing Installer (J-29376-4)	8. Rear Axle Assembly
4. Bushing Remover (J-29376-6)	9. Control Arm Bushing
5. Plate (J-29376-7)	10. Bushing Index Marks

90I04747   Courtesy of General Motors Corp.

Fig. 5: Replacing Control Arm Bushing ("J", "L" & "N" Bodies)

Installation – 1) Ensure bushing areas are clean. Install Receiver (J-29376-1) on control arm. Install bolt through Plate (J-29376-7) and receiver. See Fig. 5.
2) Install bushing on bolt and install in control arm. Align bushing installer arrow (index marks) with bushing index marks on receiver. Install nut on bolt. Tighten nut to install bushing. Control arm bushing is properly located when end flange is even with control arm surface.
3) Rotate control arm upward until mounting bolts can be installed. Bolts must be installed from inboard side of control arm. DO NOT tighten bolts at this time.

4) Install brake lines and parking brake cable. Adjust parking brake cable. Install wheels. Support vehicle at curb height. Tighten control arm-to-body mounting bolts to specification. See TORQUE SPECIFICATIONS tables at end of this article.

REAR AXLE

CAUTION: When removing rear axle, DO NOT use a twin-post type hoist. Swing arc tendency of axle, caused when certain fasteners are removed, may cause vehicle to slip from hoist.

Removal – 1) On "A", "J" and "N" bodies, raise and support vehicle under axle.
2) On "L" body, raise and support vehicle under control arms. Install jack to support front of vehicle.
3) On "J", "L" and "N" bodies, remove stabilizer bar from axle. See STABILIZER BAR ("J", "L" & "N" BODIES) under REMOVAL & INSTALLATION.
4) On all models, remove wheel and brake drum. Remove shock absorber lower mounting bolts from axle. Disconnect parking brake cable.
5) On "A" body, remove track bar attaching bolts at axle, and disconnect track bar. See TRACK BAR ("A" BODY) under REMOVAL & INSTALLATION. Disconnect brake lines from control arm. Disconnect parking brake cable from rear axle.
6) On all models, lower rear axle, and remove coil springs and insulators. See COIL SPRINGS & INSULATORS under REMOVAL & INSTALLATION. Remove hub and backing plate. Remove control arm bolts from frame bracket, and lower axle.

Installation – 1) To install, reverse removal procedure.
2) On "A" body, ensure control arm brackets are tightened at 40-44 degree angle. See COIL SPRINGS & INSULATORS under REMOVAL & INSTALLATION. Clean control arm bracket-to-body bolts and apply Loctite sealer to threads.
3) On "J" and "N" bodies, ensure coil spring upper coil is positioned in spring seat and is within 9/16" (15 mm) of spring stop. See Fig. 2.
4) On all models, tighten all bolts to specification. See TORQUE SPECIFICATIONS tables at end of this article. Adjust brakes and parking brake cable. Bleed brake system.

HUB & BEARING ASSEMBLY

Removal & Installation – 1) Raise and support vehicle. Remove wheel. Remove brake drum. Support brake assembly. Remove hub retaining bolts. On some models, top rear retaining bolt will not clear brake shoe. Hub assembly must be loosened and top rear retaining bolt removed. Remove hub and bearing assembly.

2) To install, reverse removal procedure. On models where top rear retaining bolt hits brake shoe, install retaining bolt in hub assembly before installing. Tighten bolts to specification. See TORQUE SPECIFICATIONS tables at end of article.

TORQUE SPECIFICATIONS

TORQUE SPECIFICATIONS ("A" BODY)

Application	Ft. Lbs. (N.m)
Control Arm-To-Bracket Nut	84 (114)
Control Arm-To-Underbody Bolt	28 (38)
Hub & Bearing-To-Axle Bolt	44 (60)
Shock Absorber	
Lower End Nut	44 (60)
Upper End Nut	¹ 16 (22)
Track Bar Bracket-To-Body Bolt	34 (46)
Track Bar Bracket-To-Frame Bolt	45 (61)
Track Bar-To-Axle Nut	44 (60)
Track Bar-To-Frame Nut	35 (47)
	INCH Lbs.
Brake Line Bracket-To-Frame Screw	96 (11)

¹ – Final torque at curb height.

TORQUE SPECIFICATIONS ("J", "L" & "N" BODIES)

Application	Ft. Lbs. (N.m)
Brake Line Bracket-To-Control	
Arm Screw	11 (15)
Control Arm-To-Body Bracket Nut	
"J" & "L" Bodies	¹ 67 (91)
"N" Body	¹ 61 (83)
Hub & Bearing-To-Axle Bolt	37 (51)
Shock Absorber Mount-To-Body Bolt	13 (18)
Shock Absorber-To-Axle Bolt	
"J" & "N" Bodies	35 (47)
"L" Body	
Beretta	43 (58)
Corsica	35 (47)
Shock Absorber-To-Mount Nut	
"J" Body	¹ 13 (18)
"L" Body	¹ 22 (30)
"N" Body	¹ 28 (38)
Stabilizer Bar-To-Axle Nut	10-15 (14-20)
Stabilizer Bar-To-Control Arm Nut	16 (22)
	INCH Lbs.
Brake Line Bracket-To-Frame Screw	96 (11)

¹ – Final torque at curb height.

"B" Body: Caprice, Custom Cruiser,
          Roadmaster
"D" Body: Brougham
"F" Body: Camaro, Firebird

DESCRIPTION

On Caprice, Custom Cruiser and Roadmaster models, the rear suspension is a 4-link type with coil springs, which are mounted between lower spring seats on the axle housing and upper spring seats in the frame. The axle housing is attached to the frame by 2 upper and 2 lower control arms.

The control arms maintain a geometrical relationship between the axle housing and frame, to oppose torque reaction on acceleration and braking. Two shock absorbers are attached to the frame and axle housing.

Camaro and Firebird models use an upper torque arm, 2 lower control arms and track bar to secure differential.

ADJUSTMENTS & INSPECTION

WHEEL ALIGNMENT
SPECIFICATIONS & PROCEDURES

NOTE: See SPECIFICATIONS & PROCEDURES article in WHEEL ALIGNMENT.

RIDING HEIGHT

NOTE: See SPECIFICATIONS & PROCEDURES article in WHEEL ALIGNMENT.

REMOVAL & INSTALLATION

SHOCK ABSORBERS

Removal & Installation (Camaro & Firebird) – 1) Raise and support vehicle. Support rear axle assembly. From above, pull back carpeting and remove upper shock absorber mounting nut. Remove shock absorber lower mounting nut and remove shock absorber.

CAUTION: Support axle assembly before removing upper shock absorber mounting nut to avoid damage to brake lines, track bar and propeller shaft.

2) To install shock absorber, reverse removal procedure. Tighten mounting nuts to specification.
Removal (Except Camaro & Firebird) – 1) Raise and support vehicle. Support rear axle assembly. Disconnect air line from shock absorber (if equipped). See Fig. 1.

2) Disconnect upper shock absorber mounting bolts. Use back-up wrench on upper shock absorber mounting nuts (if equipped). Disconnect lower mounting nut, using a back-up wrench to keep stud from turning.
Installation – 1) To install shock absorber, reverse removal procedure. If equipped with Electronic Level Control, left air shock has 2 line connections while right shock only has one connection.

CAUTION: DO NOT allow vehicle weight to rest on air shock until it has been inflated to at least 10 psi (.7 kg/cm²).

2) Tighten mounting nuts to specification. Connect air line and add 10 psi (.7 kg/cm²) air pressure to prevent shock absorber damage (if equipped).
3) On models with Electronic Level Control, turn ignition on and ground compressor test lead to active system and inflate shocks. Test lead is Green connector with Yellow wire located to left of power brake booster.

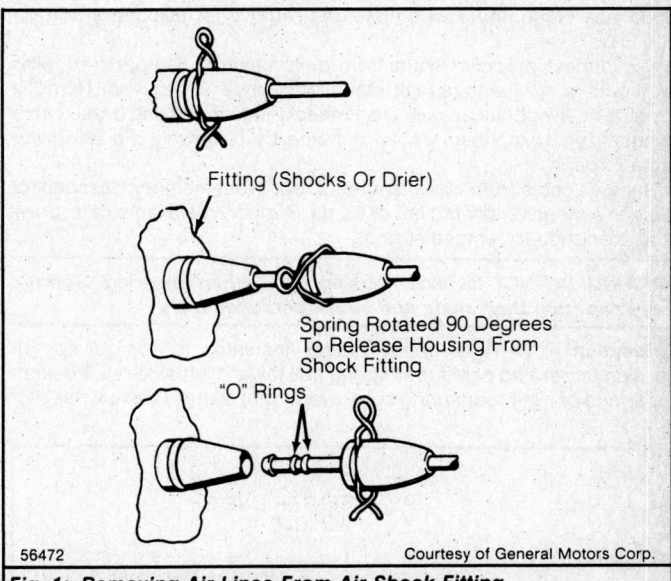

Fig. 1: Removing Air Lines From Air Shock Fitting

COIL SPRINGS & INSULATORS

CAUTION: Manufacturers recommend removing and installing coil springs one side at a time.

Removal (Caprice, Custom Cruiser, Roadmaster) – 1) Turn off ignition so Electronic Level Control system (if equipped) will not activate. Raise vehicle and support axle housing with adjustable lifting device. Disconnect trim height sensor link (if equipped). Disconnect upper control arms at axle housing.
2) Disconnect stabilizer bar (if equipped). Remove brake hose support bolt at axle housing to allow axle to drop further. Remove shock absorber lower mounts. Lower axle enough to remove spring. Remove coil springs and insulators.

NOTE: Brake lines do not have to be disconnected to let axle drop. DO NOT lower axle to a point where brake line supports axle.

Installation – To install coil spring, reverse removal procedure. Ensure coil spring is mounted correctly. See Fig. 2. Tighten all nuts and bolts to specification. See TORQUE SPECIFICATIONS tables at end of this article.

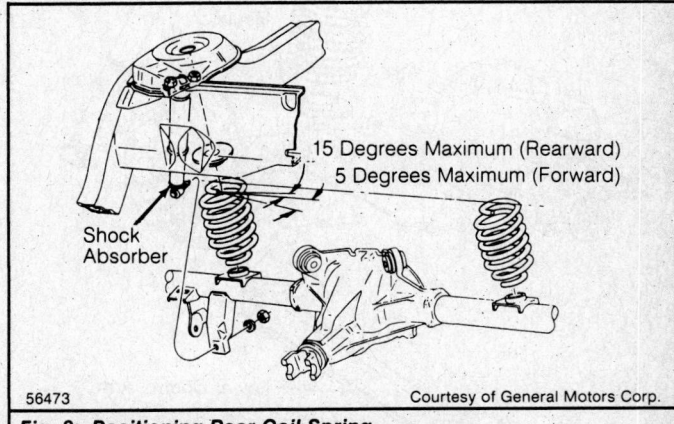

Fig. 2: Positioning Rear Coil Spring
          (Caprice, Custom Cruiser, Roadmaster)

Removal (Brougham) – 1) Raise vehicle and support frame and rear axle. Remove shock absorbers as previously described. Remove stabilizer bar-to-lower control arm bolts, and remove stabilizer bar.
2) Remove bolt securing junction block to top of rear axle. Disconnect brake lines from axle clips. Disconnect link from leveling sensor arm.

Place jack stand under axle nose and remove lower control arm-to-axle bolts.

3) Disconnect propeller shaft from pinion flange. Support propeller shaft with wire. Remove jack stand from under axle nose. Remove upper arm pivot bolts at axle. Disconnect left side parking brake cable at equalizer. Disconnect cable at frame by removing clip and slide cable through hole.

4) Remove cable from clip at center of rear crossmember. Disconnect cable at connector located left of frame. Support rear frame rails. Lower axle enough to remove springs.

WARNING: DO NOT let axle housing twist when lowering. Springs may snap from their seats and cause personal injury.

Installation – **1)** Tape upper rubber insulator to top of spring. Position upper end of left rear spring coil toward left side rail. Position upper end of right rear spring coil toward right frame side rail. *See Fig. 3.*

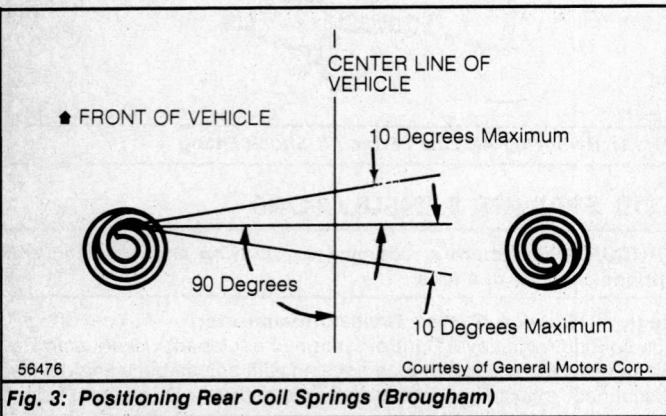

Fig. 3: Positioning Rear Coil Springs (Brougham)

2) Continue installation in reverse of removal procedure. Tighten all mounting nuts and bolts to specification. See TORQUE SPECIFICATIONS tables at end of this article. DO NOT tighten upper and lower control arms until vehicle is resting at normal standing height position.

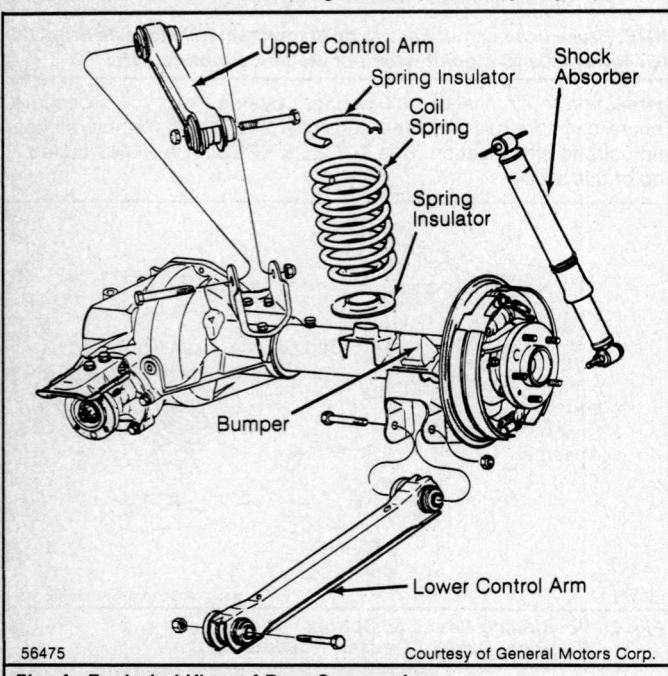

Fig. 4: Exploded View of Rear Suspension
(Typical Except Camaro & Firebird)

Removal (Camaro & Firebird) – **1)** Raise and support vehicle. Support rear axle with adjustable lifting device. Remove track bar mounting bolt at axle assembly. Loosen track bar bolt at body brace.

2) Disconnect rear brake hose clip at underbody to allow axle drop. Remove both lower shock absorber attaching nuts. Lower rear axle and remove spring.

Installation – To install coil spring, reverse removal procedure. Manufacturer recommends using NEW track bar bolt if nylon patch in threads is damaged or will not hold correct torque.

UPPER CONTROL ARM

NOTE: Remove and replace one control arm at a time to prevent rear axle from rolling or slipping. Bushings are not serviceable on Brougham.

Removal – **1)** Raise and support vehicle. If equipped with Electronic Level Control, remove height control sensor link-to-right upper control arm nut.

2) Remove stabilizer bar bolts and washers from upper control arm (if equipped). Place jack stands under rear axle. Unbolt control arm from upper and lower pivot bolt mounts. Remove control arm from vehicle.

Bushing Replacement – Except for Brougham, control arm mounted bushings may be replaced using a press. *See Fig. 5.* Axle housing mounted bushings are removed using Receiver (J-25317-2), Bushing Carrier (J-21474-6), Bolt (J-21474-19) and Nut (J-21474-18). Bushings are installed using Receiver (J-25317-2), Bushing Installer (J-25317-1), Bolt (J-21474-19) and Nut (J-21474-18).

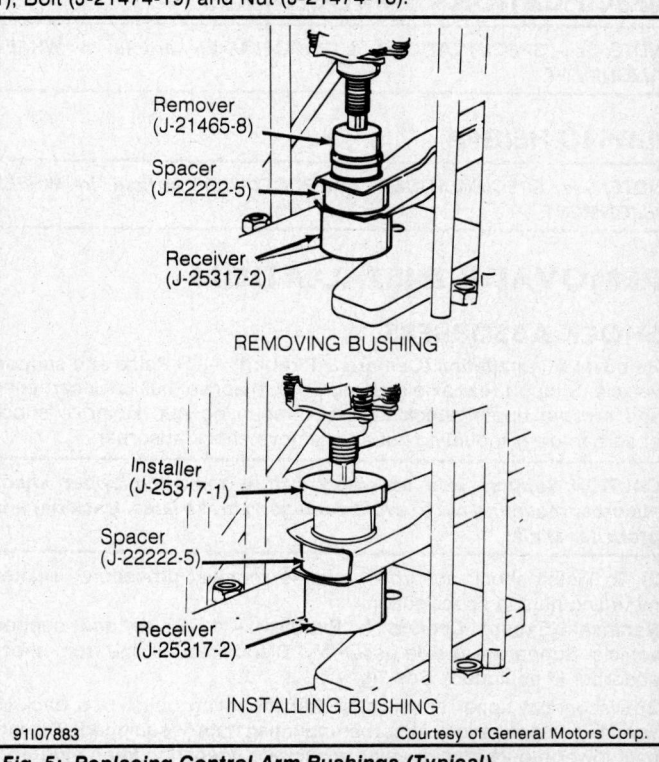

Fig. 5: Replacing Control Arm Bushings (Typical)

Installation – To install, reverse removal procedure. Tighten pivot bolts with vehicle on ground and at curb height. On Brougham, if equipped with Nylock or prevailing torque nuts, tighten nut, NOT bolt, to achieve accurate torque. On all others, tighten nut or bolt according to accessibility.

LOWER CONTROL ARM

NOTE: Remove and replace one control arm at a time to prevent rear axle from rolling or slipping.

Removal – Raise and support rear of vehicle. Support axle housing to relieve tension on control arm bolts. If equipped with stabilizer bar, disconnect bar at lower control arm. Remove lower control arm pivot bolt. Disconnect control arm from frame crossmember and remove control arm.

Bushing Replacement – Bushing replacement is similar to upper control arm mounted bushing procedure. *See Fig. 5.*

Installation – To install, reverse removal procedure. Tighten pivot bolts with vehicle on ground and at curb height. On Brougham, if equipped with Nylock or prevailing torque nuts, tighten nut, NOT bolt, to achieve accurate torque. On all others, tighten nut or bolt according to accessibility.

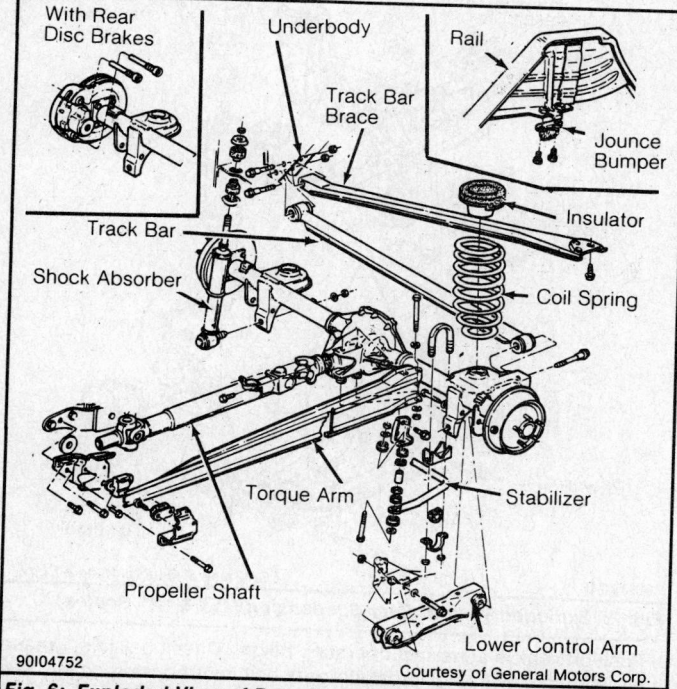

Fig. 6: Exploded View of Rear Suspension (Camaro & Firebird)

90104752 Courtesy of General Motors Corp.

TRACK BAR

Removal (Camaro & Firebird) – Raise vehicle. Support rear axle at curb height position. Remove track bar mounting bolt and nut at rear axle and body bracket. Remove track bar. *See Fig. 6.*

Installation – Thoroughly clean track bar-to-axle housing bolt and nut. Replace any nuts and bolts that are rusted or damaged. Reinstall track bar mounting bolts at axle and body bracket. Tighten to specification. See TORQUE SPECIFICATIONS tables at end of this article.

TRACK BAR BRACE

Removal (Camaro & Firebird) – Raise vehicle and support rear axle. Remove heat shield-to-track bar brace. Remove 3 track bar brace-to-body screws. Remove nut and bolt at body bracket and lift out track bar.

Installation – To install track bar, reverse removal procedure. Tighten 3 track bar brace-to-body screws before tightening nut and bolt. Tighten NUT at track bar brace, not bolt. Install heat shield and lower vehicle.

TORQUE ARM

CAUTION: Remove coil springs before removing torque arm to avoid rear axle twisting forward and damaging vehicle.

Removal (Camaro & Firebird) – **1)** Raise vehicle and support rear axle with adjustable lifting device. Remove track bar mounting bolt at axle assembly. Loosen track bar bolt at body brace.
2) Disconnect rear brake hose clips at underbody to allow more axle drop (if necessary). Remove both shock absorber lower attaching nuts.
3) Carefully lower rear axle and remove coil springs. Remove torque arm rear attaching bolts. Remove torque arm front outer bracket and remove torque arm.

Installation – **1)** Position torque arm, and loosely install rear torque arm bolts. Install torque arm front bracket, and tighten nuts to specification. Tighten torque arm rear nuts. See TORQUE SPECIFICATIONS tables at end of article.
2) Position springs and insulators in spring seats. Raise rear axle until it supports vehicle weight at curb height position.
3) Install shock absorbers to rear axle. Replace any rusted or damaged nuts and bolts. Install brake line clips. Remove adjustable lifting device, and lower vehicle.

TORQUE SPECIFICATIONS

TORQUE SPECIFICATIONS ("B" BODY)

Application	Ft. Lbs. (N.m)
Lower Control Arm-To-Axle Bolt	122 (165)
Lower Control Arm-To-Axle Nut	122 (165)
Lower Control Arm-To-Frame Bolt	92 (125)
Lower Control Arm-To-Frame Nut	122 (165)
Shock Absorber Nut (Lower Attachment)	92 (125)
Shock Absorber Nut (Upper Attachment)	48 (65)
Stabilizer Bar-To-Body Bracket Bolt	12 (16)
Stabilizer Bar-To-Control Arm Nut	52 (70)
Stabilizer Bracket-To-Body Bolt	35 (47)
Torque Arm-To-Rear Axle Nut	21 (29)
Torque Arm-To-Front Bracket Nut	98 (133)
Upper Control Arm-To-Axle Bolt	30 (41)
Upper Control Arm-To-Axle Nut	122 (165)
Upper Control Arm-To-Frame Nut	70 (95)
Wheel Lug Nuts	92 (125)
	100 (136)

TORQUE SPECIFICATIONS ("D" BODY)

Application	Ft. Lbs. (N.m)
Lower Control Arm-To-Axle Bolt	122 (165)
Lower Control Arm-To-Axle Nut	122 (165)
Lower Control Arm-To-Frame Bolt	89 (121)
Lower Control Arm-To-Frame Nut	92 (125)
Shock Absorber Nut (Lower Attachment)	65 (88)
Shock Absorber Nut (Upper Attachment)	12 (16)
Stabilizer Bar-To-Body Bracket Bolt	52 (70)
Stabilizer Bracket-To-Body Bolt	21 (29)
Torque Arm-To-Rear Axle Nut	98 (133)
Torque Arm-To-Front Bracket Nut	30 (41)
Upper Control Arm-To-Axle Bolt	85 (115)
Upper Control Arm-To-Axle Nut	70 (95)
Upper Control Arm-To-Frame Nut	92 (125)
Wheel Lug Nuts	100 (136)

TORQUE SPECIFICATIONS ("F" BODY)

Application	Ft. Lbs. (N.m)
Lower Control Arm-To-Axle Bolt	85 (115)
Lower Control Arm-To-Frame Bolt	85 (115)
Shock Absorber Nut (Lower Attachment)	70 (95)
Shock Absorber Nut (Upper Attachment)	13 (18)
Stabilizer Bar-To-Body Bracket Bolt	16 (22)
Stabilizer Bracket-To-Body Bolt	35 (47)
Track Bar-To-Body Bracket Nut	80 (108)
Track Bar-To-Axle Nut	61 (83)
Track Bar Brace-To-Body Brace Bracket	35 (47)
Torque Arm-To-Rear Axle Nut	98 (133)
Torque Arm-To-Front Bracket Nut	30 (41)
Wheel Lug Nuts	81 (110)

"C" Body: DeVille, Fleetwood, Ninety-Eight, Park Avenue, Touring Sedan
"E" Body: Eldorado, Reatta, Riviera, Toronado, Trofeo
"H" Body: Bonneville, Eighty-Eight, LeSabre
"K" Body: Seville

DESCRIPTION

The "C" and "H" bodies use an independent rear suspension, supported by 2 ball joints, control arms, coil springs, and non-serviceable struts. Air adjustable struts are standard on "C" body and optional on "H" body. Stabilizer bar is used to minimize body roll. Control arms are equipped with suspension adjustment links for toe adjustments. *See Fig. 1.*

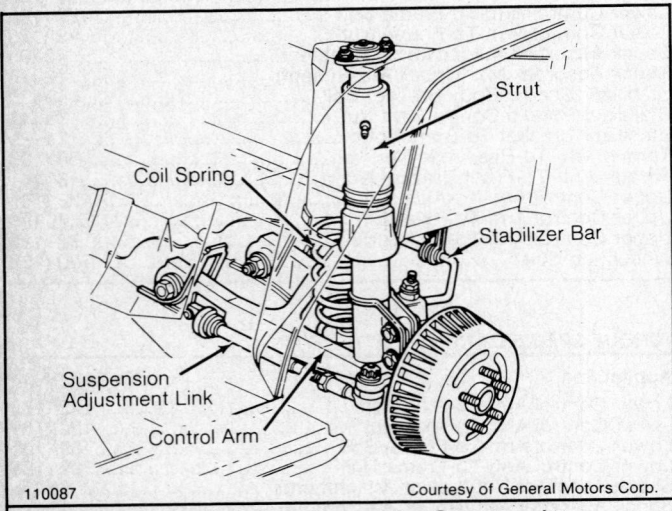

Fig. 1: Identifying Body Rear Suspension Components ("C" & "H" Bodies)

The "E" and "K" bodies use an independent transverse mounted leaf spring rear suspension. Rear suspension components are mounted on a suspension crossmember assembly mounted to the body. *See Fig. 2.*

On all bodies, hub and bearing assembly is connected to the suspension system by the knuckle and struts. Hub and bearing assembly are a complete unit and cannot be serviced individually. Some models use Electronic Level Control (ELC) to maintain proper ride height under various load conditions.

ADJUSTMENTS & INSPECTION

WHEEL ALIGNMENT
SPECIFICATIONS & PROCEDURES

NOTE: See SPECIFICATIONS & PROCEDURES article in WHEEL ALIGNMENT.

RIDING HEIGHT

NOTE: See SPECIFICATIONS & PROCEDURES article in WHEEL ALIGNMENT.

BALL JOINT CHECKING

Lower Ball Joint ("C" & "H" Bodies) – 1) Inspect ball joint stud for looseness. If looseness exists, replace ball joint and steering knuckle.

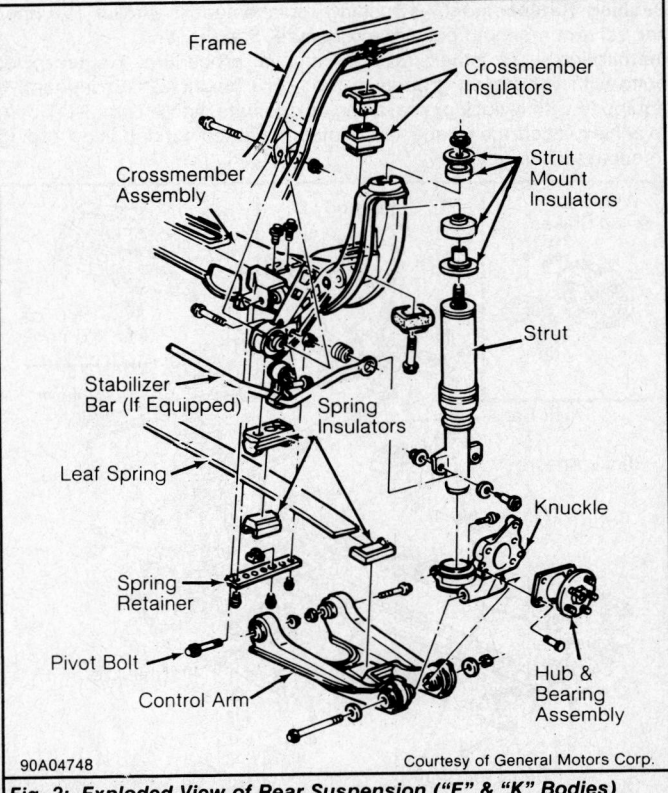

Fig. 2: Exploded View of Rear Suspension ("E" & "K" Bodies)

2) Position vehicle at normal operating height. Check ball joint grease fitting shoulder does not protrude past ball joint housing cover. *See Fig. 3.* Replace ball joint if grease fitting is even or below cover.

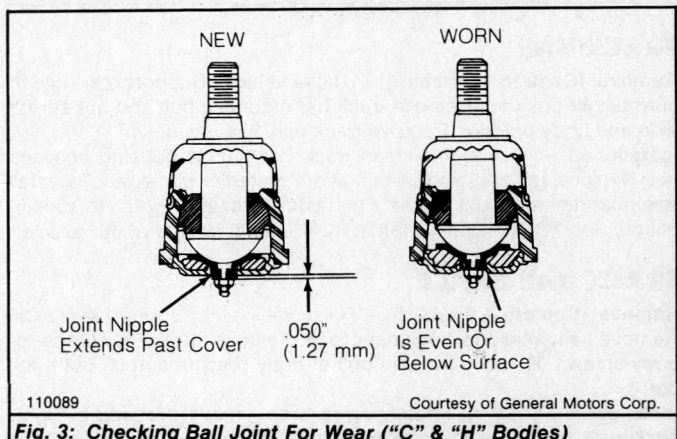

Fig. 3: Checking Ball Joint For Wear ("C" & "H" Bodies)

WHEEL BEARING

Inspection – 1) Raise and support vehicle. Remove wheel. Free disc brake pads away from rotor or remove caliper. Install 2 wheel nuts to secure rotor (if equipped).
2) Mount dial indicator with stem resting against hub. Push inward on rotor or hub. Adjust indicator to zero. Pull outward and note reading. Replace hub assembly if movement exceeds .005" (.12 mm).

ELECTRONIC LEVEL CONTROL

See REAR – ELECTRONIC LEVEL CONTROL article in SUSPENSION.

REMOVAL & INSTALLATION

COIL SPRINGS & INSULATORS

Removal ("C" & "H" Bodies) – 1) Raise and support vehicle. Allow suspension to hang freely. Remove wheel. Remove Electric Level Control (ELC) height sensor link from right control arm (if equipped). Remove parking brake cable retaining clip at left control arm. Remove stabilizer bar from bracket.

2) Place chain around spring and through control arm as a safety precaution. Position Holding Fixture (J-23028-01) to cradle the control arm. *See Fig. 4.* Raise jack to remove tension from pivot bolts.

CAUTION: To avoid injury, securely attach Holding Fixture (J-23028-01) to transmission jack.

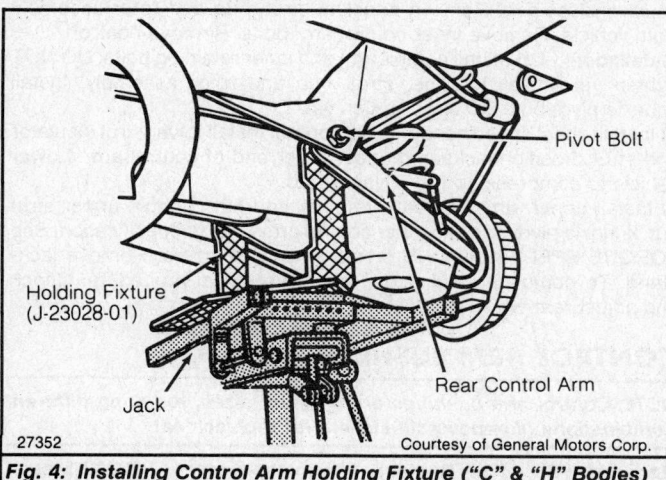

Fig. 4: *Installing Control Arm Holding Fixture ("C" & "H" Bodies)*

3) Remove rear pivot bolt from control arm. Carefully move jack to remove tension from front of control arm. Remove front pivot bolt. Slowly lower jack to allow control arm to pivot downward.

4) Once spring tension is relieved, remove safety chain, spring and insulators. DO NOT force control arm or ball joint to remove spring.

Installation – 1) Replace insulators if damaged or vehicle mileage exceeds 50,000 miles. Install upper and lower insulators on spring. Install springs. *See Fig. 5.* Ensure tightly wound coils are at top on all "C" and "H" bodies without ELC. On all bodies, use holding fixture secured to transmission jack. Install control arm.

2) Slowly move jack and raise control arm into position. Install front and then rear pivot bolts. DO NOT tighten at this time. Attach stabilizer bar to knuckle bracket. DO NOT tighten at this time.

3) To install, reverse removal procedure. Lower vehicle to normal operating height. Tighten pivot nuts, pivot bolts, and stabilizer bar bolt to specification in this order. See TORQUE SPECIFICATIONS table at end of this article.

CAUTION: Control arm pivot nuts, bolts and stabilizer bar MUST be tightened in proper sequence, with vehicle at normal operating height.

KNUCKLE

Removal ("C" & "H" Bodies) – Information is not available from manufacturer.

Removal ("E" & "K" Bodies) – 1) Raise vehicle on frame contact hoist. Remove wheel. When working on left control arm, disconnect ELC height sensor link (if equipped).

2) Remove stabilizer bar mounting bolt at strut (if equipped). Remove and support caliper. Remove rotor. Remove hub and bearing assembly.

3) Loosen outboard knuckle pivot bolt. *See Fig. 6.* DO NOT remove at this time. Use jackstand to support outer control arm and slightly compress spring. Remove strut rod cap, mounting nut, retainer, and upper insulator.

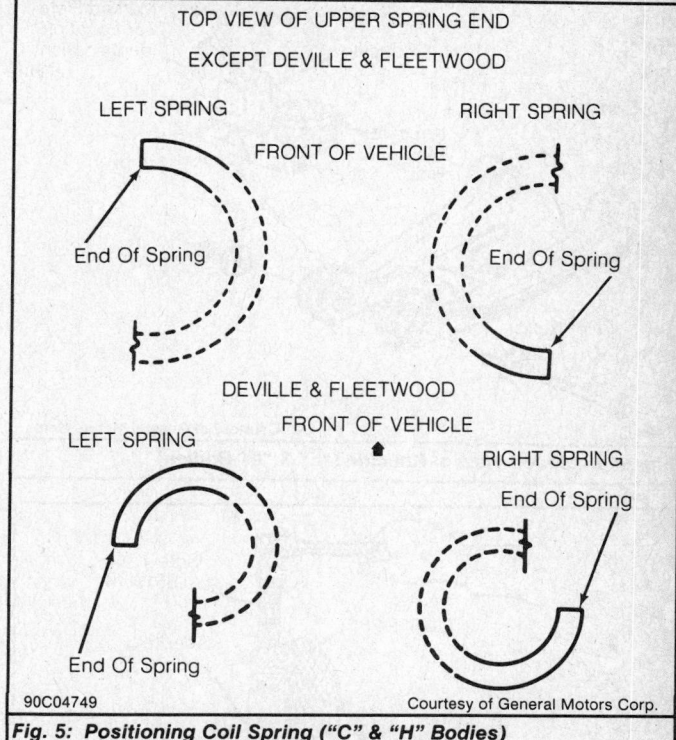

TOP VIEW OF UPPER SPRING END

EXCEPT DEVILLE & FLEETWOOD

LEFT SPRING

RIGHT SPRING

FRONT OF VEHICLE

End Of Spring

End Of Spring

DEVILLE & FLEETWOOD

LEFT SPRING

FRONT OF VEHICLE

RIGHT SPRING

End Of Spring

End Of Spring

End Of Spring

90C04749

Courtesy of General Motors Corp.

Fig. 5: *Positioning Coil Spring ("C" & "H" Bodies)*

4) Slowly release spring pressure, and remove jackstand. Compress strut, and remove lower insulator. Rotate strut and knuckle assembly outward. Remove knuckle pinch bolt. *See Fig. 6.*

5) Remove strut from knuckle. On vehicles equipped with anti-lock brake system, disconnect speed sensor from knuckle. On all models, remove knuckle pivot bolt. Remove knuckle from control arm.

Installation – 1) Knuckles are not interchangeable. Knuckles are marked on rear with "L" for left side and "R" for right side. *See Fig. 6.* Install knuckle on control arm.

2) Install knuckle pivot bolt. DO NOT tighten yet. Install wheel speed sensor (if equipped). Install strut in knuckle. Ensure strut is fully seated in knuckle, with strut tang bottomed in knuckle slot. Install knuckle pinch bolt. Tighten pinch bolt to specification. See TORQUE SPECIFICATIONS tables at end of article.

3) Rotate strut and knuckle assembly inward. Install lower insulator. Use jackstand to support outer control arm, and slightly compress spring. Install upper insulator, retainer and nut. Position strut rod in suspension crossmember.

4) To complete installation, reverse removal procedure. Tighten knuckle pivot bolt to specification with vehicle at normal riding height. See TORQUE SPECIFICATIONS tables at end of article.

BALL JOINT

Removal & Installation ("C" & "H" Bodies) – 1) Raise and support vehicle. Remove wheel. Remove height sensor link (if equipped) for right ball joint replacement. Remove parking brake cable retaining clip for left ball joint replacement.

2) Remove cotter pin and nut from outer end of suspension adjustment link. *See Fig. 1.* Separate link from knuckle. Support control arm.

3) Remove ball joint cotter pin and nut. Invert nut and install with flat portion facing upward. DO NOT tighten nut. Install Puller (J-34505) and separate ball joint from control arm by backing off inverted nut against puller.

4) Using Clamp (J-9519-23), Screw (J-9519-18) and Adapters (J-9519-7) and (J-9519-17), press ball joint from control arm. *See Fig. 7.* To install, reverse removal procedure using clamp, screw and adapters. *See Fig. 7.*

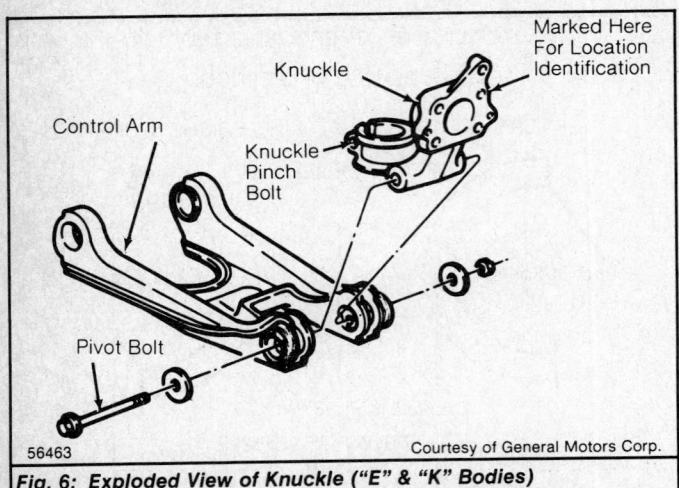

Fig. 6: Exploded View of Knuckle ("E" & "K" Bodies)

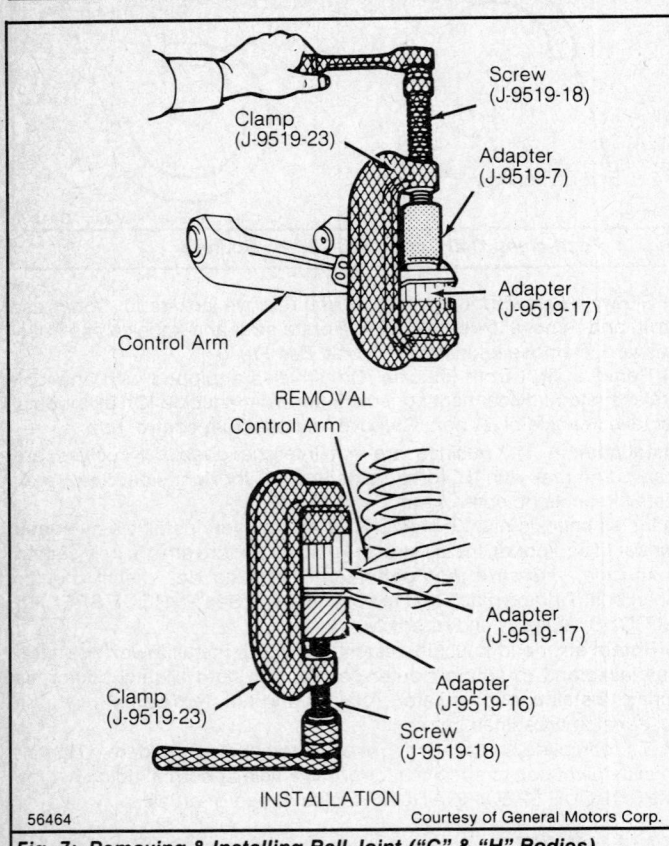

Fig. 7: Removing & Installing Ball Joint ("C" & "H" Bodies)

CONTROL ARM

Removal ("C" & "H" Bodies) – 1) Raise and support vehicle. Remove wheel. Remove ELC height sensor link from right control arm (if equipped). Remove parking brake cable retaining clip from left control arm. Separate suspension adjustment link from control arm. See SUSPENSION ADJUSTMENT LINK under REMOVAL & INSTALLATION.

2) Remove coil spring. See COIL SPRING & INSULATORS under REMOVAL & INSTALLATION. Separate ball joint from control arm. Remove ball joint cotter pin and nut. Invert nut and install with flat portion facing upward. DO NOT tighten nut.

3) Install Puller (J-34505) and separate ball joint from control arm by backing off inverted nut against puller. Remove control arm retaining bolts. Remove control arm.

Installation – To install, reverse removal procedure. With vehicle at normal operating height, tighten pivot nuts, pivot bolts and stabilizer bar bolt to specification in this order. See TORQUE SPECIFICATIONS table at end of this article.

Removal ("E" & "K" Bodies) – 1) Raise and support vehicle. Remove wheel. If working on left control arm, disconnect ELC height sensor link (if equipped). On all models, remove stabilizer bar mounting bolt at strut (if equipped).

2) Install 2 lug nuts to retain rotor. Remove brake caliper assembly. Loosen outer knuckle pivot bolt. DO NOT remove yet. Use jackstand to support outer control arm, and slightly compress spring. Remove strut rod cap, mounting nut, retainer and upper insulator.

3) Slowly release jackstand pressure. Compress strut by hand. Remove lower insulator. Remove wheel speed sensor from knuckle if equipped with anti-lock brake system. Support knuckle, and remove knuckle pivot bolt. Remove knuckle, strut, hub and rotor assembly from vehicle. Remove inner control arm bolts. Remove control.

Installation – 1) Install control arm and inner retaining bolts. DO NOT tighten yet. Install knuckle, strut, hub and rotor assembly. Install knuckle pivot bolt. DO NOT tighten yet.

2) Install wheel speed sensor (if equipped). Install lower strut insulator and strut. Position jackstand under outer end of control arm. Lower vehicle to compress spring on jackstand.

3) Install upper strut insulator, retainer and nut. Tighten upper strut nut, knuckle pivot bolt and inner control arm bolts to specification. See TORQUE SPECIFICATIONS tables at end of article. Remove jackstand. To complete installation, reverse removal procedure. Check and adjust rear wheel alignment.

CONTROL ARM BUSHING

NOTE: Control arm bushings are different sizes, requiring different combinations of removers/installers for replacement.

Removal ("C" & "H" Bodies) – 1) Install Spacer (J-22222-5 or J-33793-5), according to bushing size in control arm. Position Receiver Tube (J-25317-2) and Cap (J-29376-7) on outside of control arm. *See Fig. 8*. Ensure receiver tube does not contact bushing flange. Coat threaded portion of Bolt and Bearing (J-21474-19) with grease.

2) Install bolt through receiver, cap and bushing. Install Remover (J-22222-2 or J-28685-2) on bolt at inner side of control arm with small end contacting the bushing.

3) Place bearing on bolt and install Nut (J-21474-18). Tighten nut to remove bushing from control arm.

Installation – 1) Install new bushing in control arm with flanged end facing outward. Install proper sized spacer on bushing. Position receiver tube and cap on inside of control arm.

2) Center receiver tube over hole. Coat threaded portion of bolt and bearing with grease. Install bolt through receiver, cap and bushing. Place installer on bolt at outer side of control arm with large end contacting bushing flange.

3) Place bearing on bolt and install nut. Bearing must be positioned between nut and installer. Tighten nut and draw bushing into control arm until bushing flange seats firmly against control arm.

NOTE: On "E" & "K" bodies, outer control arm bushings can be replaced without removing control arm. If inner control arm bolts are not disturbed, rear wheel alignment will not be changed by outer bushing replacement.

Removal (Outer Control Arm Bushing – "E" & "K" Bodies) – 1) For on car service, remove control arm. See CONTROL ARM under REMOVAL & INSTALLATION. Install Spacer Set (J-35739-1) between control arm flanges. Use wide spacer for outer bushing removal.

2) Coat threads of bolt and bearing with grease. Install Remover (J-35739-2), Receiver (J-21474-5), Nut (J-21474-18) and Bolt and Bearing (J-21474-19) on control arm. *See Fig. 9*. Tighten nut to remove bushing.

Installation – 1) Position new bushing on control arm. Install bushing from outside of control arm inward. Install wide end of spacer between control arm flanges.

2) Coat threads of bolt and bearing with grease. Place installer, receiver, nut, bolt and bearing on control arm. See Fig. 9. Tighten nut until bushing flange seats against control arm.

Removal (Inner Control Arm Bushing – "E" & "K" Bodies) – 1) To remove bushing, install Spacer Set (J-35739-1) between control arm flanges. Use narrow spacer for inner bushing removal.

2) Coat threads of bolt and bearing with grease. Install Remover (J-21474-23), Receiver (J-21474-5), Nut (J-21474-18), Bolt and Bearing (J-21474-19) in control arm. See Fig. 9. Tighten nut to remove bushing.

Installation – 1) To install, position new bushing in control arm. Bushing must be installed from outside of control arm and drawn inward. Install narrow end of Spacer Set (J-35739-1) between control arm flanges.

2) Position Installer (J-28576-1), Receiver (J-21474-5), Nut (J-21474-18), Bolt and Bearing (J-21474-19). See Fig. 9. Tighten nut to install bushing until bushing flange seats against control arm.

STABILIZER BAR

Removal ("C" & "H" Bodies) – Raise and support vehicle. Remove wheels. Remove nut, support bolt, retainer, and insulators retaining stabilizer bar to knuckle. Remove bushing clip bolt. Bend open end of bushing clip downward. Remove stabilizer and bushings. See Fig. 10.

Installation – To install, reverse removal procedure. Tighten bushing clip bolt to specification with vehicle at normal operating height. See TORQUE SPECIFICATIONS table at end of this article.

NOTE: Stabilizer bar replacement may be more easily completed with vehicle at curb height and supported by wheels. Use drive-on type hoist. If using a frame contact hoist, support control arms as far outboard as possible, without allowing hoist to contact struts.

Removal & Installation ("E" & "K" Bodies) – Raise and support vehicle. Remove stabilizer bar mounting bolt and nut at strut. Remove stabilizer bracket bolt at crossmember. Remove stabilizer bar assembly from vehicle. Remove brackets, bushings and insulators from stabilizer bar. To install, reverse removal procedure. Tighten bolts to specification. See TORQUE SPECIFICATIONS table at end of this article.

STRUT ASSEMBLY

Removal ("C" & "H" Bodies) – 1) Raise and support vehicle. Remove wheel and support control arm. Disconnect ELC air tube from strut (if equipped).

2) Remove trunk side cover and remove upper strut mounting nuts. From under vehicle, remove lower strut bolts from knuckle and stabilizer bar bracket. Support knuckle to prevent damage to ball joint. Remove strut. See Fig. 11.

Installation – To install, reverse removal procedure. Tighten bolts to specification. See TORQUE SPECIFICATIONS table at end of this article. Before lowering vehicle, lightly pressurize ELC system by grounding Yellow wire of compressor test lead, located near ELC compressor in the engine compartment. Check and adjust rear wheel alignment. See SPECIFICATIONS & PROCEDURES article in WHEEL ALIGNMENT.

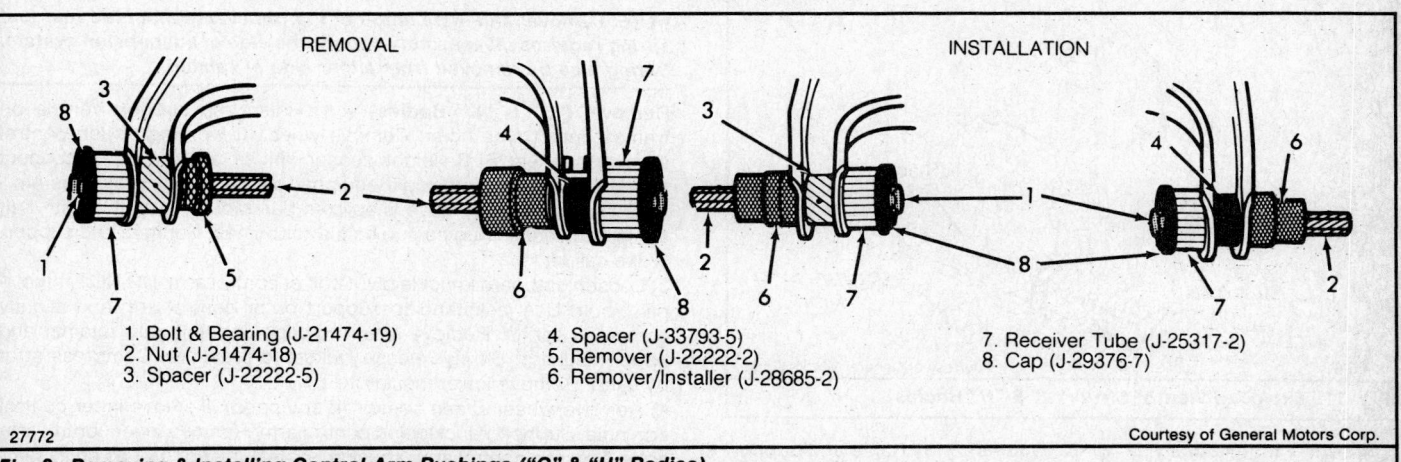

REMOVAL

INSTALLATION

1. Bolt & Bearing (J-21474-19)
2. Nut (J-21474-18)
3. Spacer (J-22222-5)
4. Spacer (J-33793-5)
5. Remover (J-22222-2)
6. Remover/Installer (J-28685-2)
7. Receiver Tube (J-25317-2)
8. Cap (J-29376-7)

27772

Courtesy of General Motors Corp.

Fig. 8: Removing & Installing Control Arm Bushings ("C" & "H" Bodies)

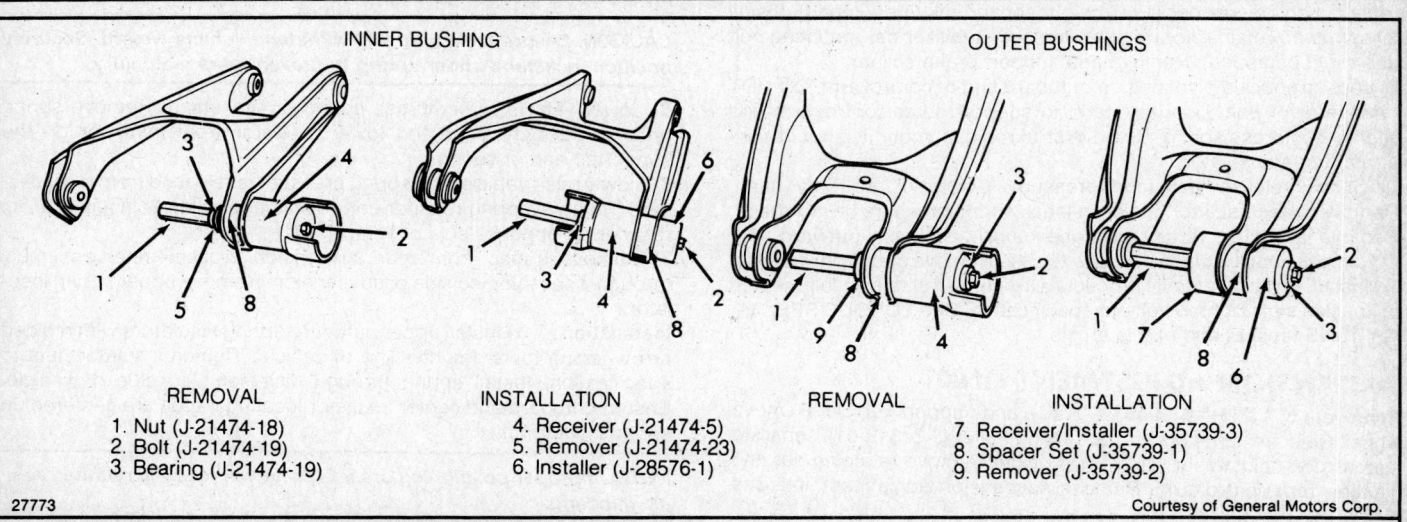

INNER BUSHING

OUTER BUSHINGS

REMOVAL

1. Nut (J-21474-18)
2. Bolt (J-21474-19)
3. Bearing (J-21474-19)

INSTALLATION

4. Receiver (J-21474-5)
5. Remover (J-21474-23)
6. Installer (J-28576-1)

REMOVAL

INSTALLATION

7. Receiver/Installer (J-35739-3)
8. Spacer Set (J-35739-1)
9. Remover (J-35739-2)

27773

Courtesy of General Motors Corp.

Fig. 9: Removing & Installing Control Arm Bushing ("E" & "K" Bodies)

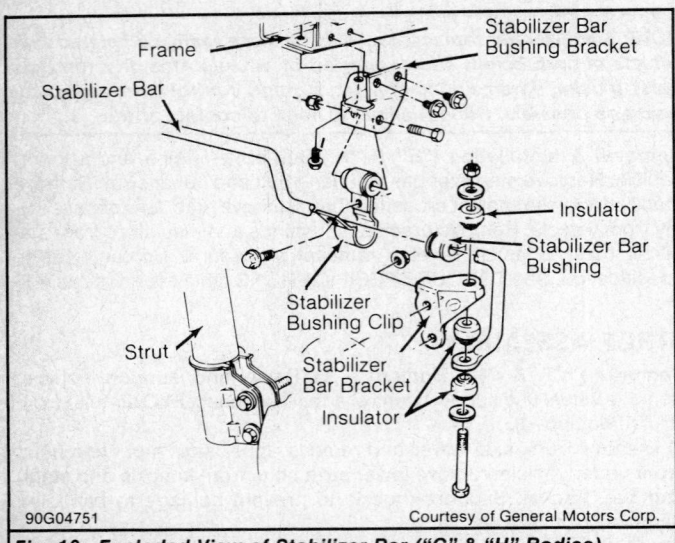

Fig. 10: **Exploded View of Stabilizer Bar ("C" & "H" Bodies)**

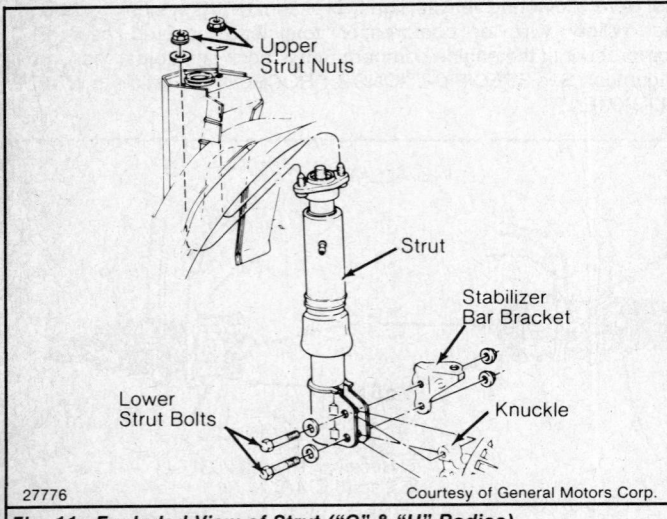

Fig. 11: **Exploded View of Strut ("C" & "H" Bodies)**

Removal & Installation ("E" & "K" Bodies) – **1)** Raise and support vehicle on frame contact hoist. Remove wheel. On left strut replacement, disconnect ELC height sensor link (if equipped). Install 2 lug nuts to retain rotor on hub. Remove stabilizer bar mounting bolt at strut (if equipped). Remove and support brake caliper.
2) Loosen knuckle pivot bolt on outboard end of control arm. DO NOT remove pivot bolt. Use jackstand to support outer control arm and slightly compress spring. Remove strut rod cap, mounting nut, retainer and upper insulator.
3) Slowly release jackstand pressure. Compress strut by hand. Remove lower insulator. Slowly release spring pressure on jackstand. Remove jackstand. Rotate strut and knuckle assembly outward.
4) Remove knuckle pinch bolt. *See Fig. 12.* Remove strut from knuckle. To install, reverse removal procedure. Ensure strut tang is fully seated in knuckle slot. Tighten bolts to specification. See TORQUE SPECIFICATIONS table at end of this article.

SUSPENSION ADJUSTMENT LINK

Removal ("C" & "H" Bodies) – Raise and support vehicle. Remove wheel. Remove cotter pin and nut. Using Puller (J-24319-01), separate suspension adjustment link from knuckle. Remove retaining nut and washer from control arm. Remove suspension adjustment link. *See Fig. 1.*

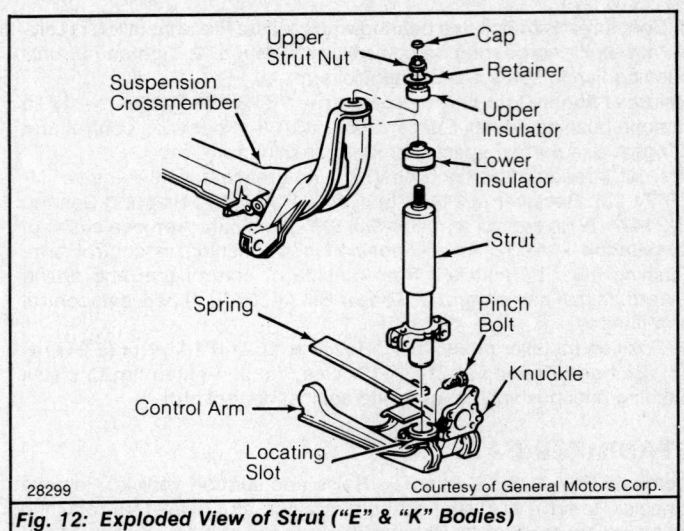

Fig. 12: **Exploded View of Strut ("E" & "K" Bodies)**

Installation – To install, reverse removal procedures. DO NOT loosen nut to align cotter pin. Lubricate adjustment link joints. Check and adjust rear alignment.

LEAF SPRING & INSULATORS

NOTE: Removal and installation of the transverse-mounted rear leaf spring requires disassembly of only one side of suspension system. Spring may be removed from either side of vehicle.

Removal ("E" & "K" Bodies) – **1)** Raise and support vehicle on frame contact type hoist. Remove wheel. If working on left control arm, disconnect ELC height sensor link (if equipped). Disconnect speed sensor from knuckle if equipped with anti-lock brake system.
2) On all models, remove stabilizer bar mounting bolt at strut (if equipped). Install 2 lug nuts to hold rotor on hub. Remove and support brake caliper.
3) Loosen outboard knuckle pivot bolt at control arm. DO NOT remove pivot bolt. Use jackstand to support outer control arm and slightly compress spring. Remove strut rod cap, mounting nut, retainer and upper insulator. Slowly release jackstand pressure. Compress strut by hand. Remove lower insulator.
4) Remove wheel speed sensor (if equipped). Remove inner control arm nuts. Support knuckle and control arm. Remove inner control arm bolts. Remove control arm, knuckle, strut, hub and rotor as an assembly. Raise vehicle and place jackstand under outboard end of spring.

CAUTION: Ensure jackstand will withstand vehicle weight. Securely position jackstand under spring to prevent personal injury.

5) Lower vehicle to compress spring on jackstand. Remove spring retainer bolts, retainer and lower insulator from insulator on the supported end of spring.
6) Slowly raise vehicle until spring pressure is released from the jackstand. Remove spring retainer bolts, retainer and lower insulator from retainer on opposite side of vehicle.
7) Remove spring from rear suspension crossmember assembly through disassembled side of suspension. Remove upper spring insulators.
Installation – **1)** Install upper outboard spring insulators with molded arrow facing toward center line of vehicle. Tighten insulator nuts to specification. Install spring through disassembled side of vehicle. Ensure outboard and center insulator locating bands are centered on spring insulators.

NOTE: Improper positioning of leaf spring will result in reduced vehicle handling.

2) Install lower insulator and spring retainer on side opposite disassembled portion of suspension system. Position jackstand under free end of spring. Slowly lower vehicle to compress spring so spring seats in suspension support.

3) Install lower insulator and spring retainer. Tighten to specification. See TORQUE SPECIFICATIONS table at end of this article. Raise vehicle and remove jackstand. Install control arm assembly. Install inner control arm bolts and nuts. DO NOT tighten bolts at this time.

4) Install wheel speed sensor (if equipped). Install lower strut insulator. Position strut rod in suspension support assembly. Use jackstand to support outer control arm and slightly compress spring.

5) Install upper strut insulator, retainer and nut. Tighten to specification. See TORQUE SPECIFICATIONS table at end of this article. To complete installation, reverse removal procedure. Tighten lower control arm nuts with weight of vehicle on ground. Check and adjust rear wheel alignment.

TRIM HEIGHT ADJUSTMENT SPACER

Removal & Installation ("E" & "K" Bodies) – Raise and support vehicle. Place jackstand and block of wood under outer end of spring. Slowly lower vehicle until clearance between spring and spacer is approximately 3/8". See Fig. 13. Using pliers, remove and install spacer.

WARNING: DO NOT allow spring to slip from jack. Spring is under pressure and may cause personal injury.

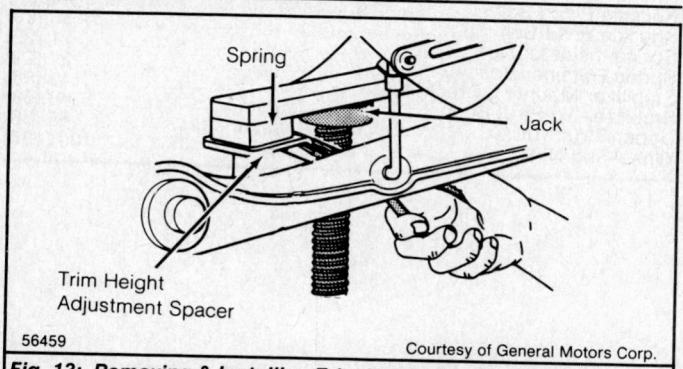

56459   Courtesy of General Motors Corp.
Fig. 13: Removing & Installing Trim Height Adjustment Spacers

REAR SUSPENSION CROSSMEMBER

NOTE: Crossmember may be removed without removing or disconnecting following components: spring, strut, control arm, knuckle, hub assembly, rotor, stabilizer bar assembly or Electronic Level Control compressor. If spring is to be removed, remove spring before to loosening any crossmember mounting bolts.

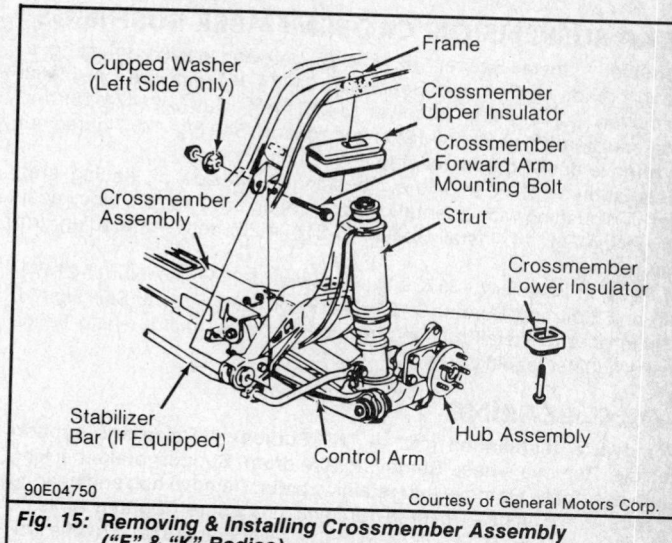

90E04750   Courtesy of General Motors Corp.
Fig. 15: Removing & Installing Crossmember Assembly ("E" & "K" Bodies)

Removal ("E" & "K" Bodies) – 1) Raise vehicle on frame contact hoist. Remove wheels. Remove and support calipers. Remove necessary suspension components as required. Remove ELC height sensor connector and ELC compressor connector from body wiring harness (if equipped).

2) Remove ELC compressor air intake filter from body (if equipped). Remove intermediate parking brake cable from equalizer. Position cable clear of crossmember assembly.

3) Remove brake crossover pipe retainer screws. Remove right rear brake hose retainer bolt and crossover pipe. Remove wheel speed sensor and brackets (if equipped).

4) Support rear crossmember assembly with jackstands. Remove crossmember forward arm mounting bolts, upper mounting bolts and lower insulators. See Fig. 15. Slowly raise vehicle. Ensure brake lines, hoses and calipers are not damaged when crossmember is lowered.

Installation – 1) Place crossmember below vehicle on jackstands. Install upper crossmember insulators on crossmember assembly. Lower vehicle onto crossmember assembly. See Fig. 15. Align crossmember, ensuring brake lines, hoses and calipers are not damaged.

2) Install crossmember forward arm bolts, nuts, washers, upper mounting bolts and insulators. See Fig. 15. To complete installation, reverse removal procedure. Tighten bolts to specification. See TORQUE SPECIFICATIONS tables at end of article.

NOTE: Both forward arm bolts must be installed with nuts on right side of arm. The cup-shaped washer is used only on left forward arm.

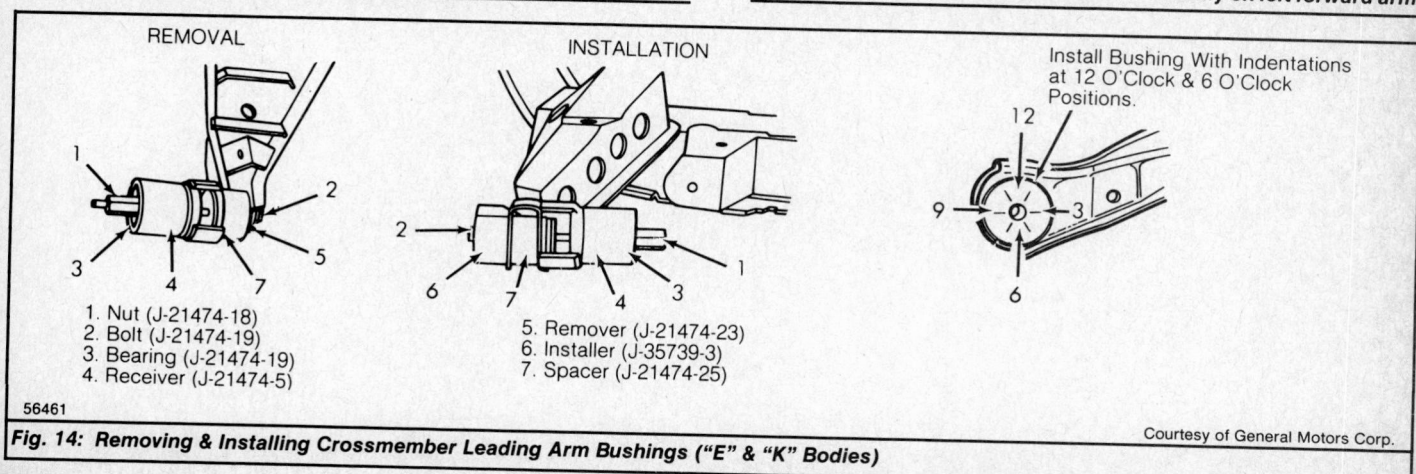

1. Nut (J-21474-18)
2. Bolt (J-21474-19)
3. Bearing (J-21474-19)
4. Receiver (J-21474-5)
5. Remover (J-21474-23)
6. Installer (J-35739-3)
7. Spacer (J-21474-25)

56461   Courtesy of General Motors Corp.
Fig. 14: Removing & Installing Crossmember Leading Arm Bushings ("E" & "K" Bodies)

REAR SUSPENSION CROSSMEMBER BUSHINGS

Removal – Install Spacer (J-21474-25) between leading arm flanges. Coat threads of Bolt and Bearing (J-21474-19) with grease. Install Remover (J-21474-23), Receiver (J-21474-5), Nut (J-21474-18) and Bolt and Bearing (J-21474-19) in control arm. See Fig. 14. Tighten nut to remove bushing from leading arm.

Installation – 1) Position new bushing in outside of leading arm. Position bushing with indentations positioned at 12 and 6 o'clock positions. See Fig. 14. Install Spacer (J-21474-25) between leading arm flanges.

2) Position Installer (J-35739-3), Receiver (J-21474-5), Nut (J-21474-18) and Bolt and Bearing (J-21474-19) on leading arm. See Fig. 14. Tighten nut to install bushing into leading arm, until bushing flange seats against leading arm.

WHEEL BEARING

Removal & Installation ("C" & "H" Bodies) – Raise and support vehicle. Remove wheel. Remove brake drum. Support brake backing plate assembly. Remove hub retaining bolts. Remove hub and bearing assembly. To install, reverse removal procedure. Tighten bolts to specification. See TORQUE SPECIFICATIONS table at end of this article.

Removal & Installation ("E" & "K" Bodies) – Raise and support vehicle. Remove wheel. Remove and support brake caliper. Remove rotor. Remove hub retaining bolts. Remove hub and bearing assembly. To install, reverse removal procedure. Tighten bolts to specification. See TORQUE SPECIFICATIONS table.

TORQUE SPECIFICATIONS

TORQUE SPECIFICATIONS ("C" & "H" BODIES)

Application	Ft. Lbs. (N.m)
Ball Joint Stud Nut	[1] 14 (10)
Control Arm Pivot Bolt	138 (187)
Control Arm Pivot Nut	85 (115)
Hub Mounting Bolt	52 (71)
Stabilizer Bushing Clip Bolt	37 (51)
Stabilizer Support Bolt	13 (18)
Strut-To-Knuckle Bolt	180 (244)
Strut-To-Upper Mount Nut	35 (47)
Suspension Adjusting Link To-Control Arm	63 (85)
Suspension Adjusting Link To-Knuckle Nut	33 (48)
Suspension Adjusting Link Lock Nut	48 (65)
Wheel Lug Nut	100 (136)

[1] – Plus an additional 2/3 turn.

TORQUE SPECIFICATIONS ("E" & "K" BODIES)

Application	Ft. Lbs. (N.m)
Caliper Mounting Bolt	83 (113)
Control Arm Bolt	66 (90)
Crossmember Forward Arm Bolt	66 (90)
Crossmember Upper Mount Bolt	66 (90)
Hub Mounting Bolt	52 (71)
Knuckle Pinch Bolt	40 (54)
Knuckle Pivot Bolt	59 (80)
Spring Insulator Nut	21 (29)
Spring Retainer Bolt	21 (29)
Stabilizer Mounting Bracket Bolt	43 (58)
Stabilizer-To-Strut Bolt	43 (58)
Upper Strut Nut	65 (88)
Wheel Lug Nut	100 (136)

DESCRIPTION

Each wheel is mounted to a 5-link independent rear suspension, composed of a drive shaft, camber control knuckle support rod, upper and lower control arms and tie rod. A fiberglass transverse mounted spring is attached to the differential carrier beam. These components along with the aluminum knuckles, differential carrier beam and driveline support beam form the rear suspension.

ADJUSTMENTS & INSPECTION

WHEEL ALIGNMENT
SPECIFICATIONS & PROCEDURES

NOTE: See SPECIFICATIONS & PROCEDURES article in WHEEL ALIGNMENT.

RIDING HEIGHT

NOTE: See SPECIFICATIONS & PROCEDURES article in WHEEL ALIGNMENT.

REAR WHEEL BEARINGS

Rear hub and wheel bearings are a sealed unit which require no adjustment. Replace hub and bearing assembly if end play is more than .005" (.127 mm).

REMOVAL & INSTALLATION

NOTE: Carefully note routing, position, mounting and location of ABS components and wiring prior to component removal. Components must be mounted in original positions. ABS components are extremely sensitive to Electro-Magnetic Interference (EMI).

REAR HUB & WHEEL BEARINGS

CAUTION: Use frame contact hoist to raise vehicle so that suspension hangs free. DO NOT allow vehicle to rest on tires or be moved until spindle nut is properly tightened.

Removal – Raise and support vehicle. Remove wheel and tire. Remove speed sensor. Use care not to damage speed sensor. Remove brake caliper and rotor. Remove hub assembly mounting bolts. Remove cotter pin, retainer, spindle nut and washer. *See Fig. 1.* Remove hub assembly.

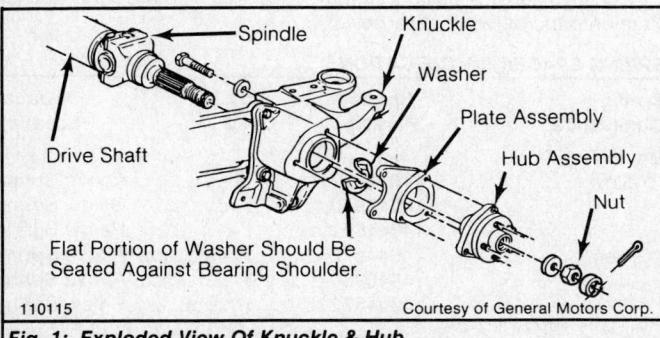

Flat Portion of Washer Should Be Seated Against Bearing Shoulder.

110115   Courtesy of General Motors Corp.

Fig. 1: Exploded View Of Knuckle & Hub

Installation – To install, reverse removal procedure. Replace spindle seal. Replace spindle washer if necessary. Flat side of washer should be seated against shoulder of bearing on yoke spindle. Lip of washer should face spindle splines. Tighten bolts to specification. See TORQUE SPECIFICATIONS table at end of this article.

REAR WHEEL SPINDLE

CAUTION: Use frame contact hoist to raise vehicle so that suspension hangs free. Do not allow vehicle to rest on tires or be moved until spindle nut is properly tightened.

Removal – 1) Raise and support vehicle. Remove wheel and tire. Remove speed sensor and bracket. Use care not to damage speed sensor. Use Spring Compressor (J-33432) to compress transverse spring. Disconnect transverse spring from knuckle. *See Fig. 2.* Remove cotter pin, retainer, spindle nut and washer. *See Fig. 1.*

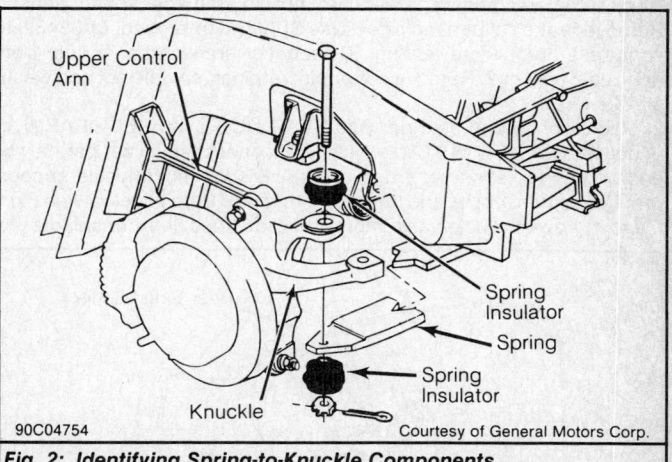

90C04754   Courtesy of General Motors Corp.

Fig. 2: Identifying Spring-to-Knuckle Components

2) Disconnect tie rod end from knuckle. Scribe mark cam bolt and knuckle for realignment. *See Fig. 3.* Remove cam bolt and separate knuckle support rod from carrier mounting bracket.

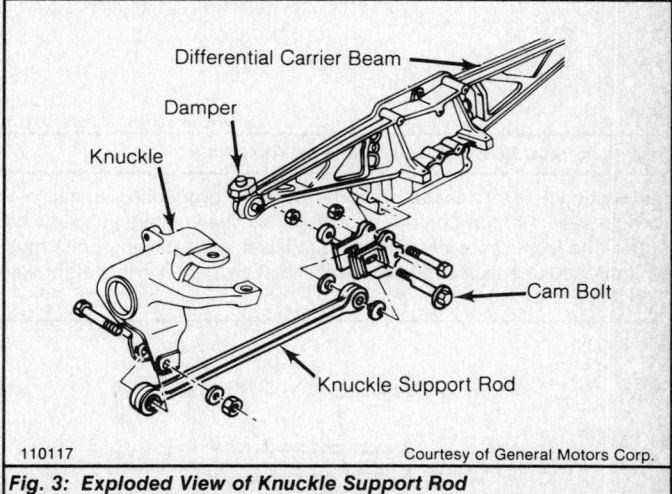

110117   Courtesy of General Motors Corp.

Fig. 3: Exploded View of Knuckle Support Rod

3) Remove driveshaft retaining straps at spindle yoke and side gear yoke. Move knuckle outward and remove driveshaft from spindle yoke. Remove spindle from hub.
Installation – To install, reverse removal procedure. Replace spindle seal. Replace spindle washer if necessary. Flat side of washer should be seated against shoulder of bearing on yoke spindle. Lip of washer should face spindle splines. Tighten bolts to specification. See TORQUE SPECIFICATIONS table at end of this article. Check and adjust rear suspension alignment. See SPECIFICATIONS & PROCEDURES article in WHEEL ALIGNMENT.

KNUCKLE SUPPORT ROD

Removal – Raise and support vehicle. Scribe mark on cam bolt and mounting bracket for reassembly reference. *See Fig. 3.* Remove cam bolt. Separate knuckle support rod from mounting bracket. Remove knuckle support rod bolt at knuckle. Remove knuckle support rod.

Installation – To install, reverse removal procedure. Tighten bolts to specification. See TORQUE SPECIFICATIONS table at end of this article. Bolt located at the knuckle must be tightened at proper "D" trim height. See REAR KNUCKLE installation steps **1)** and **2)** under REMOVAL & INSTALLATION (use jackstands as necessary). Check and adjust rear wheel alignment. See SPECIFICATIONS & PROCEDURES article in WHEEL ALIGNMENT.

REAR KNUCKLE

Removal – **1)** Raise and support vehicle. Remove wheel and tire. Remove speed sensor. Use care not to damage speed sensor. Remove brake caliper and rotor. Use Spring Compressor (J-33432) to compress transverse spring. Disconnect transverse spring from knuckle. *See Fig. 2.* Remove cotter pin, retainer, spindle nut and washer. *See Fig. 1.*

2) Remove hub and bearing. See REAR HUB & WHEEL BEARINGS under REMOVAL & INSTALLATION. Disconnect stabilizer bar, tie rod end and shock absorber from knuckle. Disconnect knuckle support rod. Disconnect upper and lower control arms from knuckle. *See Figs. 3 and 4.* Lower knuckle assembly and slide knuckle from spindle.

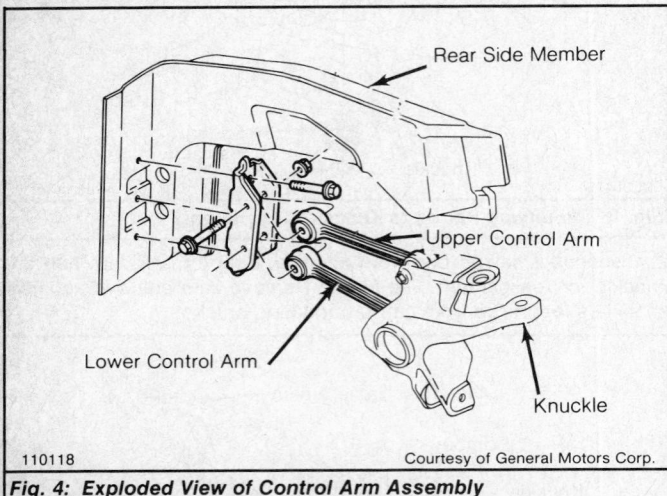

110118   Courtesy of General Motors Corp.

Fig. 4: Exploded View of Control Arm Assembly

Installation – **1)** To install, reverse removal procedure. Install new spindle seal. Tighten bolts to specification. The knuckle support rod, upper and lower control arms and stabilizer bar retaining bolts must be tightened to specification with vehicle at proper "D" trim height. *See Fig. 5.*

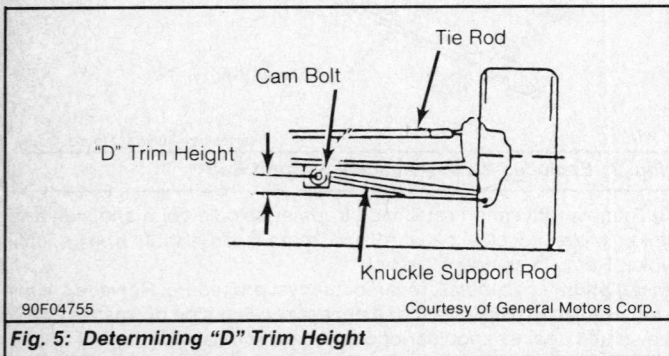

90F04755   Courtesy of General Motors Corp.

Fig. 5: Determining "D" Trim Height

2) Trim height "D" is measured between centers of outer end of knuckle support rod and inner end of knuckle support rod. See "D" TRIM HEIGHT SPECIFICATIONS table. Check and adjust rear wheel alignment. See SPECIFICATIONS & PROCEDURES article in WHEEL ALIGNMENT.

"D" TRIM HEIGHT SPECIFICATIONS [1]

Application	Suspension	Height In. (mm)
Hatchback		
Standard Suspension	[2] FE1	1.41 (55.6)
H.D Suspension	[2] FE7	1.29 (50.8)
Convertible	[2] FE1	1.60 (62.9)

[1] – P275-40ZR17 tires at recommended pressure and load.
[2] – Suspension option is listed in top of floor console lid.

REAR TRANSVERSE SPRING

CAUTION: Vehicle must be raised, allowing suspension to hang free. DO NOT use degreasers, solvents, etc. on or near fiberglass rear spring. Use care in handling to prevent scratching or other damage to spring.

Removal – **1)** Raise and support vehicle. Remove one wheel. Use Spring Compressor (J-33432) to compress transverse spring. Remove cotter pins, retaining nuts, insulators and transverse spring-to-knuckle link bolt. *See Fig. 2.*

2) Release and remove spring compressor. Remove transverse spring anchor plate bolts, spacers, insulators and transverse spring from differential carrier. *See Fig. 6.* Note shim and spacer location.

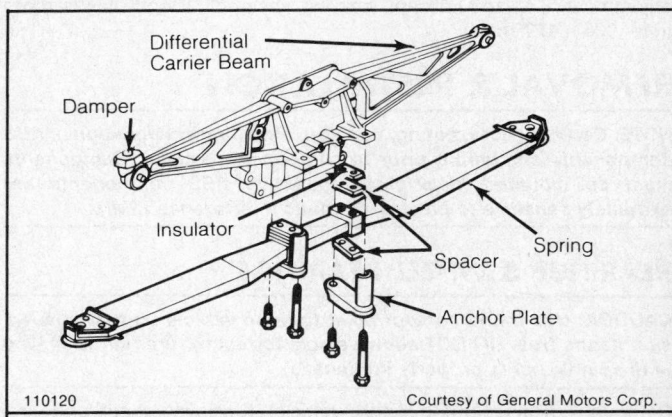

110120   Courtesy of General Motors Corp.

Fig. 6: Exploded View of Spring & Carrier Beam

Installation – **1)** Determine proper spacers, number used and location according to spring color code. See SPRING SPACER SPECIFICATIONS table. Position spring spacers, insulators, and anchor plate onto the differential carrier.

SPRING SPACER SPECIFICATIONS

Spring Color Code	Spacer Part No.	No. Used	Spacer Location
Base (FE1)			
Yellow	14044572	1	Above Spring
	14048950	1	Below Spring
	14044572	1	Below Spring
Green	14044572	1	Above Spring
	14048950	1	Above Spring
	14044572	1	Below Spring
Opt. H.D. (FE7)			
Yellow	14084056	1	Above Spring
	14048950	2	Below Spring
Green	14084056	1	Above Spring
	14048950	1	Above Spring
	14048950	1	Below Spring
Convertible			
Yellow	14044572	2	Above Spring
	14093185	1	Above Spring
	14084056	1	Below Spring

NOTE: *DO NOT add extra spacers to raise trim height. Extra spacers will overstress fiberglass spring.*

2) Install anchor plate bolts, and tighten to specification. Use Spring Compressor (J-33432) to compress transverse spring. Position transverse spring to knuckle. Install spring-to-knuckle link bolt, bushings, retaining nuts and cotter pins. Tighten bolts to specification. See TORQUE SPECIFICATIONS table at end of article.

UPPER & LOWER CONTROL ARMS

WARNING: *Vehicle must be raised, allowing suspension to hang free. Failure to do so will leave transverse spring in loaded state, and if released, could result in injury.*

Removal – Raise and support vehicle. Support suspension with jackstands. Remove control arm bolt at knuckle. Remove control arm bolt at body bracket. Remove control arm. *See Fig. 4.* Do not allow suspension to move below rebound.

Installation – To install, reverse removal procedure. Tighten all bolts to specification. See TORQUE SPECIFICATIONS table at end of article. Control arm bolts at knuckle must be tightened at proper "D" trim height. See REAR KNUCKLE installation steps under REMOVAL & INSTALLATION.

REAR SHOCK ABSORBER

CAUTION: *Shock absorbers may use oil and gas under high pressure. To avoid personal injury due to explosion, DO NOT apply heat or fire to shock absorbers.*

Removal – Raise and support vehicle. Support knuckle with jackstand. Disconnect shock absorber at knuckle. Remove upper shock absorber retaining bolt(s). Remove actuator retaining clip, actuator (if equipped), and shock absorber.

Installation – To install, reverse removal procedure. Tighten retaining nuts to specification. See TORQUE SPECIFICATIONS table at end of this article.

REAR AXLE TIE ROD

Removal – Raise and support vehicle. Loosen tie rod adjustment lock nut. Remove cotter pin and retaining nut from tie rod end at knuckle. Using Linkage Puller (J-24319-01), remove tie rod end from knuckle. Remove bolts and tie rod assembly from differential carrier beam. *See Fig. 7.*

Installation – To install, reverse removal procedure. Tighten bolts to specification. See TORQUE SPECIFICATIONS table at end of this article. Check and adjust rear suspension alignment.

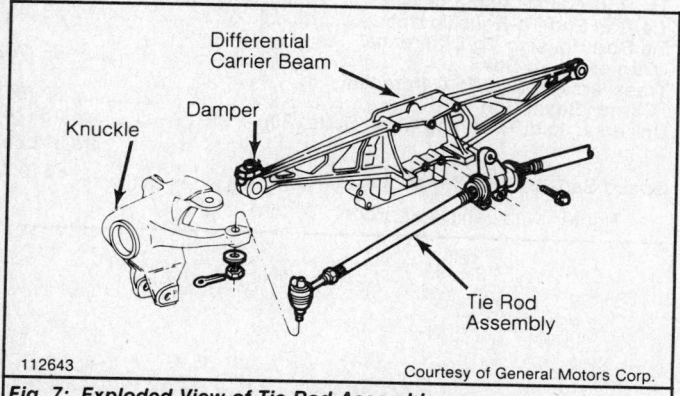

Fig. 7: **Exploded View of Tie Rod Assembly**

STABILIZER BAR

Removal – Raise and support vehicle. Remove rear wheels. Remove spare tire and carrier. Loosen stabilizer bar link bracket nuts. Disconnect stabilizer bar from knuckles. Remove nuts securing fuel tank

straps to stabilizer bushing retainers. Remove stabilizer bar bushing retainers, and stabilizer bar from vehicle. *See Fig. 8.*

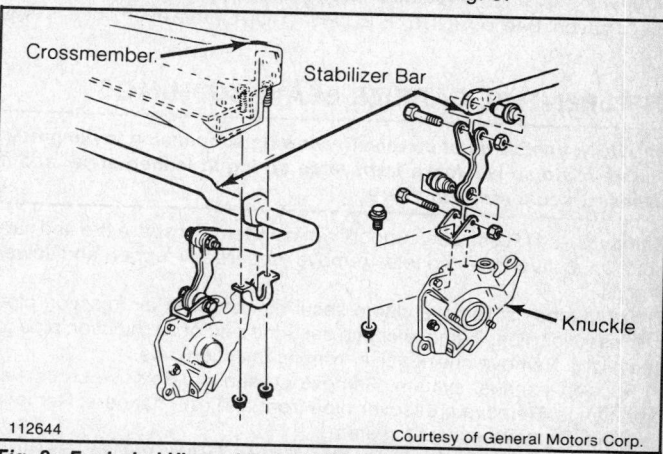

Fig. 8: **Exploded View of Rear Stabilizer Bar Assembly**

Installation – To install, reverse removal procedure. Bolt located at the knuckle must be tightened at proper "D" trim height. See REAR KNUCKLE under REMOVAL & INSTALLATION. Tighten retaining nuts to specification. See TORQUE SPECIFICATIONS table at end of this article. Check and adjust rear wheel alignment. See SPECIFICATIONS & PROCEDURES article in WHEEL ALIGNMENT.

DRIVELINE SUPPORT

Removal – 1) Raise and support vehicle. On convertible models, remove underbody braces.

2) On all models, remove clamp securing converter air injection pipe to crossover pipe. Remove clamp securing end of air injection pipe to converter. Remove check valve from air injection pipe.

3) Support exhaust system. Remove O_2 sensor. Remove crossover pipe flange. Remove crossover pipe front and rear hangers. Remove mufflers. Remove exhaust system.

4) Support transmission. Scribe mark propeller shaft to pinion yoke for reassembly reference. Remove rear propeller shaft retainers. Slide yoke from transmission and remove propeller shaft. Remove driveline support nuts and bolts. Remove driveline support from vehicle. *See Fig. 9.*

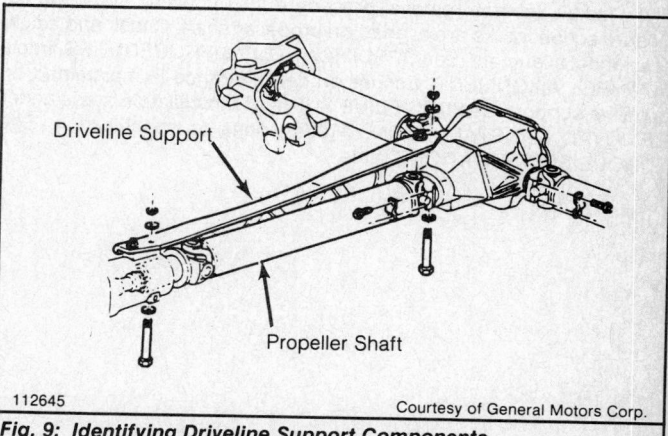

Fig. 9: **Identifying Driveline Support Components**

Installation – 1) To install, reverse removal procedure. Align propeller shaft scribe marks. To ensure proper driveline alignment, a clearance of 1.52"-2.02" (39-51 mm) must exist between top of support and the underbody.

2) A clearance of .85"-1.35" (22-34 mm) must exist from the passenger's side of the support to the side wall. Measurements should be obtained directly above and to the right of propeller shaft

front yoke. Apply sealant to mating surfaces of the transmission extension housing, differential carrier and support. Tighten bolts to specification. See TORQUE SPECIFICATIONS table at end of this article.

DIFFERENTIAL CARRIER BEAM BUSHINGS

CAUTION: Vehicle must be raised, allowing suspension to hang free. Failure to do so will leave transverse spring in loaded state, and if released, could result in injury.

Removal – 1) Raise and support vehicle. Remove spare tire and carrier. On convertible models, remove underbody upper and lower braces.

2) On all models, remove clamp securing converter air injection pipe to crossover pipe. Remove clamp securing end of air injection pipe to converter. Remove check valve from air injection pipe.

3) Support exhaust system. Remove O₂ sensor. Remove crossover pipe flange. Remove crossover pipe front and rear hangers. Remove mufflers. Remove exhaust system.

4) Remove transverse spring. See REAR TRANSVERSE SPRING under REMOVAL & INSTALLATION. Scribe alignment marks on cam bolts and mounting bracket for reassembly reference. Remove cam bolts and mounting bracket.

5) Disconnect tie rod ends at knuckles using Linkage Puller (J-24319-01). Remove drive shafts from spindle yokes. Push wheel assemblies outward so drive shafts can be removed. Scribe mark on propeller shaft and axle yoke for reassembly reference. Disconnect propeller shaft and slide forward into transmission.

6) Support transmission. Remove differential carrier beam-to-frame retaining bolts. Remove driveline support retaining bolts at front of differential. Remove differential carrier assembly.

7) Install Receiver (J-34197-1), bolt, bearing and washer on flanged side of bushing (rear side). See Fig. 10. Install Bushing Remover (J-34197-3) over bolt until fully seated on front side of bushing. Install Long Nut (J-34197-5) on bolt. While holding long nut, tighten bolt until bushing is removed. See Fig. 10.

Installation – 1) Install bolt, bearing and washer on Bushing Installer (J-34197-2). Install assembly on flanged side of bushing. Install assembly on rear side of differential carrier beam. See Fig. 10.

2) Install Receiver (J-34197-1) on the bolt. Install Long Nut (J-34197-5) on bolt. While holding long nut, tighten bolt until bushing is even with differential carrier beam surface.

3) To install, reverse removal procedure for remaining components. Ensure scribe marks are aligned on propeller shaft. Check and adjust rear wheel alignment. See SPECIFICATIONS & PROCEDURES article in WHEEL ALIGNMENT. Ensure proper clearance is maintained on driveline support. See DRIVELINE SUPPORT installation steps under REMOVAL & INSTALLATION. Tighten bolts to specification. See TORQUE SPECIFICATIONS table.

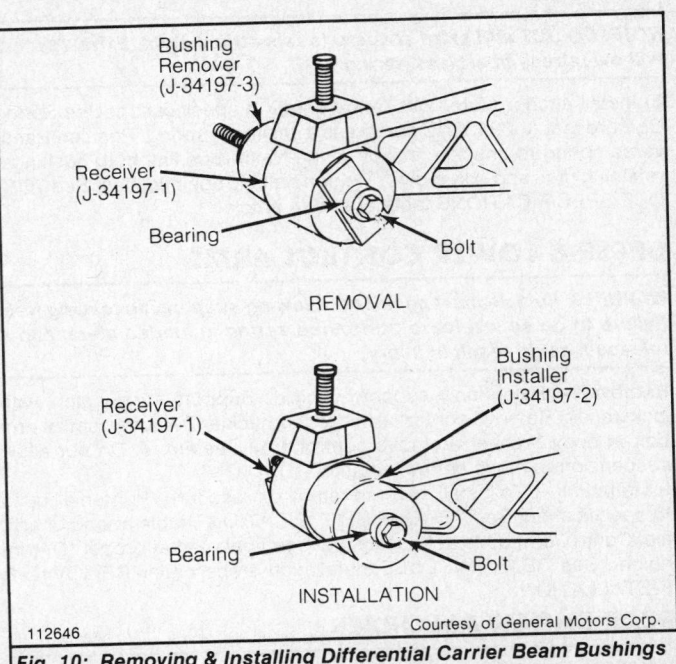

112646   Courtesy of General Motors Corp.

Fig. 10: Removing & Installing Differential Carrier Beam Bushings

TORQUE SPECIFICATIONS

TORQUE SPECIFICATIONS

Application	Ft. Lbs. (N.m)
Cam Bolt-To-Support Rod	187 (254)
Control Arm-To-Body Bracket Bolt	¹ 63 (85)
Control Arm-To-Knuckle Nut	¹ 140 (190)
Differential Carrier Beam-To-Body Bolt	60 (80)
Hub-To-Knuckle Bolt	66 (90)
Jounce Bumper-To-Body Nut	26 (35)
Knuckle Support Rod Bracket-to-Differential Carrier Bolt	60 (80)
Knuckle Support Rod-To-Knuckle Bolt	¹ 107 (145)
Shock Absorber Bracket-To-Body Bolt	¹ 22 (30)
Shock Absorber Stud-To-Knuckle Nut	89 (120)
Shock Absorber Upper Mounting Nut	19 (26)
Spindle-To-Hub Nut	164 (223)
Stabilizer Bar-To-Body Bolt	18 (24)
Stabilizer Link Bracket-To-Knuckle Bolt	18 (24)
Stabilizer Link-To-Bracket & Bar Bolt	¹ 31 (42)
Support Beam-To-Differential Carrier Bolt	60 (80)
Support Beam-To-Transmission Bolt	60 (80)
Tie Rod Adjustment Lock Nut	46 (63)
Tie Rod End-To-Knuckle Nut	33 (45)
Tie Rod Housing-To-Differential Carrier Beam Bolt	55 (75)
Transverse Spring-To-Differential Carrier Beam Bolt	37 (51)
Universal Joint Retaining Strap Bolts (All)	18 (24)
	INCH Lbs.
Speed Sensor Retaining Bolt	86 (9.7)

¹ – Tighten with vehicle at proper "D" trim height.

"W" Body: Cutlass Supreme, Grand Prix, Lumina, Regal

DESCRIPTION

The rear suspension features MacPherson struts coupled to a knuckle, trailing link, and front and rear lateral links. The suspension also includes a composite fiberglass monoleaf transverse spring. *See Fig. 1.*

Rear wheel camber is adjustable through lower strut mounting bolts. Rear wheel toe may be adjusted with cams on the inner ends of rear lateral link. The hub and bearing assembly is sealed and is serviced as a unit.

ADJUSTMENTS & INSPECTION

WHEEL ALIGNMENT SPECIFICATIONS & PROCEDURES

NOTE: See SPECIFICATIONS & PROCEDURES article in WHEEL ALIGNMENT.

WHEEL BEARING

Replace wheel bearing if end play is more than .005" (.127 mm).

RIDING HEIGHT

NOTE: See SPECIFICATIONS & PROCEDURES article in WHEEL ALIGNMENT.

REMOVAL & INSTALLATION

AUXILIARY SPRING ASSEMBLY

NOTE: DO NOT use silicone lubricants on or near auxiliary spring. These materials may damage rubber components.

Removal – 1) Raise and support vehicle. Remove tires. Remove leaf spring rear retention plate bolt. Loosen leaf spring front retention plate bolt just enough to allow leaf spring retention plate to be rotated clear of lateral link.

2) Remove dust plug from auxiliary spring upper bracket. Install Auxiliary Spring Compressor (J-37956). *See Fig. 2.* Engage pin on upper end of clamp, in hole located in auxiliary spring upper bracket.

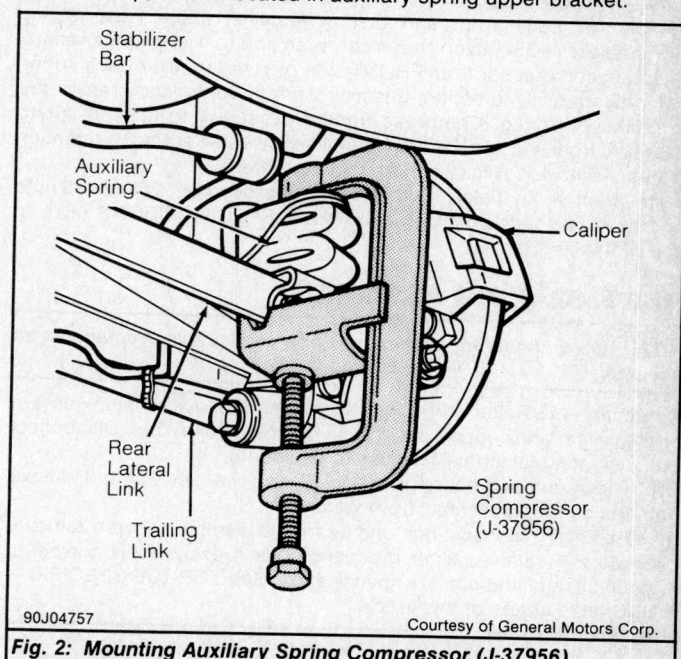

90J04757   Courtesy of General Motors Corp.

Fig. 2: Mounting Auxiliary Spring Compressor (J-37956)

3) Seat lateral link in spring compressor and hand tighten spring compressor. Remove lateral link-to-knuckle bolt. Loosen spring compressor forcing screw to allow auxiliary spring to expand.

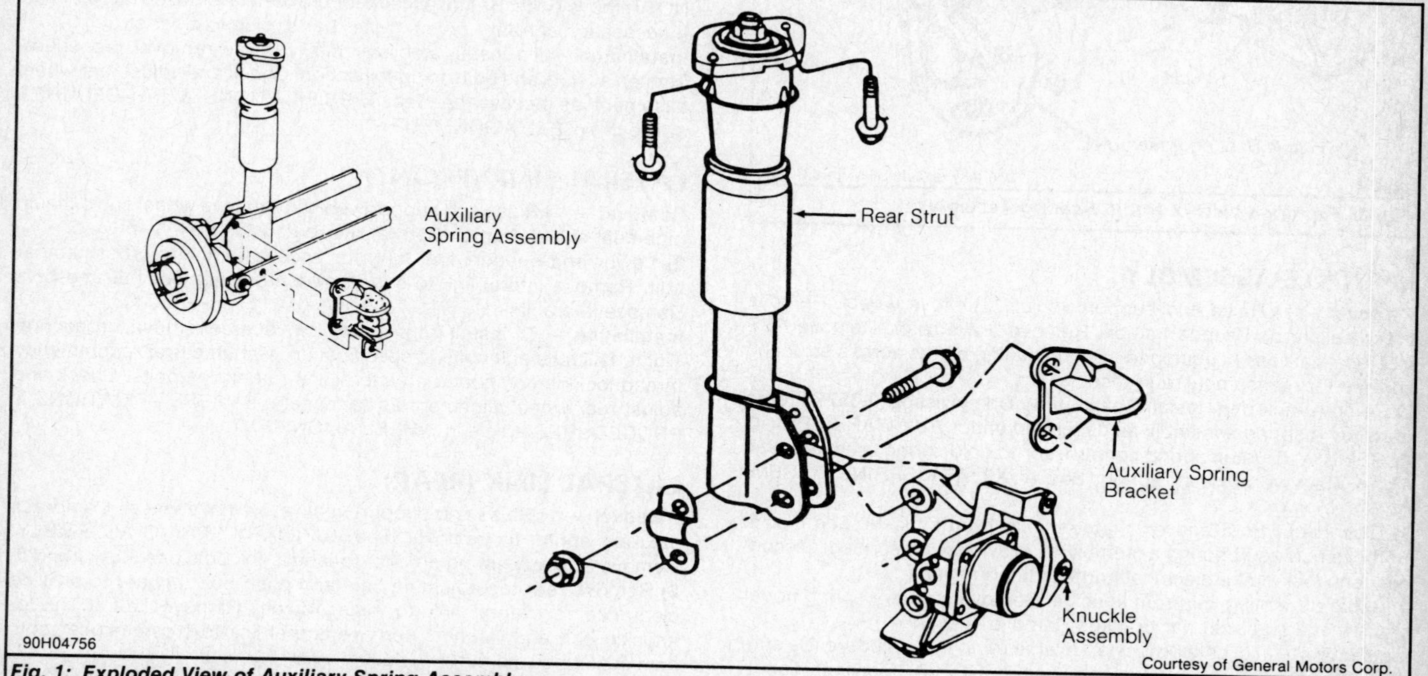

90H04756

Fig. 1: Exploded View of Auxiliary Spring Assembly

Courtesy of General Motors Corp.

4) Remove auxiliary spring with spring compressor installed. Ensure lateral link bushing clears transverse spring and knuckle boss.

5) Scribe mating lines across strut and knuckle for reassembly reference. Remove auxiliary spring lower bracket at lateral link. Remove jack pad from bottom center of crossmember. Remove 4 bolts on left and right spring anchor plates. Disconnect anti-lock brake electrical harness (if equipped).

6) Remove trailing nut and bolt at knuckle. Place Rear Spring Compressor (J-35778) on rear transverse spring. Hang center shank of spring compressor from FRONT side of vehicle only. Attach spring compressor body to spring. Ensure rollers of spring compressor are in center of spring. Compress transverse spring to release spring pressure from knuckle. Do NOT remove transverse spring or retention plates. Remove auxiliary spring upper bracket.

Installation – To install, reverse removal procedure. Tighten all nuts and bolts to specification. See TORQUE SPECIFICATIONS table at end of this article.

HUB & BEARING ASSEMBLY

NOTE: Hub and bearing assembly is non-serviceable. Replace as an assembly.

Removal – **1)** Raise and support vehicle. Remove wheel. Remove brake caliper and support out of way. Remove brake rotor. Disconnect anti-lock brake electrical harness (if equipped).

2) Remove hub and bearing retainer Torx bolts. *See Fig. 3.* Remove hub and bearing assembly from knuckle.

Installation – To install hub and bearing assembly, reverse removal procedure. Replace caliper mounting bolts if excessively corroded. Tighten all nuts and bolts to specification. See TORQUE SPECIFICATIONS table at end of this article.

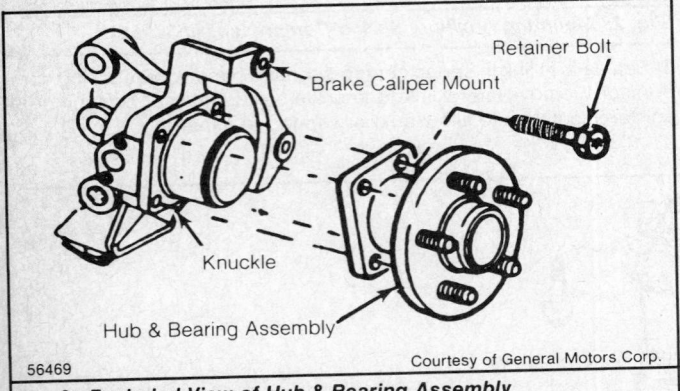

56469   Courtesy of General Motors Corp.
Fig. 3: Exploded View of Hub & Bearing Assembly

KNUCKLE ASSEMBLY

Removal – **1)** Raise and support vehicle. Remove wheel. Remove brake caliper and support aside. Remove brake rotor. Remove ABS electrical harness (if equipped). Scribe mating marks across strut and knuckle for reassembly reference.

2) Remove jack pad. Install Rear Spring Compressor (J-35778) onto transverse spring assembly as described under AUXILIARY SPRING ASSEMBLY. Tighten spring compressor to hold spring pressure. *See Fig. 4.* Remove auxiliary spring. See AUXILIARY SPRING ASSEMBLY.

3) Disconnect front and rear lateral links from knuckle. *See Fig. 5.* Remove hub and bearing assembly as previously described. Disconnect anti-lock brake electrical harness (if equipped).

4) Separate trailing link from knuckle. Remove auxiliary spring upper bracket and stabilizer bar bracket. Remove knuckle.

Installation – To install knuckle, reverse removal procedure. Be sure to align scribed marks on strut and knuckle. REPLACE caliper mounting bolts if excessively corroded. Tighten all nuts and bolts to specification. See TORQUE SPECIFICATIONS table at end of this article.

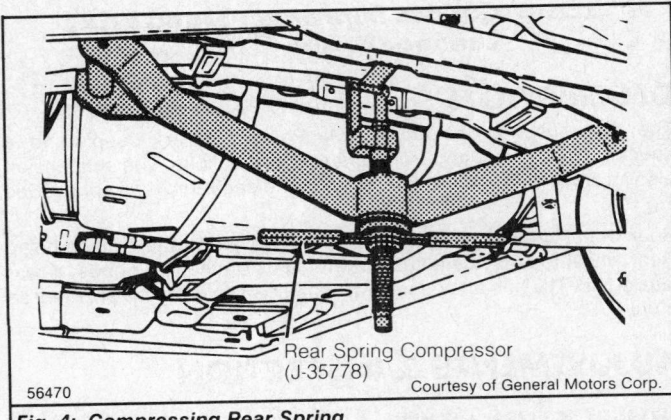

Rear Spring Compressor
(J-35778)
56470   Courtesy of General Motors Corp.
Fig. 4: Compressing Rear Spring

REAR STRUT ASSEMBLY

Removal – **1)** Raise vehicle on hoist. Remove wheel. Scribe mating marks across knuckle and strut. Remove jack pad. Install Rear Spring Compressor (J-35778) onto transverse spring assembly as described in AUXILIARY SPRING ASSEMBLY. Tighten spring compressor to hold spring pressure. *See Fig. 4.*

2) Remove auxiliary spring. See AUXILIARY SPRING ASSEMBLY. Remove brake hose bracket at strut. Remove auxiliary spring upper bracket and stabilizer bar bracket. *See Figs. 1 and 5.* Remove strut bolts at body and allow assembly to drop down. Remove strut-to-knuckle bolts. Lower strut assembly out of vehicle.

Installation – To install strut, reverse removal procedure. Tighten all nuts and bolts to specification. Check and adjust rear wheel alignment as necessary. See SPECIFICATIONS & PROCEDURES article in WHEEL ALIGNMENT.

STABILIZER BAR

Removal – **1)** Raise and support vehicle. Remove left and right side stabilizer bar bracket bolts. *See Fig. 5.* Pry open brackets to remove insulator.

2) Remove right and left strut-to-knuckle-to-stabilizer bar nuts. DO NOT remove bolts. Remove insulator brackets. Remove stabilizer bar. If necessary, carefully pry stabilizer bar to side to clear strut.

Installation – To install stabilizer bar, reverse removal procedure. Tighten all nuts and bolts to specification. Check and adjust rear wheel alignment as necessary. See SPECIFICATIONS & PROCEDURES article in WHEEL ALIGNMENT.

LATERAL LINK (FRONT)

Removal – **1)** Raise and support vehicle. Remove wheel and exhaust pipe heat shield. Remove lateral link-to-knuckle bolt. *See Fig. 5.*

2) Lower and support fuel tank for access to link-to-crossmember bolt. Remove lateral link-to-suspension crossmember nut and bolt. Remove lateral link.

Installation – To install front lateral link, reverse removal procedure. Tighten all nuts and bolts to specification. Manufacturer recommends thread locking compound on lateral link-to-knuckle bolts. Check and adjust rear wheel alignment as necessary. See SPECIFICATIONS & PROCEDURES article in WHEEL ALIGNMENT.

LATERAL LINK (REAR)

Removal – **1)** Raise and support vehicle. Remove wheel. Compress auxiliary spring for removal. See AUXILIARY SPRING ASSEMBLY. Remove auxiliary spring bracket-to-lateral link bolt. *See Figs. 1 and 5.*

2) Remove rear toe adjusting cam and push bolt forward to provide clearance for lateral link to swing down. Remove lateral link-to-knuckle bolt and washer. Remove lateral link-to-crossmember bolt, cam assembly and nut.

Installation – To install rear lateral link, reverse removal procedure. Tighten all nuts and bolts to specification. Check and adjust rear wheel alignment as necessary. See SPECIFICATIONS & PROCEDURES article in WHEEL ALIGNMENT.

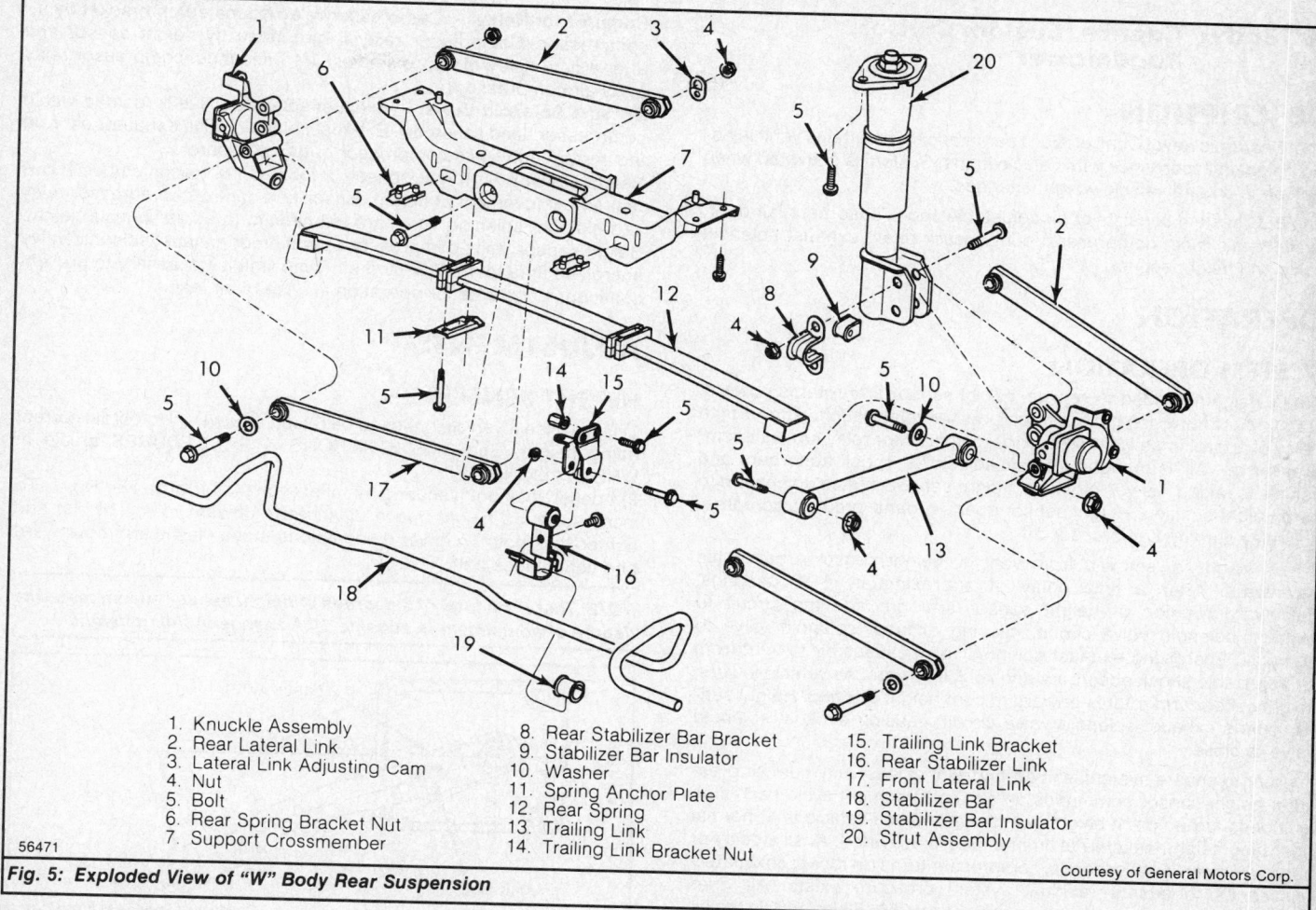

1. Knuckle Assembly
2. Rear Lateral Link
3. Lateral Link Adjusting Cam
4. Nut
5. Bolt
6. Rear Spring Bracket Nut
7. Support Crossmember
8. Rear Stabilizer Bar Bracket
9. Stabilizer Bar Insulator
10. Washer
11. Spring Anchor Plate
12. Rear Spring
13. Trailing Link
14. Trailing Link Bracket Nut
15. Trailing Link Bracket
16. Rear Stabilizer Link
17. Front Lateral Link
18. Stabilizer Bar
19. Stabilizer Bar Insulator
20. Strut Assembly

56471

Fig. 5: Exploded View of "W" Body Rear Suspension

Courtesy of General Motors Corp.

TRAILING LINK

Removal – Raise and support vehicle. Disconnect anti-lock brake electrical harness (if equipped). Remove trailing link-to-knuckle nut and bolt. Remove trailing link-to-body nut and bolt. Remove trailing link. *See Fig. 5.*

Installation – To install trailing link, reverse removal procedure. Tighten all nuts and bolts to specification. See TORQUE SPECIFICATIONS table at end of this article.

TRANSVERSE SPRING ASSEMBLY

CAUTION: DO NOT use corrosive cleaning agents, degreasers or solvents on fiberglass leaf spring. These materials could damage spring.

Removal – **1)** Raise and support vehicle. Remove jack pad located on bottom center of crossmember support. Remove 4 bolts on left and right spring anchor plates. *See Fig. 5.* Disconnect anti-lock brake electrical harness (if equipped).

2) Remove trailing link nut and bolt at knuckle. Place Rear Spring Compressor (J-35778) on rear transverse spring. *See Fig. 4.* Hang center shank of spring compressor from FRONT side of vehicle only.

3) Attach spring compressor body to spring. Ensure rollers of spring compressor are in center of spring. Compress spring. Slide spring to left side. It may be necessary to carefully pry spring to the left using a pry bar against the right knuckle for leverage.

4) Slowly relieve spring tension until there is enough clearance to slide spring out of right side of vehicle.

Installation – To install transverse spring assembly, reverse removal procedure. Tighten all nuts and bolts to specification. See TORQUE SPECIFICATIONS table at end of this article.

CAUTION: Spring anchor plates have tabs on one end. Tabs must be aligned with support crossmember to prevent fuel tank damage.

TORQUE SPECIFICATIONS

TORQUE SPECIFICATIONS

Application	Ft. Lbs. (N.m)
Brake Caliper Mounting Bolts	92 (125)
Crossmember-To-Body Bolt	85 (115)
Hub-To-Bearing Mount Bolt	52 (71)
Jack Pad Bolt	18 (24)
Lateral Links	
Cutlass Supreme, Gran Prix & Regal	
Link-To-Knuckle Bolt	[1] 66 (90)
Link-To-Support Crossmember Bolt	[2] 81 (110)
Lumina	
Link-To-Knuckle Bolt	[3] 66 (90)
Link-To-Support Crossmember Bolt	[3] 66 (90)
Stabilizer Bar	
Link Bolt	40 (54)
Link-To-Body Bracket Nut	18 (24)
Strut Assembly	
Strut-To-Knuckle Nut	133 (180)
Upper Strut Bolts	34 (46)
Trailing Link	
Link-To-Knuckle Nut	192 (260)
Link-To-Body Nut	48 (65)
Transverse Spring	
Anchor Plate Bolt	15 (20)
Wheel Lug Nut	100 (136)

[1] – Tighten to specification, then an additional 90 degrees.
[2] – Tighten to specification, then an additional 60 degrees.
[3] – Tighten to specification, then an additional 120 degrees.

"B" Body: Caprice, Custom Cruiser, Roadmaster

DESCRIPTION

The Electronic Level Control (ELC) automatically maintains vehicle riding height in accordance with vehicle loads. System is activated when ignition is on and vehicle weight changes.

The ELC system consists of air adjustable shock absorbers, air drier, air filter, air lines, compressor, compressor relay, exhaust solenoid valve and height sensor.

OPERATION

SYSTEM OPERATION

When weight is added to vehicle, height sensor arm rotates upward. Rotating arm upward grounds compressor relay circuit. After a time delay of approximately 8-15 seconds, compressor relay turns air compressor on. Air is pumped into air adjustable shock absorbers and vehicle is raised. As vehicle rises, height sensor rotates downward to curb height position. Height sensor opens ground circuit to compressor relay, turning compressor off.

When weight is removed from vehicle, height sensor arm rotates downward. After a time delay of approximately 8-15 seconds, downward rotation of height sensor arm grounds the circuit to exhaust solenoid valve circuit, causing exhaust solenoid valve to energize. Energizing exhaust solenoid valve causes air to vent from air adjustable shock absorbers and vehicle lowers. As vehicle lowers, height sensor arm rotates upward to curb height position. Height sensor opens exhaust solenoid valve circuit, causing exhaust solenoid valve to close.

In order to ensure system is operating with at least minimum air pressure, height sensor commands an air replenishment cycle each time ignition is turned on. If height sensor determines vehicle is at normal operating height, an internal timer circuit is activated. After a delay of approximately 35-40 seconds, compressor turns on for approximately 4 seconds to ensure residual system pressure exists. Air drier maintains a minimum air pressure of 8-14 psi (.56-.98 kg/cm²) in the air adjustable shock absorbers.

If weight is added or removed from vehicle during 35-40 second delay, air replenishment cycle will be overridden and vehicle will rise or lower after normal time delay.

Voltage is applied to compressor and height sensor at all times. This allows system to vent after load is removed with ignition turned off. Height sensor limits compressor operation or exhaust solenoid valve energized time to 4.5-7.0 minutes. Time limit is necessary to prevent continuous compressor operation in case of air leak. Turning ignition from off to on will reset compressor operation or exhaust solenoid valve energized time.

Low compressor motor starting current is obtained by a 1.5 second actuation of exhaust solenoid valve. This reduces air pressure in compressor cylinder, allowing for easier compressor operation.

COMPONENT OPERATION

Air Adjustable Shock Absorber – Air adjustable shock absorber is a conventional shock absorber, containing an air chamber which extends when air pressure is increased.

Air Drier – Air drier is attached to compressor output. Air drier absorbs moisture from air being delivered to air adjustable shock absorbers. Air drier contains a valve which maintains a minimum shock absorber air pressure of 8-14 psi (.56-.98 kg/cm²).

Air Filter – Air filter is mounted on rear crossmember, directly above rear axle. Air filter contains a foam filter, used to prevent contaminants from entering air system.

Compressor – The piston-type compressor is mounted on rear crossmember, near rear axle. Compressor provides air pressure for system operation.

Compressor Relay – Compressor relay is located on bracket by air compressor. Compressor relay is grounded by height sensor and after a time delay of approximately 7-14 seconds, compressor relay turns air compressor on.

Exhaust Solenoid Valve – Exhaust solenoid valve is located within compressor head assembly. Exhaust solenoid valve exhausts air from the system and limits compressor output pressure.

Height Sensor – Height sensor is located on crossmember above rear axle. Movement of height sensor arm controls compressor relay and exhaust solenoid valve ground circuits to adjust vehicle height. Height sensor limits compressor operation or exhaust solenoid valve energized time to 4.5-7.0 minutes. Time limit is necessary to prevent continuous compressor operation in case of air leak.

ADJUSTMENTS

HEIGHT SENSOR

1) Determine if vehicle needs to be raised or lowered to obtain correct riding height. See SPECIFICATIONS & PROCEDURES article in WHEEL ALIGNMENT.

2) Loosen lock bolt securing metal arm on plastic arm. *See Fig. 1.* To increase riding height, move plastic arm upward to top of slot and tighten lock bolt. To lower riding height, move plastic arm downward and tighten lock bolt.

NOTE: There is a total of 5 degrees of height sensor adjustment. One degree of adjustment is equal to 1/4" change in riding height.

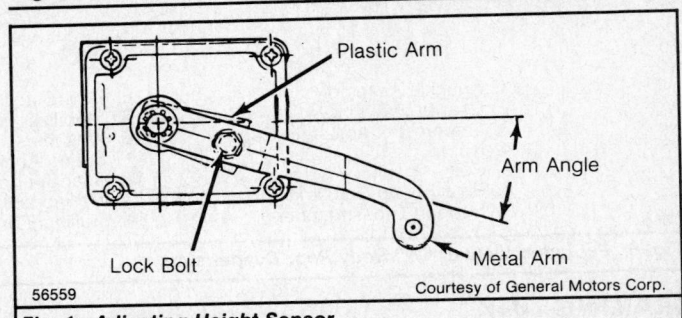

Plastic Arm

Arm Angle

Lock Bolt

Metal Arm

56559   Courtesy of General Motors Corp.

Fig. 1: Adjusting Height Sensor

RIDING HEIGHT

NOTE: See SPECIFICATIONS & PROCEDURES article in WHEEL ALIGNMENT.

SYSTEM TESTING

SYSTEM OPERATION TEST

NOTE: Ensure height sensor and link assembly are in good condition before performing system operation test.

1) Place vehicle on flat surface. Measure distance from floor to rocker panel in front of rear wheelwell opening. Turn ignition on. Add 300 lbs. (135 kg) of weight to rear of vehicle. If compressor starts within 8-15 seconds, proceed to step **4)**.

2) If compressor does not start within 8-15 seconds and vehicle is within 1" (25 mm) of distance measured in step **1)**, test air drier. See AIR DRIER TEST under COMPONENT TESTING.

3) If compressor does not start within 8-15 seconds and vehicle is not within 1" (25 mm) of distance measured in step **1)**, check height sensor adjustment, and retest. See HEIGHT SENSOR under ADJUSTMENTS. If height sensor is properly adjusted, see COMPRESSOR INOPERATIVE TEST under ELECTRICAL TESTING.

4) If compressor starts within 8-15 seconds, compressor should stop within 7 minutes. If compressor stops within 7 minutes, proceed to step **5)**. If compressor runs continuously, test height sensor. See HEIGHT SENSOR TEST under COMPONENT TESTING.

5) If compressor stops within 7 minutes and vehicle returns to within 1" (25 mm) of distance measured in step **1)**, remove load, and proceed to step **7)**. If compressor stops within 7 minutes and vehicle does not return to within 1" (25 mm) of distance measured in step **1)**, remove load, and proceed to step **6)**. If system leaks down, perform compressor leak test. See COMPRESSOR LEAK TEST under COMPONENT TESTING.

6) Check height sensor adjustment, and retest. See HEIGHT SENSOR under ADJUSTMENTS. If height sensor is properly adjusted, see VEHICLE WILL NOT LOWER TEST under ELECTRICAL TESTING.

7) With load removed, system should start to exhaust within 8-15 seconds. If system does exhaust within 8-15 seconds, proceed to step **8)**. If system does not exhaust within 8-15 seconds, see VEHICLE WILL NOT LOWER TEST under ELECTRICAL TESTING.

8) If exhaust of air starts within 8-15 seconds and, after 2 minutes, vehicle returns to within 1" (25 mm) of distance measured in step **1)**, system is operating correctly. If vehicle does not return to within 1" (25 mm) of distance measured in step **1)**, adjust height sensor. See HEIGHT SENSOR under ADJUSTMENTS.

SYSTEM LEAK TEST

CAUTION: System leak test will determine if a leak exists and if leak is internal or external to the compressor.

1) Install Pressure Gauge (J-22124-A) and Air Hose Set (J-22124-91) to air drier and air adjustable shock absorbers. *See Fig. 2.* With shut-off gauge open, apply shop air pressure through service valve on pressure gauge until pressure gauge reaches 100-120 psi (7.0-8.4 kg/cm²). *See Fig. 2.*

2) If a leak is indicated, close shut-off valve. This isolates compressor from rest of system. Check for decrease in air pressure.

3) If air pressure continues to decrease, leak is external from the compressor. Test all connections using soapy water solution and repair as necessary. If air pressure stops decreasing after shut-off valve is closed, leak is in the compressor assembly. See COMPRESSOR LEAK TEST under COMPONENT TESTING.

4) If air pressure builds up rapidly but vehicle does not rise, check for pinched air line or stuck or binding air adjustable shock absorbers.

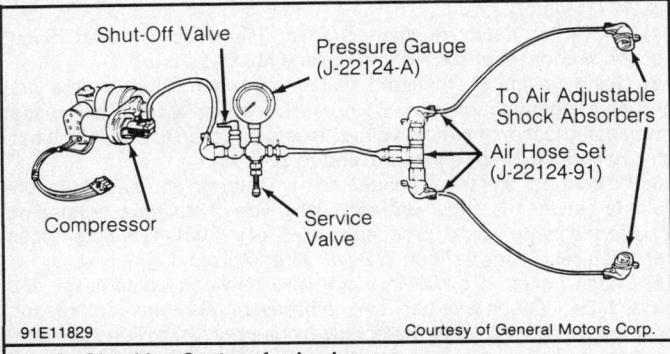

91E11829 Courtesy of General Motors Corp.

Fig. 2: Checking System for Leakage

COMPONENT TESTING

AIR DRIER TEST

NOTE: Air drier is tested to ensure valve maintains a minimum pressure of 8-14 psi (.56-.98 kg/cm²) in air adjustable shock absorbers.

1) Install Pressure Gauge (J-22124-A) and Air Hose Set (J-22124-91) to air drier and air adjustable shock absorbers. *See Fig. 2.* Turn ignition on to inflate air adjustable shock absorbers.

2) Turn ignition off to deflate air adjustable shock absorbers through pressure gauge valve. Pressure gauge should read 8-14 psi (.56-.98 kg/cm²) after air adjustable shock absorbers are deflated. If air pressure reading is not within specification, replace air drier.

COMPRESSOR OPERATION TEST

NOTE: Compressor operation will be checked by measuring current draw, compressor output and pressure leak-down.

1) Remove compressor. See COMPRESSOR under REMOVAL & INSTALLATION. Connect Pressure Gauge (J-22124-A) to air drier. *See Fig. 3.*

2) Connect ammeter to (B+) battery terminal and other lead to Dark Green wire at compressor electrical connector. Connect Black wire of compressor electrical connector to negative (-) battery terminal and note compressor motor current draw. *See Fig. 3.*

3) If compressor does not operate or current draw exceeds 14 amps, replace compressor. If current draw is 14 amps or less, allow pressure to reach 100 psi (7.0 kg/cm²) and disconnect ammeter from (B+) battery terminal.

4) If pressure held at 100 psi (7.0 kg/cm²), compressor is okay. If pressure decreases to less than 90 psi (6.3 kg/cm²), but does not continue to decrease, replace compressor head assembly. See COMPRESSOR HEAD under REMOVAL & INSTALLATION.

5) If pressure fully leaks off, or pressure built up, but would not reach 100 psi (7.0 kg/cm²), check compressor for leaks. See COMPRESSOR LEAK TEST under COMPONENT TESTING. Remove pressure gauge.

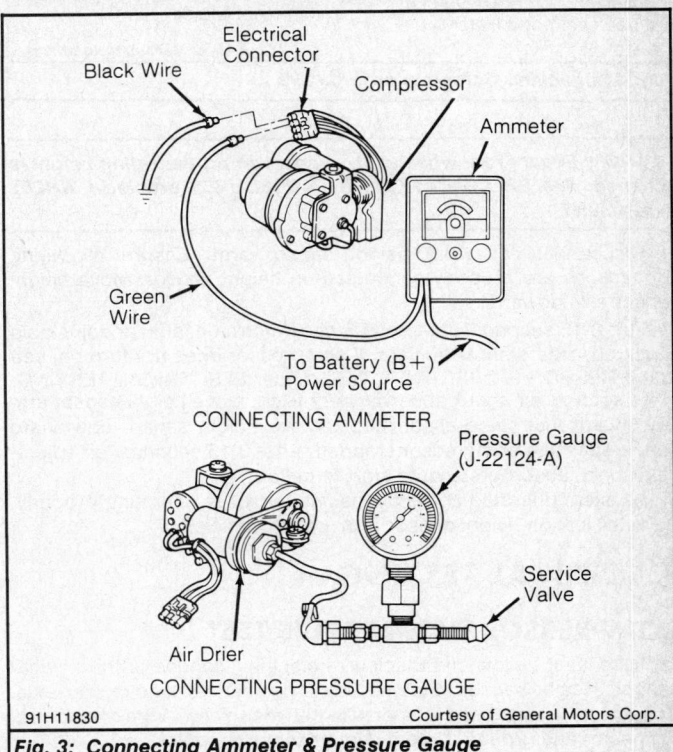

CONNECTING AMMETER

CONNECTING PRESSURE GAUGE

91H11830 Courtesy of General Motors Corp.

Fig. 3: Connecting Ammeter & Pressure Gauge

COMPRESSOR LEAK TEST

1) Remove compressor. See COMPRESSOR under REMOVAL & INSTALLATION. Connect Pressure Gauge (J-22124-A) to air drier. *See Fig. 3.* Apply shop air pressure through service valve on pressure gauge until gauge reaches 100 psi (7.0 kg/cm²).

2) Using soapy water solution, check for leaks around air drier cover, air drier "O" ring casting bore, edge of cover gasket, edge of solenoid valve housing, head casting air intake and exhaust openings and head cover. *See Fig. 4.*

3) If leak exists at cover bolts, tighten cover bolts to specification, and recheck for leaks. See TORQUE SPECIFICATIONS table at end of article. Remove pressure gauge.

HEIGHT SENSOR TEST

1) Turn ignition off and then on to reset height sensor timing circuit. Raise and support vehicle.

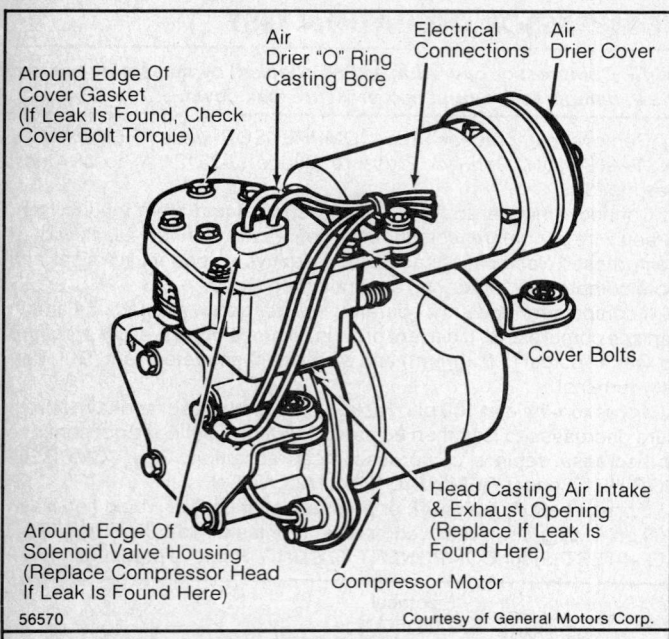

Around Edge Of Cover Gasket (If Leak Is Found, Check Cover Bolt Torque)

Air Drier "O" Ring Casting Bore

Electrical Connections

Air Drier Cover

Cover Bolts

Head Casting Air Intake & Exhaust Opening (Replace If Leak Is Found Here)

Compressor Motor

Around Edge Of Solenoid Valve Housing (Replace Compressor Head If Leak Is Found Here)

56570   Courtesy of General Motors Corp.

Fig. 4: Checking Compressor for Leaks

CAUTION: Ensure rear wheels are support so proper riding height is obtained. See SPECIFICATIONS & PROCEDURES article in WHEEL ALIGNMENT.

2) Disconnect link from height sensor arm. Ensure all wiring connections are properly connected on height sensor. Move height sensor arm upward.
3) After 8-15 seconds, compressor should turn on, and air adjustable shock absorbers should inflate. If compressor does not turn on, see COMPRESSOR INOPERATIVE TEST under ELECTRICAL TESTING.
4) As soon as air shock absorbers are filled, move height sensor arm downward until compressor stops. Move height sensor downward past area where compressor stopped. After 8-15 seconds, air adjustable shock absorbers should start to deflate.
5) If system operated correctly, height sensor is operating properly. Reinstall link on height sensor arm. Lower vehicle.

ELECTRICAL TESTING

COMPRESSOR INOPERATIVE TEST

1) Disconnect Yellow and Black wire electrical connector from height sensor. Height sensor is located on crossmember above rear axle. Connect a 10-amp fused jumper wire between Yellow wire of electrical connector and ground. Note if compressor operates.
2) If compressor operates, proceed to step **8)**. If compressor does not operate, disconnect electrical connector from compressor relay. Compressor relay is located on bracket by air compressor.
3) Connect a 25-amp fused jumper wire between Orange wire and Dark Green wire of compressor relay electrical connector. Note if compressor operates. If compressor does not operate, proceed to step **12)**. If compressor operates, proceed to step **4)**.
4) Using voltmeter, measure voltage between Orange wires of compressor relay electrical connector and ground. If battery voltage exists, proceed to step **7)**.
5) If battery voltage does not exist, check for defective connections at compressor relay. If connections are okay, check for open wire circuit in Orange wire between compressor relay and ELC fuse or defective ELC fuse. The ELC fuse is located in left front corner of engine compartment, near ABS hydraulic modulator. See Fig. 5.

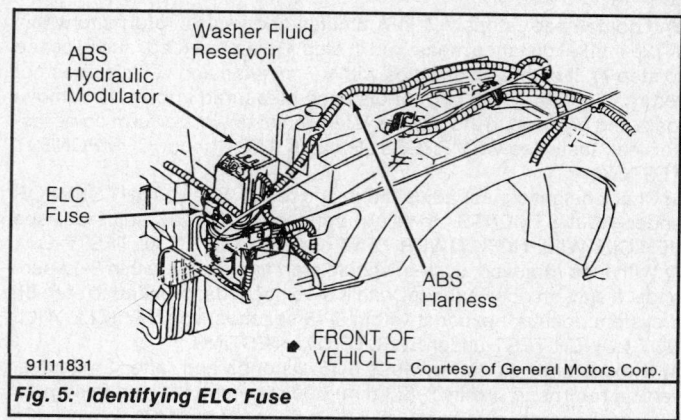

ABS Hydraulic Modulator

Washer Fluid Reservoir

ELC Fuse

ABS Harness

91I11831   FRONT OF VEHICLE   Courtesy of General Motors Corp.

Fig. 5: Identifying ELC Fuse

6) If ELC fuse and wiring are okay, check for defective connection at battery junction or defective Rust colored fusible link, located at battery junction block. Battery junction block is located on right side of engine compartment, near right wheelwell.
7) If battery voltage exists, check for defective connection at Yellow wire on compressor relay and open circuit in Yellow wire between compressor relay and height sensor. If wiring and connections are okay, replace compressor relay.
8) Using voltmeter, measure voltage between Orange wire and ground at electrical connector on height sensor. If battery voltage exists, proceed to step **9)**. If battery voltage does not exist, repair open circuit in Orange wire to height sensor.
9) Using voltmeter, measure voltage between Orange wire and Black wire at electrical connector on height sensor. If battery voltage exists, proceed to step **10)**. If battery voltage does not exist, repair open circuit in Black wire to ground at height sensor.
10) Turn ignition on. Using voltmeter, measure voltage between Pink/Black wire and ground on electrical connector at height sensor. If battery voltage exists, proceed to step **11)**. If battery voltage does not exist, repair open circuit in Pink/Black wire between height sensor and fuse block, located near left side of instrument panel or defective fuse No. 17 (15-amp).
11) Check for defective connection or Pink/Black wire at height sensor. If connections are okay, replace height sensor.
12) Using voltmeter, measure voltage between Orange wire and ground at compressor relay. Compressor relay is located on bracket by air compressor. If battery voltage exists, proceed to step **13)**. If battery voltage does not exist, proceed to step **15)**.
13) Disconnect electrical connector at compressor relay. Measure voltage between Orange wire and Black wire of electrical connector. If battery voltage exists, proceed to step **14)**. If battery voltage does not exist, repair open circuit in Black wire to ground.
14) Check for open circuit in Black wire between compressor and ground, Dark Green wire between compressor relay and compressor, or defective connection at Black wire at compressor. If wiring and connections are okay, replace compressor.
15) Remove ELC fuse, located in left front corner of engine compartment, near ABS hydraulic modulator. See Fig. 5. Using voltmeter, measure voltage between fuse socket and ground. If battery voltage exists, proceed to step **17)**. If battery voltage does not exist, proceed to step **16)**.
16) Check for defective Rust colored fusible link, located at battery junction block or defective connections at fuse block. Battery junction block is located on right side of engine compartment, near right wheelwell. If fusible link and connections are okay, repair open circuit in Red wire between fusible link and fuse block.
17) Check for defective ELC fuse or defective connection on Orange wire at compressor relay. If fuse and connections are okay, repair open circuit in Orange wire between ELC fuse and compressor relay.

VEHICLE WILL NOT LOWER TEST

NOTE: This test checks operation of exhaust solenoid valve, located within compressor head assembly. Compressor must be replaced if exhaust solenoid valve is defective.

1) Disconnect electrical connector from height sensor. Height sensor is located on crossmember above rear axle. Connect a 10-amp fused jumper wire between White wire of electrical connector and ground. Note if exhaust solenoid valve clicks and air is exhausted.

2) If exhaust solenoid valve does not operate, proceed to step **4)**. If exhaust solenoid valve operated, check for defective connection at White wire on height sensor or open in White wire near connection on height sensor.

3) If wiring and connections were okay, check height sensor adjustment. See HEIGHT SENSOR under ADJUSTMENTS. If defective connection or open in wiring circuit exists, repair as necessary.

4) Note if fused jumper was blown during testing. If fuse was not blown, proceed to step **5)**. If fuse was blown, check for short to voltage on White wire between height sensor and exhaust solenoid valve. If wiring circuit is okay, replace compressor assembly.

5) Using voltmeter, measure voltage from White wire to ground on height sensor electrical connector. If battery voltage does not exist, proceed to step **6)**. If battery voltage exists, replace compressor.

6) Disconnect electrical connector at compressor. Using voltmeter, measure voltage between Orange wires and ground on electrical connector. If battery voltage exists, proceed to step **7)**. If battery voltage does not exist, repair open circuit in Orange wire between exhaust solenoid valve and ELC fuse.

7) Check for defective connection or wiring at exhaust solenoid valve or open in White wire between height sensor and exhaust solenoid valve. If wiring and connections are okay, replace compressor.

COMPRESSOR OPERATES CONTINUOUSLY (LONGER THAN 7 MINUTES) TEST

1) Disconnect electrical connector from compressor relay. Compressor relay is located on bracket by air compressor. Note if compressor continues to operate.

2) If compressor stops, proceed to step **3)**. If compressor does not stop, check for short to battery voltage in Dark Green wire between compressor relay and compressor. If wiring is okay, replace compressor.

3) Using a test light, check for voltage between Orange wire and Yellow wire on electrical connection on compressor relay. If voltage exists, proceed to step **4)**. If voltage does not exist, replace compressor relay.

4) Disconnect electrical connector at height sensor. Height sensor is located on crossmember above rear axle. Turn ignition on. Using a test light, check for voltage between Yellow wire and Black wire on height sensor electrical connection.

5) If voltage exists, repair short to ground in Yellow wire between height sensor and compressor relay. If voltage does not exist, check Yellow wire at height sensor pigtail electrical connector for short to ground. If wiring is okay, replace height sensor.

REMOVAL & INSTALLATION

NOTE: For additional information on suspension components, see appropriate article in SUSPENSION.

AIR ADJUSTABLE SHOCK ABSORBER

Removal – 1) Raise and support vehicle. Support rear axle. Disconnect air lines by rotating spring clip and removing air line. Remove upper retaining bolts/nuts on shock absorber.

2) Remove lower retaining nut and washer. DO NOT allow lower stud to rotate when removing retaining nut. Remove air adjustable shock absorber.

Installation – To install, reverse removal procedure. Tighten bolts/nuts to specification. See TORQUE SPECIFICATIONS table at end of this article. Before installing air lines, lubricate "O" rings with petroleum jelly. Ensure air line and connector are fully seated in fitting.

AIR DRIER

Removal & Installation – 1) Remove compressor and bracket. See COMPRESSOR under REMOVAL & INSTALLATION. Remove air drier-to-compressor bolts. Rotate retaining clip on air drier 90 degrees. Rotate air drier. Remove air drier and "O" ring.

2) To install, reverse removal procedure. Lubricate "O" ring with petroleum jelly before installing. Tighten bolts to specification. See TORQUE SPECIFICATIONS table at end of this article.

AIR FILTER

Removal & Installation – 1) Air filter is mounted on rear crossmember, directly above rear axle. Disconnect hose from air filter. Remove retaining bolt and air filter.

2) To install, reverse removal procedure. Tighten bolt to specification. See TORQUE SPECIFICATIONS table at end of this article.

COMPRESSOR

Removal – 1) Disconnect negative battery cable. Raise and support vehicle. Disconnect air lines by rotating spring clip and removing air line. Remove compressor and bracket-to-crossmember bolts.

2) Disconnect anti-lock brake wheel speed sensor wiring from bracket. Disconnect electrical connection at compressor. Remove compressor and bracket from crossmember. Remove compressor-to-bracket bolts. Separate compressor from bracket.

Installation – To install, reverse removal procedure. Tighten bolts to specification. See TORQUE SPECIFICATIONS table at end of this article. Before installing air lines, lubricate "O" rings with petroleum jelly. Ensure air line and connector are fully seated in fitting.

COMPRESSOR HEAD

Removal & Installation – 1) Remove air drier. See AIR DRIER under REMOVAL & INSTALLATION. Remove 3 compressor head-to-compressor retaining bolts. Remove compressor head and "O" ring.

2) To install, reverse removal procedure, using new "O" ring. Tighten bolts to specification, starting with the center bolt and then the outer bolts. See TORQUE SPECIFICATIONS table at end of this article.

COMPRESSOR RELAY

NOTE: Compressor relay is mounted inside mounting bracket for the compressor. Compressor does not have to be removed from bracket to service compressor relay.

Removal & Installation – 1) Remove compressor and bracket. See COMPRESSOR under REMOVAL & INSTALLATION. Remove compressor relay retaining bolt. Disconnect electrical connector and remove compressor relay.

2) To install, reverse removal procedure. Tighten bolts to specification. See TORQUE SPECIFICATIONS table at end of this article.

EXHAUST SOLENOID VALVE

Removal & Installation – Exhaust solenoid valve is not serviceable. Compressor head must be replaced if exhaust solenoid valve is defective. See COMPRESSOR HEAD under REMOVAL & INSTALLATION.

HEIGHT SENSOR

Removal & Installation – 1) Disconnect negative battery cable. Raise and support vehicle. Disconnect electrical connector at height sensor. Height sensor is located on crossmember above rear axle.

2) Remove link-to-upper control arm nut. Remove retaining bolts and height sensor.

3) To install, reverse removal procedure. Tighten bolts/nuts to specification. See TORQUE SPECIFICATIONS table.

TORQUE SPECIFICATIONS

TORQUE SPECIFICATIONS

Application	Ft. Lbs. (N.m)
Air Adjustable Shock Absorber	
Lower Nut	48 (65)
Upper Bolt	20 (27)
Upper Nut	16 (22)
	INCH Lbs. (N.m)
Air Drier-To-Compressor Bolt	34 (3.8)
Air Filter Bolt	89 (10.0)
Bracket-To-Crossmember Bolt	89 (10.0)
Compressor Head Bolt	35 (3.9)
Compressor Relay-To-Bracket Bolt	34 (3.8)
Compressor-To-Bracket Bolt	44 (5.0)
Cover Bolt	35 (3.9)
Height Sensor Bolt	24 (14.0)
Height Sensor Link Nut	27 (3.0)

WIRING DIAGRAM

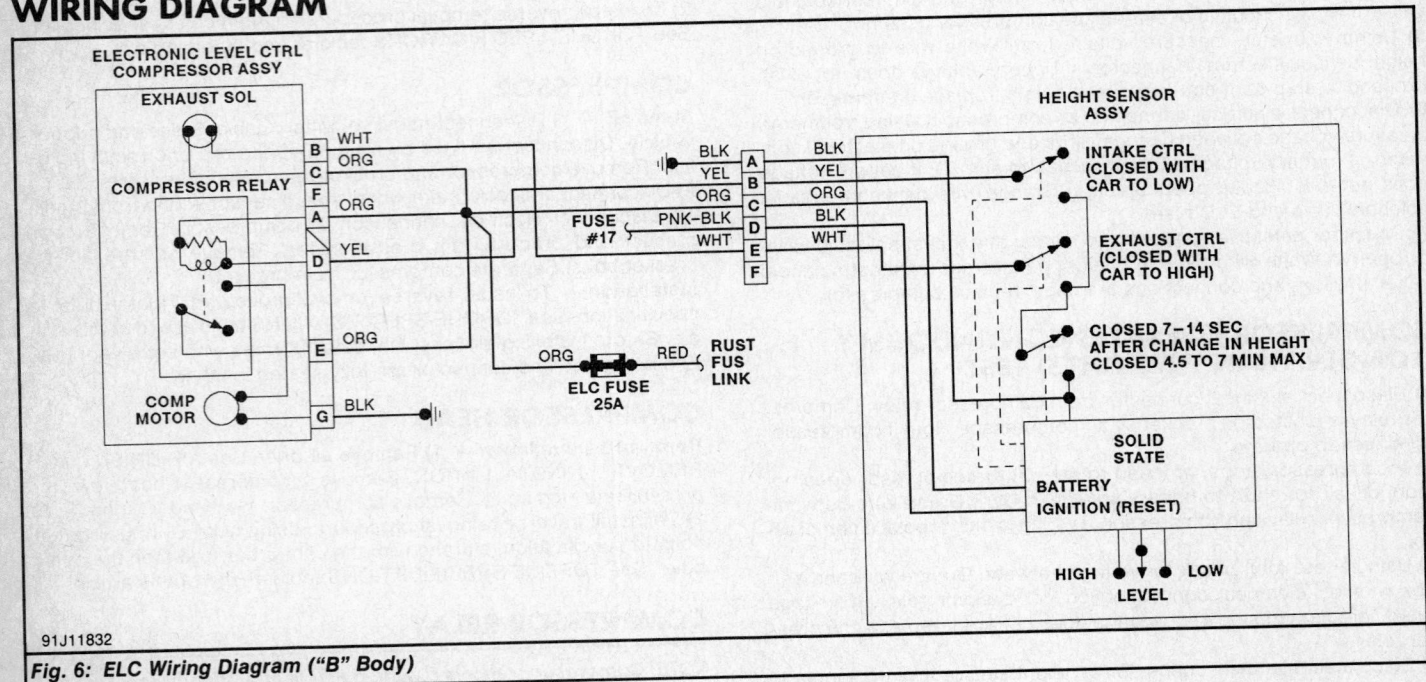

91J11832

Fig. 6: ELC Wiring Diagram ("B" Body)

DESCRIPTION

Electronic Level Control (ELC) automatically adjusts rear height of vehicle regardless of load. System is activated when ignition is on and weight is added to or removed from vehicle.

The ELC system consists of a compressor, air drier, exhaust solenoid, compressor relay, height sensor, air adjustable shock absorbers and connecting air lines.

Air drier, mounted on compressor, contains a moisture-absorbing dry chemical and valves to maintain air pressure. Valves are used for maintaining minimum system air pressure to approximately 8-14 psi (.56-.98 kg/cm²).

OPERATION

SYSTEM OPERATION

When weight is added to vehicle, height sensor arm rotates upward. Rotating arm upward grounds compressor relay circuit. After a time delay of approximately 8-15 seconds, compressor relay turns air compressor on. Air is pumped into shock absorbers and vehicle is raised. As vehicle rises, height sensor arm rotates downward to curb height position. Height sensor then opens ground circuit to compressor relay, turning compressor off.

When weight is removed from vehicle, height sensor arm rotates downward. After a time delay of approximately 8-15 seconds, downward rotation of the arm grounds exhaust solenoid valve circuit, causing air to vent. Energizing exhaust solenoid valve causes air to vent from shock absorbers and vehicle lowers. As vehicle lowers, height sensor arm rotates upward to curb height position. Height sensor opens exhaust solenoid valve circuit, causing exhaust solenoid valve to close.

In order to ensure system is operating with at least minimum air pressure, height sensor commands an air replenishment cycle each time ignition is turned on. If height sensor determines that vehicle is at normal operating height, an internal timer circuit is activated. After a delay of approximately 35-40 seconds, compressor turns on for approximately 4 seconds to ensure residual system pressure exists. Air drier maintains a minimum shock absorber air pressure of 8-14 psi (.56-.98 kg/cm²).

If weight is added or removed from vehicle during 35-40 second delay, air replenishment cycle will be overridden and vehicle will rise or lower after normal time delay.

Battery voltage is applied to compressor and height sensor at all times. This allows system to vent after load is removed with ignition turned off. Height sensor limits compressor operation or exhaust solenoid valve energized time to 4.5-7.0 minutes. Time limit is necessary to prevent continuous compressor operation in case of air leak. Turning ignition from off to on will reset compressor operation or exhaust solenoid valve energized time.

Low compressor motor starting current is obtained by a 1.5 second actuation of exhaust solenoid valve. This reduces air pressure in compressor cylinder, allowing for easier compressor operation.

COMPONENT OPERATION

Air Adjustable Shock Absorber – Air adjustable shock absorber is a conventional shock absorber that contains an air chamber which extends shock absorber when air pressure is increased to shock absorber.

Air Drier – Air drier is attached to compressor output. Air drier absorbs moisture from air being delivered to air adjustable shock absorbers. Air drier contains a valve which maintains a minimum shock absorber air pressure of 8-14 psi (.56-.98 kg/cm²).

Air Filter – Air filter is mounted on rear crossmember, directly above rear axle. Air filter contains a foam filter, used to prevent contaminants from entering air system.

Compressor – The piston-type compressor is mounted on rear crossmember, near rear axle. Compressor provides air pressure for system operation.

Compressor Relay – Compressor relay is located on bracket by air compressor. Compressor relay is grounded by height sensor and after a time delay of approximately 8-15 seconds, compressor relay turns air compressor on.

Exhaust Solenoid Valve – Exhaust solenoid valve is located within compressor head assembly. Exhaust solenoid valve exhausts air from the system and limits compressor output pressure.

Height Sensor – Height sensor is located on crossmember above rear axle. Movement of height sensor arm controls compressor relay and exhaust solenoid valve ground circuits to adjust vehicle height. Height sensor limits compressor operation or exhaust solenoid valve energized time to 4.5-7.0 minutes. Time limit is necessary to prevent continuous compressor operation in case of air leak.

ADJUSTMENTS

HEIGHT SENSOR

1) Determine if vehicle needs to be raised or lowered to obtain correct riding height. See SPECIFICATIONS & PROCEDURES article in WHEEL ALIGNMENT.

2) Vehicle should be on level surface with full gas tank and NO load in vehicle. Push bumper down and up slowly a few times to normalize suspension. Turn ignition switch to ON position.

3) To raise vehicle riding height, loosen lock bolt securing height sensor metal arm to plastic arm. Move plastic arm upward slowly until riding height is obtained and tighten lock nut. *See Fig. 1.*

4) To lower riding height, loosen lock bolt securing height sensor metal arm to plastic arm. Move plastic arm downward slowly until riding height is obtained and tighten lock nut. If adjustment cannot be made, there is a problem with rear springs or suspension. *See Fig. 1.*

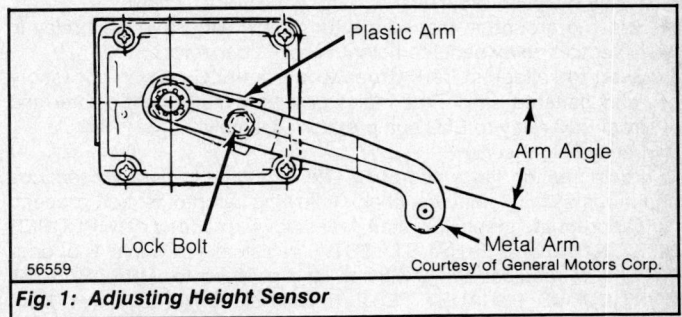

Courtesy of General Motors Corp.

56559

Fig. 1: Adjusting Height Sensor

RIDING HEIGHT

NOTE: See SPECIFICATIONS & PROCEDURES article in WHEEL ALIGNMENT.

SYSTEM TESTING

DIAGNOSTIC SYMPTOM DIRECTORY

Symptom	Perform
Compressor Does Not Run	ELC SYSTEM OPERATIONAL TEST, COMPRESSOR DOES NOT OPERATE TEST, HEIGHT SENSOR OPERATIONAL TEST
System Does Not Exhaust	NO EXHAUST TEST, HEIGHT SENSOR OPERATIONAL TEST
Compressor Runs Continuously, Vehicle Rises & Does Not Leak Down	[1] HEIGHT SENSOR OPERATIONAL TEST
Compressor Runs For Maximum Time & Turns Off. Vehicle Does Not Rise, Or Rises & Leaks Down	COMPRESSOR PERFORMANCE TEST, IMPROPER OR CONTINUOUS EXHAUST TEST, SYSTEM LEAK TEST
System Vents Continuously	IMPROPER OR CONTINUOUS EXHAUST TEST, SYSTEM LEAK TEST

[1] – Unplug ELC height sensor connector. If compressor does not run, replace ELC height sensor. If compressor runs, check Yellow wire for short to ground. If wire is okay, replace ELC relay.

ELC SYSTEM OPERATIONAL TEST

1) Unload vehicle. Open hood and trunk. Ensure ignition is off. Check riding height specifications. See SPECIFICATIONS & PROCEDURES article in WHEEL ALIGNMENT. Turn ignition on, off and back on to cycle reset systems. Add 300-350 lbs. (136-159 kg) load to trunk.

2) If compressor DOES NOT start operating after a delay of about 28 seconds and vehicle is within 1" of unloaded height, proceed to NO EXHAUST TEST.

3) If compressor DOES NOT start operating after a delay of about 28 seconds and vehicle is NOT within 1" of unloaded height, adjust height sensor, and retest. See HEIGHT SENSOR under ADJUSTMENTS. If compressor does not operate during height sensor test, proceed to COMPRESSOR DOES NOT OPERATE TEST.

4) If compressor does start operating after a delay of about 28 seconds and compressor runs continuously, check for following:
- Faulty relay (stuck).
- Short to ground in test connector Yellow wire from ELC relay in accessory relay panel to height sensor connector.
- Short to voltage in Dark Green wire from ELC relay in accessory relay panel to Level Ride Indicator light in instrument cluster and from ELC relay to ELC compressor assembly.
- Faulty height sensor.

5) If compressor starts operating after a delay of about 28 seconds and stops within 7 minutes, check following symptoms, and proceed with appropriate steps. If system leaks down, proceed to IMPROPER OR CONTINUOUS EXHAUST TEST. If vehicle in not within 1" of original height, readjust height sensor, and proceed to IMPROPER OR CONTINUOUS EXHAUST TEST. If vehicle returns to within 1" of unloaded height, proceed to next steps.

6) Remove load from trunk. If system does not exhaust after 28 seconds, proceed to NO EXHAUST TEST. If system starts to exhaust within 28 seconds and vehicle returns to within 1" of original height, system is functioning properly. If vehicle does not return to within 1" of original height, adjust or replace height sensor, and retest.

COMPRESSOR DOES NOT OPERATE TEST

1) Turn ignition to ON position. Ground ELC test connector located on Yellow wire near ELC relay. ELC Relay is located in relay center under left instrument panel. If compressor does not run, go to step 3). If compressor runs, go to next step.

2) Disconnect height sensor harness connector. Using a jumper wire, connect pins No. 3 and No. 4 of height sensor harness connector. If compressor does not run, check for an open in Yellow wire. Check compressor motor ground circuit (Black wire). If compressor runs, go to RESET CIRCUIT OPERATIONAL TEST.

3) Remove ELC relay. Check for battery voltage at pins No. 2 and No. 4 of relay cavity. If battery voltage is present, go to next step. If battery voltage is not present, check GA-TRANS fuse in fuse block. If fuse is okay, repair open in Pink/Black wire circuit to ELC relay connector and to height sensor.

4) Using a jumper wire, connect pins No. 1 and No. 4 of ELC relay cavity. If compressor does not run, go to next step. If compressor runs, check for an open in Yellow wire circuit from ELC relay to height sensor. If circuit is okay, replace ELC relay.

5) Disconnect compressor harness connector. Apply 12 volts to pin "B". Ground pin "D". If compressor runs, check for open in compressor motor ground circuit (Black wire) and check for open in Dark Green wire to ELC relay. If compressor does not run, replace compressor motor assembly.

IMPROPER OR CONTINUOUS EXHAUST TEST

1) Check for a short to ground in White wire circuit from compressor to height sensor. If a short exists, repair as required. If a short does not exist, perform COMPRESSOR PERFORMANCE TEST under COMPONENT TESTING.

2) If compressor does not operate correctly, refer to ELC COMPRESSOR DIAGNOSIS under COMPONENT TESTING. If compressor operates correctly, perform SYSTEM LEAK TEST, and repair as required. If system leak test is satisfactory, replace height sensor.

NO EXHAUST TEST

1) Cycle ignition on, off and then on to reset system. Disconnect compressor harness connector. Check for voltage at harness connector pin "A". If battery voltage is present, go to step 2). If voltage is not present, check BODY fuse. Replace fuse if blown. If fuse is okay, repair open in Orange wire circuit from fuse block to compressor assembly to height sensor.

2) Reconnect compressor harness connector. Disconnect height sensor harness connector. Using a jumper wire, connect terminals No. 2 and No. 4 of height sensor harness connector. If system does not exhaust, go to next step. If system does exhaust, check for voltage at pin No. 6. If voltage is not present, repair open in Orange wire circuit from fuse box to compressor and from compressor to height sensor. If battery voltage is present, replace height sensor.

3) Disconnect compressor harness connector. Apply 12 volts to pin "A" and ground pin "C" of compressor harness connector. If system does not exhaust, replace head assembly. If system does exhaust, repair open in White wire between compressor to height sensor and/or repair open in Black wire ground circuit from compressor motor to ground and from compressor to ELC height sensor.

RESET CIRCUIT OPERATIONAL TEST

1) Turn ignition off. Disconnect height sensor harness connector. Check for voltage at pins No. 5 and No. 6. If voltage is not present at pin No. 5 and battery voltage is present at pin No. 6, go on to next step. If voltage is present at pin No. 5, repair short to voltage in Pink/Black wire from GA-TRANS fuse to height sensor connector. If zero voltage is present at pin No. 6, check BODY fuse. If fuse is okay, repair open in Orange wire from fuse box to compressor assembly to height sensor.

2) Turn key to ON position. Check voltage at pin No. 5. If battery voltage is present, go to step 3). If zero voltage is present, check GA-TRANS fuse and replace as necessary. If fuse is okay, repair open in Pink/Black wire from GA-TRANS fuse to height sensor connector.

3) Check voltage from pin No. 6 to pin No. 4. If battery voltage is present, replace height sensor. If voltage is not present, repair open in Black wire from compressor motor to ground or from height sensor to ground.

SYSTEM LEAK TEST

1) Install Pressure Gauge (J-22124-A) in-line between drier assembly and existing air line to shocks. See Fig. 3. Install gauge so shut-off valve is on compressor side of gauge. With shut-off valve open, apply shop air pressure through the service valve until gauge reads 100-120 psi (7.03-8.43 kg/cm²).

2) If a leak is indicated, close shut-off valve to isolate compressor and continue to watch gauge for a system pressure drop. If pressure continues to drop, leak is external from the compressor. Leak test all connections. If pressure stops decreasing after shut-off valve is closed, leak is in the compressor assembly.

3) Check compressor for leaks. If pressure builds up rapidly but vehicle does not rise, check for pinched air line or stuck or binding shocks. *See Fig. 2.*

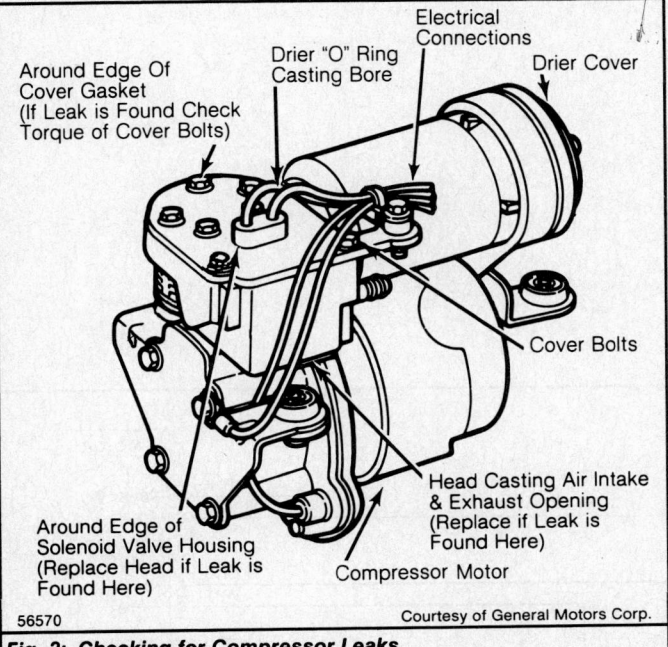

Fig. 2: *Checking for Compressor Leaks*

COMPONENT TESTING

COMPRESSOR PERFORMANCE TEST

1) Disconnect harness connectors from compressor and exhaust solenoid. Disconnect air pressure line from drier and attach Air Pressure Gauge (J-22124-A) to drier fitting. *See Fig. 3.*

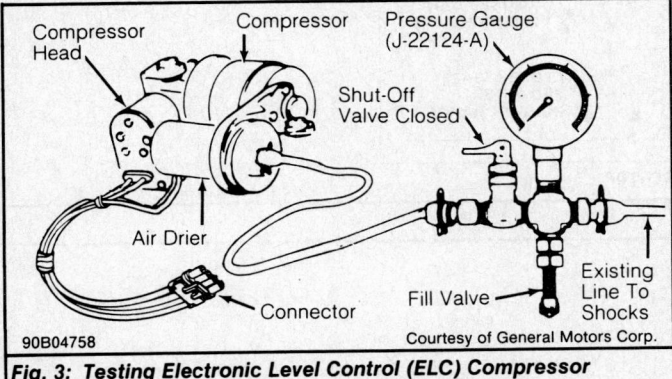

Fig. 3: *Testing Electronic Level Control (ELC) Compressor*

2) Connect 12-volt power supply to compressor through an ammeter, in order to measure current draw. Current draw must not exceed 14 amps. Allow air pressure to reach 100 psi (7.03 kg/cm²) minimum and shut off compressor. Allow air pressure to stabilize. Check for pressure leaks.

3) If compressor is allowed to run to maximum output pressure of 170 psi (12.3 kg/cm²), the solenoid exhaust valve will act as a pressure relief valve. The solenoid exhaust valve will then release pressure down to 100 psi (7.03 kg/cm²). This will give a false indication of system leakage.

4) If compressor operates correctly, reconnect wiring harnesses and air lines. If compressor does not operate correctly, refer to ELC COMPRESSOR DIAGNOSIS.

ELC COMPRESSOR DIAGNOSIS

- Compressor runs but current draw exceeds 14 amps. Replace compressor motor assembly.
- Compressor is inoperative. Remove motor end housing and inspect internal components. Repair or replace as required. If no defect is found, replace motor assembly.
- Air pressure builds up okay but leaks down to below 90 psi (kg/cm²) before holding steady. Does not leak down to zero air pressure. Replace compressor head assembly.
- Air pressure leaks down to zero psi. Perform compressor/drier leak test and repair as required.
- Air pressure build up is less than 110 psi. Perform compressor/drier leak test and repair as required. If no defect is found, replace complete air compressor assembly.

HEIGHT SENSOR OPERATIONAL TEST

1) Cycle ignition off then on. This will reset height sensor timer circuits. Raise vehicle on hoist that allows rear wheels to be as close as possible to trim height dimension. An alignment rack type hoist is ideal for this test.

2) Ensure wiring is securely connected to height sensor and ground wire is secure. Scribe reference mark on height sensor metal arm to plastic arm. Disconnect link from height sensor metal arm. Move sensor arm up. Should be 8-15 second delay before compressor turns on and shocks inflate. When shocks start to inflate, move metal arm down to stop compressor.

3) Now, move metal arm downward to just below where compressor previously stopped. After 8-15 second delay, shocks should begin to deflate. If system performs as described, move metal arm back to original position and secure lock nut. If system does not perform as described, replace height sensor and adjust to specification. See HEIGHT SENSOR under ADJUSTMENTS.

REMOVAL & INSTALLATION

ELC HEIGHT SENSOR

Removal – Disconnect negative battery cable. Raise and support vehicle. Disconnect height sensor harness. Disconnect height sensor link from height sensor actuating arm. Remove 2 height sensor mounting screws.

Installation – To install, reverse removal procedure. Tighten sensor mounting bolts to specification. Adjust height sensor. See HEIGHT SENSOR under ADJUSTMENTS.

ELC COMPRESSOR

Removal – Disconnect negative battery cable. Disconnect compressor electrical connectors. Remove air line from drier. Remove bracket-to-inner fender panel screws. Remove compressor-to-bracket screws. Remove compressor from bracket.

Installation – To install, reverse removal procedure. Pre-pressurize system by grounding test connector (Yellow wire terminal) with jumper wire. Turn ignition on and allow system to cycle. Check for leaks using soap and water solution.

AIR DRIER

Removal – Disconnect high pressure line by turning spring clip 90 degrees and removing tube assembly. Disconnect drier from compressor by turning spring clip and sliding drier and "O" ring from compressor head assembly.

Installation – Lubricate "O" ring and install in port of compressor head. Return retainer spring to its original position. Install drier on compressor head assembly. If difficulty arises when installing drier in compressor head assembly, rotate slightly while applying pressure. Check system for leaks.

1991 SUSPENSION
Rear – Electronic Level Control – Brougham (Cont.)

AIR LINE

Repair air line by splicing in a coupling at leak area. Inflate system to 100 psi (7.03 kg/cm²). Use a soap and water solution to locate leak. Deflate system through service valve, and cut out leaking area. Install coupling, and tighten tube nuts to 72 INCH lbs. (8 N.m). *See Fig. 4.* Inflate system, and check for leaks using a soap and water solution.

TORQUE SPECIFICATIONS

TORQUE SPECIFICATIONS

Application	INCH Lbs. (N.m)
Compressor Bracket Mounting Screws	62 (7.0)
Compressor Head Bolts	36 (4.0)
Compressor Mounting Screws	36 (4.0)
Height Sensor Mounting Screws	133 (15.0)

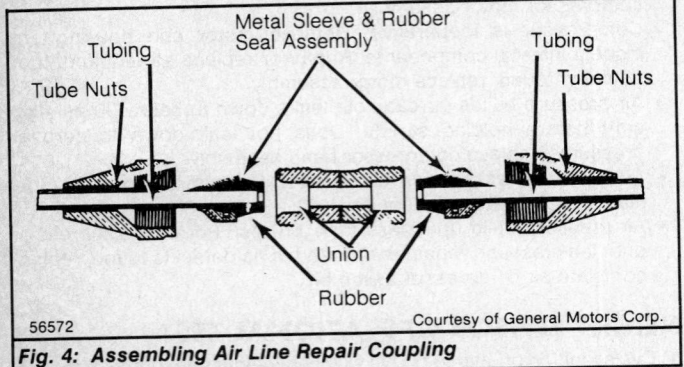

56572   Courtesy of General Motors Corp.

Fig. 4: Assembling Air Line Repair Coupling

WIRING DIAGRAM

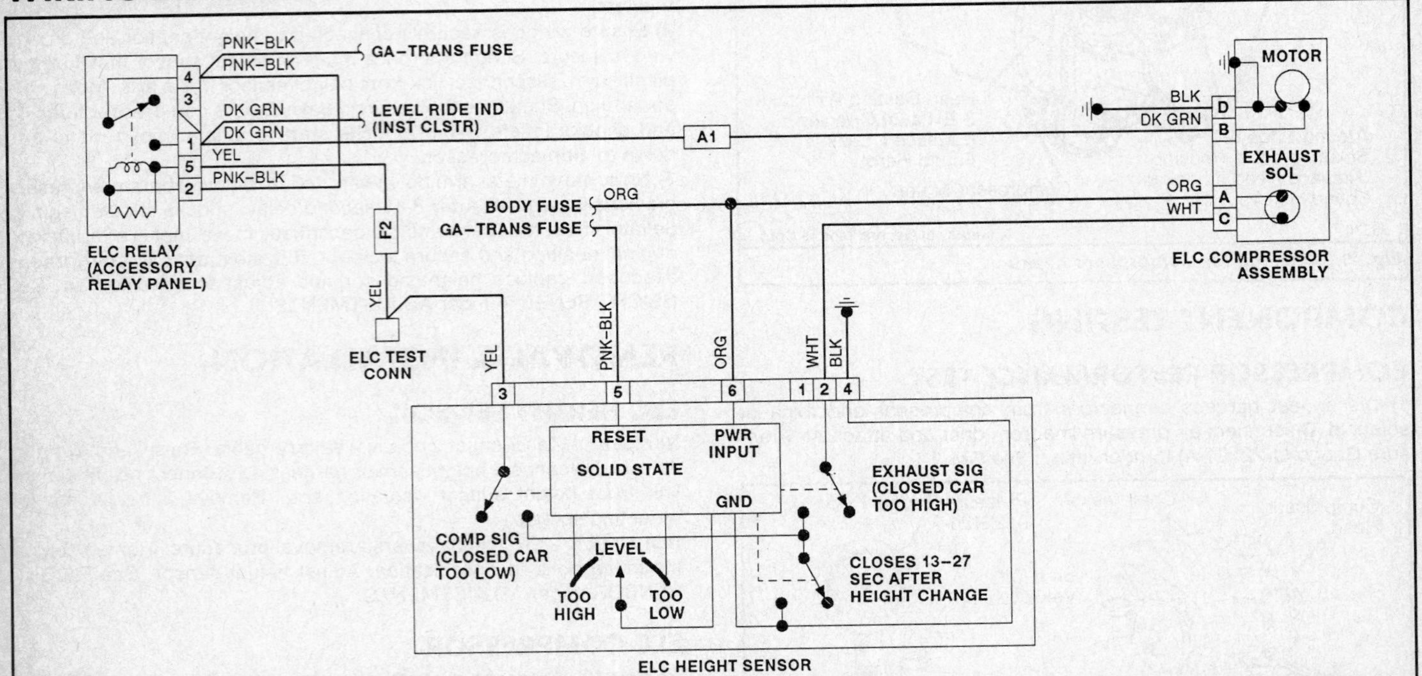

91J07831

Fig. 5: Electronic Level Control Wiring Diagram ("D" Body)

"C" Body: DeVille, Fleetwood, Ninety-Eight,
Park Avenue, Touring Sedan
"H" Body: Bonneville, Eighty-Eight, LeSabre

DESCRIPTION

The Electronic Level Control (ELC) automatically maintains vehicle riding height in accordance with vehicle loads. System is activated when ignition is on and vehicle weight changes.

The ELC system consists of a compressor, air drier, exhaust (vent) solenoid, compressor relay, height sensor, air adjustable shock absorbers, pressure limiter and connecting air lines.

OPERATION

SYSTEM OPERATION

When weight is added to vehicle, height sensor arm rotates upward. Rotating arm upward grounds compressor relay circuit. After a time delay of approximately 17-27 seconds, compressor relay turns air compressor on. Air is pumped into shock absorbers and vehicle is raised. As vehicle rises, height sensor rotates downward to curb height position. When vehicle is within 1" (25.4 mm) of curb height, height sensor opens ground circuit to compressor relay, turning compressor off.

When weight is removed from vehicle, height sensor arm rotates downward. After a time delay of approximately 17-27 seconds, downward rotation of the arm grounds exhaust solenoid valve circuit, causing air to vent. Energizing exhaust solenoid valve causes air to vent from shock absorbers and vehicle lowers. As vehicle lowers, height sensor arm rotates upward. When vehicle is within 1" (25.4 mm) of curb height, height sensor opens exhaust solenoid valve circuit causing exhaust solenoid valve to close.

In order to ensure system is operating with at least minimum air pressure, height sensor commands an air replenishment cycle each time ignition is cycled on. An internal timer circuit is activated when ignition switch is turned to ON position. After a delay of approximately 35-45 seconds, compressor turns on for 3-5 seconds to ensure residual system pressure.

If weight is added or removed from vehicle during 35-45 second delay, air replenishment cycle will be overridden and vehicle will raise or lower after normal time delay.

Voltage is applied to compressor, ELC relay, inflator timer and height sensor at all times. This allows system to vent after load is removed with ignition turned off. Height sensor limits compressor operation or exhaust solenoid energized time to 7 minutes (10 minutes on Bonneville). Time limit is necessary to prevent continuous compressor operation in case of air leak. Turning ignition from off to on will reset compressor operation or exhaust solenoid valve energized time.

Bonneville models are equipped with an air inflator feature. When air is needed to fill a tire, connecting inflator hose then turning inflator switch on activates inflator solenoid valve and compressor. The compressor pumps and air is diverted from ELC system to inflator system by inflator solenoid.

Air Adjustable Shock Absorber – Air adjustable shock absorber is a conventional shock absorber which contains an air chamber that extends when air pressure is increased in shock absorber.

Air Drier – Air drier is attached to compressor output. Air drier absorbs moisture from air being delivered to air adjustable shock absorbers. Air drier contains a valve arrangement that maintains a minimum shock absorber air pressure of 7-14 psi (.49-.98 kg/cm²).

Compressor – The piston-type compressor is located on left side of engine compartment. Compressor head casting contains intake and exhaust valves and exhaust valve solenoid. Compressor provides air pressure for system operation.

Compressor Relay – Compressor relay is located in relay center behind glove box. Compressor relay is grounded by height sensor and after a time delay of approximately 7-14 seconds, compressor relay turns air compressor on.

Exhaust Solenoid Valve – Exhaust solenoid valve is located within compressor head assembly. Exhaust solenoid valve exhausts air from the system and limits compressor output pressure.

Height Sensor – Height sensor is mounted to underbody frame in rear of vehicle. Movement of height sensor arm controls compressor relay and exhaust solenoid valve ground circuits to adjust vehicle height. Height sensor limits compressor operation or exhaust solenoid valve energized time to 2.5 minutes. Time limit is necessary to prevent continuous compressor operation in case of air leak.

Inflator Solenoid (Bonneville) – Inflator solenoid is located in right front side of trunk. When inflator switch is turned on, inflator solenoid valve and ELC compressor are activated and air is diverted from ELC system to inflator system.

Inflator Switch (Bonneville) – Inflator switch is located in right rear side of trunk. When switch is turned on, inflator solenoid and ELC compressor are activated.

ADJUSTMENTS

HEIGHT SENSOR

1) Vehicle should be on level surface with gas tank full and NO load in car. Turn ignition switch to ON position. Bounce car 3 times to normalize suspension. To increase vehicle riding height, loosen lock bolt on sensor arm. Move plastic arm upward and tighten lock nut.

2) To lower riding height, loosen lock nut, move plastic arm down and tighten lock nut. There is a total of 5 degrees of adjustment on sensor. One degree of adjustment is equal to 1/4" change in height at bumper. If adjustment cannot be made, there is a problem with rear springs or suspension. See Fig. 1.

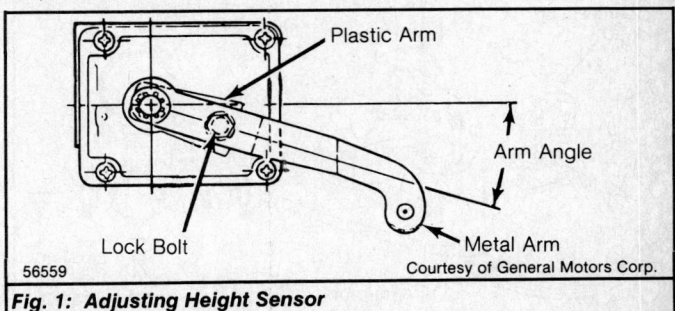

Lock Bolt · Plastic Arm · Arm Angle · Metal Arm
56559
Courtesy of General Motors Corp.

Fig. 1: Adjusting Height Sensor

RIDING HEIGHT

NOTE: See SPECIFICATIONS & PROCEDURES article in WHEEL ALIGNMENT.

TROUBLE SHOOTING

Car Loaded, Will Not Rise – Leaks in air lines, fittings or shock absorbers. Pinched lines between compressor and shock absorbers. Defective height sensor. Compressor inoperative. Loose or damaged electrical connections to sensor or compressor.

Car Loaded, Rises, Then Leaks Down – Severe leak in lines, fittings or shock absorbers. Internal leak in compressor.

Car Loaded, Rises Partially – Height sensor out of adjustment. Compressor or wiring defective.

Car Rises When Loaded, Leaks Down When Driving – Defective drier or compressor. Pinched air lines or leaks in fittings or air lines.

Car Rides High – Height sensor out of adjustment. Drier plugged or air lines pinched. Poor electrical connections.

SYSTEM TESTING

SYSTEM OPERATIONAL TEST

1) Ensure height sensor and link assembly are in good condition before performing system operation test. Place vehicle on flat surface.

Measure distance from floor to rocker panel in front of rear wheelwell opening.

2) Turn ignition on. Add 300-350 lbs. (135-159 kg) of weight to rear of vehicle. After 17-27 second delay, compressor should turn on and vehicle start to raise. Vehicle should raise within 1" (25.4 mm) of measurement made in step **1)**.

3) Remove load from vehicle. After 17-27 second delay, vehicle should start to lower. Within 3 1/2 minutes, exhaust should stop and vehicle should be within 1" (25.4 mm) of measurement made in step **1)**. If ELC system does not function as specified, see ELECTRICAL TESTING.

SYSTEM LEAK TEST

CAUTION: System leak test will determine if a leak exists and if leak is internal or external to the compressor.

1) Install Pressure Gauge (J-22124-A) and Air Hose Set (J-22124-91) to air drier and air adjustable shock absorbers. *See Fig. 2.* With shutoff gauge open, apply shop air pressure through service valve on pressure gauge until pressure gauge reaches 100 psi (7.0 kg/cm²).

2) If air leak is indicated, close shutoff valve. This isolates compressor from rest of system. Check for drop in air pressure. If air pressure continues to drop, leak is external from the compressor.

3) Test all connections using soapy water solution and repair as necessary. If air pressure stops decreasing after shutoff valve is closed, leak is in compressor assembly. See COMPRESSOR LEAK TEST under COMPONENT TESTING.

4) If air pressure builds up rapidly but vehicle does not rise, check for pinched air line or stuck or binding air adjustable shock absorbers.

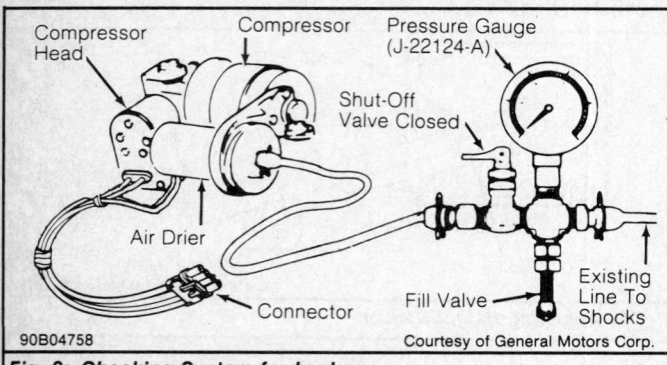

Courtesy of General Motors Corp.
90B04758
Fig. 2: Checking System for Leakage

COMPONENT TESTING

COMPRESSOR OPERATION TEST

NOTE: Compressor operation will be checked by measuring current draw, compressor output and pressure leak-down.

1) Disconnect pressure line from drier and connect Pressure Gauge (J-22124-A) to air drier. *See Fig. 3.*

2) Disconnect compressor ground wire (Black wire) from compressor bracket and install ammeter between Black wire and ground. Using a jumper wire, apply battery voltage to pin "B" (Dark Green wire) at compressor connector. Ground pin "D" (Black wire) at compressor connector. Note compressor motor current draw. *See Fig. 3.*

3) If compressor does not operate or current draw exceeds 14 amps, replace motor/cylinder assembly. If current draw is 14 amps or less, allow pressure to reach 100 psi (7.0 kg/cm²) and disconnect voltage supply.

NOTE: If compressor is allowed to run to maximum output pressure of 180 psi (12.7 kg/cm²), the solenoid exhaust valve will act as a relief valve. This gives a false indication of system leakage.

4) If pressure held at 100 psi (7.0 kg/cm²), compressor is okay. If pressure decreases to less than 60 psi (4.2 kg/cm²), but does not continue to drop, replace compressor head assembly.

5) If pressure completely leaks off, or pressure built up but would not reach 100 psi (7.0 kg/cm²), check compressor for leaks. See COMPRESSOR LEAK TEST under COMPONENT TESTING. Remove pressure gauge.

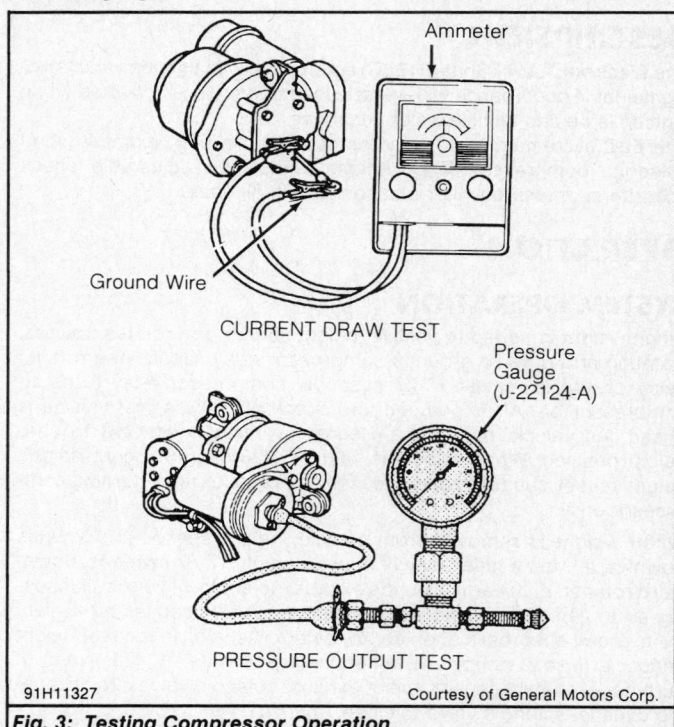

91H11327   Courtesy of General Motors Corp.
Fig. 3: Testing Compressor Operation

COMPRESSOR LEAK TEST

1) Install Pressure Gauge (J-22124-A) to air drier so shutoff valve is on compressor side of gauge. *See Fig. 4.* With shutoff valve open, apply shop air pressure through service valve on pressure gauge until gauge reaches 100-120 psi (7.0-8.4 kg/cm²).

2) If leak is indicated, close shutoff valve (down) and note pressure drop. Closing the valve isolates compressor from remainder of system. If gauge pressure continues to drop, leak is external to compressor. Using soapy water solution, check for leaks around all connections.

3) If gauge pressure does not continue to drop, leak is in compressor. Using soapy water solution, check for leaks around air drier cover, air drier "O" ring casting bore, edge of cover gasket, edge of solenoid valve housing, head casting air intake and exhaust openings and head cover. *See Fig. 4.*

4) If leak exists at cover bolts, tighten bolts to specification and in sequence. *See Fig. 8* and TORQUE SPECIFICATIONS table at end of this article. Recheck compressor for leaks. Remove pressure gauge. If pressure builds up rapidly but vehicle does not raise, check for pinched air lines or seized air adjustable shock absorbers.

COMPRESSOR RESIDUAL AIR TEST

1) Disconnect pressure line from drier and attach Air Pressure Gauge (J-22124-A) to drier fitting. Disconnect ELC relay wiring harness connector and connect 12-volt jumper wire to Dark Green wire terminal to run compressor.

2) Allow pressure to reach 100 psi (7.03 kg/cm²) minimum and shut off compressor. Disconnect compressor wiring harness connector. Connect 12-volt jumper wire to White wire terminal. This will cause system to exhaust.

3) When all air has been exhausted from system, air pressure gauge should register a residual amount of 7-14 psi (.5-.9 kg/cm²). If there is no residual pressure, replace drier cover and valve assembly.

HEIGHT SENSOR OPERATIONAL TEST

1) Turn ignition off and then on to reset height sensor timing circuit. Raise and support vehicle.

CAUTION: Ensure rear wheels are supported so proper riding height is obtained. See SPECIFICATIONS & PROCEDURES article in WHEEL ALIGNMENT.

2) Disconnect link from height sensor arm. Ensure all wiring connections are properly connected on height sensor. Move height sensor arm upward.

3) After 17-27 second delay, compressor should turn on and air adjustable shock absorbers should start to inflate. As soon as air shock absorbers start to inflate, move height sensor arm downward until compressor stops. Move height sensor downward past area where compressor stopped. After 17-27 second delay, air adjustable shock absorbers should start to deflate.

4) If system operated as described, height sensor is operating properly. Reinstall link on height sensor arm. Lower vehicle. If system does not perform as described, replace height sensor and adjust sensor to specification. See HEIGHT SENSOR under ADJUSTMENTS.

ACTUATOR ARM TEST

Raise vehicle, and ensure link is attached to actuator arm correctly and actuator arm is properly aligned. *See Fig. 1.* If actuator arm is okay, go to SYMPTOM DIRECTORY table under ELECTRICAL TESTING.

ELECTRICAL TESTING

SYMPTOM DIRECTORY

Symptom	Perform
Compressor Does Not Run	ELC RELAY & COMPRESSOR MOTOR TESTS, ACTUATOR ARM TEST, ELC HEIGHT SENSOR TESTS
System Does Not Exhaust	EXHAUST SOLENOID TESTS, ACTUATOR ARM TEST, ELC HEIGHT SENSOR TESTS
Compressor Runs Continuously, Vehicle Rises & Compressor Runs 7 Minutes & Stays At Maximum Height	[1] ACTUATOR ARM TEST.
Compressor Runs 7 Minutes & Turns Off. Vehicle Does Not Reach Proper Height	ACTUATOR ARM TEST, EXHAUST SOLENOID SHORT TEST
System Cycles On And Off Frequently	ACTUATOR ARM TEST, EXHAUST SOLENOID SHORT TEST
Compressor Inoperative For Inflator Feature	INFLATOR TIMER RELAY TESTS INFLATOR SWITCH TEST
Compressor Runs But No Air From Inflator Hose	INFLATOR TIMER RELAY TESTS INFLATOR SOLENOID TEST

[1] – Unplug ELC height sensor connector. If compressor does not run, replace ELC height sensor. If compressor runs, check Yellow wire for short to ground. If wire is okay, replace ELC relay.

ELC RELAY & COMPRESSOR MOTOR TESTS (EXCEPT BONNEVILLE)

Test No. 1 – On DeVille and Fleetwood models, disconnect ELC sensor connector and jumper terminal "B" (Yellow wire) to ground. On Eighty-Eight, Ninety-Eight and Touring Sedan models, ground ELC test lead connector, located on Yellow wire near ELC relay, with a fused jumper wire. If compressor runs, go to ELC HEIGHT SENSOR TESTS. If compressor does not run, go to TEST NO. 2 of ELC RELAY & COMPRESSOR MOTOR TESTS.

Test No. 2 – Disconnect ELC relay connector. Relay is located in relay center behind glove box. Measure voltage from terminals No. 1 and 5 (Orange wires) to ground. If voltage reads zero, check Orange wires and fuse No. 12 for an open. If reading is battery voltage, go to TEST NO. 3 of ELC RELAY & COMPRESSOR MOTOR TESTS.

Test No. 3 – Connect a fused jumper wire between terminals No. 1 (Orange wire) and 4 (Dark Green wire) of ELC relay connector. If compressor runs, check Yellow wire for an open. If wire is okay, replace ELC relay. If compressor does not run go to TEST NO. 4 of ELC RELAY & COMPRESSOR MOTOR TESTS.

Test No. 4 – 1) With fused jumper still connected to ELC relay (from previous test), disconnect ELC compressor connector. Measure voltage between terminal "B" (Dark Green wire) at compressor connector and ground.

2) If voltage reads zero, check Dark Green wire for an open. If reading is battery voltage, measure voltage between terminals "B" (Dark Green wire) and "D" (Black wire) at ELC compressor connector. If voltage reads zero, check Black wire for an open. If reading is battery voltage, repair and/or replace ELC compressor assembly.

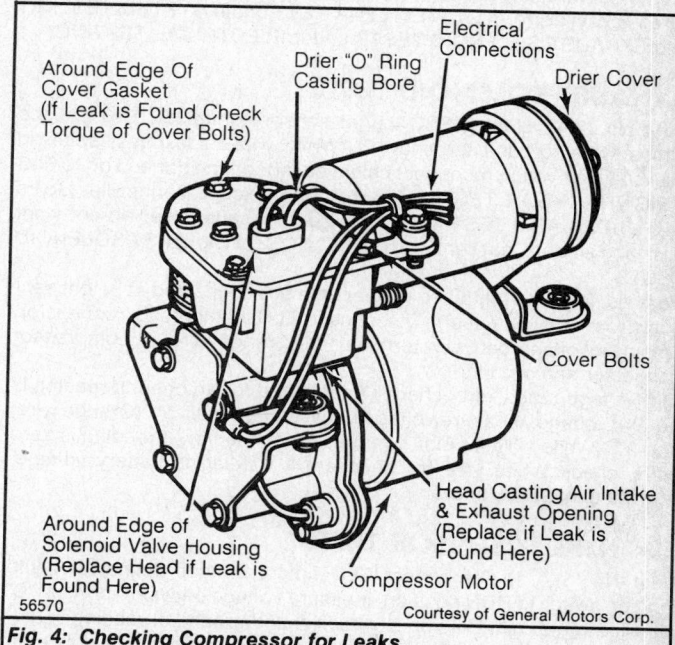

Fig. 4: Checking Compressor for Leaks

Labels: Drier "O" Ring Casting Bore; Electrical Connections; Drier Cover; Around Edge Of Cover Gasket (If Leak is Found Check Torque of Cover Bolts); Cover Bolts; Around Edge of Solenoid Valve Housing (Replace Head if Leak is Found Here); Head Casting Air Intake & Exhaust Opening (Replace if Leak is Found Here); Compressor Motor; 56570; Courtesy of General Motors Corp.

ELC RELAY & COMPRESSOR MOTOR TESTS (BONNEVILLE)

Test No. 1 – Using a fused jumper wire, ground Yellow wire at ELC test lead connector. ELC test connector is located in front of engine compartment, above ELC compressor assembly. If compressor runs, go to ACTUATOR ARM TEST under COMPONENT TESTING. If compressor does not run, go to TEST NO. 2 of ELC RELAY & COMPRESSOR MOTOR TESTS.

Test No. 2 – With fused jumper wire still connected (from previous test), remove ELC relay. Relay is located in relay center behind glove box. Measure voltage between terminals No. 1 and No. 5 (Orange wires) to ground. If voltage reads zero, check Orange wires for an open. Measure voltage between terminals No. 1 (Orange wire) and No. 2 (Yellow wire). If voltage reads zero, check Yellow wire for an open. If all test readings are battery voltage, go to TEST NO. 3 of ELC RELAY & COMPRESSOR MOTOR TESTS.

Test No. 3 – With fused jumper still connected and ELC relay removed (from previous test), connect a fused jumper wire between terminals No. 1 (Orange wire) and No. 4 (Dark Green wire) of ELC relay connector. If compressor runs, replace ELC relay. If compressor does not run go to TEST NO. 4 of ELC RELAY & COMPRESSOR MOTOR TESTS.

Test No. 4 – 1) With fused jumper still connected to ELC relay (from previous test), disconnect ELC compressor connector. Measure voltage between terminal "B" (Dark Green wire) at compressor connector and ground.

2) If voltage reads zero, check Dark Green wire for an open. If reading is battery voltage, measure voltage between terminals "B" (Dark Green wire) and "D" (Black wire) at ELC compressor connector. If volt-

GM
10-54

1991 SUSPENSION
Rear – Electronic Level Control – "C" & "H" Bodies (Cont.)

age reads zero, check Black wire for an open. If reading is battery voltage, repair and/or replace ELC compressor assembly.

EXHAUST SOLENOID SHORT TEST (BONNEVILLE)

1) Add 300 lbs. (136 kg) to luggage compartment. Disconnect ELC height sensor connector. Ground ELC test connector (terminal "B" Yellow wire) with a fused jumper. ELC test connector is located in front of engine compartment, above ELC compressor assembly. Allow compressor to run for 2 minutes.

2) If vehicle rises and maintains its height, replace ELC height sensor. If vehicle does not raise or rises and leaks down, check White wire between height sensor and compressor for short to ground.

3) If White wire is found to have a short, repair as necessary. If White wire is okay, perform SYSTEM LEAK TEST under SYSTEM TESTING and EXHAUST SOLENOID TESTS under ELECTRICAL TESTING.

EXHAUST SOLENOID TESTS

Test No. 1 – Unplug ELC height sensor connector. Using fused jumper wire, ground terminal "E" (White wire). If exhaust solenoid clicks and air vents, reconnect height sensor connector and go to ELC HEIGHT SENSOR TESTS for all models except Bonneville. Go to ACTUATOR ARM TEST for Bonneville. If exhaust solenoid does not click and air does not vent, go to TEST NO. 2 of EXHAUST SOLENOID TESTS

Test No. 2 – 1) With fused jumper wire still connected at height sensor (from previous test), Disconnect ELC compressor connector. Measure voltage between terminal "A" (Orange wire) at compressor connector and ground.

2) If voltage reads zero, check Orange wire for an open. If reading is battery voltage, measure voltage between terminals "A" (Orange wire) and "C" (White wire) at ELC compressor connector. If reading is zero volts, check White wire for an open. If reading is battery voltage, replace exhaust solenoid.

ELC HEIGHT SENSOR TESTS

Test No. 1 – 1) Disconnect ELC height sensor connector. With ignition switch in RUN position, measure voltage between terminal "C" (Orange wire, Light Blue on Bonneville) and ground. If reading is battery voltage, go to step **2)**. If reading is not battery voltage, check and/or repair open in Orange wire (Light Blue on Bonneville).

2) Measure voltage between terminals "C" (Orange wire, Light Blue on Bonneville) and "A" (Black wire). If reading is battery voltage, go to step **3)**. If reading is not battery voltage, check and/or repair open to ground in Black wire.

3) Measure voltage between terminals "D" (Brown wire) and "A" (Black wire). If reading is battery voltage, go to step **4)**. If reading is not battery voltage, check and/or repair Brown wire for an open.

4) Measure voltage between terminals "B" (Yellow wire) and "A" (Black wire). On all models except Bonneville, if reading is battery voltage, go to step **5)**. On Bonneville, if reading is battery voltage, go to TEST NO. 2 of ELC HEIGHT SENSOR TESTS. On all models, if reading is not battery voltage, check and/or repair Yellow wire for an open.

5) Measure voltage between terminal "E" (White wire) and "A" (Black wire). If reading is not battery voltage, check and/or repair open in White wire. If all test readings are battery voltage, go to TEST NO. 2 of ELC HEIGHT SENSOR TESTS.

Test No. 2 – 1) Cycle ignition switch and place in RUN position. Raise vehicle and support rear axle housing at ride height. Disconnect link from actuator arm. Move actuator arm upward.

2) If compressor begins to run but shocks DO NOT inflate after a 17-27 second delay, perform COMPRESSOR OPERATION TEST under COMPONENT TESTING and SYSTEM LEAK TEST under SYSTEM TESTING. If compressor does not begin to run after a 17-27 second delay, replace ELC height sensor.

3) If compressor begins to run and shocks begin to inflate after a 17-27 second delay, slowly move actuator arm downward until compressor stops. If compressor does not stop, replace height sensor. If compressor does stop, continue to move actuator arm downward.

4) If the shocks DO NOT start to deflate and vehicle does not begin to lower after a 17-27 second delay, replace the height sensor. If the shocks begin to deflate and the vehicle starts to lower after a 17-27 second delay, the ELC system is okay. Adjust height sensor. See HEIGHT SENSOR under ADJUSTMENTS.

INFLATOR TIMER RELAY TESTS (BONNEVILLE)

Test No. 1 – Connect a fused jumper wire between terminal "F" (White wire) of inflator timer relay and ground with connector connected. Relay is located inside of trunk toward right front. If compressor runs and high pressure air is vented from air hose as valve operates, go to INFLATOR SWITCH TEST. If compressor does not run, remove jumper and go to TEST NO. 2 of INFLATOR TIMER RELAY TESTS (BONNEVILLE). If compressor runs and no air is vented, leave jumper connected and go to TEST NO. 3 of INFLATOR TIMER RELAY TESTS (BONNEVILLE).

Test No. 2 – 1) Ensure inflator switch is in OFF position and compressor is not running. At inflator timer relay connector, measure voltage between terminal "D" (Orange wire) and ground. If battery voltage is present, go to step **2)**. If battery voltage is not present, check and/or repair open in Orange wire.

2) Measure voltage between terminals "E" (Yellow wire) and ground. If battery voltage is present, go to step **3)**. If battery voltage is not present, check and/or repair open to ground in Yellow wire.

3) Measure voltage between terminal "B" (Light Blue wire) and ground. If battery voltage is present, go to step **4)**. If battery voltage is not present, replace inflator timer relay.

4) Measure voltage between terminal "D" (Orange wire) and "H" (Black wire). If battery voltage is not present, check and/or repair open in Black wire. If all test readings are battery voltage, replace inflator timer relay.

Test No. 3 – Connect jumper wire as in INFLATOR TIMER RELAY TEST NO. 1 (BONNEVILLE). Measure voltage between connector terminal "C" (Dark Blue wire) and ground. If battery voltage is present, go to INFLATOR SOLENOID TEST (BONNEVILLE). If battery voltage is not present, replace inflator timer relay.

INFLATOR SWITCH TEST (BONNEVILLE)

1) Disconnect inflator timer relay connector located inside of trunk toward right front. With inflator switch connected and held in ON position, use ohmmeter to measure resistance between terminal "A" (White wire) and "B" (Black wire). If reading is not zero ohms, replace inflator switch. If reading is zero ohms, go to step **2)**.

2) Hold inflator switch in OFF position. Measure resistance between terminal "C" (Purple wire) and "B" (Black wire). If reading is not zero ohms, replace inflator switch. If readings in both steps were zero ohms, check White, Black and Purple wires for an open.

INFLATOR SOLENOID TEST (BONNEVILLE)

1) Disconnect inflator solenoid connector located inside of trunk toward right front. Connect a fused jumper wire between terminals "D" (Orange) and "C" (Dark Blue wire) of the inflator timer relay connector. Measure voltage between terminal "A" (Dark Blue wire) and ground. If battery voltage is present, go to step **2)**. If battery voltage is not present, check and/or repair open in Dark Blue wire.

2) Measure voltage between inflator solenoid terminal "A" (Dark Blue wire) and terminal "B" (Black wire). If battery voltage is not present, check and/or repair open in Black wire. If battery voltage is present in steps **1)** and **2)**, check air lines and fittings. If air lines and fittings are okay, replace inflator solenoid.

REMOVAL & INSTALLATION

ELC HEIGHT SENSOR

Removal & Installation – Disconnect negative battery cable. Raise and support vehicle. Disconnect height sensor harness connector. Disconnect height sensor link from height sensor actuating arm. Remove 2 height sensor mounting screws. To install, reverse removal

1991 SUSPENSION
Rear – Electronic Level Control – "C" & "H" Bodies (Cont.)

GM
10-55

procedure. Tighten sensor mounting bolts to specification. Adjust height sensor. See HEIGHT SENSOR under ADJUSTMENTS.

ELC COMPRESSOR

Removal – Disconnect negative battery cable. Disconnect compressor electrical connectors. Remove pressure limiter retaining clip from compressor bracket. Remove rear shock feed line from pressure limiter valve. Remove mounting screws. Remove compressor-to-bracket screws. Remove compressor.

Installation – To install, reverse removal procedure. Turn ignition on and allow system to cycle. Check for leaks using soap and water solution.

AIR DRIER

Removal – Disconnect high pressure line by turning spring clip 90 degrees and removing tube assembly. Disconnect drier from compressor by turning spring clip 90 degrees and pull drier and "O" ring from compressor head assembly. See Fig. 5.

Installation – Lubricate "O" ring and install in port of compressor head. Install retainer spring to its original position. Install drier on compressor head assembly. If difficulty arises when installing drier in compressor head assembly, rotate slightly while applying pressure. Install air tube to drier. Check system for leaks.

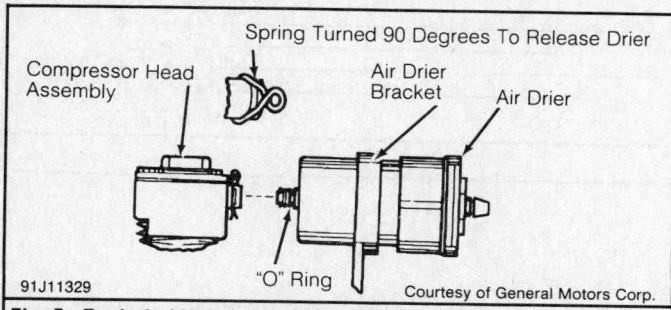

Fig. 5: Exploded View of Air Drier Assembly

AIR LINE

Repair air line by splicing in a coupling at leak area. Inflate system to 100 psi (7.03 kg/cm²). Use a soap and water solution to locate leak. Deflate system through service valve, and cut out leaking area. Install coupling, and tighten tube nuts to 72 INCH lbs. (8 N.m). See Fig. 6. Inflate system, and check for leaks using a soap and water solution.

COMPRESSOR HEAD ASSEMBLY

Removal & Installation – 1) Remove air drier assembly. See AIR DRIER under REMOVAL & INSTALLATION. Remove compressor head mounting bolts. See Fig. 7. Remove head assembly.
2) To install, reverse removal procedure. Tighten compressor head bolts to specification and in sequence. See Fig. 8. See TORQUE SPECIFICATIONS table at end of article.

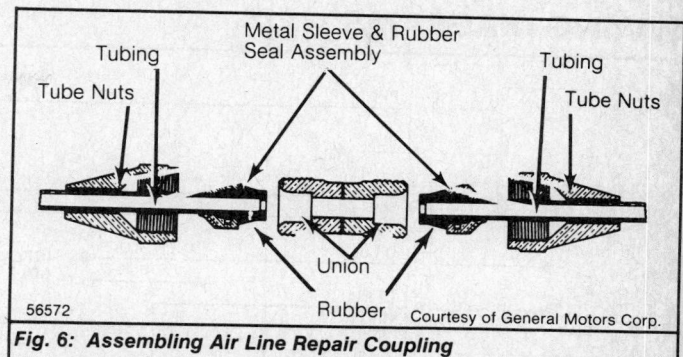

Fig. 6: Assembling Air Line Repair Coupling

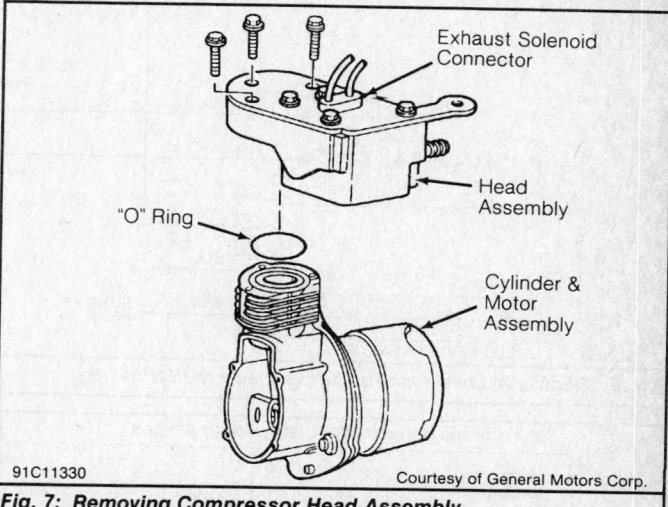

Fig. 7: Removing Compressor Head Assembly

Fig. 8: Compressor Head Tightening Sequence

TORQUE SPECIFICATIONS

TORQUE SPECIFICATIONS

Application	INCH Lbs. (N.m)
Compressor Bracket Mounting Screws	45 (5)
Compressor Head Bolts [1]	36 (4)
Compressor Mounting Screws	45 (5)
Height Sensor Mounting Screws	62 (7)

[1] – Tighten in sequence. See Fig. 8.

GM
10-56

1991 SUSPENSION
Rear – Electronic Level Control – "C" & "H" Bodies (Cont.)

WIRING DIAGRAMS

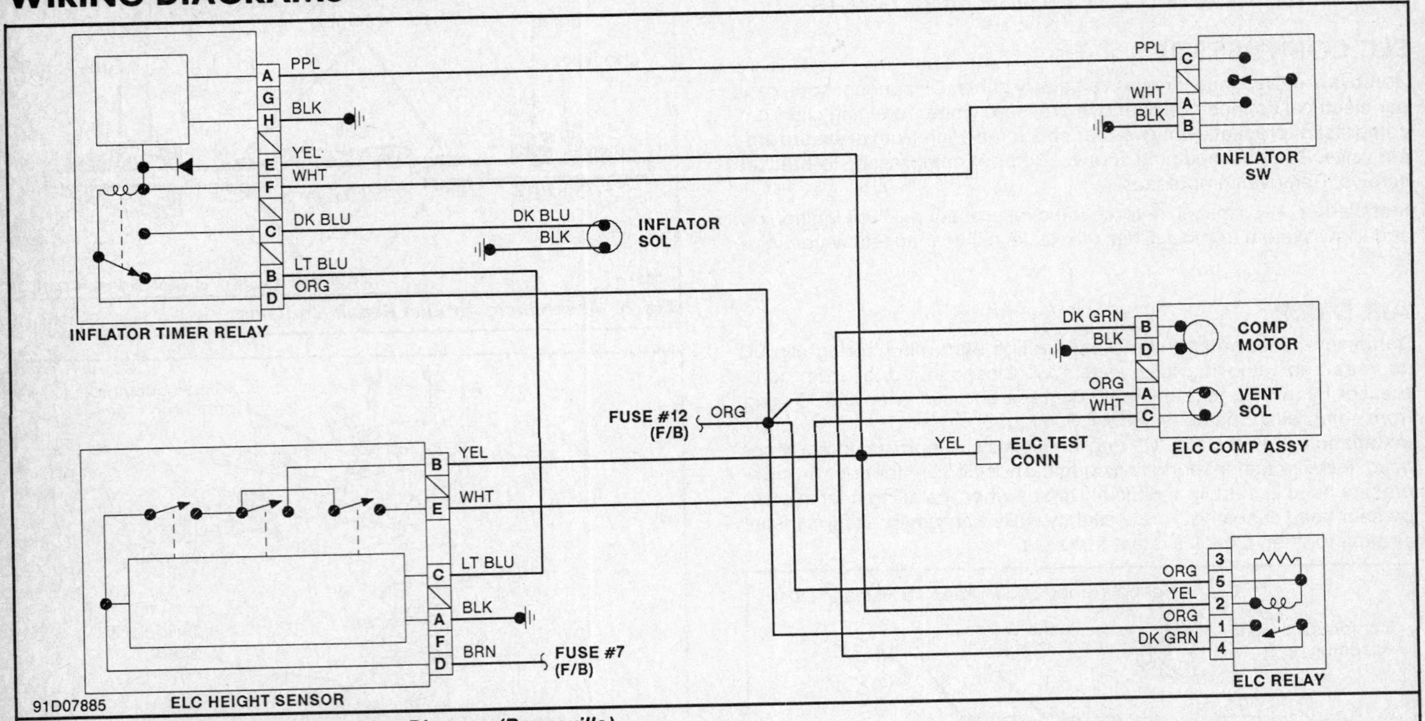

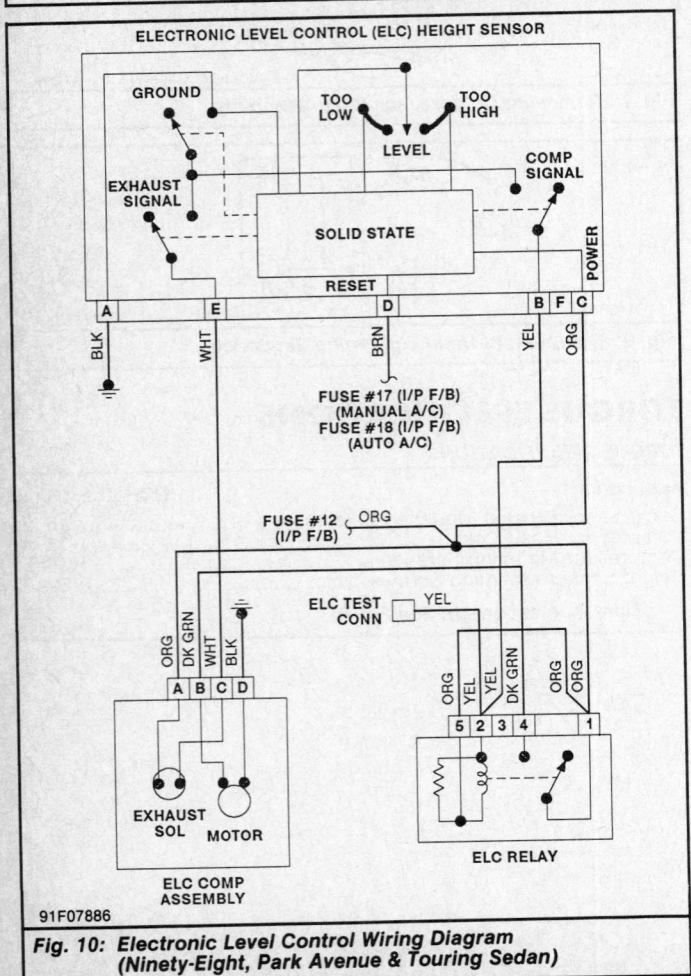

Fig. 9: *Electronic Level Control Wiring Diagram (Bonneville)*

91D07885

91F07886

Fig. 10: *Electronic Level Control Wiring Diagram (Ninety-Eight, Park Avenue & Touring Sedan)*

1991 SUSPENSION
Rear – Electronic Level Control – "C" & "H" Bodies (Cont.)

GM
10-57

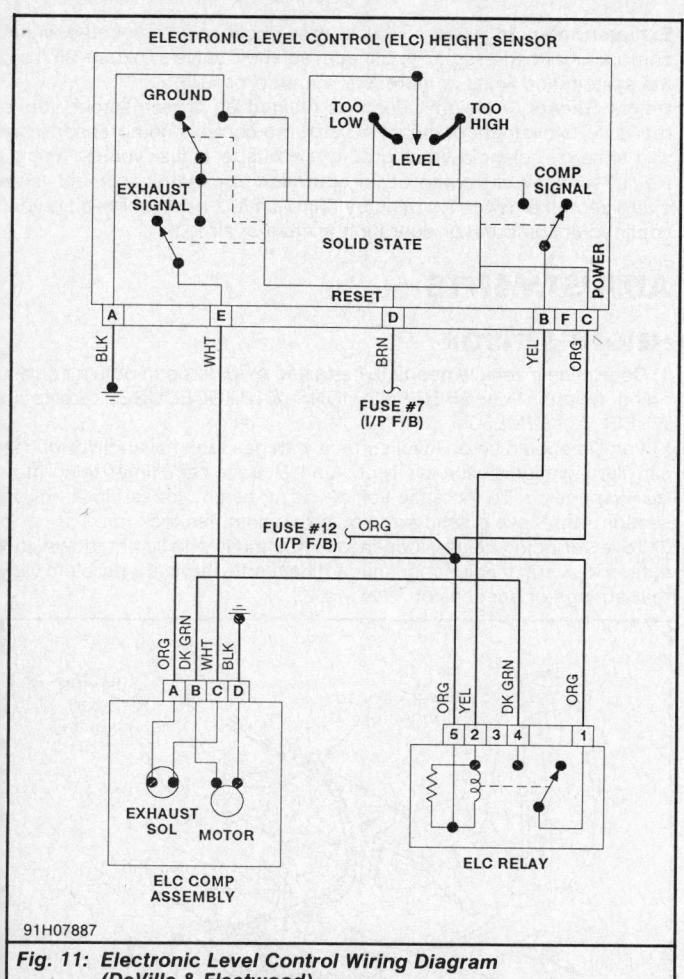

Fig. 11: Electronic Level Control Wiring Diagram (DeVille & Fleetwood)

91H07887

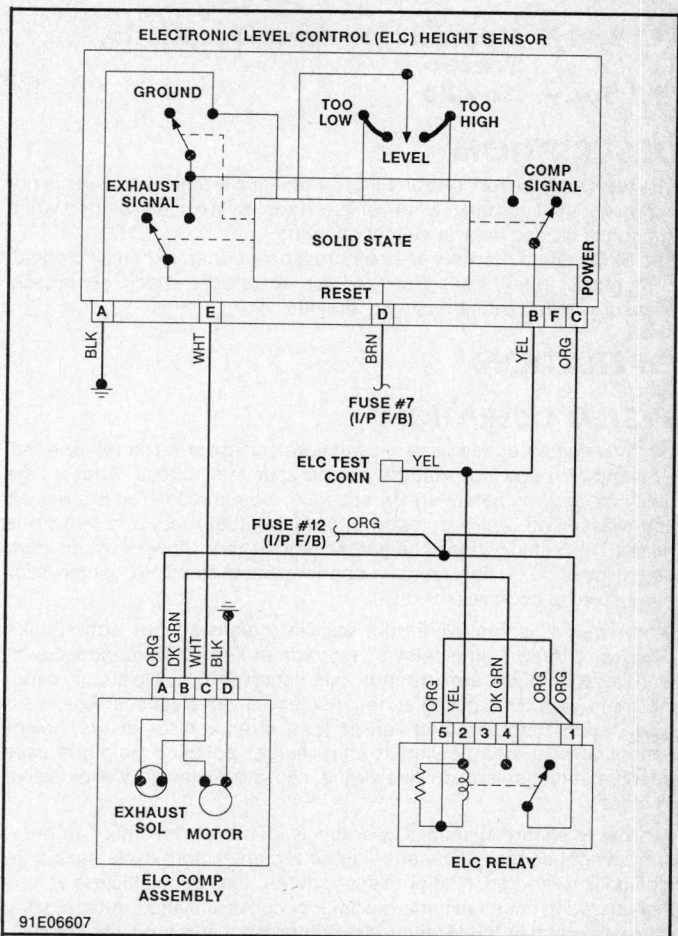

Fig. 12: Electronic Level Control Wiring Diagram (Eighty-Eight & LeSabre)

91E06607

1991 SUSPENSION
Rear – Electronic Level Control – "E" & "K" Bodies

"E" Body: Eldorado, Riviera, Toronado, Trofeo
"K" Body: Seville

DESCRIPTION

The Electronic Level Control (ELC) automatically maintains vehicle riding height in accordance with vehicle loads. System is activated when ignition is on and vehicle weight changes.

The ELC system consists of a compressor, air drier, exhaust solenoid, compressor relay, height sensor, air adjustable shock absorbers, pressure limiter and connecting air lines.

OPERATION

SYSTEM OPERATION

When weight is added to vehicle, height sensor arm rotates upward. Rotating arm upward grounds compressor relay circuit. After a time delay of approximately 13-27 seconds, compressor relay turns air compressor on. Air is pumped into shock absorbers and vehicle is raised. As vehicle rises, height sensor rotates downward to curb height position. Height sensor opens ground circuit to compressor relay, turning compressor off.

When weight is removed from vehicle, height sensor arm rotates downward. After a time delay of approximately 13-27 seconds, downward rotation of the arm grounds exhaust solenoid valve circuit, causing air to vent. Energizing exhaust solenoid valve causes air to vent from shock absorbers and vehicle lowers. As vehicle lowers, height sensor arm rotates upward to curb height position. Height sensor opens exhaust solenoid valve circuit, causing exhaust solenoid valve to close.

In order to ensure system is operating with at least minimum air pressure, height sensor commands an air replenishment cycle each time ignition is turned on. If height sensor determines that vehicle is at normal operating height, an internal timer circuit is activated. After a delay of approximately 35-45 seconds, compressor turns on for approximately 4 seconds to ensure residual system pressure exists. Air drier maintains a minimum shock absorber air pressure of 7-14 psi (.49-.98 kg/cm²).

If weight is added or removed from vehicle during 35-40 second delay, air replenishment cycle will be overridden and vehicle will raise or lower after normal time delay.

Voltage is applied to compressor and height sensor at all times. This allows system to vent after load is removed with ignition turned off. Height sensor limits compressor operation or exhaust solenoid valve energized time to 4.5-7.0 minutes. Time limit is necessary to prevent continuous compressor operation in case of air leak. Turning ignition from off to on will reset compressor operation or exhaust solenoid valve energized time.

Low compressor motor starting current is obtained by a 1.5 second actuation of exhaust solenoid valve. This reduces air pressure in compressor cylinder, allowing for easier compressor operation.

COMPONENT OPERATION

Air Adjustable Shock Absorber – Air adjustable shock absorber is a conventional shock absorber which contains an air chamber that extends when air pressure is increased in shock absorber.

Air Drier – Air drier is attached to compressor output. Air drier absorbs moisture from air being delivered to air adjustable shock absorbers. Air drier contains a valve arrangement that maintains a minimum shock absorber air pressure of 7-14 psi (.49-.98 kg/cm²).

Compressor – The piston-type compressor is mounted on top of rear suspension crossmember at right side of vehicle. Compressor provides air pressure for system operation.

Compressor Relay – Compressor relay is located on bracket by air compressor. Compressor relay is grounded by height sensor and after a time delay of approximately 7-14 seconds, compressor relay turns air compressor on.

Exhaust Solenoid Valve – Exhaust solenoid valve is located within compressor head assembly. Exhaust solenoid valve exhausts air from the system and limits compressor output pressure.

Height Sensor – Height sensor is located on crossmember above rear axle. Movement of height sensor arm controls compressor relay and exhaust solenoid valve ground circuits to adjust vehicle height. Height sensor limits compressor operation or exhaust solenoid valve energized time to 4.5-7.0 minutes. Time limit is necessary to prevent continuous compressor operation in case of air leak.

ADJUSTMENTS

HEIGHT SENSOR

1) Determine if vehicle needs to be raised or lowered to obtain correct riding height. See SPECIFICATIONS & PROCEDURES article in WHEEL ALIGNMENT.

2) Vehicle should be on level surface with gas tank full and NO load in car. Turn ignition switch to ON position. Bounce car 3 times to normalize suspension. To increase vehicle riding height, loosen lock nut on sensor arm. Move plastic arm upward and tighten lock nut.

3) To lower riding height, loosen lock nut, move plastic arm down and tighten lock nut. If adjustment cannot be made, there is a problem with rear springs or suspension. See Fig. 1.

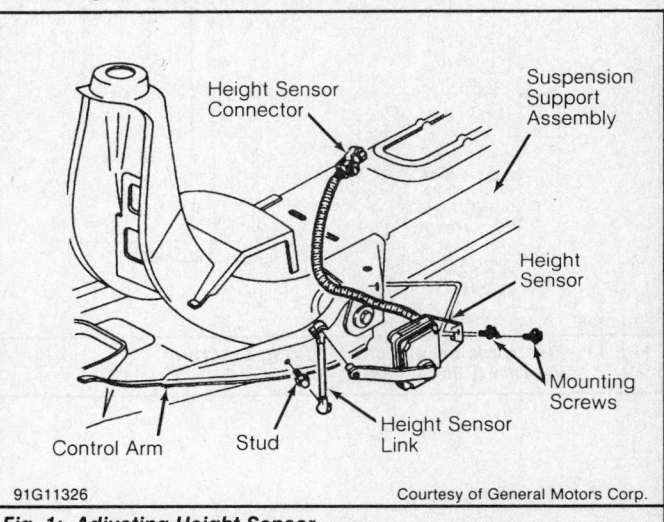

91G11326   Courtesy of General Motors Corp.

Fig. 1: Adjusting Height Sensor

RIDING HEIGHT

NOTE: See SPECIFICATIONS & PROCEDURES article in WHEEL ALIGNMENT.

SYSTEM TESTING

SYSTEM OPERATION TEST

NOTE: Ensure height sensor and link assembly are in good condition before performing system operation test.

1) Place vehicle on flat surface. Measure distance from floor to rocker panel in front of rear wheelwell opening. Turn ignition on. Add 300 lbs. (135 kg) of weight to rear of vehicle. If compressor starts within 28 seconds, proceed to step **4)**.

2) If compressor does not start within 28 seconds and vehicle is within 1" (25 mm) of distance measured in step **1)**, go to NO EXHAUST TEST under ELECTRICAL TESTING.

3) If compressor does not start within 28 seconds and vehicle is not within 1" (25 mm) of distance measured in step **1)**, check height sensor adjustment and retest. See HEIGHT SENSOR under ADJUSTMENTS.

1991 SUSPENSION
Rear – Electronic Level Control – "E" & "K" Bodies (Cont.)

GM
10-59

If compressor does not operate during height sensor test, go to COMPRESSOR DOES NOT OPERATE TEST under ELECTRICAL TESTING.

4) If compressor starts within 28 seconds, compressor should stop within 7 minutes. If compressor stops within 7 minutes, proceed to step **5)**. If compressor runs continuously, check for following:

- Stuck Electronic Level Control (ELC) relay.
- Short to ground in Yellow wire between ELC relay (terminal No. 2) and ELC height sensor (terminal "B").
- Short to voltage in Dark Green wire between ELC compressor (terminal "B") and ELC relay (terminal No. 5).
- Faulty height sensor. See HEIGHT SENSOR TEST under COMPONENT TESTING.

5) If compressor stops within 7 minutes and vehicle returns to within 1" (25 mm) of distance measured in step **1)**, remove load, and proceed to step **7)**. If compressor stops within 7 minutes and vehicle does not return to within 1" (25 mm) of distance measured in step **1)**, remove load, and proceed to step **6)**. If system leaks down, go to IMPROPER OR CONTINUOUS EXHAUST TEST under ELECTRICAL TESTING.

6) Check height sensor adjustment, and retest. See HEIGHT SENSOR under ADJUSTMENTS. If height sensor is properly adjusted, go to IMPROPER OR CONTINUOUS EXHAUST TEST under ELECTRICAL TESTING.

7) With load removed, system should start to exhaust within 28 seconds. If system exhausts within 28 seconds, proceed to step **8)**. If system does not exhaust within 28 seconds, go to NO EXHAUST TEST under ELECTRICAL TESTING.

8) If exhaust starts within 28 seconds and, after 2 minutes, vehicle returns to within 1" (25 mm) of distance measured in step **1)**, system is operating correctly. If vehicle does not return to within 1" (25 mm) of distance measured in step **1)**, adjust height sensor. See HEIGHT SENSOR under ADJUSTMENTS.

SYSTEM LEAK TEST

CAUTION: System leak test will determine if a leak exists and if leak is internal or external to the compressor.

1) Install Pressure Gauge (J-22124-A) and Air Hose Set (J-22124-91) to air drier and air adjustable shock absorbers. *See Fig. 2.* With shutoff gauge open, apply shop air pressure through service valve on pressure gauge until pressure gauge reaches 100-120 psi (7.0-8.4 kg/cm²).

2) If a leak is indicated, close shutoff valve. This isolates compressor from rest of system. Check for drop in air pressure. If air pressure continues to drop, leak is external from the compressor.

3) Test all connections using soapy water solution and repair as necessary. If air pressure stops decreasing after shutoff valve is closed, leak is in compressor assembly. See COMPRESSOR LEAK TEST under COMPONENT TESTING.

4) If air pressure builds up rapidly but vehicle does not rise, check for pinched air line or stuck or binding air adjustable shock absorbers.

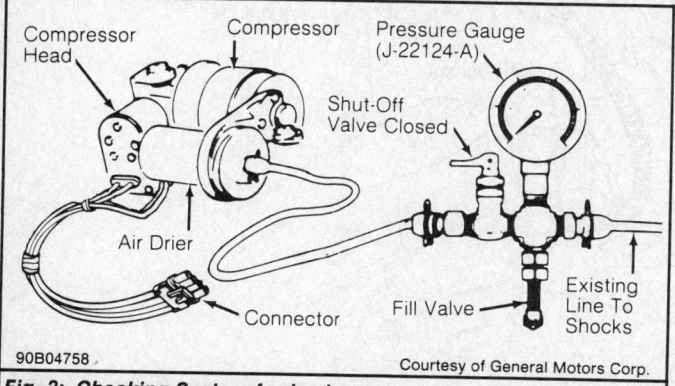

Fig. 2: Checking System for Leakage

COMPONENT TESTING

COMPRESSOR OPERATION TEST

NOTE: Compressor operation will be checked by measuring current draw, compressor output and pressure leak-down.

1) Disconnect pressure line from drier, and connect Pressure Gauge (J-22124-A) to air drier. *See Fig. 3.*

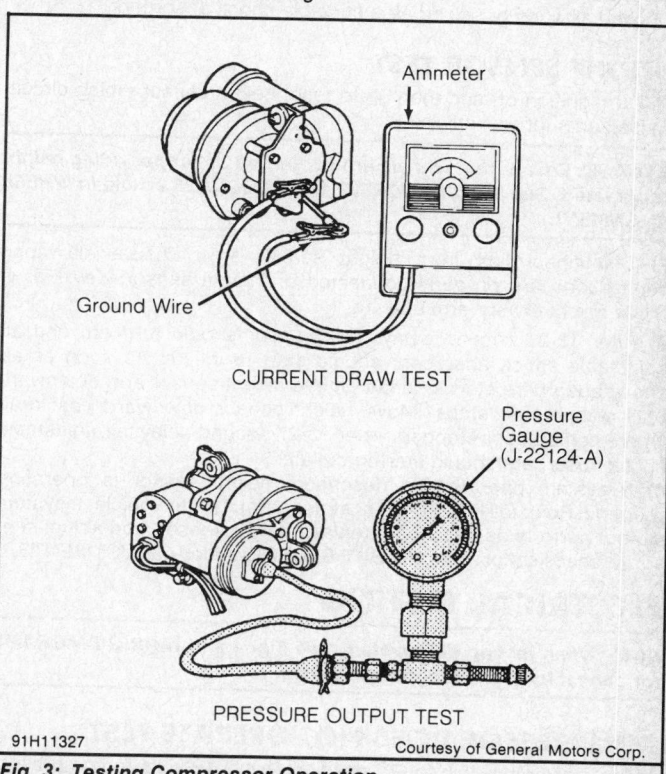

Courtesy of General Motors Corp.

Fig. 3: Testing Compressor Operation

2) Disconnect compressor ground wire (Black wire) from compressor bracket and install ammeter between Black wire and ground. Using a jumper wire, apply battery voltage to pin "B" (Dark Green wire) at compressor connector. Ground pin "D" (Black wire) at compressor connector. Note compressor motor current draw. *See Fig. 3.*

3) If compressor does not operate or current draw exceeds 10 amps, replace motor/cylinder assembly. If current draw is 10 amps or less, allow pressure to reach 100 psi (7.0 kg/cm²) and disconnect voltage supply.

4) If pressure held at 100 psi (7.0 kg/cm²), compressor is okay. If pressure decreases to less than 60 psi (4.2 kg/cm²), but does not continue to drop, replace compressor head assembly.

5) If pressure completely leaks off, or pressure built up but would not reach 100 psi (7.0 kg/cm²), check compressor for leaks. See COMPRESSOR LEAK TEST under COMPONENT TESTING. Remove pressure gauge.

COMPRESSOR LEAK TEST

1) Install Pressure Gauge (J-22124-A) to air drier so shutoff valve is on compressor side of gauge. *See Fig. 5.* With shutoff valve open, apply shop air pressure through service valve on pressure gauge until gauge reaches 100-120 psi (7.0-8.4 kg/cm²).

2) If leak is indicated, close shutoff valve (down), and note pressure drop. Closing valve isolates compressor from remainder of system. If gauge pressure continues to drop, leak is external to compressor. Using soapy water solution, check for leaks around all connections.

GM
10-60

1991 SUSPENSION
Rear – Electronic Level Control – "E" & "K" Bodies (Cont.)

3) If gauge pressure does not continue to drop, leak is in compressor. Using soapy water solution, check for leaks around air drier cover, air drier "O" ring casting bore, edge of cover gasket, edge of solenoid valve housing, head casting air intake and exhaust openings and head cover. *See Fig. 5.*

4) If leak exists at cover bolts, tighten bolts to specification and in sequence. *See Fig. 8.* See TORQUE SPECIFICATIONS table at end of article. Recheck compressor for leaks. Remove pressure gauge. If pressure builds up rapidly but vehicle does not raise, check for pinched air lines or seized air adjustable shock absorbers.

HEIGHT SENSOR TEST

1) Turn ignition off and then on to reset height sensor timing circuit. Raise and support vehicle.

CAUTION: Ensure rear wheels are supported so proper riding height is obtained. See SPECIFICATIONS & PROCEDURES article in WHEEL ALIGNMENT.

2) Disconnect link from height sensor arm. Ensure all wiring connections are properly connected on height sensor. *See Fig. 4.* Move height sensor arm upward.

3) After 13-27 second delay, compressor should turn on, and air adjustable shock absorbers should start to inflate. As soon as air shock absorbers start to inflate, move height sensor arm downward until compressor stops. Move height sensor downward past area where compressor stopped. After 13-27 second delay, air adjustable shock absorbers should start to deflate.

4) If system operated as described, height sensor is operating properly. Reinstall link on height sensor arm. Lower vehicle. If system did not perform as described, replace height sensor, and adjust sensor to specification. See HEIGHT SENSOR under ADJUSTMENTS.

ELECTRICAL TESTING

NOTE: When testing ELC system, see Fig. 4 and WIRING DIAGRAMS for connector and wiring identification.

COMPRESSOR DOES NOT OPERATE TEST

1) Turn ignition switch to ON position. Apply 12 volts to compressor pin "B" (Dark Green wire), and ground to pin "D" (Black wire). If

compressor does not run, go to step **3)**. If compressor runs, go to step **2)**.

2) Disconnect height sensor harness connector. Using a jumper wire, jump pins "A" (White wire) and "B" (Dark Green wire) of height sensor body wiring harness connector. If compressor does not run, check for an open in Yellow wire between ELC relay and height sensor or an open in Black/White wire between ground and height sensor. If compressor runs, go to RESET CIRCUIT OPERATIONAL TEST.

3) Remove ELC relay. Using a DVOM, check for battery voltage at pin No. 3 (Brown/White wire) of relay connector. If battery voltage is present, go to next step. If battery voltage is not present, check compressor fuse and replace as necessary. See IDENTIFYING ELC

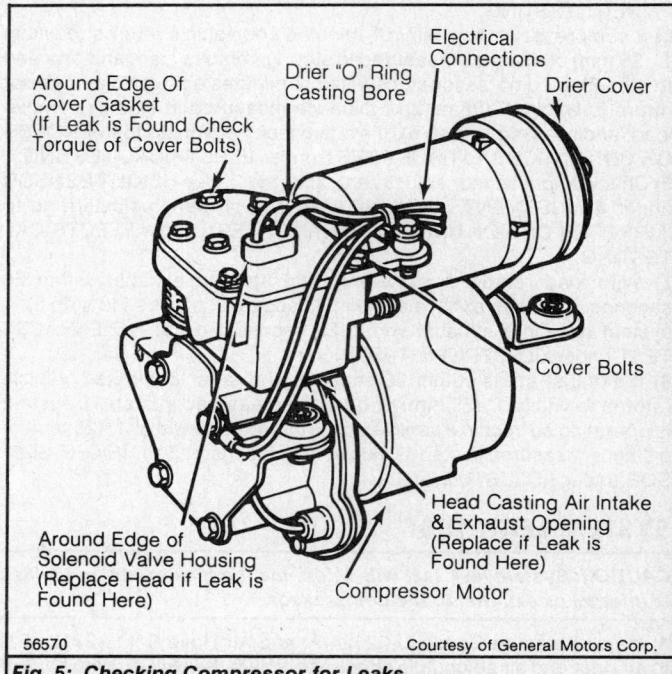

56570   Courtesy of General Motors Corp.

Fig. 5: Checking Compressor for Leaks

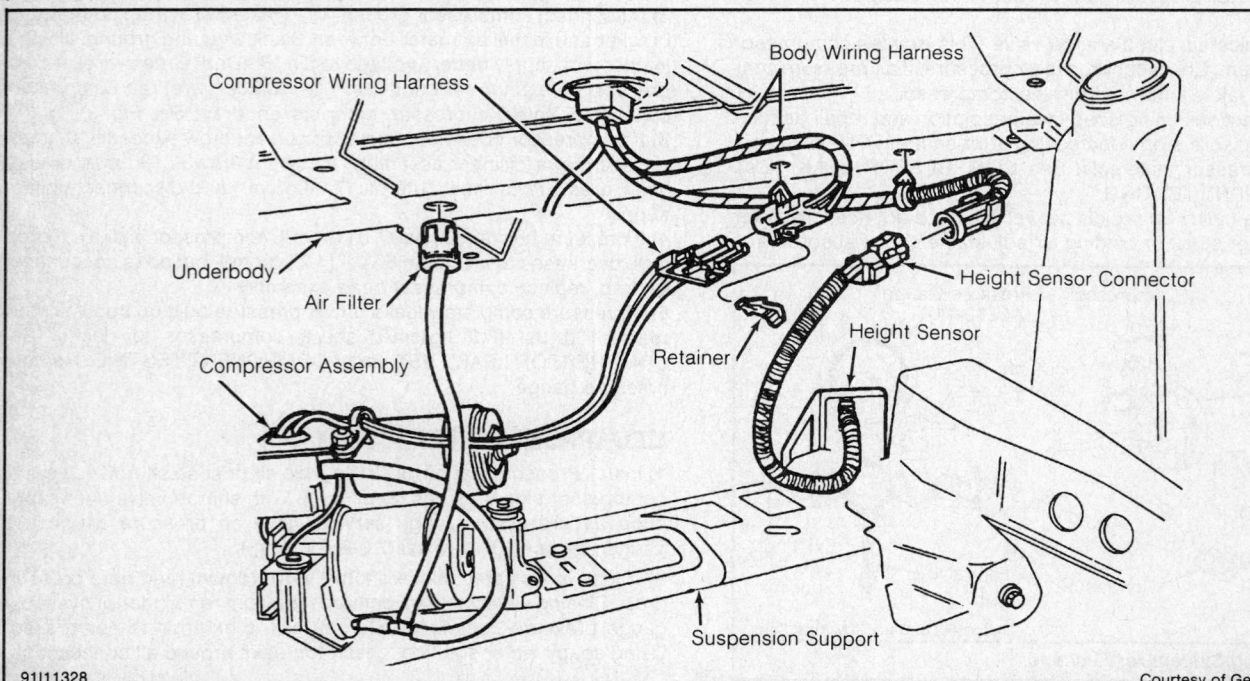

91I11328   Courtesy of General Motors Corp.

Fig. 4: Identifying Electronic Level Control (ELC) Electrical Connectors

1991 SUSPENSION
Rear – Electronic Level Control – "E" & "K" Bodies (Cont.)

GM
10-61

COMPRESSOR FUSE table and FUSE BLOCK LOCATION table. If fuse is okay, repair open in Brown/White wire between ELC relay and fuse block.

4) Using a jumper wire, jump pins No. 3 (Brown/White wire) and No. 5 (Dark Green wire) of ELC relay connector. If compressor does not run, go to next step. If compressor runs, check for an open in Yellow wire between ELC relay and height sensor. If wiring is okay, replace ELC relay.

5) Disconnect compressor harness connector. Apply 12 volts to pin "B" (Yellow wire) and ground pin "D" (Black wire). If compressor runs, check for an open in Dark Green wire between compressor and ELC relay and/or check for an open in Black wire between ground and compressor. If compressor does not run, repair or replace compressor motor.

IDENTIFYING ELC COMPRESSOR FUSE

Application	Fuse No.
Eldorado & Seville	6
Riviera	19
Toronado & Trofeo	17

FUSE BLOCK LOCATION

Application	Location
Riviera	Left Front Of Console
Except Riviera	In Glove Box

IMPROPER OR CONTINUOUS EXHAUST TEST

1) Check for a short to ground in White wire between compressor and height sensor. If a short is present, repair short. If a short is not present, perform compressor performance test. See COMPRESSOR OPERATION TEST under COMPONENT TESTING.

2) If compressor performance test is not okay, repair or replace compressor. If compressor performance tests okay, perform SYSTEM LEAK TEST under SYSTEM TESTING. If system leak test is okay, replace height sensor. If system leak test is not okay, repair leak.

NO EXHAUST TEST

1) Cycle ignition on and off to reset system. Disconnect compressor harness connector. Check for voltage at harness connector pin "C" (Orange wire). If battery voltage is present, go to step 2). If zero voltage is present, check fuse No. 1 (fuse No. 4 on Riviera) at fuse block and replace as necessary. See FUSE BLOCK LOCATION table. If fuse is okay, repair open in Orange wire between fuse block and compressor or Orange wire between compressor and height sensor.

2) Reconnect compressor harness. Disconnect height sensor harness connector. Using a jumper wire, jump terminals "A" (Black wire) and "E" (White wire). If system does not exhaust, go to next step. If system exhausts, check for voltage at pin "C" (Orange wire). If zero voltage is present, repair open in Orange wire between fuse block and compressor or Orange wire between compressor and height sensor. If voltage is present, replace height sensor.

3) Apply 12 volts to pin "C" (Orange wire) and ground pin "A" (White wire) of compressor harness connector. If system does not exhaust, replace exhaust solenoid. If system does exhaust, repair open in White wire between compressor and height sensor or Black wire between height sensor and ground.

RESET CIRCUIT OPERATIONAL TEST

1) Turn ignition off. Disconnect height sensor harness. On Toronado and Trofeo, check for voltage at pins "C" (Orange wire) and "D" (Brown/White wire). On Eldorado, Seville and Riviera, check for voltage at pins "C" (Orange wire) and "D" (Pink/Black wire). Go to next step.

2) On all models, if zero voltage is present at pin "D" and battery voltage is present at pin "C", go to next step. If voltage is present at pin "D", repair short to voltage in fuse to height sensor circuit (Pink/Black wire on Toronado and Trofeo, Brown/White wire on all other models). If zero voltage is present at pin "C", check fuse No. 1 (fuse No. 4 on

Riviera). If fuse is okay, repair open in circuit from fuse block to compressor to height sensor (Orange wires).

3) Turn ignition switch to ON position. Check voltage at pin "D" (Brown/White wire on Toronado and Trofeo, Pink/Black wire on all others). If battery voltage is present, go to next step. If zero voltage is present, check fuse No. 9 (fuse No. 17 on Toronado and Trofeo) and replace as necessary. If okay, repair open in fuse to height sensor circuit (Brown/White wire Toronado and Trofeo, Pink/Black wire on all other models).

4) Check voltage between pin "C" (Orange wire) and pin "A" (Black/White wire). If battery voltage is present, replace height sensor. If battery voltage is not present, repair open in height sensor to ground circuit (Black/White wire).

REMOVAL & INSTALLATION

ELC HEIGHT SENSOR

Removal & Installation – Disconnect negative battery cable. Raise and support vehicle. Disconnect height sensor harness connector. Disconnect height sensor link from height sensor actuating arm. Remove 2 height sensor mounting screws. To install, reverse removal procedure. Tighten sensor mounting bolts to specification. Adjust height sensor. See HEIGHT SENSOR under ADJUSTMENTS.

ELC COMPRESSOR

Removal – 1) Raise vehicle on frame contact type hoist. Loosen exhaust pipes at both sides of muffler. Remove muffler heat shield. Disconnect compressor electrical connectors and air line from drier.

2) Remove air inlet filter from underbody mount. Remove compressor bracket-to-suspension mounting screws. Remove compressor and bracket as an assembly by moving toward rear of vehicle next to exhaust pipe. Remove bracket from compressor.

Installation – To install, reverse removal procedure. Turn ignition on and allow system to cycle. Check for leaks using soap and water solution.

AIR DRIER

Removal – Disconnect high pressure line by turning spring clip 90 degrees and removing tube assembly. Disconnect drier from compressor by turning spring clip 90 degrees and pull drier and "O" ring from compressor head assembly. See Fig. 6.

Installation – Lubricate "O" ring and install in port of compressor head. Install retainer spring to its original position. Install drier on compressor head assembly. If difficulty arises when installing drier in compressor head assembly, rotate slightly while applying pressure. Install air tube to drier. Check system for leaks.

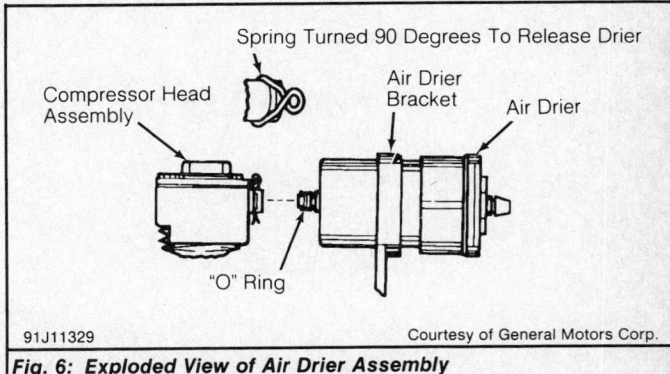

91J11329   Courtesy of General Motors Corp.

Fig. 6: Exploded View of Air Drier Assembly

COMPRESSOR HEAD ASSEMBLY

Removal & Installation – 1) Remove air drier assembly. See AIR DRIER under REMOVAL & INSTALLATION. Remove compressor head mounting bolts. See Fig. 7. Remove head assembly.

2) To install, reverse removal procedure. Tighten compressor head bolts to specification and in sequence. See Fig. 8 and TORQUE SPECIFICATIONS table at end of this article.

GM
10-62

1991 SUSPENSION
Rear – Electronic Level Control – "E" & "K" Bodies (Cont.)

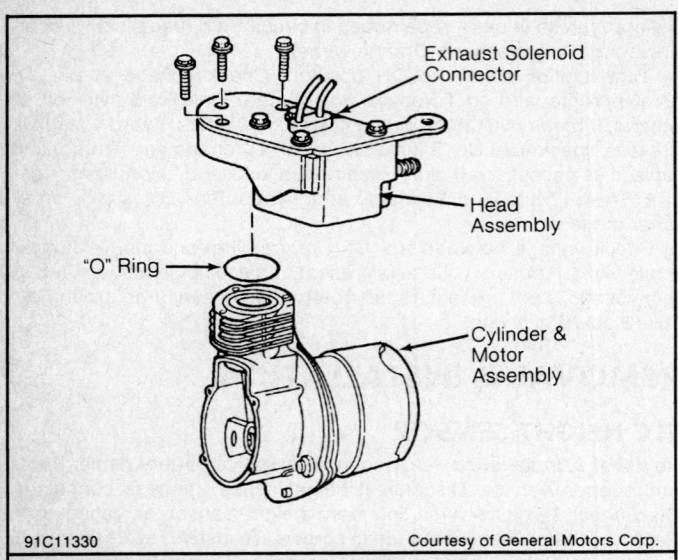

91C11330   Courtesy of General Motors Corp.

Fig. 7: Removing Compressor Head Assembly

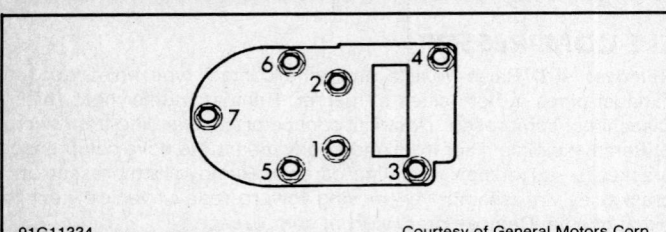

91G11334   Courtesy of General Motors Corp.

Fig. 8: Compressor Head Tightening Sequence

TORQUE SPECIFICATIONS

TORQUE SPECIFICATIONS

Application	INCH Lbs. (N.m)
Compressor Bracket Mounting Screws	133 (15)
Compressor Head Bolts [1]	36 (4)
Compressor Mounting Screws	36 (4)
Height Sensor Mounting Screws	45 (5)

[1] – Tighten in sequence. *See Fig. 8.*

WIRING DIAGRAMS

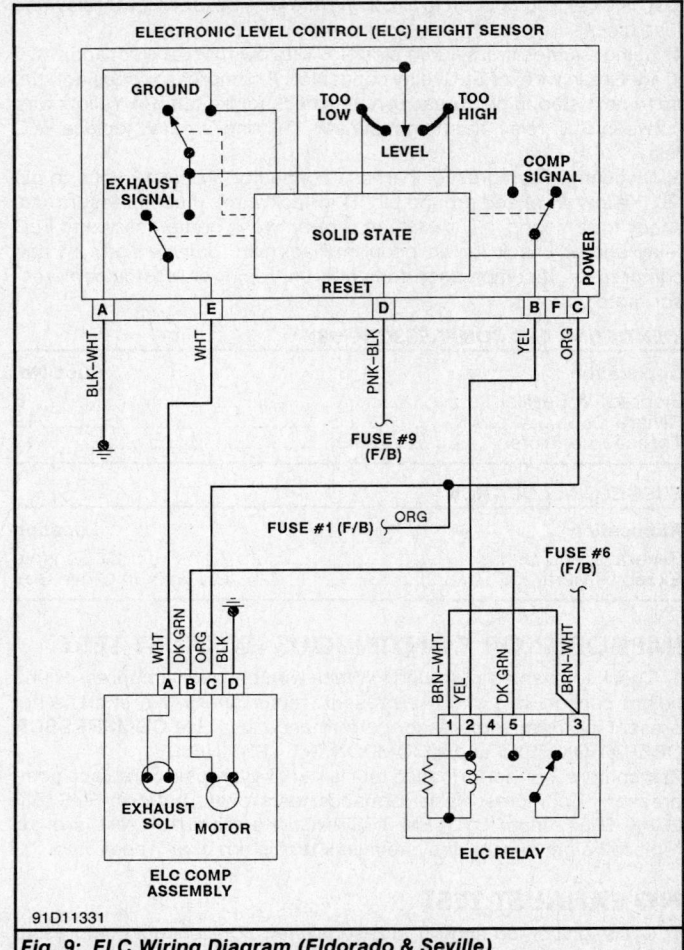

91D11331

Fig. 9: ELC Wiring Diagram (Eldorado & Seville)

1991 SUSPENSION
Rear – Electronic Level Control – "E" & "K" Bodies (Cont.)

GM
10-63

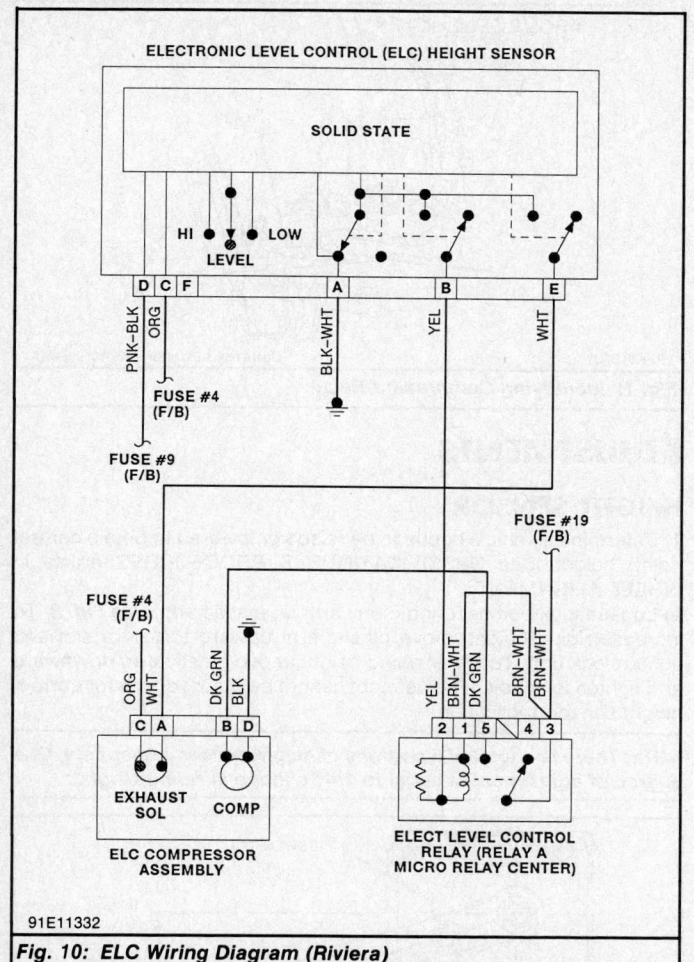

Fig. 10: ELC Wiring Diagram (Riviera)

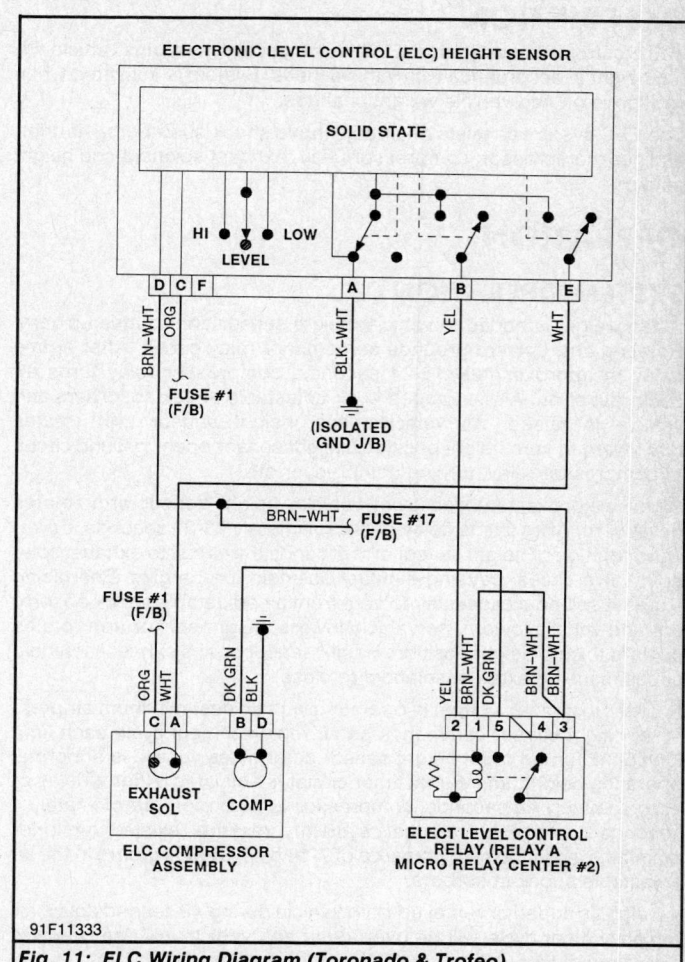

Fig. 11: ELC Wiring Diagram (Toronado & Trofeo)

DESCRIPTION

The Electronic Level Control (ELC) automatically maintains vehicle riding height in accordance with vehicle loads. System is activated when ignition is on and vehicle weight changes.

The ELC system consists of air adjustable shock absorbers, air drier, air lines, compressor, compressor relay, exhaust solenoid and height sensor.

OPERATION

SYSTEM OPERATION

When weight is added to vehicle, height sensor arm rotates upward. Rotating arm upward grounds compressor relay circuit. After a time delay of approximately 13-27 seconds, compressor relay turns air compressor on. Air is pumped in air adjustable shock absorbers and vehicle is raised. As vehicle rises, height sensor arm rotates downward to curb height position. Height sensor opens ground circuit to compressor relay, turning compressor off.

When weight is removed from vehicle, height sensor arm rotates downward. After a time delay of approximately 13-27 seconds, downward rotation of height sensor arm grounds the circuit to exhaust solenoid valve circuit, causing exhaust solenoid to energize. Energizing exhaust solenoid causes air to vent from air adjustable shock absorbers and vehicle lowers. As vehicle lowers, height sensor arm rotates upward to curb height position. Height sensor opens exhaust solenoid circuit, causing exhaust solenoid to close.

In order to ensure system is operating with at least minimum air pressure, height sensor commands an air replenishment cycle each time ignition is turned on. If height sensor determines vehicle is at normal operating height, an internal timer circuit is activated. After a delay of approximately 40 seconds, compressor turns on for approximately 4 seconds to ensure residual system pressure exists. Air drier maintains a minimum air pressure of 7-14 psi (.49-.98 kg/cm²) in the air adjustable shock absorbers.

If weight is added or removed from vehicle during 40 second delay, air replenishment cycle will be overridden and vehicle will rise or lower after normal time delay.

Voltage is applied to compressor and height sensor at all times, allowing system to vent after load is removed with ignition turned off. Height sensor limits compressor operation or exhaust solenoid energized time to 7 minutes. Time limit is necessary to prevent continuous compressor operation in case of air leak. Turning ignition from off to on will reset compressor operation or exhaust solenoid energized time.

COMPONENT OPERATION

Air Adjustable Shock Absorber – Air adjustable shock absorber is a conventional shock absorber, containing an air chamber which extends when air pressure is increased.

Air Drier – Air drier is attached to compressor output. Air drier absorbs moisture from air being delivered to air adjustable shock absorbers. Air drier contains a valve which maintains a minimum shock absorber air pressure of 7-14 psi (.49-.98 kg/cm²).

Compressor – The piston-type compressor is mounted below left side of luggage compartment on the frame. Compressor provides air pressure for system operation.

Compressor Relay – Compressor relay is located on left side of luggage compartment, behind wheelwell. *See Fig. 1.* Compressor relay is grounded by height sensor and after a time delay of approximately 13-27 seconds, compressor relay turns air compressor on.

Exhaust Solenoid – Exhaust solenoid is located within compressor head assembly. Exhaust solenoid exhausts air from the system and limits compressor output pressure.

Height Sensor – Height sensor is mounted below left side of luggage compartment on the frame. Movement of height sensor arm controls compressor relay and exhaust solenoid ground circuits to adjust vehicle height. Height sensor limits compressor operation or exhaust solenoid energized time to 7 minutes. Time limit is necessary to prevent continuous compressor operation in case of air leak.

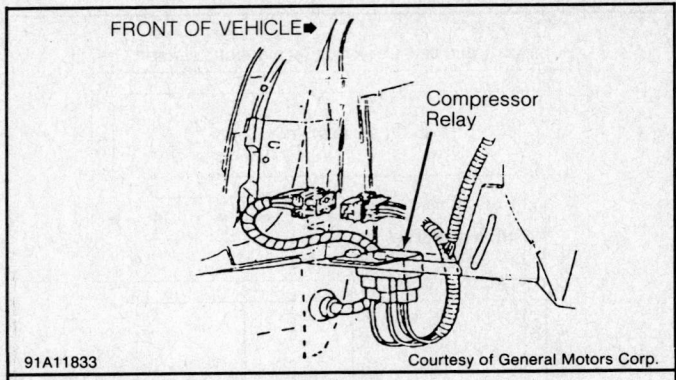

FRONT OF VEHICLE➡
Compressor Relay

91A11833   Courtesy of General Motors Corp.

Fig. 1: Identifying Compressor Relay

ADJUSTMENTS

HEIGHT SENSOR

1) Determine if vehicle needs to be raised or lowered to obtain correct riding height. See SPECIFICATIONS & PROCEDURES article in WHEEL ALIGNMENT.

2) Loosen lock bolt securing metal arm on plastic arm. *See Fig. 2.* To increase riding height, move plastic arm upward to top of slot and tighten lock bolt. To lower riding height, move plastic arm downward and tighten lock bolt. If adjustment cannot be made, check for correct height sensor application.

NOTE: There is a total of 5 degrees of height sensor adjustment. One degree of adjustment is equal to 1/4" change in riding height.

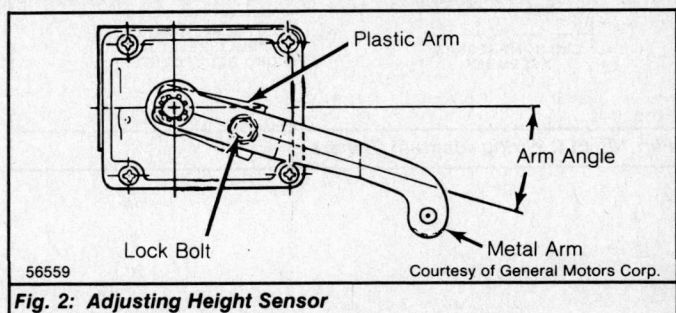

Plastic Arm

Arm Angle

Lock Bolt

Metal Arm

56559   Courtesy of General Motors Corp.

Fig. 2: Adjusting Height Sensor

RIDING HEIGHT

NOTE: See SPECIFICATIONS & PROCEDURES article in WHEEL ALIGNMENT.

TROUBLE SHOOTING

SYSTEM OPERATION

If system fails to operate correctly, check the following:
- Ensure CTSY fuse in fuse block behind right side of instrument panel is okay by checking that courtesy lights are operating.
- Ensure ELC fuse is okay. Fuse is located in convenience center, near fuse block behind right side of instrument panel.
- Ensure ground connection below left side of luggage compartment on the frame, near height sensor, is clean and tight.
- Ensure link and arm attached to height sensor is not damaged.
- If compressor operates for maximum time of 7 minutes and then shuts off, check for defective air lines or fittings.

SYSTEM TESTING

NOTE: Before performing system operation test, check items listed in SYSTEM OPERATION under TROUBLE SHOOTING.

SYSTEM OPERATION TEST

1) Turn ignition on. After an initial delay, compressor should run for a short time to charge the system.

2) Add 300 lbs. (136 kg) to luggage area. Compressor should start operating after a 13-27 second delay and vehicle should rise.

3) Remove weight from luggage area. Air should exhaust from exhaust solenoid within 13-27 seconds.

4) If system does not operate correctly, see SYMPTOM DIRECTORY under ELECTRICAL TESTING.

SYSTEM LEAK TEST

CAUTION: System leak test will determine if a leak exists and if leak is internal or external to the compressor.

1) Install Pressure Gauge (J-22124-A) in-line between air drier on compressor and air line to air adjustable shock absorbers. Compressor is mounted below left side of luggage compartment on the frame. Install pressure gauge so shut-off valve is on compressor side of pressure gauge. With shut-off gauge open, apply air pressure through service valve until pressure reaches 100 psi (7.03 kg/cm²).

2) If an air leak is found, close shut-off valve and check for a pressure decrease. If pressure continues to decrease, air leak is external from the compressor. Test all connections for leaks using soapy water solution.

3) If pressure does not decrease after shut-off valve was closed, leak is in the compressor assembly. Using soapy water solution, check for leaks around air drier cover, air drier "O" ring casting bore, edge of cover gasket, edge of solenoid valve housing, head casting air intake and exhaust openings and head cover. *See Fig. 3.*

4) If leak exists at cover bolts, tighten cover bolts to specification, and recheck for leaks. See TORQUE SPECIFICATIONS table at end of this article. If pressure builds rapidly but vehicle does not rise, check for pinched air line or defective air adjustable shock absorbers. Remove pressure gauge.

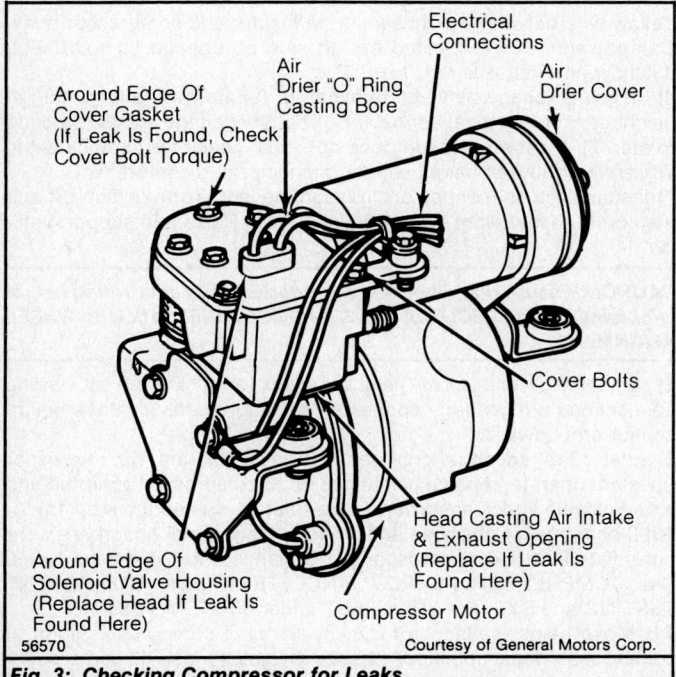

Fig. 3: *Checking Compressor for Leaks*

SYSTEM RESIDUAL AIR TEST

1) Disconnect air line from air drier on compressor. Compressor is mounted below left side of luggage compartment on the frame. Install Pressure Gauge (J-22124-A) on air drier fitting. Disconnect electrical connector from compressor.

2) Connect jumper wire from Black wire terminal on compressor to ground. Connect jumper wire from 12-volt battery power source to Dark Green wire on terminal of compressor. Compressor should operate until pressure reaches 100 psi (7.03 kg/cm²).

3) Disconnect wiring from exhaust solenoid. Exhaust solenoid is located within compressor head assembly. Connect jumper wire from White wire terminal of exhaust solenoid to ground and jumper wire from 12-volt battery power source to Orange wire terminal of exhaust solenoid. Air should exhaust from exhaust solenoid.

4) When all air has been exhausted from system, air pressure gauge should read a residual pressure of 7-14 psi (.49-.98 kg/cm²). If residual pressure was not obtained, replace air drier.

COMPONENT TESTING

COMPRESSOR PERFORMANCE TEST

NOTE: Compressor performance test checks current draw, pressure output and pressure leak-down. Test can be performed on or off vehicle.

1) Connect Pressure Gauge (J-22124-A) to air drier on compressor. *See Fig. 4.* Compressor is mounted below left side of luggage compartment on frame. Connect one ammeter lead to (B+) battery terminal and other lead to Dark Green wire at compressor electrical connector.

2) Connect Black wire of compressor electrical connector to negative (-) battery terminal, and note compressor motor current draw.

3) If compressor does not operate or current draw exceeds 14 amps, replace compressor. If current draw is 14 amps or less, allow pressure to reach at least 100 psi (7.0 kg/cm²), and disconnect ammeter from (B+) battery terminal.

NOTE: If compressor is allowed to obtain maximum output pressure of 180 psi (12.6 kg/cm², exhaust solenoid will act as a relief valve, resulting in a false indication of system leakage.

4) If pressure holds steady when compressor is shut off, compressor is okay. If pressure decreases to less than 90 psi (6.3 kg/cm²) but does not continue to decrease, replace compressor head assembly. See COMPRESSOR HEAD under REMOVAL & INSTALLATION.

5) If pressure fully leaks off or if pressure builds up but does not reach 110 psi (7.7 kg/cm²), check compressor for leaks. Using soapy water solution, check for leaks around air drier cover, air drier "O" ring casting bore, edge of cover gasket, edge of solenoid valve housing, head casting air intake and exhaust openings and head cover. *See Fig. 3.*

6) If leak exists at cover bolts, tighten cover bolts to specification, and recheck for leaks. See TORQUE SPECIFICATIONS table at end of article.

7) If pressure builds rapidly but vehicle does not rise, check for pinched air line or defective air adjustable shock absorbers. Remove pressure gauge.

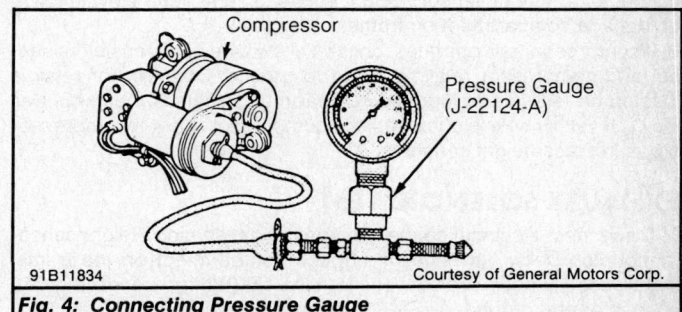

Fig. 4: *Connecting Pressure Gauge*

ELECTRICAL TESTING

NOTE: Use SYMPTOM DIRECTORY to determine test to be performed.

SYMPTOM DIRECTORY

Symptom	Test To Be Performed
Compressor Inoperative	COMPRESSOR RELAY & COMPRESSOR TEST
System Does Not Exhaust	EXHAUST SOLENOID TEST HEIGHT SENSOR TEST
Compressor Runs More Than 7 Minutes & Vehicle Stays At Maximum Height	COMPRESSOR RUNS CONTINUOUSLY (LONGER THAN 7 MINUTES) TEST
Compressor Runs For 7 Minutes & Turns Off & Vehicle Does Not Reach Proper Height	HEIGHT SENSOR TEST

COMPRESSOR RELAY & COMPRESSOR TEST

1) Install a fused jumper wire between Yellow wire of compressor relay and ground. Compressor relay is located on left side of luggage compartment, behind wheelwell. *See Fig. 1.*

2) If compressor operates, check height sensor. See HEIGHT SENSOR TEST under ELECTRICAL TESTING. If compressor does not operate, disconnect electrical connector from compressor relay.

3) Measure voltage from terminals No. 1 and 4 (Orange wires) and ground at compressor relay electrical connector.

4) If battery voltage exists, proceed to step **5)**. If battery voltage does not exist, check for open circuit in Orange wire between compressor relay and CTSY fuse or defective CTSY fuse. The CTSY fuse is located in fuse block behind right side of instrument panel.

5) Install electrical connector on compressor relay. Connect a fused jumper wire between terminals No. 1 (Orange wire) and No. 2 (Dark Green wire) on compressor relay electrical connector.

6) If compressor operates, replace compressor relay. If compressor does not operate, leave jumper wire installed and proceed to step **7)**.

7) With fused jumper still installed on compressor relay electrical connector, disconnect electrical connector from compressor. Compressor is mounted below left side of luggage compartment on the frame.

8) Measure voltage between terminal "B" (Dark Green wire) and ground at compressor electrical connector. If battery voltage exists, proceed to step **9)**. If battery voltage does not exist, check for open circuit in Dark Green wire between compressor relay and compressor.

9) Measure voltage between terminal "B" (Dark Green wire) and terminal "D" (Black wire) at compressor electrical connector. If battery voltage exists, replace compressor. If battery voltage does not exist, check for open circuit in Black wire between compressor and ground connection, located below left side of luggage compartment on frame, near height sensor.

COMPRESSOR OPERATES CONTINUOUSLY (LONGER THAN 7 MINUTES) TEST

1) Ensure arm at height sensor is not damaged. Disconnect electrical connector at height sensor. Height sensor is mounted below left side of luggage compartment on frame.

2) If compressor still operates, check Yellow wire between height sensor and compressor relay for short to ground. Compressor relay is located on left side of luggage compartment, behind wheelwell. *See Fig. 1.* If yellow wire is okay, replace compressor relay. If compressor stops, replace height sensor.

EXHAUST SOLENOID TEST

1) Disconnect electrical connector from height sensor. Height sensor is mounted below left side of luggage compartment on the frame. Install fused jumper wire between terminal "E" (White wire) of electrical connector and ground.

2) If exhaust solenoid clicks and air vents, reinstall electrical connector and check height sensor. See HEIGHT SENSOR TEST under ELECTRICAL TESTING. If exhaust solenoid does not operate, leave jumper wire installed and proceed to step **3)**.

3) With fused jumper wire installed at height sensor, disconnect electrical connector from compressor. Compressor is mounted below left side of luggage compartment on the frame.

4) Measure voltage between terminal "C" (Orange wire) and ground at compressor electrical connector. If battery voltage exists, proceed to step **5)**. If battery voltage does not exist, check for open circuit in Orange wire between compressor and CTSY fuse. The CTSY fuse is located in fuse block behind right side of instrument panel.

5) Measure voltage between terminals "C" (Orange wire) and "E" (White wire) at compressor electrical connector. If battery voltage exists, replace exhaust solenoid. See EXHAUST SOLENOID under REMOVAL & INSTALLATION. If battery voltage does not exist, check for open circuit in White wire between height sensor and compressor.

HEIGHT SENSOR TEST

1) Disconnect electrical connector at height sensor. Height sensor is mounted below left side of luggage compartment on the frame. Turn ignition on.

2) Measure voltage between terminal "C" (Orange wire) and ground at height sensor electrical connector. If battery voltage exists, proceed to step **3)**. If battery voltage does not exist, check for open circuit in Orange wire between compressor and CTSY fuse. The CTSY fuse is located in fuse block behind right side of instrument panel.

3) Measure voltage between terminals "C" (Orange wire) and "A" (Black wire) at height sensor electrical connector. If battery voltage exists, proceed to step **4)**. If battery voltage does not exist, check for open circuit in Black wire between height sensor connector and ground connection, located below left side of luggage compartment on the frame, near height sensor.

4) Measure voltage between terminal "D" (Brown/White wire) and ground at height sensor electrical connector. If battery voltage exists, proceed to step **5)**. If battery voltage does not exist, check for open circuit in Brown/White wire between height sensor connector and ELC fuse. The ELC fuse is located in convenience center, near fuse block behind right side of instrument panel.

5) Measure voltage between terminal "B" (Yellow wire) and ground at height sensor electrical connector. If battery voltage exists, proceed to step **6)**. If battery voltage does not exist, check for open circuit in Yellow wire between height sensor connector and compressor relay. Compressor relay is located on left side of luggage compartment, behind wheelwell. *See Fig. 1.*

6) Measure voltage between terminal "E" (White wire) and ground at height sensor electrical connector. If battery voltage exists, proceed to step **7)**. If battery voltage does not exist, check for open circuit in White wire between height sensor connector and compressor.

7) Install electrical connector on height sensor. Turn ignition off and then on to reset height sensor timing circuit. Raise and support vehicle.

CAUTION: Ensure rear wheels are supported so proper riding height is obtained. See SPECIFICATIONS & PROCEDURES article in WHEEL ALIGNMENT.

8) Disconnect link from height sensor arm. Ensure all wiring connections are properly connected on height sensor. Move height sensor arm upward.

9) After 13-27 seconds, compressor should operate. If compressor does not operate, replace height sensor. If compressor operated and air adjustable shock absorbers were inflated, proceed to step **11)**.

10) If compressor operated and air adjustable shock absorbers were not inflated, check compressor performance and system for leaks. See COMPRESSOR PERFORMANCE TEST under COMPONENT TESTING and SYSTEM LEAK TEST under SYSTEM TESTING.

11) Move height sensor arm downward until compressor stops. If compressor does not stop, replace height sensor. If compressor stopped, move height sensor arm downward past area where compressor stopped. After 13-27 seconds, air adjustable shock absorbers should start to deflate.

12) If air adjustable shock absorbers do not deflate, replace height sensor. If system operated correctly, height sensor is operating properly. Check height sensor adjustment. See HEIGHT SENSOR under ADJUSTMENTS.

REMOVAL & INSTALLATION

NOTE: For additional information on suspension components, see other appropriate articles in SUSPENSION.

AIR ADJUSTABLE SHOCK ABSORBER

Removal – 1) Remove trim cover and upper nut from air adjustable shock absorber. Raise and support vehicle. Support rear axle.
2) Disconnect air lines by rotating spring clip and removing air line. Remove lower bolt/nut and air adjustable shock absorber.
Installation – 1) To install, reverse removal procedure. Tighten upper nut when vehicle is lowered and vehicle weight is applied on suspension. Tighten bolts/nuts to specification. See TORQUE SPECIFICATIONS table at end of this article.
2) Before installing air lines, lubricate "O" rings with petroleum jelly. Ensure air line and connector are fully seated in fitting.

AIR DRIER

Removal & Installation – 1) Remove compressor. See COMPRESSOR under REMOVAL & INSTALLATION. Remove air drier bracket bolt. Rotate retaining clip on air drier 90 degrees. Remove air drier and "O" ring.
2) To install, reverse removal procedure. Lubricate "O" ring with petroleum jelly before installing. Tighten bolt to specification. See TORQUE SPECIFICATIONS table at end of this article.

COMPRESSOR

Removal – 1) Disconnect negative battery cable. Raise and support vehicle. Remove shield located around compressor. Compressor is mounted below left side of luggage compartment on the frame.
2) Disconnect air lines by rotating spring clip and removing air line. Disconnect electrical connections. Remove compressor-to-bracket bolts. Remove compressor.
Installation – To install, reverse removal procedure. Tighten bolts to specification. See TORQUE SPECIFICATIONS table at end of this article. Before installing air lines, lubricate "O" rings with petroleum jelly. Ensure air line and connector are fully seated in fitting.

COMPRESSOR HEAD

Removal & Installation – 1) Remove air drier. See AIR DRIER under REMOVAL & INSTALLATION. Remove 3 compressor head-to-compressor retaining bolts. Remove compressor head and "O" ring.
2) To install, reverse removal procedure, using new "O" ring. Tighten bolts to specification, starting with the center bolt and then the outer bolts. See TORQUE SPECIFICATIONS table at end of this article.

COMPRESSOR RELAY

Removal & Installation – Compressor relay is located on left side of luggage compartment, behind wheelwell. *See Fig. 1.* No other information available from manufacturer.

EXHAUST SOLENOID

Removal & Installation – Exhaust solenoid is not serviceable. Compressor head must be replaced if exhaust solenoid is defective. See COMPRESSOR HEAD under REMOVAL & INSTALLATION.

HEIGHT SENSOR

Removal & Installation – 1) Disconnect negative battery cable. Raise and support vehicle. Disconnect electrical connector at height sensor.

Height sensor is mounted below left side of luggage compartment on the frame.
2) Remove link-to-height sensor nut. Remove retaining bolts and height sensor. To install, reverse removal procedure. Tighten bolts/nuts to specification. See TORQUE SPECIFICATIONS table. Adjust height sensor. See HEIGHT SENSOR under ADJUSTMENTS.

TORQUE SPECIFICATIONS

TORQUE SPECIFICATIONS

Application	Ft. Lbs. (N.m)
Air Adjustable Shock Absorber	
Lower Bolt/Nut	44 (60)
Upper Nut	16 (22)
	INCH Lbs. (N.m)
Air Drier-To-Compressor Bolt	20 (2.3)
Compressor Head Bolt	36 (4.0)
Compressor-To-Bracket Bolt	36 (4.0)
Cover Bolt	35 (3.9)
Height Sensor Bolt	36 (4.0)
Height Sensor Link Nut	53 (5.9)

WIRING DIAGRAM

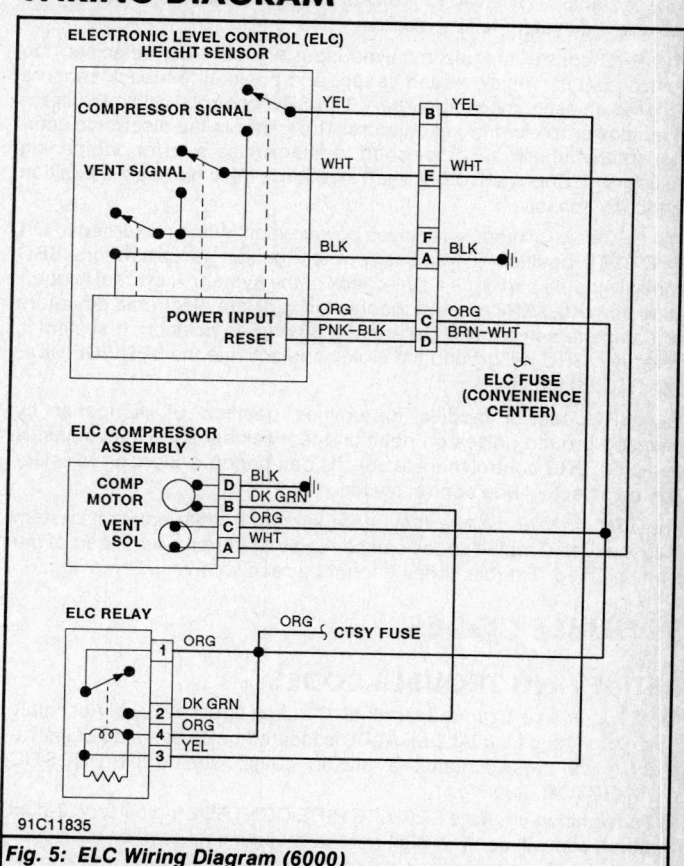

91C11835

Fig. 5: ELC Wiring Diagram (6000)

Corvette

DESCRIPTION

The Selective Ride Control (SRC) system uses electronically operated actuators to adjust suspension dampening characteristics. The system is operated by a selective ride control switch, allowing the driver to manually select desired shock absorber dampening.

The shock absorbers are installed identically as standard equipment shock absorbers. Electronic actuators, positioned on top of each shock absorber, are operated by commands received from SRC control module, located in storage compartment, behind driver's seat.

System consists of 4 shock absorbers, 4 electronic actuators, SRC control module, selective ride control switch, vehicle speed sensor (mounted at rear of transmission) and SERVICE RIDE CONTROL indicator. The SERVICE RIDE CONTROL indicator is located on the driver information center.

OPERATION

When vehicle is first started on, SERVICE RIDE CONTROL indicator should illuminate to show that indicator circuit is operating. Indicator will stay on if ignition is turned from OFF or LOCK to ON position 3 times without vehicle moving. Indicator will turn off when speed sensor signal is received to indicate vehicle movement. Indicator will activate if a system failure exists.

The SRC control module receives input signals from selective ride control switch, vehicle speed sensor and position feedback sensors (located on each shock absorber). The SRC control module then provides power to electronic actuators. The motor in the electronic actuator rotates shock absorber shaft to alter orifice size for dampening adjustment. Shock absorber shaft location is indicated by the position feedback sensor.

The SRC control module receives power when ignition is turned to ON or START position. Immediately after ignition is turned on, SRC control module performs a self-check of the system. If system is operating correctly, SRC control module will activate electronic actuators so dampeners in shocks are set at a 60 degree position. If system is defective, SRC will ground the circuit and activate the SERVICE RIDE CONTROL indicator.

The SRC control module determines position of dampener by counting ground pulses on position feedback sensor. Once signal is detected, SRC control module adjusts dampeners according to selection on selective ride control switch.

The SRC control module may store system trouble codes if system failure exists. Trouble codes can be read to determine what part of the system failed. Trouble codes cannot be read with vehicle moving.

TROUBLE CODES

RETRIEVING TROUBLE CODES

1) With ignition off, ground terminal "C" (Light Green wire) of Assembly Line Diagnostic Link (ALDL). ALDL is located below left side of instrument panel and contains a plastic cover labeled DIAGNOSTIC CONNECTOR. *See Fig. 1.*

2) Turn ignition on. Note SERVICE RIDE CONTROL indicator. A 2-digit trouble code will flash. A digit is read by counting number of flashes occurring within a half second. Second digit occurs approximately one second after first digit.

3) Each trouble code repeats 3 times before next trouble code displays, with a 3 second pause between each trouble code. Trouble codes display as long as ALDL is grounded.

4) Trouble code display starts by displaying Code 12 three times, indicating system is capable of storing trouble codes. If trouble codes cannot be displayed, see TROUBLE CODES CANNOT BE DISPLAYED TEST under TESTING & DIAGNOSIS.

5) Different trouble codes will be obtained to indicate different system failures. See TROUBLE CODE IDENTIFICATION table. Trouble codes

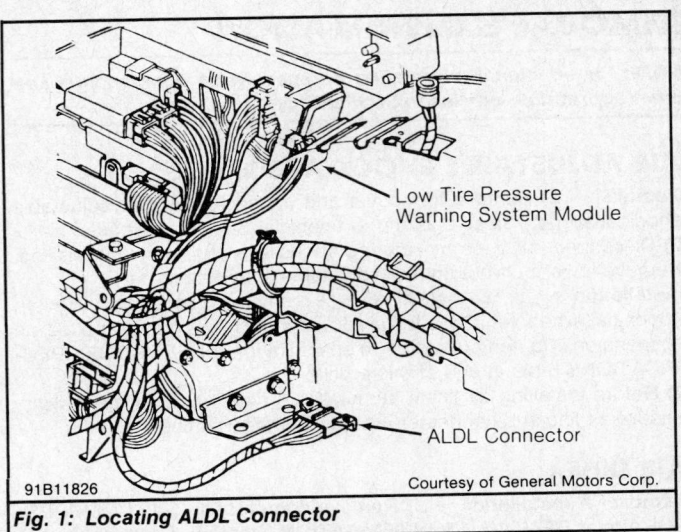

Low Tire Pressure
Warning System Module

ALDL Connector

91B11826   Courtesy of General Motors Corp.

Fig. 1: Locating ALDL Connector

must be cleared after system components are serviced. See CLEARING TROUBLE CODES under TROUBLE CODES.

TROUBLE CODE IDENTIFICATION

Code	Definition
12	Start Of Trouble Code Sequence
13	Left Rear Inoperative
14	Right Front Inoperative
21	Left Front Inoperative
22	Right Rear Inoperative
23	[1] Loss Of Speed Sensor Signal
31	Left Front Out Of Position
32	Right Front Out Of Position
33	Left Rear Out Of Position
34	Right Rear Out Of Position
41	[2] SRC Switch Shorted To Battery Voltage
42	[3] SRC Switch Contacts Open
43	[4] SRC Switch Open Circuit

[1] – Code 23 will set if ignition is cycled on/off 3 times without driving vehicle. SRC indicator light will go out when vehicle is driven. Code will remain in history and must be cleared to prevent misdiagnosis.

[2] – Code 41 will set if SRC control module senses a short to ground at terminal D11 (Pink/Black wire) of SRC control module.

[3] – Code 42 will set if poor connection exists at SRC switch terminals or SRC control module senses an open contact in the switch.

[4] – Code 43 will if SRC control module senses a open circuit at terminal D11 (Pink/Black wire) of SRC control module.

CLEARING TROUBLE CODES

Turn ignition on. Ground terminal "C" (Light Green wire) of Assembly Line Diagnostic Link (ALDL) for 2 seconds, and remove ground. Repeat procedure twice more. ALDL is located below left side of instrument panel and contains a plastic cover labeled DIAGNOSTIC CONNECTOR. *See Fig. 1.*

TESTING & DIAGNOSIS

TROUBLE CODES CANNOT BE DISPLAYED TEST

1) Disconnect wiring harness electrical connector from SRC control module, located in storage compartment, behind driver's seat. See Fig. 2. Turn ignition on with engine off.

2) Using voltmeter, measure voltage between SRC control module wiring harness connector terminal C16 (Pink/Black wire) and ground.

3) If battery voltage exists, proceed to step **4)**. If battery voltage does not exist, check for defective AIR BAG fuse, located in fuse block below right side of instrument panel. If AIR BAG fuse is okay, check for open circuit in Pink/Black wire between fuse block and SRC control module.

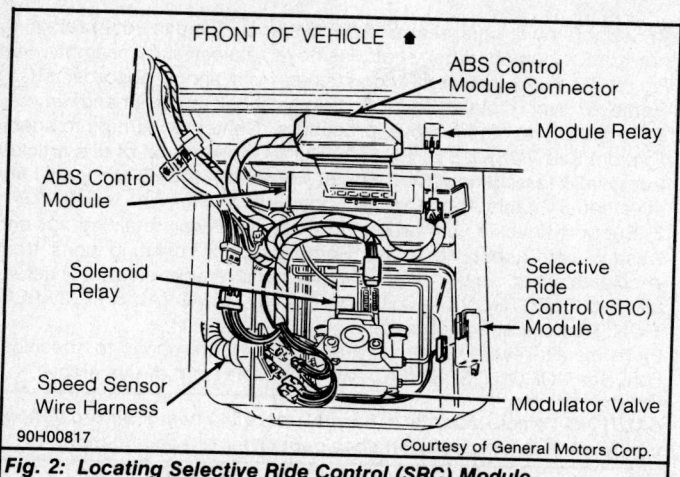

FRONT OF VEHICLE ▲

ABS Control Module Connector

Module Relay

ABS Control Module

Solenoid Relay

Selective Ride Control (SRC) Module

Speed Sensor Wire Harness

Modulator Valve

90H00817

Courtesy of General Motors Corp.

Fig. 2: Locating Selective Ride Control (SRC) Module

4) Using voltmeter, measure voltage between terminal D16 (Black/Red wire) and C16 (Pink/Black wire) of SRC control module wiring harness connector.

5) If battery voltage exists, proceed to step **6)**. If battery voltage does not exist, check for open circuit in Black/Red wire between SRC control module and ground. Ground circuit is attached at right rear of engine, near bellhousing (VIN J) or left rear of engine, near oil filter (VIN 8).

6) Using voltmeter, measure voltage between SRC control module wiring harness connector terminals D16 (Black/Red wire) and D6 (Brown/White wire).

7) If battery voltage exists, proceed to step **8)**. If battery voltage does not exist, check for open in SERVICE RIDE CONTROL indicator bulb or in Brown/White wire circuit between SRC control module and driver information center. If wiring and bulb are okay, repair/replace driver information center circuit board.

8) Turn ignition off. Using ohmmeter, check for continuity between terminal "C" (Light Green wire) of ALDL connector and terminal C8 (Light Green wire) of SRC control module wiring harness connector. The ALDL is located below left side of instrument panel and contains a plastic cover labeled DIAGNOSTIC CONNECTOR. See Fig. 1.

9) If continuity exists, replace SRC control module. If continuity does not exist, check for open circuit in Light Green between ALDL connector and SRC control module.

CODES 13, 14, 21 & 22

NOTE: Codes will be stored if SRC control module senses corresponding electronic actuator motor is moving slowly or not receiving correct feedback signal.

1) Ensure ignition is off. Remove clip and disconnect suspected electronic actuator from shock absorber assembly. Turn ignition on. Note if electronic actuator gear momentarily rotates.

2) If electronic actuator gear rotates, proceed to step **4)**. If electronic actuator gear does not rotate, disconnect electrical connector at electronic actuator. Connect test light between terminals "B" and "C" of electronic actuator wiring harness. See WIRING DIAGRAM for proper wire colors.

3) Turn ignition on and off, while checking for power at electronic actuator wiring harness. If power exists, replace defective electronic actuator. If power does not exist, check for open circuit or short to ground in wiring between SRC control module and terminals "B" and "C" of electronic actuator. The SRC control module is located in storage compartment, behind driver's seat. See Fig. 2. If wiring is okay, replace SRC control module.

4) Disconnect electrical connector at electronic actuator. Using voltmeter, check voltage at electronic actuator wiring harness at the following areas: terminal "E" and ground, terminal "E" and terminal "A", and terminal "D" and terminal "A". See WIRING DIAGRAM for proper wire colors.

5) If voltage was approximately 5 volts on all terminals, proceed to step **6)**. If voltage was not approximately 5 volts on each circuit, check for open circuit or defective wire connections. If wiring and connections are okay, replace SRC control module.

6) Attempt to rotate shaft in top of shock absorber. If shaft will not rotate easily with slight friction, replace shock absorber assembly. If shaft rotates easily with slight friction, ensure actuator wiring connector terminals are clean and tight. If wiring connection is okay, replace defective electronic actuator.

CODE 23

NOTE: Code 23 will set if ignition is cycled on/off 3 times without driving vehicle. SRC indicator light will go out when vehicle is driven. Code will remain in history and must be cleared to prevent misdiagnosis.

1) Check to see if Code 24 is set. If Code 24 is set, see SELF-DIAGNOSTICS article in ENGINE PERFORMANCE.

2) If Code 24 was not set, check for open circuit in Yellow and Purple wire between vehicle speed sensor (mounted on transmission) and SRC control module and Electronic Control Module (ECM).

3) SRC control module is located in storage compartment behind driver's seat. See Fig. 2. ECM is located in left rear corner of engine compartment, above battery. If wiring is okay, replace SRC control module.

CODES 41, 42 & 43

NOTE: Codes set under following conditions:
- *Code 41 sets if SRC control module senses a short to ground at terminal D11 (Pink/Black wire) of SRC control module.*
- *Code 42 sets if poor connection exists at SRC switch terminals or SRC control module senses an open contact in switch.*
- *Code 43 sets if SRC control module senses a open circuit at terminal D11 (Pink/Black wire) of SRC control module.*

1) Disconnect electrical connector from selective ride control switch, located on center console, between seat controls. Adjust selective ride control switch to PERF position. Using ohmmeter, measure resistance between selective ride control switch terminals "A" (Tan/White wire) and "B" (Pink/Blue wire). Resistance should be 250-350 ohms.

2) If resistance is within specifications, proceed to step **3)**. If resistance exceeds specifications, ensure selective ride control switch is not between detent positions. If switch is not between detent positions, replace selective ride control switch. If resistance is less than specifications, replace selective ride control switch.

3) Turn ignition on, with engine off. Using voltmeter, measure voltage between terminals "A" (Tan/White wire) and "D" (Black wire) of switch wiring harness electrical connector (not switch terminals).

4) If voltage is approximately 5 volts, proceed to step **5)**. If voltage is not approximately 5 volts, check for open circuit or short to ground in Tan/White wire between selective ride control switch and SRC control module. SRC control module is located in storage compartment behind driver's seat. See Fig. 2. If wiring is okay, replace SRC control module.

5) With ignition on and engine off, measure voltage between terminals "A" (Tan/White wire) and "B" (Pink/Black wire) of switch wiring harness electrical connector (not switch terminals).

6) If voltage is approximately 5 volts, replace SRC control module. If voltage is not approximately 5 volts, check for open circuit in Pink/Black wire between selective ride control switch and SRC control module. If wiring is okay, replace SRC control module. SRC control module is located in storage compartment behind driver's seat. See Fig. 2.

REMOVAL & INSTALLATION

NOTE: For additional information, see FRONT - CORVETTE or REAR - CORVETTE article in SUSPENSION.

ELECTRONIC ACTUATOR

NOTE: To remove electronic actuator from rear shock absorber, shock absorber must be removed from vehicle.

Removal (Front & Rear) – Disconnect negative battery cable. Note direction of wiring installation for reassembly reference. Remove retainer clip and retainer cup assembly. *See Fig. 3.* Remove wiring harness clip from wheelwell panel (if necessary). Disconnect electrical connector and remove electronic actuator.

Installation – 1) To install, reverse removal procedure. Ensure selector gear is positioned .20" (5.1 mm) above surface of retainer cup assembly. *See Fig. 3.*

2) Ensure retainer clip is fully seated in retainer cup assembly and ends of clip protrude away from retainer cup assembly. When installing electronic actuator on front shock absorber, maintain a .315" (8.00 mm) clearance between wheelwell panel and actuator wire harness.

CAUTION: DO NOT force electronic actuator onto retainer cup assembly. Very little effort is required to seat actuator. A "click" should be heard or felt when electronic actuator is fully seated. Electrical lead must face toward rear of vehicle on front shock applications and toward front of vehicle on rear shock applications.

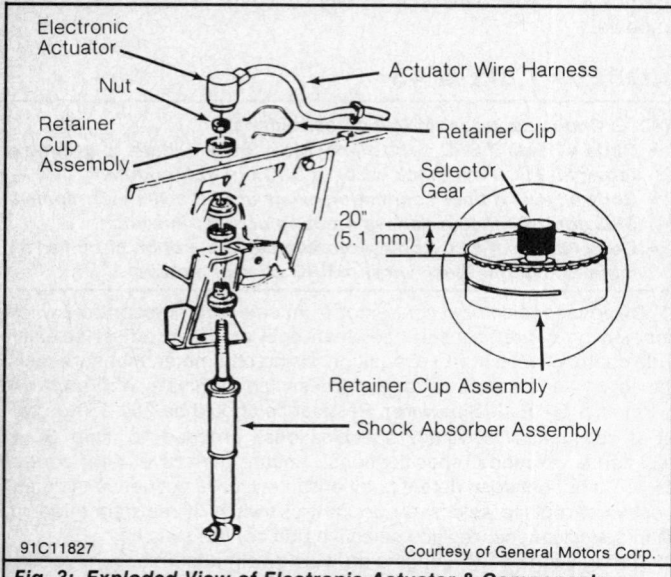

Electronic Actuator

Nut

Retainer Cup Assembly

Actuator Wire Harness

Retainer Clip

Selector Gear

.20" (5.1 mm)

Retainer Cup Assembly

Shock Absorber Assembly

91C11827   Courtesy of General Motors Corp.

Fig. 3: Exploded View of Electronic Actuator & Components (Front Shock Absorber Shown)

SELECTIVE RIDE CONTROL SWITCH

Removal & Installation – Selective ride control switch is located on center console, between the seat controls. No other information is available from manufacturer.

SHOCK ABSORBER

Removal & Installation (Front Shock Absorber) – 1) Remove electronic actuator. See ELECTRONIC ACTUATOR under REMOVAL & INSTALLATION. Raise and support vehicle. Remove wheel.

2) Support lower control arm with jackstand. Remove upper retaining nut from shock absorber shaft. Remove retainer cup assembly. *See Fig. 3.* Remove insulator and retainer from shock absorber shaft. Remove lower retaining bolts. Compress shock absorber and remove.

3) To install, reverse removal procedure. Tighten bolts/nuts to specification. See TORQUE SPECIFICATIONS table at end of this article.

Removal & Installation (Rear Shock Absorber) – 1) Disconnect negative battery cable. Raise and support vehicle. Remove wheel.

2) Support knuckle with jackstand. Remove lower retaining nut and washer from shock absorber. Remove upper retaining bolts from shock absorber. Lower shock absorber and remove electronic actuator. See ELECTRONIC ACTUATOR under REMOVAL & INSTALLATION. Remove shock absorber.

3) To install, reverse removal procedure. Tighten bolts to specification. See TORQUE SPECIFICATIONS table at end of this article.

CAUTION: Vehicle must be at normal operating height before tightening upper retaining bolts on shock absorber to specification.

SRC CONTROL MODULE

Removal & Installation – 1) Disconnect negative battery cable. Lift left side of rear floor compartment tray behind driver's seat. Remove compartment tray. Remove upper insulator.

2) Remove retaining screws from SRC control module. *See Fig. 2.* Separate SRC control module from retaining clips. Disconnect electrical connector. Remove SRC control module.

3) To install, reverse removal procedure. Tighten retaining screws to specification. See TORQUE SPECIFICATIONS table at end of this article.

VEHICLE SPEED SENSOR

Removal & Installation – 1) Disconnect negative battery cable. Raise and support vehicle. Disconnect electrical connector from vehicle speed sensor (mounted on rear of transmission). Remove retaining bolt, spacer, vehicle speed sensor and "O" ring.

2) To install, reverse removal procedure. Use new "O" ring coated with ATF. Tightening retaining bolt to specification. See TORQUE SPECIFICATIONS table.

TORQUE SPECIFICATIONS

TORQUE SPECIFICATIONS

Application	Ft. Lbs. (N.m)
Front Shock Absorber	
Lower Retaining Bolt	19 (26)
Upper Retaining Nut	31 (42)
Rear Shock Absorber	
Lower Retaining Bolt	61 (83)
Upper Retaining Bolt	22 (30)
Wheel Lug Nut	100 (136)

	INCH Lbs. (N.m)
SRC Control Module Retaining Screw	22 (2.5)
Vehicle Speed Sensor Retaining Bolt	89 (10)

WIRING DIAGRAM

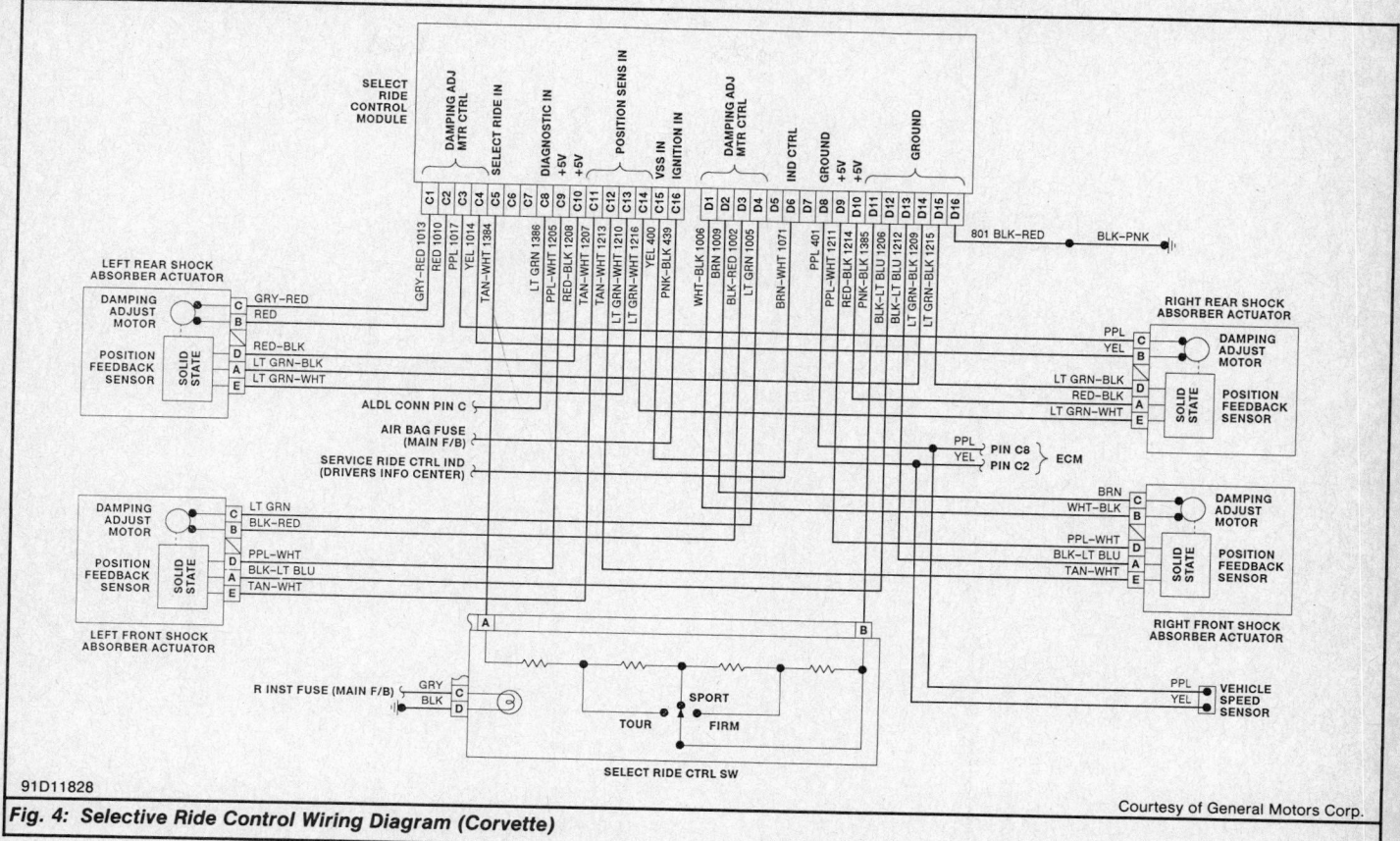

91D11828

Fig. 4: Selective Ride Control Wiring Diagram (Corvette)

Courtesy of General Motors Corp.

1991 STEERING
Fixed & Tilt Columns

"A" Body: **Century, Cutlass Ciera, Cutlass Cruiser, 6000**
"B" Body: **Caprice, Custom Cruiser, Roadmaster**
"C" Body: **DeVille, Fleetwood, Ninety-Eight, Park Avenue, Touring Sedan**
"D" Body: **Brougham**
"E" Body: **Eldorado, Reatta, Riviera, Toronado, Trofeo**
"F" Body: **Camaro, Firebird**
"H" Body: **Bonneville, Eighty-Eight, LeSabre**
"J" Body: **Cavalier & Sunbird**
"K" Body: **Seville**
"L" Body: **Beretta, Corsica**
"N" Body: **Cutlass Calais, Grand Am, Skylark**
"W" Body: **Cutlass Supreme, Grand Prix, Lumina, Regal**
"Y" Body: **Corvette**

DESCRIPTION

Steering columns are either floor shift or column shift. Column shift and floor shift steering columns are each available in 3 configurations: fixed column, tilt column and tilt/telescopic column. Design and maintenance of column shift and floor shift columns are similar. Column shift models, however, include an additionional shift lever, shift tube, tilt or tilt/telescopic mechanism and related components. *See Figs. 6-11.*

Columns have a 2-piece telescoping gear shift tube (column shift), connected by plastic inserts and shear pins. A 2-piece telescoping steering shaft features upper and lower sections, connected by plastic collars and pins. Steering columns use an integral ignition lock switch. This lock secures the steering wheel and shift linkage (column shift).

CAUTION: On models with Supplemental Inflatable Restraint (SIR), use extreme caution when servicing steering column. Air bag could deploy at any time. Before any repairs are performed, disconnect and shield battery ground cable. Ensure front wheels are in straight-ahead position. Turn ignition switch to LOCK position. Remove SIR (AIR BAG) fuse from fuse block. Disconnect the Connector Position Assurance (CPA) and Yellow 2-way SIR harness connector at base of steering column.

SAFETY PRECAUTIONS

AIR BAG SYSTEM

CAUTION: Read the following safety precautions before servicing steering columns on vehicles equipped with air bag restraint system.

ALWAYS wear safety glasses when servicing a vehicle with air bag and when handling an air bag removed from vehicle.

When carrying a live air bag, ensure bag and trim cover are pointed away from your body. In the unlikely event of an accidental deployment, bag will then deploy with minimal chance of injury. When placing a live air bag on a bench or other surface, ALWAYS face air bag and trim cover up, away from the surface. This will reduce the motion of the module if it is accidentally deployed.

Safety precautions must also be observed when handling a deployed air bag. After deployment, air bag surface may contain deposits of sodium hydroxide, a product of the gas generant combustion that irritates the skin. ALWAYS wear gloves and safety glasses when handling a deployed air bag, and wash hands with mild soap and water afterward.

Because of the critical operating requirements of system, DO NOT attempt to service air bag module or coil assembly. To correct system malfunctions, replace entire part.

After any servicing, ensure that Inflatable Restraint Indicator Light (AIR BAG light) flashes 7 to 9 times and then turns off. This ensures SIR system is working properly.

ADJUSTMENTS

IGNITION SWITCH

Move slider switch to extreme right position, and then move slider one detent to left. Adjust ignition switch by sliding switch up and down, until lock cylinder functions properly in all positions. Tighten ignition screws to 35 INCH lbs. (4 N.m).

DIMMER SWITCH

Depress dimmer switch until a 3/32" drill bit can be inserted into adjusting pin hole. *See Fig 1.* Connect dimmer switch to ignition switch but do not tighten screws. Connect dimmer switch rod to dimmer switch. Adjust dimmer switch by sliding switch up or down until a click is heard when the multi-function lever is pulled to activate high and low beam. Tighten screws to 35 INCH lbs. (4 N.m). Remove drill bit.

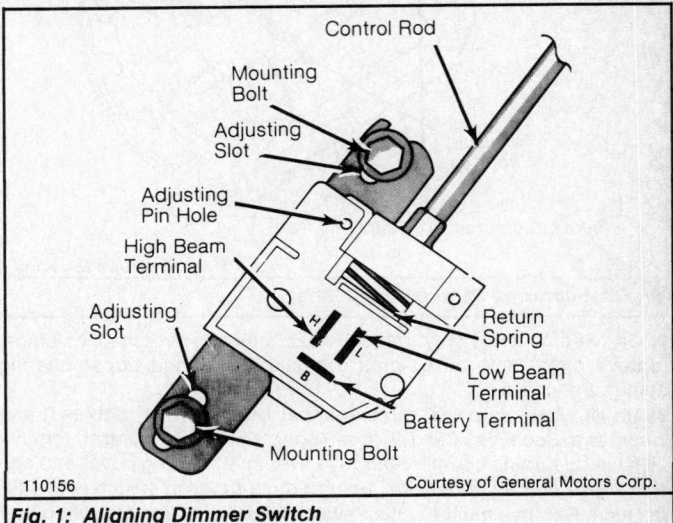

110156   Courtesy of General Motors Corp.

Fig. 1: Aligning Dimmer Switch

REMOVAL & INSTALLATION

STEERING WHEEL

CAUTION: DO NOT strike steering shaft with hammer to remove steering wheel. Hammering could loosen the plastic injections which maintain column rigidity. On vehicles with SIR, DO NOT thread puller bolts all the way through steering wheel hub. Threading puller bolts too far through steering wheel may cause damage to coil assembly.

Removal & Installation – 1) Disconnect and shield negative battery cable. Remove horn pad by pulling up. Turn ignition switch to ON position. On vehicles with SIR, ensure front wheels are in straight-ahead position. Turn ignition switch to LOCK position. Remove SIR fuse from fuse block. Disconnect the Connector Position Assurance (CPA) and Yellow 2-way SIR harness connector at base of steering column.

2) On vehicles with SIR, remove air bag module retaining screws from rear of steering wheel. Pull module away from steering wheel and disconnect coil assembly connector from module. Disconnect horn wire from steering column and remove module.

3) On all models, scribe an alignment mark on steering wheel hub in line with steering wheel shaft. Remove steering wheel nut. Using appropriate steering wheel puller, remove steering wheel. To install, reverse removal procedure. Align scribe marks on steering wheel hub and steering wheel shaft. Tighten steering wheel nut to 30 ft. lbs. (41 N.m). On vehicles with SIR, ensure that wiring is not trapped between air bag module and steering wheel. Check AIR BAG light for system faults. See AIR BAG SYSTEM under SAFETY PRECAUTIONS.

MULTI-FUNCTION SWITCH

NOTE: Multi-function switch incorporates turn signal, headlight high beam, wiper/washer, hazard warning and cruise control (if equipped).

Removal & Installation – 1) Remove steering wheel. See STEERING WHEEL under REMOVAL & INSTALLATION. On vehicles with SIR, remove coil assembly retaining ring. Pull out coil assembly and allow to hang. Remove wave washer. Using spring compressor (J-23653), remove shaft lock retaining snap ring. *See Fig. 2.*

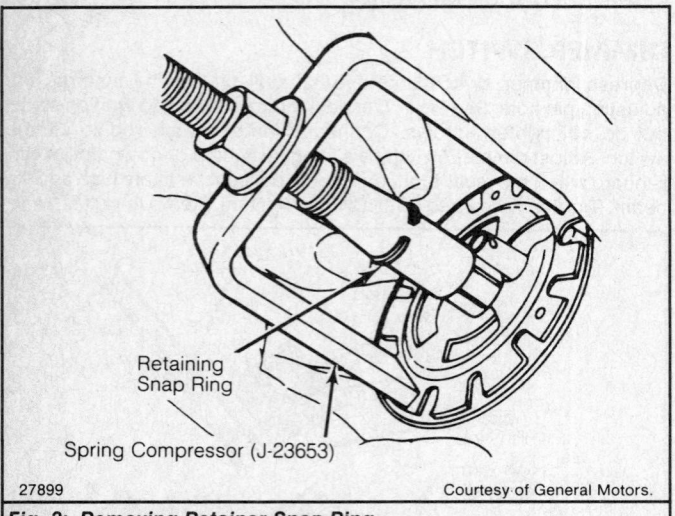

Retaining
Snap Ring

Spring Compressor (J-23653)

27899   Courtesy of General Motors.

Fig. 2: Removing Retainer Snap Ring

2) On fixed columns only, remove shaft lock spacer. On all columns, remove shaft lock, turn signal canceling cam, and upper bearing spring. *See Fig. 6.*
3) On tilt wheel columns, remove upper bearing inner race seat and inner race. *See Figs. 7 and 9.* If equipped with cruise control, remove tilt lever by turning counterclockwise. Remove housing cover end cap and cruise control connector. Ensure multi-function switch is in OFF position. Remove multi-function switch lever by pulling straight out of switch.
4) Remove signal switch arm and hazard warning assembly. Remove wiring protector from steering column. Remove switch connector from body harness connector. Remove multi-function switch retaining screws from steering column and remove switch from steering column shaft. To install, reverse removal procedure. Tighten switch retaining screws to 27 INCH lbs. (3.1 N.m). Tighten switch arm screw to 19 INCH lbs. (2.2 N.m). On vehicles with SIR, check AIR BAG light for system faults. See AIR BAG SYSTEM under SAFETY PRECAUTIONS.

TURN SIGNAL SWITCH

Removal & Installation ("W" Body) – 1) Remove steering wheel. See STEERING WHEEL under REMOVAL & INSTALLATION. Remove turn signal cancel cam assembly. Remove hazard warning knob. Remove housing cover. Remove wiring protector from opening in instrument panel bracket on jacket and bowl assembly and remove from wires. *See Figs. 10 and 11.*
2) Remove wiper switch connector from ignition and dimmer switch. Remove wiper switch assembly. Remove turn signal switch screws. Remove turn signal switch connector from ignition and dimmer switch assembly connector.
3) Remove 17-way secondary lock from turn signal connector. Remove wires on buzzer switch assembly from turn signal connector. Remove turn signal switch from steering column. To install, reverse removal procedure. Lubricate bottom side of cancel cam with lithium grease.

IGNITION SWITCH

Removal – 1) Disconnect and shield negative battery cable. Ensure front wheels are in straight ahead position. Turn ignition switch to LOCK position. On vehicles with SIR, remove SIR fuse from fuse block. Disconnect the Connector Position Assurance (CPA) and Yellow 2-way SIR harness connector at base of steering column.
2) On all models, remove knee bolster and deflector at base of steering column. Ensure ignition switch is in LOCK position. Remove shift indicator cable. Remove nuts from steering column bracket. Disconnect electrical connectors from dimmer switch and ignition switch.
3) Remove screws from dimmer switch. Remove dimmer switch from dimmer switch rod. Remove screws from ignition switch. Remove ignition switch from ignition switch rod. *See Fig. 6.*

Installation – 1) Ensure ignition switch is in LOCK position. Move slider switch to extreme right position, then move slider one detent to left. Ensure lock cylinder is in LOCK position. Connect ignition switch rod to ignition switch. Connect ignition switch to steering column jacket, but do not tighten screws.
2) Cycle ignition switch lock cylinder through all switch positions to ensure correct switch adjustment. Adjust ignition switch by sliding switch up and down until lock cylinder functions properly in all positions. Tighten ignition screws to 35 INCH lbs. (4 N.m). Depress dimmer switch until a 3/32" drill bit can be inserted into adjusting pin hole. *See Fig. 1.*
3) Connect dimmer switch to ignition switch but do not tighten screws. Connect dimmer switch rod to dimmer switch. Adjust dimmer switch by sliding switch up or down until a click is heard when the multi-function lever is pulled to activate high and low beam. Tighten screws to 35 INCH lbs. (4 N.m). Remove drill bit.
4) Connect electrical connectors. Install nuts to steering column bracket and tighten to 20 ft. lbs. (27 N.m). Install shift indicator, knee bolster and deflector. On vehicles with SIR, connect SIR system. Check AIR BAG light for system faults. See AIR BAG SYSTEM under SAFETY PRECAUTIONS.

LOCK CYLINDER

Removal & Installation – Ensure front wheels are in straight-ahead position. Turn ignition switch to LOCK position. Remove steering wheel. See STEERING WHEEL under REMOVAL & INSTALLATION. Remove multi-function switch. See MULTI-FUNCTION SWITCH under REMOVAL & INSTALLATION. On vehicles with SIR, remove coil assembly (if necessary). On all vehicles, remove buzzer switch and retaining clip. *See Fig. 6.* Insert key in lock cylinder and place in LOCK position. Remove lock cylinder screw and lock cylinder from switch actuator sector. To install, reverse removal procedure. Tighten lock cylinder screw to 22 INCH lbs. (2.5 N.m). On vehicles with SIR, connect AIR system. Check AIR BAG light for system faults. See AIR BAG SYSTEM under SAFETY PRECAUTIONS.

STEERING COLUMN

CAUTION: Columns must be handled with care when removed from vehicle. Use only fasteners of the same or equivalent part number if replacement is necessary. Improper fasteners or tightening could result in failure. Applying excessive pressure, or causing impact to mainshaft during service, may cause the column to collapse.

Removal (Except "W" Body) – 1) Disconnect and shield negative battery cable. Ensure front wheels are in straight ahead position. On vehicles with SIR, remove SIR fuse from fuse block. Disconnect the Connector Position Assurance (CPA) and Yellow 2-way SIR harness connector at base of steering column.
2) Turn ignition switch to LOCK position before disconnecting steering column or intermediate shaft from steering gear.

NOTE: Failure to lock steering shaft may cause coil assembly to become uncentered, which will cause damage to coil assembly.

3) On all models, remove steering wheel if steering column is being repaired or replaced. See STEERING WHEEL under REMOVAL & INSTALLATION. Remove stop light switch. Remove joint coupling bolt and nut attaching upper intermediate shaft to steering column. On column shift models, disconnect transmission linkage rod from lever on steering column.

4) Remove steering column lower trim panel. Remove knee bolster and deflector at base of steering column. Remove toe plate-to-cowl attaching bolts. Remove shift cable from steering column. Unplug electrical connectors from steering column. Remove steering column bracket mounting nuts. Remove steering column.

Installation – To install, reverse removal procedure. Tighten bracket mounting nuts to 20 ft. lbs. (27 N.m). Tighten joint coupling nut to 40 ft. lbs. (54 N.m). On vehicles with SIR, connect SIR system. Check AIR BAG light for system faults. See AIR BAG SYSTEM under SAFETY PRECAUTIONS.

Removal & Installation ("W" Body) – **1)** Disconnect and shield negative battery cable. Remove left side sound insulator and trim panel below steering column. With steering column unlocked, push top of intermediate shaft seal down for access to upper intermediate shaft coupling and upper coupling bolt.

2) Remove upper coupling bolt. Remove shift indicator cable end and casing from steering column (park interlock cable if floor shift). Remove upper and lower steering column bolts and lower steering column to seat. Disconnect electrical connectors. Separate upper intermediate shaft from lower steering shaft and remove steering column. To install, reverse removal procedure. Tighten coupling bolt to 35 ft. lbs. (47 N.m). Check for proper operation.

OVERHAUL

STEERING COLUMN

Preparation – Steering column removal is not necessary for shaft lock cover, shaft lock, steering shaft snap ring, canceling cam, turn signal switch, upper bearing preload spring or lock cylinder service. *See Figs. 8 and 9.* For the remaining components, steering column must be removed. Disassembly procedure for the tilt/telescopic steering column is similar to the tilt steering column and typical of all variations.

Disassembly (Non-Tilt Steering Column) – **1)** Disconnect and shield negative battery cable. Remove steering wheel. See STEERING WHEEL under REMOVAL & INSTALLATION. Remove steering column. See STEERING COLUMN under REMOVAL & INSTALLATION. Secure steering column in vise.

2) Remove multi-function switch. See MULTI-FUNCTION SWITCH under REMOVAL & INSTALLATION. Remove lock cylinder. See LOCK CYLINDER under REMOVAL & INSTALLATION. Remove lock housing cover. Remove upper bearing retainer. Remove lock bolt and spring thrust washer from ignition switch actuator. Pull pivot switch wire harness through instrument panel bracket, gearshift bowl shroud and gearshift lever bowl.

3) Remove pivot switch housing cover. Using Pivot Pin Remover (J-21854-01), remove switch actuator pin and pivot switch . *See Fig. 4.* Remove shift lever gate, bearing retaining bushing and horn contact. Remove bearing assembly, switch actuator sector and rack preload spring. Remove dimmer switch rod and dimmer switch. Remove ignition switch rod and ignition switch.

4) Remove lower bearing adapter clip, bearing adapter retainer and adapter and bearing assembly. Remove lower bearing spring, spring thrust washer and steering column shaft. *See Fig. 6.*

Disassembly (Tilt Steering Column) – **1)** Disconnect and shield negative battery cable. Remove steering wheel. See STEERING WHEEL under REMOVAL & INSTALLATION. Remove steering column. See STEERING COLUMN under REMOVAL & INSTALLATION. Secure steering column in vise.

2) Remove multi-function switch. See MULTI-FUNCTION SWITCH under REMOVAL & INSTALLATION. Remove lock cylinder. See LOCK CYLINDER under REMOVAL & INSTALLATION.

3) Remove tilt lever by turning counterclockwise. Remove lock housing cover. Remove housing cover end cap. Remove housing cover end base plate and dimmer switch rod actuator from lock housing cover. Pull pivot switch wire harness through shift lever bowl and steering column housing.

4) Remove spring retainer, tilt spring and spring guide. *See Fig. 3.* Using Pivot Pin Remover (J-21854-01), remove pivot pins. *See Fig. 4.* Install tilt lever. Pull back on tilt lever and pull steering column housing down and away from column. Remove wire abrasive shield, drive shaft and switch actuator sector. Remove switch actuator rack and rack preload spring.

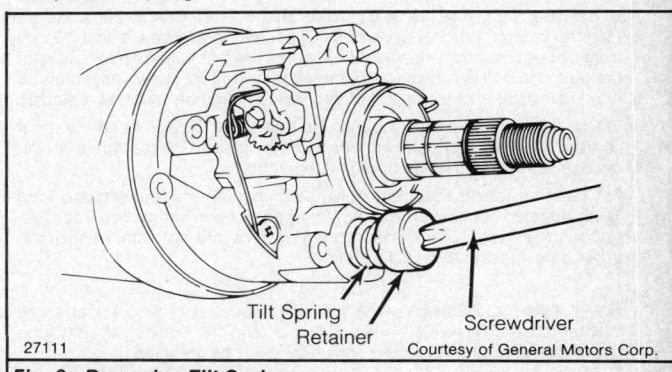

Tilt Spring
Retainer

Screwdriver

27111

Courtesy of General Motors Corp.

Fig. 3: Removing Tilt Spring

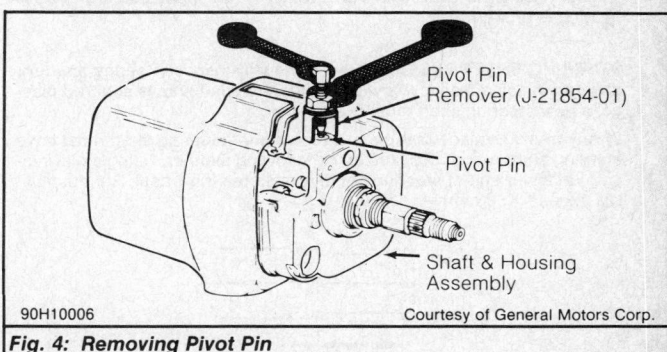

Pivot Pin
Remover (J-21854-01)

Pivot Pin

Shaft & Housing
Assembly

90H10006

Courtesy of General Motors Corp.

Fig. 4: Removing Pivot Pin

5) Remove release lever pin, shoe release lever and release lever spring. Remove dowel pin, steering wheel lock shoes, shoe springs and bearing. *See Figs. 7 and 9.* Remove lock bolt spring and bolt. Remove lower bearing adapter clip, bearing adapter retainer and adapter and bearing assembly. Remove steering column shaft.

NOTE: Scribe an alignment mark on race and upper shaft, and lower steering shaft to ensure proper assembly. Failure to assemble properly will cause steering wheel to be turned 180 degrees.

---

6) Remove race and upper shaft and lower steering shaft. Tilt one shaft 90 degrees from other and disengage shafts. Remove centering spheres from race and upper shaft, and lower steering shaft. Rotate centering spheres 90 degrees to remove. Remove joint preload spring from centering sphere. *See Figs. 7 and 9.*

7) Remove steering column housing support and dimmer switch rod from steering column jacket. Remove dimmer switch rod from steering column housing support. Remove shift lever gate, dimmer switch, ignition switch and ignition switch actuator.

8) Remove shift tube retaining ring, thrust washer, shaft lock, wave washer and shift tube. Remove gearshift lever bowl and gearshift bowl shroud. Remove gearshift bowl shroud from gearshift lever bowl. Remove shift lever spring from gearshift lever bowl.

Inspection (All Steering Columns) – *See Fig. 5.*

Reassembly (All Steering Columns) – To reassemble, reverse disassemble procedure. Apply a thin coat of lithium grease to all friction points when reassembling.

STEERING COLUMN INSPECTION

NOTE: Vehicles that have been involved in an accident which results in frame damage, major body damage, impact to the steering column or air bag deployment, may also have a damaged or misaligned steering column.

INSPECTION PROCEDURE

STEERING COLUMN JACKET ASSEMBLY – 1) Check capsules on steering column bracket assembly. Capsules should be within 1.59 mm from bottom of slots (View A). If capsules are not within specifications, bracket should be replaced if bracket is bolted to jacket assembly. If bracket is welded to jacket assembly, jacket assembly must be replaced.

2) Check contact surface "A" on capsules (View B). Bolt head must not contact surface or shear load would be increased. If contact is made, replace bracket assembly or jacket assembly.

3) Check for jacket assembly collapse by measuring the distance from lower edge of upper jacket to a defined point on lower jacket. See illustrations A through E. If measured dimensions are not within specifications, a new jacket must be installed.

SHIFT TUBE ASSEMBLY – 1) Visually inspect shift tube for sheared injected plastic (View C). (View E On "J" and "N" bodies). If shift tube shows sheared plastic, a new shift tube must be installed.

2) Check shift lever operation. If lever can be moved to PARK position without raising the lever, this is an indication that upper shift tube plastic bearing is broken.

STEERING SHAFT ASSEMBLY – 1) Visually inspect steering shaft for sheared injected plastic (View D). If steering shaft shows sheared plastic, a new steering shaft must be installed.

2) Any frame damage that could cause a bent steering shaft must have steering shaft runout checked in the following manner. Using a dial indicator at lower end of steering shaft, rotate steering wheel. Runout must not exceed 1.59 mm.

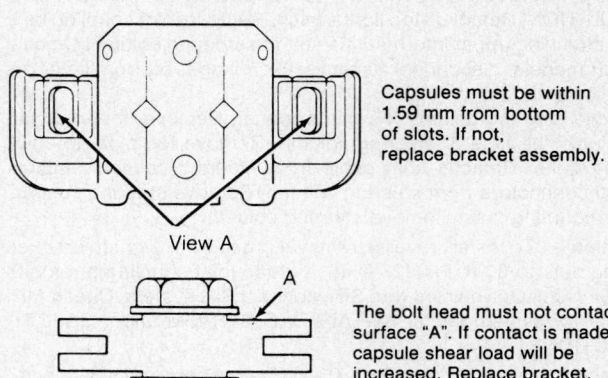

Capsules must be within 1.59 mm from bottom of slots. If not, replace bracket assembly.

View A

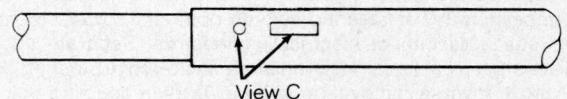

The bolt head must not contact surface "A". If contact is made, capsule shear load will be increased. Replace bracket.

View B

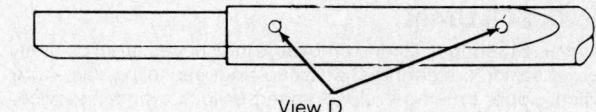

View C

View D

View E

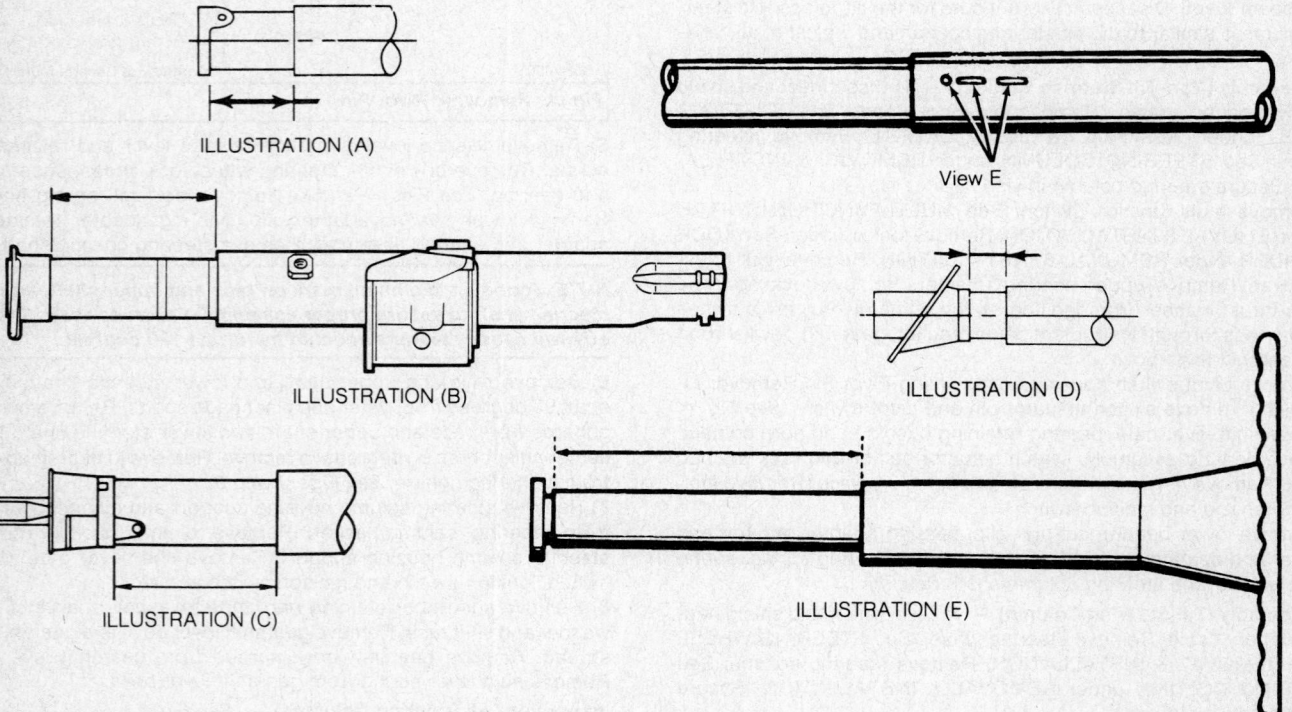

ILLUSTRATION (A)

ILLUSTRATION (B)

ILLUSTRATION (C)

ILLUSTRATION (D)

ILLUSTRATION (E)

91I09014

Courtesy of General Motors Corp.

Fig. 5: Inspecting Steering Column for Damage

STEERING COLUMN COLLAPSE MEASUREMENTS

Body [1]	[2] Illustration	In. (mm)
Standard Column		
"A" Body	(C)	4 1/2 (115)
"B" Body	(D)	7 11/64 (182)
"C" Body	(C)	4 13/16 (123)
"F" Body	(D)	7 15/64 (184)
"H" Body	(C)	5 25/64-5 15/32 (137-139)
"J" Body	(E)	5-5 3/32 (127-129)
"L" Body	(D)	3 9/64 (92.5)
"N" Body		
Column Shift	(E)	5 5/32 (127-129)
Floor Shift	(E)	5 5/32 (127-129)
"W" Body	(B)	4 1/16 (103.2)
Tilt Column		
"A" Body	(C)	4 15/32-4 17/32 (114-116)
"B" Body	(D)	7 3/16 (183)
"C" Body		
Park Avenue	(A)	4 13/64 (123)
All Other Models	(C)	5 1/8 (130)
"E" Body		
Eldorado	(C)	5 15/64 (133)
Toronado		
Column Shift	(C)	4 13/16 (123)
Floor Shift	(C)	4 13/16 (123)
Riviera	(C)	5 19/64 (134.6)
"F" Body	(D)	7 15/64-5 15/32 (137-139)
"H" Body	(C)	5 25/64 (184.6)
"J" Body	(E)	5 1/32-5 1/8 (128-130)
"K" Body	(C)	5 15/64 (133)
"L" Body	(D)	3 9/64 (92.5)
"N" Body		
Column Shift	(E)	5 1/32-5 1/8 (128-130)
Floor Shift	(E)	5 1/32-5 1/8 (128-130)
"W" Body	(B)	4 1/16 (103.2)
"Y" Body	(D)	5 43/64 (144)

[1] – "D" body information is not available.
[2] – See Fig. 5.

TORQUE SPECIFICATIONS

TORQUE SPECIFICATIONS

Application	Ft. Lbs. (N.m)
Steering Wheel Nut	30 (41)
Bracket-To-Upper Support Bolts	20 (27)
Bracket-To-Instrument Panel Stud Nuts	20 (27)
Flexible Coupling Nuts	20 (27)
Upper Intermediate Shaft-To-Steering Column	40 (54)
Intermediate Shaft-To-Steering Shaft Bolt	35 (47)
Lower Intermediate Shaft-To-Steering Gear Box	35 (47)

	INCH Lbs (N.m)
Ignition Switch Screws	35 (4)
Dimmer Switch Screws	35 (4)
Multifunction Switch Screws	27 (3.1)
Multifunction Switch Arm Screws	19 (2.2)
Lock Cylinder Screws	22 (2.5)

1991 STEERING
Fixed & Tilt Columns (Cont.)

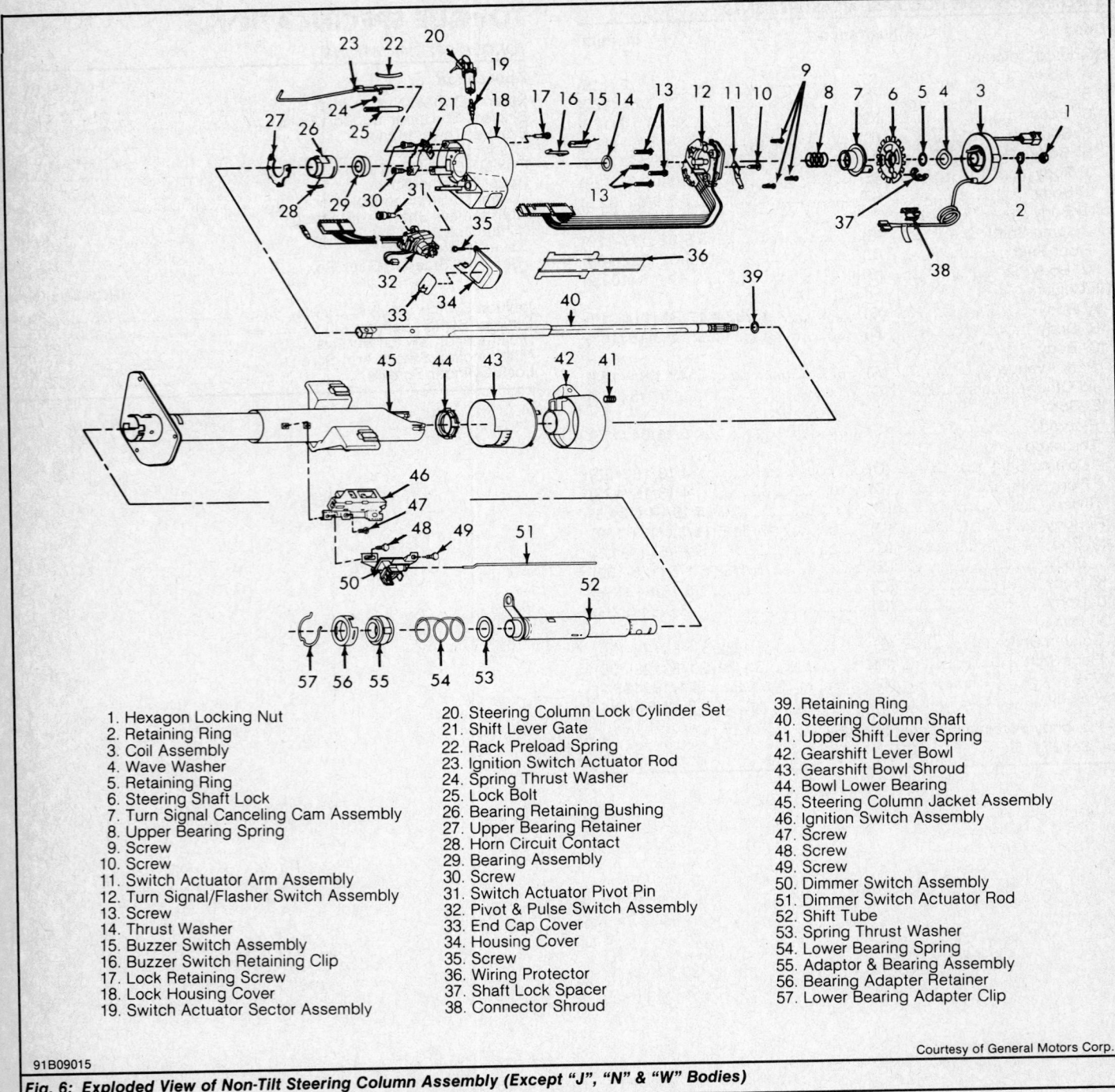

1. Hexagon Locking Nut
2. Retaining Ring
3. Coil Assembly
4. Wave Washer
5. Retaining Ring
6. Steering Shaft Lock
7. Turn Signal Canceling Cam Assembly
8. Upper Bearing Spring
9. Screw
10. Screw
11. Switch Actuator Arm Assembly
12. Turn Signal/Flasher Switch Assembly
13. Screw
14. Thrust Washer
15. Buzzer Switch Assembly
16. Buzzer Switch Retaining Clip
17. Lock Retaining Screw
18. Lock Housing Cover
19. Switch Actuator Sector Assembly

20. Steering Column Lock Cylinder Set
21. Shift Lever Gate
22. Rack Preload Spring
23. Ignition Switch Actuator Rod
24. Spring Thrust Washer
25. Lock Bolt
26. Bearing Retaining Bushing
27. Upper Bearing Retainer
28. Horn Circuit Contact
29. Bearing Assembly
30. Screw
31. Switch Actuator Pivot Pin
32. Pivot & Pulse Switch Assembly
33. End Cap Cover
34. Housing Cover
35. Screw
36. Wiring Protector
37. Shaft Lock Spacer
38. Connector Shroud

39. Retaining Ring
40. Steering Column Shaft
41. Upper Shift Lever Spring
42. Gearshift Lever Bowl
43. Gearshift Bowl Shroud
44. Bowl Lower Bearing
45. Steering Column Jacket Assembly
46. Ignition Switch Assembly
47. Screw
48. Screw
49. Screw
50. Dimmer Switch Assembly
51. Dimmer Switch Actuator Rod
52. Shift Tube
53. Spring Thrust Washer
54. Lower Bearing Spring
55. Adaptor & Bearing Assembly
56. Bearing Adapter Retainer
57. Lower Bearing Adapter Clip

Courtesy of General Motors Corp.

91B09015

Fig. 6: Exploded View of Non-Tilt Steering Column Assembly (Except "J", "N" & "W" Bodies)

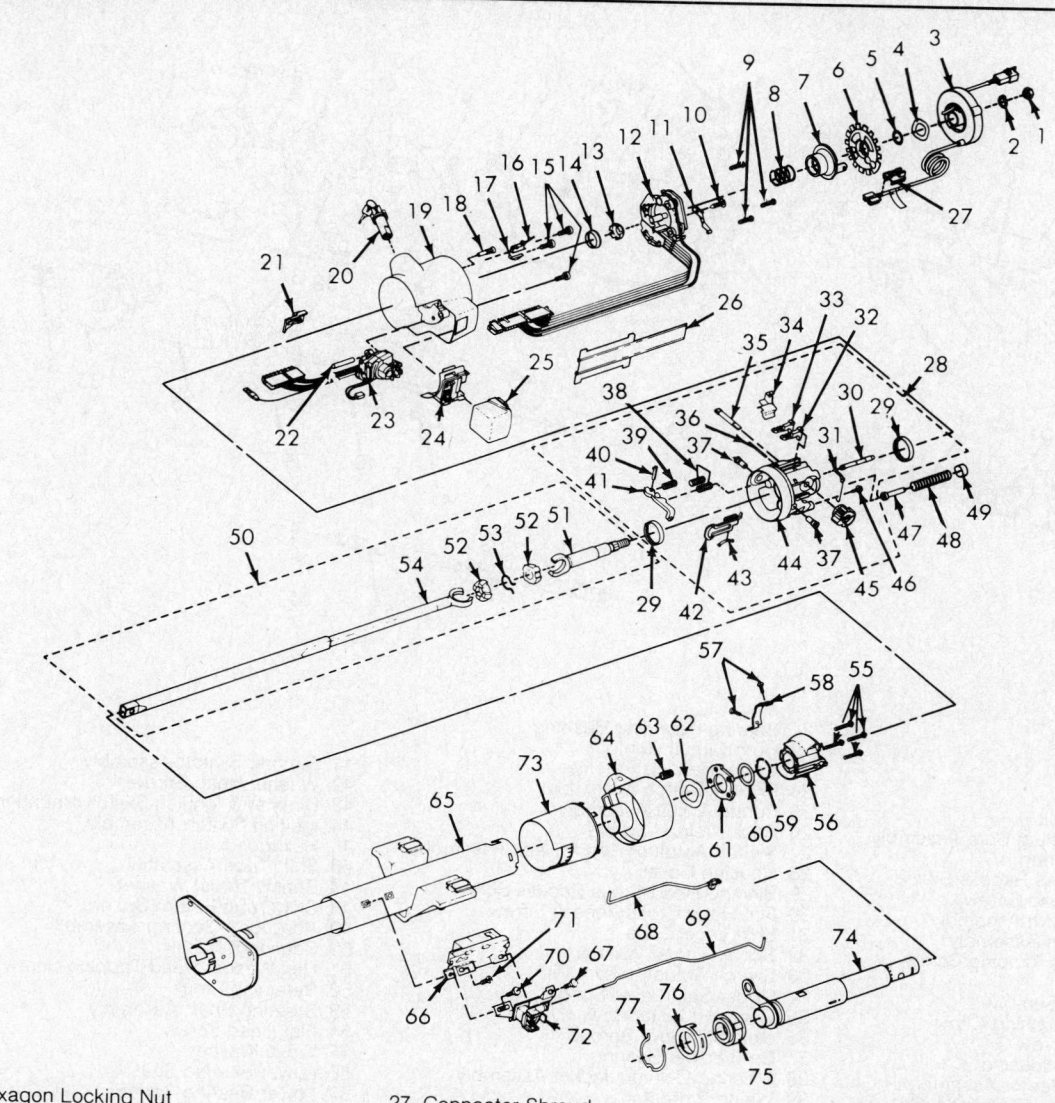

Courtesy of General Motors Corp.

Fig. 7: Exploded View of Tilt Steering Column Assembly (Except "J", "N" & "W" Bodies)

1. Hexagon Locking Nut
2. Retaining Ring
3. Coil Assembly
4. Wave Washer
5. Retaining Ring
6. Steering Shaft Lock
7. Turn Signal Canceling Cam
8. Upper Bearing Spring
9. Screw
10. Screw
11. Signal Switch Arm
12. Turn Signal/Flasher Switch
13. Upper Bearing Inner Race Seat
14. Inner Race
15. Screws
16. Buzzer Switch
17. Buzzer Switch Retaining Clip
18. Lock Retaining Screw
19. Lock Housing Cover
20. Lock Cylinder Set
21. Dimmer Switch Rod Actuator
22. Switch Actuator Pivot Pin
23. Pivot & Pulse Switch
24. Housing Cover End Base Plate
25. Housing Cover End Cap
26. Wiring Protector

27. Connector Shroud
28. Steering Column Housing Assembly
29. Bearing
30. Lock Bolt
31. Lock Bolt Spring
32. Steering Wheel Lock Shoe
33. Steering Wheel Lock Shoe
34. Wire Abrasion Shield
35. Drive Shaft
36. Dowel Pin
37. Pivot Pin
38. Shoe Spring
39. Release Lever Spring
40. Release Lever Pin
41. Shoe Release Lever
42. Switch Actuator Rack
43. Rack Preload Spring
44. Steering Column Housing
45. Switch Actuator Sector
46. Screw
47. Spring Guide
48. Wheel Tilt Spring
49. Spring Retainer
50 Steering Column Shaft
51. Race & Upper Shaft
52. Centering Sphere

53. Joint Preload Spring
54. Lower Steering Shaft
55. Screws
56. Steering Column Housing Support
57. Screws
58. Shift Lever Gate
59. Shift Tube Retaining Ring
60. Thrust Washer
61. Lock Plate
62. Wave Washer
63. Shift Lever Spring
64. Gearshift Lever Bowl
65. Steering Column Jacket
66. Ignition Switch
67. Screw
68. Ignition Switch Actuator
69. Dimmer Switch Rod
70. Screw
71. Screw
72. Dimmer Switch
73. Gearshift Bowl Shroud
74. Shift Tube
75. Adapter & Bearing Assembly
76. Bearing Adapter Retainer
77. Lower Bearing Adapter Clip

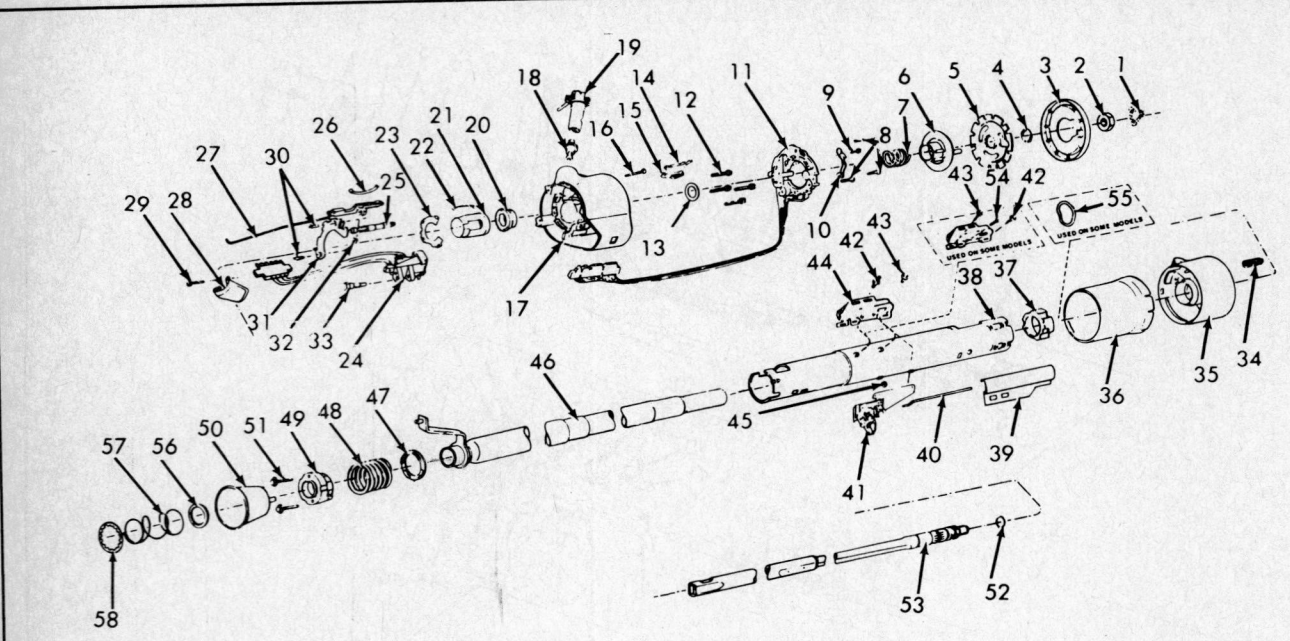

1. Retainer
2. Hexagon Nut
3. Shaft Lock Cover
4. Retaining Ring
5. Steering Shaft Lock
6. Turn Signal Canceling Cam Assembly
7. Upper Bearing Spring
8. Binding Head Cross Recess Screw
9. Round Washer Head Screw
10. Switch Actuator Arm Assembly
11. Turn Signal Switch Assembly
12. Hex Washer Head Tapping Screw
13. Thrust Washer
14. Buzzer Switch Assembly
15. Buzzer Switch Retaining Clip
16. Lock Retaining Screw
17. Steering Column Housing
18. Switch Actuator Sector Assembly
19. Steering Column Lock Cylinder Set
20. Bearing Assembly

21. Bearing Retaining Bushing
22. Horn Circuit Contact
23. Upper Bearing Retainer
24. Pivot & Switch Assembly
25. Spring & Bolt Assembly
26. Rack Preload Spring
27. Switch Actuator Rod & Rack Assembly
28. Housing Cover
29. Binding Head Cross Recess Screw
30. Flat Head Cross Recess Screw
31. Shift Lever Gate
32. Spring Thrust Washer
33. Switch Actuator Pivot Pin
34. Upper Shift Lever Spring
35. Gearshift Lever Bowl
36. Gearshift Bowl Shroud
37. Bowl Lower Bearing
38. Steering Column Jacket Assembly
39. Wiring Protector
40. Dimmer Switch Actuator Rod

41. Dimmer Switch Assembly
42. Washer Head Screw
43. Dimmer & Ignition Switch Mounting Stud
44. Ignition Switch Assembly
45. Hexagon Nut
46. Shift Tube Assembly
47. Spring Thrust Washer
48. Shift Tube Return Spring
49. Adaptor & Bearing Assembly
50. Bearing Retainer
51. Hex Washer Head Tapping Screw
52. Retaining Ring
53. Steering Shaft Assembly
54. Flat Head Screw
55. Wave Washer
56. Lower Bearing Seat
57. Lower Bearing Springs
58. Lower Spring Retainer

110152

Fig. 8: Exploded View of Non-Tilt Steering Column Assembly ("J" & "N" Bodies)

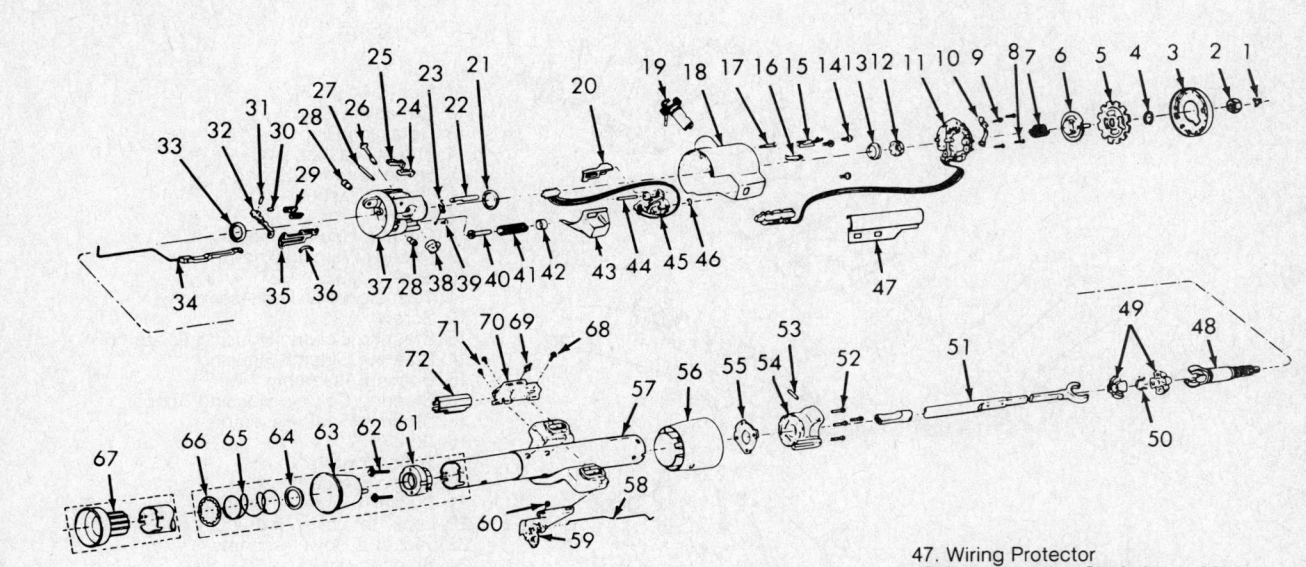

Fig. 9: Exploded View of Tilt Steering Column Assembly ("J" & "N" Bodies)

1. Retainer
2. Hexagon Nut
3. Shaft Lock Cover
4. Retaining Ring
5. Steering Shaft Lock
6. Turn Signal Canceling Cam Assembly
7. Upper Bearing Spring
8. Binding Head Cross Recess Screw
9. Round Washer Head Screw
10. Signal Switch Arm Assembly
11. Turn Signal Switch Assembly
12. Upper Bearing Inner Race Seat
13. Inner Race
14. Pan Head Cross Recess Screw
15. Buzzer Switch Assembly
16. Buzzer Switch Retaining Clip
17. Lock Retaining Screw
18. Lock Housing Cover
19. Steering Column Lock Cylinder Set
20. Dimmer Switch Rod Actuator
21. Bearing Assembly
22. Lock Bolt
23. Lock Bolt Spring

24. Steering Wheel Lock Shoe
25. Steering Wheel Lock Shoe
26. Drive Shaft
27. Dowel Pin
28. Pivot Pin
29. Shoe Spring
30. Release Lever Spring
31. Release Lever Pin
32. Shoe Release Lever
33. Bearing Assembly
34. Ignition Switch Actuator Assembly
35. Switch Actuator Rack
36. Rack Preload Spring
37. Steering Column Housing
38. Switch Actuator Sector
39. Hex Washer Head Screw
40. Spring Guide
41. Wheel Tilt Spring
42. Spring Retainer
43. Column Housing Cover End Cap
44. Switch Actuator Pivot Pin
45. Pivot & Switch Assembly
46. Pin Preload Spring

47. Wiring Protector
48. Race & Upper Shaft Assembly
49. Centering Sphere
50. Joint Preload Spring
51. Lower Steering Shaft Assembly
52. Support Screw
53. Dowel Pin
54. Steering Column Housing Support
55. Lock Plate
56. Steering Column Housing Shroud
57. Steering Column Jacket Assembly
58. Dimmer Switch Actuator Rod
59. Dimmer Switch Assembly
60. Hexagon Nut
61. Adapter & Bearing Assembly
62. Hex Washer Head Tapping Screw
63. Bearing Retainer
64. Lower Bearing Seat
65. Lower Bearing Spring
66. Lower Spring Retainer
67. Steering Column Jacket Bushing
68. Washer Head Screw
69. Dimmer & Ignition Switch Mounting Stud
70. Ignition Switch Assembly
71. Pan Head Screw
72. Ignition Switch Inhibitor Housing Assembly

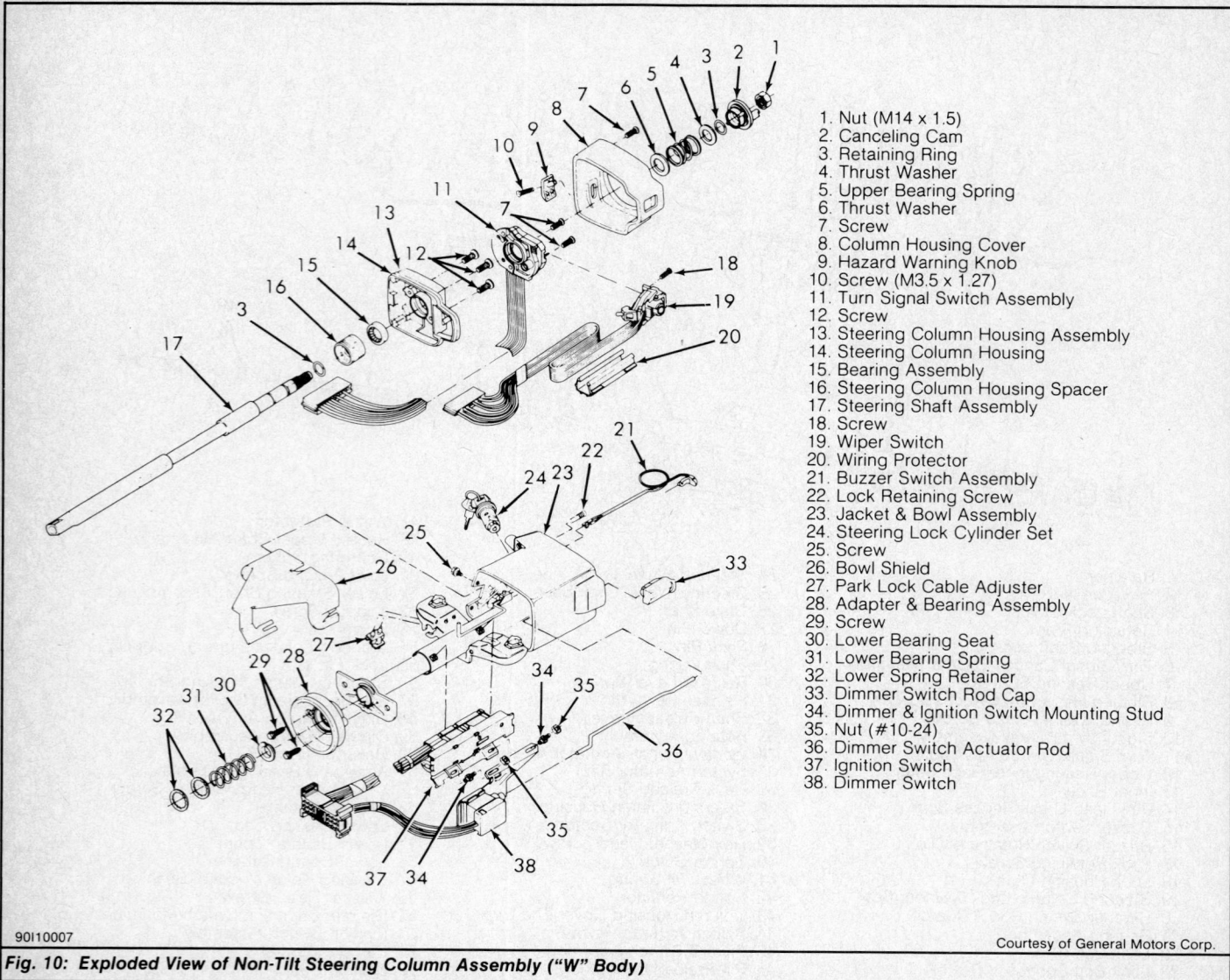

1. Nut (M14 x 1.5)
2. Canceling Cam
3. Retaining Ring
4. Thrust Washer
5. Upper Bearing Spring
6. Thrust Washer
7. Screw
8. Column Housing Cover
9. Hazard Warning Knob
10. Screw (M3.5 x 1.27)
11. Turn Signal Switch Assembly
12. Screw
13. Steering Column Housing Assembly
14. Steering Column Housing
15. Bearing Assembly
16. Steering Column Housing Spacer
17. Steering Shaft Assembly
18. Screw
19. Wiper Switch
20. Wiring Protector
21. Buzzer Switch Assembly
22. Lock Retaining Screw
23. Jacket & Bowl Assembly
24. Steering Lock Cylinder Set
25. Screw
26. Bowl Shield
27. Park Lock Cable Adjuster
28. Adapter & Bearing Assembly
29. Screw
30. Lower Bearing Seat
31. Lower Bearing Spring
32. Lower Spring Retainer
33. Dimmer Switch Rod Cap
34. Dimmer & Ignition Switch Mounting Stud
35. Nut (#10-24)
36. Dimmer Switch Actuator Rod
37. Ignition Switch
38. Dimmer Switch

90I10007

Courtesy of General Motors Corp.

Fig. 10: Exploded View of Non-Tilt Steering Column Assembly ("W" Body)

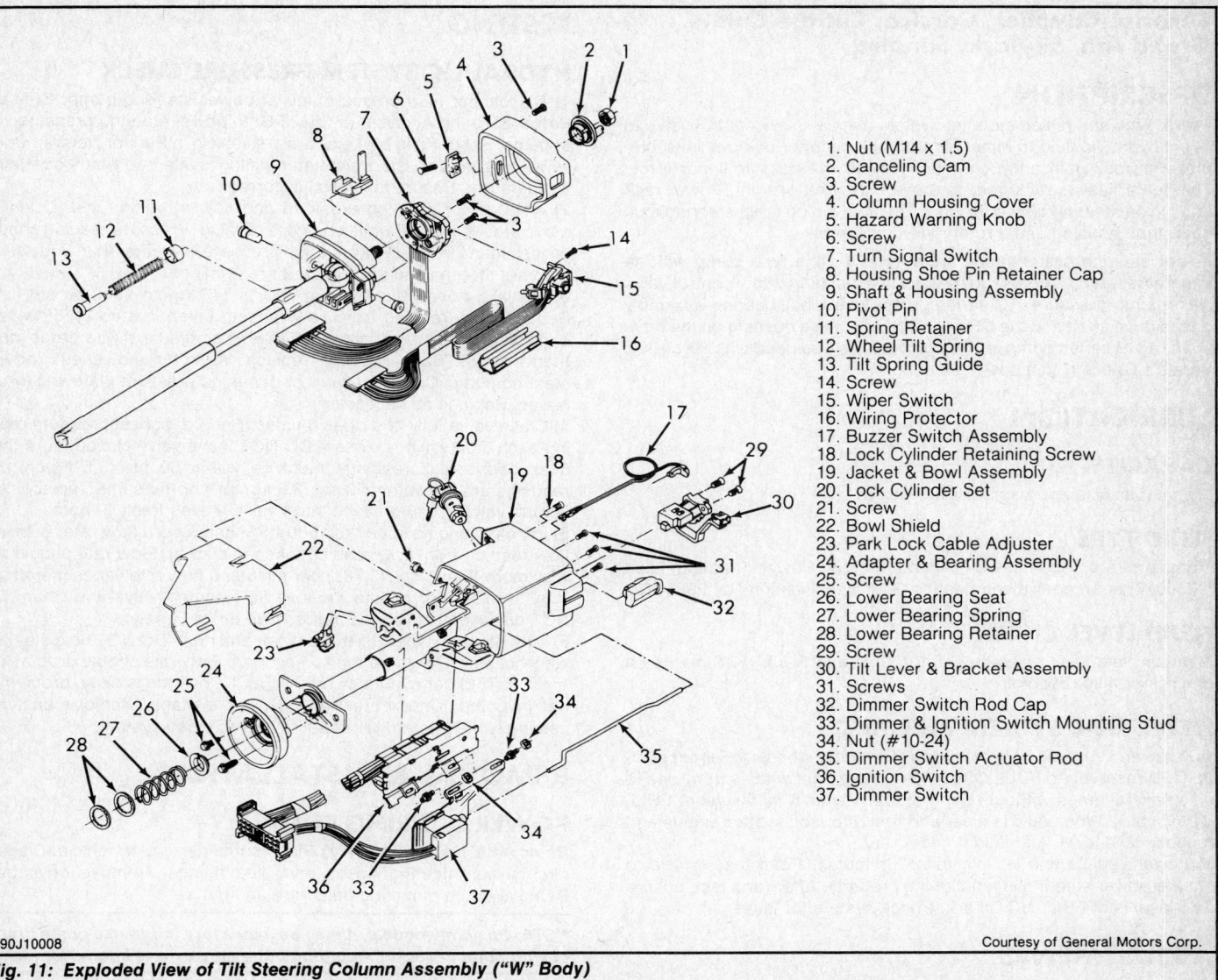

1. Nut (M14 x 1.5)
2. Canceling Cam
3. Screw
4. Column Housing Cover
5. Hazard Warning Knob
6. Screw
7. Turn Signal Switch
8. Housing Shoe Pin Retainer Cap
9. Shaft & Housing Assembly
10. Pivot Pin
11. Spring Retainer
12. Wheel Tilt Spring
13. Tilt Spring Guide
14. Screw
15. Wiper Switch
16. Wiring Protector
17. Buzzer Switch Assembly
18. Lock Cylinder Retaining Screw
19. Jacket & Bowl Assembly
20. Lock Cylinder Set
21. Screw
22. Bowl Shield
23. Park Lock Cable Adjuster
24. Adapter & Bearing Assembly
25. Screw
26. Lower Bearing Seat
27. Lower Bearing Spring
28. Lower Bearing Retainer
29. Screw
30. Tilt Lever & Bracket Assembly
31. Screws
32. Dimmer Switch Rod Cap
33. Dimmer & Ignition Switch Mounting Stud
34. Nut (#10-24)
35. Dimmer Switch Actuator Rod
36. Ignition Switch
37. Dimmer Switch

90J10008

Courtesy of General Motors Corp.

Fig. 11: Exploded View of Tilt Steering Column Assembly ("W" Body)

Beretta, Cavalier, Corsica, Cutlass Calais, Grand Am, Skylark, Sunbird

DESCRIPTION

Power rack and pinion steering system uses a rotary control valve to direct hydraulic fluid to either side of rack piston. Rack piston is integral with rack gear and converts hydraulic pressure to linear force. This force assists rack gear to move either left or right. Power rack and pinion steering gear consists of an input pinion gear, steering rack gear, tube housing and a rotary valve assembly.

Power steering system uses a belt-driven, vane type pump with an integral reservoir. A pressure relief valve inside the flow control valve limits pump pressure. TC series pumps use a ball bearing assembly on the drive shaft and the CB series pumps use a bushing on the drive shaft. A CB series pump is used on vehicles equipped with Electronic Variable Orifice (EVO) power steering.

LUBRICATION

CAPACITY

Fluid capacity is approximately 1.5 pts. (.7L).

FLUID TYPE

Manufacturers recommend General Motors Power Steering Fluid (1050017) or an equivalent meeting G.M. Specification No. 9985010.

FLUID LEVEL CHECK

Maintain fluid level between FULL COLD and FULL HOT marks on dipstick or fluid reservoir.

HYDRAULIC SYSTEM BLEEDING

1) Raise and support front of vehicle. Turn front wheels to full left position. Fill reservoir to FULL COLD mark. Turn front wheels from side to side several times without hitting stops. Maintain fluid level at FULL COLD mark. When fluid is clear and free of bubbles, start engine and recheck fluid level. Add fluid if necessary.
2) Lower vehicle and let idle for 2-3 minutes. Road test vehicle to ensure power steering is functioning properly. After road test, ensure fluid level is at FULL HOT mark. Check system for leaks.

ADJUSTMENTS

POWER STEERING PUMP BELT

Serpentine Belt – Serpentine belt is self adjusting within tensioner operating limits.
Conventional Belt – Use a belt tension gauge to check belt tension. See BELT ADJUSTMENT SPECIFICATIONS table.

BELT ADJUSTMENT SPECIFICATIONS

Application	Lbs. (kg)
2.3L	
New	191 (86.7)
Used [1]	100 (45.4)
2.5L	
New	180 (81.7)
Used [1]	90 (40.8)

[1] – Belt is considered used if it has been in operation for more than 5 minutes.

RACK BEARING PRELOAD

1) Raise and support front of vehicle. Center steering wheel. Loosen adjusting plug lock nut. Turn adjusting plug clockwise until it bottoms in housing. Back off adjusting plug 50-70 degrees on Beretta and Corsica, 35-45 degrees on all other models.
2) Tighten lock nut to specification while holding adjuster plug stationary. Check steering wheel movement for binding after adjustment.

TESTING

HYDRAULIC SYSTEM PRESSURE CHECK

1) Disconnect high pressure line at power steering pump. Connect Power Steering Analyzer (J-25323-B) to power steering pressure line at pump. Set parking brake and leave vehicle in Park or Neutral. Open valve on analyzer. Start engine and allow system to reach operating temperature. Ensure fluid level is correct.
2) Note power steering pressure and flow at engine idle. DO NOT move steering wheel while engine is running. Pressure reading should be less than 200 psi (14 kg/cm²). If pressure is greater than 200 psi (14 kg/cm²), stop engine and check for restrictions.
3) Partially close valve to build 700 psi (49 kg/cm²) and record flow. Subtract flow reading from flow reading taken in step **2)**. Flow rate should not drop more than 1 gal. (3.78L) per minute. If flow drops more than 1 gal. (3.78L) per minute, replace ring, rotor and vanes in power steering pump. Check for worn or damaged pressure plate and thrust plates. Replace as necessary.
4) Close valve fully and open 3 times. Record highest pressure reading each time valve is closed. DO NOT leave valve closed more than 5 seconds. All 3 readings must be within 50 psi (3.5 kg/cm²). If readings are not within 50 psi (3.5 kg/cm²) or the same, replace flow control valve. Ensure flow control valve moves freely in bore.
5) Increase engine speed to 1500 RPM and record flow rate. Subtract flow reading from flow reading taken in step **2)**. Flow rate should not vary more than 1 gal. (3.78L) per minute. If flow rate varies more than 1 gal. (3.78L) per minute, remove flow control valve and clean. DO NOT disassemble valve. Ensure valve moves freely.
6) Turn steering wheel all the way left and right. DO NOT hold steering wheel at stops for more than 5 seconds. Flow rate should drop below 1 gal. (3.78L) per minute at 1500 RPM. If flow rate is okay, problem is not in pump. Check steering gear for leakage. Remove analyzer assembly. Fill system to proper level and bleed system.

REMOVAL & INSTALLATION

POWER STEERING PUMP

Removal & Installation – 1) Place container under vehicle. Disconnect power steering hoses and plug fittings. Remove drive belt. Remove pump mounting hardware and pump.

NOTE: On some models, it may be necessary to remove pump bracket with pump. Bracket mounting bolts may extend into water jacket.

2) Because of different engines and air conditioning configurations, it may be necessary to remove additional components. On some models, power steering pump pulley may be removed to ease removal of pump. To install, reverse removal procedure.

POWER STEERING PUMP PULLEY

Removal & Installation – Remove drive belt from power steering pump pulley. Remove power steering pump from engine if necessary for tool clearance. Install Pulley Remover (J-25034-B). Remove pump pulley. To install, reverse removal procedure using Pulley Installer (J-25033-B).

POWER RACK & PINION

Removal – 1) Remove left side sound insulator. Remove upper pinch bolt from flexible coupling. Remove hydraulic line retainer. Raise and support vehicle. Remove front wheels. Using Separator (J-24319-01), separate tie rod ends from struts. *See Fig. 1.*
2) Lower vehicle. Remove mounting brackets and hydraulic lines from steering gear. Move gear forward. Remove lower pinch bolt from flexible coupling. Remove coupling from pinion shaft.
3) Remove dash seal from rack assembly. Raise and support vehicle. Turn left knuckle and hub assembly to full left position. Remove rack and pinion assembly through access hole in left wheel opening.

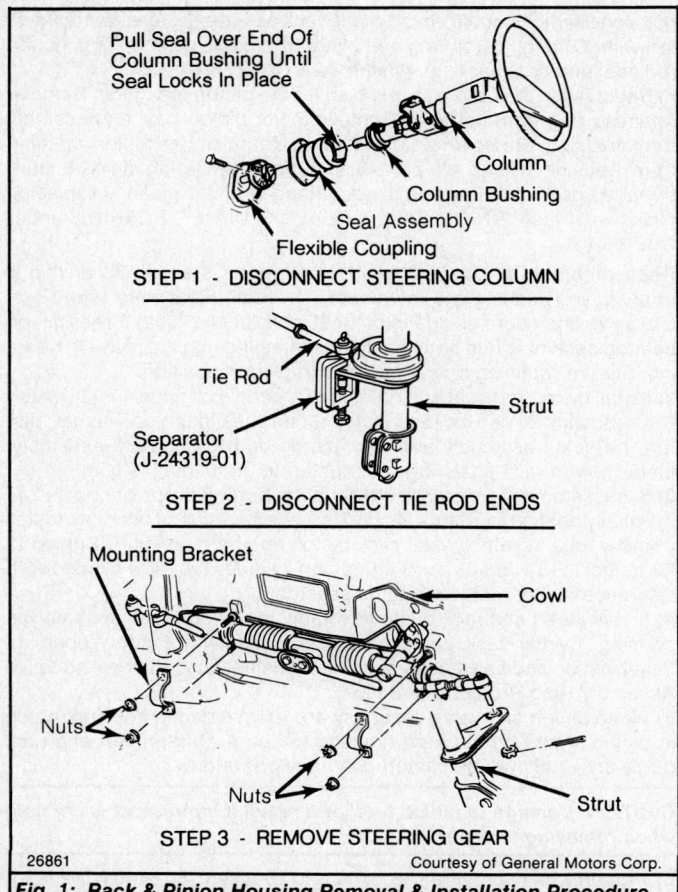

Fig. 1: Rack & Pinion Housing Removal & Installation Procedure

Installation – Reinstall studs if they were removed with mounting clamps. To install, reverse removal procedure. Tighten nuts and bolts to specification. See TORQUE SPECIFICATIONS table at end of this article.

TIE ROD END

Removal & Installation – Remove cotter pin and nut from tie rod end. Loosen tie rod end pinch bolt. Using tie rod end puller, separate tie rod end from strut. Unscrew tie rod end, counting number of turns for reassembly reference. To install, reverse removal procedure.

OVERHAUL

POWER STEERING PUMP

Disassembly – Remove drive pulley from drive shaft. Using a punch in access hole, remove retaining ring. Gently push on drive shaft to assist in removing end cover, "O" ring, pressure plate spring, pump ring, pump vanes, and drive shaft sub assembly. Remove dowel pins and "O" ring from pump housing. Remove drive shaft seal.

Inspection – Clean all parts in clean power steering fluid and dry. Inspect parts for scoring, pitting or chatter marks. Replace parts that show signs of excessive wear.

Reassembly – 1) Lubricate new drive shaft seal with power steering fluid. Using Drive Shaft Seal Installer (J-7728), install seal into pump housing. Place pump ring dowel pins into pump housing. Place thrust plate and pump rotor onto drive shaft and secure with new retaining ring. Install drive shaft sub assembly into pump housing.
2) Install pump ring onto dowel pins. Slide pump vanes into pump rotor. Lubricate new "O" ring with power steering fluid and install into groove in pump housing. Install pressure plate and pressure plate spring. Lubricate new "O" ring with power steering fluid and place into end cover.

3) Lubricate outer edge of end cover with power steering fluid and press cover into housing. Install retaining ring into groove in housing, with ring opening near access hole in housing. Ensure ring is fully seated.

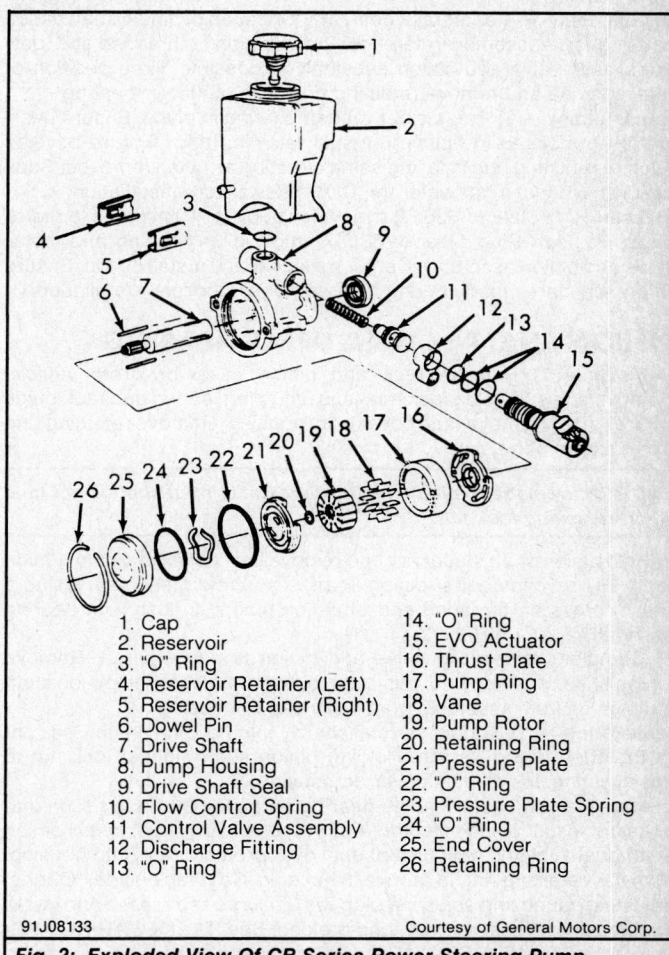

1. Cap	14. "O" Ring
2. Reservoir	15. EVO Actuator
3. "O" Ring	16. Thrust Plate
4. Reservoir Retainer (Left)	17. Pump Ring
5. Reservoir Retainer (Right)	18. Vane
6. Dowel Pin	19. Pump Rotor
7. Drive Shaft	20. Retaining Ring
8. Pump Housing	21. Pressure Plate
9. Drive Shaft Seal	22. "O" Ring
10. Flow Control Spring	23. Pressure Plate Spring
11. Control Valve Assembly	24. "O" Ring
12. Discharge Fitting	25. End Cover
13. "O" Ring	26. Retaining Ring

Fig. 2: Exploded View Of CB Series Power Steering Pump (TC Series Pump Is Similar)

INNER TIE ROD & INNER PIVOT BUSHING

Disassembly – 1) Remove and discard lock plate from inner tie rod bolts. Remove tie rod bolts, one at a time, and slide tie rod out from under support plate. See Fig. 3.
2) If removing both tie rods, reinstall first tie rod bolt to keep boot and guides properly aligned before removing second bolt. Using Bushing Driver (J-29809), remove bushing from tie rod.

Reassembly – Coat bushing with a light film of grease. Install bushing in tie rod using bushing driver. Ensure center housing cover washers are in place. Install tie rods one at a time. Tighten mounting bolts and secure bolts with lock plate tabs. See TORQUE SPECIFICATIONS table at end of this article.

PINION SHAFT SEALS & UPPER BUSHING

Disassembly – 1) Remove coupling from upper end of pinion shaft. Remove retaining ring from pinion shaft. Remove dust cap from lower end of pinion housing.

CAUTION: Damage to pinion teeth will result if input shaft is not held when removing lock nut.

2) Hold pinion shaft and remove pinion shaft lock nut. Using a press, ensure threaded end of pinion is flush with lower bearing. Remove upper pinion bushing and seal with a punch.

Reassembly – To install, reverse disassembly procedure. Use Seal Installer (J-29810) to install upper seal.

SPOOL VALVE RINGS & LOWER BEARING

Disassembly – Center rack gear. Mark location of pinion shaft flat on housing for reassembly reference. Press pinion at threaded end, until removal of valve and pinion assembly is possible. Note position of retaining ring and remove retaining ring. Tap out lower bearing.

Reassembly – **1)** Press outer race of bearing in place. Ensure bearing is not cocked in housing. Install retaining ring. Ensure beveled edge of retaining ring is facing same direction as when removed. Soak new valve rings in hot water for 10 minutes before installation.

2) Insert Ring Sizer (J-33057) over valve body for 10 minutes to resize rings. Position Ring Sizer (J-33057) into pinion housing and install valve and pinion assembly. Center rack gear and install pinion. Ensure reference marks made during disassembly procedure are aligned.

PINION SHAFT SEALS & UPPER BEARING

Removal – **1)** Remove rack and pinion assembly from vehicle. Remove adjusting plug lock nut, adjusting plug, spring and rack guide with "O" ring. Remove dust cover from housing. Remove retaining ring from bottom of housing.

CAUTION: Damage to pinion teeth will result if input shaft is not held when removing lock nut.

---

2) Hold pinion shaft stationary and remove lock nut from pinion. Pinion teeth will be damaged if pinion shaft is not held stationary. Using a press, press on threaded end of pinion until it is flush with bearing assembly.

3) Complete removal of valve and pinion is not required. Remove pinion shaft retaining ring, dust seal, pinion shaft seal and pinion shaft annulus bearing assembly from valve end of housing.

Installation – **1)** Bottom valve assembly into housing. Install lock nut to threaded end of pinion. Holding pinion shaft, tighten lock nut to specification. Install dust cover on housing.

2) Install pinion shaft annulus bearing on pinion shaft and slide into housing. Install Seal Protector (J-29810) on pinion shaft. Install pinion shaft dust seal and pinion shaft seal over protector and into housing.

3) Install retaining ring in groove in housing. Coat rack guide, "O" ring, adjusting spring and adjusting plug with lithium base grease and install into housing. Adjust rack bearing preload. See RACK BEARING PRELOAD under ADJUSTMENTS. To complete installation, reverse removal procedure.

RACK ASSEMBLY

Disassembly – **1)** Remove rack and pinion assembly from vehicle. Remove pinch bolt from flange and steering coupling. Remove steering coupling assembly. Remove dash seal from housing.

2) Remove and discard lock plate from inner tie rod end bolts. Remove inner tie rod end bolts, support plate and inner tie rod end assemblies. Remove hydraulic cylinder lines with "O" ring seals, starting at valve end of line.

3) Separate and remove mounting grommet and boot clamps. Slide boot retaining bushing from rack and pinion boot. Slide boot, boot retaining bushing and housing retaining washers as an assembly from housing. Remove insert and rack guide from housing.

4) Loosen rack bearing adjusting plug lock nut. Remove adjusting plug from housing. Remove spring, rack guide and "O" ring from housing. Remove dust cover and retaining ring. While holding pinion shaft, remove lock nut from pinion. With gear centered, mark location of pinion shaft notch on housing for reassembly reference.

5) Using a press, press on threaded end of pinion shaft until pinion and valve assembly can be removed. Remove pinion shaft dust seal, pinion shaft seal, pinion shaft upper bearing, and pinion and valve assembly with spool shaft retaining ring and valve body rings attached. Mark cylinder outer housing to ensure cylinder lines will align during reassembly.

6) Remove cylinder tube assembly from housing using Cylinder Tube Nut Wrench (J-36343). Remove rod guide rack assembly from

housing. Remove nut from rod guide rack assembly. Remove rack piston with "O" ring, piston ring and piston rod guide with "O" ring, piston rod seal and seal back-up washer. *See Fig. 3.*

7) Remove "O" ring and piston rod seal from piston rod guide. Remove retaining ring from housing. Remove lower pinion bearing assembly from housing. Remove pinion shaft seal and upper pinion bushing from housing. Clean all parts using power steering fluid. Ensure threaded portion of housing is not damaged and is clean. If replacing pinion seal, see PINION SHAFT SEALS & UPPER BEARING under OVERHAUL.

Reassembly – **1)** Coat all seals with power steering fluid. Install upper pinion bushing into valve bore in housing. Seat pinion shaft seal into valve body bore using Pinion Seal Installer (J-29822). Press pinion bearing assembly into housing. Install retaining ring in groove in housing. Ensure retaining ring is installed in proper position.

2) Install piston rod seal and "O" ring on piston rod guide. Install piston rod seal and "O" ring on rack piston. Install seal back-up washer, piston rod guide assembly and rack piston on rod and rack assembly. Install nut on rack assembly and tighten to 30 ft. lbs. (41 N.m).

3) Slide piston rod assembly into housing. Apply 3 drops of Loctite 242 in equally spaced locations around threaded portion of housing. Install cylinder tube assembly over rack piston ring onto housing. Tighten to 82 ft. lbs. (111 N.m). Ensure fittings on cylinder tube are aligned with reference marks made during disassembly.

4) Install insert and rack guide assembly to rod and rack assembly in housing. Center rack guide assembly in housing window opening. Install pinion and valve assembly into housing using Pinion And Valve Assembly Ring Protector (J-33057).

5) When pinion and valve assembly are fully seated in housing, notch in pinion shaft and mark on housing will be aligned. Insert and rack guide assembly will be centered in housing window.

CAUTION: Damage to pinion teeth will result if input shaft is not held when removing lock nut.

---

6) Tighten lock nut to threaded pinion to 26 ft. lbs. (35 N.m) while holding pinion shaft. Pinion teeth will be damaged if pinion shaft is not held stationary. Install dust cover on housing. Install pinion shaft annulus bearing assembly onto pinion shaft and slide into housing.

7) Install Seal Protector (J-29810) on pinion shaft. Install pinion shaft seals over seal protector and into housing. Install retaining ring in groove in housing. Coat rack guide, "O" ring, adjuster spring and adjuster plug with lithium base grease. Install assembly in housing.

8) With rack centered in window in housing, turn adjuster plug clockwise until it bottoms in housing, then back off plug 50-70 degrees for Beretta and Corsica, 35-45 degrees on all other models. Check pinion preload, and adjust plug if preload is not 8-16 INCH lbs. (.9-1.8 N.m). Install lock nut on adjuster plug. Tighten lock nut to specification while holding adjuster plug stationary. See TORQUE SPECIFICATIONS table at end of this article.

9) Slide boot retaining bushing from rack and pinion boot. Install new boot clamp on rack and pinion boot. Insert boot retaining bushing in boot. Coat inner lip of bushing with grease to ease installation. Slide boot assembly onto housing.

10) Ensure center housing cover washers are installed on rack and pinion boot. To ease assembly, install inner tie rod bolt through center housing cover washers, insert and rack guide. Lightly thread bolts into rod and rack assembly to keep components in proper alignment.

11) Slide rack and pinion boot and boot retaining bushing until seated in bushing groove in housing. Position boot clamps on boot and crimp clamp. Position boot clamp bridge over split in boot retaining bushing.

12) With new "O" rings on cylinder line assemblies, install lines on rack and pinion assembly. Tighten fittings at valve end of housing to 14 ft. lbs. (19 N.m). Tighten fittings at cylinder end of housing to 20 ft. lbs. (27 N.m). Remove inner tie rod bolts.

13) Install inner tie rod bolts through bolt support plate, inner tie rod assemblies, center housing cover washers, insert and rack guide assembly, and into threaded holes in rod and rack assembly. Tighten inner tie rod bolts to specification. Install new lock plate over inner tie rod bolts.

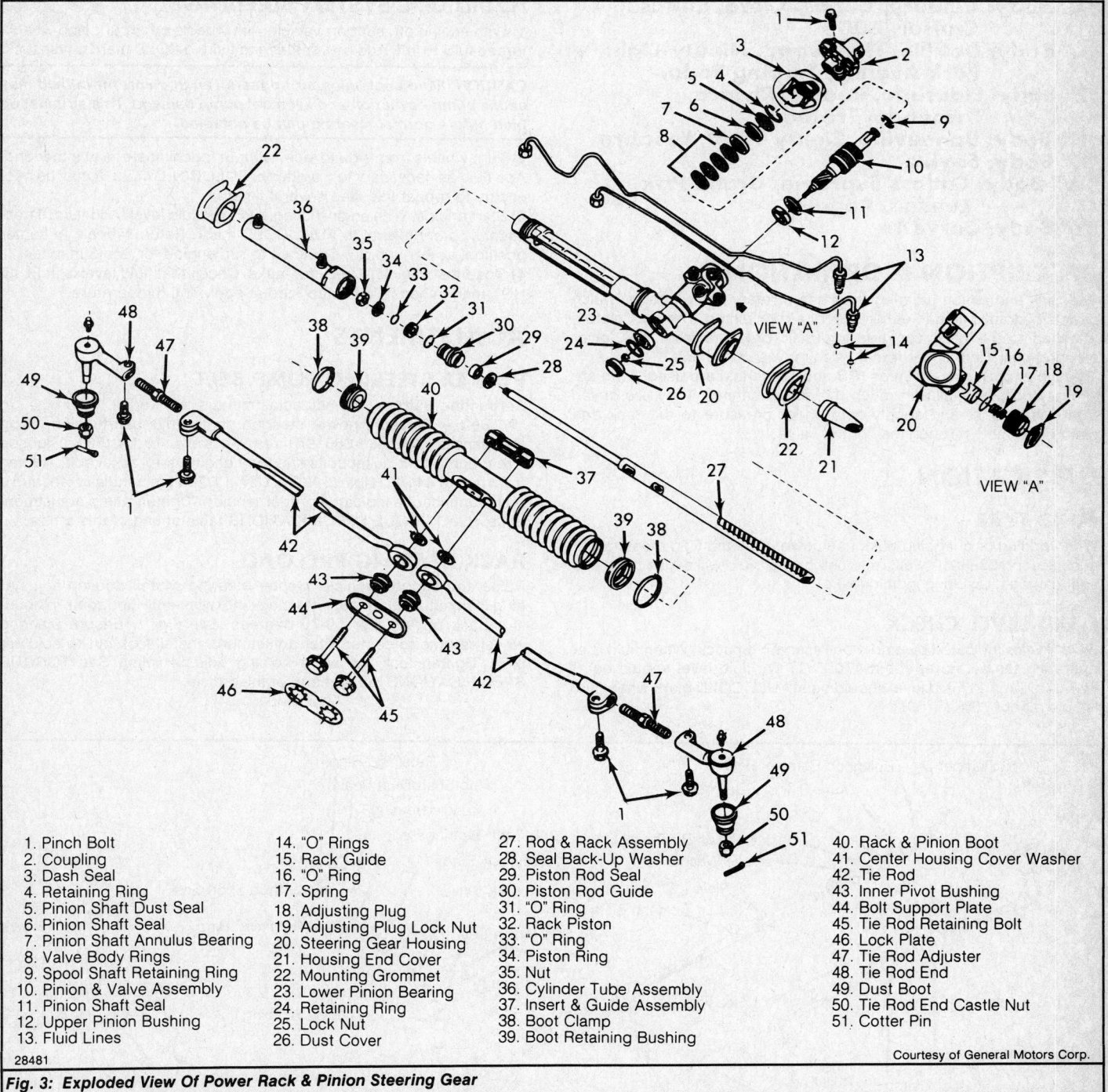

Fig. 3: Exploded View Of Power Rack & Pinion Steering Gear

Courtesy of General Motors Corp.

28481

1. Pinch Bolt	14. "O" Rings
2. Coupling	15. Rack Guide
3. Dash Seal	16. "O" Ring
4. Retaining Ring	17. Spring
5. Pinion Shaft Dust Seal	18. Adjusting Plug
6. Pinion Shaft Seal	19. Adjusting Plug Lock Nut
7. Pinion Shaft Annulus Bearing	20. Steering Gear Housing
8. Valve Body Rings	21. Housing End Cover
9. Spool Shaft Retaining Ring	22. Mounting Grommet
10. Pinion & Valve Assembly	23. Lower Pinion Bearing
11. Pinion Shaft Seal	24. Retaining Ring
12. Upper Pinion Bushing	25. Lock Nut
13. Fluid Lines	26. Dust Cover

27. Rod & Rack Assembly	40. Rack & Pinion Boot
28. Seal Back-Up Washer	41. Center Housing Cover Washer
29. Piston Rod Seal	42. Tie Rod
30. Piston Rod Guide	43. Inner Pivot Bushing
31. "O" Ring	44. Bolt Support Plate
32. Rack Piston	45. Tie Rod Retaining Bolt
33. "O" Ring	46. Lock Plate
34. Piston Ring	47. Tie Rod Adjuster
35. Nut	48. Tie Rod End
36. Cylinder Tube Assembly	49. Dust Boot
37. Insert & Guide Assembly	50. Tie Rod End Castle Nut
38. Boot Clamp	51. Cotter Pin
39. Boot Retaining Bushing	

TORQUE SPECIFICATIONS

TORQUE SPECIFICATIONS

Application	Ft. Lbs. (N.m)
Adjusting Plug Lock Nut	50 (68)
Fittings	
Housing End	20 (27)
Valve End	14 (19)
Flexible Coupling-to-Pinion Shaft Bolt	37 (50)
Flexible Coupling-to-Steering Column Bolt	34 (46)
Pinion Shaft Lock Nut	26 (35)
Piston Rod-to-Rack Gear	65 (88)

TORQUE SPECIFICATIONS (Cont.)

Application	Ft. Lbs. (N.m)
Steering Gear Mounting Nuts	22 (30)
Tie Rod-to-Rack Bolts	65 (88)
Tie Rod End Castle Nut	35 (48)
Tie Rod Pinch Bolts	41 (56)

	INCH Lbs. (N.m)
Pinion Preload	16 (1.8)

"A" Body: Century, Cutlass Ciera, Cutlass Cruiser, 6000
"C" Body: DeVille, Fleetwood, Ninety-Eight, Park Avenue, Touring Sedan
"E" Body: Eldorado, Reatta, Riviera, Toronado, Trofeo
"H" Body: Bonneville, Eighty-Eight, LeSabre
"K" Body: Seville
"W" Body: Cutlass Supreme, Grand Prix, Lumina, Regal
"Y" Body: Corvette

DESCRIPTION & OPERATION

The rack and pinion steering gear has a rotary control valve, which directs hydraulic fluid to either side of a rack piston. The rack piston, attached to the rack, converts hydraulic pressure from the power steering pump into linear force which moves the wheels.

Two types of Saginaw pumps (CB and TC series) are used. Both are similar and overhauled in much the same manner. They are driven from the engine, and supply fluid under pressure to the rack and pinion assembly through the control valve.

LUBRICATION

FLUID TYPE

When adding or changing fluid, use power steering fluid meeting GM specification 9985010. Failure to use proper fluid will cause hose and seal damage, resulting in fluid leaks.

FLUID LEVEL CHECK

Fluid level is indicated by marks on reservoir dipstick. When fluid is at operating temperature, about 170°F (77°C), fluid level should be at FULL HOT mark. Fluid level should be at FULL COLD mark when fluid is cold, about 70°F (21°C).

HYDRAULIC SYSTEM BLEEDING

1) With engine off, support vehicle with wheels off ground and wheels turned fully to left. Add power steering fluid to COLD mark on dipstick.

CAUTION: Fluid containing air appears Tan in color. Air in fluid may cause pump cavitation and eventual pump damage. This air must be bled before normal steering can be obtained.

2) Turn wheels from side to side, without touching stops at either end. Add fluid as necessary to maintain at FULL COLD mark. It may be necessary to repeat this step several times.
3) Start engine. With engine idling, recheck fluid level. Add fluid, if necessary, to bring level to FULL COLD mark. Return wheels to center position. Lower vehicle. Continue to run engine for 2 to 3 minutes.
4) Road test vehicle. Check for leaks. Check that fluid level is at FULL HOT mark when fluid is stabilized at operating temperature.

ADJUSTMENTS

POWER STEERING PUMP BELT

Serpentine Belts – No belt adjustment is required.
"V" Belt – Measure power steering pump drive belt tension, using Belt Tension Gauge (J-36018). If reading is not 110 lbs. (50 kg), loosen 2 rear pump-to-bracket bolts and front engine-to-bracket bolt. Tighten front bolt to 44 INCH lbs. (5 N.m.). Using 1/2" drive handle in tab, move pump until gauge indicates proper tension. Tighten pump adjustment bolts. See TORQUE SPECIFICATIONS table at end of this article.

RACK BEARING PRELOAD

Raise and support vehicle. Center steering wheel. Loosen adjuster plug lock nut and turn adjuster plug clockwise until it bottoms in housing. Back off adjuster 50-70 degrees. *See Fig. 1.* Ensure steering wheel returns to center after adjustment. Install lock nut to adjuster plug. Tighten lock nut while holding adjuster plug. See TORQUE SPECIFICATIONS table at end of this article.

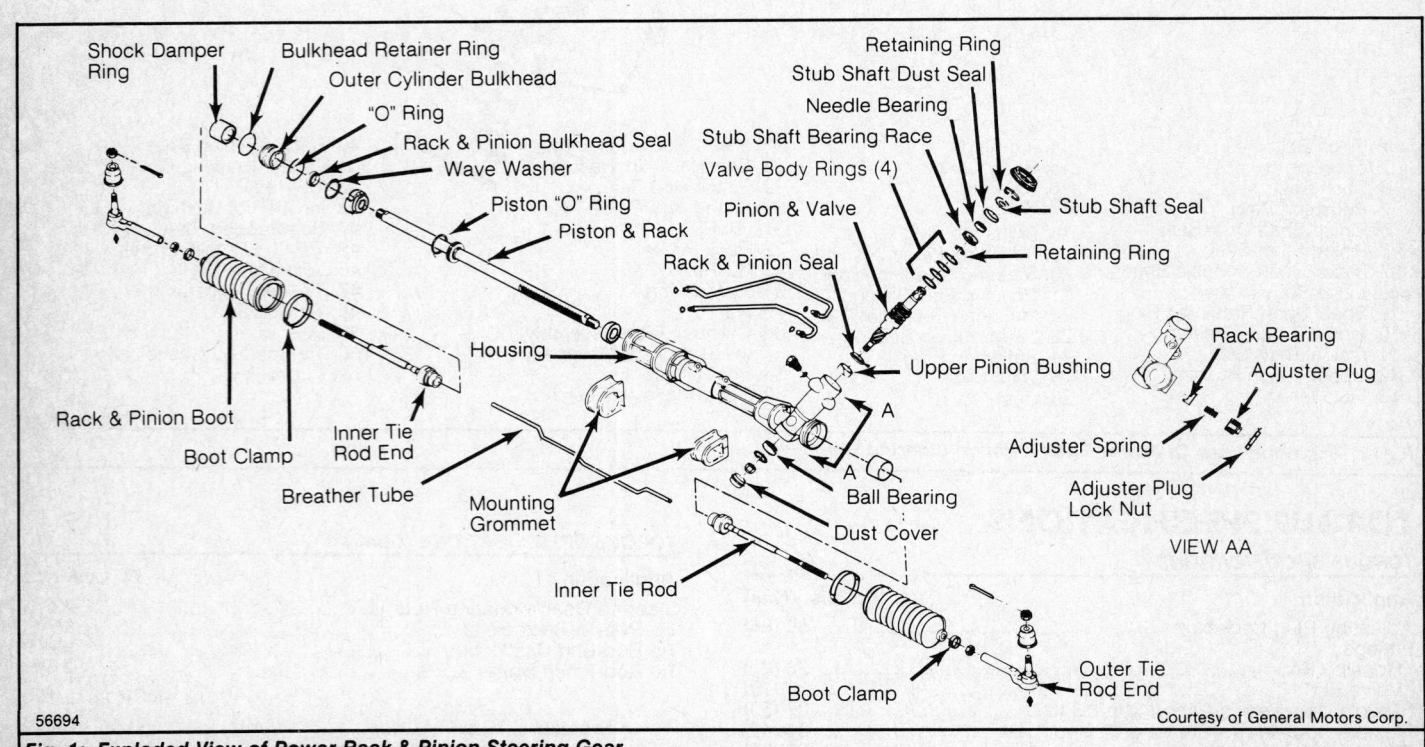

56694

Courtesy of General Motors Corp.

Fig. 1: *Exploded View of Power Rack & Pinion Steering Gear*

TESTING

PRESSURE TEST

NOTE: Before testing power steering system, check fluid level, belt tension, pump pulley, tire pressure and engine idle speed.

1) Remove high pressure line from power steering pump. Attach a spare pressure hose to pump. Connect Power Steering Pressure Tester (J-5176-D) to hose. Open valve fully.
2) Run engine until fluid reaches normal operating temperature. Check fluid level and add as necessary. With engine at operating temperature, idle pressure reading should not be higher than specified in PRESSURE TEST SPECIFICATIONS. If pressure is more than 200 psi (14 kg/cm²), inspect system for restrictions or faulty flow control valve.

CAUTION: To prevent pump damage, DO NOT hold valve closed for more than 5 seconds in step 3).

PRESSURE TEST SPECIFICATIONS

Application	Pressure psi (kg/cm²)
"A" Body	
Idle	150 (10.5)
Relief	1
"C" Body	
Idle	80-125 (5.6-8.8)
Relief	1250 (87.8)
"E" Body	
Idle	80-125 (5.6-8.8)
Relief	1250 (87.8)
"H" Body	
Idle	80-125 (5.6-8.8)
Relief	2 1000 (70.3)
"K" Body	
Idle	80-125 (5.6-8.8)
Relief	1250 (87.8)
"W" Body	
Idle	80-125 (5.6-8.8)
Relief	1
"Y" Body	
Idle	150 (10.5)
Relief	1250 (87.8)

1 – Information is not available from manufacturer.
2 – For TC Series pump, 1250 psi (87.8 kg/cm²).

3) Alternately close and open gauge valve fully 3 times while recording highest pressure obtained. Each relief measurement should be at least as high as specified in PRESSURE TEST SPECIFICATIONS.
4) If recorded pressures are all within 50 psi (3.5 kg/cm²), pump is okay. If pressures are within specifications but not within 50 psi (3.5 kg/cm²) of each other, flow control valve is sticking. If relief pressure readings are less than specifications, replace flow control valve and retest pump pressure.
5) If pump meets specifications, leave valve open. Turn steering wheel from stop to stop. Record and compare highest pressure obtained with maximum pump pressure measured in step 3). If pressure at both stops is not equal to maximum pressure, steering gear is leaking internally.

FLOW RATE TEST

1) Connect Power Steering Analyzer (J-25233-A) into system. Open analyzer valve fully. Run engine until fluid reaches normal operating temperature. Check fluid level, adding fluid as necessary. Record pressure and flow.
2) Close valve partially until pressure builds to 700 psi (49.2 kg/cm²) and record flow. Subtract flow from that measured in step 1). If flow drops more than one gal./minute (3.8L/minute), replace ring, rotor and vanes in pump.
3) Increase engine speed to 1500 RPM and read flow. Subtract flow from that measured in step 1). If flow varies more than one gal./minute, remove and clean flow control valve.

4) Turn steering wheel all the way to left and right. Flow should drop to less than one gal./minute (3.8L/minute) at each stop. If flow is within specifications, check steering gear for leakage.

REMOVAL & INSTALLATION

OUTER TIE ROD

Removal – Raise and support vehicle. Remove cotter pin and castle nut from outer tie rod end. Loosen outer tie rod end lock nut. Separate outer tie rod end from steering knuckle with Steering Linkage Remover (J-24319-01). Remove outer tie rod end from inner tie rod. Note number of turns required.

Installation – To install, reverse removal procedure. Tighten tie rod end castle nut to 90 INCH lbs. (10 N.m), then tighten nut an additional 1/3 turn. DO NOT back off nuts to install cotter pins. Ensure final torque is a minimum of 33 ft. lbs. (45 N.m).

RACK & PINION BOOTS

Removal – Remove outer tie rod end and lock nut. Cut off and discard boot clamps. Mark breather tube for reassembly reference (if equipped). Remove breather tube. Slide boot from inner tie rod.

Installation – 1) Place new inner boot clamp on housing. Align mark on breather tube and boot and install breather tube (if equipped). Slide boot onto housing. Install outer boot clamp. Secure inner boot clamp, using Banding Tool (J-22610).
2) Remove rubber band from boot seal groove. Ensure boot is not twisted. Install outer boot clamp and tie rod end. Adjust toe-in as necessary. Tighten tie rod end lock nut. See TORQUE SPECIFICATIONS table at end of this article.

POWER STEERING PUMP PULLEY

Removal – Remove drive belt. Remove pump (if necessary) for clearance. Install Pulley Remover (J-25034-B) on pulley. Hold body of tool with wrench and turn forcing bolt to remove pulley.

Installation – To install, use Pulley Installer (J-25033-B). Press pulley onto drive shaft until face of pulley hub is flush with shaft. DO NOT use arbor press to install pulley. Reinstall pump on vehicle (if removed).

POWER STEERING PUMP

Removal & Installation ("A" Body) – Remove drive belt. Disconnect hoses at pump. Remove pump retaining bolts and pump. To install, reverse removal procedure. Refill reservoir and bleed system.
Removal & Installation ("C" & "H" Bodies) – Remove drive belt. Disconnect outlet hose at pump. Remove mounting bolts. Remove pump. To install, reverse removal procedure. Tighten bolts and fittings. See TORQUE SPECIFICATIONS table at end of this article. Refill reservoir and bleed system.
Removal ("E" & "K" Bodies) – Remove belt and power steering pump pulley. See POWER STEERING PUMP PULLEY. Disconnect hoses. Remove pump mounting bolts and pump.
Installation – 1) Position pump in vehicle. Install high pressure line fitting hand tight. Tighten bolts and high pressure fitting. See TORQUE SPECIFICATIONS table at end of this article.
2) Install pump return hose. Ensure return hose has enough slack between tensioner bracket and alternator brace so it doesn't contact any moving parts. Install pump pulley and belt. See TORQUE SPECIFICATIONS table at end of this article. Refill reservoir and bleed system.
Removal & Installation ("W" Body) – Disconnect hoses at pump. Remove belt. Remove mounting bolts. Remove pump and reservoir together. Remove reservoir from pump as required. To install, reverse removal procedure. See TORQUE SPECIFICATIONS table at end of this article. Refill reservoir and bleed system.
Removal & Installation ("Y" Body) – 1) Remove negative battery cable. Remove belt. Remove power steering pump pulley. Disconnect hoses. Remove clamp from pump and bolt securing bracket to rear brace.

2) Remove engine mount bolt and rear pump brace. Remove pump and support bracket. To install, reverse removal procedure. See TORQUE SPECIFICATIONS at end of this article. Refill and bleed system.

POWER RACK & PINION

CAUTION: Before beginning this procedure on any vehicle with Supplemental Inflatable Restraint (SIR) system (air bag), read and heed all applicable cautions. See FIXED & TILT COLUMNS article in STEERING.

CAUTION: If intermediate shaft is not disconnected from rack and pinion stub shaft, steering gear and/or intermediate shaft can be damaged, causing loss of steering control.

CAUTION: Before disconnecting steering column or intermediate shaft on vehicles equipped with Supplemental Inflatable Restraint (air bag), set front wheels in straight-ahead position and the steering column in LOCK position. Failure to do so will cause damage to the SIR coil assembly in the steering column.

Removal & Installation ("A" Body) – 1) Raise vehicle with frame hoist. Place drain pan under steering gear. Remove front wheels. Position steering shaft dust seal upward. Remove intermediate shaft lower pinch bolt. Disconnect intermediate shaft from stub shaft.
2) Remove tie rod nuts and end keys. Separate tie rod ends from steering knuckles, using Tie Rod End Puller (J-24319-01). Remove brake line retaining bolts and heat shield.
3) Support engine frame at rear with jack stands. Disconnect motor mounts from frame retaining nuts. Remove rear engine frame retaining bolts. Loosen, but do not remove, front engine retaining bolts.

CAUTION: DO NOT lower rear of engine frame too far. Damage to engine components nearest to cowl may result.

4) Lower engine frame at rear. Remove rack and pinion heat shield and line-retaining clip. Disconnect hoses. Remove mounting bolts. Pull unit from vehicle through left wheel opening.
5) To install, reverse removal procedure. See TORQUE SPECIFICATIONS table at end of this article. Refill and bleed system. Check front toe and adjust as necessary. Test drive vehicle.
Removal & Installation ("C" & "H" Bodies) – 1) Place drain pan under steering gear, Raise vehicle with frame hoist and remove front wheels. Remove intermediate shaft lower pinch bolt.
2) Disconnect tie rod ends from steering knuckles. Remove line retainer and pressure switch connection. Remove outlet and pressure hoses.
3) Remove rack and pinion mounting bolts. Support body with stands to allow lowering of engine frame. Loosen front and rear engine frame bolts. Lower frame approximately 3".

CAUTION: DO NOT lower frame too far or engine components nearest the cowl will be damaged.

4) Remove rack and pinion assembly through left wheel opening. To install, reverse removal procedure. See TORQUE SPECIFICATIONS table at end of this article. Refill and bleed system. Check front toe and adjust as necessary. Test drive vehicle.
Removal & Installation ("E" & "K" Bodies) – 1) Place drain pan under steering gear. Raise vehicle with frame contact hoist. Remove left front wheel and tire assembly.
2) Remove intermediate shaft lower coupling. Disconnect tie rod ends from steering knuckles.

CAUTION: Support engine frame before lowering it. DO NOT lower it any more than needed to gain access to steering gear.

3) Drop engine frame to gain access. Remove line retainer. Disconnect hydraulic lines. Remove 5 rack and pinion attaching bolts. Pull assembly out from the side.

4) To install, reverse removal procedure. See TORQUE SPECIFICATIONS table at end of this article. Refill and bleed system. Check front toe. Adjust as necessary. Test drive vehicle.
Removal & Installation ("W" Body) – 1) Place drain pan under steering gear. Raise vehicle. Remove front wheels. Remove intermediate shaft lower pinch bolt. Remove intermediate shaft from stub shaft. Remove electrical connection at idle speed pressure switch.

NOTE: Use only specified tool for separating tie rod ends from knuckle/strut assemblies.

2) Separate tie rod ends from knuckle/strut assemblies. Support engine frame with jack stands. Remove rear frame mount bolts. Lower rear of frame approximately 5". DO NOT lower frame too far as damage to engine components may result.
3) Remove heat shield and pipe retaining clip from steering gear. Disconnect inlet and outlet lines at steering gear. Remove retaining brackets and clips. Remove rack and pinion mounting bolts and nuts. Remove rack and pinion through left wheel opening.
4) To install, reverse removal procedure. See TORQUE SPECIFICATIONS table at end of this article. Refill and bleed system. Check front toe and adjust as necessary. Test drive vehicle.
Removal & Installation ("Y" Body) – 1) Disconnect negative battery cable. Remove inlet and outlet hoses from steering gear. Disconnect cooling pipe outlet hoses from cooling pipe on vehicles so equipped. Remove steering coupling shield. Disconnect intermediate shaft from steering gear and lower steering shaft.
2) Raise vehicle. Remove front wheels. Separate outer tie rod ends from knuckles, using Tie Rod End Puller (J-24319-01). Remove power steering cooler if so equipped. Remove stabilizer shaft.
3) Remove steering gear clamp. Remove steering gear mounting bolts and nuts. Remove power steering gear. Remove cooling pipe, if so equipped. Remove outer tie rods from steering gear as necessary.
4) To install, reverse removal procedure. See TORQUE SPECIFICATIONS table at end of this article. Refill and bleed system. Check front toe and adjust as necessary. Test drive vehicle.

OVERHAUL – POWER STEERING PUMP

RETURN TUBE

Removal & Installation – 1) Plug return tube to prevent chips from entering pump. Using a 9/16 x 12 tap, a 9/16 x 12 nut and five 5/8" washers, screw tap into tube, slide washers over end of tap and turn nut to draw tube from pump body. *See Fig. 2.*
2) To install, coat end of return tube with Loctite Solvent (75559) and Loctite Adhesive (290). Press tube into housing until it bottoms.

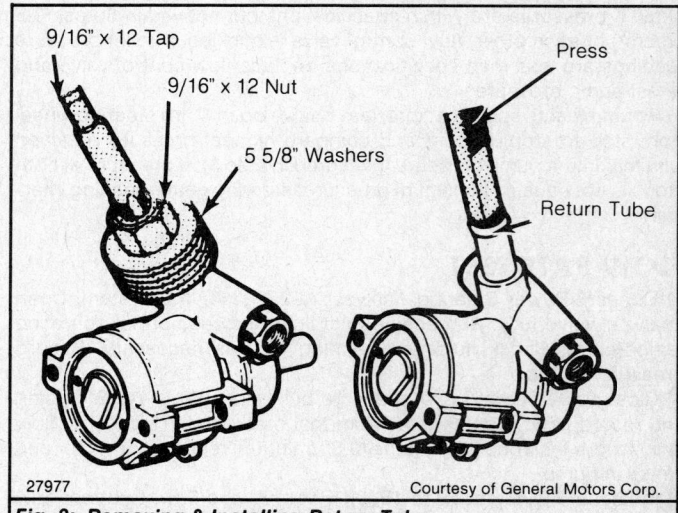

9/16" x 12 Tap
9/16" x 12 Nut
5 5/8" Washers
Press
Return Tube
27977
Courtesy of General Motors Corp.
Fig. 2: Removing & Installing Return Tube

FLOW CONTROL VALVE ASSEMBLY

Removal & Installation – With pump removed from vehicle, unscrew flow control valve line fitting. Remove "O" ring, flow control valve assembly and flow control spring. *See Fig. 3.* To install, reverse removal procedure. See TORQUE SPECIFICATIONS table at end of this article.

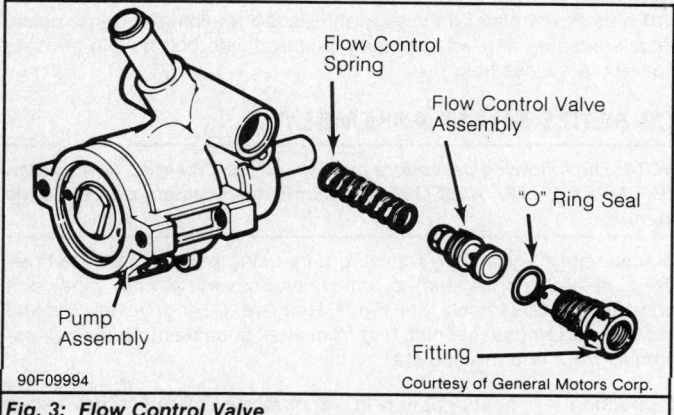

90F09994 — Courtesy of General Motors Corp.

Fig. 3: Flow Control Valve

SHAFT SEAL

Removal & Installation – 1) Remove pump from vehicle. See POWER STEERING PUMP under REMOVAL & INSTALLATION. Remove pump pulley. See POWER STEERING PUMP PULLEY under REMOVAL & INSTALLATION. Remove shaft assembly.
2) Using a screwdriver, pry old seal from housing. To install, use a suitable socket to drive oil seal into housing until bottomed. Install shaft, pump pulley and pump.

TC SERIES SHAFT ASSEMBLY

NOTE: The following procedure applies only to TC series pumps. See CB SERIES SHAFT ASSEMBLY for shaft disassembly on CB series pumps.

Removal–1) Remove pump from vehicle. See POWER STEERING PUMP under REMOVAL & INSTALLATION. Remove pump pulley. *See Fig 4.* Using a small punch in access hole, remove retaining ring. Press

on pressure plate hub from drive shaft side of housing, using a 5/8" piece of bar stock, until thrust plate can be removed. Remove "O" ring seal.

2) Remove retaining ring, shaft and bearing assembly from housing. To remove bearing from shaft, support bearing inner race and press bearing from shaft. Note and measure any clearance between shaft shoulder and bearing race before removing bearing. *See Fig. 5.*

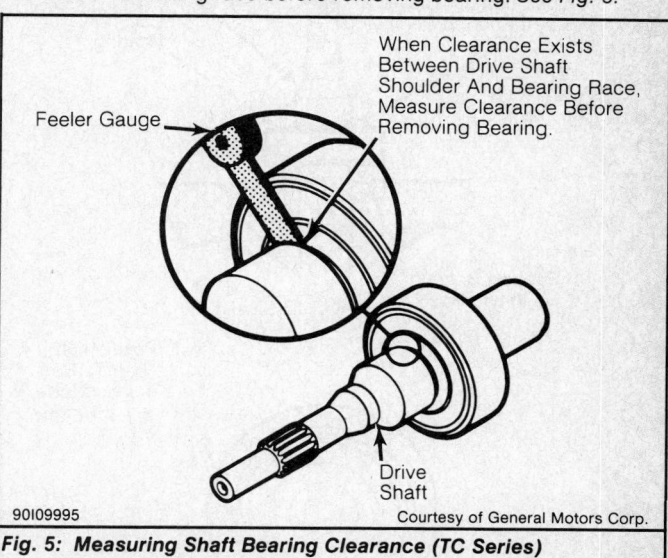

90I09995 — Courtesy of General Motors Corp.

Fig. 5: Measuring Shaft Bearing Clearance (TC Series)

3) Remove pump rotor, vanes, 2 dowel pins, cam ring and pressure plate. It may be necessary to use a press to remove pressure plate. Separate "O" ring from pressure plate. Remove dowel pin. Separate "O" ring from sleeve. Remove sleeve assembly, using punch on drive shaft side of housing.
Inspection – Clean all parts in power steering fluid. Inspect pressure plate, vanes, pump ring, drive shaft and bearing for scoring, pitting or chatter marks. Replace any worn or damaged parts.
Installation – 1) Press bearing to shoulder of shaft or to measured clearance. Slide assembly into housing while rotating shaft so shaft serrations engage with rotor. Install retaining ring with beveled side down. *See Fig. 6.*

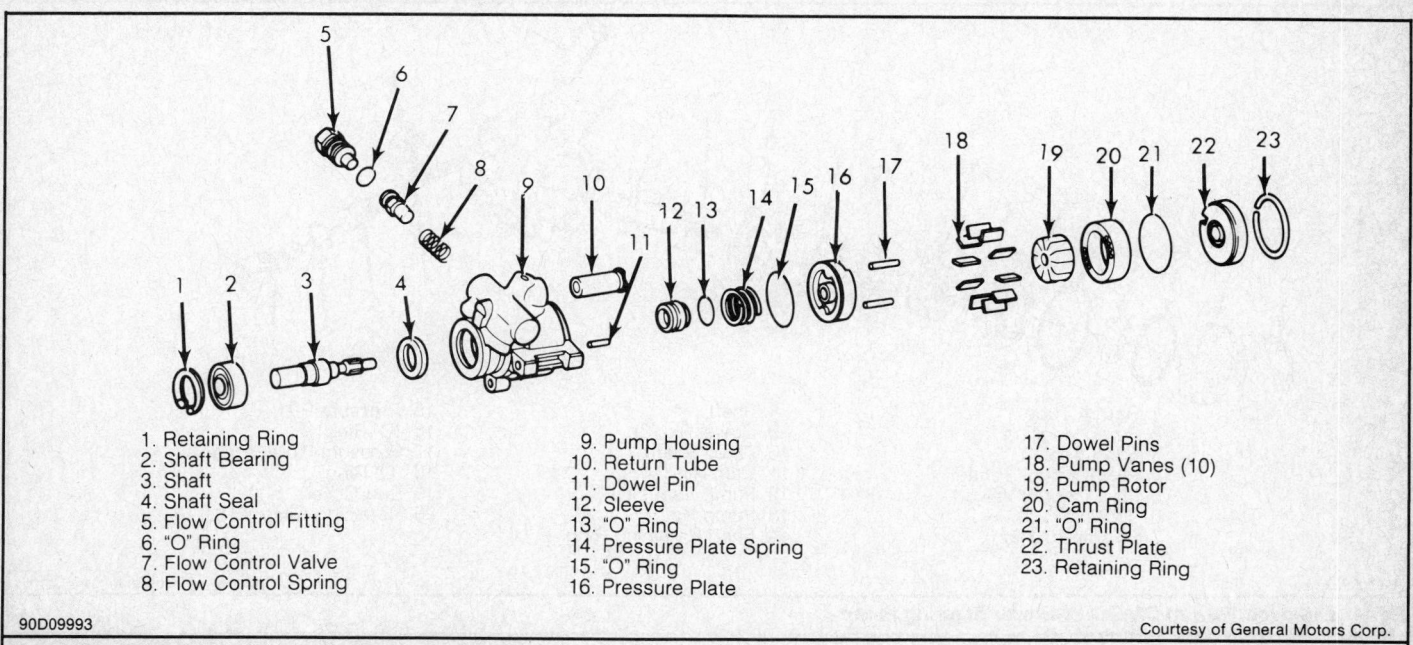

1. Retaining Ring
2. Shaft Bearing
3. Shaft
4. Shaft Seal
5. Flow Control Fitting
6. "O" Ring
7. Flow Control Valve
8. Flow Control Spring
9. Pump Housing
10. Return Tube
11. Dowel Pin
12. Sleeve
13. "O" Ring
14. Pressure Plate Spring
15. "O" Ring
16. Pressure Plate
17. Dowel Pins
18. Pump Vanes (10)
19. Pump Rotor
20. Cam Ring
21. "O" Ring
22. Thrust Plate
23. Retaining Ring

90D09993 — Courtesy of General Motors Corp.

Fig. 4: Exploded View of TC Series Power Steering Pump

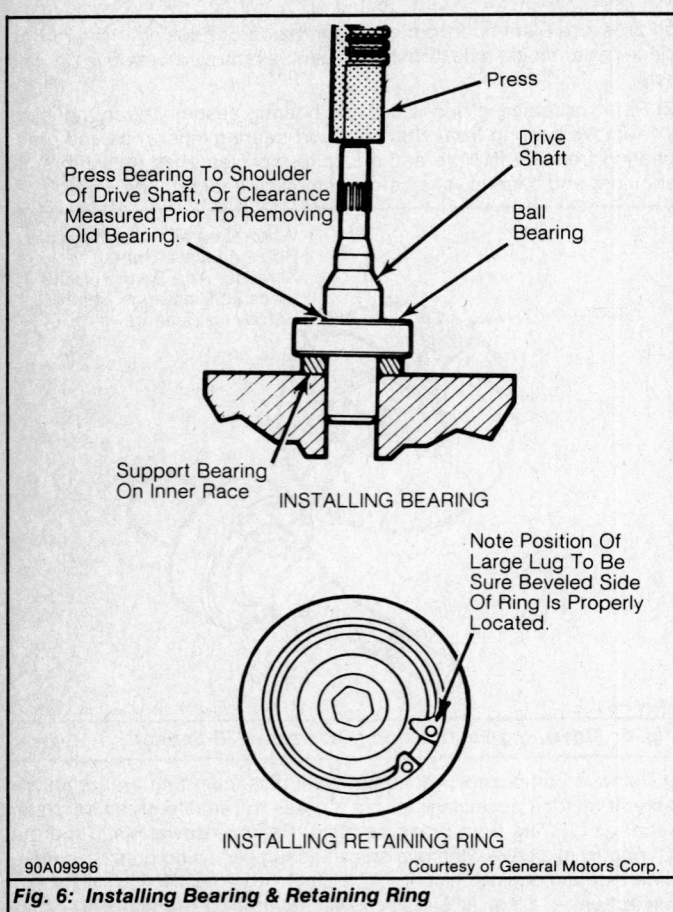

Press

Drive Shaft

Ball Bearing

Press Bearing To Shoulder Of Drive Shaft, Or Clearance Measured Prior To Removing Old Bearing.

Support Bearing On Inner Race

INSTALLING BEARING

Note Position Of Large Lug To Be Sure Beveled Side Of Ring Is Properly Located.

INSTALLING RETAINING RING

90A09996

Courtesy of General Motors Corp.

Fig. 6: Installing Bearing & Retaining Ring

2) Lubricate and install new "O" ring seal into new sleeve assembly. Insert dowel pin into housing. Install pressure plate spring. Lubricate and install new "O" ring seal into pressure plate groove.
3) Mark top of pressure plate directly over dowel pin hole in plate to help align hole with dowel pin. Install pressure plate into housing. Ensure dowel pin properly engages hole in pressure plate.

4) Install 2 pump ring dowel pins. Slide cam ring over pins. With identification marks on ring facing upward, install rotor with counterbore side toward drive shaft end of housing. Insert pump vanes.
5) Place pump ring over dowel pins. Lubricate new "O" ring and install into groove in housing. Lubricate outer edge of thrust plate. Ensure dimples in thrust plate line up with bolt holes in housing and thrust plate engages with dowel pins.
6) Press thrust plate in far enough to snap retaining ring into place. Install retaining ring with opening centered with bolt hole in housing nearest to access hole.

CB SERIES SHAFT ASSEMBLY

NOTE: The following procedure applies only to CB series pumps. See TC SERIES SHAFT ASSEMBLY for shaft disassembly on TC series pumps.

Disassembly – Remove retaining ring, using punch in access hole. Press gently on drive shaft to remove end cover, "O" ring, vanes and drive shaft subassembly. *See Fig. 7.* Remove "O" ring, dowel pins and shaft seal. Remove retaining ring from shaft subassembly, then disassemble rotor and thrust plate.

Inspection – Inspect pump ring, vanes, thrust plate and drive shaft for scoring, pitting or chatter marks. Replace any worn or damaged parts.
Reassembly – **1)** Lubricate new seal with power steering fluid. Drive seal into housing with Shaft Oil Seal Remover (J-7728). Install pump ring dowel pins into housing.
2) Assemble thrust plate, rotor, new retaining ring and drive shaft. Ensure counterbore in rotor faces drive shaft end of housing. Install drive shaft subassembly into pump housing. Insert vanes into rotor. Install pump ring. Ensure holes are positioned onto dowel pins.
3) Place pump ring over dowel pins. Lubricate new "O" ring and install into groove in housing. Lubricate outer edge of end cover. Press end cover in far enough to snap retaining ring into place. Install retaining ring with opening near access hole in housing.

OVERHAUL – RACK & PINION

STUB SHAFT SEAL & UPPER BEARING
Disassembly – **1)** Remove rack and pinion assembly from vehicle. Remove adjuster plug lock nut from plug. Remove adjuster plug from

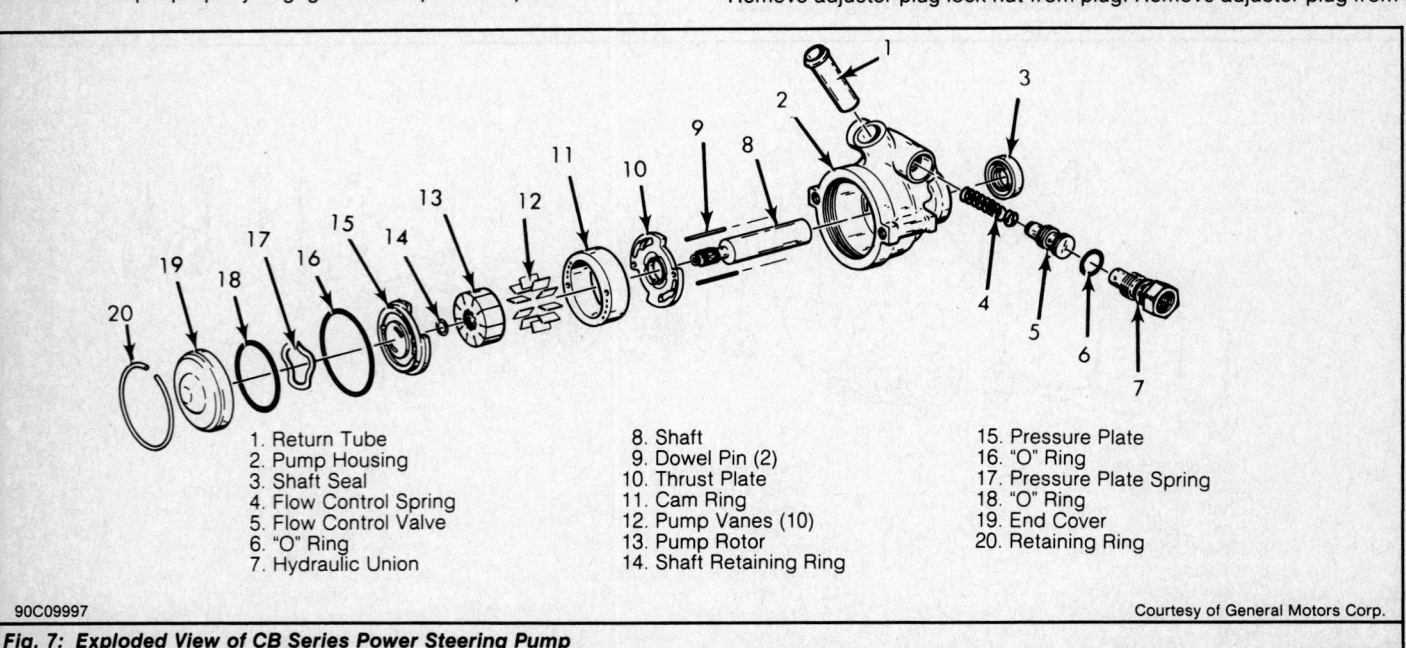

1. Return Tube
2. Pump Housing
3. Shaft Seal
4. Flow Control Spring
5. Flow Control Valve
6. "O" Ring
7. Hydraulic Union
8. Shaft
9. Dowel Pin (2)
10. Thrust Plate
11. Cam Ring
12. Pump Vanes (10)
13. Pump Rotor
14. Shaft Retaining Ring
15. Pressure Plate
16. "O" Ring
17. Pressure Plate Spring
18. "O" Ring
19. End Cover
20. Retaining Ring

90C09997

Courtesy of General Motors Corp.

Fig. 7: Exploded View of CB Series Power Steering Pump

housing. Remove adjuster spring, rack bearing and retaining ring from bore of housing. Remove dust cover.

2) Hold pinion and valve stub shaft with back-up wrench and remove lock nut from stub shaft assembly. Center rack, and mark location of pinion stub shaft notch on housing. For reassembly reference when centering rack, measure rack centering distance. *See Fig. 8.*

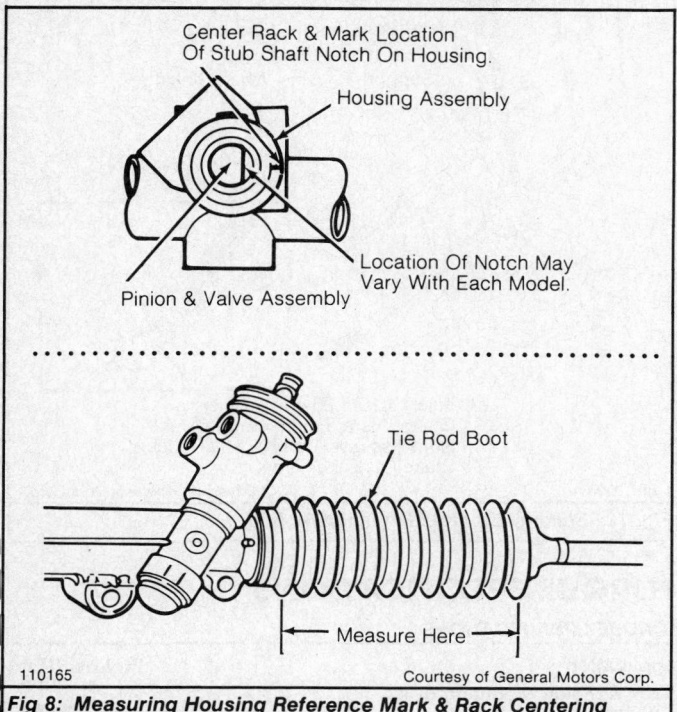

110165   Courtesy of General Motors Corp.
Fig 8: Measuring Housing Reference Mark & Rack Centering

3) Using an arbor press, press on threaded end of pinion until pinion and valve assembly will come out of housing. Before removing assembly from housing, mark second location of pinion stub shaft notch on housing. This mark will be used to position notch before reassembly.

4) Remove stub shaft dust seal, stub shaft seal and stub shaft bearing annulus (race) assembly. Remove pinion and valve assembly with retaining ring and valve body rings attached. Using care, remove valve body rings from pinion and valve assembly.

Inspection – Clean valve body ring grooves. Ensure pinion and valve assembly drive pin is not broken. If drive pin is broken, replace steering gear assembly.

Reassembly – 1) Apply grease to ring grooves and new valve body rings. Install new valve body rings on pinion and valve assembly. Install rings with split tabs engaged and staggered. *See Fig. 9.* Use care not to cut rings during installation.

2) Install pinion and valve assembly into Ring Protector (J-37090). *See Fig. 10.* Allow rings to set inside ring protector for approximately 3 minutes so valve rings will size properly.

3) Position valve assembly in ring protector so valve body is flush with bottom of protector. Ensure rings are free from cuts, nicks or other damage.

4) Using measurement taken during disassembly as a guide, center rack in housing. Clean, then apply grease to housing bore. Before reassembly, ensure stub shaft bearing annulus is not damaged and bearing is flush with annulus. *See Fig. 11.*

5) Align notch on valve stub shaft with second mark made during disassembly. Using ring protector and Pinion Seal Installer (J-29822), push pinion and valve assembly into housing bore. DO NOT hammer or use excessive force. If assembly does not fully seat in housing, ensure valve body rings are not binding in bore.

6) After assembly is seated in bore, ensure notch in stub shaft and first mark on housing line up correctly. Hold valve stub shaft to prevent damage to pinion teeth and install lock nut. See TORQUE SPECIFICATIONS table at end of this article.

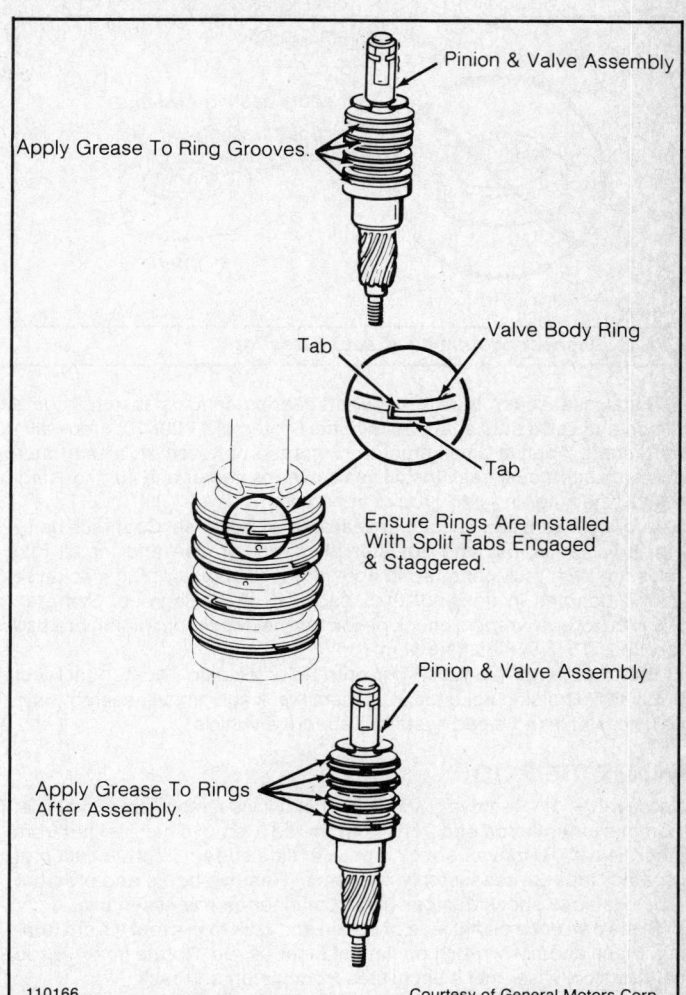

110166   Courtesy of General Motors Corp.
Fig. 9:   Installing Valve Body Rings

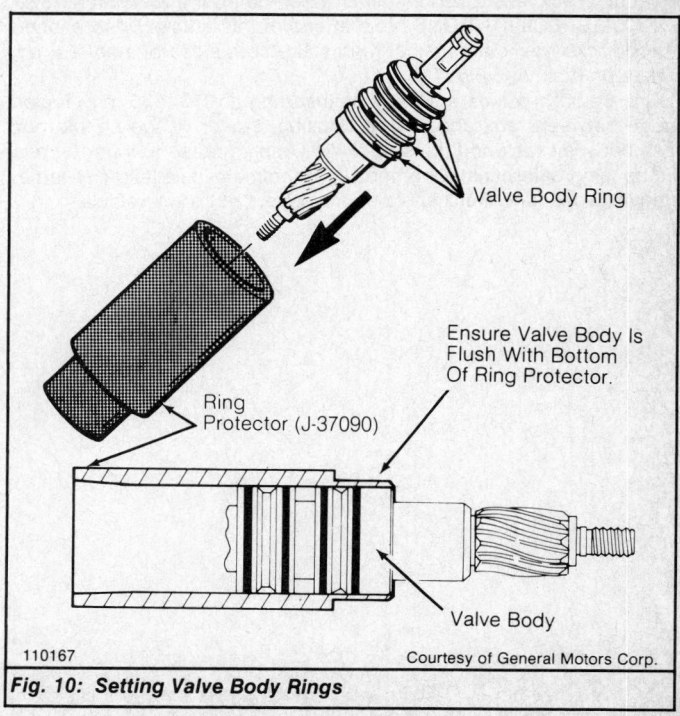

110167   Courtesy of General Motors Corp.
Fig. 10: Setting Valve Body Rings

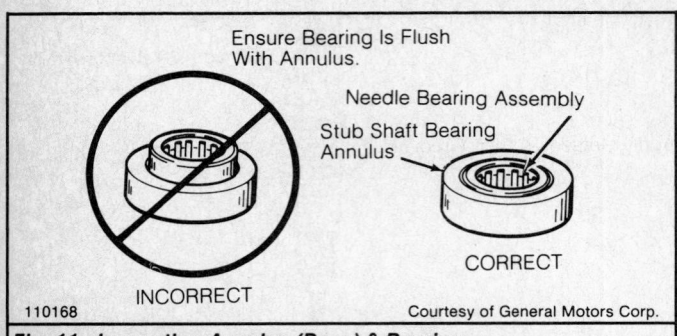

Fig. 11: Inspecting Annulus (Race) & Bearing

110168

Courtesy of General Motors Corp.

Ensure Bearing Is Flush With Annulus.

Needle Bearing Assembly

Stub Shaft Bearing Annulus

INCORRECT

CORRECT

7) Install dust cover. Install stub shaft bearing annulus assembly onto pinion and valve stub shaft. Install Seal Protector (J-29810) onto valve stub shaft. Apply a small amount of grease between stub shaft seal and stub shaft dust seal. Install seals over protector and into housing. Install retaining ring into groove in housing.

8) Lubricate stub shaft and dust seal area with grease. Coat rack bearing, adjuster spring and adjuster plug with grease and install into housing. With rack centered in housing, turn adjuster plug clockwise until it bottoms in housing, then back off 50-70 degrees. Using an INCH lb. torque wrench, check pinion torque. Maximum pinion preload torque is 16 INCH lbs. (1.8 N.m).

9) Install adjuster plug lock nut onto adjuster plug. Tighten lock nut firmly while holding adjuster plug. Install rack and pinion assembly into vehicle. Refill and bleed system. Test drive vehicle.

INNER TIE ROD

Removal – 1) Remove rack and pinion assembly from vehicle. Remove outer tie rod end from inner tie rod. Remove hex jam nut from inner tie rod. Remove boot clamps with side cutters. Mark location of breather tube for reassembly reference. Remove boots and breather tube. Remove shock damper ring from inner tie rod assembly.

2) Place a wrench on flat side of piston and rack to prevent it from turning. Place another wrench on flats of inner tie rod. Rotate inner tie rod counterclockwise until it separates from piston and rack.

Installation – 1) To prevent internal damage, hold piston and rack with a back-up wrench during tie rod installation. Install shock damper ring onto rack and piston. Install inner tie rod and tighten. See TORQUE SPECIFICATIONS table at end of this article. Ensure inner tie rod rocks freely in housing, then stake both sides of inner tie rod to flats on rack. *See Fig. 12.*

2) Ensure both stakes are okay by inserting a .010" (.25 mm) feeler gauge between rack and tie rod housing. Feeler gauge should not pass between rack and housing stake. Apply grease to inner tie rod and housing before installing boots. To complete installation, reverse removal procedure. Refill and bleed system. Test drive vehicle.

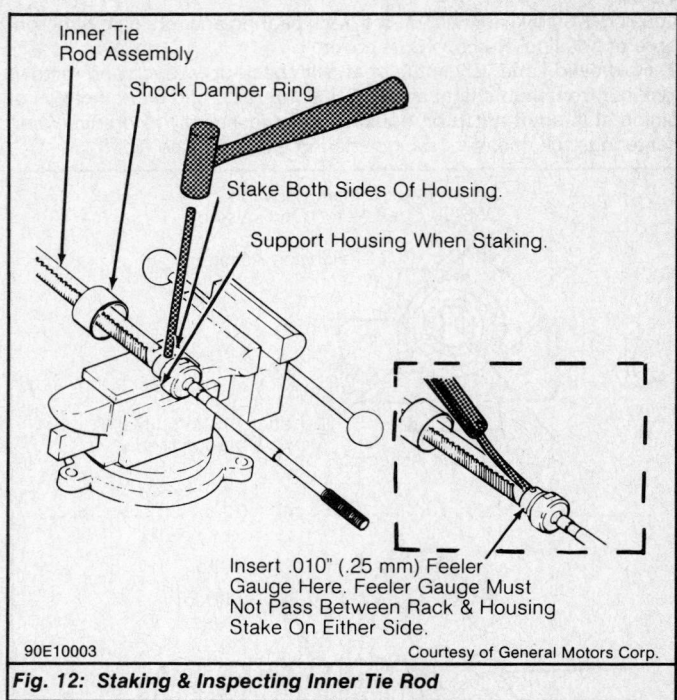

Inner Tie Rod Assembly

Shock Damper Ring

Stake Both Sides Of Housing.

Support Housing When Staking.

Insert .010" (.25 mm) Feeler Gauge Here. Feeler Gauge Must Not Pass Between Rack & Housing Stake On Either Side.

90E10003

Courtesy of General Motors Corp.

Fig. 12: Staking & Inspecting Inner Tie Rod

TORQUE SPECIFICATIONS

TORQUE SPECIFICATIONS

Application	Ft. Lbs. (N.m)
Rack & Pinion Mounting Bolts	
"A" Body	70 (95)
"W" Body	59 (80)
"Y" Body	30 (40)
All Others	50 (68)
Engine Frame Bolts	
"A" & "W" Bodies	103 (140)
All Others	76 (103)
Intermediate Shaft Coupling Bolt	35 (47)
Adjuster Plug Lock Nut	50 (68)
Tie Rod End Lock Nut	50 (68)
Tie Rod To Rack	70 (95)
Outer Tie Rod Castle Nut	33 (45)
Stub Shaft Lock Nut	26 (35)
Cylinder Line Fittings	15 (20)
Steering Line Fittings	20 (27)
Power Steering Pump Mounting Bolts	18 (25)
Power Steering Pump Line Fittings	21 (28)

Brougham, Camaro, Caprice, Custom Cruiser, Firebird, Roadmaster

DESCRIPTION & OPERATION

STEERING GEAR

Saginaw rotary valve integral power steering gears contain a control valve, which directs hydraulic pressure to either side of a rack piston. The rack piston converts this pressure into mechanical force, which is transmitted through the pitman shaft to the steering linkage.

POWER STEERING PUMP

The Saginaw vane power steering pump is a constant displacement, vane type pump with an integral fluid reservoir. When pressure exceeds set limits, a flow control pressure relief valve opens, allowing fluid to return to the inlet side of the pump.

LUBRICATION

FLUID TYPE

When adding or changing fluid, use power steering fluid meeting GM specification 9985010. Failure to use proper fluid will cause hose and seal damage, resulting in fluid leaks.

FLUID LEVEL CHECK

Fluid level is indicated by marks on reservoir dipstick. When fluid is at operating temperature, about 170°F (77°C), fluid level should be at FULL HOT mark. Fluid level should be at FULL COLD mark when fluid is cold, about 70°F (21°C).

HYDRAULIC SYSTEM BLEEDING

1) With engine off, support vehicle with wheels off ground and wheels turned fully to left. Add power steering fluid to COLD mark on dipstick.

NOTE: Fluid containing air appears tan. Air in fluid may cause pump cavitation and eventual pump damage. This air must be bled before normal steering can be obtained.

2) Turn wheels from side to side, without touching stops at either end. Add fluid as necessary to maintain at FULL COLD mark. It may be necessary to repeat this step several times.
3) Start engine. With engine idling, recheck fluid level. Add fluid, if necessary, to bring level to FULL COLD mark. Return wheels to center position. Lower vehicle. Continue to run engine for 2 to 3 minutes.
4) Road test vehicle. Check for leaks. Ensure fluid level is at FULL HOT mark when fluid is stabilized at operating temperature.

ADJUSTMENTS

POWER STEERING PUMP BELT

The power steering pump is driven by a serpentine belt. No belt adjustment is required.

WORM BEARING PRELOAD

For adjustment procedure, see WORM BEARING PRELOAD under OVERHAUL.

PITMAN SHAFT OVER-CENTER TURNING TORQUE

For adjustment procedures, see PITMAN SHAFT OVER-CENTER TURNING TORQUE under OVERHAUL.

TESTING

NOTE: Before testing power steering system, check fluid level, pump pulley, tire pressure and engine idle speed.

1) Remove high pressure line from pump. Connect spare pressure hose to pump. Connect Power Steering Pressure Tester (J-5176-D) or Power Steering System Analyzer (J-25323-A) to both hoses.
2) Open valve fully. Start and run engine until fluid reaches normal operating temperature. Check fluid level and add as necessary. With engine at operating temperature, pressure reading should be 80-125 psi (5.6-8.8 kg/cm²). If pressure is more than 200 psi (14 kg/cm²), inspect system for restrictions or faulty flow control valve.

CAUTION: To prevent pump damage, DO NOT hold valve closed for more than 5 seconds in step 3).

3) Alternately close and open gauge valve fully 3 times while recording highest pressure obtained. Each reading should be at least 1000 psi (70.3 kg/cm²).
4) If recorded pressures are all within 50 psi (3.5 kg/cm²), pump is okay. If pressures are high and not within 50 psi (3.5 kg/cm²) of each other, flow control valve is sticking.
5) If pressure readings are less than 1000 psi (70.3 kg/cm²), replace flow control valve, then repeat test. Replace rotor and vanes if pressure is still low after replacing flow control valve. See POWER STEERING PUMP under OVERHAUL.
6) If pump meets specification, leave valve open. Turn steering wheel from stop to stop. Record and compare highest pressure with maximum pump pressure. If pressure at both stops is not the same as maximum pressure recorded earlier, steering gear is leaking internally.

REMOVAL & INSTALLATION

POWER STEERING PUMP

NOTE: On some models, it may be necessary to remove pump bracket with pump. Also, bracket mounting bolts may extend into water jacket.

Removal & Installation – Place container under vehicle. Disconnect power steering hoses and plug fittings. Remove drive belt. Remove pump mounting hardware and pump. Because of different engines and air conditioning configurations, it may be necessary to remove additional components. On some models, power steering pump pulley may be removed to ease removal of pump. To install, reverse removal procedure.

POWER STEERING PUMP COMPONENTS

Pulley (Removal & Installation) – Remove drive belt. Remove pump (if necessary) for clearance. Install Pulley Remover (J-25034-B) on pulley. Remove pulley from shaft by holding body of tool with wrench and turning bolt. To install, use Pulley Installer (J-25033-B). Press pulley onto drive shaft until face of pulley hub is flush with shaft. DO NOT use arbor press to install pulley. Reinstall pump on vehicle (if removed).
Drive Shaft Seal (Removal & Installation) – Remove pump and pulley. Protect pump shaft with shim stock. Using a chisel, cut and remove seal. To install, coat shaft seal with power steering fluid. Using Shaft Oil Seal Installer (J-22670), drive new seal in place until it bottoms on shoulder.
Reservoir (Removal & Installation) – 1) Remove pump from vehicle and drain fluid. Mount pump in vise with shaft facing down. DO NOT allow vise jaws to contact reservoir.
2) Remove reservoir-to-pump mounting studs at rear of pump. Remove pressure line union bolt. Using a soft mallet, tap on filler neck of reservoir. Move reservoir back and forth until free of pump.
3) When installing reservoir, use new "O" rings. Lubricate and install pump housing "O" ring, 2 pump-to-reservoir stud "O" rings and outlet fitting "O" ring. Slide reservoir over pump. Ensure reservoir is seated properly.
4) Install pump-to-reservoir mounting studs. Install union bolt. Install pump into vehicle. Refill reservoir and bleed system. See BLEEDING HYDRAULIC SYSTEM.

STEERING GEAR

Removal & Installation – 1) Remove hoses from steering gear. Raise hoses to prevent fluid leakage. Disconnect intermediate shaft from steering gear. Remove pitman arm. Remove ABS modulator bracket nut. Remove steering gear bolts. Remove steering gear from vehicle.

2) To install, reverse removal procedure. Ensure steering gear is aligned as straight as possible with intermediate shaft. Tighten attaching bolts and hose fittings as specified. See TORQUE SPECIFICATIONS table at end of this article.

PITMAN SHAFT SEALS

NOTE: On Brougham, Caprice, Custom Cruiser and Roadmaster models, remove pitman shaft seals before removing steering gear from vehicle. For Camaro and Firebird, see step 1) in STEERING GEAR under OVERHAUL.

Removal – 1) Remove pitman arm. Clean exposed end of pitman shaft and end of housing. Remove retaining ring, using Internal Snap Ring Pliers (J-4245).

2) Place drain pan under pitman shaft. Start engine. Turn wheels fully to left to force out double lip seal and back-up washer. Stop engine. Remove single lip seal and back-up washer.

3) Check pitman shaft seal surfaces for pitting or roughness. Replace pitman shaft if pitted. Check housing for burrs and remove as necessary.

Installation – Install single lip seal and back-up washer. Using Seal Installer (J-6219), install double lip seal and back-up washer. Install retaining ring, using Internal Snap Ring Pliers (J-4245).

OVERHAUL

POWER STEERING PUMP

CAUTION: When clamping pump in vise or mounting fixture, DO NOT exert excessive force on front hub as housing may be distorted.

Disassembly – 1) Remove pulley from shaft. See POWER STEERING PUMP COMPONENTS under REMOVAL & INSTALLATION. Remove brackets from pump. Drain reservoir. Clean exterior of pump. Clamp pump in a soft-jawed vise, shaft down, between square boss and shaft housing. *See Fig. 1.*

2) Remove union bolt and "O" ring seal. Remove mounting studs. Rock filler tube back and forth gently to loosen. Work reservoir off pump housing. Remove and discard all "O" rings.

3) Using a punch, tap end cover retainer ring until one end of ring is near hole in pump housing. Insert punch in hole far enough to disengage ring from groove in pump bore. Pry ring out of pump housing.

4) Tap end cover with plastic mallet to jar it loose. Spring located under end cover should push it up. Remove pump housing from vise. Place pump in an inverted position on a clean, flat surface.

5) Tap end of drive shaft with plastic mallet to loosen pressure plate, rotor and thrust plate assembly from housing. Lift pump housing from rotor assembly.

6) Flow control valve and control valve spring should slide out of bore. *See Fig. 2.* Remove and discard end cover and pressure cover "O" rings. Remove drive shaft oil seal.

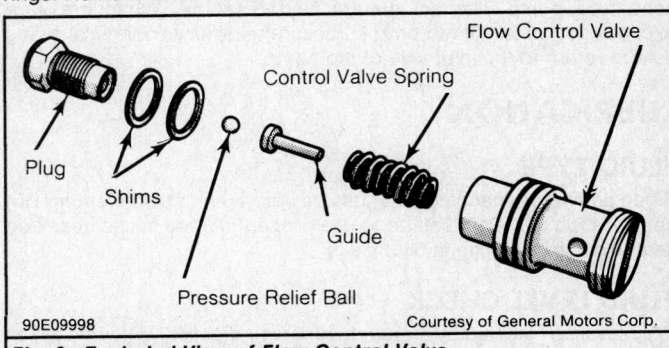

Fig. 2: **Exploded View of Flow Control Valve**

7) Lift pressure plate and cam ring from rotor. Remove 10 vanes from slots. Clamp drive shaft in soft-jawed vise with rotor and thrust plate upward.

8) Remove and discard rotor lock ring. Use care to avoid nicking rotor end face. Slide rotor and thrust plate off drive shaft. Remove drive shaft from vise.

NOTE: Individual flow control valve parts are not available. Replace flow control valve as an assembly if worn or damaged. If pump is being overhauled because of contamination in system, valve can be disassembled for cleaning.

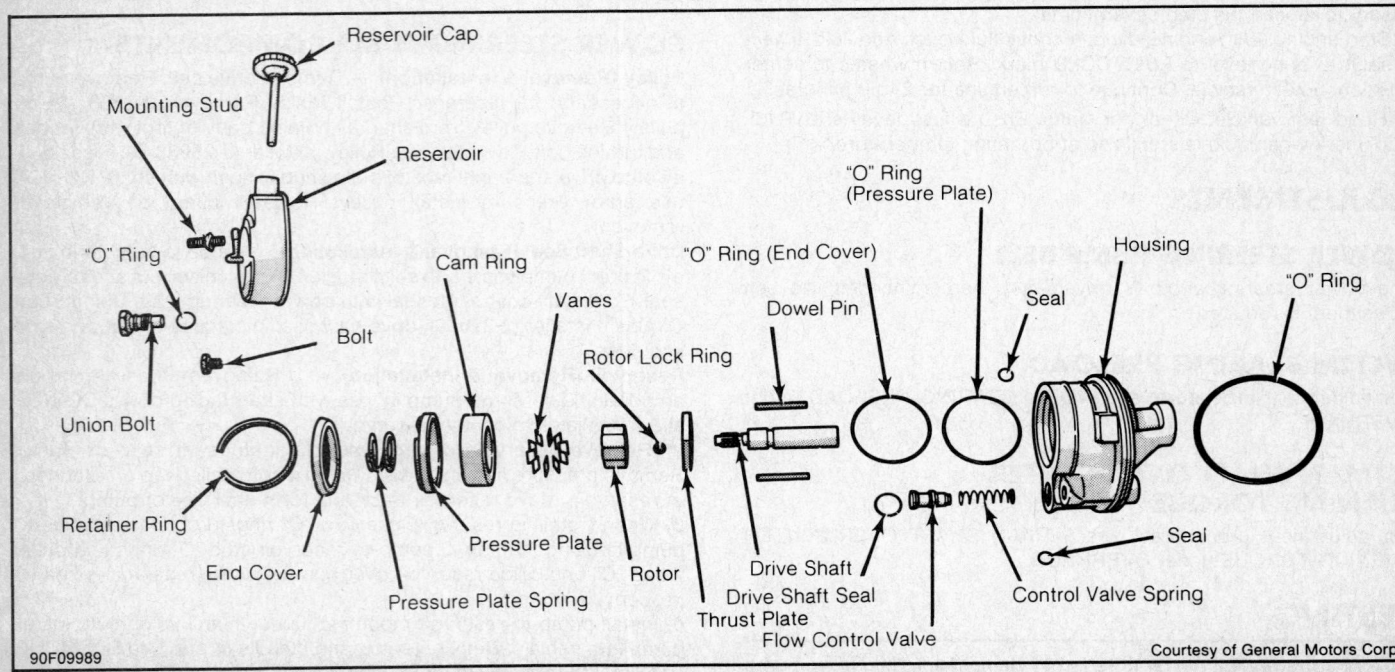

Fig. 1: **Exploded View of Saginaw Power Steering Pump**

Cleaning & Inspection – 1) Clean all parts in solvent. Inspect flow control valve for wear or damage. Inspect seal bore in housing for burrs, nicks or scoring. Inspect fit of vanes in rotor. Vanes must slide freely into rotor slots without binding.
2) Excessively loose vanes require replacement of rotor and/or vanes. Examine inner surface of cam ring for heavy scuff or chatter marks. Inspect flat surfaces of pressure and thrust plates for wear or scoring.
3) Light scoring can be removed by lapping on a flat surface. Inspect pump housing drive shaft bushing for excessive wear. Replace pump housing and bushing as an assembly if badly worn or scored. Replace any damaged or worn parts.

NOTE: If pump is equipped with magnet, ensure all residue is cleaned from magnet.

Reassembly – 1) Lubricate all "O" ring seals and seal areas with power steering fluid. Place pump housing on flat surface. Drive new shaft seal into bore using Shaft Oil Seal Installer (J-22670) until seal bottoms on shoulder. DO NOT use excessive force as seal can be distorted.
2) Clamp pump housing in vise with shaft down. Install end cover and pressure plate "O" rings in grooves in pump cavity. With drive shaft clamped, splined shaft up, install thrust plate on drive shaft with ported side up. *See Fig. 3.*

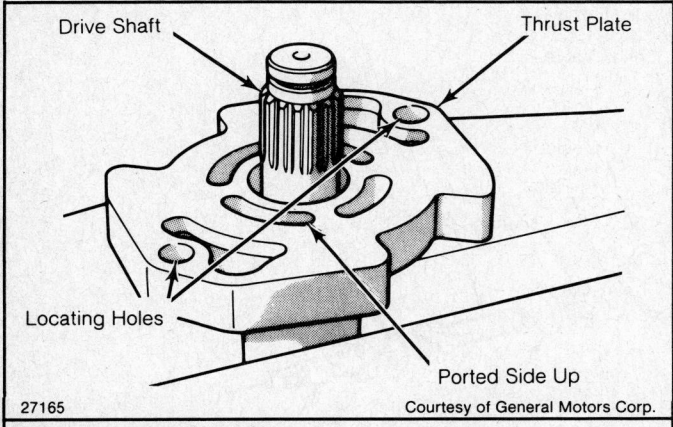

Fig. 3: **Installing Thrust Plate**

Drive Shaft | Thrust Plate | Locating Holes | Ported Side Up

27165 — Courtesy of General Motors Corp.

3) Slide rotor over splines with counterbore of rotor facing down. Install rotor lock ring. Insert both dowel pins in holes of pump cavity. Rotor must move freely on splines. Install drive shaft assembly into pump body, ensuring dowel pins are properly engaged in thrust plate.
4) Slide cam ring over rotor on dowel pins with arrow facing up. *See Fig. 4.* Install 10 vanes in rotor slots. Position pressure plate on dowel pins with plate spring groove facing upward. Place a 1 1/4" socket in groove of pressure plate. Seat entire assembly on "O" ring in pump cavity by pressing down with both thumbs.
5) Place pressure plate spring into groove in pressure plate. Position end cover lip edge up over spring. Press end cover down below retainer ring groove with thumb. Install retainer ring. Ensure ring is seated in groove. Use care to avoid cocking end cover in bore or distorting assembly.
6) Install flow control valve (if previously removed) in pump bore with control valve spring and hex end of valve facing interior of bore. Using a punch, tap retainer ring end around groove until opening is opposite flow control valve bore. This is important for maximum retention of retainer ring.
7) Replace reservoir "O" ring seal, 2 mounting stud "O" ring seals and flow control valve "O" ring seal on pump housing. Carefully position reservoir on pump housing. Visually align mounting stud holes until studs can be started into threads.
8) Press reservoir down on pump to seat on pump housing. Place new seal onto union bolt. Install union bolt in flow control valve bore. Tighten mounting studs. Install pump pulley.

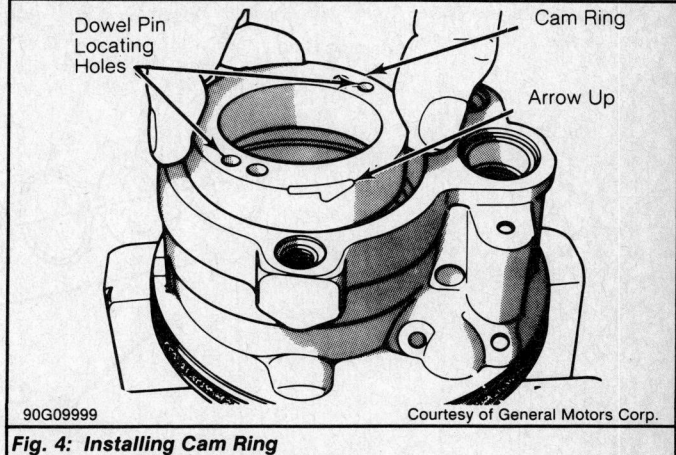

Dowel Pin Locating Holes | Cam Ring | Arrow Up

90G09999 — Courtesy of General Motors Corp.

Fig. 4: **Installing Cam Ring**

STEERING GEAR

NOTE: On Brougham, Caprice, Custom Cruiser and Roadmaster models, remove pitman shaft seals before removing steering gear from vehicle. See PITMAN SHAFT SEALS under REMOVAL & INSTALLATION.

CAUTION: DO NOT damage housing bore when prying out washer and seal.

Disassembly – 1) For Brougham, Caprice, Custom Cruiser and Roadmaster models, go to step **2)**. For Camaro and Firebird, go to step **3)**.
2) Remove pitman shaft seals before removing steering ring. See PITMAN SHAFT SEALS under REMOVAL & INSTALLATION. Remove steering gear from vehicle. Drain fluid and clean exterior. Go to step **4)**.
3) On Camaro and Firebird, remove dust seal around pitman shaft and retaining ring, using Internal Snap Ring Pliers (J-4245). Pry out washer and double lip seal. Remove steering gear from vehicle. Drain fluid and clean exterior. Go to step **4)**.
4) Mount steering gear in soft-jawed vise with pitman shaft pointing down. Remove pitman shaft adjuster lock nut. *See Fig. 5.* Remove side cover bolts. Rotate stub shaft to center gear. Remove side cover, gasket and pitman shaft as an assembly. Remove pitman shaft seal.
5) Unseat housing end plug retaining ring by inserting punch into housing access hole. Remove housing end plug and "O" ring seal.
6) Remove stub shaft adjuster lock nut, using punch against edge of slots. Using Spanner Wrench (J-7624), remove adjuster plug. Pry thrust washer bearing retainer from adjuster plug. Remove bearing spacer, races, thrust bearing, "O" ring and retaining ring.
7) Place adjuster plug on suitable support with outside face down. Using Adjuster Plug Bearing Remover and Installer (J-6221), drive needle bearing, dust seal and lip seal from adjuster plug.
8) Remove stub shaft and valve as an assembly. Tap stub shaft lightly on wooden block to loosen shaft cap. Pull cap and valve out from body 1/4" (6 mm). Disengage stub shaft pin from hole in valve spool. Pull and rotate valve spool to remove it from valve body. Remove valve spool "O" ring, valve body, Teflon rings and "O" ring seals.

NOTE: DO NOT disassemble valve body. If valve body is defective, replace entire valve body as an assembly.

9) Turn stub shaft counterclockwise until rack piston begins to emerge from housing bore. Remove rack piston plug. Insert Rack Piston Arbor (J-21552) into rack piston. Hold tool firmly against worm shaft while turning stub shaft counterclockwise to force rack piston from housing. Remove rack piston, balls and tool.
10) Remove worm shaft, thrust bearing and races. Remove worm bearing and races. Remove tool from rack piston. Remove balls, clamp, and ball guide. Remove Teflon ring and "O" ring seal. Using

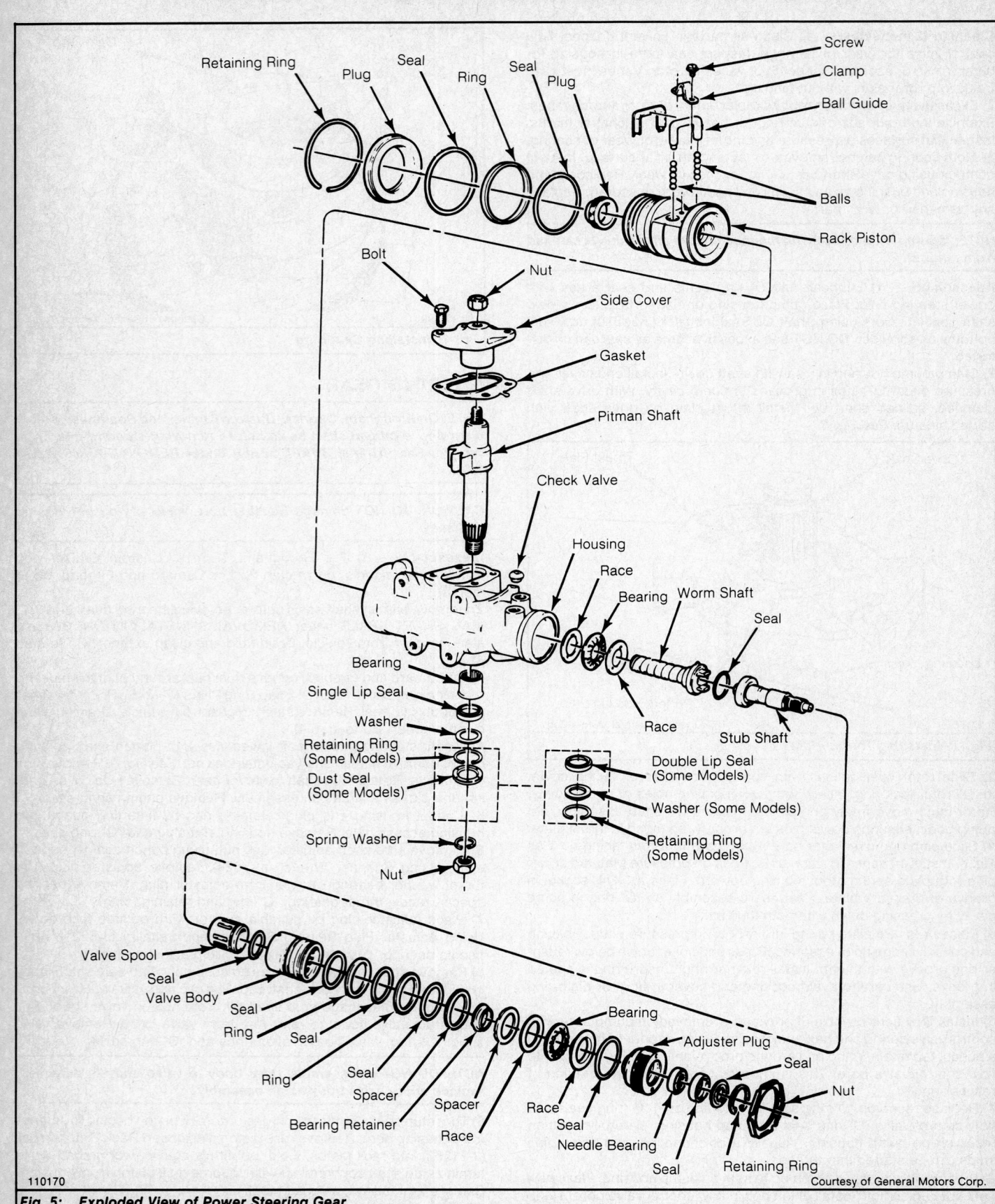

110170

Fig. 5: *Exploded View of Power Steering Gear*

Internal Snap Ring Pliers (J-4245), remove pitman shaft seal retaining ring.

CAUTION: DO NOT score housing bore when prying out seals and washers.

11) Pry back-up washer and double lip seal from housing. Pry out back-up washer and single lip seal. Insert Pitman Shaft Bearing Remover and Installer (J-6278) through hole in top of housing. Drive out bearing. Carefully pry check valve from housing.

Cleaning & Inspection – Clean housing and lubricate all internal components with power steering fluid. Replace steering gear housing if bore is damaged. Replace any worn or damaged components.

NOTE: Lubricate all "O" rings and lip seals with power steering fluid before installation.

Reassembly – 1) Drive check valve into housing, using a piece of tubing 4" (101 mm) long and 3/8" (9.5 mm) diameter. Coat pitman shaft double lip seal and washer with grease. Using Pitman Shaft Bearing Remover and Installer (J-6278), install needle bearing. Using Pitman Shaft Oil Seal Installer (J-6219), install single lip seal, then back-up washer. Install double lip seal and back-up washer. Using Internal Snap Ring Ring Pliers (J-4245), install retaining ring.

2) Install worm shaft "O" ring seal and Teflon ring. Fully seat worm shaft to rack piston. Align worm shaft groove with rack piston ball return guide hole.

NOTE: Black balls are smaller than Silver balls. Black and Silver balls must be installed alternately into rack piston and ball guide to maintain preload.

3) Lubricate balls with power steering fluid. Insert balls into ball return guide holes while turning worm shaft counterclockwise. Install remaining balls into ball guide. Use grease at each end to retain balls. Install ball guide and guide clamp. Tighten ball guide clamp screws.

4) Insert Rack Piston Arbor (J-21552) into rack piston bore while turning worm shaft counterclockwise. Install races and thrust bearing onto worm shaft. Insert worm shaft into housing.

5) Lubricate valve spool and "O" ring seal with power steering fluid. Assemble valve spool "O" ring seal and valve spool. Assemble valve spool and valve body by pushing and rotating until hole in valve spool for stub shaft pin is accessible from opposite end of valve body.

6) Assemble stub shaft and valve spool. Insert retaining pin. Ensure notch in stub shaft cap fully engages valve body pin and seats against valve body shoulder.

7) Assemble "O" ring seals, Teflon rings and valve body. Assemble stub shaft, valve assembly and worm shaft. Ensure pin on stub shaft aligns with slot in valve assembly. Install stub shaft and worm shaft into housing. Hold Rack Piston Arbor (J-21552) tightly against worm shaft while turning stub shaft clockwise until rack piston seats on worm shaft. Install rack piston plug. Use Rack Piston Teflon Ring Compressor (J-8947) to compress seals.

8) Place stub shaft adjuster plug on suitable support with outside face up. Using Adjuster Plug Bearing Remover and Installer (J-6221), assemble stub shaft needle bearing and adjuster plug. Ensure identification mark on needle bearing faces tool during installation. Using same tool, assemble lip seal and dust seal. Install retaining ring.

9) Assemble "O" ring seal, large bearing race, thrust bearing, small bearing race, bearing spacer, thrust bearing retainer and adjuster plug. Install adjuster plug assembly into housing, using Spanner Wrench (J-7624). Take care not to cut seals when installing adjuster plug.

10) Install housing end plug "O" ring seal, end plug and retaining ring into housing. Ensure open end of retaining ring is approximately 1" (25 mm) from access hole in housing.

11) Screw pitman shaft into side cover until it seats fully. Install pitman shaft lock nut. Affix gasket to side cover, bending gasket tabs around edge of side cover. Install pitman shaft and side cover into housing. Install and tighten cover bolts.

12) Using Pitman Shaft Oil Seal Installer (J-6219), install pitman shaft seal or seals, washers and retaining ring. On Camaro and Firebird, install dust seal.

13) Adjust steering gear. See WORM BEARING PRELOAD and PITMAN SHAFT OVER-CENTER TURNING TORQUE. Install steering gear. See STEERING GEAR under REMOVAL & INSTALLATION.

WORM BEARING PRELOAD

NOTE: Adjust worm bearing preload first, then adjust pitman shaft over-center turning torque.

1) Remove steering gear from vehicle. See STEERING GEAR under REMOVAL & INSTALLATION. Loosen lock nut around stub shaft, using punch. Using Spanner Wrench (J-7624), seat adjuster plug firmly in housing. Approximately 20 ft. lbs. (27 N.m) torque is required to seat adjuster plug. Mark gear housing opposite one hole in adjuster plug.

2) Measure back (counterclockwise) 1/2" (13 mm) from mark made in step 1) and make another index mark on housing. Turn adjuster plug counterclockwise until hole in adjuster plug is aligned with second mark on housing. See Fig 6. Hold adjuster plug to maintain alignment with index mark. Tighten lock nut securely.

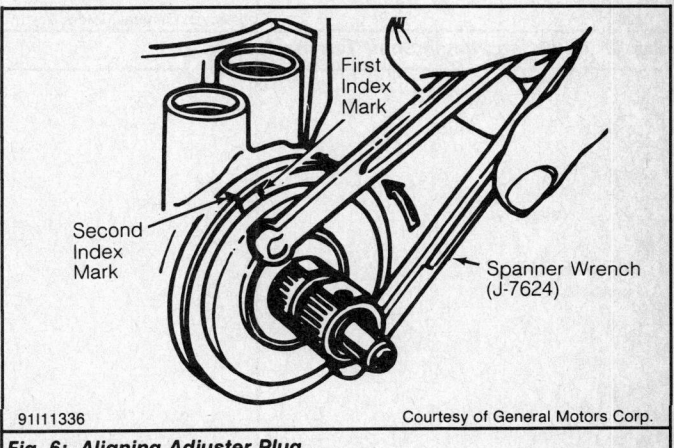

91I11336   Courtesy of General Motors Corp.

Fig. 6: Aligning Adjuster Plug

PITMAN SHAFT OVER-CENTER TURNING TORQUE

1) Remove steering gear. Rotate stub shaft back and forth to drain power steering fluid. Loosen pitman shaft adjuster lock nut. Rotate pitman shaft adjuster screw counterclockwise until fully extended, then turn back one full turn.

2) To center gear, turn stub shaft to either stop. Count number of turns required to rotate stub shaft from stop to stop. Turn shaft back 1/2 total number of turns. Once centered, flat on stub shaft should face upward, parallel to side cover, and master spline on pitman shaft should line up with adjuster screw.

3) Using an INCH lb. torque wrench with handle pointing upward, rotate stub shaft 45 degrees each side of center to measure worm bearing preload torque. See Fig. 7. Record highest turning torque measured on or near center.

4) On used steering gears (400 miles or more), add 4-5 INCH lbs. (.5-.6 N.m) torque to worm bearing preload torque measured in step 3). DO NOT exceed total steering gear preload of 13 INCH lbs. (1.5 N.m). On new steering gears (less than 400 miles), add 6-10 INCH lbs. (.7-1.1 N.m) to worm bearing preload torque measured in step 3). DO NOT exceed total steering gear preload of 18 INCH lbs. (2 N.m).

5) To adjust over-center turning torque, turn pitman shaft adjuster screw clockwise until correct pitman shaft over-center turning torque, determined in step 4), is attained. Prevent adjuster screw from turning and tighten lock nut.

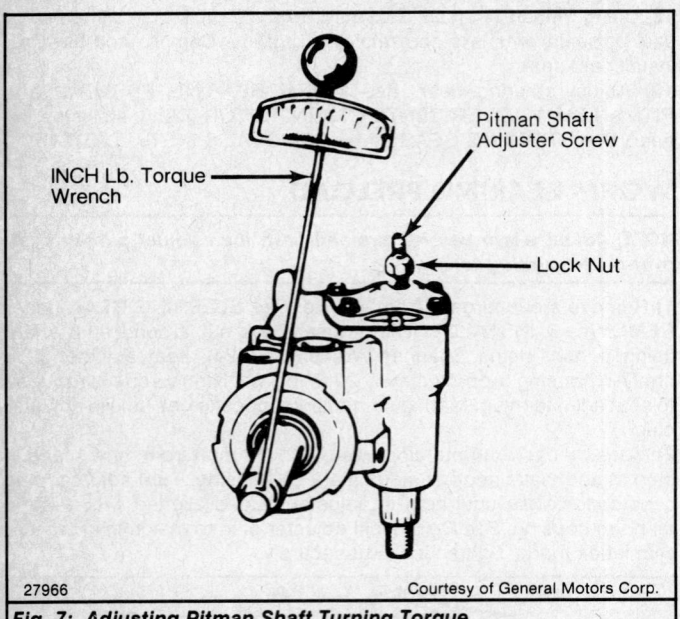

INCH Lb. Torque Wrench

Pitman Shaft Adjuster Screw

Lock Nut

27966   Courtesy of General Motors Corp.

Fig. 7: Adjusting Pitman Shaft Turning Torque

TORQUE SPECIFICATIONS

STEERING GEAR TORQUE SPECIFICATIONS

Application	Ft. Lbs. (N.m.)
Flexible Coupling Pinch Bolt	
Caprice, Custom Cruiser and Roadmaster	23 (31)
Brougham, Camaro and Firebird	30 (41)
Steering Gear Mounting Bolts	
Camaro and Firebird	66 (90)
Brougham, Caprice, Custom Cruiser and Roadmaster	70 (95)
Pitman Arm Retaining Nut	184 (250)
Side Cover Bolts	44 (60)
Pitman Shaft Adjuster Lock Nut	20 (27)
Hose Fittings	21 (28)
	INCH Lbs. (N.m.)
Ball Guide Clamp Screws	44 (5)

POWER STEERING PUMP TORQUE SPECIFICATIONS

Application	Ft. Lbs. (N.m.)
Flow Control Valve	55 (75)
High Pressure Line-to-Union Fitting	30 (41)
High Pressure Union Bolt Fitting	35 (47)
Mounting Bracket Bolts	30 (41)
Reservoir Mounting Studs	26 (35)
	INCH Lbs. (N.m.)
Flow Control Valve Plug	4 (.45)

Beretta, Bonneville, Brougham, Camaro, Caprice, Cavalier, Century, Corsica, Corvette, Custom Cruiser, Cutlass Calais, Cutlass Ciera, Cutlass Cruiser, Cutlass Supreme, DeVille, Eighty-Eight Eldorado, Firebird, Fleetwood, Grand Am, Grand Prix, LeSabre, Lumina, Ninety-Eight, Park Avenue, Reatta, Regal, Riviera, Roadmaster, Seville, Skylark, Sunbird, Toronado, Touring Sedan, Trofeo, 6000

IDENTIFICATION

The following system has been developed by the manufacturer to functionally describe its transmissions and transaxles. The designations indicate the number of speeds, type, series and major features. *See Fig. 1.*

HYDRA-MATIC			
3	**T**	**40** —	**E**
Number of Speeds:	Type:	Series:	Major Features:
3	T - Transverse	Based on	E - Electronic Controls
4	L - Longitudinal	Relative	A - All Wheel Drive
5	M - Manual	Torque Rating	HD - Heavy Duty

91B11289   Courtesy of General Motors Corp.

Fig. 1: Identifying Hydra-Matic Products

FWD TRANSAXLE APPLICATION

Model	Body	Transmission(s)
Buick		
Century	"A"	3T40 & 4T60
LeSabre	"H"	4T40
Park Avenue	"C"	4T60-E
Reatta	"E"	4T60
Regal	"W"	4T60
Riviera	"E"	4T60
Skylark	"N"	3T40
Cadillac		
DeVille	"C"	4T60
Eldorado	"E"	4T60-E
Fleetwood	"C"	4T60
Seville	"K"	4T60-E
Chevrolet		
Beretta	"L"	3T40
Cavalier	"J"	3T40
Corsica	"L"	3T40
Lumina	"W"	3T40, 4T60 & 4T60-E
Oldsmobile		
Cutlass Calais	"N"	3T40
Cutlass Ciera	"A"	3T40 & 4T60
Cutlass Cruiser	"A"	4T60
Cutlass Supreme	"W"	3T40, 4T60 & 4T60-E
Eighty-Eight	"H"	4T60
Ninety-Eight	"C"	4T60-E
Toronado	"E"	4T60-E
Trofeo	"E"	4T60-E
Pontiac		
Bonneville	"H"	4T60
Grand Am	"N"	3T40
Grand Prix	"W"	3T40, 4T60 & 4T60-E
Sunbird	"J"	3T40
Touring Sedan	C	4T60-E
6000	"A"	3T40 & 4T60

RWD TRANSMISSION APPLICATION

Manufacturer/Model	Body	Transmission(s)
Buick		
Roadmaster	"B"	4L60
Cadillac		
Brougham	"D"	4L60
Chevrolet		
Camaro	"F"	4L60
Caprice	"B"	4L60
Corvette	"Y"	4L60
Oldsmobile		
Custom Cruiser	"B"	4L60
Pontiac		
Firebird	"F"	4L60

LUBRICATION

SERVICE INTERVALS

Check transmission fluid level at every engine oil change. Transmission fluid should be changed and filter replaced every 100,000 miles under normal operating conditions.

Under continuous extreme operating conditions (trailer towing, heavy city traffic with ambient temperature over 90°F (32°C) or delivery service), fluid and filter should be changed every 15,000 miles.

CHECKING FLUID LEVEL

CAUTION: DO NOT overfill transmission. When transmission is hot, one pint of fluid will raise fluid level from "ADD 1 PT. OR .5L" mark to "FULL HOT" mark on dipstick.

1) Start engine and operate vehicle for at least 15 minutes or until reaching operating temperature. With engine at curb idle and vehicle on level ground, move gear selector lever through all ranges ending in the "P" position.

2) Remove transmission dipstick, wipe clean and fully reinsert into filler tube. Remove again and inspect fluid level. Fluid level should be between the "ADD 1 PT. OR .5L" mark and the "FULL HOT" mark on dipstick.

CAUTION: If vehicle has been driven for an extended period of time at high speeds, in city traffic, hot weather, or if vehicle has been pulling a trailer, an accurate fluid level reading cannot be made until vehicle has been parked and ATF is allowed to cool about 30 minutes.

RECOMMENDED FLUID

Use only Dexron-II Automatic Transmission Fluid (ATF).

DRAINING & REFILLING

1) With vehicle raised and large drain pan placed under transmission oil pan, remove front and side transmission oil pan bolts only. Loosen rear pan bolts about 4 turns each.

2) Carefully pry pan loose with screwdriver, allowing fluid to drain. Remove remaining bolts and remove oil pan. Discard old pan gasket. Remove filter and "O" ring or sleeve type seal. Remove any remaining gasket material left on transmission case.

3) Thoroughly clean pan, magnet and screen with solvent and dry with compressed air. Paper type filters should be replaced. Install new "O" ring on pick-up tube or new sleeve into pick-up tube recess. Lubricate with clean oil before installation.

4) Install filter assembly into pick-up tube recess. Install oil pan using new gasket and tighten pan bolts to specification. See TORQUE SPECIFICATIONS (OIL PAN BOLTS) table. Add required amount of fluid to transmission through filler tube.

5) Start engine with gear selector lever in the "P" position and parking brake applied. Engage transmission in each gear ending in the "P" position. Check fluid level with vehicle warm and add fluid if necessary. DO NOT overfill.

FLUID CAPACITY

FLUID CAPACITIES

Application Automatic Transaxle/Transmission [2]	[1] Quantity Qts. (L)
2.0L (VIN K)	4.0 (3.8)
2.2L (VIN G)	4.0 (3.8)
2.3L (VIN D)	
3T40	7.0 (6.6)
4T60	6.0 (5.7)
2.5L (VIN R)	
3T40	7.0 (6.6)
4T60	6.0 (5.7)
2.5L (VIN U)	4.0 (3.8)
3.1L (VIN T)	
3T40	7.0 (6.6)
4L60	5.0 (4.7)
3.3L (VIN N)	
3T40	7.0 (6.6)
4T60	6.0 (5.7)
3.4L (VIN X)	
3T40	7.0 (6.6)
4L60	5.0 (4.7)
3.8L (VIN C & L)	6.0 (5.7)
4.9L (VIN B)	6.0 (5.7)
5.0L (VIN E & F)	4.9 (4.6)
5.0L (VIN 8)	5.0 (4.7)
5.7L (VIN 7)	5.0 (4.7)

[1] – Fluid capacities listed are approximate. Always fill to FULL mark.
[2] – Drain and refill capacity only; does not include torque converter.

TORQUE SPECIFICATIONS

TORQUE SPECIFICATIONS (OIL PAN BOLTS)

Transmission	INCH Lbs. (N.m)
3T40	97 (11)
4T60 & 4T60-E	115 (13)
4L60	144 (16)

ADJUSTMENTS

THROTTLE VALVE (T.V.) CABLE

"N" Body (2.3L) – **1)** Rotate T.V. cable adjuster body (at transaxle) 90 degrees. Pull cable housing until slider mechanism hits stop. *See Fig. 2.*

2) Rotate adjuster body back to original position. Using a torque wrench and socket, rotate T.V. cable adjuster hex nut until 75 INCH lbs. (8.5 N.m) is reached. Road test vehicle.

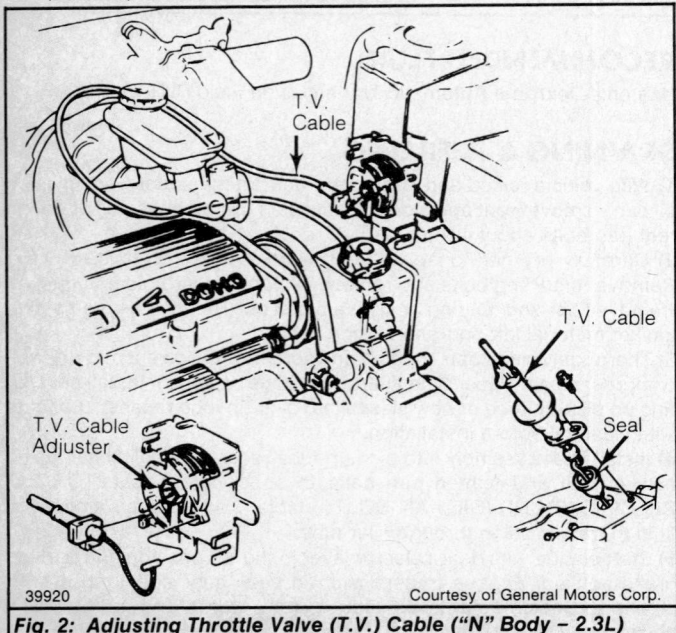

39920   Courtesy of General Motors Corp.

Fig. 2: Adjusting Throttle Valve (T.V.) Cable ("N" Body – 2.3L)

"A" Body (2.5L) – **1)** Ensure T.V. cable is in full, nonadjusted position. Ensure T.V. cable operates smoothly and connected at transaxle.

2) Accelerator cable must be installed when adjusting T.V. cable. Rotate idler pulley (cam) counterclockwise to 65 INCH lbs. (7 N.m) to place cable in adjusted position. *See Fig. 3.*

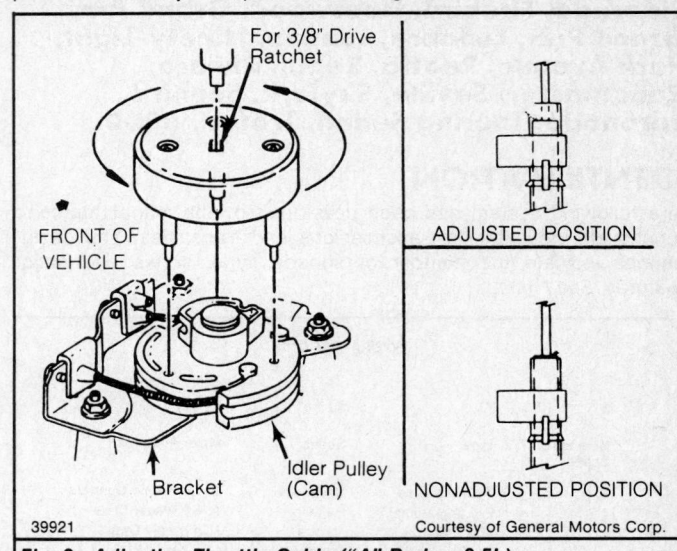

39921   Courtesy of General Motors Corp.

Fig. 3: Adjusting Throttle Cable ("A" Body – 2.5L)

Except "A" & "N" Bodies – **1)** Engine must be off. Depress metal readjust tab on cable adjuster (located at cable support bracket on engine) and hold it in this position.

2) Move cable housing slider (away from throttle lever) until it stops and is completely against fitting. Release readjust tab. *See Fig. 4.*

3) Rotate throttle lever (by hand) to its full throttle position. Slider must move (ratchet) toward lever when lever is rotated to its full throttle position. Check cable for sticking and binding.

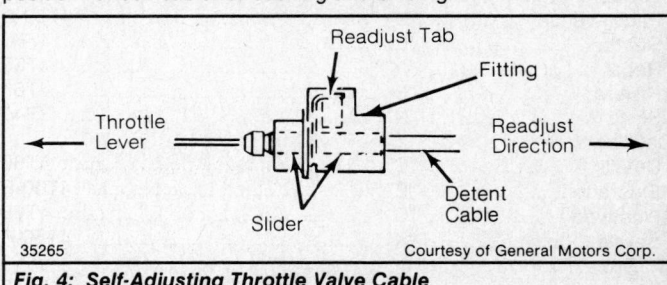

35265   Courtesy of General Motors Corp.

Fig. 4: Self-Adjusting Throttle Valve Cable (Except "A" & "N" Bodies)

GEAR SHIFT LINKAGE

1) Linkage should be adjusted so engine cannot be started in any position except Park or Neutral. If linkage is improperly adjusted, an internal hydraulic leak could occur causing internal clutch and/or band failure.

2) With selector lever in the "P" position, transmission parking pawl should engage rear/reaction internal gear lugs or output ring gear lugs. Pointer on indicator quadrant should line up properly with range indicators in all ranges.

RWD Column Shift Rod – **1)** Position steering column gear selector lever in the Neutral gate notch. Raise and support vehicle. Loosen clamp screw from below vehicle and place transmission lever in Neutral. *See Fig. 5.*

2) Hold clamp flush against equalizer lever. Tighten clamp screw finger tight, then tighten to 21 ft. lbs. (28 N.m) without applying tension on either equalizer lever or selector rod. Ensure there is no tension on either equalizer lever or selector rod after adjustment is complete. *See Fig. 5.*

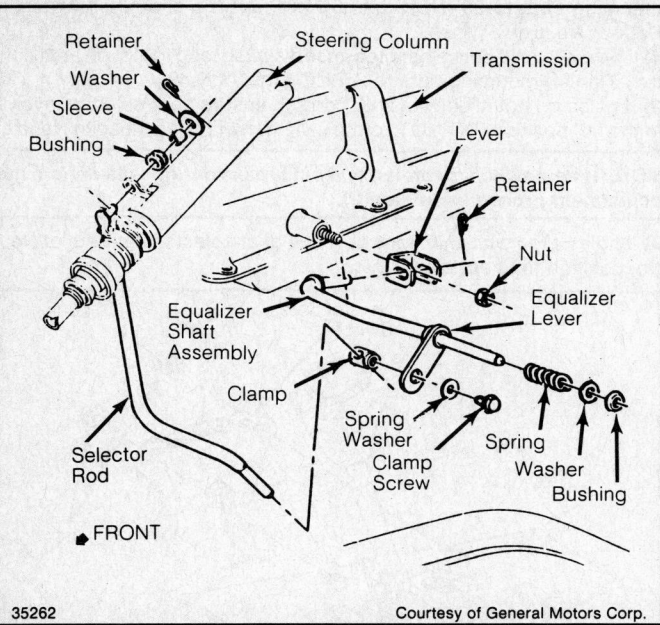

Fig. 5: Adjusting RWD Column Shift Rod

RWD Floor Shift Cable ("B" & "D" Bodies) – **1)** Place gear selector lever in "P" position. Raise and support vehicle. Ensure transmission is fully engaged in Park by rotating propeller shaft until parking pawl engages preventing rotation of shaft.

2) Loosen cable adjusting nut on transmission lever to allow pin to slide freely. With gear selector lever and transmission lever both in Park position, tighten cable adjusting nut to 15 ft. lbs. (20 N.m). See Fig. 6.

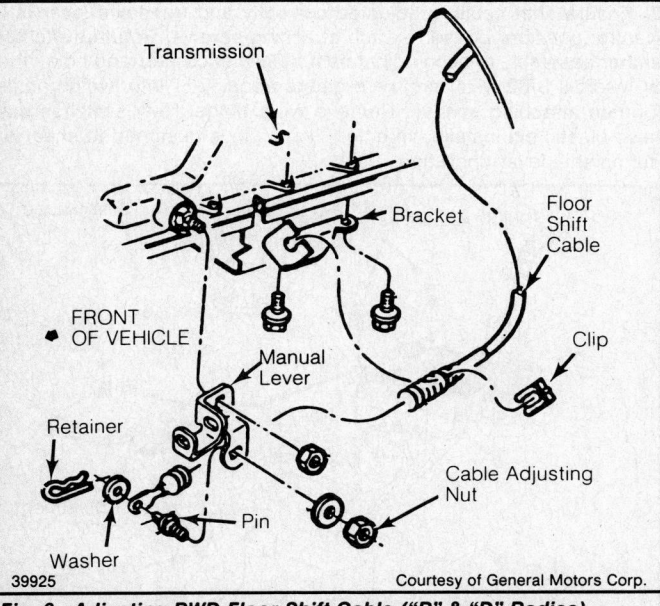

Fig. 6: Adjusting RWD Floor Shift Cable ("B" & "D" Bodies)

RWD Floor Shift Cable ("F" & "Y" Bodies) – Place gear selector lever in the "N" position. Raise and support vehicle. Loosen cable adjusting nut at transmission lever. See Fig. 7. Ensure transmission lever is in Neutral position by rotating lever clockwise to Park detent, then back (counterclockwise) 2 detents to Neutral. Tighten cable adjusting nut to 11 ft. lbs. (15 N.m).

NOTE: Lever must be held out of Park when tightening nut.

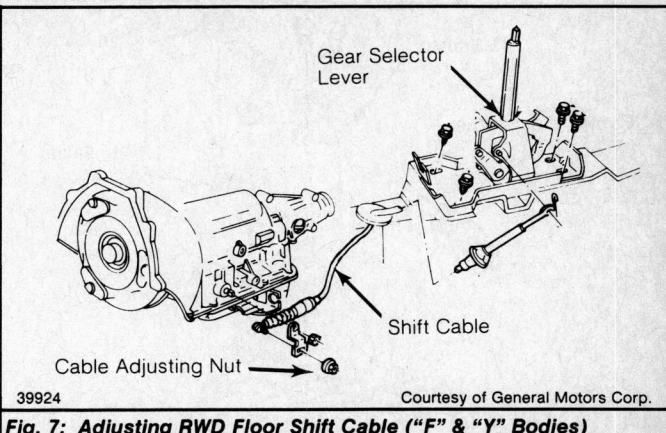

Fig. 7: Adjusting RWD Floor Shift Cable ("F" & "Y" Bodies)

FWD Floor Shift Cable (Except Self-Adjusting Type) – **1)** Place gear selector lever in the "N" position. Loosen cable adjusting nut at transaxle lever. See Fig. 8.

2) Ensure transaxle lever is in Neutral detent. Tighten cable adjusting nut. Lever MUST be held out of Park when tightening nut. DO NOT use impact tools on nut.

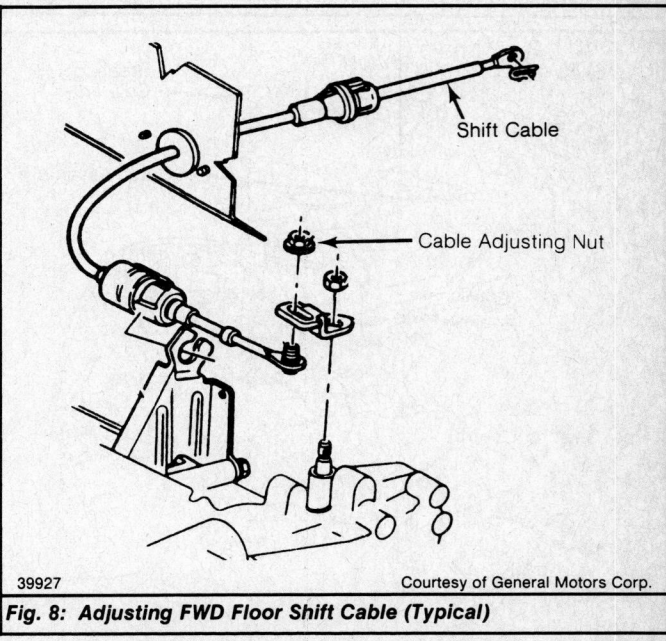

Fig. 8: Adjusting FWD Floor Shift Cable (Typical)

NOTE: Self-adjusting shift cable is commonly used on "A," "C," "H," "N" and "W" body styles.

FWD Floor Shift Cable (Self-Adjusting Type) – Place gear selector lever in the "N" position. Lift up lock button on cable adjuster at transaxle mounting bracket. See Fig. 9. Place transaxle lever in Neutral detent. Push down on lock button.

PARK/LOCK CONTROL CABLE

Floor Shift Models – **1)** With gear selector lever in the Park position and ignition key in LOCK position, gear selector lever should not be able to be moved to other gear positions. Ignition key should be removable from column.

2) With key in RUN position and gear selector lever in the Neutral position, ensure key cannot be turned to LOCK position. If system does not perform as described in steps **1)** and **2)**, go to step **3)** for adjustment procedure.

3) If key cannot be removed in Park position, snap connector lock button to up position. Move cable connector nose rearward until key can be removed from ignition. See Fig. 10. Snap lock button down.

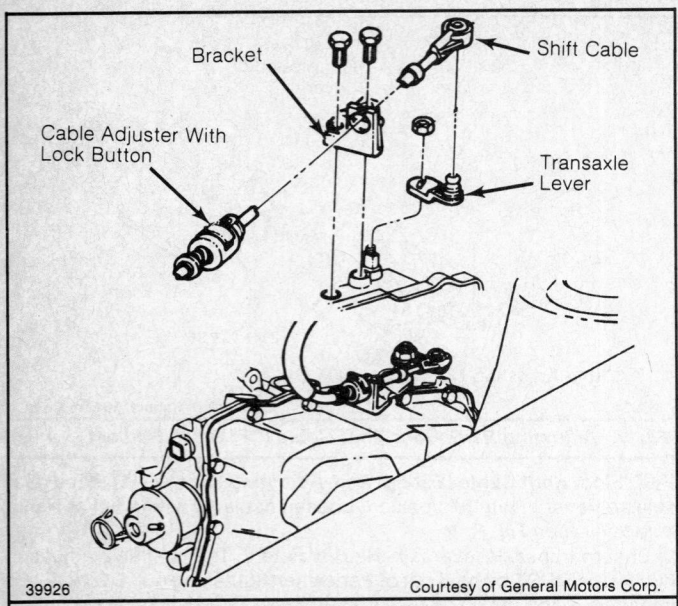

Fig. 9: FWD Self-Adjusting Floor Shift Cable

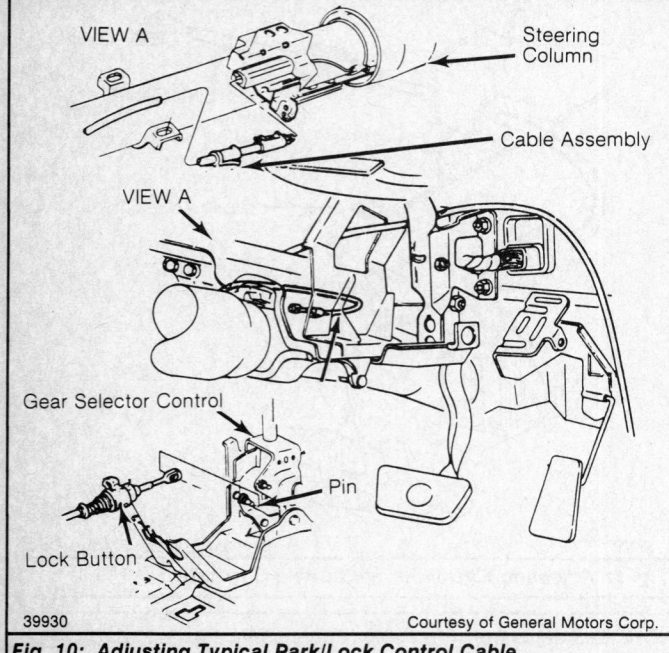

Fig. 10: Adjusting Typical Park/Lock Control Cable

NEUTRAL SAFETY SWITCH

RWD "B" & "D" Bodies – Column shift models use a mechanical interference-type neutral start system. A wedge-shaped finger, attached to the ignition switch actuator rod, blocks movement of ignition switch to the Start position in all gear selector positions except park or neutral.

RWD "F" & "Y" Bodies – **1)** Disconnect negative battery cable. Remove gear selector knob. Remove center console cover. Place gear selector lever in the "N" position. If old switch is being readjusted, go to step **2)**. If new switch is being installed, go to step **4)**.

2) Align tang on switch with tang slot on shift control. See Fig. 11. Loosen switch mounting nuts. Rotate switch to align service adjustment hole with carrier tang hole.

3) Insert a .094" (2.34 mm) wire gauge into adjustment hole in top of switch. Rotate switch until pin drops to depth of .59" (15 mm). Tighten

mounting nuts to 26 INCH lbs. (3 N.m). Vehicle should only start in Park or Neutral.

4) If new switch if being installed, insert switch tang in slot on shift control. Tighten mounting nuts to 26 INCH lbs. (3 N.m).

5) If holes do not align with shift control, ensure gear selector lever is in the "N" position. DO NOT rotate switch. Switch is pinned in Neutral.

NOTE: If new switch is rotated and pin breaks during installation, use adjustment procedure in step 2).

6) If holes align with shift control, move gear selector lever out of Neutral position to shear plastic pin.

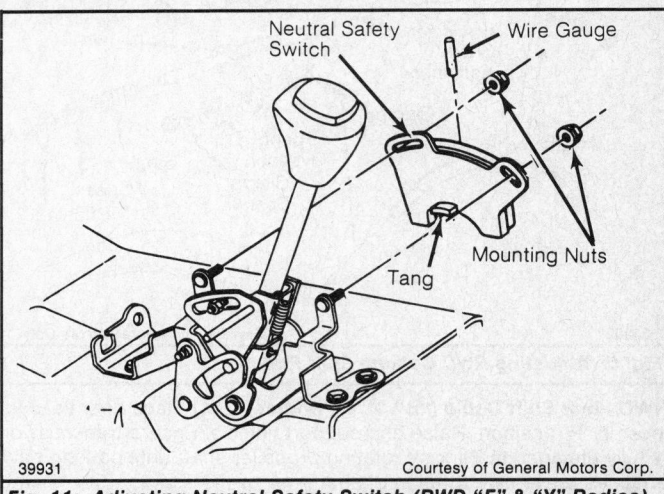

Fig. 11: Adjusting Neutral Safety Switch (RWD "F" & "Y" Bodies)

FWD Models – **1)** There are 2 different neutral safety switches used on FWD models. *See Fig. 12.* To adjust switch, place gear selector lever in the "N" position.

2) Ensure shift cable is adjusted correctly and transaxle lever is in Neutral position. Loosen switch attaching screws. Rotate switch on shifter assembly to align adjustment hole with carrier tang hole.

3) Insert a 3/32" (2.4 mm) wire gauge about 5/8" into switch holes. Tighten attaching screws. Remove wire gauge. New switches may have plastic pin installed in hole. Plastic pin is designed to shear off during shift lever operation.

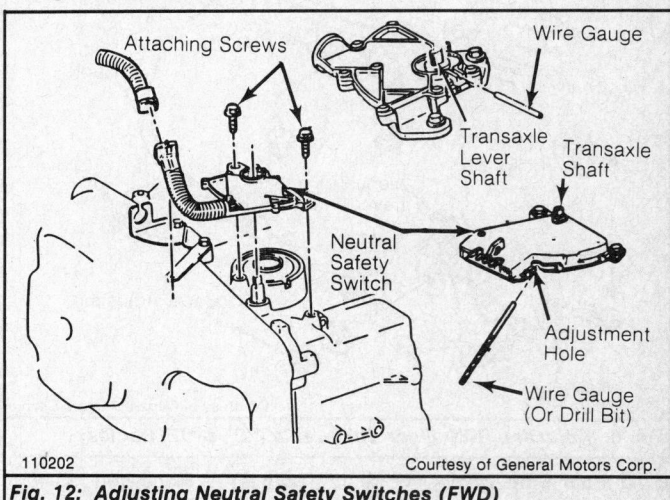

Fig. 12: Adjusting Neutral Safety Switches (FWD)

TORQUE CONVERTER CLUTCH BRAKE SWITCH

The torque converter clutch brake switch must be adjusted to prevent vehicle stalling at idle due to the clutch remaining applied. Ensure brake pedal is fully released. Adjust plunger to just touch brake pedal lever.

Beretta, Camaro, Cavalier, Corsica, Corvette, Cutlass Calais, Cutlass Supreme, Firebird, Grand Am, Grand Prix, Lumina, Sunbird

IDENTIFICATION

The following system has been developed by the manufacturer to functionally describe its transmissions and transaxles. The designations indicate the number of speeds, type, series and major features. *See Fig. 1.*

HYDRA-MATIC			
3	T	40	— E
Number of Speeds:	Type:	Series:	Major Features:
3	T - Transverse	Based on	E - Electronic Controls
4	L - Longitudinal	Relative	A - All Wheel Drive
5	M - Manual	Torque Rating	HD - Heavy Duty

90G10559   Courtesy of General Motors Corp.

Fig. 1: Identifying Hydra-Matic Products

FWD MANUAL TRANSAXLE APPLICATION

Manufacturer/Model	Transaxles
Chevrolet	
Beretta	5-Spd. Muncie 5TM40 & 5-Spd. Isuzu 76 mm
Cavalier	5-Spd. Muncie 5TM40 & 5-Spd. Isuzu 76 mm
Corsica	5-Spd. Muncie 5TM40 & 5-Spd. Isuzu 76 mm
Oldsmobile	
Cutlass Calais	5-Spd. Muncie 5TM40 & 5-Spd. Isuzu 76 mm
Cutlass Supreme	5-Spd. Getrag 284
Pontiac	
Grand Am	5-Spd. Muncie 5TM40 & 5-Spd. Isuzu 76 mm
Grand Prix	5-Spd. Getrag 284
Sunbird	5-Spd. Muncie 5TM40 & 5-Spd. Isuzu 76 mm

RWD MANUAL TRANSMISSION APPLICATIONS

Model	Transmission
Chevrolet	
Camaro	5-Spd. Borg-Warner 77 mm
Corvette	6-Spd. ZF S6-40 95 mm
Pontiac	
Firebird	5-Spd. Borg-Warner 77 mm

LUBRICATION

SERVICE INTERVALS

Corvette – Change fluid in overdrive unit every 30,000 miles.
Except Corvette – Check fluid level at 3 month/3000 mile intervals. Draining and refilling is not required, except at time of overhaul or service.

CHECKING FLUID LEVEL

CAUTION: On Camaro and Firebird, DO NOT remove reverse shift lever pin (largest hex shaped bolt) on LEFT side of case. Removal of this bolt may cause damage to transmission.

Camaro, Corvette & Firebird – Check lubricant level at filler plug hole on right side of transmission. Lubricant should be level with bottom of filler plug hole. Add lubricant as necessary to bring to correct level.
Except Camaro, Corvette & Firebird – Vehicle should be on level surface. Transaxle fluid should be COLD when checking fluid. Fluid should be at "FULL" mark on dipstick. *See Fig. 2.* Drain plug is below dipstick tube.

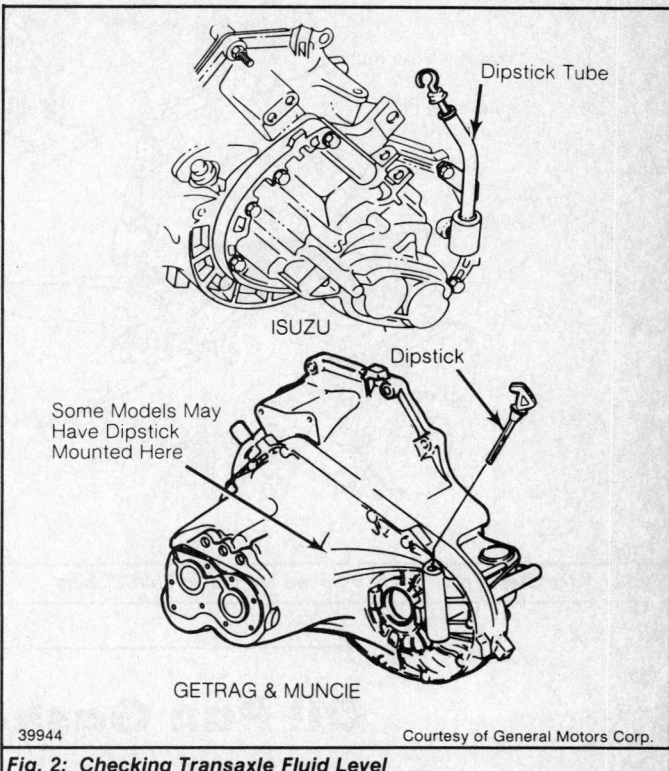

ISUZU

Dipstick Tube

Dipstick

Some Models May Have Dipstick Mounted Here

GETRAG & MUNCIE

39944   Courtesy of General Motors Corp.

Fig. 2: Checking Transaxle Fluid Level

FLUID CAPACITY & RECOMMENDED FLUID

FLUID CAPACITIES

Application	[1] Quantity Qts. (L)
2.0L (VIN K)	[2] 2.0 (1.9)
2.2L (VIN G)	[2] 2.0 (1.9)
2.3L (VIN A & D)	[2] 2.0 (1.9)
2.5L (VIN U)	[2] 2.0 (1.9)
3.1L (VIN T)	
"F" Body	[3] 3.0 (2.8)
Except "F" Body	[2] 1.9 (1.8)
3.4 (VIN X)	[2] 2.0 (1.9)
5.0L (VIN F)	[3] 3.0 (2.8)
5.7L (VIN 8)	[4] 2.2 (2.1)

[1] – Fluid capacities listed are approximate. Always fill to FULL mark.
[2] – Synchromesh Transmission Fluid (GM 12345349)
[3] – Dexron-II
[4] – SAE 5W-30

ADJUSTMENTS

SHIFT CABLE

Isuzu 76 mm 5-Speed Transaxle – 1) Disconnect negative battery cable. Shift transaxle into 3rd gear. Remove locking pin at transaxle. *See Fig. 3.* Install locking pin with tapered end down to lock transaxle into 3rd gear.
2) Loosen shift cable attaching nuts at transaxle shift levers. Remove console trim plate. Slide shifter boot up control assembly (gearshift handle). Remove console.
3) Install a 5/32" drill bit (No. 22) into alignment hole on side of control assembly. Align hole in gearshift lever assembly with slot in shifter plate and install a 3/16" drill bit.
4) Tighten cable attaching nuts at transaxle shift levers. Remove drill bits. Remove locking pin and install with tapered end up. Install console. Ensure transaxle shifts correctly.

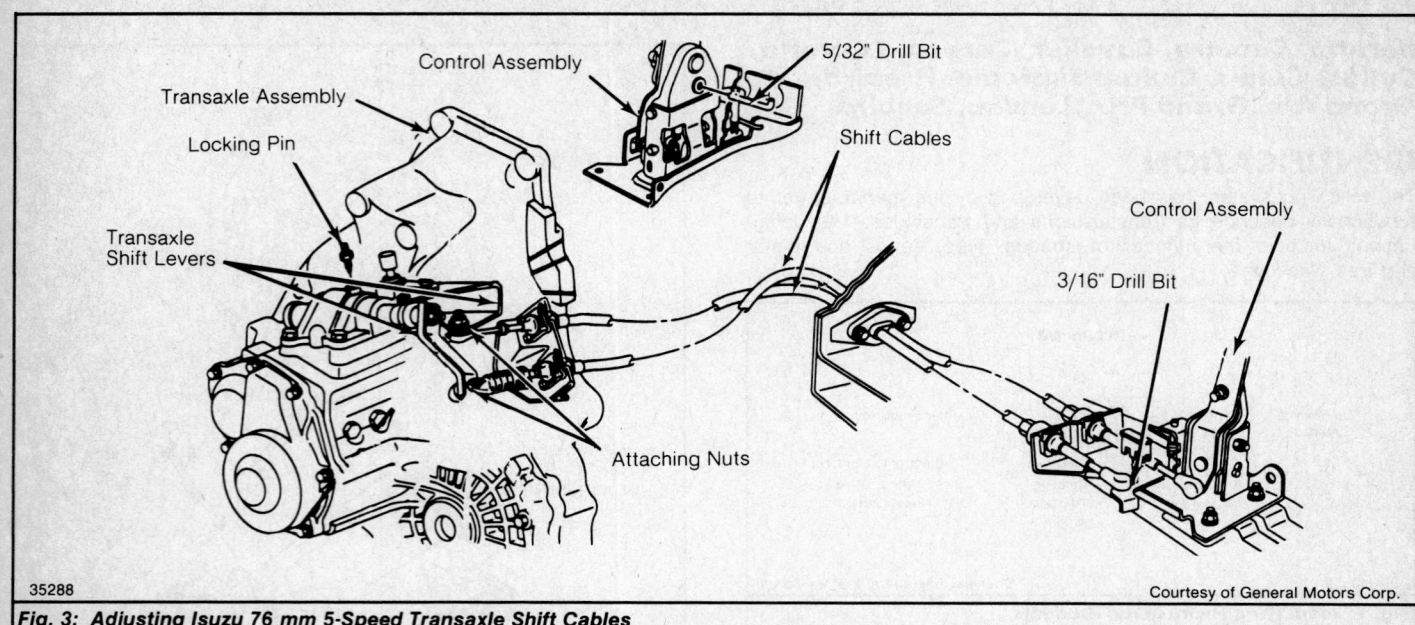

35288

Courtesy of General Motors Corp.

Fig. 3: Adjusting Isuzu 76 mm 5-Speed Transaxle Shift Cables

Oil Pan Gasket Identification

Beretta, Bonneville, Brougham, Camaro, Caprice, Cavalier, Century, Corsica, Corvette, Custom Cruiser, Cutlass Calais, Cutlass Ciera, Cutlass Cruiser, Cutlass Supreme, DeVille, Eighty-Eight Eldorado, Firebird, Fleetwood, Grand Am, Grand Prix, LeSabre, Lumina, Ninety-Eight, Park Avenue, Reatta, Regal, Riviera, Roadmaster, Seville, Skylark, Sunbird, Toronado, Touring Sedan, Trofeo, 6000

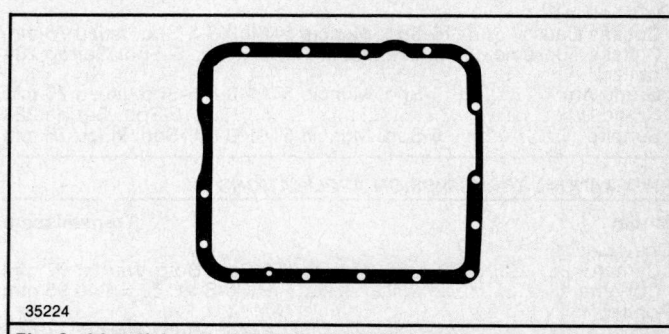

35224

Fig. 2: Identifying Hydra-Matic 4L60 Oil Pan Gasket

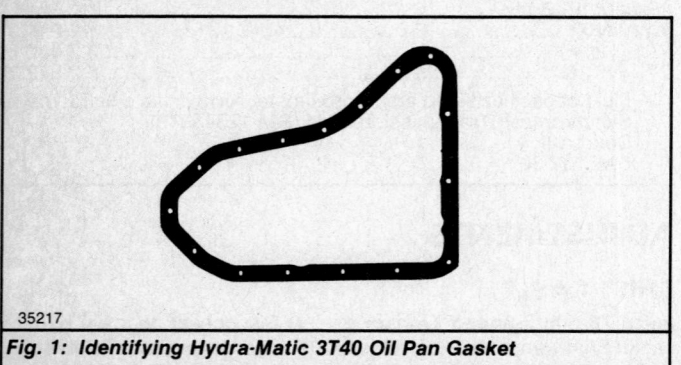

35217

Fig. 1: Identifying Hydra-Matic 3T40 Oil Pan Gasket

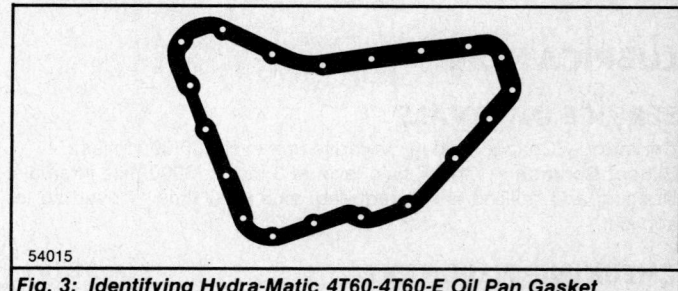

54015

Fig. 3: Identifying Hydra-Matic 4T60-4T60-E Oil Pan Gasket

"A" Body: Century, Cutlass Ciera, Cutlass Cruiser, 6000

"B" Body: Caprice, Custom Cruiser, Roadmaster

"C" Body: DeVille, Fleetwood, Ninety-Eight, Park Avenue, Touring Sedan

"D" Body: Brougham

"E" Body: Eldorado, Reatta, Riviera, Toronado, Trofeo

"F" Body: Camaro, Firebird

"H" Body: Bonneville, Eighty-Eight, LeSabre

"J" Body: Cavalier & Sunbird

"K" Body: Seville

"L" Body: Beretta, Corsica

"N" Body: Cutlass Calais, Grand Am, Skylark

"W" Body: Cutlass Supreme, Grand Prix, Lumina, Regal

"Y" Body: Corvette

MANUAL

NOTE: For manual transmission/transaxle replacement procedures, see appropriate article in CLUTCHES.

AUTOMATIC (FWD)

"A" BODY

Removal (3T40 & 4T60 Transaxles) – **1)** Disconnect and shield negative battery cable. Support engine. Remove air cleaner. Remove bolt securing Throttle Valve (T.V.) cable to transaxle. Remove shift cable and bracket from transaxle. Remove strut bracket bolts from transaxle.
2) Remove electrical wiring harness connectors as necessary. Disconnect and plug oil cooler pipes from transaxle. Remove all transaxle-to-engine bolts except bolt nearest starter motor. Raise and support vehicle. Remove stabilizer bar from lower control arm.
3) Remove steering intermediate shaft pinch bolt and shaft from steering rack. Remove left front tire and wheel assembly. Remove power steering lines from steering rack. Support steering rack and remove steering rack mounting bolts. Remove both drive axles. See FWD AXLE SHAFTS article in DRIVE AXLES.
4) Remove left lower ball joint. See BALL JOINT under REMOVAL & INSTALLATION in appropriate article in SUSPENSION. Using drill and 7/16" bit, drill through 2 spotwelds located between front and rear holes on left front stabilizer bar mounting surface. *See Fig. 1.*
5) Remove engine and transaxle mounts. Remove side-to-crossmember and left frame mount bolts. Remove left and front crossmember assembly. Remove drive axles. See FWD AXLE SHAFTS article in DRIVE AXLES.
6) Remove starter and converter shields. Remove flywheel-to-converter bolts. Secure transaxle jack under transaxle and remove remaining engine-to-transaxle bolts. Slide transaxle away from engine. Lower transaxle from vehicle.

Installation – **1)** To complete installation, reverse removal procedure. With the aid of a helper, position frame and install (but DO NOT tighten) 4 new body mount bolts.
2) Align frame to body by inserting two 8" long pins in alignment holes on right side of frame. Install frame insulators and spacers (if removed). Ensure insulators are completely seated against frame.
3) To maintain alignment, tighten right side, then left side body mount bolts. To complete installation, reverse removal procedure. Adjust T.V. cable and gear shift linkage. See ADJUSTMENTS in AUTOMATIC TRANSMISSION article. Adjust front wheel toe-in, if necessary.

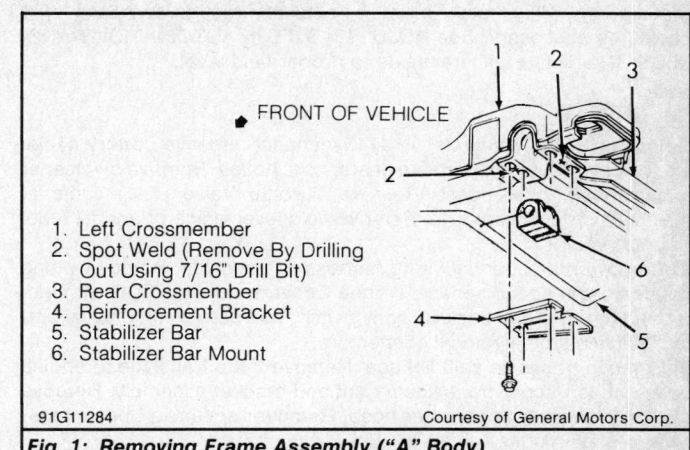

1. Left Crossmember
2. Spot Weld (Remove By Drilling Out Using 7/16" Drill Bit)
3. Rear Crossmember
4. Reinforcement Bracket
5. Stabilizer Bar
6. Stabilizer Bar Mount

91G11284   Courtesy of General Motors Corp.

Fig. 1: Removing Frame Assembly ("A" Body)

"C", "E", "H" & "K" BODIES

Removal (4T60-E Transaxle) – **1)** Disconnect negative battery cable. Remove cross brace from strut towers. Remove air duct. Disconnect cruise control cable at throttle body. Remove cruise control servo. Disconnect transaxle shift linkage. Disconnect vacuum hoses and wiring harness connectors as necessary. Remove exhaust crossover pipe, if necessary.
2) Remove fuel pipe retainers. Support engine. Raise and support vehicle. Turn steering wheel to full left position. Remove both front tire and wheel assemblies.
3) Separate both lower ball joints from steering knuckle. See BALL JOINT under REMOVAL & INSTALLATION in appropriate article in SUSPENSION. Remove right drive axle from transaxle (DO NOT remove axle from hub/knuckle assembly). See FWD AXLE SHAFTS article in DRIVE AXLES.
4) Remove left drive axle from transaxle and hub/knuckle assembly. See FWD AXLE SHAFTS article in DRIVE AXLES. Support transaxle. On Eldorado and Seville, remove power steering return line bracket and ABS pump from bracket. On all models, remove left front transaxle mount. Remove torque strut bracket from transaxle, if equipped. Remove left rear transaxle mount-to-transaxle bolts.
5) Remove transaxle brace from engine bracket. Remove stabilizer bar from control arm. Remove flywheel cover. Remove flywheel-to-converter bolts. Remove bolts attaching rear frame-to-front frame member. *See Fig. 2.*
6) Remove left frame-to-body bolts. Remove right front frame member bolts. Swing frame assembly down and support with jack stand. Remove cooler pipes from transaxle. Remove remaining transaxle-to-engine bolts. Ensure all wiring harness connectors and hoses are disconnected. Lower transaxle from vehicle.

NOTE: One transaxle-to-engine bolt is installed from the engine side. It may be necessary to use access hole located in right fenderwell and a 3-foot extension to reach bolt for removal.

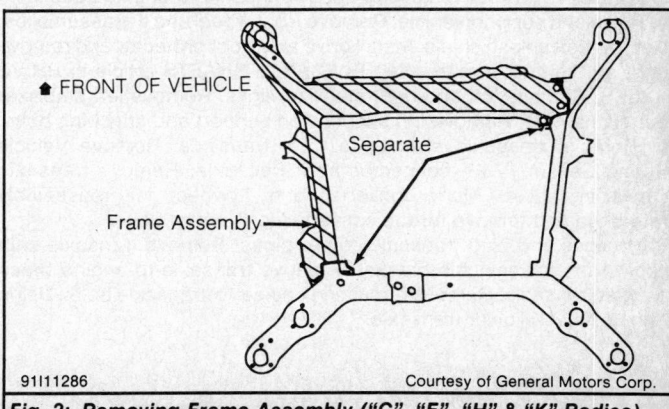

91I11286   Courtesy of General Motors Corp.

Fig. 2: Removing Frame Assembly ("C", "E", "H" & "K" Bodies)

Installation – To install, reverse removal procedure. Adjust shift cables as necessary. See ADJUSTMENTS in AUTOMATIC TRANSMISSION article. Refill transaxle to proper fluid level.

"J" BODY

Removal (3T40 Transaxle) – **1)** Disconnect negative battery cable. Drain cooling system. Remove heater core hoses. Remove air cleaner assembly/air intake duct. Remove Throttle Valve (T.V.) cable at throttle lever and transaxle. Remove fluid level indicator and fill tube. Support engine.

2) Remove nut securing wiring harness to transaxle. Remove wiring connectors at speed sensor, Torque Converter Clutch (TCC) connector and park/neutral back-up light switch. Use care when disconnecting "T" latch type electrical connectors.

3) Remove transaxle shift linkage. Remove 2 top transaxle to engine bolts and left upper transaxle mount and bracket assembly. Remove transaxle-to-vent pipe rubber hose. Remove remaining upper transaxle-to-engine bolts.

4) Raise and support vehicle. Remove front wheel and tire assemblies. Drain transaxle fluid. Remove shift linkage and bracket from transaxle. Remove both ball joints from control arms. See BALL JOINT under REMOVAL & INSTALLATION in appropriate article in SUSPENSION.

5) Remove both drive axles. See FWD AXLE SHAFTS article in DRIVE AXLES. Remove transaxle mounting strut, left stabilizer shaft link pin bolt and left stabilizer shaft frame bushing clamp nuts. Remove left suspension support assembly.

6) On 2.2L engine, remove exhaust pipe from manifold. On 3.1L engine, remove front exhaust manifold and pipe. On all vehicles, remove starter.

7) Remove transaxle converter cover. Mark torque converter-to-flywheel position and remove flywheel-to-converter bolts. Remove and plug transaxle cooler pipes. Remove transaxle-to-engine support bracket. Position transaxle jack and remove remaining engine-to-transaxle bolts. Remove transaxle.

Installation – To install, reverse removal procedure. Apply a thin film of chassis grease on torque converter pilot hub. Refill transaxle to proper fluid level. Adjust T.V. cable. See ADJUSTMENTS in AUTOMATIC TRANSMISSION article.

"L" BODY

Removal (3T40 Transaxle) – **1)** On 2.2L and 2.3L, disconnect negative battery cable. On 3.1L, remove battery. On all vehicles, remove Throttle Valve (T.V.) cable. Remove fluid level indicator and fill tube. Remove bolt securing wiring harness to transaxle. Remove wiring connectors at Torque Converter Clutch (TCC) and park/neutral back-up light switch.

2) Remove upper shift control cable bracket and disconnect cable from shift lever at transaxle. Remove transaxle-to-vent pipe rubber hose. On 3.1L engine, remove exhaust crossover.

3) On all vehicles, support engine. Remove 2 top transaxle-to-engine bolts and transaxle mounting bracket bolts. Remove transaxle mounting bracket. Remove remaining upper transaxle-to-engine bolts.

4) Raise and support vehicle. Remove front wheel and tire assemblies. Remove left splash shield. Install drive axle boot protector and remove right and left drive axles. See FWD AXLE SHAFTS article in DRIVE AXLES. Remove left and right stabilizer links. Remove left stabilizer bar clamp nuts. Remove left suspension support and attaching bolts.

5) Remove transaxle strut bolts from transaxle. Remove Vehicle Speed Sensor (VSS) connector from transaxle. Remove transaxle converter cover. Mark converter and flywheel for reassembly reference and remove torque converter-to-flywheel bolts.

6) Remove and plug transaxle cooler pipes. Remove transaxle shift cable from lower cable bracket. Remove transaxle-to-engine brace bolts at transaxle. Remove remaining engine-to-transaxle bolts. Using transaxle jack, lower transaxle.

Installation – To install, reverse removal procedure. Apply a thin film of chassis grease on torque converter pilot hub. Refill transaxle to proper fluid level. See LUBRICATION in AUTOMATIC TRANSMISSION article.

"N" BODY

Removal (3T40 Transaxle – Except 2.3L VIN D) – **1)** Disconnect negative battery cable. Drain cooling system and remove heater core hoses. Remove air cleaner assembly, mass airflow and air intake ducting (if equipped). Remove Throttle Valve (T.V.) cable at throttle lever and transaxle. Remove fluid level indicator and fill tube.

2) Support engine. On 3.3L (VIN N), insert a 1/4" x 2" bolt in hole at front right engine mount to maintain driveline alignment. On all vehicles, remove nut securing wiring harness to transaxle. Remove wiring connectors at speed sensor, Torque Converter Clutch (TCC), neutral start and back-up light switches. Use care when disconnecting "T" latch type electrical connectors.

3) Remove shift linkage from transaxle. Remove top 2 transaxle-to-engine bolts and left upper transaxle mount and bracket assembly. Remove rubber hose from transaxle to vent pipe. Remove remaining upper engine-to-transaxle bolts.

4) Raise and support vehicle. Remove both tire and wheel assemblies. Drain transaxle fluid. Remove shift linkage and bracket from transaxle. Remove both ball joints from control arms. See BALL JOINT under REMOVAL & INSTALLATION in appropriate article in SUSPENSION. Remove both drive axles. See FWD AXLE SHAFTS article in DRIVE AXLES.

5) Remove transaxle mounting strut, left stabilizer shaft link pin bolt and left stabilizer shaft frame bushing clamp nuts. Remove left suspension support assembly. Remove transaxle converter cover. Mark torque converter and flywheel for reassembly reference and remove torque converter-to-flywheel bolts.

6) Remove and plug transaxle cooler pipes. Remove transaxle-to-engine support bracket. Place jack under transaxle and remove remaining engine-to-transaxle bolts. Remove transaxle.

Installation – To install, reverse removal procedure. Apply a thin film of chassis grease on torque converter pilot hub. Adjust T.V. cable. Refill transaxle to proper fluid level. See LUBRICATION in AUTOMATIC TRANSMISSION article.

Removal (3T40 Transaxle – 2.3L VIN D) – **1)** Disconnect negative battery cable. Drain cooling system and remove heater hoses at heater core. Remove intake air duct. Remove cable control cover, throttle and Throttle Valve (T.V.) cable. Remove shift cable and bracket.

2) Remove throttle cable from throttle body. Remove vacuum lines and electrical connections. Remove power steering pump and set aside. Remove fluid fill tube. Support engine.

3) Remove top engine-to-transaxle bolts. Raise and support vehicle. Remove both front tire and wheel assemblies. Remove left inner splash shield. Remove both lower ball joints. See BALL JOINT under REMOVAL & INSTALLATION in appropriate article in SUSPENSION.

4) Remove stabilizer shaft links, front air deflector and left suspension support. Install drive axle seal protectors and remove both drive axles. See FWD AXLE SHAFTS article in DRIVE AXLES.

5) Remove flywheel cover and flywheel-to-torque converter bolts. Remove transaxle cooler pipes. Remove engine-to-transaxle ground wires. Remove cooler pipe and exhaust pipe brace. Remove bolts from engine and transaxle mount. Remove transaxle-to-body mount. Support transaxle. Remove remaining engine-to-transaxle bolts and remove transaxle assembly.

Installation – To install, reverse removal procedure. Apply a thin film of chassis grease on torque converter pilot knob. Adjust T.V. cable. Refill transaxle to proper fluid level. See LUBRICATION in AUTOMATIC TRANSMISSION article.

"W" BODY

Removal (3T40 Transaxle) – **1)** Remove air cleaner assembly. Disconnect negative battery cable. Remove shift cable at transaxle lever and remove cable from mounting bolt. Remove Throttle Valve (T.V.) cable at throttle linkage.

2) Remove throttle cable bracket and brake booster hose (if equipped). Remove both torque struts at engine. Remove left torque strut bracket and transaxle oil cooler lines at transaxle. Plug oil cooler lines.

3) Support engine and raise vehicle. Remove tire and wheel assemblies. Remove caliper/bracket assemblies and rotors. See DISC & DRUM article in BRAKES. Remove both lower engine splash shields.

4) Remove axle assemblies. See FWD AXLE SHAFTS article in DRIVE AXLES. Remove tie rod ends and ball joints. See BALL JOINT under REMOVAL & INSTALLATION in appropriate article in SUSPENSION.

5) Remove rack and pinion heat shield and electrical connector. Remove bolts holding main engine wiring harness to transaxle case. Wire rack and pinion to exhaust and remove rack and pinion bolts from frame. Remove bolts holding power steering lines to frame.

6) Remove engine and transaxle mounts from frame. Support frame with a jack stand at each end and remove frame-to-body mount bolts. Remove frame with both lower control arms and stabilizer shaft attached by working frame downward toward rear of vehicle.

7) Remove flywheel access cover and torque converter bolts. Remove starter bolts and support starter. Remove ground cable at transaxle. Remove transaxle fill tube bolt and mount bracket.

8) Lower vehicle and remove electrical connector and fill tube from transaxle. Lower left side of engine approximately 4". Raise vehicle. Remove fuel line bracket from transaxle. Install transaxle jack. Remove transaxle-to-engine bolts. Remove transaxle from vehicle.

Installation – 1) To install, reverse removal procedure. Install frame insulators and spacers, if removed. Ensure insulators are completely seated against frame.

2) Align frame to body by inserting two 8" long pins in alignment holes on right side of frame. With the aid of a helper, position frame and install (but do not tighten) new body mount bolts. To maintain alignment, tighten right side, then left side body mount bolts. Adjust T.V. and shift cables. Refill transaxle to proper fluid level. See LUBRICATION in AUTOMATIC TRANSMISSION article.

Removal (4T60 & 4T60-E Transaxle) – 1) Remove air cleaner assembly. Remove negative battery cable. Remove shift cable at transaxle lever and remove cable from mounting bracket. Remove Throttle Valve (T.V.) cable at throttle linkage.

2) On 3.1L engine, remove exhaust crossover pipe at left exhaust manifold. Remove EGR tube from crossover pipe. Remove crossover-to-exhaust pipe bolts. Loosen crossover to right exhaust manifold clamp. Swing crossover upward to gain clearance to top 2 bellhousing bolts.

3) On all vehicles, remove 4 upper bellhousing bolts, leaving 2 lower bellhousing bolts attached. Remove Torque Converter Clutch (TCC) electrical connector at transaxle (if equipped). Remove vacuum modulator pipe support nut and disconnect from valve. Remove electrical connection at neutral start switch. Raise and support vehicle.

4) Remove vehicle speed sensor at transaxle. Remove front tire and wheel assemblies. Remove wheelhouse splash shields. Remove power steering cooler lines from frame. Remove power steering rack and pinion heat shield. Remove steering rack from frame. Remove ball joints at steering knuckle. See BALL JOINT under REMOVAL & INSTALLATION in appropriate article in SUSPENSION.

5) Remove transaxle mount upper retaining nuts. Remove engine mount lower retaining nuts. Have an assistant hold frame and remove frame-to-body mount bolts. Remove frame with both lower control arms and stabilizer shaft attached by working frame downward toward rear of vehicle.

6) Remove transaxle oil cooler lines and support bracket. Remove torque converter cover. Remove and support drive axles from transaxle. See FWD AXLE SHAFTS article in DRIVE AXLES. Remove starter. Remove torque converter-to-flywheel bolts.

7) Remove engine-to-transaxle support bracket at transaxle. Support transaxle with jack stand and remove remaining transaxle retaining bolts. Remove transaxle assembly.

Installation – 1) To install, reverse removal procedure. Install frame insulators and spacers if removed. Ensure insulators are completely seated against frame.

2) Align frame to body by inserting two 8" long pins in alignment holes on right side of frame. With the aid of a helper, position frame and install (but do not tighten) new body mount bolts. To maintain alignment, tighten right side, then left side body mount bolts. Adjust T.V. and shift cables. Refill transaxle to proper fluid level. See LUBRICATION in AUTOMATIC TRANSMISSION article.

AUTOMATIC (RWD)

"B", "D", "F" & "Y" BODIES

Removal (4L60 Transmissions) – 1) Disconnect negative battery cable. Remove air cleaner. Drain transmission fluid. Disconnect upper end of T.V. cable at throttle linkage. Remove filler tube from transmission. Raise and support vehicle on a hoist. Index mark and remove drive shaft.

2) On Corvette models, remove complete exhaust system and driveline beam. On Corvette convertible, remove upper and lower body braces. On Camaro and Firebird, remove torque arm from rear suspension. To remove torque arm, remove rear brake hose retaining bracket.

3) Remove both lower shock absorber nuts. Carefully lower rear axle until coil springs can be removed. Remove coil springs. Remove front torque arm bracket and torque arm.

CAUTION: Coil springs must be removed before removing torque arm to avoid rear axle twist and damage to vehicle.

---

4) On all models, remove lower floor reinforcement (if equipped). Disconnect speedometer cable. Remove shifter linkage and disconnect all electrical connectors. Remove flexplate cover. Index mark flywheel to torque converter and remove bolts.

5) Remove catalytic converter support bracket and remove crossmember. Support transmission with transmission jack. Lower transmission slightly and disconnect oil cooler lines. Remove T.V. cable hold-down bolt.

6) Support engine. Remove transmission-to-engine bolts. Pull transmission back enough to install Torque Converter Holder (J-21366). Lower transmission from vehicle.

Installation – 1) To install transmission, reverse removal procedure. Observe index marks made during removal and align marks to original positions. Test torque converter for freedom of rotation.

2) Tighten torque converter-to-flexplate bolts finger tight, then tighten to specification. Adjust shift linkage and T.V. cable. See ADJUSTMENTS in AUTOMATIC TRANSMISSION article. Refill transmission to proper fluid level.

TORQUE SPECIFICATIONS

TORQUE SPECIFICATIONS

Application	Ft. Lbs. (N.m)
"A" Body	
Flywheel-To-Converter Bolts	46 (62)
Frame Mount Bolts	40 (54)
Shift Control Cable Bracket-To-Transaxle Bolts	18 (24)
Transaxle-To-Engine Bolts	55 (75)
Wheel Lug Nuts	100 (136)
"B","D", "F" & "Y" Bodies	
Flywheel-To-Converter Bolts	46 (62)
Torque Arm-To Rear Differential Nut	98 (133)
Transmission-To-Engine Bolts	35 (47)
Transmission-To-Frame Bolts	40 (54)
"C", "E", "H" & "K" Bodies	
Flywheel-To-Converter Bolts	46 (62)
Frame-To-Body Bolts	83 (113)
Shift Control Cable Bracket-To-Transaxle Bolts	18 (24)
Starter Mounting Bolts	32 (43)
Transaxle Brace-To-Engine Assembly Bolts	37 (50)
Transaxle-To-Engine Bolts	55 (75)
Transaxle Mount Bolts	38 (52)
Wheel Lug Nuts	100 (136)
"J" Body	
Cooler Pipes	16 (22)
Flywheel-To-Converter Bolts	46 (62)
Lower Transaxle-To-Engine Bolts	55 (75)
Transaxle Brace Bolts	37 (50)
"L" Body	
Cooler Pipes	16 (22)
Flywheel-To-Converter Bolts	46 (62)
Frame-To-Body Bolts	37 (50)
Transaxle-To-Engine Bolts	55 (75)
"N" Body	
Cooler Pipes	16 (22)
Flywheel-To-Converter Bolts	46 (62)
Starter Bolts	32 (43)
Transaxle-To-Engine Bolts	55 (75)
"W" Body	
Cooler Pipes	16 (22)
Flywheel-To-Converter Bolts	44 (60)
Frame-To-Body Bolts	103 (140)
Transaxle-To-Engine Bolts	55 (75)

NOTE: *Latest Changes and Corrections represents a collection of last minute information and relevant technical service bulletins. Read this section and make notations in appropriate manuals for easy reference later.*

GENERAL MOTORS

COMPUTERIZED ENGINE CONTROLS/ ENGINE PERFORMANCE

1 *The following is a compilation of revised General Motors engine performance mini-schematics and diagnostic procedures.*

1989 2.8L, 5.0L & 5.7L
CODE 24, VEHICLE SPEED SENSOR ("F" BODY)

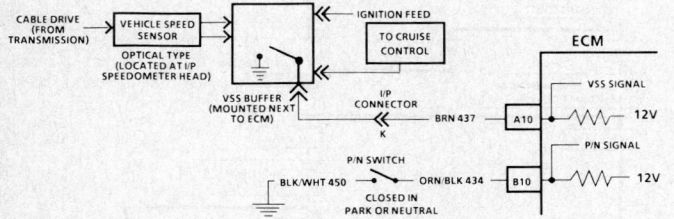

Vehicle Speed Sensor (VSS) generates voltage pulses whenever drive wheels rotate. Pulse rate (frequency) is proportionate to wheel speed. Pulses are transmitted to the ECM through circuit No. 437. The ECM calculates vehicle speed based on pulse rate. During testing procedure, "Scan" tool MPH readout should be close to speedometer reading.

NOTE: Test numbers refer to test numbers on diagnostic chart

1) Code 24 will set if voltage on circuit No. 437 is constant, engine speed is 1400-3600 RPM, TPS is less than 2 percent (closed throttle), a low load condition (high vacuum) exists, transmission is not in Park or Neutral and all conditions have been met for 4 seconds during road load deceleration.

2) Voltage of less than one volt at instrument panel 15-pin connector indicates circuit No. 437 may be shorted to ground. Disconnect circuit No. 437 at VSS buffer. If voltage remains less than 10 volts, circuit No. 437 is open or grounded. If circuit is not grounded or open, ECM connector or ECM is defective.

91G10369   91J10370

DIAGNOSTIC AIDS

"Scan" tester should indicate vehicle speed whenever vehicle is in motion. A faulty or misadjusted Park/Neutral switch can result in a false Code 24. If switch is okay, check for loose or corroded connections. Use "Scan" tester to check for a proper signal while in Drive.

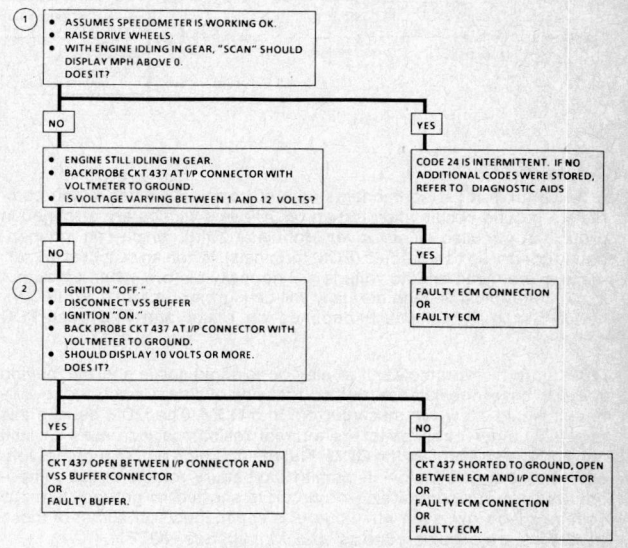

Courtesy of General Motors Corp.

1989 3.3L (VIN N)
CODE 26, QUAD-DRIVER CIRCUIT ("A" BODY)

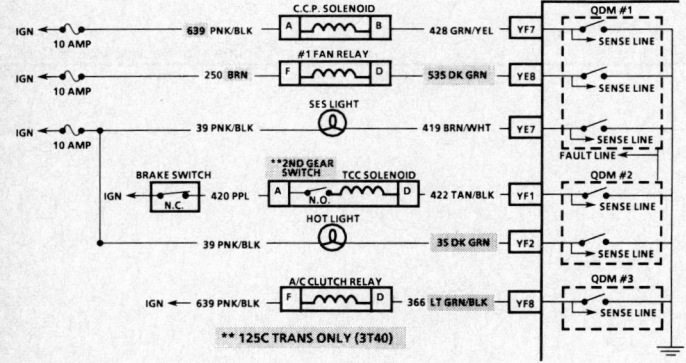

Code 26 self-diagnostic flow chart for 3.3L (VIN N) equipped with 440-T4 transaxle has been revised. Please refer to the following revision for flow chart first step procedure.
- Install "Scan" tool.
- Start engine and let idle.
- Scan Quad Driver Module No. 3.

91C10373   91D10374

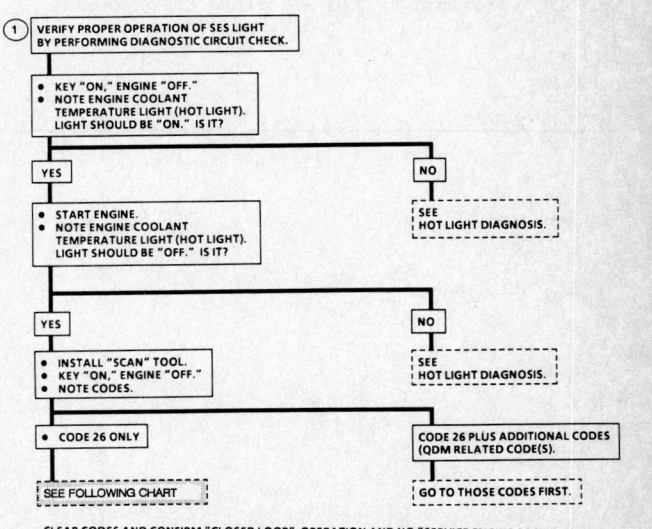

Courtesy of General Motors Corp.

1990 2.3L (VIN A & D)
CODE 26, QUAD-DRIVER CIRCUIT ("N" BODY)

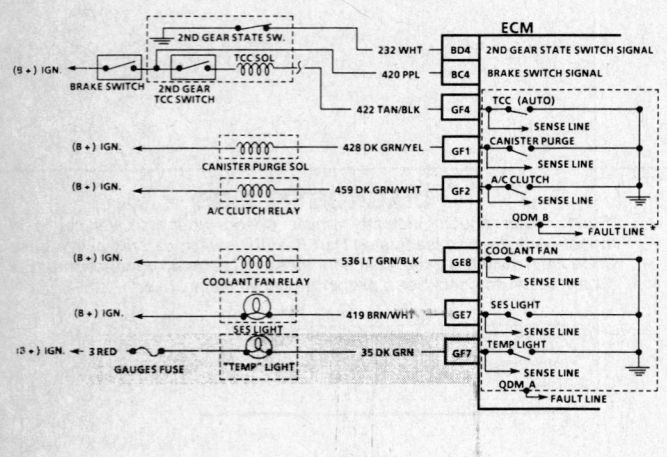

ECM controls most components with electronic switches which complete a ground circuit when turned on. These switches are arranged in groups of 4, called Quad-Driver Modules (QDM), which can independently control up to 4 outputs (ECM terminals). When an output is on, terminal is grounded and its voltage will normally be low. When an output is off, its terminal voltage normally will be high, except for Torque Converter Clutch (TCC), which depends on brake and 2nd gear TCC switches.

QDM's are fault-protected. If a relay or solenoid coil is shorted, having very low or zero resistance, or if control side of circuit is shorted to voltage, it would allow too much current into QDM. The QDM senses this and the output turns off or its internal resistance increases to limit current flow and protect the QDM. The result is high output terminal voltage when it should be low. If circuit from battery voltage or the component is open, or control side of circuit is shorted to ground, terminal voltage will be low, even when output is commanded off. Either of these conditions are considered to be a QDM fault. See NOTE.

Each QDM has a separate fault line to indicate presence of a current fault to ECM's central processor. A "Scan" tool displays the status of each of these fault lines as LOW or HIGH (LOW = okay or HIGH = fault). Because of brake and 2nd gear switches in TCC circuit, Code 26 is set under different conditions for QDM "A" and QDM "B" as follows:

- QDM "A" fault line – High for 20 seconds or more.
- QDM "B" fault line – High for 20 seconds or more AND brake switch signal indicates brake switch is closed and 2nd gear switch indicates transaxle is in 2nd or 3rd gear, OR TCC is commanded on.

NOTE: QDM "B" fault line on automatic transmission vehicles will normally be high when car is stopped. The ECM ignores QDM "B" fault line except under conditions previously stated.

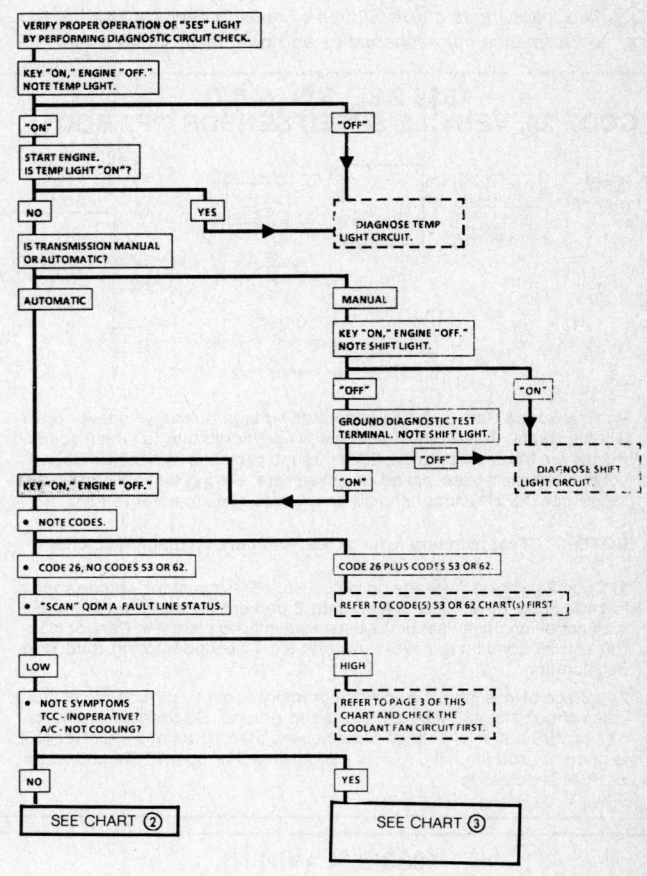

1990 3.3L (VIN N)
CODE 26, QUAD-DRIVER CIRCUIT ("A" BODY)

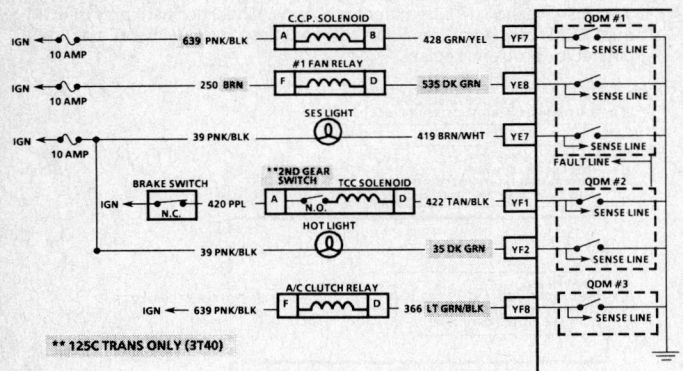

** 125C TRANS ONLY (3T40)

Quad-Driver Modules (QDM) are used to control components. When ECM commands a component on, QDM closes the switch completing circuit to ground. Each QDM has a sense line and a fault line. When a component is commanded on, voltage potential on sense line is low. When component is commanded off, voltage potential on sense line is high.

Code 26 will set when ECM is commanding component on and voltage potential on sense line is high or if the component is commanded off and voltage potential is low. QDM No. 3 will not set a Code 26. On vehicles with 3T40 (125C) transaxle, QDM status on "Scan" tool will read high until 2nd gear switch is closed. To simulate driving in 2nd gear and change QDM status to low, disconnect Torque Converter Clutch (TCC) connector and jumper terminals "A" and "D" together using a test light.

NOTE: Test numbers refer to test numbers on diagnostic chart.

1) The ECM does not know which controlled circuit caused the Code 26, so this chart will go through each of the circuits to determine which is at fault. This test checks the SERVICE ENGINE SOON (SES) light driver and SERVICE ENGINE SOON light circuit.

QDM Symptoms:
• TCC inoperative (Code 39).
• HOT light on all the time or off during bulb check.
• Coolant fan on low speed all the time or won't come on at all.
• Poor driveability due to 100 percent canister purge.

2) This test will determine which circuit is out of specification. All circuits EXCEPT YE7, YF2, SES light and HOT light should be battery voltage with ignition on, engine off. On models with 3T40 (125C) transaxle, circuit YF1 should be near zero volts. Diagnostic test terminal is not grounded.

3) This test will determine if problem is circuit or component. As factory installed ECM is protected with an internal fuse, it is highly unlikely that ECM needs to be replaced.

HOT LIGHT DIAGNOSIS

NOTE: These checks apply when vehicle is not overheating. Verify proper operation of cooling system prior to diagnosing hot light.

Hot light is powered by the 10-amp GAGES fuse. Light will turn on when ECM provides a ground for the circuit. If circuit grounds between light and ECM, light will illuminate any time the ignition is turned on.
1) Turn ignition on with engine off (bulb test position). If hot light illuminates, go to step 3). If hot light does not illuminate, check the following:
• 10-amp GAGES fuse.
• Faulty instrument cluster bulb.
• Open circuit between fuse and hot light.

2) Backprobe terminal YF2 at ECM with a test light to battery voltage. Turn ignition on. If test light does not illuminate, ECM terminal connection is bad or ECM is faulty. If test light illuminates, turn ignition off. Disconnect ECM connectors. Jumper terminal YF2 to ground. Turn ignition on. If hot light does not illuminate, check for open circuit between hot light and ECM. If light does not illuminate and all circuits are intact and power is available to light, instrument cluster must be replaced.
3) Start engine. If test light goes off, no problem is evident. See DIAGNOSTIC AIDS. If test light is on, turn ignition off. Disconnect ECM connector. Probe ECM harness terminal YF2 with a test light to battery voltage. If light is off, replace ECM. If light is on, repair short to ground in circuit No. 35. If no short is present, replace instrument cluster.

DIAGNOSTIC AIDS

Monitor voltage at each terminal while moving related harness connectors, including ECM harness. If failure is induced, voltage will change. This may help locate intermittent problems. Check for bent pins at ECM and ECM connector terminals. If code reoccurs with no apparent connector problem, replace ECM.

CIRCUIT NOT ISOLATED BY PRIOR STEPS
(VOLTAGE TEST)

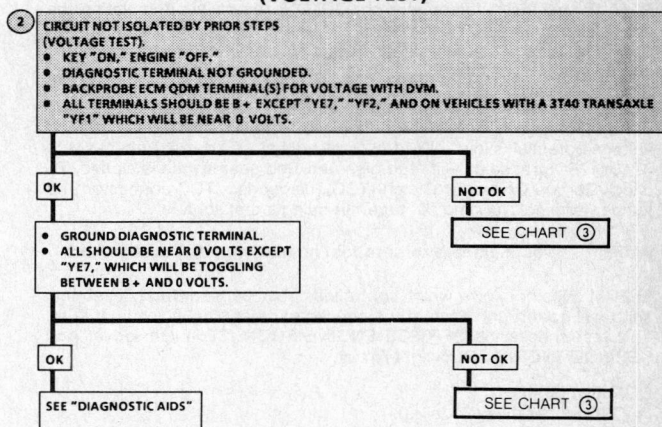

CIRCUIT ISOLATED FROM PRIOR CHARTS

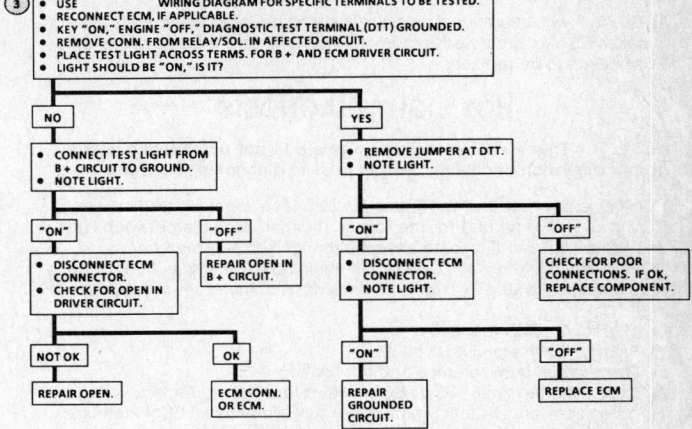

CLEAR CODES AND CONFIRM "CLOSED LOOP" OPERATION AND NO "SERVICE ENGINE SOON" LIGHT

1990 3.3L (VIN N)
CODE 26, QUAD-DRIVER CIRCUIT ("N" BODY)

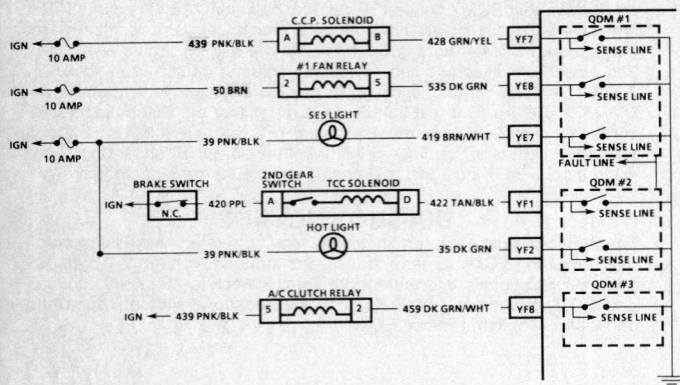

Quad-Driver Modules (QDM) are used to control components. When ECM commands a component on, QDM closes switch completing the circuit to ground. Each QDM has a sense and a fault line. When a component is commanded on, voltage potential on sense line is low. When component is commanded off, voltage potential on sense line is high.

Code 26 will set when ECM is commanding component on and voltage potential on sense line is high or if the component is commanded off and voltage potential is low. QDM No. 3 will not set a Code 26. Vehicles with 3T40 (125C) transaxle will read high until 2nd gear switch is closed. To check Torque Converter Clutch (TCC), disconnect TCC connector and jumper terminals "A" and "D" together using a test light.

NOTE: Test numbers refer to test numbers on diagnostic chart.

1) ECM does not know which controlled circuit caused Code 26, so this chart will go through each of the circuits to determine which is at fault. This test checks the SERVICE ENGINE SOON (SES) light driver and SERVICE ENGINE SOON light circuit.

QDM Symptoms:
- TCC inoperative (Code 39).
- HOT light on all the time or off during bulb check.
- Coolant fan on low speed all the time or won't come on at all.
- Poor driveability due to 100 percent canister purge.

2) This test will determine which circuit is out of specification. All circuits EXCEPT YE7, YF1, YF2, SES light and HOT light should be battery voltage with ignition on, engine off. Diagnostic test terminal is not grounded.

3) This test will determine if problem is circuit or component. As factory-installed ECM is protected with an internal fuse, it is highly unlikely that ECM needs to be replaced.

HOT LIGHT DIAGNOSIS

NOTE: These checks assume vehicle is not overheating. Verify proper operation of cooling system prior to diagnosing hot light.

Hot light is powered by the 10-amp GAGES fuse. Light will turn on when ECM provides a ground for the circuit. If circuit grounds between light and ECM, light will illuminate any time the ignition is turned on.
1) Turn ignition on with engine off (bulb test position). If hot light illuminates, go to step **3)**. If hot light does not illuminate, check the following:
- 10-amp GAGES fuse.
- Faulty instrument cluster bulb.
- Open circuit between fuse and hot light.

2) Backprobe terminal YF2 at ECM with a test light to battery voltage. Turn ignition on. If test light does not illuminate, ECM terminal connection is bad or ECM is faulty. If test light illuminates, turn ignition off. Disconnect ECM connectors. Jumper terminal YF2 to ground. Turn ignition on. If hot light does not illuminate, check for open circuit between hot light and ECM. If light does not illuminate, all circuits are intact and power is available to light, instrument cluster must be replaced.
3) Start engine. If test light goes off, no problem is evident. See DIAGNOSTIC AIDS. If test light is on, turn ignition off. Disconnect ECM connector. Probe ECM harness terminal YF2 with a test light to battery voltage. If light is off, replace ECM. If light is on, repair short to ground in circuit No. 35. If no short is present, replace instrument cluster.

DIAGNOSTIC AIDS

Monitor voltage at each terminal while moving related harness connectors, including ECM harness. If failure is induced, voltage will change. This may help locate intermittent problems. Check for bent pins at ECM and ECM connector terminals. If code reoccurs with no apparent connector problem, replace ECM.

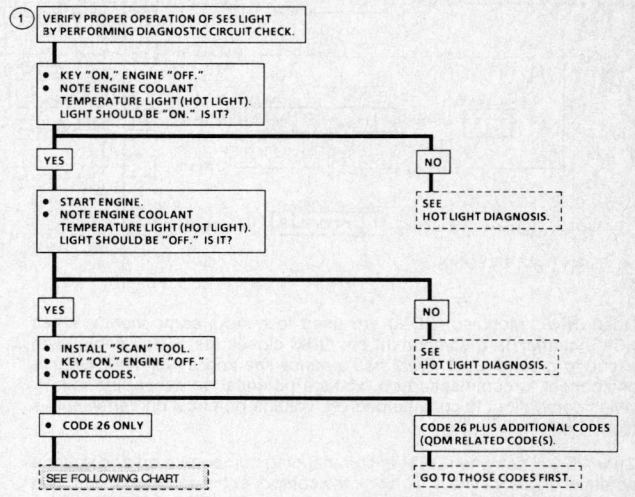

CIRCUIT NOT ISOLATED BY PRIOR STEPS
(VOLTAGE TEST)

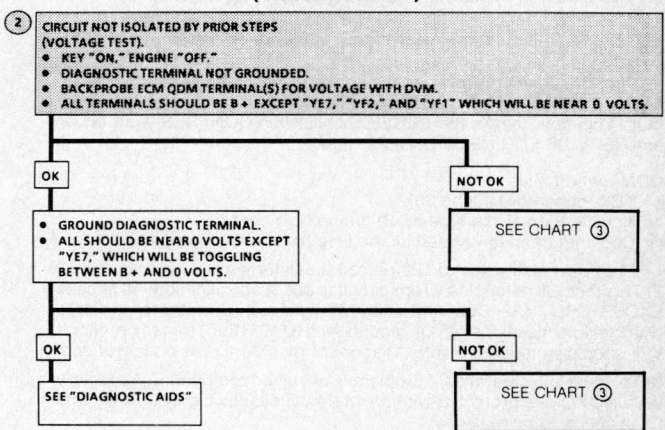

CIRCUIT ISOLATED FROM PRIOR CHARTS

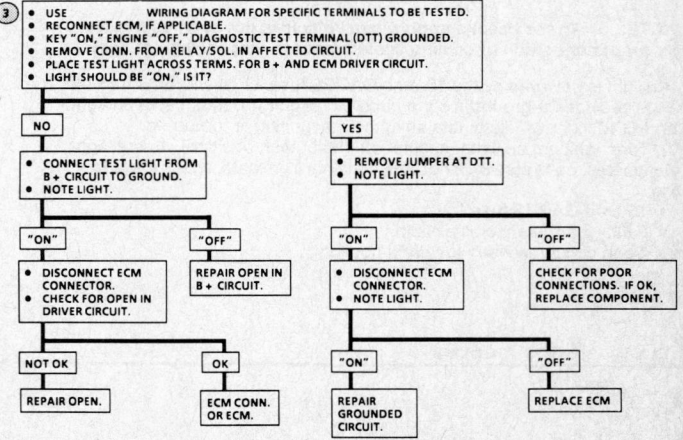

CLEAR CODES AND CONFIRM "CLOSED LOOP" OPERATION AND NO "SERVICE ENGINE SOON" LIGHT

1990 3.1L (VIN T)
CODE 32, EGR SYSTEM FAILURE ("W" BODY)

Mini-schematic for 3.1L (W body) has been revised. See the new mini-schematic for correct terminal and wire identification.

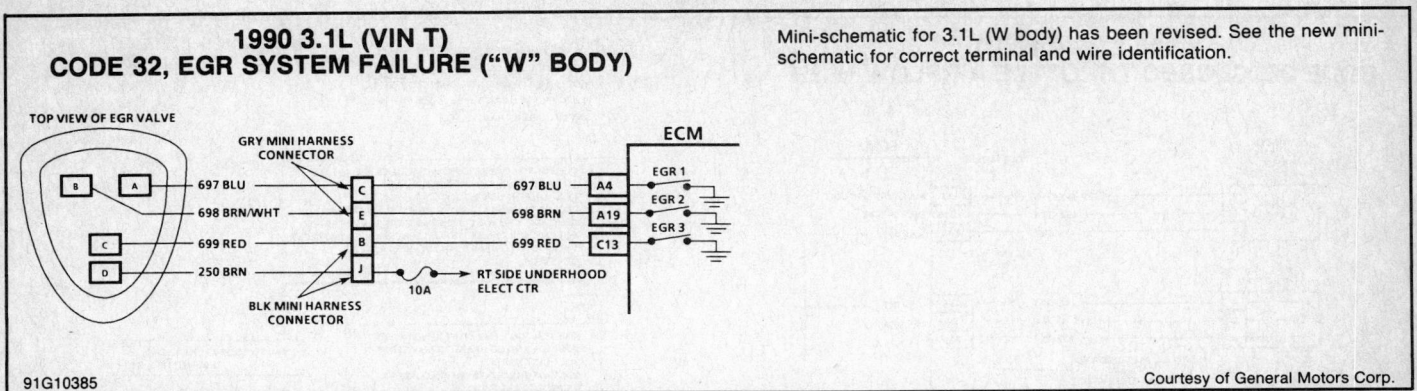

91G10385

Courtesy of General Motors Corp.

1990 5.0L & 5.7L TBI (VIN 7)
CODE 32, EGR CIRCUIT FAILURE ("D" BODY)

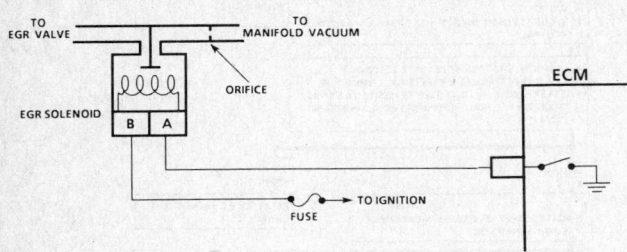

ECM operates a normally closed solenoid to regulate vacuum to EGR valve. When ECM provides a path to ground for the EGR solenoid winding, solenoid opens, allowing vacuum to pass through to EGR valve. ECM monitors EGR effectiveness by shutting off vacuum to EGR valve during a steady cruise above 50 MPH, and monitoring the change in MAP sensor vacuum signal. If vacuum signal change is not within a pre-calibrated window, Code 32 will be set.

NOTE: Test numbers refer to test numbers on diagnostic chart.

1) Plugged Intake Passage – Shut off engine and remove EGR valve. Plug exhaust side port with a shop rag or suitable plug. Attempt to start engine. If engine runs at a very high idle (up to 3000 RPM is possible) or if engine starts and stalls, EGR intake passage is not plugged. If vehicle starts and idles normally, intake-side passage is plugged.

Plugged Exhaust Passage – With EGR valve removed, plug intake manifold side passage with a suitable plug. Start engine and listen for exhaust noise. If no exhaust gas escapes from open EGR port, exhaust passage is plugged.

2) By grounding ALDL test terminal, EGR solenoid should energize and allow vacuum to be applied to gauge. Vacuum at gauge may or may not slowly bleed off; however, what is important is that gauge is able to read amount of vacuum applied.

3) When ALDL test terminal is ungrounded, gauge vacuum should bleed off through a vent in the solenoid. Vacuum pump gauge vacuum may or may not bleed off but this does not indicate a problem.

4) This test determines if electrical control part of system is at fault or if the connector or solenoid is at fault.

5) EGR valves used with this engine are stamped "P" for positive backpressure or an "N" for negative backpressure. "F" body uses negative backpressure only.

6) Remaining tests check the ability of the EGR valve to interact with the exhaust system. This system uses a negative backpressure EGR valve which should hold vacuum with the engine off.

7) When engine is started, exhaust backpressure at base of EGR valve should open the valve's internal bleed. This will vent the applied vacuum, allowing valve to seat.

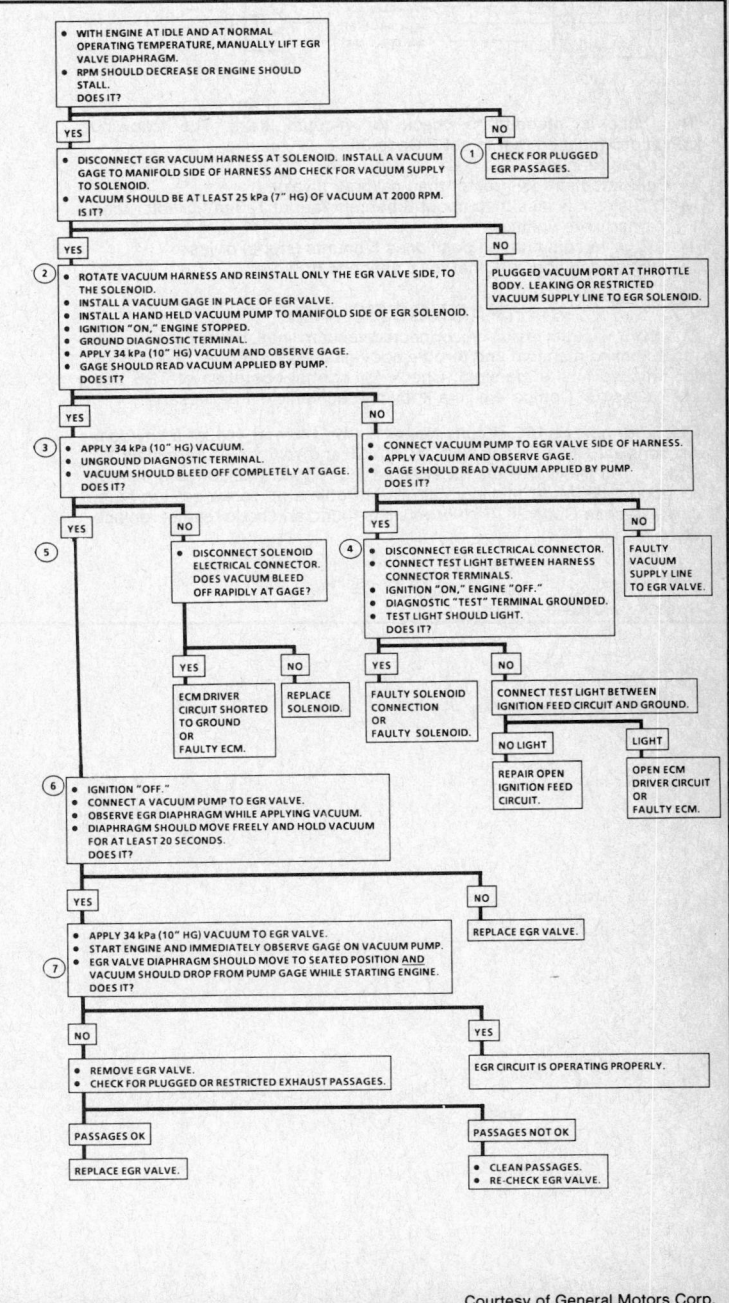

91H10386   91I10387   91J10388

Courtesy of General Motors Corp.

LATEST CHANGES & CORRECTIONS
For 1991 & Earlier Models (Cont.)

1988 2.3L (VIN D)
CODE 36, CLOSED THROTTLE AIRFLOW HIGH

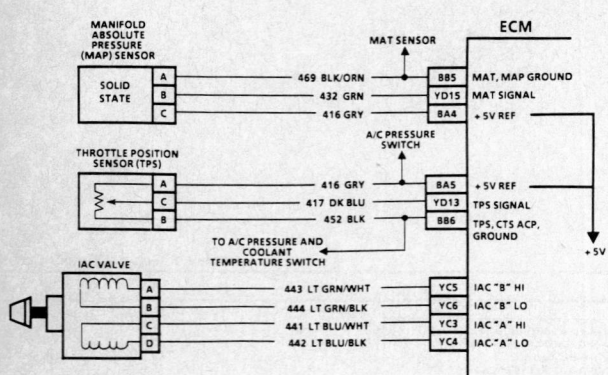

This code is intended to check for vacuum leaks. The following conditions must be met to set a Code 36:

- Engine running
- Calculated airflow greater than calibrated value
- TPS signal is less than about 3 percent (about 120 mV greater than learned zero voltage)
- IAC valve commanded position is 5 counts (steps) or less
- Above conditions are met for 5 seconds or more

DIAGNOSTIC AIDS

Check for vacuum leaks, disconnected vacuum lines, brittle hoses, cuts, etc. Examine manifold and throttle body gaskets for proper seal. Check for cracked intake manifold. Check for normal operation of TPS and MAP sensors. Compare with a known good vehicle if necessary.

Check for open in IAC circuits No. 441, 442, 443 and 444, or faulty connections at ECM terminals YC3, YC4, YC5 and YC6, or IAC terminals "A" and "C". An IAC valve that is stopped in an open position and cannot respond to ECM, or minimum air rate throttle stop screw set too high, can also set a Code 36. If no problem is found and code resets, replace ECM.

NOTE: *A VACUUM LEAK IS THE MOST PROBABLE CAUSE OF CODE 36. CHECK THOROUGHLY FOR LEAKS AT VACUUM CONNECTOR BLOCK, THROTTLE BODY AND INTAKE MANIFOLD BEFORE USING CHART.*

- DISREGARD CODE 36 IF SET WITH CODES 22 OR 33. REFER TO THOSE CODE CHARTS FIRST.
- IGNITION "ON", ENG. "OFF".
- "SCAN" TPS WHILE DEPRESSING ACCELERATOR PEDAL GRADUALLY TO WIDE OPEN THROTTLE (WOT). TPS VOLTAGE (OR PERCENT) SHOULD INCREASE FROM BELOW 1 VOLT (0%) TO NEAR 5 VOLTS (100%) AT WOT. DOES IT?

YES / **NO**

NO → REFER TO CODE 22 CHART OR "DIAGNOSTIC AIDS".

- IGNITION "ON", ENG. "OFF", "SCAN" MAP VOLTAGE AND COMPARE TO MAP SENSOR VOLTAGE CHART VOLTAGE SHOULD BE WITHIN CORRECT RANGE FOR ALTITUDE. IS IT?

YES / **NO**

NO → REFER TO CODE 34 CHART OR DIAGNOSTIC AIDS AND MAP SENSOR CHECK CHART C-1D

- START ENGINE.
- ENGINE AT NORMAL OPERATING TEMPERATURE.
- A/C "OFF"
- RECORD CLOSED THROTTLE IDLE RPM IN "PARK OR NEUTRAL".

- IGNITION "OFF" FOR AT LEAST 10 SECONDS.
- DISCONNECT IAC VALVE ELECTRICAL CONNECTOR.
- START ENGINE. NOTE CLOSED THROTTLE IDLE RPM IN "PARK OR NEUTRAL". IDLE RPM SHOULD INCREASE. DOES IT?

YES / **NO**

NO → REFER TO IAC VALVE CHECK, CHART C-2C.

- THROTTLE PLATE STOP SCREW ADJUSTMENT CHECK. IS ADJUSTMENT OK?

YES / **NO**

YES → CODE 36 IS INTERMITTENT. REFER TO "DIAGNOSTIC AIDS"

NO → ADJUST THROTTLE STOP SCREW

CLEAR CODES AND CONFIRM "CLOSED LOOP" OPERATION AND NO "SERVICE ENGINE SOON" LIGHT.

91A10389 91D10390

Courtesy of General Motors Corp.

1988-90 3.8L (VIN C) EXCEPT ECM/BCM MODELS CODE 41, CAM SENSOR CIRCUIT

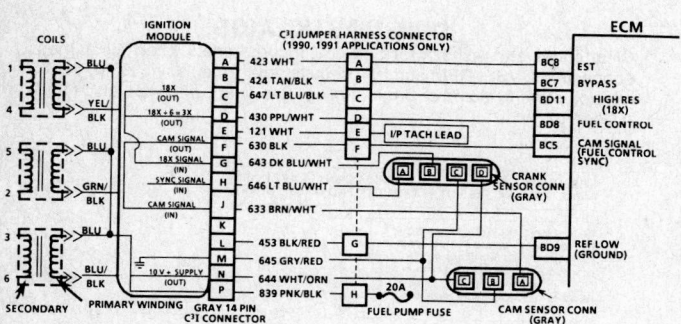

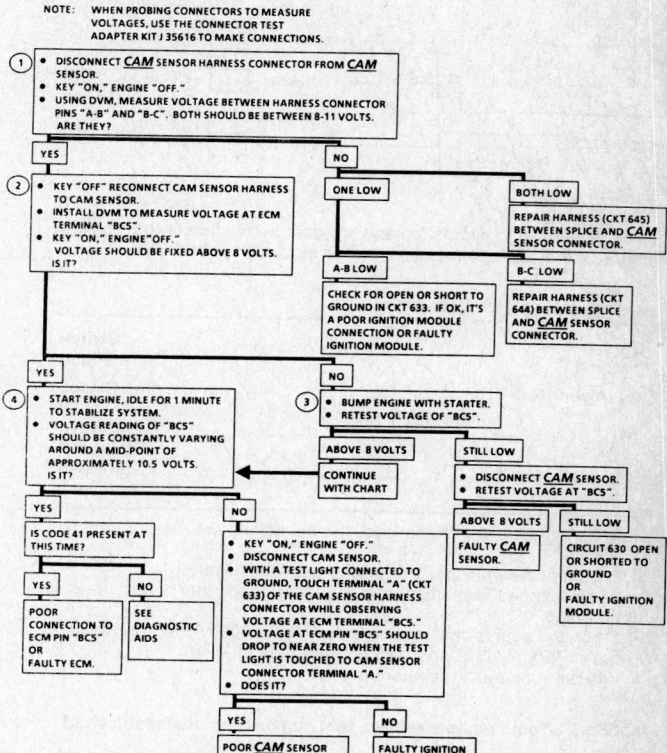

Simultaneous fuel injection is used during start-up. When 400 RPM is obtained and a cam signal has been received by ECM from C³I module, fuel injection switches to sequential injection mode. This is accomplished by use of a cam interrupter magnet and cam sensor Hall Effect switch.

The cam sensor sends a signal to the ignition module when cylinder No. 1 is 25 degrees ATDC on compression stroke. This signal is used to start sequential fuel injection with the proper cylinder. If cam signal to ECM is lost, fuel delivery will switch back to simultaneous mode of operation. The engine will continue to run and will restart after shutdown.

Code 41 is set when the following conditions are met:
* Engine is running
* Cam sensor signal is not received by ECM for last 2 seconds

NOTE: Test numbers refer to test numbers on diagnostic chart.

1) This step verifies operation of circuits No. 633, 644 and 645.
2) This step verifies the integrity of circuit No. 630 from ignition module to ECM.
3) If camshaft gear magnet is interfacing with cam sensor, voltage reading will be zero. Bumping engine eliminates condition.
4) If voltage reading at ECM terminal BC5 is constantly varying and connection to ECM is good, ECM is faulty.

DIAGNOSTIC AIDS
An intermittent may be caused by a poor connection, rubbed-through wire insulation or a wire broken inside the insulation. Check for:

* **Poor Connection or Damaged Harness** – Inspect harness connectors for backed-out terminal BC5, improper mating, broken locks, improperly formed or damaged terminals, poor terminal-to-wire connection and damaged harness.
* **Intermittent Test** – If connections and harness check okay, monitor a digital voltmeter connected from ECM terminal BC5 to ground while moving related connectors and wiring harness. If the failure is induced, voltage reading will change. This may help to isolate the location of the malfunction.

91E10391   91F10392

Courtesy of General Motors Corp.

1990 2.3L (VIN A & D)
CODE 62, GEAR SWITCH ERROR
("N" & "W" BODIES)

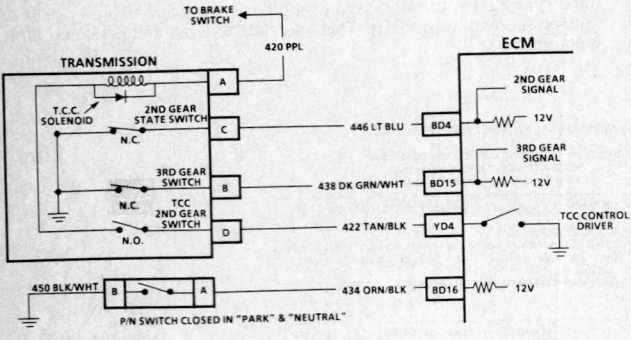

Code 62 is used to check 2nd and 3rd gear switch inputs to ECM. See INPUT SIGNALS table for transmission input signals to ECM.

INPUT SIGNALS

Gear Position	Switch Position
1st (Also P/N & R)	2nd Closed
	3rd Closed
2nd	2nd Open
	3rd Closed
3rd	2nd Open
	3rd Open

Code 62 will set if any of the following conditions are met for about 17 seconds:

- In Park or Neutral, and 2nd or 3rd gear is indicated.
- Vehicle speed less than about 5 MPH and 2nd or 3rd gear is indicated.
- 1st or 2nd gear is indicated, less than about 3000 RPM, transmission not in Park/Neutral, and VSS greater than 50 MPH.
- Vehicle at operating temperature.

NOTE: Test numbers refer to test numbers on diagnostic chart.

1) This step checks for an open or grounded circuit between transmission connector and ECM. Since ECM terminals are normally high, battery voltage should be at both terminals with connector removed.

2) Digital voltmeter reading should be near battery voltage because 2nd and 3rd gear switches should provide continuity to ground.

3) This step checks to see if transmission switches function normally. In 3rd gear both switches should have changed from their original 1st gear state.

DIAGNOSTIC AIDS

Clear codes and recheck for Code 62. If code resets, check all harness connections, VSS, RPM and P/N circuits prior to replacing ECM. Transmission starting in 2nd or 3rd or a sticky 2nd gear switch can also cause a Code 62.

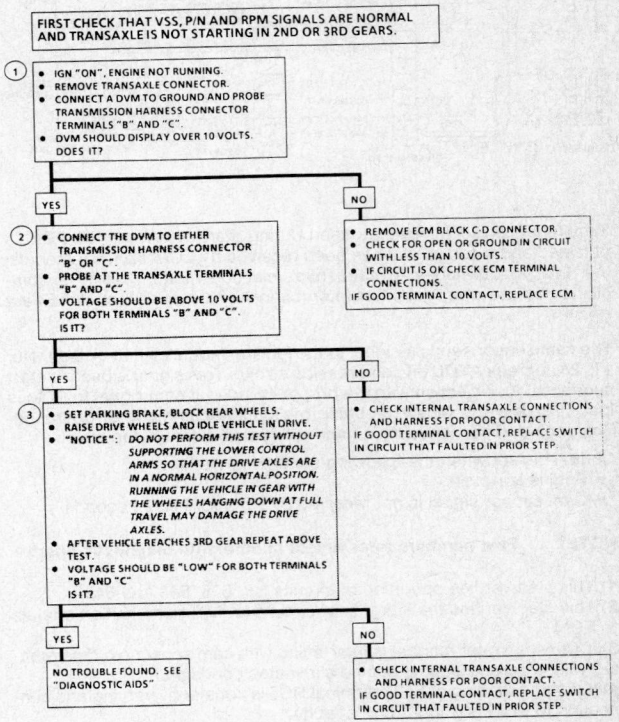

Courtesy of General Motors Corp.

1990 REATTA & RIVIERA 3.8L
CODE B333, LOSS OF SUPPLEMENTAL
INFLATABLE RESTRAINT (SIR) DATA

Code B333 chart for Reatta and Riviera models has been revised. See new flow chart for revised diagnostic procedure.

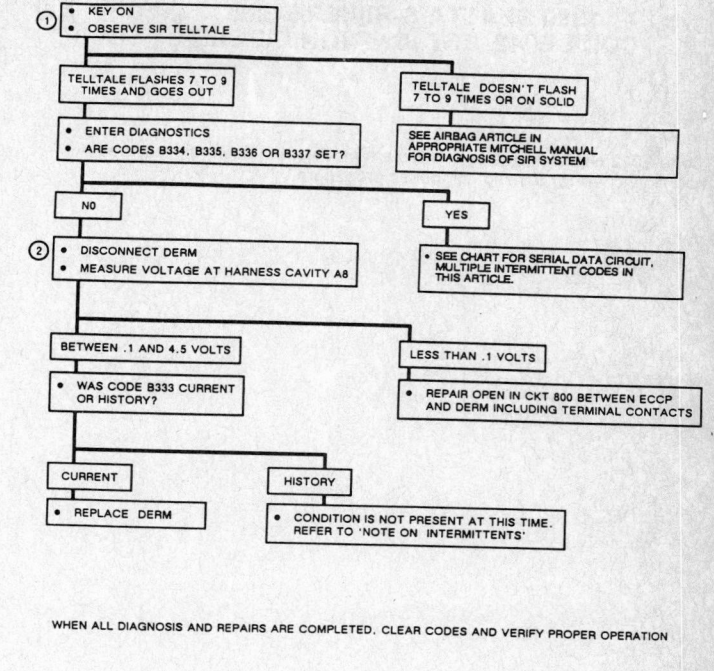

① • KEY ON
   • OBSERVE SIR TELLTALE

TELLTALE FLASHES 7 TO 9 TIMES AND GOES OUT

TELLTALE DOESN'T FLASH 7 TO 9 TIMES OR ON SOLID

• ENTER DIAGNOSTICS
• ARE CODES B334, B335, B336 OR B337 SET?

SEE AIRBAG ARTICLE IN APPROPRIATE MITCHELL MANUAL FOR DIAGNOSIS OF SIR SYSTEM

NO

YES

② • DISCONNECT DERM
   • MEASURE VOLTAGE AT HARNESS CAVITY A8

• SEE CHART FOR SERIAL DATA CIRCUIT, MULTIPLE INTERMITTENT CODES IN THIS ARTICLE.

BETWEEN .1 AND 4.5 VOLTS
• WAS CODE B333 CURRENT OR HISTORY?

LESS THAN .1 VOLTS
• REPAIR OPEN IN CKT 800 BETWEEN ECCP AND DERM INCLUDING TERMINAL CONTACTS

CURRENT
• REPLACE DERM

HISTORY
• CONDITION IS NOT PRESENT AT THIS TIME. REFER TO 'NOTE ON INTERMITTENTS'

WHEN ALL DIAGNOSIS AND REPAIRS ARE COMPLETED, CLEAR CODES AND VERIFY PROPER OPERATION

91I10395

Courtesy of General Motors Corp.

1989 3.8L ECM/BCM
CODE C553, CRT KEEP ALIVE
MEMORY ERROR (TORONADO)

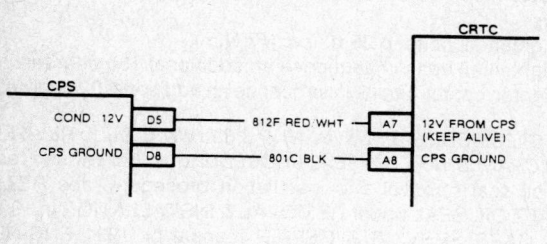

CRTC

CPS

COND 12V | D5 — 812F RED/WHT — A7 | 12V FROM CPS (KEEP ALIVE)

CPS GROUND | D8 — 801C BLK — A8 | CPS GROUND

DO NOT ATTEMPT TO DIAGNOSE THIS CODE UNLESS OWNER COMPLAINT IS OF LOSS OF CRT DISPLAY

• KEY OFF, BACKPROBE CRT CONTROLLER TERMINALS A7 AND A8. NOTE VOLTAGE AT KEY OFF, KEY ON, DURING CRANK, AND WITH ENGINE RUNNING.

REMAINS ABOVE 8 VOLTS AT ALL TIMES

ALWAYS BELOW 8 VOLTS

BELOW 8 VOLTS AT TIMES

• CHECK TERMINAL CONTACT FOR INTERMITTENTS

• CHECK FOR OPEN IN CKT 801
• CHECK FOR OPEN OR SHORT TO GROUND IN CKT 812

• REPAIR CHARGING OR STARTING SYSTEM FOR LOW VOLTAGE CONDITION

WHEN ALL DIAGNOSIS AND REPAIRS ARE COMPLETED, CLEAR CODES AND VERIFY OPERATION

Code C553 does not necessarily indicate a fault, but is a normal occurrence anytime battery power to CRTC has been interrupted. This code could set if system voltage drops below 8 volts at CRTC terminal A7. Possible causes for this are:
• Faulty charging system
• Faulty starting system
• Extreme cold weather
• Jump starting vehicle

91A10397   91B10398

Courtesy of General Motors Corp.

1990 REATTA & RIVIERA 3.8L
CODE E042, EST IGNITION CIRCUIT

Code E042 chart for Reatta and Riviera models has been revised. See new flow chart for revised diagnostic procedure.

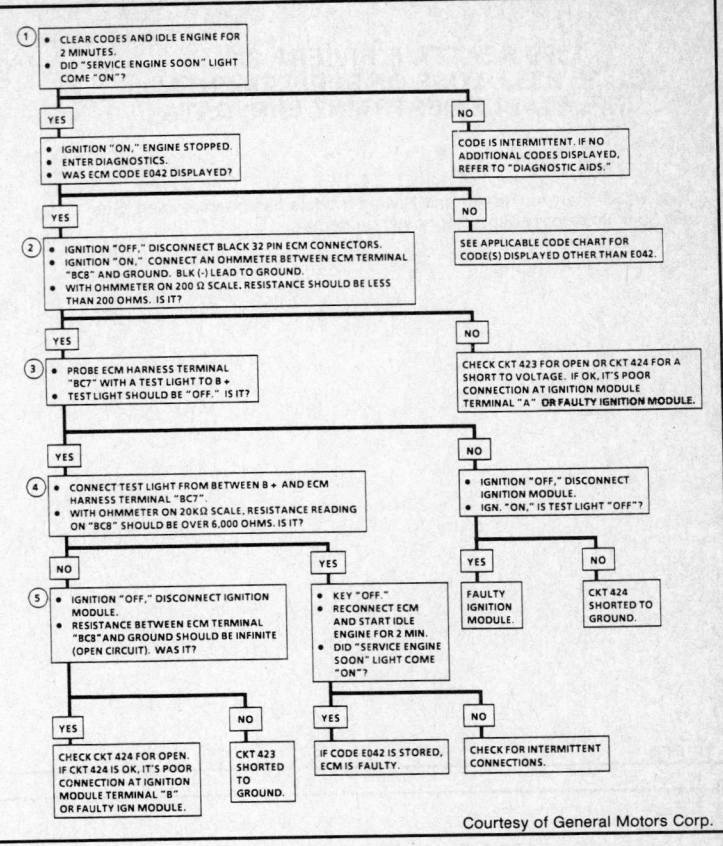

① • CLEAR CODES AND IDLE ENGINE FOR 2 MINUTES.
• DID "SERVICE ENGINE SOON" LIGHT COME "ON"?

YES → • IGNITION "ON," ENGINE STOPPED.
• ENTER DIAGNOSTICS.
• WAS ECM CODE E042 DISPLAYED?

NO → CODE IS INTERMITTENT. IF NO ADDITIONAL CODES DISPLAYED, REFER TO "DIAGNOSTIC AIDS."

② • IGNITION "OFF," DISCONNECT BLACK 32 PIN ECM CONNECTORS.
• IGNITION "ON," CONNECT AN OHMMETER BETWEEN ECM TERMINAL "BC8" AND GROUND. BLK (-) LEAD TO GROUND.
• WITH OHMMETER ON 200 Ω SCALE, RESISTANCE SHOULD BE LESS THAN 200 OHMS. IS IT?

NO → SEE APPLICABLE CODE CHART FOR CODE(S) DISPLAYED OTHER THAN E042.

③ • PROBE ECM HARNESS TERMINAL "BC7" WITH A TEST LIGHT TO B +
• TEST LIGHT SHOULD BE "OFF." IS IT?

NO → CHECK CKT 423 FOR OPEN OR CKT 424 FOR A SHORT TO VOLTAGE. IF OK, IT'S POOR CONNECTION AT IGNITION MODULE TERMINAL "A" OR FAULTY IGNITION MODULE.

④ • CONNECT TEST LIGHT FROM BETWEEN B + AND ECM HARNESS TERMINAL "BC7".
• WITH OHMMETER ON 20KΩ SCALE, RESISTANCE READING ON "BC8" SHOULD BE OVER 6,000 OHMS. IS IT?

NO → **YES** → • IGNITION "OFF," DISCONNECT IGNITION MODULE.
• IGN. "ON," IS TEST LIGHT "OFF"?

YES → FAULTY IGNITION MODULE.

NO → CKT 424 SHORTED TO GROUND.

⑤ • IGNITION "OFF," DISCONNECT IGNITION MODULE.
• RESISTANCE BETWEEN ECM TERMINAL "BC8" AND GROUND SHOULD BE INFINITE (OPEN CIRCUIT). WAS IT?

• KEY "OFF."
• RECONNECT ECM AND START IDLE ENGINE FOR 2 MIN.
• DID "SERVICE ENGINE SOON" LIGHT COME "ON"?

YES → CHECK CKT 424 FOR OPEN. IF CKT 424 IS OK, IT'S POOR CONNECTION AT IGNITION MODULE TERMINAL "B" OR FAULTY IGN MODULE.

NO → CKT 423 SHORTED TO GROUND.

YES → IF CODE E042 IS STORED, ECM IS FAULTY.

NO → CHECK FOR INTERMITTENT CONNECTIONS.

Courtesy of General Motors Corp.

91J10396

TUNE-UP/ENGINE PERFORMANCE

② *1989-90 3.1L (VIN T): REVISED SPARK PLUG TORQUE –* Please note that spark plug torque specification has been revised to 11 ft. lbs. (15 N.m).
This revision applies to the following publications:
1989 TUNE-UP SERVICE & REPAIR supplement, 1990 ENGINE PERFORMANCE SERVICE & REPAIR manual and 1990 DOMESTIC CARS SERVICE & REPAIR manual.
• 1989 – Page 1-10
• 1990 – Page 1-4

ENGINES

③ *1990 FUEL LINE TORQUE SPECIFICATION –* The following fuel line torque specification is now available for Cutlass Calais with 2.3L "QUAD 4" (VIN A or D), 2.5L (VIN U) and 3.3L (VIN N) Engines. Torque fuel line fittings between front/return hoses and front/return pipes (located at body rail in engine compartment) to 20 ft. lbs. (27 N.m).

④ *1989-90 2.5L (VIN R & U): REVISED ENGINE SPECIFICATION –* Please note on page 7-45 of the 1989 DOMESTIC CARS SERVICE & REPAIR manual and page 5-26 1990 DOMESTIC CARS SERVICE & REPAIR manual and ENGINE, CLUTCH & DRIVE AXLE SERVICE & REPAIR supplement, crankshaft main bearing oil clearance & end play specifications have been revised. See CRANKSHAFT SPECIFICATIONS table for revision.

CRANKSHAFT SPECIFICATIONS

Application	In. (mm)
End Play	
VIN R	.0059-.0100 (.13-.26)
VIN U	.0059-.0110 (.13-.28)
Main Bearing Oil Clearance	.0005-.0022 (.013-.056)

⑤ *1989 BONNEVILLE 3.8L (VIN C): REVISED CYLINDER HEAD TORQUE SPECIFICATION –* Please note that cylinder head torque listed on page 7-56 of the 1989 DOMESTIC CARS SERVICE & REPAIR manual and ENGINE, CLUTCH & DRIVE AXLE SERVICE & REPAIR supplement has been revised. Tightening procedure should be as follows:
Step 1 – Tighten all bolts to 35 ft. lbs. (47 N.m).
Step 2 – Tighten all bolts in sequence an additional 130 degrees.
Step 3 – Tighten center 4 bolts in sequence an additional 30 degrees.

⑥ *1990 OLDSMOBILE 3.3L (VIN N) & 3.8L (VIN C & L): REVISED REAR CRANKSHAFT OIL SEAL PROCEDURE –* For revised rear crankshaft oil seal removal and installation procedure, see REAR CRANKSHAFT OIL SEAL under REMOVAL & INSTALLATION in 1991 DOMESTIC CARS SERVICE & REPAIR manual or 1991 ENGINE, CLUTCH & DRIVE AXLE SERVICE & REPAIR supplement.

⑦ *1990 PONTIAC SUNBIRD, GRAND PRIX & BUICK REGAL 3.1L (VIN T): UPPER INTAKE MANIFOLD (PLENUM) TORQUE SPECIFICATION –* Please note that on page 5-31 of the 1990 DOMESTIC CARS SERVICE & REPAIR manual and ENGINE, CLUTCH & DRIVE AXLE SERVICE & REPAIR supplement upper intake manifold has been revised. Upper intake manifold bolt torque should be 88 INCH lbs. (10 N.m).

⑧ *1990 CUTLASS CIERA & CUTLASS CRUISER 3.3L RIGHT VALVE COVER REMOVAL & INSTALLATION PROCEDURE: –* Please note that on page 5-35 of the 1990 DOMESTIC CARS SERVICE & REPAIR manual, step 1) under ROCKER ARM & PUSH RODS has been revised. Please refer to the following for revised information.
Removal – 1) Disconnect negative battery cable. On 3.3L models, remove serpentine belt. On all models, for left valve cover removal, remove alternator bracket and spark plug wires.

9 ▷ 1990 OLDSMOBILE 3.3L (VIN N) & 3.8L (VIN C & L): NO. 4 (REAR) MAIN BEARING CAP – Please note that on page 5-37 of the 1990 DOMESTIC CARS SERVICE & REPAIR manual and ENGINE, CLUTCH & DRIVE AXLE SERVICE & REPAIR supplement under CRANKSHAFT & MAIN BEARINGS, the following information has been added.

CAUTION: The No. 4 main bearing cap MUST be installed flush with or .010" (.25 mm) forward of rear face of cylinder block. Misalignment of bearing cap toward transaxle may cause interference with flywheel-to-torque converter bolts.

10 ▷ 1985-91 3.0L, 3.3L, & 3.8L (VIN A, B, C, E, L, N & 3) REVISED ENGINE SPECIFICATION – Main and rod bearing clearances have been revised. The following revised bearing clearances should used:

CRANKSHAFT SPECIFICATIONS

Application	In. (mm)
3.0L, 3.3L, & 3.8L (VIN A, B, C, E, L, N & 3)	
Main Bearing Oil Clearance	.0005-.0022 (.013-.056)
Connecting Rod Bearing Clearance	.0008-.0022" (.020-.055 mm)

Please note this change in the following publications: DOMESTIC CARS SERVICE & REPAIR manual and ENGINE, CLUTCH & DRIVE AXLE SERVICE & REPAIR supplement.
- 1985 – Pages 6-201 & 6-210
- 1986 – Pages 6-201 & 6-209
- 1987 – Pages 6-193 & 6-201
- 1988 – Page 6-171
- 1989 – Page 7-61
- 1990 – Page 5-39

11 ▷ 1988 2.3L "QUAD 4" REVISED CYLINDER HEAD TORQUE PROCEDURE – Please note that on page 6-131 of the 1988 DOMESTIC CARS SERVICE & REPAIR manual and ENGINE, CLUTCH & DRIVE AXLE SERVICE & REPAIR supplement, step 3) has been revised. The secondary torque procedure of tightening cylinder head bolts an additional 30 degrees to 50 degrees has been eliminated. Step 3) now reads as follows: 3) To complete installation, reverse removal procedure.

CLUTCHES

12 ▷ 1989-90 FIREBIRD 3.1L, 5.0L & 5.7L: REVISED ENGINE TORQUE SPECIFICATIONS – Please note that bellhousing-to-engine block bolt torque specification has been revised as follows.

ENGINE TORQUE SPECIFICATION

Application	Ft. Lbs. (N.m)
Bellhousing-To-Engine Block Bolt	
3.1L	70 (95)
5.0L & 5.7L	35 (47)

Please note this change in the following publications: 1989-90 DOMESTIC CARS SERVICE & REPAIR manual and ENGINE, CLUTCH & DRIVE AXLE SERVICE & REPAIR supplement.
- 1989 – Page 8-6
- 1990 – Page 6-2

BRAKES

13 ▷ 1989-90 CUTLASS SUPREME, GRAND PRIX & REGAL: REVISED WHEEL SPEED SENSOR PROCEDURE – The front and rear wheel speed sensor removal and installation procedures have been revised as follows:
Removal & Installation (Front) – 1) Raise and support vehicle. Disconnect sensor connector, located near shock tower. Remove sensor and bracket retaining bolt. Remove sensor.
2) To install sensor, reverse removal procedure. Adjust sensor-to-rotor gap to .019-.068" (.48-1.73 mm). Ensure wiring harness is routed to avoid contact with suspension components.
Removal & Installation (Rear) – 1) Rear wheel speed sensor is integral with hub and bearing assembly. To replace sensor, the entire hub and bearing assembly must be replaced. See REAR – "W" BODY in SUSPENSION.
2) Check speed sensors for correct mounting and alignment. Inspect wire harness for correct routing. Ensure connectors are not damaged and have good contact. Check wheel speed sensor air gap for correct measurement. Gap should be .019-.068" (.48-1.73 mm).
Please note this change in the following publications: 1989-90 DOMESTIC CARS SERVICE & REPAIR manual and CHASSIS SERVICE & REPAIR supplement.
- 1989 – Pages 10-42 & 10-43
- 1990 – Page 8-10 & 8-11

14 ▷ 1990 CORVETTE ANTI-LOCK BRAKES – BOSCH 2S: CODE 36 – Please note that on page 8-69 of the 1989 DOMESTIC CARS SERVICE & REPAIR manual and CHASSIS SERVICE & REPAIR supplement, Code 36 has been revised. Components and circuitry diagnosed on Code 36 test procedure apply to the left rear toothed wheel.

15 ▷ 1990 CORVETTE ANTI-LOCK BRAKES – BOSCH 2S: CODE 45 – Please note that step 1) of Code 45 shown on page 8-70 of the 1990 DOMESTIC CARS SERVICE & REPAIR manual and CHASSIS SERVICE & REPAIR supplement has been revised. Please refer to the following for revised information.
1) Measures resistance in left front solenoid valve circuitry.

16 ▷ 1990 CORVETTE ANTI-LOCK BRAKES – BOSCH 2S: CODE 55 – Please note that step 1) of Code 45 shown on page 8-71 of the 1990 DOMESTIC CARS SERVICE & REPAIR manual and CHASSIS SERVICE & REPAIR supplement has been revised. Please refer to the following for revised information.
1) Measures resistance in rear solenoid valve circuitry.

STEERING

17 ▷ 1990 CORVETTE, ELDORADO & SEVILLE TORQUE SPECIFICATION: – Please note that on page 11-29 of the 1990 DOMESTIC CARS SERVICE & REPAIR manual, torque specification for pressure line fitting listed has been revised. Please refer to the following information for revised specification.

TORQUE SPECIFICATION

Application	Ft. Lbs. (N.m)
Pressure Line Fitting	20 (27)

NOTES

NOTES

NOTES

NOTES

NOTES

NOTES

NOTES

COMMENTS AND SUGGESTIONS

Please let us know if you have any comments or recommended changes to this book. Mail this postage-paid card today. We'd like to hear from you!

☐ Domestic Cars ☐ Imported Cars & Trucks ☐ Domestic Light Trucks ☐ Medium & Heavy Duty Trucks
☐ Engine Performance ☐ Electrical ☐ Engine ☐ Chassis ☐ Transmission
☐ Air Conditioning ☐ Electrical Component Locators ☐ Other _____

Section No. _____ Page No. _____ Vehicle Model & Year _____

Comments: _____
_____
_____

Name _____ Company _____
Address _____ City _____ State _____ Zip _____
Phone ( ) _____ Date _____ THANK YOU

ADD 91

COMMENTS AND SUGGESTIONS

Please let us know if you have any comments or recommended changes to this book. Mail this postage-paid card today. We'd like to hear from you!

☐ Domestic Cars ☐ Imported Cars & Trucks ☐ Domestic Light Trucks ☐ Medium & Heavy Duty Trucks
☐ Engine Performance ☐ Electrical ☐ Engine ☐ Chassis ☐ Transmission
☐ Air Conditioning ☐ Electrical Component Locators ☐ Other _____

Section No. _____ Page No. _____ Vehicle Model & Year _____

Comments: _____
_____
_____

Name _____ Company _____
Address _____ City _____ State _____ Zip _____
Phone ( ) _____ Date _____ THANK YOU

ADD 91

COMMENTS AND SUGGESTIONS

Please let us know if you have any comments or recommended changes to this book. Mail this postage-paid card today. We'd like to hear from you!

☐ Domestic Cars ☐ Imported Cars & Trucks ☐ Domestic Light Trucks ☐ Medium & Heavy Duty Trucks
☐ Engine Performance ☐ Electrical ☐ Engine ☐ Chassis ☐ Transmission
☐ Air Conditioning ☐ Electrical Component Locators ☐ Other _____

Section No. _____ Page No. _____ Vehicle Model & Year _____

Comments: _____
_____
_____

Name _____ Company _____
Address _____ City _____ State _____ Zip _____
Phone ( ) _____ Date _____ THANK YOU

ADD 91

Be sure to fill out this form completely.

BUSINESS REPLY MAIL

FIRST CLASS   PERMIT NO. 3701   SAN DIEGO, CA

POSTAGE WILL BE PAID BY ADDRESSEE

MITCHELL INTERNATIONAL
P.O. Box 26260
San Diego, California 92196-9984

BUSINESS REPLY MAIL

FIRST CLASS   PERMIT NO. 3701   SAN DIEGO, CA

POSTAGE WILL BE PAID BY ADDRESSEE

MITCHELL INTERNATIONAL
P.O. Box 26260
San Diego, California 92196-9984

BUSINESS REPLY MAIL

FIRST CLASS   PERMIT NO. 3701   SAN DIEGO, CA

POSTAGE WILL BE PAID BY ADDRESSEE

MITCHELL INTERNATIONAL
P.O. Box 26260
San Diego, California 92196-9984

MITCHELL'S DRIVEABILITY SEMINAR PROGRAM

Mitchell's Driveability Seminars teach technicians how to quickly diagnose and repair new import and domestic vehicles with their many computer-controlled operations. These advanced technical updates for automotive professionals will increase your knowledge, sharpen your skills, and teach you new techniques that can help you repair computerized vehicles quickly and correctly.

All Mitchell Driveability Seminars are highly concentrated sessions that tackle real-world diagnostic situations. Classes include:

- Both conventional and distributorless electronic ignition systems
- Feedback Carburetors
- Electronic Fuel Injection Systems
- On-Board Computer Diagnosis
- Using the DVOM and Scan Tool For Diagnostics

Six separate Mitchell Technical Information Seminars are offered:

Asian I
EFI Driveability
Diagnosis Seminar

Shows how to diagnose driveability problems related to Nissan, Toyota, and Mitsubishi ignition and fuel injection systems, plus how to enter and use computer diagnostics.

Asian II
EFI Driveability
Diagnosis Seminar

Shows how to diagnose driveability problems related to Acura, Honda, and Mazda ignition and fuel injection systems, plus how to enter and use computer diagnostics.

Chrysler
FBC/EFI Seminar

Answers your questions on computer-controlled fuel injected or carbureted engines. Includes information on how to diagnose the Chrysler SMEC system.

Ford
MCU/EEC Seminar

Learn to diagnose and repair both feedback carbureted and fuel injected engines, including vehicles equipped with distributorless ignition systems.

GM CCC/TBI Seminar

Gain the knowledge and confidence needed to work on computer-controlled carburetor or throttle body injected engines. An excellent program for technicians who are beginning to learn how to diagnose GM computer systems.

GM DIS/PFI Seminar

Provides answers to your toughest GM problems related to distributorless ignition systems or port fuel injected engines.

SIGN UP FOR YOUR SEMINAR TODAY

Ask your Mitchell sales representative for details, or call for more information.

**1-800-648-8010,
extension 8570** *or*
1-619-578-6550.

The Leader in Professional Estimating and Repair Information.

ADD 91

WHEN ~~EQUIP~~MENT IS DIAGNOSI~~NG~~ ~~DRIVABILI~~TY PROBLEM~~S~~ THIS IS ~~THE LIBRARY~~ YOU NEED.

To diagnose driveability problems fast, you need reliable, accurate information. Diagnostic charts. Component locations. Wiring diagrams. Vacuum circuit diagrams. Technical service bulletins. And troubleshooting tips.

Mitchell has it all...in easy-to-use manuals designed for the professional technician. We call it the Mitchell Computerized Engine Control Diagnostic Library.

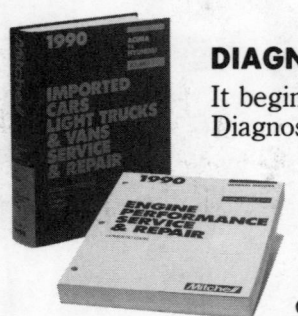

DIAGNOSTIC CHARTS

It begins with the manufacturers' Diagnostic Charts. Contained in the *Mitchell Annual Data* and *Engine Performance Manual*... guides g... manufact... diagnostic procedures for computer-controlled systems.

WIRING DIAGRAMS

Available in the *Mitchell Annual Data, Engine Performance,* and *Electrical Manuals,* these diagrams make it easy to trace complex electrical circuits. You'll also be able to verify the integrity of electrical circuits to ensure they have not been altered with the installation of stereos, cellular phones, alarms, ignition interrupt systems and other aftermarket devices.

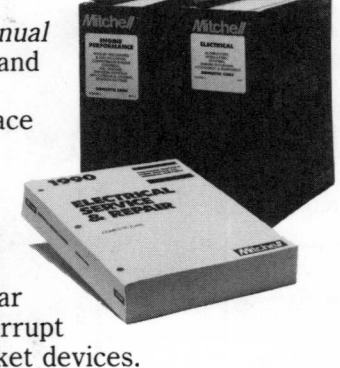

VACUUM CIRCUIT DIAGRAMS

Offered in separate books as well as in the *Mitchell Annual Data* and *Engine Performance Manuals,* these diagrams are "roadmaps" to the vacuum circuitry where emissions, driveability, and air conditioning problems often originate. You're able to pinpoint vacuum hose routing, valves, restrictors, and metered orifices quickly. And

you can verify circuit integrity to ensure that it has not been altered.

ELECTRICAL COMPONENT LOCAT~~OR~~

To speed your search for electrical components, the Mitchell Diagnostic Data Library includes two *Electrical Component Locator Manuals* – one for domestics and one for imports. With these books, you can hook up diagnostic tools and do the necessary R & R operations quickly.

~~TEC~~HNICAL SERVICE BULLETINS

Four times a year, Mitchell publishes the most significant technical service bulletins issued by manufacturers worldwide. These helpful tips can save hours of diagnostic time. Written by editors who understand real-world problems and real working solutions, *Mitchell Technical Service Bulletins* offer clear, concise descriptions that help you get the job done fast.

GUARANTEED TO PASS THE TEST

All of the books in the Mitchell Computerized Engine Control Data Diagnostic Library come with a 30-day money-back guarantee of satisfaction. And they are easy to obtain. To order, contact your Mitchell Sales Representative or call:

1-800-648-8010

(In the 619 area, call 578-6550.)

ADD 91

The Leader in Professional Estimating and Repair Informat~~ion~~